EUROPEAN RAIL

SUMMER 20

GENERAL INFORMATION

FEATURES

TIMETABLES

CONTACT DETAILS

Director and Editor-in-chief	John Potter
Editor	Chris Woodcock
Editorial Team	Peter Bass Graham Benbow Reuben Turner Peter Weller
Additional compiling	Brendan Fox Richard Stirk
Marketing, Advertising and Social Media Manager	Clare Bessent
Commercial Manager	Gemma Donaldson
Subscriptions Manager	Peter Weller

ISBN 978-0-9957998-5-1

Printed and bound by CPI Group (UK) Ltd, Croydon, CR0 4YY

Cover created by Andrea Collins website: www.millstonecreative.co.uk
Front cover: On June 21, 2015, EC144 1110 Milano - Nice, passes through Cervo, between Alassio and Diano on the Italian Riviera (Table **580**).
© Gianfranco Berto. www.duegieditricestore.it

European Rail Timetable Limited
28 Monson Way
Oundle
Northamptonshire PE8 4QG, United Kingdom
website: www.europeanrailtimetable.eu
e-mail: editorial@europeanrailtimetable.eu
sales: sales@europeanrailtimetable.eu
telephone: +44 (0)1832 270198 Mondays to Fridays 0900 - 1700

CALENDAR

2019

CALENDRIER CALENDARIO KALENDER CALENDARIO

JANUARY

M	T	W	T	F	S	S
①	②	③	④	⑤	⑥	⑦
–	1	2	3	4	5	6
7	8	9	10	11	12	13
14	15	16	17	18	19	20
21	22	23	24	25	26	27
28	29	30	31	–	–	–

FEBRUARY

M	T	W	T	F	S	S
①	②	③	④	⑤	⑥	⑦
–	–	–	–	1	2	3
4	5	6	7	8	9	10
11	12	13	14	15	16	17
18	19	20	21	22	23	24
25	26	27	28	–	–	–

MARCH

M	T	W	T	F	S	S
①	②	③	④	⑤	⑥	⑦
–	–	–	–	1	2	3
4	5	6	7	8	9	10
11	12	13	14	15	16	17
18	19	20	21	22	23	24
25	26	27	28	29	30	31

APRIL

M	T	W	T	F	S	S
①	②	③	④	⑤	⑥	⑦
1	2	3	4	5	6	7
8	9	10	11	12	13	14
15	16	17	18	19	20	21
22	23	24	25	26	27	28
29	30	–	–	–	–	–

MAY

M	T	W	T	F	S	S
①	②	③	④	⑤	⑥	⑦
–	–	1	2	3	4	5
6	7	8	9	10	11	12
13	14	15	16	17	18	19
20	21	22	23	24	25	26
27	28	29	30	31	–	–

JUNE

M	T	W	T	F	S	S
①	②	③	④	⑤	⑥	⑦
–	–	–	–	–	1	2
3	4	5	6	7	8	9
10	11	12	13	14	15	16
17	18	19	20	21	22	23
24	25	26	27	28	29	30

JULY

M	T	W	T	F	S	S
①	②	③	④	⑤	⑥	⑦
1	2	3	4	5	6	7
8	9	10	11	12	13	14
15	16	17	18	19	20	21
22	23	24	25	26	27	28
29	30	31	–	–	–	–

AUGUST

M	T	W	T	F	S	S
①	②	③	④	⑤	⑥	⑦
–	–	–	1	2	3	4
5	6	7	8	9	10	11
12	13	14	15	16	17	18
19	20	21	22	23	24	25
26	27	28	29	30	31	–

SEPTEMBER

M	T	W	T	F	S	S
①	②	③	④	⑤	⑥	⑦
30	–	–	–	–	–	1
2	3	4	5	6	7	8
9	10	11	12	13	14	15
16	17	18	19	20	21	22
23	24	25	26	27	28	29

OCTOBER

M	T	W	T	F	S	S
①	②	③	④	⑤	⑥	⑦
–	1	2	3	4	5	6
7	8	9	10	11	12	13
14	15	16	17	18	19	20
21	22	23	24	25	26	27
28	29	30	31	–	–	–

NOVEMBER

M	T	W	T	F	S	S
①	②	③	④	⑤	⑥	⑦
–	–	–	–	1	2	3
4	5	6	7	8	9	10
11	12	13	14	15	16	17
18	19	20	21	22	23	24
25	26	27	28	29	30	–

DECEMBER

M	T	W	T	F	S	S
①	②	③	④	⑤	⑥	⑦
30	31	–	–	–	–	1
2	3	4	5	6	7	8
9	10	11	12	13	14	15
16	17	18	19	20	21	22
23	24	25	26	27	28	29

2020

JANUARY

M	T	W	T	F	S	S
①	②	③	④	⑤	⑥	⑦
–	–	1	2	3	4	5
6	7	8	9	10	11	12
13	14	15	16	17	18	19
20	21	22	23	24	25	26
27	28	29	30	31	–	–

FEBRUARY

M	T	W	T	F	S	S
①	②	③	④	⑤	⑥	⑦
–	–	–	–	–	1	2
3	4	5	6	7	8	9
10	11	12	13	14	15	16
17	18	19	20	21	22	23
24	25	26	27	28	29	–

MARCH

M	T	W	T	F	S	S
①	②	③	④	⑤	⑥	⑦
30	31	–	–	–	–	1
2	3	4	5	6	7	8
9	10	11	12	13	14	15
16	17	18	19	20	21	22
23	24	25	26	27	28	29

APRIL

M	T	W	T	F	S	S
①	②	③	④	⑤	⑥	⑦
–	–	1	2	3	4	5
6	7	8	9	10	11	12
13	14	15	16	17	18	19
20	21	22	23	24	25	26
27	28	29	30	–	–	–

MAY

M	T	W	T	F	S	S
①	②	③	④	⑤	⑥	⑦
–	–	–	–	1	2	3
4	5	6	7	8	9	10
11	12	13	14	15	16	17
18	19	20	21	22	23	24
25	26	27	28	29	30	31

JUNE

M	T	W	T	F	S	S
①	②	③	④	⑤	⑥	⑦
1	2	3	4	5	6	7
8	9	10	11	12	13	14
15	16	17	18	19	20	21
22	23	24	25	26	27	28
29	30	–	–	–	–	–

PUBLIC HOLIDAYS 2019

JOURS FÉRIÉS GIORNI FESTIVI FEIERTAGE DÍAS FESTIVOS

The dates given below are those of national public holidays. They do not include regional, half-day or unofficial holidays. Passengers intending to travel on public holidays, or on days immediately preceding or following them, are strongly recommended to reserve seats and to confirm timings locally. Further information regarding special transport conditions applying on holiday dates may be found in the introduction to each country.

Austria: Jan. 1, 6, Apr. 22, May 1, 30, June 10, 20, Aug. 15, Oct. 26, Nov. 1, Dec. 8, 25, 26.

Belarus: Jan. 1, 7, Mar. 8, May 1, 7, 9, July 3, Nov. 7, Dec. 25.

Belgium: Jan. 1, Apr. 21, 22, May 1, 30, June 9, 10, July 21, Aug. 15, Nov. 1, 11, Dec. 25.

Bosnia-Herzegovina: Jan. 1, 2, Mar. 1, May 1, 2, 9, Nov. 25. *Other religious holidays are observed in certain areas.*

Bulgaria: Jan. 1, Mar. 4, Apr. 26 – 29, May 1, 6, 24, Sept. 6, 23, Dec. 24, 25, 26.

Croatia: Jan. 1, 6, Apr. 21, 22, May 1, June 20, 22, 25, Aug. 5, 15, Oct. 8, Nov. 1, Dec. 25, 26.

Czech Republic: Jan. 1, Apr. 19, 22, May 1, 8, July 5, 6, Sept. 28, Oct. 28, Nov. 17, Dec. 24, 25, 26.

Denmark: Jan. 1, Apr. 18, 19, 21, 22, May 17, 30, June 9, 10, Dec. 25, 26.

Estonia: Jan. 1, Feb. 24, Apr. 19, 21, May 1, June 9, 23, 24, Aug. 20, Dec. 24, 25, 26.

Finland: Jan. 1, 6, Apr. 19, 21, 22, May 1, 30, June 9, 22, Nov. 2, Dec. 6, 25, 26.

France: Jan. 1, Apr. 22, May 1, 8, 30, June 10, July 14, Aug. 15, Nov. 1, 11, Dec. 25.

Germany: Jan. 1, 6*, Apr. 19, 22, May 1, 30, June 10, 20*, Aug. 15*, Oct. 3, 31*, Nov. 1*, 20*, Dec. 25, 26.
** Observed in certain regions: see also page 369.*

Great Britain: *England & Wales*: Jan. 1, Apr. 19, 22, May 6, 27, Aug. 26, Dec. 25, 26.
Scotland: Jan. 1, 2, Apr. 19, May 6, 27, Aug. 5, Dec. 2, 25, 26.

Greece: Jan. 1, 6, Mar. 11, 25, Apr. 26, 28, 29, May 1, June 17, Aug. 15, Oct. 28, Dec. 25, 26.

Hungary: Jan. 1, Mar. 15, Apr. 19, 21, 22, May 1, June 10, Aug. 20, Oct. 23, Nov. 1, Dec. 25, 26.

Iceland: Jan. 1, Apr. 18, 19, 21, 22, 25, May 1, 30, June 9, 10, 17, Aug. 5, Dec. 25, 26.

Ireland (Northern): Jan. 1, Mar. 18, Apr. 19, 22, May 6, 27, July 12, Aug. 26, Dec. 25, 26.

Ireland (Republic): Jan. 1, Mar. 17, Apr. 22, May 6, June 3, Aug. 5, Oct. 28, Dec. 25, 26.

Italy: Jan. 1, 6, Apr. 21, 22, 25, May 1, June 2, Aug. 15, Nov. 1, Dec. 8, 25, 26.

Latvia: Jan. 1, Apr. 19, 21, 22, May 1, 6, June 23, 24, Nov. 18, Dec. 24, 25, 26, 31.

Lithuania: Jan. 1, Feb. 16, Mar. 11, Apr. 21, 22, May 1, June 24, July 6, Aug. 15, Nov. 1, Dec. 24, 25, 26.

Luxembourg: Jan. 1, Apr. 22, May 1, 30, June 10, 23, Aug. 15, Nov. 1, Dec. 25, 26.

North Macedonia: Jan. 1, 7, Apr. 29, May 1, 24, June 5, Aug. 2, Sept. 8, Oct. 11, 23, Dec. 8. *Other religious holidays are observed in certain areas.*

Moldova: Jan. 1, 2, 7, 8, Mar. 8, Apr. 28, 29, May 1, 6, 9, Aug. 27, 28, 31, Dec. 25.

Netherlands: Jan. 1, Apr. 21, 22, 27, May 30, June 9, 10, Dec. 25, 26.

Norway: Jan. 1, Apr. 18, 19, 21, 22, May 1, 17, 30, June 9, 10, Dec. 25, 26.

Poland: Jan. 1, 6, Apr. 21, 22, May 1, 3, June 9, 20, Aug. 15, Nov. 1, 11, Dec. 25, 26.

Portugal: Jan. 1, Apr. 19, 21, 25, May 1, June 10, 20, Aug. 15, Oct. 5, Nov. 1, Dec. 1, 8, 25.

Romania: Jan. 1, 2, 24, Apr. 26, 28, 29, May 1, June 1, 16, 17, Aug. 15, Nov. 30, Dec. 1, 25, 26.

Russia: Jan. 1 – 4, 7, 8, Feb. 25, Mar. 8, May 1, 2, 3, 9, June 12, Nov. 4.

Serbia: Jan. 1, 2, 7, Feb. 15, 16, Apr. 26 – 29, May 1, 2, Nov. 11.

Slovakia: Jan. 1, 6, Apr. 19, 22, May 1, 8, July 5, Aug. 29, Sept. 1, 15, Nov. 1, 17, Dec. 24, 25, 26.

Slovenia: Jan. 1, 2, Feb. 8, Apr. 21, 22, 27, May 1, 2, June 9, 25, Aug. 15, Oct. 31, Nov. 1, Dec. 25, 26.

Spain: Jan. 1, 6, 7*, Mar. 19*, Apr. 18*, 19, 22*, May 1, July 25*, Aug. 15, Oct. 12, Nov. 1, Dec. 6, 9, 25.
** Observed in certain regions.*

Sweden: Jan. 1, 6, Apr. 19, 21, 22, May 1, 30, June 6, 9, 22, Nov. 2, Dec. 25, 26.

Switzerland: Jan. 1, 2*, 6*, Mar. 19*, Apr. 19*, 22*, May 1*, 30, June 10*, 20*, Aug. 1, 15*, Nov. 1*, Dec. 8*, 25, 26*. *Also some local holidays.*
** Observed in certain regions.*

Turkey: Jan. 1, Apr. 23, May 1, 19, July 15, Aug. 30, Oct. 29 (also 2019 feast holiday periods June 6 – 8, Aug. 12 – 15).

Ukraine: Jan. 1, 7, 8, Mar. 8, Apr. 28, 29, May 1, 9, June 16, 17, 28, Aug. 26, Oct. 14, Nov. 21, Dec. 25.

MOVABLE HOLIDAYS

Fêtes mobiles – Feste mobile
Bewegliche Feste – Fiestas movibles

	2019	2020
Good Friday	Apr. 19 •	Apr. 10 •
Easter Monday	Apr. 22 •	Apr. 13 •
Ascension Day	May 30 •	May 21 •
Whit Monday (Pentecost)	June 10 •	June 1 •
Corpus Christi	June 20	June 11

• *One week later in the Orthodox calendar*

TIME COMPARISON

COMPARAISON DES HEURES COMPARAZIONE DELLE ORE ZEITVERGLEICH COMPARACIÓN DE LAS HORAS

West European Time	*WINTER: UTC* *SUMMER: UTC +1*	Ireland, Portugal, United Kingdom; Iceland *(UTC all year)*
Central European Time	*WINTER: UTC +1* *SUMMER: UTC +2*	Albania, Austria, Belgium, Bosnia, Croatia, Czech Rep., Denmark, France, Germany, Hungary, Italy, Luxembourg, North Macedonia, Malta, Montenegro, Netherlands, Norway, Poland, Serbia, Slovakia, Slovenia, Spain, Sweden, Switzerland
East European Time	*WINTER: UTC +2* *SUMMER: UTC +3*	Bulgaria, Estonia, Finland, Greece, Latvia, Lithuania, Moldova, Romania, Ukraine; Belarus and Western Russia *(UTC+3 all year)*, Kaliningrad *(UTC+2 all year)*, Turkey *(UTC+3 all year)*

Daylight Saving Time ('Summer Time') applies between 0100 GMT on March 31 and 0100 GMT on October 27, 2019 *(UTC = Coordinated Universal Time = GMT)*

What's new this month

WELCOME

Welcome to the Summer 2019 edition of the European Rail Timetable which includes updated schedules for most countries valid until December 14. The main exceptions are in Italy and Poland where only partial information was available as we went to press.

This expanded edition also includes the latest versions of all eight Beyond Europe sections together with our *Rail Extra* feature with 13 pages of useful transport based information presented on a country by country basis (including details of many popular tourist railways). Our regular Rail Passes feature is also expanded to seven pages with details of many domestic rail passes as well as Interrail and Eurail products.

Extracts from our timetable news page that appeared in the May digital edition will be found on page 559.

INTERNATIONAL

Thalys has introduced a new non-stop service between Brussels and Bordeaux on summer Saturdays with a journey time of just over four hours (Table **11**).

Eurostar is operating a third service from London to Amsterdam from June 11, leaving London at 1104, whilst the 0816 departure moves one hour earlier to 0716 from the same date (Table **18**). We are still awaiting news regarding the implementation of border formalities within the Netherlands which must be in place to allow direct services to run in the opposite direction. It is hoped that these will start in December this year.

Train **301/300** *Berlin Night Express* Berlin – Malmö runs on three days a week during the summer (Table **50**).

Railjet service **571/570** Praha – Břeclav has been extended to and from Bratislava and renumbered **285/284**. Train *RJ* **285** now provides a useful connection at Praha with train *EC* **177** for journeys from Hamburg and Berlin to Bratislava (Table **60**).

Train **1335/1334** *Hellas* runs between Beograd and Thessaloníki from June 14 to September 16 but passengers are conveyed by bus between Gevgelija and Thessaloníki (Table **61**).

The extension of certain WestBahn services to and from München, originally planned to commence in April, has now been delayed until later in the year, probably during the autumn (Table **65**).

The twice weekly Leo Express train **401/400** Praha – Kraków runs daily from June 29 (Table **99**).

GREAT BRITAIN

South Western Railway has added several extra services between London Waterloo and Yeovil together with an additional train to and from Bristol on weekdays (Tables **108** and **140**). The popular Saturdays only through train between London and Corfe Castle on the Swanage railway operates once again this year until September 7 (Table **114a**).

Great Western has added additional local services between Plymouth and Penzance on Mondays to Saturdays (Table **112**).

Cross Country has extended three of its services between Manchester and Bristol to run to / from Exeter on Mondays to Fridays (Table **116**).

Chiltern Railways has provided additional through trains between London and Stratford-upon-Avon by extending certain services that previously only ran as far as Banbury (Table **128a**).

The pattern of suburban services operated by West Midlands Trains along the West Coast Main Line has been completely recast. There are now five basic routes operating on weekdays as follows:

1) London to Crewe via Nuneaton (no longer running via Stoke)
2) London to Crewe via Northampton, Birmingham and Stoke-on-Trent
3) London to Liverpool via Northampton and Birmingham
4) London to Birmingham via Northampton
5) Birmingham International to Liverpool

An amended pattern runs on Sundays with the London to Birmingham and Birmingham to Liverpool sections running separately. Our Tables **142**, **143** and **144** have been adapted to reflect the new service pattern.

The service between Llandudno and Blaenau Ffestiniog is currently suspended owing to recent flood damage. A replacement bus service is provided until further notice, operating in similar timings (Table **160**).

Transport for Wales has introduced a new hourly service between Chester and Liverpool via Runcorn utilising a previously freight only chord of track between Frodsham and Runcorn (Table **163**).

There are numerous alterations to services operated by Northern. All trains between Manchester and Blackpool are now routed via Bolton (Table **156**) whilst the increased number of through services between Manchester and Windermere / Barrow-in-Furness operate via Wigan (Table **158**). A number of routes benefit from enhanced frequencies including Leeds to Harrogate (Table **175**), Hull to Scarborough (Table **177**) and Newcastle to Carlisle (Table **210**). Gainsborough Central has also gained a regular weekday service to and from Sheffield for the first time in over 30 years (Table **178**). A new direct service between Leeds and Chester has been introduced by extending certain services on the Leeds – Bradford – Halifax – Manchester Victoria route (Table **190**).

Greater Anglia has introduced two additional services in each direction between Norwich and London on Mondays to Saturdays (Table **200**). These new services complete the journey in just 90 minutes (with only one intermediate stop at Ipswich) which is the fastest ever scheduled timing between Norwich and London. The previous best was an ambitious 92 minute northbound schedule in 1992 but over subsequent years this has been gradually extended as the Great Eastern route has become more congested. However, by tweaking the schedules of certain suburban services and taking advantage of recent route upgrades, the new faster trains can now be reliably operated and other services should also benefit from journey time reductions in the near future as brand new rolling stock is introduced.

Following completion of electrification work in Scotland, Scotrail has been able to reduce journey times of services between Edinburgh and Glasgow via Falkirk High (Table **220**) and between Edinburgh and Stirling (Table **224**).

Readers planning to use the route between Aberdeen and Inverness should note that an amended timetable will be in force until August 19 with partial bus replacement in operation (Table **225**).

FRANCE

Timings in our French section are generally valid until December 14. However, some of our tables have shorter validity periods and these are clearly indicated on the relevant pages or in individual table headings. Please note that schedules in western France vary considerably during the high-summer period so, in this edition, tables covering services that radiate from Paris Montparnasse and Austerlitz stations are mostly valid from July 6 to September 1. Timings from September 2 will be included from the September edition (please refer to earlier editions for timings until July 5).

The expansion of low-cost OUIGO TGV services continues with the introduction of a daily return service between Paris Montparnasse and Toulouse from July 6 (Table **320**).

Engineering work between Paris and Troyes will cause major disruption along the route from July 13 to August 24. During this period just three through services will operate between Paris and Belfort, diverted via Châlons en Champagne. A special version of Table **380** will be found on page 210 showing the amended timings.

The latest phase of work to upgrade the route heading north from Marseille via Aix-en-Provence is expected to cause some disruption for a four month period from July 1 (Table **362**). Unfortunately, full details of amended timings along the route were not available as we went to press.

ITALY

New schedules came into effect from June 9 but only partial information was available as we went to press, mainly timings of high-speed and other long-distance trains. However, readers should be cautious of any exception dates if travelling on or around public holidays or during August. Any changes to other services are expected to be of a minor nature but it is still advisable to confirm timings before travelling.

CONTINUED ON PAGE 36

EXPLANATION OF STANDARD SYMBOLS

	EXPLANATION OF SYMBOLS	*EXPLICATION DES SIGNES*	*DELUCIDAZIONE DEI SEGNI*	*ZEICHENERKLÄRUNG*	*EXPLICACIÓN DE LOS SIGNOS*
	SERVICES	**SERVICES**	**SERVIZI**	**DIENSTE**	**SERVICIOS**
12	Through service (1st and 2nd class seats)	Relation directe (places assises 1re et 2e classe)	Relazione diretta (con posti di 1a e 2a classe)	Direkte Verbindung (Sitzplätze 1. und 2. Klasse)	Relación directa (con asientos de 1a y 2a clase)
🛏	Sleeping car	Voiture-lits	Carrozza letti	Schlafwagen	Coche-camas
━	Couchette car	Voiture-couchettes	Carrozza cuccette	Liegewagen	Coche-literas
✕	Restaurant car	Voiture-restaurant	Carrozza ristorante	Speisewagen	Coche-restaurante
🍸	Snacks and drinks available *(see page 10)*	Voiture-bar ou vente ambulante *(voir page 10)*	Carrozza bar o servizio di buffet *(vedere pagina 10)*	Imbiss und Getränke im Zug *(siehe Seite 10)*	Servicio de cafeteria o bar móvil *(véase pág. 10)*
2	Second class only	Uniquement deuxième classe	Sola seconda classe	Nur zweite Klasse	Sólo segunda clase
🚌	Bus or coach service	Service routier	Servizio automobilistico	Buslinie	Servicio de autobuses
⛴	Ferry service	Service maritime	Servizio marittimo	Schifffahrtslinie	Servicio marítimo
	DAYS OF RUNNING	**JOURS DE CIRCULATION**	**GIORNI DI EFFETTUAZIONE**	**VERKEHRSTAGE**	**DÍAS DE CIRCULACIÓN**
⚒	Mondays to Saturdays except holidays*	Du lundi au samedi, sauf les fêtes*	Dal lunedì al sabato, salvo i giorni festivi*	Montag bis Samstag außer Feiertage*	De lunes a sábado, excepto festivos*
Ⓐ	Mondays to Fridays except holidays*	Du lundi au vendredi, sauf les fêtes*	Dal lunedì al venerdì, salvo i giorni festivi*	Montag bis Freitag außer Feiertage*	De lunes a viernes, excepto festivos*
Ⓑ	Daily except Saturdays	Tous les jours sauf les samedis	Giornalmente, salvo il sabato	Täglich außer Samstag	Diario excepto sábados
Ⓒ	Saturdays, Sundays and holidays*	Les samedis, dimanches et fêtes*	Sabato, domenica e giorni festivi*	Samstage, Sonn- und Feiertage*	Sábados, domingos y festivos*
†	Sundays and holidays*	Les dimanches et fêtes*	Domenica e giorni festivi*	Sonn- und Feiertage*	Domingos y festivos*
①②	Mondays, Tuesdays	Les lundis, mardis	Lunedì, martedì	Montag, Dienstag	Lunes, martes
③④	Wednesdays, Thurdays	Les mercredis, jeudis	Mercoledì, giovedì	Mittwoch, Donnerstag	Miércoles, jueves
⑤⑥	Fridays, Saturdays	Les vendredis, samedis	Venerdì, sabato	Freitag, Samstag	Viernes, sábados
⑦	Sundays	Les dimanches	Domenica	Sonntag	Domingos
①–④	Mondays to Thursdays	Des lundis aux jeudis	Dal lunedì al giovedì	Montag bis Donnerstag	De lunes a jueves
	OTHER SYMBOLS	**AUTRES SIGNES**	**ALTRI SIMBOLI**	**SONSTIGE SYMBOLE**	**OTROS SÍMBOLOS**
IC **29**	Train number (**bold figures** above train times)	Numéro du train (en **caractères gras** au-dessus de l'horaire du train)	Numero del treno (in **neretto** sopra gli orari del treno)	Zugnummer (über den Fahrplanzeiten in **fetter Schrift** gesetzt)	Número del tren (figura en **negrita** encima del horario del tren)
◆	See footnotes (listed by train number)	Renvoi aux notes données en bas de page (dans l'ordre numérique des trains)	Vedi in calce alla pagina l'annotazione corrispondente al numero del treno	Siehe die nach Zugnummern geordneten Fußnoten	Véase al pie de la página la nota correspondiente al número del tren
R	Reservation compulsory	Réservation obligatoire	Prenotazione obbligatoria	Reservierung erforderlich	Reserva obligatoria
🏛	Frontier station	Gare frontalière	Stazione di frontiera	Grenzbahnhof	Estación fronteriza
✈	Airport	Aéroport	Aeroporto	Flughafen	Aeropuerto
|	Train does not stop	Sans arrêt	Il treno non ferma qui	Zug hält nicht	El tren no para aquí
━	Separates two trains in the same column between which no connection is possible	Sépare deux trains de la même colonne qui ne sont pas en correspondance	Separa due treni della stessa colonna che non sono in coincidenza	Trennt zwei in derselben Spalte angegebene Züge, zwischen denen kein Anschluß besteht	Separa dos trenes de la misma columna entre los cuales no hay enlace
→	Continued in later column	Suite dans une colonne à droite	Continuazione più avanti a destra	Fortsetzung weiter rechts	Continuación a la derecha
←	Continued from earlier column	Suite d'une colonne à gauche	Seguito di una colonna a sinistra	Fortsetzung von links	Continuación desde la izquierda
v.v.	Vice versa	Vice versa	Viceversa	Umgekehrt	A la inversa
	** Public holiday dates for each country are given on page 4.* *Other, special symbols are explained in table footnotes or in the introduction to each country.*	** Les dates des fêtes légales nationales sont données en page 4.* *D'autres signes particuliers sont expliqués dans les notes ou bien dans l'avant-propos relatif à chaque pays.*	** Per le date dei giorni festivi civili nei diversi paesi vedere pagina 4.* *Altri segni particolari vengono spiegati nelle note in calce ai quadri o nella introduzione attinente a ogni paese.*	** Gesetzlichen Feiertage der jeweiligen Länder finden Sie auf Seite 4.* *Besondere Symbole sind in den Fußnoten bzw. in der Einleitung zu den einzelnen Ländern erklärt.*	** Las fechas de los días festivos en cada país figuran en la página 4.* *La explicación de otros signos particulares se da en las notas o en el preámbulo correspondiente a cada país.*

What is the European Rail Timetable?

The European Rail Timetable is a concise guide to rail and ferry schedules throughout Europe, and also includes selected areas of the world outside Europe. Needless to say, it cannot be comprehensive (it would run into thousands of pages), but through our knowledge and experience, together with valuable feedback from our readers, we can select those services which we believe will satisfy the needs of most travellers.

When do the services change?

There is a major annual timetable change in mid-December affecting almost all European countries, with many countries having a second change in mid-June. There are, of course, exceptions. For example, the British summer timetable starts in late May, Sweden changes again in mid-August, whilst there are changes in Ukraine from late March (coinciding with the clock change). Many holiday areas also have separate timetables for the high-summer period, particularly areas of France, Italy and Hungary. In fact, changes can happen at any time of year, and railways issue amendments either on set dates or as and when necessary. Engineering work also causes frequent changes, and shipping schedules can change at any time.

How are the trains selected for inclusion?

People travel for many reasons, whether for leisure, business, sightseeing, visiting friends or relations, or just for the fun of it, and there are no hard and fast rules for selecting the services that we show. Naturally, major towns and inter-city services are shown as a matter of course, but the level of smaller places and local trains shown will depend on the country and even the area. It's surprising just how many minor lines we manage to squeeze in! Generally we will show a greater number of local trains in areas which are popular tourist destinations or where other services are sparse.

It is not possible to show suburban trains within cities or conurbations, or most outer-suburban routes to places close to large cities. However, where there are places of particular interest or importance in this category we do try to show brief details of frequency and journey time.

When should I use the International section?

The rail tables are divided into two sections - International (Tables **9** to **99**) and Country by Country (Tables **100** upwards). For some international services between adjacent countries (for example Stockholm - Oslo or Hamburg - Århus) it is necessary to use the relevant Country tables - the index or maps will guide you. Local trains which cross international frontiers will usually only be found in the Country sections.

Some international trains also carry passengers internally within each country and will therefore be found in the Country tables as well as the International section. Some services are primarily for international travel and will therefore only be found in the International section - this includes *Eurostar* trains (London - Paris / Brussels / Amsterdam) and *Thalys* services (Paris - Brussels - Amsterdam / Köln), as well as certain long-distance night trains.

What about places outside Europe?

The European Rail Timetable includes the whole of Turkey and Russia. Furthermore, our **Beyond Europe** section at the back of each edition features timetables from different areas of the world each month. Eight areas are featured, each appearing at least twice a year. The areas covered are **India**, **South East Asia, Australia, New Zealand, China**, **Japan**, **South America**, **North America**, **South Korea**, **Africa and the Middle East**. Details of when each region appears will be found in the introduction of the Beyond Europe section. Please note that we include **all** of the latest Beyond Europe sections in our expanded Winter and Summer editions.

What else does it contain?

A summary of international sleeper services will be found on page 35, listing types of accommodation, operators and facilities on board.

We also include a summary of European rail passes (see the list of contents on page 3 for its current location) with a more detailed version appearing in our expanded seasonal Summer and Winter editions. The seasonal editions also include a *Rail Extra* feature containing useful transport based information on a country by country basis (including details of many popular tourist railways).

Our timetables and other products may be purchased from our website **www.europeanrailtimetable.eu**.

HOW TO USE THE TIMETABLE

Using the index

Look up the two places between which you are travelling. It can often be helpful to start your search from the *smaller* of the two locations. ❺

Using the maps

The maps can be the quickest way of finding the required table number, if you already know the geographical location of the places required. ❿

COMMENT TROUVER VOTRE TRAIN

❶ Localité.
❷ Numéros des tableaux.
❸ Grande ville.
❹ Localités sélectionnées à gagner de la grande ville en haut.
❺ Cherchez les deux bouts du parcours désiré sur la liste des villes. Commencer par la ville de moindre importance peut faciliter la recherche.
❻ Ligne principale.
❼ Ligne secondaire.
❽ Ligne à grande vitesse.
❾ Liaison en autocar.
❿ La consultation des cartes – si vous savez déjà la location géographique de vos points de départ et d'arrivée – est le moyen le plus rapide de repérer les numéros des tableaux relatifs à votre parcours.

COME TROVARE IL VOSTRO TRENO

❶ Località.
❷ Numeri dei quadri-orario.
❸ Grandi città.
❹ Principali destinazione raggiungibili dalla località in neretto sopra.
❺ Cercate le localita' tra le quali dovrete viaggiare; spesso può essere di aiuto iniziare la ricerca dalla località più piccola.
❻ Principale linea ferroviaria.
❼ Linea ferroviaria secondaria.
❽ Linea ad alta velocità.
❾ Autobus.
❿ Le mappe sono il metodo più rapido per trovare i numeri dei quadri-orario di cui avete bisogno, quando gia' siete a conoscenza della collocazione geografica delle localita' di partenza e arrivo del vostro viaggio.

WIE FINDE ICH MEINEN ZUG?

❶ Ortsname.
❷ Tabellennummer.
❸ Großstadt.
❹ Knotenpunkte erreichbar von der Großstadt oben.
❺ Suchen Sie Ihre Start- und Endbahnhof im Ortsverzeichnis. Dazu empfehlen wir, Ihre Suche aus der Richtung des *kleineren* Ortes aufzunehmen.
❻ Hauptstrecke.
❼ Nebenstrecke.
❽ Hochgeschwindigkeitsstrecke.
❾ Busverbindung.
❿ Kennen Sie die geographische Lage der Ausgangs- und Bestimmungsorte Ihrer Reise, dann empfehlen wir einen Blick in die im Kursbuch enthaltene Übersichtskarte.

COMO BUSCAR SU TREN

❶ Localidad.
❷ Números de los cuadros horarios.
❸ Gran ciudad.
❹ Principales destinos accesibles a través de esta localidad.
❺ Busque los dos lugares a través de los cuales viaja. Normalmente facilita la búsqueda empezar por la localidad más pequeña.
❻ Línea principal.
❼ Línea secundaria.
❽ Línea de alta velocidad.
❾ Línea de autobuses.
❿ Los mapas pueden ser la forma más rápida de encontrar los cuadros que debe consultar, si ya conoce el punto de inicio y conclusión de su viaje.

HOW TO USE THE TIMETABLE

Numbers in circles refer to translations below

Reading the tables

Trains run daily unless otherwise shown by symbol or footnote (15)

d. = depart, a. = arrive (the first time in a column is always a departure time, the last is an arrival). (14)

Table number and route (1)

Station names in local language (2)

Distance from Praha in km (3)

Important stations are shown in **bold** for clarity (4)

Indented station: shows a branch off the main route of the table (5)

Train category (where shown) (13)

Train number (where shown) (12)

Standard symbols (e.g. Ⓐ, 🅁, ✕) are explained on page 6.

Other symbols (e.g. ⊖) and letters (**E**, **r**) are explained below the table.

♦ means footnotes are listed by train number. (11)

1150 PRAHA - BRNO - WIEN / BRATISLAVA

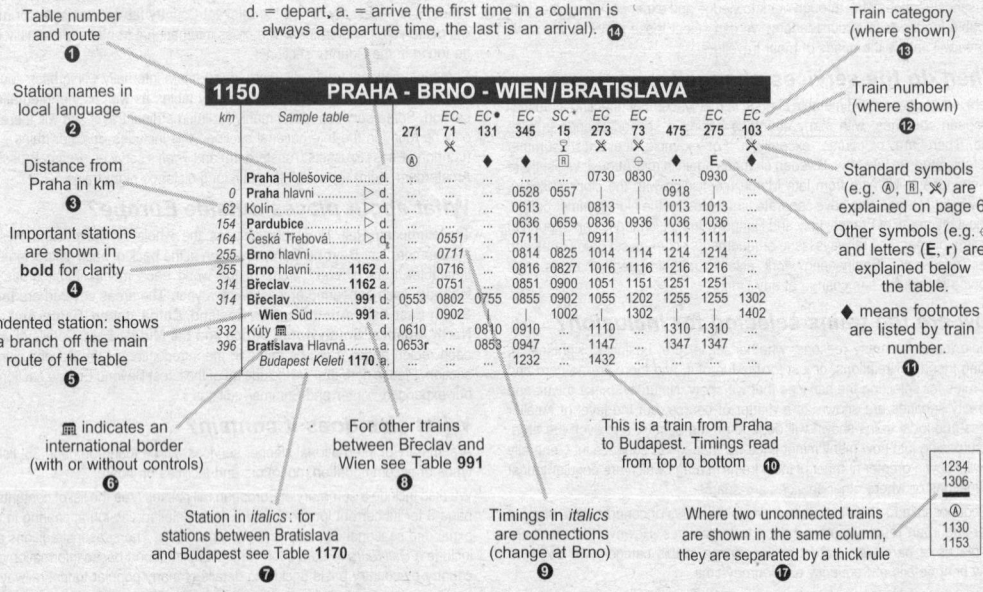

km	Sample table										
			EC	*EC*•	*EC*	*SC**	*EC*	*EC*		*EC*	*EC*
		271	71	131	345	15	273	73	475	275	103
			✕			🍷	✕	✕			✕
		Ⓐ		♦	♦	🅁		⊖	♦	E	♦
	Praha Holešovice .... d.	...	...	...	...	...	0730	0830	...	0930	...
0	**Praha** hlavni .... ▷ d.	...	...	...	0528	0557	|	|	0918	|	...
62	Kolín .... ▷ d.	...	...	...	0613	|	0813	|	1013	1013	...
154	**Pardubice** .... ▷ d.	...	...	...	0636	0659	0836	0936	1036	1036	...
164	Česká Třebová......... ▷ d.	...	*0551*	...	0711	|	0911	|	1111	1111	...
255	**Brno** hlavní.................a.	...	*0711*	...	0814	0825	1014	1114	1214	1214	...
255	**Brno** hlavní.......... **1162** d.	...	0716	...	0816	0827	1016	1116	1216	1216	...
314	**Břeclav**............... **1162** a.	...	0751	...	0851	0900	1051	1151	1251	1251	...
314	**Břeclav**................. **991** d.	0553	0802	0755	0855	0902	1055	1202	1255	1255	1302
	Wien Süd .... **991** a.	|	0902	|	|	1002	|	1302	|	|	1402
332	Kúty 🏛 ....d.	0610	...	0810	0910	...	1110	...	1310	1310	...
396	**Bratislava** Hlavná ....a.	0653**r**	...	0853	0947	...	1147	...	1347	1347	...
	Budapest Keleti **1170**.a.	...	...	...	1232	...	1432	...	...	...	...

🏛 indicates an international border (with or without controls) (6)

For other trains between Břeclav and Wien see Table **991** (8)

This is a train from Praha to Budapest. Timings read from top to bottom (10)

Station in *italics*: for stations between Bratislava and Budapest see Table **1170** (7)

Timings in *italics* are connections (change at Brno) (9)

Where two unconnected trains are shown in the same column, they are separated by a thick rule (17)

1234
1306
▬
Ⓐ
1130
1153

CLASSES OF TRAVEL:
Trains have 1st and 2nd class seats unless otherwise shown. However, local trains may only have 2nd class seats. (15)

TIME ZONES:
Times are in local time (Russian times are in Moscow time). For time zones see page 4. Timings are given in 24 hour clock (see page 11). (16)

COMMENT LIRE LES TABLEAUX

(1) Numéro et parcours du tableau.
(2) Nom de la gare en langue locale.
(3) La distance en km de Praha.
(4) Les noms de gares importantes sont imprimés en **gras** pour faciliter la lecture.
(5) La mise en retrait des noms de gares indique une ligne d'embranchement.
(6) 🏛 indique une frontière internationale (avec ou sans le contrôle).
(7) Les noms de gares imprimés en *italique*: vous trouverez des gares sur le trajet Bratislava - Budapest en consultant le tableau **1170**.
(8) Consultez le tableau **991** pour trouver des trains supplémentaires de Břeclav à Wien.
(9) Les heures en *italique* indiquent une *correspondance* et supposent dans tous les cas un changement de train.
(10) Ici un train de Praha à Budapest. Lire de haut en bas.
(11) Les signes conventionnels sont expliqués à la page 6. Les autres signes et lettres sont expliqués en bas du tableau. Le symbole ♦ à l'en-tête d'une colonne signifie qu'il faut consulter le note qui porte le numéro du train concerné.
(12) Le numéro du train (en cas échéant).
(13) Indication de catégorie (en cas échéant).
(14) d. = départ, a. = arrivée. Pour chaque train la *première* mention est toujours une heure de *départ*, la *dernière* toujours une heure d'*arrivée*.
(15) Sauf indication contraire, les trains circulent *tous les jours* et y compris des places assises de 1ère et 2ème classe.
(16) Toutes les indications horaires sont données en heures locales (voir page 4). En Russie c'est à l'heure Moskva.
(17) Deux trains de la même colonne qui ne sont pas en correspondance sont separés par une règle épaisse.

COME SI CONSULTA UN QUADRO ORARIO

(1) Numero del quadro e percorso.
(2) Nome della stazione nella lingua locale.
(3) Distanze in km da Praha.
(4) I nomi delle stazioni piu' importante sono stampati in **neretto** per renderne più facile la lettura.
(5) I nomi delle stazioni rientrati rispetto alla colonna principale indicano una diramazione dal percorso principale del quadro-orario in questione.
(6) 🏛 indica una stazione di confine (con o senza controllo).
(7) Stazioni in *corsivo*: per gli orari tra le stazione di Bratislava e Budapest bisogna consultare il quadro **1170**.
(8) Consultare il quadro **991** per ulteriori treni da Břeclav a Wien.
(9) Gli orari *in corsivo* si riferiscono a servizi *in coincidenza* che implicano un cambio di treno.
(10) Questo e' un treno da Praha a Budapest. La lettura viene fatta dall'alto verso il basso.
(11) I simboli convenzionali sono spiegate a pagina 6. Altri simboli e lettere sono spiegati sotto il quadro-orario in questione. Il simbolo ♦ all'inizio di una colonna-orario significa che bisogna fare riferimento alla nota corrispondente al numero del treno in questione.
(12) Numero del treno (quando indicato).
(13) Classificazione del treno (quando indicato).
(14) d. = partenza, a. = arrivo. Notare che l'orario che compare per *primo* nel quadro-orario è sempre un l'orario di *partenza*, mentre quello che compare per *ultimo* è sempre l'orario di *arrivo*.
(15) Se non ci sono altre indicazioni i treni si intendono giornalieri, con prima e seconda classe di viaggio.
(16) Gli orari sono sempre espressi in ora locale (in Russia e' utilizzati l'ora di Mosca). Per informazioni sui fusi orari vedere a pagina 4.
(17) Quando nella colonna-orario ci sono due treni che non sono in coincidenza tra loro, questo e' indicato dalla linea in grassetto che li separa.

WIE LESE ICH DIE FAHRPLÄNE

(1) Tabellennummer und Strecke.
(2) Bahnhof in der Landessprache.
(3) Entfernungsangabe.
(4) Wichtige Bahnhöfe sind **fett** gedruckt um das Lesen zu vereinfachen.
(5) Eingerückte Bahnhöfe befinden sich auf einer abzweigenden Strecke.
(6) 🏛 Bezeichnet eine internationale Grenze (mit oder ohne Grenzkontrolle).
(7) *Kursiv* gedruckte Bahnhofsnamen: Bahnhöfe zwischen Bratislava und Budapest finden Sie in Tabelle **1170**.
(8) Zusätzliche Züge finden Sie in Tabelle **991**.
(9) *Kursiv* gedruckte Zeitangaben weisen immer auf das Umsteigen hin.
(10) Ein Zug von Praha nach Budapest. Sie lesen von oben nach unten.
(11) Eine Erklärung der überall in dem Kursbuch verwendeten konventionellen Zeichen finden Sie auf Seite 6. Anderen Zeichen und Buchstaben finden Sie unter der Fahrplantabelle. Das Zeichen ♦ im Kopf der Zugspalte bedeutet: Sehen Sie bei der Fußnote des Zuges mit der betreffenden Zugnummer nach.
(12) Zugnummer (wo zutreffend).
(13) Zuggattung (wo zutreffend).
(14) d. = Abfahrt, a. = Ankunft. Es handelt sich stets bei der ersten für einen Zug angegebenen Zeit um eine Abfahrtzeit, bei der letzten um eine Ankunftzeit.
(15) Sofern nicht anders angemeldet, verkehren die Züge *täglich*. Im Allgemeinen führen die Züge die 1. und 2. Wagenklasse.
(16) Fahrzeiten sind immer in der jeweiligen Landeszeit angegeben (Seite 4). Russische Fahrzeiten sind auf Moskauer Zeit.
(17) Im Falle von zwei Züge in der gleichen Spalte ohne Anschlussmöglichkeit, liegt das Zeichen ▬ zwischen den Zügen.

COMO LEER LOS CUADROS

(1) Número y línea del cuadro.
(2) Nombre de las estaciones en el idioma local.
(3) Distancia en km de Praga.
(4) Los nombres de las estaciones más importantes están impresas en **negrita** facilitar la lectura.
(5) La impresión sangrada de los nombres de estas estaciones significa un ramal de la línea principal.
(6) 🏛 significa una frontera internacional (con o sin control de aduanas).
(7) Estaciones impresas en *cursiva*: para las estaciones entre Bratislava y Budapest debe consultar el cuadro **1170**.
(8) Consultar el cuadro **991** para encontrar más trenes desde Břeclav hasta Viena.
(9) Los horarios en cursiva, hacen referencia a servicios de enlace, que requieren un cambio de tren.
(10) Esto un tren desde Praga hasta Budapest. Leer de arriba a abajo.
(11) La explicación de los signos convencionales se da en la página 6. Ostros símbolos y letras se explican al pie del cuadro. El símbolo ♦ en el encabezamiento de la columna quiere decir: consulte la nota que lleva el número del tren interesado.
(12) Número de tren (si se indica).
(13) Tipo de tren (si se indica).
(14) d. = salida, a. = llegada. Nótese que el primer horario indicado en las columnas es siempre un horario de salida, y el último un horario de llegada.
(15) Salvo indicación contraria, los trenes circulan *a diario* y llevan plazas sentadas de primera y segunda clases.
(16) Todas las indicaciones horarias son en horario local (Para Rusia se utiliza la hora local de Moscú). Para comprobar las franjas horarias mirar la página 4. Los horarios utilizan el sistema horario de 24h (ver página 11).
(17) Cuando dos trenes que no tienen conexión aparecen en la misma columna, estos se encuentran separados por el símbolo ▬.

Reading the footnotes

These footnotes relate to the sample table on page 8 ❶

In certain tables, footnotes are listed by train number, shown by ◆ on relevant trains ❷

◆ –	**NOTES** (LISTED BY TRAIN NUMBERS)
102/3 –	POLONIA – (12) ✕ Warszawa - Ostrava - Břeclav - Wien and v.v.
131 –	MORAVIA – (12) Bohumin - Ostrava - Břeclav - Bratislava.
345 –	AVALA – (12) ✕ Praha - Bratislava - Budapest - Beograd. Conveys on ⑤ June 12 - Sept. 18 ▬ 2 cl. Praha - Beograd (**335**) - Thessaloniki.
475 –	JADRAN – June 19 - Sept. 4. ▬ 1, 2 cl., ▬ 2 cl., (12) Praha - Bratislava - Zagreb - Split (Table **92**); (12) Praha - Bratislava.
E –	SLOVAN, not June 19 - Sept. 4.
r –	0659 on ©.
▷ –	See also Table **1160**.
⊖ –	Runs 10 mins later on Aug. 15.
• –	*Ex* in Slovakia.
*• –	Pendolino tilting train. Classified *EC* in Austria.
	OTHER TRAIN NAMES:
71 –	GUSTAV MAHLER
73 –	FRANZ SCHUBERT

Letters and symbols may be found above the timings (e.g. **E**) or against individual times (e.g. **r**).

Symbols may also appear in the station column (e.g. ▷). ❻

Train names are sometimes listed separately. ❺

Train **345** is named 'AVALA' and runs daily from Praha to Beograd with 1st and 2nd class seats and a restaurant car. On Fridays June 12 to September 18, a through couchette car runs from Praha to Thessaloniki, attached to train **335** between Beograd and Thessaloniki. ❸

Train **475** is named 'JADRAN' and runs only from June 19 to September 4. It has a sleeper, couchettes and second class seats from Praha to Split via Bratislava and Zagreb, as well as first and second class seats only going as far as Bratislava. Further details will be found in Table **92**. ❹

Always read the footnotes; they may contain important information. Standard symbols are explained on page 6. ❼

Dates shown are where a train **starts** its journey (unless otherwise noted). Some notes show both directions of the train (e.g. **102/3**) with "and v.v." ❽

FURTHER HINTS ON READING THE TIMETABLE

- Refer to the introduction to each country for important information such as train types, supplements, compulsory reservation, and the dates of validity of the timings. Exceptions are noted in individual tables.
- For dates of public holidays see page 4.
- Please allow adequate time for changing trains, especially at large stations. Connections are not guaranteed, especially when late running occurs (connecting trains are sometimes held for late running trains).
- A Glossary of common terms appears on page 12.

LES NOTES EN BAS DU TABLEAU

❶ Ces notes se rapportent au example de tableau à la page 8.
❷ Dans certains tableaux, le symbole ◆ à l'en-tête d'une colonne signifie qu'il faut consulter le note qui porte le numéro du train concerné.
❸ Le train **345** s'appelle AVALA et circule tous les jours de Praha à Beograd avec des places assises de 1ère et 2ème classe et une voiture-restaurant. Tous les vendredis du 12 juin jusqu'au 18 sept il y a aussi une voiture-couchettes de Praha à Thessaloniki, qui se joint au train **335** entre Beograd et Thessaloniki.
❹ Le train **475** s'appelle JADRAN et circule seulement entre le 19 juin et le 4 septembre. Il compris des voitures-lits, couchettes et places assises de 2ème classe à Split via Zagreb, et des places assises de 1ère et 2ème classe jusqu'à Bratislava. Voir le tableau **92**.
❺ Les noms des trains sont parfois indiqués séparément.
❻ Les lettres et signes sont situés à l'en-tête d'une colonne ou à côté d'une heure dans la colonne. Une signe peut sortir également a côté d'un nom de gare.
❼ Les notes peuvent vous donner des informations importantes. Les signes conventionnels sont expliqués à la page 6.
❽ Sauf indication contraire, les jours et dates de circulation mentionnés sont ceux applicables à la *gare d'origine* du train (mentionnée si elle ne figure pas sur le tableau même dans les notes). Les notes peuvent expliquer les deux sens d'un train (e.g. **102/3**) utilisant "and v.v." (et vice versa).

PLUS DE CONSEILS

- Il vous est fortement recommandé de consulter aussi l'introduction à chaque section nationale: vous y trouverez des précisions concernant la classification des trains, les prestations offertes à bord des trains, les suppléments, la réservation des places, etc.
- Jours fériés - voir page 4.
- Aucune correspondance n'est garantie pourtant. N'oubliez pas non plus que dans les grandes gares les changements peuvent entraîner une longue marche et l'emprunt d'escaliers.
- Lexique - voir page 12.

NOTE ALLA FINE DEL QUADRO-ORARIO

❶ Queste note si riferiscono all' esempio a pagina 8.
❷ In certi quadri-orario, il simbolo ◆ nelle note di testa significa che bisogna fare riferimento alla nota con il numero di treno corrispondente.
❸ Il treno **345** si chiama AVALA ed e' giornaliero tra Praha a Beograd con posti di 1ª e 2ª classe e carrozza ristorante. Il venerdi dal 12 giugno fino al 18 settembre e' aggiunta a Beograd una carrozza cuccette diretta a Thessaloniki, combinandosi con il treno **335** tra Beograd e Thessaloniki.
❹ Il treno **475** si chiama JADRAN ed e' operativo solo dal 19 giugno al 4 settembre. Il treno si compone di carrozze letti, carrozze cuccette, e posti di 2ª classe tra Praha e Split, via Bratislava e Zagrabria; inoltre ci sono anche posti di 1ª e 2ª classe fino a Bratislava. Consultare anche il quadro-orario **92** al riguardo
❺ I nomi dei treni sono talvolta indicati separatamente.
❻ Lettere e simboli possono essere sia alla testa di una colonna-orario, che accanto all'orario del treno stesso. Un simbolo potrebbe anche essere accanto al nome di una stazione.
❼ E' importante leggere sempre le note a le informazioni a fine quadro. I segni convenzionali sono elencati e spiegati a pagina 6.
❽ Salvo casi in cui sia diversamente indicato, le date di circolazione dei treni si riferiscono sempre alla stazione dove il treno inizia il suo viaggio (come viene riportato nelle note a fine quadro, e Inoltre nel quadro stesso).

ALTRI CONSIGLI UTILI

- Vi consigliamo vivamente di consultare anche l'introduzione dedicata ad ogni nazione. Troverete importanti informazioni riguardanti i servizi di trasporto di ciascun paese, così come le categorie dei treni, la ristorazione, il pagamento di supplementi, le necessità di prenotazione, ecc.
- I giorni festivi suddivisi per paese sono elencati a pagina 4.
- Le coincidenze indicate non sono garantite. Tenete presente che che nelle grandi stazioni il trasferimento tra due binari potrebbe significare un lungo tratto da percorrere a piedi e con l'uso di scale.
- Il glossario si trova a pagina 12.

FUSSNOTEN

❶ Fußnoten beziehen sich auf die Beispieltabelle auf Seite 8.
❷ ◆ : Sehen Sie bei der Fußnote des Zuges mit der betreffenden Zugnummer nach.
❸ Zug **345** heißt AVALA und fährt täglich zwischen Praha und Beograd mit Sitzplätzen 1. und 2. Klasse. An Freitagen vom 12. Juni bis 18. September führt dieser Zug durchgehende Liegewagen von Praha nach Thessaloniki (mit Zug **335** vereinigt von Beograd nach Thessaloniki).
❹ Zug **475** heißt JADRAN und fährt nur von 19. Juni bis 4. September. Er führt Schlaf-, Liege und Sitzwagen 2. Klasse von Praha nach Split über Zagreb, auch Sitzwagen 1. und 2. Klasse, die nur bis Bratislava fahren. Auf Tabelle **92** finden Sie weitere Informationen.
❺ Zugnamen können besonders aufgeführt sein.
❻ Zeichen und Buchstaben finden sich im Kopf der Zugspalte oder neben einer bestimmten Zeitangabe. Zeichen sind auch in der Bahnhofsspalte möglich.
❼ In Fußnoten findet man wichtige Informationen. Standardzeichen sind auf Seite 6 erklärt.
❽ Die erwähnten Tage und Zeitabschnitte für Züge, die nicht täglich verkehren, gelten für den Ausgangsbahnhof des Zuges (wenn dieser nicht in der Tabelle steht, ist er in einer Fußnote erwähnt). Fußnoten dürfen beide Richtungen erklären (z.B. **102/3**), mit "and v.v." (und umgekehrt).

WEITERE HINWEISE

- Es ist zu empfehlen, die Einleitungen zu jedem einzelnen Land zu lesen. Darin werden Sie wichtige Informationen über die Besonderheiten jedes Landes finden: Zugcharakterisierung, Services an Bord der Züge, Zuschlagpflicht, Reservierungsbedingungen usw.
- Feiertage - siehe Seite 4.
- Anschlussversäumnisse durch Verspätung oder Ausfall von Zügen sind immer möglich. Bitte beachten Sie, dass auf Großstadtbahnhöfen häufig längere Fußwege zurückgelegt bzw. Treppen benutzen werden müssen.
- Glossar - siehe Seite 12.

LAS NOTAS AL PIE DEL CUADRO

❶ Estas notas hacen referencia al ejemplo de la página 8.
❷ El símbolo ◆ ciertas tablas horarias significa: que hay que consultar la nota a pie de página con el número correspondiente.
❸ El Tren **345** se llama AVALA y circula a diario entre Praga y Belgrado con plazas sentadas de 1ra y 2da clase, además de con coche-restaurante. Los Viernes del 12 de junio al 18 de septiembre el tren lleva coches litera desde Praga hasta Tesalónica que se combinan con el tren **335** entre Belgrado y Tesalónica.
❹ El Tren **475** se llama JADRAN y circula solamente del 19 de junio al 4 de septiembre. El Tren **475** se llama JADRAN y circula solamente del 19 de junio al 4 de sept. El tren dispone de lleva vagones de coches cama, litera, y plazas sentadas de 2da clase entre Praga y Split a través de Zagreb, también plazas sentadas de 1ra y 2da clase hasta Bratislava. Consulte el cuadro **92**.
❺ Los nombres de los Trenes a veces son enumerados por separado.
❻ Las letras y signos se encuentran en el encabezamiento de las distintas columnas horarias o adyacentes a horas de salida individuales. Los símbolos también pueden aparecer en la columna de la estación.
❼ Lea siempre las notas a pie de cuadro ya que pueden contener información importante. La explicación de los signos convencionales se da en la página 6.
❽ Salvo indicación contraria los días y fechas de circulación de los trenes son aquéllos mencionados en la estación de *origen* del tren. Algunas notas muestran ambas direcciones del tren mediante la nota "and v.v." (y viceversa).

INFORMACIÓN ADICIONAL

- Se recomienda vivamente que consulte también los preámbulos al comienzo de cada sección nacional: le proporcionarán datos importantes sobre las particularidades de cada país: tipos de trenes, restauración, pago de suplementos, y necesidades de reservación anticipada.
- Días festivos - cunsulte la página 4.
- Los trasbordos no se pueden garantizar, sobretodo en el caso de retrasos. Hay que ser consciente también que el trasbordo en las estaciones de grandes ciudades puede suponer un desplazamiento bastante largo a pie y el uso de escaleras.
- Glosario - cunsulte la página 12.

The following is designed to be an outline guide to travelling around Europe by train. For further details of types of accommodation available, catering, supplements etc., see the introduction to each country.

BUYING YOUR TICKET

Train tickets must be purchased before travelling, either from travel agents or at the station ticket office (or machine). Where a station has neither a ticket office nor a ticket machine, the ticket may usually be purchased on the train.

Tickets which are not dated when purchased (for example in France and Italy) must be validated before travel in one of the machines at the entrance to the platform.

In certain Eastern European countries foreign nationals may have to buy international rail tickets at the office of the state tourist board concerned and not at the railway station. The tickets can sometimes only be purchased in western currency and buying tickets can take a long time.

Most countries in Europe offer two classes of rail accommodation, usually 1st and 2nd class. 1st class is more comfortable and therefore more expensive than 2nd class. Local trains are often 2nd class only. In Southern and Eastern Europe, 1st class travel is advisable for visitors as fares are reasonable and 2nd class can be very overcrowded.

RESERVATIONS

Many express trains in Europe are restricted to passengers holding advance seat reservations, particularly in France, Italy, Sweden and Spain. This is indicated by the symbol 🅁 in the tables, or by notes in the introduction to each country. All *TGV, Eurostar* and *Thalys* trains require advance reservation, as do all long-distance trains in Spain.

Reservations can usually be made up to two months in advance. A small fee is charged, but where a supplement is payable the reservation fee is often included. Reservations can often be made on other long-distance services and this is recommended at busy times.

SUPPLEMENTS

Many countries have faster train services for which an extra charge is made. This supplement is payable when the ticket is purchased and often includes the price of a seat reservation. The supplement can sometimes be paid on the train, but usually at extra cost. The introduction to each country gives further information. On certain high-speed services, the first class fare includes the provision of a meal.

RAIL PASSES

Passes are available which give unlimited travel on most trains in a given area. These range from Interrail and Eurail passes which cover most of Europe for up to one month, to local passes which cover limited areas for one day. Further details of Interrail and Eurail passes appear elsewhere in this edition, and a special feature on rail passes appears in the twice-yearly Independent Travellers Edition.

FINDING YOUR TRAIN

At most stations departures are listed on large paper sheets (often yellow), and/or on electronic departure indicators. These list trains by departure, giving principal stops, and indicate from which platform they leave.

On each platform of principal European stations, a display board can be found giving details of the main trains calling at that platform. This includes the location of individual coaches, together with their destinations and the type of accommodation provided.

A sign may be carried on the side of the carriage indicating the train name, principal stops and destination and a label or sign near the door will indicate the number allocated to the carriage, which is shown on reservation tickets. 1st class accommodation is usually indicated by a yellow band above the windows and doors and/or a figure '1' near the door or on the windows

A sign above the compartment door will indicate seat numbers and which seats are reserved. In non-compartment trains, reserved seats have labels on their headrests. In some countries reserved seats are not marked and occupants will be asked to move when the passenger who has reserved the seat boards the train.

LUGGAGE & BICYCLES

Luggage may be registered at many larger stations and sent separately by rail to your destination. In some countries, bicycles may also be registered in advance and certain local and some express trains will convey bicycles (there may be a charge). The relevant railways will advise exact details on request.

✕ CATERING 🍸

Many high-quality and long-distance trains in Europe have restaurant cars serving full meals, usually with waiter service. An at-seat service may also be provided to passengers in first class accommodation. Such trains are identified with the symbol ✕ in the tables. Full meals may only be available at set times, sometimes with separate sittings, and may only be available to passengers holding first class tickets. However, the restaurant car is often supplemented by a counter or trolley service offering light snacks and drinks.

Other types of catering are shown with the symbol 🍸. This varies from a self-service buffet car serving light meals (sometimes called bistro or café) to a trolley which is wheeled through the train, serving drinks and light refreshments. Where possible, the introduction to each country gives further information on the level of catering to be expected on particular types of train.

Please note that the catering shown may not be available throughout the journey and may be suspended or altered at weekends or on holidays.

SLEEPING CARS 🛏

Sleeping cars are indicated by the symobol 🛏 in the tables. Standard sleeping car types have bedroom style compartments with limited washing facilities and full bedding. Toilets are located at one or both ends of the coach. An attendant travels with each car or pair of cars and will serve drinks, snacks and breakfast at an extra charge. Traditionally, 1st class sleeping compartments have one or two berths (in Britain and Norway two berth compartments require only 2nd class tickets) and 2nd class compartments have three berths. Some trains convey special T2 cabins, shown as 🛏 (T2) in the tables, with one berth in 1st class and two berths in 2nd class. On certain routes it is now possible to reserve a single compartment with a 2nd class ticket.

Compartments are allocated for occupation exclusively by men or by women except when married couples or families occupy all berths. Children travelling alone, or who cannot be accommodated in the same compartment as their family, are placed in women's compartments. In Russia and other countries of the CIS, however, berths are allocated in strict order of booking and men and women often share the same compartments.

Some trains have communicating doors between sleeping compartments which can be opened to create a larger room if both compartments are occupied by the same family group. Berths can be reserved up to 2 months (3 months on certain trains) before the date of travel and early reservation is recommended as space is often limited. Berths should be claimed within 15 minutes of boarding the train or they may be resold.

HOTEL TRAINS

High quality overnight trains, often referred to as Hotel trains, run on a selection of national and international routes. The facilities are of a higher standard than those offered in conventional sleeping cars, and special fares are payable. The trains fall into the following categories:

ÖBB nightjet: Many night trains radiating from Germany and Austria, are operated by Austrian Railways and are branded *ÖBB nightjet*. They operate on 17 routes serving four countries and all convey sleeping-car, couchette and seating accommodation. Standard sleeping-car compartments can be configured with one, two or three berths and have a washbasin (with toiletries provided). *Deluxe* sleeping-car compartments can also be configured with one, two or three berths and have an en-suite washroom with WC, washbasin and shower (shower gel and towels are provided). The sleeping-car fare includes a welcome drink, a bottle of water, a newspaper and a full breakfast served in the morning (including free hot drink refills). Four and six berth couchettes are available, the price of which includes a bottle of water and a small breakfast. Women only, family and wheelchair couchette compartments are provided. 2nd class seating cars (with six seat compartments) are also conveyed. Reservation is compulsory in all categories of accommodation and special all-inclusive fares are available. Please note that Interrail and Eurail pass holders must pay a special pass holders fare.

Trenhotel (Spain). These *Talgo*-type trains run on the international routes from Madrid to Lisboa and from Irún/Hendaye to Lisboa. They also operate on internal routes within Spain, from Barcelona to A Coruña, Granada and Vigo, and from Madrid to A Coruña, Ferrol and Pontevedra. The highest class of accommodation is *Gran Clase*, which has shower and toilet facilities in each compartment and can be used for single or double occupancy.

Compartments with showers are also available on some domestic overnight services in Sweden and Italy, and on certain other international routes as indicated on our international overnight services summary on page 35.

COUCHETTES ▬

Couchettes (▬) are a more basic form of overnight accommodation consisting of simple bunk beds with a sheet, blanket and pillow. The couchettes are converted from ordinary seating cars for the night, and there are usually 4 berths per compartment in 1st class, 6 berths in 2nd class. On certain trains (e.g. in Austria and Italy), 4 berth compartments are available to 2nd class passengers, at a higher supplement. Washing and toilet facilities are provided at the ends of each coach. Men and women are booked into the same compartments and are expected to sleep in daytime clothes. A small number of trains in Germany, however, have women-only couchette compartments.

INTERNATIONAL OVERNIGHT SERVICES

A summary of international overnight services will be found on page 35 which specifies the various types of accommodation and catering provided on each individual service (including details of the operator).

CAR-SLEEPERS

Trains which convey motor cars operate throughout much of Europe and are shown in Table **1** for international services and Table **2** for other services. The motor cars are conveyed in special wagons while passengers travel in sleeping cars or couchettes, usually (but not always) in the same train.

WHEELCHAIR ACCESS ♿

Most main-line domestic and international trains, together with an increasing number of local trains, are specially equipped to accommodate passengers in wheelchairs. Access ramps are available at many stations and some trains are fitted with special lifts. These trains have at least one wheelchair space, and are equipped with accessible toilets.

Most railways publish guides to accessibility, and many countries provide dedicated staff to assist disabled travellers. Wheelchair users normally need to reserve in advance, stating their requirements.

HEALTH REQUIREMENTS

It is not mandatory for visitors to Europe to be vaccinated against infectious diseases unless they are travelling from areas where these are endemic. For travellers' peace of mind, however, protection against the following diseases should be considered:

HIV	Cholera
Hepatitis A	Hepatitis B
Polio	Rabies
Tetanus	Typhoid

Full information is available from the manual published by the World Health Organisation, and travellers should seek advice from their Travel Agent.

DRINKING WATER

Tap water is usually safe to drink in most parts of Europe. The water in washrooms or toilets on trains is, however, not suitable for drinking. Those who doubt the purity of the tap water are recommended to boil it, to use sterilisation tablets, or to drink bottled water.

CLIMATE

Most of Europe lies within the temperate zone but there can be considerable differences between North and South, East and West, as illustrated in the table below. Local temperatures are also affected by altitude and the difference between summer and winter temperatures tends to be less marked in coastal regions than in areas far removed from the sea.

	Bucuresti	Dublin	Madrid	Moskva
JANUARY				
Highest	2°	8°	10°	– 6°
Lowest	– 6°	3°	3°	– 12°
Rain days	6	13	9	11
APRIL				
Highest	18°	11°	18°	10°
Lowest	6°	4°	7°	2°
Rain days	7	10	11	9
JULY				
Highest	29°	19°	31°	23°
Lowest	16°	11°	18°	14°
Rain days	7	9	3	12
OCTOBER				
Highest	18°	14°	19°	8°
Lowest	6°	8°	10°	2°
Rain days	5	11	9	10

Highest = Average highest daily temperature in °C
Lowest = Average lowest daily temperature in °C
Rain days = Average number of days with recorded precipitation

Source : World Weather Information Service

FIND US ON FACEBOOK!

www.facebook.com/EuropeanRailTimetable
and on **Twitter** @EuropeanRailTT

CURRENCY CONVERSION

The information shown below is intended to be indicative only. Rates fluctuate from day to day and commercial exchange rates normally include a commission element.

Country	unit	1 GBP =	1 USD =	1 EUR =	100 JPY =
Euro zone (‡)	**euro**	**1.13**	**0.89**	**1.00**	**0.81**
Albania	lek	138.74	109.39	122.55	99.88
Belarus	rubl	2.64	2.07	2.33	1.88
Bosnia	marka	2.21	1.75	1.96	1.59
Bulgaria	lev	2.21	1.75	1.96	1.59
Croatia	kuna	8.41	6.63	7.43	6.05
Czech Republic	koruna	29.27	23.07	25.85	21.06
Denmark	krone	8.45	6.66	7.47	6.08
Georgia	lari	3.52	2.77	3.11	2.53
Hungary	forint	369.35	291.17	326.13	265.80
Iceland	krona	156.62	123.47	138.31	112.72
Macedonia	denar	70.09	55.25	61.89	50.44
Moldova	leu	22.83	17.99	20.15	16.43
Norway	krone	11.07	8.73	9.78	7.97
Poland	złoty	4.87	3.84	4.30	3.50
Romania	leu nou	5.39	4.25	4.76	3.88
Russia	rubl	81.94	64.60	72.35	58.97
Serbia	dinar	133.56	105.28	117.95	96.13
Sweden	krona	12.17	9.59	10.74	8.75
Switzerland	franc	1.27	1.00	1.12	0.91
Turkey	yeni lira	7.74	6.11	6.84	5.57
Ukraine	hryvnya	33.38	26.32	29.47	24.02
United Kingdom	pound	1.00	0.79	0.88	0.72
United States	dollar	1.27	1.00	1.12	0.91

‡ – Austria, Belgium, Cyprus, Estonia, Finland, France, Germany, Greece, Ireland, Italy, Latvia, Lithuania, Luxembourg, Malta, the Netherlands, Portugal, Slovakia, Slovenia and Spain.

The euro is also legal tender in Andorra, Kosovo, Monaco, Montenegro, San Marino, and the Vatican City.

PASSPORTS AND VISAS

Nationals of one country intending to travel to or pass through another country normally require a valid passport and will also require a visa unless a special visa-abolition agreement has been made between the countries concerned. The limit of stay permitted in each country is usually 3 months.

Applications for visas should be made well in advance of the date of travel to the local consulate of the country concerned. Consuls usually make a charge for issuing a visa. Before issuing a transit visa, a consul normally requires to see the visa of the country of destination.

The possession of a valid passport or visa does not necessarily grant the holder automatic access to all areas of the country to be visited. Certain countries have zones which are restricted or prohibited to foreign nationals.

All border controls have been abolished, however, between those countries which have signed the **Schengen Agreement** (see list below), and a visa allowing entry to any of these countries is valid in all of them.

LIST OF SCHENGEN AREA COUNTRIES

Austria, Belgium, Czech Republic, Denmark, Estonia, Finland, France, Germany, Greece, Hungary, Iceland, Italy, Latvia, Lithuania, Luxembourg, Malta, Netherlands, Norway, Poland, Portugal, Slovakia, Slovenia, Spain, Sweden, Switzerland.

METRIC CONVERSION TABLES

The Celsius system of temperature measurement, the metric system of distance measurement and the twenty-four hour clock are used throughout this book. The tables below give Fahrenheit, mile and twelve-hour clock equivalents.

TEMPERATURE

°C	°F
–20	–4
–15	5
–10	14
–5	23
0	32
5	41
10	50
15	59
20	68
25	77
30	86
35	95
40	104

Conversion formulae :
°C = (°F – 32) x 5 / 9
°F = (°C x 9 / 5) + 32

DISTANCE

km	miles	km	miles	km	miles
1	0.62	45	27.96	300	186.41
2	1.24	50	31.07	400	248.55
3	1.86	55	34.18	500	310.69
4	2.49	60	37.28	600	372.82
5	3.11	65	40.39	700	434.96
6	3.73	70	43.50	800	497.10
7	4.35	75	46.60	900	559.23
8	4.97	80	49.71	1000	621.37
9	5.59	85	52.82	1100	683.51
10	6.21	90	55.92	1200	745.65
15	9.32	95	59.03	1300	807.78
20	12.43	100	62.14	1400	869.92
25	15.53	125	77.67	1500	932.06
30	18.64	150	93.21	2000	1242.74
35	21.75	175	108.74	3000	1864.11
40	24.85	200	124.27	4000	2485.48

TIME

Midnight departure	=	0000
1 am	=	0100
5 am	=	0500
5.30 am	=	0530
11 am	=	1100
12 noon	=	1200
1 pm	=	1300
3.45 pm	=	1545
Midnight arrival	=	2400

GLOSSARY

	FRANCAIS	*ITALIANO*	*DEUTSCH*	*ESPAÑOL*
additional trains	d'autres trains	ulteriori treni	weitere Züge	otros trenes
also	[circule] aussi	[si effettua] anche	[verkehrt] auch	[circula] también
alteration	modification	variazione	Änderung	modificación
approximately	environ	circa	ungefähr	aproximadamente
arrival, arrives (a.)	arrivée, arrive	arrivo, arriva	Ankunft, kommt an	llegada, llega
and at the same minutes past each hour until	puis toutes les heures aux mêmes minutes jusqu'à	poi ai stessi minuti di ogni ora fino a	und so weiter im Takt bis	luego a los mismos minutos de cada hora hasta
calls at	s'arrête à	ferma a	hält in	efectúa parada en
certain	déterminé	certo	bestimmt	determinado
change at	changer à	cambiare a	umsteigen in	cambiar en
composition	composition	composizione	Zugbildung	composición
confirmation	confirmation	conferma	Bestätigung	confirmación
connection	correspondance, relation	coincidenza, relazione	Anschluss, Verbindung	correspondencia, enlace
conveys	comporte, achemine	ha in composizione	befördert, führt	lleva
daily	tous les jours	giornalmente	täglich	diariamente
delay	retard	ritardo	Verspätung	retraso
departure, departs (d.)	départ, part	partenza, parte	Abfahrt, fährt ab	salida, sale
earlier	plus tôt	più presto	früher	más temprano
engineering work	travaux de voie	lavori sul binario	Bauarbeiten	obras de vía
even / uneven dates	jours pairs / impairs	giorni pari / dispari	gerade / ungerade Daten	fechas pares / impares
every 30 minutes	toutes les 30 minutes	ogni 30 minuti	alle 30 Minuten	cada 30 minutos
except	sauf	escluso	außer	excepto
fast(er)	(plus) rapide	(più) rapido	schnell(er)	(más) rápido
for	pour	per	für	para
from Rennes	(en provenance) de Rennes	(proviene) da Rennes	von Rennes	(procede) de Rennes
from Jan. 15	à partir du 15 janvier	dal 15 di gennaio	vom 15. Januar (an)	desde el 15 de enero
hourly	toutes les heures	ogni ora	stündlich	cada hora
hours (hrs)	heures	ore	Stunden	horas
journey	voyage, trajet	viaggio, percorso	Reise	viaje, trayecto
journey time	temps de parcours	tempo di tragitto	Reisezeit	duración del recorrido
later	plus tard	più tardi	später	más tarde
may	peut, peuvent	può, possono	kann, können	puede(n)
minutes (mins)	minutes	minuti	Minuten	minutos
not	ne [circule] pas	non [si effettua]	[verkehrt] nicht	no [circula]
not available	pas disponible	non disponibile	nicht erhältlich	no disponible
on the dates shown in Table **81**	les jours indiqués dans le tableau **81**	nei giorni indicati nel quadro **81**	an den in der Tabelle **81** angegebene Daten	los días indicados en el cuadro **81**
only	seulement	esclusivamente	nur	sólo
operator	entreprise de transports	azienda di trasporto	Verkehrsunternehmen	empresa de transportes
other	autre	altro	andere	otros
runs	circule	circola, si effettua	verkehrt	circula
sailing	traversée	traversata	Überfahrt	travesía
ship	bateau, navire	nave, battello	Schiff	barco
stopping trains	trains omnibus	treni regionali	Nahverkehrszüge	trenes regionales
stops	s'arrête	ferma	hält	efectúa parada
subject to	sous réserve de	soggetto a	vorbehaltlich	sujeto a
summer	été	estate	Sommer	verano
supplement payable	avec supplément	con pagamento di supplemento	zuschlagpflichtig	con pago de suplemento
then	puis	poi	dann	luego
through train	train direct	treno diretto	durchgehender Zug	tren directo
timings	horaires	orari	Zeitangaben	horarios
to York	vers, à destination de York	(diretto) a York	nach York	(continúa) a York
to / until July 23	jusqu'au 23 juillet	fino al 23 di luglio	bis zum 23. Juli	hasta el día 23 de julio
to pick up	pour laisser monter	per viaggiatori in partenza	zum Zusteigen	para recoger viajeros
to set down	pour laisser descendre	per viaggiatori in arrivo	zum Aussteigen	para dejar viajeros
unless otherwise shown	sauf indication contraire	salvo indicazione contraria	sofern nicht anders angezeigt	salvo indicación contraria
valid	valable	valido	gültig	válido
when train **44** runs	lors de la circulation du train **44**	quando circola il treno **44**	beim Verkehren des Zuges **44**	cuando circula el tren **44**
winter	hiver	inverno	Winter	invierno

INDEX OF PLACES by table number

The BEYOND EUROPE section is indexed separately - see the back of each edition

🚆 Connection by train from the nearest station shown in this timetable.
⛴ Connection by boat from the nearest station shown in this timetable.
🚌 Connection by bus from the nearest station shown in this timetable.
10/355 Consult both indicated tables to find the best connecting services.

CRUISE TRAINS

The services shown in the European Rail Timetable are the regular scheduled services of the railway companies concerned. However, a number of specialised operators also run luxurious cruise trains taking several days to complete their journey. Overnight accommodation is provided either on the train or in hotels. Cruise trains are bookable only through the operating company or its appointed agents and normal rail tickets are not valid on these trains. A selection of operators is shown below.

The Danube Express : Fully escorted holidays in central and eastern Europe by luxury private train based in Budapest. Operator: Danube Express, Offley Holes Farm, Charlton Road, Preston, Hitchin, SG4 7TD, UK; ✆ +44 (0)1462 441400. Website: www.danube-express.com

Belmond Royal Scotsman : Luxury tours of Scotland starting from Edinburgh. Operator: Belmond Royal Scotsman, Shackleton House, 4 Battle Bridge Lane, London, SE1 2HP, UK; ✆ 0845 217 0799 (UK only) or +44 (0) 20 3117 1300. Website: www.royalscotsman.com

El Transcantábrico and **El Expreso de La Robla** : Rail cruises along Spain's northern coast. Operator: Trenes Turísticos de Lujo, Plaza de los Ferroviarios s/n., 33012 Oviedo, Asturias, Spain; ✆ +34 902 555 902, fax +34 985 981 711. Website: www.trenesturisticosdelujo.com

Trans-Siberian Express : Tours by private hotel train along the Trans-Siberian Railway. Operator: Golden Eagle Luxury Trains, Denzell House, Denzell Gardens, Dunham Road, Altrincham, WA14 4QF, UK; ✆ +44 (0)16 1 928 9410, fax +44 (0)161 941 6101. Website: www.goldeneagleluxurytrains.com.

Venice Simplon-Orient-Express : This well-known luxury train runs once or twice weekly from late March to early November, mostly on its established London - Paris - Venezia route. Operator: Belmond VSOE, Shackleton House, 4 Battle Bridge Lane, London, SE1 2HP, UK; ✆ 0845 217 0799 (UK only) or +44 (0) 20 3117 1300. Website: www.vsoe.com

LIST OF ADVERTISERS

COOL CULINARIA	79, 322
EUROPE BY RAIL	38, 582
EUROPEAN RAIL TIMETABLE	12
FFESTINIOG TRAVEL	49, 54
HIDDEN EUROPE	82, 674
LOCO2	67, 121, 437
LOCOMOTIVES INTERNATIONAL	65, 80
MIDDLETON PRESS	674
MILLSTONE CREATIVE	72
RAILBOOKERS	inside back cover
TRAINSEUROPE	inside front cover

LIST OF RETAILERS

The European Rail Timetable is available for purchase direct from the retailers listed below. Some also stock the Rail Map Europe.

Great Britain

Blackwell's Bookshop	Oxford
Daunt Books	Six stores in London
Foyles	London and Birmingham
Ian Allan Bookshops	London and Birmingham
Magazine Heaven	Rushden Lakes, Northamptonshire
Oundle News	Oundle, Northamptonshire
Stanfords	London and Bristol

Austria

Buchhandlung und Antiquariat	Wien
Freytag & Berndt	Wien

Belgium

Press Shop / Relay	Brugge railway station

France

La Librairie du Voyage	Rennes
W.H. Smith Paris	248 Rue de Rivoli, Paris

Germany

FachBuchZentrum & Antiquariat Stiletto	München Neuhausen
Freytag & Berndt	Regensburg and Nürnberg
Gleisnost Reisebuero	Freiburg railway station
GVE-Verlag/BahnBuchShop	Berlin Lichtenberg railway station info@gve-verlag.de

Italy

Anglo-American Bookshop	Roma

Netherlands

Stanley & Livingstone	Den Haag
The American Book Center	Amsterdam
Treinreiswinkel	Amsterdam and Leiden

Switzerland

Fahrplancenter	Winterthur, Switzerland

United States of America

Barnes & Noble	128 locations

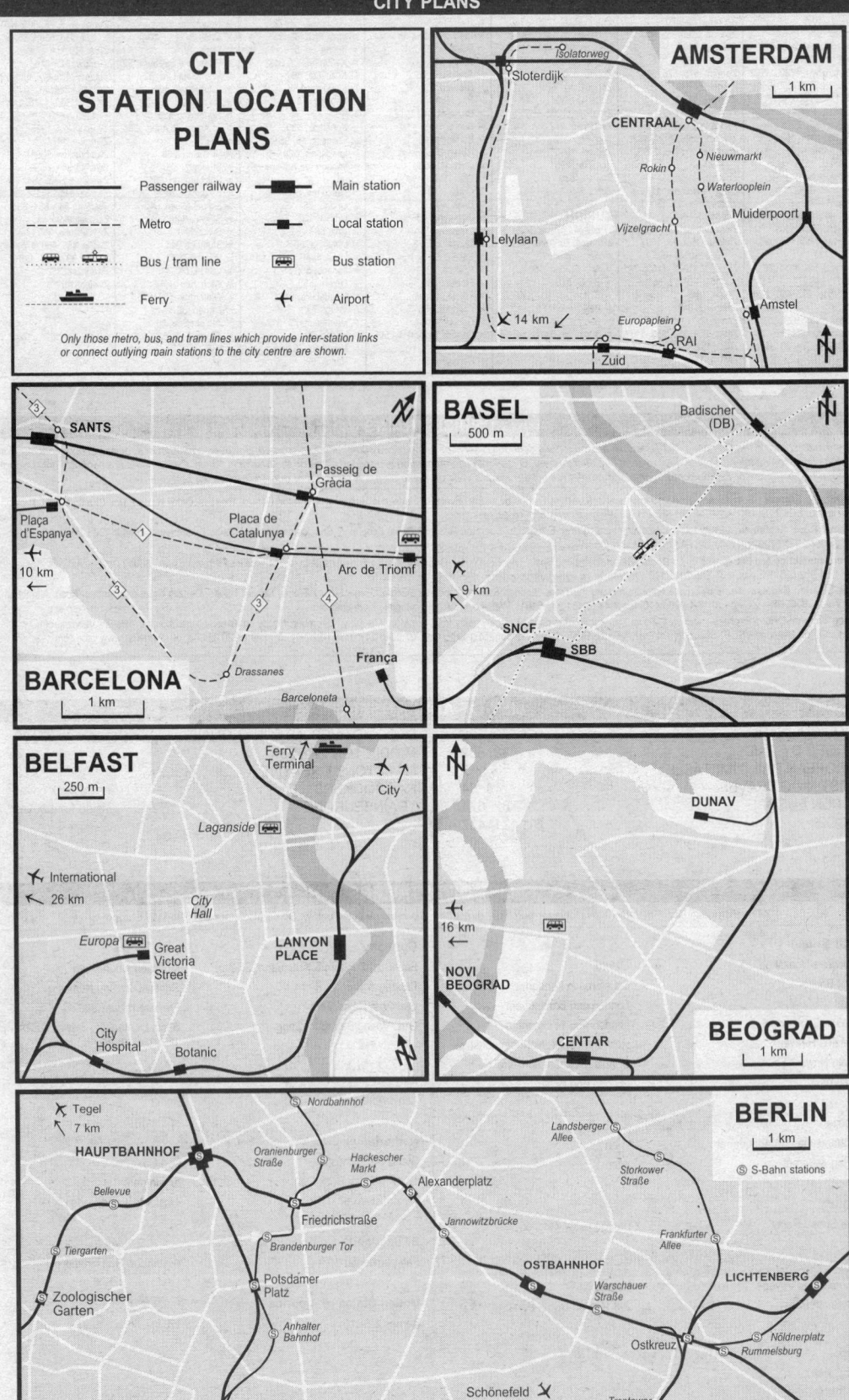

CITY STATION LOCATION PLANS

Passenger railway	Main station
Metro	Local station
Bus / tram line	Bus station
Ferry	Airport

Only those metro, bus, and tram lines which provide inter-station links or connect outlying main stations to the city centre are shown.

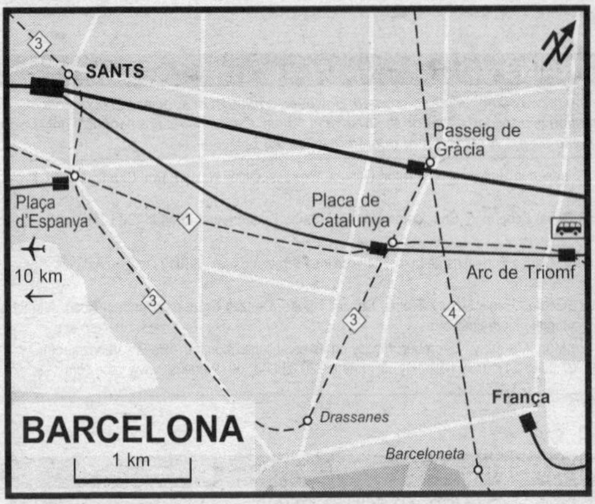

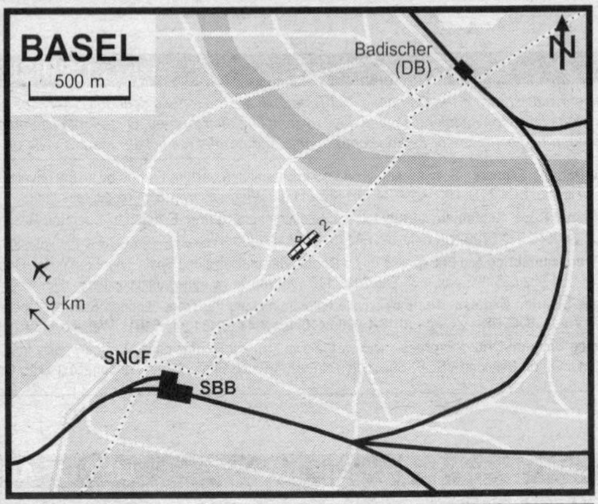

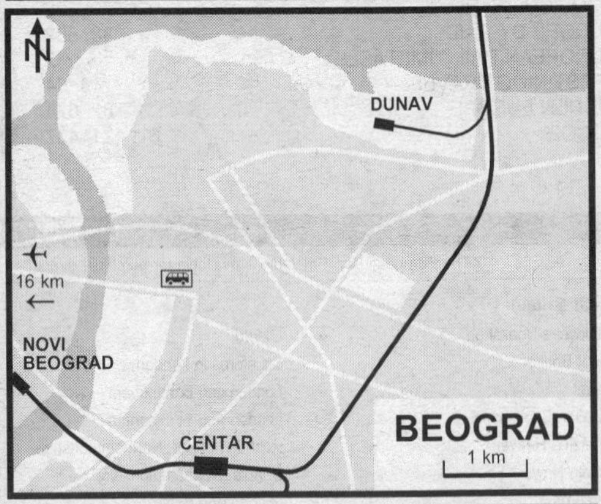

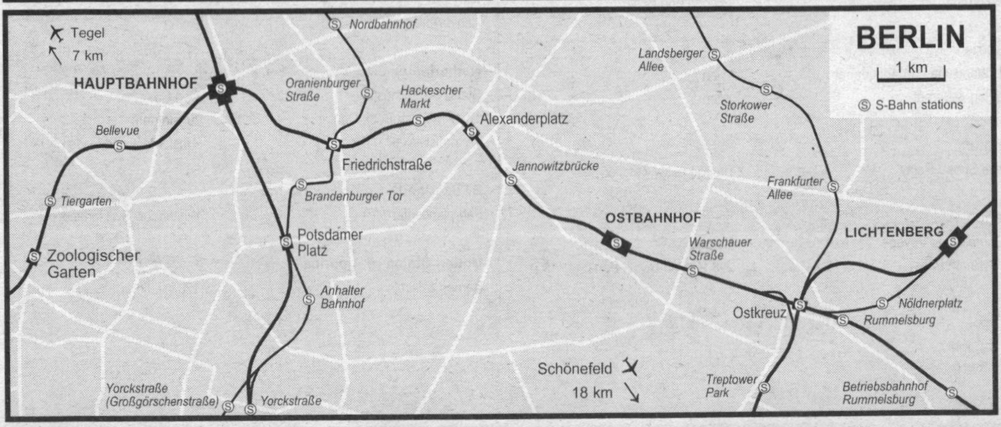

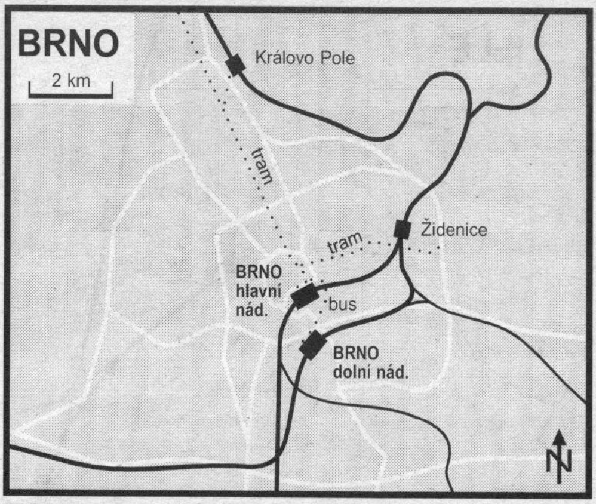
BRNO
2 km
Královo Pole
tram
Židenice
tram
BRNO hlavní nád.
bus
BRNO dolní nád.

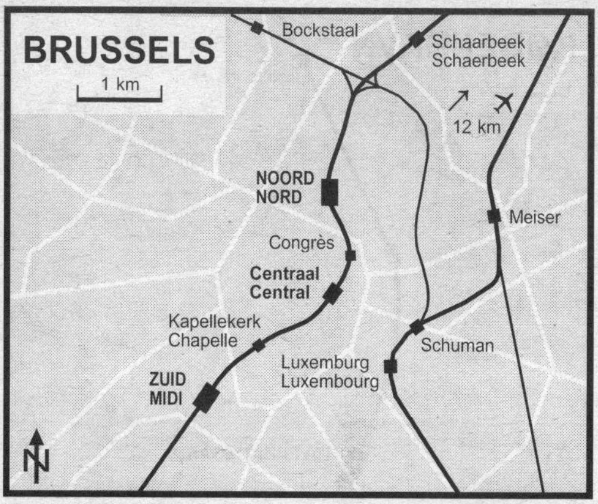
BRUSSELS
1 km
Bockstaal
Schaarbeek Schaerbeek
12 km
NOORD NORD
Meiser
Congrès
Centraal Central
Kapellekerk Chapelle
Schuman
Luxemburg Luxembourg
ZUID MIDI

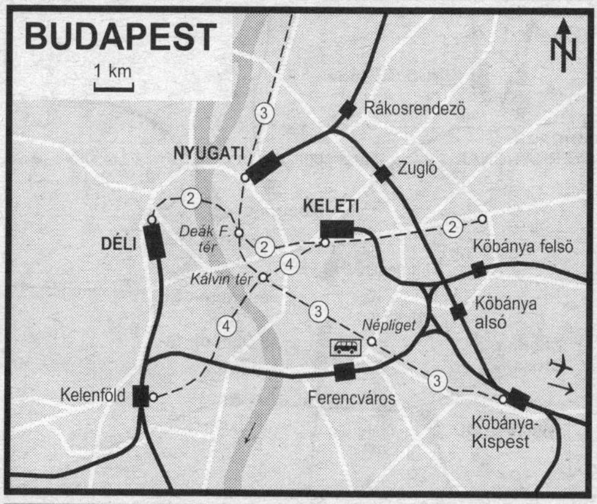
BUDAPEST
1 km
3
Rákosrendező
NYUGATI
Zugló
2
KELETI
DÉLI
Deák F. tér
2
2
Kőbánya felső
4
Kálvin tér
3
Kőbánya alsó
4
Népliget
Kelenföld
Ferencváros
3
Kőbánya-Kispest

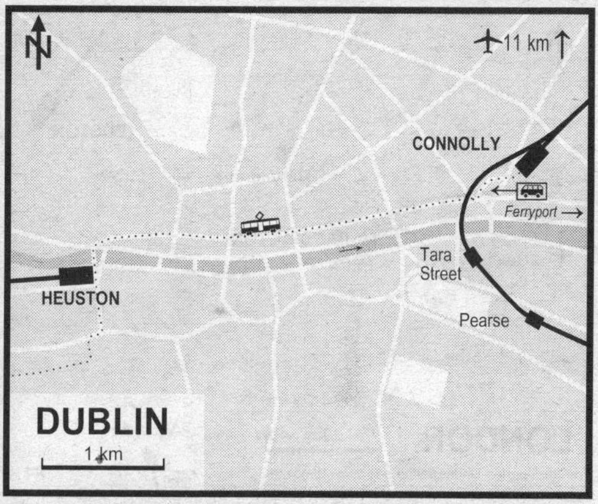
11 km
CONNOLLY
Ferryport
Tara Street
HEUSTON
Pearse
DUBLIN
1 km

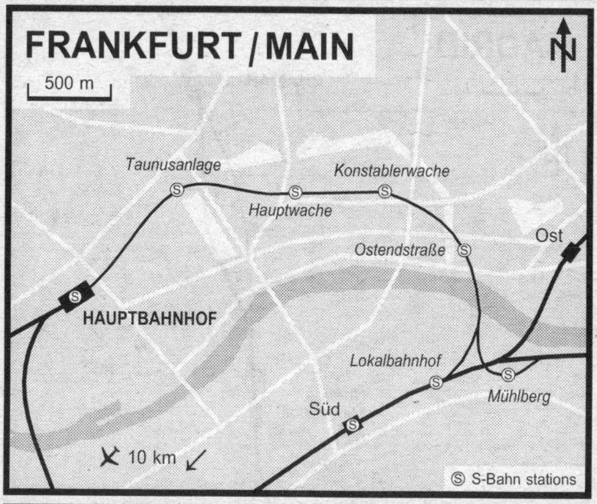
FRANKFURT / MAIN
500 m
Taunusanlage
Konstablerwache
Hauptwache
Ostendstraße
Ost
HAUPTBAHNHOF
Lokalbahnhof
Mühlberg
Süd
10 km
S-Bahn stations

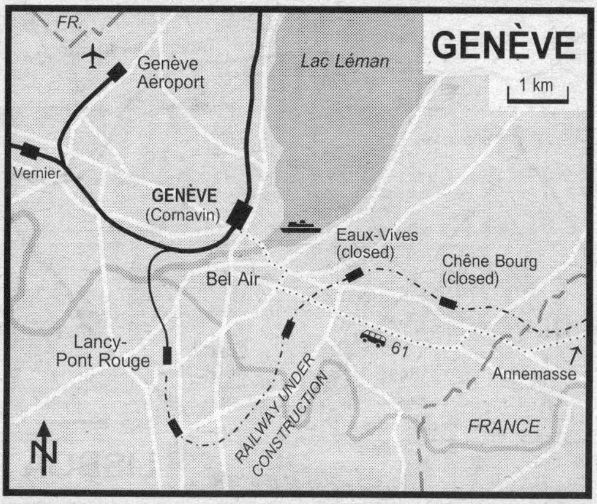
FR.
Genève Aéroport
Lac Léman
GENÈVE
1 km
Vernier
GENÈVE (Cornavin)
Eaux-Vives (closed)
Chêne Bourg (closed)
Bel Air
Lancy-Pont Rouge
61
Annemasse
RAILWAY UNDER CONSTRUCTION
FRANCE

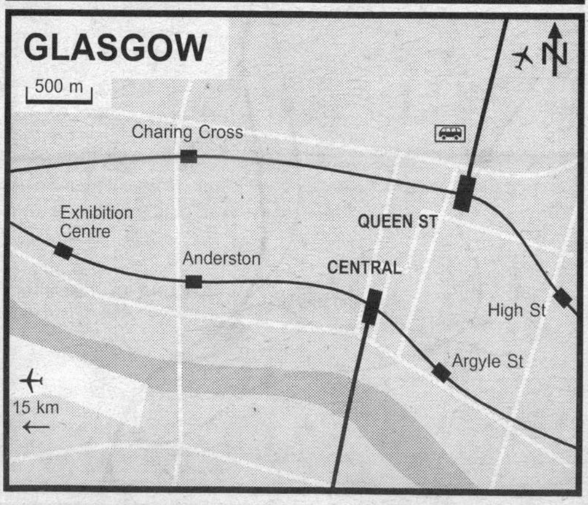
GLASGOW
500 m
Charing Cross
Exhibition Centre
QUEEN ST
Anderston
CENTRAL
High St
Argyle St
15 km

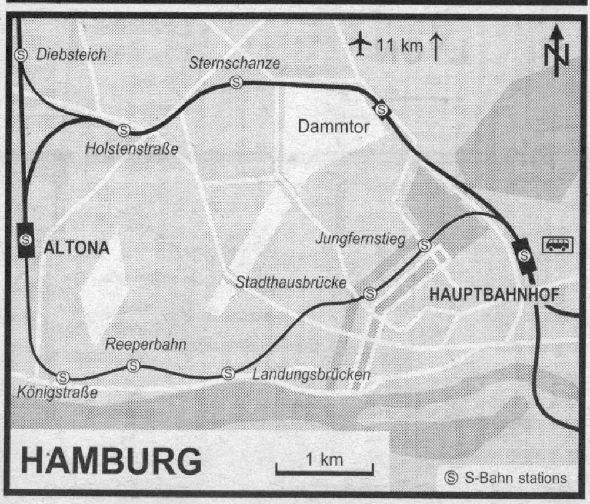
Diebsteich
11 km
Sternschanze
Dammtor
Holstenstraße
ALTONA
Jungfernstieg
Stadthausbrücke
HAUPTBAHNHOF
Reeperbahn
Landungsbrücken
Königstraße
HAMBURG
1 km
S-Bahn stations

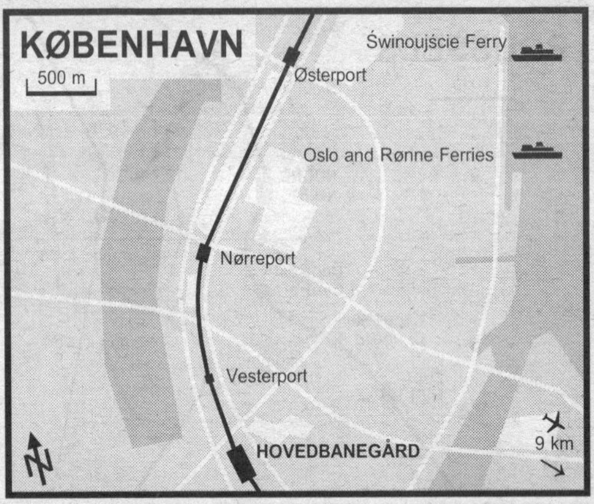
KØBENHAVN
500 m
Świnoujście Ferry
Østerport
Oslo and Rønne Ferries
Nørreport
Vesterport
HOVEDBANEGÅRD
9 km

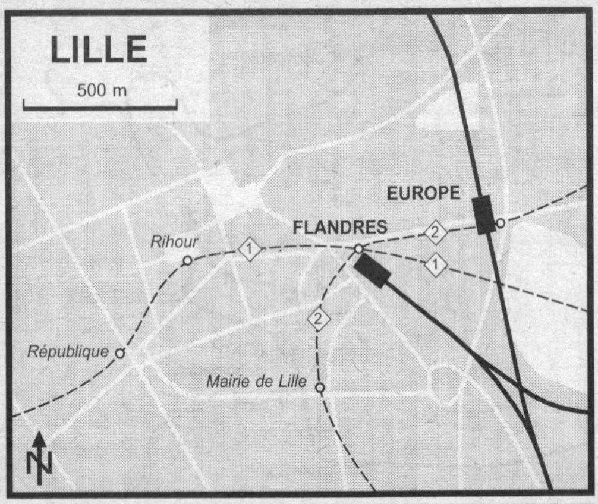
LILLE
500 m
EUROPE
FLANDRES
Rihour
République
Mairie de Lille
1
2

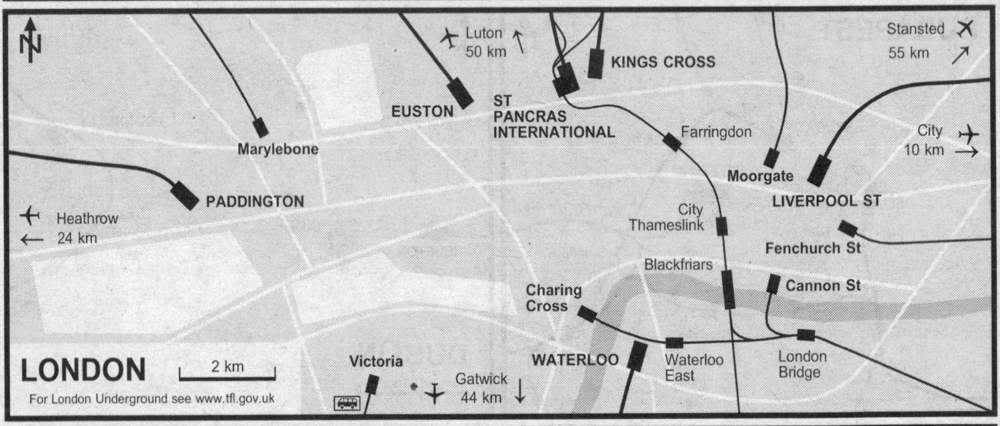
Luton
50 km
KINGS CROSS
Stansted
55 km
EUSTON
ST
PANCRAS
INTERNATIONAL
Farringdon
Marylebone
City
10 km
Moorgate
PADDINGTON
LIVERPOOL ST
Heathrow
24 km
City
Thameslink
Fenchurch St
Blackfriars
Charing
Cross
Cannon St
WATERLOO
Waterloo
East
London
Bridge
LONDON
2 km
For London Underground see www.tfl.gov.uk
Victoria
Gatwick
44 km

Entrecampos
Roma
Sete Rios
Roma-Areeiro
Sintra
Oriente
Areeiro
Campolide
Alameda
São
Sebastião
Oriente
Marquês de
Pombal
Rato
Restauradores
Rossio
SANTA
APOLÓNIA
Baixa-Chiado
Rossio
Cascais
Cais do Sodré
Terreiro
do Paço
1 km
LISBOA
Barreiro

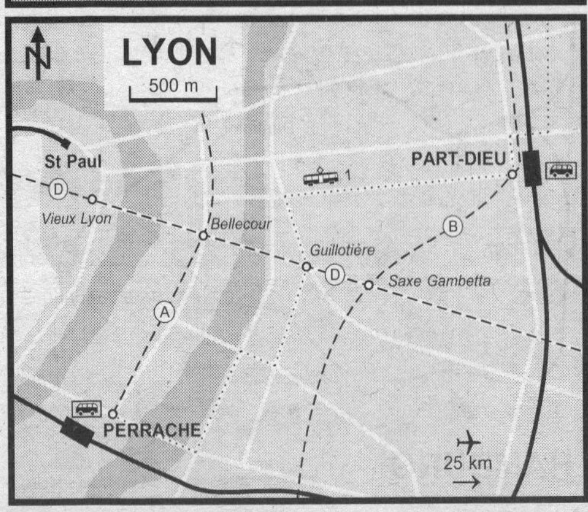
LYON
500 m
St Paul
PART-DIEU
1
D
Vieux Lyon
Bellecour
B
Guillotière
D
Saxe Gambetta
A
PERRACHE
25 km

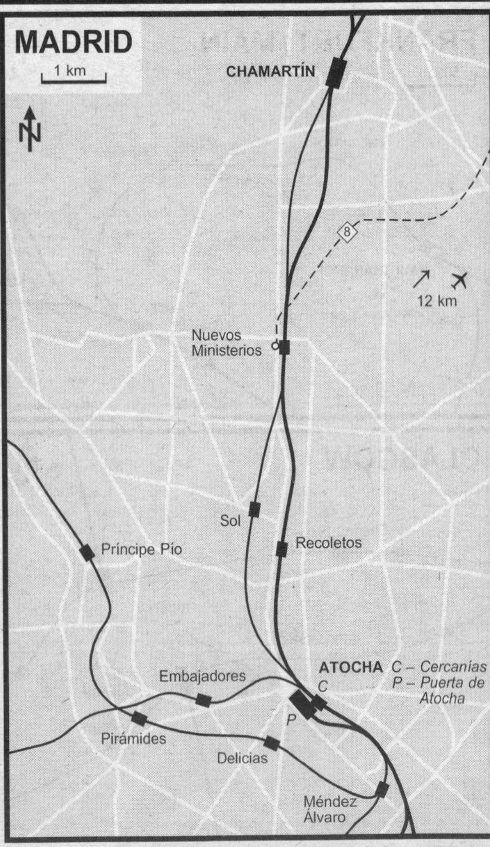
MADRID
1 km
CHAMARTÍN
8
12 km
Nuevos
Ministerios
Sol
Príncipe Pío
Recoletos
ATOCHA
C – Cercanías
P – Puerta de
Atocha
Embajadores
C
P
Pirámides
Delicias
Méndez
Álvaro

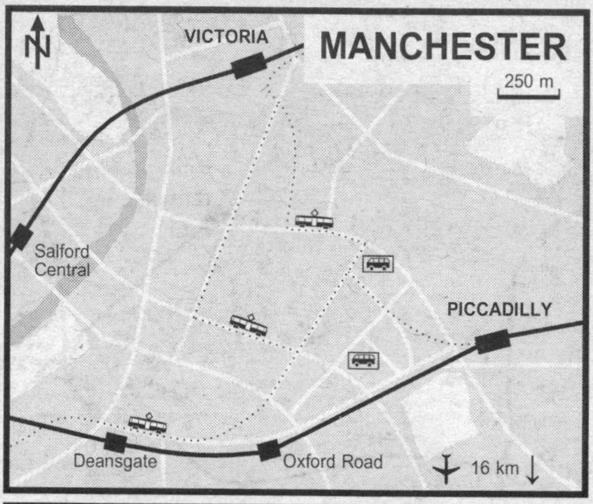
MANCHESTER
250 m
VICTORIA
Salford Central
PICCADILLY
Deansgate
Oxford Road
16 km

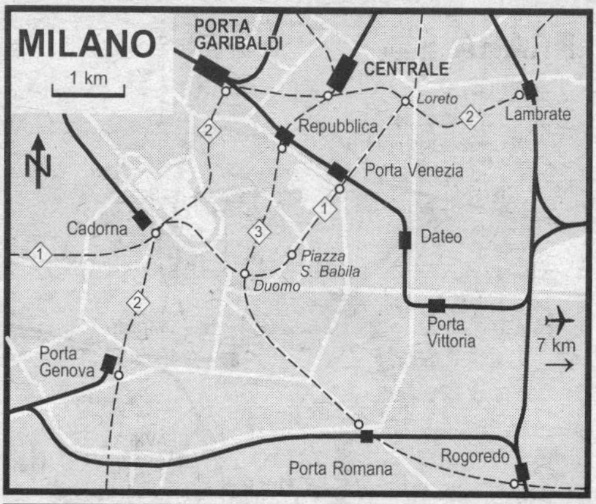
MILANO
1 km
PORTA GARIBALDI
CENTRALE
Loreto
Lambrate
Repubblica
Porta Venezia
Cadorna
Dateo
Piazza S. Babila
Duomo
Porta Vittoria
7 km
Porta Genova
Porta Romana
Rogoredo

27 km
Savyolovsky
Rizhskaya
Yaroslavskaya
BELORUSSKAYA
(Smolenskaya)
OKTYABRSKAYA
(Leningradski vokzal)
Komsomolskaya
Kazanskaya
KIYEVSKAYA
Kurskaya
Paveletskaya
MOSKVA
1 km

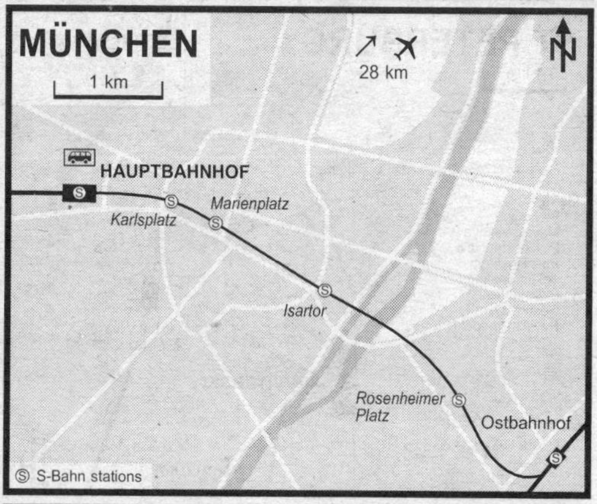
MÜNCHEN
1 km
28 km
HAUPTBAHNHOF
Marienplatz
Karlsplatz
Isartor
Rosenheimer Platz
Ostbahnhof
S-Bahn stations

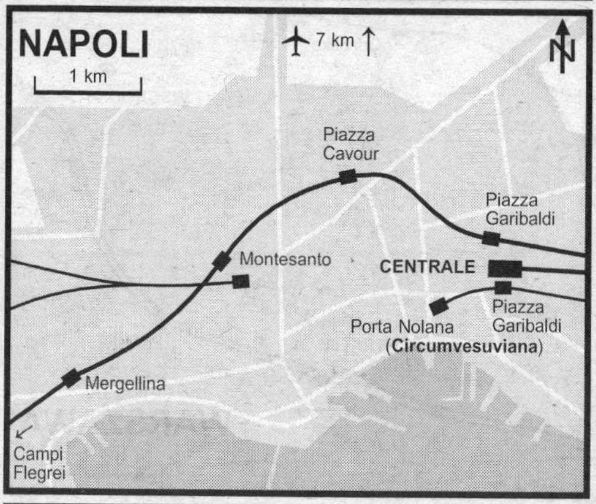
NAPOLI
1 km
7 km
Piazza Cavour
Piazza Garibaldi
Montesanto
CENTRALE
Porta Nolana
(Circumvesuviana)
Piazza Garibaldi
Mergellina
Campi Flegrei

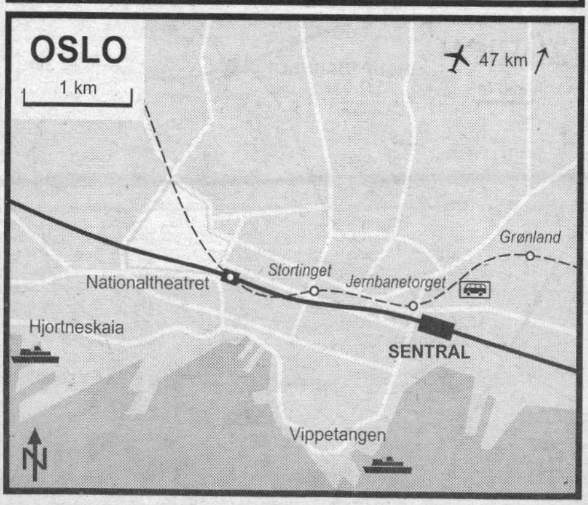
OSLO
1 km
47 km
Grønland
Stortinget
Nationaltheatret
Jernbanetorget
Hjortneskaia
SENTRAL
Vippetangen

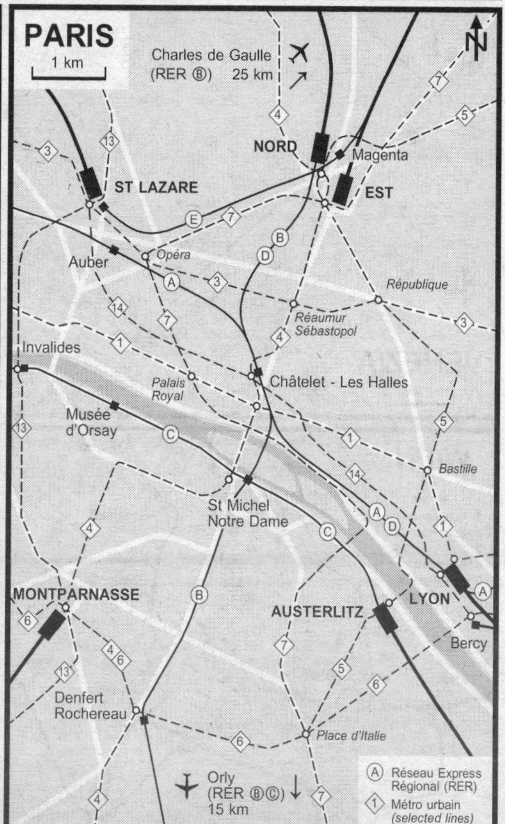
PARIS
1 km
Charles de Gaulle
(RER B) 25 km
NORD
Magenta
ST LAZARE
EST
Auber
Opéra
République
Réaumur Sébastopol
Invalides
Palais Royal
Châtelet - Les Halles
Musée d'Orsay
Bastille
St Michel Notre Dame
MONTPARNASSE
AUSTERLITZ
LYON
Bercy
Denfert Rochereau
Place d'Italie
Orly
(RER B C)
15 km
Réseau Express Régional (RER)
Métro urbain
(selected lines)

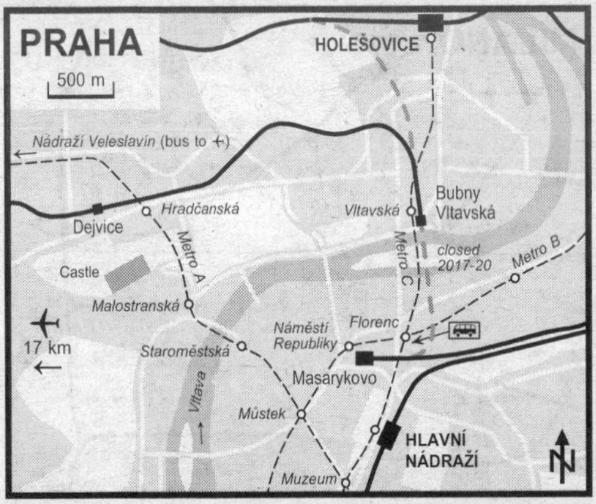
PRAHA
500 m
HOLEŠOVICE
Nádraží Veleslavín (bus to ✈)
Bubny Vltavská
Vltavská
Hradčanská
Dejvice
Metro A
Metro C
closed 2017-20
Metro B
Castle
Malostranská
17 km
Náměstí Republiky
Florenc
Staroměstská
Masarykovo
Vltava
Můstek
HLAVNÍ NÁDRAŽÍ
Muzeum

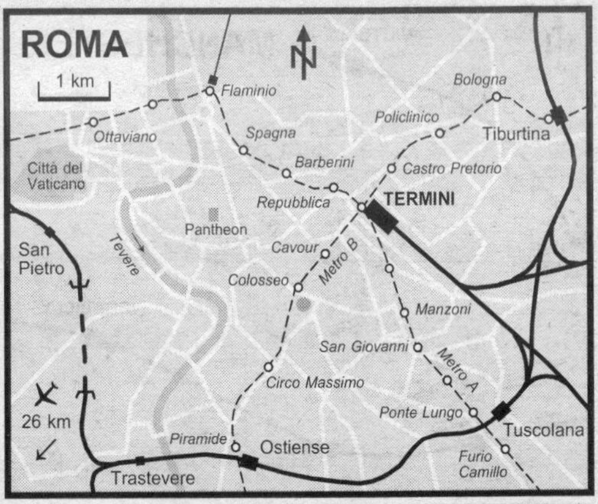
ROMA
1 km
Flaminio
Bologna
Ottaviano
Spagna
Policlinico
Tiburtina
Città del Vaticano
Barberini
Castro Pretorio
Repubblica
TERMINI
San Pietro
Pantheon
Tevere
Cavour
Metro B
Colosseo
Manzoni
San Giovanni
Metro A
Circo Massimo
26 km
Ponte Lungo
Tuscolana
Piramide
Ostiense
Furio Camillo
Trastevere

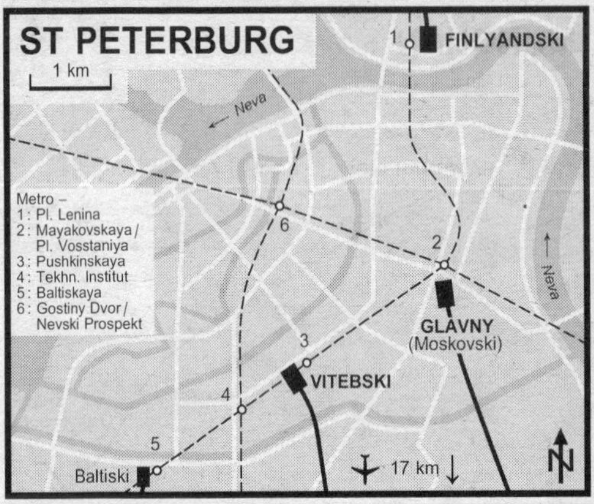
ST PETERBURG
1 km
1
FINLYANDSKI
Neva
Metro –
1: Pl. Lenina
2: Mayakovskaya / Pl. Vosstaniya
3: Pushkinskaya
4: Tekhn. Institut
5: Baltiskaya
6: Gostiny Dvor / Nevski Prospekt
6
2
Neva
GLAVNY (Moskovski)
3
VITEBSKI
4
5
Baltiski
17 km

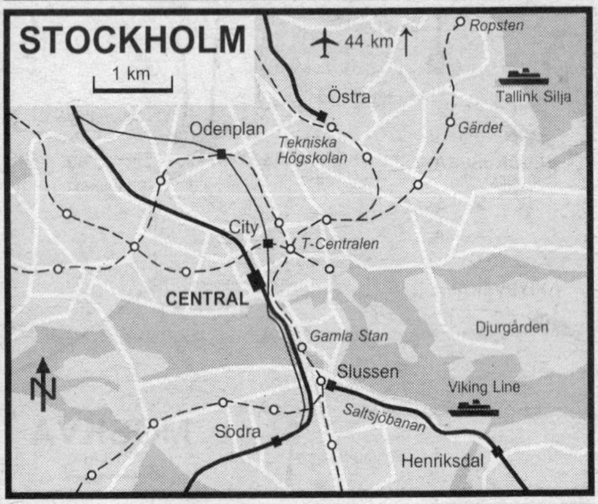
STOCKHOLM
1 km
44 km
Ropsten
Östra
Tallink Silja
Odenplan
Tekniska Högskolan
Gärdet
City
T-Centralen
CENTRAL
Gamla Stan
Djurgården
Slussen
Viking Line
Saltsjöbanan
Södra
Henriksdal

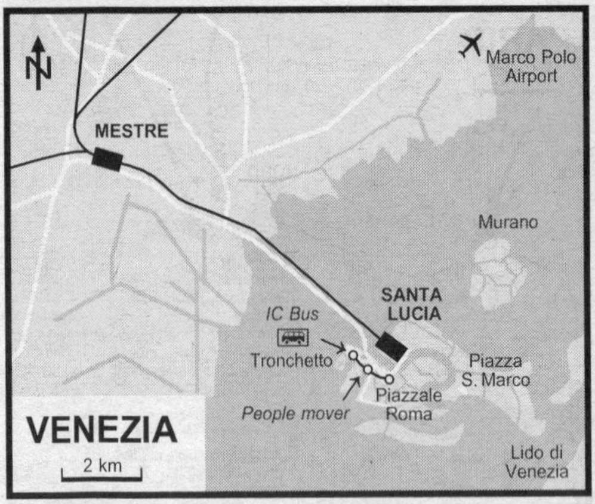
Marco Polo Airport
MESTRE
Murano
IC Bus
SANTA LUCIA
Tronchetto
Piazza S. Marco
Piazzale Roma
People mover
VENEZIA
2 km
Lido di Venezia

Gdańska
Wileńska
WSCHODNIA ▶
Ratusz Arsenał
Wisła
Stadion
Świętokrzyska
CENTRALNA
Powiśle
10 km
Centrum
Śródmieście
Ochota
WARSZAWA
1 km

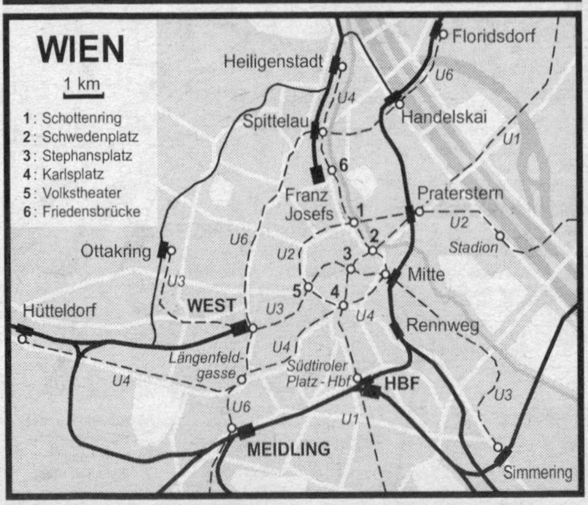
WIEN
1 km
Floridsdorf
Heiligenstadt
U6
U4
Spittelau
Handelskai
U1
1: Schottenring
2: Schwedenplatz
3: Stephansplatz
4: Karlsplatz
5: Volkstheater
6: Friedensbrücke
6
Franz Josefs
1
Praterstern
U2
Stadion
2
U6
U2
3
Ottakring
Mitte
U3
5
4
WEST
U3
U4
Hütteldorf
Rennweg
U4
Längenfeldgasse
Südtiroler Platz - Hbf
HBF
U4
U3
U6
U1
MEIDLING
Simmering

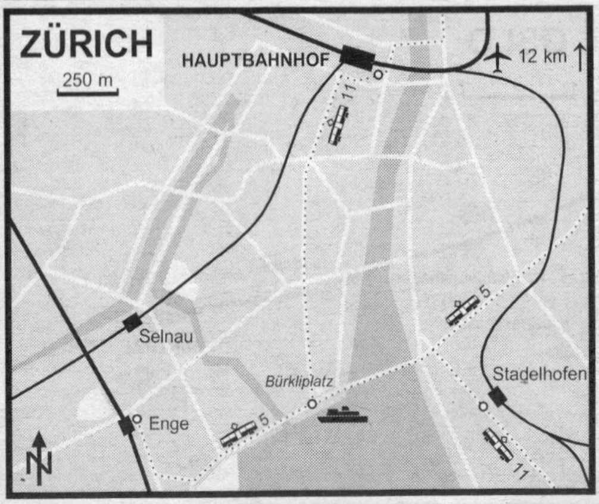
ZÜRICH
250 m
HAUPTBAHNHOF
12 km
11
Selnau
5
Stadelhofen
Bürkliplatz
Enge
5
11

SELECTED DAILY INTERNATIONAL SLEEPER SERVICES

From	To	Train Number	Brand	Facilities and owner	Train Name	International table number
Düsseldorf	Wien	40421/40490	Nightjet	🛏 1,2 cl. 🚿(öbb), ▬ 2 cl.(öbb), 🍸		28, 53, 66
Düsseldorf	Innsbruck	421/420	Nightjet	🛏 1,2 cl. 🚿(öbb), ▬ 2 cl.(öbb), 🍸		28, 53
München	Budapest	463/462	Euro Night	🛏 1,2 cl.(mav), ▬ 2 cl.(mav)	Kálmán Imre	32, 65
Wien	Bucureşti	347/346	Euro Night	🛏 1,2 cl.(cfr), ▬ 2 cl.(cfr), 🍴(cfr)	Dacia	32, 61
Budapest	Bucureşti	473/472	Euro Night	🛏 1,2 cl.(cfr), ▬ 1,2 cl.(cfr)	Ister	32, 61
Paris	Venezia	221/220	Thello Euro Night	🛏 1,2 cl.(ti), ▬ 2 cl.(ti), 🍴(ti)		44
Irún / Hendaye	Lisboa	312/310	Trenhotel talgo	🛏 1,2 cl. 🚿(renfe), 🍴(renfe)	Surex / Sud Expresso	45
Lisboa	Madrid	335/332	Trenhotel talgo	🛏 1,2 cl. 🚿(renfe), 🍴(renfe)	Lusitania	45
Zürich	Praha	50467/50466	Euro Night	🛏 1,2 cl.		52
Zürich	Hamburg	401/400	Nightjet	🛏 1,2 cl. 🚿(öbb), ▬ 2 cl.(öbb), 🍸		54, 73
Berlin	Zürich	471/470	Nightjet	🛏 1,2 cl. 🚿(öbb), ▬ 2 cl.(öbb), 🍸		54, 73
Berlin	Wien	457/456	Nightjet	🛏 1,2 cl. 🚿(öbb), ▬ 2 cl.(öbb), 🍸	Metropol	71
Berlin	Budapest	457-477 / 476-456	Nightjet	🛏 1,2 cl. 🚿(öbb), ▬ 2 cl.(öbb), 🍸	Metropol	71
Berlin	Przemyśl	60457/60456		🛏 1,2 cl.(pkp)		71
Warszawa	Kyiv	68/67		🛏 1,2 cl.(uz)	Kyiv Ekspres	56
Praha	Budapest	573-477/476-572	Euro Night	🛏 1,2 cl.(cd), ▬ 2 cl.(cd)	Metropol	60
Budapest	Beograd	341/340		🛏 1,2 cl.(zs), ▬ 2 cl.(zs)	**Suspended during 2019**	61
Beograd	Thessaloniki	335/334		▬ 2 cl.(mz)	Hellas Express	61
Bucuresti	Istanbul	461/492		▬ 2 cl. 4-berth (tcdd)	Bosphor	61
Hamburg	Wien	491/490	Nightjet	🛏 1,2 cl. 🚿(öbb), ▬ 2 cl.(öbb), 🍸		53, 64
Hamburg	Innsbruck	40491/40420	Nightjet	🛏 1,2 cl. 🚿(öbb), ▬ 2 cl.(öbb), 🍸		53, 64
München	Roma	295/294	Nightjet	🛏 1,2 cl. 🚿(db), ▬ 2 cl.(db), 🍸		70
München	Venezia	40463/40236	Nightjet	🛏 1,2 cl. 🚿(db), ▬ 2 cl.(db), 🍸		70
München	Milano	40295/40235	Nightjet	🛏 1,2 cl. 🚿(db), ▬ 2 cl.(db), 🍸		70
München	Zagreb	50463/498	Euro Night	🛏 1,2 cl.(hz), ▬ 2 cl.(hz)		86
Zürich	Zagreb	40465/414	Euro Night	🛏 1,2 cl.(hz), ▬ 2 cl.(hz)		86
Zürich	Budapest	40467/40462	Euro Night	🛏 1,2 cl.(mav), ▬ 2 cl.(mav)		86
Zürich	Graz	465/464	Nightjet	🛏 1,2 cl. 🚿(öbb), ▬ 2 cl.(öbb)		86
Zürich	Wien	467/466	Nightjet	🛏 1,2 cl. 🚿(öbb), ▬ 2 cl.(öbb)		86
Wien	Roma	40233/40294	Nightjet	🛏 1,2 cl. 🚿(öbb), ▬ 2 cl.(öbb)		88
Wien	Venezia	237/236	Nightjet	🛏 1,2 cl. 🚿(öbb), ▬ 2 cl.(öbb)		88
Wien	Milano	233/235	Nightjet	🛏 1,2 cl.(ti), ▬ 2 cl.(ti)		88
Košice	Kyiv	8813-29/81-8812		🛏 1,2 cl.(uz)		96
Wien	Kyiv	40147/40749		🛏 1,2 cl.(uz)	Hortobágy	96
Warszawa	Budapest	407-457-477 / 476-456-406		🛏 1,2 cl.(pkp), ▬ 2 cl.(pkp)		99
Warszawa	Wien	407-457 / 456-406		🛏 1,2 cl. 🚿(pkp), ▬ 2 cl.(öbb)	Chopin	99
Warszawa	Praha	407-402 / 443-406		🛏 1,2 cl.(pkp), ▬ 2 cl.(pkp)		99
Helsinki	Moskva	31/32	Firménny	🛏 1,2 cl. 🚿(rzd), 🍴	Lev Tolstoi	1910
Non daily sleepers (other seasonal services operate):						
Berlin	Malmö	301/300	Euro Night	▬ 2 cl.(bne)	Berlin Night Express	50
Paris	Moskva	453/452	Euro Night	🛏 1,2 cl. 🚿(rzd), 🍴(pkp, rzd)	Trans European Express	24
Nice	Moskva	18/17		🛏 1,2 cl. 🚿(rzd), 🍴(pkp, rzd)		25
Praha	Moskva	22/21		🛏 1,2 cl.(rzd)	Vltava	95
Warszawa	Moskva	10/9		🛏 1,2 cl.(rzd)	Polonez	56
Berlin	Moskva	14/13		🛏 1,2 cl.(rzd)		56

Key to ownership of sleeping cars:

bdz - Bulgarian, bc - Belarussian, bne - Berlin Night Express, cd - Czech, cfr - Romanian, cnl - City Night Line, db - German, hz - Croatian, mav - Hungarian, mz - Macedonian, öbb - Austrian, pkp - Polish, renfe - Spanish, rzd - Russian, sbb - Swiss, ti - Italian, uz - Ukrainian, zs - Serbian.

Note: This list excludes trains not shown in our International section (e.g. Czech Republic to Slovakia, Ukraine to Russia etc.).

🚿 – Shower. 🍴 – Restaurant car.

Steam trains in the European Rail Timetable

There are numerous tourist and heritage lines operating around Europe, most of which operate a seasonal service using steam or heritage diesel traction. Unfortunately, space limitations mean that we are unable to show timings for most of these lines. However, there are a number of routes that offer a daily service throughout the year and for these we do include timings, together with a few services hauled by steam traction on main-line rail routes. The panel below lists tourist railway **steam** train schedules that are included in our regular timetable pages.

Readers should also be aware that our expanded Summer and Winter editions (published in June and December) provide details of many other tourist railways in our special ***Rail Extra*** feature, including a brief description of selected routes and an overview of the service provided. The feature also includes other useful rail travel information on a country by country basis.

COUNTRY	RAILWAY	TABLE	NOTES
GREAT BRITAIN	The Shakespeare Express	**127**	Regular summer Sunday main-line steam excursions between Stratford upon Avon and Birmingham
	Ffestiniog / Welsh Highland Railways	**160**	Two narrow gauge railways linked at Porthmadog running through spectacular Welsh mountain landscapes
	North Yorkshire Moors Railway	**211**	Regular services run from spring to autumn, many steam-hauled through to Whitby via a link to the main line at Grosmont
	The Jacobite	**218**	A regular main-line steam excursion operating from spring to autumn over the spectacular West Highland line
FRANCE	Train des Pignes	**359**	A summer Sunday steam-hauled service running over part of the scenic Nice to Digne route
SWITZERLAND	Brienz Rothorn Bahn	**553**	A swiss mountain rack railway operating regular steam services from June to October
PORTUGAL	Comboio Historico	**694**	Enjoy a steam-hauled journey along the scenic Douro Valley between Régua and Tua at weekends from June to October
SWEDEN	Arvidsjaur Järnvägsförening	**766**	Operates twice a week from mid-July to early August over a section of the Inlandsbanan (Arvidsjaur - Slagnäs)
GERMANY	Rügensche Bäderbahn	**844a**	Daily steam services on the island of Rügen
	Lößnitzgrundbahn	**853**	Daily steam services between Radebeul Ost and Radeburg (near Dresden)
	Weißeritztalbahn	**853**	Daily steam services between Freital-Hainsberg and Kurort Kipsdorf (near Dresden)
	Zittauer Schmalspurbahn	**853**	Daily steam services between Zittau and Kurort Jonsdorf / Kurort Oybin
	Harzer Schmalspurbahnen	**867**	A famous narrow gauge network in central Germany with some services steam-hauled on a daily basis
	Fichtelbergbahn	**882**	Daily steam services between Cranzahl and Kurort Oberwiesenthal
AUSTRIA	Zillertalbahn	**955**	A single return steam service runs on selected days from May to October
	Achenseebahn	**956**	A narrow gauge steam rack railway with daily services running May to October
	Pinzgauer Lokalbahn	**957**	A single return steam service runs once or twice a week at certain times of the year
	Schneebergbahn	**984**	Most service are operated by modern diesel trains but a steam service also runs on Sundays during the summer
	Mariazellerbahn	**994**	An occasional steam service runs along this world famous mountain route (also a service hauled by heritage electric traction)
	Murtalbahn	**998**	Steam trains run between Murau and Tamsweg once or twice a week during the summer
POLAND	Koleje Wielkopolskie	**1099**	The popular scheduled steam services operating on the Wolsztyn to Poznań and Wolsztyn to Leszno routes
CZECH REPUBLIC	Jindřichohradecké Místní Dráhy	**1169**	A steam train runs on Saturdays from April to September (daily during July and August)

What's new this month *(continued from page 5)*

SPAIN

Three direct high-speed AVE services between Madrid and Granada are due to start this month, possibly on June 24. We understand that tickets were due to go on sale on June 3. Another AVE service will also be introduced between Barcelona and Granada bypassing Madrid and a new Table **678a** has been created to show the provisional timings. Madrid and Granada have been without a direct service via Antequera since April 7, 2015 and we reported at that time that we expected the line would reopen in August 2015! The future of the direct Talgo service via Linares-Baeza (Table **661**) is uncertain once the high-speed services start running.

A full service has resumed on the route between Algeciras and Bobadilla (Table **673**). This stretch of line was temporarily closed in October 2018 following storm damage.

Engineering work taking place until December 2019 in Madrid's Recoletos tunnel, between Charmartín and Atocha stations, means many Media Distancia services in Tables **679**, **681** and **689** are diverted to Madrid Principe Pio station (see the Madrid city plan on page 32).

DENMARK

Engineering work will be carried out between Odense and Frederica from June 14 to August 4 and this will result in fewer InterCity and InterCityLyn services during the periods June 30 to July 13 and July 21 to August 2. In addition, buses will replace trains from the evening of August 3 to the afternoon of August 4.

SWEDEN

From June 24 to August 18 engineering work will disrupt services in the Stockholm area, particularly affecting trains to and from the south of the country which will be unable to call at Stockholm Central. Affected trains will instead serve either Stockholm Södra or Flemingsberg and passengers wishing to travel from or to the city centre should use alternative local services.

NORWAY

Many services in the Oslo area are disrupted from June 22 to August 4. Trains in Tables **775**, **783** and **785** are replaced by buses between Oslo and Drammen or Kongsberg whilst services between Oslo and Bergen are diverted between Oslo and Hønefoss, not calling at Drammen (Drammen passengers are conveyed by bus to / from Hønefoss). The Oslo – Halden – Göteborg route (Table **770**) is also affected with buses replacing trains between Oslo and Rygge. Timings at Oslo may vary during this period so readers are strongly advised to check timings locally before travelling.

GERMANY

Various infrastructure upgrade projects will continue to disrupt both regional and long-distance services around the German network, in some cases for considerable lengths of time. We have included amended schedules where space permits but the complexity of temporary timetables often means it is not always possible to include full details.

The section of high-speed line between Hannover and Göttingen is completely closed to rail traffic from June 11 to December 14 meaning all long-distance services are diverted over the original main line via Kreiensen. Fewer services are running during this period and journey times are extended. As the amended service covers the whole of this timetable period, full details are included in the regular tables. The work on this stretch of line is the start of a programme to upgrade the country's high-speed infrastructure meaning other sections of line will be similarly affected over the next few years.

Another section of line closed until the mid-December timetable change is that between Magdeburg and Halle via Köthen. All long-distance trains in Table **866** are retimed and diverted via Dessau whilst local services are partially replaced by bus.

Services that normally use the principal Rhein-Ruhr route between Köln and Dortmund via Duisburg will be severely disrupted from July 13 to August 25 when most services are retimed with various diversions in operation. Unfortunately, the complex nature of these alterations means that it is simply not possible for us to show the amended timings so readers are advised to confirm travel arrangements beforehand if travelling to or from stations in Table **800**. Many regional services shown in Table **802** will also be affected.

Ongoing bridge renewal work in the Bielefeld area means most long distance and regional services via Bielefeld are operating to amende schedules until October 11. In this edition we have included tw versions of Table **810** with the service from October 12 located or pages 564 and 565.

Services using the main line via Eisenach and Fulda will be subject t major alterations from August 10 to October 27 with some service diverted via Kassel resulting in considerably extended journey times. A special version of Table **850** showing the amended timings will be foun on pages 566 and 567.

Readers intending to visit Germany need to be aware that there ar numerous other alterations planned during the currency of this timetabl and a summary of the most significant changes will be found in th shaded box on page 369 whilst changes to regional services are usuall indicated in the table concerned. Readers should also note that furthe short-term alterations are possible and these may not be mentioned i our tables.

Independent operator Flixtrain started operating a new service betwee Köln and Berlin from May 23 and we have revamped our specia Flixtrain table on page 369 to include the timings. Owing to engineerin work taking place at various locations along the route, the schedules wi initially be rather complex and so the timings we show will vary or certain dates. We hope to show the service with more clarity once th work along the line is completed.

Two new operators have taken over the running of certain regiona services in the Baden-Württemberg region. Go-Ahead now operates th Stuttgart – Aalen – Crailsheim (Table **925**) and Stuttgart – Pforzheim – Karlsruhe (Table **931**) routes whilst Abellio is the new operator of loca services between Stuttgart and Heidelberg (Table **931**).

POLAND

Polish Railways has issued a new timetable valid from June 9 to Augus 31. Most services between Poznań and Warszawa are no longer bein diverted via Inowrocław and so will take their normal route via Konin. However, until June 24 services are subject to extended journey time between Konin and Warszawa which is affecting *Berlin Warszaw Express* services in Tables **56** and **1001**. Unfortunately information was not available in time for all Polish timings to be checked so readers are strongly advised to verify their travel plans before visiting Poland.

CZECH REPUBLIC

Trains from Praha to Turnov and Tanvald (Table **1140**), which are currently serving Praha Masarykovo rather than Praha hlavní nádraz as an engineering work alteration, will continue to do so for the rest o the timetable year. From June 9 the Praha – Žilina *Ex* trains via Vsetin (Table **1161**) will revert to running for the full route rather than some being curtailed at Púchov, following completion of engineering work.

The morning *Arriva Express* Praha – Trenčin – Nitra train and afternoon return (Table **1163**) will not increase to daily from June 7 as originally advertised but will continue twice weekly until the end of August, becoming daily from September 1.

SLOVAKIA

The principal alteration from June 9 (apart from the extension of a Praha – Břeclav Railjet service to and from Bratislava as mentioned under the International heading) is the introduction of two fast trains each way between Košice and the Ukrainian town of Mukachevo via Chop (Table **1195**). This follows the recent opening of a standard gauge track within Ukraine, removing the gauge change requirement. Connections at Košice and Mukachevo will allow a range of new journey opportunities from Slovakia and the Czech Republic to destinations in Ukraine.

Other changes involve evening retimings on the TEŽ (Tatra Electric Railways) lines shown in Table **1182**, and some revisions to Table **1180** mostly affecting departure times from Považská Bystrica.

HUNGARY

Summer timings for trains in the area around Lake Balaton will apply from June 15 to August 25 and special versions of Tables **1220**, **1225** and **1232** will be found on pages 560 and 561. As final timings were not available by press date these tables are subject to alteration.

CONTINUED ON PAGE 37

What's new this month *(continued from page 36)*

ALBANIA

Albanian Railways amended its timetable in May. The service between Durrës and Lushnjë has been withdrawn but an additional service now runs between Durrës and Shkodër (Table **1390**).

GREECE

Services between Athina and Thessaloníki were recast from May 20 to take full advantage of the new alignment between Tithoréa and Lianokládi. Four daytime services between Athína and Thessaloníki now take exactly one hour less than before with a fifth, *IC* **51**, taking just 3 hours and 57 minutes to complete its journey.

Buses replace trains between Lianokládi and Stilída. Amfíklia station, which was planned for closure, remains open for now with one service Mondays to Saturdays and two on Sundays (Table **1400**).

BULGARIA / TURKEY

A new international service between Plovdiv and Edirne was expected to start running on Saturdays and Sundays from June 1, although only limited information was available as we went to press (Table **1550**).

LITHUANIA

Full details are now shown of the revised Vilnius – Kaunas service (Table **1811**) where all trains are terminating at Palemonas, 10 kilometres from Kaunas station, due to work on the *Rail Baltica* project. Six fast journeys each way have connections by replacement bus between Palemonas and Kaunas station organised by the railway company; on other journeys passengers will need to use local city buses.

KAZAKHSTAN

In March Kazakhstan's capital city Astana was renamed Nur-Sultan, after the former president Nursultan Nazarbayev, and our tables now refect the new name. A general timetable revision took place on May 22. The most significant alteration concerns train **85/6**, shown in Table **1980** between Nur-Sultan and Shymkent, which now serves the recently opened Nur-Sultan Nurly Zhol station rather than Nur-Sultan 1.

BEYOND EUROPE

As always in our seasonal editions, we have included all eight of our *Beyond Europe* sections. A list of the areas covered and their locations within the timetable will be found on page 583. The Africa & Middle East section has been fully updated but only limited changes have been made to the other sections since they last appeared in regular monthly editions.

We have recast the Moroccan section which will hopefully improve our presentation of services in this country. The changes have also allowed us to show services between Casablanca and Oued Zem (Table **4003**).

In Israel, electrification work on Fridays and Saturdays started on May 31 and affects services shown in Tables **4500** and **4510**. A limited service on Sundays to Thursdays between Nahariyya and Be'er Sheva recommenced on May 26 (Table **4510**).

In South Africa, the service between Cape Town and Queenstown / East London appears to have been discontinued (Table **4400**).

Various infrastructure improvement projects continue to affect services in North America until September and we have included suitable warnings in the relevant tables.

In Cuba, a new service between Habana and Holguim is expected to start in mid-June. Only limited information was available as we went to press and this has been added to Table **9920**.

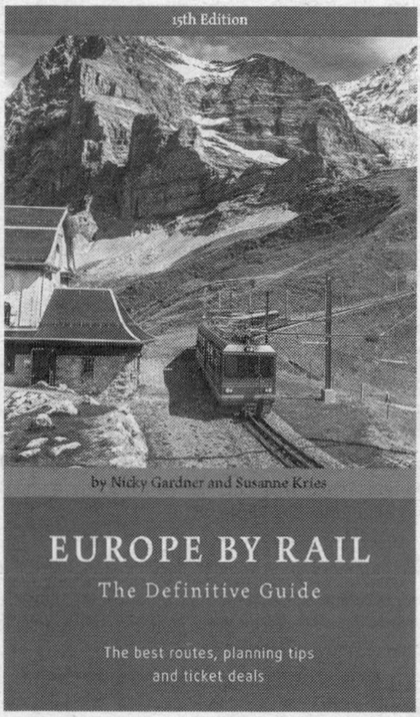

Exploring the continent by train has never been easier. Written by Nicky Gardner and Susanne Kries, authors of the *Route of the Month* in the *European Rail Timetable*, this guidebook contains all you need for planning your journey.

★ 50 routes
★ 512 pages
★ 40,000 km of journeys
★ over 30 countries
★ tips on fares and ticketing
★ detailed route descriptions
★ sketch maps for each route
★ index map which shows all routes
★ suggestions for overnight stays

... and a very fine read!

The 15th edition of *Europe by Rail* was published in November 2017 and is available directly from European Rail Timetable Ltd, all good bookshops and online retailers (including Amazon and Wordery). More at

www.EuropeByRail.eu

São Bento station, Porto (photo © Saiko3p / dreamstime.com)

AUTO-TRAIN, AUTOREISEZÜGE, MOTORAIL

Car-carrying trains are composed of special wagons or vans for the conveyance of motorcars usually with sleeping cars and couchettes enabling the driver and passengers to travel overnight in comfort in the same train. Some services (particularly in France) convey vehicles separately allowing passengers a choice of trains for their own journey. Some shorter distance services run by day and convey seating coaches.

Cars are often loaded on the trains at separate stations from the passenger station and may be loaded some time before the passenger train departs. International car-carrying trains are shown in Table **1**, Domestic car-carrying trains in Table **2**. Some services also carry passengers without cars.

Details of Channel Tunnel shuttle services may be found on page 48. Austrian and Swiss alpine tunnel car-carrying trains are shown in the relevant country section - see pages 460 and 260 respectively for details.

Readers should be careful to check that dates refer to current schedules, as old dates may be left in the table until such time as current information is received. Loading and train times may vary on some dates, but will be confirmed by the agent when booking.

Contact details:
Contact names are shown within the tables where services are operated by organisations other than the relevant national railway company for the country from which the service originates. Note that Deutsche Bahn no longer operate any international services.

BahnTouristikExpress, Vordere Cramergasse 11 - 13, 90478 Nürnberg; ✆ +49 (0)911 240 388.

ÖBB AutoZug, (booking centre); ✆ +43 (0)5 1717.

Optima Tours, Karlstrasse 56, 80333 D - München; ✆ +49 89 54880 - 111.

Urlaubs-Express, Magnusstr. 18a, 50672 Köln; ✆ +49 (0)221 800 20 820.

INTERNATIONAL CAR - CARRYING TRAINS — 1

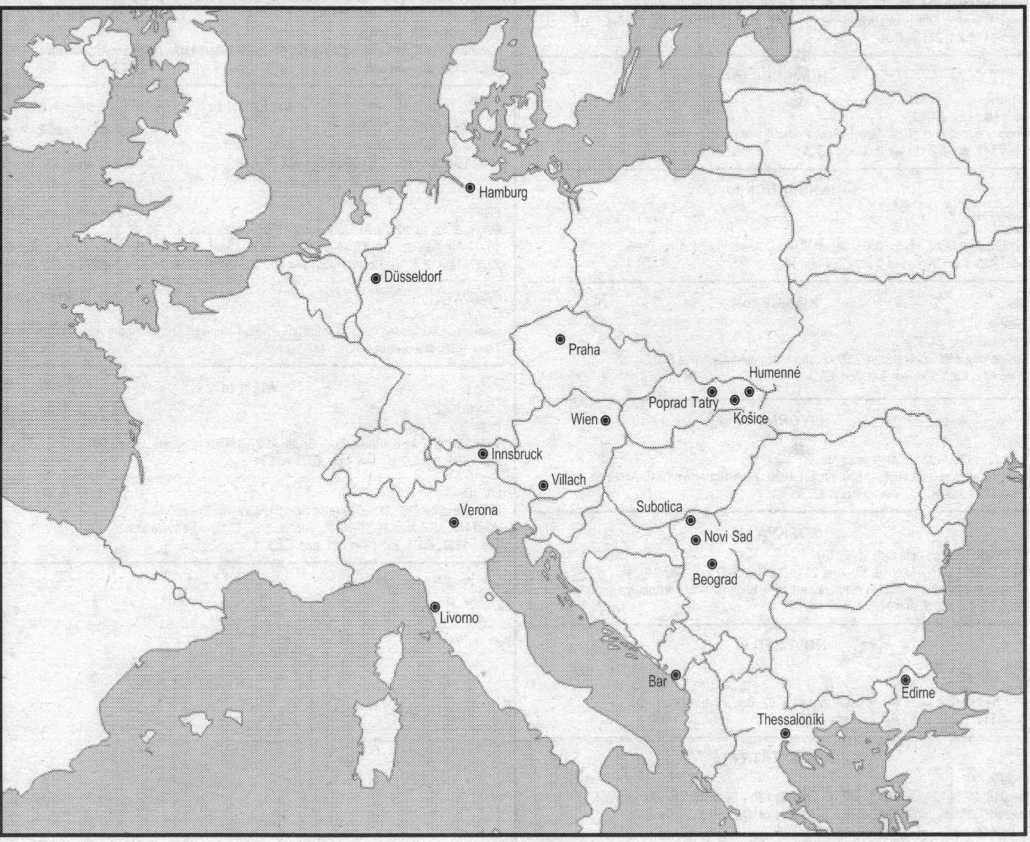

BAR to

BEOGRAD:
Daily.
Bar loading times not advised, depart 1900, Beograd arrive 0615.
Train **432**: 🛏 1, 2 cl., ▬ 2 cl. and [2].

NOVI SAD:
June 17 - Sept. 17, 2018.
Bar loading times not advised, depart 1650, Novi Sad arrive 0637.
Train **1136**: 🛏 1, 2 cl., ▬ 2 cl. and [2].

SUBOTICA:
June 17 - Sept. 17, 2018.
Bar loading times not advised, depart 1650, Subotica arrive 0930.
Train **1136**: 🛏 1, 2 cl., ▬ 2 cl. and [2].

BEOGRAD to

BAR:
Daily.
Beograd loading times not advised, depart 2110, Bar arrive 0808.
Train **433**: 🛏 1, 2 cl., ▬ 2 cl. and [2].

THESSALONÍKI:
Service suspended.
Beograd loading times not advised, depart 1810, Thessaloníki arrive 1008.
Train **335**: ▬ 2 cl. and [2].

DÜSSELDORF to

INNSBRUCK: *Contact*: ÖBB AutoZug
Daily.
Düsseldorf Hbf load 2015 - 2035, depart 2054, Innsbruck Hbf arrive 0914.
Train **421**: 🛏 1, 2 cl., ▬ 2 cl., [2] and ✕.

VERONA: *Contact*: Urlaubs-Express
⑤ June 7 - Sept. 13, 2019 (not July 5).
Düsseldorf Hbf loading times not advised, depart 1844, Verona Porta Nuova arrive 0900.
Train **1385**: 🛏, ▬ and ✕.

VILLACH: *Contact*: Urlaubs-Express
⑦ June 30 - Sept. 8, 2019.
Düsseldorf Hbf loading times not advised, depart 1912, Villach Autoverladung arrive 0845.
Train **1387**: 🛏, ▬ and ✕.

EDIRNE to

VILLACH: *Contact*: Optima Tours
May 2, 6, 10, 16, 20, 24, 29, June 6, 10, 14, 19, 23, 27, July 1, 5, 11, 15, 19, 24, 28, Aug. 1, 5, 9, 15, 16, 19, 22, 23, 26, 29, 30, Sept. 2, 5, 6, 12, 16, 20, 26, Oct. 3, 7, 11, 17, 21, 25, 31, Nov. 4, 8, 13. Timings vary. ▬ and ✕. *Contact operator for further details.*

HAMBURG to

VERONA: *Contact*: Urlaubs-Express
⑤ May 17 - Oct. 4, 2019.
Hamburg Altona loading times not advised, depart 1755, Verona Porta Nuova arrive 0955.
Train **1395**: 🛏, ▬ and ✕.

VILLACH: *Contact*: Urlaubs-Express
⑦ June 30 - Sept. 8, 2019.
Hamburg Altona loading times not advised, depart 1852, Villach Autoverladung arrive 0845.
Train **1397**: 🛏, ▬ and ✕.

WIEN: *Contact*: ÖBB AutoZug
Daily.
Hamburg Altona load 1900 - 1945, depart 2014, Wien Hbf ARZ arrive 0826.
Train **491**: 🛏 1, 2 cl., ▬ 2 cl., (2) and ✕.

HELSINKI to

MOSKVA (service until Oct. 25, 2019):
Daily to Sept. 6 (not May 18, 25, June 22); ①②③④⑤⑦ from Sept. 8.
Helsinki loading times not advised, depart 1844, Moskva Oktyabrskaya arrive 0919.
Train **31**: 🛏 1, 2 cl. and ✕.

HUMENNÉ to

PRAHA:
Daily (not Dec. 24, 31).
Humenné load until 1835, depart 1946, Praha hlavní nádraží arrive 0731.
Train **442**: 🛏 1, 2 cl., ▬ 2 cl. and (2).

INNSBRUCK to

DÜSSELDORF:
Daily.
Innsbruck Hbf load 1945 - 2005, depart 2044, Düsseldorf Hbf arrive 0842.
Train **420**: 🛏 1, 2 cl., ▬ 2 cl., (2) and ✕.

KOŠICE to

PRAHA:
Daily (not Dec. 24, 31).
Košice load until 2025, depart 2207, Praha hlavní nádraží arrive 0731.
Train **442**: 🛏 1, 2 cl., ▬ 2 cl. and (2).

LIVORNO to

WIEN:
④⑥ Apr. 13 - Oct. 12, 2019 (also Apr. 22, June 10).
Livorno Centrale load 1630 - 1800, depart 1920, Wien Hbf arrive 0840 (0922 on ⑤).
Train **1234**: 🛏 1, 2 cl., ▬ 2 cl. and (2).

MOSKVA to

HELSINKI (service until Oct. 25, 2019):
Daily to Sept. 6 (not May 18, 25, June 21); ①②③④⑤⑦ from Sept. 8.
Moskva Oktyabrskaya loading times not advised, depart 2310, Helsinki arrive 1330.
Train **32**: 🛏 1, 2 cl. and ✕.

NOVI SAD to

BAR:
June 16 - Sept. 16, 2018.
Novi Sad loading times not advised, depart 2002, Bar arrive 1001.
Train **1137**: 🛏 1, 2 cl., ▬ 2 cl. and (2).

POPRAD TATRY to

PRAHA:
Dec. 19 - 22, 26 - 29, Jan. 1 - 7, Apr. 15 - 28, May 30 - Sept. 15, Oct. 24 - Nov. 4.
Poprad Tatry load until 2045, depart 2203, Praha hlavní nádraží arrive 0616.
Train **444**: 🛏 1, 2 cl., ▬ 2 cl. and (2).

Dec. 9 - 18, Jan. 8 - Apr. 14, Apr. 29 - May 29, Sept. 16 - Oct. 23, Nov. 5 - Dec. 14.
Poprad Tatry load until 1830, depart 1938, Praha hlavní nádraží arrive 0731.
Train **764 / 442**: 🛏 1, 2 cl.

PRAHA to

HUMENNÉ:
Daily (not Dec. 24, 31).
Praha hlavní nádraží load until 1945, depart 2215, Humenné arrive 1033.
Train **443**: 🛏 1, 2 cl., ▬ 2 cl. and (2).

KOŠICE:
Daily (not Dec. 24, 31).
Praha hlavní nádraží load until 2000, depart 2215, Košice arrive 0823.
Train **443**: 🛏 1, 2 cl., ▬ 2 cl. and (2).

POPRAD TATRY:
Dec. 20 - 23, 27 - 30, Jan. 2 - 8, Apr. 16 - 29, May 31 - Sept. 16, Oct. 25 - Nov. 5.
Praha hlavní nádraží load until 2200, depart 2347, Poprad Tatry arrive 0739.
Train **445**: 🛏 1, 2 cl., ▬ 2 cl. and (2).

Dec. 9 - 19, Jan. 9 - Apr. 15, Apr. 30 - May 30, Sept. 17 - Oct. 24, Nov. 6 - Dec. 14.
Praha hlavní nádraží load until 2015, depart 2215, Poprad Tatry arrive 0833.
Train **443**: 🛏 1, 2 cl.

SUBOTICA to

BAR:
June 16 - Sept. 16, 2018.
Subotica loading times not advised, depart 1726, Bar arrive 1001.
Train **1137**: 🛏 1, 2 cl., ▬ 2 cl. and (2).

THESSALONÍKI to

BEOGRAD:
Service suspended.
Thessaloníki loading times not advised, depart 1823, Beograd arrive 0811.
Train **334**: ▬ 2 cl. and (2).

VERONA to

DÜSSELDORF: *Contact*: Urlaubs-Express
⑥ June 8 - Sept. 14, 2019.
Verona Porta Nuova loading times not advised, depart 1900, arrive 0900.
Train **1384**: 🛏, ▬ and ✕.

HAMBURG: *Contact*: Urlaubs-Express
⑥ May 18 - Oct. 5, 2019.
Verona Porta Nuova loading times not advised, depart 1800, Hamburg Altona arrive 0955.
Train **1394**: 🛏, ▬ and ✕.

VILLACH to

DÜSSELDORF: *Contact*: Urlaubs-Express
① July 1 - Sept. 9, 2019.
Villach Autoverladung loading times not advised, depart 1810, Düsseldorf arrive 0800.
Train **1386**: 🛏, ▬ and ✕.

EDIRNE: *Contact*: Optima Tours
May 4, 8, 12, 18, 22, 26, 31, June 8, 12, 16, 21, 25, 29, July 3, 7, 13, 17, 21, 26, 27, 30, Aug. 3, 7, 11, 17, 18, 21, 24, 25, 28, 31, Sept. 1, 4, 8, 14, 18, 22, 30, Oct. 5, 9, 13, 19, 23, 27, Nov. 2, 6, 10. Timings vary. ▬ and ✕. *Contact operator for further details.*

HAMBURG: *Contact*: Urlaubs-Express
① July 1 - Sept. 9, 2019.
Villach Autoverladung loading times not advised, depart 1810, Hamburg Altona arrive 0844.
Train **1396**: 🛏, ▬ and ✕.

WIEN to

HAMBURG:
Daily.
Wien Hbf ARZ load 1930 - 2010, depart 2027, Hamburg Altona arrive 0904.
Train **490**: 🛏 1, 2 cl., ▬ 2 cl., (2) and ✕.

LIVORNO:
③⑤ Apr. 12 - Oct. 11, 2019 (also Apr. 21, June 9).
Wien Hbf ARZ load 1920 - 1945, depart 2010, Livorno Centrale arrive 0850.
Train **1237**: 🛏 1, 2 cl., ▬ 2 cl. and (2).

AUSTRIA

Feldkirch - Graz: daily.
Feldkirch - Villach: daily.
Feldkirch - Wien Hbf ARZ: daily.

Graz - Feldkirch: daily.

Villach - Feldkirch: daily.

Wien Hbf ARZ - Feldkirch: daily.

CROATIA

Split - Zagreb: daily in summer.

Zagreb - Split: daily in summer.

FINLAND

to 16/06/19

Helsinki - Kemijärvi: ⑤.
Helsinki - Kolari: Daily to Apr. 22 (not Dec. 9, 11, 13, 16, 24, 31, Jan. 6, 8, 10, 13, 15, 17, 20); ③⑤ from Apr. 24 (also Apr. 27, 30, June 10, 15; not May 1).
Helsinki - Oulu: daily.
Helsinki - Rovaniemi: daily.

Kemijärvi - Helsinki: ⑥.

Kolari - Helsinki: Daily to Apr. 23 (not Dec. 9, 10, 12, 14, 17, 24, 31, Jan. 2, 7, 9, 11, 14, 16, 18, 21); ④⑥ from Apr. 25 (also Apr. 28, May 1, June 11, 16; not May 2).
Kolari - Tampere: Daily to Apr. 23 (not Dec. 9, 10, 12, 14, 17, 24, 31, Jan. 2, 7, 9, 11, 14, 16, 18, 21); ④⑥ from Apr. 25 (also Apr. 28, May 1, June 11, 16; not May 2).

Oulu - Helsinki: daily.

Rovaniemi - Helsinki: daily.
Rovaniemi - Tampere: daily.
Rovaniemi - Turku: daily (not Dec. 24).

Tampere - Kolari: Daily to Apr. 22 (not Dec. 9, 11, 13, 16, 24, 31, Jan. 6, 8, 10, 13, 15, 17, 20); ③⑤ from Apr. 24 (also Apr. 27, 30, June 10, 15; not May 1).
Tampere - Rovaniemi: daily.
Turku - Rovaniemi: daily (not Dec. 24).

Note: Helsinki trains load and unload at Pasila station (3 km north of Helsinki station)

FRANCE

to 14/12/19

2019 SERVICE

Avignon - Paris: ⑥ to May 25 (also Apr. 18, 25, May 2); ④⑥ May 30 - June 22; daily June 27 - Sept. 8; ②④⑥ Sept. 10 - Oct. 5; ④⑥ Oct. 10–26; ⑥ from Nov. 2.

Fréjus-St. Raphaël – see St. Raphaël.

Marseille - Paris: ⑥ to May 25 (also Apr. 18, 25, May 2); ④⑥ May 30 - June 22; daily June 27 - Sept. 8; ②④⑥ Sept. 10 - Oct. 5; ④⑥ Oct. 10–26; ⑥ from Nov. 2.

Nice - Paris: ⑥ to May 25 (also Apr. 18, 25, May 2); ④⑥ May 30 - June 22; daily June 27 - Sept. 8; ②④⑥ Sept. 10 - Oct. 5; ④⑥ Oct. 10–26; ⑥ from Nov. 2.

Paris - Avignon: ⑤ to May 24 (also Apr. 17, 24, May 1); ③⑤ May 29 - June 21; daily June 26 - Sept. 8; ①③⑤ Sept. 9 - Oct. 4; ③⑤ Oct. 9–25; ⑤ from Nov. 1.

Paris - Marseille: ⑤ to May 24 (also Apr. 17, 24, May 1); ③⑤ May 29 - June 21; daily June 26 - Sept. 8; ①③⑤ Sept. 9 - Oct. 4; ③⑤ Oct. 9–25; ⑤ from Nov. 1.

Paris - Nice: ⑤ to May 24 (also Apr. 17, 24, May 1); ③⑤ May 29 - June 21; daily June 26 - Sept. 8; ①③⑤ Sept. 9 - Oct. 4; ③⑤ Oct. 9–25; ⑤ from Nov. 1.

Paris - St. Raphaël: ⑤ to May 24 (also Apr. 17, 24, May 1); ③⑤ May 29 - June 21; daily June 26 - Sept. 8; ①③⑤ Sept. 9 - Oct. 4; ③⑤ Oct. 9–25; ⑤ from Nov. 1.

Paris - Toulon: ⑤ to May 24 (also Apr. 17, 24, May 1); ③⑤ May 29 - June 21; daily June 26 - Sept. 8; ①③⑤ Sept. 9 - Oct. 4; ③⑤ Oct. 9–25; ⑤ from Nov. 1.

St. Raphaël - Paris: ⑥ to May 25 (also Apr. 18, 25, May 2); ④⑥ May 30 - June 22; daily June 27 - Sept. 8; ②④⑥ Sept. 10 - Oct. 5; ④⑥ Oct. 10–26; ⑥ from Nov. 2.

Toulon - Paris: ⑥ to May 25 (also Apr. 18, 25, May 2); ④⑥ May 30 - June 22; daily June 27 - Sept. 8; ②④⑥ Sept. 10 - Oct. 5; ④⑥ Oct. 10–26; ⑥ from Nov. 2.

GERMANY

to 14/12/19

Basel (Lörrach) - Hamburg Altona: ④⑥ Apr. 13 - May 4 (also Dec. 15, 22, Jan. 5, Apr. 6); ①⑥ May 11 - June 15 (also May 30, June 6); ①④⑤⑥⑦ June 17 - Aug. 22; ①⑥ Aug. 24 - Oct. 12 (also Oct. 19). Operated by BahnTouristikExpress.

Also additional service Dec. 15 - Oct. 19 operated by Urlaubs-Express. Runs up to 5 times per week (contact operator for dates)

Hamburg Altona - Basel (Lörrach): ⑤ Apr. 5 - May 3 (also Dec. 14, 21, Jan. 4, Apr. 17, 24, 30); ⑤⑦ May 10 - June 14 (also May 29, June 5); ③④⑤⑥⑦ June 16 - Aug. 21; ⑤⑦ Aug. 23 - Oct. 11 (also Oct. 18). Operated by BahnTouristikExpress.

Also additional service Dec. 14 - Oct. 18 operated by Urlaubs-Express. Runs up to 5 times per week (contact operator for dates).

Hamburg Altona - München Ost: May 29 - Oct. 11. Operated by Urlaubs-Express (contact operator for latest running dates).

München Ost - Hamburg Altona: May 30 - Oct. 12. Operated by Urlaubs-Express (contact operator for latest running dates).

Niebüll - Westerland: Daily shuttle service; 18–28 per day in summer, 12–14 per day in winter.

Westerland - Niebüll: Daily shuttle service; 18–28 per day in summer, 12–14 per day in winter.

GREECE

Athína - Thessaloníki: daily.

Thessaloníki - Athína: daily.

RUSSIA

Moskva - Astrakhan and v.v.
Moskva - Petrozavodsk and v.v.
Moskva - Pskov and v.v.
Moskva - St. Peterburg and v.v.
Moskva - Sochi - Adler and v.v.
St. Peterburg - Astrakhan and v.v.
St. Peterburg - Sochi - Adler and v.v.

Contact operator for days and dates of running.

SLOVAKIA

Bratislava - Humenné: daily (not Dec. 24, 31).

Humenné - Bratislava: daily (not Dec. 24, 31).

SLOVENIA

Bohinjska Bistrica - Podbrdo - Most na Soči: daily.

Most na Soči - Podbrdo - Bohinjska Bistrica: daily.

Note: service operates through the Julian Alps. Passengers remain in their vehicles. Also accepts passengers without vehicles.

Scenic Rail Routes of Europe

The following is a list of some of the most scenic rail routes of Europe, timings for most of which can be found within the timetable (the relevant table number has been specified in bold). Routes marked * are some of the editorial team's favourite journeys. Please note that this list does not include specialised mountain and tourist railways.

Types of scenery: C - Coastline, F - Forest, G - Gorge, L - Lake, M - Mountain, R - River

ALBANIA

Elbasan - Pogradec	M L G R	**1390**

AUSTRIA

Bruck an der Mur - Villach	M R	**980**
Gmunden - Stainach Irdning*	M L	**961**
Innsbruck - Brennero	M	**595**
Innsbruck - Garmisch*	M	**895**
Innsbruck - Schwarzach-St Veit	M G	**960**
Krems - Emmersdorf	R	**991**
Landeck - Bludenz*	M	**951**
St Pölten - Mariazell*	M	**994**
Salzburg - Villach*	M G	**970**
Selzthal - Kleinreifling - Steyr	M G R	**976/977**
Wiener Neustadt - Graz	M	**980**

BELGIUM and LUXEMBOURG

Liège - Luxembourg*	R	**444**
Liège - Marloie	R	**447**
Namur - Dinant	R	**440**

BULGARIA

Septemvri - Dobriniste	M	**1510**
Sofia - Burgas	M	**1500**
Tulovo - Gorna Oryakhovitsa	M	**1525**

CROATIA and BOSNIA

Novi Grad - Sarajevo	M G R	**1350**
Ogulin - Split	M	**1330**
Rijeka - Ogulin	M	**1310**
Sarajevo - Ploče	M G R	**1355**

CZECH REPUBLIC

Karlovy Vary - Mariánské Lázně	R F	**1123**
Karlovy Vary - Chomutov	R	**1110**
Praha - Děčín	R	**1100**

DENMARK

Struer - Thisted	C	**716**

FINLAND

Kouvola - Joensuu	L F	**797**

FRANCE

Aurillac - Neussargues	M G	**331**
Bastia - Ajaccio	M	**369**
Bourg-en-Bresse - Bellegarde	M	**341**
Chambéry - Bourg St Maurice	M	**366**
Chambéry - Modane	M L	**367**
Chamonix - Martigny*	M G	**572**
Clermont Ferrand - Béziers	M G	**332**
Clermont Ferrand - Nîmes*	M G R	**333**
Gap - Briançon	M L	**362**
Genève - Aix les Bains	M R	**364**
Grenoble - Veynes - Marseille	M	**632**
Marseille - Ventimiglia	C	**360/361**
Mouchard - Montbéliard	R	**378**
Nice - Digne	M	**359**
Nice - Cuneo*	M G	**581**
Perpignan - Latour de Carol*	M G	**354**
Portbou - Perpignan	C	**355**
Sarlat - Bergerac	R	**318**
Toulouse - Latour de Carol	M	**312**
Valence - Veynes	M	**362**

GERMANY

Arnstadt - Meiningen	M	**870**
Dresden - Děčín	G R	**1100**
Freiburg - Donaueschingen	G F	**938**
Garmisch - Reutte - Kempten	M	**888**
Heidelberg - Neckarelz	R	**923/924**
Koblenz - Mainz*	G R	**911/914**
München - Lindau	M	**935**
Murnau - Oberammergau	M L	**897**
Naumburg - Saalfeld	R	**849/851**
Niebüll - Westerland	C	**821**

GERMANY - continued

Nürnberg - Pegnitz	G R	**880**
Offenburg - Konstanz	M F	**916**
Pforzheim - Nagold / Wildbad	F	**941**
Plattling - Bayerisch Eisenstein	F	**929**
Rosenheim - Berchtesgaden	M L	**890/891**
Rosenheim - Wörgl	M	**951**
Siegburg/Bonn - Siegen	R	**807**
Stuttgart - Singen	F	**940**
Titisee - Seebrugg	L F	**938**
Trier - Koblenz - Giessen	R	**906/915**
Ulm - Göppingen	M	**930**
Ulm - Tuttlingen	R	**938**

GREAT BRITAIN and IRELAND

Alnmouth - Dunbar	C	**180**
Barrow in Furness - Maryport	C	**159**
Coleraine - Londonderry	C	**231**
Dun Laoghaire - Wicklow	C	**237**
Edinburgh - Aberdeen	C	**224**
Exeter - Newton Abbot	C	**115/116**
Glasgow - Oban / Mallaig*	M L	**218**
Inverness - Kyle of Lochalsh*	M C	**226**
Lancaster - Carlisle - Carstairs	M G R	**151**
Liskeard - Looe	R	**118**
Llanelli - Craven Arms	M	**146**
Machynlleth - Pwllheli	M C	**148**
Perth - Inverness	M	**221**
Plymouth - Gunnislake	R	**118**
St Erth - St Ives	C	**118**
Sheffield - Chinley	M	**193/206**
Shrewsbury - Aberystwyth	M R	**147**
Skipton - Settle - Carlisle	M R	**173**

GREECE

Diakoftó - Kalávrita	M G	**1455**

HUNGARY

Budapest - Szob	R	**1255**
Eger - Szilvásvárad	M	**1299**
Székesfehérvár - Balatonszentgyörgy	L	**1220**
Székesfehérvár - Tapolca	L	**1225**

ITALY

Bologna - Pistoia	M	**609**
Bolzano - Merano	M	**597**
Brennero - Verona*	M	**595**
Brig - Arona	M L	**590**
Domodossola - Locarno*	M G	**551**
Firenze - Viareggio	M	**614**
Fortezza - San Candido	M	**596**
Genova - Pisa	C	**610**
Genova - Ventimiglia	C	**580**
Lecco - Tirano	M L	**593**
Messina - Palermo	C	**641**
Napoli - Sorrento	C	**639**
Roma - Pescara	M	**624**
Salerno - Reggio Calabria	C	**640**
Taranto - Reggio Calabria	C	**635**
Torino - Aosta	M	**586**
Ventimiglia - Cuneo*	M G	**581**

NORWAY

Bergen - Oslo*	M L	**780/781**
Bodø - Trondheim	M L	**787**
Dombås - Åndalsnes	M	**785**
Drammen - Larvik	C	**783**
Myrdal - Flåm*	M C	**781**
Oslo - Kongsvinger	R	**750**
Oslo / Røros - Trondheim	M L	**784/785**
Stavanger - Kristiansand	M	**775**

POLAND

Jelenia Góra - Wałbrzych	M	**1084**
Kraków - Zakopane	M	**1066**
Olsztyn - Ełk	L	**1035**
Olsztyn - Morąg	L	**1035**
Tarnów - Krynica	M	**1078**

PORTUGAL

Covilhã - Entroncamento	M R	**691**
Pampilhosa - Guarda	M	**692**
Porto - Coimbra	C R	**690**
Porto - Pocinho*	R	**694**
Porto - Valença	M C	**696**

ROMANIA

Brasov - Ploesti	M	**1600**
Caransebes - Craiova	M G R	**1620**
Fetesti - Constanta	R	**1680**
Oradea - Cluj Napoca	R	**1612**

SERBIA and MONTENEGRO

Kraljevo - Mitrovica / Mitrovicë	M R	**1375**
Priboj - Bar	M L	**1370**

SLOVAKIA

Banská Bystrica - Brezno - Košice	M	**1188**
Žilina - Poprad Tatry	M	**1180**

SLOVENIA

Jesenice - Sežana	M G R	**1302**
Maribor - Zidani Most	M	**1315**
Maribor - Bleiburg	M G R	**1315**
Villa Opicina - Ljubljana - Zagreb	G R	**1305**

SPAIN

Algeciras - Ronda	M R	**673**
Barcelona - Latour de Carol	M	**656**
Bilbao - San Sebastián	M	**686**
Bilbao - Santander	M	**687**
Ferrol - Gijón*	C	**687**
Granada - Almería	M	**673**
Huesca - Canfranc	M G R	**670**
León - Monforte de Lemos	M	**682**
León - Oviedo	M	**685**
Lleida - La Pobla de Segur	M L	**655**
Málaga - Bobadilla	G	**673**
Santander - Oviedo	M C	**687**
Zaragoza - València	M R	**670**

SWEDEN

Bollnäs - Ånge - Sundsvall	M L	**761**
Borlänge - Mora	M L F	**758**
Borlänge - Ludvika - Frövi	M L F	**755**
Narvik - Kiruna	M F	**765**
Östersund - Storlien	L F	**761**

SWITZERLAND

Andermatt - Göschenen	G	**576**
Basel - Delémont - Moutier	M R	**505**
Chur - Arosa	M G	**541**
Chur - Brig - Zermatt*	M	**575/576**
Chur - St Moritz*	M G	**540**
Davos - Filisur	M G	**545a**
Davos - Landquart	M	**545**
Interlaken Ost - Jungfraujoch*	M	**564**
Interlaken Ost - Luzern	M L	**561**
Interlaken West - Spiez	L	**560**
Lausanne - Brig	M L R	**570**
Lausanne - Neuchâtel - Biel	M L	**505**
Montreux - Zweisimmen - Lenk	M L G	**566**
Rorschach - Kreuzlingen	L	**532**
St Moritz - Scuol Tarasp	M	**546**
St Moritz - Tirano*	M	**547**
Spiez - Zweisimmen	G	**563**
Thun - Kandersteg - Brig*	M L	**562**
Zürich / Luzern - Chiasso	M L	**550**
Zürich - Chur	M L	**520**

City Plans are on pages 30 – 34

AIRPORT → CITY CENTRE LINKS

5

Airport code and name	City	Distance	Journey	Transport ‡	City terminal	Table
AAR Aarhus	Aarhus	37 km	40 mins	🚌 flybus, connects with flights	Banegårdspladsen, Central rail station	
ABZ Aberdeen, Dyce	Aberdeen	11 km	42 mins	🚌 **727**, ①–⑤ ± 6 per hour; ⑥⑦ ± 3 per hour	Union Square bus station.	
ALC Alacant	Alacant	12 km	30 mins	🚌 **C6**, every 20 mins 0600 - 0000	Plaza Puerta del Mar	
AMS Amsterdam, Schiphol	Amsterdam	17 km	20 mins	Train, every 10 mins	Centraal rail station	**451, 454**
	Rotterdam	65 km	45 mins	Train, every 30 mins	Centraal rail station	**450, 454**
	Den Haag	43 km	35 mins	Train, every 30 mins	Centraal rail station	**450, 454**
AOI Ancona, Falconara	Ancona	16 km	30 mins	1) 🚌 Linea **J**, 2) Train hourly at peak times: 17 mins	Main rail station	
ATH Athína, Elefthérios Venizélos	Athína	27 km	43 mins	Train, hourly	Lárisa. Also Line 3 (blue) to Syntagma	**1430**
	Pireás	41 km	90 mins	🚌 **X96**, 3 - 4 per hour	Platía Karaiskáki	
BCN Barcelona, Aeroport del Prat	Barcelona	14 km	19 mins	Train, 2 per hour	Sants. Also calls at Passeig de Gràcia rail station (26 mins)	**659**
BSL Basel - Mulhouse - Freiburg	Basel	9 km	20 mins	🚌 **50**, ①–⑤ 8 per hour; ⑥⑦ 6 per hour	SBB rail station / Kannenfeldplatz	
	Freiburg	60 km	55 mins	🚌 ①–⑤ every 1 - 2 hours; ⑥⑦ every 2 hours	Rail station	
BHD Belfast, City, George Best	Belfast	2 km	15 mins	🚌 *Airlink* **600**, ①–⑥ every 20 mins; ⑦ every 40 mins	Europa Buscentre. Also train from Sydenham rail station	
BFS Belfast, International	Belfast	26 km	40 mins	🚌 *Airbus* **300**, Ⓐ every 15 mins; ⑥ every 20; ⑦ every 30	Europa Buscentre (adjacent to Great Victoria St rail station)	
BEG Beograd, Nikola Tesla	Beograd	18 km	30 mins	🚌 **72**, every 32 minutes	Rail station	
SXF Berlin, Schönefeld	Berlin	24 km	28 mins	Train, *AirportExpress* **RE7/ RB14** 2 per hour 0631 - 2331	Hbf, also Ost, Alexanderplatz and Zoo rail stations	**847**
TXL Berlin, Tegel	Berlin	7 km	40 mins	🚌 *JetExpressBus TXL*, Ⓐ every 10 mins, Ⓒ every 20 mins	Hauptbahnhof rail station	
BIQ Biarritz - Anglet - Bayonne	Biarritz	3 km	14 mins	🚌 *Chronoplus* **14**, every 30 mins	Town centre	
	Bayonne	7 km	28 mins	🚌 *Chronoplus* **14**, every 30 mins	Town centre	
BIO Bilbao, Sondika	Bilbao	10 km	45 mins	🚌 Bizkaibus **A-3247**, every 20 mins 0620 - 0000	Plaza Moyúa (Metro station Moyúa)	
BLL Billund	Vejle	25 km	34 mins	🚌 *Sydtrafik* **43**	Town centre	
BHX Birmingham, International	Birmingham	12 km	11 mins	Train, ①–⑥ ± 9 per hour, ⑦ 6 per hour	New Street rail station from International	**129, 142, 143**
BLQ Bologna, Guglielmo Marconi	Bologna	8 km	25 mins	🚌 *Aerobus* BLQ, every 15 mins 0600 - 2315	Centrale rail station	
BOD Bordeaux, Mérignac	Bordeaux	12 km	45 mins	🚌 Jet' Bus, every 45 mins 0745 - 2245	St Jean rail station	
BOH Bournemouth, Hurn	Bournemouth	10 km	42 mins	🚌 **B 1** *Yellow Buses*, hourly 0708 - 1908	Rail station, Bus station (Travel Interchange)	
BTS Bratislava, Milan Rastislav Štefánika	Bratislava	10 km	25 mins	🚌 **61**, 3 - 4 per hour	Main rail station (Hlavná stanica)	
BRE Bremen	Bremen	3 km	20 mins	Tram **6**, ①–⑥ every 10 mins, ⑦ every 20 mins	Main rail station	
VBS Brescia, Montichiari, Verona	Verona	50 km	45 mins	🚌, connects with Ryanair flights	Main rail station	
	Brescia	18 km	20 mins	🚌, connects with Ryanair flights	Main rail station	
BRS Bristol, International	Bristol	13 km	30 mins	🚌 *International Flyer*, ①–⑥ 3 - 6 per hour; ⑦ 2 - 6 per hour	Temple Meads rail station, also bus station	
BRQ Brno	Brno	8 km	20 mins	🚌 **76**, 2 per hour	Main rail station, also bus station	
BRU Brussels, Zaventem	Brussels	12 km	25 mins	Train, 6 per hour	Midi / Zuid rail station (also calls at Central and Nord)	**401**
	Antwerpen	38 km	34 mins	Train, Ⓐ 2 per hour, Ⓒ hourly.	Centraal	**420, 432**
OTP Bucuresti, Henri Coanda, Otopeni	Bucuresti	16 km	45 mins	🚌 **783**, ①–⑤ every 15 - 30 mins; ⑥⑦ every 30 mins	Piata Victoriei (800m from Nord station or 1 stop on subway)	
BUD Budapest, Ferihegy	Budapest	16 km	40 mins	🚌 **200E**, every 10 - 20 mins	Kőbánya-Kispest metro station (Line M3 to Nyugati rail station)	
	Budapest	18 km	25 mins	Train, 2 - 6 per hour	🚌 **200E**, to Ferihegy station then train to Nyugati rail station.	
BZG Bydgoszcz	Bydgoszcz	4 km	30 mins	🚌 **80**, 2 per hour	Main rail station	
CCF Carcassonne, Salvaza	Carcassonne	5 km	10 mins	🚌, connects with Ryanair flights	Place Davilla and Carcassonne rail station	
CWL Cardiff	Cardiff	19 km	40 mins	🚌 *Airbus Xpress* **T9**, ①–⑥ hourly, ⑦ every 2 hours	Central rail station, city centre	
	Cardiff	19 km	50 mins	🚌 to Rhoose then Train: ①–⑥ hourly, ⑦ every 2 hours	Central rail station	
CRL Charleroi, Brussels South	Brussels	55 km	60 mins	🚌 *Brussels City Shuttle*, every 30 mins	Brussels Midi (corner of Rue de France / Rue de l'Instruction)	
	Charleroi		18 mins	🚌 *Line* **A**, ①–⑤ 2 per hour, ⑥⑦ hourly	Main rail station	
ORK Cork	Cork	8 km	25 mins	🚌 **226**, ①–⑥ 2 per hour, ⑦ hourly	Rail station, also Parnell Place bus station	
LDY Derry (Londonderry)	Londonderry	11 km	30 mins	🚌 connects with flights	Foyle Street bus station	
DNR Dinard - Pleurtuit - St-Malo	St Malo	14 km	20 mins	Taxis only. Dinard 6 km 10 mins		
DSA Doncaster - Sheffield	Doncaster	10 km	25 mins	🚌 **91**, ①–⑥ 2 per hour; ⑦ hourly	Frenchgate Interchange (bus station)	
DOK Donetsk	Donetsk	13 km	40 mins	Fixed-run taxi **5**	Main rail station	
DTM Dortmund, Wickede	Dortmund	10 km	25 mins	🚌 every hour, AirportExpress	Main rail station (Hbf). Also 🚌 to Holzwickede rail station	
DRS Dresden	Dresden	15 km	21 mins	Train (S-Bahn **S2**) every 30 mins	Main rail stations (Hbf and Neustadt)	**857a**
DUB Dublin	Dublin	11 km	60 mins	🚌 *Airlink* **747**, every 10 mins (15 - 20 mins on ⑦)	Bus station (Busáras) 30min, O'Connell St., Heuston rail station	
	Belfast	157 km	130 mins	🚌 **001 / 200**, hourly 0520 - 2120 also 2320, 0120, 0320	Europa Buscentre. Also 2220, 0020, 0220, 0420 June 3 - Sept. 22	
DBV Dubrovnik, Čilipi	Dubrovnik	24 km	30 mins	🚌 *Atlas Bus*, connects with flights	Bus station	
DUS Düsseldorf, International	Düsseldorf	7 km	12 mins	Train (S - Bahn **S1**) Ⓐ every 20 mins, Ⓒ every 30 mins	Main rail station (Hauptbahnhof)	**800, 802**
EMA East Midlands, Nottingham - - Leicester - Derby	East Midlands	10 km	10 mins	Taxi shuttle	East Midlands Parkway rail station	
	Nottingham	21 km	55 mins	🚌 *Skylink*, every 30 min. 0505 - 0105, also 0205, 0305, 0405	Broadmarsh bus station	
	Derby	19 km	40 mins	🚌 *Skylink* every 30 min. 0615 - 1855; (60 mins 1945 - 0545)	Bus station	
	Loughborough	8 km	25 mins	🚌 *Skylink* every 30 min. 0715 - 2017; (60 mins 2057 - 0657)	Swan Street	
	Leicester	23 km	55 mins	🚌 *Skylink* every 30 min. 0715 - 1948; (60 mins 2057 - 0657)	St Margaret's bus station	
EDI Edinburgh, Turnhouse	Edinburgh	11 km	25 mins	🚌 *Airlink* **100**, every 10 mins. **N 22** 2400 - 0600 every 30mins.	Haymarket rail station; Waverley Bridge (next to Waverley station)	
ERF Erfurt	Erfurt	6 km	22 mins	Tram, Line 4, Ⓐ 3 - 6 per hour; Ⓒ 2 per hour	Main rail station (Hauptbahnhof)	
EBJ Esbjerg	Esbjerg	12 km	21 mins	🚌 **8**, hourly	*Bybusterminal*	
EXT Exeter	Exeter	8 km	25 mins	🚌 **56, 56A, 56B**, 1 per hour	St Davids rail station	
FAO Faro	Faro	6 km	20 mins	🚌 *Proxima* **16**, 1 per hour	Rail station, Bus station	
FLR Firenze, Amerigo Vespucci	Firenze	7 km	20 mins	🚌 Ataf *Vola in bus* **62**, every 30 mins	Santa Maria Novella rail station	
HHN Frankfurt, Hahn	Frankfurt	120 km	105 mins	🚌, connects with Ryanair flights	Mannheimer Straße, adjacent to main rail station (Hauptbahnhof)	
Also 🚌 to Bingen, 60 mins; Heidelberg hbf, 140 mins; Koblenz, 70 mins; Köln hbf, 135 mins; Luxembourg, 105 mins; Mainz, 70 mins; Mannheim, 110 mins						
FRA Frankfurt	Frankfurt	10 km	15 mins	Train (S-Bahn **S8** or **S9**), 4 - 6 times hourly	Main rail station (Hauptbahnhof)	**917a**
FDH Friedrichshafen	Friedrichshafen	4 km	7 mins	1 - 2 trains per hour	Main rail station (Stadt) or Harbour (Hafen)	**933**
GDN Gdańsk, Lech Walesa	Gdańsk	10 km	22 mins	Train *PKM*, Port Lotniczy, 3 - 4 per hour	Wrzeszcz rail station, then 3 stops (every 15 mins) to Główny	
GVA Genève	Genève	6 km	6 mins	Train, 5 times hourly	Cornavin rail station	**500, 570**
GOA Genova, Cristoforo Colombo	Genova	7 km	20 mins	🚌 *Volabus*, 1 - 2 per hour	Principe rail station	
GRO Girona	Girona	12 km	25 mins	🚌, hourly	Rail / Bus station (Estación autobuses)	
	Barcelona	102 km	70 mins	🚌, connects with Ryanair flights	Estacio del Nord, corner of carrer Ali Bei 80 / Sicilia	

‡ – The frequencies shown apply during daytime on weekdays and are from the airport to the city centre. There may be fewer journeys in the evenings, at weekends and during the winter months. Extended 🚌 journey times could apply during peak hours.

5 AIRPORT → CITY CENTRE LINKS

City Plans are on pages 30 – 34

Airport code and name	City	Distance	Journey	Transport ‡	City terminal	Table
GLA Glasgow, International	Glasgow	15 km	15 mins	🚌 *GlasgowFlyer*, ①–⑥ every 10 mins, ⑦ every 15 mins.	Central rail station	
PIK Glasgow, Prestwick	Glasgow	61 km	50 mins	Train, ①–⑥ 4 per hour, ⑦ 2 per hour	Central rail station	**216**
GSE Göteborg, City	Göteborg	17 km	30 mins	🚌, connects with Ryanair, Air Berlin and Wizz Air flights	Nils Ericson Terminalen (bus station) / Central rail station	
GOT Göteborg, Landvetter	Göteborg	25 km	30 mins	🚌, ①–⑤ 3 per hour, ⑥⑦ 2 - 3 per hour	Nils Ericson Terminalen (bus station) / Central rail station	
GRZ Graz	Graz	9 km	9 mins	Train ①–⑥ 1 - 2 per hour, ⑦ every 2 hours	Main rail station (Hauptbahnhof)	**980**
GNB Grenoble, St Geoirs	Grenoble	37 km	45 mins	🚌, connects with flights	Main rail station, also bus station	
HAM Hamburg, Fuhlsbüttel	Hamburg	11 km	24 mins	Train (S-Bahn **S1**), every 10 mins	Main rail station (Hauptbahnhof)	
HAJ Hannover, Langenhagen	Hannover	15 km	17 mins	Train (S-Bahn **S5**), every 30 mins	Main rail station (Hauptbahnhof)	**809**
HEL Helsinki, Vantaa	Helsinki	19 km	35 mins	Train ①–⑥ 4 - 6 per hour, ⑦ 3 - 4 per hour	Main rail station	
NOC Ireland West Airport Knock	Ballyhaunis	22 km	30 mins	🚌 **64**, 0855, 1250	Rail station	**235**
IOM Isle of Man, Ronaldsway	Douglas	16 km	30 mins	🚌 **1**, hourly (every 30 mins in peak periods)	Lord street	
IST İstanbul, Atatürk	İstanbul	28 km	40 mins	🚌, *Havas Airport Shuttle* hourly 0400 - 2400	Taksim	
	İstanbul	28 km	60 mins	Metro to Zeytinburnu, then over bridge for Tram **T1**	Sirkeci rail station	
SAW İstanbul, Sabiha Gökcen	İstanbul	32 km	60 mins	🚌, 1–2 per hour, 0540 - 2040	Bus station. Also Pendik rail station is 4km from airport	
XRY Jerez	Jerez	10 km	9 mins	Train, 11 trains per day	Jerez de la Frontera, then to Cadiz	**671**
FKB Karlsruhe - Baden-Baden	Baden-Baden	8 km	15 mins	🚌 **205**, connects with Ryanair flights	Rail station; also 🚌 **140** to Karlsruhe Hbf, 25 mins	
KTW Katowice, Pyrzowice	Katowice	34 km	50 mins	🚌 *Lotnisko*, *PKM*, 1 per hour approx	Katowice Dworzec (main rail station)	
KUN Kaunas	Kaunas	13 km	40 mins	🚌 **120**, **29**	City centre	
	Vilnius	102 km	90 mins	🚌 connects with Ryanair flights	Hotel Panorama, close to bus and rail stations	
KLU Klagenfurt	Klagenfurt	5 km	25 mins	🚌 **45**, to Annabichl rail station, then train or 🚌 **40**	Main rail station and bus station	
CPH København, Kastrup	København	12 km	15 mins	Train, every 10 mins	Main rail station (Hovedbanegård)	**703**
	Malmö	36 km	22 mins	Train, every 20 mins	Central rail station	**703**
CGN Köln / Bonn, Konrad Adenauer	Bonn	25 km	32 mins	🚌 **SB60**, ①–⑤ 2 per hour; ⑥⑦ 1 - 2 per hour	Main rail station (Hauptbahnhof)	
	Köln	15 km	16 mins	Train **S13**, ①–⑤ every 20 mins, ⑥⑦ every 30 mins	Main rail station (Hbf). Also to Mönchengladbach, Koblenz	**802**
KRK Kraków John Paul II Airport (Balice)	Kraków	12 km	18 mins	Train, 2 per hour, from Lotnisko station	Kraków Główny	**1099**
KBP Kyiv, Boryspil	Kyiv	34 km	40 mins	Train 1 - 2 per hour	Main rail station	
LBA Leeds - Bradford	Leeds	16 km	40 mins	🚌 **757**, 2 per hour	Main rail station and bus station	
	Bradford	11 km	40 mins	🚌 **737**, **747**, 2 per hour	Interchange rail station	
AOC Leipzig, Altenburg - Nobitz	Leipzig	75 km	70 mins	🚌 **250** *ThüSac*, connects with Ryanair flights	Main rail station. Also stops at Altenburg rail station after 15 mins	
LEJ Leipzig - Halle	Leipzig	20 km	14 mins	Train, 2 - 3 per hour	Main rail station (Hauptbahnhof)	**856**
	Halle	18 km	12 mins	Train, 2 per hour	Main rail station (Hauptbahnhof)	**856**
LNZ Linz, Blue Danube	Linz	12 km	19 mins	🚌, connects with Ryanair flights	Main rail station. Also free 🚌 to Hörsching rail station, 3 mins	
LIS Lisboa, Portela	Lisboa	3 km	9 mins	Train, Red (Vermelho) line. Every 5 - 9 mins	Oriente rail station. For Santa Apolónia change at São Sebastião	
LPL Liverpool, John Lennon	Liverpool	11 km	37 mins	🚌 **500**, every 30 mins 0545 - 1945	Lime Street rail station, Liverpool One bus station	
LJU Ljubljana, Jože Pučnik, Brnik	Ljubljana	26 km	45 mins	🚌, Ⓐ hourly 0500 - 2000; © 0700, every 2 hours 1000 - 2000	Bus station (Avtobusna postaja)	
LCJ Łódź, Lublinek	Łódź	6 km	20 mins	🚌 **65**	Kaliska rail station	
LCY London, City	London	12 km	25 mins	Train (Docklands Light Railway), every 8 - 10 mins	Bank underground (tube) station	**140**
LGW London, Gatwick	London	44 km	30 mins	Train *Gatwick Express*, every 15 minutes	Victoria rail station	**103, 105, 140**
LHR London, Heathrow	London	24 km	15 mins	Train *Heathrow Express*, every 15 minutes	Paddington rail station	**140**
	London	24 km	58 mins	Underground train (tube), every 6 - 12 mins	King's Cross St Pancras rail station	**140**
LTN London, Luton	London	50 km	35 mins	6 - 7 per hour (🚌 between ✈ and Parkway rail station)	St Pancras International rail station	**103, 140, 170**
SEN London, Southend	London	64 km	55 mins	Train, 3 per hour	Liverpool Street rail station	
STN London, Stansted	London	55 km	46 mins	Train *Stansted Express*, every 15 minutes	Liverpool Street rail station	**140**
LBC Lübeck, Blankensee	Lübeck	8 km	30 mins	🚌 **6**, every 20 mins	Bus station (bus stop 5). Also train from Flughafen 300m walk	**827**
	Hamburg	59 km	75 mins	🚌 *VHHAG*, connects with Ryanair flights	Corner Adenaueralle / Brockesstrasse (ZOB) near main rail station	
LUZ Lublin	Lublin	10 km	15 mins	Train, ①–⑥ 5 per day, ⑦ 3 per day, connects with flights	Main rail station	
LUX Luxembourg, Findel	Luxembourg	7 km	25 mins	🚌 **16**, every 15 mins ①–⑥, every 30 mins ⑦	Central rail station	
LWO Lviv, Skniliv	Lvov	10 km		🚌, Taxi-bus *Marshrutka*	City Centre	
LYS Lyon, St Exupéry	Lyon	23 km	30 mins	Tram *RhôneExpress*, 4 per hour	Part Dieu rail station	
	Chambéry	87 km	60 mins	🚌 Altibus, 4 - 5 times daily	Bus station (gare routière)	
	Grenoble	91 km	65 mins	🚌 Faure Vercors, 0630 Ⓐ, hourly 0730 - 2330	Bus station (gare routière); Place de la Résistance	
MAD Madrid, Barajas T4	Madrid	12 km	16 mins	Train, Cercanías, from T4, every 15 mins 0602 - 2301, 2331.	Chamartín, also Atocha 25 mins. 🚌 from T4 to T1, T2 and T3.	
AGP Málaga	Málaga	8 km	12 mins	Train, every 30 mins	María Zambrano (Renfe) and Centro-Alameda rail stations	**662**
MMX Malmö, Sturup	Malmö	30 km	45 mins	🚌 *flygbussarna*, 1 - 2 per hour	Central rail station	
MAN Manchester	Manchester	16 km	14 mins	Train, up to 9 per hour (hourly through the night)	Piccadilly rail station	
MSE Manston	Ramsgate	3 km	9 mins	🚌 **38**, ①–⑥ hourly 0943 - 1343	Rail station	
MRS Marseille, Provence	Marseille	28 km	25 mins	🚌, every 20 mins. See also rail / bus on Table **351**	St Charles rail station; also 🚌 to Aix TGV rail stn. every 30 mins	
FMM Memmingen	Memmingen	5 km	10 mins	🚌 **2**, **810**, **811**	Bus station and rail station; also 🚌 to München, 95 mins	
LIN Milano, Linate	Milano	9 km	20 mins	1) 🚌 **73** every 10 mins; 2) 🚌 *Starfly*, every 30 mins	1) Piazza S. Babila, Metro line 1; 2) Centrale rail station	
MXP Milano, Malpensa	Milano	45 km	40 mins	1) *Malpensa Express* train, every 30 mins; 2) 1 - 2 per hour	1) Cadorna and Bovisa rail stations; 2) Centrale rail station	**583**
			50 mins	🚌 *Bus Express*, 2 per hour / *Shuttle Air* 3 per hour	Centrale rail station. Also 🚌 to Gallarate (Table **590**)	
BGY Milano, Orio al Serio, Bergamo	Milano	45 km	60 mins	🚌, 1 - 2 per hour	Centrale rail station (Air Terminal)	
	Bergamo	4 km	15 mins	🚌, 2 per hour	Rail station	
MSQ Minsk	Minsk	42 km	90 mins	🚌, **112**, **300**,	Vostochniy and Moskovskiy bus stations	
DME Moskva, Domodedovo	Moskva	35 km	47 mins	Train, *Aeroexpress*, 1 - 2 per hour approx	Paveletskaya rail station	**1901**
SVO Moskva, Sheremetyevo	Moskva	35 km	35 mins	Train, *Aeroexpress*, 1 - 2 per hour approx	Belorusskaya rail station	**1901**
VKO Moskva, Vnukovo	Moskva	28 km	40 mins	Train, *Aeroexpress*, 1 per hour approx	Kiyevskaya rail station	**1901**
MUC München, International	München	37 km	40 mins	Train **S1**, **S8** for Hbf, every 10 mins; **S8** for Ost, every 20 mins	Main rail stations (Hauptbahnhof, Ostbahnhof)	**892**
	Freising	6 km	10 mins	Train hourly 0828 - 2228	Rail station for Regensburg and connections to Passau	**892, 878**
RMU Murcia, Corvera	Murcia	25km	30 mins	🚌 connects with flights	City centre	
NTE Nantes, Atlantique	Nantes	9 km	30 mins	🚌 *Tan Air*, ± hourly; connects with flights	Main rail station	
NAP Napoli, Capodichino	Napoli	7 km	20 mins	🚌 *ANM* **3S** line, 2 per hour; *Alibus*, 2 per hour	Piazza Garibaldi (Centrale rail station)	
NCL Newcastle, International	Newcastle	9 km	25 mins	Metro train, every 12 mins	Main rail station	

‡ – The frequencies shown apply during daytime on weekdays and are from the airport to the city centre. There may be fewer journeys in the evenings, at weekends and during the winter months. Extended 🚌 journey times could apply during peak hours.

¶ – Graz Airport - Feldkirchen rail station is located about 300 metres away from the airport.

City Plans are on pages 30 – 34

AIRPORT → CITY CENTRE LINKS

5

Airport code and name		City	Distance	Journey	Transport ‡	City terminal	Table
NCE	Nice, Côte d'Azur	Nice	7 km	20 mins	🚌 **99**, 2 per hour	SNCF rail station ¶	
			7 km	24 mins	Tram **2**, ①–⑤ every 6 mins, ⑥ 8 per hour, ⑦ 6 per hour	Magnan	
FNI	Nîmes - Arles - Camargue	Nîmes	12 km	20 mins	🚌, connects with Ryanair flights	Rail station	
NWI	Norwich	Norwich	8 km	24 mins	🚌 **603**, ①–⑥ 4 per hour 0700 - 1800, 1835, 1905, 1935, 2002	Bus station	
NUE	Nürnberg	Nürnberg	6 km	12 mins	Train, U-bahn **U2**, 4 - 6 per hour	Main rail station (Hauptbahnhof)	
ODS	Odesa	Odesa	9 km	30 mins	🚌 **129**	Rail station	
OSL	Oslo, Gardermoen	Oslo	49 km	19 mins	Train *Flytoget*, 3 - 6 per hour	Central rail station	**771**
TRF	Oslo, Sandefjord Torp	Oslo	123 km	116 mins	🚌 to Torp rail station (4 mins) for train to Oslo	Also 🚌 to Oslo Bus terminal	**783**
RYG	Oslo, Rygge	Oslo	69 km	51 mins	🚌 connects with Ryanair flights, to Rygge rail station (4 km).	Sentral rail station (51 mins Rygge to Sentral)	**770**
OSR	Ostrava, Leoš Janáček	Ostrava	31km	31 mins	Train **S4**, 10 per day	Ostrava hlavní	
PMO	Palermo, Falcone-Borsellino	Palermo	24 km	45 mins	Train *Trinacria express*, ①–⑥ 2 per hour, ⑦ hourly	Centrale rail station	
PMI	Palma, Mallorca	Palma	11 km	30 mins	🚌 **1**, every 15 mins	Paseo de Mallorca, Placa d'Espanya (for rail stations), the Port	
BVA	Paris, Beauvais	Paris	80 km	75 mins	🚌, connects with Ryanair and WizzAir flights	Porte Maillot, Metro (Line 1) for Châtelet Les Halles, Gare de Lyon	
CDG	Paris, Charles de Gaulle	Paris	25 km	35 mins	RER train, (Line B), every 7 - 15 mins	Nord, Châtelet Les Halles, and St Michel rail stations	**398**
		Disneyland	23 km	45 mins	🚌 **VEA** Navette / Shuttle, every 20 minutes	Disneyland Resort, Disneyland hotels	
ORY	Paris, Orly	Paris	15 km	35 mins	🚌 to Pont de Rungis, then RER train, (Line C) 4 per hr.	Austerlitz, St Michel, Musée d'Orsay, and Invalides rail stns.	**398**
		Paris	15 km	33 mins	ORLYVAL shuttle to Antony then RER train, (Line B) 4 per hr.	Châlet-Les-Halles, Nord rail stations	**398**
PGF	Perpignan, Rivesaltes	Perpignan	5 km	15 mins	🚌, connects with flights	Rail station, bus station (gare routière)	
PSA	Pisa, Galileo Galilei	Pisa	2 km	5 mins	People Mover, every 5-8 minutes 0600 - 2400	Centrale rail station	**613**
OPO	Porto	Porto	17 km	35 mins	Metro Train, Line E, 3 per hour	Campanhã rail station	
POZ	Poznań, Ławica	Poznań	6 km	21 mins	🚌 **59** *MPK*, 2 - 3 per hour	Rail station (Główny)	
PRG	Praha, Václav Havel	Praha	19 km	46 mins	🚌 **AE** *Airport Express*, every 20 - 30 mins	hlavní rail station	
		Praha	17 km	60 mins	🚌 **119**, every 10 mins	Nádraží Veleslavín metro station, then Metro line A to muzeum	
PUY	Pula	Pula	6 km	15 mins	🚌, connects with Ryanair flights	Town centre	
REU	Reus	Reus	6 km	20 mins	🚌 **50**, *Hispano Igualadina*, hourly	Rail station	**652**
		Barcelona	90 km	90 mins	🚌 *Hispano Igualadina* connects with Ryanair flights	Sants rail station	
KEF	Reykjavík, Keflavík	Reykjavík	50 km	45 mins	🚌 *flybus*, connects with all flights	BSÍ bus terminal	
RIX	Riga	Riga	13 km	30 mins	🚌 **22**, every 10 - 30 mins	Abrenes iela (street) next to rail station	
RJK	Rijeka	Rijeka	30 km	45 mins	🚌 *Autotrans*, connects with flights	Bus station, Jelačić Square	
CIA	Roma, Ciampino	Roma	15 km	35 mins	🚌 *Airlink* 1 - 3 per hour, to Ciampino, then train	Termini rail station	**622**
FCO	Roma, Fiumicino	Roma	26 km	42 mins	Train, ①–⑥ 4 per hour, ⑦ 2 per hour	Ostiense and Tiburtina rail stations	**622**
	(also known as Leonardo da Vinci)		26 km	31 mins	*Leonardo Express* rail service, every 30 mins	Termini rail station	**622**
RTM	Rotterdam	Rotterdam	5 km	20 mins	*Airport Shuttle* **33**, ①–⑤ every 10 mins, ⑥⑦ every 15 mins	Groot Handelsgebouw (adjacent to Centraal rail station)	
RZE	Rzeszów, Jasionka	Rzeszów	15 km	20 mins	🚌 **L**, connects with flights	Main rail station and bus station	
LED	St Peterburg, Pulkovo II	St Peterburg	17 km	60 mins	🚌 **13**	Moskovskaya Metro station, Line 2 for Nevski Pr. (see City Plans)	
SZG	Salzburg, W. A. Mozart	Salzburg	5 km	22 mins	🚌 **2**, ①–⑥ every 10 - 20 mins, ⑦ every 20 mins	Main rail station	
SIP	Simferopol	Simferopol	12 km	28 mins	🚌 **9** (trolleybus), every 10–15 mins	Main rail station	
SKP	Skopje, Alexander the Great	Skopje	14 km	25 mins	🚌 Vardar Ekspres, connects with flights	Bus station	
SOF	Sofia, International	Sofia	10 km	26 mins	Train, Line **1** from Terminal 2, every 10 mins	City centre. Change at Serdika for Line **2**, for Central rail station	
SOU	Southampton	Southampton	8 km	8 mins	Train, 50 metres from terminal, 4 - 5 trains per hour	Central rail station	**108, 129**
SPU	Split, Kaštela	Split	16 km	50 mins	🚌 connects with flights	Bus station. Departs 200m from Airport terminal	
SVG	Stavanger, Sola	Stavanger	14 km	30 mins	🚌, ①–⑤ every 20 mins, ⑥ 2 per hour, ⑦ hourly	Atlantic Hotel / Fiskepiren	
ARN	Stockholm, Arlanda	Stockholm	44 km	20 mins	*Arlanda Express* train, every 15 mins	Central rail station	**747, 760**
NYO	Stockholm, Skavsta	Stockholm	103 km	80 mins	🚌, connects with Ryanair flights	Cityterminal (bus station), also 🚌 to Nyköping rail station	
VST	Stockholm, Västerås	Stockholm	107 km	75 mins	🚌, connects with Ryanair flights	Cityterminal (bus station), also 🚌 **941** to Västerås rail station	
SXB	Strasbourg, Entzheim	Strasbourg	10 km	9 mins	Train from Entzheim Aéroport (300m walk) 1 - 4 per hour	Gare Centrale (Central rail station)	**388**
STR	Stuttgart, Echterdingen	Stuttgart	20 km	27 mins	Train (S-Bahn **S2**, **S3**), 2 - 4 times hourly	Main rail station (Hauptbahnhof)	**932**
SZZ	Szczecin, Goleniów	Szczecin	35 km	35 mins	Train, 14 - 20 per day.	Szczecin Główny.	
TLL	Tallinn, Ülemiste	Tallinn	5 km	22 mins	🚌 **90K**, every 30 mins 0800 - 1800	Balti jaam (rail station)	
TMP	Tampere, Pirkkala	Tampere	18 km	25 mins	🚌, connects with Ryanair flights	Main rail station	
TBS	Tbilisi	Tbilisi	19 km	35 mins	Train	Rail station	**1995**
TIA	Tirana (Tiranë), Nënë Tereza	Tirana	12 km	45 mins	🚌 *Rinas Express*, every hour 0600 - 1800	National Museum in city centre	
TRN	Torino, Caselle	Torino	16 km	20 mins	*SATTI* train every 30 mins	Torino Dora rail station, Piazza Baldissera	
		Torino	16 km	40 mins	🚌, ①–⑥ 2 - 3 per hour; ⑦ 1 - 2 per hour	Torino Porta Nuova and Porta Susa rail stations	
TLS	Toulouse, Blagnac	Toulouse	8 km	38 mins	Tram, **T2** every 15 minutes for Arènes then Metro line **A**	for Marengo-SNCF, then 300m to Matabiau rail station	
		Toulouse	8 km	20 mins	🚌 *Aero*, every 20 minutes	Place Jeanne d'Arc / Matabiau rail / bus station (gare routière)	
TRS	Trieste, Ronchi dei Legionari	Trieste	33 km	29 mins	Train, hourly	Rail station	
		Monfalcone	5 km	5 mins	Train, hourly	Rail station	
TRD	Trondheim, Værnes	Trondheim	33 km	37 mins	Train, ①–⑤ hourly, ⑥⑦ every two hours	Rail station. Værnes rail station is 220m from Airport terminal	**787**
VLC	València	València	9 km	22 mins	Train, Lines **3**, **5**, Ⓐ every 6 - 9 mins; ⑥⑦ every 8 - 12 mins	Xátiva for Nord rail station	
VCE	Venezia, Marco Polo	Venezia	12 km	25 mins	🚌 **5**, 2 per hour	Piazzale Roma (see city plans p32)	
		Venezia		80 mins	Waterbus *Alilaguna* ± every 30 mins	Lido 53 - 63 mins / Piazza S. Marco, 72 - 80 mins	
TSF	Venezia, Treviso	Venezia	30 km	70 mins	🚌, connects with flights	Mestre rail station, Piazzale Roma (see city plans p32)	
VRN	Verona, Villafranca	Verona	12 km	20 mins	🚌, every 20 mins 0635 - 2335	Rail station	
VNO	Vilnius	Vilnius	4 km	7 mins	Train, every ± 40 minutes	Rail station	**1816**
WAW	Warszawa, Frederic Chopin, Okęcie	Warszawa	13 km	23 mins	SKM / KM train, 3 - 5 per hour	Śródmieście (2 - 3 per hr) or Centralna (1 - 2 per hr) rail stations	
WMI	Warszawa, Modlin	Warszawa	44 km	47 mins	🚌, to Modlin rail stn, then train, approx 1 - 2 per hour	Centralna or Gdánska rail stations	**1030**
NRN	Weeze, Niederhein	Düsseldorf	70 km	75 mins	🚌, connects with Ryanair flights	Main rail station (Hauptbahnhof) Worringer Street	
		Düsseldorf	74 km	82 mins	🚌 **SW1**, to Weeze rail station, then train, Table **802**	Main rail station (Hauptbahnhof)	**802**
VIE	Wien, Schwechat	Wien	21 km	16 mins	*City Airport Train (CAT)*, every 30 mins; special fares	Mitte rail station	**985**
		Wien	21 km	25 mins	S-bahn, every 30 mins	Mitte rail station	**985**
		Bratislava	54 km	60 mins	🚌 *ÖBB-Postbus / Slovak Lines*, hourly	AS Mlynské nivy (bus station) / Einsteinnova/Petrzalka	**985**
WRO	Wrocław, Copernicus	Wrocław	10 km	30 mins	🚌 **406**, ①–⑥ 2 - 3 per hour; ⑦ every 40 mins	Rail station, bus station	
ZAG	Zagreb	Zagreb	17 km	25 mins	🚌, 1 - 2 per hour	Bus station (Autobusni kolodvor), Avenija Marina Drzica	
ZAZ	Zaragoza	Zaragoza	10 km	30 mins	🚌, ①–⑥ 1 - 2 per hour 0615 - 2315; ⑦ hourly 0645 - 2245	Paseo Maria Agustín, 150m from Portillo rail station.	
ZRH	Zürich	Zürich	10 km	13 mins	Train, 7 - 8 per hour	Main rail station (HB)	**529**
ZQW	Zweibrücken	Zweibrucken	4 km	10 mins	Taxi	Rail station. Also 🚌 **199** to Saarbrücken	**918**

‡ – The frequencies shown apply during daytime on weekdays and are from the airport to the city centre. There may be fewer journeys in the evenings, at weekends and during the winter months. Extended 🚌 journey times could apply during peak hours.

¶ – Also train, from Nice St Augustin, ± hourly; 800m from Terminal 1.

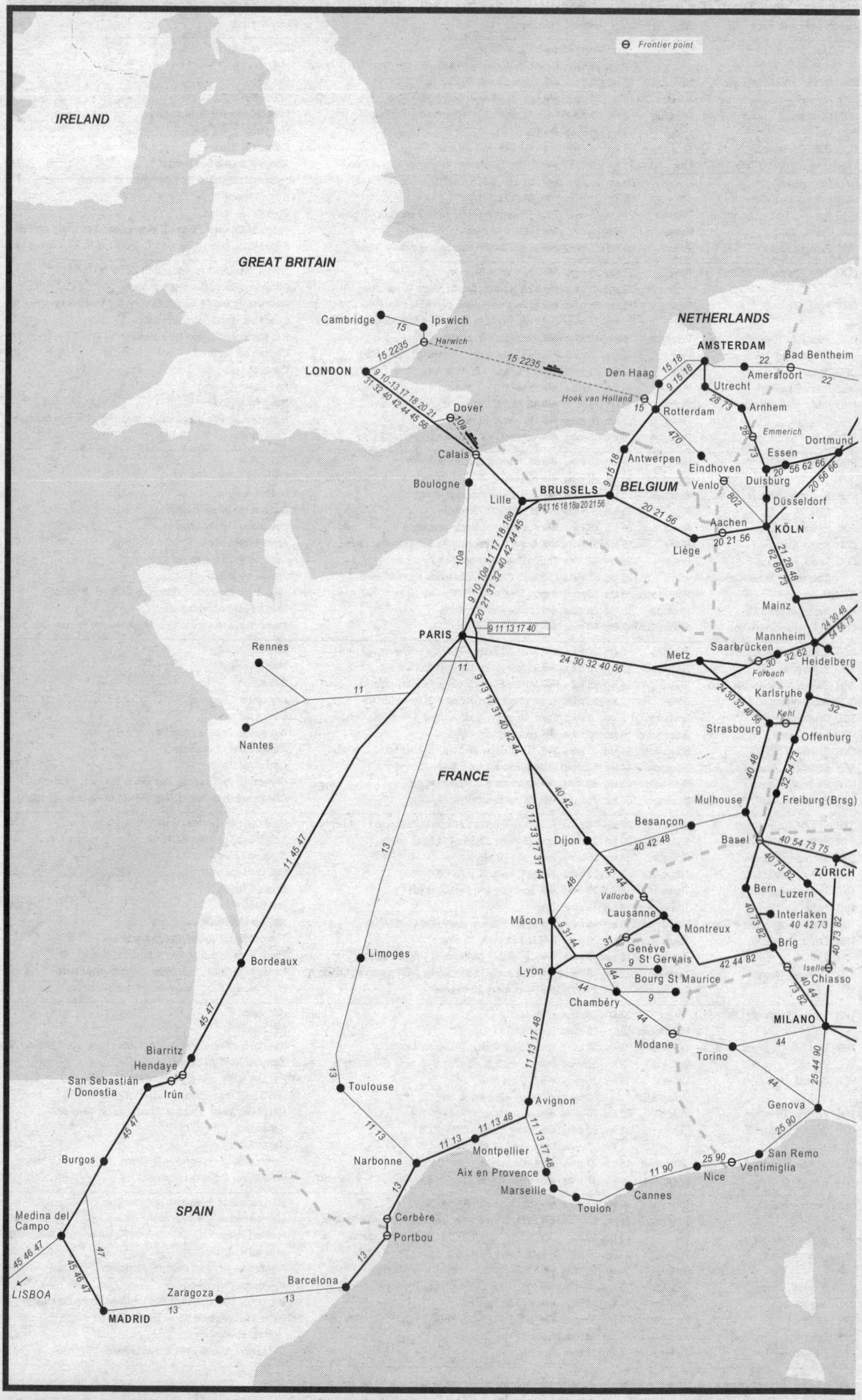
Frontier point
IRELAND
GREAT BRITAIN
NETHERLANDS
BELGIUM
FRANCE
SPAIN
Cambridge
Ipswich
Harwich
LONDON
Dover
Calais
Boulogne
Lille
BRUSSELS
PARIS
Rennes
Nantes
Bordeaux
Biarritz
Hendaye
San Sebastián / Donostia
Irún
Burgos
Medina del Campo
LISBOA
MADRID
Zaragoza
Barcelona
Portbou
Cerbère
Narbonne
Toulouse
Limoges
Montpellier
Aix en Provence
Marseille
Toulon
Cannes
Nice
Ventimiglia
San Remo
Genova
Avignon
Lyon
Mâcon
Dijon
Besançon
Chambéry
Modane
Torino
MILANO
Chiasso
Iselle
Brig
Interlaken
Bern
Luzern
ZÜRICH
Basel
Mulhouse
Freiburg (Brsg)
Offenburg
Strasbourg
Kehl
Karlsruhe
Heidelberg
Mannheim
Mainz
Saarbrücken
Forbach
Metz
Vallorbe
Lausanne
Montreux
Genève
St Gervais
Bourg St Maurice
KÖLN
Aachen
Liège
Düsseldorf
Duisburg
Essen
Dortmund
Emmerich
Arnhem
Utrecht
AMSTERDAM
Amersfoort
Bad Bentheim
Den Haag
Rotterdam
Hoek van Holland
Antwerpen
Eindhoven
Venlo

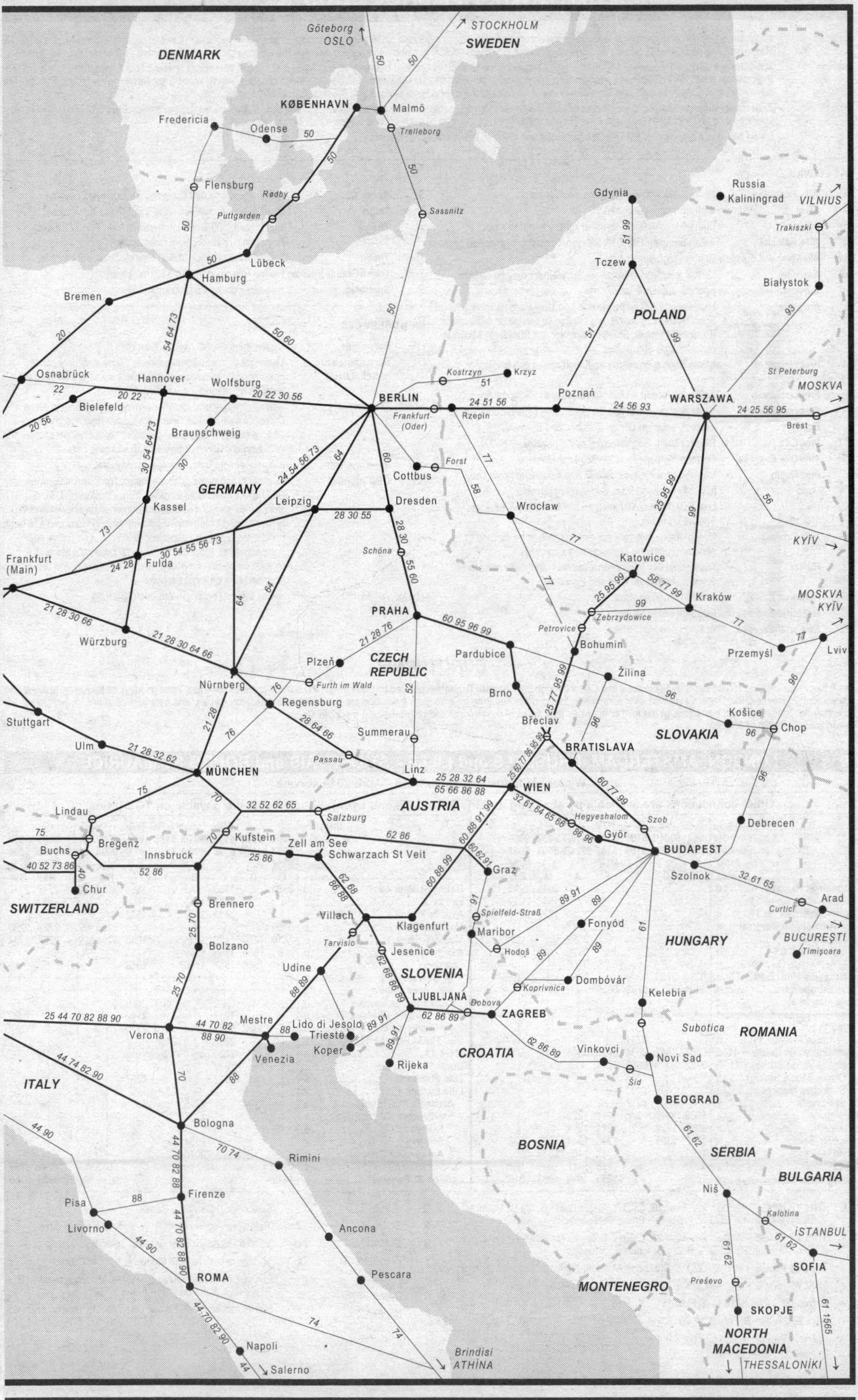

Göteborg
OSLO
STOCKHOLM
SWEDEN
DENMARK
KØBENHAVN
Malmö
Trelleborg
Fredericia
Odense
Flensburg
Rødby
Puttgarden
Sassnitz
Lübeck
Hamburg
Bremen
Osnabrück
Hannover
Wolfsburg
Bielefeld
Braunschweig
BERLIN
Kostrzyn
Krzyz
Frankfurt (Oder)
Rzepin
Poznań
WARSZAWA
Gdynia
Tczew
POLAND
Russia
Kaliningrad
VILNIUS
Trakiszki
Białystok
St Petersburg
MOSKVA
Brest
KYÏV
Cottbus
Forst
Wrocław
Kassel
GERMANY
Leipzig
Dresden
Frankfurt (Main)
Fulda
Schöna
Katowice
Kraków
Zebrzydowice
Petrovice
Bohumin
Przemyśl
Lviv
Würzburg
PRAHA
CZECH REPUBLIC
Plzeň
Furth im Wald
Pardubice
Brno
Žilina
Košice
Chop
Nürnberg
Regensburg
Stuttgart
Ulm
Summerau
Passau
Břeclav
BRATISLAVA
SLOVAKIA
MÜNCHEN
Linz
WIEN
AUSTRIA
Hegyeshalom
Győr
Szob
BUDAPEST
Debrecen
Szolnok
Curtici
Arad
BUCUREŞTI
Timişoara
Lindau
Bregenz
Buchs
Chur
Kufstein
Salzburg
Innsbruck
Zell am See
Schwarzach St Veit
Graz
SWITZERLAND
Brennero
Villach
Klagenfurt
Spielfeld-Straß
Maribor
Hodoš
Fonyód
Dombóvár
HUNGARY
Tarvisio
Jesenice
Bolzano
Udine
SLOVENIA
Koprivnica
LJUBLJANA
Dobova
ZAGREB
Kelebia
Subotica
ROMANIA
Verona
Mestre
Lido di Jesolo
Trieste
Koper
Venezia
Rijeka
CROATIA
Vinkovci
Šid
Novi Sad
BEOGRAD
ITALY
Bologna
Rimini
BOSNIA
SERBIA
BULGARIA
Niš
Kalotina
İSTANBUL
SOFIA
Pisa
Livorno
Firenze
Ancona
Pescara
ROMA
MONTENEGRO
Preševo
SKOPJE
NORTH MACEDONIA
THESSALONÍKI
Napoli
Salerno
Brindisi
ATHÍNA

INTERNATIONAL SERVICES

Services All trains convey first and second classes of seating accommodation unless otherwise noted. For information on types of sleeping car (🛏) and couchette car (🛏) see page 10. Restaurant (✕) and buffet (🍸) cars vary considerably from country to country in standard of service offered. The catering car may not be carried or open for the whole journey.

Timings **Valid June 9, 2019 – December 14, 2019.** Services can change at short notice and passengers are advised to consult the latest European Rail Timetable before travelling. International trains are not normally affected by public holidays, but may alter at Christmas and Easter - these changes (where known) are shown in the tables. Readers are advised to cross-check timings and days of running of services in the International section with the relevant country section.

Tickets **Seat reservations** are available for most international trains and are advisable as some trains can get very crowded. **Supplements** are payable on **EuroCity** (*EC*) trains in most countries and on most InterCity trains – consult the introduction at the start of each country to see which supplements apply.

Listed below is a selection of the different types of trains found in the International Section.

DAY SERVICES:

AP	***Alfa Pendular***	Portuguese high-quality tilting express train.
Alvia	***Alvia***	Spanish high-speed train.
Alta	***Altaria***	Spanish quality express using light, articulated stock.
AV	***Alta Velocità***	Italian premium fare **ETR 500** services using high-speed lines.
AVE	***Alta Velocidad Española***	Spanish high-speed train.
EC	***EuroCity***	Quality international express. Supplement may be payable.
Em	***Euromed***	Spanish 200 km/h train.
☆	***Eurostar***	High-speed (300 km/h) service London - Paris / Brussels. Special fares payable. Three classes of service on most trains: (Business Premier, Standard Premier and Standard). Minimum check-in time 30 minutes.
FA	***Frecciargento***	Italian tilting trains using both high-speed and traditional lines.
FB	***Frecciabianca***	Italian fast premium fare services using traditional lines.
FR	***Frecciarossa***	Italian fast premium fare services using high-speed lines.
Ex	***Express***	Express between Czech Republic and Slovakia.
IC	***InterCity***	Express train. Supplement may be payable.
ICE	***InterCity Express***	German high-speed (230 - 320 km/h) service.
IR	***InterRegio***	Inter-regional express usually with refurbished coaches.
ITA	***.italo***	Italian high-speed train. Supplement payable.
izy	***izy***	Low cost, high-speed international train Paris - Brussels. Special fares apply.
LE	***Leo Express***	Czech quality international express with three classes of service: (Premium, Business and Economy).
RJ *RJX*	***Railjet***	Austrian quality international express with three classes of service: (Business, First and Economy).
RB	***Regional Bahn***	German stopping train.
RE	***Regional Express***	Regional semi-fast train.
REX	***Regional Express***	Austrian semi-fast train.
SC	***Super City***	Czech Pendolino **680** tilting train, supplement payable.
Talgo	***Talgo***	Spanish quality express using light, articulated stock.
⇌	***Thalys***	High-speed (300 km/h) international train Paris - Brussels - Amsterdam / Köln. Special fares apply.
Thello	***Thello***	Jointly owned French / Italian train, supplement payable.
TGV	**Train à Grande Vitesse**	French high-speed (270 - 320 km/h) train.
Sn	***Snabbtåg***	Swedish high-speed (200 km/h) train.

NIGHT SERVICES:

EN	***EuroNight***	Quality international overnight express.
D	***Durchgangszug*** or **Schnellzug**	Overnight or international express. Some may only convey passengers to international destinations and are likely to be compulsory reservation, marked R.
Hotel	***Trenhotel***	Spanish international quality overnight train. Conveys Gran Clase / Grande Classe sleeping accommodation comprising *de luxe* (1 and 2 berth) compartments with en-suite shower and WC. Also conveys 1, 2 and 4 berth sleeping cars.
ICN	***InterCity Notte***	Italian overnight train, supplement payable.
NJ	***ÖBB nightjet***	Austrian brand name covering international services (previously City Night Line). Facilities range from *Comfortline Deluxe* sleeping cars (1, 2 and 3 berth) with en-suite shower and WC, to modernised *Comfortline Economy* sleeping cars and 4 / 6 berth couchettes. 2nd class seats are also conveyed (in six seat compartments). Most trains convey shower facilities and 🍸 (also ✕ on certain services). Special fares apply and reservation is compulsory on most services.
Thello	***Thello***	Jointly owned French / Italian overnight train.

EUROTUNNEL

The frequent car-carrying service between Folkestone and Calais through the **Channel Tunnel** is operated by Eurotunnel. The service operates up to four times hourly (less frequently at night) and takes about 35 minutes. Passengers stay with their cars during the journey. Separate less-frequent trains operate for lorries, coaches, motorcycles, and cars with caravans. Reservations are advisable but passengers can buy tickets at the toll booths when they arrive at the terminal and board the next available shuttle.
Reservations: ✆ 08443 35 35 35.

9 LONDON, AMSTERDAM, BRUSSELS and LILLE - ST GERVAIS and BOURG ST MAURICE

Winter ski trains December 2018 - April 2019 service.

Other connections are available by changing in Paris (or in Lille and Lyon). Supplements are payable on TGV trains.

train type	*TGV*	⇌	*TGV*	*TGV*	⇌	☆	☆	
train number	**964**	**9904/5**	**5108**	**5146**	**9920/1**	**9092**	**9096**	
train number	**965**	**9906/7**	**5109**	**5147**	**9924/5**	**9093**	**9097**	
notes		R 🍸	R 🍸	R 🍸	R 🍸	R ✕	R ✕	
notes	**Y**	**C**	**Y**	**F**	**A**	**M**	**E**◐	
London St Pancras d.	...	...	...	...	...	0945	1945	...
Ashford International **11** a.	...	...	...	...	...	1015	2019	...
Ashford International **11** d.	...	...	...	...	...	1028	2028	...
Amsterdam Centraal d.	...	...	...	...	0542	|	|	...
Schiphol d.	...	...	...	...	0559	|	|	...
Rotterdam CS d.	...	...	...	...	0625	|	|	...
Antwerpen Centraal d.	...	...	...	...	0705	|	|	...
Brussels Midi / Zuid d.	...	0720	...	...	0759	|	|	...
Lille Europe 11 d.	0604	|	0709	0629	|	|	|	...
Lille Flandres ◇ d.	|	|	|	|	|	|	|	...
Douai **11** d.	|	|	|	|	|	|	|	...
Arras **11** d.	|	|	|	|	|	|	|	...
TGV Haute Picardie **11** d.	|	|	0741	|	|	|	|	...
Paris Charles de Gaulle ✈ **11** d.	0707	0842	0838	0727	0916	|	|	...
Marne la Valleé Chessy § **11** d.	0722	|	0855	0744	|	|	|	...
Cluses (Haute Savoie) a.	|	|	1351	|	|	|	|	...
Salanches Megève a.	|	|	1407	|	|	|	|	...
St Gervais a.	|	|	1417	|	|	|	|	...
Chambéry a.	1008	1149	...	1111	1221	|	|	...
Albertville a.	1053	1228	...	1211	1304	|	|	...
Moûtiers-Salins a.	1142	1304	...	1246	1344	1827	0532	...
Aime la Plagne a.	1159	...	...	1307	1405	1846	0557	...
Landry a.	1209	...	...	1318	1417	|	|	...
Bourg St Maurice a.	1220	...	...	1330	1430	1903	0616	...

train type	☆	⇌	*TGV*	⇌	*TGV*	*TGV*	☆	☆	☆	☆
train number	**9095**	**9963/2**	**5174**	**9987/6**	**5178**	**970**	**9099**	**9099**	**9099**	**9099**
train number	**9094**	**9965/4**	**5175**	**9979/8**	**5179**	**971**	**9098**	**9098**	**9098**	**9098**
notes	R ✕	R 🍸	R 🍸	R 🍸	R 🍸	R 🍸	R ✕	R ✕	R ✕	R ✕
notes	**G**	**D**	**F**	**B**	**Y**	**Y**	**P**◧	**Q**◧	**R**◧	**S**◧
Bourg St Maurice d.	0934	...	1353	1541	...	1558	2212	2212	2212	2212
Landry d.	|	...	1403	1552	...	1608	|	|	|	|
Aime la Plagne d.	|	...	1412	1602	...	1618	|	|	|	|
Moûtiers-Salins a.	0959	...	|	|	...	|	2239	2239	2239	2239
Moûtiers-Salins d.	1014	1420	1429	1625	...	1643	2254	2254	2254	2254
Albertville d.	|	1509	1505	1658	...	1753	|	|	|	|
Chambéry d.	|	1555	1557	1750	...	1846	|	|	|	|
St Gervais d.	|	|	|	|	1532	|	|	|	|	|
Salanches Megève d.	|	|	|	|	1552	|	|	|	|	|
Cluses (Haute Savoie) d.	|	|	|	|	1608	|	|	|	|	|
Marne la Vallée Chessy § **11** a.	|	|	1917	|	2102	2140	|	|	|	|
Paris Charles de Gaulle ✈ **11** a.	|	1932	1933	2044	2120	2155	|	|	|	|
TGV Haute Picardie **11** a.	|	|	2010	|	2158	|	|	|	|	|
Arras **11** a.	|	|	2031	|	|	|	|	|	|	|
Douai **11** a.	|	|	2049	|	|	|	|	|	|	|
Lille Flandres ◇ a.	|	|	2112	|	|	- 2257	|	|	|	|
Lille Europe 11 a.	|	|	...	|	2229	...	|	|	|	|
Brussels Midi / Zuid a.	|	2100	...	2205	...	...	|	|	|	|
Antwerpen Centraal a.	|	...	...	2257	...	...	|	|	|	|
Rotterdam CS a.	|	...	...	2333	...	...	|	|	|	|
Schiphol a.	|	...	...	2354	...	...	|	|	|	|
Amsterdam Centraal a.	|	...	...	0010	...	...	|	|	|	|
Ashford International **11** a.	1537**f**	...	...	...	...	...	0633	|	0633**d**	0707
London St Pancras a.	1613	...	...	...	...	...	0716	0705	0728	0750

A – THALYS NEIGE – ⑥ Dec. 22 - Mar. 16: (12) 🍸 Amsterdam - Bourg St Maurice; ⑥ Dec. 22 - Apr. 13: (12) 🍸 Brussels - Bourg St Maurice.
B – THALYS NEIGE – ⑥ Dec. 29 - Mar. 23: (12) 🍸 Bourg St Maurice - Amsterdam; ⑥ Dec. 29 - Apr. 20: (12) 🍸 Bourg St Maurice - Brussels.
C – THALYS NEIGE – Mar. 2: (12) 🍸 Brussels - Moûtiers-Salins.
D – THALYS NEIGE – Mar. 9: (12) 🍸 Moûtiers-Salins - Brussels.
E – ⑤ Dec. 21 - Mar. 29 (also ⑥ Feb. 16).
F – Dec. 22, 29, Jan. 5, Feb. 9, 16, 23.
G – ⑥ Dec. 29 - Apr. 6 (also ⑦ Feb. 24).
M – ⑥ Dec. 22 - Mar. 30.
P – ⑥ Dec. 29 - Mar. 23 (not Feb. 23).
Q – ⑥ Feb. 23.
R – ⑥ Apr. 6.
S – ⑥ Mar. 30.
Y – Feb. 9, 16, 23.

d – Depart 0700.
f – Not Feb. 24.

§ – Station for Disneyland, Paris.
⇌ – *Thalys* high-speed train R 🍸. Special fares payable.
◐ – ✕ after departure from Ashford. ✕ from 0500.
◧ – ✕ after departure from Moûtiers. ✕ from 0500.
☆ – Eurostar train. Special fares payable. Minimum check-in time 30 minutes. Valid Dec. 21 - Apr. 6.
◇ – 500 metres from Lille Europe (see Lille City Plan on page 32).

LONDON - LILLE - PARIS and BRUSSELS *by Eurostar* 10

Minimum check-in time is 30 minutes, but passengers are advised to allow longer due to immigration procedures. Not available for London - Ebbsfleet - Ashford or v.v. Special fares payable that include three classes of service: business premier, standard premier and standard. All times shown are local times (France and Belgium are one hour ahead of Great Britain).
All Eurostar services are 🅁, non-smoking and convey ✗ in Business Premier and Standard Premier, 🍷 in Standard.

Service May 26 - July 27. For service from July 28 see page 50.

km	km	train number	9080	9108	9002	9110	9110	9004	9006	9008	9008	9010	9114	9010	9116	9014	9018	9128	9126	9022	9060	9024	9132	9028
		notes	①–⑤	①⑤	⑥	②③④	⑥	①–⑤	①–⑥	⑥	①–⑤	⑦	①–⑥	①–⑥							⑥			
		notes	g	f		m		h	f	k	h		A	B				D	E					
0	0	**London** St Pancras d.	0540	0613	0618	0647	0657	0701	0731	0752	0755	0819	0819	0831	0854	0922	1024	1058	1104	1131	1201	1224	1258	1331
35	35	Ebbsfleet International d.	0558	0630	|	0704	|	|	|	0812	0812	0838	|	|	0912	0955e	1042	1115	|	|	|	1242	1315	|
90	90	Ashford International d.	0624	0655	0655	0728	0728	|	|	|	|	|	|	|	|	|	|	|	|	|	|	|	|	|
166	166	Calais Fréthun a.	|	|	|	|	|	|	|	|	|	|	|	|	1056	|	|	|	|	|	|	|	1459	|
267	267	Lille Europe a.	|	|	|	0926	0926	|	|	|	|	|	|	|	1127	|	|	1326	1326	|	|	|	1530	|
	373	**Brussels** Midi / Zuid a.	|	0922	|	1005	1005	|	|	|	|	|	1112	|	1205	|	|	1404	1404	|	|	|	1608	|
492		**Paris** Nord a.	0917	...	0947	...	...	1017	1047	1117	1117	1147	...	1147	...	1247	1347	...	...	1447	1517	1547	...	1647

train number	9030	9136	9032	9140	9036	9038	9040	9042	9148	9150	9152	9046	9152	9048	9050	9054	9158	9054	9056					
notes	①⑤⑦	⑦				⑤⑦		Ⓑ	⑥	Ⓑ	⑦	①–⑥	①–⑤	①⑤⑦		①–⑤		⑥⑦	⑦					
notes	b	k				j				A	k	h	h	k		h		k	k					
London St Pancras d.	1401	1404	1422	1504	1531	1601	1622	1701	1704	1719	1755	1801	1804	1831	1901	1925	1934	2000	2031	...	...	...	...	...
Ebbsfleet International d.	|	|	|	|	|	|	|	|	|	|	|	|	|	|	|	|	|	|	|	...	...	...	...	...
Ashford International d.	|	|	|	|	|	|	1655e	|	|	|	1828e	|	|	|	|	|	|	|	|	...	...	...	...	...
Calais Fréthun a.	|	|	|	|	|	|	|	|	|	|	|	|	|	|	|	|	2129	|	|	...	...	...	...	...
Lille Europe a.	|	1626	|	1726	|	|	|	|	1926	|	2026	|	2026	|	|	|	2200	|	|	...	...	...	...	...
Brussels Midi / Zuid a.	|	1705	|	1805	|	|	|	|	2005	2012	2105	|	2105	|	|	|	2238	|	|	...	...	...	...	...
Paris Nord a.	1717	...	1747	...	1847	1920	1947	2020	...	...	...	2117	...	2147	2217	2317	...	2317	2347	...	...	...	...	...

train number	9109	9005	9007	9113	9009	9011	9117	9013	9015	9019	9121	9021	9023	9129	9025	9027	9133	9031	9033	9035	9037	9141	9141	9039
notes	①	①	①–⑥	①–⑥	①–⑤	⑥⑦		①–⑥			①–⑥	①⑤	①–⑥	⑦	⑦		①–⑥		⑦	⑥	①⑤⑦	⑦	①–⑥	
notes	f	f	y	z	h	k		h					h		k		h					k	h	
Paris Nord d.	...	0634	0701	...	0734	0804	...	0824	0904	1004	...	1034	1104	...	1134	1204	...	1301	1334	1404	1434	...	...	1504
Brussels Midi / Zuid d.	0656	|	|	0756	|	|	0852	|	|	|	1056	|	|	1156	|	|	1252	|	|	|	|	1452	1456	|
Lille Europe d.	0735	|	|	0835	|	|	0930	|	|	|	1135	|	|	1235	|	|	1330	|	|	|	|	1530	1535	|
Calais Fréthun d.	|	|	|	|	|	|	1001	|	|	|	|	|	|	|	|	|	1401	|	|	|	|	1601	|	|
Ashford International a.	|	|	|	|	|	|	|	|	|	|	|	|	1207	|	1237e	|	|	|	|	|	|	|	|	1607e
Ebbsfleet International a.	|	|	|	|	|	|	|	|	|	|	|	1148	|	|	|	|	1345	1418	|	1518	|	1545	1545	|
London St Pancras a.	0759	0802	0832	0859	0900	0930	0957	1000	1030	1130	1157	1209	1239	1257	1309	1330	1405	1439	1500	1539	1602	1605	1605	1639

train number	9145	9043	9045	9149	9047	9049	9153	9051	9157	9053	9055	9067	9059	9163	9061	9168	9063							
notes	⑦		⑦	Ⓑ	①–⑥	⑦		Ⓑ	Ⓑ	②③④		⑤⑦			⑤⑦	⑦	Ⓑ							
notes	k		k	h	h	q						k	C		q	p								
Paris Nord d.	...	1604	1634	...	1704	1734	...	1804	...	1834	1904	1934	2004	...	2034	...	2104	...	...	...	...	...	...	...
Brussels Midi / Zuid d.	1556	|	|	1656	|	|	1756	|	1856	|	|	|	|	2022	|	2126	|	...	...	...	...	...	...	...
Lille Europe d.	1635	|	|	1735	|	|	1835	|	1935	|	|	|	|	2100	|	|	|	...	...	...	...	...	...	...
Calais Fréthun d.	|	|	|	|	|	|	|	|	|	|	|	|	|	2131	|	|	|	...	...	...	...	...	...	...
Ashford International a.	|	|	|	|	|	|	1835e	|	|	|	|	2037e	2107	|	|	|	|	...	...	...	...	...	...	...
Ebbsfleet International a.	|	1718	|	1745	|	|	|	1918	|	|	2018	|	|	2115	|	|	2218	...	...	...	...	...	...	...
London St Pancras a.	1657	1739	1800	1805	1832	1906	1910	1939	1957	2002	2039	2109	2143	2133	2200	2227	2239	...	...	...	...	...	...	...

A – To Amsterdam, see Table **18**.
B – June 10 - July 27.
C – ①②③④⑥ (not May 27).
D – May 26 - June 8.
E – June 9 - July 27. To Amsterdam from June 11.
b – Not June 10.
e – Not June 16.
f – Not May 27, June 10.
g – Not May 27, 30, June 10.
h – Not May 27.
j – Also May 27, June 10.
k – Also May 27.
m – Not May 30.
p – Not May 26, June 2.
q – Also May 27; not May 26.
y – Not May 27, 30.
z – Not May 27, 30.

LONDON – PARIS *by rail – sea – rail* 10a

Other services are available by taking normal service trains between London and Dover (Tables **100**, **101**), sailings between Dover and Calais (Table **2110**) and normal service trains between Calais and Paris, by changing at Boulogne (Table **261**), passengers making their own way between stations and docks at Dover and Calais, allowing at least 1 hour for connections.

French train number	⌿	⌿	🚢	TGV⌿	2	2026				⌿	⌿	🚢	2	2	2030	2034			⌿	🚢	2	2036	
sea crossing (see below)	⑥	①–⑤	①–⑥	7254	①–⑥	①–⑥		①–⑤	⑥⑦	⑥	Ⓑ		①–⑤	⑥	①–⑤	⑥		⑦	⑦	⑦	⑦	12036	
notes		p	B	🅁 E				p										q	q	C		⑦	
London St Pancras d.	0737	0725	...	...	...	...	...	...	...	0934	0937	...	...	...	...	...	...	...	1137	...	...	...	...
London Charing Cross d.	|	|	...	...	...	...	...	0834	0840	|	|	...	...	...	...	...	...	1040	|	...	...	...	...
Dover Priory ❦ a.	0841	0839	...	...	...	...	...	1038	1033	1041	1041	...	...	...	...	...	...	1235	1241	...	...	...	...
Dover Eastern Docks 🚌 ❦ d.	...	...	1015	...	...	...	...	...	...	...	...	1205	...	...	...	...	...	...	...	1445	...	...	...
Calais Port 🚌 ✣ a.	...	...	1245	...	...	...	...	...	...	...	...	1435	...	...	...	...	...	...	...	1715	...	...	...
Calais Ville ✣ d.	...	...	...	1327	1335	...	...	...	...	...	...	...	1558	1608	...	...	...	...	...	...	1807	...	...
Boulogne Ville d.	...	...	...	|	1411	1433t	...	...	...	...	...	...	1636	1652	1645	1733	...	...	...	...	1847	1933	...
Amiens a.	...	...	...	|	...	1609	...	...	...	...	...	...	...	...	1809	1908	...	...	...	...	...	2109	...
Paris Nord a.	...	...	...	1514	...	1729	...	...	...	...	...	...	...	...	1929	2029	...	...	...	...	...	2229	...

French train number	TGV⌿	🚢	⌿		2005	2	🚢	⌿		2011	2	2	🚢		⌿	2017	2	2021	2	🚢	⌿		
sea crossing (see below)	7223	①–⑥	①–⑥	①–⑥	①–⑤	①–⑤	①–⑤	①–⑤	①–⑤	⑥⑦	⑦	⑥	⑦	⑦	⑦	Ⓑ	①–⑤	⑥	⑥⑦				
notes	🅁 A	D	p	p																			
Paris Nord d.	0946	...	...	...	0731	...	...	...	...	0928	...	...	...	...	...	1331	...	1431	...	...	...	...	...
Amiens d.	|	...	...	...	0853	...	...	...	...	1050	...	...	...	...	...	1451	...	1551	...	...	...	...	...
Boulogne Ville d.	|	...	...	...	1016	1227	...	...	...	1226	1248	1311	...	...	...	1614x	1727	1718	1723	...	...	...	...
Calais Ville ✣ a.	1132	...	...	...	...	1310	...	...	...	...	1322	1350	...	...	...	...	1810	...	1757	...	...	...	...
Calais Port 🚌 ✣ d.	...	1325	...	...	...	...	1420	...	...	...	...	...	1520	...	...	...	...	...	...	1955	...	...	...
Dover Eastern Docks 🚌 ❦ a.	...	1355	...	...	...	...	1450	...	...	...	...	...	1550	...	...	...	...	...	...	2025	...	...	...
Dover Priory ❦ d.	...	...	1449	1458	...	...	...	1549	1558	...	...	...	...	1658	1749	...	...	...	...	...	2149	...	...
London Charing Cross a.	...	...	|	1654	...	...	...	|	1754	...	...	...	...	1852	|	...	...	...	...	...	|	...	...
London St Pancras a.	...	...	1558	...	...	...	...	1654	...	...	...	...	...	...	1854	...	...	...	...	...	2254	...	...

B – Depart 0925, 0955 on certain dates.
C – Depart 1355, 1425 on certain dates.
D – Depart 1305, 1420 on certain dates.
E – ①–⑥.
p – Not Apr. 19, 22, May 6, 27, Aug. 26.
q – Also Apr. 19, 22, May 6, 27, Aug. 26.
t – 8 minutes later on ⑥.
x – 1640 on ⑦.
⌿ – Supplement payable.

🚢 – Ship service, operated by P&O Ferries. ✗ on ship. One class only on ship. For additional ferry services see Table **2110**. Check in will close 60 minutes before departure.

❦ – Passengers make their own way between Dover Priory and Dover Eastern Docks.

✣ – 🚌 service (not a guaranteed connection):
From Calais Port to Calais Ville station 1120, 1220, 1305, 1405, 1500, 1640, 1740, 1835.
From Calais Ville station to Calais Port 1040, 1135, 1235, 1320, 1420, 1515, 1655, 1755.

10 LONDON - LILLE - PARIS and BRUSSELS *by Eurostar*

Minimum check-in time is 30 minutes, but passengers are advised to allow longer due to immigration procedures. Not available for London - Ebbsfleet - Ashford or v.v. Special fares payable that include three classes of service: business premier, standard premier and standard. All times shown are local times (France and Belgium are one hour ahead of Great Britain).
All Eurostar services are Ⓡ, non-smoking and convey ✕ in Business Premier and Standard Premier, 🍸 in Standard.

Service July 28 - Aug. 31. See page 49 for service until July 27. See below for service Sept. 1 - Nov. 2.

km	km	train number	9108	9002	9110	9110	9004	9112	9008	9008	9010	9010	9116	9014	9018	9126	9022	9024	9132	9028	9030	9032	9140	
		notes	①⑤	⑥	②③④	⑥	①–⑤	①–⑥	⑥	①–⑤	⑦	①⑤⑥				①–⑥					⑤			
		notes	h				h	A		h	k	h				A								
0	0	**London** St Pancras d.	0613	0618	0647	0657	0701	0716	0752	0755	0819	0831	0855	0924	1024	1104	1131	1224	1258	1331	1401	1422	1504	...
35	35	Ebbsfleet International d.	0630	|	0704	|	|	|	0812	0812	0838	|	0912	0941	1042	|	|	1242	1315	|	|	|	|	...
90	90	Ashford International d.	0652	0655	0728	0728	|	|	|	|	|	|	|	|	|	|	|	|	|	|	|	1455	|	...
166	166	Calais Fréthun a.	|	|	|	|	|	|	|	|	|	|	1056	|	|	|	|	|	1459	|	|	|	|	...
267	267	Lille Europe a.	|	|	0926	0926	|	|	|	|	|	|	1127	|	|	1326	|	|	1530	|	|	|	1726	...
	373	**Brussels** Midi / Zuid a.	0922	|	1005	1005	|	1012	|	|	|	|	1205	|	|	1405	|	|	1608	|	|	|	1805	...
492		**Paris** Nord a.	...	0947	...	...	1017	...	1117	1117	1147	1147	...	1247	1347	...	1447	1547	...	1647	1717	1747	...	...

train number	9036	9038	9040	9042	9150	9150	9152	9046	9152	9048	9050	9158	9054	9056								
notes		⑤⑦		Ⓑ	⑥	Ⓑ	⑦	①–⑥	①–⑤	①⑤⑦				⑦								
notes		k				A	k	h	h	k				k								
London St Pancras d.	1531	1601	1622	1701	1704	1716f	1755	1801	1804	1831	1901	1934	2001	2031	...	...	...	...	...	...	...	...
Ebbsfleet International d.	|	|	|	|	|	|	|	|	|	|	|	|	|	|	...	...	...	...	...	...	...	...
Ashford International d.	|	|	|	|	|	|	1828	|	|	|	|	|	|	|	...	...	...	...	...	...	...	...
Calais Fréthun a.	|	|	|	|	|	|	|	|	|	|	|	2129	|	|	...	...	...	...	...	...	...	...
Lille Europe a.	|	|	|	|	1926	|	2026	|	2026	|	|	2200	|	|	...	...	...	...	...	...	...	...
Brussels Midi / Zuid a.	|	|	|	|	2005	2012	2105	|	2105	|	|	2238	|	|	...	...	...	...	...	...	...	...
Paris Nord a.	1847	1917	1947	2020	...	...	...	2117	...	2147	2217	...	2317	2347	...	...	...	...	...	...	...	...

train number	9109	9007	9113	9009	9011	9117	9013	9015	9015	9019	9019	9121	9021	9023	9023	9129	9025	9027	9133	9031	9033	9035	9037	
notes	①	①–⑥	①–⑥	①–⑤	⑥⑦		①	①③⑤	②④	②–⑦	①	①–⑥	⑤	①	②–⑥	⑦	⑦		①–⑥		⑦	⑥	①⑤⑦	
notes	h	h	h	h	k		h		⑥⑦	k	h			h			k		h					
Paris Nord d.	...	0713	...	0743	0813	...	0843	0904	0913	1013	1013	...	1043	1113	1113	...	1128	1213	...	1313	1328	1413	1443	...
Brussels Midi / Zuid d.	0656	|	0756	|	|	0852	|	|	|	|	|	1056	|	|	|	1156	|	|	1252	|	|	|	|	...
Lille Europe d.	0735	|	0835	|	|	0930	|	|	|	|	|	1135	|	|	|	1235	|	|	1330	|	|	|	|	...
Calais Fréthun d.	|	|	|	|	|	1001	|	|	|	|	|	|	|	|	|	|	|	|	1401	|	|	|	|	...
Ashford International a.	|	|	|	|	|	|	|	|	|	|	1107	|	|	|	1207	|	1238	|	|	|	|	|	|	...
Ebbsfleet International a.	|	|	|	|	|	|	|	1018	1018	|	|	|	1148	1218	1226	|	|	|	1345	1418	|	1518	|	...
London St Pancras a.	0759	0832	0859	0900	0930	0957	1000	1039	1039	1130	1143	1157	1209	1239	1247	1257	1309	1330	1405	1439	1500	1539	1602	...

train number	9141	9141	9039	9043	9045	9149	9149	9047	9049	9153	9153	9051	9157	9055	9067	9059	9163	9061	9063					
notes	⑦	①–⑥			⑦	①–⑤	⑦	①–⑥	⑦	⑦	①–⑥	Ⓑ	Ⓑ		⑤⑦			⑤⑦	Ⓑ					
notes					k	h	k	h	k	k	h				k	B		k						
Paris Nord d.	...	...	1513	1613	1643	...	...	1713	1743	...	...	1813	...	1913	1943	2013	...	2043	2113	...	...	...	...	...
Brussels Midi / Zuid d.	1452	1456	|	|	|	1656	1656	|	|	1756	1756	|	1856	|	|	|	2022	|	|	...	...	...	...	...
Lille Europe d.	1530	1535	|	|	|	1735	1735	|	|	1835	1835	|	1935	|	|	|	2100	|	|	...	...	...	...	...
Calais Fréthun d.	1601	|	|	|	|	|	|	|	|	|	|	|	|	|	|	|	2131	|	|	...	...	...	...	...
Ashford International a.	|	|	|	|	|	|	1734	|	|	|	1835	|	|	|	2037	2107	|	|	|	...	...	...	...	...
Ebbsfleet International a.	1545	1545	1618	1718	|	1745	1753	|	|	1845	1856	1918	|	2018	|	2127	2115	|	2218	...	...	...	...	...
London St Pancras a.	1605	1605	1639	1739	1802	1806	1814	1832	1906	1903	1915	1939	1957	2039	2109	2149	2133	2200	2239	...	...	...	...	...

A – To Amsterdam, see Table **18**. **B** – ①②③④⑥ (not Aug. 26). **f** – 1719 on ⑦. **h** – Not Aug. 26. **k** – Also Aug. 26.

10 LONDON - LILLE - PARIS and BRUSSELS *by Eurostar*

Minimum check-in time is 30 minutes, but passengers are advised to allow longer due to immigration procedures. Not available for London - Ebbsfleet - Ashford or v.v. Special fares payable that include three classes of service: business premier, standard premier and standard. All times shown are local times (France and Belgium are one hour ahead of Great Britain).
All Eurostar services are Ⓡ, non-smoking and convey ✕ in Business Premier and Standard Premier, 🍸 in Standard.

Service Sept. 1 - Nov. 2. See above for service July 28 - Aug. 31. See page 49 for service May 26 - July 27.

km	km	train number	9080	9108	9002	9110	9110	9004	9114	9008	9008	9010	9010	9116	9014	9018	9126	9022	9024	9132	9028	9030	9032	
		notes	①–⑤		⑥		⑥	①–⑤	①–⑥	⑥	①–⑤	⑦	①⑤⑥									⑤⑦		
		notes		D		C			A								A							
0	0	**London** St Pancras d.	0540	0613	0618	0647	0657	0701	0716	0752	0755	0819	0831	0854	0924	1024	1104	1131	1224	1258	1331	1401	1422	...
35	35	Ebbsfleet International d.	0558	0630	|	0704	|	|	|	0812	0812	0838	|	0912	0941	1042	|	|	1242	1315	|	|	|	...
90	90	Ashford International d.	0624	0652	0655	0728	0728	|	|	|	|	|	|	|	|	|	|	|	|	|	|	|	1455	...
166	166	Calais Fréthun a.	|	|	|	|	|	|	|	|	|	|	|	1056	|	|	|	|	|	1459	|	|	|	...
267	267	Lille Europe a.	|	|	|	0926	0926	|	|	|	|	|	|	1127	|	|	1326	|	|	1530	|	|	|	...
	373	**Brussels** Midi / Zuid a.	|	0922	|	1007	1005	|	1012	|	|	|	|	1205	|	|	1405	|	|	1608	|	|	|	...
492		**Paris** Nord a.	0917	...	0947	...	...	1017	...	1117	1117	1147	1147	...	1247	1347	...	1447	1547	...	1647	1717	1747	...

train number	9140	9036	9038	9040	9042	9150	9150	9152	9046	9152	9048	9050	9158	9054	9056							
notes			⑤⑦		Ⓑ	⑥	Ⓑ	⑦	①–⑥	①–⑤	⑤⑦				⑦							
notes							A															
London St Pancras d.	1504	1531	1601	1631	1701	1704	1716f	1755	1801	1804	1831	1901	1934	2001	2031	...	...	...	...	...	...	...
Ebbsfleet International d.	|	|	|	|	|	|	|	|	|	|	|	|	|	|	|	...	...	...	...	...	...	...
Ashford International d.	|	|	|	|	|	|	|	1828	|	|	|	|	|	|	|	...	...	...	...	...	...	...
Calais Fréthun a.	|	|	|	|	|	|	|	|	|	|	|	|	2129	|	|	...	...	...	...	...	...	...
Lille Europe a.	1726	|	|	|	|	1926	|	2026	|	2026	|	|	2200	|	|	...	...	...	...	...	...	...
Brussels Midi / Zuid a.	1805	|	|	|	|	2005	2012	2105	|	2105	|	|	2238	|	|	...	...	...	...	...	...	...
Paris Nord a.	...	1847	1920	1947	2020	...	...	...	2117	...	2147	2217	...	2317	2347	...	...	...	...	...	...	...

train number	9109	9005	9007	9113	9009	9011	9117	9013	9015	9015	9019	9019	9121	9021	9023	9023	9129	9025	9027	9133	9031	9033	9035	9037
notes	①	①	①–⑥	①–⑥	①–⑤	⑥⑦		①–⑤	①③⑤	②④	②–⑦	①	①–⑥	⑤⑦	①	②–⑥	⑦	⑦		①–⑥		⑦	⑥	⑤⑦
notes										⑥⑦														
Paris Nord d.	...	0643	0713	...	0743	0813	...	0843	0904	0913	1013	1013	...	1043	1113	1113	...	1128	1213	...	1313	1343	1413	1443
Brussels Midi / Zuid d.	0656	|	|	0756	|	|	0852	|	|	|	|	|	1056	|	|	|	1156	|	|	1252	|	|	|	|
Lille Europe d.	0736	|	|	0835	|	|	0930	|	|	|	|	|	1135	|	|	|	1235	|	|	1330	|	|	|	|
Calais Fréthun d.	|	|	|	|	|	|	1001	|	|	|	|	|	|	|	|	|	|	|	|	1401	|	|	|	|
Ashford International a.	|	|	|	|	|	|	|	|	|	|	|	1107	|	|	|	1207	|	1237	|	|	|	|	|	|
Ebbsfleet International a.	|	|	|	|	|	|	|	|	1015	1018	|	|	|	1148	1218	1228	|	|	|	1345	1418	|	1518	|
London St Pancras a.	0759	0802	0832	0857	0900	0930	0957	1000	1039	1039	1130	1143	1157	1209	1239	1247	1257	1309	1330	1405	1439	1500	1539	1602

train number	9141	9141	9039	9043	9045	9149	9149	9047	9049	9153	9153	9051	9157	9055	9067	9059	9163	9061	9063					
notes	⑦	①–⑥			⑦	①–⑤	⑦	①–⑥	⑦	⑦	①–⑥	Ⓑ	Ⓑ		⑤⑦			⑤⑦	Ⓑ					
notes															h	B								
Paris Nord d.	...	...	1513	1613	1643	...	...	1713	1743	...	...	1813	...	1913	1943	2013	...	2043	2113	...	...	...	...	...
Brussels Midi / Zuid d.	1452	1456	|	|	|	1656	1656	|	|	1756	1756	|	1856	|	|	|	2022	|	|	...	...	...	...	...
Lille Europe d.	1530	1535	|	|	|	1735	1735	|	|	1835	1835	|	1935	|	|	|	2100	|	|	...	...	...	...	...
Calais Fréthun d.	1601	|	|	|	|	|	|	|	|	|	|	|	|	|	|	|	2131	|	|	...	...	...	...	...
Ashford International a.	|	|	|	|	|	|	1734	|	|	1835	1835	|	|	|	2037	2107	|	|	|	...	...	...	...	...
Ebbsfleet International a.	1545	1545	1618	1718	|	1745	1755	|	|	|	1857	1918	|	2018	|	2128	2115	|	2218	...	...	...	...	...
London St Pancras a.	1605	1605	1639	1739	1800	1806	1813	1832	1900	1913	1916	1939	1957	2039	2113	2147	2133	2200	2239	...	...	...	...	...

A – To Amsterdam, see Table **18**. **C** – ②③④ Sept. 2 – 19. **D** – ①⑤ Sept. 2 – 16. **f** – 1719 on ⑦. **h** – Not Nov. 1.
B – ①②③④⑥ (also Nov. 1). ①–⑤ Sept. 20 - Nov. 2.

LONDON / BRUSSELS - LILLE - CHARLES DE GAULLE ✈ - WESTERN / SOUTHERN FRANCE 11

DAY TRAINS (FOR NIGHT TRAINS SEE TABLE 13). Supplements are payable on *TGV* trains. Connections at Lille are not guaranteed. Other connections available via Paris.

km	train type	*TGV*	*TGV*	*TGV*	*TGV*	*TGV*	*TGV*	*TGV*	*TGV*	*TGV*	*TGV*	*TGV*	*TGV*	*TGV*	*TGV*	⇌	*TGV*	☆	☆	*TGV*	⇌	☆	*TGV*
	train number	**5106**	**5104**	**6839**	**7669**	**7831**	**9810**	**9814**	**5111**	**6811**	**5211**	**5214**	**7867**	**9870**	**5450**	**9910**	**9812**	**9110**	**9110**	**5202**	**9926**	**9084**	**5330**
	train number	**5107**	**5105**	**6838**			**9811**	**9815**		**6810**		**5215**		**9871**	**5451**		**9813**			**5203**	**9932**	**9085**	**5332**
	notes	R 🍷 ⑥	R 🍷 ①–⑤	R 🍷	R ⊠	R ⊠	R 🍷 ①–⑤	R 🍷 ⑥⑦	R 🍷 ⑥	R 🍷	R 🍷	R 🍷	R ⊠	R 🍷	R 🍷	R 🍷	R 🍷	R ✕ ②③④	R ✕ ⑥	R 🍷	R 🍷	R ✕	R 🍷
					C				**B**							**T**		**J**			**H**	**D**	**E**
	London St Pancras d.	...	...	...	...	...	...	...	...	...	...	...	...	...	...	...	...	0647	0657	...	...	0719**t**	...
	Brussels Midi / Zuid d.	...	...	...	...	...	0609	0646	...	...	...	...	...	0717	...	0820	0817	|	|	...	0935	|	...
	Lille Europe a.	...	...	...	...	...	0650	0719	...	...	...	...	...	0752	...	|	0852	0926	0926	...	|	0951**x**	...
	Lille Europe d.	0517**f**	0517**f**	...	...	...	0652	0729	0729	...	0737	0737	...	0803	...	|	0903	...	...	1020**f**	|	|	...
	Douai d.	0543	0543	...	...	...	|	|	|	...	|	|	...	|	...	|	|	...	...	|	|	|	...
0	Arras d.	0559	0559	...	...	...	0730	|	|	...	|	|	...	|	...	|	|	...	...	|	|	|	...
	TGV Haute Picardie d.	0618	0618	...	0644	...	|	|	|	...	0815	0815	...	|	...	|	|	...	...	|	|	|	...
	Paris Charles de Gaulle ✈ a.	0648	0648	...	0714	...	0813	0822	0822	...	0844	0844	...	0853	...	|	0952	...	...	1113	|	|	...
99	Paris Charles de Gaulle ✈ d.	0657	0657	...	0719	0806	0826	0827	0827	...	0849	0849	0855	0859	0919	|	0957	...	...	1118	|	|	...
203	Marne la Vallée § d.	0710	0710	...	0732	0825	0840	0840	0840	...	0902	0902	0917	|	0932	|	1010	...	...	1132	|	|	...
203	Strasbourg a.	|	|	...	|	|	|	|	|	...	|	|	|	1049	|	|	|	...	...	|	|	|	...
227	Massy TGV d.	|	|	...	0808	|	|	|	|	...	0938	0938	|	...	1008	|	|	...	...	1208	|	|	...
	Le Mans a.	|	|	...	|	|	|	|	|	...	1026	1026	|	...	|	|	|	...	...	|	|	|	...
289	**Rennes** a.	|	|	...	|	|	|	|	|	...	1117	|	|	...	|	|	|	...	...	|	|	|	...
	Angers St Laud a.	|	|	...	|	|	|	|	|	...	...	1110	|	...	|	|	|	...	...	|	|	|	...
	Nantes a.	|	|	...	|	|	|	|	|	...	...	1150	|	...	|	|	|	...	...	|	|	|	...
	St Pierre des Corps a.	|	|	...	0858**y**	|	|	|	|	...	...	...	|	...	1058	|	|	...	...	1258	|	|	...
	Poitiers a.	|	|	...	0932	|	|	|	|	...	...	...	|	...	1132	|	|	...	...	1332	|	|	...
	Angoulême a.	|	|	...	1013	|	|	|	|	...	...	...	|	...	1213	|	|	...	...	1413	|	|	...
	Bordeaux a.	|	|	...	1052	|	|	|	|	...	...	...	|	...	1252	1231**z**	|	...	...	1452	|	|	...
	Le Creusot TGV a.	|	|	...	...	|	|	|	|	...	...	...	|	...	...	...	|	...	...	...	|	|	...
	Lyon Part Dieu a.	0900	0900	1006	...	|	1030	1030	1030	1110	...	...	|	...	...	...	1200	...	...	...	|	1300	1336
	Lyon St Exupéry ✈ a.	|	|	|	...	1008	|	|	|	|	...	...	1110	...	...	...	|	...	...	...	|	|	|
521	Valence TGV a.	0941	0946	|	...	|	1112	1112	1112	1144	...	...	|	...	...	...	1246	...	...	...	1302	|	1410
	Avignon TGV a.	1016	|	|	...	1101	1149	1149	1149	|	...	...	|	...	...	...	|	...	...	...	1337	1408	|
	Nîmes a.	|	1033	1117	...	|	|	|	|	1231	...	...	|	...	...	...	1333	...	...	...	|	|	1501
	Montpellier Saint-Roch a.	|	1104	1146	...	|	|	|	|	1301	...	...	1232	...	...	...	1404	...	...	...	|	|	1531
	Béziers a.	|	...	...	...	|	|	|	|	1343	...	...	...	...	...	...	...	...	...	...	|	|	...
	Narbonne a.	|	...	...	...	|	|	|	|	1403	...	...	...	...	...	...	...	...	...	...	|	|	...
	Toulouse Matabiau a.	|	...	...	...	|	|	|	|	1522	...	...	...	...	...	...	...	...	...	...	|	|	...
	Perpignan a.	|	...	...	...	|	|	|	|	...	...	...	...	...	...	...	...	...	...	...	|	|	...
	Aix en Provence TGV a.	1040	...	...	...	|	|	|	|	...	...	...	...	...	...	...	...	...	...	...	1401	|	...
	Marseille St Charles a.	1055	...	...	...	1138	1225	1225	1225	...	...	...	...	...	...	...	...	...	...	...	1416	1447	...
	Toulon a.	...	...	...	...	...	...	...	1318	...	...	...	...	...	...	...	...	...	...	...	...	...	...
	St Raphaël - Valescure a.	...	...	...	...	...	...	...	1414	...	...	...	...	...	...	...	...	...	...	...	...	...	...
	Cannes a.	...	...	...	...	...	...	...	1441	...	...	...	...	...	...	...	...	...	...	...	...	...	...
	Nice a.	...	...	...	...	...	...	...	1510	...	...	...	...	...	...	...	...	...	...	...	...	...	...

train type	*TGV*	*TGV*	*AVE*	*TGV*		☆	*TGV*	*TGV*	*TGV*	*TGV*	*TGV*		☆	☆	*TGV*	*TGV*	*TGV*	*TGV*	*TGV*	*TGV*			
train number	**5164**	**9826**	**9743**	**7841**		**9116**	**5226**	**5225**	**5232**	**5209**	**7835**		**9074**	**9128**	**9830**	**5228**	**5222**	**6825**	**6217**	**7845**			
train number		**9827**					**5227**		**5233**						**9831**	**5229**	**5223**	**6824**					
notes	R 🍷	R 🍷		R ⊠		R ✕	R 🍷 ①–⑥	R 🍷 ①–⑥	R 🍷 ⑦	R 🍷 ⑦	R ⊠		R ✕	R ✕	R 🍷	R 🍷	R 🍷	R 🍷	R 🍷	R ⊠			
			b										**A**			**G**							
London St Pancras d.	...	...	...	...	...	0854	...	...	...	...	...	...	1014	1058**c**	...	...	...	...	...	...	...	...	...
Brussels Midi / Zuid d.	...	1033	...	...	...	|	...	...	...	...	...	...	|	|	1309	...	...	...	...	...	...	...	...
Lille Europe a.	...	|	...	...	...	1127	...	...	...	...	...	...	1254	1326	1346	...	...	...	...	...	...	...	...
Lille Europe d.	1043	|	...	1147**f**	...	...	1152	1152	1246**f**	1246**f**	1301**f**	...	|	...	1403	...	1448**f**	...	...	1540**f**	...	...	...
Douai d.	|	|	...	|	...	...	|	|	|	|	|	...	|	...	|	...	1510	...	...	|	...	...	...
Arras d.	|	|	...	|	...	...	|	|	|	|	|	...	|	...	|	...	1527	...	...	|	...	...	...
TGV Haute Picardie d.	1124	|	...	|	...	...	|	|	|	|	|	...	|	...	|	...	1547	...	...	1622	...	...	...
Paris Charles de Gaulle ✈ a.	1152	1146	...	|	...	...	1243	1243	1343	1343	1353	...	|	...	1452	...	1616	...	...	1653	...	...	...
Paris Charles de Gaulle ✈ d.	1157	1157	...	|	...	...	1248	1248	1348	1348	1358	...	|	...	1457	1518	1621	...	...	1703	...	...	...
Marne la Vallée § d.	1210	1210	...	1246	...	...	1302	1302	1402	1402	1410	...	1403	...	1510	1532	1633	...	...	1726	...	...	...
Strasbourg a.	|	|	...	|	...	...	|	|	|	|	|	...	...	...	|	|	|	...	...	|	...	...	...
Massy TGV d.	|	|	...	|	...	...	1338	1338	1438	1445	|	...	...	...	|	1608	1708	...	...	|	...	...	...
Le Mans a.	|	|	...	|	...	...	1426	1426	|	1533	|	...	...	...	|	1658	|	...	...	|	...	...	...
Rennes a.	|	|	...	|	...	...	1523	|	1614	|	|	...	...	...	|	|	|	...	...	|	...	...	...
Angers St Laud a.	|	|	...	|	...	...	...	1514	...	1614	|	...	...	...	|	1742	|	...	...	|	...	...	...
Nantes a.	|	|	...	|	...	...	...	1554	...	1654	|	...	...	...	|	1820	|	...	...	|	...	...	...
St Pierre des Corps a.	|	|	...	|	...	...	...	...	...	...	|	...	...	...	|	...	1758	...	...	|	...	...	...
Poitiers a.	|	|	...	|	...	...	...	...	...	...	|	...	...	...	|	...	1832	...	...	|	...	...	...
Angoulême a.	|	|	...	|	...	...	...	...	...	...	|	...	...	...	|	...	1914	...	...	|	...	...	...
Bordeaux a.	|	|	...	|	...	...	...	...	...	...	|	...	...	...	|	...	1952	...	...	|	...	...	...
Le Creusot TGV a.	|	|	...	|	...	...	...	...	...	...	|	...	...	...	|	...	...	...	...	|	...	...	...
Lyon Part Dieu a.	1400	1400	1424	|	...	...	...	...	...	...	|	...	...	...	1704	...	...	1936	...	|	...	...	...
Lyon St Exupéry ✈ a.	...	|	|	1433	...	...	...	...	...	...	1556	...	...	...	...	...	...	|	...	1911	...	...	...
Valence TGV a.	...	1440	1502	|	...	...	...	...	...	...	|	...	...	...	...	...	...	|	...	|	...	...	...
Avignon TGV a.	...	|	|	1529	...	...	...	...	...	...	1658	...	...	...	...	...	...	|	...	2004	...	...	...
Nîmes a.	...	|	1547	|	...	...	...	...	...	...	|	...	...	...	...	...	...	2103	...	|	...	...	...
Montpellier Saint-Roch a.	...	|	1621	|	...	...	...	...	...	...	|	...	...	...	...	...	...	2130	2141	|	...	...	...
Béziers a.	...	|	1713	|	...	...	...	...	...	...	|	...	...	...	...	...	...	2209	2226	|	...	...	...
Narbonne a.	...	|	1730	|	...	...	...	...	...	...	|	...	...	...	...	...	...	2225	2242	|	...	...	...
Toulouse Matabiau a.	...	|	|	|	...	...	...	...	...	...	|	...	...	...	...	...	...	2341	|	|	...	...	...
Perpignan a.	...	|	1805	|	...	...	...	...	...	...	|	...	...	...	...	...	...	...	2318	|	...	...	...
Aix en Provence TGV a.	...	1536	...	1557	...	...	...	...	...	...	1727	...	...	...	...	...	...	...	...	2032	...	...	...
Marseille St Charles a.	...	1552	...	1612	...	...	...	...	...	...	1742	...	...	...	...	...	...	...	...	2046	...	...	...
Toulon a.	...	...	...	...	...	...	...	...	...	...	...	...	...	...	...	...	...	...	...	...	...	...	...
St Raphaël - Valescure a.	...	...	...	...	...	...	...	...	...	...	...	...	...	...	...	...	...	...	...	...	...	...	...
Cannes a.	...	...	...	...	...	...	...	...	...	...	...	...	...	...	...	...	...	...	...	...	...	...	...
Nice a.	...	...	...	...	...	...	...	...	...	...	...	...	...	...	...	...	...	...	...	...	...	...	...

A – ①③⑤⑦ June 3 - July 26.
①③⑤⑥⑦ July 27 - Aug. 31.
①③⑤⑦ Sept. 1 - Oct. 18.
Daily Oct. 19 - Nov. 2.
①③⑤⑦ Nov. 3 - Dec. 14. See Table **17**.

B – ⑥ Apr. 6 - Dec. 8.

C – From Tourcoing, depart 0606.

D – ①⑤⑥ May 3 - June 29 (also May 26).
①⑤⑥⑦ June 30 - Sept. 1.
①⑤⑥ Sept. 2 – 16. See Table **17**.

E – ①⑤⑥⑦.

G – ①②③④⑥⑦.

H – THALYS SOLEIL – ⑥ June 29 - Aug 31: [12] 🍷 Amsterdam - Brussels - Valence *TGV* - Marseille.

J – ②③④ (①–⑤ Sept. 20 - Nov. 2).

P – ①⑦ (daily Mar. 26 - Sept. 17).

T – ⑥ June 29 - Aug. 31.

b – To Barcelona (Table **13**).

c – 1104 from June 11.

f – Lille **Flandres** (◇).

t – 0719 on ⑦ June 30 - Sept. 1.

x – ①⑤ May 3 - Sept. 16.

y – Not June 9.

z – 1350 on Aug. 17.

§ – Marne la Vallée - Chessy (station for Disneyland).

⊖ – To St Malo on dates in Table **261**.

AVE – Alta Velocidad Española R 🍷 ✗.

☆ – Eurostar train. Special fares payable. ✕ in Business Premier and Standard Premier, 🍷 in Standard. Business Premier not available to Marne la Vallée - Chessy and Marseille. Minimum check-in time 30 minutes. Valid May 26 - Nov. 2.

◇ – 500 metres from Lille Europe (see Lille City Plan on page 32).

⊠ – OUIGO low-cost TGV service. Internet bookings only at www.ouigo.com. Timings may vary.

⇌ – *Thalys* high-speed train. R 🍷. Special fares payable.

11 LONDON / BRUSSELS - LILLE - CHARLES DE GAULLE ✈ - WESTERN / SOUTHERN FRANCE

DAY TRAINS (FOR NIGHT TRAINS SEE TABLE 13). Supplements payable on all *TGV* services. Connections at Lille are not guaranteed. Other connections available via Paris.

train type	☆	*TGV*	*TGV*	☆	*TGV*	*TGV*	*TGV*	*TGV*	*TGV*	*TGV*	*TGV*	☆	*TGV*	*TGV*	*TGV*
train number	**9132**	**9836**	**5240**	**9140**	**5237**	**5230**	**7815**	**9874**	**5124**	**5130**	**9848**	**9148**	**5234**	**9846**	**9846**
train number		**9837**	**5241**			**5231**		**9875**	**5125**	**5131**	**9849**		**5235**	**9847**	**9847**
notes	R ✕	R 🍸	R 🍸	R ✕	R 🍸	R 🍸	R	R 🍸	R 🍸	R 🍸	R 🍸	R ✕	R 🍸	R 🍸	R 🍸
							⊠		⑧		⑦	⑥	⑤⑦		⑤⑦
					△					▷				A	
London St Pancras d.	1258	...	...	1504	...	...	...	...	...	...	...	1704	...	...	...
Brussels Midi / Zuid d.	|	1617	...	|	...	...	...	1717	...	...	1830	|	...	1917	1917
Lille Europe a.	1530	1653	...	1726	...	...	...	1752	...	...	1905	1926	...	1952	1952
Lille Europe d.	...	1703	1716f	...	1752	1752	...	1803	1826	1900f	1926	...	2019f	2002	2002
Douai d.	...	|	|	...	|	|	...	|	|	|	|	...	|	|	|
Arras d.	...	|	|	...	|	|	...	|	|	|	|	...	|	2028	2032
TGV Haute Picardie d.	...	|	|	...	|	|	...	|	1855	|	|	...	|	|	2056
Paris Charles de Gaulle ✈ a.	...	1752	1809	...	1843	1843	...	1853	1922	1954	2018	...	2113	2111	2123
Paris Charles de Gaulle ✈ d.	...	1757	1814	...	1848	1848	...	1858	1927	1958	2025	...	2118	2116	2128
Marne la Vallée § d.	...	1810	1833	...	1900	1900	1909	|	1940	2007	2040	...	2132	2130	2150
Strasbourg a.	...	|	|	...	|	|	|	2058	|	...	|	...	|	|	|
Massy TGV d.	...	|	1908	...	1938	1938	|	...	|	...	|	...	2212	|	|
Le Mans a.	...	|	|	...	2026	2026	|	...	|	...	|	...	2300	|	|
Rennes a.	...	|	|	...	2117	|	|	...	|	...	|	...	|	|	|
Angers St Laud a.	...	|	|	...	...	2110	|	...	|	...	|	...	2341	|	|
Nantes a.	...	|	|	...	...	2150	|	...	|	...	|	...	0019	|	|
St Pierre des Corps a.	...	|	1958	...	...	...	|	...	|	...	|	...	...	|	|
Poitiers a.	...	|	2032	...	...	...	|	...	|	...	|	...	...	|	|
Angoulême a.	...	|	2114	...	...	...	|	...	|	...	|	...	...	|	|
Bordeaux a.	...	|	2152	...	...	...	|	...	|	...	|	...	...	|	|
Le Creusot TGV a.	...	|	...	...	...	...	|	...	|	...	|	...	...	2241	2301
Lyon Part Dieu a.	...	2000	...	...	...	...	2100	...	2130	...	2230	...	...	2324	2341
Lyon St Exupéry ✈ d.	...	|	...	...	...	...	...	...	|	...	...	...	...	...	...
Valence TGV a.	...	2046	...	...	...	...	...	...	|	...	...	...	...	...	...
Avignon TGV a.	...	|	...	...	...	...	...	...	2240	...	...	...	...	...	...
Nîmes a.	...	2133	...	...	...	...	...	...	|	...	...	...	...	...	...
Montpellier Saint-Roch a.	...	2204**x**	...	...	...	...	...	...	|	...	...	...	...	...	...
Béziers a.	...	2252**t**	...	...	...	...	...	...	|	...	...	...	...	...	...
Narbonne a.	...	2308**t**	...	...	...	...	...	...	|	...	...	...	...	...	...
Toulouse Matabiau a.	...	|	...	...	...	...	...	...	|	...	...	...	...	...	...
Perpignan a.	...	2347**t**	...	...	...	...	...	...	|	...	...	...	...	...	...
Aix en Provence TGV a.	...	...	...	...	...	...	...	...	2305	...	...	...	...	...	...
Marseille St Charles a.	...	...	...	...	...	...	...	...	2320	...	...	...	...	...	...
Toulon a.	...	...	...	...	...	...	...	...	...	...	...	...	...	...	...
St Raphaël - Valescure a.	...	...	...	...	...	...	...	...	...	...	...	...	...	...	...
Cannes a.	...	...	...	...	...	...	...	...	...	...	...	...	...	...	...
Nice a.	...	...	...	...	...	...	...	...	...	...	...	...	...	...	...

train type	*TGV*	*TGV*	*TGV*	☆	*TGV*	*TGV*	*TGV*	*TGV*	*TGV*	*TGV*	*TGV*	*TGV*	☆	☆	*TGV*	*TGV*	☆	*TGV*	☆	☆
train number	**9809**	**9852**	**9890**	**9117**	**5152**	**5252**	**5254**	**5260**	**7838**	**9854**	**5154**	**9854**	**9121**	**9129**	**5270**	**7818**	**9133**	**5265**	**9141**	**9141**
train number		**9853**	**9891**		**5153**	**5253**	**5255**	**5261**		**9855**		**9855**			**5271**			**5441**		
notes	R 🍸	R 🍸	R 🍸	R ✕	R 🍸	R 🍸	R 🍸	R 🍸	R	R 🍸	R 🍸	R 🍸	R ✕	R ✕	R 🍸	R	R ✕	R 🍸	R ✕	R ✕
	①–⑤					①–⑥	①–⑥	①–⑥	⊠	①–⑥	⑦	⑦	①–⑥	⑦	⑦	⊠	①–⑥		⑦	①–⑥
					▷						B						g		k	h
Nice d.	...	...	...	...	...	...	...	...	...	...	...	...	...	...	...	...	...	...	...	...
Cannes d.	...	...	...	...	...	...	...	...	...	...	...	...	...	...	...	...	...	...	...	...
St Raphaël - Valescure d.	...	...	...	...	...	...	...	...	...	...	...	...	...	...	...	...	...	...	...	...
Toulon d.	...	...	...	...	...	...	...	...	...	...	...	...	...	...	...	...	...	...	...	...
Marseille St Charles d.	...	...	...	...	...	...	...	...	0609	0629	0638	...	...	...	...	...	...	...	...	...
Aix en Provence TGV d.	...	...	...	...	...	...	...	...	0624	0644	0653	...	...	...	...	...	...	...	...	...
Perpignan d.	...	...	...	...	...	...	...	...	|	|	|	...	...	...	...	...	...	...	...	...
Toulouse Matabiau d.	...	...	...	...	...	...	...	...	|	|	|	...	...	...	...	...	...	...	...	...
Narbonne d.	...	...	...	...	...	...	...	...	|	|	|	...	...	...	...	...	...	...	...	...
Béziers d.	...	...	...	...	...	...	...	...	|	|	|	...	...	...	...	...	...	...	...	...
Montpellier Saint-Roch d.	...	...	...	...	...	...	...	...	|	|	|	...	...	...	...	...	...	...	...	...
Nîmes d.	...	...	...	...	...	...	...	...	|	|	|	...	...	...	...	...	...	...	...	...
Avignon TGV d.	...	...	...	...	...	...	...	...	0652	0711	0720	...	...	...	...	...	...	...	...	...
Valence TGV d.	...	...	...	...	...	...	...	...	|	0740	|	...	...	...	...	...	...	...	...	...
Lyon St Exupéry ✈ d.	...	...	...	...	...	...	...	...	0745	|	|	...	...	...	...	...	...	...	...	...
Lyon Part Dieu d.	...	0550	...	...	...	...	...	...	|	0830	0830	0830	...	...	...	0905**p**	...	...	...	...
Le Creusot TGV d.	...	0631	...	...	...	...	...	...	|	|	|	|	...	...	...	|	...	...	...	...
Bordeaux d.	...	|	...	...	...	...	...	0608	|	|	|	|	...	...	...	|	...	0908	...	...
Angoulême d.	...	|	...	...	...	...	...	0646	|	|	|	|	...	...	...	|	...	0946	...	...
Poitiers d.	...	|	...	...	...	...	...	0728	|	|	|	|	...	...	...	|	...	1028	...	...
St Pierre des Corps d.	...	|	...	...	...	...	...	0802	|	|	|	|	...	...	...	|	...	1102	...	...
Nantes d.	...	|	...	...	...	0603	...	|	|	|	|	|	...	...	0806	|	...	|	...	...
Angers St Laud d.	...	|	...	...	...	0644	...	|	|	|	|	|	...	...	0848	|	...	|	...	...
Rennes d.	...	|	...	...	...	|	0626	|	|	|	|	|	...	...	|	|	...	|	...	...
Le Mans d.	...	|	...	...	...	0733	0733	|	|	|	|	|	...	...	0933	|	...	|	...	...
Massy TGV d.	...	|	...	...	...	0825	0825	0855	|	|	|	|	...	...	1025	|	...	1155	...	...
Strasbourg d.	...	|	0607	...	...	|	|	|	|	|	|	|	...	...	|	|	...	|	...	...
Marne la Vallée § d.	...	0748	|	...	0855	0901	0901	0933	0944	1024	1024	1024	...	...	1102	1112	...	1231	...	...
Paris Charles de Gaulle ✈ a.	...	0801	0757	...	0905	0912	0912	0943	|	1034	1034	1034	...	...	1113	1123	...	1241	...	...
Paris Charles de Gaulle ✈ d.	...	0808	0808	...	0912	0917	0917	0948	|	1039	1039	1039	...	...	1118	1128	...	1246	...	...
TGV Haute Picardie d.	...	|	|	...	|	0952	0952	|	|	|	|	|	...	...	|	|	...	1322	...	...
Arras a.	...	|	|	...	|	|	|	|	|	|	|	|	...	...	|	|	...	|	...	...
Douai a.	...	|	|	...	|	|	|	|	|	|	|	|	...	...	|	|	...	|	...	...
Lille Europe a.	...	0856	0856	...	1004	1019	1019	1040**f**	1044**f**	1133	1133	1133	...	...	1208	1221**f**	...	1354**f**	...	...
Lille Europe d.	0720	0908	0908	0930	...	...	...	...	...	1155	...	1155	1135	1235	...	...	1330	...	1530	1535
Brussels Midi / Zuid a.	0755	0943	0943	|	...	...	...	...	...	1234	...	1234	|	|	...	...	|	...	|	|
London St Pancras a.	...	...	...	0957	...	...	...	...	...	...	...	...	1157	1257	...	...	1405	...	1605	1605

A – ①②③④⑥.

B – ⑦ Mar. 31 - June 30.

f – Lille **Flandres** (◇).

g – Not May 27, Aug. 26.

h – Not May 27.

k – Also May 27.

p – Lyon **Perrache**.

t – ⑤⑥⑦.

x – Stops at Montpellier **Sud de France** 2223 ①–④ Sept. 30 - Dec. 8.

▽ – To / from Le Croisic on dates in Table **288**.

△ – To / from Lorient or Quimper on dates in Table **285**.

▷ – To / from Dijon, Besancon and Mulhouse (Table **370**).

§ – Marne la Vallée - Chessy. Station for Disneyland Paris.

◇ – 500 metres from Lille Europe (see Lille City Plan on page 32).

☆ – Eurostar train. Special fares payable. ✕ in Business Premier and Standard Premier, 🍸 in Standard. Minimum check-in time 30 minutes. Valid May 26 - Nov. 2.

⊠ – OUIGO low-cost TGV service. Internet bookings only at www.ouigo.com. Timings may vary.

SOUTHERN / WESTERN FRANCE - CHARLES DE GAULLE ✈ - LILLE - BRUSSELS / LONDON 11

DAY TRAINS (FOR NIGHT TRAINS SEE TABLE 13). Supplements payable on all *TGV* services. Connections at Lille are not guaranteed. Other connections available via Paris.

train type	TGV	TGV	TGV	TGV	☆	☆		TGV	TGV	TGV	AVE	TGV	TGV	☆	⇌	☆	TGV	☆	☆			
train number	**6869**	**9862**	**5272**	**7842**	**9141**	**9141**		**5266**	**5278**	**5280**	**9736**	**9866**	**5168**	**9149**	**9963**	**9057**	**9894**	**9153**	**9057**			
train number	**6868**	**9863**	**5273**					**5267**	**5279**			**9867**					**9895**					
notes	R 🍷	R 🍷	R 🍷 △ ⑦	R ⊠	R ✕ ⑦ k	R ✕ ①–⑥ h		R 🍷	R 🍷	R 🍷 ①–⑥	b	R 🍷	R 🍷 Ⓑ	R ✕ Ⓑ	R 🍷 T	R ✕ A	R 🍷	R ✕	R ✕ S			
Nice d.	...	...	...	...	...	...	...	...	...	...	...	...	...	...	...	...	...	...	...	...	...	...
Cannes d.	...	...	...	...	...	...	...	...	...	...	...	...	...	...	...	...	...	...	...	...	...	...
St Raphaël - Valescure d.	...	...	...	...	...	...	...	...	...	...	...	...	...	...	...	...	...	...	...	...	...	...
Toulon d.	...	...	...	...	...	...	...	...	...	...	...	...	...	...	...	...	...	...	...	...	...	...
Marseille St Charles d.	...	...	...	0959	...	...	...	...	...	...	...	1210	...	...	...	...	...	...	...	...	...	...
Aix en Provence TGV d.	...	...	...	1014	...	...	...	...	...	...	...	1224	...	...	...	...	...	...	...	...	...	...
Perpignan d.	...	0708**t**	...	|	...	...	...	...	...	...	0953	|	...	...	...	...	...	...	...	...	...	...
Toulouse Matabiau d.	0540	|	...	|	...	...	...	...	...	...	|	|	...	...	...	...	...	...	...	...	...	...
Narbonne d.	0659	0745**t**	...	|	...	...	...	...	...	...	1030	|	...	...	...	...	...	...	...	...	...	...
Béziers d.	0714	0801**t**	...	|	...	...	...	...	...	...	|	|	...	...	...	...	...	...	...	...	...	...
Montpellier Saint-Roch d.	0802	0855	...	|	...	...	...	...	...	...	1130	|	1155	...	...	...	...	...	...	...	...	...
Nîmes d.	0831	0926	...	|	...	...	...	...	...	...	1201	|	1226	...	...	...	...	...	...	...	...	...
Avignon TGV d.	|	|	...	1041	...	...	...	...	...	...	|	1251	|	...	...	...	...	...	...	...	...	...
Valence TGV d.	|	1016	...	|	...	...	...	...	...	...	1246	|	1316	...	...	...	...	...	...	...	...	...
Lyon St Exupéry ✈ d.	|	|	...	1135	...	...	...	...	...	...	|	|	|	...	...	...	...	...	...	...	...	...
Lyon Part Dieu d.	0950	1100	...	|	...	...	...	...	...	...	1320	1400	1400	...	...	...	...	...	...	...	...	...
Le Creusot TGV d.	...	|	...	|	...	...	...	...	...	...	...	|	|	...	...	...	...	...	...	...	...	...
Bordeaux d.	...	|	...	|	...	...	...	1108	...	...	...	|	|	...	1346	...	...	...	...	...	...	...
Angoulême d.	...	|	...	|	...	...	...	1146	...	...	...	|	|	...	|	...	...	...	...	...	...	...
Poitiers d.	...	|	...	|	...	...	...	1228	...	...	...	|	|	...	|	...	...	...	...	...	...	...
St Pierre des Corps d.	...	|	...	|	...	...	...	1302	...	...	...	|	|	...	|	...	...	...	...	...	...	...
Nantes d.	...	|	...	|	...	...	...	|	1203	...	...	|	|	...	|	...	...	...	...	...	...	...
Angers St Laud d.	...	|	...	|	...	...	...	|	1244	...	...	|	|	...	|	...	...	...	...	...	...	...
Rennes d.	...	|	1035	|	...	...	...	|	|	1226	...	|	|	...	|	...	...	...	...	...	...	...
Le Mans d.	...	|	1133	|	...	...	...	|	1333	1333	...	|	|	...	|	...	...	...	...	...	...	...
Massy TGV d.	...	|	1225	|	...	...	...	1355	1425	1425	...	|	|	...	|	...	...	...	...	...	...	...
Strasbourg d.	...	|	|	|	...	...	...	|	|	|	...	|	|	...	|	...	1507	...	...	...	...	...
Marne la Vallée § d.	...	1252	1301	1322	...	...	...	1431	1501	1501	...	1552	1552	...	|	1655	|	...	1801	...	...	...
Paris Charles de Gaulle ✈ a.	...	1302	1312	1331	...	...	...	1441	1513	1513	...	1602	1602	...	|	|	1659	...	|	...	...	...
Paris Charles de Gaulle ✈ d.	...	1307	1317	1336	...	...	...	...	1518	1518	...	1607	1607	...	|	|	1707	...	|	...	...	...
TGV Haute Picardie d.	...	1337	|	|	...	...	...	...	|	|	...	|	|	...	|	|	|	...	|	...	...	...
Arras a.	...	1354	|	|	...	...	...	...	|	|	...	|	|	...	|	|	|	...	|	...	...	...
Douai a.	...	|	|	|	...	...	...	...	|	|	...	|	|	...	|	|	|	...	|	...	...	...
Lille Europe a.	...	1418	1408	1433**f**	...	...	...	...	1607	1607	...	1701	1701	...	|	|	1757	...	|	...	...	...
Lille Europe d.	...	1436	...	...	1530	1535	...	...	...	...	...	1707	...	1735	|	|	1808	1835	|	...	...	...
Brussels Midi / Zuid a.	...	1511	...	...	|	|	...	...	...	...	...	1717	...	|	1750	|	1843	|	|	...	...	...
London St Pancras a.	...	...	...	...	1605	1605	...	...	...	...	...	...	...	1806	...	1847	...	1910	1946	...	...	...

train type	⇌	TGV	TGV	TGV	TGV	TGV	TGV	TGV	z☆	☆	☆	⇌		TGV	TGV	TGV	TGV	TGV	TGV	TGV	TGV	
train number	**9963**	**5192**	**5256**	**7860**	**7860**	**5284**	**9864**	**9868**	**9163**	**9087**	**9087**	**9955**		**7832**	**5182**	**9882**	**5288**	**5290**	**7836**	**7806**	**5184**	
train number		**5193**	**5257**			**5285**	**9869**	**9869**		**9086**	**9086**	**9959**			**9883**	**9883**	**5289**				**5185**	
notes	R 🍷 U	R 🍷 Ⓑ	R 🍷 ⑦	R ⊠ B	R ⊠ C	R 🍷	R 🍷	R 🍷	R ✕	R ✕ M	R ✕ M	R 🍷 H		R ⊠	R 🍷 ⑥⑦	R 🍷	R 🍷	R 🍷	R ⊠	R ⊠	R 🍷 ⑦	
Nice d.	...	...	...	...	...	...	...	...	...	...	...	...	...	...	...	...	...	...	...	...	1556	...
Cannes d.	...	...	...	...	...	...	...	...	...	...	...	...	...	...	...	...	...	...	...	...	1628	...
St Raphaël - Valescure d.	...	...	...	...	...	...	...	...	...	...	...	...	...	...	...	...	...	...	...	...	1655	...
Toulon d.	...	...	...	...	...	...	...	...	...	...	...	...	...	...	...	...	...	...	...	...	1756	...
Marseille St Charles d.	...	...	...	...	...	...	1509	...	...	1522	...	1601	...	1646	...	1706	...	...	1814	1841	1857	...
Aix en Provence TGV d.	...	...	...	...	...	...	1524	...	...	|	...	1616	...	|	...	1723	...	...	1829	|	1912	...
Perpignan d.	...	...	...	...	...	...	|	...	...	|	...	|	...	|	...	|	...	...	|	|	|	...
Toulouse Matabiau d.	...	...	...	...	...	...	|	...	...	|	...	|	...	|	...	|	...	...	|	|	|	...
Narbonne d.	...	...	...	...	...	...	|	...	...	|	...	|	...	|	...	|	...	...	|	|	|	...
Béziers d.	...	...	...	...	...	...	|	...	...	|	...	|	...	|	...	|	...	...	|	|	|	...
Montpellier Saint-Roch d.	...	...	...	1431	1449**y**	...	|	1455	...	|	...	|	...	|	1652	|	...	...	|	|	|	...
Nîmes d.	...	...	...	1502	|	...	|	1528	...	|	...	|	...	|	1722	|	...	...	|	|	|	...
Avignon TGV d.	...	...	...	|	|	...	1551	|	...	1559	...	1644	...	1721	|	1751	...	...	1856	|	1935	...
Valence TGV d.	...	...	...	|	|	...	|	1616	...	|	...	1725	...	|	1813	|	...	...	|	|	2015	...
Lyon St Exupéry ✈ d.	...	...	...	1617	1617	...	|	|	...	|	...	|	...	1817	|	|	...	...	2004	|	|	...
Lyon Part Dieu d.	...	1600	...	|	|	...	1700	1700	...	1725	...	|	...	|	1900	1900	...	...	|	2020	2100	...
Le Creusot TGV d.	...	|	...	|	|	...	|	|	...	|	...	|	...	|	|	|	...	...	|	...	|	...
Bordeaux d.	1515	|	...	|	|	1508	|	|	...	|	...	|	...	|	|	|	...	...	|	...	|	...
Angoulême d.	|	|	...	|	|	1546	|	|	...	|	...	|	...	|	|	|	...	...	|	...	|	...
Poitiers d.	|	|	...	|	|	1628	|	|	...	|	...	|	...	|	|	|	...	...	|	...	|	...
St Pierre des Corps d.	|	|	...	|	|	1702	|	|	...	|	...	|	...	|	|	|	...	...	|	...	|	...
Nantes d.	|	|	...	|	|	|	|	|	...	|	...	|	...	|	|	|	1803	...	|	...	|	...
Angers St Laud d.	|	|	...	|	|	|	|	|	...	|	...	|	...	|	|	|	1844	...	|	...	|	...
Rennes d.	|	|	1531	|	|	|	|	|	...	|	...	|	...	|	|	|	|	1839	|	...	|	...
Le Mans d.	|	|	1633	|	|	|	|	|	...	|	...	|	...	|	|	|	1933	1933	|	...	|	...
Massy TGV d.	|	|	1725	|	|	1755	|	|	...	|	...	|	...	|	|	|	2025	2025	|	...	|	...
Strasbourg d.	|	|	|	|	|	|	|	|	...	|	...	|	...	|	|	|	|	|	|	...	|	...
Marne la Vallée § d.	|	1752	1803	1810	1810	1831	1852	1852	...	|	...	|	...	2011	2052	2052	2101	2101	2152	...	2252	...
Paris Charles de Gaulle ✈ a.	|	1802	1813	...	...	1842	1902	1902	...	|	...	|	...	...	2103	2103	2112	2112	2202	...	2302	...
Paris Charles de Gaulle ✈ d.	|	1807	1818	...	...	1848	1907	1907	...	|	...	|	...	...	2108	2108	2117	2117	...	...	3307	...
TGV Haute Picardie d.	|	1839	|	...	...	|	|	|	...	|	...	|	...	...	|	|	2150	2150	...	...	|	...
Arras a.	|	1856	|	...	...	|	|	|	...	|	...	|	...	...	|	|	|	|	...	...	|	...
Douai a.	|	1914	|	...	...	|	|	|	...	|	...	|	...	...	|	|	|	|	...	...	|	...
Lille Europe a.	|	1944**f**	1912**f**	...	...	1942**f**	1956	1956	...	2021	...	|	...	...	2156	2156	2216	2216	...	...	2356	...
Lille Europe d.	|	...	...	...	...	...	2008	2008	2100	...	2136	|	...	...	...	2207	...	...	...	...	...	...
Brussels Midi / Zuid a.	2013	...	...	...	...	...	2043	2043	|	...	|	2122	...	...	...	2243	...	...	...	...	...	...
London St Pancras a.	...	...	...	...	...	...	...	...	2133	...	2212	...	...	...	...	...	...	...	...	...	...	...

A – ⑤⑦ June 7 - July 19.
⑤⑥⑦ July 20 - Aug. 31.
⑤⑦ Sept. 1 - Oct. 18.
⑤⑥⑦ Oct. 19 - Nov. 2.
⑤⑦ Nov. 3 - Dec. 14. See Table **17**.

B – May 21 - July 14.

C – Dec. 9 - May 20, July 15 - Dec. 14.

H – ⑥ June 29 - Aug. 31: *THALYS* SOLEIL – (12) 🍷 Marseille - Valence *TGV* - Brussels - Amsterdam (arrive 2324; Table **18**).

M – ①⑤⑥ May 3 - June 29 (also May 26).
①⑤⑥⑦ June 30 - Sept. 1.
①⑤⑥ Sept. 2 – 16. See Table **17**.

S – ①③ June 3 - Oct. 18.
①②③④ Oct. 19 – 31.
①③ Nov. 1 - Dec. 14. See Table **17**.

T – ⑥ June 29 - Aug. 31 (not Aug. 17).

U – Aug. 17.

b – From Barcelona (Table **13**).

f – Lille **Flandres** (◇).

h – Not May 27.

k – Also May 27.

t – ①⑥⑦.

y – Montpellier **Sud de France**.

AVE – Alta Velocidad Española R 🍷 ✗.

§ – Marne la Vallée - Chessy, station for Disneyland Paris.

△ – To / from Lorient or Quimper on dates in Table **285**.

◇ – 500 metres from Lille Europe (see Lille City Plan on page 32).

⊠ – OUIGO low-cost TGV service. Internet bookings only at www.ouigo.com. Timings may vary.

☆ – Eurostar train. Special fares payable. ✕ in Business Premier and Standard Premier, 🍷 in Standard. Business Premier not available from Marne la Vallée - Chessy and Marseille. Minimum check-in time 30 minutes. Valid May 26 - Nov. 2.

⇌ – *Thalys* high-speed train. R 🍷. Special fares payable.

13 LONDON - PARIS - BARCELONA - MADRID

train type	AVE	AVE	AVE	TGV	AVE	TGV	AVE	☆	☆	☆	TGV	AVE	AVE	☆	AVE	AVE	☆		☆			AVE		
train number	9729	3122	9730	9711	3142	9713	3172	9084	9110	9110	5164	9743	3202	9014	3212	3412	9022		9040		3731	9729		
train number / notes			9731					9085	②③④	⑥					⑤⑦					Ⓐ	Ⓡ			
notes	T			C				M	P							V				2	L	T	2	
London St Pancras d.	...	...	...	...	...	...	...	0719	0647	0657	...	...	...	0922	...	...	1131	...	1622	...	...	...	...	...
Lille Europe d.	...	...	...	...	...	...	...	|	0926	0926	1043	...	...	|	...	...	|	...	|	...	...	...	...	...
Paris Nord a.	...	...	...	...	...	...	...	|	...	...	|	...	...	1247	...	...	1447	...	1947	...	...	...	...	...
								|			|			TGV 9715			TGV 9717 A S		3971 Ⓡ F					
Paris Gare de Lyon d.	...	...	...	0715	...	1007	...	|	...	...	|	...	...	1407	...	...	1607	...	...	...	...	...	...	...
Paris Austerlitz d.	...	...	...	|	...	|	...	|	...	...	|	...	...	|	...	...	|	...	2104	...	2104	...	...	...
Les Aubrais-Orléans d.	...	...	...	|	...	|	...	|	...	...	|	...	...	|	...	...	|	...	2226	...	2226	...	...	...
Lyon Part Dieu d.	...	...	...	|	...	|	...	1300	...	...	1400	1424	...	|	...	...	|	...	|	...	|	...	...	...
Valence TGV d.	...	...	...	|	...	1221	...	...	...	...	...	1505	...	1622	...	...	1822	...	|	...	|	...	...	...
Marseille St Charles d.	...	...	0801	|	...	|	...	...	...	...	...	|	...	|	...	...	|	...	|	...	|	...	...	...
Aix en Provence TGV d.	...	...	0816	|	...	|	...	...	...	...	...	|	...	|	...	...	|	...	|	...	|	...	...	...
Avignon TGV d.	...	...	0843	|	...	|	...	...	...	...	...	|	...	|	...	...	|	...	|	...	|	...	...	...
Nimes d.	...	...	0904	1008	...	1308	...	...	...	...	...	1550	...	1708	...	...	1908	...	|	...	|	...	...	...
Montpellier Saint-Roch d.	...	...	0935	1040	...	1340	...	...	...	...	...	1625	...	1740	...	...	1943	...	|	...	|	...	...	...
Béziers d.	...	...	1016	|	...	1420	...	...	...	...	...	1716	...	|	...	...	2029	...	|	...	|	...	...	...
Toulouse Matabiau d.	0807	...	|	|	...	|	...	...	...	...	...	|	...	|	...	...	|	...	0605a	...	0605a	0807	...	...
Carcassonne d.	0859	...	|	|	...	|	...	...	...	...	...	|	...	|	...	...	|	...	|	...	0743	0859	...	...
Narbonne d.	|	...	1033	1135	...	1436	...	...	...	...	...	1733	...	1835	...	...	2046	...	|	...	|	|	...	...
Perpignan d.	1000	...	1117	1213	...	1513	...	...	...	...	...	1809	...	1913	...	...	2123	...	|	...	0850	1000	...	...
Latour de Carol 🚌 a.	|	...	|	|	...	|	...	...	...	...	...	|	...	|	...	...	|	...	0915	1048	|	|	...	...
Cerbère 🚌 a.	|	...	|	|	...	|	...	...	...	...	...	|	...	|	...	...	|	...	...	|	0941	|	...	...
Portbou 🚌 a.	|	...	|	|	...	|	...	...	...	...	...	|	...	|	...	...	|	...	...	|	0950	|	1033	...
Figueres Vilafant ◇ a.	1023	...	1140	1237	...	1537	...	...	...	...	...	1834	...	1937	...	...	2147	...	...	|	...	1023	1058x	...
Girona a.	1040	...	1157	1254	...	1554	...	...	...	...	...	1851	...	1954	...	...	2204	...	...	|	...	1040	1136	...
Barcelona Sants a.	1121	...	1238	1334	...	1634	...	...	...	...	...	1930	...	2034	...	...	2244	...	...	1354	...	1121	1309	...
Barcelona Sants d.	...	1200	1250	...	1400	...	1700	...	...	...	...	...	2000	...	2100	2115	...	...	...	...	...	...	...	...
Zaragoza Delicias a.	...	1340	1423	...	1540	...	1828	...	...	...	...	...	2140	...	2240	2240	...	...	...	...	...	...	...	...
Madrid Puerta de Atocha a.	...	1510	1545	...	1710	...	1950	...	...	...	...	...	2310	...	0002	0002	...	...	...	...	...	...	...	...

train type	TGV	AVE	TGV	☆	☆	AVE	AVE	TGV	☆	AVE	TGV	AVE	TGV	AVE	AVE						☆			
train number	9708	9736	9866	9149	9153	3053	3061	9702	9055	3093	9704	3123	9706	9724	9726			3970		3730	9015			
train number / notes			9867	Ⓑ		①④⑤	①–④							19725*	31627*	Ⓐ	Ⓒ	Ⓡ		Ⓡ				
notes	Q D			h									C		E	2	2	H	2	B				
Madrid Puerta de Atocha d.	...	...	...	...	...	0550	0610	...	...	0930	...	1230	...	1325	...	...	...	...	...	...	...	...	...	...
Zaragoza Delicias d.	...	...	...	...	...	0706	|	...	...	1046	...	1346	...	1451	...	...	...	...	...	...	...	...	...	...
Barcelona Sants a.	...	...	...	...	...	0855	0840	...	...	1234	...	1530	...	1624	...	...	...	...	...	...	...	...	...	...
Barcelona Sants d.	0705	0825	...	...	...	...	...	0925	...	...	1320	...	1620	1645	1830	1501	1510	...	1516	...	...	...	...	...
Girona d.	0746	0906	...	...	...	...	...	1006	...	...	1401	...	1701	1726	1911	|	|	...	1648	...	...	...	...	...
Figueres Vilafant ◇ d.	0803	0923	...	...	...	...	...	1023	...	...	1418	...	1718	1743	1928	|	|	...	1727x	...	...	...	...	...
Portbou 🚌 d.	|	|	...	...	...	...	...	|	...	...	|	...	|	|	|	|	|	...	1753	...	...	...	...	...
Cerbère 🚌 d.	|	|	...	...	...	...	...	|	...	...	|	...	|	|	|	|	|	...	1757	1852	...	...	...	...
Latour de Carol 🚌 d.	|	|	...	...	...	...	...	|	...	...	|	...	|	|	|	1806	1817	1851	...	|	...	...	...	...
Perpignan a.	0826	0946	...	...	...	...	...	1046	...	...	1443	...	1741	1806	1951	...	...	|	...	1941	...	...	...	...
Narbonne a.	0914	1027	...	...	...	...	...	1127	...	...	1524	...	1823	1854	|	...	...	|	...	|	...	...	...	...
Carcassonne a.	|	|	...	...	...	...	...	|	...	...	|	...	|	|	2056	...	...	|	...	2045	...	...	...	...
Toulouse Matabiau a.	|	|	...	...	...	...	...	|	...	...	|	...	|	|	2142	...	...	2230	...	2230	...	...	...	...
Béziers a.	0931	|	...	...	...	...	...	1142	...	...	|	...	1839	1910	...	...	...	|	...	|	...	...	...	...
Montpellier Saint-Roch a.	1017	1123	...	...	...	...	...	1220	...	...	1617	...	1920	1952	...	...	...	|	...	|	...	...	...	...
Nimes a.	1051	1158	...	...	...	...	...	1253	...	...	1651	...	1951	2022	...	...	...	|	...	|	...	...	...	...
Avignon TGV a.	|	|	...	...	...	...	...	|	...	...	|	...	|	2042	...	...	...	|	...	|	...	...	...	...
Aix en Provence TGV a.	|	|	...	...	...	...	...	|	...	...	|	...	|	2110	...	...	...	|	...	|	...	...	...	...
Marseille St Charles a.	|	|	...	...	...	...	...	|	...	...	|	...	|	2124	...	...	...	|	...	|	...	...	...	...
Valence TGV a.	1138	1243	...	...	...	...	...	1339	...	...	1736	...	|	...	...	...	...	|	...	|	...	...	...	...
Lyon Part Dieu a.	|	1320	1400	...	...	...	...	|	...	...	|	...	|	...	...	...	...	|	...	|	...	...	...	...
Les Aubrais-Orléans a.	|	...	|	...	...	...	...	|	...	...	|	...	|	...	...	...	...	0535	...	0535	...	...	...	...
Paris Austerlitz a.	|	...	|	...	...	...	...	|	...	...	|	...	|	...	...	...	...	0649	...	0649	...	...	...	...
Paris Gare de Lyon a.	1353	...	|	...	...	...	...	1553	...	...	1953	...	2245	...	...	...	...	...	...	...	...	...	...	...
	☆ 9039		|					☆ 9051 Ⓑ																
Paris Nord d.	1504	...	|	...	...	...	...	1804	1904	...	...	...	...	...	...	...	...	...	...	...	0904	...	...	...
Lille Europe a.	|	...	1701	1735	1835	...	...	|	|	...	...	...	...	...	...	...	...	...	...	...	|	...	...	...
London St Pancras a.	1639	...	...	1805	1910	...	...	1939	2039	...	...	...	...	...	...	...	...	...	...	...	1030	...	...	...

A – June 29 - Sept. 1.
B – ⑦: 🛏 1, 2 cl., (2) (reclining) Cerbère - Toulouse - Paris.
C – June 1 - Sept. 1.
D – Calls at Agde, a. 0944, Sète, a. 0959.
E – Mar. 31 - Sept. 22.
F – 🛏 1, 2 cl., (2) (reclining) Paris - Toulouse - Latour de Carol.
H – 🛏 1, 2 cl., (2) (reclining) Latour de Carol - Toulouse - Paris.
L – ⑦: 🛏 1, 2 cl., (2) (reclining) Paris - Toulouse - Portbou.
M – ①⑤⑥ May 3 - June 29 (also May 26).
①⑤⑥⑦ June 30 - Sept. 1.
①⑤⑥ Sept. 2 - 16. See Table **17**.

P – ②③④ (①–⑤ Sept. 20 - Nov. 2).
Q – June 30 - Sept. 2.
S – Calls at Sète 1959, Agde 2015.
T – Apr. 1 - Sept. 23.
V – ①②③④⑥.

a – Arrival time.
h – Not May 27.
m – Not May 30.
x – Figueres.

TGV – *Train à Grande Vitesse* Ⓡ 🍷 supplement.
AVE – Alta Velocidad Española Ⓡ 🍷 supplement.
Supplement symbol – Supplement payable.
◇ – 🚌 connections available to Figueres bus station. (Table **657**).
☆ – Eurostar train. Ⓡ, ✕ in Business Premier and Standard Premier, 🍷 in Standard. Special fares payable. Minimum check-in time 30 minutes. Additional services are shown on Table **10**. Valid May 26 - Nov. 2.

LONDON - AMSTERDAM *by rail–sea–rail via Harwich - Hoek van Holland* 15

Engineering work is being carried out between Hoek van Holland Haven and Schiedam until mid 2019.
Bus Line 711, will convey travellers between the two points.

notes	①–⑥	⑥	①–⑤	①–⑥	①–⑤	⑥	①–⑥	①–⑥		⑦	⑦	⑦	⑦	⑦	⑦		①–⑤	⑥	①–⑥	①–⑥	⑥⑦	②–⑤	②–⑦	②–⑦		
				⛴	🚌	🚌						⛴	🚌							⛴	🚌	🚌				
London Liverpool Street d.	...	0638	0638	...	...	...	...	...	...	...	0755	...	...	...	...	...	1932	1932	...	...	...	...	...	...	...	...
Colchester d.	...	0740	0743	...	...	...	...	...	...	...	0859	...	...	...	...	...	2025	2032	...	...	...	...	...	...	...	...
Manningtree d.	...	0748	0751	...	...	...	...	...	...	...	0907	...	...	...	...	...	2034	2040	...	...	...	...	...	...	...	...
Cambridge d.	...	|	|	...	...	...	...	...	...	...	|	...	...	...	...	...	|	|	1947	...	...	...	...	...	...	...
Ipswich d.	0659	|	|	...	...	...	...	...	...	0751	|	...	...	...	...	...	|	|	2103	...	...	...	...	...	...	...
Harwich International d.	0727	0809	0810	0900	...	...	...	...	...	0816	0925	1000	...	...	...	...	2054	2056	2129	2300	...	...	...	...	...	...
Hoek van Holland Haven a.	...	...	...	1715	1749	1752	...	...	...	...	...	1815	1852	...	...	...	...	...	...	0800	0822	0831	...	...	...	...
Schiedam Centrum a.	...	...	...	...	1816	1819	1843	1847	...	...	...	...	1919	1943	1947	...	...	...	...	...	0847	0858	0913	0917	...	...
Rotterdam Centraal a.	...	...	...	...	...	...	1848	|	...	...	...	...	...	1948	|	...	...	...	...	...	...	...	0918	|	...	...
Den Haag HS a.	...	...	...	...	...	...	...	1901	...	...	...	...	...	...	2001	...	...	...	...	...	...	...	...	0931	...	...
Schiphol ✈ a.	...	...	...	...	...	...	...	|	...	...	...	...	...	...	|	...	...	...	...	...	...	...	...	|	...	...
Amsterdam Centraal a.	...	...	...	...	...	...	...	1955	...	...	...	...	...	...	2055	...	...	...	...	...	...	...	...	1025	...	...

notes	⑦	⑦	⑦	⑦	①	①	①	
				⛴	🚌			
London Liverpool Street d.	1932	...	...	...	...	...	...	...
Colchester d.	2037	2046	...	...	...	...	...	...
Manningtree d.	...	2055	...	...	...	...	...	...
Cambridge d.	...	|	1914	...	...	...	...	...
Ipswich d.	...	|	2037	...	...	...	...	...
Harwich International d.	...	2114	2105	2300	...	...	...	...
Hoek van Holland Haven a.	...	...	...	0800	0831	...	...	...
Schiedam Centrum a.	...	...	...	...	0858	0913	0917	...
Rotterdam Centraal a.	...	...	...	...	...	0918	|	...
Den Haag HS a.	...	...	...	...	...	...	0931	...
Schiphol ✈ a.	...	...	...	...	...	...	|	...
Amsterdam Centraal a.	...	...	...	...	...	...	1025	...

notes	⑦	⑦	⑦	⑦	⑦	⑦						
			🚌	⛴								
Amsterdam Centraal d.	...	1104	...	...	...	...	...	...	...	...	...	...
Schiphol ✈ d.	...	|	...	...	...	...	...	...	...	...	...	...
Den Haag HS d.	...	1159	...	...	...	...	...	...	...	...	...	...
Rotterdam Centraal d.	1206	|	...	...	...	...	...	...	...	...	...	...
Schiedam Centrum d.	1210	1213	1220	...	...	...	...	...	...	...	...	...
Hoek van Holland Haven d.	...	...	1252	1345	...	...	...	...	...	...	...	...
Harwich International a.	...	...	...	1945	2035	2110	...	...	...	...	...	...
Ipswich a.	...	...	...	...	|	2137	...	...	...	...	...	...
Cambridge a.	...	...	...	...	|	...	...	...	...	...	...	...
Manningtree a.	...	...	...	...	2048	...	...	...	...	...	...	...
Colchester a.	...	...	...	...	2057	...	...	...	...	...	...	...
London Liverpool Street a.	...	...	...	...	2202	...	...	...	...	...	...	...

notes	①–⑥	①–⑥	①–⑤	⑥	①–⑥	①–⑥	①–⑥							①–⑤	⑥	⑦	①–⑤	⑥	⑦							
			🚌	🚌	⛴							🚌	⛴													
Amsterdam Centraal d.	1104	...	...	...	...	...	...	...	...	...	1904	...	...	...	...	...	...	...	...	...	...	...	...	...	...	...
Schiphol ✈ d.	|	...	...	...	...	...	...	...	...	...	|	...	...	...	...	...	...	...	...	...	...	...	...	...	...	...
Den Haag HS d.	1159	...	...	...	...	...	...	...	...	...	1959	...	...	...	...	...	...	...	...	...	...	...	...	...	...	...
Rotterdam Centraal d.	|	1212	...	...	...	...	...	...	...	2006	|	...	...	...	...	...	...	...	...	...	...	...	...	...	...	...
Schiedam Centrum d.	1213	1217	1240	1250	...	...	...	...	...	2010	2013	2020	...	...	...	...	...	...	...	...	...	...	...	...	...	...
Hoek van Holland Haven d.	...	...	1311	1322	1415	...	...	...	...	...	...	2052	2200	...	...	...	...	...	...	...	...	...	...	...	...	...
Harwich International a.	...	...	...	...	1945	2045	2138	...	...	...	...	...	0630	0715	0720	0720	0750	0750	0830	...	...	...	...	...	...	...
Ipswich a.	...	...	...	...	...	|	2204	...	...	...	...	...	...	|	|	|	0817	0817	0853	...	...	...	...	...	...	...
Cambridge a.	...	...	...	...	...	|	...	...	...	...	...	...	...	|	|	|	0942	0940	1025	...	...	...	...	...	...	...
Manningtree a.	...	...	...	...	...	2058	...	...	...	...	...	...	...	0731	0733	0734	...	...	...	...	...	...	...	...	...	...
Colchester a.	...	...	...	...	...	2107	...	...	...	...	...	...	...	0741	0742	0743	...	...	...	...	...	...	...	...	...	...
London Liverpool Street a.	...	...	...	...	...	2214	...	...	...	...	...	...	...	0854	0846	0859	...	...	...	...	...	...	...	...	...	...

SEA CROSSING (for rail / sea / rail journeys): ⛴ – Ship operated by Stena Line. Ⓡ. Stena Plus lounge (supplement payable) and ✕ on ship. A cabin must be booked on night sailings.

LILLE - BRUSSELS (Summary Table) 16

train type	*TGV*	*TGV*	☆	*TGV*	☆	*TGV*	☆	*TGV*	☆	☆	*TGV*	☆	*TGV*	☆	*TGV*	☆	☆	*TGV*			
train number	**9809**	**9890**	**9110**	**9855**	**9116**	**9863**	**9126**	**9861**	**9132**	**9136**	**9867**	**9140**	**9895**	**9148**	**9865**	**9152**	**9158**	**9883**			
notes	①–⑤									⑦				⑥		Ⓑ					
notes			**B**							**A**											
Lille Europe d.	0720	0908	0930	1119	1130	1208	1330	1435	1533	1630	1707	1730	1808	1930	2008	2030	2203	2207	...	...	...
Brussels Midi / Zuid a.	0755	0943	1005	1153	1205	1243	1405	1512	1608	1705	1743	1805	1843	2005	2043	2105	2238	2243	...	...	...

train type	☆	*TGV*	☆	*TGV*	☆	☆	☆	*TGV*	☆	☆	☆	*TGV*	☆	*TGV*	☆	☆	☆	*TGV*	☆		
train number	**9109**	**9870**	**9113**	**9812**	**9117**	**9121**	**9129**	**9828**	**9133**	**9141**	**9141**	**9872**	**9145**	**9836**	**9149**	**9153**	**9157**	**9846**	**9163**		
notes	①		①–⑥			①–⑥	⑦		①–⑥	⑦	①–⑥		⑦		Ⓑ		Ⓑ				
notes	**f**		**h**						**h**				**A**								
Brussels Midi / Zuid d.	0656	0717	0756	0817	0852	1056	1156	1217	1252	1452	1456	1551	1556	1617	1656	1756	1856	1917	2022	...	...
Lille Europe a.	0730	0752	0830	0852	0926	1130	1230	1253	1326	1526	1530	1626	1630	1653	1730	1830	1923	1951	2056	...	...

A – ⑦ May 26 - July 27 (also May 28).

B – ②③④⑥ (①–⑥ Sept. 20 - Nov. 2).

f – Not June 10, Aug. 26.

h – Not Aug. 26.

☆ – Eurostar train. Ⓡ, ✕ in Business Premier and Standard Premier, 🍸 in Standard. Special fares payable. Minimun check-in time 30 minutes departure from Brussels. Valid May 26 - Nov. 2.

TGV– High-speed train. Ⓡ 🍸.

LONDON - MARSEILLE and MARNE LA VALLÉE 17

train type	☆	☆	☆		☆	
train number	**9084**	**9084**	**9084**		**9074**	
train number	**9085**	**9085**	**9085**			
notes	**P**	**R**	**S**		**A**	
London St Pancras d.	0715	0719	0719	...	1014	...
Ebbsfleet International d.	|	|	|	...	1034	...
Ashford International d.	0754	0755	0755	...	1058**x**	...
Lille Europe a.	|	0951	|	...	1254	...
Marne la Vallée § a.	|	|	|	...	1403	...
Lyon Part Dieu a.	1300	1300	1300	...	...	...
Avignon TGV a.	1408	1408	1408	...	...	...
Marseille St Charles a.	1447	1447	1447	...	...	...

train type	☆	☆		☆	☆	
train number	**9057**	**9057**		**9087**	**9087**	
train number				**9086**	**9086**	
notes	**B**	**C**		**M**	**M**	
Marseille St Charles d.	...	...	...	1522	...	...
Avignon TGV d.	...	...	...	1559	...	...
Lyon Part Dieu d.	...	...	...	1725	...	...
Marne la Vallée § d.	1655	1801	...	|	...	...
Lille Europe d.	|	|	...	2021	2136	...
Ashford International a.	1806**x**	1904	...	...	2134	...
Ebbsfleet International a.	1827	1926	...	...	|	...
London St Pancras a.	1847	1946	...	...	2212	...

A – ①③⑤⑦ June 3 - July 26.
①③⑤⑥⑦ July 27 - Aug. 31.
①③⑤⑦ Sept. 1 - Oct. 18.
Daily Oct. 19 - Nov. 2.
①③⑤⑦ Nov. 3 - Dec. 14.

B – ⑤⑦ June 7 - July 19.
⑤⑥⑦ July 20 - Aug. 31.
⑤⑦ Sept. 1 - Oct. 18.
⑤⑥⑦ Oct. 19 - Nov. 2.
⑤⑦ Nov. 3 - Dec. 14.

C – ①③ June 3 - Oct. 18.
①②③④ Oct. 19 – 31.
①③ Nov. 1 - Dec. 14.

M – ①⑤⑥ May 3 - June 29 (also May 26).
①⑤⑥⑦ June 30 - Sept. 1.
①⑤⑥ Sept. 2 - 16.

P – ⑦ June 30 - Sept. 1 (also May 26).

R – ①⑤ May 3 - Sept. 16.

S – ⑥ May 4 - Sept. 14.

x – Not June 16, Nov. 24.

§ – Marne la Vallée - Chessy (station for Disneyland).

☆ – Eurostar train. Ⓡ, ✕ in Standard Premier, 🍸 in Standard. Special fares payable. Minimum check-in time 30 minutes. Not available for London - Ashford or v.v. journeys.

18 LONDON / PARIS - BRUSSELS - AMSTERDAM

Eurostar service valid May 26 - Nov. 2. Thalys service Mar. 31 - Dec. 14.

train type	*ICd*	⇌	*IC*	*ICd*	⇌	⇌	*ICd*	⇌	⇌	⇌	☆	*ICd*	⇌	☆	☆	☆	⇌	*IC*	⇌	☆
train number	**9211**	**9391**	**9215**	**9219**	**9303**	**9305**	**9223**	**9309**	**9413**	**9413**	**9108**	**9227**	**9315**	**9110**	**9110**	**9112**	**9319**	**9231**	**9321**	**9114**
notes		Ⓐ			Ⓐ			⚒	⑦	⚒	①⑤			②③④	⑥	①–⑥	①⑥			①–⑥
notes						**B**					**C**			**Q**		**A**	**Dw**		**G**	**W**
London St Pancras d.	...	...	...	...	...	...	...	...	...	...	0613	...	...	0647	0657	0716	...	...	...	0816
Marne la Vallée - Chessy § d.	...	...	...	...	...	...	...	...	...	...	|	...	...	|	|	|	...	...	...	|
Paris Charles de Gaulle ✈ d.	...	...	...	...	...	...	...	...	...	...	|	...	...	|	|	|	...	...	...	|
Paris Nord d.	...	...	...	...	0613	0655	...	0725	0740	0755	|	...	0825	|	|	|	0901	...	0925	|
Lille Europe d.	...	...	...	...	|	|	...	|	|	|	|	...	|	0930	0930	|	|	...	|	|
Brussels Midi / Zuid ◧ a.	...	...	...	...	0735	0817	...	0847	0912	0917	0922	...	0947	1005	1005	1012	1024	...	1047	1112
Brussels Midi / Zuid ◧ △ d.	0544	0652	0644	0744	0752	...	0844	0852	...	...	...	0945	0952	...	...	1022	...	1044	...	1122
Brussels Airport ✈ d.	0611	|	0711	0811	|	...	0911	|	...	...	...	1011	|	...	...	|	...	1111	...	|
Mechelen d.	0625	|	0725	0825	|	...	0925	|	...	...	...	1025	|	...	...	|	...	1125	...	|
Antwerpen Centraal a.	0644	0727	0744	0844	0827	...	0944	0927	...	...	...	1044	1027	...	...	|	...	1144	...	|
Breda a.	0718	|	0818	0918	|	...	1018	|	...	...	...	1118	|	...	...	|	...	1218	...	|
Breda d.	0726	|	0826	0926	|	...	1026	|	...	...	...	1126	|	...	...	|	...	1226	...	|
Rotterdam Centraal a.	0750	0802	0850	0950	0902	...	1050	1002	...	...	...	1150	1102	...	...	1132	...	1250	...	1232
Den Haag HS a.	|	|	0920	|	|	...	|	|	...	...	...	|	|	...	...	|	...	1320	...	|
Schiphol ✈ a.	0822	0825	...	1022	0925	...	1122	1025	...	...	...	1222	1125	...	...	|	...	...	...	|
Amsterdam Centraal a.	0838	0844	...	1038	0944	...	1138	1044	...	...	...	1238	1144	...	...	1211	...	...	...	1311

train type	⇌	*ICd*	⇌	☆	*ICd*	⇌	⇌	⇌	*ICd*	⇌	⇌	☆	☆	⇌	⇌	*IC*	⇌	*ICd*	⇌	
train number	**9325**	**9235**	**9327**	**9116**	**9239**	**9933**	**9333**	**9437**	**9243**	**9939**	**9339**	**9128**	**9126**	**9341**	**9341**	**9247**	**9345**	**9251**	**9351**	
notes							①–④							①–⑤	⑥⑦		Ⓐ			
notes	**H**					**X**				**N**	**J**	**W**	**A**	**j**						
London St Pancras d.	...	...	...	0854	...	...	...	...	...	...	...	1058	1104	...	...	...	...	...	...	...
Marne la Vallée - Chessy § d.	...	...	...	|	...	1116	...	...	...	1204	...	|	|	...	...	...	...	...	...	...
Paris Charles de Gaulle ✈ d.	...	...	...	|	...	1133	...	...	...	1219	...	|	|	...	...	...	...	...	...	...
Paris Nord d.	1001	...	1025	|	...	|	1125	1155	...	|	1225	|	|	1246	1255	...	...	...	1425	...
Lille Europe d.	|	...	|	1130	...	|	|	|	...	|	|	1333	1333	|	|	...	...	...	|	...
Brussels Midi / Zuid ◧ a.	1125	...	1147	1205	...	1245	1247	1317	...	1334	1347	1405	1405	1408	1417	...	...	...	1547	...
Brussels Midi / Zuid ◧ △ d.	...	1144	1152	...	1244	1252	1252	...	1344	1352	1352	...	1422	...	...	1444	1452	1544	1552	...
Brussels Airport ✈ d.	...	1211	|	...	1311	|	|	...	1411	|	|	...	|	...	...	1511	|	1611	|	...
Mechelen d.	...	1225	|	...	1325	|	|	...	1425	|	|	...	|	...	...	1525	|	1625	|	...
Antwerpen Centraal a.	...	1244	1227	...	1344	1327	1327	...	1444	1427	1427	...	|	...	...	1544	1527	1644	1627	...
Breda a.	...	1318	|	...	1418	|	|	...	1518	|	|	...	|	...	...	1618	|	1718	|	...
Breda d.	...	1326	|	...	1426	|	|	...	1526	|	|	...	|	...	...	1626	|	1726	|	...
Rotterdam Centraal a.	...	1350	1302	...	1450	1402	1402	...	1550	1502	1502	...	1532	...	...	1650	1602	1750	1702	...
Den Haag HS a.	...	|	|	...	|	|	|	...	|	|	|	...	|	...	...	1722	|	|	|	...
Schiphol ✈ a.	...	1422	1325	...	1522	1425	1425	...	1622	1525	1525	...	|	...	...	...	1625	1822	1725	...
Amsterdam Centraal a.	...	1438	1344	...	1538	1444	1444	...	1638	1544	1544	...	1611	...	...	...	1644	1838	1744	...

train type	☆	*ICd*	⇌	⇌	*ICd*	⇌	⇌		☆	⇌	*ICd*	⇌	⇌	*ICd*	⇌	⇌				
train number	**9132**	**9255**	**9357**	**9461**	**9259**	**9363**	**9363**		**9140**	**9365**	**9263**	**9369**	**9473**	**9267**	**9375**	**9375**				
notes			Ⓑ			⑤⑦	①–④								⑤⑦	①–④				
notes										**K**										
London St Pancras d.	1258	...	...	...	...	...	...	...	1504	...	...	...	...	...	...	...	...	...	...	...
Marne la Vallée - Chessy § d.	|	...	...	...	...	...	...	...	|	...	...	...	...	...	...	...	...	...	...	...
Paris Charles de Gaulle ✈ d.	|	...	...	...	...	...	...	...	|	...	...	...	...	...	...	...	...	...	...	...
Paris Nord d.	|	...	1525	1555	...	1625	...	...	|	1655	...	1725	1755	...	1825	1825	...	...	...	...
Lille Europe d.	1533	...	|	|	...	|	...	...	1730	|	...	|	|	...	|	|	...	...	...	...
Brussels Midi / Zuid ◧ a.	1608	...	1647	1717	...	1747	...	...	1805	1817	...	1847	1917	...	1947	1947	...	...	...	...
Brussels Midi / Zuid ◧ △ d.	...	1644	1652	...	1744	1752	1752	...	...	...	1844	1852	...	1944	1952	...	...	...	...	...
Brussels Airport ✈ d.	...	1711	|	...	1811	|	|	...	...	...	1911	|	...	2011	|	...	...	...	...	...
Mechelen d.	...	1725	|	...	1825	|	|	...	...	...	1925	|	...	2025	|	...	...	...	...	...
Antwerpen Centraal a.	...	1744	1727	...	1844	1827	1827	...	...	...	1944	1927	...	2044	2027	...	...	...	...	...
Breda a.	...	1818	|	...	1918	|	|	...	...	...	2018	|	...	2118	|	...	...	...	...	...
Breda d.	...	1826	|	...	1926	|	|	...	...	...	2026	|	...	2126	|	...	...	...	...	...
Rotterdam Centraal a.	...	1850	1802	...	1950	1902	1902	...	...	...	2050	2002	...	2150	2102	...	...	...	...	...
Den Haag HS a.	...	|	|	...	|	|	|	...	...	...	2122	|	...	|	|	...	...	...	...	...
Schiphol ✈ a.	...	1922	1825	...	2022	1925	1925	...	...	...	2149	2025	...	2222	2125	...	...	...	...	...
Amsterdam Centraal a.	...	1938	1844	...	2038	1944	1944	...	...	...	2205	2044	...	2238	2144	...	...	...	...	...

train type	☆	⇌	☆	*ICd*	⇌		☆	☆	⇌	⇌	⇌			⇌	⇌	⇌	⇌			
train number	**9148**	**9377**	**9150**	**9271**	**9381**		**9152**	**9152**	**9955**	**9387**	**9985**			**9389**	**9393**	**9395**	**9399**			
notes notes	⑥		Ⓑ				⑦	①–⑤	⊗	Ⓑ						⑤	⑦			
notes		**L**					**k**	**h**	**E**	**D**	**D**			**M**	**DP**					
London St Pancras d.	1704	...	1716	...	...	...	1755	1804	...	...	...	...	...	...	...	...	...	...	...	...
Marne la Vallée - Chessy § d.	|	...	|	...	...	...	|	|	...	...	2004	...	...	...	...	...	...	...	...	...
Paris Charles de Gaulle ✈ d.	|	...	|	...	...	...	|	|	...	...	2019	...	...	...	...	...	...	...	...	...
Paris Nord d.	|	1855	|	...	1925	...	|	|	...	2025	|	...	...	2055	2125	2155	2225	...	...	...
Lille Europe d.	1930	|	|	...	|	...	2030	2030	...	|	|	...	...	|	|	|	|	...	...	...
Brussels Midi / Zuid ◧ a.	2005	2017	2012	...	2047	...	2105	2105	2122	2147	2133	...	...	2217	2247	2317	2347	...	...	...
Brussels Midi / Zuid ◧ △ d.	...	...	2022	2044	2052	...	...	...	|	...	2152	...	...	...	...	...	...	...	...	...
Brussels Airport ✈ d.	...	...	|	2111	|	...	...	...	|	...	|	...	...	...	...	...	...	...	...	...
Mechelen d.	...	...	|	2125	|	...	...	...	|	...	|	...	...	...	...	...	...	...	...	...
Antwerpen Centraal a.	...	...	|	2144	2127	...	...	...	2205	...	2227	...	...	...	...	...	...	...	...	...
Breda a.	...	...	|	2218	|	...	...	...	|	...	|	...	...	...	...	...	...	...	...	...
Breda d.	...	...	|	2226	|	...	...	...	|	...	|	...	...	...	...	...	...	...	...	...
Rotterdam Centraal a.	...	...	2132	2250	2202	...	...	...	2241	...	2302	...	...	...	...	...	...	...	...	...
Den Haag HS a.	...	...	|	|	|	...	...	...	|	...	|	...	...	...	...	...	...	...	...	...
Schiphol ✈ a.	...	...	|	2322	2225	...	...	...	2308	...	2325	...	...	...	...	...	...	...	...	...
Amsterdam Centraal a.	...	...	2211	2338	2244	...	...	...	2324	...	2344	...	...	...	...	...	...	...	...	...

A – From June 11.
B – ①–④ (not June 10, July 14 - Aug. 31).
C – ①⑤ May 26 - Sept. 26 (not May 27, June 10, Aug. 26).
D – Mar. 31 - July 13, Sept. 1 - Dec. 14.
E – *THALYS* SOLEIL – ⑥ June 29 - Aug. 31: (12) 🍸 Marseille - Valence *TGV* - Brussels - Amsterdam.
G – ②③④⑤⑦ Mar. 31 - July 13, Sept. 1 - Dec. 14 (also June 10; not June 11).
H – ① Mar. 31 - July 13, Sept. 1 - Dec. 14 (also June 11; not June 10).
J – ⑤⑥⑦ (also June 10; not June 29, July 6, 13, Aug. 16).
K – ①–⑤ (not July 14 - Aug. 31).
L – ①–④ (not July 14 - Aug. 31).
M – Daily July 14 - Aug. 31. ⑥ Sept. 1 - Dec. 14.
N – Daily Mar. 31 - July 13, Ⓑ July 14 - Aug. 31, Daily Sept. 1 - Dec. 14.
P – ①②③④⑦ Sept. 1 - Dec. 14.
Q – ②③④ (①–⑤ Sept. 20 - Nov. 2).
W – May 26 - June 10.
X – ⑥ June 29 - Aug. 31.

h – Not Aug. 26.
j – Not Aug. 16.
k – Also Aug. 26.
w – Also June 11; not June 10.

§ – Station for Disneyland.
⊗ – Calls to set down only.
◧ – Connections at Brussels are not guaranteed.
⇌ – *Thalys* high-speed train. 🅁 🍸. Valid Mar. 31 - Dec. 14. Special fares payable.
△ – All *IC* and *ICd* services call at Brussels Central 5 minutes, and at Brussels Nord 11 minutes, after Brussels Midi / Zuid.
☆ – Eurostar train. 🅁, ✕ in Business Premier and Standard Premier, 🍸 in Standard. Special fares payable. Minimum check-in time 30 minutes. Not available for London - Ebbsfleet - Ashford or v.v. journeys. Valid May 26 - Nov 2.

Brussels - Disneyland: see Table 11

AMSTERDAM - BRUSSELS - PARIS / LONDON 18

Eurostar service valid May 26 - Nov. 2. Thalys service Mar. 31 - Dec. 14.

km	km	train type	⇌	⇌	⇌	⇌	⇌	⇌	⇌	⇌	☆	⇌	⇌	⇌	☆	IC	⇌	ICd	⇌	☆
		train number	9300	9302	9302	9304	9308	9310	9916	9412	9117	9926	9316	9916	9119	9212	9322	9216	9424	9121
		notes	①–④	⑤	②③④	①	①–⑥	①–⑤		9312		⊕	①–⑤		①–⑥					①–⑥
			Q	T	S	Q			X			A		R						
0	0	**Amsterdam** Centraal d.	...	...	...	...	...	0615	0615	...	...	0715	0715	0715	0749	0555	0815	0725	...	...
17	17	Schiphol ✈ ⊕ d.	...	...	...	...	...	0634	0634	...	...	0734	0734	0734	|	0611	0834	0740	...	...
60		Den Haag HS d.	...	...	...	...	...	|	|	...	...	|	|	|	|	0640	|	|	...	...
82	70	**Rotterdam** Centraal d.	...	...	...	...	...	0658	0658	...	...	0758	0758	0758	0828	0710	0858	0810	...	...
		Breda a.	...	...	...	...	...	|	|	...	...	|	|	|	|	0734	|	0834	...	...
140		Breda d.	...	...	...	...	...	|	|	...	...	|	|	|	|	0742	|	0842	...	...
181	165	**Antwerpen** Centraal d.	...	...	...	...	...	0734	0734	...	...	0833	0833	0833	|	0816	0933	0916	...	...
		Mechelen d.	...	...	...	...	...	|	|	...	...	|	|	|	|	0836	|	0936	...	...
		Brussels Airport ✈ d.	...	...	...	...	...	|	|	...	...	|	|	|	|	0850	|	0950	...	...
229	212	**Brussels** Midi / Zuid ◧ △ a.	...	...	...	...	...	0808	0808	...	...	|	0908	0908	0938	0917	1008	1017	...	...
229	212	**Brussels** Midi / Zuid ◧ d.	0600	0630	0643	0713	0743	0813	0831	0843	0852	0935	0916	0922	...	...	1016	...	1043	1056
		Lille Europe a.	|	|	|	|	|	|	|	|	0926	...	|	|	...	...	|	...	|	1130
541	524	**Paris** Nord a.	0735	0805	0805	0835	0905	0935	|	1005	|	...	1038	|	...	...	1138	...	1205	|
		Paris Charles de Gaulle ✈ a.	...	...	...	...	...	...	0946	...	|	...	...	1033	...	...	...	...	...	|
		Marne la Vallée - Chessy § a.	...	...	...	...	...	...	1003	...	|	...	...	1053	...	...	...	...	...	|
		London St Pancras a.	...	...	...	...	...	...	...	...	0957	...	...	...	...	...	...	...	...	1157

train type	⇌	⇌	ICd	☆	⇌	ICd	⇌	☆	⇌	IC	⇌	ICd	⇌	☆	☆	⇌
train number	9328	9328	9220	9129	9334	9224	9336	9133	9340	9228	9346	9232	9448	9141	9141	9352
notes	①–⑥	⑦		⑦	⑥⑦		Ⓐ	①–⑥			Ⓐ			⑦	①–⑥	
							w	h								
Amsterdam Centraal d.	0915	...	0825	...	1015	0925	...	...	1115	...	1215	1125	...	...	...	1315
Schiphol ✈ ⊕ d.	0934	...	0840	...	1034	0940	...	...	1134	...	1234	1140	...	...	...	1334
Den Haag HS d.	|	...	|	...	|	|	...	...	|	1039	|	|	...	...	...	|
Rotterdam Centraal d.	0958	...	0910	...	1058	1010	...	...	1158	1110	1258	1210	...	...	...	1358
Breda a.	|	...	0934	...	|	1034	...	...	|	1134	|	1234	...	...	...	|
Breda d.	|	...	0942	...	|	1042	...	...	|	1142	|	1242	...	...	...	|
Antwerpen Centraal d.	1033	...	1016	...	1133	1116	...	...	1233	1216	1333	1316	...	...	...	1433
Mechelen d.	|	...	1036	...	|	1136	...	...	|	1236	|	1336	...	...	...	|
Brussels Airport ✈ d.	|	...	1050	...	|	1150	...	...	|	1250	|	1350	...	...	...	|
Brussels Midi / Zuid ◧ △ a.	1108	...	1117	...	1208	1217	...	...	1308	1317	1408	1417	...	...	...	1508
Brussels Midi / Zuid ◧ d.	1113	1113	...	1156	1216	...	1237	1252	1313	...	...	...	1443	1452	1456	1516
Lille Europe a.	|	|	...	1230	|	...	|	1326	|	...	...	...	|	1526	1530	|
Paris Nord a.	1235	1235	...	|	1338	...	1359	|	1435	...	...	...	1605	|	|	1638
Paris Charles de Gaulle ✈ a.	...	...	...	|	...	...	...	|	...	...	...	...	...	|	|	...
Marne la Vallée - Chessy § a.	...	...	...	|	...	...	...	|	...	...	...	...	...	|	|	...
London St Pancras a.	...	...	...	1257	...	...	...	1405	...	...	...	...	...	1605	1605	...

train type	ICd	⇌	☆	☆	⇌	ICd	⇌	☆	⇌	⇌	⇌	IC	⇌	☆	⇌	ICd	⇌	☆
train number	9236	9356	9145	9145	9358	9240	9360	9149	9364	9964	9364	9244	9368	9153	9370	9248	9472	9157
notes		⑤	①–⑤	⑥⑦	Ⓑ		②③④	Ⓑ	①–④		⑤⑥⑦		②③ ④⑤		Ⓑ			Ⓑ
		w	B	B			w						Q					
Amsterdam Centraal d.	1225	...	1346	1349	1415	1325	...	...	...	1515	1515	...		...	1615	1525	...	...
Schiphol ✈ ⊕ d.	1240	...	|	|	1434	1340	...	...	...	1534	1534	...	...	...	1634	1540	...	...
Den Haag HS d.	|	...	|	|	|	|	...	...	...	|	|	1439	...	...	|	|	...	...
Rotterdam Centraal d.	1310	...	1428	1428	1458	1410	...	...	...	1558	1558	1510	...	...	1658	1610	...	...
Breda a.	1334	...	|	|	|	1434	...	...	...	|	|	1534	...	...	|	1634	...	...
Breda d.	1342	...	|	|	|	1442	...	...	...	|	|	1542	...	...	|	1642	...	...
Antwerpen Centraal d.	1416	...	|	|	1533	1516	...	...	...	1633	1633	1616	...	...	1733	1716	...	...
Mechelen d.	1436	...	|	|	|	1536	...	...	...	|	|	1636	...	...	|	1736	...	...
Brussels Airport ✈ d.	1450	...	|	|	|	1550	...	...	...	|	|	1650	...	...	|	1750	...	...
Brussels Midi / Zuid ◧ △ a.	1517	...	1538	1538	1608	1617	...	...	...	1708	1708	1717	...	...	1808	1817	...	...
Brussels Midi / Zuid ◧ d.	...	1537	...	...	1613	...	1637	1656	1713	1724	1713	...	1743	1756	1813	...	1843	1856
Lille Europe a.	...	|	...	...	|	...	|	1730	|	|	|	...	|	1830	|	...	|	1930
Paris Nord a.	...	1659	...	...	1735	...	1759	|	1835	|	1835	...	1905	|	1935	...	2005	|
Paris Charles de Gaulle ✈ a.	...	...	...	...	...	...	...	|	...	1846	...	...	...	|	...	...	...	|
Marne la Vallée - Chessy § a.	...	...	...	...	...	...	...	|	...	1904	...	...	...	|	...	...	...	|
London St Pancras a.	...	...	...	...	...	...	...	1814	...	...	...	...	...	1915	...	...	...	1957

train type	☆	⇌	ICd	☆	☆	⇌	ICd	⇌	⇌	IC	⇌	⇌	ICd	ICd	ICd
train number	9177	9376	9252	9161	9163	9382	9256	9484	9388	9260	9394	9394	9264	9268	9272
notes	①–⑤	Ⓑ							Ⓑ		①–⑤	⑦			
	C			D											
Amsterdam Centraal d.	1649	1715	1625	1749	...	1815	1725	...	1915	...	2015	2015	1925	2025	2125
Schiphol ✈ ⊕ d.	|	1734	1640	|	...	1834	1740	...	1934	...	2034	2034	1940	2040	2140
Den Haag HS d.	|	|	|	|	...	|	|	...	|	1839	|	|	|	|	|
Rotterdam Centraal d.	1728	1758	1710	1828	...	1858	1810	...	1958	1910	2058	2058	2010	2110	2210
Breda a.	|	|	1734	|	...	|	1834	...	|	1934	|	|	2034	2134	2234
Breda d.	|	|	1742	|	...	|	1842	...	|	1942	|	|	2042	2142	2242
Antwerpen Centraal d.	|	1833	1816	|	...	1933	1916	...	2033	2016	2133	2133	2116	2216	2316
Mechelen d.	|	|	1836	|	...	|	1936	...	|	2036	|	|	2136	2236	2336
Brussels Airport ✈ d.	|	|	1850	|	...	|	1950	...	|	2050	|	|	2150	2250	2350
Brussels Midi / Zuid ◧ △ a.	1838	1908	1917	1938	...	2008	2017	...	2108	2117	2208	2208	2217	2317	0020
Brussels Midi / Zuid ◧ d.	...	1913	...	...	2022	2016	...	2043	2113	...	...	2216	...	...	...
Lille Europe a.	...	|	...	...	2056	|	...	|	|	...	...	|	...	...	...
Paris Nord a.	...	2035	...	...	|	2138	...	2205	2235	...	...	2338	...	...	...
Paris Charles de Gaulle ✈ a.	...	...	...	...	|	...	...	...	...	...	...	...	...	...	...
Marne la Vallée - Chessy § a.	...	...	...	...	|	...	...	...	...	...	...	...	...	...	...
London St Pancras a.	...	...	...	...	2133	...	...	...	...	...	...	...	...	...	...

A – ⑥ June 29 - Aug. 31: *THALYS* SOLEIL – (12) 🍸 Amsterdam - Brussels - Valence *TGV* - Marseille (Table **11**).
B – June 11 - Nov. 2.
C – May 26 - June 10.
D – ⑦ (Ⓑ June 11 - Nov. 2).
Q – Mar. 31 - July 13, Sept. 1 - Dec. 14.
R – Daily Mar. 31 - June 28, Ⓑ June 29 - Aug. 31, Daily Sept. 1 - Dec. 14.
S – Sept. 1 - Dec. 14.
T – ⑤ (①–⑤ Sept. 1 - Aug. 31).

X – ⑥ June 29 - Aug. 31.
h – Not Aug. 26.
w – Not July 14 - Sept. 1.
⊕ – Calls to pick up only.
§ – Station for Disneyland.

⇌ – *Thalys* high-speed train. Ⓡ 🍸. Special fares payable. Valid Mar. 31 - Dec. 14.
◧ – Connections at Brussels are not guaranteed.
△ – All *IC* and *ICd* services call at Brussels Nord 12 minutes, and at Brussels Central 5 minutes, before Brussels Midi / Zuid.
☆ – Eurostar train. Ⓡ, ✕ in Business Premier and Standard Premier, 🍸 in Standard. Special fares payable. Minimum check-in time 30 minutes. Additional services are shown on Table **10**. Valid May 26 - Nov. 2.

izy Timings may vary PARIS - BRUSSELS 18a

train type / number	izy	izy		izy	izy		izy		
train number	9600	9602		9602	9606		9606		
train number	9640	9642		9642	②③		9646		
notes	⑥	①⑤		⑤⑦	④⑤		⑦		
Brussels Midi / Zuid d.	0828	0828	...	1028	1541	...	1659	...	...
Paris Nord a.	1041	1056	...	1247	1850	...	1911	...	...

train type / number	izy	izy		izy		izy	izy		
train number	9605	9603		9605		9615	9615		
train number				9645		②③	9655		
notes	①⑤	⑥		⑦		④⑤	⑦		
Paris Nord d.	1131	1131	...	1346	...	2000	2000	...	...
Brussels Midi / Zuid a.	1344	1344	...	1612	...	2212	2212	...	...

Low-cost ***TGV*** services branded **izy**, internet booking only through www.izy.com. Timings may vary. Subject to alteration.

20 LONDON, PARIS and BRUSSELS - KÖLN, HAMBURG and BERLIN

For the full service London - Brussels see Table **10**. For Paris - Brussels see Table **18**. Connections at Brussels are not guaranteed.

train type	ICE	ICE	IC	⇌	IC	ICE	ICE	ICE	IC		⇌	⇌	ICE	IC	☆	⇌	☆	☆	ICE	ICE	IC			
train number	**11**	**545**	**2310**	**9403**	**1028**	**13**	**13**	**557**	**2216**		**9413**	**9413**	**859**	**2226**	**9108**	**9315**	**9110**	**9110**	**15**	**559**	**2218**			
notes	①-⑥			①-⑥		①-⑤	⑥⑦								①⑤		②③④	⑥						
	w										LS	KS			A		B							
London St Pancras d.	...	...	...	...	...	...	...	...	...	...	...	...	...	...	0613	...	0647	0657	...	...	...	...	...	...
Paris Nord d.	...	...	...	0613	...	...	...	...	...	...	0755x	0755x	...	...	|	0825	|	|	...	...	...	...	...	...
Brussels Midi/Zuid a.	...	...	...	0735t	...	...	...	...	...	...	0917x	0917x	...	...	0922	0947	1005	1005	...	...	...	...	...	...
Brussels Midi/Zuid d.	0625	...	...	0755	...	0823	0823	...	...	...	0925	0925	...	...	...	...	...	...	1025	...	...	...	...	...
Brussels Nord d.	0633	...	...	|	...	0832	0832	...	...	...	|	|	...	...	...	...	...	...	1034	...	...	...	...	...
Liège Guillemins d.	0712	...	...	0846	...	0914	0912	...	...	...	1013	1013	...	...	...	...	...	...	1114	...	...	...	...	...
Aachen 🏛 a.	0736	...	...	0907	...	0936	0937	...	...	...	1035	1035	...	...	...	...	...	...	1136	...	...	...	...	...
Köln Hbf a.	0815	...	...	0948	...	1015	1015	...	...	...	1116	1116	...	...	...	...	...	...	1215	...	...	...	...	...
Köln Hbf d.	...	0828	0909	...	1010	...	...	1048	1109	...	1119	1119	1148	1210	...	...	...	...	...	1248	1309	...	...	...
Wuppertal Hbf a.	...	|	|	...	1042	...	...	1114	|	...	|	|	1214	1242	...	...	...	...	...	1314	|	...	...	...
Hagen Hbf a.	...	|	|	...	1100	...	...	1133	|	...	|	|	1233	1300	...	...	...	...	...	1333	|	...	...	...
Düsseldorf Hbf a.	...	0850	0930	...	|	...	...	|	1131	...	1140	1140	|	|	...	...	...	...	...	|	1330	...	...	...
Duisburg Hbf a.	...	0908	0944	...	|	...	...	|	1144	...	1214	1201	|	|	...	...	...	...	...	|	1344	...	...	...
Essen Hbf a.	...	0921	0957	...	|	...	...	|	1157	...	|	1215	|	|	...	...	...	...	...	|	1357	...	...	...
Bochum Hbf a.	...	0933	|	...	|	...	...	|	|	...	|	|	|	|	...	...	...	...	...	|	|	...	...	...
Dortmund Hbf a.	...	0946	1021	...	1122	...	...	|	1221	...	1313	1241	|	1322	...	...	...	...	...	|	1421	...	...	...
Hamm (Westf) a.	...	1007	|	...	|	...	...	1202	|	...	...	...	1302	|	...	...	...	...	...	1402	|	...	...	...
Bielefeld Hbf a.	...	1036	|	...	|	...	...	1236	|	...	...	...	1336	|	...	...	...	...	...	1436	|	...	...	...
Münster a.	...	|	1055	...	1155	...	...	|	1255	...	...	...	|	1355	...	...	...	...	...	|	1455	...	...	...
Osnabrück Hbf a.	...	|	1121	...	1221	...	...	|	1321	...	...	...	|	1421	...	...	...	...	...	|	1521	...	...	...
Bremen Hbf a.	...	|	1216	...	1316	...	...	|	1416	...	...	...	|	1516	...	...	...	...	...	|	1616	...	...	...
Hannover Hbf a.	...	1128	|	...	|	...	...	1328	|	...	...	...	1428	|	...	...	...	...	...	1528	|	...	...	...
Hamburg Hbf a.	...	|	1314	...	1414	...	...	|	1512	...	...	...	|	1614	...	...	...	...	...	|	1714	...	...	...
Berlin Hbf a.	...	1306	...	...	...	...	...	1507	...	...	...	...	1609	...	...	...	...	...	...	1707	...	...	...	...

train type	⇌	☆	ICE	ICE	IC		⇌	⇌	⇌	ICE	IC	⇌	☆	☆	⇌	ICE	ICE	EC	⇌	ICE	ICE	ICE	EC	EC
train number	**9327**	**9116**	**211**	**651**	**2312**		**9437**	**9437**	**9437**	**1053**	**2026**	**9339**	**9128**	**9126**	**9341**	**17**	**653**	**8**	**9451**	**215**	**215**	**655**	**6**	**6**
notes								⑥	⑧	⑧					①-⑤					①-⑤	⑦		⑧	⑥
							L	K	K			QJ	D	E										
London St Pancras d.	...	0854	...	...	...	...	...	...	...	...	...	...	1058	1104	...	...	...	...	...	...	...	...	...	...
Paris Nord d.	1025	|	...	...	...	...	1155	1155	1155	...	...	1225	|	|	1246	...	...	...	1425	...	...	...	...	...
Brussels Midi/Zuid a.	1147	1205	...	...	...	...	1317	1317	1317	...	...	1347	1405	1405	1408	...	...	...	1547	...	...	...	...	...
Brussels Midi/Zuid d.	...	...	1225	...	...	...	1325	1325	1325	...	...	...	...	...	...	1425	...	...	...	1622	1625	...	...	...
Brussels Nord d.	...	...	1234	...	...	...	|	|	|	...	...	...	...	...	...	1434	...	...	...	1632	1634	...	...	...
Liège Guillemins d.	...	...	1314	...	...	...	1413	1413	1413	...	...	...	...	...	...	1514	...	...	...	1714	1714	...	...	...
Aachen 🏛 a.	...	...	1336	...	...	...	1436	1436	1436	...	...	...	...	...	...	1536	...	...	...	1736	1736	...	...	...
Köln Hbf a.	...	...	1415	...	...	...	1515	1515	1515	...	...	...	...	...	...	1615	...	...	...	1815	1815	...	...	...
Köln Hbf d.	...	...	...	1448	1509	...	...	1526	1525	1548	1610	...	...	...	...	...	1648	1709	...	...	...	1848	1909	1909
Wuppertal Hbf a.	...	...	...	1514	|	...	...	|	|	1614	1641	...	...	...	...	...	1714	|	...	...	...	1914	|	|
Hagen a.	...	...	...	1533	|	...	...	|	|	1633	1659	...	...	...	...	...	1733	|	...	...	...	1933	|	|
Düsseldorf Hbf a.	...	...	...	|	1530	...	...	1553	1552	|	|	...	...	...	...	...	|	1730	...	...	...	|	1930	1930
Duisburg Hbf a.	...	...	...	|	1544	...	...	1612	1612	|	|	...	...	...	...	...	|	1745	...	...	...	|	1944	1944
Essen Hbf a.	...	...	...	|	1557	...	...	...	1631	|	|	...	...	...	...	...	|	1758	...	...	...	|	1957	1957
Bochum Hbf a.	...	...	...	|	|	...	...	...	...	|	|	...	...	...	...	...	|	1809	...	...	...	|	2008	2009
Dortmund Hbf a.	...	...	...	|	1621	...	...	...	...	|	1721	...	...	...	...	...	|	1822	...	...	...	|	2021	2021
Hamm (Westf) a.	...	...	...	1602	|	...	...	...	...	1702	|	...	...	...	...	...	1802	|	...	...	...	2002	|	...
Bielefeld a.	...	...	...	1636	|	...	...	...	...	1736	|	...	...	...	...	...	1836	|	...	...	...	2036	|	...
Münster a.	...	...	...	|	1655	...	...	...	...	|	1755	...	...	...	...	...	|	1855	...	...	...	|	2055	...
Osnabrück a.	...	...	...	|	1721	...	...	...	...	|	1821	...	...	...	...	...	|	1921	...	...	...	|	2121	...
Bremen Hbf a.	...	...	...	|	1816	...	...	...	...	|	1916	...	...	...	...	...	|	2016	...	...	...	|	2217	...
Hannover Hbf a.	...	...	...	1728	|	...	...	...	...	1828	|	...	...	...	...	...	1928	|	...	...	...	2128	|	...
Hamburg Hbf a.	...	...	...	|	1914	...	...	...	...	|	2014	...	...	...	...	...	|	2114	...	...	...	|	2315	...
Berlin Hbf a.	...	...	...	1907	...	...	...	...	...	2009	...	...	...	...	...	...	2106	...	...	...	...	2306	...	...

train type	☆	⇌	⇌	ICE	ICE	ICE	ICE	⇌	☆	ICE	ICE	IC	ICE	ICE		⇌	⇌	ICE	ICE	ICE	IC	IC		
train number	**9132**	**9461**	**9461**	**947**	**1057**	**26**	**1212**	**9363**	**9140**	**19**	**657**	**2318**	**1102**	**102**		**9473**	**9473**	**1522**	**512**	**1119**	**2020**	**2241**		
notes					⑤⑦			⑤⑦			⑦	⑧	⑥	⑧						⑦		⚒		
		K	L	T												KG	LG			C				
London St Pancras d.	1258	...	...	...	...	...	...	...	1504	...	...	...	...	...	...	...	...	...	...	...	...	...	...	...
Paris Nord d.	|	1555	1555	...	...	...	...	1625	|	...	...	...	...	...	...	1755	1755	...	...	...	...	...	...	...
Brussels Midi/Zuid a.	1608	1717	1717	...	...	...	...	1747	1805	...	...	...	...	...	...	1917	1917	...	...	...	...	...	...	...
Brussels Midi/Zuid d.	...	1727	1727	...	...	...	...	...	...	1825	...	...	...	...	...	1925	1925	...	...	2025	...	...	...	...
Brussels Nord d.	...	|	|	...	...	...	...	...	...	1834	...	...	...	...	...	|	|	...	...	2034	...	...	...	...
Liège Guillemins d.	...	1813	1813	...	...	...	...	...	...	1914	...	...	...	...	...	2013	2013	...	...	2114	...	...	...	...
Aachen 🏛 a.	...	1836	1836	...	...	...	...	...	...	1936	...	...	...	...	...	2036	2036	...	...	2136	...	...	...	...
Köln Hbf a.	...	1915	1915	...	...	...	...	...	...	2015	...	...	...	...	...	2115	2115	...	...	2215	...	...	...	...
Köln Hbf d.	...	1918	1918	1927	1948	2010	2013z	...	...	...	2048	2109	2111	2111	...	2118	2118	2210	2211	...	0210	...	...	...
Wuppertal Hbf a.	...	|	|	|	2014	2041	|	...	...	...	2114	|	|	2141	...	|	|	2241	|	...	|	...	...	...
Hagen Hbf a.	...	|	|	|	2033	2059	|	...	...	...	2133	|	|	2159	...	|	|	2259	|	...	|	...	...	...
Düsseldorf Hbf a.	...	1940	1940	1950	|	|	2030	...	...	...	|	2130	2131	|	...	2141	2141	|	2231	...	0231	...	...	...
Duisburg Hbf a.	...	1953	2012	2008	|	|	2045	...	...	...	|	2144	2144	|	...	2202	2212	|	2245	...	0248	...	...	...
Essen Hbf a.	...	2007	|	2021	|	|	2057	...	...	...	|	2157	2157	|	...	2215	|	|	2258	...	0300	...	...	...
Bochum Hbf a.	...	|	|	2033	|	|	2107	...	...	...	|	2208	2209	|	...	|	|	|	|	...	0314	...	...	...
Dortmund Hbf a.	...	2038	2107	2046	|	2121	2121	...	...	...	|	2221	2222	2221	...	2241	2312	2320	|	...	0326	...	...	...
Hamm (Westf) a.	...	...	...	2107	2102	|	|	...	...	...	2202	|	2247	2247	...	...	...	...	|	...	|	...	...	...
Bielefeld Hbf a.	...	...	...	2136	2136	|	|	...	...	...	2235	|	2319	2319	...	...	...	...	|	...	|	...	...	...
Münster a.	...	...	...	|	|	2155	2154	...	...	...	|	2255f	|	|	...	...	...	...	2357	...	0413	0538	...	...
Osnabrück Hbf a.	...	...	...	|	|	2221	2222	...	...	...	|	...	|	|	...	...	...	...	...	...	0448	0602	...	...
Bremen Hbf a.	...	...	...	|	|	2317	2318	...	...	...	|	...	|	|	...	...	...	...	...	...	0552	|	...	...
Hannover Hbf a.	...	...	...	2228	2228	|	|	...	...	...	2328	...	0018	0018	...	...	...	...	...	...	|	0718	...	...
Hamburg Hbf a.	...	...	...	|	|	0015	0015	...	...	...	|	...	...	...	...	...	...	...	...	...	0651	|	...	...
Berlin Hbf a.	...	...	...	0010	0025	...	...	...	...	...	0112	...	...	...	...	...	...	...	...	...	...	0922	...	...

A – May 26 - Sept. 16 (not June 10).
B – ②③④ (①-⑤ Sept. 20 - Nov. 2).
C – ⑦ Until Nov. 3 (also June 10; not June 9, July 7).
D – May 26 - June 8.
E – June 9 - Dec. 14.
G – Calls at Düsseldorf Flughafen ✈ arrives 2149 (2200 July 14 - Aug. 25).
J – ⑤⑥⑦ (also June 10; not June 29, July 6, 13).
K – Mar. 31 - July 13 and Aug. 26 - Dec. 14.
L – July 14 - Aug. 25.
Q – Mar. 31 - July 13.
S – Calls at Düsseldorf Flughafen ✈, arrives 1149 (1202 July 14 - Aug. 25).
T – ①②③④⑥.

f – ⑦.
j – Not June 10.
t – 0746 on ⑥.
x – On ⑦ depart Paris 0740, arrive Brussels 0912.
w – Not June 10, 22.
z – Köln **Messe / Deutz** (Table **910**). Connections from Köln Hbf depart every 2–5 minutes, journey time 2–3 minutes.

⇌ – *Thalys* high-speed train. 🅁 🍸. Special fares payable. Valid Mar. 31 - Dec. 14.
☆ – Eurostar train. 🅁, ✕ in Business Premier and Standard Premier, 🍸 in Standard. Special fares payable. Minimum check-in time 30 minutes. Valid May 26 - Nov. 2.

BERLIN, HAMBURG and KÖLN - BRUSSELS, PARIS and LONDON 20

For the full service Brussels - London see Table **10**. For Brussels - Paris see Table **18**. Connections at Brussels are not guaranteed.

train type	*IC*	⇌	⇌	*ICE*	*IC*	*ICE*	⇌	☆		*ICE*	*EC*	⇌	⇌	☆	*EC*	*EC*	*IC*	*ICE*	*ICE*	⇌	⇌	☆	
train number	**2021**	**9412**	**9412**	**101**	**2319**	**18**	**9422**	**9121**		**1521**	**115**	**9424**	**9424**	**9129**	**7**	**7**	**119**	**656**	**214**	**9434**	**9336**	**9133**	
notes		①–⑥	①–⑥		⚒	①–⑥		①–⑥			🍷			⑦	①–⑥	⑦	**1119**	①–⑤		⑥⑦	①–⑤	①–⑥	
		R	**QY**			**w**						**R**	**Q**				🍷					**h**	
Berlin Hbf d.	...	...	...	...	...	...	...	...	...	...	...	...	...	...	...	...	...	0430	...	...	...	...	...
Hamburg Hbf d.	2246	...	...	...	...	...	...	...	...	...	...	...	...	...	0438	...	...	|	...	...	...	...	...
Hannover Hbf d.	|	...	...	...	...	...	...	...	...	...	...	...	...	...	|	...	...	0621	...	...	...	...	...
Bremen Hbf d.	2344	...	...	...	...	...	...	...	...	...	...	...	...	...	0540	...	...	|	...	...	...	...	...
Osnabrück Hbf d.	0037	...	...	...	...	...	...	...	...	...	...	...	...	...	0637	...	...	|	...	...	...	...	...
Münster d.	0105	...	...	...	0502**c**	...	...	...	...	...	0631	...	...	...	0703	...	0726	|	...	...	...	...	...
Bielefeld Hbf d.	|	...	...	...	|	...	...	...	...	...	|	...	...	...	|	...	|	0721	...	...	...	...	...
Hamm (Westf) d.	0124	...	...	...	|	...	...	...	...	...	|	...	...	...	|	...	|	0754	...	...	...	...	...
Dortmund Hbf d.	0144	0455	0520	0537	0537	...	...	...	...	0636	|	0655	0714	...	|	0737	|	|	...	...	...	...	...
Bochum Hbf d.	0156	|	|	|	0550	...	...	...	...	|	|	|	|	...	|	0750	|	|	...	...	...	...	...
Essen Hbf d.	0207	|	0542	|	0600	...	...	...	...	|	|	|	0750	...	0800	0800	0823	|	...	...	...	...	...
Duisburg Hbf d.	0220	0543	0556	|	0613	...	...	...	...	|	0734	0743	0803	...	0813	0813	0838	|	...	...	...	...	...
Düsseldorf Hbf d.	0239	0617	0617	|	0627	...	...	...	...	|	0751	0817	0818	...	0827	0827	0852	|	...	...	...	...	...
Hagen Hbf d.	|	|	|	0558	|	...	...	...	...	0657	|	|	|	...	|	|	|	0823	...	...	...	...	...
Wuppertal Hbf d.	|	|	|	0614	|	...	...	...	...	0714	|	|	|	...	|	|	|	0840	...	...	...	...	...
Köln Hbf a.	0301	0642	0642	0647	0650	...	...	...	...	0747	0815	0842	0842	...	0850	0850	0915	0909	...	...	...	...	...
Köln Hbf d.	...	0645	0645	...	...	0742	...	...	...	...	...	0845	0845	...	...	...	...	...	0943	...	...	...	...
Aachen 🚆 d.	...	0724	0724	...	...	0821	...	...	...	...	...	0924	0924	...	...	...	...	...	1021	...	...	...	...
Liège Guillemins d.	...	0753	0753	...	...	0846	...	...	...	...	...	0951	0951	...	...	...	...	...	1046	...	...	...	...
Brussels Nord a.	...	|	|	...	...	0926	...	...	...	...	...	|	|	...	...	...	...	...	1126	...	...	...	...
Brussels Midi/Zuid a.	...	0836	0836	...	...	0935	...	...	...	...	...	1035	1035	...	...	...	...	...	1135	...	...	...	...
Brussels Midi/Zuid d.	...	0843	0843	...	...	...	1016	1056	...	...	...	1043	1043	1156	...	...	...	...	...	1216	1237	1252	...
Paris Nord a.	...	1005	1005	...	...	...	1138	|	...	...	...	1205	1205	|	...	...	...	...	...	1338	1359	|	...
London St Pancras a.	...	...	...	...	...	...	...	1157	...	...	...	...	...	1257	...	...	...	...	...	...	...	1405	...

train type	*EC*	*ICE*	*ICE*	⇌	☆	☆	*IC*	*ICE*	⇌	⇌	⇌		*IC*	*ICE*	*ICE*	⇌	☆	*IC*	*ICE*	*ICE*	⇌	☆	
train number	**9**	**654**	**16**	**9448**	**9141**	**9141**	**2023**	**1054**	**9448**	**9448**	**9448**		**2313**	**652**	**210**	**9358**	**9149**	**2217**	**650**	**14**	**9370**	**9157**	
notes					⑦	①–⑥		①–⑥	⑦	⑦	①–⑥					Ⓑ	Ⓑ				Ⓑ	Ⓑ	
									S	**T**						**S**							
Berlin Hauptbahnhof d.	...	0651	...	...	...	...	...	0749	...	...	...	...	...	0851	...	...	...	...	1051	...	...	...	...
Hamburg Hbf d.	0646	|	...	...	...	...	0746	|	...	...	...	...	0846	|	...	...	...	1046	|	...	...	...	...
Hannover Hbf d.	|	0831	...	...	...	...	|	0931	...	...	...	...	|	1031	...	...	...	|	1231	...	...	...	...
Bremen Hbf d.	0744	|	...	...	...	...	0844	|	...	...	...	...	0943	|	...	...	...	1144	|	...	...	...	...
Osnabrück Hbf d.	0837	|	...	...	...	...	0937	|	...	...	...	...	1037	|	...	...	...	1237	|	...	...	...	...
Münster d.	0902	|	...	...	...	...	1002	|	...	...	...	...	1102	|	...	...	...	1302	|	...	...	...	...
Bielefeld Hbf d.	|	0922	...	...	...	...	|	1022	...	...	...	...	|	1122	...	...	...	|	1322	...	...	...	...
Hamm (Westf) d.	|	0954	...	...	...	...	|	1054	...	...	...	...	|	1154	...	...	...	|	1354	...	...	...	...
Dortmund Hbf d.	0937	|	...	...	...	...	1036	|	1053	...	...	...	1137	|	...	...	...	1337	|	...	...	...	...
Bochum Hbf d.	0950	|	...	...	...	...	|	|	|	...	...	...	|	|	...	...	...	|	|	...	...	...	...
Essen Hbf d.	1000	|	...	...	...	...	|	|	1125	...	...	...	1200	|	...	...	...	1400	|	...	...	...	...
Duisburg Hbf d.	1013	|	...	...	...	...	|	|	1138	...	...	...	1213	|	...	...	...	1413	|	...	...	...	...
Düsseldorf Hbf d.	1027	|	...	...	...	...	|	|	1154	1154	...	...	1227	|	...	...	...	1427	|	...	...	...	...
Hagen Hbf d.	|	1023	...	...	...	...	1057	1123	|	|	...	...	|	1223	...	...	...	|	1423	...	...	...	...
Wuppertal Hbf d.	|	1040	...	...	...	...	1114	1140	|	|	...	...	|	1240	...	...	...	|	1440	...	...	...	...
Köln Hbf a.	1050	1109	...	...	...	...	1146	1209	1226	1226	...	...	1250	1309	...	...	...	1450	1509	...	...	...	...
Köln Hbf d.	...	...	1143	...	...	...	...	...	1243	1243	1243	...	...	...	1343	...	...	...	...	1543	...	...	...
Aachen 🚆 d.	...	...	1221	...	...	...	...	...	1324	1324	1324	...	...	...	1421	...	...	...	...	1621	...	...	...
Liège Guillemins d.	...	...	1246	...	...	...	...	...	1351	1351	1351	...	...	...	1446	...	...	...	...	1646	...	...	...
Brussels Nord a.	...	...	1326	...	...	...	...	...	|	|	|	...	...	...	1526	...	...	...	...	1726	...	...	...
Brussels Midi/Zuid a.	...	...	1335	...	...	...	...	...	1435	1435	1435	...	...	...	1535	...	...	...	...	1735	...	...	...
Brussels Midi/Zuid d.	...	...	...	1443	1452	1456	...	...	1443	1443	1443	...	...	...	...	1613	1656	...	...	...	1813	1856	...
Paris Nord a.	...	...	...	1605	|	|	...	...	1605	1605	1605	...	...	...	...	1735	|	...	...	...	1935	|	...
London St Pancras a.	...	...	...	...	1605	1605	...	...	...	...	...	...	...	...	...	...	1814	...	...	...	...	1957	...

train type	*IC*	*ICE*	⇌	⇌		*IC*	*ICE*	*ICE*	⇌	☆		*IC*	*ICE*	⇌	⇌	*IC*	*ICE*	*ICE*	⇌		*ICE*		
train number	**2027**	**1050**	**9472**	**9472**		**2311**	**558**	**12**	**9382**	**9163**		**2229**	**858**	**9484**	**9484**	**2213**	**556**	**10**	**9394**		**1118**		
notes								Ⓑ											⑦		⑦		
			R	**Q**										**R**	**Q**						**B**		
Berlin Hauptbahnhof d.	...	1149	...	...	...	...	1251	...	...	...	...	...	1349	...	...	...	1451	...	...	...	...	...	...
Hamburg Hbf d.	1146	|	...	...	...	1246	|	...	...	...	...	1346	|	...	...	1446	|	...	...	...	...	...	...
Hannover Hbf d.	|	1331	...	...	...	|	1431	...	...	...	...	|	1531	...	...	|	1631	...	...	...	...	...	...
Bremen Hbf d.	1244	|	...	...	...	1343	|	...	...	...	...	1444	|	...	...	1544	|	...	...	...	...	...	...
Osnabrück Hbf d.	1337	|	...	...	...	1437	|	...	...	...	...	1537	|	...	...	1637	|	...	...	...	...	...	...
Münster d.	1402	|	...	...	...	1502	|	...	...	...	...	1602	|	...	...	1702	|	...	...	...	...	...	...
Bielefeld Hbf d.	|	1422	...	...	...	|	1522	...	...	...	...	|	1622	...	...	|	1722	...	...	...	...	...	...
Hamm (Westf) d.	|	1454	...	...	...	|	1554	...	...	...	...	|	1654	...	...	|	1754	...	...	...	...	...	...
Dortmund Hbf d.	1436	|	1455	1514	...	1537	|	...	...	...	...	1636	|	...	...	1737	|	...	...	...	...	...	...
Bochum Hbf d.	|	|	|	|	...	|	|	...	...	...	...	|	|	...	...	1750	|	...	...	...	...	...	...
Essen Hbf d.	|	|	|	1550	...	1600	|	...	...	...	...	|	|	...	1750	1800	|	...	...	...	...	...	...
Duisburg Hbf d.	|	|	1544	1604	...	1613	|	...	...	...	...	|	|	...	1803	1813	|	...	...	...	...	...	...
Düsseldorf Hbf d.	|	|	1618	1618	...	1627	|	...	...	...	...	|	|	...	1818	1827	|	...	...	...	...	...	...
Hagen Hbf d.	1457	1523	|	|	...	|	1623	...	...	...	...	1657	1723	...	|	|	1823	...	...	...	...	...	...
Wuppertal Hbf d.	1514	1540	|	|	...	|	1640	...	...	...	...	1714	1740	...	|	|	1840	...	...	...	...	...	...
Köln Hbf a.	1546	1609	1641	1641	...	1650	1709	...	...	...	...	1746	1809	...	1841	1850	1909	...	...	...	...	...	...
Köln Hbf d.	...	...	1644	1644	...	...	...	1743	...	...	...	...	...	1844	1844	...	...	1943	...	...	2143	...	...
Aachen 🚆 d.	...	...	1724	1724	...	...	...	1821	...	...	...	...	...	1924	1924	...	...	2021	...	...	2221	...	...
Liège Guillemins d.	...	...	1751	1751	...	...	...	1846	...	...	...	...	...	1951	1951	...	...	2046	...	...	2246	...	...
Brussels Nord a.	...	...	|	|	...	...	...	1926	...	...	...	...	...	|	|	...	...	2126	...	...	2326	...	...
Brussels Midi/Zuid a.	...	...	1835	1835	...	...	...	1935	...	...	...	...	...	2035	2035	...	...	2135	...	...	2335	...	...
Brussels Midi/Zuid d.	...	...	1843	1843	...	...	...	...	2016	2022	...	...	...	2043	2043	...	...	...	2216	...	...	...	...
Paris Nord a.	...	...	2005	2005	...	...	...	...	2138	|	...	...	...	2205	2205	...	...	...	2338	...	...	...	...
London St Pancras a.	...	...	...	...	...	...	...	...	...	2133	...	...	...	...	...	...	...	...	...	...	...	...	...

B – ⑦ Until Nov. 3 (also June 10; not June 9, 23, July 7).

Q – Mar. 31 - July 13. Aug. 26 - Dec. 14 (also Aug. 16).

R – July 14 - Aug. 25 (not Aug. 16).

S – Mar. 31 - July 13. Sept. 1 - Dec. 14.

T – July 14 - Aug. 31.

Y – Calls at Düsseldorf Flughafen ✈ departs 0607.

c – ①.

h – Not Aug. 26.

w – Not June 10.

☆ – Eurostar train. 🅁, ✕ in Business Premier and Standard Premier, 🍷 in Standard. Special fares payable. Minimum check-in time 30 minutes. Valid May 26 - Nov. 2.

⇌ – *Thalys* high-speed train. 🅁 🍷. Special fares payable. Valid Mar. 31 - Dec. 14.

21 LONDON, PARIS and BRUSSELS - FRANKFURT - MÜNCHEN

For the full service London - Brussels see Table **10**. For Paris - Brussels see Table **18**. Connections at Brussels are not guaranteed.

train type	*ICE*	*ICE*	*ICE*	🚌	⇌	*ICE*	*ICE*	🚌	*ICE*	*ICE*	*ICE*	*ICE*	*ICE*	⇌	*ICE*	*ICE*	*IC*	☆	⇌	☆	☆	*ICE*	*ICE*	*ICE*	🚌
train number	**11**	**593**	**529**	Ⓡ	**9403**	**515**	**27**	Ⓡ	**623**	**13**	**13**	**595**	**623**	**9413**	**625**	**517**	**2023**	**9108**	**9315**	**9110**	**9110**	**15**	**597**	**627**	Ⓡ
notes	①-⑥			🍷	①-⑥	**1015**		🍷		①-⑤	⑥⑦						🍷				⑥				🍷
	w						**S**											**K**		**H**					
London St Pancras ... d.	...	...	...	...	...	...	...	...	...	...	...	...	...	...	...	...	...	0613	...	0647	0657	...	...	...	...
Paris Nord ... d.	...	...	...	...	0613	...	...	...	...	...	...	...	...	0755e	...	...	...	|	0825	|	|	...	...	...	...
Brussels Midi/Zuid ... a.	...	...	...	...	0735c	...	...	...	...	...	...	...	...	0917e	...	...	...	0922	0947	1005	1005	...	...	...	...
Brussels Midi/Zuid ... d.	0625	...	...	...	0755	...	...	...	...	0823	0823	...	...	0925	...	...	...	...	...	...	...	1025	...	...	...
Brussels Nord ... d.	0633	...	...	...	|	...	...	...	...	0832	0832	...	...	|	...	...	...	...	...	...	...	1034	...	...	...
Liège Guillemins ... d.	0712	...	...	...	0846	...	...	...	...	0914	0912	...	...	1013	...	...	...	...	...	...	...	1114	...	...	...
Aachen Hbf 🏛 ... a.	0736	...	...	...	0906	...	...	...	...	0936	0937	...	...	1035	...	...	...	...	...	...	...	1136	...	...	...
Köln Hbf ... a.	0815	...	...	...	0948	...	...	...	...	1015	1015	...	...	1116	...	...	...	...	...	...	...	1215	...	...	...
Köln Hbf ... d.	0827	...	...	...	...	0955	0953	...	1034x	1028	1028	...	...	...	1130x	1155	1153	...	...	...	...	1218	...	...	...
Bonn Hbf ... a.	|	...	...	...	...	|	1012	...	|	|	|	...	...	...	|	|	1212	...	...	...	...	|	...	...	...
Koblenz Hbf ... a.	⊖	...	...	...	...	⊖	1046	...	⊖	⊖	⊖	...	...	...	⊖	⊖	1246	...	...	...	...	⊖	...	...	...
Mainz Hbf ... a.	|	...	...	...	...	|	1139	...	|	|	|	...	...	...	|	|	1339	...	...	...	...	|	...	...	...
Frankfurt Flughafen ✈ a.	0916	...	...	...	...	1049	1159	...	1133	1116	1116	...	...	...	1233	1249	1359	...	...	...	...	1316	...	...	...
Frankfurt (Main) Hbf ... a.	0931	0950	0954	...	...	|	1213	...	1148	1131	1131	1150	1154	...	1248	|	1412	...	...	...	...	1331	1350	1354	...
Würzburg Hbf ... a.	...	|	1101	...	...	|	1332	...	1304	...	...	|	1304	...	1401	|	...	...	...	...	...	...	|	1501	...
Nürnberg Hbf ... a.	...	|	1158	1250	...	|	1427	1450	1404	...	...	|	1404	...	1502	|	...	...	...	...	...	...	|	1559	1650
Praha hlavní ¶ a.	...	|	|	1625	...	|	...	1825	|	...	...	|	|	...	|	|	...	...	...	...	...	...	|	|	2025
Mannheim Hbf ... a.	...	1027	|	...	...	1123	...	...	|	...	...	1227	|	...	|	1323	...	...	...	...	...	...	1427	|	...
Stuttgart Hbf ... a.	...	1108	|	...	...	1208	...	...	|	...	...	1308	|	...	|	1408	...	...	...	...	...	...	1508	|	...
Ulm Hbf ... a.	...	1207	|	...	...	1308	...	...	|	...	...	1407	|	...	|	1508	...	...	...	...	...	...	1607	|	...
Augsburg Hbf ... a.	...	1253	|	...	...	1353	...	...	|	...	...	1453	|	...	|	1553	...	...	...	...	...	...	1653	|	...
München Hbf ... a.	...	1327	1307	...	...	1427	...	...	1509	...	...	1528	1509	...	1607	1627	...	...	...	...	...	...	1727	1705	...

train type/number	⇌	☆	*ICE*	*ICE*	*ICE*		⇌	*ICE*	*ICE*	*ICE*	*IC*		⇌	☆	☆	*ICE*	*ICE*	*ICE*	*ICE*	⇌	*ICE*	*ICE*	*ICE*	*ICE*	*ICE*
train number	**9327**	**9116**	**211**	**599**	**721**		**9437**	**125**	**723**	**611**	**2027**		**9439**	**9128**	**9126**	**17**	**17**	**691**	**725**	**9451**	**215**	**215**	**693**	**693**	**729**
notes								**155**	Ⓑ							①-⑤	⑥⑦				①-⑤	⑦	Ⓑ	⑥	
													J	**D**	**E**										
London St Pancras ... d.	...	0854	...	...	...	...	...	...	...	...	...	...	...	1058	1104	...	...	...	...	...	...	...	...	...	...
Paris Nord ... d.	1025	|	...	...	...	...	1155	...	...	...	...	...	1225	|	|	...	...	...	...	1425	...	...	...	...	...
Brussels Midi/Zuid ... a.	1147	1205	...	...	...	...	1317	...	...	...	...	...	1347	1405	1405	...	...	...	...	1547	...	...	...	...	...
Brussels Midi/Zuid ... d.	...	...	1225	...	...	...	1325	...	...	...	...	...	...	...	...	1425	1425	...	...	...	1622	1625	...	...	...
Brussels Nord ... d.	...	...	1234	...	...	...	|	...	...	...	...	...	...	...	...	1434	1434	...	...	...	1632	1634	...	...	...
Liège Guillemins ... d.	...	...	1314	...	...	...	1413	...	...	...	...	...	...	...	...	1514	1514	...	...	...	1714	1714	...	...	...
Aachen Hbf 🏛 ... a.	...	...	1336	...	...	...	1436	...	...	...	...	...	...	...	...	1536	1536	...	...	...	1736	1736	...	...	...
Köln Hbf ... a.	...	...	1415	...	...	...	1515	...	...	...	...	...	...	...	...	1615	1615	...	...	...	1815	1815	...	...	...
Köln Hbf ... d.	...	...	1428	...	...	...	...	1529	...	1555	1553	...	...	...	...	1620	1620	...	...	...	1819	1819	...	...	...
Bonn Hbf ... a.	...	...	|	...	...	...	...	|	...	|	1612	...	...	...	...	|	|	...	...	...	|	|	...	...	...
Koblenz Hbf ... a.	...	...	⊖	...	...	...	...	⊖	...	⊖	1646	...	...	...	...	⊖	⊖	...	...	...	⊖	⊖	...	...	...
Mainz Hbf ... a.	...	...	|	...	...	...	...	|	...	|	1739	...	...	...	...	|	|	...	...	...	|	|	...	...	...
Frankfurt Flughafen ✈ a.	...	...	1516	...	...	...	...	1616	...	1649	1759	...	...	...	...	1709	1726	...	...	...	1909	1909	...	...	...
Frankfurt (Main) Hbf ... a.	...	...	1531	1550	1554	...	...	1630	1654	|	1814	...	...	...	...	1722	1741	1750	1754	...	1925	1925	1950	1950	1954
Würzburg Hbf ... a.	...	...	...	|	1701	...	...	...	1801	|	1932	...	...	...	...	...	...	|	1901	...	...	...	|	|	2101
Nürnberg Hbf ... a.	...	...	...	|	1759	...	...	...	1859	|	2027	...	...	...	...	...	...	|	1959	...	...	...	|	|	2159
Praha hlavní ¶ a.	...	...	...	|	|	...	...	...	|	|	...	...	...	...	...	...	...	|	|	...	...	...	|	|	|
Mannheim Hbf ... a.	...	...	...	1627	|	...	...	...	|	1723	...	...	...	...	...	...	...	1827	|	...	...	...	2027	2027	|
Stuttgart Hbf ... a.	...	...	...	1708	|	...	...	...	|	1808	...	...	...	...	...	...	...	1908	|	...	...	...	2108	2108	|
Ulm Hbf ... a.	...	...	...	1807	|	...	...	...	|	1908	...	...	...	...	...	...	...	2007	|	...	...	...	2207	...	|
Augsburg Hbf ... a.	...	...	...	1853	|	...	...	...	|	1953	...	...	...	...	...	...	...	2053	|	...	...	...	2253	...	|
München Hbf ... a.	...	...	...	1928	1910	...	...	...	2007	2028	...	...	...	...	...	...	...	2130	2110	...	...	...	2329	...	2311

train type	☆	⇌	*IC*	*ICE*		⇌	☆	*ICE*	*ICE*	*IC*	*IC*	*NJ*		⇌	*ICE*	*ICE*	*IC*	*ICE*		*ICE*	*ICE*				
train number	**9132**	**9461**	**2029**	**615**		**9363**	**9140**	**19**	**773**	**2029**	**2315**	**421**		**9473**	**221**	**1572**	**2221**	**619**		**1119**	**619**				
notes						⑤⑦			**1073**		**2215**				**341**	**1592**	**2321**			⑦					
												A								**C**					
London St Pancras ... d.	1258	...	...	...	...	...	1504	...	...	...	...	...	...	...	...	...	...	...	...	...	...	...	...	...	...
Paris Nord ... d.	|	1555	...	...	...	1625	|	...	...	...	...	...	...	1755	...	...	...	...	...	...	...	...	...	...	...
Brussels Midi/Zuid ... a.	1608	1717	...	...	...	1747	1805	...	...	...	...	...	...	1917	...	...	...	...	...	...	...	...	...	...	...
Brussels Midi/Zuid ... d.	...	1727	...	...	...	...	...	1825	...	...	...	...	...	1925	...	...	...	...	...	2025	...	...	...	...	...
Brussels Nord ... d.	...	|	...	...	...	...	...	1834	...	...	...	...	...	|	...	...	...	...	...	2034	...	...	...	...	...
Liège Guillemins ... d.	...	1813	...	...	...	...	...	1914	...	...	...	...	...	2013	...	...	...	...	...	2114	...	...	...	...	...
Aachen Hbf 🏛 ... a.	...	1836	...	...	...	...	...	1936	...	...	...	...	...	2036	...	...	...	...	...	2136	...	...	...	...	...
Köln Hbf ... a.	...	1915	...	...	...	...	...	2015	...	...	...	...	...	2115	...	...	...	...	...	2215	...	...	...	...	...
Köln Hbf ... d.	...	...	1953	1957	...	...	...	2027	...	...	2053	2121	...	...	2128	...	2153	2229	...	...	2230	...	...	...	...
Bonn Hbf ... a.	...	...	2012	|	...	...	...	|	...	...	2112	2141	...	...	|	...	2212	|	...	...	|	...	...	...	...
Koblenz Hbf ... a.	...	...	2046	⊖	...	...	...	⊖	...	...	2146	2215	...	...	⊖	...	2246	⊖	...	...	⊖	...	...	...	...
Mainz Hbf ... a.	...	...	2142	|	...	...	...	|	...	...	2239	2309	...	...	|	...	...	|	...	...	|	...	...	...	...
Frankfurt Flughafen ✈ a.	...	...	2200	2049	...	...	...	2116	2122	...	...	2351	...	...	2216	...	...	2343	...	...	2343	...	...	...	...
Frankfurt (Main) Hbf ... a.	...	...	2213	|	...	...	...	2131	|	2221	...	0005f	...	...	2230	2308	...	2359	...	...	2359	...	...	...	...
Würzburg Hbf ... a.	...	...	2344	|	...	...	...	...	|	2344	...	0135	...	...	...	|	...	|	...	...	|	...	...	...	...
Nürnberg Hbf ... a.	...	...	0044	|	...	...	...	...	|	0044	...	0237	...	...	...	|	...	|	...	...	|	...	...	...	...
Praha hlavní ¶ a.	...	...	...	|	...	...	...	...	|	...	...	|	...	...	...	|	...	|	...	...	|	...	...	...	...
Mannheim Hbf ... a.	...	...	...	2123	...	...	...	...	2154	...	...	|	...	...	...	|	...	0104	...	...	0104	...	...	...	...
Stuttgart Hbf ... a.	...	...	...	2208	...	...	...	...	2250	...	...	|	...	...	...	0100	...	0320	...	...	0320	...	...	...	...
Ulm Hbf ... a.	...	...	...	2308	...	...	...	...	...	...	...	|	...	...	...	...	...	0440	...	...	0440	...	...	...	...
Augsburg Hbf ... a.	...	...	...	2352	...	...	...	...	...	...	...	0626	...	...	...	...	...	0530	...	...	0530	...	...	...	...
München Hbf ... a.	...	...	...	0027	...	...	...	...	...	...	...	0708	...	...	...	...	...	0602	...	...	0602	...	...	...	...

A – *ÖBB nightjet* 🛏 1, 2 cl., 🛏 2 cl. (4, 6 berth), 🚃 Düsseldorf - Köln - München - Innsbruck (Table **53**). Special fares apply.

C – ⑦ until Nov. 3 (also June 10; not June 9, July 7).

D – May 26 - June 8.

E – June 9 - Dec. 14.

H – ②③④ (①-⑤ Sept. 20 - Nov. 2).

J – ⑤⑥⑦ Mar. 31 - July 13 (also June 10; not June 29, July 6, 13).

K – ①⑤ May 26 - Sept. 16 (not June 10).

S – 🚃 ✕ Hamburg - Dortmund - Köln - Wien (Table **66**).

c – 0746 on ⑥.

e – On ⑦ depart Paris 0740, arrive Brussels 0912.

f – Frankfurt (Main) **Süd**.

t – Ⓑ.

w – Not June 10, 22.

x – Köln **Messe / Deutz** (Table **910**). Connections from Köln Hbf depart every 2 - 5 minutes journey time 2 - 3 minutes.

⊖ – Via Köln - Frankfurt high speed line.

⇌ – *Thalys* high-speed train. Ⓡ 🍷. Special fares payable. Valid Dec. 9 - July 13.

🚌 – **DB / ČD** *ExpressBus*. Ⓡ 🍷. Rail tickets valid. 🏛 is Waidhaus (Germany). (Table **76**).

¶ – For connections to Praha by train, via Nürnberg and Regensburg, see Table **76**.

☆ – Eurostar train. Ⓡ, ✕ in Business Premier and Standard Premier, 🍷 in Standard. Special fares payable. Minimum check-in time 30 minutes. Valid May 26 - Nov. 2.

MÜNCHEN - FRANKFURT - BRUSSELS, PARIS and LONDON 21

For the full service London - Brussels see Table **10**. For Paris - Brussels see Table **18**. Connections at Brussels are not guaranteed.

train type	⇌	*IC*	*ICE*	*ICE*	⇌	*IC*	*NJ*	*ICE*	*ICE*	⇌	☆	*ICE*	*ICE*	*IC*	*ICE*	⇌	⇌	*IC*	*ICE*	*ICE*	*ICE*	*ICE*	⇌	☆	☆
train number	**9412**	**2212**	**618**	**18**	**9422**	**2220**	**420**	**616**	**220**	**9424**	**9129**	**822**	**694**	**2310**	**214**	**9434**	**9336**	**2216**	**728**	**692**	**16**	**16**	**9448**	**9141**	**9141**
notes	①–⑥		**1018**	①–⑥		**2320**					⑦	①–⑥				⑥⑦	①–⑤			①–⑤	⑦	①–⑥		⑦	①–⑥
notes			🍷	**w**			**C**																		
München Hbf.....d.	...	...	0001	...	...	...	2252	0324	...	...	...	0448	...	...	...	...	...	...	0648	0629	...	...	...	...	...
Augsburg Hbf.....d.	...	...	0032	...	...	...	2330	0357	...	...	...	|	...	...	...	...	...	...	|	0706	...	...	...	...	...
Ulm Hbf.....d.	.:.	...	0116	...	...	...	|	0440	...	...	...	|	...	...	...	...	...	...	|	0751	...	...	...	...	...
Stuttgart Hbf.....d.	...	...	0230	...	...	...	|	0551	...	...	...	|	0651	...	...	...	...	0737	|	0851	...	...	...	...	...
Mannheim Hbf.....d.	...	...	0440	...	...	...	|	0636	...	...	...	|	0732	...	...	...	...	0839	|	0932	...	...	...	...	...
Praha hlavní.....¶ d.	...	...	|	...	...	...	|	|	...	...	...	|	|	...	...	...	...	|	|	|	...	...	...	...	...
Nürnberg Hbf.....d.	...	...	|	...	...	...	0246	|	...	...	...	0600	|	...	...	...	...	|	0800	|	...	...	...	...	...
Würzburg Hbf.....d.	...	...	|	...	...	...	|	|	...	...	...	0655	|	...	...	...	...	|	0855	|	...	...	...	...	...
Frankfurt (Main) Hbf...d.	...	...	0544	0627	...	...	0526**f**	|	0729	...	...	0804	0808	...	0814	...	...	|	1004	1008	1016	1029	...	...	...
Frankfurt Flughafen ✈..d.	...	...	0601	0643	...	...	0537	0709	0743	...	...	...	...	...	0831	...	...	|	...	...	1037	1043	...	...	...
Mainz Hbf.....d.	...	...	|	|	...	0617	0604	|	|	...	...	...	...	0717	|	...	...	0920	...	...	|	|	...	...	...
Koblenz Hbf.....d.	...	0605	⊖	⊖	...	0713	0707	⊖	⊖	...	...	...	...	0813	⊖	...	...	1013	...	...	⊖	⊖	...	...	...
Bonn Hbf.....d.	...	0646	|	|	...	0746	|	|	|	...	...	...	...	0846	|	...	...	1046	...	...	|	|	...	...	...
Köln Hbf.....a.	...	0705	0705	0740	...	0805	0815	0805	0833	...	...	...	...	0905	0939	...	...	1105	...	...	1133	1133	...	...	...
Köln Hbf.....d.	0645	...	...	0742	...	▬	...	...	...	0845	...	...	...	...	0943	...	...	▬	...	...	1143	1143	1243	...	...
Aachen Hbf 🚌.....d.	0724	...	...	0821	...	☆	...	...	...	0924	...	...	...	...	1021	...	...	☆	...	...	1221	1221	1324	...	...
Liège Guillemins.....d.	0753	...	...	0846	...	**9121**	...	...	...	0951	...	...	...	...	1046	...	...	**9133**	...	...	1246	1246	1351	...	...
Brussels Nord.....a.	|	...	...	0926	...	①–⑥	...	...	...	|	...	...	...	...	1126	...	...	①–⑥	...	...	1326	1326	|	...	...
Brussels Midi/Zuid.....a.	0836	...	...	0935	...		...	...	...	1035	...	...	...	...	1135	...	...	**h**	...	...	1335	1335	1435	...	...
Brussels Midi/Zuid.....d.	0843	...	...	...	1016	1056	...	...	...	1043	1156	...	...	...	...	1216	1237	1252	...	...	...	...	1443	1452	1456
Paris Nord.....d.	1005	...	...	...	1138	|	...	...	...	1205	|	...	...	...	...	1338	1359	|	...	...	...	...	1605	|	|
London St Pancras.....a.	...	...	...	...	...	1157	...	...	...	...	1257	...	...	...	...	...	...	1405	...	...	...	...	...	1605	1605

train type	*IC*	*ICE*	*ICE*	⇌		*IC*	*ICE*	*ICE*	*ICE*	*ICE*	⇌	☆		*IC*	*ICE*	*ICE*	🚌	*ICE*	*ICE*	*ICE*	⇌	☆			
train number	**2226**	**612**	**726**	**9448**		**2218**	**690**	**724**	**578**	**210**	**9358**	**9149**		**2312**	**228**	**598**	🅁	**720**	**576**	**14**	**9370**	**9157**			
notes			①–⑥								Ⓑ	Ⓑ					🍷				Ⓑ	Ⓑ			
notes																									
München Hbf.....d.	...	0728	0754	...	...	...	0828	0848	...	...	...	...	...	...	...	1028	...	1054	...	...	...	...	...	...	...
Augsburg Hbf.....d.	...	0803	|	...	...	...	0903	|	...	...	...	...	...	...	...	1103	...	|	...	...	...	...	...	...	...
Ulm Hbf.....d.	...	0850	|	...	...	...	0951	|	...	...	...	...	...	...	...	1151	...	|	...	...	...	...	...	...	...
Stuttgart Hbf.....d.	...	0951	|	...	...	0937	1051	|	1124	...	...	...	...	1137	...	1251	...	|	1324	...	...	...	...	...	...
Mannheim Hbf.....d.	...	1036	|	...	...	|	1132	|	1205	...	...	...	...	|	...	1332	...	|	1405	...	...	...	...	...	...
Praha hlavni.....¶ d.	...	|	|	...	...	|	|	|	|	...	...	...	...	|	...	|	0805	|	|	...	...	...	...	...	...
Nürnberg Hbf.....d.	0730**c**	|	0900	...	...	|	|	1000	|	...	...	...	...	|	1129	|	1140	1200	|	...	...	...	...	...	...
Würzburg Hbf.....d.	0824**c**	|	0955	...	...	|	|	1055	|	...	...	...	...	|	1227	|	...	1256	|	...	...	...	...	...	...
Frankfurt (Main) Hbf...d.	0942	|	1110	...	...	|	1208	1204	|	1229	...	...	...	|	1341	1408	...	1404	|	1429	...	...	...	...	...
Frankfurt Flughafen ✈..d.	0958	1109	1122	...	...	|	...	...	1236	1243	...	...	...	|	...	...	...	...	1436	1443	...	...	...	...	...
Mainz Hbf.....d.	1020	|	|	...	...	1120	...	...	...	|	...	...	...	1320	...	...	...	...	...	|	...	...	...	...	...
Koblenz Hbf.....d.	1113	⊖	⊖	...	...	1213	...	...	...	⊖	...	...	...	1413	...	...	...	...	...	⊖	...	...	...	...	...
Bonn Hbf.....d.	1146	|	|	...	...	1246	...	...	...	|	...	...	...	1446	...	...	...	...	...	|	...	...	...	...	...
Köln Hbf.....a.	1205	1205	1225**z**	...	...	1305	...	...	...	1333	...	...	...	1505	...	...	...	...	...	1533	...	...	...	...	...
Köln Hbf.....d.	...	...	...	1243	...	...	...	...	...	1343	...	...	...	...	...	...	...	...	...	1543	...	...	...	...	...
Aachen Hbf 🚌.....d.	...	...	...	1324	...	...	...	...	...	1421	...	...	...	...	...	...	...	...	...	1621	...	...	...	...	...
Liège Guillemins.....d.	...	...	...	1351	...	...	...	...	...	1446	...	...	...	...	...	...	...	...	...	1646	...	...	...	...	...
Brussels Nord.....a.	...	...	...	|	...	...	...	...	...	1526	...	...	...	...	...	...	...	...	...	1726	...	...	...	...	...
Brussels Midi/Zuid.....a.	...	...	...	1435	...	...	...	...	...	1535	...	...	...	...	...	...	...	...	...	1735	...	...	...	...	...
Brussels Midi/Zuid.....d.	...	...	...	1443	...	...	...	...	...	...	1613	1656	...	...	...	...	...	...	...	...	1813	1856	...	...	...
Paris Nord.....a.	...	...	...	1605	...	...	...	...	...	...	1735	|	...	...	...	...	...	...	...	...	1935	|	...	...	...
London St Pancras.....a.	...	...	...	...	...	...	...	...	...	...	...	1814	...	...	...	...	...	...	...	...	...	1957	...	...	...

train type	*IC*	*ICE*	*ICE*	⇌	*ICE*	🚌	*ICE*	*ICE*	*EC*	*ICE*	⇌	☆	*IC*	*ICE*	*ICE*	⇌	🚌	*ICE*	*ICE*	*ICE*	*ICE*	*EC*	*ICE*	⇌	*ICE*
train number	**2026**	**518**	**628**	**9472**	**28**	🅁	**596**	**626**	**8**	**12**	**9382**	**9163**	**2022**	**516**	**624**	**9484**	🅁	**26**	**594**	**622**	**572**	**6**	**10**	**9394**	**1118**
notes						🍷				Ⓑ					**1124**		🍷							⑦	⑦
notes																		**F**							**B**
München Hbf.....d.	...	1128	1151	...	...	...	1228	1250	..	...	...	...	...	1328	1354	...	...	...	1428	1450	...	...	...	...	...
Augsburg Hbf.....d.	...	1203	|	...	...	...	1303	|	...	...	...	...	...	1403	|	...	...	...	1503	|	...	...	...	...	...
Ulm Hbf.....d.	...	1250	|	...	...	...	1351	|	...	...	...	...	...	1450	|	...	...	...	1550	|	...	...	...	...	...
Stuttgart Hbf.....d.	...	1351	|	...	...	...	1451	|	...	...	...	...	...	1551	|	...	...	...	1651	|	1725	...	...	...	...
Mannheim Hbf.....d.	...	1436	|	...	...	...	1532	|	...	...	...	...	...	1636	|	...	...	...	1732	|	1806	...	...	...	...
Praha hlavní.....¶ d.	...	|	|	...	...	1005	|	|	...	...	...	...	...	|	|	...	1135	...	|	|	|	...	...	...	...
Nürnberg Hbf.....d.	...	|	1257	...	1329	1340	|	1400	...	...	...	...	...	|	1500	...	1510	1529	|	1600	|	...	...	...	...
Würzburg Hbf.....d.	...	|	1355	...	1427	...	|	1455	...	...	...	...	...	|	1555	...	...	1627	|	1655	|	...	...	...	...
Frankfurt (Main) Hbf...d.	...	|	1510	...	1536	...	1608	1604	...	1627	...	...	...	|	1710	...	...	1736	1808	1804	|	...	1827	...	2016
Frankfurt Flughafen ✈..d.	...	1509	1525	...	...	...	...	...	...	1643	...	...	...	1709	1725	...	...	...	...	...	1837	...	1843	...	2031
Mainz Hbf.....d.	1420	|	|	...	...	...	...	...	1520	|	...	...	1620	|	|	...	...	...	...	...	...	1720	|	...	|
Koblenz Hbf.....d.	1513	⊖	⊖	...	...	...	...	...	1613	⊖	...	...	1713	⊖	⊖	...	...	...	...	...	...	1813	⊖	...	⊖
Bonn Hbf.....d.	1546	|	|	...	...	...	...	...	1646	|	...	...	1746	|	|	...	...	...	...	...	...	1846	|	...	|
Köln Hbf.....a.	1605	1605	1614**z**	...	...	...	...	...	1705	1739	...	...	1805	1805	1814**z**	...	...	...	...	...	...	1905	1939	...	2140
Köln Hbf.....d.	...	...	...	1644	...	...	...	...	...	1743	...	...	...	...	...	1844	...	...	...	...	...	...	1943	...	2143
Aachen Hbf 🚌.....d.	...	...	...	1724	...	...	...	...	...	1821	...	...	...	...	...	1924	...	...	...	...	...	...	2021	...	2221
Liège Guillemins.....d.	...	...	...	1751	...	...	...	...	...	1846	...	...	...	...	...	1951	...	...	...	...	...	...	2046	...	2246
Brussels Nord.....a.	...	...	...	|	...	...	...	...	...	1926	...	...	...	...	...	|	...	...	...	...	...	...	2126	...	2326
Brussels Midi/Zuid.....a.	...	...	...	1835	...	...	...	...	...	1935	...	...	...	...	...	2035	...	...	...	...	...	...	2135	...	2335
Brussels Midi/Zuid.....d.	...	...	...	1843	...	...	...	...	...	...	2016	2022	...	...	...	2043	...	...	...	...	...	...	...	2216	...
Paris Nord.....d.	...	...	...	2005	...	...	...	...	...	...	2138	|	...	...	...	2205	...	...	...	...	...	...	...	2338	...
London St Pancras.....a.	...	...	...	...	...	...	...	...	...	...	...	2133	...	...	...	...	...	...	...	...	...	...	...	...	...

B – ⑦ until Nov. 3 (also June 10; not June 9, 23, July 7).

C – *ÖBB nightjet* – 🛏 1, 2 cl., 🛏 2 cl. (4, 6 berth), (2) Innsbruck - München - Köln - Düsseldorf (Table **53**). Special fares apply.

F – (12) ✕ Wien - Nürnberg - Frankfurt - Köln - Dortmund - Hamburg.

c – ①–⑥.

f – Frankfurt (Main) **Süd**.

h – Not Aug. 26.

w – Not June 10.

z – Köln **Messe / Deutz** (Table **910**). Connections to Köln Hbf depart every 2 - 5 minutes, journey time 2 - 3 minutes.

⊖ – Via Köln - Frankfurt high speed line.

¶ – For connections from Praha by train, via Regensburg and Nürnberg, see Table **76**.

⇌ – *Thalys* high-speed train. 🅁 🍷. Special fares payable. Valid Mar. 31 - Dec. 14.

🚌 – **DB / ČD** *ExpressBus*. 🅁 🍷. Rail tickets valid. 1st and 2nd class. 🚌 is Waidhaus (Germany). Timings subject to alteration (Table **57**).

☆ – Eurostar train. 🅁, ✕ in Business Premier and Standard Premier, 🍷 in Standard. Special fares payable. Minimum check-in time 30 minutes. Not available for London - Ebbsfleet - Ashford or v.v. journeys. Valid May 26 - Nov. 2.

22 AMSTERDAM - BERLIN

train type	*IC*	*IC*	*IC*	*IC*	*IC*	*IC*	*IC*	*IC*	*S/C*	*ICE*		*RE*	*IC*		*IC*
train number	**245**	**141**	**143**	**145**	**147**	**149**	**241**	**241**	**241**	**645**			**243**		**243**
notes	①-⑥						⑥	⑧	⑦	**655**	⑥	⑥	①-⑤	①-⑤	⑦
	J							**H**	**y**				**E**		**y**
Amsterdam Centraal d.	0502	0700	0900	1100	1300	1500	1700	1700	1700	...	...	...	1900	...	1900
Hilversum d.	0525	0722	0922	1122	1322	1522	1722	1722	1722	...	...	...	1922	...	1922
Amersfoort d.	0540	0736	0936	1136	1336	1536	1736	1736	1736	...	...	...	1936	...	1936
Apeldoorn d.	0605	0802	1002	1202	1402	1602	1802	1802	1802	...	...	...	2002	...	2002
Deventer d.	0617	0819	1019	1219	1419	1619	1819	1819	1819	...	...	...	2019	...	2019
Almelo d.	0642	0845	1045	1245	1445	1645	1845	1845	1845	...	...	...	2045	...	2045
Hengelo ▲ d.	0655	0858	1058	1258	1458	1658	1858	1858	1858	...	1934	...	2058	2134	2058
Bad Bentheim 🛃 ▲ a.	0711	0916	1116	1316	1516	1716	1916	1916	1916	...	1952	...	2116	2152	2116
Rheine ▲ a.	0733	0940	1140	1340	1540	1740	...	1940	1940	...	2012	2038	...	2212	2140
Osnabrück Hbf ▲ a.	0803	1006	1206	1406	1606	1806	...	2006	2006	...	2045	2113	...	2245	2206
Minden a.	0847	1046	1246	1446	1646	1846	...	2046	2046	...	...	2207	...	...	2246
Hannover Hbf a.	0918	1118	1318	1518	1718	1918	...	2118	2118	2131	...	2250	...	...	2321
Wolfsburg a.	0953	1153	1353	1553	1753	1953	...	...	2153	|	...	...	...	...	...
Stendal a.	1027	1227	1427	1627	1827	2025	...	...	2227	|	...	...	...	...	...
Berlin Hauptbahnhof a.	1122	1322	1522	1722	1922	2159	...	...	2322	2306	...	...	...	...	...
Berlin Ostbahnhof a.	1134	1334	1534	1734	1934	2210	...	...	2334	...	...	...	...	...	...

train type		*S/C*	*ICE*	*IC*	*RE*		*IC*	*IC*	*IC*	*IC*	*IC*	*IC*	*IC*	*IC*
train number		**244**	**646**	**242**			**240**	**240**	**240**	**148**	**146**	**144**	**142**	**140**
notes	①	①	①-⑤	①-⑥	⑦	⑦		①-⑥	①-⑥					
		D		**q**				**q**	**B**					
Berlin Ostbahnhof d.	...	...	...	...	...	...	...	0622	...	0822	1022	1222	1422	1622
Berlin Hauptbahnhof d.	...	...	0430	...	...	...	...	0634	...	0834	1034	1234	1434	1634
Stendal d.	...	...	0516	...	...	...	...	0730	...	0930	1130	1330	1530	1730
Wolfsburg d.	...	...	0548	...	...	...	...	0801	...	1001	1201	1401	1601	1801
Hannover Hbf d.	...	...	0618	0640	0709	...	...	0840	0840	1040	1240	1440	1640	1840
Minden d.	...	...	...	0711	0752	...	...	0911	0911	1111	1311	1511	1711	1911
Osnabrück Hbf ▲ d.	0614	...	...	0753	0841	0914	...	0953	0953	1153	1353	1553	1753	1953
Rheine ▲ d.	0648	...	...	0821	0921	0948	...	1021	1021	1221	1421	1620	1820	2020
Bad Bentheim 🛃 ▲ d.	0709	0744	...	0844	...	1009	1044	1044	1044	1244	1444	1644	1844	2044
Hengelo ▲ a.	0726	0801	...	0901	...	1026	1101	1101	1101	1301	1501	1701	1901	2101
Almelo a.	...	0814	...	0914	...	...	1114	1114	1114	1314	1514	1714	1914	2114
Deventer a.	...	0841	...	0941	...	...	1141	1141	1141	1341	1541	1741	1941	2141
Apeldoorn a.	...	0858	...	0958	...	...	1158	1158	1158	1358	1558	1758	1958	2158
Amersfoort a.	...	0924	...	1024	...	...	1224	1224	1224	1424	1624	1824	2024	2224
Hilversum a.	...	0938	...	1038	...	...	1238	1238	1238	1438	1638	1838	2038	2238
Amsterdam Centraal a.	...	1000	...	1100	...	...	1300	1300	1300	1500	1700	1900	2100	2300

B – ①-⑥ (daily Apr. 8 - Nov. 2).
D – ① Apr. 29 - Aug. 26 (also June 11; not June 10).
E – ①-⑤ Sept. 2 - Dec. 14.
H – ⑧ (daily Apr. 7 - Nov. 1).

J – ①-⑥ Apr. 19 - Aug. 31 (not June 10).

q – Not June 15.
y – Also June 10.

▲ – For other regional trains Hengelo – Osnabrück and v.v. see Table **811** on page 386.

24 PARIS - MOSKVA

train number	**24** *JI*	**24** *JI*
train number	**453**	**453**
notes	**AP**	**AQ**
	④	④
Paris Est d.	1858	1858
Strasbourg d.	2340	2340
Karlsruhe Hbf d.	0052	0052
Frankfurt (Main) Süd d.	0158	0158
Halle Hbf d.	0606	0606
Berlin Hbf a.	0721	0721
Berlin Hbf d.	0726	0726
Berlin Lichtenberg a.	0740	0740
Berlin Lichtenberg d.	0759	0759
Frankfurt (Oder) 🛃 d.	0905	0855
Rzepin d.	0920	0920
Poznań Gł. d.	1036	1036
Warszawa Centralna d.	|	|
Warszawa Wschodnia a.	1458	1458
Warszawa Wschodnia d.	1536	1536
Terespol a.	1744	1744
Terespol 🛃 d.	1829	1829
Brest Tsentralny 🛃 a.	2015	2115
Brest Tsentralny d.	2223	2323
Baranavichy a.	0023	0123
Minsk a.	0205	0304
Orsha Tsentralnaya § a.	0436	0536
Smolensk Tsentralny § a.	0611	0711
Vyazma a.	0759	0859
Moskva Belorusskaya a.	1058	1145

train number	**23** *JI*	**23** *JI*
train number	**452**	**452**
notes	**BP**	**BQ**
	②	②
Moskva Belorusskaya d.	1814	1912
Vyazma d.	2129	2219
Smolensk Tsentralny § d.	2311	0009
Orsha Tsentralnaya § d.	0038	0137
Minsk d.	0312	0414
Baranavichy d.	0451	0555
Brest Tsentralny a.	0642	0848
Brest Tsentralny 🛃 d.	0943	1043
Terespol 🛃 a.	0901	0901
Terespol d.	0946	0946
Warszawa Wschodnia a.	1150	1150
Warszawa Wschodnia d.	1301	1301
Warszawa Centralna d.	|	|
Poznań Gł. d.	1733	1733
Rzepin d.	1902	1902
Frankfurt (Oder) 🛃 a.	1924	1924
Berlin Lichtenberg a.	2017	2017
Berlin Lichtenberg d.	2041	2041
Berlin Hbf a.	2058	2058
Berlin Hbf d.	2103	2103
Halle Hbf d.	2217	2217
Frankfurt (Main) Süd a.	0138	0138
Karlsruhe a.	0300	0300
Strasbourg a.	0514	0514
Paris Est a.	0940	0940

25 NICE - MOSKVA

train number	**18** *BJ*	**18** *BJ*	
notes	⑦	⑦	
notes	**DP**	**DQ**	
Nice d.	0930	0930	⑦
Monaco-Monte Carlo d.	0950	0950	:
Menton d.	1001	1002	:
Ventimiglia 🛃 d.	1040	1040	:
Bordighera d.	1049	1049	:
San Remo d.	1059	1059	:
Genova Piazza Principe d.	1250	1250	:
Milano Rogoredo d.	1517	1517	:
Verona d.	1709	1735	:
Bolzano / Bozen d.	1912	2008	:
Brennero / Brenner 🛃 d.	2058	2158	:
Innsbruck Hbf d.	2231	2314	:
Jenbach d.	2252	2243	:
Kirchberg in Tirol d.	2340	0030	:
Zell am See d.	0041	0131	①
Bischofshofen d.	0131	0221	:
Linz Hbf d.	0327	0421	:
Wien Hbf d.	0605	0605	:
Břeclav 🛃 d.	0724	0724	:
Bohumin 🛃 d.	0951	0951	:
Chałupki 🛃 d.	1000	1001	:
Katowice d.	|	|	:
Warszawa Centralna d.	1500	1455	:
Warszawa Wschodnia a.	1506	1501	:
Warszawa Wschodnia d.	1536	1536	:
Terespol a.	1744	1744	:
Terespol 🛃 d.	1829	1829	:
Brest Tsentralny 🛃 a.	2015	2120	:
Brest Tsentralny d.	2223	2323	:
Baranavichy a.	0023	0123	②
Minsk a.	0205	0304	:
Orsha Tsentralnaya § a.	0436	0536	:
Smolensk Tsentralny § a.	0611	0711	:
Vyazma a.	0759	0859	:
Moskva Belorusskaya a.	1058	1145	:

train number	**17** *BJ*	**17** *BJ*	
notes	④	④	
notes	**CP**	**CQ**	
Moskva Belorusskaya d.	1814	1912	④
Vyazma d.	2129	2219	:
Smolensk Tsentralny § d.	2311	0009	⑤
Orsha Tsentralnaya § d.	0038	0137	:
Minsk d.	0312	0414	:
Baranavichy d.	0451	0555	:
Brest Tsentralny a.	0642	0848	:
Brest Tsentralny 🛃 d.	0943	1043	:
Terespol 🛃 a.	0901	0901	:
Terespol d.	0946	0946	:
Warszawa Wschodnia a.	1150	1150	:
Warszawa Wschodnia d.	1219	1219	:
Warszawa Centralna d.	1230	1230	:
Katowice d.	|	|	:
Chałupki 🛃 d.	1717	1717	:
Bohumin 🛃 d.	1800	1800	:
Břeclav 🛃 d.	2014	2014	:
Wien Hbf d.	2120	2120	:
Linz Hbf d.	2328	2328	⑥
Bischofshofen d.	0131	0131	:
Zell am See d.	0220	0220	:
Kirchberg in Tirol d.	0313	0313	:
Jenbach d.	0411	0411	:
Innsbruck Hbf d.	0457	0457	:
Brennero / Brenner 🛃 d.	0707	0707	:
Bolzano / Bozen d.	0722	0722	:
Verona d.	0936	0936	:
Milano Rogoredo d.	1108	1108	:
Genova Piazza Principe d.	1419	1419	:
San Remo d.	1653	1653	:
Bordighera d.	1705	1705	:
Ventimiglia 🛃 d.	1747	1747	:
Menton a.	1800	1800	:
Monaco-Monte Carlo a.	1811	1811	:
Nice a.	1830	1830	:

Notes for tables 24 and 25

A – TRANSEUROPEAN EXPRESS ④: 🛏 1, 2 cl. Paris (**453**) - Berlin - Brest (**24** *JI*) - Moskva (arrive ⑥). ✕ (PKP) Paris - Warszawa. ✕ (RZD) Brest - Moskva.
B – TRANSEUROPEAN EXPRESS ②: 🛏 1, 2 cl. Moskva (**23** *JI*) - Brest (**452**) - Berlin - Paris (arrive ④). ✕ (RZD) Moskva - Brest. ✕ (PKP) Warszawa - Paris.

C – ④: 🛏 1 cl. (lux), 🛏 1, 2 cl. Moskva - Nice. ✕ (RZD) Moskva - Brest and ✕ (PKP) Warszawa - Nice (journey two nights).
D – ⑦: 🛏 1 cl. (lux), 🛏 1, 2 cl. Nice - Moskva. ✕ (PKP) Nice - Warszawa and ✕ (RZD) Brest - Moskva (journey two nights).

P – Mar. 31, 2019 - Oct. 26, 2019.
Q – Oct. 27, 2019 - Dec. 14, 2019. Timings subject to confirmation.

✕ (PKP) – Polish railways restaurant car.
✕ (RZD) – Russian railways restaurant car.
§ – 🛃: Osinovka (BY) / Krasnoye (RU).

AMSTERDAM - FRANKFURT, WIEN and MÜNCHEN 28

train type		ICE	ICE	ICE		ICE	ICE	ICE	🚌		ICE	ICE	ICE	ICE	🚌		ICE	ICE	ICE		ICE	ICE	ICE			
train number		121	621	515		105	595	27	42014		123	629	519	229	42018		125	723	611		127	727	613			
notes	Ⓐ	①–⑥ p			⚒	C			🅁 🍸 2						🅁 🍸 2			Ⓑ				Ⓑ				
Amsterdam Centraal d.	...	0638	...	...	...	0808	...	...	...	...	1038	...	...	...	...	...	1238	...	...	...	1438	...	...	...	...	...
Rotterdam Centraal d.	0605	|	...	...	0735	|	...	...	...	1005	|	...	...	...	...	1205	|	...	...	1405	|	...	...	...	...	...
Utrecht Centraal d.	0642	0707	...	...	0812	0837	...	...	...	1042	1107	...	...	...	...	1242	1307	...	...	1442	1507	...	...	...	...	...
Arnhem ◐ ▲ d.	...	0737	...	...	...	0907	...	...	...	...	1137	...	...	...	...	...	1337	...	...	...	1537	...	...	...	...	...
Oberhausen Hbf ◐ ▲ d.	...	0826	...	...	...	0959	...	...	...	...	1226	...	...	...	...	...	1426	...	...	...	1626	...	...	...	...	...
Duisburg Hbf ▲ d.	...	0834	...	...	...	1008	...	...	...	...	1234	...	...	...	...	...	1434	...	...	...	1634	...	...	...	...	...
Düsseldorf Hbf ▲ d.	...	0847	...	...	...	1022	...	...	...	...	1248	...	...	...	...	...	1450	...	...	...	1651	...	...	...	...	...
Köln Hbf a.	...	0915	...	...	...	1046	...	...	...	...	1315	...	...	...	...	...	1519	...	...	...	1718	...	...	...	...	...
Köln Hbf d.	...	0928	...	...	...	1055	...	...	...	...	1328	...	...	...	...	...	1529	...	...	...	1728	...	...	...	...	...
Bonn Hbf d.	...	|	...	...	...	|	...	...	...	...	|	...	...	...	...	...	|	...	...	...	|	...	...	...	...	...
Koblenz d.	...	⊖	...	...	...	⊖	...	...	...	...	⊖	...	...	...	...	...	⊖	...	...	...	⊖	...	...	...	...	...
Mainz d.	...	|	...	...	...	|	...	...	...	...	|	...	...	...	...	...	|	...	...	...	|	...	...	...	...	...
Frankfurt Flughafen ✈ a.	...	1016	...	1052	...	1149	...	1202	...	...	1416	...	1452	...	...	...	1618	...	1652	...	1816	...	1852	...	...	...
Frankfurt (Main) Hbf a.	...	1031	1054	|	...	|	...	1213	...	...	1431	1454	|	1621	...	...	1631	1654	|	...	1831	1854	|	...	...	...
Würzburg a.	...	...	1202	|	...	|	...	1332	...	...	...	1602	|	1732	...	...	...	1802	|	...	...	2002	|	...	...	...
Nürnberg a.	...	...	1259	|	...	|	...	1427	1540	...	...	1659	|	1827	1840	...	...	1859	|	...	...	2059	|	...	...	...
Regensburg a.	...	...	|	|	...	|	...	1524	|	...	...	|	|	1924	|	...	...	|	|	...	...	|	|	...	...	...
Praha hlavní a.	...	...	|	|	...	|	...	|	1918	...	...	|	|	|	2230	...	...	|	|	...	...	|	|	...	...	...
Mannheim a.	...	...	|	1123	...	1223	1230	|	...	...	...	|	1523	|	...	...	...	|	1723	...	...	|	1923	...	...	...
Stuttgart a.	...	...	|	1208	...	...	1308	|	...	...	...	|	1608	|	...	...	...	|	1808	...	...	|	2008	...	...	...
Ulm a.	...	...	|	1308	...	...	1407	|	...	...	...	|	1707	|	...	...	...	|	1908	...	...	|	2108	...	...	...
Augsburg a.	...	...	|	1353	...	...	1453	|	...	...	...	|	1753	|	...	...	...	|	1953	...	...	|	2153	...	...	...
München Hbf a.	...	...	1407	1427	...	...	1527	|	...	...	...	1805	1827	|	...	...	...	2007	2027	...	...	2208	2226	...	...	...
Passau 🏛 a.	...	...	...	...	...	...	...	1626	...	...	...	...	...	2026	...	...	...	...	...	...	...	...	...	...	...	...
Linz Hbf a.	...	...	...	...	...	...	...	1724	...	...	...	...	...	2143	...	...	...	...	...	...	...	...	...	...	...	...
Wien Hbf a.	...	...	...	...	...	...	...	1845	...	...	...	...	...	2309	...	...	...	...	...	...	...	...	...	...	...	...

train type		ICE	ICE	ICE		ICE	NJ	NJ	
train number		129	821	615		221	40421	421	
notes			Ⓑ				A	B	
Amsterdam Centraal d.	...	1638	...	...	...	1838	...	...	...
Rotterdam Centraal d.	1605	|	...	...	1805	|	...	...	...
Utrecht Centraal d.	1642	1707	...	...	1842	1907	...	...	...
Arnhem ◐ ▲ d.	...	1737	...	...	...	1937	...	...	...
Oberhausen Hbf ◐ ▲ d.	...	1826	...	...	...	2026	...	...	...
Duisburg Hbf ▲ d.	...	1834	...	...	...	2034	...	...	...
Düsseldorf Hbf ▲ d.	...	1848	...	...	...	2048	2054	2054	...
Köln Hbf a.	...	1915	...	...	...	2112	2118	2118	...
Köln Hbf d.	...	1921	...	...	...	2128	2121	2121	...
Bonn Hbf d.	...	|	...	...	...	|	2143	2143	...
Koblenz d.	...	⊖	...	...	...	⊖	2217	2217	...
Mainz d.	...	|	...	...	...	|	2311	2311	...
Frankfurt Flughafen ✈ a.	...	2010	2035	2052	...	2218	2353**d**	2353**d**	...
Frankfurt (Main) Hbf a.	...	2026	2048	|	...	2231	|	|	...
Frankfurt (Main) Süd a.	...	...	|	|	...	...	0008**d**	0008**d**	...
Würzburg a.	...	...	2203	|	...	...	0135	0135	...
Nürnberg a.	...	...	2259	|	...	...	0237	0237	...
Regensburg a.	...	...	|	|	...	...	0410	|	...
Praha hlavní a.	...	...	|	|	...	...	|	|	...
Mannheim a.	...	...	|	2123	...	...	|	|	...
Stuttgart a.	...	...	|	2208	...	...	|	|	...
Ulm a.	...	...	|	2308	...	...	|	|	...
Augsburg a.	...	...	|	2352	...	...	|	0626	...
München Hbf a.	...	...	0007j	0028	...	...	|	0708	...
Innsbruck Hbf a.	...	...	...	...	...	...	|	0914	...
Passau 🏛 a.	...	...	...	...	...	...	0518	...	...
Linz Hbf a.	...	...	...	...	...	...	0643	...	...
Wien Hbf a.	...	...	...	...	...	...	0827	...	...

train type	ICE	ICE		NJ	NJ	ICE	ICE		ICE	ICE	ICE	
train number	222	222		420	40490	616	220		614	820	128	
notes	①–⑤ p	⑥⑦		B	A					①–⑥		
Wien Hbf d.	...	...	...	...	2041	...	...	...	...	...	...	...
Linz Hbf d.	...	...	...	...	2216	...	...	...	...	...	...	...
Passau 🏛 d.	...	...	...	...	2322	...	...	...	...	...	...	...
Innsbruck Hbf d.	...	...	...	2044	|	...	...	...	...	...	...	...
München Hbf d.	...	...	...	2252	|	0324	...	...	0527	0545	...	...
Augsburg d.	...	...	...	2330	|	0357	...	...	0601	|	...	...
Ulm d.	...	...	...	|	|	0440	...	...	0650	|	...	...
Stuttgart d.	...	...	...	|	|	0551	...	...	0751	|	...	...
Mannheim d.	...	...	...	|	|	0636	...	...	0836	|	...	...
Praha hlavní d.	...	...	...	|	|	|	...	...	|	|	...	...
Regensburg d.	...	...	...	|	0027	|	...	...	|	|	...	...
Nürnberg d.	...	...	...	0246	0246	|	...	...	|	0700	...	...
Würzburg d.	...	...	...	|	|	|	...	...	|	0755	...	...
Frankfurt (Main) Süd d.	...	...	...	0523**a**	0523**a**	|	...	...	|	|	...	...
Frankfurt (Main) Hbf d.	0529	...	...	|	|	|	0727	...	|	0904	0929	...
Frankfurt Flughafen ✈ d.	0543	...	...	0535**a**	0535**a**	0706	0743	...	0906	...	0943	...
Mainz a.	|		...	0602	0602	...	|	...	...	...	|	...
Koblenz a.	⊖	...	...	0704	0704	...	⊖	...	...	...	⊖	...
Bonn Hbf a.	|	...	...	0748	0748	...	|	...	...	...	|	...
Köln Hbf a.	0633	...	...	0815	0815	...	0833	...	...	...	1033	...
Köln Hbf d.	0641	0641	...	0817	0817	...	0841	...	...	...	1041	...
Düsseldorf Hbf ▲ a.	0706	0706	...	0842	0842	...	0906	...	...	...	1105	...
Duisburg Hbf ▲ a.	0723	0723	...	...	...	...	0923	...	...	...	1123	...
Oberhausen Hbf ◐ ▲ a.	0732	0732	...	...	...	...	0932	...	...	...	1132	...
Arnhem ◐ ▲ a.	0828	0828	...	...	...	...	1028	...	...	...	1228	...
Utrecht Centraal a.	0901	0901	0918	...	...	...	1101	1118	...	...	1301	1318
Rotterdam Centraal a.	|	|	0955	...	...	...	|	1155	...	...	|	1355
Amsterdam Centraal a.	0928	0928	...	...	...	...	1128	...	...	...	1328	...

train type	ICE	ICE	ICE		IC	ICE	ICE	ICE		EC	ICE	ICE	ICE	ICE		🚌	ICE	ICE	ICE		ICE	🚌	ICE	ICE		
train number	612	726	126		2024	610	722	124		8	28	596	626	122		42009	26	1090	104		514	42011	620	120		
notes		796 ①–⑥					792 1122						756 826			🅁 🍸 2		594	D			🅁 🍸 2		Ⓑ m		
Wien Hbf d.	...	...	...	...	...	...	...	...	...	...	0915	...	...	...	...	...	1115	...	...	...	...	...	...	...	...	...
Linz Hbf d.	...	...	...	...	...	...	...	...	...	...	1036	...	...	...	...	...	1236	...	...	...	...	...	...	...	...	...
Passau 🏛 d.	...	...	...	...	0717	...	...	...	...	...	1134	...	...	...	...	...	1337	...	...	...	...	...	...	...	...	...
München Hbf d.	0728	0754	...	...	|	0928	0951	...	...	...	|	1228	1250	...	...	...	|	1428	...	...	1528	...	1555	...	...	...
Augsburg d.	0803	|	...	...	|	1003	|	...	...	...	|	1303	|	...	...	...	|	1503	...	...	1603	...	|	...	...	...
Ulm d.	0850	|	...	...	|	1050	|	...	...	...	|	1351	|	...	...	...	|	1551	...	...	1650	...	|	...	...	...
Stuttgart d.	0951	|	...	...	|	1151	|	...	...	...	|	1451	|	...	...	...	|	1651	...	...	1751	...	|	...	...	...
Mannheim d.	1036	|	...	...	|	1236	|	...	...	1439	|	1532	|	...	...	...	|	1729	1735	...	1836	...	|	...	...	...
Praha hlavní d.	|	|	...	...	|	|	|	...	...	|	|	|	|	...	...	1042	|	...	|	...	|	1242	|	...	...	...
Regensburg d.	|	|	...	...	0827	|	|	...	...	|	1232	|	|	...	...	|	1435	...	|	...	|	|	|	...	...	...
Nürnberg d.	|	0900	...	...	0929	|	1100	...	...	|	1330	|	1400	...	...	1420	1532	...	|	...	|	1620	1700	...	...	...
Würzburg d.	|	0955	...	...	1026	|	1155	...	...	|	1424	|	1455	...	...	...	1624	...	|	...	|	...	1755	...	...	...
Frankfurt (Main) Hbf d.	|	1104	1129	...	1142	|	1304	1329	...	|	1536	1608	1604	1629	...	...	1742	...	|	...	|	...	1904	1929	...	...
Frankfurt Flughafen ✈ d.	1106	...	1143	...	1158	1306	...	1343	...	|	...	...	...	1643	...	...	1755	...	1809	...	1906	...	...	1943	...	...
Mainz a.	...	...	|	...	1218	...	...	|	...	1518	...	...	...	|	...	...	...	...	|	...	...	...	...	|	...	...
Koblenz a.	...	...	⊖	...	1311	...	...	⊖	...	1611	...	...	...	⊖	...	...	...	...	⊖	...	...	...	...	⊖	...	...
Bonn Hbf a.	...	...	|	...	1344	...	...	|	...	1644	...	...	...	|	...	...	...	...	|	...	...	...	...	|	...	...
Köln Hbf a.	...	...	1233	...	1405	...	...	1433	...	1705	...	...	...	1732	...	...	...	...	1905	...	...	...	...	2033	...	...
Köln Hbf d.	...	...	1241	...	...	...	...	1444	...	...	...	...	...	1745	...	...	...	...	1914	...	...	...	...	2042	...	...
Düsseldorf Hbf ▲ a.	...	...	1306	...	...	...	...	1510	...	...	...	...	...	1809	...	...	...	...	1936	...	...	...	...	2106	...	...
Duisburg Hbf ▲ a.	...	...	1322	...	...	...	...	1526	...	...	...	...	...	1825	...	...	...	...	1949	...	...	...	...	2122	...	...
Oberhausen Hbf ◐ ▲ a.	...	...	1332	...	...	...	...	1534	...	...	...	...	...	1832	...	...	...	...	1957	...	...	...	...	2132	...	...
Arnhem ◐ ▲ a.	...	...	1428	...	...	...	...	1628	...	...	...	...	...	1928	...	...	...	...	2057	...	...	...	...	2228	...	...
Utrecht Centraal a.	...	...	1501	1518	...	...	...	1701	1718	...	...	...	...	2001	2018	...	...	...	2130	2148	...	...	...	2301	2318	...
Rotterdam Centraal a.	...	...	|	1555	...	...	...	|	1755	...	...	...	...	|	2055	...	...	...	|	2225	...	...	...	|	2355	...
Amsterdam Centraal a.	...	...	1528	...	...	...	...	1728	...	...	...	...	...	2028	...	...	...	...	2157	...	...	...	...	2328	...	...

A – *ÖBB nightjet* 🛏 1, 2 cl., 🛌 2 cl. (4, 6 berth), (2) Düsseldorf - Wien and v.v. Special fares apply. See Table **53**.

B – *ÖBB nightjet* 🛏 1, 2 cl., 🛌 2 cl. (4, 6 berth), (2) Düsseldorf - Innsbruck and v.v. Special fares apply. See Table **53**.

C – (12) 🍸 Amsterdam - Mannheim - Basel (Table **73**).

D – (12) 🍸 Basel - Mannheim - Amsterdam (Table **73**).

a – Arrival time.

d – Departure time.

j – ④⑤⑦.

m – Not June 9.

p – Not June 10.

🚌 – **DB / ČD** *ExpressBus*. 🅁 🍸. Rail tickets valid. 2nd class only. (Table **76**).

◐ – 🏛 between Arnhem and Oberhausen is Emmerich.

⊖ – Via Köln - Frankfurt high speed line.

▲ – For other regional trains Düsseldorf – Arnhem and v.v. see Table **802** on page 379 (service *RE19*).

30 PARIS - FRANKFURT - BERLIN, LEIPZIG, DRESDEN and PRAHA

Alternative services Paris - Frankfurt are available via Brussels (Table **21**). Alternative services Paris - Berlin are available via Brussels (Table **20**).

train type	*TGV*	*ICE*	*ICE*	*EC*	*ICE*	*TGV*	*ICE*	*ICE*	*EC*	*ICE*		*ICE*	*ICE*	*ICE*	*ICE*		*ICE*	*ICE*	*ICE*	*ICE*		*ICE*	*ICE*	*IC*		*ICE*	*NJ*	
train number	**9561**	**372**	**1559**	**177**	**623**	**9551**	**370**	**1651**	**179**	**627**		**9553**	**276**	**1655**	**725**		**9563**	**274**	**1657**	**729**		**9555**	**1659**	**2029**		**9557** **9559**	**470**	
notes	[R]★	🍷	🍷	✕	🍷	[R]★	🍷	🍷	✕	🍷		[R]★	🍷	🍷	🍷		[R]★	🍷	🍷	🍷		[R]★	🍷	🍷		[R]★		
notes	①–⑥																		Ⓑ			Ⓑ	Ⓑ					
		J		A					A																		C	
Paris Est d.	0719	...	...	...	...	0906	...	...	...	...	...	1310	...	...	...	...	1521	...	...	...	...	1710	...	...	...	1906	...	...
Strasbourg d.	0913	...	...	...	...	|	...	...	...	...	...	|	...	...	...	...	1713	...	...	...	...	|	...	...	...	|	...	...
Forbach 🏛 d.	◧	...	...	...	...	1047	...	...	...	...	...	|	...	...	...	...	◧	...	...	...	...	|	...	...	...	2049	...	...
Saarbrücken d.	|	...	...	...	...	1058	...	...	...	...	...	1459	...	...	...	...	|	...	...	...	...	1859	...	...	...	2059	...	...
Kaiserlautern d.	|	...	...	...	...	1133	...	...	...	...	...	1537	...	...	...	...	|	...	...	...	...	1937	...	...	...	2137	...	...
Karlsruhe Hbf d.	0955	...	...	...	...	|	...	...	...	...	...	|	...	...	...	...	1755	...	...	...	...	|	...	...	...	|	...	...
Mannheim d.	1021	...	...	...	...	1219	...	...	...	...	...	1619	...	...	...	...	1821	...	...	...	...	2019	...	...	...	2219	2359	...
Frankfurt (Main) Hbf d.	1058	1114	1119	...	1154	1258	1314	1319	...	1354	...	1658	1714	1720	1754	...	1858	1914	1919	1954	...	2058	2119	2221	...	2258	0054**f**	...
Würzburg a.	...	|	|	...	1304	...	|	|	...	1502	...	...	|	|	1902	...	...	|	|	2102	...	...	|	2344	...	...	|	...
Nürnberg a.	...	|	|	...	1403	...	|	|	...	1559	...	...	|	|	1959	...	...	|	|	2159	...	...	|	0044	...	...	|	...
Fulda a.	...	1210	1212	...	...	...	1410	1412	...	...	...	...	1810	1812	...	...	...	2010	2012	...	...	...	2212	...	...	...	|	...
Erfurt a.	...	|	1338	...	...	...	|	1537	...	...	...	...	|	1937	...	...	...	|	2137	...	...	...	2341	...	...	...	|	...
Leipzig Hbf a.	...	|	1423	...	...	...	|	1622	...	...	...	...	|	2022	...	...	...	|	2222	...	...	...	0026	...	...	...	|	...
Dresden Hbf a.	...	|	1536	1710	...	...	|	1736	1912	...	...	...	|	2136	...	...	...	|	2336	...	...	...	0136**r**	...	...	...	|	...
Děčín (🏛 = Schöna) a.	...	|	...	1753	...	...	|	...	1953	...	...	...	|	...	...	...	...	|	...	...	...	...	...	...	...	...	|	...
Praha Holešovice a.	...	|	...	1915	...	...	|	...	2115	...	...	...	|	...	...	...	...	|	...	...	...	...	...	...	...	...	|	...
Praha hlavní a.	...	|	...	1926	...	...	|	...	2126	...	...	...	|	...	...	...	...	|	...	...	...	...	...	...	...	...	|	...
Kassel Wilhelmshöhe a.	...	1243	...	...	...	...	1443	...	...	...	...	...	1843	...	...	...	...	2043	...	...	...	...	...	...	...	...	|	...
Göttingen a.	...	1303	...	...	...	...	1503	...	...	...	...	...	1903	...	...	...	...	2103	...	...	...	...	...	...	...	...	|	...
Braunschweig a.	...	1359	...	...	...	...	1559	...	...	...	...	...	1959	...	...	...	...	2159	...	...	...	...	...	...	...	...	|	...
Wolfsburg a.	...	1417	...	...	...	...	1617	...	...	...	...	...	2017	...	...	...	...	2217	...	...	...	...	...	...	...	...	|	...
Berlin Hauptbahnhof a.	...	1528	...	...	...	...	1728	...	...	...	...	...	2128	...	...	...	...	2331	...	...	...	...	...	...	...	...	0754	...

train type	*NJ*	*ICE*	*ICE*	*ICE*	*ICE*	*ICE*	*ICE*	*ICE*	*ICE*	*ICE*	*ICE*	*ICE*	*ICE*	*ICE*	*ICE*	*ICE*	*TGV*	*TGV*	*ICE*	*ICE*	*EC*	*ICE*	*TGV*	*ICE*	*EC*	*ICE*	*ICE*	*ICE*
train number	**471**	**9558**	**9568**	**9586**	**822**	**1656**	**275**	**9566**	**9556**	**1654**	**277**	**9554**	**9554**	**724**	**1652**	**279**	**9552**	**9552**	**626**	**373**	**176**	**1558**	**9560**	**622**	**174**	**1556**	**375**	**9550**
notes		[R]★	[R]★	[R]★	🍷	🍷	🍷	[R]★	[R]★	🍷	🍷	[R]★	[R]★	🍷	🍷	🍷	[R]★	[R]★	🍷	🍷	✕	🍷	[R]★	🍷	✕	🍷	🍷	[R]★
notes		①–⑤	Ⓑ	⑥	①–⑤	①–⑥	①–⑤	⑥	①–⑤	①–⑥		⑥	⑦				Ⓑ	⑥										Ⓑ
	C						J													J	A				A			
Berlin Hauptbahnhof d.	2106	...	...	...	...	...	0430	...	...	...	0630	...	...	...	...	0830	...	...	...	1230	...	...	...	...	...	...	1430	...
Wolfsburg d.	|	...	...	...	...	...	0539	...	...	...	0739	...	...	...	...	0939	...	...	...	1339	...	...	...	...	...	...	1539	...
Braunschweig d.	|	...	...	...	...	...	0557	...	...	...	0757	...	...	...	...	0957	...	...	...	1357	...	...	...	...	...	...	1557	...
Göttingen d.	|	...	...	...	...	...	0652	...	...	...	0852	...	...	...	...	1052	...	...	...	1452	...	...	...	...	...	...	1652	...
Kassel Wilhelmshöhe d.	|	...	...	...	...	...	0714	...	...	...	0914	...	...	...	...	1114	...	...	...	1514	...	...	...	...	...	...	1714	...
Praha hlavní d.	|	...	...	...	...	...	|	...	...	...	|	...	...	...	...	|	...	...	...	|	0832	...	...	...	1032	...	|	...
Praha Holešovice d.	|	...	...	...	...	...	|	...	...	...	|	...	...	...	...	|	...	...	...	|	0842	...	...	...	1042	...	|	...
Děčín (🏛 = Schöna) d.	|	...	...	...	...	...	|	...	...	...	|	...	...	...	...	|	...	...	...	|	1002	...	...	...	1202	...	|	...
Dresden Hbf d.	|	...	...	...	...	...	|	...	...	0621	|	...	...	...	0821	|	...	...	...	|	1043	1221	...	...	1243	1421	|	...
Leipzig Hbf d.	|	...	...	...	...	0533	|	...	...	0729	|	...	...	...	0929	|	...	...	...	|	...	1329	...	...	...	1529	|	...
Erfurt d.	|	...	...	...	...	0618	|	...	...	0818	|	...	...	...	1018	|	...	...	...	|	...	1418	...	...	...	1618	|	...
Fulda d.	|	...	...	...	...	0744	0747	...	...	0944	0947	...	...	...	1144	1147	...	...	...	1547	...	1544	...	...	...	1744	1747	...
Nürnberg d.	|	...	...	...	0600	|	|	...	...	|	|	...	...	1000	|	|	...	...	1400	|	...	|	...	1600	...	|	|	...
Würzburg d.	|	...	...	...	0655	|	|	...	...	|	|	...	...	1055	|	|	...	...	1455	|	...	|	...	1655	...	|	|	...
Frankfurt (Main) Hbf d.	0402**f**	0559	0659	0658	0804	0837	0844	0859	0857	1037	1044	1059	1059	1204	1237	1244	1259	1259	1604	1644	...	1637	1659	1804	...	1837	1844	1859
Mannheim d.	0440	0639	0739	0738	...	...	...	0940	0940	...	...	1142	1142	...	..	...	1340	1340	...	...	...	...	1740	...	...	...	...	1939
Karlsruhe Hbf d.	...	|	0807	|	...	...	...	1006	|	...	...	|	|	...	...	...	|	|	...	...	...	...	1807	...	...	...	...	|
Kaiserlautern d.	...	0721	|	0822	...	...	...	|	1022	...	...	1224	1224	...	...	...	1422	1422	...	...	...	...	|	...	...	...	...	2022
Saarbrücken d.	...	0800	|	0902	...	...	...	|	1101	...	...	1305	1305	...	...	...	1501	1501	...	...	...	...	|	...	...	...	...	2101
Forbach 🏛 a.	...	0809	◧	0911	...	...	...	◧	|	...	...	|	1315	...	...	...	|	1510	...	...	...	...	◧	...	...	...	...	2110
Strasbourg a.	...	|	0847	|	...	...	...	1047	|	...	...	|	|	...	...	...	|	|	...	...	...	...	1847	...	...	...	...	|
Paris Est a.	...	0951	1037	1053	...	...	...	1237	1250	...	...	1454	1458	...	...	...	1650	1652	...	...	...	...	2037	...	...	...	...	2252

A – (12) ✕ Praha - Dresden - Berlin - Hamburg and v.v.
C – *ÖBB nightjet* – 🛏 1, 2 cl., 🛏 2 cl. (4, 6 berth), (2) Zürich - Basel - Mannheim - Frankfurt - Berlin and v.v. Special fares apply.
J – (12) 🍷 Interlaken Ost - Basel - Mannheim - Berlin and v.v.
T – Runs as *ICE* **9566** on certain dates.

f – Frankfurt (Main) **Süd**.
r – ①⑥.

◧ – 🏛 is at Kehl.
★ – *Alleo* ICE / TGV service. A DB / SNCF joint enterprise.

31 LONDON - GENÈVE

For the full service Paris - Genève, see Table **341**. 90 minutes (including Eurostar check-in time of 30 minutes) has been allowed from Paris Gare de Lyon to Paris Nord. 60 minutes has been allowed from Paris Nord to Paris Gare de Lyon. Additional Eurostar services are available, see Table **10**.

train type	☆	☆	*TGV*		☆	☆	*TGV*	*TGV*	☆	*TGV*	☆	*TGV*		☆	*TGV*	☆	*TGV*	☆	*TGV*			
train number	**9002**	**9004**	**9773**		**9110**	**9110**	**5164**	**9750**	**9018**	**9775**	**9022**	**9777**		**9028**	**9781**	**9032**	**9785**	**9036**	**9789**			
notes	⑥	①–⑤			②③④	⑥	[R]	[R]				Ⓑ							⑤**g**			
notes		**h**	♥		**J**					♥		♥			♥		♥		♥			
London St Pancras **10** d.	0618	0701	...	...	0647	0657	...	...	1024	...	1131	...	...	1331	...	1422	...	1531	...	...	...	...
Lille Europe d.	|	|	...	...	0926	0926	1043	...	|	...	|	...	...	|	...	|	...	|	...	...	...	...
Paris Nord **10** a.	0947	1017	...	...	...	...	|	...	1347	...	1447	...	...	1647	...	1747	...	1847	...	...	...	...
Paris Gare de Lyon d.	...	...	1211	...	...	...	|	...	...	1511	...	1611	...	...	1811	...	1911	...	2011	...	...	...
Lyon Part Dieu a.	...	...	|	...	...	...	1400	1534	...	|	...	|	...	...	|	...	|	...	|	...	...	...
Bellegarde a.	...	...	1458	...	...	...	...	1645	...	1748	...	1858	...	...	2058	...	2151	...	2251	...	...	...
Genève a.	...	...	1527	...	...	...	...	1718	...	1818	...	1927	...	...	2129	...	2222	...	2322	...	...	...

train type	*TGV*	☆	*TGV*	☆		*TGV*	☆		*TGV*	☆		*TGV*	*TGV*	☆	*TGV*	☆		*TGV*	☆			
train number	**9760**	**9023**	**9764**	**9031**		**9768**	**9039**		**9770**	**9047**	**96564**	**5192**	**9864**	**9163**	**9772**	**9055**		**9774**	**9059**			
notes	⚒	①–⑥							Ⓐ	①–⑥	Ⓑ				Ⓒ			Ⓐ				
notes	♥	**h**	♥			♥			♥	**h**					♥			♥	**C**			
Genève d.	0613	...	0741	...	...	0941	...	...	1141	...	1316	...	...	...	1341	...	...	1441	...	...	...	...
Bellegarde d.	0640	...	0807	...	...	1007	...	...	1207	...	1400	...	...	...	1407	...	...	1507	...	...	...	...
Lyon Part Dieu d.	|	...	|	...	...	|	...	...	|	...	1522	1600	1700	...	|	...	...	|	...	...	...	...
Paris Gare de Lyon a.	0931	...	1049	...	...	1249	...	...	1452	...	...	|	|	...	1649	...	...	1749	...	...	...	...
Paris Nord **10** d.	...	1113	...	1313	...	...	1513	...	...	1713	...	|	|	...	...	1913	...	...	2013	...	...	...
Lille Europe d.	...	|	...	|	...	...	|	...	...	|	...	1944**f**	1956	2100	...	|	...	...	|	...	...	...
London St Pancras **10** a.	...	1247	...	1439	...	...	1639	...	...	1832	...	...	...	2133	...	2039	...	...	2139	...	...	...

C – ①②③④⑥ (not Aug. 26).
H – To Lausanne on ①–④ (Table **42**).
J – ②③④ (①–⑤ Sept. 20 - Nov. 2).

f – Lille **Flandres** (◇).

g – Also May 29.
h – Not Aug. 26.

◇ – 500 metres from Lille Europe (see Lille City Plan on page 30).

♥ – *TGV Lyria* service. [R] 🍷. Special fares payable, three classes of service: Business 1ère, Standard 1ère and Standard. At-seat meal service in Business 1ère. Valid Dec. 9 - July 5.
☆ – Eurostar train. [R], ✕ in Business Premier and Standard Premier, 🍷 in Standard. Special fares payable. Minimum check-in time 30 minutes. Additional services are shown in Table **10**. Connections across Paris between *TGV* and Eurostar services are not guaranteed. Valid May 26 - Nov. 2.

LONDON - PARIS - MÜNCHEN - WIEN - BUDAPEST - BUCURESTI 32

Alternative services London - München are available via Brussels (Table **21**)

train type	*RJX*	*EN*	*EC*	*RJX*		*EC*	*RJX*	*EC*	*ICE*	*ICE*	*RJX*	*EN*	*TGV*	*ICE*	*EC*	*RJX*	*ICE*	*ICE*	*RJX*	*EC*	☆	*TGV*	*ICE*	*NJ*	*RJX*
train number	**61**	**473**	**217**	**65**		**113**	**563**	**147**	**9571**	**513**	**67**	**347**	**9551**	**595**	**219**	**167**	**9573**	**517**	**261**	**117**	**9014**	**9575**	**599**	**295**	**367**
train number/notes	✕	¶	🍷	✕		🍷	✕	✕		🍷	✕	¶	★	🍷	🍷	✕	*TGV*	🍷	✕	🍷		★	🍷	Ⓡ	✕
notes		**S**						**P**				**M**			**x**	**H**	**9593**								
London St Pancras **10** d.	...	...	...	...	...	...	...	...	...	...	...	...	...	...	...	...	...	...	...	...	0924	...	...	...	...
Paris Nord **10** a.	...	...	...	...	...	...	...	...	...	...	...	...	...	...	...	...	...	...	...	...	1247	...	...	...	...
Paris Est d.	...	...	...	...	...	...	...	...	0640	...	...	...	0906	...	...	...	1055	...	...	...	...	1355	...	...	...
Strasbourg d.	...	...	...	...	...	...	...	...	0831	...	...	...	|	...	...	...	1246	...	...	...	...	1546	...	...	...
Kehl 🛃 d.	...	...	...	...	...	...	...	...	|	...	...	...	◧	...	...	...	|	...	...	...	...	|	...	...	...
Karlsruhe Hbf d.	...	...	...	...	...	...	...	...	0911	...	...	...	|	...	...	...	1328	...	...	...	...	1628	...	...	...
Mannheim Hbf d.	...	...	0712	...	...	...	...	...	|	...	...	...	1216	1230	...	...	|	...	...	...	...	|	...	...	...
Stuttgart Hbf d.	...	...	0758	...	...	0958	...	...	0949	1014	...	...	...	1313	1358	...	1404	1414	...	1558	...	1704	1712	...	...
Ulm Hbf d.	...	...	0856	...	...	1055	...	...	...	1112	...	...	...	1409	1456	...	...	1510	...	1656	...	...	1809	...	...
Augsburg Hbf d.	...	...	0942	...	...	1142	...	...	...	1155	...	...	...	1455	1542	...	...	1555	...	1742	...	...	1855	...	...
München Pasing a.	...	...	|	...	...	|	...	...	...	1218	...	...	...	1518	|	...	...	1618	...	|	...	...	1918	...	...
München Hbf a.	...	...	1011	...	...	1211	...	...	...	1227	...	...	...	1527	1611	...	...	1627	...	1811	...	...	1927	...	...
München Hbf d.	0724	...	1018	1130	...	1218	...	...	...	...	1330	...	...	...	1618	...	...	...	1730	1818	...	...	...	2010	...
Salzburg Hbf 🛃 a.	0858	...	1159	1258	...	1359	1408	...	...	...	1458	...	...	...	1759	1808	...	...	1858	1959	...	...	...	2152	2208
Linz Hbf a.	1014	...	...	1414	...	...	1514	...	...	...	1614	...	...	...	...	1914	...	...	2014	...	...	...	...	...	2317
St Pölten Hbf a.	1100	...	...	1500	...	...	1600	...	...	...	1700	...	...	...	...	2000	...	...	2100	...	...	...	...	...	0003
Wien Hbf a.	1130	...	...	1530	...	...	1630	1642	...	...	1730	1942	...	...	...	2030	...	...	2130	...	...	...	...	...	0033
Hegyeshalom 🛃 a.	1225	...	...	1625	...	...	...	1725	...	...	1825	2025	...	...	...	...	...	...	...	...	...	...	...	...	...
Györ a.	1253	...	...	1653	...	...	...	1753	...	...	1853	2053	...	...	...	...	...	...	...	...	...	...	...	...	...
Budapest Keleti a.	1419	1910	...	1819	...	...	...	1919	...	...	2019	2220	...	...	...	...	...	...	...	...	...	...	...	...	...
Bucuresti Nord a.	...	1230	...	...	...	...	...	...	...	...	...	1606	...	...	...	...	...	...	...	...	...	...	...	...	...

train type	☆	*TGV*	*EN*	☆	*TGV*	*TGV*	*TGV*	*ICE*	☆	*ICE*	*ICE*
train number	**9018**	**9577**	**463**	**9024**	**9591**	**9579**	**9579**	**693**	**9032**	**9557**	**1093**
train number/notes		★				★	★	🍷		**9559**	**695**
notes		Ⓑ	**K**			⑥	Ⓑ	Ⓑ		★	
London St Pancras **10** d.	1024	...	...	1224	...	...	...	...	1422	...	...
Paris Nord **10** a.	1347	...	...	1547	...	...	...	...	1747	...	...
Paris Est d.	...	1555	...	...	1725	1755	1755	...	...	1906	...
Strasbourg d.	...	1746	...	...	1918	1946	1946	...	...	|	...
Kehl 🛃 d.	...	|	...	...	|	|	|	...	...	◧	...
Offenburg a.	...	|	...	...	1939	|	|	...	...	|	...
Freiburg (Brsg) Hbf a.	...	|	...	...	2030	|	|	...	...	|	...
Karlsruhe Hbf d.	...	1828	...	...	...	2028	2028	...	...	|	...
Mannheim Hbf d.	...	|	...	...	...	|	|	...	...	2217	2231
Stuttgart Hbf d.	...	1922e	...	...	...	2112	2104	2113	...	...	2308
Ulm Hbf d.	...	2020	...	...	...	2210	...	2209	...	...	...
Augsburg Hbf d.	...	2106	...	...	...	2258	...	2255	...	...	...
München Pasing a.	...	|	...	...	...	|	...	2320	...	...	...
München Hbf a.	...	2136	...	...	...	2329	...	2329	...	...	...
München Hbf d.	...	...	2335	...	...	...	...	...	...	...	...
Salzburg Hbf 🛃 a.	...	...	0118	...	...	...	...	...	...	...	...
Linz Hbf a.	...	...	0457	...	...	...	...	...	...	...	...
St Pölten Hbf a.	...	...	0600	...	...	...	...	...	...	...	...
Wien Hbf a.	...	...	0635	...	...	...	...	...	...	...	...
Hegyeshalom 🛃 a.	...	...	0723	...	...	...	...	...	...	...	...
Györ a.	...	...	0753	...	...	...	...	...	...	...	...
Budapest Keleti a.	...	...	0919	...	...	...	...	...	...	...	...
Bucuresti Nord a.	...	...	...	...	...	...	...	...	...	...	...

train type	*TGV*	*ICE*	*ICE*	☆	*TGV*	*TGV*	*ICE*	*ICE*	☆	
train number	**9590**	**616**	**9558**	**9023**	**9578**	**9584**	**9586**	**9568**	**9027**	
train number/notes			★	**h**	★	**9588**	★	★		
notes	①–⑤		①–⑤	①–⑥	①–⑥	⑥⑦	⑥	Ⓑ		
Bucuresti Nord d.	...	...	...	...	...	...	...	...	...	...
Budapest Keleti d.	...	...	...	...	...	...	...	...	...	...
Györ d.	...	...	...	...	...	...	...	...	...	...
Hegyeshalom 🛃 d.	...	...	...	...	...	...	...	...	...	...
Wien Hbf d.	...	...	...	...	...	...	...	...	...	...
St Pölten Hbf d.	...	...	...	...	...	...	...	...	...	...
Linz Hbf d.	...	...	...	...	...	...	...	...	...	...
Salzburg Hbf 🛃 d.	...	...	...	...	...	...	...	...	...	...
München Hbf a.	...	...	...	...	...	...	...	...	...	...
München Hbf d.	...	0324	...	...	...	...	...	...	...	...
München Pasing d.	...	0333	...	...	...	...	...	...	...	...
Augsburg Hbf d.	...	0357	...	...	...	...	...	...	...	...
Ulm Hbf d.	...	0440	...	...	...	...	...	...	...	...
Stuttgart Hbf d.	...	0551	...	...	0655	...	...	...	...	...
Mannheim Hbf d.	...	0628	0639	...	|	...	0738	0739	...	...
Karlsruhe Hbf d.	...	...	|	...	0732	...	|	0807	...	...
Freiburg (Brsg) Hbf d.	0624	...	|	...	|	0704	|	|	...	...
Offenburg d.	0715	...	|	...	|	0746	|	|	...	...
Kehl 🛃 d.	|	...	◧	...	|	|	◧	◧	...	...
Strasbourg a.	0740	...	|	...	0811	0809	|	|	...	...
Paris Est a.	0935	...	0951	...	1003	1005	1054	1037	...	...
Paris Nord **10** d.	...	...	...	1113	...	...	...	...	1213	...
London St Pancras **10** a.	...	...	...	1247	...	...	...	...	1330	...

train type	*EN*	*TGV*	*ICE*	*TGV*	☆	☆	*IC*	*ICE*	*TGV*	☆	*RJX*	*EC*	*ICE*	*ICE*	☆	*ICE*	*TGV*	*EN*	*RJX*	*EC*	*ICE*	*TGV*	*EN*	*RJX*	*IC*
train number	**462**	**9576**	**692**	**9576**	**9035**	**9039**	**1296**	**690**	**9574**	**9043**	**260**	**218**	**596**	**9572**	**9059**	**1090**	**9560**	**346**	**60**	**112**	**592**	**9570**	**472**	**62**	**2262**
train number/notes		★	🍷	★				🍷	★		✕	🍷	🍷	*TGV*		**594**	★	¶	✕	🍷	🍷	★	¶	✕	
notes	**K**	⑥⑦	①–⑤	①–⑤	⑥		①–⑥					**z**		**9592**	**C**	🍷		**M**					**S**		
														★											
Bucuresti Nord d.	...	...	...	...	...	...	...	...	...	...	...	...	...	...	...	...	...	1400	...	...	...	...	1745	...	...
Budapest Keleti d.	2040	...	...	...	...	...	...	...	...	...	...	...	...	...	...	...	...	0540	0740	...	...	...	0850	0940	...
Györ d.	2202	...	...	...	...	...	...	...	...	...	...	...	...	...	...	...	...	0702	0902	...	...	...	...	1102	...
Hegyeshalom 🛃 d.	2232	...	...	...	...	...	...	...	...	...	...	...	...	...	...	...	...	0732	0932	...	...	...	...	1132	...
Wien Hbf d.	2325	...	...	...	...	...	...	...	...	...	0630	...	...	...	...	...	...	0821	1030	...	...	...	...	1230	...
St Pölten Hbf d.	2359	...	...	...	...	...	...	...	...	...	0700	...	...	...	...	...	...	...	1100	...	...	...	...	1300	...
Linz Hbf d.	0103	...	...	...	...	...	...	...	...	...	0746	...	...	...	...	...	...	...	1146	...	...	...	...	1346	...
Salzburg Hbf 🛃 d.	0427	...	...	...	...	...	0545	...	...	...	0852	1000	...	...	...	...	...	...	1300	1400	...	...	...	1500	...
München Hbf a.	0610	...	...	...	...	...	0731	...	...	...	1030	1141	...	...	...	...	...	...	1430	1541	...	...	...	1630	...
München Hbf d.	...	0628	0629	...	...	...	0746	0828	...	...	...	1146	1228	...	...	1428	...	...	...	1546	1628	...	...	...	1647
München Pasing d.	...	|	0638	...	...	...	|	0837	...	...	...	|	1237	...	...	1437	...	...	...	|	1637	...	...	...	1656
Augsburg Hbf d.	...	0705	0706	...	...	...	0817	0903	...	...	...	1217	1303	...	...	1503	...	...	...	1617	1703	...	...	...	1721
Ulm Hbf d.	...	0750	0751	...	...	...	0904	0951	...	...	...	1304	1351	...	...	1551	...	...	...	1704	1751	...	...	...	1804
Stuttgart Hbf d.	...	0854	0846	0854	...	...	1001	1046	1055	...	...	1401	1446	1455	...	1651	...	...	...	1801	1846	1855	...	...	1911
Mannheim Hbf d.	...	|	...	|	...	...	...	...	|	...	...	...	...	|	...	1729	1740	...	...	...	...	|	...	...	1953
Karlsruhe Hbf d.	...	0932	...	0932	...	...	...	...	1132	...	...	...	...	1532	...	...	1807	...	...	...	...	1932	...	...	...
Kehl 🛃 d.	...	|	...	|	...	...	...	...	|	...	...	...	...	|	...	...	◧	...	...	...	...	|	...	...	...
Strasbourg a.	...	1012	...	1012	...	...	...	...	1213	...	...	...	...	1613	...	...	|	...	...	...	...	2013	...	...	...
Paris Est a.	...	1203	...	1203	...	...	...	...	1403	...	...	...	...	1803	...	...	2037	...	...	...	...	2203	...	...	...
Paris Nord **10** d.	...	...	...	...	1413	1513	...	...	...	1613	...	...	...	...	2013	...	...	...	...	...	...	...	...	...	...
London St Pancras **10** a.	...	...	...	...	1539	1639	...	...	...	1739	...	...	...	...	2139	...	...	...	...	...	...	...	...	...	...

C – ①②③④⑥ (also Nov. 1).

H – To Bratislava, arrive 2151.

K – KÁLMÁN IMRE – 🛏 1, 2 cl., couchette 2 cl. (4, 6 berth), [2] München - Budapest and v.v.

M – DACIA – 🛏 1, 2 cl., couchette 2 cl., [2] ✕ Wien - Budapest - Bucuresti and v.v.

P – [12] Wien - Budapest - Szolnok (arrive 2102) - Debrecen (2241) - Zahony (0010). Conveys 🛏 1, 2 cl. Wien - Zahony - Lviv - Kyïv (Table **96**).

S – *EuroNight* ISTER – 🛏 1, 2 cl., couchette 1, 2 cl., [2] Budapest - Bucuresti and v.v.

e – Arrive 18 minutes earlier.

h – Not Aug. 26.

x – To Graz (arrive 2214; Table **68**).

z – From Graz (depart 0536; Table **68**).

◧ – 🛃 is at Forbach.

RJ – ÖBB *Railjet* service. ✕, [1] (business class), [1] (first class), [2] (economy class).

★ – *Alleo* ICE / TGV service. A DB / SNCF joint enterprise.

TGV – Ⓡ, supplement payable, 🍷.

¶ – Compulsory reservation for international journeys between Hungary and Romania.

☆ – Eurostar train. Ⓡ, ✕ in Business Premier and Standard Premier, 🍷 in Standard. Special fares payable. Minimum check-in time 30 minutes. Additional services are shown in Table **10**. Valid May 26 - Nov. 2.

40 LONDON - PARIS - BASEL - ZÜRICH, INTERLAKEN, BRIG and MILANO

train type/number	TGV	IC	IC	IC	EC	☆	TGV	IC	IC	IC	IR	EC	☆	☆	TGV	IC	IC	IC	IR	EC
train number	9203	567	1067	967	151	9080	9211	573	1073	820	2327	21	9002	9004	9213	577	1077	824	2331	23
notes	♥ ⚒				[R] 🍷 ⊗	①–⑤ A	♥					[R] 🍷 ⊗	⑥	①–⑤ h	♥	🍷				[R] 🍷 ⊗
London St Pancras d.	...	...	...	...	...	0540	...	...	...	...	...	...	0618	0701	...	...	...	...	...	...
Paris Nord a.	...	...	...	...	...	0917	...	...	...	...	...	...	0947	1017	...	...	...	...	...	...
Paris Gare de Lyon d.	0723	...	...	...	...	...	1023	...	...	...	...	...	...	...	1223	...	...	...	...	...
Dijon d.	|	...	...	...	...	...	1201	...	...	...	...	...	...	...	1401	...	...	...	...	...
Besançon TGV ⊖ d.	|	...	...	...	...	...	|	...	...	...	...	...	...	...	|	...	...	...	...	...
Belfort TGV ⊡ d.	0941	...	...	...	...	...	|	...	...	...	...	...	...	...	|	...	...	...	...	...
Mulhouse d.	1006	...	...	...	...	...	1306	...	...	...	...	...	...	...	1507	...	...	...	...	...
Basel SBB a.	1026	...	...	...	...	...	1326	...	...	...	...	...	...	...	1526	...	...	...	...	...
Basel SBB d.	1033	...	1031	1059	1104	...	1333	...	1331	...	1404	...	...	...	1533	...	1531	...	1604	...
Zürich HB a.	1126	1137	|	|	|	...	1426	1437	|	...	|	1510	...	...	1626	1637	|	...	|	1710
Landquart a.	...	1241	|	|	|	...	...	1541	|	...	|	|	...	...	...	1741	|	...	|	|
Chur a.	...	1252	|	|	|	...	...	1552	|	...	|	|	...	...	...	1752	|	...	|	|
Luzern a.	...	...	|	|	1205	...	...	...	|	...	1505	|	...	...	...	...	|	...	1705	|
Arth Goldau a.	...	...	|	|	1246	...	...	...	|	...	1546	1547	...	...	...	...	|	...	1746	1747
Arth Goldau d.	...	...	|	|	1250	...	...	...	|	...	...	1550	...	...	...	...	|	...	...	1750
Bellinzona a.	...	...	|	|	1347	...	...	...	|	...	...	1647	...	...	...	...	|	...	...	1847
Lugano a.	...	...	|	|	1418	...	...	...	|	...	...	1718	...	...	...	...	|	...	...	1918
Chiasso 🏛 a.	...	...	|	|	1446	...	...	...	|	...	...	1746	...	...	...	...	|	...	...	1946
Bern a.	...	...	1124	1156	|	...	...	...	1424	1506	...	|	...	...	...	...	1624	1706	...	|
Thun a.	...	...	1152	1221	|	...	...	...	1452	1524	...	|	...	...	...	...	1652	1724	...	|
Spiez a.	...	...	1202	1231	|	...	...	...	1502	1534	...	|	...	...	...	...	1702	1734	...	|
Interlaken West a.	...	...	|	1251	|	...	...	...	1522	|	...	|	...	...	...	...	1722	|	...	|
Interlaken Ost a.	...	...	|	1257	|	...	...	...	1528	|	...	|	...	...	...	...	1728	|	...	|
Brig a.	...	...	1240	...	|	...	...	...	...	1611	...	|	...	...	...	...	...	1811	...	|
Como San Giovanni a.	...	...	...	...	|	...	...	...	...	...	...	|	...	...	...	...	...	...	...	|
Milano Centrale a.	...	...	...	...	1535	...	...	...	...	...	...	1835	...	...	...	...	...	...	...	2035

train type/number	☆	TGV	EC		IC	IR	EC	☆	TGV	IC	IC	ICE	IR	IC	IC	☆	TGV	RE	TGV	IR
train number	9014	9215	59		581	2335	25	9022	9219	585	1085	373	2339	1489	1489	9028	9223	3493	9225	2343
notes		♥ M	[R] 🍷 ⊗				[R] 🍷 ⊗		♥					①–⑤	⑥⑦		♥		♥ G	
London St Pancras d.	0924	...	...	...	...	...	...	1131	...	...	...	...	...	...	...	1331	...	...	...	...
Paris Nord a.	1247	...	...	...	...	...	...	1447	...	...	...	...	...	...	...	1647	...	...	...	...
Paris Gare de Lyon d.	...	1423	...	...	...	...	...	...	1623	...	...	...	...	...	...	...	1823	...	1823	...
Dijon d.	...	|	...	...	...	...	...	...	|	...	...	...	...	...	...	...	2001	...	2001	...
Besançon TGV ⊖ d.	...	|	...	...	...	...	...	...	|	...	...	...	...	...	...	...	|	...	|	...
Belfort TGV ⊡ d.	...	1641	...	...	...	...	...	...	1841	...	...	...	...	...	...	...	|	...	|	...
Mulhouse d.	...	1706	...	...	...	...	...	...	1907	...	...	...	...	...	...	...	2106	...	2106	...
Basel SBB a.	...	1726	...	...	...	...	...	...	1926	...	...	...	...	...	...	...	2126	...	2126	...
Basel SBB d.	...	...	1731	...	1733	1804	...	...	1933	...	1931	1959	2004	...	...	...	2133	...	2136	2204
Zürich HB a.	...	...	|	...	1826	|	1910	...	2026	2037	|	|	|	2110	2132	...	2226	2312	|	|
Landquart a.	...	...	|	...	1941	|	|	...	...	2141	|	|	|	|	|	...	...	0037	|	|
Chur a.	...	...	|	...	1952	|	|	...	...	2152	|	|	|	|	|	...	...	0047	|	|
Luzern a.	...	...	|	...	...	1905	|	...	...	...	|	|	2105	|	|	...	...	...	|	2305
Arth Goldau a.	...	...	|	...	...	1946	1947	...	...	...	|	|	2146	2147	2215	...	...	...	|	...
Arth Goldau d.	...	...	|	...	...	...	1950	...	...	...	|	|	...	2150	2218	...	...	...	|	...
Bellinzona a.	...	...	|	...	...	...	2047	...	...	...	|	|	...	2247	2321	...	...	...	|	...
Lugano a.	...	...	|	...	...	...	2118	...	...	...	|	|	...	2318	2350	...	...	...	|	...
Chiasso 🏛 a.	...	...	|	...	...	...	2146	...	...	...	|	|	...	2345	0017	...	...	...	|	...
Bern a.	...	...	1824	...	...	...	|	...	...	...	2024	2056	...	...	...	...	...	...	2250	...
Thun a.	...	...	1852	...	...	...	|	...	...	...	2052	2124	...	...	...	...	...	...	...	...
Spiez a.	...	...	1902	1905	...	...	|	...	...	...	2102	2134	...	...	...	...	...	...	...	...
Interlaken West a.	...	...	|	1923	...	...	|	...	...	...	|	2151	...	...	...	...	...	...	...	...
Interlaken Ost a.	...	...	|	1928	...	...	|	...	...	...	|	2157	...	...	...	...	...	...	...	...
Brig a.	...	...	1940	...	...	...	|	...	...	...	2140	...	...	...	...	...	...	...	...	...
Como San Giovanni a.	...	...	◧	...	...	...	2156	...	...	...	...	...	...	...	...	...	...	...	...	...
Milano Centrale a.	...	...	2137	...	...	...	2250	...	...	...	...	...	...	...	...	...	...	...	...	...

train type	IR	IR	IC	IC	TGV	☆	IC	IC	IR	IC	IC	TGV	☆	EC	EC	IR	IC	TGV	TGV	☆	☆
train number	2408	2308	1058	558	9206	9031	1458	1060	2312	562	1062	9210	9039	12	50	2316	566	9216	9218	9047	9049
notes					♥							♥		[R] 🍷 ⊗	[R] 🍷 ⊗		🍷	♥	♥ M	①–⑥ h	⑦ k
Milano Centrale d.	...	...	...	...	...	...	...	...	...	...	...	...	...	0725	0723	...	...	...	...	...	...
Como San Giovanni d.	...	...	...	...	...	...	...	...	...	...	...	...	...	|	◧	...	...	...	...	...	...
Brig d.	...	...	...	...	...	...	...	0720	...	...	...	...	...	|	0920	...	...	...	...	...	...
Interlaken Ost d.	...	...	0627	...	...	...	...	|	...	...	0830	...	...	|	|	...	...	...	...	...	...
Interlaken West d.	...	...	0632	...	...	...	...	|	...	...	0835	...	...	|	|	...	...	...	...	...	...
Spiez d.	...	...	0654	...	...	...	...	0754	...	...	0854	...	...	|	0954	...	...	...	...	...	...
Thun d.	...	...	0704	...	...	...	...	0804	...	...	0904	...	...	|	1004	...	...	...	...	...	...
Bern d.	...	...	0736	...	...	...	...	0836	...	...	0936	...	...	|	1036	...	...	1110	...	...	...
Chiasso 🏛 d.	...	...	|	...	...	...	0615	|	...	...	|	...	...	0815	|	...	...	|	...	...	...
Lugano d.	...	...	|	...	...	...	0643	|	...	...	|	...	...	0843	|	...	...	|	...	...	...
Bellinzona d.	...	...	|	...	...	...	0713	|	...	...	|	...	...	0913	|	...	...	|	...	...	...
Arth Goldau a.	...	...	|	...	...	...	0809	|	...	...	|	...	...	1009	|	...	...	|	...	...	...
Arth Goldau d.	0611	0614	|	...	...	...	0813	|	0814	...	|	...	...	1013	|	1014	...	|	...	...	...
Luzern d.	|	0654	|	...	...	...	|	|	0854	...	|	...	...	|	|	1054	...	|	...	...	...
Chur d.	|	|	|	0609	...	...	|	|	|	0809	|	...	...	|	|	|	1009	|	...	...	...
Landquart d.	|	|	|	0619	...	...	|	|	|	0819	|	...	...	|	|	|	1019	|	...	...	...
Zürich HB d.	0650	|	|	0723	0734	...	0850	|	|	0923	|	0934	...	1050	|	|	1123	|	1134	...	...
Basel SBB a.	...	0755	0829	...	0827	...	...	0929	0955	...	1029	1027	...	...	1129	1155	...	1227	1227	...	...
Basel SBB d.	...	...	...	...	0834	...	...	...	...	...	...	1034	...	...	...	...	...	1234	1234	...	...
Mulhouse a.	...	...	...	...	0853	...	...	...	...	...	...	1053	...	...	...	...	...	1254	1254	...	...
Belfort TGV ⊡ a.	...	...	...	...	0918	...	...	...	...	...	...	|	...	...	...	...	...	1317	1317	...	...
Besançon TGV ⊖ a.	...	...	...	...	|	...	...	...	...	...	...	|	...	...	...	...	...	|	|	...	...
Dijon a.	...	...	...	...	|	...	...	...	...	...	...	1158	...	...	...	...	...	|	|	...	...
Paris Gare de Lyon a.	...	...	...	...	1137	...	...	...	...	...	...	1337	...	...	...	...	...	1537	1537	...	...
Paris Nord d.	...	...	...	...	...	1313	...	...	...	...	...	...	1513	...	...	...	...	...	...	1713	1743
London St Pancras a.	...	...	...	...	...	1439	...	...	...	...	...	...	1639	...	...	...	...	...	...	1832	1906

A – Not July 27 - Sept. 1.

G – Calls at Olten at 2200.

M – Apr. 1 - July 5.

h – Not Aug. 26.

k – Also Aug. 26.

⊡ – Full name: Belfort Montbéliard TGV.

⊖ – Full name: Besancon Franche-Comté TGV.

◧ – 🏛 between Brig and Milano is Domodossola. Ticket point is **Iselle**.

♥ – *TGV Lyria* service. [R] 🍷. Special fares payable, three classes of service: Business 1ère, Standard 1ère and Standard. Valid Dec. 9 - July 5. At-seat meal service in Business 1ère.

⊗ – Compulsory reservation for international journeys. Supplement payable for international journeys and for internal journeys within Italy.

☆ – Eurostar train. [R], ✕ in Business Premier and Standard Premier, 🍷 in Standard. Special fares payable. Minimum check-in time 30 minutes. Valid May 26 - Nov. 2.

MILANO, BRIG, INTERLAKEN and ZÜRICH - BASEL - PARIS - LONDON 40

train type	*EC*	*IC*	*IR*	*IC*	*IC*	*TGV*	☆		*EC*	*EC*	*IR*	*IC*	*IC*	*TGV*	☆		*EC*	*IC*	*IR*	*IC*	*IC*	*TGV*	
train number	**14**	**1068**	**2320**	**1070**	**570**	**9222**	**9055**		**16**	**52**	**2324**	**1074**	**574**	**9226**	**9063**		**18**	**1076**	**2328**	**578**	**1078**	**9230**	
notes	[R] 🍷 ⊗					♥			[R] 🍷 ⊗	[R] 🍷 ⊗				♥ Ⓑ	Ⓑ		[R] 🍷 ⊗					♥	
Milano Centrale d.	0925	...	...	...	...	...	...	...	1125	1123	...	...	...	...	...	...	1325	...	...	...	...	...	...
Como San Giovanni d.	1003	...	...	...	...	...	...	...	1203	◧	...	...	...	...	...	...	|	...	...	...	...	...	...
Brig d.	|	1120	...	...	...	...	...	...	|	1320	...	...	...	...	...	...	|	1520	...	...	...	...	...
Interlaken Ost d.	|	|	...	1230	...	...	...	...	|	|	...	1430	...	...	...	...	|	|	...	...	1630	...	...
Interlaken West d.	|	|	...	1235	...	...	...	...	|	|	...	1435	...	...	...	...	|	|	...	...	1635	...	...
Spiez d.	|	1154	...	1254	...	...	...	...	|	1354	...	1454	...	...	...	...	|	1554	...	...	1654	...	...
Thun d.	|	1204	...	1304	...	...	...	...	|	1404	...	1504	...	...	...	...	|	1604	...	...	1704	...	...
Bern d.	|	1236	...	1336	...	...	...	...	|	1436	...	1536	...	...	...	...	|	1636	...	...	1736	...	...
Chiasso 🏛 d.	1015	|	...	|	...	...	...	...	1215	|	...	|	...	...	...	...	1415	|	...	...	|	...	...
Lugano d.	1043	|	...	|	...	...	...	...	1243	|	...	|	...	...	...	...	1443	|	...	...	|	...	...
Bellinzona d.	1113	|	...	|	...	...	...	...	1313	|	...	|	...	...	...	...	1513	|	...	...	|	...	...
Arth Goldau a.	1209	|	...	|	...	...	...	...	1409	|	...	|	...	...	...	...	1609	|	...	...	|	...	...
Arth Goldau d.	1213	|	1214	|	...	...	...	...	1413	|	1414	|	...	...	...	...	1613	|	1614	...	|	...	...
Luzern d.	|	|	1254	|	...	...	...	...	|	|	1454	|	...	...	...	...	|	|	1654	...	|	...	...
Chur d.	|	|	|	|	1209	...	...	...	|	|	|	|	1409	...	...	...	|	|	|	1609	|	...	...
Landquart d.	|	|	|	|	1219	...	...	...	|	|	|	|	1419	...	...	...	|	|	|	1619	|	...	...
Zürich HB d.	1250	|	|	|	1323	1334	...	...	1450	|	|	|	1523	1534	...	...	1650	|	|	1734	|	...	...
Basel SBB a.	...	1329	1355	1429	...	1427	...	...	...	1529	1555	1629	...	1627	...	...	...	1729	1755	1827	1829	...	...
Basel SBB d.	...	...	...	...	...	1434	...	...	...	...	...	...	...	1634	...	...	...	...	...	...	...	1834	...
Mulhouse a.	...	...	...	...	...	1453	...	...	...	...	...	...	...	1653	...	...	...	...	...	...	...	1853	...
Belfort TGV ⊡ a.	...	...	...	...	...	|	...	...	...	...	...	...	...	|	...	...	...	...	...	...	...	1920	...
Besançon TGV ⊖ a.	...	...	...	...	...	|	...	...	...	...	...	...	...	|	...	...	...	...	...	...	...	|	...
Dijon a.	...	...	...	...	...	1558	...	...	...	...	...	...	...	1758	...	...	...	...	...	...	...	|	...
Paris Gare de Lyon a.	...	...	...	...	...	1737	...	...	...	...	...	...	...	1937	...	...	...	...	...	...	...	2137	...
Paris Nord d.	...	...	...	...	...	...	1913	...	...	...	...	...	...	...	2113	...	...	...	...	...	...	...	...
London St Pancras a.	...	...	...	...	...	...	2039	...	...	...	...	...	...	...	2239	...	...	...	...	...	...	...	...

⊖ – Full name: Besancon Franche-Comté TGV.

⊡ – Full name: Belfort Montbéliard TGV.

◧ – 🏛 between Brig and Milano is Domodossola. Ticket point is **Iselle**.

☆ – Eurostar train. [R], ✕ in Business Premier and Standard Premier, 🍷 in Standard. Special fares payable. Minimum check-in time 30 minutes. Valid May 26 - Nov. 2.

♥ – *TGV Lyria* service. [R] 🍷. Special fares payable, three classes of service: Business 1ère, Standard 1ère and Standard. Valid Dec. 9 - July 5. At-seat meal service in Business 1ère.

⊗ – Compulsory reservation for international journeys. Supplement payable for international journeys and for internal journeys within Italy.

LONDON - PARIS - LAUSANNE - BRIG 42

train type	*TGV*	*IR*	☆	☆	*TGV*	*IR*	*TGV*		☆	*TGV*	*IR*	☆	*TGV*	*IR*	☆	*TGV*	*IR*			
train number	**9261**	**1817**	**9002**	**9004**	**9269**	**1825**	**9773**		**9014**	**9271**	**1829**	**9022**	**9273**	**1833**	**9028**	**9277**	**1837**			
notes	♥ 🍷		⑥	①–⑤ h	♥ 🍷		♥ 🍷 ①–④			♥ 🍷 †			♥ 🍷			♥ 🍷				
London St Pancras **10** d.	...	...	0618	0701	...	...	...	...	0924	...	...	1131	...	...	1331	...	...	...	...	...
Paris Nord **10** a.	...	...	0947	1017	...	...	...	...	1247	...	...	1447	...	...	1647	...	...	...	...	...
Paris Gare de Lyon d.	0757	...	...	...	1157	...	1211	...	...	1357	...	...	1557	...	...	1757	...	...	...	...
Dijon d.	0934	...	...	...	1336	...	|	...	...	1534	...	...	1734	...	...	1934	...	...	...	...
Frasne a.	1042	...	...	...	1442	...	◧	...	...	1642	...	...	1842	...	...	2042	...	...	...	...
Vallorbe 🏛 a.	1057	...	...	...	1457	...	|	...	...	1657	...	...	1857	...	...	2057	...	...	...	...
Lausanne a.	1137	...	...	...	1537	...	1615	...	...	1737	...	...	1937	...	...	2137	...	...	...	...
Lausanne d.	...	1150	...	...	...	1550	...	...	...	...	1750	...	...	1950	...	...	2150	...	...	...
Montreux a.	...	1211	...	...	...	1611	...	...	...	...	1811	...	...	2011	...	...	2211	...	...	...
Aigle a.	...	1222	...	...	...	1622	...	...	...	...	1822	...	...	2022	...	...	2222	...	...	...
Martigny a.	...	1242	...	...	...	1642	...	...	...	...	1842	...	...	2042	...	...	2243	...	...	...
Sion a.	...	1257	...	...	...	1657	...	...	...	...	1857	...	...	2057	...	...	2257	...	...	...
Sierre a.	...	1308	...	...	...	1708	...	...	...	...	1908	...	...	2108	...	...	2308	...	...	...
Visp a.	...	1324	...	...	...	1724	...	...	...	...	1924	...	...	2124	...	...	2326	...	...	...
Brig a.	...	1332	...	...	...	1732	...	...	...	...	1932	...	...	2132	...	...	2334	...	...	...

train type	*IR*	*TGV*	☆	*IR*	*IR*	*TGV*	☆	*IR*	*IR*	*EC*	*TGV*	☆	☆	*IR*	*EC*	*TGV*	*TGV*	*IR*	*TGV*	
train number	**1804**	**9260**	**9027**	**1706**	**1706**	**9264**	**9039**	**1714**	**1714**	**32**	**9268**	**9051**	**9055**	**1722**	**34**	**9270**	**9778**	**1726**	**9272**	
notes		♥ 🍷 ①–⑥		Ⓐ	Ⓒ	♥ 🍷		Ⓒ	Ⓐ	[R] 🍷 ⊗	♥ 🍷	Ⓑ			[R] 🍷 ⊗	♥ 🍷 ⑤⑦	♥ 🍷 ①–④		♥ 🍷	
Brig d.	0421	**Q**	...	0551	0557	...	...	0957	0958	1020	...	...	...	1357	1420	...	...	1557	...	...
Visp d.	0429	...	...	0559	0606	...	...	1006	1006	|	...	...	...	1406	|	...	...	1606	...	...
Sierre d.	0447	...	...	0617	0624	...	...	1024	1021	|	...	...	...	1421	|	...	...	1624	...	...
Sion d.	0459	...	...	0628	0635	...	...	1035	1032	1047	...	...	...	1432	1447	...	...	1635	...	...
Martigny d.	0513	...	...	0642	0649	...	...	1048	1046	|	...	...	...	1446	|	...	...	1649	...	...
Aigle d.	0536	...	...	0705	0709	...	...	1105	1104	|	...	...	...	1504	|	...	...	1709	...	...
Montreux d.	0547	...	...	0716	0720	...	...	1116	1115	1121	...	...	...	1515	1521	...	...	1720	...	...
Lausanne a.	0610	...	...	0739	0743	...	...	1138	1138	1142	...	...	...	1538	1542	...	...	1743	...	...
Lausanne d.	...	0623	...	...	...	0823	...	...	...	...	1223	...	...	...	...	1623	1639	...	1823	...
Vallorbe 🏛 d.	...	0700	...	...	...	0900	...	...	...	...	1300	...	...	...	...	1700	|	...	1900	...
Frasne a.	...	0713	...	...	...	0914	...	...	...	...	1314	...	...	...	...	1714	◧	...	1914	...
Dijon a.	...	0823	...	...	...	1023	...	...	...	...	1423	...	...	...	...	1823	|	...	2023	...
Paris Gare de Lyon a.	...	1003	...	...	...	1203	...	...	...	...	1603	...	...	...	...	2003	2049	...	2203	...
Paris Nord **10** d.	...	...	1213	...	...	...	1513	...	...	...	...	1813	1913	...	...	...	...	...	...	...
London St Pancras **10** a.	...	...	1330	...	...	...	1639	...	...	...	...	1939	2039	...	...	...	...	...	...	...

Q – Apr. 1 - July 5.

h – Not Aug. 26.

◧ – Via Genève.

◇ – Stopping train. 2nd class only.

♥ – *TGV Lyria* service. [R] 🍷. Special fares payable, three classes of service: business 1ère, standard 1ère and standard. Valid Dec. 9 - July 5. At-seat meal service in first class.

⊗ – Compulsory reservation for international journeys. Supplement payable for international journeys and for internal journeys within Italy.

☆ – Eurostar train. [R], ✕ in Business Premier and Standard Premier, 🍷 in Standard. Minimum check-in time 30 minutes. Special fares payable. Special fares payable. Additional Eurostar services are available, see Table **10**. Valid May 26 - Nov. 2.

44 LONDON - PARIS - TORINO - MILANO - VENEZIA and ROMA

train type		TGV	FR	FR	IC	FR		☆	TGV	FR		FR	FR	FB
train number		9241	9569	9733	597	9737		9080	9245	9755		9655	9557	8829
notes		[R] ✕	9571	[R] 🍷	ϟ	[R] 🍷			[R] ✕	[R] 🍷		[R] ✕	[R] ✕	[R] ✕
notes		♣	[R] ✕ ϟ	ϟ		ϟ		①–⑤ A	♣	ϟ		ϟ	ϟ	ϟ
London St Pancras **10 12**	d.	...	...	...	...	...	...	0540	...	...	...	...	...	...
Paris Nord **10**	a.	...	...	...	...	...	...	0917	...	...	...	...	...	...
Paris Gare de Lyon	d.	0629	...	...	...	...	...	...	1041x	...	...	...	...	...
Lyon Part Dieu	d.	0831	...	...	...	...	...	...	|	...	...	...	...	...
Lyon St Exupéry TGV ✈	d.	|	...	...	...	...	...	...	1238z	...	...	...	...	...
Chambéry	d.	0945	...	...	...	...	...	...	1345	...	...	...	...	...
Modane 🏛	d.	1055	...	...	...	...	...	...	1455	...	...	...	...	...
Oulx ▲	a.	1123	...	...	...	...	...	...	1523	...	...	...	...	...
Torino Porta Susa §	a.	1224	1320	...	...	1415	...	...	1620	...	...	1800	1822	...
Torino Porta Nuova §	a.	|	|	...	...	|	1330	...	|	...	1730	|	|	...
Novara	a.	|	|	...	...	|	|	...	1711	...	|	|	|	...
Milano Porta Garibaldi	a.	1350	1418d	...	...	|	|	...	1750	...	|	|	|	...
Milano Centrale	a.	...	|	...	...	1502	|	...	...	...	|	1850	1910	...
Milano Centrale	d.	...	|	1445	1448	1515	|	...	...	1915	|	1900	1920	1935
Alessandria	a.	...	|	|	|	|	1429	...	...	|	1829	|	|	|
Genova Piazza Principe	a.	...	|	|	|	|	1530	...	...	|	1930	|	|	|
Brescia	a.	...	|	1521	|	1551	...	...	...	|	...	|	|	|
Verona Porta Nuova	a.	...	|	1558	|	1628	...	...	...	|	...	|	|	|
Vicenza	a.	...	|	1624	|	1654	...	...	...	|	...	|	|	|
Padova	a.	...	|	1642	|	1712	...	...	...	|	...	|	|	|
Venezia Mestre	a.	...	|	1658	|	1728	...	...	...	|	...	|	|	|
Venezia Santa Lucia	a.	...	|	1710	|	...	...	...	...	1951	...	|	|	|
Piacenza	a.	...	|	...	1543	...	...	...	...	2028	...	|	|	2018
Parma	a.	...	|	...	1614	...	...	...	...	2054	...	|	|	2044
Reggio Emilia	a.	...	1509	...	1631	...	...	...	...	2112	...	|	|	2058
Modena	a.	...	|	...	1648	...	...	...	...	2128	...	|	|	2113
Bologna Centrale	a.	...	1537	...	1714	...	...	...	...	2140	...	|	2022	2138
Firenze SMN	a.	...	1615	...	1817v	...	...	...	...	...	...	|	2059	...
Roma Tiburtina	a.	...	1743	...	2112	...	...	...	...	...	...	|	2228	...
Roma Termini	a.	...	|	...	|	...	...	...	...	...	...	2159	2240	...
Napoli Centrale	a.	...	1855	...	2329	...	...	...	...	...	...	2320	...	...
Salerno	a.	...	1942	...	...	...	...	...	...	...	...	...	...	...

train type		☆		TGV		ICN	ICN	☆	EN	FR ϟ	IC	EC	IC	ITA	FR ϟ	ITA
train number		9014	17909	9249		797	799	9032	221	9503	583	141	505	9965	9509	9907
notes			83237	[R] ✕		[R] ϟ	[R] ϟ			9505	[R] 🍷	[R] 🍷	[R] 🍷	[R] ✕	[R] 🍷	[R] ✕
notes				♣		H	E		V	[R] 🍷 ⚒	ϟ	ϟ	ϟ	ϟ		ϟ
London St Pancras **10 12**	d.	0924	...	...	...	...	...	1422	...	...	...	...	...	...	...	...
Paris Nord **10**	a.	1247	...	...	...	...	...	1747	...	...	...	...	...	...	...	...
Paris Gare de Lyon	d.	...	...	1441	...	...	...	...	1915	...	...	...	...	...	...	...
Dijon	d.	...	...	|	...	...	...	...	2152	...	...	...	...	...	...	...
Lyon Part Dieu	d.	...	1550	|	...	...	...	...	|	...	...	...	...	...	...	...
Lyon St Exupéry TGV ✈	d.	...	|	1637	...	...	...	...	|	...	...	...	...	...	...	...
Chambéry	d.	...	1716	1744	...	...	...	...	|	...	...	...	...	...	...	...
Modane 🏛	d.	...	...	1855	...	...	...	...	⊙	...	...	...	...	...	...	...
Oulx ▲	a.	...	...	1923	...	...	...	...	|	...	...	...	...	...	...	...
Torino Porta Susa §	a.	...	...	2018	...	2140	...	...	|	...	...	...	...	...	...	...
Torino Porta Nuova §	a.	...	...	|	2130	|	2155	...	|	...	...	...	...	...	...	...
Novara	a.	...	...	|	|	2238d	|	...	|	...	...	...	...	...	...	...
Milano Porta Garibaldi	a.	...	...	2150	|	2317d	|	...	|	...	...	...	...	...	...	...
Milano Centrale	a.	...	...	...	|	|	|	...	0600	...	...	...	...	...	...	...
Milano Centrale	d.	...	...	...	|	|	|	...	0620	0615	0650	0705	...	0715	0720	0735
Alessandria	a.	...	...	...	2229	|	2257	...	|	|	|	|	...	|	|	|
Genova Piazza Principe	a.	...	...	...	2330	|	2350	...	|	|	|	0840	0851	|	|	|
Brescia	a.	...	...	...	...	|	|	...	0716	|	|	...	|	|	|	|
Verona Porta Nuova	a.	...	...	...	...	|	|	...	0753	|	|	...	|	|	|	|
Vicenza	a.	...	...	...	...	|	|	...	0842	|	|	...	|	|	|	|
Padova	a.	...	...	...	...	|	|	...	0903	|	|	...	|	|	|	|
Venezia Mestre	a.	...	...	...	...	|	|	...	0923	|	|	...	|	|	|	|
Venezia Santa Lucia	a.	...	...	...	...	|	|	...	0935	|	|	...	|	|	|	|
Piacenza	a.	...	...	...	...	0008	|	...	...	|	0738	...	|	|	|	|
Parma	a.	...	...	...	...	0059	|	...	...	|	0809	...	|	|	|	|
Reggio Emilia	a.	...	...	...	...	|	|	...	...	0651	0828	...	|	|	|	0821
Modena	a.	...	...	...	...	|	|	...	...	|	0846	...	|	|	|	|
Bologna Centrale	a.	...	...	...	...	0215	|	...	...	0722	0914	...	|	|	0822	0847
Firenze SMN	a.	...	...	...	...	0407t	|	...	...	0759	1011v	...	|	|	0859	0925
Roma Tiburtina	a.	...	...	...	...	0717	|	...	...	0946	1321	...	1420o	1004	1027	1053
Roma Termini	a.	...	...	...	...	|	0543o	...	...	0955c	|	...	1433	1014	1040c	1105c
Napoli Centrale	a.	...	...	...	...	0938	0817	...	...	1110	1529	...	...	...	1200	1225
Salerno	a.	...	...	...	...	1032	0912	...	...	1201	...	...	...	...	...	...

A – ①–⑤ May 26 - July 27 and Sept. 1 - Nov. 2.

E – 🛏 1, 2 cl., 🛌 2 cl., [2] Torino - Roma - Napoli - Salerno.

H – 🛏 1, 2 cl., 🛌 2 cl. (4 berth), [2] Torino - Milano - Salerno.

V – *Thello* - 🛏 1, 2 cl. (1, 2, 3 berth), 🛌 2 cl. (4, 6 berth), ✕ Paris - Milano - Venezia. For use by passengers making international journeys only. Special fares payable.

c – Depart 9 - 19 minutes later.

d – Departure time.

o – Roma **Ostiense**.

t – Firenze **Campo di Marte**.

v – Firenze **Rifredi**.

x – 1035, 1037, 1045 on certain dates.

z – 1233, 1240, 1244 on certain dates.

ϟ – Supplement payable.

♣ – *TGV* France-Italy service. [R] ✕ Special fares payable.

▲ – Station for the resorts of Cesana, Claviere and Sestriere.

☆ – Eurostar train. [R], ✕ in Business Premier and Standard Premier, 🍷 in Standard. Special fares payable. Minimum check-in time 30 minutes. Additional Eurostar services are available, see Table **10**. Valid May 26 - Nov. 2.

⊙ – Frontier / ticketing points 🏛 are Vallorbe and Domodossola. Ticket point for Domodossola is **Iselle**.

§ – Local train services (Tables **585**, **586**) and metro services run between Torino **Porta Susa** and Torino **Porta Nuova**.

ROMA and VENEZIA - MILANO - TORINO - PARIS - LONDON 44

train type		TGV			☆			ICN	ICN	IC	TGV		☆	☆						
train number		9240	83262	18550	9039			798	796	500	9244	18556	9051	9055						
notes		🅁✕						🅁⟋	🅁⟋	⟋	🅁✕	83472								
notes		♣	Ⓒ	Ⓐ				H	E	⚒	♣		Ⓑ							
											y									
Salerno d.	...	...	...	...	...	...	...	2038	2052	...	...	...	...	...	...	...	...	...	...	...
Napoli Centrale d.	...	...	...	...	...	...	...	2131	2146	...	...	...	...	...	...	...	...	...	...	...
Roma Termini d.	...	...	...	...	...	...	...	|	0011o	...	...	...	...	...	...	...	...	...	...	...
Roma Tiburtina d.	...	...	...	...	...	...	...	2353	|	...	...	...	...	...	...	...	...	...	...	...
Firenze SMN d.	...	...	...	...	...	...	...	0257t	|	...	...	...	...	...	...	...	...	...	...	...
Bologna Centrale d.	...	...	...	...	...	...	...	0418	|	...	...	...	...	...	...	...	...	...	...	...
Modena d.	...	...	...	...	...	...	...	|	|	...	...	...	...	...	...	...	...	...	...	...
Reggio Emilia d.	...	...	...	...	...	...	...	|	|	...	...	...	...	...	...	...	...	...	...	...
Parma d.	...	...	...	...	...	...	...	0521	|	...	...	...	...	...	...	...	...	...	...	...
Piacenza d.	...	...	...	...	...	...	...	0602	|	...	...	...	...	...	...	...	...	...	...	...
Venezia Santa Lucia d.	...	...	...	...	...	...	...	|	|	...	...	...	...	...	...	...	...	...	...	...
Venezia Mestre d.	...	...	...	...	...	...	...	|	|	...	...	...	...	...	...	...	...	...	...	...
Padova d.	...	...	...	...	...	...	...	|	|	...	...	...	...	...	...	...	...	...	...	...
Vicenza d.	...	...	...	...	...	...	...	|	|	...	...	...	...	...	...	...	...	...	...	...
Verona Porta Nuova d.	...	...	...	...	...	...	...	|	|	...	...	...	...	...	...	...	...	...	...	...
Brescia d.	...	...	...	...	...	...	...	|	|	...	...	...	...	...	...	...	...	...	...	...
Genova Piazza Principe d.	...	...	...	...	...	...	...	|	0606	0708	...	...	...	...	...	...	...	...	...	...
Alessandria d.	...	...	...	...	...	...	...	|	0657	0757	...	...	...	...	...	...	...	...	...	...
Milano Centrale a.	...	...	...	...	...	...	...	|	|	|	...	...	...	...	...	...	...	...	...	...
Milano Centrale d.	...	...	...	...	...	...	...	|	|	|	...	...	...	...	...	...	...	...	...	...
Milano Porta Garibaldi d.	...	0600	...	...	...	...	...	0711a	|	|	0845	...	...	...	...	...	...	...	...	...
Novara d.	...	0631	...	...	...	...	...	0805	|	|	|	...	...	...	...	...	...	...	...	...
Torino Porta Nuova § d.	...	|	...	...	...	...	...	|	0810	0855	|	...	...	...	...	...	...	...	...	...
Torino Porta Susa § d.	...	0739	...	...	...	...	...	0910	...	...	1011	...	...	...	...	...	...	...	...	...
Oulx ▲ d.	...	0836	...	...	...	...	...	...	...	...	1113	...	...	...	...	...	...	...	...	...
Modane 🏛 a.	...	0905	...	...	...	...	...	...	...	...	1144	...	...	...	...	...	...	...	...	...
Chambéry a.	...	1014	1035	1207	...	...	...	...	...	...	1250	1344	...	...	...	...	...	...	...	...
Lyon St Exupéry TGV ✈ a.	...	1123	|	|	...	...	...	...	...	...	|	|	...	...	...	...	...	...	...	...
Lyon Part Dieu a.	...	|	1210	1326	...	...	...	...	...	...	|	1510	...	...	...	...	...	...	...	...
Paris Gare de Lyon a.	...	1319	...	...	...	...	...	...	...	...	1611	...	...	...	...	...	...	...	...	...
Paris Nord **10** d.	...	...	...	...	1513	...	...	...	...	...	...	...	1813	1913	...	...	...	...	...	...
London St Pancras **10 12** a.	...	...	...	...	1639	...	...	...	...	...	...	...	1939	2039	...	...	...	...	...	...

train type		FR	FB		ITA	FR	TGV			FB	IC	FR	IC	ITA	FR	EN	☆	☆		
train number		9724	8810		9920	9622	9248			8826	728	9552	1534	9925	9654	220	9023	9025		
notes		🅁🍸	🅁🍸		🅁✕	🅁✕	🅁✕			🅁✕	🅁🍸	🅁✕	684	🅁✕	🅁✕					
notes		⟋	⟋		⟋	⟋	♣			⟋	⟋	⟋	🅁⟋	⟋	⟋	V	①–⑥	⑦		
																	h	k		
Salerno d.	...	...	...	...	...	...	...	...	...	...	1536	...	...	...	...	...	...	...	...	...
Napoli Centrale d.	...	...	...	...	0925	0940	...	...	...	...	1615	1700	...	1725	1740	...	...	...	...	...
Roma Termini d.	...	...	...	...	1045	1100	...	...	...	...	...	1820	...	1845	1900	...	...	...	...	...
Roma Tiburtina d.	...	...	...	...	1055	|	...	...	...	...	...	1829	...	1855	|	...	...	...	...	...
Firenze SMN d.	...	...	...	...	1225	|	...	...	...	...	...	2000	...	2025	|	...	...	...	...	...
Bologna Centrale d.	...	...	1118	...	1303	|	...	...	...	1918	...	2038	...	2103	|	...	...	...	...	...
Modena d.	...	...	1141	...	|	|	...	...	...	1941	...	|	...	|	|	...	...	...	...	...
Reggio Emilia d.	...	...	1154	...	1324	|	...	...	...	1954	...	|	...	2124	2116	...	...	...	...	...
Parma d.	...	...	1210	...	|	|	...	...	...	2010	...	|	...	|	|	...	...	...	...	...
Piacenza d.	...	...	1241	...	|	|	...	...	...	2041	...	|	...	|	|	...	...	...	...	...
Venezia Santa Lucia d.	...	1050	|	...	|	|	...	...	...	|	...	|	...	|	|	1920	...	...	...	...
Venezia Mestre d.	...	1102	|	...	|	|	...	...	...	|	...	|	...	|	|	1932	...	...	...	...
Padova d.	...	1118	|	...	|	|	...	...	...	|	...	|	...	|	|	1948	...	...	...	...
Vicenza d.	...	1135	|	...	|	|	...	...	...	|	...	|	...	|	|	2008	...	...	...	...
Verona Porta Nuova d.	...	1202	|	...	|	|	...	...	...	|	...	|	...	|	|	2050	...	...	...	...
Brescia d.	...	1239	|	...	|	|	...	...	...	|	...	|	...	|	|	2134	...	...	...	...
Genova Piazza Principe d.	...	|	|	1330	|	|	...	...	...	|	...	|	2018	|	|	|	...	...	...	...
Alessandria d.	...	|	|	1431	|	|	...	...	...	|	...	|	|	|	|	|	...	...	...	...
Milano Centrale a.	...	1315	1325	|	1415	1355	...	...	...	2125	...	2140	2150	2215	2202	2240	...	...	...	...
Milano Centrale d.	...	...	...	|	1428	1405	...	...	...	...	...	...	...	...	...	2310	...	...	...	...
Milano Porta Garibaldi d.	...	...	...	|	|	|	1440	...	...	...	...	...	...	...	...	|	...	...	...	...
Novara d.	...	...	...	|	|	|	|	...	...	...	...	...	...	...	...	|	...	...	...	...
Torino Porta Nuova § d.	...	...	...	1530	|	|	|	...	...	...	...	...	...	...	...	|	...	...	...	...
Torino Porta Susa § d.	...	...	...	...	1516	1452	1611	...	...	...	...	...	...	...	...	|	...	...	...	...
Oulx ▲ d.	...	...	...	...	...	...	1716	...	...	...	...	...	...	...	...	⊙	...	...	...	...
Modane 🏛 a.	...	...	...	...	...	...	1745	...	...	...	...	...	...	...	...	|	...	...	...	...
Chambéry a.	...	...	...	...	...	...	1851	...	...	...	...	...	...	...	...	|	...	...	...	...
Lyon St Exupéry TGV ✈ a.	...	...	...	...	...	...	|	...	...	...	...	...	...	...	...	|	...	...	...	...
Lyon Part Dieu a.	...	...	...	...	...	...	2028	...	...	...	...	...	...	...	...	|	...	...	...	...
Dijon a.	...	...	...	...	...	...	|	...	...	...	...	...	...	...	...	0634	...	...	...	...
Paris Gare de Lyon a.	...	...	...	...	...	...	2231f	...	...	...	...	...	...	...	...	0937	...	...	...	...
Paris Nord **10** d.	...	...	...	...	...	...	...	...	...	...	...	...	...	...	...	...	1113	1128	...	...
London St Pancras **10 12** a.	...	...	...	...	...	...	...	...	...	...	...	...	...	...	...	...	1239	1309	...	...

E – 🛏 1, 2 cl., 🛌 2 cl., (2.) Salerno - Napoli - Roma - Torino.

H – 🛏 1, 2 cl., 🛌 2 cl. (4 berth), (2.) Salerno - Torino.

V – *Thello* – 🛏 1, 2 cl. (1, 2, 3 berth), 🛌 2 cl. (4, 6 berth), ✕ Venezia - Milano - Paris. For use by passengers making international journeys only. Special fares payable.

a – Arrival time.

f – 2237 on certain dates.

h – Not Aug. 26.

k – Also Aug. 26.

o – Roma **Ostiense**.

t – Firenze **Campo di Marte**.

y – Calls at Aix les Bains at 1306, Bourg-en-Bresse 1412, Mâcon Loché TGV 1433.

⟋ – Supplement payable.

♣ – *TGV* France-Italy service. 🅁 ✕ Special fares payable.

▲ – Station for the resorts of Cesana, Claviere and Sestriere.

☆ – Eurostar train. 🅁, ✕ in Business Premier and Standard Premier, 🍸 in Standard. Minimum check-in time 30 minutes. Special fares payable. Additional Eurostar services are available, see Table **10**. Valid May 26 - Nov. 2.

⊙ – Frontier / ticketing points 🏛 are Vallorbe and Domodossola. Ticket point for Domodossola is **Iselle**.

§ – Local train services (Tables **585, 586**) and metro services run between Torino **Porta Susa** and Torino **Porta Nuova**.

45 LONDON - PARIS/MADRID - LISBOA and PORTO

train type / number	☆	TGV	Hotel	Hotel	IR
train number	**9008**	**8541**	**313**	**332**	**823**
notes	①–⑥	[R] ⚡	[R] 🍷	[R] 🍷	[R] 🍷
			A	**L**	
London St Pancras 10 .... d.	0755**f**	...	...	...	...
Paris Nord 10 .... a.	1117	...	...	...	...
Paris Montparnasse .... d.	...	1248	...	...	...
Bordeaux St Jean .... d.	...	1502	...	...	...
Biarritz .... d.	...	1704	...	...	...
Hendaye .... a.	...	1735	1835	...	...
Irún 🏛 .... a.	...	...	1845	...	...
San Sebastián / Donostia .... a.	...	...	1908	...	...
Vitoria / Gasteiz .... a.	...	...	2045	...	...
Miranda de Ebro .... a.	...	...	2107	...	...
Burgos Rosa de Lima .... a.	...	...	2158	...	...
Valladolid Campo Grande .... a.	...	...	2308	...	...
Madrid Chamartín .... d.	...	...	|	2143	...
Ávila .... d.	...	...	|	2311	...
Medina del Campo .... a.	...	...	2351	2355	...
Salamanca .... a.	...	...	0057	0057	...
Ciudad Rodrigo .... a.	...	...	0206	0206	...
Fuentes d'Oñoro .... 🏛 ES d.	...	...	0230	0230	...
Vilar Formoso .... 🏛 PT d.	...	...	0150	0150	...
Guarda .... a.	...	...	0221	0221	...
Mangualde .... a.	...	...	0323	0323	...
Coimbra-B .... a.	...	...	0445	0445	0510
Pombal .... a.	...	...	0521	0521	|
Entroncamento .... a.	...	...	0605	0605	|
Lisboa Oriente .... a.	...	...	0720	0720	|
Lisboa Santa Apolónia .... a.	...	...	0730	0730	|
Aveiro .... a.	...	...	...	...	0553
Porto Campanhã .... a.	...	...	...	...	0644

train type / number	IR	Hotel	Hotel	TGV	☆
train number	**822**	**335**	**310**	**8540**	**9059**
notes	[R] 🍷	[R] 🍷	[R] 🍷	[R] ⚡	
		L	**A**		**M**
Porto Campanhã .... d.	2153	...	...	...	...
Aveiro .... d.	2243	...	...	...	...
Lisboa Santa Apolónia .... d.	|	2125	2125	...	...
Lisboa Oriente .... d.	|	2134	2134	...	...
Entroncamento .... d.	|	2229	2229	...	...
Pombal .... d.	|	2306	2306	...	...
Coimbra-B .... d.	2325	2333	2333	...	...
Mangualde .... d.	...	0046	0046	...	...
Guarda .... d.	...	0145	0145	...	...
Vilar Formoso .... 🏛 PT d.	...	0235	0235	...	...
Fuentes d'Oñoro .... 🏛 ES d.	...	0340	0340	...	...
Ciudad Rodrigo .... d.	...	0359	0359	...	...
Salamanca .... d.	...	0456	0456	...	...
Medina del Campo .... d.	...	0618	0600	...	...
Ávila .... a.	...	0705	|	...	...
Madrid Chamartín .... a.	...	0840	|	...	...
Valladolid Campo Grande .... d.	...	...	0635	...	...
Burgos Rosa de Lima .... d.	...	...	0748	...	...
Miranda de Ebro .... d.	...	...	0848	...	...
Vitoria / Gasteiz .... d.	...	...	0912	...	...
San Sebastián / Donostia .... d.	...	...	1055	...	...
Irún .... a.	...	...	1123	...	...
Hendaye 🏛 .... a.	...	...	1133	1312	...
Biarritz .... a.	...	...	...	1349	...
Bordeaux St Jean .... a.	...	...	...	1558	...
Paris Montparnasse .... a.	...	...	...	1813	...
Paris Nord 10 .... d.	...	...	...	...	2013
London St Pancras 10 .... a.	...	...	...	...	2149

46 MADRID - LISBOA

For train services see Table 45	🚌	🚌	🚌	
	C	C	C	
		①–⑤		
Madrid Estación Sur ❖ .... d.	1000	1430	2100	...
Cáceres .... d.	|	1915	|	...
Badajoz ⊠ .... 🏛 ES d.	1530	2030	0230	...
Elvas .... 🏛 PT d.	|	|	|	...
Lisboa Oriente .... a.	1700	2200	0400	...

For train services see Table 45	🚌	🚌	🚌	
	C	C	C	
		①–⑤		
Lisboa Oriente .... d.	0915	1215	2015	...
Elvas .... 🏛 PT d.	|	|	|	...
Badajoz ⊠ .... 🏛 ES d.	1330	1630	0015	...
Cáceres .... a.	|	1800	|	...
Madrid Estación Sur ❖ .... a.	1840	2155	0530	...

NOTES FOR TABLES 45 AND 46

A – SUREX / SUD EXPRESSO *Trenhotel* – 🛏 *Gran Clase / Gran Classe* (1, 2 berths), 🛏 *Preferente* (1, 2 berths), 🛏 *Turista* (4 berths), ▭2 🍷 Hendaye (**312**) - Vilar Formoso (**313**) - Lisboa and Lisboa (**310**) - Vilar Formoso (**311**) - Hendaye.

C – 🚌 operated by Avanza, additional buses operate, rail tickets not valid; www.avanzabus.com

L – LUSITANIA *Hotel Train* – 🛏 *Gran Clase / Gran Classe* (1, 2 berths), 🛏 *Preferente* (1, 2 berths), 🛏 *Turista* (4 berths), ▭2 🍷 [R] Madrid (**332/3**) - Medina del Campo (**312**) - Lisboa and Lisboa (**310**) - Medina del Campo (**330/5**) - Madrid. Special fares apply.

M – ①②③④⑥ (also Nov. 1; not Aug. 26).

f – 0752 on ⑥.

⚡ – Supplement payable.

ES – Spain (Central European Time).

PT – Portugal (West European Time).

❖ – Madrid south bus station close to Méndez Álvaro metro (see Madrid city plan on page 30).

⊠ – Badajoz railway station is 1 km north of Badajoz city centre and Badajoz bus station is 2.5 km south of Badajoz city centre.

☆ – Eurostar train. [R], ✕ in Business Premier and Standard Premier, 🍷 in Standard. Special fares payable. Minimum check-in time 30 minutes. Additional Eurostar services are available, see Table **10**. Valid Dec. 9 - May 25.

47 PARIS - HENDAYE / IRÚN - MADRID

train type / number	TGV	TGV	MD	RE	Alvia	MD		
train number	**8571**	**8531**	**18014**	**18318**	**4166**	**18310**		
notes	[R] ⚡	[R] ⚡	2	2	🍷	2		
	①–⑥	⑤⑥						
Paris Montparnasse .... d.	0652	0752	...	...	...	...	...	...
Paris Austerlitz .... d.	|	|	...	...	...	...	...	...
Les Aubrais-Orléans .... d.	|	|	...	...	...	...	...	...
Bordeaux St Jean .... d.	0856	1002	...	...	...	...	...	...
Biarritz .... d.	*1106***z**	1204	...	...	...	...	...	...
Hendaye .... a.	*1149***z**	1235	...	...	...	...	...	...
Irún 🏛 .... a.	...	...	≋	...	≋	...	...	...
San Sebastián / Donostia .... a.	...	...	1404	...	1633	...	...	...
Vitoria / Gasteiz .... a.	...	...	1555	...	1807	...	...	...
Miranda de Ebro .... a.	...	...	1616	...	1829	...	...	...
Burgos Rosa de Lima .... a.	...	...	1713	...	1931	...	...	...
Valladolid Campo Grande .... a.	...	...	1844	1905	2048	2135	...	...
Medina del Campo .... a.	...	...	1911	1932	|	2209	...	...
Salamanca .... a.	...	...	|	2021	|	2252	...	...
Ávila .... d.	...	...	1958	...	|	...	...	...
Madrid Chamartín .... d.	...	...	2201	...	2206	...	...	...

train type / number		RE	Alvia	TGV	TGV			
train number		**18302**	**4087**	**8544**	**8550**			
notes		2	🍷	[R] ⚡	[R] ⚡			
				Ⓑ				
Madrid Chamartín .... d.	...	...	0800	...	...	...	...	...
Ávila .... d.	...	...	|	...	...	...	...	...
Salamanca .... d.	...	0712	|	...	...	...	...	...
Medina del Campo .... d.	...	0802	|	...	...	...	...	...
Valladolid Campo Grande .... d.	...	0830	0918	...	...	...	...	...
Burgos Rosa de Lima .... d.	...	...	1028	...	...	...	...	...
Miranda de Ebro .... d.	...	...	1128	...	...	...	...	...
Vitoria / Gasteiz .... d.	...	...	1151	...	...	...	...	...
San Sebastián / Donostia .... d.	...	...	1324	...	...	...	...	...
Irún .... a.	...	...	≋	...	...	...	...	...
Hendaye 🏛 .... a.	...	...	...	1514	1812	...	...	...
Biarritz .... a.	...	...	...	1551	1849	...	...	...
Bordeaux St Jean .... a.	...	...	...	1758	2058	...	...	...
Les Aubrais-Orléans .... a.	...	...	...	|	|	...	...	...
Paris Austerlitz .... a.	...	...	...	|	|	...	...	...
Paris Montparnasse .... a.	...	...	...	2008	2308	...	...	...

z – Change at Dax (arr. 1012 / dep. 1021, Table **305**).

⚡ – Supplement payable.

Alvia – [R] 🍷 ⚡.

≋ – Engineering work between Irún and San Sebastián / Donostia. No *Alvia* or *MD* services. Passengers are advised to travel on the EuskoTren (narrow-gauge) service between Hendaye and San Sebastián / Donostia, see Table **689**.

48 FRANKFURT - STRASBOURG - LYON - MARSEILLE

train type		ICE	TGV	TGV	TGV	ICE	TGV	TGV		
train number		**9568**	**9881**	**9826**	**9826**	**107**	**9580**	**9836**		
							9581			
notes		[R] ★	[R]	①–⑤	⑥⑦					
		Ⓑ		[R] f	[R] t		[R] ★	[R]		
Köln Hbf .... d.	...	...	...	...	...	1255	...	...	...	...
Frankfurt (Main) Hbf .... d.	...	0658	...	...	...	|	1358	...	...	...
Mannheim .... d.	...	0739	...		...	1423	1439	...	...	...
Karlsruhe .... d.	...	0807	...	...	...	...	1512	...	...	...
Baden-Baden .... d.	...	|	...	...	...	...	1534	...	...	...
Strasbourg .... a.	...	0846	...	...	...	...	1601	...	...	...
Strasbourg .... d.	...	...	0903	...	...	...	1612	...	...	...
Mulhouse .... a.	...	...	0948	...	...	...	1705	...	...	...
Belfort Montbéliard TGV .... a.	...	...	1021	...	...	...	1733	...	...	...
Besançon TGV ⊖ .... a.	...	...	1044	...	...	...	1755	...	...	...
Chalon sur Saône .... a.	...	...	|	...	...	...	1854	...	...	...
Lyon Part Dieu .... a.	...	...	1256	1406	1406	...	1956	2010	...	...
Avignon TGV .... a.	...	...	|	1508	|	...	2108	|	...	...
Aix en Provence TGV .... a.	...	...	|	1537	1531	...	2136	|	...	...
Marseille St Charles .... a.	...	...	|	1555	1555	...	2150	|	...	...
Nimes .... a.	...	...	1433	...	...	...	...	2133	...	...
Montpellier .... a.	...	...	1503	...	...	...	...	2204**x**	...	...

train type	TGV	TGV	ICE		AVE	TGV	TGV	ICE	ICE	
train number	**9896**	**9582**	**106**		**9866**	**6882**	**9577**	**100**	**590**	
		9583								
notes	[R]	[R] ★			[R]	[R]	[R]			
							Ⓑ			
Montpellier .... d.	0630	...	...	...	...	1130	...	...	...	...
Nimes .... d.	0700	...	...	...	...	1359	...	...	...	...
Marseille St Charles .... d.	|	0809	...	...	1210	|	...	...	...	...
Aix en Provence TGV .... d.	|	0824	...	...	1224	|	...	...	...	...
Avignon TGV .... d.	|	0851	...	...	1252	|	...	...	...	...
Lyon Part Dieu .... d.	0820	1000	...	...	1354	1528	...	...	...	...
Chalon sur Saône .... d.	...	1105	...	...	...	|	...	...	...	...
Besançon TGV ⊖ .... d.	...	1203	...	...	...	1730	...	...	...	...
Belfort Montbéliard TGV .... d.	...	1226	...	...	...	1754	...	...	...	...
Mulhouse .... d.	...	1255	...	...	...	|	...	...	...	...
Strasbourg .... a.	...	1344	...	...	...	1857	...	...	...	...
Strasbourg .... d.	...	1355	...	...	...	...	1946	...	...	...
Baden-Baden .... a.	...	1422	...	...	...	...	|	...	...	...
Karlsruhe .... a.	...	1446	...	...	...	...	2025	2101	...	...
Mannheim .... a.	...	1518	1535	...	...	...	...	2124	2132	...
Frankfurt (Main) Hbf .... a.	...	1558	|	...	...	...	...	|	2208	...
Köln Hbf .... a.	...	...	1705	...	...	...	...	2305	...	...

f – Not June 10, Aug. 15, 16, Oct. 31, Nov. 1, 11.

t – Also June 10, Aug. 15, Nov. 11.

x – Subject to alteration from Sept. 30.

★ – *Alleo* ICE / TGV service. A DB / SNCF joint enterprise.

⊖ – Full name: Besançon Franche-Comté TGV.

OSLO, STOCKHOLM and KØBENHAVN - HAMBURG - BERLIN 50

train type / train number		*EC*		*EC*	*ICE*			*EC*						*EC*		*Sn*		*EC*	*ICE*			*EC*	
train number		**438**		**38**	**1513**			**436**		**1**		**1039**		**434**		**519**		**34**	**1517**			**232**	
notes	🚌	🍷		🍷	🍷		🚌	⑤⑥⑦		Ⓡ			🚌	🍷		①–⑤		🍷	🍷		🚌	🍷	
notes	**S**	**Sc**		**Qc**			**S**	**Sc**		**A**			**S**	**Sc**		**P**		**Qc**			**S**	**Sc**	
Stockholm Central d.	...	...	...	...	...	...	...	...	...	2309	...	...	...	...	...	0525	...	...	...	...	...	...	...
Göteborg d.	...	...	...	...	...	...	...	...	...	|	...	0655	...	...	...	|	...	...	...	...	...	...	...
Malmö C ⊡ d.	...	...	0653	...	...	...	...	...	...	0655	0713	0953	...	...	...	0954	1033	...	...	...	...	...	...
København H. ⊡ d.	0710	...	0728	0735	...	...	0910	...	...	...	0748	1028	1110	...	...	...	1108	1135	...	...	1310	...	...
Rødby Ferry ⛴ d.	0925	0936	...	0938	...	...	1125	1136	...	...	...	...	1325	1336	...	...	...	1338	...	...	1525	1536	...
Puttgarden ⛴ a.	...	1042	...	1036	...	...	...	1242	...	...	...	...	...	1442	...	...	...	1436	...	...	...	1642	...
Lübeck Hbf a.	...	1137	...	1137	...	...	...	1337	...	...	...	...	...	1537	...	...	...	1537	...	...	...	1737	...
Hamburg Hbf a.	...	1216	...	1216	1236	...	...	1416	...	...	...	...	...	1616	...	...	...	1616	1636	...	...	1816	...
Berlin Hbf a.	...	...	...	...	1419	...	...	...	...	...	...	...	...	...	...	...	...	...	1819	...	...	...	...

train type / train number	**391**			*EC*	*Sn*		*EC*	*ICE*	*ICE*		*EC*		*Sn*			*EN*	**395**		*Sn*	*Sn*		*IC*	
train number	**105**	**1063**		**432**	**527**		**32**	**907**	**905**		**230**		**529**	**1075**		**301**	**117**	**1105**	**541**	**541**		**430**	
notes	①–⑥		🚌	🍷			🍷	Ⓑ		🚌	🍷					①④⑥			Ⓑ	⑥		**1130**	
notes			**S**	**Sc**			**Qc**			**J**	**Jc**					**Gb**						**L**	
Oslo Sentral d.	...	...	...	...	...	...	...	...	...	...	...	...	...	...	...	...	1301	...	...	...	...	...	...
Stockholm Central d.	0701	...	...	...	0925	...	...	...	...	...	...	...	1025	...	...	...	|	...	1624	1624	...	...	...
Göteborg d.	1040	1055	...	...	|	...	...	...	...	...	...	...	|	1255	...	...	1650	1755	|	|	...	...	...
København H. ⊡ d.	...	|	...	...	|	...	...	...	...	...	...	...	|	|	1547	...	...	|	|	|	...	...	...
Malmö C ⊡ d.	...	1353	...	...	1354	1433	...	...	...	...	...	...	1454	1551	1626	1700	...	2053	2058	2054	2133	...	...
København H. ⊡ d.	...	1428	1510	...	...	1508	1535	...	...	1710	...	...	...	...	...	|	...	2128	2131	...	2208	2300	...
Rødby Ferry ⛴ d.	...	...	1725	1736	...	...	1738	...	...	1925	1936	...	...	...	...	|	...	...	...	...	...	|	...
Puttgarden ⛴ a.	...	...	...	1842	...	...	1836	...	...	...	2036	...	...	...	...	|	...	...	...	...	...	|	...
Lübeck Hbf a.	...	...	...	1937	...	...	1937	...	...	...	2137	...	...	...	...	|	...	...	...	...	...	|	...
Hamburg Hbf a.	...	...	...	2016	...	...	2016	2034	2151	...	2217	...	...	...	...	|	...	...	...	...	...	0540	...
Berlin Hbf a.	...	...	...	...	...	...	...	2223	2353	...	...	...	...	...	...	0645	...	...	...	...	...	...	...

train type		*EN*		*Sn*		**394**	*EC*			*IC*	*EC*	*EC*			*Sn*			*EC*					
train number		**300**		**528**	**1020**	**124**	**231**			**2070**	**33**	**33**			**544**	**1068**		**235**					
notes		③⑤⑦		①–⑥			❦🍷	🚌		🍷	❦🍷	❦🍷	🚌					❦🍷	🚌				
notes		**Cb**		**M**			**Hc**	**H**			**Qc**	**Sc**	**S**					**Sc**	**S**				
Berlin Hbf d.	...	1855	...	...	...	...	...	...	...	0706	...	...	...	...	...	...	...	...	...	...	...	...	...
Hamburg Hbf d.	...	|	...	...	...	...	0726	...	...	0911	0928	0928	...	...	...	...	...	1128	...	...	...	...	...
Lübeck Hbf d.	...	|	...	...	...	...	0806	...	...	...	1006	1006	...	...	...	...	...	1206	...	...	...	...	...
Puttgarden ⛴ d.	...	|	...	...	...	...	0908	...	...	...	1108	1108	...	...	...	...	...	1308	...	...	...	...	...
Rødby Ferry ⛴ a.	...	|	...	...	...	...	1013	1025	...	...	1213	1213	1225	...	...	...	...	1413	1425	...	...	...	...
København H. ⊡ d.	...	|	...	...	...	...	...	1240	...	...	1426	...	1440	1447	...	1527	...	...	1640	...	...	...	...
Malmö C ⊡ d.	...	0725	0733	0810	0808	...	...	...	...	...	...	...	...	1526	1604	1608	...	...	...	...	...	...	...
København H. ⊡ d.	...	...	0808	|	|	...	...	...	...	...	...	...	...	...	|	|	...	...	...	...	...	...	...
Göteborg a.	...	...	...	|	1105	1300	...	...	...	...	...	...	...	...	|	1905	...	...	...	...	...	...	...
Stockholm Central a.	...	...	...	1234	...	|	...	...	...	...	...	...	...	...	2034	...	...	...	...	...	...	...	...
Oslo Sentral a.	...	...	...	...	...	1652	...	...	...	...	...	...	...	...	...	...	...	...	...	...	...	...	...

train type / train number	*ICE*	*EC*	*EC*							*EC*			*ICE*	*EC*	*EC*				*IC*			*Sn*	
train number	**696**	**35**	**35**			**1092**		**2**		**37**			**800**	**39**	**39**				**431**		**1020**	**530**	
notes	🍷	❦🍷	❦🍷	🚌				Ⓡ		❦🍷	🚌		🍷	❦	❦🍷	🚌			**1131**				
notes		**Qc**	**Sc**	**S**				**F**		**Sc**	**S**			**Qc**	**Sc**	**S**			**K**				
Berlin Hbf d.	1039	...	...	...	...	...	...	...	...	...	...	...	1439	...	...	...	...	...	...	...	...	...	...
Hamburg Hbf d.	1221	1328	1328	...	...	...	...	...	...	1528	...	...	1621	1728	1728	...	...	...	2342	...	...	...	...
Lübeck Hbf d.	...	1406	1406	...	...	...	...	...	...	1606	...	...	...	1806	1806	...	...	...	|	...	...	...	...
Puttgarden ⛴ d.	...	1508	1508	...	...	...	...	...	...	1708	...	...	...	1908	1908	...	...	...	|	...	...	...	...
Rødby Ferry ⛴ a.	...	1613	1613	1625	...	...	...	...	...	1813	1825	...	...	2013	2013	2025	...	...	|	...	...	...	...
København H. ⊡ d.	...	1826	...	1840	1847	1927	2107	...	...	...	2040	...	...	2226	...	2240	2247	...	0629	0647	0727	0823	...
Malmö C ⊡ d.	...	...	...	...	1926	2008	2146	2232	...	...	...	...	...	...	...	...	2326	...	...	0726	0808	0910	...
Göteborg a.	...	...	...	...	...	2305	...	|	...	...	...	...	...	...	...	...	...	...	...	...	1105	|	...
Stockholm Central a.	...	...	...	...	...	...	...	0555	...	...	...	...	...	...	...	...	...	...	...	...	...	1336	...

A – Ⓑ June 9 - Dec. 14: 🛏 1, 2 cl., 🛌 2 cl., (2) 🍷 Ⓡ Stockholm - Malmö.

C – BERLIN NIGHT EXPRESS – ③⑤⑦ June 26 - Aug. 18: 🛌 2 cl., 🍷 (✕ on board ferry) Berlin - Malmö. Ⓡ Special fares apply.

F – Ⓑ June 9 - Dec. 14: 🛏 1, 2 cl., 🛌 2 cl., (2) 🍷 Ⓡ Malmö - Stockholm.

G – BERLIN NIGHT EXPRESS – ①④⑥ June 24 - Aug. 17: 🛌 2 cl., 🍷 (✕ on board ferry) Malmö - Berlin. Ⓡ Special fares apply.

H – June 22 - Aug. 19.

J – June 21 - Aug. 18.

K – Mar. 30 - Sept. 16. Via Flensburg ⛴ and Padborg ⛴.

L – Mar. 30 - Sept. 16. Via Padborg ⛴ and Flensburg ⛴.

M – ①–⑥ Dec. 10 - June 15. ①–⑤ June 17 - Dec. 13.

P – ①–⑤ Jan. 7 - June 20.

Q – Sept. 17 - Dec. 14.

S – Mar. 30 - Sept. 16.

b – Train is conveyed by train-ferry Trelleborg ⛴ - Sassnitz Fährhafen ⛴ (Mukran) and v.v.

c – Passengers to / from Rødby or Puttgarden may be required to leave / board the train on board the ferry.

Sn – *Snabbtåg* high speed train. Ⓡ ✕.

⊡ – Additional services Malmö - København and v.v. are available, see Table **703**.

❦ – Compulsory reservation June 11 - Sept. 3.

BERLIN - GDYNIA 51

train type	*EC*	
train number	**55**	
notes	Ⓡ	
notes	**H**	
Berlin Hbf d.	1440	...
Berlin Ost d.	1450	...
Frankfurt (Oder) ⛴ d.	1545	...
Rzepin a.	1605	...
Poznań Gł. a.	1723	...
Gniezno a.	1751	...
Inowrocław a.	1821	...
Bydgoszcz Gł. a.	1847	...
Tczew a.	2003	...
Gdańsk Gł. a.	2023	...
Sopot a.	2042	...
Gdynia Gł. a.	2051	...

train type	*EC*	
train number	**54**	
notes	Ⓡ	
	H	
Gdynia Gł. d.	0709	...
Sopot d.	0717	...
Gdańsk Gł. d.	0734	...
Tczew d.	0751	...
Bydgoszcz Gł. d.	0901	...
Inowrocław d.	0928	...
Gniezno d.	0958	...
Poznań Gł. d.	1030	...
Rzepin d.	1152	...
Frankfurt (Oder) ⛴ a.	1212	...
Berlin Ost a.	1306	...
Berlin Hbf a.	1316	...

H – BERLIN GDANSK EXPRESS (12) ✕ Ⓡ Berlin - Poznań - Gdynia and v.v. (Table **1020**).

PRAHA - LINZ - ZÜRICH 52

train type				**1547**
train number	**1541**	**1543**	**1545**	**50466**
notes				**B**
Praha Holešovice d.	...	0948	1348	1748
Praha hlavní d.	0601	1001	1401	1801
Tábor d.	0718	1118	1518	1918
Veselí nad Lužnicí d.	|	|	|	|
České Budějovice d.	0808	1208	1608	2008
Summerau ⛴ d.	0909	1309	1709	2109
Linz Hbf a.	1007	1407	1807	2207
	RJX	*RJX*	*RJX*	|
	162	**166**	**760**	|
	✕	✕	✕	|
Linz Hbf d.	1046	1446	1846	0103
Salzburg a.	1152	1552	1952	0213
Innsbruck Hbf a.	1344	1744	2144	0423
Zürich HB a.	1720	2120	...	0820

train type	*RJX*	*EC*	*RJX*	*RJX*	*RJX*	**50467**
train number	**765**	**163**	**563**	**165**	**869**	**1540**
notes	✕	🍷	✕	🍷	✕	**A**
Zürich HB d.	...	0840	...	1040	...	2140
Innsbruck Hbf d.	0817	1211	1217	1411	1514	0128
Salzburg d.	1008	...	1408	...	1708	0350
Linz Hbf a.	1114	...	1514	...	1814	0457
						|
						|
	1542		**1544**		**1546**	|
Linz Hbf d.	1152	...	1552	...	1835	0635
Summerau ⛴ a.	1250	...	1652	...	1950	0750
České Budějovice a.	1351	...	1751	...	2051	0851
Veselí nad Lužnicí a.	|	...	|	...	2124	|
Tábor a.	1439	...	1839	...	2142	0939
Praha hlavní a.	1557	...	1957	...	2257	1057
Praha Holešovice a.	1610	...	...	...	...	1110

A – 🛏 1, 2 cl. Zürich (*EN* **50467**) - Linz (**1540**) - Praha. (12) Linz - Praha. 🍷 České Budějovice - Praha.

B – 🛏 1, 2 cl. Praha (**1547**) - Linz (*EN* **50466**) - Zürich. (12) Praha - Linz. 🍷 Praha - České Budějovice.

RJ – ÖBB *Railjet* service. (1) (premium class), (1) (first class), (2) (economy class), ✕.

53 HAMBURG / DÜSSELDORF - NÜRNBERG - INNSBRUCK / WIEN

	NJ 40421	NJ 421	NJ 491	NJ 40491
	A	B	C	D
Hamburg Altona d.	...	...	2014	2014
Hamburg Hbf d.	...	...	2029	2029
Hannover Hbf d.	...	...	2157	2157
Göttingen d.	...	...	2259	2259
Düsseldorf Hbf d.	2054	2054	|	|
Köln Hbf d.	2121	2121	|	|
Bonn Hbf d.	2143	2143	|	|
Koblenz d.	2218	2218	|	|
Mainz d.	2312	2312	|	|
Frankfurt Flughafen ✈ d.	2354	2354	|	|
Frankfurt (Main) Süd d.	0008	0008	|	|
Würzburg d.	0137	0137	0134	0134
Nürnberg a.	0237	0237	0232	0232
Nürnberg d.	0307	0340	0307	0340
Regensburg a.	0410	|	0410	|
Augsburg a.	|	0626	|	0626
München Hbf a.	|	0712	|	0712
Kufstein a.	|	0826	|	0826
Wörgl Hbf a.	|	0837	|	0837
Jenbach a.	|	0853	|	0853
Innsbruck Hbf a.	|	0914	|	0914
Passau a.	0518	...	0518	...
Wels Hbf a.	0616	...	0616	...
Linz Hbf a.	0643	...	0643	...
St Pölten Hbf a.	0746	...	0746	...
Wien Meidling a.	0820	...	0820	...
Wien Hbf a.	0827	...	0827	...

	NJ 420	NJ 40420	NJ 490	NJ 40490
	B	D	C	A
Wien Hbf d.	...	...	2041	2041
Wien Meidling d.	...	...	2049	2049
St Pölten Hbf d.	...	...	2120	2120
Linz Hbf d.	...	...	2216	2216
Wels Hbf d.	...	...	2233	2233
Passau d.	...	...	2322	2322
Innsbruck Hbf d.	2044	2044	|	|
Jenbach d.	2106	2106	|	|
Wörgl Hbf d.	2123	2123	|	|
Kufstein d.	2135	2135	|	|
München Hbf d.	2252	2252	|	|
Augsburg d.	2335	2330	|	|
Regensburg d.	|	|	0027	0027
Nürnberg a.	0116	0116	0127	0127
Nürnberg d.	0246	0200	0200	0246
Würzburg a.	|	0257	0257	|
Frankfurt (Main) Süd a.	0523	|	|	0523
Frankfurt Flughafen ✈ a.	0535	|	|	0535
Mainz a.	0602	|	|	0602
Koblenz a.	0704	|	|	0704
Bonn Hbf a.	0748	|	|	0748
Köln Hbf a.	0815	|	|	0815
Düsseldorf Hbf a.	0842	|	|	0842
Göttingen a.	...	0551	0551	...
Hannover Hbf a.	...	0649	0649	...
Hamburg Hbf a.	...	0844	0844	...
Hamburg Altona a.	...	0904	0904	...

A – *ÖBB nightjet* 1,2 cl., 2 cl. (4,6 berth), Düsseldorf - Wien and v.v. Special fares apply.
B – *ÖBB nightjet* 1,2 cl., 2 cl. (4,6 berth), Düsseldorf - Innsbruck and v.v. Special fares apply.
C – *ÖBB nightjet* 1,2 cl., 2 cl. (4,6 berth), Hamburg - Wien and v.v. Special fares apply.
D – *ÖBB nightjet* 1,2 cl., 2 cl. (4,6 berth), Hamburg - Innsbruck and v.v. Special fares apply.

54 HAMBURG - BERLIN - BASEL - ZÜRICH

	NJ 401	NJ 471
	E	G
Hamburg Altona d.	2045	...
Hamburg Hbf d.	2102	...
Berlin Lichtenberg d.	|	2033
Berlin Ost d.	|	2056
Berlin Hbf d.	|	2107
Berlin Zoo d.	|	2116
Berlin Wannsee d.	|	2128
Potsdam d.	|	2140
Brandenburg d.	|	2207
Magdeburg Hbf d.	|	2258
Braunschweig d.	|	2347
Hannover Hbf d.	2326	|
Fulda d.	0256	0256
Frankfurt (Main) Süd a.	0359	0359
Mannheim Hbf a.	0440	0440
Karlsruhe Hbf a.	0507	0507
Baden-Baden a.	0527	0527
Offenburg a.	0545	0545
Freiburg (Brsg) Hbf a.	0620	0620
Basel Bad Bf a.	0706	0706
Basel SBB a.	0720	0720
Brugg AG a.	0832	0832
Baden a.	0841	0841
Zürich HB a.	0905	0905

	NJ 470	NJ 40470
	G	E
Zürich HB d.	2000	2000
Brugg AG d.	|	|
Baden d.	|	|
Basel SBB d.	2113	2113
Basel Bad Bf d.	2122	2122
Freiburg (Brsg) Hbf d.	2158	2158
Offenburg d.	2230	2230
Baden-Baden d.	|	|
Karlsruhe Hbf d.	2304	2304
Mannheim Hbf d.	0005	0005
Frankfurt (Main) Süd d.	0054	0054
Fulda a.	0146	0146
Hannover Hbf a.	|	0604
Braunschweig a.	0457	|
Magdeburg Hbf a.	0556	|
Brandenburg a.	|	|
Potsdam a.	0706	|
Berlin Wannsee a.	0736	|
Berlin Zoo a.	0748	|
Berlin Hbf a.	0754	|
Berlin Ost a.	0810	|
Berlin Lichtenberg a.	0838	|
Hamburg Hbf a.	...	0751
Hamburg Altona a.	...	0806

E – *ÖBB nightjet* 1,2 cl., 2 cl. (4,6 berth), Hamburg -Zürich and v.v. Special fares apply.
G – *ÖBB nightjet* 1,2 cl., 2 cl. (4,6 berth), Berlin - Zürich and v.v. Special fares apply.

55 FRANKFURT - LEIPZIG - DRESDEN - PRAHA

train type	EC	IC	EC	ICE	IC	EC	ICE	IC	EC	ICE	IC	EC	ICE	IC	EC	ICE	IC	EC		
train number	**259**	**2449**	**171**	**696**	**2447**	**173**	**694**	**2445**	**379**	**692**	**2443**	**175**	**690**	**2441**	**177**	**598**	**2049**	**179**		
notes	①–⑥ J	Ⓐ	✕ D	⚒ ✕		✕ C	✕	⚒	✕ A	✕		✕ D	✕		✕ H	✕		✕ H		
Frankfurt (Main) Hbf d.	...	...	...	0614	...	...	0814	...	...	1014	...	...	1214	...	...	1413	...	...	...	...
Fulda d.	...	...	...	0709	...	...	0909	...	...	1109	...	...	1309	...	...	1510	...	...	...	...
Erfurt Hbf d.	...	...	...	0828	...	...	1028	...	...	1228	...	...	1428	...	...	1628	...	...	...	...
Leipzig Hbf d.	0555	0731	...	0909	0931	...	1109	1131	...	1309	1331	...	1509	1531	...	1709	1731	...	...	...
Dresden Hbf d.	0710	0836	0910	...	1036	1110	...	1236	1310	...	1436	1510	...	1636	1710	...	1836	1910	...	...
Bad Schandau ◧ d.	0737	...	0937	...	...	1137	...	...	1337	...	...	1537	...	...	1737	...	...	1937	...	...
Děčín ◧ d.	0758	...	0958	...	...	1158	...	...	1358	...	...	1558	...	...	1758	...	...	1958	...	...
Praha Holešovice a.	0915	...	1115	...	...	1315	...	...	1515	...	...	1716	...	...	1915	...	...	2115	...	...
Praha hlavní a.	0926	...	1126	...	...	1326	...	...	1526	...	...	1726	...	...	1926	...	...	2126	...	...

train type	EC	IC	ICE	EC	IC	ICE	EC	IC	ICE	EC	IC	ICE	EC	IC	ICE	EC	IC	ICE	ICE	EC	
train number	**178**	**2048**	**597**	**176**	**2440**	**599**	**174**	**2442**	**691**	**378**	**2444**	**693**	**172**	**2446**	**695**	**170**	**2448**	**1617**	**1627**	**258**	
notes	✕ D		✕	✕ H		✕	✕		✕	✕ A		✕	✕ C		✕	✕ D	Ⓑ	✕	✕	Ⓑ K	
Praha hlavní d.	0632	...	...	0832	...	...	1032	...	...	1232	...	...	1432	...	...	1632	...	...	...	1832	...
Praha Holešovice d.	0642	...	...	0842	...	...	1042	...	...	1242	...	...	1442	...	...	1642	...	...	...	1842	...
Děčín ◧ d.	0802	...	...	1002	...	...	1202	...	...	1402	...	...	1602	...	...	1802	...	...	...	2002	...
Bad Schandau ◧ a.	0820	...	...	1020	...	...	1220	...	...	1420	...	...	1620	...	...	1820	...	...	...	2018	...
Dresden Hbf a.	0843	0921	...	1043	1121	...	1243	1321	...	1443	1521	...	1643	1721	...	1843	1921	...	...	2043	...
Leipzig Hbf a.	...	1026	1048	...	1226	1248	...	1426	1448	...	1626	1648	...	1826	1848	...	2026	2048	...	2203	...
Erfurt Hbf a.	...	...	1128	...	...	1328	...	...	1528	...	...	1728	...	...	1929	...	...	2129	2133	...	...
Fulda a.	...	...	1248	...	...	1448	...	...	1646	...	...	1848	...	...	2048	...	...	...	2258	...	...
Frankfurt (Main) Hbf a.	...	...	1344	...	...	1544	...	...	1744	...	...	1944	...	...	2144	...	...	...	2358	...	...

A – ✕ Kiel - Berlin - Dresden - Praha and v.v.
C – HUNGARIA – ✕ Hamburg - Berlin - Dresden - Praha - Budapest and v.v.
D – ✕ Praha - Dresden - Berlin and v.v.
H – ✕ Hamburg - Berlin - Dresden - Praha and v.v.
J – ①–⑥: PORTA BOHEMICA – ✕ Leipzig - Dresden - Praha.
K – Ⓑ: PORTA BOHEMICA – ✕ Praha - Dresden - Leipzig.
◧ – Ticketing point is Schöna.

LONDON / PARIS - KÖLN - BERLIN - WARSZAWA - KYIV / MOSKVA — 56

train type	EC	☆					ICE	EC			ICE	EC	ICE	EC	⇌	ICE	EC	☆	☆	☆	ICE	ICE	441	441	
train number	41	9032	24JI	24JI	10SZ	10SZ	541	43	68KJ		845	45	847	55	9413	849	47	9108	9110	9110	15	559	14MJ	14MJ	
notes	①-⑥		453	453	②④⑥	②④⑥	①-⑥		12011		🍷		🍷			🍷				⑥		🍷	①⑥	①⑥	
	T		MY	MZ	PY	PZ	🍷	T	C			T		N			T	G	H				JY	JZ	
London St Pancras d.	...	1422	...	...	...	...	...	...	...	...	...	...	...	...	...	...	...	0613	0647	0657	...	...	...	...	...
Paris Nord d.	...	1747	...	...	...	...	...	...	...	...	...	...	...	...	0755p	...	...	|	|	|	...	...	...	...	...
Paris Est d.	...	...	1858	1858	...	...	...	...	...	...	...	...	...	...	|	...	...	|	|	|	...	...	...	...	...
Brussels Midi/Zuid d.	...	...	|	|	...	...	...	...	...	...	...	...	...	...	0925	...	...	0922	1007	1005	1025	...	...	...	...
Liège Guillemins d.	...	...	|	|	...	...	...	...	...	...	...	...	...	...	1013	...	...	...	...	...	1114	...	...	...	...
Aachen ▣ d.	...	...	|	|	...	...	...	...	...	...	...	...	...	...	1040	...	...	...	...	...	1140	...	...	...	...
Köln Hbf a.	...	...	|	|	...	...	...	...	...	...	...	...	...	...	1116	...	...	...	...	...	1215	...	...	...	...
Köln Hbf d.	...	...	|	|	...	...	0425	...	...	...	...	...	0928	...	1119	...	...	...	...	...	...	1248	...	...	...
Köln Messe / Deutz ♣ d.	...	...	|	|	...	...	|	...	...	...	0729x	...	|	...	1140x	1151x	...	...	...	...	...	|	...	...	...
Bielefeld Hbf d.	...	...	|	|	...	...	0634	...	...	...	0934	...	1134	...	...	1334	...	...	...	...	...	1434	...	...	...
Hannover Hbf d.	...	...	|	|	...	...	0731	...	...	...	1031	...	1231	...	...	1431	...	...	...	...	...	1531	...	...	...
Berlin Hbf a.	...	...	0721	0721	...	...	0906	...	...	...	1210	...	1410	...	...	1610	...	...	...	...	...	1706	...	...	...
Berlin Hbf d.	0543	...	0726	0726	...	...	...	0937	...	...	...	1237	...	1437	...	...	1643	...	...	...	...	...	...	...	...
Berlin Ostbahnhof d.	0555o	...	0759k	0759k	...	...	...	0950	...	...	...	1250	...	1450	...	...	1653	...	...	...	...	...	1924	1924	...
Frankfurt (Oder) ▣ d.	0645	...	0905	0855	...	...	...	1045	...	...	...	1345	...	1545	...	...	1745	...	...	...	...	...	2033	2033	...
Rzepin d.	0708	...	0920	0920	...	...	...	1108	...	...	...	1408	...	1608	...	...	1808	...	...	...	...	...	2057	2057	...
Poznań Gł. d.	0830	...	1036	1036	...	...	...	1231	...	...	...	1542	...	1728	...	...	1930	...	...	...	...	...	2216	2216	...
Warszawa Centralna a.	1120	...	|	|	1605	1605	...	1524	1705	...	...	1831	...	...	...	...	2220	...	...	...	...	...	|	|	...
Warszawa Wschodnia d.	1141	...	1536	1536	1613	1613	...	1546	1712	...	...	1846	...	...	...	...	2231	...	...	...	...	...	0325	0325	...
Terespol a.	...	...	1744	1744	1900	1900	...	...	|	...	...	...	...	...	...	...	...	...	...	...	...	...	0518	0518	...
Brest Tsentralny ▣ a.	...	...	2015	2115	2131	2231	...	...	|	...	...	...	...	...	...	...	...	...	...	...	...	...	0746	0838	...
Lublin a.	...	...	|	|	|	|	...	...	2031	...	...	...	...	...	...	...	...	...	...	...	...	...	|	|	...
Kyiv a.	...	...	|	|	|	|	...	...	1103	...	...	...	...	...	...	...	...	...	...	...	...	...	|	|	...
Minsk a.	...	...	0205	0304	0311	0415	...	...	...	...	...	...	...	...	...	...	...	...	...	...	...	...	1113	1213	...
Orsha Tsentralnaya § a.	...	...	0436	0536	0603	0705	...	...	...	...	...	...	...	...	...	...	...	...	...	...	...	...	1349	1449	...
Smolensk Tsentralny ▣ § a.	...	...	0611	0711	0734	0834	...	...	...	...	...	...	...	...	...	...	...	...	...	...	...	...	1516	1616	...
Moskva Belorusskaya ‡ a.	...	...	1058	1145	1225	1311	...	...	...	...	...	...	...	...	...	...	...	...	...	...	...	...	1943	2008	..

train type/number	440	440	ICE	ICE	☆	EC	ICE	ICE	☆	EC	ICE	⇌				EC	ICE		EC	ICE			☆	EC	
train number	13MJ	13MJ	652	210	9149	46	558	12	9163	54	858	9484		9SZ	9SZ	44	846	67KJ	42	552	23JI	23JI	9023	40	
notes	⑤⑦	⑤⑦			Ⓑ			Ⓑ						①③⑤	①③⑤		🍷	21010		🍷	452	452	①-⑥	Ⓑ	
	KY	KZ				T				N				QY	QZ	T		C	T		FY	FZ		T	
Moskva Belorusskaya ‡ d.	1017	1155	...	...	...	...	...	...	...	...	...	...	...	1421	1551	...	...	...	...	...	1814	1912	...	...	...
Smolensk Tsentralny ▣ § d.	1440	1544	...	...	...	...	...	...	...	...	...	...	...	1920	2020	...	...	...	...	...	2311	0009	...	...	...
Orsha Tsentralnaya § d.	1603	1706	...	...	...	...	...	...	...	...	...	...	...	2047	2145	...	...	...	...	...	0038	0137	...	...	...
Minsk d.	1824	1927	...	...	...	...	...	...	...	...	...	...	...	2343	0039	...	...	...	...	...	0312	0414	...	...	...
Kyiv d.	|	|	...	...	...	...	...	...	...	...	...	...	...	|	|	...	...	1913z	...	...	|	|	...	...	...
Lublin d.	|	|	...	...	...	...	...	...	...	...	...	...	...	|	|	...	...	0737	...	...	|	|	...	...	...
Brest Tsentralny ▣ d.	2143	2243	...	...	...	...	...	...	...	...	...	...	...	0510	0610	...	...	|	...	...	0943t	1043f	...	...	...
Terespol d.	2208	2208	...	...	...	...	...	...	...	...	...	...	...	0513	0513	...	...	|	...	...	0946	0946	...	...	...
Warszawa Wschodnia a.	2348	2348	...	...	...	0524	...	...	...	...	...	...	...	0747	0747	0849	...	1042	1214c	...	1150	1150	...	1615	...
Warszawa Centralna d.	|	|	...	...	...	0535	...	...	...	...	...	...	...	0755	0755	0906	...	1050	1225	...	|	|	...	1625	...
Poznań Gł. d.	0432	0432	...	...	...	0830	...	...	...	1029	...	...	...	...	...	1230	...	...	1529	...	1733	1733	...	1930	...
Rzepin d.	0549	0549	...	...	...	0952	...	...	...	1152	...	...	...	...	...	1352	...	...	1652	...	1902	1902	...	2052	...
Frankfurt (Oder) ▣ a.	0612	0612	...	...	...	1012	...	...	...	1212	...	...	...	...	...	1412	...	...	1712	...	|	|	...	2112	...
Berlin Ostbahnhof a.	0717	0717	...	...	...	1106	...	...	...	1306	...	...	...	...	...	1506	...	...	1806	...	2017k	2017k	...	2201o	...
Berlin Hbf a.	...	...	...	...	...	1116	...	...	...	1316	...	...	...	...	...	1516	...	...	1816	...	2058	2058	...	2216	...
Berlin Hbf d.	...	...	0850	...	...	...	1250	...	...	...	1349	...	...	...	...	...	1549	...	...	1850	2103	2103	...	...	...
Hannover Hbf a.	...	...	1028	...	...	...	1428	...	...	...	1528	...	...	...	...	...	1728	...	...	2028	|	|	...	...	...
Bielefeld Hbf a.	...	...	1124	...	...	...	1524	...	...	...	1624	...	...	...	...	...	1824	...	...	2124	|	|	...	...	...
Köln Messe / Deutz ♣ a.	...	...	|	...	...	...	|	...	...	...	|	...	...	...	...	...	|	...	...	|	|	|	...	...	...
Köln Hbf a.	...	...	1309	...	...	...	1709	...	...	...	1832	...	...	...	...	...	2036	...	...	2312	|	|	...	...	...
Köln Hbf d.	...	...	...	1343	...	...	...	1743	...	...	...	1844	...	...	...	...	2042	...	...	...	|	|	...	...	...
Aachen ▣ a.	...	...	...	1420	...	...	...	1820	...	...	...	1918	...	...	...	...	2120	...	...	...	|	|	...	...	...
Liège Guillemins a.	...	...	...	1446	...	...	...	1846	...	...	...	1946	...	...	...	...	...	...	...	...	|	|	...	...	...
Brussels Midi/Zuid a.	...	...	...	1535	1656	...	...	1935	2022	...	...	2035	...	...	...	...	...	...	...	...	|	|	...	...	...
Paris Est a.	...	...	...	...	|	...	...	...	|	...	...	|	...	...	...	...	...	...	...	...	0940	0940	...	...	...
Paris Nord a.	...	...	...	...	|	...	...	...	|	...	...	2205	...	...	...	...	...	...	...	...	...	...	1113	...	...
London St Pancras a.	...	...	...	...	1814	...	...	...	2133	...	...	...	...	...	...	...	...	...	...	...	...	...	1239	...	...

A – [12] ✕ Köln - Wuppertal - Hamm - Berlin and Düsseldorf - Hamm - Berlin and v.v. Table **810**.
C – KYIV EKSPRES / KIEV EXPRESS – 🛏 1, 2 cl. Warszawa - Kyiv and v.v.
F – TRANSEUROPEAN EXPRESS ②: 🛏 1, 2 cl. Moskva (**23** JI) - Brest (**452**) - Berlin - Paris. ✕ (RZD) Moskva - Brest. ✕ (PKP) Warszawa - Paris.
G – ①⑤ May 26 - Sept. 16.
H – ②③④ (①–⑤ Sept. 20 - Nov. 2).
J – ①⑥: 🛏 1 cl. (lux), 🛏 1, 2 cl., [1] ✕ Ⓡ Berlin - Moskva, Strizh (Swift) Talgo train.
K – ⑤⑦: 🛏 1 cl. (lux), 🛏 1, 2 cl., [1] ✕ Ⓡ Moskva - Berlin, Strizh (Swift) Talgo train.
M – TRANSEUROPEAN EXPRESS ④: 🛏 1, 2 cl. Paris (**453**) - Berlin - Brest (**24** JI) - Moskva. ✕ (PKP) Paris - Warszawa. ✕ (RZD) Brest - Moskva.
N – BERLIN GDANSK EXPRESS [12] ✕ Ⓡ Berlin - Poznań - Gdynia and v.v.
P – POLONEZ ②④⑥ – 🛏 1, 2 cl., 🍷 Warszawa - Moskva. ✕ Brest - Moskva.
Q – POLONEZ ①③⑤ – 🛏 1, 2 cl., 🍷 Moskva - Warszawa. ✕ Moskva - Brest.
T –, From June 24, ❦: BERLIN WARSZAWA EXPRESS – [12] ✕ Ⓡ Berlin - Warszawa and v.v.
Y – Mar. 31, 2019 - Oct. 26, 2019.
Z – Oct. 27, 2019 - Dec. 14, 2019. Timings subject to confirmation.

c – 1159 June 24 – 30.
e – Paris **Est**.

f – Arrive 0830.
k – Berlin **Lichtenberg**.
o – Berlin **Ostkreuz**.
p – 0740 on ⑦.
t – Arrive 0730.
x – Düsseldorf Hbf.
z – Passengers to be on board by 1848 for customs and passport control.

⇌ – *Thalys* high-speed train. Ⓡ 🍷. Special fares payable. Valid June 9 - Dec. 14.
§ – ▣: Osinovka (BY) / Krasnoye (RU).
‡ – Also known as Moskva **Smolenskaya** station.
☆ – Eurostar train. Special fares payable. ✕ in Business Premier and Standard Premier, 🍷 in Standard. Minimum check-in time 30 minutes. Valid May 26 - Nov. 2.
♣ – Köln **Messe / Deutz**. Connections from Köln Hbf depart every 2 - 5 minutes, journey time 2 - 3 minutes.
❦ – From June 24. For service until June 23 see Table **1001**.

BERLIN - WROCLAW — 58

	IRE	IRE	NJ
	5835	5839	457
	⑥	⑤	
	K	K	M
Berlin Hbf. d.	...	...	1841
Berlin Lichtenberg d.	0825	1226	|
Berlin Ostkreuz d.	0839	1231	|
Cottbus d.	0953	1353	|
Forst ▣ a.	|	|	|
Forst ▣ d.	1011	1405	|
Tuplice d.	|	|	|
Záry a.	1041	1436	|
Zagań a.	1058	1449	|
Legnica a.	1205	1555	|
Wrocław Gł. a.	1247	1647	2255

	IRE		NJ
	5832		456
	⑤⑦f		
	K		M
Wrocław Gł. d.	1718	...	0510
Legnica d.	1804	...	|
Zagań d.	1903	...	|
Záry d.	1916	...	|
Tuplice d.	|	...	|
Forst ▣ a.	1946	...	|
Forst ▣ d.	|	...	|
Cottbus a.	2005	...	|
Berlin Ostkreuz a.	2125	...	|
Berlin Lichtenberg a.	2130	...	|
Berlin Hbf. a.	...	...	0916

K – KULTURZUG - [2] Berlin - Wrocław and v.v. For International journeys only. Special fares apply. Timings subject to alteration.
M – *ÖBB nightjet* METROPOL – 🛏 1, 2 cl., ▬ 2 cl., [2] Berlin - Wrocław - Przemyśl / Wien / Budapest and v.v. (Table **71**).

f – Also June 10; not June 9.

60 HAMBURG - BERLIN - PRAHA - WIEN / BUDAPEST

train type	EC	RJ	EC	RJ	EC	RJ	EC	EC	RJ	EC	EC	RJ	EC	EC	RJ	EC	EC	RJ	EC	EC	RJ	
train number	271	71	273	73	275	75	259	277	77	171	279	79	131	173	371	379	281	373	175	283	375	
notes	✕	✕	✕	✕	✕	✕	①–⑥	✕	✕	✕	✕	✕	✕	✕	✕	✕	✕	✕	✕	✕	✕	
		A					Q						V	J		H						
Hamburg Altona d.	...	...	...	...	...	...	...	...	...	...	...	...	...	0636	...	...	...	...	...	...	...	...
Hamburg Hbf d.	...	...	...	...	...	...	...	...	...	...	...	...	...	0648	...	0851	...	...	...	...	...	...
Berlin Hbf d.	...	...	...	...	...	...	...	...	...	0716	...	...	...	0916	...	1116	...	...	1316	...	...	...
Berlin Südkreuz d.	...	...	...	...	...	...	...	...	...	0723	...	...	...	0926	...	1126	...	...	1326	...	...	...
Leipzig Hbf d.	...	...	...	...	...	...	0555	...	...	|	...	...	...	|	...	|	...	...	|	...	...	...
Dresden Hbf d.	...	...	...	...	...	...	0710	...	...	0910	...	...	...	1110	...	1310	...	...	1510	...	...	...
Bad Schandau 🏛 ⊖ d.	...	...	...	...	...	...	0737	...	...	0937	...	...	...	1137	...	1337	...	...	1537	...	...	...
Děčín d.	...	...	...	...	...	...	0758	...	...	0958	...	...	...	1158	...	1358	...	...	1558	...	...	...
Ústí nad Labem hlavní d.	...	...	...	...	...	...	0815	...	...	1015	...	...	...	1215	...	1415	...	...	1615	...	...	...
Praha Holešovice a.	...	...	...	...	...	...	0915	...	...	1115	...	...	...	1315	...	1515	...	...	1715	...	...	...
Praha hlavní a.	...	...	...	...	...	...	0926	...	...	1126	...	...	...	1326	...	1526	...	...	1726	...	...	...
Praha hlavní d.	...	0448	0550	0647	0750	0847	...	0950	1047	...	1150	1247	...	1350	1447	...	1550	1647	...	1750	1847	...
Pardubice d.	...	0546	0648	0743	0848	0943	...	1048	1143	...	1248	1343	...	1448	1541	...	1648	1741	...	1848	1943	...
Brno dolní nádraží d.	0624	0724	0824	0924	1024	1124	...	1224	1324	...	1424	1524	...	1624	1724	...	1824	1924	...	2024	2124	...
Břeclav a.	0652	0752	0852	0952	1052	1152	...	1252	1352	...	1452	1552	...	1652	1752	...	1852	1952	...	2052	2152	...
Břeclav d.	0659	0755	0859	0955	1059	1155	...	1259	1355	...	1459	1555	1559	1659	1755	...	1859	1955	...	2059	2155	...
Wien Hbf a.	|	0849	|	1049	|	1249	...	|	1449	...	|	1649	|	|	1849	...	|	2049	...	|	2249	...
Wien Meidling a.	|	0903	|	1103	|	1303	...	|	1503	...	|	1703	|	|	1903	...	|	2103	...	|	...	...
Wiener Neustadt Hbf a.	|	0928	|	1128	|	1328	...	|	1530	...	|	1730	|	|	1928	...	|	2128	...	|	...	...
Graz Hbf a.	|	1133	|	1333	|	1533	...	|	1733	...	|	1933	|	|	2133	...	|	2333	...	|	...	...
Kúty 🏛 a.	0711	...	0911	...	1111	...	...	1311	...	...	1511	...	1611	1711	...	...	1911	...	...	2111	...	...
Bratislava hlavná a.	0750	...	0950	...	1150	...	...	1350	...	...	1550	...	1650	1750	...	...	1950	...	...	2150	...	...
Štúrovo 🏛 △ a.	0917	...	1117	...	1317	...	...	1517	...	...	1717	...	1817	1917	...	...	2117	...	...	...	...	...
Budapest Nyugati a.	1020	...	1220	...	1420	...	...	1620	...	...	1820	...	1920	2020	...	...	2220	...	...	...	...	...
Budapest Keleti a.	...	...	...	...	...	...	...	...	...	...	...	...	...	...	...	...	...	...	...	...	...	...

train type	EC	RJ	EC		EN	NJ	NJ	
train number	177	285	179		573	457	457	
notes	✕	✕	✕		477	477		
					B	S	R	
Hamburg Altona d.	1239		1437	...	...	...	...	...
Hamburg Hbf d.	1251	...	1451	...	...	...	...	...
Berlin Hbf d.	1516	...	1716	...	...	1841	1841	...
Berlin Südkreuz d.	1526	...	1723	...	...	|	|	...
Leipzig Hbf d.	|	...	|	...	...	|	|	...
Dresden Hbf d.	1710	...	1910	...	...	|	|	...
Bad Schandau 🏛 ⊖ d.	1737	...	1937	...	...	|	|	...
Děčín d.	1758	...	1958	...	...	◧	◧	...
Ústí nad Labem hlavní d.	1815	...	2015	...	...	|	|	...
Praha Holešovice a.	1915	...	2115	...	...	|	|	...
Praha hlavní a.	1926	...	2126	...	...	|	|	...
Praha hlavní d.	...	1950	...	...	2156	|	|	...
Pardubice d.	...	2048	...	...	2258	|	|	...
Brno dolní nádraží d.	...	2224	...	...	0050	|	|	...
Břeclav a.	...	2252	...	...	0121	0410	0410	...
Břeclav d.	...	2254	...	...	0459	0459	0549	...
Wien Hbf a.	...	|	...	...	|	|	0700	...
Wien Meidling a.	...	|	...	...	|	|	...	...
Wiener Neustadt Hbf a.	...	|	...	...	|	|	...	...
Graz Hbf a.	...	|	...	...	|	|	...	...
Kúty 🏛 a.	...	|	...	...	0511	0511	...	...
Bratislava hlavná a.	...	2343	...	...	0550	0550	...	...
Štúrovo 🏛 △ a.	...	...	...	...	0712	0712	...	...
Budapest Nyugati a.	...	...	...	...	|	|	...	...
Budapest Keleti a.	...	...	...	...	0835	0835	...	...

train type/number	EC	EC	RJ	EC	EC	EC	EC	
train number	178	176	284	282	174	280	378	
notes	✕	✕	✕	✕	✕	✕	✕	
							G	
Budapest Keleti d.	...	...	...	...	...	...	...	...
Budapest Nyugati d.	...	...	...	...	...	0540	...	...
Štúrovo 🏛 △ d.	...	...	...	...	...	0643	...	...
Bratislava hlavná d.	...	...	0510	0610	...	0810	...	...
Kúty 🏛 d.	...	...	|	0649	...	0849	...	...
Graz Hbf d.	...	...	|	|	...	|	...	...
Wiener Neustadt Hbf d.	...	...	|	|	...	|	...	...
Wien Meidling d.	...	...	|	|	...	|	...	...
Wien Hbf d.	...	...	|	|	...	|	...	...
Břeclav a.	...	...	0601	0701	...	0901	...	...
Břeclav d.	...	...	0607	0707	...	0907	...	...
Brno dolní nádraží d.	...	...	0637	0737	...	0937	...	...
Pardubice d.	...	...	0814	0911	...	1111	...	...
Praha hlavní a.	...	...	0907	1007	...	1207	...	...
Praha hlavní d.	0632	0832	...	...	1032	...	1232	...
Praha Holešovice d.	0642	0842	...	...	1042	...	1242	...
Ústí nad Labem hlavní d.	0743	0943	...	...	1143	...	1343	...
Děčín d.	0802	1002	...	...	1202	...	1402	...
Bad Schandau 🏛 ⊖ a.	0820	1020	...	...	1220	...	1420	...
Dresden Hbf a.	0843	1043	...	...	1243	...	1443	...
Leipzig Hbf a.	|	|	...	...	|	...	|	...
Berlin Südkreuz a.	1034	1234	...	...	1434	...	1634	...
Berlin Hbf a.	1041	1241	...	...	1443	...	1641	...
Hamburg Hbf a.	...	1511	...	...	1711	...	1911	...
Hamburg Altona a.	...	1527	...	...	1724	...	...	...

train type/number	RJ	EC	EC	RJ	EC	EC	RJ	EC	EC	RJ	EC	RJ	EC	RJ	EC	RJ		EN	NJ	NJ		
train number	72	172	130	74	278	170	76	276	258	78	274	370	272	372	270	374		476	476	456		
notes	✕	✕	✕	✕	✕	✕	✕	✕	Ⓑ	✕	✕	✕	✕	✕	✕	✕		572	456			
		J	V						P									C	S	R		
Budapest Keleti d.	...	...	...	...	...	...	...	...	...	...	...	...	...	...	...	...	...	1925	1925	...	...	...
Budapest Nyugati d.	...	0740	0840	...	0940	...	...	1140	...	...	1340	...	1540	...	1740	...	...	|	|	...	...	...
Štúrovo 🏛 △ d.	...	0843	0943	...	1043	...	...	1243	...	...	1443	...	1643	...	1843	...	...	2040	2143	...	...	...
Bratislava hlavná d.	...	1010	1110	...	1210	...	...	1410	...	...	1610	...	1810	...	2010	...	...	2210	2210	...	...	...
Kúty 🏛 d.	...	1049	1149	...	1249	...	...	1449	...	...	1649	...	1849	...	2049	...	...	2249	2249	...	...	...
Graz Hbf d.	0626	|	|	0826	|	...	1026	|	...	1226	|	1426	|	1626	|	1826	...	|	|	...	...	...
Wiener Neustadt Hbf d.	0832	|	|	1032	|	...	1232	|	...	1432	|	1632	|	1832	|	2032	...	|	|	...	...	...
Wien Meidling d.	0857	|	|	1057	|	...	1257	|	...	1457	|	1657	|	1857	|	2057	...	|	|	...	...	...
Wien Hbf d.	0910	|	|	1110	|	...	1310	|	...	1510	|	1710	|	1910	|	2110	...	|	|	2210	...	...
Břeclav a.	1004	1101	1201	1204	1301	...	1404	1501	...	1604	1701	1804	1901	2004	2101	2204	...	2301	2301	2307	...	...
Břeclav d.	1007	1107	...	1207	1307	...	1407	1507	...	1607	1707	1807	1907	2007	2107	2207	...	0502	2350	2350	...	...
Brno dolní nádraží d.	1042	1137	...	1237	1337	...	1437	1537	...	1637	1737	1837	1937	2037	2137	2235	...	0534	|	|	...	...
Pardubice d.	1214	1311	...	1414	1511	...	1614	1711	...	1814	1911	2014	2114	2220	2314	...	...	0711	|	|	...	...
Praha hlavní a.	1307	1407	...	1507	1607	...	1707	1807	...	1907	2007	2107	2209	2314	0011	...	...	0807	|	|	...	...
Praha hlavní d.	...	1432	...	...	...	1632	...	...	1832	...	...	...	...	...	...	...	...	...	|	|	...	...
Praha Holešovice d.	...	1442	...	...	...	1642	...	...	1842	...	...	...	...	...	...	...	...	...	|	|	...	...
Ústí nad Labem hlavní d.	...	1543	...	...	...	1743	...	...	1943	...	...	...	...	...	...	...	...	...	|	|	...	...
Děčín d.	...	1602	...	...	...	1802	...	...	2002	...	...	...	...	...	...	...	...	...	◧	◧	...	...
Bad Schandau 🏛 ⊖ a.	...	1620	...	...	...	1820	...	...	2018	...	...	...	...	...	...	...	...	...	|	|	...	...
Dresden Hbf a.	...	1643	...	...	...	1843	...	...	2043	...	...	...	...	...	...	...	...	...	|	|	...	...
Leipzig Hbf a.	...	|	...	...	...	|	...	...	2203	...	...	...	...	...	...	...	...	...	|	|	...	...
Berlin Südkreuz a.	...	1834	...	...	...	2034	...	...	...	...	...	...	...	...	...	...	...	...	|	|	...	...
Berlin Hbf a.	...	1841	...	...	...	2041	...	...	...	...	...	...	...	...	...	...	...	...	0916	0916	...	...
Hamburg Hbf a.	...	2115	...	...	...	...	...	...	...	...	...	...	...	...	...	...	...	...	...	...	...	...
Hamburg Altona a.	...	2136	...	...	...	...	...	...	...	...	...	...	...	...	...	...	...	...	...	...	...	...

A – ①–⑥ (not July 6, Oct. 28).

B – METROPOL – 🛏 1, 2 cl., ▬ 2 cl. Praha (**573**) - Pardubice - Břeclav (**477**) - Budapest. [12] ✕ Praha - Břeclav. [12] Břeclav - Budapest.

C – METROPOL – 🛏 1, 2 cl., ▬ 2 cl. Budapest (**476**) - Pardubice - Břeclav (**572**) - Praha. [12] Budapest - Břeclav. [12] ✕ Břeclav - Praha.

G – [12] ✕ Praha - Berlin - Hamburg - Kiel (arrive 2018).

H – [12] ✕ Kiel (depart 0742) - Hamburg - Berlin - Praha.

J – HUNGARIA – [12] ✕ Hamburg - Berlin - Praha - Břeclav - Budapest and v.v.

P – Ⓑ: PORTA BOHEMICA – [12] ✕ Praha - Dresden - Leipzig.

Q – ①–⑥: PORTA BOHEMICA – [12] ✕ Leipzig - Dresden - Praha.

R – *ÖBB nightjet* METROPOL – 🛏 1, 2 cl., ▬ 2 cl., [2] Berlin - Wrocław - Bohumín - Břeclav - Wien and v.v.

S – *ÖBB nightjet* METROPOL – 🛏 1, 2 cl., ▬ 2 cl., [2] Berlin - Wrocław - Bohumín - Břeclav - Budapest and v.v.

V – BATHORY – [12] ✕ Warszawa - Katowice - Břeclav - Budapest and v.v. (Table **99**).

t – ①–⑥.

△ – Routeing point for international tickets : Szob.

⊖ – Routeing point for international tickets : Schöna.

RJ – ÖBB *Railjet* service. (business class), (first class), (economy class), ✕.

◧ – Via Wrocław and Bohumín (Table **71**).

☛ – Additional services Praha - Wien and Praha - Bratislava are operated by REGIOJET. For timings see table 1150.

WIEN - BUDAPEST - BEOGRAD / BUCUREŞTI and İSTANBUL / THESSALONÍKI — 61

Services to / from İstanbul are subject to alteration until further notice. Trains are replaced by 🚌 Halkalı - İstanbul and v.v.

Services between Budapest and Beograd are subject to alteration until December 14, 2019 due to engineering work.

train type	IC			IC	EC					EN						461	YHT		461	EN	
train number	73	1335		75	345	343	343	1491	1493	473	1095	463	465	493		465	81008	461	1461	347	
notes	[R]		🚌	[R]	✣	✣	✣		12501	[R]		2	2	12501		1493		[R]	[R]	[R]	
	H	K	K	P	A	B	B	D	AA	R	J	J	J	C		[R] S	CC	W T	M	E	
Wien Hbf d.	...	...	...	...	0842	...	...	...	...	...	...	...	...	...	...	...	...	...	...	1942	...
Budapest Keleti d.	0705	...	...	0910	1119	1157	...	...	...	1910	...	...	...	...	...	...	...	...	...	2310	...
Lökösháza a.	1010	...	...	1210	...	|	...	...	...	2210	...	...	...	...	...	...	...	...	...	0159	...
Curtici 🛃 a.	1200	...	...	1400	...	|	...	...	...	0001	...	...	...	...	...	...	...	...	...	0349	...
Arad a.	1243	...	...	1439	...	|	...	...	...	0050	...	...	...	...	...	...	...	...	...	0433	...
Timişoara a.	1333	...	...	|	...	|	...	...	...	|	...	...	...	...	...	...	...	...	...	|	...
Braşov a.	|	...	...	2338	...	|	...	...	...	0950	...	...	...	...	...	...	...	...	...	1332	...
Bucureşti Nord d.	2322	...	...	...	...	|	...	...	...	1230	1240	...	...	...	...	1240	...	1240	1240	1606	...
Videle a.	...	...	...	...	...	|	...	...	...	...	1330	...	...	...	...	1330	...	1330	1330	...	...
Giurgiu Nord 🛃 a.	...	...	...	...	...	|	...	...	...	...	1439	...	...	...	...	1439	...	1439	1439	...	...
Giurgiu Nord 🛃 d.	...	...	...	...	...	|	...	...	...	...	1500	...	...	...	...	1500	...	1500	1500	...	...
Ruse 🛃 a.	...	...	...	...	...	|	...	...	...	...	1525	...	...	...	...	1525	...	1525	1525	...	...
Ruse 🛃 d.	...	...	...	...	...	|	...	...	...	...	...	1625	...	...	...	1625	...	1625	1610	...	...
Gorna Oryakhovitsa d.	...	...	...	...	...	|	...	...	...	...	...	1830	2025	...	...	2025	...	1830	1830	...	...
Kelebia 🛃 a.	...	...	...	...	...	1511	1541	...	...	...	...	|	|	...	...	|	...	|	|	...	...
Subotica 🛃 a.	...	...	...	...	...	...	1555	...	...	...	...	|	|	...	...	|	...	|	|	...	...
Novi Sad a.	...	...	...	...	...	...	1842	...	...	...	...	|	|	...	...	|	...	|	|	...	...
Beograd Topčider a.	...	1835	...	...	...	...	...	0912	...	...	...	|	|	...	...	|	...	|	|	...	...
Niš a.	...	2308	...	...	...	...	...	1339	...	...	...	|	|	...	...	|	...	|	|	...	...
Tabanovci 🛃 a.	...	0320	...	...	...	...	...	|	...	...	...	|	|	...	...	|	...	|	|	...	...
Skopje a.	...	0425	...	...	...	...	...	|	...	...	...	|	|	...	...	|	...	|	|	...	...
Gevgelija 🛃 a.	...	0650	0723	...	...	...	...	|	...	...	...	|	|	...	...	|	...	|	|	...	...
Dimitrovgrad (Serbia) 🛃 a.	...	...	|	...	...	...	...	1648	...	...	...	|	|	...	...	|	...	|	|	...	...
Kalotina Zapad 🛃 a.	...	...	|	...	...	...	...	1828	...	...	...	|	|	...	...	|	...	|	|	...	...
Pleven a.	...	...	|	...	...	...	...	|	...	...	...	1936	|	...	...	|	...	1936	1936	...	...
Mezdra a.	...	...	|	...	...	...	...	|	...	...	...	2051	|	...	...	|	...	2051	2051	...	...
Vidin 🛃 a.	...	...	|	...	...	...	...	|	...	...	...	|	|	...	...	|	...	|	|	...	...
Sofia a.	...	...	|	...	...	...	...	2030	...	...	...	2220	|	...	...	|	...	2220	2220	...	...
Sofia d.	...	...	|	...	...	...	...	...	2130	...	...	...	|	2110	...	|	...	...	2350	...	...
Dimitrovgrad (Bulgaria) a.	...	...	|	...	...	...	...	...	0103	...	...	...	0015	0041	...	0015	...	...	|	...	...
Svilengrad a.	...	...	|	...	...	...	...	...	0223	...	...	...	...	0132	...	0223	...	...	|	...	...
Kapikule 🛃 a.	...	...	|	...	...	...	...	...	0316	...	...	...	...	0225	...	0316	...	...	|	...	...
Çerkezköy a.	...	...	|	...	...	...	...	...	0613	...	...	...	...	0517	...	0613	...	...	|	...	...
Halkalı a.	...	...	|	...	...	...	...	...	0740	...	...	...	...	0649	...	0740	1150	...	|	...	...
İstanbul Sirkeci a.	...	...	|	...	...	...	...	...	*0900**	...	...	...	...	*0800**	...	*0900**	|	...	|	...	...
İstanbul Pendik a.	...	...	|	...	...	...	...	...	...	...	...	...	...	...	...	...	1300	...	|	...	...
Ankara a.	...	...	|	...	...	...	...	...	...	...	...	...	...	...	...	...	1657	...	|	...	...
Kulata 🛃 a.	...	...	|	...	...	...	...	...	...	...	...	...	...	...	...	...	...	...	0310	...	...
Thessaloníki a.	...	...	1033	...	...	...	...	...	...	...	...	...	...	...	...	...	...	...	0630	...	...

train type/number	EN	EN	1492		1460			YHT					IC					D		IC	
train number	346	472	464	460	460	12502	1490	81011	12502	464	462	1094	74		1334	342	342	148		72	
notes	[R]	[R]	460	[R]	[R]	1492			492	2	2		[R]	🚌		✣	✣	✣		[R]	
	E	R	[R] F	W T	N	BB	D	CC	Y	J	J	J	P	L	L	B	B	Q		H	
Thessaloníki d.	...	...	...	...	2310	...	...	...	...	...	...	...	...	1851	...	...	...	...	...	...	...
Kulata 🛃 d.	...	...	...	...	0210	...	...	...	...	...	...	...	...	|	...	...	...	...	...	...	...
Ankara d.	...	...	...	...	|	...	...	1625	...	...	...	...	...	|	...	...	...	...	...	...	...
İstanbul Pendik d.	...	...	...	...	|	...	...	2021	...	...	...	...	...	|	...	...	...	...	...	...	...
İstanbul Sirkeci d.	...	...	*2000**	...	|	*2000**	...	|	*2130**	...	...	...	...	|	...	...	...	...	...	...	...
Halkalı d.	...	...	2140	...	|	2140	...	2131	2240	...	...	...	...	|	...	...	...	...	...	...	...
Çerkezköy d.	...	...	2310	...	|	2310	...	...	0014	...	...	...	...	|	...	...	...	...	...	...	...
Kapikule 🛃 d.	...	...	0230	...	|	0230	...	...	0315	...	...	...	...	|	...	...	...	...	...	...	...
Svilengrad d.	...	...	0325	...	|	0325	...	...	0405	...	...	...	...	|	...	...	...	...	...	...	...
Dimitrovgrad (Bulgaria) d.	...	...	0555	...	|	0435	...	...	0452	0555	...	...	...	|	...	...	...	...	...	...	...
Sofia a.	...	...	|	...	0551	0838	...	...	0838	|	...	...	...	|	...	...	...	...	...	...	...
Sofia d.	...	...	|	0900	0900	...	0930	...	...	|	0900	...	...	|	...	...	...	...	...	...	...
Vidin 🛃 d.	...	...	|	|	|	...	|	...	...	|	|	...	...	|	...	...	...	...	...	...	...
Mezdra d.	...	...	|	1029	1029	...	|	...	...	|	1029	...	...	|	...	...	...	...	...	...	...
Pleven d.	...	...	|	1147	1147	...	|	...	...	|	1147	...	...	|	...	...	...	...	...	...	...
Kalotina Zapad 🛃 d.	...	...	|	|	|	...	1120	...	...	|	|	...	...	|	...	...	...	...	...	...	...
Dimitrovgrad (Serbia) 🛃 d.	...	...	|	|	|	...	1100	...	...	|	|	...	...	|	...	...	...	...	...	...	...
Gevgelija 🛃 d.	...	...	|	|	|	...	|	...	...	|	|	...	...	1916	1948	...	...	...	...	...	...
Skopje d.	...	...	|	|	|	...	|	...	...	|	|	...	...	...	2219	...	...	...	...	...	...
Tabanovci 🛃 d.	...	...	|	|	|	...	|	...	...	|	|	...	...	...	2329	...	...	...	...	...	...
Niš d.	...	...	|	|	|	...	1410	...	...	|	|	...	...	...	0357	...	...	...	...	...	...
Beograd Topčider d.	...	...	|	|	|	...	1818	...	...	|	|	...	...	...	0814	...	...	...	...	...	...
Novi Sad d.	...	...	|	|	|	...	...	...	...	|	|	...	...	...	...	1057	...	...	...	...	...
Subotica 🛃 d.	...	...	|	|	|	...	...	...	...	|	|	...	...	...	...	1402	...	...	...	...	...
Kelebia 🛃 d.	...	...	|	|	|	...	...	...	...	|	|	...	...	...	...	1416	1446	...	...	...	...
Gorna Oryakhovitsa d.	...	...	1315	1315	1315	...	...	...	...	1020	1315	...	...	...	...	...	|	...	...	...	...
Ruse 🛃 a.	...	...	1515	1515	1522	...	...	...	...	...	1515	...	...	...	...	...	|	...	...	...	...
Ruse 🛃 d.	...	...	1610	1610	1610	...	...	...	...	...	...	1610	...	...	...	...	|	...	...	...	...
Giurgiu Nord 🛃 a.	...	...	1635	1635	1635	...	...	...	...	...	...	1635	...	...	...	...	|	...	...	...	...
Giurgiu Nord 🛃 d.	...	...	1655	1655	1655	...	...	...	...	...	...	1655	...	...	...	...	|	...	...	...	...
Videle d.	...	...	1803	1803	1803	...	...	...	...	...	...	1803	...	...	...	...	|	...	...	...	...
Bucureşti Nord d.	1400	1745	1855	1855	1855	...	...	...	...	...	...	1855	...	...	...	...	|	...	...	0520	...
Braşov d.	1631	2025	...	...	...	...	...	...	...	...	...	...	0525	...	...	...	|	...	...	|	...
Timişoara d.	|	|	...	...	...	...	...	...	...	...	...	...	|	...	...	...	|	...	...	1440	...
Arad d.	0122	0516	...	...	...	...	...	...	...	...	...	...	1419	...	...	...	|	...	...	1532	...
Curtici 🛃 d.	0210	0559	...	...	...	...	...	...	...	...	...	...	1458	...	...	...	|	...	...	1609	...
Lököshaza d.	0200	0549	...	...	...	...	...	...	...	...	...	...	1449	...	...	...	|	...	...	1549	...
Budapest Keleti a.	0450	0850	...	...	...	...	...	...	...	...	...	...	1750	...	...	...	1804	1840	...	1850	...
Wien Hbf a.	0821	...	...	...	...	...	...	...	...	...	...	...	...	...	...	...	...	2118	...	...	...

A – AVALA – [12] Wien - Budapest and v.v. ✣

B – IVO ANDRIC – [2] Budapest - Kelebia and v.v. and [2] Kelebia - Novi Sad and v.v. See Table **1360** ✣.

C – Dec. 9 - May 31, Oct. 8 - Dec. 14: BALKAN EXPRESS / ISTANBUL-SOFIA EXPRESS – [sleeper] 1, 2 cl., [couchette] 2 cl. Sofia - İstanbul (Halkalı).

D – June 14 - Sept. 16: BALKAN – [2] Beograd - Sofia and v.v.

E – DACIA – [sleeper] 1, 2 cl., [couchette] 2 cl., [2] ✕ Wien - Bucureşti and v.v.

F – June 2 - Oct. 8: BOSPHOR – [couchette] 2 cl. (4-berth) İstanbul (Halkalı) (**1492/12502**) - Dimitrovgrad (**464**) - Gorna Oryakhovitsa (**460**) - Ruse - Bucureşti.

H – TRAIANUS – [2] Budapest - Timişoara - Bucureşti and v.v.

J – Dec. 9 - May 31, Oct. 8 - Dec. 14.

K – June 14 - Sept. 15: HELLAS – [couchette] 2 cl., [2] Beograd - Skopje - Gevgelija. 🚌 Gevgelija - Thessaloníki.

L – June 15 - Sept. 16: HELLAS – 🚌 Thessaloníki - Gevgelija. [couchette] 2 cl., [2] Gevgelija - Skopje - Beograd.

M – ⑤ June 7 - Oct. 4: [couchette] 2 cl., [2] Bucureşti - Ruse - Sofia - Thessaloníki.

N – ⑦ June 9 - Oct. 6: [couchette] 2 cl., [2] Thessaloníki - Sofia - Ruse - Bucureşti.

P – FORARAS – [12] Budapest - Braşov and v.v.

Q – LEHÁR – [12] Budapest - Wien.

R – *EuroNight* ISTER – [sleeper] 1, 2 cl., [couchette] 1, 2 cl., [2] Budapest - Bucureşti and v.v.

S – June 1 - Oct. 7: BOSPHOR – [couchette] 2 cl. (4-berth) Bucureşti (**461**) - Ruse - Gorna Oryakhovitsa (**465**) - Dimitrovgrad (**1493/12501**) - İstanbul (Halkalı).

T – June 1 - Oct. 7.

W – [2] ROMANIA – Bucureşti - Ruse - Sofia and v.v.

Y – Dec. 9 - June 1, Oct. 9 - Dec. 14: BALKAN EXPRESS / ISTANBUL-SOFIA EXPRESS – [sleeper] 1, 2 cl., [couchette] 2 cl. İstanbul (Halkalı) - Sofia.

AA – June 1 - Oct. 7: BALKAN EXPRESS / ISTANBUL-SOFIA EXPRESS – [sleeper] 1, 2 cl., [couchette] 2 cl. Sofia - İstanbul (Halkalı).

BB – June 2 - Oct. 8: BALKAN EXPRESS / ISTANBUL-SOFIA EXPRESS – [sleeper] 1, 2 cl., [couchette] 2 cl. İstanbul (Halkalı) - Sofia.

CC – See Table **1570** for additional connections.

* – 🚌 Halkalı - İstanbul and v.v., see Table **1550**.

✣ – Engineering work is affecting services between Novi Sad and Beograd until December 2019. Passengers have to use the regular bus service between Novi Sad and Beograd (rail tickets not valid).

62 DORTMUND - FRANKFURT - MÜNCHEN - LJUBLJANA - ZAGREB - BEOGRAD - THESSALONÍKI

train type / number	*RJ*	*D*	*EC*	*EC*	*EC* 113	*EC*	*D*	*D*		*EC*	*EC*	*EN*	*EN*	*D*		
train number	111	211	217	113	*EC* 213	115	315	315	1491	219	117	60463	50463	415	1335	
notes	🍷		🍷	✕	🍷 ◧	✕		411		🍷						
		T			M	W		P	A		✕	R	L	B	G	
Dortmund Hbf d.	...	...	...	...	...	...	...	...	...	...	...	...	...	...	...	...
Münster Hbf d.	...	...	...	...	...	0631	...	...	...	...	...	...	...	...	...	...
Köln Hbf d.	...	...	...	...	...	0818	...	...	...	...	...	...	...	...	...	...
Frankfurt (Main) Hbf d.	...	...	...	0820	0822	|	...	...	...	1220	1420	...	...	...	...	...
Saarbrücken d.	...	...	0537	|	|	|	...	...	...	|	|	...	...	...	...	...
Mannheim d.	...	...	0711	|	|	1102	...	...	...	|	|	...	...	...	...	...
Heidelberg d.	...	...	|	0914	0914	|	...	...	...	1314	1514	...	...	...	...	...
Stuttgart Hbf d.	...	...	0758	0958	0958	1158	...	...	...	1359	1558	...	...	...	...	...
Ulm d.	...	...	0856	1056	1056	1256	...	...	...	1456	1656	...	...	...	...	...
Augsburg d.	...	...	0942	1142	1142	1342	...	...	...	1542	1742	...	...	...	...	...
München Hbf d.	0818	...	1017	1217	1217	1417	...	...	...	1618	1817	2335	2335	...	...	...
Salzburg Hbf ▦ d.	1012	...	1215	1412	1412	1612	...	...	...	1815	2012	0140	0140	...	...	...
Bischofshofen d.	1054	...	1313	1454	1454	1654	...	...	...	1913	2054	|	|	...	...	...
Selzthal a.	|	...	1439	|	|	|	...	...	...	2039	|	|	|	...	...	...
Graz a.	|	...	1614	|	|	|	...	...	...	2214	|	|	|	...	...	...
Schwarzach St Veit d.	1111	...	...	1511	1511	1711	...	...	...	...	2111	|	|	0423	...	...
Bad Gastein d.	1142	...	...	1542	1542	1742	...	...	...	...	2142	|	|	0501	...	...
Villach Hbf a.	1243	1253	...	1643	1643	1843	1853	...	...	...	2243	0357	0357	0625	...	...
Klagenfurt a.	1316	|	...	1718	|	1916	|	...	...	...	2316	|	|	|	...	...
Jesenice ▦ a.	...	1333	...	...	1733	...	1933	...	...	...	...	0455	0455	0705	...	...
Ljubljana a.	...	1432	...	...	1833	...	2042	2105	...	...	...	0557	0557	0811	...	...
Rijeka a.	...	|	...	...	|	...	|	|	...	...	...	0924	|	|	...	...
Dobova ▦ a.	...	1625	...	...	2007	...	2242	2242	...	...	...	...	0751	0958	...	...
Zagreb a.	...	1710	...	...	2051	...	...	2336	...	...	...	...	0835	1043	...	...
Zagreb d.	...	1742	...	...	...	...	...	2343	...	...	...	...	...	1103	...	...
Vinkovci a.	...	2110	...	...	...	...	...	0305	...	...	...	...	...	1430	...	...
Šid ▦ a.	...	...	...	...	...	...	...	0345	...	...	...	...	...	1518	...	...
Beograd Centar a.	...	...	...	...	...	...	...	0602	...	...	...	...	...	1742	...	...
Beograd Topčider d.	...	...	...	...	...	...	...	...	0912	...	...	...	...	...	1835	...
Niš a.	...	...	...	...	...	...	...	...	1339	...	...	...	...	...	2308	...
Dimitrovgrad ▦ a.	...	...	...	...	...	...	...	...	1648	...	...	...	...	...	|	...
Kalotina Zapad ▦ a.	...	...	...	...	...	...	...	...	1828	...	...	...	...	...	|	...
Sofia a.	...	...	...	...	...	...	...	...	2030	...	...	...	...	...	|	...
Tabanovci ▦ a.	...	...	...	...	...	...	...	...	...	...	...	...	...	...	0320	...
Skopje a.	...	...	...	...	...	...	...	...	...	...	...	...	...	...	0425	...
Gevgelija ▦ a.	...	...	...	...	...	...	...	...	...	...	...	...	...	...	0650	...
Thessaloníki a.	...	...	...	...	...	...	...	...	...	...	...	...	...	...	1033	...

train type	*EC*		*D*	*EN*	*EN*		*D*	*D*	*EC*	*EC*	*EC* 212	*EC*	*D*	*RJ*		
train number	218	1334	414	498	480	1490	410	314	114	112	*EC* 112	216	210	110		
notes	🍷						314		✕	✕	🍷 ◧	🍷		🍷		
		H	C	L	R	A	Q		W		M		T			
Thessaloníki d.	...	1851	...	...	...	...	...	...	...	...	...	...	...	...	...	...
Gevgelija ▦ d.	...	1948	...	...	...	...	...	...	...	...	...	...	...	...	...	...
Skopje d.	...	2219	...	...	...	...	...	...	...	...	...	...	...	...	...	...
Tabanovci ▦ d.	...	2329	...	...	...	...	...	...	...	...	...	...	...	...	...	...
Sofia d.	...	|	...	...	...	0930	...	...	...	...	...	...	...	...	...	...
Kalotina Zapad ▦ d.	...	|	...	...	...	1120	...	...	...	...	...	...	...	...	...	...
Dimitrovgrad ▦ d.	...	|	...	...	...	1100	...	...	...	...	...	...	...	...	...	...
Niš d.	...	0357	...	...	...	1410	...	...	...	...	...	...	...	...	...	...
Beograd Topčider a.	...	0814**t**	...	...	...	1818**t**	...	...	...	...	...	...	...	...	...	...
Beograd Centar d.	...	...	1035	...	...	...	2100	...	...	...	...	...	...	...	...	...
Šid ▦ d.	...	...	1346	...	...	...	0024	...	...	...	...	...	...	...	...	...
Vinkovci d.	...	...	1444	...	...	...	0105	...	...	...	...	...	0900	...	...	...
Zagreb a.	...	...	1812	...	...	...	0427	...	...	...	...	...	1210	...	...	...
Zagreb d.	...	...	1838	2123	...	...	0440	...	...	...	0655	...	1237	...	...	...
Dobova ▦ d.	...	...	1925	2206	...	...	0540	0540	...	...	0745	...	1339	...	...	...
Rijeka d.	...	...	|	|	2050	...	|	|	...	...	|	...	|	...	...	...
Ljubljana d.	...	...	2110	2355	2355	...	0718	0726	...	...	0922	...	1527	...	...	...
Jesenice ▦ d.	...	...	2209	0050	0050	...	...	0827	...	...	1017	...	1627	...	...	...
Klagenfurt d.	...	...	|	|	|	...	...	|	0842	1027	|	...	|	1642	...	...
Villach Hbf d.	...	...	2247	0131	0131	...	...	0908	0916	1058	1058	...	1709	1716	...	...
Bad Gastein a.	...	...	0027	|	|	...	...	...	1016	1216	1216	...	...	1816	...	...
Schwarzach St Veit a.	...	...	0058	|	|	...	...	...	1048	1248	1248	...	...	1848	...	...
Graz d.	0536	...	...	|	|	...	...	...	|	|	|	1145	...	|	...	...
Selzthal d.	0719	...	...	|	|	...	...	...	|	|	|	1319	...	|	...	...
Bischofshofen a.	0848	...	...	|	|	...	...	...	1103	1303	1303	1457	...	1905	...	...
Salzburg Hbf ▦ a.	0944	...	...	0404	0404	...	...	...	1148	1348	1348	1548	...	2000	...	...
München Hbf a.	1141	...	...	0610	0610	...	...	...	1341	1541	1541	1741	...	2141	...	...
Augsburg a.	1215	...	...	...	...	...	...	...	1415	1615	1615	1815	...	...	...	...
Ulm a.	1301	...	...	...	...	...	...	...	1502	1702	1702	1902	...	...	...	...
Stuttgart Hbf a.	1359	...	...	...	...	...	...	...	1601	1801	1801	2001	...	...	...	...
Heidelberg a.	1444	...	...	...	...	...	...	...	|	1844	1844	|	...	...	...	...
Mannheim a.	|	...	...	...	...	...	...	...	1657	|	|	2048	...	...	...	...
Saarbrücken a.	|	...	...	...	...	...	...	...	|	|	|	2219	...	...	...	...
Frankfurt (Main) Hbf a.	1555	...	...	...	...	...	...	...	|	1940	1940	...	...	...	...	...
Köln Hbf a.	...	...	...	...	...	...	...	...	1942	...	...	...	...	...	...	...
Münster Hbf a.	...	...	...	...	...	...	...	...	|	...	...	...	...	...	...	...
Dortmund Hbf a.	...	...	...	...	...	...	...	...	2100	...	...	...	...	...	...	...

A – June 14 - Sept. 16: BALKAN – (2) Beograd - Sofia and v.v.

B – (2) Zürich (**465**) - Schwarzach St Veit (**415**) - Zagreb - Beograd. (2) Villach - Beograd. Conveys *EN* **40465** 🛏 1, 2 cl., ▬ 2 cl. (4, 6 berth) Zürich - Zagreb (Table **86**).

C – (2) Beograd (**414**) - Zagreb - Schwarzach St Veit (**464**) - Zürich. (2) Beograd - Villach. Conveys *EN* **414** 🛏 1, 2 cl., ▬ 2 cl. (4, 6 berth) Zagreb - Zürich (Table **86**).

F – (2) Zürich (**465**) - Schwarzach St Veit (**415**) - Zagreb - Beograd and Beograd (**414**) - Zagreb - Schwarzach St Veit (**464**) - Zürich. (12) Villach - Beograd and v.v. Conveys 🛏 1, 2 cl., ▬ 2 cl. Zürich - Zagreb and v.v. (Table **86**).

G – June 14 - Sept. 15: HELLAS – ▬ 2 cl., (2) Beograd - Skopje - Gevgelija. 🚌 Gevgelija - Thessaloníki.

H – June 15 - Sept. 16: HELLAS – 🚌 Thessaloníki - Gevgelija. ▬ 2 cl., (2) Gevgelija - Skopje - Beograd.

L – LISINSKI – 🛏 1, 2 cl., ▬ 2 cl. (4, 6 berth), (2) München - Salzburg - Zagreb and v.v.

M – (12) Frankfurt - München - Zagreb and v.v. ✕ München - Villach and v.v.

P – June 22 - Sept. 15: ▬ 2 cl., (12) Ljubljana - Zagreb - Beograd.

Q – June 23 - Sept. 16: ▬ 2 cl., (12) Beograd - Zagreb - Ljubljana.

R – (2) (also 🛏 1, 2 cl., May 26 - Sept. 30) München - Salzburg - Ljubljana - Rijeka and v.v.

T – SAVA – (2) Villach - Jesenice ▦ - Ljubljana - Zagreb - Vinkovci and v.v. ✕ Jesenice ▦ - Zagreb and v.v.

W – WÖRTHERSEE – (12) ✕ Münster - Klagenfurt and Klagenfurt - Dortmund.

Z – June 2 - Oct. 1.

◧ – Supplement payable: Jesenice ▦ - Zagreb - Beograd and v.v.

HAMBURG and BERLIN - WIEN - BUDAPEST 64

For alternative services via Břeclav see Table 60

train type	ICE	ICE	ICE	ICE	ICE	RJX	ICE	ICE	RJX	ICE	RJX	ICE	ICE	ICE	EN	ICE	ICE	ICE	ICE	ICE	ICE	NJ	D	
train number	**1503**	**21**	**1505**	**783**	**23**	**65**	**1507**	**91**	**67**	**93**	**165**	**1509**	**787**	**27**	**347**	**1511**	**789**	**29**	**1513**	**881**	**229**	**491**	**345**	
notes	①–⑥	✗	✗	①–⑥	✗	✗	✗	✗	✗	✗	✗	✗	✗	✗	🅁	✗	✗	✗	**1713**	✗	✗			
	✗	...		✗		**C**			**C**						**D**				✗			**A**	**J**	
Hamburg Hbf .... d.		...	...	0555	...	...	...	0803	...	...	...	...	1001	...	...	...	1201	...	...	1401	...	2029	...	...
Hannover Hbf .... d.	...	...	...	0726	...	...	...	0926	...	...	...	...	1126	...	...	...	1326	...	...	1526	...	2157	...	...
Berlin Hbf .... d.	0430	...	0630	|	...	...	0830	|	...	1005	...	1030	|	...	...	1230	|	...	1430	|	...	|	...	...
Leipzig Hbf .... d.	0547	...	0748	|	...	...	0948	|	...	|	...	1148	|	...	...	1347	|	...	1548	|	...	|	...	...
Nürnberg Hbf .... d.	0808	0830	0952	1024	1030	...	1152	1232	...	1332	...	1354	1424	1430	...	1602	1624	1630	1753	1824	1830	0307	...	...
Passau 🏛 .... d.	...	1026	...	...	1229	...	...	1429	...	1529	...	...	...	1629	...	...	...	1829	...	...	2038	0524	...	...
Linz Hbf .... a.	...	1124	...	...	1324	1416	...	1524	1616	1624	...	...	...	1724	...	...	...	1924	...	...	2143	0643	...	...
Wien Hbf .... a.	...	1245	...	...	1445	1530	...	1645	1730	1745	1842	...	...	1845	1942	...	...	2045	...	...	2309	0827	0842	...
Budapest Keleti § .... a.	...	...	...	...	...	1819	...	...	2019	...	2119	...	...	...	2220	...	...	...	...	...	...	...	1119	...

train type	ICE	ICE	ICE	EN	ICE	ICE	ICE	RJX	ICE	RJX	ICE	ICE	ICE	RJX	ICE	ICE	RJX	ICE	ICE	ICE	D	RJX	NJ	
train number	**228**	**880**	**1510**	**346**	**28**	**788**	**1508**	**162**	**92**	**60**	**26**	**786**	**1506**	**62**	**90**	**1504**	**64**	**22**	**782**	**1502**	**344**	**42**	**490**	
notes	✗	✗	**1720**	🅁	✗	✗	✗	✗	✗	✗	✗	✗	✗	✗	✗	✗	✗	✗	✗	✗		✗		
			✗	**D**						**C**				**C**			**C**				**J**		**A**	
Budapest Keleti § .... d.	...	...	...	0540	...	...	...	0640	...	0740	...	...	...	0940	...	...	1140	...	...	...	1640	1740	...	...
Wien Hbf .... d.	0650	...	...	0821	0915	...	...	0930	1015	1030	1115	...	...	1230	1315	...	1430	1515	...	...	1921	2030	2041	...
Linz Hbf .... d.	0817	...	...	...	1036	...	...	1044	1136	1144	1236	...	...	1344	1436	...	1544	1636	...	...	...	2144	2216	...
Passau 🏛 .... a.	0922	...	...	...	1131	...	...	...	1231	...	1331	...	...	...	1531	...	...	1731	...	...	...	...	2320	...
Nürnberg Hbf .... a.	1127	1133	1205	...	1327	1333	1405	...	1427	...	1529	1534	1605	...	1729	1805	...	1927	1934	2005	...	...	0127	...
Leipzig Hbf .... a.	...	|	1410	...	...	|	1610	...	|	...	...	|	1810	...	|	2010	...	...	|	2210	...	...	|	...
Berlin Hbf .... a.	...	|	1530	...	...	|	1729	...	1758	...	...	|	1929	...	|	2129	...	...	|	2330	...	...	|	...
Hannover Hbf .... a.	...	1432	...	...	...	1632	...	...	...	...	...	1832	...	...	2032	...	...	...	2240	...	...	...	0649	...
Hamburg Hbf .... a.	...	1554	...	...	...	1753	...	...	...	...	...	1953	...	...	2154	...	...	...	0008	...	...	...	0844	...

A – *ÖBB nightjet* – 🛏 1, 2 cl., ▬ 2 cl. (4, 6 berth), [2] Hamburg - Wien and v.v. Special fares apply. See Table **53**.
C – ÖBB *Railjet* service: München - Wien - Budapest and v.v.
D – DACIA – 🛏 1, 2 cl., ▬ 2 cl., [2] ✗ Wien - Budapest - Bucuresti and v.v.
J – AVALA – [2] Wien - Budapest - Beograd and v.v.

§ – 🏛 is at Hegyeshalom.
RJ / RJX – ÖBB *Railjet* service, ✗, [1] (business class), [1] (first class), [2] (economy class).

MÜNCHEN - SALZBURG - WIEN - BUDAPEST - BUCUREŞTI 65

train type	RJX	RJX	EC	RJX	RJX	RJX	D	♣	RJX	RJ	RJX	RJX	EC	RJX	D	RJX	EN	♣	EC	RJX	EC	RJX	EC	RJX	RJX	EN
train number	**41**	**761**	**345**	**949**	**49**	**265**	**143**	**79007**	**61**	**111**	**765**	**63**	**217**	**161**	**145**	**65**	**473**	**79019**	**113**	**563**	**147**	**67**	**115**	**165**	**69**	**347**
notes	✗	✗		✗	✗	✗		**909**	✗	✗	✗	✗	🍷	✗		✗	🅁	**919**	🍷	✗	🍷	✗	🍷	✗	✗	🅁
			K				**R**					**F**			2		**C**				**G**					**D**
München Hbf .... d.	...	...	...	...	...	0624	...	0655	0724	0818	...	0930	1018	...	...	1130	...	1155	1218	...	...	1330	1418	...	1530	...
Salzburg Hbf 🏛 .... a.	...	...	...	...	...	0758	...	0842	0858	0959	...	1058	1159	...	...	1258	...	1342	1359	...	...	1458	1559	...	1658	...
Salzburg Hbf 🏛 .... d.	...	0605	...	0708	0708**r**	0808	...	0852	0908	...	1008	1108	...	1208	...	1308	...	1352	...	1408	...	1508	...	1608	1708	...
Linz Hbf .... d.	...	0716	...	0816	0816**r**	0916	...	1004	1016	...	1116	1216	...	1316	...	1416	...	1504	...	1516	...	1616	...	1716	1816	...
St Pölten Hbf .... d.	...	0802	...	0902	0902**r**	1002	...	1050	1102	...	1202	1302	...	1402	...	1502	...	1550	...	1602	...	1702	...	1802	1902	...
Wien Westbahnhof ... a.	...	|	...	|	|	|	...	1117	|	...	|	|	...	|	...	|	...	1617	...	|	...	|	...	|	|	...
Wien Meidling .... d.	...	0825	...	0925	0925**r**	1025	...	...	1125	...	1225	1325	...	1425	...	1525	...	...	...	1625	...	1725	...	1825	1925	...
Wien Hbf .... d.	0742	0830	0842	0930	0942	1030	1042	...	1140	...	1230	1340	...	1430	1442	1542	...	...	...	1630	1642	1740	...	1842	1930	1942
Hegyeshalom 🏛 .... a.	0825	...	0925	...	1025	...	1125	...	1225	...	...	1425	...	...	1525	1625	...	...	...	...	1725	1825	...	1925	...	2025
Györ .... a.	0853	...	0953	...	1053	...	1153	...	1253	...	...	1453	...	...	1553	1653	...	...	...	...	1753	1853	...	1953	...	2053
Budapest Keleti .... a.	1019	...	1119	...	1219	...	1319	...	1419	...	...	1619	...	...	1719	1819	1910	...	...	...	1919	2019	...	2119	...	2220
Bucureşti Nord .... a.	...	...	...	...	...	...	...	...	...	...	...	...	...	...	...	...	1230	...	...	...	...	...	...	...	...	1606

train type	EC	RJX	♣	RJX	EC	RJX	IC	RJX	EC	RJ	EN
train number	**219**	**167**	**79033**	**261**	**117**	**169**	**1269**	**663**	**391**	**367**	**463**
notes	🍷	✗**Q**	**929**	✗	**1217**	✗		✗		✗	
					🍷		Ⓑ		Ⓑ		**A**
München Hbf .... d.	1618	...	1655	1730	1818	...	1917	...	2018	...	2335
Salzburg Hbf 🏛 .... a.	1759	...	1842	1858	1959	...	2100	...	2202	...	0118
Salzburg Hbf 🏛 .... d.	...	1808	1852	1908	...	2008	...	2108	...	2208	0350
Linz Hbf .... d.	...	1916	2004	2016	...	2116	...	2216	...	2319	0510
St Pölten Hbf .... d.	...	2002	2050	2102	...	2202	...	2302	...	0005	0602
Wien Westbahnhof ... a.	...	|	2117	|	...	|	...	|	...	|	|
Wien Meidling .... d.	...	2025	...	2125	...	2225	...	2325	...	0026	0630
Wien Hbf .... d.	...	2030	...	2130	...	2230	...	2330	...	0033	0640
Hegyeshalom 🏛 .... a.	...	...	...	...	...	...	...	...	...	...	0723
Györ .... a.	...	...	...	...	...	...	...	...	...	...	0753
Budapest Keleti .... a.	...	...	...	...	...	...	...	...	...	...	0919
Bucureşti Nord .... a.	...	...	...	...	...	...	...	...	...	...	...

train type	RJX	EC	RJX	♣	RJX	EC	EN	RJX	RJX	EC
train number	**368**	**390**	**260**	**902**	**160**	**218**	**346**	**262**	**162**	**114**
notes	✗		✗	**79020**	✗		🅁	✗	✗	
	①–⑥				**P**		**D**			
Bucureşti Nord .... d.	...	...	...	...	...	...	1400	...	...	...
Budapest Keleti .... d.	...	...	...	...	...	...	0540	...	0640	...
Györ .... d.	...	...	...	...	...	...	0702	...	0802	...
Hegyeshalom 🏛 .... d.	...	...	...	...	...	...	0732	...	0832	...
Wien Hbf .... d.	0530	...	0630	...	0730	...	0821	0830	0930	...
Wien Meidling .... d.	0537	...	0637	...	0737	...	...	0837	0937	...
Wien Westbahnhof .... d.	|	...	|	0643	|	...	...	|	|	...
St Pölten Hbf .... d.	0600	...	0700	0710	0800	...	...	0900	1000	...
Linz Hbf .... d.	0646	...	0746	0758	0846	...	...	0946	1046	...
Salzburg Hbf 🏛 .... a.	0754	...	0852	0908	0952	...	...	1052	1152	...
Salzburg Hbf 🏛 .... d.	...	0800	0900	0915	...	1000	...	1100	...	1200
München Hbf .... a.	...	0941	1030	1106	...	1141	...	1230	...	1341

train type	RJX	EC	RJX	EC	♣	EN	RJX	RJX	EC	RJX	RJX		RJX	♣	D	RJX	RJ	RJX	EC	RJX	RJX	79050	D	NJ	IC	EN
train number	**60**	**140**	**564**	**112**	**912**	**472**	**62**	**166**	**216**	**64**	**168**	**79042**	**66**	**922**	**144**	**760**	**110**	**68**	**344**	**762**	**42**	2	**148**	**466**	**72**	**462**
notes	✗	🍷	✗		**79032**	🅁	✗	✗		✗	✗	2	**1066**	**79042**		✗		✗		✗	✗				🅁	
		J				**C**							✗**F**		**S**				**K**					**B**	**H**	**A**
Bucureşti Nord .... d.	...	...	...	...	...	1745	...	...	...	...	...	...	...	...	...	...	...	...	...	...	...	...	...	...	0520	...
Budapest Keleti .... d.	0740	0840	...	...	...	0850	0940	...	...	1140	...	...	1340	...	1440	...	...	1540	1640	...	1740	...	1840	...	1850	2040
Györ .... d.	0902	1002	...	...	...	...	1102	...	...	1302	...	...	1502	...	1602	...	...	1702	1802	...	1902	...	2002	...	...	2202
Hegyeshalom 🏛 .... d.	0932	1032	...	...	...	...	1132	...	...	1332	...	...	1532	...	1632	...	...	1732	1832	...	1932	...	2032	...	...	2232
Wien Hbf .... d.	1030	1121	1130	...	...	...	1230	1330	...	1430	1530	...	1630	...	1721	1730	...	1830	1921	1930	2030	...	2118	2127	...	2325
Wien Meidling .... d.	1037	...	1137	...	...	...	1237	1337	...	1437	1537	...	1637	...	...	1737	...	1837	...	1937	2037	...	...	2135	...	2333
Wien Westbahnhof ... d.	|	...	|	...	1143	...	|	|	...	|	|	...	|	1643	...	|	...	|	...	|	|	...	...	|	...	|
St Pölten Hbf .... d.	1100	...	1200	...	1210	...	1300	1400	...	1500	1600	...	1700	1710	...	1800	...	1900	...	2000	2100	...	...	2202	...	2359
Linz Hbf .... d.	1146	...	1246	...	1258	...	1346	1446	...	1546	1646	...	1746	1758	...	1846	...	1946	...	2046	2146	...	...	2258	...	0103
Salzburg Hbf 🏛 .... a.	1252	...	1352	...	1408	...	1452	1552	...	1652	1752	...	1852	1908	...	1952	...	2052	...	2152	2254	...	...	0024	...	0213
Salzburg Hbf 🏛 .... d.	1300	...	...	1400	1415	...	1500	...	1600	1700	...	1815	1856	1915	...	...	2000	2100	...	...	...	2300	...	...	...	0427
München Hbf .... a.	1430	...	...	1541	1606	...	1630	...	1741	1830	...	2006	2030	2115	...	...	2141	2231	...	...	...	0057	...	...	...	0610

A – KÁLMÁN IMRE – 🛏 1, 2 cl., ▬ 2 cl. (4, 6 berth), [2] 🍷 München - Wien - Budapest and v.v.

B – *ÖBB nightjet*. WIENER WALZER - 🛏 1, 2 cl., ▬ 2 cl. (4, 6 berth), [2] Wien - Salzburg - Zürich.

C – *EuroNight* ISTER – 🛏 1, 2 cl., ▬ 1, 2 cl., [2] Budapest - Bucureşti and v.v.

D – DACIA – 🛏 1, 2 cl., ▬ 2 cl., [2] ✗ Wien - Budapest - Bucureşti and v.v.

F – From / to Frankfurt (Main) Hbf on dates shown in Table **930**.

G – [12] Wien - Budapest - Szolnok (arrive 2102) - Debrecen (2241) - Zahony (0010). Conveys 🛏 1, 2 cl. Wien - Zahony - Lviv - Kyïv; see Table **96**.

H – TRAIANUS – [12] 🍷 Bucureşti - Budapest.

J – [12] Zahony (depart 0366) - Debrecen (0525) - Szolnok (0657) - Budapest - Wien. Conveys 🛏 1, 2 cl. Kyïv - Lviv - Zahony - Wien; see Table **96**.

K – AVALA – [12] Wien - Budapest - Beograd and v.v.

P – From Bratislava, depart 0610.

Q – To Bratislava, arrive 2151.

R – TRANSILVANIA – [12] Wien - Budapest - Szolnok (arrive 1502) - Cluj Napoca (2225). (Table **1275**).

S – TRANSILVANIA – [12] Cluj Napoca (depart 0740) - Szolnok (1257) - Budapest - Wien. (Table **1275**).

r – ①–⑥.

♣ – From Autumn 2019 (awaiting confirmation of start date). Services operated jointly by *WESTbahn* and Meridian. Special fares payable (ÖBB tickets not valid).

RJ / RJX – ÖBB *Railjet* service, ✗, [1] (business class), [1] (first class), [2] (economy class).

66 DORTMUND - KÖLN - FRANKFURT - WIEN - BUDAPEST

train type	ICE	ICE	ICE	ICE	ICE	ICE		NJ	D
train number	21	23	91	27	29	229		40421	345
notes	✕	✕	✕	✕	✕	✕		A	
Dortmund Hbf .... d.	...	0437	...	0837	...	...	...	...	...
Düsseldorf Hbf .... d.	...	0526	...	0929	...	...	...	2054	...
Köln Hbf .... d.	...	0553	...	0953	...	...	...	2121	...
Bonn Hbf .... d.	...	0614	...	1014	...	...	...	2143	...
Koblenz Hbf .... d.	...	0648	...	1048	...	...	...	2217	...
Mainz Hbf .... d.	...	0740	...	1141	...	...	...	2311	...
Frankfurt Flug. ✈ .... d.	...	0802	...	1202	...	...	...	2353	...
Frankfurt (M) Hbf .... d.	0621	0819	...	1221	1421	1621	...	0008**f**	...
Würzburg Hbf .... d.	0734	0934	1137	1334	1534	1734	...	0137	...
Nürnberg Hbf .... d.	0830	1030	1232	1430	1630	1830	...	0307	...
Regensburg Hbf .... d.	0926	1126	1326	1526	1726	1926	...	0413	...
Passau Hbf ▦ .... d.	1026	1229	1429	1629	1829	2038	...	0524	...
Linz .... a.	1124	1324	1524	1724	1924	2143	...	0643	...
Wien Hbf .... a.	1245	1445	1645	1845	2045	2309	...	0827	...
	RJX	*RJX*	*RJX*	*EN*					
	63	**65**	**67**	**347**					
	✕	✕	✕	**D** [R]					
Wien Hbf .... d.	1340	1542	1740	1942	...	...	...	...	0842
Hegyeshalom ▦ .... a.	1425	1625	1825	2025	...	...	...	...	0925
Budapest Keleti .... a.	1619	1819	2019	2220	...	...	...	...	1119

train type	ICE	EN	RJX	RJX	RJX	RJX	D	NJ	
train number	228	346	60	62	64	66	344	40490	
notes	✕	**D** [R]	✕	✕	✕	✕		A	
Budapest Keleti .... d.	...	0540	0740	0940	1140	1340	1640	...	...
Hegyeshalom ▦ .... d.	...	0732	0932	1132	1332	1532	1832	...	...
Wien Hbf .... a.	...	0821	1021	1221	1421	1618	1921	...	...
		ICE	*ICE*	*ICE*	*ICE*	*ICE*			
		28	**26**	**90**	**22**	**20**			
		✕	✕	✕	✕	✕			
Wien Hbf .... d.	0650	0915	1115	1315	1515	1715	...	2041	...
Linz .... d.	0817	1036	1236	1436	1636	1836	...	2216	...
Passau Hbf ▦ .... a.	0922	1131	1331	1531	1731	1934	...	2320	...
Regensburg Hbf .... a.	1030	1230	1433	1635	1830	2033	...	0024	...
Nürnberg Hbf .... a.	1127	1327	1529	1729	1927	2128	...	0127	...
Würzburg Hbf .... a.	1222	1422	1622	1822	2022	2222	...	|	...
Frankfurt (M) Hbf .... a.	1336	1536	1736	...	2136	2340	...	0523**f**	...
Frankfurt Flug. ✈ .... a.	...	...	1755	...	2157	...	...	0535	...
Mainz Hbf .... a.	...	...	1818	...	2218	...	...	0602	...
Koblenz Hbf .... a.	...	...	1911	...	2311	...	...	0704	...
Bonn Hbf .... a.	...	...	1944	...	2344	...	...	0748	...
Köln Hbf .... a.	...	...	2005	...	0005	...	...	0815	...
Düsseldorf Hbf .... a.	...	...	⊙	...	0030	...	...	0842	...
Dortmund Hbf .... a.	...	...	2121	...	0121	...	...	...	...

A – *ÖBB nightjet* – 🛏 1, 2 cl., ▬ 2 cl. (4, 6 berth), (2) Düsseldorf - Wien and v.v. Special fares apply. See Table **53**.

D – DACIA – 🛏 1, 2 cl., ▬ 2 cl., (2) ✕ Wien - Budapest - Bucureşti and v.v.

f – Frankfurt (Main) **Süd**.

⊙ – Via Hagen, Wuppertal (Table **800**).

RJ – ÖBB *Railjet* service. (1) (business class), (1) (first class), (2) (economy class), ✕.

70 MÜNCHEN - INNSBRUCK - VENEZIA and MILANO

	EC	*EC*	*EC*	*FR*	*EC*		*FR*	*FR*	*EC*	*EC*	*FA*	*EC*	*FR*	*FR*	*EC*	*FR*	*EC*	*EC*		*NJ*	*NJ*	*NJ*			
	1289	**81**	**37**	**9732**	**85**		**9738**	**9439**	**87**	**42**	**8525**	**89**	**9751**	**9756**	**83**	**9759**	**287**	**289**		**295**	**40295**	**40463**			
	♥	♥	[R]	[R]	♥		[R]	**9441**	♥	[R]	[R]	♥	[R]	[R]	♥	[R]	♥	♥							
	⑥⑦	①–⑤	⊗	⚡	**P**	2	⚡	[R] ⚡		⊗	⚡		⚡	⚡		⚡				**B**	**D**	**C**			
	✕	✕	🍷	🍷	✕		🍷	🍷	✕	🍷	🍷	✕	🍷	🍷	✕	🍷	🍷	🍷		🍷	🍷	🍷			
München Hbf .... d.	0734	0734	...	...	0934	...	...	...	1134	...	...	1334	...	...	1534	...	1734	1934	...	2010	2010	2335	...	...	...
München Ost .... d.	0743	0743	...	...	0943	...	...	...	1143	...	...	1343	...	...	1543	...	1743	1943	...	2020	2020	2346	...	...	...
Kufstein ▦ .... a.	0834	0834	...	...	1034	...	...	...	1234	...	...	1434	...	...	1634	...	1834	2034	...	|	|	|	...	...	...
Wörgl .... a.	0844	0844	...	...	1044	...	...	...	1244	...	...	1444	...	...	1644	...	1844	2044	...	|	|	|	...	...	...
Jenbach .... a.	0859	0859	...	...	1059	...	...	...	1259	...	...	1459	...	...	1659	...	1859	2059	...	|	|	|	...	...	...
Innsbruck Hbf .... a.	0918	0918	...	...	1118	...	...	...	1318	...	...	1518	...	...	1718	...	1918	2118	...	|	|	|	...	...	...
Innsbruck Hbf .... d.	0924	0924	...	...	1124	...	...	...	1324	...	...	1524	...	...	1724	...	...	...	...	|	|	|	...	...	...
Brennero / Brenner ▦ .... a.	1000	1000	...	...	1200	...	...	...	1400	...	...	1600	...	...	1800	...	...	...	...	◧	◧	◧	...	...	...
Bolzano / Bozen .... a.	1115	1127	...	...	1327	...	...	...	1527	...	...	1727	...	...	1927	...	...	...	...	|	|	|	...	...	...
Trento .... a.	1148	1202	...	...	1402	...	...	...	1602	...	...	1802	...	...	2002	...	...	...	...	|	|	|	...	...	...
Padova .... a.	|	|	...	...	|	...	...	...	|	...	...	|	...	...	|	...	...	...	...	|	0521	|	...	...	...
Verona .... a.	1237	1256	1330	1402	1458	1521	1532	...	1658	1732	1752	1858	1930	1932	2056	2130	...	...	...	|	0624	|	...	...	...
Padova .... a.	1326	|	1412	|	|	1619	|	...	1742	|	|	|	2012	|	...	2212	...	...	...	0409	|	|	...	...	...
Venezia Mestre .... a.	1344	|	1428	|	|	1636	|	...	1758	|	|	|	2028	|	...	2228	...	...	...	|	|	0812	...	...	...
Venezia Santa Lucia .... a.	1356	|	1440	|	|	1648	|	...	1810	|	|	|	2040	|	...	2240	...	...	...	|	|	0824	...	...	...
Milano Centrale .... a.	...	|	...	1515	|	...	1645	...	...	1855	|	|	...	2045	...	...	...	...	...	|	0912	...	...	...	...
Bologna Centrale .... a.	...	1407	...	...	1620	...	...	1655	...	...	1842	2030	...	...	...	...	...	...	...	0519	...	...	...	...	...
Rimini .... a.	...	...	...	...	1740**t**	...	...	|	...	...	|	...	...	...	...	...	...	...	...	|	...	...	...	...	...
Firenze SMN .... a.	...	...	...	...	...	...	...	1730	...	...	1925¶	...	...	...	...	...	...	...	...	0619	...	...	...	...	...
Roma Termini .... a.	...	...	...	...	...	...	...	1910	...	...	2045	...	...	...	...	...	...	...	...	0922	...	...	...	...	...

	EC	*EC*	*FR*	*FR*	*EC*	*FR*	*FR*	*FR*	*EC*	*FB*	*FR*	*FR*	*FR*	*EC*	*FA*	*EC*	*EC*		*FR*	*EC*	*EC*	*EC*	*NJ*	*NJ*	*NJ*
	288	**286**	**9708**	**9705**	**88**	**8504**	**9716**	**8709**	**80**	**9715**	**9717**	**9724**	**9518**	**84**	**8512**	**15**	**86**		**9737**	**10**	**82**	**1288**	**40236**	**294**	**40235**
	♥	♥	[R]	[R]	♥	[R]	[R]	[R]	♥	[R]	[R] ⚡	[R]	[R]	♥	[R]	[R]	♥		[R]	[R]	♥	♥			
			⚡	⚡		⚡	⚡	⚡		⚡	⑥⑦	⚡	⚡	**R**	⚡	⚡			⚡	⊗	①–⑤	⑥⑦	**F**	**B**	**G**
	🍷	🍷	🍷	🍷	✕	🍷	🍷	🍷	✕	🍷	🍷	🍷	🍷	✕	🍷	🍷	✕		🍷	🍷	✕	✕	🍷	🍷	🍷
Roma Termini .... d.	...	...	...	...	...	0645	...	...	...	...	...	...	0920	...	1045	...	...	...	...	...	...	...	...	1858	...
Firenze SMN .... d.	...	...	...	...	...	0803¶	...	...	...	...	...	...	1100	...	1203¶	...	...	...	...	...	...	...	...	2149	...
Rimini .... d.	...	...	...	...	...	|	...	...	...	...	...	...	|	1035**f**	|	...	...	...	...	...	...	...	...	|	...
Bologna Centrale .... d.	...	...	...	...	0740	0845	...	...	...	...	...	...	1135	1152	1245	...	...	1410	...	...	1552	...	...	2246	...
Milano Centrale .... d.	...	...	...	0715	|	|	...	0915	...	0945	1015	...	...	|	|	1305	...	|	1515	...	|	...	...	|	2040
Venezia Santa Lucia .... d.	...	...	0720	|	|	|	...	|	...	|	|	1050	...	|	|	|	1350	|	|	1520	|	1535	2104	|	|
Venezia Mestre .... d.	...	...	0732	|	|	|	0902	|	...	|	|	1102	...	|	|	|	1402	|	|	1532	|	1547	2116	|	|
Padova .... d.	...	...	0748	|	|	|	0918	|	...	|	|	1118	...	|	|	|	1418	|	|	1548	|	1606	|	0003	|
Verona .... d.	...	...	0830	0828	0904	0937	1000	1028	1102	1058	1128	1200	...	1304	1337	1428	1502	1540	1628	1630	1702	1702	|	|	2252
Padova .... d.	...	...	...	...	|	...	...	...	|	...	...	...	...	|	...	...	|	...	...	...	|	|	|	|	2344
Trento .... d.	...	...	...	...	0959	...	...	...	1159	...	...	...	...	1359	...	...	1559	...	...	...	1759	1759	|	|	|
Bolzano / Bozen .... d.	...	...	...	...	1034	...	...	...	1234	...	...	...	...	1434	...	...	1634	...	...	...	1834	1834	|	|	|
Brennero / Brenner ▦ .... d.	...	...	...	...	1200	...	...	...	1400	...	...	...	...	1600	...	...	1800	...	...	...	2000	2000	◧	◧	◧
Innsbruck Hbf .... a.	...	...	...	...	1236	...	...	...	1436	...	...	...	...	1636	...	...	1836	...	...	...	2036	2036	|	|	|
Innsbruck Hbf .... d.	0717	1040	...	...	1240	...	...	...	1440	...	...	...	...	1640	...	...	1840	...	...	...	2040	2040	|	|	|
Jenbach .... d.	0735	1101	...	...	1301	...	...	...	1501	...	...	...	...	1701	...	...	1901	...	...	...	2101	2101	|	|	|
Wörgl .... d.	0749	1116	...	...	1316	...	...	...	1516	...	...	...	...	1716	...	...	1916	...	...	...	2116	2116	|	|	|
Kufstein ▦ .... a.	0757	1124	...	...	1324	...	...	...	1524	...	...	...	...	1724	...	...	1924	...	...	...	2124	2124	|	|	|
München Ost .... a.	0849	1215	...	...	1415	...	...	...	1615	...	...	...	...	1815	...	...	2015	...	...	...	2215	2215	0557	|	|
München Hbf .... a.	0901	1226	...	...	1426	...	...	...	1626	...	...	...	...	1826	...	...	2026	...	...	...	2226	2226	0610	0819	0819

B – *ÖBB nightjet* – 🛏 1, 2 cl., ▬ 2 cl. (4, 6 berth), (2) München - Villach - Tarvisio ▦ - Roma and v.v. Special fares apply.

C – *ÖBB nightjet* – 🛏 1, 2 cl., ▬ 2 cl. (4, 6 berth), (2) München (**463**) - Villach (**237**) - Tarvisio ▦ - Venezia. Special fares apply.

D – *ÖBB nightjet* – 🛏 1, 2 cl., ▬ 2 cl. (4, 6 berth), (2) München (**295**) - Villach (**235**) - Tarvisio ▦ - Verona - Milano. Special fares apply.

F – *ÖBB nightjet* – 🛏 1, 2 cl., ▬ 2 cl. (4, 6 berth), (2) Venezia (**236**) - Tarvisio ▦ - Villach (**498**) - München. Special fares apply.

G – *ÖBB nightjet* – 🛏 1, 2 cl., ▬ 2 cl. (4, 6 berth), (2) Milano (**235**) - Verona - Tarvisio ▦ - Villach (**294**) - München. Special fares apply.

K – (1,2) 🍷 Munster - Köln - Stuttgart - Lindau ▦ - Innsbruck.

P – (1,2) ✕ München - Bologna - (Rimini ④⑤⑥).

R – (1,2) ✕ (Rimini ⑤⑥⑦) - Bologna - München.

f – ⑤⑥⑦.

t – ④⑤⑥.

⊗ – Compulsory reservation for international journeys. Supplement payable for international journeys and for internal journeys within Italy.

◧ – ▦ is Tarvisio (Table **88**).

⚡ – Supplement payable.

♥ – DB-ÖBB EuroCity service.

¶ – Firenze **Campo di Marte**.

AMSTERDAM, BERLIN, DORTMUND and KÖLN - BASEL - ZÜRICH and MILANO 73

train type	ICE	EC	ICE	ICE	IR	EC	ICE	EC	ICE	EC	ICE	EC	ICE	ICE	ICE	IR	EC	ICE	ICE	EC	ICE	EC	EC	
train number	3	15	271	5	2319	17	101	151	275	57	71	7	121	515	277	2327	21	105	73	9	279	9	23	
notes	🍷	[R] 🍷	1271	🍷		[R] 🍷	🍷	[R] 🍷	🍷	[R] 🍷	291	✕	①–⑥	🍷			[R] 🍷	🍷	1173	✕	🍷	✕	[R] 🍷	
	Ⓐ	⊗	M			⊗		⊗		⊗	🍷	C	f				⊗		🍷	D		D	⊗	
Hamburg Hbf d.	...	...	0045e	...	...	...	...	...	...	...	0618	0442v	...	...	...	...	...	...	0824	0646	...	...	...	...
Bremen Hbf d.	...	...	|	...	...	...	...	...	...	...	|	0540v	...	...	...	...	...	...	|	0744	...	...	...	...
Berlin Hbf d.	...	...	|	...	...	...	...	...	0432p	...	|	|	...	...	0630	...	...	...	|	|	0830	...	...	...
Hannover Hbf d.	...	...	0210e	...	...	...	...	...	|	...	0741	|	...	...	|	...	...	...	0941	|	|	...	...	...
Dortmund Hbf d.	...	...	|	...	...	...	0537	...	|	...	|	0737	...	0837	|	...	...	...	|	0937	|	...	...	...
Essen Hbf d.	...	...	|	...	...	...	|	...	|	...	|	0800	...	|	|	...	...	...	|	1000	|	...	...	...
Amsterdam Centraal d.	...	...	|	...	...	...	|	...	|	...	|	|	0638	|	|	...	...	0808	|	|	|	...	...	...
Utrecht Centraal d.	...	...	|	...	...	...	|	...	|	...	|	|	0707	|	|	...	...	0837	|	|	|	...	...	...
Arnhem ⊙ d.	...	...	|	...	...	...	|	...	|	...	|	|	0737	|	|	...	...	0907	|	|	|	...	...	...
Duisburg Hbf d.	...	...	|	...	...	...	h	...	|	...	|	0813	0834	h	|	...	...	1008	|	1013	|	...	...	...
Düsseldorf Hbf d.	...	...	|	...	...	...	|	...	|	...	|	0827	0847	|	|	...	...	1022	|	1027	|	...	...	...
Köln Hbf d.	...	...	|	...	...	...	0654	...	|	...	|	0853	0928	0955	|	...	...	1055	|	1053	|	...	...	...
Bonn Hbf d.	...	...	|	...	...	...	|	...	|	...	|	0914	|	|	|	...	...	|	|	1114	|	...	...	...
Koblenz Hbf d.	...	...	|	...	...	...	⊖	...	|	...	|	0948	⊖	⊖	|	...	...	⊖	|	1148	|	...	...	...
Mainz Hbf d.	...	...	|	...	...	...	|	...	|	...	|	1040	|	|	|	...	...	|	|	1240	|	...	...	...
Frankfurt Flughafen ✈ d.	...	...	|	...	...	...	0751	...	|	...	|	|	1018	1052	|	...	...	1152	|	|	|	...	...	...
Frankfurt (Main) Hbf d.	...	...	0550	0650	...	...	|	0801	0850	...	1005	|	1031	|	1050	...	...	|	1205	|	1250	...	...	...
Mannheim Hbf d.	...	...	0633	0736	...	...	0836	0846	0936	...	1045	1123	...	1123	1136	...	...	1236	1245	1323	1336	...	...	...
Karlsruhe Hbf d.	0556	...	0658	0800	...	...	0900	0910	1000	...	1110	1149	...	...	1200	...	...	1300	1310	1349	1400	...	...	...
Freiburg (Brsg) Hbf d.	0702	...	0802	0901	...	...	1007	1015	1101	...	1212	1251	...	...	1306	...	...	1400	1412	1455	1501	...	...	...
Basel Bad Bf 🏛 a.	0735	...	0834	0934	...	...	1038	1045	1134	...	1245	1322	...	...	1338	...	...	1434	1445	1527	1534	←	...	...
Basel SBB a.	0747	...	0847	0946	...	...	1047	1054	1147	...	1254	1330	...	...	1347	...	...	1447	1454	1535	1546	1535	...	...
Basel SBB ★ d.	0807	...	0907	...	1004	...	...	1104	1159	1231	1307	1359	...	...	...	1404	...	...	1507	1607	...	1607	...	...
Bern a.	|	...	|	...	|	...	...	|	1256	1324	|	1456	...	...	...	|	...	...	|	→	...	|	...	...
Interlaken Ost a.	|	...	|	...	|	...	...	|	1356	|	|	1557	...	...	...	|	...	...	|	...	...	|	...	...
Zürich HB a.	0900	0910	1000	...	|	1110	...	|	...	|	1400	...	...	...	...	|	1510	...	1600	...	...	1700	1710	...
Chur a.	...	|	1122	...	|	|	...	|	...	|	1522	...	...	...	...	|	|	...	...	...	...	...	|	...
Arth-Goldau a.	...	0947	...	...	1146	1147x	...	1246	...	|	...	...	...	...	...	1546	1547x	...	...	...	...	...	1747	...
Bellinzona a.	...	1047	...	...	...	1247	...	1347	...	|	...	...	...	...	...	...	1647	...	...	...	...	...	1847	...
Lugano a.	...	1118	...	...	...	1318	...	1418	...	|	...	...	...	...	...	...	1718	...	...	...	...	...	1918	...
Chiasso 🏛 a.	...	1146	...	...	...	1346	...	1446	...	◧	...	...	...	...	...	...	1746	...	...	...	...	...	1946	...
Como San Giovanni a.	...	|	...	...	...	1355	...	|	...	|	...	...	...	...	...	...	|	...	...	...	...	...	|	...
Milano Centrale a.	...	1235	...	...	...	1435	...	1535	...	1637	...	...	...	...	...	...	1835	...	...	...	...	...	2035	...

train type	ICE	ICE	EC	EC	ICE	ICE	ICE	ICE	ICE	ICE	ICE		NJ	NJ	IC	EC								
train number	107	75	59	25	123	371	109	77	125	373	79		401	471	665	15								
notes	🍷	1175	[R] 🍷	[R] 🍷	🍷	🍷	🍷	1277	🍷	🍷	1279		471			[R] 🍷								
		🍷	⊗	⊗				🍷			🍷		A	B		⊗								
Hamburg Hbf d.	...	1024	...	...	...	...	...	1224	...	...	1424	...	2045	...	...	...	...	...	...	...	...	...	...	...
Bremen Hbf d.	...	|	...	...	...	...	...	|	...	...	|	...	|	...	...	...	...	...	...	...	...	...	...	...
Berlin Hbf d.	...	|	...	...	...	1034	...	|	...	1230	|	...	|	2106	...	...	...	...	...	...	...	...	...	...
Hannover Hbf d.	...	1141	...	...	...	|	...	1341	...	|	1541	...	2326	|	...	...	...	...	...	...	...	...	...	...
Dortmund Hbf d.	...	|	...	...	...	|	1337c	|	...	|	|	...	|	|	...	...	...	...	...	...	...	...	...	...
Essen Hbf d.	...	|	...	...	...	|	|	|	...	|	|	...	|	|	...	...	...	...	...	...	...	...	...	...
Amsterdam Centraal d.	...	|	...	...	1038	|	|	|	1238	|	|	...	|	|	...	...	...	...	...	...	...	...	...	...
Utrecht Centraal d.	...	|	...	...	1107	|	|	|	1307	|	|	...	|	|	...	...	...	...	...	...	...	...	...	...
Arnhem ⊙ d.	...	|	...	...	1137	|	|	|	1337	|	|	...	|	|	...	...	...	...	...	...	...	...	...	...
Duisburg Hbf d.	...	|	...	...	1234	|	h	|	1434	|	|	...	|	|	...	...	...	...	...	...	...	...	...	...
Düsseldorf Hbf d.	...	|	...	...	1248	|	|	|	1450	|	|	...	|	|	...	...	...	...	...	...	...	...	...	...
Köln Hbf d.	1255	|	...	...	1328	|	1455	|	1529	|	|	...	|	|	...	...	...	...	...	...	...	...	...	...
Bonn Hbf d.	|	|	...	...	|	|	|	|	|	|	|	...	|	|	...	...	...	...	...	...	...	...	...	...
Koblenz Hbf d.	⊖	|	...	...	⊖	|	⊖	|	⊖	|	|	...	|	|	...	...	...	...	...	...	...	...	...	...
Mainz Hbf d.	|	|	...	...	|	|	|	|	|	|	|	...	|	|	...	...	...	...	...	...	...	...	...	...
Frankfurt Flughafen ✈ d.	1351	|	...	...	1418	|	1551	|	1620	|	|	...	|	|	...	...	...	...	...	...	...	...	...	...
Frankfurt (Main) Hbf d.	|	1405	...	...	1431	1450	|	1605	1631	1650	1805	...	0402z	0402z	...	...	...	...	...	...	...	...	...	...
Mannheim Hbf d.	1434	1445	...	...	...	1536	1636	1645	...	1736	1845	...	0442	0442	...	...	...	...	...	...	...	...	...	...
Karlsruhe Hbf d.	1458	1510	...	...	...	1600	1700	1710	...	1800	1910	...	0509	0509	...	...	...	...	...	...	...	...	...	...
Freiburg (Brsg) Hbf d.	1601	1612	...	...	...	1701	1801	1812	...	1901	2012	...	0622	0622	...	...	...	...	...	...	...	...	...	...
Basel Bad Bf 🏛 a.	1634	1645	...	...	...	1734	1834	1845	...	1934	2045	...	0706	0706	...	...	...	...	...	...	...	...	...	...
Basel SBB a.	1647	1654	...	...	...	1747	1847	1854	...	1947	2054	...	0720	0720	...	...	...	...	...	...	...	...	...	...
Basel SBB ★ d.	...	1707	1731	...	...	1759	...	1907	...	1959	2107	...	|	|	0804	...	...	...	...	...	...	...	...	...
Bern a.	...	|	1824	...	...	1856	...	|	...	2056	|	...	|	|	|	...	...	...	...	...	...	...	...	...
Interlaken Ost a.	...	|	|	...	...	1956	...	|	...	2156	|	...	|	|	|	...	...	...	...	...	...	...	...	...
Zürich HB a.	...	1800	|	1910	...	...	...	2000	...	...	2200	...	0905	0905	|	...	...	...	...	...	...	...	...	...
Chur a.	...	1922	|	|	...	...	...	...	...	...	...	...	...	...	|	...	...	...	...	...	...	...	...	...
Arth-Goldau a.	...	...	|	1947	...	...	...	...	...	...	...	...	...	...	0946	0950	...	...	...	...	...	...	...	...
Bellinzona a.	...	...	|	2047	...	...	...	...	...	...	...	...	...	...	...	1047	...	...	...	...	...	...	...	...
Lugano a.	...	...	|	2118	...	...	...	...	...	...	...	...	...	...	...	1118	...	...	...	...	...	...	...	...
Chiasso 🏛 a.	...	...	◧	2146	...	...	...	...	...	...	...	...	...	...	...	1146	...	...	...	...	...	...	...	...
Como San Giovanni a.	...	...	|	2156	...	...	...	...	...	...	...	...	...	...	...	|	...	...	...	...	...	...	...	...
Milano Centrale a.	...	...	2137	2250	...	...	...	...	...	...	...	...	...	...	...	1235	...	...	...	...	...	...	...	...

A – *ÖBB nightjet* – 🛏 1, 2 cl., 🛌 2 cl. (4, 6 berth), (2) Hamburg - Frankfurt - Zürich. Special fares apply.
B – *ÖBB nightjet* – 🛏 1, 2 cl., 🛌 2 cl. (4, 6 berth), (2) Berlin - Frankfurt - Zürich. Special fares apply.
C – (12) ✕ (Hamburg ①–⑥) - Dortmund - Köln - Basel - Interlaken Ost.
D – (12) ✕ Hamburg - Dortmund - Köln - Basel - Zürich.
M – (12) 🍷 (Hamburg ①) - (Frankfurt ①–⑥) - Basel - Chur.

c – Not ⑥.
e – ①.
f – Not Apr. 22, June 10.
h – Via Hagen and Wuppertal.
p – ①–⑤.

v – ①–⑥.
x – Depart 3 minutes later.
z – Frankfurt (Main) **Süd**.

⊙ – 🏛 is at Emmerich.
◧ – Via Brig. 🏛 is at Domodossola; ticket point is **Iselle**.
⊖ – Via Köln - Frankfurt high speed line.
★ – Connections at Basel are not guaranteed.
⊗ – Compulsory reservation for international journeys. Supplement payable for international journeys and for internal journeys within Italy.

CONNECTING SERVICES

Basel - Luzern - Chiasso: Table **550**, Basel - Bern - Interlaken and Brig: Table **560**.
Zürich - Landquart - Chur: Table **520**, Chur - St Moritz: Table **540**, Zürich - Bellinzona - Chiasso: Table **550**.

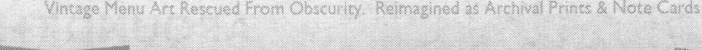

73 MILANO and ZÜRICH - KÖLN, DORTMUND, BERLIN and AMSTERDAM

train type	ICE	ICE	ICE	ICE	ICE	ICE		ICE	EC	EC	EC	ICE	EC	ICE	ICE		ICE	EC	EC	EC	ICE	ICE	
train number	**78**	**372**	**126**	**76**	**370**	**124**		**74**	**12**	**8**	**50**	**278**	**8**	**72**	**122**		**276**	**6**	**14**	**158**	**70**	**104**	
notes	**1278**	🍷	🍷	**1276**	🍷	🍷		**1274**	🅁🍷	✕	🅁🍷	🍷	✕	**1272**	🍷		🍷	✕	🅁🍷	🅁🍷	**1270**	🍷	
	🍷			🍷				🍷	⊗		⊗			🍷				**G**	⊗	⊗	🍷		
Milano Centrale d.	...	...	...	...	...	...	...	...	0725	...	0723	...	...	...	...	...	...	...	0925	1015	...	...	...
Como San Giovanni d.	...	...	...	...	...	...	...	...	|	...	|	...	...	...	...	...	...	...	1003	1103	...	...	...
Chiasso 🏛 d.	...	...	...	...	...	...	...	...	0815	...	◧	...	...	...	...	...	...	...	1015	1115	...	...	...
Lugano d.	...	...	...	...	...	...	...	...	0843	...	|	...	...	...	...	...	...	...	1043	1143	...	...	...
Bellinzona d.	...	...	...	...	...	...	...	...	0913	...	|	...	...	...	...	...	...	...	1113	1213	...	...	...
Arth-Goldau d.	...	...	...	...	...	...	...	...	1013	...	|	...	...	...	...	...	...	...	1213	1314	...	...	...
Chur d.	...	...	...	...	...	...	...	...	|	...	|	...	...	1039	...	...	...	...	|	|	1239	...	...
Zürich HB d.	0600	...	...	0800	...	...	...	1000	1050	1100	|	...	...	1200	...	...	...	...	1250	|	1400	...	...
Interlaken Ost d.	|	0600	...	|	...	...	...	|	...	|	|	1000	...	|	...	...	...	1200	...	|	|	...	...
Bern d.	|	0704	...	|	...	...	...	|	...	|	1036	1104	←	|	...	...	...	1304	...	|	|	...	...
Basel SBB ★ a.	0653	0759	...	0853	...	...	...	1053	...	1153	1129	1159	1153	1253	...	...	...	1359	...	1455	1453	...	...
Basel SBB d.	0706	0813	...	0906	1013	...	...	1106	...	1220	...	1213	1220	1306	...	...	1413	1427	...	...	1506	1513	...
Basel Bad Bf 🏛 d.	0715	0823	...	0915	1023	...	...	1115	...	→	...	1223	1230	1315	...	...	1423	1435	...	...	1515	1523	...
Freiburg (Brsg) Hbf d.	0749	0857	...	0949	1057	...	...	1149	...	...	...	1257	1304	1349	...	...	1455	1507	...	...	1549	1556	...
Karlsruhe Hbf d.	0851	1000	...	1051	1200	...	...	1251	...	...	...	1400	1412	1451	...	...	1601	1612	...	...	1651	1700	...
Mannheim Hbf a.	0914	1023	...	1114	1224	...	...	1314	...	...	...	1423	1437	1514	...	...	1624	1637	...	...	1714	1723	...
Frankfurt (Main) Hbf a.	0953	1108	1129	1153	1308	1329	...	1353	...	...	...	1508	|	1553	1629	...	1708	|	...	...	1753	|	...
Frankfurt Flughafen ✈ a.	|	|	1140	|	|	1340	...	|	...	...	...	|	|	|	1640	...	|	|	...	...	|	1806	...
Mainz Hbf a.	|	|	|	|	|	|	...	|	...	...	...	|	1518	|	|	...	|	1718	...	...	|	|	...
Koblenz Hbf a.	|	|	⊖	|	|	⊖	...	|	...	...	...	|	1611	|	⊖	...	|	1811	...	...	|	⊖	...
Bonn Hbf a.	|	|	|	|	|	|	...	|	...	...	...	|	1644	|	|	...	|	1844	...	...	|	|	...
Köln Hbf a.	|	|	1233	|	|	1433	...	|	...	...	...	|	1705	|	1732	...	|	1905	...	...	|	1905	...
Düsseldorf Hbf a.	|	|	1306	|	|	1510	...	|	...	...	...	|	1731	|	1809	...	|	1931	...	...	|	1936	...
Duisburg Hbf a.	|	|	1322	|	|	1526	...	|	...	...	...	|	1744	|	1825	...	|	1944	...	...	|	1949	...
Arnhem ⊙ a.	|	|	1428	|	|	1628	...	|	...	...	...	|	|	|	1928	...	|	|	...	...	|	2058	...
Utrecht Centraal a.	|	|	1501	|	|	1701	...	|	...	...	...	|	|	|	2001	...	|	|	...	...	|	2131	...
Amsterdam Centraal a.	|	|	1528	|	|	1728	...	|	...	...	...	|	|	|	2028	...	|	|	...	...	|	2158	...
Essen Hbf a.	|	|	...	|	|	...	...	|	...	...	...	|	1757	|	...	...	|	1957	...	...	|	...	...
Dortmund Hbf a.	|	|	...	|	|	...	...	|	...	...	...	|	1821	|	...	...	|	2021	...	...	|	...	...
Hannover Hbf a.	1217	|	...	1417	|	...	...	1617	...	...	...	|	|	1817	...	...	|	|	...	...	2017	...	...
Berlin Hbf a.	|	1528	...	|	1728	...	...	|	...	...	...	1928	|	|	...	...	2128	|	...	...	|	...	...
Bremen Hbf a.	|	...	...	|	...	...	...	|	...	...	...	...	2015	|	...	...	...	2216**x**	...	...	|	...	...
Hamburg Hbf a.	1335	...	...	1535	...	...	...	1735	...	...	...	...	2113	1935	...	...	...	2314**x**	...	...	2138	...	...

train type	EC	EC	IC	ICE	ICE	ICE	ICE		EC	ICE	ICE		EC	ICE		NJ	NJ						
train number	**52**	**16**	**776**	**274**	**120**	**376**	**102**		**18**	**272**	**100**		**20**	**4**		**470**	**470**						
notes	🅁🍷	🅁🍷		🍷	Ⓑ	**396**	**1102**		🅁🍷	**292**	🍷		🅁	🍷			**400**						
	⊗	⊗			**m**	🍷	🍷		⊗	**1172**			⊗			**A**	**B**						
Milano Centrale d.	1123	1125	...	...	...	...	...	...	1325	...	...	...	1525	...	...	...	...	...	...	...	...	...	...
Como San Giovanni d.	|	1203	...	...	...	...	...	...	|	...	...	...	1603	...	...	...	...	...	...	...	...	...	...
Chiasso 🏛 d.	◧	1215	...	...	...	...	...	...	1415	...	...	...	1615	...	...	...	...	...	...	...	...	...	...
Lugano d.	|	1243	...	...	...	...	...	...	1443	...	...	...	1643	...	...	...	...	...	...	...	...	...	...
Bellinzona d.	|	1313	...	...	...	...	...	...	1513	...	...	...	1713	...	...	...	...	...	...	...	...	...	...
Arth-Goldau d.	|	1413	...	...	...	...	...	...	1613	...	...	...	1813	...	...	...	...	...	...	...	...	...	...
Chur d.	|	|	...	...	...	...	...	...	|	...	...	...	|	...	...	...	...	...	...	...	...	...	...
Zürich HB d.	|	1450	1500	...	...	...	...	...	1650	1700	...	...	1850	1900	...	2000	2000	...	...	...	...	...	...
Interlaken Ost d.	|	...	|	...	...	1500	...	...	...	|	...	...	...	|	...	|	|	...	...	...	...	...	...
Bern d.	1436	...	|	...	...	1604	...	...	...	|	...	...	...	|	...	|	|	...	...	...	...	...	...
Basel SBB ★ a.	1529	...	1553	...	...	1659	...	...	...	1753	...	...	...	1953	...	|	|	...	...	...	...	...	...
Basel SBB d.	1538	...	...	1613	...	1706	1713	...	...	1813	1913	...	...	2013	...	2113	2113	...	...	...	...	...	...
Basel Bad Bf 🏛 d.	1551	...	...	1623	...	1715	1723	...	...	1823	1923	...	...	2023	...	2122	2122	...	...	...	...	...	...
Freiburg (Brsg) Hbf d.	|	...	...	1655	...	1749	1756	...	...	1857	1956	...	...	2055	...	2158	2158	...	...	...	...	...	...
Karlsruhe Hbf d.	1731	...	...	1801	...	1851	1900	...	...	2000	2101	...	...	2201	...	2304	2304	...	...	...	...	...	...
Mannheim Hbf a.	1810	...	...	1824	...	1914	1924	...	...	2024	2124	...	...	2233	...	2346	2346	...	...	...	...	...	...
Frankfurt (Main) Hbf a.	1859	...	...	1908	1929	1953	|	...	...	2108	|	...	...	2310	...	0051**z**	0051**z**	...	...	...	...	...	...
Frankfurt Flughafen ✈ a.	...	...	...	|	1940	|	2006	...	...	|	2206	...	...	...	...	|	|	...	...	...	...	...	...
Mainz Hbf a.	...	...	...	|	|	|	|	...	...	|	|	...	...	...	...	|	|	...	...	...	...	...	...
Koblenz Hbf a.	...	...	...	|	⊖	|	⊖	...	...	|	⊖	...	...	...	...	|	|	...	...	...	...	...	...
Bonn Hbf a.	...	...	...	|	|	|	|	...	...	|	|	...	...	...	...	|	|	...	...	...	...	...	...
Köln Hbf a.	...	...	...	|	2033	|	2105	...	...	|	2307	...	...	...	...	|	|	...	...	...	...	...	...
Düsseldorf Hbf a.	...	...	...	|	2106	|	|	...	...	|	2338	...	...	...	...	|	|	...	...	...	...	...	...
Duisburg Hbf a.	...	...	...	|	2122	|	**h**	...	...	|	2355	...	...	...	...	|	|	...	...	...	...	...	...
Arnhem ⊙ a.	...	...	...	|	2228	|	|	...	...	|	|	...	...	...	...	|	|	...	...	...	...	...	...
Utrecht Centraal a.	...	...	...	|	2301	|	|	...	...	|	|	...	...	...	...	|	|	...	...	...	...	...	...
Amsterdam Centraal a.	...	...	...	|	2328	|	|	...	...	|	|	...	...	...	...	|	|	...	...	...	...	...	...
Essen Hbf a.	...	...	...	|	...	|	|	...	...	|	0008	...	...	...	...	|	|	...	...	...	...	...	...
Dortmund Hbf a.	...	...	...	|	...	|	2221	...	...	|	0031	...	...	...	...	|	|	...	...	...	...	...	...
Hannover Hbf a.	...	...	...	|	...	2217**j**	0018	...	...	2341**f**	...	...	...	...	...	|	0604	...	...	...	...	...	...
Berlin Hbf a.	...	...	...	2330	...	|	...	...	...	|	...	...	...	...	...	0754	|	...	...	...	...	...	...
Bremen Hbf a.	...	...	...	...	...	|	...	...	...	|	...	...	...	...	...	...	|	...	...	...	...	...	...
Hamburg Hbf a.	...	...	...	...	...	2351**j**	...	...	...	0111**f**	...	...	...	...	...	...	0751	...	...	...	...	...	...

A – *ÖBB nightjet* – 🛏 1, 2 cl., ▬ 2 cl. (4, 6 berth), [2] Zürich - Frankfurt - Berlin. Special fares apply.
B – *ÖBB nightjet* – 🛏 1, 2 cl., ▬ 2 cl. (4, 6 berth), [2] Zürich - Frankfurt - Hamburg. Special fares apply.
G – [12] ✕ Interlaken Ost - Basel - Köln - Dortmund (- Hamburg Ⓑ).

f – Not ⑥.
h – Via Wuppertal, Hagen.
j – ⑤⑦.
m – Not June 9.
x – Ⓑ.
z – Frankfurt (Main) **Süd**.

⊙ – 🏛 is at Emmerich.
◧ – Via Brig. 🏛 is at Domodossola; ticket point is **Iselle**.
★ – Connections at Basel are not guaranteed.
⊖ – Via Köln - Frankfurt high speed line.
⊗ – Compulsory reservation for international journeys. Supplement payable for international journeys and for internal journeys within Italy.

CONNECTING SERVICES

Basel - Luzern - Chiasso : Table **550**, Basel - Bern - Interlaken and Brig : Table **560**.

Zürich - Landquart - Chur : Table **520**, Chur - St Moritz : Table **540**, Zürich - Bellinzona - Chiasso : Table **550**.

MILANO - PÁTRA - ATHÍNAI 74

train type	FB			IC	FB			
train number	8803			605	8809			
notes	🄡 ✕	⛴		🄡 ✕	🄡 ✕	⛴	⛴	
	⚡	SF		⚡	⚡	SF	SF	
Milano Centrale d.	0735	...	...	0705	1035	...	...	...
Bologna d.	0945	...	...	0958	1245	...	...	...
Ancona d.	1130	...	...	1228	1436	...	...	...
Ancona Marittima d.	...	1330	...	|	|	1630	...	...
Pescara Centrale d.	...	|	...	1401	1547	|	...	...
Foggia d.	...	|	...	1551	1722	|	...	...
Bari Centrale a.	...	|	...	1705	1825	|	...	...
Bari Marittima d.	...	|	...	...	...	|	1930	...
Pátra a.	...	1430	...	...	...	1500	1300	...
Athína Lárisa a.	...	✣	...	...	...	✣	✣	...

train type			FB				FB	IC		
train number			8820				8820	612		
notes		⛴	🄡 ✕	⛴		⛴	🄡 ✕	🄡 ✕		
		SF	⚡	SF		SF	⚡	⚡		
Athína Lárisa d.	...	✣	...	✣	...	✣	...	...	...	...
Pátra d.	...	1730	...	1730	...	1800	...	...	...	...
Bari Marittima a.	...	|	...	|	...	0930	...	...	...	...
Bari Centrale d.	...	|	...	|	...	...	1132	1155	...	...
Foggia d.	...	|	...	|	...	...	1239	1313	...	...
Pescara Centrale d.	...	|	...	|	...	...	1414	1502	...	...
Ancona Marittima a.	...	1400	...	1630	...	...	|	|	...	...
Ancona d.	...	...	1525	...	...	...	1525	1638	...	...
Bologna a.	...	...	1715	...	...	...	1718	1901	...	...
Milano Centrale a.	...	...	1925	...	...	...	1925	2145	...	...

⚡ – Supplement payable. ✣ – For 🚌/rail connections Pátra - Athína and v.v. see Tables **1440**, **1450**. *SF* – **Superfast Ferries**, for days of running see Tables **2715**, **2755**.

MÜNCHEN - ZÜRICH 75

train type		EC			EC			EC	
train number		196			194			190	
notes		✕			✕			✕	
München Hbf d.	...	0714	...	...	1214	...	...	1815	...
Buchloe d.	...	0758	...	...	1259	...	...	1858	...
Memmingen d.	...	|	...	...	|	...	...	|	...
Kempten Hbf d.	...	0841	...	...	1342	...	...	1941	...
Lindau 🏛 d.	...	0954	...	...	1454	...	...	2054	...
Bregenz 🏛 d.	...	1006	...	...	1506	...	...	2106	...
St Margrethen 🏛 a.	...	1018	...	...	1518	...	...	2118	...
St Gallen a.	...	1053	...	...	1553	...	...	2153	...
Winterthur a.	...	1131	...	...	1631	...	...	2231	...
Zürich Flughafen ✈ a.	...	1146	...	...	1646	...	...	2246	...
Zürich HB a.	...	1158	...	...	1658	...	...	2258	...
Basel SBB a.	...	...	...	...	...	...	...	0013	...

train type		EC			EC			EC	
train number		191			195			197	
notes		✕			✕			✕	
Basel SBB d.	...	0543	...	...	...	...	...	...	...
Zürich HB d.	...	0702	...	...	1302	...	...	1802	...
Zürich Flughafen ✈ d.	...	0714	...	...	1314	...	...	1814	...
Winterthur d.	...	0729	...	...	1329	...	...	1829	...
St Gallen d.	...	0807	...	...	1407	...	...	1907	...
St Margrethen 🏛 d.	...	0842	...	...	1442	...	...	1942	...
Bregenz 🏛 d.	...	0855	...	...	1455	...	...	1955	...
Lindau 🏛 a.	...	0905	...	...	1505	...	...	2005	...
Kempten Hbf a.	...	1019	...	...	1619	...	...	2122	...
Memmingen a.	...	|	...	...	|	...	...	|	...
Buchloe a.	...	1100	...	...	1656	...	...	2203	...
München Hbf a.	...	1147	...	...	1746	...	...	2248	...

MÜNCHEN and NÜRNBERG - PRAHA 76

Due to bus substitution Plzeň - Domažlice on most dates June 14–21 passengers leaving Praha at 0545, 0745, 0945, 1145, 1345, 1545 & 1745 for München will need to depart Praha at 0515, 0715, 0845, 1045, 1315, 1515 & 1715 respectively (on trains in Table 1120) and change at Plzen.

train type	RE	RE	ALX	ALX	🚌	🚌	RE	ALX	RE	ALX	🚌	🚌	RE		ALX	🚌	RE	ALX	🚌	🚌	RE	ALX	RE	ALX	
train number			351	351	P	P		353		355	P	P			357	P		359	P	P		361		363	
notes	①–⑥	⑥⑦	①–⑥	⑦	🄡	🄡					🄡	🄡			¶	🄡		¶	🄡	🄡		¶		¶	
notes			¶	¶				¶		¶															
München Hbf d.	...	...	0443	...	...	...	...	0643	...	0843	...	...	...	...	1043	...	...	1243	...	...	...	1443	...	1643	...
Nürnberg Hbf d.	0434	0535	|	...	0720	0850	0738	|	0943	|	1035	1120	1143	...	|	1250	1343	|	1450	1650	1543	|	1743	|	...
Regensburg d.	|	|	0614	...	|	|	|	0814	|	1014	|	|	|	...	1214	|	|	1414	|	|	|	1614	|	1814	...
Schwandorf d.	0542	0643	0651	0651	|	|	0846	0852	1046	1052	|	|	1246	...	1252	|	1446	1452	|	|	1647	1652	1846	1852	...
Furth im Wald 🏛 d.	...	...	0740	0740	◐	◐	...	0940	...	1140	◐	◐	...	...	1340	◐	...	1540	◐	◐	...	1740	...	1940	...
Plzeň hlavní a.	...	...	0849	0849	|	|	...	1049	...	1249	|	|	...	...	1449	|	...	1649	|	|	...	1849	...	2049	...
Praha hlavní a.	...	...	1019	1019	1055	1225	...	1219	...	1419	1410	1455	...	...	1619	1625	...	1819	1825	2025	...	2016	...	2216	...

train type	ALX	RE	ALX	RE	🚌	ALX	RE	🚌	ALX	RE	🚌		ALX	RE	🚌	ALX	RE	🚌	🚌	ALX	RE	🚌			
train number	362		360		P	358		P	356		P		354		P	352		P	P	350		P			
notes	¶		¶		🄡	¶		🄡	¶		🄡		¶		🄡	¶		🄡	🄡	¶		🄡			
notes	🍷		🍷			🍷			🍷							🍷									
Praha hlavní d.	0545	...	0745	...	0805	0945	...	1005	1145	...	1135	...	1345	...	1335	1545	...	1535	1605	1745	...	1735	...	...	...
Plzeň hlavní d.	0710	...	0910	...	|	1110	...	|	1310	...	|	...	1510	...	|	1710	...	|	|	1910	...	|	...	...	...
Furth im Wald 🏛 a.	0820	...	1020	...	◐	1220	...	◐	1420	...	◐	...	1620	...	◐	1820	...	◐	◐	2020	...	◐	...	...	...
Schwandorf a.	0904	0907	1104	1107	|	1304	1307	|	1504	1507	|	...	1704	1707	|	1904	1908	|	|	2104	2110	|	...	...	...
Regensburg a.	0945	|	1145	|	|	1345	|	|	1545	|	|	...	1745	|	|	1945	|	|	|	2149	|	|	...	...	...
Nürnberg Hbf a.	|	1014	|	1214	1140	|	1414	1340	|	1615	1510	...	|	1814	1710	|	2014	1910	1940	|	2222	2110	...	...	...
München Hbf a.	1118	...	1318	...	...	1518	...	...	1718	...	...	...	1918	...	...	2118	...	...	...	2321	...	...	...	...	...

P – 🚌 **DB / ČD** *IC Bus.* Rail tickets valid. 🄡 🍷. Supplement payable. 2nd class only. At Praha hlavní railway station the bus stop is located outside the old building on the upper level (access from platform one); street name is Wilsonova. At Nürnberg Hbf the bus stop is at Bahnhofvorplatz Hauptausgang (main entrance). At Plzeň the bus stop is located at Plzeň Autobusove nadrazi (Husova).

¶ – *Ex* in the Czech Republic.

◐ – 🏛 is Waidhaus (Germany).

ALX – Arriva Länderbahn Express.

BERLIN - WROCLAW - WIEN / BUDAPEST / PRZEMYŚL 77

train type / number	NJ	NJ	IC		
train number	457	457	457	89	715
notes		477	60457		
	M	M	P	A	
Berlin Hbf d.	1841	1841	1841	...	...
Berlin Ost d.	1851	1851	1851	...	...
Frankfurt / Oder d.	1945	1945	1945	...	...
Rzepin d.	2009	2009	2009	...	...
Zielona Góra d.	2057	2057	2057	...	...
Glogów d.	2132	2132	2132	...	...
Wrocław Gł d.	2300	2300	2300	...	...
Opole Gł. d.	2340	2340	2340	...	...
Kedzierzyn-Koźle d.	0027	0027	0027	...	...
Racibórz a.	0053	0053	0053	...	...
Racibórz d.	0123	0123	0120	...	...
Bohumín d.	0220	0220	|	...	...
Ostrava hlavní d.	0230	0230	|	...	...
Břeclav a.	0410	0410	|	...	...
Wien Hbf a.	0700	|	|	...	...
Bratislava hlavná a.	...	0550	|	...	...
Budapest Keleti a.	...	0835	|	...	...
Gliwice a.	...	...	0214	...	...
Katowice a.	...	...	0239	...	...
Kraków Gł. a.	...	...	0531	...	...
Rzeszów a.	...	...	0745	...	...
Przemyśl a.	...	...	0858	...	...
Przemyśl ⊖ PL d.	...	...	...	1015	1310
Lviv UA a.	...	...	...	1345	1602

train type / number			IC	NJ	NJ
train number	715	89	60456	476	456
notes			456	456	
		A	P	M	M
Lviv UA d.	1355	1600	...	...	...
Przemyśl ⊖ PL a.	1458	1746	...	...	...
Przemyśl d.	...	...	1809	...	...
Rzeszów d.	...	...	1923	...	...
Kraków Gł. d.	...	...	2139	...	...
Katowice d.	...	...	0018	...	...
Gliwice d.	...	...	0043	...	...
Budapest Keleti d.	...	...	|	1925	...
Bratislava hlavná d.	...	...	|	2210	...
Wien Hbf d.	...	...	|	|	2210
Břeclav d.	...	...	|	2350	2350
Ostrava hlavní a.	...	...	|	0130	0130
Bohumín a.	...	...	|	0139	0139
Racibórz a.	...	...	0139	0240	0240
Racibórz d.	...	...	0300	0300	0300
Kedzierzyn-Koźle a.	...	...	0330	0330	0330
Opole Gł. a.	...	...	0422	0422	0422
Wrocław Gł a.	...	...	0505	0505	0505
Glogów a.	...	...	0622	0622	0622
Zielona Góra a.	...	...	0701	0701	0701
Rzepin a.	...	...	0748	0748	0748
Frankfurt / Oder a.	...	...	0812	0812	0812
Berlin Ost a.	...	...	0906	0906	0906
Berlin Hbf a.	...	...	0916	0916	0916

A – ⑥⑦ May 11 - Sept. 1 (also June 17, 20, 28, Aug. 15, 26), ⑦ Sept. 8 - Dec. 1 (also Oct. 14, Nov. 9, 11): 🚃12 Przemyśl - Lviv and v.v.

M – *ÖBB nightjet* METROPOL – 🛏 1, 2 cl., 🛌 2 cl., 🚃2 Berlin - Wrocław - Wien / Budapest and v.v.

P – 🛏 1, 2 cl., 🚃2 Berlin (**60457/74010**) - Wrocław - Racibórz (**44172**) - Katowice (**83192**) - Przemyśl. 🄡 Frankfurt / Oder - Przemyśl.

Q – 🛏 1, 2 cl., 🚃2 Przemyśl (**38192**) - Katowice (**40171**) - Racibórz (**60456/47010**) - Wrocław - Berlin. 🄡 Przemyśl - Frankfurt / Oder.

⊖ – 🏛 = Medyka / Mostiska II.

PL – Poland (UTC + 1 winter, UTC + 2 summer).

UA – Ukraine (UTC + 2 winter, UTC + 3 summer).

82 GENÈVE, BASEL and ZÜRICH - MILANO, VENEZIA and ROMA

train type	IR	EC	IC	EC	FR	FR	IR	EC	IR	EC	FR	FR	IC	EC	FR	IC	EC	FR	IR	EC	FR	IR	EC	FR	FR
train number	**2309**	**11**	**802**	**35**	**9717**	**9521**	**2311**	**13**	**1807**	**51**	**9525**	**9723**	**806**	**37**	**9529**	**665**	**15**	**9533**	**2319**	**17**	**9541**	**2421**	**151**	**9743**	**9545**
notes		R 🍸		R 🍸	R 🍸	R ✕		R 🍸		R 🍸	R ✕	R ✕		R 🍸	R ✕		R 🍸	R ✕		R 🍸	R ✕		R 🍸	R ✕	R ✕
		⊗		⊗	⊗	⟋		⊗		⊗	⟋	⟋		⊗	⟋		⊗	⟋		⊗	⟋		⊗	⟋	⟋
					⑥⑦																		F		
Genève Aéroport ✈ d.	...	...	...	...	...	...	...	...	...	...	...	...	...	...	...	...	...	...	...	...	...	...	...	...	...
Genève d.	...	...	...	0539	...	...	...	...	0609	...	...	...	...	0739	...	...	...	...	...	...	...	...	...	...	...
Lausanne d.	...	...	...	0618	...	...	...	...	0650	...	...	...	...	0818	...	...	...	...	...	...	...	...	...	...	...
Montreux d.	...	...	...	0637	...	...	...	...	0712	...	...	...	...	0837	...	...	...	...	...	...	...	...	...	...	...
Aigle d.	...	...	...	|	...	...	...	...	0723	...	...	...	...	|	...	...	...	...	...	...	...	...	...	...	...
Martigny d.	...	...	...	|	...	...	...	...	0743	...	...	...	...	|	...	...	...	...	...	...	...	...	...	...	...
Sion d.	...	...	...	0713	...	...	...	...	0759	...	...	...	...	0913	...	...	...	...	...	...	...	...	...	...	...
Zürich HB d.	...	0610	...	|	...	...	...	0710	|	...	...	...	...	|	...	...	0910	...	...	1110	...	1210	...	...	...
Basel SBB d.	0504	|	...	|	...	...	0604	|	|	0631	...	...	...	|	...	0804	|	...	1004	|	...	|	1104	...	...
Olten d.	0530	|	...	|	...	...	0630	|	|	0657	...	...	...	|	...	0830	|	...	1030	|	...	|	1130	...	...
Bern d.	|	|	0606	|	...	...	|	|	|	0734	...	...	0806	|	...	|	|	...	|	|	...	|	|	...	...
Spiez d.	|	|	0636	|	...	...	|	|	|	0805	...	...	0836	|	...	|	|	...	|	|	...	|	|	...	...
Luzern d.	0618	|	|	|	...	...	0718	|	|	|	...	...	|	|	...	0918	|	...	1118	|	...	|	1218	...	...
Arth-Goldau d.	0646	0650	|	|	...	...	0746	0750	|	|	...	...	|	|	...	0946	0950	...	1146	1150	...	1246	1250	...	...
Bellinzona d.	...	0751	|	|	...	...	...	0851	|	|	...	...	|	|	...	...	1051	...	...	1251	...	...	1351	...	...
Lugano d.	...	0822	|	|	...	...	...	0922	|	|	...	...	|	|	...	...	1122	...	...	1322	...	...	1422	...	...
Chiasso 🏛 d.	...	0851	|	|	...	...	...	0951	|	|	...	...	|	|	...	...	1151	...	...	1351	...	...	1451	...	...
Como San Giovanni a.	...	|	|	|	...	...	...	0955	|	|	...	...	|	|	...	...	|	...	...	1355	...	...	1455	...	...
Visp d.	...	|	0703	|	...	...	...	|	0825	0832	...	...	0903	|	...	...	|	...	...	|	...	...	|	...	...
Brig d.	...	|	0711	0744	...	...	...	|	0832	0844	...	...	0911	0944	...	...	|	...	...	|	...	...	|	...	...
Domodossola 🏛 ¶ a.	...	|	...	0812	...	...	...	|	...	0912	...	...	...	1012	...	...	|	...	...	|	...	...	|	...	...
Stresa a.	...	|	...	0838	...	...	...	|	...	0938	...	...	...	|	...	...	|	...	...	|	...	...	|	...	...
Gallarate a.	...	|	...	|	...	...	...	|	...	|	...	...	...	1102	...	...	|	...	...	|	...	...	|	...	...
Milano Centrale a.	...	0935	...	0937	...	...	...	1035	...	1037	...	...	...	1137	...	...	1235	...	...	1435	...	...	1535	...	...
														|			|			*FR*					
														|			|			**9737**					
														|			|			R ✕					
														|			|			⟋					
Milano Centrale d.	...	...	...	...	1015	1020	...	...	...	...	1120	1145	...	1205	1220	...	1305	1320	...	1515	1520	...	...	1615	1615
Verona Porta Nuova a.	...	...	...	...	1128	|	...	...	...	...	|	1258	...	1328	|	...	1428	|	...	1628	|	...	...	1728	|
Venezia Mestre a.	...	...	...	...	1228	|	...	...	...	...	|	1358	...	1428	|	...	1528	|	...	1728	|	...	...	1828	|
Venezia Santa Lucia a.	...	...	...	...	...	|	...	...	...	...	|	1410	...	1440	|	...	1540	|	...	...	|	...	...	1840	|
Bologna Centrale a.	...	...	...	...	...	1122	...	...	...	...	1222	...	...	...	1322	...	...	1422	...	...	1622	...	...	...	1722
Firenze SMN a.	...	...	...	...	...	1159	...	...	...	...	1259	...	...	...	1359	...	...	1459	...	...	1659	...	...	...	1759
Roma Termini a.	...	...	...	...	...	1340	...	...	...	...	1440	...	...	...	1540	...	...	1640	...	...	1840	...	...	...	1940
Napoli Centrale a.	...	...	...	...	...	1503	...	...	...	...	1602	...	...	...	1700	...	...	1800	...	...	2000	...	...	...	2100

train type	IR	EC	IR	EC	FR	IC	IC	EC	FR	IR	EC	FR		IR	EC	IR	EC	IC	EC	IR	EC	ICN			
train number	**2323**	**19**	**1819**	**57**	**9549**	**971**	**818**	**39**	**9553**	**2327**	**21**	**9557**		**2331**	**23**	**1829**	**59**	**828**	**41**	**2335**	**25**	**797**	**2051**		
notes		R 🍸		R 🍸	R ✕			R 🍸	R ✕		R 🍸	R ✕			R 🍸		R 🍸		R 🍸		R 🍸	R	2		
		⊗		⊗	⟋			⊗	⟋		⊗	⟋			⊗		⊗		⊗		⊗	⟋			
																						A			
Genève Aéroport ✈ d.	...	...	1202	...	...	...	...	...	...	...	...	...	...	...	...	1702	...	...	...	...	...	...	...	...	...
Genève d.	...	...	1212	...	...	...	...	1339	...	...	...	...	...	...	...	1712	...	...	1839	...	...	...	...	...	...
Lausanne d.	...	...	1250	...	...	...	...	1418	...	...	...	...	...	...	...	1750	...	...	1918	...	...	...	...	...	...
Montreux d.	...	...	1312	...	...	...	...	1437	...	...	...	...	...	...	...	1812	...	...	1937	...	...	...	...	...	...
Aigle d.	...	...	1323	...	...	...	...	|	...	...	...	...	...	...	...	1823	...	...	|	...	...	...	...	...	...
Martigny d.	...	...	1343	...	...	...	...	|	...	...	...	...	...	...	...	1843	...	...	|	...	...	...	...	...	...
Sion d.	...	...	1359	...	...	...	...	1513	...	...	...	...	...	...	...	1859	...	...	2013	...	...	...	...	...	...
Zürich HB d.	...	1310	|	...	...	...	...	|	...	...	1510	...	...	...	1710	|	...	...	|	...	1910	...	...	...	...
Basel SBB d.	1204	|	|	1231	...	1259	...	|	...	1404	|	...	...	1604	|	|	1731	...	|	1804	|	...	...	...	...
Oltern d.	1230	|	|	1257	...	1329	...	|	...	1430	|	...	...	1630	|	|	1757	...	|	1830	|	...	...	...	...
Bern d.	|	|	|	1334	...	1356	1406	|	...	|	|	...	...	|	|	|	1834	1906	|	|	|	...	...	...	...
Spiez d.	|	|	|	1405	...	...	1436	|	...	|	|	...	...	|	|	|	1905	1936	|	|	|	...	...	...	...
Luzern d.	1318	|	|	|	...	...	|	|	...	1518	|	...	...	1718	|	|	|	|	|	1918	|	...	...	...	...
Arth-Goldau d.	1346	1350	|	|	...	...	|	|	...	1546	1550	...	...	1746	1750	|	|	|	|	1946	1950	...	...	...	...
Bellinzona d.	...	1451	|	|	...	...	|	|	...	...	1651	...	...	...	1851	|	|	|	|	...	2051	...	...	...	...
Lugano d.	...	1522	|	|	...	...	|	|	...	...	1722	...	...	...	1922	|	|	|	|	...	2122	...	...	...	...
Chiasso 🏛 d.	...	1551	|	|	...	...	|	|	...	...	1751	...	...	...	1951	|	|	|	|	...	2151	...	...	...	...
Como San Giovanni a.	...	|	|	|	...	...	|	|	...	...	1755	...	...	...	|	|	|	|	|	...	2156	...	...	...	...
Visp d.	...	|	1425	1432	...	...	1503	|	...	...	|	...	...	...	|	1925	1932	2003	|	...	|	...	...	...	...
Brig d.	...	|	1432	1444	...	...	1511	1544	...	...	|	...	...	...	|	1932	1944	2011	2044	...	|	...	...	...	...
Domodossola 🏛 ¶ a.	...	|	...	1512	...	...	...	1612	...	...	|	...	...	...	|	▬	2012	...	2110	...	|	...	...	...	...
Stresa a.	...	|	...	|	...	...	...	1638	...	...	|	...	...	...	|	...	|	...	2138	...	|	...	...	...	...
Gallarate a.	...	|	...	1602	...	...	...	|	...	...	|	...	...	...	|	...	2103	...	|	...	|	...	...	...	...
Milano Centrale a.	...	1635	...	1637	...	...	...	1737	...	...	1835	...	...	...	2035	...	2137	...	2237	...	2250	...	...	...	...
				FR				*FR*			*FR*				*FR* ⟋										
				9747				**9751**			**9755**				**9663**										
				R ✕				R ✕			R ✕				R ✕	**2085**	**2087**								
				⟋				⟋			⟋				⑦	2	2								
Milano Centrale d.	...	...	...	1715	1720	...	...	1815	1820	...	1915	1920	...	...	2100	2125	2225	...	...	...	...	2317**g**	0015	...	...
Verona Porta Nuova a.	...	...	...	1828	|	...	...	1928	|	...	2028	|	...	...	|	2315	0015	...	...	...	...	|	0215	...	...
Venezia Mestre a.	...	...	...	1928	|	...	...	2028	|	...	2128	|	...	...	|	...	...	...	...	...	...	|	...	...	...
Venezia Santa Lucia a.	...	...	...	...	|	...	...	2040	|	...	2140	|	...	...	|	...	...	...	...	...	...	|	...	...	...
Bologna Centrale a.	...	...	...	...	1822	...	...	...	1922	...	...	2022	...	...	|	...	...	...	...	...	...	0215	...	...	...
Firenze SMN a.	...	...	...	...	1859	...	...	...	1959	...	...	2059	...	...	|	...	...	...	...	...	...	0407**y**	...	...	...
Roma Termini a.	...	...	...	...	2040	...	...	...	2140	...	...	2240	...	...	2355	...	...	...	...	...	...	0717**t**	...	...	...
Napoli Centrale a.	...	...	...	...	2200	...	...	...	2300	...	...	...	...	...	...	...	...	...	...	...	...	0938	...	...	...

A – 🛏 1, 2 cl., 🛏 2 cl. (4 berth), 🚗 Milano - Napoli - Salerno.
F – From Frankfurt (depart 0801). Table **73**.

g – Milano **Porta Garibaldi**.
t – Roma **Tiburtina**.
y – Firenze **Campo di Marte**.

⟋ – Supplement payable.
¶ – Ticketing point is **Iselle**.

⊗ – Compulsory reservation for international journeys. Supplement payable for international journeys and for internal journeys within Italy.

ROMA, VENEZIA and MILANO - ZÜRICH, BASEL and GENÈVE 82

train type	EC	IR	EC	IR	ICN			IC	IC	FR	FR ⁄	FR ⁄	IR	FR	FR	IR	FR	FR	IR	EC	IR	FR	FR	IC	ICE
train number	12	2316	50	1814	798	2051	2122	817	968	9702	9600	9502	2320	9504	9708	2420	9508	9714	1822	16	2324	9716	9514	825	376 396
notes	R 🍷 ⊗		R 🍷 ⊗		A	2				R ✕ ⁄	R ✕ ①–⑥	R ✕ ①–⑥		R ✕ ⁄	R ✕ ⁄		R ✕ ⁄	R ✕ ⁄		R 🍷 ⊗		R ✕ ⁄	R ✕ ⁄		
apoli Centrale d.	...	...	...	...	2131	...	...	...	...	...	...	...	...	...	...	...	...	...	...	...	...	...	0700	...	...
oma Termini d.	...	...	...	...	2353t	...	...	...	...	...	0600	...	...	0620	...	...	0720	...	...	...	...	...	0820	...	...
renze SMN d.	...	...	...	...	0315y	...	...	...	...	...	|	0730	...	0800	...	...	0900	...	...	...	...	...	1000	...	...
ologna Centrale d.	...	...	...	...	|	...	0528	...	...	...	|	0808	...	0838	...	...	0938	...	...	...	...	...	1038	...	...
Venezia Santa Lucia d.	...	...	...	...	|	...	|	...	...	0620	|	|	...	|	0720	...	|	0820	...	...	...	...	|	...	...
Venezia Mestre d.	...	...	...	...	|	...	|	...	...	0632	|	|	...	|	0732	...	|	0832	...	...	...	0902	|	...	...
Verona Porta Nuova d.	...	...	...	...	|	0545	|	...	...	0732	|	|	...	|	0832	...	|	0932	...	...	...	1002	|	...	...
lano Centrale a.	...	...	...	...	0711g	0735	0800	...	...	0845	0855	0910	...	0943	0945	...	1040	1045	...	...	...	1115	1140	...	...
							EC 32 R 🍷 ⊗					EC 14 R 🍷 ⊗			EC 158 R 🍷 ⊗			EC 52 R 🍷 F ⊗					EC 34 R 🍷 ⊗		
lano Centrale d.	0725	...	0723	...	...	...	0823	...	...	...	...	0925	...	...	1015	...	...	1123	...	1125	...	...	1223	...	...
allarate d.	|	...	0757	...	...	...	|	...	...	...	...	|	...	...	|	...	...	|	...	|	...	...	|	...	...
resa d.	|	...	|	...	...	...	0921	...	...	...	...	|	...	...	|	...	...	1221	...	|	...	...	1321	...	...
omodossola 🏛 ¶ d.	|	...	0848	...	...	...	0948	...	...	...	...	|	...	...	|	...	...	1248	...	|	...	...	1348	...	...
ig a.	|	...	0916	0926	...	...	1016	1049	...	...	...	|	...	...	|	...	...	1316	1326	|	...	...	1416	1449	...
sp a.	|	...	0926	0933	...	...	|	1055	...	...	...	|	...	...	|	...	...	1326	1333	|	...	...	|	1455	...
Como San Giovanni d.	|	...	|	|	...	...	|	|	...	...	...	1003	...	...	1103	...	...	|	|	1203	...	...	|	|	...
Chiasso 🏛 a.	0810	...	|	|	...	...	|	|	...	...	...	1010	...	...	1110	...	...	|	|	1210	...	...	|	|	...
Lugano a.	0838	...	|	|	...	...	|	|	...	...	...	1038	...	...	1138	...	...	|	|	1238	...	...	|	|	...
Bellinzona a.	0910	...	|	|	...	...	|	|	...	...	...	1110	...	...	1210	...	...	|	|	1310	...	...	|	|	...
Arth-Goldau a.	1009	1014	|	|	...	...	|	|	...	...	...	1209	1214	...	1309	1313	...	|	|	1409	1414	...	|	|	...
zern a.	|	1041	|	|	...	...	|	|	...	...	...	|	1241	...	1341	|	...	|	|	|	1441	...	|	|	...
iez a.	|	|	0953	|	...	...	|	1124	...	...	...	|	|	...	|	|	...	1353	|	|	|	...	|	1524	...
rn a.	|	|	1023	|	...	...	|	1154	1204	...	...	|	|	...	|	|	...	1424	|	|	|	...	|	1554	1604
ten a.	|	1127	1102	|	...	...	|	...	1230	...	...	|	1327	...	1427	|	...	1502	|	|	1527	...	|	...	1630
asel SBB a.	|	1155	1129	|	...	...	|	...	1259	...	...	|	1355	...	1455	|	...	1529	|	|	1555	...	|	...	1659
Zürich HB a.	1050	...	...	|	...	...	|	...	...	...	...	1250	...	...	...	1350	...	...	|	1450	...	...	|	...	...
on a.	...	...	...	1000	...	...	1045	...	...	...	...	...	...	...	...	...	...	...	1400	...	...	...	1445	...	...
artigny a.	...	...	...	1015	...	...	|	...	...	...	...	...	...	...	...	...	...	...	1415	...	...	...	|	...	...
gle a.	...	...	...	1035	...	...	|	...	...	...	...	...	...	...	...	...	...	...	1435	...	...	...	|	...	...
ontreux a.	...	...	...	1046	...	...	1120	...	...	...	...	...	...	...	...	...	...	...	1446	...	...	...	1520	...	...
usanne a.	...	...	...	1110	...	...	1142	...	...	...	...	...	...	...	...	...	...	...	1510	...	...	...	1542	...	...
enève a.	...	...	...	1148	...	...	1221	...	...	...	...	...	...	...	...	...	...	...	1548	...	...	...	1621	...	...
enève Aéroport ✈ a.	...	...	...	1157	...	...	...	...	...	...	...	...	...	...	...	...	...	...	1557	...	...	...	...	...	...

train type/number	FR	EC	IR	FR	FR	EC	IR	FR	FR	EC	IC	EC	IR	FR	EC	EC	IR	EC	IR	FR	EC	IC	ICE	EC	
train number	9518	18	2328	9728	9526	20	2332	9532	9738	36	1084	22	2336	9536	10	56	1836	10	2338 692	9540	42	1088	338	24	
notes	R ✕ ⁄	R 🍷 ⊗		R ✕ ⁄	R ✕ ⁄	R 🍷 ⊗		R ✕ ⁄	R ✕ ⁄	R 🍷 ⊗		R 🍷 ⊗		R ✕ ⁄	R 🍷 ⊗	R 🍷 ⊗		R 🍷 ⊗		R ✕ ⁄	R 🍷 ⊗			R ✕ ⊗	
poli Centrale d.	0800	...	...	...	1000	...	...	1200	...	...	...	...	...	1300	...	...	...	...	...	1400	...	...	...	...	...
ma Termini d.	0920	...	...	...	1120	...	...	1320	...	...	...	...	...	1420	...	...	...	...	...	1522	...	...	...	...	...
enze SMN d.	1100	...	...	...	1300	...	...	1500	...	...	...	...	...	1600	...	...	...	...	...	1700	...	...	...	...	...
logna Centrale d.	1138	...	...	...	1338	...	...	1538	...	...	...	...	...	1638	...	...	...	...	...	1738	...	...	...	...	...
Venezia Santa Lucia d.	|	...	...	1150	|	...	...	|	1420	...	...	...	...	|	1520	...	...	...	...	|	1620	...	...	...	...
Venezia Mestre d.	|	...	...	1202	|	...	...	|	1432	...	...	...	...	|	1532	...	...	...	...	|	1632	...	...	...	...
Verona Porta Nuova d.	|	...	...	1302	|	...	...	|	1532	...	...	...	...	|	1632	...	...	←	...	|	1732	...	...	...	...
lano Centrale a.	1240	...	...	1415	1440	...	...	1645	1645	...	...	...	...	1742	1755	...	...	1755	...	1842	1855	...	...	...	...
lano Centrale d.	...	1325	...	...	...	1525	...	...	...	1723	...	1725	...	...	1825	1823	...	1825	...	...	1923	...	...	1925	...
llarate d.	...	|	...	...	...	|	...	...	...	|	...	|	...	...	→	|	...	|	...	...	1957	...	...	|	...
esa d.	...	|	...	...	...	|	...	...	...	1821	...	|	...	...	...	1921	...	|	...	...	|	...	...	|	...
modossola 🏛 ¶ d.	...	|	...	...	...	|	...	...	...	1848	...	|	...	...	...	1948	...	|	...	...	2048	...	...	|	...
g a.	...	|	...	...	...	|	...	...	...	1916	1920	|	...	...	...	2016	2023	|	...	...	2116	2120	...	|	...
sp a.	...	|	...	...	...	|	...	...	...	|	1926	|	...	...	...	2026	2029	|	...	...	|	2126	...	|	...
Como San Giovanni d.	...	|	...	...	...	1603	...	...	...	|	|	|	...	...	...	|	|	|	...	...	|	|	...	2003	...
Chiasso 🏛 a.	...	1410	...	...	...	1610	...	...	...	|	|	1810	...	...	...	|	|	1910	...	...	|	|	...	2010	...
Lugano a.	...	1438	...	...	...	1638	...	...	...	|	|	1838	...	...	...	|	|	1938	...	...	|	|	...	2038	...
Bellinzona a.	...	1510	...	...	...	1710	...	...	...	|	|	1910	...	...	...	|	|	2010	...	...	|	|	...	2110	...
Arth-Goldau a.	...	1609	1614	...	...	1809	1814	...	...	|	|	2009	2014	...	...	|	|	2109	2114	...	|	|	...	2209	...
zern a.	...	|	1641	...	...	|	1841	...	...	|	|	|	2041	...	...	|	|	|	2141	...	|	|	...	|	...
ez a.	...	|	|	...	...	|	|	...	...	|	1953	|	|	...	...	2053	|	|	|	...	|	2153	...	|	...
rn a.	...	|	|	...	...	|	|	...	...	|	2023	|	|	...	...	2123	|	|	|	...	|	2223	2236	|	...
en a.	...	|	1727	...	...	|	1927	...	...	|	2102	|	2127	...	...	2202	|	|	2227	...	|	...	2303	|	...
sel SBB a.	...	|	1755	...	...	|	1955	...	...	|	2129	|	2155	...	...	2229	|	|	2259	...	|	...	2330	|	...
Zürich HB a.	...	1650	...	...	...	1850	...	...	...	|	...	2050	...	...	...	...	|	2150	...	...	|	...	...	2250	...
n a.	...	...	...	...	...	...	...	...	...	1945	...	...	...	...	...	...	2059	...	...	...	2145	...	...	...	...
rtigny a.	...	...	...	...	...	...	...	...	...	|	...	...	...	...	...	...	2113	...	...	...	|	...	...	...	...
le a.	...	...	...	...	...	...	...	...	...	|	...	...	...	...	...	...	2136	...	...	...	|	...	...	...	...
ntreux a.	...	...	...	...	...	...	...	...	...	2020	...	...	...	...	...	...	2147	...	...	...	2220	...	...	...	...
sanne a.	...	...	...	...	...	...	...	...	...	2042	...	...	...	...	...	...	2210	...	...	...	2242	...	...	...	...
nève a.	...	...	...	...	...	...	...	...	...	2121	...	...	...	...	...	...	2307	...	...	...	2322	...	...	...	...
nève Aéroport ✈ a.	...	...	...	...	...	...	...	...	...	...	...	...	...	...	...	...	2316	...	...	...	...	...	...	...	...

- 🛏 1, 2 cl., 🛏 2 cl. (4 berth), (2) Salerno - Napoli - Milano. To Frankfurt (arrive 1826). Table **73**.

g – Milano **Porta Garibaldi**.
t – Roma **Tiburtina**.
y – Firenze **Campo di Marte**.

⁄ – Supplement payable.
¶ – Ticketing point is **Iselle**.

⊗ – Compulsory reservation for international journeys. Supplement payable for international journeys and for internal journeys within Italy.

86 ZÜRICH - INNSBRUCK - WIEN, GRAZ, ZAGREB and BUDAPEST

train type/number	RJX	RJX	IC	RJ	D	RJX	RJ	EC	EC	RJX	EC	EC	RJX	EC	D	D	IC	RJX	EC	RJX	EC	RJX	RJX	NJ	EN	EN	NJ
train number	**49**	**765**	**515**	**111**	**211**	**161**	**596**	**217**	**163**	**563**	**147**	**113**	**165**	**115**	**315**	**315**	**611**	**167**	**219**	**169**	**117**	**367**	**369**	**465**	**40465**	**40467**	**467**
notes	✕	✕	🍷	✕		✕	✕	🍷	🍷	✕		**213**	✕	🍷		**411**	🍷	✕	🍷	✕	**1217**	✕	✕				
					2				**B**		**D**	**H**				**P**		**G**			🍷			**Z**	**A**	**C**	**W**
Zürich HB d.	...	...	...	...	...	0640	...	...	0840	...	...	...	1040	...	...	...	...	1240	...	1440	...	1640	1840	2040	2040	2140	214
Sargans d.	...	...	...	...	...	0737	...	...	0937	...	...	...	1137	...	...	...	...	1337	...	1537	...	1737	1937	2137	2137	2237	223
Buchs 🛃 d.	...	...	...	...	...	0754	...	...	1000	...	...	...	1154	...	...	...	...	1354	...	1554	...	1800	1954	2205	2205	2305	230
Bregenz d.	...	0548	...	...	...	|	...	...	|	...	...	...	|	...	...	...	...	|	...	|	...	|	|	|	|	|	|
Feldkirch d.	...	0613	...	...	...	0817	...	...	1017	...	...	...	1217	...	...	...	...	1417	...	1617	...	1817	2017	2245	2245	2324	232
Bludenz d.	...	0626	...	...	...	0830	...	...	1030	...	...	...	1230	...	...	...	...	1430	...	1630	...	1830	2030	2301	2301	2340	234
Langen am Arlberg d.	...	0652	...	...	...	|	...	...	|	...	...	...	|	...	...	...	...	|	...	|	...	|	|	2335	2335	|	|
St Anton am Arlberg d.	...	0703	...	...	...	0903	...	...	1103	...	...	...	1303	...	...	...	...	1503	...	1703	...	1903	2107	2345	2345	|	|
Landeck-Zams d.	...	0727	...	...	...	0927	...	...	1127	...	...	...	1327	...	...	...	...	1527	...	1727	...	1927	2131	0009	0009	|	|
Ötztal d.	...	0751	...	...	...	0948	...	...	1148	...	...	...	1348	...	...	...	...	1548	...	1748	...	1951	2155	|	|	|	|
Innsbruck Hbf d.	0510**x**	0817	0821	...	...	1017	...	...	1221**e**	1217	...	...	1417	...	...	...	...	1617	...	1817	...	2017	2218	0056	0056	0128	012
Jenbach d.	0527**x**	|	0844	...	...	|	...	...	1244	|	...	...	|	...	...	...	...	|	...	|	...	|	...	|	|	|	|
Wörgl d.	0541**x**	0843	0900	...	...	1043	...	...	1300	1243	...	...	1443	...	...	...	...	1643	...	1843	...	2043	...	|	|	|	|
Kitzbühel d.	|	|	0930	...	...	|	...	...	1330	|	...	...	|	...	...	...	...	|	...	|	...	|	...	|	|	|	|
St Johann in Tirol d.	|	|	0938	...	...	|	...	...	1338	|	...	...	|	...	...	...	...	|	...	|	...	|	...	|	|	|	|
Saalfelden d.	|	|	1006	...	...	|	...	...	1406	|	...	...	|	...	...	...	...	|	...	|	...	|	...	|	|	|	|
Zell am See d.	|	|	1017	...	...	|	...	...	1417	|	...	...	|	...	...	...	...	|	...	|	...	|	...	|	|	|	|
Schwarzach St Veit d.	|	|	|	...	...	|	...	...	|	|	...	...	|	...	...	...	...	|	...	|	...	|	...	0324	0423	|	|
Salzburg Hbf d.	0708**x**	1008	|	1012	...	1208	1212	1215	|	1408	...	...	1608	1612	...	...	1615	1808	1815	2008	2012	2208	...	|	|	0350	043
Bischofshofen a.	|	|	|	1052	...	|	1252	1302	|	|	...	...	|	1652	...	...	1702	|	1902	|	2052	|	...	0336	|	|	|
Schwarzach St Veit a.	|	|	1046	1109	...	|	1309	|	1446	|	...	1509	|	1709	...	...	|	|	|	|	2109	|	...	|	|	|	|
Selzthal a.	|	|	1239	|	...	|	|	1439	1639	|	...	|	|	|	...	...	1839	|	2039	|	|	|	...	0504	|	|	|
Graz Hbf a.	|	|	1414	|	...	|	|	1614	1814	|	...	|	|	|	...	...	2014	|	2214	|	|	|	...	0700	|	|	|
Villach Hbf a.	|	|	▬	1243	1253	|	1443	...	...	|	...	1643	|	1843	1853	...	...	|	...	|	2243	|	...	...	0605	|	|
Klagenfurt a.	|	|	...	1316	|	|	1513	...	...	|	...	1718	|	1916	|	...	...	|	...	|	2316	|	...	...	|	|	|
Jesenice 🛃 a.	|	|	...	...	1333	|	▬	...	...	|	...	1733	|	...	1933	...	...	|	...	|	...	|	...	...	0705	|	|
Ljubljana ⊙ a.	|	|	...	...	1432	|	...	...	...	|	...	1833	|	...	2042	2105	...	|	...	|	...	|	...	...	0811	|	|
Zagreb ⊙ a.	|	|	...	...	1710	|	...	...	...	|	...	2051	|	...	...	2336	...	|	...	|	...	|	...	...	1043	|	|
Vinkovci ⊕ a.	|	|	...	...	2110	|	...	...	...	|	...	...	|	...	...	0305	...	|	...	|	...	|	...	...	1430	|	|
Beograd Centar ⊕ a.	|	|	...	...	...	|	...	...	...	|	...	...	|	...	...	0602	...	|	...	|	...	|	...	...	1742	|	|
Linz Hbf a.	0814**x**	1114	...	...	...	1314	...	...	...	1514	...	...	1714	...	...	...	...	1914	...	2114	...	2317	...	...	...	0457	055
St Pölten a.	0900**x**	1200	*RJX*	...	...	1400	*EC*	...	...	1600	...	...	1800	...	...	...	...	2000	...	2200	...	0003	...	...	...	0600	071
Wien Meidling a.	0923**x**	1223	**63**	...	...	1423	**145**	...	...	1623	...	...	1823	...	...	...	...	2023	...	2223	...	0026	...	...	...	0627	074
Wien Hbf. a.	0930**x**	1230	✕	...	...	1430	🍷	...	...	1630	...	...	1830	...	...	...	...	2030	...	2230	...	0033	...	...	...	0635	075
Wien Hbf. d.	0942	...	1340	...	...	...	1442	...	...	...	1642	...	1842	...	...	...	...	2042	...	...	...	...	...	...	...	0640	...
Bratislava hl. a.	|	...	|	...	...	...	|	...	...	...	|	...	|	...	...	...	...	|	...	...	...	...	...	...	...	|	...
Hegyeshalom 🛃 a.	1025	...	1425	...	...	...	1525	...	...	...	1725	...	1925	...	...	...	...	2151	...	...	...	...	...	...	...	0725	...
Györ a.	1053	...	1453	...	...	...	1553	...	...	...	1753	...	1953	...	...	...	...	...	...	...	...	...	...	...	...	0753	...
Budapest Keleti a.	1219	...	1619	...	...	...	1719	...	...	...	1919	...	2119	...	...	...	...	...	...	...	...	...	...	...	...	0919	...

train type/number	RJX	RJX	EC	RJ	RJX	D	D	EC	RJX	RJX	RJX	RJX	EC	EC	EC	RJX	RJX	RJX	RJX	IC	D	RJX	RJX	NJ	EN	EN	NJ
train number	**360**	**368**	**218**	**691**	**160**	**410**	**314**	**114**	**162**	**60**	**860**	**564**	**212**	**164**	**216**	**62**	**166**	**64**	**168**	**610**	**210**	**66**	**760**	**466**	**40462**	**414**	**46**
notes	✕	✕	🍷	✕	✕	**314**		🍷	✕	✕	✕	✕	**112**	🍷	🍷	✕	✕	✕	✕	🍷		✕	✕				
						Q							**H**	**B**							2			**W**	**E**	**A**	**Z**
Budapest Keleti d.	...	...	...	...	...	...	...	...	0640	0740	...	...	...	...	...	0940	...	1140	...	...	...	1340	...	...	2040	...	..
Györ d.	...	...	...	...	...	...	...	...	0802	0902	...	...	...	...	...	1102	...	1302	...	...	...	1502	...	...	2202	...	..
Hegyeshalom 🛃 d.	...	...	...	...	...	...	...	...	0832	0932	...	...	...	...	...	1132	...	1332	...	...	...	1532	...	...	2232	...	..
Bratislava hl. d.	...	...	...	...	0610	...	...	...	|	|	...	...	...	...	...	|	...	|	...	...	...	|	...	...	|	...	..
Wien Hbf a.	...	...	...	...	0718	...	...	...	0918	1021	...	...	...	...	...	1221	...	1421	...	...	...	1618	...	...	2321	...	..
Wien Hbf d.	...	0530**x**	...	...	0730	...	...	...	0930	1030	1030	1130	...	...	...	▬	1330	▬	1530	...	...	▬	1730	2127	2325	...	..
Wien Meidling d.	...	0537**x**	...	...	0737	...	...	...	0937	1037	1037	1137	...	...	...	...	1337	...	1537	...	...	...	1737	2135	2333	...	..
St Pölten d.	...	0600**x**	...	...	0800	...	...	...	1000	1100	1100	1200	...	...	...	...	1400	...	1600	...	...	...	1800	2202	2359	...	..
Linz Hbf d.	...	0646**x**	...	...	0846	...	...	...	1046	1146	1146	1246	...	...	...	...	1446	...	1646	...	...	...	1846	2258	0103	...	..
Beograd Centar ⊕ d.	...	|	...	...	|	2100	...	...	|	|	|	|	...	...	...	...	|	...	|	...	...	...	|	|	|	1035	..
Vinkovci ⊕ d.	...	|	...	...	|	0105	...	...	|	|	|	|	...	...	...	...	|	...	|	...	0855	...	|	|	|	1444	..
Zagreb ⊙ d.	...	|	...	...	|	0440	...	...	|	|	|	|	0700	...	...	...	|	...	|	...	1236	*RJ*	|	|	|	1838	..
Ljubljana ⊙ d.	...	|	...	...	|	0718	0726	...	|	|	|	|	0922	...	...	*RJ*	|	...	|	...	1527	**110**	|	|	|	2110	..
Jesenice 🛃 d.	...	|	...	...	|	▬	0827	...	|	|	|	|	1017	...	...	**793**	|	*IC*	|	...	1627	✕	|	|	|	2209	..
Klagenfurt d.	...	|	...	0645	|	*IC*	|	0842	|	|	|	|	1027	...	...	1245	|	**518**	|	...	|	1642	|	|	|	|	..
Villach Hbf d.	...	|	...	0716	|	**512**	0908	0916	|	|	|	|	1116	...	...	1316	|	🍷	|	...	1709	1716	|	|	|	2320	..
Graz Hbf d.	...	|	0536	|	|	0745	...	|	|	|	|	|	|	0945	1145	|	|	1345	|	1545	...	|	|	|	|	|	22
Selzthal d.	...	|	0719	|	|	0919	...	|	|	|	|	|	|	1119	1319	|	|	1519	|	1719	...	|	|	|	|	|	00
Schwarzach St Veit d.	...	|	|	0850	|	|	...	1050	|	|	|	|	1248	1313	|	1450	|	|	|	|	...	1850	|	|	|	|	|
Bischofshofen d.	...	|	0857	0905	|	1057	...	1105	|	|	|	|	...	|	1457	1505	|	1650	|	1857	...	1905	|	|	|	|	01
Salzburg Hbf d.	...	0756	0944	0948	0956	1144	...	1148	1156	1252	1256	1356	...	|	1544	1548	1556	|	1756	1944	...	1948	1956	0230	0230	|	|
Schwarzach St Veit d.	...	|	...	...	|	...	...	...	|	...	|	|	...	|	...	...	|	1713	|	...	...	...	|	|	|	0232	02
Zell am See d.	...	|	...	...	|	...	...	...	|	...	|	|	...	1344	...	...	|	1744	|	...	...	...	|	|	|	|	|
Saalfelden d.	...	|	...	...	|	...	...	...	|	...	|	|	...	1354	...	...	|	1754	|	...	...	...	|	|	|	|	|
St Johann in Tirol d.	...	|	...	...	|	...	...	...	|	...	|	|	...	1422	...	...	|	1822	|	...	...	...	|	|	|	|	|
Kitzbühel d.	...	|	...	...	|	...	...	...	|	...	|	|	...	1430	...	...	|	1830	|	...	...	...	|	|	|	|	|
Wörgl d.	...	0919	...	...	1119	...	...	...	1319	...	1415	1519	...	1502	...	...	1719	1902	1919	...	...	...	2119	|	|	|	|
Jenbach d.	...	|	...	...	|	...	...	...	|	...	1429	|	...	1518	...	...	|	1918	|	...	...	...	|	|	|	|	|
Innsbruck Hbf d.	0745	0948	...	...	1148	...	...	...	1348	...	1448	1544	...	1548	...	...	1748	1940	1948	...	...	...	2148	0431	0431	0453	04
Ötztal d.	0809	1012	...	...	1212	...	...	...	1412	...	|	...	...	1612	...	...	1812	...	2012	...	...	...	2212	|	|	|	|
Landeck-Zams d.	0833	1033	...	...	1233	...	...	...	1433	...	1533	...	...	1633	...	...	1833	...	2036	...	...	...	2236	|	|	0545	05
St Anton am Arlberg d.	0857	1057	...	...	1257	...	...	...	1457	...	|	...	...	1657	...	...	1857	...	2100	...	...	...	2300	|	|	0610	06
Langen am Arlberg d.	|	|	...	...	|	...	...	...	|	...	1604	...	...	|	...	...	|	...	|	...	...	...	2310	|	|	0621	06
Bludenz d.	0931	1131	...	...	1331	...	...	...	1531	...	1631	...	...	1731	...	...	1931	...	2134	...	...	...	2337	0625	0625	0706	07
Feldkirch d.	0944	1148	...	...	1348	...	...	...	1548	...	1647	...	...	1744	...	...	1948	...	2148	...	...	...	2348	0640	0640	0738	07
Bregenz a.	|	|	...	...	|	...	...	...	|	...	1717	...	...	|	...	...	|	...	|	...	...	...	0013	|	|	|	
Buchs 🛃 a.	0959	1206	...	...	1406	...	...	...	1606	...	...	...	...	1759	...	...	2006	...	2203	...	...	...	...	0656	0656	0753	07
Sargans a.	1023	1223	...	...	1423	...	...	...	1623	...	...	...	...	1823	...	...	2023	...	2223	...	...	...	...	0723	0723	0823	08
Zürich HB a.	1120	1320	...	...	1520	...	...	...	1720	...	...	...	...	1920	...	...	2120	...	2320	...	...	...	...	0820	0820	0920	09

A – *ÖBB nightjet.* ALPINE PEARLS – 🛏 1, 2 cl., ▬ 2 cl. (4, 6 berth), [2] Zürich - Zagreb and v.v. [2] Zürich - Beograd and v.v. [2] Villach - Beograd and v.v.

B – TRANSALPIN [1] (observation car), [12] 🍷 Zürich - Innsbruck - Graz and v.v.

C – 🛏 1, 2 cl., ▬ 2 cl., [2] Zürich - Wien - Budapest. Conveys 🛏 1, 2 cl. (**50467**) Zürich - Linz - Praha (Table **52**). Special fares payable.

D – HORTOBÁGY [12] ✕ Wien - Budapest - Szolnok (arrive 2102) - Debrecen (2241) - Záhony (0010). Conveys 🛏 1, 2 cl. Wien (**40147**) - Budapest - Záhony - Lviv - Kyïv (Table **96**).

E – 🛏 1, 2 cl., ▬ 2 cl., [2] Budapest - Wien - Zürich. Conveys 🛏 1, 2 cl. (**50466**) Praha - Linz - Zürich (Table **52**). Special fares payable.

H – [12] Schwarzach St Veit - Villach - Klagenfurt and Schwarzach St Veit - Villach - Ljubljana - Zagreb and v.v.

P – June 22 - Sept. 15: ▬ 2 cl., [12] Ljubljana - Zagreb - Beograd.

Q – June 23 - Sept. 16: ▬ 2 cl., [12] Beograd - Zagreb - Ljubljana.

W – *ÖBB nightjet.* WIENER WALZER – 🛏 1, 2 cl., ▬ 2 cl. (4, 6 berth), [2] Zürich - Wien and v.v. Special fares payable.

Z – *ÖBB nightjet.* ZÜRICHSEE – 🛏 1, 2 cl., ▬ 2 cl. (4, 6 berth), [2] Zürich - Graz and v.v.

e – Arrive 1211.

x – ①–⑥.

RJ – ÖBB *Railjet* service. ✕, [business] (business class, [1] (first class), [2] (economy class).

⊙ – 🛃 between Ljubljana and Zagreb is Dobova.

⊕ – 🛃 between Vinkovci and Beograd is Šid.

LJUBLJANA - SEŽANA - VILLA OPICINA - TRIESTE - UDINE 87

	1824		1896	
	2		2	
Ljubljana d.	0600	...	1610	...
Postojna d.	0656	...	1708	...
Pivka d.	0709	...	1721	...
Divača d.	0728	...	1740	...
Sežana 🛃 d.	0737	...	1751	...
Villa Opicina 🛃 a.	0747	...	1801	...
Villa Opicina 🛃 d.	0805	...	1815	...
Trieste a.	0839	...	1843	...
Trieste d.	0850	0915	...	1915
Monfalcone d.	0913	0939	...	1939
Trieste Airport d.	0918	0944	...	1944
Cervignano-Aquileia-Grado d.	0927	0952	...	1952
Udine a.	0952	|	...	|
Venezia Mestre a.	...	1108	...	2108
Venezia Santa Lucia a.	...	1120	...	2120

		1825		1897
		2		2
Venezia Santa Lucia d.	0641	...	1641	...
Venezia Mestre d.	0653	...	1653	...
Udine d.	|	...	|	1754
Cervignano-Aquileia-Grado d.	0809	...	1809	1823
Trieste Airport d.	0817	...	1817	1830
Monfalcone d.	0823	...	1823	1835
Trieste a.	0846	...	1848	1858
Trieste d.	...	0901	...	1907
Villa Opicina 🛃 a.	...	0926	...	1936
Villa Opicina 🛃 d.	...	0946	...	1958
Sežana 🛃 d.	...	0957	...	2009
Divača d.	...	1006	...	2018
Pivka d.	...	1026	...	2038
Postojna d.	...	1039	...	2051
Ljubljana a.	...	1136	...	2148

WIEN - KLAGENFURT - VENEZIA, MILANO and ROMA 88

train type / number	🚌	*REX*	*RJ*	*IC*	🚌	*RJ*	*RJ*	*EC*	*RJ*	*RJ*	*REX*	*NJ*	*NJ*	*NJ*	*NJ*
train number	**831**	**1821**	**131**	**533**	**835**	**535**	**73**	**140**	**133**	**539**	**1823**	**40233**	**233**	**1237**	**237**
notes	Ⓡ	**1817** 2	✗	✗	Ⓡ Y	✗	✗	🍷 J	✗	✗	**1819** 2	**A**	**B**	**G**	**C**
Praha hlavní d.	...	...	...	...	...	...	0650	...	...	...	...	...	...	...	...
Břeclav d.	...	...	...	...	...	...	0955	...	...	...	...	...	...	...	...
Budapest Keleti d.	...	...	...	...	...	...	|	0840	...	...	...	...	...	...	...
Györ d.	...	...	...	...	...	...	|	1002	...	...	...	...	...	...	...
Wien Hbf d.	...	...	0625	0825	...	1025	1049	1121	1225	1425	...	1923	1923	2023	2127
Wien Meidling d.	...	...	0632	0832	...	1032	...	...	1232	1432	...	1931	1931	2031	2135
Bruck an der Mur d.	...	...	0815	1015	...	1215	...	...	1415	1615	...	2127	2127	2222	|
Klagenfurt Hbf d.	0605	...	1022	1222	...	1422	...	...	1622	1822	...	2337	2337	0021	|
Linz Hbf d.	|	...	|	|	...	|	...	...	|	|	...	|	|	|	2258
Salzburg Hbf d.	|	...	|	|	...	|	...	...	|	|	...	|	|	|	0140
Villach Hbf d.	0650	0945	1050	1246	1256	1446	...	...	1649	1846	1929	0055	0134	0045	0445
Tarvisio 🛃 a.	|	1013	1112	...	|	...	...	...	1712	...	1957	0119	0157	0108	0508
Udine a.	0823	1130	1216	...	1429	...	...	...	1816	...	2113	|	|	|	0623
Trieste Centrale a.	|	1259**x**	|	...	|	...	...	...	|	...	2239**x**	|	|	|	|
Venezia Mestre a.	1000	...	1353	...	1605	...	...	...	1953	...	...	|	|	|	0812
Venezia Tronchetto ★ a.	1020	...	|	...	1625	...	...	...	|	...	...	|	|	|	|
Venezia Santa Lucia a.	...	...	1405	...	...	...	...	...	2005	...	...	|	|	|	0824
Padova a.	...								...	...	...	0409	0521	0415	...
Verona Porta Nuova a.	...								...	...	...	|	0624	|	...
Milano Centrale a.	...								...	...	...	|	0912	|	...
Bologna Centrale a.	...								...	...	...	0520	...	0541	...
Firenze SMN a.	...								...	...	...	0619	...	0653	...
Pisa Centrale a.	...								...	...	...	|	...	0831	...
Livorno Centrale a.	...								...	...	...	|	...	0850	...
Roma Termini a.	...								...	...	...	0922	...	...	...

OTHER CONNECTING SERVICES

Praha - Wien: Table **1150**
Budapest - Wien: Table **1250**
Venezia - Roma: Table **600**
Venezia - Milano: Table **605**

train type / number	*REX*	*RJ*	*RJ*	*EC*	*EC*	*RJX*	*RJ*	🚌	*IC*	*REX*	*RJ*	🚌	*NJ*	*NJ*	*NJ*	*NJ*
train number	**1816**	**534**	**132**	**100**	**272**	**165**	**372**	**832**	**632**	**1818**	**130**	**838**	**236**	**1234**	**235**	**40294**
notes	**1820** 2	✗	✗		✗	✗	✗	Ⓡ	🍷	**1822** 2	✗	Ⓡ Y	**C**	**D**	**B**	**A**
Roma Termini d.	...	...	...	...	...	...	...	...	...	...	...	...	...	...	...	1858
Livorno Centrale d.	...	...	...	...	...	...	...	...	...	...	...	...	...	1920	...	|
Pisa Centrale d.	...	...	...	...	...	...	...	...	...	...	...	...	...	1946	...	|
Firenze SMN d.	...	...	...	...	...	...	...	...	...	...	...	...	...	2105	...	2149
Bologna Centrale d.	...	...	...	...	...	...	...	...	...	...	...	...	...	2223	...	2246
Milano Centrale d.	...	...	...	...	...	...	...	...	...	...	...	...	...	|	2040	|
Verona Porta Nuova d.	...	...	...	...	...	...	...	...	...	...	...	...	...	|	2252	|
Padova d.	...	...	...	...	...	...	...	...	...	...	...	...	...	2349	2344	0003
Venezia Santa Lucia d.	...	...	0955	...	...	...	...	...	...	...	1555	...	2104	|	|	|
Venezia Tronchetto ★ d.	...	...	|	...	...	...	...	1320	...	...	|	1820	|	|	|	|
Venezia Mestre d.	...	...	1007	...	...	...	...	1340	...	...	1607	1840	2116	|	|	|
Trieste Centrale d.	0545**x**	...	|	...	...	...	...	|	...	1550**x**	|	|	|	|	|	|
Udine d.	0714	...	1146	...	...	...	...	1516	...	1722	1746	2016	2247	|	|	|
Tarvisio 🛃 d.	0827	...	1249	...	...	...	...	|	...	1840	1849	|	|	0319	0245	0305
Villach Hbf a.	0854	0914	1311	...	...	...	...	1650	1714	1907	1911	2150	0042	0341	0307	0327
Salzburg Hbf a.	...	|	|	...	...	...	...	...	|	...	|	|	0404	|	|	|
Linz Hbf a.	...	|	|	...	...	...	...	...	|	...	|	|	0558	|	|	|
Klagenfurt Hbf a.	...	0937	1337	...	...	...	...	...	1737	...	1937	2235	|	0407	0439	0439
Bruck an der Mur a.	...	1144	1544	...	...	...	...	...	1944	...	2144	...	|	0621	0639	0639
Wien Meidling a.	...	1328	1728	...	...	...	...	...	2128	...	2328	...	0744	0826	0839	0839
Wien Hbf a.	...	1335	1735	1810	...	1842	1910	...	2035	...	2335	...	0755	0832	0846	0846
Györ a.	...	...	...	|	...	1953	|	...	...	...	...	...	...	...	...	...
Budapest Keleti a.	...	...	...	|	...	2119	|	...	...	...	...	...	...	...	...	...
Břeclav a.	...	...	...	1904	1907	...	2004	...	...	...	...	...	...	...	...	...
Praha hlavní a.	...	...	...	...	2209	...	2314	...	...	...	...	...	...	...	...	...

A – *ÖBB nightjet* 🛏 1, 2 cl., 🛏 2 cl. (4, 6 berth), [2] 🍷 Wien - Roma and v.v.

B – *ÖBB nightjet* 🛏 1, 2 cl., 🛏 2 cl. (4, 6 berth), [2] 🍷 Wien - Milano and v.v.

C – *ÖBB nightjet* 🛏 1, 2 cl., 🛏 2 cl. (4, 6 berth), [2] Wien - Venezia and v.v.

D – ④⑥ Apr. 13 - Oct. 12 (also June 10): *ÖBB nightjet* 🛏 1, 2 cl., 🛏 2 cl. (4, 6 berth), [2] 🍷 Livorno - Pisa - Firenze - Wien.

G – ③⑤ Apr. 12 - Oct. 11 (also June 9): *ÖBB nightjet* 🛏 1, 2 cl., 🛏 2 cl. (4, 6 berth), [2] 🍷 Wien - Firenze - Pisa - Livorno.

J – [12] Zahony (depart 0356) - Debrecen (0525) - Szolnok (0657) - Budapest - Wien. Conveys 🛏 1, 2 cl. Kyiv (**40749**) - Lviv (**145**) - Chop (**140**) - Budapest - Wien.

Y – Apr. 13 - Sept. 29 (also Oct. 26).

x – ⑥⑦ (subject to confirmation).

⚡ – Supplement payable.

★ – See Venezia City Plan on page 32.

RJ – ÖBB *Railjet* service. [1] (business class), [1] (first class), [2] (economy class), ✗.

🚌 – **ÖBB** *IC Bus*. Rail tickets valid. Ⓡ. Supplement payable. 1st and 2nd class. 🍷 in first class. Connections to / from Wien are made at Villach.

89 VENEZIA - LJUBLJANA - ZAGREB - BUDAPEST and BEOGRAD

train type	D	D	D	D	RJ	EC	D	D	1604	480	D
train number	703	415	247	581	132	213	315	315	1247	1247	1205
notes	205			201	[R]			411	959	959	
notes	A		M	R				P	K	E	C
Venezia Santa Lucia d.	...	...	...	...	0955	...	...	...	...	...	...
Venezia Tronchetto d.	...	...	...	...	|	...	...	...	...	...	...
Venezia Mestre d.	...	...	...	...	1007	...	...	...	...	...	...
Villach Hbf a.	...	...	...	...	1311	...	...	...	...	...	...
Villach Hbf d.	...	0625	...	...	...	1653	1853	...	...	...	...
Koper a.	...	|	0525p	...	...	|	|	...	2017	...	...
Rijeka d.	...	|	|	...	...	|	|	...	|	2050	...
Ljubljana d.	...	0825	0858	...	...	1836	2040	2105	0015	0015	...
Dobova 🛃 d.	...	1013	|	...	...	2021	...	2306	|	|	...
Split d.	...	|	|	...	...	|	...	|	|	|	1830
Zagreb a.	...	1043	|	...	...	2051	...	2336	|	|	0243
Zagreb d.	0949	1103	|	1638	...	...	...	2343	|	|	0317
Vinkovci a.	|	1430	|	|	...	...	...	0305	|	|	|
Šid 🛃 a.	|	1518	|	|	...	...	...	0345	|	|	|
Beograd Centar a.	|	1742	|	|	...	...	...	0602	|	|	|
Koprivnica 🛃 d.	1122	...	|	1757	...	...	...	...	|	|	0449
Gyékényes 🛃 a.	1133	...	|	1808	...	...	...	...	|	|	0500
Nagykanizsa a.	1256	...	|	1906	...	...	...	...	|	|	0605
Hodoš 🛃 a.	|	...	1230	|	...	...	...	...	0338	0338	|
Zalaegerszeg a.	|	...	1330	|	...	...	...	...	0527	0527	|
Fonyód a.	1422	...	|	2022	...	...	...	...	|	|	0700
Siófok a.	1501	...	|	2101	...	...	...	...	|	|	0731
Székesfehérvár a.	1536	...	1641	2136	...	...	...	...	0741	0741	0813
Budapest Déli a.	1624	...	1729	2224	...	...	...	...	0829	0829	|
Budapest Keleti a.	...	...	...	...	...	...	...	...	...	...	0909

train type	D	D	RJ	EC	🚌	D	D	D	D	D	9008	9008
train number	410	314	131	212	835	200	414	246	204	1204	1246	1246
notes	314		[R]		[R]				782		481	1605
notes	Q				T	A		H	R	D	G	J
Budapest Keleti d.	...	...	...	...	...	...	...	...	...	1855	...	...
Budapest Déli d.	...	...	...	...	...	0635	...	0830	1535	|	2030	2030
Székesfehérvár d.	...	...	...	...	...	0721	...	0916	1621	1954	2116	2116
Siófok d.	...	...	...	...	...	0757	...	|	1657	2030	|	|
Fonyód d.	...	...	...	...	...	0837	...	|	1737	2101	|	|
Zalaegerszeg d.	...	...	...	...	...	|	...	1212	|	|	0012	0012
Hodoš 🛃 d.	...	...	...	...	...	|	...	1305	|	|	0103	0103
Nagykanizsa d.	...	...	...	...	...	0949	...	|	1841	2157	|	|
Gyékényes 🛃 d.	...	...	...	...	...	1044	...	|	1927	2255	|	|
Koprivnica 🛃 a.	...	...	...	...	...	1055	...	|	1938	2306	|	|
Beograd Centar d.	2100	...	...	...	...	|	1035	|	|	|	|	|
Šid 🛃 d.	0024	...	...	...	...	|	1346	|	|	|	|	|
Vinkovci d.	0105	...	...	...	...	|	1444	|	|	|	|	|
Zagreb a.	0427	...	...	...	...	1238	1812	|	2105	0022	|	|
Zagreb d.	0440	...	...	0700	...	...	1838	|	...	0038	|	|
Split a.	|	...	...	|	...	...	|	|	...	0837	|	|
Dobova 🛃 d.	0540	0540	...	0745	...	...	1925	|	...	...	|	|
Ljubljana d.	0718	0726	...	0922	...	...	2110	1639	...	...	0550	0550
Rijeka a.	...	|	...	|	...	...	|	|	...	...	0924	|
Koper a.	...	|	...	|	...	...	|	2007p	...	...	...	0833
Villach Hbf a.	...	0908	...	1058	...	...	2247	...	...	...	...	...
Villach Hbf d.	...	...	1050	...	1256	...	...	...	...	...	...	...
Venezia Mestre a.	...	...	1353	...	1605	...	...	...	...	...	...	...
Venezia Tronchetto a.	...	...	|	...	1625	...	...	...	...	...	...	...
Venezia Santa Lucia a.	...	...	1405	...	...	...	...	...	...	...	...	...

A – GRADEC June 15 - Sept. 15: [12] Budapest - Zagreb and v.v.

C – ADRIA June 15 - Sept. 7: 🛏 1, 2 cl., 🛌 2 cl., [2] Split - Zagreb - Budapest.

D – ADRIA June 14 - Sept. 6: 🛏 1, 2 cl., 🛌 2 cl., [2] Budapest - Zagreb - Split.

E – ISTRA June 22 - Aug. 31: 🛏 1, 2 cl., 🛌 2 cl., [2] Rijeka - Hodoš 🛃 - Budapest (Table **91**).

G – ISTRA June 21 - Aug. 30: 🛏 1, 2 cl., 🛌 2 cl., [2] Budapest - Hodoš 🛃 - Rijeka (Table **91**).

H – CITADELLA [12] Budapest - Hodoš - Ljubljana - (Koper June 21 - Aug. 25) (Table **91**).

J – ISTRA June 21 - Aug. 30: 🛌 2 cl. [2] Budapest - Hodoš 🛃 - Koper (Table **91**).

K – ISTRA June 22 - Aug. 31: 🛌 2 cl. [2] Koper - Hodoš 🛃 - Budapest (Table **91**).

M – CITADELLA – [12] (Koper June 21 - Aug. 25) - Ljubljana - Hodoš - Budapest (Table **91**).

P – Dec. 9 - Jan. 12, June 22 - Sept. 15: 🛌 2 cl., [12] Ljubljana - Zagreb - Beograd.

Q – Dec. 10 - Jan. 13, June 23 - Sept. 16: 🛌 2 cl., [12] Beograd - Zagreb - Ljubljana.

R – AGRAM [12] Zagreb - Budapest and v.v.

T – Apr. 13 - Sept. 29 (also Oct. 26).

p – June 21 - Aug. 25.

q – June 22 - Aug. 26.

t – Zalaegerszeg **Ola**.

🚌 – **ÖBB** *IC Bus*. [R] 🍷. Rail tickets valid. Supplement payable. 1st and 2nd class.

RJ – ÖBB *Railjet* service. [1] (business class), [1] (first class), [2] (economy class), 🍴.

90 MARSEILLE - NICE - MILANO, ROMA and VENEZIA

train type	EC	FB	IC	EC	FR				IC	IC	FA	FR	FR		EC	IC	FR	FR	FR	EC	EC	ICN	
train number	139	8613	511	15	9539		86101		745	665	8619	9737	9547		145	673	9755	9565	9665	147	147	799	
notes	140	[R] 🍷	[R] 🍷	[R] 🍷	9541			◇	746	[R]	[R] 🍷	[R] 🍷	[R] 🍴		146	35873	[R] 🍷	[R] 🍴	[R] 🍴	148	148	[R]	
notes	♣	ϟ	ϟ	ϟ	[R] 🍴		Ⓐ		[R]	ϟ	ϟ	ϟ	ϟ		♣	[R] 🍷	ϟ	ϟ	ϟ	♣	♣	ϟ	
notes					ϟ				ϟ							ϟ			Ⓑ	P		A	
Marseille St Charles d.	...	...	...	...	...	...	0558	...	...	...	...	...	...	...	...	...	...	...	...	1528	...	...	...
Toulon d.	...	...	...	...	...	...	0647	...	...	...	...	...	...	...	...	...	...	...	...	1617	...	...	...
Cannes d.	...	...	...	...	...	...	0813	0851	...	...	...	...	...	...	...	...	...	...	...	1740	...	...	...
Nice d.	0801	...	...	...	...	...	0852	0936	...	...	...	...	...	...	1402	...	...	...	...	1808	1808	...	...
Monaco - Monte Carlo d.	0825	...	...	...	...	...	0915	1003	...	...	...	...	...	...	1423	...	...	...	...	1833	1833	...	...
Ventimiglia 🛃 d.	0910	...	...	...	...	...	0938	1035	1105	...	...	...	...	...	1510	...	...	...	...	1910	1910	...	...
San Remo d.	0923	...	...	...	...	...	...	...	1122	...	...	...	...	...	1523	...	...	...	...	1923	1923	...	...
Genova Piazza Principe a.	1108	1210	1224	...	...	...	...	...	1308	1347	1502	...	...	...	1708	1747	...	...	...	2108	2108	2353	...
Milano Centrale a.	1250	|	|	1305	1320	...	...	...	1450	|	|	1515	1520	...	1850	|	1915	1920	1930	2250	2250	|	...
Verona a.	...	|	|	1428	|	...	...	...	...	|	|	1628	|	...	...	|	2028	|	|	...	...	|	...
Venezia Santa Lucia a.	...	|	|	1540	|	...	...	...	...	|	|	1728q	|	...	...	|	2140	|	|	...	...	|	...
La Spezia a.	...	1314	1350	...	|	...	...	...	...	1521	1614	...	|	...	...	1921	...	|	|	...	...	0124	...
Pisa Centrale a.	...	1404	1447	...	|	...	...	...	...	...	1704	...	|	...	...	2017	...	|	|	...	...	0216	...
Firenze SMN a.	...	|	|	...	1459	...	...	...	...	...	|	...	1659	...	...	...	...	2059	|	...	...	|	...
Roma Termini a.	...	1703	1803	...	1640	...	...	...	...	...	2003	...	1840	...	...	...	...	2240	2229	...	...	0543o	...
Napoli Centrale a.	...	...	2029	...	1800	...	...	...	...	...	...	...	2000	...	...	...	...	...	2350	...	...	0817	...

train type	ICN	IC	EC	TGV	FB	FR	FR	FR	EC		IC	IC	FR	FR	EC	EC		FR	FR	IC	IC		
train number	796	658	141	6864	8606	9606	9508	9714	143	17490	510	674	9728	9524	159	159		9532	9738	680	675		
notes	[R]	[R] 🍷	142	[R]	[R] 🍷	[R] 🍴	[R] 🍷	[R] 🍷	144		[R] 🍷	[R] 🍷	[R] 🍷	[R] 🍴	160	160		[R] 🍴	[R] 🍷	[R] 🍷	676	◇	
notes	ϟ	ϟ	♣	ϟ	ϟ	ϟ	ϟ	ϟ	♣		ϟ	ϟ	ϟ	ϟ	♣	♣		ϟ	ϟ	ϟ	[R] ϟ		
notes	A															Q							
Napoli Centrale d.	2146	...	...	...	...	0550f	...	...	...	...	0731	...	...	1000	...	...	...	1200	...	...	...	...	...
Roma Termini d.	0011o	...	...	...	0657	0700	0720	...	...	...	0957	...	...	1120	...	...	...	1320	...	...	...	...	...
Firenze SMN d.	|	...	...	...	|	|	0900	...	...	...	|	...	...	1300	...	...	...	1500	...	...	...	...	...
Pisa Centrale d.	0326	0542	...	...	0956	|	|	...	...	...	1302	1342	...	|	...	...	...	|	...	...	...	...	...
La Spezia d.	0425	0638	...	...	1046	|	|	...	...	...	1405	1438	...	|	...	...	...	|	...	1638	...	...	...
Venezia Santa Lucia d.	|	|	...	...	|	|	|	0820	...	...	|	|	1150	|	...	...	...	|	1420	|	...	...	...
Verona d.	|	|	...	...	|	|	|	0932	...	...	|	|	1302	|	...	...	...	|	1532	|	...	...	...
Milano Centrale d.	|	|	0710	...	|	0959	1040	1045	1110	...	|	|	1415	1440	1505	1505	...	1645	1645	|	1705	...	...
Genova Piazza Principe d.	0601	0815	0856	...	1150	...	...	...	1258	...	1536	1615	...	...	1658	1658	...	...	...	1815	1858	...	...
San Remo d.	...	...	1042	...	...	...	...	...	1442	...	...	...	...	...	1842	1842	...	...	...	...	2039	...	...
Ventimiglia 🛃 a.	...	...	1054	...	...	...	...	...	1454	...	...	...	...	...	1854	1854	...	...	...	...	2056	2103	...
Monaco - Monte Carlo a.	...	...	1141	...	...	...	...	...	1543	...	...	...	...	...	1940	1940	...	...	...	...	...	2131	...
Nice a.	...	...	1200	1213	...	...	...	...	1600	1623	...	...	...	...	2001	2001	...	...	...	...	...	2157	...
Cannes a.	...	...	...	1242	...	...	...	...	...	1648	...	...	...	...	...	2029	...	...	...	...	...	2246	...
Toulon a.	...	...	...	1409	...	...	...	...	...	1814	...	...	...	...	...	2145	...	...	...	...	...	...	...
Marseille St Charles a.	...	...	...	1457	...	...	...	...	...	1907	...	...	...	...	...	2231	...	...	...	...	...	...	...

A – 🛏 1, 2 cl., 🛌 2 cl.(4 berth), [2] Torino - Genova - Napoli - Salerno and v.v.

P – ①⑥⑦ (daily June 2–7, June 11 - Oct. 30, Nov. 4 - Dec. 14).

Q – ⑤⑥⑦ (daily June 2–6, June 10 - Oct. 30, Nov. 3 - Dec. 14).

f – Napoli **Afragola**.

o – Roma **Ostiense**.

q – Venezia **Mestre**.

♣ – *EC Thello*.

ϟ – Supplement payable.

◇ – Stopping train. Alternative services available, see Table **361**.

WIEN - LJUBLJANA and ZAGREB 91

Due to engineering work between Zidani Most and Pragersko 🚌 will operate on certain services

train type	*EC*			*D*	*EC*		9008	9008	
train number	**151**	**483**	**2752**	**246**	**159**¶	**523**	**1246**	**1246**	
notes	✕		2		✕✓	🚌	1605	481	
	E			G	C	X	P	J	
Vien Hbf ... d.	0758	...	...	...	1558	...	...	...	...
Vien Meidling ... d.	0805	...	...	...	1605	...	...	...	...
Viener Neustadt Hbf ... d.	0832	...	...	...	1632	...	...	...	...
Graz Hbf ... d.	1039	...	...	...	1839	...	...	...	...
Spielfeld-Straß 🛃 ... d.	1120	...	...	...	1920	...	...	...	...
Budapest Keleti ... d.	|	...	...	...	|	...	...	...	...
Budapest Déli ... d.	|	...	...	0830	|	...	2030	2030	...
Hodoš 🛃 ... d.	|	...	...	1305	|	...	0103	0103	...
Maribor ... a.	1137	...	...	|	1938	...	0225	0225	...
Pragersko ... a.	1200	...	...	1422	2011	...	0331	0331	...
Zidani Most ... a.	1317	...	...	1541	|	2040**c**	0449	0449	...
Dobova 🛃 ... a.	|	...	...	|	2156	|	|	|	...
Zagreb ... a.	|	...	...	|	2242	|	|	|	...
Ljubljana ... a.	1414	1510	1545	1639	...	2152	0550	0550	...
Koper ... a.	...	|	1812	2007**p**	...	...	0833	|	...
Rijeka ... a.	...	1803	...	...	...	...	...	0924	...

train type/number	*IC*		*EC*	*D*			*EC*	480	1604	
train number	**508**	**14**	**158**	**247**	**2751**	**482**	**150**	**1247**	**1247**	
notes		🚌	✕✓		2		✕	959	959	
		Z	C	H			E	K	Q	
Rijeka ... d.	...	...	...	...	...	1155	...	2050	...	...
Koper ... d.	0525	...	...	0525**q**	1003	|	...	|	2017	...
Ljubljana ... d.	0748	0800	...	0858	1236	1448	1545	0015	0015	...
Zagreb ... d.	...	|	0725	|	...	...	|	|	|	...
Dobova 🛃 ... d.	...	|	0813	|	...	...	|	|	|	...
Zidani Most ... d.	...	0910**c**	|	0953	...	...	1642	0108	0108	...
Pragersko ... d.	...	...	0959	1114	...	...	1756	0225	0225	...
Maribor ... d.	...	...	1019	|	...	...	1820	|	|	...
Hodoš 🛃 ... a.	...	...	|	1230	...	...	|	0338	0338	...
Budapest Déli ... a.	...	...	|	1729	...	...	|	0829	0829	...
Budapest Keleti ... a.	...	...	|	...	...	...	|	...	...	...
Spielfeld-Straß 🛃 ... a.	...	...	1036	...	...	...	1836	...	...	...
Graz Hbf ... a.	...	...	1120	...	...	...	1920	...	...	...
Wiener Neustadt Hbf ... a.	...	...	1328	...	...	...	2128	...	...	...
Wien Meidling ... a.	...	...	1355	...	...	...	2155	...	...	...
Wien Hbf ... a.	...	...	1402	...	...	...	2202	...	...	...

– CROATIA (12) ✕ Wien - Zagreb and v.v.

– EMONA (12) ✕ Wien - Ljubljana and v.v.

– CITADELLA (12) Budapest - Hodoš - Ljubljana - (Koper June 21 - Aug. 25) (Table **89**).

– CITADELLA (12) (Koper June 22 - Aug. 26) - Ljubljana - Hodoš - Budapest (Table **89**).

– ISTRA June 21 - Aug. 30: 🛏 1, 2 cl., 🛏 2 cl., (2) Budapest - Hodoš 🛃 - Rijeka (Table **89**).

– ISTRA June 22 - Aug. 31: 🛏 1, 2 cl., 🛏 2 cl., (2) Rijeka - Hodoš 🛃 - Budapest (Table **89**).

– ISTRA June 21 - Aug. 30: 🛏 2 cl., (2) Budapest - Hodoš 🛃 - Koper (Table **89**).

– ISTRA June 22 - Aug. 31: 🛏 2 cl., (2) Koper - Hodoš 🛃 - Budapest (Table **89**).

– 🚌 Celje - Ljubljana. *EC* **159** arrives Celje 2037 to connect.

Z – 🚌 Ljubljana - Celje. *EC* **158** departs Celje 0920 to connect.

c – Celje.

p – June 21 - Aug. 25.

q – June 22 - Aug. 26.

✓ – Supplement payable.

◇ – Stopping train.

¶ – Train number **1259** on ⑥⑦.

WARSZAWA - VILNIUS 93

train type				*TLK*		*IC*			
train number	**143**			**41106**		**7112**	**149**		
notes	⑥⑦			**H**		**7113**	⑤⑥⑦		
	2	2		🅁		🅁	2	2	
Warszawa Centralna ... d.	...	...	...	0755	...	1315	...	...	...
Warszawa Wschodnia ... d.	...	...	...	0802	...	1322	...	...	...
Małkinia ... d.	...	...	...	0909	...	1423	...	...	...
Białystok ... d.	0828	...	...	1050	...	1526	1549	...	...
Suwałki ... d.	1020	...	...	1240	...	...	1751	...	...
Mockava 🛃 ◐ ... a.	|	...	...	...	...	...	|	...	...
Šeštokai ... a.	|	...	...	...	...	...	|	...	...
Kaunas ... a.	1425	1435	...	...	...	...	2125	2230	...
Vilnius ... a.	...	1553	...	...	...	...	...	2346	...

train type			*TLK*		*TLK*				
train number		**141**	**53106**		**14106**		**145**		
notes		①⑥⑦			**H**		⑥⑦		
	2	2	🅁		🅁	2	2		
Vilnius ... d.	0707	...	...	...	...	1545	...	...	...
Kaunas ... d.	0842	0958	...	...	...	1704	1730	...	...
Šeštokai ... d.	...	|	...	...	...	...	|	...	...
Mockava 🛃 ◐ ... d.	...	|	...	...	...	...	|	...	...
Suwałki ... d.	...	1134	...	...	1540	...	1907	...	...
Białystok ... d.	...	1342	1434	...	1750	...	2051	...	...
Małkinia ... d.	...	...	1537	...	1905	...	...	...	...
Warszawa Wschodnia ... a.	...	...	1656	...	2012	...	...	...	...
Warszawa Centralna ... a.	...	...	1705	...	2020	...	...	...	...

– HAŃCZA – (12) 🅁 Kraków - Warszawa - Białystok - Suwałki and v.v.

◐ – 🛃 = Trakiszki (Poland) / Mockava (Lithuania); ticketing point is Mockava.

MOSKVA - WARSZAWA - PRAHA and WIEN 95

train number									23*JI*	23*JI*
train number	**13***MJ*	**13***MJ*	**9***SZ*	**9***SZ*	**21***EJ*	**21***EJ*	**17***BJ*	**17***BJ*	**452**	**452**
notes										
notes	KW	KX	GW	GX	PW	PX	HW	HX	BW	BX
	⑤⑦	⑤⑦	①③⑤	①③⑤	①	①	④	④	②	②
Moskva Belorusskaya ... d.	1017	1155	1421	1551	1814	1912	1814	1912	1814	1912
Smolensk Tsentralny 🛃§ d.	1440	1544	1920	2020	2311	0009	2311	0009	2311	0009
Orsha Tsentralnaya ... § d.	1603	1706	2047	2145	0038	0137	0038	0137	0038	0137
Minsk ... d.	1824	1927	2343	0039	0312	0414	0312	0414	0312	0414
Brest Tsentralny 🛃 ... a.	2133	2235	0310	0410	0642	0810	0642	0810	0642	0848
Brest Tsentralny 🛃 ... d.	2143	2243	0510	0610	0943	1043	0943	1043	0943	1043
Terespol 🛃 ... a.	2123	2123	0428	0428	0901	0901	0901	0901	0901	0901
Terespol 🛃 ... d.	2208	2208	0513	0513	0946	0946	0946	0946	0946	0946
Warszawa Wschodnia ... a.	2348	2348	0747	0747	1150	1150	1150	1150	1150	1150
Warszawa Centralna ... a.	...	...	0755	0755	1225	1225	1225	1225	...	...
Katowice ... a.	...	...	...	...	|	|	|	|	...	...
Bohumín 🛃 ... a.	...	...	...	...	1723	1723	1723	1723	...	...
Ostrava hlavní ... a.	...	...	...	...	1813	1813	|	|	...	...
Břeclav ... a.	...	...	...	...	|	|	1945	1945	...	...
Wien Hbf ... a.	...	...	...	...	|	|	2117	2117	...	...
Olomouc ... a.	...	...	...	..	1918	1918	...	...	...	...
Pardubice ... a.	...	...	...	...	2039	2039	...	...	...	...
Praha hlavní ... a.	...	...	...	...	2139	2139	...	...	...	...

train number										
train number	**18***BJ*	**18***BJ*	**22***AJ*	**22***AJ*	**24***JI*	**24***JI*	**10***SZ*	**10***SZ*	**14***MJ*	**14***MJ*
notes					**453**	**453**				
notes	TW	TX	QW	QX	AW	AX	RW	RX	JW	JX
	①	①	③	③	⑤	⑤	②④⑥	②④⑥	②⑦	②⑦
Praha hlavní ... d.	...	...	0624	0624	...	...	...	...	...	...
Pardubice ... d.	...	...	0723	0723	...	...	...	...	...	...
Olomouc ... d.	...	...	0846	0846	...	...	...	...	...	...
Wien Hbf ... d.	0605	0605	|	|	...	...	...	...	...	...
Břeclav ... d.	0724	0724	|	|	...	...	...	...	...	...
Ostrava hlavní ... d.	|	|	0950	0950	...	...	...	...	...	...
Bohumín 🛃 ... d.	0951	0951	1026	1026	...	...	...	...	...	...
Katowice ... d.	|	|	|	|	...	...	...	...	...	...
Warszawa Centralna ... d.	1500	1455	1515	1515	...	...	1605	1605	...	...
Warszawa Wschodnia ... d.	1536	1536	1536	1536	1536	1536	1613	1613	0325	0325
Terespol 🛃 ... a.	1744	1744	1744	1744	1744	1744	1900	1900	0518	0518
Terespol 🛃 ... d.	1829	1829	1829	1829	1829	1829	1945	1945	0603	0603
Brest Tsentralny 🛃 ... a.	2015	2115	2015	2115	2015	2115	2131	2231	0746	0838
Brest Tsentralny 🛃 ... d.	2223	2323	2223	2323	2223	2323	2338	0038	0753	0845
Minsk ... a.	0205	0304	0205	0304	0205	0304	0311	0415	1113	1213
Orsha Tsentralnaya ... § a.	0436	0536	0436	0536	0436	0536	0603	0705	1349	1449
Smolensk Tsentralny 🛃§ a.	0611	0716	0611	0711	0611	0716	0734	0834	1516	1616
Moskva Belorusskaya ... a.	1058	1145	1058	1145	1058	1145	1225	1311	1943	2008

– TRANSEUROPEAN EXPRESS ④: 🛏 1, 2 cl. Paris (**453**) - Berlin - Warszawa - Brest (**24** *JI*) - Moskva. ✕ (RZD) Brest - Moskva.

– TRANSEUROPEAN EXPRESS ②: 🛏 1, 2 cl. Moskva (**23** *JI*) - Brest (**452**) - Warszawa - Berlin - Paris. ✕ (RZD) Moskva - Brest.

– POLONEZ ①③⑤ – 🛏 1, 2 cl. 🍸 Moskva - Warszawa. ✕ Moskva - Brest.

– ④: 🛏 1 cl. (lux), 🛏 1, 2 cl. Moskva - Wien - Nice. ✕ (RZD) Moskva - Brest and ✕ (PKP) Warszawa - Nice (journey two nights).

– ①⑥: 🛏 1 cl. (lux), 🛏 1, 2 cl., (coach) ✕ 🅁 Berlin - Warszawa - Moskva, Talgo train.

– ⑤⑦: 🛏 1 cl. (lux), 🛏 1, 2 cl., (coach) ✕ 🅁 Moskva - Warszawa - Berlin, Talgo train.

– VLTAVA ①: 🛏 1, 2 cl. Moskva (**21** *EJ*) - Terespol (**404**) - Bohumín (**112**) - Praha.

– VLTAVA ③: 🛏 1, 2 cl. Praha (**113**) - Bohumín (**405**) - Brest (**22** *AJ*) - Moskva.

– POLONEZ ②④⑥ – 🛏 1, 2 cl. 🍸 Warszawa - Moskva. ✕ Brest - Moskva.

– ⑦: 🛏 1 cl. (lux), 🛏 1, 2 cl. Nice - Wien - Moskva. ✕ (PKP) Nice - Warszawa and ✕ (RZD) Brest - Moskva (journey two nights).

W – Mar. 31, 2019 - Oct. 26, 2019.

X – Oct. 27, 2019 - Dec. 14, 2019. Timings subject to confirmation.

§ – 🛃: Osinovka (BY) / Krasnoye (RU).

96 WIEN / BUDAPEST / PRAHA / BRATISLAVA - LVIV - KYIV

train number		*IC*			*SC*	8813		*EC* 147	
train number		34		603	241	29		146	
notes		[R]		✕	🍷 [R]			749	
notes		L				A		E	
Wien Hbf d.	...	...	...	...	...	...	...	1642	...
Budapest Nyugati d.	...	0723	...	...	...	...	...	|	...
Budapest Keleti d.	...	|	...	...	...	...	...	1940	...
Szolnok d.	...	0838	...	...	...	...	...	2104	...
Debrecen d.	...	0954	...	...	...	...	...	2243	...
Záhony 🏛 a.	...	1121	...	...	...	...	...	0010	...
Praha hlavní d.	...	|	...	...	0709	...	...	|	...
Bratislava hlavná d.	...	|	...	0813	|	...	...	|	...
Žilina d.	...	|	...	1044	1134	...	...	|	...
Košice a.	...	|	...	1353	1427	1510	...	|	...
Čierna nad Tisou 🏛 a.	...	|	...	...	...	1652	...	|	...
Chop 🏛 a.	...	1340	...	...	...	1847	...	0228	...
Mukachevo a.	...	1520	...	...	...	2155	...	0619	...
Lviv a.	...	...	...	...	...	0253	...	1014	...
Khmelnytsky a.	...	...	...	...	...	|	...	|	...
Vinnytsya a.	...	...	...	...	...	|	...	|	...
Kyiv a.	...	...	...	...	...	1013	...	1721	...

train number		749		81	*SC*			*IC*	
train number		145		8812	240	612		33	
notes		*EC* 140			🍷 [R]	✕		[R]	
notes		D		B				L	
Kyiv d.	...	1407	...	1830	...	...	...	...	...
Vinnytsya d.	...	|	...	2152	...	...	...	...	...
Khmelnytsky d.	...	|	...	2356	...	...	...	...	...
Lviv d.	...	2100	...	0409	...	...	...	...	...
Mukachevo d.	...	0054	...	0854	...	...	...	1230	...
Chop 🏛 d.	...	0328	...	1135	...	...	...	1410	...
Čierna nad Tisou 🏛 d.	...	|	...	1205	...	...	...	|	...
Košice d.	...	|	...	1354	1500	1607	...	|	...
Žilina a.	...	|	...	...	1752	1916	...	|	...
Bratislava hlavná a.	...	|	...	...	|	2147	...	|	...
Praha hlavní a.	...	|	...	...	2219	...	...	|	...
Záhony 🏛 a.	...	0246	...	...	...	...	...	1327	...
Debrecen a.	...	0521	...	...	...	...	...	1601	...
Szolnok a.	...	0653	...	...	...	...	...	1720	...
Budapest Keleti a.	...	0820	...	...	...	...	...	|	...
Budapest Nyugati a.	...	|	...	...	...	...	...	1837	...
Wien Hbf a.	...	1121	...	...	...	...	...	...	...

A – 🛏 1, 2 cl. Košice (**8813**) - Čierna nad Tisou (**8862**) - Chop (**29**) - Lviv - Kyiv.

B – 🛏 1, 2 cl. Kyiv (**81**) - Lviv - Chop (**8861**) - Čierna nad Tisou (**8812**) - Košice.

D – HORTOBÁGY – 🛏 1, 2 cl. Kyiv (**749**) - Lviv (**145**) - Chop (**140**) - Budapest - Wien. [12] ✕ Záhony - Budapest - Wien.

E – HORTOBÁGY – 🛏 1, 2 cl. Wien (**147**) - Budapest - Chop (**146**) - Lviv (**750**) - Kyiv. [12] ✕ Wien - Budapest - Záhony.

L – LATORCA – [12] Budapest - Záhony and v.v.

99 WARSZAWA and KRAKÓW - PRAHA, WIEN and BUDAPEST

train type/train number	*IC*¶	*EC*	*LE*	*IC*¶	*EC*	*EC*	*IC*¶	*EC*	*RJ*	*IC*¶			*IC**	*IC*	*EC*	*EC*	*EC*		*EN*	*EN*	*EN*	
train number	101	273	400	116	103	277	114	131	79	114		404	112	205	105	283	110		407	407	407	
notes/train number	✕	✕	🍷	✕	✕	✕	🍷	✕	✕	🍷		112	🍷	⊡	✕	✕	✕ [R]		457	457	442	
notes				⊡	⊡		⊡	⊡		⊡			⊡	2	⊡		Ⓑ		477			
notes	H		K		X		L	V		L		R		D	W		T		B	C	P	
Gdynia Główny d.	...	...	...	...	...	...	...	...	...	...	...	...	...	...	1112	...	...	...	...	...	...	...
Gdańsk Główny d.	...	...	...	...	...	...	...	...	...	...	...	...	...	...	1138	...	...	...	...	...	...	...
Warszawa Wschodnia d.	...	...	...	0514	0629	...	...	0849	...	...	...	1219	1319	...	1429	...	1734	...	1914	1914	1914	...
Warszawa Centralna d.	...	...	...	0525	0640	...	...	0900	...	...	...	1230	1330	...	1440	...	1747	...	1930	1930	1930	...
Kraków Główny d.	...	...	0448	|	|	...	1025	|	...	...	...	|	|	1541	|	...	|	...	2234	2234	2234	...
Oświecim d.	...	...	|	|	|	...	1153	|	...	...	...	|	|	1658	|	...	|	...	2356	2356	2356	...
Katowice d.	0505	...	0641	0829	0921	...	|	1200	...	...	...	|	1626	|	1713	...	2024	...	|	|	|	...
Zebrzydowice 🏛 d.	|	...	0737	|	1016	...	1307	|	...	←	...	|	|	1804	1816	...	|	...	0109	0109	0109	...
Bohumín 🏛 a.	0626	...	0753	0949	1036	...	1325	1322	...	1325	...	1723	1748	1828	1836	...	|	...	0129	0129	0129	...
Bohumín 🏛 d.	0651	...	0756	1006	1051	...	→	1351	...	1406	...	1806	1806	1851	1851	...	|	...	0220	0220	0323	...
Ostrava hlavní a.	0658	...	0802	1013	1058	...	...	1358	...	1413	...	1813	1813	1858	1858	...	2154	...	0227	0227	0331	...
Přerov a.	0751	...	0859	|	1151	...	...	1451	...	|	...	|	|	1951	1951	...	...	...	|	|	|	...
Olomouc a.	|	...	0915	1118	|	...	...	|	...	1518	...	1918	1918	|	|	...	...	...	|	|	0440	...
Pardubice a.	|	...	1028	1239	|	...	...	|	...	1639	...	2039	2039	|	|	...	...	...	|	|	0609	...
Praha hlavní a.	|	...	1123	1339	|	...	...	|	...	1739	...	2139	2139	|	|	...	...	...	|	|	0731	...
Břeclav a.	0847	0859	...	...	1247	1259	...	1547	1555	...	...	...	...	2047	2047	2059	...	...	0410	0410	...	...
Wien Hbf a.	0949	|	...	...	1349	|	...	|	1649	...	...	...	...	2149	2149	|	...	...	|	0700	...	...
Kúty 🏛 a.	...	0911	...	...	...	1311	...	1611	...	...	...	...	...	...	...	2111	...	...	0511	...	...	...
Bratislava hlavná a.	...	0950	...	...	...	1350	...	1650	...	...	...	...	...	...	...	2150	...	...	0550	...	...	...
Štúrovo 🏛 △ a.	...	1117	...	...	...	1517	...	1817	...	...	...	...	...	...	...	...	...	...	0712	...	...	...
Budapest Nyugati a.	...	1220	...	...	...	1620	...	1920	...	...	...	...	...	...	...	...	...	...	|	...	...	...
Budapest Keleti a.	...	...	...	...	...	...	...	...	...	...	...	...	...	...	...	...	...	...	0835	...	...	...

train type/train number	*EC*	*IC**		*EC*	*EC*	*IC*		*IC*¶	*RJ*	*EC*	*IC*¶	*EC*	*EC*	*IC*¶	*LE*	*EC*	*EC*		*EN*	*EN*	*EN*	
train number	111	113	113	280	104	204		115	74	130	115	276	102	117	401	272	100		456	476	443	
notes/train number	✕ [R]	✕	405	✕	✕	⊡		🍷	✕	✕	🍷	✕	✕	✕		✕	✕		406	456	406	
notes	①–⑥	⊡			⊡	2		⊡		⊡	⊡		⊡	⊡						406		
notes	U		S		W	D		L		V	L		X		J		H		C	F	Q	
Budapest Keleti d.	...	...	...	...	...	...	...	...	...	...	...	...	...	...	...	...	...	...	...	1925	...	...
Budapest Nyugati d.	...	...	...	0540	...	...	...	...	...	0840	...	1140	...	...	...	1540	...	...	...	|	...	...
Štúrovo 🏛 △ d.	...	...	...	0643	...	...	...	...	...	0943	...	1243	...	...	...	1643	...	...	...	2040	...	...
Bratislava hlavná d.	...	...	...	0810	...	...	...	...	...	1110	...	1410	...	...	...	1810	...	...	...	2210	...	...
Kúty 🏛 d.	...	...	...	0849	...	...	...	...	...	1149	...	1449	...	...	...	1849	...	...	...	2249	...	...
Wien Hbf d.	...	...	...	|	0810	0810	...	...	1110	|	...	|	1410	...	...	|	1810	...	2210	|	...	...
Břeclav d.	...	...	...	0901	0910	0910	...	...	1204	1210	...	1501	1510	...	...	1901	1910	...	2350	2350	...	...
Praha hlavní d.	...	0624	0624	...	|	|	...	1024	...	|	...	...	|	1424	1609	...	|	...	|	|	2215	...
Pardubice d.	...	0723	0723	...	|	|	...	1123	...	|	...	...	|	1523	1705	...	|	...	|	|	2325	...
Olomouc d.	...	0846	0846	...	|	|	...	1246	...	|	...	...	|	1648	1820	...	|	...	|	|	0107	...
Přerov d.	...	|	|	...	1008	1008	...	|	...	1308	...	...	1608	|	1838	...	2008	...	|	|	|	...
Ostrava hlavní d.	0605	0950	0950	...	1102	1102	...	1350	...	1402	←	...	1702	1752	1935	...	2102	...	0132	0132	0225	...
Bohumín 🏛 a.	|	0957	0957	...	1109	1109	...	1357	...	1409	1357	...	1709	1759	1942	...	2109	...	0139	0139	0234	...
Bohumín 🏛 d.	|	1009	1026	...	1120	1129	...	→	...	1435	1433	...	1722	1809	1949	...	2131	...	0318	0318	0318	...
Zebrzydowice 🏛 d.	|	|	|	...	1141	1148	...	...	...	|	1454	...	1743	|	2008	...	|	...	0341	0341	0341	...
Katowice a.	0735	1133	|	...	1230	|	...	...	...	1601	|	...	1832	1931	2109	...	2255	...	|	|	|	...
Oświecim a.	|	|	|	...	|	1305	...	...	...	|	1606	...	|	|	|	...	...	...	0451	0451	0451	...
Kraków Główny a.	|	|	|	...	|	1436	...	...	...	|	1728	...	|	|	2257	...	...	...	0617	0617	0617	...
Warszawa Centralna a.	1012	1430	1455	...	1507	...	...	...	...	1903	...	...	2107	2239	...	...	...	...	0923	0923	0923	...
Warszawa Wschodnia a.	1022	1446	1511	...	1531	...	...	...	...	1916	...	...	2121	2251	...	...	...	...	0941	0941	0941	...
Gdańsk Główny a.	...	...	...	...	1826	...	...	...	...	...	...	...	...	...	...	...	...	...	...	...	...	...
Gdynia Główny a.	...	...	...	...	1852	...	...	...	...	...	...	...	...	...	...	...	...	...	...	...	...	...

B – 🛏 1, 2 cl., 🛌 2 cl., [2] Warszawa (**407**) - Kraków - Bohumín (**457**) - Břeclav (**477**) - Budapest. Conveys 🛏 1, 2 cl., 🛌 2 cl., [2] Berlin (**457**) - Wrocław - Břeclav (**477**) - Budapest.

C – CHOPIN – 🛏 1, 2 cl., 🛌 2 cl. [2] Warszawa - Kraków - Wien and v.v. Conveys 🛏 1, 2 cl., 🛌 2 cl., [2] Berlin - Wrocław - Bohumín - Wien and v.v.

D – SOBIESKI – [2] [R] Kraków - Wien and v.v.

F – 🛏 1, 2 cl., 🛌 2 cl., [2] Budapest (**476**) - Břeclav (**456**) - Bohumín (**406**) - Kraków - Warszawa. Conveys 🛏 1, 2 cl., 🛌 2 cl., [2] Budapest (**476**) - Břeclav (**456**) - Bohumín - Wrocław - Berlin.

H – MORAVIA – [12] ✕ Katowice - Bohumín - Ostrava - Břeclav - Wien and v.v.

J – ⑤⑦ (daily June 29 - Sept. 1): LEO EXPRESS – [12] 🍷 Praha - Bohumín - Kraków.

K – ①⑥ (daily June 30 - Sept. 2): LEO EXPRESS – [12] 🍷 Kraków - Bohumín - Praha.

L – CRACOVIA – [12] 🍷 Kraków - Bohumín - Praha and v.v.

P – 🛏 1, 2 cl., 🛌 2 cl., [2] Warszawa (**407**) - Kraków - Bohumín (**442**) - Praha.

Q – 🛏 1, 2 cl., 🛌 2 cl., [2] Praha (**443**) - Bohumín (**406**) - Kraków - Warszawa.

R – VLTAVA ① (next day from Warszawa): 🛏 1, 2 cl. Moskva (**21***EJ*) - Terespol (**404**) - Bohumín (**112**) - Praha (Table **95**).

S – VLTAVA ③: 🛏 1, 2 cl. Praha (**113**) - Bohumín (**405**) - Brest (**22***AJ*) - Moskva (Table **95**).

T – Ⓑ: [12] ✕ Warszawa - Katowice - Ostrava.

U – ①–⑥: [12] ✕ Ostrava - Katowice - Warszawa.

V – BÁTHORY – [12] ✕ Warszawa - Budapest and v.v.

W – SOBIESKI – [12] ✕ Gdynia - Warszawa - Katowice - Wien and v.v.

X – POLONIA – [12] ✕ Warszawa - Katowice - Wien and v.v.

△ – Routeing point for international tickets : Szob.

⊡ – Supplement payable in Poland; Reservation compulsory in Poland.

* – Classified *Ex* in Czech Republic.

¶ – Classified *EC* in Czech Republic.

European Rail Timetable Price List

☐ Regular printed edition (excluding Summer and Winter): £17.99

☐ Printed Summer or Winter edition: £19.99

☐ Monthly digital edition: £11.99 (January - May, July - November), £13.99 (Summer or Winter)

Postage and packaging rates for a single printed copy are as follows:

☐ UK	£2.48	Delivery in 2 – 5 working days
☐ Europe	£5.68	Delivery in 3 – 10 working days
☐ Rest of the World	£7.98 – £8.43	Delivery in 5 – 21 working days

Subscription rates for 6 printed editions (price includes postage and packaging):

☐ UK £114 ☐ Europe £135 ☐ Rest of the World £150

Annual subscription for 12 digital editions: ☐ £100

Subscription rates for 6 printed issues and 12 digital editions (price includes postage and packaging):

☐ UK £174 ☐ Europe £195 ☐ Rest of the World £210

Order on-line at **www.europeanrailtimetable.eu**

By post to: 28 Monson Way, Oundle, Northamptonshire, PE8 4QG (cheques payable to European Rail Timetable Limited)

✆ +44 (0) 1832 270198 (Monday to Friday 0900 – 1700)

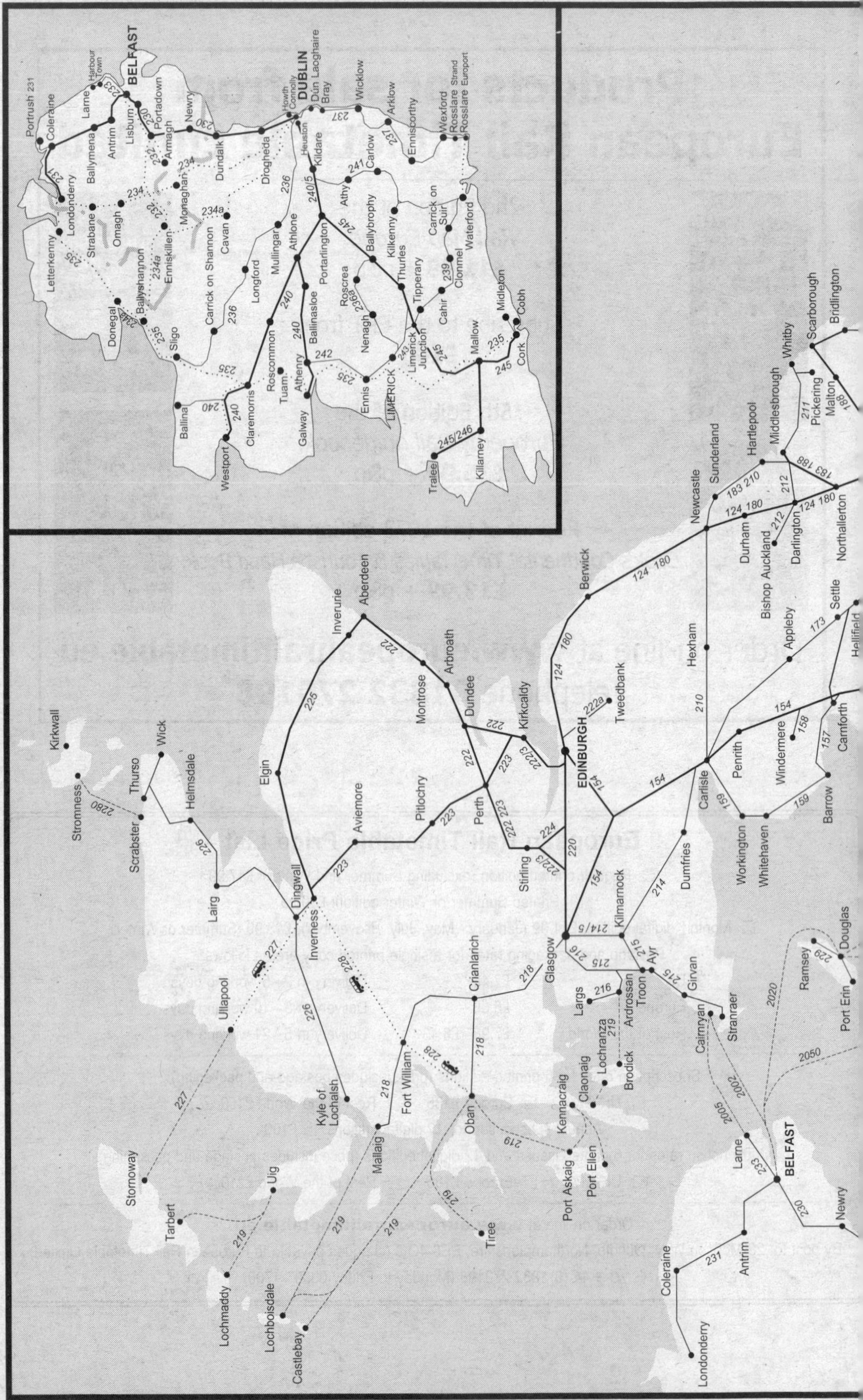
BELFAST
DUBLIN
Portrush 231
Coleraine
Larne
Harbour
Town
Ballymena
Antrim
Lisburn
Portadown
Armagh
Newry
Dundalk
Drogheda
Howth
Connolly
Dún Laoghaire
Bray
Wicklow
Arklow
Enniscorthy
Wexford
Rosslare Strand
Rosslare Europort
Heuston
Kildare
Londonderry
Strabane
Omagh
Monaghan
Enniskillen
Cavan
Letterkenny
Donegal
Ballyshannon
Sligo
Carrick on Shannon
Longford
Mullingar
Athlone
Athy
Carlow
Portarlington
Ballybrophy
Kilkenny
Thurles
Carrick on Suir
Waterford
Clonmel
Cahir
Tipperary
Roscrea
Nenagh
Ballinasloe
Roscommon
Claremorris
Ballina
Westport
Tuam
Athenry
Galway
Ennis
LIMERICK
Limerick Junction
Mallow
Cork
Cobh
Midleton
Killarney
Tralee
Kirkwall
Stromness
Thurso
Wick
Scrabster
Helmsdale
Lairg
Dingwall
Inverness
Elgin
Aviemore
Inverurie
Aberdeen
Montrose
Arbroath
Dundee
Pitlochry
Perth
Kirkcaldy
Stirling
EDINBURGH
Tweedbank
Berwick
Glasgow
Kilmarnock
Ayr
Troon
Ardrossan
Largs
Lochranza
Brodick
Claonaig
Kennacraig
Port Askaig
Port Ellen
Girvan
Cairnryan
Stranraer
Dumfries
Carlisle
Hexham
Newcastle
Sunderland
Durham
Hartlepool
Middlesbrough
Bishop Auckland
Darlington
Northallerton
Whitby
Scarborough
Pickering
Malton
Bridlington
Appleby
Settle
Hellifield
Penrith
Windermere
Carnforth
Barrow
Workington
Whitehaven
Douglas
Ramsey
Port Erin
Crianlarich
Oban
Fort William
Mallaig
Kyle of Lochalsh
Ullapool
Stornoway
Tarbert
Uig
Lochmaddy
Lochboisdale
Castlebay
Tiree
Larne
BELFAST
Newry
Antrim
Coleraine
Londonderry

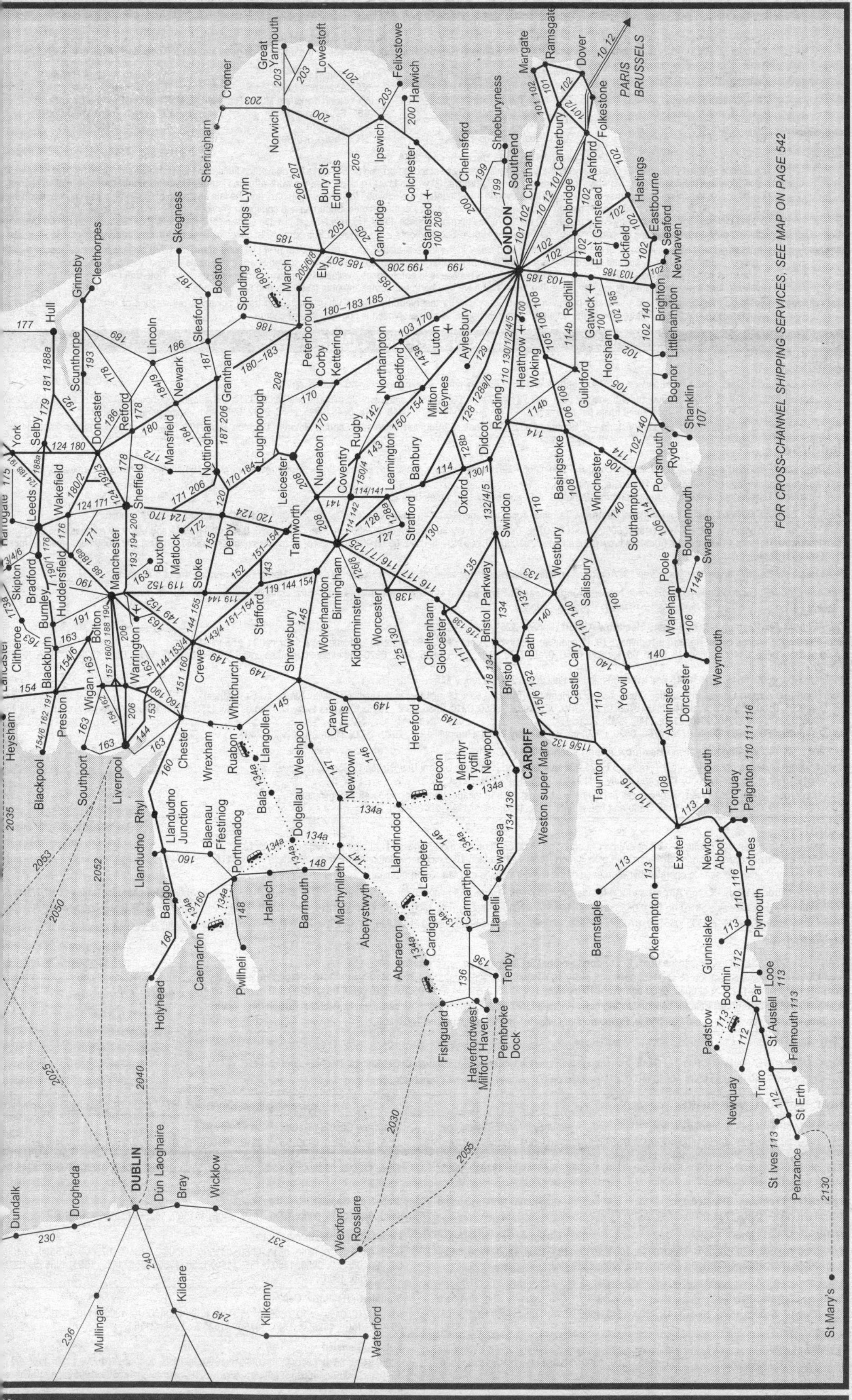
FOR CROSS-CHANNEL SHIPPING SERVICES, SEE MAP ON PAGE 542
PARIS
BRUSSELS
LONDON
CARDIFF
DUBLIN
Hull
York
Selby
Leeds
Harrogate
Skipton
Bradford
Wakefield
Huddersfield
Clitheroe
Burnley
Blackburn
Bolton
Preston
Blackpool
Heysham
Wigan
Southport
Liverpool
Warrington
Manchester
Buxton
Matlock
Stoke
Crewe
Chester
Wrexham
Whitchurch
Shrewsbury
Stafford
Derby
Tamworth
Wolverhampton
Birmingham
Kidderminster
Worcester
Hereford
Doncaster
Scunthorpe
Grimsby
Cleethorpes
Lincoln
Retford
Sheffield
Mansfield
Nottingham
Newark
Sleaford
Grantham
Boston
Skegness
Spalding
Peterborough
Leicester
Loughborough
Nuneaton
Coventry
Rugby
Leamington
Stratford
Banbury
Corby
Kettering
Northampton
Bedford
Milton Keynes
Luton
Aylesbury
Oxford
Didcot
Reading
Swindon
Bristol Parkway
Bristol
Bath
Cheltenham
Gloucester
Newport
Kings Lynn
March
Ely
Cambridge
Bury St Edmunds
Norwich
Sheringham
Cromer
Great Yarmouth
Lowestoft
Ipswich
Felixstowe
Harwich
Colchester
Chelmsford
Stansted
Southend
Shoeburyness
Chatham
Margate
Ramsgate
Canterbury
Dover
Folkestone
Ashford
Hastings
Tonbridge
East Grinstead
Uckfield
Eastbourne
Seaford
Newhaven
Brighton
Redhill
Gatwick
Horsham
Littlehampton
Bognor
Heathrow
Woking
Guildford
Basingstoke
Winchester
Southampton
Portsmouth
Ryde
Shanklin
Bournemouth
Poole
Swanage
Wareham
Weymouth
Dorchester
Westbury
Salisbury
Castle Cary
Yeovil
Axminster
Taunton
Weston super Mare
Exeter
Exmouth
Torquay
Paignton
Newton Abbot
Totnes
Barnstaple
Okehampton
Plymouth
Gunnislake
Bodmin
Looe
Par
Padstow
St Austell
Falmouth
Newquay
Truro
St Erth
St Ives
Penzance
St Mary's
Craven Arms
Welshpool
Newtown
Llandrindod
Brecon
Merthyr Tydfil
Swansea
Llanelli
Carmarthen
Tenby
Pembroke Dock
Haverfordwest
Milford Haven
Fishguard
Cardigan
Aberaeron
Lampeter
Aberystwyth
Machynlleth
Barmouth
Dolgellau
Bala
Llangollen
Ruabon
Harlech
Porthmadog
Blaenau Ffestiniog
Pwllheli
Caernarfon
Bangor
Holyhead
Llandudno
Llandudno Junction
Rhyl
Dundalk
Drogheda
Dun Laoghaire
Bray
Wicklow
Wexford
Rosslare
Kildare
Kilkenny
Waterford
Mullingar

GREAT BRITAIN

Operators: Passenger services are provided by a number of private passenger train companies operating the **National Rail** (www.nationalrail.co.uk) network on lines owned by the Britis national railway infrastructure company **Network Rail**. The following Network Rail codes are used in the table headings to indicate the operators of trains in each table:

AW	Transport for Wales	GR	London North Eastern Railway	ME	Merseyrail	SW	South Western Railway
CC	c2c	GW	Great Western Railway	NT	Arriva Rail North	TL	Thameslink Railway
CH	Chiltern Railways	HT	Hull Trains	NY	North Yorkshire Moors Railway	TP	TransPennine Express
CS	Caledonian Sleeper	IL	Island Line	SE	Southeastern	VT	Virgin Trains West Coast
EM	East Midlands Trains	LE	Greater Anglia	SN	Southern	XC	Arriva Cross Country
GC	Grand Central Railway	LM	West Midlands Trains	SR	Abellio ScotRail		

Timings: Except where indicated otherwise, timings are valid **May 19 - December 14, 2019.**
As service patterns at weekends (especially on ⑦) usually differ greatly from those applying on Mondays to Fridays, the timings in most tables are grouped by days of operatio Ⓐ = Mondays to Fridays; ⚒ = Mondays to Saturdays; ⑥ = Saturdays; ⑦ = Sundays. Track engineering work, affecting journey times, frequently takes place at weekends, s it is advisable to confirm your journey details locally if planning to travel in the period between the late evening of ⑥ and the late afternoon of ⑦. Confirm timings, too, if you inte travelling on public holidays (see page 4) as there may be alterations to services at these times. Suburban and commuter services are the most likely to be affected; the major of long-distance and cross-country trains marked Ⓐ and ⚒ run as normal on these dates. No trains (except limited Gatwick and Heathrow Express services) run on **Decemb 25**, with only a limited service on certain routes on **December 26**. In Scotland only trains between Edinburgh / Glasgow and England run on **January 1**.

Services: Unless indicated otherwise (by '2' in the train column or '2nd class' in the table heading), trains convey both **first** (1st) and **standard** (2nd) classes of seated accommodatic Light refreshments (snacks, hot and cold drinks) are available from a **buffet car** or a **mobile trolley service** on board those trains marked 🍸 and ✕: the latter also convey **restaurant car** or serve meals to passengers at their seats (this service is in some cases available to first-class ticket holders only). Note that catering facilities may not available for the whole of a train's journey. **Sleeping-cars** (🛏) have one berth per compartment in first class and two in standard class.

Reservations: Seats on most long-distance trains and berths in sleeping-cars can be reserved in advance when purchasing travel tickets at rail stations or directly from train operatir companies (quote the departure time of the train and your destination). Seat reservation is normally free of charge.

100 LONDON AIRPORT LINKS

Gatwick ✈

GATWICK EXPRESS: Daily non-stop rail service from / to **London Victoria**. Journey time: 30 minutes (30 – 40 minutes on ⑦).

From **London** Victoria: On ⚒ at 0430, 0500 and 4 trains per hour until 2214, 2244; on ⑦ at 0500 and every 30 minutes until 0900, 0914 and 4 trains per hour until 2100, 2130, 2200, 2230.
From **Gatwick Airport**: On ⚒ at 0540, 0557 and 4 trains per hour until 2311; on ⑦ at 0548, 0618, 0648, 0718, 0748, 0815, 0853, 0922, 0952 and 4 trains per hour until 2152, 2222, 2252, 23

Other rail services via Gatwick Airport: London Victoria - Eastbourne Table **102**; Bedford - Brighton Table **103**; London Victoria - Brighton Table **103**; Reading - Gatwick Airport Table **114b**.

Heathrow ✈

HEATHROW EXPRESS: Daily non-stop rail service **London** Paddington - **Heathrow** Terminal 5 and v.v. Journey times: **Heathrow** Central ♣, 15 minutes, **Heathrow** Terminal 5, 21 minute

From **London** Paddington: 0510 and every 15 minutes until 2325.
From **Heathrow** Terminal 5 (5 mins. later from Heathrow Central): 0512 and every 15 minutes until 2342.

TFL RAIL: Daily rail service **London** Paddington - **Heathrow** Terminal 4 and v.v. Journey times: **Heathrow** Central ♣, 26 minutes, **Heathrow** Terminal 4, 34 minutes.

From **London** Paddington: on ⚒ at 0442, 0457, 0500Ⓐ, 0503⑥, 0532, 0602 and every 30 minutes until 2303; on ⑦ at 0511, 0526, 0541, 0611, 0641 and every 30 minutes until 2311.
From **Heathrow** Terminal 4 (4 mins. later from Heathrow Central): on ⚒ at 0001①, 0007②–⑥, 0522, 0552, 0622 and every 30 minutes until 2322, 2357; on ⑦ at 0007, 0601 and every 30 minut until 2331, 2346.

♣ – Heathrow Central serves Terminals 2 and 3. A free rail transfer service operates every 15 minutes Heathrow Central - Heathrow **Terminals 4 and 5 and v.v.**

PICCADILLY LINE: London Underground service between **Kings Cross St Pancras** and all Heathrow terminals via Central London. Journey time: 50-58 minutes.

Frequent trains (every 4 - 10 minutes) 0530⚒/0730⑦ - 2300⚒/2330⑦.

RAILAIR LINK 🚌 **Reading** railway station - **Heathrow Airport** (Service **X25**).

From **Reading**: Services call at Heathrow Terminal 5 (±40 minutes), Heathrow Terminal 2 (±50 minutes) and Heathrow Terminal 3 (±56 minutes):
On Ⓐ at 0355, 0425, 0445, 0505, 0535, 0600, 0615, 0630, 0650, 0710, 0730, 0751, 0815, 0835, 0855, 0920 and every 20 minutes until 1720, 1745, 1805, 1830, 1900, 1930, 2000, 2030, 210 2200, 2300.
On Ⓒ at 0400, 0500, 0545, 0615, 0645 and every 30 minutes until 2045, 2115, 2200, 2300.

From **Heathrow Airport** Central Bus Station: Services call at Heathrow Terminal 5 (±14 minutes) and Reading Railway Station (±54 minutes).
On Ⓐ at 0005, 0500, 0530, 0550, 0610, 0640, 0705, 0725, 0745, 0810, 0830, 0850, 0910, 0935, 0955, 1015, 1030 and every 20 minutes until 1550, 1615, 1640 and every 20 minutes until 184 1905, 1925, 1950, 2010, 2040, 2110, 2140, 2210, 2305.
On Ⓒ at 0005, 0505, 0605, 0650, 0720, 0750, 0820, 0850, 0925 and every 30 minutes until 1955, 2020, 2050, 2120, 2150, 2220, 2305.

RAILAIR LINK 🚌 **Woking** rail station - **Heathrow Airport** (Service **701**).

From **Woking**: Services call at Heathrow Terminal 5 (±25 - 35 minutes) and Heathrow Central Bus Station (±45 - 55 minutes).
0600, 0640, 0740, 0845, 0945, 1050, 1135 and hourly until 1735, 1845, 1945, 2045, 2130, 2220.

From **Heathrow** Central Bus Station: Services call at Heathrow Terminal 5 (±15 minutes) and Woking (±45 - 65 minutes).
0545, 0645, 0745, 0845, 0950, 1040, 1140, 1230 and hourly until 1630, 1735, 1835, 1940, 2040, 2130, 2215.

Luton ✈

Thameslink Railway services Brighton - Gatwick Airport - London St Pancras - Luton Airport Parkway ◧ - Luton ◧ - Bedford: Table **103**.
East Midlands Trains services London St Pancras - Luton Airport Parkway ◧ - Luton ◧ - Leicester - Nottingham / Derby / Sheffield: Table **170**.
◧ – A frequent shuttle 🚌 service operates between each of the railway stations and the airport terminal.

🚌 service **Milton Keynes** - **Luton Airport** and v.v. (Stagecoach route **99**. Journey 55 minutes) for connections from / to **Birmingham**, **Liverpool** and **Manchester** (Tables **150/1/2/3/4**).
From **Milton Keynes** railway station: on ⚒ at 0635, 0745Ⓐ, 0755⑥, 0900 and hourly until 1600, 1710, 1740Ⓐ, 1810, 1910, 2010, 2110, 2210Ⓐ; on ⑦ at 0900 and hourly until 1900, 210
From **Luton Airport**: on ⚒ at 0535, 0655Ⓐ, 0700⑥, 0755Ⓐ, 0800⑥, 0915 and hourly until 1715, 1820, 1920, 2020, 2120Ⓐ; on ⑦ at 0815 and hourly until 2015.

Stansted ✈

STANSTED EXPRESS: Daily rail service from / to **London** Liverpool St. Journey time ± 45 minutes.

From **London** Liverpool Street: on ⚒ at 0440, 0510 and every 15 minutes until 2255, 2325; on ⑦ at 0410, 0440, 0510, 0540, 0610 and every 15 minutes until 2255, 2325.
From **Stansted Airport**: on ⚒ at 0030, 0600 and every 15 minutes until 2345, 2359; on ⑦ at 0030, 0530, 0600, 0630, 0700 and every 15 minutes until 2345, 2359.

Most trains call at **Tottenham Hale** for London Underground (Victoria Line) connections to / from Kings Cross, St Pancras, Euston, and Victoria stations.

For *Cross Country* services to / from Cambridge, Peterborough, Leicester and Birmingham see Table **208**.

City ✈

DOCKLANDS LIGHT RAILWAY from / to **Bank** (interchange with London Underground: Central, Circle, District, Northern, and Waterloo & City Lines).

Trains run every 7-10 minutes 0530 - 0030 on ⚒, 0700 - 2330 on ⑦. Journey time: ± 22 minutes.

Inter - Airport 🚌 links

Operator: National Express ✆ 08717 81 81 81. www.nationalexpress.co

Gatwick North Terminal - **Heathrow** Central. Journey time: 65 - 85 minutes
0315, 0600, 0655Ⓐ, 0710Ⓒ, 0715Ⓐ, 0720Ⓐ, 0735Ⓒ, 0740Ⓒ, 0755Ⓐ, 0815Ⓒ, 0840, 0920, 0925Ⓐ, 0935Ⓒ, 0940, 1005, 1055, 1125, 1140, 1255, 1300, 1325, 1330, 1340, 1520, 1525, 1530, 1540, 1630Ⓐ, 1640Ⓒ, 1655, 1730, 1740, 1755Ⓒ, 1840, 1900, 1930Ⓒ, 2005, 2015, 2100, 2130, 2220, 2245, 2325, 2355.

Heathrow Central - **Gatwick** North Terminal.
0255, 0320, 0330, 0435, 0500, 0540, 0635, 0705, 0715Ⓒ, 0725Ⓐ, 0740, 0840, 0910, 09 0950, 1005Ⓐ, 1045, 1110, 1140, 1220, 1245, 1305, 1335, 1355, 1435, 1505, 1545, 1605 1705, 1720Ⓒ, 1725Ⓐ, 1745Ⓒ, 1750Ⓐ, 1755Ⓒ, 1805Ⓐ, 1835, 1955, 2005Ⓐ, 2245.

Gatwick North Terminal - **Stansted**. Journey time: ± 3 hours
0920, 1125, 1330, 1530, 1730, 1930, 2130, 2325.

Stansted - **Gatwick** North Terminal.
0140, 0400 0605, 0800, 1000, 1215, 1405, 1615Ⓒ, 1625Ⓐ, 1815Ⓒ, 1825Ⓐ.

Heathrow Central - **Luton**. Journey time: 1–1½ hours
0035, 0730, 0750Ⓐ, 0800, 0805Ⓒ, 0830, 0930, 1005, 1030, 1130, 1205, 1300, 1330, 1405, 1530, 1605, 1730, 1805, 1900, 1930, 2005, 2130, 2205, 2359.

From **Luton** to **Heathrow** Central.
0255, 0350, 0410, 0450, 0515, 0550, 0635Ⓐ, 0650Ⓒ, 0735Ⓐ, 0750Ⓒ, 0755Ⓐ, 0810Ⓒ 0820Ⓐ, 0850Ⓒ, 0950, 1050, 1135, 1150, 1250, 1350, 1355, 1450, 1550, 1635Ⓒ, 1650, 1745, 1750, 1950.

Heathrow Central - **Stansted**. Journey time: 1½ hours
0055, 0705, 0745, 0905, 0945, 1055, 1145, 1300, 1345, 1505, 1545, 1705, 1745, 1905, 2105, 2145, 2305, 2359.

Stansted - **Heathrow** Central.
0140, 0240, 0400, 0510, 0605, 0725Ⓐ, 0740Ⓒ, 0800, 0940, 1000, 1140, 1215, 1340, 14 1540, 1615Ⓒ, 1625Ⓐ, 1740, 1815Ⓒ, 1825Ⓐ, 1940, 2115.

Stansted - **Luton**. Journey time: 1½ hours
0100, 0600Ⓐ,0615, 0645Ⓒ, 0920, 0930, 1115, 1200, 1300, 1400, 1445, 1630, 1830, 1900, 2015, 2200.

Luton - **Stansted**.
0300, 0430, 0630, 0810Ⓐ, 0820Ⓒ, 0910Ⓐ, 0915Ⓒ, 1000Ⓒ, 1010Ⓐ, 1130, 1155Ⓒ, 1210Ⓐ, 1355⑦, 1400, 1525Ⓒ, 1535Ⓐ, 1620Ⓒ, 1625Ⓐ, 1855Ⓒ, 1905Ⓐ, 1910Ⓒ, 1930Ⓐ, 2055, 2145.

High-speed services LONDON - MARGATE

Special fares are payable for high-speed services. For slower services see Table **102**.

Via Faversham

km			Ⓐ	ⒶF	Ⓐ	ⒶF	Ⓐ		ⒶF	Ⓐ	Ⓐ	Ⓐ	Ⓐ	Ⓐ	Ⓐ	Ⓐ		Ⓐ	Ⓐ	ⒶA	Ⓐ	Ⓐ	Ⓐ		⑥F
0	**London** St Pancras d.	Ⓐ	0655	0722	0804	0825	0855		1525	1555	1625	1655	1725	1755	1825	1855		2125	2155	2225	2255	2325	2355	⑥	0725
9	Stratford International d.		0702	0729	0811	0832	0902	and at	1532	1602	1632	1702	1732	1802	1832	1902	and at	2132	2202	2232	2302	2332	0002		0732
35	Ebbsfleet International d.		0715	0740	0823	0843	0913	the same	1543	1613	1643	1713	1743	1813	1843	1913	the same	2143	2213	2243	2313	2343	0013		0743
52	Rochester d.		0734	0758	0844	0902	0932	minutes	1602	1632	1702	1731	1758	1836	1901	1935	minutes	2202	2232	2302	2332	0002	0032		0802
54	Chatham d.		0738	0802	0847	0906	0936	past each	1605	1636	1706	1735	1802	1840	1905	1939	past each	2206	2236	2306	2336	0006	0036		0806
70	Sittingbourne d.		0755	0818	0905	0923	0954	hour until	1622	1653	1723	1754	1820	1858	1925	1956	hour until	2223	2253	2323	2353	0023	0053		0823
83	Faversham a.		0803	0827	0914	0931	1005		1630	1701	1731	1802	1832	1906	1933	2005		2231	2301	2331	0001	0031	0103		0831
100	Herne Bay a.		...	0842	...	0945	...	♣	1646	...	...	...	1844	1921	1948	...	♣	2247	...	2347	...	...	...		0845
118	**Margate** a.		...	0859	...	0959	...		1702	...	...	...	1901	1936	2002	...		2304	...	0004	...	...	...		0859

	⑥	⑥F	⑥	⑥F	⑥	★	⑥	⑥	⑥	⑥		⑦F	⑦F	⑦F	⑦F	⑦F	⑦		⑦K	⑦	⑦	⑦	⑦	⑦	⑦
London St Pancras d.	0757	0825	0857	0925	0955		2225	2255	2325	2355	⑦	0825	0925	1027	1125	1227	1252		2025	2055	2125	2155	2225	2255	2325
Stratford International d.	0804	0832	0904	0932	1002	and at	2232	2302	2332	0002		0832	0932	1034	1132	1234	1259	and at	2032	2102	2132	2202	2232	2302	2332
Ebbsfleet International d.	0815	0843	0915	0944	1013	the same	2243	2313	2343	0013		0843	0944	1045	1143	1245	1313	the same	2043	2113	2143	2213	2243	2313	2343
Rochester d.	0832	0902	0933	1002	1032	minutes	2302	2332	0002	0032		0902	1002	1103	1202	1303	1332	minutes	2102	2132	2202	2232	2302	2332	0002
Chatham d.	0836	0906	0937	1006	1036	past each	2306	2336	0006	0036		0906	1006	1106	1206	1306	1336	past each	2106	2136	2206	2236	2306	2336	0006
Sittingbourne d.	0854	0923	0954	1023	1054	hour until	2323	2353	0023	0053		0923	1023	1123	1223	1323	1353	hour until	2123	2153	2223	2253	2323	2353	0023
Faversham a.	0905	0931	1005	1031	1105		2331	0001	0031	0101		0931	1031	1131	1231	1331	1402		2131	2202	2231	2302	2331	0001	0032
Herne Bay a.	...	0945	...	1045	...	♣	2345	...	*0050*	...		0945	1045	1145	1245	1345	...	♣	2145	...	2245	...	2345	...	...
Margate a.	...	0959	...	1059	...		2359	...	*0107*	...		0959	1059	1159	1259	1359	...		2159	...	2259	...	2359	...	...

		Ⓐ	Ⓐ	Ⓐ	Ⓐ	Ⓐ	Ⓐ	Ⓐ	Ⓐ	Ⓐ	Ⓐ	ⒶG	Ⓐ	ⒶG		ⒶG	Ⓐ	Ⓐ	ⒶG	Ⓐ	Ⓐ	Ⓐ	Ⓐ	ⒶG		⑥
Margate d.	Ⓐ	...	*0436*	0523	...	0634	0703	...	*0752*	*0821*	...	0930	...	1030		1730	...	1825	1838	1930	...	2030	...	2130	⑥	*0440*
Herne Bay d.		...	*0452*	0540	...	0648	0717	...	*0808*	*0837*	...	0944	...	1044	and at	1744	...	1842	1854	1944	...	2044	...	2144		*0454*
Faversham d.		0458	0528	0556	0628	0702	0731	0759	0828	0859	0930	0958	1030	1058	the same	1758	1828	1858	1930t	1958	2030	2058	2130	2158		0530
Sittingbourne d.		0507	0537	0604	0636	0710	0739	0807	0838	0908	0938	1008	1038	1108	minutes	1808	1838	1908	1938	2008	2038	2108	2138	2208		0538
Chatham d.		0524	0554	0621	0653	0727	0756	0824	0855	0925	0955	1025	1055	1125	past each	1825	1855	1925	1955	2025	2056	2125	2155	2225		0555
Rochester d.		0528	0558	0625	0657	0730	0800	0827	0859	0929	0959	1029	1059	1129	hour until	1829	1859	1929	1959	2029	2100	2129	2159	2229		0559
Ebbsfleet International a.		0545	0615	0642	0711	0748	0817	0846	0916	0946v	1016	1046	1116	1146		1849	1916	1946	2016	2046	2118	2146	2216	2246		0616
Stratford International a.		0557	0627	0655	0724	0800	0830	0859	0928	1002	1028	1058	1129	1158	♠	1901	1928	1959	2028	2059	2132	2159	2228	2258		0628
London St Pancras a.		0605	0635	0702	0731	0808	0838	0907	0936	1010	1036	1106	1140	1206		1909	1936	2007	2036	2106	2140	2206	2236	2306		0636

	⑥	⑥	⑥	⑥H	⑥	⑥G		⑥G	⑥	⑥G	⑥	⑥G	⑥	⑥G		⑦	⑦	⑦	⑦H	⑦G	⑦	⑦G		⑦	⑦G
Margate d.	...	0630	...	0730	...	0830		1830	...	1930	...	2030	...	2130	⑦	...	...	0830	0930	1030	...	1130		...	2130
Herne Bay d.	...	0644	...	0744	...	0844	and at	1844	...	1944	...	2044	...	2144		...	...	0844	0944	1044	...	1144	and at	...	2144
Faversham d.	0630	0658	0730	0758	0830	0858	the same	1858	1930	1958	2030	2058	2130	2158		0700	0800	0858	0958	1058	1130	1158	the same	2130	2158
Sittingbourne d.	0638	0708	0738	0808	0838	0908	minutes	1908	1938	2008	2038	2108	2138	2208		0708	0808	0908	1008	1108	1138	1208	minutes	2138	2208
Chatham d.	0655	0725	0755	0825	0855	0925	past each	1925	1955	2025	2055	2125	2155	2225		0725	0825	0925	1025	1125	1155	1225	past each	2155	2225
Rochester d.	0659	0729	0759	0829	0859	0929	hour until	1929	1959	2029	2059	2129	2159	2229		0729	0829	0929	1029	1129	1159	1229	hour until	2159	2229
Ebbsfleet International a.	0716	0746	0816	0846	0916	0946		1946	2016	2046	2116v	2146	2216	2246		0746	0846	0946v	1046	1146	1216	1246		2216	2246
Stratford International a.	0728	0758	0829	0858	0929	1002	♠	1958	2028	2058	2132	2158	2228	2258		0758	0858	1002	1058	1158	1228	1258	♠	2228	2258
London St Pancras a.	0736	0806	0836	0906	0937	1010		2006	2036	2106	2140	2206	2236	2306		0806	0906	1010	1106	1206	1236	1306		2236	2306

Via Ashford and Dover

km			②–⑤	Ⓐ	Ⓐ	Ⓐ	ⒶD	Ⓐ	ⒶD	Ⓐ		Ⓐ	ⒶD	Ⓐ	Ⓐ	Ⓐ	Ⓐ	Ⓐ	Ⓐ	Ⓐ	Ⓐ	Ⓐ	Ⓐ	Ⓐ	ⒶD	Ⓐ
0	**London** St Pancras d.	Ⓐ	0012	0640	0705	0725	0737	0812	0837	0909		1610	1637	1650	1707	1720	1737	1750	1807	1820	1837	1850	1907	1920	1937	2012
9	Stratford International d.		0019	0647	0712	0732	0744	0819	0844	0916	and at	1617	1644	1657	1714	1727	1744	1757	1814	1827	1845	1857	1914	1927	1944	2019
35	Ebbsfleet International d.		0030	0659	0723	0746	0755	0830	0855	0927	the same	1630	1655	|	1725	|	1756	|	1826	|	1856	|	1926	|	1955	2030
90	Ashford International d.		0050	0719	0744	0809	0816	0852	0915	0952	minutes	1652y	1718	1726	1746	1756	1817	1826	1847	1856	1917	1927	1947	1956	2015	2052
112	**Folkestone** Central d.		...	...	|	0828	0831	|	0930	|	past each	|	1733	|	1802	|	1835	|	1903	|	1934	|	2003	|	2030	|
124	**Dover** Priory a.		...	...	|	0839	0842	|	0941	|	hour until	|	1744	|	1814	|	1845	|	1915	|	1945	|	2014	|	2041	|
112	Canterbury West d.		...	...	0801	...	|	0909	|	1009		1709	|	1744	...	1812	|	1842	...	1912	...	1943	...	2012	|	2110
140	Ramsgate a.		...	...	0822	...	0919	0927	1019	1027	♣	1731	1825	1801	...	1831	1925	1901	...	1931	...	2002	...	2031	2118	2132
149	**Margate** a.		...	...	0834	...	0929	0942	1029	1039		1742	1837	1815	...	1845	...	1915	...	1945	...	2016	...	2045	2129	2143

	Ⓐ	Ⓐ	Ⓐ	ⒶB	Ⓐ	②–⑤	①	Ⓐ		⑥	⑥D	⑥	⑥D	⑥		⑥D	⑥	⑥	⑥	⑥	⑥	⑥	⑥	⑥		⑦
London St Pancras d.	2037	2112	2137	2212	2237	2312	2312	2337	⑥	0012	...	...	0637	0707		1937	2012	2037	2112	2137	2212	2237	2312	2337	⑦	0012
Stratford International d.	2044	2119	2144	2219	2244	2319	2319	2344		0019	...	...	0644	0714	and at	1944	2019	2044	2119	2144	2219	2244	2319	2344		0019
Ebbsfleet International d.	2055	2130	2155	2230	2255	2330	2330	2355		0030	...	...	0655	0725	the same	1955	2030	2055	2130	2155	2230	2255	2330	2355		0030
Ashford International d.	2115	2152	2215	2252	2315	2352	2352	0015		0050	0615	0635	0715	0752	minutes	2015	2052	2115	2152	2215	2252	2315	2352	0015		0050
Folkestone Central d.	2130	|	2230	|	2330	|	|	0030		...	0630	|	0730	|	past each	2030	|	2130	|	2230	|	2330	|	0030		...
Dover Priory a.	2141	|	2241	|	2343	|	|	0041		...	0641	|	0741	|	hour until	2041	|	2141	|	2241	|	2341	|	0041		...
Canterbury West d.	|	2209	|	2309	|	0009	*0034*p	|		...	|	0654	|	0809		|	2109	|	2209	|	2309	|	0009	|		...
Ramsgate a.	2219	2227	2322	2330	0021	0031	0043	0123		...	0719	0715	0819	0827	♠	2119	2127	2219	2227	2321	2329	0021	0027	0123		...
Margate a.	...	2239	...	2340f	...	0042r	0058	...		...	0729	0726	0829	0839		2129	2139	...	2239	...	2340	...	0039	...		...

	⑦D	⑦D	⑦		⑦D	⑦	⑦	⑦	⑦	⑦	⑦	⑦	⑦
London St Pancras d.	...	0837	0909		1937	2012	2037	2112	2137	2212	2237	2312	2337
Stratford International d.	...	0844	0916	and at	1944	2019	2044	2119	2144	2219	2244	2319	2344
Ebbsfleet International d.	...	0855	0927	the same	1955	2030	2055	2130	2155	2230	2255	2330	2355
Ashford International d.	0815	0915	0952	minutes	2015	2052	2115	2152	2215	2252	2315	2352	0015
Folkestone Central d.	0830	0930	|	past each	2030	|	2130	|	2230	|	2330	|	...
Dover Priory a.	0841	0941	|	hour until	2041	|	2141	|	2241	|	2341	|	...
Canterbury West a.	|	|	1009		|	2109	|	2209	|	2309	|	0009	...
Ramsgate a.	0919	1019	1027	♣	2119	2127	2219	2227	2318	2327	0018	0027	...
Margate a.	0929	1029	1039		2129	2139	...	2239	...	2339	...	0039	...

		Ⓐ	Ⓐ	Ⓐ	Ⓐ	Ⓐ	Ⓐ	Ⓐ	Ⓐ
Margate d.	Ⓐ	...	...	...	0546	...	0616	...	0646
Ramsgate d.		...	0455	...	0558	...	0628	0614	0658
Canterbury West d.		...	0518	...	0618	...	0648	|	0718
Dover Priory d.		...	|	0545	|	0618	|	0648	|
Folkestone Cent. d.		...	|	0556	|	0629	|	0659	|
Ashford Int'l d.		0513	0543	0613	0636	0646	0706	0716	0736
Ebbsfleet Int'l a.		0532	0602	0632	0655	0705	|	0735	|
Stratford Int'l a.		0544	0614	0644	0707	0717	0734	0747	0804
London St Pancras a.		0551	0621	0651	0714	0725	0742	0754	0812

	Ⓐ	Ⓐ	Ⓐ	Ⓐ	Ⓐ	Ⓐ	Ⓐ	ⒶE	Ⓐ		ⒶE	Ⓐ	Ⓐ	Ⓐ	Ⓐ	Ⓐ	Ⓐ	Ⓐ	Ⓐ	Ⓐ	Ⓐ	Ⓐ		⑥	⑥	⑥
Margate d.	...	0716	0654	0748	...	0851	...	0859	0953		1702	1753	...	1853	...	1953	...	2053	2100	2153	...	2253	⑥	...	...	0553
Ramsgate d.	...	0728	0710	0801	...	0903	0935	0912	1005	and at	1713	1805	...	1905	...	2005	...	2105	2112	2205	2212	2305		0505	...	0605
Canterbury West d.	...	0748	|	0825	...	0923	0954	|	1025	the same	|	1825	...	1925	...	2025	...	2125	|	2225	|	2325		0525	...	0625
Dover Priory d.	0713	|	0746	|	0849	|	|	0949	|	minutes	1749	|	1849	|	1949	|	2049	|	2149	|	2249	|		|	0549	|
Folkestone Central d.	0724	|	0757	|	0900	|	|	1000	|	past each	1800	|	1900	|	2000	|	2100	|	2200	|	2300	|		|	0600	|
Ashford International d.	0744	0806	0816	0843	0916	0943y	1011	1016	1043	hour until	1816	1843	1916	1943	2016	2043	2116	2143	2216	2243	2316	2341		0543	0616	0643
Ebbsfleet International a.	|	|	0835	0902	0935	1002	|	1035	1102		1835	1902	1935	2002	2035	2102	2135	2202	2235	2302	2335	...		0602	0635	0702
Stratford International a.	0812	0834	0847	0914	0947	1014	1039	1047	1114	♣	1847	1914	1947	2014	2047	2114	2147	2214	2247	2314	2347	...		0614	0647	0714
London St Pancras a.	0820	0842	0854	0921	0954	1021	1047	1055	1121		1854	1921	1954	2021	2054	2121	2154	2221	2254	2321	2354	...		0621	0654	0721

	⑥	⑥	⑥	⑥	⑥	⑥	⑥E		⑥	⑥E	⑥		⑦	⑦	⑦	⑦	⑦	⑦	⑦	⑦E		⑦E	⑦	⑦E	⑦
Margate d.	...	0653	0657	0753	...	0853	0859		2153	2159	2253	⑦	...	...	0753	...	0853	...	0953	0959		2059	2153	2159	2253
Ramsgate d.	0612	0705	0712	0805	0812	0905	0912	and at	2205	2212	2305		...	0712	0805	0812	0905	0912	1005	1012	and at	2112	2205	2212	2305
Canterbury West d.	|	0725	|	0825	|	0925	|	the same	2225	|	2325		...	|	0825	|	0925	|	1025	|	the same	|	2225	|	2325
Dover Priory d.	0649	|	0749	|	0849	|	0949	minutes	|	2249	|		...	0749	|	0849	|	0949	|	1049	minutes	2149	|	2249	|
Folkestone Central d.	0700	|	0800	|	0900	|	1000	past each	|	2300	|		...	0800	|	0900	|	1000	|	1100	past each	2200	|	2300	|
Ashford International d.	0716	0743	0816	0843	0916	0943	1016	hour until	2243	2316	2341		0743	0816	0843	0916	0943	1016	1043	1116	hour until	2216	2243	2315	2341
Ebbsfleet International a.	0735	0802	0835	0902	0935	1002	1035		2302	2335	...		0802	0835	0902	0935	1002	1035	1102	1135		2235	2302	...	...
Stratford International a.	0747	0814	0847	0914	0947	1014	1047	♣	2314	2347	...		0814	0847	0914	0947	1014	1047	1114	1147		2247	2314	...	...
London St Pancras a.	0754	0821	0854	0921	0954	1021	1055		2321	2354	...		0821	0854	0921	0954	1021	1054	1121	1154		2254	2321	...	...

– ② departure from London St Pancras is operated by 🚌 after Faversham (Faversham d. 2337, Herne Bay d. 0014, Margate a. 0045).
– ② departure from London St Pancras is operated by 🚌 after Ramsgate (Ramsgate d. 2336, Margate a. 2355).
– To London St Pancras (see upper table).
– From London St Pancras (see upper table).
– To London St Pancras (see lower table).

G – From London St Pancras (see lower table).
H – From Ashford International (see lower table).
K – To Ashford International (see lower table).
f – Not ②.
p – Connection by 🚌 from Ashford; continues to Ramsgate (arr. 0112) and Margate (arr. 0131).

r – On ③ mornings connection by 🚌 (arr. 0055).
t – Arrives 1910.
v – Departs 5 minutes later.
y – Arrives 4–5 minutes earlier.
♠ – Timings may vary by up to ± 5 minutes.
♣ – Timings may vary by up to ± 3 minutes.
★ – The 2125 does not continue to London St. Pancras.

102 LONDON - THE SOUTH and SOUTH EAST SE, SN

Typical off-peak journey time in hours and minutes
READ DOWN ↓ READ UP ↑

Journey times may be extended during peak hours on Ⓐ (0600 - 0900 and 1600 - 1900) and also at weekends.

The longest journey time by any train is noted in the table heading.

LONDON VICTORIA - RAMSGATE

Longest journey: 2 hours 10 minutes SE

km	↓		↑
0	0h00	d.**London** Victoria.....a.	1h57
18	0h17	d.Bromley South ....d.	1h40
53	0h47	d.Rochester ....d.	1h12
72	1h09	d.Sittingbourne..........d.	0h50
84	1h21	d.Faversham.............d.	0h42
101	1h36	d.Herne Bay ....d.	0h26
119	1h49	d.Margate ....d.	0h10
128	1h59	a.**Ramsgate** ....d.	0h00

From London Victoria: on Ⓐ at 0010②–⑤ **f**, 0512 **g**, 0542 **g**, 0612 **g**, 0640 **g**, 0810 **g**, 0840 and hourly until 1540, 1610 **g**, 1640, 1710 **g** 1740, 1810, 1840 **g**, 1940, 2040, 2140, 2210 **f g**, 2240 **f**, 2310 **f**; on ⑥ at 0542 **g**, 0710 **g**, 0740 and hourly until 2240, 2310; on ⑦ at 0010 0740 and hourly until 2040, 2140, 2240.

From Ramsgate: on Ⓐ at 0425, 0556, 0630, 0655 **c**, 0719 **c**, 0740, 0810, 0853 and hourly until 1353, 1449, 1545, 1652, 1748, 1848, 1953 2053, 2153, 2250 **h** ②, 2315 **a**; on ⑥ at 0430, 0553 and hourly until 2153, 2315 **h**; on ⑦ at 0705 and hourly until 2105, 2120 **g**, 2235.

a – To Sittingbourne; on ② by 🚌 with extended journey time.
c – From/to London Cannon Street, not Victoria.
f – On Tuesday nights/Wednesday mornings does not call at Herne Bay or Margate.
h – To Faversham.
g – Change at Faversham.

LONDON VICTORIA - DOVER

Longest journey: 2 hours 10 minutes SE

km	↓		↑
0	0h00	d.**London** Victoria.....a.	2h02
18	0h17	d.Bromley South ....d.	1h43
53	0h47	d.Rochester ....d.	1h17
72	1h09	d.Sittingbourne..........d.	0h58
84	1h21	d.Faversham.............d.	0h47
99	1h37	d.Canterbury East.....d.	0h27
124	1h58	a.**Dover** Priory..........d.	0h00

From London Victoria: on Ⓐ at 0512, 0542, 0612, 0640, 0742, 0810, 0842 and at the same minutes past each hour until 1410, 1440 1510, 1540, 1610, 1640 **g**, 1710, 1740 **g**, 1810 **g**, 1840, 1910, 1940, 2010, 2110, 2210; on ⑥ at 0542, 0642, 0710, 0742 and at the same minutes past each hour until 1942, 2010, 2042 **e**, 2110, 2142 **e**, 2210; on ⑦ at 0740, 0810 **e**, 0840 and at the same minutes past each hou until 2010 **e**, 2040, 2140, 2240 **h**.

From Dover Priory: on Ⓐ at 0448, 0532, 0624 **g**, 0704, 0740, 0815, 0852, 0915, 0952, 1018, 1052 and at the same minutes past each hour until 1518, 1548, 1620, 1655, 1720, 1752, 1820, 1852, 1922, 1950 **g**, 2022, 2105, 2205, 2310**h**; on ⑥ at 0518, 0618, 0652 and at the same minutes past each hour until 2018, 2105, 2205, 2310**h**; on ⑦ at 0703, 0803, 0902 **e**, 0903 and at the same minutes past each hou until 2102 **e**, 2103, 2202 **e**, 2233 **g**.

b – From/to London Blackfriars, not Victoria. e – To/from Canterbury East. g – Change at Faversham. h – To Faversham.

LONDON CHARING CROSS - CANTERBURY WEST

Longest journey: 1 hour 55 minutes SE

km	↓		↑
0	0h00	d.**London** C Cross ...a.	1h46
1	0h03	d.**London** Waterloo ‡ a.	1h42
3	0h08	d.**London** Bridge ......a.	1h36
36	0h32	d.Sevenoaks.............d.	1h13
48	0h40	d.Tonbridge ....d.	1h04
90	1h20	a.Ashford Int'l ....d.	0h27
113	1h38	a.**Canterbury** West...d.	0h00

From London Charing Cross: on Ⓐ at 0530 **c**, 0632 **c**, 0709, 0737, 0816, 0902, 0940 **d**, 1010, 1040 **d** and at the same minutes past each hour until 1610, 1639, 1711, 1739, 1807 **c**, 1841, 1910, 1940 **d**, 2010, 2110, 2210 **e**; on ⑥ at 0600, 0710, 0740 **d** and at the same minutes past each hour until 1910, 2010, 2110, 2210, 2340; on ⑦ at 0810, 0840 **d** and at the same minutes past each hour until 1710 then hourly until 2210.

From Canterbury West: on Ⓐ at 0518 **d**, 0601, 0634 **c**, 0703, 0736, 0804 **d**, 0836, 0905 **d**, 0936, 1005 **d**, 1042 and at the same minutes past each hour until 1605 **d**, 1640, 1705 **d**, 1740, 1805 **d**, 1836, 1939, 2039, 2139, 2239 **k**; on ⑥ at 0537, 0637, 0737, 0805 **d**, 0840, 0905 **d** 0940, 1005 **d**, 1042 at the same minutes past each hour until 2042, 2105 **d**, 2139, 2239 **k**; on ⑦ at 0739, 0839, 0904 **d**, 0943 and at the same minutes past each hour until 1843, 1904 **d**, 1939, 2039, 2139, 2239 **k**.

c – To/from London Cannon Street.
d – Change at Ashford.
e – On ① change at Ashford for 🚌 connection to Canterbury.
h – On ②–⑤ change at Ashford.
k – To Tonbridge.
‡ – London Waterloo East.

LONDON CHARING CROSS - DOVER

Longest journey: 2 hours 06 minutes SE

km	↓		↑
0	0h00	d.**London** C Cross ...a.	1h58
1	0h03	d.**London** Waterloo ‡ a.	1h53
3	0h08	d.**London** Bridge ......a.	1h42
36	0h32	d.Sevenoaks.............d.	1h18
48	0h40	d.Tonbridge ....d.	1h06
90	1h20	d.Ashford Int'l ....d.	0h29
113	1h40	d.Folkstone Central...d.	0h12
124	1h52	a.**Dover** Priory..........d.	0h00

From London Charing Cross: on Ⓐ at 0530, 0737, 0834, 0940 and hourly until 1540, 1639, 1651 **f**, 1723 **c**, 1739 **d f**, 1801, 1831 **c**, 1910 1940, 2040, 2140, 2240; on ⑥ at 0740 and hourly until 2340; on ⑦ at 0840 and hourly until 2240, 2310 **g**, 2340 **g**.

From Dover Priory: on Ⓐ at 0430 **c**, 0529, 0559 **d**, 0630, 0725, 0758, 0825, 0858, 0925, 0958 and hourly until 1558, 1625, 1658, 1725 1758, 1825, 1858, 1958, 2058, 2158 **e**; on ⑥ at 0458 and hourly until 2058, 2158 **e**; on ⑦ at 0758 and hourly until 2058.

c – From/to London Cannon Street.
d – Change trains at Ashford.
e – To Tonbridge.
f – To/from Folkestone Central.
g – Terminates at Ashford.
‡ – London Waterloo East.

LONDON VICTORIA - ASHFORD INTERNATIONAL

Longest journey: 1 hours 40 minutes SE

km	↓		↑
0	0h00	d.**London** Victoria.....a.	1h29
18	0h17	d.Bromley South ....d.	1h14
28	0h28	d.Swanley..................d.	1h03
56	0h52	d.West Malling...........d.	0h42
64	1h03	d.Maidstone East.......d.	0h30
68	1h09	d.Bearsted.................d.	0h25
95	1h31	a.**Ashford** Int'l.............d.	0h00

From London Victoria: on Ⓐ at 0025 ②–⑤, 0550, 0625, 0655, 0755, 0825, 0855 and every 30 minutes until 1625, 1652, 1722, 1752 1822, 1852, 1925, 1955 and every 30 minutes until 2355; on ⑥ at 0025, 0625, 0725, 0755 and every 30 minutes until 2325, 2355; on ⑦ at 0025, 0725 and hourly until 2325.

From Ashford International: on Ⓐ at 0518, 0547, 0600, 0616, 0639, 0656, 0727, 0757, 0830, 0905, 0930, 1005, 1033 and at the same minutes past each hour until 1533, 1557, 1633, 1657, 1733, 1757, 1833, 1857, 1935, 2005, 2035, 2105, 2135, 2205, 2240; on ⑥ at 0527 0605, 0633 and at the same minutes past each hour until 2133, 2205, 2240; on ⑦ at 0635 and hourly until 2135.

LONDON CHARING CROSS - HASTINGS

Longest journey: 1 hour 53 minutes SE

km	↓		↑
0	0h00	d.**London** C Cross ...a.	1h43
1	0h03	d.**London** Waterloo ‡ a.	1h39
3	0h08	d.**London** Bridge .....a.	1h35
36	0h34	d.Sevenoaks...............d.	1h09
48	0h43	d.Tonbridge ....d.	1h00
55	0h55	d.Tunbridge Wells.....d.	0h49
89	1h33	d.Battle.....................d.	0h16
100	1h45	a.**Hastings** ....d.	0h00

From London Charing Cross: on Ⓐ at 0628, 0715, 0742 **c**, 0818, 0840 **c**, 0914 **c**, 0945 and every 30 minutes until 1545, 1614, 1643 1715 *, 1757 *, 1826 **c***, 1845, 1902 **c**, 1915, 1945, 2015, 2045, 2145, 2245, 2345; on ⑥ at 0715, 0745, 0815, 0845 and every 30 minutes until 2015, 2045, 2145, 2245, 2345; on ⑦ at 0825, 0855 and every 30 minutes until 1925, 1955, 2025, 2125, 2225, 2325.

From Hastings: on Ⓐ at 0518, 0548 **c**, 0605 *, 0627 *, 0644 **c** *, 0703 *, 0726 **c** *, 0744, 0804 **c** *, 0817, 0847, 0929, 0947, 1031, 1050 and a the same minutes past each hour until 1450, 1531, 1545 **c**, 1620, 1645, 1721, 1750, 1820, 1846, 1930 **g**, 1950, 2050, 2150, 2250 **g**; on ⑥ a 0548, 0619, 0650, 0719, 0750, 0819, 0850, 0931, 0950 and at the same minutes past each hour until 1650, 1719, 1750, 1818, 1850, 1950 2050, 2150, 2250 **g**; on ⑦ at 0650, 0731, 0750 and at the same minutes past each hour until 1831, 1850, 1950, 2050, 2150, 2250 **g**.

c – From/to London Cannon Street.
d – Does not call at London Bridge.
e – Change at Tonbridge.
g – To Tonbridge.
* – Does not call at Sevenoaks and Tonbridge. Frequent trains call at these stations.
‡ – London Waterloo East.

LONDON VICTORIA - EASTBOURNE

Longest journey: 1 hour 44 minutes SN

km	↓		↑
0	0h00	d.**London** Victoria.....a.	1h26
17	0h16	d.East Croydon..........d.	1h09
43	0h33	d.Gatwick Airport ....d.	0h53
61	0h50	d.Haywards Heath ....d.	0h34
81	1h06	d.Lewes.....................d.	0h19
106	1h27	a.**Eastbourne**...........d.	0h00

From London Victoria: on Ⓐ 0002 ②–⑤, 0532, 0646, 0716, 0746, 0816, 0846 and every 30 minutes until 1616, 1645, 1715, 1732 **b** 1745, 1815, 1832 **b**, 1845, 1916 and every 30 minutes unti 2246; on ⑥ at 0002, 0746 and every 30 minutes until 2316; on ⑦ at 0846 an hourly until 2246.

From Eastbourne: on Ⓐ at 0449, 0520, 0534 **b**, 0554, 0620, 0636 **b**, 0649, 0720, 0752, 0824, 0900, 0924 and at the same minutes pas each hour untill 1924, 2000, 2027, 2100, 2125, 2200, 2225; on ⑥ at 0558, 0625, 0701, 0725, 0801, 0825, 0901, 0925, 1000, 1025 and at the same minutes past each hour until 2200; on ⑦ at 0657, 0755, 0900 and hourly until 2100.

b – From/to London Bridge, not Victoria. g – Does not call at Gatwick Airport.

ASHFORD - HASTINGS - EASTBOURNE - (BRIGHTON)

Longest journey: 1 hour 25 minutes SN

km	↓		↑
0	0h00	d.**Ashford** Int'l ‡ ....a.	1h20
14	0h12	d.Appledore ‡ ....d.	1h07
25	0h23	d.Rye ‡......................d.	0h56
41	0h42	d.Ore.........................d.	0h40
42	0h45	d.**Hastings** ....d.	0h36
50	0h57	d.Bexhill.....................d.	0h25
67	1h14	a.**Eastbourne**...........d.	0h00

From Ashford International: On Ⓐ at 0615, 0722, 0824, 0845 **h**, 0924 and hourly until 1924, 1952 **h**, 2024, 2124, 2225 **h**, 2325 **h**; on ⑥ a 0624 and hourly until 2224, 2325 **h**; on ⑦ at 0825 and hourly until 2125, 2234 **h**.

From Eastbourne: on Ⓐ at 0453, 0544, 0545 **h**, 0646, 0749 and hourly until 1549, 1652, 1705 **h**, 1752, 1852, 1949, 2049, 2149; on ⑥ a 0520 **h**, 0549 and hourly until 2149; on ⑦ at 0724 **h**, 0759, 0856 and hourly until 2056.

h – Ashford - Hastings and v.v.
‡ – Additional services operate on Ⓐ: Ashford - Rye at 0645, 0745, 1755, 1855; Rye - Ashford at 0716, 0816, 1826, 1926.

☛ Local services are available Brighton/Lewes - Eastbourne - Hastings v.v.

TONBRIDGE - REDHILL

Longest journey: 36 Minutes SN

km	↓		↑
0	0h00	d.**Tonbridge**............a.	0h31
7	0h08	d.Penshurst ....d.	0h22
15	0h15	d.Edenbridge..............d.	0h16
22	0h21	d.Godstone.................d.	0h10
32	0h35	a.**Redhill** ....d.	0h00

From Tonbridge: On Ⓐ at 0440, 0528 and every 30 minutes unti 0858, 0932, 1001 and hourly until 1501, 1547 and every 30 minutes unt 1847, 1922, 2001, 2101, 2201, 2303, 2336; on ⑥ at 0533, 0603, 0701 and hourly until 2201, 2303; on ⑦ at 0700, 0735, 0829 and hourl until 2129, 2229.

From Redhill: On Ⓐ at 0016 ②–⑤, 0523, 0552, 0622, 0652, 0723, 0752, 0822, 0856, 0925, 1000 and hourly until 1500, 1530 and ever 30 minutes until 2000, 2100, 2200, 2300; on ⑥ at 0016, 0625, 0700 and hourly until 2300; on ⑦ at 0750, 0848, 0911, 1007 and hourly unt 2307.

SE, SN

LONDON - THE SOUTH and SOUTH EAST

ypical off-peak journey time in hours and minutes
READ DOWN ↓ READ UP ↑

Journey times may be extended during peak hours on Ⓐ (0600 - 0900 and 1600 - 1900) and also at weekends.

The longest journey time by any train is noted in the table heading.

LONDON BRIDGE - UCKFIELD

Longest journey: 1 hour 19 minutes SN

km					
0	0h00	↓	d.**London** Bridge......a.	↑	1h15
16	0h16		d.East Croydon.........d.		0h59
32	0h29	↓	d.Oxted.....................d.	↑	0h44
57	0h55		d.Eridge △ ....d.		0h17
70	1h01	↓	d.Crowborough ....d.	↑	0h12
74	1h15		a.**Uckfield** ....d.		0h00

From London Bridge: on Ⓐ at 0520**e**, 0607, 0637, 0707, 0807, 0837, 0907 and hourly until 1607, 1637, 1707, 1737, 1807 and hourly until 2307; on ⑥ at 0607 and hourly until 2307.

From Uckfield: on Ⓐ at 0510, 0531, 0633, 0703, 0733, 0803, 0833, 0933, 1003, 1033 and hourly until 1733, 1803, 1833, 1903, 1933, 2033, 2133, 2233; on ⑥ at 0633 and hourly until 2233.

On ⑦ services run Oxted - Uckfield and v.v. only. Connections available from / to London Victoria (see East Grinstead Table). From Oxted at 0837, 0937, 1038 and hourly until 2238. From Uckfield at 0934 and hourly until 2234**e**.

– East Croydon - Uckfield and v.v. △ – **Spa Valley Railway** (🚂 Eridge - Tunbridge Wells West: *8 km*). ✆ 01892 537715. www.spavalleyrailway.co.uk

LONDON VICTORIA - EAST GRINSTEAD

Longest journey: 60 minutes SN

km					
0	0h00	↓	d.**London** Victoria.....a.	↑	0h56
17	0h17		d.East Croydon.........d.		0h37
33	0h37	↓	d.Oxted.....................d.		0h16
42	0h43	↓	d.Lingfield.................d.	↑	0h12
48	0h54		a.**East Grinstead** ▽.d.		0h00

From London Victoria: on Ⓐ at 0520, 0537**b**, 0550, 0611**b**, 0620, 0641**b**, 0650, 0711**b**, 0720, 0741**b**, 0750, 0811**b**, 0820 and every 30 minutes until 1620, 1641**b**, 1650, 1711**b** and at the same minutes past each hour until 1920 and every 30 minutes until 2220, 2252, 2322, 2353**c**; on ⑥ at 0520, 0620 and every 30 minutes until 2320, 2353**c**; on ⑦ at 0743, 0851, 0921 and every 30 minutes until 2251.

From East Grinstead: on Ⓐ at 0536, 0545**b**, 0604, 0613**b** and at the same minutes past each hour until 0906, 0919**b**, 0936 and every 30 minutes until 1736, 1751**b**, 1806, 1821**b**, 1836, 1851**b**, 1906, 1917**b**, 1936, 1951**b**, 2006, 2017**b**, 2036, 2106, 2136, 2206, 2236, 2306; on ⑥ at 0636 and every 30 minutes until 2306; on ⑦ at 0812 and every 30 minutes until 2242, 2314.

– From / to London Bridge (not Victoria).
– To Oxted.

▽ – **Bluebell Railway** (🚂 East Grinstead - Sheffield Park: *18 km*). ✆ 01825 720800. www.bluebell-railway.com

LONDON VICTORIA - LITTLEHAMPTON

Longest journey: 1 hour 47 minutes SN

km					
0	0h00	↓	d.**London** Victoria.....a.	↑	1h42
17	0h16		d.East Croydon.........a.		1h25
43	0h33	↓	d.Gatwick Airport ......a.	↑	1h09
61	0h50		d.Haywards Heath .....a.		0h54
82	1h06	↓	d.Hove.......................a.	↑	0h35
96	1h21		d.Worthing..................d.		0h21
114	1h41	↓	a.**Littlehampton**........d.	↑	0h00

From London Victoria: on Ⓐ at 0002 ②–⑤**d**, 0746, 0846, 0916 and every 30 minutes until 1616, 1654, 1724, 1754, 1824, 1854, 1916, 1946, 2016, 2046, 2116, 2146, 2246**d**, 2316**d**; on ⑥ at 0002**d**, 0746 and every 30 minutes until 2146, 2216**d**, 2246**d**, 2316**d**; on ⑦ at 0002**d**, 0814, 0916 and hourly until 2016, 2116, 2216**d**, 2316**d**.

From Littlehampton: on Ⓐ at 0514, 0544, 0616, 0647, 0712, 0742, 0814 and every 30 minutes until 1444, 1513, 1544, 1614, 1644, 1714, 1744, 1814, 1840, 1910, 1940, 2010, 2040, 2114, 2144, 2214; on ⑥ at 0544 and every 30 minutes until 2144; on ⑦ at 0712, 0814 and hourly until 2014.

c – Change at Worthing. **d** – To Worthing.

LONDON VICTORIA - BOGNOR REGIS

Longest journey: 1 hour 57 minutes SN

km					
0	0h00	↓	d.**London** Victoria.....a.	↑	1h50
17	0h16		d.East Croydon.........d.		1h30
43	0h37	↓	d.Gatwick Airport ......d.	↑	1h08
61	1h03		d.Horsham..................d.		0h50
94	1h30	↓	d.Arundel....................d.	↑	0h16
110	1h40		d.Barnham..................d.		0h07
116	1h46	↓	a.**Bognor Regis**.......d.	↑	0h00

From London Victoria: on Ⓐ at 0554**p**, 0636, 0706, 0736, 0806, 0836 and every 30 minutes until 1636, 1702**g n**, 1706, 1736, 1802**g n**, 1806 and every 30 minutes until 2106, 2206, 2216**k**; on ⑥ at 0606 and every 30 minutes until 2036, 2106, 2206**p**, 2216**k**; on ⑦ at 0732, 0832**p**, 0933**p**, 1033 and hourly until 2033, 2133, 2233.

From Bognor Regis: on Ⓐ at 0529**p**, 0555**g n**, 0621, 0651, 0700**g n**, 0727, 0754, 0828, 0856, 0929, 0956 and at the same minutes past each hour until 1456, 1526, 1556, 1629, 1656, 1729, 1756, 1829, 1856, 1929, 1956, 2029, 2055, 2129; on ⑥ at 0629, 0656 and at the same minutes past each hour until 2129; on ⑦ at 0726, 0831 and hourly until 2131.

– Does not call at Gatwick Airport. **k** – Does not call at Arundel and Horsham. **n** – From / to London Bridge. **p** – Change at Barnham.

SEAFORD - BRIGHTON

Longest journey: 42 minutes SN

km					
0	0h00	↓	d.**Seaford**.................a.	↑	0h36
4	0h05		d.Newhaven Harbour..d.		0h30
5	0h07	↓	d.Newhaven Town ....d.	↑	0h28
15	0h19		d.Lewes......................d.		0h18
22	0h26	↓	d.Falmer.....................d.	↑	0h09
28	0h35		a.**Brighton** ....d.		0h00

From Seaford: on Ⓐ at 0450, 0525, 0555, 0625, 0650**b**, 0723, 0753, 0823, 0853, 0925, 0953 and at the same minutes past each hour until 1625 then every half hour until 1925, 1953, 2025, 2053, 2125, 2153, 2225, 2253, 2325, 2353; on ⑥ at 0504, 0625, 0653, 0725, 0753 and at the same minutes past each hour until 2353; on ⑦ at 0757, 0829, 0859 and every 30 minutes until 2129, 2157, 2229, 2257.

From Brighton: on Ⓐ at 0541, 0607, 0641 and every half hour until 1811, 1838**a**, 1911 then every half hour until 2341; on ⑥ at 0541, 0611, 0641 and every 30 minutes until 2341; on ⑦ at 0715, 0747 and every 30 minutes until 2247.

a – To Newhaven Harbour. **b** – Change at Newhaven Harbour.

BRIGHTON - PORTSMOUTH HARBOUR

Longest journey: 1 hour 49 minutes SN

km	⚒	⑦				⚒	⑦
0	0h00	0h00	↓	d.**Brighton**..............d.	↑	1h19	1h36
2	0h04	0h10		d.Hove.......................d.		1h15	1h31
16	0h22	0h31	↓	d.Worthing ....d.	↑	0h57	1h10
35	0h39	0h54		d.Barnham..................d.		0h39	0h48
45	0h47	1h02	↓	d.Chichester..............d.	↑	0h31	0h39
59	1h02	1h23		d.Havant.....................d.		0h17	0h19
71	1h14	1h37	↓	a.**Portsmouth** S ▽.d.	↑	0h04	0h04
72	1h18	1h41		a.**Portsmouth** Hbr..d.		0h00	0h00

From Brighton: on Ⓐ at 0500**t**, 0602**p t**, 0702**t**, 0741**t**, 0800**p t**, 0905**p**, 1002 and hourly until 1402, 1502**p**, 1602**p**, 1705**p**, 1802**p t**, 1902**p t**, 2002**p t**, 2102**t**, 2202**t**; on ⑥ at 0602, 0702, 0802, 0904, 1002 and hourly until 1602, 1704, 1802, 1902, 2002, 2102, 2132, 2202; on ⑦ at 0715**r**, 0730, 0820**r**, 0830 and hourly until 1430, 1630, 1830, 1930, 2030, 2146**r**, 2210**v**.

From Portsmouth Harbour: on Ⓐ at 0632, 0709, 0717**t**, 0829, 0933**p**, 1033**p**, 1129 and hourly until 1529, 1633**p** and hourly until 2133**p**, 2215**t**, 2240**t**; on ⑥ at 0455**p v**, 0629, 0650, 0729 and hourly until 2029, 2215**t**, 2240**t**; on ⑦ at 0714 and hourly until 1114, 1213, 1314, 1414, 1514, 1614, 1814, 2014, 2114, 2201.

p – To / from Portsmouth & Southsea only. **t** – Runs in ⑦ (slower) timings. ▽ – Portsmouth and Southsea.
r – Runs in ⚒ (faster) timings. **v** – Change at Hove.

BRIGHTON - SOUTHAMPTON CENTRAL

Longest journey: 2 hours 1 minute SN

km	⚒	⑦				⚒	⑦
0	0h00	0h00	↓	d.**Brighton**..............d.	↑	1h45	1h50
2	0h04	0h04		d.Hove.......................d.		1h41	1h46
16	0h18	0h25	↓	d.Worthing ....d.	↑	1h23	1h25
35	0h39	0h48		d.Barnham..................d.		1h00	1h03
45	0h46	0h56	↓	d.Chichester..............d.	↑	0h52	0h54
59	1h04	1h08		d.Havant.....................d.		0h38	0h42
75	1h19	1h25	↓	d.Fareham ....d.	↑	0h23	0h24
98	1h52	1h56		a.**Southampton** C ..d.		0h00	0h00

From Brighton: on Ⓐ at 0527**t**, 0632, 0732, 0832, 0859, 0932 and hourly until 1632, 1702, 1732, 1832, 1932, 2032;
on ⑥ at 0514, 0532, 0632, 0732, 0833, 0900, 0932 and hourly until 1632, 1700, 1732, 1832, 1932, 2032;
on ⑦ at 0800, 0900, 1000, 1100, 1110**r**, 1200, 1300, 1400, 1500, 1547**r**, 1600, 1700, 1746**r**, 1800, 1900, 2000, 2100.

From Southampton Central:
on Ⓐ at 0546, 0733, 0826, 0926, 1026, 1126, 1229, 1326, 1434, 1526 and hourly until 2026, 2113**t**;
on ⑥ at 0626, 0726, 0827, 0926 and hourly until 1326, 1434, 1526 and hourly until 2026, 2113**t**;
on ⑦ at 0730, 0831**r**, 0930, 1030, 1130, 1230, 1304**r**, 1330, 1430, 1506**r**, 1530, 1630, 1730, 1830, 1928**r**, 2028, 2130.

r – Runs in ⚒ (faster) timings. **t** – Runs in ⑦ (slower) timings.

LONDON WATERLOO - READING

Longest journey: 1 hour 35 minutes SW

km					
0	0h00	↓	d.**London** Waterloo ..a.	↑	1h22
16	0h16		d.Richmond ....d.		1h03
18	0h20	↓	d.Twickenham.............d.	↑	0h58
30	0h33		d.Staines ....d.		0h36
46	0h53	↓	d.Ascot.......................d.	↑	0h28
70	1h20		a.**Reading** ....d.		0h00

From London Waterloo: on Ⓐ at 0505, 0550, 0620, 0650, 0720, 0750, 0807, 0820, 0837, 0850 and every 30 minutes until 1550, 1605, 1620, 1635, 1650, 1720, 1735, 1750, 1805, 1820, 1835, 1850, 1905, 1920, 1935, 1950 and every 30 minutes until 2350; on ⑥ at 0505, 0550 and every 30 minutes until 2350; on ⑦ at 0709, 0809 and every 30 minutes until 2339.

From Reading: on Ⓐ at 0542, 0553, 0609, 0623, 0641, 0654, 0712, 0723, 0741, 0753, 0812, 0842, 0912, 0925, 0942, 0955, 1012 and every 30 minutes until 1712, 1723, 1742, 1756, 1812, 1842, 1912 and every 30 minutes until 2242, 2312; on ⑥ at 0542 and every 30 minutes until 2242, 2312; on ⑦ at 0754, 0824, 0854, 0924 and every 30 minutes until 2154, 2224, 2254.

LONDON WATERLOO - WINDSOR

Longest journey: 1 hour 09 minutes SW

km					
0	0h00	↓	d.**London** Waterloo ..a.	↑	0h56
16	0h20		d.Richmond ....d.		0h34
18	0h24	↓	d.Twickenham.............d.	↑	0h30
30	0h39		d.Staines ....d.		0h15
41	0h53	↓	a.**Windsor** ▷ ....d.	↑	0h00

From London Waterloo: on ⚒ at 0558 and every 30 minutes until 2328; on ⑦ at 0644, 0744, 0825, 0844 and at the same minutes past each hour until 2025, 2044, 2144, 2244.

From Windsor and Eton Riverside: on ⚒ at 0553, 0623, 0653, 0702, 0723 and every 30 minutes until 2223, 2253; on ⑦ at 0701, 0801, 0901, 0934 and at the same minutes past each hour until 2101, 2201, 2301.

▷ – Windsor and Eton Riverside.

103 BEDFORD - LONDON - GATWICK ✈ - BRIGHTON

SN, TL

km	km			②–⑥	⚒	⚒	⚒	⚒	⑥	Ⓐ	⑥	Ⓐ	⚒	⑥	Ⓐ	⚒	⚒	⑥	Ⓐ	⚒	⚒	Ⓐ	⚒	⚒	⑥	Ⓐ	⚒
0		**Bedford** 170 d.	⚒	...	0015	0115	0153	0215	...	0253	0253	...	0310	...	...	0345	0413	...	...	0443	...	...	...	0515	...	...	...
31		Luton 170 d.		...	0040	0140	0218	0240	...	0318	0318	...	0335	...	...	0410	0438	...	...	0508	...	...	...	0540	...	...	...
33		Luton Airport P ✈ ◇ 170 d.		...	0043	0143	0221	0243	...	0321	0321	...	0338	...	...	0413	0441	...	...	0511	...	...	...	0543	...	...	...
48		St. Albans d.		...	0055	0155	0233	0255	...	0333	0333	...	0350	...	...	0425	0453	...	...	0523	...	...	...	0555	...	...	...
80		**London** St Pancras 170 d.		...	0132	0232	0302	0332	...	0402	0402	...	0432	...	...	0451	0520	...	...	0550	...	...	...	0620	...	...	...
82		Farringdon 185 d.		...	|	|	|	|	...	|	|	...	|	...	...	0456	0524	...	...	0554	...	...	...	·0624	...	...	...
83		**London** Blackfriars 185 d.		...	0140	0240	0310	0340	...	0410	0410	...	0440	...	...	0501	0529	...	...	0559	...	...	...	0629	...	...	...
84		**London** Bridge 185 d.		...	|	|	|	|	...	|	|	...	|	...	...	|	0535	...	...	0605	...	...	...	0635	...	...	...
	0	**London** Victoria d.		0002	|	|	|	|	0410	|	|	0435	|	0508	0514	|	|	0544	0600	|	0613	0630	0643	|	0655	0700	071
99	17	East Croydon 185 d.		0024	0207	0307	0337	0407	0431	0437	0437	0457	0507	0531	|	0528	0549	|	|	0619	|	|	|	0649	0711	|	|
124	43	Gatwick Airport ✈ 185 d.		0044	0230	0330	0358	0430	0500	0458	0504	0528	0532	0601	0551	0548	0605	0612	0631	0635	0642	0700	0712	0705	0728	0731	0742
142	61	Haywards Heath 185 d.		0102	...	...	...	...	0517	0514	0520	...	0547	0617	|	0606	0622	0623	|	0652	0655j	|	|	0724	0741	|	|
163	82	**Brighton** 185 a.		0116	...	...	...	...	0532	0532	0538	...	0610	0637	0613	0626	0646k	0640	0656	0714f	0709k	0726	0737	0744	0802	0758	0807

	⚒	⑥	Ⓐ	⚒	⚒	⚒	⚒	⚒	⚒	Ⓐ	⚒	⚒	Ⓐ	⚒	⚒	⚒	Ⓐ	⑥	⚒	⚒	⚒	⚒	⚒	⚒	⚒	
Bedford 170 d.	0548	...	...	0618	...	...	...	0648	...	0722	0718	...	...	...	0748	...	...	...	0818	...	...	0848	...	...	0916	
Luton 170 d.	0612	...	...	0642	...	...	...	0712	...	0739	0742	...	0758	...	0812	...	...	...	0842	...	...	0912	...	...	0941	and
Luton Airport P ✈ ◇ 170 d.	0615	...	...	0645	...	...	...	0715	...	|	0745	...	0801	...	0815	...	...	...	0845	...	...	0915	...	...	0944	at the
St. Albans d.	0627	...	...	0657	...	...	...	0727	...	0748	0757	...	0812	...	0826	...	...	...	0856	...	...	0926	...	...	0955	same
London St Pancras 170 d.	0650	...	...	0720	...	...	...	0750	...	0810	0820	...	0835	...	0850	...	...	...	0920	...	...	0950	...	...	1020	minutes
Farringdon 185 d.	0654	...	...	0724	...	...	...	0754	...	0814	0824	...	0839	...	0854	...	...	...	0924	...	...	0954	...	...	1024	past
London Blackfriars 185 d.	0659	...	...	0729	...	...	...	0759	...	0819	0829	...	0844	...	0859	...	...	...	0929	...	...	0959	...	...	1029	each
London Bridge 185 d.	0705	...	...	0735	...	...	...	0805	...	0825	0835	...	0851	...	0905	...	...	...	0935	...	...	1005	...	...	1035	hour
London Victoria d.	|	0725	0730	|	0743	0755	0813	|	0825	|	|	0843	|	0855	|	0914	0925	0925	|	0944	0955	|	1014	1025	|	until
East Croydon 185 d.	0719	0741	|	0749	|	0811	|	0819	0841	0838	0849	|	0907	0911	0919	|	0941	0941	0949	|	1011	1019	|	1041	1049	
Gatwick Airport ✈ 185 d.	0735	0758	0800	0805	0812	0827	0842	0835	0858	|	0905	0912	0935	0928	0935	0942	1001	0958	1005	1012	1028	1035	1042	1058	1105	♠
Haywards Heath 185 d.	0754	0811	|	0824	|	0841	|	0854	0911	0857	0924	|	...	0941	0954	|	1013	1011	1024	|	1041	1054	|	1111	1124	
Brighton 185 a.	0812	0832	0823	0846k	0837	0902	0907	0912	0932	...	0944	0937	...	1002	1012	1007	1032	1032	1044	1037	1102	1112	1107	1132	1144	

	⚒	⚒	⚒	⚒	⚒	⚒	⑥	Ⓐ	Ⓐ	⚒	⚒	⑥	Ⓐ	⚒	⚒	⑥	Ⓐ	Ⓐ	⚒	⚒	⑥	Ⓐ	⚒	⚒	⑥	Ⓐ	⚒
Bedford 170 d.	...	1449	...	...	1519	...	...	...	1544	...	1548	...	...	...	1618	...	...	1645	...	1649	...	...	...	1718	...	...	174
Luton 170 d.	...	1513	...	...	1543	...	...	...	1606	...	1613	...	...	...	1642	...	...	1704	...	1713	...	...	...	1742	...	...	181
Luton Airport P ✈ ◇ 170 d.	...	1516	...	...	1546	...	...	...	1609	...	1616	...	...	...	1645	...	...	1707	...	1716	...	...	...	1745	...	...	181
St. Albans d.	...	1527	...	...	1557	...	...	...	1618	...	1627	...	...	...	1656	...	...	1718	...	1727	...	...	...	1756	...	...	182
London St Pancras 170 d.	...	1550	...	...	1620	...	...	...	1640	...	1650	...	...	...	1720	...	...	1740	...	1750	...	...	...	1820	...	...	185
Farringdon 185 d.	...	1554	...	...	1624	...	...	...	1644	...	1654	...	...	...	1724	...	...	1744	...	1754	...	...	...	1824	...	...	185
London Blackfriars 185 d.	...	1559	...	...	1629	...	...	...	1649	...	1659	...	...	...	1729	...	...	1749	...	1759	...	...	...	1829	...	...	185
London Bridge 185 d.	...	1605	...	...	1635	...	...	...	1655	...	1705	...	...	...	1735	...	...	1755	...	1805	...	...	...	1835	...	...	190
London Victoria d.	1555	|	1614	1625	|	1643	1655	1659	|	1713	|	1725	1729	1743	|	1755	1759	|	1813	|	1825	1829	1843	|	1855	1859	|
East Croydon 185 d.	1611	1619	|	1641	1649	|	1711	|	1708	|	1719	1741	|	|	1749	1811	|	1808	|	1819	1841	|	|	1849	1911	|	191
Gatwick Airport ✈ 185 d.	1628	1635	1642	1658	1705	1712	1728	1733	|	1742	1735	1758	1800	1812	1805	1828	1833	|	1842	1835	1858	1900	1912	1905	1928	1930	193
Haywards Heath 185 d.	1641	1654	|	1711	1724	|	1741	1745	1737	|	1754	1811	1814	|	1824	1841	1845	1837	|	1854	1911	1913	|	1924	1941	1943	195
Brighton 185 a.	1702	1712	1707	1732	1746	1737	1802	1802	...	1812d	1815	1832	1832	1842d	1846	1902	1902	...	1912d	1915	1932	1932	1942d	1946	2002	2002	201

	⚒	⚒	⚒	⚒	⚒	⚒		⚒	⚒	⚒	⚒	⚒	⚒	⚒	⚒	⚒	⚒	⚒	⚒	⑥	Ⓐ	⑦	⑦	⑦	⑦	⑦
Bedford 170 d.	...	...	1816	...	...	1846		...	...	2119	...	...	2149	...	...	2205	2217	2245	2305	2335	2345		...	...	...	055
Luton 170 d.	...	...	1842	...	...	1912	and	...	...	2143	...	...	2213	...	...	2228	2241	2310	2330	2359	0010		...	...	...	062
Luton Airport P ✈ ◇ 170 d.	...	...	1845	...	...	1915	at the	...	...	2146	...	...	2216	...	...	2231	2244	2313	2333	0003	0013		...	...	...	062
St. Albans d.	...	...	1856	...	...	1927	same	...	...	2157	...	...	2227	...	...	2241	2255	2325	2345	0015	0025		...	...	...	063
London St Pancras 170 d.	...	...	1920	...	...	1950	minutes	...	...	2220	...	...	2250	...	...	2305	2322	2351	0021	0051	0052		...	...	...	071
Farringdon 185 d.	...	...	1924	...	...	1954	past	...	...	2224	...	...	2254	...	...	2310	2327	2356	0026	|	|		...	...	...	▬
London Blackfriars 185 d.	...	...	1929	...	...	1959	each	...	...	2229	...	...	2259	...	...	2314	2331	0001	0031	0101	0102		...	...	...	...
London Bridge 185 d.	...	...	1935	...	...	2005	hour	...	...	2235	...	...	2305	...	...	2321	2337	|	|	|	|		...	...	...	⑦
London Victoria 185 d.	1914	1925	|	1944	1955	|	until	2214	2225	|	2244	2255	|	2316	2325	|	|	|	|	|	|		0002	0108	0410	050
East Croydon 185 d.	|	1941	1949	|	2011	2019		|	2241	2249	|	2311	2319	2333	2343	2337	2351	0028	0058	0128	0128		0024	0133	0431	052
Gatwick Airport ✈ 185 d.	1942	1958	2005	2012	2028	2035	♠	2242	2258	2305	2312	2328	2335	2354	0004	0001	0018	0048	0120	0158	0158		0044	0208	0458	055
Haywards Heath 185 d.	|	2011	2024	|	2041	2054		|	2311	2324	|	2341	2354	0006	0017	...	0036	0104	...	0214	0214		0102	0224	0513	060
Brighton 185 a.	2007	2032	2044	2037	2102	2112		2307	2332	2345	2337	0002	0012	...	0035	...	0056	0124	...	0228	0228		0116	0238	0528	062

	⑦	⑦	⑦	⑦	⑦	⑦	⑦	⑦	⑦	⑦	⑦	⑦	⑦	⑦	⑦		⑦	⑦	⑦	⑦	⑦	⑦	⑦	⑦	⑦	⑦
Bedford 170 d.	...	0625	...	0655	...	...	0735	...	0805	...	...	0819	...	0849	...		...	2051	...	2121	2151	...	2211	2245	2305	234
Luton 170 d.	...	0650	...	0720	...	...	0800	...	0830	...	...	0844	...	0914	...	and	...	2116	...	2146	2216	...	2236	2310	2330	001
Luton Airport P ✈ ◇ 170 d.	...	0653	...	0723	...	...	0803	...	0833	...	...	0847	...	0917	...	at the	...	2119	...	2149	2219	...	2239	2313	2333	001
St. Albans d.	...	0705	...	0735	...	...	0815	...	0845	...	...	0859	...	0929	...	same	...	2131	...	2201	2231	...	2251	2325	2345	002
London St Pancras 170 d.	...	0740	...	0810	...	...	0840	...	0910	...	...	0926	...	0956	...	minutes	...	2156	...	2226	2256	...	2326	2351	0021	005
Farringdon 185 d.	...	▬	...	▬	...	...	▬	...	▬	...	...	0930	...	1000	...	past	...	2200	...	2230	2300	...	2330	2356	0026	|
London Blackfriars 185 d.	...	...	...	...	...	...	...	...	...	...	...	0935	...	1005	...	each	...	2205	...	2235	2305	...	2335	0001	0031	010
London Bridge 185 d.	...	⑦	0711	⑦	0741	0811	⑦	0841	⑦	0911	...	0941	...	1011	...	hour	...	2211	...	2241	2311	...	2341	|	|	|
London Victoria d.	0545	0632	|	0702	|	|	0802	|	0855	|	0925	|	0955	|	1025	until	2155	|	2225	|	|	2332	|	|	|	|
East Croydon 185 d.	0609	0654	0725	0727	0755	0825	0827	0855	0912	0925	0942	0955	1012	1025	1042		2212	2225	2242	2255	2325	2357	2355	0028	0058	012
Gatwick Airport ✈ 185 d.	0633	0724	0745	0753	0815	0844	0854	0910	0928	0940	0958	1010	1028	1040	1058	♠	2228	2240	2258	2310	2344	0023	0018	0048	0120	015
Haywards Heath 185 d.	0648	0740	0801	0808	0832	0901	0913	0927	0942	0955	1012	1027	1042	1055	1112		2242	2255	2312	2327	2359	0039	0035	0104	...	021
Brighton 185 a.	0711	0801	0821	0830	0852	0921	0933	0947	1001	1015	1031	1047	1101	1115	1131		2301	2315	2331	2347	0019	0059	0054	0124	...	022

		⚒	⚒	⚒	⚒	⑥	⚒Ⓐ	⑥	Ⓐ	Ⓐ	⑥	⑥	Ⓐ	⑥	⑥	⚒	Ⓐ	⑥	Ⓐ	⑥	⚒	Ⓐ	⑥	Ⓐ	⑥	⚒	Ⓐ
Brighton 185 d.	⚒	0004	...	...	...	0412	0412	0433	0519	0526	0526	0533	0552	0558	0603	0612r	0622	0626	0629	0633	0642r	0648	0658	0657	0703	0712r	071
Haywards Heath 185 d.		0025	...	...	...	0426	0426	0447	0539	0546	0547	0551	0611	0616	0621	|	0641	0647	0647	0651	|	0711	0716	0714	0721	|	074
Gatwick Airport ✈ 185 d.		0042	0146	0246	0346	0441	0441	0503	0553	0606	0606	0603	0625	0636	0633	0642	0655	0706	0659	0703	0712	0725	0736	0729	0733	0742	075
East Croydon 185 d.		0110	0210	0310	0410	0510	0510	0530	0608	0621	0621	0619	0641	0651	0649	|	0710	0721	|	0719	|	0740	0751	|	0749	|	081
London Victoria a.		|	|	|	|	|	|	0559	0627	|	|	0635	|	|	0705	0714	|	|	0728	0735	0743	|	|	0758	0805	0813	|
London Bridge 185 d.		|	|	|	|	0526	0525	...	...	0635	0635	...	0654	0705	...	...	0724	0735	...	...	...	0754	0805	...	...	...	082
London Blackfriars 185 d.		0136	0236	0336	0436	0532	0531	...	...	0642	0642	...	0702	0712	...	...	0732	0742	...	...	...	0802	0812	...	...	...	083
Farringdon 185 d.		|	|	|	|	0536	0536	...	...	0646	0646	...	0706	0716	...	...	0736	0746	...	...	...	0806	0816	...	...	...	083
London St Pancras 170 d.		0144	0244	0344	0444	0541	0540	...	...	0651	0651	...	0711	0721	...	...	0741	0751	...	...	...	0811	0821	...	...	...	084
St Albans City a.		0219	0319	0419	0519	0600	0605	...	...	0710	0711	...	0729	0741	...	...	0759	0811	...	...	...	0829	0841	...	...	...	085
Luton Airport P ✈ ◇ 170 a.		0230	0330	0430	0530	0612	0616	...	...	0718	0723	...	0740	0753	...	...	0812	0823	...	...	...	0840	0853	...	...	...	091
Luton 170 a.		0235	0335	0435	0535	0616	0621	...	...	0722	0727	...	0744	0757	...	...	0815	0827	...	...	...	0845	0857	...	...	...	091
Bedford 170 a.		0259	0359	0501	0559	0641	0645	...	...	0742	0751	...	0811	0821	...	...	0835	0851	...	...	...	0909	0921	...	...	...	093

	⑥	Ⓐ	⑥	⚒	Ⓐ	Ⓐ	⑥	⑥	⚒	Ⓐ	Ⓐ	⑥	⑥	⚒	Ⓐ	⑥	Ⓐ	⑥	⚒	⚒	⚒c	⚒	⚒	⚒		⚒
Brighton 185 d.	0726	0727	0733	0742r	0754	0800	0758	0803	0812r	0824	0830	0826	0833	0842r	0857	0858	0902	0903	0918	0926	0933	0948	0958	1003		135
Haywards Heath 185 d.	0747	0744	0751	|	0811	0819	0816	0821	|	0841	0849	0847	0851	|	|	0916	0919	0921	|	0946	0951	|	1016	1021	and	141
Gatwick Airport ✈ 185 d.	0806	0759	0803	0812	0828	0836	0836	0833	0842	0858	0906	0906	0903	0912	0924	0936	0936	0933	0942	1006	1003	1012	1036	1033	at the	143
East Croydon 185 d.	0821	|	0819	|	|	0851	0851	0849	|	|	0921	0921	0919	|	|	0951	0951	0949	|	1021	1019	|	1051	1048	same	145
London Victoria a.	|	0828	0835	0843	0858	|	|	0905	0913	0928	|	|	0935	0943	0954	|	|	1005	1013	|	1035	1043	|	1105	minutes	|
London Bridge 185 d.	0835	...	...	...	...	0905	0905	...	...	...	0935	0935	...	...	...	1005	1005	...	...	1035	...	...	1105	...	past	150
London Blackfriars 185 d.	0842	...	...	...	...	0912	0912	...	...	...	0942	0942	...	...	...	1012	1012	...	...	1042	...	...	1112	...	each	151
Farringdon 185 d.	0846	...	...	...	...	0916	0916	...	...	...	0946	0946	...	...	...	1016	1016	...	...	1046	...	...	1116	...	hour	151
London St Pancras 170 d.	0851	...	...	...	...	0921	0921	...	...	...	0951	0951	...	...	...	1021	1021	...	...	1051	...	...	1121	...	until	152
St Albans City a.	0911	...	...	...	...	|	0941	...	...	...	|	1011	...	...	...	1041	1041	...	...	1111	...	...	1141	...		154
Luton Airport P ✈ ◇ 170 a.	0923	...	...	...	...	0949	0953	...	...	...	1019	1023	...	...	...	1053	1053	...	...	1123	...	...	1153	...	♠	155
Luton 170 a.	0927	...	...	...	...	0953	0957	...	...	...	1023	1027	...	...	...	1057	1057	...	...	1127	...	...	1157	...		155
Bedford 170 a.	0951	...	...	...	...	1016	1021	...	...	...	1044	1051	...	...	...	1121	1121	...	...	1151	...	...	1221	...		162

a – Arrives 2344.
b – Arrives 7–8 minutes earlier.
c – The 0933 from Brighton arrives London Victoria 1039 on Ⓐ.
d – Arrives 5 minutes earlier on ⑥.
f – Arrives 0706 on ⑥.

j – ⑥ only.
k – Arrives 4–5 minutes earlier on Ⓐ.
r – Departs 6 minutes later on ⑥.

◇ – Luton Airport Parkway.
♠ – Timings may vary by ± 4 minutes.

☛ Additional trains run Bedford - Gatwick Airport and v.v.
For other services London Victoria - Gatwick Airport and v.v. see Table **100**.
For other services London St Pancras - London Bridge - Brighton and v.v. see Table **185**.

SN BRIGHTON - GATWICK ✈ - LONDON - BEDFORD 103

	⚒	⚒	Ⓐ	⑥	⚒	⚒	Ⓐ	⑥	⚒	⚒	Ⓐ	⑥	⚒	⚒		⚒	Ⓐ	⑥	⚒	⚒	Ⓐ	⑥	⚒	⚒	Ⓐ
Brighton 185 d.	1403	1418	1428	1426	1433	1448	1456	1458	1503	1518	1526	1526	1533	1548		1716	1728	1726	1733	1746	1758	1758	1803	1816	1828
Haywards Heath 185 d.	1421	|	1446	1447	1451	|	1517	1516	1521	|	1547	1547	1551	|	and	|	1746	1747	1751	|	1817	1816	1821	|	1846
Gatwick Airport ✈ 185 d.	1433	1442	1506	1506	1503	1512	1536	1536	1533	1542	1606	1606	1603	1612	at the	1742	1806	1806	1803	1812	1836	1836	1833	1842	1906
East Croydon 185 d.	1449	|	1521	1521	1519	|	1551	1551	1549	|	1621	1621	1619	|	same	|	1821	1821	1818	|	1851	1851	1848	|	1921
London Victoria a.	1505	1513	|	|	1535	1543	|	|	1609	1615	|	|	1635	1643	minutes	1813	|	|	1835	1844	|	|	1905	1914	|
London Bridge 185 d.	...	...	1535	1535	...	...	1605	1605	...	...	1635	1635	...	...	past	...	1835	1835	...	...	1905	1905	...	...	1935
London Blackfriars 185 d.	...	...	1542	1542	...	...	1612	1612	...	...	1642	1642	...	...	each	...	1842	1842	...	...	1912	1912	...	...	1942
Farringdon 185 d.	...	...	1546	1546	...	...	1616	1616	...	...	1646	1646	...	...	hour	...	1846	1846	...	...	1916	1916	...	...	1946
London St Pancras 170 d.	...	...	1551	1551	...	...	1621	1621	...	...	1651	1651	...	...	until	...	1851	1851	...	...	1921	1921	...	...	1951
St Albans City d.	...	...	1614	1611	...	...	1639	1641	...	...	1709	1711	...	...		...	1909	1911	...	...	1939	1941	...	...	2009
Luton Airport P ✈ ◇ 170 d.	...	...	1625	1622	...	...	|	1652	...	...	|	1722	...	...	♠	...	|	1922	...	...	|	1952	...	...	|
Luton 170 d.	...	...	1629	1626	...	...	1650	1656	...	...	1720	1726	...	...		...	1922	1926	...	...	1952	1956	...	...	2022
Bedford 170 a.	...	...	1653	1651	...	...	1706	1721	...	...	1740	1751	...	...		...	1944	1951	...	...	2014	2021	...	...	2044

	⑥	⚒	⚒	⚒	⚒	⚒	⚒		⚒	⚒	⚒	⚒	⚒	⚒	⚒	⚒	⚒	⚒	⚒	⚒		⑦	⑦	⑦	⑦
Brighton 185 d.	1826	1833	1846	1858	1903	1916	1925		2133	2148	2158	2203	2218	2226	2233	2248	2256	2313	2324	2342	⑦	0004	0433	0542	0547
Haywards Heath 185 d.	1847	1851	|	1916	1921	|	1946	and	2151	|	2216	2221	|	2247	2251	|	2317	2330	2346	0003		0025	0447	0604	0608
Gatwick Airport ✈ 185 d.	1906	1903	1914	1936	1933	1942	2006	at the	2203	2212	2236	2233	2242	2306	2303	2311	2334	2355a	0004	0021		0042	0503	0621	0628
East Croydon 185 d.	1921	1918	|	1951	1949	|	2021	same	2219	|	2251	2249	|	2321	2319	|	2353	0016	0023	0040		0110	0530	0640	0651
London Victoria a.	|	1935	1945	|	2005	2013	|	minutes	2237	2243	|	2305	2313	|	2335	2343	|	0041	|	|		|	0559	|	0715
London Bridge 185 d.	1935	...	...	2005	...	...	2035	past	...	...	2305	...	...	2335	...	...	|	...	|	|		|	▬	0655	▬
London Blackfriars 185 d.	1942	...	...	2012	...	...	2042	each	...	...	2312	...	...	2342	...	...	0022	...	0050	0106		0136	...	...	...
Farringdon 185 d.	1946	...	...	2016	...	...	2046	hour	...	...	2316	...	...	2346	...	...	0026	...	|	|		|	⑦	...	⑦
London St Pancras 170 d.	1951	...	...	2021	...	...	2051	until	...	...	2321	...	...	2351	...	...	0031	...	0101	0116		0144	0618	...	0718
St Albans City d.	2011	...	...	2041	...	...	2111		...	...	2346	...	...	0016	...	...	0056	...	0134	0140		0217	0654	...	0754
Luton Airport P ✈ ◇ 170 d.	2022	...	...	2052	...	...	2122	♠	...	...	2357	...	...	0027	...	...	0107	...	0145	0152		0230	0705	...	0805
Luton 170 d.	2026	...	...	2056	...	...	2126		...	...	0001	...	...	0031	...	...	0111	...	0149	0156		0234	0710	...	0810
Bedford 170 a.	2051	...	...	2121	...	...	2151		...	...	0026	...	...	0058	...	...	0136	...	0214	0221		0259	0734	...	0834

	⑦	⑦	⑦	⑦	⑦	⑦	⑦	⑦	⑦	⑦	⑦	⑦		⑦	⑦	⑦	⑦	⑦	⑦	⑦	⑦	⑦	⑦	⑦	⑦
Brighton 185 d.	0608	0642	0647	0708	0717	0742	0747	0808	0827	0842	0857	0908		2042	2057	2108	2127	2142	2154	2208	2227	2242	2254	2308	2342
Haywards Heath 185 d.	0630	0704	0708	0730	0742b	0804	0813b	0830	0846	0904	0916	0930	and	2104	2116	2130	2146	2204	2216	2230	2246	2304	2316	2330	0004
Gatwick Airport ✈ 185 d.	0651	0721	0728	0751	0754	0821	0825	0847	0900	0919	0930	0949	at the	2119	2130	2149	2200	2219	2230	2249	2300	2321	2330	2350	0021
East Croydon 185 d.	0710	0740	0751	0810	0823	0840	0846	0902	0915	0934	0945	1004	same	2134	2145	2204	2215	2234	2245	2304	2315	2340	0352	0010	0040
London Victoria a.	|	|	0815	|	0846	|	0902	|	0932	|	1002	|	minutes	|	2202	|	2232	|	2302	|	2331	|	0017	|	|
London Bridge 185 d.	0725	0755	▬	0825	▬	0855	▬	0917	...	0949	...	1019	past	2149	...	2219	...	2249	...	2319	...	|	...	|	|
London Blackfriars 185 d.	...	...	...	...	...	...	...	▬	...	0955	...	1025	each	2155	...	2225	...	2255	...	2327	...	0006	...	0036	0106
Farringdon 185 d.	...	...	⑦	...	⑦	...	⑦	⑦	...	0959	...	1029	hour	2159	...	2229	...	2359	...	2331	...	0011	...	|	|
London St Pancras 170 d.	...	...	0748	...	0818	...	0848	0918	...	1004	...	1034	until	2204	...	2234	...	2304	...	2336	...	0016	...	0046	0116
St Albans City d.	...	...	0824	...	0854	...	0912	0942	...	1029	...	1059		2229	...	2259	...	2329	...	0003	...	0051	...	0121	0141
Luton Airport P ✈ ◇ 170 d.	...	...	0835	...	0905	...	0824	0953	...	1040	...	1110	♠	2240	...	2310	...	2340	...	0014	...	0102	...	0132	0152
Luton 170 d.	...	...	0840	...	0910	...	0928	0957	...	1045	...	1115		2244	...	2314	...	2345	...	0019	...	0107	...	0137	0157
Bedford 170 a.	...	...	0904	...	0934	...	0953	1022	...	1109	...	1140		2308	...	2338	...	0009	...	0043	...	0131	...	0201	0221

◄◄◄◄ FOR NOTES SEE PREVIOUS PAGE

SW 🍷 on most trains LONDON - GUILDFORD - PORTSMOUTH 105

km			①	Ⓐ	Ⓐ	Ⓐ	Ⓐ	Ⓐ	Ⓐ	Ⓐ	Ⓐ	Ⓐ	Ⓐ	Ⓐ	Ⓐ		Ⓐ	Ⓐ	Ⓐ	Ⓐ	Ⓐ	Ⓐ	Ⓐ	Ⓐ	Ⓐ
0	**London Waterloo** 108 d.	Ⓐ	0050	...	0500	0545	0615	0700	0730	0800	0830	0900	0930	1000	1030		1600	1630	1700	1730	1800	1815	1830	1900	1930
39	Woking 108 d.		0118	...	0553	0613	0643	0725	0756	0825	0855	0925	0955	1025	1055	and at	1625	1655	1725	1756u	|	|	1858	|	1955
49	Guildford d.		0126s	0509	0604	0630	0655	0733	0806	0834	0904	0934	1004	1034	1104	the same	1634	1704	1734	1808	1833	1852	1909	1934	2004
69	Haslemere d.		|	0524	0628	0655	0720	0754	0825	0854	0925	0952	1023	1052	1124	minutes	1652	1724	1754	1827	1852	1910	1928	1952	2024
88	Petersfield d.		|	0545	0645	0711	0737	0805	0836	0905	0936	1003	1034	1103	1135	past each	1704	1736	1806	1838	1903	1928	1939	2004	2036
107	Havant a.		0200s	0600	0659	0727	0752	0819	0850	0918	0951	1017	1051	1117	1151	hour until	1717	1749	1818	1852	1917	1943	1952	2017	2051
118	**Portsmouth** & Southsea 140 a.		0214s	0616	0716	0746	0808	0832	0903	0931	1004	1030	1104	1130	1204		1730	1803	1831	1907	1930	2003	2005	2030	2104
120	**Portsmouth** Harbour 140 a.		0219	0620	0721	0751	0813	0836	0908	0936	1008	1034	1108	1136	1208		1735	1809	1838	1914	1936	...	2010	2034	2108

	Ⓐ	Ⓐ	Ⓐ	Ⓐ	Ⓐ	Ⓐ	Ⓐ	Ⓐ	Ⓐ		⑥	⑥	⑥	⑥	⑥		⑥	⑥	⑥	⑥	⑥	⑥	⑥	⑥	⑥
London Waterloo 108 d.	2000	2030	2100	2130	2200	2230	2300	2330	2345	⑥	...	0520	0645	0730	0800		1930	2000	2030	2100	2130	2200	2230	2245	2315
Woking 108 d.	2025	2056	2125	2155	2225	2256	2327	2355	0013		...	0613	0713	0755	0825	and at	1955	2025	2055	2125	2155	2225	2255	2313	2343
Guildford d.	2034	2105	2134	2204	2234	2305*	2336	0004	0025		0515	0625	0725	0804	0834	the same	2004	2034	2104	2134	2204	2234	2304	2325	2352
Haslemere d.	2055	2123	2155	2225	2255	2325	0354	0022	0050		0530	0645	0745	0822	0852	minutes	2022	2052	2122	2155	2225	2255	2325	2350	0012
Petersfield d.	2106	2134	2206	2236	2306	2336	0005	0033	0106		0546	0702	0801	0833	0903	past each	2033	2103	2133	2206	2236	2306	2336	0006	0023
Havant a.	2118	2146	2218	2248	2318	2349	0018	0045	0121		0601	0722	0817	0851	0917	hour until	2051	2117	2145	2218	2248	2318	2348	0020	0036
Portsmouth & Southsea 140 a.	2131	2159	2231	2303	2331	0002	0031	0058	0138		0617	0737	0833	0903	0929		2103	2129	2158	2232	2302	2331	0002	0037	0049
Portsmouth Harbour 140 a.	2136	2203	2236	2307	2336	0007	0035	0103	...		0622	0743	0838	0908	0934		2108	2134	2203	2236	2308	2336	0007	0042	0054

	⑥		⑦	⑦	⑦	⑦	⑦	⑦	⑦		⑦	⑦	⑦	⑦	⑦	⑦	⑦	⑦	⑦	⑦	⑦	⑦	⑦	⑦	⑦
London Waterloo 108 d.	2345	⑦	...	0800	0830	0900	0930	1000	1030		1800	1830	1855	1900	1930	1955	2000	2030	2055	2100	2130	2200	2230	2300	2330
Woking 108 d.	0013		0732	0835	0904	0935	1004	1032	1102	and at	1832	1902	|	1932	2002	|	2032	2102	|	2132	2202	2232	2302	2332	0002
Guildford d.	0025		0741	0845	0914	0945	1015	1042	1112	the same	1842	1912	1934	1942	2012	2034	2042	2112	2134	2142	2212	2242	2312	2342	0012
Haslemere d.	0050		0807	0912	0932	1012	1032	1108	1130	minutes	1907	1930	|	2007	2030	|	2107	2130	|	2207	2230	2307	2330	0007	0029
Petersfield d.	0106		0823	0928	0943	1028	1043	1123	1141	past each	1923	1941	|	2023	2041	|	2123	2141	|	2223	2241	2323	2341	0023	0040
Havant a.	0121		0838	0943	0956	1043	1056	1140	1153	hour until	1940	1953	2007	2040	2053	2107	2140	2153	2207	2240	2253	2342	2353	0038	0053
Portsmouth & Southsea 140 a.	0137		0853	0958	1008	1058	1108	1155	1207		1954	2007	2022	2055	2107	2122	2155	2207	2222	2256	2307	2357	0006	0053	0105
Portsmouth Harbour 140 a.	...		0857	1004	1013	1104	1113	1200	1211		1958	2011	...	2100	2113	...	2200	2211	...	2300	2311	0001	0010	0058	0109

		Ⓐ	Ⓐ	Ⓐ	Ⓐ	Ⓐ	Ⓐ	Ⓐ		Ⓐ	Ⓐ	Ⓐ	Ⓐ	Ⓐ	Ⓐ	Ⓐ	Ⓐ		Ⓐ	Ⓐ	Ⓐ	Ⓐ	Ⓐ	Ⓐ	Ⓐ
Portsmouth Harbour 140 d.	Ⓐ	0425	0512	0519	...	0550	0615	...	...	0643	...	0714	0745	0815	0845	0915	0945	and at	1445	1515	...	1545	1615	...	1645
Portsmouth & Southsea 140 d.		0430	0517	0524	...	0555	0620	...	...	0648	...	0718	0750	0820	0850	0920	0950	the same	1450	1520	...	1550	1620	...	1650
Havant d.		0446	0530	0540	...	0611	0634	0640	...	0701	0710	0732	0804	0834	0904	0934	1004	minutes	1504	1534	1552	1604	1634	1659	1704
Petersfield d.		0503	0544	0557	0611	0628	0648	0654	...	0715	0724	0747	0818	0848	0918	0948	1018	past each	1518	1548	1606	1618	1648	1713	1718
Haslemere d.		0521	0557	0616	0629	0648	0702	0708	...	0735	0739	0801	0832	0902	0932	1001	1032	hour until	1532	1602	1624a	1637	1702	1732a	1737
Guildford d.		0550	0614	0633	0652	0707	0718	0728	...	0754	0802	0819	0853a	0919	0949	1018	1049		1549	1619	1647	1700	1719	1749	1800
Woking 108 a.		0600	0625	0641	0703	|	0725	0739	...	|	0813	0826	|	0927	0959	1025	1057	♥	1557	1626	1657	1711	1726	1758	1811
London Waterloo 108 a.		0630	0651	0712	0734	0740	0756	0807	...	0831	0841	0854	0930	0955	1029	1054	1123		1624	1653	1727	1741	1754	1827	1843

	Ⓐ	Ⓐ	Ⓐ	Ⓐ	Ⓐ	Ⓐ		Ⓐ	Ⓐ	Ⓐ	Ⓐ	Ⓐ	Ⓐ		⑥	⑥	⑥	⑥	⑥		⑥	⑥	⑥	⑥	⑥
Portsmouth Harbour 140 d.	1715	1745	1815	1845	1915	1945	...	2015	2045	2115	...	2219	2319	⑥	0443	0519	0619	0645	0715	and at	2015	2045	2119	2219	2319
Portsmouth & Southsea 140 d.	1719	1750	1820	1850	1920	1950	...	2020	2050	2120	2124	2224	2324		0448	0524	0624	0650	0720	the same	2020	2048	2124	2224	2324
Havant d.	1734	1804	1834	1904	1934	2004	...	2034	2104	2134	2140	2241	2340		0504	0540	0640	0704	0734	minutes	2034	2104	2140	2241	2340
Petersfield d.	1748	1818	1848	1918	1948	2018	...	2048	2118	2148	2157	2257	2357		0520	0557	0657	0718	0748	past each	2048	2118	2157	2257	2357
Haslemere d.	1802	1832	1902	1932	2002	2032	...	2102	2132	2202	2215	2315	0015		0539	0615	0715	0732	0802	hour until	2102	2132	2215	2315	0015
Guildford d.	1819	1853	1919	1949	2019	2049	...	2119	2149	2219	2239	2339	0037		0602	0634	0734	0749	0819		2119	2149	2239	2339	0037
Woking 108 a.	|	1903	|	1957	2026	2059	...	2126	2157	2226	2249	2349	...		0611	0644	0744	0757	0826	♣	2126	2157	2249	2349	...
London Waterloo 108 a.	1859	1929	1959	2024	2051	2129	...	2153	2227	2252	2319	0033	...		0640	0713	0813	0823	0851		2151	2227	2319	0032	...

		⑦	⑦	⑦	⑦	⑦	⑦	⑦		⑦	⑦	⑦	⑦	⑦	⑦	⑦	⑦	⑦	⑦	⑦		⑦	⑦	⑦
Portsmouth Harbour 140 d.	⑦	0648	0732	0748	0832	0848	0932	0948		1532	1548	...	1632	1648	...	1732	1748	...	1832	1848		2148	2232	2248
Portsmouth & Southsea 140 d.		0653	0737	0753	0837	0853	0937	0953	and at	1537	1553	1626	1637	1653	1726	1737	1753	1826	1837	1853	and at	2153	2237	2252
Havant d.		0707	0750	0807	0850	0907	0950	1007	the same	1550	1607	1640	1650	1707	1740	1750	1807	1840	1850	1907	the same	2207	2250	2307
Petersfield d.		0724	0804	0824	0904	0924	1004	1024	minutes	1604	1624	|	1704	1724	|	1804	1824	|	1904	1924	minutes	2224	2304	2324
Haslemere d.		0742	0817	0842	0917	0942	1017	1042	past each	1617	1642	|	1717	1742	|	1817	1842	|	1917	1942	past each	2242	2317	2342
Guildford d.		0805	0835	0905	0935	1004	1035	1105	hour until	1635	1705	1716	1735	1805	1816	1835	1905	1916	1935	2005	hour until	2305	2335	0005
Woking 108 a.		0813	0842	0915	0942	1015	1042	1114		1642	1713	|	1742	1813	|	1842	1913	|	1942	2013		2313	2342	0013
London Waterloo 108 a.		0850	0916	0949	1016	1046	1114	1144		1714	1744	1756	1814	1844	1856	1914	1944	1956	2015	2044		2344	0014	...

– Arrives 4–6 minutes earlier.

♣ – The 1115, 1215, 1315, 1415 and 1515 departures from Portsmouth Harbour arrive at London Waterloo 6 minutes later than shown.

♥ – Timings may vary by ± 3 minutes.

106 LONDON - SOUTHAMPTON - BOURNEMOUTH - WEYMOUTH

🍷 on most trains. SW

km			②–⑤	Ⓐ	Ⓐ	Ⓐ	Ⓐ	Ⓐ	Ⓐ	Ⓐ	Ⓐ	Ⓐ	Ⓐ	Ⓐ	Ⓐ		Ⓐ	Ⓐ	Ⓐ	Ⓐ	Ⓐ	Ⓐ	Ⓐ	Ⓐ	Ⓐ	Ⓐ	Ⓐ
0	**London** Waterloo . 108 d.	Ⓐ	0005	0105	...	...	...	0530	...	0630	0703	0735	0805	0835	0905		1505	1535	1605	1635	1705	1735	1805	1835	1905	1935	2005
39	Woking 108 d.		0037	0149	...	...	...	0601	...	0657	0730	0800	|	0900	|	and	|	1600	|	1700u	|	|	|	|	|	2000	|
77	Basingstoke ... 108 114 d.		0056	0216s	...	...	0540	0621	...	0718	0750	0820	0849	|	0949	at	1549	|	1649	|	|	|	|	|	1949	|	2049
107	Winchester 114 d.		0113	0233s	...	...	0559	0638	...	0734	0806	0837	0905	0933	1005	the	1605	1633	1705	1733	1800	1830	1900	1930	2005	2033	2105
120	**Southampton** ✈ ... 114 d.		0126	0246s	...	...	0613	0653	...	0749	0815	0851	0914	0942	1014	same	1614	1642	1714	1742	1810	1839	1909	1939	2014	2042	2115
128	**Southampton** Cent 114 d.		0137	0257	...	...	0626	0701	0719	0759	0827	0900	0925	0951	1024	minutes	1624	1653r	1724	1753r	1821r	1851r	1921	1951r	2025r	2051	2125
149	Brockenhurst 114 d.		0153s	...	...	0615	0645	0718	0744	0820	0846	0914	0939	1005	1038	past	1638	1709	1738	1808	|	|	|	|	2042	2108	2142
174	**Bournemouth** 114 d.		0215	...	0611	0644	0712	0746	0811	0847	0914	0933r	1004	1024r	1104r	each	1709r	1725	1809r	1825	1850	1921	1950	2022	2101r	2127r	2210
183	Poole d.		...	...	0624	0657	0725	0758	0824	0900	0926	0945	1014	1037	1114	hour	1719	1738	1819	1838	1903	1935	2003	2035	2113	2139	2222
193	Wareham 114a d.		...	...	0638	0711	0739	0812	0838	0912	0940	0957	1028	1049	1128	until	1733	1750	1833	1850	1917	1947	2017	2047	2126	2151	...
219	Dorchester South. 114a d.		...	...	0658	0731	0759	0833	0858	0933	1001	1013	1054	1105	1149		1753	1809	1857	1909	1937	2004	2037	2104	2147	2212	...
230	**Weymouth** .... 114a 140 a.		...	...	0709	0742	0810	0844	0909	0944	1012	1023	1106	1116	1202		1806	1818	1908	1925	1950	2015	2050	2115	2159	2223	...

	Ⓐ	Ⓐ	Ⓐ	Ⓐ	Ⓐ	Ⓐ		⑥	⑥	⑥	⑥	⑥	⑥	⑥	⑥	⑥	⑥	⑥	⑥		⑥	⑥	⑥	⑥	⑥	⑥	⑥
London Waterloo .. 108 d.	2035	2105	2135	2205	2235	2305	⑥	0005	0105	...	...	...	0530	...	0630	...	0735	0805	0835		1835	1905	1935	2005	2035	2105	2135
Woking 108 d.	2100	|	2200	|	2300	2333		0037	0142	...	...	...	0601	...	0657	...	0800	|	0900	and	1900	|	2000	|	2100	2132	2200
Basingstoke .... 108 114 d.	|	2149	|	2249	|	2353		0056	0209s	...	...	...	0621	...	0718	...	0821	0849	|	at	|	1949	|	2049	|	2151	|
Winchester 114 d.	2133	2205	2233	2305	2333	0013		0113	0226s	...	...	...	0641	...	0734	...	0838	0905	0933	the	1933	2005	2033	2105	2133	2207	2233
Southampton ✈ .... 114 d.	2142	2218	2242	2319	2342	0028		0126	0239s	...	...	...	0656	...	0748	...	0851	0914	0942	same	1942	2014	2042	2114	2142	2221	2242
Southampton Cent 114 d.	2151	2227	2251	2330	2351	0038		0137	0249	...	...	0621	0705	0721	0800r	0817	0900	0924	0951	minutes	1951	2024	2051	2124	2151	2230	2251
Brockenhurst 114 d.	2205	2247	2306	2349	0005	0054s		0153s	...	...	0615	0640r	0722	0740	0817	0838	0917	0938	1005	past	2005	2038	2105	2143	2205	2249	2305
Bournemouth 114 d.	2224r	2316	2327r	0016	0022	0118		0215	...	0611	0644	0711r	0749	0811r	0844	0909r	0944	1004r	1024r	each	2024r	2104r	2124r	2210	2224r	2317	2327
Poole d.	2237	2329	2340	0028	0035	0130		...	...	0624	0657	0724	0802	0824	0857	0922	0957	1014	1037	hour	2037	2114	2137	2223	2237	2329	2340
Wareham 114a d.	2249	...	2351	...	...	...		...	...	0638	0711	0738	0813	0838	0909	0935	1009	1028	1049	until	2049	2126	2149	...	2249	...	2351
Dorchester South.. 114a d.	2309	...	0012	...	...	...		...	...	0658	0731	0758	0834	0858	0929	0956	1027	1049	1105		2105	2147	2209	...	2309	...	0012
Weymouth ..... 114a 140 a.	2320	...	0023	...	...	...		...	...	0709	0742	0809	0845	0909	0940	1007	1035	1100	1116		2113	2158	2220	...	2320	...	0023

	⑥	⑥	⑥		⑦	⑦	⑦	⑦	⑦		⑦	⑦	⑦		⑦	⑦	⑦	⑦	⑦		⑦	⑦	⑦	⑦	⑦	⑦
London Waterloo .. 108 d.	2205	2235	2305	⑦	0005	0105	...	...	...	...	0751	0835	0854		1435	1454	1535	1605	1635		2005	2035	2105	2135	2205	2305
Woking 108 d.	2232	2300	2332		0037	0149	...	...	...	...	0828	0909	0928	and	1507	1528	1607	1637	1707	and	2037	2107	2137	2207	2237	2337
Basingstoke .... 108 114 d.	2252	|	2352		0056	0216s	...	0748	...	...	0848	0929	0948	at	1528	1548	1628	1657	1728	at	2057	2128	2157	2228	2257	2357
Winchester 114 d.	2308	2333	0011		0113	0233s	...	0807	...	...	0908	0946	1008	the	1544	1608	1644	1714	1744	the	2114	2144	2214	2244	2314	0014
Southampton ✈ .... 114 d.	2322	2342	0024		0126	0246s	...	0825	...	...	0927	0955	1027	same	1553	1627	1653	1727	1753	same	2127	2153	2227	2253	2327	0028
Southampton Cent 114 d.	2330	2351	0035		0137	0256	...	0834	0903	...	0935	1003	1035	minutes	1603	1635	1703	1736	1803	minutes	2136	2203	2236	2303	2336	0040
Brockenhurst 114 d.	2349	0005	0051s		0153s	...	...	0855	0917	...	0957	1018	1057	past	1617	1657	1717	1757	1817	past	2157	2217	2257	2317	2355	0056s
Bournemouth 114 d.	0016	0022	0115		0215	...	0839	0925r	0939r	...	1024	1039r	1124	each	1639r	1724	1739r	1824	1839r	each	2225	2239r	2324	2339r	0022	0120
Poole d.	0030	0035	0127		...	...	0851	0934	0951	...	1033	1051	1133	hour	1651	1733	1751	1833	1851	hour	2234	2251	2333	2351	0034	0132
Wareham 114a d.	...	...	...		...	...	0903	...	1003	...	...	1103	...	until	1703	...	1803	...	1903	until	...	2303	...	0003	...	...
Dorchester South.. 114a d.	...	...	...		...	...	0924	...	1024	...	...	1124	...		1724	...	1824	...	1924		...	2325	...	0024	...	...
Weymouth ..... 114a 140 a.	...	...	...		...	...	0935	...	1035	...	...	1135	...		1735	...	1835	...	1936		...	2336	...	0036	...	...

		Ⓐ	Ⓐ	Ⓐ	Ⓐ	Ⓐ	Ⓐ	Ⓐ	Ⓐ		Ⓐ	Ⓐ	Ⓐ	Ⓐ	Ⓐ	Ⓐ	Ⓐ	Ⓐ		Ⓐ	Ⓐ	Ⓐ	Ⓐ	Ⓐ	Ⓐ	Ⓐ	Ⓐ
Weymouth ... 114a 140 a.	Ⓐ	...	...	...	...	...	0555	...	0625	...	0655	...	0725	0755	0820	0903	0920	1003		1703	1720	1803	1820	1903	1920	2003	2010
Dorchester South. 114a d.		...	...	...	...	...	0607	...	0637	...	0707	...	0737	0807	0833	0913	0933	1013	and	1713	1733	1813	1833	1913	1937	2013	2022
Wareham 114a d.		...	...	...	...	...	0627	...	0657	...	0727	...	0757	0827	0853	0928	0953	1028	at	1728	1753	1828	1853	1928	1957	2028	2042
Poole d.		...	0500	0545	0611	...	0641	...	0711	...	0741	0755	0811	0841	0907	0940	1007	1040	the	1740	1807	1840	1907	1940	2009	2040	2054
Bournemouth 114 d.		...	0515	0557	0626	0634	0656	0700	0726	...	0759r	0810	0825	0859r	0918	0959r	1022r	1059r	same	1759r	1822r	1859r	1922r	1959r	2022	2059r	2112
Brockenhurst 114 d.		...	0538	0614	|	0703	|	0723	|	...	0815	0841	0852	0915	0941	1015	1045	1115	minutes	1815	1845	1915	1945	2015	2045	2115	2140
Southampton Cent 114 d.		0520	0555	0630	0700r	0730j	0730r	0738r	0800r	...	0830	0900	*0917*	0930	1000r	1030	1100	1130	past	1830	1900	1930	2000	2030	2100	2130	2200
Southampton ✈ .... 114 d.		0528	0603	0638	0708	0738	0738	0750	0808	...	0838	0908	*0924*	0938	1008	1038	1108	1138	each	1838	1908	1938	2008	2038	2108	2138	2208
Winchester 114 d.		0542	0618	0648	0718	0748	0748	0806	0818	...	0848	0918	*0933*	0948	1018	1048	1118	1148	hour	1848	1918	1948	2018	2048	2118	2148	2218
Basingstoke ..... 108 114 a.		0601	0635	|	|	|	|	0822	0834	...	|	0935	*0947*	|	1034	|	1135	|	until	|	1934	|	2034	|	2134	|	2234
Woking 108 a.		|	0654	|	|	|	|	|	0853	...	0922	0954	...	1020	|	1119	|	1220		1925	|	2021	|	2121	2153	2223	2254
London Waterloo ... 108 a.		0646	0724	0748	0816	0850	0850	0912	0925	...	0951	1023	...	1049	1120	1149	1223	1249		1952	2023	2049	2127	2151	2222	2250	2323

	Ⓐ	Ⓐ	Ⓐ	Ⓐ		⑥	⑥	⑥	⑥	⑥	⑥	⑥	⑥	⑥		⑥	⑥	⑥	⑥	⑥	⑥	⑥	⑥	⑥	⑥	⑥	⑥
Weymouth ... 114a 140 a.	...	2110	2210	2310	⑥	...	...	...	0542	0620	0655	0720	0803	0820		1703	1720	1803	1820	1903	1920	...	2010	...	2110	2210	2310
Dorchester South. 114a d.	...	2122	2222	2322		...	...	...	0552	0633	0707	0733	0813	0833	and	1713	1733	1813	1833	1913	1933	...	2022	...	2122	2222	2322
Wareham 114a d.	...	2142	2242	2342		...	...	...	0610	0653	0727	0753	0828	0853	at	1728	1753	1828	1853	1928	1953	...	2042	...	2142	2242	2342
Poole d.	...	2154	2254	2354		...	...	0528	0624	0707	0741	0807	0840	0907	the	1740	1807	1840	1907	1940	2007	...	2054	...	2154	2254	2354
Bournemouth 114 d.	...	2212r	2312r	0003		...	...	0542	0642r	0722r	0759r	0822r	0859r	0922r	same	1759r	1822r	1859r	1922r	1959r	2022r	2059	2112r	...	2212r	2312r	0003
Brockenhurst 114 d.	...	2240	2340	...		...	...	0610	0710	0744	0815	0845	0915	0945	minutes	1815	1845	1915	1945	2015	2045	2115	2140	...	2240	2340	...
Southampton Cent 114 d.	2230	2300	2359	...		0512	0600	0630	0730	0800	0830	0900	0930	1000	past	1830	1900	1930	2000	2030	2100	2130	2200	2230	2300	2359	...
Southampton ✈ .... 114 d.	2238	2308	0010	...		0520	0608	0638	0738	0808	0838	0908	0938	1008	each	1838	1908	1938	2008	2038	2108	2138	2208	2238	2308	0010	...
Winchester 114 d.	2255	2324	...	...		0534	0623	0652	0748	0818	0848	0918	0948	1018	hour	1848	1918	1948	2018	2048	2118	2148	2218	2256	2325	...	...
Basingstoke ..... 108 114 a.	2311	2343	...	...		0550	0639	0708	|	0834	|	0934	|	1034	until	|	1934	|	2034	|	2134	|	2234	2312	2343	...	...
Woking 108 a.	2331	0018	...	...		0628	0658	0727	0821	|	0919	|	1019	|		1919	|	2020	|	2120	|	2219	2253	2332	0018	...	...
London Waterloo ... 108 a.	0008	0104	...	...		0705	0729	0753	0849	0920	0949	1021	1051	1121		1949	2021	2049	2121	2149	2222	2249	2322	0006	0104	...	...

		⑦	⑦	⑦	⑦		⑦	⑦	⑦	⑦		⑦	⑦	⑦	⑦	⑦		⑦	⑦	⑦	⑦	⑦		⑦	⑦	⑦
Weymouth ... 114a 140 a.	⑦	...	...	...	0748	...	...	0848	...	0948		...	1248	...	1348	...		1748	...	1848	...	1958	...	2058	2158	2258
Dorchester South. 114a d.		...	...	...	0800	...	...	0900	...	1000	and	...	1300	...	1400	...	and	1800	...	1900	...	2010	...	2110	2210	2310
Wareham 114a d.		...	...	...	0820	...	...	0920	...	1020	at	...	1320	...	1420	...	at	1820	...	1920	...	2030	...	2130	2230	2330
Poole d.		...	0650	0750	0832	...	0855	0932	0955	1032	the	1255	1332	1355	1432	1455	the	1832	1855	1932	1955	2050j	...	2150j	2250j	2350
Bournemouth 114 d.		...	0706r	0806r	0850r	...	0906	0950r	1006	1050r	same	1306	1350r	1406	1450r	1506	same	1850r	1906	1950r	2006	2106	...	2208r	2308r	0003
Brockenhurst 114 d.		...	0734	0834	0909	...	0934	1009	1034	1109	minutes	1334	1409	1434	1509	1534	minutes	1909	1934	2009	2034	2134	...	2236	2336	...
Southampton Cent 114 d.		0655	0755	0855	0925	...	0955	1025	1055	1125	past	1355	1425	1455	1525	1555	past	1925	1955	2025	2055	2155	...	2255	2354	...
Southampton ✈ .... 114 d.		0703	0803	0903	0933	...	1003	1033	1103	1133	each	1403	1433	1503	1533	1603	each	1933	2003	2033	2103	2203	...	2303	...	...
Winchester 114 d.		0723	0823	0923	0942	...	1023	1042	1123	1142	hour	1423	1442	1523	1542	1617	hour	1942	2017	2042	2117	2217	...	2323	...	...
Basingstoke ..... 108 114 a.		0742	0842	0942	0958	...	1042	1058	1142	1158	until	1442	1458	1542	1558	1633	until	1958	2033	2058	2133	2234	...	2342	...	...
Woking 108 a.		0802	0902	1002	1019	...	1102	1118	1202	1218		1502	1518	1602	1618	1653		2018	2053	2118	2153	2254	...	0002	...	...
London Waterloo ... 108 a.		0846	0941	1039	1050	...	1139	1150	1237	1249		1537	1549	1637	1649	1725		2049	2124	2149	2224	2324	...	0033	...	...

Brockenhurst - Lymington Pier (for ⛴ to Isle of Wight).
Journey 11 minutes. Trains call at Lymington Town 6 minutes later:
Ⓐ: 0559 and every 30 minutes until 0929, 1012 and every 30 minutes until 1812, 1848 and every 30 minutes until 2218.
⑥: 0612, 0642 and every 30 minutes until 2112, 2148, 2218.
⑦: 0859, 0929 and every 30 minutes until 2059, 2129, 2159.

Lymington Pier - Brockenhurst.
Journey 11 minutes. Trains call at Lymington Town 2 minutes later:
Ⓐ: 0614 and every 30 minutes until 0944, 1027 and every 30 minutes until 1827, 1903 and every 30 minutes until 2203, 2236.
⑥: 0627, 0657 and every 30 minutes until 2127, 2203, 2236.
⑦: 0914, 0944 and every 30 minutes until 2114, 2144, 2214.

j – Arrives 8–9 minutes earlier.
r – Arrives 4–5 minutes earlier.
s – Calls to set down only.
u – Calls to pick up only.

☛ For ⛴ services Portsmouth / Poole – Jersey / Guernsey / St Malo and v.v., see Table **2100**.

107 PORTSMOUTH - RYDE - SHANKLIN

2nd class IL

Through fares including ferry travel are available. Allow 10 minutes for connections between trains and ferries. Operator: Wightlink ✆ 0333 999 7333. www.wightlink.co.u

Portsmouth Harbour - Ryde Pierhead: ⛴
0515Ⓐ, 0615⚒, 0715 and hourly until 1815, 1920, 2020, 2120, 2245.

Ryde Pierhead - Portsmouth Harbour Journey time: ± 22 minute
0547Ⓐ, 0647⚒, 0747 and hourly until 2147, 2310.

Additional services operate on Ⓐ and on public holidays.

Ryde Pierhead - Shanklin: Trains call at **Sandown** 18 minutes later *14 km*
⚒: 0549, 0607, 0649, 0707, 0749, 0807, 0849, 0907, 0949, 1007, 1049*, 1107, 1149*, 1207*, 1249*, 1307*, 1349, 1407, 1449*, 1507*, 1549*, 1607*, 1649, 1707, 1749, 1807, 1849, 1907, 1949, 2007, 2049, 2149.
⑦: 0649, 0749, 0849, 0907, 0949, 1007, 1049*, 1107, 1149*, 1207, 1249*, 1307*, 1349, 1407, 1449*, 1507*, 1549*, 1607*, 1649, 1707, 1749, 1807, 1849, 1907, 1949, 2049, 2149.

Shanklin - Ryde Pierhead: Trains call at **Sandown** 6 minutes later Journey time: ± 24 minute
⚒: 0618, 0638, 0718, 0738, 0818, 0838, 0918, 0938, 1018, 1038*, 1118, 1138*, 1218*, 1238*, 1318*, 1338, 1418, 1438*, 1518*, 1538*, 1618*, 1638, 1718, 1738, 1818, 1838, 1918, 1938, 2018, 2118, 2238.
⑦: 0718, 0818, 0838 0918, 0938, 1018, 1038, 1118, 1138, 1218*, 1318*, 1338, 1418, 1438*, 1518*, 1538*, 1618*, 1638, 1718, 1738, 1818, 1918, 1938, 2018, 2118, 2238

* – Also calls at Smallbrook Junction (connection with **Isle of Wight Steam Railway**, see note △) 9 minutes from Ryde / 15 minutes from Shanklin, when Steam Railway is operating.

△ – **Isle of Wight Steam Railway** (🚂 Smallbrook Junction - Wootton: *9 km*). ✆ 01983 882204. www.iwsteamrailway.co.uk

SW 🍷 on most services London - Axminster and v.v.

LONDON - SALISBURY - EXETER

km			Ⓐ	Ⓐ	Ⓐ	Ⓐ	Ⓐ	Ⓐ	Ⓐ	Ⓐ	ⒶB	Ⓐ	Ⓐ		Ⓐ	Ⓐ	ⒶB	Ⓐ	Ⓐ	Ⓐ	Ⓐ	Ⓐ	Ⓐ	ⒶB	ⒶW	Ⓐ	Ⓐ
0	**London** Waterloo . 106 d.	Ⓐ	...	...	...	...	0635	0710	0750	0820	0920	0950	1020	...	1120	1150	1220	1250	1320	1350	1420	1520	1550	1620	1650	1720	1750
39	Woking .... 106 d.		...	...	...	...	0702	0739	0817	0846	0946	1016	1046	...	1146	1216	1246	1316	1346	1416	1446	1546	1616	1646u	1716u	1746u	|
77	Basingstoke .... 106 d.		...	...	...	...	0724	0800	0838	0907	1007	1038	1107	...	1207	1238	1307	1338	1407	1438	1507	1607	1638	1707	1738	1807	1838
07	Andover .... d.		...	...	...	...	0746	0822	0900	0924	1024	1100	1124	...	1224	1300	1324	1400	1424	1500	1524	1624	1700	1730	1800	1830	1900
34	**Salisbury** .... a.		...	...	...	...	0808	0843	0920	0943	1042	1119	1142	...	1243	1320	1343	1420	1442	1520	1542	1644	1720	1750	1820	1850	1920
34	**Salisbury** .... 140 d.		...	...	0607	0738	0808	0847	0923	0947	1047	1123	1147	...	1247	1324	1347	1424	1447	1523	1547	1647	1723	1754	1823	1854	1926
69	Gillingham .... d.		...	0551	0642	0811	0837	0917	|	1017	1117	1152	1217	...	1317	1352	1417	|	1517	1552t	1617	1717	1752t	1818	1852t	1919	1956t
90	Sherborne .... d.		...	0606	0657	0826	...	0932	◧	1032	1132	1207	1232	...	1332	1407	1432	◧	1532	1607	1632	1732	1807	1833	1907	1934	2011
97	**Yeovil** Junction .... a.		...	0611	0703	0832	...	0938	|	1038	1138	1212	1238	...	1338	1412	1438	|	1538	1613	1638	1738	1813	1839	1912	1940	2016
97	**Yeovil** Junction .... d.		...	0615	0707	0839	...	0942	|	1039	1139	1219	1239	...	1339	1418	1439	|	1539	1620	1639	1739	...	1840	1917	1941	2021
00	**Yeovil** Pen Mill . 140 a.		...	|	|	|	...	|	1035	|	|	1224	|	...	|	1425	|	1535	|	1627	|	|	...	|	1925	|	2028
11	Crewkerne .... d.		...	0624	0716	0849	...	0951	...	1049	1149	...	1249	...	1349	...	1449	...	1549	▬	1649	1749	...	1850	...	1950	...
33	Axminster .... d.		0552	0656c	0737	0903	...	1005	...	1103	1203	...	1303	...	1403	...	1503	...	1603	Ⓐ	1703	1803	...	1904	...	2004	...
49	Honiton .... d.		0607	0712t	0753t	0916	...	1017	...	1116	1216	...	1316	...	1416	...	1515	...	1616	1707	1716	1816	...	1918	...	2017	...
77	**Exeter** St Davids .... △ a.		0635	0742	0821	0944	...	1043	...	1143	1243	...	1343	...	1443	...	1543	...	1643	1733	1742	1844	...	1944	...	2044	...

	ⒶC	Ⓐ	ⒶB	Ⓐ	Ⓐ	Ⓐ	①–④	⑤		⑥	⑥	⑥	⑥	⑥D	⑥	⑥	⑥B	⑥	⑥	⑥B	⑥	⑥	⑥	⑥B	⑥	⑥	⑥B
ondon Waterloo . 106 d.	1820	1850	1920	2020	2120	2220	2340	2340	⑥	...	...	...	...	0635	0710	0820	0920	1020	1120	1220	1320	1420	1520	1620	1720	1820	1920
/oking .... 106 d.	1846u	1919u	1946u	2046	2146	2249	0007	0007		...	...	...	...	0701	0736	0846	0946	1046	1146	1246	1346	1446	1546	1646	1746	1846	1946
asingstoke .... 106 d.	1907	1939	2007	2107	2207	2311	0029	0029		...	...	...	...	0723	0759	0907	1007	1107	1207	1307	1407	1507	1607	1707	1807	1907	2007
ndover .... d.	1930	2001	2030	2129	2224	2329	0051	0051		...	...	...	...	0745	0821	0924	1024	1124	1224	1324	1424	1524	1624	1724	1824	1924	2024
alisbury .... a.	1950	2021	2050	2150	2240	2346	0111	0111		...	...	...	...	0805	0842	0942	1042	1142	1242	1342	1442	1542	1642	1742	1843	1943	2043
alisbury .... 140 d.	1954	2025	2054	2206	2250	2358	...	0114		...	...	0615	0745	0810	0847	0947	1047	1147	1247	1347	1447	1547	1647	1747	1847	1947	2047
illingham .... d.	2021	2052	2120	2235	2319s	0022	...	0137s		...	...	0642	0814t	0900a	0917	1017	1117	1217	1317	1417	1517	1617	1717	1817	1919	2017	2117
herborne .... d.	2036	2107	2135	2250	2335s	...	...	0153s		...	...	0657	0829	0915	0932	1032	1132	1232	1332	1432	1532	1632	1732	1832	1934	2032	2132
eovil Junction .... a.	2041	2113	2140	2255	2341	...	...	0159		...	...	0703	0835	0920	0938	1038	1138	1238	1338	1438	1538	1638	1738	1838	1939	2038	2138
eovil Junction .... d.	2042	2117	2142	2257	...	...	...	...		...	0615	0707	0839	0935	0939	1039	1139	1239	1339	1439	1539	1639	1739	1839	1941	2039	2139
Yeovil Pen Mill .. 140 a.	|	2124	|	|	...	...	...	...		...	|	|	|	0945	|	|	|	|	|	|	|	|	|	|	|	|	|
rewkerne .... d.	2052	...	2151	2306	...	...	...	...		...	0624	0716	0849	...	0949	1049	1149	1249	1349	1449	1549	1649	1749	1849	1950	2049	2149
xminster .... d.	2106	...	2205	2320	...	...	...	...		0552	0656c	0738	0903	...	1003	1103	1203	1303	1403	1503	1603	1703	1803	1903	2005	2103	2203
oniton .... d.	2118	...	2218	2333	...	...	...	...		0607	0712t	0754t	0916	...	1016	1116	1216	1316	1416	1516	1616	1716	1816	1916	2016	2117	2217
xeter St Davids .... △ a.	2147	...	2247	0001	...	...	...	...		0635	0742	0822	0944	...	1042	1142	1242	1342	1442	1542	1642	1741	1847	1942	2045	2142	2245

	⑥	⑥	⑥	⑥		⑦	⑦	⑦	⑦B	⑦	⑦	⑦B	⑦	⑦	⑦	⑦	⑦	⑦	⑦B	⑦	⑦	⑦	⑦	⑦	⑦e	⑦	⑦
ondon Waterloo . 106 d.	2020	2120	2220	2340	⑦	...	...	0815	0915	1015	1115	1215	1315	1415	1515	1615	1715	1745	1815	1845	1915	1945	2015	2045	2115	2215	2335
/oking .... 106 d.	2046	2149	2249	0008		...	...	0847	0948	1046	1146	1246	1346	1446	1546	1646	1746	|	1846	|	1946	|	2046	|	2146	2246	0008
asingstoke .... 106 d.	2107	2213	2313	0028		...	0805	0908	1009	1107	1207	1307	1407	1507	1607	1707	1807	|	1907	|	2007	|	2107	|	2207	2307	0041
ndover .... d.	2124	2230	2335	0050		...	0827	0930	1028	1129	1226	1329	1426	1529	1626	1729	1826	1849	1929	1949	2026	2049	2129	2149	2226	2329	0103
alisbury .... a.	2144	2248	2354	0110		...	0846	0946	1048	1145	1246	1345	1446	1545	1646	1745	1846	1905	1945	2005	2046	2105	2145	2205	2247	2348	0122
alisbury .... 140 d.	2149	2255	...	...		0706	0851	0951	1051	1151	1251	1351	1451	1551	1651	1751	1851	...	1951	...	2051	...	2151	...	2252	...	...
illingham .... d.	2219	2320s	...	...		0731	0921	1021	1121	1221	1321	1421	1521	1621	1721	1821	1921	...	2021	...	2121	...	|	...	2322	...	...
herborne .... d.	2234	2335s	...	...		0746	0936	1036	1136	1236	1336	1436	1536	1636	1736	1836	1936	...	2036	...	2136	...	2236	...	2337	...	...
eovil Junction .... a.	2239	2342	...	...		0751	0941	1041	1142	1241	1341	1441	1541	1641	1741	1841	1941	...	2041	...	2141	...	2242	...	2343	...	...
eovil Junction .... d.	2240	...	...	...		0753	0943	1043	1143	1243	1343	1443	1543	1643	1743	1843	1943	...	2043	...	2143	...	...	...	2344	...	...
Yeovil Pen Mill .. 140 a.	|	...	...	...		|	|	|	|	|	|	|	|	|	|	|	|	...	|	...	|	...	...	...	|	...	...
rewkerne .... d.	2250	...	...	...		0802	0952	1052	1152	1252	1352	1452	1552	1652	1752	1852	1952	...	2052	...	2152	...	...	...	2354	...	...
xminster .... d.	2304	...	...	...		0816	1006	1106	1206	1306	1406	1506	1606	1706	1806	1906	2006	...	2106	...	2206	...	...	...	0008	...	...
oniton .... d.	2315	...	...	...		0831	1018	1118	1218	1318	1418	1518	1618	1718	1818	1918	2018	...	2118	...	2218	...	...	...	0020	...	...
xeter St Davids .... △ a.	...	...	...	...		0859	1045	1145	1245	1345	1445	1545	1645	1745	1845	1945	2045	...	2146	...	2247	...	...	...	0046	...	...

		Ⓐ	Ⓐ	Ⓐ	Ⓐ	Ⓐ	Ⓐ	Ⓐ	Ⓐ	Ⓐ	ⒶB	Ⓐ	Ⓐ	Ⓐ	Ⓐ	Ⓐ	Ⓐ	ⒶB	Ⓐ	Ⓐ	Ⓐ	Ⓐ	Ⓐ	ⒶB	Ⓐ	Ⓐ	Ⓐ
xeter St Davids .... ▽ d.	Ⓐ	...	...	0510	...	...	...	0641	0725	...	0823	...	0925	...	1025	...	1125	1225	...	1325	...	1425	...	1525	...	...	1625
oniton .... d.		...	...	0541	0619	...	...	0712	0752	...	0855	...	0955	...	1055	...	1155	1255	...	1355	...	1455	...	1555	...	...	1655
xminster .... d.		...	...	0552	0630	...	...	0723	0803	...	0906	...	1006	...	1106	...	1206	1306	...	1406	...	1506	...	1606	...	...	1706
rewkerne .... d.		...	...	0605	0643	...	...	0736	0816	...	0919	...	1019	...	1119	...	1219	1319	...	1419	...	1519	...	1619	...	...	1720
Yeovil Pen Mill .. 140 d.		...	0541	|	|	0655	...	|	|	...	|	...	|	1045	|	...	|	|	1344	|	1500	|	1544	|	1635	1653	|
eovil Junction .... a.		...	0546	0614	0652	|	...	0745	0825	...	0927	...	1027	|	1127	...	1227	1327	1349	1427	|	1527	1549	1628	1640	|	1727
eovil Junction .... d.		0514	0550	0621	0653	|	0720	0750	0829	...	0929	0953	1029	|	1129	1153	1229	1329	1353	1429	1453f	1529	1553	1629	...	1646f	1729
herborne .... d.		0520	0556	0627	0700	◧	0726	0756	0835	...	0935	0959	1035	◧	1135	1159	1235	1335	1359	1435	◧	1535	1559	1635	...	◧	1735
illingham .... d.		0536	0612	0643	0715	|	0742	0812	0851	0918	0951	1018	1051	|	1151	1218	1251	1351	1418	1451	|	1551	1618	1651	...	|	1751
alisbury .... 140 a.		0601	0639	0708	0740	0810	0806	0837	0916	0943	1016	1043	1116	1210	1217	1243	1316	1417	1443	1516	1613	1616	1643	1716	...	1817	1821
alisbury .... d.		0606	0645	0715	0745	0815	0815	0847	0921	0947	1021	1047	1121	1221	1221	1247	1321	1421	1447	1521	1621	1621	1647	1721	...	1826	1826
ndover .... d.		0626	0705	0735	0805	0835	0835	0906	0938	1006	1038	1106	1138	1238	1238	1306	1338	1438	1506	1538	1638	1638	1706	1738	...	1843	1843
asingstoke .... 106 a.		0649	0728	0758	0828	0858	0858	0928	0955	1028	1055	1128	1155	1255	1255	1328	1355	1455	1528	1555	1655	1655	1728	1755	...	1900	1900
oking .... 106 a.		|	|	0818	0848	0918	0918	0949	1015	1049	1115	1149	1215	1315	1315	1349	1415	1515	1549	1615	1715	1715	1749	1815	...	1920	1920
ondon Waterloo . 106 a.		0736	0814	0848	0917	0951	0951	1019	1049	1119	1149	1219	1249	1349	1349	1419	1449	1549	1619	1649	1749	1749	1816	1849	...	1950	1950

	Ⓐ	Ⓐ	Ⓐ	ⒶB	Ⓐ	Ⓐ	Ⓐ	Ⓐ	Ⓐ		⑥	⑥	⑥C	⑥	⑥	⑥B	⑥	⑥	⑥E	⑥	⑥B	⑥	⑥	⑥B	⑥	⑥D	⑥
xeter St Davids .... ▽ d.	1725	1746	1825	...	1925	...	2025	2125	2300	⑥	0510	...	...	0641	0725	0824	...	0925	1025	1125	1225	1325	1425	1525	1625	...	1725
oniton .... d.	1755	1819	1855	...	1955	...	2057	2157	2335f		0541	0619	...	0713	0755	0855	...	0955	1055	1155	1255	1355	1455	1555	1655	...	1756
xminster .... d.	1806	1829	1906	...	2006	...	2108	2208	2346		0552	0630	...	0724	0806	0906	...	1006	1106	1206	1306	1406	1506	1606	1706	...	1807
rewkerne .... d.	1819	...	1919	...	2019	...	2121	2220	2359		0605	0643	...	0737	0819	0919	...	1019	1119	1219	1319	1419	1519	1619	1719	...	1820
Yeovil Pen Mill .. 140 d.	|	...	|	...	|	2030	|	|	|		|	|	...	|	|	|	...	|	|	|	|	|	|	|	|	1739	|
eovil Junction .... a.	1827	...	1930	...	2027	2035	2129	2231	0007		0614	0652	...	0745	0827	0927	...	1027	1127	1227	1327	1427	1527	1627	1727	1744	1829
eovil Junction .... d.	1829	...	1931	...	2029	...	2131	2232	0009		0620	0653	...	0753	0829	0929	0953	1029	1129	1229	1329	1429	1529	1629	1729	1753	1830
herborne .... d.	1835	...	1937	...	2035	...	2137	2238	|		0626	0659	...	0759	0835	0935	0959	1035	1135	1235	1335	1435	1535	1635	1735	1759	1837
illingham .... d.	1851	...	1953	...	2052	...	2153	2255	|		0642	0715	...	0815	0851	0951	1017	1051	1151	1251	1351	1451	1551	1651	1751	1817	1852
alisbury .... 140 a.	1922	...	2022	...	2122	...	2218	2319	0045		0707	0739	...	0840	0916	1016	1042	1116	1216	1316	1416	1516	1616	1716	1816	1841	1918
alisbury .... d.	1924	...	2023	2047	2124	...	2225	...	...		0721	0747	0821	0847	0921	1021	1047	1121	1221	1321	1421	1521	1621	1721	1821	1847	1921
ndover .... d.	1947	...	2040	2106	2141	...	2244	...	...		0738	0806	0838	0906	0938	1038	1106	1138	1238	1338	1438	1538	1638	1738	1838	1906	1938
asingstoke .... 106 a.	2008	...	2058	2128	2159	...	2306	...	...		0755	0828	0855	0928	0955	1055	1128	1155	1255	1355	1455	1555	1655	1755	1855	1928	1955
/oking .... 106 a.	2030	...	2117	2149	2219	...	2326	...	...		0817	0849	0915	0949	1015	1115	1149	1215	1315	1415	1515	1615	1715	1815	1915	1950	2015
ondon Waterloo . 106 a.	2104	...	2149	2219	2249	...	2355	...	...		0849	0919	0949	1019	1049	1149	1219	1249	1349	1449	1549	1649	1749	1849	1949	2019	2049

	⑥	⑥	⑥	⑥	⑥		⑦	⑦	⑦	⑦	⑦	⑦	⑦	⑦B	⑦	⑦	⑦	⑦B	⑦	⑦	⑦E	⑦	⑦	⑦	⑦	⑦	⑦
xeter St Davids .... ▽ d.	1825	1925	2025	2125	2300	⑦	...	...	...	...	0925	1025	1125	1225	1325	1425	...	1525	...	1625	...	1725	1825	1925	2025	2125	2315
oniton .... d.	1855	1955	2056	2156	2332		...	...	0858	...	0957	1057	1157	1257	1357	1457	...	1557	...	1657	...	1757	1857	1957	2057	2157	2340s
xminster .... d.	1906	2006	2107	2207	2343		...	...	0909	...	1009	1109	1209	1309	1409	1509	...	1609	...	1709	...	1809	1909	2009	2109	2209	2351s
rewkerne .... d.	1919	2019	2120	2220	2356		...	...	0922	...	1022	1122	1222	1322	1422	1522	...	1622	...	1722	...	1822	1922	2022	2122	2222	0012s
Yeovil Pen Mill .. 140 d.	|	|	|	|	|		...	...	|	0958	|	|	|	|	|	|	...	|	...	|	...	|	|	|	|	|	|
eovil Junction .... a.	1927	2027	2129	2229	0004		...	...	0930	|	1030	1130	1230	1330	1430	1530	...	1630	...	1730	...	1830	1930	2030	2131	2231	0021s
eovil Junction .... d.	1929	2029	2130	2230	0006		0732	0832	0932	0951f	1032	1132	1232	1332	1432	1532	...	1632	...	1732	...	1832	1932	2032	2132	2232	|
herborne .... d.	1935	2035	2137	2236	|		0738	0838	0938	◧	1038	1138	1238	1338	1438	1538	...	1638	...	1738	...	1838	1938	2038	2138	2238	|
illingham .... d.	1951	2051	2152	2252	|		0754	0854	0954	|	1054	1154	1254	1354	1454	1554	1621	1654	1721	1754	...	1854	1954	2054	2154	2254	|
alisbury .... 140 a.	2016	2116	2218	2324	0041		0820	0920	1020	1116	1120	1220	1320	1420	1520	1620	1647	1720	1747	1820	...	1920	2020	2120	2220	2321	0057
alisbury .... d.	2026	2126	2226	...	...		0827	0927	1027	1127	1127	1227	1327	1427	1527	1627	1652	1727	1752	1827	1852	1927	2027	2127	2227	...	...
ndover .... d.	2045	2145	2245	...	...		0846	0946	1044	1146	1146	1244	1346	1444	1546	1644	1709	1746	1809	1844	1909	1946	2044	2146	2246	...	...
asingstoke .... 106 a.	2108	2207	2307	...	...		0908	1005	1106	1206	1206	1306	1405	1506	1605	1706	1726	1805	1826	1906	1926	2005	2106	2206	2308	...	...
/oking .... 106 a.	2130	2228	2328	...	...		0928	1028	1128	1228	1228	1328	1428	1528	1628	1728	1748	1828	1848	1928	1948	2028	2128	2228	2328	...	...
ondon Waterloo . 106 a.	2204	2257	2357	...	...		1014	1101	1201	1259	1259	1359	1459	1559	1659	1759	1819	1859	1919	1959	2019	2059	2159	2259	2358	...	...

☛ Full service **London** Waterloo - **Salisbury** and v.v.:

rom **London** Waterloo on ⚒ at 0635, 0710, 0750 and every 30 minutes until 2220, 250Ⓐ, 2340; on ⑦ at 0815 and hourly until 2215, 2335 (also 1745, 1845, 1945, 045. Please see timings above for calling points between London and Salisbury).

rom **Salisbury** on ⚒ at 0510Ⓐ, 0515⑥, 0543Ⓐ, 0547⑥ 0606Ⓐ, 0621⑥, 0645Ⓐ, 647⑥, 0715Ⓐ, 0721⑥, 0745Ⓐ, 0747⑥, 0815Ⓐ, 0821⑥, 0847, 0921, 0947 and at e same minutes past each hour until 1747, 1821⑥, 1826Ⓐ, 1847, 1921⑥, 1924Ⓐ, 947, 2023Ⓐ, 2026⑥, 2047Ⓐ, 2124Ⓐ, 2126⑥, 2225; on ⑦ at 0645, 0727 and ourly until 2227 (also 1652, 1752, 1852).

B – Conveys 🚃12 London - Bristol and v.v. (Table **140**).
C – Conveys 🚃12 London - Castle Cary and v.v. (Table **140**).
D – To / from Weymouth (Table **140**); until Sept. 7 also conveys 🚃12 to / from Corfe Castle via Wareham (Table **114a**).
E – Conveys 🚃12 London - Frome and v.v. (Table **140**).
W – To Westbury (Table **140**).

a – Arrives 0840.
c – Arrives 0643.
e – Does not call at Exeter Central.
f – Calls at Yeovil Junction before Yeovil Pen Mill.
r – Arrives 0836.

s – Calls to set down only.
t – Arrives 5–7 minutes earlier.
u – Calls to pick up only.
◧ – Via Westbury (Table **140**).
△ – Trains to Exeter St Davids also call at **Exeter Central** 5–6 minutes earlier.
▽ – Trains from Exeter St Davids also call at **Exeter Central** 4–5 minutes later.

110 LONDON - EXETER - PAIGNTON and PLYMOUTH GW

km			Ⓐ 2 B★	Ⓐ 2★	Ⓐ 2	Ⓐ	Ⓐ 2	Ⓐ	Ⓐ 🍷	Ⓐ 2 D★	Ⓐ 🍷	Ⓐ 2 Dd	Ⓐ 2 D★	Ⓐ 🍷	Ⓐ 🍷★	Ⓐ 🍷	Ⓐ 🍴	Ⓐ 🍴	Ⓐ 2	Ⓐ 🍴	Ⓐ 2	Ⓐ 2D	Ⓐ 2★	Ⓐ 🍷
0	**London** Paddington.... 130/1/2/3/4 d.	Ⓐ	...	...	...	0635	...	0703	0730	...	0903	...	g	1003	1033	1103	1203	1233	...	1303	...	...	...	140
58	**Reading**.................. 130/1/2/3/4 d.		...	...	...	0702	...	0731	0757	...	0931	...	...	1032	1100	1130	1230r	1300	...	1331r	...	...	...	143
85	Newbury.......................... d.		...	...	...	|	...	0748	|	...	|	...	...	|	1118	|	|	1316	...	|	...	...	...	|
154	Westbury.................... 140 d.		...	...	...	|	...	0827	|	...	|	...	...	|	1159	|	|	1355	...	|	...	...	...	|
186	Castle Cary................. 140 d.		...	...	...	|	...	|	|	...	1028	...	...	|	1217	|	|	1413	...	|	...	...	...	|
	Bristol Temple M 115 116 132 d.		...	0524	0643	|	...	|	0912	0855	|	0955	0956	|	|	|	|	|	...	|	...	1358	...	|
230	Taunton.................. 115 116 d.		...	0620	0739	0818	...	0904	0945	1001	1051	1100	1100	|	1240	1252	|	1434	...	1448	...	1459	...	155
253	Tiverton Parkway.............. 116 d.		...	0635	0755	|	...	0917	|	|	1104	1116	1116	|	|	1305	|	...	...	1501	...	1515	...	160
279	**Exeter** St Davids.............. 116 a.		...	0652	0812	0841	...	0931	1009	1031	1118	1132	1132	1204	1303	1319	1403	...	...	1515	...	1533	...	161
279	**Exeter** St Davids........ 111 116 d.		0628	0655	0814	0844	0926	0932	1011	1032	1119	1135	1135	1209	1305	1320	1408	...	...	1516	...	...	1551	162
311	Newton Abbot............ 111 116 d.		0654	0728	0835	|	0947	0953	1032	1101	1140	1157	1215	1230	1332	1342	1429	...	1450	1539	1555	...	1622	164
321	Torquay.................. 111 116 d.		|	|	|	|	|	1005	|	1113	|	|	|	|	1344	|	|	...	|	|	|	...	|	|
324	**Paignton**............... 111 116 a.		|	|	|	|	|	1011	|	1120	|	|	|	|	1352	|	|	...	|	|	|	...	|	|
325	Totnes.......................... 116 d.		0707	0742	0849	|	1000	...	1044	...	1153	1209	1228	|	...	1355	|	...	1502	1551	1607	...	1634	165
363	**Plymouth**....................... 116 a.		0737	0811	0918	0934	1029	...	1110	...	1220	1240	1259	1306	...	1422	1503	...	1533	1618	1638	...	1706	172
	Newquay 112.................... a.		...	1009c	|	|	|	...	|	...	1419c	|	...	|	...	...	|	...	|	|	...	...	...	|
	Penzance 112.................... a.		...	1016b	1120	1136	1234	...	1313	...	...	1439	...	1512	...	...	1709	...	1738	1830c	...	...	...	193

	⑤ 🍷c	Ⓐ 🍷	Ⓐ 🍷	Ⓐ 🍷	Ⓐ 🍷	Ⓐ 🍷★	Ⓐ 🍴	Ⓐ 🍷	①–④ 🍷	⑤ 🍷	①–④ 🍴	⑤ 🍴	Ⓐ 🍷	Ⓐ 🍷	Ⓐ 2	Ⓐ 2	Ⓐ 🍷	Ⓐ A	⑥ ♠	⑥ 2★	⑥ ★	⑥ 🍷★	⑥ 2	⑥ 🍷
London Paddington.... 130/1/2/3/4 d.	1433	1503	1603	1633	1703	1733	1803	1807	1833	1833	1903	1903	2003	2103	...	...	2145	2345‡		...	...	0702	...	073
Reading.................. 130/1/2/3/4 d.	1502u	1530r	1630	1701	1730r	1800	1830	1839	1900	1900	1930	1930u	2030	2130	...	...	2214	0046u		...	...	0730u	...	075
Newbury.......................... d.	|	|	|	1720	1747	1816	1849	1904	1916	1916	1948	1948	2046	2147	...	...	|	|		...	...	|	...	|
Westbury.................... 140 d.	1614	1623	|	1805	|	1902	|	1958	2004	2004	|	|	2127	2226	...	...	|	|		...	...	|	...	|
Castle Cary................. 140 d.	1633	1641	|	1823	|	1920	|	...	2022	2022	|	|	2145	2245	...	...	|	|		...	...	|	...	|
Bristol Temple M. 115 116 132 d.	|	|	|	|	|	|	|	...	|	|	|	|	|	|	2154	2306	2337	|		0524	0641	|	...	091
Taunton.................. 115 116 d.	1655	1704	1752	1846	1855	1943	1953	...	2045	2045	2053	2053	2207	2308	2312	0014s	0036s	0238		0620	0730	0850	...	095
Tiverton Parkway.............. 116 d.	1708	1717	1805	1859	1908	1956	|	...	2058	2058	2106	2106	2220	2321	2328	0031s	0050s	|		0635	0743	|	...	|
Exeter St Davids.............. 116 a.	1722	1732	1819	1913	1922	2010	2016	...	2112	2112	2120	2120	2234	2335	2346	0052	0105	0307		0652	0756	0912	...	101
Exeter St Davids........ 111 116 d.	...	1737	1824	...	1925	2022	2018	...	...	2114	2122	2122	2236	2337	...	...	...	0411		0655	0802	0918	0934	101
Newton Abbot............ 111 116 d.	...	1758	1845	...	1946	2100	2039	...	...	2135	2143	2143	2257	2358	...	...	...	0432		0728	0835	0947	0956	103
Torquay.................. 111 116 d.	...	|	|	...	|	2114	|	...	...	|	|	|	|	|	...	...	...	|		|	|	|	|	|
Paignton............... 111 116 a.	...	|	|	...	|	2121	|	...	...	|	|	|	|	|	...	...	...	|		|	|	|	|	|
Totnes.......................... 116 d.	...	1810	1858	...	1959	...	2051	...	...	|	2155	2155	2309	0010	...	...	...	|		0742	0848	1000	1009	105
Plymouth....................... 116 a.	...	1836	1928	...	2025	...	2117	...	...	2211	2222	2222	2336	0040	...	...	...	0515		0813	0917	1026	1038	111
Newquay 112.................... a.	...	|	|	...	|	...	|	...	...	...	|	|	...	...	...	...	...	|		...	|	|	1239	|
Penzance 112.................... a.	...	2040	2129	...	2228	...	2313	...	...	...	*0040*	0045	...	...	...	...	...	0755j		...	1126	1237	...	132

	⑥ 🍷★	⑥ 🍷	⑥ 🍷	⑥ 2★	⑥ 🍷★	⑥ 🍷	⑥ 🍷	⑥ 🍷	⑥ 🍷★	⑥ 🍷		⑥ 🍷	⑥ 🍷	⑥ 2★	⑥ 🍷	⑥ 🍷	⑥ 🍷	⑥ 🍷	⑥ 🍷	⑥ 🍷★	⑥ 2	⑥ 🍷	⑦	⑦ 2★
London Paddington.... 130/1/2/3/4 d.	0835	0903	1003	...	1035	1103	1135	1203	1233	1303	...	1403	1503	...	1603	1703	1630	1803	1903	2003	...	2030		...
Reading.................. 130/1/2/3/4 d.	0903u	0931u	1031u	...	1103u	1131u	1203u	1232u	1300u	1331u	...	1431u	1531u	...	1631u	1731u	1658	1831u	1931u	2030u	...	2058		...
Newbury.......................... d.	0920	|	|	...	|	|	|	|	1316	|	...	|	|	...	|	|	|	|	1947	2046	...	|		...
Westbury.................... 140 d.	0959	|	|	...	1156	|	1255	|	1355	|	...	|	1621	...	|	1821	|	|	2027	2126	...	|		...
Castle Cary................. 140 d.	1017	|	1129	...	1214	|	|	|	1413	|	...	|	1639	...	|	1839	|	|	2045	2144	...	|		...
Bristol Temple M. 115 116 132 d.	|	|	|	*1145*	|	|	|	|	|	|	...	|	|	*1645*	|	|	1818	|	|	|	2202	2217		072
Taunton.................. 115 116 d.	1039	1047	|	*1217*	1237	|	1332	|	1436	1447	...	1548	1702	*1717*	1747	1902	1908	1947	2107	2207	2307	2317		081
Tiverton Parkway.............. 116 d.	1053	1101	|	*1230*	1250	|	|	|	|	1500	...	1601	1715	*1730*	1800	1915	1921	|	2120	2220	2323	2330		083
Exeter St Davids.............. 116 a.	1106	1115	1209	*1244*	1303	1308	1355	1404	1458	1514	...	1615	1729	*1744*	1813	1929	1935	2010	2134	2234	2341	2346		084
Exeter St Davids........ 111 116 d.	1109	1117	1215	1251	1308	1315	1359	1410	1502	1517	...	1618	1731	1750	1817	1934	1940	2013	2137	2238	...	...		085
Newton Abbot............ 111 116 d.	1150	1140	1237	1320	1348	1338	|	1435	1535	1540	...	1639	1752	1819	1838	1956	2001	2034	2158	2306	...	...		091
Torquay.................. 111 116 d.	1203	|	|	|	1401	|	|	|	1548	|	...	|	|	|	|	|	2015	|	|	|	...	...		|
Paignton............... 111 116 a.	1210	|	|	|	1410	|	|	|	1555	|	...	|	|	|	|	|	2024	|	|	|	...	...		|
Totnes.......................... 116 d.	...	1153	|	1333	...	1351	|	|	...	1553	...	1651	1805	1833	1851	2008	...	2047	2211	2318	...	...		093
Plymouth....................... 116 a.	...	1223	1312	1403	...	1417	1454	1511	...	1619	...	1717	1835	1904	1921	2035	...	2113	2238	2345	...	...		100
Newquay 112.................... a.	...	|	|	...	...	|	1647	|	...	|	...	|	...	|	|	...	...	|	...	...	...	...		|
Penzance 112.................... a.	...	1425	1514	...	...	1618	...	1712	...	1819	...	1921	...	2110	2125	...	...	2322	...	...	...	...		115

	⑦ 2★	⑦ 🍷★	⑦ 🍷	⑦ 2h	⑦ 2k	⑦ 🍷	⑦ 🍷	⑦ 🍷★	⑦ 🍷	⑦ 🍷	⑦ 🍷	⑦ 2★	⑦ 🍷	⑦ 🍷		⑦ 🍷	⑦ 🍷	⑦ 2	⑦ 🍷	⑦ 🍷★	⑦ 🍷	⑦ 🍷	⑦ 🍷	⑦ A
London Paddington.... 130/1/2/3/4 d.	...	0805	0903	...	...	1003	1103	1142	1203	1303	1315	...	1403	1503	...	1603	1703	...	1803	1903	1915	2003	2103	235
Reading.................. 130/1/2/3/4 d.	...	0839	0932	...	...	1031	1132	1209	1232	1332	1339	...	1432	1532	...	1632	1732	...	1832	1932	1939	2032	2132	004
Newbury.......................... d.	...	|	0948	...	...	|	|	|	1248	|	|	...	1448	|	...	1648	|	...	1848	|	|	2048	|	|
Westbury.................... 140 d.	...	|	1025	...	...	|	|	1302	|	1418	|	...	|	|	...	1725	|	...	1927	|	|	2128	|	|
Castle Cary................. 140 d.	...	|	|	...	...	1134	|	1321	|	|	|	...	1537	|	...	1743	|	...	|	2031	|	2145	|	|
Bristol Temple M. 115 116 132 d.	0828	1000	|	...	...	|	|	|	|	|	1456	...	|	|	...	|	|	1830	|	|	2100	|	|	|
Taunton.................. 115 116 d.	0932	1034	1059	...	...	1155	1248	1342	1354	1455	1530	...	1558	1650	...	1806	1850	1941	2003	2052	2152	2206	2247s	|
Tiverton Parkway.............. 116 d.	0948	1047	1113	...	...	|	|	1356	1407	|	|	...	|	1703	...	1819	1903	1956	2016	2106	2206	2219	2301s	|
Exeter St Davids.............. 116 a.	1004	1101	1127	...	...	1220	1314	1412	1421	1518	1555	...	1623	1718	...	1835	1918	2014	2030	2121	2222	2235	2320	031
Exeter St Davids........ 111 116 d.	1006	1104	1130	1215	1215	1222	1315	1413	1424	1521	1556	1550	1625	1720	...	1836	1919	...	2031	2122	...	2236	...	043
Newton Abbot............ 111 116 d.	1031	1132	1148	1237	1237	1243	1337	1440	1445	1542	1619	1633	1645	1741	...	1858	1938	...	2053	2148	...	2257	...	045
Torquay.................. 111 116 d.	|	|	|	|	|	|	|	1453	|	|	|	|	|	|	...	|	|	...	|	|	...	|	...	|
Paignton............... 111 116 a.	|	|	|	|	|	|	|	1502	|	|	|	|	|	|	...	|	|	...	|	|	...	|	...	|
Totnes.......................... 116 d.	1043	1144	1201	1249	1249	1257	|	...	1457	1554	|	1646	1702	1755	...	|	1952	...	2106	2202	...	2310	...	|
Plymouth....................... 116 a.	1112	1212	1231	1319	1319	1326	1414	...	1525	1622	1656	1717	1731	1821	...	1935	2019	...	2133	2229	...	2340	...	053
Newquay 112.................... a.	|	|	|	...	|	1513h	|	...	|	|	...	|	|	|	...	...	|	...	|	...	...	...	...	|
Penzance 112.................... a.	1314	1415	1433h	...	1526	*1526*k	1611	...	1729	1824	...	1932	*1932*	2023	...	...	2222	...	2338	...	...	...	...	085

A – THE NIGHT RIVIERA – Conveys 🛏 1, 2. cl and (2).
See also note ‡.
B – Continues to Par until July 5 and from Sept. 2. (Table **112**).
D – To / from Cardiff (Table **115**).
a – Via Trowbridge (Table **140**).
b – Until July 5 and from Sept. 2.
c – July 8 - Aug. 30.
d – From Sept. 9.
g – Until Sept. 6.
h – Until Sept. 8.
j – Arrives 0750 on ⑥ mornings.
k – From Sept. 15.
r – Stops to pick up only on ⑤.
s – Stops to set down only.
t – Arrives 2339 on ⑤.
u – Stops to pick up only.
v – Arrives 1649.
z – Arrives 0503 on Ⓐ mornings.

NOTES CONTINUE ON NEXT PAGE –

111 EXETER - PAIGNTON 2nd class GW

km			Ⓐ	Ⓐ	Ⓐ	Ⓐ	Ⓐ	Ⓐ	Ⓐ	Ⓐ	Ⓐ	Ⓐ	Ⓐ	Ⓐ	Ⓐ	Ⓐ	Ⓐ	Ⓐ	Ⓐ	Ⓐ	Ⓐ	Ⓐ	Ⓐ	Ⓐ	Ⓐ
0	**Exeter** St Davids 110 116 d.	Ⓐ	0535	0611	0718	0749	0826	0900	1001	1032	1058	1158	1249	1257	1358	1501	1558	1628	1655	1728	1751	1836	1933	2022	212
20	Dawlish.............. 110 116 d.		0556	0631	0738	0810	0847	0925	1028	1048	1118	1227	|	1324	1427	1521	1619	1648	1715	1753	1812	1902	1959	2045	214
24	Teignmouth......... 110 116 d.		0601	0636	0743	0815	0852	0930	1033	1053	1123	1232	|	1329	1432	1526	1624	1653	1720	1758	1817	1907	2004	2052	215
32	Newton Abbot..... 110 116 d.		0609	0645	0752	0824	0901	0938	1041	1101	1132	1240	1311	1339	1440	1535	1632	1702	1729	1807	1826	1916	2013	2100	220
42	Torquay.............. 110 116 d.		0620	0656	0803	0836	0912	0949	1052	1113	1143	1252	1322	1352	1452	1546	1644	1713	1740	1818	1837	1927	2024	2114	221
45	**Paignton**..... 🚂 110 116 a.		0626	0706	0810	0844	0919	0956	1059	1120	1150	1300	1329	1400	1459	1553	1651	1720	1748	1825	1844	1934	2030	2121	222

	Ⓐ		⑥	⑥	⑥	⑥	⑥	⑥	⑥	⑥	⑥	⑥c	⑥d	⑥c	⑥d	⑥	⑥c	⑥d	⑥	⑥c	⑥d	⑥d	⑥c	⑥	⑥
Exeter St Davids 110 116 d.	2247	⑥	0518	0538	0611	0754	0837	0859	0958	1022	1045	1059	1100	1158	1158	1259	1358	1403	1430	1459	1506	1559	1601	1655	173
Dawlish.............. 110 116 d.	2307		0538	0558	0631	0814	0850	0926	1018	1037	|	1120	1122	1224	1219	1320	1424	1429	1445	1519	1533	1619	1621	1715	175
Teignmouth......... 110 116 d.	2312		0543	0603	0636	0819	0855	0931	1023	1042	|	1125	1127	1229	1224	1325	1429	1434	1450	1524	1538	1624	1626	1720	180
Newton Abbot..... 110 116 d.	2320		0552	0611	0645	0828	0906	0939	1033	1050	1106	1141b	1137	1237	1240b	1333	1437	1442	1459	1540b	1546	1633	1642b	1729	180
Torquay.............. 110 116 d.	2330		0603	0622	0656	0839	0916	0950	1044	1100	1117	1152	1150	1249	1251	1344	1449	1454	1510	1551	1557	1644	1653	1740	182
Paignton...... 🚂 110 116 a.	2337		0611	0631	0706	0848	0925	0959	1052	1108	1126	1201	1159	1257	1259	1352	1456	1501	1518	1600	1606	1652	1701	1750	183

	⑥	⑥		⑥	⑥	⑥	⑥		⑦	⑦	⑦	⑦	⑦	⑦	⑦	⑦	⑦	⑦	⑦	⑦	⑦	⑦	⑦	⑦	⑦
Exeter St Davids 110 116 d.	1827	1900	...	1918	2018	2150	2238	⑦	0845	0954	1053	1159	1302	1326	1359	1505	1531	1603	1657	1712	1757	1857	1957	2102	220
Dawlish.............. 110 116 d.	1847	1913	...	1938	2038	2210	2251		0912	1014	1113	1219	1317	1339	1419	1517	1543	1616	1712	1724	1817	1917	2017	2117	222
Teignmouth......... 110 116 d.	1852	1918	...	1943	2043	2215	2257		0919	1019	1118	1224	1322	1344	1424	1522	1548	1621	1717	1729	1822	1922	2022	2122	222
Newton Abbot..... 110 116 d.	1901	1925	...	1952	2052	2223	2303		0926	1037b	1127	1234	1330	1352	1435	1530	1556	1629	1726	1736	1831	1931	2031	2131	223
Torquay.............. 110 116 d.	1912	1935	...	2003	2103	2234	*2319*		0938	1048	1138	1244	1341	1404	1446	1542	1607	1640	1737	1747	1842	1942	2042	2142	224
Paignton...... 🚂 110 116 a.	1921	1943	...	2013	2110	2242	*2327*		0945	1054	1145	1252	1348	1411	1453	1550	1615	1647	1744	1754	1849	1949	2049	2149	225

b – Arrives 9 minutes earlier. c – From Sept. 14. d – Until Sept. 7. 🚂 – Dartmouth Steam Railway (Paignton - Kingswear). See page 101 for contact detail

GW PLYMOUTH and PAIGNTON - EXETER - LONDON 110

km		Ⓐ 🍷a	Ⓐ 🍷	Ⓐ 🍷	Ⓐ 2	Ⓐ 🍷☆	Ⓐ 🍷	Ⓐ 🍷	Ⓐ 🍷	Ⓐ ✕	Ⓐ 🍷☆	Ⓐ 🍷	Ⓐ 🍷	Ⓐ 2☆	Ⓐ 2D	Ⓐ 🍷	Ⓐ 🍷	Ⓐ 🍷	Ⓐ 🍷☆	Ⓐ ✕	Ⓐ2 D☆	Ⓐ ✕	Ⓐ 2☆	Ⓐ 2
	Penzance 112 d.	...	...	...	...	...	...	...	...	0505	...	0541	...	0600	...	0647	0741	0900	...	1000	...	1049c	1112	1141
	Newquay 112 d.	...	...	...	...	...	...	...	...	|	...	|	...	|	...	|	|	|	...	|	...	|	|	|
0	**Plymouth** 116 d.	...	...	0450	...	0529	0553	...	...	0653	...	0747	...	0809	...	0851	0951	1100	...	1201	...	1255	1304	1340
38	Totnes 116 d.	...	...	|	...	0556	|	...	...	|	...	0815	...	0839	...	0921	1021	|	...	1228	...	1322	1334	1409
	Paignton 111 116 d.	...	...	0527	...	|	|	...	...	|	0748	|	...	|	...	|	|	|	1132	|	1253	|	|	|
	Torquay 111 116 d.	...	...	|	...	|	|	...	...	|	0755	|	...	|	...	|	|	|	1138	|	1259	|	|	|
52	Newton Abbot 111 116 d.	...	...	|	...	0609	0629	...	...	0731	0808	0828	...	0852	...	0934	1034	|	1150	1241	1312	1335	1346	1424
84	**Exeter** St Davids 111 116 a.	...	...	0546	...	0634	0650	...	...	0750	0840	0848	...	0916	...	0953	1053	1152	1215	1300	1336	1355	1415	...
84	**Exeter** St Davids 116 d.	...	...	0552	0600	0636	0652	...	0628	0751	0842	0851	...	...	0933	0955	1055	1155	1217	1302	1338	1359	...	...
110	Tiverton Parkway 116 d.	...	...	0607	0617	0651	|	←	0643	|	|	0906	←	...	0950	1010	1111	|	1232	1317	1355	1414	...	...
133	Taunton 115 116 d.	...	...	0622	0634	0705	0717	0705	0657	0815	0907	0920	0907	...	1011	1028	1125	|	1246	1331	1411	1428	...	...
205	**Bristol** Temple M. 115 116 132 a.	0515	...	|	0741	→	|	|	0758	|	→	|	0957	...	1111	|	|	|	|	|	1514	|	...	...
	Castle Cary 140 d.	|	...	0644	...	...	|	0727	|	|	...	0941	|	...	...	|	|	|	1307	|	...	|	...	...
	Westbury 140 d.	0600	0616	0704	...	...	|	0752	|	|	...	1000	|	...	...	|	1105	|	1327	|	...	1504	...	...
	Newbury a.	0649	0706	0745	...	...	|	0830	|	|	...	|	|	...	...	|	|	|	1404	|	...	|	...	...
337	**Reading** 130/1/2/3/4 a.	0718	0737	0807	...	...	0833	0854	0915	0933	...	1051	1110	...	...	1151	1242	1331	1423	1451	...	1550	...	...
395	**London** Paddington 130/1/2/3/4 a.	0747	0809	0838	...	...	0902	0923	0943	1002	...	1121	1139	...	...	1221	1315	1401	1454	1522	...	1621	...	...

	Ⓐ 🍷	Ⓐ 🍷	Ⓐ 🍷☆	Ⓐ 🍷	Ⓐ 2	Ⓐ 🍷	Ⓐ 🍷	⑤ 2c	Ⓐ 2☆	Ⓐ ✕	Ⓐ 2☆	Ⓐ 2	Ⓐ 🍷	Ⓐ 🍷	Ⓐ 2☆	Ⓐ 2☆	Ⓐ A	⑥ ♠ 2	⑥ 🍷	⑥ 🍷	⑥ 🍷	⑥ 🍷	⑥ 🍷	⑥ 2☆
Penzance 112 d.	1204	...	...	*1256*	1256	1400	...	...	...	1600	...	1644	...	1742	...	...	2145‡	...	...	...	...	...	...	...
Newquay 112 d.	|	...	...	|	|	|	1507c	...	...	|	...	|	...	|	...	...	|	...	...	...	...	...	...	...
Plymouth 116 d.	1356	...	...	1500	1508	1559	1657	...	1735	1803	...	1843	...	1944	...	2125	2354	...	0540	...	0657	...	0750	0808
Totnes 116 d.	|	...	...	1527	1537	1626	1728	...	1806	1831	...	1912	...	2012	...	2154	0022	...	0607	...	|	...	0817	0838
Paignton 111 116 d.	|	...	1454	|	|	|	|	...	|	|	1852	|	...	|	*2035*	|	|	...	|	...	|	...	|	|
Torquay 111 116 d.	|	...	1500	|	|	|	|	...	|	|	1857	|	...	|	*2040*	|	|	...	|	...	|	...	|	|
Newton Abbot 111 116 d.	1432	...	1512	1540	1549	1639	1741	...	1819	1844	1909	1925	...	2025	*2053*	2206	0036	...	0620	...	0733	...	0830	0850
Exeter St Davids 111 116 a.	1452	...	1537	1559	...	1659	1800	...	1848	1903	1939	1947	...	2044	*2128*	2240	0057	...	0639	...	0752	...	0849	0915
Exeter St Davids 116 d.	1455	...	1539	1601	...	1702	1802	1820	...	1905	1939	...	1956	2046	2149	...	0106	0600	0643	0729	0756	...	0852	...
Tiverton Parkway 116 d.	1510	...	|	1616	...	1717	1817	|	...	1920	|	...	2011	2101	2206	...	|	0617	0659	0745	0811	←	0907	...
Taunton 115 116 d.	1524	1533	1604	1630	...	1731	1831	1844	...	1934	2010	...	2026	2115	2223	...	0142	0634	0713	0759	0825	0759	0921	...
Bristol Temple M. 115 116 132 a.	|	|	|	|	...	|	|	|	...	|	2054	...	|	2147	2313	...	|	0742	|	→	|	0856	|	...
Castle Cary 140 d.	|	1555	1625	|	...	|	1852	|	...	|	...	...	2047	|	...	...	|	...	0734	...	|	|	0942	...
Westbury 140 d.	|	1614	1645	|	...	|	1912	|	...	|	...	...	2107	|	...	...	|	...	0756	...	|	|	1002	...
Newbury a.	|	1651	|	|	...	|	1948	|	...	|	...	...	2143	|	...	...	|	...	0834	...	|	|	|	...
Reading 130/1/2/3/4 a.	1646	1716	1737	1746	...	1851	2008	2019	...	2053	...	...	2202	2307	...	...	0400s	...	0851	...	0940	1011	1052	...
London Paddington 130/1/2/3/4 a.	1716	1753	1808	1816	...	1920	2037	2051	...	2122	...	...	2237	2342t	...	...	0507z	...	0921	...	1010	1039	1121	...

	⑥ 🍷	⑥ 🍷☆	⑥ 🍷	⑥ 🍷	⑥ 🍷	⑥ 🍷	⑥ 2☆	⑥ 🍷	⑥ 🍷☆	⑥ 🍷	⑥ 🍷	⑥ 🍷☆	⑥ 🍷	⑥ 2	⑥ 🍷	⑥ 🍷☆	⑥ 2☆	⑥ 🍷	⑥ 🍷	⑥ 🍷	⑥ 2☆	⑦ 2	⑦ 🍷	⑦ 2
Penzance 112 d.	0648	...	0753	0855	0930	1000	...	1058	...	...	1200	...	1307	...	1400	...	...	1552	...	1742	1906	...	...	...
Newquay 112 d.	|	...	|	|	|	|	...	|	...	1128	|	...	|	1322	|	...	...	|	1728	|	|	...	...	...
Plymouth 116 d.	0852	...	1001	1100	1139	1205	1232	1303	...	1314	1403	...	1510	1532	1600	...	1736	1755	1925	1941	2115	...	...	...
Totnes 116 d.	0920	...	1031	|	1209	|	1302	|	...	1342	|	...	|	1601	1627	...	1805	1822	1952	2011	2144	...	...	...
Paignton 111 116 d.	|	0918	|	|	|	|	|	|	1308	|	|	1450	|	|	|	1700	|	|	|	|	|	...	...	...
Torquay 111 116 d.	|	0925	|	|	|	|	|	|	1315	|	|	1458	|	|	|	1707	|	|	|	|	|	...	...	...
Newton Abbot 111 116 d.	0933	0939	1044	|	1222	1242	1315	|	1327	1355	1440	1510	1546	1615	1640	1719	1817	1835	2005	2024	2157	...	...	...
Exeter St Davids 111 116 a.	0951	1011	1103	1152	1241	1301	1346	1400	1408	1415	1459	1543	1605	...	1659	1750	1854	1857	2028	2042	2223	...	...	...
Exeter St Davids 116 d.	0955	1015	1107	1156	1245	1308	...	1404	1411	1418	1503	1546	1608	...	1703	1802	...	1900	2030	2045	...	0801	0830	0931
Tiverton Parkway 116 d.	1010	1030	1122	|	1300	|	...	|	|	|	1519	|	1624	...	1718	1817	...	1915	|	2100	...	0818	0845	0948
Taunton 115 116 d.	1024	1045	1136	|	1314	1334	...	1430	1445	|	1534	1612	1638	...	1732	1831	...	1929	2055	2114	...	0835	0858	1003
Bristol Temple M. 115 116 132 a.	|	1120	|	|	|	|	...	|	|	|	|	|	|	...	|	|	...	|	|	2146	...	0937	|	1111
Castle Cary 140 d.	|	|	|	|	1335	|	...	|	1509	|	|	1633	|	...	1753	1853	...	1950	|	|	...	...	0920	...
Westbury 140 d.	1103	|	|	|	1355	|	...	|	1528	|	|	1653	|	...	|	1914	...	2013	|	|	...	...	0941	...
Newbury a.	|	|	|	|	|	|	...	|	1606	|	|	|	|	...	|	1948	...	|	|	|	...	...	1018	...
Reading 130/1/2/3/4 a.	1149	1246	1251	1331	1447	1451	...	1546	1629	1603	1649	1744	1752	...	1850	2004	...	2102	2213	2303	...	...	1038	...
London Paddington 130/1/2/3/4 a.	1221	1314	1321	1400	1516	1521	...	1621	1700	1631	1721	1816	1821	...	1922	2037	...	2131	2244	2343	...	...	1108	...

	⑦ 🍷☆	⑦ 🍷	⑦ 🍷	⑦ 🍷	⑦ 🍷	⑦ 🍷h	⑦ 🍷k	⑦ 2☆	⑦ 🍷	⑦ 🍷	⑦ 🍷☆	⑦ 2	⑦ 🍷		⑦ 🍷	⑦ 2☆	⑦ 🍷	⑦ 🍷k	⑦ 🍷h	⑦ 🍷	⑦ 🍷	⑦ 🍷	⑦ 🍷	⑦ 2☆	⑦ A
Penzance 112 d.	...	0805	...	0945	1100	1140	...	1204	1300	...	...	1337	...	...	...	1437	1500	...	...	1613	...	1735	...	1900	2115‡
Newquay 112 d.	...	|	...	|	|	|	...	|	|	...	...	|	...	...	...	|	|	...	1559	|	...	|	...	|	|
Plymouth 116 d.	0837	1010	1100	1146	1300	1350	1350	1406	1459	1512	...	1540	1554	...	1610	1636	1700	1740	1749	1815	1840	1934	2004	2114	2320
Totnes 116 d.	0904	1037	1127	1216	1329	1417	1417	1436	1526	|	...	1609	1620	...	1637	1704	1728	1807	1816	|	1907	2001	|	2143	2348
Paignton 111 116 d.	|	|	|	|	|	|	|	|	|	|	1545	|	|	...	|	|	|	|	|	|	|	|	|	|	|
Torquay 111 116 d.	|	|	|	|	|	|	|	|	|	|	1550	|	|	...	|	|	|	|	|	|	|	|	|	|	|
Newton Abbot 111 116 d.	0918	1051	1140	1228	1342	1430	1430	1448	1539	1547	1605	1622	1634	...	1655v	1718	1740	1821	1830	|	1921	2014	2041	2156	0001
Exeter St Davids 111 116 a.	0943	1110	1159	1248	1402	1449	1449	1514	1558	1607	1631	1643	1653	...	1715	1744	1801	1844	1849	1908	1940	2034	2100	2221	0023
Exeter St Davids 116 d.	0945	1111	1201	1249	1404	1451	1453	...	1601	1609	1633	...	1654	...	1717	1745	1801	1846	1851	1912	1942	2035	2102	...	0059
Tiverton Parkway 116 d.	|	1127	1217	|	1419	|	|	...	1616	1624	|	...	1710	...	|	|	1819	|	|	|	1957	2051	2117	...	|
Taunton 115 116 d.	1009	1140	1230	1316	1434	1515	1517	...	1630	1639	1658	...	1723	...	1741	1812	1834	1910	1915	1940	2010	2104	2131	...	|
Bristol Temple M. 115 116 132 a.	|	|	|	|	|	|	|	...	|	1720	1751	...	|	...	1821	1912	|	|	|	|	|	|	2200	...	|
Castle Cary 140 d.	|	1201	1251	|	|	1537	1539	...	|	|	|	...	1745	...	|	...	|	|	|	|	2032	2128	|	...	|
Westbury 140 d.	1045	1221	|	1359	|	1554	1557	...	|	|	|	...	1805	...	|	...	|	1947	1953	|	2052	2147	|	...	|
Newbury a.	1119	1258	|	|	|	1633	1636	...	|	|	|	...	1842	...	|	...	|	2020	2026	|	|	2222	|	...	|
Reading 130/1/2/3/4 a.	1138	1317	1353	1445	1550	1650	1653	...	1747	1836	1908	...	1859	...	1934	...	1949	2039	2045	2056	2138	2244	2326	...	0406s
London Paddington 130/1/2/3/4 a.	1208	1353	1422	1514	1621	1722	1722	...	1816	1908	1936	...	1929	...	2006	...	2021	2111	2114	2124	2216	2333	0009	...	0502

– **NOTES** (continued from previous page)

♠ – Service valid until Sept. 7.

★ – Also calls at Dawlish (10 – 15 minutes after Exeter) and Teignmouth (15 – 18 minutes after Exeter).
☆ – Also calls at Teignmouth (7 – 10 minutes after Newton Abbot) and Dawlish (12 – 15 minutes after Newton Abbot).
‡ – Passengers may occupy cabins at London Paddington from 2230 and at Penzance from 2045⑦ / 2115Ⓐ.

GW 2nd class PAIGNTON - EXETER 111

	Ⓐ	Ⓐ	Ⓐ	Ⓐ	Ⓐ	Ⓐ	Ⓐ	Ⓐ	Ⓐ	Ⓐ	Ⓐ	Ⓐ	Ⓐ	Ⓐ	Ⓐ	Ⓐ	Ⓐ	Ⓐ	Ⓐ	Ⓐ	Ⓐ	Ⓐ	Ⓐ	Ⓐ
Paignton 🚂 110 116 d.	0603	0634	0710	0748	0820	0912	0934	1021	1033	1120	1213	1308	1421	1513	1612	1629	1657	1726	1752	1834	1937	2035	2135	2245
Torquay 110 116 d.	0608	0639	0715	0755	0825	0917	0939	1026	1038	1125	1218	1313	1426	1518	1617	1634	1702	1731	1757	1839	1942	2040	2141	2250
Newton Abbot 110 116 d.	0621	0652	0734b	0808	0838	0939a	0950	1039	1051	1137	1231	1325	1439	1531	1631	1647	1715	1744	1810	1852	1954	2053	2153	2303
Teignmouth 110 116 d.	0628	0659	0741	0815	0845	0945	|	1046	1058	1145	1238	1333	1446	1538	1638	1655	1722	1751	1817	1859	2002	2100	*2213*	2310
Dawlish 110 116 d.	0633	0704	0746	0822	0850	0950	|	1051	1103	1150	1243	1338	1451	1543	1643	1700	1727	1756	1822	1904	2007	2105	*2218*	2315
Exeter St Davids 110 116 a.	0703	0733	0810	0840	0912	1014	*1021*	1113	1128	1211	1313	1408	1513	1612	1711	1717	1751	1819	1844	1932	2029	2128	*2240*	2337

	Ⓐ	⑥	⑥	⑥	⑥	⑥	⑥	⑥	⑥	⑥	⑥	⑥	⑥c	⑥d	⑥c	⑥d	⑥c	⑥d	⑥c	⑥	⑥	⑥	⑥d	⑥c
Paignton 🚂 110 116 d.	2355	0613	0634	0700	0806	0904	0918	0930	1016	1100	1121	1213	1242	1258	1326	1408	1408	1507	1513	1544	1612	1711	1750	1752
Torquay 110 116 d.	2359	0618	0639	0706	0811	0909	0925	0935	1021	1105	1126	1218	1247	1303	1331	1413	1413	1512	1518	1549	1617	1716	1755	1757
Newton Abbot 110 116 d.	0013	0630	0652	0716	0834e	0923	0939	0948	1033	1118	1139	1231	1307a	1320b	1345	1426	1438f	1525	1531	1608a	1630	1729	1807	1810
Teignmouth 110 116 d.	0021	0638	0659	0723	0841	0930	0947	0955	1040	1125	1147	1238	1315	1328	1352	1433	1445	1533	1538	1615	1638	1736	1814	1817
Dawlish 110 116 d.	0026	0643	0704	0728	0846	0935	0954	1000	1045	1130	1152	1243	1320	1333	1357	1438	1450	1538	1543	1620	1643	1741	1819	1822
Exeter St Davids 110 116 a.	0048	0705	0733	0738	0909	1004	1011	1017	1114	1147	1213	1312	1336	1357	1420	1510	1513	1602	1612	1634	1713	1810h	1842	1845

	⑥	⑥c	⑥d	⑥	⑥	⑥	⑥	⑥	⑦	⑦	⑦	⑦	⑦	⑦	⑦	⑦	⑦	⑦	⑦	⑦	⑦	⑦	⑦	⑦
Paignton 🚂 110 116 d.	1852	1924	1930	1951	2020	2120	2245	2330	0949	1058	1149	1256	1352	1418	1457	1555	1619	1653	1750	1854	1953	2053	2153	2300
Torquay 110 116 d.	1857	1929	1935	1956	2025	2125	2250	2335	0954	1103	1154	1301	1357	1423	1501	1600	1624	1658	1755	1859	1958	2058	2158	2305
Newton Abbot 110 116 d.	1910	1942	1948	2009	2037	2138	2301	2347	1007	1115	1208	1313	1409	1437	1516g	1612	1637	1711	1807	1911	2016b	2111	2210	2318
Teignmouth 110 116 d.	1917	1949	1955	2016	2045	2145	...	2354	1014	1121	1216	1320	1416	1444	1524	1619	1644	1718	1814	1918	2024	2118	2217	2325
Dawlish 110 116 d.	1922	1954	2000	2021	2050	2150	...	2359	1019	1126	1221	1325	1421	1449	1529	1624	1649	1723	1819	1923	2029	2123	2222	2330
Exeter St Davids 110 116 a.	1945	2025	2024	2037	2112	2212	...	0022	1040	1148	1242	1341	1441	1512	1542	1640	1711	1739	1839	1948	2052	2139	2242	2352

a – Arrives 9 – 11 minutes earlier.
b – Arrives 6 – 8 minutes earlier.
c – From Sept. 14.
d – Until Sept. 7.
e – Arrives 0822.
f – Arrives 1424.
g – Arrives 1512.
h – Arrives 1806 until Sept. 7.
🚂 – Dartmouth Steam Railway (Paignton - Kingswear). ✆ 01803 555 872. www.dartmouthrailriver.co.uk

112 PLYMOUTH - NEWQUAY and PENZANCE — GW, XC

km			②–⑤	①	②–⑤	①	Ⓐ	Ⓐ	Ⓐ2	Ⓐ	Ⓐ	Ⓐ	Ⓐ	Ⓐ	Ⓐ	Ⓐ	Ⓐ	Ⓐ	Ⓐ	Ⓐ	Ⓐ	Ⓐ	Ⓐ2	Ⓐ	Ⓐ
		Ⓐ	A			A	🍷	2	Ka	2b	2a	b	2	2	2a	2b	🍷	2K	2	🍷	2	🍷b	Nb	2Ba	🍷
	London Paddington **110** d.		2345p	...	...	2350p	...	...	...	...	...	...	...	...	...	...	0635	...	...	0730	...	0903	...	...	1003
	Bristol Temple M **110 116** d.		|	...	...	|	...	...	...	0524	0524	...	...	...	0643	0643	|	...	...	0912	...	|	...	0956c	|
0	**Plymouth** d.		0549	0600	0622	0628	0702	0735	0753	0814	0814	0820	...	0900	0921	0924	0945	1033	1046	1119	1215	1230	...	1242	1314
7	Saltash d.		|	|	|	|	0715	0744	0802	|	0824	0833	...	0910	0931	0934	|	1042	1057	|	1226	1240	...	1251	|
29	Liskeard d.		0615	0623	0645	0709	0736	0803	0821	0838	0843	0854	...	0929	0950	0952	1010	1103	1118	1144	1245	1300	...	1310	1339
43	Bodmin Parkway 🚌 d.		0629	0635	0658	0723	0749	0815	0833	0850	0855	|	...	0941	1002	1004	1023	1117	1132	1157	1257	1313	...	1323	1352
49	Lostwithiel d.		0635	0640	0704	0729	0755	|	0845	0855	0900	|	←	0946	1007	1009	|	|	1137	|	|	1319	...	1329	|
56	Par ❖ ♡ d.		0643	0646	0711	0738	0803	0826	0854	0904	0908	0915	0917	0954	1015	1017	|	1128	1144	1208	1308	1329	1338	1336	1403
89	**Newquay** ❖ ♡ a.		|	|	|	|	|	|	→	→	|	|	1009	|	|	|	|	|	|	|	|	1419	|	|	|
63	St Austell d.		0652	0653	0719	0746	0811	0834	...	...	0916	0923	...	1002	1022	1024	1038	1136	1151	1215	1316	...	1345	1343	1410
86	Truro d.		0710	0709	0736	0806	0829	0855	...	...	0934	0941	...	1023	1040	1041	1056	1153	1208	1233	1333	...	1402	1400	1428
101	Redruth d.		0723	0720	0748	0820	0841	0908	...	...	0947	0953	...	1036	1053	1054	1109	1207	1221	1246	1346	...	1415	1413	1440
107	Camborne d.		0731	0727	0754	0827	0848	0914	...	...	0953	1000	...	1042	1059	1100	1116	1213	1227	1253	1352	...	1421	1419	1448
119	St Erth d.		0745	0739	0807	0845	0901	0926	...	...	1008	1014	...	1053	1110	1110	1126	1225	1238	1303	1404	...	1432	1430	1502
128	**Penzance** a.		0755	0747	0817	0859	0911	0936	...	...	1016	1026	...	1102	1120	1120	1136	1234	1247	1313	1414	...	1441	1439	1512

	Ⓐ	Ⓐ	Ⓐ	Ⓐ	Ⓐ	Ⓐ	Ⓐ	Ⓐ	Ⓐ	Ⓐ	Ⓐ	Ⓐ	Ⓐ	Ⓐ	Ⓐ	Ⓐ	Ⓐ	Ⓐ	Ⓐ	⑤	①–④		⑥	⑥	⑥
	2	2	🍷	2R	2a	2b	🍷b	2	2	🍷	2	2	🍷	C	🍷	D	🍷	C	🍷	🍷	2	⑥ ♣		A	
London Paddington **110** d.	...	...	1203	...	...	...	1303	...	...	1403	...	...	1503	...	1603	...	1703	...	1803	1903	...		...	2345p	...
Bristol Temple M **110 116** d.	...	...	|	...	...	...	|	...	...	|	...	...	|	1645	|	1745	|	1845	|	|	...		...	...	...
Plymouth d.	1342	1409	1511	1534	1556	1556	1626	1645	1701	1725	1755	1817	1845	1901	1931	1951	2033	2051	2126	2229	2242		...	0540	0731
Saltash d.	|	1418	|	1543	1612	1612	|	1654	1714	1736	1804	1831	|	|	1942	|	2044	|	|	2240	2251		...	|	|
Liskeard d.	1408	1437	1537	1604	1633	1633	1654	1713	1736	1757	1823	1852	1910	1924	1958	2014	2103	2114	2151	2300	2310		...	0606	0754
Bodmin Parkway 🚌 d.	1420	1449	1550	1619	1645	...	1707	1725	...	1810	1835	...	1923	1936	2011	2026	2116	2126	2204	2314	2324		...	0620	0806
Lostwithiel d.	1426	1454	|	1624	1651	...	1713	1730	...	1816	1840	...	|	|	|	|	|	2131	|	2320	2329		...	0627	0811
Par ❖ ♡ d.	1434	1501	1601	1632	1658	...	1721	1738	...	1824	1847	...	1934	1948	2023	2036	2126	2137	2215	2329	2336		0610	0635	0819
Newquay ❖ ♡ a.	|	|	|	|	|	...	|	|	...	|	|	...	|	|	|	|	|	|	|	|	|		|	|	0909
St Austell d.	1441	1508	1608	1640	1706	...	1728	1746	...	1831	1855	...	1942	1955	2030	2042	2133	2144	2222	2336	2344		0617	0644	...
Truro d.	1458	1526	1626	1657	1723	...	1746	1803	...	1849	1911	...	2000	2016v	2048	2100	2151	2200	2240	2358v	2359		0635	0705	...
Redruth d.	1512	1539	1638	1710	1736	...	1759	1816	...	1901	1924	...	2012	2027	2100	2112	2203	2211	2252	0013	0014		0648	0718	...
Camborne d.	1518	1545	1646	1716	1742	...	1807	1822	...	1909	1930	...	2020	2034	2108	2119	|	2218	|	0021	0020		0654	0726	...
St Erth d.	1530	1557	1659	1728	1754	...	1820	1834	...	1922	1942	...	2030	2044	2119	2131	2218	2230	|	0035	0031		0705	0740	...
Penzance a.	1539	1610	1709	1738	1804	...	1830	1844	...	1932	1952	...	2040	2052	2129	2140	2228	2238	2313	0045	0040		0715	0750	...

	⑥	⑥	⑥	⑥	⑥	⑥	⑥	⑥	Ⓐ	⑥	⑥	⑥	⑥	⑥	⑥	⑥	⑥	⑥	⑥	⑥	⑥	⑥	⑥	⑥	⑥
		🍷	🍷	🍷	2	🍷	2K	🍷	2	🍷	M	🍷	H	🍷	2	🍷	🍷	2	🍷	J	🍷	C		C	2K
London Paddington **110** d.	...	...	...	...	...	0702	...	0730	...	0903	...	1003	...	1103	...	1135	1203	...	1303	...	1403	...	...	...	...
Bristol Temple M **110 116** d.	...	...	...	0641	...	|	...	0917	...	|	1020	|	1145	|	...	|	|	...	|	1445	|	1545	...	1645	...
Plymouth d.	0739	0818	0903	0921	0950	1030	1050	1125	1148	1227	1239	1316	1351	1421	1445	1503	1516	1550	1623	1650	1726	1746	1752	1854	1910
Saltash d.	|	0828	|	0932	1001	1041	1103	|	|	1238	|	|	|	|	1455	|	|	1559	|	|	|	|	1806	|	1919
Liskeard d.	0804	0848	0928	0948	1022	1102	1120	1150	1214	1254	1306	1341	1414	1446	1514	|	1541	1620	1648	1713	1751	1809	1829	1918	1938
Bodmin Parkway 🚌 d.	0817	0901	0941	1001	1034	1115	1133	1203	1225	1307	1322	1354	1430	1459	1526	|	1554	1632	1701	1728	1804	1821	1842	1930	1950
Lostwithiel d.	0823	0907	|	1008	1040	1121	|	|	1230	|	|	|	|	|	1531	|	|	1638	|	|	|	|	1849	|	1955
Par ❖ ♡ d.	0831	0915	0954	1016	1047	1130	1145	1214	1238	|	1336	1404	1441	|	1539	1548	1605	1645	|	1745	1815	1831	1857	1941	2003
Newquay ❖ ♡ a.	|	|	1047	|	|	|	1239	|	|	|	1429	|	|	|	|	1647	|	|	|	1839	|	|	|	|	|
St Austell d.	0838	0923	...	1023	1054	1137	...	1221	1246	1323	...	1412	1449	1515	1546	...	1612	1652	1716	...	1822	1837	1904	1949	2010
Truro d.	0856	0941	...	1042	1111	1156	...	1240	1303	1341	...	1430	1506	1533	1604	...	1631	1710	1735	...	1841	1854	1923	2007	2028
Redruth d.	0909	0953	...	1054	1124	1209	...	1252	1315	1353	...	1442	1518	1546	1617	...	1643	1723	1747	...	1853	1905	1935	2019	2041
Camborne d.	0916	1001	...	1102	1130	1216	...	1300	1322	1401	...	1449	1524	1554	1623	...	1651	1729	1755	...	1901	1911	1943	2026	2047
St Erth d.	0930	1015	...	1116	1142	1227	...	1314	1335	1415	...	1504	1535	1608	1635	...	1702	1741	1809	...	1911	1923	1956	2036	2101
Penzance a.	0940	1028	...	1126	1151	1237	...	1324	1345	1425	...	1514	1544	1618	1645	...	1712	1751	1819	...	1921	1932	2006	2045	2110

	⑥	⑥	⑥	⑥		⑦	⑦	⑦	⑦	⑦	⑦	⑦	⑦	⑦2	⑦	⑦	⑦	⑦	⑦	⑦	⑦	⑦	⑦	⑦	⑦
	🍷	D	2	🍷	⑦	2	2d	2	2	🍷	🍷d	F	🍷d	Kh	🍷	2	🍷	🍷	2K	🍷	E	2	🍷	C	🍷
London Paddington **110** d.	1603	...	...	1803		...	...	...	...	0805	0903	...	1003	...	1103	...	1203	1303	...	1503	...	...	1703	...	1803
Bristol Temple M **110 116** d.	|	1745	...	|		...	...	0726	0828	1000	|	1057	|	...	|	...	|	|	...	|	1645	...	|	1845	|
Plymouth d.	1930	1948	2042	2121		0900	0920	1005	1113	1214	1235	1302	1329	1331	1415	1450	1530	1625	1735	1825	1853	1943	2025	2051	2140
Saltash d.	|	|	2055	|		0912	|	1012	1122	|	|	|	|	1339	|	1459	|	|	1743	|	|	1952	|	|	|
Liskeard d.	1956	2011	2115	2147		0930	0944	1032	1141	1239	1301	1327	1354	1358	1439	1518	1555	1650	1804	1850	1916	2010	2051	2114	2204
Bodmin Parkway 🚌 d.	2009	2025	2127	2201		0942	0957	1044	1153	1252	1314	1339	1406	1410	1453	1530	1609	1703	1816	1903	1928	2022	2104	2126	2218
Lostwithiel d.	|	2030	2132	|		0947	|	1051	1158	|	|	|	1412	|	|	1536	|	|	1821	|	|	2027	|	|	|
Par ❖ ♡ d.	2020	2036	2139	2212		0954	1012e	1056	1206	1303	1325	1349	1423	1421	|	1544	1621	1714	1828	1913	1938	2034	2114	2136	2231
Newquay ❖ ♡ a.	|	|	|	|		|	1106	|	|	|	|	|	1513	|	|	|	|	|	|	|	|	|	|	|	|
St Austell d.	2027	2043	2147	2219		1001	...	1105	1216	1314	1333	1356	...	1429	1510	1551	1629	1722	1835	1921	1944	2041	2121	2142	2238
Truro d.	2045	2102	2204	2238		1017	...	1121	1234	1335	1351	1412	...	1445	1527	1610	1647	1740	1853	1937	2001	2057	2137	2159	2254
Redruth d.	2057	2113	2217	2250		1029	...	1133	1247	1346	1404	1423	...	1459	1539	1623	1659	1753	1905	1950	2012	2110	2151	2210	2308
Camborne d.	2105	2119	2223	2258		1035	...	1139	1253	1354	1411	1430	...	1506	1547	1629	1707	1801	1911	1959	2018	2116	2157	2216	2315
St Erth d.	2115	2131	2234	2312		1046	...	1150	1305	1405	1423	1440	...	1517	1558	1639	1720	1812	1921	2011	2028	2127	2210	2226	2327
Penzance a.	2125	2141	2245	2322		1055	...	1159	1314	1415	1433	1448	...	1526	1611	1650	1729	1824	1932	2023	2037	2136	2222	2235	2338

A – THE NIGHT RIVIERA – Conveys 🛏 1, 2. cl and (2). See also note ‡ on page 101.
B – From Sept. 9 from Cardiff Central (Tables **110** and **115**).
C – From/to Glasgow Central (Table **116**).
D – From Aberdeen (Tables **222**/**116**).
E – From/to Edinburgh (Table **116**).
F – From Birmingham New Street (Table **116**).
H – From York (Table **116**).
J – From/to Dundee (Tables **222**/**116**).
K – From/to Exeter St Davids (Table **110**).
M – From/to Manchester Piccadilly (Table **116**).
N – From Newquay.
P – To Leeds (Table **116**).
Q – To Penzance.
R – From/to Newton Abbot (Table **110**).
a – Until July 5 and from Sept. 2.
b – July 8 - Aug. 30.
c – From Sept. 9.
d – Until Sept. 8.
e – Arrives 1008.
f – Arrives 1411.
g – Arrives 1948.
h – From Sept. 15.
k – Arrives 2339 on ⑤.
p – Previous night.
t – Arrives 0507 on ⑥ morning
v – Arrives 5–6 minutes earlie

NOTES CONTINUE ON NEXT PAGE ►►►►

113 BRANCH LINES and BUS CONNECTIONS IN DEVON and CORNWALL — 2nd class GW

EXETER - EXMOUTH *'The Avocet Line'* *18 km*

From Exeter St Davids: on ⚒ at 0544, 0606Ⓐ, 0629, 0707Ⓐ, 0710⑥, 0736Ⓐ, 0744⑥, 0815, 0845, 0916, 0948 and at the same minutes past each hour until 1615, 1647, 1715, 1745⑥, 1753Ⓐ, 1814⑥, 1821Ⓐ, 1845⑥, 1850Ⓐ, 1932⑥, 1933Ⓐ, 2033, 2131Ⓐ, 2140⑥, 2231Ⓐ, 2240⑥, 2309⑥, 2326Ⓐ; on ⑦ at 0830, 0940, 1013, 1044, 1122**a**, 1151, 1226**a**, 1247, 1322**a**, 1349, 1446, 1518, 1546, 1622**a**, 1646, 1716, 1746, 1846, 1951, 2054, 2148, 2248, 2325.

From Exmouth: on ⚒ at 0001①, 0004②–⑥, 0614, 0643Ⓐ, 0712Ⓐ, 0718⑥, 0751, 0822, 0852, 0923, 0953 and at the same minutes past each hour until 1653, 1724, 1753⑥, 1801Ⓐ, 1823⑥, 1832Ⓐ, 1854⑥, 1859Ⓐ, 1939, 2007⑥, 2015Ⓐ, 2111Ⓐ, 2116⑥, 2207Ⓐ, 2219⑥, 2307Ⓐ, 2317⑥, 2345⑥; on ⑦ at 0910, 1019, 1054**b**, 1124, 1200**b**, 1228, 1255, 1324, 1358, 1427, 1523, 1555**b**, 1623, 1655, 1723, 1755, 1823, 1923, 2028, 2130, 2227, 2329.

Journey: 37–40 minutes. Trains call at Exeter Central 3–4 minutes from Exeter St Davids.

a – Starts from Exeter Central. **b** – Terminates at Exeter Central.

EXETER - BARNSTAPLE *'The Tarka Line'* *63 km*

From Exeter St Davids: on ⚒ at 0548Ⓐ, 0554⑥, 0648Ⓐ, 0654⑥, 0831, 0927, 1027, 1127, 1227, 1327Ⓐ, 1330⑥, 1427Ⓐ, 1430⑥, 1527, 1657, 1757, 1852⑥, 1901Ⓐ, 2100, 2253⑤; on ⑦ at 0839, 0949, 1205, 1408, 1605, 1807, 2001.

From Barnstaple: on ⚒ at 0005⑥, 0658Ⓐ, 0705⑥, 0843, 0943, 1043Ⓐ, 1045⑥, 1143, 1243, 1343, 1443, 1543, 1710⑥, 1713Ⓐ, 1811⑥, 1814Ⓐ, 1917, 2024, 2216Ⓐ, 2230⑥; on ⑦ at 0958, 1129, 1322, 1528, 1721, 1926, 2130.

Journey: 65 minutes. Trains call at ***Crediton*** *(11 minutes from Exeter/54 minutes from Barnstaple) and* ***Eggesford*** *(40 minutes from Exeter/25 minutes from Barnstaple).*

PLYMOUTH - GUNNISLAKE *'The Tamar Valley Line'* *24 km*

From Plymouth: on Ⓐ at 0506, 0641, 0840, 1054, 1254, 1454, 1637, 1823, 2131; on ⑥ at 0641, 0837, 1054, 1254, 1454, 1639, 1823, 2131; on ⑦ at 0910, 1117, 1306, 1511, 1741, 2001**c**.

From Gunnislake: on Ⓐ at 0551, 0731, 0929, 1145, 1345, 1545, 1727, 1913, 2221; on ⑥ at 0731, 0927, 1145**d**, 1151**c**, 1345, 1545, 1729, 1913**d**, 1918**c**, 2221; on ⑦ at 1010, 1207, 1358, 1604, 1835, 2050**c**.

Journey: 45–60 minutes *For notes - see below.*

LISKEARD - LOOE *°'The Looe Valley Line'* *14 km*

From Liskeard:
on Ⓐ at 0605, 0714, 0850, 1014, 1115, 1216, 1319, 1424, 1541, 1641, 1806, 1920; on ⑥ 0610, 0714, 0817, 0956, 1110, 1222, 1339, 1439**c**, 1442**d**, 1548**c**, 1551**d**, 1655, 1758, 192 2041**c**; on ⑦ until Oct. 20 at 1009, 1125, 1248, 1359**c**, 1402**d**, 1502**c**, 1523**d**, 1610**c**, 1635 1735**c** 1740**d**, 2015.

From Looe:
on Ⓐ at 0637, 0746, 0929, 1044, 1147, 1248, 1351, 1458, 1613, 1715, 1842, 1952; on ⑥ 0638, 0746, 0851**c**, 0853**d**, 1027, 1142, 1254, 1411, 1514**c**, 1517**d**, 1617**c**, 1623**d**, 172 1830, 2000, 2113**c**; on ⑦ until Oct. 21 at 1041, 1157, 1320, 1431**c**, 1434**d**, 1534**c**, 1555 1642**c**, 1707**d**, 1815, 2047.

Journey: 28–33 minutes. **c** – Until Sept. 8. **d** – From Sept. 14.

EXETER - OKEHAMPTON *Service runs only summer ⑦.* 40 km

From Exeter St. Davids: On ⑦ until Sept. 8 at 0904, 1108, 1434, 1705.
From Okehampton: On ⑦ until Sept. 8 at 0953, 1214, 1552, 1756.

Journey: 40–42 minutes. Trains call at ***Crediton*** *(approx. 10 minutes from Exeter).*

GW, XC — PENZANCE and NEWQUAY - PLYMOUTH — 112

		Ⓐ 🍸	Ⓐ 2	Ⓐ 🍸	Ⓐ 2K	Ⓐ C	Ⓐ 🍸	Ⓐ 2	Ⓐ 🍸	Ⓐ C	Ⓐ 🍸	Ⓐ J	Ⓐ 🍸	Ⓐ 2	Ⓐ 🍸b	Ⓐ 2a	Ⓐ 2K	Ⓐ 2R	Ⓐ 🍸	Ⓐ2 Qb	Ⓐ 2R	Ⓐ 2	Ⓐ 🍸	Ⓐ 2b
enzance d.	Ⓐ	0505	0519	0541	0600	0635	0647	0730	0741	0837	0900	0925	1000	1017	1049	1051	1112	1141	1204	...	1256	1325	1400	1449
t Erth d.		|	|	|	0609	0643	0657	0739	0751	0845	0910	0934	1010	1026	1059	1100	1121	1150	1214	...	1305	1334	1410	1458
amborne d.		|	0539	0558	0621	0653	0708	0750	0806	0855	0921	0948	1021	1037	1114	1113	1132	1203	|	...	1318	1318	1421	1511
edruth d.		0526	|	0605	0628	0659	0715	0756	0812	0901	0927	0954	1027	1043	1121	1119	1138	1209	1228	...	1324	1351	1428	1517
ruro d.		0538	0554	0618	0639	0711	0728	0807	0825	0913	0940	1007	1040	1054	1134	1130	1149	1220	1241	...	1335	1402	1441	1528
t Austell d.		0556	...	0635	0656	0727	0745	0824	0843	0929	0957	1024	1058	1111	1151	1147	1206	1237	1259	...	1352	1419	1458	1545
Newquay ★ ♡ d.		|	...	|	|	|	|	|	|	|	|	|	|	|	|	|	|	|	|	1240	|	|	|	|
ar ★ ♡ d.		|	...	0642	0702	0733	0753	0830	0850	0935	1004	1031	1105	1117	1158	1153	1212	1243	|	1335	1359	1425	1506	1551
ostwithiel d.		|	...	0650	0709	|	0800	|	|	|	|	1038	|	1124	|	1200	|	1250	|	...	1405	|	|	...
odmin Parkway 🚂 d.		0611	...	0657	0715	0744	0807	0841	0901	0946	1016	1044	1116	1130	1210	1206	1223	1256	1315	...	1411	1436	1517	...
iskeard d.		0624	...	0710	0728	0756	0820	0854	0914	0958	1029	1056	1129	1143	1223	1219	1236	1309	1328	...	1424	1453	1530	...
altash d.		|	...	0730	0746	|	0839	0911	0934	|	|	|	|	1201	1242	1237	1253	1328	|	...	1444	|	|	...
lymouth a.		0648	...	0740	0803	0820	0849	0920	0945	1021	1054	1120	1155	1210	1252	1248	1302	1338	1352	...	1453	1517	1555	...
Bristol Temple M 110 116 a.		|	...	|	...	1025	|	...	|	1222	|	1325	|	...	|	...	...	...	|	...	...	...	|	...
London Paddington 110 a.		1002	...	1121	...	...	1221	...	1315	...	1401	...	1522	...	1621	...	...	...	1716	...	...	...	1920	...

	Ⓐ 🍸b	Ⓐ 2a	Ⓐ 🍸	Ⓐ 2	Ⓐ 2	Ⓐ 2K	Ⓐ 2	Ⓐ 🍸		Ⓐ 2	Ⓐ 2a	Ⓐ 2b	Ⓐ 2b	①–④ 2	⑤ 🍸	Ⓐ A	Ⓐ		⑥ 2	⑥ 2	⑥ C	⑥ 🍸	⑥ 2	⑥ 🍸
enzance d.	...	1449	1600	1611	...	1644	1710	1742	...	1845	1915	1915	...	2018	2018	2145	2210	⑥	0520	0540	0630	0648	0739	0753
t Erth d.	...	1458	1610	1620	...	1653	1719	1752	...	1854	1924	1925	...	2028	2028	2159	2218		|	0549	0638	0658	0748	0803
amborne d.	...	1511	1621	1633	...	1706	1732	1807	...	1907	1937	1940	...	2043	2042	2211	2231		0537	0602	0651	0709	0802	0818
edruth d.	...	1517	1628	1639	...	1712	1738	1814	...	1913	1943	1947	...	2049	2048	2219	2238		0543	0608	0658	0716	0808	0824
ruro d.	...	1528	1641	1650	...	1725	1749	1826	...	1925	1954	2000	...	2101	2101	2232	2249	♣	0553	0619	0709	0729	0820	0837
t Austell d.	...	1545	1658	1707	...	1742	1806	1844	...	1943	2011	2018	...	2118	2117	2251	2305		...	0636	0725	0746	0837	0856
Newquay ★ ♡ d.	1507	|	|	|	...	|	|	|	...	|	|	|	...	|	|	|	|		...	|	|	|	|	|
ar ★ ♡ d.	1601	1552	1706	1715	...	1748	1813	1851	...	1950	2018	2025	...	2125	2125	2259	2312		...	0643	0732	0753	0844	0903
ostwithiel d.	1610	1558	1713	1722	...	1755	1820	|	...	|	2025	2033	...	2132	2131	|	2318		...	0650	0738	0801	0851	|
odmin Parkway 🚂 d.	1617	1604	1720	1728	...	1801	1826	1902	...	2001	2031	2039	...	2138	2138	2312	2325		...	0656	0745	0807	0857	0915
iskeard d.	1630	1617	1733	1740	1749	1814	1839	1915	...	2014	2044	2052	2104	2151	2151	2327	2337		...	0709	0757	0820	0910	0928
altash d.	|	1637	|	|	1806	1832	1856	|	...	|	2103	|	2123	2209	2209	|	|		...	0728	|	|	0931	|
lymouth a.	1654	1651	1758	1804	1818	1841	1906	1941	...	2038	2120	2117	2138	2220	2222	2353	0002		...	0745	0820	0845	0942	0952
Bristol Temple M 110 116 a.	|	...	|	...	...	...	...	2147	...	...	...	...	...	...	...	|	...		...	...	1021	|	...	|
London Paddington 110 a.	2037	...	2122	...	...	...	...	2342k	...	...	...	...	...	...	...	0503t	...		...	...	...	1221	...	1321

	⑥ C	⑥ 🍸	⑥ 🍸J	⑥ 🍸	⑥ 🍸	⑥	⑥ 🍸.	⑥ 🍸	⑥ 🍸	⑥ 2	⑥ 🍸	⑥ 2R	⑥ 🍸	⑥ 2	⑥ 🍸	⑥ M	⑥ 🍸	⑥ P	⑥ 🍸	⑥ 🍸	⑥ 🍸	⑥ 2	⑥ 2	⑥
enzance d.	0828	0855	...	0930	1000	1018	1058	...	1200	1240	1307	...	1400	1430	1500	...	1552	1630	1655	...	1742	1806	1832	...
t Erth d.	0836	0906	...	0941	1011	1029	1109	...	1211	1252	1318	...	1410	1438	1510	...	1602	1639	1705	...	1752	1815	1841	...
amborne d.	0846	0922	...	0956	1022	1043	1124	...	1226	1305	1333	...	1421	1452	1525	...	1614	1650	1720	...	1806	1828	1852	...
edruth d.	0852	0929	...	1003	1028	1050	1132	...	1234	1311	1340	...	1428	1458	1532	...	1621	1658	1727	...	1813	1834	1858	...
ruro d.	0904	0943	...	1017	1042	1103	1146	...	1247	1323	1353	...	1441	1510	1545	...	1634	1710	1740	...	1826	1846	1910	...
t Austell d.	0920	1000	...	1034	1059	1121	1204	...	1305	1340	1410	...	1459	1526	1603	...	1652	1727	1758	...	1843	1903	1927	...
Newquay ★ ♡ d.	|	|	0940	|	|	|	|	1128	|	|	|	1322	|	|	|	1535	|	|	|	1728	|	|	|	1900
ar ★ ♡ d.	0926	1007	1028	1042	1107	1128	|	1223	|	1347	1418	1427f	1506	1534	1610	1627v	1659	1735	1805	1822	1850	1910	1934	1959g
ostwithiel d.	|	|	|	|	|	1135	|	|	|	1354	|	1435	|	1541	1618	|	1706	|	1813	|	|	1917	|	|
odmin Parkway 🚂 d.	0937	1019	1039	1053	1118	1142	1220	|	1321	1400	1429	1441	1518	1546	1625	1638	1713	1745	1819	1834	1902	1923	1945	2010
iskeard d.	0949	1032	1051	1106	1131	1155	1234	|	1334	1413	1442	1454	1532	1559	1638	1652	1726	1757	1832	1847	1915	1938	1958	2022
altash d.	|	|	|	|	|	1217	|	|	|	1431	|	1514	|	1614	1658	|	|	|	1852	|	|	1956	2014	|
lymouth a.	1016	1055	1114	1130	1155	1227	1258	1308	1358	1442	1507	1525	1556	1625	1710	1716	1749	1821	1902	1918	1938	2010	2025	2046
Bristol Temple M 110 116 a.	1221	|	1324	|	|	...	|	|	|	...	|	...	|	...	...	1923	|	2023	...	|	2146	...	...	...
London Paddington 110 a.	...	1400	...	1516	1521	...	1621	1631	1721	...	1821	...	1922	...	...	...	2131	...	...	2244	2343	...	...	...

	⑥ 2K	⑥ 2	⑥		⑦ 🍸	⑦ E	⑦ 🍸	⑦ 🍸	⑦ Ed	⑦ 🍸d	⑦ 2K	⑦ M	⑦ 🍸	⑦ 2K	⑦ 2	⑦ 🍸	⑦ P	⑦ 🍸d	⑦ 🍸	⑦ 🍸	⑦ 2d	⑦ 2K	⑦ 2	⑦ A
enzance d.	1906	...	2130	⑦	0803	0930	0945	1100	...	1140	1204	1230	1300	1337	1437	1500	1530	...	1613	1735	1755	1900	2012	2115
t Erth d.	1915	...	2139		0812	0938	0954	1110	...	1149	1213	1238	1309	1347	1448v	1510	1538	...	1624	1744	1804	1909	2022	2125
amborne d.	1929	...	2149		0828	0948	1005	1122	...	1201	1224	1251	1323	1400	1500	1522	1548	...	1636	1757	1817	1920	2035	2139
edruth d.	1935	...	2156		0833	0955	1011	1128	...	1207	1230	1258	1329	1406	1506	1529	1555	...	1643	1804	1823	1926	2041	2146
ruro d.	1946	...	2208		0847	1008	1024	1142	...	1221	1241	1309	1342	1417	1517	1542	1606	...	1656	1816	1834	1938	2053	2201
t Austell d.	2003	...	2225		0904	1024	1042	1158	...	1238	1257	1326	1400	1434	1534	1600	1623	...	1714	1835	1851	1955	2110	2219
Newquay ★ ♡ d.	|	2118	|		|	|	|	|	1138	|	|	|	|	|	|	|	|	1559	|	|	|	|	|	|
ar ★ ♡ d.	2010	2212v	2232		0912	1030	1050	1205	1225	1246	1303	1332	1406	1441	1540	1607	1629	1653	1720	1842	1858	2002	2117	|
ostwithiel d.	2017	2219	|		|	|	|	|	|	|	1312	1339	|	1448	1547	|	|	|	|	|	1904	2008	2123	|
odmin Parkway 🚂 d.	2023	2225	2243		0923	1041	1102	1218	1237	1258	1316	1346	1419	1453	1553	1618	1640	1705	1731	1853	1910	2014	2129	2235
iskeard d.	2036	2238	2255		0936	1053	1115	1231	1249	1311	1332	1358	1432	1506	1606	1631	1652	1718	1745	1906	1923	2027	2142	2250
altash d.	2056	2258	|		0953	|	1127	|	|	|	1352	|	|	1524	1624	|	|	|	1802	|	1939	2046	2200	|
lymouth a.	2111	2313	2318		1002	1116	1140	1257	1312	1337	1402	1423	1456	1532	1633	1656	1715	1741	1811	1930	1955	2059	2210	2313
Bristol Temple M 110 116 a.	...	...	...		|	1321	|	|	1521	|	...	1648	|	...	1912	|	1923	|	|	|	...	...	...	|
London Paddington 110 a.	...	...	...		1352	...	1514	1621	...	1722	...	...	1816	...	...	2021	...	2114	2124	2333	...	...	...	0502

OTES (CONTINUED FROM PREVIOUS PAGE)

♣ – Service until Sept. 8 only.
♡ – Par - Newquay: *'The Atlantic Coast Line'*.
🚂 – Bodmin & Wenford Railway (Bodmin Parkway - Bodmin General - Boscarne Junction *10 km*). ✆ 01208 73555. www.bodminrailway.co.uk

✣ – Additional trains **Par - Newquay**: On Ⓐ at 1144**b**, 1211**a**, 1407**a**, 1610, 1829, 2028; on ⑥ at 2023**d**; on ⑦ at 0900**d**, 1010**h**, 1149**d**, 1315**h**, 1634**h**, 1646**d**, 1922**d**.
★ – Additional trains **Newquay - Par**: On Ⓐ at 1013, 1305**a**, 1501**a**, 1722, 1924, 2126; on ⑦ at 0958**d**, 1112**h**, 1310**d**, 1510**h**, 1745, 2020**d**.

GW 2nd class — BRANCH LINES and BUS CONNECTIONS IN DEVON and CORNWALL — 113

Rail tickets are generally not valid on 🚌 services shown in this table.

BODMIN PARKWAY - PADSTOW — *Plymouth City Bus 🚌 service 11A*

rom **Bodmin Parkway** station:
1 ⚒ at 0612, 0652**n**, 0707**p**, 0747**n**, 0807**p**, 0907**p**, 1007 and hourly until 1607⑥, 1612Ⓐ, 722, 1812;
1 ⑦ at 0756, 0956, 1156, 1356, 1556, 1751.

rom **Padstow** Bus Terminus:
1 ⚒ at 0625, 0730, 0830**p**, 0930 and hourly until 1430, 1520**n**, 1530**p**, 1630, 1730, 1830, 1920;
1 ⑦ at 0905, 1105, 1305, 1505, 1705, 1905.

*ourney: 68 minutes. Buses also make calls in Bodmin town centre and at Bodmin General ation, and call at **Wadebridge** (35 minutes after Bodmin / 25 minutes after Padstow).*

RURO - FALMOUTH DOCKS — *'The Maritime Line'* — *20 km*

om **Truro**:
1 ⚒ at 0604, 0631, 0716, 0747, 0820, 0851 and at the same minutes past each hour until 520, 1651, 1727, 1759, 1831, 1902, 2004, 2105, 2212⑥, 2244Ⓐ, ;
1 ⑦ at 0909, 1036, 1136, 1239, 1344, 1440, 1547, 1710, 1825, 1955, 2103, 2204.

om **Falmouth Docks**:
1 ⚒ at 0631, 0716, 0747, 0820, 0850 and at the same minutes past each hour until 1620, 550Ⓐ, 1652⑥, 1727, 1759, 1831, 1902, 1929Ⓐ, 1934⑥, 2031, 2132, 2239⑥, 2311Ⓐ;
1 ⑦ at 0937, 1103, 1203, 1306, 1411, 1509, 1614, 1740, 1852, 2022, 2130, 2233.

*rains call at **Falmouth Town** 22 minutes after Truro and 3 minutes after Falmouth Docks.*
ourney: 25 minutes.

– Until Sept. 8.
– From Sept. 14.
– Sept 15- Oct. 20.
– From Oct. 27.
g – Until Oct. 20.
n – Schooldays - check locally for details.
p – School holidays (check locally for details) and ⑥.

ST AUSTELL - EDEN PROJECT — *First Kernow 🚌 service 101*

From St Austell bus station:
on Ⓐ at 0846, 0928, 1042, 1151, 1243, 1413, 1502, 1553, 1645, 1739;
on ⑥ at 0846, 0928, 1040, 1140, 1243, 1411, 1504, 1558, 1645, 1739;
on ⑦ at 0846, 0928, 1031, 1125, 1220, 1330, 1441, 1539, 1632, 1739.

From Eden Project:
on Ⓐ at 0907, 1110, 1212, 1328, 1431, 1522, 1614, 1716, 1800;
on ⑥ at 0907, 1106, 1209, 1328, 1432, 1525, 1624, 1707, 1800;
on ⑦ at 0907, 0959, 1052, 1147, 1248, 1401, 1506, 1600, 1651, 1800.

Journey: 20 minutes.

ST ERTH - ST IVES — *'The St Ives Bay Line'* — *7 km*

From St Erth: on Ⓐ at 0706, 0754, 0853, 0942, 1018 and every 30 minutes until 1648, 1717, 1748 and every 30 minutes until 2048, 2123, 2158; on ⑥ at 0647, 0752, 0854, 0945**c**, 0955**d**, 1022, 1052, 1120, 1152, 1222, 1253, 1322, 1352, 1422, 1452, 1522, 1552, 1622, 1650, 1722, 1800, 1905, 2000, 2030, 2105, 2147; on ⑦ at 0853**c**, 0925**c**, 1000**c**, 1030**c**, 1036**e**, 1113**g**, 1141**g**, 1155**f**, 1218**g**, 1230**f**, 1248**g**, 1318, 1348, 1417, 1448, 1518, 1548, 1618, 1648, 1728**c**, 1730**d**, 1757**d**, 1801**c**, 1828**d** 1830**c**, 1930.

From St Ives: on Ⓐ at 0725, 0810, 0920, 0955, 1033, 1102, 1133 and every 30 minutes until 1703, 1731, 1803, 1833, 1905, 1932, 2003, 2033, 2103, 2137, 2231; on ⑥ at 0715, 0815, 0908, 0959**c**, 1008**d**, 1036, 1106, 1134, 1206 and every 30 minutes until 1636, 1704, 1736, 1820, 1925, 2015, 2044, 2120, 2205; on ⑦ at 0910**c**, 0939**c**, 1015**c**, 1045**c**, 1053**e**, 1126**g**, 1156**g**, 1210**f**, 1233**g**, 1245**f**, 1303**g**, 1333, 1402, 1431, 1503, 1533, 1603, 1633, 1703, 1741, 1811**d**, 1814**c**, 1845**c**, 1850**d**, 1945.

Journey: 15 minutes.

114 BIRMINGHAM - READING - SOUTHAMPTON - BOURNEMOUTH

Most services convey 🍸 XC

km			Ⓐ	Ⓐ	⑥	⑥	Ⓐ	⑥	Ⓐ	⑥B	Ⓐ	⚒A	Ⓐ	⑥	⚒	Ⓐ	⑥	⚒	Ⓐ	⑥	⚒	⚒E	Ⓐ	⑥	Ⓐ
	Manchester Piccadilly **119** d.		...	...	...	...	...	0511	0511	...	...	...	...	...	0727	...	...	0827	...	...	0927	...	1027	1027	...
	Newcastle **124** d.	⚒	...	...	...	...	...	|	|	...	...	...	...	...	|	0625	0623	|	0725	0735	|	0835	|	|	0935
	York **124** d.		...	...	...	...	...	|	|	...	...	...	0622	0624	|	0726	0725	|	0827	0835	|	0935	|	|	1035
	Leeds **124** d.		...	...	...	...	...	|	|	...	...	...	|	|	|	|	|	|	|	|	|	|	|	|	|
	Sheffield **124** d.		...	...	...	...	...	|	|	0545a	0559	...	0718	0718	|	0818	0818	|	0924	0924	|	1024	|	|	1124
0	**Birmingham** New St. **142 150** d.		...	0604	0604	0633	0633	0704	0704	0733	0733	0804	0833	0834	0904	0933	0933	1004	1033	1033	1104	1133	1204	1204	1233
13	Birmingham Int'l ✈. **142 150** d.		...	0614	0614	|	|	0714	0714	|	|	0814	|	|	0914	|	|	1014	|	|	1114	|	1214	1214	|
30	Coventry **141 142 150** d.		...	0625	0625	|	|	0725	0725	|	|	0825	|	|	0925	|	|	1025	|	|	1125	|	1225	1225	|
45	Leamington Spa **128 141** d.		...	0637	0637	0700	0700	0737	0737	0801	0800	0837	0900	0901	0937	1000	1003	1037	1100	1100	1137	1203	1237	1237	1300
77	Banbury **128** d.		...	0654	0654	0717	0717	0754	0754	0818	0817	0854	0917	0918	0954	1017	1020	1054	1117	1117	1154	1220	1254	1254	1320
114	Oxford a.		...	0714	0712	0740	0737	0812	0814	0839	0839	0915	0941	0941	1012	1040	1039	1112	1140	1141	1212	1240	1312	1312	1340
114	Oxford **131** d.		...	0716	0716	0742	0743	0816	0816	0843	0843	0916	0944	0944	1016	1043	1041	1116	1143	1143	1216	1241	1316	1316	1342
158	**Reading** **131** a.		...	0740	0741	0805	0809	0837	0840	0910	0908	0942	1009	1007	1042	1110	1107	1142	1206	1207	1243	1309d	1341	1342	1409
158	**Reading** d.		...	0752	0752	0822	0820	0852	0849	...	...	0952	1020	1022	1048c	...	...	1152	1222	1222	1250	...	1352	1347	1418
183	Basingstoke **106** a.		...	0809	0808	0840	0842	0911	0910	...	...	1009	1042	1040	1110	...	...	1210	1242	1242	1309	...	1410	1409	1441
213	Winchester **106** a.		...	0826	0826	0858	0857	0926	0926	...	...	1026	1058	1056	1127	...	...	1226	1258	1258	1326	...	1426	1425	1458
226	**Southampton** Airport ✈ **106** a.		...	0835	0835	0908	0908	0935	0935	...	...	1035	1108	1109	1136	...	...	1235	1308	1308	1335	...	1434	1433	1508
234	**Southampton** Central **106** a.		0756	0842	0843	0917	0917	0943	0943	...	...	1043	1117	1117	1143	...	...	1243	1317	1317	1342	...	1442	1443	1517
255	Brockenhurst **106** a.		0809	0900	0856	...	...	0958	0958	...	...	1058	...	...	1158	...	...	1258	...	...	1358	...	1457	1458	...
280	**Bournemouth** **106** a.		0824	0916	0913	...	...	1013	1013	...	...	1113	...	...	1213	...	...	1313	...	...	1413	...	1512	1513	...

	⑥	⚒	⚒	⚒	⑥	Ⓐ	⚒	Ⓐ	⑥	⚒	⚒G	⚒	⚒	⑥	Ⓐ	⚒	⚒	⚒	Ⓐ	⑥	⑥	Ⓐ	Ⓐ	⑥	Ⓐ
Manchester Piccadilly **119** d.	...	1127	...	1227	...	...	1327	...	...	1427	...	1527	...	1627	1627	...	1727	...	1827	1827	...	...	1927	1927	*2005*
Newcastle **124** d.	0935	|	1035	|	1135	1135	|	1235	1235	|	1335	|	1436	|	|	1505	|	1635	|	|	1732	1732	|	|	|
York **124** d.	1035	|	1135	|	1235	1235	|	1335	1335	|	1435	|	1535	|	|	1604	|	1735	|	|	1835	1836	|	|	|
Leeds **124** d.	|	|	|	|	|	|	|	|	|	|	|	|	|	|	|	1635	|	|	|	|	|	|	|	|	|
Sheffield **124** d.	1124	|	1224	|	1324	1324	|	1424	1424	|	1524	|	1624	|	|	1724	|	1824	|	|	1924	1924	|	|	|
Birmingham New St. **142 150** d.	1233	1304	1333	1404	1433	1433	1504	1533	1533	1604	1633	1704	1733	1804	1804	1833	1904	1933	2004	2004	2033	2033	2104	2104	2204
Birmingham Int'l ✈ .**142 150** d.	|	1314	|	1414	|	|	1514	|	|	1614	|	1714	|	1814	1814	|	1914	|	2014	2014	|	|	2114	2114	2214
Coventry **141 142 150** d.	|	1325	|	1425	|	|	1525	|	|	1625	|	1725	|	1825	1825	|	1925	|	2025	2025	|	|	2125	2125	2225
Leamington Spa **128 141** d.	1300	1337	1401	1437	1500	1500	1537	1603	1603	1637	1700	1737	1800	1837	1837	1900	1937	2002	2037	2037	2100	2100	2137	2137	2237
Banbury **128** d.	1317	1354	1420	1454	1521	1517	1554	1621	1620	1654	1717	1754	1817	1854	1855	1917	1954	2019	2054	2056	2117	2117	2154	2154	2254
Oxford a.	1341	1412	1440	1514	1542	1540	1612	1641	1639	1714	1741	1813	1840	1912	1914	1941	2012	2040	2112	2114	2135	2139	2213	2212	2312
Oxford **131** d.	1343	1415	1443	1516	1546	1543	1616	1644	1641	1716	1742	1816	1842	1916	1916	1943	2016	2040	2116	2116	2140	2149	2216	2218	2316
Reading **131** a.	1407	1440	1507	1541	1610	1610	1641	1707	1704	1740	1810d	1843	1910d	1940	1939	2007	2040	2106	2141	2139	2204	2214	2240	2239	2351
Reading d.	1422	1452	...	1552	1622	1620	1652	...	...	1752	...	1852	...	1952	1952	...	2052	...	2152	2148	2222	2222	2252	2252	...
Basingstoke **106** a.	1440	1510	...	1610	1640	1642	1710	...	...	1809	...	1909	...	2009	2009	...	2109	...	2209	2208	2241	2240	2308	2308	...
Winchester **106** a.	1458	1526	...	1626	1658	1658	1726	...	...	1825	...	1926	...	2026	2026	...	2126	...	2224	2226	2256	2258	2325	2326	...
Southampton Airport ✈ **106** a.	1508	1535	...	1635	1708	1708	1735	...	...	1834	...	1935	...	2035	2035	...	2135	...	2233	2235	2311	2311	2336	2335	...
Southampton Central **106** a.	1517	1542	...	1643	1717	1717	1742	...	...	1842	...	1942	...	2042	2043	...	2142	...	2241	2242	2320	2320	2343	2343	...
Brockenhurst **106** a.	...	1558	...	1658	...	...	1758	...	...	1858	...	1957	...	2058	2101	...	2158	...	2258	2258	...	...	...	...	...
Bournemouth **106** a.	...	1613	...	1714	...	...	1814	...	...	1913	...	2012	...	2113	2116	...	2215	...	2317	2319	...	...	...	...	...

		⑦	⑦	⑦	⑦		⑦	⑦	⑦	⑦	⑦	⑦D	⑦	⑦	⑦	⑦	⑦	⑦	⑦	⑦E	⑦	⑦	⑦	⑦G	⑦
Manchester Piccadilly **119** d.		...	...	0827	0927	...	1027	...	1127	...	1227	...	1327	...	1427	...	1527	...	1627	...	1727	...	1827	...	1927
Newcastle **124** d.	⑦	...	...	|	|	...	|	...	|	...	|	...	|	...	|	1336	|	1436	|	1524	|	1635	|	1735	|
York **124** d.		...	...	|	|	...	|	...	|	...	|	...	|	...	|	1435	|	1535	|	1625	|	1735	|	1835	|
Leeds **124** d.		...	...	|	|	...	|	...	|	...	|	...	|	...	|	|	|	|	|	|	|	|	|	|	|
Sheffield **124** d.		...	...	|	|	...	|	...	|	...	|	...	|	1422	|	1524	|	1624	|	1724	|	1824	|	1924	|
Birmingham New St. **142 150** d.		...	0904	1004	1104	...	1204	1233	1304	1333	1404	1433	1504	1533	1604	1633	1704	1733	1804	1833	1904	1933	2004	2033	2104
Birmingham Int'l ✈ .**142 150** d.		...	0914	1014	1114	...	1214	1243	1314	|	1414	1443	1514	|	1614	1644	1714	|	1814	1843	1914	1944	2014	|	2114
Coventry **141 142 150** d.		...	0925	1025	1125	...	1225	1255	1325	|	1425	1455	1525	|	1625	1655	1725	|	1825	1855	1925	1955	2025	|	2125
Leamington Spa **128 141** d.		...	0937	1037	1137	...	1237	1309	1338	1400	1437	1509	1537	1600	1637	1709	1737	1800	1837	1909	1937	2009	2037	2100	2137
Banbury **128** d.		...	0954	1054	1154	...	1254	1326	1355	1417	1454	1526	1554	1617	1654	1726	1754	1817	1854	1926	1954	2026	2054	2118	2154
Oxford a.		...	1012	1112	1212	...	1312	1344	1413	1435	1512	1544	1612	1635	1712	1744	1812	1835	1912	1944	2012	2044	2112	2137	2212
Oxford **131** d.		...	1016	1116	1216	...	1316	1346	1416	1437	1516	1546	1616	1637	1716	1746	1816	1837	1916	1946	2016	2046	2116	2139	2216
Reading **131** a.		...	1039	1139	1239	...	1339	1409	1439	1500	1539	1609	1639	1700	1739	1809	1839	1900	1939	2009	2039	2109	21389	2202	2240
Reading d.		0952	1052	1152	1252	...	1352	...	1452	...	1552	...	1652	...	1752	...	1852	...	1952	...	2052	...	2152	...	...
Basingstoke **106** a.		1010	1109	1209	1309	...	1409	...	1509	...	1609	...	1709	...	1809	...	1909	...	2009	...	2109	...	2209	...	...
Winchester **106** a.		1026	1125	1226	1326	...	1426	...	1526	...	1626	...	1724	...	1824	...	1924	...	2024	...	2126	...	2225	...	...
Southampton Airport ✈ **106** a.		1035	1133	1234	1334	...	1434	...	1534	...	1635	...	1733	...	1833	...	1933	...	2033	...	2134	...	2233	...	...
Southampton Central **106** a.		1042	1143	1243	1343	...	1443	...	1543	...	1642	...	1742	...	1842	...	1942	...	2042	...	2143	...	2243	...	...
Brockenhurst **106** a.		1107	1207	1307	1407	...	1507	...	1607	...	1706	...	1806	...	1906	...	2006	...	2106	...	2207	...	...	...	...
Bournemouth **106** a.		1126	1226	1326	1426	...	1526	...	1626	...	1726	...	1826	...	1926	....	2026	...	2126	...	2226	...	...	...	...

A – From Nottingham (Tables **117/124**).
B – Starts from Derby from Sept. 14 (Table **124**).
D – From Derby (Table **124**).
E – From Edinburgh Waverley (Table **124**).
G – To Guildford (Table **114b**).
a – Until Sept. 7.
c – Departs 1052 on Ⓐ.
d – Arrives 4–5 minutes earlier on ⑥.

114a WAREHAM - SWANAGE

SW

Service operates on ⑥ May 25 - Sept. 7, 2019. Contact Swanage Railway for steam service Norden - Swanage and v.v.

km		⑥Aa	⑥a		⑥a	
	Weymouth **106** d.	1038	...	...	...	...
	Dorchester South **106** d.	1050	...	...	...	...
0	**Wareham** **106** d.	1117	1312	...	1512	...
9	Norden 🚂 a.	|	|	...	|	...
10	Corfe Castle 🚂 a.	1135	1430	...	1530	...
18	**Swanage** 🚂 a.	...	...	...	...	...

	⑥a		⑥a	⑥Aa	
Swanage 🚂 d.	...	...	...	...	...
Corfe Castle 🚂 d.	1210	...	1445	1545	...
Norden 🚂 d.	|	...	|	|	...
Wareham **106** a.	1237	...	1504	1604	...
Dorchester South **106** a.	...	...	...	1632	...
Weymouth **106** a.	...	...	...	1643	...

A – From/to London Waterloo via Weymouth and Yeovil (Tables **140** and **108**).
a – May 25 - Sept. 7.
🚂 – Additional steam trains run Norden - Corfe Castle - Swanage and v.v www.swanagerailway.co.uk ✆ 01929 425800.

114b GATWICK AIRPORT ✈ - READING

GW

km			ⒶA	Ⓐ	Ⓐ	Ⓐ	Ⓐ	Ⓐ	Ⓐ	Ⓐ	Ⓐ	Ⓐ	Ⓐ	and at	Ⓐ	Ⓐ	Ⓐ	Ⓐ	Ⓐ	Ⓐ	Ⓐ	Ⓐ	Ⓐ2	Ⓐ2	Ⓐ	Ⓐ
0	**Gatwick** Airport ✈ **185** d.	Ⓐ	...	0510	0600	...	0703	...	0802	0903	...	1000	...	the same	...	1600	...	1700	...	1800	...	1900	2000	...	2100	...
10	Redhill **102 185** d.		...	0535	0615	0619	0714	0731	0814	0914	0933	1014	1030	minutes	1529	1614	1631	1714	1745	1814	1843	1913	2013	2034	2113	213
43	Guildford d.		0601	0606	0643	0704	0743	0813	0843	0944	1015	1044	1109	past each	1609	1644	1709	1744	1825	1843	1925	1943	2043	2117	2144	221
84	**Reading** a.		0633	0651	0726	0749	0829	0859	0918	1016	1058	1119	1152	hour until	1652	1719	1752	1823	1918	1929	2015	2024	2119	2200	2221	225

	Ⓐ	Ⓐ		⑥A	⑥	⑥	⑥	⑥	and at the	⑥	⑥	⑥	⑥		⑦	⑦	⑦	⑦	⑦	and at the	⑦	⑦	⑦	⑦	⑦
Gatwick Airport ✈. **185** d.	2200	2318	⑥	...	0524	0556	...	0700	same mins	2100	...	2216	2318	⑦	0611	0711	0818	...	0915	same mins	...	2015	2107	2218	230
Redhill **102 185** d.	2212	2332		...	0542	0613	0630	0713	past each	2113	2135	2235	2332		0620	0720	0829	0843	0928	past each	1943	2030	2119	2230	231
Guildford d.	2256	0003		0609	0615	0644	0706	0742	hour until	2144	2214	2315	0001		0651	0752	0859	0923	1000	hour until	2023	2100	2200	2301	235
Reading a.	2349	0045		0644	0701	0719	0752	0819	♠	2219	2258	0005	0037		0726	0836	0940	1006	1036	△	2107	2136	2244	2336	004

		Ⓐ	Ⓐ	Ⓐ	Ⓐ	Ⓐ	Ⓐ	Ⓐ	Ⓐ	Ⓐ	Ⓐ	and at	Ⓐ	Ⓐ	Ⓐ	Ⓐ	Ⓐ	Ⓐ	Ⓐ	ⒶA	Ⓐ	Ⓐ	Ⓐ	Ⓐ	Ⓐ2	Ⓐ
Reading d.	Ⓐ	0431	0532	0554	0632	0704	0734	0804	0832	0904	0932	the same	1504	1528	1604	1632	1704	1732	1804	1822	1831	1932	2004	2029	2126	223
Guildford d.		0510	0608	0644	0708	0753	0818	0849	0910	0948	1009	minutes	1549	1610	1650	1709	1750	1811	1848	1857	1906	2008	2047	2108	2210	232
Redhill **102 185** a.		0539	0637	0724	0737	0837	0846	0928	0941	1025	1038	past each	1627	1640	1732	1740	1830	1839	1932	...	1940	2039	2128	2140	2240	000
Gatwick Airport ✈. **185** a.		0551	0654	...	0751	0851	...	...	0951	...	1053	hour until	...	1652	...	1751	...	1850	...	...	1950	2054	...	2153	2256	002

	Ⓐ		⑥	⑥	⑥	⑥	and at the	⑥	⑥	⑥	⑥	⑥		⑦	⑦	⑦	⑦	and at	⑦	⑦	⑦	⑦	⑦A	⑦	⑦
Reading d.	2334	⑥	0431	0532	0604	0632	same mins	2004	2032	2122	2233	2335	⑦	0603	0712	0747	0817	the same	1847	1917	2017	2117	2214	2217	231
Guildford d.	0021		0510	0612	0648	0708	past each	2048	2108	2206	2320	0021		0639	0747	0831	0852	minutes	1931	1952	2102	2201	2241	2256	235
Redhill **102 185** a.	0049		0539	0640	0723	0738	hour until	2122	2142	2240	2359	0049		0708	0817	0906	0924	past each	2006	2024	2143	2235	...	2335	003
Gatwick Airport ✈. **185** a.	0107		0551	0654	...	0751	▲	...	2154	2251	0020	0105		0727	0828	...	0935	hour until	...	2035	2154	2245	...	2348	004

A – (12) Guildford - Newcastle and v.v. (Table **124**).
♠ – No departure from Gatwick at 1500; retimed to depart at 1458.
△ – Additional train on ⑦ Guildford d. 1214 - Reading a. 1245 **A**.
▲ – Additional train on ⑥ Reading d. 1822 - Guildford a. 1901 **A**.

XC Most services convey ⚲ — BOURNEMOUTH - SOUTHAMPTON - READING - BIRMINGHAM — 114

	⚒	⑥	Ⓐ	ⒶG	⑥G	Ⓐ	⑥	Ⓐ	⑥	Ⓐ	⑥	Ⓐ	⑥	Ⓐ	⑥	⑥	Ⓐ	⚒	⚒	⚒	⚒	Ⓐ	⑥	⚒	Ⓐ	⑥	Ⓐ
Bournemouth 106 d.		...	...	...	...	...	...	...	0625	0630	0638	...	...	0730	0747	...	...	0845	...	0945	...	1045	1047	...	1145	1147	...
Brockenhurst 106 d.		...	...	...	...	...	...	...	0640	0646	0653	...	...	0748	0802	...	...	0900	...	1000	...	1100	1102	...	1200	1202	...
Southampton Central 106 d.		0509	0515	...	...	0616	0620	...	0654	0714	0711	0756	0749	0812	0820	...	...	0917	0947	1017	...	1117	1120	1147	1217	1220	...
Southampton Airport ✈ 106 d.		0516	0522	...	...	0623	0627	...	0701	0722	0718	0803	0756	0819	0827	...	...	0924	0954	1024	...	1124	1127	1154	1225	1227	...
Winchester 106 d.		0525	0531	...	...	0632	0636	...	0710	0731	0729	0812	0805	0831	0836	...	...	0933	1003	1033	...	1133	1136	1203	1233	1236	...
Basingstoke 106 d.		0540	0548	...	...	0649	0651	...	0726	0747	0750b	0828	0821	0849	0851	...	...	0949	1019	1049	...	1149	1151	1219	1249	1251	...
Reading a.		0600	0605	...	...	0706	0707	...	0741	0803	0807	0845	0837	0905	0907	...	...	1007	1037	1107	...	1205	1207	1235	1306	1309	...
Reading 131 d.		0615	0615	0645	0647	0715	0715	0745	0747	0815	0815	0850	0845	0915	0915	0945	0945	1015	1045	1115	1145	1215	1215	1245	1315	1315	1345
Oxford 131 a.		0638	0637	0706	0710	0737	0738	0808	0810	0837	0838	0913	0908	0938	0938	1008	1012	1038	1109	1138	1208	1238	1238	1308	1338	1338	1410
Oxford d.		0639	0639	0708	0712	0739	0739	0810	0811	0838	0839	0914	0909	0939	0939	1009	1014	1039	1109	1139	1209	1239	1239	1309	1339	1339	1413
Banbury 128 d.		0657	0657	0726	0732	0757	0757	0828	0830	0857	0857	0933	0927	0957	0957	1027	1032	1057	1127e	1157	1227	1257	1257	1327	1357	1357	1431
Leamington Spa 128 141 d.		0715	0715	0744	0750	0815	0815	0850	0850	0915	0915	0951	0950b	1015	1015	1049b	1050	1115	1148	1215	1249b	1315	1315	1349b	1415	1415	1450
Coventry 141 142 150 d.		0727	0727	|	|	0827	0827	|	|	0927	0927	|	|	1027	1027	|	|	1127	|	1227	|	1327	1327	|	1427	1427	|
Birmingham Int'l ✈ 142 150 d.		0738	0738	|	|	0838	0838	|	|	0938	0938	|	|	1038	1038	|	|	1138	|	1238	|	1338	1338	|	1438	1438	|
Birmingham N St. 142 150 a.		0748	0748	0812	0818	0848	0848	0918	0918	0949	0948	1018	1018	1048	1048	1118	1118	1148	1218	1248	1318	1348	1348	1418	1448	1448	1518
Sheffield 124 a.		|	|	0948	0947	|	|	1046	1048	|	|	1146	1146	|	|	1246	1246	|	1348	|	1447	|	|	1547	|	|	1646
Leeds 124 a.		|	|	|	|	|	|	|	|	|	|	|	|	|	|	|	|	|	|	|	|	|	|	|	|	|	|
York 124 a.		|	|	1040	1040	|	|	1140	1140	|	|	1240	1240	|	|	1340	1340	|	1440	|	1540	|	|	1640	|	|	1741
Newcastle 124 a.		|	|	1144	1145	|	|	1243	1243	|	|	1344	1344	|	|	1443	1443	|	1545	|	1644	|	|	1744	|	|	1848
Manchester P'dilly 119 a.		0924	0924	...	...	1024	1024	...	...	1124	1124	...	...	1224	1224	...	...	1324	...	1424	...	1524	1524	...	1624	1624	...

	⑥	⚒	⑥	⚒E	Ⓐ	⑥	⚒	Ⓐ	⑥	Ⓐ	⑥	Ⓐ	⑥	⚒	Ⓐ	⑥	Ⓐ	⑥	Ⓐ	⑥g	⑥h	⚒	Ⓐ	⑥	Ⓐ	⑥	Ⓐ
Bournemouth 106 d.	...	1245	1247	...	1345	1347	...	1445	1447	...	...	1545	1547	...	1645	1647	...	...	1745	1747	1747	...	1845	1847	...	...	1945
Brockenhurst 106 d.	...	1300	1302	...	1400	1402	...	1500	1502	...	...	1600	1602	...	1700	1702	...	...	1800	1802	1802	...	1900	1902	...	...	2000
Southampton Central 106 d.	...	1316	1320	1347	1415	1420	...	1517	1520	1546	1547	1617	1620	...	1717	1720	1747	1750	1815	1820	1820	...	1916	1920	...	...	2017
Southampton Airport ✈ 106 d.	...	1323	1327	1354	1422	1427	...	1524	1527	1553	1554	1624	1627	...	1724	1727	1754	1757	1822	1827	1827	...	1924	1927	...	...	2024
Winchester 106 d.	...	1332	1336	1403	1431	1436	...	1533	1536	1602	1603	1633	1636	...	1733	1736	1803	1806	1831	1836	1836	...	1932	1936	...	...	2033
Basingstoke 106 d.	...	1349	1351	1419	1447	1451	...	1549	1551	1618	1618	1649	1651	...	1749	1751	1819	1821	1848	1851	1851	...	1949	1951	...	...	2049
Reading a.	...	1406	1407	1435	1505	1507	...	1604	1607	1634	1634	1704	1707	...	1805	1807	1834	1837	1905	1907	1907	...	2004	2008	...	...	2104
Reading 131 d.	1345	1415	1415	1445	1515	1515	1545	1615	1615	1645	1645	1715	1715	1745	1815	1815	1845	1845	1915	1915	1915	1945	2015	2015	2045	2045	2112
Oxford 131 a.	1408	1438	1438	1508	1538	1538	1608	1638	1638	1709	1708	1737	1738	1808	1838	1838	1911	1908	1938	1938	1938	2008	2037	2038	2108	2108	2135
Oxford d.	1409	1439	1439	1509	1539	1539	1609	1640	1639	1713	1709	1739	1740	1809	1839	1839	1912	1909	1939	1939	1939	2009	2039	2039	2109	2109	2136
Banbury 128 d.	1427	1457	1457	1527	1557	1557	1627	1657	1657	1731	1727	1757	1758	1827	1857	1857	1930	1927	1957	1957	1957	2027	2057	2057	2130	2127	2154
Leamington Spa 128 141 d.	1449b	1515	1515	1549b	1615	1615	1649b	1715	1715	1751	1749b	1815	1815	1848	1915	1915	1950	1950b	2015	2015	2015	2050b	2115	2115	2150	2150b	2215
Coventry 141 142 150 d.	|	1527	1527	|	1627	1627	|	1727	1727	|	|	1827	1827	|	1927	1927	|	|	2027	2028	2028	|	2127	2127	|	2202	2227
Birmingham Int'l ✈ 142 150 d.	|	1538	1538	|	1638	1638	|	1738	1738	|	|	1838	1838	|	1938	1938	|	|	2038	2039	2039	|	2138	2138	|	2212	2238
Birmingham N St. 142 150 a.	1518	1548	1548	1618	1648	1648	1718	1748	1748	1818	1818	1848	1848	1918	1948	1948	2018	2018	2048	2049	2049	2123a	2148	2148	2218	2222	2248
Sheffield 124 a.	1647	|	|	1748	|	|	1848	|	|	1943	1947	|	|	2047f	|	|	2150	2159	|	2223	|	...	|	|	...	...	...
Leeds 124 a.	|	|	|	1833	|	|	|	|	|	|	|	|	|	|	|	|	|	|	|	2326	|	...	|	|	...	...	...
York 124 a.	1740	|	|	1905d	|	|	1940	|	|	2041	2040	|	|	2142	|	|	2247	2246	|	...	|	...	|	|	...	...	...
Newcastle 124 a.	1843	|	|	2005d	|	|	2043	|	|	2146	2146	|	|	2248	|	|	...	...	|	...	|	...	|	|	...	...	...
Manchester P'dilly 119 a.	...	1724	1724	...	1824	1824	...	1924	1924	...	...	2024	2024	...	2124	2124	...	...	2225	...	2233	...	2324	2329	...	...	...

	⑥	⑥	Ⓐ	⑦	⑦	⑦	⑦	⑦	⑦G	⑦	⑦	⑦	⑦	⑦	⑦E	⑦	⑦	⑦	⑦	⑦	⑦	⑦	⑦	⑦	⑦	⑦	⑦
Bournemouth 106 d.	1947	...	...		...	...	0940	1040	...	1140	...	1240	...	1340	...	1440	...	1540	...	1640	...	1740	...	1840	...	1940	...
Brockenhurst 106 d.	2002	...	...		...	...	0955	1057	...	1155	...	1255	...	1355	...	1502j	...	1602j	...	1702j	...	1755	...	1902j	...	2002j	...
Southampton Central 106 d.	2020	...	...		...	0920	1015j	1115j	...	1213b	...	1313b	...	1413b	...	1520b	...	1620b	...	1720b	...	1814b	...	1920b	...	2020b	...
Southampton Airport ✈ 106 d.	2027	...	...		...	0927	1022	1122	...	1220	...	1320	...	1420	...	1527	...	1627	...	1727	...	1822	...	1927	...	2027	...
Winchester 106 d.	2036	...	...		...	0936	1033	1133	...	1229	...	1329	...	1429	...	1536	...	1636	...	1736	...	1830	...	1936	...	2036	...
Basingstoke 106 d.	2051	...	...		...	0951	1051	1151	...	1247	...	1349	...	1449	...	1551	...	1651	...	1751	...	1850	...	1951	...	2051	...
Reading a.	2107	...	...		...	1007	1107	1207	...	1303	...	1407	...	1507	...	1607	...	1707	...	1807	...	1907	...	2007	...	2107	...
Reading 131 d.	2115	2145	2146		0911	1012	1112	1212	1252	1312	1342	1412	1442	1512	1542	1612	1642	1712	1742	1812	1842	1912	1942	2012	2042	2112	2141
Oxford 131 a.	2138	2208	2224		0935	1037	1137	1237	1315	1337	1405	1437	1505	1537	1605	1637	1705	1737	1805	1837	1905	1937	2005	2037	2105	2135	2205
Oxford d.	2139	2209	2230		0939	1039	1139	1239	1317	1339	1406	1439	1506	1539	1606	1639	1706	1739	1806	1839	1906	1939	2006	2039	2106	2136	2206
Banbury 128 d.	2157	2227	2248		0957	1057	1157	1257	1335	1357	1424	1457	1524	1557	1624	1657	1724	1757	1824	1857	1924	1957	2024	2057	2124	2154	2224
Leamington Spa 128 141 d.	2215	2250b	2305		1015	1115	1215	1315	1352	1415	1442	1515	1542	1615	1642	1715	1742	1815	1842	1915	1942	2015	2042	2115	2142	2212	2242
Coventry 141 142 150 d.	2227	|	2317		1027	1128	1228	1327	|	1427	1454	1527	1554	1627	1654	1727	1754	1827	1854	1927	1954	2027	2054	2127	2154	2224	2254
Birmingham Int'l ✈ 142 150 d.	2238	|	2328		1038	1139	1239	1338	|	1438	1504	1538	1604	1638	1704	1738	1804	1838	1904	1938	2004	2038	2103	2138	2204	2234	2304
Birmingham N St. 142 150 a.	2248	2318	2356		1048	1150	1249	1348	1418	1448	1514	1548	1614	1648	1714	1748	1814	1848	1914	1948	2014	2048	2115	2148	2214	2243	2314
Sheffield 124 a.	...	...	...		|	|	|	|	1545	|	1641	|	1743	|	1840	|	1941	|	2041	|	...	|	...	|	...	...	...
Leeds 124 a.	...	...	...		|	|	|	|	|	|	|	|	1847	|	|	|	|	|	|	|	...	|	...	|	...	...	...
York 124 a.	...	...	...		|	|	|	|	1637	|	1740	|	1918	|	1941	|	2042	|	2144	|	...	|	...	|	...	...	...
Newcastle 124 a.	...	...	...		|	|	|	|	1741	|	1841	|	2020	|	2050	|	2145	|	2310	|	...	|	...	|	...	...	...
Manchester P'dilly 119 a.	...	...	...		1240	1330	1429	1524	...	1629	...	1729	...	1829	...	1928	...	2028	...	2129	...	2226	...	2324	...	...	...

E – To Edinburgh Waverley on Ⓐ (Table **124**).
G – From Guildford (Table **114b**).

a – Arrives 2118 on ⑥.
b – Arrives 5–6 minutes earlier.
c – Arrives 1206 on ⑥.

d – Arrives 3–4 minutes earlier on Ⓐ.
e – Departs 4 minutes later on Ⓐ.
f – Arrives 2033 on Ⓐ.

g – Until Sept. 7.
h – From Sept. 14.
j – Arrive 8 minutes earlier.

GW 2nd class — BRISTOL - TAUNTON — 115

km		Ⓐ	ⒶB	ⒶB	ⒶA	Ⓐ	Ⓐ	ⒶB	ⒶB	Ⓐ	Ⓐ	Ⓐ	ⒶB	Ⓐ	Ⓐ	Ⓐ	Ⓐ	ⒶF	Ⓐ	ⒶF	Ⓐ	Ⓐ	ⒶB	ⒶB	ⒶC	⑥	⑥B	⑥
	Cardiff Central 119 d.		...	...	...	...	...	0800	0900	1000	1100	1200	1300	1400	1500	1600	1700	...	1800	...	1900	2000	...	...	...		...	...
0	**Bristol** T M 116 132 d.		0524	0643	0717	0748	0826	0855	0956	1054	1153	1253	1358	1453	1552	1654	1754	1821	1856	1918	1955	2055	2154	2306	2337		0524	0618
31	Weston-s-Mare 132 d.		0547	0706f	0749	0824	0901	0929r	1024	1122	1221	1323	1426	1528r	1627	1728	1830	1900c	1930	2002c	2029	2135c	2229	2342	0007s		0547f	0646
43	Highbridge ‡ d.		0557	0717	0800	0835	0911	0940	1035	1133	1232	1334	1437	1538	1637	1739	1841	1911	1940	2013	2039	2145	2240	2354	0018s		0557	0657
53	Bridgwater d.		0605	0725	0808	0843	0919	0948	1043	1141	1240	1342	1445	1546	1645	1747	1849	1919	1948	2020	2047	2153	2248	0002	0025s		0605	0705
72	**Taunton** 116 132 a.		0618	0738	0823	0856	0932	1001	1059	1155	1256	1355	1458	1601	1659	1801	1903	1930	2002	2031	2101	2210	2300	0014	0036		0618	0719

	⑥B	⑥A	⑥	⑥	⑥	⑥	⑥	⑥	⑥	⑥	⑥	⑥	⑥	⑥	⑥F	⑥B	⑥C	⑦	⑦B	⑦B	⑦	⑦A	⑦	⑦	⑦F	⑦B	⑦	⑦
Cardiff Central 119 d.	...	...	0800	0901	1000	1100	1200	1300	1400	1500	1600	1700	1800	1900	...	...	...		...	...	...	...	...	...	...	...	...	...
Bristol T M 116 132 d.	0641	0718	0858	0955	1055	1153	1253	1356	1453	1555	1654	1754	1853	1953	2054	2202	2217		0726	0828	1022	1111	1309	1555	1700	1830	1907	2025
Weston-s-Mare 132 d.	0706c	0751	0932r	1024	1124	1222	1323	1425	1528c	1623	1725f	1822	1924	2023	2130	2235	2247s		0749	0859f	1053	1141	1335	1629	1730	1908c	1941	2059
Highbridge ‡ d.	|	0802	0943	1035	1135	1233	1334	1436	1538	1634	1736	1833	1935	2034	2141	2246	2258s		|	0910	1103	1152	1346	1640	1743	1918	1952	2110
Bridgwater d.	|	0810	0951	1043	1143	1241	1342	1444	1546	1642	1744	1841	1943	2042	2148	2254	2305s		0805	0918	1111	1200	1354	1648	1748	1926	1959	2118
Taunton 116 132 a.	0732a	0823	1005	1056	1156	1255	1357	1458	1600	1656	1758	1856	1957	2057	2159	2307	2316		0817	0931	1124	1213	1405	1702	1803	1940	2011	2131

	Ⓐ	Ⓐ	Ⓐ	ⒶB	ⒶC	ⒶF	Ⓐ	Ⓐ	Ⓐ	Ⓐ	ⒶB		Ⓐ	Ⓐ	Ⓐ	ⒶB	Ⓐ	Ⓐ	Ⓐ	Ⓐ	Ⓐ	ⒶA	ⒶF	Ⓐ	⑥	⑥W	⑥B	⑥F
Taunton 116 132 d.		0512	0602	0634	0657	0712	0735	0836	0916	*0935*	1011	...	1104	1204	1308	1411	1456	1607	1706	1808	1917	2035	2128	2245		0535	0634	0654
Bridgwater d.		0524	0614	0646	0707	0724	0747	0848	0928	*0947*	1023	...	1116	1218	1320	1423	1508	1619	1718	1820	1929	2047	2139	2257		0547	0646	0705
Highbridge ‡ d.		0532	0621	0654	0715	0732	0755	0856	0936	*0954*	1031	...	1124	1226	1328	1431	1515	1627	1726	1828	1936	2055	2147	2305		0555	0654	0712
Weston-s-Mare 132 d.		0546f	0636f	0708	0726	0749r	0807	0911	0948	1010	1043	...	1138f	1241	1341	1445	1544b	1639	1738	1840	1954r	2107	2158	2317		0606	0707	0724
Bristol T M 116 132 a.		0618	0708	0741	0758	0825	0842	0944	1021	1042	1111	...	1204	1310	1412	1514	1613	1713	1814	1913	2023	2139	2229	2351		0640	0742	0754
Cardiff Central 119 a.		0719	0823	...	...	...	...	...	1122	...	1219	...	1322	1413	1526	1615	1727	1813	1923	2018	...	...	...	...		...	...	...

	⑥	⑥C	⑥	⑥	⑥	⑥	⑥	⑥		⑥	⑥	⑥	⑥	⑥	⑥	⑥	⑦	⑦B	⑦B	⑦	⑦	⑦	⑦E	⑦	⑦B	⑦F	⑦	⑦
Taunton 116 132 d.	0735	0759	0912	1011t	1104	1207	1307	1407	...	1507	1607	1706	1808	1906	2017	2134		0835	1003	1136	1334	1509	1658	1713	1812	1838	2025	2136
Bridgwater d.	0747	0809	0924	1023t	1116	1219	1319	1419	...	1519	1619	1718	1820	1917	2029	2146		0847	1015	1147	1346	1521	1709	1724	1823	1848	2037	2148
Highbridge ‡ d.	0755	0817	0932	1031t	1124	1227	1327	1427	...	1527	1627	1726	1828	1925	2037	2154		0855	1023	1154	1353	1528	1717	1731	1830	1855	2044	2155
Weston-s-Mare 132 d.	0807	0829	0944	1043t	1140f	1240	1341	1439	...	1539	1639	1740	1840	1940f	2050	2206		0907	1040c	1209f	1408f	1545r	1731f	1745	1841	1917c	2059f	2207
Bristol T M 116 132 a.	0841	0856	1012	1111t	1209	1311	1411	1509	...	1609	1711	1810	1909	2010	2124	2241		0937	1111	1242	1441	1615	1751	1814	1912	1946	2132	2239
Cardiff Central 119 a.	...	...	1119	1217	1318	1417	1517	1615	...	1717	1815	1917	2013	...	2232	...		...	...	...	...	...	...	...	...	...	...	...

A – To/from Gloucester (Table **138**).
B – To/from Penzance, Paignton, Plymouth or Exeter St Davids (Table **110**).
C – [12] ⚲ London Paddington - Exeter St Davids and v.v. (Table **110**).
E – [12] ⚲ Paignton - London Paddington (Table **110**).
F – [12] ⚲ London Paddington - Taunton and v.v. (Table **132**).
W – To Westbury (Table **140**).

a – Until Sept. 7 arrives 0726.
b – Arrives 1526. An earlier arrival into Bristol (at 1557) is possible by changing trains at Weston-super-Mare.
c – Arrives 8–10 minutes earlier.
f – Arrives 4–5 minutes earlier.
r – Arrives 6–7 minutes earlier.

s – Calls to set down only.
t – Runs 5 minutes later until Sept. 7.
‡ – Highbridge and Burnham.

116 BIRMINGHAM - BRISTOL - PAIGNTON and PLYMOUTH

Most services convey 🍸 XC

km	Ⓐ	Ⓐ	Ⓐ	Ⓐ	Ⓐ	Ⓐ	Ⓐ	Ⓐ	Ⓐ	Ⓐ	Ⓐ	Ⓐ	Ⓐ	Ⓐ	Ⓐ	Ⓐ	Ⓐ	Ⓐ	Ⓐ	Ⓐ	Ⓐ	Ⓐ	Ⓐ	Ⓐ
			D					★d							A					★	B			
	Glasgow Central **124 220** ...d.	...	...	...	...	...	...	...	...	...	...	...	0601	...	...	...	0748	...	0900	...	...	...	1100	...
	Edinburgh Wav'ley **124 220** d.	...	...	...	...	...	...	...	...	...	0606	...	0710	...	0809	...	0907	...	1010	...	1106	...	1208	...
	Newcastle **124** d.	...	...	...	...	...	...	...	0645	...	0740	...	0843	...	0943	...	1043	...	1142	...	1242	...	1342	...
	York **124** d.	...	...	...	...	...	0645	...	0743	...	0844	...	0944	...	1044	...	1144	...	1244	...	1344	...	1444	...
	Leeds **124** d.	...	...	...	0611	...	0710	...	0811	...	0911	...	1011	...	1111	...	1211	...	1311	...	1411	...	1511	...
	Sheffield **124** d.	...	...	...	0653	...	0753	...	0854	...	0956	...	1056	...	1156	...	1256	...	1356	...	1456	...	1556	...
	Manchester P'dilly **119** ....d.	...	...	0600	|	0705	|	0805	|	0905	|	1005	|	1105	|	1205	|	1305	|	1405	|	1505	|	1605
0	**Birmingham** New St ...... **117** d.	...	0642	0712	0742	0812	0842	0917	0942	1017	1042	1117	1142	1217	1242	1317	1342	1417	1442	1517	1542	1612	1642	1712	1742
73	Cheltenham Spa ...... **117 138** a.	...	0720	0750	0824	0850	0924	1001	1024	1101	1124	1201	1224	1301	1324	1401	1424	1501	1524	1601	1624	1650	1724	1750	1825
135	**Bristol** Parkway .... **138** a.	...	0754	0826	0854	0925	0954	1031	1054	1130	1154	1231	1254	1331	1354	1431	1454	1531	1557	1632	1654	1723	1756	1828	1855
145	**Bristol** Temple Meads .... **138** a.	...	0805	0839	0905	0939	1005	1042	1104	1142	1204	1241	1304	1341	1404	1442	1505	1541	1611	1643	1706	1737	1809	1842	1905
145	**Bristol** Temple M .... **115 110** d.	0635	0810	0844	...	0945	...	1045	1115	1145	...	1245	1309	1345	...	1445	1510	1545	1613	1645	1713	1745	1816	1845	...
217	Taunton .... **115 110** a.	0706	0840	0915	...	1016	...	1116	1158	1215	...	1316	1339	1416	...	1516	1540	1616	1643	1716	1744	1816	1848	1916	...
240	Tiverton Parkway .... **110** a.	0718	0852	0927	...	1028	...	1129	1210	1227	...	1329	1356	1428	...	1528	1552	1628	1655	1728	1756	1828	|	1928	...
266	**Exeter** St Davids .... **110** a.	0732	0907	0942	...	1044	...	1144	1225	1243	...	1344	1413	1444	...	1544	1607	1644	1710	1744	1811	1844	1918	1943	...
298	Newton Abbot .... **110** a.	0753	0927	1002	...	1104	...	1205	1250	1303	...	1405	...	1504	...	1604	...	1704	...	1809	1836	1904	...	2003	...
308	**Torquay** .... **110** a.	|	0938	|	...	|	...	|	1300	|	...	|	...	|	...	|	...	|	...	|	1846	|	...	|	...
311	**Paignton** .... **110** a.	|	0946	|	...	|	...	|	1308	|	...	|	...	|	...	|	...	|	...	|	1854	|	...	|	...
312	Totnes .... **110** a.	0806	...	1015	...	1117	...	1217	...	1316	...	1417	...	1517	...	1617	...	1717	...	1822	...	1917	...	2015	...
350	**Plymouth** .... **110** a.	0832	...	1042	...	1145	...	1245	...	1343	...	1445	...	1544	...	1645	...	1744	...	1849	...	1944	...	2043	...
	Newquay **112** a.	...	...	...	...	...	...	...	...	...	...	...	...	...	...	...	...	...	...	|	...	|	...	|	...
	Penzance **112** a.	...	...	...	...	...	...	...	...	...	...	...	...	...	...	...	...	...	...	2052	...	2140	...	2238	...

	Ⓐ	Ⓐ	Ⓐ	Ⓐ	Ⓐ	Ⓐ	Ⓐ	Ⓐ	⑥	⑥	⑥	⑥	⑥	⑥	⑥	⑥	⑥	⑥	⑥	⑥	⑥	⑥	⑥	⑥	⑥
	b	C					c				D		f	★e	f	e		★d		f	e				f
Glasgow Central **124 220** ...d.	...	...	1300	...	...	...	1500	...	...	...	...	...	...	...	...	...	...	...	...	...	...	...	...	...	0601
Edinburgh Wav'ley **124 220** d.	1307	...	1409	...	1508	...	1606	1707	...	...	...	...	...	...	...	...	...	...	...	...	...	...	0606	...	0707
Newcastle **124** d.	1442	...	1542	...	1642	...	1742	1843	...	...	...	...	...	...	...	...	...	...	...	0645	...	...	0740	...	0841
York **124** d.	1544	...	1644	...	1745	...	1845	1945	...	...	...	...	...	...	...	...	0618h	...	...	0745	0745	...	0844	...	0945
Leeds **124** d.	1611	...	1711	...	1811	...	1911	2011	...	...	...	...	0611	0611	...	...	0711	...	...	0811	0811	...	0911	...	1011
Sheffield **124** d.	1656	...	1756	...	1856	...	1956	2058	...	...	...	...	0653	0653	...	...	0756	...	...	0854	0854	...	0956	...	1056
Manchester P'dilly **119** ....d.	|	1705	|	1805	|	1905	|	|	...	...	...	0600	|	|	0705	0705	|	0805	...	|	|	0905	|	1005	|
Birmingham New St ...... **117** d.	1812	1842	1912	1942	2012	2042	2112	2212	...	0642	0712	0742	0812	0812	0842	0842	0912	0942	...	1012	1012	1042	1112	1142	1212
Cheltenham Spa ...... **117 138** a.	1850	1924	1951	2024	2053	2125	2150	2250	...	0724	0750	0824	0850	0850	0924	0924	0950	1024	...	1050	1050	1124	1150	1224	1250
Bristol Parkway .... **138** a.	1934	1954	2030	2054	2124	2155	2231	2320	...	0754	0824	0854	0923	0923	0954	0954	1028	1054	...	1123	1123	1154	1229	1254	1321
Bristol Temple Meads .... **138** a.	1945	2009	2042	2104	2135	2205	2241	2330	...	0804	0837	0905	0934	0935	1005	1004	1042	1109	...	1138	1138	1205	1241	1304	1333
Bristol Temple M .... **115 110** d.	1948	...	2048	2113	2144	...	...	...	0608	0810	0845	...	0945	0945	...	1020	1045	1112	...	1145	1145	...	1245	...	1345
Taunton .... **115 110** a.	2019	...	2118	2144	2214	...	...	...	0714	0842	0915	...	1016	1016	...	1100	1116	1200	...	1216	1216	...	1316	...	1416
Tiverton Parkway .... **110** a.	2031	...	2130	2156	2226	...	...	...	0726	0854	0927	...	1029	1029	...	1113	1128	1212	...	1228	1229	...	1329	...	1429
Exeter St Davids .... **110** a.	2047	...	2144	2211	2241	...	...	...	0740	0908	0942	...	1044	1044	...	1129	1143	1231	...	1244	1244	...	1344	...	1444
Newton Abbot .... **110** a.	2107	...	2204	2231	2301	...	...	...	0800	0928	1003	...	1105	1115	...	1154	1204	1256	...	1305	1306	...	1405	...	1505
Torquay .... **110** a.	|	...	|	|	|	...	...	...	|	0939	|	...	|	1127	...	|	|	1306	...	|	|	...	|	...	|
Paignton .... **110** a.	|	...	|	|	|	...	...	...	|	0947	|	...	|	1137	...	|	|	1314	...	|	|	...	|	...	|
Totnes .... **110** a.	2120	...	2216	2243	2317	...	...	...	0813	...	1017	...	1117	...	...	1207	1217	...	...	1318	1319	...	1417	...	1517
Plymouth .... **110** a.	2147	...	2244	2310	2344	...	...	...	0839	...	1045	...	1145	...	...	1233	1244	...	...	1346	1346	...	1445	...	1545
Newquay **112** a.	...	...	...	...	...	...	...	...	...	...	...	...	...	...	...	1429	...	...	...	...	|	...	...	...	...
Penzance **112** a.	...	...	...	...	...	...	...	...	...	...	...	...	...	...	...	...	...	...	...	...	1544	...	...	...	...

	⑥	⑥	⑥	⑥	⑥	⑥	⑥	⑥	⑥	⑥	⑥	⑥	⑥	⑥	⑥	⑥	⑥	⑥	⑥	⑥	⑥	⑥	⑥	⑥	⑦
	e★		Af	Ae	e★	f	e	f			★f	e	B					C		e	f			c	
Glasgow Central **124 220** ...d.	0601	...	...	...	...	...	0748	0748	...	0900	...	...	...	...	1100	...	...	...	1300	...	...	...	...	1500	...
Edinburgh Wav'ley **124 220** d.	0707	...	0807	0807	...	...	0908	0908	...	1006	...	...	1108	...	1206	...	1309	...	1407	...	...	1508	...	1605	...
Newcastle **124** d.	0841	...	0942	0941	...	...	1043	1043	...	1142	...	...	1243	...	1344	...	1443	...	1545	...	...	1644	...	1744	...
York **124** d.	0945	...	1045	1044	...	...	1144	1144	...	1245	...	...	1344	...	1445	...	1545	...	1645	...	...	1745	...	1845	...
Leeds **124** d.	1011	...	1111	1111	...	...	1211	1211	...	1311	...	...	1411	...	1511	...	1611	...	1710	...	...	1811	...	1911	...
Sheffield **124** d.	1056	...	1156	1156	...	...	1256	1256	...	1356	...	...	1456	...	1556	...	1656	...	1756	...	...	1856	...	1956	...
Manchester P'dilly **119** ....d.	|	1105	|	|	1205	1205	|	|	1305	|	1405	1405	|	1505	|	1605	|	1705	|	1805	1805	|	1905	|	...
Birmingham New St ...... **117** d.	1212	1242	1312	1312	1342	1342	1412	1412	1442	1512	1542	1542	1612	1642	1712	1742	1812	1842	1912	1942	1942	2012	2042	2112	...
Cheltenham Spa ...... **117 138** a.	1250	1327	1350	1350	1424	1424	1450	1450	1524	1550	1624	1624	1650	1724	1750	1824	1850	1924	1950	2024	2024	2050	2124	2150	...
Bristol Parkway .... **138** a.	1321	1357	1423	1423	1457	1457	1523	1523	1554	1628	1654	1654	1723	1754	1828	1854	1922	1954	2029	2054	2054	2120	2157	2233	...
Bristol Temple Meads .... **138** a.	1333	1407	1435	1435	1508	1507	1538	1538	1604	1640	1704	1704	1735	1804	1840	1905	1938	2005	2041	2104	2104	2134	2212	2243	...
Bristol Temple M .... **115 110** d.	1345	...	1445	1445	1512	1510	1545	1545	...	1645	1709	...	1745	...	1845	...	1945	...	2045	...	2110	2145	...	...	0844
Taunton .... **115 110** a.	1416	...	1516	1516	1542	1540	1615	1615	...	1716	1739	...	1816	...	1916	...	2016	...	2116	...	2140	2216	...	...	0915
Tiverton Parkway .... **110** a.	1429	...	1529	1528	1554	1552	1627	1627	...	1729	1751	...	1828	...	1928	...	2028	...	2128	...	2152	2228	...	...	0927
Exeter St Davids .... **110** a.	1444	...	1544	1543	1609	1607	1642	1642	...	1744	1805	...	1844	...	1944	...	2044	...	2144	...	2207	2244	...	...	0941
Newton Abbot .... **110** a.	1512	...	1605	1606	1648	...	1702	1702	...	1811	1830	...	1904	...	2004	...	2104	...	2204	...	2227	2312	...	...	1001
Torquay .... **110** a.	1524	...	|	|	1700	...	|	|	...	|	1840	...	|	...	|	...	|	...	|	...	|	|	...	...	|
Paignton .... **110** a.	1534	...	|	|	1709	...	|	|	...	|	1848	...	|	...	|	...	|	...	|	...	|	|	...	...	|
Totnes .... **110** a.	...	...	1617	1619	...	...	1715	1715	...	1824	...	...	1917	...	2017	...	2117	...	2217	...	2239	2327	...	...	1014
Plymouth .... **110** a.	...	...	1645	1646	...	...	1742	1742	...	1852	...	...	1944	...	2044	...	2144	...	2246	...	2306	2356	...	...	1040
Newquay **112** a.	...	...	...	1839	...	...	|	...	...	|	...	...	|	...	|	...	...	...	...	...	...	...	...	...	...
Penzance **112** a.	...	...	...	...	...	...	1932	...	...	2045	...	...	2141	...	2253f	...	...	...	...	...	...	...	...	...	...

	⑦	⑦	⑦	⑦	⑦	⑦	⑦	⑦	⑦	⑦	⑦	⑦	⑦	⑦	⑦	⑦	⑦a	⑦a	⑦	⑦	⑦	⑦	⑦	⑦	⑦
									★								★n	★m	B				c		
Glasgow Central **124 220** ...d.	...	...	...	...	...	...	...	...	...	...	...	...	...	1055	...	1202	...	...	...	...	1348	...	1455	...	...
Edinburgh Wav'ley **124 220** d.	...	...	...	...	...	...	...	0908	...	1008	...	1105	...	1208	...	1308	...	...	1408	...	1508	...	1608	...	1708
Newcastle **124** d.	...	...	...	...	...	0935	...	1039	...	1140	...	1240	...	1340	...	1441	...	...	1540	...	1640	...	1740	...	1840
York **124** d.	...	...	...	...	0936	1034	...	1141	...	1245	...	1345	...	1444	...	1544	...	...	1644	...	1744	...	1845	...	1945
Leeds **124** d.	...	...	0810	0900	1001	1100	...	1211	...	1311	...	1411	...	1511	...	1611	...	...	1712	...	1811	...	1912	...	2011
Sheffield **124** d.	...	...	0855	0958	1055	1157	...	1257	...	1357	...	1455	...	1555	...	1655	...	...	1755	...	1855	...	1956	...	2054
Manchester P'dilly **118** ....d.	...	...	|	|	|	|	...	|	1305	|	1405	|	1505	|	1605	|	1705	1705	|	1805	|	1905	|	2005	|
Birmingham New St ...... **117** d.	...	0930	1030	1130	1212	1312	1342	1412	1442	1512	1542	1612	1642	1712	1742	1812	1842	1842	1912	1942	2012	2042	2112	2142	2212
Cheltenham Spa ...... **117 138** a.	...	1008	1108	1208	1250	1350	1424	1450	1524	1550	1625	1650	1724	1750	1824	1850	1924	1924	1950	2024	2050	2124	2151	2224	2250
Bristol Parkway .... **138** a.	...	1038	1138	1238	1320	1420	1454	1520	1556	1620	1656	1720	1758	1820	1854	1920	2003	2003	2020	2054	2120	2159	2233	2254	2320
Bristol Temple Meads .... **138** a.	...	1049	1149	1249	1334	1433	1504	1534	1609	1632	1707	1734	1810	1834	1908	1934	2013	2013	2034	2104	2134	2210	2244	2304	2334
Bristol Temple M .... **115 110** d.	0948	1057	1155	1255	1345	1445	...	1545	1614	1645	...	1745	...	1845	...	1945	2019	2019	2045	...	2145	...	...	...	...
Taunton .... **115 110** a.	1019	1129	1226	1326	1416	1515	...	1616	1644	1718	...	1818	...	1917	...	2015	2057	2057	2116	...	2215	...	...	...	...
Tiverton Parkway .... **110** a.	1031	1141	1238	1338	1429	1527	...	1629	1656	1730	...	1830	...	1930	...	2028	2111	2111	2128	...	2228	...	...	...	...
Exeter St Davids .... **110** a.	1045	1155	1254	1354	1444	1543	...	1644	1711	1746	...	1845	...	1945	...	2043	2127	2127	2144	...	2245	...	...	...	...
Newton Abbot .... **110** a.	1105	1215	1314	1414	1505	1604	...	1705	1735	1806	...	1905	...	2009	...	2104	2153	2153	2207	...	2306	...	...	...	...
Torquay .... **110** a.	|	|	|	|	|	|	...	|	1746	|	...	|	...	|	...	|	|	2203	|	...	|	...	...	...	...
Paignton .... **110** a.	|	|	|	|	|	|	...	|	1754	|	...	|	...	|	...	|	|	2211	|	...	|	...	...	...	...
Totnes .... **110** a.	1118	1227	1327	1427	1517	1617	...	1717	...	1819	...	1917	...	2021	...	2117	|	...	2220	...	2319	...	...	...	...
Plymouth .... **110** a.	1144	1255	1354	1454	1545	1644	...	1745	...	1846	...	1944	...	2048	...	2144	2236	...	2248	...	2346	...	...	...	...
Newquay **112** a.	...	|	...	...	...	...	...	...	...	|	...	...	...	|	...	...	...	...	...	...	...	...	...	...	...
Penzance **112** a.	...	1448	...	...	...	...	...	...	...	2037	...	...	...	2235	...	...	...	...	...	...	...	...	...	...	...

A – From Dundee (Table **222**).
B – From Aberdeen (Table **222**).
C – To Cardiff Central (Table **117**).
D – From Derby (Table **124**).

a – Also calls at Weston-super-Mare (a. 2036).
b – Also calls at Gloucester (a. 1901).
c – Also calls at Gloucester (a. 2201 on Ⓐ, 2202 on ⑥, 2203 on ⑦).
d – Also calls at Weston-super-Mare (a. 1132 on Ⓐ, 1129 on ⑥).
e – Until Sept. 7.
f – From Sept. 14.

h – Departs 0645 until Sept. 7.
m – Until Sept. 8.
n – From Sept. 15.

★ – Also calls at Dawlish (10 – 15 minutes after Exeter) and Teignmouth (15 – 18 minutes after Exeter).

XC Most services convey 🍸 PLYMOUTH and PAIGNTON - BRISTOL - BIRMINGHAM 116

Ⓐ	Ⓐ Fh	Ⓐ E	Ⓐ	Ⓐ	Ⓐ C	Ⓐ	Ⓐ ☆e	Ⓐ	Ⓐ	Ⓐ	Ⓐ	Ⓐ B	Ⓐ ☆	Ⓐ	Ⓐ	Ⓐ A	Ⓐ	Ⓐ	Ⓐ	Ⓐ	Ⓐ ☆a	Ⓐ	Ⓐ
Penzance 112 d.	...	...	...	...	...	...	...	...	...	0635	...	...	...	0837	...	0925	...	...	...	...	...	...	...
Newquay 112 d.	...	...	...	...	...	...	...	...	...	|	...	...	...	|	...	|	...	...	...	...	...	...	...
Plymouth 110 d.	...	...	...	0520	...	0625	...	0725	...	0825	...	0925	...	1025	...	1124	1150	1225	...	1325	...	1425	...
Totnes 110 d.	...	...	...	0546	...	0651	...	0751	...	0851	...	0951	...	1051	...	1150	1216	1251	...	1351	...	1451	...
Paignton 110 d.	...	...	...	|	...	|	0701	|	...	|	...	|	1007	|	...	|	|	|	...	|	1406	|	...
Torquay 110 d.	...	...	...	|	...	|	0707	|	...	|	...	|	1013	|	...	|	|	|	...	|	1412	|	...
Newton Abbot 110 d.	...	...	...	0558	...	0704	0717	0804	...	0904	...	1003	1022	1104	...	1203	1228	1304	...	1404	1423	1504	...
Exeter St Davids 110 d.	...	...	...	0624	...	0724	0744	0824	...	0924	...	1023	1047	1124	...	1223	1250	1324	...	1424	1448	1524	1555
Tiverton Parkway 110 d.	...	...	...	0637	...	0738	0757	0838	...	0938	...	1038	1100	1138	...	1239	1306	1338	...	1438	1502	1538	1609
Taunton 115 110 d.	...	...	...	0650	...	0750	0810	0850	...	0950	...	1050	1117	1150	...	1251	1321	1350	...	1450	1516	1550	1623
Bristol Temple Meads 115 110 a.	...	0621	...	0726	...	0827	0852	0925	...	1025	...	1124	1151	1222	...	1325	1355	1425	...	1523	1557	1621	1654
Bristol Temple Meads 138 d.	0613	0630	0700	0730	0800	0830	0900	0930	1000	1030	1100	1130	1200	1230	1300	1330	1400	1430	1500	1530	1600	1630	1700
Bristol Parkway 138 d.	0624	0640	0710	0740	0809	0840	0910	0940	1009	1040	1109	1140	1209	1240	1309	1340	1410	1440	1509	1540	1609	1640	1710
Cheltenham Spa 117 138 d.	0717	0711	0740	0816	0840	0916	0940	1016	1040	1116	1140	1211	1240	1316	1340	1416	1441	1511	1540	1616	1640	1716	1742
Birmingham New Street 117 a.	0815	0756	0825	0856	0925	0958	1023	1056	1125	1158	1225	1256	1325	1356	1423	1456	1523	1556	1623	1656	1723	1756	1823
Manchester P'dilly 119 a.	...	|	1000	|	1100	|	1200	|	1300	|	1400	|	1500	|	1600	|	1700	|	1800	|	1900	|	2000
Sheffield 124 a.	...	0918	...	1018	...	1118	...	1218	...	1318	...	1418	...	1518	...	1618	...	1718	...	1818	...	1919	...
Leeds 124 a.	...	1000	...	1100	...	1201	...	1300	...	1400	...	1500	...	1600	...	1701	...	1801	...	1904	...	2003	...
York 124 a.	...	1030	...	1130	...	1230	...	1330	...	1430	...	1530	...	1630	...	1730	...	1830	...	1930	...	2030	...
Newcastle 124 a.	...	1129	...	1230	...	1331	...	1432	...	1530	...	1630	...	1731	...	1832	...	1933	...	2035	...	2133	...
Edinburgh Wav'ley 124 220 a.	...	1306	...	1407	...	1508	...	1606	...	1705	...	1807	...	1906	...	2009	...	2109	...	2213	...	2303	...
Glasgow Central 124 220 a.	...	1412	...	...	...	1612	...	...	...	1811	...	...	...	2015	...	...	...	2221	...	...	...	...	...

	Ⓐ	Ⓐ	Ⓐ	Ⓐ	Ⓐ	Ⓐ b	Ⓐ	Ⓐ	Ⓐ	⑥ c	⑥	⑥	⑥ C	⑥	⑥ ☆	⑥	⑥	⑥	⑥ gk	⑥ f	⑥☆ Bg	⑥ Bf	⑥ ☆
Penzance 112 d.	...	...	...	...	...	...	...	...	...	...	...	...	...	...	...	...	...	0630	...	...	...	...	...
Newquay 112 d.	...	...	...	...	...	...	...	...	...	...	...	...	...	...	...	...	...	|	...	...	...	...	...
Plymouth 110 d.	1525	...	1625	...	1725	...	1825	...	...	...	...	0525	...	0625	...	0725	...	0825	0840	...	0915	0925	...
Totnes 110 d.	1551	...	1651	...	1751	...	1851	...	...	...	...	0551	...	0651	...	0751	...	0851	0906	...	0941	0951	...
Paignton 110 d.	|	...	|	...	|	...	|	...	2020	...	...	|	...	|	0700	|	...	|	|	...	|	|	1007
Torquay 110 d.	|	...	|	...	|	...	|	...	2026	...	...	|	...	|	0706	|	...	|	|	...	|	|	1013
Newton Abbot 110 d.	1604	...	1704	...	1804	...	1904	...	2035	...	...	0604	...	0704	0716	0804	...	0904	0919	...	0954	1004	1022
Exeter St Davids 110 d.	1624	1656	1724	1754	1824	...	1924	1952	2055	...	...	0624	...	0724	0741	0824	...	0924	0945	...	1024	1024	1056
Tiverton Parkway 110 d.	1638	1709	1738	1807	1838	...	1938	2006	2108	...	...	0637	...	0738	0755	0838	...	0938	0958	...	1038	1038	1110
Taunton 115 110 d.	1650	1722	1750	1824	1850	...	1950	2020	2121	...	...	0650	...	0750	0808	0850	...	0950	1011	...	1050	1050	1122
Bristol Temple Meads 115 110 a.	1723	1754	1821	1855	1923	...	2026	2058	2152	...	...	0722	...	0821	0856	0921	...	1021	1052	...	1125	1125	1153
Bristol Temple Meads 138 d.	1730	1800	1830	1900	1930	2000	2030	2100	2200	0612	0700	0730	0800	0830	0900	0930	1000	1030	1100	1100	1130	1130	1200
Bristol Parkway 138 d.	1740	1809	1840	1910	1940	2010	2040	2111	2209	0621	0710	0741	0810	0840	0909	0940	1009	1040	1109	1109	1140	1140	1209
Cheltenham Spa 117 138 d.	1816	1841	1916	1940	2016	2055	2116	2142	2245	0708	0741	0816	0840	0916	0940	1016	1040	1116	1140	1140	1216	1216	1240
Birmingham New Street 117 a.	1856	1923	1956	2023	2056	2137	2201	2236	2343	0756	0825	0856	0925	0956	1025	1056	1125	1156	1225	1225	1256	1256	1325
Manchester P'dilly 119 a.	...	2059	|	2200	...	...	...	...	...	|	1000	|	1100	|	1200	|	1300	|	1400	1400	|	|	1500
Sheffield 124 a.	2018	...	2120	...	2221	...	...	...	...	0918	...	1018	...	1118	...	1218	...	1318	...	...	1418	1418	...
Leeds 124 a.	2102	...	2202	...	2308	...	...	...	...	1000	...	1100	...	1200	...	1300	...	1401	...	...	1500	1500	...
York 124 a.	...	...	...	...	...	...	...	...	...	1030	...	1130	...	1230	...	1330	...	1430	...	...	1530	1530	...
Newcastle 124 a.	...	...	...	...	...	...	...	...	...	1129	...	1229	...	1329	...	1429	...	1529	...	...	1630	1630	...
Edinburgh Waverley 124 220 a.	...	...	...	...	...	...	...	...	...	1305	...	1405	...	1503	...	1606	...	1705	...	...	1806	1806	...
Glasgow Central 124 220 a.	...	...	...	...	...	...	...	...	...	1412	...	...	...	1612	...	...	...	1809	...	...	...	...	...

	⑥	⑥	⑥ A	⑥ g	⑥ f	⑥ ☆g	⑥ f	⑥	⑥	⑥ ☆a	⑥	⑥	⑥	⑥ f	⑥ g	⑥ f	⑥ ☆g	⑥	⑥ g	⑥ f	⑥ g	⑥ f	⑥ g	⑥ f
Penzance 112 d.	0828	...	...	...	0943	...	...	...	...	...	...	...	...	...	...	...	...	...	...	...	...	...	1630	...
Newquay 112 d.	|	...	0940g	...	|	...	...	...	...	...	...	...	...	...	...	...	...	...	...	...	...	...	|	...
Plymouth 110 d.	1025	...	1125	...	1148	...	1225	...	1326	...	1424	...	1525	...	...	1625	...	...	1724	1725	...	...	1825	1825
Totnes 110 d.	1051	...	1151	...	1214	...	1251	...	1352	...	1450	...	1551	...	...	1651	...	...	1750	1751	...	...	1851	1851
Paignton 110 d.	|	...	|	...	|	1233	|	...	|	1356	|	...	|	...	...	|	1640	...	|	|	1810	...	|	|
Torquay 110 d.	|	...	|	...	|	1240	|	...	|	1402	|	...	|	...	...	|	1647	...	|	|	1817	...	|	|
Newton Abbot 110 d.	1104	...	1204	...	1226	1251	1304	...	1405	1412	1503	...	1604	...	...	1704	1658	...	1803	1804	1827	...	1904	1904
Exeter St Davids 110 d.	1124	...	1224	...	1248	1324	1324	...	1426	1436	1523	...	1624	1653	...	1724	1726	...	1824	1824	1849	...	1924	1924
Tiverton Parkway 110 d.	1138	...	1238	...	1302	1338	1338	...	1440	1450	1537	...	1638	1707	...	1738	1740	...	1838	1838	1905	...	1938	1938
Taunton 115 110 d.	1150	...	1250	...	1315	1350	1350	...	1452	1502	1550	...	1650	1720	...	1751	1751	...	1851	1850	1920	...	1950	1950
Bristol Temple Meads 115 110 a.	1221	...	1324	...	1354	1425	1425	...	1525	1550	1621	...	1724	1755	...	1823	1825	...	1923	1923	1952	...	2023	2021
Bristol Temple Meads 138 d.	1230	1300	1330	1400	1400	1430	1430	1500	1530	1600	1630	1700	1730	1800	1800	1830	1830	1900	1930	1930	2000	2000	2030	2030
Bristol Parkway 138 d.	1240	1309	1340	1409	1409	1440	1440	1509	1540	1609	1640	1710	1740	1809	1809	1840	1840	1909	1940	1940	2009	2009	2040	2040
Cheltenham Spa 117 138 d.	1316	1341	1416	1440	1440	1516	1516	1541	1613	1640	1712	1740	1816	1841	1841	1916	1916	1940	2012	2012	2040	2040	2111	2111
Birmingham New Street 117 a.	1356	1425	1456	1525	1525	1556	1556	1625	1656	1725	1756	1825	1856	1925	1925	1956	1956	2025	2050	2052	2136	2136	2152	2151
Manchester P'dilly 119 a.	|	1600	|	1700	1700	|	|	1800	|	1900	|	2000	|	2059	2059	|	|	2200	2233	|	...	...	|	...
Sheffield 124 a.	1518	...	1618	...	...	1718	1718	...	1818	...	1918	...	2018	...	...	2119	2119	...	...	2223	...	...	2312	...
Leeds 124 a.	1600	...	1700	...	...	1801	1801	...	1903	...	2003	...	2102	...	...	2202	2202	...	...	2326	...	...	2355	...
York 124 a.	1630	...	1729	...	...	1831	1831	...	1930	...	2030	...	2147	...	...	...	...	...	...	...	...	...	...	...
Newcastle 124 a.	1729	...	1829	...	...	1932	1932	...	2035	...	2128	...	...	...	...	...	...	...	...	...	...	...	...	...
Edinburgh Waverley 124 220 a.	1905	...	2006	...	...	2109	2109	...	2208	...	2300	...	...	...	...	...	...	...	...	...	...	...	...	...
Glasgow Central 124 220 a.	2015	...	...	...	...	2219	2219	...	...	...	...	...	...	...	...	...	...	...	...	...	...	...	...	...

⑦	⑦ c	⑦	⑦ B	⑦	⑦ ☆a	⑦	⑦	⑦	⑦	⑦ m	⑦ n	⑦	⑦	⑦ d		⑦	⑦	⑦	⑦	⑦	⑦	⑦	⑦
Penzance 112 d.	...	...	...	...	...	0930	...	...	...	...	...	...	...	1230	...	...	...	...	...	1530	...	...	...
Newquay 112 d.	...	...	...	...	...	|	...	...	...	1138	...	...	...	|	...	...	...	...	...	|	...	...	...
Plymouth 110 d.	...	...	0924	1025	...	1125	1200	1225	1252	1325	1325	...	1425	1434	...	1523	...	1625	...	1725	...	1825	...
Totnes 110 d.	...	...	0950	1051	...	1150	|	1251	|	1351	1351	...	1451	1500	...	1549	...	1651	...	1751	...	1851	...
Paignton 110 d.	...	...	|	|	1050	|	|	|	|	|	|	...	|	|	...	|	...	|	...	|	1820	|	...
Torquay 110 d.	...	...	|	|	1056	|	|	|	|	|	|	...	|	|	...	|	...	|	...	|	1826	|	...
Newton Abbot 110 d.	...	...	1003	1104	1108	1204	1238	1304	1330	1404	1404	...	1504	1513	...	1602	...	1704	...	1804	1835	1904	...
Exeter St Davids 110 d.	...	...	1024	1124	1133	1224	1300	1324	1352	1424	1424	...	1524	1534	...	1624	...	1724	...	1825	1858	1924	...
Tiverton Parkway 110 d.	...	...	1038	1138	1147	1238	1313	1338	|	1438	1438	...	1538	1547	...	1638	...	1738	...	1839	1911	1938	...
Taunton 115 110 d.	...	...	1050	1150	1159	1250	1326	1350	|	1450	1450	...	1551	1600	...	1650	...	1751	...	1851	1924	1950	...
Bristol Temple Meads 115 110 a.	...	...	1123	1221	1246	1321	1357	1423	1445	1521	1521	...	1624	1648	...	1726	...	1827	...	1923	1955	2024	...
Bristol Temple Meads 138 d.	0915	1030	1130	1230	1300	1330	1400	1430	1500	1530	1530	1600	1630	1700	...	1730	1800	1830	1900	1930	2000	2030	2210
Bristol Parkway 138 d.	0925	1040	1140	1240	1309	1340	1409	1440	1510	1540	1540	1609	1640	1709	...	1740	1809	1840	1909	1940	2009	2040	2219
Cheltenham Spa 117 138 d.	1011	1111	1211	1311	1340	1411	1440	1511	1541	1611	1611	1640	1711	1740	...	1811	1840	1911	1940	2011	2040	2111	2250
Birmingham New Street 117 a.	1049	1149	1249	1349	1427	1449	1527	1552	1627	1649	1649	1727	1750	1827	...	1850	1927	1950	2027	2054	2118	2150	2339
Manchester P'dilly 118 a.	|	|	|	|	1559	|	1659	|	1759	|	|	1859	|	1959	...	|	2100	|	2202	|	|	|	...
Sheffield 124 a.	1218	1318	1417	1518	...	1618	...	1719	...	1819	1819	...	1920	...	...	2018	...	2118	...	2218	...	2318	...
Leeds 124 a.	1300	1400	1500	1600	...	1659	...	1801	...	1901	1901	...	2004	...	...	2102	...	2202	...	2302	...	0009	...
York 124 a.	1327	1429	1529	1629	...	1729	...	1829	...	1930	1930	...	2030	...	...	2131	...	...	...	...	...	...	...
Newcastle 124 a.	1427	1527	1627	1727	...	1827	...	1930	...	2031	2031	...	2131	...	...	...	...	...	...	...	...	...	...
Edinburgh Waverley 124 220 a.	1603	1655	1800	1859	...	1957	...	2103	...	2207	2207	...	2303	...	...	...	...	...	...	...	...	...	...
Glasgow Central 124 220 a.	...	1813	...	2020	...	...	...	2212	...	...	...	...	...	...	...	...	...	...	...	...	...	...	...

A – To Dundee (Table 222).
B – To Aberdeen (Table 222).
C – From Cardiff Central (Table 117).
E – From Bath Spa (d. 0610).
F – To Stansted Airport (Table 208).

a – Also calls at Weston-super-Mare (d. 1538 on Ⓐ, 1532 on ⑥, 1221 on ⑦).
b – Also calls at Gloucester (d. 2045).
c – Also calls at Gloucester (d. 0653 on ⑥, 1000 on ⑦).
d – Also calls at Weston-super-Mare (d. 1630).
e – Also calls at Weston-super-Mare (d. 0835).
f – From Sept. 14.
g – Until Sept. 7.

h – Also calls at Gloucester (d. 0651).
k – Also calls at Weston-super-Mare (d. 1034).
m – Until Sept. 8.
n – From Sept. 15.

☆ – Also calls at Teignmouth (7 – 10 minutes after Newton Abbot) and Dawlish (12 – 15 minutes after Newton Abbot).

117 BIRMINGHAM - CARDIFF — AW, XC

km			Ⓐ	Ⓐ	Ⓐ	Ⓐ	Ⓐ	Ⓐ	Ⓐ	Ⓐ	Ⓐ	Ⓐ	Ⓐ	Ⓐ	Ⓐ	Ⓐ	Ⓐ	Ⓐ	Ⓐ 2	Ⓐ	Ⓐ	Ⓐ
			2			2		🍸	2		🍸	2	🍸	2	🍸	🍸	2	🍸	🍸 B	🍸	🍸	2
	Nottingham 123 d.	Ⓐ	...	...	...	...	...	0600	...	0704	0809	...	0907	...	1007	1107	...	1207	...	1307	1407	...
	Derby 116 123 d.		...	...	...	...	0610	0636	...	0736	0838	...	0938	...	1038	1137	...	1237	...	1337	1437	...
0	**Birmingham** New Street 116 d.		...	0500	0537	...	0712	0730	...	0830	0930	...	1030	...	1130	1230	...	1330	...	1430	1530	...
73	Cheltenham Spa 116 135 138 d.		0537	0603	0644	0746	0752	0815	0846	0915	1015	1045	1115	1146	121	1315	1345	1415	...	1515	1615	1645
83	**Gloucester** 135 138 d.		0550	0615c	0700c	0758	...	0825	0858	0925	1025	1058	1125	1159	1225	1325	1358	1425	1448	1525	1625	1658
115	Lydney 🚂 d.		0609	0633	0718	0817	...	|	0917	|	1043	1117	|	1218	|	1343	1417	|	1507	|	1643	1717
127	Chepstow d.		0618	0643	0728	0826	...	0850	0927	0950	|	1126	1150	1227	1250	|	1426	1450	1516	1550	1653	1727
138	Caldicot d.		0626	0651	0736	0835	...	|	0935	|	|	1135	|	1236	|	|	1435	|	1525	|	|	1735
155	Newport 118 134 149 a.		0641	0706	0753	0850	...	0909	0951	1011	1110	1150	1209	1251	1309	1410	1450	1512	1540	1612	1711	1750
174	**Cardiff** Central 118 134 149 a.		0700	0721	0808	0907	...	0928	1009	1027	1129	1213	1226	1310	1330	1426	1515	1530	1558	1630	1730	1810

	Ⓐ	Ⓐ	Ⓐ	Ⓐ	Ⓐ	Ⓐ	Ⓐ	Ⓐ	Ⓐ	Ⓐ	Ⓐ	⑤	①–④		⑥	⑥	⑥	⑥	⑥	⑥	⑥	⑥
	🍸	2		2		🍸 A	2					2	2		2			2		🍸	2	
Nottingham 123 d.	1507	...	1607	...	1707	...	...	1807	1907	*1936*	*2040*	...	...	⑥	...	...	...	...	...	0559	...	0700
Derby 116 123 d.	1537	...	1637	...	1737	...	...	1840	1938	2031	2131	...	...		...	...	...	...	0610	0636	...	0736
Birmingham New Street 116 d.	1630	...	1730	...	1830	1842	...	1930	2030	2112	2212	...	...		...	0500	0542	...	0712	0730	...	0830
Cheltenham Spa 116 135 138 d.	1718	1745	1818	1845	1915	1926	1947	2015	2115	2152	2252	2300	2300		...	0603	0642	0745	0752	0815	0845	0915
Gloucester 135 138 d.	1730	1758	1831	1900	1925	|	1958	2025	2125	2201	...	2313	2313		0550	0615c	0700d	0758	...	0825	0858	0925
Lydney 🚂 d.	1749	1817	|	1919	|	|	2017	|	2143	...	...	2332	2332		0609	0633	0718	0817	...	|	0917	|
Chepstow d.	|	1826	|	1929	|	|	2027	|	2153	...	...	2342	2342		0618	0643	0728	0826	...	0850	0926	0950
Caldicot d.	|	1835	|	1936	|	|	2035	|	2201	...	...	2350	2350		0627	0651	0736	0835	...	|	0935	|
Newport 118 134 149 a.	1814	1849	1914	1953	2012	2046	2050	2111	2216	...	...	0006	0012		0642	0706	0751	0850	...	0909	0950	1009
Cardiff Central 118 134 149 a.	1830	1909	1933	2012	2028	2102	2110	2128	2237f	...	...	0026	0034		0701	0721	0806	0910	...	0924	1010	1024

	⑥	⑥	⑥	⑥	⑥	⑥	⑥	⑥	⑥ 2	⑥		⑥	⑥	⑥	⑥	⑥	⑥	⑥	⑥	⑥	⑥	⑥
	🍸	2	🍸	2	🍸	🍸	2	🍸	🍸 B	🍸		🍸	2	🍸	2		2		🍸 A	2		
Nottingham 123 d.	0806	...	0906	...	1006	1106	...	1206	...	1306	...	1406	...	1506	...	1606	...	1707	...	...	1806	1906
Derby 116 123 d.	0837	...	0936	...	1038	1137	...	1237	...	1337	...	1437	...	1537	...	1637	...	1737	...	...	1837	1939
Birmingham New Street 116 d.	0930	...	1030	...	1130	1230	...	1330	...	1430	...	1530	...	1630	...	1730	...	1830	1842	...	1930	2030
Cheltenham Spa 116 135 138 d.	1015	1045	1115	1146	1215	1315	1345	1415	...	1515	...	1615	1645	1715	1745	1818	1845	1915	1926	1945	2015	2115
Gloucester 135 138 d.	1025	1058	1125	1158	1225	1325	1358	1425	1442	1525	...	1625	1658	1725	1758	1828	1858	1925	|	1958	2025	2125
Lydney 🚂 d.	1043	1117	|	1217	|	1343	1417	|	1501	|	...	1643	1717	1743	1817	|	1917	|	|	2017	|	2143
Chepstow d.	|	1126	1150	1226	1250	|	1426	1450	1510	1550	...	1653	1726	|	1826	|	1926	|	|	2026	|	2153
Caldicot d.	|	1135	|	1235	|	|	1435	|	1519	|	...	|	1735	|	1835	|	1934	|	|	2035	|	2201
Newport 118 134 149 a.	1109	1150	1209	1250	1309	1409	1450	1510	1535	1609	...	1711	1750	1809	1850	1910	1950	2006	2045	2050	2109	2222
Cardiff Central 118 134 149 a.	1124	1205	1224	1307	1324	1424	1509	1526	1554	1624	...	1726	1810	1824	1912	1927	2010	2021	2100	2106	2124	2243

	⑥	⑥		⑦	⑦	⑦	⑦	⑦	⑦	⑦	⑦		⑦	⑦	⑦	⑦	⑦	⑦	⑦	⑦	⑦	⑦
	🍸	2		2	🍸		2	🍸	🍸	2	🍸		🍸	2			2			2		2
Nottingham 123 d.	*1929*	...	⑦	...	...	0954	...	1111	1210	...	1310	...	1410	...	1510	1610	...	1710	1810	...	*1910*	...
Derby 116 123 d.	2028	...		...	...	1018	...	1138	1236	...	1338	...	1436	...	1535	1636	...	1735	1836	...	2027	...
Birmingham New Street 116 d.	2112	...		...	1012	1112	...	1230	1330	...	1430	...	1530	...	1630	1730	...	1830	1930	...	2112	...
Cheltenham Spa 116 135 138 d.	2152	...		...	1101	1157	1221	1315	1415	1421	1515	...	1615	1621	1715	1815	1835	1915	2015	2010	2153	...
Gloucester 135 138 d.	2202	2309		1048	1111	1211	1233	1325	1425	1434	1525	...	1625	1635	1725	1825	1848	1927	2026	2033e	2203	2233
Lydney 🚂 d.	...	2328		1107	|	|	1252	|	|	1453	|	...	|	1653	|	|	1907	|	|	2052	...	2252
Chepstow d.	...	2337		1116	|	|	1301	|	|	1502	|	...	|	1703	|	|	1916	|	|	2101	...	2301
Caldicot d.	...	2346		1125	|	|	1310	|	|	1511	|	...	|	1711	|	|	1925	|	|	2110	...	2310
Newport 118 134 149 a.	...	0011		1139	1152	1252	1325	1406	1506	1526	1606	...	1706	1727	1806	1906	1947	2008	2107	2125	...	2325
Cardiff Central 118 134 149 a.	...	0038		1158	1208	1307	1345	1422	1521	1545	1621	...	1721	1745	1821	1921	2009	2023	2122	2142	...	2341

		Ⓐ	Ⓐ	Ⓐ	Ⓐ	Ⓐ	Ⓐ		Ⓐ	Ⓐ	Ⓐ	Ⓐ	Ⓐ		Ⓐ	Ⓐ	Ⓐ	Ⓐ	Ⓐ	Ⓐ	Ⓐ	Ⓐ
		C	2		2	🍸 A				2	🍸	2			🍸	2	🍸	2	🍸	🍸	2	🍸
Cardiff Central 118 134 149 d.	Ⓐ	...	0612	0640	0705	0700	0745	...	0845	0912	0945	1009	1045	...	1145	1212	1245	1312	1345	1445	1512	1545
Newport 118 134 149 d.		...	0627	0655	0723	0714	0802	...	0900	0928	0959	1027	1059	...	1159	1228	1259	1328	1359	1501	1528	1559
Caldicot d.		...	0641	0709	0736	|	|	...	|	0939	|	1040	|	...	|	1242	|	1343	|	|	1540	|
Chepstow d.		...	0650	0717	0745	|	|	...	0918	0948	1017	1049	|	...	1217	1251	1317	1352	|	1519	1549	1617
Lydney 🚂 d.		...	0659	0726	0754	|	0827	...	|	0957	|	1058	1124	...	|	1300	|	1401	1424	|	1558	|
Gloucester 135 138 d.		0707	0722	0748	0821c	|	0848	...	0952d	1020	1048c	1121	1151d	...	1244	1322	1352d	1422	1448c	1550c	1622	1646
Cheltenham Spa 116 135 138 d.		0717	0734	0759	0834	0840	0859	...	1003	1031	1059	1132	1203	...	1255	1333	1403	...	1459	1601	1631	1657
Birmingham New Street 116 a.		0815	*0825*	0845	...	0925	0945	...	1045	...	1145	...	1245	...	1345	...	1445	...	1545	1645	...	1745
Derby 116 123 a.		...	...	0932	...	...	1038	...	1136	...	1236	...	1335	...	1435	...	1535	...	1635	1735	...	1833
Nottingham 123 a.		...	...	1003	...	...	1103	...	1207	...	1303	...	1402	...	1502	...	1602	...	1702	1802	...	1905

	Ⓐ	Ⓐ	Ⓐ	Ⓐ	Ⓐ	Ⓐ	Ⓐ	Ⓐ	Ⓐ	Ⓐ	⑤	①–④		⑥	⑥	⑥	⑥	⑥	⑥	⑥	⑥	⑥
	2	🍸	2	🍸	2	🍸			2		2	2			C	2		2	🍸 A			2
Cardiff Central 118 134 149 d.	1610	1645	1712	1745	1808	1845	1949	2105	2112	2150	2320	2320	⑥	...	...	0610	0638	0707	0700	0745	0845	0910
Newport 118 134 149 d.	1627	1700	1728	1759	1824	1859	2003	2119	2127	2204	2335	2340		...	...	0626	0653	0723	0714	0801	0901	0925
Caldicot d.	1640	|	1741	|	1837	|	2017	|	2141	|	2352	0001		...	...	0639	0706	0736	|	|	|	0937
Chepstow d.	1649	|	1750	1817	1846	1917	2025	|	2150	|	0002	0010		...	...	0648	0715	0745	|	|	0919	0947
Lydney 🚂 d.	1658	1724	1759	|	1855	|	2034	|	2159	|	0011	0019		...	...	0657	0723	0754	|	0826	|	0955
Gloucester 135 138 d.	1720	1752d	1821	1844	1921c	1951d	2055c	2202	2223	2248	0031	0039		0653	0704	0721	0744	0822	|	0848	0948	1021
Cheltenham Spa 116 135 138 d.	1729	1803	1830	1855	1931	2002	2106	2213	2234	2259	...	...		0708c	0714	0734	0755	0835	0840	0859	0959	1032
Birmingham New Street 116 a.	...	1845	...	1945	...	2045	2154	2305	...	2359	...	...		0756	0806	...	0845	...	0925	0945	1045	...
Derby 116 123 a.	...	1935	...	2033	...	2132	*2353*	...	...	...	...	...		0841	...	...	0936	...	...	1037	1136	...
Nottingham 123 a.	...	2003	...	2104	...	2212	*0016*	...	...	...	...	...		...	...	...	1002	...	...	1103	1202	...

	⑥	⑥	⑥		⑥	⑥	⑥	⑥	⑥	⑥	⑥	⑥	⑥	⑥	⑥	⑥	⑥	⑥	⑥	⑥	⑥	⑥
	🍸	2			🍸	2	🍸	2 🍸	🍸	🍸	🍸	🍸	2	🍸	2	🍸	2	🍸			2	2
Cardiff Central 118 134 149 d.	0945	1010	1045	...	1145	1209	1245	1312	1345	1445	1508	1545	1608	1645	1709	1745	1808	1845	2000	2050	2111	2318
Newport 118 134 149 d.	0959	1027	1059	...	1159	1227c	1259	1327	1359	1459	1527c	1559	1624	1659	1725	1759	1827c	1859	2014	2104	2127	2337
Caldicot d.	|	1040	|	...	|	1240	|	1341	|	|	1538	|	1637	|	1740	|	1840	|	2028	|	2140	2359
Chepstow d.	1017	1049	|	...	1217	1249	1317	1350	|	1517	1547	1617	1646	|	1749	1817	1849	1917	2036	|	2149	0008
Lydney 🚂 d.	|	1058	1124	...	|	1258	|	1359	1424	|	1556	|	1655	1724	1758	|	1858	|	2045	|	2158	0017
Gloucester 135 138 d.	1048c	1122	1148c	...	1244	1322	1348c	1420	1448c	1548c	1621	1648c	1723c	1748c	1821	1844	1921	1948	2106	2148	2219	0040
Cheltenham Spa 116 135 138 d.	1059	1132	1159	...	1255	1332	1359	...	1459	1559	1632	1659	1733	1759	1831	1855	1931	1959	2117	2159	...	...
Birmingham New Street 116 a.	1145	...	1245	...	1345	...	1445	...	1545	1645	...	1745	...	1845	...	1945	...	2042	2207	2245	...	...
Derby 116 123 a.	1237	...	1335	...	1436	...	1536	...	1636	1735	...	1835	...	1932	...	2035	...	2135	2253	...	...	...
Nottingham 123 a.	1303	...	1402	...	1502	...	1603	...	1702	1802	...	1902	...	2003	...	2102	...	2208	2327	...	...	...

		⑦	⑦	⑦	⑦	⑦	⑦	⑦	⑦	⑦	⑦	⑦	⑦		⑦	⑦	⑦	⑦	⑦	⑦	⑦	⑦
			2			2			2	🍸	🍸	2	🍸		🍸	2	🍸	D		2		2
Cardiff Central 118 134 149 d.	⑦	...	1030	1045	1145	1225	1245	1345	1425	1445	1545	1625	1645	...	1745	1824	1845	1945	...	2024	2045	2226
Newport 118 134 149 d.		...	1045	1059	1159	1240	1259	1359	1440	1459	1559	1640	1659	...	1759	1839	1859	1959	...	2040	2059	2241
Caldicot d.		...	1101	|	|	1300	|	|	1458	|	|	1658	|	...	|	1859	|	|	...	2059	|	2259
Chepstow d.		...	1110	|	|	1309	|	|	1507	|	|	1707	|	...	|	1908	|	|	...	2108	|	2308
Lydney 🚂 d.		...	1119	|	|	1318	|	|	1516	|	|	1716	|	...	|	1917	|	|	...	2117	|	2317
Gloucester 135 138 d.		1000	1142	1148	1248	1340	1348	1448	1540	1548	1648	1740	1748	...	1848	1941	1948	2048	...	2142	2148	2342
Cheltenham Spa 116 135 138 d.		1011	1152	1159	1259	1352	1359	1459	1550	1559	1659	1750	1759	...	1859	1953	2959	2059	2111	...	2159	...
Birmingham New Street 116 a.		1049	...	1245	1345	...	1445	1545	...	1645	1745	...	1845	...	1945	...	2045	2145	2150	...	2245	...
Derby 116 123 a.		1137	...	1333	1433	...	1534	1634	...	1733	1834	...	1934	...	2034	...	2134	...	2240	...	...	...
Nottingham 123 a.		...	...	1357	1456	...	1559	1655	...	1757	1855	...	1958	...	2057	...	2159	...	...	...	...	...

A – (12) Manchester Piccadilly - Bristol Temple Meads - Cardiff Central and v.v. (Tables **116**/**119**).
B – (2) and 🍸 Gloucester - Fishguard Harbour (Table **136**).
C – To Stansted Airport (Table **208**).
D – (12) Cardiff - Leicester (Table **208**).

c – Arrives 4–6 minutes earlier.
d – Arrives 8 minutes earlier.
e – Arrives 2019.
f – On ⑤ arrives 2231.

🚂 – DEAN FOREST RAILWAY (Lydney Junction - Parkend. *7 km*). ✆ 01594 845840. www.deanforestrailway.co.uk. Lydney Junction station is 10 minutes walk from the National Rail station.

GW 2nd class — CARDIFF - BRISTOL — 118

km		Ⓐ	Ⓐ A	Ⓐ B	Ⓐ A	Ⓐ P	Ⓐ A	Ⓐ T	Ⓐ A	Ⓐ G	and at the same	Ⓐ A	Ⓐ G	Ⓐ A	Ⓐ A	Ⓐ	⑤	①–④	⑤	①–④	Ⓐ	⑥	⑥ R	⑥ A	⑥ B	⑥ A
0	**Cardiff** Central . ‡ d.		0630	0700	0730	0800	0830	0900	0930	1000	minutes past	1930	2000	2030	2100	2130	2204	2204	2236	2236	2327		0455	0630	0700	0730
19	Newport .... ‡ d.		0644	0714	0744	0815	0844	0915	0944	1015	each hour until	1945	2016	2044	2115	2145	2218	2220	2251	2254	2345		0509	0644	0714	0744
61	**Bristol** T Meads.. a.		0720	0747	0817	0851	0919	0954	1019	1052	▲ H	2018	2053	2117	2151	2221	2259	2309	2326	2338	0035		0553	0718	0752	0818

	⑥ G	and at the same	⑥ G	⑥ A	⑥	⑥ A	⑥ A	⑥	⑥	⑦	⑦ A	⑦ A	⑦ A	⑦ A	and	⑦ A	⑦ A	⑦ A	⑦ A	⑦ A	⑦ A	⑦ A	⑦	⑦ A	⑦
Cardiff Central .. ‡ d.	0800	minutes past	1900	1930	1954	2030	2100	2200	2247		0810	0908	1008	1108	hourly	1608	1635	1708	1740	1808	1908	2018	2118	2210	2307
Newport .... ‡ d.	0815	each hour until	1915	1944	2010	2044	2115	2215	2303		0828	0926	1022	1122	until	1622	1649	1723	1752	1822	1922	2033	2132	2228	2323
Bristol T Meads... a.	0854	▽	1950	2018	2049	2116	2152	2300	2343		0908	1012	1103	1203	▲	1703	1728	1802	1839	1904	2007	2112	2219	2310	2359

	Ⓐ	②–⑤ E	Ⓐ	Ⓐ G	Ⓐ A	Ⓐ R	Ⓐ G	Ⓐ A	Ⓐ	Ⓐ A	Ⓐ F	and at the same	Ⓐ G	Ⓐ A	Ⓐ B	Ⓐ A	Ⓐ	⑤ A	①–④ A	⑤ A	①–④ A	⑥	⑥ E	⑥	⑥	⑥
Bristol T Meads .. d.		0137	0552	0620	0651	0705	0724	0753	0824	0854	0921	minutes past	1921	1954	2014	2054	2119	2154	2154	2254	2254		0137	0651	0723	0755
Newport .... ‡ a.		0211s	0635	0701	0725	0748	0806	0826	0905	0924	0958	each hour until	2000	2025	2046	2124	2159	2227	2233	2333	2333		0211s	0727	0758	0825
Cardiff Central .. ‡ a.		0232	0651	0719	0741	0802	0823	0843	0926	0942	1016	▽ F	2018	2047	2102	2144	2215	2243	2256	2349	2355		0232	0745	0818	0842

	⑥	⑥ A	⑥ N	and at the same	⑥ G	⑥ A	⑥ B	⑥ A	⑥ G	⑥ A	⑥ A	⑦	⑦	⑦ A	⑦ A	⑦ A	⑦	⑦ A	⑦	⑦ A	⑦ A	⑦	⑦ A	and	⑦ A	⑦ A
Bristol T Meads .. d.	0823	0855	0922	minutes past	1919	1954	2010	2053	2129	2157	2255		0848	0949	1040	1147	1248	1348	1416	1448	1548	1612	1648	hourly	2149	2249
Newport .... ‡ a.	0901	0925	0958	each hour until	1955	2023	2045	2123	2209	2237	2335		0924	1021	1114	1221	1319	1419	1447	1520	1619	1644	1721	until	2224	2321
Cardiff Central .. ‡ a.	0923	0942	1018	▲ C	2013	2042	2100	2142	2232	2300	2356		0945	1036	1131	1236	1334	1435	1502	1535	1634	1701	1737	▲	2243	2335

A – To/from Portsmouth Harbour, Brighton, Frome, Westbury or Warminster (Table **140**).
B – To/from Manchester Piccadilly (Tables **114** and **119**).
C – 0922 from Bristol starts from Weston-super-Mare d. 0839; all other xx22 services from Bristol start from Taunton (Table **115**).
E – [12] and 🍸 London Paddington - Cardiff Central (Table **134**).
F – 0921 from Bristol starts from Weston-super-Mare (d. 0841); 1121 from Bristol starts from Exeter St Davids (Tables **110** and **115**); 1519 from Bristol starts from Paignton (Tables **110** and **115**); all other xx21 services start from Taunton (Table **115**).
G – To/from Taunton (Table **115**).
H – 1300 from Cardiff extended to Exeter St Davids (Tables **115** and **110**).
P – To Paignton (Table **110**).
R – [12] and 🍸 London Paddington - Swansea and v.v. (Table **134**).
T – To Plymouth (Table **110**).

s – Calls to set down only.

▽ – Timings may vary by up to 6 minutes.
▲ – Timings may vary by up to 3 minutes.
‡ – For additional services see Tables **117**, **134** and **149**.

XC Most services convey 🍸 — BIRMINGHAM - MANCHESTER — 119

km		Ⓐ	Ⓐ	Ⓐ	Ⓐ	Ⓐ	Ⓐ S	Ⓐ	Ⓐ S	Ⓐ A	Ⓐ	Ⓐ	Ⓐ	Ⓐ	Ⓐ	Ⓐ	Ⓐ	Ⓐ	Ⓐ	Ⓐ	Ⓐ	Ⓐ F	Ⓐ	Ⓐ
	Bournemouth **114** .... d.		...	...	...	...	...	...	...	...	0630	...	0730	...	0845	...	0945	...	1045	...	1145	...	1245	...
	Reading **114** .... d.		...	...	...	...	0615	...	0715	...	0815	...	0915	...	1015	...	1115	...	1215	...	1315	...	1415	...
	Paignton **116** .... d.		...	...	...	...	|	...	|	...	|	0701	|	...	|	...	|	1007	|	...	|	...	|	...
	Exeter St Davids **116** .... d.		...	...	...	...	|	...	|	...	|	0744	|	...	|	...	|	1047	|	...	|	1250	|	...
	Bristol Temple Meads **116** d.		...	...	...	...	|	0700	|	0800	|	0900	|	1000	|	1100	|	1200	|	1300	|	1400	|	1500
0	**Birmingham** New Str **144 150** d.		0557	0630	0652	0731	0757	0831	0857	0931	0957	1031	1057	1131	1157	1231	1257	1331	1357	1431	1457	1531	1557	1631
20	Wolverhampton .... **144 150** d.		0614	0648	0710	0749	0814	0848	0914	0948	1014	1048	1114	1148	1214	1248	1314	1348	1414	1448	1514	1548	1614	1648
46	Stafford .... **144** d.		0628	0702	0724	0803	0828	0902	0928	1002	1028	1102	1128	1202	1228	1302	1328	1402	1428	1502	1528	1602	1628	1702
72	Stoke on Trent .... **144 152** d.		0645	0720	|	0820	0844	0920	0944	1020	1044	1120	1144	1220	1244	1320	1344	1420	1444	1520	1544	1620	1644	1720
104	Macclesfield .... **152** d.		0706	0738	|	0837	0902	0937	1002	1037	1102	1137	1202	1237	1302	1337	1402	1437	1502	1537	1602	1637	1702	1737
123	Stockport .... **152** d.		0720	0750	0814	0850	0914	0950	1014	1050	1114	1150	1214	1250	1314	1350	1414	1450	1514	1550	1614	1650	1714	1750
132	**Manchester** Piccadilly ...... **152** a.		0730	0800	0823	0900	0924	1000	1024	1100	1124	1200	1224	1300	1324	1400	1424	1500	1524	1600	1624	1700	1724	1800

	Ⓐ	Ⓐ	Ⓐ	Ⓐ	Ⓐ	Ⓐ	Ⓐ	Ⓐ	Ⓐ	Ⓐ	Ⓐ	⑥	⑥	⑥	⑥	⑥	⑥ S	⑥	⑥ S	⑥ A	⑥	⑥	⑥	⑥
Bournemouth **114** .... d.	1345	...	1445	...	1545	...	1645	...	1745	1845	...		...	...	...	...	...	...	...	...	0638	...	0747	...
Reading **114** .... d.	1515	...	1615	...	1715	...	1815	...	1915	2015	*2045*		...	...	...	...	0615	...	0715	...	0815	...	0915	...
Paignton **116** .... d.	|	1406	|	...	|	...	|	...	|	|	|		...	...	...	...	|	...	|	...	|	0700	|	...
Exeter St Davids **116** .... d.	|	1448	|	1555	|	1656	|	1754	|	|	|		...	...	...	...	|	...	|	...	|	0741	|	...
Bristol Temple Meads **116**. d.	|	1600	|	1700	|	1800	|	1900	|	|	|		...	...	...	...	|	0700	|	0800	|	0900	|	1000
Birmingham New Str . **144 150** d.	1657	1731	1757	1831	1857	1931	1957	2031	2057	2157	2230		0557	0631	0657	0731	0757	0831	0857	0931	0957	1031	1057	1131
Wolverhampton .... **144 150** d.	1714	1748	1814	1848	1914	1948	2014	2048	2114	2214	2248		0614	0648	0714	0750	0814	0848	0914	0948	1014	1048	1114	1148
Stafford .... **144** d.	1728	1802	1828	1902	1928	2002	2028	2102	2128	2228	2302		0628	0702	0731	0804	0828	0902	0928	1004	1028	1102	1128	1202
Stoke on Trent .... **144 152** d.	1744	1820	1844	1920	1944	2020	2044	2120	2144	2244	2320		0644	0720	|	0820	0844	0920	0944	1020	1044	1120	1144	1220
Macclesfield .... **152** d.	1802	1837	1902	1937	2002	2037	2102	2137	2202	2302	|		0705	0737	|	0837	0902	0937	1002	1037	1102	1137	1202	1237
Stockport .... **152** d.	1814	1850	1914	1950	2014	2049	2114	2150	2216	2314	|		0720	0750	0816	0851	0914	0950	1014	1050	1114	1150	1214	1250
Manchester Piccadilly ...... **152** a.	1824	1900	1924	2000	2024	2059	2124	2200	2225	2324	0012		0731	0759	0829	0859	0924	1000	1024	1100	1124	1200	1224	1300

	⑥	⑥ F	⑥	⑥	⑥	⑥	⑥	⑥	⑥	⑥ H	⑥	⑥	⑥	⑥	⑥	⑥	⑥	⑥	⑥	⑥	⑥	⑥ N	⑥ b	⑥
Bournemouth **114** .... d.	0847	**a**	**b**	0947	...	1047	...	1147	**a**	**b**	1247	...	1347	...	1447	...	1547	**a**	**b**	1647	...	**a**	1747	1847
Reading **114** .... d.	1015	...	...	1115	...	1215	...	1315	...	...	1415	...	1515	...	1615	...	1715	...	...	1815	...	...	1915	2015
Paignton **116** .... d.	|	...	...	|	1007	|	...	|	...	...	|	...	|	1356	|	...	|	...	...	|	...	...	|	|
Exeter St Davids **116** .... d.	|	0945	...	|	1056	|	...	|	...	1248	|	...	|	1436	|	...	|	...	1653	|	...	1824	|	|
Bristol Temple Meads **116**. d.	|	1100	1100	|	1200	|	1300	|	1400	1400	|	1500	|	1600	|	1700	|	1800	1800	|	1900	1930	|	|
Birmingham New Str . **144 150** d.	1157	1231	1231	1257	1331	1357	1431	1457	1531	1531	1557	1631	1657	1731	1757	1831	1857	1931	1931	1957	2031	2057	2057	2157
Wolverhampton .... **144 150** d.	1214	1248	1248	1314	1348	1414	1448	1514	1548	1548	1614	1648	1714	1748	1814	1848	1914	1948	1948	2014	2048	2118	2118	2214
Stafford .... **144** d.	1228	1302	1302	1328	1402	1428	1502	1528	1602	1602	1628	1702	1728	1802	1828	1902	1928	2002	2002	2028	2102	2132	2132	2228
Stoke on Trent .... **144 152** d.	1244	1320	1320	1344	1420	1444	1520	1544	1620	1620	1644	1720	1744	1820	1844	1920	1944	2020	2020	2044	2120	2148	2148	2244
Macclesfield .... **152** d.	1302	1337	1337	1402	1437	1502	1537	1602	1637	1637	1702	1737	1802	1837	1902	1937	2002	2037	2037	2102	2137	2206	2206	2302
Stockport .... **152** d.	1314	1350	1350	1414	1450	1514	1550	1614	1650	1650	1714	1750	1814	1850	1914	1950	2014	2050	2050	2114	2150	2221r	2221r	2314
Manchester Piccadilly ...... **152** a.	1324	1400	1400	1424	1500	1524	1600	1624	1700	1700	1724	1800	1824	1900	1924	2000	2024	2059	2059	2124	2200	2233	2233	2329

	⑥	⑦	⑦	⑦	⑦	⑦ S	⑦	⑦	⑦	⑦	⑦	⑦ F	⑦	⑦ F	⑦	⑦	⑦	⑦ H	⑦	⑦	⑦	⑦	⑦	⑦
Bournemouth **114** .... d.	...		...	...	...	...	0940	...	1040	...	1140	...	1240	...	1340	...	1440	...	1540	...	1640	...	1740	1840
Reading **114** .... d.	...		...	...	0911	1012	1112	...	1212	...	1312	...	1412	...	1512	...	1612	...	1712	...	1812	...	1912	2012
Paignton **116** .... d.	...		...	...	|	|	|	...	|	1050	|	...	|	...	|	...	|	...	|	...	|	...	|	|
Exeter St Davids **116** .... d.	*1924*		...	...	|	|	|	...	|	1133	|	1300	|	1352	|	...	|	1534	|	...	|	...	|	|
Bristol Temple Meads **116**. d.	*2030*		...	...	|	|	|	...	|	1300	|	1400	|	1500	|	1600	|	1700	|	1800	|	1900	|	|
Birmingham New Str . **144 150** d.	2231		0901	1001	1101	1157	1257	1331	1357	1431	1457	1531	1557	1631	1657	1731	1757	1831	1857	1931	1957	2031	2057	2157
Wolverhampton .... **144 150** d.	2248		0918	1018	1118	1215	1314	1348	1414	1448	1514	1548	1614	1648	1714	1748	1814	1848	1914	1948	2014	2051	2114	2214
Stafford .... **144** d.	2302		0932	1033	1133	1230	1328	1402	1428	1502	1528	1602	1628	1702	1728	1802	1828	1902	1928	2002	2028	2105	2128	2228
Stoke on Trent .... **144 152** d.	2320		0952	1052	1152	1246	1344	1420	1444	1520	1544	1620	1644	1720	1744	1820	1845	1920	1944	2020	2045	2121	2144	2244
Macclesfield .... **152** d.	2339		1010	1109	1209	1306	1405	1437	1502	1537	1605	1637	1705	1737	1805	1837	1905	1937	2005	2037	2103	2140	2204	2302
Stockport .... **152** d.	2354		1027r	1123	1230r	1319	1417	1451	1515	1551	1617	1651	1717	1751	1817	1851	1918	1951	2017	2051	2116	2153	2216	2315
Manchester Piccadilly ...... **152** a.	0010		1038	1133	1241	1330	1429	1459	1524	1559	1629	1659	1729	1759	1829	1859	1928	1959	2028	2100	2129	2202	2226	2324

A – From Cardiff (Tables **117** and **118**).
F – From Plymouth (Table **116**).
H – From Penzance (Tables **112** and **116**).
N – From Newquay (Tables **112** and **116**).
S – From Southampton Central (Table **114**).
a – Until Sept. 7.
b – From Sept. 14.
r – Arrives 4 – 6 minutes earlier.

119 MANCHESTER - BIRMINGHAM

Most services convey 🍸 XC

		Ⓐ	Ⓐ	Ⓐ	Ⓐ	Ⓐ	Ⓐ	Ⓐ	Ⓐ	Ⓐ	Ⓐ	Ⓐ	Ⓐ	Ⓐ	Ⓐ	Ⓐ	Ⓐ	Ⓐ	Ⓐ	Ⓐ	Ⓐ	Ⓐ	Ⓐ	Ⓐ
Manchester Piccadilly .... **152** d.	Ⓐ	0511	0600	0627	0705	0727	0805	0827	0905	0927	1005	1027	1105	1127	1205	1227	1305	1327	1405	1427	1505	1527	1605	1627
Stockport .... **152** d.		|	0608	0636	0713	0736	0813	0836	0913	0936	1013	1036	1113	1136	1213	1236	1313	1336	1413	1436	1513	1536	1613	1636
Macclesfield .... **152** d.		|	|	0648	0726	0749	0826	0849	0926	0949	1026	1049	1126	1149	1226	1249	1326	1349	1426	1449	1526	1549	1626	1649
Stoke on Trent .... **144 152** d.		0606	|	0706	0744	0807	0844	0907	0944	1007	1044	1107	1144	1207	1244	1307	1344	1407	1444	1507	1544	1607	1644	1707
Stafford .... **144** d.		0625	0701	0724	0803	0826	0902	0926	1003	1028	1103	1128	1203	1228	1301	1328	1403	1425	1503	1528	1603	1625	1703	1725
Wolverhampton .... **144 150** d.		0639	0716	0745	0817	0840	0917	0940	1017	1042	1117	1142	1217	1242	1317	1342	1417	1439	1517	1542	1617	1639	1717	1739
Birmingham New Str. **144 150** a.		0655	0733	0807	0833	0857	0933	0958	1033	1058	1133	1158	1233	1258	1333	1358	1433	1457	1533	1558	1633	1657	1733	1757
Bristol Temple Meads **116**.. a.		|	0905	...	1005	|	1104	|	1204	|	1304	|	1404	|	1505	|	1611	|	1706	|	1809	|	1910	|
Exeter St Davids **116** .... a.		|	...	...	...	|	1225	|	...	|	1413	|	...	|	1607	|	1710	|	1811	|	1918	|	...	|
Paignton **116** .... a.		|	...	...	...	|	1308	|	...	|	...	|	...	|	|	|	...	|	1854	|	|	|	...	|
Reading **114** .... a.		0840	...	...	...	1041	...	1141	...	1243	...	1341	...	1440	...	1540	...	1639	...	1739	...	1843	...	1939
Bournemouth **114** .... a.		1013	...	...	...	1213	...	1313	...	1413	...	1512	...	1613	...	1714	...	1814	...	1913	...	2012	...	2116

	ⒶA	Ⓐ	ⒶF	Ⓐ	Ⓐ	ⒶS	Ⓐ	Ⓐ	Ⓐ	Ⓐ		⑥	⑥	⑥Na	⑥b	⑥	⑥	⑥	⑥	⑥	⑥	⑥	⑥	⑥
Manchester Piccadilly .... **152** d.	1705	1727	1805	1827	1905	1927	2005	2027	2127	2207	⑥	0511	0600	0705	0705	0727	0805	0827	0905	0927	1005	1027	1105	1127
Stockport .... **152** d.	1713	1736	1813	1836	1913	1936	2013	2036	2136	2217		|	0608	0713	0713	0736	0813	0836	0913	0936	1013	1036	1113	1136
Macclesfield .... **152** d.	1726	|	1826	|	1926	1949	2026	2049	2149	2229		|	0621	0726	0726	0749	0826	0849	0926	0949	1026	1049	1126	1149
Stoke on Trent .... **144 152** d.	1744	|	1844	1907	1944	2007	2044	2107	2207	2247		0606	0639	0744	0744	0807	0844	0907	0944	1007	1044	1107	1144	1207
Stafford .... **144** d.	1803	1827	1901	1927	2003	2026	2103	2129	2228	2306		0628	0703	0803	0803	0828	0903	0928	1003	1028	1103	1128	1203	1228
Wolverhampton .... **144 150** d.	1817	1841	1917	1941	2017	2042	2117	2143	2242	2320		0642	0717	0817	0817	0842	0917	0942	1017	1042	1117	1142	1217	1242
Birmingham New Str. **144 150** a.	1833	1857	1933	1957	2033	2058	2133	2200	2259	2337		0658	0733	0833	0833	0858	0933	0958	1033	1058	1133	1158	1233	1258
Bristol Temple Meads **116**.. a.	2009	|	2104	|	2205	|	|	...	...	...		|	0905	1004	1005	|	1109	|	1205	|	1304	|	1407	|
Exeter St Davids **116** .... a.	...	|	2211	|	...	|	|	...	...	...		|	...	1129	...	|	1231	|	...	|	...	|	...	|
Paignton **116** .... a.	...	|	...	|	...	|	|	...	...	...		|	...	...	...	|	1314	|	...	|	...	|	...	|
Reading **114** .... a.	...	2039	...	2141	...	2240	*2351*	...	...	...		0837	...	...	...	1042	...	1142	...	1239	...	1342	...	1441
Bournemouth **114** .... a.	...	2215	...	2317	...	...	...	...	...	...		1013	...	...	...	1213	...	1313	...	1412	...	1513	...	1613

	⑥a	⑥b	⑥	⑥	⑥	⑥a	⑥b	⑥	⑥	⑥		⑥	⑥	⑥A	⑥	⑥a	⑥Fb	⑥	⑥	⑥S	⑥	⑥	⑥	⑥
Manchester Piccadilly .... **152** d.	1205	1205	1227	1305	1327	1405	1405	1427	1505	1527	...	1605	1627	1705	1727	1805	1805	1827	1905	1927	2005	2027	2105	2127
Stockport .... **152** d.	1213	1213	1236	1313	1336	1413	1413	1436	1513	1536	...	1613	1636	1713	1736	1813	1813	1836	1913	1936	2013	2036	2113	2136
Macclesfield .... **152** d.	1226	1226	1249	1326	1349	1426	1426	1449	1526	1549	...	1626	1649	1726	|	1826	1826	|	1926	1949	2026	2049	2126	2149
Stoke on Trent .... **144 152** d.	1244	1244	1307	1344	1407	1444	1444	1507	1544	1607	...	1644	1707	1744	1807	1844	1844	1907	1944	2007	2044	2108	2144	2207
Stafford .... **144** d.	1303	1303	1328	1403	1428	1503	1503	1528	1603	1628	...	1703	1725	1803	1828	1903	1903	1928	2003	2028	2103	2128	2203	2230
Wolverhampton .... **144 150** d.	1317	1317	1342	1417	1442	1517	1517	1542	1617	1642	...	1717	1742	1817	1842	1917	1917	1942	2017	2042	2117	2142	2217	2244
Birmingham New Str. **144 150** a.	1333	1333	1358	1434	1458	1533	1533	1558	1633	1658	...	1733	1758	1833	1858	1933	1933	1958	2033	2058	2133	2200	2233	2300
Bristol Temple Meads **116**.. a.	1508	1507	|	1604	|	1704	1704	|	1804	|	...	1905	|	2005	|	2104	2104	|	2212	|	...	...	...	...
Exeter St Davids **116** .... a.	1609	1607	|	...	|	...	1805	|	...	|	...	...	|	...	|	...	2207	|	...	|	...	...	...	...
Paignton **116** .... a.	1709	...	|	...	|	...	1848	|	...	|	...	...	|	...	|	...	...	|	...	|	...	...	...	...
Reading **114** .... a.	...	...	1541	...	1641	...	...	1740	...	1840	...	...	1940	...	2040	...	...	2139	...	2239	...	...	...	...
Bournemouth **114** .... a.	...	...	1713	...	1813	...	...	1913	...	2012	...	...	2113	...	2215	...	...	2319	...	...	...	...	...	...

		⑦	⑦	⑦	⑦	⑦	⑦	⑦	⑦	⑦	⑦	⑦	⑦	⑦	⑦c	⑦Fb	⑦	⑦	⑦S	⑦	⑦	⑦	⑦	⑦
Manchester Piccadilly .... **152** d.	⑦	0827	0927	1027	1127	1227	1305	1327	1405	1427	1505	1527	1605	1627	1705	1705	1727	1805	1827	1905	1927	2005	2105	2205
Stockport .... **152** d.		0835	0935	1035	1135	1235	1313	1337	1413	1435	1513	1535	1613	1636	1713	1713	1735	1813	1835	1913	1935	2013	2113	2213
Macclesfield .... **152** d.		|	0948	1048	1148	1248	1326	1350	1426	1448	1526	1548	1626	1649	1726	1726	1748	1826	1848	1926	1948	2026	2126	2226
Stoke on Trent .... **144 152** d.		|	1006	1106	1206	1306	1344	1408	1444	1506	1544	1606	1644	1708	1744	1744	1806	1845	1906	1944	2006	2044	2144	2244
Stafford .... **144** d.		0928	1028	1128	1228	1328	1403	1428	1503	1528	1603	1628	1703	1725	1803	1803	1828	1903	1928	2003	2028	2103	2205	2304
Wolverhampton .... **144 150** d.		0942	1042	1143	1242	1342	1417	1442	1517	1542	1617	1642	1717	1741	1817	1817	1842	1917	1942	2017	2042	2117	2220	2318
Birmingham New Str. **144 150** a.		0958	1058	1159	1258	1358	1433	1458	1533	1558	1633	1658	1734	1759	1833	1833	1858	1933	1958	2033	2058	2133	2236	2335
Bristol Temple Meads **116**.. a.		|	|	|	|	|	1609	|	1707	|	1810	|	1908	|	2013	2013	|	2104	|	2210	|	2304	...	...
Exeter St Davids **116** .... a.		|	|	|	|	|	1711	|	...	|	...	|	...	|	2127	2127	|	...	|	...	|	...	...	...
Paignton **116** .... a.		|	|	|	|	|	1754	|	...	|	...	|	...	|	2211	...	|	...	|	...	|	...	...	...
Reading **114** .... a.		1139	1239	1339	1439	1539	...	1639	...	1739	...	1839	...	1939	...	...	2039	...	2139	...	2240	...	...	...
Bournemouth **114** .... a.		1326	1426	1526	1626	1726	...	1826	...	1926	...	2026	...	2126	...	...	2226	...	...	...	...	...	...	...

A – To Cardiff (Tables **117** and **118**).
F – To Plymouth (Table **116**).
N – To Newquay (Tables **112** and **116**).
S – To Southampton Central (Table **114**).
a – Until Sept. 7.
b – From Sept. 14.
c – Until Sept. 8.
d – Fron Sept. 15.

120 BIRMINGHAM - NOTTINGHAM

Some services convey 🍸 XC

km			Ⓐ	Ⓐ	Ⓐ	Ⓐ	Ⓐ	Ⓐ	Ⓐ	Ⓐ		Ⓐ	Ⓐ	Ⓐ	Ⓐ	Ⓐ	Ⓐ	Ⓐ		⑥	⑥	⑥	⑥	⑥
	Cardiff Central **117** .... d.	Ⓐ	...	...	...	...	...	0640	...	0745	and at	...	1645	...	1745	1845	...	*1949*	⑥	...	...	...	...	...
0	**Birmingham** New Street **124** d.		0619	0649	0719	0749	0819	0849	0919	0949	the same	1819	1849	1919	1949	2049	2203	2309		0619	0649	0719	0749	0819
28	Tamworth .... **124** d.		0639	0707	0739	0809	0836	0909	0936	1007	minutes	1836	1909	1936	2009	2109	2227	2328		0639	0707	0739	0807	0836
48	Burton-on-Trent .... **124** d.		0651	0720	0750	0821	0848	0921	0948	1019	past each	1848	1921	1948	2021	2121	2239	2340		0651	0719	0750	0819	0848
67	**Derby** .... **124** a.		0703	0735	0805	0836	0900	0932	1000	1038	hour until	1900	1935	2000	2033	2132	2253	2353		0703	0735	0805	0836	0900
67	**Derby** .... d.		0709	0744	0809	0840	0908	0941	1010	1041	▽	1908	1940	2008	2042	2145	2259	2358		0709	0743	0810	0840	0908
93	**Nottingham** .... a.		0738	0812	0834	0909	0929	1003	1029	1103		1934	2003	2028	2104	2212	2326	0016		0738	0809	0834	0906	0928

	⑥	⑥	⑥	⑥		⑥	⑥	⑥	⑥	⑥	⑥		⑦	⑦	⑦	⑦	⑦	⑦	⑦	⑦	⑦	⑦		⑦
Cardiff Central **117** .... d.	0638	...	0745	...	and at	1645	...	1745	1845	2000	...	⑦	...	1045	1145	1245	1345	1445	1545	1645	1745	1845	...	*1945*
Birmingham New Street **124** d.	0849	0919	0949	1019	the same	1849	1919	1949	2049	2210	2249		1149	1249	1349	1449	1549	1649	1749	1849	1949	2049	...	2203
Tamworth .... **124** d.	0909	0936	1007	1036	minutes	1909	1936	2009	2109	2227	2308		1207	1307	1407	1509	1607	1707	1807	1909	2007	2106	...	2219
Burton-on-Trent .... **124** d.	0921	0948	1019	1048	past each	1921	1948	2021	2121	2239	2320		1219	1319	1419	1521	1619	1719	1820	1921	2019	2119	...	|
Derby .... **124** a.	0936	0959	1037	1100	hour until	1932	2000	2035	2135	2253	2333		1233	1333	1433	1534	1634	1734	1834	1934	2034	2134	...	2240
Derby .... d.	0940	1008	1041	1108	▽	1940	2008	2040	2140	2259	...		1240	1338	1439	1539	1638	1738	1838	1938	2038	2139	...	...
Nottingham .... a.	1002	1028	1103	1128		2003	2028	2102	2208	2327	...		1259	1357	1456	1559	1655	1757	1855	1958	2057	2159	...	...

		Ⓐ	ⒶA	Ⓐ	Ⓐ	Ⓐ	Ⓐ	Ⓐ	Ⓐ	Ⓐ	Ⓐ		Ⓐ	Ⓐ	Ⓐ	Ⓐ	Ⓐ	Ⓐ	Ⓐ	Ⓐ		⑥	⑥A	⑥
Nottingham .... d.	Ⓐ	0600	0643	0704	0737	0809	0839	0907	0941	1007	1041	and at	1741	1807	1841	1907	1936	2040	2139	...	⑥	0559	0644	0700
Derby .... a.		0633	0707	0732	0802	0834	0906	0934	1003	1035	1101	the same	1807	1836	1902	1934	2004	2105	2208	...		0629	0706	0727
Derby .... **124** d.		0636	0713	0736	0806	0838	0910	0938	1010	1038	1110	minutes	1813	1840	1910	1938	2010	2110	2212	2246		0636	0712	0736
Burton-on-Trent .... **124** d.		0648	0723	0750	0818	0850	0922	0952	1021	1050	1121	past each	1827	1851	1921	1949	2021	2124	2223	2256		0648	0722	0750
Tamworth .... **124** d.		0701	0734	0803	0830	0902	0934	1003	1033	1102	1133	hour until	1838	1903	1933	2003	2033	2135	2235	2307		0701	0733	0802
Birmingham New Street **124** a.		0725	0753	0825	0855	0924	0955	1024	1055	1124	1155	▽	1857	1924	1955	2025	2055	2158	2301	2326		0725	0752	0825
Cardiff Central **117** .... a.		0928	...	1027	...	1129	...	1226	...	1330	...		...	2128	...	2237a	...	...	...	...		0924	...	1024

	⑥	⑥	⑥	⑥	⑥		⑥	⑥	⑥	⑥	⑥		⑦	⑦	⑦	⑦	⑦	⑦	⑦	⑦	⑦	⑦	⑦	⑦
Nottingham .... d.	0737	0806	0841	0906	0941	and at	1841	1906	1929	2038	2138	⑦	0954	1111	1210	1310	1410	1510	1610	1710	1810	1910	2010	2110
Derby .... a.	0802	0831	0903	0933	1002	the same	1902	1935	2003	2102	2208		1012	1131	1230	1330	1430	1530	1630	1730	1830	1930	2030	2131
Derby .... **124** d.	0806	0837	0910	0936	1010	minutes	1910	1939	2010	2110	2212		1018	1138	1236	1338	1436	1535	1636	1735	1836	1935	2036	2135
Burton-on-Trent .... **124** d.	0818	0849	0922	0950	1021	past each	1921	1950	2022	2122	2223		1029	1149	1247	1349	1447	1547	1647	1747	1847	1946	2047	2148
Tamworth .... **124** d.	0830	0903	0934	1002	1033	hour until	1933	2002	2034	2134	2235		1042	1202	1300	1401	1500	1600	1700	1800	1900	1958	2059	2200
Birmingham New Street **124** a.	0855	0925	0955	1025	1055	▽	1955	2025	2055	2155	2302		1102	1221	1321	1421	1520	1621	1719	1819	1921	2021	2118	2223
Cardiff Central **117** .... a.	...	1124	...	1224	...		...	2243	...	...	...		1307	1422	1521	1621	1721	1821	1921	2023	2122	...	...	...

A – To Bournemouth (Table **114**).
a – On ⑤ arrives 2231.
▽ – Timings may vary ± 3 minutes.

XC BIRMINGHAM - SHEFFIELD - LEEDS - YORK - NEWCASTLE - EDINBURGH - GLASGOW 124

Ⓐ

km			Ⓐ	Ⓐ	Ⓐ	Ⓐ	Ⓐ	Ⓐ	ⒶH	ⒶG	Ⓐ	Ⓐ	Ⓐ	Ⓐ	Ⓐ	Ⓐ	ⒶB	Ⓐ	ⒶC	Ⓐ	ⒶB	Ⓐ	ⒶBD	Ⓐ	Ⓐ
	Plymouth 116	d.	...	...	...	...	...	...	...	...	0520	...	0625	...	0725	...	0825	...	0925	...	1025	...	1124	...	1225
	Bristol Temple M 116	d.	...	...	...	...	...	...	0630	...	0730	...	0830	...	0930	...	1030	...	1130	...	1230	...	1330	...	1430
	Southampton Cent 114	d.	...	...	...	...	...	...	|	...	|	...	|	0756	|	...	|	0947	|	...	|	1147	|	...	|
	Reading 114	d.	...	...	...	...	...	...	|	0645	|	0745	|	0850	|	0945	|	1045	|	1145	|	1245	|	1345	|
0	**Birmingham** New Str 120	d.	...	...	0603	0630	0703	0730	0803	0830	0903	0930	1003	1030	1103	1130	1203	1230	1303	1330	1403	1430	1503	1530	1603
28	Tamworth 120	d.	...	...	|	|	0719	|	0819	|	|	|	1019	|	|	|	1219	|	|	|	1419	|	|	|	1620
48	Burton on Trent 120	d.	...	...	|	|	0731	|	0829	|	0927	|	|	|	1126	|	|	|	1328	|	|	|	1526	|	|
67	**Derby** 120 170	d.	...	0559	0644**a**	0713	0744	0816**d**	0845**c**	0921**j**	0945**b**	1016**a**	1045	1116**a**	1145**b**	1216**a**	1245**c**	1316**a**	1345**b**	1416**a**	1445**b**	1516**a**	1543	1617**a**	1643
105	Chesterfield 170	d.	...	0617	0702	0734**c**	0806**c**	0836	0903	|	1003	|	1103	|	1203	|	1303	|	1403	|	1503	|	1603	|	1704
125	**Sheffield** 170	d.	...	0634	0721**b**	0755**c**	0822	0850	0921	0951	1021	1051**b**	1121	1151**b**	1221	1251**b**	1321	1351**b**	1421	1451**b**	1521	1551**b**	1621	1651**b**	1721
154	Doncaster 180	d.	...	0703**c**	|	0819**b**	|	0919**c**	|	1018	|	1119	|	1219	|	1319	|	1419	|	1519**c**	|	1619**c**	|	1719**b**	|
171	Wakefield Westgate 180	d.	...	|	0748	|	0848	|	0947	|	1047	|	1147	|	1247	|	1347	|	1447	|	1547	|	1647	|	1747
187	**Leeds** 180	a.	...	|	0801	|	0902	|	1000	|	1100	|	1201	|	1300	|	1400	|	1500	|	1600	|	1701	|	1801
	Leeds 191	d.	0534	|	0808	|	0908	|	1008	|	1108	|	1208	|	1308	|	1408	|	1508	|	1608	|	1707	|	1807
199	**York** 191 180	a.	0600	0724	0830	0840	0930	0940	1030	1040	1130	1140	1230	1240	1330	1340	1430	1440	1530	1540	1630	1640	1730	1741	1830
	York 180	d.	0625	0732	0831	0844	0931	0946	1031	1046	1131	1146	1231	1246	1331	1346	1431	1446	1532	1546	1631	1646	1731	1748	1832
270	Darlington 180	d.	0655**c**	0800	0859	0916	1000	1013	1100	1114	1159	1213	1300	1313	1403	1413	1500	1514	1601	1614	1700	1714	1759	1816	1902
305	Durham 180	d.	0713	0818	0915	0933	1018	1030	1117	1131	1216	1230	1317	1331	1419	1430	1517	1532	1618	1631	1717	1731	1817	1833	1920
328	**Newcastle** 180	a.	0730	0834	0928	0946	1031	1043	1129	1144	1230	1243	1331	1344	1432	1443	1530	1545	1630	1644	1731	1743	1832	1848	1933
	Newcastle 180	d.	0735	...	0935	...	1035	...	1137	...	1238	...	1338	...	1435	...	1537	...	1635	...	1737	...	1835	...	1936
384	Alnmouth 180	a.	|	...	0959	...	|	...	|	...	|	...	1402	...	|	...	1601	...	1703	...	1801	...	|	...	2001
436	Berwick upon Tweed 180	a.	0820	...	1021	...	|	...	1223	...	|	...	1423	...	|	...	1623	...	|	...	1823	...	1922	...	2025
528	**Edinburgh** Wav'ley 180 220	a.	0902	...	1106	...	1203	...	1306	..	1407	...	1508	...	1606	...	1705	...	1807	...	1906	...	2009	...	2109
599	Motherwell 220	a.	0954	...	1154	...	...	...	1354	...	...	...	1555	...	...	...	1755	...	...	...	1954	...	...	...	2202
620	**Glasgow** Central 220	a.	1015	...	1212	...	...	...	1412	...	...	...	1612	...	...	...	1811	...	...	...	2015	...	...	...	2221

Station		Ⓐ	Ⓐ	Ⓐ	Ⓐ	Ⓐ	Ⓐ	Ⓐ	Ⓐ	Ⓐ	Ⓐ
Plymouth 116	d.	...	1325	...	1425	...	1525	...	1625	...	1725
Bristol Temple M 116	d.	...	1530	...	1630	...	1730	...	1830	...	1930
Southampton Cent 114	d.	1347	|	...	|	1546	|	...	|	1747	|
Reading 114	d.	1445	|	1545	|	1645	|	1745	|	1845	|
Birmingham New Str 120	d.	1630	1703	1730	1803	1830	1903	1930	2003	2030	2103
Tamworth 120	d.	|	|	|	1819	|	|	|	2019	|	2120
Burton on Trent 120	d.	|	1726	|	|	|	1929	|	|	|	2131
Derby 120 170	d.	1718**a**	1742	1817**a**	1845**b**	1909**c**	1943	2006	2048**a**	2119**a**	2146**c**
Chesterfield 170	d.	|	1803	|	1903	1928	2004	|	2106	2138	2208
Sheffield 170	d.	1751	1821	1851	1921	1951**d**	2021	2050**g**	2123	2152	2224
Doncaster 180	d.	|	|	1919	|	2020**d**	|	2120	|	2226	|
Wakefield Westgate 180	d.	1817	1850	|	1947	|	2048	|	2147	|	2255
Leeds 180	a.	1833	1904	|	2003	|	2102	|	2202	|	2308
Leeds 191	d.	1836	1907	|	2008	|	...	|	...	|	...
York 191 180	a.	1901	1930	1940	2030	2041	...	2140	...	2247	...
York 180	d.	1905	1933	1943	2032	2048	...	2146	...	...	...
Darlington 180	d.	1933	2005	2012	2101	2115	...	2213	...	...	...
Durham 180	d.	1950	2022	2029	2119	2132	...	2230	...	...	...
Newcastle 180	a.	2002	2035	2042	2133	2146	...	2248	...	...	...
Newcastle 180	d.	2004	2038	...	2135	...	...	...	...	...	...
Alnmouth 180	a.	2028	|	...	2159	...	...	...	...	...	...
Berwick upon Tweed 180	a.	|	2126	...	|	...	...	...	...	...	...
Edinburgh Wav'ley 180 220	a.	2128	2213	...	2303	...	...	...	...	...	...
Motherwell 220	a.	...	...	...	...	...	...	...	...	...	...
Glasgow Central 220	a.	...	...	...	...	...	...	...	...	...	...

⑥

		⑥	⑥	⑥	⑥	⑥	⑥	⑥	⑥G	⑥	⑥E	⑥	⑥	⑥	⑥
Plymouth 116	d.	...	...	...	...	...	...	...	...	0525	...	0625	...	0725	...
Bristol Temple M 116	d.	...	...	...	...	...	...	0612	...	0730	...	0830	...	0930	...
Southampton Cent 114	d.	...	...	...	...	...	...	|	...	|	0653	|	0749	|	...
Reading 114	d.	...	...	...	...	...	...	|	0647	|	0747	|	0845	|	0945
Birmingham New Str 120	d.	...	...	0603	0630	0703	0730	0803	0830	0903	0930	1003	1030	1103	1130
Tamworth 120	d.	...	...	0619	0646	0719	0746	0819	|	|	|	1019	|	|	|
Burton on Trent 120	d.	...	...	0630	0656	0731	0756	0829	|	0928	|	|	|	1128**c**	|
Derby 120 170	d.	...	0557	0644**b**	0713**b**	0744	0815**d**	0845**c**	0916**a**	0945**b**	1016**a**	1045**c**	1116**a**	1145**d**	1216**a**
Chesterfield 170	d.	...	0631	0702	0733	0806**c**	0834	0903	|	1003	|	1103	|	1203	|
Sheffield 170	d.	...	0652**b**	0721**b**	0752**b**	0822	0850	0921	0951**c**	1021	1051	1121	1151**d**	1221	1251**b**
Doncaster 180	d.	...	0719**b**	|	0819**b**	|	0919**c**	|	1019**c**	|	1119**b**	|	1219**b**	|	1319**b**
Wakefield Westgate 180	d.	...	|	0747	|	0847	|	0947	|	1047	|	1147	|	1247	|
Leeds 180	a.	...	|	0801	|	0901	|	1000	|	1100	|	1200	|	1300	|
Leeds 191	d.	...	|	0807	|	0908	|	1008	|	1108	|	1208	|	1308	|
York 191 180	a.	...	0741	0830	0840	0930	0940	1030	1040	1130	1140	1230	1240	1330	1340
York 180	d.	...	0751	0831	0844	0931	0946	1032	1046	1132	1147	1231	1246	1331	1346
Darlington 180	d.	...	0818	0859	0913	1000	1017	1100	1116	1200	1213	1300	1313	1400	1413
Durham 180	d.	...	0835	0915	0930	1017	1033	1117	1133	1217	1230	1317	1331	1417	1430
Newcastle 180	a.	...	0848	0928	0943	1029	1047	1129	1145	1229	1243	1329	1344	1429	1443
Newcastle 180	d.	0738	...	0935	...	1035	...	1133	...	1236	...	1335	...	1433	...
Alnmouth 180	a.	|	...	0959	...	|	...	|	...	|	...	1359	...	|	...
Berwick upon Tweed 180	a.	0823	...	1021	...	|	...	1218	...	|	...	1421	...	|	...
Edinburgh Wav'ley 180 220	a.	0907	...	1103	...	1205	...	1305	...	1405	...	1503	...	1606	...
Motherwell 220	a.	0954	...	1153	...	...	...	1354	...	...	...	1554	...	...	...
Glasgow Central 220	a.	1014	...	1212	...	...	...	1412	...	...	...	1612	...	...	...

		⑥B	⑥	⑥C	⑥	⑥B	⑥	⑥DF	⑥	⑥Jk	⑥n	⑥	⑥	⑥	⑥	⑥	⑥	⑥	⑥Jk	⑥n	⑥	⑥Ek	⑥n	⑥Bk	⑦
Plymouth 116	d.	0825	...	0925**h**	...	1025	...	1125	...	...	1225	...	1326	...	1424	...	1525	...	...	1625	...	...	1725	1825	...
Bristol Temple M 116	d.	1030	...	1130	...	1230	...	1330	...	1430	1430	...	1530	...	1630	...	1730	...	1830	1830	...	...	1930	2030	...
Southampton Cent 114	d.	|	0947	|	...	|	1147	|	...	|	|	1347	|	...	|	1547	|	...	|	|	1750	1820	|	|	...
Reading 114	d.	|	1045	|	1145	|	1245	|	1345	|	|	1445	|	1545	|	1645	|	1745	|	|	1845	1915	|	|	...
Birmingham New Str 120	d.	1203	1230	1303	1330	1403	1430	1503	1530	1603	1603	1630	1703	1730	1803	1830	1903	1930	2003	2003	2030	2103	2103	2156	...
Tamworth 120	d.	1219	|	|	|	1419	|	|	|	1619	1619	|	|	|	1819	|	|	|	2019	2019	|	2119	2119	|	...
Burton on Trent 120	d.	|	|	1327	|	|	|	1527	|	|	|	1654	1726	|	|	|	1927	|	|	|	|	2130	2130	|	...
Derby 120 170	d.	1245**b**	1316**a**	1345**d**	1416**a**	1445**d**	1516**a**	1545**b**	1616**a**	1643	1643	1716**a**	1745**d**	1816**a**	1845**b**	1916**a**	1943**c**	2016**a**	2044**c**	2044**c**	2127	2147	2147	2234**b**	...
Chesterfield 170	d.	1303	|	1403	|	1503	|	1603	|	1704	1704	|	1803	|	1905	1934	2004	2034	2105	2105	2147	2208	2208	2255	...
Sheffield 170	d.	1321	1351	1421	1451**c**	1521	1551**c**	1621	1651**c**	1721	1721	1751**b**	1821	1851**b**	1921	1951**c**	2021	2050**c**	2121	2121	2203**c**	2225	2225	2314	...
Doncaster 180	d.	|	1419**b**	|	1519	|	1619	|	1719**b**	|	|	|	|	1919**b**	|	2019**b**	|	2122	|	|	2226	2255**b**	2255**b**	|	...
Wakefield Westgate 180	d.	1348	|	1447	|	1547	|	1647	|	1747	1747	1817	1850	|	1947	|	2048	|	2148	2148	|	2312	2312	|	...
Leeds 180	a.	1401	|	1500	|	1600	|	1700	|	1801	1801	1833	1903	|	2003	|	2102	|	2202	2202	|	2327	2327	2355	...
Leeds 191	d.	1408	|	1508	|	1608	|	1707	|	1808	1808	1838	1907	|	2008	|	2109	|	...	...	|	...	...	...	...
York 191 180	a.	1430	1440	1530	1540	1630	1640	1729	1740	1831	1831	1905	1930	1940	2030	2040	2147	2142	...	...	2246	...	...	...	...
York 180	d.	1432	1446	1532	1546	1632	1646	1730	1746	1832	1832	1908	1934	1946	2032	2046	...	2145	...	...	...	...	...	...	...
Darlington 180	d.	1500	1514	1601	1614	1700	1714	1758	1814	1902	1902	1936	2005	2013	2059	2116	...	2213	...	...	...	...	...	...	...
Durham 180	d.	1517	1532	1618	1631	1717	1731	1814	1830	1919	1919	1953	2022	2030	2116	2132	...	2232	...	...	...	...	...	...	...
Newcastle 180	a.	1529	1545	1630	1644	1729	1744	1829	1843	1932	1932	2005	2035	2043	2128	2146	...	2247	...	...	...	...	...	...	...
Newcastle 180	d.	1535	...	1635	...	1735	...	1836	...	1935	1935	...	2036	...	2134	...	...	...	...	...	...	...	...	...	0945
Alnmouth 180	a.	1559	...	1704	...	1800	...	|	...	2000	2000	...	|	...	2159	...	...	...	...	...	...	...	...	...	1012
Berwick upon Tweed 180	a.	1621	...	|	...	1821	...	1918	...	2024	2024	...	2121	...	|	...	...	...	...	...	...	...	...	...	|
Edinburgh Wav'ley 180 220	a.	1705	...	1806	...	1905	...	2006	...	2109	2109	...	2208	...	2300	...	...	...	...	...	...	...	...	...	1112
Motherwell 220	a.	1754	...	...	...	1953	...	...	...	2156	2156	...	...	...	...	...	...	...	...	...	...	...	...	...	...
Glasgow Central 220	a.	1811	...	...	...	2015	...	...	...	2219	2219	...	...	...	...	...	...	...	...	...	...	...	...	...	...

		⑦	⑦	⑦	⑦	⑦	⑦	⑦	⑦C	⑦	⑦	⑦G	⑦B		⑦	⑦	⑦	⑦F	⑦	⑦	⑦	⑦	⑦	⑦	⑦B	⑦
Plymouth 116	d.	...	...	...	...	...	...	...	0924	...	1025	...	1125	...	...	1225	...	1325	...	1425	...	1523	...	1625	1725	1825
Bristol Temple M 116	d.	...	...	...	...	0915	1030	...	1130	...	1230	...	1330	...	...	1430	...	1530	...	1630	...	1730	...	1830	1930	2030
Southampton Cent 114	d.	...	...	...	...	|	|	...	|	...	|	...	|	...	...	|	...	|	...	|	...	|	...	|	|	|
Reading 114	d.	...	...	...	...	|	|	...	|	...	|	1252	|	...	1342	|	1442	|	1542	|	1642	|	1742	|	|	|
Birmingham New Str 120	d.	...	...	0903	1003	1103	1203	1230	1303	1330	1403	1430	1503	...	1530	1603	1630	1703	1730	1803	1830	1903	1930	2003	2103	2203
Tamworth 120	d.	...	...	0919	1018	|	1219	|	|	|	1420	|	|	...	|	1619	|	|	|	1819	|	|	|	2019	2119	2219
Burton on Trent 120	d.	...	...	0928	1029	1126	|	|	1326	|	|	|	1525	...	|	|	|	1725	|	|	|	1926	|	|	2129	|
Derby 120 170	d.	...	...	0945**c**	1045**b**	1146**d**	1245**d**	1311**a**	1345**d**	1411**a**	1442	1511**a**	1544**b**	...	1611**a**	1644**b**	1712**a**	1748**a**	1812**a**	1844**c**	1907**d**	1942	2009**d**	2043	2145**c**	2242
Chesterfield 170	d.	...	...	1003	1103	1204	1303	1329	1403	1429	1503	|	1602	...	|	1704	|	1806	|	1905	|	2003	|	2104	2203	2303
Sheffield 170	d.	...	0921	1021	1121	1221	1321	1352**d**	1421**c**	1452**a**	1521	1550**b**	1621	...	1652**a**	1721	1752**d**	1821	1852**a**	1921	1952**a**	2022**c**	2054**g**	2121	2221	2319
Doncaster 180	d.	...	|	|	|	|	|	1419**b**	|	1520	|	1616**c**	|	...	1719**b**	|	1817	|	1920**b**	|	2019**b**	|	2123	|	|	|
Wakefield Westgate 180	d.	...	0947	1046	1146	1246	1346	|	1447	|	1547	|	1646	...	|	1747	1833	1847	|	1951	|	2048	|	2149	2249	|
Leeds 180	a.	...	1002	1059	1159	1300	1400	|	1500	|	1600	|	1659	...	|	1801	1847	1901	|	2004	|	2102	|	2202	2302	0009
Leeds 191	d.	0918	1009	1107	1208	1305	1407	|	1507	|	1607	|	1707	...	|	1807	1856	1908	|	2009	|	2108	|	...	...	...
York 191 180	a.	0940	1031	1129	1230	1327	1429	1440	1529	1541	1629	1637	1729	...	1740	1829	1918	1930	1941	2030	2042	2131	2144	...	...	...
York 180	d.	0944	1033	1131	1232	1329	1430	1450	1531	1545	1630	1644	1731	...	1743	1831	1923	1932	1954	2032	2044	...	2146	...	...	...
Darlington 180	d.	1011	1100	1158	1259	1358	1458	1517	1558	1612	1658	1711	1758	...	1811	1900	1950	2000	2021	2101	2114	...	2225	...	...	...
Durham 180	d.	1028	1117	1219	1316	1415	1515	1534	1615	1629	1714	1728	1815	...	1827	1917	2007	2018	2038	2118	2132	...	2242	...	...	...
Newcastle 180	a.	1040	1129	1227	1328	1427	1527	1546	1627	1642	1727	1741	1827	...	1841	1930	2020	2031	2050	2131	2145	...	2310	...	...	...
Newcastle 180	d.	1042	1131	1230	1331	1431	1529	...	1629	...	1728	...	1829	...	...	1932	...	2037	2056	2134	...	...	...	...	...	...
Alnmouth 180	a.	|	|	|	1355	|	1553	...	1655	...	1755	...	|	...	...	1957	...	|	|	2159	...	...	...	...	...	...
Berwick upon Tweed 180	a.	1124	1216	|	1416	|	1614	...	|	...	1817	...	1911	...	...	2020	...	2122	|	|	...	...	...	...	...	...
Edinburgh Wav'ley 180 220	a.	1206	1258	1401	1458	1603	1655	...	1800	...	1859	...	1957	...	...	2103	...	2207	2218	2303	...	...	...	...	...	...
Motherwell 220	a.	1259	1354	...	1555	...	1752	...	...	...	2000	...	...	...	...	2154	...	...	...	...	...	...	...	...	...	...
Glasgow Central 220	a.	1319	1414	...	1612	...	1813	...	...	...	2020	...	...	...	...	2212	...	...	...	...	...	...	...	...	...	...

B – From Penzance (Tables **112**/**116**).
C – To Aberdeen (Table **222**).
D – To Dundee (Table **222**).
E – From Bournemouth (Table **114**).
F – From Newquay until Sept. 8 (Tables **112**/**116**).
G – From Guildford (Table **114b**).
H – From Bath Spa (Table **116**).
J – From Paignton (Table **116**).
a – Arrives 10 – 12 minutes earlier.
b – Arrives 5 – 6 minutes earlier.
c – Arrives 4 minutes earlier.
d – Arrives 7 – 9 minutes earlier.
g – Arrives 13 – 16 minutes earlier.
h – Departs 0915 until Sept. 7.
j – Arrives 0904.
k – Until Sept. 7.
n – From Sept. 14.

124 GLASGOW - EDINBURGH - NEWCASTLE - YORK - LEEDS - SHEFFIELD - BIRMINGHAM XC

Ⓐ	Ⓐ	Ⓐ	Ⓐ	Ⓐ	Ⓐ	Ⓐ	Ⓐ	Ⓐ	Ⓐ	Ⓐ	Ⓐ	Ⓐ	ⒶD	Ⓐ	Ⓐ	Ⓐ	ⒶB	Ⓐ	ⒶCB	ⒶG	ⒶB	Ⓐ	Ⓐ	Ⓐ
Glasgow Central 220 d.	...	...	...	...	...	...	...	...	...	...	0601	...	...	...	0748	...	0900	...	...	...	1100	...	...	...
Motherwell 220 d.	...	...	...	...	...	...	...	...	...	...	0617	...	...	...	0808b	...	0915	...	...	...	1115	...	...	...
Edinburgh Wav'ley 180 220 d.	...	...	...	...	...	...	...	...	0606	0700	0710	...	0809	...	0907	...	1010	...	1106	...	1208	...	1307	...
Berwick upon Tweed 180 d.	...	...	...	...	...	...	...	...	0650	0743	|	...	0852	...	0952	...	1051	...	1151	...	1250	...	|	...
Alnmouth 180 d.	...	...	...	...	...	...	...	...	0711	0803	|	...	|	...	|	...	|	...	1212	...	|	...	1412	...
Newcastle 180 a.	...	...	...	...	...	...	...	...	0738	0832	0836	...	0940	...	1040	...	1136	...	1238	...	1335	...	1439	...
Newcastle 180 d.	...	...	...	...	...	0625	0645	0725	0740	0835	0843	0935	0943	1035	1043	1135	1142	1235	1242	1335	1342	1436	1442	1505
Durham 180 d.	...	...	...	...	...	0638	0657	0738	0753	0848	0855	0949	0956	1048	1055	1149	1154	1248	1254	1349	1354	1448	1455	1518
Darlington 180 d.	...	...	...	...	...	0656	0715	0756	0811	0905	0912	1007	1013	1106	1113	1207	1212	1306	1312	1407	1412	1506	1513	1535
York 180 a.	...	...	...	...	...	0724	0741	0823	0841	0932	0939	1033	1040	1133	1139	1233	1239	1332	1342	1433	1439	1532	1540	1601
York 191 180 d.	...	...	...	0622	0645	0726	0743	0827	0844	0935	0944	1035	1044	1135	1144	1235	1244	1335	1344	1435	1444	1535	1544	1604
Leeds 191 a.	...	...	...	|	0708	|	0808	|	0908	|	1007	|	1108	|	1209	|	1308	|	1408	|	1507	|	1607	1629
Leeds 180 d.	...	...	0611	|	0710	|	0811	|	0911	|	1011	|	1111	|	1211	|	1311	|	1411	|	1511	|	1611	1635
Wakefield Westgate 180 d.	...	...	0623	|	0723	|	0823	|	0923	|	1023	|	1123	|	1223	|	1323	|	1423	|	1523	|	1623	1652b
Doncaster 180 d.	...	...	|	0647	|	0753	|	0853	|	0959	|	1059	|	1159	|	1259	|	1359	|	1459	|	1559	|	|
Sheffield 170 d.	...	0559	0653	0718b	0753	0818	0854	0924	0956	1024	1056	1124	1156	1224	1256	1324	1356	1424	1456	1524	1556	1624	1656	1724c
Chesterfield 170 d.	...	0626	0706	0730	0806	0830	0907	|	1009	|	1108	|	1209	|	1308	|	1408	|	1508	|	1608	|	1709	|
Derby 120 170 d.	0610	0650d	0727	0749	0828	0853b	0929b	0953	1030	1053	1132d	1153	1230	1253	1330	1353	1430b	1453	1528	1552	1630b	1653	1730	1753
Burton on Trent 120 d.	0620	0700	0738	0800	0839	|	0939	|	|	|	|	|	|	|	1341	|	|	|	1538	|	|	|	1741	|
Tamworth 120 d.	0631	0710	0750	0810	0850	|	|	|	1050	|	|	|	1250	|	|	|	1448	|	|	|	1649	|	|	|
Birmingham New Str 120 a.	0652	0728	0808	0828	0910	0927	1006	1027	1108	1127	1206	1227	1309	1327	1405	1427	1506	1527	1604	1627	1706	1727	1807	1827
Reading 114 a.	|	0908	|	1009	|	1110	|	1206	|	1309	|	1409	|	1507	|	1610	|	1707	|	1810	|	1910	|	2007
Southampton Cent 114 a.	|	...	|	1117	|	...	|	1317	|	...	|	1517	|	...	|	1717	|	...	|	...	|	...	|	...
Bristol Temple M 116 a.	0839	...	0939	...	1042	...	1142	...	1241	...	1341	...	1442	...	1541	...	1643	...	1737	...	1842	...	1945	...
Plymouth 116 a.	1042	...	1145	...	1245	...	1343	...	1445	...	1544	...	1645	...	1744	...	1849	...	1944	...	2043	...	2147	...

	Ⓐ	Ⓐ	Ⓐ	Ⓐ	Ⓐ	Ⓐ	Ⓐ	Ⓐ	Ⓐ	Ⓐ	⑥	⑥	⑥ He	⑥ g	⑥	⑥ e	⑥ g	⑥	⑥ Be	⑥ g	⑥	⑥	⑥	⑥He
Glasgow Central 220 d.	1300	...	...	...	1500	...	...	...	1700	1900	...	...			...			...			...	...	...	0601
Motherwell 220 d.	1316	...	...	...	1516	...	...	...	1716	1916	...	...	...	...	...	...	...	...	...	...	...	...	...	0616
Edinburgh Wav'ley 180 220 d.	1409	...	1508	...	1606	...	1707	...	1808	2003	...	...	...	...	...	...	...	...	...	...	...	0606	0700	0707
Berwick upon Tweed 180 d.	1450	...	|	...	|	...	1752	...	1854	2048	...	...	...	...	...	...	...	...	...	...	...	0650	0743	|
Alnmouth 180 d.	|	...	|	...	1705	...	|	...	1914	2109	...	...	...	...	...	...	...	...	...	...	...	0711	0803	|
Newcastle 180 a.	1537	...	1633	...	1734	...	1838	...	1940	2135	...	...	...	...	...	...	...	...	...	...	...	0738	0832	0838
Newcastle 180 d.	1542	1635	1642	1732	1742	1835	1843	1935	1942	2136	...	...	...	...	...	...	...	0623	...	0645	0725	0740	0835	0841
Durham 180 d.	1554	1648	1654	1748	1754	1848	1855	1950	1955	2150	...	...	...	...	...	...	...	0636	...	0657	0738	0753	0848	0855
Darlington 180 d.	1612	1706	1712	1806	1812	1907	1913	2007	2013	2209	...	...	...	...	...	...	...	0654	...	0715	0756	0811	0905	0913
York 180 a.	1639	1732	1739	1833	1838	1933	1939	2033	2040	2235	...	...	...	...	...	...	...	0723	...	0741	0823	0841	0932	0940
York 191 180 d.	1644	1735	1745	1836	1845	1936	1945	2036	2044	...	...	...	...	...	0624	0645	0618	0725	0745	0743	0827	0844	0935	0945
Leeds 191 a.	1707	|	1809	|	1909	|	2008	|	2107	...	...	...	...	...	|	0708	0659	|	0808	0808	|	0908	|	1009
Leeds 180 d.	1711	|	1811	|	1911	|	2011	|	2111	...	...	...	0611	0611	|	0711	0711	|	0811	0811	|	0911	|	1011
Wakefield Westgate 180 d.	1723	|	1823	|	1923	|	2023	|	2123	...	...	...	0623	0623	|	0723	0723	|	0823	0823	|	0923	|	1023
Doncaster 180 d.	|	1758	|	1859	|	1959	|	2101	|	...	...	...	|	|	0648	|	|	0748	|	|	0853	|	0959	|
Sheffield 170 d.	1756	1824c	1856	1924	1956	2024	2058c	2129c	2201d	...	...	0545e	0653	0653	0718	0756b	0756b	0818	0854	0854	0924	0956	1024	1056
Chesterfield 170 d.	1808	|	1911	|	2010	|	2110	2141	2225	...	...	0557e	0706	0706	0730	0808	0808	0831	0908	0907	|	1009	|	1109
Derby 120 170 d.	1829	1853	1931	1953	2027	2053	2131c	2202b	2246c	...	0610	0649a	0727	0727	0749	0828	0828	0853b	0930	0929b	0953	1030	1053	1131
Burton on Trent 120 d.	|	|	1941	|	|	|	2141	|	2256	...	0620	0659	0738	0738	0759	0838	0838	|	0941	0939	|	|	|	1142
Tamworth 120 d.	1850	|	|	|	2050	|	2151	|	2307	...	0631	0709	0749	0750	0810	0849	0849	|	|	|	|	1050	|	|
Birmingham New Str 120 a.	1908	1927	2005	2027	2107	2129	2209	2252	2326	...	0650	0727	0808	0808	0828	0908	0908	0927	1007	1006	1027	1108	1127	1207
Reading 114 a.	|	2104	|	2214	|	...	|	...	...	...	|	0910	|	|	1007	|	|	1107	|	|	1206	|	1309	|
Southampton Cent 114 a.	|	...	|	2320	|	...	|	...	...	...	|	...	|	|	1117	|	|	...	|	|	1317	|	...	|
Bristol Temple M 116 a.	2042	...	2135	...	2241	...	2330	...	...	...	0837	...	0935	0939	...	1042	1042	...	1138	1141	...	1241	...	1333
Plymouth 116 a.	2244	...	2344	...	...	...	...	...	...	...	1045	...	...	1145	...	1244	1244	...	1346	1343	...	1445	...	...

	⑥g	⑥	⑥e DH	⑥ Dg	⑥	⑥Be	⑥g	⑥	⑥B	⑥	⑥CB	⑥G	⑥e	⑥Bg	⑥	⑥	⑥	⑥	⑥	⑥	⑥	⑥	⑥	⑥	⑥
Glasgow Central 220 d.	0601	...			...	0748	0748	...	0900	...	...	...	1100	1100	...	...	...	1300	...	...	...	1500	...	...	...
Motherwell 220 d.	0617	...	...	...	...	0808b	0808b	...	0915	...	...	...	1115	1115	...	...	...	1316	...	...	...	1516	...	...	...
Edinburgh Wav'ley 180 220 d.	0710	...	0807	0809	...	0907	0907	...	1010	...	1106	...	1208	1208	...	1307	...	1407	...	1508	...	1606	...	1708	...
Berwick upon Tweed 180 d.	|	...	0848	0852	...	0952	0952	...	1051	...	1151	...	1250	1250	...	|	...	1448	...	|	...	|	...	1754	...
Alnmouth 180 d.	|	...	0910	|	...	1012	1012	...	|	...	1212	...	|	|	...	1412	...	|	...	|	...	1706	...	|	...
Newcastle 180 a.	0836	...	0937	0940	...	1040	1040	...	1136	...	1238	...	1335	1335	...	1439	...	1536	...	1633	...	1734	...	1837	...
Newcastle 180 d.	0843	0935	0941	0943	1036	1043	1043	1135	1142	1235	1242	1335	1342	1342	1436	1442	1505	1545	1635	1644	1732	1744	1836	1844	1935
Durham 180 d.	0855	0949	0954	0956	1049	1055	1055	1149	1154	1248	1254	1349	1354	1354	1448	1455	1518	1557	1648	1656	1748	1756	1849	1856	1950
Darlington 180 d.	0912	1007	1014	1013	1107	1113	1113	1207	1212	1306	1312	1407	1412	1412	1506	1513	1535	1615	1705	1714	1806	1814	1907	1914	2007
York 180 a.	0939	1033	1042	1040	1132	1139	1139	1233	1239	1332	1342	1433	1439	1439	1532	1540	1601	1641	1732	1740	1832	1840	1933	1940	2033
York 191 180 d.	0944	1035	1044	1044	1135	1144	1144	1235	1244	1335	1344	1435	1444	1444	1535	1544	1604	1645	1735	1745	1835	1845	1936	1945	2035
Leeds 191 a.	1007	|	1107	1108	|	1209	1209	|	1308	|	1408	|	1507	1507	|	1607	1629	1708	|	1808	|	1909	|	2008	|
Leeds 180 d.	1011	|	1111	1111	|	1211	1211	|	1311	|	1411	|	1511	1511	|	1611	1636	1710	|	1811	|	1911	|	2011	|
Wakefield Westgate 180 d.	1023	|	1123	1123	|	1223	1223	|	1323	|	1423	|	1523	1523	|	1623	1652b	1722	|	1823	|	1923	|	2023	|
Doncaster 180 d.	|	1059	|	|	1158	|	|	1259	|	1359	|	1459	|	|	1559	|	|	|	1758	|	1858	|	1959	|	2059
Sheffield 170 d.	1056	1124	1156	1156	1224	1256	1256	1324	1356	1424	1456	1524	1556	1556	1624	1656	1724	1756	1824c	1856	1924	1956	2024	2056	2125
Chesterfield 170 d.	1108	|	1209	1209	|	1308	1308	|	1408	|	1508	|	1608	1608	|	1709	|	1808	|	1908	|	2008	|	2108	2137
Derby 120 170 d.	1132d	1153	1229	1230	1253	1330	1330	1353	1430b	1453	1528	1552	1630b	1630b	1653	1730	1752	1828	1852	1931b	1953	2028	2053	2128	2156
Burton on Trent 120 d.	|	|	|	|	|	1341	1341	|	|	|	1538	|	|	|	|	1741	|	|	|	1941	|	|	|	2138	|
Tamworth 120 d.	|	|	1249	1250	|	|	|	|	1448	|	|	|	1649	1649	|	|	|	1847	|	|	|	2046	|	2149	|
Birmingham New Str 120 a.	1206	1227	1308	1309	1327	1405	1405	1427	1506	1527	1604	1627	1706	1706	1727	1807	1827	1907	1927	2006	2027	2104	2124	2206	2244
Reading 114 a.	|	1409	|	|	1507	|	|	1610	|	1707	|	1810	|	|	1910	|	2006	|	2106	|	2204	|	...	...	...
Southampton Cent 114 a.	|	1517	|	|	...	|	|	1717	|	...	|	...	|	|	...	|	...	|	...	|	2320	|	...	...	...
Bristol Temple M 116 a.	1341	...	1435	1442	...	1541	1541	...	1643	...	1737	...	1842	1842	...	1945	...	2041	...	2134	...	2243	...	...	...
Plymouth 116 a.	1544	...	1646	1645	...	1744	1744	...	1849	...	1944	...	2043	2043	...	2147	...	2246	...	2356	...	...	...	...	...

	⑥	⑦	⑦	⑦	⑦	⑦	⑦B	⑦	⑦	⑦	⑦B	⑦	⑦	⑦	⑦C	⑦	⑦	⑦G	⑦	⑦	⑦	⑦	⑦	⑦
Glasgow Central 220 d.	1700	...	...	...	...	...	...	...	...	...	1055	...	1202	...	...	...	1348	...	1455	...	...	...	1655	1900
Motherwell 220 d.	1716	...	...	...	...	...	...	...	...	...	1114	...	1218	...	...	...	1403	...	1513	...	...	...	1713	1916
Edinburgh Wav'ley 180 220 d.	1807	...	...	...	...	0908	1008	...	1105	...	1208	...	1308	1355	1408	...	1508	...	1608	...	1708	...	1806	2018
Berwick upon Tweed 180 d.	1853	...	...	...	...	0951	|	...	1150	...	1249	...	|	1436	1449	...	|	...	|	...	1753	...	1852	2040
Alnmouth 180 d.	1914	...	...	...	...	|	1107	...	1210	...	|	...	1411	|	|	...	|	...	1708	...	|	...	|	2104
Newcastle 180 a.	1940	...	...	...	...	1035	1136	...	1236	...	1334	...	1437	1519	1535	...	1636	...	1736	...	1836	...	1938	2148
Newcastle 180 d.	1945	...	...	...	0935	1039	1140	...	1240	1336	1340	1436	1441	1524	1540	1635	1640	1735	1740	1825	1840	1926	1941	...
Durham 180 d.	1957	...	...	...	0947	1053	1152	...	1253	1348	1353	1448	1453	1536	1552	1647	1652	1748	1753	1837	1852	1939	1953	...
Darlington 180 d.	2015	...	...	...	1005	1110	1210	...	1310	1406	1410	1506	1510	1554	1610	1705	1710	1806	1811	1855	1909	1956	2010	...
York 180 a.	2041	...	...	...	1031	1138	1236	...	1336	1432	1439	1532	1540	1622	1636	1731	1740	1833	1841	1922	1936	2024	2037	...
York 191 180 d.	2045	...	...	0936	1034	1141	1245	...	1345	1435	1444	1535	1544	1625	1644	1735	1744	1835	1845	1924	1945	2026	2045	...
Leeds 191 a.	2108	...	...	0959	1058	1210	1309	...	1409	|	1509	|	1609	|	1710	|	1810	|	1910	|	2008	|	2108	...
Leeds 180 d.	2111	0810	0900	1001	1100	1211	1311	...	1411	|	1511	|	1611	|	1712	|	1811	|	1912	|	2011	|	2111	...
Wakefield Westgate 180 d.	2123	0823	0912	1014	1112	1224	1324	...	1423	|	1523	|	1623	|	1724	|	1823	|	1924	|	2023	|	2123	...
Doncaster 180 d.	|	|	0931	1032	1130	|	|	...	|	1500c	|	1558	|	1651	|	1758	|	1858	|	1954c	|	2051	|	...
Sheffield 170 d.	2155	0855	0958	1055	1157	1257c	1357	1422	1455	1524	1555	1624c	1655	1724b	1755	1824c	1855	1924c	1956	2021b	2054	2120	2154	...
Chesterfield 170 d.	2207	0908	1011	1109	1209	1310	1409	1434	1507	|	1607	|	1707	|	1807	|	1907	|	2008	|	2106	2132	2206	...
Derby 120 170 d.	2226	0930	1033	1129	1229	1331	1429	1453	1527	1553	1627	1653	1727	1753	1827	1853	1927	1953	2027	2053b	2126	2153	2226	...
Burton on Trent 120 d.	2237	|	|	1140	|	1342	|	|	1537	|	|	|	1737	|	|	|	1937	|	|	|	2136	2203	2237	...
Tamworth 120 d.	2247	|	1052	|	1247	|	1447	|	|	|	1645	|	|	|	1845	|	|	|	2045	|	2147	2213	2247	...
Birmingham New Str 120 a.	2306	1018	1120	1206	1305	1408	1505	1527	1601	1627	1703	1727	1801	1827	1903	1927	2000	2024	2103	2124	2204	2231	2305	...
Reading 114 a.	...	|	|	|	|	|	|	1700	|	1809	|	1900	|	2009	|	2109	|	2202	|	...	|	...	...	...
Southampton Cent 114 a.	...	|	|	|	|	|	|	...	|	...	|	...	|	...	|	...	|	...	|	...	|	...	...	...
Bristol Temple M 116 a.	...	1149	1249	1334	1433	1534	1632	...	1734	...	1834	...	1934	...	2034	...	2134	...	2244	...	2334	...	...	...
Plymouth 116 a.	...	1354	1454	1545	1644	1745	1846	...	1944	...	2048	...	2144	...	2248	...	2346	...	...	...	...	...	...	...

B – To Penzance (Tables 112/116).
C – From Aberdeen (Table 222).
D – From Dundee (Table 222).
E – To Bournemouth (Table 114).
G – To Guildford (Table 114b).
H – To Paignton (Table 116).
N – To Newquay (Tables 112/116).
a – Arrives 0631.
b – Arrives 5–6 minutes earlier.
c – Arrives 4 minutes earlier.
d – Arrives 7–9 minutes earlier.
e – Until Sept. 7.
g – From Sept. 14.

LM 2nd class BIRMINGHAM - WORCESTER - HEREFORD 125

km		Ⓐ	Ⓐ	Ⓐ	Ⓐ		Ⓐ	Ⓐ	Ⓐ	Ⓐ	Ⓐ	Ⓐ	Ⓐ	Ⓐ	Ⓐ	Ⓐ	Ⓐ	⑥		⑥	⑥	⑥	⑥	⑥	⑥
0	**Birmingham** New St .... d.	0659	0720	0800	0850		1550	1620	1650	1720	1750	1820	1920	2000	2100	2200	2300	0650		1750	1850	1950	2050	2120	2220
21	Bromsgrove .... d.	0722	0744	0822	0912		1612	1642	1712	1742	1812	1842	1942	2021	2121	2221	2321	0713		1812	1913	2012	2113	2142	2241
32	Droitwich Spa .... d.	0731	0754	0832	0922	and	1621	1652	1722	1752	1822	1852	1953	2031	2131	2237	2331	0723	and	1822	1923	2022	2127a	2152	2255
40	**Worcester** Shrub Hill. 138 d.	|	0807a	|	|	hourly	|	1706c	1732	1805a	1834	|	2013c	2039	|	2245	2338	|	hourly	1832	|	|	|	|	|
41	**Worcester** Foregate St ..... d.	0742	0811	0841	0932	until	1630	1709	1735	1808	1837	1902	2016	...	2141	*2310*	...	0732	until	1835	1932	2035a	2138	2201	2304
54	Great Malvern .... 130 138 d.	0800a	0822	0854	0945		1644	1720	1747	1820	1849	1914	2028	...	2154	*2323*	...	0745		1848	1944	2048	2150	2213	2315
65	Ledbury .... 130 d.	0813	...	0907	0958		1659	...	1800	1832	1904	1927	2042	...	2209	...	...	0759		1901	...	2101	...	2226	...
87	**Hereford** .... 130 a.	0829	...	0922	1016		1715	...	1817	1847	1919	1942	2058	...	2224	...	...	0815		1916	...	2117	...	2241	...

	⑦	⑦	⑦	⑦	⑦	⑦	⑦	⑦	⑦	⑦
Birmingham New St .... d.	1000	1200	1400	1500	1600	1800	1900	2000	2100	2200
Bromsgrove .... d.	1020	1220	1420	1520	1621	1820	1920	2020	2120	2220
Droitwich Spa .... d.	1030	1232	1431	1530	1631	1832	1931	2030	2130	2236
Worcester Shrub Hill. 138 d.	1054b	1247c	1452b	1552b	1647c	1852c	1952b	2053c	2141	2251a
Worcester Foregate St...... d.	1057	1250	1455	1555	1650	1855	1955	2055	2144	2254
Great Malvern.... 130 138 d.	1109	1302	1507	1607	1702	1907	2007	*2136*	2156	2305
Ledbury .... 130 d.	1121	1315	1519	1619	1715	1919	2019	...	2209	...
Hereford .... 130 a.	1137	1332	1535	1635	1733	1940	2035	...	2227	...

	Ⓐ	Ⓐ	Ⓐ	Ⓐ	Ⓐ	Ⓐ	Ⓐ	Ⓐ		Ⓐ	Ⓐ
Hereford......... 130 d.	*0447*	*0528*	...	0709	0732	...	0845	0939		1739	1848
Ledbury.............. 130 d.	*0504*	*0545*	...	0725	0750	...	0906	0957		1758	1904
Great Malvern 130 d.	0543	*0559*	0647	0736	0807a	0838	0918	1009	and	1810	1915
Worcester F'gate Std.	0602c	*0614*	0659	0748	0824a	0850	0931	1022	hourly	1824	1928
Worcester Shrub H d.	|	0625	0705a	0754	|	|	0936	|	until	|	|
Droitwich Spa........ d.	0611	0633	0713	0802	0833	0859	0943	1033		1833	1937
Bromsgrove............ d.	0621	0643	0723	|	0842	0908	0953	1042		1842	1947
Birmingham N St . a.	0648	0710	0746	0840	0909	0939	1019	1110		1909	2019

	Ⓐ	Ⓐ	Ⓐ	Ⓐ	⑥	⑥	⑥		⑥	⑥	⑥	⑥	⑥	⑥	⑦	⑦	⑦	⑦	⑦	⑦	⑦	⑦	⑦	⑦	⑦
Hereford .... 130 d.	1950	2056	2129	2259	...	0639	0737		1739	1842	1939	*2020*	2131	2249	...	1005	1202	1402	1557	1656	1803	*1838*	2000	2100	2239
Ledbury .... 130 d.	2009	2114	2145	2315	...	0659	0758		1758	1901	1959	*2037*	2154	2305	...	1022	1218	1419	1619a	1715	1819	*1857*	2019	2117	2258
Great Malvern.... 130 138 d.	2020	2125	2157	2327	0617	0711	0810	and	1810	1911	2010	*2053*	2205	2317	...	1034	1230	1431	1631	1731a	1831	*1912*	2031	2128	2310
Worcester Foregate St...... d.	2031	2137	2210	2340	0628	0723	0824	hourly	1824	1924	2024	*2111*	2218	2329	0901	1048	1242	1443	1643	1743	1843	*1927*	2043	2140	2323
Worcester Shrub Hill 138 d.	2037	2139	|	2347	|	0731a	|	until	|	|	|	2130	2221	2336	0906	1058c	1250c	1450a	1650a	1750a	1850a	1950	2050a	|	2327
Droitwich Spa .... d.	2045	...	2219	...	0637	0739	0833		1833	1933	2033	2138	...	...	0914	1106	1258	1458	1658	1758	1858	1958	2058	2149	...
Bromsgrove .... d.	2055	...	2229	...	0647	0747	0843		1843	1943	2043	2148	...	...	0923	1116	1308	1508	1708	1808	1908	2008	2108	2158	...
Birmingham New St .... a.	2125	...	2255	...	0715	0815	0911		1909	2009	2110	2214	...	...	0946	1146	1337	1537	1737	1837	1937	2037	2139	2221	...

a – Arrives 4–6 minutes earlier. b – Arrives 12–16 minutes earlier. c – Arrives 7–10 minutes earlier.

LM 2nd class BIRMINGHAM - KIDDERMINSTER - WORCESTER 126

km		Ⓐ	⑥	Ⓐ	⑥	Ⓐ	⑥	ⒶA	Ⓐ	⑥	⚒	⚒	⚒	⚒	⚒	⚒	⚒	⚒	⚒	⚒	⚒	⚒	⑥	Ⓐ	⚒	⚒
0	**Birmingham** Moor St.. 128 d.	0604	0633	0649	0701	0719	0749	0748	0834	0845	0909	0939	1009	1039	1109	1139	1209	1239	1309	1339	1409	1439	1509	1509	1539	1609
1	**Birmingham** Snow Hill 128 d.	0607	0637	0653	0705	0723	0753	0753	0839	0853	0913	0943	1013	1043	1113	1143	1213	1243	1313	1343	1413	1443	1513	1513	1543	1613
20	Stourbridge Junction .. 128 d.	0636	0706	0722	0734	0752	0819	0822	0907	0922	0939	1009	1039	1109	1139	1209	1239	1309	1339	1409	1439	1509	1539	1539	1608	1639
31	Kidderminster .... △ 128 d.	0647	0717	0734	0745	0804	0831	0834	0918	0933	0947	1018	1047	1118	1147	1218	1247	1318	1347	1418	1447	1518	1547	1552	1618	1647
45	Droitwich Spa .... d.	0658	0731	0747	0756	0817	0842	0847	0930	0944	1000	1030	1100	1130	1200	1230	1300	1330	1400	1429	1500	1530	1600	1606	1630	1700
54	**Worcester** Shrub Hill...... a.	|	0741	|	0805	0824	|	|	0938	0952	|	1038r	|	1138	|	1238t	|	1338r	1408t	1439	1510t	1538r	|	1614	|	|
54	**Worcester** Foregate St...... a.	0709	...	0757	0813	0834	0851	0858	...	...	1009	1039t	1111	...	1209	1239r	1309	1340t	1409r	1446	1509r	1539t	1609	1625	1642	1709

	⑥	Ⓐ	⑥	Ⓐ	⑥	Ⓐ	⑥	Ⓐ	⑥A	ⒶA	⑥	⚒	⑥A	ⒶA	⑥	Ⓐ	⑥	Ⓐ	⑥	Ⓐ	⑥	⚒	⑦	⑦A	⑦A	⑦A
Birmingham Moor St. 128 d.	1639	1639	1709	1709	1729	1732	1739	1749	1819	1840	1850	1924	1947	1954	2054	2056	2118	2138	2152	2154	2218	2256	0924	1016	1116	1216
Birmingham Snow Hill 128 d.	1643	1643	1713	1713	1733	1736	1743	1753	1823	1844	1853	1928	1956	1958	2059	2100	2123	2143	2156	2158	2223	2300	0929	1022	1122	1222
Stourbridge Junction . 128 d.	1709	1710	1741	1739	1759	1802	1809	1820	1849	1910	1923	1957	2025	2027	2128	2129	2152	2209	2225	2229	2252	2330	0955	1047	1147	1247
Kidderminster........ △ 128 d.	1718	1724	1751	1752	1812	1814	1822	1832	1900	1922	1934	2009	2036	2039	2142	2141	2202	2221	2236	2241	2304	2341	1004	1059	1159	1259
Droitwich Spa .... d.	1730	1737	1804	1804	1827	1827	1837	1846	1914	1933	1946	2022f	2048	2050	2158	2154	2216	2232	2250	2254	2318	2354	1018	1111	1211	1311
Worcester Shrub Hill ..... a.	|	1745	1812	1812	1835	|	|	1856	1922	|	1954	2035r	2056	2059	2206	2201	2224	|	2300	2301	2326	0005	1025	1119	1219	|
Worcester Foregate St...... a.	1739	...	*1822*	...	...	1838	1846	...	1927	1943	...	2031t	2101	...	...	2208	...	2241	...	2310	...	...	1032	1135	...	1320

	⑦A	⑦A	⑦A	⑦A	⑦	⑦A	⑦A	⑦A	⑦A	⑦	⑦
Birmingham Moor St . 128 d.	1316	1416	1516	1616	1702	1716	1815	1915	2015	2143	2251
Birmingham Snow Hill 128 d.	1322	1422	1522	1622	1706	1722	1822	1922	2022	2146	2255
Stourbridge Junction . 128 d.	1347	1447	1547	1647	1724	1747	1847	1947	2047	2210	2322
Kidderminster........ △ 128 d.	1357	1459	1557	1657	1733	1759	1859	1957	2057	2220	2331
Droitwich Spa .... d.	1408	1511	1608	1708	1745	1811	1911	2009	2109	2231	2343
Worcester Shrub Hill ..... a.	|	|	|	|	1752	|	1919	2017	2117	2239	2351
Worcester Foregate St...... a.	1417	1520	1617	1717	...	1821	...	...	2124	...	...

⚒	Ⓐ	⑥	ⒶA	⑥	Ⓐ	⑥	Ⓐ	⑥	Ⓐ	⑥
Worcester Foregate St .. d.	...	...	...	...	...	...	...	0714	...	0747
Worcester Shrub Hill.. d.	0530	0543	0612	0621	0630	0649	0701	|	0735	|
Droitwich Spa............... d.	0538	0551	0620	0629	0639	0703	0709	0723	0743	0756
Kidderminster...........△ d.	0548	0604	0633	0643	0651	0716	0722	0736	0754	0806
Stourbridge Junction..... d.	0556	0616	0650	0657	0704	0728	0735	0748	0807	0819
Birmingham Snow Hill .. a.	0627	0645	0722	0728	0734	0803	0805	0815	0835	0845
Birmingham Moor St .... a.	0638	0653	0728	0736	0743	0807	0810	0820	0840	0850

	Ⓐ	⑥	Ⓐ	⑥A	Ⓐ	⑥	⚒	⚒	⚒	⚒	⚒	⚒	⚒	⚒	⚒	⚒	⚒	⚒	Ⓐ	⑥	Ⓐ	⑥	Ⓐ	⚒A	⑥	Ⓐ	⑥
Worcester Foregate St...... d.	0802	...	0839	0856	0903	0916	0951r	1016	...	1116t	1151	1216	1251r	...	1351	1416	...	1516r	1533	1551	1613	1614	1634	1647	...	1715	1744
Worcester Shrub Hill ..... d.	|	0815	0845	|	|	|	0952t	|	1052	1117r	|	|	1252t	1317	|	|	1452	1517t	1547	|	|	|	1640	|	1715	|	|
Droitwich Spa .... d.	0811	0823	0853	0905	0912	0925	1000	1025	1100	1125	1200	1225	1300	1325	1400	1425	1500	1525	1555	1600	1622	1623	1648	1655	1724	1725	1753
Kidderminster........ △ 128 d.	0824	0836	0906	0916	0925	0938	1010	1038	1110	1138	1210	1238	1310	1338	1410	1438	1510	1538	1606	1610	1635	1636	1701	1706	1736	1738	1803
Stourbridge Junction . 128 d.	0835	0848	0919	0927	0937	0948	1018	1048	1118	1148	1218	1248	1318	1348	1418	1448	1518	1550	1618	1618	1648	1648	1712	1718	1748	1750	1815
Birmingham Snow Hill 128 a.	0907	0915	0946	0956	1004	1015	1045	1115	1145	1215	1245	1315	1345	1415	1445	1515	1545	1616	1645	1645	1718	1715	1739	1745	1815	1817	1842
Birmingham Moor St . 128 a.	0911	0920	0950	1001	1010	1020	1050	1120	1150	1220	1250	1320	1350	1420	1450	1520	1550	1620	1650	1650	1725	1720	1745	1750	1820	1825	1846

	Ⓐ	⑥	Ⓐ	Ⓐ	⑥	⚒	Ⓐ	⚒	⚒	Ⓐ	⑥	⑦A	⑦A	⑦A	⑦A	⑦A	⑦A	⑦A	⑦	⑦A	⑦A	⑦	⑦	⑦	⑦	⑦
Worcester Foregate St...... d.	...	1812	...	1841	1851	1948	2022	2051t	2145r	2217	...	0919	1026	1118	1221	1326	1426	1528	1545	1626	1727	1826	*1927*	*2027*	2118	2223
Worcester Shrub Hill ..... d.	1755	1817	1837	|	|	|	|	2050r	2154	2227	2244	0926	|	1126	1226	|	|	|	|	|	|	|	1938	2038	2125	2229
Droitwich Spa .... d.	1805	1825	1845	1850	1900	1957	2031	2058	2202	2235	2252	0935	1035	1135	1235	1335	1435	1537	1554	1635	1736	1835	1946	2046	2133	2237
Kidderminster........ △ 128 d.	1815	1837	1855	1907	1913	2010	2044	2113	2213	2248	2305	0945	1045	1145	1245	1345	1445	1547	1604	1645	1746	1845	1956	2056	2143	2247
Stourbridge Junction . 128 d.	1825	1850	1906	1919	1925	2025	2057	2125	2225	2300	2318	0957	1057	1157	1257	1357	1457	1557	1617	1657	1759	1855	2007	2107	2153	2257
Birmingham Snow Hill 128 a.	1855	1916	1938	1951	1955	2055	2126	2155	2255	2333	2336	1022	1122	1222	1322	1422	1522	1623	1637	1722	1824	1921	2033	2133	2219	2325
Birmingham Moor St . 128 a.	1900	1920	1949	2001	2000	2100	2131	2200	2300	2337	2340	1030	1130	1230	1330	1430	1530	1630	1645	1730	1830	1924	2037	2137	2223	...

A – To/from Stratford upon Avon (Table 127). f – Departs 2027 on ⑥. r – ⑥ only. t – Ⓐ only. △ – **Severn Valley Railway** (🚂 Kidderminster - Bridgnorth: 26 km). ✆ 01299 403816. www.svr.co.uk.

LM 2nd class STRATFORD UPON AVON - BIRMINGHAM 127

km		Ⓐ	ⒶA	Ⓐ	Ⓐ	Ⓐ	Ⓐ	Ⓐ		Ⓐ	Ⓐ	Ⓐ	ⒶA	Ⓐ		Ⓐ	ⒶA	Ⓐ	Ⓐ	Ⓐ	Ⓐ	Ⓐ
0	**Stratford upon Avon**............d.	0626	0652	0720	0741	0826	0926	1003	and at the same	1603	1626	1727	1755	1827	...	1851	1903	1926	2026	2126	2233	2330
13	Henley in Arden.....................d.	0641	0707	0735	0756	0841	0941	|	minutes	|	1641	1743	1807	1843	...	1907	|	1941	2041	2139	2246	|
40	**Birmingham** Moor St.............d.	0724	0748	0808	0838	0918	1018	1049	past each	1649	1719	1818	1840	1919	...	1935	1954	2028	2118	2218	2319	0005
41	**Birmingham** Snow Hill..........a.	0726	0750	0810	0840	0920	1020	1052	hour until	1652	1721	1821	1843	1922	...	1937	1956	2028	2120	2220	2321	0008

	⑥	⑥	⑥	⑥		⑥	⑥A	⑥	⑥	⑥	⑥	⑥	⑥	⑥	⑥	⑥	⑦A	⑦A		⑦A	⑦A
Stratford upon Avon..........d.	0700	0743	0826	0903	and at the same	1703	1726	1754	1826	1848	1926	1953	2026	2126	2233	2330	0929	1029	and	1829	1929
Henley in Arden.....................d.	0715	0758	0841	|	minutes	|	1741	1808	1841	1904	1941	2007	2041	2140	2247	|	0943	1043	hourly	1843	1943
Birmingham Moor St.............a.	0755	0838	0918	0949	past each	1749	1819	1839	1918	1947	2021	2035	2118	2218	2319	0007	1016	1116	until	1915	2015
Birmingham Snow Hill..........a.	0757	0840	0920	0952	hour until	1752	1821	1843	1920	1949	2024	2038	2120	2220	2322	0010	1019	1118		1917	2017

	Ⓐ	Ⓐ	Ⓐ	ⒶA	Ⓐ	Ⓐ	Ⓐ		Ⓐ	Ⓐ	Ⓐ	Ⓐ	Ⓐ	ⒶA	Ⓐ	Ⓐ	Ⓐ	Ⓐ	Ⓐ	Ⓐ	⑥
Birmingham Snow Hill.........d.	0553	0630	0640	0725	0828	0858	0928	and at the same	1458	1528	1628	1703	1728	1747	1758	1828	1928	2028	2128	2228	0725
Birmingham Moor St.............d.	0556	0633	0643	0728	0831	0901	0931	minutes	1501	1531	1631	1706	1731	1750	1801	1831	1931	2031	2131	2231	0728
Henley in Arden.....................d.	|	0706	0720	0806	0906	|	1006	past each	|	1606	1707	1736	1807	1828	|	1907	2007	2107	2207	2307	0806
Stratford upon Avon............a.	0648	0721	0736	0823	0921	0942	1023	hour until	1541	1623	1724	1749	1824	1843	1859	1923	2023	2123	2223	2323	0821

	⑥	⑥	⑥	⑥	⑥A	⑥	⑥		⑥	⑥	⑥A	⑥	⑥	⑥	⑥	⑥	⑥	⑦	⑦	⑦A		⑦A
Birmingham Snow Hill.........d.	0758	0828	0858	0928	0958	1028	1058	and at the same	1658	1728	1747	1828	1847	1928	2028	2128	2228	0837	0927	1027	and	1827
Birmingham Moor St.............d.	0801	0831	0901	0931	1001	1031	1101	minutes	1701	1731	1750	1831	1850	1931	2031	2131	2231	|	0930	1030	hourly	1830
Henley in Arden.....................d.	|	0906	|	1006	|	1106	|	past each	|	1806	1828	1906	1929	2007	2107	2207	2307	|	1003	1103	until	1901
Stratford upon Avon............a.	0841	0923	0942	1023	1041	1123	1141	hour until	1741	1821	1843	1923	1944	2023	2123	2223	2323	0912	1017	1117		1915

A – To/from Worcester Shrub Hill or Worcester Foregate Street (Table 126).

🚂 – THE SHAKESPEARE EXPRESS – (12), ✕ (1st class only) and 🍷 Birmingham Snow Hill - Stratford upon Avon and v.v. Runs ⑦ July 21, Aug. 4, 18, Sept. 1, 15.
National Rail tickets NOT valid.
Expected timings: from Birmingham Snow Hill 1000 and 1401 (Birmingham Moor Street 5 minutes later); from Stratford upon Avon at 1241 and 1618. Journey time: 59–68 minutes.
To book and confirm timings contact Vintage Trains Ltd. ✆ 0121 708 4960. www.vintagetrains.co.uk/the-shakespeare-express.

128 LONDON - BANBURY - BIRMINGHAM
2nd class CH

From October 8 arrival times at London Marylebone (also the arrival time of trains terminating at Birmingham Moor Street) are 3 minutes later than shown.

km			②–⑤	①	Ⓐ	Ⓐ	Ⓐ	Ⓐ	Ⓐ	Ⓐ	Ⓐ	Ⓐ	Ⓐ	Ⓐ	Ⓐ	Ⓐ	Ⓐ	Ⓐ	Ⓐ	Ⓐ	Ⓐ	Ⓐ	Ⓐ	Ⓐ	Ⓐ
0	**London** Marylebone.. **128a / b** ◇ d.		0005	0005	...	...	0605	0711	0748	0814	0837	0844	0910	0940	1010	1040	1110	1140	1210	1240	1310	1340	1410	1440	1510
45	High Wycombe.......... **128a / b** ◇ d.	Ⓐ	0036	0038	...	0605	|	|	0814	|	|	0917	0936	|	1036	|	1135	|	1234	|	1334	|	1434	|	1535
88	Bicester North .... **128a** ◇ d.		0105	0108	0546	0638	0647	0754	0836	|	0926	0945	|	1029	|	1128	|	1227	|	1327	|	1427	|	1529	|
111	Banbury ....**114 128a** ◇ d.		0122	0127	0604	0652	0703	0807	0850	0908	0940	1003	1008	1043	1106	1141	1207	1240	1308	1340	1410	1440	1507	1542	1609
143	Leamington Spa.......... **114 128a** d.		...	...	0625	...	0721	0825	0908	0926	0958	...	1025	1101	1125	1159	1226	1258	1326	1358	1427	1458	1525	1559	1626
146	Warwick .... **128a** d.		...	...	0630	...	0726	0829	0912	0930	1003	...	|	1105	|	1203	|	1302	|	1402	|	1502	|	1603	|
147	Warwick Parkway ....d.		...	...	0633	...	0729	0833	0916	0934	1007	...	1032	1109	1133	1207	1232	1306	1332	1406	1433	1506	1530	1607	1632
169	Solihull ....a.		...	...	0649	...	0750	0844	0931	0945	1023	...	1044	1124	1144	1222	1244	1321	1344	1421	1444	1521	1544	1622	1644
180	**Birmingham** Moor Street..... **126** a.		...	...	0659	...	0802	0853	0942	0954	1035	...	1053	1133	1156	1233	1256	1333	1356	1433	1456	1533	1556	1633	1654
181	**Birmingham** Snow Hill......... **126** a.		...	...	0707	...	0810	0902	...	1002	...	...	1101	1141	...	1241	...	1341	...	1441	...	1541	...	1641	1702

	Ⓐ	Ⓐ	Ⓐ	Ⓐ	Ⓐ	Ⓐ	Ⓐ	Ⓐ	Ⓐ	Ⓐ	Ⓐ	Ⓐ	Ⓐ	Ⓐ	Ⓐ	Ⓐ	Ⓐ	Ⓐ		⑥	⑥	⑥	⑥	⑥	⑥
London Marylebone...**128a / b** ◇ d.	1540	1615	1621	1647	1715	1746	1815	1821	1847	1915	1947	2010	2037	2110	2140	2210	2236	2307		0020	...	0700	0810	0840	0910
High Wycombe ....**128a / b** ◇ d.	|	|	1648	|	|	|	|	1850	|	|	|	2035	|	2136	2204	2235	2302	|		0051	0612	0723	0834	|	0934
Bicester North................**128a** ◇ d.	1627	|	1711	1734	|	1835	|	1920	1937	2002	2034	2059	2124	2159	2228	2259	2327	2350	⑥	0120	0645	0750	0856	0926	|
Banbury...................**114 128a** ◇ d.	1640	1708	1724	1747	1809	1848	1909	1937	1951	2016	2047	2112	2139	2214	2241	2313	2341	0003		0135	0703	0804	0910	0940	1007
Leamington Spa........... **114 128a** d.	1658	1726	1741	1804	1827	1905	1927	...	2009	2034	2104	2130	2157	2231	2259	2331	2359	0021		0156	0721	0823	0928	0958	1025
Warwick.......................... **128a** d.	1702	|	|	1808	|	1909	|	...	2013	|	2108	|	2201	|	2303	|	0003	0025		...	0725	|	0932	1002	|
Warwick Parkway ....d.	1706	1732	1747	1812	1834	1913	1934	...	2017	2040	2112	2136	2205	2238	2307	2337	0007	0029		...	0729	0829	0935	1006	1031
Solihull......................................a.	1721	1744	1802	1826	1849	1928	1950	...	2032	2055	2133	2148	2220	2250	2330	2348	0023	0040		...	0747	0846	0950	1021	1043
Birmingham Moor Street ..... **126** a.	1736	1754	1810	1838	1859	1938	2000	...	2041	2106	2143	2157	2230	2300	2342	0001	0036	0052		...	0800	0859	1001	1033	1054
Birmingham Snow Hill .... **126** a.	1744	1757	1821	...	1902	1946	2004	...	2049	...	2151	2208	2238	2305	...	...	...	...		...	...	0907	1009	1041	...
Stourbridge Junction .... **126** a.	...	1825	...	...	1926	...	2033	...	...	...	...	2236	...	2349	...	...	...	...		...	...	...	...	...	...
Kidderminster...................△ **126** a.	...	1844	...	...	1941	...	2048	...	...	...	...	2250	...	...	...	...	...	...		...	...	...	...	...	...

	⑥	⑥	⑥	⑥	⑥	⑥	⑥	⑥	⑥	⑥	⑥	⑥	⑥	⑥	⑥	⑥	⑥	⑥	⑥	⑥	⑥	⑥	⑥	⑥	⑥
London Marylebone...**128a / b** ◇ d.	0940	1010	1040	1110	1140	1210	1240	1310	1340	1410	1440	1510	1540	1610	1640	1710	1740	1810	1840	1910	1940	2010	2040	2110	2210
High Wycombe ....**128a / b** ◇ d.	|	1034	|	1134	|	1234	|	1335	|	1434	|	1534	|	1634	|	1734	|	1834	|	1934	|	2034	|	2134	2234
Bicester North................**128a** ◇ d.	1024	|	1128	|	1224	|	1324	|	1424	|	1524	|	1624	|	1724	|	1824	|	1924	|	2024	|	2124	2157	2257
Banbury...................**114 128a** ◇ d.	1037	1107	1143	1208	1237	1307	1337	1409	1437	1507	1537	1609	1637	1707	1737	1809	1837	1907	1937	2009	2037	2107	2137	2210	2310
Leamington Spa........... **114 128a** d.	1055	1125	1201	1226	1255	1325	1355	1427	1455	1525	1555	1626	1655	1725	1755	1826	1855	1926	1955	2027	2055	2125	2155	2228	2328
Warwick.......................... **128a** d.	1059	|	1205	|	1259	|	1359	|	1459	|	1559	|	1659	|	1759	|	1859	|	1959	|	2059	|	2159	2232	2332
Warwick Parkway ....d.	1103	1132	1209	1233	1303	1332	1403	1433	1503	1532	1603	1633	1703	1732	1803	1833	1903	1933	2003	2033	2103	2132	2203	2236	2337
Solihull......................................a.	1120	1144	1224	1245	1320	1344	1420	1444	1520	1544	1620	1644	1720	1744	1820	1847	1918	1946	2018	2046	2119	2144	2218	2258	2352
Birmingham Moor Street ..... **126** a.	1133	1156	1233	1256	1333	1356	1433	1456	1533	1556	1633	1656	1733	1756	1833	1858	1929	1958	2030	2058	2127	2157	2227	2306	0004
Birmingham Snow Hill .... **126** a.	1141	...	1241	...	1341	...	1441	...	1541	...	1641	...	1741	...	1841	1902	1937	2007	...	...	2130	...	2235	2314	...
Stourbridge Junction .... **126** a.	...	...	...	...	...	...	...	...	...	...	...	...	...	...	...	1927	...	...	...	...	2156	...	...	...	...
Kidderminster...................△ **126** a.	...	...	...	...	...	...	...	...	...	...	...	...	...	...	...	1944	...	...	...	...	2212	...	...	...	...

	⑥	⑥		⑦	⑦	⑦	⑦	⑦	⑦	⑦		⑦	⑦	⑦	⑦	⑦	⑦	⑦	⑦	⑦	⑦	⑦	⑦	⑦
London Marylebone...**128a / b** ◇ d.	2315	2345		0815	0910	0940	1010	1040	1110	1140		1710	1740	1810	1840	1910	1940	2010	2040	2043	2110	2208	2240	2330
High Wycombe ....**128a / b** ◇ d.	2349	0021	⑦	0845	0934	|	1034	|	1134	|		1734	|	1835	|	1934	|	2034	|	2117	2134	2234	2309	0004
Bicester North................**128a** ◇ d.	0019	0051		0910	|	1024	|	1124	|	1224	and at	|	1826	|	1926	|	2026	|	2126	2146	|	2256	2335	0034
Banbury...................**114 128a** ◇ d.	0036	0111		0929	1007	1037	1107	1137	1207	1237	the	1808	1839	1907	1939	2008	2039	2108	2139	2203	2208	2309	2350	0052
Leamington Spa........... **114 128a** d.	...	...		0947	1025	1055	1125	1155	1225	1255	same	1826	1857	1925	1957	2026	2057	2126	2157	...	2226	2327	...	...
Warwick.......................... **128a** d.	...	...		0951	|	1059	|	1159	|	1259	minutes	|	1901	|	2001	|	2101	|	2201	...	2230	2331	...	...
Warwick Parkway ....d.	...	...		0955	1032	1103	1132	1203	1232	1303	past	1832	1905	1932	2005	2032	2105	2132	2205	...	2234	2334	...	...
Solihull......................................a.	...	...		1016	1044	1118	1144	1218	1244	1319	each	1844	1920	1943	2020	2044	2128	2144	2220	...	2257	2349	...	...
Birmingham Moor Street ..... **126** a.	...	...		1024	1053	1127	1156	1227	1256	1329	hour	1856	1929	1953	2029	2056	2137	2156	2229	...	2306	2358	...	...
Birmingham Snow Hill .... **126** a.	...	...		1032	1101	1135	...	1235	...	1337	until	...	1937	1957	2037	...	2140	...	2232	...	2314	0007	...	...
Sourbridge Junction .... **126** a.	...	...		...	...	...	...	...	...	...		...	...	2021	...	...	2204	...	2256	...	...	...	...	...
Kidderminster...................△ **126** a.	...	...		...	...	...	...	...	...	...		...	...	2036	...	...	2218	...	2310	...	...	...	...	...

		Ⓐ	Ⓐ	Ⓐ	Ⓐ	Ⓐ	Ⓐ	Ⓐ	Ⓐ	Ⓐ	Ⓐ	Ⓐ	Ⓐ	Ⓐ	Ⓐ	Ⓐ	Ⓐ	Ⓐ	Ⓐ	Ⓐ	Ⓐ	Ⓐ	Ⓐ	Ⓐ	Ⓐ
Kidderminster...................△ **126** d.		...	...	...	...	...	0609	...	...	0710	0730	...	...	0809	...	...	...	...	...	...	...	...	...	...	...
Stourbridge Junction .... **126** d.	Ⓐ	...	...	...	...	...	0618	...	0641	0721	0738	...	...	0823	...	...	...	...	...	...	...	...	...	...	...
Birmingham Snow Hill .... **126** d.		...	...	...	...	...	0650	...	0707	0750	0808	...	0822	0852	0912	...	...	1012	...	1112	...	1212	...	1312	...
Birmingham Moor Street ..... **126** d.		...	0515	0542	0610	0628	0655	...	0711	0754	0811	...	0825	0855	0915	0955	...	1015	1055	1115	1155	1215	1255	1315	1355
Solihull.......................................d.		...	0524	0551	0619	0638	0704	...	0722	0803	0820	...	0837	0907	0924	1004	...	1024	1104	1124	1204	1224	1304	1324	1404
Warwick Parkway ....d.		...	0536	0605	0634	0659	0718	...	0740	0816	0835	...	0902	0919	0939	1016	...	1039	1117	1139	1216	1239	1317	1340	1416
Warwick.......................... **128a** d.		...	|	0608	|	0702	|	...	|	|	0838	...	0906	|	0942	|	...	1042	|	1142	|	1242	|	1344	|
Leamington Spa........... **114 128a** d.		...	0541	0613	0641	0706	0724	...	0747	0821	0843	...	0912	0925	0946	1022	...	1046	1123	1146	1222	1246	1323	1349	1422
Banbury...................**114 128a** ◇ d.		0517	0559	0631	0659	0724	|	0750	0806	0841	0902	0907	0931	0944	1004	1040	1045	1104	1140	1204	1240	1304	1341	1407	1440
Bicester North................**128a** ◇ d.		0533	0611	0646	0711	0740	|	0807	|	0855	|	0930	0943	|	1016	|	1101	1116	|	1216	|	1317	|	1420	|
High Wycombe ....**128a / b** ◇ d.		0559	0635	|	|	|	|	0831	|	|	|	0957	1007	|	|	1110	1130	|	1213	|	1313	|	1413	|	1510
London Marylebone...**128a / b** ◇ a.		0631	0703	0735	0802	0833	0834	0905	0907	0938	0959	1032	1036	1040	1108	1140	1205	1208	1243	1309	1343	1409	1443	1509	1540

	Ⓐ	Ⓐ	Ⓐ	Ⓐ	Ⓐ	Ⓐ	Ⓐ	Ⓐ	Ⓐ	Ⓐ	Ⓐ	Ⓐ	Ⓐ	Ⓐ		⑥	⑥	⑥	⑥	⑥	⑥	⑥	⑥	⑥	⑥
Kidderminster...................△ **126** d.	...	...	...	...	...	...	...	...	...	...	...	...	...	...		...	...	...	...	0637	0712	...	0813	...	0910
Stourbridge Junction .... **126** d.	...	...	...	...	...	...	...	...	...	...	...	...	...	...	⑥	...	...	...	...	0645	0722	...	0824	...	0920
Birmingham Snow Hill .... **126** d.	1412	...	1512	...	...	1612	1652	1707	1752	1812	1840	1917	2015	2110		...	...	0612	0646	0712	0751	...	0853	0912	0951
Birmingham Moor Street ..... **126** d.	1415	1455	1515	1555	...	1615	1655	1710	1755	1815	1843	1920	2018	2118		...	...	0615	0649	0715	0755	0815	0856	0915	0955
Solihull.......................................d.	1424	1504	1524	1604	...	1624	1704	1719	1806	1824	1852	1929	2027	2127		...	...	0624	0702	0724	0805	0824	0905	0924	1006
Warwick Parkway ....d.	1439	1516	1540	1617	...	1639	1716	1736	1822	1845	1907	1949	2042	2147		...	...	0644	0714	0739	0818	0839	0916	0939	1020
Warwick.......................... **128a** d.	1442	|	1543	|	...	1642	1719	1739	|	1848	|	1952	2045	2150		...	...	0647	|	0742	|	0842	|	0942	|
Leamington Spa........... **114 128a** d.	1446	1522	1547	1623	...	1646	1723	1743	1828	1853	1912	1957	2050	2156		...	...	0652	0720	0746	0824	0846	0922	0946	1026
Banbury...................**114 128a** ◇ d.	1504	1542	1605	1641	1645	1704	1741	1801	1846	1913	1930	2016	2113	2213		0604	0624	0710	0739	0804	0844	0904	0940	1005	1045
Bicester North................**128a** ◇ d.	1516	|	1617	|	1703	1716	|	1814	1858	1929	1942	2030	2125	2225		0618	0639	0722	0751	0816	|	0916	|	1018	|
High Wycombe ....**128a / b** ◇ d.	1537	1614	|	1713	1731	|	1811	1838	|	|	2009	2101	2145	2245		0647	0703	0746	0811	|	0914	|	1014	|	1118
London Marylebone...**128a / b** ◇ a.	1608	1642	1712	1745	1810	1813	1839	1911	1944	2023	2037	2135	2212	2312		0724	0736	0814	0842	0911	0941	1011	1041	1111	1145

	⑥	⑥	⑥	⑥	⑥	⑥	⑥	⑥	⑥	⑥	⑥	⑥	⑥	⑥	⑥	⑥	⑥	⑥	⑥	⑥	⑥	⑥	⑥	⑥	⑥
Birmingham Snow Hill .... **126** d.	1012	...	1112	...	...	1212	...	1312	...	1412	...	1512	...	1612	...	1712	...	1812	...	1912	...	...	2012	...	...
Birmingham Moor Street ..... **126** d.	1015	1055	1115	1155	...	1215	1255	1315	1355	1415	1455	1515	1555	1615	1655	1715	1755	1815	1855	1915	1955	...	2015	2045	2118
Solihull.......................................d.	1024	1104	1124	1204	...	1224	1304	1324	1404	1424	1504	1524	1604	1624	1704	1724	1804	1824	1905	1924	2004	...	2024	2055	2127
Warwick Parkway ....d.	1039	1116	1139	1219	...	1239	1316	1338	1416	1439	1516	1539	1616	1639	1716	1739	1816	1839	1917	1939	2016	...	2039	2113	2149
Warwick.......................... **128a** d.	1042	|	1142	|	...	1242	|	1341	|	1442	|	1542	|	1642	|	1742	|	1842	|	1942	|	...	2042	2117	2152
Leamington Spa........... **114 128a** d.	1046	1121	1146	1225	...	1246	1322	1346	1422	1446	1522	1546	1622	1646	1722	1746	1822	1846	1923	1946	2022	...	2046	2122	2157
Banbury...................**114 128a** ◇ d.	1105	1139	1205	1244	1249	1305	1340	1407	1441	1505	1541	1605	1641	1705	1741	1805	1841	1905	1941	2005	2041	2045	2105	2140	2216
Bicester North................**128a** ◇ d.	1118	|	1218	|	1302	1318	|	1420	|	1518	|	1618	|	1718	|	1818	|	1918	|	2018	|	2101	2118	2152	2232
High Wycombe ....**128a / b** ◇ d.	|	1214	|	1314	1331	|	1414	|	1514	|	1614	|	1714	|	1814	|	1914	|	2014	|	2114	2130	|	2214	2302
London Marylebone...**128a / b** ◇ a.	1211	1241	1311	1341	1408	1411	1441	1511	1541	1611	1646	1711	1741	1811	1841	1911	1941	2011	2041	2111	2141	2207	2211	2241	2348

		⑦	⑦	⑦	⑦	⑦	⑦	⑦	⑦	⑦	⑦	⑦	⑦		⑦	⑦	⑦	⑦		⑦	⑦	⑦	⑦	⑦
Kidderminster...................△ **126** d.		...	...	...	...	...	...	0940	...	...	1113	...	...		...	...	...	...	...	...	...	...	...	...
Stourbridge Junction .... **126** d.	⑦	...	...	...	...	...	...	0948	...	...	1122	...	...		...	...	...	...	...	...	...	...	...	...
Birmingham Snow Hill .... **126** d.		...	...	...	...	0912	...	1012	...	1112	1149	1212	...	and at	1712	...	1812	...	...	1912	...	...	2012	2115
Birmingham Moor Street ..... **126** d.		...	...	0825	0855	0915	0955	1015	1055	1115	1155	1215	1255	the	1715	1755	1815	1855	...	1915	...	1939	2015	2118
Solihull.......................................d.		...	...	0834	0904	0924	1004	1024	1104	1124	1204	1224	1304	same	1724	1804	1824	1904	...	1924	...	1948	2024	2127
Warwick Parkway ....d.		...	...	0849	0916	0939	1016	1039	1116	1139	1216	1239	1316	minutes	1739	1816	1839	1916	...	1939	...	|	2039	2144
Warwick.......................... **128a** d.		...	...	0852	|	0942	|	1042	|	1142	|	1242	|	past	1742	|	1842	|	...	1942	...	2011	2042	2147
Leamington Spa........... **114 128a** d.		...	...	0858	0922	0946	1022	1046	1122	1146	1222	1246	1323	each	1746	1823	1846	1923	...	1946	...	2017	2046	2152
Banbury...................**114 128a** ◇ d.		0750	0849	0916	0940	1007	1040	1107	1140	1207	1240	1307	1340	hour	1807	1841	1907	1941	...	2007	2013	2036	2107	2215
Bicester North................**128a** ◇ d.		0804	0903	0929	|	1019	|	1119	|	1219	|	1319	|	until	1819	|	1919	1953	...	2019	2032	2052	2119	2231
High Wycombe ....**128a / b** ◇ d.		0833	0932	|	1013	|	1114	|	1213	|	1313	|	1412		|	1913	|	2016	...	|	2103	2116	|	2301
London Marylebone...**128a / b** ◇ a.		0923	1006	1018	1041	1109	1142	1210	1240	1310	1340	1410	1440		1910	1940	2010	2042	...	2110	2141	2153	2213	2342

◇ – Additional services operate between these stations.

△ – **Severn Valley Railway** (Kidderminster - Bridgnorth: *26 km*). ✆ 01299 403816. www.svr.co.uk.

CH 2nd class LONDON - STRATFORD UPON AVON 128a

From October 8 arrival times at London Marylebone are 3 minutes later than shown.

km		Ⓐ	Ⓐ	Ⓐ	Ⓐ	Ⓐ		Ⓐ	Ⓐ	Ⓐ	Ⓐ	⑥	⑥	⑥	⑥	⑥	⑥	⑥	⑦	⑦	⑦		⑦	⑦
0	**London** Marylebone 128/b d.	...	0617	...	0943	1143	...	1343	...	1824	2043	...	0943	...	1343	1543	1743	...	0943	1143	1343	...	1543	1743
45	High Wycombe 128/b d.	...	0701	...	1018	1216	...	1416	...	1902	2114	...	1018	...	1418	1618	1818	...	1018	1218	1418	...	1618	1818
88	Bicester North 128 d.	...	0733	...	1047	1245	...	1445	...	1944b	2143	...	1047	...	1447	1647	1847	...	1047	1247	1447	...	1647	1847
111	Banbury 128 a.	...	0749	...	1101	1303	...	1502	...	2005	2200	...	1102	...	1502	1701	1902	...	1102	1301	1501	...	1701	1902
111	Banbury 128 d.	...	0749	...	1110	1311	...	1510	...	2006	2201	...	1110	...	1510	1710	1910	...	1111	1311	1511	...	1711	1911
143	**Leamington Spa** 128 a.	...	0808	...	1129	1330	...	1529	...	2025	2219	...	1129	...	1529	1729	1929	...	1130	1330	1530	...	1730	1930
143	**Leamington Spa** 128 d.	0651	0808	0940	1132	1332	...	1532	1811	2026	2220	0830	1132	1332	1532	1732	1932	2132	1132	1332	1532	...	1732	1932
146	Warwick 128 d.	0656	0813	0945	1137	1337	...	1537	1816	|	2224	0834	1137	1337	1537	1737	1937	2137	1138	1337	1537	...	1737	1937
165	Stratford u. Avon Pkwy a.	0722	0837	1008	1157	1401	...	1601	1846	2050	2245	0901	1157	1400	1600	1758	1958	2158	1157	1356	1556	...	1756	1956
167	**Stratford upon Avon** a.	0731	0846	1017	1206	1410	...	1611	1854	2054	2256	0912	1206	1409	1609	1807	2007	2207	1207	1406	1606	...	1805	2005

	Ⓐ	Ⓐ	Ⓐ	Ⓐ	Ⓐ	Ⓐ	Ⓐ	Ⓐ	Ⓐ	ⒶB	⑥	⑥	⑥	⑥	⑥	⑥	⑥	⑥	⑦	⑦	⑦	⑦	⑦	⑦
Stratford upon Avon d.	0606	0733	0900	1040	1243	1440	1736	1912	2139	2315	0756	1040	1242	1441	1641	1841	2043	2215	0938	1219	1443	1643	1844	2038
Stratford u. Avon Pkwy. d.	0610	0737	0904	1044	1247	1444	1740	1916	2143	|	0800	1044	1245	1445	1645	1845	2047	|	0941	1223	1447	1647	1848	2042
Warwick 128 d.	0640	0804	0928	1108	1308	1508	1805	1946	2206	2334	0824	1108	1308	1508	1708	1908	2108	2235	1001	1245	1508	1708	1909	2103
Leamington Spa 128 a.	0649	0808	0937	1113	1313	1513	1809	...	2210	2338	0828	1113	1317	1513	1713	1913	2117	2240	1005	1250	1514	1714	1918	210
Leamington Spa 128 d.	...	0809	...	1115	1315	1515	1809	...	2210	2339	0829	1115	...	1515	1715	1915	...	2241	1006	1251	1515	1715	...	2108
Banbury 128 a.	...	0826	...	1134	1334	1537	1828	...	2229	2357	0847	1134	...	1535	1734	1934	...	2302	1023	1310	1534	1735	...	2127
Banbury 128 d.	...	0828	...	1148	1345	1548	1828	...	2230	...	0848	1143	...	1546	1745	1946	...	...	1024	1345	1545	1745	...	2128
Bicester North 128 d.	...	0842	...	1203	1401	1603	1845	...	2246	...	0903	1201	...	1601	1801	2001	...	...	1036	1402	1601	1801	...	2142
High Wycombe 128/b d.	...	0906	...	1230	1430	1630	|	...	2317	...	0930	1230	...	1630	1830	2030	...	...	1103	1431	1630	1830	...	2213
London Marylebone 128/b a.	...	0935	...	1305	1505	1709	1941	...	2358	...	1005	1307	...	1706	1907	2107	...	...	1139	1506	1705	1905	...	2253

B – To Oxford (arr. 0021).   a – Arrives 8 minutes earlier.   b – Arrives 1931.

CH 2nd class LONDON - HIGH WYCOMBE - OXFORD 128b

From October 8 arrival times at Oxford and London Marylebone are 3 minutes later than shown.

km		②–⑤	Ⓐ	Ⓐ	Ⓐ	Ⓐ	Ⓐ	Ⓐ	Ⓐ	Ⓐ	Ⓐ	Ⓐ	Ⓐ	Ⓐ	Ⓐ	Ⓐ	Ⓐ	Ⓐ	Ⓐ	Ⓐ	Ⓐ	Ⓐ	Ⓐ	Ⓐ	Ⓐ
0	**London** Marylebone 128 d.	0001	0609	0648	0714	0740	0811	0841	0900	0935	1006	1035	1107	1135	1207	1235	1306	1335	1406	1435	1505	1535	1600	1618	1650
45	High Wycombe 128 d.	0028	0640	0717	0738	0804	|	0906	|	1000	|	1100	|	1200	|	1259	|	1359	|	1503	|	1600	1629	|	1713
90	Bicester Village d.	0055	0708	0745	0802	0831	0854	0931	0952	1023	1053	1124	1154	1223	1254	1321	1354	1421	1454	1526	1555	1622	1654	1706	1739
103	**Oxford** Parkway a.	0104	0718	0752	0812	0840	0901	0938	1001	1030	1101	1132	1202	1230	1304	1330	1402	1430	1502	1535	1603	1629	1702	1713	1748
108	**Oxford** 131 a.	0112	0730	0801	0821	0849	0910	0947	1010	1038	1109	1139	1210	1238	1312	1337	1410	1437	1510	1543	1611	1638	1708	1721	1756

	Ⓐ	Ⓐ	Ⓐ	Ⓐ	Ⓐ	Ⓐ	Ⓐ		Ⓐ	Ⓐ	Ⓐ	①–④	⑤	Ⓐ	Ⓐ	⑥	⑥	⑥	⑥	⑥	⑥	⑥	⑥	⑥	⑥
London Marylebone 128 d.	1718	1750	1818	1850	1921	1950	2007	...	2040	2102	2132	2205	2205	2240	2310	0010	0110	0556	0644	0706	0740	0806	0835	0906	0935
High Wycombe 128 d.	|	1814	|	1916	1945	2014	|	...	2105	|	2159	|	|	2307	2339	0038	0141	0626	0707	0730	0803	|	0858	|	0958
Bicester Village d.	1805	1840	1908	1942	2011	2039	2052	...	2128	2155	2226	2253	2256	2333	0010	0105	0213	0655	0735	0756	0826	0854	0921	0954	1022
Oxford Parkway a.	1812	1847	1916	1949	2018	2046	2102	...	2135	2202	2234	2302	2306	2341	0018	0113	0221	0703	0744	0803	0835	0901	0931	1001	1029
Oxford 131 a.	1820	1854	1924	1957	2027	2056	2111	...	2145	2211	2241	2309	2313	2349	0026	0122	0229	0711	0751	0812	0843	0910	0938	1010	1037

	⑥	⑥		⑥	⑥	⑥	⑥	⑥	⑥	⑥	⑥	⑥	⑦	⑦	⑦	⑦		⑦	⑦	⑦		⑦	⑦
			and at														and at						
London Marylebone 128 d.	1006	1035	the same	1906	1935	2006	2035	2106	2135	2206	2235	2310	0735	0835	0905	0935	the same	2035	2105	2135	...	2215	2315
High Wycombe 128 d.	|	1059	minutes	|	1958	|	2058	|	2159	|	2306	2336	0805	0859	|	0958	minutes	2058	|	2159	...	|	2347
Bicester Village d.	1054	1122	past each	1954	2022	2054	2122	2154	2222	2253	2333	2359	0834	0928	0953	1021	past each	2120	2151	2222	...	2309	0018
Oxford Parkway a.	1101	1129	hour until	2001	2029	2101	2131	2201	2229	2301	2341	0009	0843	0929	1000	1030	hour until	2128	2159	2231	...	2317	0026
Oxford 131 a.	1110	1139	♥	2010	2037	2110	2139	2210	2237	2310	2347	0018	0851	0937	1009	1039	♥	2136	2208	2239	...	2326	0035

	Ⓐ	Ⓐ	Ⓐ	Ⓐ	Ⓐ	Ⓐ	Ⓐ	Ⓐ	Ⓐ	Ⓐ	Ⓐ	Ⓐ	Ⓐ	Ⓐ	Ⓐ	Ⓐ	Ⓐ		Ⓐ	Ⓐ	Ⓐ	Ⓐ	①–④	⑤
Oxford 131 d.	0536	0601	0625	0643	0717	0743	0802	0822	0840	0910	0938	1010	1041	1109	1142	1211	1241	and at	1611	1638	1656	1723	1740	1740
Oxford Parkway d.	0542	0607	0631	0650	0725	0750	0808	0828	0850	0916	0945	1017	1047	1115	1148	1217	1247	the same	1617	1644	1703	1729	1746	1746
Bicester Village d.	0552	0617	0640	0659	0735	0759	0820	0837	0859	0925	0957	1026	1056	1124	1157	1226	1256	minutes	1626	1657	1720	1738	1758	1758
High Wycombe 128 d.	0625	0646	|	0727	|	0827	0854	0902	0927	0952	|	1051	|	1151	|	1251	|	past each	1651	|	1745	1806	|	|
London Marylebone 128 a.	0700	0723	0729	0757	0820	0858	0927	0930	0956	1019	1041	1118	1146	1218	1246	1318	1346	hour until ♥	1721	1750	1826	1835	1848	1853

	Ⓐ	Ⓐ	①–④	⑤	Ⓐ	Ⓐ	Ⓐ	Ⓐ		Ⓐ	Ⓐ	Ⓐ	Ⓐ	Ⓐ	Ⓐ	⑥	⑥	⑥	⑥	⑥	⑥	⑥	⑥	
Oxford 131 d.	1804	1823	1901	1901	1928	2000	2026	2055	...	2115	2137	2215	2241	2315	2336	0612	0637	0710	0736	0811	0843	0909	0941	and at
Oxford Parkway d.	1810	1829	1907	1907	1937	2009	2032	2101	...	2121	2148	2221	2247	2321	2342	0618	0643	0716	0744	0817	0849	0915	0948	the same
Bicester Village d.	1823	1838	1918	1918	1947	2019	2041	2110	...	2130	2157	2230	2258	2331	2352	0628	0652	0727	0755	0826	0858	0926	0957	minutes
High Wycombe 128 d.	1845	1906	|	|	2013	|	2109	2138	...	|	2222	2300	2326	0007	0018	0656	|	0755	|	0851	|	0951	|	past each
London Marylebone 128 a.	1912	1933	2009	2013	2043	2110	2138	2205	...	2218	2252	2352	0011	...	0047	0727	0740	0828	0854	0918	0946	1018	1048	hour until ♥

	⑥	⑥	⑥	⑥	⑥	⑥	⑥	⑦	⑦	⑦	⑦	⑦	⑦	⑦		⑦	⑦	⑦	⑦	⑦	⑦	⑦	⑦	⑦
Oxford 131 d.	1911	1942	2011	2042	2109	2142	2209	0743	0810	0838	0901	0942	1009	1042	and at	1811	1841	1909	1942	2011	2049	2108	2154	2208
Oxford Parkway d.	1917	1948	2017	2048	2115	2148	2215	0749	0816	0844	0907	0948	1015	1048	the same	1817	1847	1915	1948	2017	2055	2114	2200	2214
Bicester Village d.	1926	1957	2026	2057	2126	2157	2226	0758	0825	0853	0918	0957	1026	1057	minutes	1826	1856	1926	1957	2026	2104	2125	2209	2223
High Wycombe 128 d.	1951	|	2051	|	2151	2222	2252	0823	0850	|	0944	|	1051	|	past each	1851	|	1951	|	2051	|	2150	|	2251
London Marylebone 128 a.	2018	2048	2118	2147	2218	2249	2325	0851	0926	0942	1011	1045	1118	1145	hour until ♥	1918	1945	2017	2048	2118	2156	2216	2256	2316

♥ – Timings may vary by up to 3 minutes.

CH 2nd class LONDON - AYLESBURY 129

From October 8 arrival times at Aylesbury Vale Parkway are 3 minutes later than shown whilst departures from Aylesbury Vale Parkway, Aylesbury and Amersham are 3 minutes **earlier** than shown.

km		Ⓐ	Ⓐ	Ⓐ		Ⓐ	Ⓐ	Ⓐ	Ⓐ	Ⓐ	Ⓐ	Ⓐ	Ⓐ	Ⓐ		Ⓐ	Ⓐ	Ⓐ	Ⓐ	Ⓐ	⑥	⑥
0	**London** Marylebone ... △ d.	0633	0652	0757	and at the same	1457	1527	1612	1642	1730	1758	1832	1859	1932	...	1956	2057	2157	2257	2357	0025	...
38	Amersham △ d.	0708	0727	0832	minutes	1532	1602	1647	1717	|	1829	|	1934	2008	...	2031	2132	2232	2332	0032	|	0702
60	**Aylesbury** △ d.	0730	0753	0854	past each	1554	1626	1709	1739	1824	1852	1925	2003	2031	...	2053	2154	2254	2354	0054	0144	0729
65	**Aylesbury** Vale Parkway a.	0739	0804	0903	hour until	1603	1634	1718	1748	1832	1901	1933	2011	2039	...	2102	2203	2303	0003	0103	...	...

	⑥	⑥	⑥	⑥	⑥		⑥	⑥	⑥	⑥	⑥	⑥	⑦	⑦	⑦	⑦		⑦	⑦	⑦	⑦	⑦
						and at											and at					
London Marylebone ... △ d.	0727	0757	0827	0857	0957	the same	1957	2027	2057	2157	2227	2257	0757	0857	0957	1057	the same	1957	2027	2057	2127	2227
Amersham △ d.	0802	0832	0902	0932	1032	minutes	2032	2102	2132	2232	2302	2332	0832	0932	1032	1132	minutes	2032	2102	2132	2202	2302
Aylesbury △ d.	0824	0854	0924	0954	1054	past each	2054	2124	2154	2254	2324	2354	0854	0954	1054	1154	past each	2054	2124	2154	2224	2324
Aylesbury Vale Parkway a.	0833	0903	0933	1003	1103	hour until	2103	2136	2203	2303	2333	0003	0903	1003	1103	1203	hour until	2103	2133	2203	2233	2333

	Ⓐ	Ⓐ	Ⓐ	Ⓐ	Ⓐ	Ⓐ	Ⓐ	Ⓐ	Ⓐ	Ⓐ		Ⓐ	Ⓐ	Ⓐ	Ⓐ	Ⓐ	Ⓐ	Ⓐ	Ⓐ	⑥	⑥	⑥
											and at											
Aylesbury Vale Parkway d.	0516	0544	0619	0653	0725	0751	0812	0839	0918	1013	the same	1613	1643	1734	*1806*	1842	1943	2048	2113	0613	0713	0813
Aylesbury ▽ d.	0521	0549	0624	0658	0730	0802	0817	0844	0923	1018	minutes	1618	1648	1750	1820	1847	1948	2053	2118	0618	0718	0818
Amersham ▽ d.	0543	0611	0647	0721	0753	0825	0839	0905	0944	1039	past each	1639	1709	1811	1842	1908	2009	2114	2139	0639	0739	0839
London Marylebone ... ▽ a.	0616	0649	0722	0753	0826	0900	0917	0944	1023	1120	hour until	1720	1748	1850	1920	1948	2049	2153	2219	0718	0818	0920

	⑥	⑥	⑥		⑥	⑥	⑥	⑥	⑥	⑥	⑦	⑦	⑦	⑦	⑦		⑦	⑦	⑦	⑦	⑦	⑦	⑦
				and at												and at							
Aylesbury Vale Parkway d.	0913	0943	1013	the same	1913	2013	2113	2143	2213	...	0713	0813	0913	1013	1113	the same	1813	1913	2013	2113	2143	2243
Aylesbury ▽ d.	0918	0948	1018	minutes	1918	2018	2118	2148	2218	2318	0718	0818	0918	1018	1118	minutes	1818	1918	2018	2118	2148	2248
Amersham ▽ d.	0939	1009	1039	past each	1939	2039	2139	2209	2239	2342	0739	0839	0939	1039	1139	past each	1839	1939	2039	2139	2209	2309
London Marylebone ... ▽ a.	1020	1050	1120	hour until	2020	2120	2220	2250	2318	...	0820	0918	1020	1120	1220	hour until	1920	2020	2120	2220	2250	2348

△ – Additional trains London Marylebone - Aylesbury on Ⓐ at 0726, 0827 and hourly until 1427, 1556, 1627, 1711, 1740, 1812, 1843, 1918, 2023, 2127, 2227, 2327; on ⑥ at 0927 and hourly until 1927, 2127, 2327, 2357; on ⑦ at 1527 and hourly until 1927, 2157, 2257, 2327.

▽ – Additional trains Aylesbury - London Marylebone on Ⓐ at 0607, 0638, 0710, 0741, 0902, 0948, 1048 and hourly until 1548, 1630, 1715, 1918, 2021, 2148, 2248; on ⑥ at 0648 , 0748, 0848, 1048 and hourly until 2048; on ⑦ at 0848, 0948, 1548 and hourly until 2048.

130 LONDON - WORCESTER - HEREFORD

Most trains convey 🍸 GW

Other services: London Paddington - Oxford see Table **131**; Worcester - Hereford see Table **125**.

km		Ⓐ	Ⓐ	Ⓐ	Ⓐ	Ⓐ	Ⓐ	Ⓐ	Ⓐ	Ⓐ	Ⓐ	Ⓐ	Ⓐ	Ⓐ	Ⓐ	Ⓐ	Ⓐ	Ⓐ	Ⓐ	Ⓐ	Ⓐ	Ⓐ	Ⓐ	⑤	⑥	⑥
0	**London** Padd .... **131 132** d.	...	0512	0547	0650	0750	...	0821	0921	1022	1120	1222	1322	1421	1522	1550	1622	1722	1752	1822	1922	2022	2148	2320	0518	0622
58	Reading .... **131 132** d.	...	0550	0619	0722	0821	0819	0853	0952	1053	1154	1253	1353	1452	1553	1622	1653u	1752	1821	1851	1953	2053	2220	0003	0554	0653
103	**Oxford** .... **131** d.	0514	0621	0652	0801	0851	0909	0923	1020	1125	1224	1323	1419	1523	1625	1650	1725	1817	1850	1923	2023	2124	2256	0036	0624	0723
148	Moreton in Marsh .... d.	0539	0645	0729	0839	0928	0942	1000	1057	1202	1302	1400	1456	1600	1702	1726	1818	1854	1931	2002	2106f	2201	2337	0111	0701	0800
172	Evesham .... a.	0557	...	0748	0858	0943	...	1020	1112	1221	1321	1419	1512	1618	1722	...	1837	1914	1947	2021	2126	2220	2356	...	0721	0819
172	Evesham .... d.	0557	...	0752	0859	0944	...	1030	1113	1222	1323	1420	1513	1623	1723	...	1838	1915	1948	2023	2131	2221	2357	...	0726	0823
194	**Worcester** Shrub Hill **138** a.	0619	...	0813	0916	0959	...	1051	1127	1244	1341	1442	1527	1644	1741	...	1857	1936	2010	2041	2149	2243	0021	...	0744	0845
195	**Worcester** Foregate St ... a.	0622	...	0817	0919	1002	...	1055	1131	1247	1344	...	...	1648	1745	...	1910	1940	...	2045	2201	2246	...	...	0749	0848
208	Great Malvern .... **125 138** a.	...	...	...	0931	1014	...	1108	...	1300t	...	...	...	...	1758	...	1924	1953	...	2058	2215e	2300	...	...	0803	0904
219	Ledbury .... **125** a.	...	...	...	...	...	...	1121	...	1320c	...	...	...	...	...	...	...	2008	...	2113	2232	...	...	...	...	...
241	**Hereford** .... **125** a.	...	...	...	...	...	...	1142	...	1347	...	...	...	...	...	...	...	2029	...	2134	2254	...	...	...	...	...

	⑥	⑥	⑥	⑥	⑥	⑥	⑥	⑥	⑥	⑥	⑥	⑥	⑥	⑥	⑦	⑦	⑦	⑦	⑦	⑦	⑦	⑦	⑦	⑦	⑦	⑦	⑦
London Padd.... **131 132** d.	0722	0822	0922	1022	1122	1222	1322	1422	1522	1622	1722	1822	1952	2148	0808	0848	0949	1049	1249	1349	1449	1549	1649	1749	1849	1949	2137
Reading .... **131 132** d.	0753	0854	0954	1054	1153	1253	1353	1453	1553	1654	1754	1854	2023	2220	0847	0920	1020	1120	1319	1419	1520	1620	1724	1823	1920	2020	2221
Oxford .... **131** d.	0823	0924	1023	1123	1223	1323	1423	1523	1623	1723	1823	1923	2049	2251	0916	0954	1050	1154	1351	1449	1550	1651	1755	1854	1950	2051	2255
Moreton in Marsh............d.	0900	1001	1100	1200	1300	1400	1504	1600	1700	1804	1900	2004	2126	2332	0954	1024	1127	1230	1426	1522	1625	1723	1832	1930	2028	2128	2331
Evesham ....a.	0919	1020	1119	1219	1319	...	1523	1619	1718	1823	1919	2023	2144	2352	1012	1040	1145	1249	1445	1540	1646	1740	1850	1951	2046	2147	2350
Evesham ....d.	0922	1024	1120	1228	1323	...	1524	1621	1720	1825	1920	2026	2145	2353	1013	1044	1152	1250	1446	1545	1648	1746	1851	1951	2050	2148	2351
Worcester Shrub Hill **138** a.	0945	1046	1140	1247	1346	...	1546	1640	1742	1848e	1942	2045	2207	0018	1036	1103	1210	1313	1510	1604	1710	1805	1914	2012	2109	2211	0016
Worcester Foregate St....a.	0949	1050	1147	1251	1350	...	1550	1644	1745	1855	1946	2049	2211	...	1039	1106	1213	1316	1512	1607	1713	1810	1917	2018	...	2214	...
Great Malvern.... **125 138** a.	1005	1103	...	1304	1403	...	1603	1700	1758	1909	...	2102	2224	...	1056	1119	1226	1328	1525	...	1726	...	1930	2031	...	2227	...
Ledbury .... **125** a.	...	1121	...	1321	...	...	...	...	...	1923	...	2116	...	...	...	1133	...	1343	1540	...	1740	...	...	2045	...	...	...
Hereford .... **125** a.	...	1141	...	1340	...	...	...	...	...	1941	...	2135	...	...	...	1151	...	1407	1558	...	1758	...	...	2102	...	...	...

	Ⓐ	Ⓐ	Ⓐ	Ⓐ	Ⓐ2	Ⓐ	Ⓐ	Ⓐ	Ⓐ	Ⓐ	Ⓐ	Ⓐ	Ⓐ	Ⓐ	Ⓐ	Ⓐ	Ⓐ	Ⓐ	Ⓐ	Ⓐ	Ⓐ	Ⓐ	⑥	⑥	⑥	⑥
Hereford .... **125** d.	...	0447	0528	...	...	0642	...	...	...	...	...	1209	...	...	...	1514	...	...	...	...	...	2151	...	0616	0713	...
Ledbury .... **125** d.	...	0504	0545	...	...	0700	...	...	...	...	...	1227	...	...	...	1531	...	...	...	...	...	2211	...	0633	0730	...
Great Malvern.... **125 138** d.	...	0517	0559	...	...	0713	...	...	0954	1100	...	1240	...	...	...	1545	...	...	1829	1942	...	2224	0552	0647	0743	0843
Worcester Foregate St....d.	...	0532	0614	...	0651	0728	0825	...	1009	1115	1157	1256	1358	...	...	1601	...	1726	1845	1957	2059	2236	0607	0702	0759	0858
Worcester Shrub Hill **138** d.	0507	0537	0619	...	0654	0732	0835e	...	1014	1121e	1201	1300	1401	1522	1552	1607	...	1733e	1850	2002	2103	2240	0611	0706	0803	0902
Evesham ....a.	0524	0557	0636	...	0713	0752	0856	...	1030	1138	1221	1320	1418	1536	1609	1623	...	1755	1906	2024	2123	2300	0631	0726	0823	0922
Evesham ....d.	0526	0558	0637	...	0714	0754	0902	...	1032	1138	1226	1321	1425	1537	1610	1624	...	1756	1907	2025	2124	2301	0632	0727	0826	0924
Moreton in Marsh............d.	0546	0614	0656	0710	0729	0815	0922	0950	1052	1153	1246	1346r	1445	1553	1626	1646	1738	1816	1927	2045	2144	2322	0652	0747	0846	0944
Oxford .... **131** a.	0623	0651	0730	0751	0811	0853	0959	1025	1129	1230	1324	1424	1524	1629	1657	1728	1804	1900	2004	2128	2225	2359	0729	0827	0924	1031
Reading .... **131 132** a.	0651	0720	0754	0819	...	0917	1024	1054	1155	1254	1354	1454	1554	1655	1723	1754	1829	1925	2029	2155	2256	0039	0754	0853	0952	1056
London Padd.... **131 132** a.	0729	0752	0828	0851	-...	0947	1057	1130	1228	1329	1427	1527	1627	1728	1800	1827	1906	1959	2105	2231	2336j	0120	0827	0928	1024	1129

	⑥	⑥	⑥	⑥	⑥	⑥	⑥	⑥	⑥	⑥	⑥	⑥	⑥	⑦	⑦		⑦	⑦	⑦	⑦	⑦	⑦	⑦	⑦	⑦		⑦
Hereford .... **125** d.	...	...	...	1213	...	...	1513	...	...	...	...	2020	...	...	...	...	...	...	1332	1432	...	1633	...	1838	...	...	...
Ledbury .... **125** d.	...	...	...	1230	...	...	1530	...	...	...	...	2037	...	...	...	...	...	...	1351	1451	...	1650	...	1857	...	...	...
Great Malvern.... **125 138** d.	0945	1045	...	1246	...	1435	1544	1635	1745	1832	...	2053	2241	...	0918	...	1113	1316	1407	1509	...	1704	...	1912	2010	...	...
Worcester Foregate St....d.	0959	1100	1204	1301	...	1457	1559	1655	1800	1846	2001	2111	2256	0828	0932	...	1128	1328	1422	1522	1627	1723	1826	1927	2027	...	...
Worcester Shrub Hill **138** d.	1003	1104	1208	1306	...	1502	1604	1659	1804	1900a	2005	2115	2300	0833	0936	...	1132	1333	1425	1526	1631	1729	1830	1931	2031	...	2130
Evesham ....a.	1024	1121	1228	1323	...	1522	1621	1720	1825	1920	2026	2136	2323	0853	0956	...	1151	1352	1447	1547	1646	1751	1851	1950	2051	...	2146
Evesham ....d.	1025	1125	1229	1326	...	1528	1622	1725	1828	1928	2028	2137	...	0853	0956	...	1155	1355	1455	1551	1655	1755	1855	1955	2054	...	2147
Moreton in Marsh............d.	1045	1145	1249	1346	1450	1548	1642	1745	1848	1948	2048	2157	...	0913	1015	...	1214	1414	1511	1609	1714	1816	1914	2014	2114	...	2206
Oxford .... **131** a.	1126	1225	1326	1427	1528	1627	1722	1822	1925	2025	2127	2234	...	0952	1052	...	1252	1449	1549	1651	1754	1851	1952	2051	2152	...	2242
Reading .... **131 132** a.	1154	1254	1352	1455	1554	1654	1754	1854	1954	2053	2156	2306	...	1021	1123	...	1322	1524	1622	1724	1822	1925	2023	2124	2220	...	2312
London Padd.... **131 132** a.	1226	1328	1426	1528	1626	1726	1829	1926	2027	2125	2229	2351	...	1053	1157	...	1359	1557	1658	1759	1857	1957	2055	2204	2307	...	2359

a – Arrives 1849.
c – Departs 1331.
e – Departs 4–5 minutes later.
f – Arrives 4–5 minutes earlier.
j – 2330 on ⑤.
r – Arrives 1340.
t – Departs 1308.
u – Calls to pick up only.

131 LONDON - READING - OXFORD

GW

km		②–⑤	Ⓐ	Ⓐ	Ⓐ	Ⓐ	Ⓐ	Ⓐ	Ⓐ	Ⓐ	Ⓐ	Ⓐ	Ⓐ	Ⓐ	Ⓐ	Ⓐ	Ⓐ	Ⓐ	Ⓐ	Ⓐ	Ⓐ	Ⓐ	Ⓐ	Ⓐ	Ⓐ
0	**London** Pad .**130 132** d.	0025	0512	0547	0620	0650	0721	0750	0821	0850	0921	0950	1022	1050	1120	1150	1222	1250	1322	1350	1421	1450	1522	1550	1622
30	Slough .... **131a** d.	0043	0530	0603	0636	0708	0737	0807	0837	0906	0937	1006	1038	1107	1136	1206	1238	1306	1338	1407	1437	1507	1538	1606	1638
58	Reading ....**130 132** d.	0103	0550	0619	0651	0722	0752	0823	0853	0921	0952	1021	1053	1123	1154f	1221	1253	1321	1353	1423	1452	1522	1553	1622	1653
85	Didcot Parkway.. **132** d.	0119	|	0635	0707	0743f	|	|	|	093	|	|	|	1138	|	|	|	1337	|	|	|	1537	|	|	|
102	**Oxford**....... **130 128b** a.	0135	0616	0650	0722	0757	0817	0848	0918	0951	1017	1049	1122	1151	1220	1248	1320	1350	1416	1448	1520	1550	1623	1646	1722

	Ⓐ	Ⓐ	Ⓐ	Ⓐ	Ⓐ	Ⓐ	Ⓐ	Ⓐ	Ⓐ	Ⓐ	Ⓐ	⑤	①–④	⑤	①–④	⑤	①–④	⑤	⑥	⑥	⑥	⑥	⑥	⑥	⑥
London Pad.**130 132** d.	1652	1722	1752	1822	1852	1922	1951	2022	2050	2118	2148	2218	2218	2250	2250	2320	2320	2342	0022	0518	0552	0622	0652	0722	0752
Slough...............**131a** d.	|	|	|	|	|	1938	2008	2038	2106	2135	2204	|	|	2307	2310	2337	2340	2359	0043	0534	0608	0638	0708	0738	0808
Reading........**130 132** d.	1719	1752	1821	1851	1919	1953	2024	2053	2121	2151	2220	2250	2259	2330	2333	0003	0004	0023	0102	0554	0623	0653	0723	0753	0823
Didcot Parkway.. **132** d.	|	|	|	|	|	|	|	|	|	|	|	|	|	|	|	|	|	0047	0118	0610	0639	|	|	|	|
Oxford ......**130 128b** a.	1743	1815	1848	1920	1943	2020	2053	2121	2149	2218	2253	2330	2329	2355	2358	0034	0032	0101	0131	0622	0652	0719	0752	0819	0851

	⑥		⑥	⑥	⑥	⑥	⑥	⑥	⑥	⑥	⑦	⑦	⑦	⑦		⑦	⑦	⑦	⑦	⑦	⑦	⑦	⑦	⑦
London Pad.**130 132** d.	0822	and at the	1952	2022	2050	2120	2148	2220	2250	2335	0808	0848	0949	1049	and	1649	1749	1849	1949	2049	2137	2203	2237	2337
Slough...............**131a** d.	0838	same	2008	2038	2106	2136	2205	2236	2306	2354	0824	0902	1005	1103	hourly	1705	1803	1905	2003	2104	2153	|	|	0001
Reading........**130 132** d.	0854	minutes	2023	2053	2121	2157	2220	2256	2330f	0020	0847	0920	1020	1120	until	1724	1823	1920	2020	2120	2221	2245	2315	0020
Didcot Parkway.. **132** d.	|	past each	|	|	2138	2213	2237	2313	2346	0036	0903	0936	1036	1135	♥	1739	1840	1937	2035	2137	2240f	2300a	2332a	0035
Oxford ......**130 128b** a.	0921	hour until ♥	2046	2120	2153	2226	2249	2327	0001	0050	0915	0946	1050	1148		1753	1852	1949	2049	2150	2254	*2350**	*0015**	*0115*

	①	②–⑤	②–⑤	Ⓐ	Ⓐ	Ⓐ	Ⓐ	Ⓐ	Ⓐ	Ⓐ	Ⓐ	Ⓐ	Ⓐ	Ⓐ	Ⓐ	Ⓐ		Ⓐ	Ⓐ	Ⓐ	Ⓐ	Ⓐ	Ⓐ	Ⓐ
Oxford ....**130 128b** d.	*0005**	0007	0026	*0454*	*0523*	...	0557	0628	0654	0731	0754	0807	0854	0901	0931	1001	and at the	1601	1631	1700	1731	1806	1831	1902
Didcot Parkway.. **132** d.	0035	0023	0048f	0517	0540	0601	0614	|	0708	|	|	0821	|	0917	|	|	same minutes	|	|	|	|	|	|	|
Reading........**130 132** a.	0050	0040	0115	0542	0554	0616	0627	0651	0720	0754	0819	0834	0917	0930	0957	1024	past each	1624	1655	1723r	1754	1829	1856	1925
Slough...............**131a** a.	0114	0059	*0245*	0613	|	|	0648	|	|	|	|	|	|	|	1012	1039	hour until	1640	1710	1741	1809	1844	1912	1940
London Pad.**130 132** a.	0141	0119	*0315*	0646	0622	0654	0706	0729	0752	0828	0851	0907	0947	0959	1031	1057	♥	1700	1728	1800	1827	1906	1931	1959

	Ⓐ	Ⓐ	Ⓐ	Ⓐ	Ⓐ	⑤	①–④	⑤	①–④	Ⓐ	⑥	⑥	⑥	⑥	⑥	⑥	⑥	⑥	⑥	⑥		⑥	⑥	⑥
Oxford ....**130 128b** d.	1932	2006	2031	2101	2131	2201	2201	2231	2231	2301	0007	0026	0400	0514	*0601*	0631	0701	0731	0801	0830	and at the	1901	1931	2001
Didcot Parkway.. **132** d.	|	|	|	|	|	2214	2214	|	|	2317	0022	0048f	0413	0532	0630	|	|	|	|	|	same minutes	|	|	|
Reading........**130 132** a.	1956	2029	2054	2126	2155	2231	2229t	2256	2256	2332r	0040	0115	0429	0557	0643	0654	0724	0754	0824	0853	past each	1924	1954	2024
Slough...............**131a** a.	2010	2044	2109	2143	2211	2249	2302	2312	2316	2355	0059	...	*0501*	*0626*	|	0709	0738	0808	0839	0910	hour until	1938	2008	2038
London Pad.**130 132** a.	2028	2105	2129	2206	2231	2309	2323	2330	2336	0021	0120	...	*0532*	*0701*	0714	0729	0756	0827	0857	0928	♥	1956	2027	2059

	⑥	⑥	⑥	⑥	⑥	⑥	⑥	⑦	⑦	⑦	⑦	⑦	⑦	⑦	⑦	⑦	⑦		⑦	⑦	⑦	⑦	⑦	⑦	⑦
Oxford ....**130 128b** d.	2030	2101	2129	2201	2235	2301	*2310*	0757	0854	0955	1055	1155	1255	1355	1455	1550	1655	...	1755	1855	1955	2055	2152	2244	2300
Didcot Parkway.. **132** d.	|	|	2143	2214	2252	2315	2334	0809	0905	1008	1108	1208	1307	1408	1510	1608	1710	...	1808	1909	2007	2108	2206	2257	2353
Reading........**130 132** a.	2053	2124	2156	2227	2306r	2331	2348	0826	0920	1021	1123	1222	1322	1423	1524	1622	1724	...	1822	1925	2023	2124	2220	2312	0019
Slough...............**131a** a.	2107	2138	2211	2242	2331	2351	|	0840	0937	1036	1139	1239	1337	1436	1539	1638	1739	...	1837	1940	2037	2135	2238	2330	004
London Pad.**130 132** a.	2125	2156	2229	2300	2351	0017	0029	0857	0956	1053	1157	1258	1359	1456	1557	1658	1759	...	1857	1957	2055	2204	2307	2359	011

a – Arrival time.
b – ②–⑤ only.
f – Arrives 4–7 minutes earlier.
r – Departs 5–8 minutes later.
t – Departs 2239.
u – Calls to pick up only.
* – Connection by 🚌.
♥ – Timings may vary by up to 3 minutes

131a SLOUGH - WINDSOR

GW 2nd class Journey time 6 minutes

From Slough:
Ⓐ: 0530, 0550, 0610, 0630, 0650, 0708, 0730, 0750, 0808, 0830 and every 20 minutes until 1730, 1751, 1810 and every 20 minutes until 2250, 2312 and 2336.
⑥: 0617 and every 30 minutes until 0947, 1011, 1030, 1050 and every 20 minutes until 1850, 1917, 1947 and every 30 minutes until 2247, 2322 and 2356.
⑦: 0822, 0852, 0922, 0952, 1012 and every 20 minutes until 1852, 1922 and every 30 minutes until 2322.

From Windsor & Eton Central:
Ⓐ: 0539, 0559, 0619, 0639, 0659, 0717, 0739, 0759, 0817, 0839 and every 20 minutes un 1739, 1800, 1819 and every 20 minutes until 2259, 2321, 2346.
⑥: 0627 and every 30 minutes until 0957, 1021, 1039 and every 20 minutes until 1859, 192 and every 30 minutes until 2127, 2156, 2227, 2257, 2331.
⑦: 0005, 0832, 0902, 0932, 1002, 1022 and every 20 minutes until 1902, 1932 and every 3 minutes until 2332.

GW Most trains convey 🍸 LONDON - BRISTOL - TAUNTON 132

km		ⒶQ	Ⓐ	Ⓐ	ⒶD	Ⓐ	Ⓐ	Ⓐ	Ⓐ	Ⓐ	Ⓐ	Ⓐ	Ⓐ	Ⓐ	Ⓐ	Ⓐ	Ⓐ	Ⓐ	Ⓐ	Ⓐ	Ⓐ	Ⓐ	Ⓐ
0	**London** Paddington... 130 131 134 d.	0502	0630	0700	0730	0800	0830	0900	0930	1000	1030	1100	1130	1200	1230	1300	1330	1400	1430	1500	1530	1600	1630
58	Reading.......... 130 131 134 d.	0542	0657	0728	0757	0828	0857	0928	0957	1027	1059	1127	1158	1228	1257	1327	1358	1427	1457	1528	1558	1627	1657
85	Didcot Parkway.......... 131 134 d.	0557	0712	0744	|	0843	|	0942	|	1041	|	1142	|	1243	|	1342	1413	|	1512	|	1612	|	1713
124	Swindon.......... 132a 134 d.	0616	0730	0802	0824	0901	0930	1000	1026	1100	1129	1200	1230a	1301	1325	1400	1431	1456	1532	1557	1630	1656	1731
151	Chippenham.......... 132a d.	0630	0745	0817	0839	0916	0945	1015	1041	1114	1143	1215	1245	1316	1340	1414	1446	1511	1546	1612	1645	1711	1746
172	Bath.......... a.	0644	0759	0831	0853	0930	0959	1029	1055	1128	1157	1229	1259	1330	1354	1428	1500	1527	1600	1626	1659	1725	1800
190	**Bristol** Temple Meads 110 116 115 a.	0658	0818	0848	0910	0944	1013	1043	1109	1143	1211	1243	1316	1344	1408	1443	1515	1541	1615	1640	1714	1739	1815
221	Weston-super-Mare.......... 116 115 a.	...	...	...	|	...	...	...	...	...	1233	...	...	...	...	...	...	...	1650	...	1750	...	1852
262	**Taunton**.......... 110 116 115 a.	...	...	...	0944	...	...	...	...	...	...	...	...	...	...	...	...	...	...	...	...	...	1930

	Ⓐ	Ⓐ	Ⓐ	Ⓐ	Ⓐ	①-④	⑤	Ⓐ	Ⓐ	Ⓐ	ⒶB	⑤	①-④	ⒶC	⑥	⑥	⑥D	⑥	⑥		⑥	⑥	⑥
London Paddington.... 130 131 134 d.	1700	1730	1800	1830	1900	1912	1912	1930	2000	2045	2145	2215	2215	2330	0630	0700	0730	0800	0830	...	0900	0930	1000
Reading.......... 130 131 134 d.	1727	1757	1828	1857	1927	|	1939	1959	2027	2112	2214	2244	2256	0010	0658	0728	0758	0830	0858	...	0928	0958	1028
Didcot Parkway.......... 131 134 d.	1742	1812	1842	1913	1942	|	1954	2013	2043	2126	2233	2301	2313	0029	0713	|	0813	|	0913	...	|	1014	|
Swindon.......... 132a 134 d.	1800	1830	1901	1931	2000	2005	2012	2032	2101	2144	2251	2319	2332	0047	0731	0756	0831	0858	0931	...	0956	1032	1056
Chippenham.......... 132a d.	1815	1845	1916	1946	2015	|	|	2047	2116	2159	2306	2334	2346	0102	0746	0811	0846	0913	0946	...	1011	1047	1111
Bath.......... a.	1829	1859	1930	1959	2029	n	k	2101	2130	2213	2320	2348	2359	0116	0759	0824	0859	0926	0959	...	1024	1100	1124
Bristol Temple Meads 110 116 115 a.	1846	1914	1944	2014	2043	2047	2059	2115	2144	2229	2334	0003	0014	0130	0814	0840	0914	0941	1014	...	1039	1115	1139
Weston-super-Mare.......... 116 115 a.	...	1952	...	2053	...	...	...	2151	...	...	0007s	...	...	...	...	...	|	...	...	...	1110t	...	...
Taunton.......... 110 116 115 a.	...	2031	...	...	...	...	...	...	...	...	0036	...	...	...	...	...	0948	...	...	...	...	...	...

	⑥	⑥	⑥	⑥	⑥	⑥	⑥	⑥	⑥	⑥	⑥	⑥	⑥A	⑥	⑥	⑥	⑥	⑥	⑥	⑥	⑥B	⑥	⑥	⑥
L**London** Paddington . 130 131 134 d.	1030	1100	1130	1200	1230	1300	1330	1400	1430	1500	1530	1600	1630	1700	1730	1800	1830	1900	1930	2000	2030	2132	2235	2330
Reading.......... 130 131 134 d.	1058	1128	1158	1229	1258	1328	1358	1428	1458	1528	1558	1628	1658	1728	1758	1828	1858	1928	1958	2028	2058	2159	2302	0005
Didcot Parkway.......... 131 134 d.	1113	|	1213	|	1313	|	1413	|	1513	|	1614	|	1713	|	1813	|	1913	|	2013	2043	2113	2214	2318	0022
Swindon.......... 132a 134 d.	1131	1156	1231	1257	1331	1358	1431	1456	1531	1556	1632	1656	1731	1756	1831	1856	1931	1956	2031	2101	2131	2232	2337	0041
Chippenham.......... 132a d.	1146	1211	1246	1312	1346	1413	1446	1511	1546	1611	1647	1711	1746	1811	1846	1911	1946	2011	2046	2116	2146	2247	2352	0056
Bath.......... a.	1159	1224	1259	1325	1359	1426	1500	1527	1559	1624	1700	1724	1759	1824	1859	1924	2000	2024	2059	2129	2159	2300	0005	0109
Bristol Temple Meads 110 116 115 a.	1214	1240	1314	1341	1414	1441	1514	1541	1614	1639	1715	1739	1814	1841	1914	1940	2014	2041	2114	2144	2214	2315	0020	0124
Weston-super-Mare.......... 116 115 a.	1240t	...	...	...	1435t	...	...	...	1635t	...	1740t	...	1836	...	1950	...	2036	2127	...	...	2247s	...	...	...
Taunton.......... 110 116 115 a.	...	...	...	...	...	...	...	...	...	...	...	...	1905	...	...	...	2101	2159	...	...	2316	...	...	...

	⑦D	⑦	⑦	⑦	⑦	⑦E	⑦	⑦	⑦	⑦	⑦	⑦	⑦	⑦	⑦	⑦	⑦B	⑦	⑦	⑦	⑦	⑦	⑦
London Paddington.... 130 131 134 d.	0805	0915	1015	1115	1215	1315	1415	1437	1515	1537	1615	1637	1715	1737	1815	1837	1915	1937	2015	2115	2203	2303	2337
Reading.......... 130 131 134 d.	0839	0939	1039	1139	1239	1339	1439	1502	1539	1602	1639	1702	1739	1802	1839	1902	1939	2002	2039	2139	2245	2348	0020
Didcot Parkway.......... 131 134 d.	0858	0954	1054	1154	1254	1354	1454	|	1554	|	1654	|	1754	|	1854	|	1954	|	2054	2154	2302	0032s	0035s
Swindon.......... 132a 134 d.	0917	1012	1113	1214	1313	1413	1513	1530	1613	1629	1713	1729	1813	1829	1913	1929	2013	2029	2113	2213	2320	0031s	0055s
Chippenham.......... 132a d.	0931	1027	1128	1228	1328	1428	1528	1546	1628	1645	1728	1745	1828	1845	1928	1945	2028	2045	2128	2228	2333	0065s	0110s
Bath.......... a.	0945	1040	1141	1241	1341	1441	1541	1600	1641	1659	1741	1759	1841	1859	1941	1959	2041	2059	2141	2241	2348	0020s	0124s
Bristol Temple Meads 110 116 115 a.	0959	1057	1156	1259	1357	1456	1557	1617	1659	1714	1757	1813	1857	1917	2000	2014	2058	2114	2157	2258	0004	0108	0139
Weston-super-Mare.......... 116 115 a.	|	1119p	1232	...	1432	|	...	...	1730	...	...	...	...	1957	...	...	2127	...	2235	...	...	...	...
Taunton.......... 110 116 115 a.	1033	...	...	...	...	1530	...	...	1803	...	...	...	...	...	...	...	2150	...	...	...	...	...	...

	Ⓐ	Ⓐ	Ⓐ	Ⓐ	Ⓐ	Ⓐ		ⒶB	ⒶT	Ⓐ	Ⓐ	Ⓐ	ⒶA	Ⓐ	Ⓐ	Ⓐ	Ⓐ	Ⓐ	Ⓐ	Ⓐ	Ⓐ	Ⓐ	Ⓐ
Taunton.......... 110 116 115 d.	...	...	...	...	...	...	...	0657	...	0712	...	...	0907	...	...	...	...	...	...	...	...	...	...
Weston-super-Mare.......... 116 115 d.	...	...	...	...	0620	0648	...	0726	...	0749	...	...	0929	...	...	...	...	...	...	1301	...	...	...
Bristol Temple Meads 110 116 115 d.	0445	0530	0600	0633	0700	0730	...	0800	0812	0830	0900	0930	1000	1030	1100	1130	1200	1230	1300	1330	1400	1430	1500
Bath.......... d.	m	0543	0613	0646	0713	0743	...	0813	0830	0843	0913	0943	1013	1043	1113	1143	1213	1243	1313	1343	1413	1443	1513
Chippenham.......... 132a d.	|	0556	0626	0659	0726	0756	...	0825	0845	0856	0926	0956	1026	1056	1125	1156	1226	1256	1326	1356	1426	1456	1526
Swindon.......... 132a 134 d.	0522	0612	0642	0715	0742	0812	...	0842	0902	0912	0942	1012	1042	1112	1141	1212	1242	1312	1342	1412	1442	1512	1542
Didcot Parkway.......... 131 134 a.	0539	0629	0659	|	0800	0829	...	0859	...	0929	|	1029	|	1129	|	1229	|	1329	|	1429	|	1529	|
Reading.......... 130 131 134 a.	0554	0643	0714	0746	0816	0845	...	0915	...	0945	1009	1043	1110	1143	1209	1243	1310	1344	1408	1444	1511	1544	1609
London Paddington.......... 130 131 134 a.	0622	0717	0744	0815	0844	0914	...	0943	...	1014	1039	1112	1139	1214	1237	1312	1337	1414	1437	1514	1538	1614	1640

	Ⓐ	Ⓐ	Ⓐ	Ⓐ		Ⓐ	Ⓐ	Ⓐ	Ⓐ	Ⓐ	ⒶD	Ⓐ	⑥	⑥Q	⑥	⑥	⑥		⑥	⑥	⑥B	⑥	⑥
Taunton.......... 110 116 115 d.	...	...	...	...	...	...	...	...	...	...	2115	2128	...	...	...	...	...	...	0654	...	0759	...	...
Weston-super-Mare.......... 116 115 d.	...	...	...	...	...	1710	...	1808	...	...	|	2158	...	...	...	0623	...	...	0724	...	0829	...	...
Bristol Temple Meads 110 116 115 d.	1530	1600	1630	1700	...	1731	1800	1830	1930	2030	2150	2235	0530	0600	0630	0700	0730	...	0800	0830	0900	0930	1000
Bath.......... d.	1543	1614	1643	1713	...	1744	1813	1843	1943	2043	2204	2248	0543	0613	0643	0713	0743	...	0813	0843	0913	0943	1013
Chippenham.......... 132a d.	1556	1627	1656	1726	...	1757	1826	1856	1956	2056	2217	2301	0556	0626	0656	0726	0756	...	0826	0856	0926	0956	1026
Swindon.......... 132a 134 d.	1612	1642	1712	1742	...	1813	1842	1912	2013	2112	2234	2317	0612	0642	0712	0742	0812	...	0842	0912	0942	1012	1042
Didcot Parkway.......... 131 134 a.	1629	|	1729	1759	...	1830	|	1929	2030	2129	2251	2335	0629	0659	0729	0759	0829	...	0900	0929	|	1029	|
Reading.......... 130 131 134 a.	1644	1710	1744	1814	...	1846	1910	1944	2044	2145	2307	2352	0643	0713	0743	0814	0844	...	0915	0943	1011	1045	1109
London Paddington.......... 130 131 134 a.	1712	1739	1814	1844	...	1916	1939	2014	2112	2213	2342	0031	0714	0741	0814	0842	0914	...	0943	1014	1039	1114	1140

	⑥	⑥	⑥A	⑥	⑥	⑥	⑥	⑥	⑥	⑥	⑥	⑥	⑥	⑥	⑥	⑥	⑥	⑥	⑥	⑥D	⑥	⑦	⑦
Taunton.......... 110 116 115 d.	...	...	1045	...	...	...	...	...	...	...	...	...	...	...	...	...	...	...	...	2114	2128	...	...
Weston-super-Mare.......... 116 115 d.	...	...	1107v	1130t	...	...	1300t	...	...	...	1500t	...	...	...	1700t	...	1800t	...	2010	|	2153	...	...
Bristol Temple Meads 110 116 115 d.	1030	1100	1130	1200	1230	1300	1330	1400	1430	1500	1530	1600	1630	1700	1730	1800	1830	1930	2035	2147	2230	0745	0814
Bath.......... d.	1043	1113	1143	1213	1243	1313	1343	1413	1443	1513	1543	1614	1643	1713	1743	1813	1843	1943	2049	2203	2245	0758	0828
Chippenham.......... 132a d.	1056	1126	1156	1226	1256	1326	1356	1426	1456	1526	1556	1626	1656	1726	1756	1826	1856	1956	2101	2216	2258	0811	0841
Swindon.......... 132a 134 d.	1112	1142	1212	1242	1312	1342	1412	1442	1512	1542	1612	1642	1712	1742	1812	1842	1912	2012	2117	2232	2314	0826	0857
Didcot Parkway.......... 131 134 a.	1129	|	1229	|	1329	|	1429	|	1529	|	1629	|	1729	|	1829	|	1929	2029	2134	2249	2332	0845	|
Reading.......... 130 131 134 a.	1144	1210	1246	1310	1343	1412	1443	1508	1543	1610	1646	1709	1743	1809	1845	1909	1943	2044	2149	2303	2348	0901	0928
London Paddington.......... 130 131 134 a.	1214	1238	1314	1338	1414	1441	1514	1541	1614	1638	1714	1738	1814	1837	1914	1937	2014	2114	2216	2343	0029	0930	0959

	⑦	⑦	⑦	⑦	⑦	⑦	⑦	⑦	⑦		⑦	⑦	⑦	⑦	⑦	⑦	⑦E	⑦A	⑦E	⑦	⑦	⑦	⑦	⑦E
Taunton.......... 110 116 115 d.	...	...	...	...	...	...	...	...	...	...	...	...	...	...	...	...	1639	1658	1741	...	...	1838	...	2131
Weston-super-Mare.......... 116 115 d.	0814	...	0946	...	...	...	1149p	...	...	...	1314	...	...	1513	...	...	1701	1731	|	...	...	1917	2026	|
Bristol Temple Meads 110 116 115 d.	0853	0953	1024	1053	1125	1153	1225	1253	1325	...	1353	1453	1525	1554	1625	1653	1725	1753	1825	1850	1925	1953	2100	2210
Bath.......... d.	0906	1006	1037	1106	1138	1206	1238	1306	1338	...	1406	1507	1538	1607	1638	1706	1738	1805	1838	1906	1938	2006	2116	2223
Chippenham.......... 132a d.	0919	1019	1049	1119	1150	1219	1250	1319	1350	...	1419	1520	1550	1619	1650	1718	1751	1817	1850	1919	1950	2019	2129	2235
Swindon.......... 132a 134 d.	0935	1035	1105	1135	1206	1234	1306	1335	1405	...	1435	1536	1606	1635	1706	1733	1807	1833	1906	1935	2006	2034	2145	2252
Didcot Parkway.......... 131 134 a.	0952	1051	|	1152	|	1252	|	1352	|	...	1452	1552	|	1652	|	1751	|	1852	|	1952	|	2051	2200	2310
Reading.......... 130 131 134 a.	1008	1108	1133	1208	1235	1308	1334	1408	1434	...	1508	1609	1634	1708	1734	1807	1836	1908	1934	2008	2036	2108	2216	2326
London Paddington.......... 130 131 134 a.	1037	1136	1201	1236	1301	1336	1402	1436	1502	...	1536	1636	1702	1736	1801	1842	1908	1936	2006	2036	2106	2137	2304	0009

A – To/from Paignton (Table 115).
B – To/from Exeter St Davids (Table 115).
C – To Cardiff Central (Table 134).
D – To/from Penzance (Tables 112/117).
E – To/from Plymouth (Table 115).
Q – To/from Swansea (Table 134).
T – From Gloucester (Table 138).
a – Arrives 1224.
k – Also calls Bristol Parkway a. 2035/d. 2037.
m – Also calls Bristol Parkway a. 0454/d. 0455.
n – Also calls Bristol Parkway a. 2035/d. 2037.
p – Until Sept. 8.
s – Calls to set down only.
t – Until Sept. 7.
v – From Sept. 14.

GW 2nd class SWINDON - WESTBURY 133

km		ⒶA	Ⓐ	Ⓐ	Ⓐ	Ⓐ	Ⓐ	Ⓐ	ⒶC	Ⓐ	⑥	⑥	⑥	⑥	⑥	⑥	⑥	⑥B	⑦	⑦	⑦D	⑦	⑦	⑦
	Gloucester 135.......... d.	0517	...	...	...	...	...	...	1754	...	...	...	...	...	...	...	...	2014	...	...	...	...	...	...
0	**Swindon**.......... 132 135 d.	0607	0853	1047	1249	1329	1519	1736	1848	2008	0836	1036	1236	1436	1522	1736	1936	2106	0922	1128	1338	1528	1752	1953
27	Chippenham.......... 132 d.	0624	0908	1102	1304	1344	1534	1751	1906	2023	0853	1053	1253	1453	1539	1753	1953	2123	0937	1143	1355	1543	1807	2008
37	Melksham.......... d.	0636	0918	1112	1314	1355	1545	1802	1915	2033	0902	1102	1302	1502	1548	1802	2002	2132	0947	1153	1404	1553	1817	2018
46	Trowbridge.......... 140 d.	0646	0934	1122	1323	1404	1554	1811	1924	2042	0912	1112	1312	1512	1559	1812	2012	2142	0956	1202	1414	1602	1828	2027
52	**Westbury**.......... 140 a.	0653	0941	1128	1331	1410	1600	1818	1931	2049	0920	1120	1320	1520	1607	1820	2020	2150	1002	1208	1420	1608	1834	2034

	ⒶB	Ⓐ	Ⓐ	Ⓐ	Ⓐ	Ⓐ	Ⓐ	Ⓐ	ⒶB	⑥	⑥	⑥	⑥	⑥	⑥	⑥	⑥	⑦	⑦	⑦D	⑦	⑦	⑦	⑦B
Westbury.......... 140 d.	0704	0733	0946	1147	1220	1424	1621	1832	1932	0733	0822	0930	1132	1332	1514	1632	1832	0820	1030	1237	1435	1652	1845	1941
Trowbridge.......... 140 d.	0710	0739	0952	1153	1226	1431	1627	1838	1938	0739	0829	0936	1138	1338	1521	1638	1838	0826	1035	1243	1440	1657	1851	1946
Melksham.......... d.	0720	0749	1002	1203	1236	1440	1637	1848	1947	0749	0838	0946	1148	1348	1531	1648	1848	0836	1046	1253	1450	1707	1900	1957
Chippenham.......... 132 a.	0730	0759	1011	1212	1245	1449	1646	1901	2000	0800	0848	1000	1200	1400	1540	1700	1900	0846	1055	1302	1500	1724	1910	2007
Swindon.......... 132 135 a.	0748	0815	1032	1232	1302	1507	1703	1921	2020	0820	0907	1020	1220	1420	1559	1722	1922	0904	1114	1320	1519	1741	1927	2024
Gloucester 135.......... a.	0852	...	...	...	...	...	...	...	2123	...	...	...	...	...	...	...	...	...	...	...	...	...	...	2126

A – To Southampton Central (Table 140).
B – From/to Cheltenham Spa (Table 135).
C – From Cheltenham Spa (Table 135) to Southampton Central (Table 140).
D – To/from Weymouth (Table 140).

134 LONDON - BRISTOL PARKWAY - CARDIFF - SWANSEA

Most trains convey 🍸 GW

km		Ⓐa	Ⓐ	Ⓐ	Ⓐ	Ⓐ	Ⓐ	Ⓐ	Ⓐ	Ⓐ	Ⓐ✕	Ⓐ	Ⓐ	Ⓐ	Ⓐ	Ⓐ	Ⓐ	Ⓐ	Ⓐ	Ⓐ	Ⓐ	Ⓐ	Ⓐ
0	**London** Paddington. 130 131 132 d.	0502c	0645	0715	0745	0815	0845	0915	0945	1015	1045	1115	1145	1215	1245	1315	1345	1415	1445	1515	1545	1615	1645
58	Reading 130 131 132 d.	0542	0712	0742	0812	0842	0912	0942	1012	1042	1112	1142	1212	1242	1312	1342	1412	1442	1512	1542	1612	1642	1712
85	Didcot Parkway 131 132 d.	0557	|	0756	|	0856	|	0956	|	1056	|	1156	|	1256	|	1356	|	1456	|	1556	|	1656	|
124	Swindon 132 d.	0616	0739	0814	0840	0914	0939	1014	1040	1114	1139	1214	1240	1314	1339	1414	1441	1514	1543	1614	1640	1714	1740
180	**Bristol** Parkway d.	0723t	0810f	0841	0909	0945f	1009f	1041	1109	1141	1209f	1241	1309	1344	1409	1441	1509	1541	1610	1641	1710	1741	1810f
215	Newport 117 118 149 a.	0748	0831	0904	0930	1006	1032	1104	1130	1203	1231	1303	1330	1405	1431	1507	1530	1603	1631	1706	1732	1802	1831
234	**Cardiff** Central 117 118 136 149 a.	0802	0850	0921	0949	1021	1048	1123	1146	1221	1247	1322	1346	1421	1447	1523	1544	1622	1645	1721	1747	1821	1849
266	Bridgend 136 a.	0824	0914	...	1011	...	1110	...	1208	...	1309	...	1409	...	1509	...	1607	...	1708	...	1810	1849	1912
286	Port Talbot 136 a.	0836	0926	...	1023	...	1122	...	1220	...	1321	...	1423	...	1521	...	1619	...	1720	...	1822	1901	1924
295	Neath 136 a.	0845	0934	...	1032	...	1130	...	1228	...	1330	...	1430	...	1529	...	1628	...	1729	...	1831	1910	1932
307	**Swansea** 136 a.	0858	0948	...	1045	...	1144	...	1242	...	1343	...	1444	...	1543	...	1641	...	1742	...	1844	1923	1946

	ⒶG	Ⓐ	Ⓐ	Ⓐ	①-④	⑤	⑤	①-④	⑤	①-④	⑤	①-④	Ⓐ
London Paddington 130 131 132 d.	1715	1745	1814	1845	1915	1915	2015	2015	2115	2115	2245	2245	2330
Reading 130 131 132 d.	1742	1812	1842	1912	1942	1948	2042	2042	2143	2143	2313	2320	0010
Didcot Parkway 131 132 d.	1756	|	1856	|	1957	|	2056	2056	2203	2203	2330	2343	0029
Swindon 132 d.	1814	1845	1914	1941	2015	2018	2114	2114	2221	2221	2348	0001	0047
Bristol Parkway d.	1841	1912	1942	2010f	2042	2045	2141	2141	2248	2248	0015	0028	0137h
Newport 117 118 149 a.	1910	1933	2006	2032	2103	2106	2204	2204	2317	2316	0036	0055	0211s
Cardiff Central 117 118 136 149 a.	1925	1948	2020	2051	2117	2121	2218	2224	2339	2341	0051	0116	0232
Bridgend 136 a.	1949	2011	2046	2115	2145	2144	2241	2249	0003	0003	0116	0141	...
Port Talbot 136 a.	2001	2024	2058	2127	2157	2156	2253	2302	0016	0016	0128	0154	...
Neath 136 a.	2010	2032	2107	2135	2206	2204	2302	2310	0025	0025	0137	0203	...
Swansea 136 a.	2023	2046	2120	2150	2220	2218	2315	2324	0039	0039	0150	0217	...

⑥	⑥F	⑥	⑥P	⑥	⑥	⑥	⑥	⑥	⑥	⑥
London Paddington 130 131 132 d.	...	0745	0845	0945	1045	1145	1245	1345	1445	1545
Reading 130 131 132 d.	...	0812	0912	1012	1112	1212	1312	1412	1512	1612
Didcot Parkway 131 132 d.	...	|	|	|	|	|	|	|	|	|
Swindon 132 d.	...	0841	0940	1041	1140	1241	1340	1441	1540	1640
Bristol Parkway d.	0709	0909f	1009f	1109f	1209f	1309f	1409f	1509f	1609f	1709f
Newport 117 118 149 a.	0731	0929	1030	1130	1230	1330	1430	1530	1630	1731
Cardiff Central 117 118 136 149 a.	0747	0946	1045	1145	1245	1345	1445	1545	1644	1746
Bridgend 136 a.	0809	1009	1107	1209	1309	1409	1509	1609	1709	1809
Port Talbot 136 a.	0822	1021	1119	1221	1321	1421	1521	1621	1721	1821
Neath 136 a.	0830	1029	1127	1229	1329	1429	1529	1629	1729	1829
Swansea 136 a.	0844	1043	1141	1243	1343	1443	1543	1643	1743	1846

	⑥	⑥G	⑥	⑥d	⑥	⑥	⑥
London Paddington 130 131 132 d.	1645	1745	1845	1915	1945	2045	2200
Reading 130 131 132 d.	1712	1812	1912	1942	2012	2112	2229
Didcot Parkway 131 132 d.	|	|	|	1957	|	|	2244
Swindon 132 d.	1741	1840	1941	2016	2041	2140	2305
Bristol Parkway d.	1809f	1909f	2009f	2043f	2109f	2212g	2334f
Newport 117 118 149 a.	1830	1931	2030	2104	2130	2244	0001
Cardiff Central 117 118 136 149 a.	1847	1945	2044	2118	2148	2305	0023
Bridgend 136 a.	1909	2009	2109	2145	2210	2328	...
Port Talbot 136 a.	1921	2021	2121	2158	2222	2340	...
Neath 136 a.	1929	2029	2129	2205	2230	2348	...
Swansea 136 a.	1943	2042	2143	2220	2244	0003	...

⑦	⑦		⑦G	⑦	⑦G	⑦	⑦G	⑦	⑦	⑦	⑦	⑦	⑦	⑦	⑦	⑦
London Paddington 130 131 132 d.	0845	...	0945	1045	1145	1245	1345	1445	1545	1645	1745	1845	1912	1945	2045	2133
Reading 130 131 132 d.	0914	...	1012	1111	1211	1312	1410	1512	1610	1712	1811	1912	1940	2012	2115	2209
Didcot Parkway 131 132 d.	0932	...	|	1125	1226	1325	1427	1527	1624	1726	1827	1926	|	2026	2129	2225
Swindon 132 d.	0950	...	1039	1144	1244	1342	1445	1545	1644f	1745	1847	1945	2006	2044	2147	2243
Bristol Parkway d.	1016	...	1104	1211	1310	1409	1511	1611	1710	1811	1913	2011	2033	2111	2214	2310
Newport 117 118 149 a.	1035	...	1124	1229	1332	1432	1531	1635	1730	1831	1935	2031	2050	2130	2236	2334
Cardiff Central 117 118 136 149 a.	1053	...	1142	1246	1350	1447	1548	1653	1747	1847	1949	2047	2109	2151	2252	2350
Bridgend 136 a.	1122	...	1205	1313	1417	1515	1619	1723	1816	1915	2015	2115	2135	2218	2319	0018
Port Talbot 136 a.	1135	...	1218	1325	1431	1527	1631	1734	1830	1929	2029	2129	2148	2231	2333	0031
Neath 136 a.	1144	...	1225	1332	1439	1536	1639	1743	1838	1938	2038	2138	2157	2239	2341	0038
Swansea 136 a.	1157	...	1239	1348	1454	1548	1654	1757	1851	1951	2053	2151	2210	2252	2355	0052

Ⓐ	ⒶS	Ⓐ	Ⓐ	Ⓐ	Ⓐ✕	Ⓐ	Ⓐ	Ⓐ	Ⓐ	ⒶG	Ⓐ	Ⓐ	Ⓐ	Ⓐ	Ⓐ	Ⓐ		Ⓐ	Ⓐ	Ⓐ	Ⓐ	Ⓐ	Ⓐ
Swansea 136 d.	...	0354	0458	0529	0559	0629	0659	0729	0759	0829	...	0929	...	1029	...	1129	...	...	1229	...	1329	...	1429
Neath 136 d.	...	0406	0510	0541	0611	0641	0711	0741	0811	0841	...	0941	...	1041	...	1141	...	...	1241	...	1341	...	1441
Port Talbot 136 d.	...	0414	0518	0549	0619	0649	0719	0749	0819	0849	...	0949	...	1049	...	1149	...	...	1249	...	1349	...	1449
Bridgend 136 d.	...	0427	0531	0602	0632	0702	0732	0802	0832	0902	...	1002	...	1102	...	1202	...	...	1302	...	1402	...	1502
Cardiff Central 117 118 136 149 d.	...	0515	0555	0626	0656	0726	0756	0826	0856	0926	0956	1026	1056	1126	1156	1226	...	1256	1326	1356	1426	1456	1526
Newport 117 118 149 d.	...	0533	0609	0640	0710	0740	0810	0840	0910	0940	1010	1040	1110	1140	1210	1240	...	1310	1340	1410	1440	1510	1540
Bristol Parkway d.	0455	0603	0631	0702	0733	0803	0832	0903	0933	1003	1033	1103	1132	1203	1233	1303	...	1333	1403	1433	1503	1533	1603
Swindon 132 d.	0522	0630	0658	0729	0800	0830	0859	0930	1000	1030	1100	1130	1159	1230	1300	1330	...	1400	1430	1500	1530	1600	1630
Didcot Parkway 131 132 a.	0539	0647	|	0746	|	|	|	|	1017	1050	1117	|	1216	1247	1317	|	...	1417	1447	1517	|	1617	1647
Reading 130 131 132 a.	0554	0702	0725	0802	|	0857	0925	1000	1032	1105	1132	1200	1231	1302	1332	1357	...	1432	1502	1532	1558	1632	1702
London Paddington 130 131 132 a.	0622	0731	0759	0832	0856	0925	0955	1037	1100	1137	1200	1230	1301	1332	1407	1430	...	1502	1530	1602	1632	1702	1730

	Ⓐ	Ⓐ	Ⓐ	Ⓐ	Ⓐ	Ⓐ	Ⓐ	Ⓐ	①-④	⑤
Swansea 136 d.	...	1529	...	1629	...	1729	1829	1929	2029	2029
Neath 136 d.	...	1541	...	1641	...	1741	1841	1941	2041	2041
Port Talbot 136 d.	...	1549	...	1649	...	1749	1849	1949	2049	2049
Bridgend 136 d.	...	1602	...	1702	...	1802	1902	2002	2102	2102
Cardiff Central 117 118 136 149 d.	1556	1626	1656	1726	1756	1826	1925	2026	2126	2126
Newport 117 118 149 d.	1610	1640	1710	1740	1810	1840	1939	2040	2140	2140
Bristol Parkway d.	1633	1703	1733	1803	1833	1903	2003	2103	2203	2203
Swindon 132 d.	1700	1730	1800	1830	1900	1930	2030	2135r	2230	2230
Didcot Parkway 131 132 a.	1717	|	1818	1847	1917	|	2047	2152	|	|
Reading 130 131 132 a.	1734	1757	1834	1903	1932	1958	2102	2209	2302	2302
London Paddington 130 131 132 a.	1804	1830	1909	1936	2005	2032	2131	2251b	2340	2337

⑥	⑥	⑥	⑥	⑥	⑥	⑥	⑥	⑥d	⑥	⑥	⑥G	⑥	⑥P
Swansea 136 d.	0359	0459	0529	0559	0629	0659	0729	0759	0829	0929	1029	1129	1229
Neath 136 d.	0411	0511	0541	0611	0641	0711	0741	0811	0841	0941	1041	1141	1241
Port Talbot 136 d.	0419	0519	0549	0619	0649	0719	0749	0819	0849	0949	1049	1149	1249
Bridgend 136 d.	0431	0532	0602	0632	0702	0732	0802	0832	0902	1002	1102	1202	1302
Cardiff Central 117 118 136 149 d.	0455	0556	0626	0656	0726	0756	0826	0855	0926	1026	1126	1226	1326
Newport 117 118 149 d.	0509	0610	0640	0710	0740	0810	0840	0910	0940	1040	1140	1240	1340
Bristol Parkway d.	0542j	0634f	0704f	0733	0804f	0833	0904f	0933	1004f	1104f	1204f	1304f	1404f
Swindon 132 d.	0642	0701	0731	0800	0830	0900	0931	1000	1031	1131	1231	1331	1431
Didcot Parkway 131 132 a.	0659	|	|	0816	|	0917	|	1017	|	|	|	|	|
Reading 130 131 132 a.	0713	0728	0758	0832	0858	0932	0957	1032	1100	1158	1258	1357	1459
London Paddington 130 131 132 a.	0741	0759	0830	0859	0930	1001	1029	1101	1131	1229	1331	1429	1530

	⑥	⑥	⑥		⑥	⑥	⑥	⑥
Swansea 136 d.	1329	1429	1529	...	1629	1729	1829	1929
Neath 136 d.	1341	1441	1541	...	1641	1741	1841	1941
Port Talbot 136 d.	1349	1449	1549	...	1649	1749	1849	1949
Bridgend 136 d.	1402	1502	1602	...	1702	1802	1902	2002
Cardiff Central 117 118 136 149 d.	1426	1526	1626	...	1726	1826	1926	2026
Newport 117 118 149 d.	1440	1540	1640	...	1740	1840	1940	2040
Bristol Parkway d.	1504	1604f	1704f	...	1804f	1903	2004f	2103
Swindon 132 d.	1531	1631	1731	...	1831	1929	2031	2130
Didcot Parkway 131 132 a.	|	|	|	...	|	|	|	2147
Reading 130 131 132 a.	1558	1658	1758	...	1858	1958	2057	2202
London Paddington 130 131 132 a.	1629	1729	1831	...	1929	2030	2129	2238

⑦	⑦	⑦		⑦	⑦	⑦	⑦	⑦	⑦	⑦	⑦G	⑦	⑦G	⑦	⑦G
Swansea 136 d.	...	0753	...	0924	1024	1124	1224	1324	1424	1524	1551	1651	1751	1851	1955
Neath 136 d.	...	0805	...	0936	1036	1136	1236	1336	1436	1536	1603	1703	1803	1903	2007
Port Talbot 136 d.	...	0812	...	0943	1043	1143	1243	1343	1443	1543	1610	1710	1810	1910	2014
Bridgend 136 d.	...	0826	...	0956	1056	1156	1256	1356	1456	1556	1623	1723	1823	1923	2028
Cardiff Central 117 118 136 149 d.	0805	0849	...	1020	1120	1220	1320	1420	1520	1620	1650	1750	1850	1950	2052
Newport 117 118 149 d.	0823	0908	...	1033	1133	1233	1335	1434	1533	1632	1703	1803	1903	2003	2109
Bristol Parkway d.	0852	0937	...	1101	1201	1301	1401	1501	1601	1701	1730	1830	1930	2030	2134
Swindon 132 d.	0925k	1004	...	1129	1229	1329	1429	1529	1629	1729	1759	1859	1959	2059	2200
Didcot Parkway 131 132 a.	|	|	...	|	|	1346	1446	1546	1646	1746	1816	1916	2016	|	|
Reading 130 131 132 a.	0953	1032	...	1157	1257	1401	1502	1602	1701	1801	1832	1932	2032	2130	2234
London Paddington 130 131 132 a.	1022	1059	...	1225	1324	1429	1529	1629	1729	1829	1900	2000	2059	2209	2324

F – From Bristol Temple Meads dep. 0645.
G – To/from Carmarthen (Table **136**).
P – Until Sept. 7 to/from Pembroke Dock (Table **136**).
S – From Bristol Temple Meads (Table **132**).

a – Also calls at Bristol Temple Meads (a.0658/d. 0705).
b – Arrives 2239 on ⑤.
c – Departs 0507 on ①.
d – From Sept. 14.
e – Also calls at Bristol Temple Meads (a. 0553/d. 0600).
f – Arrives 4 – 5 minutes earlier.
g – Arrives 2204.
h – Bristol Temple Meads (a. 0130).
j – Arrives 0536.
k – Arrives 0917.
r – Arrives 2128.
s – Calls to set down only.
t – Arrives 0717.

134a WELSH LONG DISTANCE BUS SERVICES

Traws Cymru operate several long distance bus services through Wales linking a number of main towns not served by rail services. The principal routes are shown below with the number of through journeys each way each day. For full timings and fares: ✆ +44 (0) 300 200 22 33; www.trawscymru.info

Service T1: Aberystwyth - Aberaeron - Lampeter/Llanbedr - Carmarthen and v.v.: on ⚒ 13 journeys; ⑦ 4 journeys.
Service T2: Aberystwyth - Machynlleth - Dolgellau - Minfford (for Portmeirion) - Porthmadog - Caernarfon - Bangor and v.v.: on ⚒ 8 journeys; ⑦ 3 journeys.
Service T3: Wrexham - Ruabon - Llangollen 🚂 - Corwen 🚂 - Bala 🚂 - Dolgellau - Barmouth and v.v.: on ⚒ 9 journeys; ⑦ 2 journeys.
Service T4: Newtown - Llandrindod Wells - Builth Wells - Brecon - Merthyr Tydfil * - Cardiff * and v.v.: on ⚒ 5 journeys; ⑦ 3 journeys.
Service T5: Aberystwyth - Aberaeron - New Quay - Cardigan - Fishguard - Haverfordwest and v.v.: on ⚒ 9 journeys; ⑦ 2 journeys until Sept. 28.
Service T6: Brecon - Ystradgynlais - Neath - Swansea and v.v.: on ⚒ 9 journeys; ⑦ 5 journeys.
Other short workings also operate on most services.

* – Frequent local trains also operate Merthyr Tydfil - Cardiff and v.v.
🚂 – Heritage and Tourist Railways:
Llangollen Railway: Llangollen - Corwen and v.v. (16km): ✆ +44 (0) 1978 860 979; www.llangollen-railway.co.uk
Bala Lake Railway: (narrow gauge) Bala - Llanuwchllyn and v.v. (7km): ✆ +44 (0) 1678 540 666; www.bala-lake-railway.co.uk

GW — Most London trains convey 🍷 — LONDON - CHELTENHAM — 135

km			Ⓐ	Ⓐ2	Ⓐ	Ⓐ2	Ⓐ2	Ⓐ2	Ⓐ	Ⓐ2	Ⓐ	Ⓐ2	Ⓐ	Ⓐ	Ⓐ	Ⓐ	Ⓐ2	Ⓐ	Ⓐ2	Ⓐ2		⑥2	⑥	⑥2	⑥
0	**London** Paddington 132 134 d.	Ⓐ	...	A	0736	...	0936	...	1136	...	1336	...	1536	1636	1742	1837	A	1948	...	...	⑥	...	0815	...	1015
58	Reading 132 134 d.		...	...	0803	...	1003	...	1203	...	1403	...	1603	1703	|	|	...	2020	...	...		...	0842	...	1042
85	Didcot Parkway 132 134 d.		...	...	0817	...	1017	...	1217	...	1418	...	1617	1717	1820	1917	...	2035	...	...		...	0857	...	1057
124	**Swindon** 132 134 d.		0640	0750	0836	0936	1036	1136	1236	1336	1437	1536	1636	1752t	1841	1937	2025	2055	2154	2336		0716	0916	1014	1116
164	Stroud d.		0709	0820	0907	1005	1107	1205	1307	1405	1508	1605	1707	1822	1910	2006	2053	2124	2223	0005		0745	0945	1043	1145
183	Gloucester a.		0731	0848	0930	1028	1129	1230	1329	1429	1529	1627	1730	1847	1931	2027	2115	2145	2246	0028		0805	1006	1104	1206
194	**Cheltenham** Spa 138 a.		0747	0905	0952	1046	1152	1246	1352	1445	1552	1645	1752	1902	1951	2043	2133	2200	2303	0043r		0820	1022	1120	1222
223	**Worcester** Shrub Hill 138 a.		...	...	...	...	...	...	...	...	...	...	...	...	...	...	...	2222	...	...		...	...	...	...

	⑥2	⑥	⑥2	⑥	⑥2	⑥	⑥2	⑥	⑥2	⑥	⑥2		⑦	⑦2	⑦	⑦		⑦2	⑦	⑦	⑦2	⑦	⑦2	⑦	⑦2
London Paddington 132 134 d.	...	1215	...	1415	...	1615	...	1815	...	2015	...	⑦	0837	...	1037	1237	...	...	1442	1642	...	1842	A	2037	...
Reading 132 134 d.	...	1242	...	1442	...	1642	...	1842	...	2042	...		0904	...	1104	1304	...	...	1508	1708	...	1908	...	2102	...
Didcot Parkway 132 134 d.	...	1257	...	1457	...	1656	...	1856	...	2057	...		|	...	|	|	...	...	|	|	...	|	...	|	...
Swindon 132 134 d.	1214	1316	1414	1516	1614	1716	1814	1916	2000	2118	2241		0939	1044	1135	1334	...	1425	1537	1739	1842	1936	2033	2133	2257
Stroud d.	1243	1345	1443	1545	1643	1745	1843	1945	2029	2146	2310		1007	1113	1205	1400	...	1455	1605	1808	1910	2006	2101	2201	2326
Gloucester a.	1304	1406	1503	1606	1704	1806	1903	2006	2050	2207	2331		1029	1133	1227	1431	...	1520	1629	1830	1934	2028	2120	2222	2346
Cheltenham Spa 138 a.	1320	1422	1520	1622	1720	1822	1920	2022	2104	2222	...		1044	1145	1245	1446	...	1533	1647	1847	...	2045	2134	2238	0007
Worcester Shrub Hill 138 a.	...	...	...	...	...	...	...	...	...	...	...		...	...	...	...	...	...	...	...	...	...	...	...	...

		Ⓐ2	Ⓐ	Ⓐ		Ⓐ		Ⓐ	Ⓐ	Ⓐ	Ⓐ2	Ⓐ	Ⓐ2	Ⓐ		Ⓐ2	Ⓐ	Ⓐ2	Ⓐ	Ⓐ2	Ⓐ2	Ⓐ2		⑥2	⑥
Worcester Shrub Hill 138 d.	Ⓐ	B	0528	...	...	0708	...	...	...	...	...	...	...	...	...	...	...	B	...	...	...	...	⑥	...	...
Cheltenham Spa 138 d.		...	0554	0630	...	0731	...	0832	0919	1036	1120	1236	1320	1436	...	1520	1620	1741	1833	2004	2102	2201		0530	0732
Gloucester d.		0517	0610	0646	...	0747	...	0848	0933	1051	1134	1252	1333	1452	...	1533	1643	1754	1850	2017	2121	2213		0543	0748
Stroud d.		0535	0631	0706	...	0807	...	0908	0955	1113	1155	1314	1352	1514	...	1552	1704	1812	1911	2030	2138	2232		0601	0807
Swindon 132 134 a.		0605	0700	0735	...	0836	...	0941v	1024	1142	1223	1343	1422	1543	...	1622	1733	1844	1939	2105	2209	2303		0632	0836
Didcot Parkway 132 134 a.		...	0719	0754	...	0854	...	1003	1046	1202	...	1402	...	1603	...	...	|	...	1958	...	...	...		...	0854
Reading 132 134 a.		...	0734	0812	...	0909	...	1017	1101	1216	...	1417	...	1616	...	...	1803	...	2014	...	...	...		...	0909
London Paddington 132 134 a.		...	0807	0842	...	0940	...	1045	1133	1244	...	1446	...	1644	...	...	1838	...	2043	...	...	...		...	0939

	⑥	⑥2	⑥	⑥2	⑥	⑥2	⑥	⑥2		⑥	⑥2	⑥	⑥2	⑥2		⑦2	⑦	⑦2	⑦	⑦	⑦2	⑦		⑦	⑦2
Worcester Shrub Hill 138 d.	0838	...	...	...	...	...	...	...	...	...	...	...	A	...	⑦	...	...	...	...	...	...	...	...	...	...
Cheltenham Spa 138 d.	0900	1001	1100	1201	1300	1401	1500	1601	...	1700	1801	1900	2002	2120		0924	1118	1246	1346	1546	1646	1746	...	1946	2147
Gloucester d.	0916	1014	1116	1214	1316	1414	1516	1614	...	1716	1814	1916	2014	2135		0937	1134	1304	1402	1600	1659	1802	...	2001	2159
Stroud d.	0936	1032	1135	1232	1336	1432	1535	1632	...	1736	1832	1936	2032	2153		0955	1154	1322	1422	1620	1716	1822	...	2022	2217
Swindon 132 134 a.	1004	1104	1204	1304	1404	1504	1604	1704	...	1804	1904	2004	2103	2225		1024	1222	1351	1451	1649	1749	1852	...	2050	2247
Didcot Parkway 132 134 a.	1023	...	1222	...	1423	...	1622	...	...	1823	...	2023	...	...		...	|	...	|	|	...	|	...	|	...
Reading 132 134 a.	1037	...	1237	...	1437	...	1637	...	...	1837	...	2038	...	...		...	1251	...	1519	1720	...	1919	...	2120	...
London Paddington 132 134 a.	1107	...	1307	...	1506	...	1707	...	...	1906	...	2106	...	...		...	1321	...	1553	1753	...	1953	...	2154	...

A – To/from Westbury (Table **132a**). B – To Southampton Central (Tables **132a** and **140**). r – On ②–⑤ mornings arrives 0040. t – Arrives 1735. v – Departs 0946.

AW — 2nd class — CARDIFF - SWANSEA - SOUTH WEST WALES — 136

km			②–⑤	Ⓐ	Ⓐ	Ⓐ	Ⓐ	Ⓐ	Ⓐ	Ⓐ 🍷	Ⓐ	Ⓐ	Ⓐ	Ⓐ 🍷E	Ⓐ 🍷E	Ⓐ 🍷	Ⓐ	Ⓐ 🍷	Ⓐ 🍷	Ⓐ	Ⓐ 🍷	Ⓐ 🍷	Ⓐ	Ⓐ	Ⓐ 🍷	Ⓐ 🍷	Ⓐ	Ⓐ 🍷C
	Manchester P **149** d.	Ⓐ	...	...	...	...	...	...	...	...	...	...	...	...	...	0629	...	0730	...	...	0831	0931	...	...	1031	1131	...	...
0	**Cardiff** Central 134 d.		...	...	...	...	...	...	...	0535	0637	...	0716	0750	0904	1004	...	1041	...	1112	1141	1242	...	1313	1343	1443	...	1513
32	Bridgend 134 d.		...	...	...	...	...	...	...	0607	0703	...	0736	0809	0924	1023	...	1100	...	1132	1159	1301	...	1334	1404	1502	...	1533
52	Port Talbot 134 d.		...	...	...	...	...	...	...	0622	0720	...	0756	0825	0937	1036	...	1112	...	1148	1211	1314	...	1350	1418	1515	...	1549
61	Neath 134 d.		...	...	...	...	...	...	...	0632	0732	...	0804	0835	0944	1043	...	1119	...	1159	1218	1321	...	1401	1425	1522	...	1559
73	**Swansea** 134 a.		...	...	...	...	...	...	...	0648	0748	...	0825	0852	0956	1055	...	1133	...	1218	1232	1334	...	1420	1438	1535	...	1615
73	**Swansea** 146 d.		0013	...	...	...	...	...	0545	0651	0754	0814	...	0906	1002	1104	1100	1138	1200	1222	1240	1337	1400	*1435*	1440	1539	1600	1620
91	Llanelli 146 d.		0030	...	...	...	...	...	0604	0709	0812	0831	...	0925	1021	1123	1117	1154	1219	1240	1259	1356	1416	*1451*	1459	1558	1618	1638
124	**Carmarthen** a.		0105	...	...	...	...	...	0638	0741	0843	|	...	0955	1051	1149	|	1225	1248	...	1324	1430	1447	...	1525	1630	1647	...
124	**Carmarthen** d.		...	0450	0530	0550	0558	...	0639	0746	0844	|	...	0959	*1056*	1153	|	...	1251	...	1330	...	1451	...	1529	...	1651	...
147	Whitland d.		...	0504	0547	0605	0613	...	0656	0800	0902	0910	...	1014	*1111*	1206	1151	...	1306	...	1345	...	1506	...	1544	...	1706	...
172	Tenby a.		...	|	0614f	|	|	...	0724f	|	0930g	|	...	|	*1139*f	|	|	...	1334f	...	|	...	1534f	...	|	...	1734f	...
191	**Pembroke Dock** a.		...	|	0654	|	|	...	0807	|	1018	|	...	|	*1223*	|	|	...	1419	...	|	...	1619	...	|	...	1819	...
166	Clarbeston Road d.		...	0518x	...	0620x	0627x	0720	...	0814x	...	0925x	...	1028x	...	1220x	1204x	...	...	...	1359x	...	...	...	1558x	...	...	...
174	Haverfordwest d.		...	0529	...	|	0635	|	...	0823	...	|	...	1036	...	1228	|	...	...	...	1408	...	...	...	1607	...	...	...
189	**Milford Haven** a.		...	0552	...	|	0658	|	...	0843	...	|	...	1057	...	1253	|	...	...	...	1431	...	...	...	1625	...	...	...
191	**Fishguard** Hbr a.		...	...	...	0644	...	0744	...	...	...	0950	...	...	...	...	1230	...	...	...	...	...	...	...	...	...	...	...

	Ⓐ 🍷	Ⓐ 🍷B	Ⓐ 🍷	Ⓐ 🍷	Ⓐ	Ⓐ 🍷	Ⓐ	Ⓐ A	Ⓐ 🍷	Ⓐ	①–④	⑤	Ⓐ		⑥	⑥	⑥	⑥	⑥	⑥	⑥ 🍷	⑥ 🍷a	⑥ a	⑥ b	⑥ b	⑥	⑥	⑥ 🍷E
Manchester P **149** d.	1231	...	1331	1431	...	1531	...	...	1631	...	1829	1831	1931	⑥	...	...	...	...	...	...	...	...	...	...	...	...	...	...
Cardiff Central 134 d.	1542	1604	1704	1742	1806	1904	...	1930	1946	2107	2218	2210	2315		...	...	...	...	...	...	0533	...	0642	0642	0642	...	0714	0758
Bridgend 134 d.	1601	1624	1727	1801	1830	1923	...	1950	2005	2127	2245	2237	2345		...	...	...	...	...	...	0603	...	0703	0703	0703	...	0738	0817
Port Talbot 134 d.	1614	1639	1742	1817	1847	1938	...	2003	2018	2145	2258	2249	0001		...	...	...	...	...	...	0620	...	0719	0719	0719	...	0754	0830
Neath 134 d.	1621	1646	1752	1825	1858	1948	...	2011	2025	2152	|	2256	0013		...	...	...	...	...	...	0631	...	0730	0730	0730	...	0805	0837
Swansea 134 a.	1633	1700	1807	1838	1914	2004	...	2023	2040	2205	|	2309	0028		...	...	...	...	...	...	0647	...	0746	0746	0746	...	0822	0851
Swansea 146 d.	1640	1705	1814	1842	*1934*	2011	...	2034	2048	2227	|	2313	0045		*0013*	...	...	...	...	0545	0653	0723	0752	0752	0752	0815	▬	0905
Llanelli 146 d.	1659	1724	1833	1901	*1954*	2030	...	2051	2107	2245	2329	2332	0102s		*0030*	...	...	...	...	0604	0711	0740	0810	0810	0810	0836	⑥	0924
Carmarthen a.	1728	1755	1902	1928	*2029*	2058	...	2120	2137	2318	2359	0007	0135		*0105*	...	...	...	...	0638	0743	0808	0842	0842	0842	0908	a	0953
Carmarthen d.	1731	1759	1905	1930	...	*2103*	2110	...	2141	2319	...	...	0139		0450	0530	0550	0558	...	0639	0746	0816	0843	0843	0843	...	0940	0957
Whitland d.	1746	1814	1921	1946	...	*2118*	2125	...	2156	2334	...	...	0155		0503	0546	0606	0613	...	0656	0800	0835	0859	0902r	0907r	...	0954	1014
Tenby a.	|	|	1954f	|	...	|	2152	...	|	|	...	...	|		|	0614f	|	|	...	0724f	|	0906	|	0930g	|	...	1026	|
Pembroke Dock a.	|	|	*2036*	|	...	|	2226	...	|	|	...	...	|		|	0659	|	|	...	0807	|	0944	|	1017	|	...	...	|
Clarbeston Road d.	1800x	1828x	...	2000x	...	*2133*x	...	...	2210x	2349x	...	...	0208x		0518x	...	0621x	0627x	0720	...	0815x	...	0917x	...	0922x	...	...	1028x
Haverfordwest d.	1808	|	...	2009	...	|	...	...	2223	2356	...	...	|		0530	...	|	0635	|	...	0823	...	|	...	|	...	...	1036
Milford Haven a.	1831	|	...	2032	...	|	...	...	2246	0021	...	...	|		0553	...	|	0658	|	...	0848	...	|	...	|	...	...	1058
Fishguard Hbr a.	...	1856	...	...	...	*2200*	...	...	...	...	...	...	0237		...	...	0646	...	0744	...	...	...	0943	...	0947	...	...	...

	⑥ 🍷E	⑥	⑥ 🍷	⑥ 🍷	⑥ Aa	⑥ b	⑥ 🍷	⑥	⑥ 🍷b	⑥ 🍷a	⑥ a	⑥ b	⑥ 🍷	⑥	⑥ 🍷	⑥ 🍷	⑥ b	⑥ a	⑥	⑥ 🍷	⑥🍷 Ba	⑥🍷 Bb	⑥ 🍷b	⑥ 🍷a	⑥	⑥ 🍷	⑥ 🍷	⑥
Manchester P **149** d.	...	...	0630	...	...	...	0730	...	0830	0830	...	...	0931	...	1031	1131	...	...	...	1231	...	...	1331	1331	...	1431	1531	...
Cardiff Central 134 d.	0904	0914	1000	...	1048	...	1106	1114	1204	1204	...	...	1304	1310	1404	1504	...	...	1514	1540	1604	1604	1704	1704	1738	1804	1904	...
Bridgend 134 d.	0923	0934	1019	...	1108	...	1125	1134	1223	1223	...	...	1323	1332	1423	1523	...	...	1534	1559	1624	1624	1725	1725	1758	1825	1924	...
Port Talbot 134 d.	0936	0952	1031	...	1121	...	1138	1150	1236	1236	...	...	1336	1348	1436	1536	...	...	1550	1615	1640	1640	1741	1740	1814	1841	1939	...
Neath 134 d.	0943	1003	1038	...	1129	...	1145	1201	1243	1243	...	...	1343	1359	1443	1543	...	...	1601	1622	1648	1648	1751	1750	1825	1849	1949	...
Swansea 134 a.	0955	1021	1051	...	1141	...	1159	1220	1255	1255	...	...	1357	1418	1455	1555	...	...	1617	1634	1701	1701	1806	1805	1844	1902	2005	...
Swansea 146 d.	1003	▬	1104	1100	1150	1150	1205	...	1302	1302	1335	1350	1405	...	1500	1600	1609	1607	1623	1638	1706	1706	1810	1811	...	1905	2013	...
Llanelli 146 d.	1021	⑥	1123	1117	1211t	1211t	1224	...	1322	1322	1351	1406	1424	...	1520	1619	1628	1626	1641	1657	1724	1724	1830	1832	...	1924	2032	...
Carmarthen a.	1050		1151	|	1240	1240	1253	...	1347	1347	1420	1440	1453	...	1545	1653	1657	1700	...	1726	1755	1755	1901	1905	...	1951	2057	...
Carmarthen d.	...	1055	1153	|	1246	1258	...	...	1351	1351	1438	1458	...	...	1549	...	1659	1720	...	1731	1757	1803	1905	1909	...	1958	2100	2107
Whitland d.	...	1110	1208	1151	1305	1312	...	...	1406	1415	1454	1512	...	...	1604	...	1714	1735	...	1746	1813	1819	1921	1925	...	2013	2115	2123
Tenby a.	...	1138f	|	|	1325f	1340e	...	...	|	|	1522f	1540e	...	...	|	...	1741e	1808e	...	|	|	|	1953	1957	...	|	2142	|
Pembroke Dock a.	...	1220	|	|	1412	1419	...	...	|	|	1609	1619	...	...	|	...	1821	1843	...	|	|	|	2025	2029	...	|	2218	|
Clarbeston Road d.	...	...	1222x	1204x	...	...	...	...	1420x	1429x	...	...	...	...	1618x	...	...	...	...	1800x	1827x	1833x	...	...	...	2028x	...	2137x
Haverfordwest d.	...	...	1231	|	...	...	...	...	1429	1437	...	...	...	...	1626	...	...	...	...	1808	|	|	...	...	...	2036	...	|
Milford Haven a.	...	...	1254	|	...	...	...	...	1452	1500	...	...	...	...	1649	...	...	...	...	1831	|	|	...	...	...	2059	...	|
Fishguard Hbr a.	...	...	...	1230	...	...	...	...	...	...	...	...	...	...	...	...	...	...	...	...	1854	1900	...	...	...	...	...	2204

A – From London Paddington (operated by GW, see Table **134**). Conveys 🛏12 and 🍷.
B – From Gloucester (Table **117**).
C – From Holyhead (Tables **149** and **160**).
E – From Crewe (Table **149**).

a – Until Sept. 7.
b – From Sept. 14.
e – Departs 4–6 minutes earlier.
f – Departs 7–10 minutes later.

g – Departs 0943.
r – Arrives 0859.
t – Arrives 1206.
x – Calls on request.

136 CARDIFF - SWANSEA - SOUTH WEST WALES

2nd class AW

	⑥ A	⑥ 🍷	⑥	⑥ 🍷	⑥	⑦ c	⑦ c	⑦	⑦	⑦ 🍷	⑦ 🍷	⑦ F	⑦ A	⑦ 🍷d	⑦ 🍷c	⑦	⑦ A	⑦ 🍷	⑦	⑦ A	⑦ 🍷	⑦	⑦ 🍷	⑦ 🍷	⑦	⑦	⑦
Manchester P **149** d.	...	1631	...	1831	...	...	...	...	...	...	...	...	...	...	...	...	...	1031	...	...	1232	...	1430	1430	...	...	...
Cardiff Central . **134** d.	1950	2001	2104	2208	2235	...	0710	...	...	...	0956	1119	1145	1205	1205	...	1400	1405	...	1600	1614	...	1810	1810	...	2013	2230
Bridgend **134** d.	2010	2020	2123	2235	2302	...	0732	...	...	...	1025	1139	1206	1235	1235	...	1418	1434	...	1620	1643	...	1839	1839	...	2033	2251
Port Talbot **134** d.	2023	2033	2139	2247	2319	...	0746	...	...	...	1040	1153	1219	1251	1254	...	1431	1451	...	1631	1659	...	1856	1856	...	2049	2305
Neath **134** d.	2031	|	2146	2254	2331	...	1754	...	...	...	1048	1201	1226	|	|	...	1439	1459	...	1639	1707	...	1904	1904	...	2057	2313
Swansea **134** a.	2042	|	2157	2307	2347	...	0807	...	...	...	1100	1214	1239	|	|	...	1454	1511	...	1654	1720	...	1917	1917	...	2110	2325
Swansea **146** d.	2100	|	2225	2310	2353	...	0815	...	...	1045	1104	1216	1249	|	|	1402	1503	1544	1638	1707	1725	1837	1922	1922	2058	2118	2338
Llanelli **146** d.	2117	2103	2244	2329	0012	...	0835	...	...	1102	1124	1235	1307	1324	1326	1422	1520	1603	1658	1725	1745	1857	1941	1941	2118	2137	2358
Carmarthen a.	2148	2131	2323	0003	0047	...	0907	...	...	1127	1156	1309	1336	1354	1359	1455	1548	1632	1730	1755	1815	1929	2009	2009	2149	2206	0033
Carmarthen d.	...	2205	...	...	...	0820	0910	0955	1019	1132	1206	1309	...	1357	1405	1457	...	1635	1735	...	1820	1932	2010	2010	2151	2210	...
Whitland d.	...	2220	...	...	...	0836	0926	1011	1034	1147	1222	1325	...	1413	1421	1512	...	1652	1752	...	1837	1948	2030r	2037r	2207	2226	...
Tenby a.	...	|	...	...	...	|	0954	|	1101f	|	|	|	...	|	|	1540	...	|	1820	...	|	|	|	2102	|	|	...
Pembroke Dock a.	...	|	...	...	...	|	1027	|	1141	|	|	|	...	|	|	1617	...	|	1859	...	|	|	|	2136	|	|	...
Clarbeston Road d.	...	2234x	...	...	...	0852x	...	1027x	...	1200x	1239x	1338x	...	1427x	1437x	...	...	1708x	...	...	1853x	2004x	2046x	...	2220x	2242x	...
Haverfordwest d.	...	2242	...	...	...	0900	...	1035	...	|	1247	|	...	1436	1445	...	...	1716	...	...	1901	2012	2054	...	|	2250	...
Milford Haven a.	...	2305	...	...	...	0920	...	1055	...	|	1307	|	...	1459	1509	...	...	1737	...	...	1925	...	2120	...	|	2310	...
Fishguard Hbr a.	...	...	...	...	...	...	...	...	...	1227	...	1405	...	...	...	...	...	...	...	...	...	...	...	...	2249	...	...

	Ⓐ ②–⑤	Ⓐ	Ⓐ ②–⑤	Ⓐ 🍷	Ⓐ 🍷	Ⓐ 🍷	Ⓐ 🍷	Ⓐ	Ⓐ 🍷	Ⓐ	Ⓐ 🍷	Ⓐ S	Ⓐ 🍷	Ⓐ 🍷	Ⓐ 🍷	Ⓐ 🍷	Ⓐ S	Ⓐ	Ⓐ 🍷	Ⓐ 🍷	Ⓐ 🍷	Ⓐ G	Ⓐ	Ⓐ 🍷	Ⓐ 🍷	Ⓐ	Ⓐ 🍷
Fishguard Hbr d.	...	...	0237	...	...	...	...	0650	...	...	0750	...	...	...	*0954*	...	...	...	...	1250	...	...	...	...	...	...	...
Milford Haven d.	0021	...	|	...	...	...	0555	|	0705	...	|	...	0909	...	|	1110	...	...	...	|	1308	...	...	...	1508	...	...
Haverfordwest d.	0036	...	|	...	...	...	0610	|	0720	...	|	...	0924	...	|	1125	...	...	...	|	1323	...	...	...	1523	...	...
Clarbeston Road d.	0044x	...	0259x	...	...	...	0618x	0714	0728x	...	0811x	...	0932x	...	*1017*x	1133x	...	...	...	1312x	1331x	...	...	...	1531x	...	...
Pembroke Dock d.	|	...	|	...	...	...	|	▬	|	0659	|	...	|	0909	|	|	...	1109	...	|	|	...	1309	...	|	1509	...
Tenby d.	|	...	|	...	...	...	|	...	|	0729	|	...	|	0938	|	|	...	1143t	...	|	|	...	1341t	...	|	1541	...
Whitland d.	0057	...	0311	...	...	...	0631	Ⓐ	0741	0753	0824	...	0946	1007	*1032*	1146	...	1211	...	1324	1344	...	1409	...	1544	1609	...
Carmarthen a.	0116	...	0329	...	...	...	0647	A	0755	0812	0843	...	1005	1024	*1049*	1202	...	1229	...	1340	1400	...	1427	...	1600	1627	...
Carmarthen d.	...	0259	...	0503	0546	0615	0650	0730	0801	0815	0900	...	1008	1031	1103	1208	...	1233	1302	1347	1405	...	1440	1502	1605	1631	1658
Llanelli **146** d.	...	0321	...	0528	0615	0644	0719	0805	0830	0841	0925	0939	1032	1057	1131	1233	1245	1259	1330	1409	1430	...	1505	1531	1630	1657	1726
Swansea **146** a.	...	0342	...	|	0635	0705	0738	0822	0849	0903	0951	1001	1049	1123	1150	1252	1304	1322	1349	|	1449	...	1524	1550	1649	1722	1745
Swansea **134** d.	...	*0354*	...	|	0638	0707	0742	0829	0853	*0910*	0955	1008	1055	...	1155	1256	1310	...	1355	|	1455	1510	...	1555	1655	...	1749
Neath **134** d.	...	*0406*	...	|	0653	0718	0753	0841	0904	*0925*	1006	|	1106	...	1206	1307	1325	...	1406	|	1506	1525	...	1606	1706	...	1803
Port Talbot **134** d.	...	*0414*	...	0601	0704	0725	0800	0849	0911	*0936*	1013	|	1113	...	1213	1314	1336	...	1413	1443	1513	1536	...	1613	1713	...	1814
Bridgend **134** d.	...	*0427*	...	0616	0720	0741	0815	0902	0924	*0953*	1026	|	1126	...	1226	1325	1353	...	1426	|	1526	1553	...	1626	1728	...	1829
Cardiff Central . **134** a.	...	*0512*	...	0645	0749	0804	0840	0922	0948	*1018*	1048	1110	1148	...	1248	1349	1415	...	1447	1519	1547	1614	...	1647	1748	...	1850
Manchester P **149** a.	...	...	...	1011	...	1112	1213	...	1313	...	1413	...	1513	...	1613	1713	...	...	1813	...	1913	...	...	2019	2106	...	2215

	Ⓐ	Ⓐ	Ⓐ	Ⓐ	Ⓐ	Ⓐ	Ⓐ	Ⓐ E	Ⓐ	Ⓐ	Ⓐ	Ⓐ	⑥	⑥ 🍷	⑥ 🍷	⑥	⑥ 🍷	⑥	⑥ 🍷	⑥ 🍷	⑥ S	⑥ 🍷	⑥ a	⑥ A	⑥	⑥	⑥
Fishguard Hbr d.	...	...	...	1908	...	...	...	...	...	2214	...	...	...	*0237*	...	...	...	0650	...	...	...	0750	...	...	...	...	...
Milford Haven d.	1713	...	...	|	1916	...	2038	...	...	|	...	2320	0021	|	...	...	0554	|	0706	...	...	|	...	...	0908	...	...
Haverfordwest d.	1728	...	...	|	1924	...	2053	...	...	|	...	2335	0036	|	...	...	0609	|	0721	...	...	|	...	...	0923	...	...
Clarbeston Road d.	1736x	...	...	1930x	1939x	...	2101x	...	...	2236x	...	2343x	0044x	*0259*x	...	...	0617x	0714	0729x	...	...	0811x	...	...	0931x	...	...
Pembroke Dock d.	|	1709	...	|	|	*1919*	|	...	2109	|	2227	|	|	|	...	...	|	...	|	0659	...	|	0835	...	|	...	0909b
Tenby d.	|	1738	...	|	|	957j	|	...	2153	|	2255	|	|	|	...	...	|	...	|	0729	...	|	0908t	...	|	...	0937b
Whitland d.	1749	1807	...	1942	1952	2027	2114	...	2221	2250	2325	2356	0057	*0311*	...	...	0630	...	0742	0753	...	0824	0938	...	0944	...	1005
Carmarthen a.	1805	1824	...	2002	2008	2044	2134	...	2243	2308	2344	0016	0116	*0329*	...	...	0646	...	0754	0811	...	0843	...	...	1002	...	1023
Carmarthen d.	1808	1831	1850	...	2011	2049	...	...	...	2310	...	...	*0244*	0504	0555	0620	0649	...	0801	0814	...	0900	...	0938	1004	...	1027
Llanelli **146** d.	1836	1857	1921	...	2035	2117	...	2201	...	2340	...	...	*0306*	0529	0624	0648	0718	...	0830	0842	0855	0928	...	1006	1031	...	1053
Swansea **146** a.	1856	1922	1943	...	2055	2140	...	2222	...	0008	...	...	*0329*	|	0643	0708	0737	...	0849	0902	0922	0950	...	1023	1048	...	1119
Swansea **134** d.	1900	...	1951	...	2100	2145	...	2232	...	...	...	...	...	|	0648	0711	0741	...	0854	*0910*	0933	0954	...	1029	1055	1110	...
Neath **134** d.	1914	...	2002	...	2111	2200	...	2247	...	...	...	...	...	|	0700	0726	0752	...	0906	*0925*	0945	1006	...	1041	1106	1125	...
Port Talbot **134** d.	1925	...	2009	...	2118	2211	...	2258	...	...	...	...	...	0602	0708	0737	0759	...	0913	*0936*	0952	1013	...	1049	1113	1136	...
Bridgend **134** d.	1940	...	2023	...	2131	2227	...	2315	...	...	...	...	...	0617	0723	0753	0814	...	0928	*0953*	1010	1028	...	1102	1128	1152	...
Cardiff Central . **134** a.	2003	...	2045	...	2203	2255	...	2340	...	...	...	...	...	0644	0746	0836	0841	...	0949	*1016*	1033	1048	...	1123	1148	1215	...
Manchester P **149** a.	...	...	...	...	...	...	...	...	...	...	...	...	...	1013	1113	...	1213	...	1313	...	...	1414	...	...	1515	...	...

	⑥ 🍷	⑥ Aa	⑥ 🍷	⑥ 🍷S	⑥	⑥ 🍷	⑥ 🍷	⑥ 🍷	⑥ B	⑥	⑥ 🍷	⑥ 🍷	⑥	⑥ Aa	⑥ b	⑥ 🍷	⑥	⑥ a	⑥ b	⑥	⑥	⑥ F	⑥ b	⑥ a	⑥	⑥	⑥	⑥
Fishguard Hbr d.	*0953*	...	...	...	...	...	1243	...	...	...	...	...	...	...	...	...	...	...	...	...	1902	...	...	...	...	...	...	2215
Milford Haven d.	|	...	1108	...	...	...	|	1308	...	...	...	1508	...	...	...	...	1708	...	...	...	|	1908	...	...	...	2118	...	|
Haverfordwest d.	|	...	1123	...	...	...	|	1323	...	...	...	1523	...	...	...	...	1723	...	...	...	|	1923	...	...	...	2133	...	|
Clarbeston Road d.	*1014*x	...	1131x	...	...	...	1305x	1331x	...	...	...	1531x	...	...	...	...	1731x	...	...	...	1924x	1931x	...	...	...	2141x	...	2237x
Pembroke Dock d.	|	1001	|	...	1109b	...	|	|	...	1309	...	|	...	1455	1509	...	|	1630	1712	...	|	|	1919	1919	...	|	2109	|
Tenby d.	|	1037t	|	...	1140	...	|	|	...	1342t	...	|	...	1535t	1544t	...	|	1701	1743	...	|	|	1951	1955t	...	|	2142t	|
Whitland d.	*1029*	1108	1144	...	1210	...	1317	1344	...	1411	...	1544	...	1609	1612	...	1744	1729	1811	...	1936	1944	2021	2025	...	2154	2211	2252
Carmarthen a.	*1046*	1126	1200	...	1228	...	1332	1358	...	1428	...	1600	...	1627	1630	...	1802	1747	1829	...	1954	2004	2039	2043	...	2214	2232	2308
Carmarthen d.	1109	1135	1205	...	1233	1302	1336	1405	...	1433	1503	1605	...	1631	1632	1702	1808	1833	1833	1854	...	2007	2047	2047	...	...	...	2311
Llanelli **146** d.	1137	1203	1230	1242	1258	1330	1405	1430	...	1458	1532	1630	1647	1705	1658	1730	1836	1859	1859	1925	...	2031	2117	2117	*2138*	...	...	2339
Swansea **146** a.	1156	1221	1249	1301	1319	1349	|	1449	...	1520	1551	1649	1704	1722	1720	1749	1856	1921	1921	1947	...	2051	2142	2142	*2206*	...	...	0002
Swansea **134** d.	1200	1229	1253	1307	...	1400	|	1455	1510	...	1555	1658	1711	1729	...	1754	1900	...	...	1952	...	2055	2143	2143	2220	...	...	...
Neath **134** d.	1211	1241	1304	1322	...	1411	|	1506	1525	...	1606	1709	1726	1741	...	1805	1911	...	...	2003	...	2106	2159	2159	2235	...	...	...
Port Talbot **134** d.	1218	1249	1311	1333	...	1418	1433	1513	1536	...	1613	1716	1737	1749	...	1812	1919	...	...	2010	...	2113	2210	2210	2246	...	...	...
Bridgend **134** d.	1231	1302	1326	1352	...	1431	|	1526	1553	...	1628	1731	1753	1802	...	1827	1933	...	...	2024	...	2126	2226	2226	2302	...	...	...
Cardiff Central . **134** a.	1252	1322	1348	1413	...	1452	1509	1551	1616	...	1649	1752	1820	1822	...	1847	1956	...	...	2047	...	2147	2250	2250	2326	...	...	...
Manchester P **149** a.	1615	...	1714	...	...	1815	...	1915	...	...	2013	2115	...	...	...	2214	*2349*	...	...	...	...	...	...	...	...	...	...	...

	⑥	⑥	⑦ 🚌	⑦ c	⑦	⑦ 🍷d	⑦ 🍷c	⑦	⑦ c	⑦ 🍷	⑦	⑦	⑦ 🍷	⑦ A	⑦	⑦ 🍷	⑦ A	⑦	⑦ A	⑦ S	⑦	⑦	⑦ F	⑦	⑦	⑦	⑦
Fishguard Hbr d.	...	...	0217	...	...	...	...	...	...	...	...	1240	...	...	1422	...	...	...	...	...	...	...	...	...	...	2303	...
Milford Haven d.	...	2318	|	...	...	...	0928	...	...	1123	...	|	1318	...	|	1513	...	...	*1740*	...	...	1938	...	2135	...	|	2315
Haverfordwest d.	...	2333	|	...	...	...	0943	...	...	1138	...	|	1331	...	|	1528	...	...	*1755*	...	...	1953	...	2150	...	|	2330
Clarbeston Road d.	...	2341x	|	...	...	...	0952x	...	...	1147x	...	1302x	1340x	...	1444x	1537x	...	...	*1803*x	...	...	2001x	...	2158x	...	2325x	2339x
Pembroke Dock d.	2218	|	|	...	...	...	|	...	1040	|	1200	|	|	...	|	|	...	1625	|	...	1901	|	...	|	2146	|	|
Tenby d.	2245	|	|	...	...	...	|	...	1113t	|	1228	|	|	...	|	|	...	1653	|	...	1929	|	...	|	2214	|	|
Whitland d.	2315	2354	0312	...	...	...	1006	...	1142	1203	1300	1314	1357	...	1457	1554	...	1724	*1816*	...	2000	2017	...	2213	2245	2338	2353
Carmarthen a.	2334	0013	0332	...	...	...	1026	...	1158	1221	1317	1330	1415	...	1514	1611	...	1742	*1835*	...	2017	2036	...	2230	2306	2354	0014
Carmarthen d.	...	...	...	0845	0934	1030	1030	1053	...	1224	1320	1338	1425	1458	1540	1616	1655	1747	1903	...	2021	...	2115	2235	...	2357	...
Llanelli **146** d.	...	...	...	0912	0958	1056	1057	1123	...	1250	1350	1400	1451	1527	1610	1649	1722	1818	1930	2004	2052	...	2141	2304	...	|	...
Swansea **146** a.	...	...	...	0930	1016	1118	1116	1147	...	1313	1416	|	1516	1543	1635	1715	1739	1846	1947	2025	2119	...	2204	2326	...	0037	...
Swansea **134** d.	...	...	...	0934	*1024*	1131	1132	*1224*	...	1343	...	|	1534	1551	...	1730	1751	*1851*	1955	2040	...	...	2210	2331	...	...	...
Neath **134** d.	...	...	...	0945	*1036*	1142	1143	*1236*	...	1354	...	|	1545	1603	...	1741	1803	*1903*	2007	2051	...	...	2221	2343	...	...	...
Port Talbot **134** d.	...	...	...	0952	*1043*	1149	1150	*1243*	...	1401	...	|	1552	1610	...	1748	1810	*1910*	2014	2058	...	...	2228	2350	...	...	...
Bridgend **134** d.	...	...	...	1007	*1056*	1204	1205	*1256*	...	1417	...	1444	1607	1623	...	1803	1823	*1923*	2028	2114	...	...	2245	0007	...	...	...
Cardiff Central . **134** a.	...	...	...	1030	*1118*	1233	1234	*1318*	...	1448	...	1507	1638	1645	...	1832	1845	*1945*	2049	2137	...	...	2310	0034	...	...	...
Manchester P **149** a.	...	...	...	1417	...	1614	1614	...	...	1818	...	...	2016	...	...	2219	...	...	...	...	...	...	...	...	...	...	...

A – To / from London (operated by GW, see Table **134**). Conveys 🛏12 and 🍷.
B – To Abergavenny (Table **149**).
E – To Crewe (Table **149**).
F – To / from Hereford (Table **149**).
G – To Chester (Table **149**).
S – From Shrewsbury (Table **146**).

a – Until Sept. 7.
b – From Sept. 14.
c – Until Sept. 8.
d – From Sept. 15.
f – Departs 1111.

j – Arrives 1947.
r – Arrives 2026.
s – Calls to set down only.
t – Arrives 5–7 minutes earlier.
x – Calls on request.

GW 2nd class — WORCESTER - GLOUCESTER - BRISTOL — 138

km		Ⓐ	Ⓐ	ⒶA	ⒶB	ⒶC	ⒶB	ⒶB	ⒶB	ⒶB	ⒶB	ⒶB	ⒶB	ⒶB	ⒶB	ⒶB	ⒶB	Ⓐ	Ⓐ	Ⓐ	Ⓐ	Ⓐ	Ⓐ	⑥	⑥A
	Great Malvern 125 130 d.		...	...	...	...	...	...	0850	...	1048	...	1251	...	1450	...	1648	...	1850	...	...	2136	...		...
0	**Worcester** Shrub Hill 125 130 d.		0528	...	...	...	0649	*0708*	0906	...	1107	...	1306	...	1506	...	1706	...	1907	...	...	2152	2228		...
24	Ashchurch for Tewkesbury d.		0544	...	...	*0628*	0705	|	0927	...	1125	...	1325	...	1525	...	1724	...	1925	...	...	2208	2251		...
36	Cheltenham Spa ◧ 116 d.		0554	...	0624	*0644*	0716	*0731*	0936	...	1134	...	1334	...	1534	...	1733	...	1935	2020	2121	2218	2305		*0603*
46	**Gloucester** ◧ a.		0603	...	0634	*0654*	0726	*0740*	0946	...	1144	...	1343	...	1543	...	1742	...	1943	2029	2130	2228	2317		*0611*
46	**Gloucester** d.		...	0616	0642	0705	0741	0841	0947	1041	1147	1242	1346	1441	1546	1640	1746	1842	1945	2039	2136	2231	...		0621
97	**Bristol** Parkway 116 d.		...	0657	0724	0749	0820	0919	1024	1119	1223	1319	1423	1520	1624	1720	1823	1919	2024	2119	2212	2308	...		0701
108	**Bristol** Temple Meads 116 a.		...	0713	0740	0800	0835	0935	1041	1134	1235	1336	1439	1538	1639	1736	1838	1934	2037	2131	2224	2318	...		0712

	⑥	⑥B	⑥B	⑥B	⑥B	⑥B	⑥B	⑥B	⑥B	⑥B	⑥B	⑥B	⑥B	⑥	⑥	⑥	⑥	⑦	⑦A	⑦	⑦	⑦	⑦	⑦	⑦
Great Malvern 125 130 d.	...	...	...	...	...	1057	...	...	...	1450	...	1650	...	1850	...	2112	...		...	...	...	...	...	...	...
Worcester Shrub Hill 125 130 d.	...	0649	...	0910	...	1113	...	1258	...	1507	...	1708	...	1908	...	2132	2225		...	1138	1436	1637	1840	2038	...
Ashchurch for Tewkesbury d.	*0633*	0705	...	0927	...	1129	...	1314	...	1525	...	1725	...	1925	...	2151	2241		...	1153	1451	1653	1856	2054	...
Cheltenham Spa ◧ 116 d.	0648	0716	...	0936	...	1138	...	1323	...	1535	...	1735	...	1935	2102	2202	2251		1004	1203	1501	1703	1906	2103	2201
Gloucester ◧ a.	0658	0725	...	0945	...	1147	...	1335	...	1544	...	1744	...	1945	2112	2212	2301		1014	1214	1510	1713	1916	2113	2211
Gloucester d.	0702	0741	0841	0948	1041	1150	1241	1342	1441	1547	1642	1748	1841	1948	2114	...	...		1016	1218	1512	1716	1919	2115	...
Bristol Parkway 116 d.	0743	0820	0919	1023	1120	1225	1317	1420	1519	1624	1720	1825	1920	2026	2152	...	...		1055	1258	1602	1754	1958	2154	...
Bristol Temple Meads 116 a.	0754	0833	0935	1039	1135	1238	1333	1436	1534	1639	1736	1840	1932	2037	2207	...	...		1107	1310	1613	1806	2010	2206	...

	Ⓐ	Ⓐ	Ⓐ	Ⓐ	ⒶB	ⒶB	Ⓐ	ⒶB	ⒶB	ⒶB	ⒶB	ⒶB	ⒶB	ⒶB	ⒶB	ⒶB	ⒶB	Ⓐ	Ⓐ	ⒶA	Ⓐ	⑥	⑥	⑥	⑥B
Bristol Temple Meads 116 d.		...	0613	...	0734	0841	0941	1041	1138	1242	1341	1441	1541	1641	1741	1836	1940	2041	...	2141	2242		...	...	0741
Bristol Parkway 116 d.		...	0624	...	0749	0855	0952	1053	1152	1253	1352	1453	1552	1652	1753	1848	1952	2052	...	2156	2253		...	...	0753
Gloucester a.		...	0702	...	0830	0935	1032	1133	1233	1333	1431	1533	1634	1734	1833	1927	2033	2133	...	2239	2338		...	...	0832
Gloucester ◧ d.		0600	0707	0714	...	0938	...	1137	...	1337	...	1537	...	1737	...	1935	2037	2135	2151	*2248*	...		0600	0713	...
Cheltenham Spa ◧ 116 a.		0610	0716	0724	...	0946	...	1146	...	1346	...	1546	...	1746	...	1945	2048	2146	2200	*2257*	...		0610	0723	...
Ashchurch for Tewkesbury a.		0619	0724	0733	...	0955	...	1156	...	1355	...	1556	...	1756	...	1954	...	2155	|	...	...		0619	0733	...
Worcester Shrub Hill 125 130 a.		0639	...	0753	...	1014	...	1213	...	1413	...	1614	...	1816	...	2021	...	2213	2222	...	...		0640	0753	...
Great Malvern 125 130 a.		...	...	0809	...	1031	...	1230	...	1430	...	1629	...	1835	...	2037	...	...	...	...	...		...	...	...

	⑥	⑥B	⑥B	⑥B	⑥B	⑥B	⑥B	⑥B	⑥B	⑥B	⑥B	⑥B	⑥B	⑥	⑥		⑦	⑦	⑦	⑦	⑦	⑦	⑦	⑦	⑦
Bristol Temple Meads 116 d.	0800	0840	0941	1041	1141	1242	1341	1441	1541	1641	1741	1841	1941	2041	2213	...		0920	1211	1439	1641	1837	2042	2230	...
Bristol Parkway 116 d.	0810	0853	0952	1052	1152	1255	1352	1453	1552	1652	1752	1852	1952	2052	2224	...		0929	1222	1451	1651	1846	2051	2239	...
Gloucester a.	|	0930	1033	1132	1231	1332	1434	1533	1632	1733	1832	1932	2032	2132	2302	...		1010	1304	1533	1733	1930	2134	2321	...
Gloucester ◧ d.	|	0938	...	1137	...	1337	...	1537	...	1737	...	1938	2038	2138	...	...		1012	1305	1535	1735	1933	2138	...	2356
Cheltenham Spa ◧ 116 a.	0839	0946	...	1147	...	1346	...	1547	...	1747	...	1947	2048	2148	...	...		1021	1316	1545	1745	1945	2147	...	0007
Ashchurch for Tewkesbury a.	...	0955	...	1156	...	1355	...	1556	...	1756	...	1956	...	2157	...	...		1030	1325	1555	1755	1954	...	...	...
Worcester Shrub Hill 125 130 a.	...	1014	...	1214	...	1413	...	1614	...	1816	...	2014	...	2218	...	...		1051	1342	1612	1815	2022	...	...	...
Great Malvern 125 130 a.	...	1033	...	...	...	1432	...	1632	...	1836	...	2035	...	...	...	...		...	...	...	...	...	...	...	...

A – To/from Taunton (Table **115**).
B – To/from Weymouth, Westbury, Frome, Salisbury, Southampton or Brighton (see Table **140**).
C – To Swindon (Table **132**).
◧ – See also Tables **117** and **133**.

GW, SW — BRISTOL - WESTBURY - SOUTHAMPTON, PORTSMOUTH and WEYMOUTH — 140

km		⚒	⚒	Ⓐ	⑥	ⒶP	Ⓐ	⑥	⚒	ⒶC	⑥	⚒T	Ⓐ	⑥	⚒F	⚒	⑥A	ⒶA	⚒W	Ⓐ	⑥a	ⒶD	⚒	⚒A	Ⓐ	⑥	⑥
	Cardiff Central **118** d.		...	...	...	...	...	...	...	...	...	...	0630	0630	...	0730	...	...	...	...	...	...	0830	...	0930	0930	...
0	**Bristol** Temple Meads d.		...	...	...	0515	0544	0549	...	...	...	0648	0724	0722	0747	0822	0839	0841	0848	0907	0908	...	0922	0946	1022	1022	...
19	Bath Spa d.		...	...	...	|	0603	0606	...	...	...	0706	0737	0736	0807	0836	0857	0859	0906	0925	0926	...	0935	1005	1035	1036	...
34	Bradford on Avon d.		...	...	...	0539	0619	0622	...	...	...	0722	0750	0748	0823	0848	0913	0915	0922	0937	0938	...	0947	1020	1047	1048	...
39	Trowbridge 132a d.		...	...	...	0546	0626	0628	...	0646	...	0728	0757	0754	0829	0854	0919	0921	0928	0944	0945	...	0954	1027	1053	1054	...
46	**Westbury** 132a a.		...	...	...	0554	0633	0635	...	0653	...	0736	0804	0801	0836	0901	0926	0928	0937	0951	0952	...	1001	1034	1100	1101	...
46	**Westbury** 110 d.		0524	0549	0602	...	0640	0643	0654	0701	0703t	...	0805	0802	▬	0902	0933	0932	0939	...	0954	0956	1002	1037	1101	1102	1111
	Frome d.		|	|	|	...	|	|	0703	|	0649g	...	|	|	⑥	|	0942	0942	|	...	1006	1005	|	1044	|	|	|
	Castle Cary 110 d.		|	|	|	...	|	|	0721	|	|	...	|	|	Y	|	1001	1000	|	...	1023	1022	|	1101	|	|	|
	Yeovil Pen Mill d.		|	|	|	...	|	|	0735	|	|	...	|	|	0950	|	1015	1014	|	...	1040	1035	|	1115	|	|	|
	Dorchester West d.		|	|	|	...	|	|	0809j	|	|	...	|	|	1018	|	1054	1048	|	...	1113	...	|	1153	|	|	|
	Weymouth a.		|	|	|	...	|	|	0826	|	|	...	|	|	1029	|	1109	1103	|	...	1127	...	|	1210	|	|	|
53	Warminster d.		0532	0557	0610	...	0648	0651	...	0712	0712	...	0813	0810	...	0910	...	...	0946	...	...	...	1010	...	1109	1110	1121
85	**Salisbury** d.		0555	0619	0632	...	0712	0724e	...	0736	0736	...	0833	0833	...	0933	...	...	1011	...	...	...	1032	...	1132	1133	1143
112	Romsey d.		...	0638	0651	...	0730	0743	...	0756	0754	...	0854	0852	...	0950	...	...	...	...	...	...	1050	...	1150	1151	1204
123	**Southampton** Central a.		...	0649	0702	...	0740	0755	...	0809	0807	...	0904	0902	...	1003	...	...	...	...	...	...	1104	...	1202	1203	1221
147	Fareham a.		...	0715	0727	...	0805	0823	...	...	...	...	0927	0927	...	1027	...	...	...	...	...	...	1127	...	1232	1227	...
	Brighton a.		...	|	|	...	|	|	...	...	...	...	|	|	...	|	...	...	...	...	...	...	|	...	|	|	...
164	**Portsmouth** & S'sea a.		...	0738	0746	...	0824	0845	...	...	...	...	0947	0946	...	1046	...	...	...	...	...	...	1146	...	1253	1246	...
165	**Portsmouth** Harbour a.		...	0742	0752	...	0828	0851	...	...	...	...	0951	0952	...	1052	...	...	...	...	...	...	1152	...	1257	1252	...

	⚒A	⑥W	⚒	⚒A	⚒	ⒶA	⑥A	⚒W	⚒	⑥A	ⒶA	ⒶD	⚒	⑥a	ⒶA	⑥b	ⒶG	⑥	Ⓐ	⚒A	⚒W	⑥	Ⓐ	ⒶA	⑥b	⑥a	ⒶG
Cardiff Central **118** d.	...	...	1030	...	1130	B	B	...	1230	...	...	...	1330	A	...	A	W	1430	1430	...	...	1530	1530	...	A	A	W
Bristol Temple Meads d.	1047	...	1122	1149	1222	1239	1243	1249	1322	1344	1349	...	1422	1443	1448	1449	...	1522	1522	1544	1550	1622	1622	1647	1649	1649	...
Bath Spa d.	1106	...	1135	1207	1235	1256	1301	1307	1335	1402	1407	...	1435	1501	1506	1507	...	1536	1535	1602	1608	1636	1635	1706	1707	1707	...
Bradford on Avon d.	1121	...	1147	1223	1247	1312	1313	1322	1347	1418	1423	...	1447	1517	1522	1523	...	1548	1548	1618	1625	1648	1647	1724	1723	1723	...
Trowbridge 132a d.	1128	...	1153	1229	1253	1318	1319	1328	1353	1424	1429	...	1453	1523	1528	1530	...	1554	1558	1624	1631	1654	1653	1731	1729	1729	...
Westbury 132a a.	1136	...	1201	1236	1301	1325	1326	1335	1401	1431	1436	...	1501	1532	1535	1537	...	1601	1604	1633	1639	1701	1700	1736	1736	1736	...
Westbury 110 d.	...	1143t	1201	1239	1301	1330	1329	1340	1401	1436	1439	1457	1501	1534	1538	1541	1541	1602	1606	...	1640	1702	1704	1739	1738	1738	1745
Frome d.	...	1130g	|	1248	|	|	|	|	|	1454	1448	1507	|	1543	1547	1550	|	|	|	...	|	|	|	1749	1747	1747	|
Castle Cary 110 d.	...	|	|	1305	|	|	|	|	|	...	...	1524	|	1601	1609t	1609	|	|	|	...	|	|	|	1806	1805	1805	|
Yeovil Pen Mill d.	...	|	|	1319	|	|	|	|	|	...	...	1535	|	1615	1624	1624	|	|	|	...	|	|	|	1821	1821	1821	|
Dorchester West d.	...	|	|	1356	|	|	|	|	|	...	...	...	|	1658e	1658	1658	|	|	|	...	|	|	|	1902	1855	1913e	|
Weymouth a.	...	|	|	1410	|	|	|	|	|	...	...	...	|	1710	1710	1710	|	|	|	...	|	|	|	1916	1910	1926	|
Warminster d.	...	1150	1209	...	1309	1339	1338	1347	1409	...	...	...	1509	...	...	...	1551	1610	1613	...	1647	1710	1712	...	...	...	1754
Salisbury d.	...	1211	1232	...	1331	1402	1402	1410	1432	...	...	...	1531	...	...	...	1613	1633	1634	...	1711	1733	1733	...	...	...	1817
Romsey d.	...	...	1250	...	1350	1421	1421	...	1450	...	...	...	1550	...	...	...	...	1651	1652	...	...	1751	1751	...	...	...	...
Southampton Central a.	...	...	1304	...	1404	1432	1432	...	1504	...	...	...	1604	...	...	...	...	1703	1704	...	...	1803	1804	...	...	...	...
Fareham a.	...	...	1327	...	1427	1456	1455	...	1526	...	...	...	1627	...	...	...	...	1727	1726	...	...	1827	1826	...	...	...	...
Brighton a.	...	...	|	...	|	1614	1618	...	|	...	...	...	|	...	...	...	...	|	|	...	...	|	|	...	...	...	...
Portsmouth & S'sea a.	...	...	1346	...	1446	...	...	...	1546	...	...	...	1646	...	...	...	...	1746	1746	...	...	1846	1852	...	...	...	...
Portsmouth Harbour a.	...	...	1352	...	1452	...	...	...	1552	...	...	...	1652	...	...	...	...	1752	1752	...	...	1852	1858	...	...	...	...

	Ⓐ	Ⓐ	⑥	⚒A	Ⓐ	⚒	⑥	ⒶE	⚒A	⑥	Ⓐ	ⒶW	⑥H	Ⓐ	⑥A	⑥	Ⓐ	⚒	⑥	Ⓐ	ⒶK	⚒	⚒	⑥	Ⓐ	⑦	⑦
Cardiff Central **118** d.	...	1630	1630	...	...	1730	...	...	...	1830	1830	...	...	...	...	1930	1930	...	2030	2030	...	2100	...	...	...		...
Bristol Temple Meads d.	1706	1723	1722	1749	1804	1822	...	...	1849	1922	1923	1935	1935	1949	1949	2022	2022	2048	2122	2123	...	2202	2223	2310	2320		0818
Bath Spa d.	1724	1737	1736	1807	1823	1836	...	...	1907	1936	1937	1951	1954	2007	2007	2036	2036	2107	2136	2136	...	2220	2236	2327	2338		0837
Bradford on Avon d.	1738	1750	1748	1823	1840	1848	...	...	1923	1948	1950	2002	2010	2023	2023	2048	2047	2123	2148	2148	...	2236	2247	2343	2354		0853
Trowbridge 132a d.	1745	1757	1754	1829	1847	1854	...	1924	1929	1954	1957	2008	2017	2029	2029	2054	2053	2129	2154	2155	...	2242	2253	2349	2359		0859
Westbury 132a a.	1752	1804	1801	1836	1854	1901	...	1931	1939	2001	2006	2015	2024	2037	2036	2101	2100	2136	2201	2203	...	2250	2300	2356	0008		0905
Westbury 110 d.	1753	1807	1802	1840	...	1902	1920	1940	...	2002	2009	2016	2024	2039	2037	2102	2101	2140	2202	2203	2218	...	2305	2357	0009		0906
Frome d.	|	|	|	1849	...	|	|	|	...	|	|	|	|	2049	2048	|	|	2150	|	|	|	...	|	0008	0018		0917
Castle Cary 110 d.	|	|	|	1906	...	|	|	|	...	|	|	|	|	...	...	|	|	2208	|	|	|	...	|	...	...		0935
Yeovil Pen Mill d.	|	|	|	1919	...	|	|	|	...	|	|	|	|	...	...	|	|	2223	|	|	|	...	|	...	...		0953
Dorchester West d.	|	|	|	1954	...	|	|	|	...	|	|	|	|	...	...	|	|	2258	|	|	|	...	|	...	...		1029
Weymouth a.	|	|	|	2010	...	|	|	|	...	|	|	|	|	...	...	|	|	2314	|	|	|	...	|	...	...		1042
Warminster d.	1802	1815	1810	...	...	1910	1930	1950	...	2010	2017	2024	2032	...	...	2110	2109	...	2213	2211	2226	...	2312	...	...		...
Salisbury d.	...	1837	1833	...	...	1933	1952	2011	...	2033	2039	2044	2053	...	...	2133	2132	...	2234	2232	2248	...	2338	...	...		...
Romsey d.	...	1855	1851	...	...	1951	2011	2030	...	2051	2057	...	...	...	...	2151	2150	...	2254	2253	...	...	...	...	...		...
Southampton Cent a.	...	1905	1903	...	...	2003	2022	2044	...	2103	2107	...	...	...	...	2202	2202	...	2304	2304	...	...	...	...	...		...
Fareham a.	...	1927	1927	...	...	2027	...	...	...	2127	2131	...	...	...	...	2226	2241	...	2327	2327	...	...	...	...	...		...
Brighton a.	...	|	|	...	...	|	...	...	...	|	|	...	...	...	...	|	|	...	|	|	...	...	...	...	...		...
Portsmouth & S'sea a.	...	1947	1946	...	...	2049	...	...	...	2146	2151	...	...	...	...	2245	2257	...	2345	2348	...	...	...	...	...		...
Portsmouth Harbour a.	...	1951	1952	...	...	2054	...	...	...	2152	2155	...	...	...	...	2252	2302	...	2352	2352	...	...	...	...	...		...

FOR NOTES SEE BOTTOM OF PAGE 123

140 BRISTOL - WESTBURY - SOUTHAMPTON, PORTSMOUTH and WEYMOUTH

GW, SW

	⑦	⑦	⑦	⑦G	⑦B	⑦	⑦W	⑦B	⑦S	⑦	⑦	⑦W	⑦	⑦	⑦W	⑦B	⑦	⑦	⑦		⑦	⑦	⑦	⑦	⑦	⑦	⑦
Cardiff Central **118** ...d.	0810	...	0908	W	1008	1108	...	1208	...	1308	1408	...	1508	1608	...	1635	...	1708	1740	...	1808	1908	...	2018	...	...	2210
Bristol Temple Meads .d.	0915	0920	1015	...	1110	1210	1304	1310	...	1410	1510	1604	1615	1710	...	1735	1743	1810	1845	...	1910	2015	2048	2125	2135	2215	2315
Bath Spa ....d.	0931	0939	1028	...	1126	1227	1322	1327	...	1427	1527	1622	1627	1728	...	1752	1758	1827	1858	...	1926	2027	2106	2138	2149	2233	2328
Bradford on Avon.........d.	0944	0955	1045	...	1139	1244	1334	1341	...	1444	1540	1635	1644	1740	...	1804	1813	1839	1910	...	1938	2044	2123	2150	2200	2250	2340
Trowbridge .... **132a** d.	0952	1002	1051	...	1147	1251	1340	1348	1414	1451	1547	1641	1650	1747	...	1812	1821	1847	1917	...	1946	2051	2130	2157	2206	2256	2347
Westbury .... **132a** a.	0959	1008	1058	...	1154	1257	1347	1356	1420	1458	1554	1648	1658	1754	...	1819	1828	1854	1926	...	1955	2058	2137	2204	2213	2303	2354
Westbury .... **110** d.	1000	1010	1102	1049	1201	1301	1349	1401	1425	1502	1605	1649	1701	1801	1816t	1820	1831	1901	1930	...	1959	2101	2138	2205	2215	...	2355
Frome ....d.	|	1019	|	|	|	|	|	|	1433	|	|	|	|	|	1804f	|	1839	|	|	...	|	|	2148	|	|	...	0004
Castle Cary .... **110** d.	|	1039t	|	|	|	|	|	|	1450	|	|	|	|	|	|	|	1858	|	|	...	|	|	2205	|	|	...	...
Yeovil Pen Mill ....d.	|	1054	|	|	|	|	|	|	1505	|	|	|	|	|	|	|	1912	|	|	...	|	|	2221	|	|	...	...
Dorchester West.......d.	|	1134	|	|	|	|	|	|	1540	|	|	|	|	|	|	|	1947	|	|	...	|	|	2255	|	|	...	...
Weymouth...............a.	|	1146	|	|	|	|	|	|	1554	|	|	|	|	|	|	|	2001	|	|	...	|	|	2307	|	|	...	...
Warminster ....d.	1009	...	1109	1056	1210	1309	1356	1410	...	1509	1612	1656	1710	1808	1823	1829	...	1908	1938	...	2008	2108	...	2213	2222	...	...
Salisbury ....d.	1032	...	1132	1116	1232	1332	1417	1436	...	1532	1632	1717	1732	1832	1843	1856t	...	1932	2002	...	2032	2132	...	2236	2245	...	...
Romsey ....d.	1050	...	1150	...	1250	1350	...	1454	...	1550	1650	...	1750	1850	...	1914	...	1950	2020	...	2050	2150	...	2254	...	...	...
Southampton Central .a.	1103	...	1203	...	1303	1403	...	1503	...	1603	1703	...	1803	1903	...	1927	...	2003	2030	...	2103	2203	...	2305	...	...	...
Fareham......................a.	1126	...	1226	...	1329	1426	...	1527	...	1626	1726	...	1826	1926	...	1953	...	2026	2058	...	2126	2226	...	2329	...	...	...
Brighton..................a.	|	...	|	...	1449	|	...	1644	...	|	|	...	|	|	...	2110	...	|	|	...	|	|	...	|	...	...	...
Portsmouth & S'sea ...a.	1146	...	1246	...	...	1446	...	...	...	1646	1746	...	1846	1946	...	...	...	2047	2117	...	2143	2246	...	2346	...	...	...
Portsmouth Harbour...a.	1151	...	1253	...	...	1453	...	...	...	1652	1751	...	1852	1952	...	...	...	2052	2123	...	2151	2252	...	2350	...	...	...

km		⚒	Ⓐ	⑥A	ⒶA	Ⓐ	⑥	Ⓐ	Ⓐ	⚒A	Ⓐ	⑥	⚒	⑥A	ⒶA	Ⓐ	⑥	ⒶA	⑥A	ⒶW	⚒	⚒A	⑥W	⚒	⑥W	ⒶW	ⒶA
	Portsmouth Harbour... d.		...	...	...	...	...	...	...	...	0600	0608	...	...	...	0705	0723	...	...	L	0823	...	...	0923	...	...	B
	Portsmouth & S'sea... d.		...	...	...	...	...	...	...	...	0605	0612	...	...	...	0709	0727	...	...	...	0827	...	...	0927	...	...	...
	Brighton .... d.		...	...	...	...	...	...	...	...	|	|	...	...	...	|	|	...	...	...	|	...	...	|	...	...	0859
	Fareham .... d.		...	...	...	...	...	...	...	...	0625	0632	...	...	...	0729	0747	...	...	...	0847	...	...	0947	...	...	1013
	Southampton Central. d.		...	...	...	...	...	...	...	...	0647	0657	...	...	...	0753	0810	0823	0830	...	0910	...	...	1010	...	...	1042
	Romsey......................... d.		...	...	...	...	...	...	...	...	0700	0711	...	...	...	0811	0821	0835	0841	...	0921	...	...	1021	...	...	1054
	Salisbury..................... d.		...	0607	0610	...	0640	0640	...	...	0719	0730	...	...	...	0830	0840	0903	0905	0923	0940	...	1026	1040	1052	1052	1113
	Warminster.................... d.		...	0628	0630	...	0700	0702	...	0723	0739	0750	...	...	...	0852	0901	0925	0927	0943	1001	...	1046	1101	1112	1112	1132
0	**Weymouth** .... d.		...	|	|	...	|	|	0533	|	|	|	0644	...	...	|	|	|	|	|	|	0853	|	|	|	|	|
11	Dorchester West ...... d.		...	|	|	...	|	|	0546	|	|	|	0657	...	...	|	|	|	|	|	|	0906	|	|	|	|	|
44	Yeovil Pen Mill .... d.		...	|	|	...	|	|	0621	|	|	|	0734	...	...	|	|	|	|	|	|	0941	|	|	|	|	|
63	Castle Cary....... **110** d.		...	|	|	...	|	|	0635	|	|	|	0748	...	...	|	|	|	|	|	|	0955	|	|	|	|	|
86	Frome.......................... d.		...	|	|	0640	|	|	0656	|	|	|	0807	...	...	|	|	|	|	|	|	1015	1106f	|	|	|	|
95	**Westbury**............. **110** a.		...	0637	0639	0650	0708	0710	0708	0732	0749	0800	0816	...	...	0901	0909	0935	0937	0952	1009	1026	1054	1109	1120	1120	1140
95	**Westbury**........... **132a** d.		0558	0638	0641	0655	0709	0711	0717	0738	0754	0806	0817	0838	0845	0910	0910	0938	0939	...	1010	1038	...	1110	1121	1121	1141
105	Trowbridge .... **132a** d.		0604	0644	0647	0702	0715	0717	0723	0744	0800	0812	0824	0844	0851	0916	0916	0944	0945	...	1016	1044	...	1116	1127	1127	1148
110	Bradford on Avon .... d.		0610	0650	0653	0708	0721	0723	0729	0750	0806	0818	0830	0850	0857	0922	0922	0950	0951	...	1022	1050	...	1122	1133	1133	1154
125	Bath Spa...................... a.		0626	0706	0709	0724	0733	0736	0745	0807	0821	0831	0846	0906	0913	0934	0934	1006	1006	...	1035	1106	...	1134	1150	1147	1210
144	**Bristol** Temple Meads a.		0647	0728	0729	0747	0752	0755	0806	0829	0842	0847	0907	0928	0935	0951	0948	1028	1027	...	1049	1128	...	1148	1210	1206	1229
	Cardiff Central **118**... a.		0741	...	...	0843	...	...	...	...	0942	0942	...	...	...	1043	1042	...	...	...	1142	...	...	1244	...	...	...

	⑥A	⚒	ⒶA	⑥A	⚒	⑥A	ⒶA	⚒	⚒W	⑥	ⒶA	⑥A	ⒶL	⚒	⚒A	ⒶJ	⚒	⑥A	⑥A	ⒶA	⚒	ⒶJ	ⒶA	⑥A	⑥A	⚒	⑥W
Portsmouth Harbour...d.	B	1023	...	...	1123	...	...	1223	...	...	...	...	W	1323	...	...	1423	a	b	...	1523	...	...	b	a	1623	...
Portsmouth & S'sea ...d.	...	1027	...	...	1127	...	...	1227	...	...	...	...	...	1327	...	...	1427	...	...	...	1527	...	...	...	...	1627	...
Brighton...................d.	0900	|	...	...	|	...	...	|	...	...	...	...	...	|	...	...	|	...	...	...	|	...	...	...	...	|	...
Fareham.......................d.	1017	1047	...	...	1147	...	...	1247	...	...	...	...	...	1347	...	...	1447	...	...	...	1547	...	...	...	...	1647	...
Southampton Central .d.	1042	1110	...	...	1210	1227	1227	1310	...	...	...	...	...	1410	...	...	1510	...	...	...	1610	...	...	...	...	1710	...
Romsey.........................d.	1054	1121	...	...	1221	1238	1239	1321	...	...	...	...	...	1421	...	...	1521	...	...	...	1621	...	...	...	...	1721	...
Salisbury ....d.	1113	1140	...	...	1240	1303t	1307	1339	1352	...	...	...	1424	1440	...	...	1540	...	...	...	1640	...	...	...	...	1740	1752
Warminster ....d.	1133	1201	...	...	1301	1325	1334	1400	1412	...	...	...	1444	1501	1528	...	1600	1628	...	...	1700	...	1728	1728	...	1801	1812
Weymouth...............d.	|	|	1110	1114	|	|	|	|	|	...	1310	1310	|	|	|	...	|	|	1508	1508	|	...	|	|	1608	|	|
Dorchester West.......d.	|	|	1123	1127	|	|	|	|	|	...	1322	1323	|	|	|	...	|	|	1521	1521	|	...	|	|	1621	|	|
Yeovil Pen Mill ....d.	|	|	1203	1206	|	|	|	|	|	...	1410	1410	|	|	|	1500	|	|	1556	1556	|	1653	|	|	1703	|	|
Castle Cary .... **110** d.	|	|	1218	1220	|	|	|	|	|	...	1424	1428t	|	|	|	1512	|	|	1610	1610	|	1707	|	|	1717	|	|
Frome ....d.	|	|	1237	1238	|	|	|	|	|	...	1442	1446	|	|	|	1529	|	|	1629	1629	|	1724	|	|	1736	|	|
Westbury .... **110** a.	1142	1209	1246	1247	1309	1334	1342	1409	1420	...	1451	1456	1452	1509	1537	1537	1609	1638	1638	1638	1709	1733	1736	1737	1745	1809	1820
Westbury .... **132a** d.	1144	1210	1247	1248	1310	1338	1344	1410	1421	1438	1452	1457	...	1510	1538	...	1610	1639	1639	1642	1709	...	1738	1748	1748	1810	1821
Trowbridge .... **132a** d.	1151	1216	1253	1255	1316	1344	1350	1416	1427	1444	1459	1504	...	1516	1544	...	1616	1646	1646	1647	1715	...	1744	1754	1754	1816	1827
Bradford on Avon.........d.	1157	1222	1259	1301	1322	1350	1356	1422	1433	1450	1505	1510	...	1522	1550	...	1622	1652	1652	1653	1721	...	1750	1800	1800	1822	1833
Bath Spa ....a.	1213	1234	1316	1317	1336	1406	1412	1435	1447	1506	1521	1522	...	1534	1607	...	1634	1708	1708	1709	1734	...	1806	1816	1816	1835	1847
Bristol Temple Meads .a.	1235	1248	1335	1337	1350	1428	1435	1449	1506	1528	1536	1537	...	1549	1628	...	1648	1728	1728	1731	1748	...	1828	1836	1836	1849	1906
Cardiff Central **118** ...a.	...	1342	...	...	1441	...	...	1546c	...	...	...	...	...	1642	...	...	1743	...	...	...	1843	...	...	...	...	1942	...

	ⒶW	ⒶA	⑥Y	Ⓐ	⑥	⑥	Ⓐ	ⒶB	⑥B	ⒶW	⑥	Ⓐ	⑥a	ⒶW	⚒	⚒	⚒W	Ⓐ	⑥	Ⓐ	⑥	ⒶS	Ⓐ	⑥	Ⓐ		⑦R
Portsmouth Harbour...d.	...	...	...	1723	1723	...	...	...	...	...	1823	1823	...	...	...	1923	...	...	...	2023	2023	...	...	...	2123	⑦	...
Portsmouth & S'sea ...d.	...	...	...	1727	1727	...	...	...	...	...	1827	1827	...	...	...	1927	...	...	...	2027	2027	...	...	...	2127		...
Brighton...................d.	...	...	...	|	|	...	...	1702	1700	...	|	|	...	...	...	|	...	...	...	|	|	...	...	...	|		...
Fareham.......................d.	...	...	...	1747	1747	...	...	1814	1817	...	1847	1847	...	...	...	1947	...	...	...	2046	2047	...	...	...	2144		...
Southampton Central .d.	...	...	...	1810	1810	...	...	1842	1845	...	1910	1910	...	...	...	2010	...	...	...	2111	2112	...	2122	2132	2223		...
Romsey.........................d.	...	...	...	1821	1821	...	...	1853	1856	...	1921	1921	...	...	...	2021	...	...	...	2122	2123	...	2134	2143	2234		...
Salisbury ....d.	1801	...	...	1840	1840	...	...	1913	1915	1823	1940	1940	...	1958	...	2040	2057	...	...	2140	2142	...	2154	2204	2300		...
Warminster ....d.	1821	1818	...	1859	1901	...	...	1932	1935	|	2001	2001	...	2018	...	2101	2117	...	...	2201	2203	...	2216	2225	2320		0811
Weymouth...............d.	|	|	1654	|	|	1730	1730	|	|	|	|	|	1830	|	...	|	|	2021	2023	|	|	...	|	|	|		|
Dorchester West.......d.	|	|	1707	|	|	1743	1743	|	|	|	|	|	1843	|	...	|	|	2034	2036	|	|	...	|	|	|		|
Yeovil Pen Mill ....d.	|	|	1734	|	|	1820	1823	|	|	1926	|	|	1920	|	...	|	|	2106	2111	|	|	...	|	|	|		|
Castle Cary .... **110** d.	|	|	▬	|	|	1840t	1837	|	|	1940	|	|	1935	2059f	...	|	|	2118	2125	|	|	2141	|	|	|		|
Frome ....d.	|	|	⑥	|	|	1858	1856	|	|	1957	|	|	2000	2043f	...	|	|	2137	2144	|	|	2158	|	|	|		|
Westbury .... **110** a.	1829	1826	A	1908	1909	1907	1904	1940	1944	2006	2009	2010	2013	2030	...	2109	2125	2149	2154	2209	2211	2212	2230	2235	2329		0819
Westbury .... **132a** d.	1830	1838	1846	1909	1910	1921	1921	1941	1945	...	2010	2011	2016	...	2038	2110	2125	2155	2155	2210	2212	...	*2235*	2240	...		0820
Trowbridge .... **132a** d.	1836	1844	1852	1917	1916	1927	1927	1948	1951	...	2016	2018	2022	...	2044	2116	2131	2202	2202	2216	2218	...	*2241*	2246	...		0826
Bradford on Avon.........d.	1842	1850	1858	1924	1922	1933	1933	1954	1957	...	2022	2024	2029	...	2050	2122	2137	2208	2208	2222	2224	...	*2247*	2252	...		...
Bath Spa ....a.	1854	1906	1914	1936	1934	1949	1949	2006	2009	...	2034	2036	2041	...	2107	2136	2150	2224	2224	2234	2236	...	*2303*	2308	...		...
Bristol Temple Meads .a.	1910	1929	1935	1949	1948	2009	2009	2026	2028	...	2048	2050	2103	...	2128	2150	2206	2243	2246	2248	2250	...	*2325*	2329	...		...
Cardiff Central **118** ...a.	...	...	...	2047	2042	...	...	...	...	...	2142	2144	...	...	...	2300d	...	...	...	2355r	2356	...	...	...	...		...

	⑦	⑦	⑦J	⑦	⑦W	⑦	⑦R	⑦	⑦B	⑦W	⑦	⑦	⑦	⑦	⑦	⑦	⑦	⑦B	⑦	⑦	⑦	⑦W	⑦B	⑦	⑦	⑦	⑦
Portsmouth Harbour...d.	...	...	...	0908	...	...	...	1108	...	...	1308	...	1408	1508	...	...	1608	...	1708	...	1808	...	...	1908	...	2008	2208
Portsmouth & S'sea ...d.	...	...	...	0912	...	...	...	1112	...	...	1312	...	1412	1512	...	...	1613	...	1712	...	1812	...	...	1912	...	2012	2212
Brighton...................d.	...	...	...	|	...	...	...	|	1108	...	|	...	|	|	...	...	|	1547	|	...	|	...	1746	|	...	|	|
Fareham.......................d.	...	...	...	0933	...	...	...	1133	1234	...	1332	...	1434	1534	...	...	1634	1659	1734	...	1834	...	1905	1934	...	2034	2232
Southampton Central .d.	...	...	...	0955	...	...	...	1156	1256	...	1356	...	1456	1556	...	...	1656	1722	1756	...	1856	...	1928	1957	...	2056	2257
Romsey.........................d.	...	...	...	1007	...	...	...	1207	1307	...	1407	...	1507	1607	...	...	1707	1739	1807	...	1908	...	1940	2008	...	2107	2308
Salisbury ....d.	...	...	...	1026	1055	...	...	1227	1325	1355	1427	...	1527	1627	...	1716	1727	1758	1827	...	1927	1955	2001	2026	...	2126	2328
Warminster ....d.	...	...	...	1049	1115	...	...	1244	1344	1415	1445	...	1544	1644	...	1736	1744	1818	1844	...	1946	2015	2022	2044	...	2146	2350
Weymouth...............d.	...	0807h	...	|	|	...	1105	|	|	|	|	1414	|	|	1610	|	|	|	|	1756	|	|	|	|	2009	|	|
Dorchester West.......d.	...	0819h	...	|	|	...	1118	|	|	|	|	1427	|	|	1623	|	|	|	|	1809	|	|	|	|	2022	|	|
Yeovil Pen Mill ....d.	...	0854h	0958	|	|	...	1154	|	|	|	|	1504	|	|	1658	|	|	|	|	1844	|	|	|	|	2057	|	|
Castle Cary .... **110** d.	...	0908h	1013	|	|	...	1208	|	|	|	|	1519	|	|	1713	|	|	|	|	1900t	|	|	|	|	2110	|	|
Frome ....d.	...	0925	1031	|	|	1140	1227	|	|	|	|	1537	|	|	1731	1757f	|	|	|	1918	|	|	|	|	2129	|	|
Westbury .... **110** a.	...	0934	1039	1058	1123	1149	1236	1254	1356	1423	1456	1546	1556	1656	1740	1744	1756	1826	1856	1927	1957	2023	2031	2056	2139	2156	2359
Westbury .... **132a** d.	0856	0946	...	1058	1124	1150	1237	1256	1356	1424	1500	1547	1604	1700	1741	...	1800	1828	1901	1934	2000	2023	2036	2100	2147	2200	...
Trowbridge .... **132a** d.	0902	0952	...	1105	1130	1156	1243	1303	1402	1430	1506	1553	1610	1706	1748	...	1806	1835	1906	1940	2006	2029	2042	2106	2155	2206	...
Bradford on Avon.........d.	0908	0958	...	1111	1136	1202	...	1309	1408	1436	1512	1559	1616	1712	1754	...	1812	1841	1912	1948	2012	2035	2048	2112	2201	2212	...
Bath Spa ....a.	0923	1014	...	1124	1151	1219	...	1323	1424	1449	1524	1615	1628	1724	1806	...	1829	1852	1925	2004	2025	2050	2106	2125	2218	2225	...
Bristol Temple Meads .a.	0944	1033	...	1144	1210	1240	...	1341	1444	1508	1540	1635	1641	1744	1827	...	1843	1912	1939	2025	2040	2107	2125	2141	2237	2241	...
Cardiff Central **118** ...a.	1036	1131	...	1236	...	...	...	1435	1535	...	1634	...	1737	1837	...	...	1934	...	2037	...	2134	...	...	2243	...	2335	...

FOR NOTES SEE NEXT PAGE ▶ ▶ ▶ ▶

LM NUNEATON - COVENTRY - LEAMINGTON SPA 141

km			⚒	Ⓐ	⑥	Ⓐ	⑥	⚒	⚒	⑥	Ⓐ	⚒	Ⓐ	⑥	Ⓐ	⑥	Ⓐ	⑥	⚒	⚒	⑥	Ⓐ	⚒	⚒	Ⓐ	⑥	⑥
0	**Nuneaton** d.	⚒	0619	0715	0716	0813	0816	0916	1016	1116	1116	1216	1316	1316	1414	1416	1514	1516	1616	1716	1816	1816	1916	2016	2114	2116	...
16	Coventry a.		0639	0735	0736	0834	0836	0936	1036	1136	1139	1237	1336	1337	1434	1436	1534	1536	1636	1736	1836	1836	1936	2036	2134	2137	...
			|	|	|	|	|	|	|	|	|	|	|	|	|	|	|	|	|	|	|	|	|	|	|	|	
16	Coventry 114 d.		0640	0740	0737	0835	0837	0937	1037	1137	1140	1237	1337	1338	1435	1437	1537	1537	1637	1737	1837	1837	1937	2037	2136	2137	2220
24	Kenilworth d.		0646	0748	0745	0743	0845	0645	1045	1145	1147	1248	1345	1348	1443	1445	1545	1545	1645	1745	1845	1845	1945	2045	2144	2145	2228
32	**Leamington Spa** 114 a.		0655	0755	0753	0853	0854	0953	1053	1153	1155	1256	1353	1355	1452	1454	1554	1553	1653	1753	1853	1856	1953	2053	2150	2153	2235

	⑥	Ⓐ	Ⓐ		⑦	⑦	⑦	⑦		⑦	⑦	⑦
Nuneaton d.	2220	2222	2322	⑦	...	...	1213	1313		2013	2105	2202
Coventry a.	2240	2242	2342		...	...	1233	1333	and	2033	2125	2222
		|	|				⑦	⑦	hourly	⑦	⑦	⑦
Coventry 114 d.	...	2243	2343		1036	1136	1236	1347	until	2047	2157	2257
Kenilworth d.	...	2251	2351		1044	1144	1244	1355		2055	2205	2305
Leamington Spa 114 a.	...	2257	2358		1055	1155	1255	1404		2104	2215	2315

		⑥	Ⓐ	⑥	Ⓐ	Ⓐ	⑥	Ⓐ	⑥	⚒	⚒
Leamington Spa d.	⚒	0534	0534	608	0613	0700	0702	0802	0803	0900	1002
Kenilworth d.		0541	0542	0615	0620	0707	0709	0809	0810	0907	1009
Coventry 114 a.		0549	0552	0622	0627	0714	0716	0817	0817	0915	1016
		|	|	|	|	|	|	|	|	|	|
Coventry d.		0550	0553	0624	0633	0715	0717	0818	0821	0917	1017
Nuneaton a.		0611	0614	0647	0655	0736	0738	0845	0842	0938	1038

	⚒	⚒	Ⓐ	⑥		⑥	Ⓐ	⚒	⚒	⚒	⚒	⚒	⚒	⚒	⑥	Ⓐ
Leamington Spa 114 d.	1102	1202	1301	1302	...	1402	1401	1502	1602	1701	1800	1902	2002	2101	2201	2206
Kenilworth d.	1109	1209	1309	1309	...	1409	1408	1508	1609	1708	1807	1909	2009	2109	2208	2213
Coventry 114 a.	1116	1216	1317	1316	...	1416	1419	1516	1616	1716	1816	1916	2016	2116	2215	2221
	|	|	|	|		|	|	|	|	|	|	|	|	|		|
Coventry d.	1117	1217	1317	1317	...	1417	1420	1516	1617	1717	1817	1917	2017	2117	...	2222
Nuneaton a	1138	1238	1341	1338	...	1438	1449	1538	1640	1738	1839	1938	2039	2138	...	2243

		⑦	⑦	⑦	⑦	⑦		⑦	⑦	⑦	⑦
Leamington Spa 114 d.	⑦	1000	1100	1200	...	1319		1919	2019	2119	2219
Kenilworth d.		1008	1108	1208	...	1326	and	1927	2027	2126	2227
Coventry 114 a.		1016	1116	1216	...	1339	hourly	1940	2040	2140	2237
		⑦		⑦		⑦	until	⑦	⑦		
Coventry d.		1115	...	1239	1339	1439		2039	2132	...	...
Nuneaton a		1136	...	1300	1400	1500		2100	2153	...	...

LM LONDON - NORTHAMPTON - BIRMINGHAM 142

km			Ⓐ	Ⓐ	Ⓐ L	Ⓐ	Ⓐ L	Ⓐ	Ⓐ	Ⓐ L	Ⓐ A	Ⓐ	Ⓐ L	Ⓐ A	Ⓐ	Ⓐ L	Ⓐ A	Ⓐ	Ⓐ L	Ⓐ A	Ⓐ	Ⓐ L		Ⓐ A	Ⓐ	Ⓐ L	Ⓐ A
0	**London** Euston 143 ‡ d.	Ⓐ	0005	0034	...	...	0534	...	0612	0634	0713	0723	0749	0813	0822	0849	0913	0924	0949	1015	1024	1049		1515	1524	1549	1615
28	Watford Junction 143 ‡ d.		0025	0057	...	...	0555	...	0634	0654	|	0741	0804	|	0840	0904	|	0940	1004	|	1039	1104	and	|	1539	1604	|
64	Leighton Buzzard d.		0054	0130	...	...	0628	...	0704	0726	0741	0810	|	0840	0908	|	0943	1008	|	1042	1108	|	at	1542	1609	|	1642
75	Bletchley d.		0101	0137	...	...	0635	...	0711	0733	0749	0818	|	0847	0915	0924	0950	1015	1025	1049	1115	|	the	1549	1615	|	1649
80	Milton Keynes 143 ‡ d.		0109	0146	0537	...	0640	...	0716	0738	0754	0822	0825	0853	0921	0929	0955	1021	1030	1055	1120	1124	same	1555	1921	1625	1655
106	**Northampton** 143 a.		0126	0205	0553	...	0656	...	0732	0755	0810	0838	0842	0909	0937	0944	1012	1037	1045	1112	1137	1141	minutes	1612	1637	1641	1711
106	**Northampton** 143 d.		...	*0516*	0556	0614	0657	0715	0737	0756	0814	0839	0856	0914	0938	0954	1014	1039	1056	1114	1138	1156	past	1614	1638	1655	1713
136	Rugby 143 ‡ d.		...	*0538*	0618	0650	0719	0737	0800	0818	0837	0901	0918	0936	1000	1018	1036	1101	1118	1136	1200	1218	each	1638	1700	1718	1736
154	Coventry ‡ d.		...	*0549*	0630	0706	0730	0749	0811	0830	0847	0912	0930	0947	1011	1030	1047	1111	1131	1147	1211	1230	hour	1649	1711	1730	1747
171	**Birmingham** Intl ✈ ‡ d.		...	*0607*	0646	0724	0746	0805	0828	0846	0902	0930	0946	1002	1029	1046	1102	1129	1146	1202	1229	1246	until	1704	1729	1746	1803
185	**Birmingham** New St ‡ a.		...	*0618*	0701	0736	0801	0818	0842	0901	0914	0942	1001	1013	1041	1101	1113	1141	1201	1213	1240	1301		1715	1740	1801	1814

	Ⓐ	Ⓐ A	Ⓐ	Ⓐ	Ⓐ	Ⓐ	Ⓐ A	Ⓐ	Ⓐ A	Ⓐ A	Ⓐ A	Ⓐ A	Ⓐ	Ⓐ A	Ⓐ	Ⓐ	Ⓐ	Ⓐ	Ⓐ
London Euston 143 ‡ d.	1630	1652	1713	1723	1752	1805	1813	1821	1849	1852	1915	1955	2016	2051	2113	2153	2224	2304	2322
Watford Junction 143 ‡ d.	|	|	|	1743	|	1826	|	1841	|	|	|	|	|	|	|	|	2241	2328	2341
Leighton Buzzard d.	1709	1720	|	1809	1820	1854	|	1910	|	1920	1942	2022	2044	2119	2144	2220	2307	0001	0007
Bletchley d.	1716	1727	|	1816	|	1901	|	|	|	1927	|	|	2051	|	2152	|	2314	0008	0014
Milton Keynes 143 ‡ d.	1722	1732	1749	1822	1831	1907	1845	1920	1924	1932	1956	2033	2056	2130	2156	2234	2323	0017	0022
Northampton 143 a.	1738	1748	1811	1838	1848	1925	1900	1936	1940	1953	2012	2049	2113	2148	2213	2251	2341	0034	0041
Northampton 143 d.	1739	1757	1820	1839	1857	...	1909	1938	1946	1955	2013	2055	2115	2157	2220	2256	...	...	...
Rugby 143 ‡ d.	1801	1819	1842	1901	1920	...	1936	2000	2005	2017	2037	2120	2138	2220	2242	2318	...	...	...
Coventry ‡ d.	1811	1830	1853	1911	1932	...	1948	2011	...	2030	2047	2131	2149	2231	2253	2330	...	...	...
Birmingham Int'l ✈ ‡ d.	1829	1846	1908	1929	1948	...	2003	2029	...	2046	2102	2147	2204	2247	2311	2348	...	...	...
Birmingham New St ‡ a.	1840	1901	1919	1941	2003	...	2014	2040	...	2101	2114	2202	2218	2303	2322	0008	...	...	...

		⑥	⑥	⑥ L	⑥ A	⑥	⑥ L	⑥ A	⑥
London Euston 143 ‡ d.	⑥	0005	0034	...	...	...	0534	...	0624
Watford Junction 143 ‡ d.		0025	0059	...	...	...	0553	...	0639
Leighton Buzzard d.		0054	0132	...	...	...	0625	...	0708
Bletchley d.		0101	0139	0529	...	...	0631	...	0715
Milton Keynes 143 ‡ d.		0109	0148	0537	...	...	0637	...	0720
Northampton 143 a.		0126	0205	0553	...	...	0653	...	0737
Northampton 143 d.		...	...	0556	0604	0641	0653	0714	0737
Rugby 143 ‡ d.		...	...	0618	0628	0701	0718	0737	0759
Coventry ‡ d.		...	...	0630	0639	0711	0730	0747	0810
Birmingham Int'l ✈ ‡ d.		...	...	0646	0654	0729	0746	0802	0828
Birmingham New St ‡ a.		...	...	0700	0706	0742	0801	0814	0840

	⑥ L	⑥ A	⑥	⑥ L	⑥ A	⑥	⑥ L	⑥ A	⑥	⑥ L	⑥ A	⑥	⑥ L	Q	⑥	⑥	⑥	⑥ A	⑥	⑥	⑥	⑥	⑥	⑥	⑥	⑥	⑥
London Euston 143 ‡ d.	...	...	0724	0749	0815	0824	0849	0915	0924	0949	1015	1024	1049		1815	1824	1849	1910	1920	1930	1947	2039	2042	2109	2131	2234	2340
Watford Junction 143 ‡ d.	...	...	0739	0804	|	0839	0904	|	0939	1004	|	1039	1104	and	|	1839	1904	|	1936	1951	2006	2055	2100	2129	|	2251	2359
Leighton Buzzard d.	...	...	0808	|	0842	0908	|	0943	1008	|	1042	1108	|	at	1843	1908	|	|	2001	2022	2036	2121	|	2159	2209	2318	0032
Bletchley d.	...	...	0815	|	0849	0915	0924	0951	1015	1024	1050	1115	|	the	1851	1915	|	|	|	2029	2043	|	2131	2206	2216	2325	0039
Milton Keynes 143 ‡ d.	...	...	0820	0826	0855	0920	0929	0955	1020	1030	1056	1120	1124	same	1856	1920	1925	1946	2011	2037	2050	2132	2140	2214	2225	2334	0047
Northampton 143 a.	...	...	0837	0841	0912	0937	0944	1012	1037	1046	1114	1137	1143	minutes	1912	1937	1945	2004	2025	2055	2109	2151	2157	2232	2244	2351	0104
Northampton 143 d.	0756	0814	0837	0855	0914	0937	0955	1013	1037	1056	1114	1137	1155	past	1914	1937	1956	2004	2031	2057	2118	2156	2216	...	2253	...	...
Rugby 143 ‡ d.	0818	0836	0859	0917	0936	0959	1017	1036	1059	1118	1136	1159	1217	each	1937	1959	2019	2026	2054	2118	2139	2218	2238	...	2314	...	...
Coventry ‡ d.	0830	0847	0910	0929	0947	1010	1030	1047	1110	1130	1147	1210	1230	hour	1947	2010	2031	2037	2107	2130	2150	2230	2250	...	2329	...	...
Birmingham Int'l ✈ ‡ d.	0846	0902	0928	0945	1002	1028	1046	1102	1128	1146	1202	1228	1245	until	2002	2028	2047	2055	2125	2146	2205	2246	2305	...	2344	...	...
Birmingham New St ‡ a.	0901	0913	0939	1000	1013	1039	1101	1113	1139	1201	1214	1241	1302		2014	2039	2102	2106	2142	2201	2218	2301	2317	...	0002	...	...

		⑦	⑦	⑦	⑦ L	⑦	⑦	⑦ A	⑦	⑦	⑦ A	⑦	⑦ A	⑦	⑦	⑦	⑦	⑦		⑦	⑦	⑦	⑦	⑦	⑦	⑦	⑦
London Euston 143 ‡ d.	⑦	0014	0653	0720	...	0752	0824	0855	0924	0955	1001	1031	1053	1124	1208	1231	1234	1306		1732	1734	1806	1831	1834	1911	1931	1934
Watford Junction 143 ‡ d.		0035	0712	0741	...	0810	0844	0914	0945	1011	1019	1047	1114	1142	1223	|	1250	1321	and	|	1750	1821	|	1850	|	|	1950
Leighton Buzzard d.		0106	0740	0810	...	0839	0914	0941	1014	1036	1047	1113	1142	1212	|	1258	1315	|	at	1800	1815	|	|	1915	|	1958	2015
Bletchley d.		0113	0747	0817	...	0845	0921	0948	1021	1043	|	|	1149	1219	|	1305	1322	|	the	1807	1822	|	|	1922	|	2005	2022
Milton Keynes 143 ‡ d.		0119	0757	0826	...	0851	0926	0957	1027	1051	1058	1126	1158	1228	1252j	1313	1328	1349	same	1814	1828	1847	1913j	1928	1950	2013	2028
Northampton 143 a.		0136	0814	0843	...	0908	0945	1014	1044	1105	1116	1145	1215	1244	1308	1331	1344	1407	minutes	1831	1844	1904	1930	1944	2007	2030	2044
Northampton 143 d.		...	...	...	...	0926	0959	1028	1100	1110	1130	1158	1217	1255	1315	1334	1355	1415	past	1834	1855	1907	1934	1955	2009	2034	2055
Rugby 143 ‡ d.		...	...	...	0853	0948	1021	1049	1122	1133	1151	1220	1239	1317	1337	1356	1417	1437	each	1856	1917	1937	1957	2017	2037	2057	2117
Coventry ‡ d.		...	...	...	0906	1000	1033	...	1134	1146	...	1232	...	1330	1347	1408	1430	1447	hour	1908	1930	1947	2008	2030	2048	2108	2130
Birmingham Int'l ✈ ‡ d.		...	...	...	0919	1009	1051	...	1152	1157	...	1250	...	1348	1358	1418	1448	1458	until	1918	1948	2000	2018	2048	2058	2118	2148
Birmingham New St ‡ a.		...	...	...	0930	1026	1102	...	1203	1206	...	1301	...	1359	1407	1430	1500	1507		1930	2001	2009	2030	2100	2108	2132	2159

	⑦	⑦	⑦	⑦	⑦	⑦	⑦	⑦
London Euston 143 ‡ d.	2034	2106	2131	2201	2231	2240	2259	2338
Watford Junction 143 ‡ d.	2050	2125	2147	2221	2252	2301	2319	0001
Leighton Buzzard d.	2114	2153	2217	2250	2321	2331	2352	0034
Bletchley d.	2121	2200	2224	2257	2328	2338	2359	0041
Milton Keynes 143 ‡ d.	2131	2208	2232	2306	2336	2247	0007	0049
Northampton 143 a.	2148	2225	2248	2324	2353	0002	0025	0106
Northampton 143 d.	2157	2237	2251	2333	...	...	...	...
Rugby 143 ‡ d.	2219	2258	2313	2354	...	...	...	...
Coventry ‡ d.	2232	2309	2337f	0004	...	...	...	...
Birmingham Int'l ✈ ‡ d.	2250	2318	2355	...	...	...	...	...
Birmingham New St ‡ a.	2302	2336	0007	...	...	...	...	...

		Ⓐ	Ⓐ	Ⓐ	Ⓐ	Ⓐ	Ⓐ	Ⓐ	Ⓐ	Ⓐ	Ⓐ	Ⓐ	Ⓐ	Ⓐ	Ⓐ
Birmingham New St ‡ d.	Ⓐ	...	...	...	...	0545	0533	...	...	...	0613	0634	0654	0714	0733
Birmingham Int'l ✈ ‡ d.		...	...	...	...	0555	0544	...	...	...	0630	0646	0705	0730	0745
Coventry ‡ d.		...	...	...	0538	0606	0602	...	0622	...	0648	0702	0722	0749j	0804
Rugby 143 ‡ d.		...	...	0515	0549	0620	0613	...	0633	...	0659	0712	0732	0759	0814
Northampton 143 a.		...	...	0536	0613	0639	0634	...	0654	...	0724	0733	0754	0821	0836
Northampton 143 d.		0414	0505	0545	0622	0641	0635	0651	0704	0715	0738	0742	0804	0823	0837
Milton Keynes 143 ‡ d.		0430	0521	0601	0638	|	0653	0707	0721	0732	0755	|	0821	0841	0851
Bletchley d.		0435	0526	0606	0643	|	0658	0712	|	|	0800	|	0826	0846	|
Leighton Buzzard d.		0442	0533	0613	0650	|	0706	|	0730	0741	0807	|	0832	0853	|
Watford Junction 143 ‡ d.		0513	0602	0630	0707	|	|	0746	|	|	|	|	|	|	0913
London Euston 143 ‡ a.		0538	0620	0645	0722	0728	0738	0805	0801	0813	0838	0828	0911	0924	0929

A – To Crewe (Table **144**).
L – To Liverpool Lime Street (Table **144**).
Q – The 1149 departure from London Euston departs Northampton 1251. The 1324 departure does not call at Bletchley.

f – Arrives 2323.
j – Arrives 6 – 7 minutes earlier.

‡ – For faster journeys between these stations see Table **150**.

NOTES FOR TABLE 140

A – From / to Gloucester, Cheltenham Spa, Worcester or Great Malvern (see Table **138**).
B – Also calls at Havant, Chichester, Worthing and Hove and v.v.
C – From Gloucester (Table **132a**).
D – From London Waterloo (see other direction of table).
E – From Cheltenham Spa (Table **132a**).
F – From Cheltenham Spa on Ⓐ (Table **138**).
G – From Yeovil (see other direction of table).
H – To Basingstoke (Table **108**).
J – From Yeovil Junction (Table **108**). To London Waterloo (see other direction of table).
K – From Castle Cary (see other direction of table).

L – To Yeovil Pen Mill (see other direction of table).
N – To Salisbury (see other direction of table).
P – To London Paddington (Table **110**).
R – To Swindon (Table **132a**).
S – From Swindon (Table **132a**).
T – From Taunton on ⑥ (Table **115**).
W – To / from London Waterloo (Table **108**).
Y – To / from London Waterloo (Table **108**); until Sept. 7 also conveys (1,2) to / from Corfe Castle via Wareham (Table **114a**).

a – Until Sept. 7.
b – From Sept. 14.
c – Arrives 1542 on Ⓐ.
d – Arrives 2243 on ⑤; 2256 on ①-④.
e – Arrives 9 – 12 minutes earlier.
f – Arrival time. Calls after Westbury.
g – Calls at Frome before Westbury.
h – Until Oct. 20.
j – Departs 4 minutes later on ⑥.
t – Arrives 4 – 6 minutes earlier.

142 BIRMINGHAM - NORTHAMPTON - LONDON — LM

	ⒶL	Ⓐ	Ⓐ	ⒶL	Ⓐ	ⒶA	ⒶL		Ⓐ	ⒶA	ⒶL	Ⓐ	ⒶA	ⒶL	Ⓐ	ⒶA	ⒶL	Ⓐ	ⒶA	ⒶL	Ⓐ	ⒶA	ⒶL	ⒶA	ⒶL	ⒶL	ⒶL
Birmingham New St ‡ d.	0754	0813	0833	0854	0913	0933	0954	and	1514	1533	1554	1614	1633	1654	1714	1733	1754	1814	1833	1854	1914	1933	1954	2033	2054	2134	2154
Birmingham Int'l ✈ ‡ d.	0805	0829	0845	0905	0929	0944	1005	at	1530	1544	1605	1630	1644	1705	1730	1744	1805	1830	1846	1905	1930	1944	2006	2045	2105	2145	2205
Coventry ‡ d.	0822	0848	0900	0925	0947	1001	1021	the	1549	1601	1621	1648	1701	1722	1748	1801	1822	1848	1901	1921	1948	2001	2022	2102	2121	2201	2222
Rugby 143 ‡ d.	0839	0858	0911	0938	0958	1012	1032	same	1559	1611	1632	1658	1715	1732	1758	1813	1732	1858	1912	1932	1958	2012	2033	2114	2131	2212	2232
Northampton 143 a.	0900	0920	0933	0959	1022	1035	1054	minutes	1623	1633	1657	1720	1738	1756	1823	1834	1854	1920	1937	1954	2020	2037	2055	2135	2154	2235	2254
Northampton 143 d.	0905	0924	0952	1005	1024	1037	1104	past	1624	1638	1706	1724	1739	1805	1825	1837	1905	1925	1938	2005	2022	2038	2105	2137	2204	...	2255
Milton Keynes 143 ‡ d.	0922	0941	1006	1022	1041	1051	1121	each	1642	1653	1722	1742	1753	1822	1842	1852	1922	1942	1952	2022	2044	2055	2122	2153	2221	...	2313
Bletchley d.	0927	0946	|	1027	1046	|	1126	hour	1647	|	1727	1747	|	1827	1847	|	1927	1947	|	2027	2050	|	2127	2158	2226	...	2318
Leighton Buzzard d.	0934	0953	|	1034	1053	|	1133	until	1654	|	1734	1755	|	1834	1854	|	1934	1954	|	2034	2057	|	2134	2205	2235	...	2325
Watford Junction 143 ‡ d.	0959	|	1028	1059	|	1114	1158	△	|	1715	1759	|	1815	1859	|	|	1959	|	2015	2059	|	|	2159	2234	2301	...	0001
London Euston 143 ‡ a.	1017	1023	1044	1118	1125	1130	1217		1725	1731	1817	1825	1830	1918	1924	1928	2018	2025	2030	2117	2127	2130	2224	2253	2323	...	0025

	Ⓐ	Ⓐ	Ⓐ	Ⓐ		⑥	⑥	⑥	⑥	⑥	⑥	⑥	⑥	⑥	⑥A	⑥L	⑥	⑥A		⑥	⑥A	⑥L	⑥	⑥A	⑥L	⑥	⑥A
Birmingham New St ‡ d.	2214	2234	2255	2310	⑥	...	...	...	0533	...	0614	0633	0654	0714	0734	0754	0814	0833	and	1314	1333	1354	1414	1433	1454	1514	1533
Birmingham Int'l ✈ ‡ d.	2230	2245	2306	2320		...	...	...	0544	...	0630	0645	0705	0730	0745	0805	0830	0845	at	1330	1344	1405	1430	1445	1505	1530	1544
Coventry ‡ d.	2248	2303	2322	2331		...	...	...	0602	...	0648	0701	0721	0748	0801	0821	0848	0901	the	1348	1401	1421	1448	1501	1521	1548	1601
Rugby 143 ‡ d.	2300	2314	2332	2344		...	...	...	0613	...	0659	0712	0731	0759	0812	0832	0859	0912	same	1359	1412	1432	1501	1512	1532	1559	1612
Northampton 143 a.	2321	2336	2355	0005s		...	...	...	0634	...	0720	0734	0753	0820	0833	0857	0920	0933	minutes	1420	1434	1453	1522	1533	1553	1620	1633
Northampton 143 d.	2334	...	...	|		0515	0614	0604	0638	0705	0722	0738	0805	0825	0841	0905	0925	0938	past	1422	1439	1501	1524	1538	1605	1625	1638
Milton Keynes 143 ‡ d.	2350	...	...	0024		0532	0628	0620	0655	0722	0738	0754	0822	0842	0856	0922	0942	0953	each	1438	1453	1522	1541	1553	1622	1642	1653
Bletchley d.	|	...	...	|		0537	|	0625	0700	0727	0743	|	0827	0847	|	0927	0947	|	hour	1443	|	1527	1546	|	1627	1647	|
Leighton Buzzard d.	|	...	...	|		0544	0637	0632	0707	0733	0750	|	0833	0854	|	0934	0954	|	until	1450	|	1534	1553	|	1634	1654	|
Watford Junction 143 ‡ d.	0033	...	...	0054s		0617	|	0705j	|	0759	|	0816	0859	|	0918	0959	|	1015	△	|	1515	1559	|	1615	1659	|	1715
London Euston 143 ‡ a.	0054	...	...	0113		0640	0707	0722	0739	0818	0820	0831	0917	0925	0933	1017	1025	1030		1520	1531	1619	1624	1630	1717	1724	1730

	⑥L	⑥	⑥A	⑥L	⑥	⑥A	⑥L	⑥	⑥A	⑥L	⑥	⑥A	⑥L	⑥	⑥A	⑥L	⑥A	⑥L	⑥	⑥		⑦	⑦	⑦	⑦	⑦	⑦	⑦
Birmingham New St ‡ d.	1554	1614	1633	1654	1714	1733	1754	1814	1833	1854	1914	1933	1954	2014	2033	2054	2134	2154	2214	2252	⑦	...	...	...	...	...	...	*0834*
Birmingham Int'l ✈ ‡ d.	1605	1630	1644	1705	1731	1745	1805	1830	1844	1905	1930	1944	2005	2030	2044	2105	2146	2205	2230	2303		...	...	...	...	...	...	*0846*
Coventry ‡ d.	1621	1648	1701	1721	1749	1801	1821	1848	1901	1921	1948	2001	2021	2048	2101	2121	2201	2221	2248	2319		...	...	...	...	...	...	*0902*
Rugby 143 ‡ d.	1632	1659	1715	1732	1759	1812	1832	1859	1912	1932	1959	2012	2032	2058	2112	2132	2212	2232	2259	2330		...	...	...	...	...	...	*0913*
Northampton 143 a.	1656	1720	1738	1753	1821	1837	1853	1920	1933	1953	2020	2035	2053	2119	2134	2153	2233	2253	2321	2352		...	...	...	...	...	...	*0935*
Northampton 143 d.	1705	1725	1739	1805	1825	1839	1905	1927	1933	2000	2025	2036	2100	2122	2140	2205	2240	...	2330	...		...	*0615**	0752	0815	0845	0925	1008
Milton Keynes 143 ‡ d.	1722	1742	1753	1822	1842	1853	1922	1944	1948	2016	2039	2051	2116	2138	2159	2221	2256	...	2346	...		0642	0710	0808	0831	0901	0942	1025
Bletchley d.	1727	1747	|	1827	1847	|	1927	1949	...	2021	|	2056	2120	|	2204	2226	2301	...	2351	...		0647	0715	0813	0836	0906	0947	1030
Leighton Buzzard d.	1734	1754	|	1834	1854	|	1934	1956	...	2028	2048	|	2127	2147	|	2233	2308	...	2358	...		0653	0722	0820	0843	0913	0954	1037
Watford Junction 143 ‡ d.	1759	|	1815	1859	|	1916	1959	2023	...	2050	2114	2131	2154	2219	2233	2307	2343	...	0020	...		0725	0753	0852	0908	0938	1027	1105
London Euston 143 ‡ a.	1817	1824	1830	1917	1926	1931	2017	2045	...	2110	2134	2154	2212	2240	2253	2330	0006	...	0040	...		0745	0813	0912	0927	0958	1044	1128

	⑦	⑦	⑦	⑦	⑦A	⑦	⑦	⑦	⑦	⑦	⑦		⑦	⑦	⑦	⑦	⑦	⑦	⑦	⑦	⑦	⑦A	⑦	⑦	⑦	⑦	⑦
Birmingham New St ‡ d.	0914	0937	...	1014	...	1054	1114	1154	1214	1254	1314	and	1714	1754	1814	1854	1914	1917	1954	2014	2054	...	2117	...	2214	2248	2300
Birmingham Int'l ✈ ‡ d.	0925	0955	...	1025	...	1105	1124	1205	1225	1305	1324	at	1724	1807	1824	1905	1924	1928	2005	2025	2105	...	2128	...	2225	2305	2310
Coventry ‡ d.	0944	1011	...	1044	...	1115	1136	1215	1237	1317	1337	the	1737	1817	1837	1918	1937	1947	2018	2044	2117	...	2147	...	2244	2317	2321
Rugby 143 ‡ d.	0955	1022	...	1055	1119	1127	1147	1227	1247	1328	1347	same	1750	1827	1847	1928	1947	1958	2028	2055	2127	2131	2158	...	2255	2327	2335
Northampton 143 a.	1016	1042	...	1116	1143	1148	1209	1248	1309	1348	1409	minutes	1812	1847	1908	1948	2009	2019	2048	2116	2148	2152	2218	...	2316	2349	2354s
Northampton 143 d.	1030	1104	1110	1125	1143	1148	1210	1248	1311	1348	1410	past	1813	1848	1909	1953	2011	2025	...	2129	...	2155	2225	2300	2325	...	|
Milton Keynes 143 ‡ d.	1047	1122	1126	1142	1200	1205	1227	1305	1328	1405	1427	each	1830	1905	1924	2011	2027	2041	...	2145	...	2211	2241	2316	2341	...	0013s
Bletchley d.	1052	|	1131	1147	1205	1210	1232	1310	1333	1410	1432	hour	1835	1910	1929	2016	...	2046	...	2150	...	2216	2246	2321	2346	...	|
Leighton Buzzard d.	1059	|	1138	1154	1212	1217	1239	1317	1340	1417	1439	until	1842	1917	1936	2023	...	2052	...	2157	...	2223	2252	2328	2352	...	|
Watford Junction 143 ‡ d.	1126	1154	1209	1219	1231	1239	1300	1339	1405	1439	1500		1903	1939	2002	2052	...	2123	...	2227	...	2254	2323	2359	0023	...	0043s
London Euston 143 ‡ a.	1147	1215	1229	1240	1248	1301	1318	1401	1424	1501	1518		1924	2001	2019	2114	...	2143	...	2247	...	2317	2343	0023	0043	...	0103

A – From Crewe (Table **144**).
L – From Liverpool Lime Street (Table **144**).
j – Arrives 6–7 minutes earlier.
s – Stops to set down only.
* – Connection by 🚌.
△ – Timings may vary by up to 3 minutes.
‡ – For faster journeys between these stations see Table **150**.

143 LONDON - CREWE via Trent Valley — LM

km			⑥	Ⓐ	Ⓐ	⑥	Ⓐ	Ⓐ	⑥	Ⓐ	⑥	Ⓐ	⑥	Ⓐ	⑥	⚒	Ⓐ	⑥	Ⓐ	⑥	⚒	⚒	⚒	⑥	Ⓐ
0	**London** Euston 142 150/2/3 d.	⚒	...	...	...	...	0534	0628	0629	0746	0746	0846	0846	0946	0946	1046	1146	1146	1246	1246	1346	1446	1546	1646	1646
78	Milton Keynes 142 150 152 d.		...	...	...	...	0640	0701	0702	0819	0819	0919	0919	1019	1019	1119	1219	1219	1319	1319	1419	1519	1619	1719	1719
104	Northampton 142 d.		0541	0520	0601	0637	0657	|	|	|	|	|	|	|	|	|	|	|	|	|	|	|	|	|	|
135	Rugby 142 150 d.		0602	0542	0623	0657	0719	0729	0727	0842	0842	0942	0942	1042	1042	1142	1242	1242	1349	1342	1442	1542	1642	1742	1747
158	Nuneaton d.		0621f	0555	0640f	0711	|	0741	0741	0857	0856	0954	0956	1054	1055	1155	1254	1255	1400	1355	1454	1555	1654	1755	1801
178	Tamworth (Low Level) d.		0635	0609	0702	0728	|	0755	0755	0918	0910	1008	1010	1108	1109	1209	1307	1310	1414	1410	1508	1610	1708	1810	1816
188	Lichfield Trent Valley d.		0641	0616	0721	0734	|	0802	0801	0926	0916	1016	1018	1116	1117	1216	1314	1317	1421	1417	1516	1617	1716	1817	1822
217	Stafford 153 d.		0658	0635	|	0754	0838	0818	0818	0935	0935	1035	1035	1135	1147t	1235	1341	1344	1438r	1436	1535	1635	1735	1836	1842
268	**Crewe** 152 153 a.		0716	0653	0740	0814	0856	0836	0837	0953	0953	1053	1053	1153	1208	1253	1404	1403	1457r	1454	1553	1654	1754	1854	1901

	⑥	Ⓐ	⑥	①–④	⑤	⑥	Ⓐ	⑥	Ⓐ	Ⓐ	Ⓐ		⑦	⑦	⑦	⑦	⑦		⑦	⑦	⑦	⑦	⑦	⑦	⑦
London Euston 142 150/2/3 d.	1746	1746	1846	1846	1849	1933	1946	2034	2046	2149	2200	⑦	...	0855	1001	1053	1243	...	1343	1443	1543	1646	1743	1843	1947
Milton Keynes 142 150 152 d.	1819	1819	1919	1919	1924	2006	2019	2122	2119	2222	2240		...	0957	1058	1158	1320	...	1419	1519	1619	1722	1819	1919	|
Northampton 142 d.	|	|	|	|	1946	|	|	|	|	|	|		0930	1028	1130	1217	|	...	|	|	|	|	|	|	|
Rugby 142 150 d.	1842	1848	1942	1947	2005	2030	2042	2146	2145	2243	2302		0952	1049	1151	1239	1347	...	1447	1542	1647	1755	1847	1947	2047
Nuneaton d.	1855	1900	1955	2002	2018	2043	2100	2158	2200	2257	2312		1005	1102	1203	1251	1400	...	1500	1555	1700	1808	1900	2000	2100
Tamworth (Low Level) d.	1910	1915	2010	2017	2033	2058	2114	2212	2215	2310	2326s		1020	1116	1217	1305	1415	...	1515	1610	1715	1821	1915	2015	2115
Lichfield Trent Valley d.	1917	1921	2017	2023	2039	2104	2121	2218	2222	2316	2333s		1026	1122	1223	1311	1421	...	1521	1617	1721	1828	1921	2021	2121
Stafford 153 d.	1935	1941	2035	2046	2057	2121	2142	2241	2244	2346	2348s		1047	1144	1245	1330	1440	...	1540	1636	1740	1858	1940	2059	2140
Crewe 152 153 a.	1953	2002	2053	2107	2118	2139	2200	2301	2302	0013	0016		1107	1204	1303	1348	1458	...	1558	1655	1758	1916	2000	2117	2158

		⑥	Ⓐ	⑥	Ⓐ	⑥	⑥	Ⓐ		⑥	Ⓐ	⑥	Ⓐ	⑥	⚒	⚒	⚒		⚒	⚒	⚒		⚒	Ⓐ	⑥
Crewe 152 153 d.	⚒	0538	0547	0624	0714	0725	0744	0816	...	0833	0933	0933	1033	1033	1133	1233	1332	...	1433	1533	1632	...	1732	1832	1833
Stafford 153 d.		0559	0608	0647	0739	0748	0807	0837	...	0855	0952	0956	1052	1055	1156	1256	1356	...	1456	1556	1656	...	1756	1856	1856
Lichfield Trent Valley d.		0616	0625	0704	0756	0805	0826	0854	...	0912	1010	1013	1113	1113	1213	1313	1413	...	1513	1613	1713	...	1813	1914	1912
Tamworth (Low Level) d.		0623	0634	0711	0803	0812	0832	0900	...	0919	1017	1020	1119	1120	1220	1320	1420	...	1520	1619	1720	...	1820	1921	1919
Nuneaton d.		0639	0650	0726	0818	0827	0847	0915	...	0934	1032	1035	1135	1135	1235	1335	1435	...	1535	1635	1735	...	1835	1937	1934
Rugby 142 150 d.		0655	0705	0742	0833	0842	0903	0931	...	0950	1051	1050	1152	1150	1251	1350	1451	...	1550	1651	1750	...	1851	1955	1949
Northampton 142 d.		|	|	|	|	|	|	|	...	|	|	|	|	|	|	|	|	...	|	|	|	...	|	|	2011
Milton Keynes 142 150 152 a.		|	|	0804	0855	0905	0924	0954	...	1014	1114	1114	1214	1215	1314	1414	1514	...	1614	1714	1814	...	1914	2016	...
London Euston 142 150/2/3 a.		0757	0806	0840	0936	0950	1000	1030	...	1050	1150	1150	1250	1251	1350	1450	1550	...	1652	1750	1850	...	1950	2052	...

	⑥	Ⓐ	Ⓐ	⑥		Ⓐ	Ⓐ	Ⓐ		⑦	⑦	⑦	⑦		⑦	⑦	⑦	⑦	⑦		⑦	⑦	⑦	⑦	
Crewe 152 153 d.	1933	1935	2036	2038	...	2125	2129	2153	⑦	0952	1133	1216	1316	...	1416	1516	1616	1716	1816	...	1933	2016	2124	2131	...
Stafford 153 d.	1952	1952	2103	2058	...	2144	2149	2212		1018	1141	1237	1337	...	1437	1537	1637	1734	1837	...	1951	2034	2143	2151	...
Lichfield Trent Valley d.	2009	2009	2120	2115	...	2158	2206	2229		1035	1159	1254	1354	...	1454	1554	1654	1751	1854	...	2008	2051	2200	2208	...
Tamworth (Low Level) d.	2015	2016	2127	2122	...	2205	2213	2236		1042	1206	1300	1400	...	1500	1600	1700	1758	1900	...	2014	2058	2207	2215	...
Nuneaton d.	2030	2032	2142	2137	...	2218	2228	2258		1057	1220	1315	1415	...	1515	1615	1715	1812	1915	...	2029	2113	2218	2230	...
Rugby 142 150 d.	2046	2047	2157	2152	...	2230	2241	2311		1116	1235	1330	1430	...	1530	1630	1730	1829	1930	...	2044	2130	2231	2245	...
Northampton 142 d.	2107	|	2221	|	...	|	2303	|		1143	|	|	|	...	|	|	|	|	|	...	|	2152	|	2308	...
Milton Keynes 142 150 152 a.	...	2109	...	2215	...	2253	...	2344		1158	1258	1354	1454	...	1553	1653	1753	1852	1953	...	2106	2211	2304	...	...
London Euston 142 150/2/3 a.	...	2150	...	2303	...	2344	...	0045		1248	1349	1433	1533	...	1632	1732	1832	1931	2032	...	2157	2317	2353	...	...

r – Runs 4 minutes later on ④.
t Arrives 1133.

LM BEDFORD - BLETCHLEY 143a

km		Ⓐ	⚒	⚒	⚒	Ⓐ	⑥	⚒	Ⓐ	⑥	⚒	⚒	⚒	Ⓐ	⑥	⚒	⑥	Ⓐ	Ⓐ	⑥	Ⓐ	⑥	⚒	⑥	Ⓐ
0	**Bedford** d.	0603	0729	0828	0929	1050	1055	1155	1255	1258	1355	1455	1555	1640	1640	1740	1826	1826	1930	1930	2009	2009	2112	2208	2238
20	Woburn Sands d.	0635	0801	0900	1001	1121	1126	1226	1326	1329	1426	1526	1626	1712	1712	1812	1857	1857	2002	2002	2040	2040	2143	2239	2309
27	**Bletchley** a.	0645	0812	0911	1012	1132	1136	1237	1336	1340	1437	1537	1637	1722	1722	1822	1908	1908	2013	2013	2050	2050	2153	2249	2319
	Milton Keynes 142 a.	*0700*	*0822*	*0920*	*1030*	*1148*	*1148*	*1248*	*1346*	*1355*	*1448*	*1554*	*1648*	*1732*	*1748*	*1848*	*1920*	*1925*	*2026*	*2037*	*2100*	*2139*	*2214*	*2303*	*2350*

	⑥	Ⓐ	Ⓐ	⑥	⚒	⚒		⚒	⚒	⚒	⚒	⑥	Ⓐ	⚒	⚒	⚒		⚒	⚒	Ⓐ	⑥	⚒	Ⓐ	⑥
Milton Keynes 142 d.	*0435*	*0504*	*0601*	*0620*	*0707*	*0812*	...	*0941*	*1042*	*1141*	*1242*	*1341*	*1352*	*1438*	*1541*	*1642*	...	*1722*	*1822*	*1847*	*1913*	*1944*	*2050*	*2116*
Bletchley d.	0516	0516	0624	0629	0731	0822	...	0958	1101	1201	1301	1401	1401	1501	1551	1653	...	1732	1832	1922	1922	2023	2121	2138
Woburn Sands d.	0527	0527	0636	0640	0742	0834	...	1010	1112	1212	1312	1412	1412	1512	1602	1704	...	1743	1843	1933	1933	2034	2132	2149
Bedford a.	0558	0558	0708	0715	0813	0906	...	1043	1143	1243	1343	1443	1443	1543	1633	1735	...	1814	1914	2004	2004	2105	2203	2220

LM BIRMINGHAM - CREWE - LIVERPOOL 144

km		⚒	Ⓐ	⑥	Ⓐ	Ⓐ	⑥	⑥D	ⒶA	⑥B	ⒶB	⚒	⚒C	⑥B	Ⓐ	⚒	⚒E	ⒶC	⑥B	⚒	⚒C	⚒C	⚒	⚒C	⚒C	⚒
	Birmingham Int'l ✈ ❖ d.		...	...	...	0552	0618	0646	0646	0654	0658	0718	0746	0802	...	0817	0846	0902	0902	0918	0945	1002	1017	1046	1102	1118
0	**Birmingham** N St §119 ❖ d.		0602	0607	0607	0636	0636	0704	0704	0713	0720	0736	0804	0821	0820	0836	0904	0920	0920	0936	1003	1020	1035	1104	1120	1136
19	Wolverhampton 119 ❖ d.		0621	0633	0632	0656	0656	0723	0723	|	0740	0754	0822	0841	0841	0856	0922	0940	0941	0956	1022	1040	1054	1122	1140	1154
43	Stafford 119 143 153 d.		0638	0647	0646	0713	0713	0739	0739	0748	0755	0811	0838	0857	0856	0911	0938	0955	0956	1012	1038	1056	1110	1138	1156	1210
	Stone d.		|	0656	0655	|	|	|	|	0757	0804	|	|	0906	0905	|	|	1004	1006	|	|	1105	|	|	1205	|
	Stoke on Trent 119 d.		|	0704	0714	|	|	|	|	0810f	0812	|	|	0914	0913	|	|	1012	1014	|	|	1113	|	|	1213	|
82	**Crewe** 143 153 d.		0700	0729	0743	0733	0733	0758	0759	0831	0833	0832	0857	0935	0934	0932	0958	1032	1036	1032	1058	1135	1130	1158	1235	1230
118	Runcorn 153 a.		0724	...	...	0759	0759	0823	0824	...	...	0853	0922	...	...	0952	1025	...	...	1053	1124	...	1153	1224	...	1252
131	**Liverpool** S Parkway ‡ a.		0704	...	...	0809	0810	0831	0835	...	...	0902	0931	...	...	1001	1033	...	...	1102	1132	...	1202	1233	...	1301
140	**Liverpool** Lime Street 153 a.		0729	...	...	0819	0819	0842	0844	...	...	0911	0940	...	...	1012	1044	...	...	1111	1143	...	1212	1243	...	1311

	⚒C	⚒C	⑥	Ⓐ	⚒C	⚒C	⚒	and at the same minutes past each hour until	⚒	⚒C	⚒C	⑥	Ⓐ	⚒C	⚒C	⑥	Ⓐ	⚒C	⑥C	Ⓐ	Ⓐ	⑥	⑥C	Ⓐ	Ⓐ
Birmingham Int'l ✈ ❖ d.	1146	1202	1218	1218	1246	1302	1318		1618	1646	1703	1718	1718	1746	1803	1818	1818	1846	1903	...	1918	1919	1947	2003	2018
Birmingham N St § 119 ❖ d.	1204	1220	1236	1236	1304	1320	1336		1636	1704	1721	1736	1736	1804	1820	1836	1836	1904	1921	1920	1936	1937	2004	2019	2036
Wolverhampton 119 ❖ d.	1222	1240	1254	1254	1322	1340	1354		1654	1722	1738	1754	1754	1822	1840	1854	1854	1922	1940	1940	1954	1958	2022	2040	2054
Stafford 119 143 153 d.	1238	1256	1310	1311	1338	1355	1410		1710	1738	1756	1810	1810	1838	1854	1910	1910	1938	1955	1957	2009	2013	2038	2054	2109
Stone d.	|	1305	|	|	|	1404	|		|	|	1806	|	|	|	1903	|	|	|	2004	2006	|	|	|	2104	|
Stoke on Trent 119 d.	|	1313	|	|	|	1412	|		|	|	1814	|	|	|	1911	|	|	|	2012	2015	|	|	|	2112	|
Crewe 143 153 d.	1259	1334	1330	1333	1357	1434	1431		1731	1758	1837	1830	1834	1859	1937	1931	1933	1958	2034	2036	2034f	2035	2058	2133	2132f
Runcorn 153 a.	1322	...	1350	1356	1424	...	1454	★	1752	1824	...	1851	1858	1923	...	1952	1956	...	...	...	2056	2101	2121	...	2155
Liverpool S Parkway ‡ a.	1331	...	1359	1404	1432	...	1503		1802	1832	...	1900	1908	1932	...	2001	2005	...	...	...	2106	2111	2130	...	2204
Liverpool Lime Street 153 a.	1341	...	1409	1414	1443	...	1514		1812	1842	...	1910	1919	1942	...	2011	2016	...	...	...	2116	2120	2139	...	2216

	⑥	ⒶC	⑥C	ⒶC	Ⓐ	ⒶC	⑥	ⒶC	⑦	⑦	⑦	⑦	⑦	⑦	⑦	⑦	⑦		⑦	⑦	⑦	⑦	⑦	⑦	⑦	⑦
Birmingham Int'l ✈ ❖ d.	2018	2046	2055	2102	2118	2147	...	2247		...	0919	...	...	...	...	...	...	...	...	...	...	...	...	...	...	...
Birmingham N St § 119 ❖ d.	2036	2104	2113	2120	2136	2212	2239	2310		0917	0942	1017	1042	1116	1140	1217	1235	...	1317	1335	1420	1435	1520	1535	1620	1635
Wolverhampton 119 ❖ d.	2054	2123	2133	2140	2154	2241	2305	2337		0934	1000	1035	1102	1134	1200	1233	1255	...	1334	1355	1441	1455	1541	1555	1641	1655
Stafford 119 143 153 d.	2110	2144	2147	2159	2210	2258	2321	2353		0947	1016	1049	1119	1148	1217	1247	1310	...	1348	1411	1457	1511	1556	1611	1657	1710
Stone d.	|	|	2156	2208	|	2308	|	|		0958	|	1058	|	1157	|	1256	|	...	1357	|	1507	|	1605	|	1706	|
Stoke on Trent 119 d.	|	|	2204	2216	|	2317	|	|		1006	|	1106	|	1205	|	1304	|	...	1405	|	1515	|	1613	|	1714	|
Crewe 143 153 d.	2130	2204	2225	2237	2236	2338	2341	0019		1028	1036	1127	1141	1227	1237	1326	1331	...	1427	1431	1536	1531	1635	1631	1735	1731
Runcorn 153 a.	2150	...	...	...	2300	...	...	...		...	1101	...	1203	...	1302	...	1353	...	...	1457	...	1554	...	1657	...	1756
Liverpool S Parkway ‡ a.	2159	...	...	...	2309	...	...	...		...	1110	...	1212	...	1311	...	1402	...	...	1506	...	1603	...	1706	...	1805
Liverpool Lime Street 153 a.	2208	...	...	...	2320	...	...	...		...	1120	...	1222	...	1321	...	1412	...	...	1515	...	1612	...	1715	...	1814

	⑦	⑦	⑦	⑦	⑦	⑦	⑦	⑦	⑦	⑦	⑦
Birmingham Int'l ✈ ❖ d.	...	...	...	...	...	...	...	...	...	...	...
Birmingham N St § 119 ❖ d.	1720	1735	1820	1835	1920	1935	2020	2040	2120	2142	2200
Wolverhampton 119 ❖ d.	1741	1755	1840	1855	1941	1955	2041	2100	2146	2202	2221
Stafford 119 143 153 d.	1757	1811	1855	1911	1958	2011	2057	2116	2200	2219	2237
Stone d.	1806	|	1904	|	2007	|	2106	|	2209	|	2246
Stoke on Trent d.	1814	|	1912	|	2015	|	2114	|	2217	|	2254
Crewe 143 153 d.	1835	1831	1934	1931	2037	2032	2135	2135	2239	2238	2313
Runcorn 153 a.	...	1857	...	1954	...	2058	...	...	...	2304	...
Liverpool S Parkway ‡ a.	...	1906	...	2003	...	2107	...	...	...	2314	...
Liverpool Lime Street 153 a.	...	1915	...	2012	...	2116	...	...	...	2328	...

	⚒	Ⓐ	ⒶC	⑥C	⚒C	Ⓐ	Ⓐ	⑥	⑥C
Liverpool Lime Str 153 d.		...	...	...	0610	...	0631	0634	...
Liverpool South Parkway d.		...	...	...	0620	...	0641	0644	...
Runcorn 153 d.		...	...	...	0627	...	0648	0651	...
Crewe 143 153 d.		0601	0605	0601	0649	0635	0717	0718f	0701
Stoke on Trent 119 d.		0626	|	0626	|	0656	|	|	0729
Stone d.		0634	|	0634	|	0704	|	|	0740
Stafford 119 143 153 d.		0644	0632f	0645	0709	0715	0740	0738	0751
Wolverhampton 119 ❖ a.		0658	0648	0704t	0726	0729	0758	0754	0806
Birmingham New St 119 ❖ a.		0722	0710	0727	0750	0804	0818	0821	0825
Birmingham Int'l ✈ ❖ a.		...	0729	0745	0805	...	...	...	0844

	⚒C	⚒	⚒C	⚒C	⚒	and at the same minutes past each hour until	⚒C	⚒	⚒C	ⒶC	⑥C	⚒	⚒C	⚒C	⚒	⚒C	ⒶC	⑥C	Ⓐ	⑥	⚒C	⚒C	⚒	⚒C	⚒C
Liverpool Lime Street 153 d.	0705	0735	...	0805	0832		1105	1133	...	1205	1205	1233	...	1305	1333	...	1405	1405	1431	1435	...	1505	1533	...	1605
Liverpool S Parkway ‡ d.	0715	0744	...	0815	0842		1115	1143	...	1216	1218	1243	...	1315	1343	...	1415	1417	1441	1445	...	1515	1543	...	1615
Runcorn 153 d.	0723	0752	...	0823	0849		1123	1150	...	1223	1227	1250	...	1323	1350	...	1425	1425	1449	1452	...	1524	1550	...	1623
Crewe 143 153 d.	0750	0818	0801	0849	0917		1150	1219	1201	1251	1250	1318	1301	1349	1418	1401	1451	1449f	1521	1519	1501	1549	1619	1601	1649
Stoke on Trent 119 d.	|	|	0826	|	|		|	|	1226	|	|	|	1326	|	|	1426	|	|	|	|	1526	|	|	1626	|
Stone d.	|	|	0834	|	|		|	|	1234	|	|	|	1334	|	|	1434	|	|	|	|	1534	|	|	1634	|
Stafford 119 143 153 d.	0810	0838	0845	0909	0939		1209	1240	1245	1311	1309	1339	1345	1409	1438	1445	1512	1508	1541	1539	1545	1609	1639	1645	1708
Wolverhampton 119 ❖ a.	0827	0859	0903	0927	0958	★	1226	1258	1302	1328	1326	1358	1402	1426	1500	1504	1528	1525	1557	1558	1605r	1627	1658	1702	1726
Birmingham N St § 119 ❖ a.	0850	0921r	0927	0950	1021		1250	1320	1325	1350	1351	1420	1425	1450	1520	1525	1550	1550	1617	1617	1624	1650	1721	1725	1750
Birmingham Int'l ✈ ❖ a.	0905	...	0944	1005	...		1305	...	1344	1404	1405	...	1444	1505	...	1544	1605	1605	...	...	1644	1705	...	1744	1805

	Ⓐ	⑥	⚒C	⚒C	⚒	⚒C	⚒C	⚒	⚒C	ⒶC	⑥C	⚒	ⒶB	⑥C	ⒶC	⑥B	⚒	⑥	Ⓐ	⑥	⚒	⑥	Ⓐ	Ⓐ	⑦	⑦
Liverpool Lime Street 153 d.	1633	1635	...	1705	1734	...	1805	1834	...	1912	1912	1934	...	...	2005	2004	2035	...	...	2115	2134	2203	2235	2335		...
Liverpool S Parkway ‡ d.	1643	1645	...	1715	1744	...	1815	1844	...	1922	1922	1944	...	...	2015	2014	2045	...	...	2126	2144	2214	2247	2345		...
Runcorn 153 d.	1651	1652	...	1723	1751	...	1823	1851	...	1929	1930	1951	...	...	2023	2022	2052	...	...	2134	2151	2221	2255	2352		...
Crewe 143 153 d.	1723f	1719	1701	1749	1817	1801	1849	1919	1901	1955	1953	2019	2001	2002	2048	2052	2119	2102	2114	2200	2218	2244	2325	0023		0912
Stoke on Trent 119 d.	|	|	1726	|	|	1826	|	|	1926	|	|	|	2026	2026	|	|	|	2126	2137	...	|	...	...	...		0935
Stone d.	|	|	1734	|	|	1834	|	|	1934	|	|	|	2034	2035	|	|	|	2134	2145	...	|	...	...	...		0943
Stafford 119 143 153 d.	1742	1739	1745	1808	1839	1846	1909	1940	1945	2016	2011	2040	2048f	2045	2109	2113	2138	2145	2159	...	2237	...	...	...		0956
Wolverhampton 119 ❖ a.	1758	1758	1802	1825	1858	1903	1927	1958	2002	2032	2028	2058	2102	2103	2126	2130	2157	2159	2214	...	2258	...	...	...		1012
Birmingham N St § 119 ❖ a.	1821	1820	1825	1850	1920	1926	1950	2020	2026	2050	2050	2121	2125	2124	2148	2150	2218	2225	2239	...	2318	...	...	...		1028
Birmingham Int'l ✈ ❖ a.	...	...	1845	1905	...	1944	2005	...	2045	2105	2105	...	2145	2145	2205	2205	...	...	...	...	...	...	...	...		...

	⑦	⑦	⑦	⑦	⑦	⑦	⑦	⑦	⑦		⑦	⑦	⑦	⑦	⑦	⑦	⑦	⑦	⑦	⑦	⑦	⑦	⑦	⑦	⑦	⑦
Liverpool Lime Street 153 d.	...	1012	...	1135	...	1232	...	1335	...	...	1432	...	1535	...	1632	...	1735	...	1832	...	1932	...	2035	...	2134	...
Liverpool S Parkway ‡ d.	...	1022	...	1145	...	1243	...	1345	...	...	1443	...	1545	...	1643	...	1745	...	1842	...	1942	...	2045	...	2144	...
Runcorn 153 d.	...	1029	...	1152	...	1250	...	1352	...	...	1450	...	1552	...	1650	...	1752	...	1850	...	1950	...	2052	...	2151	...
Crewe 143 153 d.	1010	1105e	1112	1219	1212	1319	1312	1419	1412	...	1519	1515	1609	1615	1719	1715	1819	1816	1919	1904	2019	2004	2119	2108	2221	2210
Stoke on Trent 119 d.	1033	|	1134	|	1234	|	1333	|	1434	...	|	1539	|	1638	|	1737	|	1839	|	1926	|	2026	|	2129	|	2231
Stone d.	1042	|	1143	|	1243	|	1342	|	1443	...	|	1547	|	1646	|	1747	|	1848	|	1935	|	2035	|	2138	|	2240
Stafford 119 143 153 d.	1058f	1130f	1153	1238	1253	1338	1353	1440	1453	...	1540	1557	1637	1657	1738	1758	1838	1858	1938	1945	2039	2045	2138	2152	2242	2250
Wolverhampton 119 ❖ a.	1112	1147	1207	1255	1307	1355	1410	1456	1511	...	1556	1611	1654	1711	1755	1813	1855	1913	1955	1959	2056	2101	2155	2206	2258	2305
Birmingham N St § 119 ❖ a.	1129	1211	1227	1315	1324	1415	1427	1515	1527	...	1616	1628	1714	1727	1815	1830	1915	1930	2015	2018	2115	2119	2215	2230	2325	2330
Birmingham Int'l ✈ ❖ a.	...	...	...	...	...	...	...	...	...	...	...	...	...	...	...	1852	...	1952	...	...	...	...	...	...	...	...

A – From Milton Keyneys (Table **142**).
B – From/to Northampton (Table **142**).
C – From/to London Euston (Table **142**).
D – From Bletchley (Table **142**).
E – From London Euston on Ⓐ; from Northampton on ⑥ (Table **142**).
H – From Rugby (Table **142**).

e – Arrives 1056.
f – Arrives 4–6 minutes earlier.
r – Arrives 4–5 minutes earlier on ⑥.
t – Departs 0709.

★ – Timings may vary ± 4 minutes.
‡ – 🚌 connections available to/from Liverpool John Lennon Airport.
§ – Birmingham New Street.
❖ – See also Tables **142** and **150**.

145 BIRMINGHAM - SHREWSBURY - CHESTER

2nd class AW

km		⚒	⑥	Ⓐ	⑥	⚒A	Ⓐ	⑥🍷	ⒶB	Ⓐ	⑥🍷	Ⓐ🍷	⚒🍷	Ⓐ🍷	⑥🍷	Ⓐ🍷	⑥🍷	⚒🍷	⑥🍷	Ⓐ🍷	⚒🍷	⚒🍷	⚒🍷	ⒶC	⚒🍷	⚒🍷	⑥C
	London Euston **150** d.		...	...	...	...	...	M	...	...	...	L	...	L	...	...	...	F	...	...	F	...	...	1023	F	...	1123
0	**Birmingham** Int'l ✈ d.		...	...	...	...	...	...	...	...	...	...	...	0709	0709	...	...	0809	0910	0910	1009	...	1110	1133	1209	...	1233
13	**Birmingham** New St. d.		...	...	...	0530	...	...	...	...	...	...	0625	0723	0724	...	...	0824	0925	0925	1025	...	1125	1152	1225	...	1252
34	Wolverhampton d.		...	...	...	0548	...	...	...	...	...	...	0643	0743	0743	...	...	0844	0944	0943	1043	...	1143	1211	1244	...	1310
59	Telford Central d.		...	...	...	|	...	...	...	...	...	...	0659	0759	0800	...	...	0900	1000	0959	1100	...	1200	1229	1300	...	1328
65	Wellington d.		...	...	...	|	...	...	...	...	...	...	0706	0806	0806	...	...	0907	1007	1005	1106	...	1206	1236	1307	...	1335
81	**Shrewsbury** a.		...	...	...	|	...	...	...	...	...	...	0721	0819	0819	...	...	0920	1019	1021	1120	...	1221	1250	1320	...	1348
	Aberystwyth **147** a.		...	...	...	|	...	...	...	...	...	...	0920	|	|	...	...	1120	|	|	1320	...	|	...	1520	...	...
	Cardiff Central **149** d.		...	...	...	|	...	...	...	...	0520	0508	...	|	|	0721	0721	...	|	|	...	0921	|	...	...	1121	...
81	**Shrewsbury** d.		0520	0520	...	|	...	0610	*0610*	0700	0725	0725	...	0825	0825	0925	0925	...	1023	1025	...	1125	1225	...	...	1325	...
110	Gobowen d.		0538	0538	...	|	...	0629	*0629*	0719	0743	0743	...	0843	0843	0943	0943	...	1041	1043	...	1142	1243	...	...	1342	...
122	Ruabon d.		0550	0550	...	|	...	0641	*0641*	0731	0755	0755	...	0855	0855	0955	0955	...	1053	1055	...	1154	1255	...	...	1354	...
129	Wrexham General d.		0556	0606b	0619	|	0635	0650	0703	0740	0801	0801	...	0902	0901	1001	1001	...	1102	1100	...	1201	1301	...	...	1401	...
149	**Chester** 160 a.		0617	0625	0638	0643	0659	0709	0720	...	0819	0820	...	0919	0917	1020	1019	...	1121	1120	...	1219	1320	...	...	1419	...
	Holyhead **160** a.		...	...	...	0819	...	...	...	...	1012	...	...	...	1105	1223	1209	...	1312	1317	...	1414	1509	...	...	1614	...

	Ⓐ🍷	⑥🍷	⚒🍷	⚒🍷	Ⓐ🍷	⑥🍷	⚒🍷	⚒🍷	ⒶE	Ⓐ🍷	⑥🍷	Ⓐ✕	⚒	⚒🍷	⑥	Ⓐ	Ⓐ🍷	Ⓐ🍷	⑥🍷	⚒C	⚒	Ⓐ	⑥J	ⒶM	⑥	⑥
London Euston **150** d.	...	...	F	...	...	...	F	...	...	L	...	...	...	...	...	...	P	...	...	1823	...	...	...	...	...	...
Birmingham International ✈ d.	1308	1310	1409	...	1509	1509	1609	...	...	1709	1709	...	...	1809	...	...	...	1905	1909	1933	2009	...	...	2106	2109	...
Birmingham New Street d.	1325	1325	1425	...	1525	1525	1625	...	...	1726	1725	...	...	1825	...	...	...	1925	1925	1950	2025	...	...	2125	2125	...
Wolverhampton d.	1344	1342	1443	...	1543	1543	1643	...	...	1744	1743	...	...	1843	...	...	...	1943	1943	2018	2043	...	...	2142	2143	...
Telford Central d.	1401	1359	1500	...	1600	1600	1659	...	...	1801	1800	...	...	1859	...	...	...	2000	2000	2035	2059	...	...	2158	2200	...
Wellington d.	1407	1406	1506	...	1606	1607	1706	...	...	1807	1807	...	...	1906	...	...	...	2006	2006	2042	2105	...	...	2206	2206	...
Shrewsbury a.	1420	1419	1520	...	1620	1620	1720	...	...	1820	1820	...	...	1920	...	...	...	2019	2020	2055	2120	...	...	2218	2223	...
Aberystwyth **147** a.	|	|	1720	...	|	|	1922	...	...	|	|	...	...	2123	...	...	...	|	|	...	2336f	...	...	|	|	...
Cardiff Central **149** d.	|	|	...	1321	|	|	...	1521	1621	|	|	1716	...	▬	1721	...	1821	|	|	...	...	1934	1934	|	|	2055
Shrewsbury d.	1425	1422	...	1529	1624	1625	...	1724	1813	1825	1825	1909	...	...	1928	1927	2014	2028	2025	...	...	2141	2139	2224	2225	2306
Gobowen d.	1443	1440	...	1546	1643	1643	...	1741	|	1843	1843	|	...	...	1945	1945	|	2046	2043	...	...	2158	2156	2242	2243	|
Ruabon d.	1455	1452	...	1558	1655	1655	...	1753	a	1855	1855	|	...	⑥	1957	1957	a	2058	2055	...	...	2210	2208	2253	2255	a
Wrexham General d.	1501	1459	...	1605	1702	1703	...	1800	|	1901	1902	1938	1909	1948	2004	2003	|	2104	2101	...	...	2217	2215	2300	2301	|
Chester 160 a.	1518	1520	...	1623	1721	1719	...	1819	1905	1920	1921	1957	1928	2006	2023	2025	2108	2123	2120	...	...	2236	2233	2317	2322	0023
Holyhead **160** a.	1716	1712	...	1821	1917	1913	...	2020	...	...	2131	2141	...	...	2225	...	...	...	...	...	...	0048	...	...	...	...

	Ⓐ	⑥H	Ⓐ	⑥	Ⓐ	⑦	⑦🍷	⑦	⑦	⑦🍷	⑦🍷	⑦🍷	⑦🍷	⑦🍷	⑦🍷	⑦	⑦🍷	⑦🍷	⑦🍷	⑦	⑦C	⑦	⑦	⑦	⑦	⑦
London Euston **150** d.	...	...	...	...	...		...	...	...	G	...	...	...	...	F	...	...	...	...	...	1900	...	...	...	...	...
Birmingham International ✈ d.	...	...	...	...	...		...	0951	1048	1207	1307	...	1407	1507	1607	...	1708	1808	1907	2008	2012	2108	...	2211	2240	2308
Birmingham New Street d.	2236	2235	2335	2335	2252		...	1004	1104	1224	1324	...	1424	1524	1624	...	1724	1824	1924	2024	2026	2124	...	2224	2255	2324
Wolverhampton d.	2258	2253	0003	2354	2327		...	1022	1122	1242	1342	...	1444	1544	1644	...	1744	1843	1944	2044	2056	2143	...	2242	2315	2346
Telford Central d.	2325	2309	0030	0022	|		...	1049	1150	1259	1358	...	1502	1600	1701	...	1801	1900	2000	2101	2113	2210	...	2309	|	0013
Wellington d.	2333	2316	0037	0030	|		...	1057	1158	1305	1404	...	1508	1607	1707	...	1806	1906	2007	2107	2120	2217	...	2316	|	0020
Shrewsbury a.	2346	2328	0053	0045	|		...	1110	1214	1319	1418	...	1522	1622	1719	...	1820	1920	2020	2121	2135	2230	...	2332	|	0036
Aberystwyth **147** a.	...	...	▬	▬	|		...	1321	|	1520	|	...	1720	|	1920	...	|	2120	|	2315	...	|	...	...	|	...
Cardiff Central **149** d.	...	...	⑥	Ⓐ	|		...	...	|	...	|	1316	...	|	...	1515	|	...	|	▬	...	|	2112	...	|	...
Shrewsbury d.	...	...	2333	2340	|		1016	...	1218	...	1420	1525	...	1630	...	1730	1824	...	2023	...	...	2232	2319	...	|	...
Gobowen d.	...	...	2352	2357	|		1034	...	1236	...	1438	1543	...	1648	...	1748	1842	...	2041	...	...	|	|	...	|	...
Ruabon d.	...	...	0004	0009	|		1046	...	1248	...	1450	1555	...	1700	...	1800	1854	...	2053	⑦	...	a	a	...	|	...
Wrexham General d.	...	...	0014	0015	|		1052	...	1254	...	1456	1602	...	1707	...	1806	1900	...	2100	2235	...	|	|	...	|	...
Chester 160 a.	...	...	0033	0035	0037		1114	...	1317	...	1518	1620	...	1726	...	1825	1918	...	2120	2255	...	2333	0034	...	0022	...
Holyhead **160** a.	...	...	...	...	0215		...	...	...	...	...	1837	...	...	...	2018	2134	...	...	...	...	...	...	...	0220	...

	⚒	⑥	Ⓐ	Ⓐ	⑥	Ⓐ	⑥	Ⓐ	⑥🍷	Ⓐ🍷	⚒🍷	⑥C	⑥🍷	Ⓐ✕	Ⓐ🍷	Ⓐ🍷	⑥🍷	⚒🍷	⑥🍷	Ⓐ🍷	Ⓐ🍷	Ⓐ🍷	⑥🍷	⚒🍷	⚒🍷	⑥🍷
Holyhead **160** d.		...	...	...	...	...	...	...	0425c	0425	...	...	0523	0534	Q	0628	0635	K	0715	L	...	0805	0820	F	0923	1033
Chester 160 d.		0422	0422	...	...	0535	0537	0545	0620	0618	...	...	0730	0716	...	0819	0820	...	0930	0927	...	1021	1019	...	1136	1219
Wrexham General d.		|	|	...	...	0550	0555	0603	0635	0634	...	...	0745	0734d	0750	0835	0834	...	0945	0942	...	1036	1034	...	1150	1233
Ruabon d.		|	|	...	...	0556	▬	▬	0641	0641	...	...	0751	|	0757	0842	0841	...	0951	0949	...	1042	1041	...	1157	1240
Gobowen d.		|	|	...	...	0608	...	...	0653	0653	...	...	0803	|	0809	0854	0853	...	1003	1001	...	1054	1052	...	1209	1251
Shrewsbury a.		|	|	...	...	0627	...	...	0712	0712	...	...	0822	0803	0828	0912	0911	...	1027	1020	...	1113	1111	...	1229	1310
Cardiff Central **149** a.		|	|	...	...	|	...	...	0918	0918	...	...	|	0958	|	1115	1114	...	|	1210	...	1319	1317	...	|	1524
Aberystwyth **147** d.		|	|	...	...	|	⑥	ⒶC	...	...	0530	...	|	...	|	...	...	0730	|	...	...	...	...	0930	|	...
Shrewsbury d.		|	|	0518	0522	0633	0633	0639	...	...	0733	0819	0833	...	0832	...	...	0933	1033	...	1034	...	...	1133	1233	...
Wellington d.		|	|	0531	0535	0646	0646	0653	...	...	0746	0833	0846	...	0845	...	...	0947	1046	...	1048	...	...	1146	1246	...
Telford Central d.		|	|	0538	0542	0653	0653	0700	...	...	0753	0840	0853	...	0852	...	...	0953	1053	...	1054	...	...	1153	1253	...
Wolverhampton a.		0539	0539	0558	0601	0711	0711	0717	...	...	0811	0900	0911	...	0910	...	...	1010	1111	...	1111	...	...	1211	1312	...
Birmingham New Street a.		0600	0609	0615	0619	0730	0730	0747	...	...	0829	0919	0928	...	0929	...	...	1030	1130	...	1130	...	...	1231	1330	...
Birmingham International ✈ a.		...	...	0649	0650	0749	0749	0759	...	...	0850	0939	0950	...	0949	...	...	1050	1150	...	1151	...	...	1250	1350	...
London Euston **150** a.		...	...	...	...	...	...	0915	...	...	...	1056	...	...	...	...	...	...	...	...	...	...	...	...	...	...

	Ⓐ🍷P	⚒🍷	⑥🍷	Ⓐ🍷	Ⓐ🍷	⑥🍷	⚒C	⚒🍷	⚒🍷	⑥🍷	Ⓐ🍷	⚒🍷	⑥🍷	Ⓐ🍷	⚒	Ⓐ🍷	⑥🍷	⚒🍷	Ⓐ🍷	⑥🍷	ⒶB	⑥	Ⓐ	Ⓐ	⚒F	ⒶD
Holyhead **160** d.	1042	F	1123	1128	1232	1238	...	F	1325	1427	1436	F	1523	1547	h	1648	1652	...	1731	1732	...	...	...	...	...	...
Chester 160 d.	1219	...	1335	1330	1420	1419	...	...	1536	1621	1622	...	1730	1734	1824	1825	1832	...	1917	1931	2021	2026	...	2055	...	2135
Wrexham General d.	1234	...	1350	1345	1434	1433	...	...	1551	1636	1637	...	1745	1750	1839	1841	1847	...	1932	1946	2038	2041	2049	|	...	|
Ruabon d.	1240	...	1356	1351	1441	1440	...	...	1557	1643	1644	...	1751	1756	...	1847	1854	...	1939	1952	...	2048	2056	a	...	|
Gobowen d.	1252	...	1408	1403	1453	1452	...	...	1609	1655	1656	...	1803	1808	...	1859	1906	...	1951	2004	...	2100	2108	|	...	|
Shrewsbury a.	1311	...	1428	1423	1511	1510	...	...	1629	1713	1714	...	1822	1827	...	1918	1924	...	2013	2026	...	2121	2128	2208	...	|
Cardiff Central **149** a.	1511	...	|	|	1716	1707	...	...	|	1915	1918	...	|	|	...	2136	2135	...	...	▬	...	...	...	0023	...	|
Aberystwyth **147** d.	...	1130	|	|	...	...	...	1330	|	...	...	1530	|	|	...	...	...	1730	...	⚒	...	...	...	...	1930	|
Shrewsbury d.	...	1334	1433	1433	...	...	1524	1533	1633	...	...	1733	1833	1833	...	...	...	1932	...	2045	...	...	...	...	2133	|
Wellington d.	...	1348	1446	1446	...	...	1538	1546	1647	...	...	1746	1846	1846	...	...	...	1946	...	2057	...	...	...	...	2146	|
Telford Central d.	...	1354	1453	1453	...	...	1544	1553	1654	...	...	1753	1853	1853	...	...	...	1953	...	2107	...	...	...	...	2153	|
Wolverhampton a.	...	1412	1511	1511	...	...	1601	1610	1709	...	...	1811	1911	1911	...	...	...	2011	...	2138	...	...	...	...	2211	2227
Birmingham New Street a.	...	1430	1530	1530	...	...	1621	1630	1730	...	...	1830	1930	1930	...	...	...	2029	...	2157	...	...	...	...	2232	2248
Birmingham International ✈ a.	...	1450	1550	1550	...	...	1639	1649	1750	...	...	1850	1949	1949	...	...	...	2049	...	...	...	...	...	...	...	...
London Euston **150** a.	...	...	...	...	...	...	1755	...	...	...	...	...	...	...	...	...	...	...	...	...	...	...	...	...	...	...

	Ⓐ	⑥	⑥	Ⓐ	⑦	⑦	⑦	⑦	⑦	⑦🍷	⑦	⑦🍷	⑦	⑦C	⑦	⑦🍷	⑦🍷	⑦	⑦	⑦🍷	⑦	⑦🍷	⑦	⑦	⑦	⑦
Holyhead **160** d.	1922	1922	...	...		...	...	...	...	...	1020	...	...	...	...	...	G	...	1625	...	...	1826	...	1917g	...	...
Chester 160 d.	2121	2122	2230	2232		0815	...	0926	...	1135	1229	...	1335	...	...	1532	...	1731	1825	...	1926	2027	...	2128	2204	2300
Wrexham General d.	2137	2137	2246	2245		0833	...	0941	...	1150	1244	...	1350	...	...	1547	...	1746	1840	...	1941	|	...	2144	2222	|
Ruabon d.	2144	2144	2253	2251		▬	...	0947	...	1157	1250	...	1357	...	...	1554	...	1753	1847	...	1947	|	...	2151	...	a
Gobowen d.	2156,	2156	2305	2303		...	...	0959	...	1210	1302	...	1409	...	...	1606	...	1805	1859	...	1959	|	...	2203	...	|
Shrewsbury a.	2214	2214	2323	2321		...	...	1018	...	1230	1323	...	1427	...	...	1624	...	1823	1918	...	2017	|	...	2222	...	0017
Cardiff Central **149** a.	|	|	|	|		...	...	|	...	|	1529	...	|	...	...	|	...	|	2131	...	|	|	...	|	...	...
Aberystwyth **147** d.	|	|	|	|		⑦	...	|	0930	|	...	1130	|	...	1330	|	1530	|	...	1730	|	|	1930	|	...	...
Shrewsbury d.	2218	2231	2326	2324		0810	0909	1020	1135	1231	...	1331	1431	1524	1532	1640	1733	1831	...	1931	2023	|	2131	2223	...	...
Wellington d.	2232	2245	2340	2338		0824	0923	1034	1149	1246	...	1345	1445	1538	1546	1654	1747	1845	...	1945	2037	|	2145	2237	...	...
Telford Central d.	2238	2251	2347	2345		0831	0930	1040	1155	1253	...	1351	1451	1544	1552	1700	1753	1851	...	1951	2044	|	2151	2245	...	...
Wolverhampton a.	2255	2308	0016	0017		0859	0958	1056	1211	1311	...	1407	1507	1601	1608	1717	1809	1907	...	2007	2111	2129	2208	2314	...	...
Birmingham New Street a.	2328	2330	...	...		0915	1014	1113	1233	1328	...	1423	1524	1620	1624	1737	1827	1926	...	2025	2129	2151	2227	...	...	...
Birmingham International ✈ a.	...	...	...	...		0932	1032	1131	1302	1357	...	1500	1557	1639	1700	1757	1900	1957	...	2101	2157	2206	2301	...	...	...
London Euston **150** a.	...	...	...	...		...	...	...	...	...	...	...	...	1757	...	...	...	...	...	...	...	...	...	...	...	...

A – [12] and 🍷 Birmingham New Street - Crewe - Holyhead (Table **151**).
B – [12] and 🍷 Wrexham - London Euston and v.v. (Table **151**).
C – [12] and 🍷 Shrewsbury - London Euston and v.v. (Table **150**).
D – [12] and 🍷 Bangor - Crewe - Birmingham New Street (Table **151**).
E – From Swansea (Table **136**).
F – Also conveys [2] Birmingham - Pwllheli and v.v. (Table **148**).
G – Until Sept. 8 also conveys [2] Birmingham - Pwllheli and v.v. (Table **148**).

H – To Crewe (Table **149**).
J – To/from Llandudno Junction (Table **165**).
K – On ⑥ also conveys [2] Barmouth - Birmingham (Table **148**).
L – To/from Llandudno (Table **165**).
M – To/from Manchester Piccadilly (Table **160**).
P – To/from Llanelli (Table **136**).
Q – Also conveys [2] Crewe - Birmingham (Table **149**).

a – Via Crewe (Table **149**).
b – Arrives 0556.
c – From Sept. 14.
d – Arrives 0730.
f – On ⑥ arrives 2330.
g – Until Sept. 8.
h – Runs 9 minutes later on Ⓐ.

AW 2nd class SHREWSBURY - SWANSEA 146

km		Ⓐ	⑥A	ⒶA	⑥A	ⒶB	⑦	⑥	Ⓐ	⑦	⑥	ⒶC
0	**Shrewsbury** .... **149** d.	0446	0516	0556	0900	1009	1204	1358	1405	1618	1757	1824
20	Church Stretton **149** d.	0504	0533	0614	0919	1027	1222	1416	1423	1636	1813	1842
32	Craven Arms .... **149** d.	0515	0547	0626	0929	1037	1233	1426	1434	1647	1824	1854
52	Knighton .... d.	0537	0612	0656f	0953	1101	1257	1450	1458	1711	1848	1918
84	**Llandrindod** .... a.	0611	0646	0734	1031	1139	1335	1528	1536	1749	1926	1956
84	**Llandrindod** .... d.	▬	0654	0735	1034	1200	1341	1540	1541	1803	1937	1956
110	Llanwrtyd .... d.	Ⓐ	0723	0809f	1107f	1231	1412	1611	1623f	1834	2008	2030
128	Llandovery .... d.	0642	0747	0834	1132	1256	1437	1636	1648	1900	2034	2056
146	Llandeilo .... d.	0703	0808	0856	1154	1318	1459	1658	1710	1921	2055	2117
159	Pantyffynnon .... d.	0721	0825	0913	1211	1335	1516	1715	1727	1939	2113	2135
178	Llanelli .... **136** a.	0741	0848	0933	1235	1358	1536	1735	1747	1959	2133	2155
196	**Swansea** .... **136** a.	0808	0922	1001	1301	1425	1603	1809	1814	2025	2206	2222

	⑥	Ⓐ	ⒶB	⑥	Ⓐ	⑦	⑥	ⒶB	⑦	⑥	Ⓐ
Swansea .... **136** d.	0431	...	0604	0915	0934	1112	1312	1435	1529	1817	1821
Llanelli .... **136** d.	0450	0520	0625	0934	0955	1132	1332	1453	1549	1840	1842
Pantyffynnon .... d.	0510	0539	0644	0955	1014	1153	1353	1512	1612	1859	1901
Llandeilo .... d.	0529	0559	0706	1015	1034	1213	1413	1532	1632	1919	1921
Llandovery .... d.	0551	0622	0728	1037	1056	1235	1435	1554	1654	1941	1943
Llanwrtyd .... d.	0616	▬	0808f	1105	1121	1300	1501	1624f	1720	2008	2031r
Llandrindod .... a.	0644	ⒶB	0838	1136	1152	1331	1531	1654	1750	2037	2102
Llandrindod .... d.	0655	0618	0845	1140	1201	1343	1542	1659	1801	2042	2119
Knighton .... d.	0732	0703f	0923	1218	1240	1422	1621	1737	1840	2118	2158
Craven Arms .... **149** a.	0753	0725	0945	1240	1302	1444	1642	1759	1902	2139	2220
Church Stretton **149** a.	0806	0742	0958	1253	1317	1457	1655	1812	1915	2152	2235
Shrewsbury .... **149** a.	0823	0757	1014	1309	1332	1512	1711	1828	1939	2208	2254

A – To Cardiff (Table **136**). B – From / to Crewe (Table **149**). C – 🚃2 Crewe - Cardiff (Tables **136** / **149**). f – Arrives 6 – 14 minutes earlier. r – Arrives 2006.

AW 2nd class SHREWSBURY - ABERYSTWYTH 147

km			⚒	Ⓐ🍷	⑥🍷	⚒🍷	⚒	⚒🍷	⚒🍷	⚒🍷	⚒🍷	⑥	Ⓐ	Ⓐ🍷	⑥🍷	⚒	⑥	Ⓐ
	Birmingham N St ◇ d.	⚒	...	0625	0625	0824	...	1025	1225	1425	1625	...	...	1825	1825	...	2025	2025
0	**Shrewsbury** .... d.		0625	0727	0729	0930	1029	1127	1329	1530	1727	1827	1831	1930	1930	2032	2143	2150
32	Welshpool .... d.		0648	0749	0752	0952	1051	1149	1351	1552	1749	1849	1853	1952	1952	2053	2205	2212
54	Newtown .... d.		0703	0803	0806	1006	1106	1203	1405	1606	1803	1903	1907	2006	2006	2108	2220	2227
63	Caersws .... d.		0710	0810	0813	1013	1113	1210	1412	1613	1810	1910	1914	2013	2013	2115	2227	2234
98	**Machynlleth** .... a.		0742	0841	0844	1044	1141	1243	1443	1644	1841	1942	1945	2047	2047	2143	2255	2302
98	**Machynlleth** ..... **148** d.		0746	0848	0849	1050	1141r	1247	1449	1650	1849	1946	1948	2049	2052	2149	2302	2307
104	Dovey Junction **148** d.		0755	0855	0856	1056	1154	1254r	1455	1656	1858	1955	1957	2057	2100	2157	2308	2313
118	Borth .... d.		0805	0905	0906	1106	1204	1304r	1505	1706	1908	2005	2007	2107	2110	2207	2318	2323
131	**Aberystwyth** .... a.		0820	0920	0920	1120	1220	1320	1520	1720	1922	2020	2020	2120	2123	2221	2330	2336

		⑦a	⑦b	⑦	⑦🍷	⑦🍷	⑦🍷	⑦🍷	⑦	⑦🍷	⑦
Birmingham N St ◇ d.	⑦	...	🚌	1004	1224	1424	...	1624	...	1824	2024
Shrewsbury .... d.		0830	0830	1128	1328	1528	1629	1727	1828	1927	2128
Welshpool .... d.		0852	0905	1150	1350	1551	1651	1749	1850	1949	2150
Newtown .... d.		0906	0930	1204	1404	1605	1705	1803	1904	2003	2204
Caersws .... d.		0913	0945	1211	1412	1612	1712	1811	1911	2010	2212
Machynlleth .... a.		0945	1025	1245	1443	1643	1742	1842	1940	2041	2240
Machynlleth ..... **148** d.		0947	1025	1250	1448	1648	1745	1848	1942	2047	2246
Dovey Junction **148** d.		0955	|	1258	1458	1655	1755	1856	1956	2055	2252
Borth .... d.		1005	1050	1308	1508	1705	1805	1906	2006	2105	2302
Aberystwyth .... a.		1020	1110	1321	1520	1720	1820	1920	2020	2120	2315

		⚒🍷	⚒	Ⓐ🍷	⑥🍷	Ⓐ	⑥	⚒🍷	Ⓐ🍷	⑥🍷	⚒	⚒🍷	⚒🍷	⑥🍷	Ⓐ🍷	Ⓐ	⑥	⑥	Ⓐ
Aberystwyth .... d.	⚒	0530	0630	0730	0730	0830	0830	0930	1130	1130	1230	1330	1530	1730	1730	1832	1833	1930	1930
Borth .... d.		0543	0643	0743	0743	0843	0843	0943	1143	1143	1243	1343	1543	1743	1743	1845	1845	1943	1943
Dovey Junction .... **148** d.		0553	0653	0753	0754	0858	0859	0953	1153	1155	1257	1353	1553	1753	1753	1856	1856	1959	1959
Machynlleth .... **148** a.		0601	0701	0800	0801	0905	0906	1000	1201	1200	1305	1400	1600	1800	1800	1903	1903	2004	2006
Machynlleth .... d.		0601	0703	0805	0808	0906	0908	1008	1204	1207	1306	1407	1608	1805	1805	1909	1905	2011	2011
Caersws .... d.		0628	0730	0828	0831	0933	0935	1035	1232	1234	1333	1434	1631	1828	1830	1932	1928	2034	2034
Newtown .... d.		0635	0737	0839	0842	0940	0942	1042	1239	1241	1340	1441	1642	1839	1841	1943	1939	2044	2044
Welshpool .... d.		0650	0752	0854	0856	0955	0956	1056	1254	1255	1354	1455	1656	1853	1856	1957	2000	2102	2059
Shrewsbury .... a.		0713	0814	0916	0918	1017	1018	1118	1316	1317	1418	1519	1720	1915	1918	2022	2022	2124	2121
Birmingham New St **145** a.		0829	...	1030	1030	...	...	1231	1430	1430	...	1630	1830	2029	2029	...	...	2232	2231

		⑦	⑦🍷	⑦🍷	⑦	⑦	⑦🍷	⑦🍷	⑦
Aberystwyth .... d.	⑦	0930	1030	1130	1330	1434	1530	1730	1930
Borth .... d.		0943	1043	1143	1343	1447	1543	1743	1943
Dovey Junction .... **148** d.		0953	1056	1153	1357	1457	1553	1753	1953
Machynlleth .... **148** a.		1000	1103	1200	1404	1507	1600	1800	2000
Machynlleth .... d.		1008	1105	1206	1406	1508	1605	1805	2005
Caersws .... d.		1031	1128	1229	1429	1531	1630	1828	2028
Newtown .... d.		1041	1138	1240	1440	1541	1641	1839	2039
Welshpool .... d.		1057	1154	1254	1455	1556	1655	1854	2053
Shrewsbury .... a.		1119	1217	1316	1517	1618	1717	1916	2116
Birmingham New St **145** a.		1233	...	1423	1624	...	1827	2025	2227

a – Until Sept. 8.
b – From Sept. 15.
r – On ⑥ departs 3 – 4 minutes later.
◇ – Birmingham New Street (see Table **145**).
▷ – Additional journeys Machynlleth - Aberystwyth and v.v.:
From Machynlleth at 0453 ⚒, 0545 Ⓐ, 0547 ⑥, 0647 ⚒, 0850 ⑦, 0947 ⑦, 1049 ⑦, 1351 ⑦, 1801 ⚒.
From Aberystwyth at 1830 ⑦, 2030 Ⓑ, 2036 ⑥, 2130 Ⓑ, 2135 ⑥, 2230 ⚒, 2320 ⑦, 2335 ⑥, 2340 Ⓐ.

AW 2nd class MACHYNLLETH - PWLLHELI 148

km			Ⓐ	Ⓐ	Ⓐ	Ⓐ	Ⓐ	Ⓐ	Ⓐ	Ⓐ	Ⓐ		⑥	⑥	⑥	⑥	⑥	⑥	⑥	⑥	⑥		⑦c	⑦c	⑦
	Birmingham New Street **145** d.	Ⓐ	...	...	*0625*	0824	1025	1225	1425	1625	*1825*	⑥	...	...	*0625*	0825	1025	1225	1425	1625	*1825*	⑦	...	1224	1624
	Shrewsbury **147** .... d.		...	...	*0727*	0930	1127	1329	1530	1729	*1930*		...	...	*0729*	0930	1129	1329	1530	1727	*1930*		...	1328	1727
0	**Machynlleth** .... **147** d.		0507	0643	0852	1055	1251	1456	1655	1904	2147		0507	0643	0853	1055	1252	1456	1655	1904	2147		1010	1454	1855
6	Dovey Junction .... **147** d.		0513	0649	0858	1101	1257	1502	1701	1910	2153		0513	0649	0859	1101	1258	1502	1701	1910	2153		1016	1500	1901
16	Aberdovey .... d.		0526	0702	0911	1114	1310	1515	1714	1923	2206		0526	0702	0912	1114	1311	1515	1714	1923	2206		1029	1513	1914
22	Tywyn .... 🚂 a.		0533	0711	0920	1123	1319	1524	1724	1932	2215		0533	0711	0921	1123	1319	1524	1724	1932	2215		1035	1519	1920
22	Tywyn .... 🚂 d.		0533	0714	0929	1130	1325	1526	1729	1933	2216		0533	0714	0929	1130	1324	1525	1729	1933	2217		1036	1531	1925
37	Fairbourne .... d.		0552	0732	0948	1149	1344	1545	1747	1951	2235		0552	0732	0948	1148	1343	1544	1747	1951	2235		1054	1549	1944
41	**Barmouth** .... d.		0604	0747	1001	1201	1357	1558	1800	2004	2247		0604	0747	1001	1200	1356	1557	1800	2004	2248		1104	1559	1954
58	Harlech .... a.		...	0811	1025	1225	1421	1622	1824	2030	2312		...	0811	1025	1225	1420	1621	1824	2030	2312		1130	1625	2020
58	Harlech .... d.		...	0825	1027	1227	1431	1629	1833	2030	2313		...	0825	1027	1228	1431	1629	1833	2030	2314		1132	1625	2022
67	Penrhyndeudraeth .... d.		...	0838	1040	1240	1444	1642	1846	2043	2326		...	0838	1040	1241	1444	1642	1846	2043	2327		1146	1639	2036
69	Minffordd .... **160** d.		...	0842	1044	1244	1448	1645	1849	2047	2330		...	0842	1044	1244	1448	1645	1849	2047	2330		1149	1642	2039
72	**Porthmadog** .... **160** d.		...	0850	1052	1252	1456	1653	1857	2055	2338		...	0850	1052	1252	1456	1653	1857	2055	2338		1157	1648	2045
80	Criccieth .... d.		...	0857	1059	1259	1503	1700	1904	2103	2346		...	0857	1059	1300	1503	1700	1904	2103	2346		1205	1655	2053
93	**Pwllheli** .... a.		...	0912	1114	1315	1520	1718	1920	2118	0001		...	0913	1114	1315	1520	1716	1919	2118	0001		1221	1714	2112

		Ⓐ	Ⓐ	Ⓐ	Ⓐ	Ⓐ	Ⓐ	Ⓐ	Ⓐ	Ⓐ		⑥	⑥	⑥	⑥	⑥	⑥		⑥	⑥	⑥		⑦c	⑦	⑦c
Pwllheli .... d.	Ⓐ	...	0629	0724	0934	1137	1338	1537	1742	2026	⑥	...	0629	0724	0934	1137	1338	...	1537	1742	2026	⑦	1128	1348	1736
Criccieth .... d.		...	0643	0738	0948	1151	1352	1551	1756	2040		...	0643	0738	0948	1151	1352	...	1551	1756	2040		1141	1402	1750
Porthmadog .... **160** d.		...	0653	0747	0957	1201	1402	1601	1806	2055b		...	0653	0747	0958	1201	1402	...	1601	1806	2056b		1157t	1412	1800
Minffordd .... **160** d.		...	0657	0752	1001	1205	1406	1605	1810	2059		...	0657	0752	1002	1205	1406	...	1605	1810	2101		1202	1416	1805
Penrhyndeudraeth .... d.		...	0701	0756	1005	1209	1410	1609	1814	2103		...	0701	0756	1006	1209	1410	...	1609	1814	2104		1206	1420	1809
Harlech .... a.		...	0715	0809	1020	1224	1425	1624	1827	2117		...	0715	0809	1021	1224	1425	...	1624	1827	2118		1218	1432	1821
Harlech .... d.		...	0717	0821	1029	1228	1428	1629	1830	2119		...	0717	0821	1028	1228	1428	...	1629	1830	2120		1219	1434	1822
Barmouth .... d.		0645	0746f	0852f	1059f	1255	1455	1656	1857	2146		0645	0746f	0852f	1059f	1255	1455	...	1656	1857	2147		1248	1501	1850
Fairbourne .... d.		0653	0754	0900	1107	1303	1503	1704	1905	2154		0653	0754	0900	1107	1303	1503	...	1704	1905	2155		1256	1509	1857
Tywyn .... 🚂 a.		0713	0812	0920	1127	1323	1524	1724	1925	2214		0713	0812	0920	1127	1323	1524	...	1724	1925	2215		1316	1527	1919
Tywyn .... 🚂 d.		0714	0816	0927	1130	1325	1526	1727	1934	2217		0714	0816	0927	1130	1325	1526	...	1727	1935	2217		1316	1528	1924
Aberdovey .... d.		0720	0822	0933	1136	1331	1532	1733	1940	2223		0720	0822	0933	1136	1331	1532	...	1733	1941	2223		1322	1535	1930
Dovey Junction .... **147** d.		0735	0838	0947	1149	1345	1546	1747	1956	2238		0735	0838	0947	1151	1345	1546	...	1747	1956	2238		1336	1549	1946
Machynlleth .... **147** a.		0743	0845	0954	1157	1352	1554	1755	2004	2245		0743	0847	0955	1158	1353	1555	...	1755	2003	2245		1346	1559	1954
Shrewsbury **147** .... a.		*0916*	*1017*	1118	1316	1519	1720	*1918*	2121	...		0918	*1018*	1118	1317	1517	1719	...	*1915*	2124	...		*1517*	1717r	*2116*
Birmingham New Street **145** a.		*1030*	...	1230	1430	1630	1830	*2029*	2231	...		1030	...	1231	1430	1630	1830	...	*2029*	2232	...		*1624*	1827r	*2227*

b – Arrives 2048.
c – Until Sept. 8.
f – Arrives 4 – 7 minutes earlier.
r – From Sept. 15 change at Machynlleth.
t – Arrives 1148.
🚂 – Talyllyn Railway (Tywyn Wharf - Abergynolwyn - Nant Gwernol: *12 km*). ✆ 01654 710472. www.talyllyn.co.uk

AW 2nd class Most trains convey 🍷 CARDIFF - HEREFORD - CREWE - MANCHESTER 149

Most Manchester trains continue to / from destinations on Table **135**

km			Ⓐ	ⒶJ	Ⓐ	ⒶR	Ⓐ	Ⓐ	Ⓐ	ⒶS	Ⓐ	Ⓐ	Ⓐ	Ⓐ	Ⓐ	ⒶS	Ⓐ	Ⓐ	Ⓐ	Ⓐ	Ⓐ	Ⓐ	Ⓐ	Ⓐ	ⒶT	Ⓐ	Ⓐ✗
0	**Cardiff** Central ... **134** § d.	Ⓐ	0435	0508	0538	...	0650	0721	0805	...	0850	0921	1005	1051	1121	...	1205	1251	1321	1405	1450	1521	1550	1621	...	1650	1716
19	Newport .... **134** § d.		0453	0527	0558	...	0704	0735	0819	...	0905	0935	1019	1105	1136	...	1219	1306	1336	1419	1504	1536	1604	1635	...	1705	1731
30	Cwmbrân .... d.		0505	0538	0608	...	0714	0746	0829	...	0915	0946	1029	1115	1146	...	1229	1316	1346	1429	1514	1546	1614	1645	...	1715	1742
35	Pontypool & New Inn .. d.		0511	0544	0614	...	|	0751	|	...	|	0951	|	|	1152	...	|	|	1352	|	|	1552	1619	|	...	1721	1749
50	Abergavenny .... d.		0522	0553	0623	...	0727	0801	0842	...	0928	1001	1042	1128	1201	...	1242	1329	1401	1443	1527	1601	1629	1658	...	1730	1800
89	**Hereford** .... d.		0547	0625g	0649	...	0753	0827	0908	...	0955	1029	1108	1153	1227	...	1308	1355	1428	1508	1555	1628	1654	1725	...	1757	1825
109	Leominster .... d.		0600	0638	0702	...	0806	|	0921	...	1008	|	1121	1208	|	...	1321	1408	|	1521	1608	1641	1707	|	...	1810	|
127	Ludlow .... d.		0611	0649	0713	...	0817	0848	0932	...	1019	1050	1132	1219	1248	...	1332	1419	1449	1532	1619	1652	1718	|	...	1822	|
138	Craven Arms .... **146** d.		0620	0657	0721	0729	0825	0857	|	0946	1027	1058	|	1227	1256	1303	|	1427	1458	|	1627	1701	1727	|	1800	1831	|
150	Church Stretton .... **146** d.		0629	0708	0730	0742	0834	0906	|	0959	1036	1107	|	1236	1305	1317	|	1436	1507	|	|	1710	1736	|	1813	1841	|
170	**Shrewsbury** .... **146** a.		0644	0725	0745	0757	0849	0921	0959	1014	1051	1122	1159	1251	1321	1332	1359	1451	1524	1559	1649	1724	1751	1811	1828	1856	1909
170	**Shrewsbury** .... ¶ d.		0645	0725	0746	0800	0852	0925	1000	1018	1055	1125	1159	1253	1326	...	1359	1452	1529	1559	1650	1725	1753	1813	1830	1857	1909
200	Whitchurch .... ¶ d.		0705	|	0806	0828	0909	|	|	1046	1112	|	|	1310	|	...	|	1509	|	|	1710	|	1810	|	1857	1914	|
223	**Crewe** .... ¶ a.		0725	|	0825	0853	0928	|	1029	1110	1129	|	1229	1328	|	...	1429	1529	|	1629	1728	|	1828	1843	1920	1934	|
	Chester **145, 160** ...... a.		|	0820	|	...	|	1020	|	...	|	1219	|	|	1419	...	|	|	1623	|	|	1819	|	1905	...	|	1957
	Holyhead **145, 160** ... a.		|	...	|	...	|	1223	|	...	|	1414	|	|	1614	...	|	|	1821	|	|	2020	|	...	...	|	2141
263	Stockport .... a.		0758	...	0859	...	0958	...	1059	...	1159	...	1259	1359	...	...	1459	1559	...	1659	1759	...	1858	...	...	2006	...
273	**Manchester** Piccadilly . a.		0810	...	0912	...	1011	...	1112	...	1213	...	1313	1413	...	...	1513	1613	...	1713	1813	...	1913	...	...	2019	...

J – To / from Llandudno (Tables **145** / **160**). L – To Llandudno Junction (Tables **145** / **160**).

For continuation of Table and additional footnotes see next page ▶ ▶ ▶

149 CARDIFF - HEREFORD - CREWE - MANCHESTER

Most trains convey 🍸 2nd class AW

Most Manchester trains continue to/from destinations on Table **135**

	Ⓐ	Ⓐ	Ⓐ	Ⓐ	Ⓐ	Ⓐ	Ⓐ	⑥	⑥	⑥	⑥	⑥	⑥	⑥	⑥	⑥	⑥	⑥	⑥	⑥	⑥	⑥	⑥	⑥	⑥	⑥
Cardiff Central ..**134** § d.	1751	1821	1855	1934	2017	2117	2155	0435	0520	0537	0652	0721	0750	0850	0921	0955	1055	1121	1155	1255	1321	1355	1455	1521	1555	1618
Newport..........**134** § d.	1804	1834	1909	1950	2031	2132	2212	0452	0534	0552	0706	0736	0804	0906	0936	1009	1109	1135	1209	1309	1334	1409	1509	1536	1609	1634
Cwmbrân..........d.	1815	1845	1919	2000	2041	2143	2223	0503	0545	0603	0716	0746	0814	0916	0946	1019	1119	1145	1219	1319	1345	1419	1519	1546	1619	1644
Pontypool & New Inn ..d.	1820	│	1924	2005	2047	│	2229	0509	0550	0608	│	0751	│	│	0952	│	│	1150	│	│	1349	│	│	1552	1624	1650
Abergavenny ....d.	1829	1858	1934	2015	2056	2157	2239	0518	0600	0618	0729	0801	0827	0929	1001	1032	1132	1159	1232	1332	1400	1432	1532	1601	1634	1702
Hereford ....d.	1855	1924	1959	2041	2122	2224	2310	0546	0625	0647d	0755	0830	0853	0955	1029	1058	1158	1228	1258	1400	1427	1458	1559	1629	1700	...
Leominster..........d.	1908	│	2012	2054	2135	2237	2323	0559	0639	0700	0808	│	0906	1008	│	1111	1211	│	1311	1413	│	1511	1612	1642	1713	...
Ludlow..........d.	1919	1945	2023	2105	2146	2249	2334	0610	0650	0711	0819	0851	0917	1019	1050	1122	1222	1249	1322	1424	1448	1522	1623	1654	1724	...
Craven Arms .... **146** d.	1927	│	2032	2114	2154	2258	2344	0618	0659	0719	0827	0859	│	1027	1058	│	1230	1257	│	1432	1457	│	1631	│	│	...
Church Stretton ... **146** d.	1936	│	2041	2123	2204	2308	2353	0627	0708	0728	0836	0908	│	1036	1108	│	1239	1306	│	1442	1506	│	1640	1708	│	...
Shrewsbury .... **146** a.	1951	2012	2056	2138	2219	2324	0009	0642	0723	0743	0852	0924	0944	1051	1124	1149	1254	1323	1349	1456	1524	1549	1654	1722	1751	...
Shrewsbury ......**145** ¶ d.	1952	2014	2057	2141	2220	2326	0012	0645	0725	0745	0852	0925	0947	1052	1125	1149	1255	1325	1349	1457	1530	1549	1657	1724	1752	...
Whitchurch ....¶ d.	│	│	2114	│	2245	2353	0038	0705	│	0805	0909	│	1004	1109	│	1206	│	│	1406	│	│	1606	│	│	1808	...
Crewe ....¶ a.	2023	2045	2133	│	2307	0017	0103	0725	│	0824	0928	│	1023	1126	│	1225	1327	│	1426	1528	│	1625	1728	│	1830	...
Chester **145, 160** .....a.	│	2108	│	2236	│	...	...	│	0819	│	│	1019	│	│	1218	│	│	1419	│	│	1623	│	│	1817	│	...
Holyhead **145, 160**...a.	│	...	│	0048	│	...	...	│	1012	│	│	1209	│	│	1413	│	│	1612	│	│	1818	│	│	2018	│	...
Stockport..........a.	2052	...	2201	...	2335	...	...	0758	...	0859	0958	...	1058	1158	...	1258	1358	...	1459	1559	...	1659	1759	...	1859	...
Manchester Piccadilly a.	2106	...	2215	...	2350	...	...	0810	...	0913	1013	...	1113	1213	...	1313	1414	...	1515	1615	...	1714	1815	...	1915	...

	⑥	⑥	⑥	⑥	⑥ L	⑥	⑥	⑥	⑦	⑦	⑦	⑦	⑦	⑦	⑦	⑦	⑦	⑦	⑦	⑦	⑦	⑦	⑦	⑦ V	⑦	⑦
Cardiff Central ..**134** § d.	1655	1721	1755	1850	1934	2010	2055	2154	...	0830	0917	1034	1135	1240	1316	1340	1456	1515	1556	1640	1735	1840	1940	...	2112	2320
Newport..........**134** § d.	1709	1734	1809	1904	1948	2026	2110	2212	...	0849	0940	1054	1153	1255	1330	1355	1514	1530	1614	1655	1750	1855	1957	...	2126	2339
Cwmbrân..........d.	1719	1745	1820	1915	1959	2037	2121	2224	...	0900	0951	1105	1206	1309	1344	1409	1524	1544	1624	1709	1804	1909	2011	...	2140	2349
Pontypool & New Inn ..d.	│	1750	1825	1920	2004	2042	│	2229	...	0906	0957	1111	1212	1315	1350	│	│	1550	│	1715	1810	│	2017	...	2146	2355
Abergavenny ....d.	1732	1800	1835	1930	2013	2052	2134	2239	...	0915	1008	1121	1223	1325	1359	1422	1538	1559	1637	1725	1820	1922	2027	...	2155	0005
Hereford ....d.	1758	1827	1900	1956	2040	2120	2200	2303	...	0941	1035	1150	1252	1352	1426	1448	1604	1627	1704	1753	1847	1950	2054	...	2221	0036
Leominster..........d.	1811	│	1913	2009	2054	2133	2214	━	...	0955	1049	1203	1305	1405	1440	1501	│	1640	│	1806	1901	2004	2108	...	2234	...
Ludlow..........d.	1822	1848	1924	2020	2105	2144	2225	...	...	1006	1100	1214	1317	1416	1451	1512	1625	1651	1726	1817	1912	2015	2119	...	2245	...
Craven Arms .... **146** d.	1830	1857	│	2029	2113	2154	2233	...	...	1014	│	1224	│	1425	1500	│	│	1659	│	1826	│	2023	2129	...	2254	...
Church Stretton ... **146** d.	1839	1906	│	2038	2122	2203	2242	⑥	...	1023	│	1233	│	1434	│	│	│	1708	│	1835	│	2032	2138	...	2303	...
Shrewsbury .... **146** a.	1854	1921	1951	2053	2137	2218	2257	V	...	1038	1130	1250	1347	1450	1523	1539	1652	1723	1753	1850	1940	2047	2155	...	2319	...
Shrewsbury ......**145** ¶ d.	1856	1928	1952	2057	2139	2219	2306	2330	0955	1041	1131	1252	1349	1452	1525	1540	1653	1730	1754	1854	1942	2050	...	2232	2319	...
Whitchurch ....¶ d.	│	│	2009	│	│	2244	2332	2355	│	1102	1158	│	│	│	│	1606	│	│	│	│	2008	│	...	│	2345	...
Crewe ....¶ a.	1927	│	2028	2128	│	2305	2354	0016	1025	1123	1224	1328	1426	1527	│	1628	1727	│	1827	1925	2030	2121	...	2303	0006	...
Chester **145, 160** .....a.	│	2023	│	│	2233	│	0023	...	│	│	*1317*t	│	*1518*t	│	1620	*1726*t	│	1825	*1918*t	│	*2120*t	│	...	2333	0034	...
Holyhead **145, 160**...a.	│	2225	│	│	...	│	...	...	│	│	│	│	│	│	1837	│	│	2018	*2134*t	│	│	│	...	...	...	...
Stockport..........a.	1958	...	2059	2159	...	2335	...	...	1058	│	1258	1359	1458	1557	...	1700	1800	...	1857	1957	2057	2201	...	...	...	...
Manchester Piccadilly a.	2013	...	2115	2214	...	2349	...	...	1117	1207	1317	1417	1515	1614	...	1717	1818	...	1916	2016	2115	2219	...	...	...	...

	Ⓐ R	Ⓐ	Ⓐ	Ⓐ	Ⓐ	Ⓐ	Ⓐ ✕	Ⓐ	Ⓐ	Ⓐ	Ⓐ S	Ⓐ J	Ⓐ	Ⓐ	Ⓐ	Ⓐ	Ⓐ	Ⓐ	Ⓐ	Ⓐ	Ⓐ	Ⓐ	Ⓐ	Ⓐ	Ⓐ T	Ⓐ
Manchester Piccadilly d.	...	...	...	...	...	0629	...	0730	...	0831	...	...	0931	...	1031	1131	...	1231	1331	...	1431	1531	...	1631	...	1731
Stockport..........d.	...	...	...	...	...	0639	...	0739	...	0839	...	...	0939	...	1039	1139	...	1239	1339	...	1439	1539	...	1639	...	1739
Holyhead **145, 160**...d.	...	...	...	...	0425	│	0534	│	0628	│	...	...	│	0805	│	│	1042	│	│	1232	│	│	1436	│	...	│
Chester **145, 160** .....d.	...	...	...	...	0618	│	0716	│	0819	│	...	0927	│	1021	│	│	1219	│	│	1420	│	│	1622	│	...	│
Crewe ....¶ d.	...	0449	...	0558	│	0708	│	0809	│	0908	0914	│	1008	│	1108	1208	│	1310	1408	│	1508	1608	│	1709	1720	1809
Whitchurch ....¶ d.	...	0508	...	0619	│	│	│	│	│	│	0937	│	│	│	│	│	│	│	1428	│	│	1628	│	│	1743	1829
Shrewsbury ......**145** ¶ a.	...	0530	...	0646	0712	0742	0803	0838	0912	0938	1006	1020	1038	1113	1138	1238	1311	1340	1446	1511	1538	1648	1714	1739	1812	1849
Shrewsbury .... **146** d.	0446	0531	0610	0648	0717	0744	0810	0840	0914	0940	1009	1025	1039	1116	1139	1239	1316	1340	1451	1515	1540	1651	1716	1741	1824	1852
Church Stretton ... **146** d.	0504	0546	0626	0703	│	0759	│	│	0930	│	1027	│	1054	│	1154	│	1331	│	1506	1530	│	1706	1731	│	1842	1907
Craven Arms .... **146** d.	0514	0554	0634	0711	│	0807	│	│	0938	│	1037	│	│	1136	│	│	1339	│	1514	1538	│	1714	1739	│	1854	1915
Ludlow..........d.	━	0602	0643	0718	0743	0815	│	0906	0945	1006	...	│	1108	1143	1208	1305	1346	1406	1521	1546	1606	1721	1746	1807	...	1922
Leominster..........d.	Ⓐ	0612	0654	0729	0753	0826	│	0916	│	1016	...	│	1118	│	1218	1315	│	1417	1532	│	1616	1732	1757	1817	...	1933
Hereford ....d.	0526	0640y	0710	0748	0810	0845	0900d	0936d	1010	1034	...	│	1135	1209	1235	1332	1411	1434	1551	1611	1633	1751	1814	1834	...	1951
Abergavenny ....d.	0551	0703	0734	0812	0833	0908	│	0958	1033	1057	...	│	1158	1232	1258	1355	1434	1457	1614	1634	1656	1814	1837	1857	...	2014
Pontypool & New Inn ..d.	0602	0714	0745	0822	0843	│	│	│	1043	│	...	│	│	1242	│	1405	│	│	1623	1644	│	1824	│	│	...	2024
Cwmbrân..........d.	0607	0719	0750	0828	0848	0921	│	1011	1048	1110	...	│	1211	1247	1311	1410	│	1509	1628	1649	1709	1829	1849	1910	...	2029
Newport..........**134** § a.	0619	0732	0801	0839	0900	0935	0941	1022	1101	1121	...	1153	1222	1256	1323	1421	1456	1521	1639	1700	1720	1839	1901	1922	...	2040
Cardiff Central ..**134** § a.	0640	0749	0817	0856	0918	0959	0958	1038	1115	1137	...	1210	1239	1319	1341	1439	1511	1540	1655	1716	1738	1856	1918	1944	...	2103

	Ⓐ	Ⓐ	Ⓐ	Ⓐ	Ⓐ	Ⓐ	Ⓐ	⑥ S	⑥	⑥	⑥	⑥	⑥	⑥	⑥	⑥	⑥	⑥	⑥	⑥	⑥	⑥	⑥	⑥	⑥	⑥
Manchester Piccadilly d.	...	1829	1931	...	2136	...	2236	...	...	...	...	...	0630	0730	...	0830	0931	...	1031	1131	...	1231	1331	...	1431	1531
Stockport..........d.	...	1837	1940	...	2145	...	2245	...	...	...	...	...	0639	0740	...	0839	0940	...	1040	1139	...	1239	1339	...	1439	1539
Holyhead **145, 160**...d.	1648	│	│	...	│	...	│	...	...	...	...	0425x	│	│	0635	│	│	0820	│	│	1033	│	│	1238	│	│
Chester **145, 160** .....d.	1825	│	│	2055	│	...	│	...	...	...	...	0620	│	│	0820	│	│	1019	│	│	1219	│	│	1419	│	│
Crewe ....¶ d.	│	1908	2010	2120	2213	...	2314	...	0454	...	0555	│	0709	0808	│	0909	1008	│	1108	1209	│	1308	1408	│	1509	1608
Whitchurch ....¶ d.	│	1929	2029	2141	2233	...	2334	...	0513	...	0616	│	0729	0828	│	│	│	│	│	1229	│	│	1427	│	│	1627
Shrewsbury ......**145** ¶ a.	1918	1956	2049	2207	2302	...	0004	...	0535	...	0642	0712	0750	0847	0911	0939	1038	1111	1138	1247	1310	1338	1446	1510	1540	1646
Shrewsbury .... **146** d.	1925	1956	2051	2208	...	2309	...	0516	0540	0613	0644	0718	0752	0850	0917	0941	1039	1116	1140	1250	1314	1340	1446	1513	1547	1646
Church Stretton ... **146** d.	1940	2011	2106	2224	...	2325	...	0533	0555	0628	0659	│	0807	0905	│	0956	1054	│	1155	1305	1329	│	1501	│	1602	1701
Craven Arms .... **146** d.	1948	2019	2114	2233	...	2333	...	0547	0603	0636	0707	│	0815	0913	│	1004	1102	│	1203	1313	1337	│	1509	│	1610	1709
Ludlow..........d.	1956	2027	2121	2241	...	2342	...	━	0610	0644	0714	0744	0822	0920	0943	1011	1109	1142	1210	1320	1344	1406	1517	1539	1617	1717
Leominster..........d.	│	2037	2132	2253	...	2353	...	⑥	0621	0655	0725	0754	0833	0931	│	1022	1120	│	1221	1331	│	1416	1527	│	1628	1727
Hereford ....d.	2022	2054	2154d	2309	...	0010	...	0542	0647z	0711	0744	0811	0851	0951	1009	1040	1140d	1207	1240	1351	1410	1433	1546	1604	1647	1750d
Abergavenny ....d.	2045	2122	2217	2333	...	0034	...	0607	0710	0734	0807	0834	0914	1014	1032	1103	1203	1230	1303	1414	1432	1456	1609	1627	1710	1813
Pontypool & New Inn ..d.	│	2132	│	2343	...	0044	...	0618	0720	0744	0817	0844	│	│	1042	│	│	1240	│	│	1443	│	│	1637	│	│
Cwmbrân..........d.	2057	2137	2229	2348	...	0049	...	0623	0725	0749	0822	0849	0926	1026	1047	1115	1215	1245	1315	1426	1448	1509	1621	1642	1722	1825
Newport..........**134** § a.	2115	2152	2242	2359	...	0101	...	0637	0737	0759	0833	0901	0938	1038	1059	1127	1228	1257	1328	1438	1504	1521	1638	1653	1735	1836
Cardiff Central ..**134** § a.	2136	2213f	2306f	0023	...	0121	...	0654	0754	0818	0850	0918	0959	1103	1114	1153	1254	1317	1353	1454	1524	1537	1654	1707	1753	1855

	⑥	⑥	⑥	⑥	⑥	⑥	⑥	⑥	⑥	⑦ 🚌	⑦	⑦	⑦	⑦	⑦	⑦	⑦	⑦	⑦	⑦	⑦	⑦	⑦	⑦	⑦	⑦
Manchester Piccadilly d.	...	1631	1731	...	1831	1931	2030	2133	2235	...	...	0930	1031	1130	...	1232	1330	1430	1530	1630	1730	...	1830	1930	2030	...
Stockport..........d.	...	1639	1739	...	1839	1940	2040	2143	2245	...	...	0940	1040	1143	...	1242	1340	1440	1540	1639	1740	...	1840	1940	2040	...
Holyhead **145, 160**...d.	1427	│	│	1652	│	│	│	│	│	...	...	│	│	│	1020	│	│	│	│	│	│	1625	│	│	│	...
Chester **145, 160** .....d.	1621	│	│	1832	│	│	│	│	│	...	...	*0926*t	│	*1135*t	1229	│	*1335*t	│	*1532*t	│	*1731*t	1825	│	*1926*t	│	2300
Crewe ....¶ d.	│	1708	1809	│	1910	2009	2109	2212	2314	...	...	1014	1111	1213	│	1313	1412	1511	1610	1713	1813	│	1913	2010	2113	2330
Whitchurch ....¶ d.	│	1727	1828	│	1931	2028	2130	2233	2334	...	...	1036	│	│	│	1334	│	│	│	1734	│	│	1934	│	2135	2351
Shrewsbury ......**145** ¶ a.	1713	1744	1848	1924	1957	2048	2153	2301	0004	...	...	1105	1142	1243	1323	1401	1443	1545	1640	1801	1844	1918	2000	2040	2204	0017
Shrewsbury .... **146** d.	1716	1746	1854	1926	1958	2048	2155	...	━	0750	...	1106	1144	1245	1323	1403	1444	1548	1640	1801	1844	1922	2003	2043	2204	...
Church Stretton ... **146** d.	│	1801	1909	1941	2013	2103	2210	...	...	0815	...	1122	│	│	1339	│	1459	│	1656	│	│	1937	│	2058	2220	...
Craven Arms .... **146** d.	│	1809	1917	1949	2021	2111	2218	...	...	0835	...	1130	│	│	1347	│	1507	│	1704	│	│	1945	│	2106	2229	...
Ludlow..........d.	1742	1816	1924	1955	2028	2119	2226	...	⑥	0855	...	1139	1211	1312	1355	1431	1515	1618	1712	1829	1912	1953	2030	2114	2237	...
Leominster..........d.	│	1827	1935	│	2039	2129	2237	...		0920	...	1150	1222	1323	1405	1441	1526	1629	1722	1839	│	2004	2041	2125	2249	...
Hereford ....d.	1807	1851d	1952	2027d	2056	2146	2255	...	2315	0950	1007	1210	1240	1340	1422	1459	1544	1647	1739	1857	1936	2022	2058	2142	2305	...
Abergavenny ....d.	1830	1914	2015	2050	2119	2209	2318	...	2338	...	1031	1234	1303	1403	1445	1522	1607	1711	1802	1920	1959	2045	2121	2205	2329	...
Pontypool & New Inn ..d.	1840	│	2024	│	2128	│	2328	...	│	...	1041	│	1313	│	1455	│	1617	│	1812	│	│	2055	│	2215	2339	...
Cwmbrân..........d.	1845	1926	2029	2102	2133	2222	2333	...	2350	...	1046	1247	1318	1416	1500	1535	1622	1724	1817	1933	2011	2100	2133	2220	2344	...
Newport..........**134** § a.	1856	1937	2041	2114	2145	2234	2344	...	0002	...	1057	1258	1330	1427	1512	1547	1633	1736	1828	1944	2028	2112	2144	2231	2356	...
Cardiff Central ..**134** § a.	1915	1953	2100	2135	2205	2300	0010	...	0033	...	1112	1315	1350	1443	1529	1606	1649	1756	1845	2002	2043	2131	2204	2248	0018	...

◄◄◄ For additional notes see previous page.

R – To/from Llandrindod (Table **146**).
S – To/from Swansea (Table **146**).
T – To/from Cardiff Central (Tables **146**/**136**).
V – To/from Birmingham (Table **145**).

d – Arrives 4–6 minutes earlier.
f – Arrives 6 minutes earlier on ⑤.
t – Change at Shrewsbury.
v – Arrives 0618.
x – From Sept. 14.

y – Arrives 0631.
z – Arrives 0637.

§ – See also Tables **117** and **118**.

¶ – Additional journeys Shrewsbury - Whitchurch - Crewe and v.v.: **From Shrewsbury** at 0012②–⑥, 0531Ⓐ, 0544⑥, 0757⑥, 1018⑥, 1224⚒, 1424⚒, 1624⚒, 1825⑥, 2032⚒. **From Crewe** at 0640Ⓐ, 0720⑥, 0734Ⓐ**V**, 0920⑥, 1120⚒, 1320⚒, 1520⑥, 1522Ⓐ, 1720⑥.

VT Most trains convey 🍸 LONDON - BIRMINGHAM - WOLVERHAMPTON 150

Certain services continue to/from destinations in Table **154**. For trains via Northampton see Table **142**.

km			Ⓐ	Ⓐ	Ⓐ	Ⓐ	Ⓐ	C	Ⓐ	Ⓐ	Ⓐ	Ⓐ	Ⓐ S		Ⓐ	Ⓐ	Ⓐ	Ⓐ	Ⓐ	Ⓐ		Ⓐ	Ⓐ	Ⓐ
0	**London** Euston 143 151/2/3 d.	Ⓐ	0620	0643	0703	0723	0743	and	1703	1723	1743	1803	1823	...	1843	1903	1923	1943	2003	2023	...	2043	2103	2143
28	Watford Junction △ d.		0634	|	|	0737	|	at the	|	1737	|	|	1837	...	|	|	1937	|	|	2037	...	|	|	2158
80	Milton Keynes 143 151/2/3 d.		|	0713	|	|	0813	same	|	|	1813u	|	|	...	1913	|	|	2013	|	|	...	2113	2135	2217
133	Rugby a.		0712	|	0751	|	|	minutes	1751	|	|	1851	|	...	|	1951	|	|	2051	|	...	|	2156	|
151	Coventry 114 a.		0722	0742	0802	0822	0842	past	1802	1822	1842	1902	1922	...	1942	2002	2022	2042	2102	2122	...	2142	2207	2245
168	Birmingham Int'l ✈ 114 a.		0733	0753	0813	0833	0853	each	1813	1833	1853	1913	1933	...	1953	2013	2033	2053	2113	2133	...	2153	2217	2259
182	**Birmingham** NS 114 119 a.		0745	0809	0825	0845	0905	hour	1825	1845	1905	1925	1944	...	2008	2026	2045	2105	2126	2145	...	2205	2230	2311
190	Sandwell & Dudley a.		...	0824	...	...	0924	until	...	...	1924	|	1958	...	2024	...	2058	2124	|	2157	...	2216	2241	2331
202	**Wolverhampton** 119 a.		...	0837	...	...	0937		...	...	1937	1959	2011	...	2037	...	2110	2137	2157	2208	...	2228	2253	2344

	Ⓐ	①–④	⑤		⑥	⑥	⑥	⑥	⑥	⑥	⑥	E	⑥	⑥	⑥	⑥	⑥ D	⑥	⑥	⑥	⑥	⑥	⑥	⑥
London Euston 143 151/2/3 d.	2230	2330	2330	⑥	0623	0703	0723	0743	0803	0823	0843	and	1703	1723	1743	1803	1823	1843	1903	1923	1943	2025	2103	2142
Watford Junction △ d.	2245	|	|		0637	|	0737	|	|	0837	|	at the	|	1737	|	|	1837	|	|	1937	|	2040	2119	2158
Milton Keynes 143 151/2/3 d.	2329	0028	0028		|	|	|	0813	|	|	0913	same	|	|	1813	|	|	1913	|	|	2020	|	2151	2230
Rugby a.	2358	0100	0105		|	0751	|	|	0851	|	|	minutes	1751	|	|	1851	|	|	1951	|	|	|	2212	2252
Coventry 114 a.	0010	0113	0118		0722	0802	0822	0842	0902	0922	0942	past	1802	1822	1842	1902	1922	1942	2002	2022	2049	2136	2223	2302
Birmingham Int'l ✈ 114 a.	0020	0123	0128		0733	0813	0833	0853	0913	0933	0953	each	1813	1833	1853	1913	1933	1953	2013	2033	2100	2149	2233	2313
Birmingham NS 114 119 a.	0032	0135	0140		0745	0824	0845	0904	0924	0945	1004	hour	1824	1845	1905	1924	1944	2006	2024	2045	2111	2205	2245	2324
Sandwell & Dudley a.	|	|	|		...	...	...	0924	...	...	1024	until	...	1858	1924	1940	1958	2024	2053	2058	|	2224	2256	2335
Wolverhampton 119 a.	0100	0204	0208		...	...	...	0937	...	...	1037		...	1910	1937	1952	2011	2037	2107	2110	2135	2237	2308	2347

		⑦	⑦	⑦	⑦	⑦	⑦	⑦	⑦		⑦	⑦	⑦	⑦	⑦ S	⑦	⑦	⑦	⑦	⑦	⑦	⑦	⑦	⑦
London Euston 143 151/2/3 d.	⑦	0850	0950	1049	1149	1220	1240	1300	1320	and	1740	1800	1820	1840	1900	1920	1940	2000	2018	2038	2054	2155	2225	2324
Watford Junction △ d.		0907	1006	1105	1205	1234	|	|	1334	at the	|	|	1834	|	|	1934	|	|	2032	|	2111	2213	2241	2339
Milton Keynes 143 151/2/3 d.		0939	1038	1138	1230	|	1313	|	|	same	1813	|	|	1913	|	|	2013	|	|	2117	2145	2247	2314	0012
Rugby a.		1013	1113	1213	1249	|	|	1351	|	minutes	|	1851	|	|	1951	|	|	2050	|	|	2205	2322	2346	0047s
Coventry 114 a.		1023	1122	1223	1259	1322	1343	1402	1422	past	1842	1901	1922	1942	2002	2022	2042	2101	2120	2146	2216	2333	2357	0059s
Birmingham Int'l ✈ 114 a.		1034	1133	1234	1310	1333	1353	1412	1433	each	1852	1912	1933	1952	2012	2033	2053	2111	2130	2156	2226	2343	0007	0109s
Birmingham NS 114 119 a.		1046	1147	1245	1322	1344	1405	1423	1445	hour	1903	1924	1944	2004	2023	2045	2105	2123	2144	2209	2239	2356	0020	0122s
Sandwell & Dudley a.		1057	1158	1258	...	1355	1425	...	...	until	1925	1947	...	2024	2034	2057	2124	...	2155	2224	2250	|	|	|
Wolverhampton 119 a.		1110	1211	1310	...	1407	1437	...	...		1937	1959	...	2037	2047	2110	2137	...	2208	2236	2302	0015	0040	0142

		Ⓐ	Ⓐ	Ⓐ	Ⓐ	Ⓐ	Ⓐ	Ⓐ	Ⓐ	Ⓐ S	Ⓐ K	Ⓐ	Ⓐ	Ⓐ	Ⓐ	F	Ⓐ	Ⓐ	Ⓐ	Ⓐ	Ⓐ	Ⓐ	Ⓐ	Ⓐ
Wolverhampton 119 d.	Ⓐ	0500	0524	0545	0604	0627	0645	0705	...	0724	0745	...	...	0845	...	and	...	1845	...	1945	...	2047	2146	2245
Sandwell & Dudley d.		|	0534	0555	0615	0638	0656	0715	...	|	0757	...	...	0855	...	at the	...	1855	...	1955	...	2057	2155	2255
Birmingham NS 114 119 d.		0529	0550	0610	0630	0650	0710	0730	...	0750	0810	0830	0850	0910	0930	same	1850	1910	1930	2010	2050	2110	2210	2310
Birmingham Int'l ✈ 114 d.		0540	0600	0620	0640	0700	0720	|	0741	0800	0820	0840	0900	0920	0940	minutes	1900	1920	1940	2020	2100	2120	2220	2320
Coventry 114 d.		0551	0611	0631	0651	0711	0731	|	0752	0811	0831	0851	0911	0931	0951	past	1911	1931	1951	2031	2111	2131	2231	2331
Rugby d.		0603	|	|	|	|	|	|	|	0822	|	|	0923	|	|	each	1923	|	2004	|	2123	|	2245	2344
Milton Keynes 143 151/2/3 d.		0626	0638	0659	|	0740s	|	|	|	|	|	0920	|	1000	|	hour	|	2000	|	2100	|	2159	2308	0024
Watford Junction ▽ a.		0647	|	|	0737	|	|	|	|	|	0916	|	|	|	1039	until	|	|	2041	2119	|	2220	2339	0054
London Euston 143 151/2/3 a.		0705	0713	0733	0753	0816	0831	0843	0850	0915	0933	0953	1013	1033	1056	☆	2015	2033	2057	2136	2212	2241	0003	0113

		⑥	⑥	⑥	⑥	⑥	⑥	⑥	⑥		⑥	⑥	⑥	⑥ S	⑥	⑥	⑥	F	⑥	⑥	⑥	⑥	⑥	⑥
Wolverhampton 119 d.	⑥	...	0545	0606	0627	0645	0705	0725	0745	...	...	...	...	0903	...	0945	...	and	...	...	1845	1945	2045	2109
Sandwell & Dudley d.		...	0555	0617	0637	0656	0715	|	0755	...	...	...	...	|	...	0955	...	at the	...	...	1855	1955	2055	2119
Birmingham NS 114 119 d.		0550	0610	0630	0650	0710	0730	0750	0810	...	0830	0850	0910	0930	0950	1010	1030	same	1830	1850	1910	2010	2110	2130
Birmingham Int'l ✈ 114 d.		0600	0620	0640	0700	0720	0740	0800	0820	...	0840	0900	0920	0940	1000	1020	1040	minutes	1840	1900	1920	2020	2120	2140
Coventry 114 d.		0611	0631	0651	0711	0731	0751	0811	0831	...	0851	0911	0931	0951	1011	1031	1051	past	1851	1911	1931	2031	2131	2151
Rugby d.		0623	|	|	0723	|	|	0823	|	...	|	0923	|	|	1023	|	|	each	|	1923	1943	2043	2144	2203
Milton Keynes 143 151/2/3 d.		|	0659	|	|	0759	|	|	0859	...	|	|	0959	|	|	1059	|	hour	|	|	2007	2105	2206	2226
Watford Junction ▽ a.		|	0719	0737	|	|	0837	|	|	...	0939	|	|	1039	|	|	1139	until	1939	|	2034	2135	2236	2312
London Euston 143 151/2/3 a.		0713	0736	0753	0817	0834	0853	0913	0936	...	0957	1015	1033	1056	1113	1133	1155	☆	1955	2023	2055	2154	2256	2333

		⑦	⑦	⑦	⑦	⑦	⑦	⑦	F	⑦	⑦	⑦	⑦	⑦	⑦	⑦	⑦	⑦	⑦	⑦		⑦	⑦	⑦
Wolverhampton 119 d.	⑦	0805	0905	1005	1105	...	1145	...	and	...	1645	...	...	1745	...	...	1845	...	1945	...	...	2106	2205	2237
Sandwell & Dudley d.		0815	0915	1015	1114	...	1155	...	at the	...	1655	...	...	1756	...	...	1855	...	1955	...	...	2117	2216	2248
Birmingham NS 114 119 d.		0830	0930	1030	1130	1150	1210	1230	same	1650	1710	1730	1750	1810	1830	1850	1910	1930	2010	2030	...	2130	2230	2300
Birmingham Int'l ✈ 114 d.		0840	0940	1040	1140	1200	1220	1240	minutes	1700	1720	1740	1800	1820	1840	1900	1920	1940	2020	2040	...	2140	2240	2310
Coventry 114 d.		0851	0951	1051	1151	1211	1231	1251	past	1711	1731	1751	1811	1831	1851	1911	1931	1951	2031	2051	...	2151	2251	2321
Rugby d.		0904	1004	1104	1205	1225	|	|	each	1725	|	|	1825	|	|	1926	|	|	|	2105	...	2204	2304	2335
Milton Keynes 143 151/2/3 d.		0938	1039	1139	1227	|	1301	|	hour	|	1758	|	|	1900	|	|	2000	|	2101	2128	...	2237	2337	0013s
Watford Junction ▽ a.		1007	1111	1208	|	|	|	1338	until	|	|	1836	|	|	1938	|	|	2039	|	2202	...	2305	0006	0043
London Euston 143 151/2/3 a.		1025	1131	1225	1304	1317	1338	1357	☆	1818	1835	1855	1917	1936	1957	2018	2037	2057	2146	2224	...	2323	0026	0103

C – The 1023 from London continues to Shrewsbury (Table **145**) calling at Wolverhampton (a. 1210).
E – The 1123 from London continues to Shrewsbury (Table **145**) calling at Wolverhampton (a. 1310).
F – The 1630 from Birmingham New Street starts from Shrewsbury (Table **145**) calling at Wolverhampton (d. 1604).

K – From Manchester (Table **152**).
S – To/from Shrewsbury (Table **145**).
s – Calls to set down only.
u – Calls to pick up only.

☆ – Timings may vary by up to 3 minutes.
△ – Trains call here to pick up only.
▽ – Trains call here to set down only.

VT Most trains convey 🍸 LONDON - CHESTER (- HOLYHEAD) 151

km			Ⓐ A	Ⓐ	Ⓐ	Ⓐ	Ⓐ	Ⓐ	Ⓐ	Ⓐ	Ⓐ	Ⓐ	Ⓐ	Ⓐ	Ⓐ G	Ⓐ	Ⓐ	Ⓐ D		⑥ A	⑥	⑥	⑥
0	**London** Euston 143 150/2/3/4 d.	Ⓐ	...	0710	0810	0910	1010	1110	1210	1310	1410	1510	1610	1710	1810	1910	2010	*2046*	⑥	...	0810	0910	1010
80	Milton Keynes 143 150/2/3/4 d.		...	0741	0841	0941	1041	1141	1241	1341	1441	1541	1641u	1741u	1841u	1941	2041	*2119*		...	0841	0941	1041
254	Crewe 143 152/3/4 160 d.		0623	0847	0952	1047	1147	1247	1350	1448	1547	1647	1748	1856	1954	2054	2148	0015		0622	0947	1048	1154
288	**Chester** 160 a.		0643	0908	1012	1112	1208	1308	1411	1508	1608	1708	1807	1915	2013	2119	2211	0037		0642	1008	1112	1215
	Bangor 160 a.		0749	*1053*	1122	1216	*1329*	*1434*	*1530*	*1642*	*1737*	*1846*	1918	2027	2125	2230	*0013*	0146		0748	*1135*	1215	*1332*
	Holyhead 160 a.		0819	*1120*	1153	1249	*1414*	*1507*	*1614*	*1716*	*1821*	*1917*	*2020*	2100	2156	2301	*0048*	0215		0819	*1209*	1246	*1413*

	⑥	⑥	⑥	⑥	⑥	⑥	⑥	⑥	⑥		⑦	⑦	⑦	⑦	⑦	⑦	⑦	⑦	⑦	⑦	⑦	⑦	⑦ C
London Euston 143 150/2/3/4 d.	1110	1210	1310	1410	1510	1610	1710	1810	*1907*	⑦	*0816*	*0847*	*0946*	*1116*	*1237*	*1337*	*1437*	1508	1608	1708	1808	1908	*2121*
Milton Keynes 143 150/2/3/4 d.	1141	1241	1341	1441	1541	1641	1741	1841	|		|	*0934*	*1033*	*1204*	|	|	|	1542	1642	1742	1842	1942	|
Crewe 143 152/3/4 160 d.	1247	1351	1448	1547	1647	1748	1850	1947	2100		1042	1127	1227	1327	1427	1527	1627	1651	1750	1900	1950	2053	0001
Chester 160 a.	1309	1413	1507	1608	1708	1808	1909	2008	2121		1102	1146	1252	1351	1451	1549	1649	1710	1810	1919	2012	2112	0022
Bangor 160 a.	*1437*	*1530*	*1634*	1715	*1841*	1919	2021	*2142*	2245		1209	1310	1417	1514	1617	1712	1817	*1912*	*1948*	2034	2121	2220	0144
Holyhead 160 a.	*1509*	*1612*	*1712*	1746	*1913*	1950	2052	*2225*	2318		1240	1340	1453	1555	1653	1757	1854	*1954*	*2018*	2103	2152	2251	0220

		Ⓐ H	Ⓐ	Ⓐ G	Ⓐ	Ⓐ	Ⓐ	Ⓐ	Ⓐ	Ⓐ	Ⓐ	Ⓐ	Ⓐ	Ⓐ	Ⓐ	Ⓐ	Ⓐ	Ⓐ B		⑥ H	⑥	⑥	⑥
Holyhead 160 d.	Ⓐ	...	0448	0551	0655	*0715*	0855	*0923*	*1042*	*1128*	1253	1358	*1436*	*1547*	*1648*	*1731*	1823	*1922*	⑥	...	*0425*	0652	0755
Bangor 160 d.		...	0514	0618	0722	*0802*	0922	*1002*	*1108*	*1201*	1321	1425	*1504*	*1626*	*1716*	*1810*	1902	2020		...	*0457*	0720	0822
Chester 160 d.		0422	0626	0735	0835	0935	1035	1135	1235	1335	1435	1535	1635	1735	1855	1935	2019	2135		0422	0717	0835	0935
Crewe 143 152/3/4 160 a.		0444	0647	0754	0854	0954	1054	1154	1254	1354	1454	1554	1654	1754	1918	1954	2041	2154		0443	0736	0854	0954
Milton Keynes 143 150/2/3/4 a.		*0651*	|	|	1002	1102	1202	1302	1402	1502	1602	1702	1802	1902	*2031*	2103	*2253*	*0023*t		*0710*	0851	1001	1101
London Euston 143 150/2/3/4 a.		*0725*	0834	0939	1037	1137	1238	1336	1439	1537	1636	1737	1836	1937	*2105*	2139	*2344*	*0113*t		*0750*	0928	1036	1136

	⑥	⑥	⑥	⑥	⑥	⑥	⑥	⑥	⑥	⑥	⑥		⑦	⑦	⑦	⑦	⑦	⑦	⑦	⑦	⑦	⑦	⑦ E
Holyhead 160 d.	0855	*0923*	*1033*	*1123*	*1238*	1358	*1427*	*1523*	*1652*	*1732*	1825	⑦	0845	...	1055	1150	1250	1355	*1430*	*1530*	*1625*	*1730*	1826
Bangor 160 d.	0922	*1002*	*1105*	*1202*	*1307*	1425	*1455*	*1602*	*1720*	*1811*	1904		0913	...	1122	1217	1318	1422	*1508*	*1558*	*1704*	*1759*	1905
Chester 160 d.	1035	1135	1235	1335	1435	1535	1635	1735	1855	1955	2020		1039	1128	1233	1330	1433	1532	1627	1735	1835	1935	2027
Crewe 143 152/3/4 160 a.	1054	1154	1254	1354	1454	1554	1654	1754	1918	2018	2041		1103	1147	1253	1350	1454	1552	1651	1753	1853	1956	2048
Milton Keynes 143 150/2/3/4 a.	1201	1302	1402	1502	1601	1701	1802	|	|	*2151*	...		|	1303	1403	1503	1603	1703	|	1903	2003	*2137*	*2304*
London Euston 143 150/2/3/4 a.	1236	1336	1436	1537	1636	1736	1836	*2001*	*2123*	*2243*	...		*1309*	1342	1440	1541	1640	1740	*1902*	1941	2041	*2227*	*2353*

A – From Birmingham New Street (d. 0530), Wolverhampton (d. 0548) and Stafford (d. 0601).
B – To Wolverhampton (a. 2227) and Birmingham New Street (a. 2248).
C – From Birmingham New Street (d. 2255), Wolverhampton (d. 2315) and Stafford (d. 2331).
D – From Birmingham New Street (d. 2252), Wolverhampton (d. 2327) and Stafford (d. 2343).
E – To Stafford (a. 2113), Wolverhampton (a. 2129) and Birmingham New Street (a. 2151).

G – Conveys 🛏12 London Euston - Wrexham and v.v. (Table **145**).
H – To Stafford (a. 0524), Wolverhampton (a. 0539) and Birmingham New Street (a. 0600 ⑥, 0609 Ⓐ).

t – ⑤ only.
u – Calls to pick up only.

152 LONDON - MANCHESTER

Most trains convey 🍷 VT

km			Ⓐ	Ⓐ	Ⓐ	Ⓐ	Ⓐ	Ⓐ	Ⓐ	Ⓐ	Ⓐ	Ⓐ	Ⓐ		Ⓐ	Ⓐ	Ⓐ	④⑤2	Ⓐ		Ⓐ	Ⓐ	Ⓐ	Ⓐ
0	**London** Euston 150/1/3/4 d.	Ⓐ	0616	0636	0655	0720	0735	0800	0820	0840	0900	0920	0940	and at	1800	1820	1840	1857	1900	...	1920	1940	2000	2040
80	Milton Keynes ...... 150/1/4 d.		0646	|	0727	0750	0806	|	0850	|	|	0950	|	the same	|	1850u	|	|	|	...	1950u	|	|	|
235	Stoke on Trent .... 119 d.		0745	|	0825	0848	|	0925	0948	|	1025	1048	|	minutes	1925	1948	|	|	2025	...	2050	|	2126	|
267	Macclesfield .... 119 d.		0802	|	0841	|	|	0941	|	|	1041	|	|	past each	1941	|	|	|	|	...	2107	|	2142	|
	Crewe .... 154 d.		|	0812	|	|	0911	|	|	1012	|	|	1111	hour until	|	|	2018	2033s	|	...	|	2123	|	2211
	Wilmslow .... d.		|	0828	|	|	0927	|	|	1027	|	|	1127		|	|	2033	|	|	...	|	2138	|	2227
287	Stockport .... 119 d.		0818	0837	0856	0918	0937	0956	1017	1037	1055	1117	1136	♡	1956	2017	2043	|	2055	...	2120	|	2155	2237
296	**Manchester** Piccadilly 119 a.		0827	0846	0905	0927	0946	1005	1027	1046	1105	1128	1146		2005	2027	2052	2109	2105	...	2128	2154	2205	2246

	Ⓐ	Ⓐ		Ⓐ	Ⓐ		⑥	⑥	⑥	⑥	⑥		⑥	⑥	⑥	⑥	⑥		⑥	⑥	⑥	⑥		⑥
London Euston . 150/1/3/4 d.	2100	2140	...	2200	2300	⑥	0636	0655	0720	0735	0800	...	0820	0840	0900	0920	0940		1900	1920	1940	2020	...	2101
Milton Keynes .... 150/1/4 d.	2131	|	...	2240	|		|	0727	0750	0806	|	...	0850	|	|	0950	|	and at	|	1950	|	2105	...	2146
Stoke on Trent .... 119 d.	2228	2308	...	|	0118s		|	0825	0848	|	0925	...	0948	|	1025	1048	|	the same	2025	2048	|	2207	...	|
Macclesfield .... 119 d.	2244	2324	...	|	0134s		|	0841	|	|	0941	...	|	|	1041	|	|	minutes	2041	|	|	2224	...	|
Crewe .... 154 d.	|	|	...	0016	|		0811	|	|	0911	|	...	|	1011	|	|	1111	past each	|	|	2120	|	...	2300
Wilmslow ....d.	|	|	...	...	|		0827	|	|	0927	|	...	|	1027	|	|	1127	hour until	|	|	2135	|	...	2316
Stockport .... 119 d.	2259	2339	...	...	0148s		0836	0856	0917	0937	0956	...	1017	1037	1056	1117	1136		2056	2122	2145	2238	...	2327
Manchester Piccadilly 119 a.	2308	2349	...	...	0159		0846	0905	0927	0946	1005	...	1027	1046	1105	1127	1146		2104	2132	2153	2250	...	2339

		⑦	⑦	⑦	⑦	⑦	⑦	⑦	⑦	⑦	⑦	⑦	⑦		⑦	⑦	⑦	⑦	⑦	⑦	⑦	⑦	⑦	⑦
London Euston . 150/1/3/4 d.	⑦	0810	0820	0920	1019	1119	1217	1237	1257	1317	1337	1357	1417		1817	1837	1857	1917	1937	1957	2015	2035	2125	2151
Milton Keynes .... 150/1/4 d.		0856	0906	1007	1107	1208	1250	|	|	1350	|	|	1450	and at	1850	|	|	1950	|	|	2048	|	2217	2242
Stoke on Trent .... 119 d.		|	1021	1123	1225	1311	1350	|	1426	1450	|	1526	1550	the same	1950	|	2026	2050	|	2126	2150	|	2333	|
Macclesfield .... 119 d.		|	1038	1139	1242	1328	|	|	1442	|	|	1542	|	minutes	|	|	2042	|	|	2143	|	|	2350	|
Crewe .... 154 d.		1019	|	|	|	|	|	1413	|	|	1513	|	|	past each	|	2013	|	|	2113	|	|	2222	|	0016s
Wilmslow ....d.		1034	|	|	|	|	|	1428	|	|	1529	|	|	until	|	2029	|	|	2129	|	|	2237	|	|
Stockport .... 119 d.		1044	1052	1153	1256	1342	1423	1439	1456	1521	1539	1556	1624		2024	2039	2057	2120	2139	2200	2222	2247	0004	0039s
Manchester Piccadilly 119 a.		1053	1100	1204	1305	1350	1432	1448	1506	1531	1548	1606	1632		2032	2048	2106	2131	2149	2209	2231	2255	0013	0048

km			Ⓐ	Ⓐ	Ⓐ	Ⓐ	Ⓐ	Ⓐ	Ⓐ	Ⓐ	Ⓐ	Ⓐ	Ⓐ	Ⓐ	Ⓐ	Ⓐ	Ⓐ	Ⓐ		Ⓐ	Ⓐ	Ⓐ	Ⓐ	Ⓐ
0	**Manchester** Piccadilly 119 d.	Ⓐ	0505	0555	0610	0635	0643	0701	0715	0627	0735	0755	0815	0835	0855	0915	0935	0955	and at	1655	1715	1735	1755	1815
9	Stockport .... 119 d.		0513	0603	0618	0643	0651	0708u	0723	0636	0743	0804	0823	0843	0904	0923	0943	1004	the same	1704	1723	1743	1804	1823
30	Wilmslow .... d.		|	0611	|	|	0659	|	|	|	|	0811	|	|	0911	|	|	1011	minutes	1711	|	|	1811	|
50	Crewe .... 154 d.		0536	0628	|	|	0718	|	|	|	|	0829	|	|	0930	|	|	1029	past each	1729	|	|	1829	|
	Macclesfield .... 119 d.		|	|	0631	0656	|	|	|	0648	0756	|	|	0856	|	|	0956	|	until	|	|	1756	|	|
	Stoke on Trent .... 119 d.		|	|	0648	0712	|	|	0750	0706	0812	|	0850	0912	|	0950	1012	|		|	1750	1812	|	1850
	Milton Keynes ...... 150/1/4 a.		0651	|	|	|	|	|	0846	b	|	|	0950	|	|	1046	|	|	♧	|	1346	|	1932	1946
304	**London** Euston 150/1/3/4 a.		0725	0810	0820	0846	0853	0900	0920	0933	0949	1016	1026	1051	1107	1120	1140	1202		1906	1920	1941	2007	2021

	Ⓐ	Ⓐ	Ⓐ	Ⓐ	Ⓐ	Ⓐ		⑥	⑥	⑥	⑥	⑥	⑥	⑥	⑥	⑥	⑥	⑥	⑥	⑥		⑥	⑥	⑥
Manchester Piccadilly 119 d.	1835	1855	1915	1955	2015	2115	⑥	0525	0555	0610	0635	0655	0715	0735	0755	0815	0835	0855	0915	0935	and at	1715	1735	1755
Stockport .... 119 d.	1843	1904	1923	2004	2023	2123		0534	0603	0619	0643	0704	0723	0743	0804	0823	0843	0904	0923	0943	the same	1723	1743	1803
Wilmslow ....d.	|	1911	|	2011	|	|		0541	0611	|	|	0711	|	|	0811	|	|	0911	|	|	minutes	|	|	1811
Crewe .... 154 d.	|	1929	|	2029	|	|		0600	0629	|	|	0729	|	|	0829	|	|	0929	|	|	past each	|	|	1828
Macclesfield .... 119 d.	1856	|	1936	|	2036	2136		|	|	0631	0656	|	|	0756	|	|	0856	|	|	0956	until	|	1756	|
Stoke on Trent .... 119 d.	1912	|	1953	|	2052	2153		|	|	0648	0712	|	0750	0812	|	0850	0912	|	0950	1012		1750	1812	|
Milton Keynes .... 150/1/4 a.	|	2031	2049	2134	2152	2300		0710	0731	|	|	|	0846	|	|	0946	|	|	1048	|	★	1848	|	|
London Euston . 150/1/3/4 a.	2039	2105	2123	2209	2230	2348		0750	0807	0823	0844	0901	0921	0940	1008	1021	1041	1104	1120	1139		1922	1938	2001

	⑥	⑥	⑥	⑥	⑥		⑦	⑦	⑦		⑦	⑦	⑦	⑦	⑦	⑦		⑦	⑦	⑦	⑦	⑦	⑦	⑦
Manchester Piccadilly 119 d.	1815	1835	1855	1935	2035	⑦	0805	0820	0920	...	1020	1035	1115	1135	1155	1215	and at	1815	1835	1855	1915	1935	2021	2055
Stockport .... 119 d.	1823	1843	1904	1943	2043		0814	0828	0928	...	1029	1046	1124	1144	1205	1221	the same	1822	1842	1903	1922	1941	2027	2103
Wilmslow ....d.	|	|	1911	|	|		0822	|	|	...	1037	|	|	|	1213	|	minutes	|	|	1911	|	|	|	|
Crewe .... 154 d.	|	|	1929	|	|		0843	|	|	...	1055	|	|	|	1230	|	past each	|	|	1929	|	|	|	|
Macclesfield .... 119 d.	|	1856	|	1956	2056		|	0841	0940	...	|	1057	|	1157	|	|	until	|	1855	|	|	1954	2040	2116
Stoke on Trent .... 119 d.	1850	1912	|	2012	2112		|	0857	1000	...	|	1115	1152	1214	|	1249		1851	1912	|	1950	2011	2058	2133
Milton Keynes .... 150/1/4 a.	1946	|	|	2110	2210		|	|	1116	...	|	1221	1250	|	|	1345	☆	1947	|	|	2047	|	2158	2249
London Euston . 150/1/3/4 a.	2034	2059	2123	2201	2300		1056	1101	1206	...	1253	1257	1328	1345	1409	1426		2025	2045	2110	2131	2201	2256	2346

b – Via Birmingham New Street (Table **150**).
s – Calls to set down only.

♡ – The 1520 from London also calls at Macclesfield (d. 1706); the 1720 Ⓐ from London calls at Milton Keynes to pick up only.

☆ – Timings may vary by up to 4 minutes.
♧ – Arrival times at London Euston may vary ± 5 minutes.
★ – Arrival times at London Euston may vary ± 3 minutes.

153 LONDON - LIVERPOOL

🍷 conveyed on most services VT

km			Ⓐ	⚒	⑥	Ⓐ	Ⓐ	⑥	⚒	⚒		⚒	⚒	⚒	⚒	⚒	⑥	Ⓐ	⑥	Ⓐ	⚒	⑥	Ⓐ
0	**London** Euston ..... 142/3 150/1/2/4 d.	⚒	0527	0707	0807	0807	0907	0907	1007	1107	...	1207	1307	1407	1507	1607	1633	1707	1707	1733	1807	1833	1833
80	Milton Keynes .... 142/3 150/1/2/4 d.		0615	|	|	0838	|	|	|	|	...	|	|	|	|	|	|	|	|	|	|	|	|
135	Rugby .... 142/3 150 d.		|	|	|	|	|	|	|	|	...	|	|	|	|	|	|	|	|	1823	|	|	1923
155	Nuneaton .... 143 d.		0645	|	|	|	|	|	|	|	...	|	|	|	|	|	|	|	1803	|	|	|	|
215	Stafford .... 143 144 d.		0708	0824	0924	0927	1024	1024	1124	1224	...	1324	1424	1524	1624	1724	1759	1824	1827	1856	1924	1959	1954
254	Crewe .... 143 144 151 152 154 d.		0728	0843	0943	|	1043	1045	1143	1243	...	1343	1443	1543	1643	1743	|	1844	1847	1916	1943	|	2016
290	Runcorn .... 144 a.		0745	0902	1000	1000	1101	1102	1200	1300	...	1400	1500	1600	1700	1800	1831	1900	1904	1935	2000	2031	2033
312	**Liverpool** Lime Street .... 144 a.		0804	0920	1019	1019	1120	1120	1221	1320	...	1419	1519	1620	1720	1820	1851	1922	1922	1952	2020	2051	2053

	Ⓐ	⑥	Ⓐ	⑥	Ⓐ		⑦	⑦	⑦	⑦		⑦	⑦	⑦	⑦	⑦	⑦		⑦	⑦	⑦	⑦	⑦
London Euston ...... 142/3 150/1/2/4 d.	1907	1907	2007	2011	2107	⑦	0816	0916	1016	1116	...	1205	1305	1405	1505	1605	1705	...	1805	1905	2005	2008	2121
Milton Keynes .... 142/3 150/1/2/4 d.	|	|	|	|	2139		|	|	|	1204	...	|	|	|	|	|	|	...	|	|	|	2041	|
Rugby .... 142 143 150 d.	|	|	|	2115	|		|	|	|	|	...	|	|	|	|	|	|	...	|	|	|	|	|
Nuneaton .... 143 d.	|	2003	2103	|	2208		0944	1045	1147	|	...	|	|	|	|	|	1804	...	|	2004	2104	|	2257
Stafford .... 143 144 d.	|	2027	2127	2146	|		1008	1115	1214	1253	...	1325	1425	1525	1625	1726	|	...	1925	2029	|	2133	2323
Crewe .... 143 144 151 152 154 d.	|	2047	2148	2206	2253		1030	1137	1234	1315	...	1345	1445	1545	1645	1746	1846	...	1945	2049	2146	2155	2347
Runcorn .... 144 a.	2050	2105	2206	2224	2311		1048	1154	1251	1332	...	1402	1502	1602	1702	1802	1902	...	2002	2106	2203	2212	0006
Liverpool Lime Street .... 144 a.	2108	2127	2223	2241	2333		1105	1211	1308	1354	...	1420	1520	1623	1721	1821	1921	...	2020	2123	2220	2229	0029

		Ⓐ	⑥	Ⓐ	⑥	Ⓐ	⑥	Ⓐ	⑥	⚒	⚒	⚒	⚒	⑥	Ⓐ	⑥	①–④	⑤	⚒	⑥	Ⓐ	Ⓐ	⑥
Liverpool Lime Street .... 144 d.	⚒	0526	0546	0605	0644	0700	0716	0747	0747	0847	0947	1047	1147	1247	1247	1347	1347	1347	1447	1547	1547	1647	1647
Runcorn .... 144 d.		0543	0603	0621	0701	0715u	0733	0803	0803	0903	1003	1103	1203	1303	1303	1403	1403	1403	1503	1603	1603	1703	1703
Crewe .... 143 144 151 152 154 d.		0602	|	|	0720	|	0756	0823	0822	0924	1022	1122	1222	1324	1324	1424	1424	1424	1522	1622	1624	|	1723
Stafford .... 143 144 d.		0621	0635	0653	0739	|	0815	0842	0841	0943	1041	1141	1241	1342	1343	1443	1444	1444	1541	1641	1644	1736	1741
Nuneaton .... 143 d.		|	0657	|	|	|	|	|	0903	|	|	|	|	|	|	|	|	|	|	|	|	|	|
Rugby .... 142 143 150 d.		0652	|	|	|	|	|	|	|	|	|	|	|	|	|	|	|	|	|	|	|	|	|
Milton Keynes .... 142/3 150/1/2/4 d.		0712	|	|	|	|	|	|	|	|	|	|	|	|	|	|	|	|	|	|	|	1823	|
London Euston ...... 142/3 150/1/2/4 a.		0750	0802	0823	0856	0903	0944	0959	1003	1101	1159	1259	1403	1459	1503	1601	1603	1605	1659	1759	1803	1859	1907

	⑥	Ⓐ	Ⓐ	⑥	Ⓐ	⑥	Ⓐ		⑦	⑦	⑦	⑦	⑦	⑦	⑦	⑦	⑦	⑦	⑦	⑦	⑦	⑦	⑦
Liverpool Lime Street .... 144 d.	1747	1747	1847	1847	1947	1948	2048	⑦	0818	0838	0938	1038	1147	1247	1347	1447	1547	1619	1647	1747	1847	1947	2047
Runcorn .... 144 d.	1803	1803	1903	1903	2003	2005	2104		0835	0854	0954	1054	1205	1305	1405	1505	1605	1635	1705	1805	1905	2004	2103
Crewe .... 143 144 151 152 154 d.	|	1824	1922	1923	2024	2023	2125		0853	0913	1014	1114	1223	1323	1423	1523	1623	1654	1723	1823	1923	2024	2124
Stafford .... 143 144 d.	1836	1843	1941	1941	|	2043	2144		|	0932	1033	1136	1243	1343	1443	1543	1643	|	1742	1843	1943	2043	2143
Nuneaton .... 143 d.	|	|	|	|	2100	|	2217		|	0954	1055	1158	|	|	|	|	|	|	|	|	|	|	2217
Rugby .... 142 143 150 d.	|	|	|	|	|	|	2230		|	|	|	|	|	|	|	|	|	|	|	|	|	|	2231
Milton Keynes .... 142/3 150/1/2/4 d.	|	|	|	|	|	|	2253		1019	|	1145	|	|	|	|	|	|	1802	|	|	|	2137	2304
London Euston ...... 142/3 150/1/2/4 a.	2001	2003	2102	2113	2204	2218	2344		1104	1134	1229	1309	1403	1503	1603	1704	1803	1839	1902	2003	2102	2227	2353

u – Calls to pick up only.

TP, VT LONDON, BIRMINGHAM and MANCHESTER - PRESTON - EDINBURGH and GLASGOW 154

km		⚒	⚒	⑥	Ⓐ	⚒	⚒	Ⓐ	⑥	Ⓐ	⑥	⚒	⚒n	⚒	⑥	Ⓐ	⚒	⚒	⚒	⚒	⚒	⚒	Ⓐ	⑥	⚒	⚒
0	**London Euston** . 143 150/1/2/3 d.		...	...	...	...	...	...	...	0531	0605	...	...	...	...	0646	0730	0643y	...	0830	0743	...	0854	0854	0930	0843
80	Milton Keynes..... 143 150/1/2/3 d.		...	...	...	...	...	...	...	0623	0641	...	...	...	...	|	|	0713y	...	|	0813	...	|	|	|	0913
	Birmingham New St . 144 150 d.		...	...	...	...	0615	...	...	|	|	0715	...	...	0721	|	|	0815	...	|	0915	...	|	|	|	1015
	Wolverhampton........... 144 150 d.		...	...	...	...	0637	...	...	|	|	0737	...	...	0740	|	|	0837	...	|	0937	...	|	|	|	1037
253	Crewe .... 143 144 151 152 153 d.		...	0557	0557	...	0709	...	...	0732	0755	0808	...	...	0819	|	|	0909	...	|	1009	...	|	|	|	1109
291	Warrington Bank Quay .... d.		...	0615	0615	...	0727	...	...	0749	0812	0827	...	...	0841	0845	0914	0927	...	1014	1027	...	1100	1059	1114	1127
	Manchester Airport ✈ 156 157 d.		...	|	|	0610	|	0710	0710	|	|	|	...	0810	|	|	|	|	0910	|	|	1010	|	|	|	|
	Manchester Piccadilly 156 157 d.		0500	|	|	0626	|	0726	0726	|	|	|	...	0826	|	|	|	|	0926	|	|	1026	|	|	|	|
	Liverpool Lime Street .162 d.		|	|	|	|	|	|	|	|	|	|	0812	|	|	|	|	|	|	|	|	|	|	|	|	|
310	Wigan North Western ..156 162 d.		|	0625	0625	|	0738	|	|	0800	0823	0838	0843	|	0852	0857	0925	0938	|	1025	1038	|	1112	1112	1125	1138
334	**Preston**......... 156 157 158 162 d.		0540r	0641	0641	0703	0753	0803	0804	0815	0838	0853	0900	0904	0911	0914	0941	0953	1005	1041	1053	1104	1128	1135f	1141	1153
	Blackpool North ...... 156 162 a.		|	|	|	|	|	|	|	|	|	|	|	|	0932	0937	|	|	|	|	|	|	1149	1157	|	|
368	Lancaster .... 157 158 d.		0556	0655	0655	0719	0808	0819	0820	0830	0853	0908	|	0920	...	...	0955	1008	1021	1055	1109	|	...	...	1155	1208
398	Oxenholme......................... 158 d.		0610	0709	0711	0732	0822	|	0833	0843	0906	|	|	0933	...	...	|	1022	1035	1109	|	|	...	...	|	1222
450	Penrith..................................... d.		0635	0735	0735	|	|	0854	0858	|	0932	0944	0950	|	...	...	1032	|	1100	|	1145	|	...	...	1231	|
478	Carlisle .... 214 d.		0652	0751	0753	0812	0901	0911	0915	0921	0949	1002	1008	1013	...	...	1047	1102	1117	1147	1202	1207	...	...	1247	1301
519	Lockerbie.................................. d.		0711	0811	0811	0831	|	0930	0934	|	|	|	|	1031	...	...	|	|	1137	|	|	|	...	...	|	|
641	**Edinburgh** Waverley .... △ a.		|	|	|	0938	1018	|	|	|	|	|	|	1138	...	...	|	1222	|	|	|	1330b	...	...	|	1417
643	**Glasgow** Central .... 214 a.		0820	0912	0916	...	...	1033	1040	1038	1059	1115	1138t	...	...	...	1159	...	1241	1259	1315	...	...	...	1359	...

	Ⓐ	⑥	Ⓐ	⑥	⚒	⚒	⚒	⚒n	⚒	⚒	⑥	Ⓐ	⚒	⚒	⚒	Ⓐ	⑥	⚒	Ⓐ	⑥	⑥	Ⓐ	⑥	Ⓐ	⚒n	⚒
London Euston .. 143 150/1/2/3 d.	...	...	1030	1030	0943	1036	...	...	1130	1043	...	...	1230	1143	...	1330	1330	1243	...	...	1430	1430	1343	1343	...	...
Milton Keynes...... 143 150/1/2/3 d.	...	...	|	|	1013	|	...	...	|	1113	...	...	|	1213	...	|	|	1313	...	...	|	|	1413	1413	...	...
Birmingham New St . 144 150 d.	...	...	|	|	1115	|	...	...	|	1215	...	...	|	1315	...	|	|	1415	...	...	|	|	1515	1515	...	...
Wolverhampton........... 144 150 d.	...	...	|	|	1137	|	...	...	|	1237	...	...	|	1337	...	|	|	1436	...	...	|	|	1536	1537	...	...
Crewe .... 143 144 151 152 153 d.	...	...	|	|	1209	|	...	...	|	1309	...	...	|	1409	...	|	|	1507	...	...	|	|	1609	1609	...	...
Warrington Bank Quay .... d.	...	...	1214	1214	1227	1234	...	...	1314	1327	...	...	1414	1427	...	1514	1514	1525	...	...	1614	1614	1627	1627	...	...
Manchester Airport ✈ 156 157 d.	1110	1110	|	|	|	|	1210	...	|	|	1310	1310	|	|	1410	|	|	|	1510	1510	|	|	|	|	...	1610
Manchester Piccadilly.. 156 157 d.	1126	1126	|	|	|	|	1226	...	|	|	1326	1326	|	|	1426	|	|	|	1526	1526	|	|	|	|	...	1626
Liverpool Lime Street.. 162 d.	|	|	|	|	|	|	|	1211	|	|	|	|	|	|	|	|	|	|	|	|	|	|	|	|	1612	|
Wigan North Western.... 156 162 d.	|	|	1225	1225	1238	1245	|	1250	1325	1338	|	|	1425	1438	|	1525	1525	1536	|	|	1625	1625	1638	1638	1643	|
Preston.......... 156 157 158 162 d.	1205	1205	1241	1241	1253	1300	1304	1309	1341	1353	1405	1405	1441	1453	1504	1541	1541	1553	1603	1604	1641	1641	1653	1653	1659	1705
Blackpool North .... 156 162 a.	|	|	|	|	|	1320	|	|	|	|	|	|	|	|	|	|	|	|	|	|	|	|	|	|	|	|
Lancaster...................... 157 158 d.	1220	1220	|	1255	1308	...	1320	1327	1355	1408	1420	1420	1456	1509	1520	|	1555	1608	1620	1620	1656	1656	1709	1709	1718	1723
Oxenholme .... 158 d.	1234	1234	|	1309	1323	...	1333	|	1409	|	1434	1434	|	1523	|	1607	1610	|	1633	1633	|	1709	1723	1723	|	1736
Penrith..................................... d.	1259	1259	1329	|	|	...	|	1407	|	1443	1459	1459	1531	|	1555	1632	|	1645	1658	1657	1730	1735	|	1748	1755	|
Carlisle .... 214 d.	1314	1317	1345	1347	1400	...	1412	1424	1447	1500	1515	1515	1546	1603	1612	1648	1649	1702	1715	1714	1747	1751	1803	1806	1812	1816
Lockerbie.................................. d.	1333	1337	|	|	|	...	1431	1443	|	|	1541	1537	|	|	1631	|	|	|	1734	|	|	|	|	|	|	1835
Edinburgh Waverley.......... △ a.	|	|	|	|	|	...	1536	|	|	1623	|	|	|	|	1737	|	|	1823	|	|	|	|	|	|	|	1939
Glasgow Central .... 214 a.	1440	1440	1459	1459	1515	...	...	1556k	1559	...	1650	1641	1659	1715	...	1759	1759	...	1842	1831	1859	1915	1915	1923	1940	...

	⚒	⑥	Ⓐ	⚒	Ⓐ	⑥	⚒	⚒	Ⓐ	Ⓐ	Ⓐ	⑥	Ⓐ	⑥	Ⓐ	⑥	Ⓐ	Ⓐ	⚒	Ⓐ	⑥	Ⓐ	⑤	Ⓐ	⑥	⚒
London Euston .. 143 150/1/2/3 d.	1530	1443	1443	...	1630	1630	1543	...	1633	1657	1730	1730	1643	1643	...	...	...	1757	1830	1743	1743	...	1846	1930	1930	1843
Milton Keynes...... 143 150/1/2/3 d.	|	1513	1513	...	|	|	1613	...	|	|	|	|	1713	1713	...	...	...	|	|	1813u	1813	...	1919	|	|	1913
Birmingham New St . 144 150 d.	|	1615	1615	...	|	|	1715	...	|	|	|	|	1815	1815	...	...	...	|	|	1915	1915	...	|	|	|	2015
Wolverhampton........... 144 150 d.	|	1637	1637	...	|	|	1737	...	|	|	|	|	1837	1837	...	...	...	|	|	1937	1937	...	|	|	|	2037
Crewe .... 143 144 151 152 153 d.	|	1708	1709	...	|	|	1809	...	1820	|	|	|	1911r	1908	...	...	...	|	|	2009	2008	...	2043	|	2105	2115d
Warrington Bank Quay .... d.	1714	1727	1727	...	1814	1814	1827	...	1837	1850	1914	1914	1929	1927	...	...	...	1950	2014	2027	2027	...	2103	2116	2123	...
Manchester Airport ✈ 156 157 d.	|	|	|	1710	|	|	|	1810	|	|	|	|	|	|	1910	1910	...	|	|	|	|	2010	|	|	|	...
Manchester Piccadilly.. 156 157 d.	|	|	|	1726	|	|	|	1826	|	|	|	|	|	|	1926	1926	...	|	|	|	|	2026	|	|	|	...
Liverpool Lime Street.. 162 d.	|	|	|	|	|	|	|	|	|	|	|	|	|	|	|	|	2012	|	|	|	|	|	|	|	|	...
Wigan North Western.... 156 162 d.	1725	1738	1738	|	1825	1825	1838	|	1848	1901	1925	1925	1940	1938	|	|	2043	2001	2025	2038	2038	|	2114	2127	2134	...
Preston.......... 156 157 158 162 d.	1741	1753	1753	1805	1841	1841	1853	1905	1905r	1915	1941	1941	1955	1952	2006	2005	2059	2016	2041	2053	2052	2105	2131	2143r	2147	...
Blackpool North .... 156 162 a.	|	|	|	|	|	|	|	|	1930	|	|	|	|	...	|	|	|	|	|	|	...	|	...	|	...	...
Lancaster...................... 157 158 d.	1755	1808	1809	1820	1858	1855	1908	1922	...	1930	1955	1955	2011	...	2021	2021	2115	2030	2055	2108	...	2121	...	2158	...	...
Oxenholme .... 158 d.	1809	1824	1824	1834	|	1908	1923	1935	...	1945	2009	2009	|	...	2035	2034	2130	...	2110	2123	...	2134	...	2211	...	...
Penrith..................................... d.	|	1849	1849	1859	1932	1934	|	2000	...	2010	|	2035	2049	...	2100	2059	...	...	2135	|	...	2159	...	2236	...	...
Carlisle .... 214 d.	1847	1904	1905	1915	1948	1951	2002	2017	...	2025	2047	2050	2106	...	2118	2115	...	...	2150	2202	...	2216	...	2251	...	...
Lockerbie.................................. d.	|	|	|	1935	|	|	|	2036	...	2044	|	|	|	...	2137	2134	...	...	2209	|	...	2235	...	|	...	...
Edinburgh Waverley.......... △ a.	|	2022	2025	|	|	|	|	2140	...	|	|	|	2222	...	|	2238	...	...	|	|	...	2339	...	|	...	...
Glasgow Central .... 214 a.	1959	...	...	2042	2059	2102	2115	...	...	2144	2210	2201	...	...	2240	...	...	...	2309	2317	...	...	...	0003	...	...

	Ⓐ	Ⓐ	Ⓐ	Ⓐ	⑥	Ⓐ	⑦	⑦e	⑦e	⑦g	⑦	⑦n	⑦	⑦	⑦	⑦	⑦	⑦	⑦	⑦	⑦	⑦	⑦	⑦	⑦	⑦
London Euston .. 143 150/1/2/3 d.	...	2030	1943	...	2031	2110		...	...	...	...	...	...	...	...	0847	...	...	0946	...	...	1046	...	...	1228	...
Milton Keynes...... 143 150/1/2/3 d.	...	|	2013	...	|	|		...	...	...	...	...	...	...	...	0934	...	...	1033	...	...	1133	...	...	|	...
Birmingham New St . 144 150 d.	...	|	2115	...	|	|		...	...	...	0845	...	0920	...	...	|	1020	...	|	1120	...	|	1220	...	|	1320
Wolverhampton........... 144 150 d.	...	|	2137	...	|	|		...	...	...	0904	...	0937	...	...	|	1037	...	|	1137	...	|	1237	...	|	1337
Crewe .... 143 144 151 152 153 d.	...	2219	2230	...	2230	2259		...	...	...	0937	...	1010	...	1027	1058	1111	...	1157	1209	...	1258	1309	...	|	1409
Warrington Bank Quay .... d.	...	2236	...	...	2247	2321		...	...	...	0954	...	1028	...	1043	1114	1129	...	1214	1227	...	1315	1327	...	1416	1427
Manchester Airport ✈ 156 157 d.	2105	|	...	2210	|	|		...	0905	0905	|	...	|	1010	|	|	|	1110	|	|	...	|	|	1310	|	|
Manchester Piccadilly.. 156 157 d.	2122	|	...	2226	|	|		0843	0922	0922	|	...	|	1026	|	|	|	1125	|	|	1231x	|	|	1326	|	|
Liverpool Lime Street.. 162 d.	|	|	...	|	|	|		|	|	|	|	1012	|	|	|	|	|	|	|	|	|	|	|	|	|	|
Wigan North Western.... 156 162 d.	|	2247	...	2258	2301	2332		|	|	|	1006	1044	1038	|	1054	1125	1140	|	1225	1238	|	1326	1338	|	1427	1438
Preston.......... 156 157 158 162 d.	2201	2300	...	2315	2316	2350		0924	1004	1019a	1021	1100	1102f	1109	1118r	1141	1155	1205	1240	1253	1305	1341	1353	1408	1442	1453
Blackpool North .... 156 162 a.	|	...	...	|	...	...		|	|	|	...	|	|	|	|	|	|	|	|	|	|	|	|	|	|	|
Lancaster...................... 157 158 d.	2220	...	...	2333	...	...		0939	1020	1035	...	|	1118	1125	1136	1156	1210	1221	1255	1308	1320	1356	1409	1423	1458	1510
Oxenholme .... 158 d.	2234	...	...	...	...	...		0953	1034	|	...	|	1133	1138	...	1209	1225	1234	1309	1322	1334	1410	|	1437	|	1524
Penrith..................................... d.	2300	...	...	...	...	...		|	1059	|	...	|	|	|	...	1235	|	1259	1335	|	|	1436	1446	1502	1532	|
Carlisle .... 214 d.	2318	...	...	...	...	...		1033	1116	1130	...	1205	1212	1218	...	1251	1303	1316	1350	1401	1413	1451	1503	1518	1548	1603
Lockerbie.................................. d.	2337	...	...	...	...	...		|	1136	|	...	|	|	|	...	|	|	1337	|	|	1431	|	|	1537	|	|
Edinburgh Waverley.......... △ a.	|	...	...	...	...	...		1153	|	|	...	|	|	1342	...	|	1421	|	|	|	1536	|	1620	|	|	|
Glasgow Central .... 214 a.	0054	...	...	...	...	...		...	1246	1256	...	1322	1327	...	...	1404	...	1442	1504	1515	...	1606	...	1642	1700	1715

	⑦n	⑦	⑦	⑦	⑦	⑦	⑦	⑦	⑦	⑦	⑦	⑦	⑦	⑦n	⑦	⑦	⑦	⑦	⑦	⑦	⑦	⑦	⑦	⑦	⑦	⑦
London Euston .. 143 150/1/2/3 d.	...	...	1328	1240	...	1428	1340	...	1528	1440	...	1628	1540	...	...	1728	1640	...	1828	1740	...	1840	1928	2025	1940	2050
Milton Keynes...... 143 150/1/2/3 d.	...	...	|	1313	...	|	1413	...	|	1513	...	|	1613	...	...	|	1713	...	|	1813	...	1913	|	|	2013	2140
Birmingham New St . 144 150 d.	...	...	|	1415	...	|	1515	...	|	1615	...	|	1715	...	...	|	1815	...	|	1915	...	2015	|	|	2115	|
Wolverhampton........... 144 150 d.	...	...	|	1437	...	|	1537	...	|	1637	...	|	1737	...	...	|	1836	...	|	1937	...	2037	|	|	2137	|
Crewe .... 143 144 151 152 153 d.	...	...	|	1509	...	|	1609	...	|	1709	...	|	1809	...	...	|	1908	...	|	2009	...	2110	|	2213	2217	2251
Warrington Bank Quay .... d.	...	...	1516	1527	...	1616	1627	...	1716	1727	...	1816	1827	...	...	1917	1926	...	2016	2027	...	...	2116	2230	2236	2308
Manchester Airport ✈ 156 157 d.	...	1410	|	|	1510	|	|	1610	|	|	1710	|	|	...	1810	|	|	1910	|	|	2010	...	|	|	|	|
Manchester Piccadilly.. 156 157 d.	...	1426	|	|	1526	|	|	1626	|	|	1726	|	|	...	1826	|	|	1926	|	|	2026	...	|	|	|	|
Liverpool Lime Street.. 162 d.	1412	|	|	|	|	|	|	|	|	|	|	|	|	1812	|	|	|	|	|	|	|	...	|	|	|	|
Wigan North Western.... 156 162 d.	1443	|	1527	1538	|	1627	1638	|	1727	1738	|	1827	1838	1843	|	1928	1938	|	2027	2038	|	...	2127	2241	2247	2319
Preston.......... 156 157 158 162 d.	1459	1505	1542	1553	1607	1642	1653	1705	1742	1753	1807	1842	1853	1859	1904	1943	1953	2007	2042	2053	2104	...	2142	2255	2302	2336
Blackpool North .... 156 162 a.	|	|	|	|	|	|	|	|	|	|	|	|	|	|	|	|	|	|	|	|	|	...	|	...	...	...
Lancaster...................... 157 158 d.	1515	1521	1558	1609	1622	1657	1708	1721	1757	1809	1822	1857	1908	1915	1920	1958	2009	2023	2057	2109	2120	...	2157	...	...	...
Oxenholme .... 158 d.	|	|	1612	|	1636	|	1723	1734	1812	1824	1836	1912	1923	|	1934	2012	|	2036	2112	2124	2133	...	2212	...	...	...
Penrith..................................... d.	|	1557	|	1645	1701	1732	|	1759	|	1849	1901	1937	|	1953	1959	2037	2046	2101	2137	|	2158	...	2237	...	...	...
Carlisle .... 214 d.	1608	1613	1649	1702	1718	1748	1802	1815	1849	1904	1917	1953	2001	2010	2015	2052	2102	2118	2152	2202	2215	...	2252	...	...	...
Lockerbie.................................. d.	|	1632	|	|	1737	|	|	1834	|	|	1937	|	|	2029	2033	|	|	2137	|	2221	|	...	|	...	...	...
Edinburgh Waverley.......... △ a.	|	1733	|	1820	|	|	|	1935	|	2022	|	|	|	|	2135	|	2219	|	|	|	2333	...	|	...	...	...
Glasgow Central .... 214 a.	1730	...	1803	...	1843	1900	1913	...	2001	...	2040	2104	2112	2135	...	2204	...	2242	2307	2321	...	...	0004	...	...	...

a – Arrives 1003.
b – Arrives 1326 on ⑥.
d – Arrives 2110 on ⑥.
e – From June 23.
f – Arrives 7–10 minutes earlier.
g – Until June 16.
h – Arrives 0912 on ⑥.
k – Arrives 1547 on ⑥.
n – From Sept. 14.
r – Arrives 4–6 minutes earlier.
t – Arrives 1128 on Ⓐ.
x – Manchester **Victoria**.
y – Ⓐ only.
△ – All trains to **Edinburgh** Waverley call at Haymarket 5–9 minutes earlier.

154 GLASGOW and EDINBURGH - PRESTON - MANCHESTER, BIRMINGHAM and LONDON — TP, VT

km			Ⓐ	⑥	Ⓐ	Ⓐ	⑥	⚒	⚒	Ⓐn	⑥n	⑥	⚒	Ⓐ	⑥	Ⓐ	⚒	⚒	⚒	⚒	⚒	Ⓐ	⑥	Ⓐ	⚒	Ⓐn
	Glasgow Central 214 d.		...	...	...	...	...	...	0426	...	...	...	0422	0540	0540	...	0549	...	0630	...	0710	...	0735	0737	0800	0745
	Edinburgh Waverley ▽ d.	⚒	...	...	...	...	...	...	|	...	...	...	|	|	|	...	|	0614	|	0652	|	...	|	|	|	|
	Lockerbie d.		...	...	...	...	...	...	|	...	...	...	0550d	|	|	...	|	0713	0726	|	0809	...	|	|	|	0902
	Carlisle 214 d.		...	...	...	...	...	...	0543	0548	0550	...	0621a	0650	0649	...	0702	0735	0746	0807	0832	...	0849	0850	0910	0924
	Penrith d.		...	...	...	...	...	...	0558	0603	0605	...	0639	|	|	...	0717	0749	0800	0822	0849	...	|	|	|	0939
	Oxenholme 158 d.		...	...	...	...	...	...	0621	0627	0629	...	0708	0725	0724	...	0741	0813	0823	|	0913	...	0923	0924	|	1003
	Lancaster 157 158 d.		0513	0538	...	...	...	0628	0636	0642	|	0658	0723	0739	0738	0658	0756	0828	0838	0857	0927	...	0938	0939	0957	1018
	Blackpool North 156 162 d.		|	|	0530	...	...	|	|	|	|	|	|	|	|	|	|	|	|	|	|	...	|	|	|	|
0	**Preston** 156 157 158 162 d.		0533	0557	0600	0617	0617	0647	0656	0705	0705	0717	0746b	0800	0759	0718	0817	0847	0859	0917	0946	0951	0959	0959	1017	1039
24	Wigan North Western 156 162 d.		0545	0609	0611	0629	0629	|	0709	0717	|	0729	|	0811	0811	0729	0829	|	0911	0929	|	1004	1011	1011	1029	1052
	Liverpool Lime Street 162 d.		|	|	|	|	|	|	|	0757	0756	|	|	|	|	|	|	|	|	|	|	|	|	|	|	1128
57	**Manchester** Piccadilly 156 157 a.		|	|	|	|	|	0724	|	...	...	|	0824	|	|	|	|	0924	|	|	1024	|	|	|	|	...
73	**Manchester** Airport ✈ 156 157 a.		|	|	|	|	|	0743	|	...	...	|	0843	|	|	|	|	0945	|	|	1043	|	|	|	|	...
—	Warrington Bank Quay d.		0556	0620	0622	0640	0640	...	0719	...	...	0741	...	0822	0822	0741	0840	...	0922	0940	...	1016	1022	1022	1040	...
0	Crewe 143 144 151 152 153 a.		|	|	0642c	0659	0657	...	|	...	...	0757	...	|	|	0757	0857	...	|	0957	...	1038	|	|	1057	...
63	Wolverhampton 144 150 a.		|	|	|	0735	0731	...	|	...	...	0835	...	|	|	0832	0933	...	|	1034	...	|	|	|	1134	...
82	**Birmingham** New St 144 150 a.		|	|	|	0756	0805	...	|	...	...	0906	...	|	|	0905	1006	...	|	1105	...	|	|	|	1205	...
	Milton Keynes 150/1/2/3 a.		|	0738	|	...	0858	...	|	...	...	...	...	|	|	0958	1058	...	|	1158	...	|	|	|	1258	...
	London Euston 143 150/1/2/3 a.		0756	0813	0834	...	0936	...	0906	...	...	...	...	1009	1011	1033	1134	...	1110	1235	...	1232	1208	1210	1333	...

	⚒	⑥n	⚒	⚒	⚒	⑥	Ⓐ	⚒	⚒	Ⓐ	⑥	⚒	⚒	⚒	⚒	⚒	Ⓐ	⑥	Ⓐn	⑥n	⚒	⚒	⚒	Ⓐ	⚒	⚒
Glasgow Central 214 d.	...	0805	0840	...	...	0907	0906	0940	1000	...	...	1040	...	...	1109	1140	1200	1200	1145e	1205	...	1240	...	...	1309	1340
Edinburgh Waverley ▽ d.	0811	|	|	0852	...	|	|	|	|	1012	1012	|	1052	...	|	|	|	|	|	|	1211	|	1252	...	|	|
Lockerbie d.	0910	0916	|	|	...	1012	1008	|	|	1111	1110	|	|	...	1208	|	|	|	|	1307	1311	|	|	...	1408	|
Carlisle 214 d.	0934	0938	0949	1008	...	1034	1034	1049	1110	1134	1134b	1149	1207	...	1234b	1249	1312	1313	1326	1329	1333	1349	1408	...	1434b	1449
Penrith d.	0949	0953	1003	|	...	1049	1049	|	1125	1149	1151	|	|	...	1249	1303	|	|	1341	1344	1347	|	1422	...	1449	|
Oxenholme 158 d.	1013	1017	|	1042	...	1112	1113	1123	|	1213	|	1223	1243	...	1313	|	|	|	1405	1408	1411	1424	|	...	1513	1523
Lancaster 157 158 d.	1028	1033	1038	1057	...	1127	1128	1138	|	1228	1228	1238	1257	...	1328	1337	1357	1400	1422	1423	1428	1439	1457	...	1528	1538
Blackpool North 156 162 d.	|	|	|	|	1054	|	|	|	|	|	|	|	|	1303	|	|	|	|	|	|	|	|	|	1502	|	|
Preston 156 157 158 162 d.	1047	1053	1059	1117	1121	1146	1147	1159	1217	1247	1247	1259	1317	1328	1347	1359	1417	1420	1443	1444	1447	1459	1517	1529b	1547	1559
Wigan North Western 156 162 d.	|	|	1111	1129	1135	|	|	1211	1229	|	|	1311	1329	1341	|	1411	1429	1432	1456	1457	|	1511	1529	1545	|	1611
Liverpool Lime Street 162 d.	|	1144	|	|	|	|	|	|	|	|	|	|	|	|	|	|	|	|	1531	1529	|	|	|	|	|	|
Manchester Piccadilly 156 157 a.	1124	...	|	|	|	1226	1224	|	|	1324	1324	|	|	|	1424	|	|	|	...	...	1524	|	|	|	1624	|
Manchester Airport ✈ 156 157 a.	1143	...	|	|	|	1245	1243	|	|	1343	1343	|	|	|	1443	|	|	|	...	...	1543	|	|	|	1649r	|
Warrington Bank Quay d.	...	...	1122	1140	1148	...	...	1222	1240	...	...	1322	1340	1352	...	1422	1440	1443	...	...	...	1522	1540	1600	...	1622
Crewe 143 144 151 152 153 a.	...	...	|	1157	|	...	...	|	1259	...	...	|	1357	|	...	|	1457	1458	...	...	...	|	1558	|	...	|
Wolverhampton 144 150 a.	...	...	|	1233	|	...	...	|	1333	...	...	|	1434	|	...	|	1535	1534	...	...	...	|	1633	|	...	|
Birmingham New St 144 150 a.	...	...	|	1305	|	...	...	|	1405	...	...	|	1505	|	...	|	1604	1605	...	...	...	|	1706	|	...	|
Milton Keynes 150/1/2/3 a.	...	...	|	1357	|	...	...	|	1458	...	...	|	1558	|	...	|	1658	1658	...	...	...	|	1758	|	...	|
London Euston 143 150/1/2/3 a.	...	...	1309	1436	1353	...	...	1410	1534	...	...	1513	1633	1559	...	1611	1734	1733	...	...	...	1710	1833	1759	...	1809

	⑥	⚒	⚒	⚒	Ⓐ	⑥	Ⓐ	⑥	⚒	Ⓐ	⑥	⚒	Ⓐ	⑥	⚒n	Ⓐ	⑥	⑥	Ⓐ	Ⓐ	⑥	Ⓐ	⑥	⑥	Ⓐ	Ⓐ
Glasgow Central 214 d.	...	1400	...	1440	...	...	1509	1509	1540	1600	1600	...	1640	1640	1629	...	...	1709	1708	1730	1740	1740	1800	...	...	1840
Edinburgh Waverley ▽ d.	...	|	1418	|	1452	1452	|	|	|	|	|	1611	|	|	|	1652	1652	|	|	|	|	|	|	1812	1812	|
Lockerbie d.	...	|	1516	|	|	|	1608	1608	|	|	|	1709	|	|	|	|	|	1808	1809	|	1833	1833	|	1910	1914	|
Carlisle 214 d.	...	1511	1539	1549	1608	1608	1631	1635h	1649	1711	1711	1735	1752	1752	1804	1810	1809	1834b	1834b	1846	1853	1857	1911	1936b	1936	1949
Penrith d.	...	|	|	|	1621	1622	1646	1650	1703	|	|	1750	1806	|	|	|	|	1849	1849	1901	1907	|	|	1950	1950	|
Oxenholme 158 d.	...	1545	1614	1624	|	|	1710	1714	|	1745	1745	1814	1830	1826	|	1844	1845	1913	1913	1925	1930	1933	|	2014	2014	2024
Lancaster 157 158 d.	...	|	1629	1638	1658	1657	1727	1728	1737	|	|	1828	1844	1841	1854	1859	1900	1927	1928	1939	1944	1947	1958	2028	2028	2038
Blackpool North 156 162 d.	1554	|	|	|	|	|	|	|	|	|	|	|	|	|	|	|	|	|	|	|	|	|	|	|	|	|
Preston 156 157 158 162 d.	1623b	1617	1648	1659	1717	1717	1746	1747	1759	1817	1817	1847	1905	1902	1914	1918	1920	1947	1948	2000	2005	2008	2018	2047	2047	2059
Wigan North Western 156 162 d.	1636	1629	|	1711	1729	1729	|	|	1811	1829	1829	|	1917	1914	|	1932	1932	|	|	2012	2017	2020	2030	|	|	2111
Liverpool Lime Street 162 d.	|	|	|	|	|	|	|	|	|	|	|	|	|	|	1958	|	|	|	|	|	|	|	|	|	|	|
Manchester Piccadilly 156 157 a.	|	|	1727	|	|	|	1823	1823	|	|	|	1924	|	|	...	|	|	2024	2024	|	|	|	|	2124	2124	|
Manchester Airport ✈ 156 157 a.	|	|	1744	|	|	|	1843	1846	|	|	|	1945	|	|	...	|	|	2039	2039	|	|	|	|	2142	2142	|
Warrington Bank Quay d.	1647	1640	...	1722	1740	1740	...	...	1822	1840	1840	...	1927	1925	...	1942	1943	...	...	2023	2028	2032	2041	...	...	2121
Crewe 143 144 151 152 153 a.	|	1657	...	|	1757	1757	...	...	|	1857	1857	...	|	|	...	2000	2002	...	...	2042	2047	2051	2101	...	...	|
Wolverhampton 144 150 a.	|	1733	...	|	1832	1833	...	...	|	1933	1934	...	|	|	...	2037	2034	...	...	|	|	2130	2134	...	...	|
Birmingham New St 144 150 a.	|	1805	...	|	1905	1906	...	...	|	2005	2006	...	|	|	...	2105	2105	...	...	|	|	2154	2153	...	...	|
Milton Keynes 150/1/2/3 a.	|	1858	...	|	1959	2005	...	...	|	2058	2104	...	2045	2043	...	2158	2204	...	...	2149	2151	...	...	...	...	2240
London Euston 143 150/1/2/3 a.	1853	1934	...	1910	2033	2055	...	...	2013	2136	2157	...	2119	2140	...	2241	2256	...	...	2227	2243	...	...	...	...	2332

	⑥	①–④	⑤	⑥	⑥	Ⓐ	Ⓐ	Ⓐ	Ⓐ		⑦	⑦	⑦	⑦	⑦	⑦m	⑦k	⑦	⑦	⑦	⑦n	⑦	⑦	⑦	⑦	⑦
Glasgow Central 214 d.	1840	...	...	...	1847	1908	2010	...	...		...	...	...	...	...	...	...	0938	...	...	1013	1038	...	1114	1138	1155
Edinburgh Waverley ▽ d.	|	1852	1852	1852	|	|	|	2011	2213	⑦	...	...	...	...	...	0916	0916	|	...	1015	|	|	1051	|	|	|
Lockerbie d.	|	|	|	|	1955	2008	2104	2112	2316		...	...	...	...	...	1014	1021	|	...	1113	1117	|	|	1216	|	|
Carlisle 214 d.	1949	2007	2007	2009b	2017	2031	2125	2135	2344		...	...	...	...	...	1036	1045	1051	...	1135	1140	1153	1207	1237	1249	1307
Penrith d.	2003	|	|	2023	2031	2045	2140	|	|		...	...	...	...	...	1150	1100	1105	...	1149	|	1207	|	1251	|	|
Oxenholme 158 d.	2026	2042	2042	2047	2055	2109	2204	2211	|		...	...	...	...	...	1114	1123	1128	...	1213	1217	1231	1243	1315	1323	|
Lancaster 157 158 d.	2041	2056	2056	2102	2109	2124	2219	2226	|		...	...	...	...	...	1129	1138	1143	1158	1228	1232	1245	1257	1330	1338	1357
Blackpool North 156 162 d.	|	|	|	|	|	|	|	|	|		...	...	...	...	...	|	|	|	|	|	|	|	|	|	|	|
Preston 156 157 158 162 d.	2102	2117	2117	2122	2128	2143	2239	2246	0057		0900	1000	1017	1058	1117	1148	1157	1204	1217	1247	1254	1306	1317	1349	1359	1418
Wigan North Western 156 162 d.	2114	2129	2130	2133	|	|	2253	|	|		0911	1012	1028	1109	1128	|	|	1215	1229	|	1308	1317	1329	|	1411	1429
Liverpool Lime Street 162 d.	|	|	|	|	|	|	|	|	|		|	|	|	|	|	|	|	|	|	|	1341	|	|	|	|	|
Manchester Piccadilly 156 157 a.	|	|	|	|	2210	2223	|	2324	0142		|	|	|	|	|	1223	1241	|	|	1325	...	|	|	1426	|	|
Manchester Airport ✈ 156 157 a.	|	|	|	|	2226	2241	|	2341	0158y		|	|	|	|	|	1238	1303	|	|	1344	...	|	|	1443	|	|
Warrington Bank Quay d.	2125	2139	2140	2144	...	...	2304	...	...		0922	1022	1039	1120	1140	...	...	1226	1240	...	...	1329	1340	...	1422	1441
Crewe 143 144 151 152 153 a.	2145	2159	2159	2204	...	...	2326	...	...		0941	1041	1059	|	1159	...	...	|	1259	...	...	|	1359	...	|	1500
Wolverhampton 144 150 a.	2222	2232	2232	2238	...	...	...	...	...		|	|	1134	|	1233	...	...	|	1332	...	...	|	1433	...	|	1534
Birmingham New St 144 150 a.	2249	2252	2306	2257	...	...	...	...	...		|	|	1153	|	1250	...	...	|	1406	...	...	|	1506	...	|	1606
Milton Keynes 150/1/2/3 a.	...	...	0023	...	...	...	...	...	...		1106	1205	...	|	...	...	...	|	1458	...	...	|	1558	...	|	1658
London Euston 143 150/1/2/3 a.	...	...	0113	...	...	...	...	...	...		1202	1242	...	1320	...	...	...	1415	1537	...	...	1518	1637	...	1611	1736

	⑦	⑦	⑦	⑦	⑦	⑦	⑦n	⑦	⑦	⑦	⑦	⑦	⑦	⑦	⑦	⑦	⑦	⑦	⑦	⑦	⑦	⑦n	⑦	⑦	⑦	⑦m
Glasgow Central 214 d.	...	1238	...	1314	1338	1355	1405	...	1438	...	1514	1538	1557	...	1638	...	1715	1738	...	1837	...	1847	1915	2008	...	...
Edinburgh Waverley ▽ d.	1212	|	1251	|	|	|	|	1412	|	1451	|	|	|	1614	|	1651	|	|	1814	|	1851	|	|	|	2015	2210
Lockerbie d.	1311	|	|	1415	|	|	|	1510	|	|	1614	|	|	1712	|	|	1814	1832	1912	|	|	|	2014	2104	2114	2308
Carlisle 214 d.	1333	1349	1407	1437	1449	1511	1523	1533	1549	1607b	1636	1649	1710	1735	1751	1807	1836	1852	1935	1948	2007b	2014	2036	2125	2136	2330
Penrith d.	1348	|	1422	1451	|	|	1538	1548	|	1622	1651	1703	|	1750	1805	|	1850	1906	1950	|	2022	2029	2050	2140	|	|
Oxenholme 158 d.	1412	1423	|	1515	1523	1545	1602	1612	1623	|	1714	|	1744	1814	1828	1842	1914	1929	2014	2023	|	2053	2114	2204	2212	|
Lancaster 157 158 d.	1427	1438	1457	1529	1538	|	1617	1627	1638	1657	1729	1738	|	1829	1843	1857	1929	1944	2029	2037	2057	2112	2129	2219	2227	|
Blackpool North 156 162 d.	|	|	|	|	|	|	|	|	|	|	|	|	|	|	|	|	|	|	|	|	|	|	|	|	|	|
Preston 156 157 158 162 d.	1446	1459	1517	1548	1559	1617	1638	1646	1659	1717	1747	1759	1817b	1848	1904	1917	1948	2005	2048	2057	2118	2132	2148	2241	2246	0037
Wigan North Western 156 162 d.	|	1511	1528	|	1611	1630	1651	|	1710	1730	|	1811	1828	|	1915	1929	|	2017	|	2108	2130	2144	|	2253	|	|
Liverpool Lime Street 162 d.	|	|	|	|	|	|	1726	|	|	|	|	|	|	|	|	|	|	|	|	|	|	2215	|	|	2323	0114
Manchester Piccadilly 156 157 a.	1524	|	|	1624	|	|	...	1725	|	|	1825	|	|	1925	|	|	2024	|	2125	|	|	...	2224	|	2339	0129
Manchester Airport ✈ 156 157 a.	1543	|	|	1643	|	|	...	1743	|	|	1843	|	|	1945	|	|	2043	|	2140	|	|	...	2239	|	...	...
Warrington Bank Quay d.	...	1522	1539	...	1622	1641	...	...	1721	1741	...	1822	1840	...	1927	1940	...	2028	...	2119	2141	...	...	2304	...	...
Crewe 143 144 151 152 153 a.	...	|	1559	...	|	1659	...	...	|	1800	...	|	1859	...	|	1959	...	2047	...	2139	2200	...	...	2322	...	...
Wolverhampton 144 150 a.	...	|	1632	...	|	1733	...	...	|	1834	...	|	1933	...	|	2033	...	|	...	2213	2232	...	...	...	...	...
Birmingham New St 144 150 a.	...	|	1705	...	|	1805	...	...	|	1906	...	|	2006	...	|	2051	...	|	...	2231	2252	...	...	...	...	...
Milton Keynes 150/1/2/3 a.	...	|	1757	...	|	1859	...	...	|	1958	...	|	2059	...	|	...	...	2152	...	...	...	...	...	...	...	...
London Euston 143 150/1/2/3 a.	...	1711	1835	...	1811	1936	...	...	1910	2037	...	2011	2146	...	2119	...	...	2253	...	...	...	...	...	...	...	...

a – Arrives 7–9 minutes earlier.
b – Arrives 4–6 minutes earlier.
c – Departs 0653.
d – Arrives 0537.
e – On ①③④⑤ departs 1205.
f – ⑥ only.
h – Arrives 1628.
k – Until June 16.
m – From June 23.
n – From Sept. 9.
r – Arrives 1643 on ⑥.
y – Not ④ mornings.
▽ – All trains from **Edinburgh** Waverley call at Haymarket 4–6 minutes later.

EM 2nd class only — CREWE - STOKE - DERBY — 155

km			Ⓐ	Ⓐ	Ⓐ	★	Ⓐ	Ⓐ		⑥	⑥	⑥		⑥	⑥		⑦	⑦	⑦	⑦	⑦	⑦	⑦	⑦
0	**Crewe** .... **143** d.	Ⓐ	0607	0658	0807	and at	1907	2045	⑥	0607	0707	0807	and at	1907	2045	⑦	1404	1505	1608	1708	1808	1908	2015	2116
24	Stoke on Trent ... **143** d.		0633	0724	0833	the same	1933	2118		0633	0733	0833	the same	1933	2119		1429	1532	1634	1734	1835	1935	2040	2142
33	Blythe Bridge .... d.		0646	0736	0845	minutes	1945	2130		0645	0745	0845	minutes	1945	2131		1441	1544	1647	1747	1847	1947	2052	2154
51	Uttoxeter .... d.		0658	0749	0858	past each	1958	2142		0658	0758	0858	past each	1958	2144		1454	1557	1659	1759	1859	1959	2105	2206
82	**Derby** .... a.		0726	0817	0926	hour until	2027	2208		0727	0828	0927	hour until	2023	2210		1519	1623	1727	1828	1928	2027	2133	2232

		Ⓐ	Ⓐ	Ⓐ	Ⓐ		Ⓐ	Ⓐ		⑥	⑥	⑥		⑥	⑥			⑦	⑦	⑦	⑦	⑦	⑦	⑦
Derby .... d.	Ⓐ	0640	0740	0842	0942	and at	1943	2042	⑥	0640	0740	0842	and at	1942	2042	...	⑦	1440	1540	1641	1741	1841	1941	2040
Uttoxeter .... d.		0706	0807	0907	1006	the same	2007	2107		0706	0807	0906	the same	2007	2107	...		1505	1605	1706	1806	1905	2006	2105
Blythe Bridge .... d.		0720	0821	0921	1021	minutes	2022	2121		0720	0821	0920	minutes	2021	2121	...		1519	1619	1720	1820	1919	2020	2119
Stoke on Trent ... **143** d.		0733	0834	0934	1034	past each	2034	2134		0733	0834	0934	past each	2034	2134	...		1532	1633	1733	1834	1933	2034	2133
Crewe .... **143** a.		0800	0902	1004	1104	hour until	2104	2204		0800	0902	1004	hour until	2104	2204	...		1602	1702	1805	1901	2002	2100	2200

★ – Arrival times at Derby may vary by up to 3 minutes.

NT 2nd Class only — MANCHESTER - PRESTON - BLACKPOOL — 156

For other trains Manchester - Preston and v.v. see Tables **154** and **157**.

km			⚒	Ⓐ	⑥	⚒	⚒	⚒	⚒	⚒	Ⓐ	⑥	⚒	⚒	♣	⚒	⚒	⚒	⚒	⚒	⚒	⚒	⚒	⚒	⚒	⚒	⚒
0	**Manchester** Airport ... d.	⚒	0446	0542	0542	...	0637	...	0739	...	0839	0839	...	0939	and at	...	1539	...	1637	...	1740	...	1839	...	...	1939	...
16	**Manchester** Piccadilly d.		0504	0601	0601	0630	0701	0730	0801	0830	0901	0901	0930	1000	the same	1530	1600	1630	1700	1731	1800	1830	1900	1905t	1930	2000	2030
34	Bolton .... d.		0523	0620	0620	0651	0721	0749	0820	0851	0921	0921	0951	1020	minutes	1551	1620	1650	1721	1751	1820	1850	1920	1925	1951	2020	2051
66	**Preston** ...... **173a 191** d.		0552	0653	0658r	0737	0752	0825	0851	0925	0951	0956	1025	1051	past each	1624	1653	1739	1754	1827	1852	1926	1951	2003	2026	2051	2127
94	**Blackpool** North. **191** a.		0618	0719	0725	0802	0819	0847	0919	0946	1017	1022	1047	1119	hour until	1648	1719	1802	1822	1851	1919	1947	2018	2029	2047	2117	2148

	Ⓐ	⑥	⚒	⚒	⑥	Ⓐ	⚒	⚒	Ⓐ		⑦🚌	⑦	⑦	⑦	⑦	⑦	⑦	⑦	⑦	⑦	⑦	♣	⑦	⑦	⑦	⑦	⑦
Manchester Airport .... d.	2038	2038	...	2138	...	...	2234	...	2347	⑦	0530	0740a	...	0842	...	0943	...	...	...	...	1339	and at	2039	...	2143	...	2243
Manchester Piccadilly d.	2057	2057	2131	2201	2230	2230	2256	2330	0009		0555	0759	0831t	0901	0951t	0959	1051t	1151t	1251t	1351t	1400	the same	2100	2148t	2201	2249t	2301
Bolton .... d.	2119	2119	2151	2220	2251	2252	2318	2349	|		0620s	0819	0847	0923	1007	1019	1107	1207	1307	1407	1419	minutes	2119	2204	2220	2305	2320
Preston .... **173a 191** d.	2150	2156	2228	2251	2327	2330	2355	0025	0101		0655s	0857	0923	0954	1043	1049	1146	1247	1347	1448	1453	past each	2151	2244	2249	2341	2357
Blackpool North.. **191** a.	2216	2222	2250	2317	2348	2352	0023	0049	0127		0735	0920	0949	1018	1109	1116	1212	1312	1413	1513	1515	hour until	2215	2309	2313	0007	0021

		⚒	⚒	⚒	Ⓐ	⑥	⚒	⚒	⚒	Ⓐ	⑥	⚒	⚒	⚒	⚒	♣	⚒	⚒	⚒	⚒	⚒	⚒	⚒	⚒	⚒	⚒	⑥
Blackpool North.. **191** d.	⚒	0333	0444	0522	0556	0556	0632	0653	0723	0745	0755	0823d	0858	0927	0958	and at	1558	1627	1653	1727	1756	1827	1856	1925	1958	2024	2058
Preston .... **173a 191** d.		0356	0510	0549	0621	0621	0700	0721	0751	0823b	0823	0855	0923	0955	1023	the same	1623	1655	1721	1755	1821	1855	1923	1953	2023	2052	2123
Bolton .... d.		|	0537	0621	0655	0651	0734	0755	0824	0854	0854	0922	0954	1022	1054	minutes	1654	1722	1755	1822	1854	1921	1954	2022	2054	2122	2154
Manchester Piccadilly a.		0446	0557	0648	0715	0712	0756	0816	0845	0915	0915	0945	1015	1045	1115	past each	1715	1745	1815	1845	1915	1945	2015	2045	2115	2144	2215
Manchester Airport .... a.		0504	0621	...	0732	0732	...	0832	...	0932	0932	...	1032	...	1132	hour until	1733	...	1833	...	1931	...	2031	...	2134	...	2234

	Ⓐ	⚒	⚒	⑥	Ⓐ		⑦🚌	⑦🚌	⑦	⑦	⑦	⑦	⑦	⑦	⑦	⑦	⑦	⑦	⑦	⑦	♣	⑦	⑦	⑦	⑦	⑦	⑦
Blackpool North.. **191** d.	2058	2121	2221	2302	2313	⑦	0320	0520	0752	0821	0900	0921	1000	1015	1100	1120	1200	1220	1300	1321	and at	2000	2021	2059	2122	2159	2222
Preston .... **173a 191** d.	2123	2149	2249	2330	2345c		0400u	0600u	0818	0848	0927	0950	1027	1042	1127	1151	1227	1250	1327	1349	the same	2027	2051	2126	2149	2226	2249
Bolton .... d.	2154	2224	2323	0004	0018		0435u	0635u	0845	0923	0953	1029	1053	1123	1153	1225	1253	1327	1353	1425	minutes	2053	2125	2152	2224	2252	2324
Manchester Piccadilly a.	2219	2247	2347	0026	0040		0500u	0700u	0902f	0941t	1013f	1046t	1113f	1142t	1211f	1242t	1315	1342t	1415	1442t	past each	2115	2142t	2219	2242t	2317	2342t
Manchester Airport .... a.	2238	2306	0015	0044a	0059		0525	0725	...	...	...	...	...	...	...	...	1332	...	1432	...	hour until	2132	...	2235	...	2335	...

a – Until Oct. 20.
b – Arrives 0811.
c – Arrives 2340.
d – Departs 0827 on ⑥.
f – Manchester **Oxford Road**.
r – Arrives 0651.
s – Calls to set down only.
t – Manchester **Victoria**.
u – Calls to pick up only.
♣ – Timings may vary by ± 3 minutes.

NT 2nd Class only — MANCHESTER - PRESTON - BARROW IN FURNESS — 157

For other trains Manchester - Preston / Lancaster and v.v. see Tables **154** and **156**.

km			⚒	⚒	⚒	Ⓐ	⑥	⚒	⚒W	⚒A	⚒	⚒	⑥A	⚒W	ⒶA	⚒	⚒	⚒A	⚒W	⚒	⚒	⑥	Ⓐ	⚒	⚒W	ⒶA	⑥C
0	**Manchester** Airport + . d.	⚒	...	0522	...	...	...	0725	0827	...	0929	1029	...	1129	...	1229	1329	...	1429	1530	...	1629	1634	...	1729	...	...
16	**Manchester** Piccadilly . d.		...	0542	...	...	...	0743	0847	...	0947	1047	...	1147	...	1247	1347	...	1447	1548	...	1647	1654	...	1747	...	...
34	Wigan North Western .. d.		...	0615	...	...	...	0816	0918	...	1020	1120	...	1218	...	1317	1418	...	1518	1618	...	1717	|	...	1819	...	...
66	**Preston** .... a.		...	0631	...	...	...	0840	0943	...	1043	1142	...	1237	...	1343	1443	...	1543	1642	...	1743	1743	...	1843	...	...
66	**Preston** .... d.		0518	0647	...	...	...	0842	...	...	1045	1144	...	1245	...	1344	1445	1532	...	1645	...	1745	1745	...	...	...	...
100	Lancaster .... **174** d.		0538	0706	0736	0823	0823	0900	...	1013	1103	1202	1301	1304	1313	1402	1503	1613f	...	1703	1738	1803	1803	1835	...	1913	1913
110	Carnforth .... **174** d.		0548	0716	0745	0832	0832	0910	...	1022	1113	1212	1310	...	1322	1412	1512	1622	...	1712	1747	1812	1812	1844	...	1922	1922
119	Arnside .... d.		0558	0726	0755	0842	0842	0920	...	1032	1122	1222	1320	...	1332	1422	1522	1632	...	1721	1757	1822	1822	1854	...	1932	1932
124	Grange over Sands ..... d.		0604	0732	0801	0848	0848	0926	...	1038	1128	1228	1326	...	1338	1428	1528	1638	...	1727	1803	1828	1828	1900	...	1938	1938
140	Ulverston .... d.		0620	0747	0817	0902	0904	0942	...	1054	1142	1244	1342	...	1354	1443	1544	1654	...	1739	1818	1844	1844	1916	...	1954	1954
156	**Barrow in Furness** ..... a.		0642	0809	0839	0922	0926	1003	...	1116	1201	1305	1404	...	1416	1505	1605	1716	...	1801	1840	1905	1905	1938	...	2016	2016

	⚒	⚒	Ⓐ	⑥a	⑥b	⑥a	⑥b	Ⓐ		⑦W	⑦A	⑦A	⑦	⑦	⑦W	⑦C	⑦	⑦	⑦A	⑦W	⑦	⑦	⑦	⑦W	⑦	⑦	⑦
Manchester Airport + . d.	1829	1929	...	...	...	...	2210	2210	⑦	0833e	t	v	0935	1035	1133	...	1241	1334	...	1433	1533	1633	...	1733	1833	1933	...
Manchester Piccadilly . d.	1847	1947	...	...	...	...	2226	2226		0853	...	...	0952	1054	1150	...	1301	1349	...	1451	1549	1649	...	1749	1848	1949	...
Wigan North Western... d.	1919	2017	...	...	...	...	|	2257		0922	...	...	1028	|	1219	...	1332	1432	...	1532	1632	1732	...	1832	1933	2020	...
Preston .... a.	1942	2041	...	...	...	...	2309	2314		0940	...	...	1044	1143	1242	...	1355	1455	...	1555	1654	1755	...	1855	1952	2038	...
Preston .... d.	1944	2044	...	...	2211	...	2310	2315		0948	...	...	1046	1147	...	...	1357	1508	...	1557	1657	1757	...	...	1957	2046	...
Lancaster .... **174** d.	2003	2102	2209	2226	2232	2328	2328	2333		1005	1011	*0945**	1106	1205	...	1313	1415	1526	1603	1615	1715	1815	1903	...	2015	2113c	2220
Carnforth .... **174** d.	2012	2112	2218	2235	2241	2337	2338	2243		...	1020	1020	1115	1214	...	1322	1425	1536	1612	...	1724	1825	1912	...	2024	2122	2229
Arnside .... d.	2022	2122	2228	2245	2251	2348	2348	2353		...	1030	1030	1125	1224	...	1332	1435	1546	1623	...	1734	1835	1922	...	2035	2132	2239
Grange over Sands ..... d.	2028	2128	2234	2251	2257	2354	2354	2359		...	1036	1036	1131	1230	...	1338	1441	1552	1629	...	1740	1841	1928	...	2041	2138	2245
Ulverston .... d.	2044	2143	2250	2307	2313	0010	0010	0016		...	1052	1052	1147	1244	...	1354	1457	1607	1645	...	1755	1856	1944	...	2056	2154	2300
Barrow in Furness ..... a.	2105	2205	2312	2331	2335	0034	0032	0037		...	1114	1114	1208	1304	...	1416	1518	1629	1707	...	1817	1918	2006	...	2118	2215	2322

		⚒	Ⓐ	⑥	⚒	⚒	⚒	⚒	⚒	⚒W	⚒A	⚒	⚒	⚒W	⚒A	⚒	⚒	⚒W	⚒A	⚒	⚒	⚒	⚒W	Ⓐ	⑥	⑥	Ⓐ
Barrow in Furness ..... d.	⚒	0453	0548	0548	0611	0647	0708	0746	0846	...	0958	1046	1146	...	1250	1353	1446	...	1550	1645	1719	1804	...	1855	1903	1934	1943
Ulverston .... d.		0509	0606	0606	0630	0705	0727	0805	0904	...	1017	1104	1204	...	1308	1409	1504	...	1608	1704	1737	1823	...	1913	1921	1953	2002
Grange over Sands ..... d.		0521	0622	0622	0645	0720	0742	0819	0920	...	1032	1120	1220	...	1324	1421	1520	...	1624	1720	1752	1838	...	1929	1937	2008	2017
Arnside .... d.		0527	0627	0627	0651	0725	0749	0825	0925	...	1039	1125	1225	...	1330	1427	1525	...	1630	1725	1758	1844	...	1935	1943	2014	2023
Carnforth .... **174** d.		0537	0640	0641	0703	0737	0801	0837	0939	...	1056	1137	1237	...	1342	1437	1537	...	1642	1737	1810	1856	...	1947	1955	2026	2035
Lancaster .... **174** d.		0546	0649	0651	0715	0746	0812	0846	0947	...	1107	1146	1246	1345	1353	1447	1546	...	1652	1746	1824	1906	1933	1956	2003	2035	2044
Preston .... a.		0606	0710	0711	...	0806	...	0906	1008	...	...	1206	1306	1406	...	1508	1606	...	...	1806	...	...	1955	2019	2026	2056	2104
Preston .... d.		0608	0711	0712	...	0808	...	0908	1010	1102r	...	1208	1312	1408	...	1509	1608	1708	...	1808	...	...	2009	...	...	2105	2106
Wigan North Western... a.		0623	0725	0726	...	0823	...	0923	1024	1120	...	1225	|	1424	...	1524	1623	1723n	...	1823	...	...	2027	...	...	|	|
Manchester Piccadilly . a.		0657	0801	0801	...	0859	...	0958	1058	1158	...	1258	1358	1458	...	1558	1658	1759	...	1858	...	...	2059	...	...	2142	2147
Manchester Airport + . a.		0721	0822	0822	...	0921	...	1021	1121	1221	...	1321	1421	1521	...	1621	1721	1821	...	1921	...	...	2120	...	...	2205	2205

	⑥b	⑥a	⚒	ⒶA	⑥b	⑥a		⑦d	⑦e	⑦t	⑦v	⑦	⑦	⑦	⑦W	⑦At	⑦Av	⑦	⑦	⑦W	⑦A	⑦	⑦A	⑦W	⑦	⑦	⑦
Barrow in Furness ..... d.	2042	2042	2042	2145	2146	2146	⑦	0840	0840	0905	0905	0947	1047	1137	...	1253	1317	1347	1447	...	1550	1647	1746	...	1851	1947	2046
Ulverston .... d.	2101	2101	2101	2204	2204	2204		0858	0858	0922	0924	1005	1106	1156	...	1311	1335	1405	1505	...	1608	1705	1805	...	1909	2005	2105
Grange over Sands ..... d.	2116	2116	2116	2219	2220	2220		0914	0914	0934	0939	1021	1121	1211	...	1324	1348	1421	1521	...	1624	1721	1820	...	1925	2021	2020
Arnside .... d.	2122	2122	2122	2226	2226	2226		0920	0920	0940	0945	1027	1127	1217	...	1330	1354	1427	1527	...	1630	1727	1827	...	1931	2027	2126
Carnforth .... **174** d.	2134	2134	2134	2238	2238	2238		0932	0932	0951	0957	1039	1140	1229	...	1342	1406	1439	1539	...	1642	1739	1841	...	1943	2039	2138
Lancaster .... **174** d.	2143	2146	2146	2247	2246	2249		0940	0940	1001	*1025*	1047	1149	1238	1346	1352	1419	1447	1547	1646	1652	1747	1849	...	1951	2047	2148
Preston .... a.	2205	...	...	...	2309	...		1002	1002	...	...	1108	1209	1259	1407	...	...	1508	1608	1706	...	1808	...	...	2014	2108	...
Preston .... d.	...	...	...	...	...	...		1008	1008	...	...	1109	1211	1309	1410	...	...	1509	1609	1709	...	1809	...	2009	...	2109	...
Wigan North Western... a.	...	...	...	...	...	...		1024	1024	...	...	1124	|	1323	1424	...	...	1523	1623	1723	...	1823	...	2023	...	2123	...
Manchester Piccadilly . a.	...	...	...	...	...	...		1055j	1101	...	...	1201	1256	1400	1501	...	...	1601	1701	1801	...	1901	...	2059	...	2201	...
Manchester Airport + . a.	...	...	...	...	...	...		...	1119	...	...	1223	1313	1417	1517	...	...	1617	1717	1817	...	1917	...	2117	...	2216	...

A – From / to Carlisle (Table **159**).
C – To Millom (Table **159**).
W – To / from Windermere (Table **158**).
a – Until June 15 and from Sept. 14.
b – June 22 - Sept. 7.
c – Arrives 2105.
d – From Sept. 15.
e – June 23 - Sept. 8.
f – Arrives 1552.
j – Manchester **Oxford Road**.
n – ⑥ only.
r – Departs 1108 on ⑥.
t – From June 23.
v – Until June 16.
* – Connection by 🚌.

158 PRESTON - OXENHOLME - WINDERMERE — 2nd Class NT

km		⚒	⚒	⚒	⚒	⑥	Ⓐ	Ⓐ	⑥	⚒	⚒	⚒	⚒	⑥	Ⓐ	⚒	⑥	Ⓐ	⚒	⑥	Ⓐ	⑥	Ⓐ	⑥ c
	Manchester Airport ✈ 157 d.		...	...	...	...	...	0827	0827	...	...	1129	...	...	...	1429	...	...	...	1729	1729	...	...	...
	Manchester Piccadilly 157 d.		...	...	...	...	...	0847	0847	...	...	1147	...	...	...	1447	...	...	...	1747	1747	...	...	...
	Preston 154 157 d.		...	...	...	...	...	0944	0944	...	...	1245	...	...	...	1545	...	...	...	1844	1908	...	...	...
	Lancaster 154 157 d.		0559	...	...	...	...	|	|	...	...	1323f	...	...	...	|	...	...	...	|	|	...	...	...
0	**Oxenholme** 154 157 d.		0619	0728	0827	0920	0930	1021	1033	1121	1239	1341	1438	1532	1532	1631	1736	1742	1829	1921	1942	2018	2039	2116
4	Kendal d.		0623	0732	0831	0924	0934	1026	1038	1125	1243	1345	1442	1536	1537	1636	1740	1746	1833	1926	1947	2022	2043	2120
16	**Windermere** a.		0639	0749	0847	0941	0951	1043	1052	1142	1300	1403	1455	1552	1554	1653	1757	1803	1850	1943	2004	2039	2100	2136

	⑥ b 🚌	Ⓐ	⑥ c	⑥ b 🚌	Ⓐ	⑦	⑦ d 🚌	⑦ h	⑦ k		⑦ d	⑦ g	⑦	⑦	⑦	⑦	⑦	⑦	⑦	⑦	⑦	⑦	⑦ d	⑦ g
Manchester Airport ✈ 157 d.	...	...	...	...	...		...	0833	...	...	...	...	...	...	1133	...	...	1433	...	...	1733	...	...	...
Manchester Piccadilly 157 d.	...	...	...	...	...		...	0853	0853	...	...	...	...	...	1150	...	...	1451	...	...	1749	...	...	...
Preston 154 157 d.	...	...	...	...	...		...	0948	0948	...	1030	...	...	...	1245	...	...	1557	...	...	1908	...	...	...
Lancaster 154 157 d.	...	...	...	...	...		...	1007	1007	...	1048	...	...	...	|	...	...	1615	...	...	|	...	...	...
Oxenholme 154 157 d.	2115	2128	2201	2200	2219		0945	1030	1030	...	1107	1118	1201	1247	1332	1423	1535	1633	1739	1830	1941	2028	2117	2118
Kendal d.	2125	2132	2205	2210	2223		0955	1034	1034	...	1111	1122	1205	1251	1337	1427	1539	1638	1743	1834	1945	2032	2121	2122
Windermere a.	2155	2145	2222	2240	2240		1025	1051	1051	...	1128	1135	1219	1304	1354	1444	1556	1655	1756	1751	2002	2049	2134	2139

	⚒	⚒	⚒	⚒	Ⓐ	⑥	⚒	⚒	⚒	⚒	⚒	⚒		⚒	⑥	Ⓐ	⚒	⑥	Ⓐ		⑥ b	⑥ c	Ⓐ	⑥ c
Windermere d.		0643	0755	0851	0956	1008	1057	1147	1306	1407	1459	1605	...	1706	1801	1807	1855	1948	2008	...	2043	2044	2104	2140
Kendal d.		0658	0810	0903	1010	1022	1112	1202	1321	1422	1514	1619	...	1721	1816	1819	1910	2003	2023	...	2055	2059	2119	2152
Oxenholme 154 157 a.		0703	0815	0908	1015	1027	1177	1207	1326	1427	1519	1624	...	1726	1821	1824	1915	2008	2028	...	2100	2104	2124	2157
Lancaster 154 157 a.		...	...	...	|	|	...	...	1344	...	...	|	...	...	...	...	1933	...	...	...	2122	...	...	...
Preston 154 157 a.		...	...	...	1052	1104	...	...	1406	...	...	1702	...	...	...	...	1954	...	...	...	...	...	...	...
Manchester Piccadilly 157 a.		...	...	...	1158	1158	...	...	1458	...	...	1759	...	...	...	...	2059	...	...	...	...	...	...	...
Manchester Airport ✈ 157 a.		...	...	...	1221	1221	...	...	1521	...	...	1821	...	...	...	...	2120	...	...	...	...	...	...	...

	⑥ b 🚌	Ⓐ	⑥ c		⑥ b 🚌	Ⓐ	⑦	⑦ d 🚌	⑦ g	⑦	⑦	⑦	⑦	⑦		⑦	⑦	⑦		⑦	⑦	⑦	⑦ d	⑦ g
Windermere d.	2140	2149	2226	...	2225	2245		1030	1055	1140	1223	1308	1358	1449	...	1606	1709	1800	...	1901	2006	2053	2138	2144
Kendal d.	2210	2201	2240	...	2255	2259		1100	1109	1152	1238	1320	1413	1504	...	1621	1724	1815	...	1916	2018	2108	2150	2159
Oxenholme 154 157 a.	2225	2206	2245	...	2310	2304		1115	1114	1157	1243	1325	1418	1509	...	1626	1729	1820	...	1921	2023	2113	2155	2204
Lancaster 154 157 a.	...	...	2305	...	2355	2323		...	...	...	...	1345	...	...	...	1645	...	...	...	|	...	...	|	2234
Preston 154 157 a.	...	...	2329	...	0035	2345		...	...	...	...	1407	...	...	...	1706	...	...	...	1959	...	...	2235	2257
Manchester Piccadilly 157 a.	...	...	...	...	...	...		...	...	...	...	1501	...	...	...	1801	...	...	...	2059	...	...	...	...
Manchester Airport ✈ 157 a.	...	...	...	...	...	...		...	...	...	...	1517	...	...	...	1817	...	...	...	2117	...	...	...	...

b – Until June 15 and from Sept.14.
c – June 22 - Sept. 7.
d – Until June 16.
f – Arrives 1304.
g – From June 23.
h – June 23 - Oct. 20.
k – From Oct. 27.

159 BARROW - WHITEHAVEN - CARLISLE — 2nd class NT

km		⚒	⑥	Ⓐ	⚒	⚒	⚒	Ⓐ	⑥	⑥	Ⓐ	⚒	⚒	⚒	⚒	⑥	Ⓐ	⚒	⚒	⑥	Ⓐ	Ⓐ	⚒ P	⚒	⑥	Ⓐ
	Lancaster 157 d.		...	...	...	...	...	...	...	...	...	...	1013	...	...	1301	1313	...	...	...	...	...	1613	...	...	...
0	**Barrow in Furness** d.		...	...	...	0558	0651	0750	0754	0917	0927	1022	1118	1206	1316	1414	1417	1449	1544	1611	1615	...	1717	1807	1857	1912
26	Millom d.		...	...	...	0627	0719	0818	0822	0944	0955	1050	1146	1234	1344	1442	1445	1517	1612	1639	1644	...	1745	1834	1925	1940
47	Ravenglass for Eskdale 🚂 d.		...	...	...	0645	0737	0835	0839	1001	1012	1107	1203	1251	1401	1459	1502	1534	1629	1656	1701	...	1802	1849	1942	1957
56	Sellafield d.		...	...	...	0700	0753	0849	0852	1014	1032	1122	1217	1303	1413	1512	1514	1547	1641	1708	1712	...	1814	1900	1953	2012
74	**Whitehaven** d.		...	...	0630	0723	0816	0909	0914	1037	1051	1145	1236	1338	1438	1539	1540	1612	1701	1729	...	1749	1835	1921	2013	2037
85	Workington d.		0548	0605	0648	0742	0834	0927	0933	1055	1109	1203	1253	1356	1456	1558	1559	1633r	1719	1747	...	1807	1853	1943r	2035r	2055
92	Maryport d.		0556	0613	0656	0750	0843	0936	0941	1103	1117	1211	1301	1404	1505	1607	1608	1643	1728	1756	...	1816	1902	1953	2044	2104
119	Wigton d.		0618	0635	0718	0812	0904	0957	1003	1124	1138	1233	1322	1426	1526	1628	1629	1705	1749	1817	...	1837	1923	2014	2105	2125
138	**Carlisle** a.		0638	0655	0739	0832	0924	1017	1023	1144	1158	1253	1340	1447	1546	1648	1651	1725	1811	1841	...	1857	1943	2034	2125	2145

	⑥	⑥	Ⓐ	⚒	⑥	Ⓐ	⚒	⑦	⑦ a	⑦ a	⑦ b	⑦	⑦	⑦	⑦ a	⑦ Ab	⑦	⑦	⑦	⑦	⑦	⑦	⑦	⑦	⑦	⑦
Lancaster 157 d.	...	1913	1913	...	...	...	...		...	...	...	...	...	...	1011	...	...	...	1313	...	...	1603	...	...	...	...
Barrow in Furness d.	1944	2018	2019	2110	...	...	2211		...	...	...	0905	...	0950	1115	1115	1218	1309	1417	1455	1558	1717	...	1825	...	1907
Millom d.	2011	2046	2046	2138	...	...	2239		...	...	...	0933	...	1017	1143	1143	1245	1336	1443	1523	1625	1746	...	1853	...	1935
Ravenglass for Eskdale 🚂 d.	2028	...	2103	...	...	...	...		...	...	...	...	...	1034	1200	1200	1302	1353	1458	1541	1642	1803	...	...	...	...
Sellafield d.	2041	...	2116	...	...	...	...		...	...	...	...	...	1046	1212	1212	1315	1405	1506	1551	1654	1815	...	...	...	...
Whitehaven d.	2102	...	2135	...	2209	2209	...		...	...	...	...	1016	1111	1234	1234	1338	1426	1529	1611	1716	1839	1938	...	2030	...
Workington d.	2120	...	2153	...	2227	2227	...		0855	0940	0957	...	1034	1129	1252	1252	1358	1444	1547	1629	1734	1857	1956	...	2048	...
Maryport d.	2128	...	2201	...	2236	2236	...		0904	0949	1006	...	1043	1137	1301	1301	1408	1453	1556	1637	1743	1906	2005	...	2057	...
Wigton d.	...	...	2222	...	...	2257	...		0925	1010	1027	...	1104	1159	1322	1322	1430	1514	1617	1659	1804	1927	2026	...	2118	...
Carlisle a.	...	...	2242	...	...	2317	...		0945	1030	1047	...	1124	1219	1342	1342	1450	1534	1637	1719	1824	1947	2046	...	2138	...

	⚒	⚒	⚒	⚒	⑥	Ⓐ	⚒	Ⓐ	⑥	Ⓐ	⑥	⚒	Ⓐ	⑥	⚒	⚒	⚒	⚒	⚒	Ⓐ	Ⓐ	⑥	⚒	⚒	Ⓐ	⚒
Carlisle d.		...	...	0553	0616	0619	0710	0808	0815	0902	0908	1013	1107	1107	1210	1307	1408	1441	1512	...	1559	1626	1707	1754	...	1846
Wigton d.		...	...	0611	0635	0636	0731	0826	0832	0920	0926	1031	1125	1125	1227	1325	1426	1458	1530	...	1617	1644	1725	1812	...	1904
Maryport d.		...	0548	0633	0659	0659	0755	0848	0853	0941	0947	1053	1146	1146	1249	1346	1447	1520	1551	...	1638	1705	1746	1833	...	1925
Workington d.		...	0558	0644	0710	0710	0806	0858	0903	0952	0958	1103	1157	1157	1259	1357	1502	1530	1602	...	1648	1715	1757	1844	...	1936
Whitehaven d.		...	0618	0704	0730	0730	0825	0916	0921	1012	1017	1123	1216	1216	1319	1416	1517	1550	1621	...	1708	1736	1818	1903	...	1956
Sellafield d.		...	0639	0724	0750	0750	0844	0939	0942	1031	1037	1145	1238	1240	1340	1441	1537	1611	1641	1725	...	1755	1840	1928	...	▬
Ravenglass for Eskdale 🚂 d.		...	0650	0734	0801	0801	0854	0949	0952	1042	1048	1155	1248	1250	1350	1451	1548	1622	1651	1735	...	1805	1849	1939	...	⑥
Millom d.		0610	0709	0753	0820	0820	0914	1008	1010	1101	1107	1214	1307	1309	1409	1511	1607	1642	1712	1754	...	1825	1905	2001	2029	2059
Barrow in Furness a.		0641	0741	0826	0853	0853	0947	1040	1041	1135	1139	1246	1339	1341	1441	1543	1639	1714	1745	1826	...	1857	1937	2036	2101	2129
Lancaster 157 a.		...	...	...	...	...	1107	...	...	...	...	1353	...	...	...	1652	...	...	...	...	...	...	...	...	...	...

	⚒ P	⑥	⚒	Ⓐ	⑥	⑥	Ⓐ	⑦	⑦	⑦	⑦ a	⑦ b	⑦ a	⑦ b	⑦	⑦	⑦	⑦	⑦ P	⑦	⑦	⑦	⑦	⑦	⑦	⑦
Carlisle d.	1909	2000	...	2055	2106	2149	2201		...	...	0945	...	1023	1041	1106	1207	1324	1401	1510	1616	...	1710	1810	1910	2010	2110
Wigton d.	1927	2018	...	2113	2124	2206	2219		...	...	1002	...	1041	1058	1124	1225	1342	1419	1528	1634	...	1728	1828	1928	2028	2128
Maryport d.	1948	2039	...	2134	2145	2227	2241		...	0917	1024	1024	1103	1120	1145	1246	1403	1440	1549	1655	...	1749	1849	1949	2049	2149
Workington d.	1959	2050	...	2145	2156	2237	2251		...	0927	1033	1033	1113	1130	1156	1258	1414	1451	1600	1706	...	1800	1900	2000	2100	2200
Whitehaven d.	2018	2109	...	2204	2215	2257	2310		...	0947	1051	1051	1133	1150	1215	1318	1433	1510	1619	1725	...	1819	1919	2019	2119	2219
Sellafield d.	2040	...	...	...	...	...	...		...	1007	1109	1109	1151	1208	1236	1337	1451	1528	1642	1744	...	1840	...	...	...	...
Ravenglass for Eskdale 🚂 d.	2050	...	...	...	...	...	...		...	1017	1119	1119	1201	1218	1246	1347	1501	1539	1652	1754	...	1850	...	...	...	...
Millom d.	2109	...	2200	...	...	...	...		0950	1036	1137	1137	1219	1236	1305	1406	1517	1556	1711	1814	1925	1909	...	...	...	...
Barrow in Furness a.	2142	...	2231	...	...	...	...		1021	1108	1209	1209	1251	1308	1337	1438	1548	1628	1743	1846	1957	1941	...	...	...	...
Lancaster 157 a.	2247f	...	...	...	...	...	...		...	...	...	...	1352	1419	...	...	1652	...	1849	...	...	...	...	...	...	...

A – From Carnforth (Table 157).
P – To/from Preston (Table 157).
a – From June 23.
b – Until June 16.
f – Ⓐ only.
r – Arrives 5–6 minutes earlier.
s – Calls to set down only.
🚂 – Ravenglass and Eskdale Railway. ✆ 01229 717171. www.ravenglass-railway.co.uk

AW, VT 2nd class

HOLYHEAD - CHESTER - MANCHESTER

km	Ⓐ	Ⓐ	Ⓐ	Ⓐ	Ⓐ	Ⓐ	Ⓐ	Ⓐ	Ⓐ	Ⓐ🍴	Ⓐ	Ⓐ	Ⓐ	Ⓐ	Ⓐ	Ⓐ	Ⓐ	Ⓐ	Ⓐ	Ⓐ	Ⓐ	Ⓐ	Ⓐ	Ⓐ	Ⓐ	Ⓐ
					🍷C	🍴A		🍷	🍴C	AW			🍷C	🍴A	🍷	🍷	🍷C	🍷	🍷C	🍴A	🍷	🍷M	🍷	🍷P	🍷	🍷M
0	**Holyhead** d.	...	...	...	0425	0448	...	0514	0534	0551	...	...	0628	0655	...	0715	...	...	0805	0855	...	0923	...	1042	...	1128
40	Bangor d.	...	...	...	0457	0514	...	0544	0602	0618	...	...	0706	0722	...	0802d	...	...	0902c	0922	...	1002	...	1108	...	1201
	Llandudno ‡ d.	...	...	...	|	|	...	|	|	|	...	0646	|	|	0745	|	0830	...	|	|	0945	|	1044	|	1144	|
64	Llandudno Junction ‡ d.	...	0438	...	0515	0532	0546	0607	0620	0636	...	0657	0725	0740	0754	0825	0839	0854	0925	0940	0954	1025	1053	1126	1153	1224
71	Colwyn Bay d.	...	0444	...	0521	0538	0552	0613	0628	0642	...	0703	0731	0747	0800	0831	0845	0900	0931	0947	1000	1031	1059	1132	1159	1230
88	Rhyl d.	...	0457	...	0530	0549	0602	0626	0639	0653	...	0716	0740	0758	0813	0841	0855	0913	0940	0958	1013	1041	1112	1141	1212	1240
94	Prestatyn d.	...	0502	...	0536	|	0608	0631	|	0658	...	0722	0746	0804	0819	0847	|	0919	0946	1004	1019	1047	1118	1147	1218	1245
136	**Chester** a.	...	0534	...	0606	0617	0639	0703	0711	0726	...	0752	0815	0831	0850	0915	0924	0950	1016	1031	1050	1116	1149	1215	1249	1314
136	**Chester 151** 190 ♥ d.	0334	0537	0538	...	0626	0643	0712	...	0735	0738	0753	...	0835	0852	0917	...	0952	...	1035	1052	...	1152	...	1252	...
170	**Crewe 151** ♥ a.	|	0558	|	...	0647	|	|	...	0754	|	0817	...	0854	|	0937	...	|	...	1054	|	...	|	...	|	...
165	Warrington Bank Quay 190 a.	|	...	0605	...	...	0710	0739	...	...	0808	...	...	...	0918	...	...	1018	...	...	1118	...	1220	...	1318	...
201	**Manchester** Piccadilly a.	0442	...	0643	...	...	0750	0812	...	...	0853	...	...	...	0953	...	...	1053	...	...	1154	...	1253	...	1353	...
217	**Manchester** Airport a.	0504	...	...	...	...	...	...	...	...	...	...	...	...	1019	...	...	1119	...	...	1219	...	1319	...	1419	...

	Ⓐ	Ⓐ	Ⓐ	Ⓐ	Ⓐ	Ⓐ	Ⓐ	Ⓐ	Ⓐ	Ⓐ	Ⓐ	Ⓐ	Ⓐ	Ⓐ	Ⓐ	Ⓐ	Ⓐ	Ⓐ	Ⓐ	Ⓐ	Ⓐ	Ⓐ	Ⓐ	Ⓐ	Ⓐ	Ⓐ	Ⓐ
	🍷	🍷C	🍷A	🍷	🍷M	🍷A	🍷	🍷	🍷C		🍷	🍷M	🍷	🍷C		🍷D						B	🍷B				M
Holyhead d.	...	1232	1253	1307	1325	1358	...	...	1436	...	...	1547	...	1648	...	1731	...	...	1823	...	...	1922	...	...	2032	...	...
Bangor d.	...	1307	1321	1334	1405	1425	...	...	1504	...	...	1626	...	1716	...	1810	...	...	1902	...	...	2001	2020	...	2101	...	...
Llandudno ‡ d.	...	|	|	|	|	|	1440	1508	|	1606	...	|	1707	|	...	|	...	1844	|	1934	...	|	|	2043	|	2145	...
Llandudno Junction ‡ d.	1254	1325	1339	1352	1430	1443	1449	1517	1528	1615	1625	1649	1717	1734	...	1833	1839	1853	1926	1946	...	2024	2038	2052	2128f	2155	...
Colwyn Bay d.	1300	1331	1345	1400	1436	1450	1455	1523	1534	1621	1631	|	1723	1740	...	|	1845	1859	1932	1954	...	2030	2044	2058	2134	2201	...
Rhyl d.	1313	1340	1356	1414	1446	1500	1508	1535	1543	1633	1643	|	1735	1749	...	|	1855	1912	1942	2009	...	2040	2055	2111	2147	2216	...
Prestatyn d.	1319	1346	1401	1420	1451	|	1514	1541	1549	1638	1648	|	1741	1755	...	|	1901	1918	1948	2016	...	2045	2101	2117	2152	2222	...
Chester a.	1350	1415	1428	1448	1524	1528	1545	1613	1618	1712	1717	1729	1814	1823	...	1913	1930	1949	2017	2045	...	2116	2128	2148	2224	2255	...
Chester 151 190 ♥ d.	1352	...	1435	1450	...	1535	1549	1620	...	1712	...	...	1816	...	1851	...	...	1952	2019	2047	2052	...	2135	2151	2230	2301	2322
Crewe 151 ♥ a.	|	...	1454	|	...	1554	|	|	...	|	...	...	|	...	|	...	...	|	2041	2107	|	...	2154	|	2252	2326	|
Warrington Bank Quay 190 a.	1420	...	...	1520	...	...	1618	1649	...	1749	...	...	1844	...	1918	...	...	2018	...	...	2119	...	...	2217	...	...	2351
Manchester Piccadilly a.	1453	...	...	1554	...	...	1654	1723	...	1827	...	...	1923	...	1953	...	...	2054	...	...	2152	...	...	2255	...	...	0025
Manchester Airport a.	1519	...	...	...	...	...	...	...	...	...	...	...	...	...	2019	...	...	2117	...	...	...	...	...	...	...	...	...

⑥	⑥	⑥	⑥	⑥	⑥b	⑥	⑥	⑥	⑥	⑥	⑥	⑥	⑥	⑥	⑥	⑥	⑥	⑥	⑥	⑥	⑥	⑥	⑥	⑥	⑥	⑥
		B			🍷C	b	a		🍷D	🍷M	🍷	🍷C	🍷A	🍷	🍷M	🍷A	🍷	🍷C	🍷A	🍷	🍷M	🍷	🍷C	🍷	🍷M	🍷
Holyhead d.	...	...	...	...	0425	...	0425	...	...	0523	...	0635	0652	...	0715	0755	...	0820	0855	...	0923	...	1033	...	1123	...
Bangor d.	...	...	...	...	0457	...	0457	...	...	0602	...	0707	0720	...	0802d	0822	...	0902f	0922	...	1002	...	1105	...	1202	...
Llandudno ‡ d.	...	...	...	...	|	...	|	...	...	|	0634	|	|	0745	|	|	0845	|	|	0945	|	1044	|	1144	|	1240
Llandudno Junction ‡ d.	...	...	0438	...	0515	...	0515	0537	...	0625	0644	0725	0738	0754	0825	0840	0854	0925	0940	0954	1025	1053	1123	1153	1225	1253f
Colwyn Bay d.	...	...	0444	...	0521	...	0521	0543	...	0631	0650	0731	0744	0800	0831	0847	0900	0931	0947	1000	1031	1059	1129	1159	1231	1259
Rhyl d.	...	...	0457	...	0531	...	0531	0556	...	0641	0703	0740	0755	0813	0841	0858	0913	0940	0958	1013	1041	1112	1139	1212	1241	1312
Prestatyn d.	...	...	0502	...	0537	...	0537	0601	...	0647	0708	0746	0801	0819	0847	0904	0919	0946	1003	1019	1047	1118	1145	1218	1247	1318
Chester a.	...	...	0534	...	0605	...	0605	0633	...	0716	0739	0815	0828	0850	0916	0931	0950	1015	1028	1050	1117	1149	1213	1249	1316	1349
Chester 151 190 ♥ d.	0336	0422	0536	0538	...	0613	0613	0635	0712	...	0741	...	0835	0852	...	0935	0952	...	1035	1052	...	1152	...	1251	...	1352
Crewe 151 ♥ a.	|	0443	0557	|	...	|	|	0700	|	...	|	...	0854	|	...	0954	|	...	1054	|	...	|	...	|	...	|
Warrington Bank Quay 190 a.	|	...	...	0605	...	0639	0639	...	0738	...	0807	...	...	0918	...	...	1018	...	...	1118	...	1220	...	1318	...	1420
Manchester Piccadilly a.	0439	...	...	0644	...	0719	0719	...	0816	...	0853	...	...	0953	...	...	1053	...	...	1154	...	1253	...	1354	...	1453
Manchester Airport a.	0505	...	...	...	...	...	...	...	...	...	0919	...	...	1019	...	...	1119	...	...	1219	...	1319	...	1419	...	1519

	⑥	⑥	⑥	⑥	⑥	⑥	⑥	⑥	⑥	⑥	⑥	⑥	⑥	⑥	⑥	⑥	⑥	⑥	⑥	⑥	⑥	⑦	⑦	⑦	⑦	⑦
	🍷C	🍷	🍷M	🍷A	🍷	🍷C	🍷	🍷M	🍷	🍷C	🍷	🍷D				B							n	p	🍷n	
Holyhead d.	1238	...	1328	1358	...	1427	...	1523	...	1652	...	1732	...	1825	...	1922	...	...	2037	...	...	...	0716	...	0750	0845
Bangor d.	1307	1333	1407	1425	...	1455	...	1602	...	1720	...	1811	...	1904	...	2001	...	...	2106	...	...	...	0743	...	0828	0913
Llandudno ‡ d.	|	|	|	|	1442	|	1544	|	1644	|	1744	|	1844	|	1942	|	2043	...	|	2145	...	...	|	...	|	|
Llandudno Junction ‡ d.	1325	1356	1425	1443	1451	1518	1553	1625	1653	1738	1753	1834	1853	1927	1951	2024	2052	...	2129	2155	...	...	0800	...	0851	0935f
Colwyn Bay d.	1331	1402	1431	1450	1457	1524	1559	1631	1659	1744	1759	1840	1859	1933	1957	2030	2058	...	2135	2201	...	...	0807	...	0857	0941
Rhyl d.	1340	1415	1441	1500	1510	1535	1612	1641	1712	1754	1812	1850	1912	1943	2010	2040	2111	...	2148	2216	...	...	0820	...	0908	0954
Prestatyn d.	1346	1421	1447	|	1516	1540	1618	1647	1718	1800	1818	1856	1918	1949	2016	2046	2117	...	2154	2222	...	...	0825	...	|	0959
Chester a.	1414	1452	1518	1527	1547	1608	1649	1716	1749	1828	1849	1925	1949	2018	2047	2115	2148	...	2224	2255	...	...	0857	...	0940	1031
Chester 151 🚌 190 ♥ d.	...	1454	...	1535	1549	...	1652	...	1751	...	1852	...	1951	2020	2050	...	...	2153	2227	2307	2322	0841	0858	0942	0942	1039
Crewe 151 ♥ a.	...	|	...	1554	|	...	|	...	|	...	|	...	|	2041	|	...	...	|	2250	2331	|	|	0921	|	|	1103
Warrington Bank Quay 190 a.	...	1520	...	...	1618	...	1719	...	1818	...	1920	...	2019	...	2119	...	...	2220	...	...	2350	0907	...	1009	1009	...
Manchester Piccadilly a.	...	1554	...	...	1652	...	1753	...	1853	...	1953	...	2056	...	2154	...	...	2255	...	...	0022	0945	...	1046	1047	...
Manchester Airport a.	...	1619	...	...	1719	...	1819	...	...	...	2019	...	...	...	...	...	...	...	...	...	...	...	...	...	...	...

	⑦	⑦	⑦	⑦	⑦	⑦	⑦	⑦	⑦	⑦	⑦	⑦	⑦	⑦	⑦	⑦	⑦	⑦	⑦	⑦	⑦	⑦	⑦	⑦	⑦	⑦	⑦
	🍷	🍷	🍷C	🍷A	🍷	🍷A		🍷A		🍷A	🍷	🍷	p	🍷n	p	🍷C		🍷		🍷M		Dn	p				
Holyhead d.	...	...	1020	1055	...	1150	...	1250	...	1355	...	1430	1530	1544	...	1625	...	1730	...	1826	...	1917	1940	...	...	2035	2140
Bangor d.	...	...	1059	1122	...	1217	...	1318	...	1422	...	1508	1558	1612	...	1704	...	1759	...	1905	...	1956	2009	...	...	2114	2209
Llandudno ‡ d.	...	...	|	|	...	|	...	|	...	|	...	|	|	|	...	|	...	|	...	|	...	|	|	...	...	|	|
Llandudno Junction ‡ d.	...	1025	1122	1140	...	1235	...	1336	...	1440	...	1528	1625f	1635	...	1725f	...	1826f	...	1924	...	2024f	2037f	...	...	2137	2227
Colwyn Bay d.	...	1031	1128	1146	...	1242	...	1342	...	1446	...	1534	1631	1641	...	1731	...	1832	...	1930	...	2030	2043	...	...	2143	2233
Rhyl d.	...	1044	1141	1157	...	1253	...	1353	...	1457	...	1547	1644	1654	...	1744	...	1845	...	1943	...	2044	2056	...	...	2156	2243
Prestatyn d.	...	1050	1146	1203	...	1259	...	1359	...	1503	...	1552	1649	1659	...	1749	...	1850	...	1948	...	2049	2101	...	...	2201	2249
Chester a.	...	1121	1219	1230	...	1324	...	1426	...	1530	...	1621	1721	1734	...	1822	...	1922	...	2020	...	2122	2133	...	...	2233	2317
Chester 151 190 ♥ d.	1036	1136	...	1233	1236	1330	1336	1433	1436	1532	1536	1636	1722	1736	1736	...	1836	1927	1936	2027	2036	...	2136	2143	2206	2235	...
Crewe 151 ♥ a.	|	|	...	1253	|	1350	|	1454	|	1552	|	|	1742	|	|	...	|	1949	|	2048	|	...	2200	|	|	2301	...
Warrington Bank Quay 190 a.	1103	1203	...	...	1303	...	1403	...	1503	...	1603	1703	...	1803	1803	...	1903	...	2003	...	2103	...	...	2210	2233	...	...
Manchester Piccadilly a.	1141	1240	...	...	1337	...	1440	...	1540	...	1640	1740	...	1837	1837	...	1937	...	2040	...	2140	...	...	2248	2306	...	...
Manchester Airport a.	...	...	...	...	...	...	...	...	...	...	...	...	...	...	...	...	...	...	...	...	...	...	...	...	...	...	...

CAERNARFON - PORTHMADOG - BLAENAU FFESTINIOG △

km	A special WHR service operates June 21–23.	🚂 GH	🚂 J	🚂 EF KN	🚂 H	🚂 K	🚂 GJ	🚂 F KN	🚂 H	🚂 EF N	🚂 K	🚂 K	🚂 F KN
0	**Blaenau Ffestiniog** d.	...	...	1135	...	1220	...	1340	...	1505	1525	1605	1720
19	Minffordd d.	...	...	1230	...	1320	...	1435	...	1600	1625	1700	1815
22	**Porthmadog** Hbr d.	0940	1050	1245	1255	1335	1415	1450	1540	1615	1640	1715	1830
35	Beddgelert d.	1025	1130	...	1335	...	1455	...	1620	...	...	...	...
42	Rhyd Ddu d.	1100	1200	...	1400	...	1525	...	1645	...	...	...	...
50	Waunfawr d.	1125	1230	...	1430	...	1555	...	1720	...	...	...	...
61	**Caernarfon** a.	1205	1310	...	1510	...	1630	...	1755	...	...	...	...

A special WHR service operates June 21–23.	🚂 EF KLN	🚂 KL	🚂 FL N	🚂 K	🚂 GH J	🚂 EF KLN	🚂 KL	🚂 H	🚂 FK LN	🚂 GJ	🚂 H
Caernarfon d.	...	...	...	...	1000	...	...	1300	...	1420	1545
Waunfawr d.	...	...	...	...	1030	...	...	1330	...	1450	1615
Rhyd Ddu d.	...	...	...	...	1100	...	...	1400	...	1525	1645
Beddgelert d.	...	...	...	...	1130	...	...	1430	...	1555	1715
Porthmadog Hbr d.	1005	1035	1125	1155	1215	1335	1430	1515	1550	1630	1800
Minffordd d.	1015	1045	1135	1205	...	1345	1440	...	1600	...	...
Blaenau Ffestiniog d.	1120	1150	1240	1320	...	1445	1550	...	1700	...	...

A – Conveys 🛏12 to/from London Euston (Table **151**).
B – To/from Birmingham New Street (Table **145** or **151**).
C – To/from Cardiff Central (Tables **145** and **149**).
D – To/from Shrewsbury (Table **145**).
E – FR Pink service: June 3, 7, 10, 14–17, 21, 28, Sept. 16, 20, 23, 27, 30, Oct. 4–7, 11–14, 18, Nov. 1, 2, 3.
F – FR Blue service: June 1, 2, 4–6, 11–13, 18–20, 22–24, 29, 30, July 1, 5–8, 12–15, 19–22, 26–28, Aug. 2, 3, 4, 9–11, 16–18, 23–25, 30, 31, Sept. 1, 2, 6–15, 17–19, 21, 22, 24–26, 28, 29, Oct.1–3, 8–10, 15–17, 19–31.
G – WHR Yellow service: June 24, 28–30, July 1, 5–7, 12–15, 26–28, Aug. 2–4, 9–11, 16–18, 23–25, 30, 31, Sept. 1, 2.
H – WHR Red service: June 25–27, July 2–4, 9–11, 16–18, 23, 24, 25, 29–31, Aug. 1, 5–8, 12–15, 19–22, 26–29, Sept. 3–5, 10–12.
J – WHR Blue service: June 1–20, Sept. 6–9, 13–30, Oct. 1–3, 5, 6, 8–10, 12, 13, 15–17, 19–31, Nov. 1, 2.
K – FR Red service §: July 16–18, 23–25, 30, 31, Aug. 1, 6–8, 13–5, 20–22, 27–29.
L – FR Yellow service: July 29, Aug. 5, 12, 19, 26.
M – To/from Birmingham International (Table **145**).
N – FR Green service ◧: June 25–27, July 2–4, 9–11, Sept. 3–5.

P – To/from Llanelli (Tables **135**, **145** and **149**).
W – Conveys 🛏12 London - Chester - Wrexham and v.v. (Tables **145** and **151**).

a – Until Sept. 7.
b – From Sept. 14.
c – Arrives 20 minutes earlier.
d – Arrives 10 minutes earlier.
f – Arrives 5–6 minutes earlier.
g – Departs 0950.
h – Departs 6–10 minutes later.
n – Until Sept. 8.
p – From Sept. 15.
r – Departs 1007.
t – Arrives 12 minutes earlier.
v – Arrives 1612.

* – Connection by 🚌.
‡ – For full service Llandudno - Llandudno Junction and v.v. see next page.
♥ – For full service Chester - Crewe and v.v. see next page.
§ – Additional trains operate at 0840 and 1805¶ from Porthmadog returning at 1010 and 1940¶ from Blaenau Ffestiniog.
¶ – These trains do not run July 16–18 and Aug. 27–29.
◧ – An additional train operates at 0840 from Porthmadog returning at 1010 from Blaenau Ffestiniog.
△ – Operators: Ffestiniog Railway and Welsh Highland Railway. www.festrail.co.uk
Ffestiniog Railway and Welsh Highland Railway ✆ 01766 516024.

160 MANCHESTER - CHESTER - HOLYHEAD

2nd class AW, VT

		① M	②–⑤ M	Ⓐ 🍷B	Ⓐ 🍷	Ⓐ 🍷	Ⓐ 🍷	Ⓐ 🍷C	Ⓐ 🍷	Ⓐ 🍷M	Ⓐ 🍷	Ⓐ 🍷	Ⓐ 🍷A	Ⓐ 🍷C	Ⓐ 🍷	Ⓐ 🍷A	Ⓐ 🍷M	Ⓐ 🍷	Ⓐ 🍷C	Ⓐ 🍷	Ⓐ 🍷M	Ⓐ 🍷	Ⓐ 🍷C	Ⓐ 🍷	Ⓐ 🍷M	Ⓐ 🍷
Manchester Airport d.	Ⓐ	...	...	...	0533	...	...	...	...	...	...	...	...	...	...	...	...	1036	...	1136	...	1236	...	1336	...	1436
Manchester Piccadilly d.		...	...	...	0547	...	0650	...	0750	...	0852	...	...	...	0953	...	...	1052	...	1152	...	1253	...	1352	...	1452
Warrington Bank Quay . **190** d.		...	...	...	0621	...	0725	...	0827	...	0927	...	...	...	1031	...	...	1127	...	1228	...	1328	...	1428	...	1528
Crewe 151 ♥ d.		0001	0015	0623	|	0656	|	...	|	...	|	...	0952	...	|	1047	...	|	...	|	...	|	...	|	...	|
Chester 151 **190** ♥ a.		0022	0037	0643	0650	0719	0753	...	0856	...	0955	...	1012	...	1102	1112	...	1155	...	1256	...	1356	...	1456	...	1555
Chester d.		0038	0040	0643	0655	0721	0755	0822	0857	0923	0959	1004	1014	1025	1103	1114	1125	1156	1223	1257	1324	1357	1424	1457	1524	1557
Prestatyn d.		0104	0106	0709	0721	0749	0823	0850	0923	0950	|	1031	1040	1052	1128	|	1151	1224	1249	1326	1350	1426	1450	1524	1551	1624
Rhyl d.		0110	0112	0715	0727	0755	0829	0856	0929	0956	|	1037	1046	1058	1134	1141	1157	1230	1256	1332	1357	1432	1456	1530	1557	1630
Colwyn Bay d.		0121	0123	0726	0738	0809	0843	0910	0940	1010	|	1051	1058	1109	|	1152	1211	1244	1306	1346	1407	1446	1507	1544	1607	1644
Llandudno Junction ‡ d.		0128	0129	0732	0744	0816	0851	0917	0946	1017	1037	1057	1104	1115	1149	1200	1218	1251	1313	1352	1413	1452	1513	1551	1620v	1651
Llandudno ‡ a.		|	|	|	0756	|	...	0926	|	1030	|	1109	|	|	|	|	|	...	|	1404	|	1504	|	1603	|	1703
Bangor d.		0144	0146	0749	...	0838	...	...	1009	...	1054	...	1124	1139	1206	1216	1236	...	1331	...	1436	...	1531	...	1644	...
Holyhead ▽ a.		0220	0215	0819	...	0922	...	...	1037	...	1120	...	1153	1223	1236	1249	1317	...	1414	...	1507	...	1614	...	1716	...

	Ⓐ 🍷C	Ⓐ 🍷	Ⓐ 🍷M	Ⓐ 🍷	Ⓐ 🍷A	Ⓐ 🍷	Ⓐ 🍷C	Ⓐ 🍷	Ⓐ 🍷A	Ⓐ 🍷M	Ⓐ	Ⓐ ✕C	Ⓐ🍷 AW	Ⓐ	Ⓐ	Ⓐ 🍷A	Ⓐ	Ⓐ	Ⓐ	Ⓐ C	Ⓐ	Ⓐ		⑥ B	⑥ 🍷B	⑥ 🍷
Manchester Airport d.	...	1536	...	...	...	...	...	...	...	...	...	...	...	...	...	...	2035	...	2132	...	...	...	⑥	...	...	0533
Manchester Piccadilly d.	...	1552	...	1650	...	1715	...	1752	...	...	1852	...	...	...	1952	...	2050	...	2150	...	2212	2314		...	...	0547
Warrington Bank Quay . **190** d.	...	1626	...	1729	...	1747	...	1828	...	...	1930	...	...	...	2027	...	2127	...	2224	...	2249	2348		...	...	0622
Crewe 151 ♥ d.	...	|	...	|	1748	|	...	|	1856	...	|	...	1954	...	|	2054	|	2140	|	...	|	|		0015	0622	|
Chester 151 **190** ♥ a.	...	1654	...	1802	1807	1819	...	1857	1915	...	1957	...	2013	...	2054	2119	2156	2201	2251	...	2319	0016		0037	0642	0654
Chester d.	1627	1655	1726	1804	1809	...	1822	1858	1923	1932	...	2002	2026	2034	...	2125	...	2204	...	2256	...	...		0040	0644	0656
Prestatyn d.	1653	1723	1754	1827	1836	...	1852	1927	1949	2000	...	|	|	2102	...	2151	...	2232	...	2324	...	...		0106	0710	0724
Rhyl d.	1659	1729	1800	1834	1842	...	1858	1933	1955	2006	...	2031	2053	2108	...	2157	...	2238	...	2330	...	...		0112	0715	0730
Colwyn Bay d.	1710	1743	1814	1844	1853	...	1912	1943	2006	2020	...	2044	2104	2122	...	2208	...	2252	...	2344	...	...		0123	0726	0744
Llandudno Junction ‡ d.	1715	1750	1825f	1851	1900	...	1918	1953f	2012	2030f	...	2051	2110	2129	...	2215	...	2259	...	2352	...	...		0129	0732	0751
Llandudno ‡ a.	|	1802	|	1904	|	...	|	|	|	2042	...	|	|	|	...	|	...	|	...	|	...	...		|	|	0803
Bangor d.	1739	...	1847	...	1918	...	1934	2017	2029	...	...	2107	2127	2152	...	2231	...	2322	...	0014	...	...		0146	0749	...
Holyhead ▽ a.	1821	...	1917	...	...	...	2020	2046	2100	...	...	2141	2156	2235	...	2301	...	0005	...	0048	...	...		0215	0819	...

	⑥ 🍷	⑥ 🍷	⑥ 🍷C	⑥ 🍷	⑥ 🍷M	⑥ 🍷	⑥ 🍷C	⑥ 🍷	⑥ 🍷A	⑥ 🍷M	⑥ 🍷	⑥	⑥ 🍷C	⑥ 🍷	⑥ 🍷M	⑥ 🍷	⑥ 🍷C	⑥ 🍷	⑥ 🍷M	⑥ 🍷	⑥ 🍷A	⑥ 🍷C	⑥ 🍷	⑥ 🍷M	⑥ 🍷	⑥ 🍷A
Manchester Airport d.	...	...	...	...	...	...	...	0936	...	...	1036	...	...	1136	...	1236	...	1336	...	1436	...	...	1536	...	1636	...
Manchester Piccadilly d.	...	0650	...	0752	...	0852	...	0953	...	...	1053	...	...	1152	...	1253	...	1353	...	1452	...	...	1553	...	1653	...
Warrington Bank Quay . **190** d.	...	0723	...	0829	...	0928	...	1027	...	...	1127	...	...	1226	...	1327	...	1428	...	1526	...	...	1627	...	1727	...
Crewe 151 ♥ d.	0703	|	...	|	...	|	...	|	1048	...	|	...	...	|	...	|	...	|	...	|	1547	...	|	...	|	1748
Chester 151 **190** ♥ a.	0723	0750	...	0858	...	0955	...	1054	1112	...	1154	...	...	1253	...	1354	...	1456	...	1553	1608	...	1654	...	1754	1808
Chester d.	0725	0755	0823	0900	0924	0957	1023	1056	1115	1126	1156	...	1223	1255	1325	1356	1423	1457	1521	1555	1610	1626	1656	1724	1756	1815
Prestatyn d.	0752	0823	0850	0928	0950	1025	1050	1124	|	1152	1224	...	1250	1323	1351	1424	1449	1526	1549	1623	1637	1653	1724	1752	1824	1841
Rhyl d.	0758	0829	0856	0934	0957	1031	1056	1130	1142	1158	1230	...	1257	1329	1358	1430	1456	1532	1556	1629	1643	1659	1730	1758	1830	1847
Colwyn Bay d.	0809	0843	0907	0948	1007	1045	1106	1144	1153	1209	1244	...	1309	1343	1408	1444	1507	1546	1606	1643	1654	1709	1744	1812	1844	1858
Llandudno Junction ‡ d.	0815	0850	0913	0954	1013	1052	1113	1151	1200	1215	1250	1257	1315	1350	1414	1451	1514	1552	1612	1650	1700	1716	1751	1819	1851	1904
Llandudno ‡ a.	|	0902	|	1006	|	1103	|	1202	|	|	|	1307	|	1401	|	1502	|	1604	|	1701	|	|	1803	|	1903	|
Bangor d.	0838	...	0937	...	1031	...	1136	...	1216	1233	1315	...	1333	...	1439	...	1531	...	1635	...	1717	1739	...	1843	...	1921
Holyhead ▽ a.	0921	...	1012	...	1105	...	1209	...	1246	1312	...	...	1413	...	1509	...	1612	...	1712	...	1746	1818	...	1913	...	1950

	⑥ 🍷C	⑥ 🍷	⑥ 🍷A	⑥ 🍷M	⑥	⑥ C	⑥	⑥	⑥	⑥ C	⑥	⑥	⑥		⑦ n	⑦ n	⑦ 🚌	⑦	⑦	⑦ 🍷	⑦	⑦	⑦ 🍷	⑦ 🍷	⑦ 🍷	⑦ 🍷
Manchester Airport d.	...	1736	...	...	1836	...	...	...	2035	...	...	...	...	⑦	...	...	...	...	...	...	...	...	...	...	...	...
Manchester Piccadilly d.	...	1753	...	...	1853	...	1952	...	2050	...	2151	2212	2314		...	...	0718	...	0948	...	1052	...	1156	...	1256	...
Warrington Bank Quay . **190** d.	...	1827	...	...	1927	...	2030	...	2130	...	2225	2249	2348		...	...	0838	...	1020	...	1126	...	1230	...	1332	...
Crewe 151 ♥ d.	...	|	1850	...	|	...	|	2100	|	...	|	|	|		...	0827	|	0925	|	1042	|	1127	|	1227	|	1327
Chester 151 **190** ♥ a.	...	1854	1909	...	1955	...	2058	2121	2158	...	2254	2320	0015		...	0849	0938	0947	1048	1102	1154	1146	1258	1252	1359	1351
Chester d.	1824	1856	1916	1927	...	2032	...	2126	...	2238	▬	...	...		0620	0900	...	0948	...	1107	...	1203	...	1302	...	1404
Prestatyn d.	1852	1924	1943	1955	...	2100	...	2154	...	2306	...	...	...		0647	0926	...	1017	...	1131	...	1231	...	1330	...	1432
Rhyl d.	1858	1930	1949	2001	...	2106	...	2200	...	2312	⑥	...	...		0653	0932	...	1023	...	1137	...	1237	...	1336	...	1438
Colwyn Bay d.	1909	1944	2000	2015	...	2119	...	2214	...	2326	🚌	...	...		0703	0943	...	1037	...	1148	...	1248	...	1350	...	1452
Llandudno Junction ‡ d.	1916	1951	2006	2027f	...	2126	...	2221	...	2338	2348	...	...		0710	0954f	...	1043	...	1154	...	1254	...	1357	...	1459
Llandudno ‡ a.	|	2002	|	|	...	|	...	|	...	...	|	...	...		|	|	...	|	...	|	...	|	...	|	...	|
Bangor d.	1933	...	2023	2048	...	2143	...	2245	...	...	0013	...	...		0726	1012	...	1106	...	1211	...	1311	...	1419	...	1516
Holyhead ▽ a.	2018	...	2052	2131	...	2225	...	2318	...	...	0048	...	...		0800	1048	...	1149	...	1240	...	1340	...	1453	...	1555

	⑦ 🍷	⑦ 🍷	⑦ 🍷	⑦	⑦ 🍷C	⑦ 🍷	⑦	⑦ 🍷A	⑦	⑦ p	⑦ 🍷A	⑦ 🍷C	⑦	⑦ 🍷	⑦ 🍷A	⑦ 🍷M	⑦	⑦ 🍷A	⑦	⑦ 🍷A	⑦	⑦	⑦	⑦	⑦	⑦
Manchester Airport d.	...	...	...	...	...	...	...	...	...	...		...	...	...	...	...	...	...	...	...	...	...	...	...	...	...
Manchester Piccadilly d.	1356	...	1456	...	...	1556	...	...	1656	...	...	...	...	1756	...	...	1856	...	1956	...	2056	...	2156	...	2256	2325
Warrington Bank Quay . **190** d.	1427	...	1528	...	...	1627	...	...	1727	...	...	...	...	1827	...	...	1930	...	2031	...	2128	...	2227	...	2331	2355
Crewe 151 ♥ d.	|	1427	|	1527	...	|	1627	1651	|	1727	1750	...	1827	|	1900	...	|	1950	|	2053	|	2128	|	2229	|	|
Chester 151 **190** ♥ a.	1455	1451	1556	1549	...	1655	1649	1710	1755	1749	1810	...	1849	1855	1918	...	1958	2012	2100	2112	2156	2151	2254	2252	2358	0024
Chester d.	...	1502	...	1602	1636	...	1702	...	...	1802	...	1830	1852	...	1929	1938	...	2016	...	2115	...	2201	...	2302	...	*0038*
Prestatyn d.	...	1530	...	1630	1704	...	1730	...	...	1830	...	1858	1921	...	1955	2011	...	2043	...	2142	...	2229	...	2330	...	*0104*
Rhyl d.	...	1536	...	1636	1710	...	1736	...	...	1836	...	1904	1927	...	2002	2017	...	2049	...	2148	...	2235	...	2336	...	*0110*
Colwyn Bay d.	...	1550	...	1650	1724	...	1750	...	...	1850	...	1918	1941	...	2013	2031	...	2100	...	2159	...	2249	...	2347	...	*0121*
Llandudno Junction ‡ d.	...	1557	...	1657	1731	...	1757	...	...	1857	...	1925	1947	...	2019	2037	...	2106	...	2205	...	2256	...	2353	...	*0128*
Llandudno ‡ a.	...	|	...	|	|	...	|	...	...	|	...	|	|	...	|	|	...	|	...	|	...	|	...	|	...	|
Bangor d.	...	1619	...	1714	1755	...	1819	...	...	1914	...	1949	2009	...	2036	2059	...	2123	...	2222	...	2313	...	0016	...	*0144*
Holyhead ▽ a.	...	1653	...	1757	1837	...	1854	...	...	1954	...	2018	2044	...	2103	2134	...	2152	...	2251	...	2355	...	0051	...	*0220*

LLANDUDNO - BLAENAU FFESTINIOG

Due to extensive storm damage the service shown is currently suspended. A replacement 🚌 is in operation in similar timings.

km		⚒	⚒	Ⓐ	⑦n	⑥	⚒	⑦n	⚒	⑦n	⑥	Ⓐ
0	**Llandudno** d.	...	*0708*	1008	1022	1022	1308	1330	1620	*1544*	1903	1905
5	**Llandudno** Junction a.	...	*0718*	1018	1030	1032	1318	1338	1630	*1554*	1911	1913
5	**Llandudno** Junction d.	0530	0726	1028	1032	1034	1330	1340	1633	1615	1919	1923
18	Llanrwst d.	0548	0749	1050	1054	1056	1352	1402	1655	1637	1941	1945
24	Betws y Coed d.	0554	0755	1056	1100	1102	1358	1408	1701	1643	1947	1951
44	**Blaenau Ffestiniog** d.	0624	0829	1130	1132	1136	1432	1440	1735	1712	2021	2023

	⚒	Ⓐ	⑥	⚒	⑦n	⑥	Ⓐ	⑦n	⑦n	Ⓐ	⑥	⚒
Blaenau Ffestiniog d.	0624	0835	0846	1135	1145	1457	1457	1503	1730	1736	1737	2023
Betws y Coed d.	0650	0902	0913	1202	1211	1524	1524	1529	1757	1803	1804	2050
Llanrwst d.	0656	0908	0919	1208	1217	1530	1530	1535	1803	1809	1810	2056
Llandudno Junction a.	0720	0933	0944	1233	1240	1555	1555	1559	1829	1834	1835	2121
Llandudno Junction d.	*0731*	0950	1007	1235	1242	1605	1605	*1604*	1831	1841	1841	2132
Llandudno a.	*0741*	0958	1017	1245	1254	1615	1617	*1614*	1843	1853	1853	2144

♥ – All trains **Chester - Crewe**. Journey time ± 23 minutes:
On ⚒: 0422, 0455⑥, 0459Ⓐ, 0536, 0540⑥, 0551, 0626Ⓐ**A**, 0635⑥, 0645Ⓐ, 0717⑥**A**, 0735Ⓐ**A**, 0753Ⓐ, 0755, 0835**A**, 0855, 0917Ⓐ, 0935**A**, 0955 and at the same minutes past each hour until 1735**A**, 1755, 1855, 1935Ⓐ**A**, 1937⑥**a**, 1955, 2019, 2035⑥, 2047Ⓐ, 2055, 2135Ⓐ, 2230Ⓐ, 2227⑥, 2301Ⓐ, 2307⑥.
On ⑦: 0756**n**, 0828**n**, 0838**p**, 0858**n**, 0927**n**, 0939**p**, 0957**n**, 1039, 1057**n**, 1128**A**, 1157**n**, 1223, 1233**A**, 1257**n**, 1322**p**, 1330**A**, 1357**n**, 1424, 1433**A**, 1457**n**, 1532**A**, 1557**n**, 1600**p**, 1627, 1657**n**, 1722, 1735**A**, 1759**n**, 1835**A**, 1900, 1927, 1935, 1952**p**, 1957**n**, 2027, 2037, 2050**p**, 2057**n**, 2127**n**, 2136**p**, 2152**p**, 2157**n**, 2235, 2300**D**.

‡ – All trains **Llandudno Junction - Llandudno**. Journey time ± 10 minutes:
On ⚒: 0540Ⓐ, 0613, 0651, 0731, 0744Ⓐ, 0751⑥, 0819Ⓐ, 0828⑥, 0850⑥, 0917Ⓐ, 0928⑥, 0950Ⓐ, 0954⑥, 1007⑥, 1017Ⓐ, 1028⑥, 1052⑥, 1057Ⓐ, 1126⑥, 1128Ⓐ, 1151⑥, 1225⑥, 1235, 1257, 1350⑥, 1352Ⓐ, 1428, 1451, 1530⑥, 1551, 1605, 1626⑥, 1650, 1728⑥, 1750, 1826, 1841, 1851, 1928⑥, 1951⑥, 1956Ⓐ, 2030, 2058Ⓐ, 2132.
On ⑦ until Sept. 8: 1000, 1050, 1125, 1200, 1242, 1258, 1339, 1402, 1502, 1530, 1604, 1639, 1705, 1740, 1831.

♥ – All trains **Crewe - Chester**. Journey time ± 23 minutes:
On ⚒: 0001①**M**, 0010①**C**, 0015②–⑥**B**, 0622**B**, 0656Ⓐ, 0703⑥, 0711Ⓐ, 0723⑥, 0823, 0847Ⓐ**A**, 0923, 0942Ⓐ, 0947⑥**A**, 0952Ⓐ**A**, 1023, 1047**A**, 1123, 1147Ⓐ**A**, 1154⑥**A**, 1223, 1247**A**, 1323, 1350**A**, 1423, 1447**A** and at the same minutes past each hour until 1823, 1845Ⓐ**C**, 1850⑥**A**, 1856Ⓐ, 1923, 1947⑥**A**, 1954Ⓐ, 2023, 2048Ⓐ**P**, 2054**A**Ⓐ, 2100⑥, 2136⑥, 2140Ⓐ, 2148Ⓐ**A**, 2223, 2321⑥, 2330Ⓐ, 2357⑥.
On ⑦: 0827**n**, 0925, 0957**n**, 1007**p**, 1042, 1057**n**, 1105**p**, 1127, 1155, 1227, 1254**p**, 1257**n**, 1327, 1357, 1427, 1457, 1527, 1557**n**, 1627, 1651**A**, 1727, 1750**A**, 1827, 1900**A**, 1924**n**, 1926**p**, 1950**A**, 2027, 2053**A**, 2128, 2157**n**, 2203**p**, 2229, 2306, 2338.

‡ – All trains **Llandudno - Llandudno Junction**. Journey time ± 10 minutes:
On ⚒: 0554Ⓐ, 0634⑥, 0646Ⓐ, 0708, 0745, 0802Ⓐ, 0808⑥, 0830Ⓐ, 0845⑥, 0908⑥, 0945, 1008Ⓐ, 1010⑥, 1022⑥, 1044, 1108⑥, 1113Ⓐ, 1144, 1208⑥, 1240⑥, 1246, 1308, 1408, 1440Ⓐ, 1442⑥, 1508, 1544⑥, 1606, 1620, 1644⑥, 1707, 1744⑥, 1808, 1844, 1903⑥, 1905Ⓐ, 1913⑥, 1934Ⓐ, 1942⑥, 2008, 2043, 2111Ⓐ, 2145.
On ⑦ until Sept. 8: 1022, 1107, 1140, 1218, 1319, 1330, 1350, 1420, 1513, 1544, 1616, 1652, 1720, 1805, 1855.

← **FOR OTHER NOTES SEE PREVIOUS PAGE**

CS ⛟ Sleeper trains LONDON - SCOTLAND 161

All trains in this table convey 🛏 1, 2 cl., (2) (reservation compulsory) ✕ and 🍷. Only available for overnight journeys.

	⑦	⑦	⑦	Ⓐ	Ⓐ	Ⓐ	⑦ ◐	⑦ ◐	Ⓐ ◐	Ⓐ ◐
London Euston **151/2/3** d.	2059**a**	2059**a**	2059**a**	2115	2115	2115	2328**r**	2328**r**	2350	2350
Watford Junction d.	2120**f**	2120**f**	2120**f**	2133	2133	2133	2349**f**	2349**f**	0010	0010
Crewe **151 152 153 154** d.	2340**f**	2340**f**	2340**f**	2350	2350	2350	|	|	|	|
Preston **154** d.	0033**f**	0033**f**	0033**f**	0056	0056	0056	|	|	|	|
Carlisle **154** a.	|	|	|	|	|	|	0445**f**	0445**f**	0513	0513
Motherwell a.	|	|	|	|	|	|	|	0700	|	0700
Glasgow Central **154** ◧ a.	|	|	|	|	|	|	|	0722	|	0722
Edinburgh Waverley **154** ◧ a.	|	|	|	|	|	|	0723**j**	...	0723	...
Dundee **222** a.	0606	|	|	0606	|	|	...	...	...	...
Aberdeen **222** ◧ a.	0739	|	|	0739	|	|	...	...	...	...
Perth **223** a.	...	0541	|	...	0541	|	...	...	...	...
Inverness **223** a.	...	0842	|	...	0842	|	...	...	...	...
Fort William **218** a.	...	...	0957	...	...	0957	...	...	...	...

	⑦	⑦	Ⓐ	Ⓐ	Ⓐ	Ⓐ	Ⓐ	⑦	⑦	⑦
Fort William **218** d.	...	...	...	...	1950	...	...	1900	...	...
Inverness **223** d.	...	...	...	...	|	2045	...	|	2026	...
Perth **223** d.	...	...	...	...	|	2331	...	|	2307	...
Aberdeen **222** d.	...	...	...	...	|	|	2143	|	|	2143
Dundee **222** d.	...	...	...	...	|	|	2308	|	|	2308
Edinburgh Waverley **154** d.	2315	...	2340	...	|	|	|	|	|	|
Glasgow Central **154** d.	|	2315**t**	|	2340	|	|	|	|	|	|
Motherwell d.	|	2330**t**	|	2359	|	|	|	|	|	|
Carlisle **154** d.	0141**f**	0141**f**	0144	0144	|	|	|	|	|	|
Preston **154** a.	|	|	|	|	0431	0428	0428	0433**f**	0433**f**	0433**f**
Crewe **151 152 153 154** a.	|	|	|	|	0537	0538	0538	0537**f**	0537**f**	0537**f**
Watford Junction a.	0639**f**	0639**f**	0643	0643	|	|	|	|	|	|
London Euston **151/2/3** ◧ a.	0707	0707	0707	0707	0749	0749	0749	0749**h**	0749**h**	0749**h**

a – Until June 16 departs 2028.
f – From June 23.
h – Arrives 0906 on mornings of ① until June 17.
j – Until June 16 arrives 0513.
r – Until June 16 departs 2134.
t – Until June 16 departs Glasgow Central 2145, Motherwell 2202.
◐ – Sleeping-car passengers may occupy their cabins from 2200.
◧ – Sleeping-car passengers may occupy their cabins until 0800 following arrival at these stations.

NT 2nd class BLACKPOOL - PRESTON - LIVERPOOL 162

km			⚒	⚒	⚒	⚒	⚒		⚒	⚒	⚒	⚒	⚒	⚒	⚒		⑦	⑦	⑦	⑦	⑦	⑦	⑦		⑦	⑦	⑦
0	**Blackpool** North **154** d.	⚒	0603	0703	0804	0903	1003	and	1605	1703	1803	1905	2003	2101	2218	⑦	0755	0832	0932	1033	1132	1224	1332	and	1925	2032	2206
28	**Preston** **154** d.		0629	0729	0830	0929	1029	hourly	1631	1732	1829	1931	2029	2130	2243		0822	0859	1000	1100	1200	1252	1359	hourly	1952	2100	2233
52	Wigan North Western **154** d.		0647	0747	0850	0950	1048	until	1650	1750	1847	1949	2047	2151	2301		0841	0919	1019	1119	1222	1313	1419	until	2012	2119	2258
70	St Helens Central **154** d.		0700	0803	0908	1007	1100	★	1704	1803	1900	2002	2100	2204	2318		0858	0935	1035	1136	1238	1333	1435	★	2028	2135	2315
89	**Liverpool** Lime Str **154** a.		0719	0828	0940	1038	1119		1726	1824	1919	2021	2119	2230	2352		0923	1006	1108	1207	1309	1403	1506		2057	2208	2345

		⚒	⚒	⚒	⚒	a	⚒	⚒	⚒	⚒	⚒	⚒	⚒	⚒	Ⓐ	⑥	⑥	Ⓐ		⑦	⑦	⑦	⑦		⑦	⑦
Liverpool Lime Street **154** d.	⚒	0636	0736	0836	0936		1537	1636	1709	1736	1835	1936	2036	2115	2215	2217	2315	2315	⑦	0828	0909	1016	1112	and	2212	2312
St Helens Central **154** d.		0653	0753	0853	0953	and	1554	1653	1731	1757	1854	1953	2053	2143	2244	2246	2343	2343		0856	0937	1042	1139	hourly	2239	2339
Wigan North Western **154** d.		0706	0806	0906	1006	hourly	1607	1706	1747	1814	1907	2006	2106	2159	2301	2306	2359	0001		0912	0953	1059	1155	until	2255	2355
Preston **154** d.		0729	0830	0930	1030	until	1630	1729	1810	1837	1930	2031	2131	2222	2324	2330	0021	0022		0934	1015	1122	1217	★	2314	0014
Blackpool North **154** a.		0752	0857	0953	1053	★	1653	1753	...	1901	1955	2054	2154	2246	2347	2353	...	...		0958	1039	1145	1241		2338	0038

a – On ⑥ the 1337 departure from Liverpool calls St. Helens d. 1358, Wigan d. 1411, Preston d. 1436, Blackpool a. 1501.
★ – Timings may vary by up to 3 minutes.

ME, NT 2nd class MANCHESTER and LIVERPOOL local services 163

MANCHESTER - CLITHEROE
Journey time: ± 76–80 minutes *57 km* NT

From Manchester Victoria:
Trains call at Bolton ± 19 and Blackburn ± 48 minutes later.
⚒: 0536, 0741, 0841 and hourly until 1841, 1909, 1941, 2041, 2140, 2215.
⑦: 0755, 0841, 0945 and hourly until 1645, 1759, 1845, 1945, 2112, 2207.

From Clitheroe:
Trains call at Blackburn ± 23 and Bolton ± 54 minutes later.
⚒: 0623, 0649, 0721 and hourly until 1623, 1725, 1751, 1823, 1908, 2023, 2123, 2252.
⑦: 0923, 1023 and hourly until 1823, 1945, 2023, 2123, 2243.

MANCHESTER - BUXTON
Journey time: ± 56–65 minutes *41 km* NT

From Manchester Piccadilly:
Trains call at Stockport ± 10, Hazel Grove ± 22 and New Mills Newtown ± 31 minutes later.
⚒: 0624, 0722, 0808, 0824, 0908, 0924, 1008, 1024 and at the same minutes past each hour until 1908, 1924, 2024, 2147⑥, 2124, 2210, 2307⑥, 2311Ⓐ.
⑦: 0850, 0945, 1043, 1149, 1248, 1351, 1449 and hourly until 2049, 2150, 2248.

From Buxton:
Trains call at New Mills Newtown ± 21, Hazel Grove ± 34 and at Stockport ± 46 minutes later.
⚒: 0556, 0629, 0657, 0732, 0756, 0830, 0930, 0958, 1030 and at the same minutes past each hour until 1530, 1556, 1632, 1656, 1731, 1756, 1856, 1944, 2047, 2150, 2252⑥, 2255Ⓐ.
⑦: 0810, 0852, 0959, 1055, 1155, 1256, 1354 and hourly until 1954, 2056, 2201, 2255.

MANCHESTER - NORTHWICH - CHESTER
Journey time: ± 90–95 minutes *73 km* NT

From Manchester Piccadilly:
Trains call at Stockport ± 13, Altrincham ± 29 and Northwich ± 57 minutes later.
⚒: 0613, 0708, 0741, 0841 and hourly until 1541, 1639Ⓐ, 1641⑥, 1741, 1841, 1940, 2041, 2137⑥, 2140Ⓐ, 2240, 2341.
⑦: 0904, 1100, 1306, 1506, 1706, 1906, 2106.

From Chester:
Trains call at Northwich ± 30, Altrincham ± 55 and Stockport ± 74 minutes later.
⚒: 0556, 0651, 0802, and hourly until 1502, 1601Ⓐ, 1602⑥, 1702, 1801, 1900, 2001, 2101⑥, 2102Ⓐ, 2201, 2248⑥, 2252Ⓐ.
⑦: 0904, 1056, 1259, 1504, 1707, 1905, 2059.

CREWE - MANCHESTER AIRPORT - ST HELENS - LIVERPOOL
Journey time: ± 130 minutes *105 km* NT

From Crewe:
Trains call at Wilmslow ± 26 minutes, Manchester Airport ± 38 minutes, Manchester Piccadilly ± 68 minutes and St Helens Junction ± 101 minutes later.
⚒: 0542**y**, 0616, 0713, 0816, 0916, 1016, 1117, 1217, 1318, 1416, 1516, 1616, 1716**t**Ⓐ, 1716⑥, 1816⑥, 1817**t**Ⓐ, 1917, 2043**y**, 2134**y**, 2234**y**Ⓐ, 2239**y**⑥.
⑦: 0838**y**, 0943**y**, 1043**y**, 1138**y**, 1243**y**, 1339**y** and hourly until 1939**y**, 2039**y**, 2137**y**, 2252**y**.

From Liverpool Lime Street:
Trains call at St Helens Junction ± 27 minutes, Manchester Piccadilly ± 63 minutes, Manchester Airport ±89 minutes and Wilmslow ± 107 minutes later.
⚒: 0519**z**, 0524, 0628, 0728 and hourly until 1628, 1729⑥, 1829**w**⑥, 1834**z**Ⓐ, 1928**w**, 1931**wz**, 2028**w**, 2129**w**⑥, 2230**r**.
⑦: 0815**w**, 0930**w**, 1030**w**, 1129**w** and hourly until 2130**w**, 2230**w**, 2330**r**.

MANCHESTER - WIGAN - SOUTHPORT
Journey time: ± 75 minutes *62 km* NT

From Manchester Victoria:
Trains call at Wigan Wallgate ± 35 minutes later.
⚒: 0636, 0725, 0755Ⓐ, 0757⑥, 0826, 0855 and at the same minutes past each hour until 1555, 1618**p**, 1655, 1719**p**, 1756, 1818**p**, 1855, 1918**p**, 2026, 2127**p**, 2155, 2240.
⑦: 0825, 0925 and hourly until 2025, 2132.

From Southport:
Trains call at Wigan Wallgate ± 30 minutes later.
⚒: 0617**p**, 0634, 0648, 0717**p**, 0747, 0817**p**, 0852, 0924, 0947, 1024, 1052, 1124, 1147, 1224, 1252, 1324, 1352, 1424, 1447, 1525, 1547, 1619Ⓐ, 1624⑥, 1652, 1724, 1752, 1824, 1847, 1924, 2018, 2108, 2218.
⑦: 0846, 0938**n**, 0947**v** and hourly until 2138**n**, 2147**v**, 2254.

LIVERPOOL - BIRKENHEAD - CHESTER
Journey time: ± 42 minutes *29 km* ME

From Liverpool Lime Street (Low Level):
Trains call at Liverpool Central ± 2 minutes and Birkenhead Central ± 9 minutes later.
⚒: 0538, 0608, 0643, 0713, 0743, 0755Ⓐ, 0813, 0821Ⓐ, 0843, 0858⑥, 0913, 0928, 0943, 0958 and every 15 minutes until 1858, 1913 and every 30 minutes until 2343.
⑦: 0813, 0843 and every 30 minutes until 2313, 2343.

From Chester:
Trains call at Birkenhead Central ± 33 minutes and Liverpool Central ± 44* minutes later.
⚒: 0555, 0630, 0700, 0722Ⓐ, 0730⑥, 0737Ⓐ, 0752Ⓐ, 0800⑥, 0807Ⓐ, 0815⑥, 0831, 0845 and every 15 minutes until 1830, 1900 and every 30 minutes until 2300.
⑦: 0800, 0830 and every 30 minutes until 2300.

LIVERPOOL - RUNCORN - CHESTER
Journey time: ± 50 minutes *43 km* AW

From Liverpool Lime Street:
Trains call at Liverpool South Parkway ± 9 minutes and Runcorn ± 19 minutes later.
⚒: 0713, 0836, 0913, 1036 and hourly until 1837, 2038, 2140, 2219⑥, 2239Ⓐ, 2219⑥, 2323Ⓐ.
⑦: 0949, 1049, 1156 and hourly until 1957, 2057, 2137, 2257, 2318.

From Chester:
Trains call at Runcorn ± 26 minutes and Liverpool South Parkway ± 35 minutes later.
⚒: 0604⑥, 0607Ⓐ, 0643⑥, 0703Ⓐ, 0810, 0927, 1012, 1132, 1230, 1327Ⓐ, 1330⑥, 1427, 1532, 1630, 1730, 1927Ⓐ, 1931⑥, 2030, 2129, 2230Ⓐ, 2322⑥.
⑦: 0831, 0931, 1047 and hourly until 1747, 1844, 1947, 2047, 2154, 2228.

LIVERPOOL - SOUTHPORT
Journey time: ± 44 minutes *30 km* ME

From Liverpool Central:
⚒: 0608, 0623, 0638, 0653, 0708 and every 15 minutes until 2308, 2323, 2338.
⑦: 0808, 0823, 0853, 0923, 0953 and every 30 minutes until 2323, 2338.

From Southport:
⚒: 0538, 0553, 0608, 0623, 0643 and every 15 minutes until 2258, 2318.
⑦: 0758, 0828, 0858, 0928, 0958 and every 30 minutes until 2258, 2318.

n – Until Sept. 8.
p – Starts / terminates at Manchester **Piccadilly**, not Victoria.
r – Terminates at Manchester Airport.
t – Terminates at Manchester Piccadilly.
v – From Sept. 15.
w – To Wilmslow.
y – From Wilmslow.
z – From Manchester Piccadilly.
* – Trains FROM Chester call at Liverpool Lime Street, then Liverpool Central.

170 LONDON - LEICESTER - NOTTINGHAM, DERBY and SHEFFIELD

Most trains convey 🍷 EM

km			②–⑥	⚒	Ⓐ	⑥	Ⓐ	⑥S	⚒	⚒	Ⓐ	⑥	⑥	Ⓐ	⚒	Ⓐ	⑥	Ⓐ	⑥	Ⓐ	⑥	Ⓐ	⑥	Ⓐ	⑥	Ⓐ	ⒶF	⑥
0	**London** St Pancras d.	⚒	0015	...	0552	0548	0623	0633	...	0648	0704	0705	...	0732	0735	...	0747	0749	0802	0802	0805	0805	0831	0831	0834	0834	...	0847
47	Luton ✈ Parkway d.		0053	...	|	|	|	|	...	0710	|	|	...	|	0756	...	|	|	|	|	0826	0828	|	|	|	|	...	|
49	Luton d.		0057	...	0615	0614	0646	0656	...	|	0727	0727	...	|	|	...	0809	|	|	|	|	|	|	|	|	|	...	0909
80	Bedford d.		0125	...	0629	0628	0700	|	...	|	0741	0740	...	|	0810	...	0824	0825	|	|	0840	0842	|	|	|	|	...	0924
105	Wellingborough d.		0136	...	0641	0640	0712	|	...	|	0754	0752	...	|	0823	...	0836	0837	|	|	0853	0855	|	|	|	|	...	0936
116	Kettering d.		0146	...	0648	0648	0719	0723	0738	|	0804	0801	...	|	0830	0832	0845	0846	|	|	0900	0902	|	|	|	|	...	0945
128	**Corby** a.		|	...	|	|	|	|	0747	|	|	|	...	|	|	0841	0855	0855	|	|	|	|	|	|	|	|	0926	0955
133	Market Harborough d.		0158	...	0658	0658	0729	0733	...	|	0815	0811	...	0827	0841	...	...	...	|	|	0911	0913	|	|	0929	0932	|	...
159	**Leicester** 184 d.		0213	...	0712	0712	0742	0748	...	0755	0832	0825	0835	0840	0854	...	...	...	0905	0907	0924	0926	0935	0938	0943	0946	|	...
180	Loughborough 184 d.		▬	...	0722	0723	0752	0758	...	0804	0843	0835	0845	0850	0903	...	...	...	|	|	0933	0935	0945	0948	|	|	|	...
191	E. Midlands Parkway d.		...	...	0729	|	|	0805	...	0813	0851	0842	0852	0858	|	...	...	...	|	|	|	|	0952	0956	1002	1003	1040	...
204	**Nottingham** 184 ‡ a.		⚒	...	|	|	|	|	...	0828	0902	0854	|	|	0923	...	...	...	|	|	0953	0957	|	|	1016	1016	|	...
207	**Derby** 124 a.		0627	0717	0744	0742	0806	0818r	...	...	...	...	0908	0914	...	...	...	...	0926	0928	...	...	1009	1010	...	...	1054	...
246	Chesterfield 124 ‡ d.		0645	0742	0811	0811	0828	0842	...	...	...	...	0927	0932	...	...	...	...	0945	0947	...	...	1026	1028	...	...	...	...
265	**Sheffield** 124 ‡ a.		0709	0800	0826	0828	0846	0856	...	...	...	...	0943	0947	...	...	...	...	0959	1003	...	...	1040	1042	...	...	...	...

	Ⓐ	⚒	⚒	⚒	⚒	⚒	⚒	⑥	Ⓐ	⚒	⚒	⚒	⚒	⚒	⚒	⚒	⚒	⚒	⚒	⚒	⚒	⚒	⚒	⚒	⚒	⚒	⚒	⚒
London St Pancras d.	0847	0902	0905	0931	0934	0947	1002	1005	1005	1031	1034	1047	1102	1105	1131	1134	1147	1202	1205	1231	1234	1247	1302	1305	1331	1334	1347	1402
Luton ✈ Parkway d.	|	|	0926	|	|	|	|	1026	1028	|	|	|	|	1126	|	|	|	|	1226	|	|	|	|	1326	|	|	|	|
Luton d.	0912	|	|	|	|	1009	|	|	|	|	|	1109	|	|	|	|	1209	|	|	|	|	1309	|	|	|	|	1409	|
Bedford d.	0927	|	0940	|	|	1024	|	1040	1042	|	|	1124	|	1140	|	|	1224	|	1240	|	|	1324	|	1340	|	|	1424	|
Wellingborough d.	0941	|	0953	|	|	1036	|	1053	1056	|	|	1135	|	1153	|	|	1236	|	1253	|	|	1336	|	1353	|	|	1436	|
Kettering d.	0953	|	1000	|	|	1045	|	1100	1103	|	|	1145	|	1200	|	|	1245	|	1300	|	|	1345	|	1400	|	|	1445	|
Corby a.	1002	|	|	|	|	1055	|	|	|	|	|	1156	|	|	|	|	1256	|	|	|	|	1354	|	|	|	|	1455	|
Market Harborough d.	...	|	1011	|	1029	...	|	1111	1115	|	1129	...	|	1211	|	1229	...	|	1311	|	1329	...	|	1411	|	1429	...	|
Leicester 184 d.	...	1005	1024	1035	1043	...	1104	1124	1130	1135	1143	...	1205	1224	1235	1243	...	1304	1324	1335	1343	...	1404	1424	1435	1443	...	1504
Loughborough 184 d.	...	|	1033	1045	|	...	|	1133	1140	1145	|	...	|	1233	1245	|	...	|	1333	1345	|	...	|	1433	1445	|	...	|
E. Midlands Parkway d.	...	|	|	1052	1100	...	|	|	|	1152	1200	...	|	|	1252	1300	...	|	|	1352	1400	...	|	|	1452	1500	...	|
Nottingham 184 ‡ a.	...	|	1054	|	1116	...	|	1152	1205	|	1216b	...	|	1252	|	1316b	...	|	1353	|	1416b	...	|	1452	|	1516b	...	|
Derby 124 a.	...	1027	...	1109b	...	...	1126	...	...	1209	...	...	1226	...	1309	...	...	1326	...	1409	...	...	1426	...	1509	...	...	1526
Chesterfield 124 ‡ d.	...	1045	...	1126	...	...	1146	...	...	1226	...	...	1245	...	1326	...	...	1345	...	1426	...	...	1445	...	1526	...	...	1545
Sheffield 124 ‡ a.	...	1101	...	1141	...	...	1201	...	...	1241	...	...	1301	...	1341	...	...	1402	...	1441	...	...	1501	...	1541	...	...	1601

	⚒	⚒	⚒	⚒	⚒	⚒	⚒	⚒	⚒	⚒	⑥	Ⓐ	⑥	Ⓐ	⑥	Ⓐ	⑥	Ⓐ	Ⓐ	⑥	Ⓐ	⑥B	⑥	Ⓐ	Ⓐ	⑥	Ⓐ	⑥
London St Pancras d.	1405	1431	1434	1447	1502	1505	1531	1534	1547	1602	1605	1605	1631	1631	1634	1634	1647	1650	1702	1702	1705	1705	1731	...	1719	1734	1734	1747
Luton ✈ Parkway d.	1426	|	|	|	|	1526	|	|	|	|	1626	1626	|	|	|	|	|	|	|	|	|	1726	|	...	1742	|	|	|
Luton d.	|	|	|	1509	|	|	|	|	1609	|	|	|	|	|	|	|	1710	|	|	|	|	|	|	...	|	|	|	1809
Bedford ★ d.	1440	|	|	1524	|	1540	|	|	1624	|	1640	|	|	|	|	|	1724	|	|	|	|	1740	|	...	|	|	|	1824
Wellingborough ★ d.	1453	|	|	1536	|	1553	|	|	1635	|	1653	1650	|	|	|	|	1736	1733	|	|	1750	1753	|	...	1806	|	|	1835
Kettering d.	1500	|	|	1545	|	1600	|	|	1645	|	1700	1658	|	|	|	|	1745	1746	|	|	1757	1800	|	1810	1815	|	|	1845
Corby a.	|	|	|	1554	|	|	|	|	1655	|	|	|	|	|	|	|	1754	1755	|	|	|	|	|	|	|	|	|	1855
Market Harborough d.	1511	|	1529	...	|	1611	|	1629	...	|	1711	1708	|	|	1729	1734	...	...	|	|	1809	1811	|	|	1826	1829	1832	...
Leicester 184 d.	1524	1535	1543	...	1605	1624	1635	1643	...	1705	1724	1722	1735	1740	1743	1748	...	...	1808	1805	1822	1824	1835	1836	1841	1843	1847	...
Loughborough 184 d.	1533	1545	|	...	|	1633	1645	|	...	|	1733	1732	1745	1750	|	|	...	...	|	|	1835	1833	1845	1845	1852	|	|	...
E. Midlands Parkway d.	|	1552	1600	...	|	|	1652	1700	...	|	|	|	1752	1759	1800	1806	...	...	|	|	1843	|	1852	1853	1901	1900	1905	...
Nottingham 184 ‡ a.	1552	|	1616b	...	|	1654	|	1716b	...	|	1755	1753	|	|	1816	1819	...	...	|	|	1857	1854	|	|	1916g	1918	1920	...
Derby 124 a.	...	1609	...	...	1626	...	1709	...	...	1726	...	...	1809	1814t	...	...	...	...	1829	1826	...	...	1909	1913	1955	...	...	...
Chesterfield 124 ‡ d.	...	1626	...	...	1645	...	1726	...	...	1745	...	...	1827	1838	...	...	...	...	1848	1845	...	...	1926	1933	...	...	...	...
Sheffield 124 ‡ a.	...	1641	...	...	1702	...	1744	...	...	1802	...	...	1840	1855	...	...	...	...	1905	1900	...	...	1943	1950	...	...	...	...

	ⒶC	⚒	⑥	ⒶB	Ⓐ	⑥	ⒶL	⑥L	Ⓐ	⑥	Ⓐ	⑥	⑥	ⒶL	⑥	Ⓐ	⑥	Ⓐ	⚒	ⒶL	⑥L	⑥	Ⓐ	⑥	Ⓐ	⑥	Ⓐ	⑥
London St Pancras d.	1750	1802	1805	1805	1819	1831	1834	1834	1847	1847	1901	1902	1905	1904	1931	1932	1934	1935	1947	2001	2002	2005	2005	2031	2031	2034	2034	2100
Luton ✈ Parkway d.	1815	|	1826	|	1842	|	|	|	|	|	|	|	1926	1928	|	|	|	|	|	|	|	2027	2029	|	|	|	|	|
Luton d.	|	|	|	|	|	|	|	|	|	1909	|	|	|	|	|	|	|	|	2010	|	|	|	|	|	|	|	|	|
Bedford ★ d.	|	|	1840	|	|	|	|	|	|	1924	|	|	1940	1943	|	|	|	|	2024	|	|	2040	2042	|	|	|	|	|
Wellingborough ★ d.	1836	|	1853	1849	|	|	1920	|	1929	1936	|	|	1953	1956	|	|	|	|	2035	|	|	2052	2055	|	|	|	2118	|
Kettering d.	1854j	|	1900	1856	|	|	1929	|	1939	1945	|	|	2000	|	|	|	|	2027	2045	|	|	2100	2103	|	|	|	2125	|
Corby a.	1904	|	|	|	|	|	|	|	1948	1955	|	|	|	|	|	|	|	|	2054	|	|	|	|	|	|	|	|	|
Market Harborough d.	...	|	1911	|	1918	|	|	1929	...	...	1958	|	2011	2012	|	2029	2029	2039	...	|	|	2110	2113	|	|	2128	2135	|
Leicester 184 d.	...	1905	1924	1921j	1933	1935	1953	1943	...	...	2010	2005	2024	2028	2035	2043	2043	2054	...	2111	2109	2123	2127	2135	2137	2141	2148	2205
Loughborough 184 d.	...	|	1933	|	1944	1945	2005	|	...	...	2023	|	2033	2038	2045	|	|	2105	...	|	|	2132	2136	2145	2148	|	|	|
E. Midlands Parkway d.	...	|	|	1937	|	1952	2013	2000	...	...	2031	|	|	|	2052	2056	2100	2114	...	|	|	2142	|	2152	2156	2158	2201	|
Nottingham 184 ‡ a.	...	|	1952	1953	|	|	2026	2017	...	...	|	|	2052	2102	|	2109	2116	|	...	|	|	2154	2154	|	|	2218	2218	|
Derby 124 a.	...	1927	...	...	2012	2009	|	|	...	...	2041	2026	...	|	2110	...	...	2130	...	2135	2132t	...	...	2212	2213	...	...	2226
Chesterfield 124 ‡ d.	...	1945	...	...	2035	2027	2110	2109	...	...	2102	2045	...	2144	...	...	...	...	...	2158	2202	...	...	...	...	...	...	2248
Sheffield 124 ‡ a.	...	2002	...	...	2049	2040	2124	2123	...	...	2119	2100	...	2158	...	...	...	...	...	2218	2218	...	...	...	...	...	...	2300

	Ⓐ	⑥	Ⓐ	Ⓐ	Ⓐ	⑥	Ⓐ	⑥	⚒	⚒	⑥	Ⓐ	Ⓐ		⑦Y	⑦	⑦	⑦	⑦	⑦	⑦	⑦	⑦	⑦	⑦	⑦	⑦	⑦
London St Pancras d.	2101	2120	2105	...	2130	2130	2150	2150	2200	...	2220	2220	2308	⑦	...	0900	0930	1000	1030	1100	1130	1210	1230	1250	1310	1330	1355	1410
Luton ✈ Parkway d.	|	|	2127	...	|	|	2213	2213	|	...	2242	2242	|		...	0929	|	1029	|	1129	1159	1232	1252	|	1332	1352	|	1432
Luton d.	|	|	|	...	2155	2154	|	|	2225	...	|	|	2347		...	|	1002	|	1102	1133	1203	1235	1254	|	1335	1354	|	|
Bedford d.	|	|	2143	...	2209	2210	2226	2229	2240	...	2258	2258	0009	❖	...	0955	1023	1054	1127	1155	1220	1249	1309	|	1349	1409	|	1446
Wellingborough d.	|	|	2155	...	2221	2223	2239	2241	2253	...	2310	2311	0023		...	1008	1036	1108	1138	1208	1232	1302	1321	|	1402	1421	|	1459
Kettering d.	|	|	2203	2211	2228	2233	2247	2249	2302	2310	2318	2319	0041		...	1016	1042	1116	1145	1216	1240	1309	1334	1339	1409	1432	|	1506
Corby a.	|	|	|	2226	|	|	|	|	|	2326	|	|	|		...	|	|	|	|	|	|	|	1344	|	|	1442	|	|
Market Harborough d.	|	2213	2213	...	2238	2244	2257	2259	2313	...	2328	2329	0052		...	1026	1053	1127	1155	1226	1250	1319	...	1350	1419	...	1451	1516
Leicester 184 d.	2207	2227	2226	...	2252	2259	2309	2312	2330	...	2341	2344	0108		1020	1041	1110	1145	1212	1242	1306	1336	...	1408	1436	...	1509	1533
Loughborough 184 d.	|	2237	2236	...	2302	|	2319	2322	2341	...	2352	2354	0119		1030	1051	1120	1156	1222	1252	1316	1346	...	1419	1446	...	1520	1543
E. Midlands Parkway d.	|	2244	2244	...	2309	2315	2328	2330	2350	...	2359	0002	0128		1037	1059	1127	1205	1229	1300	1324	1353	...	1428	1453	...	1528	1550
Nottingham 184 ‡ a.	|	2256	2254	...	|	|	|	|	0008	...	|	|	0141r		|	1112	|	1217	|	1313	|	1407	...	|	1507	...	|	1606
Derby 124 a.	2230	...	...	...	2319	2329	2343	2345	...	...	0014	0014	0206		1053	...	1143t	...	1245	...	1344f	...	...	1442r	...	...	1544r	...
Chesterfield 124 ‡ d.	2252	...	...	...	...	...	...	...	...	...	...	0036	...		1114	...	1209	...	1311	...	1411	...	...	1509	...	...	1609	...
Sheffield 124 ‡ a.	2304	...	...	...	...	...	...	...	...	...	...	0051	...		1128	...	1223	...	1327	...	1426	...	...	1529	...	...	1629	...

	⑦	⑦L	⑦	⑦	⑦	⑦	⑦	⑦	⑦	⑦	⑦	⑦	⑦	⑦	⑦L	⑦	⑦	⑦	⑦	⑦	⑦	⑦	⑦	⑦L	⑦	⑦	⑦	⑦
London St Pancras d.	1430	1455	1510	1540	1555	1610	1635	1640	1705	1710	1735	1740	1805	1810	1835	1840	1905	1910	1935	1940	2000	2010	2035	2040	2110	2130	2230	2300
Luton ✈ Parkway d.	|	|	1533	|	|	1632	|	|	|	1732	|	|	|	1832	|	|	|	1932	|	|	|	2032	|	|	2132	|	2252	2328
Luton d.	1453	|	|	1603	|	|	|	1703	|	|	|	1803	|	|	|	1903	|	|	|	2003	|	|	|	2104	|	2154	|	|
Bedford d.	1507	|	1548	1617	|	1646	|	1717	|	1746	|	1817	|	1846	|	1917	|	1946	|	2017	|	2047	|	2120	2146	2207	2311	2353
Wellingborough d.	1519	|	1602	1630	|	1659	|	1730	|	1758	|	1830	|	1858	|	1930	|	1958	|	2030	|	2058	|	2133	2159	2220	2334	0015
Kettering d.	1533	|	1611	1637	|	1706	|	1737	|	1806	|	1837	|	1906	|	1937	|	2005	|	2037	|	2106	|	2141	2206	2228	2345	0026
Corby a.	1544	|	|	|	|	|	|	|	|	|	|	|	|	|	|	|	|	|	|	|	|	|	|	|	|	|	|	|
Market Harborough d.	...	1551	1622	|	1651	1716	|	1747	|	1815	|	1847	|	1916	|	1947	|	2015	|	2047	|	2116	|	2152	2216	2238	2355	0037
Leicester 184 d.	...	1608	1638	1702	1709	1733	1744	1804	1811	1833	1842	1904	1910	1932	1945	2004	2022j	2033	2042	2104	2110	2133	2142	2210	2233	2254	0011	0053
Loughborough 184 d.	...	1619	1651	1712	|	1743	|	1814	|	1843	|	1914	|	1942	|	2014	|	2043	|	2114	2121	2143	2152	|	2247	2304	0021	0103
E. Midlands Parkway d.	...	1627	1659	1720	1725	1750	1800	1821	1826	1850	1856	1921	1926	1949	2001	2021	2039	2050	2056	2121	2129	2150	2200	2226	2258	2316	0029	0110
Nottingham 184 ‡ a.	...	|	1714	|	|	1805	|	|	1836	1905	|	|	1937	2005	|	|	2051	2105	|	|	2145	2205	|	|	2311	|	0041	|
Derby 124 a.	...	1645	...	1737	1744t	...	1812	1836	...	...	1908t	1937	...	...	2011	2037	...	...	2107	2136	...	...	2211	2240t	...	2335	...	0121
Chesterfield 124 ‡ d.	...	1714	...	...	1812	...	1834	...	...	...	1934	...	...	...	2037	...	...	...	2127	...	...	...	...	2309	...	2355	...	...
Sheffield 124 ‡ a.	...	1728	...	...	1827	...	1850	...	...	...	1950	...	...	...	2051	...	...	...	2143	...	...	...	...	2323	...	0012	...	...

B – To/from Lincoln (Table **184**).
C – To/from Melton Mowbray (see panel on page 139).
D – To/from London St. Pancras (Table **170**).
F – Via Melton Mowbray (see panel on page 139).
L – To/from Leeds (Table **171**).
S – To Doncaster (a. 0958) and York (a. 1023).
V – From York (d. 1748⑦, 1750⑥) and Doncaster (d. 1813).

Y – To Doncaster (a. 1154) and York (a. 1219).

b – Arrives 3–4 minutes earlier on Ⓐ.
f – Departs 1350.
g – Departs 1924.
h – Also calls at Doncaster (d. 0557).
j – Arrives 4–6 minutes earlier.
r – Departs 4–6 minutes later.

t – Departs 7–10 minutes later.
y – Arrives 3–6 minutes earlier on ⑥.

‡ – For additional trains Nottingham - Sheffield see Tables **171** and **206**.

FOR OTHER NOTES SEE NEXT PAGE ►►►

EM Most trains convey 🍷 SHEFFIELD, DERBY and NOTTINGHAM - LEICESTER - LONDON 170

	⚒	⑥	Ⓐ	Ⓐ	Ⓐ	⑥	⑥	Ⓐ	Ⓐ C	⑥	Ⓐ	⚒	⑥	Ⓐ	⑥	Ⓐ	⑥	Ⓐ	Ⓐ L h	⑥	⑥	Ⓐ	Ⓐ	Ⓐ	⑥	Ⓐ	Ⓐ
Sheffield 124 ‡ d.		...	...	...	...	...	0529	...	...	...	0531	...	...	...	...	0600	0627	...	0625	...	...	...	...	0649	...	0725	...
Chesterfield 124 ‡ d.		...	...	...	...	...	0541	...	...	...	0545	...	...	...	...	0613	0639	...	0640	...	...	...	...	0701	...	0737	...
Derby 124 d.		...	...	0502	0519	0521	0601	...	...	...	0605	...	0629	...	...	0634	0704j	...	0705	...	0731	...	...	0723	...	0756	0730
Nottingham 184 ‡ d.		...	...					0532	...	0612		...		0631	0640			0652		0712		0711	...		0745		
E. Midlands Parkway d.		...	...	0513		0535		0543	...		0617	...	0643	0643	0651			0704			0745	0726	...	0734	0756		
Loughborough 184 d.		...	...	0520		0542		0551	...	0627	0626	...	0650			0654			0722	0729	0753		...	0742			0751
Leicester 184 d.		0445	0442	0531	0544	0553	0624	0604	...	0638	0639	...	0701	0659	0712	0706	0725	0719	0736	0740	0803	0743	...	0755j	0813	0816	0803
Market Harborough d.				0544	0557	0607		0619	...	0652	0654	...		0712	0726			0733		0753		0758	...		0827		0818
Corby d.									0638			0706											0802				
Kettering d.		0505	0503	0555	0608	0617		0631	0648	0702	0705	0717	0722	0723		0729		0743	0759	0803		0809	0811	0817			0830
Wellingborough ★ d.		0517	0513	0603	0616	0624		0639	0657	0709	0714	...	0729	0731		0737		0751	0807	0810			...	0825			0841
Bedford ★ a.		0532	0537			0637				0723		...	0742							0823			...				
Luton a.				0625		0652						...	0756										...				
Luton ✈ Parkway a.		0549	0553					0704		0738	0744	...				0802				0838			...				
London St Pancras a.		0621	0624	0654	0708	0721	0733	0736	0755	0805	0809	...	0822	0824	0826	0828	0838	0841	0855	0907	0911	0909	...	0912	0925	0927	0942

	Ⓐ	⑥	⑥	Ⓐ B	Ⓐ	⑥ B	⑥	Ⓐ L	⑥ L	Ⓐ	⑥	Ⓐ	⑥	⚒	⚒	Ⓐ	⑥ L	⚒	⚒	⚒	Ⓐ	⑥	⚒	⚒	⚒	⚒	⚒
Sheffield 124 ‡ d.	...	0729	...	...	0746	...	...	0728	0737	0826	0829	...	...	...	0900	...	0834	0929	...	...	1000	1000	...	1029	...	...	1100
Chesterfield 124 ‡ d.	...	0741	...	...	0759	...	...	0742	0750	0838	0841	...	...	...	0912	...	0847	0941	...	...	1013	1013	...	1041	...	...	1113
Derby 124 d.	...	0804j	...	...	0819	...	0831			0858	0904j	...	...	...	0931	...		1004j	...	...	1033	1032	...	1102	...	...	1132
Nottingham 184 ‡ d.	0800		...	0805		0812		0832	0845			...	...	0912		0945	0945		...	1012			1045		...	1112	
E. Midlands Parkway d.	0809		...		0834		0845	0843	0856			...	...		0944	0956	0956		...		1046	1045	1056		...		1145
Loughborough 184 d.			...	0821	0842	0828	0853					...	...	0926	0950				...	1027	1052	1053			...	1127	1152
Leicester 184 d.	0824	0825	...	0832	0855	0839	0903	0859	0913	0918	0925	...	...	0938	1002	1013	1013	1025	...	1038	1103	1103	1113	1124	...	1138	1203
Market Harborough d.			...	0846		0852		0913	0926			...	...	0951		1026	1026		...	1051			1126		...	1151	
Corby d.			0841									0932	0941						1041						1141		
Kettering d.			0851	0856		0902						0942	0951	1001					1051	1101					1151	1201	
Wellingborough ★ d.			0900	0903		0909						0951	1000	1008					1059	1108					1200	1208	
Bedford ★ a.			0912			0923						1012	1012	1023					1112	1122					1212	1223	
Luton a.			0927									1026	1027						1127						1227		
Luton ✈ Parkway a.				0930		0937								1038						1138						1238	
London St Pancras a.	0938	0936	0951	0955	1004	1007	1010	1011	1025	1025	1035	1051	1051	1108b	1111b	1125	1125	1136	1152	1208	1209	1211	1225	1236	1251	1308	1311b

	⚒	⚒	⚒	⚒	⚒	⚒	⚒	⚒	⚒	⚒	⚒	⚒	⚒	⚒	⑥	Ⓐ	⚒	⚒	Ⓐ	⑥	⚒	⚒	⚒	⚒	Ⓐ	⑥	⚒
Sheffield 124 ‡ d.	...	1129	...	...	1200	...	1229	...	...	1300	...	1329	...	...	1400	1359	...	1429	...	...	...	1500	...	1529	...	...	...
Chesterfield 124 ‡ d.	...	1141	...	...	1213	...	1241	...	...	1312	...	1341	...	...	1413	1413	...	1441	...	...	...	1512	...	1541	...	...	...
Derby 124 d.	...	1204j	...	...	1232	...	1304j	...	...	1331	...	1404j	...	...	1432	1433	...	1504j	...	...	...	1531	...	1604j	...	...	...
Nottingham 184 ‡ d.	1145		...	1212		1245		...	1312		1345		...	1412			1445		...	...	1512		1545		...	...	1612
E. Midlands Parkway d.	1156		...		1245	1256		...		1345	1356		...		1445	1447	1456		...	...		1544	1556		...	...	
Loughborough 184 d.			...	1227	1252			...	1327	1352			...	1427	1452	1455			...	...	1527	1552			...	...	1627
Leicester 184 d.	1212	1225	...	1238	1303	1312	1325	...	1338	1403	1413	1425	...	1438	1503	1508	1513	1525	...	...	1538	1602	1613	1625	...	...	1638
Market Harborough d.	1226		...	1251		1326		...	1351		1426		...	1451			1526		...	...	1551		1626		...	...	1651
Corby d.			1241					1341					1441						1539	1541					1639	1641	
Kettering d.			1251	1301				1351	1401				1451	1501					1549	1551	1601				1649	1651	1701
Wellingborough d.			1300	1308				1400	1409				1500	1508					1558	1600	1608				1657	1700	1708
Bedford a.			1312	1323				1412	1423				1512	1522					1610	1612	1623				1710	1712	1723
Luton a.			1327					1427					1527						1626	1627					1729	1727	
Luton ✈ Parkway a.				1338					1438					1538							1638						1738
London St Pancras a.	1325	1336	1351	1408	1412	1425	1438y	1451	1507	1510	1525	1539y	1551	1611y	1610	1624	1628y	1641y	1655	1650	1712y	1712	1725	1739y	1755	1751	1808

	Ⓐ F	⑥	Ⓐ	⑥	Ⓐ	⑥	Ⓐ	Ⓐ	⑥	Ⓐ	⑥	⚒	⑥	Ⓐ	⚒	Ⓐ	⑥	⚒	⚒	⚒	⑥	Ⓐ	Ⓐ	⑥	⚒	⑥ V	Ⓐ
Sheffield 124 ‡ d.	...	1600	1600	...	...	1629	1629	...	...	...	...	1700	...	...	1729	...	...	...	1800	...	1829	1829	...	...	...	1900	1902
Chesterfield 124 ‡ d.	...	1612	1613	...	...	1641	1641	...	...	...	...	1711	...	...	1741	...	...	...	1812	...	1841	1841	...	...	...	1912	1916
Derby 124 d.	1627	1631	1632	...	...	1704j	1702	...	...	...	...	1731	...	...	1804	...	...	...	1831	...	1904j	1904j	...	...	...	1931	1935
Nottingham 184 ‡ d.				1645	1645			...	...	1712	1712		1745	1745		...	...	1812		1845			...	...	1912		
E. Midlands Parkway d.	1640	1645	1645	1656	1656			...	...			1745	1756	1757		...	...		1845	1856			...	...		1945	1950
Loughborough 184 d.		1652	1652					...	...	1726	1728	1752				...	...	1827	1852				...	...	1927	1952	1957
Leicester 184 d.		1703	1703	1713	1713	1725	1723	...	...	1737	1739	1803	1813	1814	1825	...	...	1838	1902	1913	1925	1926	...	...	1938	2003	2008
Market Harborough d.				1726	1726			...	...	1750	1752		1826	1827		...	...	1851		1926			...	...	1951		
Corby d.	1749							1739	1741							1837	1841						1939	1941			
Kettering d.	1758		1724					1749	1751	1800	1802			1839		1847	1851	1901			1947		1949	1951	2001		
Wellingborough d.	...							1757	1800	1808	1809					1856	1900	1908					1957	2000	2008		
Bedford a.	...							1810	1812	1821	1823					1911	1912	1923					2010	2012	2023		
Luton a.	...				1803			1826	1827							1927	1927						2024	2027			
Luton ✈ Parkway a.	...									1840	1838							1940							2038		
London St Pancras a.	...	1811	1814	1825	1835	1834	1839	1855	1850	1906	1908	1911	1925	1936	1939y	1957	1951	2008	2011	2025	2038	2040	2051	2052	2108	2110	2121

	⚒	⑥	Ⓐ	⚒	⚒	Ⓐ	⚒	⑥	Ⓐ	⑥	Ⓐ	⑥	Ⓐ		⑦	⑦	⑦	⑦	⑦	⑦	⑦	⑦	⑦	⑦ L	⑦ L	⑦	⑦
Sheffield 124 ‡ d.	...	1929	1929	...	...	...	...	2029	2050	...	...	...	2201	⑦	...	...	...	...	0818	...	0925	...	1025	1035	1143	...	...
Chesterfield 124 ‡ d.	...	1941	1942	...	...	...	...	2041	2102	...	...	...	2213		...	...	...	...	0831	...	0937	...	1037	1048	1155	...	...
Derby 124 d.	...	2004j	2002	...	...	...	...	2101	2122	...	...	...	2234		0650	...	0751	...	0851	...	0958	...	1057		1217	...	...
Nottingham 184 ‡ d.	1945			...	2012	2055	...			2105	2129	2130	▬	❖		0729		0822		0920		1030		1139		...	1249
E. Midlands Parkway d.	1956			...	2024	2107	...	2113	2133	2117			...		0702	0739	0805	0835	0905	0931	1012	1045	1111	1150	1234	...	1303
Loughborough 184 d.				...	2032	2115	...	2120	2139	2125	2146	2146	...				0813	0843	0912	0940	1019	1053	1119	1159	1242	...	1312
Leicester 184 d.	2013	2025	2027	...	2042	2129	...	2131	2152	2136	2157	2156	...		0720	0755	0825	0855	0924	0954	1031	1108	1130	1213	1256	...	1326
Market Harborough d.	2027			...	2055	2142	...	...		2149	2210	2209	⚒		0738	0811	0841	0911	0940	1011	1044	1122	1143	1227	1310	...	1340
Corby d.				2041			2143	...					2243													1313	
Kettering d.				2051	2104	2152	2152	...		2157	2220	2219	2252		0749	0821	0851	0921	0950	1022	1054	1133	1153	1238		1323	1351
Wellingborough d.				2100	2113	2159	...	...		2206	2227	2226	...		0757	0828	0858	0928	1002	1030	1101	1141	1201	1246		1332	1359
Bedford a.				2112	2126	2212	...	...		2219	2239	2239	...		0815	0845	0915	0945	1015	1045	1115	1157	1215	1302		1344	1415
Luton a.				2127		2227	...	...		2234	2254	2253	...		0835		0934		1033		1135		1229			1400	
Luton ✈ Parkway a.					2142	2230	...	...		2238			...			0906		1006		1106		1214		1318			1431
London St Pancras a.	2125	2135	2138	2155y	2209	2257	...	...	2301	2311	2324	2329	...		0913	0942	1011	1042	1111	1142	1212	1241	1254	1345	1409	1424	1459

	⑦	⑦	⑦	⑦	⑦	⑦	⑦	⑦	⑦	⑦ L	⑦	⑦	⑦	⑦	⑦	⑦	⑦	⑦	⑦	⑦	⑦	⑦ V	⑦	⑦	⑦	⑦	⑦
Sheffield 124 ‡ d.	1249	...	...	1343	...	...	1449	...	...	1528	1550	...	...	...	1649	...	...	...	1750	...	...	1847	...	1928	2026	...	2236
Chesterfield 124 ‡ d.	1302	...	...	1356	...	...	1501	...	...	1542	1602	...	...	...	1700	...	...	...	1802	...	...	1900	...	1941	2039	...	2248
Derby 124 d.	1322	...	...	1416	...	...	1521	...	...	1602	1626j	...	...	1657	1723j	...	...	1806	1826j	...	...	1919	...	2002	2101	...	2323
Nottingham 184 ‡ d.		...	1349		...	1452		1543	1552			1645	1650			1745	1752			1845	1852		1952			2121	...
E. Midlands Parkway d.	1335	...	1403	1430	...	1504	1535	1553	1605	1616	1637	1655	1703	1711	1735	1755	1804	1820	1837	1855	1905	1934	2005	2018	2113	2131	...
Loughborough 184 d.	1343	...	1412	1438	...	1512	1542		1612	1625			1711	1719			1812	1828		1902	1912	1942	2012	2026		2139	...
Leicester 184 d.	1354	...	1426	1455	...	1524	1555	1612	1624	1639	1655	1710	1723	1731	1754	1814	1825	1840	1854	1914	1925	1955	2024	2040	2132	2154	...
Market Harborough d.	1407	...	1440	1508	...	1537			1637	1653			1736	1744			1838	1853		1927	1938	2008	2037	2054	2146	2208	...
Corby d.		1413			1513																						...
Kettering d.		1423	1451		1523	1547			1647	1703			1746	1755			1848	1905		1937	1948	2015	2047	2105	2157	2218	...
Wellingborough d.		1431	1459		1531	1554			1655	1712			1754	1802			1855	1912		1945	1955	2025	2054	2113	2205	2225	...
Bedford a.		1445	1515		1545	1609			1709	1728			1807	1816			1909	1927		1958	2009	2038	2108	2128	2219	2239	...
Luton a.		1500			1600		1640			1746				1831				1944		2014		2055	2123	2145	2235	2254	...
Luton ✈ Parkway a.			1531			1625			1725				1824				1924				2025	2058					...
London St Pancras a.	1502	1524	1559	1604	1624	1648	1708	1723	1750	1812	1802	1817	1847	1855	1908	1925	1950	2008	2001	2039	2050	2122	2148	2211	2300	2324	...

❖ – Additional journeys **Kettering - Corby** and v.v. on ⑦. Journey time: 10 minutes.
From Kettering at 0955, 1055, 1155, 1250, 1650, 1750, 1855, 1950, 2050, 2155.
From Corby at 0930, 1025, 1125, 1220, 1620, 1720, 1820, 1920, 2020, 2125.

★ – Additional 🚌 services operate Bedford - Wellingborough and v.v. on Ⓐ.
Journey time: 40 – 50 minutes.
From Bedford at 1628, 1658, 1728, 1759, 1828, 1904.
From Wellingborough at 0626, 0650, 0724, 0748, 0814, 0848.

◄◄◄ FOR OTHER NOTES SEE PREVIOUS PAGE

CORBY - MELTON MOWBRAY - DERBY

km		Ⓐ	Ⓐ D			Ⓐ D	Ⓐ	
	Kettering **170** d.	...	1854	...	**Derby** d.	...	1627	...
0	**Corby** d.	0926	1904	...	East Mid's Parkway d.	...	1640	...
23	Oakham d.	0947	1925	...	**Melton Mowbray** d.	0603	1711	...
43	**Melton Mowbray** d.	0959	1936	...	Oakham d.	0615	1723	...
81	East Mid's Parkway d.	1040	...	...	**Corby** a.	0638	1749	...
97	**Derby** a.	1054	...	...	*Kettering* **170** a.	0647	1758	...

171 NOTTINGHAM - SHEFFIELD - HUDDERSFIELD and LEEDS — 2nd class NT

NOTTINGHAM - SHEFFIELD - LEEDS

km			⚒	⚒	⚒	⚒	⚒	⚒	⚒	⚒R	⚒	⚒L	⚒	⚒L	⚒		⚒L	⚒	⚒L	⚒	⚒L	⚒	⚒L	⚒	⑥A	ⒶA
0	**Nottingham** 170 206 d.	⚒	...	...	...	0520	...	...	0617	...	0718	...	0817	...	0916	and	...	1717	...	1817	...	1917	...	2017	2024	2033
18	Langley Mill d.		...	...	...	|	...	...	0636	...	0737	...	0836	...	0935	at	...	1736	...	1836	...	1936	...	2036	2043	2049
29	Alfreton 206 d.		...	...	...	|	...	...	0644	...	0745	...	0844	...	0943	the	...	1744	...	1844	...	1944	...	2044	2051	2057
45	Chesterfield 170 206 d.		...	...	...	0549	0625	...	0654	...	0757	...	0855	...	0954	same	...	1755	...	1855	...	1955	...	2055	2109	2110
64	**Sheffield** 170 206 a.		...	...	...	0615	0642	...	0711	...	0815	...	0913	...	1013	minutes	...	1813	...	1913	...	2013	...	2113	2123	2124
64	**Sheffield** 192 193 d.		0528	0602	0619	...	0644	0704	0718	0747	0818	0845	0918	0945	1018	past	1745	1818	1845	1918	1945	2018	2045	2118	2126	2126
70	Meadowhall 192 193 d.		0534	0608	0625	...	0651	0710	0724	0754	0824	0851	0924	0951	1024	each	1751	1824	1851	1924	1951	2024	2051	2124	|	|
90	Barnsley d.		0557	0630	0639	...	0706	0733	0742	0808	0840	0909	0940	1009	1040	hour	1809	1840	1919	1940	2009	2040	2109	2140	|	|
107	Wakefield Kirkgate d.		0615	0649	0655	...	0723	0751	0757	0824	0855	0924	0955	1024	1055	until	1825	1855	1924	1955	2024	2055	2124	2155	2158e	2159e
130	**Leeds** a.		0643	0725	0716	...	0743	0826	0817	0845	0917	0945	1015	1045	1115		1846	1915	1943	2015	2045	2115	2144	2215	2217	2220

	ⒶA	⚒A	⚒	⚒	⚒	⚒		⑦	⑦	⑦B	⑦	⑦	⑦	⑦	⑦	⑦	⑦	⑦	⑦A	⑦	⑦	⑦	⑦A	⑦	⑦	⑦	⑦A
Nottingham 170 206 d.	2108	...	2112	...	2215	2318	⑦	...	...	0918	...	1017	1118	1219	1319	1419	1520	1619	...	1719	1819	1919	...	...	2015	2133	...
Langley Mill d.	2125	...	2136	...	|	2336		...	...	0938	...	1035	1136	1237	1337	1437	1538	1637	...	1737	1837	1937	...	...	2033	2157	...
Alfreton 206 d.	2133	...	2144	...	|	2344		...	...	0946	...	1043	1144	1245	1345	1445	1546	1645	...	1745	1845	1945	...	...	2041	2205	...
Chesterfield 170 206 d.	2144	2158	2155	...	2302	2354		...	...	0956	...	1054	1155	1256	1356	1456	1557	1656	1714	1756	1856	1956	2037	...	2054	2216	2309
Sheffield 170 206 a.	2158	2218	2213	...	2325r	0015		...	...	1016	...	1113	1214	1315	1415	1515	1614	1715	1728	1815	1914	2015	2051	...	2115	2234	2323
Sheffield 192 193 d.	2204	2221	2218	2231	...	...		0839	0917	1017	1051	1116	1216	1317	1417	1517	1617	1718	1734	1817	1916	2017	2103	2048	2117	2244	2326
Meadowhall 192 193 d.	|	|	2224	2237	...	...		0845	0923	1023	1057	1122	1223	1323	1423	1523	1623	1724	|	1823	1923	2023	|	2054	2123	2250	|
Barnsley d.	|	|	2240	2259	...	...		0906	0938	1038	1112	1136	1237	1337	1437	1537	1637	1738	|	1837	1937	2037	|	2115	2137	2312	|
Wakefield Kirkgate d.	2234e	2249e	2255	2318	...	...		0923	0959	1053	1132	1152	1302	1356	1456	1555	1657	1757	1801e	1853	1953	2053	2133e	2132	2153	2332	2353e
Leeds a.	2249	2306	2314	0002	...	...		0956	1024	1113	1208	1211	1322	1418	1518	1615	1717	1817	1816	1915	2015	2114	2149	2211	2215	0007	0008

		⚒	⚒	⚒	Ⓐ	⚒	⚒	ⒶA	⑥A	⚒L	⑥	Ⓐ	⑥A	⚒	⚒L	⚒		⚒	⚒L	⚒	⚒L	⚒	⚒L	⚒	⚒	⚒
Leeds d.	⚒	...	...	...	0519	...	0555	0633	0634	0638	0703	0703	0740	0804	0838	0908	and	1604	1638	1708	1738	1803	1838	1903	1930	2003
Wakefield Kirkgate d.		...	...	...	0532e	...	0627	0647e	0646e	0656	0722	0723	0753e	0822	0855	0925	at	1622	1655	1726	1755	1822	1857	1921	2001	2021
Barnsley d.		...	*0523*	0552	|	...	0645	|	|	0713	0738	0739	|	0838	0911	0941	the	1638	1711	1742	1811	1838	1913	1937	2020	2037
Meadowhall 192 193 d.		...	*0543*	0612	|	...	0707	|	|	0727	0753	0753	|	0857	0927	0957	same	1657	1727	1757	1827	1857	1928	1957	2042	2055
Sheffield 192 193 a.		...	*0553*	0620	0623	...	0719t	0721	0722	0734	0800	0800	0824	0904	0934	1004	minutes	1704	1734	1804	1834	1904	1935	2004	2051	2103
Sheffield 170 206 d.		0515	0601	...	0625	0702	...	0728	0737	...	0803	0803	0834	0906	...	1005	past	1706	...	1805	...	1905	...	2005	...	2104
Chesterfield 170 206 d.		0530	0619	...	0635	0717	...	0742	0750	...	0819	0819	0847	0922	...	1022	each	1722	...	1821	...	1921	...	2021	...	2120
Alfreton 206 d.		0545	0629	...	...	0728	...	0753	0801	...	0829	0833	0857	0933	...	1032	hour	1732	...	1832	...	1932	...	2032	...	|
Langley Mill d.		0553	0636	...	...	0735	...	0801	0809	...	0837	0841	|	0940	...	1040	until	1740	...	1839	...	1939	...	2039	...	|
Nottingham 170 206 a.		0611	0700	...	...	0753	...	0824	0825	...	0855	0859	0919	0959	...	1058		1758	...	1857	...	1957	...	2059	...	2202

	⚒	⚒	⑥	⚒	⑥	Ⓐ	⚒	Ⓐ		⑦	⑦	⑦	⑦A	⑦	⑦	⑦	⑦	⑦	⑦A	⑦	C	⑦	⑦	⑦	⑦	⑦
Leeds d.	2030	2104	...	2137	...	...	2232	2300	⑦	...	0833	0908	0950	1008	1108	1208	1308	1408	1434	1508	and	2008	2017	2108	2208	2218
Wakefield Kirkgate d.	2101	2121	...	2153	...	...	2304	2332		...	0903	0924	1002e	1024	1124	1224	1324	1424	1447e	1524	at	2024	2046	2129	2224	2247
Barnsley d.	2120	2137	...	2211	...	...	2322	2350		...	0920	0941	|	1041	1141	1241	1341	1441	|	1541	the	2041	2107	2145	2241	2305
Meadowhall 192 193 d.	2142	2154	...	2230	...	...	2343	0012		...	0941	0956	|	1056	1156	1256	1356	1456	|	1556	same	2054	2131	2200	2255	2326
Sheffield 192 193 a.	2150	2202	...	2240	...	...	2352	0021		...	0950	1003	1030	1103	1203	1303	1403	1503	1519	1603	minutes	2102	2138	2207	2303	2335
Sheffield 170 206 d.	...	2204	2242	...	2338	2338	...	...		0905	...	1006	1035	1106	1206	1306	1406	1506	1528	1606	past	2106	...	2209	*2330*	...
Chesterfield 170 206 d.	...	2220	2256	...	2353	0002	...	...		0921	...	1022	1048	1122	1222	1322	1422	1522	1541	1622	each	2122	...	2225	*2344*	...
Alfreton 206 d.	...	2231	2307	...	|	|	...	...		0932	...	1032	|	1132	1232	1332	1432	1532	...	1632	hour	2132	...	2236	*2355*	...
Langley Mill d.	...	2238	|	...	|	|	...	...		0939	...	1040	|	1140	1240	1340	1440	1540	...	1640	until	2140	...	2243	*0002*	...
Nottingham 170 206 a.	...	2257	2328	...	0029	0045	...	...		1000	...	1100	1121	1200	1300	1400	1500	1600	...	1700		2200	...	2307	*0023*	...

SHEFFIELD - HUDDERSFIELD *'The Penistone Line'*

km			⚒	⚒	⚒		⚒	⚒	⚒	⚒	⚒	⚒	⚒		⑦	⑦	⑦L	⑦L	⑦L	⑦L	⑦L	⑦	⑦	⑦	⑦
0	**Sheffield** 192 193 d.	⚒	0537	0630	0735	and at	1635	1735	1835	1935	2035	2135	2238	⑦	0938	1038	1139	1239	1339	1439	1538	1639	1739	1839	1939
6	Meadowhall 192 193 d.		0543	0636	0741	the same	1641	1741	1841	1941	2041	2141	2244		0945	1045	1145	1245	1345	1445	1544	1645	1745	1845	1945
26	Barnsley d.		0605	0701	0803	minutes	1703	1803	1903	2003	2103	2203	2307		1006	1106	1206	1306	1406	1503	1606	1703	1809	1903	2006
38	Penistone d.		0620	0717	0819	past each	1719	1823	1919	2019	2119	2219	2326		1023	1123	1223	1323	1423	1520	1622	1720	1825	1920	2023
59	**Huddersfield** a.		0651	0748	0851	hour until	1750	1854	1950	2050	2150	2250	2357		1054	1154	1255	1354	1454	1551	1654	1752	1856	1950	2053

		⚒	⚒	⚒	⚒		⚒	⚒	⚒	⚒	⚒	⚒	⚒		⑦	⑦	⑦L	⑦L	⑦L	⑦L	⑦L	⑦L	⑦	⑦	⑦
Huddersfield d.	⚒	0613	0712	0812	0912	and at	1712	1750	1813	1912	2012	2112	2249	⑦	0910	1016	1119	1216	1319	1465	1515	1616	1715	1816	1915
Penistone d.		0644	0743	0843	0943	the same	1743	1827f	1846	1943	2043	2143	2320		0941	1047	1150	1247	1350	1447	1546	1647	1746	1847	1946
Barnsley d.		0701	0800	0900	1000	minutes	1800	1845	1902	2000	2100	2200	2338		0958	1103	1207	1304	1407	1504	1603	1704	1803	1904	2003
Meadowhall 192 193 a.		0721	0820	0920	1020	past each	1820	1907	1923	2020	2120	2220	2358		1017	1119	1226	1318	1426	1518	1622	1718	1822	1918	2022
Sheffield 192 193 a.		0729	0828	0928	1028	hour until	1828	1917	1932	2028	2129	2228	0006		1027	1127	1237	1330	1438	1529	1634	1729	1833	1927	2032

A – From/to London St. Pancras (Table **170**).
B – To Carlisle (Table **173**).
C – The 1808 departure conveys (2) from Carlisle (Table **173**).
L – To/from Lincoln (Table **178**).
R – From Retford (Table **178**)
e – Wakefield Westgate.
f – Arrives 1821.
r – Arrives 2316 on ⑥.
t – Arrives 0715 on Ⓐ.

172 NOTTINGHAM - WORKSOP and MATLOCK — 2nd class EM

NOTTINGHAM - WORKSOP *'The Robin Hood Line'*

km			⚒	⑥	Ⓐ	⑥	Ⓐ	⚒	⚒		⚒	⚒	⚒	⚒	⚒	⚒	⑥		⑦	⑦	⑦	⑦	⑦	⑦	⑦	⑦
0	**Nottingham** d.	⚒	0540	0605	0605	0703	0701	0826	0926	and	1726	1755	1855	1955	2055	2205	2305	⑦	0807	0942	1128	1328	1525	1653	1829	2024
28	Mansfield d.		0613	0638	0638	0740	0740	0900	0957	hourly	1803	1836	1929	2036	2136	2242	2343		0840	1016	1205	1401	1558	1726	1902	2058
50	**Worksop** a.		0649	0718	0720	0814	0818	0933	1033	until	1837	1908	2003	2109	2208	2319	...		...	...	...	...	...	...	...	...

		⚒		⚒	⚒	⚒		⚒	Ⓐ	⑥	⚒	⚒		⚒	⚒	⚒	⚒		⑦	⑦	⑦	⑦	⑦	⑦	⑦	⑦
Worksop d.	⚒	0549	...	0656	0738	0838	and	1538	1638	1638	1746	1841	...	1922	2022	2122	2222	⑦	...	...	...	...	...	...	...	...
Mansfield d.		0621	...	0729	0810	0910	hourly	1610	1710	1713	1818	1913	...	1953	2053	2153	2253		0855	1033	1217	1415	1612	1739	1921	2110
Nottingham a.		0656	...	0805	0846	0944	until	1643	1745	1745	1852	1948	...	2032	2125	2226	2326		0931	1107	1251	1450	1646	1813	1955	2144

NOTTINGHAM - DERBY - MATLOCK

km			⚒	Ⓐ	⑥	⚒	⚒	⚒		⚒	⚒	Ⓐ	⑥		⑦	⑦	⑦	⑦	⑦		⑦	⑦	⑦	⑦
0	**Nottingham** 123 d.	⚒	...	0617	0620	0720	0820	0920		1920	2020	*2139*	*2138*	⑦	...	0926	1127	1323	1528	...	1623	1722	1922	2124
26	**Derby** 123 a.		...	0649	0650	0751	0850	0951	and	1951	2050	*2208*	*2208*		...	0954	1154	1351	1556	...	1651	1751	1950	2152
26	**Derby** d.		0542	0651	0652	0752	0852	0952	hourly	1951	2052	2219	2216		0756	0956	1156	1356	1558	...	1656	1756	1952	2155
34	Duffield ◧ d.		0549	0658	0659	0759	0859	0959	until	1958	2059	2226	2223		0803	1003	1204	1403	1605	...	1704	1803	1959	2202
46	Whatstandwell ◧ d.		0604	0713	0714	0814	0914	1014		2013	2114	2241	2238		0818	1018	1219	1418	1620	...	1719	1818	2014	2217
50	Cromford d.		0610	0719	0720	0820	0920	1020	★	2019	2120	2247	2244		0824	1024	1224	1424	1626	...	1724	1824	2020	2223
52	Matlock Bath ◧ d.		0612	0721	0722	0822	0922	1022		2021	2122	2249	2246		0826	1026	1227	1426	1628	...	1727	1826	2022	2225
53	**Matlock** ◧ a.		0615	0726	0726	0828	0927	1027		2027	2127	2254	2250		0830	1030	1230	1430	1632	...	1730	1830	2026	2229

		⚒	⚒	⚒	⚒	⚒		⚒	⑥	Ⓐ	⚒	⚒	⚒	⚒		⑦	⑦	⑦	⑦	⑦	⑦	⑦	⑦	⑦
Matlock ◧ d.	⚒	0620	0736	0836	0936	1036		1736	1836	1836	1936	2036	2140	2254	⑦	0838	1038	1238	1441	1638	1742	1838	2038	2244
Matlock Bath ◧ d.		0622	0738	0838	0938	1038	and	1738	1838	1838	1938	2038	2142	2256		0840	1040	1240	1443	1640	1744	1840	2040	2246
Cromford d.		0625	0741	0841	0941	1041	hourly	1741	1841	1841	1941	2041	2145	2259		0843	1043	1243	1446	1643	1747	1843	2043	2249
Whatstandwell ◧ d.		0630	0746	0846	0946	1046	until	1746	1846	1846	1946	2046	2150	2304		0848	1048	1248	1451	1648	1752	1848	2048	2254
Duffield ◧ d.		0646	0803	0903	1003	1103		1803	1903	1903	2003	2103	2207	2321		0905	1104	1304	1506	1705	1809	1904	2105	2311
Derby d.		0655	0810	0910	1010	1110	★	1810	1910	1910	2010	2110	2214	2328		0912	1111	1311	1514	1712	1816	1911	2112	2318
Derby 123 d.		*0709*	0812	0911	1012	1112		1811	1912	1913	2012	2112	*2259*	2329		0914	1113	1313	1515	1714	1817	1914	2113	...
Nottingham 123 a.		*0738*	0846	0941	1041	1139		1846	1939	1943	2041	2141	*2327*	0001		0941	1141	1341	1541	1744	1845	1944	2139	...

★ – Timings may vary by up to 2 minutes.

◧ – Visitor attractions near these stations:
Duffield: Ecclesbourne Valley Railway (shares National Rail station). ✆ 01629 823076.
Whatstandwell: Crich National Tramway Museum (1.6 km walk). ✆ 01773 854321.
Matlock Bath: Heights of Abraham (short walk to cable car). ✆ 01629 582365.
Matlock: Peak Rail (shares National Rail station). ✆ 01629 580381.

NT 2nd class LEEDS - SETTLE - CARLISLE 173

km			Ⓐ	⑥		⚒	⚒	⑦		⚒	⑦B	⑦C	⑦	⚒	⑦	⚒	⑦	⚒	E	⑤	⑦	⚒	⚒A	⑦A
	London Kings Cross 180 ....d.	...	...	...	...	...	...	...	...	...	...	...	...	...	...	...	...	...	...	...	...	...	1803	1835
0	**Leeds** 174 176 d.	...	0517	0620	...	0747	0917	0859	...	1049	...	1116	1228	1318	1424	1518	1622	1648	1818	1818	1852	1949	2039	2100
27	Keighley 🚂 174 176 d.	...	0544	0647	...	0810	0942	0927	...	1113	...	1142	1251	1343	1447	1543	1647	1713	1842	1842	1916	2012	2101s	2119s
42	Skipton 174 176 d.	...	0602	0705	...	0826	0959	0945	...	1127	...	1155	1305	1357	1502	1559	1701	1727	1856	1859	1933	2027	2119	2136
58	Hellifield 173a 174 d.	...	0614	0716	...	0840	1013	0959	...	1141	1016	1207	1319	1409	1516	1613	1713	1741	1910	1913	1945	2042	...	...
66	**Settle** d.	...	0622	0726	...	0849	1022	1007	...	1151	1034	1216	1328	1417	1525	1620	1721	1749	1919	1922	1953	2050	...	...
76	Horton in Ribblesdale d.	...	0630	0734	...	0858	1031	1016	...	1159	1043	|	1337	1425	1534	1629	1730	1758	1927	1930	2002	2059	...	...
84	Ribblehead d.	...	0638	0742	...	0906	1039	1024	...	1207	1051	|	1345	1433	1542	1637	1738	1806	1935	1938	2010	2108	...	...
93	Dent d.	...	0648	0752	...	0915	1048	1034	...	1217	1101	|	1355	1443	1552	1646	1748	1815	1944	1947	2020	...	...	...
99	Garsdale d.	...	0653	0757	...	0921	1054	1040	...	1222	1107	|	1401	1448	1557	1652	1753	1821	1950	1953	2025	...	...	...
115	Kirkby Stephen d.	...	0706	0810	...	0934	1106	1053	...	1235	1120	1254	1414	1501	1610	1704	1806	1833	2002	2005	2038	...	...	...
132	Appleby d.	...	0718	0822	...	0947	1119	1106	...	1248	1133	1308	1426	1514	1623	1717	1819	1846	2015	2018	2051	...	...	...
149	Langwathby d.	...	0732	0836	...	1001	1132	1120	...	1302	1147	|	1440	1528	1637	1731	1833	1900	2028	2031	2105	...	...	...
166	Armathwaite d.	...	0746	0850	...	1014	1146	1134	...	1316	1201	|	1454	1541	1651	1744	1847	1913	2042	2045	2119	...	...	...
182	**Carlisle** a.	...	0802	0905	...	1031	1201	1152	...	1333	1218	1347	1511	1601	1708	1759	1903	1928	2059	2102	2139	...	...	...

	⑥A	ⒶA	⑥	Ⓐ	⑥	Ⓐ	⑦	⑥	⚒	⑦	⚒		⚒	⑦C	⑦	⚒	⑦	⑦B	⚒	⑦	Ⓐ	⑥	Ⓐ	⑥
Carlisle d.	...	...	...	0551	0755	0824	0925	0927	1049	1250	1340	...	1450	1502	1607	1618	1725	1748	1824	1912	2013	2015	...	...
Armathwaite d.	...	...	...	0605	0809	0838	0939	0941	1104	1304	|	...	1504	1516	|	1632	1739	1802	1838	1926	2027	2029	...	...
Langwathby d.	...	...	...	0619	0822	0852	0953	0955	1118	1318	|	...	1518	1530	|	1646	1753	1815	1852	1940	2041	2043	...	...
Appleby d.	...	...	...	0633	0837	0906	1007	1009	1133	1332	1416	...	1532	1544	1644	1700	1808	1831	1906	1954	2055	2057	...	...
Kirkby Stephen d.	...	...	...	0646	0850	0920	1021	1023	1146	1346	1429	...	1546	1558	1657	1714	1822	1844	1920	2008	2108	2111	...	...
Garsdale d.	...	...	...	0700	0904	0933	1034	1036	1205	1359	|	...	1559	1613	|	1727	1835	1857	1933	2021	2121	2124	...	...
Dent d.	...	...	...	0705	0909	0938	1040	1041	1210	1405	|	...	1604	1618	|	1732	1841	1903	1938	2027	|	|	...	...
Ribblehead d.	...	...	0714	0714	0918	0948	1049	1051	1219	1414	|	...	1614	1628	|	1742	1850	1912	1948	2036	|	|	2145	2145
Horton in Ribblesdale d.	...	...	0720	0721	0925	0954	1056	1057	1226	1421	|	...	1620	1635	|	1748	1857	1919	1954	2043	|	|	2151	2153
Settle d.	...	...	0728	0729	0933	1002	1104	1105	1234	1429	1506	...	1628	1644	1734	1756	1906	1927	2002	2052	2149	2148	2159	2201
Hellifield 173a 174 d.	...	...	0737	0737	0940	1010	1113	1113	1241	1438	1514	...	1637	1653	1742	1805	1913	1937	2011	2100	|	|	2208	2210
Skipton 174 176 a.	0655	0655	0753	0753	0955	1024	1130	1127	1255	1455	1527	...	1654	1706	1757	1821	1928	...	2027	2117	2210	2209	2225	2226
Keighley 🚂 174 176 a.	0709u	0707u	0808	0805	1009	1038	1140	1138	1309	1507	1541	...	1709	1716	1808	1839	1940	...	2039	2128	2221	2221	2241	2241
Leeds 174 176 a.	0733	0731	0835	0833	1037	1108	1206	1205	1338	1536	1608	...	1739	1746	1832	1907	2007	...	2106	2153	2248	2248	2312	2311
London Kings Cross 180 ....a.	0955	1000	...	...	...	...	...	...	...	...	...	...	...	...	...	...	...	...	...	...	...	...	...	...

A – (12) and 🍸 London Kings Cross - Skipton and v.v. (Table **180**).
B – Until Sept. 8. from / to Blackpool North (Table **173a**).
C – From / to Nottingham (Table **171**).
E – ①②③④⑥.

s – Calls to set down only.
t – On ⑥ arrives 1527.
u – Calls to pick up only.

🚂 – Keighley and Worth Valley Railway (Keighley - Haworth - Oakworth - Oxenhope, *8 km*). ✆ 01535 645214. www.kwvr.co.uk

NT 2nd class BLACKPOOL - PRESTON - CLITHEROE - HELLIFIELD 173a

km			⑦B		⑦A		⑦B	
0	**Blackpool North** 156 190 d.	...	0812	...	0840	...	...	...
29	**Preston** 156 190 d.	...	0839	...	0907	...	1535	...
48	Blackburn 163 190 d.	...	0900	...	0928	...	1556	...
63	Clitheroe 163 d.	...	0924	...	0952	...	1617	...
85	Hellifield a.	...	0947	...	1016	...	1640	...
	Carlisle 173 a.	...	*1152*	...	1218	...	*1903*	...

		⑦B		⑦B		⑦A	
Carlisle 173 d.	...	...	...	*1502*	...	1748	...
Hellifield d.	...	1030	...	1715	...	1937	...
Clitheroe 163 a.	...	1053	...	1736	...	1959	...
Blackburn 163 190 a.	...	1122	...	1801	...	2025	...
Preston 156 190 a.	...	1143	...	1821	...	2049	...
Blackpool North 156 190 a.	...	...	...	1849	...	2121	...

A – Until Sept. 8.
B – From Sept. 15.

NT 2nd class LEEDS - LANCASTER - HEYSHAM 174

km	km		⚒	⑥	Ⓐ	⚒	⚒	⚒	⚒		⚒		⚒	⑥	Ⓐ	⚒	⑦	⑦	⑦	⑦		⑦	⑦	⑦
0	0	**Leeds** 173 176 d.		...	...	0720	0819	1018	...	...	1218	...	1418	1726	1726	1918		0830	1024	...	...	1324	1524	1724
27	27	Keighley 🚂 173 176 d.		...	...	0744	0842	1043	...	...	1243	...	1443	1752	1752	1943		0857	1047	...	...	1347	1547	1747
42	42	Skipton 173 176 d.		0519	0522	0759	0856	1057	...	...	1258	...	1458	1808	1810	2000		0915	1102	...	...	1402	1602	1802
58	58	Hellifield 173 d.		0534	0537	0815	0910	1111	...	...	1312	...	1513	1822	1824	2014		0929	1116	...	...	1416	1616	1816
66	66	Giggleswick d.		0545	0548	0827	0921	1122	...	...	1323	...	1523	1833	1834	2025		0939	1126	...	...	1426	1626	1826
82	82	Bentham d.		0601	0603	0842	0935	1136	...	...	1337	...	1538	1848	1849	2040		0954	1140	...	...	1440	1640	1840
103	103	Carnforth 157 d.		0621	0623	0904	0957	1201	...	...	1401	...	1559	1910	1916	2105		1015	1202	...	...	1502	1704	1902
113		**Lancaster** 157 a.		0632	0632	0913	1005	1210	1249	...	1410	...	1608	1919	1925	2114		1025	1213	1230	...	1513	1715	1913
120	112	Morecambe a.		*0732*	*0732*	*0937*	1026	1224	1302	...	1424	...	1632	1945	1951	*2144*		*1040*	...	1243	...	*1539*	*1739*	*1939*
127	119	**Heysham** Port a.		...	...	...	...	...	1317	...	...	...	...	...	...	...		...	...	1258	...	...	...	...

	⚒	⚒	⚒		⚒	⚒		⚒	⚒		⚒	⚒	⚒	⑦	⑦	⑦		⑦	⑦		⑦		⑦
Heysham Port d.		...	...	...	...	...	...	1320	...	...	...	...	...		...	...	...	1305	...	...	...	...	...
Morecambe d.		*0558*	*0854*	...	1033	1232	...	1339	1432	...	1731	2007	*2108*		*1000f*	*1150*	...	1325	*1457*	...	*1657*	...	*1857*
Lancaster 157 d.		0648	0941	...	1046	1245	...	1348	1447	...	1745	2030	2130		1041	1239	...	1335	1541	...	1741	...	1951
Carnforth 157 d.		0659	0950	...	1055	1255	...	...	1456	...	1755	2040	2143		1051	1251	...	...	1551	...	1751	...	2001
Bentham d.		0719	1010	...	1115	1314	...	...	1516	...	1815	2100	2202		1111	1311	...	...	1611	...	1811	...	2021
Giggleswick d.		0735	1027	...	1132	1331	...	...	1533	...	1832	2117	2219		1126	1326	...	...	1626	...	1826	...	2036
Hellifield 173 d.		0746	1037	...	1141	1340	...	...	1542	...	1842	2126	2228		1137	1337	...	...	1637	...	1837	...	2047
Skipton 173 176 a.		0803	1053	...	1157	1356	...	...	1557	...	1858	2141	2244		1154	1354	...	...	1654	...	1854	...	2104
Keighley 🚂 173 176 a.		0817	1109	...	1209	1409	...	...	1609	...	1909	2155	...		1206	1406	...	...	1706	...	1906	...	2117
Leeds 173 176 a.		0841	1138	...	1238	1437	...	...	1639	...	1938	2222	...		1236	1436	...	...	1739	...	1938	...	2144

f – From June 23.

🚂 – Keighley and Worth Valley Railway (Keighley - Haworth - Oakworth - Oxenhope, *8 km*). ✆ 01535 645214. www.kwvr.co.uk

NT 2nd class LEEDS - HARROGATE - YORK 175

km		⚒	⚒	⚒	⚒	⚒	⚒	⚒	⚒	⚒	⚒	⚒	⚒	and at	⚒	⚒	⚒	⚒		⚒	⚒	⚒	⚒	⚒
0	**Leeds** 124 188 d.		0605	0623	0633	0700	0715	0745	0808	0829	0859	0914	0929	the same	1559	1615	1629	1659	...	1709	1729	1738	1749	1809
29	**Harrogate** d.		0642	0651	0710	0740	0752	0822	0844	0907	0936	0944	1004	minutes	1636	1646	1706	1735	...	1749f	1806	1816	1830f	1846
36	Knaresborough d.		0651	...	0720	0751	0801	0831	0856	0916	0947	...	1015	past each	1647	...	1715	1745	...	1758	1815	1827	1839	1857
62	**York** 124 188 a.		0721	...	0750	...	0830	0901	...	0946	...	...	1046	hour until	...	...	1747	...	...	...	1845	...	1907	...

	⚒	⚒	⚒	ⒶA	⚒	⑥A	⚒	⚒	⚒	⑦	⑦	⑦	⑦	⑦	⑦	C and at	⑦	⑦	⑦	⑦A	⑦	⑦	⑦	⑦
Leeds 124 188 d.	1829	1901	1929	2001	2030	2101	2129	2239	2339		0902	1005	1035	1105	1136	the same	1905	1936	2005	2031	2105	2131	2226	2315
Harrogate d.	1906	1938	2004	2027	2107	2128	2206	2317	0016		0943	1042	1113	1142	1213	minutes	1942	2013	2042	2057	2142	2208	2305	2354
Knaresborough d.	1915	1949	2015	...	2116	...	2215	...	...		0952	1052	1124	1152	1224	past each	1952	2024	2052	...	2152	2219	...	...
York 124 188 a.	1946	...	2048	...	2146	...	2247	...	...		1020	1120	...	1220	...	hour until	2021	...	2120	...	2220	...	...	...

	⚒	⚒	⚒	⚒	⚒	⚒	ⒶA	⑥A	⚒	⚒	⚒	⚒	⚒	⚒	⚒	⚒	⚒	⚒	and at	⚒	⚒	⚒	⚒	⚒
York 124 188 d.		...	...	...	...	0649	...	...	...	...	...	0756	...	0847	0911	...	...	1011	the same	...	...	1611	...	...
Knaresborough d.		...	...	...	0655	0714	...	...	0737	...	0806	0821	0900	0913	0936	...	1006	1036	minutes	...	1606	1636	...	1706
Harrogate d.		0603	0632	0655	0704	0723	0734	0735	0746	0805	0815	0831	0910	0923	0945	1002	1015	1045	past each	1602	1615	1645	1702	1715
Leeds 124 188 a.		0640	0710	0728	0742	0801	0804	0807	0824	0842	0852	0906	0947	1001	1023	1033	1053	1124	hour until	1635	1653	1723	1732	1750

	⚒	⚒	⚒	⚒	⚒	⚒	⚒	⚒	⚒	⚒	⚒	⚒	⑦	⑦	⑦	⑦	⑦	⑦	⑦	B and at	⑦	⑦	⑦	⑦
York 124 188 d.	1711	...	1742	1811	...	1911	...	2011	...	2111	2211	2244		...	...	...	...	1047	...	the same	...	2047	2143	...
Knaresborough d.	1736	...	1809	1837	1906	1936	2006	2036	2106	2136	2236	2309		...	...	...	1042	1112	1142	minutes	2042	2112	2211	...
Harrogate d.	1745	1810	1818	1846	1915	1945	2015	2045	2115	2145	2245	2318		0922	0952	1022	1051	1121	1151	past each	2051	2121	2220	2312
Leeds 124 188 a.	1823	1849	1853	1922	1953	2024	2053	2124	2153	2224	2323	2357		1000	1030	1100	1130	1200	1229	hour until	2129	2200	2259	2351

A – (12) and 🍸 Harrogate - Leeds - London Kings Cross and v.v. (Table **180**).
B – Additional train Harrogate d. 1707 - Leeds a. 1733 **A**.
C – The 1305 and 1805 departures from Leeds arrive York at 1424 and 1925 respectively.
f – Arrives 5–6 minutes earlier.

176 WEST YORKSHIRE local services — 2nd class NT

BRADFORD FORSTER SQUARE - SKIPTON
Journey: ± 38 minutes 30 km

From Bradford Forster Square: Trains call at **Keighley** ± 22 minutes later.

⚒: 0603, 0641, 0711, 0741, 0811, 0841, 0911 and every 30 minutes until 2011, 2048, 2111, 2211, 2311.

⑦: 0948, 1048 and hourly until 2248.

From Skipton: Trains call at **Keighley** ± 14 minutes later.

⚒: 0604, 0634, 0709, 0736, 0815, 0834, 0904 and every 30 minutes until 1734, 1803, 1841, 1904, 1934, 2004, 2034, 2133, 2234.

⑦: 0842, 0942 and hourly until 2142.

LEEDS - SKIPTON
See also Tables 173/174 — Journey: ± 45 minutes 42 km

From Leeds: Trains call at **Keighley** ± 24 minutes later.

⚒: 0517Ⓐ, 0620⑥, 0626, 0656, 0723, 0752, 0826, 0854, 0926 and every 30 minutes until 1826, 1855, 1926 and every 30 minutes until 2126, 2152⑥, 2156Ⓐ, 2226, 2256, 2320.

⑦: 0830, 0859, 1016, 1126, 1216, 1316, 1416, 1516, 1612, 1716 and hourly until 2116, 2220, 2322.

From Skipton: Trains call at **Keighley** ± 13 minutes later.

⚒: 0545, 0618, 0640, 0701, 0717, 0730, 0744, 0809, 0847, 0917, 0947 and every 30 minutes until 2117, 2148, 2226, 2249.

⑦: 0832, 0912, 1012 and hourly until 1612, 1714, 1812, 1912, 2012, 2122, 2212, 2312.

LEEDS - BRADFORD FORSTER SQUARE
For Leeds - Bradford Interchange see Table 190 — Journey: ± 21 minutes 22 km

From Leeds:

⚒: 0630, 0710, 0741, 0812 and every 30 minutes until 1712, 1735, 1812, 1842, 1912.

⑦: 0836, 0941 and hourly until 1641, 1745, 1841, 1942, 2041, 2142, 2241.

From Bradford Forster Square:

⚒: 0558, 0630, 0655, 0730, 0754, 0831, 0900, 0930 and every 30 minutes until 1930.

⑦: 0913 and hourly until 1713, 1814, 1913, 2013, 2113, 2213, 2315.

HUDDERSFIELD - WAKEFIELD KIRKGATE
Journey: ± 30 minutes 25 km

From Huddersfield:

⚒: 0603, 0703 and hourly until 1703, 1806, 1903, 2003, 2103, 2208, 2303.

From Wakefield Kirkgate:

⚒: 0617, 0708 and hourly until 1208, 1309, 1408, 1508, 1608, 1707, 1808, 1908, 2008, 2108, 2209, 2316.

177 HULL - BRIDLINGTON - SCARBOROUGH — 2nd class NT

km			⚒	⚒	⚒	⚒	⚒	⚒	⚒	⚒	⚒	⚒	⚒	⚒	⚒	⚒	⚒		⑦	⑦A	⑦A	⑦A	⑦A	⑦A
0	**Hull** △ d.	⚒	0533	0639	0725	0827	0930	1030	1130	1230	1330	1430	1530	1630	1736	1833	1930	⑦	0835	1003	1048	1157	1307	1400
13	Beverley △ d.		|	0653	0739	0841	0944	1044	1144	1244	1344	1444	1544	1644	1750	1847	1944		0849	1019	1102	1213	1321	1416
31	Driffield △ d.		|	0707	0753	0855	0958	1059	1156	1256	1356	1458	1556	1656	1806	1859	1956		0906	1034	1117	1228	1336	1431
50	**Bridlington** △ a.		0606	0723	0809	0911	1014	1115	1210	1310	1410	1514	1610	1710	1821	1913	2010		0923	1049	1135	1244	1351	1447
50	**Bridlington** d.		0606	0733	0815	0914	1015	1118	1213	1313	1413	1515	1613	1713	1822	1916	2013		0924	1053	1137	1253	1353	1453
71	Filey d.		0626	0755	0837	0936	1037	1139	1236	1336	1436	1537	1636	1736	1844	1939	2036		0946	1117	1159	1317	1417	1517
87	**Scarborough** a.		0644	0812	0855	0954	1055	1159	1254	1354	1454	1555	1654	1754	1902	1957	2054		1005	1133	1218	1333	1433	1533

	⑦A	⑦A	⑦A	⑦		⑦A	⑦A	⑦A	⑦A
Scarborough d.	1500	1600	1659	1726	...	1800	1907	1953	2051
Filey d.	1508	1616	1716	1740	...	1816	1921	2007	2106
Bridlington a.	1531	1631	1731	1755	...	1831	1936	2022	2120
Bridlington △ d.	1547	1647	1747	1815	...	1847	1951	2038	2135
Driffield △ d.	1553	1653	1753	...	...	1853	1953	...	...
Beverley △ d.	1617	1717	1817	...	...	1917	2017	...	...
Hull △ a.	1633	1733	1833	...	...	1933	2033	...	...

		⚒A	⚒	⚒	⚒	⚒	⚒	⚒	⚒	⚒
Scarborough d.	⚒	0655	0822	0920	1020	1120	1220	1320	1420	1520
Filey d.		0710	0839	0937	1037	1137	1237	1337	1437	1537
Bridlington a.		0732	0901	0959	1059	1159	1259	1359	1459	1559
Bridlington △ d.		0734	0904	1000	1104	1204	1304	1404	1500	1604
Driffield △ d.		0750	0918	1016	1118	1218	1318	1418	1516	1618
Beverley △ d.		0805	0930	1030	1130	1230	1330	1430	1530	1630
Hull △ a.		0821	0947	1047	1147	1247	1348	1447	1547	1648

	⚒	⚒	⚒	⚒A	⚒	⚒	⚒	⚒		⑦	⑦	⑦	⑦A	⑦A	⑦A	⑦A	⑦A	⑦A	⑦	⑦A	⑦A	⑦A	⑦	⑦
Scarborough d.	1620	1720	1820	1920	2018	2111	...	...	⑦	...	1013	1059	1204	1302	1402	1502	1602	1702	...	1802	1902	2002	...	2126
Filey d.	1637	1736	1837	1935	2035	2128	...	...		...	1028	1114	1219	1317	1417	1517	1617	1717	...	1817	1917	2017	...	2141
Bridlington a.	1659	1758	1859	1956	2057	2150	...	...		...	1050	1136	1240	1338	1438	1538	1638	1728	...	1838	1938	2038	...	2204
Bridlington △ d.	1702	1759	1904	2002	2102	2153	2233	2306		0941	1051	1138	1242	1340	1440	1540	1640	1740	1823	1840	1940	2040	2127	2205
Driffield △ d.	1715	1815	1918	2015	2116	2207	2249	2322		0956	1107	1154	1257	1355	1455	1555	1655	1755	1838	1855	1955	2055	2143	2220
Beverley △ d.	1732	1829	1930	2027	2128	2221	2304	2337		1013	1122	1209	1312	1410	1510	1610	1710	1810	1855	1910	2010	2110	2158	2234
Hull △ a.	1748	1846	1947	2045	2144	2237	2320	2353		1026	1138	1224	1325	1423	1523	1623	1723	1823	1914	1923	2023	2123	2213	2251

A – From/to Sheffield (Table **192**).

△ – All trains Hull - Bridlington and v.v. on ⚒:

From Hull on ⚒ at 0533, 0557, 0613, 0639, 0725, 0747, 0801, 0827, 0901 **A**, 0930, 1001 **A**, 1030, 1056 **A**, 1130, 1156 **A**, 1230, 1256 **A**, 1330, 1356 **A**, 1430, 1455 **A**, 1530, 1556 **A**, 1630, 1656 **A**, 1718, 1736, 1757 **A**, 1833, 1904 **A**, 1930, 2001 **A**, 2057 **A**, 2157 **A**.

From Bridlington on ⚒ at 0645, 0703, 0734 **A**, 0751, 0832 **A**, 0904, 0935 **A**, 1000, 1035 **A**, 1104, 1135 **A**, 1204, 1232 **A**, 1304, 1335 **A**, 1404, 1435 **A**, 1500, 1535 **A**, 1604, 1633 **A**, 1702, 1735 **A**, 1759, 1817, 1835 **A**, 1904, 1927, 2002 **A**, 2035 **A**, 2102, 2136, 2153, 2233, 2306.

178 LINCOLN and CLEETHORPES - SHEFFIELD — 2nd class NT

km			⚒	⚒L	⚒	⚒L	⚒	⚒L	⚒	⚒L	⚒	⚒L	⚒	⚒L	⑥C	Ⓐ	⚒L	⚒	⚒L	⚒	⚒L	⚒	⚒L	⑥C	Ⓐ	⚒L	⚒
0	**Lincoln** d.	⚒	...	...	0643	0723	...	0826	...	0929	...	1029	...	1129	...	...	1229	...	1326	...	1427	...	1529	...	...	1629	...
	Gainsborough Central d.		...	...	|	|	0816	|	0917	|	1016	|	1116	|	1210	1212	|	1316	|	1416	|	1516	|	1610	1616	|	1716
26	Gainsborough Lea Road d.		...	...	0704	0744	|	0847	|	0950	|	1050	|	1150	|	|	1250	|	1347	|	1448	|	1550	|	|	1650	|
40	Retford d.		0613	0656	0717	0757	0832	0900	0932	1005	1032	1105	1132	1205	1230	1230	1305	1331	1402	1431	1504	1531	1605	1631r	1631	1705	1731
52	Worksop d.		0625	0708	0729	0808	0843	0911	0944	1017	1043	1117	1143	1217	1242	1242	1317	1343	1414	1443	1515	1543	1617	1642	1643	1717	1742
78	**Sheffield** a.		0656	0743	0804	0841	0917	0942	1017	1042	1117	1141	1217	1242	1317	1317	1342	1417	1442	1517	1542	1617	1642	1717	1717	1742	1817

	⚒L	⚒	⚒L	⚒	⚒L	⑥C	⚒	⚒	⚒	⚒	⚒		⑦	⑦H	⑦H	⑦H	⑦H	⑦	⑦H	⑦	⑦	⑦	⑦	⑦	⑦	⑦	⑦
Lincoln d.	1723	...	1823	...	1926	...	2019	2129	...	...	2244	⑦	...	1014	1114	1214	1314	...	1414	1512	1612	1715	1812	1919	2017	2120	2151
Gainsborough Central d.	|	1816	|	1912	|	2015	|	|	...	...	|		...	|	|	|	|	...	|	|	|	|	|	|	|	|	|
Gainsborough Lea Road d.	1744	|	1844	|	1948	|	2040	2150	...	...	2305		...	1035	1135	1235	1335	...	1435	1533	1633	1736	1837	1940	2038	2141	2212
Retford d.	1757	1831	1857	1927	2001	2032	2053	2204	2251	...	2318		0912	1050	1150	1250	1350	1414	1450	1548	1648	1751	1852	1955	2053	2156	2227
Worksop d.	1808	1846	1908	1939	2012	2043	2105	2216	2303	2321	2330		0926	1102	1202	1302	1402	1428	1502	1559	1700	1803	1904	2007	2105	2207	2238
Sheffield a.	1841	1924	1941	2012	2041	2115	2138	2248	2336	2359	0002		0959	1134	1234	1334	1436	1501	1535	1631	1733	1836	1933	2040	2135	2241	2312

km			⚒	Ⓐ	⑥	⚒	⚒	⚒L	Ⓐ	⑥C	⚒L	⚒	⚒L	⚒	⚒L	⚒	⚒L	Ⓐ	⑥C	⚒L	⚒	⚒L	⚒	⚒L	⚒	⚒L	Ⓐ
0	**Sheffield** d.	⚒	0545	0610	0613	0638	0658	0738	0759	0759	0837	0853	0937	0954	1037	1054	1137	1154	1154	1237	1254	1337	1354	1437	1454	1537	1554
25	Worksop d.		0614	0634	0636	0710	0729	0759	0829	0828	0858	0923	1000	1024	1058	1125	1158	1224	1224	1258	1324	1358	1424	1458	1524	1559	1624
38	Retford d.		0624	0649	0652	0720	0739	0809	0839	0841	0908	0933	1010	1034	1108	1135	1208	1234	1239f	1308	1334	1408	1434	1510	1534	1609	1634
	Gainsborough Lea Road d.		0639	...	...	0735	|	0824	|	|	0923	|	1030	|	1124	|	1223	|	|	1324	|	1423	|	1524	|	1624	|
54	Gainsborough Central a.		|	...	...	|	0755	|	0855	0858	|	0949	|	1052	|	1151	|	1250	1258	|	1350	|	1450	|	1550	|	1650
	Lincoln a.		0707	...	...	0801	...	0847	...	...	0948	...	1055	...	1149	...	1248	...	...	1349	...	1448	...	1548	...	1649	...

	⑥C	⚒L	⚒	⚒L	⚒	⚒L	⚒L	⚒	⚒	⚒		⑦	⑦	⑦	⑦	⑦H	⑦	⑦H	⑦H	⑦H		⑦H	⑦H	⑦	⑦	⑦	⑦
Sheffield d.	1554	1637	1654	1737	1754	1837	1938	2053	2143	2241	⑦	0845	0941	1041	1141	1241	1314	1336	1441	1542	...	1637	1738	1842	1934	2020	2123
Worksop d.	1625	1708	1724	1808	1824	1913	2008	2122	2214	2314		0908	1012	1106	1211	1307	1345	1406	1507	1608	...	1708	1805	1913	2000	2051	2154
Retford d.	1641j	1718	1734	1818	1834	1923	2018	2133	2228	...		0919	1022	1117	1222	1318	1359	1416	1518	1618	...	1719	1815	1924	2010	2101	2205
Gainsborough Lea Road d.	|	1732	|	1833	|	1938	2033	2147	...	...		0933	1036	1131	1236	1332	...	1431	1532	1633	...	1733	1830	1938	2025	2115	2219
Gainsborough Central a.	1658	|	1750	|	1850	|	|	|	...	...		|	|	|	|	|	...	|	|	|	...	|	|	|	|	|	|
Lincoln a.	...	1756	...	1857	...	2006	2058	2210	...	...		0957	1100	1156	1300	1356	...	1455	1557	1657	...	1758	1854	2004	2049	2141	2245

C – To/from Cleethorpes (See panel below main table).
H – To/from Huddersfield (Table **171**).
L – To/from Leeds (Table **171**).

f – Arrives 1235.
j – Arrives 1635.
r – Arrives 1625.
t – Arrives 4 minutes earlier.

CLEETHORPES - GAINSBOROUGH - SHEFFIELD

km		⑥	⑥	⑥
0	**Cleethorpes** 193 d.	1114	1151	1917
5	Grimsby Town 189 193 d.	1121	1518	1924
28	Barnetby 189 193 d.	1142	1838	1943
34	Brigg d.	1148	1543	1948
61	**Gainsborough** Central d.	1210	1610	2015
114	*Sheffield* 178 d.	1317	1717	2115

	⑥	⑥	⑥
Sheffield 178 d.	0759	1154	1554
Gainsborough Central d.	0858	1258	1658
Brigg d.	0924t	1320	1724t
Barnetby 189 193 d.	0936	1331	1734
Grimsby Town 189 193 d.	0959	1353	1757
Cleethorpes 193 a.	1008	1403	1808

NT 2nd class HULL - YORK 179

km		Ⓐ	⑥	⚒	⚒	⚒	⚒	⚒	⚒	⚒	⚒	⚒	⚒	Ⓐ	⑥	⚒	⚒	⚒	⚒	⚒	⑦	⑦	⑦	⑦
0	Hull ..... 181 189 d.	0619	0622	0706	0808	0910	1010	1110	1210	1310	1409	1518	1610	1715	1715	1810	1916	2010	2110	2154	0831	1035	1131	1233
50	Selby ..... 181 189 d.	0656	0659	0755	0847	0947	1047	1147	1247	1356	1447	1557	1647	1803	1803	1847	1956	2047	2147	2234	0907	1111	1207	1307
84	York ..... a.	0731	0735	0831	0919	1020	1112	1222	1319	1420	1511	1629	1723	1933	1836	1920	2027	2126	2220	2310	0942	1141	1228	1340

	⑦	⑦	⑦	⑦	⑦	⑦	⑦	⑦	⑦
Hull ..... 181 189 d.	1335	1425	1535	1635	1735	1835	1935	2023	2135
Selby ..... 181 189 d.	1409	1504	1609	1709	1809	1909	2009	2103	2209
York ..... a.	1436	1529	1642	1741	1836	1941	2038	2128	2241

	⚒	Ⓐ	⑥	⚒	⚒	⚒	⚒	⚒	⚒	⚒
York ..... d.	0540	0615	0620	0721	0848	0947	1050	1148	1250	1347
Selby ..... 181 189 d.	0606	0649	0652	0750	0920	1017	1117	1217	1317	1417
Hull ..... 181 189 a.	...	0738	0740	0839	1002	1100	1200	1300	1400	1500

	⚒	⑥	Ⓐ	⚒	⚒	⚒	⚒	⚒	⚒	⚒	⑦	⑦	⑦	⑦	⑦	⑦	⑦	⑦	⑦	⑦	⑦	⑦	⑦	⑦
York ..... d.	1450	1547	1547	1648	1748	1850	1950	2048	2150	2247	0851	1001	1049	1151	1250	1351	1454	1551	1651	1751	1851	1956	2052	2219
Selby ..... 181 189 d.	1517	1717	1620	1718	1819	1918	2021	2119	2220	2318	0921	1020	1117	1214	1320	1419	1515	1619	1719	1813	1917	2017	2113	2238
Hull ..... 181 189 a.	1600	1700	1703	1801	1900	1959	2101	2205	2300	0005	0959	1056	1200	1252	1358	1457	1559	1658	1757	1850	1959	2056	2200	2325

GR Most services convey 🍷 LONDON - LEEDS, YORK, NEWCASTLE and EDINBURGH 180

For additional services see Tables **124**, **181**, **182**, **183**, **185** and **188**.

km		⑥	Ⓐ	⑥	Ⓐ	⚒ A	⚒	⚒	⑥	Ⓐ	Ⓐ	⑥	⚒	⑥	Ⓐ	⚒	⚒	Ⓐ	⑥	⚒	Ⓐ	⑥	⚒	Ⓐ	⑥	⚒
0	**London** Kings Cross ... d.	...	...	...	...	...	0555	0615	0630	0633	0700	0700	0703	0706	0706	0730	0733	0800	0800	0803	0830	0830	0833	0900	0900	0903
44	Stevenage ..... d.	...	...	...	...	...	0617	0637	0652	0655	|	|	|	0728	0728	|	0755	|	|	|	|	|	0855	|	|	|
123	Peterborough ..... d.	...	...	...	...	...	0647	0708	0722	0725	0748	0748	0753	0758	0800	0818	|	|	|	0851	0918	0918	|	0948	0948	0952
170	Grantham ..... d.	...	...	...	...	...	0706	0727	0741	0744	|	|	|	0817	0819	|	0841	|	|	|	|	|	0941	|	|	|
193	Newark North Gate ..... d.	...	...	...	...	...	0719	0741	|	|	|	|	|	0830	0832	0846	|	|	|	|	0946	0946	|	|	|	|
223	Retford ..... d.	...	...	...	...	...	0734	0756	|	|	|	|	|	0845	0847	|	|	|	|	|	|	|	|	|	|	|
251	Doncaster ..... d.	...	...	0612	0615	...	0750	0811	0818	0817	|	|	0843**h**	0901	0902	0911	0915	|	|	0944**f**	1010	1010	1015	|	|	1042
283	Wakefield Westgate . a.	...	...	|	|	...	0806	|	0834	0834	|	|	0859	|	|	|	0931	|	|	1000	|	|	1031	|	|	1100
299	**Leeds** ..... a.	...	...	|	|	0708	0822	|	0851	0851	|	|	0916	|	|	|	0947	|	|	1016	|	|	1047	|	|	1116
303	**York** ..... d.	...	...	0636	0639	0736**f**	...	0834	...	...	0855**f**	0900**t**	...	0924	0925	0935	...	0954	0955	...	1035	1036**n**	...	1054	1054	...
351	Northallerton ..... d.	...	...	0655	|	|	...	0854	...	...	|	|	...	...	...	|	...	|	|	...	1055	1055	...	|	|	...
374	Darlington ..... d.	...	...	0710	0708	0806	...	0908	...	...	0924	0929	...	...	...	1005	...	1023	1024	...	1109	1109	...	1123	1123	...
409	Durham ..... d.	...	...	0726	0726	0824	...	0926	...	...	|	|	...	...	...	1022	...	|	|	...	1126	1127	...	|	|	...
432	**Newcastle** ..... a.	0620	0622	0740	0739**r**	0837	...	0939**g**	...	...	0951	0955	...	...	...	1036**g**	...	1050	1052	...	1141	1140**r**	...	1150	1150**g**	...
488	Alnmouth ..... a.	0650	0653	0809	0808	|	...	|	...	...	|	|	...	...	...	1107	...	|	|	...	...	|	...	|	|	...
540	Berwick upon Tweed ... a.	0715	0717	0832	0830	0928	...	|	...	...	1036	1040	...	...	...	|	...	1135	1137	...	...	|	...	1235	1238	...
632	**Edinburgh** Waverley ... a.	0807	0807	0920	0922	1019	...	1112**a**	...	...	1122	1128	...	...	...	1210	...	1220	1226	...	...	1310	...	1320	1326	...

	⚒	Ⓐ	⑥	⚒	⚒ A	⚒	⑥	Ⓐ	⚒	⚒	⚒	⚒	⚒	⑥	Ⓐ	⚒	⚒ B	⚒	⚒	Ⓐ	⑥	⚒	Ⓐ	⑥	⚒	⑥	Ⓐ
London Kings Cross ... d.	0906	0930	0930	0933	1000	1003	1006	1006	1030	1033	1100	1103	1106	1130	1130	1133	1200	1203	1206	1230	1230	1233	1300	1300	1303	1306	1306
Stevenage ..... d.	0928	|	|	0956	|	|	1029	1028	|	1056	|	|	1128	|	|	1156	|	|	1228	|	|	1256	|	|	|	|	1328
Peterborough ..... d.	0959	1018	1018	|	|	1051	1059	1101**f**	1118	|	|	1153	1159	1218	1218	|	|	1251	1300	1318	1318	|	1348	1348	1352	1355	1359
Grantham ..... d.	1020	|	|	1041	|	|	1120	1121	|	1141	|	|	1218	|	|	1241	|	|	1321	|	|	1341	|	|	|	1416	1420
Newark North Gate ..... d.	1033	1046	1046	|	|	|	1134	1135	1146	|	|	|	1231	1246	1246	|	|	|	1336	1346	1346	|	|	|	|	1433**f**	1433
Retford ..... d.	1049	|	|	|	|	|	...	...	|	|	|	|	1246	|	|	|	|	|	...	|	|	|	|	|	|	1449	1448
Doncaster ..... d.	1105	1110	1110	1115	|	1143	...	...	1210	1215	|	1243	1305	1310	1310	1315	|	1343	...	1411	1410	1415	|	|	1443**f**	1505	1504
Wakefield Westgate .. a.	|	|	|	1131	|	1200	...	...	|	1232	|	1300	|	|	|	1332	|	1359	...	|	|	1431	|	|	1459	|	|
Leeds ..... a.	|	|	|	1148	|	1216	...	...	|	1249	|	1316	|	|	|	1349	|	1416	...	|	|	1448	|	|	1516	|	|
York ..... d.	1130	1135	1135	...	1154	...	...	...	1235**f**	...	1254	...	1329	1335**f**	1335	...	1354	...	...	1435	1435**f**	...	1454	1454	...	1529	1529
Northallerton ..... d.	...	|	|	...	|	...	...	...	1254	...	|	...	...	|	|	...	|	...	...	1455	1455	...	|	|	...	...	...
Darlington ..... d.	...	1205	1206	...	1223	...	...	...	1308	...	1323	...	...	1406	1408	...	1423	...	...	1509	1509	...	1523	1523	...	...	...
Durham ..... d.	...	1222	1223	...	|	...	...	...	1326	...	|	...	...	1423	1425	...	|	...	...	1526	1527	...	|	|	...	...	...
Newcastle ..... a.	...	1238	1236	...	1250**r**	...	...	...	1339**g**	...	1350	...	...	1437	1440**r**	...	1451	...	...	1541	1540**g**	...	1549	1549**j**	...	...	...
Alnmouth ..... a.	...	1311	1307	...	|	...	...	...	|	...	|	...	...	1505	1509	...	|	...	...	...	|	...	|	|	...	...	...
Berwick upon Tweed .... a.	...	|	|	...	1339	...	...	...	|	...	1435	...	...	|	|	...	1539	...	...	...	|	...	1634	1641	...	...	...
Edinburgh Waverley ... a.	...	1415	1410	...	1425**d**	...	...	...	1516**e**	...	1527**p**	...	...	1613	1614	...	1624**d**	...	...	...	1710	...	1723	1730	...	...	...

	⚒	Ⓐ	⑥	Ⓐ A	⑥ A	⚒	⚒	Ⓐ	⑥	Ⓐ	⑥	Ⓐ K	⑥	Ⓐ	⑥	⑥	Ⓐ	⑥	Ⓐ C	Ⓐ	⑥	⑥	Ⓐ A	⚒	⚒	⑥	Ⓐ
London Kings Cross ... d.	1330	1333	1335	1400	1400	1403	1406	1430	1430	1433	1435	1500	1500	1503	1503	1506	1506	1530	1530	1533	1535	1600	1600	1603	1606	1630	1630
Stevenage ..... d.	|	1356	1358	|	|	|	1428	|	|	1456	1457	|	|	|	|	1528	1528	|	|	1556	1557	|	|	|	1628	|	|
Peterborough ..... d.	1418	|	|	|	|	1451	1459	1519	1518	|	|	|	|	1551	1554**f**	1559	1559	1618	1618	|	|	|	|	1652	1701	1718	1718
Grantham ..... d.	|	1442	1441	|	|	|	1519	|	|	1542	1542	|	|	|	|	1618	1619	|	|	1641	1642	|	|	|	1722	|	|
Newark North Gate ..... d.	1446	|	|	|	|	|	1534	1547	1546	|	|	|	|	|	|	1632	1633	1646	1646	|	|	|	|	|	1736	1747	1746
Retford ..... d.	|	|	|	|	|	|	...	|	|	|	|	|	|	|	|	1647	1648	|	|	|	|	|	|	|	...	|	|
Doncaster ..... d.	1510	1515	1514	|	|	1543	...	1611	1610	1615	1615	|	|	1643	1644	1702	1704	1710	1710	1717	1716	|	|	1741	...	1812	1816**n**
Wakefield Westgate .. a.	|	1531	1530	|	|	1559	...	|	|	1631	1632	|	|	1659	1700	|	|	|	|	1733	1734	|	|	1759	...	|	|
Leeds ..... a.	|	1548	1548	|	|	1616	...	|	|	1649	1649	|	|	1716	1716	|	|	|	|	1750	1750	|	|	1816	...	|	|
York ..... d.	1535**f**	...	...	1555	1553	...	...	1635	1635	...	...	1654	1654	...	...	1725	1727	1734	1735**n**	...	...	1754**f**	1756**f**	...	...	1835	1839
Northallerton ..... d.	1555	...	...	|	|	...	...	1655	1655	...	...	|	|	...	...	...	...	1754	1755	...	...	|	|	...	...	1858	1858
Darlington ..... d.	1609	...	...	1624	1623	...	...	1709	1709	...	...	1723	1723	...	...	...	...	1808	1810	...	...	1823	1825	...	...	1912	1912
Durham ..... d.	1626	...	...	|	|	...	...	1726	1727	...	...	|	|	...	...	...	...	1825	1827	...	...	|	|	...	...	1929	1930
Newcastle ..... a.	1639	...	...	1651**r**	1650**g**	...	...	1741	1740**r**	...	...	1750	1749**b**	...	...	...	...	1838**g**	1840**r**	...	...	1849	1851	...	...	1943	1943
Alnmouth ..... a.	1710	...	...	|	|	...	...	...	|	...	...	|	|	...	...	...	...	1908	1909	...	...	|	|	...	...	|	|
Berwick upon Tweed .... a.	|	...	...	1739	1740	...	...	...	|	...	...	1836	1843	...	...	...	...	|	|	...	...	1935	1937	...	...	|	|
Edinburgh Waverley ... a.	1816	...	...	1822	1825	...	...	...	1910	...	...	1918	1928	...	...	...	...	2013	2013	...	...	2021	2020	...	...	2114	2114

	⚒	⑥	Ⓐ	⚒	⚒ D	⑥	Ⓐ	Ⓐ E	⑥	Ⓐ	Ⓐ	⑥	⑥ F	Ⓐ F	Ⓐ	⑥	Ⓐ	⑥	⑥ E	Ⓐ G	Ⓐ	⑥	⚒	⚒ H	①–④	⑤	⑥
London Kings Cross ... d.	1633	1700	1700	1703	1718	1730	1730	1733	1733	1748	1800	1800	1803	1803	1818	1818	1830	1830	1833	1833	1900	1900	1903	1906	1930	1930	1930
Stevenage ..... d.	1655	|	|	|	|	|	|	1755	1755	|	|	|	|	|	|	|	|	|	1855	1855	|	|	|	1928	|	|	|
Peterborough ..... d.	|	|	|	1751	1809	1818	1819	|	|	1838	|	|	1851	1855**f**	1909	1910	1918	1918	|	|	|	|	1951	1959	2018	2018	2018
Grantham ..... d.	1741	|	|	|	1829	|	|	1842	1842	1906	|	|	|	|	1928	1929	|	|	1942	1942	|	|	|	2020	|	|	|
Newark North Gate ..... d.	|	|	|	|	1842	1847	1847	|	|	|	|	|	1922	1924	|	|	1947	1948	|	|	|	|	|	2034	2046	2046	2046
Retford ..... d.	1804	|	|	|	|	|	|	|	|	1929	|	|	|	|	|	1952	|	|	2006	2005	|	|	|	...	|	|	|
Doncaster ..... d.	1819	|	|	1843	1909**c**	|	|	1916	1916	1945	|	|	1950	1950	|	2007	2016	2014	2022	2022	|	|	2042	...	2110	2110	2112
Wakefield Westgate .. a.	1836	|	|	1900	...	|	|	1932	1932	2001	|	|	2006	2006	|	2023	|	|	2039	2038	|	|	2059	...	|	|	|
Leeds ..... a.	1853	|	|	1917	...	|	|	1947	1949	2017	|	|	2020	2021	|	2041	|	|	2054	2053	|	|	2116	...	|	|	|
York ..... d.	...	1855**f**	1853**f**	...	...	1930	1930	...	...	...	1952	1953	...	...	2019	...	2039	2037	...	...	2057	2054**f**	...	...	2133	2133	2135
Northallerton ..... d.	...	|	|	...	...	|	|	...	...	...	|	|	...	...	2038	...	|	2056	...	...	|	|	...	...	2153	2153	2155
Darlington ..... d.	...	1926	1922	...	...	1959	1959	...	...	...	2022	2023	...	...	2052	...	2108	2110	...	...	2126	2123	...	...	2207	2207	2209
Durham ..... d.	...	|	|	...	...	2017	2016	...	...	...	|	|	...	...	2110	...	2125	2128	...	...	|	|	...	...	2224	2224	2226
Newcastle ..... a.	...	1952	1949**r**	...	...	2030	2029**r**	...	...	...	2048	2050	...	...	2125	...	2138	2143	...	...	2153	2152	...	...	2239	2239	2241
Alnmouth ..... a.	...	|	|	...	...	|	2100	...	...	...	|	2123	...	...	...	...	2210	...	...	...	|	...	...	...	...	2309	...
Berwick upon Tweed .... a.	...	2038	2036	...	...	|	|	...	...	...	2134	2147	...	...	...	...	|	...	...	...	2238	...	...	...	...	2333	...
Edinburgh Waverley ... a.	...	2122	2121	...	...	2158	2210	...	...	...	2219	2238	...	...	...	...	2318	...	...	...	2331	...	...	...	...	0028	...

A – To Aberdeen (Table **222**).
B – To Inverness (Table **224**).
C – To Glasgow Central (Table **220**).
D – To Hull (Table **181**).
E – To Harrogate (Table **175**).
F – To Skipton (Table **173**).
G – To Bradford Forster Square (Table **182**).
H – To Lincoln (Table **189**).

J – To Sunderland (a. 2323).
K – To Stirling (Table **222**).

a – Arrives 1109 on ⑥.
b – Departs 1800.
c – Arrives 1904 on ⑥.
d – Arrives 4–5 minutes earlier on Ⓐ.
e – Arrives 1509 on ⑥.

f – Arrives 3–6 minutes earlier.
g – Departs 6–8 minutes later.
h – Arrives 0839 on ⑥.
j – Departs 1559.
p – Arrives 1519 on Ⓐ.
r – Departs 4–5 minutes later.
s – Calls to set down only.
t – Arrives 8 minutes earlier.

180 LONDON - LEEDS, YORK, NEWCASTLE and EDINBURGH

Most services convey 🍷 GR

For additional services see Tables **124, 181, 182, 183, 185** and **188**.

	⚒	Ⓐ	⑥	Ⓐ	⑥	⑥	Ⓐ	⑥	Ⓐ	Ⓐ	⑥	Ⓐ	Ⓐ	Ⓐ		⑦	⑦	⑦	⑦	⑦	⑦	⑦	⑦	⑦	⑦	⑦
		J																							A	
London Kings Cross d.	1933	2000	2000	2003	2003	2030	2033	2100	2100	2133	2200	2200	2300	2333	⑦	...	...	...	...	0848	0900	0903	0922	0930	1000	1003
Stevenage d.	1955	|	|	|	|	|	2055	|	2122	2156	|	|	|	|		...	...	...	...	|	|	0925	|	|	|	|
Peterborough d.	|	|	2048	2052	2052	2118	2126	2148	2153	2228	2248	2249	2344s	0016s		...	...	...	...	|	|	0955	1010	1018	|	1051
Grantham d.	2041	|	|	|	2112	2138	2145	|	|	2248	2307	2309	0013s	0045s		...	...	...	...	|	|	1014	|	|	|	|
Newark North Gate d.	|	|	2116	2120	|	2151	2158	|	2221	2302	2320	2323	0025s	0057s		...	...	...	...	|	|	1027	|	|	|	|
Retford d.	|	|	|	|	|	2207	|	|	|	2317	2334	|	|	|		...	...	...	...	|	|	|	|	1056	|	|
Doncaster d.	2114	|	2140	2145	2145	2223	2223	|	2249f	2337	2350	2352	0058s	0124s		...	...	...	0937	|	|	1052	1058	1111	|	1143f
Wakefield Westgate a.	2130	|	|	2205	2205	2240	2239	|	|	2354	0006	|	|	|		...	...	...	|	|	|	1108	1121	|	|	|
Leeds a.	2147	|	|	2221	2221	2257	2257	|	|	0010	0022	|	|	0236		...	...	0830	|	|	|	1126	|	|	|	|
York d.	...	2153f	2205	...	...	...	...	2257	2312	...	...	0041	0134	...		...	...	0900f	1000	1037	1050	...	1153	1134	1155t	1208f
Northallerton d.	...	|	|	...	...	...	...	2318	2343	...	...	0109s	...	...		...	...	0921	|	|	|	...	|	|	|	|
Darlington d.	...	2223	2234	...	...	...	...	2332	2357	...	...	0123s	...	...		...	...	0935	1029	1106	1119	...	|	1203	1224	1239
Durham d.	...	2241	2251	...	...	...	...	2350	0014	...	...	0142s	...	...		...	...	0954	1046	1124	|	...	1211	1221	|	1256
Newcastle a.	...	2254	2306	...	...	...	...	0005	0043	...	...	0215	...	...		0845	0915	1009	1059	1137	1145g	...	1226	1234r	1251	1310r
Alnmouth a.	...	...	...	...	...	...	...	...	...	...	...	...	...	...		0914	|	1042	|	|	|	...	...	1303	|	|
Berwick upon Tweed a.	...	...	...	...	...	...	...	...	...	...	...	...	...	...		0938	0957	1106	1144	|	1234	...	...	|	1337	|
Edinburgh Waverley a.	...	...	...	...	...	...	...	...	...	...	...	...	...	...		1028	1045	1158	1229	1308	1319	...	...	1418	1420	1438

	⑦	⑦	⑦	⑦	⑦	⑦	⑦		⑦	⑦	⑦	⑦	⑦	⑦	⑦	⑦	⑦	⑦	⑦	⑦	⑦	⑦	⑦	⑦	⑦	⑦
							B										A								C	
London Kings Cross d.	1007	1030	1100	1103	1122	1130	1200	...	1203	1222	1230	1233	1300	1303	1330	1333	1400	1403	1430	1500	1503	1530	1600	1605	1630	1635
Stevenage d.	|	|	|	1125	|	|	|	...	|	|	|	1256	|	1325	|	1355	|	|	|	|	1525	|	|	|	|	1657
Peterborough d.	1057	1118	|	1155	|	1218	|	...	1251	1311	1318	|	|	1355	1418	1426	|	1452	1518	|	1555	1618	|	1653	1718	|
Grantham d.	1116	|	|	1214	1224	|	|	...	1310	|	|	1342	|	1415	|	1452f	|	1511	|	|	1614	1638	|	1712	|	1741
Newark North Gate d.	1130	1146	|	1227	|	|	|	...	1323	|	1346	|	|	1428	|	|	|	1524	1546	|	1627	|	|	1726	1746	|
Retford d.	|	|	|	|	|	1256	|	...	|	|	|	|	|	|	1456	1520	|	|	|	|	1642	|	|	|	|	1804
Doncaster d.	1155	1210	|	1252	|	1311	|	...	1348	1359	1410	1420	|	1454	1511	1536	|	1550	1610	|	1658	1712	|	1752	1810	1821
Wakefield Westgate a.	1211	|	|	1308	|	|	|	...	1404	|	|	1436	|	1510	|	1559	|	1606	|	|	1714	|	|	1808	|	1837
Leeds a.	1228	|	|	1326	|	|	|	...	1420	|	|	1454	|	1526	|	1617	|	1623	|	|	1730	|	|	1826	|	1855
York d.	...	1235f	1251f	...	1315	1334	1350	...	...	1423f	1433	...	1453f	...	1534	...	1553f	...	1633	1652f	...	1735	1749	...	1835	...
Northallerton d.	...	1255	|	...	1334	|	|	...	...	|	1453	...	|	...	|	...	|	...	1654	|	...	|	|	...	1855	...
Darlington d.	...	1309	1320	...	1348	1403	1419	...	...	1452	1507	...	1522	...	1603	...	1622	...	1707	1721	...	1804	1818	...	1909	...
Durham d.	...	1326	|	...	1406	1421	|	...	...	1509	1524	...	|	...	1621	...	|	...	1724	|	...	1822	|	...	1926	...
Newcastle a.	...	1339	1346	...	1419g	1434g	1446r	...	...	1524	1537g	...	1549	...	1634r	...	1648r	...	1739r	1747	...	1835	1845r	...	1939	...
Alnmouth a.	...	|	|	...	|	1505	|	...	...	...	|	...	|	...	1703	...	|	...	|	|	...	1904	|	...	|	...
Berwick upon Tweed a.	...	|	1431	...	|	|	1534	...	...	...	|	...	1636	...	|	...	1735	...	|	1833	...	|	1932	...	|	...
Edinburgh Waverley a.	...	1508	1516	...	1558	1609	1618	...	...	...	1708	...	1720	...	1808	...	1818	...	1908	1918	...	2009	2019	...	2112	...

	⑦	⑦	⑦	⑦	⑦	⑦	⑦	⑦	⑦		⑦	⑦	⑦	⑦	⑦	⑦	⑦	⑦	⑦	⑦	⑦	⑦	⑦		⑦	⑦
			D				E				F			H												
London Kings Cross d.	1700	1705	1722	1730	1735	1800	1803	1827	1830	...	1835	1900	1903	1906	1930	1935	2000	2005	2035	2100	2105	2135	2200	...	2205	2235
Stevenage d.	|	|	|	|	1757	|	|	|	|	...	1857	|	|	1928	|	1957	|	|	2057	|	|	2157	|	...	|	|
Peterborough d.	|	1753	|	1818	|	1848	1852	|	|	...	|	|	1951	2001	2018	2027	2048	2053	2127	2148	2153	2227	2248	...	2253	2325s
Grantham d.	|	|	1826	1837	1843	|	|	|	|	...	1941	|	|	2022	|	2047	|	|	2146	|	|	2248	|	...	2312	2346s
Newark North Gate d.	|	1821	1839	|	|	|	1921	|	1946	...	|	|	2019	2036	2047	|	|	|	2159	|	2221	2301	|	...	2325	2358s
Retford d.	|	|	|	|	|	|	|	|	|	...	2004	|	|	...	|	|	|	2132	|	|	|	2317	|	...	|	|
Doncaster d.	|	1845	1903	1912	1918	|	1950	|	2010	...	2020	|	2044	...	2116f	2121	|	2148	2224	|	2250	2337	2343	...	2354	0028s
Wakefield Westgate a.	|	1903	...	|	1934	|	2006	|	|	...	2038	|	2102	...	|	2137	|	2205	2240	|	2308	2357	|	...	|	|
Leeds a.	|	1921	...	|	1950	|	2021	|	|	...	2052	|	2119	...	|	2154	|	2221	2258	|	2326	0014	|	...	|	0133
York d.	1850	...	...	1937f	...	1959f	...	2024f	2036f	...	...	2052f	...	...	2139	...	2156	...	...	2302f	...	...	0012f	...	0019	...
Northallerton d.	|	...	...	|	...	|	...	|	2056	...	...	|	...	...	|	...	2230	...	...	2337	...	...	0045s	...	...	...
Darlington d.	1919	...	...	2007	...	2028	...	2055	2110	...	...	2122	...	...	2220	...	2243	...	...	2350	...	...	0059s	...	...	...
Durham d.	|	...	...	2025	...	|	...	2112	2127	...	...	|	...	...	2238	...	2301	...	...	0007	...	...	0117s	...	...	...
Newcastle a.	1946r	...	...	2038	...	2055r	...	2127	2140r	...	...	2150	...	...	2309	...	2332	...	...	0038	...	...	0150	...	...	...
Alnmouth a.	|	...	...	2110	...	|	...	...	|	...	...	2223	...	...	...	...	...	...	...	...	...	...	...	...	...	...
Berwick upon Tweed a.	2034	...	...	|	...	2143	...	...	2227	...	...	2247	...	...	...	...	...	...	...	...	...	...	...	...	...	...
Edinburgh Waverley a.	2119	...	...	2215	...	2227	...	...	2312	...	...	2338	...	...	...	...	...	...	...	...	...	...	...	...	...	...

		⑥	Ⓐ	⚒	Ⓐ	⑥	⚒	⚒	⚒	Ⓐ	⑥	⚒	Ⓐ	⑥	Ⓐ	⑥	⚒	Ⓐ	⑥	Ⓐ	Ⓐ	⑥	Ⓐ	⑥	Ⓐ	Ⓐ
												G	J		H	H						D	D	F	F	
Edinburgh Waverley d.	⚒	...	...	...	...	...	...	...	...	...	...	...	...	...	...	...	...	...	...	...	0540	...	...	...	...	...
Berwick upon Tweed d.		...	...	...	...	...	...	...	...	...	...	...	...	...	...	...	...	...	...	0600	|	...	...	...	...	...
Alnmouth d.		...	...	...	...	...	...	...	...	...	...	...	...	...	...	...	...	...	...	0621	|	...	...	...	...	...
Newcastle d.		...	...	...	...	...	0444	...	0526	...	...	...	0558	0559	...	...	...	0630	0630	0655	0705	...	...	...	...	...
Durham d.		...	...	...	...	...	0459	...	0539	...	...	...	0612	0612	...	...	...	0644	0643	0708	|	...	...	...	...	←
Darlington d.		...	...	...	...	...	0517	...	0558	...	...	...	0631	0632	...	...	...	0703	0702	0732f	|	...	...	...	...	0732
Northallerton d.		...	...	...	...	...	0528	...	0609	...	...	...	|	|	...	...	...	0715	0714	→	|	...	...	...	...	|
York d.		0440	0440	...	...	...	0559	...	0631	...	...	...	0701	0701	...	...	...	0737	0739f	...	|	...	...	...	...	0802
Leeds d.		|	|	0505	0530	0530	|	0605	|	0640	0640	0700	|	|	...	...	0715	|	|	...	|	...	...	0738	0740	|
Wakefield Westgate d.		|	|	0518	0543	0543	|	0618	|	0653	0653	0713	|	|	...	...	0728	|	|	...	|	...	...	|	0753	|
Doncaster d.		0507	0507	0537	0602	0603	0622	0637	0654	0714	0714	|	|	|	...	...	0747	|	|	...	|	0758	0758	0810	0814	|
Retford d.		|	|	0551	|	|	|	0651	|	|	|	|	|	|	...	...	|	|	|	...	|	|	|	|	|	0835
Newark North Gate d.		0535	0536	0606	0626	0627	0646	0706	|	0737	0737	|	|	|	0758	0757	|	|	|	...	|	0825	0824	0833	0839	|
Grantham d.		0548	0549	0618	0638	0640	0658	0718	0726	|	|	|	|	|	|	|	0818	|	|	...	|	0838	0836	|	|	|
Peterborough d.		0610	0610	0639	0700	0703	0719	0740	0749	|	|	|	0812	0820t	0829	0830	|	0844	0850	...	|	0900	|	0903	0908	|
Stevenage d.		|	|	|	|	|	|	|	|	|	|	|	|	|	0859	0859	0904	|	|	...	|	|	|	|	|	|
London Kings Cross a.		0700	0701	0730	0749	0753	0810	0831	0840	0851	0853	0901	0909	0910	0926	0923	0931	0937	0940	...	0940	0949	0953	0955	1000	1003

	⚒	⑥	Ⓐ	⑥	Ⓐ	⚒	⚒	⑥	Ⓐ	⚒	Ⓐ	⑥	Ⓐ	⑥	Ⓐ	⑥	Ⓐ	⑥	Ⓐ	⑥	⚒	⑥	Ⓐ	⚒	⑥	Ⓐ
	E				K												C	C								
Edinburgh Waverley d.	...	0548	0548	0626	0626	...	...	0655	0656	0730	...	...	...	...	...	...	0800	0800	0830	0830	...	...	...	...	0900	0900
Berwick upon Tweed d.	...	0634	0634	0709	0710	...	...	|	|	0812	...	...	...	...	...	...	|	|	0912	0912	...	...	...	...	|	|
Alnmouth d.	...	0655	0655	|	|	...	...	|	|	|	...	...	...	...	...	...	0900	0901	|	|	...	...	...	...	|	|
Newcastle d.	...	0727	0729	0756f	0757f	...	...	0825	0825	0858	...	...	...	...	...	...	0929	0930	0958	0959	...	...	...	...	1026	1026
Durham d.	...	0740	0742	|	|	...	...	0838	0838	|	...	...	...	...	...	...	0942	0943	|	|	...	...	...	...	1039	1039
Darlington d.	...	0759	0801	0825	0827	...	...	0857	0857	0927	...	...	...	...	...	...	1001	1002	1028	1029	...	...	...	...	1058	1057
Northallerton d.	...	|	|	|	|	...	...	0908	0908	|	...	...	...	...	...	...	|	|	|	|	...	...	...	...	1110	1109
York d.	...	0830f	0831	0856	0857	...	...	0930	0930	0957	...	...	1002	1004	...	...	1032	1031	1057	1059	...	...	...	...	1132	1131
Leeds d.	0815	|	|	|	|	0845	0915	|	|	|	0945	0945	|	|	1015	1015	|	|	|	|	1045	...	...	1115	|	|
Wakefield Westgate d.	0830	|	|	|	|	0858	0929	|	|	|	0958	0958	|	|	1028	1028	|	|	|	|	1058	...	...	1128	|	|
Doncaster d.	0849	0853	0856	|	|	0919f	0948	0956f	0953	|	1018	1018	1025	1032f	1047	1049f	1057	1057f	|	|	1119f	...	...	1147	1155	1155
Retford d.	|	|	|	|	|	|	|	|	|	|	|	|	1039	1047	|	|	|	|	|	|	|	...	...	|	|	|
Newark North Gate d.	|	0918	0920	|	|	|	|	1020	1018	|	|	|	1055	1102	|	|	1121	1121	|	|	|	1154	1156	|	1218	1218
Grantham d.	0921	|	|	|	|	|	1019	|	|	|	|	|	1107	1114	1118	1121	|	|	|	|	|	1206	1208	1218	|	|
Peterborough d.	|	0950f	0950	|	|	1009	|	1049	1049	|	1110	1110	1129	1136	|	|	1150	1151	|	|	1210	1230	1230	|	1247	1247
Stevenage d.	1006	|	|	|	|	|	1104	|	|	|	|	|	1158	1205	1203	1208	|	|	|	|	|	1259	1259	1304	|	|
London Kings Cross a.	1031	1039	1040	1049	1049	1101	1132	1139	1139	1149	1159	1203	1222	1230	1230	1233	1240	1246	1249	1252	1301	1323	1323	1331	1339	1339

A – To/from Aberdeen (Table **222**).
B – To/from Inverness (Table **224**).
C – To/from Glasgow Central (Table **220**).
D – To/from Hull (Table **181**).
E – To/from Harrogate (Table **175**).

F – To/from Skipton (Table **173**).
G – From Bradford Forster Square (Table **182**).
H – To/from Lincoln (Table **189**).
J – From Sunderland (d. 0540).
K – From Stirling (Table **222**).

f – Arrives 3–6 minutes earlier.
g – Departs 6–8 minutes later.
r – Departs 4–5 minutes later.
s – Calls to set down only.
t – Arrives 0810.

GR Most services convey 🍷 EDINBURGH - NEWCASTLE - YORK and LEEDS - LONDON 180

For additional services see Tables **124, 181, 182, 183, 185** and **188**.

	⚒	⚒	⚒	⚒	⑥	Ⓐ	⚒A	⚒	⚒	⚒	⑥	Ⓐ	ⒶB	⑥B	⚒	Ⓐ	⚒	⑥	⑥	Ⓐ	⑥	⚒A	⚒	⑥	Ⓐ	⚒
Edinburgh Waverley . d.	0930	...	...	...	1000	1000	1030	...	...	...	1100	...	1130	1130	...	...	...	...	...	1200	1200	1230	...	...	...	...
Berwick upon Tweed.. d.	1012	...	...	...	|	|	1113	...	...	...	|	...	|	|	...	...	...	...	...	|	|	1312	...	...	...	...
Alnmouth .... d.	|	...	...	...	1100	1100	|	...	...	...	|	...	|	|	...	...	...	...	...	1300	1300	|	...	...	...	...
Newcastle .... d.	1058	...	...	...	1129	1129	1159	...	...	...	1225	1225	1256	1256	...	...	...	...	...	1329	1329	1359	...	...	...	...
Durham .... d.	|	...	...	...	1142	1142	|	...	...	...	1238	1238	|	|	...	...	...	...	...	1342	1342	|	...	...	...	...
Darlington .... d.	1127	...	...	...	1201	1202	1229	...	...	...	1257	1257	1326	1325	...	...	...	...	...	1401	1401	1428	...	...	...	...
Northallerton .... d.	|	...	...	...	|	|	|	...	...	...	1309	1308	|	|	...	...	...	...	...	|	|	|	...	...	...	...
York .... d.	1158f	...	1202	...	1231	1232	1258	...	...	...	1331	1330	1358f	1357	...	1402	...	...	1405	1432	1431	1458	...	...	...	...
Leeds .... d.	|	1145	|	1215	|	|	|	1245	...	1315	|	|	|	|	1345	|	1415	1415	|	|	|	|	1445	...	...	1515
Wakefield Westgate d.	|	1158	|	1228	|	|	|	1258	...	1328	|	|	|	|	1358	|	1428	1428	|	|	|	|	1458	...	...	1528
Doncaster .... d.	|	1218	1225	1247	1255	1257	|	1318	...	1347	1354	1355	|	|	1418	1426	1447	1447	1430	1456	1454	|	1519f	...	...	1547
Retford .... d.	|	|	1240	|	|	|	|	|	...	|	|	|	|	|	|	1441	|	|	1445	|	|	|	|	...	...	|
Newark North Gate .... d.	|	|	1255	|	1319	1321	|	|	1354	|	1418	1419	|	|	|	1456	|	|	1500	1520	1518	|	|	1554	1556	|
Grantham .... d.	|	|	1307	1318	|	|	|	|	1406	1418	|	|	|	|	|	1508	1518	1519	1512	|	|	|	|	1606	1608	1618
Peterborough .... d.	|	1310	1330	|	1350f	1350	|	1410	1430	|	1448	1449	|	|	1510	1530	|	|	1534	1549	1551f	|	1610	1630f	1629	|
Stevenage .... d.	|	|	1359	1404	|	|	|	|	1459	1504	|	|	|	|	|	1559	1604	1607	1603	|	|	|	|	1659	1659	1704
London Kings Cross . a.	1349	1401	1423	1431	1439	1439	1451	1501	1523	1531	1539	1540	1549	1550	1601	1623	1633	1633	1630	1639	1646	1652	1701	1723	1723	1731

	⑥	Ⓐ	⑥	Ⓐ	⚒	⑥	Ⓐ	Ⓐ	⑥	Ⓐ	⑥	Ⓐ	⑥	Ⓐ	⑥	⚒	⚒	⑥	Ⓐ	⑥	Ⓐ	⚒	⚒	Ⓐ	⑥	Ⓐ
Edinburgh Waverley . d.	1300	1300	1330	1330	...	...	...	...	...	1400	1400	1430	1430	...	...	...	...	1500	...	1530	1530	...	...	...	...	1600
Berwick upon Tweed.. d.	|	|	1411	1412	...	...	...	...	...	|	|	1512	1511	...	...	...	...	|	...	1612	1612	...	...	...	...	|
Alnmouth .... d.	|	|	|	|	...	...	...	...	...	1500	1500	|	|	...	...	...	...	|	...	|	|	...	...	...	...	|
Newcastle .... d.	1425	1425	1459f	1459f	...	...	...	...	...	1533	1532	1559f	1557	...	...	...	...	1625	1625	1659f	1659f	...	...	...	...	1726f
Durham .... d.	1438	1438	|	|	...	...	...	...	...	1546	1545	|	|	...	...	...	...	1638	1638	|	|	...	...	...	...	1739
Darlington .... d.	1457	1457	1527	1527	...	...	...	...	...	1605	1604	1628	1626	...	...	...	...	1657	1657	1727	1727	...	...	...	...	1758
Northallerton .... d.	1509	1508	|	|	...	...	...	...	...	|	|	|	|	...	...	...	...	1709	1709	|	|	...	...	...	...	1809
York .... d.	1531	1531	1557	1559f	...	1602	1603	...	...	1635	1634	1658	1658f	...	...	...	...	1731	1731	1758f	1758f	...	1802	...	...	1831
Leeds .... d.	|	|	|	|	1545	|	|	1615	1615	|	|	|	|	1645	1645	...	1714	|	|	|	|	1745	|	1815	1815	|
Wakefield Westgate d.	|	|	|	|	1558	|	|	1628	1628	|	|	|	|	1658	1658	...	1727	|	|	|	|	1758	|	1828	1828	|
Doncaster .... d.	1554	1556	|	|	1617	1628	1626	1647	1649f	1658	1657	|	|	1718	1720f	...	1746	1755	1756f	|	|	1818	1825	1847	1847	1855
Retford .... d.	|	|	|	|	|	1643	1641	|	|	|	|	|	|	|	|	...	1800	|	|	|	|	|	1839	|	|	|
Newark North Gate .... d.	1618	1620	|	|	|	1658	1656	|	|	1721	1721	|	|	|	|	1754	|	1820	1820	|	|	|	1855	|	|	1919
Grantham .... d.	|	|	|	|	|	1710	1708	1719	1721	|	|	|	|	|	|	1806	1823	|	|	|	|	|	1907	1919	1919	|
Peterborough .... d.	1650f	1649	|	|	1710	1734	1730	|	|	1750	1751	|	|	1809	1810	1829	|	1851	1849	|	|	1910	1930	|	|	1951f
Stevenage .... d.	|	|	|	|	|	1803	1759	1805	1807	|	|	|	|	|	|	1859	1907	|	|	|	|	|	1959	2006	2004	2020
London Kings Cross . a.	1739	1740	1749	1751	1801	1829	1825	1831	1832	1839	1846	1849	1852	1901	1901	1923	1933	1946	1940	1949	1955	2001	2023	2031	2031	2046

	⑥	⚒	Ⓐ	⑥	⚒	Ⓐ	⑥	Ⓐ	⑥	ⒶA	⑥A	⑥	Ⓐ	⑥	Ⓐ	⑥	Ⓐ	⑥	ⒶA	⑤	⑦	⑦	⑦	⑦	⑦	⑦
Edinburgh Waverley . d.	1600	1630	...	...	...	1700	1700	...	...	1731	1731	...	...	1830	1830	1900	1936	2000	2100	2200		...	...	...	...	...
Berwick upon Tweed.. d.	|	1712	...	...	...	|	|	...	...	1818	1818	...	...	1912	1918	1945	2017	2046	2148	2246		...	...	...	...	...
Alnmouth .... d.	|	|	...	...	...	1800	1800	...	...	|	|	...	...	|	1942	2008	2040	2109	2211	2309		...	...	...	...	...
Newcastle .... d.	1725	1758	...	...	...	1829	1829	...	...	1905	1904	...	...	1957	2017	2043	2115f	2143	2245	2354		...	...	0754	...	...
Durham .... d.	1738	|	...	...	...	1842	1842	...	...	|	|	...	...	...	2030	2058	2129	...	2259	...		...	...	0808	...	...
Darlington .... d.	1757	1826	...	...	...	1901	1901	...	...	1934	1934	...	...	...	2049	2118	2148	...	2320	...		...	...	0827	...	...
Northallerton .... d.	1809	|	...	...	...	|	|	...	...	|	|	...	...	...	|	2131	2159	...	2346s	...		...	...	|	...	...
York .... d.	1831	1856f	...	...	...	1931	1931	...	...	2004	2003	...	...	...	2119	2155	2221	...	0016	...		0800	...	0858f	...	...
Leeds .... d.	|	|	1845	1845	1916	|	|	1945	1945	|	|	2015	2045	...	|	|	|	...	0045	...		|	0805	|	0843	0905
Wakefield Westgate d.	|	|	1858	1858	1929	|	|	1958	1958	|	|	2028	2058	...	|	|	|	...	...	...		|	0818	|	0856	0918
Doncaster .... d.	1856	|	1919	1923a	1948	1954	1954	2017	2017	2027	2027	2048	2117	...	2142	2221	2244	...	...	...		0823	0837	|	0920f	0938
Retford .... d.	|	|	|	|	|	|	|	|	|	|	|	2102	2132	...	|	...	|	...	...	...		|	0851	|	|	|
Newark North Gate .... d.	1920	|	|	|	|	2017	2019	|	|	|	|	2117	|	...	2205	...	2308	...	...	...		|	0907	|	|	1002
Grantham .... d.	|	|	|	|	2019	|	|	|	|	|	|	2129	2155	...	2217	...	2320	...	...	...		|	0919	|	|	1015
Peterborough .... d.	1951	|	2011	2014	|	2046	2051f	2105	2105	2116	2120f	2150	2216	...	2239	...	2347	...	...	...		0911	0942	1005	1011f	1036
Stevenage .... d.	2020	2029	|	|	2104	2115	2120	|	|	2145	2150	|	2245	...	2308	...	0028s	...	...	...		0940	|	|	|	1106
London Kings Cross . a.	2047	2053	2059	2109	2131	2139	2144	2159	2154	2210	2215	2239	2309	...	2332	...	0105	...	...	...		1006	1033	1054	1108	1133

	⑦	⑦	⑦	⑦	⑦	⑦	⑦	⑦	⑦	⑦	⑦	⑦	⑦	⑦	⑦	⑦	⑦	⑦	⑦	⑦	⑦	⑦A	⑦	⑦	⑦	⑦
Edinburgh Waverley . d.	...	...	...	...	...	...	...	...	0900	0930	...	1000	1030	...	1100	1120	1130	...	...	1200	1220	1230	...	...	1300	1319
Berwick upon Tweed.. d.	...	...	...	...	...	...	...	...	|	1013	...	|	1112	...	|	|	1212	...	...	|	|	1313	...	...	1343	|
Alnmouth .... d.	...	...	...	...	...	...	...	...	|	|	...	1100	|	...	|	|	|	...	...	1300	|	|	...	...	|	|
Newcastle .... d.	0825	0855	...	...	0925	1000	...	...	1028f	1059	...	1129	1158	...	1225	1251	1259	...	1315	1329	1350	1359	...	1420	1431f	1445
Durham .... d.	0838	0908	...	...	0938	|	...	...	1041	|	...	1142	|	...	1238	1305	|	...	1328	1342	1404	|	...	1433	|	1458
Darlington .... d.	0857	0928	...	...	0957	1028	...	...	1100	1128	...	1201	1227	...	1257	1324	1329	...	1349	1401	|	1430	...	1452	1500	1518
Northallerton .... d.	|	|	...	...	1008	|	...	...	1112	|	...	|	|	...	1310	|	|	...	1402	|	|	|	...	|	|	1532
York .... d.	0927	0957	...	...	1030	1058	...	...	1134	1158	...	1231	1256	...	1332	1356	1400	...	1424	1431	1450f	1459	...	1523	1530	1557
Leeds .... d.	|	|	0940	1005	|	|	1045	1105	|	|	1205	|	|	1305	|	|	|	1405	|	|	|	|	1505	|	|	|
Wakefield Westgate d.	|	|	0953	1018	|	|	1058	1118	|	|	1218	|	|	1318	|	|	|	1418	|	|	|	|	1518	|	|	|
Doncaster .... d.	|	|	|	1037	1053	|	1117	1139f	1157	|	1237	1254	|	1337	1355	|	|	1437	1448	1454	|	|	1537	1546	1553	|
Retford .... d.	|	|	1020	1052	|	|	1134	|	1211	|	|	|	|	|	1409	|	|	|	|	|	|	|	|	|	1608	|
Newark North Gate .... d.	1008	|	1040f	1107	1118	|	|	1203	|	|	1300	1318	|	1400	|	|	|	1500	|	1518	|	|	1600	1609	|	|
Grantham .... d.	1020	|	|	1120	|	|	|	1215	|	|	1312	|	|	1412	|	|	|	1512	|	|	1540	|	1612	|	|	|
Peterborough .... d.	1042	1104	1109	1142	1151f	1204	|	1239	1251	|	1334	1350f	|	1434	1451	|	|	1534	1538	1551f	|	|	1634	1642	1651	|
Stevenage .... d.	1111	|	|	|	|	|	|	1308	|	|	|	|	|	1503	|	|	|	|	|	|	|	|	1703	|	|	|
London Kings Cross . a.	1136	1153	1158	1233	1240	1253	1259	1333	1340	1349	1423	1439	1445	1527	1540	1547	1551	1623	1628	1640	1644	1650	1728	1736	1741	1748

	⑦B	⑦	⑦	⑦A	⑦	⑦	⑦	⑦	⑦	⑦	⑦E	⑦	⑦	⑦	⑦A	⑦	⑦	⑦	⑦	⑦	⑦	⑦	⑦	⑦	⑦	⑦
Edinburgh Waverley . d.	1330	...	1400	1430	...	...	...	1450	1500	1530	...	...	1600	1620	1630	...	...	1700	1730	...	1800	...	1830	1900	2000	2100
Berwick upon Tweed.. d.	1413	...	|	|	...	...	...	1533	|	1612	...	...	|	|	1713	...	...	|	1816	...	|	...	1913	1946	2047	2147
Alnmouth .... d.	|	...	1500	|	...	...	...	|	|	|	...	...	1700	|	|	...	...	|	|	...	1901	...	|	|	2110	2209
Newcastle .... d.	1459	...	1531	1556	...	1604	...	1620f	1627f	1701f	...	...	1729	1752f	1800f	...	...	1829f	1902	...	1930	...	2000f	2033f	2144	2238
Durham .... d.	|	...	1544	|	...	1617	...	1633	1640	|	...	...	1742	|	|	...	...	1842	|	...	1944	...	|	2046	2158	...
Darlington .... d.	1528	...	1603	|	...	1635	...	1652	1659	1729	...	...	1801	1821	1830	...	...	1901	1929	...	2003	...	2029	2105	2217	...
Northallerton .... d.	|	...	|	|	...	1647	...	|	|	|	...	...	|	1833	|	...	...	1913	|	...	|	...	|	|	2231	...
York .... d.	1601	...	1632	1659v	...	1710	...	1723	1730	1759	...	...	1831	1855	1901	...	...	1935	2000	...	2032	...	2100f	2135	2307f	...
Leeds .... d.	|	1616	|	|	1645	|	1716	|	|	|	1747	1815	|	|	|	1845	1916	|	|	1946	|	2045	|	|	2335	...
Wakefield Westgate d.	|	1629	|	|	1658	|	1729	|	|	|	1800	1828	|	|	|	1859	1929	|	|	1959	|	2058	|	|	...	...
Doncaster .... d.	|	1648	1656	|	1719	1736	1748	|	1757f	|	1818	1847	1855	|	|	1921	1948	1958	|	2020	2055	2117	2126f	2158	...	...
Retford .... d.	|	|	|	|	|	|	1802	|	|	|	|	|	|	|	|	|	2002	|	|	|	|	2131	|	|	...	...
Newark North Gate .... d.	|	|	1720	|	1744	|	|	1804	|	|	1844	|	1919	|	|	1946	|	2021	|	2045	2119	|	2150	2221	...	...
Grantham .... d.	|	1719	|	|	|	1807	1825	|	1831	|	|	1918	|	1944	|	|	2025	|	2049	|	|	2154	2202	2233	...	...
Peterborough .... d.	|	|	1751f	|	1814	|	|	1833	1852	|	1914	|	1951f	|	|	2015	|	2051	2110	2114	2150	2215	2224	2255	...	...
Stevenage .... d.	|	1804	|	|	|	|	1909	|	|	|	|	2003	|	|	|	|	2109	|	|	|	|	2244	2253	2333s	...	...
London Kings Cross . a.	1754	1828	1840	1850	1905	1918	1934	1922	1942	1947	2005	2027	2040	2048	2053	2107	2133	2140	2159	2207	2239	2310	2317	2359	...	...

A – From Aberdeen (Table **222**).
B – From Inverness (Table **224**).
E – From Harrogate (Table **175**).
a – Arrives 1915.
f – Arrives 4–6 minutes earlier.
s – Calls to set down only.
v – Arrives 1647.

First Excel service XL 🚌 PETERBOROUGH - KINGS LYNN 🚌 180a

From **Peterborough** railway station to **Kings Lynn** bus station: Journey 75 minutes. Buses call at **Wisbech** bus station ± 39 minutes later.

⚒: 0704, 0734, 0809, 0844 and every 30 minutes until 1844, 1944, 2044, 2249.

⑦: 0944, 1044 and hourly until 1944.

From **Kings Lynn** railway station to **Peterborough** bus station: Journey 80 minutes. Buses call at **Wisbech** bus station ± 32 minutes later.

⚒: 0532Ⓐ, 0602, 0632, 0702, 0732, 0802, 0832, 0902, 0932, 1007 and every 30 minutes until 1707, 1737**a**, 1807, 1907, 2007**a**, 2127.

⑦: 0807 and hourly until 1807, 1907**a**.

a – Terminates at Wisbech.

181 LONDON - HULL

All trains 🍸 HT

km		Ⓐ	Ⓐ	Ⓐ	Ⓐ	Ⓐ	Ⓐ	Ⓐ△	Ⓐ	Ⓐ	⑥	⑥	⑥	⑥	⑥	⑥	⑥△	⑥	⑥	⑦	⑦	⑦	⑦	⑦△	⑦	⑦
0	**London** Kings Cross **180** d.	Ⓐ	0726	0948	1148	1348	1548	1718	1848	2030	⑥	0727	0948	1147	...	1448	1718	1748	1948	⑦	1049	1248	1448	1722	1748	1952
170	Grantham **180** d.		0826	1050	1250	1450	1650	1829	1952	2130		0828	1049	1250	...	1550	1829	1850	2052		1149	1348	1549	1826	1852	2052
223	Retford **180** d.		0851	1111	1311	1513	1712	|	2013	2153		0851	1111	1311	...	1611	|	1912	2114		1211	1410	1610	|	1914	2114
251	Doncaster **180** a.		0906	1125	1325	1526	1725	1909	2027	2206		0904	1124	1325	...	1625	1904	1925	2127		1227	1423	1626	1903	1927	2127
280	Selby a.		0925	1140	1342	1543	1742	1926	2043	2225		0925	1141	1341	...	1641	1925	1942	2144		1244	1440	1646	1922	1944	2144
330	**Hull** a.		1006	1218	1417	1618	1817	2005	2118	2304		1005	1218	1417	...	1725	2005	2017	2219		1322	1518	1721	2004	2019	2221
330	**Hull** **177** d.		...	...	...	...	...	...	2128	...		...	...	...	...	...	...	2025	...		...	...	...	...	2026	...
343	Beverley **177** a.		...	...	...	...	...	...	2141	...		...	...	...	...	...	...	2038	...		...	...	...	...	2039	...

		Ⓐ	Ⓐ△	Ⓐ	Ⓐ		Ⓐ	Ⓐ	Ⓐ	Ⓐ		⑥	⑥△	⑥	⑥	⑥		⑥	⑥		⑦	⑦	⑦		⑦	⑦
Beverley **177** d.	Ⓐ	0604	...	...	...	...	...	...	...	...	⑥	0557	...	...	...	...	...	...	...	⑦	...	1052	...	...	...	...
Hull **177** a.		0618	...	...	...	...	...	...	...	...		0612	...	...	...	...	...	...	...		...	1105	...	...	...	...
Hull d.		0626	0700	0823	1033	...	1233	1512	1709	1912		0617	0700	0823	1033	1331	...	1531	1834		0907	1112	1436	...	1625	1847
Selby d.		0700	0734	0857	1107	...	1307	1548	1743	1947		0652	0734	0857	1107	1405	...	1605	1908		0941	1146	1510	...	1703	1921
Doncaster **180** d.		0722	0758	0924	1124	...	1325	1605	1802	2004		0710	0758	0927	1125	1425	...	1624	1928		0959	1204	1528	...	1727	1940
Retford **180** d.		0741	|	0939	1138	...	1339	1619	1816	2018		|	|	0941	1139	1439	...	1638	1942		1013	1218	1542	...	1741	1954
Grantham **180** d.		0803	0836	1001	1200	...	1400	1641	1837	2040		0740	0838	1002	1201	1501	...	1700	2004		1035	1239	1606	...	1802	2015
London Kings Cross **180** a.		0915	0953	1109	1308	...	1509	1746	1946	2148		0847	0949	1108	1307	1609	...	1809	2114		1139	1342	1714	...	1909	2118

△ – Operated by GR (Table **180**).

182 LONDON - BRADFORD

All trains 🍸 GC

km			Ⓐ	Ⓐ		Ⓐ	Ⓐ△	Ⓐ		⑥	⑥		⑥	⑥		⑥△		⑦	⑦	⑦		⑦	
0	**London** Kings Cross **180** d.	Ⓐ	1057	1448	...	1627	1833	1954	⑥	1048	1548	...	1627	1957	...	1933	⑦	1150	1550	1853	...	1922	...
251	Doncaster **180** a.		1227a	1623	...	1804	2020	2124		1222	1722	...	1805	2134	...	2113		1321	1722	2039	...	2100	...
278	Pontefract Monkhill a.		1258	1654	...	|	|	|		|	|	...	|	2203	...	|		|	|	|	...	|	...
292	Wakefield Kirkgate a.		1315	1711	...	1831	2040e	2151		1250	1747	...	1831	2221	...	2131e		1345	1751	2100	...	2124	...
306	Mirfield a.		1328	1726	...	1843	|	2203		1302	1759	...	1843	2233	...	|		1358	1803	2113	...	2139	...
313	Brighouse a.		1336	1735	...	1851	|	2211		1310	1809	...	1850	2241	...	|		1406	1811	2121	...	2146	...
322	Halifax **190** a.		1348	1747	...	1904	|	2226		1322	1822	...	1904	2253	...	|		1421	1825	2132	...	2158	...
335	**Bradford** Interchange **190** a.		1403	1801	...	1919	2129f	2241		1337	1838	...	1919	2308	...	2220f		1437	1840	2146	...	2213	...

		Ⓐ△	Ⓐ				Ⓐ	Ⓐ		⑥△	⑥		⑥	⑥		⑥		⑦	⑦		⑦		⑦
Bradford Interchange **190** d.	Ⓐ	0630f	0653	...	0756	...	1022	1451	⑥	0630f	0653	...	0852	1022	...	1522	⑦	0757	1205	...	1508	...	1559
Halifax **190** d.		|	0706	...	0809	...	1036	1505		|	0706	...	0905	1036	...	1535		0811	1219	...	1521	...	1612
Brighouse d.		|	0718	...	0824	...	1047	1517		|	0718	...	0916	1048	...	1548		0821	1230	...	1536	...	1622
Mirfield d.		|	0724	...	0832	...	1055	1524		|	0725	...	0924	1055	...	1556		0828	1239	...	1545	...	1630
Wakefield Kirkgate d.		0713e	0742	...	0855	...	1114	1539		0713e	0743	...	0940	1114	...	1614		0845	1256	...	1602	...	1644
Pontefract Monkhill d.		|	0800	...	|	...	1134	1555		|	0800	...	0957	1132	...	1635		|	|	...	|	...	|
Doncaster **180** d.		|	0831	...	0930	...	1204	1622		|	0832	...	1025	1204	...	1708		0911	1321	...	1627	...	1713
London Kings Cross **180** a.		0859	1009	...	1115	...	1344	1807		0901	1009	...	1158	1344	...	1847		1040	1454	...	1756	...	1845

a – Departs 1235. **e** – Wakefield Westgate. **f** – Bradford Forster Square. △ – Operated by GR (Table **180**).

183 LONDON - YORK - SUNDERLAND

All trains 🍸 GC

km			Ⓐ	Ⓐ	Ⓐ	Ⓐ	Ⓐ	Ⓐ△		⑥	⑥		⑥	⑥	⑥			⑦	⑦		⑦	⑦	
0	**London** Kings Cross **180** d.	Ⓐ	0806	1127	1257	1648	1927	2000	⑥	0806	1127	...	1318	1648	1927	...	⑦	0955	1348	...	1653	1822	...
303	**York** **180** d.		1007	1322	1451	1842	2122	2153		1008	1321	...	1514	1842	2123	...		1142	1538	...	1841	2012	...
339	Thirsk d.		1024	1338	1514	1859	2138	|		1025	1337	...	1537	1859	2139	...		1159	1555	...	1900	2029	...
351	Northallerton **180** d.		1032	1348	1527	1908	2147	|		1034	1347	...	1546	1910	2148	...		1207	1606	...	1911	2043	...
375	Eaglescliffe a.		1051	1404	1546	1926	2203	|		1051	1403	...	1602	1927	2205	...		1224	1626	...	1932	2101	...
399	Hartlepool a.		1115	1423	1613	1951	2226	|		1114	1423	...	1623	1957	2227	...		1244	1646	...	1955	2126	...
428	**Sunderland** a.		1140	1452	1638	2022	2252	2323		1138	1451	...	1651	2021	2251	...		1308	1710	...	2021	2151	...

		Ⓐ△	Ⓐ	Ⓐ	Ⓐ	Ⓐ	Ⓐ			⑥	⑥		⑥	⑥	⑥			⑦	⑦		⑦	⑦	
Sunderland d.	Ⓐ	0540	0642	0842	1229	1530	1730	...	⑥	0642	0828	...	1218	1529	1729	...	⑦	0923	1212	...	1412	1812	...
Hartlepool d.		|	0707	0908	1254	1554	1756	...		0709	0853	...	1242	1553	1754	...		0947	1236	...	1439	1840	...
Eaglescliffe d.		|	0729	0928	1314	1615	1817	...		0730	0916	...	1301	1613	1814	...		1007	1304	...	1506	1900	...
Northallerton **180** d.		|	0751	0950	1333	1633	1841	...		0748	0941	...	1320	1631	1832	...		1025	1324	...	1524	1920	...
Thirsk d.		|	0800	0959	1344	1643	1851	...		0757	0953	...	1329	1643	1843	...		1034	1333	...	1533	1929	...
York **180** d.		0701	0821	1027d	1406	1706	1912	...		0819	1012	...	1351	1706a	1902	...		1054	1352	...	1552	1951	...
London Kings Cross **180** a.		0909	1014	1232	1609	1907	2108	...		1018	1210	...	1544	1908	2059	...		1241	1541	...	1743	2141	...

a – Arrives 1659. **c** – Arrives 1204. **d** – Arrives 1016. △ – Operated by GR (Table **180**).

184 LINCOLN - NEWARK - NOTTINGHAM - LEICESTER

2nd class EM

km			ⒶN	Ⓐ	Ⓐ	ⒶP	ⒶS	Ⓐ	Ⓐ	Ⓐ	Ⓐ	Ⓐ	Ⓐ	Ⓐ	Ⓐ	Ⓐ	Ⓐ	Ⓐ	Ⓐ	Ⓐ	Ⓐ		⑥N	⑥	⑥P	⑥S	⑥	⑥
0	**Lincoln** d.	Ⓐ	0526	...	0646	0704	0736	0836	0937	1036	1140	1234	1337	1436	1536	1634	1726	1835	2031	2140	2226	⑥	0526	...	0704	0735	0835	0936
27	Newark Castle ♧ d.		0608	...	0714	0730	0806	0907	1007	1106	1206	1305	1407	1506	1607	1704	1756	1903	2058	2207	2254		0610	...	0729	0805	0904	1006
55	**Nottingham** ♧ a.		0647	...	0740	0756	0834	0930	1032	1132	1230	1332	1432	1532	1630	1731	1832	1932	2129	2239	2330		0648	...	0757	0830	0933	1032
55	**Nottingham** **170** d.		...	0730	...	0805	0836	0933	1035	1136	1235	1336	1436	1536	1632	1733	1836	1932	*2201*	*2310*	...		...	0733	0812	0836	0936	1035
68	East Mid. P'kway **170** d.		...	0744	...	|	0850	0947	1050	1150	1250	1350	1450	1550	1648	1749	1852	1948	*2216*	*2323*	...		...	0750	|	0850	0950	1050
79	Loughborough **170** d.		...	0756	...	0821	0858	0956	1058	1158	1258	1358	1458	1559	1657	1758	1900	1957	*2224*	*2331*	...		...	0758	0828	0858	0958	1058
99	**Leicester** **170** a.		...	0818	...	0831	0923	1022	1123	1223	1323	1423	1523	1623	1723	1823	1923	2023	*2250*	*2347*	...		...	0823	0837	0925	1023	1123

	⑥	⑥	⑥	⑥	⑥	⑥	⑥	⑥	⑥	⑥	⑥	⑥
Lincoln d.	1036	1140	1236	1337	1432	1526	1635	1726	1830	1939	2045	...
Newark Castle ♧ d.	1104	1204	1305	1405	1504	1559	1704	1754	1859	2004	2110	...
Nottingham ♧ a.	1132	1229	1331	1430	1530	1629	1732	1831	1926	2032	2137	...
Nottingham **170** d.	1135	1235	1335	1435	1534	1633	1733	1835	1936	*2105*	...	2305
East Mid. P'kway **170** d.	1149	1249	1349	1450	1549	1649	1748	1849	1950	*2117*	...	2318
Loughborough **170** d.	1158	1257	1357	1458	1558	1658	1757	1858	1958	*2125*	...	2326
Leicester **170** a.	1223	1323	1423	1523	1623	1723	1823	1923	2023	*2135*	...	2345

		Ⓐ	ⒶQ	Ⓐ	Ⓐ	Ⓐ	Ⓐ	Ⓐ	Ⓐ	Ⓐ	Ⓐ
Leicester **170** d.	Ⓐ	...	...	*0626*	0826	0930	1030	1130	1230	1330	1430
Loughborough **170** d.		...	...	*0648*	0851	0953	1153	1153	1253	1353	1453
East Mid. P'kway **170** d.		...	...	*0656*	0859	1005	1105	1203	1304	1403	1504
Nottingham **170** a.		...	...	*0716*	0923	1022	1122	1223	1321	1421	1521
Nottingham ♧ d.		0554	0653	0812	0925	1029	1129	1229	1329	1429	1529
Newark Castle ♧ d.		0630	0727	0840	0952	1051	1153	1253	1352	1453	1553
Lincoln a.		0704	0756	0908	1017	1130	1223	1325	1425	1524	1625

	ⒶS	Ⓐ	Ⓐ	Ⓐ	Ⓐ	ⒶP	Ⓐ	ⒶN	Ⓐ		⑥	⑥Q	⑥	⑥	⑥	⑥	⑥		⑥	⑥	⑥	⑥	⑥	⑥	⑥P	⑥	⑥N	⑥
Leicester **170** d.	1530	1630	...	1727	1826	1921	2030	...	2130	⑥	...	...	*0626*	0826	0926	1026	1126	...	1226	1326	1426	1526	1626	1726	1824	1926	2026	2126
Loughborough **170** d.	1553	1653	...	1751	1848	|	2053	...	2153		...	...	*0648*	0848	0948	1048	1148	...	1248	1348	1448	1548	1648	1748	1833	1948	2048	2148
East Mid. P'kway **170** d.	1602	1702	...	1759	1856	1937	2102	...	2203		...	...	*0656*	0856	0956	1056	1156	...	1256	1356	1456	1556	1656	1756	|	1956	2056	2156
Nottingham **170** a.	1621	1721	...	1815	1913	1953	2119	...	2224		...	...	*0715*	0911	1014	1114	1214	...	1314	1414	1514	1614	1714	1814	1854	2013	2114	2215
Nottingham ♧ d.	1627	1721	1750	1817	1919	2000	2120	2226	...		0555	0650	0811	0922	1029	1129	1229	...	1329	1419	1528	1621	1729	1817	1929	2030	2124	...
Newark Castle ♧ d.	1653	1752	1818	1853	1954	2024	2153	2257	...		0630	0726	0842	0951	1051	1155	1253	...	1351	1442	1554	1643	1750	1843	1953	2104	2157	...
Lincoln a.	1719	1826	1851	1924	2023	2052	2222	2340	...		0703	0758	0909	1020	1127	1228	1324	...	1425	1513	1627	1710	1825	1925	2026	2133	2242	...

		⑦N	⑦	⑦	⑦	⑦	⑦	⑦N	⑦	⑦	⑦	⑦	⑦	⑦N	⑦
Lincoln d.	⑦	0847	0959	1110	1156	1301	1417	1508	1615	1656	1805	1903	2005	2100	2210
Newark Castle d.		0929	1024	1142	1224	1329	1448	1550	1646	1724	1834	1933	2035	2140	2238
Nottingham a.		1008	1053	1221	1257	1357	1527	1620	1726	1753	1911	2005	2102	2209	2315

		⑦	⑦	⑦	⑦	⑦	⑦	⑦a	⑦b	⑦	⑦	⑦N	⑦	⑦	⑦N
Nottingham d.	⑦	0930	1030	1130	1230	1330	1435	1529	1530	1633	1727	1836	1935	2039	2228
Newark Castle d.		1006	1055	1206	1254	1354	1513	1556	1559	1659	1801	1902	1958	2103	2303
Lincoln a.		1040	1124	1241	1325	1424	1550	1626	1626	1731	1833	1957	2030	2135	2348

♧ – Additional journeys Newark Castle - Nottingham and v.v. Journey time: 28 – 36 minutes.
From Newark Castle at 0642Ⓐ, 0739Ⓐ, 0741⑥, 0841Ⓐ, 0843⑥, 0938⚒, 1047⚒, 1139⚒, 1247⚒, 1347Ⓐ, 1349⑥, 1439⚒, 1547⚒, 1638⚒, 1739⚒, 1847⑥, 1947⚒.
From Nottingham at 0756Ⓐ, 0758⑥, 0851Ⓐ, 0854⑥, 0949⚒, 1047Ⓐ, 1054⑥, 1151Ⓐ, 1153⑥, 1249⚒, 1348⚒, 1450⚒, 1549Ⓐ, 1551⑥, 1648⑥, 1650Ⓐ, 1747⑥, 1851Ⓐ, 1857⑥.

N – Via Newark North Gate (Table **189**).
P – 12 🍸 Lincoln - London St Pancras and v.v. (Table **170**).
Q – To Peterborough (Table **186**).
S – From/to Sleaford (Table **186**).
a – Until Sept. 8; to Grimsby Town (Table **189**).
b – From Sept. 15.

KINGS LYNN, CAMBRIDGE and PETERBOROUGH - LONDON - GATWICK - BRIGHTON 185

KINGS LYNN - CAMBRIDGE - LONDON

km			Ⓐ	⑥	⑥	Ⓐ	Ⓐ	Ⓐ	⑥	Ⓐ	⑥	Ⓐ	Ⓐ	⑥	Ⓐ	⑥	Ⓐ	Ⓐ	Ⓐ	⑥	Ⓐ	⑥	Ⓐ	⚒	⑥
0	**Kings Lynn** d.	⚒	0443	...	...	...	0517	0540	0544	0609	...	0618	0640	0644	...	...	0705	0716	...	0744	0748	...	0812	0844	0913
14	Downham Market d.		0457	...	...	...	0531	0554	0558	0624	...	0632	0654	0658	...	...	0719	0728	...	0758	0803	...	0826	0858	0925
42	Ely **207 208** d.		0515	0512	0547	...	0550	0612	0617	0642	0647	0650	0712	0717	0730	0747	0741	0746	0800	0817	0825	0847	0845	0917	0947
62	Cambridge North .. **207** d.		0530	0526	0600	...	0604	0627	0632	0655	0701	0704	|	0732	0742	0801	|	0758	0814	0832	0840	0901	0900	0931	1001
66	**Cambridge** **207 208** a.		0534	0531	0605	...	0610	0634	0637	0700	0706	0710	0730	0736	0747	0805	0759	0803	0820	0837	0844	0905	0904	0937	1005
66	**Cambridge** d.		0540	0537	0614	0610	0618	0640	0644	0709	0714	0717	0739	0744	0751	0814	0809	0809	0821	0844	0849	0914	0910	0941	1014
15	Stevenage d.		|	|	|	|	|	|	|	|	|	|	|	|	|	|	|	|	|	|	|	|	|	|	|
59	**London** Kings Cross .. a.		0632	0633	0703	0702	0725**d**	0733	0732	0802	0803	0825**d**	0834	0833	0921**d**	0903	0904	0904	0950**d**	0933	0946	1005	1005	1035	1104

	Ⓐ	⚒	Ⓐ	⑥	⚒	⚒	⚒		⚒	⚒	Ⓐ	⑥	⚒	⑥	Ⓐ	⚒	⑥	Ⓐ	Ⓐ	⑥	⚒	⚒	⚒	⚒
ngs Lynn d.	0910	0944	...	1013	1044	...	1144	and at	...	1544	...	...	1644	...	1715	1744	...	...	1840	1844	...	1944	...	2044
›wnham Market d.	0928**b**	0958	...	1025	1058	...	1158	the same	...	1558	...	...	1658	...	1729	1758	...	...	1854	1858	...	1958	...	2058
y **207 208** d.	0948	1017	1047	1047	1117	1147	1217	minutes	1545	1617	1647	1647	1717	1747	1746	1817	1847	1857	1917	1917	1947	2017	2047	2117
ambridge North .. **207** d.	1003	1031	1101	1101	1131	1201	1231	past each	1600	1631	1701	1701	1731	1801	|	1832	1901	1909	1932	1932	2001	2032	2101	2131
ambridge **207 208** a.	1007	1037	1105	1105	1137	1205	1237	hour	1605	1637	1705	1705	1737	1806	1802	1837	1905	1913	1936	1937	2005	2038	2105	2137
ambridge d.	1014	1044	1114	1114	1144	1214	1244	until	1614	1644	1708	1714	1743	1814	1808	1844	1914	1914	1944	1944	2014	2044	2114	2144
evenage d.	|	|	|	|	|	|	|		|	|	|	|	|	|	|	|	|	|	|	|	|	|	|	|
ndon Kings Cross .. a.	1105	1134	1202	1205	1235	1303	1333		1704	1733	1803	1802	1834	1903	1905	1935	2003	2002	2033	2033	2103	2133	2203	2233

	⚒	⚒	⚒	Ⓐ	⑥	⑥	⚒	Ⓐ	⑥	⚒		⑦	⑦	⑦	⑦		⑦	⑦	⑦	⑦	⑦	⑦	⑦	⑦
ngs Lynn d.	...	2144	...	...	...	...	...	2244	2257	...	⑦	...	...	...	0826		1726	1754	1826	1926	2026	2126	...	2226
›wnham Market d.	...	2158	...	...	...	...	...	2258	2311	...		...	...	...	0840	and at	1740	1808	1840	1940	2040	2140	...	2240
/ **207 208** d.	2147	2217	...	2246	2252	...	...	2317	2329	...		...	...	...	0857	the same	1757	1826	1857	1957	2057	2157	...	2257
ambridge North .. **207** d.	2200	2231	...	2301	2305	...	...	2331	2343	...		...	...	...	0912	minutes	1812	1838	1912	2012	2012	2212	...	2312
ambridge **207 208** a.	2205	2237	...	2306	2309	...	...	2338	2347	...		...	...	...	0916	past each	1816	1842	1916	2016	2116	2216	...	2316
ambridge d.	2214	2244	2254	2314	2314	2324	2335	...	...	2354		0641	0728	0821	0922	hour until	1822	1843	1922	2022	2122	2222	2228	2320
evenage d.	|	|	2332	|	|	0002	0016	...	...	0032		0717	0804	|	|		|	|	|	|	|	|	2304	0007
ndon Kings Cross .. a.	2303	2334	2358	0008	0007	0035	0057	...	...	0106		0750	0831	0909	1011		1913	1936	2010	2109	2210	2313	2331	0049

	①	②–⑥	Ⓐ	⚒	⚒	Ⓐ	Ⓐ	Ⓐ	⑥	⑥	Ⓐ	⚒		⚒	Ⓐ	⑥	⚒	⚒	⚒		⚒	⚒	Ⓐ	⚒
ndon Kings Cross . d.	0002	0032	...	0503	0542	...	0603	0642	0642	0712	0712	0742	...	0812	0842	0842	0912	0942	1012		1442	1512	...	1542
evenage d.	0044	0113	...	0534	|	...	0632	|	|	|	|	|	...	|	|	|	|	|	|	and at	|	|	...	|
ambridge a.	0132	0144	...	0614	0630	...	0713	0730	0730	0802	0804	0830	...	0902	0930	0930	1003	1030	1102	the same	1530	1602	...	1630
ambridge **207 208** d.	...	...	0614	...	0635	0710	*0725*	0735	0735	0804	0812	0835	...	0904	0935	0935	1004	1035	1104	minutes	1535	1604	1620	1635
ambridge North .. **207** d.	...	...	0618	...	0638	0714	*0729*	0739	0738	0808	0818	0838	...	0908	0939	0938	1008	1038	1108	past each	1538	1608	|	1638
/ **207 208** d.	...	...	0633	...	0654	0728	...	0802**a**	0755	0823	0832	0855	...	0923	0956	0955	1024	1055	1123	hour until	1555	1623	1637	1655
›wnham Market d.	...	...	0650	...	0717**b**	0749	...	0821	0817	...	0848	0917	...	...	1017	1022**b**	...	1117	...		1617	...	1653	1717
ngs Lynn a.	...	...	0704	...	0732	0804	...	0835	0831	...	0902	0934	...	...	1031	1036	...	1131	...		1631	...	1707	1731

	⚒	Ⓐ	⑥	Ⓐ	⑥	Ⓐ		⑥	Ⓐ	⑥	Ⓐ	Ⓐ	⑥	Ⓐ	⑥	Ⓐ	Ⓐ	⑥	Ⓐ	⑥	Ⓐ	⚒	⑥	⚒	⑥
ndon Kings Cross . d.	1612	1639	1642	1709	1712	1707**d**	...	1742	1739	1812	1809	1807**d**	1842	1839	1912	1912	1907**d**	1942	1939	2012	2009	2039	2112	2109	2142
evenage d.	|	|	|	|	|	|	...	|	|	|	|	|	|	|	|	|	|	|	|	|	|	|	|	|	|
mbridge a.	1704	1733	1730	1805	1802	1817	...	1830	1832	1902	1903	1917	1930	1932	2002	2005	2015	2030	2033	2104	2103	2132	2204	2203	2230
mbridge **207 208** d.	1704	1738	1735	1807	1804	1819	...	1835	1837	1904	1908	1919	1935	1941	2004	2007	2016	2035	2038	2105	2108	2137	2205	2208	2235
mbridge North .. **207** d.	1708	1743	1738	1811	1808	|	...	1838	1841	1908	1912	|	1938	1945	2008	2011	|	2038	2042	2109	2112	2141	2209	2212	2238
/ **207 208** d.	1723	1759	1755	1824	1823	1835	...	1855	1856	1925	1930**b**	1935	1955	2002	2023	2024	2033	2055	2058	2125	2129	2157	2223	2227	2255
wnham Market d.	...	1817	1817	...	...	1852	...	1917	1913	1946	1947	1957	2017	2019	2046**c**	...	2051	2117	2118	2146	2147	2217	...	...	2311
ngs Lynn a.	...	1831	1831	...	...	1909	...	1931	1928	2000	2001	2014	2031	2033	2100	...	2108	2131	2132	2200	2201	2231	...	...	2325

	Ⓐ	⑥	Ⓐ		⑥	Ⓐ	⚒	⚒	⚒		⑦	⑦	⑦	⑦	⑦	⑦	⑦		⑦	⑦	⑦		⑦	⑦
ndon Kings Cross . d.	2139	2212	2209	...	2242	2239	2309	2342	2351	⑦	0001	0032	0631	0702	0752	0839	0911		1911	2011	2111	...	2211	2311
evenage d.	|	|	|	...	|	|	|	|	0040		0034	0104	0703	0744	0820	0906	|	and at	|	|	|	...	|	|
mbridge a.	2233	2304	2304	...	2330	2333	0004	0035	0128		0114	0144	0745	0830	0858	0947	0959	the same	2000	2058	2158	...	2258	0002
mbridge **207 208** d.	2238	2305	2309	...	2335	2338	0008	...	...		...	...	...	...	0904	...	1004	minutes	2005	2104	2204	...	2304	0004
mbridge North .. **207** d.	2242	2309	2313	...	2338	2342	0013	...	...		...	...	...	...	0908	...	1008	past each	2009	2108	2208	...	2308	0008
/ **207 208** d.	2258	2323	2328	...	2355	2358	0027	...	...		...	...	...	...	0922	...	1022	hour until	2023	2122	2222	...	2322	0022
wnham Market d.	2317	...	...	...	0012	0015	0043	...	...		...	...	...	...	0938	...	1038		2039	2138	2238	...	2338	0038
ngs Lynn a.	2331	...	...	...	0026	0029	0057	...	...		...	...	...	...	0952	...	1052		2053	2152	2252	...	2352	0052

PETERBOROUGH and CAMBRIDGE - STEVENAGE - LONDON - GATWICK AIRPORT - HORSHAM and BRIGHTON

m			Ⓐ	⚒	Ⓐ	Ⓐ	Ⓐ	⚒	Ⓐ		Ⓐ	Ⓐ	⚒	Ⓐ	Ⓐ	⚒	Ⓐ	Ⓐ	⚒	Ⓐ	Ⓐ	⚒	Ⓐ			⑦		⑦
0	**Peterborough** d.	⚒	0420	...	0454	...	0524	...	0554	A	...	1824	...	1852	1924	...	1954	2024	...	2054	2124	...	2154	...	⑦	...	B	...
28	Huntingdon d.		0435	...	0511	...	0541	...	0611		...	1841	...	1911	1941	...	2011	2041	...	2111	2141	...	2211	...		...		...
	Cambridge d.		|	0454	|	0524	|	0554	|	and at	1824	|	1853	|	|	1954	|	|	2054	|	|	2154	|	...		0828		2128
79	Stevenage d.		0513	0532	0547	0602	0617	0632	0647		1902	1917	1932	1947	2017	2032	2047	2117	2132	2247	2217	2232	2247	...		0904		2204
9	Finsbury Park d.		0537	0552	0608	0622	0638	0652	0708	the same	1922	1938	1952	2008	2038	2052	2108	2138	2152	2208	2237	2252	2307	...		0927	and	2227
2	**London** St Pancras **103** d.		0545	0600	0615	0630	0645	0700	0715		1930	1945	2000	2015	2045	2100	2115	2145	2200	2215	2245	2300	2315	...		0935		2235
4	Farringdon **103** d.		0549	0604	0619	0634	0649	0704	0719	minutes	1934	1949	2004	2019	2049	2104	2119	2149	2204	2219	2249	2304	2319	...		0939	hourly	2239
6	**London** Blackfriars **103** d.		0554	0609	0624	0639	0654	0709	0724		1939	1954	2009	2024	2054	2109	2124	2154	2209	2224	2254	2309	2324	...		0944		2244
7	**London** Bridge **103** d.		0600	0615	0630	0645	0700	0715	0730	past each	1945	2000	2015	2030	2100	2115	2130	2200	2215	2230	2300	2315	2330	...		0951	until	2251
3	East Croydon **102 103** d.		0616	0629	0646	0700	0716	0730	0746		1959	2016	2029	2046	2116	2130	2146	2216	2230	2246	2316	2329	2346	...		1007		2308
	Redhill **102 114b** d.		0637	|	0707	|	0734	|	0807	hour until	|	2033	|	2303	2233	|	2203	2233	|	2303	2333	|	2359	...		1019		2323
3	Gatwick ✈ **102 103** d.		0651	0645	0721	0715	0747	0745	0817		2015	2044	2045	2114	2144	2145	2214	2244	2245	2314	2341	2347	0012	...		1027		2333
5	**Horsham** **102** a.		0713	|	0745	|	0811	|	0842	♠	|	2108	|	2138	2208	|	2238	2308	|	2338	0006	|	0036	...		...		...
	Haywards Heath **103** d.		...	0659	...	0730	...	0800	...		2029	...	2059	...	...	2201	...	...	2301	...	...	2359	...	...		...		...
	Brighton **103** a.		...	0722	...	0749	...	0819	...		2049	...	2119	...	...	2220	...	...	2320	...	...	0023	...	...		...		...

m			⚒	Ⓐ	Ⓐ	Ⓐ	⚒	Ⓐ	Ⓐ	Ⓐ	⚒		Ⓐ	Ⓐ	⚒	Ⓐ	Ⓐ	⚒	Ⓐ		⚒	Ⓐ	Ⓐ		⑦		⑦
0	**Brighton** **103** d.	⚒	0506	...	0538	...	0605	...	0637	...	0707	C	1838	...	1908	...	...	2008	...		2208	...	...	⑦	...	B	...
1	Haywards Heath **103** d.		0528	...	0601	...	0631	...	0701	...	0731		1901	...	1931	...	...	2031	...		2231	...	...		...		...
	Horsham **102** d.		|	0525	|	...	|	0624**r**	|	0655**r**	|	and at	|	1855	|	1925	1955	|	2025	and at	|	2225	2311		...		...
5	Gatwick ✈ **102 103** d.		0546	0549	0616	0613	0646	0643	0716	0713	0746		1916	1919	1946	1949	2019	2046	2049		2246	2249	2335		0846		2146
	Redhill **102 114b** d.		|	0559	|	0629	|	0659	|	0729	|	the same	|	1929	|	1959	2029	|	2059	the same	|	2304	2349		0854	and	2154
5	East Croydon **102 103** d.		0601	0616	0631	0646	0701	0716	0731	0746	0801		1931	1945	2001	2015	2045	2101	2115		2301	2315	0009		0907		2207
1	**London** Bridge **103** d.		0616	0631	0646	0701	0716	0731	0746	0801	0816	minutes	1946	2001	2016	2031	2101	2116	2131	minutes	2316	2331	|		0925	hourly	2225
2	**London** Blackfriars **103** d.		0622	0637	0652	0707	0822	0737	0752	0807	0822		1952	2007	2022	2037	2107	2122	2137		2322	2337	0037		0931		2231
4	Farringdon **103** d.		0626	0641	0656	0711	0726	0741	0756	0811	0826	past each	1956	2011	2026	2041	2111	2126	2141	past each	2326	2341	0041		0935	until	2235
6	**London** St Pancras **103** d.		0631	0646	0701	0716	0731	0746	0801	0816	0831		2001	2016	2031	2046	2116	2131	2146		2331	2346	0046		0940		2240
0	Finsbury Park d.		0642	0654	0712	0724	0742	0754	0812	0824	0842	hour until	2009	2024	2039	2054	2124	2139	2154	hour until	2342	2354	0054		0947		2247
0	Stevenage d.		0703	0714	0733	0744	0802	0814	0833	0844	0903		2030	2044	2100	2114	2174	2200	2214		0003	0014	0122		1007		2307
9	**Cambridge** d.		0743	|	0812	|	...	|	0913	|	0942	♣	2114	|	2140	|	|	2240	|	♣	0041	|	|		1048		2345
	Huntingdon d.		...	0749	...	0819	...	0849	...	0919	...		...	2119	...	2149	2219	...	2249		...	0051	0159		...		...
	Peterborough a.		...	0806	...	0840	...	0905	...	0935	...		...	2135	...	2205	2235	...	2305		...	0109	0217		...		...

⑥ and ⑦ service LONDON BRIDGE - GATWICK AIRPORT - HORSHAM

		⑥	⑥	B	⑥		⑦	⑦	⑦	⑦	B	⑦
ndon Bridge d.	⑥	0600	0630	and	2330	⑦	0719	0819	0919	1021		2221
st Croydon... d.		0616	0646	every	2346		0735	0837	0937	1037	and	2237
dhill d.		0637	0703	30	2359		0753	0855	0953	1053	hourly	2253
twick ✈ d.		0651	0714	minutes	0014		0809	0909	1003	1103	until	2303
rsham a.		0714	0738	until	0036		0831	0931	1025	1125		2325

		⑥	B	⑥	⑥		⑦	⑦	⑦	B	⑦
Horsham d.	⑥	0525	and	2225	2311	⑦	0639	0735	0848		2148
Gatwick ✈ d.		0549	every	2249	2334		0702	0758	0911	and	2211
Redhill d.		0559	30	2304	2349		0716	0812	0921	hourly	2225
East Croydon d.		0615	minutes	2315	0009		0732	0832	0937	until	2247
London Bridge . d.		0633	until	2333	0036**t**		0750	0850	0957		2305

- On Ⓐ no departure from Cambridge at 0824 (starts from Stevenage d. 0902).
- There is no through service on ⑥⑦ Peterborough - London Bridge and v.v. (see the next page for other GN / TL services between Peterborough and London Kings Cross).
- On Ⓐ the 0805 from Brighton terminates at Stevenage.

a – Arrives 0753.
b – Arrives 4–5 minutes earlier.
c – Arrives 2039.
d – London Liverpool Street.

r – No departures from Horsham at 0655, 0723, 0755 and 0823 (these trains start from Gatwick Airport).
t – London Blackfriars.
♠ – Timings London Bridge - Horsham / Brighton and v.v. may vary by up to 4 minutes.
♣ – Timings St. Pancras - Cambridge / Peterborough may vary by up to 3 minutes.

185 KINGS LYNN, CAMBRIDGE and PETERBOROUGH - LONDON - GATWICK - BRIGHTON GN, T

Other services PETERBOROUGH - HUNTINGDON - LONDON KINGS CROSS *See Table 180 for fast trains operated by GR*

		Ⓐ	Ⓐ	Ⓐ	Ⓐ		Ⓐ	Ⓐ	Ⓐ	Ⓐ	Ⓐ	Ⓐ	Ⓐ	Ⓐ	Ⓐ	Ⓐ	Ⓐ	Ⓐ		⑥	⑥	⑥		⑥	⑥	⑥		⑥
Peterborough d.	Ⓐ	0324	0542	0605	0636	...	0705	0714	0735	0804	0917	1832	1942	2018	2141	2224	2254	2320	⑥	0324	0418	0454	and	0754	0804	0824	...	08
Huntingdon d.		0339	0556	0620	0650	...	0720	0730	0749	0820	0932	|	1956	2032	2155	2241	2311	2335		0339	0432	0511	every	0811	0820	0841	...	09
Stevenage d.		0417	|	0649	0720	...	0751	|	0821	0853	|	1923	|	|	2224	2317	2350	0012		0417	0510	0547	30	0847	|	0917	...	09
Finsbury Park a.		0445	|	|	|	...	|	|	|	|	|	|	|	|	|	2336	0010	0038		0445	0534	0608	minutes	0910	|	0937	...	10
London Kings Cross a.		0451	0644	0714	0744	...	0814	0817	0846	0918	1020	1950	2047	2120	2246	2344	0018	0045		0451	0842	0614	until	0917	0911	0946	...	10

	⑥	⑥		⑥	⑥	⑥	⑥		⑥	⑥	⑥	⑥		⑦	⑦	⑦	⑦	⑦	⑦	⑦		⑦	⑦	⑦		⑦	⑦
Peterborough d.	0904	0924	...	0954	1004	1024	1053	and at	2154	2224	2254	2320	⑦	0545	0645	0745	0845	0915	0945	1015	...	1045	1115	1145		2145	22
Huntingdon d.	0920	0941	...	1011	1020	1041	1111	the same	2211	2241	2311	2335		0600	0701	0801	0901	0929	1000	1029	...	1101	1129	1201	and	2201	23
Stevenage d.	|	1017	...	1047	|	1117	1147	minutes	2247	2317	2350	0012		0640	0737	0835	0936	|	1036	|	...	1136	|	1236	hourly	2236	23
Finsbury Park a.	|	1037	...	1110	|	1137	1208	past each	2306	2336	0013	0039		0713	0800	0855	0956	|	1056	|	...	1156	|	1256	until	2256	23
London Kings Cross a.	1012	1046	...	1118	1111	1146	1216	hour until	2314	2344	0022	0045		0723	0809	0903	1003	1017	1103	1118	...	1203	1217	1303		2303	00

		①	Ⓐ	Ⓐ	Ⓐ	Ⓐ	Ⓐ	Ⓐ	Ⓐ	Ⓐ	Ⓐ	Ⓐ	Ⓐ	Ⓐ	Ⓐ	Ⓐ		⑥	⑥	⑥	⑥	⑥	⑥	⑥		⑥	⑥	⑥
London Kings Cross d.	Ⓐ	0032	0132	0518	0548	0618	1642	1712	1742	1812	1842	1918	2012	2112	2212	2312	⑥	0136	0514	0548	0616	0716	0745	0813	and at	1546	1616	16
Finsbury Park d.		0039	0139	0524	0554	0624	|	|	|	|	|	|	|	|	|	|		0144	0520	0554	0622	0724	0754	0824	the same	1554	1623	
Stevenage d.		0113s	0212	0549	0614	0644	1705	1735	1805	1835	1905	|	2034	2134	2234	2335		0212	0546	0614	0642	0744	0814	0844	minutes	1614	1643	|
Huntingdon d.		0156s	0249	0627	0649	0719	1736	1806	1836	1906	1936	2006	2103	2203	2303	0004		0249	0625	0649	0719	0819	0849	0921	past each	1650	1718	17
Peterborough a.		0212	0316	0642	0709	0734	1753	1822	1853	1922	1953	2022	2122	2219	2319	0022		0307	0641	0707	0735	0840	0905	0942	hour until	1706	1733	17

	⑥	♥	⑥	⑥	⑥	⑥		⑥	⑥		⑦	⑦	⑦	⑦		⑦	⑦	⑦	⑦	⑦	⑦	⑦		⑦	⑦
London Kings Cross d.	1646	and at	1836	1846	1916	1945	and	2316	2346	⑦	0012	0046	0735	0813		1613	1655	1713	1755	1813	1855	1913		2213	23
Finsbury Park d.	1654	the same	|	1854	1924	1954	every	2324	2354		0020	0054	0742	0819	and	1619	|	1719	|	1819	|	1919	and	2219	23
Stevenage d.	1713	minutes	|	1913	1944	2014	30	2344	0014		0056	0122	0807	0840	hourly	1640	|	1740	|	1840	|	1940	hourly	2239	23
Huntingdon d.	1748	past each	1927	1948	2021	2049	minutes	0019	0053		0131	0159	0848	0913	until	1713	1743	1813	1842	1913	1943	2013	until	2312	00
Peterborough a.	1804	hour until	1943	2004	2040	2104	until	0039	0111		0149	0219	0904	0929		1729	1801	1829	1859	1929	2001	2029		2330	00

s – Stops to set down only.

♥ – Arrival times in Peterborough may vary by up to 4 minutes.

186 PETERBOROUGH - LINCOLN - DONCASTER 2nd class EI

km		⑥Q	ⒶQ	⚒T	⚒	⚒	ⒶD	Ⓐ	⑥	⑥	Ⓐ	Ⓐ	ⒶD	⑥	⚒	Ⓐ	⚒	Ⓐ	⑥	⑥	ⒶD	⚒	⚒D	⚒	Ⓐ	⑥	⚒
0	**Peterborough** d.	...	...	0630	...	0730	...	0833	0833	0932	0935	1040	1150	1152	1241	1341	1511	1625	1625	...	...	1732	...	1836	...	...	20
27	Spalding d.	...	...	0653	...	0752	...	0854	0854	0953	0956	1101	1213	1213	1302	1404	1532	1646	1647	...	...	1755	...	1859	...	...	20
57	Sleaford d.	0650	0653	...	0743	...	0840	0918	0919	1020	1021	1125	1242	1241	1326	1429	1614t	1716	1719	1754	1756	...	1900	...	2005	2010	...
91	**Lincoln** a.	0722	0726	...	0815	...	0913	0953	0956	1053	1053	1157	1314	1314	1403	1500	1647	1748	1751	1827	1829	...	1932	...	2039	2044	...

	Ⓐ	⚒	Ⓐ	⑥	⚒	⚒N	Ⓐ	Ⓐ	⑥	⚒	Ⓐ	ⒶR	⑥R	⚒	Ⓐ	ⒶR	⑥R	⚒	⑥	ⒶQ	⚒	⚒	⑥	Ⓐ	⚒L	⑥T	Ⓐ
Lincoln d.	0617	...	...	...	0705	0800	0911	1018	1018	1110	1210	1330	1333	1441	1512	1600	1601	...	1715	1718	1810	...	1905	1915	2048	...	..
Sleaford d.	0646	...	...	...	0737	0835f	0943	1051	1051	1142	1242	1403	1406	1516	1544	1634	1634	...	1747	1752	1842	...	1937	1947	2120	...	..
Spalding d.	...	0700	0800	0805	...	0900	1007	1113	1119j	1204	1307	1425	1429	1538	...	1656	1657	1808	...	...	...	1959	...	...	...	2103	21
Peterborough a.	...	0722	0820	0827	...	0924	1031	1134	1143	1228	1328	1446	1451	1602a	...	1718	1723	1831a	...	...	...	2022	...	...	...	2125	21

km		⚒	ⒶS	⑥	⚒	ⒶP	⑥	⑥	ⒶS	⚒S
0	**Lincoln** d.	0643	0915	0915	1154	1315	1410	1510	1831	1932
26	Gainsborough Lea Road d.	0704	0935	0935	1215	1335	1430	1530	1855	1951
60	**Doncaster** a.	*0748*r	1002	1005	1245	1404	1458	1600	1925	2021

	⚒	⑥	Ⓐ	Ⓐ	⑥	Ⓐ	⑥	⑥	Ⓐ	⑥	Ⓐ
Doncaster d.	*0722*b	1024	1024	1301	1305	1427	1507	1627	1939	2033	20
Gainsborough Lea Road d.	0824	1048	1048	1330	1330	1455	1531	1652	2002	2056	21
Lincoln a.	0847	1110	1117	1353	1354	1517	1558	1719	2024	2124	21

D – To/from Doncaster (lower panel).
L – To Boston (Table **187**).
N – From Nottingham (Table **184**).
P – To/from Peterborough (upper panel).
Q – To/from Leicester (Table **184**).
R – From Newark North Gate (Table **189**).
S – To/from Sleaford (upper panel).
T – From/to Nottingham (Table **206**).
V – To Nottingham (Tables **206** and **208**).
a – Arrives 3 minutes earlier on Ⓐ.
b – Change trains at Retford (a. 0741, d. 0809).
f – Arrives 0832.
j – Arrives 1112.
r – Change trains at Retford (a. 0717, d. 0734).
t – Arrives 1556 on Ⓐ; 1600 on ⑥.

187 SKEGNESS - NOTTINGHAM 2nd class EI

km			⚒	⚒	⚒	Ⓐ	⑥	Ⓐ	⑥	⚒	⚒	⑥	Ⓐ	⑥	⑥	⚒	⚒	⚒	⚒	⑥	Ⓐ	⚒	Ⓐ	⑥	⑥	Ⓐ	⚒
0	**Skegness** d.	⚒	...	...	0709	0810	0815	0906	0915	1015	1115	1140	1215	1215	1235	1315	1415	1509	1611	1724	1730	1814	1914	1919	2015	2015	21
8	Wainfleet d.		...	...	0719	0818	0823	0914	0923	1023	1123	|	1223	1223	|	1323	1423	1517	1621	1732	1738	1822	1922	1927	2023	2023	21
38	Boston d.		...	0613	0746	0845	0850	0941	0950	1050	1150	1225t	1250	1250	1315	1350	1450	1544	1648	1759	1805	1848	1949	1954	2050	2050	21
66	Sleaford d.		...	0635	0811	0907	0912	1003	1014	1112	1212	1247	1313	1312	1339	1413	1512	1610	1713	1821	1827	1913	2013	2018	2112	2118	22
89	Grantham a.		...	0707	0842	0938	0941	1031	1043	1142	1241	|	1342	1341	|	1442	1541	1641	1742	|	|	1941	2040	2045	2142	2145	
89	Grantham 206 d.		0610	0710	0845	0944	0945	1036	1046	1145	1245	|	1348	1346	|	1445	1545	1645	1745	|	|	1945	2044	2048	2146	2149	
126	**Nottingham** 206 a.		0654	0753	0920	1020	1021	1113	1123	1222	1323	1344	1422	1424	1438	1523	1625	1720	1822	1922	1921	2025	2120	2124	2224	2226	22

		⑦	⑦a	⑦a	⑦a	⑦b	⑦a	⑦	⑦a	⑦b	⑦a	⑦	⑦	⑦a	⑦b
Skegness d.	⑦	...	...	1014	1115	...	1227	1410	1515	1610	1622	1807	1915	2043	...
Wainfleet d.		...	...	1022	1123	...	1235	1418	1523	1618	1630	1815	1923	2051	...
Boston d.		...	0906	1049	1149	1213	1302	1445	1552	1645	1657	1842	1950	2118	...
Sleaford d.		...	0928	1111	1211	1235	1324	1507	1620	1707	1719	1904	2012	2142	2142
Grantham a.		...	0957	1140	1240	1304	|	1535	1646	1741	|	1932	2041	2210	2210
Grantham 206 d.		0900	1001	1146	1244	...	|	1540	1650	1745	|	1936	2045	2213	2213
Nottingham 206 a.		0933	1037	1226	1320	...	1416	1616	1722	1820	1811	2011	2120	2249	2249

		⚒	⚒	⚒	⑥	Ⓐ	⑥	
Nottingham 206 d.	⚒	0507	0550	0641	0731	0735	0824	08
Grantham 206 a.		0546	0627	0719	0809	0812	|	09
Grantham d.		—	0631	0723	0817	0816	|	09
Sleaford d.		⚒	0657	0750	0846	0845	0919	09
Boston d.		0625	0725	0817	0911	0912	0951t	10
Wainfleet d.		0649	0751	0842	0935	0936	|	10
Skegness a.		0703	0805	0856	0948	0949	1033	11

	Ⓐ	⑥	⚒	⚒	⚒	⚒	⚒	⚒	⚒	⚒	⚒	⚒	⚒A	⚒
Nottingham 206 d.	0845	0943	0955	1045	1145	1245	1345	1445	1545	1645	1744	1844	...	2051
Grantham 206 a.	0926	1015	|	1123	1219	1325	1423	1522	1625	1728	1825	1923	...	2132
Grantham d.	0932	1021	|	1127	1225	1327	1427	1526	1629	1732	1829	1926	...	2136
Sleaford d.	1001	1057	1044	1153	1250	1354	1452	1552	1655	1800	1855	1955	2120	2201
Boston d.	1025	1127r	1111	1219	1315	1421	1517	1620	1721	1826	1921	2018	2153	2229
Wainfleet d.	1049	|	1135	1244	1340	1446	1542	1645	1748	1850	1946	2042	...	...
Skegness a.	1100	1207	1150	1258	1354	1500	1556	1659	1800	1905	1959	2057	...	...

		⑦	⑦a	⑦a	⑦a	⑦	⑦b	⑦a	⑦	⑦	⑦a	⑦b	
Nottingham 206 d.	⑦	0815	0900	0941	1109	1157	*1240*	1357	1456	1623	1816	1831	19
Grantham 206 a.		0849	|	1015	1144	1229	*1313*	1431	1531	1703	1850	1908	20
Grantham d.		—	|	1020	1150	1233	1350	1435	1536	1707	1854	1913	20
Sleaford d.		⑦a	0949	1046	1215	1259	1416	1508	1602	1736	1920	1941	20
Boston d.		0931	1016	1111	1241	1324	1445r	1532	1629	1802	1950r	2009	21
Wainfleet d.		0955	1040	1136	1306	1349	1509	1557	1653	1827	2014	...	
Skegness a.		1007	1054	1150	1320	1400	1524	1611	1708	1838	2026	...	

A – From Lincoln (Table **186**). a – Until Sept. 8. b – From Sept. 15. r – Arrives 4–5 minutes earlier. t – Arrives 7–9 minutes earlier.

188 THE NORTH EAST and YORKSHIRE - MANCHESTER and LIVERPOOL Most trains convey 🍸

km			⑥	②–⑤	①	⑥	②–⑤	①	Ⓐ	⑥	⚒	⚒	⚒	⚒	⚒	⚒	⚒	⚒	⚒	⚒	⚒	⚒		⚒	⑥	Ⓐ	
0	**Newcastle** 124 180 d.	⚒	...	...	...	...	...	...	...	...	...	...	...	...	...	0448	...	...	...	0603	...	...	...	...	0700	0708	07
23	Durham 124 180 d.		...	...	...	...	...	...	...	...	...	...	...	...	...	0504	...	...	...	0619	...	...	...	...	0718	0721	07
34	**Middlesbrough** d.		...	...	...	...	...	...	...	...	...	...	...	...	...	|	...	0543	...	|	0622	...	...	0650	|	|	
58	Darlington 124 180 d.		...	...	...	...	...	...	...	...	...	...	...	...	...	0523	...	|	...	0637	|	...	...	|	|	|	07
81	Northallerton 124 180 d.		...	...	...	...	...	...	...	...	...	...	...	...	...	0542	...	0613	...	|	0651	...	...	0719	|	|	
93	Thirsk d.		...	...	...	...	...	...	...	...	...	...	...	...	...	0550	...	0622	...	|	0700	...	...	0729	|	|	
◧	**Scarborough** d.		...	...	...	...	...	...	...	...	...	...	...	...	...	|	...	|	0600	|	|	0642	...	|	|	|	
◧	Malton d.		...	...	...	...	...	...	...	...	...	...	...	...	...	|	...	|	0624	|	|	0707	...	|	|	|	
129	**York** 124 180 a.		...	...	...	...	...	...	...	...	...	...	...	...	...	0607	...	0640	0649	0707	0717	0732	...	0748	0804	0806	0
129	**York** 124 d.		0138	0138	0138	0252	0247	0252	0350	0353	...	...	0505	0538	0547	0609	0623	0641	0653	0709	0721	0738	...	0750	0809	0809	0
170	**Leeds** 124 a.		0218	0218	0205	0318	0330	0319	0415	0436	...	...	0542	0603	0612	0632	0647	0704	0715	0731	0746	0803	...	0815	0831	0831	0
170	**Leeds** 188a d.		0218	0220	0205	0319	0335	0320	0416	0439	...	...	0545	0605	0614	0632	0650	0706	0718	0734	0748	0806	...	0818	0834	0834	0
185	Dewsbury 188a d.		|	|	|	|	|	|	|	|	...	...	0557	|	0627	|	|	|	0729	|	0759	|	...	0829	|	|	
198	Huddersfield 188a d.		0256	0241	0241	0355	0358	0358	0453	0512	...	...	0607	0623	0636	0651	0708	0724	0738	0752	0808	0824	...	0839	0852	0852	0
	Manchester Victoria d.		|	|	|	|	|	|	0539	0544	0555	0625	0640	0657	0710	0724	0739	0755	0810	0825	0839	0854	...	0910	0924	0924	0
239	**Manchester** Picc 188a a.		0329	0341	0341	0427	0456	0456	0549	0553	|	|	0653	|	0720	|	0749	|	0820	|	0849	|	...	0919	|	|	0
255	**Manchester** Airport ✈ a.		0349	0357	0357	0448	0513	0513	0609	0614	|	|	0708	|	0737	|	0807	|	0838	|	0906	|	...	0935	|	|	1
295	**Liverpool** Lime Street a.		...	...	...	...	...	...	...	...	0632	0700	...	0734	...	0800	...	0831	...	0901	...	0932	...	...	1000	1000	

◧ – Distances: York (*0 km*) - Malton (*33 km*) - Scarborough (*67 km*).

TP Most trains convey 🍷 THE NORTH EAST and YORKSHIRE - MANCHESTER and LIVERPOOL 188

	⑥	⚒	⚒	⚒	⚒	⚒	⚒	⚒	⚒	⚒	⚒	⚒	⚒	⚒	⚒	⚒	⚒	⚒	⚒	⚒	⚒	⚒	⚒	⚒	⚒	⚒
Newcastle 124 180 d.	0718	...	...	0801	0817	...	...	0900	0920	...	...	1002	1018	...	...	1102	1117	...	...	1203	1218	...	...	1300	1317	...
Durham 124 180 d.	0731	...	...	0815	0833	...	...	0915	0934	...	...	1016	1034	...	...	1116	1133	...	...	1216	1231	...	...	1316	1333	...
Middlesbrough d.	|	...	0755	|	|	...	0854	|	|	...	0955	|	|	...	1055	|	|	...	1155	|	|	...	1255	|	|	...
Darlington 124 180 d.	0748	...	|	0833	0851	...	|	0934	0951	...	|	1034	|	...	|	1134	|	...	|	1234	1249	...	|	1334	1351	...
Northallerton 124 180 d.	|	...	0824	0845	|	...	0924	0945	|	...	1026	1045	|	...	1125	1145	|	...	1224	1245	|	...	1325	1345	|	...
Thirsk d.	|	...	0833	|	|	...	0932	|	|	...	1034	|	|	...	1133	|	|	...	1233	|	|	...	1333	|	|	...
Scarborough d.	|	0738	|	|	|	0845	|	|	|	0941	|	|	|	1041	|	|	|	1141	|	|	|	1244	|	|	|	1344
Malton d.	|	0803	|	|	|	0908	|	|	|	1007	|	|	|	1107	|	|	|	1207	|	|	|	1307	|	|	|	1407
York 124 180 a.	0820	0828	0849	0907	0922	0936	0948	1007	1022	1035	1050	1107	1120	1135	1152	1207	1218	1235	1249	1307	1322	1335	1349	1407	1422	1435
York 124 d.	0822	0837	0852	0909	0923	0937	0952	1009	1023	1038	1053	1109	1122	1138	1153	1209	1222	1238	1252	1309	1324	1337	1352	1409	1423	1438
Leeds 124 a.	0848	0903	0915	0931	0947	1003	1015	1031	1046	1103	1116	1131	1146	1205	1216	1231	1245	1304	1315	1331	1346	1405	1415	1432	1447	1503
Leeds 188a d.	0850	0906	0918	0934	0950	1006	1018	1034	1050	1106	1118	1134	1150	1206	1218	1234	1250	1306	1318	1333	1350	1406	1418	1434	1450	1505
Dewsbury 188a d.	|	|	0929	|	|	|	1029	|	|	|	1129	|	|	|	1229	|	|	|	1329	|	|	|	1429	|	|	|
Huddersfield 188a d.	0908	0924	0939	0952	1008	1024	1039	1052	1108	1124	1139	1152	1208	1224	1239	1252	1308	1324	1339	1352	1408	1424	1439	1452	1508	1523
Manchester Victoria d.	0939	0955	1010	1024	1039	1056	1110	1124	1139	1156	1210	1224	1239	1256	1310	1324	1339	1356	1410	1424	1439	1455	1510	1524	1540	1555
Manchester Picc. 188a a.	0949	|	1019	|	1049	|	1119	|	1150	|	1220	|	1249	|	1320	|	1349	|	1420	|	1449	|	1520	|	1549	|
Manchester Airport ✈ a.	1007	|	1035	|	1107	|	1135	|	1207	|	1235	|	1307	|	1335	|	1407	|	1435	|	1507	|	1535	|	1609	|
Liverpool Lime Street a.	...	1032	...	1100	...	1131	...	1201	...	1232	...	1300	...	1332	...	1400	...	1431	...	1500	...	1534	...	1600	...	1632

	⑥	Ⓐ	⚒	⚒	⚒	⚒	⚒	⚒	⚒	Ⓐ	⑥	⚒	⚒	⚒	⚒	⚒	⚒	⚒	⚒	⚒	⚒	⚒	⚒	⚒	⚒	⚒
Newcastle 124 180 d.	...	...	1403	1415	...	...	1452	1515	...	...	...	1603	1616	...	...	1702	1717	...	...	1803	1817	...	...	1853	...	...
Durham 124 180 d.	...	...	1416	1432	...	...	1505	1528	...	...	...	1616	1633	...	...	1716	1733	...	...	1816	1833	...	...	1906	...	...
Middlesbrough d.	1355	1355	|	|	...	1455	|	|	...	1555	1555	|	|	...	1655	|	|	...	1755	|	|	...	1855	|	...	1957
Darlington 124 180 d.	|	|	1434	1450	...	|	1523	1546	...	|	|	1633	1651	...	|	1733	1751	...	|	1833	1851	...	|	1923	...	|
Northallerton 124 180 d.	1425	1425	1445	|	...	1525	|	1558	...	1624	1624	1644	|	...	1724	1744	|	...	1824	1845	|	...	1924	1934	...	2025
Thirsk d.	1433	1433	|	|	...	1533	|	|	...	1633	1633	|	|	...	1733	|	|	...	1832	|	|	...	1932	|	...	2034
Scarborough d.	|	|	|	|	1444	|	|	|	1544	|	|	|	|	1644	|	|	|	1744	|	|	|	1842	|	|	1944	|
Malton d.	|	|	|	|	1507	|	|	|	1607	|	|	|	|	1707	|	|	|	1807	|	|	|	1905	|	|	2008	|
York 124 180 a.	1450	1450	1507	1521	1535	1551	1604	1620	1635	1649	1649	1707	1722	1735	1750	1807	1822	1835	1849	1907	1922	1933	1949	1957	2035	2054
York 124 d.	1452	1452	1509	1522	1538	1552	1607	1622	1638	1652	1652	1709	1723	1738	1751	1809	1823	1841	1851	1909	1923	1940	1952	2009	2038	...
Leeds 124 a.	1515	1515	1531	1546	1603	1615	1632	1646	1703	1715	1715	1731	1746	1804	1815	1831	1849	1905	1914	1931	1948	2005	2015	2031	2102	...
Leeds 188a d.	1518	1518	1534	1550	1606	1618	1634	1650	1706	1718	1718	1734	1749	1806	1818	1834	1851	1905	1916	1934	1950	2007	2018	2034	2105	...
Dewsbury 188a d.	1529	1529	|	|	|	1629	|	|	|	1729	1729	|	|	|	1829	|	|	|	1928	|	|	|	2029	|	|	...
Huddersfield 188a d.	1539	1539	1552	1608	1623	1639	1652	1708	1723	1739	1739	1752	1808	1823	1839	1852	1908	1924	1939	1952	2008	2024	2039	2052	2123	...
Manchester Victoria d.	1610	1610	1624	1639	1655	1710	1725	1739	1755	1810	1810	1824	1840	1855	1910	1924	1939	1955	2011	2024	2039	2100	2109	2124	2154	...
Manchester Picc. 188a a.	1620	1620	|	1649	|	1720	|	1749	|	1819	1819	|	1849	|	1919	|	1949	|	2020	|	2049	2119	...	|	2205	...
Manchester Airport ✈ a.	1635	1641	|	1709	|	1736	|	1807	|	1835	1843	|	1909	|	1934	|	2009	|	2036	|	2109	2137	...	|	2222	...
Liverpool Lime Street a.	...	...	1700	...	1731	...	1802	...	1833	...	...	1900	...	1934	...	2001	...	2033	...	2100	...	...	...	2200	...	...

	⑥	Ⓐ	⚒	⚒	⚒	⑥	Ⓐ	⚒	Ⓐ	⑥	⑥	⑥	⑥p	Ⓐ	Ⓐ		⑦	⑦	⑦	⑦	⑦	⑦	⑦	⑦	⑦	⑦
Newcastle 124 180 d.	1958	2000	...	...	2100	...	...	...	2200	2200	...	2230	...	...	...		a	b	a	b	a	b	a	b	...	a
Durham 124 180 d.	2016	2016	...	...	2116	...	...	...	2214	2214	...	2246	...	...	...	⑦	🚌	...	🚌	...	🚌	...	🚌	...	...	🚌
Middlesbrough d.	|	|	...	2055	|	...	...	2157	|	|	2243	▬	...	...	2257		...	...	...	...	...	...	...	...	...	...
Darlington 124 180 d.	2033	2033	...	|	2133	...	...	|	2231	2231	|	...	...	...	|		...	...	...	...	...	...	...	...	...	...
Northallerton 124 180 d.	2044	2044	...	2124	2144	...	...	2225	2243	2243	2310	...	...	...	2325		...	...	...	...	...	...	...	...	...	...
Thirsk d.	|	|	...	2133	|	...	...	2233	|	|	|	⑥n	...	...	|		...	...	...	...	...	...	...	...	...	...
Scarborough d.	|	|	2044	|	|	2146	2146	|	|	|	|	2246	2246	2246	|		...	...	...	...	...	...	...	...	...	...
Malton d.	|	|	2108	|	|	2211	2212	|	|	|	|	2312	2312	2312	|		...	...	...	...	...	...	...	...	...	...
York 124 180 a.	2107	2107	2135	2151	2207	2236	2236	2253	2306	2306	2332	2336	2336	2336	0007		...	...	...	...	...	...	...	...	...	...
York 124 d.	2109	2109	2140	2152	2209	2238	2238	...	2307	2307	...	...	2339	2339	...		0130	0225	0330	0400	0455	0515	0555	0619	...	0655
Leeds 124 a.	2132	2132	2203	2215	2231	2300	2301	...	2330	2330	...	...	0004	0004	...		0220	0250	0420	0425	0545	0540	0645	0644	...	0745
Leeds 188a d.	2134	2134	2205	2216	2234	2303	2303	...	2335	2335	...	...	0009	0009	...		0220	0253	0420	0428	0545	0543	0645	0646	...	0745
Dewsbury 188a d.	|	|	|	2229	|	2314	2314	...	2346	2346	...	...	|	|	...		|	|	|	|	0610	0554	0710	0657	...	0810
Huddersfield 188a d.	2152	2152	2223	2239	2252	2323	2323	...	2355	0003t	...	...	|	|	...		0255	0311	0455	0446	0635	0603	0735	0707	...	0835
Manchester Victoria d.	2225	2225	2254	2312	2323	|	2353	...	0027	|	...	...	|	|	...		|	|	|	|	|	|	|	|	0825	|
Manchester Picc. 188a a.	|	|	|	2328	|	2355	...	...	0036	0036	...	...	0056	0118	...		0355	0342	0555	0517	0745	0633	0845s	0738	|	0945
Manchester Airport ✈ a.	|	|	|	2344	|	...	...	...	0050	0053f	...	...	...	...	...		0420	0400	0620	0534	0810	0658	0910	0804	|	...
Liverpool Lime Street a.	2301	2313	2337	...	0001	...	...	...	...	...	...	...	...	...	...		...	...	...	...	...	...	...	...	0900	...

	⑦	⑦	⑦	⑦	⑦	⑦	⑦	⑦	⑦	⑦	⑦	⑦	⑦	⑦	⑦	⑦	⑦	⑦	⑦	⑦	⑦	⑦	⑦	⑦	⑦	⑦
Newcastle 124 180 d.	b	a	b	a	a	b	a	b	...	0800	...	...	...	0903	0917	...	...	1004	1020	...	...	1103	1117	...	...	1203
Durham 124 180 d.	...	...	...	🚌	...	...	...	...	...	0813	...	...	...	0916	0933	...	...	1017	1033	...	...	1116	1133	...	...	1216
Middlesbrough d.	...	...	...	...	...	...	...	...	...	|	...	...	0855	|	|	...	0953	|	|	...	1055	|	|	...	1155	|
Darlington 124 180 d.	...	...	...	...	...	...	...	...	...	0831	...	...	|	0934	0951	...	|	1035	1051	...	|	1134	1151	...	|	1234
Northallerton 124 180 d.	...	...	...	...	...	...	...	...	...	0842	...	...	0924	0945	|	...	1021	1046	|	...	1124	1145	|	...	1224	1245
Thirsk d.	...	...	...	...	...	...	...	...	...	0850	...	...	0933	|	|	...	1030	|	|	...	1133	|	|	...	1233	|
Scarborough d.	...	...	...	...	...	...	...	...	...	|	...	0844	|	|	|	0944	|	|	|	1041	|	|	|	1142	|	|
Malton d.	...	...	...	...	...	...	...	...	...	|	...	0908	|	|	|	1008	|	|	|	1104	|	|	|	1207	|	|
York 124 180 a.	...	...	...	...	...	...	...	...	...	0908	...	0936	0949	1007	1022	1035	1048	1108	1122	1132	1150	1207	1222	1235	1249	1307
York 124 d.	0717	...	0753	...	0810	0822	0839	0839	0852	0909	0920	0941	0952	1009	1024	1038	1052	1110	1124	1138	1152	1209	1224	1238	1252	1310
Leeds 124 a.	0743	...	0818	...	0832	0845	0905	0902	0914	0932	0945	1004	1016	1031	1046	1101	1115	1132	1146	1204	1215	1231	1247	1304	1315	1332
Leeds 188a d.	0745	...	0821	0825	...	0848	▬	0904	0916	0934	0948	1006	1018	1034	1050	1106	1118	1134	1150	1206	1218	1234	1250	1306	1318	1334
Dewsbury 188a d.	0756	...	|	0908	...	0859	⑦	|	0928	|	|	|	1029	|	|	|	1129	|	|	|	1229	|	|	|	1329	|
Huddersfield 188a d.	0805	...	0839	0939	...	0908	a	0922	0937	0952	1008	1024	1039	1052	1108	1124	1139	1152	1208	1224	1239	1252	1308	1324	1338	1352
Manchester Victoria d.	0838	0910	0910	...	...	0939	0956	0956	1009	1024	|	1056	1109	1124	1139	1156	1210	1225	1240	1256	1310	1324	1340	1356	1410	1424
Manchester Picc. 188a a.	0849	|	|	...	...	0950	|	|	...	|	1042	|	...	|	1149	|	1219k	|	1252	|	1320	|	1350	|	1420	|
Manchester Airport ✈ a.	0910	|	|	...	...	1005	|	|	...	|	...	|	...	|	1206	|	1235k	|	1308	|	1338	|	1407	|	1437	|
Liverpool Lime Street a.	...	0946	0946	...	...	...	1031	1031	...	1100	...	1141	...	1159	...	1233	...	1303	...	1332	...	1359	...	1432	...	1500

	⑦	⑦	⑦	⑦	⑦	⑦	⑦	⑦	⑦	⑦	⑦	⑦	⑦	⑦	⑦	⑦	⑦	⑦	⑦	⑦	⑦	⑦	⑦	⑦	⑦	⑦
Newcastle 124 180 d.	1217	...	...	1303	1310	...	...	1403	1415	...	...	1503	1514	...	...	1600	1612	...	...	1705	1713	...	...	1803	1813	...
Durham 124 180 d.	1233	...	...	1316	1323	...	...	1416	1428	...	...	1516	1530	...	...	1613	1628	...	...	1718	1726	...	...	1816	1830	...
Middlesbrough d.	|	...	1246	|	|	...	1355	|	|	...	1448	|	|	...	1555	|	|	...	1655	|	|	...	1755	|	|	...
Darlington 124 180 d.	1251	...	|	1334	1344	...	|	1434	1446	...	|	1534	1548	...	|	1630	1646	...	|	1735	1743	...	|	1834	1848	...
Northallerton 124 180 d.	|	...	1315	1345	1355	...	1424	1445	|	...	|	1545	|	...	1624	1641	|	...	1724	|	1755	...	1824	1845	|	...
Thirsk d.	|	...	1324	|	|	...	1433	|	|	...	1528	|	|	...	1634	|	|	...	1733	|	|	...	1832	|	|	...
Scarborough d.	|	1241	|	|	|	1344	|	|	|	1444	|	|	|	1544	|	|	|	1644	|	|	|	1744	|	|	|	1842
Malton d.	|	1307	|	|	|	1408	|	|	|	1507	|	|	|	1607	|	|	|	1707	|	|	|	1806	|	|	|	1907
York 124 180 a.	1322	1335	1342	1407	1417	1435	1451	1507	1517	1535	1545	1607	1619	1635	1653	1703	1717	1735	1751	1807	1817	1837	1855	1907	1919	1935
York 124 d.	1324	1338	1353	1409	1424	1438	1452	1509	1524	1538	1548	1609	1624	1638	1654	1709	1724	1738	1752	1809	1824	1838	1857	1909	1920	1940
Leeds 124 a.	1346	1404	1415	1432	1446	1504	1515	1531	1546	1604	1615	1632	1646	1704	1717	1731	1747	1804	1815	1832	1846	1905	1919	1933	1946	2004
Leeds 188a d.	1350	1406	1418	1434	1450	1506	1518	1534	1550	1606	1618	1634	1650	1706	1718	1734	1750	1806	1818	1834	1850	1906	1921	1935	1950	2005
Dewsbury 188a d.	|	|	1429	|	|	|	1529	|	|	|	1629	|	|	|	1730	|	|	|	1829	|	|	|	1932	|	|	|
Huddersfield 188a d.	1408	1424	1439	1452	1508	1524	1539	1552	1608	1624	1639	1652	1708	1724	1739	1752	1808	1824	1839	1852	1908	1924	1941	1952	2008	2024
Manchester Victoria d.	1440	1456	1510	1524	1540	1556	1610	1624	1640	1656	1710	1724	1740	1756	1810	1824	1840	1856	1910	1924	1940	1956	2012	2024	2040	2056
Manchester Picc. 188a a.	1450	|	1519	|	1550	|	1620	|	1649	|	1720	|	1750	|	1820	|	1850	|	1920	|	1950	|	2021	|	2050	|
Manchester Airport ✈ a.	1509	|	1537	|	1607	|	1637	|	1707	|	1737	|	1807	|	1837	|	1907	|	1937	|	2007	|	2036	|	2109	|
Liverpool Lime Street a.	...	1532	...	1600	...	1632	...	1700	...	1732	...	1800	...	1832	...	1900	...	1932	...	2000	...	2032	...	2101	...	2132

- From Oct. 27.
- Until Oct. 20.
- From Oct. 26 change at Manchester Piccadilly for conecting 🚌 arriving 0115.

k – Until Sept. 8.
n – From Oct. 26.
p – Until Oct. 19.

r – ⑥ only.
t – Arrives 2355.

188 THE NORTH EAST and YORKSHIRE - MANCHESTER and LIVERPOOL

Most trains convey 🍷 TP

	⑦	⑦	⑦	⑦	⑦	⑦	⑦	⑦	⑦	⑦	⑦	⑦	⑦
Newcastle 124 180 d.	...	1906	1920	...	...	2004	...	...	2100	...	...	2200	...
Durham 124 180 d.	...	│	1933	...	...	2017	...	...	2116	...	...	2214	...
Middlesbrough d.	1855	│	│	...	1957	│	...	2057	│	...	2157	│	2257
Darlington 124 180 d.	│	1934	1950	...	│	2035	...	│	2133	...	│	2231	│
Northallerton 124 180 d.	1925	1945	│	...	2025	2046	...	2126	2144	...	2226	2243	2326
Thirsk d.	1934	│	│	...	2034	│	...	2135	│	...	2235	│	│
Scarborough d.	│	│	│	1944	│	│	2042	│	│	2142	│	│	│
Malton d.	│	│	│	2007	│	│	2105	│	│	2205	│	│	│
York 124 180 a.	1951	2007	2023	2035	2054	2108	2135	2154	2208	2233	2256	2311	2356
York 124 d.	1954	2009	...	2038	...	2110	2141	...	2209	2239	...	2313	...
Leeds 124 a.	2016	2033	...	2104	...	2132	2204	...	2232	2302	...	2339	...
Leeds 188a d.	2018	2034	...	2105	...	2134	2206	...	2234	2304	...	2340	...
Dewsbury 188a d.	2029	│	...	│	...	│	│	...	│	2315	...	2351	...
Huddersfield 188a d.	2039	2052	...	2123	...	2152	2224	...	2252	2324	...	0001	...
Manchester Victoria d.	2110	2123	...	2156	...	2225	2255	...	2324	2356	...	0032	...
Manchester Picc 188a a.	2120	│	...	│	...	│	2309	...	│	0003	...	0039	...
Manchester Airport ✈ a.	2135	│	...	│	...	│	2323	...	│	0021	...	0056	...
Liverpool Lime Street a.	...	2201	...	2232	...	2302	...	...	0001	...	...	...	...

		②–⑤	⑥	①	Ⓐ	⑥	⚒	⚒	⑥
Liverpool Lime Street d.	⚒	...	...	...	...	...	...	...	...
Manchester Airport ✈ d.		0038	0038	0045	...	...	...	...	0412
Manchester Picc. 188a d.		0053	0101	0100	0242	0242	...	...	0426
Manchester Victoria d.		│	│	│	│	│	...	...	│
Huddersfield 188a d.		│	0131	│	0350c	0351e	...	...	0540c
Dewsbury 188a d.		│	│	│	│	│	...	...	│
Leeds 188a a.		0204	0208	0206	0409	0430	...	...	0559
Leeds 124 d.		0213	0217	0211	0420	0432	...	...	0600
York 124 a.		0253	0255	0238	0500	0457	...	...	0623
York 124 180 d.		...	...	...	...	...	0506	0625	0629
Malton d.		...	...	...	...	...	│	0648	│
Scarborough a.		...	...	...	...	...	│	0715	│
Thirsk d.		...	...	...	...	...	0533	...	│
Northallerton 124 180 d.		...	...	...	...	...	0538	...	0650
Darlington 124 180 d.		...	...	...	...	...	0605d	...	0702
Middlesbrough a.		...	...	...	...	...	0629	...	│
Durham 124 180 d.		...	...	...	...	...	...	...	0718
Newcastle 124 180 a.		...	...	...	...	...	...	...	0736

	Ⓐ	⑥	Ⓐ	⚒	⚒	⚒	⚒	⚒		⚒	⚒	⚒	⚒	⚒		⚒	⚒	⚒	⚒	⚒	⚒	⚒	⚒	⚒	⚒	⚒	⚒
Liverpool Lime Street d.	...	...	...	...	0520	...	0556	...	...	0625	...	0656	...	0725	...	...	0754	...	0825	...	0856	...	0925	...	0956	...	1025
Manchester Airport ✈ d.	0422	0454	0503	...	│	0548	│	0617	...	│	0644	│	0717	│	...	0747	│	0817	│	0847	│	0917	│	0946	│	1017	│
Manchester Picc 188a d.	0436	0510	0517	...	│	0605	│	0634	...	│	0705	│	0735	│	...	0805	│	0835	│	0905	│	0935	│	1005	│	1035	│
Manchester Victoria d.	│	0520	0527	...	0559	0617	0632	0647	...	0702	0717	0732	0747	0802	...	0817	0832	0847	0902	0916	0932	0947	1002	1017	1032	1047	1102
Huddersfield 188a d.	0540	0554c	0556	...	0627	0645	0700	0715	...	0730	0745	0800	0815	0830	...	0843	0900	0915	0930	0943	1000	1015	1030	1043	1100	1115	1130
Dewsbury 188a d.	│	│	│	...	0636	0654	│	│	...	│	0754	│	0824	│	...	0853	│	│	│	0954	│	│	│	1054	│	│	│
Leeds 188a a.	0559	0614	0615	...	0649	0708	0719	0734	...	0749	0807	0819	0837	0849	...	0907	0919	0934	0949	1007	1019	1035	1049	1107	1119	1135	1149
Leeds 124 d.	0600	0618	0618	...	0654	0711	0721	0735	...	0752	0812	0821	0839	0852	...	0912	0921	0939	0952	1012	1021	1038	1052	1112	1121	1138	1152
York 124 a.	0623	0640	0640	...	0717	0735	0743	0801	...	0816	0836	0843	0902	0916	...	0934	0943	1001	1016	1035	1043	1102	1116	1135	1143	1201	1216
York 124 180 d.	0629	0643	0643	0646	0718	0738	0747	0804	...	0818	0838	0847	0903	0918	...	0940	0947	1002	1018	1039	1047	1103	1119	1139	1147	1202	1218
Malton d.	│	│	│	│	│	│	0814	│	...	│	│	0915	│	│	...	│	1014	│	│	│	1114	│	│	│	1214	│	│
Scarborough a.	│	│	│	│	│	│	0840	│	...	│	│	0940	│	│	...	│	1040	│	│	│	1140	│	│	│	1242	│	│
Thirsk d.	│	│	│	0704	0735	0756	...	│	...	│	0855	...	│	│	...	0956	...	│	│	1057	...	│	│	1156	...	│	│
Northallerton 124 180 d.	0650	0704	0704	0714	0743	0804	...	│	...	0839	0903	...	│	0939	...	1007	...	│	1039	1107	...	│	1140	1207	...	│	1240
Darlington 124 180 d.	0702	0716	0716	│	0755	│	...	0835	...	0851	│	...	0935	0951	...	│	...	1034	1052	│	...	1135	1152	│	...	1234	1253
Middlesbrough a.	│	│	│	0746	│	0837	...	│	...	│	0939	...	│	│	...	1038	...	│	│	1138	...	│	│	1238	...	│	│
Durham 124 180 d.	0718	0733	0733	...	0811	...	...	0852	...	0907	...	...	0951	1007	...	...	...	1051	1108	...	...	1151	1208	...	...	1251	1309
Newcastle 124 180 a.	0736	0751	0751	...	0829	...	...	0906	...	0925	...	...	1006	1024	...	...	...	1106	1125	...	...	1205	1223	...	...	1304	1326

	⚒	⚒	⚒	⚒	⚒	⚒	⚒	⚒	⚒	⚒	⚒		⚒	⚒	⚒	⚒	⚒	⚒	⚒	⚒	⑥	Ⓐ	⚒	⚒	⚒	⚒	⚒
Liverpool Lime Street d.	...	1056	...	1125	...	1156	...	1225	...	1256	...	...	1325	...	1356	...	1425	...	1456	...	1525	1525	...	1556	...	1625	...
Manchester Airport ✈ d.	1047	│	1117	│	1147	│	1217	│	1247	│	1317	...	│	1347	│	1417	│	1447	│	1517	│	│	1547	│	1617	│	1642
Manchester Picc 188a d.	1105	│	1135	│	1205	│	1235	│	1305	│	1335	...	│	1405	│	1435	│	1505	│	1535	│	│	1605	│	1635	│	1705
Manchester Victoria d.	1117	1132	1147	1202	1217	1232	1247	1302	1317	1332	1347	...	1402	1417	1433	1447	1502	1517	1532	1547	1602	1602	1617	1632	1647	1702	1717
Huddersfield 188a d.	1143	1200	1215	1230	1245	1300	1315	1330	1344	1400	1415	...	1430	1443	1500	1515	1530	1543	1600	1615	1630	1630	1645	1700	1715	1730	1745
Dewsbury 188a d.	1154	│	│	│	1254	│	│	│	1354	│	│	...	│	1454	│	│	│	1554	│	│	│	│	1654	│	│	│	1754
Leeds 188a a.	1207	1219	1235	1249	1307	1319	1335	1349	1407	1419	1437	...	1449	1507	1519	1535	1549	1607	1618	1634	1649	1649	1707	1720	1734	1749	1807
Leeds 124 d.	1211	1221	1238	1252	1312	1321	1337	1352	1412	1421	1439	...	1452	1512	1521	1539	1552	1612	1621	1636	1652	1652	1711	1721	1735	1752	1812
York 124 a.	1235	1243	1301	1316	1336	1343	1401	1417	1434	1443	1501	...	1517	1534	1543	1601	1617	1637	1643	1701	1716	1717	1737	1743	1801	1816	1837
York 124 180 d.	1238	1247	1302	1318	1339	1347	1402	1419	1438	1447	1502	...	1519	1538	1547	1602	1619	1639	1647	1703	1718	1719	1738	1746	1802	1818	1846
Malton d.	│	1314	│	│	│	1414	│	│	│	1514	│	...	│	│	1614	│	│	│	1714	│	│	│	│	1815	│	│	│
Scarborough a.	│	1340	│	│	│	1440	│	│	│	1540	│	...	│	│	1640	│	│	│	1740	│	│	│	│	1843	│	│	│
Thirsk d.	1256	...	│	│	1356	...	│	│	1456	...	│	...	│	1556	...	│	│	1656	...	│	│	│	1755	...	│	│	1904
Northallerton 124 180 d.	1307	...	│	1339	1407	...	│	1440	1507	...	│	...	1540	1607	...	│	1640	1706	...	│	1739	1740	1807	...	│	1839	1917
Darlington 124 180 d.	│	...	1334	1351	│	...	1434	1453	│	...	│	...	1553	│	...	1634	1653	│	...	│	1751	1752	│	...	1834	1851	│
Middlesbrough a.	1338	...	│	│	1438	...	│	│	1539	...	│	...	│	1639	...	│	│	1738	...	│	│	│	1840	...	│	│	1950
Durham 124 180 d.	...	...	1351	1409	...	...	1451	1509	...	...	1547	...	1609	...	...	1650	1709	...	...	1749	1807	1811	...	...	1850	1907	...
Newcastle 124 180 a.	...	...	1407	1425	...	...	1504	1526	...	...	1601	...	1623	...	...	1704	1728	...	...	1802	1824	1827	...	...	1903	1926	...

	⚒	Ⓐ	⑥	Ⓐ	⑥	⚒	⚒	⚒	⑥	Ⓐ	Ⓐ	⑥	⚒	⚒	⚒	⚒	⚒	⚒		Ⓐ	⑥	Ⓐ	⑥	Ⓐ	⑥	⚒	⚒
Liverpool Lime Street d.	1656	...	...	1725	1724	...	1756	...	1825	1825	...	...	1856	...	...	1925	...	1956	...	2025	2025	...	...	2124	2124	...	...
Manchester Airport ✈ d.	│	1717	1717	│	│	1747	│	1817	│	│	1847	1847	│	...	1917	│	1947	│	2019	│	│	2044	2105	│	│	2206	...
Manchester Picc 188a d.	│	1735	1735	│	│	1805	│	1835	│	│	1905	1905	│	...	1935	│	2005	│	2035	│	│	2105	2122	│	│	2222	2247
Manchester Victoria d.	1731	1747	1747	1802	1802	1817	1832	1847	1902	1902	1917	1917	1932	...	1947	2002	2017	2032	2047	2102	2102	2117	2132	2202	2202	2232	│
Huddersfield 188a d.	1801	1815	1815	1830	1830	1844	1900	1915	1930	1930	1943	1943	2000	...	2015	2030	2043	2100	2116	2130	2130	2146	2200	2230	2230	2300	2322
Dewsbury 188a d.	│	│	│	│	│	1854	│	│	│	│	1954	1954	│	...	│	│	2054	│	│	│	│	│	│	│	│	2309	2331
Leeds 188a a.	1820	1834	1834	1849	1849	1908	1919	1934	1949	1949	2007	2007	2019	...	2034	2049	2107	2119	2135	2149	2149	2207	2219	2249	2249	2322	2345
Leeds 124 d.	1821	1839	1835	1852	1852	1913	1921	1939	1952	1952	2012	2012	2021	...	2039	2052	2112	2121	2137	2152	2152	2209	2221	2252	2252	2323	...
York 124 a.	1843	1905	1901	1916	1916	1934	1943	2003	2016	2016	2034	2034	2043	...	2103	2116	2137	2143	2202	2216	2216	2231	2243	2316	2317	2350	...
York 124 180 d.	1845	1908	1914	1918	1918	1936	1945	...	2018	2023	2036	2041	2046	2105	...	2118	2139	2145	...	2218	2221	2245	2245	2317	...	...	...
Malton d.	1914	│	│	│	│	│	2013	...	│	│	│	│	2114	2128	...	│	│	2208	...	│	│	2308	2308	│	...	...	...
Scarborough a.	1944	│	│	│	│	│	2042	...	│	│	│	│	2138	2154	...	│	│	2235	...	│	│	2335	2335	│	...	...	...
Thirsk d.	...	1926	│	│	1935	1956	...	...	│	│	2059	2104	...	...	...	│	2157	...	...	│	│	...	...	2340	...	...	...
Northallerton 124 180 d.	...	│	1935	1939	│	2007	...	...	2039	2044	2110	2116	...	...	...	2139	2206	...	...	2239	2242	...	...	2348	...	...	...
Darlington 124 180 d.	...	1945	1948	1951	1953	│	...	...	2051	2056	│	│	...	...	...	2151	│	...	...	2251	2255	...	...	0002	...	...	...
Middlesbrough a.	...	│	│	│	│	2038	...	...	│	│	2142	2145	...	...	...	│	2237	...	...	│	│	...	...	│	...	...	...
Durham 124 180 d.	...	2002	2005	2007	2010	...	...	...	2107	2114	...	...	...	...	...	2207	...	...	...	2307	2311	...	...	0025t	...	...	...
Newcastle 124 180 a.	...	2015	2020	2021	2024	...	...	...	2124	2130	...	...	...	...	...	2222	...	...	...	2324	2330	...	...	0056	...	...	...

	⑥	Ⓐ	⑥g	⑤	①–④	⑥h	
Liverpool Lime Street d.	2224	2224	...	...	...	🚌	
Manchester Airport ✈ d.	│	│	2319	2319	2319	2320	...
Manchester Picc 188a d.	│	│	2335	2335	2335	2345	...
Manchester Victoria d.	2302	2302	2347	2345	2345	│	...
Huddersfield 188a d.	2330	2330	0015	0013	0039	0045	...
Dewsbury 188a d.	│	│	0024	0021s	0048s	0110	...
Leeds 188a a.	2349	0007	0037	0035	0101	0135	...
Leeds 124 d.	2352	0011	0042	0036	0111	0135	...
York 124 a.	0024	0051	0108	0104	0151	0225	...
York 124 180 d.	...	...	...	...	...	...	...
Malton d.	...	...	...	...	...	...	...
Scarborough a.	...	...	...	...	...	...	...
Thirsk d.	...	...	...	...	...	...	...
Northallerton 124 180 d.	...	...	...	...	...	...	...
Darlington 124 180 d.	...	...	...	...	...	...	...
Middlesbrough a.	...	...	...	...	...	...	...
Durham 124 180 d.	...	...	...	...	...	...	...
Newcastle 124 180 a.	...	...	...	...	...	...	...

		⑦	⑦a	⑦a	⑦	⑦	⑦a	⑦	⑦	⑦	⑦	⑦a	⑦	⑦	⑦	⑦a	⑦	⑦	⑦	⑦
Liverpool Lime Street d.	⑦	b	🚌	🚌	b	b	🚌	a	b	...	...	🚌	b	a	b	🚌	a	b	a	0812
Manchester Airport ✈ d.		0100	0100	0330	0422	...	0455	...	0627	...	...	0605	0726	...	0746	0700	...	0822	...	│
Manchester Picc 188a d.		0123	0125	0355	0440	0545	0520	...	0644	...	...	0630	0743	...	0806	0725	...	0836	...	│
Manchester Victoria d.		│	│	│	│	│	│	...	│	...	...	│	│	...	0825	│	...	0848	...	0857
Huddersfield 188a d.		0153	0225	0455	0510	0614	0620	...	0716	...	...	0740	0815	...	0900	0825	...	0915	...	0930
Dewsbury 188a d.		│	│	│	│	│	0645	...	0725	...	...	0805	0824	...	│	│	...	│	...	│
Leeds 188a a.		0212	0300	0530	0529	0633	0710	...	0738	...	...	0830	0837	...	0919	0910	...	0935	...	0947
Leeds 124 d.		0213	0300	0530	0531	0636	0710	...	0741	...	...	...	0842	0841	0921	...	0921	0938	0938	0952
York 124 a.		0240	0350	0620	0558	0703	0800	...	0806	...	...	...	0904	0903	0944	...	0944	1002	1002	1016
York 124 180 d.		...	...	...	...	...	...	0814	0814	0838	0840	...	0914	0914	0947	...	0946	1004	1004	1018
Malton d.		...	...	...	...	...	...	│	│	│	0903	...	│	│	1014	...	1014	│	│	│
Scarborough a.		...	...	...	...	...	...	│	│	│	0930	...	│	│	1040	...	1040	│	│	│
Thirsk d.		...	...	...	...	...	...	│	│	0855	...	...	│	│	...	...	...	1021	1021	│
Northallerton 124 180 d.		...	...	...	...	...	...	│	│	0904	...	...	│	│	...	...	...	1029	1029	1039
Darlington 124 180 d.		...	...	...	...	...	...	0846	0846	│	...	...	0945	0945	...	...	...	│	│	1052
Middlesbrough a.		...	...	...	...	...	...	│	│	0934	...	...	│	│	...	...	...	1101	1101	│
Durham 124 180 d.		...	...	...	...	...	...	0902	0902	...	...	...	1002	1002	...	...	...	...	...	1108
Newcastle 124 180 a.		...	...	...	...	...	...	0916	0916	...	...	...	1019	1019	...	...	...	...	...	1124

a – From Oct. 27.
b – Until Oct. 20.
c – Arrives 7–9 minutes earlier.
d – Arrives 0553.
e – Arrives 0326.
f – Departs 1647 on ⑥.
g – Until Oct. 19.
h – From Oct. 26.
s – Stops to set down only.
t – Arrives 0018.

TP Most trains convey 🍷 LIVERPOOL and MANCHESTER - YORKSHIRE and THE NORTH EAST 188

	⑦	⑦	⑦	⑦	⑦	⑦	⑦	⑦	⑦	⑦	⑦	⑦	⑦	⑦		⑦	⑦	⑦	⑦	⑦	⑦	⑦	⑦	⑦	⑦	⑦	⑦
Liverpool Lime Street ... d.	0856	...	0923	...	0955	...	1024	...	1052	...	1125	...	1152	...	...	1224	...	1252	...	1325	...	1352	...	1425	...	1452	...
Manchester Airport ✈ d.	|	0919	|	...	|	1020	|	...	|	...	|	...	|	1219	...	|	1245r	|	1319	|	1346	|	1419	|	1447	|	1519
Manchester Picc 188a d.	|	0933	|	...	|	1037	|	...	|	1140	|	...	|	1235	...	|	1305r	|	1335	|	1405	|	1435	|	1505	|	1535
Manchester Victoria ... d.	0932	0946	1002	1016	1032	1047	1102	1117	1132	|	1202	1217	1230	1247	...	1302	1317	1332	1347	1402	1417	1432	1447	1502	1517	1532	1547
Huddersfield ... 188a d.	1000	1015	1030	1043	1100	1115	1130	1145	1200	1215	1230	1245	1300	1315	...	1330	1345	1400	1415	1430	1445	1500	1515	1530	1543	1600	1615
Dewsbury ... 188a d.	|	|	|	1054	|	|	|	1157	|	|	|	1254	|	|	...	|	1354	|	|	|	1456	|	|	|	1556	|	|
Leeds ... 188a a.	1019	1034	1049	1107	1119	1134	1149	1209	1219	1234	1250	1307	1319	1334	...	1349	1407	1419	1434	1449	1509	1519	1534	1549	1609	1619	1634
Leeds ... 124 d.	1021	1039	1052	1112	1121	1136	1151	1211	1221	1238	1252	1312	1321	1339	...	1352	1412	1421	1439	1452	1512	1521	1539	1551	1612	1621	1637
York ... 124 a.	1043	1101	1114	1134	1143	1201	1214	1235	1243	1300	1315	1335	1343	1401	...	1414	1434	1443	1501	1515	1535	1544	1601	1614	1634	1643	1700
York ... 124 180 d.	1047	1102	1115	1138	1147	1202	1218	1239	1247	1302	1320	1338	1347	1402	...	1415	1439	1447	1502	1518	1542	1547	1602	1615	1639	1645	1702
Malton ... d.	1114	|	|	|	1214	|	|	|	1314	|	|	|	1414	|	...	|	|	1514	|	|	|	1614	|	|	|	1713	|
Scarborough ... a.	1140	|	|	|	1240	|	|	|	1340	|	|	|	1440	|	...	|	|	1540	|	|	|	1640	|	|	|	1741	|
Thirsk ... d.	...	|	|	|	...	|	|	1256	...	|	|	1355	...	|	...	|	1457	...	|	|	1605	...	|	|	1659	...	|
Northallerton ... 124 180 d.	...	|	1136	1201	...	|	1239	1304	...	|	1341	1403	...	|	...	|	1506	...	|	1539	1614	...	|	1636	|	...	|
Darlington ... 124 180 d.	...	1134	1148	|	...	|	1252	|	...	1334	1353	|	...	|	...	1446	|	...	1534	1551	|	...	1634	1649	|	...	1734
Middlesbrough ... a.	...	|	|	1231	...	|	|	1334	...	|	|	1433	...	|	...	|	1536	...	|	|	1650	...	|	|	1738	...	|
Durham ... 124 180 d.	...	1150	1205	...	...	|	1308	...	...	1350	1410	...	...	1448	...	1502	...	...	1550	1607	...	...	1651	1706	...	...	1751
Newcastle ... 124 180 a.	...	1204	1219	...	...	1259	1324	...	...	1404	1423	...	...	1507	...	1515	...	...	1604	1621	...	...	1704	1723	...	...	1804

	⑦	⑦	⑦	⑦	⑦	⑦	⑦	⑦	⑦	⑦	⑦	⑦	⑦	⑦	⑦	⑦	⑦	⑦		⑦	⑦	⑦	⑦	⑦	⑦	⑦	⑦
Liverpool Lime Street ... d.	1525	...	1552	...	1625	...	1652	...	1725	...	1752	...	1825	...	1852	...	1925	...	...	2011	2025	2052	...	2124	...	2220	...
Manchester Airport ✈ d.	|	1547	|	1619	|	1647	|	1719	|	1747	|	1819	|	1847	|	1919	|	1953	...	|	|	|	2104	|	2206	|	2335
Manchester Picc 188a d.	|	1605	|	1635	|	1705	|	1735	|	1807	|	1835	|	1905	|	1935	|	2013	...	|	|	|	2122	|	2223	|	2349
Manchester Victoria ... d.	1602	1617	1632	1647	1702	1717	1732	1747	1802	1817	1832	1847	1902	1917	1932	1947	2002	2032	...	2047	2102	2127	2132	2202	2233	2302	2359
Huddersfield ... 188a d.	1630	1643	1700	1715	1729	1745	1800	1815	1830	1843	1900	1915	1930	1943	2000	2015	2030	2100	...	2115	2130	...	2200	2231	2300	2330	0026
Dewsbury ... 188a d.	|	1656	|	|	|	1756	|	|	|	1856	|	|	|	1956	|	|	|	|	...	|	|	...	|	|	2309	|	0035s
Leeds ... 188a a.	1649	1709	1719	1734	1746	1809	1819	1834	1850	1909	1919	1934	1949	2009	2019	2034	2049	2119	...	2134	2147	...	2219	2250	2322	0014	0046
Leeds ... 124 d.	1652	1712	1721	1738	1752	1812	1821	1838	1852	1912	1921	1939	1951	2012	2021	2039	2052	2121	...	2139	2151	...	2221	2252	2324	0015	0048
York ... 124 a.	1715	1734	1743	1801	1816	1834	1843	1901	1914	1934	1943	2002	2013	2034	2043	2103	2116	2143	...	2202	2213	...	2243	2316	2351	0045	0114
York ... 124 180 d.	1717	1736	1746	1802	1818	1835	1847	1902	1918	1940	1947	2003	2016	2038	2047	...	2118	2149	...	2204	2218	...	2247	2318	...	...	...
Malton ... d.	|	|	1813	|	|	|	1914	|	|	|	2014	|	|	|	2112	...	|	|	...	2231	|	...	2314	|	...	...	...
Scarborough ... a.	|	|	1839	|	|	|	1940	|	|	|	2040	|	|	|	2138	...	|	|	...	2301	|	...	2342	|	...	...	...
Thirsk ... d.	|	1800	...	|	|	1856	...	|	|	1958	...	|	|	2104	...	...	|	2212	...	...	|	...	...	2341	...	...	...
Northallerton ... 124 180 d.	1738	1810	...	|	1839	1903	...	|	1944	2006	...	|	2037	2115	...	...	2146	2222	...	...	2246	...	...	2349	...	...	...
Darlington ... 124 180 d.	1750	|	...	1834	1851	|	...	1936	1956	|	...	2035	2049	|	...	...	2158	|	...	...	2258	...	...	0002	...	...	...
Middlesbrough ... a.	|	1840	...	|	|	1934	...	|	|	2038	...	|	|	2143	...	...	|	2252	...	...	|	...	...	|	...	...	...
Durham ... 124 180 d.	1806	...	...	1851	1907	...	...	1953	2012	...	...	2052	2106	...	...	...	2215	...	...	...	2315	...	...	0018	...	...	...
Newcastle ... 124 180 a.	1820	...	...	1904	1921	...	...	2008	2028	...	...	2109	2122	...	...	...	2230	...	...	...	2346	...	...	0048	...	...	...

– Until Sept. 8.

s – Stops to set down only.

TP HULL - MANCHESTER 188a

km		⚒	⚒A	⚒	⚒	⚒	⚒	⚒	⚒		⚒	⚒	⚒	⚒	⑥	Ⓐ	⑦	⑦C	⑦R	⑦C	⑦R	⑦C	⑦R	⑦R	⑦	⑦
0	Hull ... d.		...	...	0535	...	0640	...	0738		2040	...	2140	...	2224	2240		A	A	A	A	A	...	...	...	0841
34	Selby ... d.		...	...	0612	...	0712	...	0812	and at	2112	...	2212	...	2256	2312		...	...	...	...	...	...	...	...	0915
83	Leeds ... a.		...	...	0638	...	0738	...	0838	the same	2137	...	2237	...	2318	2334		...	...	...	...	...	...	...	...	0937
83	Leeds ... 188 d.		0545	...	0640	...	0740	...	0840	minutes	2139	...	2240	2253	2324	2340		0545	0646	0645	0745	0745	...	...	...	0940
98	Dewsbury ... 188 d.		0557	...	0651	...	0751	...	0852	past each	2151	...	2256	2310	2335	2351		0610	0657	0710	0756	0810	...	...	...	0951
111	Huddersfield ... 188 d.		0607	0628	0659	0728	0800	0828	0901	hour until	2201	2228	2311	2333	2345	0004		0635	0707	0735	0805	0835	0828	0900	0928	1001
140	Stalybridge ... d.		0625	0653	0721	0753	0821	0853	0922		2222	2253	2332	0001	|	|		0720	0725	0820	0824	0920	0857	0922	0957	1022
152	Manchester Piccadilly 188 a.		0653	0709	0736	0808	0836	0908	0938	▽	2238	2308	2352	0017	0020	0055		0745	0738	0845s	0849	0945	0912	0935f	1012	1038
168	Manchester Airport ✈ a.		0708	...	...	...	...	...	...		2302r	...	...	...	...	...		0810	0804	0910	0910	...	...	...	...	...

	⑦	⑦	⑦		⑦	⑦	⑦	⑦	⑦	⑦
Hull ... d.	...	0943	...	...	...	2041	...	2143	...	2227
Selby ... d.	...	1015	...	and at	...	2114	...	2215	...	2302
Leeds ... a.	...	1037	...	the same	...	2137	...	2239	...	2324
Leeds ... 188 d.	...	1040	...	minutes	...	2139	...	2240	...	2330
Dewsbury ... 188 d.	...	1051	...	past each	...	2150	...	2256	...	2341
Huddersfield ... 188 d.	1028	1100	1128	hour until	2128	2159	2228	2311	2328	2354
Stalybridge ... d.	1053	1122	1153		2153	2221	2253	2332	2353	...
Manchester Piccadilly 188 a.	1108	1137	1209	▽	2208	2236	2308	2351	0008	...
Manchester Airport ✈ a.	...	...	...		...	...	...	...	...	...

	⚒	Ⓐ	⚒	⚒	⚒	P	⚒	⚒	⚒	⚒	⚒
Manchester Airp't ✈ d.		...	...	...	...		...	...	...	...	...
Manchester Pic 188 d.		...	0545	0617	0645	and at	1817	1847	1917	1947	2017
Stalybridge ... d.		...	0557	0630	0700	the same	1830	1900	1930	2000	2030
Huddersfield ... 188 d.		...	0620	0655	0722	minutes	1855	1922	1955	2023	2054
Dewsbury ... 188 d.		...	0631	...	0733	past each	...	1931	...	2032	...
Leeds ... 188 a.		...	0645	...	0746	hour until	...	1945	...	2045	...
Leeds ... d.		0621	0648	...	0748		...	1948	...	2048	...
Selby ... d.		0645	0711	...	0811	▽	...	2011	...	2115	...
Hull ... a.		0723	0748	...	0845		...	2048	...	2152	...

	⚒	⚒	⚒	⚒	⚒	⑥	Ⓐ	⑦	⑦C	⑦F	⑦R	⑦C	⑦F	⑦C	⑦R	⑦	⑦	⑦	⑦	⑦		⑦	⑦	⑦	⑦	⑦
Manchester Airport ✈ d.	...	...	...	...	...	...	...		0605	0627	...	0700	0726	...	...	...	...	...	...	...		...	...	...	...	...
Manchester Piccadilly 188 d.	2047	2117	2147	2217	2247	2317	2317		0630	0644	0717	0725	0743	0800	0815	0852f	0917	0950f	1017	1047	and at	2117	2147	2217	2247	2317
Stalybridge ... d.	2100	2130	2200	2230	2300	2330	2330		0655	0657	0730	0750	0756	0825	0830	0903	0930	1001	1030	1100	the same	2130	2200	2230	2300	2329
Huddersfield ... 188 d.	2122	2155	2223	2255	2322	2357	0002		0740	0716	0748	0825	0815	0945	0855	0923	0955	1025	1055	1122	minutes	2155	2223	2255	2320	2356
Dewsbury ... 188 d.	2131	...	2232	...	2331	...	...		0805	0725	...	|	0824	...	...	0932	...	1034	...	1131	past each	...	2232	...	2329	...
Leeds ... 188 a.	2146	...	2246	...	2345	...	...		0830	0738	...	0910	0837	...	...	0945	...	1045	...	1143	hour until	...	2245	...	2342	...
Leeds ... d.	2148	...	2248	...	...	...	...		...	...	...	...	...	...	...	0948	...	1048	...	1147		...	2247	...	...	...
Selby ... d.	2211	...	2311	...	...	...	...		...	...	...	...	...	...	...	1010	...	1109	...	1208	▽	...	2308	...	...	...
Hull ... a.	2246	...	2345	...	...	...	...		...	...	...	...	...	...	...	1048	...	1142	...	1241		...	2341	...	...	...

– From York (Table **188**).
– Also calls Manchester Victoria (d. 2337).
– From Oct. 27 by 🚌.

F – Until Oct. 20; to Newcastle (Table **188**).
P – The 1647 from Manchester Piccadilly departs Selby 1812 and arrives Hull 1849.
R – Until Oct 20.
f – Manchester **Victoria**.
r – Arrives 2257 on Ⓐ.
s – Stops to set down only.
▽ – Timings may vary by up to 2 minutes.

EM 2nd class GRIMSBY - LINCOLN - NEWARK 189

km		Ⓐ	ⒶN	Ⓐ	ⒶL	Ⓐ	Ⓐ	Ⓐ		Ⓐ	Ⓐ	Ⓐ		Ⓐ	Ⓐ		Ⓐ	Ⓐ	Ⓐ	⑥	⑥N	⑥L	⑥
0	Grimsby Town ... 178 193 d.		...	0556	...	0703	...	0920	...	...	1128	1349	...	...	1545	...	...	1828	2117		...	...	0650
22	Barnetby ... 178 193 d.		...	0616	...	0722	...	0939	...	...	1147	1409	...	...	1605	...	...	1847	2144		...	...	0709
47	Market Rasen ... d.		...	0632	...	0739	...	0955	...	...	1203	1425	...	...	1622	...	...	1902	2200		...	...	0726
71	Lincoln ... d.		0526	0654	0730	0759	0907	1016	...	1135	1223	1446	...	1542	1643	...	1818	1923	2219		0526	0730	0746
97	Newark North Gate ... a.		0555	0722	0755	0824	0932	1040	...	1200	1250	1511	...	1611	1711	...	1846	1953	...		0555	0756	0812

	⑥	⑥		⑥	⑥	⑥		⑥	⑥	⑥	⑦	⑦N	⑦	⑦	⑦Nt	⑦Nv	⑦	⑦	⑦t	⑦v	⑦N	⑦t	⑦v
Grimsby Town ... 178 193 d.	...	0920	...	...	1128	1349	...	1600	1828	1945		...	...	...	1403	...	...	...	1825	...	...	2022	...
Barnetby ... 178 193 d.	...	0939	...	...	1147	1409	...	1619	1847	2004		...	...	...	1422	...	...	...	1844	...	...	2042	...
Market Rasen ... d.	...	0955	...	...	1203	1425	...	1635	1902	2020		...	...	...	1437	...	...	...	1859	...	...	2057	...
Lincoln ... d.	0901	1015	...	1135	1223	1446	...	1655	1923	2039		0847	1105	1245	1508f	1508	1544	1709	1922	1922	2100	2123c	2126
Newark North Gate ... a.	0925	1044	...	1158	1252	1511	...	1722	1951	...		0915	1130	1310	1536	1536	1609	1734	1946	1946	2127	2152	2155

	Ⓐ	Ⓐ	Ⓐ	Ⓐ	Ⓐ		Ⓐ	ⒶP	Ⓐ	ⒶP	Ⓐ	Ⓐ	Ⓐ	Ⓐ	ⒶL	ⒶN	⑥	⑥	⑥	⑥	⑥	⑥	
Newark North Gate ... d.		0742	0831	0957	1050	...	1206	1302	...	1528	1646	1728	1935	2004	2036	2310		...	...	0820	0935	1049	...
Lincoln ... d.		0815	0902	1025	1114	...	1238	1330	1437	1555	1722r	1800	2002	2029	2103	2340		0540	0808	0855	1006j	1117	...
Market Rasen ... d.		0832	...	1042	...	...	1254	...	1454	...	1739	...	2019	...	...	...		0556	0825	...	1023	...	...
Barnetby ... 178 193 d.		0849	...	1058	...	...	1310	...	1510	...	1755	...	2035	...	...	...		0613	0849	...	1039	...	...
Grimsby Town ... 178 193 a.		0912	...	1122	...	...	1335	...	1534	...	1818	...	2056	...	...	...		0641	0912	...	1102	...	...

	⑥	⑥P		⑥	⑥P	⑥		⑥	⑥	⑥L	⑥N	⑦	⑦v	⑦t	⑦	⑦Nt	⑦	⑦v	⑦t	⑦N	⑦	⑦L	⑦
Newark North Gate ... d.	1205	1302	...	...	1528	...	...	1807	2030	2036	2209		1140	1140	1335	...	1645	1755	1755	1928	1953	2037	2210
Lincoln ... d.	1236	1330	...	1452	1556	1722	...	1835	2056	2103	2243		1207	1207	1402	1628	1716	1820	1822	1957	2019	2103	2237
Market Rasen ... d.	1254	...	...	1510	...	1738	...	1852	2113	...	...		...	1223	...	1644	...	...	1838	...	...	...	...
Barnetby ... 178 193 d.	1310	...	...	1526	...	1754	...	1908	...	...	...		...	1238	...	1659	...	...	1853	...	...	...	...
Grimsby Town ... 178 193 a.	1334	...	...	1550	...	1818	...	1934	...	...	...		...	1304	...	1721	...	...	1915	...	...	...	...

– [12] and 🍷 Lincoln - London Kings Cross and v.v. (Table **180**).
– To/from Nottingham (Table **184**).

P – To Peterborough (Table **186**).
c – Arrives 2115.
f – Arrives 1456.
j – Arrives 0959.
r – Arrives 1713.
t – Until Sept. 8.
v – From Sept 15.

190 LEEDS - BRADFORD - HALIFAX - MANCHESTER - CHESTER

2nd class NT

km			⚒	⚒	⚒	⚒	⚒	⚒	⚒	⚒	⚒	⚒	⚒	⚒	⚒	⚒	⚒		⚒	⚒	⚒	⚒	⚒	⚒	⚒	⚒	⚒
0	**Leeds** d.	⚒	0512	0519	0539	0617	0621	0637	0719	0721	0736	0818	0821	0839	0918	0920	0938		1338	1418	1420	1438	1518	1520	1538	1618	1620
15	**Bradford** Interchange d.		0537	|	0602	0641	|	0701	0745	|	0805f	0842	|	0902	0941	|	1003	and	1403	1441	|	1503	1541	|	1603	1641	|
28	Halifax d.		0550	|	0614	0654	|	0715	0757	|	0816	0854	|	0914	0954	|	1015	at the	1415	1545	|	1515	1554	|	1615	1654	|
	Dewsbury d.		|	0538	|	|	0638	|	|	0738	|	|	0838	|	|	0938	|	same	|	|	1438	|	|	1538	|	|	1638
	Brighouse d.		|	0555	|	|	0653	|	|	0754	|	|	0854	|	|	0954	|	minutes	|	|	1454	|	|	1554	|	|	1655
42	Hebden Bridge d.		0605	0615	0631	0705	0714	0730	0809	0815	0832	0905	0915	0931	1006	1015	1032	past	1432	1506	1515	1532	1606	1615	1632	1703	1716
49	Todmorden d.		0614	0622	0639	0714	0721	0737	0817	0823	0839	0914	0923	0939	1015	1023	1039	each hour	1439	1515	1523	1539	1615	1623	1639	1714	1723
63	Rochdale d.		0627	0639	0650	0727	0738	0749	0830	0839	0850	0925	0939	0950	1026	1039	1050	until	1450	1526	1539	1550	1626	1639	1650	1729	1739
81	**Manchester** Victoria a.		0642	0654	0705	0743	0753	0805	0848	0854	0905	0942	0954	1005	1042	1054	1105		1505	1542	1554	1605	1642	1654	1705	1745	1753
113	Warrington Bank Q **160** a.		...	...	0744	...	...	0844	...	...	0946	...	...	1044	...	...	1138	❖	1538	...	...	1638	...	...	1734t	...	...
142	**Chester** **160** a.		...	...	0809	...	...	0909	...	...	1016	...	...	1109	...	...	1203		1616	...	...	1706	...	...	1805t	...	...

		⚒	⚒	⚒	⚒	⚒	⚒	⚒	⚒	⚒	⚒	⚒	⚒	⚒	⚒	⚒	⚒	⚒	⚒	⚒		⑦	⑦	⑦		⑦	⑦	⑦
Leeds	d.	1639	1718	1720	1737	1818	1823	1839	1919	1921	1939	2018	2021	2039	2118	2121	2138	2218	2221	2239	⑦	0818	0918	1015		2118	2211	2319
Bradford Interchange	d.	1703	1741	|	1802	1841	|	1902	1944	|	2002	2041	|	2103	2141	|	2203	2241	|	2303		0841	0942	1042	and	2142	2238	2342
Halifax	d.	1715	1754	|	1814	1854	|	1914	1956	|	2014	2054	|	2115	2154	|	2215	2254	|	2315		0853	0954	1054	at the	2154	2250	2354
Dewsbury	d.	|	|	1738	|	|	1840	|	|	1938	|	|	2038	|	|	2138	|	|	2238	|		|	|	|	same	|	|	|
Brighouse	d.	|	|	1754	|	|	1856	|	|	1954	|	|	2054	|	|	2154	|	|	2255	|		|	|	|	minutes	|	|	|
Hebden Bridge	d.	1732	1806	1815	1830	1906	1915	1931	2007	2015	2031	2105	2115	2132	2205	2215	2232	2305	2314	2327		0908	1009	1109	past	2208	2304	0008
Todmorden	d.	1739	1814	1822	0838	1915	1923	1939	2014	2023	2038	2114	2123	2139	2214	2223	2239	2314	...	2334		0915	1017	1017	each hour	2216	2312	0016
Rochdale	d.	1750	1824	1839	1849	1926	1939	1950	2026	2039	2049	2126	2139	2150	2225	2239	2250	2325	...	2350		0930	1031	1031	until	2230	2326	0030
Manchester Victoria	a.	1805	1844	1854	1905	1942	1954	2005	2042	2054	2104	2147	2154	2206	2243	2254	2310	2342	...	0005		0946	1047	1047		2246	2342	0046
Warrington Bank Q **160**	a.	1839	...	...	1937	...	...	2042	...	...	2149	...	...	...	...	...	...	...	...	...		...	...	...	❖	...	...	...
Chester **160**	a.	1914	...	...	2005	...	...	2107	...	...	2216	...	...	...	...	...	...	...	...	...		...	...	...		...	...	...

			⚒	⚒	⚒	⚒	⚒	⚒	⚒	⚒	⚒	⚒	⚒	⚒	⚒	⚒	⚒	⚒	⚒	⚒	⚒	⚒	⚒	⚒		⚒	⚒	⚒
Chester **160**	d.	⚒	...	...	...	...	0617r	...	...	0720t	...	...	0821	...	...	0921	...	...	1023	...	...	1124	...	...		1517	...	...
Warrington Bank Q **160**	d.		...	...	...	...	0644	...	...	0748t	...	...	0849	...	...	0946	...	...	1046	...	...	1147	...	...	and	1541	...	...
Manchester Victoria	d.		0545	0622	0637	0655	0719	0736	0756	0820	0837	0857	0920	0937	0958	1020	1037	1058	1120	1136	1158	1219	1237	1258	at the	1619	1637	165
Rochdale	d.		0606	0635	0651	0709	0733	0750	0811	0834	0851	0911	0933	0951	1012	1033	1051	1112	1133	1150	1212	1233	1251	1312	same	1635	1651	170
Todmorden	d.		0623	0645	0708	0724	0743	0806	0826	0844	0907	0925	0944	1007	1023	1043	1107	1123	1143	1206	1223	1245	1307	1323	minutes	1646	1707	172
Hebden Bridge	d.		0631	0652	0715	0730	0749	0813	0833	0850	0915	0931	0951	1014	1030	1051	1114	1132	1150	1214	1231	1252	1314	1330	past	1653	0714	173
Brighouse	d.		|	|	0733	|	|	0831	|	|	0932	|	|	1032	|	|	1132	|	|	1231	|	|	1332	|	each hour	|	0732	|
Dewsbury	d.		|	|	0745	|	|	0846	|	|	0944	|	|	1044	|	|	1144	|	|	1244	|	|	1344	|	until	|	0744	|
Halifax	d.		0645	0707	|	0742	0805	|	0844	0905	|	0943	1007	|	1043	1107	|	1144	1207	|	1242	1307	|	1343		1709	|	174
Bradford Interchange	d.		0659	0723	|	0758	0820	|	0900	0920	|	0959	1024	|	1059	1124	|	1200	1223	|	1258	1322	|	1359	❖	1725	|	175
Leeds	a.		0722	0745	0804	0820	0846	0904	0926	0943	1004	1021	1045	1103	1121	1145	1203	1222	1244	1303	1321	1344	1403	1421		1746	1803	181

		⚒	⚒	⚒	⚒	⚒	⚒	⚒	⚒	⚒		⚒	⚒	⚒	⚒	⚒	⚒	⚒		⑦	⑦	⑦	⑦		⑦	⑦	⑦	⑦
Chester **160**	d.	1614	...	...	1716	...	...	1825t	...	...	...	1920	...	...	2020	...	...	...	⑦	...	...	...	...		...	...	...	...
Warrington Bank Q **160**	d.	1644	...	...	1744	...	...	1848t	...	...	...	1944	...	...	2048	...	...	...		...	...	...	...	and	...	...	...	...
Manchester Victoria	d.	1719	1737	1758	1820	1837	1858	1918	1937	1958	...	2019	2039	2058	2119	2158	2258	2319		0854	0956	1056	1156	at the	1957	2057	2157	225
Rochdale	d.	1737	1751	1813	1838	1851	1913	1934	1951	2013	...	2033	2053	2113	2132	2212	2311	2333		0908	1009	1110	1210	same	2010	2110	2210	231
Todmorden	d.	1748	1807	1828	1848	1907	1928	1944	2007	2024	...	2043	2109	2124	2142	2223	2322	2349		0924	1025	1125	1225	minutes	2025	2126	2225	232
Hebden Bridge	d.	1754	1814	1835	1854	1914	1935	1950	2014	2030	...	2049	2116	2130	2149	2230	2329	2356		0930	1031	1131	1231	past	2031	2132	2231	233
Brighouse	d.	|	1831	|	|	1932	|	|	2032	|	...	|	2134	|	|	|	|	|		|	|	|	|	each hour	|	|	|	|
Dewsbury	d.	|	1844	|	|	1944	|	|	2044	|	...	|	2146	|	|	|	|	|		|	|	|	|	until	|	|	|	|
Halifax	d.	1809	|	1847	1909	|	1946	2005	|	2042	...	2104	|	2142	2206	2241	2340	0011		0945	1046	1146	1246		2046	2147	2246	234
Bradford Interchange	d.	1825	|	1904	1925	|	2004	2021	|	2058	...	2119	|	2158	2221	2257	2357	0027		1001	1102	1202	1302		2101	2203	2302	000
Leeds	a.	1846	1902	1926	1946	2003	2028	2041	2103	2122	...	2143	2205	2223	2243	2320	0019	0046		1021	1122	1222	1322		2124	2223	2322	002

f – Arrives 0757. r – On ⑥ departs 0624. t – ⑥ only. ❖ – Timings may vary by ± 3 minutes.

191 YORK - LEEDS - BLACKBURN - BLACKPOOL and MANCHESTER - BLACKBURN

2nd class NT

km			⚒	⚒	⚒	⚒	⚒	⚒	⚒		⚒	⚒	⚒	⚒	⚒		⑦	⑦	⑦	⑦		⑦	⑦	⑦	⑦
0	**York** **124 188** d.	⚒	...	0512	...	0612	...	0712	...	❖	2012	...	...	...	2217	⑦	...	...	...	...	⊡	...	...	...	...
41	**Leeds** **124 188** d.		...	0555	...	0651	...	0749	...		2051	...	2200	...	2300		...	...	...	0947		...	2049	...	214
56	**Bradford** Interchange d.		...	0616	...	0712	...	0814	...	and	2112	...	2220	...	2320		...	...	...	1010	and	...	2111	...	221
69	Halifax d.		...	0627	...	0724	...	0825	...	at the	2124	...	2232	...	2332		...	...	...	1022	at the	...	2123	...	222
83	Hebden Bridge d.		...	0643	...	0740	...	0841	...	same	2141	...	2249	...	2349		...	...	...	1039	same	...	2138	...	224
	Manchester Victoria d.		0600	|	0704	|	0804	|	0904	minutes	|	2204	|	2304	|		0833	0859	1000	|	minutes	2102	|	2202	|
	Rochdale d.		0614	|	0718	|	0818	|	0918	past	|	2218	|	2318	|		0854	0920	1021	|	past	2122	|	2222	|
	Todmorden d.		0629	|	0735	|	0835	|	0933	each	|	2235	|	2333	|		0909	0935	1036	|	each	2137	|	2237	|
103	Burnley Manchester Road d.		0645	0703	0751	0803	0851	0903	0951	hour	2203	2251	2310	2349	0009		0925	0951	1052	1100	hour	2153	2203	2253	230
113	Accrington d.		0655	0712	0801	0812	0901	0912	1001	until	2212	2301	2319	0001	0018		0936	1002	1103	1109	until	2203	2212	2303	231
123	**Blackburn** **191** d.		0706	0722	0812	0821	0912	0922	1012		2221	2313	2328	0013	0028		0952	1016	1117	1122		2217	2221	2317	232
142	**Preston** **156 191** a.		...	0745	...	0844	...	0941	...		2239	...	2348	...	...		...	...	...	1139		...	2239	...	234
171	**Blackpool** North **156 191** a.		...	0809	...	0908	...	1007	...		2305	...	0014	...	...		...	...	...	1203		...	2305	...	000

			⚒	⚒	⚒	⚒	⚒	⚒		⚒	⚒	Ⓐ	⚒		⑦	⑦	⑦	⑦		⑦	⑦	⑦	⑦	⑦	⑦	⑦
Blackpool North. **156 191**	d.	⚒	0519	...	0620	...	0720	...	★	2117	...	2215	...	⑦	...	...	...	0918	⊡	1917	...	2017	...	2117	...	...
Preston **156 191**	d.		0546	...	0648	...	0746	...		2145	...	2246	...		...	...	...	0947		1942	...	2044	...	2144	...	...
Blackburn **191**	d.		0603	0619	0705	0714	0803	0819	and	2203	2219	2302	2319		0748	0812	0912	1007	and	2004	2016	2104	2113	2201	2213	230
Accrington	d.		0611	0627	0713	0721	0811	0827	at the	2211	2227	2310	2327		0756	0821	0921	1015	at the	2012	2025	2112	2122	2211	2222	230
Burnley Manchester Road	d.		0620	0638	0722	0732	0820	0838	same	2220	2238	2319	2338		0807	0832	0932	1024	same	2021	2036	2121	2133	2221	2233	231
Todmordon	d.		|	0655	|	0749	|	0855	minutes	|	2255	|	2355		0824	0849	0949	|	minutes	|	2055	|	2150	|	2250	233
Rochdale	d.		|	0709	|	0806	|	0909	past	|	2311	|	0009		0838	0903	1003	|	past	|	2109	|	2204	|	2304	234
Manchester Victoria	a.		|	0724	|	0824	|	0924	each	|	2333	|	0023		0859	0924	1024	|	each	|	2130	|	2225	|	2325	001
Hebden Bridge	d.		0642	...	0743	...	0842	...	hour	2242	...	2340	...		...	...	...	1046	hour	2043	...	2143	...	2243	...	...
Halifax	d.		0658	...	0759	...	0858	...	until	2257	...	|	...		...	...	...	1101	until	2058	...	2203	...	2258	...	...
Bradford Interchange	d.		0712	...	0814	...	0912	...		2310	...	|	...		...	...	...	1118		2113	...	2220	...	2314	...	...
Leeds **124 188**	a.		0734	...	0837	...	0935	...		2332	...	0011	...		...	...	...	1138		2134	...	2242	...	2334	...	...
York **124 188**	a.		0811	...	0911	...	1009	...		0021	...	...	...		...	...	...	...		...	...	...	...	...	...	...

⊡ – Timings may vary by ± 4 minutes.

★ – Timings may vary by ± 4 minutes. The 2021 departure from Blackpool North arrives York 2320.

❖ – Timings may vary by ± 4 minutes. York d. 1806 (not 1812).

192 HULL - DONCASTER - SHEFFIELD

2nd class NT

km			⑥	Ⓐ	⚒	⚒	⚒B	⚒	⚒A	⚒		⚒	⚒A	⑥	Ⓐ	⚒A	⚒	⚒B	⚒A	⚒		⑦	⑦	⑦A
0	**Hull** **181** d.	⚒	0524	0524	0630	0725	0826	0853	0927	0951	and at	1752	1827	1854	1854	1927	1955	2048	2125	2248	⑦	0845	0927	1029
17	Brough d.		0541	0541	0643	0737	0841	0910	0939	1010	the same	1809	1839	1911	1911	1939	2012	2104	2138	2304		0902	0939	104
38	Goole d.		0601	0559	0658	0752	0856	0928	0954	1028	minutes	1829	1854	1929	1929	|	2029	2120	2153	2320		0918	0954	1056
66	**Doncaster** **181** a.		0631	0631	0719	0819	0919	1000	1019	1059	past each	1859	1919	1958	2004	2019	2102f	2149	2223	2347		0943	1019	1119
66	**Doncaster** **193** d.		0635	0635	0719	0820	0920	1004	1020	1104	hour until	1904	1920	2003	2005	2021	2104	2149	2226	2349		...	1021	1122
90	Meadowhall **193** d.		0703	0710	0738	0839	0938	1034	1039	1134		1934	1938	2034	2035	2039	2135	2210	2244	0008		...	1039	1144
96	**Sheffield** **193** a.		0712	0718	0747	0848	0949	1044	1048	1144	▽	1944	1949	2044	2043	2049	2143	2219	2255	0018		...	1049	1151

		⑦	⑦	⑦B		⑦B	⑦	⑦
Hull **181**	d.	1127	1229	1329		2129	2159	2254
Brough	d.	1139	1241	1341	and	2141	2211	2311
Goole	d.	1154	1256	1356	hourly	2156	2228	2327
Doncaster **181**	a.	1217	1321	1419	until	2219	2257	2357
Doncaster **193**	d.	1219	1323	1421		2221	...	...
Meadowhall **193**	d.	1239	1341	1439	▽	2242	...	...
Sheffield **193**	a.	1248	1350	1448		2250	...	...

			⚒	⚒	⚒A		⚒A	⚒	⚒A	⚒	⚒A	
Sheffield **193**	d.	⚒	0542	0627	0724	...	0825	0830	0925	0929	1025	and at
Meadowhall **193**	d.		0548	0633	0732	...	0832	0836	0932	0936	1032	the same
Doncaster **193**	a.		0611	0704	0757	...	0856	0908	0954	1008	1056	minutes
Doncaster **181**	d.		0613	0706	0759	...	0857	0908	0956	1008	1059	past each
Goole	d.		0638	0732	0819	...	0919	0941	1019	1035	1119	hour until
Brough	d.		0701	0753	0840	...	0937	0959	1037	1052	1137	
Hull **181**	a.		0721	0813	0859	...	0958	1024	1052	1114	1153	▽

A – From/to Bridlington (Table **177**).
B – From/to Scarborough (Table **177**).

f – Arrives 2058 on ⑥.

▽ – Timings may vary by ± 3 minutes.

The table continues on the next page ► ► ► ►

NT 2nd class · SHEFFIELD - DONCASTER - HULL 192

	⚒A	⚒	⚒A	⚒	⚒A	⚒	⚒A	⚒	⚒	⚒		⑦	⑦B	⑦B	⑦B	⑦B	⑦B		⑦B	⑦A	⑦A	⑦	⑦	⑦
heffield .... 193 d.	1724	1730	1825	1830	1925	1930	2025	2030	2130	2228	⑦	0806	0836	0925	1025	1134	1225		1725	1825	1925	2025	2125	2225
leadowhall .... 193 d.	1732	1736	1832	1836	1933	1937	2032	2036	2136	2234		0812	0843	0931	1031	1141	1231	and	1731	1831	1931	2031	2131	2231
oncaster .... 193 a.	1758	1808	1857	1908	1954	2009	2054	2108	2157	2255		0843	0903	0950	1050	1200	1250	hourly	1750	1850	1950	2050	2150	2250
oncaster .... 181 d.	1800	1808	1859	1909	2000	2009	2058	2108	2159	2257		0846	0905	0952	1054	1203	1255	until	1802	1852	1951	2052	2152	2252
oole .... d.	1822	1835	1918	1935	|	2036	2118	2136	2218	2318		0912	0924	1011	1117	1225	1319		1824	1916	2015	2115	2215	2315
rough .... d.	1842	1856	1936	1956	2037	2053	2133	2157	2239	2335		0931	0938	1026	1133	1242	1334	▽	1841	1934	2032	2131	2233	2334
ull .... 181 a.	1857	1915	1956	2014	2053	2114	2149	2216	2254	2349		0945	0953	1040	1146	1256	1349		1856	1949	2048	2147	2248	2354

A – From Bridlington (Table **177**). **B** – From Scarborough (Table **177**). ▽ – Timings may vary by ± 3 minutes.

TP · CLEETHORPES - DONCASTER - SHEFFIELD - MANCHESTER 193

km			②–⑥	①	⚒	⚒	⚒	⚒	⚒		⚒	Ⓐ	⑥	⚒	⚒		⑦	⑦	⑦	⑦	⑦		⑦	⑦	⑦
0	**Cleethorpes** .... 178 d.	⚒	...	...	...	...	0505	0626	0726		1726	1826	1826	1926	2026	⑦	...	...	...	0926	1026		1829	1926	2026
5	Grimsby Town ..... 178 189 d.		...	...	...	...	0513	0634	0734	and	1734	1834	1834	1934	2034		...	...	...	0934	1034	and	1837	1934	2034
29	Barnetby .... 178 189 d.		...	...	...	...	0532	0653	0753	at	1753	1853	1853	1953	2053		...	...	...	0953	1053	at	1856	1953	2053
48	Scunthorpe .... d.		...	...	...	...	0547	0708	0808	the	1808	1909	1908	2008	2108		...	...	...	1009	1108	the	1908	2008	2108
85	**Doncaster** .... a.		...	...	...	...	0624	0738	0838	same	1838	1939	1940	2038	2138		...	...	...	1039	1138	same	1941	2038	2141
85	**Doncaster** .... 192 d.		...	...	...	0534	0625	0742	0842	minutes	1842	1942	1942	2042	2142		...	...	0945	1043	1143	minutes	1942	2042	2144
109	Meadowhall .... 192 d.		...	...	...	0557	0654	0759	0902	past	1902	2002	2002	2104	2202		...	...	1005	1102	1202	past	2001	2102	2203
115	**Sheffield** .... 192 a.		...	...	...	0608	0705	0806	0908	each	1909	2009	2009	2109	2208		...	...	1012	1110	1208	each	2008	2108	2210
115	**Sheffield** .... 206 d.		0324	0345	0511	0609	0708	0808	0911	hour	1911	2011	2011	2111	2211		0751	0911	1014	1111	1211	hour	2011	2111	2213
175	Stockport .... 206 a.		|	|	|	0653	0752	0852	0953	until	1953	2052	2052	2152	2252		0832	0953	1055	1156	1252	until	2053	2156	2303
184	**Manchester** Piccadilly 206 a.		0452	0437	0603	0703	0802	0902	1002		2002	2101	2101	2204	2301		0842	1003	1106	1210	1304		2104	2205	2314
200	**Manchester** Airport ✈ .... a.		0510	0510	0626	0725	0825	0925	1025		2024	2126	2124	...	2322		0902	1025	1124	1229	1324		2125	2223	...

		⚒	⚒	⚒	⚒		⚒	⚒	⚒	⚒	⚒	⚒	⚒	Ⓐ		⑦	⑦	⑦	⑦	⑦		⑦	⑦	⑦	⑦
lanchester Airport ✈ .... d.	⚒	0555	0653	0753	0853		1553	1653	1753	1853	1953	2055	2153	2330	⑦	0749b	0846b	0956	1055	1156		1956	2055	2156	2256
lanchester Piccadilly . 206 d.		0615	0718	0819	0918	and	1618	1718	1818	1918	2019	2118	2219	2350		0813	0910	1014	1119	1219	and	2018	2119	2219	2320
tockport .... 206 d.		0626	0728	0828	0928	at	1628	1728	1828	1928	2028	2128	|	|		0823	0918	1022	1129	1228	at	2028	2128	2227	2328
heffield .... 206 a.		0706	0809	0909	1009	the	1709	1810	1908	2008	2108	2208	2309	0120		0908	1008	1105	1209	1308	the	2109	2211	2309	0010
heffield .... 192 d.		0708	0810	0911	1011	same	1711	1811	1911	2011	2111	2211	2309	...		0910	1010	1110	1210	1310	same	2111	2212	2311	...
leadowhall .... 192 d.		0714	0816	0917	1017	minutes	1717	1817	1917	2017	2117	2217	|	...		0916	1016	1116	1216	1316	minutes	2117	2218	|	...
oncaster .... 192 a.		0732	0838	0937	1035	past	1735	1835	1937	2035	2145	2235	2350t	...		0936	1036	1136	1234	1334	past	2135	2236	2340	...
oncaster .... d.		0733	0840	0939	1037	each	1737	1837	1939	2037	2147	2237	...	...		0938	1038	1139	1237	1337	each	2137	2239	...	...
cunthorpe .... d.		0800	0906	1005	1103	hour	1803	1903	2003	2103	2213	2311	...	...		1004	1104	1205	1303	1403	hour	2203	2305	...	...
arnetby .... 178 189 d.		0816	0921	1020	1118	until	1818	1918	2018	2118	2228	2326	...	...		1018	1119	1219	1317	1417	until	2217	2319	...	...
rimsby Town ...... 178 189 a.		0844	0939	1041	1139		1841	1940	2039	2139	2249	2347	...	...		1040	1141	1241	1339	1441		2239	2343	...	...
leethorpes .... 178 a.		0853	0952	1053	1151		1854	1950	2051	2151	2301	2359	...	...		1053	1151	1253	1349	1451		2251	2353	...	...

– From Oct. 27 a replacement 🚌 services operate between Manchester Airport and Manchester Piccadilly departing at 0735 and 0835. **t** – Arrives 2333 on ⑥.

NT 2nd class only · SHEFFIELD - MANCHESTER (Hope Valley service) 194

km			⚒	Ⓐ	⑥	Ⓐ	⑥	⚒	⑥	Ⓐ	⚒	⚒	⚒	⚒	⑥	Ⓐ	⚒	⑥	Ⓐ	⚒	⚒	⚒	⚒	⚒	⚒	⑥
0	**Sheffield** .... d.	⚒	...	0618	0620	0712	0714	0732	0813	0833	0914	1014	1114	1214	1314	1314	1414	1514	1545	1614	1714	1814	1914	2014	2114	2224
16	Grindleford .... d.		...	0633	0635	0728	0728	|	0827	|	0929	1029	1128	1228	1328	1326	1429	1528	|	1629	1729	1829	1929	|	2127	2238
18	Hathersage .... d.		...	0638	0639	0732	0732	|	0831	|	0932	1032	1132	1232	1332	|	1432	1532	|	1632	1732	1832	1932	2032	2131	2242
24	Hope .... d.		...	0646	0647	0740	0739	|	0838	|	0940	1040	1139	1239	1339	1335	1440	1539	1606	1640	1740	1840	1940	2038	2138	2249
32	Edale .... d.		...	0653	0654	0747	0747	|	0846	0857	0947	1047	1147	1247	1347	|	1447	1547	|	1647	1747	1847	1947	|	2145	2256
41	Chinley .... d.		0648	0701	0702	0756	0755	0803	0854	0905	0955	1055	1155	1255	1355	1348	1455	1555	1619	1655	1755	1855	1955	2051	2153	2304
67	**Manchester** Piccadilly a.		0733	0738	0739	0828	0833	0837	0931	0940	1033	1133	1233	1333	1431	1433	1533	1631	1658	1731	1831	1933	2033	2128	2232	2341

	Ⓐ	Ⓐ		⑦	⑦		⑦	⑦
heffield .... d.	2247	2327	⑦	0814	0914		2014	2216
rindleford .... d.	2302	2342		0827	0928	and	2027	2230
athersage .... d.	2306	2346		0831	0932	hourly	2031	2234
ope .... d.	2313	2354		0838	0939	until	2038	2241
dale .... d.	2321	0001		0846	0947		2046	2249
hinley .... d.	2329	0009		0854	0955	▽	2054	2257
anchester Piccadilly a.	0015	0035		0935	1033		2132	2337

		⚒	⚒	Ⓐ	⑥	⚒	Ⓐ	⑥	⚒		⚒
Manchester Piccadilly ...... d.	⚒	0546	0638	0711	0749	0849	0941	0949	1049		1549
Chinley .... d.		0615	0713	0748	0824	0923	1015	1024	1122	and	1623
Edale .... d.		0623	0722	0757	0832	0932	1024	1032	1131	hourly	1632
Hope .... d.		0630	0729	0804	0839	0938	1031	1039	1137	until	1638
Hathersage .... d.		0637	0736	0810	0846	0945	1039	1046	1144		1645
Grindleford .... d.		0641	0740	0814	0850	0949	1043	1050	1148	▽	1649
Sheffield .... a.		0656	0804	0832	0905	1005	1104	1105	1204		1704

	⚒	⚒	⑥	Ⓐ	⚒	Ⓐ	⚒	⑥	Ⓐ	⚒	⑥	Ⓐ	⚒		⑦	⑦a	⑦b	⑦b	⑦a		⑦	⑦	A	⑦	⑦
lanchester Piccadilly d.	1642	1649	1742	1742	1749	1819	1849	1949	1949	2049	2119	2119	2228	⑦	0742	0831	0845	0931	0945	...	1045	1142		2042	2145
hinley .... d.	1709	1724	1810	1809	1824	1858	1924	2024	2024	2122	2156	2212	2253		0821	0906	0921	1007	1020	...	1120	1219	and	2117	2220
dale .... d.	|	1733	|	|	1832	...	1932	2032	|	2130	|	|	2301		0830	0915	0930	1016	1029	...	1129	1228	hourly	2126	2229
ope .... d.	|	1739	|	|	1839	...	1939	2039	|	2137	|	2225	2307		0837	0922	0937	1023	1036	...	1136	1235	until	2132	2236
athersage .... d.	|	1746	|	|	1846	...	1946	2046	|	2143	|	2232	2315		0845	0929	0944	1030	1043	...	1143	1242		2139	2243
rindleford .... d.	|	1750	|	|	1850	...	1950	2050	|	2147	|	|	2319		0849	0933	0947	1033	1047	...	1147	1246	▽	2142	2247
heffield .... a.	1739	1810	1837	1847	1905	...	2005	2105	2056	2209	2228	2252	2336		0904	0948	1002	1048	1102	...	1202	1302		2159	2302

– From Sept. 15 the 1245 departure from Manchester is retimed to depart at 1252. **a** – Until Sept. 8. **b** – From Sept. 15. ▽ – Timings may vary by ± 4 minutes.

CC, LE · LONDON - SOUTHEND and CAMBRIDGE 199

ypical off-peak journey time in hours and minutes
READ DOWN ↓ READ UP ↑

Journey times may be extended during peak hours on Ⓐ (0600 - 0900 and 1600 - 1900) and also at weekends.
The longest journey time by any train is noted in the table heading.

LONDON FENCHURCH STREET - SOUTHEND CENTRAL — Longest journey: 1 hour 08 minutes CC

km	A				
0	0h00	↓	d.**London** F Street....a.	↑	1h04
8	0h09		d.West Ham..........d.		0h56
12	0h14	↓	d.Barking..........d.	↑	0h50
39	0h34		d.Basildon..........d.		0h29
56	0h53	↓	a.**Southend** Central..d.	↑	0h10
63	1h03		a.Shoeburyness........d.		0h00

From London Fenchurch Street: 0500⚒/0638⑦ and at least every 30 minutes (every 10 - 15 minutes 0840Ⓐ - 2204Ⓐ) until 2349.

From Southend Central*: 0424⚒/0544⑦ and at least every 30 minutes (every 15 minutes 0424Ⓐ - 2020Ⓐ) until 2249⑦, 2336⚒.

A – During peak hours on Ⓐ (0600 - 0900 and 1600 - 1900) trains may not make all stops.

* – Trains depart Shoeburyness 10 minutes before Southend Central.

LONDON LIVERPOOL STREET - SOUTHEND VICTORIA — Longest journey: 1 hour 14 minutes LE

km					
0	0h00	↓	d.**London** L Street....a.	↑	0h58
6	0h07		d.Stratford..........d.		0h49
32	0h25	↓	d.Shenfield..........d.	↑	0h35
53	0h43		d.Rayleigh..........d.		0h16
64	0h54	↓	a.**Southend** Airport....d.	↑	0h05
66	1h01		a.**Southend** Victoria .d.		0h00

From London Liverpool Street: 0535⚒/0714⑦ and at least every 30 minutes (every 20 minutes 0635⚒ - 2213⚒) until 2342.

From Southend Victoria: 0400⚒/0615⑦ and at least every 30 minutes (every 20 minutes 0626⚒ - 2130⚒) until 2254⑦/2300⚒.

LONDON LIVERPOOL STREET - CAMBRIDGE — Longest journey: 1 hour 39 minutes LE

km					
0	0h00	↓	d.**London** L Street....a.	↑	1h23
10	0h12		d.Tottenham Hale .....d.		0h57
36	0h29	↓	d.Harlow Town..........d.	↑	0h38
48	0h42		d.Bishops Stortford ...d.		0h28
67	0h54	↓	d.Audley End..........d.	↑	0h15
89	1h23		a.**Cambridge**..........d.		0h00

From London Liverpool Street: on Ⓐ at 0528, 0558 and every 30 minutes until 1628, 1643, 1707, 1713, 1737, 1743, 1807, 1813, 1837, 1843, 1907, 1911, 1928 and every 30 minutes until 2258, 2328, 2358⑤; on ⑥ at 0520, 0558, 0628, 0658 and every 30 minutes until 2328, 2358; on ⑦ at 0742, 0828, 0857 and at the same minutes past each hour until 2228, 2257.

From Cambridge: on Ⓐ at 0448, 0520, 0548, 0551, 0618, 0621, 0647, 0651, 0717, 0721, 0747, 0751, 0818, 0821, 0848, 0920, 1004, 1021 and at the same minutes past each hour until 1521, 1551 and every 30 minutes until 1851, 1920, 2004, 2021, 2104, 2121, 2204, 2221, 2251; on ⑥ at 0438, 0521, 0604, 0621 and at the same minutes past each hour until 2221, 2251; on ⑦ at 0732, 0751 and at the same minutes past each hour until 2132, 2232.

200 LONDON - HARWICH, IPSWICH and NORWICH

Most Norwich trains convey 🍸 LE

For Rail - Sea - Rail services London - Amsterdam and v.v. via Harwich and Hoek van Holland see Table **15a**.

km		⚒	⚒ P	⑥	Ⓐ	Ⓐ	⑥	Ⓐ	Ⓐ	⑥	⚒ C	⑥	Ⓐ	⑥	Ⓐ	⚒	⚒	⚒	⚒	Ⓐ	⑥	⚒	⚒	⚒	⚒	⚒
0	**London** Liverpool St d.		...	...	...	...	0534	0600	0625	0630	...	0638	0638	0700	0700	0730	0755a	0830	0900	0836	...	0930	1000	1030	1100	1102
48	Chelmsford d.		...	...	...	...	0610	0630	0658	0703	...	0712	0710	|	|	0802	|	0903	|	0912	...	1003	|	1103	|	|
84	Colchester d.		0540	0553	0610	...	0640	0650	0723	0723	...	0740	0743v	0747	0751	0823	0847	0923	0947	0951f	0951	1023	1047	1123	|	1148
97	Manningtree ★ d.		0549	0601	0618	...	0648	0658	0731	0731	...	0748	0751	0755	0759	0831	0855	0931	0955	1000	1000	1031	1055	1131	|	1156
112	**Harwich** Int'l ★ d.		|	0618	0636	...	|	|	|	|	0750	0809	0810	|	|	|	|	|	|	1017	1017	|	|	|	|	|
115	**Harwich** Town ★ a.		|	0623	0641	...	|	|	|	|		...	0815	|	|	|	|	|	|	1022	1022	|	|	|	|	|
111	**Ipswich** 205 d.		0600	...	...	0639	0700	0712	0744	0744	0821	...	...	0808	0812	0844	0908	0944	1008	...	...	1044	1108	1144	1155	1209
130	Stowmarket 205 d.		0611	...	...	0650	*0721*	0723	0755	0755	0834	...	...	|	0823	0855	|	0955	|	...	...	1055	|	1155	|	|
153	Diss d.		...	...	...	0703	*0734*	0735	0808	0808	...	...	...	0829	0836	0908	0929	1008	1029	...	...	1108	1129	1208	|	1230
185	**Norwich** a.		...	...	...	0724	*0753*	0755	0827	0827	...	...	...	0850	0856	0927	0950	1027	1051	...	...	1127	1150	1227	1230	1252

	⚒	⚒		⚒	⚒	Ⓐ	⚒	⚒	Ⓐ	⑥	Ⓐ	Ⓐ	⑥	⑥	Ⓐ	Ⓐ	⑥	Ⓐ	⑥	Ⓐ	Ⓐ	⑥	⚒	⑥	Ⓐ
London Liverpool St. d.	1130	1200	and	1430	1500	...	1530	1600	1630	1630	1644	1700	1700	...	1702	1730	1730	1750	1800	1810	1830	1830	1900	1902	1902
Chelmsford d.	1203	|	at	1503	|	...	1600	|	|	1703	1715	|	|	...	1736	|	1803	|	|	|	|	1903	|	|	|
Colchester d.	1223	1247	the	1523	1547	1614	1621	1647	1717	1723	1747t	|	1747	1751	1801	|	1823	1843	1847	1902	1920	1923	|	1948	1948
Manningtree ★ d.	1231	1255	same	1531	1555	1623	1629	1655	|	1731	1757	|	1755	1800	1809	1827	1831	1852	1855	1911	1929	1931	|	1956	1956
Harwich Int'l ★ d.	|	|	minutes	|	|	1641	|	|	|	|	1815	|	|	1817	|	|	|	|	|	|	|	|	|	|	|
Harwich Town ★ a.	|	|	past	|	|	1646	|	|	|	|	1822	|	|	1822	|	|	|	|	|	|	|	|	|	|	|
Ipswich 205 d.	1244	1308	each	1544	1608	...	1641	1708	1736	1744	...	1800	1808	...	1825	1839	1844	1904	1908	1923	1941	1944	1955	2009	2009
Stowmarket 205 d.	1255	|	hour	1555	|	...	1652	1719	1747	1755	...	|	|	...	1836	1850	1855	1916	|	1934	1953	1955	|	|	2021
Diss d.	1308	1329	until	1608	1629	...	1708	1732	1800	1808	...	1821	1829	...	1848	1904	1908	1930	1929	1947	2006	2008	|	2030	2034
Norwich a.	1327	1350		1627	1650	...	1727	1753	1822	1827	...	1842	1850	...	1909	1925	1927	1950	1950	2009	2027	2027	2030	2051	2053

	Ⓐ	⑥	Ⓐ	⑥	Ⓐ	⚒	⚒ L	⑥	Ⓐ	⚒	⚒	⚒	⚒	⚒	⚒	⑦	⑦ C	⑦	⑦	⑦	⑦	⑦ P	⑦	⑦	⑦	⑦
London Liverpool St. d.	1930	1930	1932	2000	2000	2030	...	2100	2100	2102	2130	2200	2230	2302	2330		...	...	0757	0800	0827	...	0908	0930	0908	0930
Chelmsford d.	|	2003	2002	|	|	2103	...	|	|	2134	2203	2228	2303	2334	0003		...	...	0842	0846	|	...	0956	|	0943	|
Colchester d.	2020	2023	2025	2047	2047	2123	...	2148	2147	2204	2223	2247	2323	0004	0023		...	0818	0905	0916	0928	0932	1013	1020	1013	1020
Manningtree ★ d.	2028	2031	2034	2055	2055	2132	...	2156	2156	2212	2232	2255	2332	0012	0032		...	0826	0914	0924	|	0940	1021	1029	1021	1029
Harwich Int'l ★ d.	|	|	2054	|	|	|	2138	2156	|	2228	|	|	|	|	|		0830	0843	0930	|	|	|	|	|	|	|
Harwich Town ★ a.	|	|	...	|	|	|	|	|	|	...	|	|	|	|	|		|	0848	*0948*	|	|	|	|	|	|	|
Ipswich 205 d.	2041	2044	...	2108	2108	2145	2204	2208	2209	...	2245	2308	2345	0030	0045		0902	...	...	0936	0946	0955v	1034	1041	1034	1041
Stowmarket 205 d.	2052	2055	...	|	2119	2156	...	...	2220	...	2257	...	2357	...	0057		0917	...	...	...	0957	1006	...	1053	...	1053
Diss d.	2105	2108	...	2129	2132	2209	...	...	2233	...	2311	...	0011	...	0111		...	...	...	...	1010	...	...	1106	...	1106
Norwich a.	2124	2127	...	2150	2151	2229	...	...	2253	...	2330	...	0036c	...	0136		...	...	...	...	1030	...	...	1127	...	1127

	⑦	⑦	⑦	⑦	⑦		⑦	⑦	⑦	⑦	⑦		⑦	⑦	⑦	⑦	⑦	⑦	⑦	⑦	⑦	⑦	⑦	⑦	⑦
London Liverpool St. d.	1008	1030	1100	1108	1130	and	1708	1730	1800	1808	1830	...	1900	1908	1930	2000	2008	2030	...	2108	2130	2208	2230	2308	2330
Chelmsford d.	1043	|	|	1143	|	at	1743	|	|	1843	|	...	|	1943	|	2033	2043	|	...	2143	|	2243	|	2343	|
Colchester d.	1113	1120	1147	1213	1220	the	1813	1820	1847	1913	1920	...	1947	2013	2020	2056	2113	2120	...	2213	2220	2313	2320	0013	0026
Manningtree ★ d.	1121	1129	|	1221	1229	same	1821	1829	|	1921	1929	...	1956	2021	2029	2107	2121	2129	...	2221	2230	2321	2330	0021	0036
Harwich Int'l ★ d.	|	|	|	|	|	minutes	|	|	|	|	|	...	|	|	|	2124	|	|	2120	|	|	|	|	|	|
Harwich Town ★ a.	|	|	|	|	|	past	|	|	|	|	|	...	|	|	|	...	|	|	|	|	|	|	|	|	|
Ipswich 205 d.	1134	1141	1205	1234	1241	each	1835	1841	1905	1934	1941	...	2008	2034	2041	...	2134	2141	2145	2234	2242	2334	2342	0039	0048
Stowmarket 205 d.	...	1153	1217	...	1253	hour	...	1853	1916	...	1953	...	2019	...	2053	...	...	2153	...	...	2254	...	2354	...	0100
Diss d.	...	1206	1230	...	1306	until	...	1906	1929	...	2006	...	2032	...	2106	...	...	2206	...	...	2307	...	0007	...	0113
Norwich a.	...	1227	1252	...	1327		...	1927	1951	...	2027	...	2054	...	2127	...	...	2227	...	...	2330	...	0027	...	0138

	Ⓐ	Ⓐ	Ⓐ	⑥	Ⓐ		⑥	Ⓐ	⑥	⚒ L	Ⓐ		⑥	Ⓐ	Ⓐ	Ⓐ	⑥	Ⓐ		⑥	Ⓐ	Ⓐ	Ⓐ	⑥	Ⓐ	⚒
Norwich d.		...	0455r	0500	0525r	...	0530	0555r	0600	...	0622	...	0630	...	...	0645	0700	0703	...	0730	0740	...	...	0800	0800	0830
Diss d.		...	0514r	0517	0544r	...	0547	0614r	0617	...	0640	...	0647	...	...	0704	0717	0721	...	0747	0758	...	...	0817	0817	0847
Stowmarket 205 d.		...	0527	0529	0557	...	|	0627	0629	...	0652	...	|	0703	...	0717	0729	0734	...	|	|	...	0810	0829	0829	|
Ipswich 205 d.		0512	0542	0543	0612	...	0609	0642	0643	0659	0707	...	0709	0717	...	0732	0743	0749	...	0809	0820	...	0826	0843	0843	0909
Harwich Town ★ d.		|	|	|	|	...	|	|	|	|	|	...	|	|	0716	|	|	|	...	|	|	0758	|	|	|	|
Harwich Int'l ★ d.		|	|	|	|	...	|	|	|	0727	|	...	|	|	0721	|	|	|	...	|	|	0803	|	|	|	|
Manningtree ★ d.		0524	0553	0553	0623	...	0619	0653	0653	...	0718	...	0719	0727	0738	0743	0753	0759	...	0819	|	0820	0836	0853	0853	0919
Colchester d.		0534	0605	0603	0635	...	0930	0705	0703	...	0730	...	0730	0738	0754t	|	0803	0810	...	0830	|	0837t	0845	|	0903	093
Chelmsford d.		0558	|	0621	|	...	|	|	0721	...	|	...	|	|	0819	|	0821	|	...	|	|	0859	0904	|	0921	|
London Liverpool St. a.		0634	0654	0655	0727	...	0719	0758	0755	...	0824	...	0819	0840	0858	0842	0855	0904	...	0919	0924	0936	0939	0952	1000	102

	⚒	⚒	⚒	⚒		⑥	Ⓐ	⚒	⚒		⚒	⚒	⚒	⚒	⚒		⚒	⚒	⚒	⚒		⑥	Ⓐ	⚒	⚒
Norwich d.	0900	...	0903	0930	...	1000	1000	1030	1100	and	1600	1630	1700	...	1703	...	1730	1800	1830	1900	...	...	1930	2000	...
Diss d.	|	...	0921	0947	...	1017	1017	1047	1117	at	1617	1647	|	...	1721	...	1747	1817	1847	1917	...	...	1947	2017	...
Stowmarket 205 d.	|	...	0933	|	...	1029	1029	|	1129	the	1629	|	|	...	1733	...	1759	1829	|	1929	...	...	|	2029	...
Ipswich 205 d.	0933	...	0947	1009	...	1043	1043	1109	1143	same	1643	1709	1733	...	1747	...	1813	1843	1909	1943	...	2009	2010	2043	...
Harwich Town ★ d.	|	0928	|	|	...	|	|	|	|	minutes	|	|	|	1728	|	...	|	|	|	|	...	|	|	|	...
Harwich Int'l ★ d.	|	0933	|	|	...	|	|	|	|	past	|	|	|	1733	|	...	|	|	|	|	...	|	|	|	2045
Manningtree ★ d.	|	0950	|	1019	...	1053	1053	1119	1153	each	1653	1719	|	1750	|	...	|	1853	1919	1953	...	2019	2020	2053	2058
Colchester d.	|	0959	1004	1030	...	|	1103	1130	1203	hour	1703	1730	|	1800	1804	...	1830	1903	1930	2003	...	2030	2030	2103	2112
Chelmsford d.	|	...	1021	|	...	|	1121	|	1221	until	1721	|	|	...	1821	...	|	1921	|	2021	...	|	|	2121	2140
London Liverpool St. a.	1030	...	1056	1119	...	1152	1155	1219	1255		1758	1819	1830	...	1858	...	1919	1955	2020	2055	...	2117	2119	2155	221

	⚒ C	⑥	Ⓐ	⚒ P	⚒		⑥	⚒	⚒	⚒ P	⚒	⚒	⑦	⑦	⑦	⑦	⑦		⑦	⑦	⑦	⑦		⑦	⑦
Norwich d.	...	...	2030	...	2100	...	...	...	2200	...	...	2305		...	0652	...	...	...	0800	0820	...	0900	and	...	1500
Diss d.	...	...	2047	...	2117	...	...	...	2217	...	...	2323		...	0709	...	...	...	0817	0838	...	0917	at	...	1517
Stowmarket 205 d.	2046	...	|	2114	2129	...	...	...	2229	2308	...	2336		...	0721	...	...	...	0829	0850	...	0929	the	...	1529
Ipswich 205 d.	2101	2109	2109	2128	2143	...	2152	2223	2243	2322	...	2349		...	0735	0751	0809	...	0843	0904	0909	0943	same	1509	1543
Harwich Town ★ d.	|	|	|	|	|	...	|	|	|	|	2328	...		...	|	|	...	...	|	|	|	|	minutes	|	|
Harwich Int'l ★ d.	2129	|	|	|	|	...	|	|	|	|	2333	...		0720	|	0816	|	...	|	|	|	|	past	|	|
Manningtree ★ d.	...	2119	2119	2138	2153	...	2202	2233	2253	2332	2350	...		0733	0745	...	0819	...	0853	|	0919	0953	each	1519	1553
Colchester d.	...	2130	2130	2151	2203	...	2212	2243	2303	2343	2359	...		0742	0755	...	0830	...	0903	0922	0930	1003	hour	1530	1603
Chelmsford d.	...	|	|	...	2221	...	2240	2309	2325	...	...	...		0804	|	...	0859	...	|	|	0959	|	until	1559	|
London Liverpool St. a.	...	2217	2219	...	2255	...	2314	2348	0003	...	...	...		0858	0900	...	0937	...	0955	1010	1037	1055		1637	1655

	⑦	⑦	⑦		⑦	⑦	⑦	⑦		⑦	⑦	⑦ P	⑦	⑦		⑦	⑦ C	⑦	⑦	⑦ P	⑦		⑦	⑦	⑦	⑦
Norwich d.	1522	...	1600	...	1620	...	1700	...	...	1800	...	...	1900	...	...	...	...	2000	...	...	2100	...	...	2200	...	2305
Diss d.	1540	...	1617	...	1638	...	1717	...	...	1817	...	...	1917	...	...	...	...	2017	...	...	2117	...	...	2217	...	2323
Stowmarket 205 d.	1552	...	1629	...	1650	...	1729	...	...	1829	...	1911	1929	...	...	...	2020	2029	...	2111	2129	...	...	2229	...	2336
Ipswich 205 d.	1616	1609	1643	...	1704	1709	1743	1809	...	1843	1909	1925	1943	2009	...	...	2037	2043	2109	2125	2143	...	2209	2243	...	2351
Harwich Town ★ d.	|	|	|	...	|	|	|	|	...	|	|	|	|	|	...	...	|	|	|	|	|	...	|	|	2253	...
Harwich Int'l ★ d.	|	|	|	...	|	|	|	|	...	|	|	|	|	|	...	2030	2105	|	|	|	|	...	|	|	2258	...
Manningtree ★ d.	|	1619	1653	...	|	1719	1753	1819	...	1853	1919	1935	1953	2019	...	2043	...	2053	2119	2135	2153	...	2219	2253	2315	...
Colchester d.	1623	1630	1703	...	1722	1730	1803	1830	...	1903	1930	1945	2003	2030	...	2052	...	2103	2130	2145	2203	...	2230	2303	2324	...
Chelmsford d.	|	1659	|	...	|	1759	|	1859	...	|	1959	...	|	2059	...	2110	...	|	2159	...	|	...	2259	2325	...	...
London Liverpool St. a.	1711	1737	1755	...	1810	1837	1855	1937	...	1955	2037	...	2055	2137	...	2146	...	2155	2237	...	2255	...	2337	0006	...	...

C – To/from Cambridge (Table **205**).
P – To/from Peterborough (Table **205**).
L – To/from Lowestoft (Table **201**).

a – Departs 0800 on ⑥.

c – Arrives 0030 on ②–⑥ mornings.
f – Arrives 0940.
r – Departs 4–5 minutes later until Oct. 4.
t – Arrives 7–8 minutes earlier.
v – Arrives 4–5 minutes earlier.

★ – All trains Manningtree - Harwich International - Harwich Town and v.v.
Manningtree - Harwich Town: on Ⓐ at 0558, 0618, 0724, 0751, 0900 and hourly until 1600, 1623, 1700, 1724, 1757, 1835, 1902, 1938, 2000, 2038, 2100, 2200, 2300, 2336; on ⑥ at 0700 and hourly until 2300, 2336; on ⑦ at 0926 and hourly until 2226.
Harwich Town - Manningtree on Ⓐ at 0524, 0624, 0652, 0716, 0758, 0828 and hourly until 1628, 1653, 1728, 1800, 1826, 1905, 1928, 2005, 2028, 2104, 2128, 2228, 2328; on ⑥ at 0628 and hourly until 2328; on ⑦ at 0853 and hourly until 2153.

LE 2nd class only IPSWICH - LOWESTOFT 201

km			Ⓐ	⑥	Ⓐ	⑥	⚒		⚒	Ⓐ	⑥	⚒	Ⓐ	⑥	⚒	⚒	⚒	⚒ H		⑦	⑦	⑦	⑦	⑦	⑦	⑦	⑦
0	**Ipswich** d.	⚒	0620	0717	0735	0817	0917	and at	1517	1554	1617	1717	1813	1817	1917	2017	2117	2217	⑦	1002	1202	1402	1602	1802	1908	2002	2202
17	Woodbridge d.		0637	0732	0753	0832	0932	the same	1532	1618f	1632	1732	1830	1832	1932	2032	2132	2232		1019	1219	1419	1619	1819	1925	2019	2219
36	Saxmundham d.		0744r	0754	0815	0854	0954	minutes	1554	1640	1654	1754	1851	1854	1954	2054	2154	2254		1040	1240	1440	1640	1840	1946	2040	2240
65	Beccles d.		0816	0825	0846	0925	1025	past each	1625	1719f	1725	1825	1925	1925	2025	2125	2225	2325		1112	1312	1512	1721g	1912	2021	2112	2312
79	**Lowestoft** a.		0833	0843	0906	0943	1043	hour until	1643	1736	1751	1843	1943	1943	2043	2143	2243	2343		1130	1330	1530	1739	1930	2039	2130	2330

		Ⓐ H	⑥	Ⓐ	Ⓐ	⑥	Ⓐ	⑥	⚒		⚒	⑥	Ⓐ	Ⓐ	⑥	⚒	⚒	⚒	⚒		⑦		⑦	⑦	⑦	⑦
owestoft d.	⚒	0525	0607	0614	0641	0707	0727	0807	0907	and at	1507	1607	1607	1702	1707	1807	1907	2007	2107	⑦	0805	and every	1605	1705	1805	2005
eccles d.		0541	0625	0630	0657	0725	0743	0825	0925	the same	1525	1625	1625	1725f	1725	1825	1925	2025	2125		0821	**two** hours	1621	1721	1821	2021
axmundham d.		0613	0657	0703	0729	0757	0816	0857	0957	minutes	1557	1657	1707t	1757	1757	1857	1957	2057	2157		0853	until	1653	1753	1853	2053
oodbridge d.		0635	0718	0725	0751	0818	0838	0918	1018	past each	1618	1718	1728	1818	1818	1918	2018	2118	2218		0914		1714	1814	1914	2114
swich a.		0653	0736	0744	0809	0836	0856	0936	1036	hour until	1636	1736	1746	1836	1836	1936	2037	2136	2236		0932		1732	1832	1932	2132

– To/from Harwich International (Table **200**). f – Arrives 8 minutes earlier. g – Arrives 1711. r – Arrives 0658. t – Arrives 1701.

LE 2nd class NORWICH and IPSWICH local services 203

NORWICH - GREAT YARMOUTH

Journey time ± 32 minutes *30 km (33 km via Reedham)*

ue to re-signalling works there are no trains Reedham - Great Yarmouth until further notice.

om Norwich: Trains noted 'r' call at **Reedham** 18 - 21 minutes later.

: 0506, 0611, 0652, 0743, 0809, 0836, 0906**a**, 0936, 1036, 1106**a**, 1136, 1236, 1306**a**, 1336, 1440, 1503**a**, 1536, 1638, 1706, 1736, 1804, 1840, 1940, 2038, 2140, 2300.

: 0532, 0636, 0706, 0736, 0809, 0836, 0909**b**, 0936, 0957**b**, 1036, 1106**b**, 1136, 1157**b**, 1236, 1306**b**, 1336, 1357**b**, 1436, 1515**b**, 1536, 1640, 1706, 1736, 1806, 1840, 1933, 2040, 2140, 2300.

: 0736, 0845 and the service repeats at the same times **every 2 hours** until 2136, 2236.

From Great Yarmouth: Trains noted 'r' call at **Reedham** 12 - 14 minutes later.

Ⓐ: 0543, 0624, 0658, 0730, 0818, 0846, 0917, 0945**a**, 1017, 1117, 1144**a**, 1217, 1317, 1345**a**, 1417, 1517, 1545**a**, 1617, 1717, 1747, 1817, 1847, 1917, 2017, 2117, 2217, 2334.

⑥: 0615, 0717, 0745, 0817, 0847, 0917, 0946**b**, 1017, 1047**b**, 1117, 1147**b**, 1217, 1247**b**, 1317, 1347**b**, 1417, 1447**b**, 1517, 1547**b**, 1617, 1717, 1747, 1817, 1847, 1917, 2017, 2117, 2217, 2334.

⑦: 0821, 0922 and hourly until1722, 1820, 1922, 2022, 2122, 2222, 2322.

NORWICH - LOWESTOFT

Journey time ± 43 minutes *38 km*

om Norwich: Trains noted 'r' call at **Reedham** 18 - 21 minutes later.

: 0536r, 0627r, 0645r, 0755r, 0855, 1005r, 1058, 1205r, 1258, 1405r, 1455r, 1550r, 1658r, 1750r, 1902r, 2005r, 2105r, 2205r, 2240r.

: 0540r, 0650r, 0750r, 0855, 1007r, 1058, 1205r, 1258, 1405r, 1458r, 1550r, 1657r, 1750r, 1905r, 2005r, 2105r, 2205r, 2240r.

: 0725, 0805cr, 0858r, 1005cr, 1058r, 1205cr, 1258r, 1405cr, 1458r, 1605cr, 1658r, 1805cr, 1858r, 2005cr, 2058r.

From Lowestoft: Trains noted 'r' call at **Reedham** 20 - 23 minutes later.

Ⓐ: 0542r, 0635r, 0735r, 0747r, 0850r, 0948r, 1057, 1148r, 1257, 1348r, 1457, 1548r, 1648r, 1748r, 1848r, 1955r, 2057, 2148r, 2248r, 2330r.

⑥: 0638r, 0740r, 0848r, 0948r, 1057, 1148r, 1257, 1348r, 1457, 1548r, 1648r, 1748r, 1848r, 1955r, 2057, 2148r, 2248r, 2330r.

⑦: 0856cr, 0946r, 1056cr, 1146r, 1256cr, 1346r, 1456cr, 1546r, 1656cr, 1746r, 1856cr, 1946r, 2056cr, 2146r, 2335r.

NORWICH - SHERINGHAM (🚂)

Journey time ± 57 minutes *49 km*

om Norwich:

ains call at **Hoveton and Wroxham** 🚂 ± 15 minutes, and **Cromer** ± 45 minutes later.

: 0510Ⓐ, 0520⑥, 0540Ⓐ, 0545⑥, 0715, 0821, 0945, 1045, 1145, 1245, 1345, 1445, 1545, 1645, 1745, 1855, 1955, 2115, 2245①-④, 2305⑤⑥.

: 0836, 0945, 1036, 1145, 1236, 1345, 1436, 1545, 1636, 1745, 1836, 1945, 2036.

From Sheringham:

Trains call at **Cromer** ± 11 minutes, and **Hoveton and Wroxham** 🚂 ± 39 minutes later.

⚒: 0007⑥, 0621⑥, 0631Ⓐ, 0716, 0822, 0944, 1047, 1144, 1247, 1344, 1447, 1546, 1649, 1749, 1852, 1956, 2110, 2217, 2347①-④ (also 0553Ⓐ from Cromer).

⑦: 0007, 0942, 1041, 1142, 1241, 1342, 1441, 1542, 1641, 1742, 1841, 1942, 2041, 2142.

IPSWICH - FELIXSTOWE

Journey time ± 25 minutes *25 km*

om Ipswich:

: 0504, 0604, 0714, 0825, 0857, 0958 and hourly until 2058, 2228.

: 0558, 0658, 0758 and hourly until 2058, 2228.

: 0955c, 1055 and hourly until 1955.

From Felixstowe:

Ⓐ: 0534, 0636, 0747, 0854, 0928 and hourly until 2128, 2301.

⑥: 0628, 0728, 0828 and hourly until 2128, 2258.

⑦: 1025c, 1125 and hourly until 2025.

– ①⑤ July 22 - Sept. 6.
– Until Sept. 7.
c – Until Sept. 8.
r – Via Reedham.

🚂 –Heritage and Tourist railways:
NORTH NORFOLK RAILWAY: Sheringham - Holt and v.v. *8 km.* ✆ 01263 820800. www.nnrailway.co.uk
BURE VALLEY STEAM RAILWAY: Wroxham - Aylsham and v.v. ✆ 01253 833858. www.bvrw.co.uk

LE 2nd class only IPSWICH - CAMBRIDGE and PETERBOROUGH 205

km			⚒	⚒ C	⚒	Ⓐ	⑥	⑥	Ⓐ	⑥ H	Ⓐ H	⚒	⚒	⚒	⚒	⚒	⚒	⚒	⚒	⚒	⚒	⑥	Ⓐ	⑥	Ⓐ	⚒
0	**Ipswich** 200 d.	⚒	0510	0600	0616	0654	0720	0800	0803	0821	0821	0920	0958	1020	1120	1201	1220	1320	1358	1420	1520	1558	1600	1620	1620	1720
19	Stowmarket 200 d.		0526	0612	0631	0709	0735	0812	0816	0835	0835	0935	1011	1035	1135	1213	1235	1335	1411	1435	1535	1611	1612	1635	1635	1735
42	Bury St Edmunds d.		0549	0629	0654	0733b	0757	0829	0833	0857	0858	0957	1029	1057	1157	1231	1257	1357	1429	1457	1557	1629	1629	1657	1657	1757
65	Newmarket d.		0609	|	0715	0752	0819	|	|	0918	0918	1019	|	1118	1219	|	1318	1419	|	1518	1619	|	|	1719	1719	1819
88	**Cambridge** 208 a.		0633	|	0740	0819	0840	|	|	0940	0942	1041	|	1141	1241	|	1341	1441	|	1541	1641	|	|	1740	1744	1843
82	Ely 208 d.		...	0657	...	...	...	0858	0859	...	...	...	1058	...	...	1258	...	...	1458	...	...	1658	1659	...	...	...
108	March 208 d.		...	0715	...	...	...	0916	0917	...	...	...	1116	...	...	1316	...	...	1516	...	...	1716	1717	...	...	...
132	**Peterborough** 208 a.		...	0739	...	...	...	0939	0940	...	...	...	1139	...	...	1339	...	...	1539	...	...	1739	1740	...	...	...

	Ⓐ	⑥	Ⓐ	⑥	Ⓐ	⑥	⑥	Ⓐ	⚒	⚒	⚒		⑦	⑦ p	⑦ H	⑦ C	⑦	⑦	⑦	⑦	⑦	⑦	⑦	⑦	⑦	⑦
swich 200 d.	1741	1758	1817	1820	1913	1920	2001	2001	2020	2117	2219	⑦	0732	0755	0902	0955	1102	1155	1302	1355	1502	1555	1702	1755	1910	2102
owmarket 200 d.	1758	1811	1832	1835	1928	1935	2013	2013	2035	2133	2235		0748	0807	0918	1007	1118	1207	1318	1407	1518	1607	1718	1807	1923	2118
ury St Edmunds d.	1828f	1829	1857b	1857	1957c	1957	2031	2030	2057	2156	2257		0811	0824	0941	1024	1141	1224	1341	1424	1541	1624	1741	1824	1944	2141
Newmarket d.	|	|	1918	1918	2019	2019	|	|	2116	2219	...		0831	|	1001	|	1201	|	1401	|	1601	|	1801	|	2003	2201
Cambridge 208 a.	|	|	1941	1940	2041	2040	|	|	2142	2243	...		0857	|	1025	|	1225	|	1425	|	1625	|	1825	|	2026	2224
y 208 d.	1858	1858	...	...	...	...	2058	2101	...	...	...		...	0852	...	1052	...	1252	...	1452	...	1652	...	1852	...	...
arch 208 d.	1916	1916	...	...	...	...	2116	2118	...	...	...		...	0908	...	1108	...	1308	...	1508	...	1708	...	1908	...	...
eterborough 208 a.	1939	1939	...	...	...	...	2139	2140	...	...	...		...	0931	...	1131	...	1331	...	1531	...	1731	...	1931	...	...

		Ⓐ	Ⓐ	⑥	⚒	Ⓐ	⑥	Ⓐ	⑥	⑥	Ⓐ	⚒	⚒	⚒	⚒		⚒	⚒	⚒	⚒	⑥	Ⓐ	⚒	⚒	⚒	⚒
eterborough 208 d.	⚒	...	...	...	...	...	...	0749	0750	...	...	...	0950	...	...	...	1150	...	...	1350	...	...	...	1550	...	...
arch 208 d.		...	...	...	...	...	...	0808	0809	...	...	...	1009	...	...	...	1209	...	...	1409	...	...	...	1609	...	...
y 208 d.		...	...	...	...	...	...	0830	0832	...	...	...	1032	...	...	...	1232	...	...	1432	...	...	...	1632	...	...
Cambridge 208 d.		...	...	...	0642	0744	0747	|	|	0847	0848	0947	|	1047	1147	...	|	1247	1347	|	1447	1447	1547	|	1647	1747
Newmarket d.		...	...	...	0702	0805	0808	|	|	0907	0907	1008	|	1107	1208	...	|	1307	1408	|	1507	1507	1608	|	1708	1808
ury St Edmunds d.		0531	0621	0623	0723	0824	0826	0856	0858	0926	0927	1026	1058	1126	1226	...	1258	1326	1426	1458	1526	1526	1626	1658	1728	1828
owmarket 200 d.		0552	0642	0646	0745	0845	0847	0912	0914	0947	0947	1047	1114	1147	1247	...	1314	1347	1447	1514	1547	1547	1647	1714	1748	1848
swich 200 a.		0607	0700	0702	0802	0903	0902	0926	0928	1002	1003	1104	1128	1202	1304	...	1328	1402	1504	1529	1602	1606	1704	1728	1804	1903

	⚒	⑥	Ⓐ	⚒ H	⚒ C	⚒	Ⓐ	⑥	⚒ C	⚒		⑦	⑦ p	⑦	⑦	⑦	⑦	⑦		⑦	⑦	⑦ C	⑦ H	⑦ C	⑦	⑦
eterborough 208 d.	1750	...	...	...	1950	...	...	...	2145	...	⑦	...	0950	...	1150	...	1350	...	...	1547	...	1745	...	1947	...	...
arch 208 d.	1809	...	...	...	2009	...	...	...	2204	...		...	1009	...	1209	...	1409	...	...	1606	...	1804	...	2006	...	...
y 208 d.	1831	...	...	...	2031	...	...	...	2226	...		...	1032	...	1232	...	1432	...	...	1629b	...	1829b	...	2028	...	...
Cambridge 208 d.	|	1847	1847	1947	|	2047	2147	2147	|	2247		0914	|	1114	|	1314	|	1514	...	|	1714	|	1914	|	2114	2250
Newmarket d.	|	1907	1907	2008	|	2107	2209	2208	|	2308		0936	|	1136	|	1336	|	1536	...	|	1736	|	1936	|	2136	2312
ury St Edmunds d.	1858	1926	1927	2026	2058	2126	2227	2226	2252	2329		0957	1058	1157	1258	1357	1458	1557	...	1655	1757	1855	1957	2055	2157	2333
owmarket 200 d.	1914	1947	1948	2046	2114	2147	2248	2246	2308	2351		1020	1114	1220	1314	1420	1514	1620	...	1711	1820	1911	2020	2111	2220	2355
swich 200 a.	1928	2002	2004	2101	2128	2204	2303	2303	2322	0008		1038	1128	1236	1328	1436	1528	1636	...	1725	1836	1925	2036	2125	2238	0011

– To/from Colchester (Table **200**).
– To/from Harwich International (Table **200**).
b – Arrives 4–7 minutes earlier.
c – Arrives 1948.
f – Arrives 1820.
p – Until Sept. 8.

206 NORWICH - NOTTINGHAM - SHEFFIELD - MANCHESTER - LIVERPOOL 2nd class EM

km		Ⓐ	Ⓐ	Ⓐ	Ⓐ	Ⓐ	Ⓐ	Ⓐ	Ⓐ	Ⓐ	Ⓐ	Ⓐ	Ⓐ	Ⓐ	Ⓐ	Ⓐ	Ⓐ	Ⓐ	Ⓐ
0	**Norwich** 207 d.	...	...	...	0550	0651	0757	0856	0957	1057	1157	1257	1357	1457	1548	1656	1754	1857	**AD**
49	Thetford 207 d.	...	...	...	0624	0719	0824	0924	1024	1124	1224	1324	1424	1524	1623	1727	1827	1924	...
86	Ely 205 207 208 d.	...	...	...	0651	0744	0851	0951	1048	1151	1250	1350	1449	1548	1650	1752	1852	1952	...
111	March 205 208 d.	...	...	...	0707	0800	0907	|	|	1208	|	|	|	|	|	|	1908	|	...
135	**Peterborough** 180 205 208 d.	...	...	...	0729r	0825	0927	1028	1128	1226	1326	1426	1530	1627	1726	1826	1926	2027	2131
181	Grantham 180 194 d.	...	...	...	0758	0856	0958	1100	1202	1259	1358	1458	1603	1658	1757	1857	1959	2100	|
218	**Nottingham** 194 a.	...	...	...	0840	0927	1035	1134	1235	1336	1435	1534	1635	1735	1835	1936	2031	2136	2300
218	**Nottingham** 171 d.	0523	0639	0746	0847	0947	1051	1147	1247	1347	1447	1547	1647	1747	1847	1939	*2112*	...	...
247	Alfreton 171 d.	|	0700	0810	0908	1008	1111	1208	1310	1409	1508	1610	1708	1810	1908	2000	*2144*	...	...
264	Chesterfield 171 d.	0551	0710	0820	0920	1020	1122	1221	1320	1420	1520	1620	1720	1820	1920	2011	*2155*	...	...
283	**Sheffield** 171 193 d.	0618	0732r	0841	0940	1041r	1141	1241	1340	1441	1540	1640	1739	1839	1940	2031	*2213*	...	...
343	Stockport 193 a.	0724	0825	0925	1025	1125	1225	1325	1425	1525	1625	1725	1825	1925	2025	2125	...	...	...
352	**Manchester** Piccadilly 193 a.	0738	0837	0937	1037	1137	1237	1337	1437	1537	1637	1737	1837	1937	2038	2136	...	...	...
378	Warrington Central 188 a.	0758	0858	0958	1058	1158	1258	1358	1458	1558	1658	1803	1858	1958	2058	...	...	...	...
399	**Liverpool** SP ▷ 188 a.	0820	0915	1015	1115	1215	1315	1415	1515	1615	1715	1822	1920	2016	2120	...	...	...	...
408	**Liverpool** Lime Street 188 a.	0834	0928	1031	1131	1232	1332	1432	1532	1632	1732	1836	1935	2034	2136	...	...	...	...

	⑥	⑥	⑥	⑥	⑥	⑥
Norwich 207 d.	...	...	...	0550	0653	075
Thetford 207 d.	...	...	...	0623	0722	082
Ely 205 207 208 d.	...	...	...	0651	0748	084
March 205 208 d.	...	...	...	0707	0804	090
Peterborough 180 205 208 d.	...	...	...	0727	0829	092
Grantham 180 194 d.	...	...	...	0758	0859	095
Nottingham 194 a.	...	...	...	0839	0935	103
Nottingham 171 d.	0520	0640	0746	0848	0947	104
Alfreton 171 d.	|	0700	0809	0909	1008	110
Chesterfield 171 d.	0549	0711	0819	0920	1020	112
Sheffield 171 193 d.	0620r	0732r	0840	0940	1040	114
Stockport 193 a.	0726	0825	0925	1026	1125	122
Manchester Piccadilly 193 a.	0739	0837	0937	1037	1137	123
Warrington Central 188 a.	0758	0858	0958	1058	1158	125
Liverpool SP ▷ 188 a.	0820	0915	1015	1115	1215	131
Liverpool Lime Street 188 a.	0833	0930	1030	1132	1232	133

	⑥	⑥	⑥	⑥	⑥	⑥	⑥	⑥	⑥	⑥	⑥	⑥
Norwich 207 d.	0856	0957	1057	1157	1257	1357	1457	1552	1654	1750	1857	**D**
Thetford 207 d.	0924	1024	1124	1224	1324	1424	1524	1623	1724	1823	1924	...
Ely 205 207 208 d.	0946	1048	1148	1251	1348	1450	1547	1647	1747	1848	1948	...
March 205 208 d.	|	|	1205	|	|	|	|	|	|	1905	|	...
Peterborough 180 205 208 d.	1022	1123	1224	1328	1426	1524	1627	1725	1826	1930r	2026	2127
Grantham 180 194 d.	1055	1156	1257	1358	1456	1557	1658	1759	1858	2003r	2058	2202
Nottingham 194 a.	1136	1235	1335	1433	1535	1635	1735	1834	1931	2036	2132	2232
Nottingham 171 d.	1147	1247	1347	1447	1547	1644	1744	1847	1936	...	...	...
Alfreton 171 d.	1208	1310	1408	1508	1610	1705	1808	1908	2001	...	...	...
Chesterfield 171 d.	1220	1322	1420	1520	1620	1715	1818	1920	2011	...	...	...
Sheffield 171 193 d.	1240	1341r	1441r	1541r	1641r	1738r	1837	1940	2034r	...	...	...
Stockport 193 a.	1325	1425	1525	1625	1725	1825	1925	2025	2119	...	...	...
Manchester Piccadilly 193 a.	1337	1437	1537	1637	1737	1837	1937	2037	2129	...	...	...
Warrington Central 188 a.	1358	1458	1558	1658	1803	1858	1958	2058	...	...	...	...
Liverpool SP ▷ 188 a.	1415	1515	1715	1715	1822	1919	2017	2119	...	...	...	...
Liverpool Lime Street 188 a.	1432	1530	1732	1732	1836	1935	2033	2132	...	...	...	...

	⑦	⑦	⑦	⑦	⑦	⑦	⑦	⑦	⑦	⑦	⑦	⑦	⑦	⑦
Norwich 207 d.	...	...	...	0947t	1047	...	...	1347	1453	1554	1654	1754	1856	205
Thetford 207 d.	...	...	...	1015t	1114	...	...	1414	1520	1621	1721	1821	1923	211
Ely 205 207 208 d.	...	...	...	1041t	1139	...	...	1440	1546	|	1749	1847	1949	214
March 205 208 d.	...	...	...	|	|	...	...	|	1603	|	|	|	|	|
Peterborough 180 205 208 d.	...	...	...	1114t	1216r	...	1431	1523f	1624r	1719r	1826r	1922	2030r	222
Grantham 180 194 d.	...	...	...	1156t	1252r	...	1509	1555	1656	1755r	1858	1957r	2102	225
Nottingham 194 a.	...	...	...	1230t	1330	...	1539	1624	1731	1827	1933	2031	2134	232
Nottingham 171 d.	0947	1048	1144	1240	1342	1447	1547	1642	1739	1840	1942	...	...	...
Alfreton 171 d.	1004	1108	1207	1304	1405	1510	1607	1711	1804	1903	2003	...	...	...
Chesterfield 171 d.	1018	1119	1218	1317	1416	1521	1618	1721	1815	1914	2012	...	...	...
Sheffield 171 193 d.	1041r	1139r	1239r	1338r	1437	1543r	1639r	1744r	1837r	1935r	2035r	...	...	...
Stockport 193 a.	1126	1225	1325	1426	1525	1625	1728	1825	1925	2026	2125	...	...	...
Manchester Piccadilly 193 a.	1137	1237	1337	1437	1537	1637	1738	1837	1937	2038	2136	...	...	...
Warrington Central 188 a.	1158	1258	1358	1458	1558	1658	1758	1858	1959	...	...	...	...	...
Liverpool SP ▷ 188 a.	1216	1316	1416	1516	1616	1716	1816	1916	2017	...	...	...	...	...
Liverpool Lime Street 188 a.	1231	1331	1432	1530	1628	1732	1830	1930	2031	...	...	...	...	...

	Ⓐ	Ⓐ	Ⓐ	Ⓐ	Ⓐ	Ⓐ	Ⓐ	Ⓐ	Ⓐ		Ⓐ	Ⓐ	Ⓐ	Ⓐ	Ⓐ	Ⓐ	Ⓐ	Ⓐ
Liverpool Lime Street 187 d.	**A**	**D**	**A**	...	...	0647	0742	0852	0951		1351	1451	1551	1650	1751	1851	1951	2137
Liverpool SP ▷ 188 d.	...	...	...	...	...	0658	0753	0903	1002		1402	1502	1602	1701	1802	1902	2002	2147
Warrington Central 188 d.	...	...	...	...	...	0715	0813	0919	1018	and	1418	1518	1618	1717	1818	1918	2018	2204
Manchester Piccadilly 193 d.	...	...	...	...	...	0742	0843	0943	1042	at	1442	1542	1642	1742	1842	1942	2042	2228
Stockport 193 d.	...	...	...	...	...	0754	0854	0954	1054	the	1454	1554	1654	1755	1854	1954	2053	2239
Sheffield 171 193 d.	...	...	...	*0603*	*0728*	0839	0938	1037	1138	same	1537	1637	1743r	1851r	1937	2041	2137	2338
Chesterfield 171 d.	...	...	...	*0619*	*0742*	0854	0952	1054	1154	minutes	1553	1653	1801	1907	1952	2056	2155	0002
Alfreton 171 d.	...	...	...	*0629*	*0753*	0905	1002	1105	1205	past	1605	1704	1811	1919	2003	2108	2205	|
Nottingham 171 a.	...	...	...	*0700*	*0824*	0928	1027	1126	1229	each	1627	1727	1831	1940	2027	2134	2231	0045
Nottingham 194 d.	0456	0507	0609	0752	0835	0934	1034	1134	1234	hour	1635	1734	1837	...	2034	...	...	...
Grantham 180 194 d.	|	0551r	|	0827r	0910r	1011r	1110	1212	1309	until	1711r	1811	1910	...	2110	...	...	...
Peterborough 180 205 208 d.	0627r	0626a	0738r	0905r	0940r	1045	1141	1242	1341		1744	1845r	1942	...	2139	...	...	...
March 205 208 a.	0642	...	0753	|	|	|	|	|	|	♤	|	1859	|	...	|	...	...	...
Ely 205 207 208 a.	0702c	...	0812c	0942c	1013c	1119	1213	1314	1413		1819	1919c	2015	...	2213c	...	...	...
Thetford 207 a.	0733	...	0838	1009	1039	1143	1238	1340	1438		1843	1944	2038	...	2238	...	...	...
Norwich 207 a.	0813	...	0915	1044	1112	1215	1313	1413	1511		1916	2019	2113	...	2318	...	...	...

	⑥	⑥	⑥	⑥	⑥	⑥
Liverpool Lime Street 187 d.	**A**	**D**	**A**	...	...	064
Liverpool SP ▷ 188 d.	...	...	...	...	...	065
Warrington Central 188 d.	...	...	...	...	...	07
Manchester Piccadilly 193 d.	...	...	...	...	...	074
Stockport 193 d.	...	...	...	...	...	075
Sheffield 171 193 d.	...	...	...	*0601*	*0737*	083
Chesterfield 171 d.	...	...	...	*0619*	*0750*	085
Alfreton 171 d.	...	...	...	*0629*	*0801*	090
Nottingham 171 a.	...	...	...	*0700*	*0825*	092
Nottingham 194 d.	0505	0507	0607	0745	0835	093
Grantham 180 194 d.	|	0551r	|	0820r	0910r	101
Peterborough 180 205 208 d.	0627	0625	0735	0900f	0945f	104
March 205 208 a.	0642	...	0752	|	|	|
Ely 205 207 208 a.	0703	...	0813	0935g	1019	11
Thetford 207 a.	0730	...	0837	1006	1043	11
Norwich 207 a.	0813	...	0915	1043	1115	12

	⑥	⑥	⑥		⑥	⑥	⑥	⑥	⑥	⑥	⑥	⑥
Liverpool Lime Street 187 d.	0742	0852	0951	**B**	1451	1551	1651	1751	1851	1952	2049	2137
Liverpool SP ▷ 188 d.	0752	0903	1002		1502	1602	1702	1802	1902	2003	2100	2147
Warrington Central 188 d.	0813	0919	1018	and	1518	1618	1718	1818	1918	2019	2116	2204
Manchester Piccadilly 193 d.	0843	0943	1043	at	1542	1642	1742	1842	1942	2043	2141	2229
Stockport 193 d.	0855	0955	1055	the	1555	1655	1755	1855	1955	2055	2152	2238
Sheffield 171 193 d.	0937	1037	1138	same	1638	1741r	1840	1937	2039r	2138r	2242f	2338
Chesterfield 171 d.	0952	1052	1152	minutes	1654	1757	1858	1953	2054	2154	2256	2353
Alfreton 171 d.	1003	1102	1203	past	1705	1808	1909	2004	2105	2205	2307	|
Nottingham 171 a.	1027	1127	1227	each	1727	1829	1929	2028	2133	2234	2328	0029
Nottingham 194 d.	1034	1134	1234	hour	1734	1837	...	2035	...	...	...	...
Grantham 180 194 d.	1105	1213r	1311r	until	1811	1910	...	2108	...	...	...	...
Peterborough 180 205 208 d.	1141r	1244r	1340		1844r	1941	...	2140	...	...	...	...
March 205 208 a.	|	|	|	♤	1900	|	...	|	...	...	...	...
Ely 205 207 208 a.	1213	1319	1413		1919	2014	...	2213c	...	...	...	...
Thetford 207 a.	1238	1343	1437		1943	2038	...	2237	...	...	...	...
Norwich 207 a.	1313	1412	1513		2016	2113	...	2319	...	...	...	...

	⑦	⑦	⑦	⑦	⑦	⑦	⑦	⑦	⑦	⑦	⑦	⑦	⑦
Liverpool Lime Street 187 d.	t	...	...	...	1252	1352	1452	1552	1652	1752	1852	1952	21
Liverpool SP ▷ 188 d.	...	...	...	...	1303	1403	1503	1603	1703	1803	1903	2003	21
Warrington Central 188 d.	...	...	...	...	1319	1419	1519	1619	1719	1819	1919	2019	21
Manchester Piccadilly 193 d.	...	...	...	1243	1343	1443	1543	1642	1743	1843	1943	2044	22
Stockport 193 d.	...	...	...	1255	1351	1454	1554	1654	1754	1853	1954	2053	22
Sheffield 171 193 d.	1048	...	1243	1348f	1441r	1539r	1643r	1740r	1840r	1940r	2040r	2140r	23
Chesterfield 171 d. ★	1104	...	1257	1402	1455	1553	1657	1754	1854	1954	2054	2156	23
Alfreton 171 d.	1114	...	1308	1412	1508	1604	1707	1805	1905	2005	2105	2206	23
Nottingham 171 a.	1139	...	1334	1435	1532	1628	1730	1834	1933	2030	2133	2236	00
Nottingham 194 d.	1139	1240	1347	1445	1550	1645	1736	1846	...	2045	...	...	...
Grantham 180 194 d.	1223f	1315	1422	1520r	1622	1721r	1817	1923	...	2120	...	...	...
Peterborough 180 205 208 d.	1256	1343	1458r	1558r	1659r	1757r	1849	1957	...	2154	...	...	...
March 205 208 a.	|	|	|	|	|	1812	|	|	...	|	...	...	...
Ely 205 207 208 a.	1331	1416	1531g	1631	1732c	1831c	1922g	2032	...	2227	...	...	...
Thetford 207 a.	1355	1443	1601	1655	1756	1855	1951	2056	...	2251	...	...	...
Norwich 207 a.	1428	1523	1635	1726	1830	1928	2026	2137	...	2325	...	...	...

A – Via Melton Mowbray (Table **208**).
B – The 1151 from Liverpool departs Peterborough 1545r, arrives Ely 1619 and Thetford 1643.
D – From/to Spalding (Table **186**).
a – Arrives 0622 on ②–⑤.
c – Departs 4–6 minutes later.
d – Arrives 2216.
f – Arrives 9–11 minutes earlier.
g – Departs 8–11 minutes later.
h – Departs 1930.
r – Arrives 4–7 minutes earlier.
t – Until Sept. 8.
♤ – Timings may vary by up to 3 minutes.
▷ – **Liverpool** South Parkway.
★ – An additional train operates until Sept. Nottingham d. 0952, Grantham d. 1029, Peterborough d. 1109, March d. 1125, E a. 1143, Thetford a. 1212, Norwich a. 125

207 CAMBRIDGE - NORWICH 2nd Class L

km		⚒	Ⓐ	⑥	⚒	⚒	Ⓐ	⑥	⚒	⚒	⚒		⚒	⚒	⑥	Ⓐ	⑥	Ⓐ	⑥	Ⓐ	⚒	⚒
0	**Cambridge** d.		0602	0605	0700	0809	0909	0909	1009	1109	1209	and at	1709	1809	1909	1922	2009	2019	2109	2115	...	2255
4	Cambridge North d.		0606	0609	0704	0813	0914	0913	1013	1113	1213	the same	1713	1813	1913	1926	2013	2023	2113	2120	...	2259
24	Ely 206 d.		0619	0622	0717	0828	0927	0928	1028	1128	1228	minutes	1728	1828	1929	1939	2028	2037	2128	2133	2217	2312
63	Thetford 206 d.		0644	0647	0746	0853	0952	0953	1053	1155	1253	past each	1753	1853	1954	2004	2053	2101	2153	2157	2238	2337
84	Attleborough d.		0703	0706	0805	0908	1007	1008	1108	1211	1308	hour until	1808	1908	2009	2019	2108	2116	2208	2212	2252	2352
94	Wymondham d.		0711	0714	0815	0915	1016	1015	1115	1219	1315		1815	1915	2016	2027	2115	2124	2215	2220	2259	2359
110	**Norwich** 206 a.		0725	0728	0830	0930	1030	1030	1130	1237	1331		1830	1930	2034	2041	2130	2138	2232	2235	2319	0014

	⑦	⑦	⑦
Cambridge d.	0850	1050	115
Cambridge North d.	0854	1054	115
Ely 206 d.	0907	1107	120
Thetford 206 d.	0934	1134	123
Attleborough d.	0949	1149	124
Wymondham d.	0957	1157	125
Norwich 206 a.	1013	1213	131

	⑦	⑦	⑦	⑦	⑦	⑦	⑦	⑦	⑦	⑦	⑦
Cambridge d.	1250	1350	1450	1550	1650	1750	1850	1950	*2005*	2150	*2204*
Cambridge North d.	1254	1354	1454	1554	1654	1754	1854	1954	|	2154	*2208*
Ely 206 d.	1307	1407	1507	1607	1707	1807	1907	2007	2035	2207	2230
Thetford 206 d.	1334	1432	1532	1634	1732	1832	1932	2032	2056	2232	2251
Attleborough d.	1349	1447	1547	1649	1747	1847	1947	2047	2110	2247	2305
Wymondham d.	1357	1454	1554	1657	1754	1854	1954	2054	2117	2254	2312
Norwich 206 a.	1413	1513	1613	1713	1813	1910	2013	2110	2137	2313	2325

	⚒	Ⓐ	⑥	⚒	Ⓐ	⑥	Ⓐ	⑥	⚒	⑥	Ⓐ	⚒
Norwich 206 d.		0533	0537	0550	0633	0640	0734	0740	0840	0938	0940	104
Wymondham d.		0545	0549	0602	0645	0652	0746	0752	0852	0950	0952	105
Attleborough d.		0552	0556	0609	0652	0659	0753	0759	0859	0957	0959	105
Thetford 206 d.		0606	0610	0623	0706	0713	0807	0813	0913	1011	1013	11
Ely 206 d.		0631	0635	0646	0733	0738	0833	0838	0938	1038	1038	113
Cambridge North d.		0644	0648	...	0746	0751	0845	0851	0951	1051	1051	115
Cambridge a.		0652	0656	...	0753	0759	0852	0859	0959	1059	1059	115

	⚒	⚒	⚒	⚒	⑥	Ⓐ	⚒	⑥	Ⓐ	⑥	Ⓐ	⑥	Ⓐ	Ⓐ	⑥	⑥	Ⓐ	⚒
Norwich 206 d.	1140	1240	1340	1440	1535	1540	1638	1735	1735	1750	1754	1838	1840	1935	1935	2110	2115	2240
Wymondham d.	1152	1252	1352	1452	1547	1552	1650	1747	1747	1802	1806	1850	1852	1948	1948	2122	2127	2252
Attleborough d.	1159	1259	1359	1459	1554	1559	1659	1754	1754	1809	1813	1857	1859	1955	1955	2129	2134	2259
Thetford 206 d.	1213	1313	1413	1513	1613	1613	1713	1813	1812	1823	1827	1911	1913	2010	2010	2143	2148	2313
Ely 206 d.	1238	1338	1438	1538	1638	1638	1738	1838	1838	1845	1848	1938	1940	2037	2038	2210	2213	2338
Cambridge North d.	1251	1351	1451	1551	1651	1651	1751	1851	1854	|	|	1951	1954	2049	2051	2223	2226	2351
Cambridge a.	1259	1359	1459	1559	1659	1659	1759	1856	1859	*1908*	*1907*	1959	1959	2057	2057	2231	2232	2359

	⑦		⑦	⑦	⑦	⑦	⑦
Norwich 206 d.	0903	and at	1803	1856	2003	2052	220
Wymondham d.	0915	the same	1815	|	2015	|	22
Attleborough d.	0922	minutes	1822	|	2022	|	22
Thetford 206 d.	0936	past each	1836	1923	2036	2119	22
Ely 206 d.	1003	hour until	1903	1945	2103	2140	23
Cambridge North d.	1016		1916	|	2116	|	23
Cambridge a.	1022		1922	*2008*	2122	*2287*	23

XC STANSTED AIRPORT - CAMBRIDGE - PETERBOROUGH - LEICESTER - BIRMINGHAM 208

km		Ⓐ	⑥	⑥	Ⓐ	Ⓐ	⑥	⚒🍷	⚒🍷	⚒🍷	⚒🍷	⚒🍷	⚒🍷	⚒🍷	⚒🍷	⑥🍷	Ⓐ🍷	⚒🍷	⚒🍷	⚒	⚒	ⒶB	Ⓐ	⑦
0	**Stansted Airport** ▽ d.	...	...	0525	0525	0612	0627	0721a	0821a	0921a	1027	1127	1227	1327	1427	1527	1527	1627	1727	1821a	1921a	...	2021	1025
40	**Cambridge** ▽ d.	0515	0515	0556	0556	0656	0658	0801	0901	1000	1101	1201	1301	1401	1501	1601	1601	1701	1801	1900	2001	...	2101	1101
64	Ely **205** d.	0530	0530	0611	0611	0712	0713	0816	0916	1015	1116	1216	1316	1416	1516	1616	1616	1716	1816	1916	2016	...	2116	1116
89	March **205** d.	0546	0546	0629	0629	0729	0729	0832	0932	1032	1132	1232	1332	1432	1532	1632	1632	1732	1834	1932	2032	...	2133	1132
113	**Peterborough** **205** d.	0610	0610	0652	0652	0752	0752	0852	0952	1052	1152	1252	1352	1452	1552	1652	1652	1752	1852	1952	2052	2131	2200b	1153
131	Stamford d.	0623	0623	0705	0705	0805	0805	0905	1005	1105	1205	1305	1405	1505	1605	1705	1705	1805	1905	2005	2105	2145	2213	1206
154	Oakham d.	0637	0637	0719	0719	0819	0819	0919	1019	1119	1219	1319	1419	1519	1619	1719	1719	1819	1919	2019	2119	2201	2227	1220
174	Melton Mowbray d.	0648	0648	0730	0730	0830	0830	0930	1030	1130	1230	1330	1430	1530	1630	1730	1730	1830	1930	2030	2130	2214	2238	1231
197	**Leicester** d.	0710	0708	0748	0748	0848	0848	0948	1048	1148	1248	1348	1448	1548	1648	1751f	1748	1848	1948	2048	2148	...	2256	1250
227	Nuneaton d.	0730	0730	0810	0815	0910	0910	1010	1110	1210	1310	1410	1510	1610	1710	1810	1816	1910	2010	2110	2210	...	2315	1310
244	Coleshill Parkway △ d.	0745	0747	0825	0830	0924	0925	1025	1125	1225	1325	1425	1525	1625	1725	1825	1831	1925	2025	2125	2225	...	2330	1325
259	**Birmingham** New St. a.	0758	0803	0838	0844	0938	0938	1038	1138	1238	1338	1438	1538	1638	1738	1838	1844	1938	2038	2138	2238	...	2343	1338

	⑦	⑦🍷	⑦🍷	⑦🍷	⑦🍷	⑦🍷	⑦	⑦	⑦
tansted Airport ▽ d.	1125	1225	1325	1425	1525	1625	1725	1825	1925
ambridge ▽ d.	1201	1301	1401	1501	1601	1701	1801	1901	2001
ly **205** d.	1216	1316	1416	1516	1616	1716	1816	1916	2016
arch **205** d.	1232	1332	1432	1532	1632	1732	1832	1932	2032
eterborough **205** d.	1253	1353	1453	1553	1653	1753	1853	1953	2053
tamford d.	1306	1406	1506	1606	1706	1806	1906	2006	2106
akham d.	1320	1420	1520	1620	1720	1820	1920	2020	2120
elton Mowbray d.	1331	1431	1531	1631	1731	1831	1931	2031	2131
eicester d.	1350	1450	1550	1650	1750	1850	1950	2050	2150
uneaton d.	1410	1510	1610	1710	1810	1910	2010	2110	2210
oleshill Parkway △ d.	1425	1525	1625	1725	1825	1925	2025	2125	2225
irmingham New St. a.	1438	1538	1638	1738	1838	1938	2038	2138	2238

	ⒶA	⑥A	Ⓐ	⑥	⚒A	⑥🍷	Ⓐ🍷	⚒🍷	⚒C	⚒🍷	⚒🍷	⚒🍷
Birmingham New St d.	...	...	0519	0522	...	0622	0622	0722	0822	0922	1022	1122
Coleshill Parkway △ d.	...	...	0533	0536	...	0636	0636	0735	0836	0936	1036	1136
Nuneaton d.	...	...	0548	0551	...	0651	0651	0751	0851	0951	1051	1151
Leicester d.	...	...	0615	0615c	...	0718	0718	0818	0919c	1018b	1118c	1218b
Melton Mowbray d.	0536	0540	0631	0632	0653	0734	0734	0834	0935	1034	1134	1234
Oakham d.	0549	0552	0643	0643	0705	0746	0746	0846	0947	1046	1146	1246
Stamford d.	0605	0608	0657	0657	0719	0800	0800	0900	1001	1100	1200	1300
Peterborough **205** d.	0627b	0627	0713	0713	0735	0819c	0819c	0919c	1019c	1119c	1219c	1319c
March **205** d.	0643	0643	0732	0732	0753	0834	0834	0934	1034	1134	1234	1334
Ely **205** d.	0702	0703	0753	0753	0813	0853	0854	0953	1053	1153	1253	1353
Cambridge ▽ d.	...	...	0811	0811	...	0911	0914	1011	1111	1211	1311	1411
Stansted Airport ▽ a.	...	...	0842	0841	...	0941	0944	1041	1141	1241	1341	1441

	⚒🍷	⚒🍷	⚒🍷	⚒🍷	⚒🍷	Ⓐ	⑥	⚒	⚒	⚒	⑥	Ⓐ	⚒
irmingham New St. d.	1222	1322	1422	1522	1622	1652	1652	1722	1822	1922	2022	2025	2222
oleshill Parkway △ d.	1236	1336	1436	1536	1636	1706	1707	1736	1836	1936	2036	2039	2236
uneaton d.	1251	1351	1451	1551	1651	1721	1724	1751	1851	1954	2052	2054	2251
eicester d.	1318c	1418c	1518b	1618b	1718	1753	1749	1818g	1918c	2018	2117c	2118	2317
elton Mowbray d.	1334	1434	1534	1634	1734	1816	...	1834	1934	2034	2133	2134	...
akham d.	1346	1446	1546	1646	1746	1829	...	1846	1946	2046	2145	2146	...
tamford d.	1400	1500	1600	1700	1800	1843	...	1900	2000	2100	2159	2200	...
eterborough **205** d.	1419c	1519c	1619c	1719c	1818c	1859	...	1919c	2019c	2118c	2214	2219c	...
arch **205** d.	1434	1534	1634	1738	1833	1914	...	1934	2034	2134	2229	2234	...
ly **205** d.	1453	1553	1653	1800	1852	1934	...	1953	2053	2153	2248	2253	...
ambridge ▽ d.	1511	1611	1711	1817	1911	1950	...	2011	2111	2211	2303	2309	...
tansted Airport ▽ a.	1541	1641	1741	1854	1941	...	...	2041	2154h	2241	...	...	...

⑦	⑦🍷	⑦🍷	⑦🍷	⑦🍷	⑦🍷	⑦	⑦	⑦	⑦	⑦	⑦	⑦D
Birmingham New St. d.	1122	1222	1322	1422	1522	1622	1722	1822	1922	2022	2052	2152
Coleshill Parkway △ d.	1136	1236	1336	1436	1536	1636	1736	1836	1936	2036	2106	2206
Nuneaton d.	1151	1251	1351	1451	1551	1651	1751	1851	1951	2051	2121	2221
Leicester d.	1218	1318b	1418c	1519c	1618b	1716	1818	1918c	2018b	2118c	2147	2247
Melton Mowbray d.	1234	1334	1434	1534	1634	1734	1834	1934	2034	2134	...	...
Oakham d.	1246	1346	1446	1546	1646	1746	1846	1946	2046	2146	...	...
Stamford d.	1300	1400	1500	1600	1700	1800	1900	2000	2100	2200	...	...
Peterborough 205 d.	1319c	1419c	1519c	1619c	1719c	1819c	1919c	2019c	2119c	2217c	...	...
March 205 d.	1334	1434	1534	1634	1734	1834	1934	2034	2134	2232	...	...
Ely 205 d.	1353	1453	1553	1653	1753	1853	1953	2053	2153	2251	...	...
Cambridge ▽ d.	1415	1515	1615	1715	1815	1915	2015	2113	2215	2306	...	...
Stansted Airport ▽ a.	1445	1545	1645	1745	1845	1945	2045	2145	2245	...	...	...

A – 2 Nottingham - Norwich (Table **206**).
B – 2 Spalding - Nottingham (Tables **186** and **206**).
C – From Bristol Temple Meads on Ⓐ (Table **116**); From Gloucester on ⑥ (Table **117**).
D – From Cardiff Central (Table **117**).

a – Departs 6 minutes later on ⑥.
b – Arrives 8–9 minutes earlier.
c – Arrives 4–6 minutes earlier.
– Arrives 0758 on Ⓐ.
f – Arrives 1746.
g – Arrives 1810 on ⑥; 1817 on Ⓐ.
h – Arrives 2141 on ⑥.

☛ **Full service Leicester - Birmingham New Street and v.v.**

From Leicester: On Ⓐ at 0618, 0648, 0710, 0722, 0748, 0820, 0848, 0913, 0948, 1018 and every 30 minutes until 2018, 2048, 2116, 2148, 2227, 2256.
On ⑥ at 0548, 0648, 0708, 0748 and every 30 minutes until 2118, 2220.
On ⑦ at 1020, 1120, 1220 and every 30 minutes until 1650, 1719, 1750 and every 30 minutes until 2050, 2150, 2220.

From Birmingham New Street: On Ⓐ at 0519, 0550, 0622 and every 30 minutes until 1552, 1609, 1622, 1652, 1709, 1722 and every 30 minutes until 1952, 2025, 2052, 2222.
On ⑥ at 0522, 0552 and every 30 minutes until 2222.
On ⑦ at 0952, 1052, 1122, 1152 and every 30 minutes until 2022, 2052, 2152.

△ – 🚌 connections available to the National Exhibition Centre (NEC) and Birmingham International Airport.

▽ – **Full service Cambridge - Stansted Airport and v.v.**

From Cambridge:
On Ⓐ at 0444, 0517, 0635, 0735, 0811, 0914, 0931, 1011, 1030 and at the same minutes past each hour until 1611, 1711, 1817, 1911, 2011, 2111, 2130, 2211.
On ⑥ at 0451, 0540, 0610, 0640, 0709, 0740, 0811, 0830 and at the same minutes past each hour unti 1730, 1817, 1830, 1911, 1930, 2011, 2030, 2111, 2130, 2211.
On ⑦ at 0739, 0824, 0915, 0925, 1015, 1025, 1115, 1125, 1215, 1225, 1315, 1325, 1410, 1425 and at the same minutes past each hour until 2110, 2124, 2210.

From Stansted Airport:
On Ⓐ at 0525, 0612 0721, 0821, 0921, 1010, 1027 and at the same minutes past each hour until 1627, 1727, 1821,1921, 2021, 2027, 2127, 2210, 2227, 2257.
On ⑥ at 0525, 0627, 0648, 0727, 0748, 0827, 0910, 0927 and at the same minutes past each hour until 2227, 2327.
On ⑦ at 0840, 0909, 1009, 1025 and at the same minutes past each hour until 2025, 2103, 2112, 2209, 2225, 2304.

NT 2nd class MIDDLESBROUGH - NEWCASTLE - CARLISLE 210

km		⚒	⚒	⚒	⚒	⚒S	⚒	⚒	⚒S	⚒	⚒	⚒	⚒	⑥	Ⓐ	⚒	⚒	⚒	⚒	⚒	⚒	⚒	⚒	⚒	⚒	⚒	Ⓐ	⑥
0	**Middlesbrough** d.	...	...	0547r	...	0645	0659	0735	0745	...	...	0834	...	...	...	0935	...	...	1035	...	...	1135	...	...	1235	...	...	...
9	Stockton d.	...	...	|	...	|	0710	0746	|	...	...	0845	...	...	...	0946	...	...	1046	...	...	1145	...	...	1246	...	...	...
28	Hartlepool **183** d.	...	...	b	0650	b	0730	0805	b	...	...	0904	...	...	...	1005	...	...	1104	...	...	1204	...	...	1305	...	...	...
57	Sunderland **183** d.	...	...	|	0716	|	0756	0830	|	...	...	0930	...	...	...	1030	...	...	1130	...	...	1230	...	...	1330	...	...	...
76	**Newcastle** a.	...	...	0659r	0742	0800	0819	0853	0901	...	...	0953	...	...	...	1053	...	...	1152	...	...	1253	...	...	1353	...	...	...
	Newcastle d.	0542	0620	0702	0744	0805	...	0855	...	0923	0946	0955	1023	1031	1046	1055	1122	1151	1200	1223	1239	1255	1323	1339	1355	1420	1433	1440
81	Metrocentre d.	0549	0629	0710	0752	0814	...	0904	...	0931	0954	1004	1031	1043	1054	1104	1130	1201	1209	1231	1247	1304	1331	1347	1404	1428	1441	1448
95	Prudhoe d.	0604	0644	0725	0759	0825	...	0919	...	0942	1007	1019	1042	1054	1105	1119	1141	1212	1224	1242	1259	1319	1342	1358	1419	1439	1452	1459
111	Hexham d.	0624	0659	0744	0819	0838	...	0938	...	0955	1022	1038	1055	1109	1118	1138	1154	1232	1243	1255	1311	1338	1355	1411	1438	1452	1505	1512
137	Haltwhistle d.	0643	0721	0803	...	0857	...	...	...	1014	1042	...	1114	1131	1142	...	1213	1253	...	1314	1333	...	1414	1431	...	1511	1527	1534
174	**Carlisle** a.	0713	0758	0834	...	0932f	...	...	...	1044	1115	...	1143	1204	1213	...	1242	1326	...	1346	1404	...	1443	1504	...	1543	1558	1605

	⚒	⚒	⚒	⚒	⚒	⚒	⚒	⚒	⚒Y	⚒	⚒	⚒◇	⚒	⚒	⚒	⑥	⚒	⑦	⑦	⑦	⑦		⑦	⑦	⑦	⑦	⑦	⑦
iddlesbrough d.	1335	...	...	1535	...	...	1635	...	1734	...	1835	...	1935	...	2036	...	2135		...	0832	0934	❖W	1635	1733	1833	1935	2033	2133
tockton d.	1346	...	...	1546	...	...	1646	...	1745	...	1846	...	1946	...	2047	...	2145		...	0844	0946		1646	1744	1844	1946	2044	2144
artlepool **183** d.	1405	...	...	1605	...	...	1706	...	1804	...	1905	...	2005	...	2106	...	2204		...	0904	1005	and at	1705	1804	1904	2005	2104	2204
underland **183** d.	1430	...	...	1630	...	...	1731	...	1829	...	1930	...	2030	...	2132	...	2229		...	0930	1030	the	1730	1830	1929	2030	2129	2229
ewcastle a.	1453	...	...	1652	...	...	1753	...	1850	...	1949	...	2051	...	2155	...	2251		...	0950	1050	same	1749	1850	1950	2050	2150	2250
ewcastle d.	1458	1620	1640	1655	1705	1723	1755	1821	1855	1923	1951	2023	2053	2124	2156	2236	2253r		0845	0955	1055	minutes	1755	1855	1955	2100	...	...
etrocentre d.	1507	1628	1648	1703	1713	1731	1804	1829	1904	1931	2004	2031	2101	2132	2205	2245	2302r		0853	1003	1103	past	1803	1903	2003	2109	...	...
rudhoe d.	1522	1639	1703	...	1728	1746	1819	1844	1919	1946	2019j	2046	...	2147	...	2300	2317r		0907	1017	1115	each	1817	1915	2017	2123	...	...
exham d.	1541	1652	1722	...	1747	1805	1838	1903	1938	2005	...	2105	...	2206	...	2319	2336r		0927	1037	1135	hour	1837	1935	2037	2143	...	...
altwhistle d.	...	1711	1745	...	...	1828	...	1926	...	2028	...	2126	...	2229	...	...	...		0949	1059	1157	until	1857	1957	2059	2205	...	...
arlisle a.	...	1740	1816	...	...	1900	...	1958	...	2100	...	2155	...	2301	...	...	...		1022	1132	1229		1935	2027	2132	2238	...	...

	Ⓐ	⑥	ⒶS	⑥S	⑥	Ⓐ	⚒	⚒D	⚒	⚒	⚒E	⚒	⚒	⚒	⚒	⚒	⚒	⚒	⚒Y	⚒	⚒	⚒	⚒	⚒	⚒	⚒	⚒	⚒
arlisle d.	...	...	...	...	0544	0544	0632	0657	...	0802	0820	0850	...	0922	0952	...	1023	1054	...	1125	1152	...	1225	1253	...	1332	1354	...
altwhistle d.	...	...	...	...	0621	0621	0707	0729	...	0833	0852	0920	...	0957	1020	...	1053	1122	...	1157	1221	...	1255	1321	...	1404	1422	...
exham d.	...	...	0610	0610	0647	0647	0731	0752	0826	0856	0913	0942	0956	1018	1040	1056	1118	1142	*1156*	1217	1240	1256	1318	1341	1356	1425	1442	1456
rudhoe d.	...	...	0628	0628	0704	0704	0749	0809	0844	0914	0925	0954	1013	1030	1052	1113	1130	1154	*1213*	1230	1252	1313	1330	1353	1413	1437	1454	1513
etrocentre d.	...	...	0643	0643	0722	0722	0805	0825	0856	0929	0937	1006	1029	1044	1104	1129	1144	1206	*1229*	1244	1304	1329	1344	1405	1429	1449	1506	1529
ewcastle a.	...	...	0652	0652	0733	0733	0815	0835	0906	0945e	0949	1014	1039	1054	1112	1139	1155	1215	*1239*	1253	1313	1339	1353	1413	1439	1457	1514	1539
ewcastle d.	0600	0600	0654	0654	0735	0741	*0833c*	...	*0941*	...	...	...	1041	...	...	1141	...	...	1241	...	...	1341	...	...	1441	...	...	1541
underland **183** d.	0625	0622	0714	0721	0802t	0802	*0854c*	...	*1003*	...	...	...	1101	...	...	1201	...	...	1301	...	...	1402	...	...	1502	...	...	1602
artlepool **183** d.	0656	0701	0737	0744	0825	0825	*0925*	...	*1026*	...	...	...	1125	...	...	1225	...	...	1325	...	...	1426	...	...	1525	...	...	1625
tockton d.	0715	0720	0756	0803	0844	0844	*0944*	...	*1044*	...	...	...	1143	...	...	1244	...	...	1343	...	...	1444	...	...	1544	...	...	1644
iddlesbrough a.	0730	0731	0811	0814	0855	0854	*0956*	...	*1055*	...	...	...	1155	...	...	1255	...	...	1355	...	...	1456	...	...	1555	...	...	1655

D – From Dumfries (Table **214**).
E – From Dumfries on Ⓐ (Table **214**).
S – To / from Saltburn (Table **212**).
W – The 1434 and 1733 departures from Middlesbrough start from Whitby (Table **211**).
Y – From / to Whitby (Table **211**).

b – Via Darlington (Table **212**).
c – Departs 7 minutes later on Ⓐ.
e – Arrives 0939 on ⑥.
f – Arrives 0928 on Ⓐ.
j – ⑥ only.

r – Ⓐ only.
t – Arrives 0755.
◇ – Runs 10 minutes later to Haltwhistle on ⑥ and arrives Carlisle 2210.
❖ – Timings may vary by ± 2 minutes.

210 MIDDLESBROUGH - NEWCASTLE - CARLISLE

2nd class NT

	⚒	⚒	⚒Y	⚒◇	⚒	⚒	⚒	⚒	⚒	⚒	⚒	⚒	ⒶG	⑥G	⚒	⚒	⚒	⚒	⑥	Ⓐ	⑦	⑦	⑦Y	⑦	⑦	✣W	⑦	⑦
Carlisle d.	1431	1454	...	1521	1552	...	1623	1654	...	1725	1753	...	1839	1849	...	2009	2107	2204	...	...		...	...	0850	0955		1950	2038
Haltwhistle d.	1504	1522	...	1553	1620	...	1653	1722	...	1757	1821	...	1912	1921	...	2038	2139	2236	...	...		...	...	0922	1024		2022	2110
Hexham d.	1529	1542	1553	1614	1640	1654	1716	1742	1759	1820	1841	1856	1934	1943	2000	2100	2200	2258	2325	2341		...	...	0945	1047	and at	2045	2132
Prudhoe d.	1541	1554	1610	1626	1652	1711	1728	1754	1817	1832	1853	1913	1946	1955	2018	2118	2218	2316	2343	2359		...	...	1003	1104	the	2103	2149
Metrocentre d.	1554	1606	1626	1638	1704	1727	1741	1806	1832	1844	1905	1929	1958	2007	2033	2133	2233	2331	2355	0013		...	...	1018	1118	same	2118	2204
Newcastle a.	1604	1614	1639	1648	1712	1736	1751	1816	1842	1852	1913	1939	2007	2016	2042	2142	2242	2341	0005	0023		...	...	1027	1127	minutes	2127	2215
Newcastle d.	...	...	1641	...	...	1741	...	...	1845	...	...	1945	...	...	*2045*	2145	2245	...	...	...		0830	0932	1030	1130	past	2130	...
Sunderland .. **183** d.	...	...	1701	...	...	1802	...	...	1908	...	...	2008	...	...	*2106*	2206	2308	...	...	...		0850	0952	1050	1151	each	2151	...
Hartlepool .... **183** d.	...	...	1725	...	...	1825	...	...	1932	...	...	2031	...	...	*2130*	2229	2332r	...	...	...		0913	1016	1115	1214	hour	2214	...
Stockton d.	...	...	1743	...	...	1844	...	...	1950	...	...	2050	...	...	*2148*	2248	...	...	...	...		0932	1034	1134	1233	until	2233	...
Middlesbrough a.	...	...	1754	...	...	1855	...	...	2001	...	...	2101	...	...	*2202*	2259	...	...	...	...		0943	1046	1144	1244		2245	...

G – From Glasgow Central (Table **214**).
W – The 1054 and 1355 departures from Carlisle continue to Whitby (Table **211**).
Y – To Whitby (Table **211**).
r – Ⓐ only.
✣ – Timings may vary by ± 2 minutes.
◇ – Runs 4 – 5 minutes later on ⑥.

211 MIDDLESBROUGH and PICKERING - WHITBY

2nd class NT

km		⚒D	⑦D	⚒	⑦B	⑦C	⚒B	⑦C	⚒B	⑤
0	**Middlesbrough** d.	0705	0841	1020	1046	1345	1402	1645	1756	2120
18	Battersby d.	0735	0910	1050	1125f	1418	1436	1720	1825	2149
41	Glaisdale d.	0809	0944	1124	1159	1452	1510	1754	1858	2223
46	Grosmont d.	0817	0952	1132	1207	1500	1518	1802	1906	2231
56	**Whitby** a.	0837	1011	1151	1225	1518	1537	1821	1925	2250

	⚒	⑦D	⚒	⑦C	⑦C	⚒H	⑦	⚒	⑤
Whitby d.	0845	1019	1158	1246	1548	1600	1828	1934	2257
Grosmont d.	0902	1036	1215	1303	1605	1618	1845	1951	2314
Glaisdale d.	0913	1047	1226	1314	1616	1629	1856	2002	2325
Battersby d.	0947	1121	1300	1349	1651	1705	1930	2036	2359
Middlesbrough a.	1015	1148	1330	1416	1719	1732	1958	2106	0025

km		🚂	🚂		🚂	🚂		🚂	🚂	🚂
0	**Pickering** d.	...	0925	...	1100	1200	...	1400	1500	1600
29	Grosmont a.	...	1030	...	1205	1305	...	1505	1605	1705
29	Grosmont d.	0915	1040	...	...	1315	...	...	1630	...
39	**Whitby** a.	0945	1110	...	...	1345	...	...	1700	...

	🚂		🚂	🚂		🚂		🚂	🚂
Whitby d.	1000	...	...	1245	...	1400	...	...	1710
Grosmont a.	1025	...	...	1315	...	1425	...	...	1735
Grosmont d.	1030	...	1230	1330	...	1430	...	1630	1745
Pickering a.	1140	...	1340	1440	...	1540	...	1735	1855

B – From Newcastle (Table **210**).
C – To/from Carlisle (Tables **210**).
D – To/from Darlington (Table **212**).
H – To/from Hexham (Table **210**).
f – Arrives 1113.
🚂 – Until November 3. National rail tickets **not** valid. An amended service operates on most ⑦ and on certain other dates - please confirm with operator. The North Yorkshire Moors Railway (✆ 01751 472508. www.nymr.co.uk)

212 BISHOP AUCKLAND - DARLINGTON - MIDDLESBROUGH - SALTBURN

2nd class NT

km		⚒	⚒A	⑥	Ⓐ	⚒B	⚒		⚒	⚒	⚒		⚒	⚒	⚒	⑦	⑦A	⑦		⑦	⑦		⑦	⑦
0	**Bishop Auckland** d.		...	0707	0709	...	0811		1611	1711	1811	...	1911	2011	2111		...	0811	...	0911	1011		1911	2011
4	Shildon d.		...	0712	0714	...	0816	and at	1616	1716	1816	...	1916	2016	2116		...	0816	...	0916	1016	and at	1916	2016
8	Newton Aycliffe d.		...	0717	0719	...	0821	the same	1621	1721	1821	...	1921	2021	2121		...	0821	...	1921	1021	the same	1921	2021
19	**Darlington** a.		...	0734	0737	...	0838	minutes	1638	1738	1838	...	1938	2038	2138		...	0838	...	1938	1038	minutes	1938	2038
19	**Darlington** ▶ d.		0634	0736	0738	...	0840	past each	1640	1740	1840	...	1940	2040	2140		0810	0840	...	1940	1039	past each	1940	2040
43	**Middlesbrough** ▶ d.		0700	0804	0806	0815	0907	hour until	1707	1807	1907	...	2007	2109	2207		0837	0907	...	1007	1107	hour until	2007	2107
55	Redcar Central ▶ d.		*0751*	0816	0818	0829	0919		1719	1821	1919	...	2019	2121	2219		...	0919	...	1019	1119		2019	2119
63	**Saltburn** ▶ a.		*0806*	0831	0833	0844	0934		1734	1836	1934	...	2034	2136	2234		...	0934	...	1034	1134		2034	2134

	⚒	⚒a	⚒C	⚒	⚒C	⚒	⚒		⚒	⚒	⚒	⚒	⚒	⑦	⑦	⑦	⑦	⑦	⑦	⑦A	⑦		⑦	⑦
Saltburn ▷ d.		D	0618	...	0718	0741	0844		1544	1642	1744	1844	1944		...	...	...	0944	1044	...	1144		1744	1844
Redcar Central ▷ d.		...	0631	...	0731	0754	0857	and at	1557	1655	1757	1857	1957		...	...	...	0957	1057	...	1157	and at	1757	1857
Middlesbrough ▷ d.		0547	0645	...	0745	0810	0910	the same	1610	1710	1810	1910	2010		...	...	0910	1010	1110	1150	1210	the same	1810	1910
Darlington ▷ a.		0618	0720	...	0820r	0838	0939	minutes	1638	1738	1839	1939	2038		...	...	0939	1038	1138	1219	1238	minutes	1838	1938
Darlington d.		0624	...	0740	...	0840	0940	past each	1640	1740	1841	1941	2040		0735	0840	0941	1040	1140	...	1239	past each	1840	1940
Newton Aycliffe d.		0638	...	0754	...	0854	0954	hour until	1654	1754	1855	1955	2054		0749	0854	0955	1054	1154	...	1254	hour until	1854	1954
Shildon d.		0643	...	0759	...	0859	0959		1659	1759	1900	2000	2059		0754	0859	1000	1059	1159	...	1259		1859	1958
Bishop Auckland a.		0650	...	0806	...	0906	1007		1706	1806	1907	2007	2106		0801	0906	1007	1106	1206	...	1207		1906	2004

A – To/from Whitby (Table **211**).
B – From Hexham (Table **210**).
C – To Carlisle (Table **210**).
D – To Carlisle on Ⓐ (Table **210**).

a – Change at Darlington on Ⓐ.
f – Arrives 0855.
r – Arrives 0817 on Ⓐ.
t – Change at Middlesbrough.

▶ – All trains Darlington - Middlesbrough - Redcar - Saltburn:
⚒: 0614, 0712, 0736⑥, 0738Ⓐ, 0816⑥, 0818Ⓐ, 0840, 0918, 0940, 1017, 1040, 1119, 1140, 1218, 1240 and at the same minutes past each hour until 2018, 2040, 2140.
⑦: 0840, 0940, 1040, 1140, 1240, 1339, 1440 and hourly until 2040, 2157.

▷ – All trains Saltburn - Redcar - Middlesbrough - Darlington:
⚒: 0618, 0659, 0718, 0741, 0817, 0844 and at the same minutes past each hour until 1617, 1642, 1717, 1744, 1817, 1844, 1917 1944, 2017, 2047, 2118Ⓐ, 2144Ⓐt, 2144⑥, 2244.
⑦: 0944, 1044 and hourly until 2144, 2256.

214 CARLISLE - DUMFRIES - GLASGOW

2nd class SR

At the time of going to press 🍷 service is subject to confirmation.

km		⚒	Ⓐ	⑥	⚒		⚒	⑥🍷	Ⓐ🍷	⑥🍷	Ⓐ	⚒	⚒	⚒	⚒🍷	⚒	⚒🍷		⚒	⑥	Ⓐ	⚒🍷	⚒🍷	⚒
	Newcastle **210** d.		...	...	...	...	...	...	...	...	...	...	...	...	...	...	...	...	...	...	...	...	...	...
0	**Carlisle** **154** d.		...	...	...	...	0531	0608	0608	0806	0806	0958	1112	1220	1308	1430	1505	...	1617	1721	1727	1757	1920	2020
16	Gretna Green d.		...	...	...	...	0542	0619	0619	0817	0817	1009	1123	1232	1320	1441	1517	...	1628	1732	1741	1808	1931	2031
28	Annan d.		...	...	...	...	0553	0627	0627	0825	0825	1017	1131	1240	1328	1449	1526	...	1636	1740	1751	1817	1939	2039
53	**Dumfries** d.		0513	0513	0545	...	0610	0646	0646	0844	0854j	1035	1150	1258	1347	1507	1550	...	1654	1758	1808	1835	1958	2057
124	Auchinleck d.		0601	0601	0634	...	...	0734	0734	0932	0942	...	1238	...	1435	...	1638	...	...	...	...	1924	2046	...
146	**Kilmarnock** ▽ d.		0620	0620	0652	...	...	0755	0755	0950	1000	...	1259	...	1459	...	1656	...	...	...	...	1957f	2104	...
185	**Glasgow** Central **154** ▽ a.		0707	0711	0732	...	...	0834	0837	1033	1038	...	1335	...	1537	...	1737	...	...	...	...	2037	2142	...

	⑥🍷	Ⓐ🍷	⚒	⑦	⑦🍷	⑦	⑦	⑦🍷	⑦
Newcastle **210** d.	...	...	...		...	...	...	...	...
Carlisle **154** d.	2109	2112	2310		1312	1512	1712	1912	2126
Gretna Green d.	2120	2124	2321		1324	1523	1723	1923	2137
Annan d.	2128	2132	2329		1332	1531	1731	1931	2145
Dumfries d.	2151	2151	2347		1351	1549	1749	1950	2203
Auchinleck d.	2239	2239	...		1439	...	...	2038	...
Kilmarnock ▽ d.	2257	2257	...		1457	...	...	2057	...
Glasgow Central **154** ▽ a.	2336	2336	...		1543	...	...	2135	...

	⚒	⚒	⚒	Ⓐ	Ⓐ	⑥	⚒🍷		⚒🍷	⚒
Glasgow Central .... **154** ▽ d.		...	...	...	...	...	0707	...	0837	...
Kilmarnock ▽ d.		...	...	...	...	...	0754a	...	0918	...
Auchinleck d.		...	...	...	...	...	0811	...	0935	...
Dumfries d.		0458	0618	0714	0741	0741	0901	...	1025	1102
Annan d.		0513	0633	0729	0756	0756	0916	...	1040	1117
Gretna Green d.		0522	0642	0738	0805	0805	0925	...	1049	1126
Carlisle **154** a.		0535	0655	0753	0818	0818	0942	...	1102	1139
Newcastle **210** a.		...	0835	...	0948	...	...	...	...	...

		⚒🍷	⚒	⚒🍷	⚒🍷	⚒	⚒	Ⓐ🍷	⑥🍷	⚒	⚒🍷	⚒🍷	⑥	⑥	Ⓐ	Ⓐ	⑥	Ⓐ	⑦	⑦	⑦	⑦🍷	⑦	⑦🍷
Glasgow Central **154** ▽ d.	...	1013	...	1213	1313	...	...	1613	1613	...	1742	1913	2013	...	2013	2113	2213	2313		...	...	1503	...	2212
Kilmarnock ▽ d.	...	1051	...	1250	1350	...	...	1652	1652	...	1825	1952	2058b	...	2058b	2156	2253	0002		...	...	1551	...	2249
Auchinleck d.	...	1108	...	1307	1407	...	...	1709	1709	...	1842	2009	2114	...	2125	2213	2309	0020		...	...	1608	...	2306
Dumfries d.	...	1158	1304	1357	1457	1602	1707	1759	1759	1841	1933	2100	2210	2220	2222	2303	2359	0115		1301	1501	1700	1901	2356
Annan d.	...	1213	1319	1413	1512	1617	1722	1814	1814	1856	1948	2115	...	2235	...	2318	0014	...		1316	1516	1715	1916	0011
Gretna Green d.	...	1222	1328	1421	1521	1626	1731	1823	1823	1905	1957	2124	...	2244	...	2327	0023	...		1325	1525	1724	1925	0020
Carlisle **154** a.	...	1235	1341	1435	1534	1639	1746	1837	1837	1918	2011	2139	...	2257	...	2342	0036	...		1338	1538	1738	1938	0033
Newcastle **210** a.	...	...	...	...	...	...	...	2007	2016	...	...	...	...	...	...	...	...	...		...	...	...	...	...

a – Arrives 0749. b – Arrives 2052. f – Arrives 1941. j – Arrives 0843. ▽ – Frequent additional services are available (half-hourly on ⚒, hourly on ⑦).

SR 2nd class GLASGOW and KILMARNOCK - STRANRAER 215

For ⛴ Cairnryan - Belfast and v.v. see Table 2002.

km		⚒	⚒	⚒	⚒	⚒	⚒	⑦	⚒	⚒	⑦	⚒	⚒	⑦	⚒	⚒	⚒	⑦	⚒	⚒	⑦	⚒	⚒	⚒	Ⓐ	⑥
0	**Glasgow** Central . **216** d.	...	...	...	...	0808	...	...	...	...	...	...	...	...	1413	...	...	...	1713	1813	...	...	...	...	2213	...
39	**Kilmarnock 214** ......a.	...	...	...	...	0849	...	...	...	...	...	...	...	...	1450	...	...	...	1752	1852	...	...	...	...	2252	...
39	**Kilmarnock** ......d.	...	...	...	0801	0900	...	...	1104	...	...	1303	...	...	1457	...	1700	...	1803	1904	...	...	2101	...	2305	2305
56	Troon ...... **216** d.	...	...	...	0814	0912	...	...	1116	...	...	1315	...	...	1510	...	1712	...	1816	1916	...	...	2116	...	2317	2317
64	**Ayr** 🚌 ...... **216** a.	...	...	...	0827	0923	...	...	1129	...	...	1328	...	...	1524	...	1723	...	1828	1927	...	...	2127	...	2330	2330
64	**Ayr** ......d.	0525	0621	0717	0828	0923	1028	1106	1131	1226	1227	1329	1424	1505	1525	1625	1723	1805	1829	1927	1927	2032	2128	2230	2331	2331
97	Girvan ......d.	0552	0648	0756g	0855	0954f	1055	1136f	1201f	1253	1253	1359f	1451	1535f	1555f	1652	1754f	1835f	1856	1958f	1953	2059	2153	2257	0001f	0001f
121	Barrhill ......d.	...	...	0816	...	1013	...	1155	1220	...	1318f	1418	...	1554	1614	...	1813	1854	...	2017	2017f	...	...	...	0020	0020
162	**Stranraer** ......a.	...	...	0852	...	1049	...	1231	1256	...	1354	1454	...	1630	1650	...	1849	1930	...	2053	2053	...	...	...	0056	0056

	⚒	⚒	⚒	⚒	⚒	⚒	⚒	⑦	⚒	⑦	⚒		⚒	⑦	⚒	⚒	⚒	⑦	⚒	⚒	⚒	⑦	⑥	Ⓐ	⚒	⚒
Stranraer ......d.	...	...	0700	...	0859	...	1106	1041	...	1241	1304	...	...	1440	1500	...	1659	1740	...	1903	...	1940	2103	2103	...	...
Barrhill ......d.	...	...	0734	...	0933	...	1140	1116	...	1316	1338	...	...	1514	1534	...	1733	1814	...	1937	...	2015	2137	2137	...	...
Girvan ......d.	0557	0653	0752	0900	0951	1100	1159	1134	1300	1334	1357	...	1501	1533	1553	1659	1751	1833	1901	1956	2104	2033	2157	2157	2229	2302
Ayr ......a.	0625	0721	0821	0928	1020	1128	1229	1202	1328	1402	1428	...	1529	1601	1623	1728	1820	1901	1929	2026	2132	2101	2225	2225	2308	2330
Ayr 🚌 ...... **216** d.	...	0722	0822	...	1021	...	1229	...	...	...	1430	...	...	...	1627	1728	1821	...	...	2027	...	...	2226	2226	...	...
Troon ...... **216** d.	...	0733	0836	...	1029	...	1238	...	...	...	1441	...	...	...	1638	1739	1829	...	...	2038	...	...	2239	2239	...	...
Kilmarnock ......a.	...	0749	0852	...	1044	...	1254	...	...	...	1456	...	...	...	1653	1756	1844	...	...	2055	...	...	2256	2301	...	...
Kilmarnock 214 ......d.	...	...	0856	...	...	...	...	...	...	...	...	...	...	...	...	...	1857	...	...	...	...	...	...	...	...	...
Glasgow Central . **216** a.	...	...	0937	...	...	...	...	...	...	...	...	...	...	...	...	...	1937	...	...	...	...	...	...	...	...	...

– Arrives 5 minutes earlier. **g** – Arrives 0742. ☛ 🚌 connections to / from Cairnryan are available from Ayr for pre-booked Rail & Sail ticket holders - www.stenaline.co.uk/rail

SR GLASGOW - AYR, ARDROSSAN and LARGS 216

Typical off-peak journey time in hours and minutes
READ DOWN ↓ READ UP ↑

Journey times may be extended during peak hours on Ⓐ (0600 - 0900 and 1600 - 1900) and also at weekends.
The longest journey time by any train is noted in the table heading.

GLASGOW CENTRAL - AYR — Longest journey: 1 hour 04 minutes SR

km	△				△
0	0h00	↓	**Glasgow** Central ......d.		0h49
43	0h25	↓	Kilwinning ......d.	↑	0h22
48	0h29	↓	Irvine ......d.		0h18
56	0h37	↓	Troon ......d.	↑	0h11
61	0h41	↓	Prestwick Airport ✈ ..d.		0h07
67	0h52	↓	**Ayr** ......a.	↑	0h00

From Glasgow Central: On ⚒ at 0015②–⑥, 0600, 0630, 0700, 0730, 0746, 0800, 0830, 0838, 0900, 0931, 1000, 1030 and every 30 minutes until 1600, 1628, 1640, 1701, 1716Ⓐ, 1730, 1747Ⓐ, 1800, 1830, 1901, 1930 and every 30 minutes until 2330.
On ⑦ at 0900 and every 30 minutes until 1900, 2000, 2100, 2200, 2300.

From Ayr: On ⚒ at 0513, 0540, 0602, 0620Ⓐ, 0650, 0705, 0717, 0734Ⓐ, 0740, 0805, 0829, 0851, 0924, 0950, 1025, 1050, 1124, 1152, 1223, 1250, 1325, 1350, 1426, 1450, 1525, 1548, 1623, 1654, 1706, 1724, 1753, 1825, 1850, 1915 and every 30 minutes until 2215, 2300.
On ⑦ at 0845 and every 30 minutes until 1945, 2045, 2145, 2300.

△ – Trains at 0015⚒ - 0838⚒ and 1900⚒ - 2330⚒ and all day on ⑦ call additionally at Paisley Gilmour Street.

GLASGOW CENTRAL - ARDROSSAN - LARGS — Longest journey: 1 hour 10 minutes SR

km					
0	0h00	↓	**Glasgow** Central ......d.	↑	0h59
12	0h10		Paisley Gilmour St ....d.		0h46
43	0h29	↓	Kilwinning ......d.	↑	0h25
50	0h38		**Ardrossan** Sth Beach ..d.		0h17
64	0h49	↓	Fairlie ......d.	↑	0h05
69	0h56		**Largs** ......a.		0h00

From Glasgow Central:
On ⚒ at 0615, 0715, 0848 and hourly until 1548, 1630, 1714⑥, 1723Ⓐ, 1749, 1850, 1945, 2045, 2145, 2245, 2315①–④⑥, 2345⑤.
On ⑦ at 0940 and hourly until 2140, 2242.

From Largs:
On ⚒ at 0642, 0722Ⓐ, 0742, 0833Ⓐ, 0853⑥, 0953 and hourly until 1553, 1648, 1733, 1852, 1954, 2052, 2152, 2252.
On ⑦ at 0854 and hourly until 2154, 2300.

SR 2nd class GLASGOW - OBAN, FORT WILLIAM and MALLAIG 218

Most trains convey 🍸

km		⚒	⚒	⚒A	Ba	⚒	⚒	⑦	⑦c	⑦	⚒	Bb	⑦	⑦	⚒	⚒		Ⓐ	⚒	⑦	⑦	⚒	①–④	⑤	⑥
	Edinburgh **220** ......d.	...	...	0450	...	*0715*	*0715*	...	0808	*0830*	*0930*	...	*1100*	*1100*	*1115*	*1115*	...	...	*1530*	*1701*	*1701*	*1715*	*1715*	*1715*	*1715*
0	**Glasgow** Queen St ......d.	...	0520	0548‡	...	0823	0822	...	|	0956	1033	...	1220	1220	1224	1224	...	...	1636	1821	1821	1823	1823	1823	1823
16	Dalmuir ......d.	...	0539	0604	...	0842	0842	...	0927**u**	1016	1055	...	1234	1234	1243	1243	...	...	1656	1836	1836	1842	1842	1842	1842
26	Dumbarton Central ......d.	...	0548	0615	...	0852	0852	...	|	1026	1105	...	1247	1247	1253	1253	...	...	1707	1847	1847	1851	1851	1851	1851
40	Helensburgh Upper ......d.	...	0603	0632	...	0907	0907	...	0952	1041	1127	...	1306f	1306f	1308	1308	...	...	1722	1905f	1905f	1906	1906	1906	1906
51	Garelochhead ......d.	...	0614	0645	...	0918	0918	...	1003	1052	1140	...	1318	1318	1319	1319	...	...	1733	1916	1916	1917	1917	1917	1917
68	Arrochar & Tarbet ......d.	...	0634	0709	...	0938	0938	...	1023	1112	1200	...	1338	1338	1339	1339	...	...	1757f	1936	1936	1937	1937	1937	1937
81	Ardlui ......d.	...	0652f	0724x	...	0951	0951	...	1037	1128	1214	...	1356f	1356f	1356f	1356f	...	...	1810	1951	1951	1951	1951	1951	1951
95	**Crianlarich** ......a.	...	0708	0745	...	1007	1007	...	1053	1145	1230	...	1412	1412	1412	1412	...	...	1826	2007	2007	2007	2007	2007	2007
95	**Crianlarich** ......d.	...	0718	0746	...	1015	1021	...	1056	1147	1233	...	1418	1424	1418	1424	...	...	1829	2014	2020	2014	2020	2020	2020
	Dalmally ......d.	...	0751f	|	...	1042	|	...	1122	1215	1259	...	1444	|	1444	|	...	1705	1855	2040	|	2040	|	|	|
	Taynuilt ......d.	...	0811	|	...	1103	|	...	1142	1238	1320	...	1504	|	1505	|	...	1724	1919	2100	|	2100	|	|	|
162	**Oban** ......a.	...	0835	|	...	1127	|	...	1206	1304	1343	...	1527	|	1528	|	...	1747	1942	2124	|	2124	|	|	|
115	Bridge of Orchy ......d.	...	...	0817	...	...	1048	...	...	...	...	...	...	1449	...	1449	...	...	...	...	2047f	...	2045	2045	2045
140	Rannoch ......d.	...	...	0844	...	...	1109	...	...	...	...	...	...	1512	...	1512	...	...	...	...	2108	...	2108	2108	2108
177	Roy Bridge ......d.	...	...	0931x	...	...	1148	...	...	...	...	...	...	1550	...	1550	...	...	...	...	2146	...	2146	2146	2146
183	Spean Bridge ......d.	...	...	0938	...	...	1155	...	...	...	...	...	...	1556	...	1556	...	...	...	...	2153	...	2153	2156	2153
197	**Fort William** ......a.	...	...	0957	...	...	1208	...	...	...	...	...	...	1609	...	1609	...	...	...	...	2206	...	2206	2209	2206
197	**Fort William** ......d.	0830	...	...	1015	...	1212	1212	...	...	...	1430	...	1619	...	1619	...	...	...	...	2214	...	2211	2216	2211
223	Glenfinnan ......d.	0905	...	...	1122	...	1246	1246	...	...	...	1545	...	1655	...	1655	...	...	...	...	2247	...	2247	2250	2247
251	Arisaig ......d.	0938	...	...	|	...	1319	1319	...	...	...	|	...	1727	...	1727	...	...	...	...	2320	...	2320	2323	2320
259	Morar ......d.	0946	...	...	|	...	1327	1327	...	...	...	|	...	1736	...	1736	...	...	...	...	2328	...	2328	2331	2328
264	**Mallaig** ......a.	0953	...	...	1225	...	1334	1334	...	...	...	1629	...	1743	...	1743	...	...	...	...	2335	...	2335	2338	2335

	⚒	⚒	⚒	⚒	⚒	⑦	⑦	Ⓐ	Ba	⑦	⑥	Ⓐ	⑦c	⚒	⚒	⑦	⑦	⑦A	⑦d	⚒	Ⓐ	⑥	ⒶA	Bb
lallaig ......d.	...	0603	...	...	1010	...	1010	...	1410	...	...	...	...	1605	...	1605	...	...	1815	1815	...	...	...	1838
lorar ......d.	...	0609	...	...	1017	...	1017	...	|	...	...	...	...	1612	...	1612	...	...	1822	1822	...	...	...	|
risaig ......d.	...	0619	...	...	1027	...	1026	...	|	...	...	...	...	1621	...	1621	...	...	1831	1831	...	...	...	|
ilenfinnan ......d.	...	0651	...	...	1059	...	1059	...	1518	...	...	...	...	1654	...	1654	...	...	1904	1904	...	...	...	1947
ort William ......a.	...	0725	...	...	1132	...	1132	...	1600	...	...	...	...	1728	...	1728	...	...	1937	1937	...	...	...	2031
ort William ......d.	...	0744	...	...	1140	...	1140	...	...	...	...	...	...	1737	...	1737	...	1900	...	...	...	...	1950	...
pean Bridge ......d.	...	0757	...	...	1156	...	1156	...	...	...	...	...	...	1751	...	1751	...	1919	...	...	...	...	2009	...
oy Bridge ......d.	...	0804	...	...	1202	...	1202	...	...	...	...	...	...	1757	...	1757	...	1925x	...	...	...	...	2017x	...
annoch ......d.	...	0847f	...	...	1242	...	1242	...	...	...	...	...	...	1838	...	1838	...	2014	...	...	...	...	2108	...
ridge of Orchy ......d.	...	0907	...	...	1303	...	1303	...	...	...	...	...	...	1858	...	1858	...	2047	...	...	...	...	2137	...
Oban ......d.	0521	|	0857	1211	|	1211	|	1441	...	1611	1611	1611	1711	|	1811	|	1811	|	...	...	2037	2037	|	...
Taynuilt ......d.	0544	|	0920	1235	|	1238	|	1506	...	1638	1634	1634	1737	|	1833	|	1833	|	...	...	2101	2101	|	...
Dalmally ......d.	0603	|	0940	1300f	|	1259	|	1526	...	1658	1654	1654	1758	|	1856	|	1856	|	...	...	2120	2120	|	...
rianlarich ......a.	0631	0931	1008	1332	1327	1326	1332	1554	...	1726	1722	...	1825	1922	1927	1922	1927	2116	...	...	2148	2148	2206	...
rianlarich ......d.	0633	0933	1014	1337	1337	1337	1337	1556	...	1727	1724	...	1826	1932	1932	1932	1932	2118	...	...	2148	2148	2208	...
rdlui ......d.	0651	0952	1029	1355	1355	1355	1355	1611	...	1743	1742	...	1841	1952	1952	1952	1952	2138x	...	...	2204	2204	2228x	...
rrochar & Tarbet ......d.	0710f	1006	1043	1409	1409	1409	1409	1627	...	1757	1756	...	1855	2006	2006	2006	2006	2157	...	...	2218	2218	2246	...
arelochhead ......d.	0730	1032f	1104	1431	1431	1429	1429	1649	...	1819	1819	...	1917	2026	2026	2026	2026	2223	...	...	2238	2238	2312	...
lelensburgh Upper ......d.	0742	1044	1116	1443	1443	1440	1440	1700	...	1831	1831	...	1929	2037	2037	2040	2040	2239	...	...	2249	2249	2326	...
umbarton Central ......a.	0756	1059	1129	1459	1459	1453	1453	1713	...	1847	1844	...	|	2051	2051	2053	2053	2254	...	...	2302	2302	2340	...
almuir ......a.	|	1112	1138	1512	1512	1505	1505	1724	...	1858	1853	...	1955s	2103	2103	2104	2104	2306	...	...	2311	2311	2352	...
lasgow Queen St ......a.	0837	1136	1203	1536	1536	1526	1526	1749	...	1918	1918	...	|	2124	2124	2119	2119	2329¶	...	...	2333	2336	0015¶	...
Edinburgh **220** ......a.	*0944*	*1243*	*1303*	*1636*	*1636*	*1648*	*1648*	*1844*	...	*2018*	*2018*	...	2109	*2234*	*2234*	*2223*	*2223*	0024	...	...	*0032*	...	0111	...

– [R]. (12) (limited accommodation), 🛏 1, 2 cl. and ✕ London Euston - Fort William and v.v. (Table **161**).
– THE JACOBITE – 🚂. [R]. National Rail tickets **not** valid. To book ✆ 0844 850 4685 or visit www.westcoastrailways.co.uk.

a – Ⓐ until Oct. 25 (also ⑥⑦ until Sept. 29).
b – Ⓐ until Sept. 13 (also ⑥⑦ June 15 - Sept. 1).
c – June 23 - Aug. 25.
f – Arrives 5–7 minutes earlier.
s – Calls to set down only.
u – Calls to pick up only.
x – Calls on request.
‡ – Low-level platforms. Calls to pick up only.
¶ – Low-level platforms. Calls to set down only.

219 SCOTTISH ISLAND FERRIES

Caledonian MacBrayne Ltd operates numerous ferry services linking the Western Isles of Scotland to the mainland and to each other. Principal routes – some of which are seasonal – are liste below (see also the map on page **90**). Service frequencies, sailing-times and reservations: ✆ +44 (0)800 066 5000 ; fax +44 (0)1475 635 235 ; www.calmac.co.uk

Ardrossan – Brodick (Arran)
Ardrossan – Campbeltown (Kintyre)
Barra – Eriskay
Claonaig – Lochranza (Arran)
Colintraive – Rhubodach (Bute)
Fionnphort – Iona (Iona)
Gallanach - Kerrera (Kerrera)
Gourock - Dunoon
Kennacraig – Port Askaig (Islay)
Kennacraig – Port Ellen (Islay)
Kilchoan – Tobermory (Mull)
Largs – Cumbrae (Cumbrae)
Leverburgh (Harris) – Berneray (North Uist)
Lochaline – Fishnish (Mull)
Mallaig – Armadale (Skye)
Mallaig – Eigg, Muck, Rum and Canna
Mallaig – Lochboisdale (South Uist)
Oban – Castlebay (Barra)
Oban – Coll and Tiree
Oban – Colonsay, Port Askaig (Islay) and Kennacraig
Oban – Craignure (Mull)
Oban – Lismore
Portavadie (Cowal & Kintyre) – Tarbert (Loch Fyne)
Sconser (Skye) – Raasay
Tayinloan – Gigha
Tobermory (Mull) – Kilchoan
Uig (Skye) – Lochmaddy (North Ulst
Uig (Skye) – Tarbert (Harris)
Ullapool – Stornoway (Lewis)
Wemyss Bay – Rothesay (Bute)

220 EDINBURGH - GLASGOW

GR, SR, XC

EDINBURGH - FALKIRK - GLASGOW QUEEN STREET

🍸 on all trains 0700–1900 on ⚒; 0800–1930 on ⑦

km			⚒	⚒	Ⓐ	⚒	Ⓐ	⑥	⑥	Ⓐ	⚒	⑥	Ⓐ	⚒	⚒	⚒	⚒	☆	⚒	⚒	⚒	⚒	⚒	⚒
0	**Edinburgh** Waverley d.	⚒	0600	0630	0645	0700	0715	0715	0730	0730	0745	0800	0800	0815	0830	0845	0900	and at	1815	1830	1845	1900	1915	1930
2	Haymarket d.		0604	0634	0649	0704	0719	0719	0735	0735	0749	0805	0806	0819	0836	0850	0905	the same	1819	1834	1849	1904	1919	1934
28	Linlithgow d.		0617	0646	0702	|	0732	0732	0747	0748	0802	|	|	0832	|	0904	|	minutes	1832	|	1902	|	1932	1949
41	Falkirk High d.		0626	0655	0709	0724	0739	0739	0756	0757	0810	0828	0832	0842	0855	0913	0922	past each	1841	1851	1911	1921	1941	1956
76	**Glasgow** Queen Street a.		0648	0718	0737	0744	0800	0803	0817	0823	0834	0850	0853	0904	0915	0934	0943	hour until	1904	1913	1931	1943	1959	2016

	⚒	⚒	⚒	⚒	⚒	⚒	⑥	Ⓐ	⚒	⚒		⑦	⑦	⑦	⑦		⑦	⑦	☆	⑦	⑦	⑦	⑦	⑦
Edinburgh Waverley d.	1945	2015	2045	2115	2145	2215	2245	2245	2315	2345	⑦	0800	0830	0900	0930	...	1030	1100	and at	2130	2200	2230	2300	2330
Haymarket d.	1949	2020	2049	2120	2149	2219	2249	2249	2320	2349		0804	0834	0904	0934	...	1034	1104	the same	2134	2204	2234	2304	2334
Linlithgow d.	2001	2033	2102	2133	2202	2232	2302	2306	2333	0002		0824	0854	0924	0952	...	1047	1117	minutes	2147	2217	2247	2316	2346
Falkirk High d.	2010	2042	2111	2142	2211	2241	2311	2315	2342	0011		0833	0901	0933	0959	...	1054	1126	past each	2154	2226	2254	2325	2355
Glasgow Queen Street a.	2033	2103	2132	2206	2232	2302	2331	2337	0007	0033		0854	0922	0953	1020	...	1115	1147	hour until	2215	2246	2315	2348	0017

		⚒	⚒	Ⓐ	⚒	⚒	⚒	⚒	⚒	⚒	⚒	⚒	⚒	⚒	⚒	⚒	☆a	⚒	⚒	⚒	⚒	Ⓐ	⑥	⚒
Glasgow Queen Street d.	⚒	0600	0630	0645	0700	0715	0730	0745	0800	0815	0830	0845	0900	0915	0930	0945	and at	1745	1800	1815	1830	1845	1845	1900
Falkirk High d.		0618	0652	0705	0720	0733	0751	0803	0820	0832	0851	0904	0919	0933	0949	1003	the same	1803	1820	1833	1850	1903	1903	1919
Linlithgow d.		0627	0702	0712	0729	0742	0758	0813	|	0840	|	0913	|	0942	|	1012	minutes	1815	|	1842	|	1912	1912	|
Haymarket ▽ a.		0642	0718	0725	0747	0758	0813	0830	0842	0855	0912	0928	0938	1001	1008	1029	past each	1831	1839	1857	1908	1928	1925	1939
Edinburgh Waverley a.		0647	0724	0730	0755	0804	0818	0838	0848	0905	0918	0933	0944	1006	1015	1036	hour until	1837	1844	1902	1913	1933	1931	1946

	⚒	⚒	⚒	⚒	⚒	⚒	⚒	⚒	⚒	⚒	⚒		⑦	⑦	⑦	⑦	⑦	⑦	⑦	★d	⑦	⑦	⑦	⑦
Glasgow Queen Street d.	1915	1930	1945	2015	2045	2115	2145	2215	2245	2315	2345	⑦	0756	0830	0900	0930	1000	1030	1100	and at	2200	2230	2300	2330
Falkirk High d.	1933	1948	2004	2035	2105	2135	2206	2235	2304	2334	0004		0816	0849	0919	0949	1020	1049	1120	the same	2220	2250	2320	2350
Linlithgow d.	1942	1958	2014	2044	2115	2144	2216	2244	2314	2344	0014		0826	0859	0927	0959	1028	1059	1130	minutes	2227	2259	2327	2359
Haymarket ▽ a.	2000	2014	2029	2057	2128	2200	2229	2301	2331	2359	0027		0850	0919	0945	1017	1043	1112	1145	past each	2240	2312	2340	0012
Edinburgh Waverley a.	2005	2019	2036	2103	2133	2206	2234	2306	2336	0004	0032		0855	0925	0950	1022	1049	1117	1150	hour until	2245	2317	2345	0017

EDINBURGH - MOTHERWELL - GLASGOW CENTRAL

km			⚒	⚒	Ⓐ2	⑥2	⚒A	Ⓐ2	⑥2	⚒A	⚒2	⚒A	⚒2	⚒A	Ⓐ2	⑥2	⚒A	⚒2	⚒2	⚒A	ⒶB	⑥A	ⒶA	⚒2
0	**Edinburgh** Waverley d.	⚒	0624	0727	0742	0754	0912	1020	1023	1111	1151	1313	1353	1512	1549	1549	1712	1742	1828	1911	2017	2114	2114	2313
2	Haymarket d.		|	0731	0746	0758	0916	1024	1028	1116	1156	1317	1357	1517	1553	1553	1718	1747	1833	1916	2022	2119	2119	2318
71	Motherwell a.		0705	0814	0833	0900	0955	1123e	1132	1154	1309	1354	1503	1554	1632	1704	1755	1832	1933	1954	2103	2156	2204	0021
92	**Glasgow** Central a.		0722	0831	0855	0919	1015	1155	1154	1212	1324	1412	1525	1612	1651	1723	1811	1853	1954	2015	2127	2219	2221	...

		⑦	⑦A	⑦A	⑦A	⑦A	⑦A	⑦A	⑦B
Edinburgh Waverley d.	⑦	1023	1217	1313	1510	1711	1918	2112	2122
Haymarket d.		|	1221	1318	1514	1715	1923	2117	2126
Motherwell a.		1103	1259	1354	1555	1752	1959	2155	2204
Glasgow Central a.		1128	1319	1414	1612	1813	2020	2212	2226

		⚒A	⚒B	⑥2	Ⓐ2	⚒A	⚒A	Ⓐ2	⑥2
Glasgow Central d.	⚒	0601	0648	0703	0705	0748	0900	0933	0930
Motherwell d.		0616	0704	0721	0721	0808	0915	0957	0957
Haymarket d.		0657	0748	0822	0828	0853	0958	1049	1050
Edinburgh Waverley a.		0701	0752	0826	0834	0857	1002	1053	1055

	⚒A	⚒2	⚒A	⚒2	⚒A	⚒2	⚒A	ⒶA	⑥A	⚒2		⑥	Ⓐ			⑦A	⑦A	⑦A	⑦A		⑦A	⑦A	⑦
Glasgow Central d.	1100	1145	1300	1406	1500	1546	1700	1900	1900	1945	...	2105	2105	...	⑦	1055	1202	1348	1455	...	1655	1900	2058
Motherwell d.	1115	1204	1316	1425	1516	1603	1716	1916	1915	2004	...	|	2123	...		1114	1218	1403	1513	...	1713	1916	2118
Haymarket d.	1154	1250	1355	1519	1556	1704	1755	1955	1953	2051	...	2155	|	...		1153	1256	1442	1552	...	1751	1959	2204
Edinburgh Waverley a.	1158	1255	1359	1525	1602	1712	1801	1959	2000	2055	...	2200	2221	...		1157	1301	1447	1557	...	1755	2003	2208

EDINBURGH - BATHGATE - AIRDRIE - GLASGOW

2nd class only

km			⚒	⚒	⚒	⚒	⚒	⚒	⑥	Ⓐ	⚒	⚒	⚒	⚒	♣	⚒	⚒	⚒	⚒	⚒	⚒	Ⓐ	⑥	⚒	⚒
0	**Edinburgh** Waverley d.	⚒	...	...	0607	0636	0649	0720	0751	0755	0824	0849	0922	0952	and at	1453	1522	1552	1622	1651	1722	1753	1750	1822	1852
2	Haymarket d.		...	...	0611	0641	0654	0724	0755	0759	0829	0854	0926	0957	the same	1457	1526	1557	1626	1657	1726	1757	1755	1827	1858
30	Bathgate d.		0605	0619	0635	0705	0718	0749	0823	0823	0851	0918	0948	1019	minutes	1520	1549	1619	1650	1721	1749	1820	1820	1849	1920
53	Airdrie d.		0628	0635	0657	0727	0734	0805	0839	0839	0908	0934	1005	1036	past each	1536	1607	1636	1706	1737	1806	1836	1836	1906	1941
71	**Glasgow** Queen Street ✣ a.		0655	0701	0725	0751	0759	0830	0902	0902	0932	1000	1029	1100	hour until	1600	1631	1700	1729	1800	1829	1902	1902	1933	2003

	⚒	⚒	⚒	⚒	⚒	⚒	⚒	⚒	⚒		⑦	⑦	⑦	⑦	⑦	⑦	⑦		⑦	⑦	⑦	⑦	⑦	⑦	⑦
Edinburgh Waverley d.	1922	1952	2022	2054	2120	2152	2219	2252	2309	⑦	...	0838	0905	0938	1006	1040	1109	and at	1740	1809	1840	1940	2040	2140	2240
Haymarket d.	1926	1957	2027	2058	2126	2156	2225	2256	2313		...	0842	0909	0942	1010	1044	1113	the same	1744	1813	1844	1944	2044	2144	2244
Bathgate d.	1949	2019	2052	2119	2149	2219	2250	2317	2335		0806	0909	0937	1008	1036	1106	1136	minutes	1806	1836	1906	2006	2106	2206	2306
Airdrie d.	2017	2047	2117	2147	2217	2247	2317	2339	2355		0827	0930	0958	1029	1057	1127	1157	past each	1827	1857	1927	2027	2127	2227	2327
Glasgow Queen Street ✣ a.	2048	2118	2147	2217	2247	2317	2354	0005	...		0854	0956	1025	1055	1124	1154	1225	hour until	1854	1924	1954	2054	2154	2254	2354

		⚒	⚒	⚒	⚒	Ⓐ	⑥	⚒	⚒	⚒	⚒	⑥	Ⓐ	⚒	⚒	⚒	⚒	⚒	★⊡	⚒	⚒	⚒	⚒	⚒	⚒
Glasgow Queen Street ✣ d.	⚒	0545	0601	0638	0707	0738	0738	0809	0839	0911	0940	1009	1009	1038	1112	1140	1210	1239	and at	1810	1838	1907	1938	2023	2053
Airdrie d.		0609	0629	0702	0731	0802	0803	0834	0905	0936	1005	1033	1034	1104	1136	1205	1234	1304	the same	1835	1903	1926	1958	2050	2121
Bathgate d.		0630	0645	0717	0747	0818	0823	0853	0922	0952	1022	1048	1052	1122	1152	1223	1252	1322	minutes	1852	1921	1947	2018	2113	2144
Haymarket d.		0651	0707	0738	0809	0839	0848	0916	0943	1017	1045	1110	1112	1144	1213	1246	1313	1346	past each	1915	1943c	2009	2039	2137	2208
Edinburgh Waverley a.		0656	0713	0744	0815	0845	0855	0921	0948	1024	1051	1114	1118	1150	1223f	1250	1321	1351	hour until	1922	1952f	2015	2045	2144	2214

	⚒	⑥	Ⓐ	⑥	Ⓐ	⚒	⚒	⚒		⑦	⑦	⑦		⑦	⑦	⑦	⑦	⑦	★	⑦	⑦	⑦	⑦	⑦	⑦
Glasgow Queen Street ✣ d.	2123	2153	2153	2225	2225	2253	2323	2353	⑦	0811	0845	0915	...	0945	1015	1045	1115	1145	and at	1815	1845	1945	2045	2145	2245
Airdrie d.	2150	2221	2221	2252	2252	2320	2350	0020		0838	0912	0942	...	1012	1042	1112	1142	1212	the same	1842	1912	2012	2112	2212	2312
Bathgate d.	2211	2242	2242	2313	2313	2341	0011	0041		0859	0934	1004	...	1034	1104	1134	1204	1234	minutes	1904	1934	2034	2134	2234	2333
Haymarket d.	2236	2305	2306	2334	2337	...	...	...		0928	1003	1033	...	1057	1124	1200	1224	1256	past each	1924	1955	2057	2157	2256	...
Edinburgh Waverley a.	2241	2309	2312	2342	2342	...	...	...		0932	1008	1038	...	1101	1129	1204	1229	1300	hour until	1929	1959	2101	2201	2301	...

A – To/from destinations on Tables **116** and **124**.
B – To/from London Kings Cross (Table **180**).
a – The 1730 from Glasgow also calls at Linlithgow (d. 1759).
c – Departs 4 minutes later on Ⓐ.
d – The 1230, 1530, 1730 and 2130 departures arrive Haymarket and Edinburgh 6–8 minutes later than shown.
e – Departs 1130.
f – Arrives 4–5 minutes earlier on ⑥.
g – Arrives 2010.
♣ – Timings may vary by ± 2 minutes.
☆ – Timings may vary by ± 5 minutes.
★ – Timings may vary by ± 4 minutes.
▽ – Trains call to set down only.
✣ – Low Level station.
⊡ – On Ⓐ the 1510 departure from Glasgow arrives Haymarket and Edinburgh 6 minutes later than shown.

GLASGOW and EDINBURGH - DUNDEE - ABERDEEN 222

GR, SR, XC . 🍸 on most trains

km		Ⓐ 2G	⑥ 2G	⚒ A	⚒	⚒	⚒	⚒	⚒	⚒ 2	⚒ 2	⚒	⚒	⚒ 2	⚒ 2	⑦	Ⓐ	⑥	⚒	⚒ 2	⑦	⚒	⑦	⚒	⑦	⚒ 2
0	**Edinburgh** Waverley .. 223 d.	...	...	...	...	...	0530	...	...	0628	0700	0729	...	...	0759	0804	0831	0828	...	0858	0910	0928	0913	...	...	0959
2	Haymarket .... 223 d.	...	...	...	...	...	0535	...	...	0632	0704	0735	...	...	0807	0808	0836	0833	...	0902	0915	0933	0919	...	...	1007
42	Kirkcaldy .... 223 d.	...	...	0519s	...	...	0604	...	...	0706	0736	0804	...	...	0839	0840	|	|	...	0938	0950	|	1003	...	...	1039
54	Markinch .... 223 d.	...	...	|	...	...	0613	...	...	0715	0745	|	...	...	0848	|	|	|	...	0946	|	|	1012	...	...	1047
82	Leuchars .... △ d.	...	...	0546s	...	...	0634	...	...	|	0806	0827	...	...	0911	0907	0927	0927	...	1007	1014	1022	1034	...	...	1108
	Glasgow Queen St .. 223 d.	...	...	|	...	...	|	...	0553	|	|	|	0741	...	|	|	|	|	0839	|	|	|	|	0940	0937	|
	Stirling .... 223 d.	...	...	|	...	...	|	...	0623	|	|	|	0809u	...	|	|	|	|	0908	|	|	|	|	1008	1011	|
	Perth .... 223 d.	...	...	|	0600	...	|	0642	0702	0746	|	|	0845	...	|	|	|	|	0943	|	|	|	|	1040	1048	|
95	**Dundee** .... d.	0539	...	0606s	0625	0642	0649	0705	0725	0812	0824	0843	0908	...	0928	0920	0947	0947	1006	1024	1029	1036	1053	1107f	1111	1125
112	Carnoustie .... d.	0556	...	0623s	0640	|	0703	0722	0737	▬	0841	|	|	...	0945	|	|	|	|	1038	|	|	|	|	1126	1141
123	Arbroath .... d.	0603	...	0632s	0647	0659	0712	0730	0744	⚒2	0849	0900	0924	...	0954	0936	1006	1006	1022	1046	1046	1057	1109	1124	1134	1150
145	Montrose .... d.	0626f	0626	0649s	0703	0715	0727	...	0758	0858	...	0916	0938	0946	...	0950	1020	1020	1042	...	1102	1111	1125	1149	1148	...
184	Stonehaven .... d.	0651	0651	0714s	0725	0737	0750	...	0818	0923	...	0936	|	1011	...	1011	1042	1042	1102	...	1125	1131	1147	1214	1211	...
210	**Aberdeen** .... a.	0714	0714	0741	0748	0758	0814	...	0837	0946	...	0956	1015	1033	...	1029	1101	1101	1121	...	1147	1151	1210	1234	1233	...

	⚒ C	⚒	⚒ 2	⑦	⑦	⚒ 2	⑥	Ⓐ	⑦ 2	⚒	⚒ 2	⑦	⚒ 2	⚒	⚒	⑦	⑦	⚒ 2	⚒	⑦ 2	⚒	⑦	⚒ 2	⚒ 2	⚒ C	⑦ C
Edinburgh Waverley ... 223 d.	1028	...	...	...	1050	1102	1130	1132	1132	...	...	...	1159	1230	...	1241	...	1259	1330	1334	...	...	...	1403	1429	1433
Haymarket .... 223 d.	1033	...	...	...	1054	1106	1135	1137	1136	...	...	...	1204	1235	...	1246	...	1304	1334	1338	...	...	...	1407	1434	1439
Kirkcaldy .... 223 d.	1105	...	...	...	1123	1138	|	|	1208	...	...	...	1237	|	...	1315	...	1337	|	1410	...	...	...	1440	1508	1511
Markinch .... 223 d.	|	...	...	...	|	1147	|	|	1217	...	...	...	1246	|	...	|	...	1346	|	1419	...	...	...	1449	|	|
Leuchars .... △ d.	1130	...	...	...	1147	1207	1221	1223	1239	...	...	...	1306	1323	...	1338	...	1406	1424	1441	...	...	...	1509	1532	1536
Glasgow Queen St .... 223 d.	|	1040	...	1045	|	|	|	|	|	1137	...	1145	|	|	1239	|	1243	|	|	|	1339	1345	...	|	|	|
Stirling .... 223 d.	|	1108	...	1111	|	|	|	|	|	1208	...	1211	|	|	1307	|	1310	|	|	|	1406	1412	...	|	|	|
Perth .... 223 d.	|	1139	...	1142	|	|	|	|	|	1240	...	1246	|	|	1341	|	1343	|	|	|	1440	1450	...	|	|	|
Dundee .... d.	1144	1202	...	1210f	1210r	1224	1235	1237	1255	1303	...	1310	1324	1337	1404	1352	1408	1423	1439	1457	1503	1512	...	1526	1548	1552
Carnoustie .... d.	|	|	...	|	|	1242	|	|	...	|	...	|	1338	|	|	|	|	1440	|	...	|	1524	...	1540	|	|
Arbroath .... d.	1202	1218	...	1227	1227	1250	1300	1300	...	1319	...	1326	1346	1357	1420	1408	1424	1448	1458	...	1521	1531	...	1549	1605	1610
Montrose .... d.	1218	1232	1242	1241	1241	...	|	|	...	1333	1342	1341	...	1411	1434	1422	1438	...	|	...	1542	1545	1550	...	1621	1626
Stonehaven .... d.	1241	|	1307	1303	1303	...	1331	1331	...	|	1407	1402	...	1431	1454	1445	1458	...	1531	...	|	1605	1615	...	1644	1649
Aberdeen .... a.	1305	1312	1329	1323	1323	...	1352	1352	...	1410	1429	1422	...	1450	1514	1505	1518	...	1551	...	1622	1627	1637	...	1706	1706

	⚒ F	⑦	⚒ 2	⚒ 2	⚒	⑦ 2	⚒	⑦	⑥ 2	Ⓐ 2	⑦	⚒	⚒	⚒	⑦	⚒ 2	⑦	⑦ 2	⚒	⚒	⑦	Ⓐ 2	⑥ D	Ⓐ D	⑦ D	⑥ C
Edinburgh Waverley ... 223 d.	...	...	...	1500	1528	1534	...	...	1559	1603	1605	1628	...	...	...	1701	1705	1734	1736	...	...	1804	1811	1811	1813	1833
Haymarket .... 223 d.	...	...	...	1504	1533	1538	...	...	1605	1607	1610	1633u	...	...	...	1706	1710	1738	1742	...	...	1808	1815	1817	1818	1838
Kirkcaldy .... 223 d.	...	...	...	1537	|	1610	...	...	1638	1639	1640	|	...	...	...	1739	1740	1810	|	...	...	1840	1844	1849	1850	1903
Markinch .... 223 d.	...	...	...	1546	|	1621	...	...	1646	1648	1649	|	...	...	...	1748	|	1819	|	...	...	1849	1853	1859	1859	|
Leuchars .... △ d.	...	...	...	1606	1621	1642	...	...	1707	1708	1708	1725	...	...	...	1812	1802	1841	1838	...	...	1910	1914	1923	1920	1940
Glasgow Queen St .... 223 d.	1439	1450	...	|	|	|	1538	1545	|	|	|	|	1609	1642	1645	|	|	|	|	1740	1745	|	|	|	|	|
Stirling .... 223 d.	1506	1517	...	|	|	|	|	1612	|	|	|	|	1637	1713t	1712	|	|	|	|	1811	1813	|	|	|	|	|
Perth .... 223 d.	1539	1556	...	|	|	|	1638	1647	|	|	|	|	1719	1746	1742	|	|	|	|	1850	1846	|	|	|	|	|
Dundee .... d.	1602	1619	...	1623	1638f	1658	1701	1710	1724	1725	1722	1739	1749f	1809	1805	1829	1816	1857	1851	1913	1910	1926	1930	1936	1935	1955
Carnoustie .... d.	|	|	...	1640	|	...	1713	|	1741	1742	1737	|	1811	1823	|	1851	|	...	|	1924	1922	...	|	|	|	|
Arbroath .... d.	1619	1635	...	1648	1659	...	1720	1726	1749	1750	1745	1806	1819	1830	1821	1859	1835	...	1909	1932	1929	...	1948	1952	1951	2012
Montrose .... d.	1633	1649	1649	...	1713	...	1734	1741	...	...	1759	1821	...	1845	1835	...	1849	...	1923	1946	1944	...	2003	2006	2005	2028
Stonehaven .... d.	|	1709	1714	...	1734	...	1758	1805	...	...	1819	1846	...	|	1855	...	1910	...	1943	2006	2009	...	2023	2027	2026	2051
Aberdeen .... a.	1719j	1731	1736	...	1754	...	1817	1825	...	...	1838	1905	...	1927	1915	...	1932	...	2005	2026	2029	...	2042	2048	2045	2113

	Ⓐ C	⑦ C	⚒	⚒ 2	⚒ 2	⑦ 2	⚒	⚒	⑦	⚒ 2	⑥ D	Ⓐ D	Ⓐ C	⚒	⑦	⑥ 2	Ⓐ 2	⚒	⚒	⑦	⚒ 2	⑦ 2	⚒ 2	⚒ 2	⑦ 2	⚒ 2
Edinburgh Waverley ... 223 d.	1833	1836	...	1900	...	1915	1934	...	...	1958	2012	2014	2032	...	2100	2105	2108	2143	...	...	2211	2226	...	...	...	2306
Haymarket .... 223 d.	1838	1841	...	1905	...	1919	1939	...	...	2004	2017	2018	2037	...	2105	2109	2112	2147	...	...	2215	2230	...	...	...	2312
Kirkcaldy .... 223 d.	1913	1913	...	1937	...	2002	|	...	...	2047	2052	|	2111	...	2134	2151	2154	2215	...	...	2258	2313	...	...	...	2356
Markinch .... 223 d.	|	|	...	1946	...	2011	|	...	...	2056	2102	2105	|	...	2143	2200	2203	|	...	...	2307	2322	...	...	...	0005
Leuchars .... △ d.	1940	1937	...	2007	...	2032	2029	...	...	2116	2128	2128	2139	...	2204	2222	2223	2239	...	...	2331	2343	...	...	...	0025
Glasgow Queen St .... 223 d.	|	|	1840	|	1907	|	|	1938	1944	|	|	|	|	2040	|	|	|	|	2140	2144	|	|	2309	2337	2345	|
Stirling .... 223 d.	|	|	1907	|	1937	|	|	2010	2011	|	|	|	|	2106	|	|	|	|	2209	2211	|	|	2338	0006	0020	|
Perth .... 223 d.	|	|	1945	|	2012	|	|	2041	2048	|	|	|	|	2146	|	|	|	|	2240	2248	|	|	0015	0045	0100	|
Dundee .... d.	1956	1952	2008	2023	2038	2048	2044	2107	2112	2133	2143	2143	2153	2212	2218	2238	2239	2253	2302	2310	2347	2359	0036a	...	...	0041
Carnoustie .... d.	|	|	|	▬	...	...	|	|	|	...	...	...	|	2223	|	▬	...	|	2320	2322	...	...	...	...	...	...
Arbroath .... d.	2014	2009	2024	⚒2	...	...	2100	2124	2128	...	...	...	2211	2231	2238	⚒2	...	2311	2330	2329	...	...	...	...	...	...
Montrose .... d.	2031	2025	2038	2050	...	...	2114	2138	2142	...	...	...	2227	2245	2252	2302	...	2326	2344	2343	...	...	...	...	...	...
Stonehaven .... d.	2054	2048	|	2115	...	...	|	2201	2205	...	...	...	2250	|	2312	2327	...	2347	0007	0003	...	...	...	...	...	...
Aberdeen .... a.	2116	2110	2120	2137	...	...	2153	2220	2224	...	...	...	2312	2321	2335	2349	...	0007	0030	0025	...	...	...	...	...	...

km		Ⓐ C	⑥ 2	⚒ 2	⚒ 2	⚒ 2	⚒ 2	⚒ 2	⚒	⚒	⚒ 2	⚒ 2	⚒ 2	⚒	⚒	⚒ J	⚒ 2	⑦ 2	⑦ 2	⑦	⚒	⚒ C	⚒ D	⚒ 2	⚒ 2	⚒
0	**Aberdeen** .... d.	...	...	...	...	...	0505	...	0539	0549	...	...	0619	0638	...	0707	...	...	...	...	0735	0752	0820	0827	...	0849
26	Stonehaven .... d.	...	...	...	...	...	0524	...	|	0605	...	...	0638	0654	...	0727	...	...	...	...	0753	0810	0838	0846	...	|
65	Montrose .... d.	...	...	...	...	...	0550	...	0612	0625	...	...	0704	0714	...	0747	...	...	...	...	0813	0833	0859	0912	...	0922
87	Arbroath .... d.	...	...	...	...	...	▬	0606	0627	0640	...	0712	▬	0729	...	0801	0744	...	...	...	0827	0849	0915	▬	0923	0936
97	Carnoustie .... d.	...	...	...	...	...	⚒D	0613	|	0647	...	0718	⑦2	|	...	|	0751	...	...	...	0834	|	|	⑦2	0930	|
115	**Dundee** .... d.	...	...	...	0553	0602	0632	0636	0653f	0659	0709	0737	0724	0749	0817	0822	0827c	...	...	0845	0850	0907	0933	0924	0945	0956
149	**Perth** .... 223 d.	...	...	0518	0619	|	|	...	0715	|	|	|	|	0810	0839	|	|	...	0850	0906	0914	|	|	|	|	1018
202	Stirling .... 223 d.	0526	0542	0553	0655	|	|	...	0753	|	|	|	|	0843	0914	|	|	0910	|	0940	0943	|	|	|	|	1047
249	**Glasgow** Queen St .. 223 a.	|	|	0636	0733	|	|	...	0830	|	|	|	|	0911	0954j	|	|	|	|	1014	1010	|	|	|	|	1118
	Leuchars .... △ d.	|	|	...	...	0615	0646	...	...	0711	0722	0750	0737	...	...	|	0842	|	|	...	...	0921	0946	0937	0958	...
	Markinch .... 223 d.	|	|	...	...	0637	0711	...	...	|	0746	0811	0759	...	...	|	0903	|	0919	...	...	|	1007	0959	1020	...
	Kirkcaldy .... 223 d.	|	|	...	...	0647	0721	...	...	0736	0756	0821	0809	...	...	|	0913	|	0929	...	...	0945	1017	1009	1029	...
	Haymarket .... 223 a.	0611	0624	...	...	0730	0758	...	...	0818	0841	0900	0858	...	...	0925	0957	0955	1018	...	...	1019	1049	1055	1108	...
	Edinburgh .... 223 a.	0617	0629	...	...	0737	0804	...	...	0824	0848	0908k	0903	...	...	0931	1002	1000	1023	...	...	1026	1055	1101	1113	...

	⚒	⚒ 2	⚒ 2	⑦	⚒	⑦ C	⚒ C	⚒ 2	⑦ 2	⚒	⑦	⚒	⚒	⚒	⑦ D	⚒ 2	⑦ E	⚒	⑦ C	⚒	⚒ 2	⚒ 2	⑦	⚒	⑦	⚒
Aberdeen .... d.	0904	...	0918	0922	0942	0947	0952	1024	...	...	1031	1046	1102	...	1110	...	1127	1145	1147	1207	1225	...	1229	1247	1245	1312
Stonehaven .... d.	0920	...	0937	0939	|	1005	1010	1043	...	...	1047	|	1119	...	1127	...	1143	|	1205	1223	1244	...	1246	|	1306	|
Montrose .... d.	0945f	...	1003	1002	1020f	1028	1033	1109	...	...	1107	1119	1139	...	1148	...	1203	1221	1228	1245	1310	...	1307	1321	1329	1345
Arbroath .... d.	0959	1006	▬	1016	1035	1044	1049	▬	...	1103	1122	1137	1153	...	1204	1208	1218	1235	1244	1259	▬	1309	1322	1335	1343	1359
Carnoustie .... d.	|	1013	⚒	1023	|	|	|		...	1109	|	|	|	...	|	1214	|	|	|	|	⑦2	1315	|	|	1350	|
Dundee .... d.	1021f	1031	2	1042	1055	1103	1107	⑦	1120	1128	1142	1157	1210	1215	1224	1236f	1238	1254	1302	1318f	1320	1334	1343	1355	1406	1421f
Perth .... 223 d.	|	|	1102	1104	1117	|	|	2	|	|	1206	1218	|	1239	|	|	1303	1316	|	|	|	|	1406	1417	|	|
Stirling .... 223 d.	|	|	|	1139	1148	|	|	1149	|	|	1245	1247	|	1315	|	|	1337	1345	|	|	|	|	1440	1446	|	|
Glasgow Queen St .... 223 a.	|	|	|	1206	1218	|	|	|	|	|	1313	1318	|	1352	|	|	1405	1418	|	|	|	|	1509	1518	|	|
Leuchars .... △ d.	1033	1044	|	...	...	1117	1123	|	1133	1142	...	...	1222	...	1237	1249	...	...	1317	1331	1333	1347	...	...	1418	1433
Markinch .... 223 d.	|	1106	1131	...	...	|	|	|	1155	1203	...	...	1241	...	1258	1310	...	...	|	|	1355	1408	...	...	|	|
Kirkcaldy .... 223 d.	|	1115	1141	...	...	1141	1147	|	1205	1213	...	...	|	...	1307	1320	...	...	1342	|	1405	1418	...	...	1440	|
Haymarket .... 223 a.	1131	1152	1216	...	...	1216	1220	1228	1240	1254	...	...	1323k	...	1337	1357	...	...	1420	1425	1440	1455	...	...	1516	1528
Edinburgh .... 223 a.	1137	1158	1223	...	...	1222	1226	1233	1247	1259	...	...	1328	...	1343	1408h	...	...	1426	1436j	1445	1501	...	...	1524	1534

– ®. 🛏 1, 2 class and 🛋2 London Euston - Aberdeen. Departs London previous day. Train stops to set down only. See also Table 161.
– From/to destinations on Table **180**.
– From/to destinations on Table **124**.
– From Dyce until Aug. 18; from Inverurie from Aug. 25 (Table **225**).
– On Ⓐ to Dyce until Aug. 16; to Inverness from Aug. 19 (Table **225**).
– To Dyce until Aug. 16; to Inverness from Aug. 19 (Table **225**).

H – To/from Inverurie (Table **225**).
J – From Inverness from Aug. 19 (Table **225**).

c – Arrives 0813.
f – Arrives 4–7 minutes earlier.
h – Arrives 1400 on ⑥.
j – Arrives 4–6 minutes earlier on Ⓐ.
k – Arrives 5 minutes earlier on ⑥.

r – Arrives 8–10 minutes earlier.
s – Stops to set down only.
t – ⑥ only.
u – Stops to pick up only.
△ – Frequent 🚌 connections available to/from **St Andrews.** Journey 10 minutes. Operator: Stagecoach (routes 42, 94, 99).

222 ABERDEEN - DUNDEE - EDINBURGH and GLASGOW

🍷 on most trains GR, SR, XC

	⚒ 2	⚒ 2	⑦	⚒	⑦ C	⚒ 2	⚒	⚒ 2	Ⓐ 2	⑥ 2	⑦	⚒	⚒ C	⑦	⑦	⚒ 2	⚒	⚒	⚒	⑦ 2	⚒ 2	⑦	⚒	⑦	⑥	Ⓐ	⚒ 2
Aberdeen d.	...	1325	1332	1348	1347	...	1357	1422	...	...	1431	1442	1452	1509	1528	1516	...	1538	1602	...	...	1629	1630	1709	1715	1715	...
Stonehaven d.	...	1344	1348	|	1405	...	1415	1441	...	...	1448	|	1510	1529	1544	1535	...	|	1618	...	...	1645	|	1725	|	|	...
Montrose d.	...	1410	1408	1421	1428	...	1435	1507	...	...	1509	1517	1533	1550	1609	1602	...	1611	1643f	...	...	1705	1712f	1745	1754	1754	...
Arbroath d.	1407	...	1423	1435	1444	...	1450	▬	1505	1508	1524	1531	1549	1604	1623	...	1559	1626	1700	...	1709	1720	1727	1800	1808	1808	1818
Carnoustie d.	1413	...	|	|	|	...	|	⑦2	1511	1514	|	|	|	1610	|	...	1606	|	1707	...	1716	|	|	|	|	|	1825
Dundee d.	1433	...	1443	1457	1502	1513	1509f	1515	1530	1533	1545	1551	1607	1624	1643	...	1649g	1646	1724f	1721	1734	1740	1749f	1817	1824	1824	1846f
Perth ‡ d.	|	...	1504	1519	|	1537	|	|	|	|	1609	1613	|	|	1705	...	|	1713	|	|	|	1801	1811	|	|	|	|
Stirling ‡ d.	|	...	1540	1548	|	1615	|	|	|	|	1643	1644s	|	|	1740	...	|	1747	|	|	|	1832	1843	|	|	|	|
Glasgow Queen St. ‡ a.	|	...	1612	1618	|	1648	|	|	|	|	1712	1717	|	|	1809	...	|	1823	|	|	|	1909	1910	|	|	|	|
Leuchars △ d.	1446	...	...	...	1516	...	1521	1528	1543	1547	...	...	1621	1637	...	...	1703	...	1736	1734	1747	...	...	1829	1837	1837	1859
Markinch 223 d.	1507	...	...	...	|	...	|	1550	1604	1608	...	...	|	|	...	...	1725	...	|	1756	1811	...	...	|	|	|	1920
Kirkcaldy 223 d.	1517	...	...	...	1541	...	|	1600	1614	1618	...	...	1646	1702	...	...	1735	...	|	1806	1820	...	...	1851	|	|	1930
Haymarket 223 a.	1553	...	...	...	1618	...	1622	1635	1655	1653	...	...	1720	1734	...	...	1820	...	1828	1841	1855	...	...	1921	1931	1939	2005
Edinburgh 223 a.	1558	...	...	...	1624	...	1631k	1640	1700	1658	...	...	1726	1740	...	...	1828	...	1834	1846	1900	...	...	1926	1937	1944	2010

	⚒ 2H	⚒	⑦	⑥	Ⓐ C	⑦ 2	⚒	⚒	⑦	⚒ 2	⑦	⚒	⚒ 2	⑦		⑥	Ⓐ	⚒	⚒	⚒ 2	⑦	⚒	Ⓑ B	⑦ 2	①–④	⑥	⑤
Aberdeen d.	1725	1739	1744	1818	1818	...	1838	1916	1907	...	1936	1943	...	2006	...	2009	2010	2044	2107	...	2129	2131	2143	2227	2226	2226	2323
Stonehaven d.	1744	1756	1801	1836	1836	...	|	1932	1924	...	1952	|	...	2026	...	2025	2026	2100	|	...	2146	2149	2201u	2246	2246	2246	2343
Montrose d.	1809	1821	1824	1859	1859	...	1911	1952	1946	...	2012	2017	...	2049	...	2049	2050	2122	2142	...	2207	2212	2226u	2310	2310	2310	0007
Arbroath d.	...	1836	1838	1914	1915	...	1926	2010f	2000	...	2027	2037	2049	2103	...	2103	2104	2137	2156	2207	2223	2228	2244u	2324	2324	2326	0021
Carnoustie d.	...	|	|	|	|	...	|	2017	2007	...	|	|	2056	|	...	|	|	|	|	2214	|	|	2253u	2331	2331	2333	0028
Dundee d.	...	1856	1858	1933	1933	1916	1946	2030	2022	2042	2050f	2201	2113	2120	...	2120	2121	2156	2213	2232	2241	2248f	2308u	2349	2349	2350	0046
Perth ‡ d.	...	1918	1920	|	|	|	2010	|	|	|	2115f	2122	...	|	...	|	|	2217	|	...	|	|	|	0013	0012	...	0110
Stirling ‡ d.	...	1949	1952	|	|	|	2046	|	|	|	2150	2151	...	|	...	|	|	2250	|	...	|	|	|	...	...	...	...
Glasgow Queen St. ‡ a.	...	2026	2021	|	|	|	2116	|	|	|	2223	2221	...	|	...	|	|	2321	|	...	|	|	|	...	...	...	...
Leuchars △ d.	...	...	...	1946	1947	1929	...	2042	2035	2055	...	...	...	2132	...	2133	2133	...	2225	...	2254	2301	2327u	...	...	...	...
Markinch 223 d.	...	...	...	|	|	1951	...	|	|	2116	...	...	...	2154	...	2155	2155	...	2247	...	2316	2322	|	...	...	...	...
Kirkcaldy 223 d.	...	...	...	2011	2011	2001	...	|	2101	2126	...	...	...	2203	...	2203	2203	...	2256	...	2324	2331	2356u	...	...	...	...
Haymarket 223 a.	...	...	...	2044	2044	2047	...	2129	2133	2213	...	...	...	2233	...	2236	2242	...	2324	...	2357	0003	...	...	...	...	...
Edinburgh 223 a.	...	...	...	2049	2050	2052	...	2136	2138	2218	...	...	...	2238	...	2242	2247	...	2329	...	0002	0008	...	...	...	...	...

B – Ⓡ. 🛏 1, 2 class and (2) Aberdeen - London Euston. Train stops to pick up only. See also Table **161**.
C – To destinations on Table **180**.
H – From Dyce until Aug. 16; from Inverurie from Aug. 19 (Table **225**).

f – Arrives 4–7 minutes earlier.
g – Arrives 1624 on ⑥; 1626 on Ⓐ.
j – Arrives 4–6 minutes earlier on Ⓐ.
k – Arrives 4 minutes earlier on ⑥.
s – Stops to set down only.

u – Stops to pick up only.
‡ – See also Table **223**.
△ – Frequent 🚌 connections available to / from **St Andrews**. Journey 10 minutes. Operator: Stagecoach (routes 94, 96, 99).

222a EDINBURGH - TWEEDBANK

2nd class SR

km		⚒	Ⓐ	⑥	⚒	⚒	⚒	⚒	⚒	⊠	⚒	⚒	⚒	Ⓐ	⑥	Ⓐ	⑥	⚒	⚒		⑦	⑦	✥	⑦
0	**Edinburgh** Waverley d.		0544	0555	0621	0649	0722	0751	0823	and then	1854	1924	1953	2051	2056	2153	2156	2254	2354	...		0911	and	2311
13	Eskbank d.		0608	0614	0641	0711	0742	0812	0843	two trains	1914	1943	2014	2116	2115	2212	2215	2314	0013	...		0930	hourly	2330
15	Newtongrange d.		0612	0617	0644	0714	0745	0815	0846	per hour	1917	1946	2017	2119	2118	2215	2218	2317	0016	...		0933	until	2333
53	Galashiels d.		0644	0646	0715	0745	0816	0846	0917	until	1948	2017	2048	2150	2149	2246	2248	2348	0047	...		1004		0004
57	**Tweedbank** a.		0648	0650	0719	0750	0820	0853	0922		1954	2024	2052	2154	2153	2250	2253	2355	0053	...		1008		0009

	⚒	Ⓐ	⑥	⚒	⚒	⚒	Ⓐ	⑥	⚒	⚒	❦	⚒ a	⚒	⚒	⚒	⚒	⚒	⚒	⑥		⑦	⑦	✥	⑦
Tweedbank d.		0520	0528	0558	0628	0658	0726	0730	0828	0859	and then	1828	1859	1931	2029	2129	2229	2328	2331	...		0845	and	2246
Galashiels d.		0524	0532	0602	0632	0702	0730	0734	0832	0903	two trains	1832	1903	1935	2033	2133	2233	2332	2335	...		0849	hourly	2250
Newtongrange d.		0553	0601	0631	0701	0731	0800	0803	0901	0931	per hour	1901	1931	2004	2102	2202	2302	0001	0004	...		0918	until	2319
Eskbank d.		0556	0604	0634	0704	0734	0803	0806	0904	0934	until	1904	1934	2007	2105	2205	2305	0004	0007	...		0921		2322
Edinburgh Waverley a.		0615	0626	0655	0729	0757	0821	0830	0928	0955		1923	2000	2028	2130b	2232	2326	0026	0026	...		0940		2342

a – Runs 5 minutes later on ⑥ to Eskbank then Edinburgh arr. 1932.
b – Arrives 2124 on Ⓐ.
⊠ – Timings may vary by up to 6 minutes (earlier departures possible).

✥ – Timings may vary by 1–2 minutes.
❦ – Departure times may vary by up to 5 minutes (earlier departures possible). Edinburgh arrival times may vary by up to 7 minutes.

223 EDINBURGH and GLASGOW - PERTH - INVERNESS

SR

Most Inverness trains convey 🍷.

km		⚒ 2		⚒ A	⚒ 2C	⚒	⚒ 2	⚒	⚒	⑦	⑦	⚒ 2	⚒	⚒	⚒	⑦ 2	⑦	⚒ 2	⚒	⚒ 2	⚒	⚒	⑦	⑦	⑦ P
0	**Edinburgh** Waverley 222 d.	...	...	...	0628	...	0734	...	0833	...	0929	0936	...	...	1037	1035	...	1135	...	1235	...	1333	...	1356	...
2	Haymarket 222 d.	...	...	...	0632	...	0738	...	0838	...	0934	0940	...	...	1041u	1039	...	1139	...	1239	...	1338u	...	1400	...
42	Kirkcaldy 222 d.	...	...	...	0706	...	0811	...	0910	...	1010	1013	...	...	1113u	|	...	1214	...	1313	...	1408u	...	1432	...
54	Markinch 222 d.	...	...	...	0715	...	0820	...	0919	...	1019	1023	...	...	1122	|	...	1224	...	1323	...	1417	...	|	...
	Glasgow Queen St 222 d.	...	...	...	|	0707	|	0839	|	0937	|	|	1010	1039	|	|	1111	|	1208	|	1339	|	1345	|	1438
	Stirling 222 d.	...	...	0457	|	0734	|	0908	|	1011	|	|	1036	1107	|	1118	1141	|	1235	|	1406	|	1412	|	1508
91	**Perth** 222 d.	0503	...	0541	0745	0811	0851	0944	0951	1047	1053	1055	1116	1138	1156	...	1219	1257	1314	1355	1439	1450	1449	1512	1546
116	Dunkeld & Birnam d.	0521	...	0603	...	0831	...	...	|	...	1110	...	1138b	...	|	...	1237	...	1331	...	...	1506	...	1529	|
137	Pitlochry d.	0534	...	0618	...	0845	...	...	1021	...	1124	...	1151	...	1224	...	1251	...	1345	...	...	1520	...	1542	1614
148	Blair Atholl d.	0544	...	0630	...	0855	...	...	1031	...	1134	...	|	...	1234	...	|	...	1355	...	...	1530	...	1552	|
186	Dalwhinnie d.	0610	...	0701	...	0920	...	...	1055	...	1159	...	|	...	1300	...	|	...	|	...	...	1555	...	1621b	|
202	Newtonmore d.	0620	...	0712	...	0931	...	...	|	...	1210	...	|	...	1310	...	|	...	|	...	...	|	...	1632	|
207	Kingussie d.	0650f	...	0720	...	0936	...	...	1108	...	1215	...	1237	...	1316	...	1334	...	1429	...	...	1609	...	1637	1656
226	Aviemore d.	0703	...	0744b	...	0949	...	...	1127j	...	1227	...	1248	...	1333b	...	1346	...	1441	...	...	1620	...	1648	1708
237	Carrbridge d.	0723c	...	0757	...	1000	...	...	|	...	1236	...	|	...	1342	...	1401b	...	|	...	...	|	...	1657	|
282	**Inverness** a.	0754	...	0842	...	1029	...	...	1201	...	1317	...	1324	...	1413	...	1429	...	1522	...	...	1655	...	1725	1746

	⚒ 2	⚒	⑦	⚒ 2	⑦	⚒	Ⓐ 2	⑥ 2	⚒ K	⑦	⑦ K	⚒	⚒	⑦ 2	⑦ P	⚒	⑦ 2	⚒ 2	⑦ 2	⚒	⑥	Ⓐ	⚒ 2	⚒ 2	⑦ 2
Edinburgh Waverley 222 d.	1436	...	...	1535	1550	...	1635	1637	1634	...	1632	...	1742	1750	...	...	1806	1840	1855	...	1939	1939	2040	2237	2235
Haymarket 222 d.	1441	...	...	1540	1555	...	1639	1641	1639	...	1637	...	1747u	1754	...	...	1811	1846	1859	...	1944	1944	2044	2241	2241
Kirkcaldy 222 d.	1514	...	...	1613	1628	...	1713	1713	|	...	|	...	1817	1826	...	...	|	1919	|	...	2016	2016	2117	2324	|
Markinch 222 d.	1523	...	...	1622	1637	...	1722	1723	|	...	|	...	1827	1836	...	...	|	1929	2003	...	2025	2025	2126	2333	|
Glasgow Queen St 222 d.	|	1508	1545	|	|	1642	|	|	|	1645	|	1740	|	|	1811	1806	|	|	|	1938	|	|	|	|	|
Stirling 222 d.	|	1535	1612	|	|	1713r	|	|	1724	1712	1722	1811	|	|	1841	1839	1900	|	|	2010	|	|	|	|	2328
Perth 222 d.	1555	1617	1646	1656	1711	1742	1754	1754	1801	1740	1801b	1849	1901	1906	1917	1921	1936	2001	2035	2040	2058	2058	2158	0005	0008
Dunkeld & Birnam d.	...	1635	...	...	1727	...	...	...	|	...	|	...	1919	...	1933	1937	...	...	...	...	2115	2115	...	...	...
Pitlochry d.	...	1649	...	...	1741	...	...	...	1831	...	1832	...	1933	...	1946	1950	...	...	...	...	2135a	2135a	...	...	...
Blair Atholl d.	...	1659	...	...	|	...	...	...	|	...	|	...	|	...	1956	1959	...	...	...	...	2145	2145	...	...	...
Dalwhinnie d.	...	|	...	...	|	...	...	...	|	...	|	...	|	...	2020	2024	...	...	...	...	2209	2216a	...	...	...
Newtonmore d.	...	1732	...	...	|	...	...	...	|	...	|	...	|	...	2031	2034	...	...	...	...	2220	2227	...	...	...
Kingussie d.	...	1737	...	...	1824	...	...	...	1916	...	1917	...	2016	...	2036	2039	...	...	...	...	2225	2232	...	...	...
Aviemore d.	...	1748	...	...	1836	...	...	...	1928	...	1931	...	2027	...	2047	2050	...	...	...	...	2236	2243	...	...	...
Carrbridge d.	...	1757	...	...	|	...	...	...	|	...	|	...	|	...	2056	|	...	...	...	...	2245	2252	...	...	...
Inverness a.	...	1826	...	...	1910	...	...	...	2005	...	2008	...	2101	...	2125	2128	...	...	...	...	2314	2321	...	...	...

A – Ⓡ. 🛏 1, 2 class and (2) London Euston - Inverness. Departs London previous day. Train stops to set down only to Newtonmore. See Table **161**.

C – To Dundee (Table **222**).
K – From London Kings Cross (Table **180**).
P – To Elgin (Table **225**).

a – Arrives 7–8 minutes earlier.
b – Arrives 4–6 minutes earlier.
c – Arrives 0712.
f – Arrives 0625.

j – Arrives 1118.
k – Arrives 1621.
r – ⑥ only.
u – Calls to pick up only.

ɜR INVERNESS - PERTH - GLASGOW and EDINBURGH 223

Most Inverness trains convey 🍷.

	Ⓐ 2	⑥ 2	Ⓐ 2	⚒ 2	⚒ 2	⚒	⚒	⑦ 2	⚒	⑦ 2	⑦ 2	⚒ K	⚒ 2	⑦ 2	⚒	⚒ 2	⑦ K	⑦	Ⓐ	⑥	⚒	⚒	⚒	⑦	⑦	⚒ 2	⑦
verness d.	...	...	...	...	0536	...	0650	...	...	...	...	0755	...	...	0845	...	0940	...	0944	0944	...	1046	...	1053	...	...	1241
rrbridge d.	...	...	...	...	|	...	|	...	...	...	...	|	...	...	0913	...	1011	...	|	|	...	|	...	|	...	...	1312
iemore d.	...	...	...	...	0612	...	0725	...	...	...	...	0830	...	...	0921	...	1019	...	1027	1027	...	1123	...	1127	...	...	1320
igussie d.	...	...	...	...	0627	...	0737	...	...	...	...	0843	...	...	0936	...	1032	...	1039	1039	...	1136	...	1138	...	...	1336
wtonmore d.	...	...	...	...	|	...	|	...	...	...	...	|	...	...	0941	...	1037	...	|	|	...	|	...	|	...	...	1341
lwhinnie d.	...	...	...	...	0640	...	|	...	...	...	...	|	...	...	|	...	|	...	1052	1052	...	|	...	1151	...	...	|
air Atholl d.	...	...	...	...	0712r	...	|	...	...	...	...	|	...	...	|	...	1110	...	1115	1115	...	|	...	|	...	...	1412
lochry d.	...	...	...	...	0726	...	0818	...	...	...	...	0925	...	...	1020	...	1124b	...	1125	1125	...	1224t	...	1222	...	...	1422
nkeld & Birnam d.	...	...	...	...	0739	...	0831	...	...	...	...	|	...	...	1033	...	1138	...	1138	1138	...	1238	...	1237	...	...	1435
rth 222 d.	0513	0535	0614	0655	0758	0810	0851	0850	0914	0916	0936	0957	1005	1010	1053	1102	1159	1206	1158	1158	1218	1302c	1316	1258	1303	1400	1454
Stirling 222 d.	|	|	|	|	|	0843	|	|	0943	0951	|	1032	|	1046	1132	|	1235	1245	|	|	1247	|	1345	|	1337	|	1524
Glasgow Queen St. 222 a.	|	|	|	|	|	0911	|	|	1010	|	|	|	|	|	1207	|	|	1313	|	|	1318	|	1418	|	1405	|	1556
rkinch 222 d.	0546	0605	0646	0738	0828	...	|	0919	...	|	1005	|	1034	|	...	1131	|	...	|	|	...	1331	...	1326	...	1431	...
kcaldy 222 d.	0555	0614	|	0747	0837	...	0926	0929	...	|	|	|	1044	|	...	1141	|	...	1231	1231	...	1341	...	1335	...	1441	...
aymarket 222 a.	0642	0701	0754	0824	0913	...	1000	1018	...	1040	1111	1115	1128	1135	...	1216	1315	...	1312	1309	...	1422	...	1409	...	1524	...
dinburgh Waverley 222 a.	0647	0706	0801	0829	0918	...	1007	1023	...	1046	1116	1121	1133	1140	...	1223	1321	...	1320	1325	...	1428	...	1415	...	1529	...

	⚒	⚒	⑦	Ⓐ 2	⑥ 2	⑦	⚒	⚒ 2	⑦	⑦	⑥	Ⓐ	⚒	⑦	⑦ 2	⚒ 2	⚒	⚒ 2	Ⓐ	⑥	⚒	⑦	⑦	⚒	⚒	⑦ B	Ⓐ B
verness d.	1248	...	1333	...	...	...	1448	...	1523	...	1554	1554	...	1624	...	...	1727	...	1854	1845	...	1852	...	2016	...	2026	2045
rrbridge d.	1325	...	|	...	...	...	|	...	|	...	1627	1627	...	1658	...	...	1800c	...	1921	1912	...	1924	...	2100b	...	|	|
iemore d.	1335	...	1406	...	...	...	1524	...	1557	...	1635	1635	...	1709	...	...	1808	...	1933b	1927c	...	1932	...	2108	...	2117	2133
igussie d.	1346	...	1418	...	...	...	1537	...	1608	...	1647	1647	...	1721	...	...	1820	...	1945	1939	...	1944	...	2120	...	2131	2154
wtonmore d.	1351	...	|	...	...	...	|	...	|	...	1652	1652	...	|	...	...	|	...	1950	1944	...	1949	...	2124	...	2137	2200
lwhinnie d.	|	...	|	...	...	...	1551	...	|	...	|	|	...	|	...	...	|	...	2001	1955	...	2000	...	2136	...	2152	2214
air Atholl d.	1422	...	|	...	...	...	|	...	|	...	1723	1723	...	1754	...	...	|	...	2024	2018	...	2023	...	2158	...	2217	2240
lochry d.	1432	...	1459	...	...	...	1620	...	1649	...	1733	1733	...	1804	...	...	1901	...	2034	2028	...	2033	...	2208	...	2231	2252
nkeld & Birnam d.	1445	...	|	...	...	...	1635	...	1703	...	1747	1747	...	1819	...	...	1918	...	2048	2042	...	2047	...	2221	...	2245	2306
rth 222 d.	1507b	1519	1531	1606	1606	1609	1655	1703	1722	1801	1806	1806	1811	1839	...	1911	1937	2002	2107	2107	2122	2110b	2115	2241	2246	2307	2331
Stirling 222 d.	|	1548	|	|	|	1643	1732	|	|	1832	|	|	1843	1909	1918	|	2017	|	|	|	2151	|	2150	2314	|	2353	0017
Glasgow Queen St. 222 a.	|	1618	|	|	|	1712	1809	|	|	1909	|	|	1910	1943	|	|	2045	|	|	|	2221	|	2223	2345	|	...	...
rkinch 222 d.	1542	...	1600	1644	1645	...	...	1732	1751	...	1836	1837	...	...	|	1940	...	2032	2136	2136	...	2140	...	...	2315	...	...
kcaldy 222 d.	1551	...	1609	1653	1655	...	...	1747	1759	...	1844	1849	...	...	|	1950	...	2041	2145	2145	...	2148	...	...	|	...	...
ymarket 222 a.	1626	...	1643	1732	1736	...	...	1824	1835	...	1919	1926	...	...	2002	2026	...	2117	2218	2217	...	2222	...	...	0023	...	...
inburgh Waverley 222 a.	1634	...	1649	1737	1741	...	...	1831	1842	...	1926	1934	...	...	2007	2032	...	2122	2223	2222	...	2228	...	...	0028	...	...

– Ⓡ. 🛏 1,2 class and (2) Inverness - London Euston. Train stops to pick up only. See Table 161.
K – From/to London Kings Cross (Table 180).
a – Arrives 6–8 minutes earlier on Ⓐ.
b – Arrives 4–5 minutes earlier.
c – Arrives 6–8 minutes earlier.
r – Arr. 0702.
t – Arr. 1216.

R EDINBURGH - STIRLING 224

n			⚒	⚒	⚒	⚒	⚒	⚒	⚒	⚒	⚒	⚒		⚒	⚒	⚒	⚒	⚒	Ⓐ	⑥	⚒	⚒	A ★	⚒	⚒	⚒
0	Edinburgh Waverley d.	⚒	0518	0549	0619	0648	0720	0746	0818	0849	0919	0948	...	1018	1048	1119	1148	1219	1248	1249	1319	1348	and at	1848	1919	1949
2	Haymarket d.		0523	0553	0623	0652	0724	0752	0822	0853	0923	0953	...	1023	1052	1123	1152	1223	1253	1253	1323	1352	the same	1852	1923	1954
8	Linlithgow d.		|	|	|	|	|	|	|	|	|	|	...	|	|	|	|	|	|	|	|	|	minutes	|	|	2009
1	Falkirk Grahamston d.		0545	0615	0645	0715	0746r	0816	0847	0917	0948	1015	...	1046	1115	1145	1215	1247	1319	1316	1346	1415	past each	1916	1945	2019
8	Stirling a.		0559	0630	0700	0729	0803	0832	0904	0934	1002	1029	...	1102	1129	1201	1229	1301	1337	1330	1401	1430	hour until	1930	1959	2037

	⚒	⚒	⚒	⚒	⚒	⚒	⚒	⚒		⑦	⑦	⑦	⑦	⑦	⑦	⑦	★	⑦	⑦	⑦	⑦	⑦	⑦	⑦	⑦	⑦
inburgh Waverley d.	2001	2033	2103	2133	2201	2233	2303	2333	⑦	0935	1035	1107	1134	1206	1236	1305	and at	1636	1704	1735	1806	1835	1936	2035	2135	2235
ymarket d.	2007	2037	2107	2137	2207	2237	2307	2337		0939	1039	1111	1138	1211	1240	1309	the same	1641	1709	1739	1811	1839	1940	2039	2139	2241
lithgow d.	2022	2052	2122	2152	2222	2254	2323	2352		0959	1054	1126	1156	1226	1256	1324	minutes	1658	1726	1754	1828	1854	1955	2054	2154	2258
kirk Grahamston d.	2032	2102	2132	2202	2232	2304	2333	0002		1009	1104	1136	1206	1236	1306	1334	past each	1710	1738	1804	1840	1904	2005	2104	2204	2310
rling a.	2045	2115	2145	2215	2246	2318	2347	0020		1023	1118	1154	1220	1254	1320	1354	hour until	1725	1752	1818	1859	1918	2019	2118	2218	2328

		⚒	⚒	⚒	⚒	⚒	⚒		⚒	⚒	⚒	⚒	⚒	⚒	♣	⚒	⚒	⚒	⚒	⚒	⚒	⚒	⚒	⚒	⚒	⚒
rling d.	⚒	0542	0611	0641	0711	0742	0808	...	0838	0911	0932	1011	1041	1111	and at	1611	1640	1707	1740	1812	1838	1909	1941	2011	2041	2111
kirk Grahamston d.		0556	0625	0655	0725	0757	0826	...	0857	0925	0955	1025	1055	1125	the same	1625	1655	1725	1755	1826	1857	1925	1955	2025	2055	2125
lithgow d.		0607	|	|	|	|	|	...	|	|	|	|	|	|	minutes	|	|	|	|	|	|	|	|	2036	2105	2136
ymarket d.		0624	0647	0722	0751	0820	0851	...	0921	0950	1021	1049	1120	1147	past each	1650	1719	1752	1820	1850	1919	1950	2022	2051	2123	2151
inburgh Waverley a.		0629	0653	0727	0759	0828	0858	...	0927	0956	1028	1058	1126	1152	hour until	1655	1725	1757	1827	1856	1925	1957	2028	2057	2127	2158

	⚒	Ⓐ	⑥	⚒	⚒		⑦	⑦	⑦	⑦	⑦	⑦	⑦	⑦	⑦	⑦	⑦	⑦	⑦	⑦	⑦	⑦	⑦	⑦	⑦	⑦	⑦
rling d.	2141	2210	2214	2241	2319	⑦	0910	0951	1046	1109	1149	1209	1249	1309	1349	1410	1449	1510	1549	1609	1649	1710	1809	1918	2009	2109	2209
kirk Grahamston d.	2155	2225	2228	2255	2333		0924	1008	1103	1124	1203	1224	1303	1324	1403	1427	1503	1527	1603	1624	1703	1725	1824	1933	2024	2124	2224
lithgow d.	2206	2240	2239	2306	2348		0935	1021	1116	1135	1214	1234	1314	1334	1414	1440	1514	1540	1614	1634	1714	1738	1834	1943	2034	2134	2234
ymarket d.	2221	2257	2254	2321	0004		0955	1040	1136	1156	1229	1249	1330	1349	1429	1450	1533	1601	1629	1650	1732	1755	1849	2003	2050	2150	2251
inburgh Waverley a.	2228	2302	2258	2325	0011		1000	1046	1140	1201	1233	1254	1336	1354	1433	1506	1537	1606	1633	1654	1738	1800	1854	2007	2054	2155	2258

– The 1648 departure from Edinburgh departs Falkirk 1719 and arrives Stirling 1733.
f – Arrives 2207 on ⑥.
r – Ⓐ only.
★ – Timings may vary by ± 2 minutes.
♣ – Timings at Haymarket and Edinburgh may vary by up to 5 minutes.

R ABERDEEN - ELGIN - INVERNESS 225

Until August 19 the line between Dyce and Inverurie is closed for track re-doubling work. The timings shown between Inverness and Huntly are valid throughout the current timetable period whilst those between Inverurie and Huntly are valid until June 14 and from August 19. During the work an amended rail service operates between Aberdeen and Dyce with 🚌 services operating Aberdeen - Inverurie and v.v. and Inverurie - Huntly and v.v. Please confirm timings locally.

m			⚒2	⚒2	⚒		⚒2D	⚒	⚒	⚒🍷	⚒2	⚒🍷	⚒2	⚒🍷	⚒2🍷	Ⓐ	⑥	⚒🍷	⚒2🍷	⚒2🍷	⚒		⑦🍷	⑦🍷	⑦🍷	⑦🍷	⑦2🍷
0	Aberdeen ¶ d.	⚒	...	...	0613	...	0715	0822	0847	1013	...	1159	...	1338	1527	1619	1644	1724	1822	2014	2200	⑦	1000	1300	1522	1801	2127
10	Dyce ✈ ¶ d.		...	...	0622	...	0727	0831	0855	1022	...	1208	...	1347	1536	1629	1652	1733	1831	2023	2209		1008	1309	1531	1810	2136
27	Inverurie ¶ d.		...	...	0637g	...	0743	0843	▬	1034	...	1220	...	1359	1548	...	▬	1750g	1844	2035	2221		1021	1321	1543	1822	2148
44	Insch d.		...	...	0649	...	0755	0856	...	1047	...	1234	...	1412	1601	...	...	1803	1857	2048	2234		1034	1334	1556	1835	2201
55	Huntly d.		...	...	0714k	...	0812	0912	⚒	1105	...	1250	...	1428	1617	...	⚒	1820	1913	2105	2251		1050	1351	1612	1852	2221
35	Keith d.		...	...	0729	...	0826	0927	2	1119	...	1305	...	1443	1637	...	2	1834	1928	2119	2306		1107	1405	1634	1908	2235
14	Elgin d.		0707	0730	0755g	...	0852g	0950	1054	1140	1238	1326	1441	1519t	1702g	...	1806	1855	1949	2147g	2326		1128	1426	1700g	1929	2256
37	Forres d.		0720	0743	0808	...	0905	1003	1107	1153	1251	1339	1455	1532	1715	...	1819	1908	2002	2200	2339		1141	1439	1713	1942	2309
49	Nairn d.		0732	0754	0818	...	0917	1016	1119	1204	1302	1350	1506	1543	1731g	...	1830	1919	2013	2211	2350		1151	1450	1724	1954	2320
73	Inverness a.		0750	0812	0836	...	0936	1034	1137	1223	1320	1408	1526	1601	1750	...	1849	1938	2031	2229	0008		1210	1509	1742	2012	2339

		⚒ A	⚒🍷	Ⓐ2	⚒2	⚒2🍷	⚒2	⚒🍷	⚒2	⚒2🍷	⚒2	⚒🍷	⚒2🍷	⚒2	⚒🍷	⚒2	⚒2	⚒2	⚒2		⑦🍷	⑦🍷	⑦🍷	⑦🍷	⑦B	⑦🍷	⑦B
erness d.	⚒	0453	0600	...	0715	0901	0959	1102	1148	1244	1333	1428	1527	1649	1715	1814	1903	2032	2133	⑦	0959	1233	1529	1708	1800	2103	2142
rn d.		0509	0616	...	0731	0918	1015	1119	1204	1302	1350	1444	1544	1705	1732	1830	1920	2048	2149		1015	1249	1544	1724	1816	2118	2157
res d.		0520	0627	...	0742	0929	1026	1129	1215	1313	1401	1455	1555	1716	1742	1841	1931	2059	2200		1026	1300	1554	1735	1827	2128	2208
in d.		0532	0639	...	0756	0952k	1041	1142	1230	1326	1415	1508	1613g	1730	1800g	1855	1945	2114	2213		1039	1312	1607	1748	1838	2141	2224
th d.		0553	0700	...	0818	1013	...	1202	...	1347	...	1529	1634	...	1821	1917	...	...	2234		1100	1333	1628	1810	...	2203	...
tly d.		0607	0714	0746	0839	1028	...	1216	...	1402	...	1543	1648	...	1847	1942	...	...	2250		1120	1351g	1644	1824	...	2221	...
ch d.		0622	0730	0802	0856	1048g	...	1234	...	1418	...	1601	1705	...	1903	1958	...	...	2306		1136	1407	1700	1840	...	2237	...
erurie ¶ d.		0637	0743	0818	0908	1100	...	1246	...	1430	...	1615	1720	...	1916	2010	...	...	2319		1148	1419	1712	1852	...	2249	...
ce ✈ ¶ d.		0650	0758	0831	0921	1113	...	1300	...	1442	...	1630	1733	...	1930	2023	...	...	2332		1200	1434	1725	1906	...	2301	...
rdeen ¶ a.		0701	0808	0841	0931	1124	...	1310	...	1453	...	1640	1744	...	1940	2034	...	...	2342		1211	1445	1736	1916	...	2311	...

– To Edinburgh (Table 222)
From Glasgow (Table 223).
From Dundee on Ⓐ / Montrose on ⑥ (Table 222).
g – Arrives 4–7 minutes earlier.
k – Arrives 9–10 minutes earlier.
t – Arrives 1503.
¶ – Additional trains Aberdeen - Dyce - Inverurie and v.v. from Aug. 19: **From Aberdeen** on ⚒ at 0749 **E**, 0958, 1103, 1250, 1457, 1553, 1655Ⓐ, 1756, 1918, 2057, 2250; on ⑦ at 1034, 1225, 1426, 1550, 1649, 2035.
From Inverurie on ⚒ at 0713, 0818⑥, 0846Ⓐ, 1035, 1134, 1333, 1523, 1638⑥, 1652Ⓐ **M**, 1752, 1845, 1951, 2125; on ⑦ at 1103, 1255, 1458, 1620, 1730, 2122.

226 INVERNESS - THURSO, WICK and KYLE OF LOCHALSH

2nd class S

km		⚒ 🍷	⚒ 🍷	⚒ 🍷	⚒ 🍷	⚒	⚒ b	⚒ 🍷	⚒	⚒		⚒	⚒ 🍷	⚒	⑤⑥
0	**Inverness** d.	0700	0855	1041	1056	1142	1335	1400	1450	1712	...	1754	1831	2106	2333
16	Beauly d.	0715	0910	|	1113	1157	1350	1415	1505	1727	...	1809	1849	2121	2348
21	Muir of Ord d.	0723	0916	1101	1119	1207	1356	1423	1511	1733	...	1815	1857	2127	2354
30	Dingwall d.	0739	0929	1112	1132	1219	1411	1437	1524	1747	...	1829	1905	2140	0007
49	Garve d.	|	0952	|	1155	...	1433	|	|	|	...	1853	|	|	|
75	Achnasheen d.	|	1018	|	1221	...	1500	|	|	|	...	1920	|	|	|
104	Strathcarron d.	|	1048	|	1253	...	1530	|	|	|	...	1949	|	|	|
116	Stromeferry d.	|	1105	|	1310	...	1547	|	|	|	...	2006	|	|	|
124	Plockton d.	|	1117	|	1322	...	1559	|	|	|	...	2018	|	|	|
133	**Kyle of Lochalsh** a.	|	1130	|	1335	...	1612	|	|	|	...	2031	|	|	|
51	Invergordon d.	0758	...	1130	...	...	...	1454	1541	1804	...	...	1926	2157	0024
71	Tain d.	0817	...	1149	...	...	...	1513	...	1824	...	...	1945	2216	0043
93	Ardgay d.	0833	...	1205	...	...	...	1529	...	1839	...	...	2001	...	...
108	Lairg d.	0853	...	1221	...	...	...	1545	...	...	...	...	2017	...	...
136	Golspie d.	0918	...	1246	...	...	...	1610	...	...	...	...	2042	...	...
146	Brora d.	0929	...	1257	...	...	...	1621	...	...	...	...	2052	...	...
163	Helmsdale d.	0947	...	1312	...	...	...	1636	...	...	...	...	2108	...	...
201	Forsinard d.	1021	...	1346	...	...	...	1712	...	...	...	...	2142	...	...
237	Georgemas Jcn a.	1045	...	1410	...	...	...	1736	...	...	...	...	2206	...	...
248	**Thurso** a.	1059	...	1424	...	...	...	1750	...	...	...	...	2220	...	...
248	**Thurso** d.	1102	...	1427	...	...	...	1753	...	...	...	...	2223	...	...
237	Georgemas Jcn d.	1114	...	1439	...	...	...	1805	...	...	...	...	2235	...	...
260	**Wick** a.	1131	...	1456	...	...	...	1822	...	...	...	...	2252	...	...

	⑦	⑦ 🍷	⑦		⑦	⑦ 🍷	⑦ c	⑦
Inverness d.	0940	1059	1253	...	1533	1754	1754	210
Beauly d.	0955	1115	1308	...	1548	1809	1809	212
Muir of Ord d.	1001	1121	1314	...	1556	1815	1815	212
Dingwall d.	1014	1134	1327	...	1603	1831	1833	214
Garve d.	|	1158	|	...	|	|	1855	|
Achnasheen d.	|	1225	|	...	|	|	1922	|
Strathcarron d.	|	1255	|	...	|	|	1951	|
Stromeferry d.	|	1312	|	...	|	|	2008	|
Plockton d.	|	1324	|	...	|	|	2020	|
Kyle of Lochalsh a.	|	1337	|	...	|	|	2033	|
Invergordon d.	1032	...	1345	...	1626	1848	...	220
Tain d.	1050	...	1403	...	...	1907	...	221
Ardgay d.	...	...	...	...	...	1923	...	...
Lairg d.	...	...	...	...	...	1942	...	...
Golspie d.	...	...	...	...	...	2007	...	...
Brora d.	...	...	...	...	...	2018	...	...
Helmsdale d.	...	...	...	...	...	2033	...	...
Forsinard d.	...	...	...	...	...	2107	...	...
Georgemas Jcn a.	...	...	...	...	...	2131	...	...
Thurso a.	...	...	...	...	...	2145	...	...
Thurso d.	...	...	...	...	...	2148	...	...
Georgemas Jcn d.	...	...	...	...	...	2200	...	...
Wick a.	...	...	...	...	...	2217	...	...

	⑥	⚒	⚒	⚒ m	⚒ 🍷	⚒ 🍷	⚒	⚒ 🍷	⚒ b	⚒	⚒ 🍷	⚒ b	⚒ 🍷	⚒	⚒
Wick d.	...	...	...	...	0618	0802	...	...	...	...	1234	...	1600	...	...
Georgemas Jcn. d.	...	...	...	...	0636	0820	...	...	...	...	1252	...	1618	...	...
Thurso a.	...	...	...	...	0646	0830	...	...	...	...	1302	...	1628	...	...
Thurso d.	...	...	...	...	0650	0834	...	...	...	...	1306	...	1632	...	...
Georgemas Jcn. d.	...	...	...	...	0703	0847	...	...	...	...	1319	...	1645	...	...
Forsinard d.	...	...	...	...	0727	0913	...	...	...	...	1347	...	1711	...	...
Helmsdale d.	...	...	...	...	0800	0946	...	...	...	...	1421	...	1744	...	...
Brora d.	...	...	...	...	0816	1002	...	...	...	...	1436	...	1800	...	...
Golspie d.	...	...	...	...	0825	1012	...	...	...	...	1447	...	1810	...	...
Lairg d.	...	...	0626	...	0852	1038	...	...	...	...	1512	...	1836	...	...
Ardgay d.	...	0614	0643	...	0907	1054	...	...	...	...	1530	...	1852	1928	...
Tain d.	0048	0630	0659	...	0923	1110	...	...	...	...	1546	...	1908	1946	2221
Invergordon d.	0105	0649	0719	...	0942	1131	...	...	...	1551	1606	...	1925	2005	2240
Kyle of Lochalsh d.	|	|	|	0611	|	|	...	1208	1346	|	|	1713	|	|	|
Plockton d.	|	|	|	0627	|	|	...	1221	1359	|	|	1726	|	|	|
Stromeferry d.	|	|	|	0639	|	|	...	1233	1411	|	|	1738	|	|	|
Strathcarron d.	|	|	|	0658	|	|	...	1252	1430	|	|	1757	|	|	|
Achnasheen d.	|	|	|	0726	|	|	...	1320	1501	|	|	1825	|	|	|
Garve d.	|	|	|	0753	|	|	...	1347	1527	|	|	1852	|	|	|
Dingwall d.	0121	0708	0738	0816	1001	1153	1245	1410	1550	1611	1626	1919	1941	2024	2258
Muir of Ord d.	0131	0722	0751	0830	1014	1206	1258	1422	1603	1624	1639	1931	1952	2037	2311
Beauly d.	...	0728	0757	0835	1020	1211	1304	1427	1609	1629	1645	1936	|	2042	2316
Inverness a.	...	0743	0812	0850	1035	1226	1319	1442	1626	1646	1702	1954	2010	2057	2331

	⑦	⑦	⑦ c	⑦	⑦ 🍷	⑦	⑦ 🍷	⑦
Wick d.	...	...	...	...	1158	...	...	...
Georgemas Jcn. d.	...	...	...	...	1216	...	...	...
Thurso a.	...	...	...	...	1226	...	...	...
Thurso d.	...	...	...	...	1230	...	...	...
Georgemas Jcn. d.	...	...	...	...	1243	...	...	...
Forsinard d.	...	...	...	...	1309	...	...	...
Helmsdale d.	...	...	...	...	1342	...	...	...
Brora d.	...	...	...	...	1358	...	...	...
Golspie d.	...	...	...	...	1408	...	...	...
Lairg d.	...	...	...	...	1433	...	...	...
Ardgay d.	...	...	...	...	1449	...	...	...
Tain d.	0048	1055	...	1408	1505	...	...	222
Invergordon d.	0105	1114	...	1427	1524	1631	...	224
Kyle of Lochalsh d.	|	|	1020	|	|	|	1512	|
Plockton d.	|	|	1033	|	|	|	1525	|
Stromeferry d.	|	|	1045	|	|	|	1537	|
Strathcarron d.	|	|	1103	|	|	|	1556	|
Achnasheen d.	|	|	1131	|	|	|	1624	|
Garve d.	|	|	1157	|	|	|	1651	|
Dingwall d.	0121	1135	1220	1445	1543	1649	1714	230
Muir of Ord d.	0131	1148	1232	1457	1555	1702	1726	231
Beauly d.	...	1153	1237	1502	1601	1707	1732	231
Inverness a.	...	1208	1252	1517	1616	1722	1747	233

a – Arrives 1955 on Ⓐ. b – 🍷 until Sept. 28. c – Until Sept. 29. m – 🍷 on Ⓐ.

227 🚌 INVERNESS - ULLAPOOL - STORNOWAY

Valid until Sept. 29, 201

	①-⑥ 🚌	①-⑥ ⛴	⑦ 🚌	⑦ ⛴	①-⑤ 🚌	①-⑤ ⛴	⑦ 🚌	⑦ ⛴		⑥ 🚌	⑥ ⛴
Inverness d.	0810	...	0910	...	1500	...	1610	...	...	1640	...
Garve d.	0844	...	0944	...	1534	...	1644	...	...	1714	...
Ullapool a.	0930	...	1030	...	1620	...	1730	...	...	1800	...
Ullapool d.	...	1030	...	1130	...	1730	...	1830	...	...	1900
Stornoway a.	...	1300	...	1400	...	2000	...	2100	...	...	2130

	①-⑥ ⛴	①-⑥ 🚌	⑦ ⛴	⑦ 🚌		①-⑤ ⛴	①-⑤ 🚌	⑦ ⛴	⑥⑦ 🚌		⑥ ⛴	⑥
Stornoway d.	0700	...	0800	...	...	1400	...	1500	...	...	1530	..
Ullapool a.	0930	...	1030	...	...	1630	...	1730	...	...	1800	..
Ullapool d.	...	0950	...	1050	...	...	1650	...	1750	...	...	18
Garve d.	...	1032	...	1132	...	...	1732	...	1832	...	...	19
Inverness a.	...	1110	...	1210	...	...	1810	...	1910	...	...	19

☛ Latest passenger check-in for ⛴ is 30 minutes before departure.

Operators: 🚌 Scottish Citylink (service **961**). www.citylink.co.uk. ✆ +44 (0) 871 266 3333.
⛴ Caledonian MacBrayne. www.calmac.co.uk. ✆ +44 (0) 800 066 5000.

228 🚌 INVERNESS - FORT WILLIAM - OBAN

Valid until Sept. 29, 201

Service number	915	919	919	919	915	919	919	919	916	919	920 ①-⑤
Inverness bus station d.	...	0900	1000	1115	...	1200	1300	1500	...	1715	2015
Fort Augustus bus stance d.	...	1006	1106	1221	...	1306	1406	1606	...	1821	2117
Invergarry Jct. bus bay A82 d.	0948j	1021	1121	1236	1238j	1321	1421	1621	1738j	1836	2128
Fort William bus station a.	1030	1105	1205	1320	1320	1405	1505	1705	1820	1920	2205
Service number		918 ①-⑥						918 ①-⑥			
Fort William bus station d.	...	1200	...	...	...	...	...	1750	...	...	...
Ballachulish Tourist Office d.	...	1230	...	...	...	...	...	1820	...	...	...
Oban Station Road a.	...	1330	...	...	...	...	...	1920	...	...	...

Service number	920 ①-⑥	919	916	919	918 ①-⑥	919	915	919	19	918 ①-⑥	91
Oban Station Road d.	...	...	...	...	0950	...	...	...	...	1555	..
Ballachulish Tourist Office d.	...	...	...	...	1051	...	...	...	...	1656	..
Fort William bus station a.	...	...	...	...	1122	...	...	...	...	1727	..
Service number					919 ①-⑦					919 ①-⑦	
Fort William bus station d.	0730	0840	1015	1030	1200	1330	1400	1430	1530f	1740	18
Invergarry Jct. bus bay A82 d.	0814	0924	1054j	1114	1244	1414	1439j	1514	1627	1824	19
Fort Augustus bus stance d.	0829	0939	...	1129	1259	1429	...	1529	1642	1839	..
Inverness bus station a.	0935	1045	...	1235	1405	1535	...	1635	1748	1945	..

f – Departs 1543 on ⑤ during school term and ①-⑦ during school holidays. Check locally for school dates.
j – On A87 at Invergarry Hotel.

Operator: Scottish Citylink. www.citylink.co.uk. ✆ +44 (0) 871 266 33

229 ISLE OF MAN RAILWAYS

✆ +44 (0) 1624 66252

For more information please call ✆ +44 (0) 1624 662525

km	*Manx Electric Railway*	A	A	A	A	A	A	A		
0	**Douglas** Derby Castle ‡ d.	0940	1010	1040	1140	1240	1410	1510	...	...
4	Groudle d.	0952	1022	1052	1152	1252	1422	1522	...	...
11	Laxey d.	1010	1040	1110	1210	1310	1440	1540	...	...
29	**Ramsey** a.	1055	...	1155	1255	1355	1525	1625	...	...

	A	A	A	A	A	A	A	
Ramsey d.	...	1110	1210	1340	1440	1540	1640	...
Laxey d.	1055	1155	1255	1425	1525	1625	1725	...
Groudle d.	1113	1213	1313	1443	1543	1643	1743	...
Douglas Derby Castle ‡ a.	1125	1225	1325	1455	1555	1655	1755	...

km	*Snaefell Mountain Railway*	B		B		B	B	B	B	B
0	**Laxey** d.	1015	...	1115	...	1215	1315	1400	1455	1545
8	**Summit** a.	1045	...	1145	...	1245	1345	1430	1525	1615

	B	B	B	B	B	B	B	
Summit d.	1110	1215	1315	1415	1500	1555	1645	...
Laxey a.	1140	1245	1345	1445	1530	1625	1715	...

km	*Isle of Man Steam Railway*	C	C	C	C			D✕		
0	**Douglas** Railway Station ‡ d.	0950	1150	1350	1550	...	...	1900	...	...
9	Santon d.	1011x	1211x	1411x	1611x	...	...	|	...	...
13	Ballasalla d.	1020	1220	1420	1620	...	...	1940	...	...
16	Castletown d.	1027	1227	1427	1627	...	...	1947	...	...
25	**Port Erin** a.	1050	1250	1450	1650	...	...	2015	...	...

	C	C	C	C		D✕		
Port Erin d.	1000	1200	1400	1600	...	2115	...	...
Castletown d.	1027	1227	1427	1627	...	2142	...	...
Ballasalla d.	1035	1235	1435	1635	...	2149	...	...
Santon d.	1047x	1247x	1447x	1647x	...	|	...	...
Douglas Railway Station ‡ a.	1105	1305	1505	1705	...	2230	...	...

A – Until Nov. 3 (not Oct. 4, 7, 11, 14, 18, 21, 25, 28, Nov. 1). Minimum service shown. Additional services operate on most dates April - September (check locally).
B – Until Nov. 3 (not Oct. 4, 7, 11, 14, 18, 21, 25, 28, Nov. 1). Minimum service shown. Additional services operate on most dates April - September (check locally).
C – Until Nov. 3 (not Oct. 1, 2, 8, 9, 15, 16, 22, 23, 29, 30). Minimum service shown. Additional services operate on selected dates (check locally).
D – ④ June 13, July 11, 18, 25, Aug. 1, 8, 15, 22, 29, Sept. 12, Oct. 17. Reservation essential.
x – Calls on request.
‡ – 🚌 services **1**, **1H**, 2, **2A**, 10, 11, **12**, **12A**, 13 connect Derby Castle and Lord Street Bus Station which is near the Steam Railway Station.

IRELAND

SEE MAP PAGE 90

perators: Iarnród Éireann (**IÉ**), www.irishrail.ie Northern Ireland Railways (**NIR**), www.translink.co.uk Bus Éireann, www.buseireann.ie Ulsterbus, www.translink.co.uk and Dublin Area Rapid Transit (**DART**), www.irishrail.ie Most cross-border services are jointly operated.

mings: **Rail**: **NIR** services are valid until further notice. **IÉ** services are valid from December 10, 2017 until further notice. **DART** services are valid until further notice.
Bus: **Ulsterbus** services are valid until further notice. **Bus Éireann** services are valid until further notice.

ail services: Except for *Enterprise* cross-border expresses (for details, see Table **230** below), **all trains** convey *Standard* (2nd) class seating. Most express trains in the Republic of Ireland, as noted in the tables, also have first class accommodation.
On public holiday dates in the **Republic of Ireland**, DART trains run as on Sundays; outer-suburban services to or from Drogheda and Dundalk do not run. Other services may be amended, though most main-line trains run normally. All services are subject to alteration during the Christmas, New Year and Easter holiday periods.

us services: **Bus Éireann** and **Ulsterbus**: services are shown in detail where there is no comparable rail service; only basic information is given for other routes. Buses do not always call at the rail station, but usually stop nearby. Where possible the stop details are given in the station bank or as a footnote. On longer routes, a change of bus may be required – please check with the driver. At holiday times bus travellers should consult detailed leaflets or seek further information from the operator. **Bus Éireann**: ✆ +353 1 836 6111 (Dublin) or + 353 21 450 8188 (Cork); **Ulsterbus**: ✆ + 028 9033 3000 (Translink, Belfast). **Dublin Busáras** (bus station) is a 5 minute walk from Dublin Connolly station.

The Dublin Tram service (Luas) connects Dublin Connolly and Heuston stations at frequent intervals. Journey time is 14 minutes, depending on traffic conditions.
See Dublin City Plan on page 31.

NIR, IÉ BELFAST - DUNDALK - DUBLIN 230

Enterprise express trains (**E**) convey Standard (2nd) class and Plus (1st) class seating, 🍸 (Café Bar and trolley service) and ✕ (at-seat meal service in Plus)

km		Ⓐ	Ⓐ	Ⓐ 2	⑥	Ⓐ	⚒ (E)	⑥	⚒	⚒ (E)	⚒	⚒	⚒	⚒ (E)	⚒	⚒	⚒ (E)	⚒	⚒	⚒ (E)	⚒	⑤ 2	⑥	Ⓐ	⚒ (E)	⚒	Ⓐ
0	**Belfast** LP ♣.. § d.	...	...	...	...	0625t	0645	...	0735x	0800	...	...	1010z	1035	...	1210z	1235	...	1340z	1405	...	...	1600t	1601t	1605	...	1709
13	Lisburn............ § d.	...	...	...	...	0648	|	...	0758	|	...	...	1032	|	...	1232	|	...	1402	|	...	...	1610	1612	|	...	1732
42	Portadown........ § d.	...	...	...	...	0714	0721	...	0825	0836	...	...	1058	1109	...	1258	1309	...	1428	1441	...	...	1636	1638	1641	...	1802
71	Newry ....d.	...	...	0630	...	▬	0742	...	▬	0857	...	...	...	1130	...	...	1330	...	...	1502	...	...	▬	▬	1702	...	1825
95	**Dundalk** ....d.	0540	0630	0700	0705	⚒	0800	0815	Ⓐ	0915	1010	1100	...	1147	1250	...	1347	...	...	1520	...	1605	⚒	⚒	1720	...	...
31	Drogheda ....d.	0604	0655	0722	0729	0800	0822	0839	0835	|	1034	1124	...	1208	1314	...	1408	1417	...	1541	1605	1630	1700	1730	1741	1800	...
48	Balbriggan...........d.	0619	0712	|	0746	0815	|	0854	0851	|	1049	1138	...	|	1329	...	|	1433	...	|	1621	|	1716	|	|	1815	...
54	Skerries ....d.	0626	0719	|	0752	0821	|	0900	0857	|	1055	1144	...	|	1335	...	|	1439	...	|	1627	|	1722	|	|	1821	...
68	Malahide ....d.	|	0736	|	0809	0837	|	0915	0912	|	1111	1159	...	|	1350	...	|	1454	...	|	1642	|	1737	|	|	1838	...
83	**Dublin** Connolly..a.	0658	0759	0818	0830	0858	0900	0931	0930	1005	1130	1215	...	1243	1416	...	1443	1515	...	1620	1700	1714	1758	1813	1815	1857	...

	Ⓐ	⚒ (E)	⚒	⚒ (E)	⚒	⑦	⑦ (E)	⑦ (E)	⑦ (E)	⑦ (E)	⑦ (E)
elfast LP ♣ ... § d.	1801t	1805	1940t	2005	...	...	0900	1105	1305	1605	1905
sburn .... § d.	1812	|	2002	|	...	...	0913	|	|	|	|
ortadown .... § d.	1838	1841	2028	2041	...	...	0940	1136	1336	1636	1936
ewry..................d.	▬	1902	▬	2102	...	...	1001	1158	1358	1658	1958
undalk...............d.	⚒	1920	⚒	2120	...	0920	1019	1217	1417	1717	2017
ogheda..............d.	1850	1941	2005	2141	2205	0945	1040	1240	1440	1740	2040
lbriggan ....d.	1905	|	2021	|	2220	1000	|	|	|	|	|
erries.................d.	1911	|	2027	|	2226	1006	|	|	|	|	|
alahide...............d.	1926	|	2042	|	2241	1021	|	|	|	|	|
ublin Connolly ..a.	1945	2015	2100	2215	2301	1041	1120	1315	1515	1815	2115

	⑥	Ⓐ	Ⓐ	⚒ (E)	⚒	⚒ (E)	⚒	⚒	⚒ (E)	⚒	⚒	⚒ (E)
Dublin Connolly...d.	...	...	0715	0735	0848	0930	1006	1035	1120	1122	1236	1320
Malahide.............d.	...	...	0730	|	0908	|	1025	1053	|	1144	1252	|
Skerries..............d.	...	...	0744	|	0923	|	1040	1108	|	1158	1307	|
Balbriggan ....d.	...	...	0750	|	0927	|	1045	1113	|	1204	1312	|
Drogheda.............d.	...	...	0804	0809	0945	1006	1103	1130	1156	1220	1329	1356
Dundalk..............d.	...	...	...	0831	1010	1028	▬	...	1218	1245	▬	1418
Newry..................d.	...	*0715*	...	0848	...	1046	⚒	...	1236	...	⚒	1436
Portadown .... § d.	0645	0740	...	0909	...	1108	1115	...	1258	...	1315	1458
Lisburn .... § a.	0708	0805	...	|	...	|	1138	...	|	...	1338	|
Belfast LP ♣ ... § a.	0740	0826	...	0945	...	1145	1159t	...	1335	...	1359t	1535

	⚒	⚒	⚒ (E)	⚒	⚒	⚒ (E)	⚒	Ⓐ	Ⓐ	⑥	⚒	⚒	⚒ (E)	⚒	⚒	⚒ (E)	⚒	Ⓐ	⑥	Ⓐ	⚒	⑦ (E)	⑦ (E)	⑦ (E)	⑦ (E)	⑦ (E)	⑦
ublin Connolly ..d.	1336	1452	1520	1550	1621	1650	1655	...	1721	1721	1802	1840	1900	1920	2020	2050	...	2137	2207	2237	2337	1000	1200	1400	1600	1900	2122
alahide..............d.	1354	1509	|	1609	1639	|	1712	...	|	1742	1827	|	|	1939	2038	|	...	2155	2225	2255	2356	|	|	|	|	|	2140
erries.................d.	1408	1524	|	1623	1654	|	1726	...	1752	1757	1841	1906	|	1953	2053	|	...	2209	2239	2309	0010	|	|	|	|	|	2155
lbriggan..............d.	1414	1530	|	1629	1659	|	1732	...	1757	1802	1847	1912	|	1959	2058	|	...	2215	2245	2315	0016	|	|	|	|	|	2200
ogheda...............d.	1431	1547	1554	1648	1716	|	1750	...	1814	1819	1904	1927	1934	2016	2115	2129	...	2231	2302	2332	0032	1032	1232	1432	1632	1933	2220
undalk................d.	...	...	1616	▬	▬	1748	▬	...	1839	1845	1928f	...	1955	▬	...	2151	...	2256e	...	2356	*0059*	1054	1254	1454	1654	1955	2243
ewry...................d.	...	...	1633	Ⓐ	⑥	1806	⚒	1850	1905	...	...	...	2013	⚒	...	2208	...	...	...	...	...	1112	1312	1512	1712	2013	...
ortadown .... § d.	...	...	1654	1705	1715	1828	1845	1915	...	...	...	...	2033	2045	...	2229	2235	...	...	...	...	1133	1333	1533	1733	2033	...
sburn .... § a.	...	...	|	1730	1738	|	1908	1938	...	...	...	...	|	2108	...	|	2258	...	...	...	...	|	|	|	|	|	...
elfast LP ♣ ... § a.	...	...	1729	1739t	1748t	1905	1929t	2010	...	...	...	...	2110	2129t	...	2303	2319t	...	...	...	...	1208	1408	1608	1808	2108	...

- ⑤ only.
- Not ⑥.

t – Belfast **Great Victoria Street**.
x – Belfast **Great Victoria Street**. On ⑥ depart 0740.
z – Belfast **Great Victoria Street**. On ⑥ depart 20 minutes later.

§ – Other local trains run Belfast - Lisburn - Portadown and v.v.
♣ – Belfast Lanyon Place (formerly Central Station).

NIR BELFAST - LONDONDERRY and PORTRUSH 231

km		Ⓐ	⚒	⚒	⚒		⚒	⚒	⚒	⚒	⚒		Ⓐ	Ⓐ		⑦	⑦	⑦		⑦	⑦	⑦	⑦	
	Belfast GVSt. ★....... d.	0605	...	0710	...	and at the	2010	...	2110	...	2240		...	...	...	0910	...	1010	and at the	1910	...	2010	2110	...
0	**Belfast** LP ♣.......... d.	0615	...	0720	...	same	2020	...	2120	...	2250		1646	1746	...	0920	...	1020	same	1920	...	2020	2120	...
33	Antrim...................... d.	0643	...	0747	...	minutes	2047	...	2147	...	2317	addi-	1714	1814	...	0947	...	1047	minutes	1947	...	2047	2147	...
52	Ballymena................. d.	0657	...	0803	...	past each	2103	...	2203	...	2330	tional	1728	1828	...	1003	...	1103	past every	2003	...	2103	2200	...
97	**Coleraine** .... d.	0743	0745	0843	0845	hour	2143	2145	2243	2245	0005	trains	1810	1910	...	1043	1045	1143	**two** hours	2043	2045	2143	2235	...
07	Portrush .... a.	|	0757	|	0857	until	|	2157	|	2257	...	→	...	...	...	|	1057	1155	until	|	2057	2155	...	...
51	**Londonderry**........... a.	0822	...	0922	...		2222	...	2322	...	...		...	...	...	1122	...	...		2122	...	...	...	...

	Ⓐ	Ⓐ	⑥	Ⓐ	⑥	Ⓐ	⚒	⚒		⚒	⚒	⚒	Ⓐ	⑥		⑦	⑦	⑦		⑦	⑦	⑦	⑦	
ndonderry .... d.	...	...	...	0612	0638	...	...	0738	and at the	...	2038		2138	2138	...	...	...	0938	and at the	...	...	1938	...	...
Portrush .... d.	...	0605	0610	|	|	0705	0803	|	same	2103	|	2203	|	|	...	0905	1003	|	same	1905	2003	|	2105	...
leraine.................. d.	0550	0621	0623	0652	0721	0719	0815	0819	minutes	2115	2119	2215	2219	2216	...	0919	1015	1019	minutes	1919	2015	2019	2119	...
llymena................. d.	0626	0700	0700	0730	0800	0800	...	0900	past each	...	2200	...	2300	...	...	1000	...	1100	past every	2000	...	2100	2200	...
trim....................... d.	0642	0714	0714	0747	0814	0814	...	0914	hour	...	2214	...	2316	...	...	1014	...	1114	**two** hours	2014	...	2114	2214	...
lfast LP ♣ .... a.	0710	0739	0739	0816	0839	0839	...	0939	until	...	2239	...	2341	...	...	1039	...	1139	until	2039	...	2139	2239	...
lfast GVSt. ★ .... a.	0719	0750	0750	0825	0850	0851	...	0950		...	2250	...	...	...	...	1050	...	1150		2050	...	2150	...	...

km		Ⓐ	⑥	⚒	⚒	⚒	⚒		⚒	⚒			⑦	⑦	⑦	⑦		⑦	⑦			
0	Coleraine .... d.	0550	0555	0645	0745	0845	0945	and at the same minutes past	2145	2245	...	...	0845	0945	1045	1143	and at the same minutes past	2045	2143	...	...	...
10	Portrush.................... a.	0600	0605	0657	0757	0857	0957	each hour	2157	2257	...	...	0857	0957	1057	1155	every **two** hours	2057	2155	...	...	...

	Ⓐ	⑥	⑥	Ⓐ	⚒	⚒		⚒	⚒	⚒			⑦	⑦	⑦	⑦		⑦	⑦			
rtrush..................... d.	0605	0610	0703	0705	0803	0903	and at the same minutes past	2103	2203	2303	...	...	0905	1003	1105	1203	and at the same minutes past	2105	2203	...	...	...
leraine.................... a.	0617	0621	0715	0716	0815	0915	each hour	2115	2116	2314	...	...	0916	1015	1116	1215	every **two** hours	2116	2215	...	...	...

- Belfast GVSt. (Belfast Great Victoria St.) is the nearest station to Belfast City Centre and the Europa Buscentre is adjacent.
- Belfast Lanyon Place (formerly Central Station).

sterbus 212 express 🚌 service, Belfast - Londonderry. Journey time: 1 hour 40 minutes.
0630, 0700 and every 30 minutes until 1900, 1930 then 2030, 2130, 2300.
0645, 0900, 1000, 1030 and every 30 minutes until 1900, 1930 then 2030, 2130, 2300.
0830, 1030, 1100 and every 30 minutes until 1930 then 2030, 2130, 2215, 2300.

Ulsterbus 212 express 🚌 service, Londonderry - Belfast. Journey time: 1 hour 45 minutes.
Ⓐ: 0415, 0530, 0600, and every 30 minutes until 1700 then 1800, 1930, 2100, 2200, 2300.
⑥: 0645, 0730, 0800 and every 30 minutes until 1630, 1700 then 1800, 1930, 2100, 2200, 2300.
⑦: 0700, 0800, 0900, 0930 and every 30 minutes to 1730, 1800, 1900, 2100.

232 BELFAST - ENNISKILLEN and ARMAGH

Ulsterbus 251, 26

From Belfast ★ to Enniskillen (Bus Stn) (journey time 2 hours 15 mins)

Ⓐ: 0805, 0905 and hourly until 1905, 2005.
⑥: 1005, 1205, 1405, 1505, 1605, 1805, 2005.
⑦: 1605, 2005.

From Enniskillen (Bus Stn) to Belfast ★

Ⓐ: 0725, 0825, and hourly until 1625, 1725, 1825 ◧.
⑥: 0725, 0925, 1125, 1225, 1325, 1525, 1725.
⑦: 1225, 1525, 1725.

From Belfast ★ to Armagh (Bus Stn) (journey time 1 hour 25 mins)

Ⓐ: 0800, 0945, 1045, 1145, 1245, 1345, 1445, 1645, 1715, 1745, 1845, 1945, 2115.
⑥: 1045, 1245, 1445, 1745, 1845, 2005.
⑦: 1335, 1735, 2015, 2200.

From Armagh (Bus Stn) to Belfast ★.

Ⓐ: 0630, 0715, 0805, 0905, 1005, 1105, 1205, 1305, 1505, 1605, 1705, 1805.
⑥: 0730, 0905, 1105, 1305, 1605, 1705.
⑦: 1210, 1410, 1610, 1830, 2015.

Buses call at Portadown (Market Street) 40 - 75 minutes from Belfast and Portadown (Northern Ban
20–30 minutes from Armagh (Bus Stn).

◧ – Change at Dungannon; arrive Europa Buscentre 2140.

★ – Europa Buscentre / Great Victoria St. Rail Station.

233 BELFAST - LARNE and BANGOR

NI

From Belfast LP ♣ – Ⓐ: 0550, 0655, 0745 **H**, 0855 **H**, and hourly until 1355 **H**, 1455 **H**, 1525, 1555 **H**, 1644 **H**, 1716 **H**, 1744, 1825 **H**, 2025 **H**, 2320 **H**.
⑥: 0725 **H**, and every **two** hours until 2125 **H**, 2320 **H**. ⑦: 0955 **H**, and every **two** hours until 2155 **H**.

From Larne Town – Ⓐ: 0653 **S**, 0735 **S**, 0800, 0858 **S**, 0958 **S** and hourly until 1558 **S**, 1623, 1706 **S**, 1738 **S**, 1828, 1928 **S**, 2128 **S**.
⑥: 0628 **S**, and every **two** hours until 2228 **S**. ⑦: 0858 **S**, and every **two** hours until 2058 **S**.

Trains call at: Carrickfergus 27 - 29 minutes from Belfast and 28 - 31 minutes from Larne and Whitehead 38 - 40 minutes from Belfast, 18 - 21 minutes from Larne.

Trains marked **H** arrive Larne **Harbour** 4 minutes after Larne **Town**. Trains marked **S** depart Larne **Harbour** 3 minutes before Larne **Town**. Journey time Belfast Central - Larne Harbour 57 - 65 mi

A frequent train service operates between Belfast Central and Bangor. Journey time 30–31 minutes. 20 km. Approximate timings from Belfast ①–⑥: 2 per hour at xx12 and xx42 minutes past ea hour, ⑦: xx42. Approximate timings from Bangor ①–⑥: 2 per hour at xx27 and xx57 minutes past each hour, ⑦: xx27.

♣ – Belfast Lanyon Place (formerly Central Station

234 DUBLIN - LONDONDERRY

Ulsterbus X3, X

	X4	X3	X4	X3	X4	X4	X3	X4	
Dublin Busáras d.	0630	1000	1100	1215	1515	1800	2015	2230	...
Dublin Airport ✈ △ d.	0650	1020	1120	1235	1535	1820	2035	2250	...
Monaghan d.	|	1205	|	1420	|	|	2220	|	...
Omagh ▽ a.	|	1300	|	1515	|	|	2315	|	...
Strabane ▽ a.	|	1330	|	1545	|	|	2345	|	...
Londonderry a.	1035	1400	1505	1615	1920	2155	0015	0155	...

	X4	X4	X4	X3	X4	X3	X3	X4	
Londonderry d.	0130	0415	0550	0700	0950	1200	1500	1730	...
Strabane △ d.	|	|	|	0730	|	1230	1530	|	...
Omagh △ d.	|	|	|	0800	|	1300	1600	|	...
Monaghan d.	|	|	|	0905	|	1405	1705	|	...
Dublin Airport ✈ ▽ a.	0500	0800	0935	1040	1335	1540	1840	2115	...
Dublin Busáras a.	0520	0820	0955	1100	1355	1600	1900	2135	...

△ – Buses call here to pick up only. ▽ – Buses call here to set down only. ☛ The calling point in each town is the bus station unless otherwise indicate

234a DUBLIN - DONEGAL

Bus Éireann 30, X3

Dublin Busáras d.	0630	0800	0930	1100	1230	1400	1530	1700	1830	2000	2300	0030
Dublin Airport ✈ △ d.	0650	0820	0950	1120	1250	1420	1550	1720	1850	2020	2320	0050
Virginia d.	0755	0925	1055	1225	1355	1525	1655	1825	1955	2125	0025	0155
Cavan d.	0835	0955	1135	1255	1435	1555	1735	1855	2035	2155	0055	0235
Enniskillen d.	0925	1040	1225	1340	1525	1640	1825	1940	2125	2240	0140	0325
Ballyshannon d.	1010	1120	1310	1420	1610	1720	1910	2020	2210	2320	0220	0410
Donegal ⊡ a.	1030	1135	1330	1435	1630	1735	1930	2035	2230	2335	0235	0430

Donegal ⊡ d.	0100	0400	0530	0700	0830	1000	1130	1300	1430	1600	1730	190
Ballyshannon d.	0120	0420	0550	0720	0850	1020	1150	1320	1450	1620	1750	192
Enniskillen d.	0200	0500	0635	0800	0935	1100	1235	1400	1535	1700	1835	200
Cavan d.	0240	0540	0735	0840	1035	1140	1335	1440	1635	1740	1935	204
Virginia d.	0310	0610	0805	0910	1105	1210	1405	1510	1705	1810	2005	211
Dublin Airport ✈ ▽ a.	0415	0715	0910	1015	1210	1315	1510	1615	1810	1915	2110	221
Dublin Busáras a.	0435	0735	0930	1035	1230	1335	1530	1635	1830	1935	2130	223

△ – Buses call here to pick up only. ▽ – Buses call here to set down only. ⊡ – Donegal **Abbey Hotel**.

235 LONDONDERRY - GALWAY and GALWAY - CORK

Bus Éireann 51, 64, 48

	⚒									⑤⑦
Londonderry d.	...	...	...	0715	0915	1110	...	1530	1830	...
Letterkenny d.	...	...	...	0755	0957	1150	...	1610	1910	...
Donegal (Abbey Hotel) d.	...	0635	...	0840	1040	1240	...	1655	1955	...
Ballyshannon d.	...	0655	...	0900	1100	1300	...	1715	2015	...
Sligo d.	0600	0740	0800	1000	1200	1400	1600	1815	2105	2115
Ireland West Airport Knock d.	|	...	0905	1105	1305	1500	1705	|	...	|
Knock d.	0724	...	0924	1125	1324	1520	1725	1920	...	2230
Claremorris (Dalton St.) d.	|	...	|	1135	|	1530	1735	|	...	2240
Galway (Bus Station) ✥ a.	0900	...	1045	1240	1445	1635	1840	2040	...	2345

Galway (Bus Station) ✥ d.	...	...	0705	0805		1705	1805	1905	2005
Ennis d.	...	...	0820	0920		1820	1920	2020	2120
Shannon Airport ✈ d.	...	...	0850	0950	and	1850	1950	2050	2150
Limerick (Colbert Rail Station) a.	...	...	0920	1020	hourly	1920	2020	2120	2220
Limerick (Colbert Rail Station) d.	0725	0835	0935	1035	until	1935	2035	...	...
Mallow (Town Park) d.	0830	0940	1040	1140		2040	2140	...	...
Cork a.	0915	1025	1125	1225		2125	2225	...	...

Cork d.	...	...	0725	0825		1725	1825	1925	205
Mallow (Town Park) d.	...	...	0800	0900		1800	1900	2000	213
Limerick (Colbert Rail Station) a.	...	...	0910	1010	and	1910	2010	2110	224
Limerick (Colbert Rail Station) d.	0725	0825	0925	1025	hourly	1925	2025	...	...
Shannon Airport ✈ d.	0755	0855	0955	1055	until	1955	2055	...	...
Ennis d.	0825	0925	1025	1125		2025	2125	...	...
Galway (Bus Station) ✥ a.	0945	1045	1145	1245		2145	2245	...	...

	⚒	⚒		⚒						⑤
Galway (Bus Station) ✥ d.	0600	...	0845	1030	...	1200	*1410*	1600	1810	...
Claremorris (Dalton St.) d.	0700	...	|	1135	...	1305	|	|	1911	...
Knock d.	0710	...	1005	1145	...	1315	*1530*	1725	1921	...
Ireland West Airport Knock d.	0730	...	1025	1205	...	1335	*1550*	1745	|	...
Sligo d.	0845	0855	1145	1310	1330	1500	1710	1905	2040	210
Ballyshannon d.	...	0945	1232	...	1417	1547	1757	1952	...	214
Donegal (Abbey Hotel) d.	...	1015	1252	...	1437	1607	1817	2012	...	220
Letterkenny d.	...	1110	1340	...	1525	1655	1905	2100	...	225
Londonderry a.	...	1145	1420	...	1605	1735	1945	2140	...	233

✥ – Change buses at Galway. Minimum connection time 45 minutes. ☛ The calling point in each town is the bus station unless otherwise indicated.

236 DUBLIN - SLIGO

I

km		Ⓐ 🍷		⚒ 🍷	⚒ 🍷	⚒ 🍷	⚒ 🍷	⚒ 🍷	⚒ 🍷	Ⓐ	Ⓐ	⚒ 🍷	⑦ 🍷		⑦ 🍷		⑦ 🍷	⑦ 🍷	⑦ 🍷		⑦ 🍷		
0	**Dublin** Connolly d.	0655	...	0905	1105	1305	1505	1600	1705	1717	1805	1905	0905	...	1305	...	1505	1600	1705	...	1905	...	...
26	Maynooth d.	0731	...	0931	1140	1341	1541	1633	1741	1803	1837	1939	0932	...	1333	...	1534	1629	1733	...	1933	...	...
83	Mullingar d.	0817	...	1017	1221	1422	1622	1724	1823	1850	1926	2030	1013	...	1413	...	1614	1714	1819	...	2016	...	...
125	**Longford** d.	0847	...	1047	1251	1452	1652	1754	1854	1922	1958	2059	1043	...	1443	...	1644	1750	1849	...	2045	...	...
143	Dromod d.	0903	...	1103	1306	1507	1706	1808	1909	...	...	2112	1056	...	1456	...	1656	1802	1904	...	2057	...	...
159	Carrick on Shannon d.	0916	...	1116	1320	1521	1719	1822	1923	...	...	2125	1113	...	1512	...	1712	1817	1920	...	2114	...	...
173	Boyle d.	0928	...	1128	1337	1537	1730	1841	1934	...	...	2136	1134	...	1534	...	1729	1836	1933	...	2127	...	...
219	**Sligo** a.	1009	...	1209	1413	1613	1807	1917	2010	...	...	2212	1210	...	1610	...	1808	1910	2008	...	2204	...	...

	Ⓐ	Ⓐ	Ⓐ 🍷	⚒ 🍷	⚒ 🍷	⚒ 🍷	⚒ 🍷	⚒ 🍷	Ⓐ 🍷	⑥ 🍷	⚒ 🍷		⑦ 🍷		⑦ 🍷		⑦ 🍷		⑦ 🍷		⑦ 🍷		⑦ 🍷
Sligo d.	...	...	0545	0640	0900	1100	1300	1500	1655	1700	1900	...	0900	...	1100	...	1300	...	1500	...	1630	...	180
Boyle d.	...	...	0621	0717	0937	1139	1339	1539	1741	1741	1941	...	0933	...	1133	...	1333	...	1533	...	1704	...	183
Carrick on Shannon d.	...	...	0632	0728	0949	1152	1351	1551	1752	1752	1952	...	0945	...	1145	...	1345	...	1545	...	1717	...	184
Dromod d.	...	...	0644	0740	1002	1205	1404	1604	1808	1808	2008	...	1000	...	1200	...	1400	...	1600	...	1732	...	190
Longford d.	0535	0615	0658	0755	1017	1220	1419	1619	1831	1831	2031	...	1015	...	1215	...	1415	...	1615	...	1748	...	191
Mullingar d.	0609	0649	0731	0827	1049	1300	1500	1700	1907	1907	2107	...	1051	...	1246	...	1452	...	1652	...	1819	...	195
Maynooth d.	0652	0730	0814	0910	1130	1341	1541	1741	1948	1948	2148	...	1131	...	1327	...	1533	...	1733	...	1900	...	203
Dublin Connolly a.	0734	0818	0847	0937	1201	1413	1612	1819	2020	2020	2220	...	1203	...	1355	...	1606	...	1800	...	1932	...	210

236a BALLYBROPHY - ROSCREA - LIMERICK

I

km		Ⓐ	⚒ 🍷	⚒		⚒h ◇✖	⚒	⑦ 🍷	⑦		
0	**Dublin** Heuston d.	...	0900	...	...	1800	...	1825	...	...	...
107	Ballybrophy d.	...	0958	1005	...	1856	1905	1936	1945	...	...
123	Roscrea d.	...	...	1028	...	...	1928	|	2008	...	...
154	Nenagh d.	0745	...	1110	...	...	2011	|	2051	...	...
199	**Limerick** Colbert a.	0845	...	1210	...	...	2115	2043	2153	...	...

	⚒	⚒ 🍷		⚒	⚒ ◇🍷	⑦	⑦ 🍷			
Limerick Colbert d.	0630	0740	...	1655	...	1720	1820	...	...	...
Nenagh d.	0738	|	...	1751	...	1817	|	...	...	...
Roscrea d.	0818	|	...	1831	...	1857	|	...	...	...
Ballybrophy d.	0842	0849	...	1854	1901	1922	1924	...	...	...
Dublin Heuston a.	...	0953	...	...	2000	...	2031	...	...	...

h – ✖ on Ⓐ, 🍷 on

◇ – Also conveys 1st class.

DUBLIN - ROSSLARE 237

km		⑥	Ⓐ	⚒ 🍷	Ⓐ	Ⓐ	Ⓐ 🍷	⑥ 🍷		⑦	⑦ 🍷	⑦ 🍷
0	**Dublin Connolly** ▲ d.	0805	0940	1336	1637	1738	1838	1838	...	1025	1345	1830
11	Dún Laoghaire ....▲ d.	0823	0958	1355	1658	1758	1857	1857	...	1041	1402	1847
21	Bray ▲ d.	0843	1017	1417	1717	1818	1919	1919	...	1101	1423	1904
47	Wicklow d.	0905	1040	1443	1744	1846	1952	1952	...	1129	1447	1931
80	Arklow d.	0930	1108	1511	1814	1918	2020	2020	...	1157	1515	1959
97	Gorey d.	0945	1121	1524	1827	1936	2033	2033	...	1210	1528	2012
26	Enniscorthy d.	1005	1140	1544	1849	1957	2052	2052	...	1229	1549	2031
50	**Wexford** d.	1025	1201	1605	1908	2017	2113	2113	...	1251	1611	2052
60	Rosslare Strand d.	1042	1218	1621	1922	2034	...	2130	...	1307	1627	2109
66	**Rosslare** Europort a.	1050	1225	1628	1928	2041	...	2137	...	1314	1633	2116

	Ⓐ	Ⓐ y	⑥ y	⚒ 🍷		⚒ 🍷		⚒		⑦ 🍷	⑦ 🍷	⑦	
Rosslare Europort d.	...	0535	...	0720	...	1255	...	1800	...	0940	1420	1740	...
Rosslare Strand d.	...	0541	...	0726	...	1301	...	1806	...	0946	1426	1746	...
Wexford d.	...	0558	...	0743	...	1317	...	1823	...	1002	1445	1803	...
Enniscorthy d.	...	0621	...	0805	...	1339	...	1850	...	1024	1504	1825	...
Gorey d.	0555	0644	0645	0827	...	1401	...	1911	...	1046	1530	1847	...
Arklow d.	0608	0659	0700	0840	...	1414	...	1924	...	1059	1543	1900	...
Wicklow d.	0638	0734	0734	0907	...	1441	...	1951	...	1130	1611	1930	...
Bray ▲ d.	0704	0804	0804	0933	...	1504	...	2016	...	1153	1634	1954	...
Dún Laoghaire .... ▲ d.	0722	0821	0821	0951	...	1521	...	2034	...	1207	1649	2012	...
Dublin Connolly ▲ a.	0746	0847	0847	1015	...	1544	...	2100	...	1230	1710	2036	...

– To Dundalk; see table **230**. ▲ – Additional surburban trains (*DART*) run Howth - Dublin Connolly - Dún Laoghaire - Bray. Trains run every 10 - 15 mins. on ⚒, every 20 - 30 mins. on ⑦.

LIMERICK - WATERFORD 239

km			⚒ 🍷	⚒			⚒	⚒		
0	**Limerick Colbert** d.	...	0855	...	...	...	1750	...	...	...
35	**Limerick Junction** d.	...	0921	0940	...	...	1822	1840	...	...
40	Tipperary d.	...	...	0954	...	...	...	1854	...	...
62	Cahir d.	...	...	1019	...	...	...	1919	...	...
79	Clonmel d.	...	...	1038	...	...	...	1938	...	...
101	Carrick on Suir d.	...	...	1103	...	...	...	2003	...	...
124	**Waterford** a.	...	...	1129	...	...	...	2030	...	...

		⚒	⚒			⚒	⚒		
Waterford d.	...	0720	...	...	...	1625	...	...	...
Carrick on Suir d.	...	0747	...	...	...	1650	...	...	...
Clonmel d.	...	0812	...	...	...	1715	...	...	...
Cahir d.	...	0831	...	...	...	1734	...	...	...
Tipperary d.	...	0853	...	...	...	1756	...	...	...
Limerick Junction a.	...	0908	0936	...	...	1811	1833	...	...
Limerick Colbert a.	...	...	1003	...	...	...	1858	...	...

DUBLIN - GALWAY, BALLINA and WESTPORT 240

km		⚒	⚒ 🍷	⚒ 🍷	⚒ 🍷	⚒ 🍷	⚒ 🍷	⚒ 🍷	⚒ 🍷	⚒ 🍷	⚒ 🍷	⚒	⚒ 🍷	⚒ 🍷	⚒ 🍷	⚒ 🍷	⑦ 🍷	⑦	⑦ 🍷	⑦ 🍷	⑦ 🍷	⑦ 🍷	⑦ 🍷	⑦ 🍷	⑦ 🍷	⑦
0	**Dublin Heuston 245** d.	...	0735	0735f	0925	1125	1245	1325	1445	1535	1633	1710	1730	1815	1830	1935	0800	...	1140	1340	1440	1540	1635	1830	1845	2030
48	Kildare **245** d.	...	0800	0800f	|	|	|	|	|	|	1658	1738	|	|	|	|	0825	...	1205	1409	|	|	|	1901	1914	|
67	Portarlington **245** d.	...	0814	0814f	1001	1200	1321	1402	1522	1613	|	1755	1812	|	1913	2009	0839	...	1219	1423	1516	|	1713	1915	1928	2107
93	Tullamore d.	...	0830	0831f	1018	1217	1338	1419	1541	1631	1726	1812	1829	1907	|	2031	0856	...	1244	1447	1540	1633	1731	1932	1953	2123
129	**Athlone** d.	0730	0905	0908	1050	1241	1404	1442	1605	1659	1749	1848	1858	1929	1952	2102	0922	0940	1309	1512	1605	1658	1802	2000	2022	2149
152	Ballinasloe d.	0744	0920k	|	1105	1258	|	1457	|	1714	1808	|	1914	|	2008	2118	0938	|	1324	|	1622	|	1819	|	2037	2204
187	Athenry **242** d.	0817	0948k	|	1127	1322	|	1521	|	1738	1832	|	1936	|	2029	2141	1004	|	1346	|	1645	|	1848	|	2059	2224
208	**Galway 242** a.	0835	1008k	|	1148	1343	|	1540	|	1758	1850	|	1957	|	2050	2158	1024	|	1404	|	1710	|	1906	|	2119	2243
160	Roscommon d.	▬	...	0931	▬	...	1429	▬	1629	▬	...	1935f	...	1958	▬	...	...	1002	▬	1537	▬	1732	▬	2023	▬	...
186	Castlerea d.	...	...	0950	...	...	1448	...	1648	...	...	1954f	...	2017	...	...	...	1021	...	1556	...	1751	...	2042	...	...
204	Ballyhaunis d.	...	...	1003	...	...	1501	...	1702	...	...	2008f	...	2030	...	...	...	1034	...	1610	...	1804	...	2055	...	...
222	Claremorris d.	⚒	...	1018	⚒	...	1515	⚒	1716	⚒	...	2021f	...	2044	⚒	...	...	1048	⑦	1626	⑦	1820	⑦	2109	⑦	...
240	Manulla Junction § d.	0737	...	1031	1036	...	1528	1532	1729	1732	...	|	...	2057	2100	...	...	1102	1105	1640	1642	1834	1837	2122	2125	...
273	**Ballina** a.	0805	...	|	1104	...	|	1600	|	1800	...	|	...	|	2128		...	|	1133	|	1710	|	1905	|	2153	...
246	Castlebar d.	...	...	1037	...	...	1535	...	1736	...	...	2039f	...	2104	...	...	...	1109	...	1647	...	1841	...	2129	...	...
264	**Westport** a.	...	...	1055	...	...	1554	...	1754	...	...	2054f	...	2121	...	...	...	1130	...	1706	...	1859	...	2147	...	...

	Ⓐ	Ⓐ	Ⓐ 🍷	⚒ 🍷	⚒	⚒ 🍷	⚒	⚒ 🍷	⚒ 🍷	⚒	⚒ 🍷	⚒ 🍷	⚒	⚒ 🍷	⚒ 🍷	⚒	⑦	⑦ 🍷	⑦ 🍷	⑦	⑦ 🍷	⑦	⑦ 🍷	⑦ 🍷	⑦	⑦ 🍷
Westport d.	...	...	0520	...	...	0715	...	0945	...	...	1310	...	...	1815	...	...	...	0750	...	...	1320	...	1545	...	...	1745
Castlebar d.	...	...	0532	...	...	0728	...	0957	...	...	1323	...	...	1827	...	...	...	0803	...	...	1333	...	1558	...	...	1758
Ballina d.	...	...	|	...	0705	|	0935	|	...	1300	|	...	1805	|	...	2027	0740	|	...	1310	|	1535	|	...	1735	|
Manulla Junction § d.	...	...	|	...	0733	0736	1003	1005	...	1328	1330	...	1833	1835	...	2055	0808	0811	...	1338	1341	1603	1606	...	1803	1806
Claremorris d.	...	...	0550	...	▬	0750	▬	1020	...	▬	1344	...	▬	1849	...	▬	▬	0825	...	▬	1355	▬	1624	...	▬	1820
Ballyhaunis d.	...	...	0603	...	...	0804	...	1033	...	...	1357	...	...	1902	...	...	...	0839	...	...	1409	...	1637	...	...	1834
Castlerea d.	...	...	0616	...	⚒	0818	⚒	1046	...	⚒	1410	...	⚒	1915	...	...	⑦	0853	...	⑦	1423	⑦	1651	...	⑦	1848
Roscommon d.	...	...	0634	...	🍷	0838	🍷	1105	...	🍷	1432	...	🍷	1934	...	Ⓐ	🍷	0913	...	🍷	1443	🍷	1710	...	🍷	1908
Galway 242 d.	...	0530	|	0630	0730	|	0930	|	1105	1305	|	1505	1720	|	1920	2215	0805	|	1100	1300	|	1505	|	1700	1800	|
Athenry 242 d.	...	0549	|	0647	0748	|	0948	|	1127	1323	|	1523	1740	|	1937	2234	0821	|	1118	1317	|	1523	|	1718	1818	|
Ballinasloe d.	...	0612	|	|	0809	|	1012	|	1150	1347	|	1548	1808	|	2010	2300	0845	|	1141	1346	|	1546	|	1743	1845	|
Athlone d.	0520	0630	0700j	0725	0826	0903	1028	1131	1207	1405	1458	1606	1824	2005	2027	2315	0902	0938	1159	1403	1511	1606	1741	1804	1903	1934
Tullamore d.	0544	0655	0723j	0748	0850	0930	1056	1156	1238	1435	1524	1632	1849	2032	2054	...	0933	1002	1223	1429	1540	1633	1809	1830	1933	2012
Portarlington **245** d.	0602	0713	0741j	|	0908	0949	1114	1224	1257	1504	1548	1652	1913	2050	2111	...	0951	1022	1243	1447	1559	1651	1828	1849	1955	2030
Kildare **245** d.	0614	0723	0754j	|	|	|	|	|	|	|	|	1703	1923	|	|	...	1001	|	1255	|	|	1701	1838	1900	|	|
Dublin Heuston **245** a.	0659	0759	0830j	0841	0947	1027	1152	1302	1337	1542	1627	1738	1954	2129	2148	...	1031	1100	1325	1525	1637	1731	1909	1934	2034	2108

– An additional journey runs on ⑦: Galway depart 1925, Athenry 1942, Ballinasloe 2005, arrive Athlone 2021.

f – ⑤ only.

j – Also runs on ⑥.

k – Change at Athlone on ⑤.

§ – Passenger transfer point only.

DUBLIN - KILKENNY - WATERFORD 241

km		⚒ 🍷	⚒ 🍷	⚒ 🍷	⚒ 🍷	⑤ 🍷	⚒ 🍷	⚒ 🍷	⚒ 🍷	Ⓐ	⑦ 🍷	⑦ 🍷	⑦ 🍷	⑦ 🍷
0	**Dublin H** ◧ .. △ d.	0725	1015	1315	1510	1615	1640	1735	1835	2015	0910	1410	1745	1840
48	Kildare △ d.	0752	1040	|	1538	|	1715	1805	1903	2100	0939	1438	1813	1904
72	Athy d.	0814	1100	1356	1555	1703	1735	1825	1922	2114	0957	1457	1832	1927
90	Carlow d.	0825	1112	1409	1606	1716	1747	1837	1938	2127	1010	1509	1844	1939
6	Muine Bheag d.	0843	1123	1421	1618	|	1759	1848	1949	...	1024	1521	1858	1951
0	**Kilkenny** a.	0900	1140	1438	1635	|	1817	1905	2007	...	1042	1541	1917	2009
30	**Kilkenny** d.	0905	1144	1443	1640	|	1821	1910	2012	...	1047	1545	1921	2014
47	Thomastown d.	0915	1155	1453	1650	|	1831	1920	2022	...	1057	1556	1932	2024
79	**Waterford** a.	0939	1218	1524	1713	1810	1900	1944	2046	...	1120	1620	1956	2049

	Ⓐ	⚒ 🍷	⚒ 🍷	⚒ 🍷	⚒ 🍷	⚒ 🍷	⚒ 🍷	⑤⑥	⚒ 🍷	Ⓐ	⑦ 🍷	⑦ 🍷	⑦ 🍷	⑦ 🍷
Waterford d.	...	0600	0710	0750	1100	1305	1450	1600	1825	...	0905	1240	1510	1805
Thomastown d.	...	0619	|	0809	1119	1324	1511	|	1846	...	0924	1259	1530	1824
Kilkenny a.	...	0634	|	0824	1134	1339	1525	|	1900	...	0939	1314	1544	1839
Kilkenny d.	...	0637	|	0828	1141	1343	1530	|	1902	...	0943	1318	1548	1843
Muine Bheag d.	...	0651	|	0844	1155	1357	1545	|	1921	...	0957	1332	1603	1859
Carlow d.	0630	0703	0757	0856	1207	1411	1609	1653	1935	2135	1010	1343	1615	1910
Athy d.	0641	0715	0810	0908	1219	1423	1620	1704	1949	2146	1024	1355	1627	1926
Kildare △ d.	0659	0734	|	0927	1238	1441	1637	1721	2008	2200	1043	1414	1646	1946
Dublin H ◧ .. △ a.	0743	0807	0858	0958	1310	1515	1706	1750	2038	2246	1116	1448	1718	2019

◧ – Full name is **Dublin Heuston**. △ – For additional trains Dublin - Kildare and v.v, see Tables **240**, **245**.

LIMERICK JUNCTION - LIMERICK - GALWAY 242

km		⚒	⚒		⚒	⚒	⚒		⑦	⑦	⑦	⑦
0	**Limerick Jct** . 243 d.	...	...	...	1336	...	...	...	...	1137	...	...
35	**Limerick** ¶ .... 245 d.	0555	0920	...	1420	1805	1950	...	0900	1225	1555	1815
74	Ennis **245** d.	0650x	1000	...	1501	1909	2030	...	0942	1309	1636	1856
03	Gort d.	0713	1022	...	1523	1935	2052	...	1004	1331	1702	1923
32	Athenry **240** d.	0743	1054	...	1554	2007	2123	...	1035	1402	1733	1954
52	**Galway** **240** a.	0810	1114	...	1614	2028	2145	...	1056	1422	1753	2014

	⚒	⚒		⚒	⚒	⚒	⚒	⑦	⑦	⑦	⑦
Galway **240** d.	0620	1030	...	1345	1750	1840	...	0830	1155	1610	1830
Athenry **240** d.	0641	1056	...	1408	1817	1908	...	0851	1217	1633	1853
Gort d.	0715	1123	...	1435	1844	1933	...	0918	1244	1703	1924
Ennis **245** d.	0745	1147	...	1503	1908	1956	2110	0942	1308	1726	1947
Limerick ¶ **245** a.	0826	1227	...	1544	1947	...	2150	1022	1349	1807	2027
Limerick Jct .. **243** a.	...	...	...	1622	2023	...	...	...	1422	...	...

x – Arrive 0635. ¶ – Limerick Colbert.

LIMERICK JUNCTION - LIMERICK 243

Shuttle service connecting with main-line trains. *35 km.* Journey time: 25 - 40 minutes. For through services to or from Dublin Heuston see Table **245**.

From Limerick Junction ⚒: 0807, 0836, 0936, 1040, 1136, 1238, 1336, 1436, 1540, 1627, 1735, 1813, 1833, 1937, 2041, 2236.
⑦: 1008, 1137, 1335, 1443, 1532, 1644, 1733, 1844, 1936, 2047.

From Limerick Colbert ⚒: 0530, 0615, 0725, 0855, 0950, 1055, 1150, 1250, 1350, 1455, 1550, 1650, 1750, 1850, 1954, 2055.
⑦: 0930, 1050, 1250, 1354, 1445, 1550, 1645, 1750, 1845, 1950.

245 DUBLIN - LIMERICK, TRALEE and CORK — IÉ

km		⚒h ◇✗	⚒	⚒ ◇🍷	⚒	⚒ ◇🍷	⚒	⚒ ◇🍷	⚒	⚒ ◇🍷	⚒	⚒ ◇🍷	⚒	⚒ ◇🍷	⚒	⚒ ◇🍷	⚒	⚒ ◇🍷	⚒ 🍷	⚒	⚒ ◇🍷	⚒	⚒ 🍷	⚒h ◇✗	⚒
0	**Dublin Heuston** .. **240** d.	0700	...	0800	...	0900	...	1000	...	1100	...	1200	...	1300	...	1400	...	1500	1530	...	1600	...	1625	1700	...
48	Kildare **240** d.	|	...	|	...	|	...	|	...	|	...	|	...	|	...	|	...	|	1554	...	|	...	|	|	...
67	Portarlington **240** d.	|	...	|	...	|	...	|	...	|	...	|	...	|	...	|	...	|	1606	...	|	...	1700	|	...
82	Portlaoise d.	0741	...	|	...	0941	...	1041	...	1141	...	1241	...	1341	...	1441	...	|	1618	...	|	...	1712	|	...
107	Ballybrophy d.	|	...	|	...	0958	...	|	...	|	...	|	...	|	...	1458	...	|	1635	...	|	...	1729	|	...
127	Templemore d.	|	...	0904	...	|	...	|	...	1206	...	|	...	|	...	|	...	|	1646	...	|	...	1740	|	...
139	Thurles d.	0813	...	0913	...	1015	...	1113	...	1215	...	1313	...	1413	...	1516	...	1609	1657	...	1711	...	1750	|	...
172	**Limerick Junction** .. § d.	0833**x**	0836	0933**x**	0936	1036**x**	1040	1133**x**	1136	1235**x**	1238	1333**x**	1336	1433**x**	1436	1536**x**	1540	|	|	...	1732**x**	1735	1813	1830	1833
208	**Limerick** ¶ .... § **242** a.	|	0904	|	1003	|	1107	|	1204	|	1305	|	1404	|	1504	|	1608	|	1741	1805	|	1803	1840	|	1858
**	Ennis **242** a.	|	*0959*	|	...	|	...	|	1310	|	...	|	1455	|	...	|	1710	|	...	1843	|	...	...	|	...
208	Charleville d.	|	...	|	...	1055	...	|	...	1254	...	|	...	|	...	|	...	1643	...	...	|	...	...	|	...
232	**Mallow** **246** d.	0905	...	1005	...	1112	...	1205	...	1310	...	1405	...	1505	...	1609	...	1700	...	...	1805	...	...	1902	...
	Tralee **246** a.	|	...	|	...	|	...	|	...	|	...	|	...	|	...	|	...	|	...	...	|	...	...	|	...
266	**Cork** **246** a.	0930	...	1030	...	1138	...	1230	...	1337	...	1430	...	1530	...	1635	...	1725	...	...	1829	...	...	1925	...

	⚒h ✗f	⚒	⚒ 🍷	⚒h ◇✗	⚒	Ⓐ ◇🍷	⚒	⚒	⚒	⑦ ◇🍷	⑦	⑦	⑦ ◇🍷	⑦	⑦ 🍷	⑦ ◇🍷	⑦	⑦ ◇🍷	⑦ 🍷	⑦ ◇🍷	⑦ ◇🍷	⑦ 🍷	⑦ ◇🍷	⑦ ◇🍷	⑦ 🍷
Dublin Heuston ... **240** d.	1705	...	1725	1800	...	1900	...	2100	...	0830	...	...	1000	...	1125	1200	...	1300	1325	1400	1500	1525	1600	1700	1800
Kildare **240** d.	|	...	1752	|	...	|	...	|	...	|	...	...	|	...	1149	|	...	|	1349	|	|	1549	|	|	|
Portarlington **240** d.	|	...	1805	|	...	|	...	|	...	|	...	...	|	...	1202	|	...	|	1402	|	|	1602	|	|	|
Portlaoise d.	|	...	1817	|	...	1942	...	2141	...	0911	...	...	1041	...	1214	|	...	|	1414	|	|	1614	|	|	|
Ballybrophy d.	1802	...	1834	1856	...	1959	...	|	...	|	...	...	|	...	1231	|	...	|	1431	|	|	1631	|	|	|
Templemore d.	1814	...	1846	|	...	2009	...	|	...	|	...	...	|	...	1244	|	...	|	1443	|	|	1643	|	|	|
Thurles d.	1825	...	1857	1913	...	2018	...	2213	...	0944	...	...	1113	...	1254	1309	...	1409	1454	1509	1608	1654	1709	1809	1909
Limerick Junction ... § d.	|	...	|	1933**x**	1937	2038**x**	2041	2233**x**	2236	1004**x**	1008	...	1135**x**	1137	|	1333**x**	1335	|	|	1529**x**	|	|	1729**x**	|	1933
Limerick ¶ ..... § **242** a.	|	...	1940	|	2005	|	2109	|	2304	|	1035	...	|	1205	1340	|	1403	|	1540	*1600*	|	1740	*1801*	|	*2004*
Ennis **242** a.	|	...	*2029*	|	2110	|	...	|	...	|	1125	...	|	1303	...	|	*1450*	|	*1636*	|	|	...	*1855***z**	|	|
Charleville d.	1858	...	...	|	...	2057	...	|	...	1022	...	...	|	...	...	|	...	1443	...	|	|	...	1748	|	|
Mallow **246** d.	1916	1925	...	2005	...	2113	...	2305	...	1038	...	1045	1205	...	...	1405	...	1500	...	1602	1657	...	1805	1857	2004
Tralee **246** a.	2058	|	...	|	...	|	...	|	...	1221	...	|	|	...	...	|	...	|	...	|	|	...	|	|	|
Cork **246** a.	...	1950	...	2030	...	2140	...	2330	...	...	...	1111	1230	...	...	1427	...	1525	...	1625	1720	...	1830	1920	2027

	⑦ 🍷	⑦	⑦ ◇🍷	⑦	⑦	⑦ 🍷	⑦	⑦
Dublin Heuston .. **240** d.	1825	...	1900	1905	...	1925	2100	2110
Kildare **240** d.	1853	...	|	|	...	1950	|	2138
Portarlington **240** d.	1907	...	|	1940	...	2011	2134	2150
Portlaoise d.	1919	...	|	|	...	2023	|	2202
Ballybrophy d.	1936	...	|	|	...	2040	|	|
Templemore d.	1947	...	|	|	...	2052	|	|
Thurles d.	1957	...	2009	2021	...	2103	2213	2235
Limerick Junction .. § d.	|	...	|	2043**x**	2047	|	2233**x**	|
Limerick ¶ .... § **242** a.	2043	2050	|	|	2114	2149	|	2320
Ennis **242** a.	...	2129	|	|	▬	...	|	...
Charleville d.	...	...	|	2059	⑦	...	|	...
Mallow **246** d.	...	...	2057	2115	2125	...	2306	...
Tralee **246** a.	...	...	|	2248	|	...	|	...
Cork **246** a.	...	...	2120	...	2150	...	2330	...

	⚒	⚒ 🍷	Ⓐ 🍷	⚒ 🍷	⚒	⚒h ◇✗	⚒	⚒ 🍷	⚒	⚒h ✗f	⚒	⚒ 🍷
Cork **246** d.	...	0550	0615	...	...	0700	...	...	0800	...	...	...
Tralee **246** d.	...	|	|	...	...	|	...	...	|	0705	...	...
Mallow **246** d.	...	0612	|	...	...	0724	...	...	0825	0842	...	...
Charleville d.	...	0626	|	...	...	|	...	...	...	0856	...	...
Ennis **242** d.	...	|	|	...	...	|	0650	...	...	|	0745	...
Limerick Colbert .. § **242** d.	0530	*0615*	|	0640	0725	|	0730	0740	...	|	0826	0855
Limerick Junction § d.	0558	0645	|	|	0753	0756	...	|	...	0917	...	0922
Thurles d.	0619	|	|	0726	...	0816	...	0825	...	|	...	0945
Templemore d.	0628	|	|	0735	...	|	...	0836	...	|	...	|
Ballybrophy d.	0641	|	|	0747	...	|	...	0849	...	|	...	|
Portlaoise d.	0656	|	|	0802	...	|	...	0905	...	|	...	|
Portarlington **240** d.	|	|	|	0812	...	|	...	|	...	|	...	|
Kildare **240** d.	0717	|	|	0822	...	|	...	|	...	|	...	|
Dublin Heuston **240** a.	0750	0820	0830	0854	...	0928	...	0953	...	1047	...	1056

	⚒	⚒ ◇🍷	⚒	⚒ ◇🍷	⚒	⚒ ◇🍷	⚒	⚒ ◇🍷	⚒	⚒ ◇🍷	⚒	⚒	⚒ ◇🍷	⚒	⚒ ◇🍷	⚒	⚒ ◇🍷	⚒	⚒ ◇🍷	⚒	⚒	⚒ ◇🍷	⚒	Ⓐ ◇🍷	⚒ ◇🍷
Cork **246** d.	...	0925	...	1025	...	1125	...	1225	...	1325	...	...	1425	...	1525	...	1625	...	1725	...	...	1825	...	1925	2025
Tralee **246** d.	...	|	...	|	...	|	...	|	...	|	...	...	|	...	|	...	|	...	|	...	...	|	...	|	|
Mallow **246** d.	...	0949	...	1049	...	1149	...	1249	...	1349	...	...	1449	...	1549	...	1649	...	1749	...	...	1849	...	1949	2049
Charleville d.	...	|	...	1104	...	|	...	|	...	|	...	...	1504	...	|	...	1704	...	|	...	...	1904	...	|	|
Ennis **242** d.	...	|	1000	|	...	|	*1147*	|	...	|	1325	...	|	1503	|	...	|	...	|	1720	...	|	1908	|	|
Limerick ¶ ..... § **242** d.	0950	|	1055	|	1150	|	1250	|	1350	|	1407	1455	|	1550	|	1650	|	1750	|	1800	1850	|	1954	|	*2055*
Limerick Junction ... § d.	1019	1022	1123	1124	1220	1222	1331	1322	1420	1422	...	1524	1525	1622	1623	1718	1724	1822	1823	...	1918	1924	2023	2024	2125
Thurles d.	...	1041	...	|	...	1241	...	|	...	1441	...	...	1544	...	1641	...	1744	...	1841	...	...	1944	...	2042	2143
Templemore d.	...	|	...	1150	...	|	...	1347	...	|	...	...	|	...	|	...	1753	...	|	...	...	1953	...	|	|
Ballybrophy d.	...	|	...	|	...	1301	...	|	...	|	...	...	|	...	|	...	|	...	1901	...	...	|	...	|	|
Portlaoise d.	...	1113	...	|	...	1316	...	1413	...	1513	...	...	|	...	1713	...	1819	...	1916	...	...	2019	...	2113	2214
Portarlington **240** d.	...	|	...	|	...	|	...	|	...	|	...	...	|	...	|	...	|	...	|	...	...	|	...	|	|
Kildare **240** d.	...	|	...	|	...	|	...	|	...	|	...	...	|	...	|	...	|	...	|	...	...	|	...	|	|
Dublin Heuston ... **240** a.	...	1157	...	1256	...	1400	...	1456	...	1557	...	...	1657	...	1757	...	1902	...	2000	...	...	2102	...	2156	2257

	⑦ 🍷	⑦ 🍷	⑦	⑦ 🍷	⑦ ◇🍷	⑦ 🍷	⑦ ◇🍷	⑦ 🍷	⑦	⑦ ◇🍷	⑦ 🍷	⑦ ◇🍷	⑦ 🍷	⑦	⑦ ◇🍷	⑦ 🍷	⑦ ◇🍷	⑦	⑦ ◇🍷	⑦ 🍷	⑦	⑦ ◇🍷	⑦ 🍷	⑦	⑦ ◇🍷
Cork **246** d.	...	0825	...	...	1025	...	1225	...	...	1325	...	1425	...	...	1525	...	1625	...	1725	...	...	1825	...	...	192
Tralee **246** d.	...	|	...	...	|	...	|	1150	...	|	...	|	1345	...	|	...	|	...	|	...	...	|	1750	...	|
Mallow **246** d.	...	0849	...	...	1049	...	1249	1321	...	1349	...	1449	1527	...	1549	...	1649	...	1749	...	...	1849	1927	...	194
Charleville d.	...	0904	...	...	1104	...	1304	1336	...	|	...	1504	1543	...	|	...	1704	...	|	...	...	1904	|	...	|
Ennis **242** d.	*0740*	|	0942	...	|	*1135*	|	|	1308	|	...	|	|	...	|	*1515*	|	...	|	*1726*	...	|	|	1900	|
Limerick ¶ ..... § **242** d.	0825	|	1022	1025	*1050*	1225	*1250*	|	1354	|	1420	|	|	1550	|	1620	|	1750	|	1820	1845	|	|	1950	|
Limerick Junction ... § d.	|	0924	...	|	1124	|	1323	1354	1422	1423	|	|	|	1618	1622	|	|	1819	1822	|	1914	1924	1959	2018	2022
Thurles d.	0907	|	...	1110	1143	1307	1343	1415	...	1441	1504	1541	1618	...	1641	1702	1740	...	1841	1902	...	1943	2019	...	2041
Templemore d.	0916	|	...	1118	|	1316	|	|	...	|	1513	|	|	...	|	1711	|	...	|	1911	...	|	|	...	|
Ballybrophy d.	0928	|	...	1130	|	1328	|	|	...	|	1526	|	|	...	|	1724	|	...	|	1924	...	|	|	...	|
Portlaoise d.	0943	|	...	1145	|	1343	|	|	...	|	1542	|	|	...	|	1740	|	...	|	1940	...	|	|	...	|
Portarlington **240** d.	0955	|	...	1154	|	1352	|	|	...	|	1551	|	1657	...	|	1749	|	...	|	1949	...	|	|	...	|
Kildare **240** d.	1008	|	...	1205	|	1403	|	|	...	|	1601	|	1707	...	|	1759	|	...	|	1959	...	|	|	...	|
Dublin Heuston ... **240** a.	1038	1051	...	1236	1254	1433	1455	1530	...	1553	1632	1653	1738	...	1753	1831	1852	...	1953	2031	...	2055	2133	...	2153

h – ✗ on Ⓐ, 🍷 on ⑥.
f – Conveys [1] on Ⓐ.
x – Arr 1 - 2 mins. earlier.
z – Change at Limerick C.
◇ – Also conveys [1].
§ – Also Table **243**.
** – Limerick - Ennis : *39 km.*
¶ – Limerick Colber

246 (DUBLIN -) CORK - MALLOW - TRALEE — IÉ

km		⚒	⚒	⚒	⚒	⚒	⚒	⚒h ✗f	⚒		⑦	⑦ ◇🍷	⑦	⑦	⑦	⑦	⑦
0	**Cork** **245** d.	0625	0855	*1025*	*1225*	*1425*	*1655*	*1845*	2055	...	0855	*1010*	1215	1450	*1625*	1850	*2045*
	Dublin **245** d.	|	*0700*	*0900*	*1100*	*1300*	*1500*	1705	*1900*	...	|	0830	*1000*	*1300*	*1500*	*1700*	1905
34	**Mallow** **245** d.	0651	0921	1120	1320	1520	1725	1916	2121	...	0921	1038	1251	1529	1725	1930	2115
66	Millstreet d.	0716	0944	1143	1343	1543	1747	1940	2144	...	0944	1104	1316	1553	1748	1953	2139
100	Killarney d.	0747	1020	1220	1420	1620	1820	2020	2214	...	1014	1136	1347	1625	1826	2031	2210
134	**Tralee** a.	0825	1058	1258	1458	1658	1858	2058	2251	...	1051	1221	1423	1703	1901	2108	2248

	①	②–⑤	⚒h ✗f	⚒	⚒	⚒	⚒	⚒	⚒		⑦	⑦ 🍷	⑦ 🍷	⑦	⑦	⑦ 🍷	⑦
Tralee d.	0445	0555	0705	0905	1105	1305	1505	1705	1905	...	0710	1150	1345	1510	1710	1750	1915
Killarney d.	0519	0629	0744	0939	1139	1339	1539	1739	1939	...	0746	1224	1430	1543	1744	1828	1948
Millstreet d.	0545	0655	0814	1010	1210	1410	1610	1810	2010	...	0814	1253	1459	1614	1810	1857	2016
Mallow **245** d.	0609	0729**z**	0842	1038	1238	1438	1638	1843	2043	...	0851	1321	1527	1643	1846	1927	2049
Dublin **245** a.	*0820*	*0928*	1047	*1256*	*1456*	*1657*	*1902*	*2102*	*2257*	...	*1051*	1530	1738	*1852*	*2055*	2133	|
Cork **245** a.	*0720*	0750	*0915*	*1138*	*1337*	*1530*	*1725*	1905	2104	...	0917	*1352*	*1625*	*1720*	1911	*2027*	2111

CORK - COBH Journey time: 24 minutes *19 km*

⚒ 0530 Ⓐ, 0600 ⑥, 0630 Ⓐ, 0700, 0730 Ⓐ, 0800, 0830 Ⓐ, 0900, 1000, then hourly until 1600, 1630, 1700, 1730, 1800, 1830, 1900 Ⓐ, 2000, 2100, 2230.

† 0800, 0900, 1100, 1200, 1300, 1430, 1600, 1700, 1800, 1940, 2100, 2200.

COBH - CORK

⚒ 0600 Ⓐ, 0630 ⑥, 0700 Ⓐ, 0730, 0800 Ⓐ, 0830, 0900 Ⓐ, 0930, 1030, then hourly until 1630, 1700, 1730, 1800, 1830, 1900, 1930 Ⓐ, 2030, 2130, 2300.

† 0830, 0930, 1130, 1230, 1330, 1500, 1630, 1730, 1830, 2030, 2130, 2230.

f – Conveys [1] on Ⓐ.
h – ✗ on Ⓐ, 🍷 on ⑥.
z – Arrive 0718.
◇ – Also conveys [1] on ①–⑤

CORK - MIDLETON Journey time: 24 mins. *19 km.*

⚒ 0545, 0615, 0645 Ⓐ, 0715, 0745 Ⓐ, 0815, 0845 Ⓐ, 0915, 1015, then hourly until 1715, 1745,Ⓐ, 1815, 1915, 2015, 2115, 2215.

† 0815, 0915, 1115, 1215, 1415, 1615, 1715, 1815, 2015.

MIDLETON - CORK

⚒ 0615, 0645, 0715 Ⓐ, 0745, 0815 Ⓐ, 0845, 0915 Ⓐ, 0945, 1045 then hourly until 1745, 1815 Ⓐ, 1845, 1945, 2045, 2145, 2245.

† 0845, 0945, 1145, 1245, 1445, 1645, 1745, 1845, 2045.

FRANCE

SEE MAP PAGES 170/1

Operator: Société Nationale des Chemins de Fer Français (SNCF), unless otherwise shown.

Services: Most trains convey first and second classes of accommodation; many purely local services are second class only (it is not possible to show classes in the tables). *TGV* (*train à grande vitesse*) high-speed trains have a bar car selling drinks and light refreshments (some short-distance services have only vending machines). Selected *TGV* trains have an at-seat meal service in first class. Certain other long-distance trains have refreshments available on certain days, often a trolley wheeled through the train. Regional and local trains (outside Paris) are classified *TER* (*Train Express Regional*). The few remaining domestic night trains have sleeping accommodation which consists of modern four-berth couchettes (first class) or six-berth couchettes (second class). Women-only compartments are available on request. Note that all luggage placed on luggage racks must be labelled.
The *TGV* network is being rebranded ***inOui***, apart from trains with special low-cost fares which are branded ***Ouigo***.

Timings: Valid until **December 14, 2019** except where shown. Amended services operate on and around public holidays; whilst we try to show holiday variations, passengers are advised to confirm train times locally before travelling during these periods. Public holidays in 2019 are Jan. 1, Easter Monday (Apr. 22), May 1, May 8, Ascension Day (May 30), Whit Monday (June 10), July 14, Aug. 15, Nov. 1, Nov. 11, Dec. 25. Services are subject to alteration Dec. 24 - Jan. 1.
Engineering work can often affect schedules; major changes are shown in the tables where possible but other changes may occur at short notice.

Tickets: **Seat reservations** are **compulsory** for travel by all *TGV* and night trains (also other trains shown with Ⓡ), and are also available for a small fee on many other long distance trains. Advance reservations are recommended for travel to ski resorts during the winter sports season. **Supplements** (which include the cost of seat reservation) are payable for travel in *TGV* trains and night trains. All rail tickets (except passes) must be date-stamped before boarding the train using the self-service validating machines (composteurs) at the platform entrances. Note that where two *TGV* units are coupled together, they will often carry different train numbers for reservation purposes.

Note: The *TGV* services **Lille Europe - Charles de Gaulle ✈ - Marne-la-Vallée - Lyon / Bordeaux / Rennes / Nantes** are shown in the International section (Table **11**).

PARIS - LILLE - TOURCOING — 250

TGV Nord high-speed trains

For slower trains via Douai see Table **256**. For **Charles de Gaulle ✈ - Lille** see Table **11**. Certain trains continue to Dunkerque, Calais or Boulogne - see Table **265**.

km		TGV 7205*	TGV 7007	TGV 7511*	TGV 7015	TGV 7021	TGV 7519	TGV 7223	TGV 7029	TGV 7033	TGV 7535*	TGV 7043	TGV 7037	TGV 7045	TGV 7049	TGV 7053	TGV 7559*	TGV 7061	TGV 7264*	TGV 7065	TGV 7067	TGV 7269*	TGV 7271	TGV 7277	TGV 7281
		Ⓐ	Ⓐ	⚒	Ⓐ	⚒	⑦	①–⑥	⑦			Ⓐ	Ⓒ	Ⓐ		⑤		Ⓐ	①–⑥	⑦	Ⓐ		Ⓐ		Ⓐ
			J	v	L	Lt	v	n	e	B			L	L		N		J	u	Lv	L			D	J
0	**Paris** Nord ▷ d.	0646	0716	0746	0816	0846	0846	0946	0946	1046	1146	1231	1246	1316	1446	1516	1546	1616	1646	1646	1716	1746	1816	1846	1916
	Arras ▷ d.	|	|	|	|	|	|	|	|	|	|	|	|	|	|	|	|	|	|	|	|	|	|	|	|
227	**Lille** Europe a.	0745	|	0845	|	|	0945	1045	|	|	1245	|	|	|	|	|	1645	|	1745	|	|	1845	|	1945	|
227	**Lille** Flandres 415 a.	...	0818	...	0918	0948	...	...	1048	1148	...	1333	1348	1418	1548	1618	...	1718	...	1748	1818	...	1918	...	2018
237	Roubaix ◇ 415 a.	...	...	...	...	...	...	...	...	...	...	...	...	...	...	...	...	...	...	...	...	...	1942	...	2041
240	**Tourcoing** 415 a.	...	...	...	...	...	...	...	...	...	...	...	...	...	...	...	...	...	...	...	...	...	1948	...	2048

	TGV 7279	TGV 7079	TGV 7283	TGV 7083	TGV 7089	TGV 7085	TGV 7091	TGV 7093	TGV 7097	TGV 7097
	Ⓐ	⑦	†	①–⑥	⑤	⑦	⚒	⑤⑦	①–⑥	⑦
	S	Jv		E	f	s		d	z	
Paris Nord ▷ d.	1916	1916	1946	1946	2016	2046	2052	2146	2222	2246
Arras ▷ d.	|	|	|	|	|	|	2144	|	2318	|
Lille Europe a.	|	|	|	|	|	|	|	|	|	|
Lille Flandres 415 a.	2018	2018	2048	2048	2118	2148	2207	2248	2339	2348
Roubaix ◇ 415 a.	...	...	2111	...	...	...	...	...	...	...
Tourcoing 415 a.	...	...	2117	...	...	...	...	...	...	...

	TGV 7000	TGV 7206*	TGV 7214	TGV 7208	TGV 7020	TGV 7228*	TGV 7530	TGV 7536	TGV 7036	TGV 7040	TGV 7546
	Ⓐ	Ⓐ	Ⓐ	⑥	Ⓐ		Ⓐ	①–⑥	⑦		Ⓐ
		L		h				n	Jv	B	
Tourcoing 415 d.	...	0610	...	...	...	...	...	...	...	...	...
Roubaix ◇ 415 d.	...	0615	...	...	...	...	...	...	...	...	...
Lille Flandres 415 d.	0551	0641	...	0711	0741	...	...	...	...	1011	...
Lille Europe d.	|	|	0713	|	|	0813	0842	0913	0913	|	1113
Arras ▷ d.	0617	|	|	|	|	|	|	|	|	|	|
Paris Nord ▷ a.	0708	0744	0814	0814	0844	0914	0944	1014	1014	1114	1214

	TGV 7046	TGV 7248	TGV 7050	TGV 7550*	TGV 7550*	TGV 7550*	TGV 7254*	TGV 7058	TGV 7066	TGV 7070	TGV 7572*	TGV 7072	TGV 7074	TGV 7076	TGV 7082	TGV 7288*	TGV 7288*	TGV 7290	TGV 7293	TGV 7592	TGV 7094	TGV 7098	TGV 7096	TGV 7298	
	Ⓒ	Ⓐ	⑦	Ⓐ	⑥	Ⓐ				⑤	①–⑥	⑦	Ⓑ		Ⓐ	Ⓐ	Ⓒ	Ⓐ	⑦	⑥	⑤	⑦	①–⑥	⑦	
	w	L⊡	Jv	L	t	M		F	b	P	u	k	G	w	L	L			s	t	P	bv	u	s	
Tourcoing 415 d.	...	1111	...	...	...	...	...	...	...	...	...	...	...	...	...	...	...	...	...	...	...	...	...	...	...
Roubaix ◇ 415 d.	...	1116	...	...	...	...	...	...	...	...	...	...	...	...	...	...	...	...	...	...	...	...	...	...	...
Lille Flandres 415 d.	1111	1141	1211	...	...	...	...	1511	1611	1641	...	1711	1741	1811	1841	...	...	...	...	...	2041	2111	2120	...	...
Lille Europe d.	|	|	|	1313	1313	1320	1413	|	|	|	1711	|	|	|	|	1913	1913	1935	2011	2011	|	|	|	2213	...
Arras ▷ d.	|	|	|	|	|	1353	|	|	|	|	|	|	|	|	|	|	|	|	|	2039	|	|	2147	|	...
Paris Nord ▷ a.	1214	1244	1314	1414	1414	1444	1514	1614	1714	1744	1814	1814	1844	1914	1944	2014	2014	2041	2111	2129	2144	2214	2238	2314	...

- **B** – Daily to July 28 / from Aug. 26; ⑥ Aug. 3 - 24.
- **D** – Daily to July 28 / from Aug. 24; ⑥⑦ Aug. 3 - 18 (also Aug. 15).
- **E** – ①–⑥ to July 27 / from Aug. 26; ⑥ Aug. 3 - 24.
- **F** – Daily to July 28 / from Aug. 25, also Aug. 4, 11, 15, 18.
- **G** – Ⓑ to July 5 / from Aug. 26 (not Nov. 1); ⑤ July 12 - 26.
- **J** – Not July 6 - Aug. 25.
- **L** – Not July 29 - Aug. 25.
- **M** – Ⓐ July 29 - Aug. 23.
- **N** – ⑤ to July 5 / from Sept. 6 (also Oct. 31).
- **P** – ⑤ to July 5 / from Aug. 30 (also Oct. 31; not Nov. 1).
- **S** – Ⓐ July 29 - Aug. 23.
- **b** – Not Aug. 4, 11, 15, 18, 25.
- **d** – Also Aug. 14, 15, Oct. 31, Nov. 11; not Nov. 1.
- **e** – Also June 10, Aug. 15, Nov. 11.
- **f** – Also Oct. 31; not Aug. 2 - 23, Nov. 1.
- **h** – Also Aug. 15, Nov. 1.
- **k** – Also June 10, Nov. 11; not Aug. 4, 11, 18, 25.
- **n** – Not Nov. 11.
- **s** – Also Aug. 15, Nov. 11.
- **t** – Also runs Nov. 1.
- **u** – Not Aug. 15, Nov. 11.
- **v** – Also runs Nov. 11.
- **w** – Not Aug. 3, 10, 17, 24.
- **z** – Not Aug. 15.
- *TGV* – Ⓡ to / from Paris, supplement payable. Lille - Arras and v.v. requires TER-GV supplement, €3 all day.
- ◇ – Also calls at Croix Wasquehal.
- ⊡ – Starts from Lille on Ⓐ Oct. 21 - Nov. 15.
- ▷ – For Paris - Arras see also Tables **256** and **264**.
- * – Different train numbers may apply on certain days.

PARIS - SOISSONS - LAON — 251

km																									
		Ⓐ	Ⓐ	Ⓐ	Ⓐ	Ⓐ	Ⓐ	Ⓐ	Ⓐ	Ⓐ	Ⓐ	Ⓐ	Ⓐ	Ⓐ	Ⓐ	Ⓐ	Ⓒ	⑥	Ⓒ	Ⓒ	Ⓒ	⑥	Ⓒ	Ⓒ	⑥	Ⓒ
0	**Paris** Nord d.	Ⓐ	0634	0734	0834	1131	1231	1331	1431	1531	1634	1734	1834	1931	2031	2131	Ⓒ	0731	0831	0931	1331	1431	1631	1731	1831	2031
61	Crépy-en-Valois d.		0712	0813	0911	1210	1310	1410	1517	1610	1711	1813	1913	2010	2112	2210		0811	0910	1010	1408	1517	1710	1810	1910	2110
105	Soissons d.		0740	0840	0941	1239	1339	1439	1544	1640	1738	1840	1941	2039	2140	2239		0839	0941	1039	1439	1544	1739	1839	1939	2139
140	**Laon** a.		0805	0905	1005	1305	1405	1505	1609	1705	1805	1905	2005	2105	2205	2305		0905	1006	1105	1505	1609	1805	1905	2005	2205

		Ⓐ	Ⓐ	Ⓐ	Ⓐ	Ⓐ	Ⓐ	Ⓐ	Ⓐ	Ⓐ	Ⓐ	Ⓐ	Ⓐ	Ⓐ	Ⓐ		⑥	Ⓒ	†	⑥	Ⓒ	Ⓒ	Ⓒ	Ⓒ	Ⓒ	
Laon d.	Ⓐ	0511	0541	0639	0741	0941	1141	1241	1341	1540	1641	1741	1841	1941	2041	Ⓒ	0639	0741	0841	0941	1141	1241	1541	1741	2041	...
Soissons d.		0536	0607	0705	0807	1007	1207	1307	1407	1607	1707	1807	1907	2007	2107		0704	0806	0907	1007	1207	1307	1607	1805	2107	...
Crépy-en-Valois d.		0604	0635	0733	0835	1035	1235	1335	1435	1634	1735	1835	1935	2035	2135		0732	0835	0935	1035	1235	1335	1635	1835	2135	...
Paris Nord a.		0640	0710	0810	0910	1113	1313	1413	1513	1710	1810	1911	2013	2113	2213		0813	0913	1013	1113	1313	1413	1713	1913	2213	...

Subject to alteration on June 2, Sept. 21, 22.

AMIENS - TERGNIER - LAON - REIMS — 252

km		Ⓐ	⑥	Ⓐ	ⒶJ	Ⓐ	Ⓒ	Ⓐ	Ⓑ	⑥	Ⓐ	Ⓐ	†	⚒	Ⓐ	ⒶJ	⚒	Ⓑ	Ⓐ	⑥	⑥B	⑦B	H	⑤f	†
0	**Amiens** d.	...	0627	0627	0727	0827	0857	...	1227	1327	1457	...	1557	1627	...	1727	1757	1827	1857	1857	1929	1929	1927	1927	2000
59	Ham (Somme) d.	...	0712	0715	0815	0915	0942	...	1315	1415	1543	...	1644	1714	...	1815	1843	1915	1942	1943	2005	2005	2015	2015	2046
80	Tergnier d.	0705	0726	0733	0833	0933	1005	1233	1333	1433	1605	1654	1705	1733	1805	1833	1905	1933	1956	2005	2020	2020	2034	2033	2108
108	**Laon** a.	0731	0746	0759	0859	0959	1028	1259	1359	1459	1626	1715	1727	1800	1826	1859	1926	2000	...	2026	2038	2038	...	2059	2129

	Ⓐ	⚒	ⒶJ	⚒	⚒	Ⓐ	⑦B	⑥B	†		Ⓐ	†	⚒		ⒶJ	Ⓐ	Ⓒ	Ⓐ	Ⓐ	ⒶJ	Ⓐ	⑥	†	⑤f	H
Laon d.	...	0557	0634	0657	0734	0809	0817	0828r	0827	...	1158	1224	1334	...	1557	1657	1657	1734	1755	1834	1850	1923	1933	1955	1955
Tergnier d.	0605	0625	0705	0725	0805	0836	0838	0856	0859	...	1226	1257	1405	...	1625	1725	1725	1757	1825	1905	1918	1958	1958	2025	2024
Ham (Somme) d.	0619	0647	0718	0747	0818	...	0854	0912	0914	...	1247	1311	1418	...	1647	1747	1747	1818	1847	1918	1936	2014	2014	2047	...
Amiens a.	0703	0733	0803	0833	0903	...	0928	0946	1003	...	1333	1403	1503	...	1733	1831	1833	1903	1935	2003	2025	2103	2103	2133	...

LAON - REIMS

km		⚒	ⒶN	Ⓐ	Ⓐu	⑥	†	⚒u	ⒶN	Ⓐ		△
0	Laon d.	0630	0706	0740	0816	1045	1233	1333	1712	1733	1833	2045
52	Reims a.	0717	0750	0824	0900	1120	1320	1420	1750	1820	1920	2120

	⚒	Ⓐ	ⒸS	†	⚒u	⚒u	ⒶN	Ⓑ	Ⓐ		Ⓐ
Reims d.	0640	0707	0733	1110	1240	1510	1640	1710	1740	1840	1940
Laon a.	0727	0748	0809	1157	1327	1545	1727	1757	1827	1927	2028

- **B** – July 6 - Aug. 11. From / to Boulogne (Table **261**).
- **H** – ①–④ (not holidays).
- **J** – Not July 8 - Aug. 23.
- **N** – Not July 15 - Aug. 23.
- **S** – ⑥⑦ July 6 - Aug. 25 (also Aug. 15).
- **f** – Not Aug. 16.
- **r** – 0824 on Aug. 10.
- **u** – By 🚌 on June 17 - 21, Sept. 23 - 27, Sept. 30 - Oct. 4 in revised timings.
- △ – On ⑦ June 30 - Aug. 25 dep. 2111, arr. 2146.

Amiens - Laon and v.v. is subject to alteration on Aug. 16, 17, 24, 31, Oct. 5, Nov. 2, 9

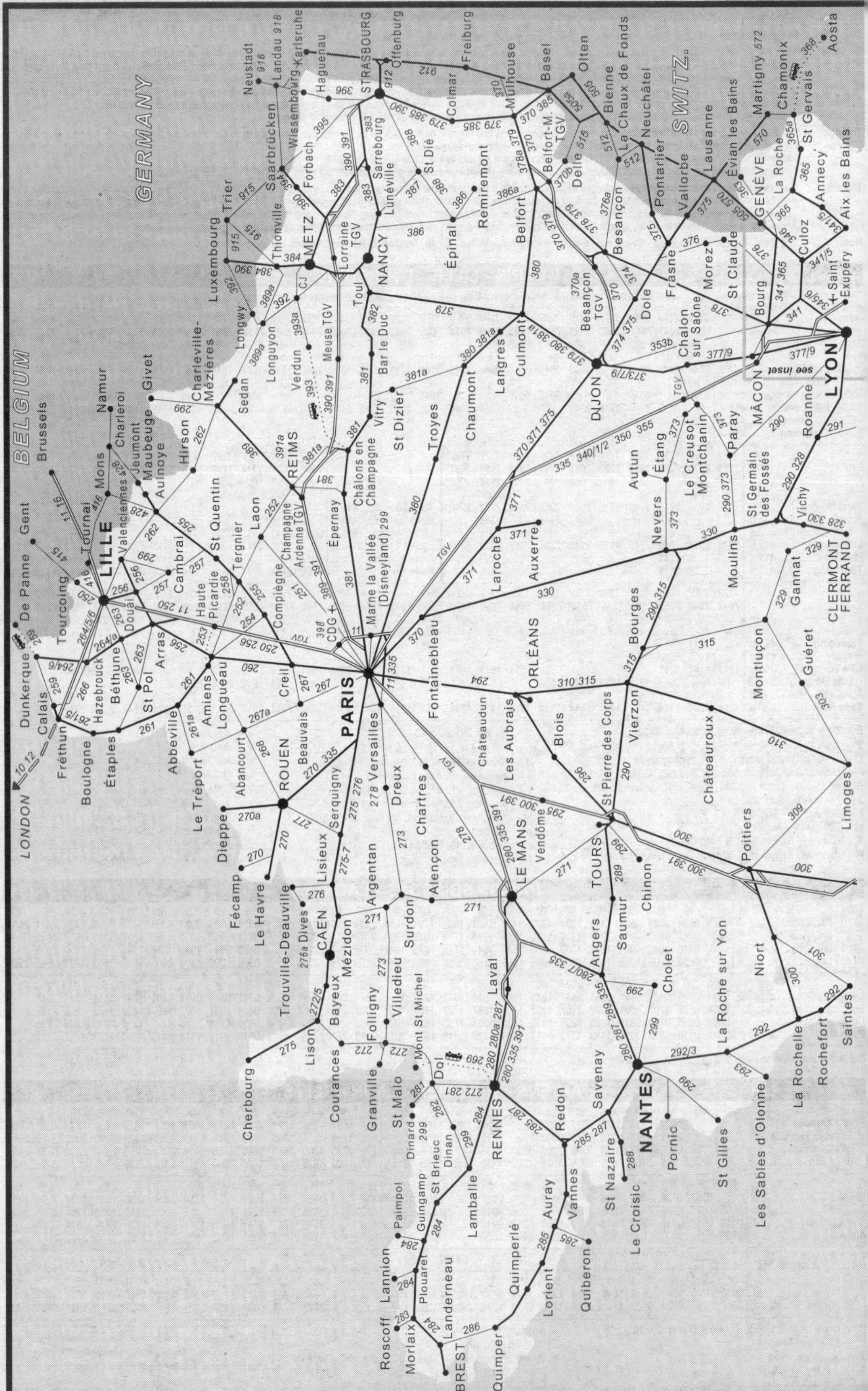
BELGIUM
GERMANY
SWITZ.
LONDON
PARIS
LILLE
ROUEN
CAEN
RENNES
NANTES
LE MANS
TOURS
ORLÉANS
REIMS
METZ
NANCY
STRASBOURG
DIJON
LYON
CLERMONT FERRAND
Brussels
Gent
De Panne
Dunkerque
Calais
Fréthun
Boulogne
Étaples
Hazebrouck
Béthune
Tourcoing
Tournai
Mons
Namur
Charleroi
Jeumont
Maubeuge
Aulnoye
Valenciennes
Douai
Arras
St Pol
Cambrai
Haute Picardie
St Quentin
Tergnier
Laon
Hirson
Charleville-Mézières
Givet
Sedan
Longwy
Longuyon
Luxembourg
Trier
Thionville
Saarbrücken
Forbach
Wissembourg
Landau
Neustadt
Karlsruhe
Haguenau
Offenburg
Freiburg
Colmar
Mulhouse
Basel
Olten
Bienne
La Chaux de Fonds
Neuchâtel
Lausanne
Vallorbe
Pontarlier
Frasne
Évian les Bains
Genève
Martigny
Chamonix
St Gervais
Aosta
La Roche
Annecy
Aix les Bains
Culoz
Bourg
Saint Exupéry
Mâcon
Roanne
Vichy
Gannat
Moulins
St Germain des Fossés
Paray
Le Creusot Montchanin
Chalon sur Saône
Étang
Autun
Nevers
Dole
Besançon
Besançon TGV
Morez
St Claude
Belfort
Belfort-M. TGV
Delle
Culmont
Langres
Chaumont
Troyes
St Dizier
Vitry
Bar le Duc
Toul
Lunéville
Sarrebourg
St Dié
Épinal
Remiremont
Lorraine TGV
Meuse TGV
Verdun
Châlons en Champagne
Épernay
Champagne Ardenne TGV
Compiègne
Creil
CDG
Marne la Vallée (Disneyland)
Fontainebleau
Laroche
Auxerre
Amiens
Longueau
Abbeville
Le Tréport
Beauvais
Abancourt
Dieppe
Fécamp
Le Havre
Serquigny
Lisieux
Trouville-Deauville
Dives
Versailles
Dreux
Chartres
Argentan
Mézidon
Bayeux
Lison
Cherbourg
Coutances
Folligny
Granville
Villedieu
Surdon
Alençon
Châteaudun
Les Aubrais
Blois
Vendôme
St Pierre des Corps
Vierzon
Bourges
Châteauroux
Montluçon
Guéret
Limoges
Poitiers
Chinon
Saumur
Angers
Laval
Cholet
Niort
La Roche sur Yon
La Rochelle
Rochefort
Saintes
Les Sables d'Olonne
St Gilles
Pornic
Savenay
St Nazaire
Le Croisic
Redon
Vannes
Auray
Quiberon
Lorient
Quimperlé
Quimper
Brest
Landerneau
Morlaix
Roscoff
Plouaret
Lannion
Guingamp
Paimpol
St Brieuc
Lamballe
Dinan
Dinard
St Malo
Dol
Mont St Michel
see inset
TGV

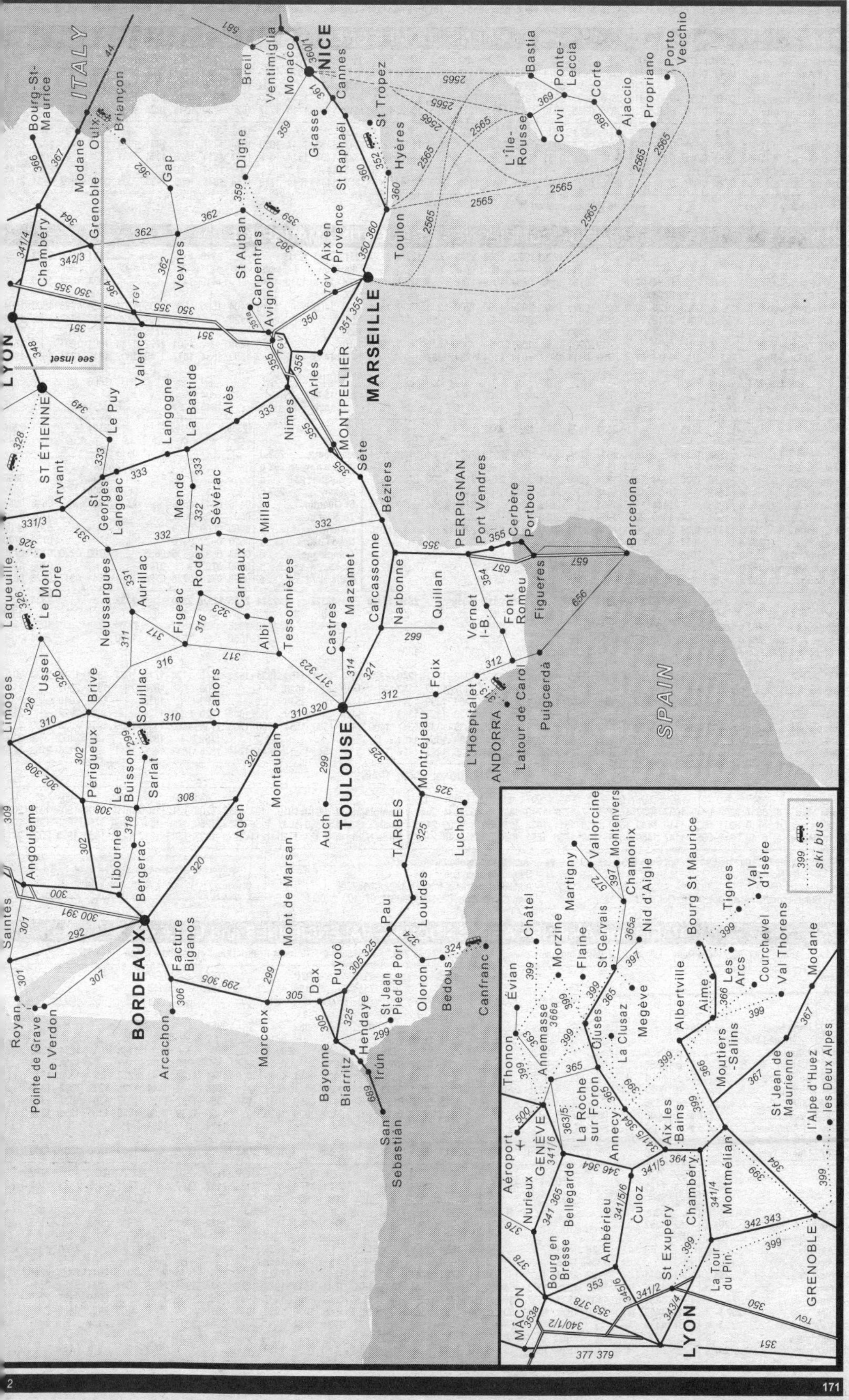
ITALY
SPAIN
ANDORRA
see inset
LYON
MARSEILLE
TOULOUSE
BORDEAUX
NICE
ST ÉTIENNE
MONTPELLIER
PERPIGNAN
TARBES
GENÈVE
GRENOBLE
MÂCON
Bourg-St-Maurice
Modane
Oulx
Briançon
Chambéry
Grenoble
Valence
Gap
Veynes
Digne
St Auban
Carpentras
Avignon
Aix en Provence
Arles
Nimes
Alès
La Bastide
Langogne
Le Puy
Breil
Ventimiglia
Monaco
Cannes
Grasse
St Raphaël
St Tropez
Hyères
Toulon
Bastia
Ponte-Leccia
Calvi
L'Île-Rousse
Corte
Ajaccio
Propriano
Porto Vecchio
Sète
Béziers
Narbonne
Carcassonne
Quillan
Port Vendres
Cerbère
Portbou
Figueres
Barcelona
Vernet I-B.
Font Romeu
Puigcerdà
Latour de Carol
L'Hospitalet
Foix
Castres
Mazamet
Albi
Tessonnières
Carmaux
Rodez
Millau
Sévérac
Mende
St Georges Langeac
Arvant
Neussargues
Aurillac
Figeac
Cahors
Montauban
Agen
Auch
Montréjeau
Luchon
Lourdes
Pau
Oloron
Bedous
Canfranc
Puyoô
Dax
St Jean Pied de Port
Hendaye
Irún
San Sebastián
Biarritz
Bayonne
Morcenx
Mont de Marsan
Facture Biganos
Arcachon
Royan
Pointe de Grave
Le Verdon
Saintes
Angoulême
Libourne
Bergerac
Le Buisson
Sarlat
Souillac
Périgueux
Brive
Limoges
Ussel
Laqueuille
Le Mont Dore
Thonon
Évian
Châtel
Annemasse
Morzine
Martigny
Vallorcine
Montenvers
Chamonix
Flaine
St Gervais
Nid d'Aigle
Cluses
La Clusaz
Megève
La Roche sur Foron
Annecy
Aéroport
Nurieux
Bellegarde
Bourg en Bresse
Ambérieu
Culoz
Aix les Bains
Albertville
Bourg St Maurice
Aime
Les Arcs
Tignes
Val d'Isère
Courchevel
Val Thorens
Moutiers -Salins
St Jean de Maurienne
l'Alpe d'Huez
les Deux Alpes
Montmélian
La Tour du Pin
St Exupéry
ski bus
TGV

253 AMIENS - TGV HAUTE-PICARDIE

SNCF 🚌 service

TGV departures and arrivals at TGV Haute-Picardie (Table **11**) have 🚌 connections from / to Amiens and St Quentin. Departs 50 - 60 mins before the train; journey 40 minutes, Ⓡ.

254 AMIENS - COMPIÈGNE

km		Ⓐ	Ⓐ	⑥	Ⓐ	†	Ⓐ	⑥	†	Ⓐ J	†	⑥ J	Ⓐ	⑥	†	Ⓐ J	Ⓒ	Ⓐ	Ⓐ	† J	⑥	Ⓐ	Ⓐ J	†	⑥	Ⓐ	Ⓒ d
0	**Amiens** d.	0547	0617	0659	0734	0735	0855	0914	0932	1054	1118	1126	1229	1246	1330	1443	1619	1640	1703	1733	1734	1752	1818	1835	1926	1931	2019
5	Longueau d.	|	|	|	0740	|	|	0920	0938	|	|	|	1235	1252	1336	|	|	|	1709	1739	1740	|	1825	1843	|	|	2025
36	Montdidier d.	0618	0653	0730	0814	0806	0930	0951	1010	1124	1148	1156	1308	1324	1406	1513	1649	1710	1743	1811	1812	1827	1903	1907	1956	2002	2056
76	**Compiègne** a.	0647	0728	0759	0850	0835	0955	1030	1042	1151	1217	1225	1342	1359	1440	1540	1718	1737	1820	1843	1845	1904	1937	1937	2025	2028	2130

	Ⓐ	Ⓐ J	Ⓐ	⑥	†	Ⓐ	Ⓐ J	Ⓐ	⑥	†	Ⓐ	⑥	†	Ⓐ J	⑥ J	†	Ⓐ	Ⓒ	Ⓐ J	Ⓒ	Ⓐ	Ⓐ	⑥	Ⓐ	† J	†	⑥
Compiègne d.	0544	0620	0659	0700	0738	0744	0825	0903	0918	0936	1059	1106	1119	1232	1247	1333	1447	1620	1644	1737	1751	1831	1904	1910	1913	2022	2042
Montdidier d.	0619	0653	0741	0729	0807	0813	0856	0931	0952	1009	1125	1133	1147	1307	1323	1407	1514	1648	1711	1811	1828	1904	1931	1938	1941	2057	2116
Longueau d.	0653	|	0819	|	0832	|	|	|	1023	1040	|	|	|	1338	1353	1438	|	|	|	1841	1900	|	|	|	|	2128	2146
Amiens a.	0658	0726	0826	0759	0839	0845	0930	1000	1028	1046	1156	1203	1218	1343	1359	1444	1544	1719	1744	1848	1906	1933	2003	2007	2012	2134	2152

J – Not July 6 - Aug. 25. **d** – Runs 18 minutes later on ⑥.

255 PARIS - COMPIÈGNE - ST QUENTIN - MAUBEUGE

km				2301			12303	12305	2307	2309		12311		12313	2317	12315			2319				2321	12321	2323	
		Ⓐ	Ⓐ	Ⓐ	⑥	Ⓑ	Ⓐ		Ⓒ	Ⓐ u	Ⓑ	⑥	⑥	Ⓑ	Ⓐ	†	⑥	⑥	⑥	Ⓐ	Ⓐ	Ⓐ	⑥	Ⓑ		⑥
0	**Paris** Nord d.	...	0634	0719	...	0734	0819	0834	1019	1119	...	1219	...	1234	1319	1319	1249	...	1419	1434	...	...	1634	1634	1719	...
51	Creil d.	...	0705	|	...	0805	|	0905	|	|	...	|	...	1305	|	|	1321	...	|	1501	...	...	1705	1705	|	...
84	**Compiègne** d.	0625	0728	0800	0804	0828	0900	0928	1100	1200	1235	1300	1304	1328	1405	1400	1356	1404	1500	1524	1635	1704	1728	1728	1800	1804
108	Noyon d.	0647	0742	|	0829	0842	|	0942	|	|	1259	|	1329	1342	|	|	...	1429	|	1540	1701	1729	1742	1742	|	1829
124	Chauny d.	0701	0753	|	0840	0853	|	0953	|	|	1313	|	1343	1353	|	|	...	1443	|	1553	1715	1742	1753	1753	|	1843
131	Tergnier d.	0709	0801	|	0849	0901	|	1001	|	|	1319	|	1349	1401	|	|	...	1449	|	1601	1722	1748	1801	1801	|	1849
154	**St Quentin** 257 d.	0728	0814	0834	0909	0914	0932	1014	1134	1234	1337	1332	1409	1414	1438	1432	...	1509	1534	1617	1740	1807	1815	1814	1834	1909
181	Busigny 257 d.	...	...	|	...	...	...	...	|	|	...	...	...	...	|	...	...	...	|	...	...	...	1833	...	|	...
207	*Cambrai* 257 a.	...	...	|	...	...	...	...	|	|	...	...	...	...	|	...	...	...	|	...	...	...	1856	...	|	...
217	Aulnoye Aymeries 262 a.	...	...	0904	...	...	...	...	1209	1304	...	...	...	...	1508	...	...	...	1604	...	...	...	...	...	1904	...
229	**Maubeuge** 262 a.	...	...	0915	...	...	...	...	1220	1315	...	...	...	...	1520	...	...	...	1615	...	...	...	...	...	1915	...

		2325			2327	2329		12331	2333				
	Ⓐ	Ⓐ	⚒	Ⓐ	†			Ⓐ	⑦ d	Ⓐ	Ⓑ v	⑥	⊕
Paris Nord d.	1734	1819	...	1834	1834	1919	...	1934	2019	2034	2134	2149	2234
Creil d.	1804	|	...	1904	1902	|	...	2005	|	2104	2207	2222	2306
Compiègne d.	1828	1900	1904	1928	1925	2000	2004	2028	2100	2128	2229	2251	2329
Noyon d.	1842	|	1930	1942	1940	|	2030	2042	|	2142	2243	...	2343
Chauny d.	1853	|	1944	1953	1951	|	2043	2053	|	2153	2254	...	2354
Tergnier d.	1901	|	1950	2001	1959	|	2050	2101	|	2201	2301	...	0001
St Quentin 257 d.	1914	1934	2009	2014	2014	2034	2109	2114	2134	2214	2315	...	0015
Busigny 257 d.	...	1951	...	...	2033	|	...	...	|	...	...	...	...
Cambrai 257 a.	...	2015	...	...	2056	|	...	...	|	...	...	...	...
Aulnoye Aymeries 262 a.	...	...	...	...	...	2104	...	...	2204	...	...	...	...
Maubeuge 262 a.	...	...	...	...	...	2115	...	...	2215	...	...	...	...

	12300		12302			2304			2306
	Ⓐ	⑥	Ⓐ	†	Ⓐ	Ⓐ	Ⓐ	Ⓑ	⑥
Maubeuge 262 d.	...	...	...	...	0514	...	...	...	...
Aulnoye Aymeries 262 d.	...	...	...	...	0532	...	...	...	...
Cambrai 257 d.	...	...	...	...	|	0536	...	...	0606
Busigny 257 d.	...	...	...	...	0600	0608	...	...	0632
St Quentin d.	0446	0547	0546	...	...	0624	...	0646	0647
Tergnier d.	0502	0602	0602	...	...	|	...	0702	0701
Chauny d.	0509	0609	0609	...	...	|	...	0709	0709
Noyon d.	0520	0622	0620	...	...	|	...	0720	0720
Compiègne d.	0535	0637	0635	0638	...	0700	0720	0735	0735
Creil d.	0559	0702	|	0700	...	|	|	0759	0759
Paris Nord a.	0626	0726	0726	0726	...	0741	0817	0826	0826

	2308			2312	2310				2316	12318		2318	12320		12322		2324	2326	12328	2330		2332			2334	
	Ⓐ	Ⓑ	⚒	⚒	†	Ⓐ	⑥	Ⓐ	⚒	Ⓐ	⑥	†	Ⓐ	⑥	⑥	†	†	Ⓐ		†	Ⓐ			⚒	†	†
Maubeuge 262 d.	0642	...	...	0742	0842	...	...	...	1042	...	...	...	...	...	...	...	1442	1538	...	1637	...	1737r	...	...	1952	...
Aulnoye Aymeries 262 d.	0653	...	...	0753	0854	...	...	...	1053	...	...	...	...	...	...	...	1454	1550	...	1649	...	1750	...	...	2004	...
Cambrai 257 d.	|	...	...	|	|	...	...	...	|	...	...	1206	...	...	...	...	|	|	...	|	...	|	...	...	|	...
Busigny 257 d.	|	...	...	|	|	...	...	...	|	...	...	1232	...	...	...	...	|	|	...	|	...	|	...	...	|	...
St Quentin d.	0724	0746	0751	0824	0924	0927	0950	1046	1124	1246	1247	1248	1324	1351	1424	1451	1524	1621	1646	1724	1746	1824	1851	1946	2034	2046
Tergnier d.	|	0802	0810	|	|	0944	1005	1102	|	1302	1302	1303	|	1410	|	1510	|	|	1700	|	1806	|	1910	2002	|	2100
Chauny d.	|	0809	0816	|	|	0950	1013	1109	|	1309	1309	1311	|	1416	|	1516	|	|	1708	|	1813	|	1919	2010	|	2108
Noyon d.	|	0820	0829	|	|	1000	1024	1120	|	1320	1321	1323	|	1429	|	1529	|	1645	1720	|	1824	|	1931	2022	|	2122
Compiègne d.	0800	0835	0854	0900	1000	1014	1038	1135	1200	1335	1335	1337	1400	1454	1500	1554	1600	1700	1735	1800	1838	1900	1954	2038	2109	2138
Creil d.	|	0859	...	|	|	...	1102	1159	|	1359	1359	1401	|	...	|	...	|	|	1759	|	1859	|	...	2100	|	2200
Paris Nord a.	0841	0926	...	0941	1044	...	1126	1226	1241	1426	1423	1426	1441	...	1541	...	1641	1741	1826	1841	1926	1941	...	2126	2153	2226

ADDITIONAL LOCAL TRAINS

▽	⚒	†	⚒	Ⓐ	Ⓐ	Ⓐ	⚒	Ⓒ	Ⓐ	⑥	Ⓐ	Ⓒ	†
Paris Nord d.	0637	0837	0849	1037	1337	1537	1637	1737	1749	1837	1840	1934	2040
Creil d.	0710	0911	0922	1110	1410	1610	1710	1811	1823	1911	1913	2009	2113
Compiègne a.	0749	0945	0951	1147	1450	1649	1749	1850	1851	1950	1953	2048	2148

▽		Ⓐ	†	⑥	Ⓒ	Ⓐ	⑥	Ⓑ		Ⓑ	⚒	Ⓐ
Compiègne d.	0810	1019	1107	1117	1208	1212	1520	1612	1709	1809	1910	2008
Creil d.	0850	1047	1136	1152	1250	1250	1547	1650	1750	1850	1950	2038
Paris Nord a.	0923	1120	1211	1223	1323	1323	1617	1723	1823	1923	2023	2111

d – Also June 10, Aug. 15, Oct. 31; not Sept. 8, 15, 29, Oct. 6 - Nov. 10.
r – 1742 on Ⓐ.
u – Subject to alteration Sept. 9 - 20, Oct. 7 - Nov. 15.
v – Subject to alteration from Sept. 7.
⊕ – Subject to alteration.
▽ – Additional journeys: from Paris Nord 1822Ⓐ; from Compiègne: 0505Ⓐ, 0609⚒, 0704Ⓐ, 0706⑥.

Subject to alteration on Sept. 7, 8, 14, 15, 28, 29, Oct. 5, 6, 26, Nov. 9 - 11

256 PARIS and AMIENS - ARRAS - DOUAI - VALENCIENNES and LILLE

For *TGV* trains Paris - Lille and v.v. (including trains calling at Arras) see Table **250**. For additional *TGV* trains Arras - Douai - Lille and v.v. see Table **11**.

km ★			◇				◇					*TGV* 7151		*TGV* 7155			*TGV* 7157		*TGV* 7159					
		Ⓐ	Ⓐ	⑥	Ⓐ	⚒	Ⓐ		†	Ⓐ ⊕	⑥	Ⓐ J	Ⓐ	⑥ t	⑥	⑦	⑦ d	⑥	N	Ⓑ	⑥	Ⓐ	Ⓒ	
0	**Paris** Nord 264 d.	...	...	...	...	...	...	...	...	...	...	0752	...	0852	...	...	0952	...	1052	...	...	...	...	...
	Rouen 268 d.	...	...	...	...	...	...	...	...	0617	...	|	...	|	0817	...	|	...	|	...	...	...	...	...
131	**Amiens** d.	0536	...	...	...	0636	...	...	...	0738	0738	|	0838	|	0938	0938	|	1038	|	1138	...	1234	1235	...
162	Albert d.	0557	...	...	...	0659	...	...	...	0759	0759	|	0859	|	0959	0958	|	1059	|	1159	...	1256	1255	...
199	Arras 264 a.	0621	...	...	...	0723	...	...	...	0823	0822	0841	0923	0941	1023	1020	1041	1123	1141	1223	...	1320	1318	...
199	Arras d.	0623	0647	...	...	0725	0745	...	*0757*	0825	0823	0844	0925	0944	1024	1021	1044	1124	1144	1225	1239	1322	1319	...
224	Douai a.	0636	|	...	...	0737	|	...	*0826*	0837	0837	0859	0937	0959	1037	1035	1059	1137	1159	1237	1304	1337	1332	...
224	Douai 257 ▶ d.	0638	|	0644	0708	0739	|	...	0834	0839	0839	0908	0939	1008	1039	1037	1108	1139	1208	1239	1306	1339	1334	...
260	Valenciennes ▶ a.	|	|	|	|	|	|	...	|	|	|	0934	|	1034	|	|	1134	|	1234	|	|	|	|	...
257	**Lille** Europe a.	|	0708	|	|	|	0808	...	|	|	|	...	|	...	|	|	...	|	...	|	|	|	|	...
257	**Lille** Flandres 257 a.	0658	...	0725	0730	0758	...	...	0913	0859	0858	...	0959	...	1058	1058	...	1158	...	1259	1330	1358	1358	...

	TGV 7163	*TGV* 7165					*TGV* 7169			*TGV* 7173	◇		*TGV* 7181	*TGV* 7179		*TGV* 7185	*TGV* 7187	*TGV* 7187		*TGV* 7191	*TGV* 7193		*TGV* 7197	
	①–④ L	⑤⑥ e	†	⑥	Ⓐ	Ⓒ	H	Ⓐ		Ⓐ	Ⓐ	Ⓑ	Ⓐ n	⑦ d	Ⓐ	Ⓐ J	Ⓐ K	F		①–④ M	⑤–⑦ P	Ⓐ	⑦ w	
Paris Nord 264 d.	1252	1252	...	...	...	...	1452	...	...	1652	...	...	1752	1752	...	1837	1852	1852	...	1952	1952	...	2152	...
Rouen 268 d.	|	|	...	...	...	...	|	...	...	|	...	...	|	|	...	|	|	|	1816	|	|	...	|	...
Amiens d.	|	|	...	1338	1438	...	|	1536	1638	|	...	1738	|	|	1836	|	|	|	1939	|	|	2038	|	...
Albert d.	|	|	...	1359	1458	...	|	1558	1659	|	...	1759	|	|	1859	|	|	|	2000	|	|	2059	|	...
Arras 264 a.	1341	1341	...	1422	1523	...	1541	1621	1723	1741	...	1823	1841	1841	1923	1926	1941	1941	2023	2041	2041	2123	2241	...
Arras d.	1344	1344	1408	1423	1525	1523	1544	1623	1725	1744	1800	1825	1844	1844	1925	1929	1944	1944	2025	2044	2044	2124	2244	...
Douai a.	1359	1359	1426	1437	1537	1537	1559	1637	1737	1759	|	1837	1859	1859	1937	1944	1959	1959	2037	2059	2059	2137	2259	...
Douai 257 ▶ d.	1408	1408	1428	1439	1539	1539	1608	1639	1739	1808	|	1839	1908	1908	1939	1954	2010	2008	2039	2108	2108	2139	2308	...
Valenciennes ▶ a.	1434	1434	|	|	|	|	1634	|	|	1834	|	|	1934	1934	|	2022	2044	2034	|	2134	2134	|	2334	...
Lille Europe a.	...	...	|	|	|	|	...	|	|	...	1821	|	...	...	|	...	...	...	|	...	...	|	...	...
Lille Flandres 257 a.	...	...	1458	1458	1559	1559	...	1700	1758	...	...	1859	...	...	1959	...	...	...	2059	...	...	2159	...	...

LILLE and VALENCIENNES - DOUAI - ARRAS - AMIENS and PARIS 256

Lille - Paris: see **250**

			TGV 7100	*TGV* 7102		*TGV* 7104	*TGV* 7106			*TGV* 7110	*TGV* 7110						*TGV* 7116					*TGV* 7120		
	Ⓐ	⑥	Ⓐ	Ⓐ J	⚒	Ⓐ	⑥ J	⑥	Ⓑ	⑥ K	⑦ d	Ⓐ E	⑥	Ⓐ	⑥	†	Ⓒ	Ⓐ		⚒	†	⚒ J		⑥
Lille Flandres **257** d.	0559	0602	...	...	0702	...	...	0802	0802	...	...	0902	0902	1002	1002	1002	...	1101	...	1202	1202	...	1302	1406
Lille Europe d.	|	|	...	...	|	...	...	|	|	...	...	|	|	|	|	|	...	|	...	|	|	...	|	|
Valenciennes ▶ d.	|	|	0549	0615	|	0652	0715	|	|	0815	0815	|	|	|	|	|	1015	|	...	|	|	1215	|	|
Douai **257** ▶ a.	0617	0621	0614	0640	0721	0717	0740	0821	0821	0840	0840	0921	0921	1021	1021	1020	1040	1121	...	1221	1221	1240	1321	1438
Douai d.	0619	0623	0626	0651	0723	0730	0751	0823	0823	0851	0851	0923	0923	1023	1023	1022	1051	1123	...	1223	1223	1251	1323	*1455*
Arras a.	0632	0636	0644	0705	0735	0744	0805	0835	0835	0905	0905	0935	0937	1042	1036	1034	1105	1136	...	1236	1236	1305	1335	*1515*
Arras **264** d.	0633	0637	0656	0717	0737	0756	0817	0837	0837	0917	0917	0937	...	...	1038	1036	1117	1137	...	1238	...	1317	1337	...
Albert d.	0653	0701	|	|	0801	|	|	0902	0901	|	|	1011	...	...	1101	1100	|	1159	...	1301	...	|	1401	...
Amiens a.	0717	0721	|	|	0819	|	|	0921	0921	|	|	1037	...	...	1121	1121	|	1219	...	1321	...	|	1421	...
Rouen **268** a.	0833	...	|	|	...	|	|	1046	...	|	|	...	...	...	...	...	|	...	...	...	...	|	...	...
Paris Nord **264** a.	...	...	0747	0808	...	0847	0908	...	...	1008	1008	...	...	...	...	...	1208	...	...	...	...	1408	...	...

	TGV 7126	*TGV* 7126		*TGV* 7130				◇	*TGV* 7136				◇		*TGV* 7142	*TGV* 7144						*TGV* 7160		
	⑤ b	Ⓒ		Ⓑ h	Ⓐ	Ⓐ	⑥ B	Ⓐ	z	Ⓐ	Ⓐ	Ⓒ	Ⓐ	Ⓐ	Ⓐ J	⑦ d	†	⑥ c	Ⓐ	Ⓑ	⑥	⑦ Jv	Ⓐ	
Lille Flandres **257** d.	...	...	1602	...	1630	1702	1702	...	...	1732	1802	1802	...	1902	...	...	1935	1935	2002	2102	2106	...	2209	...
Lille Europe d.	...	...	|	...	|	|	|	1721	...	|	|	|	1837	|	...	...	|	|	|	|	|	...	|	...
Valenciennes ▶ d.	1415	1415	|	1615	|	|	|	|	1715	|	|	|	|	|	1915	1915	|	|	|	|	|	2115	|	...
Douai **257** ▶ a.	1440	1440	1621	1640	1650	1721	1721	|	1740	1755	1821	1820	|	1921	1940	1940	2019	2017	2021	2121	2136	2140	2241	...
Douai d.	1451	1451	1623	1651	1659	1723	1723	|	1751	...	1823	1822	|	1923	1951	1951	2022	*2034*	2023	2123	2138	2151	2243	...
Arras a.	1505	1505	1636	1705	1713	1736	1736	1743	1805	...	1837	1835	1859	1935	2005	2005	2036	*2103*	2035	2138	2152	2205	2259	...
Arras **264** d.	1517	1517	1637	1717	...	1737	...	...	1817	...	1838	1837	...	1937	2017	2017	...	...	2037	...	...	2217	...	...
Albert d.	|	|	1700	|	...	1800	...	...	|	...	1901	1859	...	2001	|	|	...	...	2101	...	...	|	...	...
Amiens a.	|	|	1720	|	...	1820	...	...	|	...	1922	1921	...	2021	|	|	...	...	2120	...	...	|	...	...
Rouen **268** a.	|	|	...	|	...	1942	...	...	|	...	...	2043	...	...	|	|	...	...	...	...	...	|	...	...
Paris Nord **264** a.	1608	1608	...	1808	...	...	...	...	1908	...	...	...	...	...	2108	2108	...	...	...	...	...	2308	...	...

B – Not July 6 - Aug. 24.
E – To July 5.
F – ⑥⑦ June 1 - 30 (also June 10; not June 9), also Aug. 25, 31, Sept. 1.
H – Will not run on ①–④ July 29 - Aug. 22 (runs Aug. 14, 15).
J – Not July 29 - Aug. 24.
K – July 29 - Aug. 24.
L – ①–④ July 29 - Aug. 22 (not Aug. 14, 15).
M – ①–④ to July 4 / from Aug. 26 (not June 10, Oct. 31, Nov. 11).
N – ⚒ to July 27 / from Aug. 24 (also ⑥ Aug. 3 - 17).
P – ⑤⑥⑦ to June 30 (also June 10).

b – Also Oct. 31; not July 12 - Aug. 23.
c – By 🚌 Douai - Arras (a. 2144) ⑥ July 6 - Aug. 24.
d – Also June 10, Aug. 15, Nov. 11.
e – Also Aug. 14, Oct. 31; not July 12, 19, 26.
h – Not Nov. 1.
n – Not on ⑤ June 7 - July 5 or ⑤ from Aug. 30.
t – Also Nov. 1; not Nov. 2.
v – Also June 10, Nov. 11.
w – Also June 10; not June 9, Aug. 4 - 18, Nov. 3.
z – Not Nov. 2, 3.

TGV – Ⓡ, supplement payable.
▶ – Additional trains run Douai - Valenciennes (journey 30 - 40 mins).
★ – Paris - Arras via high-speed line is *179 km*.
◇ – TER à Grande Vitesse (via high-speed line). Supplement *Grande Vitesse* payable (€3 per day).
⊕ – Subject to alteration from Oct. 28.

Subject to alteration on Nov. 2, 3, 9, 10, Dec. 8

LILLE - DOUAI - CAMBRAI - ST QUENTIN 257

km																									
		Ⓐ P	⑥ Pv	Ⓐ	⑥	Ⓐ	Ⓐ	⑥ J	⚒	Ⓐ J	†	⑥	† Pv	†	Ⓐ J	Ⓐ	⑥	Ⓐ	†	⑥	⑥	Ⓐ J	⑥ J	Ⓐ	⚒
0	**Lille** Flandres **256** d.	...	...	...	*0602*	0606	0706	0736	0806	*0902*	0906	1006	...	1110	1136	1206	1206	1236	*1302*	*1302*	1406	...	1506	1536	1606
34	Douai **256** a.	...	...	...	*0621*	0638	0738	0808	0838	*0921*	0938	1038	...	1142	1208	1238	1238	1308	*1321*	*1321*	1438	...	1538	1608	1638
34	Douai d.	...	...	...	0637	0640	0740	0811	0840	0940	0940	1040	...	1144	1211	1240	1240	1311	1331	1340	1440	...	1540	1611	1640
66	**Cambrai** Ville a.	...	...	...	0713	0713	0813	0844	0913	1013	1012	1112	...	1213	1244	1313	1313	1344	1401	1413	1514	...	1613	1643	1713
66	**Cambrai** Ville d.	0536	0606	0632	0715	0715	0815	...	0915	...	1014	1114	1206	...	1255	1315	1315	...	1403	...	1516	1532	...	...	1715
82	Caudry d.	0554	0620	0646	0727	0727	0827	...	0927	...	1026	1127	1220	...	1309	1329	1328	...	1416	...	1528	1544	...	...	1727
92	Busigny **255** d.	0608	0632	0658	0736	0738	0838	...	0938	...	1036	1137	1232	...	1320	1338	1339	...	1425	...	1537	1555	...	...	1738
119	**St Quentin** **255** a.	0622	0645	0718	0757	0758	0857	...	0957	...	1057	1157	1246	...	...	1358	1358	...	...	...	1557	1614	...	...	1758
	Paris Nord **255** a.	0741	0826	...	...	...	...	...	...	...	...	...	1426	...	...	...	...	...	...	...	...	...	...	...	...

	Ⓐ J	Ⓐ	†	Ⓐ	Ⓑ	⑥	⑥ J	Ⓐ	Ⓐ	⑥	Ⓐ u
Lille Flandres **256** d.	1636	1706	1706	1732	1806	*1802*	*1802*	1836	1906	1935	2006
Douai **256** a.	1709	1738	1738	1755	1838	*1820*	*1820*	1908	1938	2017	2038
Douai d.	1711	1740	1740	1757	1840	1840	1840	1911	1940	2019	2040
Cambrai Ville a.	1743	1814	1816	1834	1913	1913	1913	1944	2013	2052	2113
Cambrai Ville d.	...	1816	1817	...	1915	...	1915	...	2015	2054	2115
Caudry d.	...	1828	1829	...	1929	...	1928	...	2029	2109	2128
Busigny **255** d.	...	1839	1838	...	1938	...	1937	...	2039	2119	2138
St Quentin **255** a.	...	1857	1857	...	1958	...	1957	...	2058	...	2158
Paris Nord **255** a.	...	...	...	...	...	...	...	...	...	...	...

	Ⓐ J	Ⓐ	Ⓐ	⚒	Ⓐ	Ⓐ	⑥	Ⓐ	⚒	†
Paris Nord **255** d.	...	...	...	...	...	...	...	...	...	...
St Quentin **255** d.	...	0505	...	0604	...	0704	...	...	0804	...
Busigny **255** d.	...	0525	...	0624	...	0724	0725z	...	0824	...
Caudry d.	...	0536	...	0635	...	0735	0735z	...	0835	...
Cambrai Ville a.	...	0547	...	0646	...	0746	0747z	...	0846	...
Cambrai Ville d.	0506	0549	0617	0648	0717	0748	0749	0817	0848	0848
Douai a.	0535	0620	0649	0720	0749	0820	0820	0850	0920	0920
Douai **256** d.	*0541*	0622	0652	0722	0752	0822	0822	...	0922	0922
Lille Flandres **256** a.	*0621*	0655	0725	0755	0825	0855	0855	...	0955	0955

	Ⓐ	⑥	Ⓐ	Ⓐ	⑥	†	Ⓐ	⑥	†	Ⓐ J	Ⓐ J	Ⓐ	⑥	Ⓒ	Ⓐ	†		⑥ Pv	Ⓐ	Ⓐ	⑥	†	Ⓐ P	† Pv	
Paris Nord **255** d.	...	...	...	...	...	...	...	...	...	...	...	...	...	...	...	...	...	1634	...	...	...	...	1819	1834	...
St Quentin **255** d.	0842	1004	...	1203	1205	1205	...	1406	...	1442	...	1605	1605	...	...	1705	1807r	1815	1847	1906	...	1905	1934	2014	2042
Busigny **255** d.	0902	1024	...	1224	1225	1225	1338	1426	1435	1501	...	1626	1626	...	...	1726	1824	1833	1906	1925	...	1925	1951	2033	2101
Caudry d.	0912	1035	...	1235	1236	1236	1352	1437	1445	1512	...	1635	1635	...	...	1738	1835	1844	1916	1935	...	1936	2002	2044	2113
Cambrai Ville a.	0924	1046	...	1246	1247	1247	1408	1448	1457	1524	...	1646	1646	...	...	1750	1846	1856	1927	1946	...	1947	2015	2056	2124
Cambrai Ville d.	...	1048	1148	1248	1249	1249	1418	1449	1459	...	1548	1648	1648	1717	1748	1752	1848	...	...	1948	1948	1949	...	...	...
Douai a.	...	1120	1220	1320	1320	1320	1450	1521	1529	...	1619	1720	1720	1749	1820	1820	1920	...	...	2020	2020	2020	...	...	...
Douai **256** d.	...	1122	1222	1322	*1334*	1323	...	1522	*1539*	...	*1639*	1722	*1739*	1752	1822	1822	1922	...	...	2022	2022	*2039*	...	...	...
Lille Flandres **256** a.	...	1155	1255	1355	*1358*	1355	...	1556	*1559*	...	*1700*	1755	*1758*	1831	1855	1855	1955	...	...	2055	2055	*2059*	...	...	...

J – Not July 6 - Aug. 24.
P – For train numbers see Table **255**.
r – 1804 on †.
u – Subject to alteration Cambrai - St Quentin Sept. 9 - Oct. 4.
v – Not St Quentin - Paris and v.v. Sept. 7, 8, 14, 15, 28, 29, Oct. 5, 6, 26, Nov. 9, 10.
z – Not July 6 - Aug. 24.

AMIENS - ST QUENTIN 258

km		Ⓐ	⚒	†	⚒		Ⓐ	Ⓐ	Ⓐ J	Ⓒ	Ⓐ	
0	**Amiens** d.	0649	0749	1049	1249	...	1649	1749	1847	1847	1949	...
59	Ham (Somme) d.	0723	0824	1129	1325	...	1726	1826	1926	1926	2026	...
76	**St Quentin** a.	0745	0845	1150	1345	...	1745	1848	1945	1945	2045	...

	Ⓐ	⚒	Ⓐ	†		⚒ u		Ⓐ J	⚒	†	
St Quentin d.	0616	0716	0816	0908	...	1216	...	1716	1816	2023	...
Ham (Somme) d.	0638	0737	0838	0933	...	1238	...	1738	1838	2046	...
Amiens a.	0711	0812	0912	1012	...	1312	...	1812	1912	2120	...

J – Not July 8 - Aug. 23. **u** – Subject to alteration Nov. 25 - Dec. 6. *Subject to alteration on Nov. 2, 3, 9, 10, Dec. 7, 8.*

CALAIS - DUNKERQUE - DE PANNE 259

No Sunday service

km		Ⓐ	Ⓐ	⑥ t	Ⓐ	Ⓐ J	⑥ t	Ⓐ J	Ⓐ K	Ⓐ J	Ⓐ	Ⓐ
0	Calais Ville d.	0541	0643	0712	0741	0812	1241	1300	1320	1612	1741	1841
23	Gravelines d.	0601	0700	0732	0801	0831	1301	1321	1341	1631	1801	1901
46	Dunkerque a.	0624	0719	0754	0824	0850	1330	1343	1403	1650	1826	1926

	⚒ t	Ⓐ J	Ⓐ	Ⓐ	⑥ J	⑥ t	Ⓐ J	Ⓐ	Ⓐ	Ⓐ	
Dunkerque d.	0635	0710	0810	1219	1236	1344	1709	1736	1836	1936	...
Gravelines d.	0659	0731	0831	1244	1302	1409	1729	1800	1902	2000	...
Calais Ville a.	0719	0747	0847	1305	1320	1429	1746	1819	1921	2019	...

🚌 **DUNKERQUE - LEFFRINCKOUCKE - ADINKERKE (DE PANNE STATION)** Operator: DK'BUS www.dkbus.com

Route C2 runs Dunkerque Gare - Leffrinckoucke (Fort Des Dunes). Every 10 mins (every 30 mins on Sundays). Journey 20 minutes.

Route 20 runs Leffrinckoucke (Fort Des Dunes) - Bray Dunes - Gare d'Adinkerke - De Panne. Every 30 mins (hourly on Sundays). Journey 30 minutes. Connects at De Panne station with coastal tram service (Table **406**).

J – Not July 6 - Aug. 24. **K** – July 8 - Aug. 23. **t** – Not Aug. 17.

260 PARIS - AMIENS

Trains numbered **2xxx** continue to / from Boulogne (Table **261**)

km		12001	12003	2005			12007					2011	2013			12015			2017	2017	12019	2021	12023		2025	
		Ⓐ	⚒	Ⓐ	⑦K	⑥L	Ⓑ	⑥	†	Ⓐ	⑥	Ⓒ	⚒	†	⚒	⚒	†	⑥	Ⓐ	†	Ⓐ	⑥	Ⓐ	⑥	Ⓐ	Ⓐ
0	**Paris** Nord d.	0604	0704	0731	0748	0759	0804	0807	0907	0907	0910	0931	1031	1101	1107	1149	1204	1307	1331	1331	1404	1431	1604	1604	1631	1704
51	Creil d.	0631	0731	0758	0818	0827	0831	0841	0941	0941	0942	|	|	1134	1140	1219	1231	1340	|	|	1431	|	|	1631	1658	1731
66	Clermont-de-l'Oise d.	0642	0742	|	0829	0841	0842	0856	0957	0957	0956	|	|	1149	1157	|	1242	1355	|	|	1442	|	1642	1642	|	1741
81	St Just en Chaussée d.	0653	0753	|	0840	0853	0853	0914	1014	1007	1013	|	|	1200	1207	|	1253	1408	|	|	1453	|	1653	1653	|	1752
126	Longueau d.	0716	0816	0835	|	|	0916	0945	1047	1038	1042	1033	1133	1230	...	1257	1316	1438	1433	1444	1516	1533	1717	1717	1735	1816
131	**Amiens** a.	0722	0822	0840	0910	0930	0922	0950	1052	1044	1047	1037	1138	1235	...	1302	1322	1443	1438	1449	1522	1538	1723	1724	1740	1822

		12027	2027		12029	12031				2035	12037	12039		
	Ⓒ	Ⓐ	Ⓒ	⚒	†	Ⓐ	Ⓐ			⚒	†		u	
Paris Nord d.	1710	1731	1731	1804	1804	1831	1904	1907	1931	2004	2031	2107	2228	
Creil d.	1741	|	|	1831	1830	|	1931	1940	|	2031	|	2141	2303	
Clermont-de-l'Oise d.	1755	|	|	1841	1842	|	1941	1956	|	2043	|	2157	2313	
St Just en Chaussée d.	1815	|	|	1852	1853	|	1952	2014	|	2054	|	2206	2322	
Longueau d.	1846	1833	1833	1915	1920	1933	2015	2045	2033	2117	2133	2238	2345	
Amiens a.	1852	1838	1838	1922	1926	1938	2022	2051	2038	2123	2138	2243	2351	

			12000			12002			12006
	Ⓐ	⚒	Ⓐ	Ⓐ	Ⓒ	Ⓐ	⚒	Ⓐ	Ⓐ
Amiens d.	0414	0517	0538	0606	0613	0621	0638	0706	0721
Longueau d.	0420	0523	0545	0612	0619	0628	0645	0712	0728
St Just en Chaussée d.	0454	0553	0610	0640	0648	|	0710	0742	|
Clermont-de-l'Oise d.	0505	0603	0620	0700	0704	|	0720	0801	|
Creil d.	0520	0620	0631	0722	0720	|	0731	0819	|
Paris Nord a.	0553	0653	0656	0754	0753	0729	0758	0853	0829

		2008	12010			12012	2014	12016	12018	12020	2022			12024		2026	12028	2030	12032	2034					2036	
		⚒	Ⓑ	⑥	†	⑥		Ⓐ	Ⓐ	⑥	Ⓐ	†	†	Ⓐ	Ⓒ			Ⓑ	Ⓐ	Ⓒ	Ⓒ	⑥L	⑦K	Ⓑ	†	Ⓐ
Amiens d.	0738	0823	0838	0910	0913	1034	1123	1221	1236	1321	1423	...	1538	1538	1606	1623	1737	1823	1838	1922	1936	2012	2029	2038	2123	2156
Longueau d.	0746	0830	0845	0916	0919	1041	1130	1228	1245	1328	1430	...	1545	1545	1612	1630	1745	1830	1845	1930	1945	|	|	2044	2130	2203
St Just en Chaussée d.	0810	|	0910	0948	0949	1104	|	|	1310	|	|	1450	1608	1610	1641	|	1810	|	1910	|	2008	2049	2057	2110	|	2228
Clermont-de-l'Oise d.	0820	|	0920	0959	1000	1115	|	|	1320	|	|	1502	1619	1620	1701	|	1820	|	1920	|	2020	2100	2107	2120	|	2239
Creil d.	0831	|	0931	1020	1021	1126	|	|	1331	|	|	1518	1631	1631	1720	|	1831	|	1931	|	2031	2113	2119	2131	|	2249
Paris Nord a.	0856	0929	0956	1053	1053	1152	1229	1329	1356	1429	1529	1553	1656	1656	1753	1729	1856	1929	1956	2029	2056	2144	2144	2156	2229	2314

K – ⑦ July 7 - Aug. 25 (also Aug. 15). *TER* train Paris - Boulogne and v.v.
L – ⑥ July 6 - Aug. 24. *TER* train Paris - Boulogne and v.v.
u – Runs 3-5 minutes later on Ⓐ.

261 AMIENS - BOULOGNE - CALAIS

For *TGV* service Paris - Étaples / Boulogne / Calais see Table **265**. Faster services Paris - Calais are available by changing at Lille (Tables **250** / **266**) or Hazebrouck (Tables **264** / **266**).

km												2005									2011			2013	
		Ⓐ	⑥	Ⓐu	⚒	Ⓐ	†	⚒	⚒	Ⓐ	⑥	Ⓐ	⑦K	†	⑦P	⑥L	⑥Q	†	⑥	Ⓐ	Ⓒ	†	⑥	⚒	Ⓐ
	Paris Nord **260** d.	...	...	...	...	...	...	...	...	...	...	0731	0748	...	...	0759	...	...	...	...	0931	...	...	1031	...
0	**Amiens** d.	...	...	...	...	0626	...	0713	...	...	0846	0853	0912	...	0930	0932	0948	0947	...	...	1050	...	...	1151	...
45	Abbeville d.	...	...	...	...	0659	...	0756	...	...	0919	0921	0938	...	0955	0957	1013	1019	...	...	1118	...	...	1218	...
58	Noyelles sur Mer d.	...	...	...	...	0708	...	0805	...	...	0928	|	0948	...	1006	1007	1023	1028	...	...	1130	...	...	1231	...
85	Rang du Fliers ⊙ d.	...	...	0604	...	0726	...	0823	...	...	0946	0946	1007	...	1025	1027	1044	1047	...	...	1155	...	...	1255	...
96	Étaples-Le Touquet ‡ d.	...	...	0615	0700	0734	...	0832	...	...	0955	0957	1021	...	1034	1040	1052	1056	1153	...	1206	...	...	1306	1313
123	**Boulogne** Ville ‡ a.	...	...	0642	0726	0758	...	0849	...	...	1010	1016	1036	...	1049	1055	1107	1110	1219	...	1226	...	...	1326	1331
123	**Boulogne** Ville d.	0546	0627	0643	0727	0805	0811	0850	0911	0947	1012	...	...	1048	...	...	...	1112	1222	1227	...	1248	1311	...	1333
130	Wimille-Wimereux d.	0554	0635	0652	0735	0812	0820	0857	0920	0955	1021	...	...	1057	...	...	...	1120	1230	1235	...	1255	1320	...	1340
140	Marquise-Rinxent d.	0602	0643	0700	0742	0820	0829	0905	0928	1003	1029	...	...	1105	...	...	...	1129	1237	1243	...	1302	1329	...	1349
157	Calais Fréthun **265** d.	0613	0702	0713	0800	0831	0841	0915	0941	1014	1041	...	...	1117	...	...	...	1141	1254	1301	...	1313	1341	...	1400
165	**Calais** Ville **265** a.	0622	0710	0722	0810	0840	0850	0924	0950	1022	1050	...	...	1126	...	...	...	1150	1304	1310	...	1322	1350	...	1408

							2017		2017		2021									2025		2027			2035
	†	⑥	Ⓐ	⑥	Ⓐ	⑥	Ⓐ	†	†	⑥	⑥	Ⓒ	Ⓐ	Ⓐ	Ⓐ	⑥	†	⑥	Ⓐ	Ⓐ	Ⓐ	Ⓒ	⑥	Ⓑd	
Paris Nord **260** d.	...	...	...	...	...	...	1331	...	1331	...	1431	...	...	...	...	...	...	...	...	1631	...	1731	...	...	1931
Amiens d.	...	...	1347	...	...	1447	1451	...	1502	...	1551	...	...	...	1647	...	...	1750	...	1753	1847	1851	...	1947	2051
Abbeville d.	...	...	1419	...	...	1519	1518	...	1529	...	1618	...	...	...	1719	...	...	1822	...	1820	1919	1918	...	2019	2118
Noyelles sur Mer d.	...	...	1429	...	...	1528	|	...	1542	...	|	...	...	...	1729	...	...	1831	...	1832	1928	1931	...	2028	2131
Rang du Fliers ⊙ d.	...	*1402*	1446	...	...	1546	1544	...	1606	...	1644	...	...	1718	1748	...	...	1850	...	1856	1947	1955	...	2047	2155
Étaples-Le Touquet ‡ d.	...	*1411*	1454	1521	...	1553	1555	1615	1621	1630	1655	...	1700	1727	1756	1755	1820	1859	1835	1907	1956	2006	...	2056	2206
Boulogne Ville ‡ a.	...	*1427*	...	1541	...	...	1614	1633	1640	1648	1714	...	1726	1744	1810	1820	1845	1913	1901	1927	2011	2025	...	2111	2226
Boulogne Ville d.	1448	1456	...	1543	1611	...	...	1634	...	1650	...	1723	1727	1746	1812	1821	1846	1915	1922	...	2013	...	2036	2120z	...
Wimille-Wimereux d.	1455	1504	...	1551	1620	...	...	|	...	1658	...	1731	1735	1754	1819	1829	1854	1924	1930	...	2021	...	2044	2129	...
Marquise-Rinxent d.	1502	1511	...	1559	1629	...	...	1644	...	1706	...	1739	1743	1802	1827	1836	1902	1932	1938	...	2029	...	2051	2137	...
Calais Fréthun **265** d.	1512	1523	...	1610	1641	...	...	1655	...	1717	...	1749	1801	1813	1840	1847	1914	1944	1957	...	2041	...	2102	2149	...
Calais Ville **265** a.	1522	1531	...	1619	1650	...	...	1703	...	1724	...	1757	1810	1823	1850	1856	1921	1953	2005	...	2050	...	2110	2158	...

			2008							2014		2014						2022							2026
	Ⓐ	Ⓐ	⚒	⚒	⑥	Ⓐ	Ⓐ	Ⓐ	Ⓒ	†	⑥	⚒	Ⓐd	Ⓐ	⑥	†	Ⓐ	Ⓐ	⑥	⑥	Ⓐ	⑥	†	⚒	Ⓐ
Calais Ville **265** d.	...	0509	...	0609	0648	0659	0729	0809	0809	...	0901	...	0929	1009	1106	1106	1145	...	1148	1209	1216	1309	1309	1335	...
Calais Fréthun **265** d.	...	0519	...	0620	0658	0710	0738	0818	0821	...	0911	...	0940	1022	1116	1116	1154	...	1157	1220	1225	1318	1322	1343	...
Marquise-Rinxent d.	...	0531	...	0631	0715	0723	0757	0830	0832	...	0921	...	0952	1033	1129	1130	1212	...	1215	1232	1244	1331	1334	1354	...
Wimille-Wimereux d.	...	0540	...	0640	0724	0733	0805	0838	0840	...	0930	...	1001	1042	1139	1140	1221	...	1224	1240	1252	1340	1342	1403	...
Boulogne Ville a.	...	0547	...	0648	0732	0740	0812	0846	0847	...	0938	...	1009	1050	1148	1147	1228	...	1232	1248	1259	1348	1350	1411	...
Boulogne Ville ‡ d.	0449	0549	0633	...	...	0742	0813	...	0849	0933	...	0945	1040	...	*1220*	1148	1230	1240	1233	1250	1300	...	...	...	1433
Étaples-Le Touquet ‡ d.	0506	0606	0653	...	...	0757	0839	...	0905	0953	...	1006	1101	...	*1239*	1208	1255	1300	1259	1306	1316	...	...	...	1453
Rang du Fliers ⊙ d.	0515	0615	0704	...	...	0806	...	...	0914	1004	...	1017	1111	...	*1247*	...	...	1311	...	1315	1324	...	...	...	1504
Noyelles sur Mer d.	0532	0632	0728	...	...	0827	...	...	0931	1028	...	|	1128	...	...	...	...	|	...	1332	...	...	...	...	1528
Abbeville d.	0542	0641	0741	...	...	0837	...	...	0940	1041	...	1043	1138	...	...	...	...	1343	...	1342	...	...	...	...	1541
Amiens a.	0614	0713	0809	...	...	0913	...	...	1013	1109	...	1109	1213	...	...	...	...	1409	...	1413	...	...	...	...	1609
Paris Nord **260** a.	...	...	0929	...	...	...	...	...	...	1229	...	1229	...	...	...	...	...	1529	...	...	...	...	...	...	1729

	2026				2030		2030		2034											2036					
	Ⓒ	Ⓐ	†	⚒	†	Ⓐ	Ⓐ	⑥	Ⓒ	Ⓐ	Ⓐ	†	ⒸN	Ⓐ	⑥L	†	⑥	⑦K	Ⓐ	†	Ⓐ	†	⑥	Ⓐ	Ⓒ
Calais Ville **265** d.	...	1438	1440	1509	...	1558	...	1608	...	1648	1709	1712	...	1736	...	1807	1809	...	1830	...	1930	2009	2009	2038	2208
Calais Fréthun **265** d.	...	1447	1450	1521	...	1608	...	1618	...	1657	1719	1720	...	1745	...	1817	1819	...	1841	...	1940	2019	2019	2048	2218
Marquise-Rinxent d.	...	1458	1504	1532	...	1618	...	1635	...	1716	1729	1731	...	1803	...	1830	1831	...	1852	...	1953	2031	2031	2059	2231
Wimille-Wimereux d.	...	1507	1514	1540	...	1627	...	1644	...	1724	1739	1739	...	1812	...	1839	1840	...	1901	...	2002	2040	2041	2107	2240
Boulogne Ville a.	...	1515	1522	1548	...	1634	...	1651	...	1732	1746	1746	...	1819	...	1847	1848	...	1908	...	2010	2048	2048	2115	2248
Boulogne Ville ‡ d.	1445	*1527*	1523	1550	1633	1636	1645	1652	1733	1733	1748	1747	1802	1820	1845	...	1903	1905r	1909	1933	...	...	...	2116	...
Étaples-Le Touquet ‡ d.	1506	*1554*	1545	1606	1653	1656	1706	1715	1754	1758	1804	1803	1819	1845	1902	...	1919	1922	1927	1953	...	...	...	2134	...
Rang du Fliers ⊙ d.	1517	...	...	1615	1704	1704	1717	...	1805	...	1813	...	1828	1852	1911	...	1928	1931	...	2004	...	...	...	2142	...
Noyelles sur Mer d.	|	...	...	1632	1728	...	|	...	1829	...	1831	...	1851	...	1934	...	1945	1954	...	2028	...	...	...	...	...
Abbeville d.	1543	...	...	1642	1741	...	1742	...	1842	...	1841	...	1903	...	1945	...	1955	2005	...	2041	...	...	...	...	...
Amiens a.	1609	...	...	1713	1809	...	1809	...	1908	...	1913	...	1927	...	2010	...	2026	2027	...	2109	...	...	...	...	...
Paris Nord **260** a.	1729	...	...	...	1929	...	1929	...	2029	...	...	...	...	...	2144	...	...	2144	...	2229	...	...	...	...	...

ADDITIONAL LOCAL TRAINS AMIENS - ABBEVILLE

ALSO:	Ⓐ	Ⓐ	Ⓐ	†	Ⓐ	⑥	Ⓐ		⚒	Ⓐ	Ⓑ	⚒	Ⓐ
Amiens d.	0646	0747	0812	0850	0946	1116	1247	1312	1612	1722	1812	1912	2012
Abbeville a.	0730	0820	0856	0922	1020	1159	1320	1356	1656	1807	1856	1956	2056

	Ⓐ	⚒	Ⓐ	⚒	⚒	⑥	Ⓑ	⚒	Ⓐ	Ⓑ	Ⓐ
Abbeville d.	0604	0647	0704	0726	0804	1221	1304	1604	1704	1751	1947
Amiens a.	0649	0729	0749	0800	0849	1306	1349	1649	1749	1831	2029

K – ⑦ July 7 - Aug. 25 (also Aug. 15). *TER* train.
L – ⑥ July 6 - Aug. 24. *TER* train.
N – ⑥⑦ July 6 - Aug. 11. To Laon (Table **252**).
P – ⑦ July 7 - Aug. 11. From Laon (Table **252**).
Q – ⑥ July 6 - Aug. 10. From Laon (Table **252**).

d – Change trains at Boulogne.
r – 1910 on ⑦ July 7 - Aug. 4.
u – Additional journey on Ⓐ: Boulogne d. 0711 - Calais Ville a. 0752.
z – 2124 on Ⓐ.

⊙ – Full name: Rang du Fliers-Verton-Berck.
‡ – See also Table **263**.

From Sept. 9 certain Paris - Boulogne and v.v. trains arrive earlier into Boulogne and depart later for Paris.

🚌 ABBEVILLE - LE TRÉPORT 261a

km		Ⓐ	Ⓐ	Ⓐ	Ⓐ	Ⓐ	Ⓐ	Ⓐ	⑤		⑥	⑥n	⑥	⑥	⑥	⑥	⑥		†n	†	†	†
0	Abbeville d.	0641	0830	1228	1406	1529	1730	1930	2028	...	0805	1126	1228	1406	1529	1630	1930	...	1030	1128	1537	1930
37	Le Tréport a.	0758	0947	1345	1523	1646	1847	2047	2145	...	0922	1211	1345	1523	1646	1747	2047	...	1115	1245	1654	2047

🚌	①	Ⓐ	Ⓐ	Ⓐ	Ⓐ	Ⓐ	Ⓐ			⑥	⑥	⑥	⑥	⑥	⑥			†	†	†n	†	
Le Tréport d.	0439	0558	0709	0914	1214	1614	1715	...	...	0558	0813	0914	1220	1715	1828	...	...	0914	1614	1646	1713	...
Abbeville a.	0532	0715	0826	1031	1331	1731	1832	...	...	0715	0930	1031	1337	1832	1945	...	...	1031	1731	1731	1830	...

n – Non-stop journey.

☛ All journeys are currently by 🚌 (rail tickets and passes valid).

LILLE - VALENCIENNES - MAUBEUGE and CHARLEVILLE MÉZIÈRES 262

km		Ⓐ	⑥	Ⓐ	⑥	Ⓐu	⑥J	Ⓐu	Ⓒ	†	ⒶJu	⑥J	Ⓐ	Ⓐu	⑥	†	Ⓐu	⚒		Ⓐ	Ⓒ	Ⓐ	Ⓐ	Ⓐ	Ⓐ
0	**Lille** Flandres ▷ d.	0535	*0536*	0705	0735	0805	0835	0905	0935	*1135*	1201	1201	1205	1235	1305	1335	1335	1435	...	1605	1635	1701	1705	1801	1805
48	Valenciennes ▷ d.	0621	*0620*	0750	0823	0843	0921	0944	1023	*1223*	1231	1232	1249	1320	1349	1418	1420	1520	...	1643	1722	1732	1745	1832	1843
82	Aulnoye Aymeries a.	0649	*0648*	0817	0850	0909	0949	1009	1050	*1250*	1253	1253	1315	1349	1415	1445	1449	1549	...	1709	1749	1753	1811	1853	1909
82	Aulnoye Aymeries d.	0652	0711	0819	0853	0911	0952	1011	1053	1258	1255	1255	1317	1355	1417	1454	1455	1555	...	1711	1752	1755	1813	1855	1911
94	**Maubeuge** d.	0703	0725	0832	0905	0923	1004	1024	1105	1312	1304	1305	1332	1406	1433	1505	1506	1606	...	1725	1804	1805	1826	1905	1924
104	Jeumont a.	0710	0735	0839	0912	0931	1012	1031	1112	1320	...	1312	1342	1413	1442	1512	1513	1613	...	1735	1812	1812	1838	1912	1931

	†	ⒶJ	Ⓐ	⑥	Ⓐ			Ⓐv		
Lille Flandres ▷ d.	*1835*	1901	1905	...	1935	...	2035	2135	...	...
Valenciennes ▷ d.	*1922*	1931	1943	...	2020	...	2120	2220	...	...
Aulnoye Aymeries a.	*1949*	1953	2009	...	2049	...	2149	2249	...	...
Aulnoye Aymeries d.	1958	1955	2011	2017	2055	...	2155	2255	...	...
Maubeuge d.	2013	2005	2024	2033	2106	...	2206	2306	...	...
Jeumont a.	2024	2012	2035	2042	2113	...	2213	2313	...	...

	Ⓐ	ⒶJ	⑥	Ⓐ	Ⓐ	†	⚒	Ⓐ	⚒	
Jeumont d.	0527	0549	0618	0623	0648	0718	0723	0749	0827	...
Maubeuge d.	0536	0558	0630	0637	0656	0730	0737	0758	0836	...
Aulnoye Aymeries a.	0548	0606	0642	0648	0704	0742	0748	0806	0848	...
Aulnoye Aymeries d.	0550	0608	0644	0650	0706	0744	0750	0808	0850	...
Valenciennes ▷ d.	0618	0631	0712	0718	0728	0812	0818	0831	0917	...
Lille Flandres ▷ a.	0655	0659	0755	0755	0759	0855	0855	0859	0955	...

	Ⓑ	⑥	Ⓐu	Ⓐu	⑥J	†	Ⓐu	⑥	†	Ⓐr	Ⓐ	Ⓐu	Ⓒ	Ⓐ		Ⓐ	Ⓒ	Ⓐ	†	Ⓐ	†	ⒶK	⑥J	ⒶJ	
Jeumont d.	0849	0922	0949	1049	1122	1122	1149	1218	1418	1410	...	1549	1549	1627	...	1723	1748	1849	1914	1949	2048	2104	2138	2149	...
Maubeuge d.	0857	0931	0957	1057	1131	1131	1157	1231	1426	1425	...	1557	1557	1637	...	1737	1756	1857	1927	1957	2056	2112	2147	2157	...
Aulnoye Aymeries a.	0907	0942	1009	1107	1142	1142	1207	1243	1442	1458	...	1607	1607	1648	...	1748	1807	1907	1941	2007	2107	2122	2159	2207	...
Aulnoye Aymeries d.	0911	0944	1011	1111	1144	1144	1211	1245	1444	...	1511	1611	1611	1650	...	1750	1809	1911	1943	2011	*2125*	2126	*2213*	2211	...
Valenciennes ▷ d.	0941	1011	1041	1141	1211	1211	1241	1313	1513	...	1541	1641	1641	1718	...	1818	1843	1941	2010	2041	*2156*	2155	*2242*	2241	...
Lille Flandres ▷ a.	1025	1055	1125	1225	1255	1255	1325	1355	1555	...	1625	1725	1725	1755	...	1855	1925	2025	2055	2125	*2239*	2241	*2325*	2330	...

LILLE - VALENCIENNES - HIRSON - CHARLEVILLE

km		Ⓐ	⑥	ⒶL	⑥	ⒶL	†	⑥J	†	⑥K	⑥J	ⒶL	†	Ⓐ	⑥	Ⓐ	†	⑥	Ⓐ	Ⓐ	Ⓐ	ⒶJ	Ⓒ	Ⓐ	z
0	**Lille** Flandres ▷ d.	*0536*	0635	0635	*0735*	0935	*0935*	*0935*	1135	*1205*	1235	*1235*	*1335*	*1435*	*1435*	1535	*1635*	*1635*	*1701*	1731	*1801*	1831	1835	*1935*	*2035*
48	Valenciennes ▷ d.	*0620*	0723	0720	*0823*	1020	*1023*	*1023*	1223	*1249*	1321	*1320*	*1418*	*1520*	*1520*	1620	*1722*	*1722*	*1732*	1802	*1832*	1902	1922	*2020*	*2120*
82	Aulnoye Aymeries a.	*0648*	0750	0749	*0850*	1048	*1050*	*1050*	1250	*1315*	1348	*1349*	*1445*	*1549*	*1549*	1649	*1749*	*1749*	*1753*	|	*1853*	|	1949	*2049*	*2149*
82	Aulnoye Aymeries d.	0701	0801	0801	0903	1058	1101	1101	1302	1327	1400	1401	1452	1601	1601	1701	1801	1801	1801	|	1901	|	2001	2101	2201
94	Avesnes d.	0717	0818	0817	0919	1109	1112	1117	1313	1343	1410	1412	1503	1612	1618	1713	1811	1818	1813	1827	1916	1928	2012	2112	2212
123	Hirson a.	0746	0844	0846	0947	1133	1134	1145	1336	1409	1434	1438	1527	1638	1645	1738	1833	1848	1838	1846	1946	1950	2035	2138	2236
123	Hirson d.	...	0845	*0905*r	...	*1138*r	1135	...	...	*1439*r	*1439*r	...	...	*1658*r	...	...	1834	...	...	1847	*1955*r	*1955*r	*2040*r	...	...
184	**Charleville-Mézières** a.	...	0925	*1005*r	...	*1238*r	1215	...	...	*1550*r	*1550*r	...	...	*1758*r	...	...	1915	...	...	1928	*2055*r	*2055*r	*2140*r	...	...

	Ⓐ	Ⓐ	⚒	Ⓐ	†	ⒶL	⑥	†J	ⒶL	⑥K	⑥J	ⒶL	†	†	ⒶL	ⒶL	Ⓐ	†	⑥J	Ⓐ	Ⓐ	†	Ⓐ	†	⑥J
Charleville-Mézières d.	...	0625	...	...	...	*0755*r	*0917*r	...	*1015*r	1122	1140	...	...	1320	...	...	...	...	...	*1550*r	...	*1751*r	*1815*r	1940	*1935*r
Hirson a.	...	0712	...	...	...	*0855*r	*1017*r	...	*1115*r	1158	1225	...	...	1356	...	...	...	...	...	*1650*r	...	*1851*r	*1912*r	2025	*2035*r
Hirson d.	0525	0713	0716	0816	0825	0925	1027	1050	1125	1159	1227	1216	1227	1358	1425	1525	1616	1718	1725	1716	1816	1901	1925	2027	2127
Avesnes d.	0550	0734	0741	0844	0851	0950	1050	1116	1150	1225	1250	1243	1250	1424	1450	1550	1644	1744	1751	1745	1844	1925	1950	2050	2150
Aulnoye Aymeries a.	0600	|	0758	0900	0900	1000	1059	1125	1200	1235	1259	1300	1259	1435	1500	1600	1659	1759	1800	1800	1900	1935	2000	2059	2159
Aulnoye Aymeries d.	0611	|	*0808*	*0911*	*0911*	*1011*	1113	*1144*	*1211*	*1245*	1313	1311	1313	*1444*	*1511*	*1611*	1711	*1809*	*1809*	1811	*1911*	*1943*	*2011*	2125	2213
Valenciennes ▷ d.	0639	0759	*0831*	*0941*	*0941*	*1041*	1143	*1211*	*1241*	*1313*	1342	1341	1343	*1513*	*1541*	*1641*	1741	*1843*	*1843*	1841	*1941*	*2010*	*2041*	2156	2242
Lille Flandres ▷ a.	0725	0828	*0859*	*1025*	*1025*	*1125*	1225	*1255*	*1325*	*1355*	1425	1425	1425	*1555*	*1625*	*1725*	1825	*1925*	*1925*	1925	*2025*	*2055*	*2125*	2239	2325

ADDITIONAL TRAINS LILLE - VALENCIENNES

	Ⓐ	ⒶJ	Ⓐ	Ⓐ	Ⓒ	Ⓐ	Ⓐ	Ⓐ	⑥J	†	Ⓐ	⑥J	ⒶJ		Ⓐ	ⒶJ	Ⓐ	†	⑥		Ⓐ	ⒶJ	Ⓒ	Ⓐ	Ⓒ	ⒶJ	
Lille Flandres d.	0512	0812	0912	1012	1035	1112	1205	1212	1235	1235	1312	1335	1412	...	1612	1712	1735	1735	1740	...	1812	1912	1935	2012	2135	2230	...
Valenciennes a.	0558	0855	0955	1055	1125	1201	1243	1255	1325	1325	1355	1418	1455	...	1655	1756	1820	1819	1830	...	1855	1955	2025	2055	2225	2323	...

	⑥J	Ⓐ	Ⓐ	ⒶJ	Ⓐ	⑥	Ⓐ	ⒶJ	Ⓐ	Ⓐ	†	Ⓐ	⑥J	Ⓐ		⑥	Ⓐ	†		Ⓐ	Ⓒ	ⒶJ	Ⓐ	Ⓐ	⑥		
Valenciennes d.	0434	0440	0539	0605	0703	0740	0802	0905	1041	1105	1137	1203	1230	1303	...	1530	1603	1605	...	1703	1728	1802	1903	2004	2005	...	...
Lille Flandres a.	0526	0526	0625	0648	0749	0825	0848	0948	1125	1148	1227	1248	1321	1348	...	1621	1648	1656	...	1748	1821	1848	1948	2048	2057	...	...

J – Not July 6 - Aug. 24.
K – July 6 - Aug. 24.
L – Not June 10 - Aug. 9 (there are 🚌 connections Aulnoye - Hirson and v.v. June 10 - Aug. 9 with extended journey times).
r – By 🚌 (rail tickets and passes valid).
u – Subject to alteration on Ⓐ June 11 - Aug. 9 with partial 🚌 substitution.
v – By 🚌 Aulnoye - Jeumont (a. 2347) July 8 - Aug. 23.
z – By 🚌 Aulnoye - Hirson (a. 2314) July 8 - Aug. 23.
▷ – For additional trains see panel below main table.

Subject to alteration Aug. 26 - 30.
Additional trains or buses run Aulnoye - Hirson and v.v.

BOULOGNE - ÉTAPLES - ST POL - ARRAS 263

km		🚌	🚌	🚌	🚌	🚌	🚌	🚌	🚌	🚌		🚌	🚌	🚌	🚌		🚌	🚌	🚌	🚌	🚌	🚌	🚌	🚌	🚌
		⚒	ⒶJ	ⒶK	Ⓐ	⑥	Ⓐ	Ⓐ	†J	†K	Ⓐ	†	⑥	Ⓐ	†	Ⓐ	ⒶK	ⒶJ	⑥J	⑥K	†	⑥	†	Ⓐ	Ⓐ
0	**Boulogne** Ville 261 d.	0437	0530	0530	...	0612	...	...	0822	0822	...	1200	...	...	1452	...	...	...	1615	1615	...	1705	1711	...	...
27	Étaples Le Touquet 261 d.	0510	0602	0602	0625	0645	...	0816	0855	0855	...	1233	1310	1330	1525	...	1605	1605	1650	1650	1705	1738	1744	1806	1940
39	Montreuil d.	0530	0621	0621	0645	0707	...	0836	0915	0915	...	1255	1332	1351	1547	...	1627	1627	1710	1710	1727	1800	1806	1828	1958
60	Hesdin d.	0610	0700	0700	0724	0745	...	0916	0955	0955	...	1333	1410	1430	1625	...	1714	1714	1748	1748	1805	1838	1834	1906	2036
88	St Pol sur Ternoise a.	0640	0730	0730	0753	0815	...	0943	1023	1023	...	1400	1438	1500	1655	...	1744	1744	1816	1816	1835	1908	1914	1936	2107
88	St Pol sur Ternoise d.	*0653*r	*0748*r	*0745*r	0753	*0833*r	0840	*0956*r	*1033*r	*1038*r	1328	1400	1438	1500	*1704*r	1713	*1759*	*1825*	*1826*r	*1831*r	1835	*1919*r	*1922*r	*1942*r	...
127	**Arras** a.	*0742*r	*0830*r	*0905*r	0845	*0913*r	0953	*1031*r	*1108*r	*1137*r	1410	1443	1525	1545	*1743*r	1802	*1909*	*1901*	*1908*r	*1935*r	1915	*1954*r	*1953*r	*2021*r	...

	🚌	🚌	🚌	🚌	🚌	🚌	🚌	🚌	🚌	🚌	🚌	🚌	🚌	🚌	🚌	🚌	🚌	🚌	🚌	🚌	🚌	🚌	🚌	🚌	🚌
	Ⓐ	⑥	⑥	Ⓐ	Ⓐ	†	⑥	†K	†J	⑥	Ⓐ	Ⓐ	⑥K	⑥J	†	Ⓐ	†K	†J	⑥K	⑥J	Ⓐ	Ⓐ	Ⓒ	Ⓐ	⑥
Arras d.	0544	...	0732	0734	*0905*r	0925	0945	*1141*r	*1158*r	*1221*r	*1228*r	1324	*1246*r	*1328*r	1600	*1620*r	*1606*r	*1623*r	*1652*r	*1721*r	*1734*r	*1821*r	*1828*r	*1935*r	*2008*r
St Pol sur Ternoise a.	0627	...	0815	0820	*0946*r	1038	1029	*1300*r	*1240*r	*1303*r	*1311*r	1415	*1405*r	*1410*r	1642	*1703*r	*1649*r	*1654*r	*1755*r	*1757*r	*1821*r	*1906*r	*1909*r	*2023*r	*2043*r
St Pol sur Ternoise d.	0627	0645	0815	0820	0952	1038	1029	1315	1315	1315	1320	1415	1420	1420	1642	1713	1704	1704	1810	1810	1830	1920	1925	2035	2115
Hesdin d.	0713	0713	0843	0847	1016	1106	1058	1340	1340	1345	1344	1443	1448	1448	1706	1741	1732	1732	1837	1837	1856	1948	1950	2103	2143
Montreuil d.	0750	0750	0922	0924	1053	1145	1134	1418	1418	1418	1424	1522	1525	1525	1738	1816	1812	1812	1917	1917	1934	2024	2031	2140	2222
Étaples Le Touquet 261 d.	0810	0815	0945	0947	1115	1208	1158	1445	1445	1443	1447	1543	1547	1547	1801	1841	1834	1834	1940	1940	1956	2046	2052	2203	2245
Boulogne Ville 261 a.	0855	...	...	...	1155	1240	1230	1518	1518	1518	1524	...	1622	1622	1836	...	...	...	2012	2012	2032	2122	2128	2235	2317

ST POL - BÉTHUNE - LILLE

km		Ⓐ	Ⓐ	⚒	ⒶK	ⒶJ	⑥K	⑥J	†	Ⓐ	†	⑥	ⒶJ	Ⓐ	Ⓒ	ⒶJ	Ⓐ		Ⓐ	†	⑥	Ⓐ	⑥	†	Ⓐu
0	St Pol sur Ternoise d.	0500	0556	0656	*0732*u	0756	*0800*u	0826	...	*1003*u	1049	1056	*1101*u	*1130*u	...	...	1456	...	*1658*u	1712	1723	...	1923	1936	1942
32	Béthune a.	0552	0648	0748	*0835*u	0848	*0903*u	0917	...	*1106*u	1140	1150	*1204*u	*1233*u	...	...	1548	...	*1801*u	1803	1814	...	2010	2028	2045
32	Béthune ▷ d.	0608	0650	0750	0850	0850	0918	0918	0918	1123	1142	1152	1224	1253	1318	1321	1550	1718	1821	1805	1825	1946	2012	2030	...
74	**Lille** Flandres ▷ a.	0658	0725	0829	0928	0925	0953	0953	0958	1200	1221	1225	1314	1345	1358	1358	1625	1758	1858	1841	1902	2021	2047	2107	...

	Ⓐ	Ⓐ	Ⓐ	⑥	Ⓒ	Ⓐ	Ⓒ	†	Ⓐ	⑥	z	Ⓐ	ⒶJ	Ⓒ	Ⓐ	Ⓐ	Ⓒz	⑥K	Ⓐ	⑥J	⑥K	ⒶK	ⒶJ	Ⓐ	Ⓒ
Lille Flandres ▷ d.	0544	0636	0736	0802	0842	0836	1002	1129	1210	1235	1402	1526	1602	1602	1636	1736	1742	1742	1836	1920	1920	1915	1936	2044	2102
Béthune ▷ a.	0636	0710	0812	0844	0922	0910	1045	1213	1252	1312	1446	1602	1639	1646	1712	1812	1824	1842	1912	2013	2008	2007	2010	2141	2144
Béthune d.	*0656*u	*0730*u	*0832*u	...	0922	*0930*u	...	1213	1252	1312	...	1602	...	...	1712	1812	1824	1842	1912	2013	*2023*u	*2030*u	*2030*u	...	...
St Pol sur Ternoise a.	*0802*u	*0836*u	*0938*u	...	1015	*1036*u	...	1304	1344	1407	...	1654	...	...	1804	1904	1915	1934	2004	2104	*2129*u	*2136*u	*2136*u	...	...

J – Not July 6 - Aug. 25.
K – July 6 - Aug. 25.
r – By train.
u – By 🚌.
z – Not on ⑥ July 6 - Aug. 24.
▷ – Additional trains run Béthune - Lille and v.v.

Étaples - St Pol is by 🚌 due to track reconstruction

264 PARIS and LILLE - DUNKERQUE *High-speed trains*

VIA LILLE **For local trains Lille Flandres - Dunkerque see Table 266**

km		◇	TGV 7205	TGV 7511	◇	TGV 7533		◇	TGV 7567	TGV 7269*	
		Ⓐ	Ⓐ	Ⓐ	†	⚒		Ⓐ	Ⓐ		
			u	u					u		
	Paris Nord **250** d.	...	0646	0746	...	1146	...	...	1646	1746	...
0	**Lille** Europe ◧ d.	0712	0750	0850	1150	1250	...	1650	1751	1851	...
76	**Dunkerque** ◧ a.	0744	0823	0923	1222	1323	...	1723	1823	1923	...

	TGV 7214	TGV 7528	◇	TGV 7530	◇	TGV 7552	TGV 7552	TGV 7570	TGV 7288*	TGV 7298	
	Ⓐ	Ⓐ	Ⓐ	Ⓐ	†		Ⓐ	Ⓐ		†	
		Ku				M	K				
Dunkerque ◧ d.	0630	0722	0722	0757	1034	1232	1232	1627	1832	2132	...
Lille Europe ◧ a.	0703	0754	0754	0832	1104	1305	1305	1703	1905	2205	...
Paris Nord **250** a.	0814	0914	...	0944	...	1414	1444	1814	2014	2314	...

VIA BÉTHUNE **For local trains Arras - Béthune - Hazebrouck see Table 264a**

km		TGV 7351	TGV 7357	TGV 7363*	TGV 7369	TGV 7371	TGV 7373*	TGV 7381*	TGV 7385	TGV 7387	TGV 7389	TGV 7393
		⚒	Ⓒ	⚒		⑤		Ⓐ	Ⓐ	⑦	Ⓐ	
		⊡	⊙	d	b	g	n	K	w	E	J	F
0	**Paris** Nord **256** d.	0752	0952	1252	1452	1552	1652	1752	1837	1852	1922	1952
179	Arras **256** a.	0841	1041	1342	1541	1641	1741	1841	1926	1941	2012	2041
179	Arras d.	0850	1050	1350	1550	1647	1750	1850	1935	1950	2015	2050
199	Lens d.	0904	1105	1404	1604	1703	1804	1905	1950	2004	2029	2105
218	Béthune d.	0918	1119	1418	1619	1718	1819	1919	2004	2018	2043	2119
252	Hazebrouck a.	0938	1139	1438	1641	1738	1839	1940	2024	2039	2104	2139
292	**Dunkerque** a.	1004	1204	1504	...	1802	1904	...	2055	2105	...	2204

	TGV 7300	TGV 7302	TGV 7304	TGV 7310	TGV 7314*	TGV 7324*	TGV 7330*	TGV 7336	TGV 7344	TGV 7346
	Ⓐ	Ⓐ	Ⓐ	⑥					†	⑤⑦
	K	J		t		G	k			v
Dunkerque d.	0523	0556	...	0753	0953	1354	1554	...	...	1954
Hazebrouck d.	0549	0619	0653	0820	1020	1420	1620	1720	1919	2020
Béthune d.	0620	0642	0719	0843	1043	1443	1643	1743	1943	2043
Lens d.	0633	0655	0734	0856	1055	1455	1655	1756	1955	2056
Arras a.	0647	0709	0748	0910	1109	1509	1709	1809	2009	2109
Arras **256** d.	0656	0717	0756	0917	1117	1517	1717	1817	2017	2117
Paris Nord **256** a.	0747	0808	0847	1008	1208	1608	1808	1908	2108	2208

E – ⑦ to June 30 / from Aug. 25 (also June 10, Nov. 11; not June 9).
F – ⑥⑦ (also ⑤ to July 5 / from Sept. 6), also June 10, Aug. 15, Oct. 31, Nov. 11. Additional train **7395** runs one hour later on ⑤ (also Aug. 14, Oct. 31; not Nov. 1).
G – Not on Ⓐ July 29 - Aug. 23.
J – Not July 29 - Aug. 23.
K – July 29 - Aug. 23.
M – ⚒ to July 6 / from Aug. 26 (also ⑦ July 20 - Aug. 24).
b – Not on ①–④ July 29 - Aug. 22.

d – Not July 12, 19, 26.
g – Also Oct. 31; not Aug. 2 - 23, Nov. 1.
k – Not July 12, 19, 26, Aug. 3, 10, 17, 24.
n – Not Aug. 4, 11, 18, 25.
t – Also Nov. 1.
u – Not Aug. 16.
v – Also Nov. 11; not on ⑤ July 12 - Aug. 23, Nov. 1.
w – Runs 10 - 15 mins later (train **7387**) July 29 - Aug. 23.

TGV – Ⓡ, supplement payable. See note ◧.

◇ – TER à Grande Vitesse (TER-GV) via high-speed line (1, 2 class). See note ◧.
⊡ – Runs one hour later on ⑥ **t** (train **7355**).
⊙ – Runs one hour later on ⑥ **t** (train **7359**).
◧ – Between Lille and Dunkerque trains are classified *TER-GV*, supplement *Grande Vitesse* payable, €3 valid all day, Ⓡ not necessary.
* – A different train number applies on certain days.

264a ARRAS - BÉTHUNE - HAZEBROUCK *For TGV trains see Table 264*

km		⚒	ⒶJ	⚒	†	Ⓐ	⚒	Ⓒ	ⒶJ	Ⓐ	⑥	ⒶJ	Ⓐ	†	ⒶJ	†	⚒	ⒶJ	Ⓐ	Ⓐd	Ⓐ	Ⓒ	Ⓐ	Ⓐ	Ⓐ	Ⓒ	Ⓐ
0	**Arras** d.	0722	0804	0822	0856	0904	0923	1056	1204	1222	1256	1257	1323	1356	1456	1556	1604	1617	1651	1714	1722	1756	1757	1822	1915	1956	2000
20	Lens d.	0740	0818	0840	0912	0918	0942	1112	1218	1246	1313	1313	1342	1413	1513	1613	1618	1636	1707	1728	1745	1813	1813	1846	1933	2013	2015
39	Béthune d.	0759	0835	0859	0930	0935	1001	1129	1235	1305	1331	1335	1401	1431	1531	1631	1635	1655	1728	1743	1805	1830	1831	1906	1953	2031	2032
51	Lillers d.	0808	0844	0908	0939	0944	1009	1139	1244	1317	1340	1347	1410	1440	1540	1640	1644	1703	1740	|	1816	1839	1840	1918	2002	2040	2041
73	**Hazebrouck** a.	0826	0900	0925	0956	1000	1026	1156	1300	1336	1356	1406	1426	1456	1556	1656	1700	1719	1759	1803	1836	1856	1900	1936	2018	2056	2057

	Ⓐ	ⒶJd	⑥d	Ⓐ	⚒	Ⓐ	⑥Jd	†	ⒶJ	⑥	Ⓐ	⑥J	Ⓐ	L	Ⓐ	ⒶJ	L	Ⓐ	Ⓐ	Ⓒ	ⒶJ	Ⓐ	Ⓒ	Ⓐ	Ⓒ	ⒶJ	Ⓐ
Hazebrouck d.	0623	0700	0704	0734	0834	0934	0934	1004	1034	1134	1201	1234	1253	1434	1501	1604	1634	1653	1723	1734	1803	1823	1834	1901	1934	2001	2107
Lillers d.	0644	0720	0721	0750	0850	0950	0950	1022	1050	1150	1218	1253	1313	1450	1518	1621	1651	1713	1744	1750	1822	1846	1851	1918	1952	2018	2123
Béthune d.	0658	0732	0731	0801	0901	1001	1000	1031	1101	1200	1228	1304	1328	1500	1528	1631	1701	1728	1758	1800	1832	1858	1901	1927	2002	2028	2132
Lens d.	0718	0751	0749	0821	0921	1021	1022	1049	1121	1222	1245	1324	1348	1521	1545	1649	1721	1749	1816	1821	1850	1921	1922	1944	2022	2044	2149
Arras a.	0739	0807	0803	0838	0938	1038	1039	1103	1138	1239	1300	1339	1403	1539	1600	1703	1739	1804	1839	1839	1903	1939	1939	1956	2039	2058	2203

J – Not July 6 - Aug. 24.
L – Ⓒ (daily to July 7 / from Aug. 24).
d – To / from Dunkerque (Table **266**).

ADDITIONAL TRAINS Arras - Hazebrouck: 0604Ⓐ, 0622⚒, 0657Ⓐ, 1225⑥, 2056Ⓒ, 2104Ⓐ, 2156Ⓒ.
Hazebrouck - Arras: 0506Ⓐ, 0553Ⓐ **J**, 0604⑥, 0634⑥ **J**.

265 (PARIS) - LILLE - CALAIS / BOULOGNE *High-speed trains*

For Paris - Boulogne via Amiens see Table **261**. For local trains Lille - Calais see Table **266**. For local trains Calais - Boulogne - Rang du Fliers see Table **261**.

km		TGV 7505		TGV 7513	TGV 7515		🚌	TGV 7519	🚌	TGV 7223	TGV 7535			🚌	🚌	TGV 7559	TGV 7559		TGV 7264	TGV 7565			TGV 7569	
		Ⓐ	Ⓐ	Ⓐ	⑥	⚒	Ⓒ	⑦	†	⚒	⚒	⑥	Ⓐ	⑥	†	Ⓐ	⑦	†	Ⓐ	⑥	Ⓐ	⑥	Ⓐ	Ⓐ
					t	u	§	e⊕		⊕				§	§		d			t				
	Paris Nord **250** d.	0646	...	0746	0746	...	...	0846	...	0946	1146	...	...	...	...	1546	1546	...	1646	1646	...	...	1746	...
0	**Lille** Europe d.	0755	...	0855	0855	...	...	0955	...	1054	1255	...	...	...	...	1655	1655	...	1756	1755	...	...	1856	...
99	Calais Fréthun a.	0824	...	0923	0923	...	...	1023	...	1122	1323	...	...	...	...	1723	1723	...	1824	1823	...	...	1924	...
99	Calais Fréthun **261** d.	0832	0831	0932	0932	0941	1012	1032	1030	1124	1332	1341	1400	1412	1612	1735	1732	1749	1833	1832	1840	1847	1933	1957
107	**Calais** Ville **261** a.	|	0840	|	|	0950	1027	|	1045	1132	|	1350	1408	1427	1627	|	|	1757	|	|	1850	1856	|	2005
133	**Boulogne** Ville a.	0854	...	0954	0953	...	...	1053	...	...	1354	...	...	...	...	1757	1753	...	1854	1854	...	...	1955	...
160	Étaples-Le Touquet a.	...	...	...	1012	...	...	1112	...	...	1412	...	...	...	...	...	|	...	1912	...	...	...	2014	...
171	Rang du Fliers ⊙ a.	...	...	...	1024	...	...	1124	...	...	1424	...	...	...	...	...	1819	...	1924	...	...	...	2025	...

	TGV 7569	🚌	TGV 7277	TGV 7277	🚌			🚌	◇	🚌
	⑦	†	⚒	⑦	†	Ⓐ	⑥	Ⓒ	†	†
	d		m	d				§		
Paris Nord **250** d.	1746	...	1846	1846	...	...	...	...	...	...
Lille Europe d.	1915r	...	1955	1955	...	...	...	...	2055	...
Calais Fréthun a.	1943	...	2023	2023	...	...	...	...	2123	...
Calais Fréthun **261** d.	1953	1958	2032	2032	2039	2041	2102	2112	2132	2132
Calais Ville **261** a.	|	2013	|	|	2054	2050	2110	2127	|	2147
Boulogne Ville a.	2014	...	2055	2054	...	...	...	...	2155	...
Étaples-Le Touquet a.	...	...	...	2113	...	...	...	...	...	...
Rang du Fliers ⊙ a.	...	...	...	2125	...	...	...	...	...	...

	TGV 7216		🚌	TGV 7229	🚌	TGV 7536	TGV 7537		TGV 7546
	Ⓐ	Ⓐ	⑥	⚒	⚒	Ⓐ	⑥	Ⓐ	Ⓐ
								u	
Rang du Fliers ⊙ d.	...	...	...	0630	...	0714z	...	...	...
Étaples-Le Touquet d.	...	...	...	0642	...	0725	...	...	...
Boulogne Ville d.	...	...	...	0701	...	0745	0745	...	1001
Calais Ville **261** d.	0617	0659	0702	|	0745	|	|	1009	|
Calais Fréthun **261** a.	0626	0708	0717	0722	0800	0807	0807	1021	1023
Calais Fréthun d.	0629	...	...	0731	...	0815	0815	...	1032
Lille Europe a.	0657	...	...	0801	...	0845	0845	...	1101
Paris Nord **250** a.	0814	...	...	0914	...	1014	1014	...	1214

	🚌		TGV 7550		TGV 7550	🚌		TGV 7555	TGV 7254	🚌			TGV 7573	🚌		TGV 7586		TGV 7290	🚌	TGV 7292	TGV 7592	🚌	🚌	◇
	Ⓒ	Ⓐ	Ⓐ	⑥	⑥	†	†	⑦	⚒	Ⓒ	Ⓐ	⑥	⚒	†	†	⑦	Ⓐ	Ⓐ	Ⓒ	⑦	⑥	Ⓒ	†	†
	§	u‡			t			e		§	u					d				d	t	§		
Rang du Fliers ⊙ d.	...	...	...	...	1130x	...	...	1228	...	...	...	...	1523	...	...	...	...	...	...	1830	...	...	...	...
Étaples-Le Touquet d.	...	...	...	...	1142	...	...	1242	...	...	...	...	1535	...	...	...	...	...	...	1842	...	...	...	...
Boulogne Ville d.	...	...	1201	...	1201	...	...	1301	...	...	...	...	1554	...	...	1801	...	1827	...	1901	1909	...	...	2035
Calais Ville **261** d.	1032	1216	|	1209	|	1302	1309	|	1327	1432	1556	1608	|	1800	1807	|	1830	|	1902	|	|	2032	2032	|
Calais Fréthun **261** a.	1047	1224	1223	1217	1223	1317	1321	1323	1335	1447	1607	1617	1620	1815	1816	1823	1840	1848	1917	1923	1928	2047	2047	2058
Calais Fréthun d.	...	...	1232	...	1232	...	...	1332	1337	...	...	...	1628	...	...	1832	...	1901	...	1932	1937	...	...	2106
Lille Europe a.	...	...	1301	...	1301	...	...	1401	1405	...	...	...	1657	...	...	1901	...	1930	...	2001	2006	...	...	2134
Paris Nord **250** a.	...	...	1414s	...	1414	...	...	1514	1514	...	...	...	1814	...	...	2014	...	2041	...	2114	2129	...	...	...

d – Also June 10, Aug. 15, Nov. 11.
e – Also June 10, Nov. 11.
m – On Ⓐ July 29 - Aug. 23 Paris d. 1915, Lille **Flandres** a. 2018 / d. 2039, Calais Fréthun a. 2116 / d. 2125, Boulogne a. 2148.
r – Arrive 1845.
s – 1444 on Ⓐ July 29 - Aug. 23.
t – Also Nov. 1.
u – Not on Ⓐ July 8 - Aug. 23.
x – 1125 Aug. 10 - 31.
z – 0709 Aug. 5 - Sept. 6.

TGV – Ⓡ to / from Paris. Supplement payable (see panel).
⊙ – Full name: Rang du Fliers - Verton - Berck.
◇ – TER à Grande Vitesse (TER-GV) via high-speed line (1, 2 class), see panel below.
⊕ – Not Aug. 25 - 30.

TGV journeys to / from Paris are Ⓡ with supplement. West of Lille, TGV trains and trains marked ◇ are classified TER-GV and require only a Grande Vitesse supplement, €3 valid all day, Ⓡ is not required.

🚌 – TER bus service. Rail tickets valid.
§ – Connects with *Eurostar* trains to / from Brussels (Table **10**).
‡ – Runs 5 minutes earlier Aug. 26 - Sept. 6.

ALTERNATIVE ROUTES PARIS - CALAIS
Via Lille (Tables **250** and **266**)
Via Hazebrouck (Tables **264** and **266**)
Via Amiens, Boulogne (Tables **260** and **261**)

Local trains — LILLE - DUNKERQUE and CALAIS — 266

For trains via high-speed line see Table **264** Lille - Dunkerque and Table **265** Lille - Calais

km		Ⓐ	Ⓐ	Ⓐ	⑥	⑥	Ⓐ	Ⓐ	Ⓐ	⑥	Ⓐ	⑥	Ⓐ	⑥	Ⓐ	Ⓐ	Ⓐ	Ⓒ	Ⓐ	†	Ⓐ	Ⓐ	Ⓒ	Ⓒ	Ⓐ	Ⓐ	Ⓒ
				b		J							J				J							v			
0	**Lille** Flandres d.	...	...	...	...	...	0615	0635	0645	0645	0700	...	0715	0735	0735	...	0800	0815	0835	...	0845	0900	0935	...	1000	1015	1015
22	Armentières d.	...	...	...	...	...	0629	0649	0701	0659	0714	...	|	0749	0751	...	0814	0829	0849	...	0902	0914	0950	...	1014	|	1029
47	Hazebrouck d.	0543	0618	0633	0635	0647	0648	0713	0722	0718	0735	0747	0748	0811	0814	0818	0835	0848	0913	0915	0918	0935	1013	1017	1035	1048	1048
87	**Dunkerque** a.	|	0652	|	|	0720	0720	|	0756	0752	|	0820	0819	|	|	0852	|	0920	|	|	0952	|	|	1050	|	1120	1120
68	St Omer d.	0557	...	0651	0654	...	...	0726	...	...	0753	...	...	0826	0827	...	0853	...	0926	0929	...	0953	1025	...	1053	...	...
109	**Calais** Ville a.	0626	...	0726	0726	...	...	0756	...	...	0826	...	...	0853	0856	...	0927	...	0956	0958	...	1026	1056	...	1126	...	...

	Ⓒ	Ⓒ	Ⓐ	Ⓐ	⑥	Ⓐ	Ⓐ	Ⓐ	⑥	⑥	Ⓐ	Ⓐ	⑥	†	⑥	⑥	Ⓐ	Ⓐ	Ⓐ	Ⓒ	†		Ⓐ	Ⓐ	Ⓐ		†
						J					J		J												J		
Lille Flandres d.	1135	...	1200	1215	1215	1219	1235	1245	1245	...	...	1315	...	1315	1335	...	1345	1400	...	1435	...	1545	1600	1615	1619	1635	...
Armentières d.	1150	...	1214	|	1229	1234	1249	1302	1259	...	...	|	...	1329	1350	...	1401	1414	...	1451	...	1559	1614	|	1634	1649	...
Hazebrouck d.	1213	1217	1235	1248	1248	1253	1313	1318	1321	1333	1334	1348	1348	1348	1413	1419	1418	1435	1447	1513	1519	1617	1635	1648	1653	1713	1719
Dunkerque a.	|	1253	|	1319	1319	|	|	1352	1355	|	|	1420	1420	1420	|	1455	1452	|	1520	|	1545	1652	|	1719	|	|	1743
St Omer d.	1225	...	1253	...	...	1305	1326	...	...	1352	1354	...	...	...	1426	...	...	1453	...	1526	...	...	1652	...	1705	1726	...
Calais Ville a.	1255	...	1324	...	...	...	1356	...	...	1424	1426	...	...	...	1456	...	...	1526	...	1556	...	...	1723	...	...	1756	...

	⑥	Ⓐ	Ⓐ	Ⓐ	Ⓒ	Ⓐ	Ⓐ	Ⓐ	Ⓐ	Ⓐ	Ⓐ	Ⓐ		Ⓐ	Ⓐ	Ⓐ	Ⓒ	Ⓐ	Ⓐ	Ⓐ		†	⑥	Ⓐ	Ⓒ	Ⓐ	†
	J					J	Ju					J											J	J		◧	◧
Lille Flandres d.	...	1645	1700	1715	1715	1719	...	1735	1745	1800	1815	1819	1835	1845	1900	...	1915	1919	1935	2015	2035	...	...	2115	2115	2215	2300
Armentières d.	...	1702	1714	|	1731	1734	...	1749	1802	1813	|	1834	1849	1902	1914	...	1931	1934	1949	|	2049	...	...	2129	2129	2229	2314
Hazebrouck d.	1719	1718	1735	1748	1748	1753	1806	1812	1817	1835	1848	1853	1913	1918	1935	1947	1950	1953	2017	2048	2114	2119	2118	2148	2148	2247	2335
Dunkerque a.	1753	1752	|	1819	1820	|	1828	|	1852	|	1919	|	|	1952	|	2020	2021	|	2051	2120	|	2145	2152	2220	2220	2320	|
St Omer d.	...	...	1753	...	...	1805	...	1825	...	1853	...	1905	1926	...	1953	...	...	2005	...	...	2126	...	...	...	...	...	2347
Calais Ville a.	...	...	1826	...	...	...	...	1856	...	1926	...	...	1956	...	2026	...	...	...	...	...	2156	...	...	...	...	...	0014

	Ⓐ	Ⓐ	Ⓐ	Ⓐ	Ⓐ	⑥	Ⓐ	Ⓐ	⑥	Ⓐ	⑥	Ⓐ	Ⓐ	Ⓐ	⚒	Ⓐ	⑥	Ⓐ	Ⓐ	⑥	Ⓐ	Ⓐ	⑥	Ⓐ	Ⓒ	Ⓐ	
				J		J					u	Ju		J					J	J							
Calais Ville d.	...	0453	...	...	...	...	0534	...	...	0605	...	...	...	...	0635	...	...	0705	...	...	...	0734	0735	...	...	0833	...
St Omer d.	...	0523	...	0554	...	...	0607	...	...	0635	...	...	0654	...	0708	...	...	0735	0754	...	...	0808	0808	...	...	0909	...
Dunkerque d.	...	|	0507	|	0540	0540	|	0608	0608	|	0630	0637	|	0640	|	0708	0708	|	|	0739	0740	|	|	0808	0839	|	...
Hazebrouck d.	0448	0538	0543	0608	0613	0613	0626	0642	0642	0649	0702	0658	0708	0713	0726	0743	0743	0749	0808	0811	0813	0826	0826	0843	0915	0926	...
Armentières d.	0511	...	0600	0626	|	0630	0645	0657	0659	0711	...	...	0726	|	0745	0757	0800	0811	0826	...	|	0845	0844	0857	0932	0945	...
Lille Flandres a.	0525	...	0614	0640	0644	0644	0659	0714	0714	0725	...	...	0740	0744	0759	0814	0814	0825	0840	...	0844	0859	0859	0914	0946	0959	...

	⑥	Ⓐ	†		Ⓐ	Ⓒ	Ⓐ	Ⓐ	Ⓐ	Ⓒ		⑥	Ⓐ	Ⓐ	Ⓐ	Ⓐ	Ⓐ	⑥	Ⓐ	Ⓒ	Ⓑ	†	⑥	⑥	⑥	Ⓐ	Ⓐ
	Ju													J	J				J				J				
Calais Ville d.	...	...	...	0906	...	...	1034	...	1106	1135	...	...	...	1206	...	...	1234	1235	...	...	...	1335	...	1338	...	1434	...
St Omer d.	...	...	...	0935	...	...	1108	...	1135	1209	...	...	...	1235	1254	...	1308	1307	...	...	...	1410	...	1410	...	1508	...
Dunkerque d.	0856	0908	0908	|	1040	1039	|	1108	|	|	...	1208	1213	...	|	1240	|	|	1308	1308	1339	|	1339	|	1439	|	1508
Hazebrouck d.	0932	0943	0942	0949	1113	1111	1126	1143	1149	1225	...	1244	1248	...	1308	1313	1325	1326	1343	1342	1411	1427	1411	1425	1513	1526	1543
Armentières d.	...	0957	...	1011	|	1128	1145	1157	1211	1245	...	1306	1302	...	1326	|	...	1345	1357	1359	...	1446	...	1445	1530	1545	1557
Lille Flandres a.	...	1014	...	1025	1144	1144	1159	1214	1225	1259	...	1325	1320	...	1340	1344	...	1359	1414	1414	...	1459	...	1459	1544	1559	1614

		Ⓐ	Ⓒ	Ⓐ	Ⓐ	Ⓒ	Ⓐ	Ⓐ	Ⓐ	Ⓐ	Ⓒ	Ⓐ	Ⓒ	Ⓐ	Ⓒ	Ⓒ	Ⓐ	⑥	†	Ⓒ	Ⓐ	Ⓐ	Ⓒ	Ⓐ	Ⓐ	Ⓒ	
									J																		
Calais Ville d.	...	1534	1539	...	...	...	1634	...	1706	...	...	1733	1735	...	...	...	1834	1835	1835	...	...	1906	1935	...	2034	...	...
St Omer d.	...	1608	1611	...	...	...	1707	...	1735	...	...	1806	1810	...	...	...	1911	1910	1908	...	...	1935	2010	...	2111	...	...
Dunkerque d.	1539	|	|	1608	1640	1639	|	1708	|	1740	1740	|	|	1808	1808	1849	|	|	|	1908	1908	|	|	2008	|	2108	...
Hazebrouck d.	1611	1625	1626	1643	1713	1709	1726	1743	1749	1813	1811	1826	1826	1843	1842	1921	1926	1926	1925	1937	1942	1949	2026	2043	2126	2142	...
Armentières d.	...	1645	1645	1658	|	1727	1745	1757	1811	|	...	1845	1845	1857	1859	...	1945	1945	1945	1956	...	2011	2045	2100	2145	2159	...
Lille Flandres a.	...	1659	1659	1714	1744	1744	1759	1814	1825	1844	...	1859	1859	1914	1914	...	1959	1959	1959	2014	...	2025	2059	2114	2159	2214	...

J – Not July 6 - Aug. 24.
b – From Bethune, depart 0602.
u – To/from Arras (Table **264a**).
v – Not on ⑥ July 6 - Aug. 24.
◧ – By 🚌 on certain dates.

Lille - Calais and v.v.: subject to alteration 0900 - 1600 with partial 🚌 substitution on Ⓐ June 17 - 28, Ⓐ Oct. 14 - Nov. 15.

PARIS - BEAUVAIS — 267

km		Ⓐ	⑥	Ⓐ	Ⓐ	⑥	†	Ⓐ	Ⓒ	Ⓐ			⚒		⑥	Ⓐ	Ⓐ	Ⓒ	Ⓐ	Ⓐ	⑥	Ⓐ	Ⓐ	†	⑥	
0	**Paris** Nord d.	0607	0631	0637	0737	0801	0801	0850	0901	1001	1101	1201	1301	1401	1601	1607	1637	1701	1707	1737	1801	1807	1837	1844	1901	...
80	**Beauvais** a.	0720	0751	0751	0851	0918	0919	1005	1018	1118	1218	1318	1418	1518	1720	1720	1747	1820	1820	1847	1920	1920	1947	2009	2020	...

	Ⓐ	Ⓐ	⚒	Ⓑ	Ⓒ	
Paris Nord d.	1907	1937	2001	2101	2201	...
Beauvais a.	2020	2047	2119	2219	2319	...

	Ⓐ	Ⓐ	⑥	Ⓐ	Ⓒ	Ⓐ	Ⓐ	Ⓐ	Ⓒ	Ⓐ	⑥	†		⚒		⚒	
Beauvais d.	0513	0540	0540	0613	0627	0640	0713	0740	0740	0840	0840	0937	1037	1137	1237	1337	1437
Paris Nord a.	0625	0655	0658	0725	0743	0755	0823	0855	0858	0955	0958	1057	1157	1257	1357	1457	1557

	Ⓐ	⑥	Ⓐ	Ⓐ	Ⓒ	Ⓐ	Ⓐ	Ⓒ	⑥	Ⓐ	†	Ⓒ	†		
Beauvais d.	1640	1640	1710	1740	1740	1811	1840	1840	1937	2010	2015	2037	2137	...	...
Paris Nord a.	1755	1758	1825	1855	1858	1925	1955	1957	2057	2127	2127	2157	2257	...	...

Journey times are extended July 6, 7 and July 13 - Aug. 31 with 🚌 substitution July 13 - Aug. 31

Most trains call at Persan-Beaumont (30 mins from Paris).

CREIL - BEAUVAIS: 14 journeys on Ⓐ, 7 on ⑥, 4 on †.

BEAUVAIS - LE TRÉPORT — 267a

km		🚌	🚌	🚌	🚌	🚌	🚌	🚌	🚌	🚌	🚌	🚌
		Ⓐ	Ⓒ	⚒	⚒	Ⓐ	Ⓐ	†	⑥	†	⑤	⑥
	Paris Nord **267** d.	...	...	...	...	...	...	...	...	...	...	...
0	**Beauvais** ▷ d.	0740	0930	1230	1330	1650	1759	1830	1840	2020	2030	2030
49	Abancourt ⊖ ▷ d.	0843	1028	1330	1430	1750	1859	1930	1940	2120	2130	2128
103	Eu (Lycée) d.	0951	1136	1438	...	...	2007	2038	2048	2228	2238	...
106	**Le Tréport** a.	1006	1151	1453	...	...	2022	2053	2103	2243	2253	...

	🚌	🚌	🚌	🚌	🚌	🚌	🚌	🚌	🚌	🚌
	Ⓐ	⑥	Ⓐ	⑥	†	⚒	†	⑥	†	Ⓐ
Le Tréport d.	0507	0612	...	0802	0807	1200	1207	1702	1717	1720
Eu (Lycée) d.	0522	|	...	0817	|	1215	|	1717	1732	1735
Abancourt ⊖ ▷ d.	0630	0730	0830	0925	0925	1323	1325	1825	1840	1843
Beauvais ▷ a.	0730	0830	0930	1025	1025	1423	1425	1925	1940	1943
Paris Nord **267** a.	...	...	...	...	...	...	...	...	...	...

▷ – Additional 🚌 journeys: Beauvais - Abancourt at 1740⑥, 1830Ⓐ, 1857Ⓐ, 1935Ⓐ;
Abancourt - Beauvais at 0600Ⓐ, 0625⑥, 0702Ⓐ, 1130Ⓐ, 1645Ⓐ, 1745Ⓐ.

⊖ – For connections from/to Rouen see Table **268**.

☛ All journeys are by 🚌 until December 2019 during railway modernisation.

AMIENS - ROUEN — 268

Service June 29 - September 15. *For service to June 28 see page 561. Subject to alteration on Aug. 15, 16.*

km		①	Ⓐ	⑥	⑥	†	†		Ⓐ	Ⓐ	⑥	†		①–④	⑤	Ⓐ	†	⑥		Ⓐ	Ⓐ	Ⓒ	Ⓒ	
		g		K	J	K	J		b	b				n								K	J	
	Lille Flandres **256** d.	...	0559	0802	0802	...	...	...	...	...	...	...	...	...	...	...	...	...	...	1702	...	1802	1802	...
0	**Amiens** d.	0554	0715	0923	0927	0920	0926	...	1027	1235	1244	1422	...	1655	1655	1725	1725	1733	...	1822	1919	1923	1927	...
31	Poix de Picardie d.	0613	0733	0940	0945	0938	0944	...	1106	1314	1305	1439	...	1745	1745	1744	1744	1754	...	1840	1940	1940	1944	...
52	Abancourt d.	0625	0745	0952	0957	0950	0956	...	1137	1345	1320	1452	...	1823	1823	1756	1756	1808	...	1852	1954	1952	1956	...
73	Serqueux d.	0645	0803	1011	1012	1011	1014	...	1203	1411	1336	1512	...	1855	1855	1815	1813	1826	...	1913	2013	2010	2011	...
121	**Rouen** Rive-Droite a.	0724	0832	1045	1046	1044	1047	...	1256	1504	1423	1543	...	...	1948	1844	1844	1907	...	1942	...	2043	2043	...

	Ⓐ	①	②–⑤	Ⓐ	Ⓐ	Ⓐ	⑥		†	Ⓐ		⑥	⑤	⑤	①–④		Ⓐ	Ⓐ	Ⓒ	Ⓐ	Ⓐ	⑤	†	
	J	Lg	Lb	M						b				b	bn			b						
Rouen Rive-Droite d.	...	...	...	...	0617	0717	0817	...	0913	0934	...	1217	1217	...	1217	...	1617	...	1816	1816	1834	1917	1917	...
Serqueux d.	0611	0611	0611	0611	0647	0746	0846	...	0946	1036	...	1248	1247	1300	1319	...	1649	1659	1850	1850	1916	1950	1950	...
Abancourt d.	0628	0628	0643	0628	0701	0800	0901	...	1000	1106	...	1301	...	1326	1349	...	...	1725	1903	1904	1936	2002	2003	...
Poix de Picardie d.	0642	0642	0721	0642	0713	0813	0914	...	1012	1137	...	1313	...	1357	1420	...	...	1756	1915	1918	...	2014	2015	...
Amiens a.	0709	0709	0816	0709	0736	0835	0936	...	1035	1219	...	1335	...	1436	1502	...	...	1835	1937	1937	...	2037	2035	...
Lille Flandres **256** a.	...	...	...	...	0859	...	1058	...	...	...	...	...	...	...	...	...	...	...	2059	2059	...	...	...	...

J – June 29 - July 5.
K – July 6 - Sept. 15.
L – July 6 - Aug. 25.
M – From Aug. 26.
b – By 🚌.
g – Also Aug. 16.
n – Not holidays.

269 RENNES / DOL - MONT ST MICHEL

Keolis Emeraude

68 km	WINTER Apr. 22 - July 5						SUMMER July 6 - Sept. 1					
				Ⓒ								
Rennes ⊡ .... d.	0945	...	1145	...	1245	1645	0945	...	1145	...	1245	1645
Dol ⊡ .... d.	|	1055	|	1225	|	|	|	1055	|	1225	|	|
Mont St Michel .. a.	1055	1125	1255	1255	1355	1755	1055	1125	1255	1255	1355	1755

	WINTER Apr. 22 - July 5					SUMMER July 6 - Sept. 1						
									Ⓑ	⑥		⑦
Mont St Michel .. d.	1005	1120	1405	1605	1805	1005	1120	1405	1525	1605	1820	1825
Dol ⊡ .... a.	|	|	|	1640	|	|	|	|	1600	1640	|	1900
Rennes ⊡ .... a.	1115	1230	1515	...	1915	1115	1230	1515	...	...	1930	...

⊡ – Adjacent to rail station.

Operator: Keolis Emeraude, St Malo. ✆ 02 99 26 16 00. www.keolis-emeraude.com Connections (not guaranteed) at Rennes or Dol with *TGV* services to / from Paris. Combined rail / bus tickets available from rail stations. Rail passes not valid. At Mont St Michel the coach terminates close to the tourist information office. A free *Passeur* shuttle service operates along the causeway to Mont St Michel itself, allow 25 mins (or 45 mins walk, *2.4 km*). Horse-drawn shuttles (*Maringotes*) are also available, fee payable.

270 PARIS - ROUEN - LE HAVRE

km								3101		13101		3103	3103	13103	3105	3105	50005	13105	13191	3107	13193		50001		
		⚒	⑥	Ⓐ	Ⓐ	Ⓐ	⚒	Ⓐ	⑥	Ⓐ	⑦	⑥	Ⓐ		Ⓒ	Ⓐ	⑦	⚒	⑦	Ⓐ	⑥	Ⓒ	⑥	⑥	Ⓐ
			L					J		J	d	b					R⊡		d		b		N⊡		
0	**Paris** St Lazare §........d.	...	...	...	...	...	0608	0651	...	0718	...	0750	0750	0819	0850	0852	0933	1017	1034	1047	1048	...	1102	...	...
57	Mantes la Jolie §........d.	...	...	...	0627	...	0643	|	0737	0753	...	|	|	0853	|	|	|	1052	1108	|	|	...	|	...	...
79	Vernon-Giverny...........d.	...	...	...	0645	...	0705	|	0750	0808	...	|	|	0907	|	|	1024	1107	1124	|	|	...	1148	...	...
111	Val de Reuil...............d.	...	...	...	0705	...	0726	|	0810	0828	...	|	|	0928	|	|	|	1128	1145	|	|	...	|	...	...
126	Oissel.........................d.	...	...	...	0717	...	0735	|	0822	0837	...	|	|	0937	|	|	|	1137	1156	|	|	...	|	...	...
140	**Rouen** Rive-Droite......a.	...	...	...	0730	...	0750	0802	0837	0848	...	0900	0902	0948	1003	1003	1053	1148	1207	1200	1200	...	1217	...	...
140	**Rouen** Rive-Droite......d.	0629	0700	0700	...	0740	...	0805	...	...	0904	0903	0905	...	1006	1006	1055	...	...	1203	...	1219	1220	1250	1250
178	Yvetot.........................d.	0654	0732	0732	...	0807	...	0827	...	...	0927	0926	0927	...	1029	1029	|	...	...	1226	...	1241	1242	1322	1325
203	Bréauté-Beuzeville.. ▶ d.	0707	0751	0749	...	0822	...	0842	...	...	0940	0940	0942	...	1043	1043	|	...	...	1240	...	1255	1256	1340	1344
228	**Le Havre**................ ▶ a.	0724	0807	0813	...	0837	...	0856	...	...	0955	0955	0956	...	1057	1057	1140	...	...	1255	...	1310	1310	1355	1359

	13107	3109	3113	13195	13109	3115	3117		3119		13111		3121		3123	13113	13115	3125		13197	3129	13117	13119		3131
		⚒	⑥	⑤				⑥	⑥	Ⓐ	Ⓑ	†	Ⓐ	Ⓐ	Ⓐ	Ⓒ	Ⓐ		Ⓐ	①–④	⑤	Ⓒ	Ⓐ	Ⓒ	Ⓐ
			b	Jv			B		t		h				J					▽	f	E			
Paris St Lazare §.........d.	1219	1246	1348	1349	1417	1448	1549	...	1618	...	1618	...	1648	1652	1723	1718	1728	1749	1752	1824	1824	1818	1829	...	1850
Mantes la Jolie §.........d.	1254	|	|	|	1453	|	|	...	1652	...	1653	...	|	1725	|	1753	|	|	1826	|	|	1852	|	...	|
Vernon-Giverny............d.	1307	|	|	|	1507	|	|	...	1707	...	1707	...	|	1746	|	1807	1814	|	1846	|	|	1907	1915	...	1937
Val de Reuil................d.	1328	|	|	|	1528	|	|	...	1728	...	1728	...	|	1809	|	1828	1833	|	1909	|	|	1928	1934	...	|
Oissel.........................d.	1337	|	|	|	1537	|	|	...	1737	...	1737	...	|	1819	|	1837	1841	|	1919	|	|	1937	1943	...	|
Rouen Rive-Droite.......a.	1348	1358	1500	1500	1548	1600	1700	...	1748	...	1748	...	1800	...	1834	1848	1850	1902	...	1938	1936	1948	1952	...	2005
Rouen Rive-Droite.......d.	...	1401	1503	...	...	1603	1703	1704	1751	1750	...	1804	1803	...	1837	...	...	1905	...	...	1939	...	...	2004	2008
Yvetot.........................d.	...	1424	1526	...	...	1626	1726	1727	1814	1831	...	1829	1826	...	1900	...	...	1928	...	...	2002	...	...	2029	2031
Bréauté-Beuzeville... ▶ d.	...	1438	1540	...	...	1640	1740	1740	1828	1849	...	1842	1840	...	1914	...	...	1942	...	...	2016	...	...	2042	2046
Le Havre................ ▶ a.	...	1453	1555	...	...	1655	1755	1755	1842	1904	...	1856	1857	...	1928	...	...	1957	...	...	2030	...	...	2056	2101

		13121	13123	3133	5376	13125	3135	3137	3137	13127	3141	13199	13129	3141	13131
	Ⓐ	⑦	Ⓐ		*TGV*	Ⓐ	⑥	Ⓐ	⑦	⑤	⑤	⑦	①–④	⑦	⑥
		d		C	♥	J	t		d	g	n	d‡	⊕	e	w
Paris St Lazare §.........d.	1853	1918	1928	1948	...	2019	2018	2050	2050	2115	2204	2218	2310	2348	2346
Mantes la Jolie §.........d.	1926	1952	|	|	2035	2054	2053	|	2129	2150	2238	|	2352	0022	0022
Vernon-Giverny............d.	1946	2007	2013	|	|	2107	2107	2134	2142	2207	2253	2304	0007	0036	0037
Val de Reuil................d.	2006	2028	2032	|	|	2128	2128	|	2201	2228	2313	2324	0028	0057	0058
Oissel.........................d.	2015	2037	2040	|	|	2137	2137	|	2210	2237	2323	2334	0037	0106	0107
Rouen Rive-Droite.......a.	2026	2048	2049	2101	2114	2148	2148	2205	2220	2248	2333	2343	0048	0115	0118
Rouen Rive-Droite.......d.	...	...	...	2103	2118	...	2151	2208	2223	...	2336	...	...	0118	...
Yvetot.........................d.	...	...	...	2126	|	...	2213	2231	2244	...	2359	...	...	0141	...
Bréauté-Beuzeville... ▶ d.	...	...	...	2140	|	...	2228	2245	2258	...	0013	...	...	0155	...
Le Havre................ ▶ a.	...	...	...	2156	2202	...	2242	2259	2312	...	0027	...	...	0209	...

		13100	13102	3100	
	Ⓐ	Ⓐ	⑥	Ⓐ	Ⓐ
			b		
Le Havre........................ ▶ d.	...	...	...	0529	...
Bréauté-Beuzeville......... ▶ d.	...	...	...	0545	...
Yvetot.................................d.	...	...	...	0559	...
Rouen Rive-Droite............a.	...	...	...	0623	...
Rouen Rive-Droite............d.	0526	0557	0612	0626	...
Oissel.................................d.	0538	0608	0623	|	0639
Val de Reuil........................d.	0549	0617	0632	|	0648
Vernon-Giverny...................d.	0610	0639	0653	|	0708
Mantes la Jolie §.................d.	0631	0654	0707	|	0728
Paris St Lazare §..............a.	0708	0736	0740	0740	0809

	13104	13106	3104	13108	3102			3106	13110		5316	3108	13112		13114	3110		3112	13116	3114	13118	3116	3118	13120	3120
	Ⓐ	Ⓐ	⑥	⑦	Ⓐ	Ⓐ	⑥	Ⓐ	⚒	Ⓐ	*TGV*		⚒	Ⓐ	Ⓑ	⑥		⚒	⑥	⑦		⚒	Ⓐ		
			b	d				G			♥		J		h	b			b	d			J		
Le Havre................ ▶ d.	...	...	0612	...	0629	...	0640	0702	...	0725	0753	0802	...	0903	...	0914	...	1002	...	1100	...	1201	1302	...	1400
Bréauté-Beuzeville... ▶ d.	...	...	0628	...	0645	...	0704	0718	...	0740	|	0818	...	0918	...	0930	...	1018	...	1116	...	1218	1318	...	1416
Yvetot.........................d.	...	...	0642	...	0659	...	0723	0732	...	0756	|	0832	...	0931	...	0944	...	1032	...	1130	...	1232	1332	...	1430
Rouen Rive-Droite.......a.	...	...	0707	...	0725	...	0756	0756	...	0824	0840	0856	...	0955	...	1008	...	1056	...	1154	...	1256	1356	...	1454
Rouen Rive-Droite.......d.	0648	0658	0710	0712	0728	0712	...	0759	0812	...	0845	0859	0912	...	1012	1011	...	1059	1111	1157	1212	1259	1359	1412	1457
Oissel.........................d.	|	0708	0719	0723	|	0739	...	|	0822	...	|	|	0922	...	1022	1021	...	|	1122	|	1222	|	|	1423	|
Val de Reuil................d.	0703	0717	0729	0732	|	0748	...	|	0831	...	|	|	0931	...	1031	1030	...	|	1131	|	1231	|	|	1432	|
Vernon-Giverny............d.	0724	0739	0751	0751	|	0810	...	|	0851	...	|	|	0951	...	1051	1051	...	|	1151	|	1251	|	|	1453	|
Mantes la Jolie §.........d.	|	0756	0805	0806	|	0831	...	|	0907	...	0928	|	1006	...	1106	1106	...	|	1206	|	1307	|	|	1507	|
Paris St Lazare §.........a.	0817	0837	0840	0840	0841	0910	...	0917	0941	...	...	1015	1042	...	1140	1140	...	1212	1242	1311	1341	1412	1513	1541	1610

	13196		13122	3124	13190	13124	13192	3126	3128	50008		13126		3130		13128	50422	13194		3132	3134		13130	3136	
	⑤	Ⓐ	⑦	Ⓐ	⑦	Ⓐ	⑥	⑦		⑥	Ⓐ	⑦	⑥	Ⓑ	⑥	Ⓐ	⑦	⑦	Ⓐ		Ⓑ	⑥	⑦	⑦	
	z		d		d		b	d		N⊡		d		D	b		R⊡	d		H	h	L	d	d	
Le Havre................ ▶ d.	...	...	...	1600	...	...	...	1613	1701	1720	...	...	...	1802	1803	...	1906	...	1851	1915	2002	2000	...	2115	...
Bréauté-Beuzeville... ▶ d.	...	...	...	1616	...	...	...	1629	1717	|	...	...	...	1818	1817	...	|	...	1909	1931	2018	2015	...	2131	...
Yvetot.........................d.	...	...	...	1630	...	...	...	1643	1731	|	...	...	...	1832	1831	...	|	...	1929	1945	2032	2031	...	2145	...
Rouen Rive-Droite.......a.	...	...	...	1654	...	...	...	1707	1755	1805	...	...	...	1856	1855	...	1954	...	2002	2009	2056	2053	...	2209	...
Rouen Rive-Droite.......d.	1556	1607	1612	1657	1659	1712	1712	1710	1758	1812	1810	1812	1823	1859	...	1912	...	1959	...	2012	2059	...	2110	2212	...
Oissel.........................d.	|	1617	1622	|	|	1722	1722	1721	|	|	1819	1822	1837	|	...	1922	...	|	...	2023	|	...	2123	2223	...
Val de Reuil................d.	|	1626	1631	|	|	1731	1731	1730	|	|	1829	1831	1849	|	...	1932	...	|	...	2032	|	...	2132	2232	...
Vernon-Giverny............d.	|	1647	1651	|	|	1752	1751	1751	|	1849	1850	1851	1911	|	...	1952	...	|	...	2053	|	...	2153	2253	...
Mantes la Jolie §.........d.	|	1703	1707	|	|	1806	1807	1806	|	|	1905	1908	1925	|	...	2007	...	|	...	2108	|	...	2208	2308	...
Paris St Lazare §.........a.	1713	1740	1740	1814	1812	1840	1840	1841	1914	1943	1942	1942	...	2012	...	2041	...	2112	...	2142	2210	...	2245	2342	...

B – Ⓐ to July 5 / from Sept. 2; ⑤ July 12 - Aug. 30 (also Aug. 14).
C – Will not run on ⑥ July 6 - Aug. 31 (or Aug. 15).
D – Ⓑ to July 7 / from Sept. 2; ⑤⑦ July 12 - Sept. 1 (also Aug. 14).
E – Will not run on ⑦ Aug. 4 - Sept. 1.
G – Not July 22 - Aug. 23.
H – Daily to Aug. 4; Ⓑ from Aug. 5 (also Aug. 31).
J – Not July 8 - Aug. 30.
L – Not July 13 - Aug. 17.
N – ⑥ Apr. 13 - Sept. 28.
R – ⑦ Apr. 14 - Sept. 29.
b – Also Aug. 15, Nov. 1.
d – Also June 10, Nov. 11.

e – Also June 10, Aug. 15, Nov. 11.
f – Also Aug. 14, Oct. 31; not Nov. 1.
g – Also Aug. 14; not Nov. 1.
h – Not Aug. 15.
n – Also Aug. 14; not Nov. 1.
t – Also Aug. 15.
v – Also Oct. 31; not Nov. 1.
w – Also Aug. 15, Nov. 1; not Aug. 17.
z – Also Oct. 31; not Aug. 16, Nov. 1.
TGV – [R], supplement payable, 🍸.
▶ – Additional trains run 3-7 times per day Le Havre - Bréauté-Beuzeville - Fécamp and v.v.

♥ – To/from Lyon and Marseille (Table **335**). Cancelled on certain dates.
▽ – Not June 10, July 22 - Aug. 22, Oct. 31, Nov.11.
⊡ – Train de l'impressionnisme.
⊕ – Subject to alteration.
§ – Frequent suburban trains run Paris - Mantes-la-Jolie.
‡ – Subject to alteration Sept. 15, 22.

On ⑥⑦ June 1 - 16, July 6 - 14, 27, 28 (also June 10, Nov. 1, 2) trains depart Paris up to 40 mins earlier and arrive Paris up to 35 mins later.

270a ROUEN - DIEPPE

km		⑥	Ⓐ	Ⓐ	Ⓐ	†	⚒		⚒	†	⑥	Ⓐ	⑦S	⑥b	⑥	Ⓐ	Ⓐ	Ⓐ		Ⓐr	Ⓐ		Ⓐ	⚒	†
0	**Rouen** Rive-Droite......d.	0640	0640	0712	0730	0841	0912	1012	1212	1225	1242	1341	1341	1412	1512	1612	1641	1712	1741	1812	1841	1912	2013	2124	2130
63	**Dieppe**.......................a.	0740	0743	0758	0844	0940	0958	1058	1258	1310	1344	1443	1441	1458	1558	1658	1743	1758	1843	1858	1943	1958	2058	2209	2216

	Ⓐ	⚒	Ⓐ	Ⓐ	Ⓒ	Ⓐ	⚒		⚒		Ⓐ		†	Ⓐ	⑥	⑦S	Ⓐ	†	⚒	⑦K	Ⓐ	⚒	†	⑦S	
Dieppe.......................d.	0532	0617	0700	0713	0751	0800	0813	1000	1200	1313	1400	...	1556	1600	1609	1700	1713	1802	1813	1844	1900	2000	2013	2101	...
Rouen Rive-Droite.......a.	0616	0719	0745	0819	0835	0848	0919	1048	1248	1419	1448	...	1642	1647	1655	1746	1819	1847	1919	1929	1948	2048	2113	2146	...

K – ⑦ July 7 - Aug. 25 (also Aug. 15).
S – ⑦ June 9 - Sept. 15 (also June 10, Aug. 15).

b – Also Aug. 15, Nov. 1.
r – Also ⑥ June 8 - Sept. 14.

CAEN - ALENÇON - LE MANS - TOURS 271

km		①	Ⓐ	⑦	⑥	Ⓐ		Ⓐ	Ⓒ	Ⓐ	⑥		⑤–⑦	Ⓑ	⑥	Ⓐ	Ⓑ	Ⓐ	⑥	⚒	⑦	Ⓐ	Ⓐ	⑦	①–④	⑤–⑦
		x		d	t		⊕	🚌			t	⊗			t		h		t		d			d□	🚌	
0	**Caen** .... **275/7** d.	0512	0546	...	0708	0723	0901	...	...	1046	1046	1251	...	...	...	...	1648	...	...	1743	1745	1846	2000	2029	m	...
23	Mézidon .... **275/7** d.	0528	0601	...	0723	0738	0917	...	...	1101	1101	1307	...	...	...	...	1703	...	...	1759	1801	1900	2015	2044	...	...
67	Argentan .... **273** d.	0553	0630	...	0752	0806	0942	◇	◇	1130	1130	1330	◇	...	...	...	1733	...	...	1831	1835	1934	2042	2108	◇	◇
82	Surdon .... **273** d.	|	0641	...	0803	0816	|	0924	1042	1141	1141	1340	1545	...	...	...	|	...	...	1842	1846	1944	2052	|	2143	2150
91	Sées .... d.	0608	0648	...	0810	0824	|	0934	1049	1149	1149	1348	1552	...	...	...	1750	...	...	1850	1854	1953	2059	2123	2153	2157
111	Alençon .... d.	0621	0703	0810	0824	0837	1008	0958	1102	1203	1203	1402	1605	1621	1643	1721	1803	1824	1843	1904	1909	2005	2113	2136	2217	2211
166	**Le Mans** .... a.	0714	0741	0841	0914	0914	1039	...	...	1241	1241	1431	...	1714	1714	1814	1841	1914	1914	1941	1944	...	...	2214	...	...
	Tours (below) .... a.	...	...	...	...	...	1153	...	...	1353	1353	1547	...	...	...	...	2016f	...	...	...	2049	...	...	...	...	...

	①	⑥	Ⓐ	⑦	Ⓐ	⑥	Ⓐ	⑥	Ⓐ	Ⓐ	⑥	⑦	Ⓐ	⑥	Ⓐ	⑦	Ⓐ	①–④	⑤		⚒	⑦	⑤	①–④	⑦	⑦
	x□	🚌		d□		t		🚌			t	d	🚌	t		d□		m	f			d□	f	m	d	d
Tours (below) .... d.	...	□	...	...	...	...	0624	□	...	0815	0903	0903	...	...	...	...	1416	...	1519	1634	...	...	...	...	...	1903
Le Mans .... d.	...	...	0612x	...	0712	0735	0752	...	0852	0943	1027	1026	...	1324	1331	...	1520	...	1623	1737	1824	...	1930	1953	1953	2025
Alençon .... d.	0551	0641	0657	0757	0759	0831	0847	0943	0948	1021	1107	1112	1241r	1422	1417	1458	1607	1716	1716	1820	1909	1950	2020	2051	2035	2104
Sées .... d.	0602	0705	0710	0809	0812	0843	...	1007	...	1034	1119	1124	1305	1435	1429	1510	1621	1729	1729	1835	1922	2002	2033	2104	2048	2116
Surdon .... **273** d.	0610	0715	0717	0816	0820	0851	...	1017	...	1041	1126	1132	1315	1442	1437	1517	|	1736	1736	1843	1929	2009	2040	2111	2055	|
Argentan .... **273** d.	0619	◇	0727	◇	0830	0901	...	◇	...	1050	1136	1143	◇	1452	1447	◇	1635	1746	1746	1852	1940	◇	2050	2122	2105	2130
Mézidon .... **275/7** d.	0649	...	0754	...	0859	0928	...	...	...	1113	1159	1210	...	1520	1514	...	1659	1816	1816	1916	2007	...	2118	...	2132	|
Caen .... **275/7** a.	0704	...	0809	...	0915	0943	...	...	...	1129	1213	1226	...	1535	1530	...	1714	1831	1831	1931	2022	...	2132	...	2146	2205

LE MANS - TOURS

km		⚒	Ⓐ	Ⓐ			⚒	Ⓐ	⑥	⑦				Ⓐ	Ⓐ	①–④	⑤	⑦	⑦	Ⓐ	⑥	⑥	⑦	Ⓐ	
						⊕			t	d	⊗					m	f	d	d		t	🚌	d		
	Caen (above) .... d.	...	...	...	...	0901	...	1046	1046	...	1251	...	...	...	...	...	1648	...	...	...	...	...	1745	...	...
0	**Le Mans** .... d.	0618	0647	0735	...	1042	1207	1250	1251	1251	1434	...	1651	1716	1817	1851	1851	1851	1912	1916	1917	...	1947	1951	...
49	Château du Loir .... d.	0649	0737	0806	...	1111	1257	1322	1322	1322	1502	...	1723	1807	1907	1924	1924	1923	1959	2007	2007	2015	2018	2022	...
96	St Pierre des Corps .... a.	|	...	|	...	1140	...	|	|	|	1532	...	|	...	...	|	1958	1954	|	...	...	|	|	|	...
99	**Tours** .... a.	0731	...	0835	...	1153	...	1353	1353	1354	1547	...	1755	...	...	1954	2016	2007	2038	...	...	2105	2049	2104	...

	①	①	②–⑤	Ⓐ	Ⓐ	⑥	Ⓐ	Ⓐ	⑥	⑦		⑦	Ⓐ	⑥	Ⓐ		Ⓐ	⑤		Ⓐ		⑦	⑦	⑤	⑦
	x	x	m			t			t	d		d		t				f				d	d	f	d
Tours .... d.	0522	0559	...	0624	...	0737	0754	0815	0903	0903	...	1029	1229	1229	...	...	1416	1519	1634	1726	1829	...	1903	2129	2129
St Pierre des Corps .... d.	|	|	...	|	...	|	|	0833	0918	0917	...	|	|	|	...	...	|	|	|	|	|	...	1921	|	|
Château du Loir .... d.	0552	0631	0630	0702	0753	0807	0825	0909	0949	0948	...	1100	1300	1311	1313	...	1447	1550	1705	1807	1900	1920	1953	2201	2201
Le Mans .... a.	0639	0721	0721	0749	0841	0853	0856	0939	1019	1018	...	1131	1332	1359	1400	...	1518	1621	1732	1855	1932	2011	2021	2232	2232
Caen (above) .... a.	...	...	...	...	...	...	...	1129	1213	1226	...	...	...	...	...	...	1714	1831	1931	...	...	...	2205	...	...

– Also June 10, Nov. 11.
– ⑤ (also Aug. 14, Oct. 31; not Nov. 1).
– Not Aug. 15.
m – Not holidays.
– By train d. 1252 on ⑤ (1247 from Oct. 18).

t – Also Aug. 15, Nov. 1.
x – ① (also June 11, Nov. 12; not June 10, Nov. 11).
⊕ – Runs later June 3 - 7 (Caen d. 1012, Tours a. 1324). Will not run Le Mans - Tours on June 9 or Ⓐ Oct. 7 - 31.
⊗ – Not Oct. 7 - 11 Le Mans - Tours.

◇ – Connects from / to Paris at Surdon (Table **273**).
□ – Runs up to 13 mins earlier from Oct. 14.

CAEN - COUTANCES - GRANVILLE - RENNES 272

km		Ⓐ	Ⓐ	Ⓐ	Ⓐ	Ⓐ	Ⓐ	⑥	Ⓐ	†	⑥	Ⓐ	⑦	E	⑥	Ⓐ	†	Ⓐ	Ⓒ	⑥	Ⓐ	Ⓒ	Ⓐ	Ⓐ	⑦
		🚌 b			🚌	🚌			🚌	e	t		d		S		S			🚌 t				🚌	🚌 d
0	**Caen** .... **275** d.	...	0606	0709	...	0730	0744	0813	*0901*r	0916	1013	1113	1119	1213	...	1242	...	1411	1413	*1503*r	1548	1601	1613	1615	1715
30	Bayeux .... **275** d.	...	0629	0725	...	|	0805	0830	0929	0933	1030	1130	1136	1230	...	1304	...	1432	1430	*1521*r	1609	1624	1630	|	|
57	Lison .... **275** d.	...	0644	0743	0807	|	0822	0844	|	0947	1044	1145	1150	1244	...	1322	...	1449	1444	1543	1626	1642	1644	|	|
75	Saint Lô .... d.	...	0659	0757	0827	|	0838	0859	1016	1001	1059	1158	1203	1259	...	1338	...	1501	1459	1603	1639	1659	1659	|	|
105	Coutances .... d.	...	0724	0820	0901	|	...	0922	1052	1024	1122	1219	1225	1321	...	...	...	...	1522	1637	...	1722	1722	|	|
143	**Granville** .... a.	...	0751	...	...	|	...	0949	...	1052	1149	...	1251	1349	...	...	...	...	1549	...	...	1749	...	|	|
143	**Granville** .... d.	0630	0801	...	...	|	...	1000	...	1101	...	...	...	1400	1400	...	1439	...	...	...	...	*1759**	...	|	|
157	Folligny .... **273** d.	|	0812	...	...	|	...	1011	...	1111	...	...	...	1411	1411	...	1450	...	...	...	...	|	...	|	|
176	Avranches .... d.	0700	0825	...	...	0900	...	1024	...	1125	...	...	...	1424	1424	...	1503	...	...	...	...	*1829**	...	1745	1845
198	Pontorson □ .... d.	|	0842	...	...	|	...	1041	...	1142	...	...	...	1441	1442	...	1521	...	...	...	...	|	...	|	|
219	Dol de Bretagne .. **281** d.	|	0859	...	...	|	...	1058	...	1158	...	...	...	1457	1458	...	1537	...	...	...	...	|	...	|	|
277	**Rennes** .... **281** a.	0820	0936	...	...	1020	...	1133	...	1235	...	...	...	1533	1535	...	1614	...	...	...	...	*1949**	...	1905	2005

	Ⓐ	Ⓐ	Ⓐ	⑥	⑦	Ⓐ		Ⓐ	⑤–⑦	Ⓑ
				t	d			🚌	🚌	🚌 u
Caen .... **275** d.	1713	1744	1804	1811	1813	1844	1912x	*2000*r	*2101*r	*2249*r
Bayeux .... **275** d.	1730	1806	1826	1833	1830	1905	1930	*2017*r	*2118*r	*2306*r
Lison .... **275** d.	1744	1824	1844	1851	1844	1922	1944	2040	2142	2328
Saint Lô .... d.	1759	1837	1859	1905	1859	1940	1959	2100	2202	2348
Coutances .... d.	1826	*1923*z	1927	1929	1920	...	2020	2134	2236	0022
Granville .... a.	1853	...	1954	1956	...	...	2048	...	...	...
Granville .... d.	*1903**	...	...	...	...	...	...	...	...	...
Folligny .... **273** d.	|	...	...	...	...	...	...	...	...	...
Avranches .... d.	*1933**	...	...	...	...	...	...	...	...	...
Pontorson □ .... d.	|	...	...	...	...	...	...	...	...	...
Dol de Bretagne .... **281** d.	|	...	...	...	...	...	...	...	...	...
Rennes .... **281** a.	*2053**	...	...	...	...	...	...	...	...	...

	Ⓐ	⑥	Ⓐ	Ⓐ	Ⓐ	Ⓒ	Ⓐ	Ⓒ	Ⓐ	⑦	⑥
									🚌	d	k
Rennes .... **281** d.	...	...	...	...	...	...	...	...	0730	*0756**	...
Dol de Bretagne **281** d.	...	...	...	...	...	...	...	...	|	|	...
Pontorson □ .... d.	...	...	...	...	...	...	...	...	|	|	...
Avranches .... d.	...	...	...	...	...	...	...	...	0851	*0916**	...
Folligny .... **273** d.	...	...	...	...	...	...	...	...	|	|	...
Granville .... a.	...	...	...	...	...	...	...	...	|	*0946**	...
Granville .... d.	...	...	0609	...	0657	...	...	0807	|	0956	1007
Coutances .... d.	0605	0617	0636	...	0732	*0706**	0834	0834	|	1025	1034
Saint Lô .... d.	0625	0638	0658	0717	0756	*0747**	0854	0858	|	1046	1058
Lison .... **275** d.	0640	0652	0711	0730	0809	0817	0907	0914	|	1059	1111
Bayeux .... **275** d.	0657	0706	0728	0747	0823	0833	0922	0931	|	1117	1126
Caen .... **275** a.	0720	0723	0745	0810	0843	0854	0938	0954	1020	1140	1143

	①–④	⑤	①–④	Ⓐ	⑥	Ⓒ	⑥	⑦	Ⓐ	†	Ⓐ	Ⓒ	Ⓐ	Ⓐ	⑤	Ⓐ	Ⓐ	Ⓐ	⑦	⑥	Ⓒ	Ⓐ	Ⓐ	Ⓒ	Ⓐ
	m	f	m		t	🚌	S	d	n	S					🚌 b		🚌		d	t⊕		🚌			
Rennes .... **281** d.	...	...	...	0956	*1007**	...	1155	...	...	1257	...	...	...	...	1506	...	1615	...	...	...	1655	1659	...	...	1856
Dol de Bretagne .... **281** d.	...	...	...	1031	|	...	1231	...	...	1333	...	...	...	...	|	...	|	...	...	...	1731	|	...	...	1931
Pontorson □ .... d.	...	...	...	1047	|	...	1246	...	...	1348	...	...	...	...	|	...	|	...	...	...	1747	|	...	...	1946
Avranches .... d.	...	...	...	1104	*1127**	...	1304	...	...	1406	...	...	...	...	1626	...	1735	...	...	...	1804	1820	...	...	2004
Folligny .... **273** d.	...	...	...	1117	|	...	1317	...	...	1419	...	...	...	...	|	...	|	...	...	...	1817	|	...	...	2017
Granville .... a.	...	...	...	1128	*1157**	...	1328	...	...	1430	...	...	...	...	|	...	|	...	...	...	1828	1850	...	...	2028
Granville .... d.	...	...	...	1204	1207	1230	▬	1408	...	...	...	1607	...	...	|	...	|	*1732**	1807	1815	...	...	1900	1901v	2038
Coutances .... d.	*1015**	*1117**	*1127**	1236	1234	1306	...	1435	...	...	*1512**	1634	1636	...	1726	1736	|	*1808**	1834	1842	...	...	1932	1934	2104
Saint Lô .... d.	*1049**	1201	1211	1258	1258	1346	...	1458	1508	...	1603	1658	1658	1714	...	1758	|	1859	1858	1904	...	...	1958	1958	...
Lison .... **275** d.	1119	1214	1227	1311	1311	1406	1419	1511	1521	...	1619	1711	1711	1730	...	1811	|	1912	1911	1917	...	...	2011	2011	...
Bayeux .... **275** d.	|	1230	1243	1326	1326	...	1432	1526	1535	...	1636	1726	1725	1746	...	1826	|	1930	1926	1933	...	...	2026	2026	...
Caen .... **275** a.	1151	1251	1304	1343	1343	...	1454	1543	1550	...	1658	1743	1742	1807	...	1843	1905	1952	1943	1949	...	...	2044	2043	...

– ⚒ to Granville, Ⓐ Granville - Rennes.
– Mar. 30 - Sept. 29.
– Until July 5.
– Also June 10, Nov. 11.
– Not Nov. 10.
– Also Aug. 14, Oct. 31; not Nov. 1.
– Also Aug. 15, Nov. 1 (d. 0956).
– Not holidays or June 14, Oct. 31.
– To Lisieux (Table **275**).
– Connection by train.
– Also Aug. 15, Nov. 1.

u – Not ①–④ in Sept.
v – 1908 on ⑦ **d**.
x – 1913 on Ⓒ.
z – By 🚌. Runs ①–④ (not June 10, Aug. 14, 15, Oct. 31, Nov. 11).
□ – Pontorson - Mont St Michel (10 km from Mont St Michel).
⊕ – Runs up to 8 mins earlier from Oct. 19.
* – By 🚌.
🚌 – Bus service, rail tickets valid. At Caen and Rennes 🚌 services start and finish at the Gare Routière (bus station), adjacent to the railway station.

ADDITIONAL 🚌 SERVICES:
On ⑤ to July 5 : Rennes d. 1745 - Coutances a. 2000 (non-stop).
On ⑤ to July 5 : Rennes d. 1745 - Saint Lô a. 2000 (non-stop).
On ⑤ to July 5 : Coutances d. 1745 - Avranches 1845 - Pontorson a. 1910.
On ⑦ to June 30 : Saint Lô d. 1745 - Rennes a. 2000 (non-stop).
On ⑦ to June 30 : Coutances d. 1800 - Rennes a. 2015 (non-stop).

273 PARIS - DREUX - GRANVILLE

km			3411		3413	16513	16511	3417		3421		3431	3435	16547		3441	3443	3445		16515		3451	3453	
		G	Ⓐ		Ⓒ	Ⓐ	†e	⑥K					⑤f	⑥t		Ⓐ	Ⓒ	⑤f		Ⓐ		Ⓐ	Ⓒ	
0	**Paris Montparnasse** ⊖ d.	...	0738	...	0850	0927	0927	0944	...	1055	...	1355	1528	1527	...	1643	1655	1713	...	1813	...	1943	1955	...
17	Versailles Chantiers ▲ d.	...	|	...	0902	|	|	|	...	|	...	|	|	|	...	|	|	|	...	1827	...	|	2007	...
82	**Dreux** ▶ d.	0525	0825	...	0938	1014	1014	1033	...	|	...	1443	|	1614	...	|	|	|	...	1914	...	2044	2044	...
118	Verneuil sur Avre d.	0548	0845	...	0957	1036	1036	1055	...	1158	...	1503	|	1636	...	1801	1800	|	...	1936	...	2104	2103	...
142	L'Aigle d.	0601	0858	...	1011	1049	1049	1108	...	1211	...	1516	1640	1650	...	1814	1814	1840	...	1950	...	2118	2117	...
183	Surdon 271 d.	0628	0919	...	1032	1118	1116	1135	...	|	...	1537	|	1715	...	1835	1836	1901	...	2016	...	2138	2138	...
198	Argentan 271 d.	0638	0931	...	1043	1127	1126	1146	...	1242	...	1548	1711	1725	...	1847	1847	1913	...	2026	...	2149	2148	...
226	Briouze d.	0653	0947	...	1100	...	1142	1201	...	|	...	1605	|	...	...	|	|	1929	...	...	...	2205	2205	...
243	Flers d.	0704	0958	...	1110	...	1153	1212	...	1305	...	1616	1734	...	...	1910	1913	1946	...	...	...	2216	2215	...
272	Vire d.	0720	1015	...	1127	...	1210	1229	...	1322	...	1632	1751	...	...	1927	1930	2002	...	...	...	2232	2232	...
298	Villedieu les Poêles d.	0734	1030	...	1142	...	1224	1243	...	1337	...	1647	1806	...	...	1942	1946	2018	...	...	...	2247	2247	...
313	Folligny 272 d.	0746	1040	...	1152	...	1235	|	...	|	...	|	|	...	...	|	|	2028	...	...	...	|	|	...
328	**Granville** 272 a.	0757	1051	...	1203	...	1246	1303	...	1355	...	1704	1824	...	...	1959	2004	2038	...	...	...	2305	2304	...

	16510				3410	3410		3412	3420		16546	3430	16516	3432	3440		3444	3444		13272		3450	3454	
	①g	Ⓐ	⑥t		⑥t	Ⓐ		⑦v			⑥t	⚒	Ⓐ	⑦v			⑥K	†	⑤u	†v			†	
Granville 272 d.	0451	...	...	...	0555	0555	...	0655	0900	...	...	1154	...	1356	1504	...	1705	1705	1710	...	...	1845	1954	...
Folligny 272 d.	|	...	...	...	|	|	...	|	|	...	...	|	...	|	|	...	|	|	1721	...	...	1856	2005	...
Villedieu les Poêles d.	0508	...	...	...	0613	0613	...	0714	0918	...	...	1212	...	1414	1523	...	1724	1724	1731	...	...	1906	2015	...
Vire d.	0525	...	...	...	0629	0629	...	0730	0934	...	...	1228	...	1430	1539	...	1740	1740	1747	...	...	1922	2031	...
Flers d.	0541	...	...	...	0646	0646	...	0746	0951	...	...	1245	...	1447	1555	...	1757	1757	1803	...	...	1939	2048	...
Briouze d.	0552	...	...	...	0657	0657	...	0758	|	...	...	1256	...	1458	|	...	1808	1808	1819	...	...	1950	2059	...
Argentan 271 d.	0609	0609	0609	...	0715	0715	...	0816	1017	...	1209	1315	1404	1516	1621	...	1825	1825	1835	1926	...	2009	2117	...
Surdon 271 d.	0619	0619	0619	...	0725	0725	...	0826	1027	...	1219	1325	1415	1527	|	...	|	|	...	1936	...	2019	|	...
L'Aigle d.	0642	0642	0642	...	0746	0746	...	0847	1048	...	1243	1346	1442	1548	1649	...	1853	1853	...	2004	...	2041	2145	...
Verneuil sur Avre d.	0656	0656	0656	...	0759	0759	...	0900	1101	...	1256	1359	1456	1601	1702	...	|	|	...	2019	...	2055	2158	...
Dreux ▶ d.	0718	0718	0719	...	0820	0820	...	0921	|	...	1319	1420	1519	|	|	...	|	|	...	2043	...	2116	2219	...
Versailles Chantiers ▲ a.	0803	0803	|	...	|	|	...	|	|	...	|	|	|	|	|	...	|	|	...	2118	...	|	2253	...
Paris Montparnasse ⊖ a.	0816	0816	0805	...	0905	0916	...	1006	1205	...	1405	1505	1605	1705	1815	...	2006	2006	...	2131	...	2205	2307	...

G – June 3, 11, 17, 24, July 1; ① Aug. 26 - Oct. 7.
K – ⑥ Apr. 20 - Aug. 31 (also Aug. 15).
e – Not June 9.
f – Also Aug. 14, Oct. 31; not Nov. 1.
g – Also June 11, Aug. 16, Nov. 12; not June 10, Nov. 11.
t – Also Aug. 15.
u – Also Oct. 31; not July 12 - Aug. 23, Nov. 1.

v – Also June 10; not Nov. 10.
▲ – Local travel between Paris and Versailles not permitted on some trains (see Table **278** for local services).
▶ – Suburban trains run Paris - Dreux approx hourly.
⊖ – Most trains use **Vaugirard** platforms (5-10 mins walk from Montparnasse main concourse).

Subject to alteration on Sept. 21. Departures from Granville are up to 5 mins earlier Aug. 26 - Sept. 30. Journey times are extended by up to 25 mins from Oct. 14 (earlier departures towards Paris).

275 PARIS - CAEN - CHERBOURG

km		3325							3331	3301			3333			3335		3303	3337		3305		3341		3307	3309
		①g	Ⓐ	Ⓐ	⚒	ⒶJ	⚒	⚒	Ⓐ	Ⓐ	Ⓒ		⑥t	⑥t	Ⓐ	Ⓐ	Ⓐ	Ⓒ	Ⓒ	⑥t	Ⓐ	Ⓐ	Ⓒ	Ⓒ	Ⓐ	⑥
0	**Paris** St Lazare ▷ d.	0026	...	...	...	...	...	...	0644	0705	...	...	0743	...	...	0844	...	0908	0942	...	1007	...	1142	...	1208	1310
108	Evreux ▷ d.	0133	...	...	...	0609	...	...	0745	|	...	...	0844	...	...	0944	...	|	1043	...	|	...	1243	...	|	|
160	Bernay ▷ d.	0211	...	...	...	0647	...	...	0812	|	...	...	0911	...	...	1011	...	|	1110	...	|	...	1310	...	|	|
191	Lisieux ▷ d.	0243	...	*0610*	0651	0703	...	0751	0830	|	...	0851	0929	...	0951	1028	...	|	1128	...	|	...	1328	...	|	|
216	Mézidon 271 277 d.	|	...	*0624*	0705	0716	...	0805	|	|	...	0905	|	...	1005	|	...	|	|	...	|	...	|	...	|	|
239	**Caen** 271 277 a.	0320	...	*0644*	0725	0735	...	0825	0855	0858	...	0925	0954	...	1025	1054	...	1104	1153	...	1200	...	1353	...	1403	1500
239	**Caen** 272 d.	0323	0559	0703	...	...	0803	...	...	0901	0903	...	...	1003	...	...	1103	1107	...	1203	1203	1303	...	1403	1406	1503
269	Bayeux 272 d.	0350	0616	0719	...	...	0819	...	...	0918	0919	...	...	1019	...	...	1119	1125	...	1219	1221	1319	...	1419	1423	1521
296	Lison 272 d.	0411	0630	0734	...	...	0834	...	...	|	0934	...	...	1034	...	...	1134	1140	...	1234	1236	1334	...	1434	1438	1536
314	Carentan d.	0425	0640	0744	...	...	0844	...	...	0941	0944	...	...	1044	...	...	1144	1152	...	1244	1248	1344	...	1444	1450	1548
343	Valognes d.	0445	0655	0800	...	...	0900	...	...	0957	1000	...	...	1100	...	...	1200	1207	...	1300	1303	1400	...	1500	1506	1603
371	**Cherbourg** a.	0501	0711	0815	...	...	0915	...	...	1013	1015	...	...	1115	...	...	1215	1223	...	1315	1319	1415	...	1515	1521	1619

		3343		3345	3329	3347	3311			3313			3349	3315			3351	3317		3353	3319	3321	3355	3323	3357	3359
	Ⓐ	Ⓐ	Ⓐ	⑤s	⑦d	⑥t	Ⓐ	Ⓐ	Ⓐ	Ⓒ	Ⓐ	Ⓒ	Ⓐ	Ⓐ	Ⓒ	Ⓐ		Ⓐ	Ⓒ	Ⓐ	⑤f	Ⓒu	△	Ⓑh	⑥v	⑤z
Paris St Lazare ▷ d.	...	1343	...	1410	1442	1443	1505	...	...	1608	...	...	1642	1708	...	...	1743	1804	...	1843	1904	1909	1959	2042	2042	2143
Evreux ▷ d.	...	1444	...	1511	1545	1543	|	...	...	|	...	...	1743	|	...	...	1845	|	...	1945	|	|	2108	2143	2144	2244
Bernay ▷ d.	...	1511	...	1538	1612	1610	|	...	...	|	...	...	1812	|	...	...	1912	|	...	2012	|	|	2135	2210	2211	2311
Lisieux ▷ d.	1451	1529	...	1556	1630	1628	|	1653	1721	|	1751	1751	1830	|	...	1851	1930	|	...	2030	|	|	2154	2227	2229	2329
Mézidon 271 277 d.	1505	|	...	|	|	|	|	1707	1735	|	1805	1805	|	|	...	1905	|	|	...	|	|	|	|	|	|	|
Caen 271 277 a.	1525	1554	...	1621	1654	1653	1657	1727	1753	1803	1824	1824	1855	1903	...	1925	1955	1959	...	2055	2101	2103	2219	2249	2254	2353
Caen 272 d.	...	...	1603	...	1657	...	1700	...	1756	1806	1827	...	...	1906	1903	...	...	2002	2005	...	2104	2106	...	2252	...	...
Bayeux 272 d.	...	...	1619	...	1715	...	1720	...	1813	1824	1843	...	...	1924	1919	...	...	2020	2021	...	2121	2123	...	2309	...	...
Lison 272 d.	...	...	1634	...	1731	...	1736	...	1829	1839	1858	...	...	1939	1934	...	...	2035	2036	...	2137	2138	...	2324	...	...
Carentan d.	...	...	1644	...	1743	...	1748	...	1839	1851	1908	...	...	1951	1944	...	...	2047	2046	...	2149	2150	...	2337	...	...
Valognes d.	...	...	1700	...	1759	...	1804	...	1854	1906	1923	...	...	2006	2000	...	...	2103	2102	...	2204	2206	...	2352	...	...
Cherbourg a.	...	...	1715	...	1815	...	1819	...	1910	1922	1939	...	...	2022	2015	...	...	2118	2117	...	2219	2221	...	0007	...	...

	3330	3332		3300			3334				3302		3338	3360			3340	3304	3304		3306	3342			3344	
	Ⓐ	⚒	Ⓐ	Ⓐ	⑥u	Ⓐ	▽x	⑥k	Ⓐ	⑦d		Ⓐ	Ⓐ	Ⓒ	⚒		⑤f	H	⑥	⑦d	⑤f	Ⓒ	Ⓐq	⚒	Ⓐ	
Cherbourg d.	...	...	...	0543	0620	0620	...	...	0720	...	0733	...	...	0849	0943	...	...	1035	1035	1143	1151	...	...	1243	...	...
Valognes d.	...	...	...	0601	0635	0635	...	...	0735	...	0750	...	...	0906	0958	...	...	1052	1052	1158	1209	...	...	1258	...	...
Carentan d.	...	...	...	0616	0651	0651	...	...	0751	...	0806	...	...	0921	1014	...	...	1108	1108	1214	1224	...	...	1314	...	...
Lison 272 d.	...	...	...	0628	0702	0702	...	...	0802	...	0817	0907	...	0933	1025	...	...	1119	1119	1225	|	...	...	1325	...	...
Bayeux 272 d.	...	...	...	0644	0716	0715	...	...	0816	...	0834	0922	...	0948	1039	...	...	1135	1136	1239	|	...	...	1339	...	...
Caen 272 a.	...	...	...	0659	0732	0737	...	...	0832	...	0849	0938	...	1005	1055	...	...	1151	1151	1255	1259	...	...	1355	...	...
Caen 271 277 d.	0505	0607	0635	0702	...	...	0741	0822	0835	0835	0852	...	1007	1007	...	1107	1150	1154	1154	...	1302	1306	1307	...	1403	...
Mézidon 271 277 d.	|	|	0654	|	...	...	|	0841	0854	0854	|	...	|	|	...	1126	|	|	|	...	|	|	1326	...	|	...
Lisieux ▷ d.	0531	0633	0708	|	...	...	0808	0855	0908	0908	|	...	1034	1034	...	1140	|	|	|	...	1334	1333	1340	...	1433	...
Bernay ▷ d.	0549	0651	...	|	...	...	0826	...	...	...	|	...	1053	1053	...	...	|	|	|	...	1352	1351	...	...	1451	...
Evreux ▷ d.	0616	0718	...	|	...	...	0853	...	...	...	|	...	1120	1120	...	...	|	|	|	...	1418	1418	...	...	1518	...
Paris St Lazare ▷ a.	0717	0820	...	0901	...	...	1000	...	...	...	1049	...	1221	1219	...	...	1349	1355	1357	...	1520	1519r	...	...	1618	...

	3308		3346				3348			3312	3310			3314		3350	3316		3318		3320	3320			3322	
		Ⓐ	Ⓒ	Ⓐ	Ⓐ	Ⓒ		Ⓐ	⚒	⑦d	Ⓐ	ⒶJ	Ⓐ	Ⓐ	⑦d	⑦d	⑥t	Ⓐ	⑦d		Ⓐ	⑦d	⑥t	Ⓐ	⑦d	
Cherbourg d.	1332	...	...	...	1520	1525	...	...	1620	1635	1651	...	...	1733	1743	...	1751	1820	1834	...	1905	1917	1920	1947	2005	...
Valognes d.	1349	...	...	...	1535	1540	...	...	1635	1652	|	...	...	1750	1759	...	1809	1835	1852	...	1923	1934	1935	2002	2022	...
Carentan d.	1405	...	...	...	1551	1556	...	...	1651	1708	|	...	...	1806	1814	...	1824	1851	1907	...	1938	1950	1951	2018	2038	...
Lison 272 d.	1416	1521	...	...	1602	1607	...	...	1702	1719	|	...	...	1817	1825	...	1836	1902	1919	...	1950	2002	2002	2029	2049	...
Bayeux 272 d.	1432	1535	...	...	1616	1621	...	...	1716	1735	|	...	...	1834	1839	...	1852	1916	1935	...	2006	2018	2016	2043	2105	...
Caen 272 a.	1448	1550	...	...	1632	1637	...	...	1731	1751	1749	...	...	1850	1855	...	1907	1932	1950	...	2021	2033	2032	2059	2121	...
Caen 271 277 d.	1451	1552	1607	1635	...	...	1707	1725	1734	1754	1752	1804	1835	1853	...	1907	1910	1935	1952	...	2024	2036	...	...	2124	...
Mézidon 271 277 d.	|	1605	|	1654	...	...	|	1745	1752	|	|	1824	1854	|	...	|	|	1954	|	...	|	|	...	...	|	...
Lisieux ▷ d.	|	1619	1634	1708	...	...	1734	1759	1806	|	|	1838	1908	|	...	1934	1935	2008	|	...	2049	2101	...	...	|	...
Bernay ▷ d.	|	...	1653	...	...	...	1752	...	...	|	|	1855	...	|	...	1953	1952	...	|	...	|	2119	...	...	|	...
Evreux ▷ d.	|	...	1720	...	...	...	1819	...	...	|	|	1933	...	|	...	2020	2019	...	|	...	|	2146	...	...	|	...
Paris St Lazare ▷ a.	1649	...	1819	...	...	...	1919	...	...	1951	1949	...	...	2050	...	2119	2119	...	2146	...	2226	2249	...	...	2318	...

H – ①-④ (not holidays).
J – Not July 8 - Aug. 23.
d – Also June 10, Nov. 11.
f – Also Aug. 14, Oct. 31; not Nov. 1.
g – Also June 11, Nov. 12; not June 10, Nov. 11.
h – Not Aug. 15.
k – Runs 13 mins later on ⑥ June 1-29.
q – On ③ (not July 10 - Aug. 21) runs 28 minutes later.

r – 1543 on Aug. 3 and ⑥ from Sept. 7.
s – Not Nov. 1.
t – Also Aug. 15.
u – Runs 16 mins earlier to July 13 (also Nov. 2).
v – Also Aug. 15, 16.
x – Departs up to 8 mins earlier on Ⓒ to July 28.
z – Also Aug. 14; not Nov. 1.
△ – Also calls at Mantes-la-Jolie (d. 2038).

▽ – Also calls at Mantes-la-Jolie (a. 0922).
▷ – For other trains Paris - Lisieux (- Trouville-Deauville) se[e] Table **276**; for (Rouen-) Lisieux - Caen see Table **277**. Local trains run Paris - Mantes la Jolie - Evreux.

Times may vary by up to 10 minutes. On Ⓒ to July 28 (als[o] Nov. 1, 2) departures from Paris may be up to 40 mins earlier and arrivals at Paris up to 30 mins later.

PARIS - LISIEUX - TROUVILLE DEAUVILLE 276

km				3371		3373	3375		3377		3379		3395	3381			3383		3385			3387	3389	3391	3393
		⚒	Ⓑ	Ⓐ	⑥	Ⓒ		Ⓐ		⚒	Ⓐ	Ⓒ			Ⓐ		⑤	①–④	⑤			⑤	⑦	⑥	Ⓐ
			h		t		S		F	u			Y	T			f	m	G	B	b	L	Q	P	
0	**Paris** St Lazare ..... ▷ d.	...	...	0740	...	0843r	0943	...	1010s	...	1142	...	1210c	1344c	...	...	1543	...	1633	...	...	1809	1818c	1843c	1909
108	Evreux ..... ▷ d.	...	...	0843	...	0943	|	...	1111	...	1243	...	|	1443	...	...	1644	...	|	...	...	|	1922	1943	2013
160	Bernay ..... ▷ d.	...	...	0910	...	1010	|	...	1138	...	1310	...	|	1510	...	...	1711	...	|	...	...	|	1949	2010	2042
191	**Lisieux** ..... ▷ d.	0735	0837	0928	0935	1028	|	1037	1156	1230	1328	1337	|	1528	1535	1635	1730	1735	1830	1835	1935	1950	2008	2028	2102
209	Pont l'Évêque ..... d.	0748	0850	0940	0948	1040	|	1049	1208	1243	1340	1348	|	1540	1547	1648	1741	1748	1841	1847	1946	2001	2019	2040	2113
221	**Trouville-Deauville** ..... a.	0757	0859	0948	0956	1048	1132	1059	1217	1251	1348	1358	1408	1548	1557	1700	1750	1757	1850	1902	2000	2010	2029	2048	2122

	🚌		3370				3372	3372					3374	3376		3378			3380	3382	3384			3386	3388
	Ⓐ	⚒	Ⓐ	†			Ⓐ	⑥	⑥	Ⓐ	Ⓒ	Ⓐ				⑦		Ⓐ	Ⓒ	⑦	Ⓐ	⑦	Ⓐ	⑦	⑦
					B			P	t		⊡		E	S		n		b		V		n	z	H	W
Trouville-Deauville ..... d.	0540	0700	0711	0738	0808	1000	1110	1110	1157	1204	1259	1403	1410	1414	1600	1638	1704	1807	1810	1853	1910	2004	2013	2029	2056
Pont l'Évêque ..... d.	0557	0709	0722	0747	0817	1008	1120	1120	1207	1213	1308	1412	1420	1424	1608	1649	1713	1816	1820	|	1921	2013	2022	|	2107
Lisieux ..... ▷ d.	0623	0722	0734	0800	0830	1022	1132	1132	1223	1226	1321	1425	1432	1440	1624	1702	1726	1829	1832	|	1933	2026	2035	|	2119
Bernay ..... ▷ d.	...	...	0753	...	...	...	1151	1151	...	...	...	...	1451	1459	...	1720	...	...	1851	|	1951	...	...	|	2137
Evreux ..... ▷ d.	...	...	0820	...	...	...	1219	1219	...	...	...	...	1518	1526	...	1747	...	...	1918	|	2019	...	...	|	2205
Paris St Lazare ..... ▷ a.	...	...	0920	...	...	...	1319	1319	...	...	...	...	1619	1627	...	1850	...	...	2048	2049	2119	...	...	2226	2304

B – ①–⑤ (also ⑥ July 6 - Aug. 24).
E – ⑥⑦ June 15 - Sept. 1 (also June 2, 10, Aug. 15).
F – ⑥ June 1 - Sept. 19; ⑦ June 23 - Sept. 1 (also Aug. 15, 16).
G – ⑤ May 24 - Sept. 27 (also Aug. 14).
H – ⑦ July 7 - Sept. 1.
L – ⑤ June 7 - Aug. 30 (also Aug. 14).
P – ⑥ June 22 - Aug. 31 (also Aug. 15).
Q – ⑦ July 14 - Sept. 1.
S – ①–⑤ June 24 - Aug. 30 (not Aug. 15).
T – ⑥ June 1 - Sept. 21 (also Aug. 15).
V – ⑦ June 2 - Sept. 22.

W – ⑦ June 2 - Sept. 22 (also June 10, Aug. 15).
Y – ⑥ Apr. 20 - Aug. 25.

b – Not on ⑤ July 12 - Aug. 23; not Aug. 14.
c – 34-40 mins earlier on June 1, 8, 15, July 6, 13, 27.
f – Also Aug. 14, Oct. 31; not Nov. 1.
h – Not Aug. 15.
m – Not Aug. 14, 15, Oct. 31, Nov. 11.
n – Also June 10, Nov. 11.
r – 0802 on June 1, 2, 8-10, 15, 16, July 6, 7, 13, 14, 27.
s – 0935 on June 1, 8, 15, July 6, 7, 13, 14, 27, 28.

t – Also Aug. 15, Nov. 1.
u – Runs 5 minutes later on Ⓐ.
z – Runs 7 minutes later on ①–④.
⊡ – Also runs on ⑤f (depart 1303, arrive 1325).
▷ – For other trains see Table **275**.

Timings may vary by up to 10 mins (Paris arrivals on dates in note **r** *may be up to 25 mins later).*

TROUVILLE DEAUVILLE - DIVES CABOURG 276a

24 km Journey 30 minutes

June 1 - 21 and September 2 - 29

From Trouville Deauville: 1100⑥, 1106⑦, 1225⑥, 1419⑥**D**, 1419⑦, 1604⑥, 1645⑦, 2133④⑤.
From Dives Cabourg: 0620①**g**, 1140⑥, 1144⑦, 1315⑥, 1514⑥, 1558⑦**u**, 1731Ⓒ.

June 22 - September 1

From Trouville Deauville: 0833Ⓐ, 0956Ⓐ, 1100Ⓒ, 1143Ⓐ, 1225Ⓒ, 1359Ⓐ**b**, 1406⑥⑦**n**, 1604⑥**t**, 1609Ⓐ, 1645⑦, 1750Ⓐ**c**, 1900⑦, 2005⑥**t**, 2009Ⓐ**d**, 2038⑦, 2111⑥**t**, 2133Ⓐ.
From Dives Cabourg: 0620Ⓐ, 0913Ⓐ, 1023Ⓒ, 1033Ⓐ, 1140Ⓒ, 1315, 1514Ⓐ, 1514⑥**t**, 1558⑦**u**, 1710Ⓐ, 1731Ⓒ, 1828Ⓐ, 1949⑦, 2046Ⓐ**d**.

D – ⑥ June 1 - 15.
b – Runs 8 minutes later on ⑤**f**.
c – Runs 6 minutes later on ⑤.
d – Runs 11 minutes later on ⑤.
f – Also Aug. 14; not Aug. 16.
g – Also June 11; not June 10.
n – Also Aug. 16. Depart 1419 on certain dates.
t – Also Aug. 15.
u – 1510 on ⑦ June 2 - 23.

ROUEN - LISIEUX - CAEN 277

km		Ⓐ	⑥	Ⓐ	Ⓐ	Ⓐ			⑦	Ⓐ	⑥	Ⓐ	⑤	⑤	①–④	⑦		Ⓐ	⑥	Ⓐ	Ⓒ	Ⓐ	†	
						🚌			u		t	🚌	f	v	m	u			t					
0	**Rouen** Rive Droite ..... d.	0604	0704	0707	0808	0904	1004	...	1204	1204	1304	1404	1504	1603	1612	1604	...	1704	1704	1804	1804	1904	1904	...
23	Elbeuf-St Aubin ..... d.	0620	0719	0724	|	|	1019	...	1219	1219	1319	|	1519	1619	|	1619	...	1719	1719	1819	1819	1919	1919	...
73	Serquigny ..... d.	0651	|	|	|	|	|	...	|	1254	|	|	|	1649	|	|	...	1746	1746	1854	1852	|	|	...
83	Bernay ..... ▷ d.	0659	0753	0757	|	|	1053	...	1253	1303	1353	|	1553	1657	|	1653	...	1754	1755	1903	1901	1953	1954	...
114	Lisieux ..... ▷ d.	0715	0809	0813	|	|	1109	...	1309	1319	1409	|	1609	1714	|	1709	...	1810	1811	1919	1917	2009	2012	...
139	Mézidon **271** ..... ▷ d.	0728	0823	0827	|	|	1123	...	1323	1333	1423	|	1623	1728	|	1723	...	1823	1825	1933	1930	2023	2026	...
162	**Caen 271** ..... ▷ a.	0742	0836	0840	0932	1044	1136	...	1336	1346	1436	1544	1636	1741	1735	1736	...	1837	1838	1946	1944	2036	2039	...

	Ⓐ	⚒	Ⓐ	Ⓐ	⑥	Ⓑ		Ⓐ	Ⓒ	Ⓐ		Ⓐ	Ⓐ	Ⓒ	⑦	Ⓐ	⑥	Ⓐ		⑤	⑥	⑦		
				🚌	t	h				🚌					u		t			v	S	u		
Caen 271 ..... ▷ d.	0554	0717	0801	0915	1016	1020	...	1211	1220	1415	...	1617	1720	1720	1815	1819	1819	1922	...	2013	2020	2024	...	...
Mézidon **271** ..... ▷ d.	0608	0731	|	|	1030	1034	...	1225	1234	|	...	|	1734	1734	1829	1833	1833	1936	...	2027	2034	2038	...	...
Lisieux ..... ▷ d.	0622	0744	|	|	1043	1047	...	1238	1247	|	...	|	1747	1747	1842	1846	1847	1949	...	2041	2047	2052	...	...
Bernay ..... ▷ d.	0638	0800	|	|	1059	1103	...	1254	1303	|	...	|	1803	1803	1858	1902	1904	2005	...	2057	2103	2109	...	...
Serquigny ..... d.	0645	0808	|	|	1107	|	...	1302	|	|	...	|	|	|	1906	1910	|	|	...	|	|	|	...	...
Elbeuf-St Aubin ..... d.	0721	0837	|	|	1137	1137	...	1337	1337	|	...	|	1837	1837	1938	1940	1937	2039	...	2135	2137	2142	...	...
Rouen Rive Droite ..... a.	0738	0853	0925	1055	1153	1153	...	1353	1353	1555	...	1740	1855	1853	1953	1956	1953	2055	...	2153	2153	2157	...	...

S – ⑥ Apr. 6 - Sept. 14 (also May 30, Aug. 15).
f – Not Nov. 1.
h – Not Aug. 15, Nov. 1.
m – Not June 10, Aug. 14, 15, Oct. 31, Nov. 11.
t – Also Aug. 15, Nov. 1.
u – Also June 10, Nov. 11.
v – Also Aug. 14, Oct. 31; not Nov. 1.
▷ – See also Table **275**.
🚌 – TER bus service, rail tickets valid. At Caen buses leave from the Gare Routière (bus station) adjacent to the railway station.

Times may vary by 2 - 4 minutes on certain dates

PARIS - CHARTRES - LE MANS 278

For *TGV* trains Paris - Le Mans via the high-speed line see Table **280**

km		Ⓐ	Ⓐ	⚒	⚒	Ⓐ	Ⓐ		n								Ⓐ	Ⓐ	Ⓐ	†	⑥	Ⓑ	Ⓐ	Ⓐ	Ⓑ
0	**Paris** Montparnasse ..... ▷ d.	0533	...	0610	0636	0709	0740	0809	0906	1009	1106	1209	1306	1409	1506	1609	1624	1639	1706v	1706	1706	1709	1724	1754	1806
17	Versailles Chantiers ..... ▷ d.	0547	...	0624	0652	0725	0754	0825	0920	1025	1122	1225	1322	1425	1522	1625	1640	1655	1722*	1722	1722	1725	1740	1809	1822*
48	Rambouillet ..... d.	0604	...	0646	0710	0744	0812	0845	0937	1045	1143	1245	1343	1445	1543	1644	1700	1715	|	|	1742	1745	1800	1830	|
88	**Chartres** ..... a.	0642	0648	0725	0737	0824	0851	0924	1005	1124	1209	1324	1411	1524	1609	1724	1727	1754	1807	1806	1807	1824	1827	1857	1905
149	Nogent le Rotrou ..... a.	...	0736	...	0813	0922	...	...	1041	...	1245	...	1450	...	1645	...	1822	...	1845	1844	1844	...	1922	...	1942
211	**Le Mans** ..... a.	...	0824	...	0852	...	...	...	1122	...	1324	...	1531r	...	1723	...	1914	...	1925	1925	1923	...	...	...	2022

		Ⓐ	Ⓐ		Ⓐ		Ⓑ		Ⓐ‡	①⑦
Paris Montparnasse ..... ▷ d.	1809	1824	1854	1906	1939	2009	2106	2209	2302	0002
Versailles Chantiers ..... ▷ d.	1825	1840	1910	1924	1955	2025	2122	2225	2321	0017
Rambouillet ..... d.	1845	1900	1930	1944	2014	2043	2145	2245	2342	0044
Chartres ..... a.	1924	1929	1957	2012	2054	2124	2209	2324	0021	0121
Nogent le Rotrou ..... a.	...	2023	...	2048	...	...	2245	...	...	...
Le Mans ..... a.	...	...	...	2131	...	...	2322r	...	...	...

	Ⓐ	Ⓐ	⑥	Ⓐ	⚒	Ⓐ		Ⓐ	Ⓐ	
Le Mans ..... d.	...	0338s	...	...	...	...	...	0535	...	...
Nogent le Rotrou ..... d.	...	0416	...	...	...	0534	...	0616	...	...
Chartres ..... d.	0404	0452	0450	0535	0603	0629	0635	0655	0702	...
Rambouillet ..... d.	0447	0520	0519	0616	0646	0701	0716	|	0731	...
Versailles Chantiers ..... ▷ d.	0507	0541	0541	0638	0708	0723	0738	0741*	0753	...
Paris Montparnasse ..... ▷ a.	0519	0553	0553	0650	0720	0735	0750	0753	0805	...

	⚒	Ⓐ	Ⓐ	⑥		Ⓐ	⚒	Ⓐ												Ⓐ				Ⓑ	†
Le Mans ..... d.	...	0558	...	...	...	0627	...	0640	0733r	...	...	0922	...	1133	...	1338r	...	1548	...	...	1738	...	1937	...	2136
Nogent le Rotrou ..... d.	...	0633	0637	0637	...	0708	...	0731	0813	0836	...	1010	...	1211	...	1416	...	1628	1637	...	1816	1837	2017	...	2214
Chartres ..... d.	0705	0725	0732	0730	0735	0749	0805	0832	0849	0925	0934	1051	1135	1248	1334	1452	1534	1704	1735	1805	1851	1935	2052	2131	2250
Rambouillet ..... d.	0746	|	0803	...	0816	0820	0846	0901	0919	...	1016	1119	1216	1319	1416	1520	1616	1734	1816	1846	1919	2016	2120	2210	2319
Versailles Chantiers ..... ▷ d.	0808	0811*	0823	...	0838	0841	0908	0923	0942	...	1037	1141	1238	1341	1437	1541	1637	1758	1838	1908	1941	2038	2141	2226	2341
Paris Montparnasse ..... ▷ a.	0820	0823	0835	...	0850	0853	0920	0935	0954	...	1049	1153	1250	1353	1449	1553	1649	1812	1850	1920	1953	2050	2153	2238	2353

Suburban trains PARIS - VERSAILLES: Paris St Lazare - Versailles Rive Droite (journey 28 - 35 minutes); Paris Montparnasse - Versailles Chantiers (journey 12 - 28 minutes).
RER (express Métro) Line C: **Paris Austerlitz** - St Michel Notre Dame - **Versailles Rive Gauche** (for Château) [some journeys to Versailles Chantiers]; every 15 - 30 mins; journey 40 mins.

r – ⚒ only.
n – Runs up to 13 mins earlier on Ⓒ to Apr. 7.
r – Subject to alteration on ①–④ June 3 - 27.
s – Subject to alteration on June 3, 11, 17, 24.
v – Departs from Montparnasse Vaugirard platforms.
▷ – For additional suburban and RER trains see note below table.
‡ – Subject to alteration on Ⓐ June 21 - July 26.
* – Will not convey passengers travelling Paris - Versailles or v.v.

Subject to alteration - times may vary

280 TGV BRETAGNE - PAYS DE LA LOIRE

SERVICE JULY 6 - SEPTEMBER 1 (see earlier editions for service to July 5)

PARIS - LE MANS - RENNES

km		TGV 7601	TGV 8605	TGV 8081	TGV 8707	TGV 8611	TGV 8691		TGV 8711	TGV 8715	TGV 8717		TGV 8085	TGV 8615	TGV 7603		TGV 8719	TGV 8719	TGV 8617		TGV 8091	TGV 8623		TGV 8055
			①-⑥						⑤	⑥							⑥	⑦	①-⑤					①-④
		⊠			L				f	r	D				⊠		r		h					m
0	**Paris** Montparnasse d.	0706•	0735	0809	0852	0952	0952	...	1052	1052	1052	...	1152	1152	1214	...	1252	1252	1252	...	1409	1452	...	1552
	Le Mans d.		0839	0912	|	|	|	...	|	|	|	...	|	|	|	...	|	|	|	...	1512	|	...	|
	Laval d.	0827	|	0943	|	|	|	...	|	|	|	...	|	|	1329	...	|	|	|	...	1543	|	...	|
	Vitré d.	0847	|	|	|	|	|	...	|	|	|	...	|	|	|	...	|	|	|	...	|	|	...	|
364	**Rennes** a.	0907	0925	1007	1025	1125	1125	...	1225	1225	1225	...	1325	1325	1353	...	1423	1425	1425	...	1607	1625	...	1725
	To:	—	*Bre*	*Mal*	*Qui*	*Bre*	*Lan*	...	*Qui*	*Qui*	*Qui*	...	*Mal*	*Bre*	—	...	*Qui*	*Qui*	*Bre*	...	*Mal*	*Bre*	...	—

km		TGV 8055	TGV 8055	TGV 8629	TGV 8631	TGV 8729		TGV 8057		TGV 8639	TGV 8639	TGV 8731	TGV 8735		TGV 8093		TGV 8641	TGV 8739		TGV 8059	TGV 8071		TGV 8649	TGV 8751
		⑤⑥	①-④		⑤			⑤-⑦		①-④	⑦	⑦	⑤		Ⓑ					①-⑤	⑥		⑤	
		t	m	A	f	A		t		m			f		h		A	G		h	r		f	D
0	**Paris** Montparnasse d.	1609	1626	1652	1652	1652	...	1709	...	1752	1752	1752	1752	...	1809	...	1852	1852	...	1909	1909	...	1952	1952
202	**Le Mans** d.	1712	1729	|	|	|	...	1812	...	|	|	|	|	...	|	...	|	|	...	2012	2012	...	|	|
	Laval d.	|	|	|	|	|	...	1843	...	|	|	|	|	...	1927	...	|	|	...	2043	2043	...	|	|
	Vitré d.	|	|	|	|	|	...	|	...	|	|	|	|	...	1948	...	|	|	...	|	2103	...	|	|
371	**Rennes** a.	1755	1812	1825	1825	1825	...	1907	...	1922	1925	1925	1925	...	2007	...	2025	2025	...	2107	2123	...	2125	2125
	To:	—	—	*Bre*	*Bre*	*Qui*	...	—	...	*Bre*	*Bre*	*Qui*	*Qui*	...	*Mal*	...	*Bre*	*Qui*	...	—	—	...	*Bre*	*Qui*

	TGV 8097	TGV 8073	TGV 8655	TGV 8755	TGV 8063		TGV 8065	TGV 8791	
	⑤	⑦	⑤	⑤			⑦	⑤	
	f		f	f	A			f	
Paris Montparnasse d.	2009	2009	2052	2052	2109	...	2209	2209	...
Le Mans d.	2112	2112	|	|	2212	...	2312	2312	...
Laval d.	2143	2143	|	|	2243	...	2343	2343	...
Vitré d.	|	2203	|	|	|	...	|	0003	...
Rennes a.	2207	2224	2225	2225	2307	...	0007	0024	...
To:	*Mal*	—	*Bre*	*Qui*	—	...	—	*Lor*	

	TGV 8072	TGV 8680	TGV 8050	TGV 8080		TGV 8602	TGV 8702	TGV 8052	TGV 8054
	①-⑤	①	⑥	①-⑤			①-⑥	Ⓑ	①
	h		r	h		G		h	
From:	—	*Bri*	—	*Mal*		*Bre*	*Qui*	—	—
Rennes d.	0536	0635	0650	0703	...	0735	0735	0752	0835
Vitré d.	0557	|	|	|	...	|	|	|	|
Laval d.	0619	0703	0719	|	...	|	|	0819	|
Le Mans d.	0651	|	0751	0751	...	|	|	0851	|
Paris Montparnasse a.	0752	0821	0852	0857	...	0910	0910	0952	1009

	TGV 8606	TGV 8706	TGV 7606		TGV 8610	TGV 8710		TGV 8084	TGV 8720	TGV 8620		TGV 7608		TGV 8722	TGV 8622		TGV 8792	TGV 8010	TGV 8630	TGV 8628	TGV 8694	TGV 8682		TGV 8086
	①-⑥	①-⑥													①-⑤		①-④	⑥		⑤⑦	⑤	⑦		Ⓑ
			⊠						H			⊠		¶	h		m	r	G	f	f			h
From:	*Bre*	*Qui*	—		*Bre*	*Qui*		*Mal*	*Qui*	*Bre*		—		*Qui*	*Bre*		*Lor*	—	*Bre*	*Bre*	*Lan*	*Bri*		*Mal*
Rennes d.	0935	0935	0952	...	1135	1135	...	1252	1337	1337	...	1435	...	1535	1535	...	1635	1635	1635	1635	1635	1635	...	1652
Vitré d.	|	|	|	...	|	|	...	|	|	|	...	|	...	|	|	...	|	|	|	|	|	|	...	|
Laval d.	|	|	1021	...	|	|	...	1319	|	|	...	|	...	|	|	...	|	|	|	|	|	|	...	1719
Le Mans d.	|	|	|	...	|	|	...	1351	|	|	...	|	...	|	|	...	|	|	|	|	|	|	...	1751
Paris Montparnasse a.	1108	1108	1135	...	1309	1309	...	1452	1509	1509	...	1604	...	1709	1709	...	1809	1809	1809	1809	1809	1809	...	1852

	TGV 8088	TGV 8728		TGV 8062	TGV 8636	TGV 8690	TGV 8064	TGV 8640	TGV 8642	TGV 8090	TGV 8734	TGV 8092	TGV 8094	TGV 8074	TGV 8692		TGV 8646	TGV 8746	TGV 8646	TGV 8746		TGV 8096	TGV 8652	TGV 8752
	⑥	Ⓑ							⑤	⑤	⑦	⑦		⑤	⑦		⑦	⑤⑥	①-④	①-④		⑦	⑦	⑦
	r	h				A	E	D	f	f			G	f				t	m	m				
From:	*Mal*	*Qui*		—	*Bre*	*Lan*	—	*Bre*	*Bre*	*Mal*	*Qui*	*Mal*	*Mal*	—	*Lan*		*Bre*	*Qui*	*Bre*	*Qui*		*Mal*	*Bre*	*Qui*
Rennes d.	1735	1735	...	1752	1835	1835	1905	1935	1935	1935	1935	1952	1952	1952	2035	...	2135	2135	2135	2135	...	2152	2235	2235
Vitré d.	|	|	...	|	|	|	|	|	|	|	|	2012	2012	2012	|	...	|	|	|	|	...	|	|	|
Laval d.	|	|	...	1819	|	|	|	|	|	|	|	2033	2033	2033	|	...	|	|	|	|	...	2219	|	|
Le Mans d.	|	|	...	1851	|	|	|	|	|	|	|	|	2106	2106	|	...	|	|	|	|	...	2251	|	|
Paris Montparnasse a.	1909	1909	...	1952	2009	2009	2039	2109	2109	2109	2109	2152	2209	2209	2209	...	2309	2309	2312	2312	...	2352	0009	0009

PARIS - LE MANS - NANTES

km		TGV 7621	TGV 8911	TGV 8803	TGV 8913	TGV 8973	TGV 8869	TGV 8871	TGV 8917	TGV 8807	TGV 8975	TGV 8921	TGV 8921	TGV 8809	TGV 8977	TGV 8923	TGV 8815	TGV 7623	TGV 7623	TGV 8817	TGV 8885	TGV 8927	TGV 8905	TGV 8819	TGV 8921
			①-⑥	①-⑥				Ⓑ	⑥	⑤⑥	①-④	①-⑥	⑦	①-④	⑤-⑦		⑤	⑥⑦	①-⑤	①-⑤	⑤	⑤	①-④	⑥⑦	⑤
		⊠						h	r	t	m			m	t		f	⊠	⊠	z	f	f	m	r	f
0	**Paris** Montparnasse d.	0634•	0643	0740	0843	0843	0926	1034	1034	1218	1218	1236	1236	1336	1336	1443	1618	1648	1648	1718	1734	1743	1743	1743	1818
	Le Mans d.	0736	|	|	|	|	1029	1136	1136	|	|	1337	1337	|	|	|	|	|	|	|	1840	|	|	|	|
254	Sablé d.	|	|	0851	|	|	|	|	|	|	|	|	|	1449	1449	|	|	|	|	|	|	|	|	|	|
302	Angers St Laud d.	0817	|	0913	1013	1013	1113	1217	1217	1348	1348	|	1418	1513	1513	1613	|	1813	1817	|	1919	|	1913	1913	|
390	**Nantes** a.	0854	0850	0950	1050	1050	1150	1254	1254	1424	1424	1450	1454	1550	1550	1650	1819	1850	1854	1919	...	1950	1950	1950	2019
	To:	—	*Cro*	—	*Cro*	*Sab*	—	—	*Cro*	—	*Sab*	*Cro*	*Cro*	—	*Sab*	*Cro*	—	—	—	—	—	*Cro*	*Naz*	—	—

	TGV 8897	TGV 8931	TGV 8985	TGV 8823	TGV 8887	TGV 8935	TGV 8825	TGV 8937	TGV 8827	TGV 8939	TGV 8827
				⑤		⑤	⑥⑦	⑤	①-④	⑤	⑦
				f	D	f	r	f	m◇	f	
Paris Montparnasse d.	1834	1843	1843	1918	1934	1934	2043	2043	2116	2143	2143
Le Mans d.	1940	|	|	|	2036	2036	|	|	|	|	|
Sablé d.	2002	|	|	|	|	|	|	|	|	|	|
Angers St Laud d.	2023	|	|	|	2119	2119	2213	2213	2246	2313	2313
Nantes a.	...	2048	2048	2123	2156	...	2250	2250	2323	2350	2350
To:	—	*Cro*	*Sab*	—	—	*Cro*	—	*Cro*	—	*Cro*	—

km		TGV 8860	TGV 8860	TGV 8900	TGV 8802	TGV 8804	TGV 8910		TGV 8864	TGV 8912
		①	②-⑤	①-⑤	①-④	②-⑦	①		①-⑥	
			h	h	v					
	From:	—	—	*Naz*	—	—	*Cro*		—	*Cro*
0	**Nantes** d.	0500	0500	0606	0640	0706	0709	...	0806	0906
88	Angers St Laud d.	0540	0540	0648	|	0748	|	...	0848	0948
136	Sablé d.	0601	0601	|	|	|	|	...	|	|
191	**Le Mans** d.	0624	0624	|	|	|	|	...	0933	|
393	**Paris** Montparnasse a.	0726	0729	0817	0843	0918	0918	...	1035	1116

	TGV 7628		TGV 8972	TGV 8916	TGV 8872		TGV 8876	TGV 8876	TGV 8922	TGV 8880	TGV 8984	TGV 8816	TGV 8926	TGV 8818	TGV 8928	TGV 8986	TGV 7626	TGV 8930	TGV 8932		TGV 8826	TGV 8988		TGV 8934	TGV 8936
					①-⑤		①-⑤	⑥⑦		⑥⑦		Ⓑ		⑦	⑦	①-⑥		⑦	①-⑥		⑤	⑦		⑦	⑦
	⊠				h		h	r		r		h					⊠				f				
From:	—		*Sab*	*Cro*			—	—	*Cro*		*Sab*		*Cro*	—	*Cro*	*Sab*	—	*Cro*	*Cro*		—	*Sab*		*Cro*	*Cro*
Nantes d.	0931	...	1103	1209	1258	...	1407	1407	1503	1602	1706	1740	1806	1840	1856	1906	1939	2003	2006	...	2106	2106	...	2206	2240
Angers St Laud d.	1010	...	1144	|	1340	...	1448	1448	1544	1644	1748	|	1848	|	1940	1948	2018	2044	2048	...	2148	2148	...	2248	|
Sablé d.	|	...	|	|	|	...	|	|	|	|	|	|	1910	|	|	|	|	|	|	...	|	|	...	|	|
Le Mans d.	1051	...	1225	|	1421	...	1529	1529	1625	1724	|	|	|	|	2025	|	|	2125	|	...	|	|	...	|	|
Paris Montparnasse a.	1157*	...	1327	1417	1523	...	1631	1635	1727	1826	1917	1943	2021	2043	2126	2117	2143	2227	2217	...	2317	2317	...	0017	0043

To / From:

Bre – Brest (Table **284**).
Bri – St Brieuc (Table **284**).
Cro – Le Croisic (Table **288**).
Lan – Lannion (Table **284**).
Lor – Lorient (Table **285**).
Mal – St Malo (Table **281**).
Naz – St Nazaire (Table **288**).
Qui – Quimper (Table **285**).
Sab – Les Sables-d'Olonne (Table **293**).

A – ①②③④⑥⑦ (also Aug. 16; not Aug. 14).
D – ①②③④⑦ (not Aug. 14, 15).
E – ①②③④⑥ (not Aug. 14).
G – ①②③④⑥ (also Aug. 16; not Aug. 14).
H – ①⑥⑦ (also Aug. 15, 16).
L – ②③④⑥⑦ (also Aug. 16; not Aug. 14). Train number **8193** on ⑥ (also Aug. 15, 16).

f – Also Aug. 14; not Aug. 16.
h – Not Aug. 15, 16.
m – Not Aug. 14, 15.
r – Also Aug. 15, 16.

t – Also Aug. 14, 15.
v – Not July 22 - Aug. 15.
z – Not July 29, 30, 31, Aug. 1, 5–8, 12, 13, 15, 16.

TGV – Ⓡ, supplement payable, 🍷.

• – Also calls at Massy TGV (11 – 12 minutes later).
* – Also calls at Massy TGV (a. 1140).
¶ – Train number **8190** on ⑥ (also Aug. 15, 16).
◇ – Runs 20 – 22 minutes **earlier** July 8 – 11.
⊠ – OUIGO low-cost TGV service. Internet bookings only at www.ouigo.com.

TER (regional) services LE MANS - NANTES / RENNES 280a

See Table **280** for *TGV* services.

LE MANS - NANTES

km		Ⓐ	Ⓐ	⑥ k	Ⓐ	Ⓐ	Ⓒ L	⑥ k	Ⓐ	Ⓒ		Ⓐ	⑤ v	①-⑥	Ⓐ	①-④ m	⑤ vL	Ⓒ	Ⓐ	⑥ k	⑦	Ⓐ	Ⓐ	⑦
0	**Le Mans** d.	0542	0641	0642	0703	0740	0741	*0942*	1041	1141	1227	1313	1541	1642	1701	1741	1742	1747	1800	*1831*	1901	1905	1944	2001
49	Sablé sur Sarthe **287** d.	0607	0713	0710	0731	0813	0804	1024	1105	1213	1259	1338	1613	1711	1733	1813	1813	1819	1831	1911	1934	1933	2017	2033
97	Angers St Laud **287 289** d.	0632	0733	0746	0806	0833	0826	1046	1130	1233	1335	1402	1633	1732	1809	1832	1832	1858	1906	1933	1954	2006	2038	2054
185	**Nantes** **287 289** a.	0716	0816	0830	...	0916	0906	1127	1216	1316	...	1445	1717	1817	...	1916	1916	...	...	2016	2036	...	2120	2135

	Ⓐ	①-⑥	Ⓐ	Ⓐ	⑥ k	Ⓐ	Ⓐ	Ⓒ	Ⓐ	Ⓒ	Ⓐ	⑥ k	⑦	⑥ k	Ⓑ w	Ⓐ	Ⓐ	Ⓑ w	Ⓑ w	⑥ k	Ⓐ	Ⓐ	Ⓐ	Ⓒ L
Nantes **287 289** d.	...	...	0644	...	...	0744	...	...	1143	1144	...	...	...	1543	1544	1644	...	1744	...	...	1844	...	1944	2111
Angers St Laud **287 289** d.	0552	...	0726	0752	0752	0826	0852	...	1226	1226	1252	1252	...	1626	1626	1726	1752	1826	1852	1852	1926	1952	2026	2155
Sablé sur Sarthe **287** d.	0628	0713	0748	0825	0828	0854	0927	0939	1253	1251	1328	1330	1539	1651	1654	1751	1828	1854	1928	1930	1952	2028	2054	2218
Le Mans a.	0655	0746	0815	0859	0855	0916	0953	1012	1315	1315	1359	1403	1612	1714	1716	1815	1859	1916	1955	2003	2015	2055	2116	2240

LE MANS - RENNES

km		Ⓐ	Ⓐ ◇	Ⓐ	Ⓐ	⑥ k	Ⓐ	Ⓐ	⑥ k	Ⓐ	Ⓐ ◇	⑥ k◇	Ⓐ ◇	⑦	Ⓒ ◇		Ⓐ ◇	①-⑥		Ⓐ ◇	⑤ v	⑦	Ⓑ w◇	Ⓐ	Ⓒ
0	**Le Mans** d.	...	...	0631	0650	0704	...	0719	...	0820	...	...	...	1115	...	...	...	1217	...	...	1531	1620	...	1639	...
	Sablé sur Sarthe **287** d.	...	0656	|	|	|	...	|	...	|	0858	0958	1058	|	1158	...	1258	|	...	1458	|	|	1658	|	...
90	Laval **287** d.	0638	0718	0725	0754	0755	0803	0811	0903	0911	0920	1020	1120	1206	1220	1303	1320	1332	...	1520	1619	1711	1720	1732	1803
125	Vitré **287** d.	0704	0738	0747	...	...	0828	...	0929	...	0940	1040	1140	...	1240	1329	1341	...	...	1540	1637	...	1741	1759	1829
163	**Rennes** **287** a.	0734	0801	0817	...	...	0858	...	0958	...	1001	1101	1201	...	1301	1358	1401	...	...	1601	1711	...	1802	1830	1858

	Ⓐ	Ⓐ	Ⓐ	①-⑥	⑥ k◇	Ⓑ w◇	Ⓐ	Ⓑ w	⑦ ◇	
Le Mans d.	1720	1750	...	1820	...	...	1920	2020	...	...
Sablé sur Sarthe **287** d.	|	|	...	|	1857	1858	|	|	2058	...
Laval **287** d.	1814	1855	1904	1911	1920	1920	2020	2111	2120	...
Vitré **287** d.	...	...	1929	...	1941	1941	...	...	2140	...
Rennes **287** a.	...	...	1959	...	2002	2002	...	...	2201	...

	Ⓐ	Ⓐ	①-⑥	Ⓐ	Ⓐ ◇	Ⓐ	Ⓐ	⑥ k	⑦	Ⓐ
Rennes **287** d.	...	...	...	0630	0654	0659	0749	0759	...	...
Vitré **287** d.	...	...	...	0653	0714	0729	0821	0829	...	...
Laval **287** d.	0603	0643	0659	0724	0734	0755	0847	0855	0925	0945
Sablé sur Sarthe **287** a.	|	|	|	|	0800	...	...	...	|	|
Le Mans a.	0708	0736	0804	0814	...	...	...	...	1015	1035

	①-⑥ ◇		◇	⑥ k	Ⓐ		Ⓐ ◇		Ⓐ ◇	⑤ v	⑦ ◇	Ⓐ	Ⓐ ◇	Ⓐ	Ⓐ	⑥ k◇	⑥ k	Ⓐ	Ⓐ	⑦ ◇	⑦	Ⓐ ◇	Ⓐ	⑦ ◇	⑦
Rennes **287** d.	0912	...	1053	...	...	1159	1257	...	1457	...	1557	...	1657	...	1701	1755	...	1800	...	1821	...	1901	...	1921	...
Vitré **287** d.	0938	...	1113	...	...	1229	1317	...	1517	...	1617	...	1717	...	1731	1815	...	1830	...	1841	...	1922	...	1941	...
Laval **287** d.	0957	...	1132	1245	1245	1255	1336	...	1537	1545	1637	1645	1737	1750	1757	1835	1845	1856	1903	1900	1908	1941	1945	2000	2008
Sablé sur Sarthe **287** a.	1020	...	1200	|	|	...	1400	...	1600	|	1700	|	1800	|	...	1900	|	...	|	1921	|	2005	|	2020	|
Le Mans a.	...	...	...	1335	1359	...	...	...	...	1635	...	1735	...	1852	...	...	1935	...	2013	...	1958	...	2035	...	2058

L – To / from Le Croisic (Table **288**).

k – ⑥ (also Aug. 15).

m – Not Aug. 14, 15.
v – Also Aug. 14.
w – Not Aug. 15.

◇ – From / to Nantes via Angers (Table **287**).

RENNES - ST MALO 281

km	*TGV trains*, Ⓡ, 🍸	*TGV* 8081		*TGV* 8085		*TGV* 8091		*TGV* 8093 Ⓑ h	*TGV* 8097 ⑤ f	
	Paris Montparnasse **280** d.	0809	...	1152	...	1409	...	1809	2009	...
0	**Rennes** **272** d.	1011	...	1332	...	1611	...	2011	2211	...
58	Dol **272** d.	1045	...	|	...	|	...	2046	2246	...
81	**St Malo** a.	1059	...	1416	...	1655	...	2059	2259	...

TGV trains, Ⓡ, 🍸	*TGV* 8080 ①-⑤ h		*TGV* 8084	*TGV* 8086 Ⓑ h	*TGV* 8088 ⑥ r	*TGV* 8090 ⑤ f	*TGV* 8092 ⑦	*TGV* 8094 G	*TGV* 8096 ⑦
St Malo d.	0608	...	1201	1556	1637	1841	1856	1901	2101
Dol **272** d.	0624	...	|	1612	1652	|	1911	|	|
Rennes **272** a.	0657	...	1246	1646	1725	1925	1946	1946	2146
Paris Montparnasse **280** a.	0857	...	1452	1852	1909	2109	2152	2209	2352

	Ⓐ	①-⑥		Ⓒ	Ⓐ				⑦	①-⑥		Ⓐ	⑥ k	Ⓐ	①-⑥	⑦	⑦	Ⓐ	⑥ k	Ⓐ	⑦	Ⓐ	⑥ k	Ⓐ		Ⓒ
Rennes **272** d.	0635	0729	...	0935	0935	...	1135	...	1235	1235	...	1435	1435	1535	1635	1637	1735	1735	1735	1803	1835	1835	1835	1935	...	2039
Dol **272** d.	0716	0810	...	1013	1016	...	1216	...	1313	1321	...	1516	1523	1618	1716	1718	1813	1816	1819	1846	1916	1919	1923	2016	...	2120
St Malo a.	0732	0826	...	1027	1032	...	1232	...	1327	1337	...	1532	1537	1635	1732	1734	1827	1832	1835	1906	1930	1935	1937	2032	...	2136

	⑥ k	Ⓐ	Ⓐ	Ⓐ	⑥ k	⑦	Ⓐ				①-⑥		⑥ k	Ⓑ w		Ⓐ		Ⓒ	Ⓐ	Ⓒ	Ⓐ	Ⓐ	Ⓒ		Ⓐ	Ⓒ
St Malo d.	0620	0621	0656	0756	0825	0832	0835	...	1028	...	1219	...	1320	1328	...	1428	...	1532	1628	1723	1728	1823	1830	...	2028	2030
Dol **272** d.	0636	0637	0715	0815	0841	0846	0849	...	1044	...	1236	...	1337	1344	...	1444	...	1546	1644	1739	1744	1839	1844	...	2044	2044
Rennes **272** a.	0725	0721	0756	0856	0925	0925	0925	...	1125	...	1319	...	1425	1425	...	1525	...	1625	1725	1820	1825	1920	1925	...	2125	2125

G – ①②③④⑥ (also Aug. 16; not Aug. 14).

f – Also Aug. 14; not Aug. 16.
h – Not Aug. 15, 16.

k – Also Aug. 15.
r – Also Aug. 15, 16.

w – Not Aug. 15.

DOL - DINAN 282

2nd class

km		Ⓐ	⑥ k		①-⑥			Ⓐ	⑥ k	Ⓑ z	⑤ f
0	Dol d.	0821	0850	1052	1326	...	1723	1852	1928	2051	2250
32	Dinan a.	0848	0915	1117	1351	...	1755	1919	1953	2116	2315

	Ⓐ	Ⓐ	⑥ k	Ⓒ	Ⓐ	①-⑥		Ⓑ w	⑥ k	Ⓐ	⑥ k	⑦	①-⑤ z
Dinan d.	0550	0733	0758	1003	1010	1201	...	1543	1621	1806	1808	1839	2012
Dol a.	0615	0805	0830	1035	1035	1226	...	1608	1646	1833	1833	1904	2037

f – Also Aug. 14; not Aug. 16.
k – Also Aug. 15.

w – Not Aug. 15.
z – Not Aug. 15, 16.

MORLAIX - ROSCOFF 283

SERVICE UNTIL JULY 5 (subject to alteration from July 6)

km		🚌 Ⓐ		🚌 Ⓐ		🚌 ⚒		🚌 ⚒		🚌		🚌 †	🚌 ⚒		🚌 Ⓐ		🚌 †	🚌 ⚒		🚌	🚌 ⑤				
0	**Morlaix** d.	0655	...	0800	...	0950	...	1115	...	1315	...	1540	1540	...	1655	...	1820	1820	...	2015	2055	...	...	...	...
21	St Pol de Léon d.	0720	...	0825	...	1010	...	1135	...	1335	...	1600	1605	...	1720	...	1840	1847	...	2035	2117	...	...	...	...
28	**Roscoff** a.	0740	...	0845	...	1030	...	1155	...	1350	...	1615	1620	...	1735	...	1900	1907	...	2055	2132	...	...	...	...

	🚌 ⚒	🚌 Ⓐ		🚌 ⚒		🚌 †	🚌 ⚒		🚌		🚌 ⚒	🚌 †	🚌 Ⓐ		🚌 Ⓒ	🚌 Ⓐ								
Roscoff d.	0700	0745	...	0845	...	1205	1205	...	1400	...	1600	1650	1715	...	1900	1900	...	...	...	...	...	...	...	...
St Pol de Léon d.	0715	0800	...	0905	...	1220	1220	...	1415	...	1615	1705	1735	...	1915	1920	...	...	...	...	...	...	...	...
Morlaix a.	0740	0825	...	0925	...	1240	1247	...	1435	...	1635	1725	1800	...	1935	1940	...	...	...	...	...	...	...	...

284 RENNES - ST BRIEUC - MORLAIX - BREST

km										TGV 8605						TGV 8611	TGV 8691						TGV 8615		
		Ⓐ	⑥	Ⓐ	Ⓐ	Ⓐ	Ⓐ	Ⓐ		①–⑥	⑥	①–⑥	Ⓐ	⑥	⑦			Ⓐ	Ⓒ		Ⓐ	⑥			⑤⑦
		L	k								k			k					L			k		H	v
	Paris Montparnasse **280** d.	...	...	...	...	...	...	...	...	0735	...	...	...	...	...	0952	0952	...	...	...	...	...	1152	...	...
0	**Rennes** d.	...	...	...	...	0635	0702	0735	...	0929	0935	...	1035	1035	1035	1129	1133	...	...	1235	1239	1239	1329	...	...
80	Lamballe **299** d.	...	...	...	...	0728	0744	0831	...	|	1028	...	1114	1114	1125	|	1212	...	...	1314	1337	1340	1407	...	...
101	**St Brieuc 299** d.	...	...	...	0736	0743	0756	0845	...	1016	1043	...	1127	1127	1137	|	1227	...	...	1327	1352	1354	1421	...	...
132	Guingamp d.	...	...	...	0755	...	0813	...	...	1034	...	1048	1144	1144	...	|	1244	...	...	1343	...	...	1438	...	...
158	Plouaret-Trégor d.	0627	...	...	0809	...	|	...	...	|	...	1102	|	1158	...	|	|	...	1300	|	...	...	1453	1459	1508
175	Lannion a.	|	...	...	0826	...	|	...	...	|	...	1119	|	|	...	|	1313	...	|	|	...	...	|	1516	1525
189	Morlaix d.	0650	0710	0800	...	...	0842	...	...	1103	...	...	1213	1216	...	1253	...	1310	1317	1413	...	...	1511	...	...
215	Landivisiau d.	0707	0726	0822	...	...	0858	...	...	|	...	...	1229	1232	...	|	...	1327	1332	1429	...	...	|	...	...
230	Landerneau **286** d.	0719	0737	0834	...	...	0908	...	...	|	...	...	1239	1242	...	|	...	1338	1342	1439	...	...	|	...	...
248	**Brest 286** a.	0735	0751	0850	...	...	0920	...	...	1135	...	...	1251	1254	...	1325	...	1354	1354	1451	...	...	1543	...	...

	TGV 8617											TGV 8623	TGV 8623												
	①–⑤	Ⓐ	⑦	⑥	Ⓒ	⑤	⑦	⑤	⑥	①–④	⑤		⑤	Ⓐ	⑦	Ⓐ	⑥	①–⑥	⑦	⑦	Ⓐ	Ⓐ	Ⓒ	⑥	Ⓐ
	h			k		v		v	k	m	v	A	f				k			L	L			kL	
Paris Montparnasse **280** d.	1252	...	...	...	...	...	...	...	...	...	...	1452	1452	...	...	...	...	...	...	...	...	...	...	...	...
Rennes d.	1429	...	1435	1439	...	1435	1439	...	...	...	1535	1629	1628	...	...	...	...	1635	1643	...	...	1735	1735	...	1739
Lamballe **299** d.	|	...	1514	1518	...	1524	1529	...	...	...	1614	|	|	...	...	...	...	1727	1733	...	...	1814	1814	...	1837
St Brieuc 299 d.	1516	...	1527	1531	...	1537	1541	...	...	...	1627	1716	1717	...	...	1730	1732	1740	1745	...	...	1827	1827	...	1849
Guingamp d.	1534	...	1544	1548	...	...	...	...	...	...	1644	1734	1735	...	1742	1753	1750	...	...	...	...	1844	1844	...	...
Plouaret-Trégor d.	|	...	1558	1602	1610	...	...	...	...	...	|	|	|	...	1756	1809	1805	...	...	1830	1846	|	1858	1912	...
Lannion a.	|	...	|	|	1627	...	...	...	...	...	|	|	|	...	1813	1826	1822	...	...	1847	1903	|	|	1929	...
Morlaix d.	1603	1610	1616	1620	...	...	...	1657	1710	1710	1713	1803	1804	1809	...	...	...	...	...	...	...	1913	1916	...	...
Landivisiau d.	|	1626	1632	1636	...	...	...	1713	1726	1726	1729	|	|	1826	...	...	...	...	...	...	...	1929	1932	...	...
Landerneau **286** d.	|	1637	1642	1646	...	...	...	1725	1737	1737	1739	|	|	1837	...	...	...	...	...	...	...	1939	1942	...	...
Brest 286 a.	1635	1654	1654	1658	...	...	...	1741	1751	1754	1752	1835	1836	1849	...	...	...	...	...	...	...	1951	1954	...	...

	TGV 8629	TGV 8631					TGV 8635	TGV 8695	TGV 8639	TGV 8639						TGV 8645	TGV 8641			TGV 8649			TGV 8655		TGV 8657
		⑤	Ⓐ		Ⓐ	⑥	⑤	⑤	①–④	⑦	①–④	⑦	⑤⑥	⑤	⑦	⑤			⑤	⑤	⑤	⑦	⑤		⑦
	A	f				k	f	f	m		m		t	v		f	A	A	f	f	f		f		
Paris Montparnasse **280** d.	1652	1652	...	...	...	...	1739	1739	1752	1752	...	...	...	...	...	1901	1852	...	...	1952	...	...	2052	...	2359
Rennes d.	1829	1829	...	...	1835	1837	|	|	1926	1929	...	...	1935	...	1936	|	2029	...	2035	2129	...	2135	2229	...	|
Lamballe **299** d.	|	1907	...	...	1927	1932	|	|	|	|	...	...	2014	...	2026	|	2108	...	2115	2208	...	2214	|	...	|
St Brieuc 299 d.	1916	1921	...	...	1940	1944	2000	2006	2013	2017	2023	...	2027	...	2038	2114	2122	...	2127	2222	...	2227	2316	...	0423
Guingamp d.	1934	1938	...	1945	...	...	|	2024	2031	2035	2039	2044	2044	2053	...	|	2139	...	2144	2239	...	2244	2334	...	0440
Plouaret-Trégor d.	|	|	...	1959	...	...	|	|	|	|	2053	2058	2058	2108	...	|	2154	2158	2158	2254	2258	2258	|	...	|
Lannion a.	|	|	...	2016	...	...	|	2053	|	|	2110	2115	|	2125	...	|	|	2215	|	|	2315	|	|	...	|
Morlaix d.	2003	2007	2014	...	...	...	2042	...	2100	2104	...	...	2116	...	...	|	2212	...	2216	2312	...	2316	0003	...	0516
Landivisiau d.	|	|	2030	...	...	...	|	...	|	|	...	...	2132	...	...	|	|	...	2232	|	...	2332	|	...	|
Landerneau **286** d.	|	|	2041	...	...	...	|	...	|	|	...	...	2142	...	...	|	2236	...	2242	2336	...	2342	|	...	0540
Brest 286 a.	2035	2039	2053	...	...	...	2114	...	2131	2135	...	...	2154	...	...	2219	2248	...	2254	2348	...	2354	0035	...	0552

	TGV 8680		TGV 8602								TGV 8606				TGV 8610						TGV 8620	TGV 8620	TGV 8620	TGV 8620	
	①	Ⓐ		Ⓐ	Ⓐ	Ⓐ	⑥	Ⓐ	⑥	Ⓐ	①–⑥	⑥	Ⓐ			⑥	Ⓑ	①–⑥	⑥	Ⓐ	⑥	⑦	①	②–⑤	Ⓒ
			G	L			k		k			k				k	w		k		r			h	
Brest 286 d.	...	...	0518	...	0538	...	...	...	...	0700	0718	0800	0800	...	0905	0954	1031	...	...	...	1117	1121	1130	1127	...
Landerneau **286** d.	...	...	|	...	0550	...	...	...	...	0716	|	0814	0816	...	0919	1006	1043	...	...	...	|	|	|	|	...
Landivisiau d.	...	...	|	...	0600	...	...	...	...	0728	|	0826	0828	...	|	1016	1053	...	...	...	|	|	|	|	...
Morlaix d.	...	...	0552	...	0616	...	...	...	...	0743	0752	0841	0843	...	0943	1032	1109	...	...	...	1151	1155	|	1201	...
Lannion d.	...	...	|	0604	|	0632	...	0731	0740	...	|	▬	...	0937	|	|	|	...	1136	1140	|	|	|	|	...
Plouaret-Trégor d.	...	...	|	0620	0634	0647	...	0747	0755	...	|	...	...	0953	1001	1049	1127	...	1152	1155	1209	|	|	|	...
Guingamp d.	...	...	0621	...	0649	0704	...	0802	0810	...	0821	⑦	...	...	1017	1104	1142	...	...	1209	1224	1224	|	1230	...
St Brieuc 299 d.	0543	0616	0639	...	0706	0727	0813	...	0828	...	0839	0915	...	...	1034	1122	1159	1206j	...	1225	1242	1242	1242	1248	1305z
Lamballe **299** d.	0555	0627	|	...	0718	...	0824	...	...	...	|	0926	...	...	1046	1134	1211	1220j	...	...	|	|	|	|	1319z
Rennes a.	0631	0721	0725	...	0757	...	0921	...	...	...	0925	1017	...	...	1125	1213	1250	1319	...	...	1327	1327	1327	1334	1421
Paris Montparnasse **280** a.	0821	...	0910	...	...	...	...	...	...	...	1108	...	...	...	1309	...	...	...	...	...	1509	1509	1509	1509	...

						TGV 8622		TGV 8622				TGV 8682	TGV 8694	TGV 8630	TGV 8628	TGV 8628							TGV 8690	TGV 8636	TGV 8636
	Ⓐ	Ⓒ	Ⓐ	Ⓒ	①–④	①–④	⑤	⑤	Ⓒ	①–④	⑥	⑦	⑤		⑦	⑤	Ⓐ	Ⓒ	Ⓒ	⑤	Ⓐ	⑤		⑤	
		L			m	m	v	f	¶	m	k		f	G		f				v		f	A	f	A
Brest 286 d.	1208	...	1255	1302	...	1313	...	1318	...	...	1400	...	...	1417	1422	1431	...	...	1506	1508	1604	...	...	1619	1622
Landerneau **286** d.	1220	...	1312	1314	...	|	...	|	...	...	1415	...	...	|	|	|	...	...	1518	1520	1616	...	...	|	|
Landivisiau d.	1230	...	1324	1324	...	|	...	|	...	...	1427	...	...	|	|	|	...	...	1528	1530	1628	...	...	|	|
Morlaix d.	1246	...	1338	1340	...	1347	...	1352	...	...	1441	...	...	1451	1456	1505	...	...	1544	1546	1643	...	...	1650	1656
Lannion d.	|	1236	...	|	1334	|	1340	|	1429	1435	...	...	1445	|	|	|	...	1534	|	|	▬	1634	1646	|	|
Plouaret-Trégor d.	|	1252	...	1358	1350	1405	1356	|	1445	1450	...	...	|	|	1514	|	...	1550	1601	|	...	1650	|	1707	|
Guingamp d.	1316	...	...	1413	...	1421	1410	1421	...	1505	...	...	1515	1520	1530	|	...	...	1616	1616	Ⓑw	...	1715	1722	|
St Brieuc 299 d.	1334	...	...	1430	...	1439	...	1439	...	...	...	1533	1533	1538	|	|	1614	...	1634	1634	1714y	...	1744	1744	1744
Lamballe **299** d.	1345	...	...	1442	...	|	...	|	...	...	...	1545	1545	1550	|	|	1628	...	1646	1645	1728	...	|	|	|
Rennes a.	1425	...	...	1521	...	1525	...	1525	...	...	...	1625	1625	1629	1629	1629	1721	...	1725	1725	1823y	...	1830	1830	1830
Paris Montparnasse **280** a.	...	...	...	...	...	1709	...	1709	...	...	...	1809	1809	1809	1809	1809	...	...	...	...	...	...	2009	2009	2009

						TGV 8640		TGV 8642			TGV 8644				TGV 8692						TGV 8648	TGV 8646	TGV 8646		TGV 8652
	⑦	Ⓐ	Ⓒ	Ⓐ	⑤		⑥	⑤	⑦	Ⓐ	⑦	Ⓐ	⑦	⑥	⑦	⑦	①–④	⑤	Ⓒ	Ⓐ	⑤⑥	①–④	⑦	⑦	⑦
					v	D	k	f	L	L				kL			m	v			t	m			
Brest 286 d.	1640	1648	...	...	1706	1713	1713	1730	1730	1740	1802	1806	1809	1812	...	...	...	...	...	1855	1918	1918	1918	...	2014
Landerneau **286** d.	1652	1705	...	...	1719	|	1725	|	1742	1753	|	1818	1821	1824	...	...	...	...	...	1909	|	|	|	...	|
Landivisiau d.	1702	1717	...	...	1729	|	1735	|	1752	1803	|	1828	1831	1834	...	...	...	...	...	1921	|	|	|	...	|
Morlaix d.	1718	1734	...	...	1744	1747	1751	|	1806	1818	|	1844	1847	1848	...	...	...	...	...	1943	1952	1952	1952	...	2048
Lannion d.	|	▬	1734	1737	|	|	|	|	|	|	|	|	|	|	1855	...	1932	1932	1937	...	|	|	|	2037	|
Plouaret-Trégor d.	1735	①–⑥	1750	1752	1802	|	1810	|	1823	1839	|	1902	|	1905	|	...	1947	1947	1952	...	|	|	|	2052	|
Guingamp d.	1750	◧	1805	1806	1817	1816	1825	|	...	...	|	1917	1917	...	1926	...	2001	2003	2008	...	2021	2021	2021	2107	2117
St Brieuc 299 d.	1808	1809	...	1825	1834	1833	1842	1842	...	...	1913	1934	1934	...	1944	2018	2017	...	...	...	2039	2039	2039	...	2134
Lamballe **299** d.	1820	1823	...	...	1845	1845	1853	|	...	...	|	1946	1945	...	|	2029	...	...	...	...	2052	|	|	...	2146
Rennes a.	1859	1916	...	...	1925	1925	1932	1929	...	...	|	2025	2025	...	2029	2121	...	...	...	...	|	2125	2127	...	2225
Paris Montparnasse **280** a.	...	...	...	...	...	2109	...	2109	...	...	2130	...	...	...	2209	...	...	...	...	...	2301	2312	2309	...	0009

GUINGAMP - PAIMPOL

km		Ⓐ					⑦	①–⑥	⑦	Ⓐ	⑤ v
0	Guingamp d.	0817	...	1253	1501	...	1737	1740	1950	2007	2202
47	Paimpol a.	0904	...	1340	1548	...	1824	1827	2037	2054	2249

	Ⓐ							⑦	Ⓐ	⑥ k
Paimpol d.	0720	...	0916	...	1404	1615	...	1832	1906	1916
Guingamp a.	0807	...	1003	...	1451	1702	...	1919	1953	2003

A – ①②③④⑥⑦ (also Aug. 16; not Aug. 14).
D – ①②③④⑦ (not Aug. 14, 15).
G – ①②③④⑥ (also Aug. 16; not Aug. 14).
H – ①②③④⑥ (not Aug. 14).
L – Brest - Lannion and v.v.

f – Also Aug. 14; not Aug. 16.
h – Not Aug. 15, 16.
j – 3 minutes earlier on ⑥ (also Aug. 15).
k – Also Aug. 15.
m – Not Aug. 14, 15.
r – Also Aug. 15, 16.
t – Also Aug. 14, 15.
v – Also Aug. 14.

w – Not Aug. 15.
y – On ⑦ St Brieuc d. 1717, Rennes a. 1820.
z – On ⑦ St Brieuc d. 1318, Lamballe d. 1329.

TGV – ®, supplement payable, 🍸.

¶ – Runs 13 minutes later on ⑦.
◧ – Runs 4–6 minutes later on ⑥ (also Aug. 15).

RENNES and NANTES - QUIMPER 285

km								TGV 8703						TGV 8709	TGV 8707						TGV 8715	TGV 8717	TGV 8711		
		Ⓐ	Ⓐ	Ⓐ	Ⓐ	Ⓐ	⑥	⑥	Ⓐ	⑥	⑥	⑦	⑦	①⑤		Ⓐ	⑦	⑥	Ⓐ	Ⓐ	⑥		⑤	⑥	Ⓐ
							k	r△	⊙	k	k	Q		f	L			k			r	D	f	k	
0	*Paris Montparnasse 280* d.	...	...	...	...	...	...	0757	...	...	...	...	...	0852	0852	...	...	...	...	...	1052	1052	1052	...	...
365	**Rennes** d.	0621	...	...	0705	...	0840	|	0935	...	0941	0950	...	|	1028	...	1135	...	...	1135	1232	1229	1229	...	1240
	Nantes 288 d.	|	0614	0645	|	0714	|	|	|	0925	|	|	0940	|	|	...	|	1114	1118	|	|	|	|	1226	|
	Savenay 288 d.	|	0640	0707	|	0740	|	|	|	0947	|	|	1005	|	|	...	|	1140	1140	|	|	|	|	1249	|
437	Redon d.	0706	0713	0747z	0747	0813	0924	|	1012	1023z	1023	1032	1039	1101	1104	...	1212	1213	1217z	1217	|	|	|	1320	1325
492	Vannes d.	0737	▬	0816	0816	...	0954	1031	1038	1052	1052	1103	...	1129	1131	...	1241	...	1246	1246	1331	1330	1331	...	1356
511	Auray d.	...	Ⓐ	0828	0828	...	...	1045	1050	1104	1104	1114	...	1142	1145	...	1254	...	1258	1258	1345	1344	1345	...	...
545	Lorient d.	...	0656	0851	0851	...	...	1104	1108	1125	1125	...	...	1202	1205	1211	1314	...	1319	1319	1404	1404	1404	...	...
565	Quimperlé d.	...	0711	0903	0903	...	...	1117	1120	1137	1137	...	...	|	|	1226	1326	...	1331	1331	|	1417	1417	...	...
612	**Quimper** a.	...	0740	0930	0930	...	...	1141	1147	1204	1204	...	...	1241	1244	1255	1353	...	1359	1359	1437	1440	1440	...	...

									TGV 8719	TGV 8719	TGV 8721				TGV 8725	TGV 8725									
	Ⓒ	Ⓐ	⑦	⑦	Ⓐ	⑥	⑥	⑤	⑥	⑦	①-⑤	⑤	⑦	Ⓐ		⑤	Ⓐ	⑦	Ⓐ	⑥	Ⓒ	Ⓐ	Ⓐ		Ⓑ
						k	k	v	r		h	v			E	f				k	B				w¶
Paris Montparnasse 280 d.	...	...	...	...	...	...	...	...	1252	1252	1300	...	...	...	1500	1503	...	...	...	...	...	...	...	...	...
Rennes d.	1240	...	...	1335	...	...	1335	1340	1431	1429	|	1440	1440	1605	|	|	...	1640	1640	1640	...	...	1705	1735	...
Nantes 288 d.	|	1250	1256	|	1314	1319	|	|	|	|	|	|	|	|	|	|	...	|	|	|	1658	1649	|	|	1714
Savenay 288 d.	|	|	|	|	1340	1340	|	|	|	|	|	|	|	|	|	|	...	|	|	|	|	1710	|	|	1740
Redon d.	1330	1336	1342	1412	1413	1417z	1417	1425	|	|	|	1517	1530	1641	|	|	...	1717	1725	1730	1743	1747z	1747	1810	1813
Vannes d.	1401	1406	1412	1441	...	1446	1446	1456	1528	1531	1531	1546	1601	1711	1731	1734	...	1746	1756	1801	1812	1816	1816	1838	...
Auray d.	...	1418	|	1453	...	1458	1458	...	1541	1545	1545	1600	...	1723	1745	1748	...	1758	...	...	|	1828	1828	1850	...
Lorient d.	...	1439	1438	1514	...	1519	1519	...	1600	1604	1604	1620	...	1743	1804	1807	1811	1820	...	...	1840	1851	1851	1910	...
Quimperlé d.	...	1451	|	1526	...	1531	1531	...	|	|	|	1632	...	1755	|	|	1826	1832	...	...	|	1903	1903	1922	...
Quimper a.	...	1520	1512	1553	...	1558	1558	...	1633	1637	1637	1700	...	1825	1837	1840	1855	1900	...	...	1915	1930	1930	1950	...

			TGV 8727		TGV 8729						TGV 8731	TGV 8735						TGV 8739	TGV 8747			TGV 8751	TGV 8753	TGV 8755	TGV 8791
	Ⓐ	Ⓐ	⑤	Ⓐ		⑤	①-④	⑥	⑦	⑤	⑦	⑤	Ⓐ	⑥	⑥	Ⓐ	⑦		⑤	Ⓑ	⑤		⑤	⑤	⑤
		B	f		A	v	m	k		v		f		k	k			G	f	w	v	D	f	f	f
Paris Montparnasse 280 d.	...	...	1639	...	1652	...	...	...	...	...	1752	1752	...	...	...	...	...	1852	1914	...	...	1952	2005	2052	2209
Rennes d.	1740	...	|	...	1832	1840	1840	1840	1841	1844	1932	1930	...	...	1935	1940	1940	2032	|	...	2046	2132	|	2232	0028
Nantes 288 d.	|	1758	|	1814	|	|	|	|	|	|	|	|	1914	1920	|	|	|	|	|	2026	|	|	|	|	|
Savenay 288 d.	|	|	|	1840	|	|	|	|	|	|	|	|	1940	1942	|	|	|	|	|	2054	|	|	|	|	|
Redon d.	1825b	1842	1853	1913	|	1918	1925	1930	1934	1941	|	|	2013	2018z	2018	2025	2030	2108	|	2127	2132	2208	2215	|	|
Vannes d.	1856b	1909	1921	...	1931	1944	1956	2001	2005	2012	2031	2031	...	2047	2047	2056	2101	2135	2139	...	2203	2235	2243	2331	0128
Auray d.	...	1922	1934	...	1945	1957	...	...	...	...	|	2045	...	2059	2059	...	...	2148	|	...	...	2248	2257	2345	0142
Lorient d.	...	1941	1954	...	2004	2014	...	...	...	...	2058	2104	...	2120	2120	...	...	2206	2204	...	...	2306	2318	0004	0157
Quimperlé d.	...	|	2007	...	|	2026	...	...	...	...	|	|	...	2132	2132	...	...	2219	|	...	...	2320	2331	|	...
Quimper a.	...	2015	2035	...	2037	2053	...	...	...	...	2130	2137	...	2159	2159	...	...	2248	2235	...	...	2348	2359	0037	...

			TGV 8702									TGV 8706				TGV 8710							TGV 8720		
	Ⓐ	Ⓐ	①-⑥	Ⓐ	Ⓐ	Ⓐ	①-⑥	Ⓐ	⑥	Ⓐ	Ⓐ	①-⑥		Ⓒ	Ⓐ		Ⓐ		⑥	Ⓐ	⑦	Ⓐ		⑥	⑦
									k					B	B				k				H	k	
Quimper d.	...	...	0511	0535	0535	...	...	0638	...	...	0703	0724	...	0850	0852	0911	0936	...	1038	...	...	...	1131	...	1201
Quimperlé d.	...	...	0540	0601	0601	...	...	0704	...	...	0733	|	...	|	|	0940	1003	...	1105	...	...	...	|	...	1227
Lorient d.	...	...	0555	0615	0615	...	...	0718	...	...	0748	0800	...	0927	0927	0955	1016	...	1118	...	...	...	1206	...	1241
Auray d.	...	...	0613	0636	0636	...	...	0739	...	...	...	0818	...	|	|	1013	1037	...	1139	...	...	...	|	...	1302
Vannes d.	0601	...	0627	0648	0648	0704	...	0752	0800	...	...	0832	...	0954	0954	1027	1050	...	1151	1150	1158	...	1232	1300	1315
Redon d.	0632	0644	0653	0721	0727z	0735	0744	0821	0831	0844	...	|	...	1022	1021	1053	1122	...	1221	1221	1229	1244	|	1331	1345
Savenay 288 d.	|	0718	|	|	0752	|	0818	|	|	0918	...	|	...	|	|	|	|	...	|	|	|	1318	|	|	|
Nantes 288 a.	|	0742	|	|	0815	|	0842	|	|	0942	...	|	...	1105	1104e	|	1206	...	|	|	|	1342	|	|	|
Rennes a.	0721	...	0729	0756	...	0821	...	0856	0921	...	...	0929	...	...	...	1129	...	...	1256	1308	1319	...	1331	1421	1420
Paris Montparnasse 280 a.	...	...	0910	...	...	...	...	...	...	...	...	1108	...	...	...	1309	...	...	...	...	...	...	1509	...	...

					TGV 8722	TGV 8722	TGV 8722	TGV 8190					TGV 8792				TGV 8726	TGV 8728							TGV 8732
	Ⓐ	Ⓐ	⑥	Ⓐ	①-④	⑤	⑦	⑥	⑦	⑤	Ⓒ	⑦	①-④	⑦	⑥	Ⓐ	⑥	Ⓑ	⑦	Ⓐ	Ⓐ	Ⓐ	Ⓒ	Ⓒ	⑦
			k		m	f		r		v			m		k		r	h							
Quimper d.	1204	1204	1236	1245	1319	1324	1324	1324	1336	1402	1408	...	...	...	...	...	1511	1513	...	...	1557	...	1608	...	1656
Quimperlé d.	1230	1230	1303	1315	|	|	|	|	1403	1428	1435	...	...	...	...	...	1540	1543	...	...	1624	...	1635	...	|
Lorient d.	1244	1244	1316	1330	1355	1400	1400	1400	1416	1442	1449	...	1458	...	...	...	1600	1602	...	...	1637	...	1649	...	1731
Auray d.	1305	1305	1337	...	1414	1418	1418	1418	1437	1503	1507	...	1516	...	...	...	1618	1620	...	...	1658	...	1707	...	|
Vannes d.	1317	1317	1350	...	1427	1432	1432	1432	1450	1515	1519	...	1529	1556	1607	...	1632	1634	1655	1657	1710	...	1719	...	1757
Redon d.	1350	1353	1422	...	1453	|	1456	1456	1522	1545	1545	1549	|	1627	1638	1644	|	|	1726	1728	1740	1744	1745	1759	|
Savenay 288 d.	|	1419	|	...	|	|	|	|	|	|	|	1617	|	|	|	1717	|	|	|	|	|	1817	|	1832	|
Nantes 288 a.	|	1445	1506	...	|	|	|	|	1606	|	|	1642	|	|	|	1742	|	|	|	|	|	1842	|	1853	|
Rennes a.	1425	...	...	...	1529	1529	1529	1529	...	1620	1620	...	1625	1717	1721	...	|	1731	1816	1814	1820	...	1820	...	|
Paris Montparnasse 280 a.	...	...	...	...	1709	1709	1709	1709	...	...	...	...	1809	...	...	...	1903	1909	...	...	...	...	...	...	2025

						TGV 8734			TGV 8740	TGV 8740				TGV 8742						TGV 8744	TGV 8746	TGV 8746		TGV 8794	TGV 8752
	Ⓐ	⑦	⑥	Ⓑ	Ⓐ	⑦	⑤	⑦	⑤		⑥	⑥	Ⓐ	⑦	Ⓐ	Ⓐ	⑦	⑦		⑦	⑤⑥	①-④		⑦	⑦
			k	w			v	Q	f	G	k	k									t	m			
Quimper d.	...	...	...	...	1703	1711	1716	...	1747	1750	1755	1755	...	1820	1835	1835	1835	1835	...	1907	1920	1920	...	...	2024
Quimperlé d.	...	...	...	...	1733	1740	1743	...	|	|	1822	1822	...	|	1901	1901	1901	1901	...	|	|	|	...	...	|
Lorient d.	...	...	...	...	1748	1755	1757	...	1822	1825	1835	1835	...	1856	1915	1915	1915	1915	...	1943	1955	1955	...	2030	2100
Auray d.	...	...	...	...	...	1813	1818	1832	1841	1844	1856	1856	...	1915	1936	1936	1936	1936	...	2001	2013	2013	...	2048	2118
Vannes d.	1804	1805	1811	...	...	1826	1831	1844	1854	1857	1908	1908	...	1929	1948	1948	1948	1948	...	2014	2026	2026	...	2101	2132
Redon d.	1835	1836	1842	1844	...	1853	1854	1917	1921	|	1941	1944	1944	|	2021	2027z	2021y	2034y	...	2042	2053	2053	...	|	|
Savenay 288 d.	|	|	|	1917	...	|	|	|	|	|	|	2010	2017	|	|	2053	|	2107	...	|	|	|	...	|	|
Nantes 288 a.	|	|	|	1942	...	|	|	|	|	|	|	2032	2042	|	|	2115	|	2129	...	|	|	|	...	|	|
Rennes a.	1921	1921	1925	...	...	1929	1929	1956	|	|	2016	...	...	|	2056	...	2056	...	...	|	2129	2129	...	|	2229
Paris Montparnasse 280 a.	...	...	...	...	...	2109	...	...	2130	2130	...	...	...	2200	...	...	...	...	...	2252	2309	2312	...	2331	0009

AURAY - QUIBERON *Valid July 6 - August 30 (service runs summer only); see note* ⊠

km													
									Ⓐ	Ⓒ			
				R									
0	Auray d.	0831	1017	1116	1205	1402	1507	1612	1735	1751	1911	2010	...
28	Quiberon a.	0916	1102	1207	1250	1447	1552	1657	1820	1836	1956	2101	...

							Ⓐ	Ⓒ			
								R			
Quiberon d.	0924	1112	1309	1352	1457	1602	1725	1741	1901	2006	2122
Auray a.	1007	1155	1352	1441	1551	1651	1814	1830	1950	2049	2205

A – ①②③④⑥⑦ (also Aug. 16; not Aug. 14).
B – To/from Brest (Table 286).
D – ①②③④⑦ (not Aug. 14, 15).
E – ①②③④⑥⑦ (not Aug. 14).
G – ①②③④⑥ (also Aug. 16; not Aug. 14).
H – ①⑥⑦ (also Aug. 15, 16).
L – ②③④⑥⑦ (also Aug. 16; not Aug. 14). Train number **8193** on ⑥ (also Aug. 15, 16).
Q – ⑦ to Aug. 25. To/from Quiberon (see panel).
R – To/from Rennes on ⑦ (see main table).

b – 5 minutes later on ⑤ (also Aug. 14).
e – 1108 on July 8, 22, Aug. 5, 19.
f – Also Aug. 14; not Aug. 16.
h – Not Aug. 15, 16.
k – Also Aug. 15.
m – Not Aug. 14, 15.
r – Also Aug. 15, 16.
t – Also Aug. 14, 15.
v – Also Aug. 14.
w – Not Aug. 15.
y – Arrives 2016.

z – Arrives 11 minutes earlier.

TGV – Ⓡ, supplement payable, 🍸.

△ – Runs 43–44 minutes **earlier** on Aug. 16.
⊙ – Runs 2–5 minutes later on Aug. 16.
¶ – On ⑦ Nantes d. 1719, Savenay d. 1741, Redon a. 1815.
⊠ – A limited service also runs on Ⓒ June 8–23, daily June 29 - July 5 and ⑥⑦ Aug. 31 - Sept. 8 as follows:
From Auray at 1205, 1402, 1606 and 1804.
From Quiberon at 1309, 1512, 1709 and 1907.

286 BREST - QUIMPER

km		Ⓐ	Ⓒ N	Ⓐ N	Ⓐ		Ⓐ	⑥ k	⑦	Ⓐ	⑦	⑥ k	⑥ k	⑦	⑥ k	Ⓐ		Ⓐ	⑦	⑥ k	Ⓐ		Ⓐ	⑦
0	**Brest** 284 d.	0631	0747	0749	0835	...	1000	1056	1156	1233	1335	1340	1432	1527	1626	1626	...	1734	1745	1757	1839	...	1942	2002
18	Landerneau 284 d.	0643	|	|	0847	...	1012	1108	1208	1245	1347	1352	1444	1539	1638	1639	...	1746	1757	1809	1851	...	1954	2014
72	Châteaulin d.	0729	|	|	0931	...	1052	1148	1248	1331	1431	1432	1528	1623	1718	1720	...	1832	1837	1849	1937	...	2044	2054
102	**Quimper** a.	0750	0848	0850	0952	...	1113	1209	1309	1352	1452	1453	1549	1644	1739	1741	...	1853	1858	1910	1958	...	2105	2115

	Ⓐ		Ⓐ	⑥ k	Ⓐ	⑥ k	⑦		Ⓐ	⑥ k	Ⓐ	⑦	⑥ k	⑦	⑦	⑥ k	Ⓐ		Ⓐ	Ⓐ	Ⓒ N	Ⓐ N		⑦
Quimper d.	0605	...	0706	0802	0908	1000	1030	...	1207	1219	1308	1408	1505	1600	1653	1655	1657	...	1809	1914	1917	2022	...	2141
Châteaulin d.	0626	...	0731	0832	0929	1021	1051	...	1228	1240	1333	1429	1526	1621	1714	1720	1722	...	1830	1935	|	|	...	2202
Landerneau 284 d.	0706	...	0820	0911	1004	1100	1130	...	1308	1319	1412	1508	1605	1700	1753	1759	1809	...	1915	2017	|	|	...	2241
Brest 284 a.	0719	...	0833	0923	1016	1112	1142	...	1321	1331	1424	1520	1617	1712	1805	1811	1822	...	1928	2030	2018	2123	...	2253

N – To/from Nantes (Table **285**).

k – Also Aug. 15.

287 RENNES - NANTES

NON-STOP SERVICES. Other journeys are possible by changing trains at Redon (see both directions of Table **285**).

km		Ⓐ	①–⑥		Ⓒ		①–⑥	Ⓐ	⑦		⑥ k	Ⓐ	⑦	①–⑥	⑦	⑥ k	Ⓑ w
0	**Rennes** d.	0737	0837	...	1037	...	1237	1337	1437	...	1637	1730	1746	1836	1837	1930	1936
145	**Nantes** a.	0852	0952	...	1152	...	1352	1452	1554	...	1752	1852	1901	1952	1952	2052	2052

	Ⓐ	⑥ k		Ⓒ		①–⑥	⑦	Ⓐ		⑥ k	Ⓐ	Ⓐ	Ⓒ	Ⓑ w	①–⑥	⑦	
Nantes d.	0710	0810	...	1010	...	1210	1310	1350	...	1510	1610	1710	1713	1810	1910	2010	...
Rennes a.	0825	0925	...	1125	...	1325	1425	1505	...	1625	1725	1825	1830	1925	2025	2125	...

k – Also Aug. 15.
w – Not Aug. 15.

SERVICES VIA LAVAL AND ANGERS. See also Table **280**.

km		Ⓐ		①–⑥	Ⓐ	Ⓒ		Ⓐ		Ⓐ	⑦	Ⓐ	⑥ k	⑦	Ⓐ	⑦	
0	**Rennes** d.	0654	...	0912	1053	1053	...	1257	...	1457	1557	1657	1755	1821	1901	1921	...
38	Vitré d.	0714	...	0938	1113	1113	...	1317	...	1517	1617	1717	1815	1841	1922	1941	...
73	Laval d.	0734	...	0957	1132	1132	...	1336	...	1537	1637	1737	1835	1900	1941	2000	...
126	Sablé sur Sarthe a.	0800	...	1020	1200	1200	...	1400	...	1600	1700	1800	1900	1921	2005	2020	...
126	Sablé sur Sarthe d.	0813	...	1024	1211	1213	...	1405	...	1613	1711	1813	1911	1934	2017	2033	...
174	Angers St Laud 289 d.	0833	...	1046	1233	1233	...	1435	...	1633	1732	1832	1933	1954	2038	2054	...
262	**Nantes** 289 a.	0916	...	1127	1316	1316	...	1516	...	1717	1816	1916	2016	2036	2120	2135	...

	Ⓐ		Ⓐ	⑥ k	Ⓐ	Ⓒ	Ⓐ		Ⓐ		Ⓑ w		⑥ k	Ⓑ w		⑦	
Nantes 289 d.	0544	...	0744	0844	0944	1047	1143	...	1344	...	1544	...	1744	1744	...	1944	...
Angers St Laud 289 d.	0627	...	0826	0926	1026	1129	1226	...	1429	...	1626	...	1826	1826	...	2026	...
Sablé sur Sarthe a.	0649	...	0849	0949	1049	1149	1248	...	1449	...	1649	...	1848	1849	...	2049	...
Sablé sur Sarthe d.	0656	...	0858	0958	1058	1158	1258	...	1458	...	1658	...	1857	1858	...	2058	...
Laval d.	0718	...	0920	1020	1120	1220	1320	...	1520	...	1720	...	1920	1920	...	2120	...
Vitré d.	0738	...	0940	1040	1140	1240	1341	...	1540	...	1741	...	1941	1941	...	2140	...
Rennes a.	0801	...	1001	1101	1201	1301	1401	...	1601	...	1802	...	2002	2002	...	2201	...

288 NANTES - ST NAZAIRE - LE CROISIC

km		Ⓐ	Ⓐ	Ⓐ	⑥ k	Ⓐ	Ⓐ	*TGV* **8911** ①–⑥	Ⓒ M	Ⓐ	Ⓒ O	*TGV* **8913**		Ⓒ	Ⓐ	*TGV* **8917** ⑥ r	Ⓐ		Ⓒ	*TGV* **8921** ①–⑥	*TGV* **8921** ⑦	Ⓐ		Ⓐ
	Paris Montparnasse 280 d.	...	...	...	...	...	...	0643	...	...	...	0843	...	...	...	1034	...	...	...	1236	1236	...	...	...
0	**Nantes** 285 d.	0632	0704	0732	0750	0804	0832	0854	0909	1004	1004	1054	...	1204	1232	1258	1304	...	1404	1454	1458	1504	...	1632
39	Savenay 285 d.	0700	0726	0800	0825	0826	0900	|	0931	1026	1026	|	...	1226	1300	|	1326	...	1426	|	|	1527	...	1700
64	**St Nazaire** d.	0723	0744	0823	0848	0845	0923	0932	0945	1044	1042	1132	...	1244	1323	1335	1344	...	1444	1532	1536	1544	...	1723
79	Pornichet d.	...	0758	...	0900	0858	...	0944	0958	1058	1056	|	...	1258	...	1347	1358	...	1458	|	|	1558	...	...
83	La Baule Escoublac d.	...	0806	...	0907	0906	...	0951	1006	1105	1108	1150	...	1306	...	1357	1406	...	1506	1550	1554	1606	...	...
90	**Le Croisic** a.	...	0819	...	0920	0919	...	1004	1023	1119	1132	1159	...	1319	...	1410	1419	...	1519	1559	1603	1619	...	...

	TGV **8923**	Ⓐ	Ⓐ	⑦ T	①–⑥ T	Ⓐ	⑥ k	①–④ m	⑦	⑤ vM	⑤ v	①–④ m	*TGV* **8905** ①–④ m	*TGV* **8927** ⑤ f	⑤⑥ vO	*TGV* **8931**	⑤ v	*TGV* **8935** ⑤ f	A		*TGV* **8937** ⑤ f		*TGV* **8939** ⑤ f
Paris Montparnasse 280 d.	1443	...	...	...	...	...	...	...	...	...	...	...	1743	1743	...	1843	...	1934	...	...	2043	...	2143
Nantes 285 d.	1654	1703	1732	1804	1804	1832	1839	1904	1904	1919	1923	1932	1954	1954	2005	2054	2132	2203	2213	...	2254	...	2354
Savenay 285 d.	|	1725	1800	1826	1826	1900	1913	1926	1926	1947	1956	2000	|	|	2026	|	2202	|	2240	...	|	...	|
St Nazaire d.	1730	1744	1823	1844	1844	1923	1935	1944	1947	2012	2020	2023	2029	2033	2044	2128	2219	2241	2255	...	2332	...	0032
Pornichet d.	1742	1758	...	1854	1858	...	1946	1958	1958	2022	...	...	...	2045	2058	|	2229	2253	2305	...	|	...	|
La Baule Escoublac d.	1751	1806	...	1905	1906	...	1953	2006	2005	2029	...	...	...	2052	2105	2146	2236	2300	2312	...	2350	...	0050
Le Croisic a.	1804	1819	...	1919	1923	...	2011	2019	2019	2042	...	...	...	2105	2122	2156	2249	2313	2329	...	2359	...	0059

	TGV **8900** ①–⑤ h	①–⑥	*TGV* **8910** ①	Ⓐ	Ⓐ	Ⓐ	Ⓐ	Ⓒ O	*TGV* **8912**	Ⓐ	Ⓒ		*TGV* **8916**		Ⓐ	Ⓒ	Ⓐ	Ⓐ	*TGV* **8922** ⑥ r	*TGV* **8922** Ⓑ h	Ⓐ	Ⓐ	⑦
Le Croisic d.	...	0536	0556	...	0636	...	0736	0725	0756	0836	0936	...	1051	...	...	1210	1236	...	1346j	1355	1436	1536	1536
La Baule Escoublac d.	...	0549	0608	...	0649	...	0749	0745	0808	0849	0949	...	1106	...	...	1223	1249	...	1400j	1407	1449	1549	1552
Pornichet d.	...	0557	|	...	0657	...	0757	0757	|	0857	0957	...	1112	...	...	1230	1257	...	|	|	1457	1557	1559
St Nazaire d.	0525	0610	0625	0633	0710	0733	0810	0812	0825	0910	1010	...	1125	...	1233	1243	1310	1333	1423	1423	1510	1610	1610
Savenay 285 d.	|	0624	|	0657	0724	0757	0824	0828	|	0924	1024	...	|	...	1257	1306	1324	1357	|	|	1527	1624	1624
Nantes 285 a.	0559	0648	0659	0721	0748	0821	0848	0850	0859	0948	1048	...	1159	...	1321	1340	1348	1421	1457	1457	1551	1648	1648
Paris Montparnasse 280 a.	0817	...	0918	...	...	...	...	...	1116	...	...	...	1417	...	...	...	...	...	1727	1727	...	...	...

	Ⓐ	Ⓐ	*TGV* **8926**	Ⓐ	⑦	⑥ k	*TGV* **8928** ⑦	Ⓐ	⑦	⑥ kO	Ⓐ	*TGV* **8930** ⑦	*TGV* **8932** ①–⑥	⑦ O	Ⓐ	⑦ M	⑥ kM	⑥ k	⑦	⑤ v	*TGV* **8934** ⑦		*TGV* **8936** ⑦
Le Croisic d.	...	1632	1656	...	1720	1736	1741	...	1811	1819	1836	1848	1856	1859	1932	1950	1950	2036	2036	...	2048	...	2133
La Baule Escoublac d.	...	1649	1708	...	1733	1749	1757	...	1824	1843	1849	1904	1908	1919	1949	2006	2007	2049	2049	...	2104	...	2144
Pornichet d.	...	1657	|	...	1741	1757	|	...	1831	1856	1857	1910	|	1931	1957	2014	2016	2057	2057	...	2111	...	|
St Nazaire d.	1633	1710	1725	1733	1753	1810	1813	1833	1843	1909	1910	1923	1925	1946	2010	2025	2028	2110	2110	2110	2128	...	2200
Savenay 285 d.	1657	1724	|	1757	1807	1824	|	1857	1902	1925	1924	|	|	2003	2024	2042	2043	2124	2124	2124	|	...	|
Nantes 285 a.	1721	1748	1759	1821	1830	1848	1847	1921	1938	1948	1948	1957	1959	2025	2048	2106	2106	2148	2152	2158	2202	...	2234
Paris Montparnasse 280 a.	...	...	2021	...	...	...	2126	...	...	...	...	2227	2217	...	...	...	...	...	...	...	0017	...	0043

A – ①②③④⑤⑥⑦ (not Aug. 14).
M – To/from Le Mans (Table **280a**).
O – To/from Orléans (Tables **289/296**).
T – From Tours (Table **289**).

f – Also Aug. 14; not Aug. 16.
h – Not Aug. 15, 16.
j – 7–8 minutes earlier on Aug. 16.
k – Also Aug. 15.
m – Not Aug. 14, 15.

r – Also Aug. 15, 16.
v – Also Aug. 14.

TGV – ®, supplement payable, 🍷.

NANTES - ANGERS - TOURS 289

SERVICE JULY 6 - SEPTEMBER 1 (see earlier editions for service to July 5). See Table **335** for *TGV* trains Nantes - Angers - Lyon via Le Mans.

km		Ⓐ	4402	Ⓐ		Ⓒ C	Ⓐ	Ⓐ		Ⓐ			4406	⑤ v	*TGV* 5326 w♠	Ⓐ	Ⓒ	Ⓐ	Ⓐ	⑦		⑥ kC	⑦ C		⑦
0	**Nantes** 280 d.	...	0625	0713	...	0911	0917		...	1107		...	1433	...	1551	1611	...	1710	1810	1908	...	2011	2035	...	2211
88	Angers St Laud 280 d.	0635	0710	0757	...	1002	1002	1035	...	1149	1236	...	1517	1533	1632	1657	1736	1757	1857	1954	...	2101	2123	...	2255
132	Saumur Rive Droit d.	0710	0739	0819	...	1026	1026	1109	...	1210	1327z	...	1540	1608	1657	1722	1819	1821	1919	2014	...	2126	2147	...	2317
196	St Pierre des Corps a.	|	0814	|	...	|	...	|	...	|	|	...	1620	|	1729	|	|	|	|	|	...	|	|	...	|
199	**Tours** a.	0750	|	0851	...	1057	...	1159	...	1240	1420	...	|	1659	|	1800	1859	1900	1951	2053	...	2200	2217	...	2350
202	St Pierre des Corps a.	...	|	0905	...	1112	...	...	...	1255	...	...	|	...	|	...	...	...	2005	...	...	2215	2232	...	...
	Orléans **296** a.	...	|	1012	...	1208	...	...	...	1400	...	...	|	...	◐	...	...	...	2102	...	...	2311	2325	...	...
	Lyon Part Dieu **290** a.	...	1325p	...	...	...	...	...	...	...	...	...	2128p	...	2030	...	...	...	...	...	...	...	...	...	...

	Ⓐ	Ⓐ	Ⓐ	Ⓒ C	Ⓐ	*TGV* 5352 Ⓐ a		Ⓐ	Ⓐ	⑥ k	*TGV* 5370 m♠		4504	Ⓐ	Ⓒ	C		⑤⑥ vC	①–④ m	①–⑥	⑦		4506	⑤ v	*TGV* 5380 w♣
Lyon Part Dieu **290** d.	...	...	...	...	...	0629	...	...	...	...	1030	...	0932p	...	...	...	...	...	...	...	...	...	1532p	...	1830
Orléans **296** d.	...	...	0655	0656	...	◐	...	1103	...	...	◐	...	|	...	...	...	...	1701	1701	...	1804	...	|	...	◐
St Pierre des Corps d.	...	...	0758	0756	...	|	...	1206	...	...	|	...	|	...	...	...	...	1756	1756	...	1855	...	|	...	|
Tours d.	...	0657	0811	0812	0901	|	...	1221	1225	1240	|	...	|	...	1500	1600	...	1809	1810	1840	1909	...	|	2100	|
St Pierre des Corps d.	...	|	|	|	|	0933	...	|	|	|	1333	...	1430	...	|	|	...	|	|	|	|	...	2029	|	2134
Saumur Rive Droit d.	0620	0737	0841	0846	0940	|	...	1254	1333z	1334	|	...	1506	1538	1541	1641	...	1841	1842	1947z	1941	...	2101	2139	2207
Angers St Laud 280 d.	0658	0802	0906	0917z	1017	1026	...	1320	1410	1410	1427	...	1529	1604	1605	1704	...	1904	1904	2027	2004	...	2123	2215	2230
Nantes 280 a.	0747	0847	0947	0959	...	1102	...	1420	...	...	1503	...	1610	1646	1647	1747	...	1946	1946	...	2045	...	2209	...	2306

C – To / from Le Croisic (Table **288**).

a – Not Aug. 16, Sept. 9 - Oct. 4.
k – Also Aug. 15.
m – Not Aug. 14.
p – Lyon **Perrache**.

v – Also Aug. 14.
w – Not Aug. 15 – 17.
z – Arrives 11 – 16 minutes earlier.

TGV –Ⓡ, supplement payable, 🍸.

♠ – To / from Marseille (Table **335 / 350**).
♣ – From Montpellier (Table **355**).
◐ – Via Massy (Table **335**).

☛ Additional local trains operate Saumur - Tours and v.v. Frequent connecting services operate St Pierre des Corps - Tours and v.v. (journey time 5 minutes).

TOURS - BOURGES - NEVERS - MOULINS - LYON 290

See Table **335** for faster *TGV* trains Nantes / Tours - Massy - Lyon and v.v. **Warning!** Subject to alteration June 8 – 10, Nov. 9 – 11.

km		Ⓐ	①–⑥ b		4402 A	4402 B	⑥ k	E		16840				4406		Ⓑ h	⑥ k		D	⑤ f			u	⑦ e
	Nantes **289** d.	...	...	...	0625	0625	...	...	...	...	...	...	...	1433	...	...	...	...	...	...	...	...	...	...
0	**Tours** d.	0616	0651	...	|	|	0910	0915	...	1157	...	1316	...	|	...	1716	1716	...	1818	1818	1918	...	2050	2050
3	St Pierre des Corps d.	0623	0658	...	0824	0824	0917	0922	...	1204	...	1323	...	1629	...	1723	1723	...	1825	1825	1925	...	2057	2057
113	Vierzon 315 d.	0749	0827	...	0931	0930	1041	1041	...	1328	...	1447	...	1736	...	1844	1844	...	1951	1951	2058	...	2224	2226
145	**Bourges** 315 d.	0807	0847	...	0950	0948	1100	1100	...	1347	...	1507	...	1758	...	1901	1903	...	2011	2019j	2117	...	...	2244
214	**Nevers** 315 a.	...	0924t	...	1027	1026	...	...	...	1425	...	1544	...	1836	...	...	1939	...	2103	2107	2158	...	...	...
214	**Nevers** 330 d.	...	...	...	1035	1034	...	...	...	1433	...	...	...	1847	...	...	...	...	...	...	...	...	...	...
274	**Moulins-sur-Allier** 330 d.	...	...	...	1108	1108	...	...	...	1504	...	...	...	1919	...	...	...	...	...	...	...	...	...	...
	Digoin d.	...	...	...	|	|	...	...	...	1547	...	...	...	|	...	...	...	...	...	...	...	...	...	...
	Paray le Monial d.	...	...	...	|	|	...	...	...	1559	...	...	...	|	...	...	...	...	...	...	...	...	...	...
315	St Germain des Fossés 330 d.	...	...	...	1132	1135	...	...	...	|	...	...	...	1940	...	...	...	...	...	...	...	...	...	...
381	Roanne 328 d.	...	...	...	1212	1214	...	...	...	|	...	...	...	2019	...	...	...	...	...	...	...	...	...	...
474	**Lyon** Part Dieu 328 a.	...	...	...	|	|	...	...	...	1748	...	...	...	|	...	...	...	...	...	...	...	...	...	...
479	**Lyon** Perrache 328 a.	...	...	...	1325	1325	...	...	...	1759	...	...	...	2128	...	...	...	...	...	...	...	...	...	...

	① g	Ⓐ	Ⓐ	Ⓐ	Ⓒ		Ⓐ △	⑥ k	⑦		Ⓐ ▽	⑥ k	4504 A◇	4504 B◇		⑤ f	16848		①–④ m	⑤–⑦ p		4506	Ⓑ y	⑦ e
Lyon Perrache 328 d.	...	...	...	...	...	...	...	...	...	...	...	...	0932	0932	...	...	1142	...	...	...	...	1532	...	...
Lyon Part Dieu 328 d.	...	...	...	...	...	...	...	...	...	...	...	...	|	|	...	...	1156	...	...	...	...	|	...	...
Roanne 328 d.	...	...	...	...	...	...	...	...	...	...	...	...	1039	1039	...	...	|	...	...	...	...	1639	...	...
St Germain des Fossés 330 d.	...	...	...	...	...	...	...	...	...	...	...	...	1118	1118	...	...	|	...	...	...	...	1719	...	...
Paray le Monial d.	...	...	...	...	...	...	...	...	...	...	...	...	|	|	...	...	1345	...	...	...	...	|	...	...
Digoin d.	...	...	...	...	...	...	...	...	...	...	...	...	|	|	...	...	1354	...	...	...	...	|	...	...
Moulins-sur-Allier 330 d.	...	...	...	...	...	...	...	...	...	...	...	...	1140	1140	...	...	1442	...	...	...	...	1741	...	...
Nevers 330 a.	...	...	...	...	...	...	...	...	...	...	...	...	1207	1210	...	...	1514	...	...	...	...	1809	...	...
Nevers 315 d.	...	...	0515r	0608r	0716r	...	0934r	0934r	0934r	...	...	...	1217	1220	...	...	1521	...	1638	1641	...	1822	...	1920c
Bourges 315 d.	0513	...	0554	0647	0754	...	1014	1014	1014	...	1151	1155	1253	1300	...	1459	1601	...	1718	1718	...	1859	1914	1959c
Vierzon 315 d.	0532	0532	0613	0706	0814	...	1035	1035	1035	...	1215	1215	1313	1320	...	1519	1622	...	1738	1738	...	1918	1938	2018
St Pierre des Corps a.	0703	0703	0737	0835	0941	...	1201	1201	1204	...	1335	1335	1420	1420	...	1635	1746	...	1903	1903	...	2023	2107	2135
Tours a.	0710	0710	0744	0842	0948	...	1208	1211	1211	...	1342	1342	|	|	...	1643	1753	...	1910	1910	...	|	2114	2142
Nantes **289** a.	...	...	...	...	...	...	...	...	...	...	...	...	1610	1610	...	...	...	...	...	...	...	2209	...	...

– Until Sept. 1.
– From Sept. 2.
– ①②③④⑦ (not Aug. 14, 15, Oct. 31).
– Ⓑ to Oct. 13 (not Aug. 15); ⑦ Oct. 20 - Nov. 24; Ⓑ from Dec. 1.

– Not June 10, Nov. 11.
– From Sept. 8 departs Nevers 1916, Bourges 1957.
– Also June 10, Nov. 11.
– Also Aug. 14, Oct. 31; not Nov. 1.
– Also June 11, Nov. 12; not June 10, Nov. 11.
– Not Aug. 15, Nov. 1.
– Arrives 2009.
– Also Aug. 15, Nov. 1.

m – Not June 10, Aug. 14, 15, Oct. 31, Nov. 11.
p – Also June 10, Aug. 14, 15, Oct. 31, Nov. 11.
r – 2 minutes earlier from Sept. 2.
t – 0927 from Sept. 2.
u – Not June 11 – 13, 17 – 20.
y – Not Aug. 15.

◇ – Runs up to 28 minutes later Nevers - Nantes June 17 – 20, 26, 27, Sept. 16 – 19, 23 – 26. Subject to alteration on June 21, 24, 25, 28, Sept. 20, 27, Oct. 1, 10, 14, 21.
△ – Subject to alteration Oct. 7 - Nov. 29 (also on Oct. 3).
▽ – Subject to alteration on Oct. 10, 11, 18, 25, Nov. 8, 15, 22, 29.

☛ Frequent connecting services operate St Pierre des Corps - Tours and v.v. (journey time 5 minutes).

Subject to alteration on August 16, 17

ROANNE - ST ÉTIENNE 291

km		Ⓐ	Ⓐ n	①–⑥ b	Ⓐ n	①–⑥ b	Ⓐ	Ⓒ	Ⓐ nd	kd		d		Ⓐ	Ⓐ n	Ⓑ h	A	Ⓐ		z	⑦ w			
0	**Roanne** d.	0524	0554	0624	0654	0724	0824	0854	0954	1054	...	1224t	...	1354t	1454	1554	1654	1724	1824	1924	2024	...	...	...
80	**St Étienne** Châteaucreux a.	0637r	0707	0737	0807	0837	0937	1007	1107	1207r	...	1337	...	1507	1607	1707	1807	1837	1937	2037	2137	...	...	...

	Ⓐ n	①–⑥ b	①–⑥ b	z	Ⓐ n	①–⑥ bd		Ⓐ d	d		x	Ⓐ n	c	Ⓐ	①–⑥ b	n	Ⓐ		z				
St Étienne Châteaucreux d.	0553	0623	0723	0823	0853	0953	...	1153t	1223	...	1453t	1553	1653	1723	1753	1823	1853	1953	2053	...	...	...	...
Roanne a.	0706	0736	0836	0936	1006	1106	...	1306	1336	...	1606	1706	1806	1836	1906	1936	2006	2106	2206	...	...	...	...

– Daily to July 13; ⑥ July 20 - Aug. 24 (also Aug. 15; not Aug. 17); daily from Aug. 26.

– Not June 10, Nov. 11.
– Aug. 12 – 23 St Étienne d. 1649, Roanne a. 1804.

d – Not ①–⑤ Sept. 30 - Oct. 18.
h – Not Aug. 15, Nov. 1.
k – Not July 14, 20, 21, 27, 28, Aug. 3, 4, 10, 11, 15 – 18, 24, 25.
n – Not July 14 - Aug. 25.
r – 2 minutes later Aug. 12 – 23.

t – 2 minutes earlier Aug. 12 – 23.
w – Also June 10, Nov. 11; not July 14 - Aug. 25.
x – Not ⑦ July 14 - Aug. 25.
z – Not ①–⑥ July 15 - Aug. 24.

292 NANTES - LA ROCHELLE - BORDEAUX

km													3831			3833								
		Ⓐ	Ⓐ	①–⑥	Ⓐ	Ⓐ	Ⓐ		①–⑥	Ⓐ	⑤			①–⑥			Ⓐ		Ⓐ	Ⓐ	Ⓐ	Ⓒ		Ⓐ
					A						v										A			
0	**Nantes** 293 d.	...	...	...	...	...	...	...	...	...	...	...	0825	...	...	1121	...	...	...	...	...	...	...	...
77	La Roche sur Yon 293 d.	...	...	...	...	...	...	...	...	...	...	...	0911	...	...	1205	...	...	...	...	...	...	...	...
113	Luçon d.	...	...	...	...	...	...	...	...	...	...	...	0951	...	...	1247	...	...	...	...	...	...	...	...
	La Rochelle Porte Dauphine d.	...	...	...	...	0702	0732	...	0839	...	...	...	|	...	1224	|	1430	...	...	1546	...	1619	...	1707
180	**La Rochelle** Ville d.	...	...	0544	0631	0712	0740	0740	0847	0913	...	...	1104	1136	1232	1404	1438	...	...	1554	1621	1626	1659	1715
209	Rochefort d.	...	...	0606	0653	0741	0802	0802	0916	0936	...	...	1124	1159	1302	1425	1507	...	...	1624	1642	1654	1721	1744
253	Saintes d.	0500	0543	0638	0729	...	0835	0835	...	1006	1031	...	1155	1231	...	1454	...	...	1640	...	1716	...	1750	...
376	**Bordeaux** St Jean a.	0704	0736	0833	...	...	1024	1024	...	...	1217	...	1326j	1420	...	1627	...	...	1834	...	...	...	1937	...

					3835	3835			
	⑦	①–⑥	⑦	Ⓐ	①–⑥	⑦	Ⓐ	⑦	
Nantes 293 d.	...	...	...	...	1625	1625	...	...	...
La Roche sur Yon 293 d.	...	...	...	...	1709	1711	...	...	...
Luçon d.	...	...	...	...	1749	1751	...	...	...
La Rochelle Porte Dauphine d.	...	1806	1823	1834	|	|	2014	2043	...
La Rochelle Ville d.	1749	1815	1831	1842	1904	1905	2022	2051	...
Rochefort d.	1812	1843	1859	1910	1929	1925	2051	2119	...
Saintes d.	1844	1920	...	...	1957	1956	2126	2154	...
Bordeaux St Jean a.	2030	...	...	...	2131	2132	...	...	...

								3852	
	Ⓐ	Ⓐ		⑥	Ⓐ	Ⓐ	Ⓐ		Ⓐ
				k		A			
Bordeaux St Jean d.	...	...	...	...	...	...	...	0733	0743
Saintes d.	0526	0607	...	0714	...	0740	...	0906	0922
Rochefort d.	0554	0645	...	0751	0752	0817	0850	0936	...
La Rochelle Ville d.	0624	0716	...	0821	0823	0840	0921	0959	...
La Rochelle Porte Dauphine a.	0631	0722	...	0827	0829	...	0927	|	...
Luçon d.	...	...	...	...	...	...	...	1108	...
La Roche sur Yon 293 d.	...	...	...	...	...	...	...	1150	...
Nantes 293 a.	...	...	...	...	...	...	...	1232	...

						3854									3856									
	Ⓐ	Ⓒ	①–⑥		Ⓐ		Ⓒ	Ⓐ	①–⑥	Ⓐ	Ⓐ	Ⓒ	Ⓐ	⑤			Ⓐ	⑦	Ⓑ	Ⓐ		⑦	①–④	⑤†
														v		A			h				m	
Bordeaux St Jean d.	...	0840	...	...	...	1133	...	...	1340	...	...	...	...	1543	1638	...	...	...	1725	1801	1840	1950	2040	2040
Saintes d.	1013	1021	...	...	...	1303	...	...	1518	1600	...	...	...	1724	1804	1837	...	...	1906	1953	2021	2127	2219	2221
Rochefort d.	1044	1055	1138	...	1312	1335	1400	1513	1548	1630	1649	1710	1751	...	1833	1912	1931	1956	...	...	2052	2157	...	2252
La Rochelle Ville d.	1107	1120	1208	...	1343	1359	1431	1600	1612	1653	1720	1741	1821	...	1857	1934	2001	2027	...	...	2115	2224	...	2315
La Rochelle Porte Dauphine a.	...	...	1214	...	1349	|	1437	1606	...	...	1726	1747	1827	...	|	...	2007	2033	...	...	...	...	...	...
Luçon d.	...	...	...	...	...	1508	...	...	...	...	...	...	...	...	2006	...	...	...	...	...	...	...	...	...
La Roche sur Yon 293 d.	...	...	...	...	...	1550	...	...	...	...	...	...	...	...	2048	...	...	...	...	...	...	...	...	...
Nantes 293 a.	...	...	...	...	...	1632	...	...	...	...	...	...	...	...	2130	...	...	...	...	...	...	...	...	...

A – To/from Angoulême (Table **301**).
h – Not Aug. 15.
j – 1335 on ⑤ (also Aug. 14).
k – Also Aug. 15.
m – Not Aug. 14, 15.
v – Also Aug. 14.

293 NANTES - LES SABLES D'OLONNE

km								*TGV* 8973						*TGV* 8975		*TGV* 8977						*TGV* 8985		
		Ⓐ	Ⓐ		Ⓒ	Ⓐ	Ⓒ		①–④	Ⓒ	①–⑥		⑤	①–④		⑤–⑦	①–④	Ⓐ	⑦	①–⑥	⑤–⑦			⑤⑦
									m				v	m		t	m				t			v
	Paris Montparnasse **280** d.	...	...	...	...	...	...	0843	...	...	...	...	...	1218	...	1336	...	...	...	...	...	1843	...	...
0	**Nantes** 292 d.	0632	0731	...	0918	0932	1032	1103	1205	1205	1305	...	1434	1436	...	1603	1640	1731	1805	1905	2005	2104	...	2213
77	La Roche sur Yon 292 a.	0723	0826	...	1011	1023	1121	1142	1256	1257	1356	...	1518	1516	...	1642	1733	1823	1857	1957	2057	2143	...	2305
77	La Roche sur Yon d.	0725	0837	...	1013	1024	1123	1145	1257	1259	1357	...	1520	1519	...	1645	1738	1825	1903	1959	2059	2146	...	2307
114	**Les Sables d'Olonne** a.	0757	0906	...	1047	1058	1150	1211	1331	1332	1431	...	1545	1543	...	1711	1816	1859	1933	2032	2132	2212	...	2335

					TGV 8972								*TGV* 8984					*TGV* 8986					*TGV* 8988	
	①	Ⓐ		Ⓐ		⑥	Ⓐ							Ⓐ	①–④	⑦	⑤	①–⑥	Ⓐ	⑦	Ⓐ	⑥	⑦	⑦
						k									m		v					k		
Les Sables d'Olonne d.	0523	0621	0723	0806	0944	1017	1023	...	1223	...	1357	...	1549	1604	1653	1718	1723	1748	1824	1825	1923	1925	1947	2023
La Roche sur Yon a.	0553	0651	0753	0833	1007	1044	1053	...	1253	...	1427	...	1614	1631	1723	1747	1753	1813	1853	1855	1953	1954	2010	2054
La Roche sur Yon 292 d.	0555	0655	0755	0835	1010	1049	1055	...	1255	...	1429	...	1617	1633	1725	1749	1755	1816	1855	1858	1955	1957	2013	2057
Nantes 292 a.	0650	0750	0850	0928	1054	1143	1150	...	1350	...	1523	...	1656	1725	1821	1842	1850	1857	1950	1950	2050	2050	2057	2150
Paris Montparnasse **280** a.	...	...	...	...	1327	...	...	...	...	...	...	...	1917	...	...	...	...	2117	...	...	...	...	2317	...

k – Also Aug. 15.
m – Not Aug. 14, 15.
t – Also Aug. 14, 15.
v – Also Aug. 14.

TGV – Ⓡ, supplement payable, 🍷.

PARIS - LES AUBRAIS - ORLÉANS 294

km		Ⓐ	①–⑥		Ⓐ	①–⑥	⑦		Ⓐ	⑥ k	n			①–⑥	Ⓑ h		Ⓐ				Ⓐ	Ⓒ		A	B
0	**Paris** Austerlitz ▷ d.	0625	0652	...	0825	0925	1020	1125	1223	1223	1325	...	1525	1625	1722	1725	1754	1825	1925	1935r	2025	2125	...	2255	2255
119	Les Aubrais-Orléans ▷ a.	0726	0825	...	0926	1026	1158	1226z	1354	1358	1426	...	1625	1728	1827	1853	1855	1924	2025	2103	2126	2226	...	2357	2400
121	**Orléans** a.	0734	0833	...	0934	1033	1204	1234z	1404	1404	1434	...	1634	1736	1835	1901	1903	1933	2034	2110	2134	2234	...	0005	0008

	①–⑥ ◇	Ⓐ	Ⓐ	Ⓐ	Ⓐ	Ⓐ	⑥ k	①–⑥		⑦		①–⑥ n△	⑥ k	Ⓐ	①–⑥ n			⑤⑦ f	①–⑥		⑦		Ⓐ	⑦	①–⑥
Orléans d.	0458	0558	0628	0658	0728	0737	0737	0828	0928	1011	...	1124	1235	1247	1328	...	1531	1628	1728	1823	1828	1928	1939	2028	2128
Les Aubrais-Orléans ▷ d.	0505	0605	0635	0705	0735	0743	0743	0835	0935	1017	...	1131	1241	1253	1335	...	1538	1635	1735	1831	1835	1935	1945	2035	2135
Paris Austerlitz ▷ a.	0604	0705	0735	0808	0836	0905	0915	0936	1035e	1149	...	1235	1407	1416	1435t	...	1638	1735	1835	2006	1935	2036	2118	2136	2242

A – July 15–18, 22, 23, 25, Aug. 5–8 only.
B – Aug. 26–29 only.

e – 1039 Aug. 12–14, 19–23.
f – Also Aug. 14.
h – Not Aug. 15.
k – Also Aug. 15.
n – Not Aug. 5–8.

r – 1928 on Ⓒ July 20 - Aug. 18.
t – 1438 on Aug. 12–14, 19–23.
z – 6 minutes later on July 9, Aug. 5–8.

◇ – On July 8 Orléans d. 0457, Les Aubrais d. 0504, Paris a. 0608.
△ – On Aug. 12–14, 19–23 Orléans d. 1128, Les Aubrais d. 1135, Paris a. 1246.
▷ – See also Tables **296** and **315**.

PARIS - TOURS 295

TGV services via high-speed line.
See Table **300** for other *TGV* services Paris - Vendôme-Villiers - St Pierre des Corps and v.v. See Table **296** for regional services from/to Paris Austerlitz via Blois.

km		*TGV* 8301 ⑥ k	*TGV* 8303 ◇	*TGV* 8311 ⑤ f	*TGV* 8313 ①–⑥	*TGV* 8343 ①–⑤ a	*TGV* 8317 ①–⑤ a	*TGV* 8319 ⑤⑦ f	*TGV* 8321 ①–⑥	*TGV* 8323 ⑦
0	**Paris** Montparnasse d.	0730	1232	1526	1630	1726	1800	1826	1926	2035
162	Vendôme-Villiers TGV d.	0820	1322	1617	1720	1818	1850	1917	2017	2126
221	St Pierre des Corps a.	0839	1342	1639	1739	1839	1909	1939	2039	2145
221	St Pierre des Corps d.	0843	1346	1642	1742	1842	1912	1942	2042	2156
224	**Tours** a.	0848	1351	1647	1747	1847	1917	1947	2047	2201

	TGV 8302 ①–⑤ a	*TGV* 8306 ①–⑤ a	*TGV* 8308 Ⓐ n	*TGV* 8310 ⑥ t	*TGV* 8314		*TGV* 8316 ⑤ f	*TGV* 8318 ⑤⑦ f	*TGV* 8320	*TGV* 8324 ⑦
Tours d.	0612	0642	0746	0808	1208	...	1612	1708	1812	2108
St Pierre des Corps a.	0617	0648	0751	0814	1214	...	1617	1714	1817	2113
St Pierre des Corps d.	0620	0654	0754	0820	1220	...	1620	1720	1820	2120
Vendôme-Villiers TGV d.	0641	0716	|	0841	1241	...	1645	1742	1841	2141
Paris Montparnasse a.	0739j	0805	0906	0932	1331	...	1735	1830	1931	2231

a – Not Aug. 15, 16.
f – Also Aug. 14; not Aug. 16.
j – 0736 on ①.

k – Also Aug. 15, 16.
n – Not July 8–12, Aug. 19–30.
t – Also Aug. 15.

TGV –🅁, supplement payable, 🍷.

◇ – Train number **8335** on ①–④ (not Aug. 14, 15).

ORLÉANS and PARIS - BLOIS - TOURS 296

See Table **295** for direct *TGV* services Paris Montparnasse - Tours and v.v. See Table **300** for other *TGV* services Paris Montparnasse - St Pierre des Corps and v.v.
Timings of services to/from Nantes may vary by up to 3 minutes until July 7.

km		Ⓐ	⑥ k	Ⓐ	Ⓒ L	Ⓐ	①–⑥	Ⓑ h		Ⓒ	Ⓒ	Ⓐ	Ⓐ		Ⓒ	Ⓐ	⑥ k	Ⓐ n			Ⓐ		
0	**Orléans** d.	0636	0637	0655	0656	0710	0741	...	0841	...	1042	1042	1103	...	1242	1242	...	...	1442	...	1542	...	1642
	Paris Austerlitz 294 315 d.	|	|	|	|	|	|	0734	|	0834	|	|	|	...	|	|	1237	1245	|	...	|	...	|
	Les Aubrais-Orléans 294 315 d.	|	|	|	|	|	|	0837	|	0937	|	|	|	...	|	|	1337	1359	|	...	|	...	|
27	Beaugency d.	0654	0656	0715	|	0730	0800	|	0900	|	1100	1100	|	...	1300	1300	|	|	1501	...	1600	...	1700
59	Blois d.	0717	0716	0731	0726	0753	0819	0904	0919	1003	1120	1119	1133	...	1320	1324	1404	1431	1523	...	1620	...	1720
91	Amboise d.	0735	0735	|	|	0811	0838	0923	0938	1023	1139	1141	|	...	1338	1345	1423	1452	1542	...	1638	...	1739
112	St Pierre des Corps a.	0746	0746	0756	0751	0827	0850	0935	0950	1036	1150	1153	1204	...	1352	1359	1436	1506	1555	...	1650	...	1750
115	**Tours** a.	0755	0755	0803	0801	0834	0857	0944	0957	1043	1157	1200	1211	...	1359	1406	1443	1513	1602	...	1657	...	1757
	Nantes 289 a.	...	...	0947	0959	...	...	...	...	...	...	...	1420	...	...	...	...	...	...	...	...	...	...

km		①–④ m	⑤⑥ s L	Ⓐ	⑦	Ⓒ	Ⓐ	Ⓐ	⑥	†	Ⓐ	N	Ⓐ P				Ⓑ h		⑤–⑦ v				
	Orléans d.	1701	1701	1744	1804	...	...	1842	1842	1844	...	1942	1942	...	2041	...	2142	...	...	...	...	...	...
0	**Paris** Austerlitz 294 315 d.	|	|	|	|	1737	1737	|	|	|	1837	|	|	...	|	...	|	...	2235	...	...	...	...
119	Les Aubrais-Orléans 294 315 d.	|	|	|	|	1838	1838	|	|	|	1937	|	|	...	|	...	|	...	2335	...	...	...	...
146	Beaugency d.	1716	1716	1803	|	|	|	1900	1900	1902	|	2000	2003	...	2059	...	2200	...	|	...	...	...	...
178	Blois d.	1732	1732	1823	1831	1903	1909	1919	1924	1922	2003	2019	2022	...	2122	...	2222	...	0003	...	...	...	...
210	Amboise d.	|	|	1842	|	1920	1924	1938	1943	1940	2019	2037	2040	...	2140	...	2241	...	0023	...	...	...	...
231	St Pierre des Corps a.	1754	1754	1853	1853	1932	1936	1950	1954	1954	2031	2050	2051	...	2151	...	2252	...	0035	...	...	...	...
234	**Tours** a.	1801	1801	1900	1900	1939	1943	1957	2001	2001	2038	2057	2058	...	2158	...	2259	...	0042	...	...	...	...
	Nantes 289 a.	1946	1946	...	2045	...	...	...	...	...	...	...	...	...	...	...	...	...	...	...	...	...	...

	Ⓐ		①–⑥	⑥ k	Ⓐ	Ⓐ	Ⓐ	⑥	†		Ⓐ	Ⓒ	Ⓐ z	Ⓒ		Ⓒ L	Ⓒ	Ⓐ Q	⑥ k	Ⓐ	Ⓐ		
Nantes 289 d.	...	...	...	...	...	...	...	...	...	...	0713	...	...	...	...	0911	...	...	...	...	1107	...	...
Tours d.	0503	...	0603	0620	0620	0657	0740	0800	0802	...	0901	0922	0936	0953	...	1107	1122	1122	1203	1203	1250	...	1400
St Pierre des Corps d.	0510	...	0610	0627	0627	0704	0747	0807	0809	...	0907	0929	0943	1000	...	1116	1129	1129	1210	1210	1257	...	1407
Amboise d.	0522	...	0621	0638	0640	0715	0758	0819	0821	...	0921	0942	0956	1011	...	|	1142	1142	1221	1223	|	...	1423
Blois d.	0543	...	0641	0656	0658	0737	0818	0839	0841	...	0939	0959	1019	1032	...	1143	1159	1200	1241	1244	1326	...	1443
Beaugency d.	0602	...	0701	|	|	0756	0837	0900	0859	...	|	|	1041	1050	...	|	|	|	1301	1306	|	...	1503
Les Aubrais-Orléans 294 315 a.	|	...	|	0723	0726	|	|	|	|	...	|	1027	|	|	...	|	1224	1233	|	|	|	...	|
Paris Austerlitz 294 315 a.	|	...	|	0823	0833	|	|	|	|	...	|	1130	|	|	...	|	1325	1350	|	|	|	...	|
Orléans a.	0620	...	0719	...	...	0816	0855	0918	0918	...	1012	...	1102	1107	...	1208	...	...	1321	1327	1400	...	1523

	⑤⑦ s	Ⓐ	①–⑥	⑦	Ⓑ h		⑥	Ⓐ	†		⑥ k	Ⓑ h	Ⓐ		Ⓑ h	⑥ k L	⑦ L	Ⓐ					
Nantes 289 d.	...	...	...	...	...	...	...	...	...	...	...	...	1810	...	...	2011	2035	...	...	...	...	...	...
Tours d.	1503	1522	1603	1618	1703	1719	1801	1802	1803	...	1857	1907	2000	...	2101	2210	2227	2214	...	...	...	...	...
St Pierre des Corps d.	1510	1529	1610	1625	1710	1726	1808	1809	1810	...	1905	1914	2007	...	2108	2218	2234	2221	...	...	...	...	...
Amboise d.	1522	1542	1621	1637	1722	1740	1820	1821	1821	...	1919	1925	2018	...	2120	|	|	2232	...	...	...	...	...
Blois d.	1543	1603	1641	1659	1742	1800	1840	1841	1841	...	1939	1945	2035	...	2140	2246	2258	2252	...	...	...	...	...
Beaugency d.	1601	|	1659	|	1801	|	1901	1902	1902	...	1957	2005	|	...	2200	|	|	2310	...	...	...	...	...
Les Aubrais-Orléans 294 315 a.	|	1628	|	1728	|	1824	|	|	|	...	|	|	|	...	|	|	|	|	...	...	...	...	...
Paris Austerlitz 294 315 a.	|	1732	|	1832	|	1932	|	|	|	...	|	|	|	...	|	|	|	|	...	...	...	...	...
Orléans a.	1619	...	1720	...	1821	...	1920	1920	1920	...	2017	2023	2102	...	2219	2311	2325	2328	...	...	...	...	...

L – To/from Le Croisic (Table **288**).
N – Daily to July 14; Ⓒ July 20 - Aug. 18; daily from Aug. 24.
P – July 15 - Aug. 23.
Q – Ⓐ Aug. 5–30 (not Aug. 9). Arrives Paris 1339 Aug. 26–30.

h – Not Aug. 15.
k – Also Aug. 15.
m – Not Aug. 14.

n – Not Aug. 5–8.
s – Also Aug. 14.
v – Also Aug. 14, 15.
z – Not July 29, 30, Aug. 1.

☛ Frequent trains run St Pierre des Corps - Tours and v.v. (journey time 5 minutes) and Les Aubrais-Orléans - Orléans and v.v. (journey time 4 minutes).

299 OTHER LOCAL SERVICES

ANGERS - CHOLET — Journey 41 – 53 minutes — *60 km*

From Angers at 0617 Ⓐ, 0722 Ⓐ, 0825 Ⓐ, 0922 ⑥ **k**, 1022 Ⓐ, 1122, 1254 ①–⑥ **a**, 1619 Ⓐ **n**, 1621 **D**, 1722 Ⓐ **n**, 1758 Ⓐ, 1822 Ⓐ, 1825 ⑥ **k**, 1928 Ⓐ, 1948 ⑦ **e**, 2031 **E**, 2048 ⑤ **f**, 2128 **G** and 2234 **H**.

From Cholet at 0549 Ⓐ, 0610 Ⓐ, 0647 Ⓐ, 0649 ⑥ **k**, 0715 Ⓐ, 0749 Ⓐ, 0849 **d**, 1049 Ⓐ, 1149 ⑥ **k**, 1235 Ⓐ, 1351 ⑦ **e**, 1353 ①–⑥ **a**, 1647 Ⓑ **o**, 1749 §, 1842 ⑦ **e**, 1853 Ⓐ, 1920 Ⓒ, 1921 Ⓐ and 2154 ⑦ **e**.

BAYONNE - ST JEAN PIED DE PORT — *Service June 11 - Sept. 1* — *50 km*

No service Aug. 23 – 26	q		p				L		J	...
Bayonne d.	0742	...	1159	...	1452	...	1830	...	2110	...
Cambo les Bains d.	0805	...	1221	...	1514	...	1857	...	2132	...
St Jean Pied de Port a.	0840	...	1252	...	1550	...	1936	...	2208	...

No service Aug. 23 – 26	L		q						M	
St Jean Pied de Port d.	0605	...	0851	...	1302	...	1631	...	1941	...
Cambo les Bains d.	0644	...	0927	...	1335	...	1706	...	2017	...
Bayonne a.	0710	...	0949	...	1358	...	1729	...	2038	...

BORDEAUX - MONT DE MARSAN — *Service until Sept. 1* — *147 km*

	Ⓐ	Ⓐ			①–⑥ r	Ⓒ	Ⓐ			Ⓑ u
Bordeaux 305 d.	0550	...	0818	1018	1318	1528	1618	1739	*1845*	2118
Morcenx 305 d.	0651	0802	0920	1120	1420	1640	1718	1848	1956	2220
Mont de Marsan a.	0721	0831	0945	1145	1445	1704	1741	1911	2026	2245

	Ⓐ	①–⑥ r		①–⑥ r		Ⓐ	Ⓒ	Ⓐ	Ⓒ	Ⓑ u
Mont de Marsan d.	0513	0734	1015	1215	1515	1711	1717	1810	1813	1917
Morcenx 305 d.	0537	0759	1039	1240	1539	1744	1742	1840	1843	1941
Bordeaux 305 a.	0642	0901	1142	1342	1642	...	1842	1942	...	2042

CARCASSONNE - LIMOUX - QUILLAN

km		🚌 Ⓐ	⚒	🚌 ⚒	🚌 Ⓒ	⚒ v	🚌 †	⚒ v	🚌	⚒	⚒	🚌 ⑥
0	Carcassonne d.	0635	0719	0800	0915	1036	1230	1231	1415	1600	1728	...
26	Limoux a.	0724	0749	0847	0955	1104	1310	1301	1450	1629	1756	1810
54	Quillan a.	0813	...	0927	1035	*1205**	1400	*1350**	1535	*1725**	...	1900

	🚌 Ⓐ	⚒	🚌 †	
Carcassonne d.	1820	1901	1905	...
Limoux a.	1915	1929	1945	...
Quillan a.	2005	*2018**	2035	...

	⚒	🚌 Ⓐ	🚌 Ⓐ	⚒
Quillan d.	*0549**	0620	0705	...
Limoux d.	0643	0655	0750	0802
Carcassonne a.	0712	0750	...	0831

	🚌 Ⓒ	🚌 Ⓐ	⚒ v	🚌 †	🚌	⚒ v		⚒	🚌 Ⓑ	🚌 ⑥	⚒	🚌 ⚒
Quillan d.	0745	0820	*1026**	1100	1245	*1356**	...	*1545**	1710	1725	...	1820
Limoux d.	0819	0900	1120	1135	1319	1450	...	1647	1745	1800	1813	1854
Carcassonne a.	0910	0950	1148	1220	1410	1520	...	1716	1840	...	1842	1950

CHARLEVILLE MÉZIÈRES - GIVET — Journey 69 – 81 minutes — *64 km*

Warning! Subject to alteration June 17 - August 30

From Charleville Mézières at 0557 ⚒, 0643 ⚒, 0841 Ⓐ, 0850 †, 0955 ⚒◇, 1051 †, 1246 ⚒◇, 1350◇, 1526 Ⓑ◇, 1635, 1739 ⚒, 1821 Ⓐ, 1855 Ⓐ, 1939, 2025 Ⓐ and 2058.

From Givet at 0434 Ⓐ, 0523 Ⓐ, 0555 ⚒, 0613 Ⓐ, 0636, 0715 ⚒, 0823 Ⓐ, 1024 Ⓐ◇, 1046 Ⓒ, 1222 ⚒◇, 1411 ⚒◇, 1435 †, 1536 Ⓑ◇, 1712, 1758 Ⓐ and 1912.

DINARD - ST MALO

🚌 : 7 – 10 times per day (fewer on †), journey 24 minutes. Operator: TIV. *11 km*

⛴ : *Le Bus de Mer* passenger ferry operates 12 – 15 times daily from April to October. Journey time 10 minutes. Operator: Compagnie Corsaire.

LILLE - LENS — *Service July 6 - Aug. 25* — Journey 28 – 56 minutes — *39 km*

From Lille Flandres at 0626 Ⓐ, 0642 Ⓐ, 0645 ⑥, 0715 Ⓐ, 0726 Ⓐ, 0730 Ⓐ, 0819 Ⓐ, 0824 ⑥, 0919 ⚒, 1019 Ⓐ, 1019 †, 1026 †, 1118 ⑥, 1126 Ⓐ, 1219 Ⓐ, 1226 Ⓒ, 1242 Ⓐ, 1318, 1326 Ⓐ, 1518 ⑥, 1519 †, 1542 Ⓐ, 1619 Ⓑ, 1626 Ⓐ, 1642 Ⓐ, 1715 Ⓐ, 1719 Ⓒ, 1726 ⚒, 1742 Ⓐ, 1819, 1826 Ⓑ, 1842 Ⓐ, 1919, 1926 ⚒, 2018 Ⓒ, 2019 Ⓐ and 2119 Ⓐ.

From Lens at 0454 Ⓐ, 0554 Ⓐ, 0639 Ⓐ, 0644 ⚒, 0655 ⚒, 0709 Ⓐ, 0740 ⚒, 0744 Ⓐ, 0758 ⚒, 0836 Ⓐ, 0838 †, 0854 Ⓐ, 0944 Ⓐ, 0954 ⑥, 1044 †, 1110 Ⓐ, 1116 †, 1144 Ⓐ, 1154 ⑥, 1210 Ⓐ, 1244 Ⓑ, 1254 ⚒, 1328 †, 1344 ⚒, 1354 ⑥, 1454 †, 1546 Ⓐ, 1554 ⑥, 1639 Ⓐ, 1644 Ⓐ, 1654 Ⓒ, 1709 Ⓐ, 1744 Ⓐ, 1754, 1844, 1856 Ⓑ, 1944 Ⓐ, 1948 Ⓒ and 2010 Ⓐ.

NANTES - CHOLET — *Service from July 6* — Journey 58 – 70 minutes — *65 km*

From Nantes at 0635 Ⓐ 🚌, 0735 Ⓐ, 1100 ⑥ **k** 🚌, 1245 ⑦ **w**, 1255 ①–⑥ **z**, 1405 ⑥ **k** 🚌, 1500 ⑤ **F** 🚌, 1620 Ⓐ 🚌, 1735 Ⓐ, 1815 Ⓐ 🚌, 1840 ⑦ **N** 🚌, 1858 Ⓐ, 1929 ⑥ **k** and 1952 ⑦ **w**.

From Cholet at 0606 Ⓐ, 0710 Ⓐ, 0810 ⑥ **k**, 0930 ⑥ **k** 🚌, 1245 Ⓐ 🚌, 1250 ⑥ **k** 🚌, 1410 ⑦ **w**, 1625 ⑤ **F** 🚌, 1710 Ⓐ, 1715 ⑦ **N** 🚌, 1745 Ⓐ 🚌, 1837 Ⓐ, 1910 ⑦ **w** and 1920 Ⓐ 🚌.

NANTES - PORNIC — *Service July 6 - Sept. 1*

km		Ⓐ	⑥t	⑦	Ⓐ	⑥t	Ⓒ	Ⓐ	Ⓐ	⑦	⑥t	Ⓐ	⑦
0	**Nantes** d.	0707	0919	0941	1009	1109	1209	1229	1511	1519	1521	1616	1709
24	Ste Pazanne a.	0742	0950	1012	1041	1141	1239	1301	1542	1551	1553	1649	1742
54	**Pornic** a.	0815	1023	1043	1110	1210	1308	1330	1611	1620	1623	1725	1810

	Ⓐ	⑥t	Ⓐ	⑤g	R¶	⑤g
Nantes d.	1738	1809	1847	1935	2015	2035
Ste Pazanne a.	1808	1841	1918	2007	2045	2105
Pornic a.	1839	1910	1949	2036	2114	2134

	Ⓐ	Ⓐ	⑥t
Pornic d.	0625	0716	0740
Ste Pazanne d.	0657	0745	0818
Nantes a.	0728	0816	0850

	Ⓐ	⑦	Ⓒ	Ⓐ	⚒	⑦	Ⓐ	Ⓒ	Ⓐ	⑦	Ⓐ	⑦	⑥m
Pornic d.	0825	0939	1050	1150	1348	1441	1625	1650	1741	1850	1849	2125	2230
Ste Pazanne d.	0853	1018	1118	1218	1416	1509	1655	1718	1809	1918	1923	2153	2256
Nantes a.	0924	1050	1150	1250	1450	1541	1729	1750	1835	1950	1955	2225	2325

NANTES - ST GILLES CROIX DE VIE — *Service July 6 - Sept. 1*

km		Ⓐ	⑦	⑥t	⑥t	Ⓑu¶		Ⓐ	Ⓒ	Ⓐ	①–⑥	⑦
0	**Nantes** d.	0707	0917	0919	1009	1113	1309	1429	1609	1616	1708	1805
24	Ste Pazanne d.	0750	0949	0958	1042	1146	1342	1459	1642	1654	1739	1838
63	Challans d.	0814	1014	1021	1106	1210	1405	1522	1705	1716	1804	1901
84	**St Gilles Croix** a.	0831	1031	1038	1122	1227	1422	1538	1722	1733	1822	1918

	Ⓐ	⑥t	Ⓐ	⑤g	Ⓑu
Nantes d.	1814	1909	1915	2009	2109
Ste Pazanne d.	1851	1942	1948	2040	2141
Challans d.	1916	2005	2011	2103	2204
St Gilles Croix a.	1934	2022	2028	2120	2220

	Ⓐ	Ⓐ	⚒	⑥t
St Gilles Croix d.	0539	0639	0733	0807
Challans d.	0555	0656	0749	0823
Ste Pazanne d.	0618	0718	0813j	0846
Nantes a.	0650	0751	0844j	0918

	⑥t	⑦	Ⓐ	Ⓐ		⑥t	Ⓒ	Ⓐ	Ⓑ◧	Ⓐ	⑥t	⑦	⑦
St Gilles Croix d.	0917	0933	0939	1042	1239	1433	1539	1547	1744	1834	1839	1939	2039
Challans d.	0934	0949	0955	1058	1256	1449	1556	1603	1802	1850	1856	1956	2056
Ste Pazanne d.	0957	1018	1018	1121	1318	1511	1618	1625	1824	1923	1918	2018	2118
Nantes a.	1030	1050	1050	1153	1350	1542	1650	1656	1856	1955	1950	2050	2150

PARIS - DISNEYLAND (Marne la Vallée - Chessy) — *32 km*

Trains run approximately every 15 minutes 0500 - 2400 on RER Line A:
Châtelet les Halles - Gare de Lyon - Marne la Vallée Chessy (for Disneyland).
Operator: RATP. For *TGV* services serving Marne la Vallée see Tables **11** and **391**.

Journey: 39 minutes.

ST BRIEUC - DINAN — *Service from July 6*

km		①–⑥ z ⊖		Ⓐ c		Ⓒ		Ⓐ		Ⓒ	
0	St Brieuc 284 d.	0846	...	1325	...	1620	...	1751	...	1859	...
21	Lamballe 284 d.	0902	...	1341	...	1636	...	1807	...	1915	...
62	Dinan a.	0951	...	1430	...	1725	...	1856	...	2004	...

	①–⑥ z		c		Ⓐ		Ⓒ			
Dinan d.	0714	...	1212	...	1621	...	1743	...	...	...
Lamballe 284 d.	0804	...	1302	...	1711	...	1833	...	...	...
St Brieuc 284 a.	0820	...	1318	...	1727	...	1849	...	...	...

SOUILLAC - SARLAT 🚌 — *30 km*

From Souillac (rail station) at 0645 Ⓐ, 0910 ⑥, 1355, 1945 †, 2245 ⑤.

From Sarlat (rail station) at 1122, 1310 ③, 1638 ①②④⑤, 1720 †, 1722 ③⑥, 1815 ①②④⑤.

Journey 41 minutes. Service by 🚌 (Trans Périgord Ligne 6).

Warning! Service is amended during school holiday periods.

TOULOUSE - AUCH — Journey 85 – 95 minutes — *88 km*

From Toulouse Matabiau at 0624 ⚒, 0724 Ⓐ, 0822 ◇, 1024 ⊙, 1224 ⊙, 1424 ◇, 1520 Ⓐ◇, 1624, 1724 Ⓐ, 1824 and 2025.

From Auch at 0603 ⚒, 0707 Ⓐ, 0809, 0909 Ⓐ⊙, 1007 ⊙, 1206 ⊙, 1405 ◇, 1604 ◇, 1706 Ⓐ, 1808 and 2009.

TOURS - CHINON — Journey 46 – 54 minutes — *49 km*

Chinon departures may be up to 3 minutes earlier June 10 – 21

From Tours at 0727 Ⓐ, 0932 ①–⑥ **b** △, 1232 ①–⑥ **b** △, 1505 **Q**, 1630 Ⓐ, 1736 Ⓐ, 1904 and 1955 Ⓑ **h**.

From Chinon at 0625 Ⓐ, 0652 ①–⑥ **b**, 0739 Ⓐ **y**, 0839 Ⓐ, 1109 ①–⑥ **b** △, 1339 △, 1608 Ⓐ **y**, 1744 ①–⑥ **b**, 1843 Ⓑ **h** and 2004 ⑦ **e**.

VALENCIENNES - CAMBRAI — Journey 35 – 47 minutes — *40 km*

SERVICE JULY 6 - AUGUST 25. 🚌 services are subject to extended journey times.

From Valenciennes at 0604 Ⓐ, 0630 Ⓐ, 0733 Ⓐ, 0836 ⑥, 1206 Ⓐ⊗, 1306 Ⓐ⊗, 1311 ⑥, 1703 Ⓐ, 1730 ⑥, 1733 Ⓐ 🚌, 1735 † 🚌, 1758 Ⓐ 🚌, 1910 Ⓐ 🚌 and 2040 † 🚌.

From Cambrai at 0517 Ⓐ 🚌, 0650 Ⓐ, 0742 Ⓐ, 0744 ⑥, 1212 Ⓐ⊗, 1215 ⑥, 1312 Ⓐ⊗, 1629 Ⓐ 🚌, 1722 ⑥ 🚌, 1745 † 🚌, 1812 Ⓐ, 1849 † 🚌, and 1912 Ⓐ.

D – Ⓒ to June 30; Ⓐ July 8 - Aug. 30; Ⓒ from Sept. 7.
E – ①②③④⑥⑦ (also Nov. 1; not Aug. 14, Oct. 31).
F – ⑤ from Sept. 6 (also Oct. 31; not Nov. 1).
G – Ⓐ to July 5; ⑤ July 12 - Aug. 23 (also Aug. 14); Ⓐ from Aug. 30.
H – ⑤† to July 7; ⑦ July 14 - Aug. 25; ⑤⑦ from Sept. 1 (also Oct. 31, Nov. 11; not Nov. 1).
J – ⑤† (daily from July 7).
L – ⚒ (daily from July 1).
M – † (daily from July 7).
N – ⑦ from Sept. 8 (also Nov. 11).
Q – Daily to July 14; Ⓒ July 20 - Aug. 18; daily from Aug. 24.
R – ①②③④⑦ (not Aug. 14, 15).

a – Not June 10, Sept. 16 – 20, 23 – 27, Nov. 11.
b – Not June 10, Nov. 11.
c – Not Sept. 30, Oct. 1 – 4, 7 – 11.
d – Not June 9, Nov. 10.
e – Also June 10, Nov. 11.
f – Also Aug. 14, Oct. 31; not Nov. 1.
g – Also Aug. 14.
h – Not Aug. 15, Nov. 1.
j – On ⑥ (also Aug. 15) Ste Pazanne d. 0818, Nantes a. 0850.
k – Also Aug. 15, Nov. 1.
m – Not July 6, 13.
n – Not July 8 - Aug. 30.
o – Not July 7 - Sept. 1, Nov. 1.
p – Not June 16, 23, 30.
q – Not June 20.
r – Not June 10.
t – Also Aug. 15
u – Not Aug. 15.
v – Not Nov. 25 – 29, Dec. 2 – 6, 9 – 13.
w – Also Nov. 11.
y – Not July 15 - Aug. 23.
z – Not Nov. 11.

¶ – 4 – 6 minutes **earlier** on ⑦.
◧ – 8 – 10 minutes **earlier** on ⑦.
⊖ – 17 minutes **earlier** on ①–⑤ Nov. 18 - Dec. 6.
§ – Departs 1718 on June 30.
⊗ – Subject to alteration July 29 - Aug. 9.
◇ – Subject to alteration Oct. 21 – 25, 28 – 31.
⊙ – Subject to alteration Oct. 7 – 11, 21 – 25, 28 – 31
△ – Subject to alteration Oct. 14 – 18, 21 – 25, 28 – 31, Nov. 4 – 8.
* – By 🚌 from / to Limoux.

PARIS - POITIERS - LA ROCHELLE and BORDEAUX 300

PARIS - BORDEAUX non-stop services

km		TGV 8501	TGV 8571		TGV 8531		TGV 8405	TGV 8503	TGV 8471		TGV 8572	TGV 8535		TGV 8473	TGV 8255		TGV 8507	TGV 8537		TGV 8541	TGV 8574		TGV 8511	TGV 8261
		①–⑥	①–⑥		①–⑥		①–⑤	⑥⑦	⑥												⑤			
							a	c	c												f			
0	**Paris** Montparnasse d.	0647	0647	...	0747	...	0847	0847	0847	...	0947	0947	...	1047	1047	...	1147	1147	...	1247	1247	...	1347	1347
537	**Bordeaux** St Jean a.	0856	0856	...	0956	...	1056	1056	1056	...	1156	1156	...	1256	1256	...	1356	1356	...	1456	1456	...	1556	1556
	To:	*Tou*	*Tar*		*Hen*		—	*Tou*	*Arc*		*Tar*	*Hen*		*Arc*	—		*Tou*	*Hen*		*Hen*	*Tar*		*Tou*	—

	TGV 8413	TGV 8547		TGV 8590	TGV 8549		TGV 8513		TGV 8417		TGV 8593	TGV 8551		TGV 8477		TGV 8515	TGV 8273		TGV 8517	TGV 8553		TGV 8421	
		⑤							⑤					⑤					⑤	⑤		Ⓑ	
	A	f							d					f			G		f	f		a	
Paris Montparnasse d.	1447	1447	...	1547	1547	...	1647	...	1714	...	1747	1747	...	1814	...	1847	1847	...	1947	1947	...	2047	...
Bordeaux St Jean a.	1656	1656	...	1756	1756	...	1856	...	1927	...	1956	1956	...	2027	...	2056	2056	...	2156	2156	...	2258	...
To:	—	*Hen*		*Tar*	*Hen*		*Tou*		—		*Tar*	*Hen*		*Arc*		*Tou*	—		*Tou*	*Hen*		—	

PARIS - POITIERS - LA ROCHELLE and BORDEAUX

km		TGV 8481	TGV 8481	TGV 8481	TGV 8371	TGV 8331	TGV 8483	TGV 8373	TGV 8375	TGV 5450	TGV 8433		TGV 5202	TGV 8377	TGV 8333	TGV 8333	TGV 7651	TGV 8365	TGV 8485	TGV 7653	TGV 8383		TGV 5222	TGV 5452
		②–⑤	①⑥												⑤⑥	①–④		⑤–⑦						
		a	b	E				H		wS			zL		n	m	⊠	n		⊠			zL	zS
0	**Paris** Montparnasse 295 d.	0600	0604	0710	0722	0730	0822	0822	0907	...	1019•	...	...	1222	1232	1232	1305	1341	1356	1517	1522	...	...	...
	Vendôme-Villiers TGV 295 d.	|	|	|	|	0820	|	|	|	...	|	...	...	|	1322	1322	|	|	|	|	|	...	...	...
	St Pierre des Corps 295 a.	0707	0706	0812	|	0839	|	|	1009	...	1121	...	...	|	1342	1342	|	|	1458	1620	|	...	...	...
	St Pierre des Corps d.	0711	0710	0816	|	0846	|	|	1013	1102	1125	...	1302	|	1352	1345	|	|	1502	1626	|	...	1802	1802
	Tours d.	|	|	|	|	|	|	|	|	|	|	...	|	|	|	1408	|	|	|	|	|	...	|	|
	Châtellerault d.	|	|	|	|	0915	|	|	|	|	|	...	|	|	1422	1438	|	|	|	|	|	...	|	|
	Futuroscope d.	|	|	|	|	0928	|	|	|	|	|	...	|	|	1437	1451	|	|	|	|	|	...	|	|
318	**Poitiers** a.	0741	0741	0848	0845	0937	0945	0945	1045	1132	1157	...	1332	1345	1448	1459	1433	|	1532	|	1645	...	1832	1832
318	**Poitiers** d.	0750	0750	0851	0848	...	0949	0954	1048	1135	1200	...	1335	1348	...	...	1442j	|	1536	|	1648	...	1835	1835
398	Niort d.	|	|	|	0935	...	|	1040	1139	|	|	...	|	1435	...	...	|	1543	|	|	1735	...	|	|
465	**La Rochelle** Ville a.	|	|	|	1015	...	|	1116	1219	|	|	...	|	1515	...	...	|	1618	|	|	1815	...	|	|
	Angoulême d.	0832	0832	0931	...	...	1031	...	...	1216	1248	...	1416	...	...	...	1524	...	1617	1732	...	...	1917	1917
	Libourne d.	0915	0915	|	...	...	1115	...	...	|	|	...	|	...	...	...	|	...	1704	|	...	...	|	|
540	**Bordeaux** St Jean a.	0937	0937	1008	...	...	1137	...	...	1252	1326	...	1452	...	...	...	1601	...	1726	1808	...	...	1952	1952

km		TGV 8491	TGV 8389	TGV 8341	TGV 8343	TGV 8451	TGV 8391	TGV 8391	TGV 8493	TGV 8391	TGV 8345	TGV 8453	TGV 5240	TGV 5454	TGV 8393	TGV 8455	TGV 8393		TGV 8395	TGV 8347	TGV 8457	TGV 8495		TGV 8461
				⑦	①–⑤	①–④	①–④	⑦	⑤	⑤	①–⑥	⑤			⑤				⑤	⑤⑦	①–④	⑤⑦		⑤⑦
					a	m	m		f	f		f	zL	zS	f	A	A		f	f	m	f		f
0	**Paris** Montparnasse 295 d.	1722	1722	1726	1726	1814	1822	1822	1822	1822	1826	1856	...	...	1922	1922	1922	...	2022	2035	2052	2104	...	2156
	Vendôme-Villiers TGV 295 d.	|	|	1818	1818	|	|	|	|	|	1917	|	...	...	|	|	|	...	|	2126	2142	|	...	|
	St Pierre des Corps 295 a.	|	|	1839	1839	|	|	|	|	|	1939	1958	...	...	|	|	|	...	|	2145	2201	2206	...	2258
	St Pierre des Corps d.	|	|	1846	1842	|	|	|	|	|	1946	2001	2010	2010	|	|	|	...	|	2150	2205	2210	...	2302
	Tours d.	|	|	|	1900	|	|	|	|	|	|	|	|	|	|	|	|	...	|	|	|	|	...	|
	Châtellerault d.	|	|	1915	1930	|	|	|	|	|	2015	|	|	|	|	|	|	...	|	2219	|	|	...	|
	Futuroscope d.	|	|	|	|	|	|	|	|	|	|	|	|	|	|	|	|	...	|	|	|	|	...	|
	Poitiers a.	1845	1845	1932	1949	|	1945	1945	1945	1945	2036	|	2039	2039	2045	2045	2045	...	2145	2236	2235	|	...	2332
	Poitiers d.	1849	1854	...	...	|	1948	1948	1949	1954	...	|	2042	2042	2048	2049	2054	...	2148	...	2239	|	...	2336
394	Niort d.	|	1941	...	...	|	2038	2043	|	2044	...	|	|	|	2135	|	2140	...	2239	...	|	|	...	|
461	**La Rochelle** Ville a.	|	2017	...	...	|	2119	2123	|	2119	...	|	|	|	2215	|	2220	...	2319	...	|	|	...	|
	Angoulême d.	1931	...	...	...	2005	...	...	2031	...	...	2104	2126	2126	...	2131	...	...	...	...	2321	2310	...	0018
	Libourne d.	2015	...	...	...	|	...	...	2115	...	...	|	|	|	...	|	...	...	...	...	|	2353	...	|
	Bordeaux St Jean a.	2037	...	...	...	2042	...	...	2137	...	...	2147	2206	2206	...	2210	...	...	...	...	2359	0014	...	0054

TER (regional) services TOURS - POITIERS - ANGOULÊME - BORDEAUX and POITIERS - LA ROCHELLE

TOURS - POITIERS

km		①–⑥	①–⑥	①–⑥		Ⓐ	⑦				Ⓐ	⚒	Ⓐ	Ⓐ		①–⑥		⑦						
0	**Tours** d.	...	0615	...	...	...	...	...	1221	...	1620	...	1723	...	1820	...	...	2023	...	...	...	...	...	...
68	Châtellerault d.	0650	0710	0733	...	0833	0927	...	1310	...	1708	1735	1812	1833	1908	1933	...	2113	...	...	...	...	...	...
90	Futuroscope d.	0711	0722	0754	...	0854	0940	...	1332	...	1720	1756	1827	1854	1920	1954	...	2125	...	...	...	...	...	...
101	**Poitiers** a.	0720	0729	0803	...	0903	0948	...	1342	...	1728	1805	1836	1903	1928	2003	...	2132	...	...	...	...	...	...

POITIERS - LA ROCHELLE

km		Ⓐ	Ⓐ		Ⓐ	⑥		Ⓒ				Ⓐ	Ⓐ				⑤⑦	①–④						
						k											p	m						
0	**Poitiers** d.	0600	0648	...	0757	0757	...	1003	...	1224	...	1553	1619	1713	1806	...	1906	1921	...	...	...	...	...	...
80	Niort d.	0650	0748	...	0851	0851	...	1052	...	1319	...	1641	1726	1816	1904	...	2006	2018	...	...	...	...	...	...
147	**La Rochelle** Ville a.	0735	0835	...	0934	0938	...	1136	...	1404	...	1723	1810	1903	1949	...	2047	2059	...	...	...	...	...	...

POITIERS - ANGOULÊME

km		Ⓐ		Ⓐ	Ⓐ		Ⓒ		Ⓐ	⑥		Ⓐ		⑦	①–⑥		Ⓑ		Ⓐ					
										k							h							
0	**Poitiers** d.	0611	...	0723	0811	...	0915	...	1220	1309	...	1602	...	1708	1719	...	1811	...	1911	...	...	...	...	...
65	Ruffec d.	0646	...	0758	0849	...	0953	...	1319	1400	...	1646	...	1752	1804	...	1857	...	1955	...	...	...	...	...
112	**Angoulême** a.	0713	...	0825	0917	...	1020	...	1346	1426	...	1712	...	1818	1831	...	1922	...	2021	...	...	...	...	...

ANGOULÊME - BORDEAUX

km		Ⓐ		①–⑥	Ⓐ		Ⓐ		⑥	⑦		Ⓐ		⑥		Ⓐ		Ⓒ	Ⓐ					
									k					k										
0	**Angoulême** d.	...	...	...	0558	...	0728	...	0858	0928	...	1232	...	...	...	1723	...	1828	1834	...	...	...	...	...
82	Coutras 302 d.	0535	...	0635	0648	...	0819	...	0949	1019	...	1323	...	1535	...	1817	...	1918	1922	...	...	...	...	...
98	Libourne 302 d.	0548	...	0647	0703	...	0832	...	1002	1032	...	1337	...	1548	...	1831	...	1931	1934	...	...	...	...	...
135	**Bordeaux** St Jean 302 a.	0622	...	0722	0728	...	0900	...	1030	1100	...	1404	...	1622	...	1900	...	2001	2005	...	...	...	...	...

To:
Arc – Arcachon (Table **306**).
Hen – Hendaye (Table **305**).
Iru – Irun (Table **305**).
Tar – Tarbes (Table **305**).
Tou – Toulouse (Table **320**).

A – ①②③④⑥⑦ (also Aug. 16; not Aug. 14).
E – Runs on Aug. 10, 15, 24 only.
G – ②③④⑤⑦ (not Aug. 15, 16).
H – ①⑤⑥⑦ (also Aug. 14, 15).
L – From Lille (Table **11**).
S – From Strasbourg (Table **391**).

a – Not Aug. 15, 16.
b – Also Aug. 16; not Aug. 10, 24.
c – Also Aug. 15, 16.
d – Also Aug. 14; not Aug. 16, 23, 30.
f – Also Aug. 14; not Aug. 16.
h – Not Aug. 15.
j – 1436 on ⑥ (also Aug. 15, Nov. 1).
k – Also Aug. 15.
m – Not Aug. 14, 15.
n – Also Aug. 14, 15.
p – Also Aug. 14.
w – Not Aug. 15–18.
z – Not Aug. 15–17.

TGV – 🅁, supplement payable, 🍸.

• – 1014 on ⑥ July 6 - Aug. 10 (also Aug. 24, 31).
⊠ – OUIGO low-cost TGV service. Internet bookings only at www.ouigo.com.

☛ Frequent connecting services operate St Pierre des Corps - Tours and v.v. (journey: 5 minutes).

300 BORDEAUX and LA ROCHELLE - POITIERS - PARIS

BORDEAUX - PARIS non-stop services

	TGV	*TGV*	*TGV*	*TGV*		*TGV*	*TGV*		*TGV*	*TGV*		*TGV*	*TGV*		*TGV*	*TGV*		*TGV*		*TGV*	*TGV*	*TGV*	*TGV*	*TGV*
	8400	**8402**	**8404**	**8406**		**8500**	**8408**		**8561**	**8530**		**8504**	**8504**		**8581**	**8534**		**8412**		**8536**	**8508**	**8414**	**8416**	**8470**
	②–⑤	①–⑥	①	①–⑥		①–⑥	⑦		①–⑥			①–⑥	⑦					⑤–⑦		①–⑤	⑤⑦	⑥	Ⓑ	⑥
	a																	n		a	f	c	h¶	k
From:	—	—	—	—		*Tou*	—		*Tar*	*Hen*		*Tou*	*Tou*		*Tar*	*Hen*		—		*Hen*	*Tou*	—	—	*Arc*
Bordeaux St Jean d.	0634	0704	0734	0804	...	0904	0904	...	1004	1004	...	1104	1104	...	1204	1204	...	1304	...	1404	1404	1404	1504	1504
Paris Montparnasse a.	0847	0914	0947	1013	...	1112	1112	...	1213	1213	...	1313	1317	...:	1413	1413	...	1517	...	1613	1613	1613	1713	1713
	TGV	*TGV*	*TGV*	*TGV*	*TGV*	*TGV*	*TGV*	*TGV*	*TGV*	*TGV*	*TGV*	*TGV*	*TGV*		*TGV*		*TGV*	*TGV*	*TGV*	*TGV*	*TGV*		*TGV*	*TGV*
	8540	**8510**	**8418**	**8583**	**8542**	**8264**	**8420**	**8514**	**8544**	**8474**	**7658**	**8516**	**8585**		**8518**		**8520**	**8550**	**8424**	**8520**	**8550**		**8587**	**8522**
		⑥⑦	⑤⑦		⑤–⑦	①–④	⑦								⑦		⑤⑥	⑤⑥	⑦	①–④	①–④		⑦	⑦
			f		n	m					⊠						n	n		m	m			
From:	*Hen*	*Tou*	—	*Tar*	*Hen*	—	—	*Tou*	*Hen*	*Arc*	—	*Tou*	*Tar*		*Tou*		*Tou*	*Hen*	—	*Tou*	*Hen*		*Tar*	*Tou*
Bordeaux St Jean d.	1604	1604	1634	1704	1704	1704	1734	1804	1804	1834	1852	1904	1904	...	2004	...	2104	2104	2104	2104	2104	...	2204	2204
Paris Montparnasse a.	1813	1813	1847	1913	1913	1913	1947	2013	2013	2047	2104	2113	2113	...	2213	...	2313	2313	2313	2316	2316	...	0013	0013

BORDEAUX and LA ROCHELLE - POITIERS - PARIS

km		*TGV*	*TGV*	*TGV*	*TGV*	*TGV*	*TGV*	*TGV*	*TGV*	*TGV*		*TGV*	*TGV*	*TGV*	*TGV*	*TGV*	*TGV*	*TGV*	*TGV*	*TGV*	*TGV*	*TGV*	*TGV*	*TGV*
		8350	**8430**	**8330**	**8370**	**8480**	**8332**	**5260**	**5260**	**8432**		**8372**	**8434**	**8372**	**5265**	**5440**	**8376**	**8486**	**8364**	**5443**	**7656**	**8364**	**8450**	**8378**
		①	①		①–⑥	①–⑤	①–⑤	⑥	①–⑤				⑤				⑥⑦		Ⓐ			Ⓒ		
						a	a	zL	zL			F	f	D	wL	wS	c			S	⊠			
0	**Bordeaux** St Jean d.	...	0547	...	...	0523	...	0603	0608	0708	...	...	0855	...	0908	0908	...	1023	...	1108	1158	...	1308	...
	Libourne d.	...	|	...	...	0548	...	|	|	|	...	...	|	...	|	|	...	1047	...	|	|	...	|	...
114	Angoulême d.	...	0622	...	...	0630	...	0641	0646	0746	...	...	0933	...	0946	0946	...	1129	...	1146	1240	...	1346	...
	La Rochelle Ville d.	...	|	...	0539	|	...	|	|	|	...	0851	|	0851	|	|	1047	|	1121	|	|	1251	|	1444
	Niort d.	...	|	...	0621	|	...	|	|	|	...	0933	|	0933	|	|	1125	|	1203	|	|	1332	|	1525
	Poitiers a.	...	|	...	0705	0709	...	0720	0725	0825	...	|	1016	1014	1025	1025	1205	1209	|	1224	|	|	1425	1612
	Poitiers d.	0519	|	0628	0715	0715	0723	0723	...	0828	...	|	1020	1020	1028	1028	1215	1215	|	1228	|	|	1428	1615
	Futuroscope d.	|	|	|	|	|	|	|	...	|	...	|	|	|	|	|	|	|	|	|	|	|	|	|
	Châtellerault d.	|	|	0647	|	|	0742	|	...	|	...	|	|	|	|	|	|	|	|	|	|	|	|	|
	Tours a.	|	|	|	|	|	|	|	...	|	...	|	|	|	|	|	|	|	|	|	|	|	|	|
	St Pierre-des-Corps a.	0550	|	0716	|	|	0810	0754	...	0858	...	1036	|	1050	1058	1058	|	|	|	1258	1339	|	1458	|
	St Pierre des Corps **295** d.	0554	|	0720	|	|	0820	...	...	0902	...	1040	|	1054	...	...	|	|	|	...	1342	|	1502	|
	Vendôme-Villiers TGV **295** d.	|	|	0745	|	|	0842	...	...	|	...	|	|	|	...	...	|	|	|	...	|	|	|	|
542	**Paris** Montparnasse **295** a.	0657	0813	0835	0839	0839	0932	...	...	1004	...	1144	1149	1201	...	...	1339g	1339g	1356	...	1444	1526	1604	1739

	TGV	*TGV*	*TGV*	*TGV*	*TGV*	*TGV*	*TGV*	*TGV*	*TGV*	*TGV*	*TGV*	*TGV*	*TGV*	*TGV*	*TGV*	*TGV*	*TGV*	*TGV*	*TGV*	*TGV*	*TGV*	*TGV*	*TGV*	*TGV*
	5284	**5445**	**5284**	**5445**	**8452**	**8342**	**8342**	**8380**	**8384**	**8488**	**8454**	**8346**	**8386**	**8490**	**8388**	**8390**	**8492**	**8456**	**8476**	**8392**	**8494**	**8392**	**8494**	**8394**
	⑥⑦	⑥⑦	①–⑤	①–⑤	⑦	⑥⑦	①–⑤				⑦		⑤⑦	⑤⑦	⑦			⑤	⑦	⑤	⑤	⑦	⑦	⑦
	zL	zS	zL	zS		r	t						f	f		B	B	f	N	f	f			
Bordeaux St Jean d.	1456	1456	1508	1508	1512	...	...	...	...	1623	1812	...	...	1823	...	...	1935	2012	2012	...	2023	...	2023	...
Libourne d.	|	|	|	|	|	...	...	...	...	1647	|	...	...	1847	...	...	1959	|	|	...	2047	...	2047	...
Angoulême d.	1533	1533	1546	1546	1551	...	...	...	...	1729	1851	...	...	1929	...	...	2040	2051	2051	...	2129	...	2129	...
La Rochelle Ville d.	|	|	|	|	|	...	...	1549	1644	|	|	...	1847	|	1951	1951	|	|	|	2044	|	2044	|	2155
Niort d.	|	|	|	|	|	...	...	1626	1725	|	|	...	1925	|	2033	2033	|	|	|	2125	|	2125	|	2233
Poitiers a.	1617	1617	1625	1625	|	...	...	1712	1805	1809	|	...	2005	2009	2112	2112	2121	|	|	2205	2209	2205	2209	2312
Poitiers d.	1620	1620	1628	1628	|	1610	1618	1715	1815	1815	|	1923	2015	2015	2115	2128	2128	|	|	2219	2219	2219	2219	2315
Futuroscope d.	|	|	|	|	|	1623	1628	|	|	|	|	1934	|	|	|	|	|	|	|	|	|	|	|	|
Châtellerault d.	|	|	|	|	|	1641	1642	|	|	|	|	1948	|	|	|	|	|	|	|	|	|	|	|	|
Tours a.	|	|	|	|	|	|	|	|	|	|	|	|	|	|	|	|	|	|	|	|	|	|	|	|
St Pierre-des-Corps a.	1650	1650	1658	1658	1658	1711	1711	|	|	|	1950	2017	|	|	|	2158	2158	2150	2150	|	|	2250	2250	|
St Pierre des Corps **295** d.	...	...	...	...	1702	1720	1720	|	|	|	1954	2020	|	|	|	2202	2202	2154	2154	|	|	2254	2254	|
Vendôme-Villiers TGV **295** d.	...	...	...	...	|	1742	1742	|	|	|	|	|	|	|	|	|	|	|	|	|	|	|	|	|
Paris Montparnasse **295** a.	...	...	...	...	1804	1830	1830	1839	1939	1939	2057	2122	2139	2139	2239	2308j	2308j	2257	2257	2349	2349	2357	2357	0039

TER (regional) services BORDEAUX - ANGOULÊME - POITIERS - TOURS and LA ROCHELLE - POITIERS

BORDEAUX - ANGOULÊME

km		Ⓐ		①–⑥		⑥ k	⑦		Ⓐ				Ⓐ	Ⓐ										
0	**Bordeaux** St Jean **302** d.	0600	...	0700	...	0938	0946	...	1300	...	1438	...	1656	1738	...	1858	...	2038	...	...	...	...	...	...
37	Libourne **302** d.	0629	...	0728	...	1013	1014	...	1327	...	1512	...	1723	1813	...	1927	...	2113	...	...	...	...	...	...
53	Coutras **302** d.	0642	...	0741	...	1025	1027	...	1340	...	1524	...	1736	1825	...	1940	...	2125	...	...	...	...	...	...
135	**Angoulême** a.	0733	...	0832	...	...	1118	...	1432	...	...	...	1832	...	...	2032	...	...	...	...	...	...	...	...

ANGOULÊME - POITIERS

km		Ⓐ		①–⑥		⑦		Ⓐ	⑥ k		Ⓑ h		Ⓐ				Ⓐ							
0	**Angoulême** d.	0738	...	0855	...	1045	...	1251	1334	...	1645	...	1738	...	1845	...	1945	...	...	...	...	...	...	...
47	Ruffec d.	0803	...	0921	...	1111	...	1318	1401	...	1711	...	1802	...	1911	...	2011	...	...	...	...	...	...	...
112	**Poitiers** a.	0849	...	1006	...	1152	...	1412	1452	...	1748	...	1840	...	1948	...	2048	...	...	...	...	...	...	...

LA ROCHELLE - POITIERS

km		①	Ⓐ	Ⓐ	⑥ k	Ⓐ					Ⓐ			Ⓑ h	J	⑤ v		Ⓑ h	⑤⑦ v					
0	**La Rochelle** Ville d.	0552	...	0635	0650	0716	0747	...	1224	...	1559	...	1710	1755	1838	1854	...	1936	1936	...	...	...	...	...
67	Niort d.	0634	0634	0723	0731	0757	0833	...	1310	...	1641	...	1756	1842	1924	1939	...	2020	2022	...	...	...	...	...
147	**Poitiers** a.	0733	0733	0815	0815	0853	0918	...	1402	...	1736	...	1850	1941	2014	2034	...	...	2108	...	...	...	...	...

POITIERS - TOURS

km		Ⓐ	①–⑥	①–⑥	Ⓐ	⑦				①–⑥		Ⓐ		①–⑥		Ⓐ	⑦		Ⓑ h 🚌					
0	**Poitiers** d.	0609	0655	0736	0755	0839	...	1237	...	1655	1737	1755	...	1855	...	1949	1949	...	2055	...	...	...	.	...
11	Futuroscope d.	0617	0704	0744	0804	0847	...	1246	...	1704	1745	1804	...	1904	...	1959	1959	...	|	...	...	...	...	...
33	Châtellerault d.	0630	0725	0756	0825	0900	...	1311	...	1725	1757	1825	...	1925	...	2019	2020	...	2139	...	...	...	...	...
101	**Tours** a.	0722	...	0845	...	...	...	1404q	...	...	1852	...	...	...	...	2056	2058	...	...	...	...	...	...	...

From:

Arc – Arcachon (Table **306**).
Hen – Hendaye (Table **305**).
Tar – Tarbes (Table **305**).
Tou – Toulouse (Table **320**).

B – ①②③④⑥ (also Aug. 16; not Aug. 14).
D – ①②③④⑥⑦ to Aug. 25 (also Aug. 16; not Aug. 14); ⑥⑦ from Aug. 31.
F – ⑤ to Aug. 23 (also Aug. 14; not Aug. 16); ①–⑤ from Aug. 26.
J – ①②③④⑥ (not Aug. 14).
L – To Lille (Table **11**).
N – From Arcachon (Table **306**).
S – To Strasbourg (Table **391**).

a – Not Aug. 15, 16.
c – Also Aug. 15, 16.
f – Also Aug. 14; not Aug. 16.

g – 1345 on ⑦.
h – Not Aug. 15.
j – 2305 on ⑥ (also Aug. 15, 16).
k – Also Aug. 15.
m – Not Aug. 14, 15.
n – Also Aug. 14, 15.
q – 1409 on July 12, 26, Aug. 2, 14.
r – Not Aug. 17.
t – Also Aug. 17.
v – Also Aug. 14.
w – Not Aug. 15 - 18.
z – Not Aug. 15 - 17.

¶ – Train number **8470** on Aug. 16.
⊠ – OUIGO low-cost TGV service. Internet bookings only at www.ouigo.com.

TGV – Ⓡ, supplement payable, 🍸.

☛ Frequent connecting services operate St Pierre des Corps - Tours and v.v. (journey: 5 minutes).

ANGOULÊME and NIORT - SAINTES - ROYAN — 301

SERVICE JULY 6 - SEPTEMBER 1 (see earlier editions for service to July 5).

km		Ⓐ	Ⓐ	Ⓐ	Ⓐ		⑥ p		Ⓒ z	Ⓐ	Ⓐ			①–⑥	Ⓐ			⑤⑦ v	B	Ⓐ	⑤ f	①–④ m		⑤⑦ v	⑤ d	A
0	**Angoulême** d.	0630	...	...	0733	0844	...	1036	...	...	1257	...	...	1439	1630	1630	1727	...	...	1838	...	...	1948	...	2133	2142
49	Cognac d.	0711	...	...	0813	0927	...	1114	...	...	1340	...	...	1522	1709	1709	1809	...	...	1920	...	...	2037	...	2211	2220
	Niort d.	|	...	0638	|	|	0940	|	1143	1206	|	...	1446	|	|	|	|	1739	1751	|	1840	1853	|	2054	|	|
75	**Saintes** a.	0732	...	0800	0833	0947	1053	1133	1254	1319	1400	...	1600	1542	1729	1729	1829	1905	1915	1940	2026	2019	2056	2208	2230	2240
75	**Saintes** d.	0740	0735	...	0840	0957	1056	1139	1257	1326	...	...	...	1605	...	1749	1837	1912	1918	...	...	...	2102	2211	2237	2248
	La Rochelle Ville **292** a.	0840	|	...	|	|	|	|	|	|	...	...	...	|	...	|	1934	|	|	...	...	...	|	|	|	|
111	**Royan** a.	...	0804	...	0908	1024	1123	1208	1323	1352	...	...	...	1632	...	1816	...	1938	1944	...	...	...	2129	2238	2307	2315

km		Ⓐ	Ⓐ	①–⑥	Ⓐ	Ⓐ	Ⓐ	①–⑥ z		Ⓐ	Ⓒ ◇	Ⓐ	⑥ k	①–⑥			Ⓑ h	Ⓐ	⑦	Ⓐ	⑦	B	Ⓐ		⑤⑦ v	⑦
	Royan d.	...	0550	...	0629	0650	...	0747	...	1006	1106	1151	...	1332	1405	1524	...	...	1651	1712	1730	...	...	1834	...	1945
	La Rochelle Ville **292** d.	...	|	...	|	|	0631	|	...	|	|	|	...	|	|	|	...	1621	|	|	|	...	...	|	...	|
	Saintes a.	...	0621	...	0655	0716	0729	0813	...	1034	1134	1218	...	1405	1431	1550	...	1716	1717	1738	1757	...	...	1901	...	2010
0	**Saintes** d.	0555	0628	0628	0659	...	0731	0816	1012	1040	1154	1236	1236	1406	1437	1604	1603	1724	1725	*1800*f	1800	1815	1818	1927	1926	2016
77	Niort a.	0716	|	|	0828	...	|	0926	|	1154	1318	|	|	1518	|	|	1716	|	|	*1918*f	1917	1832	|	|	2042	|
	Cognac d.	...	0648	0648	...	...	0750	...	1031	...	...	1255	1257	...	1458	1625	...	1746	1745	...	...	...	1837	1947	...	2036
	Angoulême a.	...	0727	0727	...	...	0828	...	1112	...	...	1335	1335	...	1536	1706	...	1826	1826	...	...	...	1915	2026	...	2113

A – ①②③④⑥⑦ (not Aug. 14).
B – ①②③④⑥ (not Aug. 14).

d – Also Aug. 14; not Aug. 16.
f – ⑤ (also Aug. 14).
h – Not Aug. 15.
k – Also Aug. 15.
m – Not Aug. 14, 15.
p – Also Aug. 15; not July 6.
v – Also Aug. 14.
z – Not July 6.

◇ – On July 6 Royan d. 1056, Saintes a. 1122, d. 1126, Niort a. 1241.

BORDEAUX - PÉRIGUEUX - BRIVE and LIMOGES — 302

SERVICE JUNE 9 - SEPTEMBER 1

km		Ⓐ	Ⓐ M	①–⑥ b	Ⓒ M	Ⓐ Q	⑦ e	Ⓐ	⑥ k	Ⓒ	Ⓐ	Ⓐ	Ⓐ	R	⑤ S	⑤ Q	①–④ T	Ⓐ	Ⓐ	Ⓒ	Ⓐ		Ⓐ	⑦ e		⑤⑦ q
0	**Bordeaux** St Jean **300** d.	0540	0612	0656	0727	0727	0822	0828	0828	1028	1122	1228	1521	1628	1628	1654	1656	...	1728	1728	1756	1828	1856	1928	2028	...
37	Libourne **300** d.	0606	0638	0719	0748	0748	0845	0852	0851	1051	1144	1252	1544	1652	1651	1716	1717	...	1752	1752	1819	1851	1919	1952	2052	...
53	Coutras **300** d.	0616	0648	0730	0759	0759	0856	0902	0902	1101	1154	1302	1554	1702	1702	1731	1727	...	1802	1802	1830	1901	1930	2002	2102	...
93	Mussidan d.	0647	0712	0759	0822	0826	0935	0928	0932	1124	1218	1331	1618	1731	1731	1758	1755	...	1831	1832	1858	1925	1959	2030	2131	...
129	**Périgueux** a.	0718	0731	0829	0841	0848	1006	0950	0956	1143	1237	1355	1639	1755	1755	1820	1817	...	1855	1857	1921	1944	2024	2055	2153	...
129	**Périgueux** ▷ d.	0720	0737	...	0847	0853	1009	...	0958	1150	1244	*1426*	1646	...	1820	1822	1819	1829	...	1859	...	1950	...	...	...	2200
203	**Brive la Gaillarde 326** ▷ a.	0820	|	...	|	0950	1105	...	1059	|	|	|	|	...	1935	1935	1922	|	...	1955	...	|	...	...	...	|
	Tulle **326** a.	0851	|	...	|	...	1137	...	1132	|	|	|	|	...	2004	2004	1951	|	...	...	...	|	...	...	...	|
	Ussel **326** a.	...	|	...	|	...	...	...	1250	|	|	|	|	...	2124	2124	...	|	...	...	...	|	...	...	...	|
166	Thiviers d.	...	0759	...	0909	...	...	...	...	1212	1307	*1452*	1708	...	...	...	...	1911	...	...	...	2012	...	...	...	2222
228	**Limoges** ▷ a.	...	0840	...	0950	...	...	...	...	1252	1347	*1538*	1748	...	...	...	...	1959	...	...	...	2052	...	...	...	2304

	Ⓐ Q	Ⓐ	①–⑥ b	Ⓐ	Ⓐ	Ⓐ	⑥ k	Ⓐ	Ⓒ	①–⑥ b	⑥ k		Ⓒ	Ⓐ		Ⓒ	Ⓐ	Ⓑ h	Ⓐ Q	①–⑥ b	⑦ e	M	⑤ f	⑦ e	①–⑥ b	⑦ e
Limoges ▷ d.	...	...	...	...	0607	...	0706	0715	...	...	...	1014	1229	1234	...	...	1513	...	...	...	...	1815	...	...	1930	2020
Thiviers d.	...	...	...	...	0653	...	0754	0800	...	...	...	1054	1316	1329	...	...	1553	...	...	...	...	1855	...	...	2013	2105
Ussel **326** d.	...	...	...	...	|	...	|	|	...	...	...	|	|	|	...	...	|	...	...	...	1546	|	1708	1708	|	|
Tulle **326** d.	...	...	...	...	|	0602	|	|	...	...	...	|	|	|	...	...	|	...	...	...	1707	|	1829	1829	|	|
Brive la Gaillarde . **326** ▷ d.	...	...	...	...	|	0630	|	|	...	...	0905	|	|	|	...	...	|	...	...	1739r	1739	|	1901	1909	|	|
Périgueux ▷ a.	...	...	...	...	0724	0736	0822	0821	...	...	1001	1114	1342	1359	...	...	1613	...	...	1834	1834	1915	2000	2008	2034	2126
Périgueux d.	0537	0605	0641	0705	...	0742	...	0827	0838	1005	1005	1121	...	...	1405	1610	1620	1708	1810	1835	1835	1925	2005	2011	2042	2133
Mussidan d.	0559	0630	0703	0730	...	0804	...	0846	0903	1030	1030	1141	...	...	1430	1632	1640	1730	1832	1905	1906	1946	2027	2032	2103	2152
Coutras **300** d.	0623	0658	0731	0758	...	0831	...	0909	0932	1058	1058	1204	...	...	1458	1658	1704	1758	1858	1934	1935	2012	2053	2056	2128	2215
Libourne **300** d.	0634	0709	0745	0809	...	0842	...	0919	0943	1109	1109	1215	...	...	1509	1709	1714	1809	1909	1944	1945	2025	2107	2107	2139	2226
Bordeaux St Jean **300** a.	0654	0733	0804	0833	...	0904	...	0944	1004	1133	1133	1236	...	...	1533	1733	1735	1833	1933	2005	2006	2048	2130	2130	2202	2246

ADDITIONAL TRAINS **PÉRIGUEUX - BRIVE**

	Ⓐ	Ⓒ	Ⓐ Z		Ⓐ	Ⓒ		⑤ f	①–④ m	①–④ Y	⑤ Q	①–④ T🚌	
Périgueux d.	0619	0718	0855	...	1253	1410	...	1702	1715	1819	1953	1953	...
Brive la Gaillarde a.	0720	0814	0951	...	1351	1506	...	1808	1823	1921	2049	2118	...

	Ⓒ	Ⓐ	⑦ e	Ⓐ		⑤ f	①–④ m	①–④ T🚌	Ⓒ	⑤ Q
Brive la Gaillarde d.	0731	0734	0907	1010	1246	1811	1834	2003	2004	2005
Périgueux a.	0828	0843	1003	1107	1343	1913	1933	2128	2100	2108

ADDITIONAL TRAINS **PÉRIGUEUX - LIMOGES**

	Ⓐ	Ⓐ	Ⓐ	⑥ k	Ⓐ	Ⓐ A	Ⓐ	Ⓒ A	⑦ e	Ⓐ	⑦ eA	Ⓐ	Ⓒ
Périgueux d.	0447	0601	0658	0731	0837	0936	1258	1356	1520	1530	1641	1717	1823
Thiviers d.	0509	0629	0728	0753	0901	0959	1330	1419	1551	1554	1706	1745	1856
Limoges a.	0554	0732	0822	0839	0949	1043	1424	1457	1640	1640	1755	1831	1944

	Ⓐ	Ⓒ A	Ⓐ	Ⓐ A	Ⓒ	Ⓐ	Ⓐ	Ⓐ	⑥ k	Ⓑ ⊡
Limoges d.	0816	1329	1404	1620	1653	1730	1840	2020	2105	2312
Thiviers d.	0902	1420	1451	1709	1746	1826	1934	2105	2149	2356
Périgueux a.	0925	1448	1520	1741	1814	1900	2018	2126	2211	0017

A – To / from Agen (Table **308**).
M – To / from Montluçon (Table **303**).
Q – Until July 5.
R – Ⓑ to July 11; ①②③④⑦ from July 14 (not Aug. 14, 15).
S – ⑤ July 12 - Aug. 30 (also Aug. 14).
T – ①–④ to July 4 (not June 10).
Y – ①–④ July 8 - Aug. 29 (not Aug. 14, 15).
Z – July 8 - Aug. 30.

b – Not June 10.
e – Also June 10.
f – Also Aug. 14.
h – Not Aug. 15.
k – Also Aug. 15.
m – Not June 10, Aug. 14, 15.
q – Also June 10, Aug. 14. Runs 15 minutes later on ⑤ (also Aug. 14).
r – 1736 on ⑤ (also Aug. 14).

⊡ – Runs 3–4 minutes later on ⑦ (also June 10, Aug. 15).
Runs 17–18 minutes later on ⑤ (also Aug. 14).
▷ – See panels below main table for other trains Périgueux - Brive and Périgueux - Limoges.

LIMOGES - MONTLUÇON — 303

SERVICE JUNE 9 - SEPTEMBER 1

km		①–④ m	Ⓒ		⑤ f	Ⓐ	ⒶQ 🚌			
	Bordeaux St Jean **302** d.	0612	0727	...	...	...	...	...	...	...
0	**Limoges** d.	0845	0955	...	1213	1309	...	...	1627	...
78	Guéret d.	0944	1054	...	1316	1419	1421	...	1736	...
156	**Montluçon** a.	1036	1147	...	1410	...	1529	...	1837	...

	Ⓐ 🚌	Ⓐ	⑥ k	⑤ w	①–④ U				⑦ e
Montluçon d.	0622	...	0722	0859	0906	...	1602	...	1850
Guéret d.	0728	0741	0824	0958	1010	...	1655	...	1953
Limoges a.	...	0850	0933	1105	1118	...	1805	...	2105
Bordeaux St Jean **302** a.	...	...	...	...	...	...	2048	...	...

Q – 4 minutes later from July 8.
U – ①–④ to July 18 (not June 10).

e – Also June 10.
f – Also Aug. 14.
k – Also Aug. 15.
m – Not June 10, Aug. 14, 15.
w – Not July 26, Aug. 2, 9, 23, 30.

305 BORDEAUX - TARBES, HENDAYE and IRÚN

Warning! Services to/from Hendaye are subject to alteration Aug. 23–26.

km																									
										TGV					*TGV*		*TGV*	*TGV*	*TGV*				*TGV*	*TGV*	
										8571					**8531**		**8533**	**8533**	**8533**				**8535**	**8572**	🚌
		Ⓐ	Ⓐ	Ⓐ	①–⑥	Ⓐ				①–⑥	①–⑥	⑥	⑦	⑦	①–⑥			⑤	⑥	①–⑥	⑤	①–⑥			⚒
					z							r					B	g	d	z	v				
	Paris Montparnasse **300**	d.	...	...	...	...	...	...	...	...	0647	...	...	...	...	0747	...	0900	0901	0901	...	...	...	0947	0947	...
0	**Bordeaux** St Jean **306**	d.	...	0520	...	...	...	0745	0745	...	0902	...	0950	0950	...	1002	...	|	|	|	...	...	...	1202	1202	...
40	Facture Biganos **306**	d.	...	0543	...	...	...	0809	0809	...	|	...	1012	1014	...	|	...	|	|	|	...	...	...	|	|	...
109	Morcenx	d.	...	0620	...	...	...	0844	0844	...	|	...	1043	1045	...	|	...	|	|	|	...	...	...	|	|	...
148	Dax	a.	...	0647	...	...	...	0912	0912	...	1017	...	1111	1113	...	1118	...	1224	1228	1228	...	...	...	1318	1318	...
148	Dax	d.	0623	0652	0723	0753	0821	0917	0921	...	1020	1027	1114	1118	1123	1122	...	1227	1231	1231	1230	1230	1253	1322	1328	...
179	Puyoô **325**	d.	|	|	|	|	0840	|	0940	...	|	|	|	|	1143	|	...	|	|	|	1249	1249	|	|	|	...
193	Orthez **325**	d.	|	|	|	|	0851	|	0951	...	|	|	|	|	1153	|	...	|	|	|	1300	1300	|	|	1358	...
233	Pau **325**	d.	|	|	|	|	0915	|	1015	...	1109	|	|	|	1218	|	...	|	|	|	1325	1326	|	|	1422	1430
272	Lourdes **325**	d.	|	|	|	|	...	|	...	...	1144	|	|	|	1247	|	...	|	|	|	...	1354	|	|	1447	|
293	**Tarbes 325**	a.	|	|	|	|	...	|	...	...	1158	|	|	|	1302	|	...	|	|	|	...	1409	|	|	...	1529
199	**Bayonne**	d.	0708	0735	0808	0838	...	0948	...	...	...	1111	1145	1209	...	1155	...	1259	1302	1302	...	...	1338	1355	...	...
209	Biarritz	d.	0717	0745	0817	0847	...	0958	...	...	...	1121	1155	1219	...	1206	...	1310	1311	1314	...	...	1347	1406	...	...
222	St Jean de Luz	d.	0731	0800	0831	0901	...	1013	...	...	...	1136	1210	1234	...	1218	...	1325	...	1328	...	...	1401	1420	...	...
235	Hendaye	a.	0748	0815	0848	0918	...	1028	...	...	...	1151	1225	1249	...	1233	...	1340	...	1342	...	...	1418	1435	...	...
237	**Irún**	a.	...	...	...	...	...	...	...	...	...	...	...	...	...	...	...	...	...	...	...	...	...	...	...	...

				TGV				*TGV*	*TGV*							*TGV*		*TGV*	*TGV*					*TGV*	*TGV*	*TGV*
				8537				**8541**	**8574**	🚌						**8547**		**8549**	**8590**					**8551**	**8593**	**8553**
							⑤		⑤	⑤	Ⓐ	Ⓐ		①–⑥	⑦	⑤	Ⓐ			⑥						⑤
		z	z		z	Az	v		f	f						f				k△						f
Paris Montparnasse **300**	d.	...	...	1147	...	...	...	1247	1247	...	...	...	...	...	...	1447	...	1547	1547	...	...	...	...	1747	1747	1947
Bordeaux St Jean **306**	d.	1250	...	1402	1450	1450	1450	1502	1502	...	...	...	1645	1645	...	1702	...	1802	1802	...	1845	1845	...	2002	2002	2202
Facture Biganos **306**	d.	1313	...	|	1513	1513	1513	|	|	...	...	...	1709	1709	...	|	...	|	|	...	1910	1910	...	|	|	|
Morcenx	d.	1344	...	|	1544	1544	1544	|	|	...	...	...	1746	1746	...	|	...	|	|	...	1947	1947	...	|	|	|
Dax	a.	1412	...	1518	1612	1612	1612	1618	1618	...	...	...	1813	1813	...	1818	...	1918	1918	...	2015	2015	...	2118	2118	2318
Dax	d.	1417	1421	1522	1617	1621	1638	1622	1628	...	1653	1725	1818	1822	1822	1822	1853	1922	1928	1932	2020	2024	...	2122	2126	2322
Puyoô **325**	d.	|	1440	|	|	1640	1657	|	|	...	|	|	|	1841	1841	|	|	|	|	|	|	2044	...	|	|	|
Orthez **325**	d.	|	1450	|	|	1651	1708	|	|	...	|	|	|	1852	1852	|	|	|	1958	|	|	2055	...	|	2156	|
Pau **325**	d.	|	1515	|	|	1716	1733	|	1719	1730	|	|	|	1917	1917	|	|	|	2022	|	|	2119	...	|	2220	|
Lourdes **325**	d.	|	...	|	|	...	...	|	1745	|	|	|	|	...	...	|	|	|	2057	|	|	2146	...	|	2255	|
Tarbes 325	a.	|	...	|	|	...	...	|	...	1829	|	|	|	...	...	|	|	|	2112	|	|	2201	...	|	2310	|
Bayonne	d.	1448	...	1555	1648	...	...	1655	...	...	1738	1810	1853	...	...	1856	1938	1955	...	2016	2051	...	...	2155	...	2355
Biarritz	d.	1458	...	1606	1658	...	...	1706	...	...	1747	1819	1904	...	...	1908	1947	2006	...	2026	2101	...	...	2206	...	0006
St Jean de Luz	d.	1513	...	1620	1713	...	...	1720	...	...	1801	1833	1919	...	...	1924	2001	2020	...	2040	2116	...	...	2220	...	0020
Hendaye	a.	1528	...	1635	1728	...	...	1735	...	...	1818	1850	1933	...	...	1937	2018	2035	...	2057	2131	...	...	2235	...	0035
Irún	a.	...	...	...	...	...	...	...	...	...	...	...	...	...	...	...	...	...	...	...	...	...	...	...	...	...

											TGV	*TGV*				*TGV*	*TGV*			*TGV*	*TGV*			*TGV*		
											8561	**8530**				**8581**	**8534**			**8536**	**8538**			**8540**		
		Ⓐ	Ⓐ	①	②–⑤	①–⑥	①–⑥	Ⓐ	Ⓐ	Ⓐ	①–⑥		Ⓐ	Ⓐ	Ⓒ			Ⓐ	①–⑥	①–⑤	⑥⑦				Ⓐ	
					p														z	a	c					z
Irún	d.	...	...	...	...	...	...	...	...	...	...	...	...	...	...	...	...	...	...	...	...	...	...	...	...	...
Hendaye	d.	...	0440	...	...	0548	...	0641	...	0702	...	0721	...	0830	...	...	0921	1008	1031	1121	1137	1211	...	1330	...	1335
St Jean de Luz	d.	...	0453	...	...	0601	...	0654	...	0715	...	0735	...	0843	...	...	0934	1021	1044	1135	1151	1224	...	1343	...	1348
Biarritz	d.	...	0505	...	...	0613	...	0706	...	0727	...	0749	...	0855	...	...	0947	1033	1055	1149	1205	1236	...	1356	...	1400
Bayonne	d.	...	0519	...	...	0627	0720	0720	...	0741	...	0803	...	0909	...	...	1001	1046	1109	1203	1220	1250	...	1411	...	1414
Tarbes 325	d.	...	|	0531	...	|	|	|	0633	|	0651	|	...	|	...	0847	|	|	|	|	|	|	...	|	1303	|
Lourdes **325**	d.	...	|	0546	...	|	|	|	0648	|	0708	|	...	|	...	0911	|	|	|	|	|	|	...	|	1319	|
Pau **325**	d.	0455	|	0614	0614	|	|	|	0722	|	0735	|	0842	|	0849	0938	|	|	|	|	|	|	...	|	1347	|
Orthez **325**	d.	0520	|	0640	0640	|	|	|	0748	|	0801	|	0908	|	0915	|	|	|	|	|	|	|	...	|	1412	|
Puyoô **325**	d.	0530	|	0650	0650	|	|	|	0758	|	|	|	0918	|	0925	|	|	|	|	|	|	|	...	|	1422	|
Dax	a.	0549	0553	0708	0708	0712	0804	0804	0817	0824	0827	0831	0937	0941	0943	1027	1031	1130	1141	1233	1248	1337	...	1438	1441	1446
Dax	d.	0558	0558	...	0717	0717	...	...	...	...	0836	0836	0946	0946	0946	1036	1036	...	1146	1236	1251	...	...	1442	1451	1451
Morcenx	d.	0627	0627	...	0747	0747	...	...	...	...	|	|	1015	1015	1015	|	|	...	1215	|	|	...	...	|	1519	1519
Facture Biganos **306**	d.	0705	0705	...	0818	0818	...	...	...	...	|	|	1047	1047	1047	|	|	...	1247	|	|	...	...	|	1551	1551
Bordeaux St Jean **306**	a.	0732	0732	...	0842	0842	...	...	...	...	0958	0958	1110	1110	1110	1158	1158	...	1310	1358	|	...	...	1558	1613	1613
Paris Montparnasse **300**	a.	...	...	...	...	...	...	...	...	...	1213	1213	...	...	...	1413	1413	...	...	1613	1631	...	...	1813	...	...

		TGV	*TGV*		*TGV*			*TGV*			*TGV*							*TGV*	*TGV*				*TGV*			
		8583	**8542**		**8544**		🚌	**8585**			**8546**							**8548**	**8550**				**8587**			
			⑤–⑦			Ⓐ	⚒			Ⓐ		①–⑥	Ⓐ	⑦	⑦	Ⓐ	Ⓐ	⑦	①–⑥	⑤	⑤		⑦	⑥	⑥⑦	①–⑥
			n						z		D		w							v	v			z	z	z
Irún	d.	...	...	...	...	...	...	...	...	...	...	...	...	...	...	...	...	...	...	...	...	...	...	...	...	...
Hendaye	d.	...	1425	...	1523	...	...	...	1629	1704	1724	...	1730	...	1741	1805	...	1821	1824	...	1831	...	...	...	1932	2011
St Jean de Luz	d.	...	1438	...	1536	...	...	...	1642	1717	1737	...	1743	...	1755	1818	...	1835	1837	...	1844	...	...	...	1945	2024
Biarritz	d.	...	1451	...	1548	...	...	...	1656	1730	1749	...	1756	...	1808	1831	...	1848	1849	...	1856	...	...	...	1958	2037
Bayonne	d.	...	1505	...	1603	...	...	...	1709	1743	1804	...	1810	...	1823	1844	...	1903	1904	...	1909	...	...	...	2011	2050
Tarbes 325	d.	1346	|	...	|	...	1515	...	|	|	|	...	|	1658	|	|	...	|	|	...	|	...	1907	1901	|	|
Lourdes **325**	d.	1410	|	...	|	...	|	1609	|	|	|	...	|	1713	|	|	...	|	|	...	|	...	1924	1915	|	|
Pau **325**	d.	1437	|	...	|	1617	1620	1641	|	|	|	1743	|	1742	|	|	1829	|	|	...	|	...	1951	1943	|	|
Orthez **325**	d.	1503	|	...	|	1642	...	1705	|	|	|	1809	|	1809	|	|	1855	|	|	...	|	...	|	2008	|	|
Puyoô **325**	d.	|	|	...	|	1652	...	|	|	|	|	1819	|	1819	|	|	1905	|	|	←	|	...	|	2019	|	|
Dax	a.	1530	1533	...	1632	1711	...	1733	1739	1827	1832	1837	1841	1841	1857	1928	1924	1931	1932	1924	1943	...	2038	2038	2042	2134
Dax	d.	1538	1538	...	1637	...	...	1738	1743	...	1835	...	1846	1846	1900	...	1948v	1934	1937	1948	1948	...	2041	2047	2047	...
Morcenx	d.	|	|	...	|	...	...	|	1812	...	|	...	1915	1915	1930	...	→	|	|	2017	2017	...	|	2116	2116	...
Facture Biganos **306**	d.	|	|	...	|	...	...	|	1848	...	|	...	1946	1946	2005	...	...	|	|	2049	2049	...	|	2148	2148	...
Bordeaux St Jean **306**	a.	1658	1658	...	1758	...	...	1858	1914	...	|	...	2010	2010	2030	...	...	|	2058	2111	2111	...	2158	2210	2210	...
Paris Montparnasse **300**	a.	1913	1913	...	2013	...	...	2113	...	...	2204	...	...	...	...	...	...	2305	2316j	...	...	...	0013	...	...	...

A – ①②③④⑥⑦ (not Aug. 14).
B – Runs on Aug. 14 only.
D – ①⑤⑦ (also Aug. 14; not Aug. 16, 25, 26).

TGV –Ⓡ, supplement payable, 🍷.

△ – Runs 6 minutes earlier on July 6.

a – Not Aug. 15, 16.
c – Also Aug. 15, 16.
d – Also Aug. 15, 23.
f – Also Aug. 14; not Aug. 16.
g – Not Aug. 23.
j – 2313 on ⑤⑥ (also Aug. 14, 15).
k – Also Aug. 15.
n – Also Aug. 14, 15.
p – Not Aug. 15.
r – Also Aug. 15; not July 6.
v – ⑤ (also Aug. 14).
w – Also July 6.
z – Not July 6.

BORDEAUX - ARCACHON 306

TGV services 🅁

km		TGV 8471 ⑥ c		TGV 8473		TGV 8477 ⑤ f				
	Paris Montparnasse **300** d.	0847	...	1047	...	1814	...	...	...	...
0	**Bordeaux** St Jean d.	1105	...	1302	...	2031	...	...	...	...
40	Facture Biganos d.	1127	...	1325	...	2054	...	...	...	...
56	La Teste a.	|	...	|	...	2105	...	...	...	...
59	**Arcachon** a.	1143	...	1340	...	2112	...	...	...	...

	TGV 8470 ⑥ k		TGV 8474		TGV 8476 ⑦			
Arcachon d.	1417	...	1748	...	1920	...	...	...
La Teste d.	|	...	|	...	1927	...	...	...
Facture Biganos d.	1433	...	1805	...	1941	...	...	...
Bordeaux St Jean a.	1456	...	1828	...	2006	...	...	...
Paris Montparnasse **300** a.	1713	...	2047	...	2257	...	...	...

Local TER services

	⑥		Ⓐ	Ⓐ												Ⓐ		Ⓐ		Ⓐ					D
Bordeaux St Jean **305** d.	0024	...	0635	0706	0735	...	0835	0935	1035	1135	1235	1335	1435	1535	1635	1706	1735	1806	1835	1906	1935	2035	2135	2235	2306
Facture Biganos **305** d.	0054	...	0705	0736	0805	...	0905	1005	1105	1205	1305	1405	1505	1605	1705	1736	1805	1836	1905	1936	2005	2105	2205	2305	2336
La Teste d.	0111	...	0723	0753	0823	...	0923	1023	1123	1223	1323	1423	1523	1623	1723	1753	1823	1853	1923	1953	2023	2123	2223	2323	2353
Arcachon a.	0116	...	0728	0758	0828	...	0928	1028	1128	1228	1328	1428	1528	1628	1728	1758	1828	1858	1928	1958	2028	2128	2228	2328	2358

	①	①–⑥		Ⓐ	①–⑥	①–⑥	Ⓐ								Ⓒ			Ⓐ			Ⓐ			E	E
Arcachon d.	0502	0533	0633	0648	0702	0733	0802	0833	0933	1033	1133	1233	1333	1433	1533	1633	1733	1802	1833	1933	2002	2033	...	2133	2233
La Teste d.	0506	0537	0637	0652	0706	0737	0806	0837	0937	1037	1137	1237	1337	1437	1537	1637	1737	1806	1837	1937	2006	2037	...	2137	2237
Facture Biganos **305** d.	0523	0555	0655	0710	0723	0755	0823	0855	0955	1055	1155	1255	1355	1454	1555	1655	1755	1823	1855	1955	2024	2055	...	2155	2255
Bordeaux St Jean **305** a.	0554	0625	0725	0740	0754	0825	0854	0925	1025	1125	1225	1325	1425	1525	1625	1725	1825	1854	1925	2025	2054	2125	...	2225	2325

D – ①–⑥ July 8 - Aug. 31.
E – July 7 - Sept. 1.
c – Also Aug. 15, 16.
f – Also Aug. 14; not Aug. 16.
k – Also Aug. 15.

BORDEAUX - LE VERDON - POINTE DE GRAVE 307

SERVICE JULY 7 - SEPTEMBER 1

km		Ⓐ	Ⓐ								Ⓐ		⑦	Ⓐ											
0	**Bordeaux** St Jean d.	0729	0829	0929	...	1129	...	1329	...	1629	1729	1829	1929	1929	...	...	...	...	...	...	...	...	...	...	...
19	Blanquefort d.	0755	0855	0955	...	1155	...	1355	...	1655	1755	1855	1955	1955	...	...	...	...	...	...	...	...	...	...	...
35	Margaux d.	0814	0914	1013	...	1214	...	1414	...	1714	1814	1914	2014	2014	...	...	...	...	...	...	...	...	...	...	...
57	Pauillac d.	0836	0936	1036	...	1236	...	1436	...	1736	1836	1936	2036	2036	...	...	...	...	...	...	...	...	...	...	...
76	Lesparre d.	0852	0951	1052	...	1252	...	1452	...	1752	1851	1952	2051	2052	...	...	...	...	...	...	...	...	...	...	...
102	Soulac sur Mer d.	0913	...	1113	...	1313	...	1513	...	1813	...	2013	...	2113	...	...	...	...	...	...	...	...	...	...	...
109	**Le Verdon** a.	0920	...	1120	...	1320	...	1520	...	1820	...	2020	...	2120	...	...	...	...	...	...	...	...	...	...	...
112	Pointe de Grave a.	0925	...	1125	...	1325	...	1525	...	1825	...	...	...	...	...	...	...	...	...	...	...	...	...	...	...

	⚒	Ⓐ									Ⓐ													
Pointe de Grave d.	...	...	...	...	0946	...	1146	...	1346	...	...	1646	...	1846	...	...	...	...	...	...	...	...	...	...
Le Verdon d.	...	0651	0751	...	0951	...	1151	...	1351	...	...	1651	...	1851	...	...	...	...	...	...	...	...	...	...
Soulac sur Mer d.	...	0658	0758	...	0958	...	1158	...	1359	...	...	1658	...	1858	...	...	...	...	...	...	...	...	...	...
Lesparre d.	0629	0720	0820	...	1020	...	1220	...	1420	...	1627	1720	...	1920	...	...	...	...	...	...	...	...	...	...
Pauillac d.	0644	0737	0837	...	1037	...	1237	...	1437	...	1642	1737	...	1937	...	...	...	...	...	...	...	...	...	...
Margaux d.	0703	0800	0900	...	1100	...	1300	...	1500	...	1701	1800	...	2000	...	...	...	...	...	...	...	...	...	...
Blanquefort d.	0721	0821	0921	...	1121	...	1321	...	1521	...	1721	1821	...	2021	...	...	...	...	...	...	...	...	...	...
Bordeaux St Jean a.	0746	0846	0946	...	1146	...	1346	...	1546	...	1746	1846	...	2046	...	...	...	...	...	...	...	...	...	...

POINTE DE GRAVE - ROYAN

January - March and October - December: Up to 7 sailings daily.

April - June and September: Up to 9 sailings daily.

July - August: Every 40–50 minutes 0630 - 2030 (0715 - 2115 from Royan).

Sailing time is approximately 20 minutes. ✆ 0974 500 033. www.transgironde.fr

PÉRIGUEUX - LE BUISSON - AGEN 308

km		Ⓐ	⑥ k	⑦	Ⓐ		Ⓒ	Ⓐ	Ⓐ	⑦	⑥ k	⑤⑦ v
	Limoges **302** d.	...	...	...	...	...	1329	...	1620	...	...	...
0	**Périgueux** d.	0751	0846	0958	1152	...	1451	1536	1743	1812	1844	2010
40	Les Eyzies d.	0822	0917	1028	1225	...	1522	1608	1822	1853	1921	2045
57	Le Buisson d.	0839	0935	1046	1243	...	1540	1626	1840	1912	1939	2103
108	Monsempron Libos d.	0931	1028	1138	1334	...	1633	1716	1932	2006	2032	2156
152	**Agen** a.	1019	1113	1223	1419	...	1717	1802	2019	2052	2118	2242

	Ⓐ	Ⓐ	Ⓒ		⑦	Ⓐ	⑥ k	Ⓐ	⑦	⑥ k
Agen d.	0710	1029	1121	...	1414	1458	1546	1700	1734	1806
Monsempron Libos d.	0756	1113	1212	...	1500	1544	1634	1750	1827	1855
Le Buisson d.	0848	1206	1307	...	1552	1636	1726	1846	1920	1948
Les Eyzies d.	0906	1224	1324	...	1610	1654	1744	1911	1939	2005
Périgueux a.	0935	1253	1354	...	1639	1724	1814	1946	2019	2035
Limoges **302** a.	1043	...	1457	...	1755	...	...	...	...	...

k – Also Aug. 15.
v – Also Aug. 14.

309 LIMOGES - ANGOULÊME and POITIERS

km		Ⓐ	⑥ k		Ⓐ	⑥ k	⑦ e	⑤ f	⑦ e	
0	**Limoges** d.	0618	0755	...	1210	1619	1719	1738	1815	1840
	St Junien a.	0658	0832	...	1249	1655	1801	1817	1857	1919
	Saillat Chassenon a.	0709	0839	...	1256	*1733**	1807	1824	1906	1926
122	**Angoulême** a.	*0852**	*1022**	...	*1439**	*1906**	*1950**	*2007**	*2049**	*2109**

	...	Ⓐ	D	⑥ k	Ⓐ	Ⓒ	①–⑥ b	Ⓐ	⑦ e	⑤ f	⑦
Angoulême d.	...	*0545**	*0720**	*1118**	*1158**	*1525**	*1705**	*1810**	*1835**	*2035**	*2100**
Saillat Chassenon d.	...	0729	0901	1303	1341	1708	1852	1952	2019	2218	2238
St Junien d.	...	0736	0908	1310	1348	1715	1859	1958	2026	2225	2245
Limoges a.	...	0815	0945	1346	1426	1756	1938	2039	2105	2303	2322

km		Ⓐ	Ⓐ		⑥ k		Ⓐ m		⑦	⑥ k		Ⓐ m		⑥⑦ k		Ⓐ m	⑥⑦ k		Ⓐ	⑦ e		Ⓐ		⑤⑦ B	⑦ A
0	**Limoges** d.	0452	0600	...	0745	...	0851	...	0959	1021	...	1240	...	1408	...	1535	1606	...	1737	1751	...	1835	...	2008	2012
139	**Poitiers** a.	0700	0756	...	0941	...	1042	...	1158	1217	...	1443	...	1604	...	1755	1755	...	1944	2000	...	2039	...	2201	2205

	Ⓐ		⑥ k	Ⓐ m		⑦		⑥ k		Ⓐ m		⑥⑦ k	Ⓐ m		⑥⑦ k	Ⓐ		Ⓐ	⑥ k		Ⓑ h				
Poitiers d.	0545	...	0808	0835	...	0940	...	1100	...	1228	...	1357	1417	...	1642	1728	...	1822	1904	...	2014	...	...	...	...
Limoges a.	0745	...	1006	1034	...	1144	...	1258	...	1428	...	1551	1622	...	1842	1931	...	2100	2104	...	2225	...	...	...	...

A – ⑦ to June 30.
B – ⑤⑦ from June 28 (also Aug. 14; not June 30).
D – Ⓐ to July 5; ① from July 8.

b – Not June 10.
e – Also June 10.
f – Also Aug. 14.
h – Not Aug. 15.
k – Also Aug. 15.
m – From June 24.

* – By 🚌.

310 PARIS - LIMOGES - TOULOUSE

SERVICE JUNE 11 - SEPTEMBER 1. **Warning!** *INTERCITÉS* (★) services are subject to minor, but complex, variations and so timings shown may vary by up 6 minutes on certain dates (earlier departures possible; please check your reservation for confirmed timings). See Table **320** for *TGV* services Paris - Agen - Toulouse and v.v.

km		⚒	Ⓐ	⚒	Ⓐ	†	Ⓐ	①–⑥	①–⑥	⑥ k	Ⓐ	★ 3605 Q	⑦	★ 3605 Ⓐ T	①–⑥	★ 3615 Ⓐ n⊗	Ⓐ	★ 3617 ⑦	①–⑥	①–⑤ ⊙	⑥	Ⓒ	★ 3625	★ 3629 ⑦	★ 3635 D
0	**Paris** Austerlitz **294 315** d.	...	...	...	...	...	...	...	...	...	...	0638	...	0639	...	0740	...	0738	...	...	...	...	1038j	1133	1229
	Orléans 315 d.	...	...	...	...	...	...	...	...	...	0645	|	...	|	0751	|	...	|	...	...	...	1050	|	|	|
119	Les Aubrais-Orléans **294 315** d.	...	...	...	...	...	...	...	...	...	|	0738	...	0740	|	|	...	|	...	...	...	|	|	1240	|
200	Vierzon **315** d.	...	...	...	...	...	...	...	0645	...	0745	0815	...	0817	0848	0916	...	0914	...	1051	1133	1148	1214	|	|
236	Issoudun d.	...	...	...	...	...	...	...	0710	...	0809	|	...	|	0911	|	...	|	...	1111	1154	1211	1232	|	|
263	Châteauroux d.	...	...	...	...	...	...	...	0729	...	0827	0846	...	0857	0929	0946	...	0945	...	1125	1208	1230	1249	1346	1442
294	Argenton sur Creuse d.	...	...	...	...	...	...	...	0751	...	0844	|	...	|	0951	|	...	1002	...	1141	1224	1248	|	|	1500
341	La Souterraine d.	...	...	...	...	...	...	...	0820	...	...	|	...	|	...	1023	...	1028	...	1210	1253	...	|	1426	1526
400	**Limoges** a.	...	...	...	...	...	...	...	0854	...	...	0956	...	1017	...	1058	...	1103	...	1257	1340	...	1357	1502	1557
400	**Limoges** d.	...	...	...	0602	...	0702	0735	...	0907	...	0959	1007	1020	...	1101	...	1106	1225	...	...	...	1400	1505	1600
459	Uzerche d.	...	...	...	0652	...	0739	0825	...	0956	...	|	1056	|	...	1138	...	1143	1314	...	...	...	1436	|	|
499	**Brive la Gaillarde** a.	...	...	...	0721	...	0806	0855	...	1024	...	1058	1124	1119	...	1203	...	1208	1342	...	...	...	1502	1604	1700
499	**Brive la Gaillarde** d.	...	0555	0701	...	0801	▬	...	...	...	...	1101	...	1122	...	...	1206	...	...	...	...	...	...	...	1703
536	Souillac d.	...	0621	0724	...	0824	...	...	...	...	...	1128	...	1147	...	...	1230	...	...	...	...	...	...	...	1730
559	Gourdon d.	...	0637	0740	...	0839	⚒	...	...	...	...	1145	...	1203	...	...	1245	...	...	...	...	...	...	...	1746
600	Cahors d.	0607	0706	0806	...	0906	1007	...	...	...	...	1212	...	1230	...	...	1311	...	...	...	...	...	...	...	1812
639	Caussade d.	0636	0733	0835	...	0935	1036	...	...	...	...	1239	...	1256	...	...	1338	...	...	...	...	...	...	...	...
662	Montauban **320** d.	0652	0751	0852	...	0952	1052	...	...	...	...	1254	...	1312	...	...	1352	...	...	...	...	...	...	...	...
713	**Toulouse** Matabiau **320** a.	0733	0832	0932	...	1035	1132	...	...	...	...	1319	...	1340	...	...	1432	...	...	...	...	...	...	...	...
	Portbou **355** a.	...	...	...	...	...	...	...	...	...	...	...	...	...	...	...	...	...	...	...	...	...	...	...	...

	★ 3635 Ⓒ	⑤ f	①–⑥	E	★ 3635 A	Ⓐ	★ 3645	Ⓐ	Ⓐ	⑦	†	Ⓐ	Ⓐ	⑦	⑥ k	★ 3655 J	★ 3655 z	⑦	Ⓐ	★ 3665	Ⓐ	Ⓐ	★ 3675 Ⓐ n	★ 3685 △	3731 ■ Ⓡ
Paris Austerlitz **294 315** d.	1240	...	...	...	1251	...	1438	...	...	...	...	...	...	...	...	1628	1638	...	...	1741	...	...	1841	1938	2208
Orléans 315 d.	|	...	...	...	|	...	|	...	...	...	...	...	...	1639	1646	|	|	...	...	|	...	1848	|	|	|
Les Aubrais-Orléans **294 315** d.	|	...	...	...	|	...	1540	...	...	...	...	...	...	|	|	|	|	...	...	|	...	|	|	|	2317
Vierzon **315** d.	|	...	...	...	|	...	1617	1645	...	...	...	...	1733	1746	1746	|	|	...	1821	1914	1933	1947	2014	2114	|
Issoudun d.	|	...	...	...	|	...	|	1708	...	...	...	...	1754	1809	1808	1828	1828	...	1843	|	1954	2008	2032	|	|
Châteauroux d.	1441	...	...	...	1502	...	1648	1727	...	...	...	...	1808	1830	1827	1845	1845	←	1908	1945	2008	2025	2048	2146	|
Argenton sur Creuse d.	1459	...	...	...	1519	...	|	1751	...	...	...	...	1824	1855	1851	|	|	1902	1924	2002	2024	...	|	2204	|
La Souterraine d.	1525	...	...	...	1545	...	|	...	...	...	...	...	1853	→	...	1924	1924	1935	...	|	2053	...	2129	2231	|
Limoges a.	1559	...	...	...	1621	...	1758	...	...	...	...	...	1939	...	...	1956	2001	2017	...	2058	2140	...	2204	2306	|
Limoges d.	1602	...	1607	...	1630	1707	1801	...	1810	1837	...	1907	...	...	...	1959	2004	...	...	2101	...	...	2207	2309	|
Uzerche d.	|	...	1656	...	|	1756	|	...	1859	1925	...	1959	...	...	...	2037	2041	...	...	|	...	...	2244	|	|
Brive la Gaillarde a.	1702	...	1724	...	1730	1824	1901	...	1927	1954	...	2027	...	...	...	2102	2106	...	...	2201	...	...	2310	0008	|
Brive la Gaillarde d.	1705	1718	...	1728	1733	...	1904	...	...	...	2018	...	...	...	...	2106	...	...	...	2204**z**	...	...	...	...	|
Souillac d.	1732	1742	...	1752	1800	...	1930	...	...	...	2041	...	...	...	...	2132	...	...	...	2229**z**	...	...	...	...	|
Gourdon d.	1748	1758	...	1808	1816	...	1946	...	...	...	2057	...	...	...	...	2148	...	...	...	2246**z**	...	...	...	...	|
Cahors d.	1814	1824	...	1834	1842	...	2014	...	...	...	2123	...	...	...	...	2214	...	...	...	2312**z**	...	...	...	...	|
Caussade d.	...	1851	...	1902	...	...	2040	...	...	...	2151	...	...	...	...	...	...	...	...	...	...	...	...	...	|
Montauban **320** d.	...	1908	...	1919	...	...	2056	...	...	...	2208	...	...	...	...	...	...	...	...	...	...	...	...	...	0533
Toulouse Matabiau **320** a.	...	1935	...	1959	...	...	2123	...	...	...	2235	...	...	...	...	...	...	...	...	...	...	...	...	...	0601
Portbou **355** a.	...	...	...	...	...	...	...	...	...	...	...	...	...	...	...	...	...	...	...	...	...	...	...	...	0947

	★ 3604 Ⓐ n	Ⓐ	① M	N	★ 3614	N	★ 3624 ①–⑥	①–⑥	Ⓐ	Ⓐ	★ 3628 ⑦	①–⑥	★ 3634 ①–⑥	⚒	★ 3638 ⑦	Ⓑ	①⑦ q	★ 3644 ①–⑥	Ⓐ c	⑥ k	★ 3648 ⑦	Ⓐ ⊡		★ 3656 ⑦	★ 3654 R
Cerbère **355** d.	...	...	...	...	...	...	...	...	...	...	...	...	...	...	...	...	...	...	...	...	...	...	...	...	...
Toulouse Matabiau **320** d.	...	...	...	...	...	...	...	...	...	...	...	...	...	0625	...	0715	0715	0740	...	...	...	...	...	...	...
Montauban **320** d.	...	...	...	...	...	...	...	...	...	...	...	...	...	0653	...	0757	0757	0807	...	...	...	...	...	...	...
Caussade d.	...	...	...	...	...	...	...	...	...	...	...	...	...	0710	...	0815	0815	0822	...	...	...	...	...	...	...
Cahors d.	...	...	...	...	...	...	...	...	...	...	...	...	0641	0737	0746	0841	0842	0849	...	...	...	...	...	1240	...
Gourdon d.	...	...	...	...	...	...	...	...	...	...	...	...	0709	0803	0814	...	0908	0917	...	...	...	...	...	1307	...
Souillac d.	...	...	...	...	...	...	...	...	...	...	...	...	0727	0819	0831	...	0924	0934	...	...	...	...	...	1325	...
Brive la Gaillarde a.	...	...	...	...	...	...	...	...	...	...	...	...	0752	0842	0856	...	0947	0958	...	...	...	...	...	1349	...
Brive la Gaillarde d.	0355	...	...	...	0456	...	0558	...	0609	0650	0701	...	0755	...	0859	...	...	1001	...	...	1058	...	1226	1352	1358
Uzerche d.	|	...	...	...	0522	...	|	...	0639	0717	|	...	0821	...	0924	...	...	|	...	...	1124	...	1255	1416	1423
Limoges a.	0455	...	...	...	0559	...	0658	...	0728	0755	0801	...	0859	...	1001	...	...	1100	...	...	1201	...	1343	1453	1459
Limoges d.	0458	...	0539	...	0602	...	0701	0717	...	...	0804	...	0902	...	1004	...	...	1103	...	...	1204	1319	...	1500	1502
La Souterraine d.	0535	...	0615	...	|	...	0739	0808	...	...	|	...	0938	...	1040	...	...	|	...	...	|	1408	...	1535	1539
Argenton sur Creuse d.	|	...	0644	0644	0658	←	|	0836	...	...	0900	0920	1002	...	|	...	...	|	1204	...	1259	1436	...	|	|
Châteauroux d.	0613	0635	0708	0708	0717	0721	0818	0852	...	...	0918	0938	1020	...	1118	...	...	1215	1220	1235	1317	1452	...	1614	1618
Issoudun d.	0629	0652	→	→	|	0739	|	0907	...	...	|	0957**c**	|	...	1134	...	...	|	1238	1254	1333	1506	...	1630	|
Vierzon **315** d.	0649	0717	...	...	0749	0802	0849	0927	...	...	|	1022**c**	|	...	|	...	...	1247	1301	1318	|	1527	...	1649	1649
Les Aubrais-Orléans **294 315** a.	|	|	...	...	|	|	|	...	...	...	1021	|	|	...	|	...	...	1319	|	|	|	...	...	|	|
Orléans 315 a.	|	0813	...	...	|	0902	|	...	...	...	|	1117	|	...	|	...	...	|	1349	1414	|	...	...	|	|
Paris Austerlitz **294 315** a.	0821**v**	...	...	...	0921**v**	...	1020**v**	...	...	...	1121	...	1221**x**	...	1321**v**	...	...	1420**v**	...	...	1522**v**	...	...	1821	1821

FOR NOTES SEE NEXT PAGE

TOULOUSE - LIMOGES - PARIS 310

SERVICE JUNE 11 - SEPTEMBER 1. **Warning!** *INTERCITÉS* (★) services are subject to minor, but complex, variations and so timings shown may vary by up 6 minutes on certain dates (earlier departures possible; please check your reservation for confirmed timings). See Table **320** for *TGV* services Paris - Agen - Toulouse and v.v.

	★ 3654 ①–⑥ s◇	Ⓑ p		Ⓒ	★ 3664 ⑦	⚒ W	⑤ f	Ⓐ	G	★ 3674 R	★ 3674 s	Ⓐ	①–⑥	★ 3686 ⑥ d	★ 3684 Ⓑ h¶	★ 3694 L	⑤ f	Ⓑ p	★ 3694 t	Ⓑ	Ⓑ p	Ⓐ	Ⓒ	Ⓐ	3730 ■ Ⓡ
Cerbère **355** d.	...	...	...	...	...	...	...	...	...	...	...	...	...	...	...	...	...	...	...	...	...	...	...	...	1910
Toulouse Matabiau **320** d.	...	...	...	1228	...	...	1325	...	1428	...	...	...	...	...	...	1547	1559	...	1632	1728	...	1828	1930	1928	2230
Montauban **320** d.	...	...	...	1311	...	...	1359	...	1511	...	...	...	...	...	...	1615	1640	...	1702	1811	...	1911	1958	2011	2311
Caussade d.	...	...	...	1328	...	...	1413	...	1525	...	...	...	...	...	...	1630	1656	...	1717	1828	...	1928	2016	2030	|
Cahors d.	1246	...	...	1354	...	...	1437	...	1549	1544	...	...	...	...	...	1655	1721	...	1744	1855	...	1955	2042	2058	|
Gourdon d.	1313	...	...	▬	...	...	1503	...	1616	1610	...	...	...	...	...	1721	1748	...	1811	1922	...	2021	2108	...	|
Souillac d.	1330	...	...	...	...	...	1519	...	1631	1626	...	...	...	...	...	1737	1804	...	1828	1938	...	2037	2124	...	|
Brive la Gaillarde a.	1355	...	...	...	...	...	1542	...	1655	1651	...	...	...	...	...	1805	1829	...	1853	2004	...	2100	2147	...	|
Brive la Gaillarde d.	1358	...	...	...	1601	...	...	1650	...	1654	1659	...	1732	1754	1759	1811	...	1832	1858	...	2014	...	...	...	|
Uzerche d.	1423	...	...	⑥	|	...	...	1718	...	|	|	...	1801	1819	1824	|	...	1901	|	...	2042	...	...	...	|
Limoges a.	1500	...	...	u	1701	...	...	1755	...	1759	1759	...	1849	1857	1901	1911	...	1949	1958	...	2118	...	...	...	|
Limoges d.	1503	...	...	1619	1704	1719	...	...	...	1802	1802	...	...	1900	1904	1914	...	...	2001	...	...	...	...	...	|
La Souterraine d.	1537	...	...	1708	|	1808	...	...	...	|	|	...	...	1936	1939	|	...	...	|	...	...	...	...	...	|
Argenton sur Creuse d.	|	1610	...	1736	1802	1836	...	...	...	|	|	1914	...	1959	|	|	...	...	|	...	...	...	...	...	|
Châteauroux d.	1618	1633	1735	1752	1820	1852	...	...	...	1912	1912	1934	...	2017	2018	2028	...	...	2113	...	...	...	...	...	|
Issoudun d.	|	1650	1752	1806	|	1906	...	...	...	1928	1928	1951	...	|	|	|	...	...	|	...	...	...	...	...	|
Vierzon **315** d.	1649	1715	1817	1827	1851	1927	...	...	...	1947	1947	2017	...	2048	2047	2102	...	...	2145	...	...	...	...	...	|
Les Aubrais-Orléans **294 315** a.	|	|	|	...	|	...	...	...	...	|	|	|	...	|	|	2138	...	...	2218	...	...	...	...	...	0538
Orléans **315** a.	|	1812	1912	...	|	...	...	...	...	|	|	2116	...	|	|	|	...	...	|	...	...	...	...	...	|
Paris Austerlitz **294 315** a.	1821v	...	...	...	2022v	...	...	...	...	2121	2121g	...	...	2221v	2225r	2249	...	...	2327	...	...	...	...	...	0652

A – ①–⑤ July 22 - Aug. 13 (also Aug. 19–22).
D – ①–⑤ June 11 - July 19 (also Aug. 14, 16, 23, 26–30). Aug. 26–29 Brive a. 1720, d. 1736, Souillac d. 1802, Gourdon d. 1819, Cahors a. 1844.
E – ①②③④⑦ (not Aug. 14).
G – ①②③④⑥ (not June 10, Aug. 14, 15).
J – June 17–20 only.
L – June 11, 12, 13, 17–20 only.
M – ① to July 1 (also June 11; not June 10).
N – Daily to July 6; ②–⑥ from July 9.
Q – ①–⑥ June 11 - July 20; ⑥ from July 27 (also Aug. 15).
R – Aug. 26–29 only.
T – From July 22.
W – Until July 6.

c – Departures are up to 5 minutes earlier June 11–21.
d – ⑥ (also Aug. 15, 16). Runs 4–15 minutes later on Aug. 16.
f – Also Aug. 14.
g – 2140 June 22–30.
h – Not Aug. 15, 16.
j – 1028 on ①–④ to Aug. 13 (also Aug. 19–22).
k – Also Aug. 15.
n – Not Aug. 16.
p – Not Aug. 15.
q – Also June 11, Aug. 15.
r – 11–12 minutes later on ①–⑤ June 11–28 and ①–⑤ July 22 - Aug. 23 (not Aug. 9, 15, 16). Arrives 2258 Aug. 26–29.
s – Not Aug. 26–29.
t – Not June 11, 12, 13, 17–20.
u – Not ①–⑤ July 22 - Aug. 23.
v – 10–14 minutes later until June 30.
x – 10–12 minutes later until June 29, Aug. 5–8, 12–14, 19–23.
z – Not June 17–20.

△ – Runs 6–12 minutes later Vierzon - Brive on June 15, 16, 22–30.
◇ – Timings Cahors - Limoges are 8 minutes earlier on ⑥ from July 27 (also Aug. 15, 16, 30). Timings Cahors - La Souterraine are 16–20 minutes earlier on Aug. 14, 23.
¶ – Timings Brive - Vierzon are up to 9 minutes earlier on June 16, 23, 30 and 13–16 minutes later Aug. 26–29.
⊙ – Not Aug. 26–30. Runs 31–32 minutes later July 22 - Aug. 23.
⊡ – Runs 45–48 minutes later from July 22.
⊗ – Subject to alteration on Aug. 1.
★ – *INTERCITÉS*. Ⓡ. Timings may vary by up to 6 minutes.
■ – *INTERCITÉS DE NUIT*. 🛏 1, 2 cl. and (2). Conveys portions to / from Latour de Carol (**3970/1**; Table **312**) and Rodez (**3755/4**; Table **316**). Overnight journeys only. **Timings may vary**. For days of running and confirmed timings please consult the SNCF journey planner: www.oui.sncf/billet-train

BRIVE - AURILLAC 311

Service July 6 - October 20

km		Ⓐ	⑥ k	⚒	†		Ⓒ			
0	**Brive la Gaillarde** **316** d.	1130	1211	1402	1425	...	1801	...	2216	...
27	St Denis-près-Martel **316** d.	1157	1243	1430	1454	...	1835	...	2242	...
102	**Aurillac** a.	1324	1406	1553	1618	...	2001	...	0005	...

	Ⓐ	①–⑥		Ⓒ	Ⓐ	⑦	† B	A	
Aurillac d.	0515	0746	...	1049	1158	1456	1553	1556	1710
St Denis-près-Martel **316** d.	0637	0911	...	1212	1325	1627	1723	1718	1836
Brive la Gaillarde **316** a.	0705	0937	...	1242	1355	1653	1749	1745	1900

A – ⚒ to Aug. 24; ⑤ from Aug. 30.
B † to Aug. 25.
k – Also Aug. 15.

TOULOUSE - LATOUR DE CAROL 312

km		3971 ■ Ⓡ		Ⓐ	Ⓐ ⊙	Ⓒ		Ⓒ	Ⓐ ⊡	Ⓒ		Ⓐ ⊡	Ⓒ	Ⓒ	Ⓐ ⊙		Ⓐ	Ⓒ	Ⓐ	Ⓐ	Ⓒ		Ⓐ	Ⓒ
	Paris Austerlitz **310** d.	2208	...	...	...	...	...	...	...	...	...	...	...	...	...	...	...	...	...	...	...	...	...	...
0	**Toulouse** Matabiau d.	|	...	0649	0749	0749	...	0852	0949	1050	...	1219	1249	1349	1349	...	1549	1550	1649	1748	1749	...	1853	1949
65	Pamiers d.	0717	...	0749	0850	0851	...	0947	1050	1147	...	1322	1350	1449	1446	...	1649	1650	1750	1850	1848	...	1953	2056
83	Foix d.	0731	...	0805	0908	0908	...	1005	1104	1203	...	1342	1407	1510	1505	...	1705	1706	1807	1907	1905	...	2010	2113
123	Ax-les-Thermes d.	0819	...	0843	0948	0958	...	1044	1144	1244	...	1420	1446	1552	1549	...	1749	1749	1847	1946	1950	...	2052	2154
144	L'Hospitalet ⊖ d.	0847	...	...	1014	1023	...	...	1211	1315	...	...	...	1622	1620	...	1820	1820	...	...	2014	...	2116	...
163	**Latour de Carol** ★ a.	0915	...	...	1036	1051	...	...	1234	1339	...	...	...	1642	1651	...	1844	1840	...	...	2035	...	2137	...

	⚒	Ⓐ	⊙		Ⓐ ⊡	Ⓒ	Ⓐ ⊡	Ⓒ	Ⓐ ⊡	Ⓒ		Ⓒ	Ⓐ ⊙		Ⓐ	Ⓒ	Ⓒ	Ⓐ	Ⓒ	Ⓐ	3970 ■ Ⓡ		† ♥
Latour de Carol ★ d.	...	...	0721	...	...	...	1008	1023	...	...	...	1307	1324	...	...	1524	...	1624	1724	1815	1851	...	2040
L'Hospitalet ⊖ d.	...	...	0751	...	...	...	1053	1051	...	...	...	1354	1351	...	...	1551	...	1651	1751	1853	1920	...	2107
Ax-les-Thermes d.	0617	0723	0821	...	0925	1023	1123	1120	1220	1222	...	1424	1423	...	1623	1622	1723	1723	1820	1922	1949	...	2134
Foix d.	0659	0804	0907	...	1007	1107	1207	1202	1302	1305	...	1509	1504	...	1704	1705	1806	1808	1904	2009	2042	...	2212
Pamiers d.	0719	0821	0921	...	1023	1121	1224	1221	1321	1323	...	1523	1521	...	1720	1721	1820	1822	1921	2023	2057	...	2227
Toulouse Matabiau a.	0818	0916	1016	...	1118	1216	1317	1317	1414	1417	...	1615	1616	...	1815	1816	1916	1919	2016	2115	|	...	2314
Paris Austerlitz **310** a.	...	...	...	...	...	...	...	...	...	...	...	...	...	...	...	...	...	...	...	...	0652	...	...

♥ – † July 7 - Aug. 25.
⊡ – Subject to alteration Oct. 7–11, 21–25, 28–31.
⊙ – Subject to alteration Oct. 21–25, 28–31.
★ – See Table **656** for Latour de Carol - Barcelona and v.v.
⊖ – Full name: L'Hospitalet-près-l'Andorre. For 🚌 connections to / from Andorra see Table **313**.
■ – *INTERCITÉS DE NUIT*. 🛏 1, 2 cl. and (2). **Timings may vary**. For days of running and confirmed timings please consult the SNCF journey planner: www.oui.sncf/billet-train

ANDORRA 🚌 313

						⊖		
Andorre-L'Hospitalet (Gare) d.	0850	...	1945	...	...	and	...	...
Pas de la Casa d.	0910	...	2000	...	0845	hourly	2045	...
Soldeu ⊙ d.	0920	...	2010	...	0910	until	2110	...
Andorra la Vella a.	0955	...	2040	...	0940	...	2140	...

						⊖		
Andorra la Vella d.	0630	...	1645	...	0745	and	1945	...
Soldeu ⊙ d.	0650	...	1735	...	0825	hourly	2025	...
Pas de la Casa d.	0710	...	1815	...	0840	until	2040	...
Andorre-L'Hospitalet (Gare) a.	0730	...	1845	...	...	...	...	...

⊙ – Also calls at Canillo, Encamp and Escaldes.
⊖ – Additional journeys operated by Cooperativa Interurbana (service L4) run from Andorra hourly 0720 - 2020, from Pas de la Casa at 0715 then hourly 0820 - 2120.

Operator: La Hispano Andorrana, Av. Santa Coloma, entre 85 - 87, Andorra la Vella. ✆ + 376 821 372. www.andorrabus.com. Subject to cancellation when mountain passes are closed by snow.

TOULOUSE - CASTRES - MAZAMET 314

km		Ⓐ	Ⓐ n	⚒	†	§	§	Ⓐ	Ⓐ	Ⓐ r	L		
0	**Toulouse** Matabiau d.	0542	0643	0750	0838	1144	1344	1543	1644	1722	1740	1847	2042
86	Castres a.	0655	0758	0901	0950	1251	1451	1653	1750	1833	1853	1957	2154
105	**Mazamet** a.	0722	0825	0928	1014	1318	1519	1716	1817	1902	1924	2024	2217

	Ⓐ	Ⓐ	Ⓐ		Ⓐ n §	Ⓑ §	⚒ §	¶		Ⓐ	n
Mazamet d.	0530	0553	0635	0738	0841	1031	1231	1432	1730	1822	1938
Castres d.	0553	0616	0659	0802	0905	1054	1255	1455	1754	1857	2001
Toulouse Matabiau a.	0701	0730	0806	0908	1011	1201	1402	1602	1906	2005	2112

L – Daily to July 14; ⑤–⑦ July 19 - Aug. 25 (also Aug. 15); daily from Aug. 30.
n – Not Ⓐ July 15 - Aug. 30.
r – Not July 19, 26, Aug. 2, 9, 16, 23, 30.
§ – Subject to alteration Oct. 7–11, 14–18, Nov. 18–22, 25–29, Dec. 2–6.
¶ – Subject to alteration Oct. 7–11, 14–18.

315 PARIS and ORLÉANS - VIERZON - BOURGES - MONTLUÇON and NEVERS

SERVICE JUNE 11 - SEPTEMBER 22

km				3903					3909								3913/5						3917		3921	
		Ⓐ	①–⑥	①–⑥	⑥		①–⑥	⑤			⑤	①–④	Ⓑ	Ⓐ	Ⓐ	Ⓐ	Ⓑ	⑤		①–④	⑦	Ⓐ			⑤⑦	⑤⑦
					k						f	m	h				h	f		m					w	
0	**Paris** Austerlitz .... **310** d.	...	...	0658	...	...	...	...	1206**c**	...	...	...	...	...	...	...	1707**e**	...	...	...	...	...	1858	...	2056	...
	Orléans .... **310** d.	0612	0713	|	...	0904	...	1213	|	...	1413	1413	1609	...	1644	1713	|	...	1813	...	...	1913	|	...	|	...
119	Les Aubrais-Orléans ... **310** d.	|	|	0807	...	|	...	|	1308	...	|	|	|	...	|	|	1807	...	|	...	...	|	2007	...	2207	...
178	Salbris .... d.	0652	0751	0836	...	0943	...	1252	|	...	1454	1456	1650	...	1724	1752	1834	...	1851	...	...	1951	2034	...	2234	...
200	Vierzon .... **290 310** d.	0705	0805	0852	0902	1007**x**	1017	1313**t**	1348	...	1510	1516	1703	...	1740	1805	1850	...	1905	1922	...	2005	2050	...	2250	2300
232	**Bourges** .... **290** a.	0734	0827	0911	|	1027	|	1333	1405	...	1537	1544	1723	...	1807	1823	1909	...	1927	|	...	2025	2109	...	2309	|
	Bourges .... **290** d.	0736	...	...	|	...	|	...	...	1417	...	...	1726**a**	1741	...	1826	...	1924	...	|	1941	...	...	2119	...	|
	Nevers .... **290** a.	0824**z**	...	...	|	...	|	...	...	|	...	...	1813**a**	|	...	1914	...	|	...	|	|	...	...	|	...	|
291*	St Amand-Montrond-Orval . d.	...	...	...	0956	...	1111	...	...	1502	...	...	...	1834	...	...	...	2011	...	2020	2032	...	...	2205	...	2353
341*	**Montluçon** .... a.	...	...	...	1030	...	1146	...	...	1536	...	...	...	1917	...	...	...	2045	...	2054	2114	...	...	2239	...	0028

						3904					🚌			3908			3916	3914					3920			3924
	Ⓐ	Ⓐ	⑥	Ⓐ	①–⑥	①–⑥	Ⓐ	⑥	Ⓐ	⑥	Ⓐ	Ⓐ			⚒	Ⓐ	⑦	①–⑥	Ⓐ	Ⓐ	Ⓐ	Ⓒ		Ⓐ	Ⓐ	⑦
			k				n	k		k				d		⊗										
Montluçon .... d.	...	...	...	...	0536	...	...	0613	...	...	0630	...	0821	...	1036	...	...	...	...	...	...	...	*1716*	1735	...	*1913*
St Amand-Montrond-Orval ... d.	...	...	...	...	0609	...	0627	0649	...	...	0738	...	0857	...	1109	...	...	...	...	...	...	...	*1751*	1833	...	*1953*
Nevers .... **290** d.	...	...	...	...	|	...	|	|	0643**v**	...	|	0741**v**	|	...	|	1245**v**	...	...	...	1645**v**	1743	...	|	|	1843	|
Bourges .... **290** a.	...	...	...	...	|	...	0714	|	0732	...	|	0829	0942	...	|	1333‡	...	...	...	1734	1834	...	*1842*	1921	1934	*2042*
Bourges .... **290** d.	...	...	...	0637	|	0652	...	|	0735	0736‡	|	0832	...	0952	|	1336‡	1352	1552	1637	1737	1836	1837‡	1852	...	1937	2052
Vierzon .... **290 310** d.	0551	0617‡	0651‡	0658	0701	0711	...	0742	0758‡	0758‡	0835	0855	...	1011	1202	1358‡	1411	1611	1658	1756	1858‡	1858‡	1909	...	1958	2111
Salbris .... d.	0603	0632‡	0703‡	0710	...	0725	...	...	0810	0810‡	...	0907	...	|	...	1411	1425	1627	1711	1809	1910‡	1910	1923	...	2010	2125
Les Aubrais-Orléans .... **310** a.	|	|	|	|	...	0752	...	...	|	|	...	|	...	1052	...	|	1451	1653	|	|	|	|	1951	...	|	2153
Orléans .... **310** a.	0640	0711	0739	0747	...	|	...	...	0847	0847	...	0947	...	|	...	1447	|	|	1747	1847	1947	1947	|	...	2048	|
Paris Austerlitz .... **310** a.	...	...	...	...	...	0854**r**	...	...	...	...	...	...	....	1154**j**	...	...	1553**r**	1802**r**	...	...	...	...	2053**r**	...	...	2302**r**

a – Ⓐ only. Arrives Nevers 1818 from Sept. 2.
c – 1159 June 11 – 30; 1127 on ①–⑤ Sept. 9 – 27.
d – Not July 31.
e – 1659 until June 30.
f – Also Aug. 14.
h – Not Aug. 15.
j – 1203 until June 30 (also Aug. 12 – 14, 19 – 23).
k – Also Aug. 15.
m – Not Aug. 14, 15.
n – Not July 15 - Aug. 23.
r – 4 – 13 minutes later until June 30.
t – Arrives 1303.
v – 1 – 2 minutes **earlier** from Sept. 2.
w – Also Aug. 14.
x – Arrives 0955. Departs 0957 on ⑤ (also Aug. 14, 26 – 29, Sept. 2, 3, 5, 9, 16, 17).
z – 0826 from Sept. 2.
‡ – 1 – 3 minutes **earlier** until June 21.
⊗ – Subject to alteration on Sept. 2, 3, 11, 12.
* – Via Bourges (Montluçon is *327* km for trains not calling at Bourges).

316 BRIVE - FIGEAC - RODEZ

Service from June 15

km		3755	3755							
			⑤f	⚒	Ⓑ	Ⓐ		Ⓐ		Ⓑ
		■ R	■ R		⊕	⊕	⊙			
	Paris Austerlitz **310** ...... d.	2208	2208	...	...	...	...	...	...	...
0	**Brive la Gaillarde** .... **311** d.	|	|	0550	0753	1117	1328	1714	1936	2224
27	St Denis-près-Martel . **311** d.	0409	0409	0616	0818	1142	1353	1743	2006	2248
45	Rocamadour-Padirac .... d.	0426	0426	0631	0833	1157	1409	1758	2021	2303
53	Gramat .... d.	0433	0433	0638	0840	1205	1416	1805	2028	2311
88	Figeac .... **317** d.	0503	0503	0706	0908	1235	1443	1833	2055	2338
94	Capdenac .... **317** d.	0512	0512	0714	0915	1245	1452	1842	2103	2346
109	Viviez-Decazeville .... d.	0528	0528	0728	0929	1259	1507	1857	2117	0000
161	**Rodez** .... **323** a.	0617	0617	0816	1017	1344	1552	1942	2203	0046
	Carmaux .... **323** a.	...	0739	...	...	...	...	...	...	...
	Albi .... **323** a.	...	0759	...	...	...	...	...	...	...

									3754	3754
	⚒	†	Ⓐ	†	⚒				⑦	
	⊙		⊕		⊕				■ R	■ R
Albi .... **323** d.	...	...	...	...	...	...	...	...	2056	...
Carmaux .... **323** d.	...	...	...	...	...	...	...	...	2116	...
Rodez .... **323** d.	0726	0814	1053	1140	1140	1420	1624	1738	2241	2241
Viviez-Decazeville .... d.	0812	0859	1138	1227	1227	1508	1710	1825	2329	2329
Capdenac .... **317** d.	0828	0916	1155	1244	1244	1525	1727	1843	2347	2347
Figeac .... **317** d.	0835	0924	1202	1252	1252	1532	1734	1850	2356	2356
Gramat .... d.	0904	0952	1230	1327	1327	1558	1806	1918	0027	0027
Rocamadour-Padirac...... d.	0911	1000	1237	1336	1336	1606	1813	1925	0034	0034
St Denis-près-Martel **311** d.	0926	1015	1252	1354	1354	1621	1829	1940	0051	0051
Brive la Gaillarde . **311** a.	0951	1040	1315	1417	1429	1646	1853	2005	|	|
Paris Austerlitz **310**.... a.	...	...	...	...	...	...	...	...	0652	0652

f – Also Aug. 14, Oct. 31; not Aug. 16, Nov. 1.
⊕ – Subject to alteration on ①–⑤ Sept. 30 - Oct. 31.
⊙ – Subject to alteration Oct. 21 – 25, 28 – 31.
■ – *INTERCITÉS DE NUIT*. **Timings may vary - please check your reservation**. Only for overnight journeys from / to Paris. For days of running and confirmed timings please consult the SNCF journey planner: www.oui.sncf/billet-train

317 AURILLAC - FIGEAC - TOULOUSE

km		Ⓐ			Ⓐ					⑤v
			⊗	⊗	⊗	⊙	🚌		🚌 §	🚌
	Clermont Ferrand **331** ...... d.	...	...	...	...	...	...	...	...	...
0	**Aurillac** .... d.	...	*0629*r	*0829*r	...	...	*1306*	*1630**	1831	2117
65	Figeac .... **316** d.	...	*0753*r	*0949*r	...	...	*1426*	*1750**	1951	2237
71	Capdenac .... **316** d.	0614	0814	1014	1212	1415	1451	1815	2006	2253
100	Villefranche de Rouergue .... d.	0641	0845	1044	1239	1445	1536	1844	...	...
117	Najac .... d.	0656	0900	1058	1254	1500	|	1859	...	...
170	Gaillac .... **323** d.	0742	0949	1143	1340	1546	|	1947	...	...
224	**Toulouse** Matabiau ..... **323** a.	0831	1031	1221	1421	1623	1736	2029	...	...

	⚒	Ⓐ	Ⓐ				⑤v	Ⓐ		Ⓒ
	🚌	🚌	⊙	⊗	⊗		🚌			🚌
Toulouse Matabiau .. **323** d.	...	...	0654	0858	1303	1704	...	1811	1909	...
Gaillac .... **323** d.	...	...	0742	0937	1340	1743	...	1853	1947	...
Najac .... d.	...	...	0829	1028	1428	1828	...	1939	2035	...
Villefranche de Rouergue . d.	...	...	0844	1043	1444	1843	...	1954	2049	...
Capdenac .... **316** a.	0556	0820	0912	1109	1511	1909	1919	2021	2115	2138
Figeac .... **316** a.	0611	0835	...	*1137*r	*1540**	...	1934	*2049**	...	2153
Aurillac .... a.	0731	0955	...	*1257*r	*1700**	...	2054	*2205**	...	2313
Clermont Ferrand **331**... a.	...	...	...	...	...	...	...	...	...	...

r – ⚒ only. By 🚌 Aurillac - Capdenac and v.v.
v – Also Aug. 14.
* – By 🚌 Aurillac - Capdenac and v.v.
§ – On ⑤ (also Aug. 14): Aurillac d. 1830, Figeac d. 1947, Capdenac a. 1958.
⊗ – Subject to alteration on Ⓐ Nov. 4 - Dec. 6.
⊙ – Subject to alteration Nov. 4 – 8, 12 – 15.

Trains are replaced by 🚌 between Aurillac and Capdenac until further notice

318 BORDEAUX - LIBOURNE - BERGERAC - SARLAT

SERVICE UNTIL SEPTEMBER 29. All services Libourne - Sarlat and v.v. are operated by 🚌. Rail services operate Bordeaux - Libourne and v.v.

km			Ⓐ	⚒	Ⓐ★		Ⓐ	Ⓒ★	Ⓒ	Ⓐ				Ⓐ		Ⓐ¶	Ⓐ	Ⓐ¶	d★	⑥k★		⑦★	⑤f	Ⓑh
0	**Bordeaux** St Jean . **300 302** Train d.	...	0605	0711	0828	0907	1008	1028	1111	1206	...	1411	...	1611	1711	1728	1811	1828	1828	1828	1911	1928	2011	2212
37	Libourne .... **300 302** Train a.	...	0632	0739	0851	0934	1035	1050	1141	1236	...	1438	...	1637	1739	1751	1838	1850	1850	1850	1940	1951	2038	2237
		Ⓐ	Ⓐ	⚒	|		Ⓐ	|	Ⓒ	Ⓐ	Ⓐ		Ⓐ	Ⓐ		|	Ⓐ	|	|	|		|	⑤f	Ⓑh
37	Libourne .... 🚌 d.	...	0640	0745	0852	0940	1040	1051	1146	1241	1330	1445	...	1645	1745	1752	1845	1851	1851	1851	1945	1952	2045	2245
45	St Émilion .... 🚌 d.	...	0659	0804	|	0959	1059	|	1205	1300	1349	1504	...	1704	1804	|	1904	|	|	|	2004	|	2104	2304
77	Ste Foy la Grande .... 🚌 d.	...	0739	0849	|	1039	1139	|	1245	1340	1440	1544	...	1744	1844	|	1944	|	|	|	2044	|	2144	2344
99	**Bergerac** .... 🚌 a.	...	0823	0933	|	1123	1223	|	1329	1424	1524	1628	...	1828	1928	1908	2028	2002	|	|	2128	|	2228	0028
99	**Bergerac** .... 🚌 d.	0605	0845	0944	|	1135**c**	1235	|	1340	...	...	1640**c**	1730	1840	1940**c**	...	...	...	|	|	2140	|	2240	...
135	Le Buisson .... 🚌 d.	0656	0936	1035	1103	1226**c**	1326	1257	1431	...	...	1731**c**	1821	1931	2031**c**	...	...	...	2057	2119	2231	2158	2331	...
168	**Sarlat** .... 🚌 a.	0739	1019	1118	1134	1309**c**	1409	1327	1514	...	...	1814**c**	1904	2014	2114**c**	...	...	...	2127	2149	2314	2229	0014	...

	Ⓐ	Ⓐ‡	⚒	Ⓐ‡	Ⓐ	Ⓐ	Ⓒ	Ⓐ★		Ⓐ	Ⓒ	Ⓐ	⑦★	n	⑥k★	Ⓐ★	⚒		Ⓑh	Ⓒ	Ⓐ	⑦★	⑥k★	⑤⑦f
Sarlat .... 🚌 d.	...	...	...	...	0445	0535	0545	0643	0745	0845	0945	...	1034	1150	1344	1431	...	...	...	1635	1645	1651	1734	1745
Le Buisson .... 🚌 d.	...	...	...	...	0531	0621	0631	0714	0831	0931	1031	...	1104	1234	1416	1503	...	...	...	1721	1731	1723	1806	1831
Bergerac .... 🚌 a.	...	...	...	...	0621	0711	0721	|	0921	1031	1121	...	|	1324	|	|	...	...	...	1811	1821	|	|	1921
Bergerac .... 🚌 d.	0440	0514	0520	0545	0635	0725	0735	|	0935	1035	1135	1219	|	1335	|	|	1535	1635	1720	1825	1835	|	|	1935
Ste Foy la Grande .... 🚌 d.	0512	|	0554	|	0707	0757	0807	|	1007	1107	1207	1253	|	1407	|	|	1607	1709	1754	1857	1907	|	|	2007
St Émilion .... 🚌 d.	0552	|	0647	|	0747	0837	0847	|	1047	1147	1247	1346	|	1447	|	|	1647	1749	1847	1937	1947	|	|	2047
Libourne .... 🚌 a.	0612	0633	0707	0708	0807	0857	0907	0918	1107	1207	1307	1406	1508	1507	1708	1713	1707	1809	1907	1957	2007	1944	2024	2107
	Ⓐ	|	⚒	|	Ⓐ	Ⓐ	Ⓒ	|		Ⓐ	Ⓒ		|		|	|	⚒		Ⓑh	Ⓒ	Ⓐ	|	|	⑤⑦f
Libourne .... **300 302** Train d.	0622	0634	0722	0709	0817	0915	0924	0919	1122	1222	1322	1415	1509	1522	1709	1714	1721	1822	1931	2015	2020	1945	2025	2119
Bordeaux St Jean.. **300 302** Train a.	0649	0654	0749	0733	0849	0937	0951	0944	1151	1249	1349	1443	1533	1549	1733	1735	1749	1849	2005	2037	2049	2006	2048	2143

c – Ⓒ only.
d – ①–④ (not June 10, Aug. 14, 15).
f – Also Aug. 14.
h – Not Aug. 15.
k – Also Aug. 15.
n – Not ③.
¶ – By train Bordeaux - Libourne - Mussidan (Table **302**), then 🚌 Mussidan - Bergerac.
‡ – By 🚌 Bergerac - Mussidan, then train Mussidan - Libourne - Bordeaux (Table **302**).
★ – Rail service Bordeaux - Sarlat and v.v. via Périgueux (change trains).

BORDEAUX - TOULOUSE 320

Timings of long-distance services may vary by a few minutes until July 5; *TGV* services from / to Paris are subject to minor timing variations (please check your seat reservation). Local TER services Bordeaux - Agen and v.v. are valid July 5 - September 1. Certain services are subject to alteration on Oct. 26, 27, Nov. 2, 9 – 11.

km		★ 4655 Ⓐ	★ 4657	*TGV* 8501 ①–⑥ b	⑥ k	★ 4659 ⊖	*TGV* 7671 ①–⑤ ⊠	*TGV* 8503 T	*TGV* 7671 ⑥⑦ ⊠		★ 4661 Ⓑ	★ 4661 ⑥	*TGV* 8505 ①–④ A	*TGV* 8507 B	★ 4663	*TGV* 8511	★ 4665 Ⓑ	★ 4667 ⑥ N		★ 4669 Ⓑ N	*TGV* 8513 D		*TGV* 8515	Ⓑ h	*TGV* 8517 ⑤ f
	*Paris Montparnasse **300*** d.	...	...	0647**r**	...	...	0838	0847	0938	...	...	...	1148	1147	...	1347	...	...	...	...	1647	...	1847	...	1947
0	**Bordeaux** St Jean d.	0634	0832	0905	0910	1030	|	1102	|	1110	1232	1230	1402	1405	1432	1602	1630	1630	1810	1832	1902	1910	2102	2110	2205
79	Marmande d.	|	|	|	0958	1110	|	|	|	1158	|	1310	|	|	|	|	1710	1710	1858	|	|	2014	|	2158	|
136	Agen d.	0744	|	1009	1034	1141	1205**s**	1208	|	1233	1341	1341	|	1510	|	1709	1741	1741	1934	1945	2011	2049	2210	2234	2310
206	Montauban d.	|	|	|	...	1217	1242**s**	1245	|	...	1418	1418	|	|	|	1745	1817	1817	...	|	2046	...	2246	...	|
257	**Toulouse** Matabiau a.	0848	1043	1111	...	1243	1311	1314	1437	...	1443	1443	1603	1611	1643	1811	1843	1843	...	2043	2114	...	2314	...	0010
	*Narbonne **321*** a.	1012	|	...	...	1401	...	...	...	...	1601	1601	...	...	|	...	2001	2001	...	2201	...	...	...	...	...
	*Montpellier Sud-de-F **355*** a.	|	1249	...	...	|	...	...	...	...	|	|	...	...	1849	...	|	|	...	|	...	...	...	...	...
	*Montpellier St Roch **355*** a.	1111	|	...	...	1500	...	...	...	...	1700	1700	...	...	|	...	2100	2100	...	2300**j**	...	...	...	...	...
	*Marseille St Charles **355*** a.	1254	1426	...	...	1642	...	...	...	...	1904	1904	...	...	2037	...	2242	...	...	...	...	...	...	...	...

	TGV 8500 ①–⑥ b	★ 4752 Ⓐ N	*TGV* 8504	★ 4756 Ⓐ ⊗	★ 4754 Ⓒ N	*TGV* 8508 Y	★ 4758 ⑥	★ 4758 Ⓑ ⊙	*TGV* 8510 ⑥⑦ c	*TGV* 7672 ①–⑤ ⊠	*TGV* 8512 Ⓐ E	★ 4760		*TGV* 8514 F	*TGV* 7672 ⑦ ⊠	*TGV* 7672 ⑥ ⊠	★ 4762	Ⓑ h	*TGV* 8516	★ 4764 ⚒	★ 4764 †	*TGV* 8518 ⑦ e	*TGV* 8520 ①–⑥ b	*TGV* 8522 ⑦ e	★ 4766 Ⓑ
*Marseille St Charles **355*** d.	...	...	...	0614	...	...	0818	0834	...	...	...	1018**t**	...	...	...	...	1214	...	...	1418	1418	...	...	...	1614
*Montpellier St Roch **355*** d.	...	0608**g**	...	0758	0758	...	|	|	...	...	...	1158	...	...	...	...	1358	...	...	|	|	...	...	...	1758•
*Montpellier Sud-de-F **355*** d.	...	|	...	|	|	...	0944	1005	...	...	...	|	...	...	...	...	|	...	...	1547	1547	...	...	...	|
*Narbonne **321*** d.	...	0658	...	0858	0858	...	|	|	...	...	...	1300	...	...	...	...	|	...	...	|	|	...	...	...	1858
Toulouse Matabiau d.	0648	0819	0847	1019	1019	1146	1157	1215	1345	1348	1353	1419	...	1549	1559	1606	1619	...	1645	1754	1754	1756	1849	1948	2019
Montauban d.	0714	|	0914	|	1045	1213	|	|	1412	1417	|	1445	...	|	|	|	|	...	1711	|	|	|	|	|	2045
Agen d.	0751	0920	0952	1119	1121	1249	|	|	1448	1456	|	1521	1625	1649	|	|	1719**q**	1728	1748	1854**q**	1907	|	1949	2048	2121
Marmande d.	|	|	|	1148	1150	|	|	|	|	|	|	1550	1701	|	|	|	|	1804	|	|	|	|	|	|	2150
Bordeaux St Jean a.	0858	1026	1058	1228	1230	1358	1400	1430	1554	1557	1554	1630	1747	1754	1807	1818	1828	1850	1854	1958	2012	1958	2054	2154	2230
*Paris Montparnasse **300*** a.	1112	...	1313§	...	...	1613	...	...	1813	1821	1813	...	...	2013	2033	2043	...	...	2113	...	...	2213	2313‡	0013	...

Other local TER services **BORDEAUX - AGEN**

	①	⑥	①–⑤	Ⓐ	Ⓐ	⑥ k	⑦	①–⑥	Ⓐ	Ⓑ h
Bordeaux St Jean d.	0553	0623	0623	0710	1310	1352	1410	1510	1610	1710
Marmande d.	0641	0721	0729	0758	1358	1500	1458	1558	1658	1758
Agen a.	0716	0801	0804	0834	1434	1535	1534	1634	1734	1834

	Ⓐ	⑥ k	Ⓐ	Ⓐ	⑦	①–⑥	⑦	Ⓐ	⑥	Ⓑ h	①–⑥	⑦	⑦
Agen d.	0528	0608	0630	0726	0828	0928	1028	1128	1306	1328	1828	1928	2028
Marmande d.	0603	0644	0705	0802	0904	1004	1104	1204	1342	1404	1904	2004	2104
Bordeaux St Jean a.	0650	0750	0752	0848	0950	1050	1150	1250	1445	1450	1950	2050	2150

FOR NOTES SEE TABLE 321 BELOW

TOULOUSE - CARCASSONNE - NARBONNE 321

Timings of long-distance services may vary by a few minutes until July 5 (please check your seat reservation). *TGV / INTERCITÉS* services are subject to alteration on Oct. 26, 27, Nov. 2, 9 – 11.

km		★ 4651 Ⓐ	3731 ■ 🅁	⚒	*TGV* 6859	Ⓒ R		★ 4655 Ⓐ	★ 4653 ⑥	★ 4653 ⑦	Ⓐ	★ 4657		★ 4659 ⊖	Ⓒ	*TGV* 6861	★ 4661	★ 4663	M	*TGV* 6857	Ⓐ	★ 4665 Ⓑ	★ 4667 ⑥ N	Ⓐ	★ 4669 Ⓑ N
	*Paris Austerlitz **310*** d.	...	2208	...	...	...	...	...	...	...	...	...	...	...	...	...	...	...	...	...	...	...	...	...	...
	*Bordeaux **320*** ⊠ d.	...	|	...	...	...	...	0634	...	...	...	0832	...	1030	...	...	1232**z**	1432	...	...	...	1630	1630	...	1832
0	**Toulouse** Matabiau d.	0648	|	0715	0741	0755	0811**d**	0853	0853	0853	0915	1048	1115	1248	1315	1443	1448	1648	1658	1750	1755	1848	1848	1855	2048
55	Castelnaudary d.	|	0711	0755	|	0842	0905	|	|	|	0956	|	1156	|	1405	|	|	|	1737	|	1836	|	|	1936	|
91	**Carcassonne** d.	0733	0735	0817	0824	0905	0927	0939	0939	0939	1018	|	1218	1333	1427	1527	1533	|	1759	1834	1858	1933	1933	1958	2133
128	Lézignan d.	|	0754	0835	|	0923	0945	|	|	|	1036	|	1235	|	1445	|	|	|	1816	|	1916	|	|	2016	|
150	**Narbonne** a.	0801	|	0848	0852	0935	0957	1012	1012	1007	1048	|	1248	1401	1457	1554	1601	|	1829	1901	1928	2001	2001	2028	2201
	*Montpellier Sud-de-F **355*** a.	|	|	...	|	|	...	|	|	|	|	1249	|	|	...	|	|	1849	|	|	|	|	|	...	|
	*Montpellier St Roch **355*** a.	0900	|	...	0949	|	...	1111	1111	1111	|	|	|	1500	...	1653	1700	|	1931	1959	|	2100	2100	...	2300**j**
	*Marseille St Charles **355*** a.	1042	|	...	|	|	...	1254	1254	1254	|	1426	|	1642	...	|	1904	2037	...	|	|	2242	...	...	...
	*Lyon Part Dieu **350*** a.	...	|	...	1144**p**	|	...	...	...	...	|	...	|	...	...	1901**p**	...	...	...	2150**p**	|	...	...	...	...
	*Perpignan **355*** ◇ a.	...	0849	...	...	1023	...	...	...	...	1140	...	1340	...	...	...	...	...	...	...	2011	...	...	...	...
	*Cerbère **355*** ◇ a.	...	0938	...	...	1101	...	...	...	...	...	...	...	...	...	...	...	...	...	...	...	...	...	...	...
	*Portbou **355*** ◇ a.	...	0947	...	...	...	...	...	...	...	...	...	...	...	...	...	...	...	...	...	...	...	...	...	...

	★ 4752 Ⓐ N	⚒ N	w	★ 4756 Ⓐ ⊗	★ 4754 Ⓒ N	*TGV* 6809	★ 4758 ⑥	★ 4758 Ⓑ ⊙		★ 4760	★ 4762	*TGV* 6811 Ⓒ	*TGV* 6811 Ⓐ		★ 4764 ⚒	★ 4764 †	L N		★ 4766 Ⓑ	★ 4768 ⑥	Ⓒ R◇	S	3730 ■ 🅁	★ 4770 Ⓑ	*TGV* 6817
*Cerbère **355*** ◇ d.	...	...	0637	...	...	...	...	...	...	...	...	...	...	1437**v**	...	...	...	...	...	...	1726	...	1910	...	...
*Perpignan **355*** ◇ d.	...	...	0721	...	...	...	...	...	...	...	...	...	...	1521	...	...	...	...	...	...	1806	...	2000	...	...
*Lyon Part Dieu **350*** d.	...	...	|	...	...	0706	...	...	...	...	...	1138**x**	1210	|	...	...	...	...	...	...	|	...	|	...	1807**p**
*Marseille St Charles **355*** d.	...	...	|	0614	...	|	0818	0834	...	1018**t**	1214	|	|	|	1418	1418	...	...	1614	1618	|	...	|	1818	|
*Montpellier St Roch **355*** d.	0608**g**	0619	|	0758	0758	0900	|	|	...	1158	1358	1352	1408	|	|	|	1620**y**	...	1758•	1758	|	...	|	1958	2008
*Montpellier Sud-de-F **355*** d.	|	|	|	|	|	|	0944	1005	...	|	|	|	|	|	1547	1547	|	...	|	|	|	...	|	|	|
Narbonne d.	0658	0732	0812	0858	0858	0958	|	|	1232	1300	|	1449	1504	1612	|	|	1732	1803	1858	1859	1904	1917	|	2058	2105
Lézignan d.	|	0745	0825	|	|	|	|	|	1245	|	|	|	|	1625	|	|	1745	1816	|	|	1917	1930	2046	|	|
Carcassonne d.	0730	0804	0846	0930	0930	1029	|	|	1304	1330	|	1520	1535	1646	|	|	1805	1835	1930	1930	1936	1949	2107	2130	2136
Castelnaudary d.	|	0825	0906	|	|	|	|	|	1325	|	|	|	|	1706	|	|	1825	1856	|	|	1955	2010	2127	|	|
Toulouse Matabiau a.	0814	0905	0945	1014	1014	1110	1152	1210	1405	1414	1614	1603	1617	1745	1749	1749	1905**o**	1945	2014	2014	2033	2059	|	2214	2217
*Bordeaux **320*** ⊠ a.	1026	...	...	1228	1230	...	1400	1430	...	1630	1828	...	...	...	1958	2012	...	...	2230	...	...	...	|	...	...
*Paris Austerlitz **310*** a.	...	...	...	...	...	...	...	...	...	...	...	...	...	...	...	...	...	...	...	...	...	...	0652	...	...

OTHER LOCAL TRAINS

	Ⓐ	Ⓐ			Ⓒ	Ⓐ	Ⓐ w	Ⓐ	Ⓒ	
Toulouse Matabiau d.	...	0615	0657	...	...	1015	1215	1555	1815	1958
Castelnaudary d.	0555	0705	0738	...	...	1105	1305	1636	1905	2048
Carcassonne d.	0617	0727	0758	...	1113	1127	1327	1658	1927	2109
Lézignan d.	0635	0744	...	...	1132	1145	1345	1716	1945	...
Narbonne a.	0647	0757	...	...	1145	1157	1357	1728	1957	...

	Ⓐ		Ⓐ	Ⓐ	Ⓐ w	Ⓒ		Ⓐ	Ⓒ	Ⓐ
Narbonne d.	...	...	0632	0703	0910	1010**n**	...	1510	...	1631
Lézignan d.	...	...	0645	0716	0923	1023	...	1523	...	1644
Carcassonne d.	0602	0635	0704	0735	0943	1042	1202	1542	1550	1709
Castelnaudary d.	0624	0656	0725	0756	...	...	1224	1603	1611	1733
Toulouse Matabiau a.	0704	0745	0804	0845	...	...	1304	1652	1701	1822

A – ①–④ to July 4 / from Sept. 2 (not June 10, Oct. 31, Nov. 11).
B – ⑤–⑦ to June 30 (also June 10); daily July 5 - Sept. 1; ⑤–⑦ from Sept. 6 (also Oct. 31, Nov. 11).
D – Ⓑ (not Nov. 1); runs daily June 30 - Sept. 6.
E – Ⓐ to July 5.
F – ⑤ (also Oct. 31; not Nov. 1); runs daily July 5 - Sept. 1.
L – Ⓐ (daily July 1 - Sept. 6).
M – To Nîmes on Ⓒ / Avignon on Ⓐ (Table **355**).
N – To / from Nîmes (Table **355**).
R – Ⓒ June 29 - Sept. 1.
S – Daily to July 6; Ⓐ July 8 - Aug. 30; daily from Sept. 2.
T – Daily to July 7; Ⓒ from July 13 (also Aug. 16).
Y – Ⓑ to July 7; ⑤⑦ July 12 - Aug. 25 (also Aug. 14; not Aug. 16); Ⓑ from Aug. 30 (not Nov. 1, 18 – 22, 25 – 29).

b – Not June 10, Nov. 11.
c – Also June 10, Nov. 1, 11.
d – 0815 on ⑥⑦.
e – Also June 10, Nov. 11.
f – Also Aug. 14, Oct. 31; not Aug. 16, Nov. 1.
g – Ⓐ to Sept. 30; ① from Oct. 7 (not Nov. 11).
h – Not Aug. 15.
j – Ⓑ to July 14; ⑦ from July 21 (also Aug. 16).
k – Also Aug. 15.
n – 1008 on ⑦ July 7 - Sept. 1.
o – 1858 on ⑤ (also Aug. 14, Oct. 31).
p – Lyon **Perrache**.
q – ⑥ only.
r – 0642 on ①–⑤ Sept. 16 - Oct. 4.
s – Calls to set down only.
t – 1013 on Sept. 28, 29.
v – ⚒ only.
w – Not Nov. 18 – 22, 25 – 29.
x – Lyon **Perrache** (from Lyon Part-Dieu d. 1150 on ⑥ to June 29). Departs 1150 on †.
y – Ⓐ only.
z – 1230 on ⑥.

TGV – 🅁, supplement payable, 🍷.

‡ – 2316 on ①–④ to Aug. 29 (not Aug. 14, 15).
§ – 1317 on ⑦.
⊗ – Not Nov. 18 – 29.
⊙ – Not July 8 – 12, 15 – 19, 22 – 26.
⊖ – Not ①–⑤ Nov. 18 - Dec. 6.
◇ – Runs 2 – 5 minutes later Lezignan - Toulouse on June 29, July 6, Aug. 31. Runs 21 – 31 minutes later throughout on June 30, Sept. 1.
• – June 10 – 23 and Aug. 1 – 25 service is diverted via Montpellier Sud-de-France, d. 1756 (not Saint-Roch).
★ – *INTERCITÉS*. 🅁.
⊠ – From July 6. OUIGO low-cost TGV service. Internet bookings only at www.ouigo.com.
■ – *INTERCITÉS DE NUIT*. **Timings may vary.** Overnight journeys only. For days of running and confirmed timings please consult the SNCF journey planner: www.oui.sncf/billet-train

323 TOULOUSE - ALBI - RODEZ

km																									
		Ⓐ				⊗	A⊗	⊗		Ⓐ⊗	⊗	⊗			Ⓐ		Ⓐ	Ⓐ		Ⓑ	†	⚒		
0	**Toulouse** Matabiau .... **317** d.	0606	...	0727	...	0917	1005	1116	...	1231	1307	1411	...	1637	1712	1736	1752	1815	1837	1914	1914	1928	...	2123
54	Gaillac .... **317** d.	0647	...	0811	...	1004	1050	1158	...	1320	1357	1459	...	1726	1757	1822	1842	1906	1922	2004	2004	2020	...	2209
75	**Albi Ville** .... d.	0703	...	0825	...	1024	1104	1217	...	1341	1416	1513	...	1745	1819	1836	1901	1925	1936	2028	2029	2039	...	2230
92	Carmaux .... d.	0721	...	0843	...	1041	1122	1234	...	1357	1433	1530	...	1802	...	1854	1918	...	1954	...	2046	2056	...	2246
158	**Rodez** .... a.	0823	...	0946	...	...	1221	1336	...	...	...	1632	...	...	...	1957	...	...	2054	...	2145	2155	...	...

	Ⓐ	⚒	Ⓐ		Ⓐ	⚒⊗	†	⊗		⊗	⊗		Ⓐ⊗		Ⓐ					Ⓐ			†	⚒
Rodez .... d.	...	...	...	...	0621	0739	...	0833	...	1023	...	...	1224	...	...	1431	...	...	1635	1727	1844	...	2101	2111
Carmaux .... d.	0520	0557	0616	0644	0722	0844	0844	0933	...	1123	1144	...	1322	...	1454	1531	...	1649	1734	1825	1955	...	2210	2212
Albi Ville .... d.	0538	0615	0634	0704	0742	0903	0903	0951	...	1141	1201	...	1342	...	1514	1549	...	1707	1754	1845	2012	...	2231	2231
Gaillac .... **317** d.	0556	0633	0656	0725	0756	0919	0919	1004	...	1158	1222	...	1357	...	1533	1602	...	1726	1808	1906	2032	...	2244	2244
Toulouse Matabiau .... **317** a.	0646	0720	0743	0820	0836	1000	1000	1044	...	1237	1310	...	1436	...	1619	1641	...	1818	1850	1954	2118	...	2324	2324

A – ①⑤ (also June 11).

⊗ – Subject to alteration on ①–⑤ Nov. 18 - Dec. 6.

324 PAU - OLORON - CANFRANC

SERVICE JUNE 11 - SEPTEMBER 1 (subject to alteration on July 19)

km																							
		🚌		🚌			🚌		Ⓐ t			🚌		n	🚌			🚌					
0	**Pau** .... d.	...	0715	...	...	0920	...	...	1222	...	1352	...	...	1520	...	...	1740	...	...	1906	...	2029	...
36	Oloron-Ste-Marie .... d.	0700	0751	...	...	0956	...	...	1257	...	1428	...	...	1556	...	...	1816	...	...	1942	...	2105	...
61	Bedous (Gare) .... d.	0733	0821	0850	...	1026	1035	...	...	...	1458	1510	...	1626	1640	...	1846	1855	...	2012	...	...	...
77	Urdos (Douane) 🏛 .... d.	0758	...	0913	...	...	1100	...	...	...	...	1535	...	...	1710	...	...	1920	...	...	...	...	...
96	**Canfranc** (Gare) .... **670** a.	0829	...	0946	...	...	1131	...	...	...	...	1553	...	...	1723	...	...	1938	...	...	...	...	...

	①–⑥				🚌			🚌	r		Ⓐ		🚌			🚌			🚌			🚌	
Canfranc (Gare) .... **670** d.	...	...	...	...	0830	...	...	1140	...	...	...	...	1420	...	...	1600	...	...	1725	...	...	1945	...
Urdos (Douane) 🏛 .... d.	...	...	...	...	0847	...	...	1157	...	...	...	...	1450	...	...	1630	...	...	1755	...	...	2015	...
Bedous (Gare) .... d.	...	...	0722	...	0913	0927	...	1223	1229	...	...	...	1516	1527	...	1656	1747	...	1821	1913	...	2041	...
Oloron-Ste-Marie .... d.	0629	...	0755	...	...	1000	...	...	1302	...	1432	...	...	1600	...	...	1820	...	...	1946	...	2117	...
Pau .... a.	0705	...	0831	...	...	1036	...	...	1338	...	1508	...	...	1636	...	...	1856	...	...	2022	...	...	...

n – Not June 15, 22, 29, July 6.
r – Not June 19.
t – Also June 15, 22, 29, July 6; not June 19.

325 TOULOUSE - TARBES - PAU - BAYONNE

SERVICE UNTIL SEPTEMBER 29. Warning! Until July 21 certain timings vary by up to 6 minutes (earlier departures possible).
Services Pau - Bayonne and v.v. are subject to alteration Aug. 23 – 26.

km																									
		⊖	⊖		⊖		**14141**		**14143**				**14151**	⊖				**14155**	⊖						
		Ⓐ	①–⑥	Ⓐ						Ⓐ	⑤	Ⓒ		Ⓐ	⑤	Ⓐ	Ⓒ				Ⓐ	Ⓒ	Ⓐ	⑤†	E
			r		B		⊗				f				f				D					f	
0	**Toulouse** Matabiau .... d.	...	...	0630**b**	...	0730	0833	0930	1035	1241	1241	1330	1433	...	1441	1526	1526**t**	1633	...	1730	1830	1830	1930	2030	2030
91	St Gaudens .... d.	...	...	0733	...	0835	|	1029	1128	1356	1356	1429	1527	...	1556	1631	1631	|	...	1830	1931	1930	2035	2131	2133
104	Montréjeau .... d.	...	...	0742	...	0845	0935	1039	|	1406	1406	1439	|	...	1607	1641	1641	|	...	1839	1941	1940	2044	2140	2143
121	Lannemezan .... d.	...	...	0754	...	0857	|	1051	|	1418	1418	1451	|	...	1619	1654	1654	1746	...	1851	1953	1953	2056	2152	2156
158	**Tarbes** .... **305** d.	...	0616	0822	...	0922	1014	1118	1213	1445	1447	1520	1610	...	1641	1724	1724	1814	1845	1920	2019	2021	2121	2218	2222
179	Lourdes .... **305** d.	...	0632	0837**y**	...	...	1031	...	1231	...	1503	1538**k**	1629	...	...	1740	1743	1831	1901	1951	...	2036	2139	2233	...
218	**Pau** .... **305** d.	0605	0706	0906**y**	0916	...	1059	...	1258	...	1530	1609**k**	1655	1719	...	1808	1813	1859	1936	2022	...	2107	2210	...	...
258	Orthez .... **305** d.	0630	0732	...	0942	...	1124	...	1322	...	...	...	1719	1745	...	...	...	1924	2003	...	...	...	...	...	...
272	Puyoô .... **305** d.	0641	0743	...	0952	...	|	...	|	...	...	...	|	1755	...	...	...	|	2014	...	...	...	...	...	...
323	**Bayonne** § .... a.	0723	0822	...	1031	...	1206	...	1405**c**	...	...	...	1805	1832	...	...	...	2006	2101**v**	...	...	...	...	...	...

						⊖	**14140**	⊖		**14142**							**14148**		**14150**		⊖	⊖	⊖	⊖	⊖
	Ⓐ	⑥	Ⓐ	Ⓒ	Ⓐ	Ⓐ		①–⑥			Ⓒ	Ⓐ	†		⑤	Ⓐ				Ⓒ	Ⓐ	⑦			Ⓒ
								rw							f		⊙					G	H	A	G
Bayonne § .... d.	...	...	...	...	...	0601	0653	0731	...	1056	...	...	...	...	...	...	1455	...	1653**z**	...	1734	1810	1839	1850	2010
Puyoô .... **305** d.	...	...	...	...	...	0637	|	0811	...	|	...	...	...	...	...	...	|	...	|	...	1820	1846	1916	1927	2050
Orthez .... **305** d.	...	...	...	...	...	0648	0739	0821	...	1140	...	...	...	...	...	...	1538	...	1739**z**	...	1831	1857	1927	1938	2102
Pau .... **305** d.	...	...	0552	0656	...	0720	0805	0846	0952**x**	1205	...	1257	...	...	1545	...	1604	1656**a**	1806**z**	1852	1855	1922	1951	2003	2133
Lourdes .... **305** d.	0523**g**	0621	0623	0725	...	0753	0832	...	1023**x**	1232	...	1325	...	...	1613	...	1631	1724**a**	1833**z**	1923	1929	1955	2024	...	2208
Tarbes .... **305** d.	0542	0637	0639	0742	0816	0810	0854	...	1042	1254	1340	1342	1438	1539	1629	1629	1651	1741	1854	1942	1945	2012	2041	...	2225
Lannemezan .... d.	0610	0703	0706	0809	0843	...	|	...	1110	|	1406	1410	1504	1605	1654	1654	|	1809	1919	2010	...	...	...	...	...
Montréjeau .... d.	0622	0714	0719	0821	0855	...	|	...	1122	1329	1418	1422	1516	1617	1706	1706	|	1821	|	2022	...	...	...	...	...
St Gaudens .... d.	0632	0724	0729	0831	0904	...	0937	...	1133	|	1428	1432	1526	1627	1716	1716	1734	1830	|	2032	...	...	...	...	...
Toulouse Matabiau .... a.	0730	0830	0830	0930	1021	...	1030	...	1230	1427	1530	1530	1630	1730	1819	1819	1827	1933	2029	2130	...	...	...	...	...

🚌 MONTRÉJEAU - LUCHON

	🚌	🚌	🚌	🚌	🚌	🚌		🚌	🚌	🚌	🚌
	⑥	Ⓐ	⚒			†		⑥	Ⓐ		
Montréjeau .... d.	0727	0732	0800	0940	1132	1337	...	1622	1628	1846	2051
Luchon .... a.	0815	0820	0848	1030	1220	1425	...	1710	1716	1935	2139

	🚌	🚌	🚌	🚌	🚌	🚌	🚌	🚌	🚌	🚌	🚌	🚌
	⑥	Ⓐ	⚒		Ⓐ	†	⚒	⚒	Ⓒ	⑥	Ⓐ	†
Luchon .... d.	0617	0622	0848	0937	1056	1228	1455	1605	1704	1736	1800	1953
Montréjeau .... d.	0707	0712	0938	1027	1147	1318	1545	1655	1755	1826	1850	2043

A – Ⓐ to July 5; ①–④ July 8 - Aug. 29 (not Aug. 14, 15); Ⓐ from Sept. 2.
B – Ⓑ (not June 17 – 21, 24 – 28) to July 5; daily July 7 - Sept. 6; Ⓑ from Sept. 8.
D – ⑤† to June 30; Ⓑ July 5 - Sept. 1 (not Aug. 15); ⑤† from Sept. 6.
On June 16, 23, 30 and ①–④ July 18 - Aug. 29 (not Aug. 14) Tarbes d. 1840, Lourdes d. 1856, Pau d. 1933, Orthez d. 2001, Puyoô d. 2012, Bayonne a. 2052.
E – ①②③④⑥ (not June 10, Aug. 14, 15).
G – July 7 - Sept. 1.
H – Ⓒ to July 6; ⑤ July 12 - Aug. 30 (also Aug. 14); Ⓒ from Sept. 7.

a – Ⓐ only.
b – 0609 July 15 - Aug. 30.
c – 1423 on ①–⑤ June 17 – 28.
f – Also Aug. 14.
g – ① (also June 11; not June 10).
k – ⑥ only.

r – Not June 10.
t – 1530 on †.
v – 2058 on ⑤ (also Aug. 14).
w – Not June 17 – 21, 24 – 28.
x – Not June 17 – 21, 24 – 28, Sept. 16 – 20, 23 – 27.
y – Does not run Tarbes - Pau June 17 – 28.
z – Not June 10 – 14.

⊗ – Does not run Tarbes - Bayonne June 10 – 14, Sept. 16 – 20, 23 – 27 (Toulouse d. 0833, Montréjeau d. 0932, Tarbes a. 1006).
⊙ – On ①–⑤ June 10 – 28 and ①–⑤ Sept. 16 – 27 Bayonne d. 1425, Orthez d. 1539, Pau d. 1606, Lourdes d. 1635, Tarbes d. 1654, St Gaudens d. 1737, Toulouse a. 1827.
⊖ – Subject to confirmation from Sept. 2.
§ – 🚌 service available to / from Biarritz town.

BRIVE LA GAILLARD and LIMOGES - USSEL - CLERMONT FERRAND 326

BRIVE - USSEL *Service until September 1*

km		Ⓐ	⑦	⑥	⑦	Ⓐ	⑦	①–⑥	⑦	⑤
			e	k	e		e	b	e	f
	Bordeaux 302 d.	...	...	0828	...	...	...	...	...	1654c
0	**Brive la Gaillarde** ◨ d.	0609	0950	1106	1323	1633	1711	1803	1832	1925	1939
26	Tulle ◨ d.	0648	1025	1138	1357	1705	1748	1834	1914	2002	2011
79	Meymac d.	0748	1127	1238	1458	1814	1850	1936	2021	2107	2112
92	**Ussel** a.	0801	1139	1250	1511	1827	1902	1948	2033	2119	2124

	Ⓐ	⑥		⑦	⑤	⑤	①–④	⑤⑦	⑥	Ⓑ
		k		e	f	fP	m	s	k	h
Ussel d.	0533	0939	1224	1546	1546	1628	1628	1708	1708	2007
Meymac d.	0546	0952	1240	1559	1600	1641	1641	1721	1721	2020
Tulle ◨ d.	0653	1058	1352	1707	1707	1746	1747	1829	1829	2128z
Brive la Gaillarde ◨ a.	0722	1126	1422	1733	1733	1808	1816	1857	1857	2155z
Bordeaux 302 a.	...	...	...	2006	...	...	...	2130	...	...

LIMOGES - USSEL *Service June 11 - September 1*

km				①–④	⑤–⑦					Ⓐ	Ⓑ
		G		H	d		w				h
0	**Limoges** d.	0555	...	1000	1008	...	1303	...	1811	1911	2114
98	Meymac d.	0733	...	1136	1143	...	1438	...	1951	2047	2241
111	**Ussel** a.	0746	...	1148	1155	...	1451	...	2003	2100	2253

	Ⓐ	⑥		①–④	⑤–⑦				⑤⑦	
		k	L	H	d	N	w		y	
Ussel d.	0633	0703	0813	1034	1042	1204	1254	...	1603	1801
Meymac d.	0646	0716	0826	1047	1055	1217	1307	...	1616	1814
Limoges a.	0822	0850	1000	1224	1230	1348	1445	...	1749	1953

🚌 USSEL and LE MONT DORE - CLERMONT FERRAND 🚌

	🚌	🚌		🚌	🚌		🚌	🚌		🚌	🚌	🚌	🚌		🚌		🚌	🚌		🚌		🚌	🚌		🚌
	①	①–⑥		①–⑥	①–⑥		†				Ⓑ	①–⑥	⑥				Ⓒ					⑤	⑤		Ⓑ
	g	b		b	b					F	h	b	k		E							t	t		h
Ussel d.	0537	...	...	0818	...	...	1008	...	...	...	1204	...	1300	...	...	...	1521	...	...	...	...	...	1915	...	2042
Le Mont Dore d.	|	0559	...	|	0840	...	|	1042	...	1215	|	1307	|	...	1447	...	|	1541	...	1747	...	1927	|	...	|
Laqueuille d.	0617	0622	...	0858	0903	...	1048	1105	...	1239	1244	1332	1340	...	1511	...	1600	1605	...	1810	...	1950	1955	...	2122
Clermont Ferrand a.	...	0722	...	...	1003	...	...	1205	...	...	1344	1432	1440	...	...	...	...	1705	...	1915	...	...	2055	...	2222

	🚌	🚌	🚌		🚌	🚌	🚌	🚌	🚌	🚌	🚌	🚌	🚌	🚌		🚌	🚌	🚌	🚌		🚌	🚌		🚌	🚌
			①–⑥					⑦	⑥	Ⓐ	⑤†		①–⑥	①–⑥			①–⑥				Ⓐ	⑤		⑤	⑤
			b		E			e	k		u	D	b	b		J	b					t		t	t
Clermont Ferrand d.	1010	...	1045	...	...	1246	...	...	...	...	1416	...	1517	...	...	1645	1742	1804	...	...	1948	...	...	2126	...
Laqueuille d.	1110	1115	1145	...	1252	1346	1351	1351	1419	1436	1516	1529	1617	1627	...	1745	1842	1904	1909	...	2048	2053	...	2226	2231
Le Mont Dore a.	|	1141	1210	...	1318	...	1415	|	|	|	|	1556	|	1654	...	1812	1909	|	1936	...	2115	|	...	...	2258
Ussel a.	1150	...	...	...	...	...	...	1431	1458	1516	1556	...	1657	...	...	...	...	1944	...	...	...	2131	...	...	...

D – ⑤† to June 30; Ⓑ July 5 - Sept. 1; ⑤† from Sept. 6 (also Oct. 21 – 24, 28 – 31).
E – ⑤† to June 30; Ⓑ July 5 - Sept. 1; ⑤⑦ from Sept. 6 (also Oct. 21 – 24, 28 – 31; not Nov. 1).
F – ⑤ to July 5; Ⓐ July 8 - Aug. 30; ⑤ from Sept. 6 (also Oct. 21 – 24, 28 – 31; not Nov. 1).
G – Runs on June 11, 17, 24, July 1 only.
H – ①–④ to Aug. 22 (not Aug. 14, 15).
J – July 6 - Sept. 1.
L – ① to July 1 (also June 11); Ⓐ July 8 - Aug. 23.
N – ①②③④⑥ (not Aug. 14, 26 – 29).
P – To Perigueux (a. 1913).

b – Not June 10, Nov. 11.
c – 1628 July 12 - Aug. 30.
d – Not Aug. 30; also Aug. 14, 15.
e – Also June 10, Nov. 11.
f – Also Aug. 14.
g – Also June 11, Nov. 12; not June 10, July 8 - Aug. 26, Nov. 11.
h – Not Aug. 15, Nov. 1.
k – Also Aug. 15, Nov. 1.
m – Not June 10, Aug. 14, 15.
s – Also June 10, Aug. 14.
t – Also Aug. 14, Oct. 31; not Nov. 1.
u – Also Aug. 14, Oct. 31.
w – Not Aug. 26 – 30.
y – Also Aug. 14; not Aug. 30.
z – 5 minutes later on ⑤ (also Aug. 14).

◨ – Additional local trains run Brive - Tulle and v.v.

CLERMONT FERRAND - LYON and ST ÉTIENNE 328

Timings of services from / to Clermont Ferrand may vary by up to 3 minutes until Sept. 1.

km		Ⓐ	①–⑥		Ⓐ	①–⑥	⑦	①–⑥	①–⑥	①–⑥	Ⓐ							Ⓐ	⑦	①–⑥	Ⓑ			Ⓑ	⑦
			b			b	e	b	b	b	⊗		⊗						e	b	h			h	w
0	**Clermont Ferrand** 329 330 d.	...	...	...	...	...	...	...	0658	...	0757	...	0856	...	...	1201	1354	1501	1501	...	...	1702	...	1804	1957
14	Riom-Châtel-Guyon 329 330 d.	...	...	...	...	...	...	...	0707	...	0807	...	0906	...	...	1210	1403	1510	1510	...	...	1712	...	1814	2007
55	Vichy 330 d.	...	...	...	...	...	...	...	0732	...	0833	...	0931	...	...	1235	1425	1533	1534	...	...	1735	...	1835	2029
129	Roanne 290 d.	0536	0550	0619	0633	0719	0722	0736	0817	0836	0920	0936	1017	1136	1250	1321	1512	1619	1619	1650	1750	1821	1850	1921	2118
171	Tarare d.	0609	0630	0654	0708	0754	0802	0809	0848	0909	0951	1009	1047	1209	1330	1352	1543	1648	1648	1730	1830	1856	1930	1952	2148
222	**Lyon** Part Dieu 290 a.	|	|	0735	|	0835	0852	|	0922	|	1026	|	1120	|	|	1426	1617	1726	|	|	|	1934	|	2026	2222
227	**Lyon** Perrache 290 a.	0653	0724	0748	0753	0851	0903	0853	0935	0953	1039	1053	1131	1253	1424	1437	1628	...	1728	1824	1924	1948	2024	2037	2233
	Lyon Part Dieu a.	0705	...	...	0807	...	...	...	...	1007	...	1105a	...	1305a	...	...	...	...	...	...	...	...	...	...	...

	①–⑥		①–⑥					Ⓐ		Ⓐ	⑥			Ⓐ	①–⑥					Ⓐ	Ⓐ		Ⓑ		
	b		b		⊙						k				b								h		
Lyon Part Dieu d.	...	...	0751	0955b	...	1154c	...	...	...	1455	...	...	...	...	1654	...	...	1755	...	...	1855	...	1955a	...	2054
Lyon Perrache 290 d.	0632	0658	0805	1007	1132	1207	1236	1400	1427	1507	1507	1607	1625	1636	1707	1726	1736	1807	1826	1836	1907	1936	2007	2026	2107
Lyon Part Dieu 290 d.	|	|	|	|	1143	|	|	|	1439	|	|	|	1638	|	|	1738	|	|	1838	|	|	|	|	2038	|
Tarare d.	0710	0752	0849	1050	1216	1250	1331	1457	1513	1550	1550	1650	1713	1731	1753	1812	1831	1851	1914	1932	1951	2031	2051	2113	2151
Roanne 290 d.	0741	0830	0923	1123	1251	1324	1409	1536	1545	1624	1626	1723	1747	1809	1827	1844	1909	1926	1947	2010	2026	2109	2126	2144	2226
Vichy 330 d.	0823	...	...	...	1337	...	...	...	1630	...	...	...	1831	...	...	1930	...	...	2033	...	...	...	...	2231	...
Riom-Châtel-Guyon 329 330 d.	0848	...	...	...	1400	...	...	...	1655	...	...	...	1858	...	...	1952	...	...	2056	...	...	...	...	2254	...
Clermont Ferrand 329 330 a.	0857	...	...	...	1410	...	...	...	1706	...	...	...	1908	...	...	2002	...	...	2106	...	...	...	...	2303	...

🚌 CLERMONT FERRAND - ST ÉTIENNE 🚌

km		🚌	🚌	🚌		🚌	🚌	🚌		🚌	
							⑦	⑤			
							e	v			
0	**Clermont Ferrand** d.	0720	0925	1051	...	1450	1654	1715	...	1920	...
145	**St Étienne** Châteaucreux a.	0940	1110	1420	...	1635	2008	1954	...	2105	...

	🚌		🚌	🚌	🚌		🚌	🚌	🚌
					⑤		⑦	①–⑥	
					v		e	b	
St Étienne Châteaucreux d.	0720	...	1020	1216	1320	...	1715	1720	1800
Clermont Ferrand a.	0905	...	1205	1530	1615	...	1900	1905	2132

a – Ⓐ only.
b – ①–⑥ (not June 10, Nov. 11).
c – 1153 on ①–⑤ June 11 - July 5.
e – Also June 10, Nov. 11.
h – Not Aug. 15, Nov. 1.
k – Also Aug. 15, Nov. 1.
v – Also Oct. 31; not July 19 - Aug. 23, Nov. 1.
w – Also June 10, Nov. 11; not June 9, Nov. 10.
⊗ – Subject to alteration Oct. 28 – 31, Nov. 4 – 8, 12 – 15.
⊙ – Subject to alteration Oct. 21 – 24, 28 – 31, Nov. 1, 4 – 8, 12 – 15.

MONTLUÇON - CLERMONT FERRAND 329

km		①–⑥	Ⓐ	Ⓐ		Ⓐ		🚌	Ⓑ		⑦
		b			E	z	z	A	h		w
0	**Montluçon 327** d.	...	0601	0700	0828	1042	1223	1223	1700	1843	1936
13	Commentry d.	...	0612	0711	0840	1053	1236	1248	1713	1856	1948
67	Gannat **327** d.	0706	0706	0803	0926	1139	1329	1351	1804	1949	2043
94	Riom-Châtel-Guyon ▷ d.	0729	0729	0824	0941	1158	1348	1427	1831	2009	2102
108	**Clermont Ferrand** ▷ a.	0742	0742	0834	0951	1207	1358	1452	1840	2019	2111

	Ⓐ	①			①–⑥	Ⓑ	①–⑥	Ⓑ	⑤	⑦
		g	z		bz	h	b	h	t	e
Clermont Ferrand ▷ d.	0604	0635	0747	...	1218	1648	1746	1910	2004	2012
Riom-Châtel-Guyon ▷ d.	0614	0644	0801	...	1230	1701	1758	1922	2015	2022
Gannat **327** d.	0631	0707	0821	...	1250	1727	1825	1950	2034	2044
Commentry d.	0722	0811	0910	...	1345	1821	1916	2040	2124	2134
Montluçon 327 a.	0734	0823	0921	...	1356	1832	1927	2051	2135	2145

A – ①–⑤ Sept. 23 - Oct. 11.
E – ①⑥⑦ (also June 11, Aug. 15, Nov. 1, 12).

b – Not June 10, Nov. 11.
e – Also June 10, Nov. 11.
g – Also June 11, Nov. 12; not June 10, Nov. 11.
h – Not Aug. 15, Nov. 1.
t – Also Aug. 14, Oct. 31; not Nov. 1.
w – Also June 10, Nov. 11; not June 9, Nov. 10.
z – Not ①–⑤ Sept. 23 - Oct. 11.

▷ – See also Tables **328** and **330**.

330 PARIS - NEVERS - CLERMONT FERRAND

Certain southbound timings Nevers - Moulins - Clermont Ferrand vary by up to 5 minutes from Sept. 2. Certain northbound *INTERCITÉS* (★) timings may vary by up to 8 minutes Aug. 12–30 and by up to 11 minutes from Sept. 2. Timings of northbound *TER* (regional) services Clermont Ferrand - Moulins - Nevers may vary by 1–2 minutes from Sept. 2.

km							5951		5955				5959	5963			5967		5971	5973		5977	5979	5983	5981
							R★		R★				R★	R★			R★		R★	R★		R★	R★	R★	R★
		⚒	①–⑥	Ⓐ	①–⑥	Ⓑ	①–⑥	①–⑥		①–⑥	⚒	Ⓐ				Ⓐ	⑤	Ⓑ		Ⓐ	⑦	Ⓐ			⑤
			b		b		b	b♠		b	D⊙		⊗				f	d		J	s	J	L	H	v
0	**Paris** Bercy ▶ d.	...	...	...	...	...	0701	...	0901	...	...	...	1301	1401	...	...	1501	...	1601	1657	...	1757	1757	1857	1857
254	**Nevers** ⊡ ▶ d.	...	...	...	0700	...	0903	...	1104	...	...	...	1503	1603	...	...	1703	...	1803	1904	...	|	2004	2104	2104
314	Moulins sur Allier ⊡ d.	0602	0641	0714	0740	0817	0932	...	1133	1212	1306	1412	1532	1633	1640	1710	1733	1808	1832	1933	1939	|	2033	2133	2133
355	St Germain des Fossés ⊡ d.	0627	0709	0742	0807	0842	|	1138	|	1235	1335	1436	|	|	1706	1736	|	1836	|	|	2002	|	|	|	2154
365	Vichy ▷ d.	0637	0719	0752	0817	0851	1001	1148	1202	1247	1345	1446	1600	1701	1717	1748	1802	1847	1901	2003	2012	|	2102	2202	2205
406	Riom - Châtel-Guyon ▷ d.	0659	0742	0814	0839	0913	1024	1211	1225	1310	1407	1510	1624	1725	1740	1811	1825	1909	1925	2026	2034	|	2125	2225	2229
420	**Clermont Ferrand** ▷ a.	0707	0751	0823	0848	0922	1033	1223	1234	1319	1419	1519	1633	1733	1750	1821	1834	1918	1933	2035	2042	2114	2134	2234	2237

	5948	5950	5954		5958			5962		5966			5970	5974		5978			5982			5986		5990	
	R★	R★	R★		R★			R★		R★			R★	R★		R★			R★			R★		R★	
	①	②–⑤	Ⓐ	Ⓐ	⑥	Ⓐ	①–⑥		⑥	①–⑥	①–⑥	①–⑥		⑦	Ⓐ		Ⓐ	Ⓐ	Ⓑ	⑥	Ⓑ	⑦			
	g	p	J		t		b		k	b⊗	b	b		e					h‡	k	dD	e		❦	◇
Clermont Ferrand ▷ d.	0516	0519	0552	0612	0627	0641	0743	0827	0842	1022	1042	1242	1327	1427	1540	1629	1642	1712	1726	1741	1741	1827	1842	1931	2026
Riom - Châtel-Guyon ▷ d.	0527	0530	|	0621	0638	0651	0752	0838	0851	1033	1051	1251	1339	1438	1549	1640	1651	1721	1737	1750	1750	1838	1851	1942	2036
Vichy ▷ d.	0551	0555	|	0643	0701	0713	0815	0901	0913	1056	1114	1313	1402	1501	1611	1703	1713	1743	1802	1813	1813	1901	1913	2005	2058
St Germain des Fossés ⊡ d.	0601	|	|	0653	|	0723	0825	|	0924	|	1124	1324	|	|	1622	|	1724	1755	|	1823	1823	|	1924	|	2109
Moulins sur Allier ⊡ d.	0622	0622	|	0721	0729	0750	0848	0929	0949	1124	1151	1349	1430	1529	1648	1731	1750	1817	1831	1850	1850	1929	1950	2032	2132
Nevers ⊡ ▶ d.	0652	0652	|	0756	0758	...	0920	0958	...	1153	...	...	1458	1558	...	1759	...	...	1900	...	...	1958	...	2101	...
Paris Bercy ▶ a.	0858	0858	0903	...	0957	...	...	1159	...	1353z	...	...	1657	1757	...	1957	...	...	2057	...	...	2158	...	2257	...

ADDITIONAL TRAINS PARIS - NEVERS *(timings may vary by up to 5 minutes on certain dates)*

km			5901	5905		5909		5911	5915	5917	5919	5921
			Ⓐ			①–⑥		Ⓐ	Ⓐ	Ⓒ	Ⓐ	⑦
						bn						e
0	**Paris** Bercy d.	...	0711	0911	...	1411	...	1702	1802	1802	1902	2002
119	Montargis d.	...	0810	1011	...	1511	...	1809	1905	1905	2009	2106
155	Gien d.	...	0834	1033	...	1533	...	1832	1928	1926	2030	2128
196	Cosne d.	0736	0900	1100	1236	1559	1747	1900	1956	1954	2058	2156
228	La Charité d.	0801	0920	1119	1300	1618	1812	1916	2012	2013	2117	2212
254	**Nevers** a.	0825	0940	1139	1328	1638	1836	1937	2033	2033	2137	2233

	5900	5904	5906	5908			5910	5912	5914		5916	
	Ⓐ	Ⓐ	⑥	Ⓐ	Ⓐ	⑥		Ⓐ	⑦	⚒		
			k			◐			e			♥
Nevers d.	0453	0553	0622	0725	0835	0925	1022	1422	1622	1635	1821	1924
La Charité d.	0515	0615	0644	0747	0859	0948	1044	1444	1644	1659	1843	1951
Cosne d.	0532	0631	0704	0807	0924	1013	1104	1504	1704	1724	1902	2016
Gien d.	0556	0655	0728	0831	...	...	1128	1528	1728	...	1925	...
Montargis d.	0619	0719	0752	0855	...	...	1150	1552	1752	...	1951	...
Paris Bercy a.	0727	0827	0849	0952	...	...	1248	1649	1849	...	2049	...

D – From / to Dijon (Table **373**).
H – ①②③④⑥⑦ (also Aug. 16; not Aug. 14, Oct. 31). Subject to alteration on ①–④ June 17 - July 25.
J – To July 5 and from Aug. 26.
L – ⑦ to June 30 (also June 10); Ⓑ July 7 - Aug. 25 (not Aug. 15, 16); ⑦ from Sept. 1 (also Nov. 11).

b – Not June 10, Nov. 11.
d – Not Aug. 15, Nov. 1.
e – Also June 10, Nov. 11.
f – Also Aug. 14, Oct. 31; not Aug. 16, Nov. 1.
g – Also June 11, Nov. 12; not June 10, Nov. 11.
h – Not Aug. 15, 16, Nov. 1.
k – Also Aug. 15, Nov. 1.
n – Not June 24–27, July 1–4.
p – Not June 11, Aug. 15, 16, Nov. 1, 12.
s – Also June 10, Nov. 11; not June 9, Nov. 10.
t – Also Aug. 15, 16, Nov. 1.
v – Also Aug. 14, Oct. 31; not Aug. 16.
z – 1421 on Nov. 30.

★ – *INTERCITÉS*. R.
♥ – Runs 9–10 minutes later on Ⓐ.
◐ – Runs 9 minutes later from Sept. 7.
◇ – Runs 6–12 minutes **earlier** on Sept. 23.
♠ – Runs 11–12 minutes **earlier** on ⑥ (also Aug. 15, Nov. 1).
⊗ – Subject to alteration Sept. 16–20, Nov. 25–29, Dec. 2–6.
⊙ – Subject to alteration June 15 - July 6.
‡ – Departures are up to 17 minutes earlier on Aug. 18, 25.
❦ – **Warning!** Subject to frequent timing alterations (by over 60 minutes on certain dates). Readers intending to use this service are strongly advised to check timings beforehand.
▶ – For additional trains see below main table.
▷ – See also Tables **328** and **329**.
⊡ – See also Table **290**.

331 CLERMONT FERRAND - NEUSSARGUES - AURILLAC

Service until October 17

km		Ⓐ	⑥k				Ⓐ	⑦	Ⓐ	†	Ⓐ	⑤A	B
		🚌	🚌	🚌	x	🚌	🚌¶	e		w		🚌	🚌
0	**Clermont Ferrand** ‡ d.	*0544*t	*0732*t	*1040*t	1303	*1648*t	*1748*t	1757	1842	1957	2012	*2127*t	*2143*t
36	Issoire ‡ d.	*0612*t	*0800*t	*1108*t	1329	*1717*t	*1816*t	1825	1910	2025	2040	*2206*t	*2221*t
61	Arvant ‡ d.	0636	0824	1136	1349	1747	*1838*t	1845	1929	2045	2059	2236	2252
85	Massiac-Blesle d.	0652	0840	1152	1410	1803	1907	1905	1950	2106	2120	2252	2308
111	**Neussargues** a.	0723	0911	1223	1430	1834	1938	1925	2010	2126	2140	2323	2339
111	**Neussargues** d.	0723	0911	1223	*1438**	1834	1938	*1935**	*2020**	*2136**	*2150**	2323	2339
120	Murat (Cantal) d.	0738	0926	1238	*1453**	1849	1953	*1950**	*2035**	*2151**	*2205**	2338	2354
131	Le Lioran d.	0750	0938	1250	*1505**	1901	2005	*2002**	*2047**	*2203**	*2217**	2350	0006
168	**Aurillac** a.	0837	1025	1337	*1552**	1948	2052	*2049**	*2134**	*2250**	*2304**	0037	0053

	①–⑥	Ⓐ				Ⓐz	D	Ⓐ	⑦
	r	🚌	🚌	x	🚌	🚌	🚌		e
Aurillac d.	*0520**	0713	0954	*1313**	1607	1711	1715	*1851**	*1920**
Le Lioran d.	*0607**	0800	1041	*1400**	1654	1758	1802	*1938**	*2007**
Murat (Cantal) d.	*0619**	0812	1053	*1412**	1706	1810	1814	*1950**	*2019**
Neussargues a.	*0634**	0827	1108	*1427**	1721	1825	1829	*2005**	*2034**
Neussargues d.	0644	0827	1108	1437	1721	1825	1829	2015	2044
Massiac-Blesle d.	0706	0858	1139	1458	1752	1856	1900	2036	2107
Arvant ‡ d.	0726	0914	1155	1518	1808	*1926*t	1916	2055	2128
Issoire ‡ d.	0745	*0947*t	*1224*t	1537	*1836*t	*1945*t	*1945*t	2114	2146
Clermont Ferrand ‡ a.	0818	*1015*t	*1254*t	1602	*1905*t	*2013*t	*2013*t	2142	2214

A – ⑤ to July 5 / from Aug. 30.
B – ⑦ to July 7 (also June 10; not June 9); ⑤⑦ July 12 - Aug. 25; ⑦ from Sept. 1.
D – ①–⑤ Aug. 19–30.
e – Also June 10; not June 9.
k – Also Aug. 15.
r – Not June 10.
t – Connection is by train.
w – Not June 9.
x – Not July 8 - Aug. 30.
z – Not Aug. 19–30.
* – By 🚌.
¶ – Aug. 19–30 operated by train Clermont - Arvant, then by 🚌 Arvant (d. 1846) - Aurillac (🚌 timings are 5 minutes earlier).

332 (CLERMONT FERRAND -) NEUSSARGUES - MILLAU - BÉZIERS

km		⚒	⚒	②–⑤	⚒			⑤	⑤	†	⑦
				D	⊡		x	d	d		w
0	**Clermont Ferrand 331** d.	...	...	...	...	...	1303	...	...	...	...
111	**Neussargues** **331** d.	...	...	...	...	...	1436	...	...	...	...
130	St Flour ⊖ d.	...	...	...	...	...	1459	*1557*z	...	...	...
168	St Chély d'Apcher d.	...	...	...	1131	...	1540	1630	...	...	...
201	Marvejols d.	...	...	0700	1208	...	1617	1707	1720	...	2228
236	Mende a.	...	...	0749	|	...	|	|	1807	...	2311
243	Sévérac le Château d.	...	...	...	1257	...	1703	1757	...	...	...
273	Millau d.	0551	...	...	1327	...	1738	1827	...	2102	...
352	Bédarieux △ d.	0713	0847	...	1446	1731	1854	1945	...	2225	...
394	**Béziers** △ a.	0746	0921	...	1519	1805	1928	2019	...	2259	...

	⚒	⚒		⑤	⑤			⑦	⑦v	⑤
	⊡		x	d	d		A	w	▽	d
Béziers △ d.	0638	0800	0937	...	...	1643	1818	...	1858	1856
Bédarieux △ d.	0714	0834	1010	...	...	1718	1855	...	1940	1946
Millau d.	0837	...	1128	1345	...	▬	2016	...	2055	2104
Sévérac le Château d.	0906	...	1159	1414	...	E	...	...	2127	...
Mende d.	|	...	|	|	1615	1730	...	2127	|	...
Marvejols d.	0952	...	1247	1459	1702	1817	...	2209	2221	...
St Chély d'Apcher d.	1030	...	1326	1538	...	...	...	...	2258	...
St Flour ⊖ d.	...	...	1405	...	...	...	...	...	*2336*z	...
Neussargues **331** a.	...	...	1426	...	...	...	...	...	...	...
Clermont Ferrand **331** a.	...	...	1602	...	...	...	...	...	...	...

	🚌	🚌	🚌	🚌		🚌	🚌	🚌	🚌	
	Ⓐ	Ⓐ	⑥k			⑤f		Ⓑh	⑤f	
Clermont Ferrand **331 333** d.	...	...	...	...	...	...	...	...	...	...
Arvant **331 333** d.	*0636*	0741	0824	...	...	...	...	...	...	...
Massiac-Blesle **331** d.	0711	0758	0841	1147	...	...	1808	1910	2124	...
St Flour ⊖ d.	0735	0824	0907	1211	...	1557	1833	1935	2149	...
St Chély d'Apcher a.	...	...	...	...	...	1620	...	...	...	...

	🚌	🚌		🚌	🚌	🚌	🚌		🚌
	H			B	⑤t	⑤f	Ⓐ		⑦u
St Chély d'Apcher d.	...	...	...	...	1653	...	...	...	2306
St Flour ⊖ d.	0634	1104	...	1718	1718	1728	1825	...	2336
Massiac-Blesle **331** a.	0659	1128	...	1742	1742	|	1850	...	...
Arvant **331 333** a.	...	...	...	...	...	1808	...	...	...
Clermont Ferrand **331 333** a.	...	...	...	...	...	...	...	...	...

A – ①②③④⑥⑦ (also Oct. 25, Nov. 1); runs daily June 29 - Sept. 5.
B – ①②③④⑥⑦ (also Nov. 1; not Aug. 14, Oct. 31).
D – ②–⑤ from June 18 (not Aug. 15, 16, Nov. 1, 12).
E – ①–④ June 17–27; ⚒ July 1 - Aug. 31; ①–④ from Sept. 2 (also Oct. 25; not Nov. 11).
H – ①–⑥ (not June 10, Nov. 11).

d – Not July 5 - Aug. 30, Oct. 25, Nov. 1.
f – Also Aug. 14, Oct. 31; not Nov. 1.
h – Not Aug. 15, Nov. 1.
k – Also Aug. 15, Nov. 1.
t – Also Oct. 31; not July 12 - Aug. 30, Nov. 1.
u – Also June 10, Nov. 11.
v – Also June 10, Nov. 11; not June 9, July 7 - Sept. 1, Oct. 20, 27, Nov. 10.
w – Also Nov. 11; not June 9, July 7 - Sept. 1, Oct. 20, 27, Nov. 10.
x – Not July 8 - Aug. 30.
z – By 🚌 to / from St Chély d'Apcher.

⊡ – Does not run Millau - St Chély d'Apcher and v.v. July 8 - Aug. 30, Sept. 16–19, 23–26.
⊖ – St Flour - Chaudes Aigues.
▽ – From Montpellier (Table **355**).
△ – Additional 🚌 journeys Bédarieux - Béziers and v.v.:
From Bédarieux at 0618⚒, 0715†, 1217†, 1315⚒, 1606† and 1630⚒.
From Béziers at 1049†, 1215⚒, 1445†, 1540⚒, 1730⚒ and 2045⑤**f**.

☛ *Bus services in this table are operated on behalf of SNCF. Rail tickets valid.*

CLERMONT FERRAND - LE PUY EN VELAY and NÎMES 333

SERVICE FROM JUNE 16. Services Alès - Nîmes and v.v. are subject to alteration Nov. 1–3, 9–11.

km						🚌		🚌	🚌			🚌		🚌				🚌			🚌		🚌		
		Ⓐ	Ⓐ	D	Ⓐ	Ⓐ	⑦ c	⑥ k	⑥ k			⊗				Ⓒ	Ⓐ			①–⑥ b	⑤ f	Ⓐ	⑥ k¶	⑤ f	⑦ e	Ⓑ ⊡
0	**Clermont Ferrand** ▷ d.	...	0544	...	0645	...	...	0732	...	...	...	0949	...	1250	...	1430	1448	1640	...	1758	1854	1901	1950	*2012*t	2118	2127
36	Issoire ▷ d.	...	0612	...	0714	...	...	0800	...	...	...	1017	...	1319	...	1509	1520	1708	...	1826	1922	1941	2030	*2040*t	2146	2206
61	Arvant ▷ d.	...	0631	...	0737	...	...	0820	...	...	...	1037	...	1340	...	1531	1541	1727	...	1846	1942	2028	2050	2103	2205	2227
71	Brioude d.	...	0642	...	0746	...	...	0829	...	...	...	1047	...	1351	1355	1540	1550	1737	...	1855	1951	2045	2058	2118	2215	2235
95	St Georges d'Aurac d.	...	0708	...	0805	...	...	0847	...	...	...	1112	...	|	|	▬	▬	1759	1802	1918	2015	|	...	|	2238	...
103	Langeac d.	...	|	...	0813	0817	...	0855	0859	...	...	|	...	1418	|	...	...	1808	|	|	|	|	...	2156	|	...
147	**Le Puy en Velay** a.	...	0756	...	|	0903	...	|	0945	...	...	1200	...	|	1503	...	...	|	1854	2006	2102	2205	...	2242	2326	...
170	Langogne d.	...	▬	...	0936	...	...	1020	...	1230	...	...	...	1541	...	B	◧	1942	...	...	...	...	...	...	...	...
47•	**Mende** d.	0446	⑥y	0838	|	...	*0844*r	|	...	|	1146	...	1445	|	...	1650	1832	|	...	...	...	...	...	...	...	...
188	La Bastide-St Laurent d.	0601	0706	0948	1003‡	...	1014	1040	...	1255	1305	...	1553	1605	...	1805	1942	2011	...	...	...	...	...	...	...	...
241	Grand Combe la Pise d.	0709	0808	...	1101‡	...	1112	1137	...	...	1407	...	...	1708	...	1909	...	2109	...	...	...	...	...	...	...	...
254	Alès a.	0724	0824	...	1116‡	...	1127	1152	...	...	1422	...	...	1723	...	1924	...	2123	...	...	...	...	...	...	...	...
254	Alès ▶ d.	0726	0826	...	1123v	...	1129	1158	...	...	1425	...	...	1725	...	1926	...	2125	...	...	...	...	...	...	...	...
303	**Nîmes 355** ▶ a.	0800	0858	...	1155v	...	1202	1231	...	...	1457	...	...	1757	...	1958	...	2158	...	...	...	...	...	...	...	...

							🚌				🚌		🚌		🚌		🚌	🚌					🚌		🚌
	Ⓐ	⑥ k	① g	②–⑤ d	①–⑥ b⊗	①–⑥ b⊗	① a	⑦ u		✥	⑥ k	Ⓐ							Ⓑ h	Ⓐ ⊖	⑦ e	Ⓑ	◇		⑤ w	⑤ w
Nîmes 355 ▶ d.	...	...	...	...	...	...	0715	...	0811	...	...	...	1218	...	...	...	1412	...	...	...	...	1658	1811z	...	2118	...
Alès ▶ a.	...	...	...	...	...	...	0749	...	0843	...	...	...	1250	...	...	...	1444	...	...	...	...	1735	1846z	...	2150	...
Alès d.	...	...	...	...	...	...	0751	...	0845	...	...	...	1252	...	...	...	1447	...	...	...	...	1746	1852	...	2155	...
Grand Combe la Pise d.	...	...	...	...	...	...	0809	...	0901	...	...	...	1308	...	...	...	1502	...	...	...	...	1806	1908	...	2211	...
La Bastide-St Laurent d.	...	...	...	...	...	...	0913	...	0959	1003	...	...	1415	1417	...	...	1603	1612	...	...	...	1912	2014j	2014	2313	2318
Mende a.	...	...	...	...	...	...	|	...	|	1111	...	...	1523	|	...	...	|	1720	...	...	...	|	2123	|	...	|
Langogne d.	...	...	...	...	...	...	0933	...	1023	...	...	...	...	1441	...	...	1624	...	...	...	...	1938	...	2039	...	2343
Le Puy en Velay d.	...	...	0526	0616	0808	...	...	1059	|	...	1210	1218	...	...	1606	1654	|	...	1910	...	1954	|	...	...	...	...
Langeac d.	...	...	|	|	|	...	...	|	1147	...	|	|	...	...	|	|	1747	...	|	...	|	2103	...	...	...	...
St Georges d'Aurac d.	...	...	0616	0705	0856	...	...	|	1155	...	1259	|	...	...	1655	1747	1757	...	|	...	2043	2111	...	...	...	...
Brioude d.	0557	0630	0641	0726	0916	1104	...	1203	1213	...	1319	1324	...	...	1716	...	1821	...	2018	...	2103	2129	...	...	...	...
Arvant ▷ d.	0606	0638	0649	0736	0924	1112	...	...	1222	...	1331	1339	...	...	1725	...	1830	...	2035	2055	2113	2138	...	...	...	...
Issoire ▷ d.	0626	0658	0710	0756	0944	1133	...	...	1243	...	1351	1421	...	...	1746	...	1849	...	...	2114	2133	2157	...	...	...	...
Clermont Ferrand ▷ a.	0657	0738	0742	0826	1015	1212	...	...	1310	...	1419	1501	...	...	1815	...	1916	...	...	2142	2200	2226	...	...	...	...

A – ①②③④⑥ (also ⑤ July 5 - Aug. 30, Oct. 25; not Aug. 15, Nov. 11).
B – ⑤⑦ to June 30; ⑦ July 7 - Aug. 25 (also Aug. 15); ⑤⑦ from Sept. 1 (also Nov. 11; not Oct. 25).
D – Ⓐ (daily July 1 - Sept. 6). By 🚌 to July 5 / from Sept. 2; by train (d. 0840, a. 0949) July 6 - Sept. 1.

a – Also Nov. 12; not July 8 - Sept. 2, Oct. 21, 28, Nov. 4, 11.
b – Not Nov. 11.
c – Also Aug. 15.
d – Not Aug. 15, Nov. 1, 12.
e – Also Nov. 11; not Nov. 10.
– Also Aug. 14, Oct. 31; not Nov. 1.
g – Also Nov. 12; not Nov. 11.
h – Not Aug. 15, Nov. 1.
– Arrives 2009.

k – Also Aug. 15, Nov. 1.
r – *0840* July 7 - Sept. 1.
t – By train Clermont Ferrand - Arvant.
u – Also Nov. 11.
v – Not Sept. 30, Oct. 1–4, 7–11, 14–18.
w – Not July 5 - Aug. 30, Oct. 25, Nov. 1.
y – Not July 6 - Aug. 31, Oct. 26 - Nov. 9.
z – On ⑦ (also Nov. 11; not July 7 - Sept. 1, Oct. 20, 27, Nov. 10) departs Nîmes 1815, arrives Alès 1849.

‡ – 2 minutes earlier on Sept. 30 - Oct. 18.
§ – 1523 on July 14, Aug. 15.
¶ – Runs 12 minutes later on Aug. 15.
⊖ – Runs 2 minutes earlier from Oct. 18.
⊗ – Subject to alteration Oct. 28–31, Nov. 4–8.
◇ – From Narbonne and Montpellier on Ⓐ (Table 355).

⊡ – Ⓑ (not Aug. 15, Nov. 1, 10). Runs 15–16 minutes later on ⑦ to June 30, Ⓑ July 7 - Aug. 25 and ⑦ from Sept. 1 (also Nov. 11).
◧ – Daily except Nov. 1. By train on ⑤ (not July 5 - Aug. 30, Oct. 25); by 🚌 (d. 1834) on all other dates.
✥ – Runs daily. By train on ⚒ July 6 - Aug. 31 (La Bastide d. 1006, Mende a. 1112); by 🚌 on all other dates.
• – Distance from La Bastide.
▷ – See also Table **331**.
▶ – Other trains Alès - Nîmes (journey time 32–40 minutes; subject to alteration Nov. 1–3, 9–11):
From Alès at 0557 Ⓐ, 0625 Ⓐ, 0652, 0755 ⚒, 0826, 0925 Ⓐ v, 1225 Ⓐ, 1251, 1525 §, 1640 Ⓐ, 1822 Ⓐ and 1925 A. **From Nîmes** at 0614 Ⓐ, 0649 Ⓐ, 0715 ⚒, 0747 Ⓐ, 0918 Ⓐ v, 1018 v, 1125 Ⓐ v, 1318 Ⓐ, 1518 Ⓐ, 1614, 1733 ⚒, 1918 Ⓐ and 2118.

TGV services LYON - MASSY - LE MANS - RENNES and NANTES 335

SERVICE FROM JUNE 10. See Table **290** for slower services via Bourges. **Warning!** Certain services are subject to alteration Aug. 14–18, Nov. 1, 2, 3, 9, 10.

	TGV **5352** Ⓐ a	*TGV* **5351** ①–④ J	*TGV* **5370** G	*TGV* **5354** P	*TGV* **5358** ⑥k	*TGV* **5372*** G	*TGV* **5356** ① M	*TGV* **5356** ②–⑤ L	*TGV* **5378**	*TGV* **5374** A	*TGV* **5380** A	*TGV* **5383** B	*TGV* **5383** ①–④ H	*TGV* **5360** ②–④ N	*TGV* **5363** ②–④ N
Marseille St Charles **350** d.	...	...	0838	...	...	1138	...	...	1439	1439	...	...	...	...	...
Avignon TGV **350** d.	...	...	0914	...	...	1220	...	...	1521	1521	...	...	...	...	...
Montpellier St-Roch **355** d.	...	...	|	...	...	|	...	...	|	|	1628f	1628f	1628	...	...
Valence TGV **355** d.	...	...	0949	...	...	|	...	...	|	|	1747	1747	1747	...	...
Lyon Perrache d.	0616	0616	|	1012	1312	|	1312	1316	|	|	|	|	|	1813	1813
Lyon Part Dieu d.	0630	0630	1030	1030	1330	1330	1330	1330	1630	1630	1830	1830	1830	1830	1830
Massy TGV d.	0837	0841	1235	1235	1537	1537	1537	1537	1837	1837	2037	2041y	2041	2037	2041
St Pierre des Corps a.	0930x	|	1330	1330	|	|	|	|	|	|	2131	|	|	2131	|
Le Mans **280** a.	|	0934	|	|	1629	1629	1629	1629	1929	1929	|	2133y	2134	|	2134
Laval **280** a.	|	1003	|	|	|	|	|	|	|	2004z	|	|	2204	|	2204
Rennes **280** a.	|	1030	|	|	|	1717	1717	1717	|	2031z	|	2220y	2231	|	2231
Saumur Rive Droit a.	|	...	|	|	|	...	...	...	|	...	2205	...	...	2204	...
Angers St Laud **280** a.	1023	...	1424	1424	1711	...	...	...	2014	...	2227	...	...	2227	...
Nantes **280** a.	1102	...	1503	1503	1753	...	...	...	2054	...	2306	...	...	2306	...

	TGV **5300** ②–⑤ L	*TGV* **5300** ① Q	*TGV* **5320**	*TGV* **5302** ②–④ U	*TGV* **5322** A❦	*TGV* **5330** A	*TGV* **5332** A	*TGV* **5306** R	*TGV* **5304** ②–④ N	*TGV* **5324** T§	*TGV* **5312** Ⓐ n	*TGV* **5326** T¶	*TGV* **5314** S	*TGV* **5328** ⑤⑦ w	*TGV* **5318** ⑤⑦ w
Nantes **280** d.	0445v	0455	0702	...	...	0902	...	1302v	...	...	...	1551	1551	1902	...
Angers St Laud **280** d.	0528v	0534	0744	...	...	0944	...	1344v	...	...	...	1632	1632	1944	...
Saumur Rive Droit d.	|	0558	|	...	...	|	...	|	...	...	...	1657	1657	|	...
Rennes **280** d.	|	|	|	0739	0745	|	0939	|	1318v	1318v	1539	|	|	|	1939
Laval **280** d.	|	|	|	|	|	|	|	|	1346v	1346v	|	|	|	|	|
Le Mans **280** d.	|	|	0825v	0833	|	1033	1033j	1429v	1429v	1429v	1633	|	|	2033	2033
St Pierre des Corps d.	0619v	0632	|	|	|	|	|	|	|	|	|	1732	1732	|	|
Massy TGV d.	0725	0725	0925	0925	0925	1125	1125	1525	1525	1525	1725	1825j	1825j	2125	2125
Lyon Part Dieu a.	0930	0930	1130	1130	1130	1330	1330	1730	1730	1730	1930	2030	2030	2347•	2347•
Lyon Perrache a.	0943	0943	|	1149	|	|	|	1743	1743	|	1944	|	2044	0001•	0001•
Valence TGV **355** a.	...	...	|	...	|	1411	1411	...	...	1809	...	2110	...	...	...
Montpellier St-Roch **355** a.	...	...	|	...	|	1532	1532	...	...	|	...	|	...	...	...
Avignon TGV **350** a.	...	...	1236	...	1236	...	...	...	...	1846	...	2145	...	...	...
Marseille St Charles **350** a.	...	...	1319	...	1319	...	...	...	...	1926	...	2227	...	...	...

LYON - LE HAVRE	*TGV* **5376** ⊖
Marseille **350** d.	1539
Avignon TGV **350** d.	1614
Valence TGV **350** d.	1649
Lyon Part Dieu d.	1730
Massy-Palaiseau a.	1937
Versailles Chantiers a.	1955
Mantes la Jolie a.	2032
Rouen Rive Droite a.	2114
Le Havre a.	2202

LE HAVRE - LYON	*TGV* **5316** △
Le Havre d.	0753
Rouen Rive Droite d.	0845
Mantes la Jolie d.	0931
Versailles Chantiers d.	1002
Massy-Palaiseau d.	1020
Lyon Part Dieu a.	1227
Valence TGV **350** a.	1310
Avignon TGV **350** a.	1346
Marseille **350** a.	1430

TGV – Ⓡ, supplement payable, 🍸.

A – ①⑤⑥⑦ to July 1 (also June 11); daily July 5 - Sept. 2; ①⑤⑥⑦ from Sept. 6 (also Oct. 31, Nov. 12).
B – ①⑤⑥⑦ to July 7 (also June 11); ⑤–⑦ July 12 - Aug. 25 (also Aug. 14); ①⑤⑥⑦ from Aug. 30 (also Oct. 31, Nov. 12).
G – ①⑥⑦ to July 1 (also June 11); daily July 6 - Sept. 2; ①⑥⑦ from Sept. 7 (also Nov. 1, 12).
H – ①–④ July 8 - Aug. 29 (not Aug. 14, 15).
J – ①–④ to July 4 / from Sept. 2 (not June 10, Oct. 31, Nov. 11).
L – ②–⑤ to July 5 / from Sept. 3 (not June 11, Nov. 1, 12).
M – ① July 8 - Aug. 26.
N – ②–④ to July 4 / from Sept. 3 (not June 11, Oct. 31, Nov. 12).

P – ②–⑥ to July 5 (not June 11); ①⑤⑦ July 7 - Sept. 1 (not Aug. 16, 18); ②–⑥ from Sept. 3 (not Nov. 1, 2, 12).
Q – ① to July 1 / from Sept. 2 (also June 11, Nov. 12; not June 10, Nov. 11).
R – ②–④ to July 4 (not June 11); Ⓐ July 8 - Aug. 30 (not Aug. 16); ②–④ from Sept. 3 (not Oct. 31, Nov. 12).
S – ①–④ to July 4 (not June 10); ⑦ July 7 - Sept. 1; ①–④ from Sept. 2 (not Oct. 31, Nov. 11).
T – ⑤–⑦ to June 30 (also June 10); daily July 5 - Sept. 1; ⑤–⑦ from Sept. 6 (also Oct. 31).
U – ②–④ from Oct. 8 (not Oct. 31, Nov. 12).

a – Not Aug. 16.
f – 2–3 minutes earlier from Sept. 6.
j – From Oct. 7.
k – Also ⑦ July 7 - Sept. 1; not Aug. 17, Nov. 2, 9.
n – Also ⑥ July 6–27, Aug. 3, 10, 24, 31; not Aug. 16.
v – 4–13 minutes later from Oct. 7.
w – Also June 10, Aug. 14, Oct. 31, Nov. 11; not Aug. 16, Nov. 1.
x – Not Sept. 9 - Oct. 4.
y – 5–8 minutes later on ⑤⑦ to Oct. 6 (also June 10, Aug. 14; not Aug. 16).
z – On ⑤ to Oct. 4 (also Aug. 14; not Aug. 16) Laval a. 2006, Rennes a. 2039. On ⑤ from Oct. 11 (also Oct. 31; not Nov. 1) Laval a. 1957, Rennes a. 2023. On ①⑥⑦ from Oct. 7 (also Nov. 12) Laval a. 1957, Rennes a. 2029. On ①–④ July 8 - Aug. 29 (not Aug. 14, 15) does not call at Laval, arrives Rennes 2020.

* – Train number **5368** on ⑥ (also ⑦ July 7 - Sept. 1 and on Nov. 1).
• – Arrival times vary (usually a few minutes earlier). Terminates at Lyon Part Dieu on ⑦ Aug. 18 - Sept. 8.
❦ – From Oct. 7 departs Rennes 0739 and calls additionally at Le Mans (d. 0833). On ① June 17 - Sept. 30 (also June 11, ⑤ June 14 - July 5, ⑤ Sept. 6 - Oct. 4 departs Rennes 0540 and operates via Nantes (as *TGV* **5339**).
¶ – July 8–11, 16–18 service is diverted via Avignon Centre (not calling at Avignon TGV; extended journey).
§ – Departs Rennes 1329, Laval 1355 on ⑤–⑦ to July 7 (also June 10) and ⑥⑦ Juuly 13 - Aug. 24.
⊖ – Subject to alteration Oct. 12, 19. Does not run from Versailles to Le Havre on July 26, 27, Aug. 14.
△ – Subject to alteration on Oct. 12, 13, 19, 20. Does not run from Le Havre to Versailles on June 10, July 27, 28.

Timings Marseille - Lyon and v.v. may vary by a few minutes until June 23 (also Nantes timings until July 7). Other timings may also vary by a few minutes during certain periods; please check your TGV reservation for confirmed timings.

340 PARIS - LYON *TGV trains*

For Charles de Gaulle ✈ - Marne la Vallée - Lyon see Table **11**. For Paris - Lyon St Exupéry ✈ see Table **342**. Timings may vary by up to 3 minutes on certain dates.

km		TGV 6601	TGV 6641	TGV 6603	TGV 6643	TGV 6681	TGV 6681	TGV 6605	TGV 6607	TGV 6607	TGV 6609	TGV 6609	TGV 6611	TGV 6613	TGV 6615	TGV 6685	TGV 6617	TGV 6657	TGV 6619	TGV 6619	TGV 6621	TGV 6621	TGV 6659	TGV 6623	TGV 6687
		Ⓐ	Ⓐ	①–⑥	Ⓐ	Ⓐ	⑥			Ⓒ	①–⑥	⑦						⑤g			①–④	⑤–⑦	①–④		
		a	J	b	J	a◇	k◇	C					D		E	◇		⊗	♥	♣			m⊗	H	◇
0	**Paris** Gare de Lyon .. **341/2** d.	0550	0629	0659	0729	0753	0753	0753	0859	0859	0959	0959	1059	1153	1259	1259	1353	1429	1459	1459	1548	1553	1619	1659	1659
303	Le Creusot TGV .... d.	0716	|	|	|	0915	0915	0915	|	|	|	|	|	1315	|	|	1515	|	|	|	1710	1715	|	|	|
363	Mâcon Loché TGV .... **341/2** a.	|	|	|	|	|	0933	0933	|	|	|	|	|	|	|	|	|	|	|	|	1728	|	|	|	|
427	**Lyon** Part-Dieu .... a.	0756	0826	0856	0926	0956	1000	1000	1056	1056	1156	|	1256	1356	1456	1456	1556	1626	1656	|	1756	1756	1816	1856	1856
432	**Lyon** Perrache .... a.	0809	0843	0909	0939	...	...	1013	...	1109	1209	1211	1309	1409	1509	...	1609	1643	1709	1721	1809	1809	...	1909	...

	TGV 6663	TGV 6627	TGV 6665	TGV 6689	TGV 6629	TGV 6669	TGV 6631	TGV 6633	TGV 6635
	Ⓐ					Ⓑ		Ⓑ	⑤⑦
	L		M	◇	B	q⊗		h	t△
Paris Gare de Lyon ... **341/2** d.	1729	1753	1841	1859	1859	1929	1958	2059	2159
Le Creusot TGV .... d.	|	1915	|	|	|	|	2120	|	|
Mâcon Loché TGV ..... **341/2** a.	|	|	|	|	|	|	2138	|	|
Lyon Part-Dieu .... a.	1926	1956	2040	2056	2056	2126	2205	2256	2356
Lyon Perrache .... a.	1939	2009	2053	...	2109	2139	2218	2309	0009

	TGV 6640	TGV 6602	TGV 6642	TGV 6644	TGV 6604	TGV 6690	TGV 6648	TGV 6693	TGV 6608	TGV 6610	TGV 6612
	①	Ⓐ	Ⓐ	①–④		①–⑥	①⑥				
	v⊗	a	S	m⊗	A	d◇	p	◇	x		
Lyon Perrache .... d.	0521	0551	0621	0638	0646	...	0720	...	0751	0851	0951
Lyon Part-Dieu .... d.	0534	0604	0634	0651	0704	0704	0734	0734	0804	0904	1004
Mâcon Loché TGV .. **341/2** d.	0601	0631	|	|	|	|	|	|	0832	|	1032
Le Creusot TGV .... d.	0622	0652	|	|	|	|	|	|	0854	|	1054
Paris Gare de Lyon **341/2** a.	0743	0813	0831	0849	0901	0901	0934	0934	1015	1101	1218

	TGV 6614	TGV 6616	TGV 6616	TGV 6618	TGV 6695	TGV 6620	TGV 6622	TGV 6624	TGV 6624	TGV 6664	TGV 6626	TGV 6668	TGV 6697	TGV 6628	TGV 6638	TGV 6697	TGV 6630	TGV 6630	TGV 6674	TGV 6674	TGV 6634	TGV 6634	TGV 6672	TGV 6676	TGV 6678
		Ⓐ	Ⓒ						②–⑤	Ⓑ		⑤⑦			①–④		⑥			⑥	Ⓐ	⑦	⑤	⑦	⑦
	P	a	z	R	◇			N	r⊗	h⊗		j⊙	G◇		m⊗	F◇	n	G	Q	o	a	y	f	y	y⊙
Lyon Perrache .... d.	1046	...	1151	1246	...	1351	1451	1551	1551	1621	1651	1716	...	1751	...	...	1846	1851	2016	2016	2051	2055	2148	2151	2221
Lyon Part-Dieu .... d.	1104	1134	1204	1304	1304	1404	1504	1604	1604	1634	1704	1734	1734	1804	1834	1904	1904	1904	2034	2034	2104	2108	2204	2204	2234
Mâcon Loché TGV ..... **341/2** d.	|	|	|	|	|	|	|	|	1630	|	|	|	|	|	|	|	|	|	|	|	|	|	|	2231	|
Le Creusot TGV .... d.	|	|	|	|	|	1446	|	1646	1650	|	|	|	|	1846	|	|	|	|	|	2116	2146	2150	2246	2252	|
Paris Gare de Lyon ... **341/2** a.	1301	1331	1401	1501	1501	1607	1701	1807	1811	1831	1901	1931	1931	2007	2031	2101	2101	2101	2231	2237	2307	2311	0008	0013	0031

A – ①–⑥ to July 19 (not June 10, July 6, 13); ① July 22 - Aug. 26; ①–⑥ from Sept. 2 (not Nov. 2, 11).
B – ⑥ to June 29; ⑤ July 5 - Aug. 30 (also Aug. 14; not Aug. 16); ⑥ from Sept. 7 (also Nov. 1).
C – Ⓒ to June 30; ⑦ July 7 - Aug. 25; Ⓒ from Sept. 1.
D – Daily to July 22; ①⑤⑥⑦ July 26 - Aug. 26 (also Aug. 14, 15); daily from Aug. 30.
E – Daily to July 6; ⑤ July 12 - Aug. 30 (also July 8, 13, 15, 20, Aug. 14; not Aug. 16); daily from Sept. 2.
F – ⑥ to July 6; ①②③④⑥ July 8 - Aug. 31 (also Aug. 16; not Aug. 14); ⑥ from Sept. 7 (also Nov. 1; not Nov. 2).
G – Ⓑ to July 5; ⑤⑦ July 12 - Aug. 25 (also Aug. 14; not Aug. 16); Ⓑ from Aug. 30 (not Nov. 1).
H – ②–⑦ to July 19 (also June 10; not June 11, July 6, 7, 13, 14); ②–⑦ from Sept. 3 (also Nov. 11; not Nov. 12)
J – To July 19 and from Sept. 2.
L – Ⓐ to July 8 / from Sept. 2 (also July 12, 15, 19).
M – Ⓑ to July 21; ⑤⑦ July 26 - Aug. 25 (also Aug. 14; not Aug. 16); Ⓑ from Aug. 30 (not Nov. 1).

N – ①⑥⑦ to July 1 (also June 11); daily July 16 - Sept. 2; ①⑥⑦ from Sept. 7 (also Nov. 1, 12).
P – Daily to July 21; ⑥⑦ July 27 - Aug. 25 (also Aug. 15, 16); daily from Aug. 31.
Q – Ⓑ to July 21; ⑦ July 28 - Aug. 25 (not Aug. 11); Ⓑ from Sept. 1 (not Nov. 1, 10).
R – Daily to July 19 (not July 6, 13); ⑦ July 21 - Aug. 25; daily from Sept. 1.
S – Ⓐ to July 18 / from Sept. 2 (not July 12).

a – Not Aug. 16.
b – Not June 10, Nov. 11.
d – Not June 10, Nov. 2, 11.
f – Also Aug. 14, Oct. 31; not Aug. 16, Nov. 1.
g – Also Oct. 31; not Nov. 1.
h – Not Aug. 15, 16, Nov. 1.
j – Also June 10, Oct. 31, Nov. 11; not Nov. 1.
k – Also Aug. 15, 16, Nov. 1.
m – Not June 10, Oct. 31, Nov. 11.

n – Also Nov. 1; not July 6 - Aug. 31, Nov. 2.
o – Also Aug. 15, Nov. 1; not Aug. 10, 17, 31, Nov. 2.
p – Also June 11, Aug. 15, 16, Nov. 1, 12; not June 10, July 22, 29, Aug. 5, 12, 19, 26, Nov. 11.
q – Also July 12, 14, 19, 21; not Nov. 1.
r – Not June 11, Nov. 1, 12.
t – Also June 10, Aug. 14, Nov. 11; not Aug. 16.
v – Also Nov. 12; not June 10, Nov. 11.
x – Not July 26, Aug. 2, 9, 14, 23, 30.
y – Also June 10, Nov. 11.
z – Also Aug. 16.

TGV –Ⓡ, supplement payable, 🍸.

♥ – From Aug. 31.
♣ – Until Aug. 30.
⊙ – Not July 7 - Sept. 1.
⊗ – Not July 8 - Sept. 1.
◇ – To / from St Étienne (Table **348**).
△ – Runs 7 minutes earlier on July 21, Sept. 15, Oct. 6, Nov. 3, Dec. 1. Departs Paris 2154 on June 10, Aug. 14, Nov. 1, 11.

341 PARIS - GENÈVE, CHAMBÉRY and ANNECY *Service from June 11*

km		TGV 9241	TGV 9761	TGV 6933	TGV 9763		TGV 9765	TGV 9765	TGV 6937	TGV 9245	TGV 6939	TGV 6503	TGV 6503		TGV 9773	TGV 6941		TGV 9249	TGV 9775		TGV 9777	TGV 6947	TGV 6949
			①–⑤	①–⑤	⑥		①–⑤	⑦				⑦	⑥								Ⓑ	⑤–⑦	Ⓑ
		M	a	a	k		a	p		M▲	S	L			Q			M			d⊙		n
0	**Paris** Gare de Lyon .... **340 342 366** d.	0629	0711	0749	0811	...	0911	0911	0949	1037	1041	1041	1041	...	1211	1245	...	1441	1511	...	1611	1645	1749
363	Mâcon Loché TGV .... **340 342** d.	|	|	0927	|	...	|	|	1127	|	|	|	|	...	|	1423	...	|	|	...	|	1823	1927
406	Bourg-en-Bresse .... **365** d.	|	0903	0950	1005	...	|	1103	1150	|	1235	1239	1239	...	1405	|	...	|	|	...	1805	|	1950
	Lyon St Exupéry TGV ✈ .... **342** d.	◧	|	|	|	...	|	|	|	1233	|	|	|	...	|	|	...	1637	|	...	|	|	|
439	Nurieux Brion .... a.	|	|	|	|	...	|	|	|	|	|	|	|	...	|	|	...	|	|	...	|	|	|
470	Bellegarde .... **346** a.	|	0949	|	1058	...	1147	1149	|	|	|	1328	1346	...	1458	|	...	|	1748	...	1858	|	|
503	**Genève** .... **346** a.	|	1019	|	1127	...	1218	1219	|	|	|	⊖	⊖	...	1527	|	...	|	1818	...	1929	|	|
	Chambéry .... **345 364 366** a.	0940	...	|	...	...	...	...	|	1340	1344	...	...	...	...	1538	...	1738	...	...	...	1939	|
511	Aix les Bains .... **345 364** a.	...	...	1052	...	...	...	...	1251	...	1331z	...	...	...	...	1600	...	...	...	...	...	2000	2052
550	**Annecy** .... **345 364** a.	...	...	1130	...	...	...	...	1329	...	1429	...	...	...	...	1629	...	...	...	...	...	2031	2129

	TGV 9781	TGV 6511	TGV 6951	TGV 9785		TGV 9789	TGV 6953	
		⑤				⑤	⑤	
	⊕	f	D			j	t	
Paris Gare de Lyon .... **340 342 366** d.	1811	1815	1845	1911	...	2011	2019	...
Mâcon Loché TGV .... **340 342** d.	|	|	2023	|	...	|	2157	...
Bourg-en-Bresse .... **365** d.	|	|	|	2105	...	2205	2221	...
Lyon St Exupéry TGV ✈ .... **342** d.	|	|	2047	|	...	|	|	...
Nurieux Brion .... a.	2030	|	|	|	...	|	|	...
Bellegarde .... **346** a.	2058	2111	|	2151	...	2251	|	...
Genève .... **346** a.	2129	⊖	|	2222	...	2322	|	...
Chambéry .... **345 364 366** a.	...	...	2143	...	...	...	2338	...
Aix les Bains .... **345 364** a.	...	...	2204	...	...	...	2324z	...
Annecy .... **345 364** a.	...	...	2234	...	...	...	...	...

km		TGV 6960	TGV 9760		TGV 6962	TGV 9764	TGV 9764		TGV 9768
			①–⑥			①–⑥			
		N	b⊙		E	b⊙	T		
0	**Annecy** .... **345 364** d.	0532	...	...	0621	...	...	...	...
39	Aix les Bains .... **345 364** d.	0602	...	...	0649	...	...	...	...
53	Chambéry .... **345 364 366** d.	0625	...	...	0719	...	...	...	...
	Genève .... **346** d.	|	0613	...	|	0741	0741	...	0941
	Bellegarde .... **346** d.	|	0643	...	|	0810	0810	...	1010
	Nurieux Brion .... d.	|	0709	...	|	|	0835	...	|
144	Lyon St Exupéry TGV ✈ .... **342** d.	|	|	...	0830	|	|	...	|
	Bourg-en-Bresse .... **365** d.	|	0737	...	|	0859	0902	...	|
	Mâcon Loché TGV .... **340 342** d.	|	|	...	|	|	|	...	|
585	**Paris** Gare de Lyon .... **340 342 366** a.	0915	0931	...	1023	1049	1051	...	1249

	TGV 6964	TGV 9240		TGV 9770	TGV 9244	TGV 6972	TGV 9772		TGV 6508	TGV 9774	TGV 6976		TGV 9776		TGV 9778	TGV 6980	TGV 6506	TGV 6504	TGV 9780	TGV 6984	TGV 9248	TGV 9248	TGV 9784
				①–⑤			⑥⑦		⑦	①–⑤			⑤–⑦		①–④	⑤⑦	⑦	⑥	Ⓑ		Ⓑh	⑥w	
		M		a	M△		u		p	a			r		mR	v	L	L	d⊕	G	M	M¶	
Annecy .... **345 364** d.	0931	...	...	...	...	1232	...	...	...	...	1435	...	...	...	...	1732	...	...	...	1832	...	...	...
Aix les Bains .... **345 364** d.	1001	...	...	...	1313y	1313	...	...	...	...	1551y	...	...	...	...	1802	...	...	...	1909	...	...	...
Chambéry .... **345 364 366** d.	1024	1024	...	...	1255	|	...	...	...	...	1537	...	...	...	...	1825	...	...	...	|	1856	1856	...
Genève .... **346** d.	|	|	...	1141	|	|	1341	...	⊖	1441	|	...	1629	...	1741	|	⊖	⊖	1829	|	|	|	1941
Bellegarde .... **346** d.	|	|	...	1210	|	|	1410	...	1502	1510	|	...	1700	...	1810	|	1818	1900	1900	|	|	|	2010
Nurieux Brion .... d.	|	|	...	|	|	|	|	...	|	|	|	...	|	...	|	|	|	|	|	|	|	|	|
Lyon St Exupéry TGV ✈ .... **342** d.	1126	1126	...	|	|	|	|	...	|	|	|	...	|	...	|	|	|	|	|	|	◧	◧	|
Bourg-en-Bresse .... **365** d.	|	|	...	|	1415	1415	|	...	1556	1559	|	...	1757	...	1859	|	1934	1949	|	2012	|	|	|
Mâcon Loché TGV .... **340 342** d.	|	|	...	|	1436	1436	|	...	|	|	|	...	|	...	|	|	1956	|	|	2034	|	|	|
Paris Gare de Lyon .... **340 342 366** a.	1319	1319	...	1452	1611	1611	1649	...	1749	1749	1845	...	1949	...	2049	2115	2133	2141	2149	2211	2231	2237	2249

D – Ⓑ to July 7; ⑦ July 14 - Aug. 25; Ⓑ from Sept. 1 (not Nov. 1). Does not call at Lyon St Exupéry on ①–④ to July 4.
E – ⑤ (also ①②③④⑥ July 6 - Aug. 31, Oct. 31; not Nov. 1).
G – ①②③④⑦ (not Aug. 14, 15, Oct. 31).
L – July 6 - Sept. 1.
M – [12] Paris - Modane - Milano and v.v. (Table **44**). Special fares payable.
N – ①②③④⑥ (also Nov. 1; not July 6 - Aug. 31, Oct. 31, Nov. 11).
Q – To Lausanne (a. 1615) on ①–④ **m**.
R – From Lausanne (d. 1639).

S – ⑥ to June 29; ⑥⑦ July 6 - Sept. 1 (also Aug. 15; not Aug. 17); ⑥ from Sept. 7 (also Nov. 1).
T – ⑦ (also Nov. 11); runs daily July 6 - Sept. 1.

a – Not Aug. 15, 16, Nov. 1, 11.
b – Not Nov. 11.
d – Not Nov. 1.
f – Also Aug. 14, Oct. 31; not Aug. 16, Nov. 1.
h – Not Aug. 15, 16, Nov. 1.
j – Not July 5, Aug. 2–23, Nov. 1.
k – Also Aug. 15, 16, Nov. 1.
m – Not Aug. 14, 15, Oct. 31, Nov. 11.

n – Not July 7, 14, 21, 28, Aug. 4, 11, 15–18, 25, Sept. 1, Nov. 1.
p – Also Nov. 11.
r – Also Aug. 14, 15, Oct. 31, Nov. 11.
t – Not Aug. 16, Nov. 1.
u – Also Aug. 15, Nov. 1, 11.
v – Also Aug. 14, Oct. 31, Nov. 11; not Aug. 16, Nov. 1.
w – Also Aug. 15, Nov. 1; not Nov. 2.
y – Calls after Chambéry.
z – Calls before Chambéry.

TGV –Ⓡ, supplement payable, 🍸.

▲ – Subject to alteration until June 23. Paris and Lyon St Exupéry departures are 4–8 minutes later on certain dates
△ – Subject to alteration until July 5.
⊙ – Not July 6 - Sept. 1.
⊕ – Not July 29 - Aug. 25.
¶ – Also calls at Le Creusot TGV (d. 2116)
⊖ – To / from Évian les Bains (Table **363**).
◧ – Via Lyon Part Dieu.

Certain services are subject to alteration on Aug. 10, 11, 15–17 and Nov. 10

PARIS - GRENOBLE 342

km	All trains convey 🍷	TGV 6901 ① g	TGV 6905 L	TGV 6911 K	TGV 6917	TGV 6919	TGV 6921 ①-④ B	TGV 6923 Ⓑ h	TGV 6925 Ⓐ J⊙	TGV 6925 ⑤ E	TGV 6927 N	TGV 6929 ⑤⑦ w
0	**Paris** Gare de Lyon ..... **350/1** d.	0641	0741	0941	1141	1441	1641	1741	1845	1849	1941	2045
363	Mâcon Loché TGV ..... d.	|	|	|	|	|	|	|	2023	|	|	|
441	Lyon St Exupéry ✈ ..... **350/1** a.	0834	0934	1134	1334	1633	1834	1934	2043	2050	2134	2238
441	Lyon St Exupéry ✈ ..... d.	0838	0939	1138	1339	1641	1838	1939	2054	2054	2138	2242
553	**Grenoble** ..... a.	0941	1041	1241	1441	1745	1941	2041	2154	2154	2241	2345

	TGV 6900 ①-④ B	TGV 6902 P	TGV 6906 ①-⑥ Q	TGV 6908		TGV 6910	TGV 6920 D	TGV 6922 ⑥⑦ ⊡	TGV 6922 ①-⑤	TGV 6924 H	TGV 6924 ⑤ f	TGV 6928 ⑦ e
Grenoble ..... d.	0516	0616	0816	1016	...	1316	1518	1716	1716	1916	1916	2116
Lyon St Exupéry ✈ ..... a.	0621	0721	0921	|	...	1421	1621	|	1822	2021	2021	2221
Lyon St Exupéry ✈ ..... **350/1** d.	0626	0726	0926	|	...	1430	1626	|	1826	2026	2026	2226
Mâcon Loché TGV ..... d.	|	|	|	|		|	|	1844	|	|	2050	|
Paris Gare de Lyon ..... **350/1** a.	0819	0919	1119	1315	...	1626	1819	2019	2019	2219	2224	0019

☛ See Tables **340** and **341** for other services Paris - Mâcon-Loché and v.v.

B – ①-④ to July 4 / from Sept. 2 (not June 10, Oct. 31, Nov. 11).
D – Ⓑ to July 5 / from Sept. 2 (not Nov. 1).
E – ⑤ July 12 - Aug. 30 (also Aug. 14; not Aug. 16).
H – ①②③④⑥⑦ to July 4; ①②③④⑦ July 7 - Sept. 5 (not Aug. 15); ①②③④⑥⑦ from Sept. 7.
J – To July 5 and from Sept. 2.
K – Daily to July 7; Ⓒ July 13 - Aug. 25 (also Aug. 16); daily from Aug. 31.
L – Daily to July 6; ①-⑥ July 8 - Aug. 31; daily from Sept. 2.
N – Daily to July 5; Ⓑ July 7 - Aug. 30 (not Aug. 15, 16); daily from Sept. 1.
P – Ⓐ to June 28; ①-⑥ July 1 - Aug. 30; Ⓐ from Sept. 2.
Q – ①-⑥ to July 5 / from Sept. 2 (not June 10, Nov. 11).

e – Also June 10, Nov. 11.
f – Not Aug. 16.
g – Also June 11, Nov. 12; not June 10, July 8 - Aug. 26, Nov. 11.
h – Not Aug. 15, 16, Nov. 1.
w – ⑤⑦ to July 7 (also June 10); ⑦ July 14 - Aug. 25; ⑤⑦ from Sept. 1 (also Nov. 11; not Sept. 15, 22, 29, Nov. 1). Runs 9 – 10 minutes later on ⑤. Timings may vary by a few minutes on ⑦ to July 7 (also June 10).

TGV – 🅁, supplement payable, 🍷.

LYON - GRENOBLE 343

Subject to alteration on Nov. 2, 3, 10

km		①-⑥ b	Ⓐ		Ⓐ			c							Ⓐ		Ⓐ		Ⓐ					⑥d 🚌	🚌
	Lyon Perrache ..... d.	...	0644	...	0744	...	...	...	...	...	...	...	...	...	1644	...	1744	...	1844	...	...	...	...	...	...
0	**Lyon** Part-Dieu ..... **344** d.	0612	|	0713	|	0814	0914	1014	1114	1214	1314	1414	1514	1614	|	1714	|	1814	|	1914	2014	2114	...	2206	2314
41	Bourgoin-Jallieu ..... **344** d.	0642	0714	0742	0814	0842	0942	1042	1142	1242	1342	1442	1542	1642	1712	1742	1812	1842	1912	1942	2042	2143	...	2257	0005
56	La Tour du Pin ..... **344** d.	0651	0724	0751	0824	0851	0951	1051	1151	1251	1351	1451	1551	1651	1724	1751	1824	1851	1921	1951	2051	2152	...	|	|
104	Voiron ..... d.	0722	0752	0821	0852	0921	1021	1121	1221	1322	1421	1522	1621	1721	1752	1821	1852	1921	1950	2022	2122	2221	...	|	|
129	**Grenoble** ..... a.	0738	0808	0838	0908	0938	1038	1138	1238	1338	1438	1538	1638	1738	1808	1838	1908	1938	2008	2038	2138	2238	...	0005	0110

	①-⑥ b	Ⓐ		Ⓐ					c				Ⓐ			Ⓐ		Ⓐ			🚌			Ⓑ n	⑥d 🚌
Grenoble ..... d.	0522	0552	0622	0652	0722	0822	0922	1022	1122	1222	1322	1422	1452	1522	1622	1652	1722	1752	1822	1922	1947	2023	...	2122	2123
Voiron ..... d.	0539	0609	0639	0709	0739	0839	0939	1038	1139	1239	1339	1439	1509	1539	1639	1709	1739	1809	1839	1939	|	2039	...	2139	2153
La Tour du Pin ..... **344** d.	0608	0637	0708	0737	0808	0908	1008	1108	1208	1308	1408	1508	1537	1608	1708	1737	1808	1837	1908	2008	|	2108	...	2208	2238
Bourgoin-Jallieu ..... **344** d.	0619	0647	0719	0749	0819	0919	1019	1119	1219	1319	1419	1519	1547	1619	1719	1747	1819	1847	1919	2019	|	2119	...	2219	2300
Lyon Part-Dieu ..... **344** a.	0646	|	0746	|	0846	0946	1046	1147	1246	1346	1446	1546	|	1646	1746	|	1846	|	1946	2046	2116	2146	...	|	2400
Lyon Perrache ..... a.	...	0716	...	0816	...	...	...	...	...	...	...	...	1616	...	...	1816	...	1916	...	...	...	...	...	2247	...

b – Not June 10, Nov. 11.
c – Not Nov. 4 – 8, 12 – 15.
d – Also Aug. 15, Nov. 1.
n – Not July 14, Aug. 15, Nov. 1, 11.

LYON - CHAMBÉRY 344

Subject to alteration on June 29, Aug. 16, 17, Nov. 10

SERVICE FROM JUNE 10. Certain journeys continue to / from Bourg St Maurice (Table **366**) or Modane (Table **367**).

km		Ⓐ	🚌 Ⓐ	①-⑥ b	⚒	①-⑥ b	⊗		🚌	Ⓐ a	Ⓒ c					Ⓑ h	Ⓐ					Ⓐ		Ⓐ			△
0	**Lyon Part Dieu** . **343** d.	...	0625	...	0708	0808	0908	1008	1100	1142	...	1208	1308	1408	1508	...	...	1608	1650	1708	1750	1808	1908	...	2008	2108	2208
41	Bourgoin-Jallieu . **343** d.	0620	|	0720	|	|	|	|	|	1205	1218	|	|	|	|	1546	1612	|	1718	|	1818	|	|	1957	|	2137	|
56	La Tour du Pin .. **343** d.	0630	|	0730	|	|	|	|	|	1216	1230	|	|	|	|	1557	1624	|	1730	|	1830	|	|	2009	|	2147	|
	Ambérieu ..... d.	|	|	|	0733	0833	0933	1033	|	|	|	1233	|	1433	|	|	|	1633	|	1733	|	1833	1933	|	|	|	|
	Aix les Bains ..... a.	|	|	|	0819	0918	1018	1118	|	|	|	1318	1418	1518	1618	|	|	1718	|	1818	|	1918	2018	|	2118	|	2318z
106	**Chambéry** ..... a.	0738	0745	0816	0832	*0937*	1032	1132	1220	1301	1316	*1337*	1432	1532	1632	1645	1707	*1737*r	1816	*1837*	1918	*1937*	2032	2103	2132	2229	2332

	①-⑥ b	Ⓐ	①-⑥ b			Ⓐ ⊗	Ⓐ a	Ⓒ	①-⑥ b⊗	Ⓒ	Ⓐ				Ⓐ			Ⓐ		Ⓐ	Ⓑ h	Ⓐ	⑦ e		Ⓐ	Ⓒ	⑦ e
Chambéry ..... d.	0544	*0622*	0636	0728	*0822*	0928	0957	*1022*	1127k	*1222*	1228	1328	1413	1428	1506	1528	*1623*	1718	1726	1740	1828	1844	1844	1928	2028	2031	*2122*
Aix les Bains ..... d.	|	0641	|	0741	0842	0941	|	1041	1140	1241	1241	1341	|	1441	|	1541	1641	|	1739	|	1841	|	|	1941	2041	|	2141
Ambérieu ..... d.	|	0728	|	0828	0928	|	|	1128	1228	1328	1328	|	|	1528	|	|	1728	|	1828	|	1928	|	|	2028	|	|	2228
La Tour du Pin ... **343** d.	0629	|	0726	|	|	|	1040	|	|	|	|	|	1458	|	1552	|	|	1820	|	1858	|	1934	1939	|	|	2116	|
Bourgoin-Jallieu . **343** d.	0641	|	0742	|	|	|	1051	|	|	|	|	|	1509	|	1601	|	|	1830	|	1907	|	1944	1948	|	|	2130	|
Lyon Part Dieu .. **343** a.	0711	0752	0810	0852	0952	1052	1115	1152	1252	1352	1352	1452	...	1552	...	1652	1752	...	1852	...	1952	2011	...	2052	2152	2154	2252

a – Not July 25, Nov. 7.
b – Not June 10, Nov. 11.
c – Also July 25, Nov. 7.
e – Also June 10, Nov. 11.
h – Not Aug. 15, 16, Nov. 1.
k – Not Nov. 25 – 29.
r – *1744* on ⑥ (also Aug. 15, Nov. 1).
z – Not July 14 – 18, Oct. 20, 27 – 31.
⊗ – Subject to alteration Sept. 9 – 13, 16 – 20, Nov. 18 – 22.
△ – Not Aug. 15 – 17, Oct. 13 – 17, 21 – 24. On ①②③④⑦ June 23 - July 11 operated by 🚌 (not calling at Aix les Bains).

LYON - AIX LES BAINS - ANNECY 345

Subject to alteration on June 29, Aug. 16, 17, Nov. 10

km		Ⓐ	🚌 Ⓐ	D	⚒	🚌 ⑦ e	①-⑥ b	⊗		🚌 Ⓐ	Ⓐ s					Ⓐ		Ⓑ h	Ⓐ s		Ⓐ				z
0	**Lyon Part Dieu** ..... **344 346** d.	...	0608	...	0708	0708	0808	0908	1008	...	...	1208	1308	1408	1508	...	1608	...	...	1708	1808	...	1908	2008	2208
46	Ambérieu ..... **346** d.	0612	|	0714	0733	|	0833	0933	1033	...	1214	1233	|	1433	|	1614	1633	...	...	1733	1833	1914	1933	|	|
96	Culoz ..... **346** d.	0650	|	0752	0804	|	|	|	|	...	1252	|	|	|	|	1652	|	...	1752	|	|	1952	|	|	|
118	Aix les Bains ..... a.	0709	|	0811	0819	0835	0918	1018	1118	...	1311	1318	1418	1518	1618	1712	1718	...	1811	1818	1918	2011	2018	2118	2318
118	Aix les Bains ..... **364** d.	0711	|	0813	*0825*	0835	0925	*1025*r	*1125*c	1130	1313	1325	*1436*	*1525*	*1636*	...	1728	1726	1813	1825	1925	2013	*2025*	*2136*	*2325**
132	**Chambéry** ..... **344 364** a.	0724	|	0826	|	|	|	|	|	|	1327	|	|	|	|	...	|	1737	1825	|	|	2025	|	|	|
157	**Annecy** ..... **364** a.	...	0759	...	*0908*	0910	1008	*1108*r	*1208*c	1205	...	1408	*1516*	*1608*	*1717*	...	1808	...	...	1908	2008	...	*2108*	*2216*	*2357**

	Ⓐ	Ⓐ	①-⑥ b		Ⓐ		🚌 Ⓐ	Ⓒ		①-⑥ b⊗	🚌 Ⓐ		D					Ⓐ s			Ⓑ h	Ⓐ s			⑦ e
Annecy ..... **364** d.	...	0553	0653	...	...	0753	0900	0953	1039	*1053*a	1121	1153c	...	*1245*	*1353*	*1439*	1553	...	*1653*	...	*1739*	...	*1853*	*1939*	2053
Chambéry ..... **344 364** d.	0533	|	|	...	0733	|	|	|	|	|	|	|	1233	|	|	|	|	1633	|	1733	|	1836	|	|	|
Aix les Bains ..... **364** a.	0547	0634	0734	...	0747	0836	|	1034	1124	*1134*a	1231	1234c	1247	*1324*	*1435*	*1524*	1634	1647	*1727*	1747	*1824*	1848	*1935*	*2024*	2134
Aix les Bains ..... d.	0549	0641	...	0741	0749	0842	|	1041	...	1140	...	1241	1249	1341	1441	1541	1641	1649	1739	1749	1841	1849	1941	2041	2141
Culoz ..... **346** d.	0608	|	...	|	0808	|	|	|	...	1157	...	|	1308	|	|	|	|	1707	1756	1808	|	1908	|	|	|
Ambérieu ..... **346** d.	0646	0728	...	0828	0846	0928	|	1128	...	1228	...	1328	1346	|	1528	|	1728	...	1828	1846	1928	1946	2028	|	2228
Lyon Part Dieu ..... **344 346** a.	...	0752	...	0852	...	0952	1052	1152	...	1252	...	1352	...	1452	1552	1652	1752	...	1852	...	1952	...	2052	2152	2252

D – ⚒ to July 13; ⑥ July 20 - Aug. 24 (also Aug. 15); ①-⑥ from Aug. 26 (not Nov. 11).

a – Ⓐ only.
b – Not June 10, Nov. 11.
c – Ⓒ only.
e – Also June 10, Nov. 11.
h – Not Aug. 15, 16, Nov. 1.
r – On Ⓒ Aix les Bains d. *1036*, Annecy a. *1116*.
s – Not July 15 - Aug. 23.
z – Not June 23 – 27, 29, 30, July 1 – 4, 7 – 11, 14 – 18, Aug. 15 – 17, Oct. 13 – 17, 20 – 24, 27 – 31.

* – By 🚌.
⊗ – Subject to alteration Sept. 9 – 13, 16 – 20, Nov. 18 – 22.

346 LYON - BELLEGARDE - GENÈVE

Subject to alteration on June 29

km												TGV 9750											
		①-⑤	①-⑤	⑥	①-⑤	①-⑥				①-⑤				①-⑤		①-⑤	Ⓑ	①-⑤			①-⑤	①-⑤	⑤
		a	a		a	k				a			M	a		a	h△	a			a	a	f△	R
0	**Lyon** Perrache d.	...	...	...	...	...	...	...	...	...	...	...	...	...	...	...	...	...	...	...	...	...	...	...
4	**Lyon** Part Dieu **345** d.	...	...	...	...	0638	...	0838	1038	...	1238	1438	1532	...	1638	...	1738	...	...	1838	...	...	2038	2038
54	Ambérieu **345** d.	...	...	...	...	0703	...	0903	1103	...	1303	1503	|	...	1703	...	|	...	...	|	...	...	2103	2103
106	Culoz **345** d.	...	...	...	...	0734	...	0934	1134	...	1334	1534	|	...	1734	...	1837	...	...	1937	...	...	2140	2140
139	Bellegarde **341 364** d.	0553	0623	0653	0725	0801	...	1001	1201	1253	1401	1601	1643**s**	1723	1801	1823	1900	1925	1933	2001	2027	2129	2204	2206
172	**Genève** **341 364** a.	0628	0656	0728	0758	0829	...	1029	1229	1328	1429	1629	1718	1756	1829	1856	...	1958	2001	2029	2059	2202	...	2233

								TGV 9758															
	①-⑤	①-⑥	①-⑥	①-⑥								①-⑤				①-⑤	①-⑤		①-⑤	⑦	①-⑤		①-⑤	Ⓑ
	a	b	a	b△				M	⊙		⊡	a				a	a		a	e△	a		a	r
Genève **341 364** d.	0502	...	0556	...	...	0730	...	0841	0931	...	1131	1202	1330	...	1531	1602	1702	1722	1802	...	1902	1931	2019	2059
Bellegarde **341 364** d.	0535	0555	0631	0701	...	0801	...	0910**u**	1001	...	1201	1235	1401	...	1601	1635	1735	1801	1835	1901	1935	2001	2054	2126
Culoz **345** d.	...	0619	...	0725	...	0826	...	|	1026	...	1226	...	1426	...	1626	...	...	1826	...	1926	...	2026	...	...
Ambérieu **345** d.	...	0652	...	|	...	0858	...	|	1058	...	1258	...	1458	...	1658	...	...	1858	...	1958	...	2058	...	...
Lyon Part Dieu **345** a.	...	0722	...	0822	...	0922	...	1022	1122	...	1322	...	1522	...	1722	...	...	1922	...	2022	...	2122	...	...
Lyon Perrache a.	...	...	...	...	...	...	...	...	...	...	...	...	...	...	...	...	...	...	...	...	...	...	...	...

M – (12) Genève - Lyon - Marseille and v.v. (Table **350**).
R – ①②③④⑥⑦ (also Nov. 1; not Aug. 14, Oct. 31).

a – Not June 10, Aug. 1.
b – Not June 10, Nov. 11.
e – Also June 10, Nov. 11.

f – Also Aug. 14, Oct. 31; not Nov. 1.
h – Not Aug. 15, Nov. 1.
k – Not June 10.
r – Not June 9, Nov. 10.
s – Calls to set down only.
u – Calls to pick up only.

TGV – Ⓡ, supplement payable, 🍸.

⊙ – Subject to alteration Sept. 9 – 13, 16 – 20, Nov. 18 – 22.
⊡ – Subject to alteration Oct. 14 – 18, 21 – 25.
△ – To / from Évian les Bains (Table **363**).

348 LYON - ST ÉTIENNE

TGV trains Paris - Lyon - St Étienne

	TGV 6681	TGV 6681		TGV 6685		TGV 6687		TGV 6689	
	Ⓐ	⑥							
	a	k							
Paris Gare de Lyon **340** d.	0753	0753	...	1259	...	1659	...	1859	...
Lyon Part-Dieu d.	1005	1009	...	1505	...	1905	...	2105	...
St Étienne Châteaucreux a.	1047	1051	...	1547	...	1947	...	2147	...

	TGV 6691	TGV 6693		TGV 6695		TGV 6697		TGV 6697	
	①-⑥								
	d					G		F	
St Étienne Châteaucreux d.	0613	0643	...	1213	...	1643	...	1813	...
Lyon Part-Dieu a.	0658	0724	...	1258	...	1728	...	1858	...
Paris Gare de Lyon **340** a.	0901	0934	...	1501	...	1931	...	2101	...

Local Trains Lyon - St Étienne

km		①-⑥	Ⓐ	①-⑥	①-⑥	Ⓐ	Ⓐ			Ⓐ	Ⓐ	①-⑥		Ⓐ			①-⑥					Ⓒ	Ⓐ	Ⓐ
		b		b	b							b					b							
0	**Lyon** Part-Dieu d.	...	0624	...	0654	...	0724	...	0754	...	0824	...	0854	0924	...	0954	...	1054	...	...	1154	...	1224	...
	Lyon Perrache d.	0532	|	0631	|	0701	|	0731	|	0801	|	0831	|	|	0931	|	1031	|	...	1131	|	1207	|	1227
22	Givors Ville d.	0559	0642	0658	0712	0728	0742	0758	0812	0828	0842	0858	0912	0942	0958	1012	1059	1112	...	1158	1212	|	1242	|
47	St Chamond d.	0617	0700	0717	0730	0747	0801	0817	0830	0847	0900	0917	0930	1001	1017	1030	1117	1131	...	1217	1230	|	1301	|
59	**St Étienne** Châteaucreux a.	0626	0710	0726	0740	0756	0810	0826	0840	0856	0910	0926	0940	1010	1026	1040	1126	1140	...	1226	1240	1249	1310	1315

	①-⑥						①-⑥					Ⓐ	Ⓐ	①-⑥		Ⓐ	⑥	Ⓐ			Ⓐ	Ⓐ	①-⑥	
	b						b							b			v						b	
Lyon Part-Dieu d.	...	1254	...	...	1354	...	...	1454	1524	...	1554	...	1624	...	1654	...	...	1724	...	1754	...	1824	...	1854
Lyon Perrache d.	1231	|	...	1331	|	...	1431	|	|	1531	|	1601	|	1631	|	1701	1702	|	1731	|	1801	|	1831	|
Givors Ville d.	1258	1312	...	1358	1412	...	1458	1512	1541	1558	1612	1628	1642	1658	1712	1728	|	1742	1758	1812	1828	1842	1859	1912
St Chamond d.	1317	1330	...	1417	1430	...	1517	1530	1600	1617	1630	1647	1700	1717	1730	1747	|	1801	1817	1830	1847	1900	1917	1930
St Étienne Châteaucreux a.	1326	1340	...	1426	1440	...	1526	1540	1610	1626	1640	1656	1710	1726	1740	1756	1747	1810	1826	1840	1856	1910	1926	1940

	Ⓐ	Ⓐ			①-⑥		Ⓑ			
					b		h		z	
Lyon Part-Dieu d.	...	1924	...	1954	...	2054	2154	...	2254	...
Lyon Perrache d.	1901	|	1931	|	2031	|	|	...	|	...
Givors Ville d.	1928	1942	1958	2012	2059	2112	2211	...	2311	...
St Chamond d.	1947	2000	2017	2030	2117	2130	2230	...	2330	...
St Étienne Châteaucreux a.	1956	2010	2026	2040	2126	2140	2240	...	2340	...

	Ⓐ	Ⓐ	Ⓐ	Ⓐ	①-⑥	Ⓐ	Ⓐ	①-⑥	Ⓐ
					b			b	
St Étienne Châteaucreux d.	0520	0534	0550	0604	0620	0634	0650	0704	0711
St Chamond d.	0529	0543	0600	0613	0630	0643	0700	0713	|
Givors Ville d.	0548	0602	0618	0632	0648	0702	0718	0732	|
Lyon Perrache a.	|	0629	|	0659	|	0729	|	0759	0756
Lyon Part-Dieu a.	0606	...	0636	...	0706	...	0736	...	...

		Ⓐ	Ⓐ		⑥		Ⓐ	Ⓐ	①-⑥		Ⓐ			①-⑥				Ⓐ	①-⑥			Ⓒ		①-⑥
					v				b					b					b					b
St Étienne Châteaucreux d.	0720	0735	0750	0804	0812	0820	0834	0850	0904	0920	0950	1004	1020	1104	1120	1204	1220	1250	1304	1320	1404	1411	1420	1504
St Chamond d.	0730	0744	0800	0813	|	0829	0843	0859	0913	0930	0959	1013	1029	1113	1130	1213	1230	1259	1313	1330	1413	|	1430	1513
Givors Ville d.	0748	0802	0818	0832	|	0848	0902	0918	0932	0948	1018	1032	1047	1132	1148	1232	1248	1317	1332	1348	1432	|	1448	1532
Lyon Perrache a.	|	0829	|	0859	0856	|	0929	|	0959	|	|	1059	|	1159	|	1259	|	|	1359	|	1459	|	|	1559
Lyon Part-Dieu a.	0806	...	0836	...	...	0906	...	0936	...	1006	1036	...	1106	...	1206	...	1306	1336	...	1406	...	1454	1506	...

		Ⓐ			Ⓐ	Ⓐ	①-⑥		Ⓐ	Ⓐ			Ⓐ	Ⓐ	①-⑥	⑦	Ⓐ					Ⓑ		
							b								b	e						h		w
St Étienne Châteaucreux d.	1520	1550	1604	1620	1634	1650	1704	1720	1734	1750	1804	1820	1834	1850	1904	1911	1912	1920	2004	2020	...	2120	...	2220
St Chamond d.	1530	1600	1613	1630	1643	1700	1713	1730	1743	1800	1813	1830	1843	1900	1913	|	|	1930	2013	2030	...	2129	...	2230
Givors Ville d.	1548	1618	1632	1648	1702	1718	1732	1748	1802	1818	1832	1848	1902	1918	1932	|	|	1948	2032	2048	...	2148	...	2248
Lyon Perrache a.	|	|	1659	|	1729	|	1759	|	1829	|	1859	|	1929	|	1959	|	1956	|	2059	|	...	|	...	|
Lyon Part-Dieu a.	1606	1636	...	1706	...	1736	...	1806	...	1836	...	1906	...	1936	...	1954	...	2006	...	2106	...	2206	...	2306

F – ⑥ to July 6; ①②③④⑥ July 8 - Aug. 31 (also Aug. 16; not Aug. 14); ⑥ from Sept. 7 (also Nov. 1; not Nov. 2).
G – Ⓑ to July 5; ⑤⑦ July 12 - Aug. 25 (also Aug. 14; not Aug. 16); Ⓑ from Aug. 30 (not Nov. 1).

a – Not Aug. 16.

b – Not June 10, Nov. 11.
d – Not June 10, Nov. 2, 11.
e – Also June 10, Nov. 1.
h – Not Aug. 15, Nov. 1.
k – Also Aug. 15, 16, Nov. 1.
v – Also Aug. 15, Nov. 1.

w – Not June 16, July 28, Aug. 26 – 30, Sept. 1 – 6, 22, Oct. 7 – 10, 13 – 18, 21 – 25, 28 – 31, Nov. 17 – 22, 25 – 29, Dec. 1 – 6, 9 – 13.
z – Not June 16, July 28, Sept. 1, 22, 30, Oct. 1 – 3, 7 – 10, 13, Nov. 1, 9, 17, Dec. 1.

TGV – Ⓡ, supplement payable, 🍸.

349 ST ÉTIENNE - LE PUY

km		Ⓐ	①-⑥	①-⑥		①-⑥		Ⓒ	Ⓐ		Ⓐ		Ⓐ		
			b	b		b⊗			⊗						
	Lyon Part Dieu **348** d.	...	...	...	...	...	...	...	...	...	...	...	...	...	...
	Lyon Perrache **348** d.	...	0532	...	...	...	...	1207	1227	...	...	1702v	...	...	...
0	**St Étienne** Châteaucreux d.	0531	0630	0646	0852	0959	...	1252	1319	1557	1717	1750	1853	2006	2200
15	Firminy d.	0549	0651	0711	0909	1015	...	1309	1335	1613	1733	1807	1910	2029	2222
88	**Le Puy en Velay** a.	0723	...	0825	1021	1121	...	1424	1445	1720	1849	1917	2017	2134	2325

	Ⓐ	Ⓐ	①-⑥	Ⓐ			Ⓒ	Ⓐ	⑦	Ⓐ	⑥	Ⓐ	⑦	⑦	
			b			⊗		⊗	e		v		e	e	
Le Puy en Velay d.	0430	0542	0642	0739	0842	1043	1237	1237	1547	1619	1642	1738	1738	1840	1936
Firminy d.	0536	0648	0753	0851	0949	1148	1351	1355	1654	1727	1749	1852	1852	1950	2051
St Étienne Châteaucreux a.	0559	0708	0809	0908	1005	1204	1408	1411	1710	1743	1805	1908	1908	2007	2108
Lyon Perrache **348** a.	...	0756	0856v	...	...	...	|	...	...	...	...	1956	|	...	...
Lyon Part Dieu **348** a.	...	...	...	...	...	...	1454	...	...	...	...	...	1954	...	...

b – Not June 10, Nov. 11.
e – Also June 10, Nov. 11.
v – ⑥ (also Aug. 15, Nov. 1).

⊗ – Subject to alteration on ①-⑤ Oct. 7 – 25.

TGV Méditerranée

PARIS / LYON - AVIGNON - MARSEILLE - TOULON - NICE

For *TGV* trains Paris - Valence Ville - Avignon Centre see Table **351**. Certain Paris - Toulon trains continue to Hyères (Table **360**).
Timings may vary by a few minutes until June 23 (please check your *TGV* reservation). **Warning!** Services to Toulon / Nice are subject to alteration June 8 – 10, Nov. 1 – 3.

km	All *TGV* trains are 🅁	*TGV* 6805	*TGV* 6805	*TGV* 7801	*TGV* 7801		*TGV* 6101	*TGV* 7829	*TGV* 6101	*TGV* 6801		*TGV* 7851		*TGV* 5106	*TGV* 5103		*TGV* 6105	*TGV* 6155	*TGV* 6173	*TGV* 9758	*TGV* 9810	*TGV* 9814	*TGV* 5111
		①–⑤	⑥⑦				①–⑤		①–⑤					⑥	①–⑤						①–⑤	⑥⑦	⑥
		d	g	Z ⊠	L ⊠		a	⊠	a			⊠		k	a						a	c	
	Brussels Midi **11** d.	...	...	...	...	...	...	...	...	...	...	...	...	...	...	...	...	...	...	...	0609	0636	...
	Lille Europe **11** d.	...	...	...	...	...	...	...	...	...	...	...	...	0517f	0600j	...	...	...	...	...	0702	0729	0729
	Charles de Gaulle ✈ **11** d.	...	...	...	...	...	...	...	...	...	...	...	...	0657	0657	...	...	...	...	...	0826	0827	0827
	Marne la Vallée-Chessy § **11** d.	...	...	...	...	...	...	...	...	...	...	...	...	0710	0710	...	...	...	...	...	0840	0840	0840
0	**Paris** Gare de Lyon ▶ d.	...	...	...	...	...	0607	0612	...	...	...	0707	...	|	|	...	0837	0907	0907	...	|	|	|
	Metz **379** d.	...	...	...	...	...	|	|	...	...	...	|	...	|	|	...	|	|	|	...	|	|	|
	Strasbourg **379** d.	...	...	...	...	...	|	|	...	...	...	|	...	|	|	...	|	|	|	...	|	|	|
	Dijon **379** d.	...	...	...	...	...	|	|	...	...	...	|	...	|	|	...	|	|	|	...	|	|	|
	Genève **346** d.	...	...	...	...	...	|	|	...	...	...	|	...	|	|	...	|	|	|	0841	|	|	|
◧	**Lyon** Part Dieu ▶ d.	0628	0702	0708**p**	0708**p**	...	|	|	...	0806	...	|	...	0906	0910	...	|	|	|	1028	1036	1036	1036
	Lyon St Exupéry ✈ ▶ d.	|	|	|	|	...	|	|	←	|	...	0908	...	|	|	...	1032	|	|	|	|	|	|
527	Valence TGV ▶ d.	0704	|	|	|	...	0817	|	0827	0843	...	|	...	0943	0957	...	|	|	|	|	1117	1117	1117
657	**Avignon** TGV d.	0739	0806	0820	0822	...	→	0852	0902	0918	...	|	...	1017	1032	...	1125	|	|	1133	1151	1151	1151
731	Aix en Provence TGV d.	0807	0834	0848	0852	...	...	|	0930	|	...	1022	...	1047	1100	...	|	|	|	1206	|	|	|
750	**Marseille** St Charles a.	0819	0846	0901	0904	...	...	0926	0942	0953	...	|	...	1059	1112	...	1159	1214	1214	1218	1225	1225	1225
750	**Marseille** St Charles **360** d.	0831	0858	...	...	...	...	...	...	...	...	|	...	...	...	...	...	1228	1228	...	...	...	1232
817	**Toulon** **360** a.	0918	0944	...	...	...	...	...	...	...	...	1113	...	...	...	...	...	1313	1313	...	...	...	1318
885	Les Arcs-Draguignan **360** a.	0955	1022	...	...	...	...	...	...	...	...	|	...	...	...	...	...	...	|	...	...	...	1358
911	St Raphaël-Valescure **360** a.	1011	1039	...	...	...	...	...	...	...	...	1204	...	...	...	...	...	...	1404	...	...	...	1414
944	**Cannes** **360** a.	1041	1109	...	...	...	...	...	...	...	...	1233	...	...	...	...	...	...	1433	...	...	...	1441
955	Antibes **360** a.	1053	1121	...	...	...	...	...	...	...	...	1245	...	...	...	...	...	...	1445	...	...	...	1454
975	**Nice** **360** a.	1110	1139	...	...	...	...	...	...	...	...	1306	...	...	...	...	...	...	1506	...	...	...	1517

	TGV 6107	*TGV* 5320	*TGV* 6175	*TGV* 6109	*TGV* 6109	*TGV* 5316	*TGV* 6165	*TGV* 6111		*TGV* 9826	*TGV* 9826	*TGV* 7825	*TGV* 7825		*TGV* 6163	*TGV* 7827	*TGV* 6177		*TGV* 6117	*TGV* 6169	*TGV* 5324	*TGV* 6827	*TGV* 6121
					①–④					①–⑤	⑥⑦												
		N‡		T	S	H	K			n	m	Z ⊠	L ⊠		K	⊠	M				R	E	Y
Brussels Midi **11** d.	...	...	...	...	...	...	...	...	...	1033	1033	...	...	...	...	...	...	...	...	...	...	...	...
Lille Europe **11** d.	...	...	...	...	...	...	...	...	...	|	|	...	...	...	...	...	...	...	...	...	...	...	...
Charles de Gaulle ✈ **11** d.	...	...	...	...	...	...	...	...	...	1157	1157	...	...	...	...	...	...	...	...	...	...	...	...
Marne la Vallée-Chessy § **11** d.	...	...	...	...	...	...	...	...	...	1210	1210	...	...	...	...	...	...	...	...	...	...	...	...
aris Gare de Lyon ▶ d.	0937	...	1019	1037	1037	...	1119	1137	...	|	|	1237	1237	...	1418	1437	1507	...	1537	1602v	...	...	1637
Metz **379** d.	|	...	|	|	|	...	|	|	...	|	|	|	|	...	|	|	|	...	|	|	...	...	|
Strasbourg **379** d.	|	...	|	|	|	...	|	|	...	|	|	|	|	...	|	|	|	...	|	|	...	1347	|
Dijon **379** d.	|	...	|	|	|	...	|	|	...	|	|	|	|	...	|	|	|	...	|	|	...	1620	|
Genève **346** d.	|	...	|	|	|	...	|	|	...	|	|	|	|	...	|	|	|	...	|	|	...	|	|
yon Part Dieu ▶ d.	|	1136	|	|	|	1236	|	|	...	1406	1406	|	|	...	|	|	|	...	|	|	1736	1806	|
Lyon St Exupéry ✈ ▶ d.	|	|	|	|	1236	|	|	|	...	|	|	|	|	...	|	|	|	...	|	|	|	|	|
alence TGV ▶ d.	|	|	|	|	|	1313	|	|	...	|	1443	|	|	...	|	|	|	...	|	|	1812	|	|
vignon TGV d.	1222	1239	1258	1322	1330	1351	1400	1422	...	1511	|	1524	1524	...	1702	1718	|	...	1820	|	1852	1911	1922
ix en Provence TGV d.	1250	1307	|	1350	1400	|	|	1450	...	1539	1539	|	|	...	|	1746	|	...	1848	|	|	1939	1950
arseille St Charles a.	1301	1319	|	1401	1412	1430	|	1501	...	1555	1555	1558	1604	...	|	1800	1818	...	1900	1921	1926	1951	2001
arseille St Charles **360** d.	...	...	|	...	...	...	|	...	...	...	...	...	...	...	|	...	1830	...	...	1932	...	2003	...
oulon **360** a.	...	...	1412	...	...	...	1513	...	...	...	...	...	...	...	1813	...	1915	...	...	2017	...	2048	...
es Arcs-Draguignan **360** a.	...	...	1449	...	...	...	|	...	...	...	...	...	...	...	|	...	|	...	...	|	...	2125	...
t Raphaël-Valescure **360** a.	...	...	1506	...	...	...	1604	...	...	...	...	...	...	...	1907	...	2007	...	...	2112	...	2142	...
annes **360** a.	...	...	1533	...	...	...	1633	...	...	...	...	...	...	...	1933	...	2033	...	...	2138	...	2209	...
ntibes **360** a.	...	...	1545	...	...	...	1645	...	...	...	...	...	...	...	1945	...	2045	...	...	2149	...	2220	...
ice **360** a.	...	...	1606	...	...	...	1704	...	...	...	...	...	...	...	2004	...	2104	...	...	2208	...	2241	...

	TGV 7853	*TGV* 6123	*TGV* 6153	*TGV* 9580	*TGV* 6127	*TGV* 5134	*TGV* 5326	*TGV* 6187	*TGV* 6129		*TGV* 5124	*TGV* 6131	*TGV* 6131	*TGV* 6831		*TGV* 6137
			Ⓑ				Q	⑤			Ⓑ	②–④	⑤–①			
	⊠		h	F	B		N△	w	△		h△	q△	u△			J
Brussels Midi **11** d.	...	...	...	...	...	...	...	...	...	...	...	...	...	...	...	...
Lille Europe **11** d.	...	...	...	...	...	1703	...	...	...	...	1826	...	...	...	...	...
Charles de Gaulle ✈ **11** d.	...	...	...	...	...	1757	...	...	...	...	1927	...	...	...	...	...
Marne la Vallée-Chessy § **11** d.	...	...	...	...	...	1810	...	...	...	...	1940	...	...	...	...	...
aris Gare de Lyon ▶ d.	1712	1737	1819	...	1837	|	...	1919	1937	...	|	2019	2037	...	...	2137
Metz **379** d.	|	|	|	...	|	|	...	|	|	...	|	|	|	1700	...	|
Strasbourg **379** d.	|	|	|	1612	|	|	...	|	|	...	|	|	|	1803	...	|
Dijon **379** d.	|	|	|	|	|	|	...	|	|	...	|	|	|	2029	...	|
Genève **346** d.	|	|	|	|	|	|	...	|	|	...	|	|	|	|	...	|
yon Part Dieu ▶ d.	|	|	|	2006	|	2010	2036	|	|	...	2136	|	|	2214	...	|
Lyon St Exupéry ✈ ▶ d.	1906	|	|	|	|	|	|	|	|	...	|	|	|	|	...	|
alence TGV ▶ d.	|	|	|	|	|	2054	2113	|	|	...	|	|	|	2254	...	|
vignon TGV d.	|	2018	|	2111	2122	2130	2152	2200	2218	...	2241	2306	2318	2331	...	0023
ix en Provence TGV d.	2020	2046	2122	2139	2150	2158	|	|	2246	...	2308	2335	2348	2359	...	0052
arseille St Charles a.	|	2058	2134	2150	2201	2209	2227	|	2258	...	2320	2347	2359	0012	...	0104
arseille St Charles **360** d.	|	...	2149**r**	...	2219**y**	...	...	|	2310**t**	...	...	...	...	...	...	...
oulon **360** a.	2113	...	2239**r**	...	2307**y**	...	...	2314	2356**t**	...	...	...	...	...	...	...
es Arcs-Draguignan **360** a.	2151	...	...	...	...	...	...	|	...	...	...	...	...	...	...	...
t Raphaël-Valescure **360** a.	|	...	...	...	...	...	...	0004	...	...	...	...	...	...	...	...
annes **360** a.	2233	...	...	...	...	...	...	0033	...	...	...	...	...	...	...	...
ntibes **360** a.	2245	...	...	...	...	...	...	0046	...	...	...	...	...	...	...	...
ice **360** a.	2304	...	...	...	...	...	...	0103	...	...	...	...	...	...	...	...

– Daily to Sept. 1; ①–⑤ from Sept. 16 (not Oct. 31, Nov. 1, 11).
– From Nancy (d. 1227).
– From Frankfurt (Table **47**).
– 🚌12 Le Havre - Rouen - Massy - Lyon - Marseille (Table **335**). Subject to alteration on July 27, 28, Aug. 3, 4, 15 – 18, Oct. 12, 13, 19, 20, Nov. 1, 2, 3, 9, 10.
– ⑤⑦ to June 30 (also June 10); ⑤ July 5 - Aug. 30 (not Aug. 16); ⑤⑦ from Sept. 6 (not Nov. 1).
– July 6 - Sept. 1.
– Until Oct. 31.
– To Menton (Table **360**).
– From Nantes via Massy TGV (Table **335**).
– ⑤–⑦ to June 30 (also June 10); daily July 5 - Sept. 1; ⑤–⑦ from Sept. 6 (also Oct. 31). Subject to alteration Aug. 15 – 17, Nov. 1, 2, 9.
– ⑤–⑦ to June 30 (also June 10); daily July 5 - Sept. 1; ⑤–⑦ from Sept. 6 (also Oct. 31, Nov. 11). From Rennes via Massy TGV (Table **335**). Subject to alteration Aug. 15 – 17, Nov. 1, 2.
– ①–④ to July 4 / from Sept. 2 (not June 10, Oct. 31, Nov. 11).
– ⑤–⑦ to June 30 (also June 10); daily July 5 - Sept. 1; ⑤–⑦ from Sept. 6 (also Oct. 31, Nov. 11).
– Ⓑ to June 28; daily June 30 - Sept. 6; Ⓑ from Sept. 8 (not Nov. 1).
– From Nov. 1.

– Not June 10, Aug. 15, 16, Nov. 1, 11.
– Also June 10, Aug. 15, 16, Nov. 1, 11.
– Not June 10, Nov. 1, 11.
– Lille **Flandres**.
– Also Nov. 11.

h – Not Aug. 15, 16, Nov. 1.
j – 0527 on ②–⑤ June 18 - July 12.
k – Also Aug. 15, 16, Nov. 1.
m – Also June 10, Aug. 15, Nov. 11.
n – Not June 10, Aug. 15, 16, Oct. 31, Nov. 1, 11.

p – Lyon **Perrache**.
q – Not Aug. 14, 15, Oct. 31, Nov. 12.
r – Not June 9, Oct. 31.
t – Daily to Sept. 15; ⑥⑦ from Sept. 21 (also Nov. 11; not Nov. 2).
u – Also Aug. 14, 15, Oct. 31.
v – 1615 until July 5; 1611 on ⑥ July 6 - Aug. 31.
w – Also Aug. 14; not Aug. 16, Nov. 1.
y – ①–⑤ from Sept. 16 (not Oct. 31, Nov. 1, 11).

TGV – 🅁, supplement payable, 🍸.

△ – July 8 – 11, 16 – 18 service is diverted via Avignon Centre (not calling at Avignon TGV or Aix en Provence TGV; extended journey time).
‡ – Subject to alteration Aug. 15 – 18, Nov. 1, 2, 3, 10.
⊠ – OUIGO low-cost TGV service. Internet bookings only at www.ouigo.com.
▶ – For Paris to Lyon see Table **340** (for Paris to Lyon St Exupéry ✈ see Table **342**). For other trains from Paris and Lyon to Valence TGV see Table **355**. For Lyon to Valence Ville see Table **351**.
◧ – Lyon Part Dieu to Valence TGV is 104 km.
§ – Station for Disneyland Paris.

*See Table **11** for low-cost 'Ouigo' TGV services from Lille via Marne la Vallée*

350 NICE - TOULON - MARSEILLE - AVIGNON - LYON / PARIS *TGV Méditerranée*

For *TGV* trains Avignon Centre - Valence Ville - Paris see Table **351**. Certain Toulon - Paris trains start from Hyères (Table **360**).
Timings may vary by a few minutes until June 23 (please check your *TGV* reservation). **Warning!** Services from Nice / Toulon are subject to alteration June 8 – 10, Nov. 1 – 3.

All *TGV* trains are [R]	*TGV* **6102** Ⓐ a		*TGV* **6136** ⑦ K	*TGV* **6136** ①–④ m	*TGV* **6150** Ⓐ a	*TGV* **9854** ①–⑥ b	*TGV* **5154** ⑦ e	*TGV* **6106**		*TGV* **9582** F	*TGV* **7858** ⊠	*TGV* **5370** G N	*TGV* **6112**		*TGV* **7822** ⊠	*TGV* **6814**	*TGV* **9898** X		*TGV* **6188** L		*TGV* **5368** **5372** R	*TGV* **6116**	*TGV* **9866**
Nice 360 d.	...	...	...	...	...	...	...	...	...	...	0557	...	...	...	...	0657	...	...	0757	...	...	...	...
Antibes 360 d.	...	...	...	...	...	...	...	...	...	...	0614	...	...	...	...	0712	...	...	0814	...	...	...	...
Cannes 360 d.	...	...	...	...	...	...	...	...	...	...	0626	...	...	...	...	0725	...	...	0826	...	...	...	...
St Raphaël-Valescure 360 d.	...	...	...	...	...	...	...	...	...	...	|	...	...	...	...	0750	...	...	0852	...	...	...	...
Les Arcs-Draguignan 360 d.	...	...	...	...	...	...	...	...	...	...	0705	...	...	...	...	0807	...	...	|	...	...	...	...
Toulon 360 d.	...	...	...	...	0538	...	...	...	...	...	0746	...	...	...	...	0848	...	...	0948	...	...	...	...
Marseille St Charles 360 a.	...	...	...	...	|	...	...	...	...	...	|	...	...	...	...	0934	...	...	|	...	...	...	...
Marseille St Charles d.	0517	...	0600	0601	|	0625	0638	0656	...	0809	|	0838	0902	...	0936	0946	1007	...	|	...	1138	1201	1210
Aix en Provence TGV d.	0532	...	0615	0616	0633	0639	0653	0711	...	0824	0840	|	0917	...	|	|	1024	...	|	...	1153	1216	1224
Avignon TGV d.	0559	...	0642	0644	0700	0711	0720	0738	...	0851	|	0914	0944	...	1011	1019	|	...	1102	...	1220	1243	1252
Valence TGV ▶ d.	|	...	|	|	|	0749	|	|	...	|	|	0949	|	...	1046	1054	1119	...	|	...	|	|	|
Lyon St Exupéry ✈ ▶ d.	|	...	|	|	|	|	|	|	...	|	0954	|	|	...	1112	|	|	...	|	...	|	|	|
Lyon Part Dieu ▶ a.	|	...	|	|	|	0824	0824	|	...	0954	|	1024	|	...	|	1128	1154	...	|	...	1324	|	1354
Genève **346** a.	|	...	|	|	|	|	|	|	...	|	|	...	|	...	|	|	|	...	|	...	...	|	|
Dijon **379** a.	|	...	|	|	|	|	|	|	...	|	|	...	|	...	|	1326	1335	...	|	...	...	|	|
Strasbourg **379** a.	|	...	|	|	|	|	|	|	...	1344	|	...	|	...	|	...	1556	...	|	...	...	|	|
Metz **379** a.	|	...	|	|	|	|	|	|	...	...	|	...	|	...	|	...	1649	...	|	...	...	|	|
Paris Gare de Lyon ▶ a.	0841	...	0923	0923	0942	|	|	1019	...	...	1145	...	1223	...	1305	...	...	...	1341	...	...	1523	|
Marne la Vallée-Chessy § **11** a.	...	...	...	...	...	1020	1020	...	...	...	...	...	...	...	...	...	...	...	...	...	...	...	1547
Charles de Gaulle ✈ **11** a.	...	...	...	...	...	1034	1034	...	...	...	...	...	...	...	...	...	...	...	...	...	...	...	1602
Lille Europe **11** a.	...	...	...	...	...	1127	1127	...	...	...	...	...	...	...	...	...	...	...	...	...	...	...	1656
Brussels Midi **11** a.	...	...	...	...	...	1234	...	...	...	...	...	...	...	...	...	...	...	...	...	...	...	...	1743

	TGV **6174** M	*TGV* **7820** ⊠		*TGV* **6176**	*TGV* **9750**	*TGV* **6120** B	*TGV* **6170** K	*TGV* **5378** N	*TGV* **6122**	*TGV* **9864**		*TGV* **5376** H	*TGV* **6124**	*TGV* **6866**	*TGV* **7856** Z⊠	*TGV* **7856** ⑥ Y⊠		*TGV* **6128**	*TGV* **9882** ⑦	*TGV* **9882** ①–⑥		*TGV* **7824** ⑥⑦ ⊠	*TGV* **7824** ①–⑤ ⊠
Nice 360 d.	1000	...	...	1057	...	...	1157	...	...	...	...	...	...	...	1357	1357	...	...	...	...	...	...	...
Antibes 360 d.	1017	...	...	1114	...	...	1214	...	...	...	...	...	...	...	1414	1414	...	...	...	...	...	...	...
Cannes 360 d.	1029	...	...	1126	...	...	1226	...	...	...	...	...	...	...	1426	1426	...	...	...	...	...	...	...
St Raphaël-Valescure 360 d.	1054	...	...	1152	...	...	1252	...	...	...	...	...	...	...	1452	1452	...	...	...	...	...	...	...
Les Arcs-Draguignan 360 d.	|	...	...	|	...	...	|	...	...	...	...	...	...	...	|	|	...	...	...	...	...	...	...
Toulon 360 d.	1148	...	...	1246	...	...	1346	...	...	...	...	...	1449	...	1542	1546	...	...	...	...	...	...	...
Marseille St Charles 360 a.	1236	...	...	1332	...	...	|	...	...	...	...	...	1534	...	|	|	...	...	...	...	...	...	...
Marseille St Charles d.	1249	1305	...	1344	1348	1401	|	1439	1457	1509	...	1539	1548	1610	|	|	...	1659	1706	1709	...	1741	1741
Aix en Provence TGV d.	1304	|	...	|	1402	1416	|	1454	1513	1524	...	|	1603	1625	1638	1642	...	1714	1723	1724	...	|	|
Avignon TGV d.	1331	1341	...	|	1429	1443	1502	1521	1543	1551	...	1614	|	1652	|	|	...	1742	1751	1751	...	1818	1818
Valence TGV ▶ d.	|	|	...	|	|	|	|	|	|	|	...	1649	1657	|	|	|	...	|	|	|	...	|	|
Lyon St Exupéry ✈ ▶ d.	|	1439	...	|	|	1536	|	|	|	|	...	|	|	|	1751	1804	...	|	|	|	...	1915j	1926j
Lyon Part Dieu ▶ a.	|	|	...	|	1529	|	|	1624	|	1654	...	1724	|	1754	|	|	...	|	1854	1854	...	|	|
Genève **346** a.	|	|	...	|	1718	|	|	...	|	|	...	...	|	|	|	|	...	|	|	|	...	|	|
Dijon **379** a.	|	|	...	|	...	|	|	...	|	|	...	...	|	1938	|	|	...	|	|	|	...	|	|
Strasbourg **379** a.	|	|	...	|	...	|	|	...	|	|	...	...	|	2157	|	|	...	|	|	|	...	|	|
Metz **379** a.	|	|	...	|	...	|	|	...	|	|	...	...	|	...	|	|	...	|	|	|	...	|	|
Paris Gare de Lyon ▶ a.	1615	1632	...	1653	...	1731	1741	...	1823	|	...	...	1915	...	1943	1957	...	2023	|	|	...	2111	2119
Marne la Vallée-Chessy § **11** a.	...	...	...	...	...	...	...	...	...	1848	...	...	...	...	...	...	...	...	2048	2048	...	...	...
Charles de Gaulle ✈ **11** a.	...	...	...	...	...	...	...	...	...	1902	...	...	...	...	...	...	...	...	2103	2103	...	...	...
Lille Europe **11** a.	...	...	...	...	...	...	...	...	...	1956	...	...	...	...	...	...	...	...	2156	2156	...	...	...
Brussels Midi **11** a.	...	...	...	...	...	...	...	...	...	2043	...	...	...	...	...	...	...	...	2243	2243	...	...	...

	TGV **6802**		*TGV* **6168**	*TGV* **7806** ⊠	*TGV* **5184** ⑦ w		*TGV* **6180**		*TGV* **6134**	*TGV* **6806** ✣		*TGV* **6186** ⑦	*TGV* **6144** ⑦										
Nice 360 d.	1457	...	1541	...	1556	...	1657	...	...	1723	...	1757	...	...	...	...	...	...	...	...	...	...	...
Antibes 360 d.	1514	...	1557	...	1616	...	1714	...	...	1739	...	1814	...	...	...	...	...	...	...	...	...	...	...
Cannes 360 d.	1525	...	1611	...	1628	...	1726	...	...	1753	...	1826	...	...	...	...	...	...	...	...	...	...	...
St Raphaël-Valescure 360 d.	1552	...	1639	...	1655	...	|	...	...	1818	...	1852	...	...	...	...	...	...	...	...	...	...	...
Les Arcs-Draguignan 360 d.	1609	...	1655	...	1712	...	1808	...	...	1835	...	|	...	...	...	...	...	...	...	...	...	...	...
Toulon 360 d.	1648	...	1738	...	1753	...	1846	...	...	1913	...	1946	...	...	...	...	...	...	...	...	...	...	...
Marseille St Charles 360 a.	1734	...	1823	...	1841	...	1932	...	...	1958	...	|	...	...	...	...	...	...	...	...	...	...	...
Marseille St Charles d.	1746	...	1835	1841	1857	...	1946	...	2001	2010	...	|	2102	...	...	...	...	...	...	...	...	...	...
Aix en Provence TGV d.	1801	...	|	|	1912	...	|	...	2016	2025	...	|	2117	...	...	...	...	...	...	...	...	...	...
Avignon TGV d.	1828	...	|	|	1939r	...	|	...	2043	2051	...	2102	2144	...	...	...	...	...	...	...	...	...	...
Valence TGV ▶ d.	|	...	|	|	2016r	...	|	...	|	2125	...	|	|	...	...	...	...	...	...	...	...	...	...
Lyon St Exupéry ✈ ▶ d.	|	...	|	|	|	...	|	...	|	|	...	|	|	...	...	...	...	...	...	...	...	...	...
Lyon Part Dieu ▶ a.	1930p	...	|	2020	2050	...	|	...	|	2200p	...	|	|	...	...	...	...	...	...	...	...	...	...
Genève **346** a.	...	...	|	...	|	...	|	...	|	...	...	|	|	...	...	...	...	...	...	...	...	...	...
Dijon **379** a.	...	...	|	...	|	...	|	...	|	...	...	|	|	...	...	...	...	...	...	...	...	...	...
Strasbourg **379** a.	...	...	|	...	|	...	|	...	|	...	...	|	|	...	...	...	...	...	...	...	...	...	...
Metz **379** a.	...	...	|	...	|	...	|	...	|	...	...	|	|	...	...	...	...	...	...	...	...	...	...
Paris Gare de Lyon ▶ a.	...	...	2145	...	|	...	2253	...	2327	...	...	2341	0023	...	...	...	...	...	...	...	...	...	...
Marne la Vallée-Chessy § **11** a.	...	...	...	...	2248	...	...	...	...	...	...	...	...	...	...	...	...	...	...	...	...	...	...
Charles de Gaulle ✈ **11** a.	...	...	...	...	2302	...	...	...	...	...	...	...	...	...	...	...	...	...	...	...	...	...	...
Lille Europe **11** a.	...	...	...	...	2356	...	...	...	...	...	...	...	...	...	...	...	...	...	...	...	...	...	...
Brussels Midi **11** a.	...	...	...	...	...	...	...	...	...	...	...	...	...	...	...	...	...	...	...	...	...	...	...

B – Daily to June 28; Ⓑ June 30 - Aug. 30 (not Aug. 15, 16); daily from Sept. 1.
F – To Frankfurt (Table **47**).
G – ①⑥⑦ to July 1 (also June 11); daily July 6 - Sept. 2; ①⑥⑦ from Sept. 7 (also Nov. 1, 12). Subject to alteration on Aug. 14, Nov. 2, 3, 10.
H – (12) Marseille - Lyon - Massy - Rouen - Le Havre (Table **335**). Subject to alteration on July 27, Aug. 3, 15, 16, 17, Oct. 12, 19, Nov. 1, 2, 9, 10.
K – July 6 - Sept. 1.
L – July 6 - Sept. 13.
M – From Menton (Table **360**).
N – To Nantes via Massy TGV (Table **335**).
R – ①⑥⑦ to July 1; daily July 6 - Sept. 2; ①⑥⑦ from Sept. 7 (also Nov. 1, 12). Subject to alteration on Aug. 15, 16, 17, Nov. 2, 9, 10. To Rennes via Massy TGV (Table **335**).
X – To Luxembourg (Table **379**).
Y – ⑥ June 29 - Aug. 31.
Z – Daily to June 28; Ⓑ June 30 - Aug. 30; daily from Sept. 1.

a – Not Aug. 16.
b – Not June 10, Nov. 11.
e – Also June 10, Nov. 11.

j – Arrives 1910.
m – Not June 10, Aug. 14, 15, Oct. 31, Nov. 11.
p – Lyon **Perrache**.
r – Departs Avignon 1935, Valence 2015 June 10 – 23 and July 14 - Aug. 11
w – Also June 10, Nov. 11; not June 9, Nov. 10.

TGV – [R], supplement payable, 🍸.

✣ – Subject to confirmation from Sept. 2.
‡ – Subject to alteration on Aug. 15, 16, 17, Nov. 1, 2, 9, 10.
⊠ – OUIGO low-cost TGV service. Internet bookings only at www.ouigo.com.
▶ – For Lyon - Paris see Table **340** (for St Exupéry ✈ - Paris see Table **342**). For other trains Valence TGV - Lyon and Paris see Table **355**. For Valence Ville - Lyon see Table **351**.
§ – Station for Disneyland Paris.

*See Table **11** for low-cost 'Ouigo' TGV services to Lille via Marne la Vallée*

LYON - VALENCE - AVIGNON - MARSEILLE via 'classic' line 351

See Table **350** for *TGV* services Paris / Lyon - Valence TGV - Avignon TGV - Marseille, Table **355** for *TGV* services Paris / Lyon - Valence TGV - Montpellier.
Subject to alteration on June 9, 15, 16, Aug. 7, 8, Nov. 1, 2. Timings Avignon - Marseille may vary by up to 5 minutes June 10 – 23 and July 29 - Aug. 25.

km		Ⓐ	Ⓐ	⚒	⚒	Ⓐ	①–⑥ b		①–⑥ b	Ⓐ	17705	Ⓐ		C	*TGV* 6191 H	17709	Ⓐ	E	①–⑤ S	17713 C	*TGV* 6193 ⑥⑦ R	C	Ⓐ	*TGV* 6193 D	①–⑤ S
	Paris Gare de Lyon § d.	...	...	...	...	...	...	...	...	...	...	...	...	...	0741	...	...	...	...	...	1045	...	...	1141	...
	Lyon St Exupéry TGV ✈ § d.	...	...	...	...	...	...	...	...	...	...	...	...	...	0943	...	...	...	...	...	1251	...	...	1343	...
	Lyon Perrache d.	...	...	...	...	...	0538	...	...	0638	...	0738	...	...	|	...	...	...	...	...	|	...	...	|	...
0	**Lyon** Part-Dieu d.	...	...	...	...	...	|	...	0620	|	0720	|	...	0820	|	0920	...	1020	1020	1120	|	1220	...	|	1218
32	Vienne d.	...	...	...	...	...	0559	...	0641	0659	0742	0759	...	0841	|	0942	...	1041	|	1142	|	1241	...	|	|
87	Tain-l'Hermitage-Tournon d.	...	...	...	...	...	0641	...	0720	0739	0815	0838	...	0920	|	1015	...	1120	|	1215	|	1320	...	|	|
105	**Valence** Ville a.	...	...	...	...	...	0652	...	0730	0750	0825	0848	...	0930	1013	1025	...	1130	|	1225	1321	1330	...	1412	|
105	**Valence** Ville d.	...	...	0612	0632	0632	...	0702	...	...	0828	...	0932	...	1016	1028	...	1132	|	1228	1324	1332	...	1415	|
150	Montélimar d.	...	...	0635	0700	0700	...	0730	...	...	0850	...	1000	...	1038	1050	...	1200	|	1250	1347	1400	...	1438	|
202	Orange d.	...	...	0706	0735	0735	...	0805	...	...	0924	...	1035	...	1104	1124	...	1235	|	1324	1414	1435	...	1503	|
230	**Avignon** Centre a.	...	...	0729	0758	0758	...	0828	...	...	0938	...	1058	...	1121	1138	...	1258	1320	1338	1431	1458	...	1516	1527
230	**Avignon** Centre d.	0541	0641	0731	...	0801	...	...	...	...	0941	...	...	...	...	1141	1218	...	...	1341	1435	...	1517	1521	...
265	Arles **355** d.	0600	0700	0750	...	0822	...	...	...	...	1001	...	...	...	...	1201	1236	...	...	1401	1453	...	1536	1542	...
299	Miramas **355** d.	0620	0720	0809	...	0844	...	...	...	...	1018	...	...	...	...	1218	1257	...	...	1418	1518	...	1557	1604	...
328	Vitrolles (for ✈) ⊖ **355** d.	0638	0738	0826	...	0901	...	...	...	...	1036	...	...	...	...	1236	1320	...	...	1436	...	...	1618	...	...
351	**Marseille** St Charles **355** a.	0652	0752	0842	...	0915	...	...	...	...	1050	...	...	...	...	1250	1340v	...	...	1451	...	...	1638	...	...

	17717 C	Ⓐ	17717 ①–⑤ S	J		17721	Ⓐ	†	Ⓐ	⚒ ⊙		Ⓐ	17725	⑤ F			Ⓐ		Ⓑ m	*TGV* 6195 Ⓑ h	Ⓐ	17729			
Paris Gare de Lyon § d.	...	...	...	...	...	...	...	...	...	...	...	...	...	...	...	...	...	...	...	1741	...	...	...	...	...
Lyon St Exupéry TGV ✈ § d.	...	...	...	...	...	...	...	...	...	...	...	...	...	...	...	...	...	...	...	1943	...	...	...	...	...
Lyon Perrache d.	...	...	...	1338	...	...	...	...	1538	...	1638	1711	...	...	...	1739	1810	...	1838	|	1910	...	1938	...	...
Lyon Part-Dieu d.	1320	...	1320	|	1420	1520	...	...	|	1620	|	|	1720	...	...	|	|	1820	|	|	|	1920	|	2020	2120
Vienne d.	1342	...	|	1400	1440	1542	...	...	1559	1639	1659	1732	1742	...	...	1801	1831	1841	1859	|	1931	1942	2000	2041	2141
Tain-l'Hermitage-Tournon d.	1415	...	|	1438	1520	1615	...	...	1642	1718	1741	1810	1815	...	...	1843	1911	1919	1938	|	2011	2014	2038	2120	2220
Valence Ville a.	1425	...	|	1448	1530	1625	...	...	1653	1728	1753	1822	1825	...	...	1854	1922	1929	1948	2011	2022	2025	2048	2130	2230
Valence Ville d.	1428	...	|	...	...	1628	...	1702	1702	1730	*1802*a	...	1828	1856	...	1902	...	1942	...	2014	...	2028	...	...	...
Montélimar d.	1450	...	|	...	...	1650	...	1730	1731	1759	*1830*a	...	1850	1921	...	1931	...	2014	...	2037	...	2050	...	...	...
Orange d.	1524	...	|	...	...	1724	...	1805	1805	1835	*1905*a	...	1924	1952	...	2005	...	2047	...	2103	...	2124	...	...	...
Avignon Centre a.	1538	...	1634	...	...	1738	...	1828	1828	1858	*1928*a	...	1938	2006	...	2028	...	2115	...	2118	...	2138	...	...	...
Avignon Centre d.	1541	1616	1644	...	...	1741	1806	...	...	...	...	...	1941r	...	2015	...	...	...	...	2122	...	2141	...	...	...
Arles **355** d.	1601	1635	1709	...	...	1800	1828	...	...	...	...	...	2001r	...	2035	...	...	...	...	2140	...	2203	...	...	...
Miramas **355** d.	1619	1657	1733	...	...	1819	1852	...	...	...	...	...	2019r	...	2057	...	...	...	...	2159k	...	2219	...	...	...
Vitrolles (for ✈) ⊖ **355** d.	1637	1717	1800	...	...	1836	1912	...	...	...	...	...	|	...	2118	...	...	...	...	...	...	2237	...	...	...
Marseille St Charles **355** a.	1650	1737	1832	...	...	1851	1940	...	...	...	...	...	2050r	...	2138	...	...	...	...	...	...	2251	...	...	...

	Ⓐ	Ⓐ	①–⑥ b	①–⑥ b	⚒	n	17702 ⚒	①–⑥ b	*TGV* 6194 ①–⑥ b	Ⓑ	Ⓐ	⚒		Ⓐ	17706 C	17706 ①–⑤ S	Ⓐ T	17704 ①–⑤ S	17704 M	17704 ⑥⑦ N	C		17714 C	*TGV* 6196 C	①–⑥ b
Marseille St Charles **355** d.	...	...	...	...	...	...	0503	...	...	...	...	...	...	0605	0710	0710	...	...	0910	0914	...	...	1110	...	...
Vitrolles (for ✈) ⊖ **355** d.	...	...	...	...	...	...	|	...	...	...	...	...	...	0625	0726	0726	...	...	0925	0929	...	...	1126	...	...
Miramas **355** d.	...	...	...	...	...	...	0533	...	0549	...	...	...	...	0647	0744	0744	...	...	0942	0947	...	...	1144	...	...
Arles **355** d.	...	...	...	...	...	...	0551	...	0609	...	...	...	...	0709	0801	0801	...	...	0959	1003	...	...	1201	...	...
Avignon Centre a.	...	...	...	...	...	...	0608	...	0625	...	...	...	...	0727	0818	0818	...	...	1018	1019	...	...	1218	...	...
Avignon Centre d.	...	...	...	...	0533	...	0621	...	0629	0633	0633	0702	0733	0733	0821	0825	...	0938	1021	1022	...	...	1221	1228	...
Orange d.	...	...	...	...	0556	...	0637	...	0649	0656	0656	0725	0756	0756	0837	|	...	|	1038	1039	...	...	1237	1247	...
Montélimar d.	...	0533	...	...	0631	...	0711	...	0719	0731	0731	0800	0831	0831	0912	|	...	|	1112	1113	...	...	1310	1317	...
Valence Ville a.	...	0601	...	...	0658	...	0732	...	0740	0758	0758	0827	0858	0858	0932	|	...	|	1132	1133	...	...	1332	1338	...
Valence Ville d.	0540	0608	0629	0640	0712	0712	0735	0740	0743	...	0812	0829	...	...	0935	|	1029	|	1135	1136	1229	...	1335	1341	1429
Tain-l'Hermitage-Tournon d.	0551	0619	0640	0651	0723	0723	0747	0751	|	...	0823	0840	...	...	0947	|	1040	|	1147	1148	1240	...	1347	|	1440
Vienne d.	0629	0658	0720	0729	0802	0802	0820	0829	|	...	0902	0920	...	...	1020	|	1120	|	1220	1220	1320	...	1420	|	1520
Lyon Part-Dieu a.	|	|	0740	|	|	|	0840	|	|	...	|	0940	...	...	1040	1154	1140	1219	1240	1240	1340	...	1440	|	1540
Lyon Perrache a.	0650	0720	...	0750	0822	0822	...	0850	|	...	0922	...	...	...	...	...	...	...	...	...	...	...	...	|	...
Lyon St Exupéry TGV ✈ § a.	...	...	...	...	...	...	...	...	0817	...	...	...	...	...	...	...	...	...	...	...	...	...	...	1419	...
Paris Gare de Lyon § a.	...	...	...	...	...	...	...	...	1026	...	...	...	...	...	...	...	...	...	...	...	...	...	...	1626	...

		Ⓑ m	17716	①–⑥ b	Ⓑ m	17718			*TGV* 6198 ①–⑤ ¶	*TGV* 6198 ⑥⑦	Ⓐ	Ⓑ m	⑦ w	Ⓐ	17724 ①–⑥ P	17724 ⑦ Q	⑦ eA		Ⓐ	⚒		Ⓑ	⑦ e		
Marseille St Charles **355** d.	...	...	1310	...	...	1505t	...	...	...	...	...	...	...	1640	1703	1710	...	...	1810	...	...	1902	...	...	2021
Vitrolles (for ✈) ⊖ **355** d.	...	...	1326	...	...	1526	...	...	...	...	...	...	...	1656	1725	1727	...	...	1826	...	...	1920	...	...	2042
Miramas **355** d.	...	...	1344	...	...	1544	...	...	1700	1700	...	...	...	1713	1744	1744	...	...	1848	...	...	1939	...	...	2104
Arles **355** d.	...	...	1401	...	...	1601	...	...	1721	1721	...	...	...	1734	1801	1801	...	...	1911	...	...	1958	...	...	2126
Avignon Centre a.	...	...	1418	...	...	1618	...	...	1738	1738	...	...	...	1752	1818	1818	...	...	1928j	...	...	2014	...	...	2144
Avignon Centre d.	1302	...	1421	...	...	1621	...	1702	1741	1741	1726	...	...	...	1821	1821	1843	1900	...	1933	1933	2016	...	...	...
Orange d.	1325	...	1437	...	...	1637	...	1725	1758	1758	1749	...	...	...	1837	1837	1858	1923	...	1956	1956	2031	...	...	...
Montélimar d.	1401	...	1512	...	...	1712	...	1800	1823	1823	1832	...	...	...	1912	1912	1931	1959	...	2031	2031	2102	...	...	...
Valence Ville a.	1428	...	1532	...	...	1732	...	1827	1844	1844	1858	...	...	...	1932	1932	1953	2025	...	2058	2058	2128	...	...	...
Valence Ville d.	...	1508	1535	1608	1712	1735	1810	1829	1847	1847	...	1912	1921	...	1935	1935	...	2027	...	2112	...	...	2140	...	...
Tain-l'Hermitage-Tournon d.	...	1519	1547	1619	1723	1747	1821	1840	|	|	...	1923	1934	...	1947	1947	...	2038	...	2124	...	...	2150	...	...
Vienne d.	...	1559	1620	1658	1802	1820	1859	1920	|	|	...	2002	2009	...	2020	2020	...	2122	...	2202	...	...	2229	...	...
Lyon Part-Dieu a.	...	|	1640	|	|	1840	|	1940	|	|	...	|	2030	...	2040	2041	...	2141	...	|	...	...	2250	...	...
Lyon Perrache a.	...	1622	...	1720	1822	...	1922	...	|	|	...	2022	...	...	...	...	...	...	...	2222	...	...	...	...	...
Lyon St Exupéry TGV ✈ § a.	...	...	...	...	...	...	...	...	|	1920	...	...	...	...	...	...	...	...	...	...	...	...	...	...	...
Paris Gare de Lyon § a.	...	...	...	...	...	...	...	...	2114	2122	...	...	...	...	...	...	...	...	...	...	...	...	...	...	...

A – To Annecy (Table **364**).
C – Ⓒ to June 30; daily from July 6.
D – Ⓒ to June 30; Ⓐ July 8 - Aug. 30; daily from Sept. 2.
E – ⑥ to June 29; ⚒ from July 6.
F – ⑤ (also Aug. 14, Oct. 31; not Nov. 1). From Annecy (Table **364**). From Sept. 13 departs Orange 1954, arrives Avignon 2012.
H – Daily to July 6; ①–⑥ July 8 - Aug. 31; daily from Sept. 2.
J – ⑥ to June 29; ①–⑥ from July 6 (not Nov. 11).
M – Ⓒ to June 30; ①–⑤ from July 8.
N – ⑥⑦ from July 6.
P – ①–⑥ from June 24 (also June 15, 30; not Nov. 1, 2).
Q – ⑦ (also June 10 – 14, 17 – 22; not June 30).
R – Ⓒ July 6 - Aug. 25 (not Aug. 10, 11, 17).
S – ①–⑤ June 11 - July 5.
T – From July 8.

a – Ⓐ only.
b – Not June 10, Nov. 11.

e – Also June 10, Nov. 11.
h – Not Aug. 15, 16, Nov. 1.
j – 1936 June 11 – 21 and July 29 - Aug. 23.
k – 3 – 6 minutes later until Sept. 1.
m – Not Aug. 15, Nov. 1.
n – Not Aug. 15, Nov. 1, 2.
r – Not ⑥.
t – 5 – 7 minutes later until July 5.
v – 1351 on July 8, Aug. 12, Sept. 9, Nov. 18.
w – Also June 10, Nov. 11; not June 9, Nov. 10.

TGV – Ⓡ, supplement payable, 🍸.

⊙ – Timings Vienne - Montélimar are 1 – 2 minutes later until Oct. 5.
¶ – Also calls at Mâcon-Loché TGV (d. 1934).
§ – See Table **342** for full service Paris - Lyon St Exupéry and v.v.
⊖ – Vitrolles Aéroport Marseille-Provence ✈. A shuttle bus runs to the airport terminal (journey 5 minutes) connecting with trains.

380 PARIS - TROYES - MULHOUSE

SPECIAL VERSION OF TABLE 380 VALID JULY 13 - AUGUST 24. During this period no direct services run Paris - Troyes and v.v. (please check locally for alternative arrangements). See page 228 from service to July 12 and from August 25.

km		Ⓐ	⑥	Ⓐ	Ⓐ a	Ⓐ a	⑥	Ⓒ	⚒		Ⓒ	Ⓐ	Ⓐ a	Ⓐ	Ⓒ		Ⓐ	◧	⑥	†	Ⓐ	Ⓑ	⑥	Ⓐ	Ⓒ
0	**Paris** Est d.	...	...	...	...	...	...	...	0836	...	...	...	...	...	...	...	...	...	1420	1424	1436	...	...	1736	1736
110	Nogent sur Seine d.	...	...	...	0640	0739	...	...	|	...	...	...	1341	...	...	...	...	...	|	|	|	...	...	|	|
129	Romilly sur Seine d.	...	...	...	0652	0750	...	...	|	...	...	...	1352	...	...	...	...	...	|	|	|	...	...	|	|
166	**Troyes** d.	0515	0631	...	0712	0814	0814	0912	▽	...	1312	1313	1409	1512	1513	...	...	1643	▽	▽	▽	1814	1814	▽	▽
221	Bar sur Aube d.	0546	0705	...	0742	0844	0845	0942	|	...	1342	1344	▬	1543	1544	...	...	1715	|	|	|	1844	1844	|	|
262	Chaumont **381a** d.	0607	0727	...	0802	0905	0905	1002	1141	...	1403	1405	...	1605	1606	...	...	1735	1751	1721	1741	1905	1905	2042	2034
296	Langres **381a** d.	0627	0746	...	▬	0924	0924	▬	1201	...	1423	1425	...	1624	1625	...	...	1755	1810	1740	1800	1925	1924	2059	2053
307	Culmont Chalindrey **379 381a** d.	0636	0754	...	...	0933	0932	...	1211	...	1432	1435	...	1634	1635	...	...	1802	1817	1746	1812	1932	1933	2106	2102
	Dijon Ville **379 381a** a.	0726	...	...	⚒	|	...	Ⓐ	|	...	1520	1522	Ⓐ	|	|	...	...	...	|	|	|	...	|	|	|
380	Vesoul d.	...	...	0639	0739	1011	...	1239	1311	1339	...	...	1639	1711	1712	1739	1830	...	1859	1828	1858	...	2008	2140	2137
410	Lure **386a** d.	...	...	0656	0756	1028	...	1256	1328	1356	...	...	1656	1728	1729	1756	1847	...	1916	1845	1915	...	2025	2156	2155
442	**Belfort** Ville **378a 386a** d.	...	...	0725	0825	1047	...	1325	1353	1425	...	...	1725	1746	1747	1825	1916	...	1936	1905	1935	...	2044	2213	2214
490	**Mulhouse** **378a** a.	...	...	...	...	1114	...	...	1427	...	...	...	...	...	...	...	...	...	2003	1945	2005	...	2113	2237	2243

	⑤⑥	①–④ b	Ⓐ	Ⓒ	Ⓐ	Ⓐ a	⚒		Ⓐ	Ⓒ	Ⓐ a	Ⓐ	⑥	†	Ⓐ	⚒	Ⓒ	Ⓐ	Ⓐ	Ⓐ			Ⓑ	Ⓐ	†
Mulhouse **378a** d.	...	...	0522	0522	...	...	...	0749	...	...	...	...	...	1240	...	...	1444	...	...	...	...	...	...	...	...
Belfort Ville **378a 386a** d.	...	...	0549	0549	...	...	0735	0816	0935	...	...	1235	...	1312	1320	1335	1511	1510	...	1635	1735	1812	1835	...	...
Lure **386a** d.	...	...	0606	0606	...	...	0803	0834	1003	...	...	1303	...	1331	1337	1403	1528	1528	...	1703	1803	1830	1903	...	...
Vesoul d.	...	...	0623	0623	...	...	0821	0851	1021	...	...	1321	...	1349	1355	1421	1546	1545	...	1721	1821	1848	1921	...	...
Dijon Ville **379 381a** d.	...	...	|	|	0833	...	...	|	...	...	...	▬	...	|	|	...	|	|	1631	▬	...	|	...	...	...
Culmont Chalindrey **379 381a** d.	0610	0621	0658	0658	0921	...	...	0930	...	1130	1230	...	1431	1432	1432	...	1623	1623	1720	...	...	1927	...	2000	2108
Langres **381a** d.	0619	0632	0707	0707	0929	...	...	0938	...	1139	1240	...	1440	1441	1441	...	1632	1632	1730	...	...	1936	...	2008	2117
Chaumont **381a** d.	0639	0659	0727	0727	0949	...	...	0958	...	1158	1301	1356	1459	1500	1500	...	1652	1652	1749	Ⓐ	...	1956	...	2028	2136
Bar sur Aube d.	0701	0717	|	|	1012	...	...	|	...	1219	1321	1416	1520	1520	1520	...	|	|	1809	a	...	2016	...	2048	2156
Troyes d.	0735	0743	▽	▽	1043	1151	...	▽	...	1248	1352	1445	1549	1549	1549	...	▽	▽	1838	1947	...	2045	...	2119	2226
Romilly sur Seine d.	...	...	|	|	...	1209	...	|	...	...	1411	...	...	...	...	...	|	|	...	2008	...	...	...	...	...
Nogent sur Seine d.	...	...	|	|	...	1218	...	|	...	...	1422	...	...	...	...	...	|	|	...	2018	...	...	...	...	...
Paris Est a.	...	...	1000	1024	...	...	...	1243	...	...	...	...	...	...	...	...	1954	1953	...	...	...	...	...	...	...

a – Does not run Nogent - Troyes and v.v. on Aug. 16.
b – Not Aug. 15.
◧ – Timings may vary by 1–2 minutes on certain dates.
▽ – Diverted via Châlons en Champagne.

AVIGNON TGV - AVIGNON CENTRE - CARPENTRAS 351a

km																									
		Ⓐ	Ⓐ	Ⓐ	Ⓐ		Ⓐ‡	‡	‡	‡	‡	Ⓐ	Ⓒ	Ⓐ	Ⓒ		Ⓐ		Ⓐ		Ⓐ		Ⓐ		†
0	**Avignon** TGV .... ◇ d.	...	...	0657	0727	0757	0827	0857	0957	1157	1257	1327	1357	1427	1457	1557	1627	1657	1727	1757	1827	1857	1926	2027	2227
4	**Avignon** Centre .... ◇ d.	0607	0637	0707	0737	0807	0837	0907	1007	1207	1307	1337	1407	1437	1507	1607	1637	1707	1737	1807	1837	1907	1937	2037	2237
31	**Carpentras** .... a.	0637	0707	0736	0806	0836	0906	0936	1036	1236	1336	1406	1436	1506	1536	1636	1706	1736	1806	1836	1906	1936	2006	2106	2306

	Ⓐ	⚒	Ⓐ	Ⓐ		Ⓐ		‡		‡	Ⓒ	Ⓐ‡	Ⓒ	Ⓐ‡	Ⓒ	‡		Ⓐ		Ⓐ		Ⓐ		Ⓐ	
arpentras .... d.	0517	0623	0653	0723	0753	0823	0853	0953	...	1153	1153	1223	1253	1323	1353	1453	1553	1623	1653	1723	1753	1823	1853	1923	1953
vignon Centre ..... ◇ a.	0543	0654	0724	0754	0824	0854	0924	1024	...	1224	1224	1254	1324	1354	1424	1524	1624	1654	1724	1754	1824	1854	1924	1954	2024
vignon TGV .... ◇ a.	0551	0703	0733	0803	0833	0903	0933	1033	...	...	1233	1303	1333	1403	1433	1533	1633	1703	1733	1803	1833	1903	1933	2003	2033

– Not Nov. 16, 23, 30.
– Not Oct. 14 – 18, 21 – 25.
– Not Oct. 28 - Nov. 27.

– Subject to alteration June 11 – 14.

◇ – **Full service** Avignon TGV - Avignon Centre and v.v. (journey 5 – 6 minutes):
From Avignon TGV at 0610 Ⓐ, 0657, 0710 Ⓐ, 0727, 0757, 0827, 0857, 0910, 0957, 1010, 1040, 1127, 1157, 1257, 1327, 1357, 1427 Ⓐ, 1457, 1527, 1540, 1557, 1627, 1657, 1710 Ⓒ, 1727 Ⓐ, 1740 **b**, 1757, 1810 Ⓐ, 1827, 1842 Ⓐ, 1857, 1910, 1926, 1957, 2027, 2057, 2127, 2157, 2227, 2257 **c** and 2327 **c**.
From Avignon Centre at 0546 Ⓐ, 0627, 0657, 0727, 0744 Ⓐ, 0757, 0827, 0844 Ⓐ, 0857, 0927, 0957 Ⓐ, 1013 Ⓒ, 1027, 1057, 1127, 1157, 1214 Ⓐ **d**, 1227 Ⓒ, 1257 Ⓐ, 1314, 1327 Ⓒ, 1357 Ⓐ, 1414, 1427, 1508 Ⓐ, 1527, 1557, 1627, 1657, 1714, 1727, 1745 Ⓐ, 1757, 1814 Ⓐ, 1827, 1844, 1857, 1927, 1957, 2027, 2057, 2113, 2144, 2227 and 2257 **c**.

🚌 TOULON - ST TROPEZ 352

🚌 route **7802**: **Toulon** Gare Routière (adjacent to railway station) → Hyères-les-Palmiers → **St Tropez** Gare Routière. *84 km.* Journey 1 hr 40 mins - 1 hr 45 mins.
om Toulon: 0620 ⚒, 0650 ⚒ ⊙, 0830 ⊙, 0900 ⚒, 1030 ⚒ ⊙, 1130, 1300 ⊙, 1430 ⊙, 1530 ⚒, 1630 ⊗ ⊙, 1730 ⊗ ⊙ and 1815.
om St Tropez at 0600 ⚒, 0640 ⚒ ⊙, 0845 ⊙, 1010 ⊖ ⊙, 1040 ⊗ ⊙, 1230 ⚒, 1230 ⊗ ⊙, 1440 ⊗ ⊙, 1630, 1730 ⚒, 1830 ⚒ and 1930 ⊙.

– Not July 6 - Sept. 1. ⊖ – July 6 - Sept. 1 only. ⊙ – Slower route **7801** via Le Lavandou; journey 2 hrs 5 mins - 2hrs 40 mins.

perator: Groupement SUMA, 13340 Rognac ✆ (in France) 0 810 006 177 www.varlib.fr

LYON - BOURG EN BRESSE 353

Local stopping trains via Villars-les-Dombes. See Table **378** for faster regional services via Ambérieu. Subject to alteration on Aug. 16, 17.

km																									
		Ⓐ	①–⑥	Ⓐ	†	Ⓐ	①–⑥	Ⓐ		Ⓐ	①–⑥	Ⓐ		Ⓐ	⑥	①–⑥	Ⓐ		Ⓐ	①–⑥	①–⑥		⑦	⑤	Ⓐ
			b		🚌	🚌	b				b				k	b				b	b	A	e	v	🚌
0	**Lyon** Perrache .... d.	0557	0657	0759	...	...	0959	1057	1159	1257	1359	1459	1559	1629	1631	1659	1731	1759	1830	1857	1957	2057	2113	2113	...
5	**Lyon** Part Dieu .... d.	0612	0712	0812	0812	0912	1012	1112	1212	1312	1412	1512	1612	1642	1642	1712	1742	1812	1842	1912	2012	2112	2125	2125	2220
65	**Bourg en Bresse** .... a.	0714	0814	0914	0933	1033	1114	1214	1314	1414	1514	1614	1714	1744	1744	1814	1844	1914	1944	2016	2114	2214	2227	2230	2341

	①–⑥	†	Ⓐ	①–⑥	Ⓐ	⑦	①–⑥		①–⑥	Ⓐ			Ⓐ	①–⑥	Ⓐ	Ⓐ			①–⑥		Ⓐ		Ⓐ	⑦
	b	🚌		b		e	b		b	🚌				b		🚌			b					e
urg en Bresse .... d.	0547	0557	0618	0647	0718	0747	0747	...	0847	0927	...	1047	1147	1247	1347	1427	...	1547	1647	1747	1847	1947	2047	2047
on Part Dieu .... a.	0648	0718	0718	0748	0818	0848	0849	...	0948	1048	...	1148	1248	1349	1449	1548	...	1650	1752	1850	1950	2050	2149	2148
on Perrache .... a.	0703	...	0732	0759	0829	0859	0903	...	1003	...	...	1203	1303	1403	1503	...	...	1703	1803	1903	2003	2102	2201	2203

– ①②③④⑥ (also Nov. 1; not June 10, Nov. 11).
b – Not June 10, Nov. 11.
e – Also June 10, Nov. 11.
k – Also Aug. 15, Nov. 1.
v – Also Aug. 14; not Aug. 16, Nov. 1.

MÂCON - BOURG EN BRESSE 353a

km											
				🚌			🚌				
		Ⓐt	Ⓐt		Ⓐt	Ⓐt		Ⓐt	Ⓐt	Ⓐt	Ⓐt
0	**Mâcon** Ville .... ▷ d.	0704	0757	0904	...	1304	1504	...	1704	1804	1904
37	Bourg en Bresse .... ▷ a.	0732	0827	1006	...	1333	1606	...	1732	1832	1932
37	Bourg en Bresse .... d.	0734	*0844*	*1016*h	1224	...	...	1624	1734	1834	1934
68	**Ambérieu** .... a.	0757	*0901*	*1055*h	1250	...	...	1650	1757	1857	1958

			🚌			🚌				
	Ⓐt	Ⓐt		Ⓐt	Ⓐt		Ⓐt	Ⓐt	Ⓐt	Ⓐt
Ambérieu .... d.	0652	0805	*0905*r	...	1305	...	...	1705	1805	1905
Bourg en Bresse ...... a.	0716	0828	*0945*r	...	1328	...	...	1728	1828	1928
Bourg en Bresse . ▷ d.	0717	...	0950	1228	...	1350	1628	1729	1829	1929
Mâcon Ville .... ▷ a.	0741	...	1053	1257	...	1453	1657	1758	1857	1959

– Runs daily July 13 - Aug. 25, Oct. 19 - Nov. 3.
– Not Ⓐ July 15 - Aug. 23.
r – ①–⑥ (not June 10, Nov. 11).
t – Not July 15 - Aug. 23, Oct. 21 – 31.
▷ – Additional journeys by 🚌 Mâcon Ville - Bourg en Bresse and v.v.:
From Mâcon Ville at 0727 Ⓒ **d**, 1104 Ⓐ, 1704 Ⓒ **d**, 1804 Ⓒ **d**, 2004 Ⓐ and 2104 Ⓒ **d**.
From Bourg en Bresse at 0650 Ⓐ, 0750, 1050 Ⓐ, 1650 Ⓒ **d** and 1950 Ⓒ **d**.

DIJON - BOURG EN BRESSE 353b

km										
		Ⓐ		Ⓒ		c		Ⓐ		
0	**Dijon** .... d.	0644	...	0842	...	1244	...	1744	1846	...
30	St Jean de Losne .... d.	0711	...	0916	...	1311	...	1818	1916	...
86	Louhans .... d.	0749	...	0956	...	1348	...	1856	1953	...
40	**Bourg en Bresse** .... a.	0821	...	1029	...	1420	...	1928	2025	...

	Ⓐ			B				†	
Bourg en Bresse .... d.	0529	0632	...	1136	...	1737	...	1830	...
Louhans .... d.	0601	0705	...	1208	...	1810	...	1905	...
St Jean de Losne .... d.	0640	0744	...	1246	...	1847	...	1944	...
Dijon .... a.	0711	0814	...	1314	...	1915	...	2014	...

– ⑥ to July 13 (also June 11 – 14); ⚒ July 20 - Sept. 28 (not Sept. 16 – 20); ⑥ Oct. 5 - Nov. 16; ①–⑥ from Nov. 23.
– Not June 17 – 21, 24 – 28, July 1 – 5, Sept. 16 – 20, Oct. 14 – 18, 21 – 25, 28 – 31, Nov. 4 – 8.

PERPIGNAN - VILLEFRANCHE - LATOUR DE CAROL 354

The rail service between Perpignan and Villefranche is suspended until further notice

km	RAIL SERVICE – SUSPENDED								
		⚒				Ⓐ		Ⓑ	
0	**Perpignan** .... d.	0726	0826	1226	1426	1646	1746	1846	1946
40	Prades-Molitg les Bains .... d.	0811	0911	1309	1509	1731	1831	1931	2031
46	**Villefranche-Vernet les Bains** .... a.	0819	0919	1317	1517	1739	1839	1939	2039

RAIL SERVICE – SUSPENDED								
	⚒		Ⓐ				Ⓑ	
Villefranche-Vernet les Bains .... d.	0625	0725	0825	1125	1325	1525	1745	1845
Prades-Molitg les Bains .... d.	0633	0733	0833	1133	1333	1533	1753	1853
Perpignan .... a.	0713	0813	0913	1213	1413	1613	1833	1933

The following 🚌 service operates until further notice

km									
		🚌	🚌	🚌	🚌	🚌	🚌	🚌	🚌
		⚒				Ⓐ		Ⓑ	
0	**Perpignan** .... d.	0708	0816	1236	1426	1623	1746	1846	1946
40	Prades-Molitg les Bains .... d.	0807	0907	1327	1525	1722	1845	1945	2045
46	**Villefranche-Vernet les Bains** .... a.	0820	0920	1340	1538	1735	1858	1958	2058

	🚌	🚌	🚌	🚌	🚌	🚌	🚌	🚌
	⚒		Ⓐ				Ⓑ	
Villefranche-Vernet les Bains .... d.	0609	0709	0825	1125	1325	1525	1745	1845
Prades-Molitg les Bains .... d.	0622	0722	0838	1138	1338	1538	1758	1858
Perpignan .... a.	0713	0813	0937	1229	1437	1637	1857	1957

VILLEFRANCHE - LATOUR DE CAROL *Petit Train Jaune* Narrow gauge, 2nd class. In summer most trains include open sightseeing carriages.

SERVICE MAY 30 - SEPTEMBER 29

km									
								A	
0	**Villefranche-Vernet les Bains** .... d.	0900	1004	...	1350	1546	...	1749	...
28	Mont Louis la Cabanasse .... d.	1023	1128	...	1505	1708	...	1908	...
35	Font Romeu-Odeillo-Via .... d.	1044	1155	...	1525	1727	...	1934	...
56	Bourg Madame .... d.	...	1253	...	...	...	...	2030	...
63	**Latour de Carol** .... a.	...	1309	...	...	...	...	2046	...

Latour de Carol .... d.	0828	...	...	...	1513	...	...	...
Bourg Madame .... d.	0848	...	...	...	1534	...	...	...
Font Romeu-Odeillo-Via .... d.	1000	1106	...	1540	1645	1750	...	...
Mont Louis la Cabanasse .... d.	1030	1135	...	1609	1715	1818	...	...
Villefranche-Vernet les Bains .... a.	1140	1249	...	1722	1829	1928	...	...

SERVICE OCTOBER 25 - DECEMBER 14

km									
		B		B		†			
0	**Villefranche-Vernet les Bains** .... d.	0937	...	1357	...	1552	...	1748	...
28	Mont Louis la Cabanasse .... d.	1050	...	1506	...	1715	...	1857	...
35	Font Romeu-Odeillo-Via .... d.	1116	...	1525	...	1734	...	1918	...
56	Bourg Madame .... d.	1213	...	...	...	...	...	2013	...
63	**Latour de Carol** .... a.	1231	...	...	...	...	...	2029	...

	B		B	B	†			
Latour de Carol .... d.	0814	...	...	1535	...	...	...	...
Bourg Madame .... d.	0832	...	...	1553	...	...	...	...
Font Romeu-Odeillo-Via .... d.	0934	...	1556	1651	1749	...	...	...
Mont Louis la Cabanasse .... d.	0959	...	1617	1713	1813	...	...	...
Villefranche-Vernet les Bains .... a.	1107	...	1731	1827	1924	...	...	...

– Until Sept. 28.
B – From Oct. 26.

355 PARIS - MONTPELLIER - PERPIGNAN - PORTBOU

Timings of long-distance services may vary by a few minutes until July 5 (please check your seat reservation). Subject to alteration on Oct. 26, 27, Nov. 2, 9–11.
Marseille services are subject to alteration on June 15, 16, Aug. 7, 8. Timings of services from Marseille may vary by up to 6 minutes June 10–23 and July 29 - Aug. 25.

km					4752				3731						4756	4754				TGV 6809			AVE 9731	4758	475
		Ⓐ	Ⓐ	⚒	E ★	⚒	Ⓐ	Ⓐ	B R	Ⓐ	⚒	Ⓐ	†	Ⓒ	Ⓐw ★	Ⓒ ★	Ⓐ ☆	Ⓐ	⊗	⊡	Ⓐ		■	⑥ ★	Ⓑ ★
0	**Paris** Gare de Lyon ▶ d.	...	...	...	...	...	...	...	2208z	...	...	...	...	...	...	...	...	...	...	...	...	...	...	...	...
	Brussels Midi **11** d.	...	...	...	...	...	...	...	|	...	...	...	...	...	...	...	...	...	...	...	...	...	...	...	...
	Lille Europe **11** d.	...	...	...	...	...	...	...	|	...	...	...	...	...	...	...	...	...	...	...	...	...	...	...	...
	Charles de Gaulle ✈ **11** d.	...	...	...	...	...	...	...	|	...	...	...	...	...	...	...	...	...	...	...	...	...	...	...	...
	Marne la Vallée § **11** d.	...	...	...	...	...	...	...	|	...	...	...	...	...	...	...	...	...	...	...	...	...	...	...	...
	Dijon **379** d.	...	...	...	...	...	...	...	|	...	...	...	...	...	...	...	...	...	...	...	...	...	...	...	...
	Lyon Part Dieu ▶ d.	...	...	...	...	...	...	...	|	...	...	...	...	...	...	...	...	...	...	0706	...	...	...	...	...
527	Valence TGV ▶ d.	...	...	...	...	...	...	...	|	...	...	...	...	...	...	...	...	...	...	0743	...	...	...	...	...
∆128	**Marseille** St Charles **351** d.	...	...	...	...	...	...	...	|	...	...	...	...	...	0614	...	...	...	...	|	0718	0718	0801	0818	083
∆105	Vitrolles Aéroport Marseille ‡ d.	...	...	...	...	...	...	...	|	...	...	...	...	...	|	...	...	...	...	|	0734	0734	|	|	|
∆76	Miramas **351** d.	...	...	...	...	...	...	...	|	...	...	...	...	...	|	...	...	...	...	|	0751	0751	|	|	|
∆42	Arles **351** d.	...	...	...	...	...	...	...	|	...	...	...	...	...	0702	...	...	...	...	|	0811	0811	|	|	|
∆49	**Avignon** Centre d.	...	...	...	...	...	...	...	|	...	0609t	0638	...	...	|	...	...	0711	0738	|	|	|	0843v	|	|
∆28	Tarascon-sur-Rhône d.	...	...	...	...	...	...	...	|	...	0622t	0652	...	...	|	...	...	0724	0752	|	0821	0821	|	|	|
686	**Nîmes** d.	...	0501g	...	0535	0542h	...	0612	|	0641	0645	0712	0712	...	0728	0728	0742	0747	0810	0829	0842	0842	0904	|	|
712	Lunel d.	...	0519g	...	|	0601h	...	0631	|	0656	0705	0731	0731	...	|	|	0800	0807	0831	|	0900	0900	|	|	|
736	**Montpellier** Saint-Roch a.	...	0534g	...	0604	0615h	...	0646	|	0709	0730	0746	0746	...	0754	0754	0815	0832	0846	0855	0915	0915	0931j	|	|
736	**Montpellier** Saint-Roch d.	...	0544	...	0608	0619	...	0650	|	0712	...	0750	0750	0750	0758	0758	0820	▬	0850	0900	0920	...	0935j	|	|
730	**Montpellier** Sud-de-France a.	...	|	...	|	|	...	|	|	|	...	|	|	|	|	|	|	...	|	|	|	...	|	0941	10
	Montpellier Sud-de-France d.	...	|	...	|	|	...	|	|	|	...	|	|	|	|	|	|	...	|	|	|	...	|	0944	10
756	Frontignan d.	...	0555	...	|	0636	...	0702	|	0729	...	0802	0802	0802	|	|	0832	...	0902	|	0932	...	|	|	|
763	Sète d.	...	0609	...	|	0642	...	0709	|	0736	...	0809	0809	0809	0817	0817	0839	...	0909	0916	0939	...	|	|	|
786	Agde d.	...	0623	...	|	0658	...	0723	|	0752	...	0823	0823	0823	|	|	0856	...	0923	|	0956	...	|	|	|
807	Béziers d.	...	0637	...	|	0713	...	0737	|	0807	...	0837	0837	0837	0842	0842	0911	...	0937	0942	1010	...	1016	|	|
833	**Narbonne** a.	...	0649	...	0654	0729	...	0749	|	0824	...	0850	0850	0850	0855	0855	0927	...	0949	0955	1027	...	1030	|	|
833	**Narbonne** d.	...	0656	0656	0658	0732	0734	0756	|	...	...	0856	0856	0856	0858	0858	...	...	0956	0958	...	...	1033	|	|
	Toulouse Matabiau **321** a.	...	|	|	0814	0905	|	|	|	...	...	|	|	|	1014	1014	...	...	|	1110	...	...	|	1152	12
	Bordeaux St Jean **320** a.	...	|	|	1026	...	|	|	|	...	...	|	|	|	1228	1230	...	...	|	...	...	...	|	1400	14
854	Port la Nouvelle d.	...	0709	0709	...	...	0746	0809	|	...	...	0909	0909	0909	...	...	...	Ⓒ R	1011	...	...	...	|	...	...
896	**Perpignan** a.	...	0740	0740	...	...	0816	0840	0849	...	...	0940	0940	0940	...	...	...	T	1040	...	...	...	1106	...	...
896	**Perpignan** d.	0620	0745	0745	...	...	...	0845	|	...	...	...	0945	0945	...	...	...	1026	1045	...	...	...	...	...	...
918	Argelès sur Mer d.	0635	0801	0801	...	...	...	0901	0909	...	...	...	1001	1001	...	...	...	1042	1101	...	...	...	...	...	...
923	Collioure d.	0640	0806	0806	...	...	...	0906	0919	...	...	...	1006	1006	...	...	...	1047	1106	...	...	...	...	...	...
926	Port Vendres d.	0643	0810	0810	...	...	...	0910	0924	...	...	...	1010	1010	...	...	...	1050	1110	...	...	...	...	...	...
931	Banyuls sur Mer d.	0648	0815	0815	...	...	...	0915	0930	...	...	...	1015	1015	...	...	...	1055	1115	...	...	...	...	...	...
938	Cerbère **657** a.	0654	0822	0822	...	...	...	0922	0938	...	...	...	1022	1022	...	...	...	1101	1122	...	...	...	...	...	...
940	**Portbou** **657** a.	...	...	...	...	...	...	...	0947	...	...	...	...	...	...	...	...	...	1136	...	...	...	...	...	...

	TGV 6201	TGV 6201			TGV 9711		TGV 5104	TGV 6203			4760			TGV 6207			TGV 9713		TGV 6811	4762	4762	TGV 6811	TGV 9812	TGV 6209	TG 62
	D	Ⓐ H	Ⓐ	Ⓐ T	N ♠	⊗	Ⓐ a	L	Ⓐ	T	★	†	⚒	G		Ⓐ	♠		Ⓒ	①–④ m★	⑤–⑦ k★	Ⓐ ▽		Q	P
Paris Gare de Lyon ▶ d.	0607	0607	...	...	0715	...	...	0807	...	...	...	...	...	0925	...	...	1007	...	...	...	...	...	...	1107	11
Brussels Midi **11** d.	|	|	...	...	|	...	...	|	...	...	...	...	...	|	...	...	|	...	...	...	...	...	0817	|	
Lille Europe **11** d.	|	|	...	...	|	...	0517f	|	...	...	...	...	...	|	...	...	|	...	...	...	...	...	0903	|	
Charles de Gaulle ✈ **11** d.	|	|	...	...	|	...	0657	|	...	...	...	...	...	|	...	...	|	...	...	...	...	...	0957	|	
Marne la Vallée § **11** d.	|	|	...	...	|	...	0710	|	...	...	...	...	...	|	...	...	|	...	...	...	...	...	1010	|	
Dijon **379** d.	|	|	...	...	|	...	|	|	...	...	...	...	...	|	...	...	|	...	...	...	...	...	|	|	
Lyon Part Dieu ▶ d.	|	|	...	...	|	...	0910	|	...	...	...	...	...	|	...	...	|	...	1138r	...	...	1210	1210	|	
Valence TGV ▶ d.	0822	0822	...	...	|	...	0950	1021	...	...	...	...	...	|	...	...	1221	...	1235	...	...	1251	1251	1321	
Marseille St Charles **351** d.	|	|	...	...	|	...	|	|	...	...	1018c	...	...	|	1118	...	|	...	|	1214	1214	|	|	|	
Vitrolles Aéroport Marseille ‡ d.	|	|	...	...	|	...	|	|	...	...	|	...	...	|	1134	...	|	...	|	|	|	|	|	|	
Miramas **351** d.	|	|	...	...	|	...	|	|	...	...	|	...	...	|	1151	...	|	...	|	|	|	|	|	|	
Arles **351** d.	|	|	...	...	|	...	|	|	...	...	|	...	...	|	1211	...	|	...	|	|	1301	|	|	|	
Avignon Centre d.	|	|	0838	...	|	0938	|	|	...	...	|	1138	1138	|	|	1211	|	...	|	|	|	|	|	|	
Tarascon-sur-Rhône d.	|	|	0852	...	|	0952	|	|	...	...	|	1152	1152	|	1221	1224	|	...	|	|	|	|	|	|	
Nîmes d.	0908	0908	0912	...	1008	1012	1036	1108	...	...	1121	1212	1212	1218	1241	1247	1308	...	1322	1328	1328	1336	1336n	1408	14
Lunel d.	|	|	0930	...	|	1031	|	|	...	...	|	1230	1230	|	1259	1307	|	...	|	|	|	|	|	|	
Montpellier Saint-Roch a.	0935	0935	0946	...	1036	1046	1104	1136	...	...	1154	1246	1246	1251	1314	1332	1336j	...	1348	1354	1354	1404	1404n	1436	14
Montpellier Saint-Roch d.	0939	0939	0950	...	1040	1050	...	1143	1150	...	1158	1250	1250	...	1318	...	1340j	...	1352	1358	1358	1408	...	1443	14
Montpellier Sud-de-France a.	|	|	|	...	|	|	...	|	|	...	|	|	|	...	|	...	|	...	|	|	|	|	...	|	
Montpellier Sud-de-France d.	|	|	|	...	|	|	...	|	|	...	|	|	|	...	|	...	|	...	|	|	|	|	...	|	
Frontignan d.	|	|	1002	...	|	1102	...	|	1202	...	|	1302	1302	...	1336	...	|	...	|	|	|	|	...	|	
Sète d.	0956	0956	1009	...	|	1109	...	1200	1209	...	1217	1309	1309	...	1342	...	|	...	|	|	1417b	|	...	1500	14
Agde d.	1011	1011	1023	...	|	1123	...	1216	1223	...	|	1323	1323	...	1359	...	|	...	|	|	|	|	...	1516	15
Béziers d.	1022	1024	1037	...	|	1137	...	1232	1237	...	1244	1337	1337	...	1414	...	1420	←	1432	|	1442b	1448	...	1528	15
Narbonne a.	...	1037	1049	...	1132	1149	...	1245	1249	...	1257	1349	1349	...	1430	...	1433	1430	1446	|	|	1501	...	...	15
Narbonne d.	...	1040	...	1056	1135	1156	...	1251	...	1256	1300	1356	1356	...	→	...	1436	1440	1449	|	|	1504	...	...	15
Toulouse Matabiau **321** a.	...	|	...	|	|	|	...	|	...	|	1414	|	|	...	...	...	|	|	1603	1614	1614	1617	...	...	
Bordeaux St Jean **320** a.	...	|	...	|	|	|	...	|	...	|	1630	|	|	...	...	...	|	|	▬	1828	1828	...	...	...	
Port la Nouvelle d.	...	|	...	1109	|	1209	...	|	...	1309	...	1409	1409	...	...	...	|	1454	...	...	...	...	...	...	
Perpignan a.	...	1112	...	1140	1208	1240	...	1323	...	1340	...	1440	1440	...	...	...	1508	1526	Ⓐ	...	...	...	...	...	16
Perpignan d.	...	...	...	...	...	1245	...	...	...	...	...	*1445*	1445	...	...	...	...	...	1545	...	...	...	...	...	
Argelès sur Mer d.	...	...	...	...	...	1301	...	...	...	...	...	*1501*	1501	...	...	...	...	...	1601	...	...	...	...	...	
Collioure d.	...	...	...	...	...	1306	...	...	...	...	...	*1506*	1506	...	...	...	...	...	1606	...	...	...	...	...	
Port Vendres d.	...	...	...	...	...	1310	...	...	...	...	...	*1510*	1510	...	...	...	...	...	1610	...	...	...	...	...	
Banyuls sur Mer d.	...	...	...	...	...	1315	...	...	...	...	...	*1515*	1515	...	...	...	...	...	1615	...	...	...	...	...	
Cerbère **657** a.	...	...	...	...	...	1322	...	...	...	...	...	*1522*	1522	...	...	...	...	...	1622	...	...	...	...	...	
Portbou **657** a.	...	...	...	...	...	1336	...	...	...	...	...	...	1536	...	...	...	...	...	...	...	...	...	...	...	

B – *INTERCITÉS DE NUIT*. Conveys 🛏 1, 2 cl. and (2). See also Table **310**. **Timings may vary**. Overnight journeys only. For days of running and confirmed timings please consult the SNCF journey planner: www.oui.sncf/billet-train
D – Ⓐ to June 28; ①–⑥ July 8 - Aug. 31.
E – Ⓐ to Sept. 30; ① from Oct. 7 (not Nov. 11).
G – Daily to Sept. 1; ⑥ from Sept. 7.
H – From Sept. 2.
L – ①–⑥ to June 29 (not June 10); daily July 1 - Sept. 7; ①–⑥ from Sept. 9 (not Nov. 11).
N – June 1 - Sept. 1.
P – ⑥ July 6 - Aug. 31 (also Aug. 15, 16).
Q – Daily to July 5; Ⓑ July 7 - Aug. 30 (not Aug. 15, 16); daily from Sept. 1.
R – Ⓒ June 29 - Sept. 1.
T – From Toulouse (Table **321**).

a – Not Aug. 16.
b – Not ⑥.
c – 1013 on Sept. 28, 29.
f – Lille **Flandres** (starts from Lille Europe, d. 0527, on ②–⑤ June 18 - July 12).
g – Ⓐ to Sept. 30; ① from Oct. 7 (not Nov. 11).
h – ⚒ to Oct. 4; Ⓐ from Oct. 7.
j – 2 minutes later from Sept. 2.
k – Also June 10, Aug. 15, Nov. 11.
m – Not June 10, Aug. 15, Nov. 11.
n – 2–7 minutes later on ⑥ (also Aug. 15, 16, Nov. 1).
r – Lyon **Perrache** (from Lyon Part-Dieu d. 1150 on ⑥ to June 29). Departs 1150 on †.
t – Ⓐ only.
v – Avignon **TGV**.
w – Not Nov. 18–29.
y – Not July 8–12, 15–19, 22–26.
z – Paris **Austerlitz**.

TGV – R, supplement payable, 🍸.
AVE – Spanish high-speed train. R, supplement payable, 🍸.

☆ – Also runs Nîmes - Montpellier on ⑥.
⊗ – Does not run Perpignan - Portbou on ①–⑤ Nov. 18 - Dec. 13.
⊡ – Subject to alteration Nov. 18–29.
▽ – Subject to alteration on Aug. 16.
♠ – To Barcelona (Table **13**).
■ – (12) Marseille - Barcelona - Madrid. Also calls at Aix en Provence TGV (d. 0816).
★ – *INTERCITÉS*. R.
∆ – Distance from Nîmes. Marseille to Nîmes via Avignon TGV is *135 km*.
§ – Marne la Vallée - Chessy (station for Disneyland Pa
‡ – Vitrolles Aéroport Marseille-Provence. A shuttle bus runs to the airport terminal (journey time 5 minutes). For additional trains see Table **351**.
▶ – For additional trains from Paris and Lyon to Valence TGV see Table **350**. For Lyon to Valence Ville see Table **351**.

PARIS - MONTPELLIER - PERPIGNAN - PORTBOU

Timings of long-distance services may vary by a few minutes until July 5 (please check your seat reservation). Subject to alteration on Oct. 26, 27, Nov. 2, 9–11.
Marseille services are subject to alteration on June 15, 16, Aug. 7, 8. Timings of services from Marseille may vary by up to 6 minutes June 10–23 and July 29 - Aug. 25.

		⑤ f		TGV 9881 L	TGV 5330 N	Ⓐ	Ⓐ	4764 Ⓐ ★	4764 ⑥ ★	4764 † ★	TGV 5165 Ⓒ e	Ⓐ	AVE 9743 ♠		Ⓐ	Ⓐ	TGV 9715 ♠	Ⓑ	4766 Ⓑ ★	4768 ⑥ ★	⑦ d	Ⓐ n	Ⓐ n	C	Ⓐ
aris Gare de Lyon ▶ d.	...	...	...	...	...	...	...	...	...	...	...	...	...	...	...	...	1407	...	...	...	...	...	...	...	...
Brussels Midi 11 d.	...	...	...	...	...	...	...	...	...	...	...	...	...	...	...	...	|	...	...	...	...	...	...	...	...
Lille Europe 11 d.	...	...	...	...	...	...	...	...	...	...	1043	...	...	...	...	...	|	...	...	...	...	...	...	...	...
Charles de Gaulle ✈ 11 d.	...	...	...	...	...	...	...	...	...	...	1157	...	...	...	...	...	|	...	...	...	...	...	...	...	...
Marne la Vallée § 11 d.	...	...	...	...	...	...	...	...	...	...	1210	...	...	...	...	...	|	...	...	...	...	...	...	...	...
Dijon 379 d.	...	...	...	1122	...	...	...	...	...	...	|	...	...	...	...	...	|	...	...	...	...	...	...	...	...
Lyon Part Dieu ▶ d.	...	...	...	1310	1336	...	...	...	...	...	1406	...	1424	...	...	...	|	...	...	...	...	...	...	...	...
alence TGV ▶ d.	...	...	...	1351	1414	...	...	...	...	...	1451	...	1505	...	...	...	1622	...	...	...	...	...	...	...	...
Marseille St Charles 351 d.	...	...	...	|	|	...	...	1418	1418	1418	|	...	|	...	...	...	|	...	1614	1618	...	...	1606	1606	...
Vitrolles Aéroport Marseille ‡ d.	...	...	...	|	|	...	...	|	|	|	|	...	|	...	...	...	|	...	|	|	...	...	1622	1622	...
Miramas 351 d.	...	...	...	|	|	...	...	|	|	|	|	...	|	...	...	...	|	...	|	|	...	...	1639	1639	...
Arles 351 d.	...	...	...	|	|	...	...	|	1502	1502	|	...	|	...	...	...	|	...	1702	1702	...	...	1705	1705	...
Avignon Centre △ d.	1338	1338	...	|	|	...	...	|	|	|	|	...	|	1538	...	...	|	1638t	|	|	...	...	|	|	1711
Tarascon-sur-Rhône d.	1352	1352	...	|	|	...	...	|	|	|	|	...	|	1552	...	...	|	1652t	|	|	...	...	1719	1719	1724
îmes d.	1412	1412	...	1436	1504	1512	...	|	|	|	1536	1542	1550	1611	...	1642	1707	1712	1727◊	1728	...	...	1742	1742	1747
unel d.	1431	1431	...	|	|	1530	...	|	|	|	|	1600	|	1630	...	1700	|	1731	|	|	...	...	1800	1800	1812
ontpellier Saint-Roch a.	1446	1446	...	1503	1532	1546	...	|	|	|	1604	1615	1621	1646	...	1715	1737	1746	1754◊	1754	...	...	1815	1815	1826
ontpellier Saint-Roch d.	1450	1450	...	...	...	1550	...	|	|	|	...	1620	1625	1650	1705	1720	1740	1750	1758◊	1758	1803	1805	1820	1819	▬
Montpellier Sud-de-France a.	|	|	...	...	...	|	...	1544	1544	1544	...	|	|	|	|	|	|	|	|	|	|	|	|	|	...
Montpellier Sud-de-France d.	|	|	...	...	...	|	...	1547	1547	1547	...	|	|	|	|	|	|	|	|	|	|	|	|	|	...
rontignan d.	1502	1502	...	...	...	1602	...	|	|	|	...	1632	|	1702	1722	1732	|	1802	|	|	1816	1822	1832	1837	...
ète d.	1509	1509	...	...	...	1609	...	|	|	|	...	1639	|	1709	1729	1739	|	1809	1817	1817	1823	1829	1839	1844	...
gde d.	1523	1523	...	...	...	1623	...	|	|	|	...	1656	|	1723	1744	1756	|	1823	|	|	1836	1844	1856	1901	...
éziers d.	1537	1537	...	...	...	1637	...	|	|	|	...	1711	1716	1737	1800	1811	|	1837	1842	1842	1848	1900	1911	1917	Ⓐ
arbonne a.	1550	1550	...	...	...	1649	...	|	|	|	...	1727	1730	1750	1816	1827	1832	1849	1855	1856	...	1916	1927	1934	T
arbonne d.	1557	1557	...	...	...	1656	1719	|	|	|	...	1732	1733	1756	1819	...	1835	1856	1858	1859	...	...	...	...	1939
Toulouse Matabiau 321 a.	|	|	...	...	...	|	|	1749	1749	1749	...	1905g	|	|	|	...	|	|	2014	2014	...	...	...	...	|
Bordeaux St Jean 320 a.	|	|	...	...	...	|	|	1958	1958	2012	...	...	|	|	|	...	|	|	2230	...	...	...	...	...	|
ort la Nouvelle d.	1609	1609	...	...	...	1709	1731	...	...	...	...	...	|	1809	1832	...	|	1909	...	...	...	...	...	...	|
erpignan a.	1640	1640	...	...	...	1740	1801	...	...	...	...	...	1805	1840	1901	...	1908	1940	...	...	...	...	...	...	2011
erpignan d.	...	1645	1710	...	...	1745	...	...	...	...	...	...	...	1845	...	...	...	1945	...	...	...	...	...	...	...
rgelès sur Mer d.	...	1701	1725	...	...	1801	...	...	...	...	...	...	...	1901	...	...	...	2001	...	...	...	...	...	...	...
ollioure d.	...	1706	1730	...	...	1806	...	...	...	...	...	...	...	1906	...	...	...	2006	...	...	...	...	...	...	...
ort Vendres d.	...	1710	1733	...	...	1810	...	...	...	...	...	...	...	1910	...	...	...	2010	...	...	...	...	...	...	...
anyuls sur Mer d.	...	1715	1739	...	...	1815	...	...	...	...	...	...	...	1915	...	...	...	2015	...	...	...	...	...	...	...
erbère 657 a.	...	1722	1745	...	...	1822	...	...	...	...	...	...	...	1922	...	...	...	2022	...	...	...	...	...	...	...
ortbou 657 a.	...	...	1759	...	...	...	...	...	...	...	...	...	...	1931	...	...	...	...	...	...	...	...	...	...	...

	TGV 6235 F		TGV 9879 L	Ⓐ	Ⓑ	TGV 9717 Y♠	TGV 6231 Z		Ⓐ	4770 Ⓑ ★	TGV 6817	TGV 6215 B		①–⑥ s	⑦	TGV 6217	TGV 9836 ⑤–⑦ k	TGV 9836	TGV 6219 B⊠	⑥⑦ q	G	TGV 6221 A	TGV 6221 ①–⑤ E	TGV 6225 ⑦ D	TGV 6225 ⑤ H
aris Gare de Lyon ▶ d.	1515	...	...	...	...	1607	1607	...	...	...	...	1707	...	...	...	1807	...	...	1907	...	...	2015	2015	2107	2107
Brussels Midi 11 d.	|	...	...	...	...	|	|	...	...	...	...	|	...	...	...	|	1617	1617	|	...	...	|	|	|	|
Lille Europe 11 d.	|	...	...	...	...	|	|	...	...	...	...	|	...	...	...	|	1703	1703	|	...	...	|	|	|	|
Charles de Gaulle ✈ 11 d.	|	...	...	...	...	|	|	...	...	...	...	|	...	...	...	|	1757	1757	|	...	...	|	|	|	|
Marne la Vallée § 11 d.	|	...	...	...	...	|	|	...	...	...	...	|	...	...	...	|	1810	1810	|	...	...	|	|	|	|
Dijon 379 d.	|	...	1525	...	...	|	|	...	...	...	...	|	...	...	...	|	|	|	|	...	...	|	|	|	|
Lyon Part Dieu ▶ d.	|	...	1708p	...	...	|	|	...	...	...	1807p	|	...	...	...	|	2010	2010	|	...	...	|	|	|	|
alence TGV ▶ d.	|	...	1750	...	...	1822	1822	...	...	...	1851	1921	...	...	...	2022	2051	2051	2121	...	...	2228	2228	2322	2322
Marseille St Charles 351 d.	|	...	|	...	1737	|	|	...	...	1818	|	|	...	1848	1852	|	|	|	|	...	...	|	|	|	|
Vitrolles Aéroport Marseille ‡ d.	|	...	|	...	1753	|	|	...	...	|	|	|	...	1905	1909	|	|	|	|	...	...	|	|	|	|
Miramas 351 d.	|	...	|	...	1810	|	|	...	...	|	|	|	...	1924	1926	|	|	|	|	...	...	|	|	|	|
Arles 351 d.	|	...	|	...	1830	|	|	...	...	|	|	|	...	1947	1947	|	|	|	|	...	...	|	|	|	|
Avignon Centre △ d.	|	1738	|	1811	|	|	|	1838	1838	|	|	|	1938	|	|	|	|	|	|	...	2138	|	|	|	|
Tarascon-sur-Rhône d.	|	1752	|	1824	1840	|	|	1852	1852	|	|	|	1952	1957	1957	|	|	|	|	...	|	|	|	|	|
îmes d.	1808	1812	1836	1847	1855	1908	1908	1912	1912	1928	1936	2008	2009	2016	2016	2108	2136	2136•	|	2212	2212	2313	2324r	0009	0020r
unel d.	|	1831	|	1914	...	|	|	1931	1931	|	|	|	...	2034	2034	|	|	|	|	2230	2230	|	|	|	|
ontpellier Saint-Roch a.	1836	1846	1904	1927	...	1936	1936	1946	1946	1954	2003	2036	...	2049	2049	2136	2204	2204•	|	2246	2246	2341	|	0036	|
ontpellier Saint-Roch d.	1843	1850	...	1930	...	1943	1943	1950	1950	1958	2008	...	...	2053	2053	2143	2208	...	|	2250	2250	...	|	...	|
Montpellier Sud-de-France a.	|	|	...	|	...	|	|	|	|	|	|	...	...	|	|	|	|	...	2216	|	|	...	2356	...	0103
Montpellier Sud-de-France d.	|	|	...	|	...	|	|	|	|	|	|	...	...	|	|	|	|	...	2220	|	|	...	...	...	...
rontignan d.	|	1902	...	1947	...	|	|	2002	2002	|	|	...	...	2104	2105	|	|	...	|	2302	2302	...	...	...	...
ète d.	1900	1909	...	1953	...	1959	2000	2009	2009	|	2024	...	...	2111	2111	2200	2225	...	2238	2309	2309	...	...	...	...
gde d.	1916	1923	...	2008	...	2015	2016	2023	2023	|	|	...	...	2125	2126	2216	2241	...	2254	2323	2323	...	...	...	...
éziers d.	1931	1937	...	2024	...	2029	2031	2037	2037	|	2049	...	...	2139	2139	2231	2254	...	2309	2337	2337	...	...	...	...
arbonne a.	1944	1949	...	2039	...	2043	2044	2049	2049	2054	2102	...	...	2152	2153	2244	2308	...	2322	2352	2352	...	...	...	...
arbonne d.	1947	1956	...	...	...	2046	2047	...	2056	2058	2105	...	...	2156	2157	2247	2311	...	2325	...	...	...	...	...	...
Toulouse Matabiau 321 a.	|	|	...	...	...	|	|	...	|	2214	2217	...	...	|	|	|	|	...	|	...	...	...	...	...	...
Bordeaux St Jean 320 a.	|	|	...	...	...	|	|	...	|	...	...	...	...	|	|	|	|	...	|	...	...	...	...	...	...
ort la Nouvelle d.	|	2009	...	...	...	|	|	...	2109	...	...	...	...	2210	2210	|	|	...	|	...	...	...	...	...	...
erpignan a.	2020	2040	...	...	...	2118	2120	...	2140	...	...	...	...	2240	2240	2320j	2347	...	0002	...	...	...	...	...	...
erpignan d.	...	...	...	...	...	...	...	...	2145	...	...	...	...	...	...	...	...	...	...	...	...	...	...	...	...
gelès sur Mer d.	...	...	...	...	...	...	...	...	2201	...	...	...	...	...	...	...	...	...	...	...	...	...	...	...	...
llioure d.	...	...	...	...	...	...	...	...	2206	...	...	...	...	...	...	...	...	...	...	...	...	...	...	...	...
rt Vendres d.	...	...	...	...	...	...	...	...	2210	...	...	...	...	...	...	...	...	...	...	...	...	...	...	...	...
anyuls sur Mer d.	...	...	...	...	...	...	...	...	2215	...	...	...	...	...	...	...	...	...	...	...	...	...	...	...	...
rbère 657 a.	...	...	...	...	...	...	...	...	2222	...	...	...	...	...	...	...	...	...	...	...	...	...	...	...	...
rtbou 657 a.	...	...	...	...	...	...	...	...	...	...	...	...	...	...	...	...	...	...	...	...	...	...	...	...	...

– ①–⑥ to June 29 (not June 10); daily July 1–14; ⑥⑦ July 20 - Sept. 1 (also Aug. 15, 16); ⑥ from Sept. 7.
– Ⓑ (daily June 30 - Sept. 6; not Nov. 1).
– Ⓒ (daily July 6 - Sept. 1).
– ⑦ (also June 10, 14, 21, 28, July 5, 12).
– ①–⑤ from July 15 (not Nov. 11). Subject to confirmation Sept. 23 - Nov. 1.
– ⑤ to June 28; ⑤⑥ July 5 - Aug. 31 (also Aug. 15); ⑤ from Sept. 6 (also Oct. 31; not Nov. 1). Also runs on Aug. 14 between Paris and Montpellier only.
– Ⓐ to Sept. 27; ⑤ from Oct. 4 (not Oct. 18, Nov. 1, 8, 15).
– ⑤ from July 19 (also Oct. 31; not Aug. 16, Nov. 1). Sept. 27 - Oct. 31 Nîmes d. 0008, Montpellier Sud-de-France a. 0050. Subject to confirmation Sept. 27 - Oct. 31.
– From Luxembourg via Strasbourg (Table **379**).
– ①⑤⑥⑦ to July 1 (also June 11); daily July 5 - Sept. 2; ①⑤⑥⑦ from Sept. 6 (also Oct. 31, Nov. 12). From Nantes and Rennes (Table **335**). Subject to alteration Aug. 15–18, Nov. 1–3.
– From Toulouse (Table **321**).
– June 29 - Sept. 1.
– To June 28 and from Sept. 2.

d – ⑦ (also June 10, Nov. 11; not June 9, July 7 - Sept. 1, Oct. 20, 27, Nov. 10). To St Chély d'Apcher (Table **332**).
e – Also Aug. 16.
f – Also Aug. 14, Oct. 31; not Nov. 1.
g – 1858 on ⑤ (also Aug. 14, Oct. 31).
j – 2328 on Ⓐ from Oct. 14 (also Oct. 26, Nov. 2).
k – Also June 10, Aug. 14, 15, Oct. 31.
n – Not July 8 - Aug. 30.
p – Lyon **Perrache**.
q – Also June 10, Aug. 15, Nov. 1.
r – Arrives 14 minutes earlier.
s – Not Aug. 15.
t – Ⓐ only.

TGV – Ⓡ, supplement payable, 🍷.
AVE – Spanish high-speed train. Ⓡ, supplement payable, 🍷.

◊ – June 10–23 and Aug. 1–25 service is diverted via Montpellier Sud-de-France, d. 1756 (not calling at Nîmes or Montpellier Saint-Roch).
⊠ – June 24 - July 14 service is diverted via Montpellier Saint-Roch (not calling at Montpellier Sud de France) running later beyond Montpellier. Terminates at Béziers June 24–27, July 1–4, 7–11, 14.
• – On ①–④ from Sept. 30 (not Oct. 31) Nîmes a. 2134, d. 2148 and is diverted via Montpellier Sud de France (a. 2226), Montpellier Saint-Roch a. 2318.
♠ – To Barcelona (Table **13**).
★ – *INTERCITÉS*. Ⓡ. Subject to alteration Nov. 9–11.
§ – Marne la Vallée - Chessy (station for Disneyland Paris).
‡ – Vitrolles Aéroport Marseille-Provence. A shuttle bus runs to the airport terminal (journey time 5 minutes). For additional trains see Table **351**.
▶ – For additional trains from Paris and Lyon to Valence TGV see Table **350**. For Lyon to Valence Ville see Table **351**.

355 CERBÈRE - PERPIGNAN - MONTPELLIER - PARIS

Timings of long-distance services may vary by a few minutes until July 5 (please check your seat reservation). Subject to alteration on Oct. 26, 27, Nov. 2, 9–11.
Marseille services are subject to alteration on June 15, 16, Aug. 7, 8. Timings Tarascon-sur-Rhône - Arles - Marseille may vary by up to 4 minutes June 10–23 and July 29 - Aug. 25.

	TGV 6202 Ⓐ a	Ⓐ ⊖	Ⓐ	*TGV* 6230 ①–⑥ N	*TGV* 6230 ①–⑥ d	*TGV* 9896 L	E⊖	⑥ J	Ⓐ ⊖	Ⓐ ⊖	*TGV* 6204 ⑦ e◇	*TGV* 6204 Db	*TGV* 6204 ①–⑥ b	Ⓐ A	Ⓐ B	⑥	⚒	Ⓐ n	© ⊖	Ⓐ ⊖	Ⓐ U⊖	Ⓐ	*TGV* 9862	*TGV* 9862 G	4651 Ⓐ ★
Cerbère d.	...	...	...	...	...	...	...	...	...	...	...	...	...	...	...	...	...	...	...	0537	...	...	...	...	...
Banyuls sur Mer d.	...	...	...	...	...	...	...	...	...	...	...	...	...	...	...	...	...	...	...	0544	...	...	...	...	...
Port Vendres d.	...	...	...	...	...	...	...	...	...	...	...	...	...	...	...	...	...	...	...	0549	...	...	...	...	...
Collioure d.	...	...	...	...	...	...	...	...	...	...	...	...	...	...	...	...	...	...	...	0553	...	...	...	...	...
Argelès sur Mer d.	...	...	...	...	...	...	...	...	...	...	...	...	...	...	...	...	...	...	...	0558	...	...	...	...	...
Perpignan a.	...	...	...	...	...	...	...	...	...	...	...	...	...	...	...	...	...	...	...	0614	...	...	...	...	...
Perpignan d.	...	...	...	...	...	...	...	...	...	...	0540	0540r	...	0526	0545	...	...	...	0613	0621	...	0640	...	0708	...
Port la Nouvelle d.	...	...	...	...	...	...	...	...	...	...	|	|	...	0557	0615	...	...	...	0644	0652	...	0711	...	|	...
Bordeaux St Jean **320** d.	...	...	...	...	...	...	...	...	...	...	|	|	...	|	|	...	...	...	|	|	...	|	...	|	...
Toulouse Matabiau **321** d.	...	...	...	...	...	...	...	...	...	...	|	|	...	|	|	...	...	...	|	|	...	|	...	|	0648
Narbonne a.	...	...	...	...	...	...	...	...	...	...	0614	0614r	...	0610	0627	...	...	...	0656	0705	...	0724	...	0742	0801
Narbonne d.	...	...	...	...	...	...	0532	0539	...	0602	0617	0617r	...	0620	0632	0632	...	0644	0659	0711	0719	...	...	0745	0805
Béziers d.	0428r	0447	...	...	...	...	0547	0555	...	0617	0632	0633	...	0639	0647	0647	...	0701	0716	0727	0739	...	...	0801v	|
Agde d.	0443r	0459	...	...	...	...	0559	0608	...	0632	0645	0646	...	0651	0659	0659	...	0715	0732	0740	0753	...	...	0814v	|
Sète d.	0500r	0514	...	...	...	...	0614	0621	...	0647	0700	0702	...	0708	0713	0713	...	0732	0748	0754	0810	...	...	0830v	|
Frontignan d.	|	0520	...	...	...	...	0619	0627	...	0653	|	|	...	0713	0719	0719	...	0738	0754	0800	0816	...	...	|	|
Montpellier Sud-de-France a.	|	|	...	...	...	...	|	|	...	|	|	|	...	|	|	|	...	|	|	|	|	...	...	|	|
Montpellier Sud-de-France d.	|	|	...	...	0644	...	|	|	...	|	|	|	...	|	|	|	...	|	|	|	|	...	...	|	|
Montpellier Saint-Roch a.	0517r	0531	...	...	|	...	0630	0637	...	0710	0714	0717	...	0730	0730	0730	...	0755	0810	0810	0833	...	...	0846v	0900
Montpellier Saint-Roch d.	0524	0535	...	0624	|	0630	0634	0641	0639	0714	0721	0724	0724	0734	0733	...	0739	...	0814	0814	0837	...	0856	0856	0904
Lunel d.	|	0550	...	|	|	|	0647	0654	0654	0731	|	|	|	0749	0749	...	0754	...	0831	0831	0850	...	|	|	|
Nîmes d.	0554	0607	0648	|	|	0700	0708	0718	0724	0751	0751	0754	0754	0807	0807	...	0824j	...	0851	0851	0905	...	0926	0926	0933
Tarascon-sur-Rhône d.	|	0623	0709	|	|	|	0723	0742	0744	0809	|	|	|	0823	0823	...	0844j	...	0909	0909	...	...	|	|	|
Avignon Centre a.	|	|	0722	|	|	|	|	|	0757	0822	|	|	|	|	|	...	0856j	...	0922	0922	...	...	|	|	|
Arles **351** d.	|	0632	...	|	|	|	0732	0758	...	...	|	|	|	0832	0832	...	...	...	...	...	...	...	|	|	|
Miramas **351** d.	|	0653	...	|	|	|	0753	0818	...	...	|	|	|	0853	0853	...	...	...	...	...	...	...	|	|	|
Vitrolles Aéroport Marseille ‡ d.	|	0710	...	|	|	|	0810	0836	...	...	|	|	|	0910	0910	...	...	...	...	...	...	...	|	|	|
Marseille St Charles **351** a.	|	0726	...	|	|	|	0826	0850	...	...	|	|	|	0930	0930	...	...	...	...	...	...	...	|	|	1042
Nice **360** a.	|	...	...	|	|	|	...	...	...	...	|	|	|	...	...	...	...	...	...	...	...	...	|	|	...
Valence TGV ▶ d.	0641	...	...	|	|	|	...	...	...	...	0837	0841	0841	...	...	...	...	...	...	...	...	...	1016	1016	...
Lyon Part Dieu ▶ a.	|	...	...	|	|	0820	...	...	...	...	|	|	|	...	...	...	...	...	...	...	...	...	1050	1050	...
Dijon **379** a.	|	...	...	|	|	0956	...	...	...	...	|	|	|	...	...	...	...	...	...	...	...	...	|	|	...
Marne la Vallée § **11** a.	|	...	...	|	|	...	...	...	...	...	|	|	|	...	...	...	...	...	...	...	...	...	1248	1248	...
Charles de Gaulle ✈ **11** a.	|	...	...	|	|	...	...	...	...	...	|	|	|	...	...	...	...	...	...	...	...	...	1302	1302	...
Lille Europe **11** a.	|	...	...	|	|	...	...	...	...	...	|	|	|	...	...	...	...	...	...	...	...	...	1418	1418	...
Brussels Midi **11** a.	|	...	...	|	|	...	...	...	...	...	|	|	|	...	...	...	...	...	...	...	...	...	1511	1511	...
Paris Gare de Lyon ▶ a.	0853	...	...	0947	0947	...	...	...	...	...	1047	1053	1053	...	...	...	...	...	...	...	...	...	...	...	...

	T	Ⓐ ⊖	© ⊖	*TGV* 6206	*TGV* 6206 Q	Ⓐ	*TGV* 6858	Ⓐ ⊖	⊖	*TGV* 9708 Y♠	*TGV* 6208 Z	4653 ⑦ ★	4653 ⑥ ★	4655 Ⓐ ★	*TGV* 6234 ⑦ K	*AVE* 9736 ♠	*TGV* 5168 Ⓑh	⊗	*TGV* 9702 ♠	Ⓐ	4657 ★	*TGV* 6210 H	*TGV* 6210 Ⓐ Ka	*TGV* 6882 M	Ⓐ ⊗
Cerbère d.	0637	...	...	...	...	0707	...	0737	...	...	...	...	...	...	...	...	...	0937	...	...	...	...	...	...	1037
Banyuls sur Mer d.	0644	...	...	...	...	0714	...	0744	...	...	...	...	...	...	...	...	...	0944	...	...	...	...	...	...	1044
Port Vendres d.	0649	...	...	...	...	0719	...	0749	...	...	...	...	...	...	...	...	...	0949	...	...	...	...	...	...	1049
Collioure d.	0653	...	...	...	...	0722	...	0753	...	...	...	...	...	...	...	...	...	0953	...	...	...	...	...	...	1053
Argelès sur Mer d.	0658	...	...	...	...	0727	...	0758	...	...	...	...	...	...	...	...	...	0958	...	...	...	...	...	...	1058
Perpignan a.	0714	...	...	...	...	0743	...	0814	...	...	...	...	...	...	...	...	...	1014	...	...	...	...	...	...	1114
Perpignan d.	0721	...	...	...	0740	0745	...	0821	0821	0838	...	...	...	...	0940	0953	...	1021	1051	...	...	...	...	...	...
Port la Nouvelle d.	0752	...	...	...	|	0815	...	0852	0852	|	...	...	...	...	|	|	...	1052	|	...	...	...	...	...	...
Bordeaux St Jean **320** d.	|	...	...	...	|	|	...	|	|	|	...	...	...	0634	|	|	...	|	|	...	0832	...	...	...	...
Toulouse Matabiau **321** d.	|	...	...	...	|	|	0741	|	|	|	...	0853	0853	0853	|	|	...	|	|	...	1048	...	...	...	...
Narbonne a.	0805	...	...	...	0814	0827	0852	0905	0905	0914	...	1007	1012	1012	1014	1027	...	1105	1126	...	|	...	...	...	...
Narbonne d.	...	0811	0811	...	0817	0831	0855	0911	0911	0917	...	1011	1016	1016	1017	1030	...	1111	1128	...	|	...	...	...	...
Béziers d.	...	0827	0827	...	0833	0847	0910	0927	0927	0933	...	1026	1032	1032	1033	|	...	1127	1144	...	|	...	1231	...	...
Agde d.	...	0840	0840	...	0846	0859	|	0940	0940	0946	...	|	|	|	1046	|	...	1140	|	...	|	...	1247	...	...
Sète d.	...	0854	0854	...	0902	0914	0934	0954	0954	1001	...	1054	1056	1056	1102	|	...	1154	|	...	|	...	1302	...	...
Frontignan d.	...	0900	0900	...	|	0920	|	1000	1000	|	...	|	|	|	|	|	...	1200	|	...	|	...	|	...	...
Montpellier Sud-de-France a.	...	|	|	...	|	|	|	|	|	|	...	|	|	|	|	|	...	|	|	...	1249	...	|	...	...
Montpellier Sud-de-France d.	...	|	|	...	|	|	|	|	|	|	...	|	|	|	|	|	...	|	|	...	1252	...	|	...	...
Montpellier Saint-Roch a.	...	0910	0910	...	0917	0931	0949	1010	1010	1017	...	1111	1111	1111	1117	1123x	...	1210	1219	...	|	...	1317	...	...
Montpellier Saint-Roch d.	...	0914	0914	0924	0924	...	0952	1014	1014	1024	1024	1115	1115	1115	1124	1130x	1157	1214	1223	1238	|	1324	1324	1330	...
Lunel d.	...	0931	0931	|	|	...	|	1031	1031	|	|	|	|	|	|	|	|	1231	|	1301	|	|	|	|	...
Nîmes d.	...	0948	0951	0954	0954	...	1020	1051	1051	1054	1054	1144	1144	1144	1154	1201	1226	1251	1254	1325j	|	1354	1354	1359	...
Tarascon-sur-Rhône d.	...	...	1009	|	|	...	|	1109	1109	|	|	|	|	|	|	|	|	1309	|	1344j	|	|	|	|	...
Avignon Centre a.	...	...	|	|	|	...	|	1122	1122	|	|	|	|	|	|	|	|	1322	|	1356j	|	|	|	|	...
Arles **351** d.	...	...	1020	|	|	...	|	...	...	|	|	1208	1208	1208	|	|	|	...	|	...	|	|	|	|	...
Miramas **351** d.	...	...	1040	|	|	...	|	...	...	|	|	|	|	|	|	|	|	...	|	...	|	|	|	|	...
Vitrolles Aéroport Marseille ‡ d.	...	...	1057	|	|	...	|	...	...	|	|	|	|	|	|	|	|	...	|	...	|	|	|	|	...
Marseille St Charles **351** a.	...	...	1112	|	|	...	|	...	...	|	|	1254	1254	1254	|	|	|	...	|	...	1426	|	|	|	...
Nice **360** a.	...	...	...	|	|	...	|	...	...	|	|	...	...	...	|	|	|	...	|	...	...	|	|	|	...
Valence TGV ▶ d.	...	...	...	|	|	...	1105	...	...	1141	1141	...	...	...	|	1246	1316	...	1341	...	...	|	|	1448	...
Lyon Part Dieu ▶ a.	...	...	...	|	|	...	1144p	...	...	|	|	...	...	...	|	1320	1350	...	|	...	...	|	|	1522	...
Dijon **379** a.	...	...	...	|	|	...	...	...	...	|	|	...	...	...	|	...	|	...	|	...	...	|	|	1652	...
Marne la Vallée § **11** a.	...	...	...	|	|	...	...	...	...	|	|	...	...	...	|	...	1548	...	|	...	...	|	|	...	...
Charles de Gaulle ✈ **11** a.	...	...	...	|	|	...	...	...	...	|	|	...	...	...	|	...	1602	...	|	...	...	|	|	...	...
Lille Europe **11** a.	...	...	...	|	|	...	...	...	...	|	|	...	...	...	|	...	1656	...	|	...	...	|	|	...	...
Brussels Midi **11** a.	...	...	...	|	|	...	...	...	...	|	|	...	...	...	|	...	...	...	|	...	...	|	|	...	...
Paris Gare de Lyon ▶ a.	...	...	...	1245	1245	...	...	...	...	1353	1353	...	...	...	1445	...	...	...	1553	...	...	1645	1645	...	...

A – Ⓐ July 8 - Aug. 30.
B – Ⓐ to July 5/from Sept. 2.
D – ①–⑥ to July 8; ①⑥ July 13 - Aug. 26 (also Aug. 15, 16); ①–⑥ from Aug. 31.
E – Daily to Oct. 4; Ⓑ from Oct. 6 (also Nov. 9).
G – ①⑥⑦ (also June 11, Aug. 15, 16, Nov. 1).
H – Daily to Sept. 1; ⑦ from Sept. 8 (also Nov. 11).
J – ⑥ from Oct. 5 (not Oct. 26 - Nov. 9).
K – July 7 - Sept. 1.
L – To Luxembourg via Strasbourg (Table **379**). Subject to confirmation on ⑥ from Oct. 5.
M – To Metz via Strasbourg (Table **379**).
N – June 24 - July 13.
Q – Daily to July 9; ①②⑥⑦ July 13 - Aug. 27 (also Aug. 15, 16); daily from Aug. 31.
T – To Toulouse (Table **321**).
U – From Carcassonne (d. 0645) and Lezignan (d. 0705).
Y – June 30 - Sept. 2.
Z – To June 29 and from Sept. 3.

a – Not Aug. 16.
b – Not June 10, Nov. 11.
d – Not June 10, 24–29, July 1–6, 8–13, Nov. 11.
e – Also June 10, Nov. 11.
h – Not Aug. 15, 16, Nov. 1.

j – 3 minutes later from Sept. 3.
n – Not July 8 - Aug. 30.
p – Lyon **Perrache**.
r – Not ① July 8 - Aug. 26.
v – 3–4 minutes later on ⑥ (also June 11, Aug. 15, 16; not Oct. 5 - Nov. 30).
x – 3 minutes earlier from Sept. 2.

TGV –Ⓡ, supplement payable. 🍷.
AVE –Spanish high-speed train. Ⓡ, supplement payable, 🍷.

⊖ – Departures may be up to 5 minutes **earlier** from Sept. 3.
¶ – Departures Béziers - Lunel are up 1–2 minutes **earlier** from Sept. 2.
⊗ – Does not run Cerbère - Perpignan on ①–⑤ Nov. 18 - Dec. 13.
◇ – Nov. 3 – 11 Béziers d. 0633, Agde d. 0646, Sète d. 0702, Montpellier Saint-Roch a. 0716, d. 0723, Nîmes d. 0755, Valence d. 0843, Paris a. 1057.
♠ – From Barcelona (Table **13**).
★ – *INTERCITÉS*. Ⓡ. Subject to alteration Nov. 9 – 11.
▶ – For additional trains from Valence TGV to Lyon and Paris see Table **350**. For Valence Ville to Lyon see Table **351**.
‡ – Vitrolles Aéroport Marseille-Provence. A shuttle bus runs to the airport terminal (journey time 5 minutes). For additional trains see Table **351**.
§ – Marne la Vallée - Chessy (station for Disneyland Paris).

CERBÈRE - PERPIGNAN - MONTPELLIER - PARIS 355

Timings of long-distance services may vary by a few minutes until July 5 (please check your seat reservation). Subject to alteration on Oct. 26, 27, Nov. 2, 9–11.
Marseille services are subject to alteration on June 15, 16, Aug. 7, 8. Timings Tarascon-sur-Rhône - Arles - Marseille may vary by up to 4 minutes June 10–23 and July 29 - Aug. 25.

				TGV 6212	TGV 6212	TGV 9864	4659		TGV 6214	TGV 6214		TGV 9704	TGV 5380 5383				TGV 5182	TGV 6860	4661			TGV 6218			
	Ⓐ	Ⓐ	Ⓐ						⑥⑦	⑤						Ⓐ	Ⓒ						Ⓐ	⚒	Ⓒ
				S			w★		C	f		♠	N	H					★	T⊕		Q	M		
erbère d.	...	...	...	...	...	...	...	1237	...	...	...	...	...	...	...	...	...	...	...	1437	...	...	...	...	1537
anyuls sur Mer d.	...	...	...	...	...	...	...	1244	...	...	...	...	...	...	...	...	...	...	...	1444	...	...	...	...	1544
ort Vendres d.	...	...	...	...	...	...	...	1249	...	...	...	...	...	...	...	...	...	...	...	1449	...	...	...	...	1549
ollioure d.	...	...	...	...	...	...	...	1253	...	...	...	...	...	...	...	...	...	...	...	1453	...	...	...	...	1553
rgelès sur Mer d.	...	...	...	...	...	...	...	1258	...	...	...	...	...	...	...	...	...	...	...	1458	...	...	...	...	1558
erpignan a.	...	...	...	...	...	...	...	1314	...	...	...	...	...	...	...	...	...	...	...	1514	...	...	...	...	1614
erpignan d.	1121	...	1221	1240	...	...	...	1322	1340	...	1422	1450	...	...	...	...	...	...	...	1521	...	...	...	...	1621
ort la Nouvelle d.	1152	...	1252	|	...	...	...	1352	|	...	1452	|	...	...	...	...	...	...	...	1552	...	...	...	...	1652
Bordeaux St Jean **320** d.	|	...	|	|	...	...	1030	|	|	...	|	|	...	...	...	...	...	...	1232t	|	...	...	...	...	|
Toulouse Matabiau **321** d.	|	...	|	|	...	...	1248	|	|	...	|	|	...	...	...	...	...	1443	1448	|	...	...	...	...	|
arbonne a.	1205	...	1305	1314	...	...	1401	1405	1414	...	1505	1524	...	...	...	...	...	1554	1601	1605	...	...	...	...	1705
arbonne d.	1211	1244	...	1317	...	...	1405	1411	1417	...	1511	1527	...	1532	...	...	...	1557	1605	...	1611	...	1632	...	1711
éziers d.	1227	1301	...	1333	1333r	...	1421	1427	1433	...	1527	|	...	1547	...	...	...	1613	1621	...	1627	...	1647	...	1727
gde d.	1240	1315	...	1346	1346r	...	|	1440	1446	...	1540	|	...	1559	...	...	...	|	|	...	1640	...	1659	...	1740
ète d.	1254	1332	...	1402	1402r	...	1445	1454	1502	...	1554	|	...	1614	...	...	...	1637	1645	...	1654	...	1714	...	1754
rontignan d.	1300	1338	...	|	|	...	|	1500	|	...	1600	|	...	1620	...	...	...	|	|	...	1700	...	1719	...	1800
Montpellier Sud-de-France a.	|	|	...	|	|	...	|	|	|	...	|	|	...	|	...	...	...	|	|	...	|	...	|	...	|
Montpellier Sud-de-France d.	|	|	...	|	|	...	|	|	|	...	|	|	...	|	...	...	...	|	|	...	|	...	|	...	|
ontpellier Saint-Roch a.	1310	1357	...	1417	1417r	...	1500	1510	1517	...	1610	1617	...	1630	...	...	...	1653	1700	...	1710	...	1730	...	1810
ontpellier Saint-Roch d.	1314	...	...	1424	1424	1456	1504	1514	1524	1524	1614	1624x	1628	1634	1634	1639	1652	1657	1704	...	1714	1724	1734	1739	1814
unel d.	1331	...	...	|	|	|	|	1531	|	|	1631	|	|	1649	1649	1702	|	|	|	...	1731	|	1749	1802	1831
îmes d.	1351	...	...	1454	1454	1526	1533	1551	1554	1554	1651	1654	1658	1707	1707	1722	1722	1729	1737	...	1751	1754	1804	1823	1851
Tarascon-sur-Rhône d.	1409	...	...	|	|	|	|	1609	|	|	1709	|	|	1722	1722	1744	|	|	|	...	1809	|	...	1843	1909
Avignon Centre a.	1422	...	...	|	|	|	|	1622	|	|	1722	|	|	|	|	1756	|	|	|	...	1822	|	...	1856	1922
Arles **351** d.	...	...	...	|	|	|	1558	...	|	|	...	|	|	1732	1732	...	|	|	1807	...	...	|	...	...	...
Miramas **351** d.	...	...	...	|	|	|	|	...	|	|	...	|	|	1753	1753	...	|	|	|	...	...	|	...	...	...
Vitrolles Aéroport Marseille ‡ d.	...	...	...	|	|	|	|	...	|	|	...	|	|	1810	1810	...	|	|	|	...	...	|	...	...	...
Marseille St Charles **351** a.	...	...	...	|	|	|	1642	...	|	|	...	|	|	1828	1828	...	|	|	1904	...	...	|	...	...	...
Nice **360** a.	...	...	...	|	|	|	...	...	|	|	...	|	|	...	...	...	|	|	...	...	...	|	...	...	...
alence TGV ▶ d.	...	...	...	1541	1541	1616	...	...	1641	1641	...	1739	1747	...	...	...	1813	1823	...	...	...	1841	...	...	...
Lyon Part Dieu ▶ a.	...	...	...	|	|	1650	...	...	|	|	...	|	1824	...	...	...	1850	1901p	...	...	...	|	...	...	...
Dijon **379** a.	...	...	...	|	|	|	...	...	|	|	...	|	...	...	...	...	|	...	...	...	...	|	...	...	...
Marne la Vallée § **11** a.	...	...	...	|	|	1848	...	...	|	|	...	|	...	...	...	...	2048	...	...	...	...	|	...	...	...
Charles de Gaulle ✈ **11** a.	...	...	...	|	|	1902	...	...	|	|	...	|	...	...	...	...	2103	...	...	...	...	|	...	...	...
Lille Europe **11** a.	...	...	...	|	|	1956	...	...	|	|	...	|	...	...	...	...	2156	...	...	...	...	|	...	...	...
Brussels Midi **11** a.	...	...	...	|	|	2043	...	...	|	|	...	|	...	...	...	...	...	...	...	...	...	|	...	...	...
aris Gare de Lyon ▶ a.	...	...	...	1753	1753	...	...	...	1853	1853	...	1953	...	...	...	...	...	...	...	...	...	2053	...	...	...

		TGV 6220		4663		TGV 6222				AVE 9724	TGV 6856		TGV 6224	TGV 6224	4667	4665	4665					TGV 6228	3730		4669
							Ⓒ	Ⓐ	ⒸR			Ⓑ	⑦	⑤	⑥	①–⑤	⑦	Ⓐ	⑤			⑦			
				★		♥			T	■			e	f	★	★	★	G	D	E	F	d	B🅁		L★
erbère d.	...	...	...	...	1637	...	...	...	1726	...	...	1737	...	...	...	...	...	1828	1837	1837	...	...	1910	1937	...
anyuls sur Mer d.	...	...	...	...	1644	...	...	...	1733	...	...	1744	...	...	...	...	...	1835	1844	1844	...	...	1918	1944	...
ort Vendres d.	...	...	...	...	1649	...	...	...	1738	...	...	1749	...	...	...	...	...	1840	1849	1849	...	...	1925	1949	...
llioure d.	...	...	...	...	1653	...	...	...	1741	...	...	1753	...	...	...	...	...	1844	1853	1853	...	...	1931	1953	...
gelès sur Mer d.	...	...	...	...	1658	...	...	...	1746	...	...	1758	...	...	...	...	...	1849	1858	1858	...	...	1938	1958	...
erpignan a.	...	...	...	...	1714	...	...	...	1802	...	...	1814	...	...	...	...	...	1905	1914	1914	...	...	|	2014	...
erpignan d.	1621	1628h	...	...	1721	1748	...	...	1806	1815	...	1821	1840	...	...	...	...	1912	...	1921	1921	...	2000	2021	...
rt la Nouvelle d.	1652	|	...	...	1752	|	...	...	1835	|	...	1852	|	...	...	...	...	1943	...	1952	1952	...	|	2052	...
Bordeaux St Jean **320** d.	|	|	...	1432	|	|	...	...	|	|	...	|	|	...	1630	1630	1630	|	...	|	|	...	|	|	1832
Toulouse Matabiau **321** d.	|	|	...	1648	|	|	1658	1658	|	|	1750	|	|	...	1848	1848	1848	|	...	|	|	...	|	|	2048
arbonne a.	1705	1712h	...	|	1805	1823	1829	1829	1847	1854	1901	1905	1914	...	2001	2001	2001	1956	...	2005	2005	...	|	2105	2201
arbonne d.	1711	1715h	1719	|	1811	1826	1832	1832	...	1857	1904	1911	1917	...	2005	2005	2005	2000	...	2011	2011	...	|	2111	2205
ziers d.	1727	1733	1739	|	1827	1842	1848	1848	...	1913	1920	1927	1933	...	2021	2021	2021	2015	...	2027	2027	...	|	2127	|
de d.	1740	1746	1754	|	1840	|	1900	1900	...	|	|	1940	1946	...	|	|	|	2035	...	2040	2040	...	|	2140	|
te d.	1754	1802	1810	|	1854	|	1914	1914	...	|	1944	1954	2002	...	2045	2045	2045	2049	...	2054	2054	...	|	2154	|
ontignan d.	1800	|	1815	|	1900	|	1920	1920	...	|	|	2000	|	...	|	|	|	2055	...	2100	2100	...	|	2200	|
Montpellier Sud-de-France a.	|	|	|	1849	|	|	|	|	...	|	|	|	|	...	|	|	|	|	...	|	|	...	|	|	|
Montpellier Sud-de-France d.	|	|	|	1852	|	|	|	|	...	|	|	|	|	...	|	|	|	|	...	|	|	...	|	|	|
ontpellier Saint-Roch a.	1810	1817	1831	|	1910	1920	1931	1931	...	1952x	1959	2010	2017	...	2100	2059	2100	2105	...	2110	2110	...	|	2210	2300
ontpellier Saint-Roch d.	1814	1824	1835	|	1914	1924	1935	1935	...	1956x	2004	2014	2024	2024	2104	2103	2104	2109	...	2114	2114	2124	|	2214y	2304
nel d.	1831	|	1850	|	1931	|	1949	1958	...	|	|	2031	|	|	|	|	|	2127	...	2131	2131	|	|	2231y	|
mes d.	1851	1854	1907	|	1951	1954	2004	2017	...	2025	2033	2048	2054	2054	2130	2133	2133	2144	...	2148	2148	2154	|	2248y	2330
Tarascon-sur-Rhône d.	1909	|	1923	|	2009	|	...	2038	...	|	|	...	|	|	...	|	|	...	...	...	...	|	|	...	...
Avignon Centre a.	1922	|	|	|	2022	|	...	2050	...	2042v	|	...	|	|	...	|	|	...	...	...	...	|	|	...	...
Arles **351** d.	...	|	1932	|	...	|	...	...	...	|	|	...	|	|	...	2158	2158	...	...	...	...	|	|	...	...
Miramas **351** d.	...	|	1953	|	...	|	...	...	...	|	|	...	|	|	...	|	|	...	...	...	...	|	|	...	...
Vitrolles Aéroport Marseille ‡ d.	...	|	2010	|	...	|	...	...	...	|	|	...	|	|	...	|	|	...	...	...	...	|	|	...	...
Marseille St Charles **351** a.	...	|	2025	2037	...	|	...	...	...	2124	|	...	|	|	...	2242	2242	...	...	...	...	|	|	...	...
Nice **360** a.	...	|	...	...	...	|	...	...	...	...	|	...	|	|	...	...	...	...	...	...	...	|	|	...	...
lence TGV ▶ d.	...	1941	...	...	...	|	...	...	...	...	|	...	2141	2141	...	...	...	...	...	...	...	2241	|	...	...
Lyon Part Dieu ▶ a.	...	|	...	...	...	|	...	...	...	...	2150p	...	|	|	...	...	...	...	...	...	...	|	|	...	...
Dijon **379** a.	...	|	...	...	...	|	...	...	...	...	...	...	|	|	...	...	...	...	...	...	...	|	|	...	...
Marne la Vallée § **11** a.	...	|	...	...	...	|	...	...	...	...	...	...	|	|	...	...	...	...	...	...	...	|	|	...	...
Charles de Gaulle ✈ **11** a.	...	|	...	...	...	|	...	...	...	...	...	...	|	|	...	...	...	...	...	...	...	|	|	...	...
Lille Europe **11** a.	...	|	...	...	...	|	...	...	...	...	...	...	|	|	...	...	...	...	...	...	...	|	|	...	...
Brussels Midi **11** a.	...	|	...	...	...	|	...	...	...	...	...	...	|	|	...	...	...	...	...	...	...	|	|	...	...
ris Gare de Lyon ▶ a.	...	2153	...	...	...	2245	...	...	...	...	...	...	2353	2354	...	...	...	...	...	...	...	0053	0652z	...	...

– *INTERCITÉS DE NUIT*. Conveys 🛏 1, 2 cl. and (2). See also Table **310**. **Timings may vary**. Overnight journeys only. For days of running and confirmed timings please consult the SNCF journey planner: www.oui.sncf/billet-train
– ⑥⑦ July 6 - Sept. 1 (also Aug. 15, 16).
– Until July 5.
– ①–④ to July 4 (not June 10); Ⓐ July 8 - Sept. 27 (also Oct. 31).
– Daily to Sept. 29; Ⓒ from Oct. 5.
– From Sept. 30.
– Ⓐ (daily July 1 - Sept. 6).
– Ⓑ to July 14; ⑦ from July 21 (also Aug. 16).
– To Mende (Table **333**).
– ①⑤⑥⑦ to July 1 (also June 11); daily July 5 - Sept. 2; ①⑤⑥⑦ from Sept. 6 (also Oct. 31, Nov. 12). To Nantes and Rennes (Table **335**). Subject to alteration Aug. 15–17, Nov. 1. Departure times from Montpellier / Nîmes may vary by up to 4 minutes.
– Ⓑ (daily June 30 - Sept. 6; not Nov. 1).
– Ⓒ June 29 - Sept. 1. Runs 22–23 minutes later on June 30, Sept. 1.
– ②③④⑤⑦ July 7 - Sept. 1 (not Aug. 15, 16).
– To Toulouse (Table **321**).

– Also June 10.
– Also June 10, Nov. 11.
Also Oct. 31; not July 12 - Aug. 30, Nov. 1.
– Also Aug. 14, Oct. 31; not Aug. 16.

h – ②③⑥ July 6 - Aug. 31 (also Aug. 15, 16; not Aug. 14).
p – Lyon **Perrache**.
r – Not ① July 8 - Aug. 26.
t – 1230 on ⑥.
v – Avignon **TGV** station.
w – Not ①–⑤ Nov. 18 - Dec. 6.
x – 3–4 minutes earlier from Sept. 2.
y – Daily to Sept. 29; ⑤–⑦ from Oct. 4 (also Oct. 31).
z – Paris **Austerlitz**.

TGV – 🅁, supplement payable. 🍷.
AVE – Spanish high-speed train. 🅁, supplement payable, 🍷.

⊕ – Change trains at Perpignan on †.
♠ – From Barcelona (Table **13**).
♥ – June 1 - Sept. 1 runs as **9706** and starts from Barcelona (Table **13**).
■ – (12) Madrid - Barcelona - Marseille. Also calls at Aix en Provence TGV (a. 2110).
★ – *INTERCITÉS*. 🅁. Subject to alteration Nov. 9–11.
▶ – For additional trains from Valence TGV to Lyon and Paris see Table **350**. For Valence Ville to Lyon see Table **351**.
‡ – Vitrolles Aéroport Marseille-Provence. A shuttle bus runs to the airport terminal (journey time 5 minutes). For additional trains see Table **351**.
§ – Marne la Vallée - Chessy (station for Disneyland Paris).

359 NICE - ANNOT - DIGNE

2nd class only

km	CP ▲					
0	**Nice** (Gare CP) d.	0655	0925	1305	1715	1813
	Plan du Var d.	0741	0957	1341	1757	1854
41	Villars sur Var d.	0801	1017	1401	1818	1915
58	Puget Théniers d.	0821	1038	1421	1839	1937
64	Entrevaux d.	0830	1046	1429	1847	1945
78	Annot d.	0851	1106	1449	1908	2001
96	Thorame Haute d.	0915	1130	1512	1932	...
106	St André les Alpes d.	0927	1144	1523	1945	...
150	**Digne** a.	1020*	1239*	1620*	2041*	...

CP ▲	⚒	†				
Digne d.	...	...	0715*	1045*	1425*	1735*
St. André les Alpes d.	...	...	0812	1143	1524	1830
Thorame Haute d.	...	...	0824	1156	1536	1842
Annot d.	0540	0750	0850	1219	1600	1910
Entrevaux d.	0558	0810	0908	1238	1619	1929
Puget Théniers d.	0606	0822	0916	1246	1627	1938
Villars sur Var d.	0627	0842	0937	1306	1648	1957
Plan du Var d.	0649	0903	0958	1328	1710	2018
Nice (Gare CP) a.	0731	0940	1030	1400	1745	2057

TRAIN DES PIGNES steam train, 2019
⑦ June 2 - Oct. 27 ⊠
Puget Théniers 1055 → Annot 1205
Annot 1615 → Puget Théniers 1700
Also calls at Entrevaux
www.traindespignes.fr

🚌 service Digne - Sisteron - Veynes and v.v. LER routes 33/37, operated by Autocars Payan or SCAL. For rail connections at Sisteron and Veynes see Table **362**.

	🚌 ⚒	🚌 n	🚌 ⚒	🚌	🚌 ⑤	🚌 L	🚌 n	🚌 ⑥	
Digne △ d.	0750	1140	1240	1430	1605	1715	1830	1950	...
Digne (Gare) d.	0755	1145	1245	1435	1610	1720	1835	1953	...
Château Arnoux (Mairie) a.	0835	1225	1313	1504	1650	1800	1915	2019	...
Sisteron (Gare) a.	0850	1240	1325	1520	1705	1815	1935	2035	...
Veynes (Gare) a.	...	...	...	1620	...	...	...	2130	...

	🚌 ⚒	🚌		🚌 ⚒	🚌 n		🚌 n		🚌 n
Veynes (Gare) d.	...	0645	...	...	1300	...	...	...	...
Sisteron (Gare) d.	0640	0750	...	1250	1400	...	1605	...	184
Château Arnoux (Mairie) d.	0655	0807	...	1305	1417	...	1620	...	185
Digne (Gare) a.	0740	0840x	...	1345	1445x	...	1700	...	193
Digne △ a.	0745	0845	...	1350	1450	...	1705	...	194

🚌 service Digne - Manosque-Gréoux - Aix en Provence TGV - Aéroport Marseille ✈ and v.v. LER route 26, operated by Autocars Payan. No service on May 1.

	🚌 ⚒	🚌		🚌		🚌		🚌	
Digne △ d.	0450	0735	...	1035	...	1330	...	1730	...
Digne (Gare) d.	0455	0745	...	1045	...	1340	...	1740	...
Manosque-Gréoux (Gare) d.	0550	0850	...	1150	...	1445	...	1850	...
Aix en Provence TGV a.	0650	0950	...	1250	...	1545	...	1950	...
Aéroport Marseille ✈ a.	0705	1005	...	1305	...	1600	...	2005	...

	🚌 ⚒		🚌		🚌		🚌		🚌
Aéroport Marseille ✈ d.	0920	...	1255	...	1545	...	1845	...	211
Aix en Provence TGV d.	0950	...	1325	...	1615	...	1915	...	213
Manosque-Gréoux (Gare) a.	1055	...	1430	...	1720	...	2020	...	222
Digne (Gare) a.	1155	...	1530	...	1820	...	2115	...	231
Digne △ a.	1205	...	1540	...	1830	...	2120	...	232

L – ①②③④⑥⑦ (not May 1).
n – Not May 1.
x – Request stop.

* – By 🚌 St André les Alpes - Digne and v.v. until further notice.
△ – Gare Routière (bus station).
▲ – Narrow gauge railway, operated by Chemins de Fer de Provence.

⊠ – Also July 12, 19, 26, Aug. 1, 2, 8, 9, 15, 16, 22, 23, 29, 30, Oct. 26, Nov. On June 23, Nov. 2 runs Puget - Annot - Le Fugeret (a. 1245) and v. (return train departs Le Fugeret 1515).

360 MARSEILLE - TOULON - NICE - VENTIMIGLIA

TGV timings may vary by a few minutes until June 23 (please check your reservation). **Warning!** Subject to alteration June 8–10, Nov. 1–3.

km	All *TGV* trains are Ⓡ	139 Ⓡ♥		①–⑤	Ⓐ	17471		17473 Ⓐ	*TGV* 6805 ①–⑤ d	*TGV* 6805 ⑥⑦ g		17475	*TGV* 7851 ⊠		145 Ⓡ♥		17477	*TGV* 6173	*TGV* 6155	*TGV* 5111 ⑥		*TGV* 6175	
	Brussels Midi **11** d.	...	...	...	...	...	...	...	...	...	...	...	...	...	...	...	...	...	...	...	...	...	...
	Lille Europe **11** d.	...	...	...	...	...	...	...	...	...	...	...	...	...	...	...	...	...	...	0729	...	...	...
	Paris Gare de Lyon **350** ▶ d.	...	...	...	...	...	...	...	...	...	...	...	0707	...	...	...	...	0907	0907	|	...	1019	...
	Strasbourg **379** d.	...	...	...	...	...	...	...	...	...	...	...	|	...	...	...	...	|	|	|	...	|	...
	Metz **379** d.	...	...	...	...	...	...	...	...	...	...	...	|	...	...	...	...	|	|	|	...	|	...
	Dijon **379** d.	...	...	...	...	...	...	...	...	...	...	...	|	...	...	...	...	|	|	|	...	|	...
	Lyon Part-Dieu **350** d.	...	...	...	...	...	...	...	0628	0702	...	...	|	...	...	...	...	|	|	|	...	|	...
0	**Marseille** St Charles ▶ d.	...	...	0558	...	0658	...	0758	0831	0858	...	0958	|	...	...	...	1158	1228	1228	1232	...	|	135
67	**Toulon** ▶ a.	...	...	0644	...	0744	...	0844	0918	0944	...	1044	1113	...	...	...	1244	1313	1313	1318	...	1412	144
67	**Toulon** ▶ d.	...	0622	0648	0722	0748	...	0848	0922	0948	...	1048	1117	1122	...	1222	1248	1317	1326	1322	...	1416	144
	Hyères ▶ a.	...	|	|	|	|	...	|	|	|	...	|	|	|	...	|	|	|	1340	|	...	|	|
100	Carnoules d.	...	0654	0706	0754	|	...	|	|	|	...	1105	|	1155	...	1254	|	|	...	|	...	|	150
135	Les Arcs-Draguignan ▷ d.	...	0720	0726	0820	0827	...	0927	0958	1025	...	1127	|	1220	...	1320	1327	|	...	1401	...	1452	152
162	St Raphaël-Valescure ▷ d.	...	...	0743	...	0843	...	0943	1014	1042	...	1143	1207	...	...	...	1343	1407	...	1417	...	1509	154
195	**Cannes** ▷ d.	...	...	0812	...	0912	...	1012	1045	1113	...	1212	1237	...	...	...	1412	1437	...	1444	...	1537	161
206	Antibes ▷ d.	...	...	0824	...	0923	...	1023	1056	1124	...	1223	1248	...	...	...	1423	1448	...	1459	...	1548	162
229	**Nice** Ville ▷ a.	...	...	0846	...	0938	...	1038	1110	1139	...	1238	1306	...	...	...	1438	1506	...	1517	...	1606	164
229	**Nice** Ville ▷ d.	0801	...	0851	...	...	...	...	...	...	...	...	...	...	1402	...	...	...	...	...	...	...	165
245	Monaco-Monte Carlo ▷ a.	0822	...	0913	...	...	...	...	...	...	...	...	...	...	1421	...	...	...	...	...	...	...	171
252	Menton ▷ a.	|	...	0926	...	...	...	...	...	...	...	...	...	...	|	...	...	...	...	...	...	...	172
262	**Ventimiglia** ▷ a.	0852	...	0940	...	...	...	...	...	...	...	...	...	...	1452	...	...	...	...	...	...	...	...

	TGV 6165 K		147 Ⓡ♥	Ⓐ			Ⓐ	17479	*TGV* 6163 K	Ⓐ	Ⓐ	Ⓐ	*TGV* 6177	Ⓐ	Ⓒ	17481	*TGV* 6169	*TGV* 6827 N	*TGV* 7853 ⊠		17483 ⑤–⑦ r		*TG* 618 ⑤ w
Brussels Midi **11** d.	...	...	...	...	...	...	...	...	...	...	...	...	...	...	...	...	...	...	...	...	...	...	...
Lille Europe **11** d.	...	...	...	...	...	...	...	...	...	...	...	...	...	...	...	...	...	...	...	...	...	...	...
Paris Gare de Lyon **350** ▶ d.	1119	...	...	...	...	...	...	...	1418	...	...	...	1507	...	...	...	1602v	...	1712	...	...	...	191
Strasbourg **379** d.	|	...	...	...	...	...	...	...	|	...	...	...	|	...	...	...	|	1347	|	...	...	...	|
Metz **379** d.	|	...	...	...	...	...	...	...	|	...	...	...	|	...	...	...	|	|	|	...	...	...	|
Dijon **379** d.	|	...	...	...	...	...	...	...	|	...	...	...	|	...	...	...	|	1620	|	...	...	...	|
Lyon Part-Dieu **350** d.	|	...	...	...	...	...	...	...	|	...	...	...	|	...	...	...	|	1806	|	...	...	...	|
Marseille St Charles ▶ d.	|	...	1528	...	...	...	1614	1656	|	1714	1742	1811	1830	...	...	1858	1932	2003	|	...	2058	...	|
Toulon ▶ a.	1513	...	1615	...	...	...	1709	1744	1813	1809	1840	1909	1915	←	...	1944	2017	2048	2113	...	2144	...	231
Toulon ▶ d.	1517	...	1617	1622	...	1722	1722	1748	1817	1822	1852	1923	1919	1923	1923	1948	2021	2052	2117	...	2148	...	231
Hyères ▶ a.	|	...	|	|	...	|	|	|	|	|	|	→	|	|	|	|	|	|	|	...	|	...	|
Carnoules d.	|	...	|	1654	...	1754	1754	|	|	1854	1924	...	|	1955	1955	|	|	|	|	...	|	...	|
Les Arcs-Draguignan ▷ d.	|	...	|	1720	...	1820	1820	1827	|	1920	1950	...	|	2021	2021	2028	|	2128	2154	...	2227	...	|
St Raphaël-Valescure ▷ d.	1607	...	1714	...	...	...	...	1843	1910	...	...	...	2010	...	...	2044	2115	2145	|	...	2243	...	000
Cannes ▷ d.	1637	...	1740	...	...	...	...	1912	1937	...	...	...	2037	...	...	2112	2142	2212	2237	...	2312	...	003
Antibes ▷ d.	1648	...	1750	...	...	...	...	1923	1948	...	...	...	2048	...	...	2123	2152	2223	2248	...	2323	...	004
Nice Ville ▷ a.	1704	...	1804	...	...	...	...	1938	2004	...	...	...	2104	...	...	2138	2208	2241	2304	...	2338	...	010
Nice Ville ▷ d.	...	...	1808	...	...	...	...	...	...	...	...	...	2114	...	...	...	...	...	...	...	...	...	...
Monaco-Monte Carlo ▷ a.	...	...	1831	...	...	...	...	...	...	...	...	...	2130	...	...	...	...	...	...	...	...	...	...
Menton ▷ a.	...	...	|	...	...	...	...	...	...	...	...	...	2143	...	...	...	...	...	...	...	...	...	...
Ventimiglia ▷ a.	...	...	1852	...	...	...	...	...	...	...	...	...	...	...	...	...	...	...	...	...	...	...	...

K – July 6 - Sept. 1.
N – From Nancy (d. 1227).

d – Not June 10, Nov. 1, 11.
g – Also Nov. 11.
r – Also June 10, Nov. 11.
v – 1615 until July 5; 1611 on ⑥ July 6 - Aug. 31.
w – Also Aug. 14; not Aug. 16, Nov. 1.

TGV – Ⓡ, supplement payable, 🍸.

⊠ – OUIGO low-cost TGV service. Internet bookings only at www.ouigo.com.
▷ – For local trains Les Arcs - Cannes - Nice - Ventimiglia see Table **361**.
▶ – For complete *TGV* service Paris - Marseille - Toulon see Table **350**. For local trains Marseille - Toulon - Hyères see separate panel on next page.
♥ – International service to Italy. Operated by *Thello*. See Table **90**.

VENTIMIGLIA - NICE - TOULON - MARSEILLE 360

TGV timings may vary by a few minutes until June 23 (please check your reservation). **Warning!** Subject to alteration June 8 – 10, Nov. 1 – 3.

All *TGV* trains are 🅁	⚒	Ⓐ	17470 Ⓐ	⑥	Ⓐ	*TGV* 7858 ⊠	Ⓐ	Ⓐ	17472 Ⓑ	17472 ⑥	Ⓒ	Ⓐ	*TGV* 6814	Ⓐ	⊖	*TGV* 6188 L			*TGV* 6174	*TGV* 6176	17474		*TGV* 6170 K
Ventimiglia ▷ d.	...	...	...	...	...	...	...	...	...	...	...	...	...	...	...	...	...	...	...	...	...	...	...
Menton ▷ d.	...	...	...	...	...	...	...	...	...	...	...	...	...	...	...	...	0735	...	0922	...	...	...	...
Monaco-Monte Carlo ▷ d.	...	...	...	...	...	...	...	...	...	...	...	...	...	...	...	...	0749	...	0933	...	...	...	...
Nice Ville ▷ a.	...	...	...	...	...	...	...	...	...	...	...	...	...	...	...	...	0810	...	0950	...	...	...	...
Nice Ville ▷ d.	...	...	0522	...	...	0557	...	...	0623	0623	...	...	0657	...	...	0757	0813	...	1000	1057	1123	...	1157
Antibes ▷ d.	...	...	0537	...	...	0614	...	...	0639	0639	...	...	0712	...	...	0814	0837	...	1017	1114	1139	...	1214
Cannes ▷ d.	...	...	0549	...	...	0626	...	...	0652	0653	...	...	0725	...	...	0826	0850	...	1029	1126	1152	...	1226
St Raphaël-Valescure ▷ d.	...	...	0615	...	...	|	...	...	0718	0718	...	...	0750	...	...	0852	0918	...	1054	1152	1219	...	1252
Les Arcs-Draguignan ▷ d.	0549	0609	0632	0640	0640	0705	...	0709	0735	0735	0740	0740	0807	...	0838	|	0935	...	|	|	1235	1240	|
Carnoules d.	0616	0637	|	0708	0708	|	...	0737	|	|	0808	0808	|	...	0907	|	0954	...	|	|	|	1309	|
Hyères ▶ d.	|	|	|	|	|	|	←	|	|	|	|	|	|	←	|	|	|	...	|	|	|	|	|
Toulon ▶ a.	0646	0707	0712	0738	0738	0742	0738	0806	0812	0812	0838	0838	0844	0838	0936	0944	1012	...	1144	1242	1312	1338	1342
Toulon ▶ d.	0648	...	0716	...	→	0746	0750	...	0816	0816	...	→	0848	0856	...	0948	1016	...	1148	1246	1316	...	1346
Marseille St Charles ▶ a.	0742	...	0810	...	...	|	0843	...	0901	0903	...	...	0934	0957	...	|	1102	...	1236	1332	1401	...	|
Lyon Part-Dieu **350** a.	...	...	...	...	...	|	...	...	...	...	...	...	1128	...	...	|	...	...	|	|	...	...	|
Dijon **379** a.	...	...	...	...	...	|	...	...	...	...	...	...	1326	...	...	|	...	...	|	|	...	...	|
Metz **379** a.	...	...	...	...	...	|	...	...	...	...	...	...	...	...	...	|	...	...	|	|	...	...	|
Strasbourg **379** a.	...	...	...	...	...	|	...	...	...	...	...	...	...	...	...	|	...	...	|	|	...	...	|
Paris Gare de Lyon **350** ▶ a.	...	...	...	...	...	1145	...	...	...	...	...	...	...	...	...	1341	...	...	1615	1653	...	...	1741
Lille Europe **11** a.	...	...	...	...	...	...	...	...	...	...	...	...	...	...	...	...	...	...	...	...	...	...	...
Brussels Midi **11** a.	...	...	...	...	...	...	...	...	...	...	...	...	...	...	...	...	...	...	...	...	...	...	...

	TGV 6124	142 🅁♥		*TGV* 7856 Z⊠	*TGV* 7856 ⑥ Y⊠	17478	*TGV* 6802	17482 N	N	17482 M	M	*TGV* 6168	*TGV* 5184 ⑦ w	144 🅁♥	17484		*TGV* 6180	*TGV* 6806 ❖	①–⑤	*TGV* 6186 ⑦	⑦		160 🅁♥
Ventimiglia ▷ d.	...	1112	...	...	...	...	...	...	...	...	...	...	...	1512	...	...	...	...	...	...	...	...	1912
Menton ▷ d.	...	|	...	...	...	...	...	...	...	...	...	...	...	|	...	...	...	...	1704	...	1735	1835	|
Monaco-Monte Carlo ▷ d.	...	1141	...	...	...	...	...	...	...	...	...	...	...	1543	...	...	...	...	1716	...	1749	1849	1940
Nice Ville ▷ a.	...	1200	...	...	...	...	...	...	...	...	...	...	...	1600	...	...	...	...	1737	...	1810	1910	1959
Nice Ville ▷ d.	...	...	...	1357	1357	1423	1457	1512	...	1523	...	1541	1556	...	1623	...	1657	1723	1740	1757	1813	1913	2001
Antibes ▷ d.	...	...	...	1414	1414	1439	1514	1529	...	1539	...	1557	1616	...	1639	...	1714	1739	1804	1814	1837	1937	2017
Cannes ▷ d.	...	...	...	1426	1426	1452	1525	1541	...	1552	...	1611	1628	...	1652	...	1726	1753	1817	1826	1850	1950	2029
St Raphaël-Valescure ▷ d.	...	...	...	1452	1452	1519	1552	1608	...	1619	...	1639	1655	...	1719	...	|	1818	1845	1852	1918	2018	2055
Les Arcs-Draguignan ▷ d.	...	...	...	|	|	1535	1609	1628	1632	1635	1639	1655	1712	...	1735	1740	1808	1835	1902	|	1935	2035	|
Carnoules d.	...	...	...	|	|	1554	|	|	1659	|	1707	|	|	...	|	1808	|	|	1923	|	1954	2054	|
Hyères ▶ d.	1432	...	...	|	|	|	|	|	|	|	|	|	|	...	|	|	|	|	|	|	|	|	|
Toulon ▶ a.	1445	...	...	1538	1542	1613	1644	1709	1730	1712	1737	1734	1749	...	1812	1838	1842	1909	1942	1942	2012	2112	2143
Toulon ▶ d.	1449	...	...	1542	1546	1617	1648	1713	...	1716	...	1738	1753	...	1816	...	1846	1913	1946	1946	2016	2116	2145
Marseille St Charles ▶ a.	1534	...	...	|	|	1702	1734	1803	...	1801	...	1823	1841	...	1908	...	1932	1958	2032	|	2102	2202	2231
Lyon Part-Dieu **350** a.	|	...	...	|	|	...	1930**p**	...	...	...	...	|	|	...	...	...	|	2200**p**	...	|	...	...	...
Dijon **379** a.	|	...	...	|	|	...	...	...	...	...	...	|	|	...	...	...	|	...	...	|	...	...	...
Metz **379** a.	|	...	...	|	|	...	...	...	...	...	...	|	|	...	...	...	|	...	...	|	...	...	...
Strasbourg **379** a.	|	...	...	|	|	...	...	...	...	...	...	|	|	...	...	...	|	...	...	|	...	...	...
Paris Gare de Lyon **350** ▶ a.	1915	...	...	1943	1957	...	...	...	...	...	...	2145	|	...	...	...	2253	...	...	2341	...	...	...
Lille Europe **11** a.	...	...	...	...	...	...	...	...	...	...	...	...	2356	...	...	...	...	...	...	...	...	...	...
Brussels Midi **11** a.	...	...	...	...	...	...	...	...	...	...	...	...	...	...	...	...	...	...	...	...	...	...	...

LOCAL TRAINS MARSEILLE - TOULON - HYÈRES

km			Ⓐ	Ⓐ		Ⓐ		Ⓐ	◇			Ⓒ		Ⓐ	Ⓑ	⑥	Ⓐ			Ⓐ			Ⓐ		
0	**Marseille** St Charles d.	...	0532	0602	0632	0702	0732	0802	0835	0932	1002	1032	1132	1202	1232	1236	1302	1332	1432	1502	1532	1602	1614	1632	1702
27	Cassis • d.	...	0555	0625	0655	0725	0755	0825	0859	0955	1025	1055	1155	1225	1255	1259	1325	1355	1455	1525	1555	1625	|	1655	1725
37	La Ciotat d.	...	0602	0632	0702	0732	0802	0832	0906	1002	1032	1102	1202	1232	1302	1306	1332	1402	1502	1532	1602	1632	1643	1702	1732
51	Bandol d.	...	0614	0644	0714	0744	0814	0844	0919	1014	1044	1114	1214	1244	1314	1318	1344	1414	1514	1544	1614	1644	|	1714	1744
67	**Toulon** a.	...	0634	0704	0734	0804	0834	0904	0936	1034	1104	1134	1234	1304	1334	1338	1404	1434	1534	1604	1634	1704	1709	1734	1804
67	**Toulon** d.	0636	0636	0706	0736	0806	0836	...	0939	1036	...	1136	1236	...	1336	1340	...	...	1536	1606	1636	1706	...	1736	1806
87	**Hyères** a.	0657	0657	0727	0757	0827	0857	...	0959	1057	...	1157	1257	...	1357	1400	...	...	1557	1627	1657	1727	...	1757	1827

	Ⓐ		Ⓐ			Ⓐ		⊡		Q	R	S
Marseille St Charles d.	1714	1732	1742	1802	1834**k**	1902	1932	2007	2032	2102	2202	2232
Cassis • d.	|	1755	|	1825	1857**k**	1925	1956	2030	2055	2125	2225	2255
La Ciotat d.	1742	1802	1813	1832	1904**k**	1932	2003	2037	2102	2132	2232	2302
Bandol d.	|	1814	|	1844	1918**k**	1944	2014	2051	2114	2144	2244	2314
Toulon a.	1809	1834	1840	1904	1934	2004	2034	2109	2134	2204	2302	2334
Toulon d.	...	1836	...	...	1936	2006	2036	...	2136	...	...	...
Hyères a.	...	1857	...	...	1957	2027	2057	...	2157	...	...	...

	⊕	Ⓐ	Ⓐ		⚒	Ⓐ	Ⓐ		Ⓐ
Hyères ⊡ d.	...	...	...	0603	...	0633	...	0703	...
Toulon a.	...	...	...	0624	...	0654	...	0724	...
Toulon d.	0518	0556	0620	0626	0648	0656	0716	0726	0750
Bandol d.	0533	0610	|	0641	|	0712	|	0741	|
La Ciotat d.	0545	0621	0641	0653	0708	0724	0737	0753	0810
Cassis • d.	0553	0628	|	0701	|	0731	|	0801	|
Marseille St Charles a.	0619	0656	0715	0727	0742	0757	0810	0827	0843

	Ⓐ		Ⓐ				Ⓐ		Ⓐ		Ⓐ		Ⓐ	⊙			Ⓐ	⊙	Ⓐ		⊙				T
Hyères ⊡ d.	0733	0803	...	0903	0933	1103	...	1203	...	1303	...	1403	...	...	...	1603	1633	1659	1733	1803	...	1903	2003	2103	2203
Toulon a.	0754	0824	...	0923	0954	1124	...	1224	...	1324	...	1422	...	...	...	1624	1654	1717	1752	1824	...	1924	2024	2124	2224
Toulon d.	0756	0826	0856	0926	0956	1126	1156	1226	1256	1326	1356	1424	1456	1522	1556	1626	1656	1719	1754	1826	1852	1926	2026	2126	2226
Bandol d.	0812	0841	0912	0941	1012	1141	1212	1241	1312	1341	1412	1439	1512	1537	1612	1641	1712	1734	1810	1841	1908	1941	2041	2141	2241
La Ciotat d.	0824	0853	0924	0953	1024	1153	1224	1253	1324	1353	1424	1451	1524	1549	1624	1653	1724	1746	1822	1853	1920	1953	2053	2153	2253
Cassis • d.	0831	0901	0931	1001	1031	1201	1231	1301	1331	1401	1431	1458	1531	1557	1631	1701	1731	1753	1834	1901	1927	2001	2101	2201	2301
Marseille St Charles a.	0857	0927	0957	1027	1057	1227	1257	1327	1357	1427	1457	1524	1557	1623	1657	1727	1757	1820	1900	1927	1953	2027	2128	2227	2327

– July 6 - Sept. 1.
– July 6 - Sept. 13.
– Until July 5.
– From July 6.
– Daily to Sept. 15; ⑥⑦ from Sept. 21.
– ①-④ (not June 10, Aug. 15, Nov. 11).
– ⑤-⑦ to Sept. 15 (also June 10, Aug. 15); ⑥⑦ from Sept. 21 (also Nov. 11).
– ⑥⑦ to Sept. 15 (also June 10).
– ⑥ June 29 - Aug. 31.
– Daily to June 28; Ⓑ June 30 - Aug. 30; daily from Sept. 1.

– 2 – 4 minutes earlier until July 5.
– Lyon **Perrache**.
– Also June 10, Nov. 11; not June 9, Nov. 10.

TGV – 🅁, supplement payable, 🍸.

❖ – Subject to confirmation from Sept. 2.
⊠ – OUIGO low-cost TGV service. Internet bookings only at www.ouigo.com
⊖ – Runs 3 minutes earlier July 7 - Aug. 31.
◇ – Runs up to 5 minutes earlier until July 5.
⊡ – Runs 5 – 7 minutes earlier until June 23.
⊕ – Runs 8 minutes later on ⑥⑦.
⊙ – Runs 4 – 5 minutes later until June 23.
▷ – For local trains Ventimiglia - Nice - Cannes - Les Arcs see Table **361**.
▶ – For complete *TGV* service Toulon - Marseille - Paris see Table **350**.
For local trains Hyères - Toulon - Marseille see separate panel below main table.
♥ – International service from Italy. Operated by *Thello*. See Table **90**.
• – Cassis station is located 4 km from Cassis town.

361 LES ARCS - ST RAPHAEL - CANNES - NICE - MONACO - VENTIMIGLIA *Local TER services*

Warning! Subject to alteration June 8 – 10, Nov. 1 – 3.

km			Ⓑ				①–⑤	①–⑤	⑥	Ⓑ		Ⓑ	⑥		①–⑤	①–⑤	⑦	⑥	①–⑤		⑥⑦	①–⑤			
		k		d	k																	◇			
0	**Les Arcs-Draguignan** d.	...	...	...	...	...	...	...	...	...	0558	...	...	0608	...	...	...	...	0658	...	...	0726	...	...	0808
23	Fréjus d.	...	...	...	...	...	...	...	...	...	0611	...	...	0621	...	...	...	...	0711	...	...	0739	...	...	0821
27	St Raphaël-Valescure d.	...	...	...	...	...	...	...	...	...	0615	...	...	0625	...	...	...	...	0715	...	...	0743	...	...	0825
31	Boulouris sur Mer d.	...	...	...	...	...	...	...	...	...	|	...	...	0629	...	...	...	...	|	...	...	|	...	...	0829
◧	Grasse d.	...	...	...	...	...	...	...	...	...	|	0623	...	|	...	0653	...	0656	|	0723	0723	|	0753	0823	|
60	**Cannes** d.	...	0519	0519	...	...	0554	0611	0617	0624	0644	0655	0657	0703	0712	0721	0722	0723	0744	0754	0754	0812	0819	0854	0903
69	Juan les Pins d.	...	0530	0530	...	...	0605	0619	0629	0635	0652	0705	0707	...	0720	0731	0733	0733	0752	0805	0805	0820	0830	0905	...
71	Antibes d.	...	0533	0533	...	...	0608	0624	0632	0638	0656	0708	0710	...	0724	0735	0736	0736	0756	0808	0808	0824	0833	0908	...
80	Cagnes sur Mer d.	...	0545	0545	...	...	0619	0632	0645	0649	0704	0719	0721	...	0732	0746	0748	0748	0804	0819	0819	0832	0845	0919	...
94	**Nice** Ville a.	...	0600	0600	...	...	0634	0646	0703	0704	0717	0735	0737	...	0746	0801	0803	0803	0817	0835	0835	0846	0900	0935	...
94	**Nice** Ville d.	0537	...	0607	0607	0637	0637	0652	0706	0707	0722	0738	0740	...	0752	0807	0807	0807	0822	0838	0838	0851	0907	0938	...
99	Villefranche sur Mer d.	0546	...	0615	0615	0646	0646	0701	0715	0716	0731	0746	0748	...	0801	0816	0815	0815	0831	0846	0846	0900	0915	0946	...
101	Beaulieu sur Mer d.	0549	...	0619	0619	0650	0650	0705	0718	0720	0735	0750	0752	...	0805	0819	0819	0819	0835	0850	0850	0904	0919	0950	...
104	Eze d.	0554	...	0623	0623	0654	0654	|	0723	0724	|	0755	0757	...	|	|	0824	0824	|	0855	0855	|	0924	0955	...
110	**Monaco-Monte Carlo** d.	0606	...	0635	0635	0706	0706	0716	0734	0735	0746	0806	0807	...	0816	0835	0835	0835	0846	0903	0906	0916	0935	1006	...
114	Cap Martin-Roquebrune d.	0612	...	0640	0640	0711	0711	|	0740	0740	|	0811	0812	...	|	0840	0840	0840	|	...	0911	|	0940	1011	...
117	Menton d.	0619	...	0649	0649	0719	0719	0726	0753	0753	0756	0819	0819	...	0826	0848	0848	0848	0856	...	0919	0927	0948	1019	...
127	**Ventimiglia** a.	0634	...	0705	0705	0734	0734	...	0803	0802	...	0834	0834	...	...	0903	0903	0903	...	...	0934	0940	1003	1034	...

				Ⓐ				⑥⑦	⑥⑦							①–⑤									
	◇			◇							◇							◇						◇	
Les Arcs-Draguignan d.	0827	...	...	0927	...	...	...	...	...	...	1127	...	...	1208	...	...	...	1327	...	...	1408	...	...	1526	...
Fréjus d.	|	...	...	|	...	...	...	...	...	...	|	...	...	1221	...	...	...	|	...	...	1421	...	...	1539	...
St Raphaël-Valescure d.	0843	...	...	0943	...	0955	...	...	...	...	1143	...	...	1225	...	...	...	1343	...	...	1425	...	...	1543	...
Boulouris sur Mer d.	|	...	...	|	...	0959	...	...	...	...	|	...	...	1229	...	...	...	|	...	...	1429	...	...	|	...
Grasse d.	|	0853	...	|	0953	|	1023	...	...	...	|	1153	...	|	1253	...	...	|	1353	...	|	1453	...	|	1553
Cannes d.	0912	0919	0954	1012	1019	1033	1054	1119	1154	...	1212	1219	1254	1303	1319	1344	1354	1412	1419	1454	1503	1519	1554	1612	1619
Juan les Pins d.	|	0930	1005	|	1030	...	1105	1130	1205	...	|	1230	1305	...	1330	1352	1405	|	1430	1505	...	1530	1605	1620	1630
Antibes d.	0923	0933	1008	1023	1033	...	1108	1133	1208	...	1223	1233	1308	...	1333	1356	1408	1423	1433	1508	...	1533	1608	1624	1633
Cagnes sur Mer d.	|	0945	1019	|	1045	...	1119	1145	1219	...	|	1245	1319	...	1345	1404	1419	|	1445	1519	...	1545	1619	1631	1645
Nice Ville a.	0938	1000	1034	1038	1100	...	1134	1200	1234	...	1238	1300	1334	...	1400	1417	1434	1438	1500	1534	...	1600	1634	1645	1700
Nice Ville d.	...	1007	1037	...	1107	...	1137	1207	1237	1237	...	1307	1337	...	1407	1422	1437	...	1507	1537	...	1607	1637	1651	1707
Villefranche sur Mer d.	...	1015	1046	...	1115	...	1146	1215	1246	1246	...	1315	1346	...	1415	1431	1446	...	1515	1546	...	1615	1646	1659	1715
Beaulieu sur Mer d.	...	1019	1050	...	1119	...	1150	1219	1249	1249	...	1319	1350	...	1419	1435	1450	...	1519	1550	...	1619	1650	1703	1719
Eze d.	...	1024	1054	...	1124	...	1154	1224	1255	1255	...	1324	1354	...	1424	|	1454	...	1524	1554	...	1624	1654	|	1724
Monaco-Monte Carlo d.	...	1035	1106	...	1135	...	1206	1235	1306	1306	...	1335	1406	...	1435	1446	1506	...	1535	1606	...	1635	1706	1715	1735
Cap Martin-Roquebrune d.	...	1040	1111	...	1140	...	1211	1240	1311	1311	...	1340	1411	...	1440	|	1511	...	1540	1611	...	1640	1711	|	1740
Menton d.	...	1049	1119	...	1149	...	1219	1249	1319	1319	...	1349	1419	...	1449	1456	1519	...	1549	1619	...	1649	1719	1725	1749
Ventimiglia a.	...	1105	1134	...	1205	...	1234	1305	1334	1334	...	1405	1434	...	1505	...	1534	...	1605	1634	...	1705	1734	...	1805

	①–⑤			①–⑤					①–⑤	⑥⑦						Ⓒ							⑤–⑦	⑤–⑦	⑥⑦
												◇							◇				r	r ◇	r
Les Arcs-Draguignan d.	...	...	1608	...	...	...	1708	...	...	...	1808	1827	...	...	...	...	...	2008	2028	...	...	...	...	2227	...
Fréjus d.	...	...	1621	...	...	...	1721	...	...	...	1821	|	...	...	...	...	...	2021	|	...	...	...	...	|	...
St Raphaël-Valescure d.	...	...	1625	...	...	...	1725	...	...	...	1825	1843	...	...	...	...	...	2025	2044	...	...	...	...	2243	...
Boulouris sur Mer d.	...	...	1629	...	...	...	1729	...	...	...	1829	|	...	...	...	...	...	2029	|	...	...	...	...	|	...
Grasse d.	...	...	|	...	1653	1723	|	1753	1823	...	|	|	1853	1923	1953	1953	...	|	|	2053	2123v	2153	...	|	232
Cannes d.	1644	1657	1703	1711	1719	1754	1803	1819	1854	1856	1903	1912	1919	1954	2019	2019	2054	2103	2112	2119	2154	2219	2254	2312	2354
Juan les Pins d.	1652	1707	...	1719	1730	1805	...	1830	1905	1907	...	|	1930	2005	2030	2030	2105	...	|	2130	2205	2230	2305	|	000
Antibes d.	1656	1710	...	1724	1733	1808	...	1833	1908	1910	...	1923	1933	2008	2033	2033	2108	...	2123	2133	2208	2233	2308	2323	000
Cagnes sur Mer d.	1704	1722	...	1732	1745	1819	...	1845	1919	1921	...	|	1945	2019	2044	2044	2119	...	|	2149	2219	2245	2319	|	001
Nice Ville a.	1717	1737	...	1746	1800	1834	...	1900	1934	1934	...	1938	2000	2034	2100	2100	2134	...	2138	2204	2234	2300	2334	2338	003
Nice Ville d.	1722	1740	...	1751	1802	1837	...	1907	1937	1937	...	...	2007	2037	2102	2102	2137	...	...	2207**e**	2237**f**	2303**c**	2337**h**	...	...
Villefranche sur Mer d.	1731	1748	...	1801	1810	1846	...	1915	1946	1946	...	...	2015	2046	2110	2110	2146	...	...	2215**e**	2246**f**	2311**c**	2346**h**	...	...
Beaulieu sur Mer d.	1735	1752	...	1805	1814	1850	...	1919	1950	1950	...	...	2019	2050	2114	2114	2150	...	...	2219**e**	2250**f**	2315**c**	2350**h**	...	...
Eze d.	|	1757	...	|	1818	1854	...	1924	1954	1954	...	...	2024	2054	2118	2118	2154	...	...	2224**e**	2254**f**	|	2354**h**	...	...
Monaco-Monte Carlo d.	1746	1807	...	1816	1839**j**	1906	...	1935	2006	2006	...	...	2035	2106	2126	2139	2206	...	...	2235**e**	2306**f**	2326**c**	0006**h**	...	...
Cap Martin-Roquebrune d.	|	1812	...	|	1844	1911	...	1940	2011	2011	...	...	2040	2111	...	2145	2211	...	...	2240**e**	2311**f**	2331**c**	0011**h**	...	...
Menton d.	1756	1820	...	1826	1852	1919	...	1949	2019	2019	...	...	2048	2118	...	2152	2219	...	...	2248**e**	2318**f**	2338**c**	0019**h**	...	...
Ventimiglia a.	...	1834	...	...	1905	1934	...	2005	2034	2034	...	...	2103	2133	...	2205	2234	...	...	2303**e**	...	...	0034**h**	...	...

	Ⓐ	①–⑤		⑥			Ⓑ	⑥		⑥			①–⑤												⑥⑦
	◇		d		◇				p	N					◇										
Ventimiglia d.	...	...	0502	...	...	...	0524	0528	0557	0557	...	0624	...	0657**b**	...	...	0724**k**	...	0756	0824	0846	...	0924	...	095
Menton d.	...	...	0520	...	...	...	0542	0546	0616	0621	...	0642	0705	0716	0735	...	0743**z**	0805**p**	0816	0842	0906	...	0943	...	101
Cap Martin-Roquebrune d.	...	...	0526	...	...	...	0549	0553	0622	0628	...	0649	|	0723	|	...	0749**z**	|	0823	0849	0913	...	0949	...	102
Monaco-Monte Carlo d.	...	...	0533	...	...	...	0556	0600	0629	0635	...	0656	0716	0730	0749	...	0757	0816	0830	0856	0920	...	0956	...	103
Eze d.	...	...	0542	...	...	...	0605	0609	0639	0643	...	0705	|	0739	|	...	0806	|	0839	0905	0928	...	1005	...	103
Beaulieu sur Mer d.	...	...	0546	...	...	...	0609	0613	0643	0648	...	0709	0726	0743	0759	...	0810	0826	0843	0910	0933	...	1010	...	104
Villefranche sur Mer d.	...	...	0549	...	...	...	0613	0617	0647	0651	...	0713	0729	0747	0802	...	0814	0829	0847	0913	0936	...	1013	...	104
Nice Ville a.	...	...	0556	...	...	...	0620	0624	0654	0659	...	0720	0737	0754	0810	...	0821	0837	0854	0921	0944	...	1021	...	105
Nice Ville d.	0522	0526	0601	0601	0623	...	0627	0627	0701	0701	...	0727	0740	0801	0813	...	0827	0840	0857	0927	0948	...	1027	1101	110
Cagnes sur Mer d.	|	0542	0617	0617	|	...	0643	0643	0717	0717	...	0743	0755	0817	0828	...	0843	0855	0913	0943	1004	...	1043	1117	111
Antibes d.	0537	0556	0628	0630	0639	...	0654	0654	0728	0728	...	0754	0804	0828	0837	...	0854	0904	0925	0954	1022	...	1054	1128	112
Juan les Pins d.	|	0600	0631	0634	|	...	0657	0657	0732	0732	...	0757	0807	0831	0840	...	0857	0907	0928	0957	1026	...	1057	1131	113
Cannes d.	0549	0611	0642	0646	0652	0656	0708	0708	0743	0743	0757	0808	0815	0841	0850	0857	0908	0915	0939	1008	1035	1057	1106	1141	114
Grasse a.	|	0638	0708	0710	|	|	0738	0741	0808	0808	|	0838	...	...	|	|	0938	...	1009	1038	...	|	...	...	...
Boulouris sur Mer d.	|	...	...	...	|	0732	...	...	...	...	0832	...	...	...	|	0932	...	...	...	...	...	1132	...	...	...
St Raphaël-Valescure d.	0615	...	...	...	0718	0737	...	...	...	...	0836	...	...	...	0918	0936	...	...	...	...	...	1137	...	...	...
Fréjus d.	|	...	...	...	|	0741	...	...	...	...	0840	...	...	...	0922	...	...	...	...	...	...	1141	...	...	...
Les Arcs-Draguignan a.	0629	...	...	...	0732	0754	...	...	...	...	0853	...	...	...	0934	...	...	...	...	...	...	1154	...	...	...

						⑥⑦							M	L	L	L	M	M	L						
	◇									◇					◇		◇				◇				
Ventimiglia d.	...	1024	1057	...	1125	1157	1157	1224	1257	...	...	1325	1357	1357	...	...	...	1425	1427	1457	...	...	1525	1557	...
Menton d.	...	1042	1116	...	1143	1216	1216	1243	1316	...	...	1343	1416	1415	...	...	...	1443	1445	1516	...	...	1543	1616	...
Cap Martin-Roquebrune d.	...	1049	1123	...	1150	1223	1223	1249	1323	...	...	1350	1423	1422	...	...	...	1450	1453	1523	...	...	1550	1623	...
Monaco-Monte Carlo d.	...	1056	1130	...	1157	1230	1230	1256	1330	...	...	1357	1430	1430	...	...	...	1457	1500	1530	...	...	1557	1630	...
Eze d.	...	1105	1139	...	1205	1239	1239	1305	1339	...	...	1405	1439	1439	...	...	...	1505	1509	1539	...	...	1605	1639	...
Beaulieu sur Mer d.	...	1110	1143	...	1210	1243	1243	1309	1343	...	...	1410	1443	1443	...	...	...	1510	1513	1543	...	...	1610	1643	...
Villefranche sur Mer d.	...	1113	1147	...	1213	1247	1247	1313	1347	...	...	1413	1447	1447	...	...	...	1513	1516	1547	...	...	1613	1647	...
Nice Ville a.	...	1121	1154	...	1221	1254	1254	1320	1354	...	...	1421	1454	1454	...	...	...	1521	1524	1555	...	...	1621	1654	...
Nice Ville d.	1123	1127	1201	...	1227	1301	...	1327	1401	1423	...	1427	1501	1501	1512	←	1523	1527	1527	1601	1623	...	1627	1701	...
Cagnes sur Mer d.	|	1143	1217	...	1243	1317	...	1343	1417	|	...	1443	1517	1516	|	1517	|	1543	1544	1617	|	...	1643	1717	...
Antibes d.	1139	1154	1228	...	1254	1328	...	1354	1428	1439	...	1454	1528	→	1529	1533	1539	1554	1602	1628	1639	...	1654	1728	...
Juan les Pins d.	|	1157	1231	...	1257	1331	...	1357	1431	|	...	1457	1531	...	|	1537	|	1557	1606	1631	|	...	1657	1731	...
Cannes d.	1152	1208	1241	1257	1308	1341	...	1408	1441	1452	1457	1508	1541	...	1541	1547	1552	1608	1617	1643	1652	1658	1708	1743	175
Grasse a.	|	1238	...	|	1338	...	...	1438	...	|	|	1538	...	...	|	...	|	1638	1641	1708	|	|	1738	1808**a**	|
Boulouris sur Mer d.	|	...	...	1332	...	...	...	...	...	|	1532	...	...	...	|	...	|	...	...	...	|	1736	...	...	183
St Raphaël-Valescure d.	1219	...	...	1337	...	...	...	...	...	1519	1537	...	...	...	1608	...	1619	...	...	...	1719	1740	...	...	183
Fréjus d.	|	...	...	1341	...	...	...	...	...	|	1541	...	...	...	|	...	|	...	...	...	|	1744	...	...	184
Les Arcs-Draguignan a.	1232	...	...	1354	...	...	...	...	...	1532	1554	...	...	...	1625	...	1632	...	...	...	1732	1757	...	...	185

FOR NOTES SEE NEXT PAGE

ocal TER services — VENTIMIGLIA - MONACO - NICE - CANNES - ST RAPHAEL - LES ARCS — 361

Warning! Subject to alteration June 8 – 10, Nov. 1 – 3.

		①–⑤ ◇		⑦ ◇	①–⑤		①–⑤		◇			①–⑤			①–⑤				©	Ⓐ	⑤	© t		⑥⑦	⑤–⑦
entimiglia d.	1625	...	1657	...	...	1724	...	1757	...	...	1824	...	1857	...	...	1924	1957	2024	2057	2057	...	...	...	2241	2312
enton d.	1643	1704	1716	1735	1735	1743	1805	1816	1835	...	1843	1905	1916	...	1935	1943	2016	2043	2116	2116	...	...	2300	2300	2331
ap Martin-Roquebrune d.	1650	|	1723	|	|	1749	|	1823	|	...	1849	|	1923	...	|	1949	2023	2049	2123	2123	...	...	2306	2306	2338
onaco-Monte Carlo d.	1657	1716	1730	1749	1749	1756	1816	1830	1849	...	1856	1916	1930	...	1949	1956	2030	2056	2130	2130	...	...	2313	2313	2345
ze d.	1705	|	1739	|	|	1805	|	1839	|	...	1905	|	1939	...	|	2005	2039	2105	2139	2139	...	...	2322	2322	2354
eaulieu sur Mer d.	1710	1725	1743	1759	1759	1809	1826	1843	1859	...	1909	1926	1943	...	1959	2009	2043	2109	2143	2143	...	...	2326	2326	2358
llefranche sur Mer d.	1713	1729	1747	1802	1802	1813	1829	1847	1902	...	1913	1929	1947	...	2002	2013	2047	2113	2147	2147	...	...	2330	2330	0002
ce Ville a.	1721	1737	1755	1810	1810	1820	1837	1854	1910	...	1920	1937	1954	...	2010	2020	2054	2120	2154	2154	...	...	2337	2337	0009
ce Ville d.	1727	1740	1801	1813	1813	1827	1840	1901	1913	...	1927	1940	2005	...	...	2024	2101	2127	2158	2201	2227	2227	...	2344	...
agnes sur Mer d.	1743	1755	1817	1828	1828	1843	1855	1917	1928	...	1943	1955	2021	...	...	2039	2117	2143	2214	2217	2243	2243	...	0000	...
ntibes d.	1754	1804	1828	1837	1837	1854	1904	1928	1937	...	1954	2004	2032	...	...	2053	2128	2154	2225	2228	2254	2254	...	0011	...
an les Pins d.	1757	1807	1831	1840	1840	1857	1907	1931	1940	...	1957	2007	2036	...	...	2057	2131	2157	2228	2231	2257	2257	...	0014	...
annes d.	1808	1817	1843	1850	1850	1908	1917	1943	1950	1957	2008	2015	2045	2059	...	2108	2141	2206	2240	2241	2306	2308	...	0023	...
Grasse a.	1838	|	1908	|	|	1938	|	2008v	|	|	2038	...	...	|	...	2138	...	...	2305	...	...	2338	...	...	...
oulouris sur Mer d.	...	|	...	|	|	...	|	...	|	2032	...	...	...	2134	...	...	...	...	...	...	...	...	...	...	...
Raphaël-Valescure d.	...	1845	...	1918	1918	...	1946	...	2018	2037	...	...	...	2139	...	...	...	...	...	...	...	...	...	...	...
éjus d.	...	1849	...	1922	1922	...	1950	...	2022	2041	...	...	...	2143	...	...	...	...	...	...	...	...	...	...	...
s Arcs-Draguignan a.	...	1901	...	1934	1935	...	2003	...	2034	2054	...	...	...	2156	...	...	...	...	...	...	...	...	...	...	...

– From July 6.
– Until July 5.
– Until Sept. 21.

– ①–⑤ only.
– Not ⑥.
– ⑥⑦ (daily from Sept. 21).

d – ①⑦ (Ⓑ from Sept. 22).
e – ⑥⑦ (daily Sept: 21 - Oct. 13 and from Oct. 26).
f – ⑥⑦ (also ⑤ from Sept. 27).
h – Nice - Ventimiglia on ⑥⑦ (also June 10, ⑤ from Oct. 11; not Sept. 28, 29, Oct. 19, 26).
j – Arrives 13 minutes earlier.
k – ①⑦ (daily from Sept. 22).
p – Ⓑ (daily from Sept. 22).

r – Also June 10, Nov. 11.
t – Not Aug. 15.
v – ⑤–⑦ only.
z – ①⑥⑦ (daily from Sept. 21).

◇ – To / from Marseille (Table **360**).
◧ – Grasse - Cannes is *17 km*.

BRIANÇON - GAP - GRENOBLE, VALENCE and MARSEILLE — 362

SERVICE JULY 1 - NOVEMBER 3. Timings on the route Veynes-Dévoluy - Aix en Provence - Marseille are revised during this period with partial bus replacement in operation. Confirmed timings were not available as we went to press.

km																								
		⚒	②–⑤ d	① g	⑥		①–⑤ ⊗	⑦		⊗	L	⑥	⑥ k			G			5790 5792 N 🄁					
0	**Briançon** d.	...	...	0444	0541	...	0612	0654	0803	0930	...	1117	...	1448	...	...	1722	...	2005	...	...	...	...	...	...
13	L'Argentière les Écrins d.	...	...	0457	0554	...	0625	0707	0822	0943	...	1130	...	1504	...	...	1735	...	2022	...	...	...	...	...	...
28	Montdauphin-Guillestre d.	...	...	0508	0605	...	0636	0719	0833	0954	...	1141	...	1516	...	...	1747	...	2037	...	...	...	...	...	...
45	Embrun d.	...	...	0523	0620	...	0650	0734	0847	1009	...	1156	...	1533	...	...	1805	...	2054	...	...	...	...	...	...
82	**Gap** a.	...	...	0555	0653	...	0727	0807	0921	1041	...	1235	...	1623	...	...	1837	...	|	...	...	...	...	...	...
82	**Gap** d.	...	...	0557	0655	0717	0730	0808	0924	1048	1205	1238	1332	1625	1735	...	...	...	2134	...	...	...	...	...	...
09	Veynes-Dévoluy a.	...	...	0616	0720	0736	0749	0827	0943	1108	1225	1258	1354	1644	1755	...	...	...	|	...	...	...	...	...	...
09	Veynes-Dévoluy d.	0540	0610	0619	0721	0737	0752	0828	0946	1111	1226	1301	1357	1647	1758	1913	...	...	2208	...	...	...	...	...	...
	Grenoble a.	0750	|	|	|	0949	|	|	|	|	1440	|	1634	|	2019	2132	...	...	|	...	...	...	...	...	...
72	Die d.	...	0715	0725	0827	...	0857	0933	|	1221	...	1414	...	1753	...	...	...	...	2317	...	...	...	...	...	...
09	Crest d.	...	0748	0758	0900	...	0931	1006	|	1254	...	1446	...	1826	...	...	...	...	2352	...	...	...	...	...	...
44	**Valence** Ville **364** a.	...	0816	0823	0926	...	1008	1030	|	1318	...	1513	...	1851	...	...	...	...	|	...	...	...	...	...	...
	Valence TGV a.	...	0833	0833	0938	...	1027	1038	|	1329	...	1527	...	1902	...	...	...	...	|	...	...	...	...	...	...
	Paris Austerlitz a.	...	...	...	...	...	...	...	|	...	...	...	...	...	...	...	...	...	0658	...	...	...	...	...	...
59	Sisteron d.	...	...	...	...	...	...	...	1028	...	...	...	...	...	...	...	...	...	...	...	...	...	...	...	...
76	Château Arnoux - St Auban d.	...	...	...	...	...	...	...	1043	...	...	...	...	...	...	...	...	...	...	...	...	...	...	...	...
09	Manosque-Gréoux d.	...	...	...	...	...	...	...	1119	...	...	...	...	...	...	...	...	...	...	...	...	...	...	...	...
	Meyrargues a.	...	...	...	...	...	...	...	1141	...	...	...	...	...	...	...	...	...	...	...	...	...	...	...	...
	Meyrargues 🚌 d.	...	...	...	...	...	...	...	...	...	...	...	...	...	...	...	...	...	...	...	...	...	...	...	...
	Aix en Provence 🚌 a.	...	...	...	...	...	...	...	...	...	...	...	...	...	...	...	...	...	...	...	...	...	...	...	...
78	Aix en Provence ▷ 🚌 d.	...	...	...	...	...	...	...	...	...	...	...	...	...	...	...	...	...	...	...	...	...	...	...	...
15	**Marseille** St Charles ▷ 🚌 a.	...	...	...	...	...	...	...	...	...	...	...	...	...	...	...	...	...	...	...	...	...	...	...	...

km																								
		5789 5799 N 🄁		L			⚒ ⊗	⑥			⊗		⑤ v	©			⑥	Ⓐ	⑤ f	Ⓑ	⑤⑦ w			
	Marseille St Charles ▷ 🚌 d.	...	...	...	...	...	...	...	...	...	...	...	...	...	...	...	...	...	...	...	...	...	...	...	...
	Aix en Provence ▷ 🚌 a.	...	...	...	...	...	...	...	...	...	...	...	...	...	...	...	...	...	...	...	...	...	...	...	...
	Aix en Provence 🚌 d.	...	...	...	...	...	...	...	...	...	...	...	...	...	...	...	...	...	...	...	...	...	...	...	...
	Meyrargues 🚌 a.	...	...	...	...	...	...	...	...	...	...	...	...	...	...	...	...	...	...	...	...	...	...	...	...
	Meyrargues d.	...	...	...	...	...	...	...	1349	...	...	...	...	...	...	...	...	...	...	...	...	...	...	...	...
	Manosque-Gréoux d.	...	...	...	...	...	...	...	1411	...	...	...	...	...	...	...	...	...	...	...	...	...	...	...	...
	Château Arnoux - St Auban d.	...	...	...	...	...	...	...	1435	...	...	...	...	...	...	...	...	...	...	...	...	...	...	...	...
	Sisteron d.	...	...	...	...	...	...	...	1449	...	...	...	...	...	...	...	...	...	...	...	...	...	...	...	...
	Paris Austerlitz d.	2050	...	...	...	...	...	...	|	...	...	...	...	...	...	...	...	...	...	...	...	...	...	...	...
	Valence TGV d.	|	...	...	...	...	1027	1209	|	...	1432	...	...	1633	...	...	...	1834	1834	1953	1953	...	...	...	...
	Valence Ville **364** d.	|	...	...	...	...	1035	1219	|	...	1450	...	...	1643	...	...	...	1843	1843	2003	2003	...	...	...	...
	Crest d.	0431	...	...	...	...	1101	1255	|	...	1517	...	...	1714	...	...	...	1908	1908	2029	2029	...	...	...	...
	Die d.	0505	...	...	...	...	1134	1326	|	...	1551	...	...	1755	...	...	...	1942	1942	2102	2102	...	...	...	...
0	**Grenoble** d.	|	...	0807	...	1010	|	|	|	1410	|	1605	1605	|	...	1810	1810	|	|	|	|	...	...	...	...
09	Veynes-Dévoluy a.	0620	...	1024	...	1222	1248	1432	1530	1624	1657	1827	1827	1859	...	2030	2030	2052	2052	2208	2208	...	...	...	...
	Veynes-Dévoluy d.	|	...	1027	...	1228	1302	1434	1531	1645	1704	...	1831	1901	...	...	2033	...	2059	2211	2211	...	...	...	...
	Gap a.	0651	...	1047	...	1249	1331	1453	1552	1706	1728	...	1900	1920	...	...	2053	...	2120	2231	2231	...	...	...	...
	Gap d.	|	...	...	1201	...	1333	1455	1555	...	1730	...	...	1921	2016	...	...	...	2132	...	2234	...	...	...	...
	Embrun d.	0732	...	...	1238	...	1406	1532	1630	...	1807	...	...	1956	2052	...	...	...	2206	...	2307	...	...	...	...
	Montdauphin-Guillestre d.	0751	...	...	1253	...	1421	1547	1646	...	1822	...	...	2011	2108	...	...	...	2221	...	2321	...	...	...	...
	L'Argentière les Écrins d.	0805	...	...	1305	...	1432	1559	1657	...	1834	...	...	2021	2120	...	...	...	2231	...	2333	...	...	...	...
	Briançon a.	0835	...	...	1319	...	1446	1613	1712	...	1848	...	...	2035	2134	...	...	...	2245	...	2346	...	...	...	...

- ①②③④⑥⑦ (not Aug. 14, Oct. 31).
- Daily to Sept. 21; ①–⑥ from Sept. 23.
- Conveys 🛏 1, 2 cl. and 2 (reclining). For overnight journeys only. For days of running and confirmed timings please consult the SNCF journey planner: www.oui.sncf/billet-train

- Not Aug. 15, 16, Nov. 1.
  Not Nov. 1.
- Also Aug. 16, Nov. 2.
- Also Aug. 15, Nov. 1.
- Also Aug. 14, Oct. 31; not Nov. 1.
- Also Aug. 15.

⊗ – Subject to alteration July 1 – 5 between Crest and Valence (operated by 🚌 in amended timings; earlier departures from Valence).
▷ – For other local trains see panel below main table.

🚌 BRIANÇON - OULX

🄁					
Briançon rail station d.	0700	0925	...	1515	1755
Oulx rail station a.	0805	1030	...	1620	1900
🄁					
Oulx rail station d.	0855	1145	...	1545	1945
Briançon rail station a.	0955	1245	...	1645	2045

Operator: 05 voyageurs ✆ +33 (0)4 92 502 505
www.05voyageurs.com

363 BELLEGARDE - ANNEMASSE - ÉVIAN LES BAINS

Trains from Lyon / Bellegarde may divide at Belllegarde and / or Annemasse - take care to travel in the correct portion. For connections Paris - Bellegarde and v.v. see Table **341**.
Subject to alteration on Aug. 16, 17, Sept. 7, 8, 21, 22.

km								*TGV* **6503**	*TGV* **6503**												*TGV* **6511**			
		①–⑤	Ⓐ	①–⑥		①–⑤		⑦	⑥			①–⑤	①–⑤	①–⑤		①–⑤	Ⓑ		⑤H	⑤J	⑤	⑤	C	D
		w		b		w⊗	⊗	B		⊗	⊗	w	w	w		w	h		V	V	f	k		
	Paris Gare de Lyon **341** d.	...	...	...	...	...	...	1041	1041	...	...	...	...	...	...	...	...	...	...	...	1815	...	...	...
	Lyon Part-Dieu **346** d.	...	...	...	...	...	...	|	|	...	...	...	...	...	...	...	1738	...	...	...	|	2038	...	...
0	**Bellegarde** **365** d.	...	0709	0809	1009	...	1209	1343	1352	1409	1609	...	...	...	1809	...	1909	2009	...	...	2116	2209	2212	221
38	Annemasse **365** a.	...	0744	0842	1043	...	1243	1429	1424	1443	1643	...	...	...	1843	...	1944	2043	...	...	2200	2243	2246	224
38	Annemasse d.	0717	0748	0853	1053	1220	1253	1435	1434	1453	1653	1716	1757	1820	1853	1920	1953	2053	2128	2138	2210	2253	...	225
68	Thonon les Bains d.	0746	0825	0930	1130	1250	1332	1505	1505	1530	1731	1748	1830	1850	1930	1950	2030	2130	2153	2206	2235	2330	...	233
77	**Évian les Bains** a.	0754	...	0939	1138	1258	1340	1512	1512	1538	1739	1757	1838	1858	1938	1958	2038	2138	2202	2213	2242	2338	...	233

										TGV **6508**		*TGV* **6508**			*TGV* **6506**		*TGV* **6504**						
	①–⑥	①–⑥		①–⑤	①–⑤	①–⑤	Ⓒ					①–⑤	⑦			⑦	①–⑤	⑥	⑦	⑦	Ⓐ			Ⓑ
	t	b		w	w	w				⊗	E	w⊗	e	⊗	⊗	B	w⊗	B		G				h
Évian-les-Bains d.	0502	0522	0622	0654	0715	0800	0822	...	1021	1221	1302	1305	1321	1421	1621	1656	1703	1720	1721	1740	1802	1821	...	204
Thonon-les-Bains d.	0510	0530	0630	0706	0725	0808	0832	0832	1030	1230	1313	1313	1335	1430	1631	1706	1712	1731	1731	1749	1810	1831	...	205
Annemasse a.	0539	0607	0707	0735	0804	0836	0907	0907	1107	1307	1347	1342	1357	1507	1707	1734	1750	1759	1807	1815	1839	1907	...	212
Annemasse **365** d.	0544	0617	0717	...	...	...	0917	0917	1117	1317	1352	...	1413	1517	1717	1745	...	1814	1817	...	...	1918	...	213
Bellegarde **365** a.	0620	0650	0750	...	...	...	0950	0950	1150	1350	1441	...	1457	1550	1750	1815	...	1856	1850	...	...	1950	...	220
Lyon Part-Dieu **346** a.	...	0822	...	...	...	...	...	...	...	...	|	...	|	...	...	|	...	|	2022	...	...	...	...	...
Paris Gare de Lyon **341** a.	...	...	...	...	...	...	...	...	...	...	1749	...	1749	...	...	2133	...	2141	...	...	...	...	...	...

B – July 6 - Sept. 1.
C – ①②③④⑥⑦ (also Nov. 1; not Aug. 14, Oct. 31, Nov. 23, 30).
D – ①②③④⑥⑦ (also Nov. 1; not July 8 – 11, 15 – 18, 22 – 25, Aug. 14, Sept. 2 – 5, 9 – 12, 16 – 19, 23 – 26, Oct. 31, Nov. 4 – 7, 11 – 14, 18 – 23, 25 – 30).
E – Runs on June 9, 10 only.
G – ⑦ to June 16 (also June 10); ⑦ from Aug. 11 (also Nov. 11; not Nov. 10). To Grenoble (Tables **365** and **364**).
H – ⑤ from Sept. 20 (also Oct. 31; not Nov. 1).
J – ⑤ Aug. 23 - Sept. 13 (also June 14, Aug. 14).
V – From Valence (Tables **364** and **365**).

b – Not June 10, Nov. 11.
e – Also June 10, Nov. 11; not June 9.
f – Also Aug. 14, Oct. 31; not Aug. 16, Nov. 1.
h – Not Aug. 15, Nov. 1.
k – Also Aug. 14, Oct. 31; not Nov. 1.
t – Not June 10, July 9 – 12, 16 – 19, 23 – 26, Sept. 3 – 6, 10 – 13, 17 – 20, 24 – 27, Nov. 5 – 8, 11 – 15, 19 – 22, 26 – 29.
w – Not June 10.

TGV –Ⓡ, supplement payable, 🍸.

⊗ – Subject to alteration on ①–⑤ Sept. 16 - Oct. 4.

364 GENÈVE and ANNECY - CHAMBÉRY - GRENOBLE - VALENCE

Subject to alteration on Aug. 16, 17. Journeys from / to Annecy are subject to alteration on Nov. 10.

km		Ⓐ	①–⑥	Ⓐ	①–⑥		①–⑥	①–⑥	Ⓐ	①–⑥			Ⓒ	Ⓐ	Ⓒ				Ⓒ					Ⓐ		Ⓑ
			b		b		b	r		b	⊗					⊗	⊗	⊗							A	h
0	**Genève** **341 346** d.	...	...	...	...	...	...	...	...	0657	...	...	...	...	...	1000	...	...	...	1159	...	...	...	1459	...	...
33	Bellegarde **341 346** d.	...	...	...	...	...	...	...	...	0729	...	...	...	...	...	1029	...	...	...	1229	...	...	...	1529	...	...
66	Culoz **346** d.	...	...	...	...	...	...	...	...	|	...	...	...	...	...	|	...	...	...	|	...	...	...	|	...	...
	Annecy **341 345** d.	...	...	...	0539	...	0639	0653	0653	|	0746	0839	0839	0939	0953	|	1039	...	1139	|	1245	1339	1439	|	1539	16
88	Aix les Bains **341 345** d.	...	...	...	0626	...	0726	0734	0742	0807	0826	0926	0926	1026	1034	1105	1126	...	1226	1307	1326	1426	1526	1607	1626	17
102	**Chambéry** **341 345** a.	...	...	...	0637	...	0737	...	0753	0818	0837	0937	0937	1037	...	1115	1136	...	1237	1318	1337	1437	1537	1618	1637	17
102	**Chambéry** d.	...	0540	*0601*r	0640	...	0740	...	...	0821	0840	...	0940	*1045**	...	1118	1139	1240	1240	1321	1340	1440	1540	1621	1640	17
116	Montmélian d.	...	0551	*0611*r	0651	...	0751	...	...	|	0851	...	0951	|	...	|	1151	1251	1251	|	1351	1451	1551	|	1651	17
165	**Grenoble** a.	...	0627	*0654*r	0727	...	0827	...	...	0902	0927	...	1027	*1145**	...	1202	1227	1327	1327	1402	1427	1528	1627	1702	1728	18
165	**Grenoble** d.	0601	0630	0707	0730	0730	0830	...	...	...	0930	...	1030	...	...	1205	1230	1330	1330	...	1430	1531	1630	1705	1730	18
242	Romans-Bourg de Péage d.	0658	0728	0758	0828	0828	0928	...	...	...	1028	...	1128	...	...	1258	1328	1428	1428	...	1528	1628	1728	1758	1829	19
249	Valence TGV ⊙ a.	0705	0735	0805	0835	0835	0935	...	...	...	1035	...	1135	...	...	1305	1335	1435	1435	...	1535	1635	1735	1805	1837	19
259	**Valence** Ville ⊙ a.	0715	0745	0815	0845	0845	0945	...	...	...	1045	...	1145	...	...	1315	1345	1445	1445	...	1545	1645	1745	1815	1846	19

		Ⓐ		⑤–⑦		①–⑥				
				d		b				E
Genève **341 346** d.	...	...	1641	1641	...	...	...	...	1841	...
Bellegarde **341 346** d.	...	...	1709	1709	...	...	...	...	1909	...
Culoz **346** d.	...	...	1746	1746	...	...	...	...	1946	...
Annecy **341 345** d.	1653	1653	|	|	1739	...	1839	1853	|	1939
Aix les Bains **341 345** d.	1727	1738	1807	1807	1826	...	1926	1935	2007	2026
Chambéry **341 345** a.	...	1749	1818	1818	1837	...	1937	...	2018	2037
Chambéry d.	...	...	1821	1821	1840	...	1940	...	2021	2040
Montmélian d.	...	...	|	|	1851	...	1951	...	|	2051
Grenoble a.	...	...	1902	1902	1927	...	2028	...	2102	2127
Grenoble d.	...	...	...	1905	1930	1940	2031	...	...	...
Romans-Bourg de Péage d.	...	...	...	1958	2030	2058	2128	...	...	...
Valence TGV ⊙ a.	...	...	...	2005	2036	2105	2136	...	...	...
Valence Ville ⊙ a.	...	...	...	2015	2045	2115	2146	...	...	...

	①–⑤	①–⑥	①–⑥	Ⓐ	Ⓐ	①–⑥	①–⑥	①–⑥	①–⑥		Ⓐ
	w	b	t			b	b	w	b		
Valence Ville ⊙ d.	...	...	...	...	...	...	0524	...	...	...	06
Valence TGV ⊙ d.	...	...	...	...	...	...	0534	...	...	...	06
Romans-Bourg de Péage d.	...	...	...	...	...	...	0543	...	...	...	06
Grenoble a.	...	...	...	...	...	...	0648	...	...	...	07
Grenoble d.	0507	...	0536	...	0632	0636	...	0658	...	0732	07
Montmélian d.	0544	...	0620	...	0710	0720	...	|	...	0810	08
Chambéry a.	0554	...	0629	...	0719	0728	...	0739	...	0819	08
Chambéry **341 345** d.	0557	0622	...	0645	0722	...	...	0742	0806a	0822	08
Aix les Bains **341 345** d.	0610	0635	...	0659	0736	...	...	0755	0825	0838	08
Annecy **341 345** a.	|	0716	...	0744	0816	...	...	|	0908	0916	09
Culoz **346** d.	0632	...	...	...	...	...	...	|	...	...	...
Bellegarde **341 346** d.	0702	...	...	...	...	...	...	0833	...	...	...
Genève **341 346** a.	0730	...	...	...	...	...	...	0901	...	...	...

		①–⑥	Ⓐ	Ⓑ	Ⓐ		Ⓐ																⑦	Ⓐ		Ⓑ
		b		h								⊗	⊗	⊗	⊗				E				eA			h
Valence Ville ⊙ d.	0645	...	...	...	0715	0815	0915	1015	...	...	...	1215	1315	1345	1415	1515	1615	1645	1715	1745	1815	1915	2015	2015	2115	22
Valence TGV ⊙ d.	0656	...	...	...	0725	0825	0925	1024	...	...	...	1224	1324	1356	1425	1524	1625	1656	1725	1756	1825	1925	2025	2025	2125	22
Romans-Bourg de Péage d.	0705	...	...	...	0734	0833	0933	1032	...	...	...	1232	1332	1405	1433	1532	1633	1705	1733	1805	1833	1934	2034	2033	2134	22
Grenoble a.	0755	...	...	...	0830	0930	1030	1129	...	...	...	1330	1430	1455	1530	1630	1730	1755	1829	1855	1930	2030	2130	2130	2230	23
Grenoble d.	0758	...	0806	...	...	0933	...	1132	1158	...	1233v	1333	1433	1458	1533	1633	1733	1758	1832	*1903*	1933	2033	2133	2133	2233c	
Montmélian d.	|	...	0850	...	...	1010	...	1210	|	...	1311	1410	1510	|	1610	1710	1810	|	1910	*1949*	2010	2110	2210	2210	2310c	
Chambéry a.	0839	...	0859	...	...	1019	...	1219	1239	...	1320	1419	1519	1539	1620	1719	1819	1840	1919	*1959*	2019	2119	2219	2219	2319c	
Chambéry **341 345** d.	0842	...	...	0922	...	1022	...	1222	1242	...	1323	1422	1522	1542	1623	1722	1822	1843	1922	...	2022	2122	2222j	2234	...	
Aix les Bains **341 345** d.	0855	0925	...	0935	...	1036	...	1236	1255	1325	1336	1436	1536	1555	1636	1736	1836	1855	1936	...	2036	2136	2236j	2248	...	
Annecy **341 345** a.	|	1008	...	1016	...	1116	...	1316	|	1408	1416	1516	1616	|	1717	1816	1916	|	2016	...	2116	2216	2316j	2327	...	
Culoz **346** d.	|	...	...	...	...	...	...	...	|	...	...	...	...	|	...	...	...	|	...	...	...	...	...	...	...	
Bellegarde **341 346** d.	0933	...	...	...	...	...	...	...	1333	...	...	...	...	1633	...	...	...	1933	...	...	...	...	...	...	...	
Genève **341 346** a.	1010	...	...	...	...	...	...	...	1401	...	...	...	...	1701	...	...	...	2001	...	...	...	...	...	...	...	

A – To / from Avignon on dates in Table **351**.
E – To / from Évian-les-Bains on dates in Tables **363** and **365**.

a – Ⓐ only.
b – Not June 10, Nov. 11.
c – Ⓒ only.
d – Also June 10, Aug. 14, 15, Oct. 31, Nov. 11.
e – Also June 10, Nov. 11.
h – Not Aug. 15, Nov. 1.

j – 7 – 13 minutes later on June 9, 10, 16, Nov. 11.
r – Not July 15 - Aug. 23.
t – Not June 10, July 15 - Aug. 24, Nov. 11.
v – 1237 on ①–⑤ June 11 - July 5.
w – Not June 10.

* – By 🚌.
⊗ – Subject to alteration on ①–⑤ June 11 - July 5.
⊙ – 🚌 runs 2 – 3 times per hour.

PARIS / ANNECY - LA ROCHE SUR FORON - ST GERVAIS 365

Trains from Lyon / Bellegarde may convey portions for Évian les Bains. Subject to alteration on Sept. 7, 8, 21, 22.

See Table **341** for *TGV* connections Paris - Bellegarde and v.v. For connections Genève Eaux-Vives - Annemasse / La Roche sur Foron see Table **366a**.

km							*TGV* **6467**					*TGV* **6473**									🚌			
		①–⑥	Ⓐ	①–⑥	Ⓒ	Ⓐ	⑥		Ⓐ			⑥		Ⓐ				Ⓑ			Ⓑ	⑤		
		d	R	b	R	p	L	⊗	R⊗	⊗	R⊙	L	⊡	R⊙	v⊡	R		h	◇		h	f		
0	**Paris** Gare de Lyon .... **341** d.	...	...	...	...	...	0711	...	...	...	...	1011	...	...	...	...	...	...	...	...	...	...	...	...
406	Bourg en Bresse .... **341** d.	...	...	...	...	...	|	...	...	...	...	1205	...	...	...	...	...	...	...	...	...	...	...	...
	Lyon Perrache **346** .... d.	...	...	...	...	...	|	...	...	...	...	|	...	...	...	...	...	...	...	...	...	...	...	...
	Lyon Part-Dieu **346** .... d.	...	...	*0638*	...	...	|	*0838*	...	*1038*	...	|	*1238*	...	*1438*	...	*1638*	1738	*1838*	...	...	2038	...	...
470	Bellegarde .... **341** a.	...	...	*0758*	...	...	0948**s**	*0958*	...	*1158*	...	1300	*1358*	...	*1558*	...	*1758*	1900	*1958*	...	...	2204	...	...
470	Bellegarde .... **363** d.	...	...	0809	...	...	|	1009	...	1209	...	1313	1409	...	1609	...	1809	1909	2009	...	2115	2209	...	...
508	Annemasse .... **363** a.	...	...	0842	...	...	1028**s**	1043	...	1243	...	1355	1443	...	1643	...	1843	1944	2043	...	|	2243	...	...
508	Annemasse .... ▷ d.	0650	...	0850	...	...	|	1050	...	1250	...	1406	1450	...	1650	...	1850	1951	2050	...	|	2250	...	...
•	**Annecy** .... ▷ d.	|	0732	|	0932	0932	|	|	1132	|	1332	|	|	1532	|	1732	|	|	|	...	|	|	...	...
525	La Roche sur Foron .... ▷ a.	0707	0807	0907	1007	1007	|	1107	1207	1307	1407	|	1507	1607	1707	1807	1907	2007	2107	...	2205	2307	...	...
525	La Roche sur Foron .... d.	0712	0812	0912	1012	...	|	1112	1212	1312	1412	|	1512	1612	1712	1812	1912	2012	2112	...	2205	2309	...	...
547	Cluses (Haute-Savoie) .... d.	0737	0837	0937	1037	...	1109**s**	1137	1237	1337	1437	1454	1538	1637	1737	1837	1938	2037	2138	...	2245	2333	...	...
566	Sallanches Megève .... d.	0751	0850	0951	1050	...	1136**s**	1151	1250	1351	1450	1511	1551	1650	1751	1850	1951	2051	2151	...	2300	2347	...	...
572	**St Gervais** .... **365a** a.	0756	0856	0956	1056	...	1145	1156	1256	1356	1456	1518	1556	1656	1756	1856	1956	2056	2156	...	2315	2353	...	...
	Chamonix .... **365a** a.	...	...	...	...	...	...	...	...	...	...	...	...	...	...	...	...	...	...	...	2345	...	...	...

									TGV **6482**			🚌			🚌	*TGV* **6486**							
	①–⑥				Ⓐ		Ⓒ	Ⓐ		⑥	Ⓐ		⑦			Ⓐ	⑥	Ⓐ	⑦		Ⓑ			
	bz		R		R	⊗	R	p⊙	△	L	R⊗	⊡	e	R⊙			L	R	e		Rr		B⊖	E⊖
hamonix .... **365a** d.	...	...	...	...	...	...	...	...	...	...	...	...	1350	...	...	1550	...	...	...	...	...	...	...	...
t Gervais .... **365a** d.	0504	0604	0704	0804	0904	1004	1104	...	1204	1247	1304	1404	1417	1504	1604	1617	1658	1704	1704	1804	1904	...	2004	2016
allanches Megève .... d.	0509	0609	0710	0809	0910	1009	1110	...	1209	1255	1310	1409	1430	1510	1609	1630	1706**u**	1710	1710	1809	1910	...	2009	2022
luses (Haute-Savoie) .... d.	0523	0623	0724	0823	0924	1024	1124	...	1224	1309	1324	1424	1452	1524	1624	1652	1720**u**	1724	1724	1824	1924	...	2024	2038
a Roche sur Foron .... a.	0547	0647	0747	0847	0947	1047	1147	...	1247	|	1347	1447	1534	1547	1647	1734	|	1747	1747	1847	1947	...	2047	2102
a Roche sur Foron .... ▷ d.	0553	0653	0752	0853	0952	1053	1152	1208	1253	|	1352	1453	1534	1552	1653	1734	|	1752	1753	1853	1952	...	2053	2108
Annecy .... ▷ a.	|	|	0829	|	1029	|	1229	1240	|	|	1429	|	|	1629	|	|	|	1829	|	|	2029	...	|	|
nnemasse .... ▷ a.	0610	0710	...	0910	...	1110	...	...	1310	1347	...	1510	|	...	1710	|	|	...	1810	1910	...	...	2110	2125
nnemasse .... **363** d.	0617	0717	...	0917	...	1117	...	...	1317	1403	...	1517	|	...	1717	|	1814**u**	...	1817	1918	...	...	2130	2132
ellegarde .... **363** a.	0650	0750	...	0950	...	1150	...	...	1350	1457	...	1550	1634	...	1750	1834	|	...	1850	1950	...	...	2203	2203
ellegarde .... **341** d.	0701	*0801*	...	*1001‡*	...	*1201§*	...	...	*1401*	1502	...	*1601*	...	...	*1801*	...	1900**u**	...	1901	*2001*	...	...	...	...
Lyon Part-Dieu **346** .... a.	0822	*0922*	...	*1122‡*	...	*1322§*	...	...	*1522*	|	...	*1722*	...	...	*1922*	...	|	...	2022	*2122*	...	...	...	...
Lyon Perrache **346** .... a.	...	...	...	...	...	...	...	...	...	|	...	...	...	...	...	...	|	...	...	...	...	...	...	...
ourg en Bresse .... **341** d.	...	...	...	...	...	...	...	...	...	1556	...	...	...	...	...	...	1949**u**	...	...	...	...	...	...	...
aris Gare de Lyon .... **341** a.	...	...	...	...	...	...	...	...	...	1749	...	...	...	...	...	...	2141	...	...	...	...	...	...	...

ANNECY - ANNEMASSE direct trains

	①–⑥		①–⑥		①–⑥	Ⓐ	Ⓑ	Ⓐ	⑤	⑤
	bp		bp		bp	p	ph	p	C	D
		...	⊙		⊙	⊙			A	A
nnecy .... d.	0632	...	1032	...	1432	1632	1832	1932	2032	2032
a Roche sur Foron .... a.	0707	...	1107	...	1507	1707	1907	2007	2107	2111
a Roche sur Foron .... d.	0710	...	1110	...	1510	1710	1910	2010	2110	2116
nnemasse .... a.	0726		1126	...	1526	1726	1926	2026	2126	2136

	Ⓐ	①–⑥		①–⑥	Ⓑ	⑦	Ⓑ		
	p	bp		bp	ph	w	H	J	K
				⊙	⊙	A			
Annemasse .... d.	0633	0833	...	1233	1633	1827	2033	2103	2103
La Roche sur Foron .... a.	0649	0849	...	1249	1649	1843	2049	2122	2131
La Roche sur Foron .... d.	0652	0852	...	1252	1652	1852	2052	2125	2134
Annecy .... a.	0729	0929	...	1329	1729	1930	2129	2202	2212

– 🚌 (12) Grenoble - Chambéry - Annecy - Évian les Bains and v.v. See Tables **363** and **364**.
– Ⓑ June 16 - July 21; Ⓑ from Sept. 15 (also Sept. 8; not Nov. 1).
– ⑤ from Sept. 20 (also Oct. 31; not Nov. 1).
– ⑤ Aug. 23 - Sept. 13 (also June 14, Aug. 14).
– Ⓑ Aug. 11 - Sept. 13 (also June 9, 11–14; not Sept. 8).
– Ⓑ from Sept. 15 (also June 9, 16, Aug. 11, Sept. 8; not Nov. 1).
– Aug. 18, 25, Sept. 1 only.
– Ⓐ Aug. 12 - Sept. 13 (also June 10–14).
– ⑥ July 6 - Aug. 31.
– From Sept. 9.

– Not June 10, Nov. 11.
– Not June 10.
– Also June 10, Nov. 11.
– Also Oct. 31; not Nov. 1.
– Not Aug. 15, Nov. 1.
– Not June 17 - Aug. 9.
– Not Nov. 1.
– Calls to set down only.

u – Calls to pick up only.
v – Not Aug. 11, 18, 25, Sept. 1, 8.
w – Also June 10, Nov. 11; not June 23 - Aug. 4, Sept. 8, 22, Nov. 10.
z – Not July 1–5.

TGV – 🄡, supplement payable, 🍷.

‡ – Subject to alteration Sept. 9–13, 16–20, Nov. 18–22.
§ – Subject to alteration Oct. 21–25.
⊗ – Subject to alteration on ①–⑤ Sept. 23 - Oct. 18.
⊙ – Subject to alteration on ①–⑤ Sept. 23 - Oct. 11.
⊡ – Subject to alteration on ①–⑤ Sept. 16 - Oct. 4.
△ – Subject to alteration on ①–⑤ Sept. 16 - Oct. 18.
◇ – Subject to alteration June 30 - July 4, Sept. 7, 8, 21, 22.
⊖ – Change trains at Annemasse on Ⓐ.
▷ – For other trains Annemasse - La Roche sur Foron - Annecy see panel below main table.
• – Annecy to La Roche sur Foron is 39 km.

ST GERVAIS - CHAMONIX 365a

SERVICE JUNE 22 - SEPTEMBER 8 AND FROM NOVEMBER 9. Many journeys continue to / from Le Châtelard or Martigny (Table **572**).

km									S			
0	**St Gervais** ..... d.	0705	0805	0905	1005	1205	1305	1405	1505	1605	and	2005
9	Les Houches .. d.	0733	0833	0933	1033	1233	1333	1433	1533	1633	hourly	2033
20	**Chamonix** ...... a.	0748	0848	0948	1048	1248	1348	1448	1548	1648	until	2048

								S			
Chamonix .. d.	0715	0815	0915	1015	1215	1315	1415	1515	1615	and	2015
Les Houches d.	0732	0832	0932	1032	1232	1332	1432	1532	1632	hourly	2032
St Gervais .. a.	0756	0856	0956	1056	1256	1356	1456	1556	1656	until	2056

SERVICE SEPTEMBER 9 - NOVEMBER 8 (subject to confirmation)

km		🚌	🚌	🚌	🚌	🚌	🚌	🚌	🚌	🚌	🚌	🚌	🚌
0	**St Gervais** ..... d.	0706	0806	0906	1006	1206	1306	1406	1606	1706	1806	1906	2006
9	Les Houches .. d.	0722	0822	0922	1022	1222	1322	1422	1622	1722	1822	1922	2022
20	**Chamonix** ...... a.	0738	0838	0938	1038	1238	1338	1438	1638	1738	1838	1938	2038

	🚌	🚌	🚌	🚌	🚌	🚌	🚌	🚌	🚌	🚌	🚌	🚌
Chamonix .. d.	0718	0818	0918	1018	1218	1318	1418	1618	1718	1818	1918	2018
Les Houches d.	0733	0833	0933	1033	1233	1333	1433	1633	1733	1833	1933	2033
St Gervais .. a.	0755	0855	0955	1055	1255	1355	1455	1655	1755	1855	1955	2055

– June 22 - Sept. 8.

366 (PARIS -) CHAMBÉRY - ALBERTVILLE - BOURG ST MAURICE

For Paris - Chambéry, see Table **341**. Journeys from / to Aix les Bains are subject to alteration on Aug. 16, 17.

km											*TGV*													
		🚌		🚌	🚌	🚌					6429	🚌											🚌	🚌
		Ⓐ	Ⓐ	①–⑥	Ⓐ	Ⓐ				①–⑥	⑥	Ⓐ				Ⓐ	①–⑥		Ⓐ	①–⑥			①–⑥	⑤⑦
				b				⊙		b ⊙	D			⊙			b			b			b	v
0	**Paris Gare de Lyon** 341 d.	...	...	...	...	...	...	...	...	...	0845	...	...	...	...	...	...	...	...	...	...	...	...	...
	Lyon Part Dieu 344 d.	...	...	...	...	...	...	...	...	...	|	...	...	...	...	...	...	...	...	...	...	...	...	...
	Aix les Bains d.	...	...	...	...	...	...	0934	...	...	|	...	...	1337	...	...	...	...	1837	...	...	...	...	...
532	**Chambéry** 341 367 d.	0601	0652	...	...	0805	...	0952	...	1144	1200	1250	...	1352	...	1552	1652	1752	1852	1952	2052	...	2153	2245
545	Montmélian 367 d.	0621	0702	...	...	0825	...	1002	...	1154	|	|	...	1402	...	1602	1703	1802	1902	2002	2102	...	2213	|
557	St Pierre d'Albigny 367 d.	0639	0710	...	...	0840	...	1010	...	1202	|	|	...	1410	...	1610	1712	1810	1910	2010	2110	...	2228	|
580	Albertville a.	0717	0740	...	...	0905	...	1032	...	1224	1233	1340	...	1436	...	1635	1739	1833	1938	2038	2137	...	2253	2335
580	Albertville d.	0717	0747n	0750	...	0905	...	1039	...	1231	1247	1340	...	1443	...	1642	1746	1840	1945	2045	2145	...	2253	2335
608	**Moûtiers-Salins** d.	0747	0815n	0835	0845	0935	...	1113	...	1301	1318	1410	...	1518	...	1717	1816	1917	2016	2118	2216	...	2328	0010
623	Aime la Plagne d.	0802	...	...	0900	0950	...	1129	...	1315	1336	|	...	1532	...	1732	1833	1932	2030	2132	2231	...	|	0025
630	Landry d.	0812	...	...	0910	1000	...	1138	...	1324	1347	|	...	1540	...	1739	1842	1940	2038	2140	2239	...	|	0035
637	**Bourg St Maurice** a.	0824	...	...	0922	1012	...	1146	...	1331	1354	1440	...	1548	...	1747	1849	1947	2045	2148	2246	...	0008	0050

														TGV	*TGV*								
	🚌			🚌		🚌		🚌						6436	6436			🚌					🚌
	Ⓐ	①–⑥		⑦	Ⓐ	Ⓐ	Ⓐ	Ⓐ			①–⑥			Ⓐ	⑥	⑥	Ⓐ	Ⓐ		⑦	①–⑥		⑤⑦
		b		e	H		m		⊙		b ⊙		⊙	⊙	G	E				e	b		v
Bourg St Maurice d.	0426	0514	0617	0717	...	0757	...	0856	1014	...	1214	...	1414	1514	1558	1603	1638	1638	1702	...	1814	1814	...	1940
Landry d.	|	0522	0625	0724	...	0809	...	0903	1022	...	1221	...	1421	1522	1608	1613	1645	1645	1709	...	1821	1821	...	1947
Aime la Plagne d.	|	0531	0633	0733	...	0818	...	0912	1031	...	1229	...	1430	1532	1617	1623	1655	1655	1718	...	1830	1832	...	1956
Moûtiers-Salins d.	0456	0545	0646	0802	...	0837	0847n	0936	1046	...	1243	...	1444	1545	1635	1642	1710	1710	1742	...	1845	1845	...	2020
Albertville a.	0531	0616	0716	0847	...	...	0916n	1011	1120	...	1317	...	1516	1613	|	|	1738	1738	1817	...	1916	1916	...	2055
Albertville d.	0531	0623	0723	0847	0858	...	0923	1011	1127	...	1324	...	1523	1620	1719	1721	1745	1745	1817	...	1923	1923	...	2055
St Pierre d'Albigny 367 d.	0551	0650	0750	0915	0925	...	0950	1041	1152	...	1350	...	1550	1650	|	|	1807	1807	1843	...	1950	1950	...	2115
Montmélian 367 d.	0606	0658	0758	0930	0933	...	0958	1056	1200	...	1358	...	1558	1658	|	|	1814	1814	1858	...	1958	1958	...	2130
Chambéry 341 367 a.	0626	0708	0808	0950	0943	...	1008	1116	1208	...	1408	...	1607	1708	1825*	1825*	1823	1823	1918	...	2008	2008	...	2150
Aix les Bains a.	...	...	0828	...	...	...	...	...	1223	...	...	...	1623	...	|	|	1838	...	...	...	|	...	...	...
Lyon Part Dieu 344 a.	...	...	...	...	...	...	...	...	...	...	...	...	...	...	|	|	1952	...	...	...	2154	...	...	...
Paris Gare de Lyon 341 a.	...	...	...	...	...	...	...	...	...	...	...	...	...	...	2115	2115	...	...	...	...	...	...	...	...

D – ⑥ July 6 - Aug. 31 (not Aug. 17).
E – July 6, 13, 20 only.
G – July 27 - Aug. 31.
H – Nov. 4 – 15 only.

b – Not June 10, Nov. 11.
e – Also June 10, Nov. 11.
m – Not Nov. 4 – 15.
n – Not Sept. 23 - Nov. 29.
v – Also June 10, Aug. 14, Oct. 31, Nov. 11; not Nov. 1.

TGV – Ⓡ, supplement payable, 🍷.

* – Departure time.
⊙ – Subject to alteration on Ⓐ Sept. 23 - Nov. 29.

366a 🚌 GENÈVE - ANNEMASSE

🚌 GENÈVE EAUX VIVES - ANNEMASSE - ANNECY

SNCF 🚌 service	🚌	🚌	🚌	🚌	🚌	🚌	🚌	🚌	🚌	🚌	🚌
		①–⑥					Ⓒ		①–⑥		
		b							r		
Genève Eaux-Vives d.	0645	0845	1045	1045	1245	1445	1645	1724	1800	1925	2112
Annemasse ▷ a.	0710	0910	|	1110	1310	1510	1710	|	|	|	2132
La Roche sur Foron ▷ a.	0741	0941	1115	1141	1341	1541	1741	1759	1840	1955	2202
Annecy ▷ a.	...	...	1152	...	...	...	...	1834	...	...	2237

	🚌	🚌	🚌	🚌	🚌	🚌	🚌	🚌	🚌	🚌	🚌
	①–⑥		Ⓐ	Ⓒ					①–⑥		
	r								b ▲		
Annecy ▷ d.	0615	0700	...	...	...	...	...	...	1640	...	...
La Roche sur Foron ▷ d.	0652	0735	0812	0812	1012	1212	1412	1612	1715	1812	2012
Annemasse ▷ d.	|	|	|	0847	1042	1242	1442	1647	|	1847	2042
Genève Eaux-Vives a.	0742	0825	0858	0912	1102	1302	1502	1712	1805	1912	2102

🚌 TPG route 61 provides a frequent service between Genève Cornavin and Annemasse rail stations (journey time: 45 minutes). Please note that, owing to work in the Annemasse station area services currently run to / from the nearby Chablais-Parc stop in Annemasse. On Ⓐ services run approximately every 15 – 30 minutes (from Cornavin 0638 - 2232; from Chablais-Parc 0554 - 2143); on ⑥ services run approximately every 30 minutes (from Cornavin 0643 - 2146; from Chablais-Parc 0547 - 2047); on ⑦ services run approximately every 30 minutes (from Cornavin 0834 - 2143; from Chablais-Parc 0750 - 2052).

b – Not June 10, Nov. 11.
r – Not June 10.
▲ – Runs 14 minutes **earlier** on ⑥ (also Aug. 15, Nov. 1).
▷ – See also Table **365**.

367 CHAMBÉRY - MODANE

Warning! Subject to alteration on Aug. 10, 11, 16, 17.

km					*TGV*							*TGV*			*TGV*		*TGV*								
				🚌	9241					🚌		9245			6407		9249					🚌		🚌	🚌
		①–⑥	Ⓐ	Ⓐ			Ⓐ	⑥⑦	Ⓐ	Ⓐ	Ⓒ			Ⓐ	⑥	Ⓐ		①–⑥			⑤⑦	①–④	Ⓑ	⑥	⑤
		b			M		P	t	P	R	n	M ▲	c	D	A		M	b			v	m	d	k	f
	Paris Gare de Lyon 341 d.	...	...	...	0629	...	...	...	...	...	...	1037z	...	...	1145	...	1441	...	...	...	...	...	...	...	...
	Lyon St Exupéry ✈ 342 d.	...	...	...	|	...	...	...	...	...	...	1233z	...	...	|	...	1637	...	...	...	...	...	...	...	...
	Lyon Part Dieu 344 d.	...	...	...	0831	...	...	...	...	...	...	|	...	...	|	1508	|	...	...	...	...	...	...	...	...
	Aix les Bains 364 d.	...	...	...	|	...	1049	1133	...	...	...	|	...	...	|	1621	|	1730	...	...	...	...	...	...	...
0	**Chambéry** 364 366 d.	0635	0748	0842	0945	...	1104	1148	1237	1237	1248	1345	1448	1522	1502s	1648	1744	1748	1848	1948	2048	2042	2148	2142	2243
14	Montmélian 364 366 d.	0644	0757	|	|	...	1114	1157	1247	|	1259	|	1457	1535	|	1657	|	1757	1857	1957	2057	|	2157	2202	2303
26	St Pierre d'Albigny 366 d.	0653	0806	|	|	...	1124	1206	1258	|	1307	|	1506	1544	|	1706	|	1806	1906	2006	2106	|	2206	2218	2319
61	St Avre la Chambre d.	0722	0835	0955	|	...	1200	1234	1327	1334	1336	|	1537	1612	1542s	1734	|	1835	1934	2034	2134	2155	2235	2253	2354
71	St Jean de Maurienne d.	0730	0842	1010	|	...	1217	1242	1335	1349	1344	|	1545	1620	1553s	1742	1824	1842	1942	2042	2142	2210	2242	2308	0009
83	St Michel-Valloire d.	0739	0853	1026	|	...	1228	1254	1345	1405	1355	|	1556r	1631	1610s	1753	|	1853	1953	2053	2153	2226	2253	2324	0025
99	**Modane** a.	0754	0907	1046	1050	...	1243	1310	1359	1425	1410	1450	1610r	1645	1632	1807	1847	1907	2007	2107	2207	2246	2307	2344	0045

						TGV				*TGV*									*TGV*	*TGV*	*TGV*				
			🚌		🚌	9240				9244		🚌	🚌						6414	9248	9248				
	①–⑥	Ⓐ	⑦	①–⑥	Ⓐ							Ⓐ	Ⓐ					Ⓐ	⑥	Ⓑ h	⑥ w	①–⑥			Ⓑ
	b		e	b		M			Q	M △	Q		R	N					A	M	M	b			h
Modane d.	0554	0554	0553	0704	0753	0914	0958	...	1138	1152	...	1200	1330	1358	...	1555r	...	1716r	1729	1752	1752	1756	1756	...	1953
St Michel-Valloire d.	0609	0609	0613	0722	0813	|	1012	...	1155	|	←	1220	1350	1413	...	1610r	...	1732r	1745	|	|	1811	1811	...	2009
St Jean de Maurienne d.	0620	0620	0629	0733	0829	0937	1027	...	1204	|	1220	1236	1406	1427	...	1621	...	1743	1800	|	|	1822	1822	...	2020
St Avre la Chambre d.	0627	0627	0644	0740	0844	|	1035	...	→	|	1229	1251	1421	1436	...	1629	...	1751	1810	|	|	1830	1830	...	2027
St Pierre d'Albigny 366 d.	0656	0656	0735	0807	|	|	1105	...	...	|	1257	1342	|	1505	...	1657	...	1818	|	|	|	1857	1857	...	2055
Montmélian 364 366 d.	0703	0703	0751	0816	|	|	1113	...	...	|	1305	1358	|	1514	...	1705	...	1825	|	|	|	1905	1905	...	2103
Chambéry 364 366 a.	0712	0712	0811	0826	0957	1016	1122	...	...	1252	1314	1418	1518	1523	...	1713	...	1837	1848*	1851	1851	1913	1913	...	2112
Aix les Bains 364 a.	...	0738	0831	...	...	|	...	...	...	1306	...	...	...	...	...	...	...	...	|	|	|	1938x	...	...	...
Lyon Part Dieu 344 a.	...	0852	...	...	...	|	...	...	...	|	...	...	...	...	...	...	...	...	|	2028	2028	2052x	...	...	...
Lyon St Exupéry ✈ 342 a.	...	...	...	...	...	1123	...	...	...	|	...	...	...	...	...	...	...	...	|	|	|	...	...	...	...
Paris Gare de Lyon 341 a.	...	...	...	...	...	1319	...	...	...	1611	...	...	...	...	...	...	...	...	2211	2231	2237	...	...	...	...

A – ⑥ July 6 - Aug. 31 (not Aug. 10, 17).
D – Ⓐ June 24 - July 12. On June 28, July 12 St Pierre d'Albigny d. 1543, St Avre la Chambre d. 1610, St Jean de Maurienne d. 1630, St Michel-Valloire d. 1641, Modane a. 1655.
M – 12 and 🍷 Paris - Torino - Milano and v.v. (Table **44**). Ⓡ and special fares payable.
N – Ⓒ to July 7; daily from July 13.
P – Ⓐ from July 15 (not Oct. 28 - Nov. 22).
Q – Modane - St Jean de Maurienne on Ⓒ (daily July 13 - Oct. 27 and from Nov. 23). St Jean de Maurienne - Chambéry daily except ①–⑤ Oct. 28 - Nov. 22.
R – Ⓐ to July 12.

b – Not June 10, Nov. 11.
c – Not June 24 – 28, July 1 – 5, 8 – 12.
d – Not Aug. 9, 11, 15, 16, Nov. 1.
e – Also June 10, Nov. 11.
f – Also Aug. 14, Oct. 31; not Nov. 1.
h – Not Aug. 15, 16, Nov. 1.
k – Also Aug. 15, Nov. 1.
m – Not June 10, Aug. 14, 15, Oct. 31, Nov. 11.
n – Not Nov. 11.
r – Not June 11 – 14, 17 – 21.
s – Arrival time (calls to set down only).
t – Also June 10, Aug. 15.

v – Also June 10, Aug. 14, Oct. 31, Nov. 11; not Nov. 1.
w – Also Aug. 15, Nov. 1; not Nov. 2.
x – On June 29 does not call at Aix les Bains, arrives Lyon 2110.
z – On certain dates departs Paris 1041 or 1045, Lyon St Exupéry 1238, 1240 or 1244.

TGV – Ⓡ, supplement payable, 🍷.

* – Departure time.
▲ – Subject to alteration until June 23.
△ – Subject to alteration until July 5.

SAT / SAVDA — CHAMONIX - MONT BLANC TUNNEL - COURMAYEUR — 368

y 🚌, journey 45 minutes. Reservation compulsory by 1700 on previous day through SAT, Chamonix station ✆ +33 (0) 450 530 115 or SAVDA, Aosta bus station ✆ +39 0165 367 039.

ec. 22 - Apr. 14: From Chamonix (Avenue de Courmayeur) at 0830, 0930, 1100, 1500, 1615, 1730. From Courmayeur (Piazzale Monte Bianco) at 0815, 0945, 1200, 1400, 1615, 1730.
pr. 15 - June 28: From Chamonix (Avenue de Courmayeur) at 0830, 1145, 1530, 1715. From Courmayeur (Piazzale Monte Bianco) at 0945, 1045, 1545, 1700.
une 29 - Sept. 15: From Chamonix (Avenue de Courmayeur) at 0830, 1030, 1230, 1430, 1600, 1800. From Courmayeur (Piazzale Monte Bianco) at 0900, 1100, 1200, 1400, 1600, 1800.
ept. 16 - Dec. 6: From Chamonix (Avenue de Courmayeur) at 0830, 1815. From Courmayeur (Piazzale Monte Bianco) at 0945, 1700.

SAVDA — 🚌 COURMAYEUR - PRÉ ST DIDER - AOSTA

ourmayeur △ .... d.	0645	0735	0835	0935	and	1935	2035	2135	...	...
ré St Didier .... d.	0653	0743	0843	0943	hourly	1943	2043	2143	...	...
osta ⊡ .... a.	0745	0835	0935	1035	until	2035	2135	2235	...	...

Aosta ⊡ .... d.	0645	0745	0845	0945	1045	1145	1245	1335	1445	and	2145
Pré St Didier .... d.	0737	0837	0937	1037	1137	1237	1337	1427	1537	hourly	2237
Courmayeur △...... a.	0745	0845	0945	1045	1145	1245	1345	1436	1545	until	2245

– P. le Monte Bianco.

⊡ – Autostazione (bus station).

Narrow gauge. 2nd class. — CORSICAN RAILWAYS — 369

SERVICE APRIL 1 - JUNE 30

km		Ⓐ	Ⓐ	⑥	Ⓐ	†	⑥	⑥	Ⓐ	†	⑥	Ⓐ	Ⓐ	⑥	†	Ⓐ	†	⑥	⑥	Ⓐ	Ⓐ	†c	†b	Ⓐ	⑥	Ⓐ
0	**Bastia** .... ▷ d.	0603	0617	0622	0754	0855	0913	...	0946	1008	1054	1116	1509	1526	1535	1638	1650	1651	...	1656	...	...	1813	1833	1924	1930
10	Biguglia .... ▷ d.	0618	|	0635	0808	0909	0927	...	1000	1021	1108	1130	1523	1539	1548	1656	1703	|	...	|	...	...	1830	1851	1939	1945
22	Casamozza .. ▷ d.	0632	0642	0648	0823	0923	0941	...	1016	1038	1122	1146	1538	1554	1602	1711	1721	1715	...	1721	...	...	1848	1908	1953	1959
47	Ponte Leccia..... d.	...	0720	0725	0903	1001	1019	1026	1057	1119	1156	1222	1613	1628	1641	...	1801	1757	1800	1801	1805	...	1922	1945	...	...
98	Ile Rousse. ▶ d.	...	|	|	|	|	|	1143	1213	1235	|	|	|	|	|	...	1917	|	1915	|	1920	...	|	|	...	...
120	**Calvi** .... ▶ a.	...	|	|	|	|	|	1218	1248	1310	|	|	|	|	|	...	1952	|	1950	|	1955	...	|	|	...	...
74	Corté .... d.	...	0803	0803	0939	1040	1054	...	...	...	1235	1311	1649	1707	1722	...	...	1843	...	1839	...	1900	1955	2019	...	...
90	Vivario .... d.	...	0835	0833	1017	1110	1124	...	...	...	1305	1343	1726	1737	1752	...	...	1913	...	1911	...	1930	...	...	...	...
107	Vizzavona......... d.	...	0853	0854	1035	1128	1147	...	...	...	1323	1401	1748	1757	1812	...	...	1931	...	1929	...	1948	...	...	...	...
145	Mezzana....... △ d.	...	0944	0940	1125	1214	1235	...	...	...	1409	1448	1836	1843	1858	...	...	2017	...	2016	...	2034	...	...	...	...
158	**Ajaccio** .... △ a.	...	1002	0958	1143	1232	1253	...	...	...	1427	1506	1854	1901	1916	...	...	2035	...	2031	...	2052	...	...	...	...

	Ⓐ	⑥	Ⓐ	⑥	†	Ⓐ	⑥	Ⓐ	Ⓐ	†	⑥	⑥	Ⓐ	†	⑥	Ⓐ	†	⑥	Ⓐ	⑥	†	Ⓐ	Ⓐ	⑥	†c	Ⓐ
jaccio .... △ d.	...	...	...	...	...	...	0604	0604	...	...	...	0743	0812	0842	1034	1100	...	...	...	1511	1522	1525	1635	1645	1700	...
ezzana........ △ d.	...	...	...	...	...	...	0623	0620	...	...	...	0802	0831	0901	1053	1124	...	...	...	1530	1541	1544	1654	1704	1719	...
zzavona.......... d.	...	...	...	...	...	...	0714	0711	...	...	...	0855	0925	0951	1146	1215	...	...	...	1620	1631	1635	1749	1756	1811	...
vario .... d.	...	...	...	...	...	...	0729	0727	...	...	...	0910	0941	1006	1201	1231	...	...	...	1635	1646	1651	1805	1811	1826	...
orté .... d.	...	...	0621	0647	...	...	0804	0800	...	...	...	0940	1018	1041	1234	1310	...	...	...	1709	1721	1724	1842	1844	1854	...
Calvi .... ▶ d.	...	...	|	|	...	0640	|	|	...	0800	0820	|	|	|	|	|	1440	1550	1550	|	|	|	|	|	▬	...
Ile Rousse.. ▶ d.	...	...	|	|	...	0717	|	|	...	0837	0856	|	|	|	|	|	1517	1626	1627	|	|	|	|	|	...	...
onte Leccia..... d.	...	...	0656	0724	...	0831	0839	0838	0937	1000	1010	1020	1056	1118	1308	1345	1640	1740	1741	1751	1758	1802	1918	1919	⑥	...
asamozza.... ▷ d.	0640	0714	0735	0758	0854	...	0914	0915	1017	1039	...	1055	1131	1153	1343	1420	1720	...	...	1825	1833	1838	1959	1954	2000	2004
guglia .... ▷ d.	0656	0729	0753	0813	0909	...	0927	0928	1031	1051	...	1108	1144	1205	1356	1432	1732	...	...	1837	1846	1851	|	|	2014	2018
astia .... ▷ a.	0712	0747	0813	0830	0924	...	0940	0941	1047	1104	...	1121	1157	1218	1409	1445	1745	...	...	1850	1859	1904	2021	2016	2029	2033

– Not Apr. 21, June 9.
– Not Apr. 21, 22, 28, May 1, 30, June 9.

– **Additional journeys** Ajaccio - Mezzana and v.v.: **From Ajaccio** at 0635 Ⓐ, 0645 ⑥, 0721 Ⓐ, 1010 Ⓐ, 1215 ⚒, 1725 ⚒, 1815 ⚒ and 1927 ⚒. **From Mezzana** at 0658 Ⓐ, 0710 ⑥, 0744 Ⓐ, 1033 Ⓐ, 1330 ⚒, 1748 ⚒, 1902 Ⓐ, 1904 ⑥ and 1950 ⚒.

▶ – **Additional journeys** Ile Rousse - Calvi and v.v.: **From Ile Rousse** at 0900 ⚒, 1020 †, 1100 ⚒, 1320 †, 1400 ⚒, 1620 †, 1630 ⚒, 1820 † and 1830 ⚒. **From Calvi** at 0730 ⑥, 0800 Ⓐ, 0920 †, 1000 ⚒, 1120 †, 1300 Ⓐ, 1305 ⑥, 1500 ⚒, 1520 †, 1720 † and 1730 ⚒.

▷ – **Additional journeys** Bastia - Casamozza and v.v.: **From Bastia** at 0624 Ⓐ, 0640 ⑥, 0717 Ⓐ, 0725 ⑥, 0815 †, 0821 Ⓐ, 0835 ⑥, 0857 Ⓐ, 1020 ⑥, 1026 Ⓐ, 1210 ⑥, 1213 Ⓐ, 1225 †, 1325 Ⓐ, 1340 ⑥, 1400 †, 1450 Ⓐ, 1500 ⑥, 1604 Ⓐ, 1634 ⑥, 1718 Ⓐ, 1755 Ⓐ and 1750 ⑥. **From Casamozza** at 0718 Ⓐ, 0809 Ⓐ, 0824 ⑥, 0858 Ⓐ, 0935 Ⓐ, 0945 ⑥, 1105 Ⓐ, 1126 ⑥, 1301 †, 1306 ⑥, 1316 Ⓐ, 1400 Ⓐ, 1422 ⑥, 1445 †, 1524 Ⓐ, 1555 ⑥, 1641 Ⓐ, 1716 ⑥, 1720 Ⓐ, 1758 Ⓐ, 1841 ⑥ and 1854 Ⓐ.

SUMMER SERVICE DURING JULY AND AUGUST (subject to confirmation – 2018 service shown below)

km		Ⓐ	⚒							⚒	⚒		⚒			⚒		⚒	⚒				Ⓐ		Ⓑ	Ⓐ
0	**Bastia** .... d.	...	0641	0715	0755	...	0831	...	0906	0941	1105	1215	1340	...	...	1450	1509	...	1614	1648	...	...	1730	1811	1811	1938
10	Biguglia .... d.	...	0656	0730	0811	...	0846	...	0921	0956	1120	1231	1355	...	...	1505	1523	...	1629	1703	...	...	1745	1827	1827	1954
22	Casamozza .... d.	...	0710	0745	0825	...	0908	...	0936	1010	1134	1245	1409	...	...	1519	1538	...	1643	1718	...	...	1759	1841	1842	2009
47	Ponte Leccia..... a.	...	▬	0819	▬	...	0943	...	1014	▬	...	▬	...	...	...	▬	1612	...	▬	1757	...	...	...	...	1916	...
47	Ponte Leccia..... d.	...	...	0824	...	...	0948	...	1015	...	...	...	...	...	...	...	1613	...	...	1800	1804	...	...	...	1920	...
98	Ile Rousse..... d.	...	...	|	0815	1015	1104	1245	|	...	...	...	...	1440	1715	...	|	...	...	|	1920	2000	...	...	|	...
120	**Calvi** .... a.	...	...	|	0900	1100	1139	1330	|	...	...	⚒	...	1525	1800	...	|	...	...	|	1955	2045	...	...	|	...
74	Corté .... d.	...	...	0906	...	...	...	...	1054	...	...	1330	...	...	...	...	1655	...	...	1840	...	...	...	...	1954	...
90	Vivario .... d.	...	...	0938	...	...	...	...	1126	...	...	1402	...	...	...	...	1727	...	...	1912	...	...	...	...	...	...
107	Vizzavona.......... d.	...	Ⓐ	1001	...	...	...	...	1148	⚒	...	1421	...	...	...	⚒	1749	...	Ⓐ	1930	...	...	...	...	...	...
145	Mezzana.......... d.	0727	0813	1051	...	...	...	...	1236	1330	...	1511	...	...	...	1748	1837	1902	1948	2017	...	...	...	...	...	...
158	**Ajaccio** .... a.	0745	0831	1109	...	...	...	...	1254	1348	...	1529	...	...	...	1806	1855	1920	2006	2035	...	...	...	...	...	...

	⚒	⚒					Ⓐ		Ⓐ				⚒	⚒	⚒	⚒	⚒				⚒		⚒	⚒	⚒	Ⓐ
accio .... d.	...	...	...	...	...	...	0643	0704	0750	0846	...	...	1030	1215	...	...	...	...	...	1450	...	1635	...	1725	1815	1925
ezzana............ d.	...	...	...	...	...	...	0659	0724	0808	0906	...	...	1052	1233	...	...	...	...	...	1512	...	1655	...	1743	1833	1943
zzavona........... d.	...	...	...	...	...	...	▬	0815	▬	1000	...	...	1147	...	...	...	...	...	...	1604	...	1750	...	▬	▬	...
vario .... d.	...	...	...	...	...	...	...	0831	...	1016	...	...	1203	...	...	...	...	...	...	1620	...	1806	...	...	...	...
orté .... d.	...	0634	...	...	...	...	...	0907	...	1055	...	...	1232	...	...	...	...	...	...	1656	...	1841	...	...	...	...
Calvi .... d.	...	|	...	0625	0715	0915	...	|	...	|	...	1150	...	...	...	...	...	1340	1535	|	...	|	...	1615	1815	...
Ile Rousse...... d.	...	|	...	0702	0800	1000	...	|	...	|	...	1235	...	...	...	...	...	1425	1612	|	...	|	...	1700	1900	...
onte Leccia...... a.	...	0708	...	0816	...	...	...	0941	...	1129	...	...	...	...	...	...	...	...	1726	1730	...	1915	...	...	...	...
onte Leccia..... d.	...	0709	...	0828	...	...	⚒	0949	⚒	1131	...	...	...	...	...	...	...	...	...	1732	...	1921	...	...	...	...
asamozza........ d.	0715	0745	0831	0907	...	...	1015	1029	1140	1207	1305	...	...	...	1415	1539	1648	...	...	1813	1854	1956	2014	...	...	...
guglia .... d.	0730	0800	0846	0921	...	...	1029	1041	1154	1220	1319	...	...	...	1429	1553	1703	...	...	1827	1908	2009	2028	...	...	...
astia .... a.	0745	0816	0901	0935	...	...	1044	1055	1209	1234	1334	...	...	...	1444	1608	1718	...	...	1840	1924	2022	2043	...	...	...

370 PARIS - DIJON - BESANÇON - MULHOUSE - BASEL *TGV Rhin-Rhône*

Local services: Tables **371** Paris - Dijon, **374** Dijon - Besançon, **378** Besançon - Belfort, **370b** Belfort - Mulhouse, **385** Mulhouse - Basel.

WARNING! Timings may vary by up to 4 minutes from Sept. 2 (please check you *TGV* reservation). Certain services are subject to alteration on June 23, Sept. 21, 22, 28, 29, Oct. 5, 6, 12, 13

km		*TGV* 6701	*TGV* 9203	*TGV* 6747	*TGV* 9211	*TGV* 6703	*TGV* 9213	*TGV* 6755	*TGV* 9215	*TGV* 6755	*TGV* 6755	*TGV* 6741	*TGV* 9219	*TGV* 6759	*TGV* 6759	*TGV* 6785	*TGV* 6705	*TGV* 9223	*TGV* 6757	*TGV* 6783	*TGV* 6707	*TGV* 6707	*TGV* 6709	*TGV* 6753	*TGV* 6753
		①–⑤	①–⑥	⑥⑦				⑤		①–④	⑦	⑤		Ⓑ	⑥	⑥	Ⓑ			⑤		⑤⑥		⑦	⑤
		a	b	c	w	w		f	n	m	v	f		p	r△	r△	p	B	G	f	E	t	H	e	f
0	**Paris** Gare de Lyon ..... **375** d.	0649	0723	0953	1023	1123	1223	1357	1423	1453	1453	1523	1623	1653	1653	1653	1723	1823	1853	1853	1923	1923	2023	2053	2123
212	Montbard d.	0759	|	1059	|	|	|	1503	|	1559	1559	|	|	1759	1759	1759	|	|	1959	1959	|	|	|	2159	2229
287	**Dijon** **375** a.	0833	|	1132	1158	1257	1358	1536	|	1632	1632	1657	|	1832	1832	1832	1857	1958	2032	2032	2057	2057	2157	2232	2302
287	**Dijon** **375 379** d.	0837	|	1135	1201	1301	1401	...	|	1635	...	...	|	1835	1835	1844	1901	2001	2035	2044	2101	2101	2206	2235	2308
	Chalon sur Saône **377** a.	|	|	|	|	|	|	...	|	|	...	...	|	|	|	1922	|	|	|	2125	|	|	|	|	|
333	Dole **375** a.	|	|	|	|	|	|	...	|	|	...	...	|	|	|	...	|	|	|	...	2124	|	|	2257	2330
364	**Besançon** F-Comté TGV **379** d.	0908	|	1208	|	1331	|	...	|	1708	...	...	|	1908	1908	...	1931	|	2105	...	|	2131	2235	|	|
377	Besançon Viotte a.	|	|	1220	|	|	|	...	|	1720	...	...	|	1920	|	...	|	|	|	...	2150	|	|	2326	2356
446	Belfort Montbéliard TGV. **379** d.	0933	0941	...	|	1355	|	...	1641	...	...	...	1841	...	1932	...	1955	|	2131	...	...	2155	2259	...	...
491	**Mulhouse** **379** d.	0956	1006	...	1306	1417	1507	...	1706	...	...	...	1907	...	1955	...	2017	2106	2153	...	...	2217	2320	...	...
525	**Basel** a.	...	1026	...	1326	...	1526	...	1726	...	...	...	1926	...	...	...	...	2126	...	...	...	...	...	...	...
	Zürich HB **510** a.	...	1126	...	1426	...	1626	...	...	...	...	...	2026	...	...	...	...	2226	...	...	...	...	...	...	...

	TGV 6750	*TGV* 6700	*TGV* 6745	*TGV* 6702	*TGV* 9206		*TGV* 9210		*TGV* 6704	*TGV* 9216	*TGV* 9218		*TGV* 9222	*TGV* 6742	*TGV* 6706	*TGV* 6784	*TGV* 6740	*TGV* 9226	*TGV* 6708	*TGV* 6765	*TGV* 6765	*TGV* 9230		*TGV* 676
	①–⑤													⑤	Ⓑ	⑦	⑤	Ⓑ		①–④	⑦			⑦
	a	J					w			D	u			f	p	e	f	p		m	e			e
Zürich HB **510** d.	...	...	...	...	0734	...	0934	...	...	...	1134	...	1334	...	...	...	...	1534	...	...	...	...	...	...
Basel d.	...	...	...	...	0834	...	1034	...	...	1234	1234	...	1434	...	...	...	...	1634	...	...	...	1834	...	...
Mulhouse **379** d.	...	0542	...	0740	0856	...	1056	...	1158	1257	1257	...	1456	...	1537	...	...	1656	1742	...	...	1856	...	...
Belfort Montbéliard TGV **379** d.	...	0606	...	0805	0921	...	|	...	1223	1321	1321	...	|	...	1602	...	...	|	1807	...	...	1923	...	...
Besançon Viotte d.	0533	|	0639	|	|	...	|	...	|	|	|	...	|	...	|	...	...	|	|	1837	1837	|	...	204
Besançon Franche-Comté TGV **379** d.	|	0629	0653	0829	|	...	|	...	1247	|	|	...	|	...	1626	...	...	|	1830	1852	1852	|	...	210
Dole **375** d.	0559	|	|	|	|	...	|	...	|	|	|	...	|	...	|	...	...	|	|	|	|	|	...	|
Chalon sur Saône **377** d.	|	|	|	|	|	...	|	...	|	|	|	...	|	...	|	1633	...	|	|	|	|	|	...	|
Dijon **375 379** a.	0623	0655	0720	0856	|	...	1158	...	1314	|	|	...	1558	...	1655	1715	...	1758	1856	1922	1922	|	...	212
Dijon **375** d.	0626	0702	0724	0900	|	...	1201	...	1317**d**	|	|	...	1601	1624	1658	1726	1726	1801	1900	1926	1926	|	...	213
Montbard d.	0701	|	0801	|	|	...	|	...	1404	|	|	...	|	|	1734**j**	1803	1803	|	|	|	2002	|	...	|
Paris Gare de Lyon **375** a.	0805	0837	0905	1037	1137	...	1337**y**	...	1507	1538	1538	...	1737	1801	1837	1907	1907	1937	2037	2107	2107	2137	...	230

LOCAL CONNECTING TRAINS MULHOUSE - FREIBURG

km		①–⑤ k		①–⑥ s		①–⑤ k	①–⑤ s	⑥⑦ z			
0	**Mulhouse** d.	0631	0830	...	1024	1251	1434	1534	1751	1923	...
19	Neuenburg 🏛 d.	0658	0851	...	1044	1311	1505	1601	1812	1944	...
22	Müllheim (Baden) **912** a.	0702	0856	0906	1048	1316	1509	1605	1817	1949	...
51	**Freiburg** (Brsg) Hbf **912** a.	*0736*	0916**z**	0934	*1122*	*1344*	1529	1628	*1844*	*2021*	...

	①–⑤ k				①–⑤ k				
Freiburg (Brsg) Hbf **912** d.	*0628*	0915	0926**z**	*1115*	*1315*	...	1645	*1815*	*193*
Müllheim (Baden) **912** d.	0707	0935	0945	1140	1341	...	1705	1840	200
Neuenburg 🏛 d.	0711	...	0950	1145	1345	...	1710	1844	201
Mulhouse a.	0730	...	1011	1205	1406	...	1730	1904	203

B – Also conveys [12] (**9225**) Paris - Basel - Bern (Table **40**).
D – Not July 29 - Aug. 26. From Bern (Table **40**).
E – ①②③④⑦ (not Aug. 14, 15, Oct. 31).
G – Ⓑ to July 5; ①–⑤ July 8 - Aug. 30 (not Aug. 15, 16); Ⓑ from Sept. 2 (not Nov. 1).
H – Ⓑ to July 7; ⑤⑦ July 12 - Aug. 25 (also Aug. 14; not Aug. 16; Ⓑ from Aug. 30 (not Nov. 1).
J – ①–⑥ to July 8 (not June 10); ①⑥ July 13 - Aug. 26 (also Aug. 15, 16); ①–⑥ from Aug. 31 (not Nov. 11).
L – ⑥ (also ①–④ July 8 - Aug. 13, Aug. 15, 16, 19–22, 26–29, Nov. 1).
M – ⑦ (also June 10, ②–⑤ July 9 - Aug. 14, Aug. 20–23, 27–30, Nov. 11).

a – Not June 10, Aug. 15, 16, Nov. 1, 11.
b – Not June 10, Nov. 11.
c – Also June 10, Aug. 15, 16, Nov. 1, 11.
d – 1326 on Ⓒ to Sept. 1 (also Aug. 16); 1324 from Sept. 2.
e – Also June 10, Nov. 11.
f – Also Aug. 14, Oct. 31; not Aug. 16, Nov. 1.
j – Until Sept. 1 (not June 9, 10, 16, 23, 30).
k – Not June 10, Nov. 1.
m – Not June 10, Aug. 14, 15, Oct. 31, Nov. 11.
n – Not July 29 - Aug. 24.
p – Not Aug. 15, 16, Nov. 1.
r – Also Aug. 15, 16, Nov. 1.
s – Not June 10, 20, Oct. 3, Nov. 1.
t – Also Aug. 14, 15, Oct. 31.
u – Not July 30 - Aug. 25.
v – Also June 10, Nov. 11; not July 7 - Sept. 1.
w – Not Oct. 21–25, 28–31.

LILLE - DIJON - MULHOUSE

	TGV 5130	*TGV* 5130
	L	H
Lille Flandres **11** d.	1857	1857
Charles de Gaulle ✈ **11** d.	1957	1957
Marne la Vallée **11** d.	2011	2011
Montbard d.	2109	2109
Dijon a.	2143	2153
Dijon d.	2149	2206
Besançon F-Comté TGV d.	2223	2235
Belfort Montbéliard TGV d.	2247	2259
Mulhouse d.	2310	2320

	TGV 5152	*TG* 515
	J	M
Mulhouse d.	0542	055
Belfort Montbéliard TGV d.	0606	062
Besançon F-Comté TGV d.	0629	064
Dijon a.	0656	071
Dijon d.	0705	071
Montbard d.	0753	075
Marne la Vallée **11** a.	0848	084
Charles de Gaulle ✈ **11** a.	0902	090
Lille Europe **11** a.	0958	095

y – 4–9 minutes later on Ⓐ from Aug. 26 (not Sept. 16–27, Oct. 14–18).
z – ⑥⑦ (also June 10, 20, Oct. 3, Nov. 1).

TGV – Ⓡ, supplement payable.
△ – Timings Dijon - Mulhouse / Chalon vary by a few minutes on Aug. 16

370a BESANÇON VIOTTE - BESANÇON FRANCHE-COMTÉ TGV *Local connecting service*

km		⚒n	†m		Ⓐ	Ⓐ	Ⓒ							Ⓑp			⑥	Ⓑ		Ⓐ	⑥	⑥k	Ⓑ
0	Besançon Viotte d.	0604	0620	0806	0835	0955	1012	1140	1223	...	1338	1415	1519	1605	1703	1807	1837	1903	1929	2043	2106	2159	221
13	Besançon Franche-Comté TGV a.	0619	0635	0819	0851	1010	1027	1153	1236	...	1353	1428	1532	1618	1720	1822	1852	1920	1942	2055	2121	2214	222

	⚒n	†m		Ⓐ								Ⓑp			⑥	Ⓑ	⑥	Ⓑ		Ⓐ	⑥	⑥	Ⓑ
Besançon Franche-Comté TGV d.	0638	0652	0836	0915	...	1100	1218	1339	1428	1454	1550	1633	...	1808	1838	1838	1915	1946	2022	2112	2138	2231	224
Besançon Viotte a.	0658	0706	0851	0929	...	1115	1235	1354	1442	1509	1602	1648	...	1822	1851	1855	1927	2001	2037	2125	2152	2244	225

h – Not ①–④ July 8 - Aug. 29. k – Also ①–④ July 8 - Aug. 29. m – Also ②–⑤ July 9 - Aug. 30. n – Not ②–⑤ July 9 - Aug. 30. p – Not Aug. 16, Nov. 1.

370b BELFORT - BELFORT MONTBÉLIARD TGV - DELLE *Subject to alteration June 21–23*

km		A	⚒n		Ⓐn	Ⓐn	⑥k			Ⓐn		n	⚒	Ⓐn		†	Ⓐn	⚒n	Ⓑ			Ⓑ	Ⓐn		Ⓑ
0	Belfort Ville d.	0445	0547	...	0704	0748	0748	0848	...	1002	...	1202	1249	1348	...	1543	1543	1627	1723	...	1844	1948	2021	...	214
7	Meroux TGV ⊡ ... **515** d.	0455	0556	...	0715	0759	0757	0857	...	1011	...	1211	1258	1357	...	1551	1552	1636	1736	...	1853	1957	2030	...	215
21	Delle **515** a.	0511	*0618*	...	0731	0815	*0818*	*0918*	...	...	...	...	*1318*	*1418*	...	...	1610	1656	1756	...	*1918*	*2018*	...	...	221

	Ⓐn		⚒	Ⓐn	⑥k	Ⓐn	Ⓒc	Ⓐn	⚒n	Ⓐn		Ⓐn		†	⚒n	Ⓑ		Ⓑ	Ⓐn		Ⓑ	†	Ⓐ			
Delle **515** d.	*0540*	...	0656	0740	*0740*	*0840*	*0940*	*1040*	*1140*	*1240*	*1340*	1444	...	*1640*	1642	1742	*1840*	*1940*	...	...	*2140*	2226	2248	...	...	...
Meroux TGV ⊡ ... **515** d.	0602	...	0714	0758	0802	0938	1001	1102	1223	1320	1402	1502	...	1702	1702	1800	1902	2006	2047	...	2202	2307	2307	...	...	...
Belfort Ville a.	0611	...	0723	0807	0811	0946	1010	1111	1233	1329	1411	1511	...	1711	1711	1810	1911	2015	2056	...	2211	2316	2316	...	...	...

A – ①–⑤ (not June 10).
c – Ⓒ (daily July 6 - Sept. 1 and Oct. 19 - Nov. 3).
k – ⑥ (⚒ July 6 - Aug. 31; ⚒ Oct. 19–31).
n – Does not run on Ⓐ July 8 - Aug. 30, Oct. 21–31.
⊡ – Meroux station is a short walk to / from Belfort-Montbéliard TGV station.

371 PARIS - SENS - AUXERRE and DIJON *TER service*

For *TGV* services Paris - Dijon see Table **370**. Certain services are subject to alteration on ⑥⑦ Sept. 7 - Oct. 13. See also shaded box note on next page.

km		Ⓐ	⚒	⚒	Ⓐ	Ⓐ			⑥	Ⓐ	Ⓐ d	Ⓒ	j	d	Ⓒ	d	Ⓑ ◇	⚒		Ⓐ	Ⓑ			Ⓐ	Ⓒ	Ⓑ
0	**Paris** Bercy d.	...	...	...	0611	...	0737	...	0833	0838	0921	0927	...	1033	...	1233	...	1333	...	1433	...	1533•	...	1627•	1633	...
113	Sens d.	...	0622	...	0721	...	0834	...	0931	0936	1025	1032	...	1131	...	1331	...	1430	...	1531	...	1632	...	1731	1731	...
147	Joigny d.	...	0649	...	0745	...	0851	...	0948	0952	1043	1049	...	1148	...	1347	...	1449	...	1548	...	1649	...	1748	1748	...
	Auxerre d.	0533	|	...	|	...	|	...	|	|	|	|	...	|	...	|	...	|	...	|	1536**a**	|	...	|	|	17
156	Laroche Migennes a.	0551	0656	...	0752	...	0858	...	0954	0959	1056	1056	...	1154	...	1354	...	1456	...	1554	1551**a**	1656	...	1754	1754	17
156	Laroche Migennes d.	0559	0700	0707	0755	0801	0901	0906	1004	1008**j**	1100**y**	1100	1106	1156**q**	1212	1404	1403	1459	1512	1604	1559	1659	1705	1804	1758**p**	17
175	**Auxerre** a.	|	|	0724	0810	|	|	0919	1018	1022**j**	|	|	1123	1209**q**	|	1417	|	|	1529	1617	|	|	1722	1818	1812**p**	|
197	Tonnerre d.	0626	0723	...	...	0824	0926	...	...	...	1123**y**	1123	...	...	1239	...	1430	1523	...	...	1626	1723	...	...	...	18
243	Montbard d.	0651	0750	...	...	0850	0951	...	...	...	1150**y**	1150	...	...	1305	...	1456	1549	...	...	1651	1749	...	...	...	18
315	**Dijon** a.	0727	0827	...	...	0927	1031	...	...	...	1233**y**	1227	...	...	1341	...	1532	1628	...	...	1727	1827	...	...	...	19
	Lyon Part Dieu **377** a.	...	1044	...	...	...	1244	...	...	...	1444**y**	1444	...	...	...	...	...	1844	...	...	...	2044	...	...	...	...

CONTINUED ON NEXT PAGE (including notes and other local services Paris Gare de Lyon - Laroche Migennes).

TER services — PARIS - SENS - AUXERRE and DIJON — 371 (continued)

For *TGV* services Paris - Dijon see Table **370**. Certain services are subject to alteration on ⑥⑦ Sept. 7 - Oct. 13. See also shaded box note below.

		⚒	†	Ⓐ	Ⓒ	Ⓐ	Ⓐ	†		s	
Paris Bercy	d.	1727v	...	...	1827	1833	...	...	...	1927v	...	2027
Sens	d.	1832	...	...	1932	1931	...	...	...	2032	...	2128
Joigny	d.	1849	...	...	1949	1947	...	...	...	2049	...	2144
Auxerre	d.	|	...	...	|	|	...	...	...	|	...	|
Laroche Migennes	a.	1856	...	...	1956	1954	...	...	...	2056	...	2151
Laroche Migennes	d.	1859	1906	1916	...	1958p	2010	2008	2010	2059	2106	2155
Auxerre	a.	|	1919c	1934	...	2012p	2025	|	|	|	2123r	2209
Tonnerre	d.	1923	...	...	...	...	...	2038	2037	2123	...	...
Montbard	d.	1949	...	...	...	...	...	2103	2102	2149	...	...
Dijon	a.	2027	...	...	...	...	...	2139	2138	2227	...	...
Lyon Part Dieu **377**	a.	2251t	...	...	...	...	...	...	...	...	...	...

		Ⓐ	Ⓐ	⑥	⚒	⑥	Ⓐ	Ⓑ	⚒	†		⚒
Lyon Part Dieu **377**	d.	...	...	...	...	...	...	...	...	...	...	0512g
Dijon	d.	...	...	...	...	0533	0535	0633	...	...	...	0733
Montbard	d.	...	...	...	...	0610	0612	0710	...	...	...	0809
Tonnerre	d.	...	...	...	...	0637	0639	0735	...	...	...	0835
Auxerre	d.	0450	*0533*	0550	0636	|	|	|	0738	0750	0836	|
Laroche Migennes	a.	0504	*0551*	0604	0654	0700	0702	0801	0752	0805	0854	0859
Laroche Migennes	d.	0506	0604	0606	...	0704	0706	0809	0806	0806	...	0902
Auxerre	a.	|	|	|	...	|	|	0825	|	|	...	|
Joigny	d.	0514	0612	0614	...	0712	0714	...	0815	0814	...	0910
Sens	d.	0531	0630	0631	...	0730	0732	...	0831	0831	...	0927
Paris Bercy	a.	0634	0735	0727	...	0827	0835	...	0931	0931	...	1027

		Ⓐ	⑥	⚒	⑥	Ⓑ j	u	w	Ⓐ e	Ⓒ			Ⓒ	Ⓐ	Ⓒ			Ⓑ		Ⓒ ¶	Ⓐ			Ⓑ			Ⓑ
Lyon Part Dieu **377**	d.	...	...	...	...	...	0716n	...	...	...	...	...	1116	1116	...	...	1316	...	...	...	...	1516	...	...	...	1716	...
Dijon	d.	0830	0833	...	...	...	0933n	...	1205	1225	...	...	1333	1332	...	...	1532	1628	...	...	...	1732	1833	...	...	1933	2033
Montbard	d.	0907	0910	...	...	...	1009n	...	1306	1302	...	...	1411	1417	...	...	1608	1706	...	...	...	1808	1910	...	...	2009	2126
Tonnerre	d.	0932	0935	...	...	...	1035n	...	1331	1327	...	...	1437	1442	...	...	1635	1733	...	...	...	1835	1935	...	...	2035	2151
Auxerre	d.	|	|	0950	1036	1039	|	1143j	|	|	1340j	1436	|	|	1536	1635	|	|	1742	1832	1840h	|	|	1947z	2036‡	|	|
Laroche Migennes	a.	0955	1001	1004	1053	1054	1058n	1156j	1357	1354	1356j	1454	1500	1505	1552	1653	1659	1757	1754	1846	1854	1859	2001	2003z	2054	2058	2217
Laroche Migennes	d.	...	1012	1006	...	...	1102	1204	...	...	1404	...	1504	1506	1602	...	1703	...	1803	...	...	1903	2009k	2006	...	2102	2224
Auxerre	a.	...	1028	|	...	...	|	|	...	...	|	...	|	|	|	...	|	...	|	...	...	|	2025k	|	...	|	2240
Joigny	d.	...	...	1014	...	...	1111	1212	...	...	1412	...	1512	1514	1611	...	1712	...	1812	...	...	1912	...	2014	...	2111	...
Sens	d.	...	...	1031	...	...	1128	1229	...	...	1429	...	1530	1531	1629	...	1730	...	1829	...	...	1930	...	2041	...	2128	...
Paris Bercy	a.	...	...	1135f	...	...	1227	1327	...	...	1527•	...	1627	1637	1724	...	1824	...	1924	...	...	2024	...	2150	...	2227	...

LOCAL TRAINS PARIS - LAROCHE MIGENNES

For faster trains see the main part of Table **371** above and on the previous page.

km					⊗			†	⚒⊗				Ⓐ	Ⓒ	Ⓐ	Ⓐ	Ⓒ	Ⓐ	Ⓐ	Ⓒ	Ⓐ		Ⓐ	Ⓒ			
0	**Paris** Gare de Lyon	d.	0646	0746	0846	1046	1146	1246	1246	1346	1446	1546	1621	1646	1712	1721	1746	1812	1821	1846	1912	1946	2046	2046	2146	2233b	2246
45	Melun	d.	0712	0813	0912	1112	1213	1312	1312	1412	1512	1612	1648	1712	|	1748	1812	|	1848	1912	|	2012	2113	2112	2213	|	2312
60	Fontainebleau-Avon	d.	0725	0826	0925	1125	1226	1325	1325	1425	1525	1625	1701	1725	|	1801	1825	|	1901	1925	|	2025	2126	2125	2226	|	2325§
79	Montereau	d.	0745	0844	0945	1145	1244	1345	1345	1443	1545	1643	1722	1745	1804	1822	1845	1905	1922	1945	2005	2045	2144	2145	2244	|	2343
113	Sens	d.	0833x	...	1035x	1215d	...	1415	1433x	...	1633x	...	1752	1833x	1835	1852	1933x	1935	1952	2033x	2035	2133x	...	2215	...	2348	...
147	Joigny	d.	0900	...	1101	1243d	...	1443	1500	...	1701	...	1820	1900	1902	1920	2000	2002	2020	2100	2102	2200	...	2243	...	0017	...
156	**Laroche Migennes**	a.	0908	...	1109	1250d	...	1450	1508	...	1708	...	1827	1908	1909	1927	2008	2009	2027	2108	2109	2208	...	2250	...	0024	...

			Ⓐ	⑥	Ⓐ	Ⓐ	Ⓒ	Ⓐ	Ⓐ	†	⑥							⚒	†		Ⓐ	⚒	†	Ⓐ	Ⓒ		
Laroche Migennes	d.	0410	0450	0510	0541	0550	0610	0639	0655	...	0650	0747	1010o	...	1210d	...	1410	...	1450	1550	1601	...	1650	1750	1810	...	...
Joigny	d.	0417	0458	0517	0548	0558	0617	0646	0702	...	0658	0755	1018o	...	1218d	...	1418	...	1458	1558	1610	...	1658	1758	1817	...	...
Sens	d.	0445	0527	0545	0615	0627	0645	0716	0731	...	0745x	0845x	1045o	...	1245d	...	1445	...	1545x	1645x	1628	...	1745x	1845x	1845	...	...
Montereau	d.	0514	0557	0615	0645	0657	0716	0746	0801	0813	0816	0916	1116	1213	1316	1413	1516	1613	1616	1716	|	1813	1816	1916	1916	2015	2113
Fontainebleau-Avon	d.	0532	|	0633	0703	|	0734	0804	|	0832	0834	0934	1134	1232	1334	1432	1534	1632	1634	1734	|	1832	1833	1934	1934	2033	2133
Melun	d.	0547	|	0647	0717	|	0747	0817	|	0845	0847	0947	1147	1245	1347	1445	1547	1645	1647	1747	|	1845	1846	1947	1947	2046	2146
Paris Gare de Lyon	a.	0613	0648	0713	0747	0748	0813	0845	0849	0913	0913	1012	1213	1312	1413	1513	1615	1713	1713	1813	1724b	1913	1913	2013	2013	2117	2214

– Ⓐ only.
– Paris **Bercy**.
– 1923 on Ⓐ July 1 - Aug. 23.
– Not Oct. 21–25.
– Not Oct. 21–25, 28–31.
– 11–12 minutes later Sept. 23–28, Oct. 14–18, Nov. 4–8, 16, 23.
– ① (also June 11, Nov. 12; not June 10, Nov. 11).
– 1835 July 1 - Aug. 23.
– Not Sept. 30 - Oct. 4, Nov. 25–29.
– ⑥ only.

n – Ⓒ (also ①–⑤ June 24–28, Aug. 12–30, Sept. 9–20, Sept. 30 - Oct. 4, Oct. 14–18, Nov. 12–15, 25–29).
o – Not Sept. 9–13, 23–27, 30, Oct. 1–4, 21–25.
p – 9 minutes later on †.
q – Not Sept. 30 - Oct. 4, Nov. 25–29. 8 minutes later on Ⓒ.
r – 2119 on ⑤⑥†.
s – Not Aug. 14, Oct. 31.
t – Not ⑥. 2244 on †. Change trains at Dijon on ⑤ (also Aug. 14, Oct. 31).

u – Not Sept. 23–27, Oct. 21–25.
v – 6 minutes later on Ⓒ.
w – Not Sept. 9–13, 23–27, Oct. 21–25.
x – Arrives 20–22 minutes earlier.
y – June 24–28, Aug. 12–30, Sept. 2–20, 30, Oct. 1–4, 14–18, Nov. 12–15, 25–29, Dec. 9–13 only.
z – On † Auxerre d. 1943, Laroche a. 1957.

§ – Does not call Ⓐ July 1 - Aug. 16, ①–⑤ Aug. 26 - Sept. 13, Ⓐ Sept. 23 - Nov. 22.
¶ – On ⑥ Auxerre d. 1837, Laroche a. 1852.

‡ – 2035 on Ⓐ July 1 - Aug. 23; 2038 on †.
⊗ – Subject to alteration Montereau - Laroche Oct. 21–25, Nov. 4–8.
• – Serves Paris **Gare de Lyon** (not Bercy) on July 9, 10, Oct. 29, 30.
◇ – 8–9 minutes later on †. 11–12 minutes later on Ⓐ June 17 - Aug. 30.

Warning! *Timings may vary by a few minutes on ⑥⑦ June 15 - July 7, ⑥⑦ July 20–28, Aug. 31, Sept. 1, Oct. 19, 20.*

DIJON and CHALON SUR SAÔNE - MONTCHANIN - NEVERS — 373

Warning! Subject to alteration on ⑥⑦ June 15–30. Timings may vary by up to 5 minutes June 17 - July 7.

km			Ⓐ	Ⓐ	Ⓐ	⚒	⚒	Ⓑ		⚒ ⊖⊗	⚒		¶	Ⓐ ¶	⚒ k¶	⚒	Ⓑ n	Ⓑ	⚒	⚒	Ⓐ	Ⓑ k	†	Ⓐ		
0	**Dijon** 377	d.	...	0612	0646	...	0712	0812	...	1012	1012	...	1212	1246	...	1412	...	1612	...	1711	1748	...	1811	1812	...	1911
37	Beaune 377	d.	...	0631	0705	...	0731	0831	...	1031	1031	...	1231	1305	...	1431	...	1632t	...	1730	1807	...	1830	1831	...	1930
	Chalon sur Saône 377	d.	...	|	|	0710	|	|	...	|	|	...	|	|	1410	|	1610	|	1710	|	|	1809	|	|	1910	|
	Chagny 377	d.	...	|	|	0721	|	|	...	|	|	...	|	|	1421	|	1621	|	1721	|	|	1820	|	|	1921	|
81	**Montchanin**	d.	...	0658	0731	0747	0758	0857	...	1055	1100	...	1257	1331	1447	1458	1647	1658	1747	1757	1833	1847	1857	1857	1947	1957
89	Le Creusot	d.	...	0705	0738	...	0805	0903	...	...	1107	...	1304	1338	...	1505	...	1705	...	1804	1840	...	1904	1904	...	2004
111	Étang ★	d.	0605	0721	|	...	0820	0920	...	...	1123	...	1320	|	...	1521	...	1721	...	1820	|	...	1920	1925	...	2020
	Autun ★	a.	|	|	|	...	|	|	...	...	|	...	|	|	...	|	...	|	...	|	|	...	|	1943	...	|
179	Decize	d.	0647	0803	0830	...	0903	1003	...	...	1206	...	1402	1430	...	1603	...	1803	...	1902	1932	...	2002	...	...	2102
216	**Nevers**	a.	0719	0829	0853	...	0929	1029	...	...	1233	...	1429	1453	...	1629	...	1829	...	1928	1955	...	2028	...	...	2128

km			Ⓐ	⚒	⚒	⚒	Ⓐ	Ⓑ	Ⓐ k		§	§	Ⓐ §	Ⓐ	Ⓐ k		Ⓑ	⑥	Ⓑ	Ⓑ	Ⓐ	⑥	⑥	Ⓐ	Ⓑ	Ⓑ b⊖
	Nevers	d.	0531g	...	0631	...	0705f	0731	...	0931	...	1131	1157	1331	...	1531	...	...	1731	...	1829	1829	...	1846	1942	...
	Decize	d.	0557g	...	0657	...	0728f	0757	...	0957	...	1157	1220	1357	...	1557	...	...	1757	...	1853	1857	...	1918	2010	...
0	Autun ★	d.	0612h	...	|	...	|	|	...	|	...	|	|	|	...	|	...	...	|	...	|	|	...	|	|	...
15	Étang ★	d.	0639	...	0740	...	|	0840	...	1040	...	1241	|	1440	...	1640	...	...	1840	...	|	1940	...	2000	2053	...
—	Le Creusot	d.	0654	...	0756	...	0820	0856	...	1056	...	1256	1312	1456	...	1656	...	...	1856	...	1945	1956	...	...	2108	...
0	**Montchanin**	d.	0701	0711	0804	0811	0827	0903	0911	1103	1111	1304	1318	1503	1511	1703	1711	1811	1903	1911	1952	2003	2011	...	2119	2119
29	Chagny 377	d.	|	0738	|	0838	|	|	0938	|	1138	|	|	|	1538	|	1738	1838	|	1938	|	|	2038	...	|	|
44	**Chalon sur Saône** 377	a.	|	0750	|	0850	|	|	0950	|	1150	|	|	|	1550	|	1750	1850	|	1950	|	|	2050	...	|	|
	Beaune 377	d.	0728	...	0830	...	0854	0930	...	1130	...	1331	1344	1530	...	1730	...	...	1930	...	2018	2030	...	...	2145	2145
	Dijon 377	a.	0748	...	0848	...	0915	0948	...	1148	...	1353	1405	1548	...	1748	...	...	1948	...	2037	2048	...	...	2209	2209

MONTCHANIN - PARAY LE MONIAL - MOULINS SUR ALLIER

km			Ⓐ	⚒ ‡	†	⚒ ⊗	k	⚒	Ⓑ		Ⓑ k	
	Dijon (see above)	d.	...	...	...	1012	...	...	...	...	...	...
0	**Montchanin** ▷	d.	0708	0808	0908	1108	1254	1508	1708	1808	1908	2008
15	Montceau les Mines ▷	d.	0722	0822	0922	1122	1309	1522	1722	1822	1922	2022
50	Paray le Monial 290 ▷	d.	0751	0851	0951	1159	1339	1552	1752	1851	1951	2051
61	Digoin 290	d.	...	...	...	1208	...	...	...	...	...	...
117	**Moulins sur Allier** 290	a.	...	...	...	1254	...	...	...	...	...	...
	Clermont Ferrand **330**	a.	...	...	...	1419	...	...	...	...	...	...

		Ⓐ	⚒		‡	⚒ k		Ⓑ		Ⓑ b
Clermont Ferrand **330**	d.	...	...	...	...	...	...	...	...	1741
Moulins sur Allier 290	d.	...	...	...	...	...	...	...	...	1903
Digoin 290	d.	...	...	...	...	...	...	...	...	1948
Paray le Monial 290 ▷	d.	0608	0708	1008	1204	1408	1608	1808	1902	2008
Montceau les Mines ▷	d.	0638	0738	1038	1234	1438	1638	1838	1933	2039
Montchanin ▷	a.	0651	0751	1051	1247	1451	1651	1851	1946	2052
Dijon (see above)	a.	...	...	...	...	...	...	...	...	2209

– Not Aug. 15, Nov. 1.
– Aug. 26–30 departs Nevers 0703, Decize 0727.
– ① (also June 11, Nov. 12; not June 10, Nov. 11).
– ②–⑤ (not June 11, Aug. 15, Nov. 1, 12).
– Does not run Ⓐ July 1 - Aug. 23.
– Not Sept. 3–11, Nov. 19–29.
– ①②③④⑦ (also Nov. 1; not Aug. 14, Oct. 31).

¶ – Subject to alteration Nov. 4–8, 11–15.
§ – Subject to alteration Oct. 21–25, 28–31.
‡ – Subject to alteration Oct. 7–11, 14–18.
⊖ – (12) Dijon - Clermont Ferrand and v.v. (see panel below main table for further details).
▷ – Additional services Montchanin - Paray and v.v. on Ⓐ: From Montchanin at 1608, from Paray le Monial at 1708.

⊗ – Subject to alteration June 15 - July 6.
★ – Connecting trains Étang - Autun and v.v. (journey time 18–19 minutes): **From Étang** at 0725 Ⓐ, 0925, 1045 Ⓐ, 1245 Ⓒ, 1645 ⑥, 1725 Ⓑ, 1845 Ⓑ, 1945 ⑥, 2008 Ⓐ and 2025 †. **From Autun** at 0545 Ⓐ, 0617 ① **g**, 0756 Ⓐ, 0856 †, 1016 ⚒, 1216 †, 1616, 1756 ⑥, 1816 Ⓑ, 1946 Ⓐ and 1957 †. Additional 🚌 services operate.

374 DIJON - DOLE - BESANÇON

For *TGV* services see Table **370** (Paris - Dijon - Besançon - Basel) and Table **379** (Strasbourg - Besançon - Dijon).

km		Ⓐ		Ⓐ		Ⓐ						Ⓐ		Ⓐ	Ⓐ		Ⓐ		Ⓐ		Ⓐ	△		Ⓑ			
0	**Dijon** ....**375** d.	0509	0614	0640	0709	0740	0809	0909	1009	1109	1209	1319	1350	1409	1509	1541	1609	1640	1709	1740	1809	1842	1909	1950	2009	2109	2211
32	Auxonne..............d.	0529	0636	0700	0731	0800	0829	0929	1029	1129	1231	1338	1412	1429	1529	1602	1629	1701	1729	1801	1829	1903	1929	2012	2029	2129	2232
46	Dole..............**375** d.	0539	0646	0711	0740	0811	0839	0939	1039	1139	1240	1349	1421	1439	1539	1612	1639	1711	1739	1811	1839	1913	1939	2022	2039	2139	2242
91	**Besançon** Viotte..a.	0605	0722	0738	0815	0838	0905	1005	1105	1205	1314	1415	1455	1505	1605	1646	1705	1746	1805	1845	1905	1947	2005	2053	2105	2205	2316

	Ⓐ		Ⓐ	Ⓐ		B	①g		Ⓐ			Ⓐ		Ⓐ					Ⓑ		Ⓐ		Ⓐ		Ⓐ		C
Besançon Viotte .. d.	0456	0556	0625	0656	0712	0756	0756	0856	0912	0956	1056	1206	1225	1256	1356	1456	1552	1618	1656	1716	1756	1813	1856	1912	1956	2056	2156
Dole.............. **375** d.	0530	0622	0700	0723	0745	0822	0823	0923	0945	1023	1123	1233	1259	1323	1423	1523	1619	1651	1723	1749	1822	1846	1923	1945	2023	2123	2223
Auxonne .... d.	0539	0630	0709	0732	0754	0830	0832	0932	0954	1032	1132	1242	1308	1332	1432	1532	1628	1700	1732	1758	1831	1855	1932	1954	2032	2132	2232
Dijon .... **375** a.	0602	0650	0730	0752	0815	0850	0852	0951	1015	1051	1151	1301	1330	1351	1451	1551	1647	1721	1751	1819	1850	1916	1951	2015	2051	2151	2251

B – ②–⑦ (also June 10, Nov. 11; not June 11, Nov. 12).
C – Ⓒ (daily from Sept. 28).
g – Also June 11, Nov. 12; not June 10, Nov. 11.
△ – Runs 2 minutes **earlier** on ⑥.

375 PARIS - DIJON - LAUSANNE and NEUCHÂTEL

See Table **970** for other *TGV* services Paris - Dijon and v.v.

km		①–⑤ a⊖	Ⓐ	⚒	Ⓐ	Ⓐ	*TGV* 9261 n		⚒	†	*TGV* 9269 D	◇	*TGV* 9773 ①–④ m	*TGV* 9271 ⑦ e	①–⑤ ‡⊖	Ⓐ	*TGV* 9273 r				*TGV* 9277 ①–⑥ d	*TGV* 9277 ⑦ e	⑤† w△	
0	**Paris** Gare de Lyon....... **370** d.	...	...	...	...	...	0757	...	...	...	1157	...	1211	1357	...	...	1557	...	...	...	1757	1757	...	...
287	**Dijon**........................ **370** a.	...	...	...	...	...	0931	...	...	...	1333	...	|	1531	...	...	1731	...	...	...	1931	1931	...	...
287	**Dijon**........................ **374** d.	...	0509	...	...	*0640*	0934	1009	...	...	1336	...	|	1534	...	...	1734	1740	...	1909	1934	1934	...	...
333	Dole .... **374 376** d.	...	0537	0614	...	0722j	0959	1037	1116	1116	1400	...	|	1559	...	...	1759	1809	1814	1937	1958	1959	...	2014
365	Mouchard .... **376** d.	...	...	0645	...	0740	|	▬	1143	1143	|	...	|	|	...	...	|	...	1844	...	2016	|	...	2037
389	Andelot..................... **376** d.	...	...	0706	...	...	|	...	1204	1206	|	...	◐	|	...	...	|	...	1906	...	|	|	...	...
410	Frasne.............................d.	0529	...	0721	0817	...	1044	1053	1218	1221	1444	1453	|	1644	1715	1802	1843	...	1920	...	2044	2044	2053	...
426	Pontarlier 🏛........................a.	|	...	0737	0833	...	|	1104	1234	1236	|	1504	|	|	1725	1818	|	...	1936	...	|	|	2104	...
490	**Neuchâtel 511**..................a.	|	...	...	...	...	|	1153	...	...	|	1553	|	|	...	...	|	...	...	...	|	|	2153	...
434	Vallorbe 🏛 ....a.	0548	...	...	...	...	1057	...	...	...	1457	...	|	1657	...	...	1857	...	...	...	2057	2057	...	...
480	**Lausanne** ....a.	...	...	...	...	...	1137	...	...	...	1537	...	1615	1737	...	...	1937	...	...	...	2137	2137	...	...

	①–⑤ a⊖	Ⓐ	Ⓐ	*TGV* 9260 ①–⑥ b	Ⓐ		*TGV* 9264 E		⚒	z		◇	*TGV* 9268 D	①–⑤ ‡⊖	*TGV* 9270 ⑤⑦ v	*TGV* 9778 ①–④ m	Ⓐ	⊡		H		*TGV* 9272 r	⑤† w⊗	C
Lausanne..............................d.	...	...	...	0623	...	...	0823	...	...	...	...	...	1223	...	1623	1639	...	...	...	...	...	1823	...	...
Vallorbe 🏛 ....d.	...	...	...	0700	...	...	0900	...	...	...	...	...	1300	1652	1700	|	...	...	...	...	...	1900	...	...
Neuchâtel 511.......................d.	...	...	...	|	...	0806	|	...	...	...	...	1206	|	|	|	|	...	...	...	...	1806	|	...	...
Pontarlier 🏛.............................d.	0515	0555	...	|	0742	0855	|	...	1128	...	...	1255	|	|	|	|	1742	1825	...	1825	1855	|	...	...
Frasne..d.	0525	0611	...	0715	0758	0906	0916	...	1145	...	...	1306	1316	1710	1716	|	1758	1843	...	1843	1906	1916	...	...
Andelot.......................... **376** d.	...	0624	...	|	...	...	|	...	1204	1204	...	...	|	...	|	◐	...	1901	...	1901	...	|	...	...
Mouchard .... **376** d.	...	0648	...	0743	...	...	|	...	1221	1221	...	...	|	...	|	|	...	1917	...	1944	...	|	2121	...
Dole........................ **374 376** d.	...	0711	0723	0801	...	...	1000	...	1245	1245	1259	...	1400	...	1800	|	...	1940	1945	2013	...	1959	2145	2223
Dijon............................. **374** a.	...	...	0752	0823	...	...	1023	...	...	...	1330	...	1423	...	1823	|	...	...	2015	...	...	2023	...	2251
Dijon............................. **370** d.	...	...	...	0826	...	...	1026	...	...	...	...	...	1426	...	1826	|	...	...	...	...	...	2026	...	...
Paris Gare de Lyon .... **370** a.	...	...	...	1003	...	...	1203	...	...	...	...	...	1603	...	2003	2049	...	...	...	...	...	2203	...	...

C – Ⓒ (daily from Sept. 28).
D – Daily to Sept. 20; ①–⑤ from Sept. 23 (also Oct. 19, 20; not Nov. 1, 11).
E – Daily to Oct. 20 (not Sept. 22, 29, Oct. 6, 13); ①–⑤ from Oct. 21 (not Nov. 1, 11).
H – Aug. 15–30 only. On Aug. 17, 24 Pontarlier d. 1804, Frasne d. 1821. On Aug. 21 Andelot d. 1912.

a – Not June 10, Aug. 1.
b – Not June 10, Nov. 11.
d – Not June 10, Sept. 21, 28, Oct. 5, 12, Nov. 11.
e – Also June 10, Nov. 11.
j – 0715 July 15, Aug. 16–30, Oct. 7.
m – Not June 10, Aug. 14, 15, Oct. 31, Nov. 11.
n – Not Sept. 22, 29, Oct. 6, 13.
r – Not Sept. 21, 28, Oct. 5, 12.
v – Also June 10, Aug. 14, Oct. 31, Nov. 11; not Aug. 16, Nov. 1.
w – Also Aug. 14, Oct. 31.
z – Not June 30.

‡ – Not June 10, Aug. 1, Nov. 11. Subject to alteration Oct. 14–17, 21–24.
◇ – Subject to alteration Sept. 23–27.
⊡ – Not Aug. 15–30. On ⑥ July 13 - Aug. 10 Pontarlier d. 1804, Frasne d. 182'. On ③ July 10 - Aug. 7 Andelot d. 1912, Mouchard d. 1930, Dole a. 1953.
⊗ – Runs 12 minutes **earlier** on ⑤ to Sept. 27.
◐ – Via Genève (Table **341**).
⊖ – 🚌12 Pontarlier - Frasne - Vallorbe and v.v.
△ – 8–9 minutes later Aug. 15–30.
TGV – *TGV Lyria*, 🅁, supplement payable, 🍷. Special 'global' fares including the reservation fee are payable for international journeys.

376 DOLE / BESANÇON - MOREZ - ST CLAUDE

km		Ⓐ	z				⑤ f	Ⓐ n		⑤† w	🚌 ⊖	🚌 ⑤† w
0	**Dole**.................**375** d.	...	*0614*r	...	1014	*1116*	*1615*b	...	1814	...	...	*2014*t
	Besançon ◊...**378** d.	0601	|	1004	|	|	1640	1751	|	...	...	|
32	Mouchard... **375 378** d.	0641	*0645*r	1034	1039	*1143*	1712	1820	1844	...	...	2044
56	Andelot..............**375** d.	...	0709	...	1103	1209	1735	...	1903	1910	1910	|
70	Champagnole ....d.	...	0740	...	1118	1221	1746	...	...	1923	1930	2126
105	Morez.........................d.	...	0832	...	1212	1313	1844	...	...	2015	2017	2208
128	**St Claude** ....a.	...	0859	...	1240	1340	1912	...	...	2042	2057	2248

	① g	⚒ s	Ⓐ	z		⑤ f	①–④ p	🚌 Ⓐ		⑤† w	①–④ m
St Claude ....d.	0443	0620	...	0954	...	1510	1551	...	1725	1725	...
Morez.......................d.	0516	0652	...	1029	...	1545	1626	...	1759	1759	...
Champagnole........d.	0602	0738	...	1147v	...	1632	1712	1740	1845	1845	...
Andelot .... **375** d.	0618	0759	...	1158	...	1647	...	1800	1856	1909	...
Mouchard **375 378** a.	0636	0817	0841	*1220*	1225	1705	...	1830	*1916*‡	1925	1926
Besançon ◊ **378** a.	|	|	0909	|	1256	1738	...	|	|	1959	1956
Dole.............. **375** a.	*0711*	0845	...	*1245*	...	*1804*b	...	1917	*1940*‡	...	...

ST CLAUDE - OYONNAX - BOURG EN BRESSE

km		D	D	🚌	🚌 D	Ⓐ	🚌 Ⓒ	🚌	🚌 Ⓐ	🚌 Ⓐ	⑦e	🚌
0	**St Claude** ....d.	*0540**	*0635**	0825	1040	*1230**	1340	1610	1625	1710	*1730**	1840
32	Oyonnax ....d.	0631	0725	0910	1125	1324	1425	1655	1710	1755	1822	1925
45	Brion Montréal § ....d.	0646	0740	0935	1150	1340	1450	1718	1730	1820	1838	1950
48	Nurieux Brion .... ◧ d.	0649	0744	0942	|	1344	|	1727	|	1827	1842	|
81	**Bourg en Bresse** ....a.	0725	0822	1035	1235	1422	1535	1819	1815	1919	1922	2035
	Lyon P. Dieu **353**...a.	0830c	...	...	...	...	...	...	...	...	...	...

	🚌 Ⓐ	🚌 D	🚌 Ⓒ	Ⓐ	🚌	🚌	🚌	Ⓑh		🚌	🚌 Ⓐ
Lyon P. Dieu **353** d.	...	...	...	...	...	...	...	...	...	...	...
Bourg en Bresse .d.	0610	0740	1030	1038	1225	1325	1605	1719	1821	1950	2125
Nurieux Brion .... ◧ d.	0701	|	|	1119	1321	|	|	1800	1901	2038	|
Brion Montréal § .....d.	0708	0825	1113	1123	1328	1410	1650	1804	1904	2043	2210
Oyonnax ....d.	0733	0850	1138	1138	1353	1435	1715	1818	1919	2103	2235
St Claude ....a.	0809	0926	1214	*1221**	1429	1511	1751	*1901**	*2001**	2139	...

D – ①–⑥ (not June 10, Nov. 11).

b – Connection by 🚌 to / from Mouchard.
c – ⑥ to July 6 (not June 29); ①–⑥ July 13 - Aug. 24; ⑥ from Aug. 31 (also Nov. 1).
e – Also June 10, Nov. 11.
f – Also Aug. 14, Oct. 31; not Nov. 1.
g – Also June 11, Nov. 12; not June 10, Nov. 11.
h – Not Aug. 15, Nov. 1.
m – Not June 10, Aug. 14, 15, Oct. 31, Nov. 11.
n – Not July 1 - Aug. 23.
p – Not June 10, July 1 - Aug. 22, Oct. 21–31, Nov. 11.
r – ⚒ only.
s – By 🚌 ①–⑤ July 1 - Aug. 23 and ①–⑤ Oct. 21–31 (departures are up to 67 minutes **earlier**).
t – Not Aug. 15–30. By train Dole - Mouchard.
v – Arrives 1115.
w – Also Aug. 14, Oct. 31.
z – Not June 30.

* – By 🚌.
‡ – Runs later on ③ July 10 - Aug. 7 and daily Aug. 15–30 (see Table **375**).
⊖ – ①②③④⑥ (not June 10, Aug. 14, 15, Oct. 31, Nov. 11).
◧ – For *TGV* connection Paris - Nurieux Brion see Table **341**.
§ – Brion Montréal la Cluse.
◊ – Besançon-Viotte.

376a BESANÇON - LE LOCLE - LA CHAUX DE FONDS

km		①–⑤ a	①–⑤ a		Ⓐ	⑥ ⊡			⊗	Ⓐ	
0	**Besançon** Viotte..........d.	...	...	...	0700	0728	0934	...	1400	1725	1932
67	Morteau ....d.	0509	0618	0729	0828	1000	1102	...	1528	1857	2102
80	Le Locle.................**512** d.	0529	0639	0750	...	...	1140j	...	1551	...	2121
88	**La Chaux de Fonds 512** a.	0538	0648	0759	...	...	1148	...	1559	...	2129

	①–⑤ a		①–⑤ a			⚒ ⊗			Ⓐ	
La Chaux de Fonds.. **512** d.	0542	...	0656	0809	...	...	1608	1701	...	2143
Le Locle ....**512** d.	0551	...	|	0817	...	...	1617	1710	...	2151
Morteau...........................d.	0610	0633	0721	0836	...	1241	1637	1732	1936	2209
Besançon Viotte ....a.	...	0801	...	1007	...	1412	1802	1903	2105	...

a – Not June 10, Aug. 1.
j – Arrives 1126.
⊡ – Includes a long stop at Le Valdahon (a. 0818, d. 0920).
⊗ – Subject to alteration on ①–⑤ Oct. 14–25.

cal Services — DIJON - CHALON SUR SAÔNE - LYON — 377

For faster *TGV* services, see Table **379**. Paris timings may vary on ⑥⑦ Sept. 7 - Oct. 13.

m		Ⓐ	①–⑥ b	Ⓐ		⚒	Ⓐ	s	Ⓐ			Ⓐ	⑥⑦ ★🅁	Ⓐ	Ⓒ	Ⓐ		⑦ e	Ⓐ	Ⓐ	⚒			Ⓐ	
	Paris Bercy **371** d.	...	...	...	...	...	...	...	...	0737	...	...	0916	0921**t**	0927	...	...	...	...	...	1333	...	...	...	...
0	**Dijon** **373** d.	...	...	0540	0640	0725	0740	0840	0940	1041	...	1140	|	1240	1240	1340	1440	...	1540	...	1640	1640	...	1740	1752
7	Beaune **373** d.	...	...	0600	0700	0751	0800	0900	1000	1101	...	1200	1205	1300	1300	1400	1500	...	1600	...	1700	1700	...	1800	1822
2	Chagny d.	...	...	0611	0711	0800	0811	0911	1011	1112	...	1211	|	1311	1311	1411	1511	...	1611	...	1711	1711	...	1811	1833
7	**Chalon sur Saône** d.	...	...	0623	0723	0815	0823	0923	1023	1124	...	1223	1224	1323	1323	1423	1523	...	1623	...	1723	1723	...	1823	1847
5	Mâcon Ville d.	0558	0632	0657	0757	...	0857	0957	1057	1157	1232	1257	1253	1357	1357	1457	1557	1656	1657	1735	1757	1757	1835	1857	...
3	Villefranche sur Saône d.	0631	0705	0721	0821	...	0921	1021	1121	1221	1305	1321	|	1421	1421	1521	1621	1720	1721	1805	1821	1821	1906	1921	...
7	**Lyon** Part Dieu a.	0700	|	0744	0844	...	0944	1044	1144	1244	|	1344	1333	1444	1444	1544	1644	1744	1744	|	1844	1844	|	1944	...
	Lyon Perrache a.	...	0735	...	...	...	...	...	...	...	1335	...	...	...	...	...	...	...	...	1835	...	...	1935	...	...

		⑥w ♥🅁	Ⓐ	⑥	Ⓐ	†	⑤f ♥🅁	⚒	
aris Bercy **371** d.	1533•	1653**p**	...	...	1727**z**	1733	1853**p**	...	...
on **373** d.	1840	1844	1940	1950	2040	2040	2044	2050	2212
une **373** d.	1900	1905	2000	2017	2100	2100	2107	2119	2242
agny d.	1910	|	2011	2029	2111	2111	|	2131	2255
alon sur Saône d.	1923	1922	2023	2043	2123	2123	2125	2143	2307
con Ville d.	1957	...	2057	...	2157	2157	...	...	...
efranche sur Saône d.	2021	...	2121	...	2221	2221	...	...	...
n Part Dieu a.	2044	...	2144	...	2251	2244	...	...	...
n Perrache a.	2057	...	...	...	...	2257	...	...	...

	⚒	Ⓑ	① g	②–⑥ d	⚒	Ⓐ	Ⓐ			Ⓐ	Ⓐ
Lyon Perrache d.	...	...	0500	...	...	0604	...	...	...	0725	...
Lyon Part Dieu d.	...	...	0512	...	...	0616	...	0716	...	|	0820
Villefranche sur Saône d.	...	...	0537	...	...	0641	...	0741	...	0754	0846
Mâcon Ville d.	...	...	0602	0604	...	0704	...	0804	...	0825	0911
Chalon sur Saône d.	0556	0616	0635	0638	0716	0739	0816	0839	0913	...	0943
Chagny d.	0606	0626	0645	0649	0726	0749	0831	0849	0923	...	0953
Beaune **373** d.	0614	0638	0656	0700	0739	0800	0842	0900	0941	...	1004
Dijon **373** a.	0639	0709	0715	0720	0809	0819	0911	0919	1010	...	1023
Paris Bercy **371** a.	...	...	1027	1027	...	...	...	1227**v**	...	...	...

	k			Ⓐ		Ⓐ		Ⓐ	Ⓐ	⑦e ♥🅁			⑥⑦ ★🅁	Ⓐ	Ⓐ		Ⓒ	①–⑥ b	Ⓐ	Ⓐ			Ⓐ		Ⓐ
n Perrache d.	0825	...	...	...	...	...	...	1325	...	...	...	...	1626	...	1635	...	...	1725	...	1825	...	1925	...	2104	2218‡
n Part Dieu d.	|	0916	...	1016	1116	1216	1316	|	1416	...	1516	...	|	1616	1646	1716	...	|	1816	|	1916	|	2016	2116	2206
efranche sur Saône d.	0856	0941	...	1041	1141	1241	1341	1355	1441	...	1541	...	|	1642	1711	1741	...	1756	1841	1856	1941	1958	2041	2140	2241
con Ville d.	0928	1004	...	1104	1204	1304	1404	1425	1504	...	1604	...	1702	1704	1735	1804	1823	1825	1904	1928	2004	2028	2104	2202	2305
alon sur Saône d.	...	1039	1117	1139	1238	1339	1439	...	1539	1633	1637	1717	1731	1739	...	1839	1914**j**	...	1939	...	2039	...	2139	...	...
agny d.	...	1049	1127	1149	1249	1349	1449	...	1549	|	1648	1727	|	1749	...	1849	1928	...	1949	...	2049	...	2149	...	...
une **373** d.	...	1100	1140	1200	1300	1400	1500	...	1600	1653	1700	1740	1748	1800	...	1859	1940	...	2000	...	2100	...	2200	...	...
on **373** a.	...	1119	1210	1219	1319	1419	1519	...	1619	1715	1719	1810	|	1819	...	1919	2009	...	2020	...	2119	...	2219	...	...
aris Bercy **371** a.	...	...	...	...	1637**h**	...	1824	...	...	1907**p**	2024	...	2101	...	...	2227	...	...	...	...	...	...	...	...	...

Not June 10, Nov. 11.
Not June 11, Aug. 15, Nov. 1, 12.
Also June 10, Nov. 11.
Also Aug. 14, Oct. 31; not Aug. 16, Nov. 1.
Also June 11, Nov. 12; not June 10, Nov. 11.
1627 on Ⓒ.
Arrives 1900.
Not Aug. 15, Nov. 1, 2.
Paris **Gare de Lyon**.
From Sens on ⚒ (Table **371**).

t – June 24 – 28, Aug. 12 – 30, Sept. 2 – 20, 30, Oct. 1 – 4, 14 – 18, Nov. 12 – 15, 25 – 29, Dec. 9 – 13 only.
v – Ⓒ (also ①–⑤ June 24 – 28, Aug. 12 – 30, Sept. 9 – 20, Sept. 30 - Oct. 4, Oct. 14 – 18, Nov. 12 – 15, 25 – 29).
w – Also Aug. 15, 16, Nov. 1. On Aug. 16 Dijon d. 1835, Beaune d. 1904, Chalon a. 1925.
z – Change trains at Dijon on ⑤ (also Aug. 14, Oct. 31).

‡ – Calls at Lyon Perrache after Part-Dieu.
• – On July 9, 10, Oct. 29, 30 departs Paris **Gare de Lyon** (not Paris Bercy).
♥ – *TGV* train (see Table **370** for train number).
★ – *INTERCITÉS 100% ÉCO.* Train number **5757** from Paris, **5756** from Lyon. Low-cost service. Internet bookings only at www.oui.sncf.

LYON - LONS-LE-SAUNIER - BESANÇON - BELFORT — 378

See Table **379** for *TGV* services Lyon - Besançon Franche-Comté TGV - Belfort Montbéliard TGV (- Strasbourg). **Warning!** Subject to alteration on June 21, 22, 23, 29, Aug. 15 – 18.

m		⚒	⚒	Ⓐ	Ⓐ		Ⓐ	Ⓒ				⚒	⚒	①–⑥ b	Ⓒ	Ⓐ		Ⓐ		Ⓐ	Ⓒ	Ⓑ	Ⓐ	Ⓒ	⑤⑦ v
0	**Lyon** Perrache .... **353** d.	...	...	...	...	0712**r**	...	...	...	...	...	...	...	1359	...	...	...	...	...	1617	1617	1712	1816	1817	2113
5	**Lyon** Part-Dieu .... **353** d.	...	...	...	...	0725**r**	0941**k**	0941	...	...	...	...	...	1412	...	...	...	...	...	1630	1630	1730	1830	1830	2125
	Ambérieu d.	...	...	...	...	|	|	|	...	...	...	...	...	|	...	...	...	...	...	|	|	1759	1859	1859	|
5	Bourg-en-Bresse.. **353** d.	...	...	...	0717	0817	1020**k**	1022	...	...	...	...	...	1514	1521	1521	...	...	...	1719	1719	1817	1919	1919	2232
9	**Lons-le-Saunier** d.	0544	0613	0643**n**	0759	0859	1101	1102	...	...	1218	...	1501	▬	1605	1605	...	1701	1713	1801	1802	1857	2002	2002	2312
8	Mouchard d.	0627	0702	0722**n**	0841	0937	1138	1139	...	1225	1302	...	1539	...	1641	1642	...	1737	1802	1841	1841	...	2041	2041	...
8	**Besançon** Viotte a.	0710	0742	0755**n**	0909	1009	1208	1209	...	1256	1342	...	1609	...	1709	1712	...	1810	1842	1909	1909	...	2109	2109	...
8	**Besançon** Viotte ... ▷ d.	0712	...	0811	...	1011	1211	...	1232	...	...	1511	...	1614	...	1714	1732	1811**n**	...	1912	...	...	...	2115	...
7	Montbéliard ▷ d.	0808	...	0908	...	1109	1310	...	1342	...	...	1608	...	1712	...	1812	1842	1908**n**	...	2010	...	...	...	2213	...
5	**Belfort** Ville ▷ a.	0824	...	0924	...	1125	1328	...	1356	...	...	1624	...	1729	...	1827	1856	1924**n**	...	2026	...	...	...	2229	...

	⚒	Ⓐ	Ⓐ		Ⓐ	⚒ k	†			⚒					⑥	Ⓐ	†	Ⓑ	Ⓐ		⑥	Ⓐ	Ⓐ		
ort Ville ▷ d.	...	...	0531	...	0634**n**	0735	...	...	0935	0935	...	1204	...	1335	1536	1536	1536	...	1636	...	...	1734	...	1838	1938
tbéliard ▷ d.	...	...	0547	...	0650**n**	0750	...	...	0952	0952	...	1218	...	1351	1553	1552	1552	...	1653	...	...	1749	...	1853	1954
ançon Viotte ..... ▷ a.	...	...	0645	...	0746**n**	0848	...	...	1048	1048	...	1328	...	1448	1649	1649	1649	...	1749	...	...	1849	...	1951	2050
ançon Viotte d.	...	0601	...	0651	0748	0851	0851	1004	...	1051	1251	...	1351	1451	1651	1651	1651	1726	1751**n**	1817	1850	1851	1925	1953	...
chard d.	...	0642	...	0722	0822	0920	0920	1034	...	1121	1330	...	1423	1521	1721	1720	1721	1806	1822**n**	1900	1924	1922	2004	2022	...
s-le-Saunier d.	0600	0730	...	0759	0858	1001	1001	...	...	1200	1412	...	1500	1603	1800	1802	1802	...	1900**n**	1944	2001	2000	...	2102	...
rg-en-Bresse... **353** d.	0642	...	...	0844	...	1045	1045	...	...	...	1452	...	...	1646	...	1843	1846	...	...	...	...	...	...	2146	...
érieu d.	|	...	...	0904	...	|	|	...	...	...	...	...	...	|	...	|	|	...	...	...	...	...	...	|	...
n Part-Dieu ..... **353** a.	0731	...	...	0930	...	1126	1126	...	...	...	...	...	...	1726	...	*1948*	1926	...	...	...	...	...	...	2230**t**	...
n Perrache .... **353** a.	0743	...	...	0947**a**	...	1139	1139	...	...	...	...	...	...	1738	...	*2003*	1938**j**	...	...	...	...	...	...	2243**t**	...

ADDITIONAL LOCAL TRAINS BESANÇON - BELFORT

	Ⓐ	Ⓐ	Ⓑ	†		Ⓐ	Ⓐ	Ⓒ			Ⓐ
ançon Viotte d.	0532	0611	0632	0711	0732	1111	1311	1332	1632	1834	2011
tbéliard d.	0642	0714	0742	0808	0842	1208	1408	1442	1740	1940	2108
ort Ville a.	0656	0729	0756	0824	0856	1224	1424	1456	1755	1955	2124

		Ⓐ	Ⓐ	Ⓐ	Ⓐ				▲	⚒
Belfort Ville d.	0604	0704	0836	1136	1236	1304	1704	1819	2036	2119
Montbéliard d.	0618	0718	0853	1153	1253	1318	1718	1833	2053	2134
Besançon Viotte a.	0728	0828	0950	1250	1350	1428	1828	1943	2150	...

Ⓐ only.
Not June 10, Nov. 11.
1952 on June 10, Nov. 1, 11.
Not Oct. 14 – 18, 21 – 25, 28 – 31.

n – Not July 1 - Aug. 23.
r – Not July 3, 4, 5.
t – Not July 2, 3, 4.
v – Also June 10, Aug. 14, Nov. 11; not Aug. 16, Nov. 1.

▲ – Runs 18 minutes **earlier** on Ⓐ until Sept. 20.
▷ – For additional trains Besançon - Belfort and v.v. see panel below main table.

e also Table 380 — Local trains BELFORT - MULHOUSE — 378a

Subject to alteration June 21 – 23

	Ⓐ	⚒	Ⓐd	⚒	Ⓐ	Ⓒ	Ⓐd	Ⓐ	Ⓒ	Ⓐd	Ⓐ	Ⓒ	Ⓐ	Ⓒ	Ⓐd	Ⓐ	d	Ⓐ	†	Ⓐ	⚒d	†	Ⓐ	Ⓐd	⑥	†	Ⓐ🚌
ort Ville d.	0531	0558	0631	0701	0732	0736	0806	0906	1004	1006	1206	1212	1304	1404	1506	1606	1706	1737	1800	1806	1847	1900	1905	2006	2016	2052	2052
rch d.	0552	0620	0654	0724	0755	0759	0827	0927	1025	1027	1227	1234	1326	1428	1525	1627	1726	1759	1823	1828	1910	1923	1927	2026	2036	2114	2143
house a.	0609	0637	0710	0740	0810	0815	0839	0939	1039	1039	1239	1247	1339	1442	1539	1639	1740	1810	1839	1840	1922	1939	1939	2040	2050	2128	2208

	Ⓐ	⚒	Ⓐd	Ⓐ		Ⓐd	Ⓐd	Ⓒ	Ⓐ	Ⓐd	Ⓒ		Ⓐ		†	⚒	Ⓐd	Ⓐ	d	Ⓐ	Ⓐ	⚒d	†	Ⓐ	d		Ⓐ🚌
house d.	0620	0650	0723	0801	0823	0923	1023	1122	1220	1310	1315	...	1423	...	1559	1619	1650	1719	1750	1821	1850	1929	1930	2020	2056	...	2220
rch d.	0632	0704	0735	0815	0835	0935	1035	1136	1235	1322	1332	...	1435	...	1616	1636	1708	1736	1807	1836	1915	1947	1947	2037	2110	...	2245
ort Ville a.	0653	0726	0757	0838	0856	0956	1056	1159	1256	1343	1354	...	1456	...	1639	1659	1730	1759	1830	1858	1938	2009	2009	2059	2130	...	2337

Not July 15 – 19, 22 – 26, 29 – 31, Aug. 1, 2, 5 – 9, 12 – 14, 16, 19 – 23.

379 LUXEMBOURG - METZ - STRASBOURG - DIJON - LYON

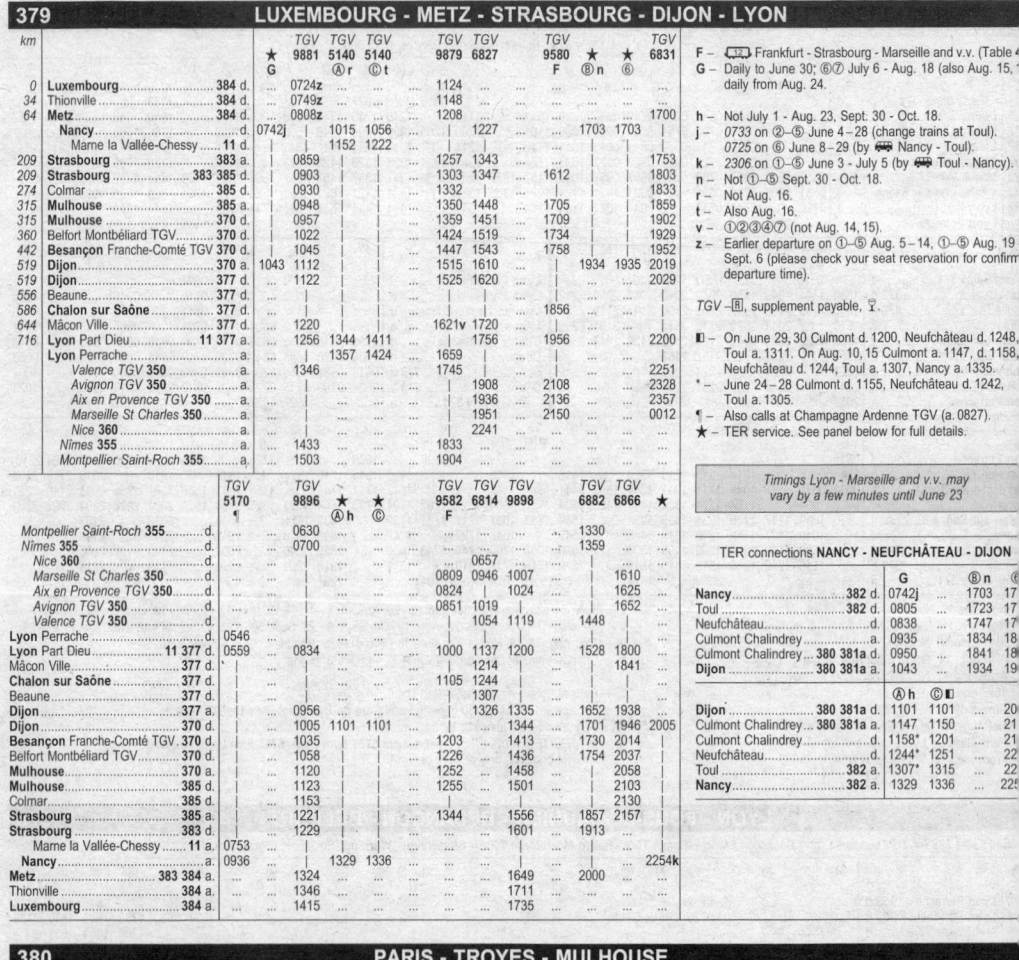

km		★ G	TGV 9881	TGV 5140 Ⓐr	TGV 5140 ©t		TGV 9879	TGV 6827		TGV 9580 F	★ Ⓑn	★ ⑥	TGV 6831
0	**Luxembourg** 384 d.	...	0724z	...	...	...	1124	...	...	...	...	...	...
34	Thionville 384 d.	...	0749z	...	...	...	1148	...	...	...	...	...	...
64	**Metz** 384 d.	...	0808z	...	...	...	1208	...	...	...	...	...	1700
	Nancy d.	0742j	|	1015	1056	...	|	1227	...	...	1703	1703	|
	Marne la Vallée-Chessy 11 d.	|	|	1152	1222	...	|	|	...	...	|	|	|
209	**Strasbourg** 383 a.	|	0859	|	|	...	1257	1343	...	...	|	|	1753
209	**Strasbourg** 383 385 d.	|	0903	|	|	...	1303	1347	...	1612	|	|	1803
274	Colmar 385 d.	|	0930	|	|	...	1332	|	...	|	|	|	1833
315	**Mulhouse** 385 a.	|	0948	|	|	...	1350	1448	...	1705	|	|	1859
315	**Mulhouse** 370 d.	|	0957	|	|	...	1359	1451	...	1709	|	|	1902
360	Belfort Montbéliard TGV 370 d.	|	1022	|	|	...	1424	1519	...	1734	|	|	1929
442	**Besançon** Franche-Comté TGV 370 d.	|	1045	|	|	...	1447	1543	...	1758	|	|	1952
519	**Dijon** 370 a.	1043	1112	|	|	...	1515	1610	...	|	1934	1935	2019
519	**Dijon** 377 d.	...	1122	|	|	...	1525	1620	...	|	...	...	2029
556	Beaune 377 d.	...	|	|	|	...	|	|	...	|	...	...	|
586	**Chalon sur Saône** 377 d.	...	|	|	|	...	|	|	...	1856	...	...	|
644	Mâcon Ville 377 d.	...	1220	|	|	...	1621v	1720	...	|	...	...	|
716	**Lyon** Part Dieu 11 377 a.	...	1256	1344	1411	...	|	1756	...	1956	...	...	2200
	Lyon Perrache a.	...	|	1357	1424	...	1659	|	...	|	...	...	|
	Valence TGV **350** a.	...	1346	...	...	...	1745	|	...	|	...	...	2251
	Avignon TGV **350** a.	...	|	...	...	...	|	1908	...	2108	...	...	2328
	Aix en Provence TGV **350** a.	...	|	...	...	...	|	1936	...	2136	...	...	2357
	Marseille St Charles **350** a.	...	|	...	...	...	|	1951	...	2150	...	...	0012
	Nice **360** a.	...	|	...	...	...	|	2241	...	...	...	...	...
	Nîmes **355** a.	...	1433	...	...	...	1833	...	...	...	...	...	...
	Montpellier Saint-Roch **355** a.	...	1503	...	...	...	1904	...	...	...	...	...	...

	TGV 5170 ¶		TGV 9896	★ Ⓐh	★ ©		TGV 9582 F	TGV 6814	TGV 9898		TGV 6882	TGV 6866	★
Montpellier Saint-Roch **355** d.	...	...	0630	...	...	...	...	...	...	...	1330	...	...
Nîmes **355** d.	...	...	0700	...	...	...	...	...	...	...	1359	...	...
Nice **360** d.	...	...	|	...	...	...	...	0657	...	...	|	...	...
Marseille St Charles **350** d.	...	...	|	...	...	...	0809	0946	1007	...	|	1610	...
Aix en Provence TGV **350** d.	...	...	|	...	...	...	0824	|	1024	...	|	1625	...
Avignon TGV **350** d.	...	...	|	...	...	...	0851	1019	|	...	|	1652	...
Valence TGV **350** d.	...	...	|	...	...	...	|	1054	1119	...	1448	|	...
Lyon Perrache d.	0546	...	|	...	...	...	|	|	|	...	|	|	...
Lyon Part Dieu 11 377 d.	0559	...	0834	...	...	...	1000	1137	1200	...	1528	1800	...
Mâcon Ville 377 d.	|	...	|	...	...	...	|	1214	|	...	|	1841	...
Chalon sur Saône 377 d.	|	...	|	...	...	...	1105	1244	|	...	|	|	...
Beaune 377 d.	|	...	|	...	...	...	|	1307	|	...	|	|	...
Dijon 377 a.	|	...	0956	...	...	...	|	1326	1335	...	1652	1938	...
Dijon 370 d.	|	...	1005	1101	1101	...	|	...	1344	...	1701	1946	2005
Besançon Franche-Comté TGV 370 d.	|	...	1035	|	|	...	1203	...	1413	...	1730	2014	|
Belfort Montbéliard TGV 370 d.	|	...	1058	|	|	...	1226	...	1436	...	1754	2037	|
Mulhouse 370 a.	|	...	1120	|	|	...	1252	...	1458	...	|	2058	|
Mulhouse 385 d.	|	...	1123	|	|	...	1255	...	1501	...	|	2103	|
Colmar 385 d.	|	...	1153	|	|	...	|	...	|	...	|	2130	|
Strasbourg 385 a.	|	...	1221	|	|	...	1344	...	1556	...	1857	2157	|
Strasbourg 383 d.	|	...	1229	|	|	...	...	...	1601	...	1913	...	|
Marne la Vallée-Chessy 11 a.	0753	...	|	|	|	...	...	...	|	...	|	...	|
Nancy a.	0936	...	|	1329	1336	...	...	...	|	...	|	...	2254k
Metz 383 384 a.	...	...	1324	...	...	...	...	...	1649	...	2000	...	...
Thionville 384 a.	...	...	1346	...	...	...	...	...	1711	...	...	...	...
Luxembourg 384 a.	...	...	1415	...	...	...	...	...	1735	...	...	...	...

F – (12) Frankfurt - Strasbourg - Marseille and v.v. (Table 4
G – Daily to June 30; ⑥⑦ July 6 - Aug. 18 (also Aug. 15, daily from Aug. 24.

h – Not July 1 - Aug. 23, Sept. 30 - Oct. 18.
j – *0733* on ②–⑤ June 4–28 (change trains at Toul). *0725* on ⑥ June 8–29 (by 🚌 Nancy - Toul).
k – *2306* on ①–⑤ June 3 - July 5 (by 🚌 Toul - Nancy).
n – Not ①–⑤ Sept. 30 - Oct. 18.
r – Not Aug. 16.
t – Also Aug. 16.
v – ①②③④⑦ (not Aug. 14, 15).
z – Earlier departure on ①–⑤ Aug. 5–14, ①–⑤ Aug. 19 Sept. 6 (please check your seat reservation for confirm departure time).

TGV –🅁, supplement payable, 🍷.

◧ – On June 29, 30 Culmont d. 1200, Neufchâteau d. 1248, Toul a. 1311. On Aug. 10, 15 Culmont a. 1147, d. 1158, Neufchâteau d. 1244, Toul a. 1307, Nancy a. 1335.
* – June 24–28 Culmont d. 1155, Neufchâteau d. 1242, Toul a. 1305.
¶ – Also calls at Champagne Ardenne TGV (a. 0827).
★ – TER service. See panel below for full details.

Timings Lyon - Marseille and v.v. may vary by a few minutes until June 23

TER connections **NANCY - NEUFCHÂTEAU - DIJON**

	G		Ⓑn	⑥
Nancy 382 d.	0742j	...	1703	17
Toul 382 d.	0805	...	1723	17
Neufchâteau d.	0838	...	1747	17
Culmont Chalindrey a.	0935	...	1834	18
Culmont Chalindrey 380 381a d.	0950	...	1841	18
Dijon 380 381a a.	1043	...	1934	19
	Ⓐh	**©◧**		
Dijon 380 381a d.	1101	1101	...	20
Culmont Chalindrey 380 381a a.	1147	1150	...	21
Culmont Chalindrey d.	1158*	1201	...	21
Neufchâteau d.	1244*	1251	...	22
Toul 382 a.	1307*	1315	...	22
Nancy 382 a.	1329	1336	...	225

380 PARIS - TROYES - MULHOUSE

SERVICE TO JULY 12 AND FROM AUGUST 25. Timings may vary by up to 6 minutes on certain dates (earlier departures possible). Subject to alteration on June 22, 23, Oct. 5, 6, 12,
An amended service operates July 13 - August 24 with no direct trains Paris - Troyes and v.v. See page 210 for schedules during this period.

km		Ⓐ	⚒	Ⓐ	Ⓐ	D	Ⓐ	©	Ⓐ ♥	©	Ⓐ	C	♣	Ⓐ	●	Ⓐ		♠	Ⓐ	Ⓐ			Ⓑ	▲	⑥
0	**Paris** Est d.	...	...	...	0542	0642	0742	0742	0842	0842	0942	...	1142	1242	1342	...	1512	1642	1712	1742	1812	1842	1942	2042	22
110	Nogent sur Seine d.	...	...	...	0642	0739	0839	0839	0939	0939	1039	...	1240	1339	1439	...	1609	1739	1812	1839	1911	1942	2039	2138	23
129	Romilly sur Seine d.	...	...	...	0653	0750	0851	0852	0950	0950	1051	...	1251	1351	1450	...	1621	1750	1823	1851	1922	1953	2051	2149	23
166	**Troyes** d.	...	...	0515	0713	0811	0909	0912	1010	1010	1109	...	1314	1409	1513	...	1644	1813	1841	1909	1941	2013	2109	2212	23
221	Bar sur Aube d.	...	...	0546	0743	0841	...	0942	1040	1040	▬	...	1344	▬	1543	...	1714	1843	...	...	...	2043	...	2242	
262	Chaumont 381a d.	...	...	0607	0803	0902	...	1002	1101	1101	...	...	1405	...	1605	...	1736	1904	...	...	...	2104	...	2303	
296	Langres 381a d.	...	...	0627	...	0922	...	...	1121	1121	...	...	1426	...	1625	...	1755	1924	...	...	...	2124	...	2323	
307	Culmont Chalindrey 379 381a d.	...	...	0636	...	0931	...	...	1132	1132	...	...	1435	...	1634	...	1802	1933	...	...	...	2133	...	2331	
	Dijon Ville 379 381a a.	...	...	0726	...	|	...	...	|	|	Ⓐ	...	1522p	Ⓐ	|	...	...	|	...	...	...	|	..	...	
380	Vesoul d.	0639	0739	...	...	1008	...	...	1209	1209	1239	1339	...	1639	1712	1830	...	2011	...	...	...	2210	...	...	
410	Lure 386a d.	0656	0756	...	...	1025	...	...	1226	1226	1256	1356	...	1656	1729	1847	...	2028	...	...	...	2228	...	...	
442	**Belfort** Ville 378a 386a d.	0725	0825	...	...	1045	...	...	1245	1247	1325	1425	...	1725	1747	1916	...	2048	...	...	...	2247	...	...	
490	**Mulhouse** 378a a.	...	...	...	...	1114	...	...	...	1315	...	...	...	...	...	...	...	2112	...	...	...	2314	...	...	

	Ⓐ	⚒	Ⓐ	Ⓐ	⚒	⑥	Ⓐ	†	⚒	©	Ⓐ	Ⓐ	Ⓐ	©	Ⓐ ⊡	◇	⑥	†	Ⓐ ⊗	⚒	⊖			A	
Mulhouse 378a d.	...	...	...	...	...	...	0522	0521	...	0745f	...	0749	...	...	...	...	...	1240	...	...	1545	...	...	...	
Belfort Ville 378a 386a d.	...	...	...	...	...	...	0548	0548	0735	0815f	...	0816	...	...	...	...	...	1312	1314	...	1614	1735	1812	...	
Lure 386a d.	...	...	...	...	...	...	0606	0605	0803	0834	...	0834	...	...	...	...	...	1331	1333	...	1632	1803	1830	...	
Vesoul d.	...	...	...	...	...	...	0624	0622	0821	0851	...	0851	...	...	...	...	...	1349	1351	...	1650	1821	1848	...	
Dijon Ville 379 381a d.	...	...	...	...	...	...	|	|	▬	|	0833	|	...	...	...	...	...	|	|	1631	|	▬	|	...	
Culmont Chalindrey 379 381a d.	...	...	...	0555	...	0659	0704	0701	...	0928	0919	0935t	...	1128	1228	...	1428	1432t	1430	1719	1732	...	1927	2000	21
Langres 381a d.	...	...	...	0604	...	0708	0712	0709	...	0937	...	0944	...	1137	1237	...	1437	1441	1439	▬	1741	...	1936	2008	21
Chaumont 381a d.	...	...	...	0624	...	0727	0731	0729	...	0957	...	1003	...	1156	1256	1356	1456	1500	1458	...	1800	...	1956	2028	21
Bar sur Aube d.	...	...	...	0644	...	0748	0752	0750	⚒	1017	...	1024	...	1217	1317	1417	1517	1519	1519	...	1819	Ⓑ	2016	2048	21
Troyes d.	0517	0616	0647	0718	0747	0822	0822	0827t	0947	1052	...	1052	1147	1247	1347	1447	1547	1549	1549	1747	1851	1947	2050	2119	22
Romilly sur Seine d.	0536	0635	0706	0736	0806	0841	0840	0846	1006	1110	...	1111	1206	1306	1406	1506	1606	1609	1609	1806	1908	2006	2109	...	
Nogent sur Seine d.	0548	0646	0718	0747	0818	0852	0851	0857	1018	1121	...	1121	1217	1318	1417	1518	1618	1620	1620	1817	1919	2018	2121	...	
Paris Est a.	0646	0746	0816	0846	0916e	0946	0946	1015y	1116	1216	...	1216	1316	1416	1516	1616	1716	1716	1716	1916	2026h	2116	2216	...	

A – ①–⑤ to Aug. 23 (also Sept. 18–20, 23, 24, Nov. 13–15, 18–20; not Aug. 15).
B – † to Aug. 18; Ⓑ from Aug. 25 (not Sept. 18–20, 23, 24, Nov. 13–15, 18–20). Does not run Culmont - Chaumont on Sept. 16, 17.
C – Daily to Nov. 11 (not June 21, 22); ⑥⑦ from Nov. 16.
D – Runs on ⚒ Paris - Culmont, Ⓐ Culmont - Mulhouse.

e – 0936 Nov. 18–22.
f – On ⑥ Mulhouse d. 0749, Belfort d. 0816.
h – 2017 on ©.
p – ⚒ only.
t – Arrives 7–8 minutes earlier.
y – 1025 on June 10, Sept. 29.

♥ – Does not run Troyes - Belfort Oct. 7 - Nov. 8.
♣ – Does not run Troyes - Dijon on Ⓐ Oct. 7 - Nov. 8.
● – Does not run Culmont - Belfort Oct. 7–11, 14–18.
♠ – Does not run Culmont - Mulhouse on June 21.
▲ – Does not run Chaumont - Culmont June 17–22, 24–28, July 1–5, 8–12.
⊡ – Does not run Culmont - Troyes Oct. 7 - Nov. 8.
◇ – Does not run Chaumont - Troyes on Ⓐ Oct. 7 - Nov. 8.
⊗ – Does not run Belfort - Culmont Oct. 7 - Dec. 13. Does not run Culmont - Troyes Oct. 7 - Nov. 8.
⊖ – Does not run Mulhouse - Culmont on ①–⑤ Nov. 12 - Dec. 13.

PARIS / REIMS - CHÂLONS EN CHAMPAGNE - BAR LE DUC / ST DIZIER 381

Warning! Subject to alteration on Ⓒ June 9 – 16 and Ⓒ Nov. 1 – 24. Timings may vary by 1 – 2 minutes until July 16.

km		Ⓐ	Ⓐ		Ⓐ	⑥	†	Ⓐ △	Ⓒ	Ⓒ	†	⑥	Ⓐ ⊡	⚒ ▽	†	2777 ♥		Ⓐ	Ⓐ	†	Ⓐ	⑥	⑥	Ⓐ
0	**Paris Est** 390 d.	...	0636	...	0706	...	...	0836	0836	...	1036	1036	1036	1236	1236	1428	...	1436	...	1636	1636	1636	...	1736
95	Château Thierry d.	...	0724	...	0801	...	...	0924	0924	...	1124	1124	1124	1324	1324	|	...	1524	...	1724	1724	1724	...	1831
	Reims 381a ♠ d.	0552	|	0736	|	0741	0743	|	|	...	|	|	|	|	|	|	1506	|	...	|	|	|	1738	|
142	Épernay ♠ a.	0627	0748	|	0826	0810	0809	0948	0950	...	1149	1150	1150	1348	1350	|	|	1549	...	1748	1749	1750	1820	1856
142	Épernay d.	0644	0750	|	0828	0819	0819	0950	0952	...	1151	1152	1152	1350	1352	|	|	1550	1614v	1749	1751	1752	1825	1858
	Champagne-Ardenne TGV 390 d.	|	|	|	|	|	|	|	|	...	|	|	|	|	|	1513	|	|	|	|	|	|	|	|
172*	**Châlons en Champagne** 381a d.	0704	0805	0815	0845	0841	0841	1010	1009	...	1207	1209	1209	1407	1409	1537	1546	1612j	1632	1806	1808	1810	1842	1934c
205	Vitry le François 381a d.	0723	...	0837	0903	0858	0858	1027	1026	1035	...	1227	1227	1423	1427	1557	1606	1635j	1650	1822	1825	1828	1859	1954
234	**St Dizier** 381a a.	|	...	0857	◐	|	|	|	|	1054	...	1246	|	1441	1446	|	1624	1652j	|	◐	◐	◐	|	2011
255	**Bar le Duc** a.	0753	...	...	0926	0926	0923	1050	1050	...	...	...	1252	...	...	1620	...	...	1714	1847	1848	1852	1924	...
	Nancy 382 a.	0854	...	...	1026	1025	1021	...	...	...	...	...	...	...	...	...	...	...	...	...	1944	...	2024	...
	Strasbourg 383 a.	...	...	...	1159	...	...	...	...	...	...	...	...	...	...	...	...	...	...	...	2111	...	...	...

	†		2785 ①–⑤ a♥		Ⓐ	⑤ f	2787 ⑦ e♥	Ⓒ	Ⓐ	⑤ f	† ◇
Paris Est 390 d.	...	1836	1925	...	1936	1936	2028	2036	2136	2136	2236
Château Thierry d.	...	1931	|	...	2031	2031	|	2124	2224	2224	2324
Reims 381a ♠ d.	1835	|	|	...	|	|	|	|	|	|	|
Épernay ♠ a.	1913	1957	|	...	2055	2055	|	2149	2248	2248	2349
Épernay d.	1923	1959	|	...	2057	2057	|	2151	2250	2250	2351
Champagne-Ardenne TGV 390 d.	|	|	2007	...	|	|	2111	|	|	|	|
Châlons en Champagne 381a d.	1939	2016	2035	2046	2112	2121	2134	2206	2305	2307	0007
Vitry le François 381a d.	1955	2034	2055	2106	...	2137	2154	...	...	2323	...
St Dizier 381a a.	|	2052	|	2125	...	2155	|	...	...	◐	...
Bar le Duc a.	2020	...	2119	...	...	...	2219	...	...	2347	...
Nancy 382 a.	2123	...	...	...	...	...	...	...	...	...	...
Strasbourg 383 a.	...	...	...	...	...	...	...	...	...	...	...

	Ⓐ	⚒	2778 ①–⑥ b♥	Ⓐ	⚒	Ⓐ ♣	Ⓒ
Strasbourg 383 d.	...	...	...	...	...	...	...
Nancy 382 d.	...	...	...	...	...	0615	...
Bar le Duc d.	...	...	0610	...	...	0714	...
St Dizier 381a d.	...	0535	|	0635	0711	|	0737
Vitry le François 381a d.	...	0558	0636	0656	0732	0739	0758
Châlons en Champagne 381a d.	0517	0616	0655	0714	0752	0801	0816
Champagne-Ardenne TGV 390 a.	|	|	0714	|	|	|	|
Épernay a.	0532	0631	|	0729	|	0816	0831
Épernay ♠ d.	0534	0633	|	0731	|	0818	0833
Reims 381a ♠ a.	|	|	|	|	0829	|	|
Château Thierry d.	0600	0700	|	0759	...	0851	0901
Paris Est 390 a.	0653	0754	0801	0853	...	0955	0954

	Ⓑ w	Ⓑ	⑥	⑥	Ⓐ ⊙	Ⓒ	Ⓐ ⊡	⊗	Ⓒ	†	Ⓑ	⚒	†	2784 ♥	Ⓐ	†	⑥	†	Ⓑ	①–④ d	⑤ h	Ⓐ	Ⓒ	⑤ f
Strasbourg 383 d.	...	...	...	...	...	...	...	...	...	...	...	...	...	...	...	...	...	...	...	1613	1619k	...	...	...
Nancy 382 d.	...	...	...	...	...	...	...	...	1434	...	...	...	...	...	...	...	1734	1734	...	1747	1746	...	...	2034
Bar le Duc d.	...	...	...	0937	1136	1136	1337	...	1533	...	...	...	...	1713	...	...	1833	1833	...	1851	1851	...	1936	2133
St Dizier 381a d.	0928	...	0933	|	◐	◐	|	1537	|	1630	...	1654	1658	|	1739	1836	|	|	1847	|	|	...	◐	|
Vitry le François 381a d.	0949	...	0952	1000	1158	1200	1401	1557	1602	1650	...	1717	1718	1739	1758	1857	1901	1901	1907	1915	1914	...	2001	2201
Châlons en Champagne 381a d.	1008	1016t	...	1017	1214	1217	1418	1614	1621	1710	1718	1739	1739	1757	1816	1915	1918	1920	1924	1932	1932	...	2018	2220
Champagne-Ardenne TGV 390 a.	...	|	...	|	|	|	|	|	|	...	|	|	|	1818	|	|	|	|	...	|	|	...	|	|
Épernay a.	...	1031t	...	1032	1230	1232	1433	1630	1639	...	1732	|	|	|	1831	1930	1933	1935	...	1949	1947	...	2032	2235
Épernay ♠ d.	...	1033	...	1033	1232	1234	1434	1632	1646	...	1734	|	|	|	1833	1932	1940	2002	...	1951	1949	2002	2033	...
Reims 381a ♠ a.	...	|	...	|	|	|	|	|	1716	...	|	1829	1828	|	|	|	2007	2037	...	|	|	2038	|	...
Château Thierry d.	...	1101	...	1100	1301	1301	1501	1659	...	...	1801	...	...	|	1901	2000	...	...	...	2021	2020	...	2100	...
Paris Est 390 a.	...	1152	...	1153	1353	1353	1553	1753	...	...	1853	...	...	1902	1953	2053	...	...	...	2119	2128	...	2153	...

– Not June 10, Aug. 15, 16, Nov. 1, 11.
– Not June 10, Nov. 11.
– Arrives 1915.
– Also ⑤ July 5 - Aug. 30; not June 10, Aug. 15, Nov. 1.
– Also June 10, Nov. 11; not June 9.
– Not Nov. 1.
– Not July 5 - Aug. 30, Nov. 1.
– 5 – 12 minutes earlier July 15 - Aug. 23.
– 1616 until June 28.
– Not Ⓐ July 15 - Aug. 23.
– Not Oct. 3, 4.
– From July 8.

w – Not ①–⑤ Sept. 30 - Nov. 22.
⊡ – Ⓐ July 8 - Aug. 30. Does not run Châlons - Bar le Duc and v.v. July 29 - Aug. 2.
△ – Subject to alteration Sept. 2 – 27. Terminates at Châlons July 29 - Aug. 2 and from Sept. 30.
▽ – Not ①–⑤ June 17 - July 16. Subject to alteration on ①–⑤ Sept. 2 - Oct. 4 and ①–⑤ from Oct. 21. Terminates at Châlons Oct. 7 – 11, 14 – 18.
⊙ – Does not run Bar le Duc - Châlons July 29 - Aug. 2, Oct. 7 – 18. Subject to alteration Sept. 2 - Oct. 4 and from Oct. 21.
⊗ – Subject to alteration on ①–⑤ Sept. 2 – 27. Does not run St Dizier - Châlons on Ⓐ Sept. 30 - Nov. 22.

◇ – Runs 8 minutes earlier on Nov. 1, 11.
♥ – *TGV* train, Ⓡ, supplement payable.
♣ – From Sarrebourg (Table **383**).
* – *188 km* via high-speed line.
◐ – See Table **381a** for St Dizier connection.

♠ – Local trains Épernay - Reims and v.v. (*31 km*; journey 26 – 40 minutes).
From Épernay at 0531 Ⓐ, 0622 Ⓐ, 0647 ⚒ n, 0719 ⚒ n, 0802 Ⓐ, 0833 Ⓐ, 0933 ⑥, 0939 Ⓐ t, 1003 †, 1109 Ⓐ t, 1203 †, 1214 Ⓐ n t, 1228 ⚒ t, 1403 t, 1533 ⑥, 1609 Ⓐ, 1637 Ⓐ n, 1704 Ⓐ, 1732 Ⓐ, 1803 n, 1828 Ⓐ, 1903 Ⓐ, 2101 Ⓐ, 2202 Ⓒ and 2355 †.
From Reims at 0452 Ⓐ, 0652 ⚒, 0721 Ⓐ n, 0750 Ⓐ, 0822 Ⓐ n, 0949 Ⓒ, 1022 Ⓐ n t, 1050 Ⓐ t, 1152 t, 1223 ⑥, 1252 Ⓐ t, 1322 Ⓐ t, 1351 Ⓐ t, 1422 ⚒ n t, 1552, 1650 Ⓑ, 1720 Ⓐ, 1750 Ⓐ n, 1822 Ⓐ, 1922 Ⓐ, 1952 ⑥⑦, 2022 Ⓐ, 2050 Ⓐ n, 2152 Ⓐ and 2222 ⑥.

REIMS - CHÂLONS EN CHAMPAGNE - DIJON 381a

Subject to alteration on June 22

km		Ⓐ	⑥	⊡		Ⓐ	Ⓐ	⑥	Ⓐ n	†	Ⓐ n	Ⓐ m		⊖		Ⓐ	†	⑥	Ⓐ	Ⓒ d	Ⓐ			†	⑤ f
0	**Reims** 381 d.	*0614*	0636	...	0736	0806	0836n	0836	1006	1036	1136	...	1236	1306	1506	1655	1736	1736	1806	1836	1936	...	2036	2236	2236
58	**Châlons en Champagne** 381 d.	0708	0727	...	0815	0844	0914	0917	1043	1118	1211	1216	1326	1345	1546	1735	1813	1818	1843	1930	2018	2046	2118j	2313	2317
91	Vitry le François 381 d.	0728	0751	...	0837	...	0935v	...	...	...	...	1233	...	1406	1606	1753	1835	1837	1906	1948	...	2106	...	2334	2338
120	St Dizier 381 d.	0748	0810	...	0859	...	0954v	...	...	...	...	1253	...	1426	1625	1813	1856	1856	1924	2007	...	2127	...	2353	2357
193	Chaumont 380 d.	0833	0853	...	0943e	...	...	...	...	...	...	...	...	1511	1716	1859	1943	...	...	...	...	2214	...	...	...
227	Langres 380 d.	0854	0915	...	...	...	...	...	...	...	...	...	...	1532	...	1920	2003	...	...	...	...	2237a	...	...	...
238	Culmont Chalindrey 379 380 d.	0903	0922	0950	...	...	...	...	...	...	...	...	...	1541	...	1928	2012	...	...	...	...	2246a	...	...	...
315	**Dijon** 379 380 a.	...	...	1043	...	...	...	...	...	...	...	...	...	1630	...	...	2104	...	...	...	...	...	...	...	...

	⚒	⚒	Ⓐ	Ⓒ	Ⓐ	Ⓐ k	Ⓐ w	Ⓒ	w	⊡ c	Ⓐ m	⑥	Ⓒ	Ⓐ n	⚒	Ⓐ	†	†	⚒	Ⓑ		†	⚒		★
Dijon 379 380 d.	...	...	...	...	...	...	...	...	...	1101	...	...	...	...	...	...	...	...	...	...	...	...	...	1805	2005
Culmont Chalindrey 379 380 d.	...	0552z	0649	...	...	...	...	...	...	1150	...	1215	...	...	...	...	...	...	...	...	...	...	...	1859	2101
Langres 380 d.	...	0600z	0658	...	...	...	...	...	...	...	...	1225	...	...	...	...	...	...	...	...	...	...	...	1909	...
Chaumont 380 d.	...	0620	0718	...	...	...	...	1140	...	...	1245	1246	...	...	...	...	1540	...	1605	1738	...	1830	1834	1930	...
St Dizier 381 d.	...	0711	0807	...	1015k	1122	...	1228	...	...	1330	1333	...	...	...	...	1630	1658	1654	1847	...	1931	1935	2012	...
Vitry le François 381 d.	...	0732	0830	...	1036k	1142	...	1250	...	...	1351	1355	...	...	...	...	1650	1718	1717	1907	...	1952	1956	2033	...
Châlons en Champagne 381 d.	0637	0752	0854	0939t	1054	1202	1207	1310	1318	...	1410	1410	1448	1452	1552	1654	1710	1739	1739	1924	1939h	2012	2013	2054	...
Reims 381 a.	0728	0829	0929	1029	1129	...	1259	...	1359	...	...	...	1531	1529	1629	1729	...	1828	1829	...	2029	...	...	2129	...

– Not ①–⑤ June 17 – 28, July 1 – 12, 25, 26.
– Not ①–⑤ Sept. 30 - Oct. 18.
– Runs daily Reims - Châlons.
– Not Oct. 7 – 11, 14 – 18.
– Also July 13, Aug. 14, Oct. 31; not Nov. 1.

h – 1952 on Ⓐ.
j – 2111 on Ⓒ.
k – Not Sept. 30 - Nov. 22.
m – Not Sept. 30 - Nov. 29.
n – Not July 15 - Aug. 23.

t – 0954 on ⑥.
v – Not Oct. 7 - Nov. 8.
w – Not Nov. 4 – 8.
z – Not June 18 - July 6, July 9 – 13, 26, 27.

⊡ – Daily to June 30; ⑥⑦ July 6 - Aug. 18 (also Aug. 15, 16); daily from Aug. 24. See also note ★.
⊖ – Subject to alteration on Ⓐ Sept. 30 - Nov. 8 and ①–⑤ Nov. 18 – 29. June 18 - July 2 departures Vitry - Langres are up to 3 minutes earlier.
★ – To / from Nancy via Neufchâteau (see Table **379** for timings).

BAR LE DUC - NANCY 382

Timings may vary by up to 6 minutes until July 1

km		Ⓐ	Ⓐ	⑥	Ⓐ	Ⓐ	†	⑥	Ⓐ P	Ⓐ	⑥	Ⓐ ‡	Ⓐ ‡	†	Ⓐ n ‡	⚒ n ‡	Ⓐ n ‡	†	Ⓐ	⑥	Ⓐ	†	Ⓐ P	†	⑥	†	Ⓐ r n
	Reims 381 d.	...	...	...	...	0552	0743	0741	...	...	...	...	...	...	...	...	...	...	...	...	...	...	...	...	1738	1835	...
0	**Bar le Duc** d.	0554	0613	0726	0726	0754	0924	0927	0928	1003	1113	1126	1213	1226	1306	1426	1525	1526	1626	1713	1726	1821	1849	1913	1925	2021	2126
40	Commercy d.	0614	0639	0746	0746	0814	0943	0946	0950	1024	1138	1146	1238	1246	1326	1446	1545	1546	1646	1738	1746	1841	1910	1938	1945	2044	2146
66	Toul d.	0629	0658	0800	0801	0830	0957	1000	1005	1038	1157	1201	1257	1301	1341	1501	1559	1601	1701	1757	1801	1856	1924	1957	1959	2100	2201
99	**Nancy** a.	0653	0725	0825	0825	0854	1021	1025	1026	1102	1225	1225	1325	1325	1405	1525	1625	1625	1725	1826	1825	1920	1944	2025	2024	2123	2225

	Ⓐ S	⑥	Ⓐ	⚒ n	Ⓐ n	n ‡	Ⓐ n ‡	Ⓐ ‡	Ⓒ	Ⓐ ‡	Ⓐ n ‡	Ⓒ	Ⓐ n	†	⑥	Ⓐ	Ⓐ	⑥	†	F P	A P	†	Ⓐ	⑥	Ⓐ r	D	⑤ E
Nancy d.	0615	0646	0734	0834	0934	1032	1134	1234	1234	1334	1434	1434	1534	1559	1607	1634	1707	1734	1734	1746	1747	1833	1834	1934	1934	2034	2034
Toul d.	0635	0710	0758	0858	0958	1051	1158	1258	1300	1359	1458	1458	1558	1624	1630	1658	1734	1758	1758	1810	1810	1857	1858	1959	2000	2058	2058
Commercy d.	0652	0724	0812	0912	1012	1105	1212	1312	1319	1418	1512	1513	1612	1644	1645	1712	1753	1812	1812	1830	1829	1911	1912	2018	2018	2112	2112
Bar le Duc a.	0712	0744	0832	0932	1032	1125	1232	1332	1343	1444	1532	1532	1632	1708	1705	1732	1819	1832	1832	1850	1850	1931	1932	2043	2043	2132	2132
Reims 381 a.	...	...	...	...	...	...	...	...	...	...	...	1716	...	...	...	...	...	2007	2037	...	...	...	...	...	...	...	...

– ①–④ (also ⑤ July 5 - Aug. 30; not June 10, Aug. 15, Nov. 1).
– ①②③④⑦ (also Nov. 1).
– ⑤ (not Nov. 1). To Épernay (Table **381**).

F – ⑤ (not July 5 - Aug. 30, Nov. 1).
P – 🚌12 Paris - Strasbourg and v.v. (Tables **381** and **383**).
S – 🚌12 Sarrebourg - Paris (Tables **381** and **383**).

n – Not Ⓐ July 15 - Aug. 23.
r – From July 8.
‡ – Subject to alteration on Ⓐ Sept. 30 - Nov. 15.

383 METZ and NANCY - STRASBOURG

See Table **390** for fast *TGV* services Paris - Nancy / Strasbourg. Certain services from / to Nancy are subject to alteration on ⑥⑦ June 9–23. Eastbound Lunéville departure times may by up to 3 minutes later until Sept. 1.

km									*TGV* 9881								*TGV* 2587		*TGV* 9879						
		Ⓐ	Ⓐ	⑥	Ⓐ	Ⓐ	⚒	⚒	⚒	🅁	Ⓐ	†		Ⓐ	Ⓒ	⑥	Ⓐ	⑦ e🅁	†	🅁	Ⓐ	⚒	⑥	Ⓐ	Ⓐ	†
0	**Metz** d.	...	...	...	...	0617	0642	...	0747	0808	...	...	...	0934	0943	...	...	...	...	1208	...	1247	...	1342	...	...
	Paris Est **381** d.	...	...	...	...	|	|	...	|	|	...	...	...	|	|	...	0706	0910	...	|	...	|	...	|	...	...
Δ	**Nancy** **387** d.	...	...	...	0612	|	|	0714	|	|	0814	0816	...	|	|	1016	1032	1053	1116	|	1212	|	1316	|	1415	141
	Lunéville **387** d.	...	...	...	0631	|	|	0732	|	|	0832	0834	...	|	|	1034	1052	|	1134	|	1230	|	1332	|	1433	143
88	Sarrebourg d.	0535	0623	0633	0656	0719	|	0758	0849	|	0855	0857	...	|	|	1057	1116	1134	1157	|	1256	1349	1355	|	1456	145
91	Réding d.	0539	0627	0637	0700	...	0729	|	...	|	0859	|	...	1022	1030	|	|	|	|	|	|	...	1359	1430	1500	|
114	Saverne d.	0555	0644	0653	0715	...	0746	0816	...	|	0915	0915	...	1039	1046	1118	1133	1152	1214	|	1313	...	1414	1445	1515	151
159•	**Strasbourg** a.	0634	0711	0734	0742k	...	0811	0842	...	0859	0941n	0941	...	1111	1111	1144	1159	1215	1241k	1257	1339	...	1441n	1511	1541n	154

										TGV 6831																*TGV* 258
	Ⓐ	⑥	Ⓐ z	Ⓐ	†	† v	Ⓐ	Ⓑ	⑥	🅁	⚒	Ⓐ	Ⓐ	Ⓐ	†	Ⓐ	Ⓐ	†	⚒	Ⓐ	⑥	Ⓑ	Ⓐ	†	†	Ⓑ h🅁
Metz d.	...	...	...	...	1547	...	1617	1643	1647	1700	...	1724	1747	...	...	1817	1843	1843	...	...	1934	1947	...	...	2043	...
Paris Est **381** d.	...	...	...	...	|	...	|	|	|	|	...	|	|	...	...	|	|	|	...	1636	|	|	...	...	|	191
Nancy **387** d.	...	1516	...	1614	|	1616	|	|	|	|	1715	|	|	1814	1816	|	|	|	1916	1948	|	|	...	2016	|	204
Lunéville **387** d.	...	1533	...	1633	|	1634	|	|	|	|	1733	|	|	1832	1834	|	|	|	1934	2006	|	|	...	2033	|	211
Sarrebourg d.	1551	1559	1618	1655	1649	1658	1719	|	1749	|	1759	1826	1849	1858	1856	1919	|	|	1957	2031	2035	2049	2055	2057	|	213
Réding d.	1555	|	1623	1659	...	|	...	1730	...	|	|	1830	...	|	|	...	1931	1933	|	|	|	...	|	|	2130	|
Saverne d.	1611	1615	1639	1715	...	1715	...	1746	...	|	1816	1846	...	1915	1915	...	1946	1949	2016	2049	2051	...	2111	2115	2144	215
Strasbourg a.	1641k	1641	1711	1741	...	1741	...	1813	...	1753	1841j	1911k	...	1941n	1941n	...	2012	2016	2042p	2111	2116	...	2142	2141	2209	221

		TGV 2584																*TGV* 9896							*TGV* 2545	*TGV* 989
	Ⓐ	①–⑥ b🅁	⚒	Ⓐ	Ⓐ	Ⓐ	Ⓐ k	⚒	⑥ ⊡	Ⓑ k	†	Ⓐ	Ⓒ ⊖	⑥	Ⓐ	⚒		🅁	Ⓑ ◇	Ⓐ	⑥	Ⓐ	⑥	Ⓐ z	⑦ e🅁	🅁
Strasbourg d.	...	0541	...	0617	...	0649k	0719	0749r	0819x	0819	0949t	1017	1019	...	...	1149t	1217t	1229	1249	1319	...	1419	1519	1519	1551	160
Saverne d.	...	0606	...	0643	...	0715	0744	0814	0844	0845	1015t	1043	1044	...	...	1215	1243	|	1315	1346	...	1445	1544	1549	1615	|
Réding d.	...	|	...	|	...	0729	|	0828	|	|	1028	1058	|	...	...	1229	|	|	1329	1359	...	|	|	1605	|	|
Sarrebourg d.	0525	0624	0636	0700	0703	|	0800	|	0901	0904	|	1102	1100	1111	1136	|	1302	|	|	1404	1411	1503	1600	1609	1633	|
Lunéville **387** d.	0551	0649	|	0725	|	|	0826	|	0925	0927	|	1125	1125	|	|	|	1325	|	|	...	|	1526	1625	...	|	|
Nancy **387** a.	0612	0709	|	0744	|	|	0845	|	0945	0946	|	1145	1145	|	|	|	1345	|	|	...	|	1544	1644	...	1712	|
Paris Est **381** a.	0955	0846	|	...	|	|	...	|	...	...	|	...	...	|	|	|	...	|	|	...	|	...	...	...	1846	|
Metz a.	...	...	0736	...	0752	0815	...	0915	...	...	1115	...	...	1211	1236	1315	...	1324	1415	...	1511	...	...	...	...	164

																			TGV 6882							
	Ⓐ	①–④ d	⑤ f	† k	†	Ⓐ k	Ⓐ	⑥ ⊡	⑥	Ⓐ	†	Ⓐ	† k	Ⓐ	†	Ⓐ	⑥ ⊙	†	🅁	Ⓐ ⊗	Ⓐ	†	⑥	Ⓐ	Ⓐ	†
Strasbourg d.	...	1613	1619*	1619	...	1649	1719v	1719	...	1749	1749	...	1755	1816v	1819v	1849t	1849	1849v	1913	1919	...	1949	1949t	1949y	2105	210
Saverne d.	...	1641	1643*	1645	...	1714	1744	1745	...	1815k	1822	...	1837	1844	1845	1921	1915	1917	|	1945	...	2015	2015	2019	2132	214
Réding d.	...	|	|	|	...	1729	|	1759	...	1831k	1839	...	1851	1858	|	1937	1929	|	|	2000	...	|	|	2035	|	|
Sarrebourg d.	1636	1658	1700*	1703	1711	1740	1803	1804	1811	|	|	1836	1855	1903	1903	1940	|	1942v	|	2004	2008	2030	2033	2038	2148	215
Lunéville **387** d.	|	1724	1724	1725	|	|	1829	1825	|	|	|	|	...	1925	1925	...	|	|	|	2025	|	2056	2055	...	...	...
Nancy **387** a.	|	1744	1744	1745	|	|	1848	1844	|	|	|	|	...	1945	1944	...	|	|	|	2045	|	2115	2116	...	...	...
Paris Est **381** a.	|	2119	2128	...	|	|	...	...	|	|	|	|	...	...	...	...	|	|	|	...	|	...	...	...	...	...
Metz a.	1736	...	...	...	1811	1830	...	...	1911	1918	1924	1936	...	...	...	...	2015	2031	2000	...	2057	...	...	...	...	...

b – Not June 10, Nov. 11.
d – Also ⑤ July 5 - Aug. 30; not June 10, Aug. 15, Nov. 1.
e – Also June 10, Nov. 11.
f – Not July 5 - Aug. 30, Nov. 1.
h – Not Aug. 15, 16, Nov. 1.
j – 1846 on Ⓐ July 1 - Aug. 30.
k – 2–4 minutes later July 1 - Aug. 30.
n – 5–7 minutes later July 1 - Aug. 30.
p – 2046 on Ⓐ July 1 - Aug. 30; 2050 on ⑥ July 6 - Aug. 24.
r – 0751 on Ⓐ July 1 - Aug. 30; 0747 on ⑥ July 6 - Aug. 24.
t – 1–2 minutes earlier July 1 - Aug. 30.
v – 3–6 minutes earlier July 1 - Aug. 30.
x – 0817 from Oct. 26.
y – 1937 July 1 - Aug. 30.
z – Not July 1 - Aug. 30.
TGV –🅁, supplement payable, 🍸.
◇ – Runs 3–9 minutes later Sept. 2–6, 9–13.
* – 1–3 minutes earlier until June 28.
⊖ – 2–4 minutes earlier on † July 7 - Aug. 25
⊙ – 14–17 minutes later July 6 - Aug. 24.
⊡ – 8–12 minutes later July 6 - Aug. 24.
⊗ – 5–9 minutes later July 1 - Aug. 30.
Δ – Nancy - Sarrebourg: *80 km*.
• – Metz - Strasbourg for *TGV* services: *145 k*

384 Regional trains NANCY - METZ - LUXEMBOURG

French holiday dates apply, although service may vary on June 23 and Nov. 11 (see shaded box below). See Table **390** for *TGV* trains Paris - Metz - Luxembourg.

km		Ⓐ	Ⓐ	⚒	Ⓐ		Ⓐn	Ⓐ		⚒	Ⓐn	n	Ⓐ	⑥	Ⓐn		❖	Ⓐn			Ⓐn	⑥	Ⓒ♣
0	**Nancy** d.	0528	0620	0650	0720	0750	0806	0820	0828	0850	0920	0950	1020	1050	1120	1150	and at the same	2020	2050	2150	2237	2250	232
28	Pont-à-Mousson d.	0553	0637	0707	0737	0807	0824	0837	0853	0907	0937	1007	1037	1107	1137	1207	minutes past	2037	2107	2207	2302	2307	001
37	Pagny sur Moselle d.	0602	0644	0714	0744	0814	0830	0845	0902	0914	0944	1014	1044	1114	1144	1214	each hour until	2044	2114	2214	2310	2314	|
57	**Metz** a.	0621	0657	0727	0758	0827	0844	0900	0921	0927	0957	1027	1057	1127	1157	1227		2057	2128	2228	2330	2328	011

	Ⓐ	⚒	Ⓐ		Ⓐ		Ⓐn	⚒	Ⓐn	¶	Ⓐn	⚒	Ⓐn		Ⓐn	⊠		Ⓐn		Ⓑn	Ⓐw	Ⓒ	Ⓒ♣
Metz ▷ d.	0602	0632	0702	0732j	0802	0832	0902	0932	1002	1032	1102	1132	1202	1232	1302	and at the same	1932	2002	2032	2132	2225	2232	233
Pagny sur Moselle ▷ d.	0617	0647	0716	0747	0816	0846	0916	0946	1016	1047	1116	1147	1216	1247	1316	minutes past	1947	2016	2046	2146	2243	2246	000
Pont-à-Mousson ▷ d.	0624	0654	0723	0754	0823	0853	0923	0953	1023	1054	1123	1154	1223	1254	1323	each hour until	1954	2023	2053	2153	2249	2253	002
Nancy ▷ a.	0641	0711	0740	0811	0840	0911	0941	1011	1041	1111	1140	1211	1240	1311	1340		2011	2040	2111	2211	2313z	2311	01

(NANCY -) METZ - LUXEMBOURG

km		Ⓐ	Ⓐn	⚒	Ⓐ	⚒	Ⓐ	Ⓐ	Ⓒ	Ⓐn	⚒	†	†¶	Ⓐ¶	⑥¶	⚒				Ⓐ	n	Ⓐ		Ⓐn	¶	Ⓐ
	Nancy ★ d.	...	...	...	0620	0650	0720	0750	0750	...	0850k	...	0950	...	...	1050k	1150	1250	1350	1450	...	...	1550	...	1650	172
0	**Metz** d.	0533	0603	0633	0703	0733	0803	0831	0833	0903	0933	0946•	1030	1033	1042	1133	1233	1333	1433	1533	1546	1603	1633	1703	1730	180
18	Hagondange d.	0545	0615	0645	0715	0745	0815	0843	0845	0918	0945	1002	1046	1045	1102	1145	1245	1345	1445	1545	1602	1615	1645	1715	1745	181
30	Thionville d.	0557	0627	0658	0727	0757	0827	0853	0857	0936	0957	1017	1057	1057	1117	1157	1257	1357	1457	1557	1617	1636	1657	1727	1757	182
64	**Luxembourg** a.	0621	0651	0721	0751	0821	0851	...	0921	1003	1021	1045	1121	1121	1145	1221	1321	1421	1521	1621	1645	1705	1721	1751	1821	185

	n	Ⓐ			⚒n	†r	Ⓒ	Ⓐ	†	⑤⑥§
Nancy ★ d.	1750c	1820	1850c	1950c	2050k	...	2150	...	...	...
Metz d.	1833	1903	1933	2033	2133	2146	2233	2246	2316	2316
Hagondange d.	1845	1915	1945	2045	2145	2202	2245	2302	2332	2332
Thionville d.	1857	1934	1957	2057	2157	2217	2257	2317	2344	2348
Luxembourg a.	1921	2003	2021	2121	2221	2245	2321	2345	...	0015

	Ⓐ	⚒	Ⓐ	Ⓐ	⑥	Ⓐ	Ⓐ		Ⓐm		⚒	Ⓐn	¶
Luxembourg d.	0516	0539k	0546	...	0628	0628	0709	0739	0809	0816	0839	...	093
Thionville d.	0546	0604	0613	0634	0702	0706	0735	0804	0834	0844	0904	0924‡	100
Hagondange d.	0557	0616	0624	0646	0714	0716	0746	0815	0845	0857	0916	0936‡	101
Metz a.	0614	0627	0641	0658	0732	0727	0757	0827	0857	0914	0927	0952	102
Nancy ★ ▷ a.	...	0711	...	0740	0811	0811	0840	0911c	...	...	1011k	1041	111

	Ⓒ¶	Ⓐ		Ⓐn		Ⓐn		Ⓐn	Ⓑn	⚒		Ⓐ		Ⓐ		Ⓑ	⑥	Ⓐ		Ⓐn	Ⓐn	Ⓐ	n	Ⓐ	Ⓐn	Ⓒ
Luxembourg d.	1016	1039	1139	1209	1239	1258	1339	1358	1416	1439	1539	1558	1639	1658	1739	1839	1839	1858	1939	2009	2039	2116	2139	2216	2239	231
Thionville d.	1044	1104	1204	1234	1304	1334	1404	1438	1444	1504	1604	1625	1704	1734	1804	1904	1909	1929	2004	2034	2104	2146	2204	2246	2304	234
Hagondange d.	1055	1116	1216	1245	1316	1346	1416	1449	1455	1516	1616	1644	1716	1745	1816	1916	1921	1940	2016	2046	2116	2157	2216	2257	2316	235
Metz a.	1118	1129	1229	1257	1329	1358	1429	1500	1514	1527	1627	1658	1727	1757	1827	1927	1934	1957	2028	2057	2127	2214	2227	2314	2327	001
Nancy ★ ▷ a.	...	1211	1311	...	1411	...	1511c	...	...	1611k	1711c	...	1811	...	1911	2011	2014	...	2111c	...	2211	...	2311c	...	...	...

c – Ⓒ only.
j – 0734 on ⑥.
k – ⑥ only.
m – Not Aug. 16.
n – Not Ⓐ July 15 - Aug. 23.
r – Not June 16, 23, 30.
w – Not Aug. 19–30.
z – 2319 July 1 - Oct. 11.
• – 0945 on June 10, July 14, Aug. 15, Nov. 1, 11.
♣ – Ⓒ to Nov. 10 (not June 16, 23, 30, Aug. 4, 11, Sept. 15, 22, 29, Oct. 6, Nov. 1, 11).
§ – Not Nov. 1. Terminates at Thionville on ⑤ Aug. 23 - Oct. 4, Nov. 8–29.
‡ – Departs 4 minutes earlier on Sept. 16, 23, 30, Nov. 25.
¶ – Timings may vary by up to 4 minutes on certain dates.
⊠ – The 1432 from Metz runs on Ⓒ only. The 1702, 1802 and 1902 from Metz also run on Ⓐ July 15 - Aug. 23. On ⑥ Metz d. 1936 (not 1932) and then Pagny d. 1950, Pont-à-Mousson d. 1957, Nancy a. 2014.
❖ – The 1620, 1720, 1820 and 1920 from Nancy also run on Ⓐ July 15 - Aug. 23.
★ – See panel above for full service Nancy - Metz and v
▷ – Southbound timings Metz - Nancy may vary by up 3 minutes until July 1.

On Nov. 11 (a public holiday in France) certain services to / from Luxembourg operate as on Ⓐ / ⚒. On June 23 (a public holiday in Luxembourg) certain services to / from Luxembourg operate as on Ⓒ / †. ***Please check locally if travelling on these days.***

STRASBOURG - MULHOUSE - BASEL 385

RVICE FROM JUNE 24. For *TGV* trains Paris - Strasbourg - Colmar see Table **390**. For *TGV* trains Luxembourg - Metz - Strasbourg - Mulhouse - Lyon - Marseille / Montpellier see Table **379**.

km		Ⓐ	Ⓐ	Ⓐ	⑥ 2	Ⓐ	⚒ 2	Ⓐ	Ⓒ 2	Ⓐ	Ⓐ	Ⓒ 2	Ⓐ	2		Ⓐ 2	Ⓐ	Ⓒ 2	Ⓐ	2		Ⓐ 2	⚒	† 2	Ⓐ 2	2
0	**Strasbourg** d.	...	0514	0551	0547	0618	...	0651	0651	0721	0751	0751	0821	...	0851	0921	0951	0951	1021	...	1051	1121	1151	1151	1221	...
43	Sélestat d.	...	0539	0611	0614	0638	...	0710	0711	0740	0810	0816	0841	...	0910	0942	1010	1016	1041	...	1110	1142	1210	1216	1241	...
65	Colmar d.	...	0550	0623	0626	0651	...	0723	0723	0753	0823	0828	0853	...	0923	0955	1023	1028	1053	...	1123	1154	1223	1228	1253	...
06	**Mulhouse** ▷ d.	0546	0616	0646	0654	0716	0719	0746	0746	0816	0846	0855	0916	0919	0946	1017	1046	1056	1114	1119	1146	1214	1245	1255	1316	1319
33	St Louis (Haut Rhin) ▷ d.	0601	0631	0701	...	0731	0742	0801	0812	0831	0901	...	0931	0942	1001	...	1101	...	...	1142	1201	...	1301	...	...	1342
40	**Basel** ▷ a.	0609	0639	0709	...	0739	0750	0809	0820	0839	0909	...	0939	0950	1009	...	1109	...	...	1150	1209	...	1309	...	...	1350

		Ⓐ	Ⓐ	Ⓒ 2		Ⓐ	Ⓑ	⑥ 2	Ⓑ		Ⓐ	⑥ 2	Ⓑ		Ⓑ	⑥ 2	Ⓑ	†		†	Ⓐ	⚒	† 2	2	†	⚒ 2
rasbourg d.	1251	1321	1351	1351	1451	1521	1551	1551	1621	1651	1721	1745	1751	1821	1851	1851	1921	1921	1951	2021	2051	2121	2121	2221	2251	2320
lestat d.	1310	1340	1410	1416	1510	1540	1610	1616	1640	1711	1741	1810	1810	1841	1911	1916	1941	1941	2011	2040	2117	2141	2147	2246	2311	2346
lmar d.	1323	1353	1423	1429	1523	1553	1622	1627	1654	1723	1753	1822	1823	1854	1923	1928	1954	1954	2023	2053	2130	2153	2200	2300	2324	2359
lhouse ▷ d.	1346	1414	1446	1456	1546	1616	1646	1654	1716	1746	1816	1849	1846	1916	1946	1956	2014	2016	2046	2116	2158	2216	2221	2321	2344	0021
Louis (Haut Rhin) ▷ d.	1401	...	1501	...	1601	1631	1701	...	1731	1801	1831	...	1901	1931	2001	...	...	2031	2101	2131	...	2231	...	...	...	...
sel ▷ a.	1409	...	1509	...	1609	1639	1710	...	1739	1809	1839	...	1909	1939	2009	...	...	2039	2109	2139	...	2239	...	...	...	...

	Ⓐ 2	⑥ 2	Ⓐ	Ⓐ	Ⓐ		Ⓐ	Ⓒ 2	Ⓐ	Ⓐ		2	Ⓐ	Ⓒ 2	Ⓐ		2	Ⓐ 2	Ⓒ 2	Ⓐ	Ⓐ		Ⓐ 2		Ⓐ 2	Ⓒ 2
sel ▷ d.	...	...	0521	0537	...	0621	0651	...	0721	0751	0821	0839	0851	...	0921	1021	1039	...	...	1121	...	1221	...	1321	...	...
Louis (Haut Rhin) ▷ d.	...	...	0530	0545	...	0630	0700	...	0730	0800	0830	0847	0900	...	0930	1030	1048	...	...	1130	...	1230	...	1330	...	...
lhouse ▷ d.	0458	0533	0546	0600	0616	0646	0716	0735	0746	0816	0846	0910	0916	0935	0946	1046	1111	1114	1135	1146	1215	1246	1314	1346	1414	1434
lmar d.	0519	0600	0606	0629	0645	0707	0737	0802	0807	0837	0907	...	0937	1002	1007	1107	...	1135	1204	1207	1237	1307	1335	1407	1435	1501
lestat d.	0532	0611	0618	0642	0657	0719	0749	0813	0819	0849	0919	...	0949	1014	1019	1119	...	1147	1216	1219	1249	1319	1347	1419	1447	1513
asbourg a.	0558	0637	0639	0709	0725	0739	0809	0840	0839	0909	0939	...	1009	1040	1039	1139	...	1209	1241	1239	1309	1339	1409	1439	1509	1539

	Ⓐ	Ⓐ	†	⚒	Ⓐ		†	Ⓐ	⑥ 2	Ⓑ	Ⓑ		Ⓐ	⑥ 2	Ⓑ	Ⓑ	⑤†	† 2		⚒	Ⓐ 2	†	⑥ 2	①-⑤ 2	Ⓐ 2	† 2
sel ▷ d.	1421	...	*1439*z	1521	1551	1621	1639	1651	*1639*	1721	1751	1821	1851	*1839*	1921	1951	1951	...	2021	2021	2039	2121	...	2239	...	...
Louis (Haut Rhin) ▷ d.	1430	...	*1447*z	1530	1600	1630	1648	1700	*1647*	1730	1800	1830	1900	*1847*	1930	2000	2000	...	2030	2030	2047	2130	...	2247	...	...
lhouse ▷ d.	1446	1516	1534	1546	1616	1646	1702	1716	1735	1746	1816	1846	1916	1935	1946	2014	2016	2033	2044	2046	2116	2146	2235	2310	2330	2338
lmar d.	1507	1537	1602	1607	1637	1707	1730	1737	1802	1807	1837	1907	1937	2002	2007	...	2037	2102	...	2107	2136	2207	2301	...	2358	0006
lestat d.	1519	1549	1613	1619	1648	1719	1742	1749	1814	1819	1849	1919	1949	2014	2019	...	2049	2114	...	2119	2148	2219	2313	...	0012	0021
rasbourg a.	1539	1609	1639	1639	1709	1739	1809	1809	1839	1839	1909	1939	2009	2039	2039	...	2109	2139	...	2139	2214	2239	2339	...	0040	0048

- Not Aug. 15, Nov. 1, 11.

▷ – Additional stopping trains run Mulhouse - Basel and v.v.

NANCY - ÉPINAL - REMIREMONT 386

ubject to alteration on ⑥⑦ to June 23

km		Ⓐ	Ⓐ	⚒ n	⚒ p	Ⓐ n	k	B	⑥	Ⓐ w	⑦ z	Ⓐ w	⚒ w	Ⓐ w	L	N	†	⚒ N	2571 ♥	⑥	Ⓐ	n	Ⓐ		Ⓐ n	
	Paris Est 390 d.	...	...	...	...	...	...	...	...	...	...	...	...	...	...	...	...	...	1228	...	...	...	...	...	...	...
0	**Nancy** d.	0555	0620	0654	0720	0753	0820	0854	0920	0931	1020	1053	1120	1154	1220	1253	1320	1320	1403	1420	1420	1520	1553	1620	1653	1720
74	Épinal a.	0653	0720	0753	0818	0853	0918	0953	1018	1022	1118	1153	1218	1251	1318t	1353	1418	1418	1444	1518	1518	1618	1653	1718	1753	1818
74	Épinal d.	...	0722	...	0820k	...	0920x	...	...	1024	1120	...	1220	...	1320t	...	...	1420	1447	...	1520	1620	...	1720a	...	1820
00	**Remiremont** a.	...	0754	...	0854k	...	0954x	...	...	1054	1152	...	1254	...	1354t	...	...	1454	1508	...	1554	1654	...	1754a	...	1854

		⚒	Ⓐ n		2573 ♥	Ⓑ		⑥	Ⓐ ⊠	†
Paris Est 390 d.	...	...	...	...	1809	...	...	...	...	...
ncy d.	1754	1820	1855	1920	1955	2020	2120	2205	2226	2254
inal a.	1853	1918	1954	2018	2036	2118	2218	2304	2324	2358
inal d.	...	1920r	...	2020n	2039	...	2220	...	...	...
miremont a.	...	1954r	...	2050n	2105	...	2250	...	...	...

	Ⓐ	⚒ n	2574 Ⓐ s♥	†	⚒	2576 ⑥ ♥	Ⓐ	⑥	⚒	Ⓐ		Ⓐ n
Remiremont d.	...	0511a	0600	...	0615	0639	...	...	0711a	...	0811	...
Épinal a.	...	0541a	0620	...	0642	0700	...	...	0741a	...	0841	...
Épinal d.	0500	0543	0623	0643	0644	0703	0703	0708	0743	0803	0843	0903
Nancy a.	0600	0640	0705	0740	0740	0746	0804	0806	0841	0902	0940	1003
Paris Est 390 a.	...	...	0846	...	...	0931	...	...	...	...	...	...

	2578 ⑦ e♥	⚒ w	Ⓐ w	⑥⑦ z	Ⓐ w	⑥	Ⓐ w	Ⓐ w	L	Ⓐ w	L	Ⓐ n	†		Ⓐ	2580 Ⓒ ♥	2580 Ⓐ s♥	⚒	Ⓐ n	Ⓑ			Ⓐ n	⑥	Ⓐ n	†
miremont d.	0906	0911a	1011	1033	...	...	...	...	1211	1311	1411	1511	...	1611	...	1656	1656	1711	...	1811	...	1911	...	...	2010	...
inal a.	0926	0941a	1041	1102	...	...	...	...	1241	1341	1441	1541	...	1641	...	1717	1717	1741	...	1841	...	1941	...	...	2040	...
inal d.	0928	0943	1043	1104	1103	1139	1143	1208	1243v	1343	1443	1543	1543	1643	1703	1720	1720	1743	1803	1843	1903	1943	2003	2043	2043	2143
ncy a.	1014	1041	1140	1200	1203	1241	1240	1303	1340	1441	1541	1640	1640	1741	1803	1802	1812	1841	1903	1941	2003	2041	2103	2140	2148	2240
Paris Est 390 a.	1146	...	...	...	...	...	...	...	...	...	...	...	...	...	...	1950	1956	...	...	...	...	...	...	...	...	...

- Ⓑ to July 7; † July 14 - Aug. 25; Ⓑ from Sept. 1 (not Oct. 21–31).
- Daily to July 7; ⑥⑦ July 13 - Aug. 25; daily from Aug. 31 (not Oct. 21–25, 28–31).
- ⚒ to July 6; ⑥ July 13 - Aug. 24; ⚒ from Aug. 31 (not Oct. 21–25, 28–31).
- Ⓐ only.
- Also June 10, Nov. 11.
- Not July 15–19, 22–26, 29–31, Aug. 1, 2, 5–9, Oct. 21–31.
- Not July 15–19, 22–26, 29–31, Aug. 1, 2, 5–9, 12–14, 16, 19–23.

p – Not July 15–19, 22–26, 29–31, Aug. 1, 2, 5–9.
r – Not July 20, 27, Aug. 3, 10, 17, 24.
s – Not Aug. 16.
t – 3 minutes later on ⑥.
v – 1241 on †.
w – Not July 8 - Aug. 31, Oct. 21–31.
x – Not July 8–12.
z – Also Nov. 1, 11.

⊠ – By 🚌 Sept. 2 - Oct. 11 (Nancy d. 2220, Épinal a. 0013).
♥ – *TGV* train. Ⓡ. Supplement payable. Conveys 🍸.

ÉPINAL - BELFORT 386a

km		ⒶD	ⒶD	B	A🚌	E
0	**Épinal** d.	0627	0959	1455	1455	1854
58	Luxeuil les Bains d.	0713	1043	1539	1615	1943
76	Lure 380 d.	0726	1056	1553	1639	1956
08	**Belfort** Ville 380 a.	0758	1128	1623	1750	2028

	ⒶD	B	A🚌	ⒷE	E
Belfort Ville 380 d.	0605	1105	1100	1705	2005
Lure 380 d.	0636	1136	1209	1736	2036
Luxeuil les Bains d.	0650	1150	1234	1750	2050
Épinal a.	0737	1237	1408	1837	2137

A – Ⓐ from Oct. 21 (not Nov. 4–8).
B – Daily Aug. 31 - Oct. 20; Ⓒ from Oct. 26 (also Nov. 4–8).
D – From Sept. 2.
E – From Aug. 30.

NANCY - LUNÉVILLE - ST DIÉ 387

ubject to alteration on ⑥⑦ to June 23

km		Ⓐ n	Ⓐ		⑥	Ⓐ n	Ⓒ	Ⓐ	Ⓒ	Ⓐ		Ⓐ n	⚒	2591 ⑦ e♥	Ⓐ n	†	Ⓐ	⚒	†	Ⓐ	⑥	Ⓐ	2593 Ⓐ s♥	Ⓒ	Ⓐ	2594 ⑦ e♥	Ⓐ
	Paris Est 390 d.	...	...	...	...	...	...	...	...	...	...	...	...	1410	...	...	...	...	...	...	...	...	1809	...	...	2010	...
0	**Nancy** 383 d.	0542	0649	0749	0854	0926	0954	1027	1249	1309	1410	1448	1548j	1552	1648	1652	1709	1748	1758	1849	1850	1911	1951	2000	2000	2150	2159
33	Lunéville 383 d.	0604	0710	0811	0914	0951	1014	1100	1311	1331	1429	1511	1610j	1613	1710	1710	1729	1810j	1818	1911	1910	1930	|	2019	2030	2212	2220
84	**St Dié** a.	0705	0755	0855	0953	1031	1055	1142	1353	1415	1513	1554	1655	1643	1755	1759	1831	1855	1900	1953	1950	2029	2044	2103	2114	2242	2258

	Ⓐ	⑥	Ⓐ	Ⓐ s	2596 ⑥ ♥	⑦ e	2596 Ⓐ s♥	Ⓐ	Ⓐ	⑥	Ⓐ n	Ⓒ	Ⓐ	Ⓒ	Ⓐ	Ⓒ	Ⓐ	†	Ⓐ n	⑥	Ⓐ	⚒ n	2598 ⑦ e♥	⚒ j	†	Ⓐ	n△
Dié d.	0505	0557	0606	0631	0659	0702	0715	0729	0805	0807	0905	0907	1046	1107	1226	1253	1442	1555	1557	1610	1629	1705	1713	1805	1922	1930	2007
néville 383 d.	0544	0638	0652	0728	|	0744	|	0829	0848	0850	0951	0950	1132	1149	1310	1348	1530	1640	1639	1652	1729	1749	1746	1849	2007	2030	2048
ncy 383 a.	0605	0658	0714	0750	0750	0804	0810	0849	0910	0910	1013	1010	1152	1211	1333	1409	1550	1700	1658	1712	1748	1810	1807	1909	2029	2050	2108
Paris Est 390 a.	...	...	...	...	0931	...	0946	...	...	...	...	...	...	...	...	...	...	...	...	...	...	...	1950	...	...	...	...

Also June 10, Nov. 11.
2–5 minutes later on ⑥.

n – Not July 15–19, 22–26, 29–31, Aug. 1, 2, 5–9, 12–14, 16, 19–23.
s – Not Aug. 16.

△ – On † St Dié d. 2006, Lunéville d. 2049, Nancy a. 2111. On ⑥ St Dié d. 2015, Lunéville d. 2100, Nancy a. 2121.
♥ – *TGV* train. Ⓡ. Supplement payable. Conveys 🍸.

388 STRASBOURG - ST DIÉ - ÉPINAL

km		Ⓐ		⑥		†	ⒶE		Ⓐz	⑥	†		Ⓐ	Ⓐ	†	Ⓐ	⑥						
0	**Strasbourg** ▷ d.	0701	...	0825	...	0950	0955	...	1205	1225	1350	...	1557	1655	1750	1755	1825	...	...	...	...	...	...
9	Entzheim Aéroport ✈ ▷ d.	0710	...	0833	...	1001	1003	...	1213	1233	1401	...	1605	1704	1801	1806	1835	...	...	...	...	...	...
19	Molsheim ▷ d.	0718	...	0841	...	1009	1011	...	1222	1242	1409	...	1615	1715	1815	1815	1843	...	...	...	...	...	...
87	**St Dié** a.	0838z	...	1000	...	1120	1120	...	1337	1353	1527	...	1735	1839	1929	1926f	1953	...	...	...	...	...	...

	Ⓐ		Ⓐ		Ⓐz	†	⑥		⑥	Ⓐz		ⒶE	⑥	†	Ⓐ	†	⑥		†				
St Dié d.	0546	...	0735n	...	0900	0903	0917	...	1207	1212	...	1552	1637	1708	1755	1801	1829	...	2009	...	...	...	...
Molsheim ▷ d.	0720	...	0846	...	1010	1014	1028	...	1318	1324	...	1705	1748	1821	1911	1916	1943	...	2121	...	...	...	...
Entzheim Aéroport ✈ ▷ d.	0729	...	0854	...	1018	1027	1036	...	1326	1332	...	1713	1801	1828	1919	1928	1957	...	2128	...	...	...	...
Strasbourg ▷ a.	0738	...	0901	...	1027	1039	1047	...	1335	1340	...	1721	1812	1839	1928	1939	2008	...	2139	...	...	...	...

ST DIÉ - ÉPINAL *60 km*. Operated by 🚌. Journey time: 89 – 105 minutes (65 minutes for services marked ¶). **Subject to confirmation**.
From St Dié at 0625 Ⓐ ¶, 0725 Ⓐ ¶, 0850 Ⓐ ¶, 1010 ⑥, 1225 Ⓐ ¶, 1350 Ⓐ, 1408 ⑥, 1657 †, 1700 ⑥, 1710 Ⓐ ¶, 1845 Ⓐ ¶, 1940 ⑤ **v**, 1957 † and 2007 ⑥.
From Épinal at 0615 Ⓐ ¶, 0923 ⑥, 1010 Ⓐ, 1235 Ⓐ ¶, 1404 Ⓐ, 1450 ⑥, 1500 †, 1630 ⑥, 1635 Ⓐ ¶, 1735 Ⓐ ¶, 1805 †, 1835 Ⓐ ¶ and 1840 ⑥.

E – Until July 12.
f – 1932 on ⑤.
n – Not July 15 - Aug. 23.
v – Not Nov. 1.
z – Not Oct. 7 – 31.
▷ – Regular trains run Strasbourg - Entzheim Aéroport (300 metres from terminal) - Molsheim and v.v. 2 – 3 per hour on ⚒, 1 per hour on †.

389 PARIS - REIMS - CHARLEVILLE MÉZIÈRES - SEDAN

km				TGV 2707			TGV 2709	TGV 2711	TGV 2715				TGV 2719		TGV 2721		TGV 2733				TGV 2777			TGV 274
		Ⓐ	⚒	Ⓐ d	Ⓐ		⑥ k	Ⓐ d△	⑦ e	†	Ⓐ n⊗	⑥	⑥ k	⚒ ⊗	⑦ e	⊗	①–⑥ b	Ⓐ	Ⓒ	Ⓐ		n	Ⓐ	Ⓑ h
0	**Paris** Est d.	...	...	0658	...	...	0828	0858	0928	...	...	...	1058	...	1128	...	1258	...	...	...	1428	...	...	152
136	Champagne Ardenne TGV. § d.	...	...	|	...	...	|	|	|	...	...	...	|	...	|	...	|	...	...	...	1510	1521	...	|
147	**Reims** § a.	...	...	0744	...	...	0914	0944	1014	...	...	...	1144	...	1214	...	1344	...	...	...	▬	1531	...	161
147	**Reims** d.	0630	0651	...	0751	0851	0919	0949	1019	...	1021	1051	...	1151	▬	1232	...	1405	1405	1451	...	1533	...	...
186	Rethel d.	0653	0714	...	0814	0914	0942	1012	1042	...	1045	1114	...	1214		1255	...	1427	1428	1519	Ⓐ	1558	...	...
235	**Charleville-Mézières** a.	0725	0746	...	0846	0945	1011	1042	1101o	...	1111	1141	...	1241	nz	1327	...	1500	1500	1544	x◇	1625	...	...
235	**Charleville-Mézières** ... **389a** d.	0730	*0751*	...	0851	0953z	1020	1052	...	1120	...	...	...	...	1246	1335c	...	1505z	*1505*	...	1550	...	1631	...
255	**Sedan** **389a** a.	0748	*0808*	...	0909	1012z	1035	1107	...	1138	...	...	...	...	1311	1355c	...	1530z	*1534*	...	1605	...	1655	...

						TGV 2747				TGV 2753	TGV 2751		TGV 2785				TGV 2757		TGV 2787		TGV 2759		TG 276
			⚒	Ⓐ	Ⓒ	Ⓐ n		Ⓑ s	⑤ ⊙	Ⓐ n	⑤ f	N		Ⓐ d	Ⓐ	⑤ j	①–④ m	⑤⑦ v	⑤† u	⑦ e	†	R	B	⑤⑥ v¶
Paris Est d.	...	...	...	...	...	...	1728	...	...	...	1828	1828		1925	...	...	...	1958	...	2028	...	2058	...	212
Champagne Ardenne TGV.. § d.	...	1639	...	1708	...	...	|	1813	...	...	|	|	...	2004	2012	...	...	|	...	2108	2116	|	...	|
Reims § a.	...	1649	...	1718	...	...	1814	1820	...	...	1914	1914	...	...	2026	...	...	2044	...	...	2127	2144	...	221
Reims d.	1621	1651	...	1720	1721	1751	...	1822	...	1851	1919	1920	1951	...	...	2041	2041	...	2051	...	2129	...	2151	221
Rethel d.	1644	1713	...	1744	1743	1815	...	1844	...	1913	1941	1943	2016	...	...	2104	2105	...	2115	...	2154	...	2214	224
Charleville-Mézières a.	1715	1746	...	1816	1815	1848	...	1915	...	1941	2011	2010	2048	...	...	2136	2136	...	2146	...	2227	...	2246	231
Charleville-Mézières .... **389a** d.	...	...	1751	1821	1820	...	...	1920r	1935	...	...	2022	2053	...	...	2141	...	...	2151y	...	2232	...	2251	232
Sedan **389a** a.	...	...	1807	1846	1846	...	...	1938r	1951	...	...	2037	2111	...	...	2159	...	...	2208y	...	2251	...	2308	233

		TGV 2706		TGV 2778		TGV 2712		TGV 2714					TGV 2720			TGV 2722		TGV 2724	TGV 2726				TGV 2730	TG 273
	Ⓐ	Ⓐ d	⚒	①–⑥ q	⚒	Ⓐ d	Ⓐ n	①–⑥ b	Ⓐ	†	⑥	Ⓐ ⊡	Ⓒ w	⚒	⑥	Ⓐ d	†	⑦ e	⑥ k	⊗	Ⓑ ⊗	Ⓑ n⊗	Ⓐ d▽	⑦ e
Sedan **389a** d.	...	...	0528	...	0604	0624	...	...	*0708*	0739	0734‡	0739g	0749¦	0806	0906	...	1017	...	1052	1116z	1203z	...	1251	...
Charleville-Mézières .... **389a** a.	...	...	0549	...	0621	0638	...	...	*0734*	0757	0753‡	0800	0805¦	0831	0931	...	1034	...	1106	1133z	1229z	...	1305	...
Charleville-Mézières d.	0537	...	0558	...	0626	0646	0709	...	0739	0802	0758	0805	0816	0839	...	...	1039	...	1115	1138	1234	1304	1314	...
Rethel d.	0610	...	0629	...	0700	0716	0740	...	0810	0834	0833	0838	0846	0911	...	...	1108	...	1145	1211	1308	1331	1344	...
Reims a.	0632	...	0653	...	0724	0740	0804	...	0834	0900	0904‡	0903	0910	0934	...	...	1134	...	1210	1234	1334	1404	1410	...
Reims § d.	...	0645	0655	...	...	0745	0806	0815	...	0902	0906‡	0905	0913	...	...	1115	...	1145	1215	...	...	...	1415	141
Champagne Ardenne TGV.. § d.	...	|	0708	0717	...	|	0818	|	...	0914	0917‡	0917	|	...	...	|	...	|	|	...	...	...	|	|
Paris Est a.	...	0734	...	0801	...	0831	...	0901	...	...	...	...	1001	...	...	1202	...	1231	1301	...	...	...	1501	150

				TGV 2750					TGV 2752	TGV 2754			TGV 2784		TGV 2756		TGV 2760	TGV 2762						TG 276
	nz	Ⓐ n⊗	⑥	⑥ k	Ⓐ	†	†	Ⓐ	Ⓐ d	⑦ e	⚒			Ⓑ	⑤⑦ v		R	⑤⑦ v	Ⓒ	Ⓐ n				⑦ e
Sedan **389a** d.	1316	...	1440	...	1517p	1517	1537	1541x	...	...	1633	...	...	1716	...	1745	...	...	1835	1851	*1904*a	2034	...	205
Charleville-Mézières .... **389a** a.	1340	...	1504	...	1534p	1534	1555	1600x	...	...	1655	...	...	1734	...	1803	...	...	1851	1908	*1921*a	2052	...	210
Charleville-Mézières d.	...	1346	1509	...	1539	1539	1600	1605	...	1615	1700	...	...	1739	...	1808	...	...	...	1913	1939	...	2109t	211
Rethel d.	...	1413	1540	...	1608	1612	1633	1638	...	1645	1731	...	...	1810	...	1840	...	...	...	1942	2012	...	2138t	214
Reims a.	...	1437	1604	...	1634	1634	1702	1703	...	1710	1755	...	...	1834	...	1905	...	...	...	2004	2034	...	2204	221
Reims § d.	...	...	1608	1615	1636	...	1704	1706	1715	1715	...	1801	...	...	1845	1907	1915	1945	...	...	...	...	...	221
Champagne Ardenne TGV.. § d.	...	...	1620	|	1648	...	1717	1718	|	|	...	1812	1821	...	|	1919	|	|	...	...	...	...	...	|
Paris Est a.	...	...	...	1701	...	...	...	...	1801	1803	...	...	1902	...	1931	...	2001	2031	...	...	...	...	...	230

B – ①②③④⑥ (not June 10, July 13, Aug. 14, 15, Oct. 31, Nov. 11).
N – ①②③④⑥⑦ (also Aug. 16, Nov. 1; not Aug. 14, Oct. 31).
R – ①②③④⑥ (also Aug. 16, Nov. 1; not June 10, Aug. 14, Oct. 31, Nov. 11).

a – Ⓐ only.
b – Not June 10, Nov. 11.
c – Ⓒ only.
d – Not Aug. 16.
e – Also June 10, Nov. 11.
f – ⑤ (also Aug. 14, Oct. 31; not Aug. 16, Nov. 1).
g – 0734 July 15 - Aug. 23.
h – Not Aug. 15, 16, Nov. 1.
j – Also June 9, July 13, Aug. 14, Oct. 31, Nov. 10; not Nov. 1.
k – Also Aug. 15, 16, Nov. 1.
m – Not June 10, Aug. 14, 15, Oct. 31, Nov. 11.
n – Not ①–⑤ July 15 - Aug. 23.
o – 1111 until June 30.
p – From Aug. 26 (not Oct. 28 – 31).
q – Not June 10, Aug. 15, Nov. 11.
r – ①②③④⑦ (not June 9, Aug. 14, Oct. 30, 31, Nov. 10).
s – Also July 13.
t – On † Charleville d. 2106, Rethel d. 2134.
u – Also July 13, Aug. 14, Oct. 30, 31.
v – Also June 10, Aug. 14, Oct. 31, Nov. 11; not Aug. 16, Nov. 1.
w – Also Aug. 16; not Aug. 15.
x – Not July 8 – 19, Oct. 28 – 31.
y – Not July 12, 13, 19, 21, 26, 28, Aug. 2, 4, 9, 11, 14, 16, 18, 23.
z – On ①–⑤ June 11 - July 19 and Ⓐ Sept. 30 - Dec. 6 operated by 🚌 in modified timings.

TGV – Ⓡ, supplement payable, 🍸.
⊙ – Also Aug. 14, Oct. 31, Nov. 10.
⊡ – On Aug. 16 Sedan d. 0728, Charleville a. 0753, d. 0758, Rethel d. 0833 and then as shown.
‡ – July 20 - Aug. 24 Sedan d. 0707, Charleville a. 0732, Reims a. 0901, d. 0903, Champagne Ardenne a. 0913.
¦ – On ⑥ (also Aug. 16) Sedan d. 0753, Charleville a. 080
• – 2126 June 10 - July 7.
¶ – Terminates at Reims on Oct. 31.
⊗ – Subject to alteration Oct. 28 – 31.
△ – Terminates at Charleville July 8 – 19, Sept. 30 - Oct. 25 and Nov. 4 - Dec. 6. Terminates at Reims Oct. 28 – 31.
▽ – Starts from Charleville June 11 - July 19, Sept. 30 - Oct. and Nov. 4 - Dec. 6. Starts from Reims Oct. 28 – 31.
◇ – Runs 5 – 6 minutes later June 11 - July 5, Sept. 30 - Oct. and Nov. 4 - Dec. 6.
§ – For full service see Table **391a**.

389a CHARLEVILLE MÉZIÈRES - THIONVILLE

km		Ⓐ ◧	Ⓐ	⑥	†	Ⓒ	Ⓐ ⊡	Ⓐ n	⚒	†	⑤ f
0	**Charleville-Mézières 389** d.	...	0607	0751	1120	1505	1550	...	1751	1812	1935
20	**Sedan** d.	...	0626	0809	1139	1540	1606	...	1808	1828	1952
69	Montmédy d.	...	0657	0840	1215	1611	1637	...	1839	1859	2022
91	Longuyon d.	0616	0711	0854	1232	1625	1652	1736	1855	1914	2037
132	Hayange d.	0647	0741	0924	1309	1656	1724	1807	1927	1944	2108
140	**Thionville** a.	0655	0749	0932	1319	1703	1733	1815	1935	1952	2116

	Ⓐ	Ⓒ ⊖	Ⓐ n	⑥	Ⓐ n	Ⓒ	Ⓐ	Ⓐ ◐	
Thionville d.	0530	0610	0702	0920	1648	1712	1740	1823	191
Hayange d.	0538	0618	0710	0928	1656	1720	1748	1831	191
Longuyon d.	0613	0651	0741	1002	1727	1750	1819	1903	194
Montmédy d.	0629	0707	...	1016	...	1804	1833	...	200
Sedan **389** d.	0708	0745	...	1046	...	1835	1904	...	203
Charleville-Mézières . **389** a.	0734	...	...	...	...	1851	1921	...	205

f – Also Aug. 14, Oct. 31, Nov. 10.
n – Not July 15 - Aug. 23.
◧ – From Longwy (d. 0602).
◐ – To Longwy (a. 1917).
⊡ – Subject to alteration Charleville - Longuyon June 11 - July 19 and Sept. 30 - Dec.
⊖ – Runs 10 – 12 minutes later on June 2, 16, 30.

TGV EST EUROPÉEN 390

PARIS - STRASBOURG - COLMAR

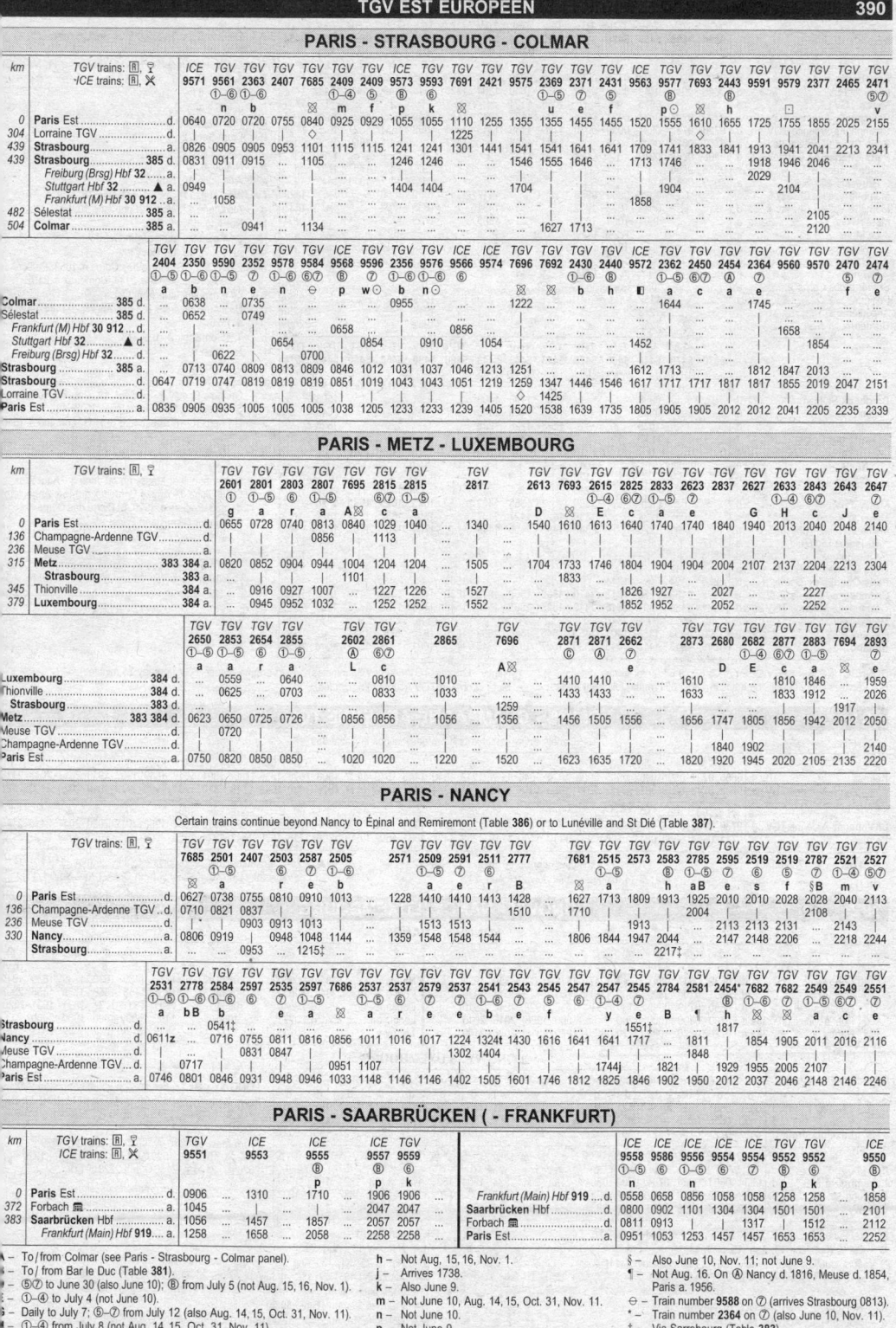

km	*TGV* trains: Ⓡ, 🍷 / *ICE* trains: Ⓡ, ✕	*ICE* 9571	*TGV* 9561	*TGV* 2363	*TGV* 2407	*TGV* 7685	*TGV* 2409	*TGV* 2409	*ICE* 9573	*TGV* 9593	*TGV* 7691	*TGV* 2421	*TGV* 9575	*TGV* 2369	*TGV* 2371	*TGV* 2431	*ICE* 9563	*TGV* 9577	*TGV* 7693	*TGV* 2443	*TGV* 9591	*TGV* 9579	*TGV* 2377	*TGV* 2465	*TGV* 2471
			①-⑥	①-⑥			①-④	⑤	Ⓑ	⑥				①-⑤	⑦	⑤		Ⓑ		Ⓑ					⑤⑦
			n	b		☒	m	f	p	k	☒			u	e	f		p⊙	☒	h		⊡			v
0	**Paris** Est d.	0640	0720	0720	0755	0840	0925	0929	1055	1055	1110	1255	1355	1355	1455	1455	1520	1555	1610	1655	1725	1755	1855	2025	2155
304	Lorraine TGV d.	│	│	│	│	◇	│	│	│	│	1225	│	│	│	│	│	│	│	◇	│	│	│	│	│	│
439	**Strasbourg** a.	0826	0905	0905	0953	1101	1115	1115	1241	1241	1301	1441	1541	1541	1641	1641	1709	1741	1833	1841	1913	1941	2041	2213	2341
439	**Strasbourg** 385 d.	0831	0911	0915	...	1105	...	...	1246	1246	...	...	1546	1555	1646	...	1713	1746	...	...	1918	1946	2046	...	...
	Freiburg (Brsg) Hbf **32** a.	│	│	│	...	│	...	...	│	│	...	...	│	│	│	...	│	│	...	...	2029	│	│	...	...
	Stuttgart Hbf **32** ▲ a.	0949	│	│	...	│	...	...	1404	1404	...	...	1704	│	│	...	│	1904	...	...	...	2104	│	...	...
	Frankfurt (M) Hbf **30 912** a.	...	1058	│	...	│	...	...	...	...	...	...	...	│	│	...	1858	...	...	...	...	...	│	...	...
482	Sélestat 385 a.	...	...	│	...	│	...	...	...	...	...	...	...	│	│	...	...	...	...	...	...	...	2105	...	...
504	**Colmar** 385 a.	...	...	0941	...	1134	...	...	...	...	...	...	...	1627	1713	...	...	...	...	...	...	...	2120	...	...

	TGV 2404	*TGV* 2350	*TGV* 9590	*TGV* 2352	*TGV* 9578	*TGV* 9584	*ICE* 9568	*TGV* 9596	*TGV* 2356	*TGV* 9576	*ICE* 9566	*ICE* 9574	*TGV* 7696	*TGV* 7692	*TGV* 2430	*TGV* 2440	*ICE* 9572	*TGV* 2362	*TGV* 2450	*TGV* 2454	*TGV* 2364	*TGV* 9560	*TGV* 9570	*TGV* 2470	*TGV* 2474
	①-⑤	①-⑥	①-⑤	⑦	①-⑥	⑥⑦	Ⓑ	⑦	①-⑥	①-⑥	⑥				①-⑥	Ⓑ		①-⑤	⑥⑦	Ⓐ	⑦			⑤	⑦
	a	b	n	e	n	⊖	p	w⊙	b	n⊙			☒	☒	b	h	◧	a	c	a	e			f	e
Colmar 385 d.	...	0638	...	0735	...	...	...	...	0955	...	...	...	1222	...	...	...	...	1644	...	...	1745	...	...	...	...
Sélestat 385 d.	...	0652	...	0749	...	...	...	...	│	...	...	...	│	...	...	...	...	│	...	...	│	...	...	...	...
Frankfurt (M) Hbf **30 912** d.	...	│	...	│	...	...	0658	...	│	...	0856	...	│	...	...	...	...	│	...	...	│	1658	...	...	...
Stuttgart Hbf **32** ▲ d.	...	│	...	│	0654	...	│	0854	│	0910	│	1054	│	...	...	...	1452	│	...	...	│	│	1854	...	...
Freiburg (Brsg) Hbf **32** d.	...	│	0622	│	│	0700	│	│	│	│	│	│	│	...	...	...	│	│	...	...	│	│	│	...	...
Strasbourg 385 a.	...	0713	0740	0809	0813	0809	0846	1012	1031	1037	1046	1213	1251	...	...	...	1612	1713	...	...	1812	1847	2013	...	...
Strasbourg d.	0647	0719	0747	0819	0819	0819	0851	1019	1043	1043	1051	1219	1259	1347	1446	1546	1617	1717	1717	1817	1817	1855	2019	2047	2151
Lorraine TGV d.	│	│	│	│	│	│	│	│	│	│	│	│	◇	1425	│	│	│	│	│	│	│	│	│	│	│
Paris Est a.	0835	0905	0935	1005	1005	1005	1038	1205	1233	1233	1239	1405	1520	1538	1639	1735	1805	1905	1905	2012	2012	2041	2205	2235	2339

PARIS - METZ - LUXEMBOURG

km	*TGV* trains: Ⓡ, 🍷	*TGV* 2601	*TGV* 2801	*TGV* 2803	*TGV* 2807	*TGV* 7695	*TGV* 2815	*TGV* 2815		*TGV* 2817		*TGV* 2613	*TGV* 7693	*TGV* 2615	*TGV* 2825	*TGV* 2833	*TGV* 2623	*TGV* 2837	*TGV* 2627	*TGV* 2633	*TGV* 2843	*TGV* 2643	*TGV* 2647
		①	①-⑤	⑥	①-⑤		⑥⑦	①-⑤						①-④	⑥⑦	①-⑤	⑦			①-④	⑥⑦		⑦
		g	a	r	a	A☒	c	a				D	☒	E	c	a	e		G	H	c	J	e
0	**Paris** Est d.	0655	0728	0740	0813	0840	1029	1040	...	1340	...	1540	1610	1613	1640	1740	1740	1840	1940	2013	2040	2048	2140
136	Champagne-Ardenne TGV d.	│	│	│	0856	│	1113	│	...	│	...	│	│	│	│	│	│	│	│	│	│	│	│
236	Meuse TGV a.	│	│	│	│	│	│	│	...	│	...	│	│	│	│	│	│	│	│	│	│	│	│
315	**Metz** 383 384 a.	0820	0852	0904	0944	1004	1204	1204	...	1505	...	1704	1733	1746	1804	1904	1904	2004	2107	2137	2204	2213	2304
	Strasbourg 383 a.	...	│	│	│	1101	│	│	...	│	...	...	1833	...	│	│	...	│	...	...	│	...	...
345	Thionville 384 a.	...	0916	0927	1007	...	1227	1226	...	1527	...	...	...	...	1826	1927	...	2027	...	...	2227	...	...
379	**Luxembourg** 384 a.	...	0945	0952	1032	...	1252	1252	...	1552	...	...	...	...	1852	1952	...	2052	...	...	2252	...	...

	TGV 2650	*TGV* 2853	*TGV* 2654	*TGV* 2855		*TGV* 2602	*TGV* 2861		*TGV* 2865		*TGV* 7696		*TGV* 2871	*TGV* 2871	*TGV* 2662		*TGV* 2873	*TGV* 2680	*TGV* 2682	*TGV* 2877	*TGV* 2883	*TGV* 7694	*TGV* 2893
	①-⑤	①-⑤	⑥	①-⑤		Ⓐ	⑥⑦						Ⓒ	Ⓐ	⑦				①-④	⑥⑦	①-⑤		⑦
	a	a	r	a		L	c				A☒				e			D	E	c	a	☒	e
Luxembourg 384 d.	...	0559	...	0640	...	...	0810	...	1010	...	...	...	1410	1410	...	...	1610	...	...	1810	1846	...	1959
Thionville 384 d.	...	0625	...	0703	...	...	0833	...	1033	...	...	...	1433	1433	...	...	1633	...	...	1833	1912	...	2026
Strasbourg 383 d.	...	│	...	│	...	...	│	...	│	...	1259	...	│	│	...	...	│	...	...	│	│	1917	│
Metz 383 384 d.	0623	0650	0725	0726	...	0856	0856	...	1056	...	1356	...	1456	1505	1556	...	1656	1747	1805	1856	1942	2012	2050
Meuse TGV d.	│	0720	│	│	...	│	│	...	│	...	│	...	│	│	│	...	│	│	│	│	│	│	│
Champagne-Ardenne TGV d.	│	│	│	│	...	│	│	...	│	...	│	...	│	│	│	...	│	1840	1902	│	│	│	2140
Paris Est a.	0750	0820	0850	0850	...	1020	1020	...	1220	...	1520	...	1623	1635	1720	...	1820	1920	1945	2020	2105	2135	2220

PARIS - NANCY

Certain trains continue beyond Nancy to Épinal and Remiremont (Table **386**) or to Lunéville and St Dié (Table **387**).

km	*TGV* trains: Ⓡ, 🍷	*TGV* 7685	*TGV* 2501	*TGV* 2407	*TGV* 2503	*TGV* 2587	*TGV* 2505		*TGV* 2571	*TGV* 2509	*TGV* 2591	*TGV* 2511	*TGV* 2777		*TGV* 7681	*TGV* 2515	*TGV* 2573	*TGV* 2583	*TGV* 2785	*TGV* 2595	*TGV* 2519	*TGV* 2519	*TGV* 2787	*TGV* 2521	*TGV* 2527
			①-⑤		⑥	⑦	①-⑥			①-⑤	⑦	⑥				①-⑤		Ⓑ	①-⑤	⑦	⑥	⑤	⑦	①-④	⑤⑦
		☒	a		r	e	b			a	e	r	B		☒	a		h	aB	e	s	f	§B	m	v
0	**Paris** Est d.	0627	0738	0755	0810	0910	1013	...	1228	1410	1410	1413	1428	...	1627	1713	1809	1913	1925	2010	2010	2028	2028	2040	2113
136	Champagne-Ardenne TGV d.	0710	0821	0837	│	│	│	...	│	│	│	│	1510	...	1710	│	│	│	2004	│	│	│	2108	│	│
236	Meuse TGV d.	│	│	0903	0913	1013	│	...	│	1513	1513	│	...	...	│	│	1913	│	...	2113	2113	2131	...	2143	│
330	**Nancy** a.	0806	0919	│	0948	1048	1144	...	1359	1548	1548	1544	...	...	1806	1844	1947	2044	...	2147	2148	2206	...	2218	2244
	Strasbourg a.	...	...	0953	...	1215‡	...	...	...	...	...	...	...	...	...	...	...	2217‡	...	...	...	...	...	...	...

	TGV 2531	*TGV* 2778	*TGV* 2584	*TGV* 2597	*TGV* 2535	*TGV* 2597	*TGV* 7686	*TGV* 2537	*TGV* 2537	*TGV* 2579	*TGV* 2537	*TGV* 2541	*TGV* 2543	*TGV* 2545	*TGV* 2547	*TGV* 2547	*TGV* 2545	*TGV* 2784	*TGV* 2581	*TGV* 2454*	*TGV* 7682	*TGV* 7682	*TGV* 2549	*TGV* 2549	*TGV* 2551
	①-⑤	①-⑥	①-⑥	⑥	⑦	①-⑤		①-⑤	⑥	⑦	⑦	①-⑥	⑦	⑤	⑥	①-④	⑦			Ⓑ	①-⑥	⑦	①-⑤	⑥⑦	⑦
	a	bB	b		e	a	☒	a	r	e	e	b	e	f		y	e	B	¶	h	☒	☒	a	c	e
Strasbourg d.	...	...	0541‡	...	...	...	...	...	...	...	...	...	...	...	...	...	1551‡	...	...	1817	...	...	...	...	...
Nancy d.	0611z	...	0716	0755	0811	0816	0856	1011	1016	1017	1224	1324t	1430	1616	1641	1641	1717	...	1811	│	1854	1905	2011	2016	2116
Meuse TGV d.	│	...	│	0831	0847	│	│	│	│	│	1302	1404	│	│	│	│	│	...	1848	│	│	│	│	│	│
Champagne-Ardenne TGV d.	│	0717	│	│	│	│	0951	1107	│	│	│	│	│	│	│	1744j	│	1821	│	1929	1955	2005	2107	│	│
Paris Est a.	0746	0801	0846	0931	0948	0946	1033	1148	1146	1146	1402	1505	1601	1746	1812	1825	1846	1902	1950	2012	2037	2046	2148	2146	2246

PARIS - SAARBRÜCKEN (- FRANKFURT)

km	*TGV* trains: Ⓡ, 🍷 / *ICE* trains: Ⓡ, ✕	*TGV* 9551		*ICE* 9553		*ICE* 9555		*ICE* 9557	*TGV* 9559	
						Ⓑ		Ⓑ	⑥	
						p		p	k	
0	**Paris** Est d.	0906	...	1310	...	1710	...	1906	1906	...
372	Forbach 🚌 a.	1045	...	│	...	│	...	2047	2047	...
383	**Saarbrücken** Hbf a.	1056	...	1457	...	1857	...	2057	2057	...
	Frankfurt (Main) Hbf **919** a.	1258	...	1658	...	2058	...	2258	2258	...

	ICE 9558	*ICE* 9586	*ICE* 9556	*ICE* 9554	*ICE* 9554	*TGV* 9552	*TGV* 9552		*ICE* 9550
	①-⑤	⑥	①-⑤	⑥	⑦	Ⓑ	⑥		Ⓑ
	n		n			p	k		p
Frankfurt (Main) Hbf **919** d.	0558	0658	0856	1058	1058	1258	1258	...	1858
Saarbrücken Hbf d.	0800	0902	1101	1304	1304	1501	1501	...	2101
Forbach 🚌 d.	0811	0913	│	│	1317	│	1512	...	2112
Paris Est a.	0951	1053	1253	1457	1457	1653	1653	...	2252

– To / from Colmar (see Paris - Strasbourg - Colmar panel).
– To / from Bar le Duc (Table **381**).
– ⑤⑦ to June 30 (also June 10); Ⓑ from July 5 (not Aug. 15, 16, Nov. 1).
– ①-④ to July 4 (not June 10).
– Daily to July 7; ⑤-⑦ from July 12 (also Aug. 14, 15, Oct. 31, Nov. 11).
– ①-④ from July 8 (not Aug. 14, 15, Oct. 31, Nov. 11).
– Ⓐ to July 5; ⑤ from July 12 (also Aug. 14, Oct. 31; not Aug. 16, Nov. 1).
– Ⓐ to July 11 / from Sept. 2 (not July 9).

– Not June 10, Aug. 15, 16, Nov. 1, 11.
– Not June 10, Nov. 11.
– Also June 10, Aug. 15, 16, Nov. 1, 11.
– Also June 10, Nov. 11.
– Also Aug. 14, Oct. 31; not Aug. 16, Nov. 1.
– Also June 11, Nov. 12; not June 10, Nov. 11.

h – Not Aug, 15, 16, Nov. 1.
j – Arrives 1738.
k – Also June 9.
m – Not June 10, Aug. 14, 15, Oct. 31, Nov. 11.
n – Not June 10.
p – Not June 9.
r – Also Aug. 15, 16, Nov. 1.
s – Also Aug. 15, 16.
t – 1328 on ⑥ (also Aug. 15, Nov. 1).
u – Not June 10, Aug. 15, 16, Nov. 11.
v – Also June 10, Aug. 14, Oct. 31, Nov. 11; not Aug. 16, Nov. 1.
w – Also June 10.
y – Also Aug. 16; not June 10, Aug. 14, Nov. 11.
z – 0609 June 11 - July 1.

§ – Also June 10, Nov. 11; not June 9.
¶ – Not Aug. 16. On Ⓐ Nancy d. 1816, Meuse d. 1854, Paris a. 1956.
⊖ – Train number **9588** on ⑦ (arrives Strasbourg 0813).
* – Train number **2364** on ⑦ (also June 10, Nov. 11).
‡ – Via Sarrebourg (Table **383**).
◧ – On ⑥ (also June 9) runs as *TGV* **9592** and departs Stuttgart 1454.
⊙ – To / from München (Table **32**).
⊡ – To München on ⑥ (Table **32**).
◇ – Via Metz (see Paris - Metz - Luxembourg panel).
▲ – Stuttgart timings may vary on certain dates (please check your reservation).
☒ – OUIGO low-cost TGV service. Internet bookings only at www.ouigo.com.

391 STRASBOURG - BRUSSELS, NANTES, RENNES and BORDEAUX

	TGV 9890	TGV 9890	TGV 5450	TGV 5486	TGV 5470	TGV 5420	TGV 5420	TGV 5484	TGV 5422	TGV 5452	TGV 5488	TGV 9894	TGV 9894	TGV 5454
		①				⑦	①–⑥	⑤			Ⓑ	Ⓑ	⑥	
	C	g		A		e	b	f		D	h	h	k	
Strasbourg d.	0607	0607	0659**v**	0759	0759	0959	0959	1225	1247**r**	1431	1459**y**	1459**y**	1501**z**	1631
Lorraine TGV d.	0645	0645	0745	0842	0842	1037	1040	1304	1325	1514	1543**y**	1543**y**	1543**z**	1711
Meuse TGV d.	|	|	0810	|	|	1058	1104	|	|	|	|	|	|	1731
Champagne-Ardenne TGV a.	0723	0724	0834	0924	0924	1123	1129	1342	1402	1549	1623	1623	1626	1754
Champagne-Ardenne TGV d.	0726	0732	0837	0930	0930	1129	1135	1345	1406	1552	1631	1627	1629	1757
Paris Charles de Gaulle ✈ a.	0757	0802	0908	|	|	1202	1206	|	1437	|	|	1659	1659	|
Paris Charles de Gaulle ✈ d.	0808	0808	0919	|	|	...	...	|	...	|	|	1707	1707	|
Lille Europe a.	0856	0856	|	|	|	...	...	|	...	|	|	1757	1757	|
Brussels Midi/Zuid a.	0943	0943	|	|	|	...	...	|	...	|	|	1843	1843	|
Marne la Vallée - Chessy § a.	...	...	0928	0958	0958	...	...	1417	...	1622	1659	...	...	1829
Marne la Vallée - Chessy § d.	...	...	0932	1002	1002	...	...	1431	...	1633	1703	...	...	1833
Massy TGV a.	...	...	1004	1034	1034	...	...	1503	...	1702	1734	...	...	1904
Le Mans a.	...	...	|	1129**j**	1129**j**	...	...	1558	...	|	1829**j**	...	...	|
Angers a.	...	...	|	1210	|	...	...	1640	...	|	1914	...	...	|
Nantes a.	...	...	|	1250	|	...	...	1720	...	|	1954	...	...	|
Rennes a.	...	...	|	...	1221**j**	...	...	...	...	|	...	...	...	|
St Pierre des Corps a.	...	...	1058**t**	...	...	...	...	...	...	1758	...	...	...	2007**n**
Poitiers a.	...	...	1132	...	...	...	...	...	...	1832	...	...	...	2039**n**
Angoulême a.	...	...	1213	...	...	...	...	...	...	1914	...	...	...	2123**n**
Bordeaux St Jean a.	...	...	1252	...	...	...	...	...	...	1952	...	...	...	2206**n**

	TGV 9870	TGV 5478	TGV 5440	TGV 5400	TGV 5476	TGV 5443	TGV 5443	TGV 5443	TGV 5406	TGV 5480	TGV 5460	TGV 5460	TGV 5445	TGV 9874
		①–⑥			⑦	⑦	①–⑥	①–⑥						
		b			e	D	E	F		A	H	G	⊙	
Bordeaux St Jean d.	...	...	0908	...	...	1108	1108	1108	...	...	...	...	1508	...
Angoulême d.	...	...	0946	...	...	1146	1146	1146	...	...	...	...	1546	...
Poitiers d.	...	...	1028	...	...	1228	1228	1228	...	...	...	...	1628	...
St Pierre des Corps d.	...	...	1102**t**	...	...	1302	1302	1302	...	...	...	...	1702	...
Rennes d.	...	...	|	...	...	|	|	|	...	...	1439	1444	|	...
Nantes d.	...	0802**p**	|	...	1042	|	|	|	...	1407**q**	|	|	|	...
Angers d.	...	0844**p**	|	...	1120	|	|	|	...	1448**q**	|	|	|	...
Le Mans d.	...	0925**p**	|	...	1210	|	|	|	...	1533**q**	1533	|	|	...
Massy TGV d.	...	1025	1155**x**	...	1309	|	1355	1403	...	1625	1625	1625	1755	...
Marne la Vallée - Chessy § a.	...	1057	1224	...	1339	1427	1427	1437	...	1657	1657	1657	1827	...
Marne la Vallée - Chessy § d.	...	1101	1228	...	1343	1435	1435	1444	...	1701	1701	1701	1835	...
Brussels Midi/Zuid d.	0717	|	|	...	|	|	|	|	...	|	|	|	|	1717
Lille Europe d.	0803	|	|	...	|	|	|	|	...	|	|	|	|	1803
Paris Charles de Gaulle ✈ a.	0853	1112	|	...	|	|	|	|	...	|	|	|	|	1853
Paris Charles de Gaulle ✈ d.	0859	1124	|	1244	|	|	|	|	1507	|	|	|	|	1858
Champagne-Ardenne TGV a.	0928	1153	1258	1313	1410	1502	1502	1519	1539	1730	1730	1730	1903	1929
Champagne-Ardenne TGV d.	0931	1156	1301	1316	1413	1505	1505	1522	1542	1736	1736	1736	1909	1935
Meuse TGV a.	|	|	|	1340	|	|	|	|	|	|	|	|	1934	|
Lorraine TGV a.	1009	1233	1338	1401	1450	1546	1546	1602	1620	1814	1814	1814	2002	2016
Strasbourg a.	1049	1313	1418	1445	1530	1627	1627	1645	1701	1901	1901	1901	2045	2058

A – Daily to Sept. 1; ⑤–⑦ from Sept. 6 (also Oct. 31, Nov. 11).
C – ②–⑦ (also June 10, Nov. 11; not June 11, Nov. 12).
D – July 6 - Sept. 1.
E – Aug. 5 – 31.
F – July 6 - Aug. 3.
G – Until Sept. 1.
H – From Sept. 2.

b – Not June 10, Nov. 11.
e – Also June 10, Nov. 11.
f – Also Aug. 14, Oct. 31; not Aug. 16, Nov. 1.
g – Also June 11, Nov. 12; not June 10, Nov. 11.
h – Not Aug. 15, 16, Nov. 1.
j – 3 – 4 minutes earlier from Oct. 7.
k – Also Aug. 15, 16, Nov. 1.
n – From Oct. 7 St Pierre des Corps a. 1958, Poitiers a. 2032, Angoulême a. 2114, Bordeaux a. 2152.
p – 4 – 8 minutes later from Oct. 7.
q – Until Aug. 4 Nantes d. 1402, Angers d. 1444, Le Mans d. 1525.
r – 1245 on Sept. 2 – 6, 9 – 13.
t – Not June 9.
v – 0707 on ⑥⑦.
x – From Oct. 7.
y – On June 9, July 4, 18, Sept. 19, Oct. 24, Nov. 28 Strasbourg d. 1507, Lorraine d. 1547.
z – On Aug. 15, 16 Strasbourg d. 1511, Lorraine d. 1548.

TGV – Ⓡ, supplement payable, 🍸.

⊙ – Does not call at Massy on Ⓐ June 3 - Aug. 2. On Ⓒ June 8 - Aug. 4 Bordeaux d. 1456, Angoulême d. 1533, Poitiers d. 1620, St Pierre des Corps d. 1654.
§ – Station for Disneyland Paris.

Warning! *Services via Massy are subject to alteration Aug. 15 – 18 and Nov. 1, 2, 3, 10, 11*

CONNECTING 🚌 SERVICES (✆ 03 87 78 67 09 for further details).
Bus services connect with the trains in Table **391** on the following routes: Nancy - Lorraine TGV (journey 35 minutes); Metz - Lorraine TGV (journey 25 minutes); Verdun - Meuse TGV (journey 25 minutes).

391a REIMS - CHAMPAGNE ARDENNE TGV

Certain trains continue to / from destinations in Table **389**

	⚒	⚒		†	Ⓐ	⑥¶			‡	Ⓐ				Ⓑ	⑥	†	Ⓐ			†	⚒				†	†
Reims d.	0655	0730	0806	0902	0905	0906	1026	1044	1131	1243	1342	1445	1515	1607	1608	1626	1636	1706**c**	1801	1848	1849	1907	1938	2017	2048	2116
Champagne-Ardenne TGV a.	0708	0743	0818	0914	0917	0917	1038	1056	1143	1251	1354	1457	1529	1619	1620	1639	1648	1718	1813	1901	1903	1919	1949	2029	2100	2128

	⚒	Ⓐ	⑥	Ⓐ	Ⓒ					Ⓐ					†	Ⓐ			⑥	Ⓑ		Ⓐ	Ⓒ	▲	†	†
Champagne-Ardenne TGV d.	0730	0755	0755	0830	0844	0940	1058	1118	1201	1321	1419	1521	1557	1639	1657	1708	1813	1828	1910	1937	1952	2012	2020	2047	2116	2145
Reims a.	0741	0804	0808	0841	0856	0952	1110	1130	1210	1332	1431	1531	1609	1649	1709	1718	1820	1843	1924	1950	2003	2026	2032	2059	2127	2157

c – 1704 on †; 1705 on ⑥.
‡ – Runs 3 – 4 minutes later on Ⓐ Sept. 30 - Nov. 22.
¶ – 3 – 4 minutes earlier July 20 - Aug. 24.
▲ – 24 – 25 minutes later on ①②④⑤ to July 26 (not June 10), Ⓐ July 29 - Oct. 18, ①②④⑤ from Oct. 21 (not Nov. 1, 11).

392 LONGWY - NANCY / LUXEMBOURG

LONGWY - NANCY

km		Ⓐ	⚒	Ⓐ	Ⓒ	Ⓐ	Ⓒ	⑦	Ⓐ	⑦	
		n				F		rv		z	
0	**Longwy** d.	0532	0647	0847	1047	1247**y**	1647	...	1859	1921	...
16	Longuyon d.	0551	0700	0900	1100	1301**y**	1700	...	1913	1936	...
57	Conflans-Jarny d.	0630	0730	0930	1130	1330	1730	1928	1946	2010	...
100	Pont-à-Mousson .. **384** d.	0700	0800	1000	1200	1400	1800	1958**j**	2016	2040	...
128	**Nancy** **384** a.	0720	0820	1020	1220	1420	1820	2015**j**	2036	2100	...

	Ⓐ		⚒		Ⓒ	Ⓐ	⑦	Ⓐ		⑤
			p			F	e			bv
Nancy **384** d.	0554	...	0839	...	1239	1439	1639	1739	1839	1945
Pont-à-Mousson **384** d.	0613	...	0858	...	1258	1458	1658	1758	1858	2002
Conflans-Jarny d.	0649	...	0931	...	1331	1531	1731	1831	1931	2030
Longuyon d.	0721	...	1000	...	1400	1600**y**	1800	1900	2000	...
Longwy a.	0735	...	1012	...	1412	1612**y**	1812	1912	2012	...

LONGWY - LUXEMBOURG

km		①–⑤	①–⑥	①–⑤	①–⑥	①–⑤	①–⑤		①–⑤	①–⑤	①–⑤	①–⑤	①–⑤	①–⑤	①–⑥	①–⑤	①–⑥
		d	d	d	d	d	d		w	w	d	d	d	d	d	d	d
0	**Longwy** d.	0621	0651	0721	0751	0821	0851	...	1321	1351	1651	1721	1751	1821	1851	1921	1951
8	Rodange 🛃 d.	0629	0659	0729	0759	0829	0859	...	1329	1359	1659	1729	1759	1829	1859	1929	1959
27	**Luxembourg** a.	0657	0727	0757	0827	0857	0927	...	1357	1427	1727	1757	1827	1857	1927	1957	2027

	①–⑤	①–⑥	①–⑤	①–⑥	①–⑤	①–⑤		①–⑤	①–⑤	①–⑤	①–⑤	①–⑤	①–⑤	①–⑥	①–⑤	①–⑥
	d	d	d	d	d	d		w	w	d	d	d	d	d	d	d
Luxembourg d.	0534	0604	0634	0704	0733	0804	...	1204	1234	1604	1633	1704	1733	1804	1833	1904
Rodange 🛃 d.	0602	0632	0702	0732	0802	0832	...	1232	1302	1632	1702	1732	1802	1832	1902	1932
Longwy a.	0609	0639	0709	0739	0809	0839	...	1239	1309	1639	1709	1739	1809	1839	1909	1939

LONGWY - METZ 🚌 service (journey 55 minutes):
From Longwy at 0505 Ⓐ, 0645 Ⓐ, 0745, 0945 ⚒, 1245 ⚒, 1445 Ⓐ, 1545 Ⓐ, 1635 Ⓐ, 1745 ⑥, 1825 Ⓐ 1925 **H** and 1930 **J**.
From Metz at 0630 Ⓐ, 0830 Ⓐ, 0920 ⚒, 1020 †, 1220 ⚒, 1520 Ⓐ, 1620 Ⓐ, 1720 Ⓐ, 1820 Ⓐ, 1920 ⑥, 2020 Ⓐ, 2120 †, 2150 **G** and 2220 ⑤⑥ **k**.

F – Ⓐ June 24 - July 12, Aug. 26 - Sept. 13 and from Oct. 28.
G – ①–④ (not June 10, Aug. 15, Nov. 11).
H – Ⓐ to July 12; Ⓑ from July 15 (not Aug. 15, Nov. 1, 11).
J – † to July 14 (also Aug. 15, Nov. 1, 11).

b – Not July 12 - Aug. 30, Oct. 25, Nov. 1.
d – Not June 10, Aug. 15, Nov. 1.
e – Also June 10.
j – 3 – 4 minutes later until July 7.
k – Not Nov. 1.
n – Not July 15 - Aug. 23.
p – Not ①–⑤ July 15 - Aug. 23.
r – Also June 10, Nov. 11; not July 14 - Aug. 25, Oct. 20, 27.
t – 2035 until July 5.
v – From / to Verdun (Table **393a**).
w – Not June 10, Aug. 15, 26 – 30, Sept. 16 - Oct. 18, Nov. 1, 25 – 29, Dec. 2 – 6.
y – Not Aug. 26 – 30, Nov. 25 – 29, Dec. 2 – 6.
z – Also Aug. 15, Nov. 1.

393 🚌 CHÂLONS EN CHAMPAGNE - VERDUN

km		Ⓐ 🚌	Ⓒ 🚌	Ⓐ 🚌	🚌	Ⓐ 🚌	† 🚌	Ⓒ 🚌	Ⓐ 🚌	
0	**Châlons en Champagne** d.	0818	1020	1222	1420	1820	1936	2030	2040	...
107	**Verdun** a.	1006	1208	1410	1608	2008	2124	2218	2228	...

	Ⓐ 🚌	Ⓒ 🚌		Ⓐ 🚌	🚌		Ⓐ 🚌		🚌
Verdun d.	0542	0612	...	1010	1212	...	1517	...	1817
Châlons en Champagne a.	0730	0800	...	1158	1400	...	1705	...	2005

VERDUN - METZ 393a

Subject to alteration on Aug. 3, 4, 24, 25

km		⑥	Ⓐ	Ⓐ	△	Ⓐn ▲	Ⓐn ▲	Ⓐn	⑥	Ⓐ	⑦m N	†
0	**Verdun** d.	...	0641	0737	1037	1237	1437	1637	1637	1813	1850	1938
40	Conflans-Jarny d.	0625	0720	0815	1115	1315	1515	1715	1715	1850	1927	2015
66	Hagondange . **384** d.	0705	|	0848	1148	1348	1548	1742	1748	|	...	|
84	**Metz** **384** a.	0716	0754z	0901	1207	1414	1601	1814	1801	1924z	...	2049z

	Ⓐ	Ⓐ ▲	⑥	Ⓐn ▲	Ⓐn ▲	Ⓒv	Ⓐ	†	Ⓐ	⑥	⑤f N
Metz **384** d.	0605	0831	0855	1038	1238	1255	1637	1637	1821	1855	...
Hagondange **384** d.	|	0911	0910	1051	1250	1310	1651	1653r	|	1910	...
Conflans-Jarny d.	0643	0943	0943	1123	1323	1343	1724	1730r	1853	1943	2036
Verdun a.	0723	1019	1019	1159	1359	1419	1759	1819	1929	2019	2111

– To/from Nancy (Table **392**).
– Not July 12 - Aug. 30, Oct. 25, Nov. 1. Runs 5 minutes later until July 5.
– Also June 10, Nov. 11; not July 14 - Aug. 25, Oct. 20, 27.
– Not July 15 - Aug. 23.
– 2–3 minutes earlier on Oct. 6, 13, Nov. 10, 11, 17, 24, Dec. 1, 8.

v – Not Oct. 13, 20.
z – 3–7 minutes later until July 24.
▲ – Subject to frequent alteration (including 🚌 substitution for all or part of journey). Please check locally.
△ – Note ▲ (above) applies on Ⓐ.

METZ - FORBACH - SAARBRÜCKEN 394

French holiday dates apply

km		Ⓐn	⑥	Ⓐ	Ⓐ	Ⓐ	⑥	⚒	†	Ⓐn	⑥	Ⓐ⊙	Ⓒ	Ⓐn⊙	Ⓒ	Ⓐ⊙	⚒⊙	Ⓐn	Ⓐ	⑥	†	⚒n		Ⓐ	Ⓐ	Ⓒ
0	**Metz** d.	0538	0608	0636	0704	0738	0738	0838	0838	0938	0938	1038	1038	1138	1238	1238	1338	1438	1538	1538	1538	1638	...	1713	1738	1738
50	St Avold d.	0610	0639	0708	0739	0810	0812	0910	0910	1010	1012	1110	1113	1210	1313	1312	1410	1510	1610	1613	1613	1710	...	1748	1810	1813
70	Forbach a.	0626	0656	0724	0753	0826	0826	0926	0926	1026	1026	1126	1126	1226	1326	1326	1426	1524	1626	1626	1627	1726	...	1802	1826	1826
70	Forbach d.	0632	0659	0732	...	0832	...	0930	0932	1032	...	1130	1132	1232	1330	1332	1432	1532	1632	1632	1632	...	1732	...	1832	1832
81	**Saarbrücken** a.	0642	0709	0742	...	0842	...	0940	0942	1042	...	1140	1142	1242	1340	1342	1442	1542	1642	1642	1642	...	1742	...	1842	1842

	Ⓐ		Ⓑ	Ⓐn	Ⓐ	Ⓒ	Ⓐ	Ⓒ	†	Ⓐ	
etz d.	1813	1838	...	1910	1938	1938	2038	2138	2238	2238	...
t Avold d.	1852	1910	...	1945	2011	2012	2110	2210	2310	2310	...
orbach a.	1905	1926	...	1959	2026	2026	2126	2226	2326	2326	...
orbach d.	...	...	1932	...	2032	2032	2132	...	2331	2345	...
aarbrücken a.	...	...	1942	...	2042	2042	2142	...	2341	2355	...

	Ⓐz	⑥y	②–⑤M	⑥L	Ⓐ	Ⓐ	⚒	Ⓐ	Ⓑ	⑥	Ⓐ	Ⓐ
Saarbrücken d.	0446	0450	0446	0450	...	0616	...	...	0716	0721	...	0816
Forbach a.	0456	0500	0456	0500	...	0626	...	...	0726	0731	...	0826
Forbach d.	0503	0503	0520	0520	0607	...	0633	0707	0733	0733	0801	...
St Avold d.	0518	0518	0535	0535	0620	...	0646	0722	0748	0749	0814	...
Metz a.	0550	0550	0607	0607	0656	...	0720	0756	0820	0820	0846	...

	⚒n	Ⓐ	n	Ⓐ⊙	Ⓐ⊙	Ⓒ	Ⓐn⊙	⑥	⑥	Ⓐ⊙	†	Ⓐ	⑥	Ⓐ	†		Ⓐn	Ⓒ	Ⓐ		Ⓑn	⑥	Ⓑ	Ⓐ	Ⓐ	Ⓐ
aarbrücken d.	...	0921	1016	1116	1221	...	1316	1321	1416	1416	1421	1516	1521	1616	1616	1716	...	1816	1816	1916	2016	2016	2116	...	2225	2325
orbach a.	...	0931	1026	1126	1231	...	1326	1331	1426	1426	1431	1526	1531	1626	1626	1726	...	1826	1826	1926	2026	2026	2126	...	2235	2335
orbach d.	0833	0933	1033	1133	1233	1233	1333	1333	1433	1433	1433	1535	1533	1633	1633	1733	1807	1833	1837	1933	2033	2033	...	2133	...	...
t Avold d.	0848	0948	1048	1148	1247	1247	1348	1348	1446	1448	1447	1549	1547	1648	1646	1748	1822	1846	1852	1948	2048	2046	...	2148	...	...
etz a.	0920	1020	1120	1220	1320	1320	1420	1420	1520	1520	1520	1620	1620	1720	1721	1820	1858	1921	1924	2020	2120	2121	...	2220	...	...

– ⑥ Sept. 7 - Oct. 12 (also July 13, Nov. 30, Dec. 7).
– ②–⑤ Sept. 3 - Oct. 11 (also July 9–12, Nov. 26–29, Dec. 3–6).
– Not Ⓐ July 15 - Aug. 23.

y – Not July 13, Sept. 7 - Oct. 12, Nov. 30, Dec. 7.
z – Not July 9–12, Sept. 3–6, 10–13, 17–20, 24–27, Oct. 1–4, 8–11, Nov. 26–29, Dec. 3–6.
⊙ – Subject to alteration Aug. 26–30, Sept. 16–20, 23–27, Nov. 4–8, 12–15.

STRASBOURG - SAARBRÜCKEN 395

French holiday dates apply

SERVICE FROM SEPTEMBER 1. No rail service July 1 - August 31 (see 🚌 service below).

km		Ⓐ	Ⓐ	⑥	Ⓐ	†	⚒⊡		Ⓐ⊡	⊡¶		Ⓑ⊡¶	Ⓐ	⑥	Ⓑ	Ⓐ	⚒	†	Ⓐ	⑥	Ⓐ	†			
0	**Strasbourg** d.	0545	0645	0745	0745	0845	0945	...	1145	1245	...	1445	1545	1545	1645	1715	1745	1815	1845	1945	1955	2000	...	...	...
71	Diemeringen d.	0638	0736	0836	0837	0937	1036	...	1237	1337	...	1537	1637	1637	1737	1807	1837	1907	1937	2038	2048	2056	...	...	...
97	Sarreguemines 🏛 ▲ a.	0703	0803	0902	0903	1004	1102	...	1303	1403	...	1603	1703	1704	1803	1834	1904	1933	2003	2104	2114	2122	...	...	...
115	**Saarbrücken** Hbf ▲ a.	...	...	0922	0927	1027	...	...	1327	...	...	...	...	1727	...	...	...	...	...	2129	...	...	...	...	...

	Ⓐ	Ⓐ	⚒	Ⓐ	⚒⊡	⑦e	⚒⊡		†	⚒⊡		⑥	†	Ⓐ⊡¶		⑥	Ⓐ⊡	Ⓐ	Ⓑ	Ⓑ	ⒷD	⑥	ⒷC	⑥🚌
aarbrücken Hbf ▲ d.	...	...	...	...	...	0654	...	...	...	0954	...	...	1154	...	...	...	1354	...	...	...	...	1754	...	...
arreguemines 🏛 ▲ d.	0500	0550	0620	0650	0720	0723	0820	...	1020	1022	...	1221	1222	1228	...	1420	1420	1520	1620	1720	1820	1820	1827	1910
iemeringen d.	0523	0613	0644	0714	0744	0745	0844	...	1044	1044	...	1245	1244	1252	...	1444	1444	1544	1644	1744	1843	1844	1851	1941
trasbourg a.	0620f	0707	0737	0808	0837	0838	0937	...	1137	1137	...	1338	1338	1345	...	1537	1537	1637	1737	1837	1937	1937	1945	2115

RAIL REPLACEMENT 🚌 SERVICE JULY 1 - AUGUST 31

km		⑥🚌	†🚌	⑥🚌	⚒🚌		⑥🚌	⑥🚌	†🚌		†🚌	⑤🚌	⑥🚌	†🚌	⑥🚌	⑥🚌	†🚌	Ⓐ🚌	Ⓐ🚌	⑥🚌	Ⓐ🚌	†🚌			
0	**Strasbourg** d.	0740	0845	0945	0945	...	1245	1245	1255	...	1445	1545	1545	1652	1745	1745	1815	1850	1850	1942	1955	2000	...	...	...
71	Diemeringen d.	0911	1016	|	1116	...	|	1416	1426	...	1616	|	1716	1823	|	1916	1946	|	2021	2113	2126	2131	...	...	...
97	Sarreguemines 🏛 ▲ a.	0954	1059	1120	1159	...	1420	1459	1509	...	1659	1720	1759	1906	1820	1959	2029	2025	2104	2156	2209	2214	...	...	...
115	**Saarbrücken** Hbf ▲ a.	1026	1131	...	...	...	...	...	...	...	...	...	1831	...	...	...	...	...	...	2228	...	...	...	...	...

	⑥🚌	†🚌	⑥🚌	⚒🚌		🚌	Ⓐ🚌	⑥🚌		⚒🚌	†🚌		⑥🚌	Ⓐ🚌		†🚌	†🚌	†🚌	†🚌	⑥🚌	†🚌	†🚌		⑥🚌
aarbrücken Hbf ▲ d.	...	0539	...	...	...	...	0837	0930	...	...	1038	...	...	...	...	...	...	...	...	1637	...	...	...	...
arreguemines 🏛 ▲ d.	0509	0611	0618	0709	...	0909	0909	1002	...	1109	1110	...	1309	1409	...	1517	1610	1609	1702	1709	1717	1810	...	1910
emeringen d.	0548	0650	0657	0748	...	0948	0948	|	...	1148	1149	...	1348	1448	...	1556	|	1648	|	1748	1756	|	...	1941
trasbourg a.	0737	0839	0846	0937	...	1137	1137	1137	...	1337	1338	...	1537	1637	...	1745	1745	1837	1837	1937	1945	1945	...	2115

SAARBAHN LIGHT RAIL SERVICE **S1 SARREGUEMINES - SAARBRÜCKEN** ⊖

	⚒	Ⓐ	⚒	Ⓐ				
arreguimes (Bahnhof) d.	0516	0546	0616	0646	0716	hourly ◐	2316	0016
aarbrücken Hbf a.	0545	0615	0645	0715	0745	until	2345	0045

	⚒	Ⓐ	⚒	Ⓐ	⚒	Ⓐ			
Saarbrücken Hbf d.	0440	0510	0540	0610	0640	0710	0740	hourly ◧	2340
Sarreguimes (Bahnhof) a.	0510	0540	0610	0640	0710	0740	0810	until	0010

– To Oct. 20.
– From Oct. 21.
– Also Nov. 1; not Sept. 1.
– 0615 from Oct. 21.

⊡ – Subject to alteration Oct. 21–25, 28–31.
¶ – Timings may vary by up to 4 minutes Sept. 2–6, 9–13.
◐ – Every 30 minutes 0716 - 0916 and 1216 - 2116 on Ⓐ, 0816 - 1816 on ⑥, 1216 - 1816 on †.
◧ – Every 30 minutes 0740 - 0840 and 1140 - 2040 on Ⓐ, 0740 - 1740 on ⑥, 1140 - 1740 on †.
▲ – For additional light rail service Sarreguemines - Saarbrücken see below main table.
⊖ – Operated by Saarbahn (www.saarbahn.de). In Saarbrücken also serves city centre.

STRASBOURG - WISSEMBOURG 396

Additional trains run Strasbourg - Haguenau and v.v.

See Table **918** for connecting trains Wissembourg - Neustadt (Weinstr) and v.v. Certain timings vary by up to 3 minutes until June 30.

km		⚒	Ⓐ	⑥	⑥	†	Ⓐw	⑥	Ⓐw	⑥	Ⓐw	†	⑥	Ⓐw	†	⑥	Ⓐ	†	⚒	†	Ⓐn	Ⓐ	Ⓑ	Ⓑ	⑥	Ⓐ	Ⓐ🚌
0	**Strasbourg** d.	0618t	0735	0751	0848	0921	0935	1055	1121	1205	1251v	1251	1351	1405	1451	1551	1621	1651	1721	1721	1751	1821	1851	1921	1951	2035	...
34	Haguenau d.	0640t	0811	0827	0914	0944	0958	1118	1145	1231	1314	1315	1416	1429	1516	1616	1644	1715	1742	1757	1817	1848	1916j	1948z	2015	2109	2114
66	**Wissembourg** a.	0717	0841h	0853	0941	1010	1025b	1144	1212e	1309	1346b	1341	1442	1456b	1543	1642	1713	1742	1816	1823	1854	1914	1953j	2021z	2048	...	2151

	Ⓐ	Ⓐk	⑥	Ⓐ	⑥	†	Ⓐw	⑥	⑥	Ⓐw	†	†	Ⓐw	⑥	Ⓒ	Ⓐw	⑥	Ⓐw	†	Ⓐ	⑥	Ⓐ	⑥	†	Ⓐ	†
issembourg d.	0607	0640	0641	0730	0744	0844	0848	0948	1037	1040c	1045	1147	1230f	1237	1348r	1402c	1546	1551c	1647	1741	1744	1821	1837	1838	1921	2049
aguenau d.	0643	0714	0715	0804	0813	0915	0917	1014	1104	1106	1114	1214	1302	1303	1414r	1429	1613	1618	1714p	1818	1813	1847	1902	1913	1947	2115
trasbourg a.	0711k	0741	0738	0830	0838	0938	0939	1038	1138	1141	1138	1237	1324	1338	1437	1453	1637	1645	1737p	1845	1838	1909	1937	1937	2009n	2138

– By 🚌 from Haguenau on Sept. 30, Oct. 1–4, 7–11 (arrives 16–41 minutes later).
– By 🚌 to Haguenau on Sept. 30, Oct. 1–4, 7–11 (departs 23–24 minutes **earlier**).
– By 🚌 from Haguenau on Sept. 30, Oct. 1, 3, 4, 7, 8, 10, 11 (a. 1228).
– By 🚌 (d. 1153) to Haguenau on Sept. 30, Oct. 1, 3, 4, 7, 8, 10, 11.
– By 🚌 from Haguenau until Aug. 30 (arrives 0854).
– 4 minutes later on Ⓐ July 1 - Aug. 30. Arrives Wissembourg 1942 on †.
– 2–4 minutes later July 1 - Aug. 30.

n – Not July 1 - Aug. 30.
p – 8–9 minutes later July 7 - Aug. 25.
r – 2 minutes earlier on ⑥ from July 6.
t – 3 minutes later on Ⓐ July 1 - Aug. 30.
v – 1249 Sept. 2–6, 9–13.
w – From Sept. 2.
z – 2–3 minutes earlier on †.

397 PRIVATE TOURIST RAILWAYS

MER DE GLACE - TRAIN DE MONTENVERS

✆ 04.50.53.22.75. www.compagniedumontblanc.fr

From Chamonix (200 metres from SNCF station) to Montenvers 'Mer de Glace' (altitude 1913 metres). Journey 20 minutes.

A cable car takes visitors to the ice grotto inside the glacier (closed Sept. 28 - Dec. 14).

Dec. 15 - Mar. 15: from Chamonix 1000 - 1600; returning until 1630. Runs every 30 mins.

Mar. 17 - Apr. 30: from Chamonix 1000 - 1630; returning until 1700. Runs every 30 mins.

May 1 - July 12: from Chamonix 0830 - 1630 ‡; returning until 1700. Runs every 30 mins.

July 13 - Aug. 25: from Chamonix 0800 - 1800; returning until 1830. Runs every 20 – 30 mins.

Aug. 26 - Sept. 8: from Chamonix 0830 - 1700 ‡; returning until 1730. Runs every 30 mins.

Sept. 9 – 29: from Chamonix 0830 - 1630 ‡; returning until 1700. Runs every 30 mins.

Sept. 30 - Oct. 18: CLOSED

Oct. 19 - Dec. 13: from Chamonix 1000, 1130, 1300, 1400, 1500, 1600; returning 1100, 1200, 1330, 1430, 1530, 1630.

‡ – Departure from Chamonix at 0900 (also 0930 return service) runs if sufficient demand.

PANORAMIQUE DES DÔMES

Electric rack railway from the foot to the summit of Le puy de Dôme. Journey: 15 minutes.
No service Mar. 25 – 29 and Oct. 14 – 18. www.panoramiquedesdomes.fr

To Mar. 24 and from Nov. 6 (does **not** run on ①②): Hourly departures 1000 - 1700, returning 1030 - 1730.

Mar. 30 - June 30 and Sept. 2 - Nov. 3: Departures every 40 minutes 0900 - 1900, returning 0920 - 1920.

July 1 - Sept. 1: Departures every 20 minutes 0900 - 2040, returning 0920 - 2100.

TRAMWAY DU MONT BLANC

The highest rack railway in France. www.compagniedumontblanc.fr
✆ 04.50.53.22.75.

Winter season : December 22, 2018 - March 31, 2019

Runs from St Gervais Le Fayet (opposite SNCF station) to Bellevue (altitude 1794 metres). Journey 60 minutes.

Mondays to Fridays (not school holidays):

Depart St Gervais : 0900, 1100, 1310, 1430.

Depart Bellevue : 1000, 1200, 1430, 1620 (to Feb. 8), 1640 (from Feb. 9).

Saturdays and Sundays (also during school holidays):

Depart St Gervais : 0900, 1000, 1100, 1310, 1410, 1510.

Depart Bellevue : 1000, 1100, 1200, 1410, 1510, 1620 (to Feb. 8), 1640 (from Feb. 9).

Summer season : June 15 - September 22, 2019

From St Gervais Le Fayet (opposite SNCF station) to Nid d'Aigle (altitude 2372 metres). Journey 70 – 80 minutes.

June 15 - July 12 and August 26 - September 22

Depart St Gervais : 0820, 0930, 1030, 1100, 1220, 1330, 1430, 1510.

Depart Nid d'Aigle : 0935, 1040, 1155, 1225, 1335, 1445, 1600, 1700.

July 13 - August 25 :

Depart St Gervais : 0720, 0830, 0930, 1000, 1110, 1220, 1330, 1400, 1520, 1620, 1700.

Depart Nid d'Aigle : 0835, 0940, 1050, 1125, 1230, 1340, 1455, 1525, 1640, 1755, 1830.

398 PARIS - PARIS AÉROPORTS

See page 31 for plan of central Paris

CHARLES DE GAULLE - PARIS

VAL shuttle train : air terminals - RER / TGV station.

Roissyrail (RER line B) : Aéroport Charles de Gaulle 2 TGV - Paris Châtelet les Halles. Frequent service 0450 - 2400.

Journey time from Charles de Gaulle :

Gare du Nord	35 minutes
Châtelet les Halles ★	38 minutes
St Michel Notre Dame	40 minutes
Antony (for Orly , see middle panel)	58 minutes

★ Cross - platform interchange with *RER* for Gare de Lyon.

ORLY - PARIS (*VAL + RER B*)

VAL light rail : Orly Sud - Orly Ouest - Antony (7 minutes). Frequent service ① - ⑤: 0600 - 2230; ⑦: 0700 - 2300. Cross platform interchange with RER line B (below).

RER line B : Antony - Paris. Frequent service 0510 - 0010.

Journey time from Antony :

St Michel Notre Dame	20 minutes
Châtelet les Halles ☆	25 minutes
Gare du Nord	29 minutes

☆ Interchange with *RER* for Gare de Lyon.

ORLY - PARIS (*Orlyrail*)

🚌 : Orly (Ouest and Sud) - Pont de Rungis Aéroport d'Orl station. Frequent shuttle service.

RER line C : Pont de Rungis Aéroport d'Orly - Paris. Ever 15 minutes approx. 0500 - 2330 (0530 - 2400 from Paris).

Journey time from Pont de Rungis Aéroport d'Orly :

Paris Austerlitz	24 minutes
St Michel Notre Dame	27 minutes
Musée d'Orsay	31 minutes
Champ de Mars Tour Eiffel	39 minutes

399 🚌 SAVOIE SKI BUSES

Winter 2018 / 2019

A network of bus services links the airports at Genève and Lyon with most ski resorts in the Savoie area during the ski season. A selection of services is shown below but details should be confirme before booking. Further details of services from Genève can be found on the Genève bus station website www.gare-routiere.com where online bookings can be made; for telephone bookings ✆ +41 22 732 02 30. Bookings can also be made through the websites and offices of the operators and at tourist offices in the ski resorts.

A minimum of one hour should be allowed between aircraft and bus and vice versa. Reservation is recommended or compulsory, and in most cases journeys from the resort to the airport should b confirmed at the local tourist office or bus station (generally 24 or 48 hours in advance) when timings will be given. Most services do not operate on December 25.

🚌 GENÈVE AÉROPORT - ST GERVAIS - CHAMONIX

Departures from Genève Gare Routière and Genève (Arrivals terminal) to St Gervais (Gare SNCF) and Chamonix Sud (Ave Courmayeur) at least six times daily. Journey 2 hours 10 mins. Operator: www.ouibus.com. Connections at St Gervais Gare SNCF are available to / from St Gervais (Le Pont), Combloux, Megève, Praz sur Arly and Les Contamines.

🚌 GENÈVE AÉROPORT - TARENTAISE SKI RESORTS

🚌 Genève (Secteur International) - Moûtiers - Aime - Bourg St Maurice - Tignes - Val d'Isère. Journey approx 4 hours.

Departures Dec. 1, 2018 to Apr. 14, 2019: 3 journeys on ①–⑤, 8 journeys on ⑥, 4 journeys on ⑦. Reservations : www.altibus.com

Connections (with through fares) are available to most ski resorts in the area, including Pralognan, Brides les Bains, St Martin de Belleville, Les Ménuires, Val Thorens, Méribel, La Tania, Le Praz Courchevel, Plagne and Les Arcs. Additional direct services are operated by Voyages Loyet to St Martin de Belleville, Les Ménuires and Val Thorens.

🚌 OTHER SERVICES FROM GENÈVE AÉROPORT ✈

GRENOBLE See Table **364a** for daily services to Grenoble. Connections available to l'Alpe d'Huez, Stations de l'Isère, Briancon and Serre Chevalier. Reservations: www.aerocar.fr

AVORIAZ via Thonon (connections for Abondance and Châtel), Saint Jean d'Aulps, Morzine. Runs on ⑥ Dec. 22 - Apr. 6. Reservations www.sat-autocars.com

LA CLUSAZ via Le Grand Bornand, St Jean de Sixt. Runs on ⑤⑥⑦ during ski season. Operator: Ballanfat Autocars.

For further ski resorts see www.altibus.com

🚌 LYON ✈ / CHAMBÉRY ✈ - SAVOIE SKI RESORTS

Bus services operate from Lyon St Exupéry airport and Chambéry airport to most Savoie ski resorts from late December to mid April. Book on-line at www.altibus.com or ✆ +33 479 68 32 9
Reservations are compulsory, at least 48 hours in advance.

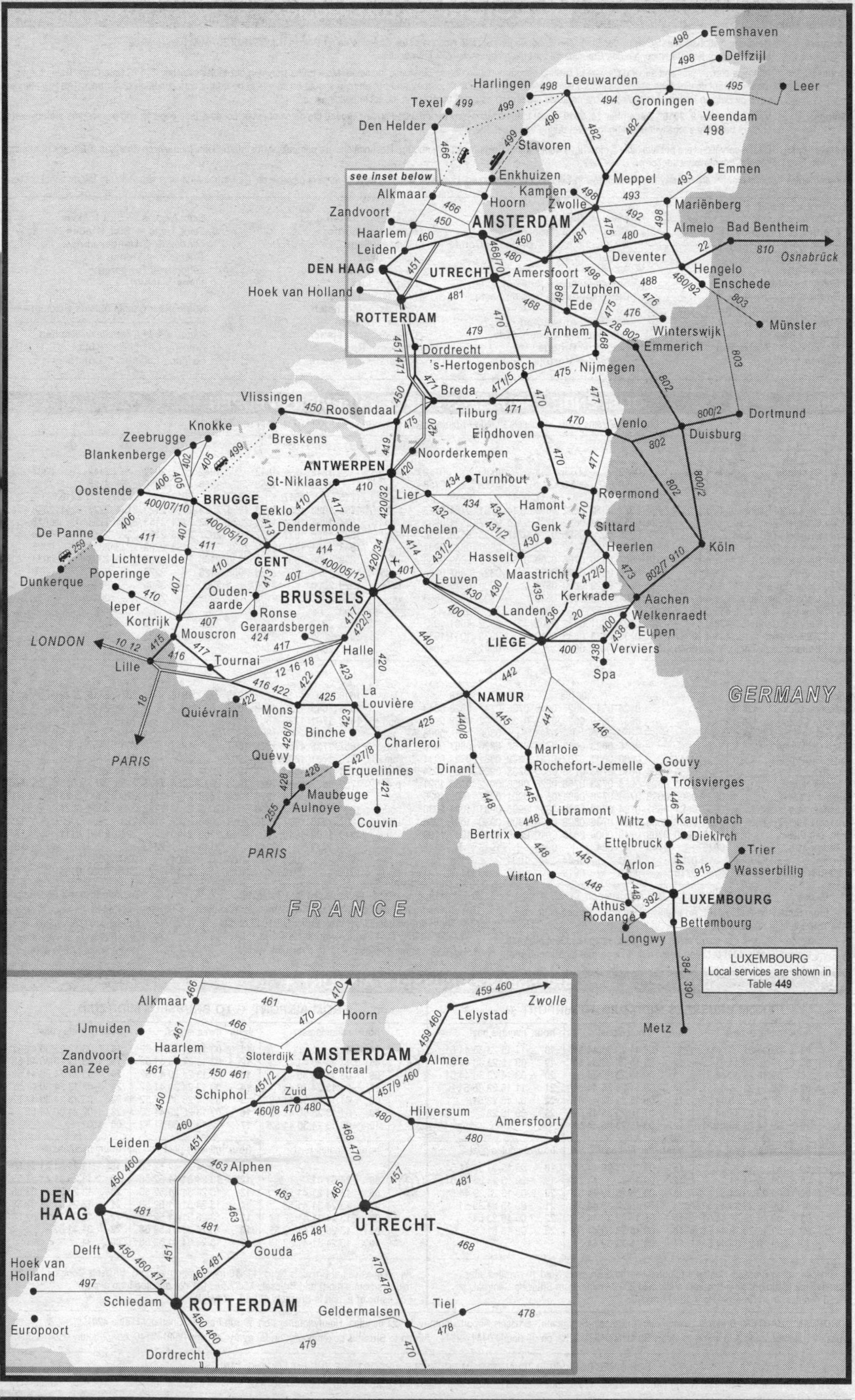
see inset below
Eemshaven
Delfzijl
Harlingen
Leeuwarden
Groningen
Leer
Texel
Den Helder
Veendam
Stavoren
Enkhuizen
Emmen
Meppel
Alkmaar
Hoorn
Kampen
Zwolle
Mariënberg
Zandvoort
AMSTERDAM
Almelo
Bad Bentheim
Haarlem
Leiden
Osnabrück
DEN HAAG
UTRECHT
Amersfoort
Deventer
Hengelo
Enschede
Hoek van Holland
Zutphen
Ede
Münster
ROTTERDAM
Arnhem
Winterswijk
Emmerich
Dordrecht
's-Hertogenbosch
Nijmegen
Vlissingen
Roosendaal
Breda
Tilburg
Dortmund
Knokke
Breskens
Eindhoven
Venlo
Duisburg
Zeebrugge
Noorderkempen
Blankenberge
ANTWERPEN
St-Niklaas
Turnhout
Oostende
Lier
Hamont
BRUGGE
Eeklo
Roermond
Dendermonde
Genk
De Panne
Mechelen
Sittard
Heerlen
Köln
Lichtervelde
GENT
Hasselt
Dunkerque
Poperinge
Maastricht
Oudenaarde
Leuven
BRUSSELS
Ieper
Ronse
Kerkrade
Aachen
Kortrijk
Geraardsbergen
Landen
Welkenraedt
LONDON
Mouscron
Eupen
Lille
Tournai
Halle
LIÈGE
Verviers
Spa
Quiévrain
Mons
La Louvière
NAMUR
GERMANY
Binche
Charleroi
Marloie
PARIS
Quévy
Rochefort-Jemelle
Gouvy
Erquelinnes
Dinant
Troisvierges
Maubeuge
Aulnoye
Couvin
Libramont
Wiltz
Kautenbach
PARIS
Bertrix
Diekirch
Ettelbruck
Trier
Arlon
Wasserbillig
Virton
FRANCE
Athus
LUXEMBOURG
Rodange
Bettembourg
Longwy
LUXEMBOURG
Local services are shown in
Table 449
Metz
Alkmaar
Hoorn
Lelystad
Zwolle
IJmuiden
Haarlem
Zandvoort
aan Zee
Sloterdijk
AMSTERDAM
Centraal
Almere
Schiphol
Zuid
Hilversum
Amersfoort
Leiden
Alphen
DEN
HAAG
UTRECHT
Gouda
Delft
Hoek van
Holland
Schiedam
ROTTERDAM
Geldermalsen
Tiel
Europoort
Dordrecht

BELGIUM and LUXEMBOURG

Operators: **Belgium**: Nationale Maatschappij der Belgische Spoorwegen / Société Nationale des Chemins de fer Belges (NMBS / SNCB). www.belgianrail.be
Luxembourg: Société Nationale des Chemins de fer Luxembourgeois (CFL). www.cfl.lu

Services: All trains convey first and second classes of seating accommodation unless otherwise indicated. Most trains shown in our tables are classified *IC* (InterCity). Trains for two or more different destinations are sometimes linked together for part of their journey and passengers should be careful to board the correct portion of the train. The line numbers used by Belgian Railways in their public timetables are shown as small numbers in the table headings.

Timings: Valid **December 9, 2018 - December 14, 2019**. Local train services may be amended on and around the dates of public holidays (see page 4), and passengers are advised to confirm train times locally if planning to travel during these periods.

Reservations: Seat reservations are not available for journeys wholly within Belgium or Luxembourg. Reservations are compulsory for international journeys on *Thalys* or *ICE* trains (for timings see the International section).

Supplements: Supplements are not payable for journeys in Belgium or Luxembourg. However, a higher level of fares is payable on *Thalys* trains (timings shown in the International section).

Dutch-language forms of some **French-language** Belgian names

Aarlen = **Arlon**
Aat = **Ath**
Bergen = **Mons**
Doornik = **Tournai**
Duinkerke = **Dunkerque** (France)
Hoei = **Huy**
Luik = **Liège**
Moeskroen = **Mouscron**
Namen = **Namur**
Nijvel = **Nivelles**
Rijsel = **Lille** (France)
's Gravenbrakel = **Braine le Comte**
Wezet = **Visé**

French-language forms of some **Dutch-language** Belgian names

Anvers = **Antwerpen**
Audenarde = **Oudenaarde**
Bruges = **Brugge**
Courtrai = **Kortrijk**
Dixmude = **Diksmuide**
Furnes = **Veurne**
Gand = **Gent**
Hal = **Halle**
La Panne = **De Panne**
Lierre = **Lier**
Louvain = **Leuven**
Malines = **Mechelen**
Menin = **Menen**
Ostende = **Oostende**
Renaix = **Ronse**
Roulers = **Roeselare**
Saint Nicolas = **Sint Niklaas**
Saint Trond = **Sint Truiden**
Termonde = **Dendermonde**
Tirlemont = **Tienen**
Tongres = **Tongeren**
Ypres = **Ieper**

Some other places outside Belgium

Aken / Aix la Chapelle = **Aachen**
Keulen / Cologne = **Köln**
Londen / Londres = **London**

400 OOSTENDE - BRUSSELS - LIÈGE - VERVIERS - EUPEN

Lines 50a, 36, 37

For *Thalys* trains Paris - Brussels - Liège - Köln and *ICE* trains Brussels - Köln - Frankfurt see Table **21**

km			Ⓐ		Ⓐ		Ⓐ	Ⓐ ♠		Ⓐ ⊡			Ⓐ		Ⓐ		Ⓐ		Ⓐ		Ⓐ	△	Ⓐ	△	
0	**Oostende** ▶ d.	...	...	0442	...	0535r	...	...	0636r	...	0742		...	1742	...	1842	...	1942	...	2042	...	2142	...	2307	...
22	Brugge ▷ d.	...	...	0458	...	0551r	...	...	0652r	...	0758		...	1758	...	1858	...	1958	...	2058	...	2158	...	2323	...
	Kortrijk **410** d.	...	0417	|	0517	|	0617	0641	|	0715	|	and	1715	|	1817	|	1917	|	2018	|	2117	|	2216	|	...
62	Gent Sint-Pieters ▷ d.	...	0454	0523	0554	0622	0655	0714	0721	0754	0823	at	1754	1823	1854	1923	1954	2023	2054	2123	2154	2223	2251	2348	...
114	**Brussels** Midi / Zuid ▷ a.	...	0524	0553	0624	0652	0725	0744	0752	0824	0853	the	1824	1853	1924	1953	2024	2053	2124	2153	2224	2253	...	0018	...
114	**Brussels** Midi / Zuid d.	...	0527	0556	0628	0655	0728	0747	0755	0828	0856	same	1828	1856	1927	1957	2027	2057	2128	2157	2228	2257	...	0020	...
116	Brussels Central d.	...	0532	0601	0633	0700	0733	0752	0800	0833	0901	minutes	1833	1901	1932	2002	2032	2102	2133	2202	2233	2302	...	0025	...
118	Brussels Nord d.	...	0538	0607	0639	0706	0739	0756	0806	0839	0908	past	1839	1908	1938	2008	2038	2108	2137	2208	2237	2308	...	0031	...
148	Leuven d.	...	0555	0626	0657	0726	0757	♤	0827	0857	0926	each	1857	1926	1955	2026	2055	2126	♤	2226	♤	2327	...	0050	...
221	**Liège** Guillemins a.	...	...	0702	0729	0800	0829	...	0900	0929	1000	hour	1929	2000	...	2100	...	2200	...	2300	...	0018	...	0141	...
221	**Liège** Guillemins d.	...	...	0704	0735	0803	0836	...	0903	0934	1003	until	1934	2003	...	2103	...	2203	...	2303	...	0021	...	...	...
241	Pepinster **438** d.	...	...	|	0752	|	0854	...	|	0953	|		1953	|	...	|	...	|	...	|	...	|	...	...	...
245	**Verviers** Central **438** d.	...	...	0723	0801	0822	0902	...	0922	1001	1022		2001	2022	...	2122	...	2222	...	2322	...	0040	...	...	...
258	Welkenraedt **438** d.	0637	...	0736	0813	0835	0912	...	0935	1011	1035		2011	2035	...	2135	...	2233	...	2333	...	0050	...	...	...
264	**Eupen** a.	0645	...	0743	...	0842	...	...	0942	...	1042		...	2042	...	2142	...	...	...	...	...	...	...	...	...

	Ⓐ	△	Ⓐ	•	Ⓐ	•	Ⓐ	•	Ⓐ	•	Ⓐ ⊙		•	Ⓐ	•	Ⓐ	•	Ⓐ	•	Ⓐ	•	•	△		Ⓐ ♥
Eupen d.	...	...	...	...	...	0618a	...	0718	...	0818	...		1618	...	1718	...	1818	...	1918	...	2018	2118	2222		...
Welkenraedt **438** d.	...	...	...	0524	0547	0627	0649	0726	0747	0826	0849		1626	1649	1726	1749	1826	...	1926	...	2026	2126	2230		...
Verviers Central **438** d.	...	...	...	0537	0559	0639	0701	0739	0802	0839	0901	and	1639	1701	1739	1801	1839	...	1939	...	2039	2139	2242		...
Pepinster **438** d.	...	...	...	|	0606	|	0708	|	0809	|	0908	at	|	1708	|	1808	|	...	|	...	|	|	|		...
Liège Guillemins a.	...	...	...	0555	0623	0657	0725	0757	0826	0857	0925	the	1657	1725	1757	1825	1857	...	1957	...	2057	2157	2301		...
Liège Guillemins d.	...	0443	...	0600	0631	0702	0731	0802	0831	0902	0931	same	1702	1731	1802	1831	1902	...	2002	...	2102	2202	2306	A	...
Leuven d.	♤	0534	0604	0635	0703	0735	0806	0835	0905	0934	1004	minutes	1734	1804	1834	1904	1934	2004	2034	2104	2134	2234	2358	L	♤
Brussels Nord d.	0521	0555	0623	0655	0723	0756	0826	0856	0922	0955	1021	past	1755	1821	1855	1921	1955	2023	2055	2123	2155	2255	0018	S	1704
Brussels Central d.	0526	0600	0628	0700	0728	0801	0831	0901	0927	1000	1026	each	1800	1826	1900	1925	2000	2028	2100	2128	2200	2300	0023	O	1709
Brussels Midi / Zuid a.	0530	0604	0632	0704	0732	0805	0835	0905	0931	1004	1030	hour	1804	1830	1904	1930	2004	2032	2104	2132	2204	2304	0027		1713
Brussels Midi / Zuid ▷ d.	0536	0607	0636	0707	0736	0808	0838	0908	0936	1007	1036	until	1807	1836	1907	1936	2007	2036	2107	2136	2207	2307	0029		1715
Gent Sint-Pieters ▷ d.	0609	0640	0709	0740	0809	0840	0910	0940	1009	1040	1109		1840	1909	1940	2009	2040	2109	2140	2209	2240	2340	0111		1748
Kortrijk **410** a.	0643	|	0743	|	0843	|	0944	|	1043	|	1143		|	1943	|	2043	|	2143	|	2243	|	|	|		1819
Brugge ▷ d.	...	0704	...	0804	...	0904	...	1004	...	1104	...		1904	...	2004	...	2104	...	2204	...	2304	0006	0136		...
Oostende ▶ a.	...	0718	...	0818	...	0918	...	1018	...	1118	...		1918	...	2018	...	2118	...	2218	...	2318	0020	0150		...

a – Ⓐ only.
r – Runs 6 - 7 minutes later on Ⓒ.
♠ – From Poperinge (Table **410**). An additional journey runs one hour later.
♥ – To Poperinge (Table **410**).
▶ – Oostende - Brugge: see also Tables **407**, **410**; Oostende - Gent also **410**.
△ – Via Landen (Table **430**) between Leuven and Liège (not high-speed line).
▷ – For Brugge - Gent - Brussels see also Table **405**.
⊡ – Trains from Kortrijk at 0815 and 1015 terminate at Leuven.
⊙ – There are no trains from Welkenraedt at 1049 or 1349 (instead they start from Leuven at 1204 and 1504).
• – On Ⓒ certain timings are up to 5 minutes earlier.
♤ – To / from Brussels Schaarbeek.

For slower trains Brussels - Liège via Landen see Table ***430***.

For Aachen change at Verviers or Welkenraedt (Table ***438****).*

401 BRUSSELS - BRUSSELS AIRPORT ✈

Line 36c

FROM BRUSSELS MIDI / ZUID TO AIRPORT ✈

	hour	minutes past	hour	minutes past	hour	minutes past
Ⓐ	**04**	09 36 51	**11**	09 14 23 36 44 51	**18**	11 15 23 36 44 51
	05	09 15 36 44 51	**12**	09 15 23 36 44 51	**19**	09 15 23 36 44 51
	06	09 15 23 36 44 51	**13**	09 15 23 36 44 51	**20**	09 14 23 36 44 51
	07	06 15 23 36 44 51	**14**	09 14 23 36 44 51	**21**	11 15 23 36 51
	08	06 15 23 36 44 53	**15**	09 15 23 32 44 51	**22**	09 15 23 51
	09	09 15 23 36 44 51	**16**	07 15 23 35 45 52	**23**	09 15 23
	10	09 14 23 36 44 51	**17**	09 15 23 36 44 51		
	hour	minutes past	hour	minutes past	hour	minutes past
Ⓒ	**04**	51	**11**	09 15 23 39 44 51	**18**	09 15 23 39 44 51
	05	09 39 44 51	**12**	09 15 23 39 44 51	**19**	09 15 23 39 44 51
	06	09 23 39 44 51	**13**	09 15 23 39 44 51	**20**	09 15 23 39 44 51
	07	09 15 23 39 44 51	**14**	09 15 23 39 44 51	**21**	09 15 23 39 51
	08	09 15 23 39 44 51	**15**	09 15 23 39 44 51	**22**	09 15 23 51
	09	09 15 23 39 44 51	**16**	09 15 23 39 44 51	**23**	09 15 51
	10	09 15 23 39 44 51	**17**	09 15 23 39 44 51		

All services call at Brussels Central 4 minutes later and Brussels Nord 10 minutes later.
Journey time to airport: from Brussels Midi / Zuid 20 - 27 mins, from Brussels Centraal 16 - 23 minutes, from Brussels Nord 10 - 17 minutes.

FROM AIRPORT ✈ TO BRUSSELS MIDI / ZUID

	hour	minutes past	hour	minutes past	hour	minutes past
Ⓐ	**04**	41	**11**	03 13 24 30 41 52	**18**	03 13 25 30 41 52
	05	13 24 30 41	**12**	03 13 24 30 41 52	**19**	03 13 25 30 41 52
	06	03 13 24 30 41	**13**	03 13 24 30 41 52	**20**	03 13 24 30 41 52
	07	01 13 24 30 41	**14**	03 13 24 30 41 52	**21**	03 13 24 30 41 52
	08	01 14 24 30 41 52	**15**	03 13 25 30 41 52	**22**	03 13 24 30 41 52
	09	01 13 25 30 41 52	**16**	02 13 25 29 41 52	**23**	02 24 30 41 52
	10	03 13 24 30 41 52	**17**	02 13 25 30 41 52	**00**	02
	hour	minutes past	hour	minutes past	hour	minutes past
Ⓒ			**11**	13 24 31 41 52 58	**18**	13 25 31 41 52 58
	05	24 31 41	**12**	13 24 31 41 52 58	**19**	13 25 31 41 52 58
	06	13 24 31 41 58	**13**	13 24 31 41 52 58	**20**	13 24 31 41 52 58
	07	13 24 31 41 58	**14**	13 24 31 41 52 58	**21**	13 24 31 41 52 58
	08	13 24 31 41 52 58	**15**	13 25 31 41 52 58	**22**	13 24 31 41 52 58
	09	13 25 31 41 52 58	**16**	13 24 31 41 52 58	**23**	31 41 52
	10	13 24 31 41 52 58	**17**	13 24 31 41 52 58	**00**	31

All services call at Brussels Nord (11 - 18 minutes from airport), Brussels Centraal (16 - 23 minutes from airport) and Brussels Midi / Zuid (21 - 28 minutes from airport).
Full name of airport is Brussels Airport - Zaventem.

EUROPEAN QUARTER: Brussels Luxembourg - Brussels Schumann - Brussels Airport. Journey 18 - 21 minutes. Hourly journeys on Ⓐ run from / to Charleroi (Table **420**).
Brussels Luxembourg to Airport: on Ⓐ every 30 mins 0652 – 2252, on Ⓒ hourly 0441 – 2341. Airport to Brussels Luxembourg: on Ⓐ every 30 mins 0546 – 2146, on Ⓒ hourly 0604 – 2304.

FOR DIRECT SERVICES TO AND FROM BRUSSELS AIRPORT SEE THE FOLLOWING TABLES:
Aalst **412**, Antwerpen **420** / **432**, Brugge **405**, Charleroi **420**, Denderleeuw **412**, Gent **405**, Hasselt **432**, Kortrijk **407**, Leuven **430** / **432**, Mechelen **432**, Mons **422**, Namur **440**, Tournai **417**.

Line 50a

ZEEBRUGGE - BRUGGE 402

km			Ⓐ	ⒶN	Ⓐ	Ⓐ		Ⓐ	Ⓐ	ⒶN	Ⓐ	Ⓐ	Ⓐ	Ⓐ			Ⓒ	Ⓒ	Ⓒ	Ⓒ	Ⓒ	Ⓒ	Ⓒ	
0	Zeebrugge Strand ❦ d.	Ⓐ	...	...	...	...	and	...	...	...	...	...	...	...	...	Ⓒ	0806	1006	1206	1406	1606	1806	2006	...
0	Zeebrugge Dorp ❦ d.		0706	0732	0806	0906	hourly	1506	1606	1632	1706	1806	1906	2006	...		|	|	|	|	|	|	|	...
15	Brugge a.		0725	0752	0825	0925	until	1526	1625	1652	1725	1825	1925	2025	...		0825	1025	1225	1425	1625	1825	2025	...

		Ⓐ	ⒶN	Ⓐ	Ⓐ		Ⓐ	Ⓐ	ⒶN	Ⓐ	Ⓐ	Ⓐ				Ⓒ	Ⓒ	Ⓒ	Ⓒ	Ⓒ	Ⓒ	Ⓒ	
Brugge d.	Ⓐ	0636	0706	0736	0836	and	1536	1636	1716	1736	1836	1936	...	...	Ⓒ	0736	0936	1136	1336	1536	1736	1936	...
Zeebrugge Dorp ❦ a.		0655	0722	0755	0855	hourly	1555	1655	1736	1755	1855	1955	...	...		|	|	|	|	|	|	|	...
Zeebrugge Strand ❦ a.		...	...	...	...	until	...	...	...	...	...	...	...	...		0756	0956	1156	1356	1556	1756	1956	...

N – Not Dec. 24 - Jan. 4, Apr. 8-22, July 1 - Aug. 30.
❦ – On Ⓐ July 1 - Aug. 30 trains serve Zeebrugge Strand not Zeebrugge Dorp.

Most trains continue beyond Brugge as stopping services to Gent (not shown).
Change at Brugge for Brussels and faster service to Gent (Tables ***400*** */* ***405****).*

Line 50a

KNOKKE and BLANKENBERGE - BRUGGE - GENT - BRUSSELS 405

For additional trains Brugge - Gent - Brussels see Table **400**. For Brugge - Gent (- Antwerpen) see Table **410**.

km		Ⓐ	Ⓐ		Ⓐ		Ⓐ	Ⓒ	Ⓐ		Ⓐ	Ⓐ	Ⓒ	Ⓐ		Ⓐ ◧	Ⓒ			Ⓐ	Ⓒ			
0	**Knokke** d.	...	...	...	0506	...	0606	...	0640	...	...	0706	0706	0740	...	0806	0806	and	...	2006	2006	...	2121	2221
•	Blankenberge d.	...	...	...	|	0552a	|	...	|	0652a	0707	|	|	|	0752	|	|	at	1952	|	|	2052	|	|
22	Brugge a.	...	...	...	0528	0605a	0628	...	0702	0705a	0720	0728	0728	0802	0805	0828	0828	the	2005	2028	2028	2105	2143	2243
22	Brugge d.	0405	0430	0508	0531	0608	0631	...	...	0708	...	0731	0731	...	0808	0831	0831	same	2008	2031	2031	2108	...	...
62	**Gent** Sint-Pieters d.	0437	0500	0537	0600	0638	0700	0701	...	0738	...	0803	0801	...	0837	0900	0901	minutes	2037	2100	2101	2137	...	...
119	**Brussels** Midi / Zuid a.	0508	0530	0607	0630	0708	0730	0731	...	0808	...	0833	0831	...	0907	0930	0931	past	2107	2130	2131	2207	...	...
121	Brussels Central a.	0515	0540	0615	0640	0715	0740	0743	...	0815	...	0840	0843	...	0915	0940	0943	each	2115	2140	2143	2215	...	...
123	Brussels Nord a.	0520	0545	0620	0645	0720	0745	0748	...	0820	...	0845	0848	...	0920	0945	0948	hour	2120	2145	2148	2220	...	...
135	**Brussels Airport** ✈ a.	▽	0557	▽	0657	▽	0759	0802	...	▽	...	0859	0902	...	▽	0957	1002	until	▽	2157	2202	▽	...	...

	Ⓐ	Ⓐ		Ⓐ d	Ⓐ k	Ⓐ d	Ⓒ	Ⓐ	Ⓒ	Ⓐ	Ⓒ	Ⓐ ❦			Ⓒ	Ⓐ		Ⓒ	Ⓐ		Ⓐ		Ⓐ	Ⓒ
Brussels Airport ✈ d.	...	...	...	▽	0603	▽	0658	0701	▽	▽	0758	0801	▽	and	1958	2003	▽	2058	2103	▽	2203	▽	2302	▽
Brussels Nord d.	...	...	...	0540	0615	0640	0712	0715	0740	0744	0812	0815	0840	at	2012	2015	2040	2112	2115	2140	2215	2240	2315	2340
Brussels Central d.	...	...	...	0545	0620	0645	0717	0720	0745	0749	0817	0820	0845	the	2017	2020	2045	2117	2120	2145	2220	2245	2320	2345
Brussels Midi / Zuid d.	...	...	...	0553	0629	0653	0726	0729	0752	0755	0826	0828	0853	same	2026	2028	2053	2126	2129	2153	2230	2252	2332	2352
Gent Sint-Pieters d.	...	...	...	0626	0702	0726	0802	0802	0824	0829	0902	0902	0926	minutes	2102	2102	2126	2202	2202	2226	2302	2326	0003	0024
Brugge a.	...	...	...	0651	0730	0751	0830	0830	0849	0854	0930	0930	0951	past	2130	2130	2151	2230	2230	2251	2330	2351	0030	0049
Brugge d.	0533	0554	0633	0654	0733	0754	0833	0833	0852	0856	0933	0933	0954	each	2133	2133	2154	2233	2233	2252c	...	...	...	...
Blankenberge a.	|	0607	|	0707	|	0807	|	|	0905	0909	|	|	1007	hour	|	|	2207	|	|	2305c	...	...	...	...
Knokke a.	0554	...	0654	...	0754	...	0854	0854	...	...	0954	0954	...	until	2154	2154	...	2254	2254	...	...	...	...	...

a – Ⓐ only.
c – Ⓒ only.
d – Also Brugge - Blankenberge on Ⓒ (d. 0652, 0752).
k – Runs daily Brugge - Knokke.

• – Blankenburg - Brugge: *15 km*.
▽ – To / from Leuven, Hasselt / Genk (Table **430**).
◧ – No journeys on Ⓐ at 1006, 1106 (local trains run Knokke to Brugge at 1005, 1106).

❦ – 1203Ⓐ and 1303Ⓐ from Brussels Airport require a change at Brugge for Knokke.
Additional local trains: Blankenberge - Brugge 1708Ⓐ, 2152, 2252; Brugge - Blankenberge 0454Ⓐ, 1627Ⓐ.

De Lijn 'Kusttram'

KNOKKE - OOSTENDE - DE PANNE (Coastal Tramway) 406

KNOKKE railway station - **OOSTENDE** railway station *Journey 63 mins*

Apr. 6 - June 30: 0458⚒, 0558, 0658, 0730, 0745Ⓐ, 0758⚒, 0825, 0840⚒, 0855, 0910 and every 15 minutes until 1855, 1920, 1940, 2005, 2026, 2126, 2226, 2326.

July 1 - Aug. 31: 0458⚒, 0558, 0658, 0729, 0749, 0759 and every 10 minutes until 2009, 2024, 2054, 2124, 2154, 2224, 2254, 2324, 2354, 0024**N**.

Calls at Heist (+6 mins), Zeebrugge (+13 mins), Blankenberge (+25 mins).

OOSTENDE railway station - **DE PANNE** railway station *Journey 79 mins*

Apr. 6 - June 30: 0505⚒, 0605⚒, 0700⚒, 0710, 0735, 0750⚒, 0805, 0820, 0835, 0850, 0910, 0930 and every 15 minutes until 1830, 1900, 1930, 2000, 2030, 2130, 2230, 2330.

July 1 - Aug. 31: 0505⚒, 0605, 0632, 0705, 0720, 0735, 0745 and every 10 minutes until 1915, 1935, 1955, 2015, 2035, 2055, 2115, 2130, 2200, 2230, 2300, 2330, 0000**N**, 0030**N**.

Calls at Middelkerke (+23 mins), Nieuwpoort (+41 mins), Koksijde (+60 mins).

DE PANNE railway station - **OOSTENDE** railway station *Journey 79 mins*

Apr. 6 - June 30: 0419⚒, 0519⚒, 0619, 0712, 0739⚒, 0816, 0831, 0846⚒, 0901 and every 15 minutes until 1746, 1803, 1819, 1836, 1854, 1906, 1924, 1949, 2024, 2124, 2224, 2324.

July 1 - Aug. 31: 0419⚒, 0519, 0619, 0712, 0729; 0749, 0809, 0819 and every 10 minutes until 2009, 2024, 2044, 2114, 2144, 2214, 2244, 2314, 2344, 0014**N**, 0044**N**.

Calls at Koksijde (+19 mins), Nieuwpoort (+38 mins), Middelkerke (+56 mins).

OOSTENDE railway station - **KNOKKE** railway station *Journey 65 mins*

Apr. 6 - June 30: 0458⚒, 0540⚒, 0640⚒, 0705, 0718Ⓐ, 0740, 0756, 0827, 0840, 0857, 0920, 0937, 0952, 1007 and every 15 minutes until 1907, 1937, 2007, 2037, 2137, 2237, 2337.

July 1 - Aug. 31: 0456⚒, 0540, 0610, 0640, 0710, 0740, 0800, 0810 and every 10 minutes until 1930, 1950, 2010, 2030, 2050, 2110, 2135, 2205, 2235, 2305, 2335, 0005, 0035.

Calls at Blankenberge (+37 mins), Zeebrugge (+47 mins), Heist (+58 mins).

N – Not Monday mornings. A change of tram is necessary at Oostende; connections not guaranteed. *Service from July 1 is subject to confirmation.*
Connections with rail services are available at Knokke (Table **405**), Zeebrugge (Table **402**), Blankenberge (Table **405**), Oostende (Tables **400/07/10**) and De Panne (Table **411**).

Lines 66, 89

OOSTENDE - BRUGGE - KORTRIJK - BRUSSELS 407

For direct trains Oostende - Brugge - Brussels via Gent (also Kortrijk - Gent - Brussels) see Table **400**. For direct trains Brugge - Brussels - Brussels Nationaal ✈ see Table **405**.

km			Ⓐ	Ⓐ	Ⓐ	Ⓐ	Ⓐ	Ⓐ N	Ⓐ	Ⓐ	Ⓐ	Ⓐ		Ⓐ	Ⓐ	Ⓐ		Ⓒ	Ⓒ	Ⓒ	Ⓒ		Ⓒ	Ⓒ
0	**Oostende** ▷ d.	Ⓐ	...	...	...	...	0556	0627	0656	...	0757	0857		1957	2057	2157	Ⓒ	...	...	...	0646		1946	2046
22	Brugge ▷ d.		...	...	...	...	0613	0645	0713	...	0814	0914		2014	2114	2214		...	...	...	0705		2005	2105
39	Torhout d.		...	...	...	...	0630	0700	0731	...	0831	0931		2031	2131	2231		...	...	...	0721		2021	2121
44	Lichtervelde § d.		...	...	...	...	0636	0705	0736	...	0836	0936		2036	2136	2236		...	...	...	0735		2035	2135
52	Roeselare d.		...	...	...	...	0645	0713	0745	...	0844	0944	and	2044	2144	2244		...	...	...	0742	and	2042	2142
73	**Kortrijk** a.		...	...	...	...	0706	0731	0806	...	0905	1005		2105	2205	2305		...	...	...	0802		2102	2202
73	**Kortrijk** d.		0511	0544	0611	0644	0711	0744	0815	0811	0912	1012	hourly	2112	2212	...		0505	0605	0705	0805	hourly	2105	...
98	Oudenaarde d.		0532	0603	0630	0703	0730	0803	|	0832	0932	1032		2132	2232	...		0523	0623	0723	0823		2123	...
115	Zottegem d.		0547	0618	0645	0719	0745	0827	◇	0847	0947	1047	until	2147	2247	...		0540	0640	0740	0840	until	2140	...
136	Denderleeuw d.		0605	0638	0705	0740	0805	0846	|	0905	1005	1105		2205	2305	...		0605	0705	0805	0905		2205	...
158	**Brussels** Midi / Zuid a.		0620	0656	0720	0756	0820	0902	0924	0920	1020	1120		2220	2320	...		0620	0720	0820	0920		2220	...
160	Brussels Central a.		0627	0705	0727	0804	0827	0911	0932	0927	1027	1127		2227	2327	...		0627	0727	0827	0927		2227	...
162	Brussels Nord a.		0632	0710	0732	0809	0832	0916	0937	0932	1032	1132		2232	2332	...		0632	0732	0832	0932		2232	...
174	**Brussels Airport** ✈ a.		0647	♤	0747	♤	0847	♤	...	0947	1047	1147		2247	2347	...		0647	0747	0847	0947		2247	...

		Ⓐ	Ⓐ	Ⓐ	Ⓐ		Ⓐ	Ⓐ	Ⓐ	Ⓐ	Ⓐ	Ⓐ	Ⓐ	Ⓐ	Ⓐ	Ⓐ		Ⓒ	Ⓒ		Ⓒ	Ⓒ	Ⓒ	Ⓒ
Brussels Airport ✈ d.	Ⓐ	...	...	0513	0613		1613	♤	1713	1813	...	1913	2013	2113	2213	...	Ⓒ	...	0613		1913	2013	2113	2213
Brussels Nord d.		...	...	0527	0627		1627	1653	1727	1827	1921	1927	2027	2127	2227	2319		...	0627		1927	2027	2127	2227
Brussels Central d.		...	...	0532	0632		1632	1658	1732	1832	1926	1932	2032	2132	2232	2323		...	0632		1932	2032	2132	2232
Brussels Midi / Zuid d.		...	...	0539	0639		1639	1705	1739	1839	1936	1939	2039	2139	2241	2329		...	0639		1939	2039	2139	2239
Denderleeuw d.		...	...	0557	0657		1657	1724	1757	1857	|	1957	2057	2157	2259	2346		...	0658		1958	2058	2158	2258
Zottegem d.		...	...	0615	0715	and	1715	1744	1815	1915	◇	2015	2115	2215	2316	0012		...	0724	and	2024	2124	2224	2324
Oudenaarde d.		...	...	0631	0731		1731	1759	1831	1931	|	2031	2131	2231	2331	0028		...	0738		2038	2138	2238	2338
Kortrijk a.		...	...	0648	0748	hourly	1748	1816	1848	1948	2043	2048	2148	2248	2349	...		...	0755	hourly	2055	2155	2255	2356
Kortrijk d.		0455	0554	0655	0755		1755	...	1855	1955	2055	...	2155	...	...	...		0658	0758		2058	...	...	...
Roeselare d.		0515	0614	0715	0816	until	1816	...	1916	2016	2116	...	2216	...	...	...		0718	0818	until	2118	...	...	...
Lichtervelde § d.		0522	0622	0723	0824		1824	...	1924	2024	2124	...	2224	...	...	...		0735	0835		2135	...	...	...
Torhout d.		0527	0627	0728	0829		1829	...	1929	2029	2129	...	2229	...	...	...		0740	0840		2140	...	...	...
Brugge ▷ a.		0543	0643	0745	0846		1846	...	1946	2046	2146	...	2246	...	...	...		0755	0855		2155	...	...	...
Oostende ▷ a.		0558	0659	0801	0902		1902	...	2002	2102	2202	...	2302	...	...	...		0811	0911		2211	...	...	...

N – Will not run Kortrijk - Brussels Dec. 24 - Jan. 4, Apr. 8-22, July 1 - Aug. 30.
◇ – Via Gent (Table **400**). To Leuven / from Welkenraedt.

▷ – See also Tables **400** and **410**.
♤ – To / from Brussels Schaarbeek.
§ – On Ⓒ arrives 10 mins earlier.

ADDITIONAL TRAINS Journey 47 mins
Brugge - Kortrijk: Ⓐ hourly 0558-2258; Ⓒ every 2 hours 0738-2138.
Kortrijk - Brugge: Ⓐ hourly 0516-2116; Ⓒ every 2 hours 0635-2035.

410 POPERINGE - KORTRIJK - GENT - ANTWERPEN

Lines 69, 75, 59

km		Ⓐ	Ⓐ	Ⓐ	Ⓐ				Ⓐ										Ⓐ	Ⓐ	Ⓐ		Ⓐ N	
0	**Poperinge** d.	...	0408	...	...	0508	...		...	1908	...	2008	...	2108	...	2208	...		0551	0651	0736	...	1636	...
10	Ieper d.	...	0416	...	...	0516	...		...	1916	...	2016	...	2116	...	2216	...		0559	0659	0744	...	1644	...
23	Comines / Komen d.	...	0426	...	...	0526	...	and	...	1926	...	2026	...	2126	...	2226	...		0609	0709	0754	...	1654	...
32	Menen d.	...	0435	...	...	0535	...	at	...	1935	...	2035	...	2135	...	2235	...		0619	0719	0803	...	1703	...
43	**Kortrijk** a.	...	0450	...	...	0550	...	the	...	1950	...	2050	...	2150	...	2250	...	A	0634	0735	0818	...	1716	...
43	**Kortrijk** d.	...	0458	...	...	0558	...	same	...	1958	...	2058	...	2158	...	2258	...	L	0641	0741	...	...	...	...
	Oostende ▷ d.	...	|	...	...	|	0609	minutes	...	|	2009	|	2109	|	2209	|	...	S	|	|	...	...	...	...
	Brugge ▷ d.	...	|	...	△	|	0625	past	△	|	2025	|	2125	|	2225	|	...	O	|	|	...	...	...	...
85	**Gent** Sint-Pieters ▷ a.	...	0524	...	0607	0624	0649	each	2007	2024	2049	2124	2149	2224	2249	2324	...		0711	0811	...	...	...	...
85	**Gent** Sint-Pieters d.	0427	0527	0553	0611	0627	0652	hour	2011	2027	2053	2127	2153	2227	2253	2327	...		0714	0814	...	...	...	...
112	Lokeren d.	0450	0550	0616	0634	0650	0716	until	2034	2050	2116	2150	2216	2250	2316	2350	...		▽	▽	...	...	...	...
125	Sint-Niklaas d.	0500	0600	0626	0645	0700	0726		2045	2100	2126	2200	2226	2300	2326	0000	...		...	...	...	...	...	...
148	Antwerpen Berchem a.	0517	0617	0648	0704	0717	0748		2104	2117	2148	2217	2248	2317	2348	0018	...		...	...	...	...	...	...
151	**Antwerpen** Centraal a.	0523	0623	0654	0709	0723	0754		2109	2123	2154	2223	2254	2323	2354	0023	...		...	...	...	...	...	...

	Ⓐ					Ⓐ			Ⓐ				Ⓐ				Ⓐ	Ⓒ			Ⓐ N	Ⓐ	Ⓐ	Ⓐ
Antwerpen Centraal d.	0437	0506	0537	0606	0637	0648	0706	0737	0751		2006	2037	2051	2106	2137	2237	2337	2337	...		...	...	...	...
Antwerpen Berchem d.	0442	0512	0543	0612	0643	0653	0712	0743	0756		2012	2043	2056	2112	2143	2243	2343	2343	...		...	...	...	...
Sint-Niklaas d.	0502	0536	0602	0636	0702	0713	0736	0802	0816	and	2036	2102	2116	2136	2202	2302	0002	0002	...		...	...	...	...
Lokeren d.	0512	0546	0612	0646	0712	0723	0746	0812	0826	at	2046	2112	2126	2146	2212	2312	0012	0012	...		...	...	▽	▽
Gent Sint-Pieters a.	0533	0607	0633	0707	0733	0744	0807	0833	0847	the	2107	2133	2147	2207	2233	2333	0033	0033	...	A	...	...	1638	1744
Gent Sint-Pieters ▷ d.	0536	0611	0636	0710	0736	0753	0811	0836	0853	same	2111	2136	2153	2211	2236	2336	...	0039	...	L	...	...	1641	1748
Brugge ▷ a.	|	0635	|	0734	|	△	0835	|	△	minutes	2135	|	△	2235	|	|	...	|	...	S	...	...	|	|
Oostende ▷ a.	|	0651	|	0750	|		0851	|		past	2151	|		2251	|	|	...	|	...	O	...	...	|	|
Kortrijk a.	0602	...	0702	...	0802	...	...	0902	...	each	...	2202	...	...	2302	0011	...	0113	...		...	...	1711	1819
Kortrijk d.	0605	...	0710	...	0810	...	...	0910	...	hour	...	2210	...	...	2310	...	...	...	...		0736	1642	1719	1822
Menen d.	0620	...	0725	...	0825	...	...	0925	...	until	...	2225	...	...	2325	...	...	...	...		0751	1657	1734	1837
Comines / Komen d.	0629	...	0734	...	0834	...	...	0934	...		...	2234	...	...	2334	...	...	...	...		0800	1706	1745	1848
Ieper d.	0639	...	0744	...	0844	...	...	0944	...		...	2244	...	...	2344	...	...	...	...		0816	1716	1755	1858
Poperinge a.	0647	...	0752	...	0852	...	...	0952	...		...	2252	...	...	2352	...	...	...	...		0823	1723	1803	1906

ADDITIONAL TRAINS KORTRIJK - GENT

		Ⓐ§		Ⓐ§		Ⓒ		Ⓒ
Kortrijk d.	Ⓐ	0417	hourly	2216	Ⓒ	0522	hourly	2222
Gent Sint-Pieters a.		0451	until	2251		0554	until	2254

		Ⓐ§		Ⓐ§		Ⓒ		Ⓒ
Gent Sint-Pieters d.	Ⓐ	0609	hourly	2309	Ⓒ	0606	hourly	2306
Kortrijk a.		0643	until	2343		0638	until	2338

N – Not Dec. 24 - Jan. 4, Apr. 8-22, July 1 - Aug. 30.
△ – From / to De Panne (Table **411**).
▽ – To / from Brussels (Table **400**).
▷ – See also Table **400** (also **407** Oostende - Brugge).
§ – Most journeys continue to / from Brussels (Table **400**).

*Between Kortrijk and Antwerpen most trains are attached to Lille - Kortrijk - Antwerpen trains (Table **415**).*

411 DE PANNE - LICHTERVELDE - GENT

Line 73

km			Ⓐ		Ⓐ ◧		Ⓒ △		Ⓒ △
0	**De Panne** § d.	Ⓐ	0452		1852	Ⓒ	0652		2052
5	Veurne d.		0501	and	1901		0701	and	2101
20	Diksmuide d.		0513		1913		0713		2113
39	Lichtervelde d.		0530	hourly	1930		0730	hourly	2130
56	Tielt d.		0542		1942		0742		2142
86	**Gent** Sint-Pieters a.		0607	until	2007		0807	until	2207
	Antwerpen 410 a.		0709		2109		|		|
	Brussels Midi / Zuid a.		...		...		0912		2312
	Brussels Airport ✈ a.		...		...		0935		2335

		Ⓐ ◐		Ⓐ		Ⓒ △		Ⓒ △
Brussels Airport ✈ d.	Ⓐ	...		...	Ⓒ	0524		1925
Brussels Midi / Zuid d.		...		...		0548		1948
Antwerpen 410 d.		0648	and	2051		|	and	|
Gent Sint-Pieters d.		0753		2153		0653		2053
Tielt d.		0819	hourly	2219		0719	hourly	2119
Lichtervelde d.		0832		2232		0732		2132
Diksmuide d.		0849	until	2249		0749	until	2149
Veurne d.		0901		2301		0801		2201
De Panne § a.		0908		2308		0808		2208

N – Not Dec. 24 - Jan. 4, Apr. 8-22, July 1 - Aug. 30.
△ – To / from Leuven or Landen (Table **430**). Runs Gent - Brussels and v.v. via Aalst (Table **412**).
◧ – Also De Panne - Gent at 1952Ⓐ, 2052Ⓐ.
◐ – Also Gent - De Panne at 0553Ⓐ, 0653Ⓐ.
§ – De Panne railway station is situated in Adinkerke. Connection available with the coastal tramway (Table **406**).

ADDITIONAL TRAINS
De Panne - Gent - Brussels Midi - Nord: 0525Ⓐ, 0623Ⓐ.
Brussels Nord - Midi - Gent - De Panne: 1634Ⓐ, 1734Ⓐ.
De Panne - Gent: 0724Ⓐ **N**. Gent - De Panne: 1620Ⓐ **N**.

412 GENT - AALST - DENDERLEEUW - BRUSSELS

Line 50

For direct trains Gent - Brussels see Tables **400** and **405**

km		Ⓐ	Ⓐ △	Ⓐ	Ⓒ	△		Ⓐ	Ⓒ	△
0	**Gent** Sint-Pieters d.	0441	0512	0538	0541	0612	and at	2140	2141	2212
28	Aalst d.	0514	0543	0613	0612	0643	the same	2214	2212	2243
35	Denderleeuw d.	0523	0554	0622	0625	0654	minutes	2223	2225	2254
58	**Brussels** Midi / Zuid a.	0541	0612	0641	0642	0712	past	2241	2242	2312
60	Brussels Central a.	0548	0618	0648	0649	0718	each	2248	2249	2318
62	Brussels Nord a.	0553	0623	0653	0654	0723	hour	2253	2254	2323
74	**Brussels Airport ✈** a.	⊡	0635	⊡	...	0735	until	⊡	...	2335

	Ⓐ △	Ⓐ	Ⓒ	△	Ⓐ		Ⓒ	△	Ⓐ
Brussels Airport ✈ d.	0524	⊡	...	0624	⊡	and at	...	2224	⊡
Brussels Nord d.	0536	0607	0606	0637	0707	the same	2206	2237	2307
Brussels Central d.	0540	0612	0610	0641	0712	minutes	2210	2241	2312
Brussels Midi / Zuid d.	0548	0619	0618	0648	0719	past	2218	2248	2319
Denderleeuw d.	0609	0639	0642	0709	0739	each	2242	2309	2339
Aalst d.	0619	0648	0650	0719	0748	hour	2250	2319	2348
Gent Sint-Pieters a.	0648	0719	0719	0747	0819	until	2319	2348	0019

△ – To / from Leuven or Landen (Table **430**). On Ⓒ most journeys run from / to De Panne (Table **411**).
⊡ – To / from Hasselt or Tongeren (Table **431**).

413 EEKLO - GENT - OUDENAARDE - RONSE

Line 86

km			Ⓐ	Ⓐ		Ⓐ ‡		Ⓒ		Ⓒ ‡
0	**Eeklo** d.	Ⓐ	0511	0617		2017	Ⓒ	0711		2011
27	**Gent** St-Pieters a.		0545	0652	and	2052		0746	and	2046
27	**Gent** St-Pieters d.		0557	0657	hourly	2057		0757	hourly	2057
52	Oudenaarde a.		0627	0727	until	2127		0827	until	2127
52	Oudenaarde d.		0634	0734	△	2134		0841		2141
66	**Ronse** a.		0645	0745		2145		0852		2152

		Ⓐ		Ⓐ		Ⓒ		Ⓒ §
Ronse d.	Ⓐ	0515		2015	Ⓒ	0708		2008
Oudenaarde a.		0526	and	2026		0719	and	2019
Oudenaarde d.		0533	hourly	2033		0733	hourly	2033
Gent St-Pieters a.		0603	until	2103		0803	until	2103
Gent St-Pieters d.		0615	▽	2115		0814		2114
Eeklo a.		0650		2150		0847		2147

N – Not Dec. 24 - Jan. 4, Apr. 8-22, July 1 - Aug. 30.
△ – Also Gent - Ronse at 1628Ⓐ, 1728Ⓐ, 1828Ⓐ **N**.
▽ – Also Ronse - Gent at 0547Ⓐ **N**, 0647Ⓐ, 0747Ⓐ, 2115Ⓐ, 2215Ⓐ.
‡ – Also Eeklo - Gent - Oudenarde at 2111Ⓒ, 2117Ⓐ, 2217Ⓐ.
§ – Also Ronse - Gent at 2108Ⓒ.

414 GENT - MECHELEN - LEUVEN

Line 53

For Mechelen - Leuven via Brussels Nationaal ✈ see Table **432**

km			Ⓐ	Ⓐ	Ⓐ	Ⓐ	Ⓐ	Ⓐ	Ⓐ		Ⓐ	Ⓐ	Ⓐ	Ⓐ	Ⓐ
0	**Gent** St-Pieters d.	Ⓐ	0422	...	...	0522	0557	...	0622	and at the same	2057	...	2122	2157	...
30	Dendermonde d.		0500	0523	...	0600	0623	...	0700	minutes	2123	...	2200	2223	←
57	Mechelen d.		0528	0548	0621	0628	0648	0721	0728	past each	2148	2221	2228	2246	2303
82	**Leuven** a.		...	0614	0653	...	0714	0753	...	hour until	2214	2253	...	→	2329

		Ⓒ	Ⓒ	Ⓒ	Ⓒ		Ⓒ	Ⓒ	Ⓒ
Gent St-Pieters d.	Ⓒ	...	0700	...	0800	and at the same	...	2200	...
Dendermonde d.		...	0728	...	0828	minutes	...	2228	...
Mechelen d.		0736	0754	0836	0854	past each	2236	2254	2336
Leuven a.		0804	...	0904	...	hour until	2304	...	0004

		Ⓐ	Ⓐ	Ⓐ	Ⓐ	Ⓐ	Ⓐ	Ⓐ		Ⓐ	Ⓐ	Ⓐ	Ⓐ
Leuven d.	Ⓐ	0506	0546	...	0607	0646	...	0707	and at the same	2146	...	2207	2246
Mechelen d.		0539	0614	0631	0639	0714	0731	0739	minutes	2214	2231	2239	2314
Dendermonde d.		...	0641	0703	...	0740	0803	...	past each	2240	2303	...	2337
Gent St-Pieters a.		...	0704	0739	...	0804	0839	...	hour until	2304	2339	...	...

		Ⓒ	Ⓒ	Ⓒ	Ⓒ	Ⓒ		Ⓒ	Ⓒ	Ⓒ	Ⓒ
Leuven d.	Ⓒ	...	...	0656	...	0756	and at the same	...	2056	2156	2256
Mechelen d.		0606	0706	0724	0806	0824	minutes	2106	2124	2224	2324
Dendermonde d.		0634	0734	...	0834	...	past each	2134	...	...	...
Gent St-Pieters a.		0700	0800	...	0900	...	hour until	2200	...	...	...

Line 75 — LILLE - MOUSCRON - KORTRIJK - (GENT - ANTWERPEN) — 415

A change at Kortrijk may be necessary on certain journeys. Lille - Mouscron is subject to alteration on French and Belgian public holidays

km		Ⓐ	⚒	Ⓐ	⚒	Ⓐ						Ⓒ	Ⓐ	Ⓒ		Ⓑ	⑥	Ⓐ		Ⓐ		⚒	†		
0	**Lille** Flandres ▷ d.	0628	0708	0728	0808	0826	0908	1008	1108	1208	1308	1403	1408	1508	1608	1708	1708	1728	1808	1828	1908	2008	2008	2108	2208
10	Roubaix ▷ d.	0642	0718	0742	0818	0841	0918	1018	1118	1218	1318	1417	1418	1518	1618	1721	1721	1742	1818	1842	1918	2018	2018	2118	2218
12	Tourcoing 🏛 ▷ d.	0646	0722	0746	0822	0845	0922	1023	1122	1222	1322	1421	1422	1522	1622	1726	1726	1746	1822	1846	1922	2022	2022	2122	2222
18	Mouscron a.	...	0728	...	0828	...	0928	1032	1128	1228	1328	1428	1428	1528	1628	1732	1732	...	1828	...	1928	2028	2028	2128	2228
18	Mouscron **417** d.	...	0735	...	0835	...	0935	1035	1135	1235	1335	1435	1435	1535	1635	1735	1735	...	1835	...	1935	2035	2035	2135	2235
30	**Kortrijk** **417** a.	...	0745	...	0845	...	0945	1045	1145	1245	1345	1445	1445	1545	1645	1745	1745	...	1845	...	1945	2045	2045	2145	2245
	Gent Sint-P. **410** a.	...	0824	...	0924	...	1024	1124	1224	1324	1424	1524	1524	1624	1724	...	1824	...	1924	...	2024	2124	...	2224	2324
	Antwerpen **410** a.	...	0923	...	1023	...	1123	1223	1323	1423	1523	1623	1623	1723	1823	...	1923	...	2023	...	2123	2223	...	2323	0023

	⚒	Ⓐ	⑥	Ⓐ	Ⓑ	⑥	Ⓐ		Ⓒ	⚒	†		Ⓐ			Ⓐ	Ⓒ	Ⓐ	Ⓒ		Ⓐ				
Antwerpen **410** d.	...	...	0537	...	0637	...	...	0737	0837	0937	...	1037	...	1137	1237	...	1337	...	1437	1537	...	1637	1737	1837	1937
Gent Sint-P. **410** d.	...	...	0636	...	0736	...	...	0836	0936	1036	...	1136	...	1236	1336	...	1436	...	1536	1636	...	1736	1836	1936	2036
Kortrijk **417** d.	0613	0713	0713	...	0813	0813	...	0913	1013	1113	1113	1213	...	1313	1413	1513	1513	1613	1613	1713	...	1813	1913	2013	2113
Mouscron **417** a.	0624	0724	0724	...	0824	0824	...	0924	1024	1124	1122	1224	...	1324	1424	1524	1524	1624	1624	1724	...	1824	1924	2024	2124
Mouscron d.	0629	0730	0729	...	0830	0830	...	0930	1030	1131	1129	1230	...	1330	1430	1530	1530	1630	1630	1730	...	1830	1930	2030	2130
Tourcoing 🏛 ▷ d.	0635	0736	0736	0815	0836	0836	0915	0936	1036	1137	1136	1236	1313	1336	1436	1536	1536	1637	1637	1736	1815	1836	1936	2036	2136
Roubaix ▷ d.	0640	0741	0740	0819	0841	0841	0919	0941	1040	1141	1140	1241	1319	1340	1440	1541	1541	1641	1641	1741	1819	1841	1940	2041	2141
Lille Flandres ▷ a.	0650	0750	0754	0832	0850	0850	0933	0950	1050	1151	1151	1250	1333	1350	1450	1550	1550	1650	1654	1750	1833	1850	1950	2050	2150

▷ – Frequent services Lille Flandres - Lille Europe - Roubaix and Tourcoing are operated by the Lille *VAL* métro (Line 2) or by tram. For *TGV* trains see Table **250**.

Lines 78, 118 — LILLE - TOURNAI - MONS — 416

km			Ⓐ	Ⓐ	Ⓐ	Ⓐ	Ⓐ	Ⓐ	Ⓐ	Ⓐ	Ⓐ	Ⓐ	Ⓐ	Ⓐ	Ⓐ	Ⓐ	Ⓐ	Ⓐ	Ⓐ	Ⓐ	Ⓐ	Ⓐ	Ⓐ	Ⓐ	Ⓐ
					d		d										◇	◇		◇	◇				
0	**Lille** Flandres § d.	Ⓐ	...	0603	...	0702	...	0731	0808	0905	1006	...	1205	1306	...	1508	1608	1708	1736	1808	1908	2006	...	...	2206
	Mouscron **417** d.		0522	|	0621	|	0722	|	|	|	|		|	|		|	|	|	|	|	|	|			|
25	**Tournai** **417** a.		0539	0633	0636	0733	0738	0758	0837	0937	1037	...	1237	1337	...	1537	1637	1737	1810	1837	1937	2037	...	...	2234
25	**Tournai** d.		0544	...	0644	0744	0744	...	0844	0944	1044	1144	1244	1344	1444	1544	1644	1744	...	1844	1944	2044	2144	2228	...
64	Saint-Ghislain d.		0605	...	0705	0805	0805	...	0905	1005	1105	1205	1305	1405	1505	1605	1705	1805	...	1905	2005	2105	2205	2259	...
73	**Mons** a.		0613	...	0713	0813	0813	...	0913	1013	1113	1213	1313	1413	1513	1613	1713	1813	...	1913	2013	2113	2213	2312	...
	Charleroi Sud **425** a.		0648	...	0748	0848	0848	...	0948	1048	1148	1248	1348	1448	1548	1648	1748	1848	...	1948	2048	2148	2248	...	...
	Namur **425** a.		0721	...	0821	0921	0921	...	1021	1121	1221	1321	1421	1521	1621	1721	1821	1921	...	2021	2121	2221	2321	...	...

		Ⓐ	Ⓐ	Ⓐ	Ⓐ	Ⓐ	Ⓐ	Ⓐ	Ⓐ	Ⓐ	Ⓐ	Ⓐ	Ⓐ	Ⓐ	Ⓐ	Ⓐ	Ⓐ	Ⓐ	Ⓐ	Ⓐ	Ⓐ	Ⓐ	Ⓐ	Ⓐ	Ⓐ
				◇	◇		◇		◇		◇	◇			◇		k		k		◇	◇	◇		
Namur **425** d.	Ⓐ	...	...	...	0540	...	0640	0740	0840	0940	1040	1140	1240	1340	1440	...	1540	...	1640	...	1740	1840	1940	2040	2140
Charleroi Sud **425** d.		...	...	...	0612	...	0712	0812	0912	1012	1112	1212	1312	1412	1512	...	1612	...	1712	...	1812	1912	2012	2112	2212
Mons d.		0453	...	0551	0647	...	0747	0847	0947	1047	1147	1247	1347	1447	1547	...	1647	...	1747	...	1847	1947	2047	2147	2247
Saint-Ghislain d.		0506	...	0604	0656	...	0756	0856	0956	1056	1156	1256	1356	1456	1556	...	1656	...	1757	...	1857	1956	2056	2156	2256
Tournai a.		0533	...	0634	0715	...	0815	0915	1015	1115	1215	1315	1415	1515	1615	...	1715	...	1818	...	1918	2015	2115	2215	2320
Tournai **417** d.		...	0622	0647	0721	0809	0821	0921	1021	1121	1221	1321	...	1521	1621	1649	1719	1723	1821	1825	1923	2021	2121	...	...
Mouscron **417** a.		...	|	|	|	|	|	|	|	|	|	|	...	|	|	|	1736	|	1838	|	|	|	|	...	...
Lille Flandres § a.		...	0651	0721	0751	0835	0851	0951	1051	1151	1251	1351	...	1552	1652	1723	...	1752	...	1856	1953	2052	2151	...	...

		Ⓒ	Ⓒ	Ⓒ		Ⓒ	Ⓒ	Ⓒ	
Mouscron **417** d.	Ⓒ	0613	0713	0813		2013	2113	2213	...
Tournai **417** d.		0629	0729	0829	and	2029	2129	2229	...
Saint-Ghislain d.		0700	0800	0900	hourly	2100	2200	2300	...
Mons a.		0712	0812	0912	until	2112	2212	2312	...
Charleroi Sud **425** a.		0751	0851	0951		2151	2251	...	...
Namur **425** a.		0830	0930	1030		2230	2330	...	...
Liège Guillemins **442** a.		0920	1020	1120		2320	...	...	...

		Ⓒ	Ⓒ	Ⓒ	Ⓒ		Ⓒ	Ⓒ	
Liège Guillemins **442** d.	Ⓒ	...	...	0640	0740		1940	2040	...
Namur **425** d.		...	0630	0730	0830	and	2030	2130	...
Charleroi Sud **425** d.		0609	0709	0809	0909	hourly	2109	2209	...
Mons d.		0648	0748	0848	0948	until	2148	2248	...
Saint-Ghislain d.		0700	0800	0900	1000	△	2200	2300	...
Tournai **417** a.		0730	0830	0930	1030		2230	2330	...
Mouscron **417** a.		0746	0846	0946	1046		2246	2346	...

		⑥	⑥	Ⓒ		Ⓒ	Ⓒ	Ⓒ	
Lille Flandres § d.	Ⓒ	0649	0749	0849	and hourly	1949	2049	2149	...
Tournai a.		0721	0821	0921	until	2021	2121	2221	...

		⑥	⑥	Ⓒ		Ⓒ	Ⓒ	Ⓒ	
Tournai d.	Ⓒ	0636	0736	0836	and hourly	1936	2036	2144	...
Lille Flandres § a.		0708	0809	0908	until	2008	2108	2213	...

d – From Kortrijk (depart 0609 and 0709).
k – To Kortrijk (arrive 1748 and 1849).
◇ – Change trains at Tournai.

△ – Mouscron arrivals at 0846, 1246, 1346, 1446, 1646, 1746, 2046 are 9 minutes later on ⑦.
§ – 🏛 between Lille and Tournai = Blandain.

Subject to alteration May 25, 26

Lines 94, 60 — KORTRIJK - MOUSCRON - TOURNAI - BRUSSELS - SINT NIKLAAS — 417

For direct trains Kortrijk - Brussels see Table **400** (via Gent) and Table **407** (via Oudenaarde)

km			Ⓐ	Ⓐ	Ⓐ	Ⓐ	Ⓐ	Ⓐ	Ⓐ	Ⓐ	Ⓐ	Ⓐ	Ⓐ	Ⓐ	Ⓐ		Ⓐ	Ⓐ	Ⓐ		Ⓒ		Ⓒ
0	**Kortrijk** **415** d.	Ⓐ	...	...	...	...	...	...	...	...	0639	...	...	0738	...		2038	...	2138	Ⓒ	...		...
13	Mouscron **415/6** d.		...	...	...	...	0548	0606	...	...	0650	0706	...	0749	...		2049	...	2149		...		...
32	**Tournai** **416** d.		0444	0509	0544	0600	0609	0628	0644	0657	0709	0729	0744	0809	0844	and	2109	2144	2209		0544		2244
50	Leuze d.		0457	0522	0557	0613	0622	0641	0657	0710	0722	0742	0757	0822	0857	at	2122	2157	2222		0556		2256
62	Ath d.		0508	0534	0608	0624	0634	0652	0708	0721	0734	0752	0808	0834	0908	the	2134	2208	2234		0608	and	2308
100	Halle d.		0537	0603	0637	|	0703	|	0737	|	0803	|	0837	0903	0937	same	2203	2237	2303		0637		2337
116	**Brussels** Midi/Zuid a.		0548	0615	0648	0700	0715	0728	0748	0800	0815	0828	0848	0915	0948	minutes	2215	2248	2315		0648	hourly	2348
116	**Brussels** Midi/Zuid d.		0551	0618	0651	0702	0718	0730	0751	0802	0818	0830	0853	0918	0951	past	2218	2251	2318		0651		2351
118	Brussels Central d.		0556	0623	0656	0707	0723	0735	0756	0807	0823	0835	0858	0923	0956	each	2223	2256	2323		0656	until	2356
120	Brussels Nord d.		0604	0629	0704	0711	0729	0739	0800	0811	0829	0839	0905	0929	1004	hour	2229	2304	2329		0704		0004
132	**Brussels Airport** ✈ a.		0624	|	0724	n	|	♤	0824	n	|	♤	0924	|	1024	until	|	2324	|		0724		0024
154	Dendermonde a.		...	0656	...	...	0756	...	...	...	0856	...	...	0956	...		2256	...	0012		...		...
168	Lokeren **410** a.		...	0721	...	...	0821	...	...	...	0921	...	...	1021	...		2321	...	...		...		...
181	**Sint-Niklaas** **410** a.		...	0736	...	...	0836	...	...	...	0936	...	...	1036	...		2336	...	...		...		...

		Ⓐ	Ⓐ	Ⓐ	Ⓐ	Ⓐ		Ⓐ	Ⓐ	Ⓐ	Ⓐ	Ⓐ	Ⓐ	Ⓐ		Ⓐ	Ⓐ	Ⓐ	Ⓐ		Ⓒ		Ⓒ
Sint-Niklaas **410** d.	Ⓐ	...	...	0524	...	0624		...	1924	...	2024	...	2124	2224		...	...	...	...	Ⓒ	...		...
Lokeren **410** d.		...	...	0539	...	0639		...	1939	...	2039	...	2139	2239		...	...	...	...		...		...
Dendermonde d.		...	...	0603	...	0703	and	...	2003	...	2103	...	2203	2303		...	...	...	...		...		...
Brussels Airport ✈ d.		0441	0541	|	0641	|	at	1941	|	2041	|	2141	|	|		n	♤	n	♤		0541		2241
Brussels Nord d.		0501	0601	0633	0701	0732	the	2001	2033	2101	2133	2201	2233	2333	A	1549	1616	1649	1717		0600	and	2300
Brussels Central d.		0506	0606	0638	0706	0737	same	2006	2038	2106	2138	2206	2238	2338	L	1554	1621	1654	1722		0605		2305
Brussels Midi/Zuid a.		0510	0610	0642	0710	0741	minutes	2010	2042	2110	2142	2210	2242	2342	S	1558	1625	1658	1726		0609	hourly	2309
Brussels Midi/Zuid d.		0513	0613	0647	0713	0746	past	2013	2047	2113	2145	2213	2247	2345	O	1600	1627	1700	1728		0613		2313
Halle d.		0524	0624	0658	0724	0758	each	2024	2058	2124	2158	2224	2258	2357		|	|	|	|		0624	until	2324
Ath d.		0553	0653	0729	0753	0829	hour	2053	2129	2153	2226	2253	2329	0026		1640	1706	1740	1806		0654		2354
Leuze d.		0603	0703	0739	0803	0839	until	2103	2139	2203	...	2303	2339	...		1649	1715	1750	1815		0704		0004
Tournai **416** d.		0616	0716	0753	0816	0853		2116	2152	2216	...	2316	2351	...		1703	1730	1803	1830		0716		0016
Mouscron **415/6** d.		...	...	0812	...	0912		...	2211	...	...	...	...	...		...	1750	...	1850		...		...
Kortrijk **415** a.		...	...	0822	...	0922		...	2220	...	...	...	...	...		...	...	...	...		...		...

n – To Namur and Liège via Brussels Luxembourg (Table **440**).

♤ – To/from Brussels Schaarbeek.

419 ROOSENDAAL - ESSEN - ANTWERPEN — Line 12

km			Ⓐ ♡	Ⓐ	Ⓐ ♡	Ⓐ	Ⓐ	Ⓐ ♡	Ⓐ ⊡		Ⓐ	Ⓐ ♡	Ⓐ			Ⓒ	Ⓒ	Ⓒ		Ⓒ	Ⓒ
0	**Roosendaal** d.	Ⓐ	...	...	...	...	0652	...	...	and at the	2152	...	2252	...	Ⓒ	...	0723	0823	and	2123	2224
8	Essen ▦ d.		0504	0600	0619	0637	0700	0719	0737	same minutes	2200	2219	2300	...		0633	0733	0833	hourly	2133	2233
26	Kapellen d.		0521	0621	0636	0655	0721	0736	0755	past each	2221	2236	2321	...		0654	0754	0854	until	2154	2254
41	**Antwerpen** Centraal a.		0536	0639	0652	0710	0739	0752	0810	hour until	2239	2252	2339	...		0710	0810	0910		2210	2310

		Ⓐ	Ⓐ ♡	Ⓐ	Ⓐ ⊙	Ⓐ ♡	Ⓐ		Ⓐ ♡	Ⓐ	Ⓐ ♡	Ⓐ	Ⓐ		Ⓒ	Ⓒ	Ⓒ		Ⓒ	Ⓒ	Ⓒ
Antwerpen Centraal d.	Ⓐ	0552	0608	0621	0652	0708	0721	and at the	2108	2121	2208	2221	2321	Ⓒ	0550	0650	0750	and	2150	2250	2350
Kapellen d.		0607	0625	0640	0707	0725	0740	same minutes	2125	2140	2225	2240	2340		0608	0708	0808	hourly	2208	2308	0008
Essen ▦ d.		0624	0642	0701	0724	0742	0801	past each	2142	2201	2242	2300	0000		0635	0730	0830	until	2230	2328	0028
Roosendaal a.		...	...	0708	...	...	0808	hour until	...	2208	...	...	...		0642	0737	0837		2237	...	...

♡ – To/from Brussels (Table **420**); most continue to/from Charleroi. ⊡ – No journey at 2137. ⊙ – No journey at 2052.

420 BREDA - ANTWERPEN - BRUSSELS - CHARLEROI — Lines 25, 124

For *Thalys* services Paris - Brussels - Antwerpen - Amsterdam see Table **18**. For additional trains Antwerpen - Brussels Nationaal ✈ see Table **432**.

km			Ⓐ	Ⓐ	Ⓐ ♡	Ⓐ	Ⓐ	Ⓐ	Ⓐ ♡	Ⓐ	Ⓐ	Ⓐ	Ⓐ	Ⓐ ♡	Ⓐ ◇	Ⓐ ♥	Ⓐ	Ⓐ	Ⓐ ♡		Ⓐ ♥	Ⓐ	Ⓐ	Ⓐ ♡
0	**Breda** ▦ d.	Ⓐ	...	...	...	...	...	...	...	...	...	...	...	...	...	0742	...	...	...		2042	...	...	...
33	Noorderkempen (Brecht) d.		...	...	...	...	*0555*	...	*0630*	...	0701	...	...	*0730*	...	0801	...	...	...		2101	...	...	...
57	**Antwerpen** Centraal a.		...	...	...	...	*0609*	...	*0645*	...	0715	...	...	*0745*	...	0815	...	...	...	and	2115	...	...	...
57	**Antwerpen** Centraal d.		0455	...	0538	0555	0625	0638	0655	0708	0717	0725	0738	0755	0808	0818	0825	0838	0855	at	2118	2125	2138	2155
59	Antwerpen Berchem d.		0501	...	0543	0601	0630	0643	0701	0713	0723	0730	0743	0801	0813	0824	0830	0843	0901	the	2124	2130	2143	2201
81	Mechelen d.		0515	...	0604	0615	0644	0704	0715	0734	0738	0744	0804	0815	0834	0838	0844	0904	0915	same	2138	2144	2204	2215
	Brussels Airport ✈ a.		|	...	|	|	|	|	|	|	0749	|	|	|	|	0849	|	|	|	minutes	2149	|	|	|
101	Brussels Nord d.		0532	0602	0624	0632	0702	0724	0732	0756	...	0802	0824	0832	0856	0908	0902	0924	0932	past	2208	2202	2224	2232
103	Brussels Central d.		0537	0607	0629	0637	0707	0729	0737	0801	...	0807	0829	0837	0901	0913	0907	0929	0937	each	2213	2207	2229	2237
105	**Brussels** Midi/Zuid a.		0541	0611	0633	0641	0711	0733	0741	0805	...	0811	0833	0841	0905	0917	0911	0933	0941	hour	2217	2211	2233	2241
105	**Brussels** Midi/Zuid d.		0545	0615	...	0645	0715	...	0745	...	...	0815	...	0845	...	...	0915	...	0945	until	...	2215	...	2245
134	Nivelles d.		0611	0641	...	0711	0741	...	0811	...	...	0841	...	0911	...	...	0941	...	1011		...	2241	...	2311
160	**Charleroi** Sud a.		0635	0705	...	0735	0805	...	0835	...	...	0905	...	0935	...	...	1005	...	1035		...	2305	...	2335

	Ⓐ ♥	Ⓐ ⊙	Ⓐ ♡	Ⓐ ♥	Ⓐ ⊡	Ⓐ	②–⑥ ⊡‡		Ⓒ	Ⓒ	Ⓒ	Ⓒ	Ⓒ	Ⓒ	Ⓒ	Ⓒ ♥	Ⓒ		Ⓒ	Ⓒ ♥	Ⓒ	Ⓒ	Ⓒ ♥	⑦ ⊡‡
Breda ▦ d.	2142	...	...	2242	...	...	...	Ⓒ	...	...	...	...	...	...	...	0742	...		...	2142	...	...	2242	...
Noorderkempen (Brecht) d.	2201	...	...	2301	...	...	...		...	...	...	...	...	...	...	0801	...		...	2201	...	...	2301	...
Antwerpen Centraal a.	2215	...	...	2315	...	...	...		...	...	...	...	...	...	...	0815	...	and	...	2215	...	...	2315	...
Antwerpen Centraal d.	2218	2225	2255	2318	2305	2325	0010		...	0540	0609	0640	0709	0740	0809	0818	0840	at	2209	2218	2240	2309	2318	0005
Antwerpen Berchem d.	2224	2230	2301	2324	2310	2330	0015		...	0546	0614	0646	0714	0746	0814	0824	0846	the	2214	2224	2246	2314	2324	0010
Mechelen d.	2238	2244	2315	2338	2346	2344	0047		...	0605	0634	0705	0734	0805	0834	0838	0905	same	2234	2238	2305	2334	2338	0044
Brussels Airport ✈ a.	2249	|	|	2349	|	|	|		...	|	|	|	|	|	|	0849	|	minutes	|	2249	|	|	2349	|
Brussels Nord d.	2308	2302	2332	0008	0013	0002	0119		0555	0623	0655	0723	0755	0823	0855	0907	0923	past	2255	2307	2323	2355	0007	0110
Brussels Central d.	2313	2307	2337	0013	0017	0007	|		0559	0627	0659	0727	0759	0827	0859	0912	0927	each	2259	2312	2327	2359	0012	0114
Brussels Midi/Zuid a.	2317	2311	2341	0017	0021	0011	0131		0603	0631	0703	0731	0803	0831	0903	0916	0931	hour	2303	2316	2331	0003	0016	0118
Brussels Midi/Zuid d.	...	...	...	...	...	...	...		0606	...	0706	...	0806	...	0906	...	...	until	2306	...	...	...	...	...
Nivelles d.	...	...	...	...	...	...	...		0633	...	0733	...	0833	...	0933	...	...		2333	...	...	...	...	...
Charleroi Sud a.	...	...	...	...	...	...	...		0655	...	0755	...	0855	...	0955	...	...		2355	...	...	...	...	...

		Ⓐ	Ⓐ ♡	Ⓐ	Ⓐ ⊡	Ⓐ ♥	Ⓐ	Ⓐ	Ⓐ ♡	Ⓐ	Ⓐ ♥	Ⓐ	Ⓐ	Ⓐ ♡	Ⓐ	Ⓐ ♥	Ⓐ		Ⓐ	Ⓐ ♡	Ⓐ	Ⓐ ♥	Ⓐ	Ⓐ ♡
Charleroi Sud d.	Ⓐ	...	...	...	0428	...	...	...	0525	...	...	0555	...	0625	...	...	0655		...	1925	...	...	1955	2025
Nivelles d.		...	...	...	0457	...	...	...	0550	...	...	0620	...	0650	...	...	0720		...	1950	...	...	2020	2050
Brussels Midi/Zuid a.		...	...	...	0535	...	...	...	0615	...	...	0645	...	0715	...	...	0745	and	...	2015	...	...	2045	2115
Brussels Midi/Zuid d.		0449	0519	0526	0538	0545	0549	0556	0619	0626	0645	0649	0656	0718	0726	0745	0747	at	1956	2018	2026	2045	2049	2119
Brussels Central d.		0454	0524	0531	0542	0550	0554	0601	0624	0631	0650	0654	0701	0723	0731	0749	0752	the	2001	2023	2031	2050	2054	2124
Brussels Nord d.		0502	0530	0537	0549	0556	0602	0608	0630	0637	0656	0702	0708	0730	0737	0756	0802	same	2008	2030	2037	2056	2102	2130
Brussels Airport ✈ d.		|	|	|	|	0611	|	|	|	|	0711	|	|	|	|	0811	|	minutes	|	|	|	2111	|	|
Mechelen d.		0517	0547	0558	0621	0625	0618	0629	0647	0658	0725	0718	0729	0747	0758	0825	0818	past	2029	2047	2058	2125	2118	2147
Antwerpen Berchem d.		0532	0601	0619	0651	0639	0632	0650	0701	0719	0739	0732	0750	0801	0819	0839	0832	each	2050	2101	2119	2139	2132	2201
Antwerpen Centraal a.		0536	0605	0623	0655	0643	0636	0654	0705	0723	0743	0736	0754	0805	0823	0843	0836	hour	2054	2105	2123	2143	2136	2205
Antwerpen Centraal d.		...	...	...	...	0645	...	...	...	...	0745	...	...	...	...	0845	...	until	...	...	...	2145	...	...
Noorderkempen (Brecht) d.		...	...	...	...	0701	...	...	...	...	0801	...	...	...	...	0901	...		...	...	...	2201	...	...
Breda ▦ a.		...	...	...	...	0718	...	...	...	...	0818	...	...	...	...	0918	...		...	...	...	2218	...	...

	Ⓐ	Ⓐ	Ⓐ	Ⓐ	Ⓐ	Ⓐ	Ⓐ	Ⓐ ⊡		Ⓒ ♥	Ⓒ	Ⓒ	Ⓒ ♥	Ⓒ	Ⓒ		Ⓒ ♥	Ⓒ	Ⓒ	Ⓒ	Ⓒ	Ⓒ	Ⓒ	⑥ ⊡
Charleroi Sud d.	...	2055	2125	...	2155	2225	...	...	Ⓒ	...	0505	...	...	0605	...		...	2005	...	2105	...	2205	...	...
Nivelles d.	...	2120	2150	...	2220	2250	...	2255		...	0529	...	...	0629	...		...	2029	...	2129	...	2229	...	2304
Brussels Midi/Zuid a.	...	2145	2215	...	2245	2315	...	2335		...	0554	...	...	0654	...	and	...	2054	...	2154	...	2255	...	2340
Brussels Midi/Zuid d.	2126	2149	2219	2226	2249	2319	2326	2339		0544	0600	0628	0644	0700	0728	at	2044	2100	2128	2200	2228	2300	2328	2342
Brussels Central d.	2131	2154	2224	2231	2254	2324	2331	2343		0549	0604	0632	0649	0704	0732	the	2049	2104	2132	2204	2232	2304	2332	2346
Brussels Nord d.	2137	2202	2230	2237	2302	2328	2337	2349		0556	0610	0638	0656	0710	0738	same	2056	2110	2138	2210	2238	2310	2338	2353
Brussels Airport ✈ d.	|	|	|	|	|	...	|	|		0611	|	|	0711	|	|	minutes	2111	|	|	|	|	|	|	|
Mechelen d.	2158	2218	2247	2258	2318	...	2358	0021		0625	0629	0656	0725	0729	0756	past	2125	2129	2156	2229	2256	2329	2356	0021
Antwerpen Berchem d.	2219	2232	2301	2319	2332	...	0019	0051		0639	0647	0713	0739	0747	0813	each	2139	2147	2213	2247	2313	2347	0013	0051
Antwerpen Centraal a.	2223	2236	2305	2323	2336	...	0023	0055		0643	0651	0717	0743	0751	0817	hour	2143	2151	2217	2251	2317	2351	0017	0055
Antwerpen Centraal d.	...	...	...	...	...	...	...	...		0645	...	...	0745	...	...	until	2145	...	...	...	...	...	...	...
Noorderkempen (Brecht) d.	...	...	...	...	...	...	...	...		0701	...	...	0801	...	...		2201	...	...	...	...	...	...	...
Breda ▦ a.	...	...	...	...	...	...	...	...		0718	...	...	0818	...	...		2218	...	...	...	...	...	...	...

♥ – From/to Amsterdam or Den Haag via Rotterdam (Table **18**).
♡ – From/to Essen (Belgium), Table **419**.
◇ – No journey at 2108.
⊙ – Additional journey runs at 2238.
⊡ – Local train.
‡ – Runs mornings of days shown.

BRUSSELS AIRPORT ✈ - CHARLEROI — Runs Ⓐ only

	Ⓐ		Ⓐ	
Brussels Airport ✈ d.	0546		2146	...
Brussels Schuman d.	0603	and	2203	...
Brussels Luxembourg d.	0610	hourly	2210	...
Nivelles d.	0652	until	2252	...
Charleroi Sud a.	0721		2321	...

	Ⓐ		Ⓐ	
Charleroi Sud d.	0537		2137	...
Nivelles d.	0606	and	2206	...
Brussels Luxembourg d.	0652	hourly	2252	...
Brussels Schuman d.	0657	until	2257	...
Brussels Airport ✈ a.	0712		2312	...

421 CHARLEROI - MARIEMBOURG - COUVIN — Line 132

km			Ⓐ	Ⓐ	Ⓐ		Ⓐ	Ⓐ		Ⓒ		Ⓒ
0	**Charleroi** Sud d.	Ⓐ	0553	0700	0811		2011	2140	Ⓒ	0815		2215
18	Berzée d.		0617	0724	0831	every	2031	2203		0838	every	2238
22	Walcourt d.		0623	0733	0836	hour	2036	2212		0846	**two**	2246
35	Philippeville d.		0637	0747	0850	until	2050	2227		0900	hours	2300
48	Mariembourg ▲ d.		0648	0800	0901	△	2101	2238		0911	until	2311
53	**Couvin** a.		0656	0808	0910		2110	2246		0919		2319

		Ⓐ	Ⓐ		Ⓐ	Ⓐ		Ⓒ		Ⓒ
Couvin d.	Ⓐ	0615	0750		1950	2051	Ⓒ	0638		2038
Mariembourg ▲ d.		0626	0801	every	2001	2101		0649	every	2049
Philippeville d.		0638	0812	hour	2012	2112		0703	**two**	2103
Walcourt d.		0652	0826	until	2026	2126		0718	hours	2118
Berzée d.		0656	0830	▽	2030	2133		0724	until	2124
Charleroi Sud a.		0716	0850		2050	2157		0745		2145

△ – Also at 1640, 1721, 1737, 1823 (no journey at 1711).
▽ – Also from Couvin at 0432, 0547, 1629, 1759 (no journeys at 1650, 1750).
▲ – For MARIEMBOURG - TREIGNES heritage railway operated by Chemin de Fer à Vapeur des 3 Vallées (CFV3V). For days of running and timings see www.cfv3v.com

ENGINEERING WORK: Mariembourg - Couvin is by 🚌 Apr. 1 - Oct. 31.
Arrivals at Couvin are 9 minutes later; departures from Couvin are 9 minutes earlier.

BRUSSELS - MONS - QUIÉVRAIN 422
Lines 96, 97

km		Ⓐ	Ⓐ ◇	Ⓐ	Ⓐ ◇	Ⓐ		Ⓐ ◇	Ⓐ	Ⓐ ◇	Ⓐ	Ⓐ ◇	Ⓐ	Ⓐ ◇	Ⓐ	Ⓐ ◇	Ⓐ		Ⓒ		Ⓒ
0	**Brussels Airport** ✈ d.	0530	...	0630	...	0730		...	1930	...	2030	...	2130	...	2230	...	2330	...	0531		2231
12	Brussels Nord **423** d.	0543	0613	0643	0713	0743	and	1913	1943	2013	2043	2113	2143	2213	2243	2313	2343	...	0543		2243
14	Brussels Central **423** d.	0548	0617	0648	0717	0748	at	1917	1948	2017	2048	2117	2148	2217	2248	2317	2348	...	0548		2248
16	**Brussels** Midi / Zuid **423** d.	0556	0624	0655	0724	0755	the	1924	1956	2024	2056	2124	2156	2224	2256	2324	2356	...	0556	and	2256
32	Halle **423** d.	|	0634	|	0734	|	same	1934	|	2034	|	2134	|	2234	|	2334	|	...	|	hourly	|
45	Braine-le-Comte **423** d.	0618	0648	0719	0748	0818	minutes	1948	2018	2048	2118	2148	2218	2248	2318	2348	0018	...	0617	until	2317
51	Soignies d.	0624	0654	0725	0754	0824	past	1954	2024	2054	2124	2154	2224	2254	2324	2354	0024	...	0623		2323
76	**Mons** a.	0643	0712	0744	0812	0844	each	2012	2043	2112	2143	2212	2243	2312	2343	0012	0043	...	0641		2341
76	**Mons** d.	...	0714	...	0814	...	hour	2014	...	2114	...	2214	...	2314	...	...	...	...	⊡		⊡
86	Saint-Ghislain a.	...	0728	...	0828	...	until	2028	...	2128	...	2228	...	2328	...	...	...	...	⊡		⊡
96	**Quiévrain** a.	...	0746	...	0846	...		2046	...	...	...	...	...	...	...	...	...	...	⊡		⊡

	Ⓐ	Ⓐ ◇	Ⓐ	Ⓐ ◇	Ⓐ	Ⓐ ◇	Ⓐ	Ⓐ ◇	Ⓐ		Ⓐ ◇	Ⓐ	Ⓐ ◇	Ⓐ	Ⓐ			Ⓒ		Ⓒ	
Quiévrain d.	...	...	...	0514	...	0614	...	0714	...		1914	...	2014	...	...	...	...	⊡		⊡	...
Saint-Ghislain d.	...	...	...	0533	...	0633	...	0733	...	and	1933	...	2033	...	...	...	...	⊡		⊡	...
Mons a.	...	...	...	0547	...	0647	...	0747	...	at	1947	...	2047	...	...	...	...	⊡		⊡	...
Mons d.	0420	0449	0520	0549	0618	0649	0718	0749	0818	the	1949	2018	2049	2119	2220	...	...	0519		2219	...
Soignies d.	0439	0508	0539	0608	0638	0708	0738	0808	0839	same	2008	2039	2108	2138	2239	...	...	0538		2238	...
Braine-le-Comte **423** d.	0447	0515	0547	0615	0644	0715	0744	0815	0847	minutes	2015	2047	2115	2145	2247	...	...	0547	and	2247	...
Halle **423** d.	|	0527	|	0627	|	0727	|	0827	|	past	2027	|	2127	|	|	...	...	|	hourly	|	...
Brussels Midi / Zuid **423** a.	0506	0536	0606	0636	0703	0736	0804	0836	0906	each	2036	2106	2136	2207	2306	...	...	0606	until	2306	...
Brussels Central **423** a.	0513	0542	0613	0642	0710	0742	0810	0842	0913	hour	2042	2113	2142	2213	2313	...	...	0613		2313	...
Brussels Nord **423** a.	0518	0547	0618	0647	0715	0747	0815	0847	0918	until	2047	2118	2147	2218	2318	...	...	0618		2318	...
Brussels Airport ✈ d.	0531	...	0631	...	0728	...	0828	...	0931		...	2131	...	2231	2331	...	...	0631		2331	...

◇ – From / to Liège via Landen (Table **430**).

⊡ – MONS - QUIÉVRAIN LOCAL TRAINS ON Ⓒ: from Mons hourly 0654Ⓒ - 2054Ⓒ, from Quiévrain hourly 0737Ⓒ - 2137Ⓒ.

BRUSSELS - LA LOUVIÈRE - BINCHE 423
Lines 96, 108

For additional trains Brussels - Halle - Braine-le-Comte see Table **422**

km		Ⓐ		Ⓐ	Ⓐ	Ⓐ	Ⓒ		Ⓒ
0	**Brussels** Nord d.	0618		2018	2118	2218	0618		2218
2	Brussels Central d.	0623		2023	2123	2223	0622		2222
4	**Brussels** Midi / Zuid d.	0630	and	2030	2130	2230	0630	and	2230
20	Halle d.	0640	hourly	2040	2140	2240	0641	hourly	2241
33	Braine-le-Comte d.	0657	until	2057	2157	2257	0700	until	2300
52	**La Louvière** Centre a.	0717		2117	2217	2317	0720		2320
55	La Louvière Sud a.	0722		2122	2222	2322	0725		2325
64	**Binche** a.	0740		2140	...	...	0748		2348

	Ⓐ		Ⓐ	Ⓒ	Ⓒ		Ⓒ
Binche d.	0523		2123	0512	0612		2212
La Louvière Sud d.	0538		2138	0535	0635		2235
La Louvière Centre d.	0543	and	2143	0540	0640	and	2240
Braine-le-Comte d.	0605	hourly	2205	0605	0705	hourly	2305
Halle d.	0620	until	2220	0620	0720	until	2320
Brussels Midi / Zuid a.	0630		2230	0630	0730		2330
Brussels Central a.	0637		2237	0636	0736		2336
Brussels Nord a.	0642		2242	0641	0741		2341

)n Ⓐ trains run beyond Brussels to / from Turnhout (Table **434**). On Ⓒ trains run beyond Brussels Nord to / from Brussels Schaarbeek.

BRUSSELS - GERAARDSBERGEN 424
Lines 94, 123 (S6)

km		Ⓐ		Ⓐ	Ⓒ		Ⓒ
0	**Brussels** Nord d.	0442		2042	0742		2042
2	Brussels Centraal d.	0446	and	2046	0746	and	2046
4	**Brussels** Midi / Zuid d.	0453	hourly	2053	0753	hourly	2053
18	Halle d.	0504	until	2104	0804	until	2104
33	Edingen d.	0515		2115	0815		2115
49	**Geraardsbergen** a.	0534		2134	0834		2134

	Ⓐ		Ⓐ	Ⓒ		Ⓒ
Geraardsbergen d.	0425		2025	0725		2025
Edingen d.	0446	and	2046	0746	and	2046
Halle d.	0458	hourly	2058	0758	hourly	2058
Brussels Midi / Zuid a.	0507	until	2107	0807	until	2107
Brussels Centraal a.	0513		2113	0813		2113
Brussels Nord a.	0518		2118	0818		2118

MONS - CHARLEROI - NAMUR 425
Lines 118, 130

km		Ⓐ	Ⓐ	Ⓐ	Ⓐ ♡	Ⓐ	Ⓐ ◇	Ⓐ		Ⓐ ◇	Ⓐ	Ⓐ ◇	Ⓐ	Ⓐ	Ⓐ	Ⓒ	Ⓒ ♡	Ⓒ ♡		Ⓒ ♡	Ⓒ ♡
	Tournai **416** d.	...	...	...	0544	...	0644	...	and at	1944	...	2044	...	2144	...	...	0629	0729		2029	2129
0	**Mons** d.	0437	...	0539	0615	0639	0715	0739	the same	2015	2039	2115	2139	2215	2239	0612	0714	0814		2114	2214
20	La Louvière Sud d.	0454	...	0558	0632	0658	0732	0758	minutes	2032	2058	2132	2157	2232	2258	0633	0733	0833	and	2133	2233
41	**Charleroi** Sud d.	0513	0550	0618	0650	0718	0750	0818	past	2050	2118	2150	2216	2250	2316	0653	0754	0854	hourly	2154	2254
56	Tamines d.	0527	0602	0629	0702	0729	0802	0829	each	2102	2129	2202	2229	2302	...	0706	0807	0907	until	2207	2307
78	**Namur** a.	0549	0621	0649	0721	0749	0821	0849	hour	2121	2149	2221	2251	2321	...	0729	0830	0930		2230	2330
	Liège Guillemins **442** a.	0636	...	0736	...	0836	...	0936	until	...	2236	...	...	...	...	0820	0920	1020		2320	...

	Ⓐ	Ⓐ	Ⓐ ◇	Ⓐ	Ⓐ	Ⓐ	Ⓐ ◇		Ⓐ	Ⓐ	Ⓐ	Ⓐ	Ⓐ	Ⓐ	Ⓐ	Ⓒ ♡	Ⓒ ♡	Ⓒ ♡		Ⓒ ♡	Ⓒ
Liège Guillemins **442** a.	...	...	...	0524	...	0624	...	and at	1924	...	2024	...	2124	...	2224	...	...	0640		2040	2140
Namur d.	...	0508	0540	0612	0640	0712	0740	the same	2012	2040	2112	2140	2211	2240	2311	...	0630	0730		2130	2231
Tamines d.	...	0529	0558	0630	0658	0730	0758	minutes	2030	2058	2130	2158	2232	2258	2332	...	0654	0754	and	2154	2255
Charleroi Sud d.	0444	0544	0612	0644	0712	0744	0812	past	2044	2112	2144	2212	2247	2310	2346	0609	0709	0809	hourly	2209	2307
La Louvière Sud d.	0505	0605	0630	0705	0730	0805	0830	each	2105	2130	2205	2230	2306	...	...	0630	0730	0830	until	2230	...
Mons a.	0521	0621	0645	0721	0745	0821	0845	hour	2121	2145	2221	2245	2322	...	...	0646	0746	0846		2246	...
Tournai **416** a.	...	...	0715	...	0815	...	0915	until	...	2215	...	2320	...	...	...	0730	0830	0930		2330	...

› – Certain journeys run from / to Lille Flandres (Table **416**).

♡ – From / to Mouscron (Table **416**).

MONS - QUÉVY 426
Line 96

km		Ⓐ	Ⓐ	Ⓐ		Ⓐ	Ⓐ §	Ⓐ §	Ⓐ	Ⓐ	Ⓐ
0	Mons d.	0723	0822	0922	hourly	1622	1729	1810	1856	1922	2022
18	Quévy d.	0738	0838	0938	until	1638	1747	1829	1911	1938	2038

	Ⓐ	Ⓐ ‡	Ⓐ	Ⓐ	Ⓐ ‡	Ⓐ	Ⓐ		Ⓐ	Ⓐ
Quévy d.	0522	0559	0622	0655	0717	0822	0922	hourly	1822	1922
Mons a.	0539	0616	0639	0711	0734	0839	0939	until	1839	1939

– From Brussels (depart Brussels Midi 1640 and 1717).

‡ – To Brussels (arrive Brussels Midi 0703 and 0820).

No service on Ⓒ.

CHARLEROI - ERQUELINNES 427
Line 130a

km		Ⓐ		Ⓐ	Ⓒ		Ⓒ
0	**Charleroi** Sud d.	0553	and	1953	0614	every	2014
14	Thuin d.	0610	hourly	2010	0629	**two**	2029
16	Lobbes d.	0615	until	2015	0634	hours	2034
29	**Erquelinnes** a.	0631		2031	0652	until	2052

	Ⓐ		Ⓐ	Ⓒ		Ⓒ
Erquelinnes d.	0500	and	2000	0705	every	2105
Lobbes d.	0517	hourly	2017	0724	**two**	2124
Thuin d.	0520	until	2020	0727	hours	2127
Charleroi Sud a.	0539		2039	0745	until	2145

ɜumont (France) is approximately 2 km from Erquelinnes station (for Jeumont - Lille see Table **262**).

CROSS-BORDER SERVICES 428

	Ⓐ	Ⓐ	⑥	⑥	⑦	⑦			
amur d.	0519r	...	0619r	...	0719r	...	...	1607r	...
harleroi Sud d.	0550	...	0650	...	0750	...	...	1649	...
ons d.	|	0615	|	0715	|	0815	...	|	...
aubeuge 🏛 a.	0626	|	0726	|	0826	|	...	1726	...
ulnoye-Aymeries 🏛 a.	...	0642	...	0744	...	0842	...	...	...

	Ⓐ	Ⓐ		Ⓒ	Ⓒ				
Aulnoye-Aymeries 🏛 d.	...	0917	...	...	1220	...	...	...	...
Maubeuge 🏛 d.	0930	|	...	1232	|	...	2132	...	...
Mons a.	|	0945	...	|	1250	...	|	...	...
Charleroi Sud a.	1007	...	...	1307	...	...	2207	...	...
Namur a.	1054r	...	...	1340r	...	...	2240r	...	...

– Not Apr. 8 - Nov. 3 due to engineering work.

Trains call only at the stations shown. For connections Maubeuge - Paris and Aulnoye - Paris see Table **255**.

430 BRUSSELS - LANDEN - HASSELT, GENK and LIÈGE

Lines 36, 21

For direct services Brussels - Liège via high-speed line see Table **400**. For other services Brussels - Hasselt on Ⓐ (via Aarshot) see Table **431**.

km			Ⓐ	Ⓐ	Ⓐ	Ⓐ	Ⓐ	Ⓐ		Ⓐ	Ⓐ	Ⓐ	Ⓐ	Ⓐ	Ⓐ	Ⓐ	Ⓐ		Ⓐ	Ⓐ	Ⓐ	Ⓐ	Ⓐ	Ⓐ
			♡		•	♡	△	•		♡	△	•	♡	△	b	△u	bv		N					
0	**Brussels** Midi / Zuid d.	Ⓐ	0511	0515	0539	0611	0615	0639		2112	2115	2139	2211	2215	2257	2315	0020		1547	1603	1631	1707	1731	1800
2	Brussels Central d.		0516	0519	0543	0616	0619	0643	and	2116	2119	2143	2216	2219	2302	2319	0025		1552	1608	1636	1712	1736	1805
4	Brussels Nord d.		0522	0525	0549	0622	0625	0649	at	2122	2126	2149	2222	2225	2308	2325	0031		1602	1614	1642	1718	1742	1812
16	**Brussels Airport** ✈ d.		|	0537	|	|	0637	|	the	|	2138	|	|	2237	|	2337	|	A	|	|	|	|	|	|
33	Leuven d.		0543	0553	0610	0643	0653	0710	same	2143	2153	2210	2243	2253	2327	2353	0050	L	1621	1635	1703	1738	1803	1832
64	Tienen d.		0556	0608	0624	0656	0708	0724	minutes	2156	2208	2224	2256	2308	2340	0008	0102	S	1638	1649	1717	1752	1817	1845
64	Landen d.		0606	0622	0635	0706	0722	0735	past	2206	2222	2235	2306	2322	2349	0022	0111	O	1653	1700	1729	1802	1829	1855
75	Sint-Truiden d.		0615	...	|	0715	...	|	each	2215	...	|	2315	...	|	...	|		1704	|	1745	|	1845	...
92	**Hasselt** a.		0630	...	|	0730	...	|	hour	2230	...	|	2330	...	|	...	|		1719	|	1801	|	1903	...
108	Genk a.		0652	...	|	0752s	...	|	until	2252	...	|	...	...	|	...	|		...	|	...	|	1923	...
103	**Liège** Guillemins a.		...	...	0707	...	...	0806		...	...	2306	...	...	0018	...	0141		...	1733	...	1835	...	...

		Ⓒ	Ⓒ	Ⓒ	Ⓒ	Ⓒ	Ⓒ	Ⓒ	Ⓒ		Ⓒ	Ⓒ	Ⓒ	Ⓒ	Ⓒ	Ⓒ	Ⓒ	Ⓒ						
		♡		♡		△	♡		△		♡		△	♡	△	b	△	b						
Brussels Midi / Zuid d.	Ⓒ	0612	...	0712	...	0715	0812	...	0815		2112	...	2115	2212	2215	2256	2315	0020	...	...	...	...	...	...
Brussels Central d.		0617	...	0717	...	0719	0817	...	0819	and	2117	...	2119	2217	2219	2301	2319	0025	...	...	...	...	...	...
Brussels Nord d.		0623	...	0723	...	0725	0823	...	0825	at	2123	...	2125	2223	2225	2307	2325	0031	...	...	...	...	...	...
Brussels Airport ✈ d.		|	...	|	...	0738	|	...	0838	the	|	...	2138	|	2238	|	2338	|	...	...	...	...	...	...
Leuven d.		0644	...	0744	...	0754	0844	...	0854	same	2144	...	2154	2244	2254	2327	2352	0050	...	...	...	...	...	...
Tienen d.		0657	...	0757	...	0809	0857	...	0909	minutes	2157	...	2209	2257	2309	2340	...	0102	...	...	...	...	...	...
Landen d.		0707	0712	0807	0812	0823	0907	0912	0923	past	2207	2212	2223	2307	2323	2349	...	0113	...	...	...	...	...	...
Sint-Truiden d.		0716	|	0816	|	...	0916	|	...	each	2216	|	...	2316	...	|	...	|	...	...	...	...	...	...
Hasselt a.		0731	|	0831	|	...	0931	|	...	hour	2231	|	...	2331	...	|	...	|	...	...	...	...	...	...
Genk a.		0752	|	0852	|	...	0952	|	...	until	2252	|	...	2352	...	|	...	|	...	...	...	...	...	...
Liège Guillemins a.		...	0750	...	0850	...	...	0950	...		...	2250	...	...	...	0018	...	0144	...	...	...	...	...	...

		Ⓐ	Ⓐ	Ⓐ	Ⓐ	Ⓐ	Ⓐ	Ⓐ	Ⓐ	Ⓐ	Ⓐ	Ⓐ	Ⓐ	Ⓐ		Ⓐ	Ⓐ	Ⓐ	Ⓐ		Ⓐ	Ⓐ	Ⓐ	Ⓐ
		△	♡	b	•	△	♡	N	•		△	♡	•	△		♡	•		b					N
Liège Guillemins d.	Ⓐ	...	...	0440	0456	...	...	...	0556	...	...	...	0656	...		...	2156	...	2306		0626	...	0726	...
Genk d.		...	...	|	|	...	0507	...	|	0533	...	0607r	|	...	and	2107	|	...	|		|	0626	|	1537
Hasselt d.		...	0421	|	|	...	0528	...	|	0557	...	0628	|	...	at	2128	|	...	|		|	0657	|	1557
Sint-Truiden d.		...	0437	|	|	...	0544	...	|	0615	...	0644	|	...	the	2144	|	...	|	A	|	0715	|	1615
Landen d.		...	0447	0509	0527	0537	0554	0604	0626	0630	0634	0654	0726	0737	same	2154	2226	2237	2334	L	0701	0730	0801	1630
Tienen d.		...	0503	0519	0538	0551	0605	0615	0637	0642	0648	0705	0737	0751	minutes	2205	2237	2251	2344	S	0712	0742	0812	1642
Leuven d.		0508	0520	0536	0552	0608	0619	0629	0652	0658	0708	0719	0752	0808	past	2219	2252	2308	2358	O	0727	0758	0827	1656
Brussels Airport ✈ a.		0524	|	|	|	0624	|	|	|	|	0724	|	|	0824	each	|	|	2324	|		|	|	|	...
Brussels Nord a.		0534	0538	0553	0611	0634	0638	0647	0711	0717	0734	0738	0811	0834	hour	2238	2311	2334	0016		0745	0817	0845	...
Brussels Central a.		0539	0544	0559	0616	0640	0644	0653	0716	0723	0739	0744	0816	0839	until	2244	2316	2340	0022		0751	0823	0851	...
Brussels Midi / Zuid a.		0544	0549	0604	0621	0645	0649	0658	0721	0728	0744	0749	0821	0844		2249	2321	2345	0027		0756	0828	0856	...

		Ⓒ	Ⓒ	Ⓒ	Ⓒ	Ⓒ	Ⓒ	Ⓒ	Ⓒ	Ⓒ	Ⓒ	Ⓒ	Ⓒ		Ⓒ	Ⓒ	Ⓒ	Ⓒ	Ⓒ	Ⓒ	Ⓒ	Ⓒ		
		△	b	△	△	♡	△		♡	△		♡	△			♡	△		♡		♡	b		
Liège Guillemins d.	Ⓒ	...	0441	...	...	...	...	0708	...	...	0808	...	...		2008	...	...	2108	...	2208	...	2306	...	...
Genk d.		...	|	...	...	...	...	|	0706	...	|	0808	...	and	|	2008	...	|	2108	|	2204	|	...	...
Hasselt d.		...	|	...	...	0630	...	|	0730	...	|	0830	...	at	|	2030	...	|	2130	|	2230	|	...	...
Sint-Truiden d.		...	|	...	...	0645	...	|	0745	...	|	0845	...	the	|	2045	...	|	2145	|	2245	|	...	...
Landen d.		...	0509	0537	0637	0654	0737	0746	0754	0837	0846	0854	0937	same	2046	2054	2137	2146	2154	2246	2254	2334	...	...
Tienen d.		...	0520	0551	0651	0705	0751	...	0805	0851	...	0905	0951	minutes	...	2105	2151	...	2205	...	2305	2344	...	...
Leuven d.		0508	0533	0608	0708	0719	0808	...	0819	0908	...	0919	1008	past	...	2119	2208	...	2219	...	2319	2358	...	...
Brussels Airport ✈ a.		0524	|	0624	0724	|	0824	...	|	0925	...	|	1024	each	...	|	2224	...	|	...	|	|	...	...
Brussels Nord a.		0534	0549	0634	0735	0738	0834	...	0838	0935	...	0938	1034	hour	...	2138	2234	...	2238	...	2338	0016	...	...
Brussels Central a.		0540	0555	0640	0740	0744	0840	...	0844	0940	...	0944	1040	until	...	2144	2240	...	2244	...	2344	0022	...	...
Brussels Midi / Zuid a.		0545	0600	0645	0745	0749	0845	...	0849	0945	...	0949	1045		...	2149	2245	...	2249	...	2349	0027	...	...

N – Not Dec. 24 - Jan. 4, Apr. 8-22, July 1 - Aug. 30.
b – From / to Brugge and Oostende (Table **400**).
r – Variations: 1007 departs 1005 (change at Hasselt); 1307 departs at 1300; 1807 departs at 1805; 1907 departs at 1903.
s – 1311 from Brussels requires change at Hasselt.
u – On ①–④ to Dec. 13 terminates at Leuven (🚌 connection to Landen).
v – On ①–④ to Dec. 13 diverted via high-speed line, not calling at Tienen or Landen.
♡ – From / to Brugge and Gent, Table **405** (most trains also from / to Blankenberge).
△ – From / to Gent via Aalst, Table **412** (on Ⓒ most trains also from / to De Panne, Table **411**
• – From / to Mons (Table **422**).

431 BRUSSELS - AARSCHOT - HASSELT - TONGEREN

Line 35

km			Ⓐ	Ⓐ		Ⓐ	Ⓐ	Ⓐ	
	Gent 412 ▷ d.	Ⓐ	0441	0540		1940	2040	2140	...
0	**Brussels** Midi / Zuid d.		0544	0644		2044	2144	2244	...
2	Brussels Central d.		0549	0649	and	2049	2149	2249	...
4	Brussels Nord d.		0555	0655	hourly	2055	2155	2255	...
46	Aarschot **432** d.		0621	0721	until	2121	2221	2321	...
63	Diest **432** d.		0634	0734		2134	2234	2334	...
84	**Hasselt** **432** a.		0649	0749		2149	2249	2349	...
110	Tongeren **435** a.		0724	0820s		2220	...	...	...

		Ⓐ	Ⓐ	Ⓐ		Ⓐ	Ⓐ	
Tongeren **435** d.	Ⓐ	...	0539	0639r		2039	2139	...
Hasselt **432** d.		0511	0611	0711		2111	2211	...
Diest **432** d.		0527	0627	0727	and	2127	2227	...
Aarschot **432** d.		0541	0641	0741	hourly	2141	2241	...
Brussels Nord a.		0605	0705	0805	until	2205	2305	...
Brussels Central a.		0611	0711	0811		2211	2311	...
Brussels Midi / Zuid a.		0616	0716	0816		2216	2316	...
Gent 412 ▷ a.		0719	0819	0919		2319	0019	...

r – Journeys from Tongeren at 0939Ⓐ and 1939Ⓐ require a change at Hasselt.
s – 1240Ⓐ from Gent (1344Ⓐ from Brussels Midi) requires a change at Hasselt.
▷ – Gent to Brussels is via Aalst and Denderleeuw (Table **412**).
☛ No service on Ⓒ via this route. For other trains Brussels - Hasselt (via Landen) see Table 43

432 ANTWERPEN - BRUSSELS NATIONAAL ✈ - AARSCHOT - HASSELT

Lines 35, 36c, 1

For Antwerpen - Hasselt via Mol see Table **434**. For additional trains Brussels Nationaal ✈ - Leuven see Table **430**.

km	*Via Airport*		Ⓐ		Ⓐ		Ⓒ		Ⓒ	Ⓒ
0	**Antwerpen** Centraal . **420** d.	Ⓐ	0448		2248	Ⓒ	0536	hourly	2136	2236
24	Mechelen **420** d.		0508		2308		0556	on ⑥	2156	2256
40	**Brussels Airport** ✈ . **420** d.		0521	and	2321		0610		2210	2310
59	Leuven d.		0542	hourly	2342		0634	**two**	2234	2334
75	Aarschot d.		0555	until	2355		0647	hourly	2247	2347
92	Diest d.		0608		0008		0706	on ⑦	2306	0006
113	**Hasselt** a.		0622		0022		0723	♠	2323	0023

		Ⓐ		Ⓐ		Ⓒ ‡	Ⓒ		Ⓒ
Hasselt d.	Ⓐ	0438		2238	Ⓒ	...	0637	hourly	223
Diest d.		0453		2253		...	0654	on ⑥	225
Aarschot d.		0507	and	2307		...	0714		231
Leuven d.		0524	hourly	2324		0536	0736	**two**	233
Brussels Airport ✈ .. **420** a.		0539	until	2339		0550	0750	hourly	235
Mechelen **420** a.		0552		2352		0604	0804	on ⑦	000
Antwerpen Centraal .. **420** a.		0612		0012		0624	0824	♥	002

km	*Via Lier*		Ⓐ		Ⓐ		Ⓒ		Ⓒ	Ⓒ ◇
0	**Antwerpen** Centraal d.	Ⓐ	0630		2230	Ⓒ	0631		1931	2031
14	Lier d.		0648	and	2248		0649		1949	2049
41	Aarschot d.		0712	hourly	2312		0717	and	2017	2117
57	**Leuven** a.		0724	until	2324		|	hourly	|	|
59	Diest d.		...		...		0730	until	2030	2130
80	**Hasselt** a.		...		...		0744	⊡	2044	2144
	Tongeren 435 a.		...		...		0812		2112	2212
	Liège Guillemins 435 a.		...		...		0850		2150	...

		Ⓐ		Ⓐ		Ⓒ	Ⓒ		Ⓒ
Liège Guillemins 435 d.	Ⓐ	...		...	Ⓒ	...	0611		211
Tongeren 435 d.		...		...		...	0648		214
Hasselt d.		...		...		0616	0716	and	221
Diest d.		...		...		0631	0731	hourly	223
Leuven d.		0636	and	2036		|	|	until	|
Aarschot d.		0650	hourly	2050		0650	0750	⊡	225
Lier d.		0714	until	2114		0713	0813		231
Antwerpen Centraal a.		0730		2130		0729	0829		232

♠ – On ⑦ runs **hourly** to Leuven and every **two** hours 0536-2136 to Hasselt (also 2236).
♥ – On ⑦ runs every **two** hours from Hasselt; Leuven - Antwerpen runs **hourly** 0536-2336.
◇ – Also at 2131 to Tongeren, 2231 to Hasselt.
⊡ – On Ⓒ additional local trains run hourly Antwerpen - Aarschot - Leuven (journey 64 mins from Antwerpen 0645-2245, from Leuven 0611-2211.
‡ – Also at 0636.

Line 15 BRUSSELS and ANTWERPEN - LIER - TURNHOUT / HASSELT / HAMONT 434

km			Ⓐ	Ⓐ	Ⓐ	Ⓐ	Ⓐ	Ⓐ		Ⓐ	Ⓐ	Ⓐ	Ⓐ	Ⓐ	Ⓐ 🚌	Ⓐ	Ⓐ	Ⓐ	Ⓐ	Ⓐ	Ⓐ	Ⓐ	Ⓐ
	Brussels Midi / Zuid ▷ d.	Ⓐ	...	...	...	0633	...	...		1833	...	...	1933	...	...	...	2033	...	...	2133	...	2233	...
	Brussels Centraal ▷ d.		...	...	...	0638	...	...		1838	...	...	1938	...	...	...	2038	...	...	2138	...	2238	...
	Brussels Nord ▷ d.		...	...	...	0644	...	...	and	1844	...	...	1944	...	...	...	2044	...	...	2144	...	2244	...
	Mechelen ▷ d.		...	...	...	0704	...	...	at	1904	...	...	2004	...	...	...	2104	...	...	2204	...	2304	...
0	**Antwerpen** Centraal d.		...	0609	0647	|	0709	0748	the	|	1909	1948	|	2009	...	2048	|	2109	2148	|	2225	|	2325
2	Antwerpen Berchem d.		...	0615	0653	|	0715	0753	same	|	1915	1953	|	2015	...	2053	|	2115	2153	|	2230	|	2330
15	Lier d.		...	0627	0704	0722	0727	0804	minutes	1922	1927	2004	2022	2027	...	2104	2122	2127	2204	2222	2245	2322	2346
34	Herentals d.		...	0643	0722	0738	0743	0822	past	1938	1943	2022	2038	2043	...	2122	2138	2143	2222	2238	2309	2338	0009
	Turnhout a.		...	|	0738	0754	|	0838	each	1954	|	2038	2054	|	...	2138	2154	|	2238	2254	|	2354	|
46	Geel d.		...	0655	...	...	0755	...	hour	...	1955	...	...	2055	...	...	...	2155	...	...	2321	...	0021
56	Mol a.		0607	0702	...	...	0802	...	until	...	2002	...	...	2102	2110	...	...	2202	...	...	2328	...	0028
99	**Hasselt** a.		0652	0752r	...	...	0852r	...		...	2052r	...	...	2152r	|	...	...	2252	...	...	...	...	...
77	Overpelt a.		...	0726	...	...	0826	...		...	2026	...	...	...	2145	...	...	...	...	...	...	...	...
79	Neerpelt a.		...	0729	...	...	0829	...		...	2029	...	...	...	2149	...	...	...	...	...	...	...	...
87	**Hamont** a.		...	0739	...	...	0839	...		...	2039	...	...	...	2205	...	...	...	...	...	...	...	...

km			Ⓐ	Ⓐ	Ⓐ	Ⓐ	Ⓐ	Ⓐ	Ⓐ	Ⓐ	Ⓐ	Ⓐ	Ⓐ		Ⓐ	Ⓐ	Ⓐ	Ⓐ	Ⓐ	Ⓐ	Ⓐ	Ⓐ	
	Hamont d.	Ⓐ	...	...	...	...	...	...	0619	...	...	0719	...		...	1919	...	...	2019	...	2119	...	...
	Neerpelt d.		...	...	...	...	...	...	0630	...	...	0730	...		...	1930	...	...	2030	...	2130	...	...
	Overpelt d.		...	...	...	...	...	...	0633	...	...	0733	...	and	...	1933	...	...	2033	...	2133	...	...
	Hasselt d.		...	...	...	...	...	...	0608s	...	...	0708s	...	at	...	1908s	...	...	2008s	...	2108s	2208	...
	Mol d.		0458	...	...	0558	...	...	0658	...	...	0758	...	the	...	1958	...	...	2058	...	2159	2253	...
	Geel d.		0506	...	...	0606	...	...	0706	...	...	0806	...	same	...	2006	...	...	2106	...	2207	...	...
0	**Turnhout** d.		|	0458	0522	|	0605	0622	|	0705	0722	|	0805	minutes	1922	|	2005	2022	|	2105	|	...	...
18	Herentals d.		0519	0523	0542	0619	0623	0640	0719	0723	0741	0819	0823	past	1942	2019	2023	2042	2119	2123	2220	...	...
38	Lier d.		0535	0539	0557	0635	0639	0657	0735	0739	0758	0835	0839	each	1957	2035	2039	2057	2135	2139	2235	...	...
	Antwerpen Berchem a.		0545	|	0607	0645	|	0707	0745	|	0808	0845	|	hour	2007	2045	|	2107	2145	|	2245	...	...
	Antwerpen Centraal a.		0551	|	0612	0651	|	0712	0751	|	0813	0851	|	until	2012	2051	|	2112	2151	|	2251	...	...
55	Mechelen ▷ d.		...	0559	...	...	0659	...	...	0759	...	...	0859		...	...	2059	...	...	2159	...	...	...
75	Brussels Nord ▷ a.		...	0616	...	...	0716	...	...	0816	...	...	0916		...	...	2116	...	...	2216	...	...	...
77	Brussels Central ▷ a.		...	0622	...	...	0722	...	...	0822	...	...	0922		...	...	2122	...	...	2222	...	...	...
79	**Brussels** Midi / Zuid ▷ a.		...	0627	...	...	0727	...	...	0827	...	...	0927		...	...	2127	...	...	2227	...	...	...

		Ⓒ	Ⓒ	Ⓒ	Ⓒ		Ⓒ	Ⓒ	Ⓒ △	Ⓒ ▽
Antwerpen C. d.	Ⓒ	0609	0709	0752	0809		1952	2009	2052	2109
Ant. Berchem d.		0615	0715	0758	0815	and	1958	2015	2058	2115
Lier d.		0627	0727	0810	0827	at	2010	2027	2110	2127
Herentals d.		0643	0743	0832	0843	the	2032	2043	2132	2143
Turnhout a.		|	|	0847	|	same	2047	|	2147	|
Geel d.		0655	0755	...	0855	minutes	...	2055	...	2155
Mol a.		0702	0802	...	0902	past	...	2102	...	2202
Hasselt a.		0752x	0852x	...	0952x	each	...	2152x	...	|
Overpelt a.		0726	0826	...	0926	hour	...	2126	...	2226
Neerpelt a.		0729	0829	...	0929	until	...	2129	...	2229
Hamont a.		0739	0839	...	0939		...	2139	...	2239

		Ⓒ ⊙	Ⓒ ⊡	Ⓒ	Ⓒ	Ⓒ		Ⓒ	Ⓒ	Ⓒ	Ⓒ	Ⓒ
Hamont d.	Ⓒ	0628	...	0719	...	0819		...	2019	...	2119	...
Neerpelt d.		0637	...	0730	...	0830	and	...	2030	...	2130	...
Overpelt d.		0640	...	0733	...	0833	at	...	2033	...	2133	...
Hasselt d.		|	...	|	...	0808z	the	...	2008z	...	2108z	...
Mol d.		0658	...	0758	...	0858	same	...	2058	...	2159	...
Geel d.		0706	...	0806	...	0906	minutes	...	2106	...	2207	...
Turnhout d.		|	0713	|	0813	|	past	2013	|	2113	|	2213
Herentals d.		0719	0730	0819	0830	0919	each	2030	2119	2130	2220	2230
Lier d.		0735	0752	0835	0852	0935	hour	2052	2135	2152	2235	2252
Ant. Berchem a.		0745	0802	0845	0902	0945	until	2102	2145	2202	2245	2302
Antwerpen C. a.		0751	0808	0851	0908	0951		2108	2151	2208	2251	2308

r – Portion for Hasselt is detached from main train at Mol (departs Mol xx07; Hamont portion departs xx10).
s – Portion from Hasselt attaches to main train at Mol (arrives Mol xx53; Hamont portion arrives xx49).
x – Hourly on ⑥. On ⑦ Hasselt is served every **two** hours (from Antwerpen even hours 0609 - 2009). Note **r** applies.
z – Hourly on ⑥. On ⑦ Hasselt is served every **two** hours (departing on even hours 0808 - 2008). Note **s** applies.
▷ – See also Table **420**.
△ – Also at 2152, 2252, 2352.

▽ – Also at 2209, 2309.
⊡ – Also at 0613.
⊙ – Also runs Mol - Antwerpen at 0458 and 0558.

*On Ⓐ Turnhout trains run beyond Brussels to / from Binche (Table **423**).*

Line 34 LIÈGE - HASSELT 435

km			Ⓐ ◇		Ⓐ ◇		Ⓒ ♡		Ⓒ ♡
0	**Liège** Guillemins d.	Ⓐ	0722	and	2022	Ⓒ	0611	and	2111
27	Tongeren 431 d.		0800	hourly	2100		0648	hourly	2148
53	**Hasselt** 431 a.		0822	until	2122		0710	until	2210

		Ⓐ ◇		Ⓐ ◇		Ⓒ ♡		Ⓒ ♡	Ⓒ ♡	Ⓒ ♡
Hasselt 431 d.	Ⓐ	0638	and	2038	Ⓒ	0550	and	2050	2150	2250
Tongeren 431 d.		0701	hourly	2101		0613	hourly	2113	2212	2312
Liège Guillemins a.		0739	until	2139		0650	until	2150	...	...

◇ – From / to Maastricht (Table **436**).

♡ – Most journeys on Ⓒ run beyond Hasselt to / from Antwerpen (Table **432**).

Line 40 LIÈGE - MAASTRICHT 436

km			Ⓐ	Ⓐ	Ⓐ ◇	Ⓐ ◇		Ⓐ ◇	Ⓐ ◇	Ⓐ					⑥	Ⓒ	Ⓒ	Ⓒ		Ⓒ	Ⓒ		
0	**Liège** Guillemins d.	Ⓐ	0609	0640	0740	0840	and	2040	2140	2240	...	...	...	Ⓒ	0608	0708	0808	0908	and	2108	2208	...	...
19	Visé 🏛 d.		0627	0658	0758	0858	hourly	2058	2158	2258	...	...	...		0627	0727	0827	0927	hourly	2127	2227	...	...
32	**Maastricht** a.		0642	0712	0812	0912	until	2112	2212	2312	...	...	...		0642	0742	0842	0942	until	2142	2242	...	...

		Ⓐ	Ⓐ ◇	Ⓐ ◇	Ⓐ ◇		Ⓐ ◇		Ⓐ	Ⓐ	Ⓐ			⑥	Ⓒ	Ⓒ	Ⓒ		Ⓒ	Ⓒ			
Maastricht d.	Ⓐ	...	0649	0749	0849	and	1949	...	2149	2249	2349	...	Ⓒ	0719	0819	0919	1019	and	2219	2319	...	...	...
Visé 🏛 d.		0615	0703	0803	0903	hourly	2003	...	2203	2303	0003	...		0733	0833	0933	1033	hourly	2233	2333	...	...	...
Liège Guillemins a.		0633	0721	0821	0921	until	2021	...	2221	2321	0021	...		0753	0853	0953	1053	until	2253	2351	...	...	...

◇ – To / from Hasselt (Table **435**).

Lines 37, 44 SPA - VERVIERS - AACHEN 438

For international trains Brussels - Aachen and beyond see Tables **20 / 21**.

km		Ⓐ	Ⓐ	Ⓐ ⊡				Ⓐ	Ⓒ	Ⓒ
0	Spa Géronstère d.	...	0604	0647	0747		1947	2047	2047	2147
1	**Spa** d.	...	0607	0650	0750	and	1950	2050	2050	2150
13	Pepinster d.	...	0626	0710	0810	hourly	2010	2110	2110	2210
17	**Verviers** Central a.	...	0630	0716	0816	until	2016	2116	2116	2216
17	**Verviers** Central 400 d.	...	...	0726	0827		2027	2127	2127	2227
31	Welkenraedt 🏛 400 d.	0641	...	0741	0841		2041	2140	2141	2240
50	**Aachen** Hbf a.	0656	...	0756	0856		2056	...	2156	...

		Ⓐ	Ⓒ				Ⓐ	Ⓒ △
Aachen Hbf d.	...	0704	...	0804		2004	2104	2104
Welkenraedt 🏛 400 d.	0621	0721	0721	0821	and	2021	2119	2121
Verviers Central 400 a.	0635	0735	0735	0835	hourly	2035	...	2135
Verviers central d.	0644	0744	0744	0844	until	2044	...	2144
Pepinster d.	0651	0751	0751	0851		2051	...	2151
Spa a.	0710	0810	0810	0910		2110	...	2210
Spa Géronstère a.	0713	0813	0813	0913		2113	...	2213

△ – Also 2204Ⓒ to Welkenraedt.

⊡ – Runs daily Welkenraedt - Aachen.

440 BRUSSELS - NAMUR - DINANT

Lines 161, 154

km			Ⓐ	Ⓐ	Ⓐ	Ⓐ	Ⓐ	Ⓐ	Ⓐ	Ⓐ		Ⓐ	Ⓐ	Ⓐ	Ⓐ	Ⓐ			Ⓐ N	Ⓐ N	Ⓐ	Ⓐ	Ⓐ N
	Brussels Airport ✈ d.	Ⓐ	...	...	...	0616	...	...	0716	...		...	2116	...	...	...	...		...	...	...	...	...
0	**Brussels** Midi/Zuid d.		...	0533	0603	|	0633	0702	|	0733	and	2103	|	2133	2203	2233	...		1307	1540	1608	1641	1807
2	Brussels Central d.		...	0538	0608	|	0638	0707	|	0738	at	2108	|	2138	2208	2238	...	A	1312	1545	1613	1646	1812
4	**Brussels** Nord d.		...	0544	0613	|	0644	0713	|	0744	the	2113	|	2144	2213	2244	...	L	1321	1552	1621	1652	1821
9	Brussels Schuman d.		...	0552	0621	0633	0652	0721	0733	0752	same	2121	2133	2152	2221	2252	...	S	1329	1600	1629	1700	1829
10	Brussels Luxembourg d.		...	0556	0626	0637	0656	0726	0738	0756	minutes	2126	2137	2156	2226	2256	...	O	1334	1604	1634	1704	1834
33	Ottignies d.		...	0616	0648	0701	0716	0748	0801	0816	past	2148	2201	2216	2248	2317	...		|	1624	1656	1725	1855
48	Gembloux d.		...	0629	0702	0714	0729	0802	0814	0829	each	2202	2214	2229	2302	2331	...		|	1637	1709	1738	1910
65	**Namur** a.		...	0640	0714	0725	0740	0814	0825	0841	hour	2214	2225	2240	2314	2343	...		1417	1651	1721	1751	1922
65	**Namur** ▷ d.		0628	0642	0718	0728	0742	0818	0828	0843	until	2218	2228	2242	2318	2348	...		1419	...	1723	...	1924
	Liège Guillemins **442** a.		|	◇	0809	|	◇	0909	|	◇		2309	|	◇	0009	◇	...		◇	...	◇	...	◇
93	**Dinant** ▷ a.		0657	...	...	0757	...	...	0857	...		...	2257	...	...	...	...		...	...	...	...	...

		Ⓐ	Ⓐ	Ⓐ	Ⓐ	Ⓐ	Ⓐ	Ⓐ	Ⓐ	Ⓐ		Ⓐ	Ⓐ	Ⓐ	Ⓐ	Ⓐ			Ⓐ	Ⓐ	Ⓐ	Ⓐ N	Ⓐ N
Dinant ▷ d.	Ⓐ	...	...	...	...	0603	...	...	0703	...		...	2103	...	2140	...	...		...	...	...	...	...
Liège Guillemins **442** d.		...	◇	0451	◇	|	0551	◇	|	0651	and	◇	|	2051	|	◇	...		◇	...	◇	◇	◇
Namur ▷ a.		...	0515	0543	0617	0633	0643	0717	0733	0743	at	2118	2133	2143	2209	2218	...	A	0639	...	0738	0839	0941
Namur d.		0427	0518	0546	0619	0636	0646	0719	0736	0746	the	2120	2136	2146	...	2220	...	L	0641	0711	0740	0841	0943
Gembloux d.		0439	0532	0601	0632	0649	0701	0733	0749	0801	same	2134	2149	2201	...	2234	...	S	0654	0725	0754	0854	|
Ottignies d.		0450	0544	0614	0644	0701	0714	0745	0801	0814	minutes	2146	2201	2214	...	2246	...	O	0706	0737	0806	0908	|
Brussels Luxembourg a.		0518	0604	0633	0703	0721	0733	0804	0821	0833	past	2204	2221	2233	...	2304	...		0725	0756	0825	0926	1026
Brussels Schuman a.		0521	0608	0638	0707	0724	0738	0808	0824	0838	each	2208	2224	2238	...	2308	...		0729	0800	0829	0930	1030
Brussels Nord a.		0529	0617	0647	0716	|	0747	0817	|	0847	hour	2217	|	2247	...	2317	...		0738	0809	0838	0940	1040
Brussels Central a.		0534	0623	0652	0722	|	0752	0823	|	0852	until	2223	|	2252	...	2323	...		0744	0815	0844	0948	1048
Brussels Midi/Zuid a.		0539	0628	0657	0727	|	0757	0828	|	0857		2228	|	2257	...	2328	...		0749	0820	0849	0953	1053
Brussels Airport ✈ a.		...	...	...	...	0743	...	...	0843	...		...	2243	...	...	...	...		...	...	...	...	...

		Ⓒ	Ⓒ	Ⓒ	Ⓒ		Ⓒ	Ⓒ	Ⓒ	Ⓒ	Ⓒ
Brussels Midi/Zuid d.	Ⓒ	0603	0633	0703	0733	and	2103	2133	2203	2233	2333
Brussels Central d.		0607	0638	0707	0738	at	2107	2138	2207	2238	2338
Brussels Nord d.		0614	0644	0714	0744	the	2114	2144	2214	2244	2344
Brussels Schuman d.		0622	0652	0722	0752	same	2122	2152	2222	2252	2352
Brussels Luxembourg d.		0627	0656	0727	0756	minutes	2127	2156	2227	2256	2356
Ottignies d.		0647	0716	0747	0816	past	2147	2216	2247	2317	0017
Gembloux d.		0701	0729	0801	0829	each	2201	2229	2301	2331	0031
Namur a.		0713	0740	0813	0840	hour	2213	2240	2313	2343	0043
Namur ▷ d.		0716	0742	0816	0842	until	2216	2242	...	...	...
Dinant ▷ a.		0745	◇	0845	◇		2245	◇	...	...	...

		Ⓒ	Ⓒ	Ⓒ	Ⓒ	Ⓒ		Ⓒ	Ⓒ
Dinant ▷ d.	Ⓒ	...	...	...	0616	◇	and	2116	◇
Namur ▷ a.		...	...	...	0644	0718	at	2144	2218
Namur d.		0518	0547	0620	0647	0720	the	2147	2220
Gembloux d.		0531	0601	0633	0701	0733	same	2201	2233
Ottignies d.		0543	0615	0645	0715	0745	minutes	2215	2245
Brussels Luxembourg a.		0604	0634	0704	0734	0804	past	2234	2304
Brussels Schuman a.		0608	0638	0708	0738	0808	each	2238	2308
Brussels Nord a.		0617	0646	0717	0746	0817	hour	2246	2317
Brussels Central a.		0623	0652	0723	0752	0822	until	2252	2322
Brussels Midi/Zuid a.		0628	0657	0728	0757	0828		2257	2328

N – Not Dec. 24 - Jan. 4, Apr. 8-22, July 1 - Aug. 30. ◇ – To/from Luxembourg or other destinations in Table **445**. ▷ – See also Table **448**.

442 NAMUR - LIÈGE

Line 125

km			Ⓐ	Ⓐ	Ⓐ	Ⓐ	Ⓐ	Ⓐ		Ⓐ	Ⓐ	Ⓐ	Ⓐ	Ⓐ		Ⓒ	Ⓒ	Ⓒ ▽	Ⓒ ▽		Ⓒ ▽	Ⓒ ▽	Ⓒ ▽
	Mons **425** d.	Ⓐ	0437	...	0539	...	0639	...	and at	1939	...	2039	...	...	Ⓒ	...	0612	0714	0814		1914	2014	2114
	Charleroi Sud **425** d.		0513	...	0618	...	0718	...	the	2018	...	2118	...	...		...	0653	0754	0854		1954	2054	2154
	Brussels Midi/Zuid **440** § d.		|	...	|	0603	|	0702	same	|	2003	|	2103	2203		...	|	|	|	and	|	|	|
0	**Namur** d.		0551	0618	0651	0718	0751	0818	minutes	2051	2118	2151	2218	2318		0632	0732	0832	0932	hourly	2032	2132	2232
20	Andenne d.		0605	0632	0705	0732	0805	0832	past	2105	2132	2205	2232	2332		0645	0746	0846	0946	until	2046	2146	2246
31	Huy d.		0615	0645	0715	0745	0815	0845	each	2115	2145	2215	2245	2345		0658	0758	0858	0958		2058	2158	2258
60	**Liège** Guillemins a.		0636	0709	0736	0809	0836	0909	hour	2136	2209	2236	2309	0009		0720	0820	0920	1020		2120	2220	2320
63	Liège St Lambert a.		...	0718	...	0824	...	0924	until	...	2224	2247	2324	0024		0729	0829	0929	1029		2129	2229	2329

		Ⓐ	Ⓐ	Ⓐ	Ⓐ	Ⓐ	Ⓐ	Ⓐ		Ⓐ	Ⓐ	Ⓐ	Ⓐ	Ⓐ		Ⓒ ▽	Ⓒ ▽	Ⓒ ▽	Ⓒ ▽		Ⓒ ▽	Ⓒ	Ⓒ
Liège St Lambert d.	Ⓐ	0437	0513	0537	0613	0637	...	0737	and at	...	2037	...	2137	...	Ⓒ	0630	0730	0830	0930		2030	2130	2230
Liège Guillemins d.		0451	0524	0551	0624	0651	0724	0751	the	2024	2051	2124	2151	2224		0640	0740	0840	0940		2040	2140	2240
Huy d.		0514	0546	0614	0646	0714	0746	0814	same	2046	2114	2146	2214	2246		0702	0802	0902	1002	and	2102	2203	2302
Andenne d.		0527	0555	0627	0655	0727	0755	0827	minutes	2055	2127	2155	2227	2255		0713	0813	0913	1013	hourly	2113	2214	2313
Namur a.		0543	0610	0643	0710	0743	0810	0843	past	2110	2143	2210	2243	2310		0728	0828	0928	1028	until	2128	2229	2328
Brussels Midi/Zuid **440** § a.		0657	|	0757	|	0857	|	0957	each	|	2257	|	...	|		|	|	|	|		|	|	...
Charleroi Sud **425** a.		...	0642	...	0742	...	0842	...	hour	2142	...	2246	...	2346		0806	0906	1007	1107		2207	2307	...
Mons **425** a.		...	0721	...	0821	...	0921	...	until	2221	...	2322	...	...		0846	0946	1046	1146		2246	...	...

▽ – From/to Mouscron via Tournai (Table **416**).
§ – For direct trains Brussels - Liège see Table **400**.

On Ⓐ July 1 - Aug. 30 the 0637 train from Liège extends to Oostende (a. 1013) and the 2124 arrival at Liège starts from Oostende (d. 1736).

On Ⓒ trains continue beyond Liège to/from Liers.

445 (BRUSSELS) - NAMUR - LUXEMBOURG

Line 162

km			Ⓐ	Ⓐ	Ⓐ ⊡		Ⓐ ⊡	Ⓐ	Ⓐ	Ⓐ	Ⓐ		Ⓐ N	Ⓐ	Ⓐ	Ⓐ	Ⓐ N		Ⓒ ⊡		Ⓒ ⊡	Ⓒ	Ⓒ
	Brussels Midi/Zuid **440** d.	Ⓐ	...	...	0533		1833	1933	2033	2133	2233		1307	...	1608	...	1807	Ⓒ	0633		1933	2033	2133
	Brussels Nord **440** d.		...	...	0544		1844	1944	2044	2144	2244		1321	...	1621	...	1821		0644		1944	2044	2144
	Brussels Luxembourg **440** d.		...	...	0556		1856	1956	2056	2156	2256		1334	...	1634	...	1834		0656		1956	2056	2156
0	**Namur** d.		0539	0609	0642	and	1943	2042	2142	2242	2348	A	1419	1621	1723	1821	1924		0742	and	2042	2142	2242
29	Ciney d.		0557	0628	0700	hourly	2002	2100	2200	2300	0007	L	|	1639	1742	1840	1943		0800	hourly	2101	2201	2300
52	Marloie d.		0611	0643	0714	until	2016	2114	2214	2314	0021	S	|	1653	1757	1855	1959		0814	until	2115	2215	2314
58	Rochefort-Jemelle d.		0617	0649	0720	⊡	2022	2120	2220	2320	0026	O	|	1658	1802	1900	2004		0820	⊡	2121	2221	2320
90	Libramont d.		0651	0719	0751		2052	2152	2245	2345	▬		1521	...	...	...	...		0851		2152	2245	2352
137	Arlon a.		0723	0755	0823		2123	2223	...	...	Ⓐ		1550	...	...	...	...		0923		2223	▬	...
137	Arlon ▷ d.		0729	0758	0829		2129	2229	...	...	2329		1554	...	...	...	...		0929		2229	2329	...
165	**Luxembourg** ▷ a.		0750	0823	0850		2150	2250	...	...	2350		1614	...	...	...	...		0950		2250	2350	...

		Ⓐ	Ⓐ	Ⓐ	Ⓐ	Ⓐ	Ⓐ	Ⓐ N	Ⓐ	Ⓐ N	Ⓐ ♡		Ⓐ ♡	Ⓐ ♡	Ⓐ	Ⓐ	Ⓐ		Ⓒ	Ⓒ ♡		Ⓒ ♡	Ⓒ
Luxembourg ▷ d.	Ⓐ	...	...	...	*0510*	...	*0610*	...	0710	0740	0810		1910	*2010*	2110	2210	2310	Ⓒ	...	0610		2010	2110
Arlon ▷ a.		...	...	...	*0531*	...	*0631*	...	0731	0801	0831		1931	*2031*	2131	2231	2331		...	0631		2031	2131
Arlon d.		...	0437	...	0536	...	0636	...	0737	0804	0837		1937	2037	2137	...	...		...	0637		2037	...
Libramont d.		...	0514	...	0613	...	0716	...	0816	0843	0916	and	2016	2116	2216	...	...		...	0716	and	2116	...
Rochefort-Jemelle d.		0433	0539	0559	0638	0659	0740	0759	0841	|	0941	hourly	2041	2141	2241	...	...		0641	0741	hourly	2141	...
Marloie d.		0439	0545	0606	0644	0705	0746	0806	0847	|	0947	until	2047	2147	2247	...	...		0647	0747	until	2147	...
Ciney d.		0458	0559	0621	0659	0721	0800	0821	0901	|	1001	♡	2101	2201	2301	...	...		0701	0801	♡	2201	...
Namur a.		0515	0617	0639	0717	0738	0818	0839	0918	0941	1018		2118	2218	2320	...	...		0718	0818		2218	...
Brussels Luxembourg **440** a.		0604	0703	0725	0804	0825	0904	0926	1004	1026	1104		2204	2304	...	...	...		0804	0904		2304	...
Brussels Nord **440** a.		0617	0716	0738	0817	0838	0917	0940	1017	1040	1117		2217	2317	...	...	...		0817	0917		2317	...
Brussels Midi/Zuid **440** a.		0628	0727	0749	0828	0849	0928	0953	1028	1053	1128		2228	2328	...	...	...		0828	0928		2328	...

N – Not Dec. 24 - Jan. 4, Apr. 8-22, July 1 - Aug. 30.
⊡ – The following departures from Brussels require a change of train at Arlon: Ⓐ – 0733 to 1033, 1533 to 1833; ⑥ – 0633, 0933, 1133, 1233, 1733, 1933; ⑦ – 0633, 0933, 1033, 1233 to 1533, 1733 to 1933.
♡ – The following departures from Luxembourg require a change of train at Arlon: Ⓐ: –1110 to 1410, 1910, 2010; ⑥ – 0710, 0810, 1010, 1310, 1510 to 1710; ⑦ – 0610, 0810 to 1010, 1310 to 1910.
▷ – Additional local trains run Arlon - Kleinbettingen 🚍 - Luxembourg (journey 20-30 mins).

OOSTENDE JOURNEYS on Ⓒ June 29 - Sept 1:
1833 and 1933 Brussels - Luxembourg journeys start from Oostende at 1711 and 1811 calling at Brugge and Gent. 0641 from Rochefort-Jemelle and 0610 from Luxembourg continue to Oostende arriving 0945 and 1046, calling at Gent and Brugge.

Line 43/L10 LIÈGE - GOUVY - CLERVAUX - LUXEMBOURG 446

km																									
						Ⓐ N										Ⓐ N		Ⓐ		Ⓐ		Ⓐ			
	Liège St Lambert d.	...	...	0551	...	...	0751	...	0951	...	...	...	1351	...	...	...	...	...	1751	...	...	...	1951	...	2151
0	**Liège** Guillemins **447** d.	...	...	0608	...	0728	0808	...	1008	...	1208	...	1408	...	1608	1629	...	1708	1808	...	...	1908	2008	...	2208
23	Rivage **447** d.	...	...	0630	...	0751	0830	...	1030	...	1230	...	1430	...	1630	1653	...	1731	1830	...	...	1931	2030	...	2230
31	Aywaille d.	...	...	0639	...	0759	0839	...	1039	...	1239	...	1439	...	1639	1701	...	1739	1839	...	...	1939	2039	...	2239
58	Trois-Ponts d.	...	...	0701	...	0822	0901	...	1101	...	1301	...	1501	...	1701	1729	...	1802	1901	...	...	2002	2101	...	2301
70	Vielsalm d.	...	...	0713	...	0834	0913	...	1113	...	1313	...	1513	...	1713	1741	...	1814	1913	...	...	2014	2113	...	2313
81	Gouvy 🏛 d.	0526**a**	0626**a**	0726	...	0844	0926	...	1126	...	1326	...	1526	...	1726	1751	1815**a**	1824	1926	1955	...	2024	2126	...	2323
91	Troisvierges d.	0535	0635	0735	0835	...	0935	1035	1135	1235	1335	1435	1535	1635	1735	...	1835	...	1935	2005	2035	...	2135	2235	...
99	**Clervaux** d.	0544	0644	0744	0844	...	0944	1044	1144	1244	1344	1444	1544	1644	1744	...	1844	...	1944	2014	2044	...	2144	2244	...
114	Kautenbach d.	0601	0701	0801	0901	...	1001	1101	1201	1301	1401	1501	1601	1701	1801	...	1901	...	2001	2031	2101	...	2201	2301	...
129	Ettelbruck d.	0615	0716	0815	0915	...	1015	1115	1215	1315	1415	1515	1615	1715	1815	...	1915	...	2015	2045	2115	...	2215	2315	...
141	Mersch d.	0626	0726	0826	0926	...	1026	1126	1226	1326	1426	1526	1626	1726	1826	...	1926	...	2026	2056	2126	...	2226	2326	...
160	**Luxembourg** a.	0643	0743	0843	0943	...	1043	1143	1243	1343	1443	1543	1643	1743	1843	...	1943	...	2043	2115	2143	...	2243	2343	...

	Ⓐ	Ⓐ		Ⓐ N													Ⓐ								
Luxembourg d.	...	...	...	...	0516	0616	0716	0816	0916	1016	1116	1216	1316	1416	1516	1616	1644	1716	1816	1916	2016	2116	2216	2316	2344
Mersch d.	...	...	...	...	0532	0633	0733	0833	0933	1033	1133	1233	1333	1433	1533	1633	1703	1733	1833	1933	2033	2133	2233	2333	0003
Ettelbruck d.	...	...	...	...	0545	0645	0745	0845	0945	1045	1145	1245	1345	1445	1545	1645	1715	1745	1845	1945	2045	2145	2245	2345	0015
Kautenbach d.	...	...	...	...	0600	0700	0800	0900	1000	1100	1200	1300	1400	1500	1600	1700	1730	1801	1900	2000	2100	2200	2300	0000	0030
Clervaux d.	...	...	...	...	0616	0716	0816	0916	1016	1116	1216	1316	1415	1516	1616	1716	1746	1816	1916	2016	2116	2216	2316	0016	0046
Troisvierges d.	...	...	...	...	0624	0724	0826	0924	1026	1124	1226	1324	1426	1524	1626	1724	1756	1826	1924	2026	2124	2226	2324	0024	0054
Gouvy 🏛 d.	0506	0547	0639	0707	...	...	0839	...	1039	...	1239	...	1439	...	1639	...	1805	1839	1945**a**	2039	...	2239	...	...	...
Vielsalm d.	0517	0558	0649	0718	...	...	0849	...	1049	...	1249	...	1449	...	1649	...	...	1849	...	2049	...	2249	...	...	...
Trois-Ponts d.	0528	0609	0701	0729	...	...	0901	...	1101	...	1301	...	1501	...	1701	...	...	1901	...	2101	...	2301	...	...	...
Aywaille d.	0550	0631	0723	0751	...	...	0923	...	1123	...	1323	...	1523	...	1723	...	...	1923	...	2123	...	2323	...	...	...
Rivage **447** d.	0559	0640	0732	0800	...	...	0932	...	1132	...	1332	...	1532	...	1732	...	...	1932	...	2132	...	2332	...	...	...
Liège Guillemins ... **447** a.	0622	0701	0754	0823	...	...	0954	...	1154	...	1354	...	1554	...	1754	...	...	1954	...	2154	...	2354	...	...	...
Liège St Lambert a.	...	...	0811	...	...	...	1011	...	1211	...	1411	...	1611	...	1811	...	...	2011	...	2211	...	...	...	...	...

a – Ⓐ only.
N – Not Dec. 24 - Jan. 4, Apr. 8 - 22, July 1 - Aug. 30.

ADDITIONAL TRAINS TROISVIERGES - CLERVAUX - LUXEMBOURG:
From Troisvierges hourly 0405Ⓐ - 2205Ⓐ. From Luxembourg hourly 0544Ⓐ - 2244Ⓐ.

CONNECTIONS KAUTENBACH - WILTZ (journey 12 minutes):
From Kautenbach: on Ⓐ every 30 minutes 0532 - 2302; on Ⓒ 0602, 0702, hourly 0804 - 2304.
From Wiltz: on Ⓐ every 30 minutes 0416 - 2246; on Ⓒ 0546, 0646, 0746, hourly 0842 - 2242.

☛ Trains serving Liège St Lambert (formerly Liège Palais) continue to/from Liers.

Line 43 LIÈGE - MARLOIE - ROCHEFORT JEMELLE 447

km																								
		Ⓐ	Ⓐ		Ⓐ	Ⓒ **S**		Ⓐ		Ⓐ		Ⓐ		Ⓐ	Ⓐ		Ⓐ	Ⓐ	Ⓒ	Ⓐ				
	Liège St Lambert ◇ d.	0606	...	0806**a**	...	...	1006**a**	...	1206**a**	...	1406**a**	...	1606**a**	...	...	1806**a**	1906	2006	...	...	2206**a**	...	...	...
0	**Liège** Guillemins **446** d.	0616	0716	0816	0916	0914	1016	1116	1216	1316	1416	1516	1616	1649	1716	1816	1916	2016	2016	2116	2216	...	...	...
23	Rivage **446** d.	0643	0743	0843	0943	0941	1043	1143	1243	1343	1443	1543	1643	1718	1743	1843	1943	2043	2043	2143	2243	...	...	...
43	Barvaux d.	0705	0805	0905	1005	1004	1105	1205	1305	1405	1505	1605	1705	1740	1805	1905	2005	2105	2105	2205	2305	...	...	...
65	Marloie **445** a.	0723	0823	0923	1023	1022	1123	1223	1323	1423	1523	1623	1723	1800	1823	1923	2023	2123	2123	2223	2324	...	...	...
71	**Rochefort-Jemelle** **445** a.	...	...	...	...	1028	...	...	...	...	...	...	...	1806	...	...	...	2130	...	2229	2329	...	...	...

	Ⓐ	Ⓐ	Ⓐ	Ⓐ	Ⓐ	Ⓒ	Ⓐ		Ⓐ		Ⓐ		Ⓐ		Ⓐ		Ⓐ		Ⓐ	Ⓒ				
Rochefort-Jemelle **445** d.	0429	0529	0607	0629	...	0729	...	...	...	...	...	...	...	...	...	...	...	...	...	...	...	...	...	...
Marloie **445** d.	0435	0535	0613	0635	0735	0735	0835	0935	1035	1135	1235	1335	1435	1535	1635	1735	1835	1935	2035	2135	...	...	...	...
Barvaux d.	0452	0552	0631	0652	0752	0752	0852	0952	1052	1152	1252	1352	1452	1552	1652	1752	1852	1952	2052	2152	...	...	...	...
Rivage **446** d.	0515	0615	0654	0715	0815	0815	0915	1015	1115	1215	1315	1415	1515	1615	1715	1815	1915	2015	2115	2215	...	...	...	...
Liège Guillemins **446** a.	0543	0643	0722	0743	0843	0843	0943	1043	1143	1243	1343	1443	1543	1643	1743	1843	1943	2043	2143	2243	...	...	...	...
Liège St Lambert ◇ a.	0555	...	...	0755	...	...	0955	...	1155	...	1355	...	1555	...	1755	1855**a**	1955	...	2155	...	...	...	...	...

S – June 29 - Sept. 1. **a** – Ⓐ only. ◇ – Most trains continue beyond Liège St Lambert (formerly Liège Palais) to/from Liers.

Lines 154, 166, 165 ARDENNES LOCAL SERVICES 448

km										
			Ⓐ	Ⓐ		Ⓐ		Ⓒ	⇓	Ⓒ
0	**Namur** **440** d.	Ⓐ	0558	0658		1958	Ⓒ	0558		1958
28	Dinant **440** d.		0627	0727		2027		0627	and	2027
43	Houyet d.		0646	0746	and	2046		0646	every	2046
52	Beauraing d.		0654	0754	hourly	2054		0654	**two**	2054
100	Bertrix a.		0732	0832	until	2132		0732	hours	2132
100	Bertrix d.		0738	0838		2138		0738	until	2138
108	**Libramont** a.		0747	0847		2147		0747		2147

		Ⓐ	Ⓐ		Ⓐ		Ⓒ	♥	Ⓒ
Libramont d.	Ⓐ	...	0614		1914	Ⓒ	0714		1914
Bertrix a.		...	0623		1923		0723	and	1923
Bertrix d.		0529	0629	and	1929		0729	every	1929
Beauraing d.		0605	0705	hourly	2005		0805	**two**	2005
Houyet d.		0613	0713	until	2013		0813	hours	2013
Dinant **440** d.		0632	0732		2032		0832	until	2032
Namur **440** a.		0702	0802		2102		0902		2102

km										
			Ⓐ		Ⓐ	Ⓐ‡		Ⓒ		Ⓒ
0	**Libramont** d.	Ⓐ	0656		2056	2156	Ⓒ	0756	and	2156
8	Bertrix a.		0706	and	2106	2205		0806	every	2206
33	Florenville d.		0719	hourly	2119	...		0819	**two**	2219
57	Virton d.		0738	until	2138	...		0837	hours	2237
85	Athus ▷ d.		0801		2201	...		...	until	...
98	**Arlon** a.		0816		2216	...		...		...

		Ⓐ	Ⓐ		Ⓐ		Ⓒ		Ⓒ
Arlon d.	Ⓐ	...	0643		2143	Ⓒ	...		...
Athus ▷ d.		...	0701	and	2201		...	and	...
Virton d.		0622	0722	hourly	2222		0622	every	2022
Florenville d.		0640	0740	until	2240		0640	**two**	2040
Bertrix d.		0654	0754		2254		0654	hours	2054
Libramont a.		0703	0803		2303		0703	until	2103

▷ – Athus - Luxembourg: see Table **449**.
‡ – Also 2256Ⓐ to Bertrix.
⇓ – Journeys at 0958, 1158, 1358 run 12 mins **earlier**.
♥ – 0914, 1114, 1314 run 12 mins later.

Arlon - Athus is subject to alteration until June 17

Operator: CFL LUXEMBOURG – local services 449

		⚒				
Luxembourg d.	0455	0525	0555	every 30 mins on ⚒	2255	2325
Ettelbruck d.	0535	0605	0635	hourly on ⑦ and holidays	2335	0005
Diekirch a.	0540	0610	0640	(every 30 mins from 1155)	2340	0010

	⚒	⚒				
Diekirch d.	...	0450	0520	0550	every 30 mins on ⚒	2320
Ettelbruck d.	0425	0455	0525	0555	hourly on ⑦ and holidays	2325
Luxembourg a.	0505	0535	0605	0635	(every 30 mins from 1050)	0005

		⚒				
Luxembourg d.	...	0520	0550	every 30 mins on ⚒	2320	2350
Pétange d.	...	0545	0615	hourly on ⑦ and holidays	2345	0015
Rodange d.	...	0550	0620	(every 30 mins from 1150)	2350	0020
Athus (Belgium) ▷ a.	...	0555	0625		2355	0025

	⚒	⚒	⚒			
Athus (Belgium) ▷ d.	0505	0535	0605	0635	every 30 mins on ⚒	2335
Rodange d.	0510	0540	0610	0640	hourly on ⑦ and holidays	2340
Pétange d.	0515	0545	0615	0645	(every 30 mins from 1135)	2345
Luxembourg a.	0540	0610	0640	0710		0010

Luxembourg → Bettembourg → Esch-sur-Alzette → Pétange → **Rodange** (journey 12 mins to Bettembourg, 25 mins to Esch, 45 - 50 mins to Pétange, 50 - 55 mins to Rodange):
⚒: 0521 and approx every 30 minutes to 1921, 1932 and every 30 minutes to 2332, 0002.
†: 0118, 0318, 0502 and hourly to 1202 then every 30 minutes to 2332, 0002.

Rodange → Pétange → Esch-sur-Alzette → Bettembourg → **Luxembourg** (5 - 7 mins to Pétange, 26 - 32 mins to Esch, 39 - 45 mins to Bettembourg, 50 - 55 mins to Luxembourg):
⚒: 0451, 0551, 0621 and every 30 mins to 1921, 2032 then every 30 mins to 2332.
†: 0132, 0232, 0432, 0532 and hourly to 1232 then every 30 minutes to 2332.

Luxembourg → **Wasserbillig** (journey 35 - 42 minutes):
Trains run approx every 30 mins (some continue to Trier, Table **915**).

Wasserbillig → **Luxembourg** (journey 35 - 42 minutes):
Trains run approx every 30 mins (some from Trier, Table **915**).

Luxembourg → **Kleinbettingen** (journey 18 - 19 minutes):
Ⓐ: 0522 and approx every 30 mins to 2025, 2055, 2119 (not 0922, 1122, 1922).
Ⓒ: 0545 and hourly to 2245, 2355.

Kleinbettingen → **Luxembourg** (journey 18 - 19 minutes):
Ⓐ: 0445 and approx every 30 mins to 1916, 1946, 2045, 2116, 2150 (not 1015, 1215).
Ⓒ: 0615 and hourly to 2315.

Bettembourg → Dudelange → **Volmerange-les-Mines** (journey 17 minutes):
Approx every 30 mins. On † runs only to Dudelange Usines, hourly (afternoon every 30 mins).

Volmerange-les-Mines → Dudelange → **Bettembourg** (journey 14 minutes):
Approx every 30 mins. On † runs from Dudelange Usines, hourly (afternoon every 30 mins).

▷ – For connections to/from Arlon see Table **448**.

NETHERLANDS

SEE MAP PAGE 237

Operator: **NS** – Nederlandse Spoorwegen (unless otherwise indicated) www.ns.nl

Services: Trains convey first- and second-class seated accommodation, unless otherwise indicated in the tables. Some trains consist of portions for two or more destinations, and passengers should be careful to join the correct part of the train. The destination of each train portion is normally indicated beside the entrance doors.

Timings: Valid **December 9**, 2018 - **December 14**, 2019.

Holidays: Unless otherwise indicated, services marked ⚒ do not run on ⑦ or on Dec. 25, 26, Jan. 1, Apr. 22;
those marked Ⓐ do not run on ⑥⑦ or on Dec. 25, 26, Jan. 1, Apr. 22, May 30, June 10;
those marked † run on ⑦ and on Dec. 25, 26, Jan. 1, Apr. 22;
those marked Ⓒ run on ⑥⑦ and on Dec. 25, 26, Jan. 1, Apr. 22, May 30, June 10.
No trains, other than international services, will run between ± 2000 hours on Dec. 31 and ± 0200 on Jan. 1.

Tickets: A nationwide smartcard system called *OV-chipkaart* is used for all public transport in the Netherlands. Personalised and anonymous cards are available (€7.50) which can be loaded and topped up with travel credit. Disposable single use cards can also be purchased from ticket machines and ticket offices for full fare single / return journeys and day tickets (a €1 supplement is payable for single use cards). You must always check-in and check-out your OV-chipkaart for each journey. Alternatively, e-tickets for full fare single and return journeys may be purchased on-line and printed yourself.

Supplements: A supplement is payable for journeys on *Intercity direct* services (except for local journeys Amsterdam - Schiphol and Rotterdam - Breda), also for internal journeys on *ICE* trains between Amsterdam and Arnhem. In both cases the single journey supplement is €2.40. Supplements may be purchased from special Supplement Pillars (using your OV-chipkaart) or from ticket machines.

450 AMSTERDAM - DEN HAAG - ROTTERDAM - ROOSENDAAL - VLISSINGEN

For *Intercity direct* services via the high-speed line, see Table **451**. For services via Amsterdam Zuid and Schiphol ✈, see Table **460**.
For Night Network services Amsterdam - Rotterdam and v.v., see Table **454**. For International services to / from Brussels, see Table **18**.

km			⊗	⊖	④⑤n	⑥⑦p		Ⓐ	⚒	Ⓐ	Ⓐ	⚒	⚒	⚒		Ⓐ		Ⓐ		Ⓐ		Ⓐ		⚒
0	**Amsterdam** Centraal ...... **461** d.	0004	0034	0034	0034	0104	...	...	...	...	...	...	0534	0604	...	0619	0634	0649	0704	0719	0734	0749	0804	0819
5	Amsterdam Sloterdijk .... d.	0010	0040	0040	0040	0110	...	...	...	...	...	...	0540	0610	...	0625	0640	0655	0710	0725	0740	0755	0810	0825
19	**Haarlem** .... **461** d.	0020	0050	0050	0050	0120	...	...	...	...	...	...	0550	0620	...	0637	0650	0707	0720	0737	0750	0807	0820	0837
47	Leiden Centraal .... a.	0040	0110	0110	0110	0140	...	...	...	...	...	...	0610	0640	...	0656	0710	0726	0740	0756	0810	0826	0840	0856
47	Leiden Centraal .... **460** d.	0043	0115	0116	0116	0145	...	...	...	...	...	...	0615	0645	...	0701	0715	0731	0745	0801	0815	0831	0845	0901
	Den Haag Centraal **460 471** a.	|	|	|	|	|	...	...	...	...	...	...	|	|	...	0712	|	0742	|	0812	|	0842	|	0912
63	**Den Haag** HS.......... **460 471** d.	0056	0129	0129	0131	0157	...	...	...	...	...	...	0629	0659	...	...	0729	...	0759	...	0829	...	0859	...
71	Delft .... **460 471** d.	0102	0135	0135	...	...	...	...	...	...	...	...	0635	0705	...	...	0735	...	0805	...	0835	...	0905	...
81	Schiedam Centrum .... **460** d.	0110	0143	0143	...	...	...	...	...	...	...	...	0643	0713	...	...	0743	...	0813	...	0843	...	0913	...
85	**Rotterdam** Centraal **460 471** a.	0115	0148	0150	...	...	...	...	...	...	...	...	0648	0718	...	...	0748	...	0818	...	0848	...	0918	...
85	**Rotterdam** Centraal **460 471** d.	...	...	...	...	...	...	...	...	...	0621	...	0651	0721	...	...	0751	...	0821	...	0851	...	0921	...
105	Dordrecht .... **460 471** d.	...	...	...	...	...	...	...	0553	...	0637	...	0707	0737	...	...	0807	...	0837	...	0907	...	0937	...
143	**Roosendaal** .... a.	...	...	...	...	...	...	...	0623	...	0700	...	0731	0800	...	...	0831	...	0900	...	0930	...	1000	...
143	**Roosendaal** .... d.	...	...	...	...	...	...	0606	...	0636	0706	0706	0736	0806	0806	...	0836	...	0906	...	0936	...	1006	...
156	Bergen op Zoom .... d.	...	...	...	...	...	...	0616	...	0646	0716	0716	0746	0816	0816	...	0846	...	0916	...	0946	...	1016	...
193	Goes .... d.	...	...	...	...	...	...	0646	...	0716	0746	0746	0816	0846	0846	...	0916	...	0946	...	1016	...	1046	...
212	Middelburg .... d.	...	...	...	...	...	...	0700	...	0730	0800	0800	0830	0900	0900	...	0930	...	1000	...	1030	...	1100	...
218	**Vlissingen** .... a.	...	...	...	...	...	...	0708	...	0738	0808	0808	0838	0908	0908	...	0938	...	1008	...	1038	...	1108	...

		⚒		⚒		⚒		⚒		⚒													
Amsterdam Centraal ...... **461** d.	0834	0849	0904	0919	0934	0949	1004	1019	1034	1049	1104	1119	1134	1149	and at the same minutes past each hour until	2104	2119	2134	2149	2204	2234	2304	2334
Amsterdam Sloterdijk .... d.	0840	0855	0910	0925	0940	0955	1010	1025	1040	1055	1110	1125	1140	1155		2110	2125	2140	2155	2210	2240	2310	2340
Haarlem .... **461** d.	0850	0907	0920	0937	0950	1007	1020	1037	1050	1107	1120	1137	1150	1207		2120	2137	2150	2207	2220	2250	2320	2350
Leiden Centraal .... a.	0910	0926	0940	0956	1010	1026	1040	1056	1110	1126	1140	1156	1210	1226		2140	2156	2210	2226	2240	2310	2340	0010
Leiden Centraal .... **460** d.	0915	0931	0945	1001	1015	1031	1045	1101	1115	1131	1145	1201	1215	1231		2145	2201	2215	2232	2245	2315	2345	0015
Den Haag Centraal **460 471** a.	|	0942	|	1012	|	1042	|	1112	|	1142	|	1212	|	1242		|	2212	|	2242	|	|	|	|
Den Haag HS.......... **460 471** d.	0929	...	0959	...	1029	...	1059	...	1129	...	1159	...	1229	...		2159	...	2229	...	2259	2329	2359	0029
Delft .... **460 471** d.	0935	...	1005	...	1035	...	1105	...	1135	...	1205	...	1235	...		2205	...	2235	...	2305	2335	0005	0035
Schiedam Centrum .... **460** d.	0943	...	1013	...	1043	...	1113	...	1143	...	1213	...	1243	...		2213	...	2243	...	2313	2343	0013	0043
Rotterdam Centraal **460 471** a.	0948	...	1018	...	1048	...	1118	...	1148	...	1218	...	1248	...		2218	...	2248	...	2318	2348	0018	0048
Rotterdam Centraal **460 471** d.	0951	...	1021	...	1051	...	1121	...	1151	...	1221	...	1251	...		2221	...	2251	...	2321	2351	0021	0051
Dordrecht .... **460 471** d.	1007	...	1037	...	1107	...	1137	...	1207	...	1237	...	1307	...		2237	...	2307	...	2337	0007	0037	0107
Roosendaal .... a.	1030	...	1100	...	1130	...	1200	...	1230	...	1300	...	1330	...		2330	...	2330	...	0000	0030	0109**j**	0139**k**
Roosendaal .... d.	1036	...	1106	...	1136	...	1206	...	1236	...	1306	...	1336	...		2306	...	2336	...	0006	...	...	...
Bergen op Zoom .... d.	1046	...	1116	...	1146	...	1216	...	1246	...	1316	...	1346	...		2316	...	2346	...	0016	...	...	...
Goes .... d.	1116	...	1146	...	1216	...	1246	...	1316	...	1346	...	1416	...		2346	...	0016	...	0046	...	...	...
Middelburg .... d.	1130	...	1200	...	1230	...	1300	...	1330	...	1400	...	1430	...		0000	...	0030	...	0100	...	...	...
Vlissingen .... a.	1138	...	1208	...	1238	...	1308	...	1338	...	1408	...	1438	...		0008	...	0038	...	0108	...	...	...

km		Ⓐ	⚒	Ⓐ	⚒	Ⓐ	Ⓐ		Ⓐ	Ⓐ		Ⓐ	⚒		⚒	⚒	Ⓐ		⚒		⚒		Ⓐ	⚒
	Vlissingen .... d.	...	...	...	...	...	...	...	...	0521	...	...	0552	...	...	0622	0641	...	...	0652	...	0722	0741	...
	Middelburg .... d.	...	...	...	...	...	...	...	...	0528	...	...	0600	...	...	0630	0646	...	...	0700	...	0730	0746	...
	Goes .... d.	...	...	...	...	...	...	...	...	0542	...	...	0614	...	...	0644	0658	...	...	0714	...	0744	0758	...
	Bergen op Zoom .... d.	...	...	...	...	...	0544	...	...	0614	...	...	0644	...	...	0714	0718	...	...	0744	...	0814	0818	...
	Roosendaal .... a.	...	...	...	...	...	0554	...	...	0624	...	...	0654	...	...	0724	0728	...	...	0754	...	0824	0828	...
	Roosendaal .... d.	...	...	...	0531**t**	...	0601	...	...	0631	0631**r**	...	0701	...	...	0731	0731	...	...	0801	...	0831	0831	...
	Dordrecht .... **460 471** d.	...	...	...	0554	...	0624	0624	...	0654	0654	...	0724	0724	...	0754	0754	0754	...	0824	...	0854	0854	...
	Rotterdam Centraal **460 471** a.	...	...	...	0609	...	0639	0639	...	0709	0709	...	0739	0739	...	0809	0809	0809	...	0839	...	0909	0909	...
	Rotterdam Centraal **460 471** d.	0512**z**	0542	...	0612	...	0642	0642	...	0712	0712	...	0742	0742	...	0812	0812	0812	...	0842	...	0912	0912	...
	Schiedam Centrum .... **460** d.	0517**z**	0547	...	0617	...	0647	0647	...	0717	0717	...	0747	0747	...	0817	0817	0817	...	0847	...	0917	0917	...
	Delft .... **460 471** d.	0524**z**	0554	...	0624	...	0654	0654	...	0724	0724	...	0754	0754	...	0824	0824	0824	...	0854	...	0924	0924	...
	Den Haag HS.......... **460 471** d.	0533**z**	0603	...	0633	...	0703	0703	...	0733	0733	...	0803	0803	...	0833	0833	0833	...	0903	...	0933	0933	...
0	**Den Haag** Centraal **460 471** d.	|	|	0617	|	0647	|	|	0717	|	|	0747	|	|	0817	|	|	|	0847	|	0917	|	|	0947
15	Leiden Centraal .... **460** a.	0545**z**	0615	0629	0645	0359	0715	0715	0729	0745	0745	0759	0815	0815	0829	0845	0845	0845	0849	0915	0929	0945	0945	0959
15	Leiden Centraal .... d.	0550	0620	0634	0650	0704	0720	0720	0734	0750	0750	0804	0820	0820	0834	0850	0850	0850	0904	0920	0934	0950	0950	1004
43	**Haarlem** .... **461** d.	0610	0640	0655	0710	0725	0740	0740	0755	0810	0810	0825	0840	0840	0855	0910	0910	0910	0925	0940	0955	1010	1010	1025
57	Amsterdam Sloterdijk .... d.	0619	0649	0704	0719	0734	0749	0749	0804	0819	0819	0834	0849	0849	0904	0919	0919	0919	0934	0949	1004	1019	1019	1034
62	**Amsterdam** Centraal ...... **461** a.	0625	0655	0710	0725	0740	0755	0755	0810	0825	0825	0840	0855	0855	0910	0925	0925	0925	0940	0955	1010	1025	1025	1040

Vlissingen .... d.	0752	...	0822	...	...	0852	...	0922	...	and at the same minutes past each hour until	1852	...	1922	...	1952	...	2022	2052	2122	2152	2222	2252	2322
Middelburg .... d.	0800	...	0830	...	...	0900	...	0930	...		1900	...	1930	...	2000	...	2030	2100	2130	2200	2230	2300	2330
Goes .... d.	0814	...	0844	...	...	0914	...	0944	...		1914	...	1944	...	2014	...	2044	2114	2144	2214	2244	2314	2344
Bergen op Zoom .... d.	0844	...	0914	...	...	0944	...	1014	...		1944	...	2014	...	2044	...	2114	2144	2214	2244	2314	2344	0014
Roosendaal .... a.	0854	...	0924	...	...	0954	...	1024	...		1954	...	2024	...	2054	...	2124	2154	2224	2254	2324	2354	0024
Roosendaal .... d.	0901	...	0931	...	...	1001	...	1031	...		2001	...	2031	...	2101	...	2131	2201	2231	2301	2331	0001	...
Dordrecht .... **460 471** d.	0924	...	0954	...	...	1024	...	1054	...		2024	...	2054	...	2124	...	2154	2224	2254	2324	2354	0024	...
Rotterdam Centraal **460 471** a.	0939	...	1009	...	...	1039	...	1109	...		2039	...	2109	...	2139	...	2210	2239	2309	2339	0009	0039	...
Rotterdam Centraal **460 471** d.	0942	...	1012	...	...	1042	...	1112	...		2042	...	2112	...	2142	...	2212	2242	2312	2342	0012	...	...
Schiedam Centrum .... **460** d.	0947	...	1017	...	...	1047	...	1117	...		2047	...	2117	...	2147	...	2217	2247	2317	2347	0017	...	...
Delft .... **460 471** d.	0954	...	1024	...	...	1054	...	1124	...		2054	...	2124	...	2154	...	2224	2254	2324	2354	0024	...	...
Den Haag HS.......... **460 471** d.	1003	...	1033	...	...	1103	...	1133	...		2103	...	2133	...	2203	...	2233	2303	2333	0003	0033	...	...
Den Haag Centraal **460 471** d.	|	1017**r**	|	1047**r**	...	|	1117	|	1147		|	2117	|	2147	|	2217	|	|	|	|	|	...	...
Leiden Centraal .... **460** a.	1015	1029**r**	1045	1059**r**	...	1115	1129	1145	1159		2115	2129	2145	2159	2215	2229	2245	2315	2345	0015	0045	...	...
Leiden Centraal .... d.	1020	1034**r**	1050	1104**r**	...	1120	1134	1150	1204		2120	2134	2150	2204	2220	2234	2250	2320	2350	0020	0050	...	...
Haarlem .... **461** d.	1040	1055	1110	1125	...	1140	1155	1210	1225		2140	2155	2210	2225	2240	2255	2310	2340	0010	0040	0110	...	...
Amsterdam Sloterdijk .... d.	1049	1104	1119	1134	...	1149	1204	1219	1234		2149	2204	2219	2234	2249	2304	2319	2349	0019	0049	0119	...	...
Amsterdam Centraal ...... **461** a.	1055	1110	1125	1140	...	1155	1210	1225	1240		2155	2210	2225	2240	2255	2310	2325	2355	0025	0055	0125	...	...

j – Mornings of ①–③ (also Dec. 27; not June 11).
k – Mornings of ④–⑦ (also June 11; not Dec. 27).
n – Not Dec. 27, May 31.
p – Also May 31, June 11.
r – ⚒ only.
t – Ⓐ only.
z – 1–3 minutes later on ④⑤.
⊗ – ①⑥⑦ (also Dec. 26, 27, Jan. 2, Apr. 23, May 31, June 11).
⊖ – ②③ (not Dec. 25, 26, Jan. 2, Apr. 23, June 11).

AMSTERDAM - ROTTERDAM - BREDA 451

Intercity direct services via the high-speed line. Supplement payable (except for local journeys Amsterdam - Schiphol and Rotterdam - Breda).

km		1010	910	9212	912	1014	914	9216	916	1018	918	9220	920	1022	922	9224	924	1026	926	9228	928	1030	930	9232	932
		⚒	⚒	B	⚒	⚒		B		⚒		B		⚒		B		⚒		B		⚒		B	
0	**Amsterdam** Centraal .. d.	0552	0608	*0622*r	0638	0653	0708	0725	0738	0753	0808	0825	0838	0853	0908	0925	0938	0953	1008	*1022*r	1038	1053	1108	1125	1138
17	**Schiphol** ✈ ... d.	0608	0623	*0637*r	0653	0708	0723	0740	0753	0808	0823	0840	0853	0908	0923	0940	0953	1008	1023	*1037*r	1053	1108	1123	1140	1153
70	**Rotterdam** Centraal ... a.	0634	0649	*0703*r	0719	0734	0749	0807	0819	0834	0849	0907	0919	0934	0949	1007	1019	1034	1049	*1103*r	1119	1134	1149	1207	1219
70	**Rotterdam** Centraal ... d.	...	0651	0710	0721	...	0751	0810	0821	...	0851	0910	0921	...	0951	1010	1021	...	1051	1110	1121	...	1151	1210	1221
117	**Breda** ... a.	...	0715	0734	0745	...	0815	0834	0845	...	0915	0934	0945	...	1015	1034	1045	...	1115	1134	1145	...	1215	1234	1245

	1034	★	1070	970	9272	972	974	976	978
					B				
Amsterdam Centraal ... d.	1153	and at the same minutes past each hour until	2053	2108	2125	2138	2208	2238	2307
Schiphol ✈ ... d.	1208		2108	2123	2140	2153	2223	2253	2323
Rotterdam Centraal ... a.	1234		2134	2149	2207	2219	2249	2319	2349
Rotterdam Centraal ... d.	...		...	2151	2210	2221	2251	...	2351
Breda ... a.	...		...	2215	2234	2245	2315	...	0015

	1003	1005	905	1007	907	907	9211	909	1011	911
	⚒	⚒	⚒	⚒	⚒		B		⚒	
Breda ... d.	...	...	0645	...	0715	...	0726	0745	...	0815
Rotterdam Centraal ... a.	...	...	0709	...	0739	...	0750	0809	...	0839
Rotterdam Centraal ... d.	0626	0655	0711	0726	0741	0741	0758	0811	0826	0841
Schiphol ✈ ... a.	0651	0719	0735	0751	0805	0805	0822	0835	0851	0905
Amsterdam Centraal ... a.	0707	0735	0751	0807	0821	0821	0838	0851	0907	0921

	9215	913	1015	915	9219	917	1019	919	9223	921	1023	923	9227	925	1027	♥	963	9267	965	1067	967	9271	969	971
	B		⚒		B		⚒		B		⚒		B					B				B		
Breda ... d.	0826	0845	...	0915	0926	0945	...	1015	1026	1045	...	1115	1126	1145	...	and at the same minutes past each hour until	2115	2126	2145	...	2215	2226	2245	2315
Rotterdam Centraal ... a.	0850	0909	...	0939	0950	1009	...	1039	1050	1109	...	1139	1150	1209	...		2139	2150	2209	...	2239	2250	2309	2339
Rotterdam Centraal ... d.	*0855*r	0911	0926	0941	0958	1011	1026	1041	1058	1111	1126	1141	1158	1211	1226		2141	2158	2211	2226	2241	2258	2311	2341
Schiphol ✈ ... d.	*0919*r	0935	0951	1005	1022	1035	1051	1105	1122	1135	1151	1205	1221	1235	1251		2205	2222	2235	2251	2305	2322	2335	0005
Amsterdam Centraal ... a.	*0935*r	0951	1007	1021	1038	1051	1107	1121	1138	1151	1207	1221	1238	1251	1307		2221	2238	2251	2307	2321	2338	2351	0021

B – To/from Brussels (Table **18**). ★ – No direct service from Amsterdam to Breda at 1425 and 1825. ♥ – No direct service from Breda to Amsterdam at 1426 and 1826.
r – ⚒ only.

Local trains AMSTERDAM CENTRAAL - SCHIPHOL 452

See Table **451** for *Intercity direct* trains (which can be used without payment of a supplement between Amsterdam Centraal and Schiphol)

From Amsterdam Centraal

0001, 0011, 0031, 0042, 0512⑥**k**, 0515Ⓐ, 0530⚒, 0542Ⓐ, 0543⑥**k**, 0600⚒, 0612, 0630, 0642, 0700, 0712, 0730, 0742 and at 00, 12, 30 and 42 minutes past each hour until 2300, 2312, 2330 and 2342.

k – Also May 30, June 10.

From Schiphol Journey time: 17 – 18 minutes

0001, 0011, 0041, 0531Ⓐ, 0541, 0552Ⓐ, 0611, 0631⚒, 0641, 0701, 0711, 0731, 0741 and at 01, 11, 31 and 41 minutes past each hour until 2301, 2311, 2331 and 2341.

UTRECHT - AMSTERDAM - ROTTERDAM - EINDHOVEN Night Network 454

	⑥⑦	⑥⑦		H	④⑤	④⑤	③	③		H	④⑤	④⑤	③	③		H	④⑤	④⑤	③	③		L	③	③	†	†
Utrecht Centraal ... d.	...	...	...	0101	0101	...	*0101*b	0101	...	0211	0211	...	*0217*b	0217	...	0311	0311	...	*0317*b	0317	...	0411	*0417*b	0417	0506	0605
Amsterdam Centraal . d.	...	...	...	0145	0145	...	|	0145	...	0246	0247	...	|	0252	...	0346	0348	...	|	0346	...	0446	|	0446	0542	0639
Schiphol ✈ ... d.	...	...	...	0205	0205	...	0203	|	...	0305	0305	...	0303	|	...	0405	0405	...	0403	|	...	0505	0503	|	0557	...
Leiden Centraal ... d.	...	...	...	0223	0223	🚌	0219	0223j	...	0323	0323	🚌	0319	0326	...	0423	0423	🚌	0419	0423j	...	0523	0519	0524j	0614	...
Den Haag HS ... d.	...	...	...	0238	0244j	0242	...	0238	...	0338	0344j	0342	...	0339	...	0438	0444j	0442	...	0438	...	0539	...	0540	0627	...
Delft ... d.	...	...	...	0245	|	0302	...	0245	...	0345	|	0402	...	0346	...	0445	|	0502	...	0445	...	0546	...	0547	0633	...
Rotterdam Centraal .. d.	0002	0102	...	0256	0326	...	...	0258	...	0356	0426	...	...	0359	...	0456	0526	...	...	0459	...	0601	...	0558	0644	...
Dordrecht ... d.	0017	0117	...	...	...	...	...	...	...	...	...	...	...	...	...	...	...	...	...	...	...	...	...	...	...	...
Breda ... d.	0036	0137	...	...	...	...	...	...	...	...	...	...	...	...	...	...	...	...	...	...	...	...	...	...	...	...
Tilburg ... d.	0054	0154	...	...	...	...	...	...	...	...	...	...	...	...	...	...	...	...	...	...	...	...	...	...	...	...
Eindhoven ... a.	0117	0217	...	...	...	...	...	...	...	...	...	...	...	...	...	...	...	...	...	...	...	...	...	...	...	...

		③	④⑤	H	③	④⑤	④⑤	⑥⑦	H	③	③		④⑤	④⑤	⑥⑦	H	③	③	④⑤	④⑤	H	③	③	⑥	†	†
Eindhoven ... d.	...	...	...	...	...	...	...	0030	...	...	...	...	...	...	0130	...	...	...	...	...	...	...	...	...	...	...
Tilburg ... d.	...	...	...	...	...	...	...	0102	...	...	...	...	...	...	0202	...	...	...	...	...	...	...	...	...	...	...
Breda ... d.	...	...	...	...	...	...	...	0119	...	...	...	...	...	...	0219	...	...	...	...	...	...	...	...	...	...	...
Dordrecht ... d.	...	...	...	...	...	...	...	0141	...	...	...	...	...	...	0241	...	...	...	...	...	...	...	...	...	...	...
Rotterdam Centraal .. d.	...	...	0056	0100	0100	🚌	0132	0155	0200	0200	...	...	🚌	0232	0255	0300	0300	...	🚌	0332	0400	0400	...	0500	0500	0600
Delft ... d.	...	...	0106	0112	0112	0158	|	...	0212	0212	...	...	0258	|	...	0312	0312	...	0358	|	0412	0412	...	0511	0512	0612
Den Haag HS ... d.	...	...	0132t	0129j	0130j	0218	0223j	...	0221	0221	...	...	0318	0323j	...	0321	0321	...	0418	0423j	0421	0421	...	0528j	0521	0628j
Leiden Centraal ... d.	...	0146	0145	0145	0145	...	0245j	...	0245j	0245j	0240	...	...	0345j	...	0345j	0345j	0340	...	0445j	0445	0445j	0440	0545	0545	0646
Schiphol ✈ ... a.	...	0202	0200	0200	|	...	0300	...	0300	|	0257	...	...	0400	...	0400	|	0357	...	0500	0500	|	0457	0600	0600	0702
Amsterdam Centraal. a.	0118	|	0216	0216	0217	...	0316	...	0316	0317	|	...	...	0417	...	0416	0417	|	...	0516	0517	0517	|	0617	0616	0721
Utrecht Centraal ... a.	0145	*0248*b	0258	0247	0248	...	0358	...	0354	0349	*0349*b	...	...	0459	...	0454	0448	*0448*b	...	0600	0554	0548	*0548*b	0654	0702	...

H – ①②⑥⑦. L – Not ③. b – Change trains at Amsterdam Bijlmer Arena. j – Arrives 7 – 10 minutes earlier. t – Arrives 0113.

ALMERE - UTRECHT 457

km		Ⓐ	Ⓐ	Ⓐ	⚒	⚒	†	Ⓐ			⚒				⚒								
0	**Almere** Centrum ... d.	0552	0622	0652	...	0722	0722	0752	...	0822	0852	...	and at the same minutes past each hour until	1922	1952	...	2022	...	2122	...	2222	...	2322
	Weesp ... **480** d.	|	|	|	0713	|	|	|	0813	|	|	0913		|	|	2013	|	...	|	...	|	...	|
20	Naarden-Bussum . **480** d.	0612	0642	0712	0720	0742	0742	0812	0820	0842	0912	0920		1942	2012	2020	2042	...	2142	...	2242	...	2341
26	Hilversum ... **480** d.	0619	0649	0719	0730	0749	0749	0819	0830	0849	0919	0930		1949	2019	2030	2049	2119	2149	2219	2249	2319	2349
43	**Utrecht** Centraal ... a.	0638	0705	0735	0749	0805	0808	0835	0849	0905	0935	0949		2005	2035	2049	2108	2138	2208	2238	2308	2338	0008

	⑥⑦c		Ⓐ		⚒	Ⓐ		⚒			⚒				⚒								
Utrecht Centraal ... d.	0044	...	0622	0641	0652	0722	0741	0752	0822	0841	0852	and at the same minutes past each hour until	1922	1941	1952	2014	2044	2114	2144	2214	2244	2314	2344
Hilversum ... **480** d.	0112	...	0642	0701	0712	0742	0801	0812	0842	0901	0912		1942	2001	2012	2042	2107	2142	2207	2242	2307	2342	0012
Naarden-Bussum .. **480** d.	0120	...	0650	0710	0720	0750	0810	0820	0850	0910	0920		1950	2010	2020	2050	...	2150	...	2250	...	2350	0020
Weesp ... **480** a.	|	...	|	0717	|	|	0817	|	|	0917	|		|	2017	|	|	...	|	...	|	...	|	|
Almere Centrum ... a.	0138	...	0708	...	0738	0808	...	0838	0908	...	0938		2008	...	2038	2108	...	2208	...	2308	...	0008	0038

c – Also May 31, June 11.

AMSTERDAM CENTRAAL - ALMERE - ZWOLLE 459

For fast services via Amsterdam Zuid, see Table **460**

km		Ⓐ	Ⓐ	⑥k	Ⓐ	Ⓐ	⚒	⚒	†	⚒	⚒														
0	**Amsterdam** Centraal d.	...	...	...	0553	0607	0623a	0637	...	0653	0707	0723	0737	0753	0807	and at the same minutes past each hour until	2223	2237	2253	2307	2323	2337	2353	0007	0023
14	Weesp ... d.	...	...	...	0610	|	0640a	|	...	0710	|	0740	|	0810	|		2240	|	2310	|	2340	|	0010	|	0040
30	**Almere** Centrum ... d.	...	...	...	0625	0628	0655a	0658	...	0725	0728	0755	0758	0825	0828		2255	2258	2325	2328	2355	2358	0024	0028	0055
36	Almere Buiten ... d.	...	...	...	0631	...	0701a	...	...	0731	...	0801	...	0831	...		2301	...	2331	...	0001	...	0030	...	0101b
54	**Lelystad** Centrum ... d.	0542	0611	0640	0654	...	0724	...	0741	0754	...	0824	...	0854	...		2324	...	2354	...	0020	...	0044	...	0119b
75	Dronten ... d.	0553	0623	0652	0706	...	0736	...	0753	0806	...	0836	...	0906	...		2336	...	0006	...	...	...	...	...	...
88	Kampen Zuid ... d.	0602	0632	0701	0714	...	0744	...	0802	0814	...	0844	...	0914	...		2344	...	0014	...	...	...	...	...	...
104	**Zwolle** ... a.	0613	0643	0712	0724	...	0754	...	0813	0824	...	0854	...	0924	...		2354	...	0024	...	...	...	...	...	...

	Ⓐ	Ⓐ		Ⓐ		Ⓐ		⚒		⚒															
Zwolle ... d.	...	...	...	...	0537a	...	0607a	...	0637a	...	0707r	...	0737r	...	0807	...	0837	and at the same minutes past each hour until	...	2237	...	2307	...	2337	0007
Kampen Zuid ... d.	...	...	...	...	0546a	...	0616a	...	0646a	...	0716r	...	0746r	...	0816	...	0846		...	2246	...	2316	...	2346	0016
Dronten ... d.	...	...	...	...	0555a	...	0625a	...	0655a	...	0725r	...	0755r	...	0825	...	0855		...	2255	...	2325	...	2355	0025
Lelystad Centrum ... d.	0510	0544	0540	...	0610	...	0640	...	0710	...	0740	...	0810	...	0840	...	0910		...	2310	...	2340	...	0010	0037
Almere Buiten ... d.	0528	|	0558	...	0628	...	0658	...	0728	...	0758	...	0828	...	0858	...	0928		...	2328	...	2358	...	0028	...
Almere Centrum ... d.	0536	0602	0606	0632	0636	0702	0706	0732	0736	0802	0806	0832	0836	0902	0906	0932	0936		2332	2336	0002	0006	0032	0036	...
Weesp ... d.	0551	|	0621	|	0651	|	0721	|	0751	|	0821	|	0851	|	0921	|	0951		|	2351	|	0021	|	0051	...
Amsterdam Centraal. a.	0607	0623	0637	0653	0707	0723	0737	0754	0807	0823	0837	0853	0907	0923	0937	0953	1007		2353	0007	0023	0037	0053	0109	...

a – Ⓐ only. b – On the mornings of ④⑤ (not Dec. 27) Weesp - Lelystad is by 🚌 (arriving Lelystad 0144). k – Also May 30, June 10. r – ⚒ only.

460 DEN HAAG - SCHIPHOL - AMSTERDAM ZUID - ALMERE - ZWOLLE

For services Amsterdam Centraal - Almere - Zwolle and v.v., see Table **459**. For services via Amersfoort and Utrecht, see Table **481**.

km				⑥k	Ⓐ	⚒	Ⓐ	⚒	Ⓐ		Ⓐ		Ⓐ		⚒		⚒		⚒		⚒		⚒	
	Dordrecht 450 d.	...	...	...	...	...	...	...	0608	...	0639	...	0709	...	0739	...	0809	...	0839	...	0908	...	0939	...
	Rotterdam Centraal 450 d.	...	...	...	...	...	0557	...	0627	...	0657	...	0727	...	0757	...	0827	...	0857	...	0927	...	0957	...
	Schiedam Centrum 450 d.	...	...	...	...	...	0602	...	0632	...	0702	...	0732	...	0802	...	0832	...	0902	...	0932	...	1002	...
	Delft 450 d.	...	...	...	...	...	0609	...	0639	...	0709	...	0739	...	0809	...	0839	...	0909	...	0939	...	1009	...
	Den Haag HS 450 d.	...	...	...	...	...	0618	...	0648	...	0718	...	0748	...	0818	...	0848	...	0918	...	0948	...	1018	...
0	**Den Haag** Centraal 450 d.	0003	0033	...	0533	0603	|	0633	|	0703	|	0733	|	0803	|	0833	|	0903	|	0933	|	1003	|	1033
15	Leiden Centraal 450 d.	0017	0047	...	0547	0617	0631	0647	0701	0717	0731	0747	0801	0817	0831	0847	0901	0917	0931	0947	1001	1017	1031	1047
42	**Schiphol** ✈ d.	0032	0102	...	0604	0634	0648	0704	0718	0734	0748	0804	0818	0834	0848	0904	0918	0934	0948	1004	1018	1034	1048	1104
51	**Amsterdam** Zuid d.	▬	▬	...	0612	0642	0656	0712	0726	0742	0756	0812	0826	0842	0856	0912	0926	0942	0956	1012	1026	1042	1056	1112
56	Duivendrecht d.	...	...	...	|	|	0701	|	0731	|	0801	|	0831	|	0901	|	0931	|	1001	|	1031	|	1101	|
80	**Almere** Centrum 459 d.	...	...	...	0633	0703	0720	0733	0750	0803	0820	0833	0850	0903	0920	0933	0949	1003	1020	1033	1050	1103	1120	1133
86	**Almere** Buiten 459 d.	Ⓐ	Ⓐ	...	|	|	0725	|	0755	|	0825	|	0855	|	0925	|	0955	|	1025	|	1055	|	1125	|
104	**Lelystad** Centrum 459 d.	0541	0611	0640	0647	0717	0736	0747	0806	0817	0836	0847	0906	0917	0936	0947	1006	1017	1036	1047	1106	1117	1136	1147
154	**Zwolle** 459 a.	0613	0643	0712	0713	0743	...	0813	...	0843	...	0913	...	0943	...	1013	...	1043	...	1113	...	1143	...	1213
	Leeuwarden 482 a.	|	0744	|	|	0845v	...	|	...	0944	...	|	...	1044	...	|	...	1144	...	|	...	1244	...	|
	Groningen 482 a.	0723	...	0833	0813	...	...	0913	...	...	...	1013	...	...	...	1113	...	...	...	1213	...	...	...	1313

	⚒				♥	♥																	
Dordrecht 450 d.	1009	...	1039	...	1108		...	1839	...	1908	...	1939	...	2008	...	2039	...	2108	...	2139	...	...	...
Rotterdam Centraal 450 d.	1027	...	1057	...	1127		...	1857	...	1927	...	1957	...	2027	...	2057	...	2127	...	2157	...	...	...
Schiedam Centrum 450 d.	1032	...	1102	...	1132		...	1902	...	1932	...	2002	...	2032	...	2102	...	2132	...	2202	...	...	...
Delft 450 d.	1039	...	1109	...	1139	and at	...	1909	...	1939	...	2009	...	2039	...	2109	...	2139	...	2209	...	...	...
Den Haag HS 450 d.	1048	...	1118	...	1148		...	1918	...	1948	...	2018	...	2048	...	2118	...	2148	...	2218	...	...	...
Den Haag Centraal 450 d.	|	1103	|	1133	|	the same	1903	|	1933	|	2003	|	2033	|	2103	|	2133	|	2203	|	2233	2303	2333
Leiden Centraal 450 d.	1101	1117	1131	1147	1201		1917	1931	1947	2001	2017	2031	2047	2101	2117	2131	2147	2201	2217	2231	2247	2317	2347
Schiphol ✈ d.	1118	1134	1148	1204	1218	minutes	1934	1948	2004	2018	2034	2048	2104	2118	2134	2148	2204	2218	2234	2248	2304	2334	0002
Amsterdam Zuid d.	1126	1142	1156	1212	1226		1942	1956	2012	2026	2042	2056	2112	2127	2142	2156	2212	2226	2242	2256	2312	2342	...
Duivendrecht d.	1131	|	1201	|	1231	past each	|	2001	|	2031	|	2100	|	2131	|	2200	|	2230	|	2300	|	|	...
Almere Centrum 459 d.	1150	1203	1220r	1233	1250r	hour until	2003	2020r	2033	2050r	2103	...	2133	...	2203	...	2233	...	2303	...	2333	0003	...
Almere Buiten 459 d.	1155	|	1225r	|	1255r		|	2025r	|	2055r	|	...	|	...	|	...	|	...	|	...	|	|	...
Lelystad Centrum 459 d.	1206	1217	1236r	1247	1306r		2017	2036r	2047	2106r	2117	...	2147	...	2217	...	2247	...	2317	...	2347	0017	...
Zwolle 459 a.	...	1243	...	1313	...		2043	...	2113	...	2143	...	2213	...	2243	...	2313	...	2343	...	0015	0043	...
Leeuwarden 482 a.	...	1344	...	|	...		2144	...	|	...	2244	...	|	...	2351	...	|	...	0051	...	|	0151c	...
Groningen 482 a.	...	...	...	1413	...		...	...	2213	...	...	...	2313	...	...	...	0022	...	...	...	0123	...	...

	⚒	Ⓐ	Ⓐ		Ⓐ		Ⓐ	⚒d	⚒		⚒		⚒		⚒		⚒		⚒					
Groningen 482 d.	...	...	...	...	...	...	...	0533b	...	...	...	0648h	...	...	...	0748j	...	...	...	0848	...	...	...	0948
Leeuwarden 482 d.	...	...	...	...	...	0507a	...	|	...	0607a	...	|	...	0716e	...	|	...	0816j	...	|	...	0916	...	|
Zwolle 459 d.	...	...	...	0547a	...	0617a	...	0647	...	0717r	...	0747	...	0817	...	0847	...	0917	...	0947	...	1017	...	1047
Lelystad Centrum 459 d.	...	...	...	0613a	0624	0643a	0654	0713	0724a	0743r	0754a	0813	0824	0843	0854	0913	0924	0943	0954	1013	1024r	1043	1054r	1113
Almere Buiten 459 d.	...	...	...	|	0636	|	0706	|	0736a	|	0806a	|	0836	|	0906	|	0936	|	1006	|	1036r	|	1106r	|
Almere Centrum 459 d.	...	...	...	0629a	0642	0659	0712	0729	0742a	0759	0812a	0829	0842	0859	0912	0929	0942	0959	1012	1029	1042r	1059	1112r	1129
Duivendrecht d.	...	...	...	|	0659	|	0729	|	0759a	|	0829a	|	0859	|	0929	|	0959	|	1029	|	1059	|	1129	|
Amsterdam Zuid d.	...	...	...	0649a	0705	0719	0735	0749	0805a	0819	0835a	0849	0905	0919	0935	0949	1005	1019	1035	1049	1105	1119	1135	1149
Schiphol ✈ d.	0557	0627	0643	0657	0713	0727	0743	0757	0813	0827	0843	0857	0913	0927	0943	0957	1013	1027	1043	1057	1113	1127	1143	1157
Leiden Centraal 450 d.	0615	0645	0700	0715	0730	0745	0800	0815	0830	0845	0900	0915	0930	0945	1000	1015	1030	1045	1100	1115	1130	1145	1200	1215
Den Haag Centraal 450 a.	0626	0656	|	0726	|	0756	|	0826	|	0856	|	0926	|	0956	|	1026	|	1056	|	1126	|	1156	|	1226
Den Haag HS 450 d.	...	...	0714	...	0744	...	0814	...	0844	...	0914	...	0944	...	1014	...	1044	...	1114	...	1144	...	1214	...
Delft 450 d.	...	...	0720	...	0750	...	0820	...	0850	...	0920	...	0950	...	1020	...	1050	...	1120	...	1150	...	1220	...
Schiedam Centrum 450 d.	...	...	0728	...	0758	...	0828	...	0858	...	0928	...	0958	...	1028	...	1058	...	1128	...	1158	...	1228	...
Rotterdam Centraal 450 d.	...	...	0736	...	0806	...	0836	...	0907	...	0936	...	1006	...	1036	...	1107	...	1136	...	1206	...	1236	...
Dordrecht 450 a.	...	...	0752	...	0822	...	0852	...	0923	...	0952	...	1023	...	1052	...	1123	...	1152	...	1223	...	1252	...

																							⑤⑥k
Groningen 482 d.	...		1648	...	...	...	1748	...	...	...	1848	...	...	...	1948	...	...	2048	...	2148	...	2248	2326
Leeuwarden 482 d.	...		|	...	1716	...	|	...	1816	...	|	...	1916	...	|	...	2016	|	2116	|	2216	|	|
Zwolle 459 d.	...		1747	...	1817	...	1847	...	1917	...	1947	...	2017	...	2047	...	2117	2147	2217	2247	2317	2347	0037
Lelystad Centrum 459 d.	1124r	and at	1813	1824r	1843	1854r	1913	...	1943	...	2013	...	2043	...	2113	...	2143	2213	2243	2313	2343	0013	0108
Almere Buiten 459 d.	1136r		|	1836r	|	1906r	|	...	|	...	|	...	|	...	|	...	|	|	|	|	|	|	|
Almere Centrum 459 d.	1142r	the same	1829	1842r	1859	1912r	1929	...	1959	...	2029	...	2059	...	2129	...	2159	2229	2259	2329	2359	0029	0122
Duivendrecht d.	1159		|	1859	|	1929	|	1959	|	2029	|	2059	|	2129	|	2159	|	|	|	|	|	|	|
Amsterdam Zuid d.	1205	minutes	1849	1905	1919	1935	1949	2005	2019	2035	2049	2105	2119	2135	2149	2205	2219	2249	2319	2349	0019	0049	0142‡
Schiphol ✈ d.	1213		1857	1913	1927	1943	1957	2013	2027	2043	2057	2113	2127	2143	2157	2213	2227	2257	2327	2357	0026	0057	...
Leiden Centraal 450 d.	1230	past each	1915	1930	1945	2000	2015	2030	2045	2100	2115	2130	2145	2200	2215	2230	2245	2315	2345	0015	0045	0115	...
Den Haag Centraal 450 a.	|		1926	|	1956	|	2026	|	2056	|	2126	|	2156	|	2226	|	2256	2326	2356	0026	0056	0126c	...
Den Haag HS 450 d.	1244	hour until	...	1944	...	2014	...	2044	...	2114	...	2144	...	2214	...	2244	...	...	...	...	...	...	...
Delft 450 d.	1250		...	1950	...	2020	...	2050	...	2120	...	2150	...	2220	...	2250	...	...	...	...	...	...	...
Schiedam Centrum 450 d.	1258		...	1958	...	2028	...	2058	...	2128	...	2158	...	2228	...	2258	...	...	...	...	...	...	...
Rotterdam Centraal 450 d.	1307		...	2006	...	2036	...	2107	...	2136	...	2206	...	2236	...	2306	...	...	...	...	...	...	...
Dordrecht 450 a.	1323		...	2023	...	2052	...	2123	...	2152	...	2223	...	2252	...	2324	...	...	...	...	...	...	...

a – Ⓐ only.
b – 0548 on ⑥ (also May 30, June 10).
c – Mornings of ⑥⑦ (also May 31 June 11).
d – Runs daily Schiphol - Den Haag.
e – 0707 on †.
h – 0637 on ⑥ (also May 30, June 10).
j – 8 – 10 minutes earlier on †.
k – Also May 30, June 10.
r – ⚒ only.
v – 0842 on ⑥ (also May 30, June 10).
♥ – Certain trains depart Dordrecht at xx09 (not xx08); other timings follow the same pattern.
‡ – Amsterdam **Centraal**.

461 AMSTERDAM - HAARLEM - HOORN and ZANDVOORT AAN SEE

km		Ⓐ	Ⓐ	Ⓐ	⚒	⚒	⚒			⚒														
	Amsterdam C ⊙ 450 d.	...	...	0611	...	0641	0711	...	0741	0741	0811	0841	✥	1811	1841	1911	1941	2011	2041	2111	2141	2211	2241	2311	2341
0	**Haarlem** 450 d.	...	...	0631	...	0701	0731	...	0801	0801	0831	0901	and every	1831	1901	1931	2001	2031	2101	2131	2201	2231	2301	2331	0001
11	Beverwijk d.	...	...	0647	...	0717	0747	...	0817	0817	0847	0917		1847	1917	1947	2017	2047	2117	2147	2217	2247	2317	2347	0017
22	Castricum 466 d.	...	...	0700	...	0730	0800	...	0830	0830	0900	0930	30 minutes	1900	1930	2000	2030	2100	2130	2200	2230	2300	2330	0000	0030
34	**Alkmaar** 466 a.	...	...	0711	...	0741	0811	...	0841	0841	0911	0941	until	1911	1941	2011	2041	2111	2141	2211	2241	2311	2341	0011	0041
34	**Alkmaar** 466 d.	0613	0643	0713	0713	0743	0813	0813	...	0843	0913	0943		1913	1943	2013	...	2113	...	2213	...	2313	...	0013	...
40	Heerhugowaard 466 d.	0621	0651	0721	0721	0751	0821	0821	...	0851	0921	0951		1921	1951	2021	...	2121	...	2221	...	2321	...	0021	...
57	**Hoorn** a.	0640	0710	0740	0740	0810	0840	0840	...	0910	0940	1010		1940	2010	2040	...	2140	...	2240	...	2340	...	0040	...

	Ⓐ	Ⓐ	⚒	Ⓐ	⚒	Ⓐ	⚒	⚒		⚒		⚒														
Hoorn d.	...	...	...	0551	...	0621	...	0651	0721	0751	0821	0851	0921	0951	⊡	1921	1951	...	2051	...	2151	...	2251	...	2351
Heerhugowaard 466 d.	...	...	...	0608	...	0638	...	0708	0738	0808	0838	0908	0938	1008	and every	1938	2008	...	2108	...	2208	...	2308	...	0008
Alkmaar 466 a.	...	...	...	0616	...	0646	...	0716	0746	0816	0846	0916	0946	1016		1946	2016	...	2116	...	2216	...	2316	...	0016
Alkmaar 466 d.	0458	0519	0549	0619	0619	0649	0649	0719	0749	0819	0849	0919	0949	1019	30 minutes	1949	2019	2049	2119	2149	2219	2249	2319	2349	0019
Castricum 466 d.	0508	0529	0559	0629	0629	0659	0659	0729	0759	0829	0859	0929	0959	1029	until	1959	2029	2059	2129	2159	2229	2259	2329	2359	0029
Beverwijk d.	0521	0542	0612	0642	0642	0712	0712	0742	0812	0842	0912	0942	1012	1042		2012	2042	2112	2142	2212	2242	2312	2342	0012	0042
Haarlem 450 d.	0540	0601	0631	0701	0701	0731	0731	0801	0831	0901	0931	1001	1031	1101		2031	2101	2131	2201	2231	2301	2331	0001	0031	0101
Amsterdam C ⊙ 450 a.	0559	0620	0650	0720	0720	0750	0750	0820	0850	0920	0950	1020	1050	1120		2050	2120	2150	2220	2250	2320	2350	0020	0050	0120

AMSTERDAM - HAARLEM - ZANDVOORT AAN SEE ☒

		⚒								
Amsterdam C ⊙ 450 d.	0026	*0619*a	0656a	0726r	0756r	0826	0856	and every	2326	2356
Haarlem 450 d.	0046	0646	0716	0746	0816	0846	0916	30 minutes	2346	0016
Zandvoort aan See a.	0056	0658	0726	0758	0826	0856	0926	until	2357	0026

	Ⓐ	⚒	⚒						
Zandvoort aan See d.	0604	0634	0704	0734	0804	0834	and every	2304	2334
Haarlem 450 d.	0616	0646	0716	0746	0816	0846	30 minutes	2316	2346
Amsterdam C ⊙ 450 a.	0635	0705	0735	0805	0835	0905	until	2335	0005

a – Ⓐ only.
r – ⚒ only.
⊙ – Amsterdam Centraal. All trains also call at Amsterdam Sloterdijk (5 minutes from Centraal).
✥ – On Ⓐ the 1441, 1511, 1541, 1611 and 1641 from Amsterdam run 1 – 4 minutes earlier Alkmaar - Hoorn.
⊡ – On Ⓐ Hoorn d. 1548 (not 1551), 1618 (not 1621), 1648 (not 1651), 1718 (not 1721), 1748 (not 1751).
☒ Haarlem - Zandvoort is *8 km*.

LEIDEN - ALPHEN - UTRECHT and GOUDA 463

km		Ⓐ	⚒	⚒								
0	**Leiden** Centraal d.	0552	0622	0652	0722	0752	0822	0852	and every	2322	2352	0022
15	Alphen a/d Rijn d.	0607	0637	0707	0737	0807	0837	0907	30 minutes	2337	0007	0037
34	Woerden d.	0625	0655	0725	0755	0825	0855	0925	until	2355	0025	0055
50	**Utrecht** Centraal a.	0635	0705	0735	0805	0835	0905	0935		0005	0035	0105

	Ⓐ	⚒	⚒									
Utrecht Centraal d.	0555	0625	0655	0725	0755	and every	2325	2355	0025	...	...	...
Voerden d.	0606	0636	0706	0736	0806	30 minutes	2336	0006	0036	...	...	...
Alphen a/d Rijn d.	0623	0653	0723	0753	0823	until	2353	0023	0053	...	...	...
Leiden Centraal a.	0637	0707	0737	0807	0837		0007	0037	0107	...	...	...

ALPHEN A/D RIJN - GOUDA and v.v. *17 km*. Journey: 22–28 minutes. Additional services run on Ⓐ.

From Alphen a/d Rijn at 0609 Ⓐ, 0639 Ⓐ, 0709 ⚒, 0739 ⚒, 0809, 0839 and every 30 minutes until 2309, 2339, 0009, 0039 and 0109.

From Gouda at 0551 Ⓐ, 0627 ⚒, 0657 ⚒, 0727, 0757, 0821, 0857, 0927, 0957, 1021, 1057, 1127, 1157, 1221, 1257, 1327, 1357, 1421, 1457, 1527, 1557, 1621, 1657, 1727, 1757, 1821, 1857, 1927, 1957, 2021, 2057, 2127, 2157, 2221 Ⓐ, 2227 Ⓒ. 2257, 2327, 2357 and 0027.

AMSTERDAM - GOUDA - ROTTERDAM 465

For fast trains **Amsterdam - Rotterdam**, see Tables **450** and **451**. For other trains **Gouda - Rotterdam**, see Table **481**.

km		Ⓐ	⚒	⚒	⚒					
0	**Amsterdam** Centraal d.	0549	0619	0649	0719	0749	0819	and every	2319	2349
6	Amsterdam Amstel d.	0558	0628	0658	0728	0758	0828	30 minutes	2328	2358
9	Duivendrecht d.	0601	0631	0701	0731	0801	0831	until	2331	0001
27	Breukelen d.	0620	0650	0720	0750	0820	0850		2350	0020
40	Woerden d.	0628	0658	0728	0758	0828	0858		2358	0028
56	**Gouda** d.	0641	0711	0741	0811	0841	0911		0011	0041
70	Rotterdam Alexander d.	0654	0724	0754	0824	0854	0924		0024	0054
80	**Rotterdam** Centraal a.	0704	0734	0804	0834	0904	0934		0034	0104

	Ⓐ	Ⓐ	⚒	⚒					
Rotterdam Centraal d.	0525	0555	0625	0655	0725	0755	and every	2255	2325
Rotterdam Alexander d.	0535	0605	0635	0705	0735	0805	30 minutes	2305	2335
Gouda d.	0549	0619	0649	0719	0749	0819	until	2319	2349
Woerden d.	0601	0631	0701	0731	0801	0831		2331	0001
Breukelen d.	0612	0642	0712	0742	0812	0842		2342	0012
Duivendrecht d.	0628	0658	0728	0758	0828	0858		2358	0028
Amsterdam Amstel d.	0632	0702	0732	0802	0832	0902		0002	0032
Amsterdam Centraal a.	0641	0711	0741	0811	0841	0911		0011	0041

AMSTERDAM - ALKMAAR - DEN HELDER 466

km		⑥⑦c	⑥⑦c	Ⓐ	Ⓐ	⚒	Ⓐ					†	⚒									
	Nijmegen 468 d.	2343p	...	...	...	...	...	0537a	0613r	0643r	0713	0737	0743	0813	0843	0913	and every	2043	2113	2143	2213	2243
	Arnhem Centraal 468 d.	0001	...	...	...	...	...	0601a	0631r	0701r	0731	0801	0801	0832	0901	0931	30 minutes	2102	2131	2201	2231	2301
0	**Amsterdam Centraal 459 470** d.	0109	0114	...	0609	...	0639	0709	0739	0809	0839	0909	0909	0939	1009	1039	until	2209	2239	2309	2339	0009
5	Amsterdam Sloterdijk **459 470** d.	0115	0120	...	0615	...	0645	0715	0745	0815	0845	0915	0915	0945	1015	1045		2215	2245	2315	2345	0015
12	Zaandam **459** d.	0122	0126	...	0622	...	0652	0722	0752	0822	0852	0922	0922	0952	1022	1052		2222	2252	2322	2352	0022
29	Castricum **461** d.	0134	0147	...	0634	...	0704	0734	0804	0834	0904	0934	0934	1004	1034	1104		2234	2304	2334	0004	0034
41	**Alkmaar 461 470** a.	0146	0159	...	0646	...	0716	0746	0816	0846	0916	0946	0946	1016	1046	1116		2246	2317	2346	0017	0046
41	**Alkmaar 461** d.	...	0200	0619	0649	0649	0719	0749	0819	0849	0919	0949	0949	1019	1049	1119		2249	2319	2349	0019	0049b
48	Heerhugowaard **461** d.	...	0207	0627	0657	0657	0727	0757	0827	0857	0927	0957	0957	1027	1057	1127		2257	2327	2357	0027	0057b
83	**Den Helder** a.	...	0235	0656	0727	0727	0756	0827	0857	0927	0957	1027	1027	1057	1127	1157		2327	2356	0033	0057	0127b

		Ⓐ	†	Ⓐ	Ⓐ	†	⚒																
Den Helder d.	...	0504	...	0534	0604	...	0634	0704	0734	and every	1804	1834	1904	1934	2004	2034	2104	2134	2204	2304	...	2357
Heerhugowaard **461** d.	...	0531	...	0601	0631	...	0701	0731	0801	30 minutes	1831	1901	1931	2001	2031	2101	2131	2201	2231	2331	...	0023
Alkmaar 461 a.	...	0541	...	0611	0641	...	0711	0741	0811	until	1841	1911	1941	2011	2041	2111	2141	2211	2241	2341	...	0031
Alkmaar 461 470 d.	0502	0544	0602	0614	0644	0702	0714	0744	0814		1844	1914	1944	2014	2044	2114	2144	2214	2244	2344	...	0032
Castricum **461** d.	0511	0555	0612	0625	0655	0712	0725	0755	0825		1855	1925	1955	2025	2055	2125	2155	2225	2255	2355	...	0043
Zaandam **459** d.	0535	0608	0635	0639	0709	0735	0739	0809	0839		1909	1939	2009	2039	2109	2139	2209	2239	2309	0009	...	0104
Amsterdam Sloterdijk **459 470** d.	0541	0615	0641	0645	0715	0741	0745	0815	0845		1915	1945	2015	2045	2115	2145	2215	2245	2315	0015	...	0110
Amsterdam Centraal **459 470** a.	0547	0621	0647	0651	0721	0747	0751	0821	0851		1921	1951	2021	2051	2121	2151	2221	2251	2321	0021	...	0116
Arnhem Centraal 468 a.	...	0729	...	0759	0830	...	0859	0929	0959		2029	2059	2129	2159	2229	2259	2330	2400	0030	0130	...	...
Nijmegen 468 a.	...	0747	...	0817	0847	...	0917	0947	1017		2047	2117	2147	2217	2247	2317	2347	0020	0049	0149n	...	...

– Ⓐ only.
– Operated by 🚌 Alkmaar - Den Helder on the mornings of ②③ (not Dec. 26, Jan. 1, 2) arriving Den Helder 0221.
c – Also May 31, June 11.
n – *0211* (by 🚌 from Arnhem) on the mornings of ④⑤ (not May 11).
p – Previous day.
r – ⚒ only.

AMSTERDAM and SCHIPHOL ✈ - ARNHEM - NIJMEGEN 468

Many trains from / to Amsterdam Centraal start from / continue to Den Helder (see Table **466**). For international trains **Amsterdam – Arnhem – Köln**, see Table **28**.

km			④j				Ⓐ		Ⓐ	Ⓐ	Ⓐ	⚒	Ⓐ	Ⓐ	⚒	⚒	Ⓐ		⚒		⚒		⚒	
0	Amsterdam Centraal **470** d.	0021	...	0057	...	...	...	...	...	0539	...	...	0624	...	...	0654	...	0724	...	0754	...	0824	...	0854
6	Amsterdam Amstel **470** d.	0033	...	0106	...	...	...	...	...	0548	...	...	0633	...	...	0703	...	0733	...	0803	...	0833	...	0903
	Schiphol ✈ 470 d.	|	...	|	...	...	...	...	...	|	...	...	|	...	...	|	0700	|	0730	|	0800	|	0830	|
	Amsterdam Zuid 470 d.	|	...	|	...	...	...	...	...	|	...	...	|	...	...	|	0709	|	0739	|	0809	|	0839	|
39	**Utrecht** Centraal **470** a.	0052	...	0140	...	...	...	...	...	0622	...	...	0652	...	...	0722	0735	0752	0805	0822	0837	0852	0905	0922
39	**Utrecht** Centraal d.	0054	...	...	...	...	0554	...	0624	...	0639	0654	0654	0709	0709	0724	0739	0754	0809	0824	0839	0854	0909	0924
79	Ede-Wageningen d.	0119	...	...	...	...	0619	...	0648	...	0703	0718	0718	0733	0733	0748	0803	0819	0833	0848	0903	0918	0933	0948
96	**Arnhem** Centraal a.	0130	🚌	...	...	...	0630	...	0659	...	0714	0729	0729	0744	0743	0759	0813	0830	0843	0859	0913	0929	0943	0959
96	**Arnhem** Centraal **475** d.	0135t	0140	...	...	...	0635	...	0705	...	0720	0735	0735	0750	...	0805	0820	0835	0850	0905	0920	0935	0950	1005
114	**Nijmegen 475** a.	0149t	0211	...	...	...	0655	...	0717	...	0732	0747	0747	0802	...	0817	0832	0847	0902	0917	0932	0947	1002	1017

	⚒		⚒																				
msterdam Centraal **470** d.	...	0924	...	0954	...	1024	...	1054	and at	...	2122	...	2151	...	...	...	2224	...	2254	...	2324	...	2354
msterdam Amstel **470** d.	...	0933	...	1003	...	1033	...	1103	the same	...	2133	...	2203	...	...	...	2233	...	2303	...	2333	...	0003
Schiphol ✈ 470 d.	0900	|	0930	|	1000	|	1030	|	minutes	2100	|	2130	|	...	2200	2218	|	2248	|	2318	|	2348	|
Amsterdam Zuid 470 d.	0909	|	0939	|	1009	|	1039	|	past each	2109	|	2139	|	...	2209	2226	|	2256	|	2326	|	2356	|
trecht Centraal **470** a.	0935	0952	1006	1022	1035	1052	1107	1122	hour until	2134	2152	2204	2222	...	2234	2248	2252	2319	2322	2348	2352	0018	0022
trecht Centraal d.	0939	0954	1009	1024	1039	1054	1109	1124		2139	2154	2209	2224	...	2239	...	2254	...	2324	...	2354	...	...
de-Wageningen d.	1003	1019	1033	1048	1103	1118	1133	1148		2203	2218	2233	2248	...	2303	...	2319	...	2349	...	0019	...	...
rnhem Centraal a.	1013	1030	1043	1100	1113	1129	1143	1159		2213	2229	2243	2259	...	2313	...	2330	...	0000	...	0030	...	...
rnhem Centraal **475** d.	1020	1035	1050	1105	1120	1135	1150	1205		2220	2235	2250	2305	...	2320	...	2335	...	0005	...	0035	...	...
ijmegen **475** a.	1032	1047	1102	1117	1132	1147	1202	1217		2232	2247	2302	2317	...	2332	...	2347	...	0020	...	0049	...	...

km		Ⓐ	Ⓐ	⚒	Ⓐ	Ⓐ	⚒	†	⚒	⚒	†	⚒		⚒	†	⚒	⚒	⚒	†	⚒					
	Nijmegen 475 d.	...	...	...	0537	...	0613	...	0628a	0643	...	0658a	0713	0728a	0737	0743	0758a	0813	0813	0828	0843	0858	0913	0928	0943
	Arnhem Centraal **475** a.	...	...	...	0556	...	0626	...	0640a	0656	...	0710a	0726	0740a	0756	0756	0810a	0826	0826	0840	0856	0910	0926	0940	0956
	Arnhem Centraal d.	...	0546	...	0601	0616	0631	...	0646	0701	...	0716	0731	0746	0801	0801	0816	0832	0832	0846	0901	0916	0931	0946	1001
	Ede-Wageningen d.	...	0556	...	0611	0626	0641	...	0656	0711	...	0726	0741	0756	0811	0811	0826	0843	0842	0856	0911	0926	0941	0956	1011
	Utrecht Centraal a.	...	0621	...	0636	0651	0706	...	0721	0736	...	0751	0807	0821	0838	0836	0851	0906	0908	0921	0936	0951	1006	1021	1036
0	**Utrecht** Centraal **470** d.	0555	0626	0638	0638	0656	0708	0708	0725	0738	0738	0755	0809	0825	0838	0838	0855	0908	0909	0925	0937	0955	1008	1025	1038
36	**Amsterdam Zuid 470** d.	0623	0653	|	|	0723	|	|	0753	|	|	0823	|	0853	|	|	0923	|	|	0953	|	1023	|	1053	|
45	**Schiphol ✈ 470** a.	0629	0659	|	|	0729	|	|	0759	|	|	0829	|	0859	|	|	0929	|	|	0959	|	1029	|	1059	|
	Amsterdam Amstel **470** d.	...	...	0657	0657	...	0727	0727	...	0757	0758	...	0827	...	0857	0857	...	0927	0928	...	0957	...	1027	...	1057
	Amsterdam Centraal **470** a.	...	...	0705	0705	...	0736	0736	...	0806	0806	...	0835	...	0905	0905	...	0935	0936	...	1005	...	1035	...	1105

	❖										†			†										⑤⑥k
ijmegen **475** d.		1858	1913	1928	1943	1958	2013	2028	2043	...	2058	2113	...	2128	2143	...	2213	...	2243	...	2313	...	2343	2343
rnhem Centraal **475** a.	and at	1910	1926	1940	1956	2010	2026	2040	2056	...	2110	2126	...	2140	2156	...	2226	...	2256	...	2326	...	2356	2356
rnhem Centraal d.	the same	1916	1932	1946	2001	2016	2031	2046	2102	...	2116	2131	...	2146	2201	...	2231	...	2301	...	2331	...	0001	0001
de-Wageningen d.	minutes	1926	1943	1956	2011	2026	2041	2056	2111	...	2126	2141	...	2156	2211	...	2241	...	2311	...	2341	...	0011	0011
trecht Centraal a.	past each	1951	2006	2021	2036	2051	2106	2121	2138	...	2151	2208	...	2221	2238	...	2308	...	2338	...	0008	...	0036	0036
trecht Centraal **470** d.	hour until	1955	2008	2025	2038	2055	2108	2125	2139	2142	2156	2209	2212	2226	2239	2242	2309	2312	2339	2342	...	0023	...	0038
Amsterdam Zuid 470 d.		2023	|	2053	|	2123	|	2153	|	2205	2223	|	2235	2253	|	2305	|	2335	|	0005	...	|	...	|
Schiphol ✈ 470 a.		2029	|	2059	|	2129	|	2159	|	2211	2229	|	2241	2259	|	2311	|	2341	|	0011	...	|	...	|
msterdam Amstel **470** d.		...	2027	...	2057	...	2127	...	2158	...	...	2227	...	...	2257	...	2327	...	2357	...	...	0043	...	0057
msterdam Centraal **470** a.		...	2035	...	2105	...	2137	...	2206	...	...	2235	...	...	2305	...	2336	...	0005	...	...	0052	...	0106

– Ⓐ only.
j – Not July 18.
k – Also May 30, June 10.
t – ①②③⑤⑥⑦ (also May 30).
❖ – Timings may vary by 1–2 minutes.

NETHERLANDS

470 ENKHUIZEN - AMSTERDAM - EINDHOVEN - MAASTRICHT, VENLO and HEERLEN

ENKHUIZEN / ALKMAAR - AMSTERDAM CENTRAAL - EINDHOVEN - MAASTRICHT / HEERLEN

km		Ⓐ	Ⓐ	Ⓐ	⚒	Ⓐ	⚒	Ⓐ	⑥k	Ⓐ◇	Ⓐ	Ⓒ	Ⓐ◇	Ⓐ	Ⓒ	Ⓐ◇	⚒	†	⚒◇	⚒	†	⚒◇	⚒	†	⚒◇	⚒
0	**Enkhuizen** d.	...	...	0509	...	0539	0539	...	0609	0609	...	0639	0639	...	0709k	0709	...	0739	0739	...	0809	0809	...	0839	0839	...
18	Hoorn d.	...	...	0535	...	0605	0605	...	0635	0640	...	0705	0710	...	0735k	0740	...	0805	0810	...	0835	0840	...	0905	0910	...
	Alkmaar 466 d.	...	...	|	...	|	|	0627	|	|	0657	|	|	0727	|	|	0757	|	|	0827	|	|	0857	|	|	0927
57	Amsterdam Sloterdijk 466 d.	...	...	0601	...	0631	0631	0655	0701	0705	0725	0731	0735	0755	0801k	0805	0826	0831	0835	0855	0901	0905	0925	0931	0936	0955
62	**Amsterdam** Centraal 466 a.	...	...	0607	...	0637	0637	0701	0707	0711	0731	0737	0741	0801	0807k	0811	0832	0837	0841	0902	0907	0911	0932	0937	0941	1002
62	**Amsterdam** Centraal 468 d.	...	...	0610	...	0641	—	0705	0710	0714	0735	0740	0745	0804	0811	0816	0835	0840	0845	0905	0910	0914	0935	0940	0945	1005
68	Amsterdam Amstel 468 d.	...	...	0618	...	0649	...	0713	0718	0722	0743	0748	0753	0811	0819	0824	0843	0848	0853	0913	0918	0922	0943	0948	0953	1013
101	**Utrecht** Centraal 468 d.	...	0609	0639	...	0709	...	0733	0739	0744	0803	0809	0814	0833	0839	0844	0903	0909	0914	0933	0939	0944	1003	1009	1014	1033
149	's-Hertogenbosch d.	...	0639	0709	...	0739	...	0806	0809	0815	0835	0839	0845	0906	0909	0915	0936	0939	0945	1006	1009	1015	1035	1039	1045	1106
181	**Eindhoven** a.	...	0658	0728	...	0758	...	0824	0828	0834	0854	0858	0904	0924	0928	0934	0954	0958	1004	1024	1028	1034	1054	1058	1104	1124
181	**Eindhoven** d.	0630	0700	0730	0730	0800	0800	0827	0830	0838	0857	0900	0908	0927	0930	0938	0957	1000	1008	1027	1030	1038	1057	1100	1108	1127
210	Weert d.	0647	0717	0747	0747	0817	0817	0844	0847	0855	0914	0917	0925	0944	0947	0955	1014	1017	1025	1044	1047	1055	1114	1117	1125	1144
234	Roermond d.	0701	0731	0801	0801	0831	0831	0900	0901	0910	0930	0931	0940	1000	1001	1010	1030	1031	1040	1100	1101	1110	1130	1131	1140	1200
258	Sittard ★ a.	0716	0746	0816	0816	0846	0846	0915	0916	0925	0945	0946	0955	1015	1016	1025	1045	1046	1055	1115	1116	1125	1145	1146	1155	1215
277	**Heerlen** ★ a.	|	|	|	|	|	|	|	|	0941	|	|	1011	|	|	1041	|	|	1111	|	|	1141	|	|	1211	|
280	**Maastricht** a.	0731	0801	0831	0831	0901	0901	0930	0931	...	1000	1001	...	1030	1031	...	1100	1101	...	1130	1131	...	1200	1201	...	1230

	†	⚒◇											†	⚒	†	†	⚒	†								
Enkhuizen d.	0909	0909	...	0939	...	1009	and at	...	1739	...	1809	...	1839	1839	...	1909	1909	1939	2009	2039	2109	2139	2209	2239	2309
Hoorn d.	0935	0940	...	1010	...	1040	the	...	1810	...	1840	...	1905	1910	...	1935	1940	2005	2035	2105	2135	2205	2235	2305	2335
Alkmaar 466 d.	|	|	0957	|	1027	|	same	1757	|	1827	|	1857	|	|	1927	|	|	|	|	|	|	|	|	|	|
Amsterdam Sloterdijk 466 d.	1001	1005	1025	1035	1056	1105	minutes	1825	1835	1855	1905	1926	1931	1935	1956	2001	2005	2031	2101	2131	2201	2231	2301	2331	0001
Amsterdam Centraal 466 a.	1007	1011	1031	1041	1102	1111	past	1831	1841	1902	1911	1932	1937	1941	2002	2007	2011	2037	2107	2137	2207	2237	2307	2337	0007
Amsterdam Centraal 468 d.	1010	1014	1034	1045	1105	1114	each	1834	1845	1905	1914	1935	1940	1945	2005	2010	2014	2040	2110	2140	2210	2240	2310	2340	...
Amsterdam Amstel 468 d.	1018	1022	1042	1054	1113	1122	hour	1842	1854	1913	1922	1943	1948	1953	2013	2018	2022	2048	2118	2148	2218	2248	2318	2348	...
Utrecht Centraal 468 d.	1039	1044	1103	1114	1133	1144	until	1903	1914	1933	1944	2003	2009	2014	2033	2039	2044	2109	2139	2209	2239	2309	2339	0009	...
's-Hertogenbosch d.	1109	1115	1135	1145	1206	1215		1935	1945	2006	2015	2035	2039	2045	2106	2109	2115	2139	2209	2239	2309	2339	0009	0039	...
Eindhoven a.	1128	1134	1154	1204	1224	1234		1954	2005	2025	2034	2054	2058	2104	2124	2128	2134	2158	2228	2258	2328	2358	0028	0058	...
Eindhoven d.	1130	1138	1157	1208	1227	1238		1957	2008	2027	2038	2057	2100	2108	2127	2130	2138	2200	2230	2300	2330	0000	...	...	...
Weert d.	1147	1155	1214	1225	1244	1256		2014	2025	2044	2055	2114	2117	2125	2144	2147	2155	2217	2247	2317	2347	0017	...	...	...
Roermond d.	1201	1210	1230	1240	1300	1310		2030	2040	2100	2110	2130	2131	2140	2200	2201	2210	2231	2301	2331	0001	0031	...	...	...
Sittard ★ a.	1216	1225	1245	1255	1315	1325		2045	2055	2115	2125	2145	2146	2155	2215	2216	2225	2246	2316	2346	0016	0046	...	...	...
Heerlen ★ a.	|	1241	|	1311	|	1341		|	2111	|	2141	|	|	2211	|	|	2241	|	|	|	|	|	...	...	...
Maastricht a.	1231	...	1300	...	1330	...		2100	...	2130	...	2200	2201	...	2230	2231	...	2301	2331	0001	0031	0101	...	...	...

	Ⓐ	Ⓐ	Ⓐ	Ⓐ	Ⓐ	Ⓒ	Ⓐ	Ⓐ	Ⓒ	Ⓐ	Ⓐ	Ⓒ	Ⓐ	⚒	†	⚒	⚒	†	⚒	⚒	†	⚒				
Maastricht d.	...	...	...	0531	...	...	0601	...	0631k	0631	...	0701k	0701	...	0731	0731	...	0801	0801	...	0831	0831	...	0901	...	0931
Heerlen ★ d.	...	...	...	|	0549	...	|	0619	|	|	0649	|	|	0719	|	|	0749	|	|	0819	|	|	0849	|	0919	|
Sittard ★ d.	...	...	...	0547	0605	...	0617	0635	0647k	0647	0705	0717k	0717	0735	0747	0747	0805	0817	0817	0835	0847	0847	0905	0917	0935	0947
Roermond d.	...	...	...	0602	0621	...	0632	0651	0702k	0702	0721	0732k	0732	0751	0802	0802	0821	0832	0832	0851	0902	0902	0921	0932	0951	1002
Weert d.	...	...	...	0616	0635	...	0646	0705	0716k	0716	0735	0746k	0746	0805	0816	0816	0835	0846	0846	0905	0916	0916	0935	0946	1005	1016
Eindhoven a.	...	...	...	0632	0651	...	0702	0721	0732k	0732	0751	0802k	0802	0821	0832	0832	0851	0902	0902	0921	0932	0932	0951	1002	1021	1032
Eindhoven d.	0534	0604	0627	0637	0657	0704k	0707	0727	0734	0737	0757	0804	0807	0827	0834	0837	0857	0904	0907	0927	0934	0937	0957	1007	1027	1037
's-Hertogenbosch d.	0553	0623	0648	0658	0718	0723k	0728	0748	0753	0758	0818	0823	0828	0848	0853	0858	0918	0923	0928	0948	0953	0958	1018	1028	1048	1058
Utrecht Centraal 468 d.	0623	0653	0718	0728	0748	0753k	0758	0818	0823	0828	0848	0853	0858	0918	0923	0928	0948	0953	0958	1018	1023	1028	1048	1058	1118	1128
Amsterdam Amstel 468 d.	0641	0711	0737	0747	0807	0811k	0817	0837	0841	0847	0907	0911	0917	0937	0941	0947	1007	1011	1017	1037	1041	1047	1107	1117	1137	1147
Amsterdam Centraal 468 a.	0649	0719	0745	0755	0815	0819k	0825	0844	0849	0855	0915	0919	0925	0945	0949	0955	1015	1019	1025	1045	1049	1055	1115	1125	1145	1155
Amsterdam Centraal 466 ◧ d.	0653	0723	0749	0759	0819	0823	0829	0849	0853	0859	0919	0923	0929	0949	0953	0959	1019	1023	1029	1049	1053	1059	1119	1129	1149	1159
Amsterdam Sloterdijk 466 ◧ d.	0658	0728	0755	0805	0825	0828	0835	0855	0858	0905	0925	0928	0935	0955	0958	1005	1025	1028	1035	1055	1058	1105	1125	1135	1155	1205
Alkmaar 466 a.	|	|	|	0833	|	|	0903	|	|	0933	|	|	1003	|	|	1033	|	|	1103	|	|	1133	|	1203	|	1233
Hoorn ◧ d.	0726	0756	0826	...	0856	0856	...	0926	0926	...	0956	0956	...	1026	1026	...	1056	1056	...	1126	1126	...	1156	...	1226	...
Enkhuizen ◧ a.	0752	0822	0852	...	0922	0922	...	0952	0952	...	1022	1022	...	1052	1052	...	1122	1122	...	1152	1152	...	1222	...	1252	...

						†⊙	⚒	†	†⊙	⚒	†	†⊙	⚒	†	†⊙	⚒	†	†	⚒	†					
Maastricht ◐ d.		...	1631	...	1701	...	1731	1731	...	1801	1801	...	1831	1831	...	1901	1901	...	1931	1931	2001	2031	2101	2131	2201
Heerlen ★ d.	and at	1619	|	1649	|	1719	|	|	1749	|	|	1819	|	|	1849	|	|	1919	|	|	|	|	|	|	|
Sittard ★ ◐ d.		1635	1647	1705	1717	1735	1747	1747	1805	1817	1817	1835	1847	1847	1905	1917	1917	1935	1947	1947	2017	2047	2117	2147	2217
Roermond ◐ d.	the	1651	1702	1721	1732	1751	1702	1802	1821	1832	1832	1851	1902	1902	1921	1932	1932	1951	2002	2002	2032	2102	2132	2202	2232
Weert ◐ d.		1705	1716	1735	1746	1805	1816	1816	1835	1846	1846	1905	1916	1916	1935	1946	1946	2005	2016	2016	2046	2116	2146	2216	2246
Eindhoven ◐ a.	same	1721	1733	1751	1802	1821	1832	1832	1851	1902	1902	1921	1932	1932	1951	2002	2002	2021	2032	2032	2102	2132	2202	2232	2302
Eindhoven d.	minutes	1727	1737	1757	1807	1827	1834	1837	1857	1904	1907	1927	1934	1937	1957	2004	2007	2027	2034	2037	2104	2134	2204	2234	2304
's-Hertogenbosch d.		1748	1758	1818	1828	1848	1853	1858	1918	1923	1928	1948	1953	1958	2018	2023	2028	2048	2053	2058	2123	2153	2223	2253	2323
Utrecht Centraal 468 d.	past	1818	1828	1848	1858	1918	1923	1928	1948	1953	1958	2018	2023	2028	2048	2053	2058	2118	2121	2128	2153	2223	2253	2323	2353
Amsterdam Amstel 468 d.	each	1837	1847	1907	1917	1937	1941	1947	2007	2011	2017	2037	2041	2047	2107	2111	2117	2137	2123	2147	2211	2241	2313	2343	0013
Amsterdam Centraal 468 a.		1845	1855	1915	1925	1945	1949	1955	2015	2019	2025	2045	2049	2055	2115	2119	2125	2145	2141	2155	2219	2249	2321	2351	0021
Amsterdam Centraal 466 d.	hour	1849	1859	1919	1929	1949	1953	1959	2019	2023	2029	2049	2053	2059	2119	2123	2129	2149	2149	2159	2223	2253	2323	2353	0023
Amsterdam Sloterdijk 466 d.	until	1855	1905	1925	1935	1955	1958	2005	2025	2028	2035	2055	2058	2105	2125	2128	2135	2155	2153	2205	2228	2258	2328	2358	0028
Alkmaar 466 a.		|	1933	|	2003	|	|	2033	|	|	2103	|	|	2133	|	|	2203	|	|	2233	|	|	|	|	|
Hoorn d.		1926	...	1956	...	2026	2026	...	2056	2056	...	2126	2126	...	2156	2156	...	2226	2226	...	2256	2326	2356	0024	0104
Enkhuizen a.		1952	...	2022	...	2052	2052	...	2122	2122	...	2152	2152	...	2222	2222	...	2252	2252	...	2322	2352	0022	...	0127

SCHIPHOL - AMSTERDAM ZUID - EINDHOVEN - VENLO

km		Ⓐ	Ⓐ	⚒	⚒	Ⓐ		Ⓐ	⚒															
0	**Schiphol** ✈ 468 d.	...	...	...	...	0619	...	0648	0648	0748	0818	0848	and at	2018	2048	2118	2148	2218	...	2248	2318	2348	...	...	...
9	**Amsterdam** Zuid 468 d.	...	...	...	...	0626	...	0656	0656	0756	0826	0856		2026	2056	2126	2156	2226	...	2256	2326	2356	...	...	...
45	**Utrecht** Centraal 468 a.	...	...	...	...	0648	...	0718	0718	0818	0848	0918	the same	2048	2118	2148	2218	2248	...	2319	2348	0018	...	...	...
45	**Utrecht** Centraal d.	...	...	...	...	0654	...	0724	...	0824	0854	0924	minutes	2054	2124	2154	2224	2254	...	...	...	...	...	...	...
93	's-Hertogenbosch d.	...	...	...	...	0725	...	0755	...	0855	0925	0955		2125	2155	2225	2255	2325	...	...	...	...	...	...	...
125	**Eindhoven** a.	...	...	...	...	0744	...	0814	...	0914	0944	1014	past each	2144	2214	2244	2314	2344	...	...	...	...	...	...	...
125	**Eindhoven** d.	0619	0649	0719	0749	0749	0819	0819	...	0919	0949	1019	hour until	2149	2219	2249	2319	...	0019	...	...	...	...	...	...
138	Helmond d.	0628	0658	0728	0458	0728	0828	0828	...	0928	0958	1028		2158	2228	2258	2328	...	0028	...	...	...	...	...	...
176	**Venlo** a.	0658	0728	0758	0828	0828	0858	0858	...	0958	1028	1058		2228	2258	2328	2358	...	0058	...	...	...	...	...	...

	Ⓐ	Ⓐ	Ⓐ	⚒	⚒														†			†			
Venlo d.	...	0533	0603	...	0633	0703	0733	...	0803	0833	and at	1803	1833	1903	1933	2003	...	2033	2033	...	2103	2103	...	...	...
Helmond d.	...	0601	0631	...	0701	0731	0801	...	0831	0901		1831	1901	1931	2001	2031	...	2101	2101	...	2131	2131	...	...	...
Eindhoven a.	...	0611	0641	...	0711	0741	0811	...	0841	0911	the same	1841	1911	1941	2011	2041	...	2111	2111	...	2141	2141	...	...	...
Eindhoven d.	0547	0617	0647	...	0717	0747	0817	...	0847	0917	minutes	1847	1917	1947	2017	2047	...	...	2117	...	...	2147	...	...	...
's-Hertogenbosch d.	0608	0638	0708	...	0738	0808	0838	...	0908	0938		1908	1938	2008	2038	2108	...	...	2138	...	...	2208	...	...	...
Utrecht Centraal a.	0635	0705	0735	...	0805	0835	0905	...	0935	1005	past each	1935	2005	2035	2105	2135	...	...	2205	...	...	2235	...	...	...
Utrecht Centraal 468 d.	0641	0711	0741	0741	0811	0841	0911	...	0941	1011	hour until	1941	2011	2041	2111	2142	...	...	2212	2212	...	2242	2242	2312	234
Amsterdam Zuid 468 d.	0705	0735	0805	0805	0835	0905	0935	...	1005	1035		2005	2035	2105	2135	2205	...	...	2235	2235	...	2305	2305	2335	000
Schiphol ✈ 468 a.	0711	0741	0811	0811	0841	0911	0941	...	1011	1041		2011	2041	2111	2141	2211	...	...	2241	2241	...	2311	2311	2341	001

Local stopping trains **SITTARD - HEERLEN - KERKRADE** (operated by Arriva)

km		⚒									
0	Sittard d.	0618a	0648r	0718r	0748	0818	0848	and every	2318	2348	0018
19	Heerlen a.	0638a	0708r	0738r	0808	0838	0908	30 minutes	2338	0008	0038
19	Heerlen d.	0640	0713	0740	0813	0840	0913	until	2340	0013	...
28	Kerkrade Centrum a.	0655	0727	0755	0827	0855	0927		2355	0027	...

	Ⓐ	⚒	⚒							
Kerkrade Centrum d.	...	0608a	0638	0708r	0738	0808	0838	and every	2308	233
Heerlen a.	...	0622a	0652	0722r	0752	0822	0852	30 minutes	2322	235
Heerlen d.	0552	0622	0652	0722	0752	0822	0852	until	2322	235
Sittard a.	0613	0643	0713	0743	0813	0843	0913		2343	001

a – Ⓐ only.
c – Mornings of ⑥⑦ (also May 31, June 11).
k – ⑥ (also May 30, June 10).
r – ⚒ only.

◇ – Runs daily Eindhoven - Heerlen.
⊙ – Runs daily Heerlen - Eindhoven.
★ – See also Sittard - Heerlen - Kerkrade panel.
◧ – Additional trains Amsterdam - Hoorn - Enkhuizen: From Amsterdam Centraal at 0623 Ⓐ, 0723 Ⓒ, 0753 ⑥ k.
◐ – Additional trains Maastricht - Eindhoven: From Maastricht at 2301 and 0001.

For traffic arrangements on Dutch holiday dates, see page 248

DEN HAAG - EINDHOVEN 471

km		Ⓐ	⚒	Ⓐ	⚒	⚒	⚒															
0	**Den Haag** Centraal d.	...	...	0547	...	...	0617	...	0647r	...	0717	...	0747	and at	...	2217	...	2247	...	...	...	...
2	**Den Haag** HS 450 460 d.	0523	...	0553	...	...	0623	...	0653r	...	0723	...	0753	the same	...	2223	...	2253	...	...	...	...
10	Delft 450 460 d.	0531	...	0601	...	...	0631	...	0701r	...	0731	...	0801	minutes	...	2231	...	2301	...	...	...	...
24	**Rotterdam** Centraal 450 451 460 d.	0544	...	0614	0614	...	0644	...	0714	...	0744	...	0814	past each	...	2244	...	2314	...	...	2351	...
	Dordrecht 450 460 ★ d.	|	0558	|	|	0628	|	0658	|	0728	|	0758	|	hour until	2228	|	2258	|	2328	...	|	2358
71	**Breda** 451 ★ a.	0607	0621	0637	0637	0651	0707	0721	0737	0751	0807	0821	0837		2251	2307	2321	2337	2351	...	0015	0021
71	Breda 475 d.	0609	0623a	0639	0639	0653	0709	0723r	0739	0753	0809	0823	0839		2253	2309	2323	2339	2353	...	...	0023
92	Tilburg 475 d.	0624	0643a	0654	0654	0713	0724	0743r	0754	0813	0824	0843	0854		2313	2324	2343	2354	0013	0038	...	0043
	's-Hertogenbosch 475 a.	|	0659a	|	|	0729	|	0759r	|	0829	|	0859	|		2329	|	2359	|	0029	|	...	0059
129	**Eindhoven** a.	0646	...	0716	0716	...	0746	...	0816	...	0846	...	0916		...	2346	...	0016	...	0106	...	...

km		Ⓐ	⚒	Ⓐ	⚒	Ⓐ	⚒	⚒	⚒	⚒												
	Eindhoven d.	...	...	0544	...	0614	...	0644	...	0714	...	0744	...	0814	...	and at	2244	...	2314	...	2344	...
	's-Hertogenbosch 475 d.	...	...	|	0603a	|	0633a	|	0703	|	0733r	|	0803	|	0833	the same	|	2303	|	2333	|	...
	Tilburg 475 d.	...	0549a	0609	0619a	0639	0649a	0709	0719	0739	0749r	0809	0819	0839	0849	minutes	2309	2319	2339	2349	0009	...
	Breda 475 a.	...	0607a	0622	0637a	0652	0707a	0722	0737	0752	0807r	0822	0837	0852	0907	past each	2322	2337	2352	0007	0022	...
0	Breda 451 ★ d.	0539	0609	0623	0639	0653	0709	0723	0739	0753	0809	0823	0839	0853	0909	hour until	2323	2339	2353	0009	0023	0039
30	Dordrecht 450 460 ★ a.	0602	0632	|	0702	|	0732	|	0802	|	0832	|	0902	|	0932		|	0002	|	0032	|	0102
	Rotterdam Centraal 450 451 460 d.	...	...	0648	...	0718	...	0748	...	0818	...	0848	...	0918	...		2348	...	0018	...	0052	...
	Delft 450 460 d.	...	...	0700	...	0730	...	0800	...	0830	...	0900	...	0930	...		0000	...	0030	...	...	...
	Den Haag HS 450 460 d.	...	...	0708	...	0738	...	0808	...	0838	...	0908	...	0938	...		0008	...	0038	...	...	...
	Den Haag Centraal a.	...	...	0712	...	0742	...	0812	...	0842	...	0912	...	0942	...		0012	...	0042	...	...	...

a – Ⓐ only.
r – ⚒ only.

★ – Other fast shuttle services Dordrecht - Breda and v.v. (journey 21 – 22 minutes):
From Dordrecht at 0733 Ⓐ, 0833 Ⓐ, 1633Ⓐ, 1733Ⓐ.
From Breda at 0806 Ⓐ, 0906 Ⓐ, 1606 Ⓐ, 1706 Ⓐ.

MAASTRICHT - HEERLEN 472

Operated by **Arriva** (NS tickets valid)

See also Table **473**

km		Ⓐ	⚒	⚒						
0	**Maastricht** d.	0538	0608	0638	0708	0738	and every	0008	0038	...
11	Valkenburg d.	0552	0622	0652	0722	0752	30 minutes	0022	0052	...
24	**Heerlen** d.	0608	0638	0708	0738	0808	until	0038	0108	...

	Ⓐ	⚒	⚒						
Heerlen d.	0523	0553	0623	0653	0723	and every	2353	0023	...
Valkenburg d.	0539	0609	0639	0709	0739	30 minutes	0009	0039	...
Maastricht a.	0555	0622	0655	0725	0755	until	0025	0055	...

MAASTRICHT - HEERLEN - AACHEN 473

km		A	E						
	Maastricht 472 d.	0519	0619	0719		2219	2319	...	...
	Valkenburg 472 d.	0531	0631	0731	and	2231	2331	...	...
0	**Heerlen** 472 d.	0543	0643	0743	hourly	2243	2343	...	...
10	Herzogenrath 🏛 802 a.	0600	0700	0800	until	2300	0000	...	...
24	**Aachen** Hbf 802 a.	0614	0714	0814		2314	0014	...	...

	A	E						
Aachen Hbf 802 d.	0546	0646	0746		2246	2346	...	...
Herzogenrath 🏛 802 d.	0600	0700	0800	and	2300	0000	...	...
Heerlen 472 d.	0618	0718	0818	hourly	2318	0018	...	...
Valkenburg 472 a.	0629	0729	0829	until	2329	0029	...	...
Maastricht 472 a.	0640	0740	0840		2340	0040	...	...

A – ①–⑤ (not Dec. 25, 26, Jan. 1, Apr. 22, May 30, June 10).
E – ①–⑥ (not Dec. 25, 26, Jan. 1, Apr. 22).

ROOSENDAAL - 's-HERTOGENBOSCH - NIJMEGEN - ARNHEM - ZWOLLE 475

km		Ⓐ	Ⓐ	Ⓐ	Ⓐ	⚒	Ⓐ	⚒	†	⚒	Ⓐ	†	⚒	†	⚒									
0	**Roosendaal** d.	...	...	...	...	...	0527	...	...	...	0557	...	0627	0654	0657	0727	0757		2127	2157	2227	...	2257	2327
23	Breda 471 d.	...	...	...	...	...	0550	...	...	...	0620	...	0650	0713	0720	0750	0820		2150	2220	2250	...	2320	2350
44	Tilburg 471 d.	...	...	...	...	...	0604	...	...	...	0634	...	0704	0734	0734	0804	0834		2204	2234	2304	...	2334	0004
67	**'s-Hertogenbosch** 471 a.	...	...	...	...	...	0619	...	...	...	0649	...	0719	0749	0750	0820	0850		2219	2249	2319	...	2349	0020
67	**'s-Hertogenbosch** d.	...	...	0532	...	...	0624	...	...	...	0654	...	0724	0754	0754	0824	0854	and every	2224	2254	2324	...	2354	...
86	Oss d.	...	...	0550	...	...	0636	...	...	...	0706	...	0736	0806	0806	0836	0906	30 minutes	2236	2306	2336	...	0006	...
110	**Nijmegen** a.	...	...	0614	...	...	0651	...	...	...	0721	...	0751	0821	0821	0851	0921	until	2251	2321	2351	...	0021	...
110	**Nijmegen** 468 d.	...	...	0616	0624	...	0654	0654	*0713*	*0716*	0724	*0746*	0754	0824	0824	0854	0924		2254	2324	2354	0001	0024	...
129	**Arnhem** Centraal 468 a.	...	...	0634	0637	...	0707	0707	*0726*	*0734*	0737	*0804*	0807	0837	0837	0907	0937		2307	2337	0007	0019	0037	...
129	**Arnhem** Centraal d.	...	0559	...	0641	...	0711	0711	0730	0741	0741	0811	0811	0841	0841	0911	0941		2311	2341	...	0025	...	...
145	Dieren d.	...	0619	...	0653	...	0723	0723	0750	0753	0753	0823	0823	0853	0853	0923	0953		2323	2353	...	0043	...	...
159	Zutphen d.	0604	0634	...	0704	0704	0734	0734	0804	0804	0804	0834	0834	0904	0904	0934	1004		2334	0004	...	0054	...	...
174	Deventer d.	0617	0647	...	0717	0717	0747	0747	0817	0817	0817	0847	0847	0917	0917	0947	1017		2347	0017	...	...	...	...
204	**Zwolle** a.	0641	0711	...	0741	0741	0811	0811	0841	0841	0841	0911	0911	0941	0941	1011	1041		0011	0041	...	...	...	...

	Ⓐ	Ⓐ	Ⓐ	Ⓐ	Ⓐ	⚒		⚒		⚒														
Zwolle d.	...	...	...	...	...	...	...	0620a	...	0650a	...	0720r	0750	0820	0850	0920	0950		2120	2150	2220	2250	2320	2350
Deventer d.	...	...	...	...	...	...	...	0646a	...	0716a	...	0746r	0815	0846	0915	0945	1015		2145	2215	2246	2316	2346	0016
Zutphen d.	...	...	...	0551	0608	...	...	0658	...	0728	...	0758	0828	0858	0928	0958	1028		2158	2228	2258	2328	2358	0028
Dieren d.	...	...	...	0602	0619	...	...	0709	...	0739	...	0809	0839	0909	0939	1009	1039		2209	2239	2309	2339	0009	0039
Arnhem Centraal a.	...	...	...	0622	0638	...	...	0721	...	0751	...	0821	0851	0921	0951	1021	1051		2221	2251	2321	2351	0021	0051
Arnhem Centraal 468 d.	...	...	0553	0623	0641	0653	...	0723	...	0753	0753	0823	0853	0923	0953	1023	1053	and every	2223	2253	2323	2353	*0035*	...
Nijmegen 468 a.	...	...	0606	0636	0659	0706	...	0736	...	0806	0806	0836	0906	0936	1006	1036	1106	30 minutes	2236	2306	2336	0006	*0049*	...
Nijmegen d.	...	...	0609	0639	▬	0709	...	0739	...	0809	0809	0839	0909	0939	1009	1039	1109	until	2239	2309	2339	*0022*v	...	...
Oss d.	...	...	0625	0655	...	0725	...	0755	...	0825	0825	0855	0925	0955	1025	1055	1125		2255	2325	2355	*0044*v	...	...
's-Hertogenbosch a.	...	...	0637	0707	...	0737	...	0807	...	0837	0837	0907	0938	1008	1038	1108	1137		2307	2337	0007	*0101*v	...	...
's-Hertogenbosch 471 d.	...	0612	0642	0712	0712r	0742	0742	0812	0812	0842	0842	0912	0942	1012	1042	1112	1142		2312	2342	0012	...	...	...
Tilburg 471 d.	*0549*	0628	0658	0728	0728r	0758	0758	0828	0828	0858	0858	0928	0958	1028	1058	1128	1158		2328	2358	0028	...	...	...
Breda 471 d.	0615	0645	0715	0745	0745	0815	0815	0845	0845	0915	0915	0945	1015	1045	1115	1145	1215		2345	0015	0049	...	...	...
Roosendaal a.	0633	0703	0733	0803	0803	0833	0833	0903	0903	0933	0933	1003	1033	1103	1133	1203	1233		0003	0033	0105	...	...	...

a – Ⓐ only.
r – ⚒ only.
v – 1 minutes later on the mornings of ⑦ (also May 31, June 11).

ARNHEM and ZUTPHEN - WINTERSWIJK 476

Operated by **Arriva** (NS tickets valid) 2nd class only

Arnhem - Winterswijk

km		H		Ⓐ	Ⓐ	Ⓐ	Ⓐ	⑥k	†	Ⓐ																	
0	**Arnhem** Cen... d.	0004	...	0602	0632	0702	0731	0731	0734	0802	0832t	0901	0932t	1032t	1131	1232t	1331	1432t	1531	1632t	1731	1832t	1931	2034	2134	2234	2334
14	Zevenaar d.	0018	...	0617	0646	0716	0746	0748	0748	0816	0846t	0916	0946t	1046t	1146t	1246t	1346	1446t	1548	1646t	1746t	1846t	1946t	2048	2148	2248	2348
30	Doetinchem d.	0037	...	0637	0707	0737	0807	0807	0807	0837	0907	0937	1007	1107	1207	1307	1407	1507	1607	1707	1807	1907	2007	2107	2207	2307	0007
64	**Winterswijk** a.	0110	...	0710	0740	0810	0840	0840	0840	0910	0940	1010a	1040	1140	1240	1340	1440	1540	1640	1740	1842	1910	2040	2140	2240	2342	0042

	⑦w		Ⓐ	⚒	Ⓐ																					
Winterswijk d.	0020	...	0520	0550	0620	0650	0720a	0750	0820a	0850	0920a	0950	1050	1150	1250	1350	1450	1550	1650	1750	1850	1950	2050	2150	2250	2320a
Doetinchem d.	0052	...	0552	0622	0652	0722	0752	0822	0852	0922	0952	1022	1122	1222	1322	1422	1522	1622	1722	1822	1922	2022	2122	2222	2322	2352
Zevenaar d.	0111	...	0611	0641	0711	0741	0811	0841	0911	0941	1011	1041	1141	1241	1341	1441	1541	1641	1741	1841	1941	2041	2141	2241	2341	0011
Arnhem Centraal a.	0126	...	0626	0656	0726	0756	0823	0856	0926	0956	1025	1055	1156	1256	1356	1456	1556	1655	1756	1856	1955	2055	2156	2255	2356	0026

Zutphen - Winterswijk

km		K	Ⓐ	Ⓐ	Ⓐ	Ⓐ	Ⓒ	Ⓐ				
0	**Zutphen** d.	0007	0632	0702	0732	0802	0807	0837	0907	and	2307	...
22	Ruurlo d.	0022	0648	0718	0748	0818	0822	0852	0922	hourly	2322	...
43	**Winterswijk** a.	0039	0708	0737	0807	0840	0840	0910	0940	until	2340	...

	Ⓐ	Ⓐ	⑥k	Ⓐ	Ⓐ	Ⓒ				⑥k
Winterswijk d.	0617	0647	0650	0717	0747	0750	0850	and	2250	2350
Ruurlo d.	0635	0705	0708	0735	0805	0808	0908	hourly	2308	0008
Zutphen a.	0651	0721	0723	0751	0821	0823	0923	until	2323	0023

H – ②–⑥ (not Dec. 26, 27, Jan. 2, Apr. 23, May 31, June 11).
K – ②–⑦ (Not Dec. 26, 27, Jan. 2, Apr. 23).
a – Ⓐ only.
k – Also May 30, June 10.
t – 2 minutes later on Ⓒ.
w – Also May 31, June 11.
☛ Additional trains run on Ⓐ.

477 NIJMEGEN - VENLO - ROERMOND

Operated by **Arriva** (NS tickets valid)

km		Ⓐh	Ⓐh	⚒d	⚒d						
0	**Nijmegen** d.	0538	0608	0638	0708	0738	0808	and every 30 minutes until	2238	2308	2338
24	Boxmeer d.	0601	0631	0701	0731	0801	0831		2301	2331	0001
39	Venray d.	0615	0645	0715	0745	0815	0845		2315	2345	0015
61	**Venlo** d.	0633	0703	0733	0803	0833	0903		2333	0003	0031
84	**Roermond** a.	0655	0725	0755	0825	0855	0925		2355	0025	...

	⚒	⚒								
Roermond d.	...	0604a	0634a	0704r	0734r	0804	0834	and every 30 minutes until	2234	2304
Venlo d.	0559	0629	0659	0729	0759	0829	0859		2259	2329
Venray d.	0616	0646	0716	0746	0816	0846	0916		2316	2346
Boxmeer d.	0630	0700	0730	0800	0830	0900	0930		2330	0000
Nijmegen a.	0652	0722	0752	0822	0852	0922	0952		2352	0022

☛ Additional journeys: **Venlo** → **Roermond** at 0533 Ⓐ, 0603 Ⓐ; **Nijmegen** → **Venlo** at 0008; **Venlo** → **Nijmegen** at 0459 Ⓐ, 0529 Ⓐ; **Roermond** → **Venlo** at 2334, 0004, 0034.

a – Ⓐ only. d – Runs daily Venlo - Roermond. h – Also runs on ⑥ Venlo - Roermond. r – ⚒ only.

478 ARNHEM - TIEL - GELDERMALSEN - UTRECHT

km		Ⓐ	Ⓐ	Ⓐ	⑥k	Ⓐ	⑥k	△	△			
0	**Tiel** d.	0536	0604	0634	0636	0704	0706	0734	0804	and every 30 minutes until	2334	0004
12	Geldermalsen a.	0548	0616	0646	0648	0716	0718	0748	0818		2346	0016
38	**Utrecht** Centraal a.	0619	0649	0719	0719	0749	0749	0819	0849		0019	0049

Local connecting trains run every 30 minutes Geldermalsen - 's-Hertogenbosch and v.v. Journey time: 15–16 minutes.

	Ⓐ	Ⓐ	Ⓐ	Ⓐ	⑥k	Ⓐ	Ⓒ															
Utrecht Centraal d.	0541	0611	0641	0711	0711	0741	0741	0811	0841	0911	0941	1011	1041	and every 30 minutes until	1741	1811	1841	1911	and every 30 minutes until	2311	2341	0011
Geldermalsen d.	0613	0643	0711	0741	0743	0811	0813	0843	0911	0941	1011	1041	1111		1811	1841	1913	1943		2343	0013	0036
Tiel a.	0626	0656	0723	0753	0756	0823	0826	0856	0926	0956	1026	1054	1124		1824	1854	1926	1956		2356	0026	

ARNHEM - TIEL and v.v. Operated by ***Arriva*** (NS tickets valid). 2nd class only. *44 km*. Journey time: 35–36 minutes.

From Arnhem at 0638 Ⓐ, 0708 Ⓐ, 0738 Ⓐ, 0808 Ⓐ, 0838 ⚒, 0908 Ⓐ, 0938, 1008 Ⓐ, 1038, 1138, 1238, 1338, 1438, 1508 Ⓐ, 1538, 1608 Ⓐ, 1638, 1708 Ⓐ, 1738, 1808 Ⓐ, 1838, 1938, 2038, 2138, 2238, 2338 and 0038 ⑦ **n**. **From Tiel** at 0617 Ⓐ, 0647 Ⓐ, 0717 Ⓐ, 0747 ⚒, 0817 Ⓐ, 0847, 0917 Ⓐ, 0947, 1047, 1147, 1247, 1347, 1417 Ⓐ, 1447, 1517 Ⓐ, 1547, 1617 Ⓐ, 1647, 1717 Ⓐ, 1747, 1817 Ⓐ, 1847, 1947, 2047, 2147, 2247 and 2347 ⑥ **k**.

k – Also May 30, June 10. n – Also May 31, June 11. △ – Tiel departures may be 2 minutes later.

479 DORDRECHT - GELDERMALSEN

Operated by **Arriva** (NS tickets valid); 2nd class only

km						Ⓐ	Ⓐ	⑥k	Ⓐ	⑥k	Ⓐ	⑥k	†	Ⓐ	Ⓒ	Ⓐ	Ⓒ	Ⓐ	Ⓒ					
0	**Dordrecht** d.	0011	0041	0111	...	0446	0510	0515	0538	0541	0607	0611	0615	0638	0641	0709	0711	0740	0741	0811	0841	and every 30 minutes until	2311	2341
10	Sliedrecht d.	0023	0053	0122	...	0457	0521	0523	0550	0553	0619	0623	0627	0650	0653	0721	0723	0752	0753	0823	0853		2323	2353
24	Gorinchem d.	0039	0107	0139	...	0512	0539	0539	0609	0609	0639	0639	0642	0709	0709	0739	0739	0809	0809	0839	0909		2339	0009
49	**Geldermalsen** a.	0103	...	...	...	0535	0603	0603	0633	0633	0703	0703	0705	0733	0733	0803	0803	0833	0833	0903	0933		0003	0033

					Ⓐ	Ⓐ	Ⓐ	⑥k	Ⓐ	⑥k	Ⓒ	Ⓐ	Ⓒ										
Geldermalsen d.	0009	0039	0106	...	...	0539	0609	0609	0639	0639	...	0709	0709	0739	...	0809	0839	and every 30 minutes until	2309	2339	...	...	...
Gorinchem d.	0039	0108	0129	...	0535	0604	0635	0639	0705	0709	0709	0736	0739	0809	...	0839	0909		2339	0009	...	...	...
Sliedrecht d.	0053	0122	0144	...	0550	0619	0650	0653	0721	0723	0723	0752	0753	0823	...	0853	0923		2353	0023	...	...	...
Dordrecht a.	0105	0134	0155	...	0601	0631	0702	0705	0733	0735	0735	0804	0805	0835	...	0905	0935		0005	0035	...	...	...

k – Also May 30, June 10.

480 AMSTERDAM and SCHIPHOL ✈ - AMERSFOORT - DEVENTER - ENSCHEDE

AMSTERDAM CENTRAAL - AMERSFOORT

km		D	②③j	⑥⑦c		Ⓐ	Ⓐ	Ⓐ	⚒			Ⓐ		⚒										
0	**Amsterdam** Centraal d.	0010	0010	0030	...	0600	0610	0630	0640	0700	0710	0730	0740	0800	0810	0830	0840	0900	0910	and at the same minutes past each hour until	2300	2310	2330	2340
14	Weesp 457 d.	0029	0029	│	...	│	0629	│	0659	│	0729	│	0759	│	0829	│	0859	│	0929		│	2329	│	2359
23	Naarden-Bussum 457 d.	0036	0036	│	...	│	0636	│	0706	│	0736	│	0806	│	0836	│	0906	│	0936		│	2336	│	0006
29	Hilversum 457 d.	0046	0045	0052	...	0622	0646	0652	0716	0722	0746	0752	0816	0822	0846	0852	0916	0922	0946		2322	2346	2352	0016
36	Baarn d.	0052	*0104**	│	...	│	0652	│	0722	│	0752	│	0822	│	0852	│	0922	│	0952		│	2352	│	0022
45	**Amersfoort** a.	0059	*0124**	0103	...	0634	0659	0704	0729	0734	0759	0804	0829	0834	0859	0904	0929	0934	0959		2334	2359	0004	0029

		Ⓐ	Ⓐ	Ⓐ		Ⓐ		⚒		⚒		⚒										⑤⑥k		
Amersfoort d.	0448	0531	0601	0625	0631	0655	0701	0725	0731	0755	0801	0825	0831	0855	0901	0925	and at the same minutes past each hour until	2231	2255	2301	2325	2331	2355	0001
Baarn d.	0455	0538	0608	│	0638	│	0708	│	0738	│	0808	│	0838	│	0908	│		2238	│	2308	│	2338	│	0008
Hilversum 457 d.	0502	0545	0615	0639	0645	0709	0715	0739	0745	0809	0815	0839	0845	0909	0915	0939		2245	2309	2315	2339	2345	0009	0015
Naarden-Bussum 457 d.	0511	0554	0624	│	0654	│	0724	│	0754	│	0824	│	0854	│	0924	│		2254	│	2324	│	2354	│	0024
Weesp 457 d.	0521	0604	0634	│	0704	│	0734	│	0804	│	0834	│	0904	│	0934	│		2304	│	2334	│	0004	│	0034
Amsterdam Centraal a.	0537	0620	0650	0700	0720	0730	0751	0800	0820	0830	0850	0900	0920	0930	0950	1000		2320	2330	2350	2400	0020	0030	0050

SCHIPHOL ✈ - AMSTERDAM ZUID - AMERSFOORT - ENSCHEDE

km		Ⓐ	Ⓐ	⚒H	⚒	⚒	H			H			H				H			H			H		⑤⑥k
0	**Schiphol** ✈ d.	0536	0606	...	0636	0706	...	0736	0806	...	0836	0906	...	0936	and at the same minutes past each hour until	2106	...	2136	2206	...	2236	2306	...	2336	2336
9	Amsterdam Zuid d.	0545	0615	...	0645	0715	...	0745	0815	...	0845	0915	...	0945		2115	...	2145	2215	...	2245	2315	...	2345	2345
14	Duivendrecht d.	0550	0620	...	0650	0720	...	0750	0820	...	0850	0920	...	0950		2120	...	2150	2220	...	2250	2320	...	2350	2350
37	Hilversum d.	0608	0638	...	0708	0738	...	0808	0838	...	0908	0938	...	1008		2138	...	2208	2238	...	2308	2338	...	0008	0008
53	**Amersfoort** d.	0622	0650	0652	0722	0750	0752	0822	0850	0852	0922	0950	0952	1022		2150	2152	2222	2250	2252	2322	2350	2352	0020	0022
96	Apeldoorn d.	0647	...	0717	0747	...	0817	0847	...	0917	0947	...	1017	1047		...	2217	2247	...	2317	2347	...	0017	...	0047
111	**Deventer** d.	0700	...	0730	0800	...	0830	0900	...	0930	1000	...	1030	1100		...	2230	2300	...	2330	0000	...	0030	...	0100
149	Almelo 492 d.	0726	...	0755	0826t	...	0855	0925	...	0955	1025	...	1055	1125		...	2255	2325	...	2355	0025	...	0055	...	0125
164	**Hengelo** 492 a.	0738	...	0805	0838t	...	0905	0935	...	1005	1035	...	1105	1135		...	2305	2335	...	0005	0035	...	0105	...	0135
172	**Enschede** 492 a.	0746	...	0814	0846t	...	0914	0944	...	1014	1044	...	1114	1144		...	2314	2344	...	0014	0044	...	0114	...	0144

	ⒶH	Ⓐ	Ⓐ	⚒	ⒶH	⚒H		⚒		H			H				H			H			U	
Enschede 492 d.	0446	...	0516	...	0546	...	...	0616	...	0646r	...	0716r	0746	...	0816	and at the same minutes past each hour until	2046	...	2116	2146	...	2216	2246	...
Hengelo 492 d.	0454	...	0524	...	0554	...	...	0624	...	0654r	...	0724r	0754	...	0824		2054	...	2124	2154	...	2224	2254	...
Almelo 492 d.	0506	...	0536	...	0606	...	...	0636	...	0706r	...	0736r	0806	...	0836		2106	...	2136	2206	...	2236	2306	...
Deventer d.	0532	...	0603	...	0633	0633	...	0703	...	0733	...	0803	0833	...	0903		2133	...	2203	2233	...	2303	2333	...
Apeldoorn d.	0543	...	0614	...	0644	0644	...	0714	...	0744	...	0814	0844	...	0914		2144	...	2214	2244	...	2314	2344	...
Amersfoort d.	0607	0610	0640	0640	0708	0708	0710	0740	0740	0808	0810	0840	0908	0910	0940		2208	2210	2240	2308	2310	2340	0008	0010
Hilversum d.	...	0623	0653	0653	...	...	0723	0753	0753	...	0823	0853	...	0923	0953		...	2223	2253	...	2323	2353	...	0023
Duivendrecht d.	...	0640	0710	0710	...	...	0740	0810	0810	...	0840	0910	...	0940	1010		...	2240	2310	...	2340	0010	...	0040
Amsterdam Zuid a.	...	0645	0715	0715	...	...	0745	0815	0815	...	0845	0915	...	0945	1015		...	2245	2315	...	2345	0015	...	0045
Schiphol ✈ a.	...	0653	0723	0723	...	...	0753	0823	0823	...	0853	0923	...	0953	1023		...	2253	2323	...	2353	0023	...	0053

Through trains AMSTERDAM CENTRAAL - DEVENTER - HENGELO

	F♥	♥	Ⓐ	♥	Ⓐ	♥	Ⓐ	♥	Ⓐ	♥	Ⓐ	♥	Ⓐ	E♥	⑥k
Amsterdam Centraal d.	0502	0700	0800	0900	1000	1100	1200	1300	1400	1500	1600	1700	1800	1900	1900
Hilversum d.	0525	0722	0822	0922	1022	1122	1222	1322	1422	1522	1622	1722	1822	1922	1922
Amersfoort d.	0540	0736	0836	0936	1036	1136	1236	1336	1436	1536	1636	1736	1836	1936	1936
Apeldoorn d.	0605	0802	0902	1002	1102	1202	1302	1402	1502	1602	1702	1802	1902	2002	2002
Deventer d.	0617	0819	0912	1019	1112	1219	1312	1419	1512	1619	1712	1819	1912	2019	2019
Almelo d.	0642	0845	...	1045	...	1245	...	1445	...	1645	...	1845	...	2045	2046
Hengelo a.	0653	0856	...	1056	...	1257	...	1456	...	1656	...	1856	...	2056	2056

	Ⓐ	G♥	⚒♥	†	Ⓐ	♥	Ⓐ	♥	Ⓐ	♥	Ⓐ	♥	Ⓐ	♥	♥
Hengelo d.	...	0803	0903	0904	...	1103	...	1303	...	1503	...	1703	...	1903	2103
Almelo d.	...	0816	0916	0916	...	1116	...	1316	...	1516	...	1716	...	1917	2116
Deventer d.	0648	0848	0948	0948	1048	1148	1248	1348	1448	1548	1648	1748	1818	1948	2148
Apeldoorn d.	0700	0900	1000	1000	1100	1200	1300	1400	1500	1600	1700	1800	1830	2000	2200
Amersfoort d.	0725	0925	1026	1026	1125	1226	1326	1426	1526	1626	1726	1826	1856	2026	2226
Hilversum d.	0739	0939	1039	1039	1139	1239	1339	1439	1539	1639	1739	1839	1909	2039	2239
Amsterdam Centraal a.	0800	1000	1100	1100	1200	1300	1400	1501	1600	1701	1800	1900	1930	2100	2300

D – ①④⑤⑥⑦ (also Dec. 26, Jan. 2, Apr. 23, June 11).
E – Ⓑ to Apr. 17 (not Dec. 24, 25, 31); ⑦ Apr. 28 - Sept. 1 (also Apr. 22 May 30; not June 9); Ⓑ from Sept. 2.
F – ①–⑥ Apr. 19 - Aug. 31 (not Apr. 22, June 10).
G – ① Apr. 29 - Aug. 28 (also Apr. 23, June 11; not June 10).
H – From / to Den Haag (Table **481**).
U – 12 Enschede - Utrecht (- Den Haag ⑤⑥ **k**).

c – Also May 31, June 11.
e – Not June 9.
j – Not Dec. 26, Jan. 1, 2,
k – Also May 30, June 10.
r – ⚒ only.
t – 1–3 minutes earlier on ⑥ (also May 30, June 10).

* – By 🚌 from Hilversum.
♥ – *IC* service to / from Germany via Bad Bentheim. Conveys 🍸. See Table **22** for further details.

ROTTERDAM and DEN HAAG - UTRECHT - ZWOLLE 481

km			⑥⑦c		Ⓐ	Ⓐ	⚒	Ⓐ	Ⓐ	⚒	Ⓐ	Ⓐ	⚒		⚒	⚒	⚒	⚒	⚒	⚒		⚒	⚒	⚒	
0	**Rotterdam** Centraal d.	0005	0005	...	...	...	...	...	0605	...	0620	...	...	...	...	0635	0650	...	...	0705	...	0720	...	...	0735
10	Rotterdam Alexander d.	0013	0013	...	...	...	...	...	0613	...	0628	...	...	...	...	0643	0658	...	...	0713	...	0728	...	...	0743
	Den Haag Centraal d.	|	|	...	...	0555	...	0610	|	...	|	0625	...	...	0640	|	|	0655	0710	|	...	|	0725	0740	|
24	Gouda d.	0024	0024	...	...	0614	...	0629	0624	...	0639	0644	...	...	0659	0654	0709	0714	0729	0724	...	0739	0744	0759	0754
56	**Utrecht** Centraal a.	0042	0042	...	...	0632	...	0647	0642	...	0658	0702	...	...	0717	0712	0728	0732	0747	0742	...	0757	0802	0817	0812
56	**Utrecht** Centraal d.	0048	0048	...	0619	0637	0637	...	0649	0649	...	0707	0707	...	...	0719	...	0737	...	0749	...	...	0807	...	0819
77	**Amersfoort** a.	0102	0102	...	0632	0650	0650	...	0702	0702	...	0720	0720	...	...	0732	...	0750	...	0802	...	...	0820	...	0832
77	**Amersfoort** d.	...	0105	...	0635	0652	0652	...	0705	0705	...	...	...	...	...	0735	...	0752	...	0805	0805	...	...	...	0835
	Deventer 480 a.	...	|	...	|	0727	0727	...	|	|	...	...	...	...	...	|	...	0827	...	|	|	...	...	...	|
	Enschede 480 a.	...	|	...	|	0814	0814	...	|	|	...	...	...	...	...	|	...	0914	...	|	|	...	...	...	|
144	**Zwolle** a.	...	0140	...	0710	...	...	...	0740	0740	...	...	...	...	...	0810	...	...	...	0840	0840	...	...	...	0910
	Leeuwarden 482 a.	...	|	...	0815	...	...	...	|	|	...	...	...	...	...	0915t	...	...	...	|	|	...	...	...	1014
	Groningen 482 a.	...	0253k	...	...	...	...	...	0843	0843	...	...	...	...	...	...	...	...	...	0943	0943	...	...	...	...

	⚒		⚒			⚒		⚒		⚒				⚒		⚒		⚒		⚒		⚒		⚒	
Rotterdam Centraal d.	0750	...	...	0805	...	0820	...	...	0835	0850	...	...	0905	0920	...	...	0935	0950	...	...	1005	1020	...	...	1035
Rotterdam Alexander d.	0758	...	...	0813	...	0828	...	...	0843	0858	...	...	0913	0928	...	...	0943	0958	...	...	1013	1028	...	...	1043
Den Haag Centraal d.	|	0755	0810	|	...	|	0825	0840	|	|	0855	0910	|	|	0925	0940	|	|	0955	1010	|	|	1025	1040	|
Gouda d.	0809	0814	0829	0824	...	0839	0844	0859	0854	0909	0912	0929	0924	0939	0944	0959	0954	1009	1014	1029	1024	1039	1044	1059	1054
Utrecht Centraal a.	0827	0832	0847	0842	...	0858	0900	0917	0912	0927	0932	0947	0942	0958	1002	1017	1012	1027	1032	1047	1042	1058	1102	1117	1112
Utrecht Centraal d.	...	0837	...	0849	...	...	0907	...	0919	...	0937	...	0949	...	1007	...	1019	...	1037	...	1049	...	1107	...	1119
Amersfoort a.	...	0850	...	0902	...	...	0920	...	0932	...	0950	...	1002	...	1020	...	1032	...	1050	...	1102	...	1120	...	1132
Amersfoort d.	...	0852	...	0905	...	...	...	...	0935	...	0952	...	1005	...	...	...	1035	...	1052	...	1105	...	...	...	1135
Deventer 480 a.	...	0927	...	|	...	...	...	...	|	...	1027	...	|	...	...	...	|	...	1127	...	|	...	...	...	|
Enschede 480 a.	...	1014	...	|	...	...	...	...	|	...	1114	...	|	...	...	...	|	...	1214	...	|	...	...	...	|
Zwolle a.	...	...	...	0940	...	...	...	...	1010	...	...	...	1040	...	...	...	1110	...	...	...	1140	...	...	...	1210
Leeuwarden 482 a.	...	...	...	|	...	...	...	...	1114	...	...	...	|	...	...	...	1214	...	...	...	|	...	...	...	1314
Groningen 482 a.	...	...	...	1043	...	...	...	...	...	...	...	...	1143	...	...	...	...	...	...	...	1243	...	...	...	...

	⚒																							
Rotterdam Centraal d.	1050	...	...	1105	1120	...	...	1135	1150	...		...	2005	2020	...	...	2035	2050	...	2105	...	2135	...	2205
Rotterdam Alexander d.	1058	...	...	1113	1128	...	...	1143	1158	...		...	2013	2028	...	...	2043	2058	...	2113	...	2143	...	2213
Den Haag Centraal d.	|	1055	1110	|	|	1125	1140	|	|	1155	and at	2010	|	|	2025	2010	|	|	2055	|	2125	|	2155	|
Gouda d.	1109	1114	1129	1124	1139	1144	1159	1154	1209	1214		2029	2024	2039	2044	2059	2054	2109	2114	2124	2144	2154	2214	2224
Utrecht Centraal a.	1127	1132	1147	1142	1158	1202	1217	1212	1228	1232	the same	2047	2042	2058	2102	2117	2112	2128	2132	2142	2202	2212	2232	2242
Utrecht Centraal d.	...	1137	...	1149	...	1207	...	1219	...	1237	minutes	...	2049	...	2107	...	2119	...	2137	2149	2207	2219	2237	2249
Amersfoort a.	...	1150	...	1202	...	1220	...	1232	...	1250		...	2102	...	2120	...	2132	...	2150	2202	2220	2232	2250	2302
Amersfoort d.	...	1152	...	1205	...	...	...	1235	...	1252	past each	...	2105	...	...	...	2135	...	2152	2205	...	2235	2252	2305
Deventer 480 a.	...	1227	...	|	...	...	...	|	...	1327	hour until	...	|	...	...	...	|	...	2227	|	...	|	2327	|
Enschede 480 a.	...	1314	...	|	...	...	...	|	...	1414		...	|	...	...	...	|	...	2314	|	...	|	0014	|
Zwolle a.	...	...	...	1240	...	...	...	1310	...	...		...	2140	...	...	...	2210	...	...	2240	...	2310	...	2340
Leeuwarden 482 a.	...	...	...	|	...	...	...	1414	...	...		...	|	...	...	...	2314	...	...	|	...	0015	...	|
Groningen 482 a.	...	...	...	1343	...	...	...	...	...	...		...	2243	...	...	...	...	...	...	2343	...	...	...	0043

					⚒			
Rotterdam Centraal d.	...	2235	...	2305	2305	...	2335	...
Rotterdam Alexander d.	...	2243	...	2313	2313	...	2343	...
Den Haag Centraal d.	2225	|	2255	|	|	2325	|	2355
Gouda d.	2244	2254	2314	2324	2324	2344	2354	0014
Utrecht Centraal a.	2302	2312	2332	2342	2342	0002	0012	0032
Utrecht Centraal d.	2307	2319	2337	2349	2349	0007	0019	0037
Amersfoort a.	2320	2332	2350	0002	0002	0020	0032	0050
Amersfoort d.	...	2335	2352	0005	0005	...	...	...
Deventer 480 a.	...	|	0027	|	|	...	...	...
Enschede 480 a.	...	|	0114	|	|	...	...	...
Zwolle a.	...	0010	...	0046	0046	...	...	...
Leeuwarden 482 a.	...	...	...	...	|	...	...	...
Groningen 482 a.	...	...	...	...	0202	...	...	...

km		Ⓐ	Ⓐ	Ⓐ	Ⓐ	Ⓐ	Ⓐ	Ⓐ	Ⓐ	⚒	⚒	⚒
	Groningen 482 d.	...	...	...	...	...	...	...	...	...	...	...
	Leeuwarden 482 d.	...	...	...	...	...	...	...	...	...	...	...
	Zwolle d.	...	...	...	...	...	...	0550	...	...	...	...
	Enschede 480 d.	...	...	...	...	0446	...	|	...	...	...	...
	Deventer 480 d.	...	...	...	...	0533	...	|	...	...	...	...
	Amersfoort a.	...	...	...	...	0608	...	0625	...	...	...	...
	Amersfoort d.	...	...	...	...	0610	...	0627	...	0640a	...	...
	Utrecht Centraal a.	...	...	...	...	0624	...	0641	...	0654a	...	...
0	**Utrecht** Centraal d.	0558	0603	0613	0618	0628	0633	0648	0643	0658	0703	0718
32	Gouda d.	0617	0622	0632	0637	0647	0652	0707	0702	0717	0722	0737
60	**Den Haag** Centraal a.	0636	|	0651	|	0706	|	|	0721	0736	|	|
	Rotterdam Alexander d.	...	0631	...	0646	...	0701	0716	...	...	0731	0746
	Rotterdam Centraal a.	...	0640	...	0655	...	0710	0725	...	...	0740	0755

	Ⓐ	⚒	⚒	⚒	⚒	⚒	⚒	⚒		⚒	⚒		⚒		⚒		⚒		⚒		⚒		⚒		⚒
Groningen 482 d.	0500j	...	...	...	...	...	...	...	...	0605	...	...	...	...	...	...	...	0716y	...	...	...	...	...	...	...
Leeuwarden 482 d.	|	...	...	...	0545a	...	...	...	...	|	...	...	...	0646r	...	...	...	|	...	...	...	0746v	...	...	...
Zwolle d.	0620	...	...	...	0650	...	...	...	...	0720	...	...	...	0750	...	...	...	0820	...	...	...	0850	...	...	...
Enschede 480 d.	|	...	0546a	...	|	...	...	...	...	|	...	0646r	...	|	...	...	...	|	...	0746	...	|	...	...	...
Deventer 480 d.	|	...	0633	...	|	...	...	...	...	|	...	0733	...	|	...	...	...	|	...	0833	...	|	...	...	...
Amersfoort a.	0655	...	0708	...	0725	...	...	...	...	0755	...	0808	...	0825	...	...	...	0855	...	0908	...	0925	...	...	...
Amersfoort d.	0658	...	0710	...	0727	...	0740	...	...	0758	...	0810	...	0827	...	0840	...	0858	...	0910	...	0928	...	0940	...
Utrecht Centraal a.	0711	...	0724	...	0741	...	0754	...	...	0811	...	0824	...	0841	...	0854	...	0911	...	0924	...	0941	...	0954	...
Utrecht Centraal d.	0718	0713	0728	0733	0748	0743	0758	0803	0818	0818	0813	0828	0833	0848	0843	0858	0903	0918	0913	0928	0933	0948	0943	0958	1003
Gouda d.	0737	0732	0747	0752	0807	0802	0817	0822	0837	0837	0834	0847	0852	0907	0902	0917	0922	0937	0932	0947	0952	1007	1002	1017	1022
Den Haag Centraal a.	|	0751	0806	|	|	...	0821	0836	|	|	0852	0908	|	|	0921	0936	|	|	0951	1006	|	|	1021	1036	|
Rotterdam Alexander d.	0746	...	...	0801	0816	...	...	0831	0846	0846	...	...	0901	0916	...	...	0931	0946	...	...	1001	1016	...	...	1031
Rotterdam Centraal a.	0755	...	...	0810	0825	...	...	0840	0855	0855	...	...	0910	0925	...	...	0940	0955	...	...	1010	1025	...	...	1040

		⚒		⚒		⚒		⚒																
Groningen 482 d.	0818	...	...	...	...	...	...	...	0918h	...	...	...	...	...	...	...	1018	...		1718	...	...	...	...
Leeuwarden 482 d.	|	...	...	...	0846	...	...	...	|	...	...	...	0946	...	...	...	|	...		|	...	...	...	1746
Zwolle d.	0920	...	...	...	0950	...	...	...	1020	...	...	...	1050	...	...	...	1120	...		1820	...	...	...	1850
Enschede 480 d.	|	...	0846	...	|	...	...	...	|	...	0946	...	|	...	...	...	|	...	and at	|	...	1746	...	|
Deventer 480 d.	|	...	0933	...	|	...	...	...	|	...	1033	...	|	...	...	...	|	...	the same	|	...	1833	...	|
Amersfoort a.	0955	...	1008	...	1025	...	...	...	1055	...	1108	...	1125	...	...	...	1155	...		1855	...	1908	...	1925
Amersfoort d.	0957	...	1010	...	1027	...	1040	...	1057	...	1110	...	1127	...	1140	...	1157	...	minutes	1857	...	1910	...	1927
Utrecht Centraal a.	1011	...	1024	...	1041	...	1054	...	1111	...	1124	...	1141	...	1154	...	1211	...	past each	1911	...	1924	...	1941
Utrecht Centraal d.	1018	1013	1028	1033	1048	1043	1058	1103	1118	1113	1128	1133	1148	1143	1158	1203	1218	1213		1918	1913	1928	1933	1948
Gouda d.	1037	1032	1047	1052	1107	1102	1117	1122	1137	1132	1147	1152	1207	1202	1217	1222	1237	1232	hour until	1937	1932	1947	1952	2007
Den Haag Centraal a.	|	1051	1106	|	|	1121	1136	|	|	1151	1206	|	|	1221	1236	|	|	1251		|	1951	2006	|	|
Rotterdam Alexander d.	1046	...	...	1101	1116	...	...	1131	1146	...	...	1201	1216	...	...	1231	1246	...		1946	...	...	2001	2016
Rotterdam Centraal a.	1055	...	...	1110	1125	...	...	1140	1155	...	...	1210	1225	...	...	1240	1255	...		1955	...	...	2011	2025

Groningen 482 d.	...	...	...	1805z	...	...	...	...	...	...	1918	...	...	...	2018	...	...	...	2118	...	...	...	2218	...	...
Leeuwarden 482 d.	...	...	...	|	...	...	...	1846	...	...	|	...	1946	...	|	...	2046	...	|	...	2146	...	|	...	2236
Zwolle d.	...	...	...	1920	...	...	...	1950	...	...	2020	...	2050	...	2120	...	2150	...	2220	...	2250	...	2320	...	2350
Enschede 480 d.	...	...	...	|	...	1846	...	|	...	...	|	1946	|	...	|	2046	|	...	|	2146	|	...	|	2246	|
Deventer 480 d.	...	...	...	|	...	1933	...	|	...	...	|	2033	|	...	|	2133	|	...	|	2233	|	...	|	2333	|
Amersfoort a.	...	...	...	1955	...	2008	...	2025	...	...	2055	2108	2125	...	2155	2208	2225	...	2255	2308	2325	...	2355	0008	0025
Amersfoort d.	...	1940	...	1958	...	2010	...	2027	...	2040	2057	2110	2127	2140	2157	2210	2227	2240	2257	2310	2327	2340	2357	0010	0027
Utrecht Centraal a.	...	1954	...	2011	...	2024	...	2041	...	2054	2111	2124	2141	2154	2211	2224	2241	2254	2311	2324	2341	2354	0011	0024	0041
Utrecht Centraal d.	1943	1958	2003	2018	2013	2028	2033	2048	2043	2058	2118	2128	2148	2158	2218	2228	2248	2258	2318	2328	2348	2358	0018	0028c	...
Gouda d.	2002	2017	2022	2037	2032	2047	2052	2107	2102	2117	2137	2147	2207	2217	2237	2247	2307	2317	2337	2347	0007	0017	0037	0047c	...
Den Haag Centraal a.	2021	2036	|	|	2051	2106	|	|	2121	2136	|	2206	|	2236	|	2306	|	2336	|	0006	|	0036	|	0106c	...
Rotterdam Alexander d.	...	...	2031	2046	...	...	2101	2116	...	...	2146	...	2216	...	2246	...	2316	...	2346	...	0016	...	0046	...	...
Rotterdam Centraal a.	...	...	2040	2055	...	...	2110	2125	...	...	2155	...	2225	...	2255	...	2325	...	2355	...	0025	...	0055	...	...

a – Ⓐ only.
c – Mornings of ⑥⑦ (also May 31, June 11).
h – 0916 on †.
j – 0505 on ①④⑤ (not May 30, June 10).
k – ⑥ only.
r – ⚒ only.
t – 0914 on ⑥ (also May 30, June 10).
v – 0736 on †.
y – 0705 on ©.
z – 1818 on ©.

482 ZWOLLE - GRONINGEN and LEEUWARDEN

km		⑥		Ⓐ	Ⓐ	ⒶL	Ⓐ	Ⓐ	Ⓐ	⚒L	⚒	Ⓐ		⑥k	Ⓐ	Ⓐ	⚒		⑥k	Ⓐ	†		⚒	†M
	Rotterdam Centraal **481** d.	0005	...	...	...	...	...	...	...	...	...	...	...	...	...	...	0605a	...	...	...	...	...	...	...
	Utrecht Centraal **481** d.	0049	...	...	...	...	...	...	...	...	...	...	...	...	0619	...	0649	...	...	...	...	...	...	...
	Amersfoort **481** d.	0105	...	...	...	...	...	...	...	...	...	...	...	...	0635	...	0705	...	...	...	...	...	...	...
	Den Haag Centraal **460** d.	|	...	...	...	...	...	...	...	...	...	0533	...	...	|	...	|	...	0603	0603	...	...	0633	...
	Schiphol + **460** d.	|	...	...	...	...	...	...	...	...	...	0604	...	...	|	...	|	...	0634	0634	...	...	0704	...
	Amsterdam Zuid **460** d.	|	...	...	...	...	...	...	...	...	...	0612	...	...	|	...	|	...	0642	0642	...	...	0712	...
	Zwolle **460 481** a.	0140	...	...	...	...	...	...	...	...	...	0713	...	...	0710	...	0740	...	0743	0743	...	...	0813	...
0	**Zwolle** d.	0145	...	0548	0554	0615	0618	0624	0645	0648	0654	0715	...	0718	0721	0724	0745	0745	0748	0751	0748	0754	0815	0815
27	Meppel d.	0201	...	0604	0610	0631	0635	0640	|	0704	0710	|	...	0734	|	0740	|	|	0804	|	0804	0810	|	|
41	Steenwijk d.	|	...	0613	|	|	0644	|	|	0713	|	|	...	0743	0744	|	|	|	0813	0814	0813	|	|	|
65	Heerenveen d.	|	...	0629	|	|	0700	|	|	0726	|	|	...	0756	0757	|	|	|	0826	0827	0829	|	|	|
94	**Leeuwarden** a.	|	...	0651	|	|	0724	|	|	0744	|	|	...	0814	0815	|	|	|	0844	0845	0850	|	|	|
47	Hoogeveen d.	0213	...	...	0622	0643	...	0652	|	...	0722	|	...	...	...	0752	|	|	...	...	...	0822	|	|
77	Assen d.	0232	...	...	0642	0702	...	0712	0726	...	0742	0756	...	...	...	0812	0826	0826	...	...	...	0842	0856	0856
104	**Groningen** a.	0253	...	...	0703	0723	...	0733	0743	...	0803	0813	...	...	...	0833	0843	0843	...	...	...	0903	0913	0913

	⑥k	Ⓐ	⚒						⚒						⚒◐								
Rotterdam Centraal **481** d.	0635	0635	...	0705r	...	...	...	0735	...	0805	...	...	...	0835	...	and at the same minutes past each hour until	1805	...	...	...	1835	...	1905
Utrecht Centraal **481** d.	0719	0719	...	0749r	...	...	...	0819	...	0849	...	...	...	0919	...		1849	...	...	...	1919	...	1949
Amersfoort **481** d.	0735	0735	...	0805	...	...	...	0835	...	0905	...	...	...	0935	...		1905	...	...	...	1935	...	2005
Den Haag Centraal **460** d.	|	|	...	|	0703	...	0733	|	...	|	0803	...	0833	|	...		|	1803	...	1833	|	...	|
Schiphol + **460** d.	|	|	...	|	0734	...	0804	|	...	|	0834	...	0904	|	...		|	1834	...	1904	|	...	|
Amsterdam Zuid **460** d.	|	|	...	|	0742	...	0812	|	...	|	0842	...	0912	|	...		|	1842	...	1912	|	...	|
Zwolle **460 481** a.	0810	0810	...	0840	0843	...	0913	0910	...	0940	0943	...	1013	1010	...		1940	1943	...	2013	2010	...	2040
Zwolle d.	0818	0821	0824	0845	0848	0854	0915	0918	0924	0945	0948	0954	1015	1018	1024		1945	1948	1954	2015	2018	2024	2045
Meppel d.	0834	|	0840	|	0904	0910	|	0934	0940	|	1004	1010	|	1034	1040		|	2004	2010	|	2034	2040	|
Steenwijk d.	0843	0844	|	|	0913	|	|	0943	|	|	1013	|	|	1043	|		|	2013	|	|	2043	|	|
Heerenveen d.	0856	0858	|	|	0926	|	|	0956	|	|	1026	|	|	1056	|		|	2026	|	|	2056	|	|
Leeuwarden a.	0914	0915	|	|	0944	|	|	1014	|	|	1044	|	|	1114	|		|	2044	|	|	2114	|	|
Hoogeveen d.	...	...	0852	|	...	0922	|	...	0952	|	...	1022	|	...	1052		|	...	2022	|	...	2052	|
Assen d.	...	...	0912	0926	...	0942	0956	...	1012	1026	...	1042	1056	...	1112		2026	...	2042	2056	...	2112	2126
Groningen a.	...	...	0933	0943	...	1003	1013	...	1033	1043	...	1103	1113	...	1133		2043	...	2103	2113	...	2133	2143

																						⚒⊖	⑤⑥k
Rotterdam Centraal **481** d.	...	...	...	1935	...	2005	...	...	...	2035	...	2105	...	...	...	2135	...	2205	...	...	...	...	2305	...
Utrecht Centraal **481** d.	...	...	...	2019	...	2049	...	...	...	2119	...	2149	...	...	...	2219	...	2249	...	...	...	...	2349	...
Amersfoort **481** d.	...	...	...	2035	...	2105	...	...	...	2135	...	2205	...	...	...	2235	...	2305	...	...	...	...	0005	...
Den Haag Centraal **460** d.	1903	...	1933	|	...	|	2003	...	2033	|	...	|	2103	...	2133	|	...	|	2203	...	2233	...	|	2303
Schiphol + **460** d.	1934	...	2004	|	...	|	2034	...	2104	|	...	|	2134	...	2204	|	...	|	2234	...	2304	...	|	2334
Amsterdam Zuid **460** d.	1942	...	2012	|	...	|	2042	...	2112	|	...	|	2142	...	2212	|	...	|	2242	...	2312	...	|	2342
Zwolle **460 481** a.	2043	...	2113	2110	...	2140	2143	...	2213	2210	...	2240	2243	...	2313	2310	...	2340	2343	...	0013	...	0046	0043
Zwolle d.	2048	2054	2115	2118	2124	2145	2148	2154	2215	2218	2224	2245	2248	...	2315	2318	...	2345	2348	...	0015	...	0049	0048
Meppel d.	2104	2110	|	2134	2140	|	2204	2210	|	2234	2240	|	2304	...	2331	2335	...	|	0004	...	0031	...	0105	0104
Steenwijk d.	2113	|	|	2143	|	|	2213	|	|	2243	|	|	2313	...	|	2344	...	|	0013	...	|	...	|	0113
Heerenveen d.	2126	|	|	2156	|	|	2226	|	|	2256	|	|	2329	...	|	2357	...	|	0029	...	|	...	|	0129
Leeuwarden a.	2144	|	|	2214	|	|	2244	|	|	2314	|	|	2351	...	|	0015	...	|	0051	...	|	...	|	0151
Hoogeveen d.	...	2122	|	...	2152	|	...	2222	|	...	2252	|	...	...	2343	...	...	|	...	...	0043	...	0117	...
Assen d.	...	2142	2156	...	2212	2226	...	2242	2256	...	2312	2326	...	...	0002	...	...	0026	...	...	0102	...	0137	...
Groningen a.	...	2203	2213	...	2233	2243	...	2303	2313	...	2333	2343	...	...	0022	...	...	0045	...	...	0123	...	0202	...

	Ⓐ	Ⓐ	Ⓐ	Ⓐ	⑥k	Ⓐ	⚒	Ⓐ	⚒	⑥k	Ⓑ	Ⓐ	†		⚒	Ⓒ	Ⓐ	⚒	†	⚒	†	⚒	⚒	†
Groningen d.	...	0503t	...	0533t	0548	...	0605	0623	...	0637	0648	0653	...	...	...	0705	0716	0724	...	...	0737	0748	0753	...
Assen d.	...	0526t	...	0556t	0605	...	0627	0645	...	0658	0705	0715	...	...	...	0727	0735	0745	...	...	0758	0805	0815	...
Hoogeveen d.	...	0546	...	0617	|	...	0646	0705	...	0717	|	0735	...	...	...	0746	|	0805	...	...	0817	|	0835	...
Leeuwarden d.	0507	|	0545	|	|	0607	|	|	0646	|	|	|	0707	...	0716	|	|	|	0736	0746	|	|	|	0807
Heerenveen d.	0529	|	0601	|	|	0629	|	|	0702	|	|	|	0729	...	0732	|	|	|	0758	0802	|	|	|	0829
Steenwijk d.	0546	|	0615	|	|	0646	|	|	0716	|	|	|	0746	...	0746	|	|	|	0815	0816	|	|	|	0846
Meppel d.	0555	0559	0625	0629	|	0655	0659	0717	0726	0730	|	0747	0755	...	0756	0759	|	0817	0825	0826	0829	|	0847	0855
Zwolle a.	0611	0615	0641	0645	0645	0711	0715	0733	0742	0745	0745	0803	0811	...	0812	0815	0815	0833	0842	0842	0845	0845	0903	0911
Zwolle **460 481** d.	0617	0620	0650	0647	0647	0717	0720	...	0750	0747	0747	...	0817	...	0817	0820	0820	...	0850	0850	0847	0847	...	0917
Amsterdam Zuid **460** a.	0718	|	|	0748	0748	0818	|	...	|	0848	0848	...	0918	...	0918	|	|	...	|	|	0948	0948	...	1018
Schiphol + **460** a.	0725	|	|	0755	0755	0825	|	...	|	0855	0855	...	0925	...	0925	|	|	...	|	|	0955	0955	...	1025
Den Haag Centraal **460** a.	0756	|	|	0826	0826	0856	|	...	|	0926	0926	...	0956	...	0956	|	|	...	|	|	1026	1026	...	1056
Amersfoort **481** a.	...	0657	0725	...	...	...	0755	...	0825	...	...	...	...	...	...	0855	0855	...	0925	0925	...	...	...	...
Utrecht Centraal **481** a.	...	0711	0741	...	...	...	0811	...	0841	...	...	...	...	...	...	0911	0911	...	0941	0941	...	...	...	...
Rotterdam Centraal **481** a.	...	0755	0825	...	...	...	0855	...	0925	...	...	...	...	...	...	0955	0955	...	1025	1025	...	...	...	...

	⚒	◇				⚒◧									Ⓐ	Ⓒ							
Groningen d.	...	0818	0823	...	0848	0853	...	and at the same minutes past each hour until	1718	1723	...	1748	1753	...	1805	1818	1823	...	1848	1853	...	1918	1923
Assen d.	...	0835	0845	...	0905	0915	...		1735	1745	...	1805	1815	...	1827	1835	1845	...	1905	1915	...	1935	1945
Hoogeveen d.	...	|	0905	...	|	0935	...		|	1805	...	|	1835	...	1846	|	1905	...	|	1935	...	|	2005
Leeuwarden d.	0816	|	|	0846	|	|	0916		|	|	1746	|	|	1816	|	|	|	1846	|	|	1916	|	|
Heerenveen d.	0832	|	|	0902	|	|	0932		|	|	1802	|	|	1832	|	|	|	1902	|	|	1932	|	|
Steenwijk d.	0846	|	|	0916	|	|	0946		|	|	1816	|	|	1846	|	|	|	1916	|	|	1946	|	|
Meppel d.	0856	|	0917	0926	|	0947	0956		|	1817	1826	|	1847	1856	1900	|	1917	1926	|	1947	1956	|	2017
Zwolle a.	0911	0915	0934	0942	0945	1003	1012		1815	1833	1842	1845	1903	1912	1915	1915	1933	1942	1945	2003	2012	2015	2033
Zwolle **460 481** d.	0917	0920	...	0950	0947	...	1017		1820	...	1850	1847	...	1917	1920	1920	...	1950	1947	...	2017	2020	...
Amsterdam Zuid **460** a.	1018	|	...	|	1048	...	1118		|	...	|	1948	...	2018	|	|	...	|	2048	...	2118	|	...
Schiphol + **460** a.	1025	|	...	|	1055	...	1125		|	...	|	1955	...	2025	|	|	...	|	2055	...	2125	|	...
Den Haag Centraal **460** a.	1056	|	...	|	1126	...	1156		|	...	|	2026	...	2056	|	|	...	|	2126	...	2156	|	...
Amersfoort **481** a.	...	0955	...	1025	...	...	...		1855	...	1925	...	...	...	1955	1955	...	2025	...	...	...	2055	...
Utrecht Centraal **481** a.	...	1011	...	1041	...	...	...		1911	...	1941	...	...	...	2011	2011	...	2041	...	...	...	2111	...
Rotterdam Centraal **481** a.	...	1055	...	1125	...	...	...		1955	...	2025	...	...	...	2055	2055	...	2125	...	...	...	2155	...

																							⊡	⑤⑥k
Groningen d.	...	1948	1953	...	2018	2023	...	2048	2053	...	2118	2123	...	2148	2153	...	2218	2223	...	2248	...	...	2323	2326
Assen d.	...	2005	2015	...	2035	2045	...	2105	2115	...	2135	2145	...	2205	2215	...	2235	2245	...	2305	...	...	2345	2348
Hoogeveen d.	...	|	2035	...	|	2105	...	|	2135	...	|	2205	...	|	2235	...	|	2305	...	|	...	...	0005	0007
Leeuwarden d.	1946	|	|	2016	|	|	2046	|	|	2116	|	|	2146	|	|	2216	|	|	2236	|	2324	...	|	|
Heerenveen d.	2002	|	|	2032	|	|	2102	|	|	2132	|	|	2202	|	|	2232	|	|	2258	|	2346	...	|	|
Steenwijk d.	2016	|	|	2046	|	|	2116	|	|	2146	|	|	2216	|	|	2246	|	|	2316	|	0003	...	|	|
Meppel d.	2026	|	2047	2056	|	2117	2126	|	2147	2156	|	2217	2226	|	2247	2256	|	2317	2326	|	0013	...	0017	0019
Zwolle a.	2042	2045	2103	2112	2115	2133	2142	2145	2203	2212	2215	2233	2242	2245	2303	2312	2315	2333	2342	2345	0028	...	0033	0035
Zwolle **460 481** d.	2050	2047	...	2117	2120	...	2150	2147	...	2217	2220	...	2250	2247	...	2317	2320	...	2350	2347	...	...	...	0037
Amsterdam Zuid **460** a.	|	2148	...	2218	|	...	|	2248	...	2318	|	...	|	2348	...	0018	|	...	|	0048	...	...	...	0142‡
Schiphol + **460** a.	|	2155	...	2225	|	...	|	2255	...	2325	|	...	|	2355	...	0025	|	...	|	0055	...	...	...	...
Den Haag Centraal **460** a.	|	2226	...	2256	|	...	|	2326	...	2356	|	...	|	0026	...	0056	|	...	|	0126c	...	...	...	...
Amersfoort **481** a.	2125	...	...	...	2155	...	2225	...	...	...	2255	...	2325	...	...	...	2355	...	0025	...	...	...	...	...
Utrecht Centraal **481** a.	2141	...	...	...	2211	...	2241	...	...	...	2311	...	2341	...	...	...	0011	...	0041	...	...	...	...	...
Rotterdam Centraal **481** a.	2225	...	...	...	2255	...	2325	...	...	...	2355	...	0025	...	...	...	0055	...	...	...	...	...	...	...

L – From Lelystadt Centrum (Table **460**).
M – From Lelystadt Centrum (d. 0741).

a – Ⓐ only.
c – Mornings of ⑥⑦ (also May 31, June 11).
k – Also May 30, June 10.
r – ⚒ only.
t – 2–5 minutes later on ①④⑤.

⊡ – ①②③④⑦ (not May 30, June 10).
◇ – Groningen departure variations: 0916 (not 0918).
⊖ – Timings Zwolle - Groningen may vary by up to 3 minutes (earliest departures shown).
◐ – The 1524, 1624, 1724, 1824 and 1924 from Zwolle run daily.
◧ – The 1553 and 1653 from Groningen run daily.
‡ – Amsterdam **Centraal**.

OLDENZAAL - HENGELO - ZUTPHEN 488

Operated by **Blauwnet** (NS tickets valid) 2nd class only

km		H	Ⓐ	Ⓐ	Ⓑ	⚒			⚒								Ⓑ		⚒	†		⚒	†	
0	**Oldenzaal**... ★ d.	0002	0032	0602	0632	...	0702	0732	and at	1402	1432	1502	1532	and at	2002	2032	2102	2132	2132	2202	2232	2232	2302	2332	2332
11	**Hengelo** ..... ★ a.	0012	0042	0612	0642	...	0712	0742	the same	1412	1442	1512	1542	the same	2012	2042	2112	2142	2142	2212	2242	2242	2312	2342	2342
11	**Hengelo** .... d.	0016	0046	0616	0646	...	0716	0746	minutes	1416	1446	1516	1546	minutes	2016	2046	2116	2146	...	2216	2246	...	2316	2346	...
26	Goor .... d.	0031	0100	0631	0701	0701	0731	0801	past each	1431	1501	1531	1601	past each	2031	2101	2131	2201	...	2231	2301	...	2331	2400	...
39	Lochem........... d.	0039	...	0639	0709	0709	0739	0809	hour until	1439	1509	1539	1609	hour until	2039	2109	2139	2209	...	2239	2309	...	2339	...	...
56	**Zutphen** .... a.	0053	...	0653	0723	0723	0753	0823		1453	1523	1553	1623		2053	2123	2153	2223	...	2253	2323	...	2353	...	...

	H	Ⓐ	Ⓐ	Ⓐ	⚒	Ⓐ		⚒		⚒			⚒									Ⓐ			
Zutphen...........d.	0006	...	...	0608	...	0636	...	0706j	0736t	0806	0836t	and at	1306	1336t	1406	1436t	1506	1536	and at	2006	2036	2106	2136	2236t	2336t
Lochem ....d.	0019	...	...	0621	...	0651	...	0721	0751	0821	0851	the same	1321	1351	1421	1451	1521	1551	the same	2021	2051	2121	2151	2251	2351
Goor...................d.	0029	0530	0600	0630	0630	0700	0700	0730	0800	0830	0900	minutes	1330	1400	1430	1500	1530	1600	minutes	2030	2100	2130	2200	2300	0000
Hengelo.............a.	...	0544	0614	0644	0644	0714	0714	0744	0814	0844	0914	past each	1344	1414	1444	1514	1544	1614	past each	2044	2114	2144	2214	2314	0014
Hengelo ...... ★ d.	...	0548	0618	0648	0648	0718	0718	0748	0818	0848	0918	hour until	1348	1418	1448	1518	1548	1618	hour until	2048	2118	2148	2218	2318	0018
Oldenzaal ... ★ a.	...	0558	0628	0658	0658	0728	0728	0758	0828	0858	0928		1358	1428	1458	1528	1558	1628		2058	2128	2158	2228	2328	0028

H – ②–⑦ (not Dec. 26, 27, Jan. 2, Apr. 23).
j – 0708 on ⑥ (also May 30, June 10).
t – 2 minutes later on †.
★ – See Table **811** for other journeys Bad Bentheim - Oldenzaal - Hengelo and v.v.

ZWOLLE - ENSCHEDE 492

Operated by **Blauwnet** (NS tickets valid)

km		Ⓐ	Ⓐ	⚒	⚒						
0	**Zwolle**.............d.	0552	0622	0652	0722	0752	0822	and at	2252	2322	2352
18	Raalte...............d.	0608	0636	0708	0736	0808	0836	the same	2308	2336	0008
32	Nijverdal ....d.	0618	0647	0718	0747	0818	0847	minutes	2318	2347	0018
44	Almelo .... 480 d.	0630	0700	0730	0800	0830	0900	past each	2330	0000	0030
59	Hengelo...... **480** d.	0647	0717	0747	0817	0847	0917	hour until	2347	0017	0044
67	**Enschede** . **480** a.	0656	0726	0756	0826	0856	0926		2356	0026	0056

	Ⓐ	Ⓐ	Ⓐ	⚒	⚒					
Enschede 480 d.	0505	0535	0605	0635	0705	0735	0805	and at	2305	2335
Hengelo ... **480** d.	0516	0546	0616	0646	0716	0746	0816	the same	2316	2346
Almelo ..... **480** d.	0531	0601	0631	0701	0731	0801	0831	minutes	2331	0001
Nijverdal ....d.	0543	0616	0643	0716	0743	0816	0843	past each	2343	0016
Raalte ....d.	0555	0625	0655	0725	0755	0825	0855	hour until	2355	0025
Zwolle ....a.	0608	0638	0708	0738	0808	0838	0908		0008	0038

ZWOLLE - EMMEN 493

Operated by **Blauwnet** (NS tickets valid)

km		⚒								⚒	⚒
0	**Zwolle**........ d.	0651	0748j	0818t	0851	0921	and at	2221	2251	2321	2351
23	Ommen .... d.	0708	0808	0838	0908	0938	the same	2238	2308	2338	0008
34	Mariënberg . d.	0715	0815	0845	0915	0945	minutes	2245	2315	2345	0015
55	Coevorden .. d.	0734	0834	0900	0934	1000	past each	2300	2334	0000	0035
75	**Emmen** ...... a.	0753	0853	0915	0953	1015	hour until	2315	2354	0015	0053

	Ⓐ	Ⓐ	⚒	⚒						⚒	⚒
Emmen ....d.	0512	0615	0638z	0715	0738	0815	and at	2215	2238	2315	2338
Coevorden.....d.	0530	0631	0659	0731	0759	0831	the same	2231	2259	2331	2359
Mariënberg.....d.	0546	0646	0716	0746	0816	0846	minutes	2246	2316	2346	0016
Ommen ....d.	0553	0653	0723	0753	0823	0853	past each	2253	2323	2353	0023
Zwolle............a.	0609	0709	0739	0809	0840	0910	hour until	2310	2340	0010	0040

j – 3 minutes later on ⑥.
t – 3 minutes later on Ⓒ.
v – Not Dec. 26, 27, Jan. 2, Apr. 23.
z – 0640 on ⑥ (also May 30, June 10).
☛ Other journeys Zwolle - Emmen and v.v.: **From Zwolle** at 0021 ②–⑦ **v**, 0551 Ⓐ, 0621 Ⓐ and 0718 Ⓐ. **From Emmen** at 0020 ②–⑦ **v** and 0538 Ⓐ.

LEEUWARDEN - GRONINGEN 494

Operated by **Arriva** (NS tickets valid)

km			Ⓐ	Ⓐ	⑥k	Ⓐ	⚒	Ⓐ	Ⓐ	⚒		Ⓐ	⚒		⚒	⚒		⚒	⚒			⚒			
0	**Leeuwarden**... d.	0021	0551	0620	0621	0644	0651	0721	0744	0751	0821	0844	0851	0921	0944	0951	1021	1044	1051	1121	1144	1151	and at the same	1821	1844
25	Buitenpost........ d.	0046	0616	0646	0646	0700	0716	0746	0800	0816	0846	0900	0916	0946	1000	1016	1046	1100	1116	1146	1200	1216	minutes past	1846	1900
54	**Groningen** ...... a.	0109	0639	0710	0709	0718	0739	0809	0818	0839	0909	0918	0939	1009	1018	1039	1109	1118	1139	1209	1218	1239	each hour until	1909	1918

	⚒			⚒			⚒		†		
Leeuwarden......d.	1851	1921	1944	1951	2021	2044	2051	2121	2144	2221	2321
Buitenpost ....d.	1916	1946	2000	2016	2046	2100	2116	2146	2200	2246	2346
Groningen ....a.	1939	2009	2018	2039	2109	2118	2209	2209	2218	2309	0009

			Ⓐ	⚒	Ⓐ	Ⓐ	⑥k	Ⓐ	Ⓐ	Ⓐ	⑥k
Groningen ....d.	0029	...	0550	0621	0642	0649	0651	0721	0742	0749	0751
Buitenpost..................d.	0051	...	0614	0645	0700	0715	0715	0745	0800	0815	0815
Leeuwarden.............a.	0116	...	0638	0710	0716	0740	0740	0811	0816	0840	0840

		Ⓐ	Ⓐ	⑥k		⚒	⚒		⚒	⚒			⚒				⚒			⚒		†		
Groningen ....d.	0821	0842	0849	0851	0921	0942	0951	1021	1042	1051	1121	1142	1151	and at the same	1921	1942	1951	2021	2042	2051	2121	2142	2221	2321
Buitenpost ....d.	0845	0900	0915	0915	0945	1000	1015	1045	1100	1115	1145	1200	1215	minutes past	1945	2000	2015	2045	2100	2115	2145	2200	2245	2345
Leeuwarden........a.	0910	0916	0940	0940	1010	1016	1040	1110	1116	1140	1210	1216	1240	each hour until	2010	2016	2040	2110	2116	2140	2210	2216	2310	0010

k – Also May 30, June 10.

GRONINGEN - BAD NIEUWESCHANS - LEER 495

Operated by **Arriva** (NS tickets valid)

km		⑥⑦c		Ⓐ	Ⓐ	⚒	Ⓐ	Ⓒ	Ⓐ	⚒	Ⓒ	Ⓐ	⚒			⚒						
0	**Groningen** .... **498** d.	0023	...	0509	0521	0553	0621	0653	0655	0723	0753	0755	0823	0853	and at the same	1823	1853	1953	2053	2153	2253	2353
15	Hoogezand-Sappemeer .. **498** d.	0038	...	0524	0536	0608	0636	0708	0710	0738	0808	0810	0838	0908	minutes past	1838	1908	2008	2108	2208	2308	0008
34	Winschoten............................a.	0059	...	0544	0555	0627	0655	0727	0728	0757	0827	0828	0857	0927	each hour until	1857	1927	2027	2127	2227	2327	0027
46	**Bad Nieuweschans** ....a.	0108	...	0553	...	0642	...	0742	*0744*	...	0842	*0844*	...	0942		...	1942	2042	2142	2242	2342	0037

		⑥⑦c		Ⓐ	Ⓐ	⑥k	Ⓐ	⑥k	Ⓑ	⚒	Ⓐ	Ⓒ	⚒			⚒						
Bad Nieuweschans ....d.	0048	0112	...	...	0620	...	...	*0718*	*0718*a	0745a	*0818*	0818	...	0918	and at the same	...	1918	2018	2118	2218	2318	2352
Winschoten...............................d.	0102	0121	...	0600	0630	0632	0700	0732	0732	0802	0832	0832	0902	0932	minutes past	1902	1932	2032	2132	2232	2332	0002
Hoogezand-Sappemeer .. **498** d.	0120	0140	...	0618	0648	0650	0718	0750	0750	0820	0850	0850	0920	0950	each hour until	1920	1950	2050	2150	2250	2350	0020
Groningen ....a.	0137	0157	...	0635	0705	0707	0735	0807	0807	0837	0907	0907	0937	1007		1937	2007	2107	2207	2307	0007	0037

Service to / from Leer. Dutch holiday dates apply (see page 248). See panel above for full service Groningen - Bad Nieuweschans and v.v.

	Ⓐ	⊡	Ⓒ	Ⓐ	Ⓒ	Ⓐ							⊡🚌	🚌	🚌	🚌	🚌	🚌	🚌	🚌			
Groningen ....d.	0509	0553	0653	0655v	0753	0755v	...	0853	and	2153	...	A	0630	0830	1030	1230	1430	1630	1830	2030	...	...	...
Bad Nieuweschans 🚌..d.	0554	0643	0743	0745	0843	0843	...	0943	hourly	2243	...	L	|	|	|	|	|	|	|	|	...	...	...
Weener.........................a.	0603	0652	0752	0754	0852	0852	...	0952	until	2252	...	S	|	|	|	|	|	|	|	|	...	...	...
Leer ....a.	*0627**	*0723**	*0823**	*0823**	*0923**	*0923**	...	*1023**		*2323**	...	O	0725	0925	1125	1325	1525	1725	1925	2125	...	...	...

	Ⓐ	⑥h	Ⓐ		Ⓐ	Ⓒ							⊡🚌	🚌	🚌	🚌	🚌	🚌	🚌	🚌			
Leer ....d.	*0530**	*0630**	*0630**	...	*0730**	*0730**	...	*0830**	and	*2230**	...	A	0730	0930	1130	1330	1530	1730	1930	2130	...	...	...
Weener.........................d.	0608	0708	0708	...	0808	0808	...	0908	hourly	2308	...	L	|	|	|	|	|	|	|	|	...	...	...
Bad Nieuweschans 🚌..a.	0617	0717	0717	...	0817	0817	...	0917	until	2317	...	S	|	|	|	|	|	|	|	|	...	...	...
Groningen ....a.	0705	0807	0809v	...	0907v	0907	...	1007		0007	...	O	0825	1025	1225	1425	1625	1825	2025	2225	...	...	...

a – Ⓐ only.
c – Also May 31, June 11.
h – ⑥ (also May 30).
k – ⑥ (also May 30, June 10).
v – Change trains at Winschoten (see upper panel).
* – By 🚌 from / to Weener.
⊡ – ①–⑥ (not Dec. 25, 26, Jan. 1, Apr. 22, June 10).

LEEUWARDEN - STAVOREN 496

Operated by **Arriva** (NS tickets valid); 2nd class only

km		Ⓐ	Ⓐ	Ⓐ	⑥k	Ⓐ	Ⓐ	⑥k	Ⓐ	†	⑥k	Ⓐ	Ⓐ	⑥k	Ⓐ	Ⓒ	Ⓐ	Ⓐ	⑥k		Ⓐ	Ⓒ	Ⓐ	Ⓐ	⑥k
0	**Leeuwarden**.... d.	0532	0542	0602	0622	0622	0642	0652	0702	0720	0722	0722	0742	0752	0802	0822	0822	0842	0852	and at the same	1802	1822	1822	1842	1852
22	Sneek .... a.	0551	0603	0621	0642	0641	0703	0712	0722	0738	0742	0743	0803	0812	0822	0842	0843	0903	0912	minutes past	1822	1842	1843	1903	1912
22	Sneek .... d.	0552	...	0623	0645	0653	...	...	...	...	0745	0750	...	...	...	0845	0850	...	...	each hour until	...	1845	1850	...	...
51	**Stavoren** .... a.	0619	...	0649	0712	0719	...	...	...	...	0812	0816	...	...	...	0912	0916	...	...		...	1912	1916	...	...

	Ⓐ	Ⓒ	Ⓐ	Ⓒ	Ⓐ	Ⓐ	Ⓒ	Ⓑb	⑤	⑥k		
Leeuwarden.....d.	1902	1922	1922	2022	2022	2122	2122	2222	2222	2222	2322	...
Sneek...............a.	1922	1942	1943	2042	2043	2143	2142	2241	2241	2242	2341	...
Sneek...............d.	...	1945	1947	2045	2047	2145	2145	...	2242	2245	...	...
Stavoren..........a.	...	2012	2013	2112	2113	2211	2212	...	2308	2312	...	...

	Ⓐ	Ⓐ	Ⓐ	Ⓐ	⑥k	Ⓐ	†	⑥k	Ⓐ	Ⓐ	⑥k	Ⓐ
Stavoren ......d.	...	...	0624	...	...	0654	...	0719	0724	...	...	...
Sneek ....a.	...	...	0651	...	...	0725	...	0745	0750	...	...	...
Sneek ....d.	0616	0636	0656	0716	0718	0736	0743	0748	0756	0816	0818	0836
Leeuwarden.a.	0637	0657	0717	0737	0738	0757	0803	0808	0817	0837	0838	0857

	†	⑥k	Ⓐ	Ⓐ	⑥k	Ⓐ	Ⓒ	Ⓐ		Ⓒ	Ⓐ	Ⓐ	⑥k	Ⓐ	Ⓒ	Ⓐ	Ⓒ	Ⓐ	Ⓐ	Ⓒ	Ⓐ	Ⓒ	⑤	⑥k	f
Stavoren..........d.	...	0819	0824	...	...	...	0919	0924	and at the same	1819	1824	...	...	...	1919	1921	2019	2021	2117	2119	2215	2219	2315	2319	...
Sneek...............a.	...	0845	0850	...	...	...	0945	0950	minutes past	1845	1850	...	...	...	1945	1947	2045	2047	2143	2145	2241	2245	2341	2345	...
Sneek...............d.	0846	0848	0856	0916	0918	0936	0948	0956	each hour until	1848	1856	1916	1918	1936	1948	1948	2046	2048	2144	2146	2242	2246	2342	2346	2346
Leeuwarden.....a.	0907	0908	0917	0937	0938	0957	1008	1017		1908	1917	1937	1938	1957	2008	2008	2106	2108	2204	2206	2302	2306	0002	0006	0006

b – Not May 30, June 10.
f – Daily except ⑤.
k – Also May 30, June 10.

497 SCHIEDAM - HOEK VAN HOLLAND

Interim service. Operated by 🚌 before reopening as an extension of the Rotterdam Metro lines A and B (awaiting confirmation for the exact date).
Services are operated by *Rotterdamse Elektrische Tram N.V.* (RET), the local transport provider in the Rotterdam area. Local RET fares apply (rail passes are valid).

Bus **711**: Fast service (journey time ±30 minutes).

Departures from Schiedam Centrum: On Ⓐ at 0030, 0532, 0544, 0604, 0624, 0644, 0659, 0715 and every 15 minutes until 0900, 0920 and every 20 minutes until 1520, 1535 and every 15 minutes until 1820, 1850 and every 30 minutes until 2350. On Ⓒ at 0030, 0650⑥, 0720⑥, 0750, 0816⑦, 0820⑥, 0850 and every 30 minutes until 2350.

Departures from Hoek van Holland Haven: On Ⓐ at 0006, 0051, 0531, 0546, 0606, 0626, 0646, 0701, 0716, 0724, 0731, 0746, and every 15 minutes until 0946 and every 20 minutes until 1526, 1549, and every 15 minutes until 1811, 1836, and every 30 minutes until 2336. On Ⓒ at 0022, 0102⑥, 0722⑥, 0752⑥, 0822, 0848⑦, 0852⑥, 0922 and every 30 minutes until 2352.

Bus **713** provides a stopping service via Vlaardingen and Maassluis (additional journeys operate between Schiedam and Vlaardingen on ⚒). Overall journey time on bus **713** between Schiedam and Hoek van Holland is approximately 70 minutes, so the fast service **711** (above) is recommended for direct journeys between Schiedam and Hoek van Holland.

Departures from Schiedam Centrum: On Ⓐ at 0533, 0603, and every 30 minutes until 2333, 0003. On Ⓒ at 0700⑥, 0730⑥, 0800, 0830 and every 30 minutes until 0000.

Departures from Hoek van Holland Haven: On ⚒ at 0536Ⓐ, 0606Ⓐ, 0635Ⓐ, 0701, 0731, 0801, 0830Ⓐ, 0831⑥, 0901 and every 30 minutes until 2331, 0003. On ⑦ 0008, 0801, 0831, 0901, 0930 and every 30 minutes until 2330.

498 OTHER BRANCH LINES

ALMELO – MARIËNBERG Operated by **Blauwnet** (NS tickets valid) *19 km.* Journey time: 17–19 minutes.

From Almelo:
0618Ⓐ, 0648Ⓐ, 0718Ⓐ, 0748⚒, 0818Ⓐ, 0848, 0948, 1048, 1148, 1248, 1318⚒, 1348, 1418⚒, 1448, 1518⚒, 1548, 1618⚒, 1648, 1718⚒, 1748, 1818⚒, 1848, 1948, 2048, 2148, 2248 and 2357.

From Mariënberg:
0555Ⓐ, 0625Ⓐ, 0655Ⓐ, 0725⚒, 0755Ⓐ, 0825, 0855Ⓐ, 0925, 1025, 1125, 1225, 1325, 1355⚒, 1425, 1455⚒, 1525, 1555⚒, 1625, 1655⚒, 1725, 1755⚒, 1825, 1925, 2025, 2125, 2225 and 2325.

AMERSFOORT – EDE-WAGENINGEN Operated by **Connexxion** (NS tickets valid) *34 km.* Journey time: 35–38 minutes.

From Amersfoort:
0009⊖, 0039⑦**w**, 0109⑦**w**, 0507Ⓐ, 0535⚒, 0609⚒, 0639⚒, 0709, 0739, 0809, 0839 and every 30 minutes until 2339.
All trains call at Barneveld Centrum (17 minutes from Amersfoort)

From Ede-Wageningen:
0023, 0053⊖, 0123⑦**w**, 0153⑦**w**, 0549Ⓐ, 0623⚒, 0653⚒, 0723⚒, 0753, 0823, 0853 and every 30 minutes until 2353.
All trains call at Barneveld Centrum (20 minutes from Ede-Wageningen)

APELDOORN – ZUTPHEN Operated by **Arriva** (NS tickets valid) *18 km.* Journey time: 19–20 minutes.

From Apeldoorn:
0005, 0635Ⓐ, 0705Ⓐ, 0735Ⓐ, 0805⚒, 0835, 0905 and every 30 minutes until 2335.

From Zutphen:
0612Ⓐ, 0636Ⓐ, 0706Ⓐ, 0736⚒, 0806, 0836 and every 30 minutes until 2336.

GRONINGEN – DELFZIJL Operated by **Arriva** (NS tickets valid) *38 km.* Journey time: 37–39 minutes.

From Groningen:
0033, 0518Ⓐ, 0548⚒, 0618, 0648⚒, 0718, 0748⚒ and at 18 and 48⚒ minutes past each hour until 1718, 1748⚒; then 1818, 1848Ⓐ, 1919, 2018, 2048④**d**, 2118, 2218 and 2318.

From Delfzijl:
0004, 0113, 0530①**m**, 0600Ⓐ, 0630⚒, 0700, 0730⚒, 0800, 0830⚒ and at 00 and 30⚒ minutes past each hour until 1800, 1830⚒; then 1900, 1930Ⓐ, 2000, 2100, 2200 and 2300.

GRONINGEN – EEMSHAVEN ⊡ Operated by **Arriva** (NS tickets valid) *36 km.* Journey time: 51 minutes.

From Groningen:
1052⚒, 1422†.

From Eemshaven:
1150⚒, 1520†.

GRONINGEN – VEENDAM 🚂 Operated by **Arriva** (NS tickets valid) *29 km.* Journey time: 30–32 minutes.

From Groningen:
0023 ①–⑤**e**, 0038⑥⑦**w**, 0458Ⓐ, 0538Ⓐ, 0608⑥**k**, 0610Ⓐ, 0640Ⓐ, 0708⑥**k**, 0710Ⓐ, 0723†, 0738⑥**k**, 0740Ⓐ, 0808⑥**k**, 0810Ⓐ, 0823†, 0838⚒, 0908⚒, 0923†, 0938⚒ and at 08⚒, 23† and 38⚒ minutes past each hour until 1808⚒, 1823†, 1838⚒; then 1923, 2023, 2123, 2223 and 2323.
All trains call at Hoogezand-Sappemeer (15 minutes from Groningen)

From Veendam:
0057①–⑤**e**, 0100⑥⑦**c**, 0533Ⓐ, 0619Ⓐ, 0647Ⓐ, 0651⑥**k**, 0720Ⓐ, 0751⚒, 0805†, 0821⚒, 0851⚒ and at 05†, 21⚒ and 51⚒ minutes past each hour until 1805†, 1821⚒, 1851⚒; then 1905†, 1921⚒, 2005, 2105, 2205, 2305 and 2358.
All trains call at Hoogezand-Sappemeer (15 minutes from Veendam)

LEEUWARDEN – HARLINGEN Haven ★ Operated by **Arriva** (NS tickets valid) *26 km.* Journey time: 25–28 minutes. 2nd class.

From Leeuwarden:
0545Ⓐ, 0609Ⓐ, 0612⑥**k**, 0645Ⓐ, 0712⑥**k**, 0720Ⓐ, 0745, 0820, 0845, 0920, 0945⚒, 1020, 1045⚒, 1120, 1145, 1220, 1245⚒, 1320, 1345, 1420, 1445, 1520, 1545⚒, 1620, 1645, 1720, 1745⚒, 1820, 1845, 1920, 1945, 2020, 2120, 2220 and 2320.

From Harlingen Haven:
0614Ⓐ, 0640Ⓐ, 0641⑥**k**, 0714Ⓐ, 0741⑥**k**, 0749Ⓐ, 0814, 0849, 0914, 0949⚒, 1014, 1049⚒, 1114, 1149, 1214, 1249⚒, 1314, 1349, 1414, 1449, 1514, 1549⚒, 1614, 1649, 1714, 1749⚒, 1814, 1849, 1914, 1949, 2014, 2048, 2148, 2249 and 2349.

ZWOLLE – KAMPEN Operated by **Blauwnet** (NS tickets valid) *13 km.* Journey time: 10 minutes.

From Zwolle:
0019, 0549Ⓐ, 0619Ⓐ, 0649⚒, 0719, 0749 and every 30 minutes until 2349.

From Kampen:
0002, 0032, 0602Ⓐ, 0632Ⓐ, 0702⚒, 0732, 0802, 0832 and every 30 minutes until 2332.

d – Not May 30.
e – Not May 31, June 11.
k – Also May 30, June 10.
m – Not Apr. 22, June 10.
w – Also May 31, June 11.

⊖ – ④–⑦ (also June 11; not Dec. 27).
⊡ – For ⛴ to/from Borkum. See www.ag-ems.de for latest timings. Additional trains run Groningen - Roodeschool and v.v.
★ – For ⛴ to/from Terschelling and Vlieland. All trains also call at Harlingen (station for the town centre), 3 minutes from Harlingen Haven.
🚂 – Station for *Museumspoorlijn S.T.A.R.* Steam trains operate to/from Stadskanaal on ⑦ May - September. www.stadskanaalrail.nl

499 OTHER 🚌 and ⛴ LINES

ALKMAAR – LEEUWARDEN 🚌 *Arriva Qliner* route **350** Journey time: 1 hr 44 m – 1 hr 58 m

From Alkmaar rail station:
On Ⓐ at 0524, 0624, 0720, 0823, 0927, 1027, 1127, 1227, 1327, 1423, 1523, 1618, 1718, 1827, 1927, 2027 and 2127.
On ⑥ at 0627, 0727, 0827, 0926 and hourly until 1626; then 1727 and hourly until 2127.
On † at 0827 and hourly until 2227.

From Leeuwarden bus station:
On Ⓐ at 0612, 0712, 0815 and hourly until 1615; then 1717, 1817, 1918, 2018, 2118 and 2218.
On ⑥ at 0715 and hourly until 1615; then 1717, 1817, 1918, 2018, 2118 and 2218.
On † at 0817 and hourly until 1817; then 1918, 2018, 2118 and 2218.

DEN HELDER – TEXEL ⛴ *TESO*: ✆ +31 (0) 222 36 96 00 Journey time: 20 minutes

🚌 route **33**: Den Helder rail station (departs 18 minutes before ships sail) to Havenhoofd.
From Den Helder Havenhoofd: 0630⚒, 0730⚒**d**, 0830 and hourly until 2030; 2130**n**.

From Texel ('t Horntje ferryport): 0600⚒, 0700⚒**d**, 0800 and hourly until 2000; 2100**n**.
🚌 route **33**: Den Helder Havenhoofd to rail station (journey: 7 minutes).

ENKHUIZEN – STAVOREN ⛴ *Rederij V&O* ▲: ✆ +31 (0) 228 32 66 67 Journey time: ± 90 minutes

From Enkuizen Spoorhaven: 0845**A**, 1245**B**, 1545**C**, 1645**B**.

From Stavoren: 1025**A**, 1425**B**, 1725**C**, 1825**B**.

VLISSINGEN – BRESKENS ⛴ *Westerschelde Ferry* ▲ Journey time: 23 minutes
0545Ⓐ, 0645Ⓐ, 0748, 0848 and hourly until 2048; then 2148Ⓐ.
Additional sailings operate June 8 - Aug. 30.

BRESKENS ferryport – **BRUGGE** rail station 🚌 *Connexxion* **42** Journey time: 84 minutes
0614Ⓐ, 0714Ⓐ, 0716⑥, 0816⚒, 0916, 1016 and hourly until 1916; then 2016⚒.

BRUGGE rail station – **BRESKENS** ferryport 🚌 *Connexxion* **42** Journey time: 82 minutes
0648⚒, 0748⚒, 0848, 0948 and hourly until 1948; then 2048⚒.

BRESKENS – VLISSINGEN ⛴ *Westerschelde Ferry* ▲ Journey time: 23 minutes
0612Ⓐ, 0712Ⓐ, 0818, 0918 and hourly until 2118; then 2218Ⓐ.
Additional sailings operate June 8 - Aug. 30.

A – Daily May 1 - Sept. 30 (also Apr. 13, 14, 20, 21, 27–30); ⑥⑦ Oct. 5–27 (also Oct. 22–25).
B – Daily May 1 - Sept. 30.
C – Apr. 13, 14, 20, 21, 27–30; ⑥⑦ Oct. 5–27 (also Oct. 22–25).

d – Runs daily Mar. 1 - Nov. 1.
n – Not Dec. 31.

▲ – Conveys foot passengers, cycles and mopeds only.

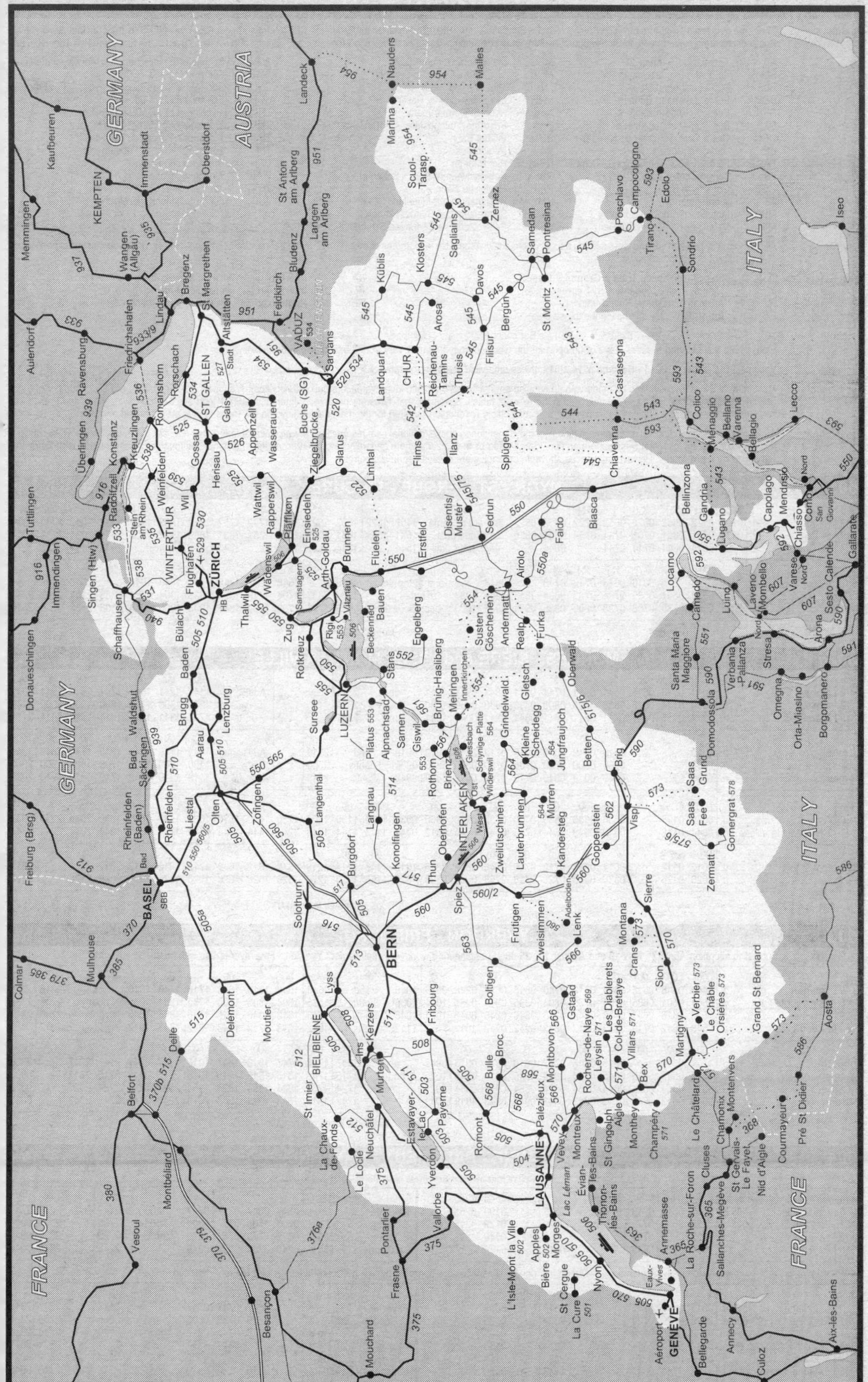

GERMANY
AUSTRIA
ITALY
FRANCE
BASEL
ZÜRICH
BERN
LUZERN
LAUSANNE
GENÈVE
ST GALLEN
CHUR
WINTERTHUR
INTERLAKEN
BIEL/BIENNE
Schaffhausen
Konstanz
Kreuzlingen
Romanshorn
Rorschach
Friedrichshafen
Lindau
Bregenz
St Margrethen
Feldkirch
Buchs (SG)
Sargans
VADUZ
Landquart
Davos
Klosters
Arosa
Filisur
Thusis
Bergün
Samedan
Pontresina
St Moritz
Zernez
Scuol-Tarasp
Martina
Nauders
Landeck
Tirano
Poschiavo
Chiavenna
Bellinzona
Lugano
Locarno
Chiasso
Como
Varese
Domodossola
Brig
Visp
Zermatt
Saas Fee
Sierre
Sion
Martigny
Montreux
Vevey
Aigle
Bex
Gstaad
Zweisimmen
Spiez
Thun
Olten
Aarau
Baden
Brugg
Zug
Arth-Goldau
Brunnen
Flüelen
Göschenen
Andermatt
Airolo
Biasca
Disentis/Mustér
Glarus
Rapperswil
Einsiedeln
Fribourg
Neuchâtel
Yverdon
Vallorbe
Pontarlier
Nyon
Morges
Delémont
Solothurn
Burgdorf
Langenthal
Mulhouse
Belfort
Besançon
Chamonix
Annemasse
Aosta
Domodossola
For list of Scenic Rail Routes in Switzerland see contents page

SWITZERLAND

Operators: There are numerous operators of which Schweizerische Bundesbahnen (SBB)/Chemins de fer Fédéraux (CFF)/Ferrovie Federali Svizzere (FFS) is the principal: www.sbb.ch. Bus services are provided by PostAuto/Autopostale (PA): www.postauto.ch. Table headings show the operators' initials; abbreviations used in the European Rail Timetable are:

AB	Appenzeller Bahnen	MGB	Matterhorn Gotthard Bahn	SGV	Schifffahrtsgesellschaft des Vierwaldstättersees
BLM	Bergbahn Lauterbrunnen - Mürren	MOB	Montreux - Oberland Bernois	SMC	Sierre - Montana - Crans
BLS	BLS Lötschbergbahn	MThB	Mittelthurgau Bahn	SNCF	Société Nationale des Chemins de Fer Francais
BOB	Berner Oberland Bahnen	MVR	Montreux - Vevey Riviera	SOB	Schweizerische Südostbahn
BRB	Brienz - Rothorn Bahn	NStCM	Nyon-St Cergue-Morez	THURBO	an alliance of MThB and SBB
BSB	Bodensee-Schiffsbetriebe	PA	PostAuto / Autopostale / AutoDaPosta	TMR	Transports de Martigny et Régions
CGN	Compagnie Générale de Navigation	PB	Pilatus Bahn	TPC	Transports Publics du Chablais
CP	CarPostal Suisse	RA	RegionAlps	TPF	Transports Publics Fribourgeois
FART	Ferrovie Autolinee Regionali Ticinesi	RB	Rigi Bahnen	URh	Untersee und Rhein
FS	Ferrovie dello Stato	RBS	Regionalverkehr Bern - Solothurn	WAB	Wengernalpbahn
GGB	Gornergrat Bahn	RhB	Rhätische Bahn	ZB	Zentralbahn
JB	Jungfraubahn	RM	Regionalverkehr Mittelland	ZSG	Zürich Schifffahrtsgesellschaft
MBC	Morges - Bière - Cossonay	SBB	Schweizerische Bundesbahnen		
MIB	Meiringen - Innertkirchen Bahn	SBS	Schweizerische Bodensee-Schifffahrtsgesellschaft		

Services: All trains convey first and second class seating except where shown otherwise in footnotes or by a '1' or '2' in the train column. For most local services you must be in possession of a valid ticket before boarding your train.

Train Categories:
TGV French high-speed **Train à Grande Vitesse**;
ICE German high-speed **InterCity Express** train;
RJ Austrian high-speed **Railjet** train;
EC **EuroCity** quality international express train;
IC **InterCity** quality internal express train;
IR **InterRegio** fast inter-regional trains;
RE **RegioExpress** semi-fast regional trains.

Catering: ✕ – Restaurant; ⊗ – Bistro; (🍸) – Bar coach; 🍸 – Minibar.
Please note that catering facilities may not be open for the whole journey and may vary from those shown in our tables.

Timings: Valid until **December 9**, 2018 - **December 14**, 2019 unless otherwise stated in the table.

Supplements: Most internal Swiss journeys can be made without supplement (including domestic journeys on international services). A supplement is payable on a small number of trains (mainly tourist services) and these are indicated in the relevant tables. Special 'global' fares are payable for international *TGV* journeys between Switzerland and France with compulsory reservation. A supplement is payable and compulsory reservation required for international journeys on *EC* trains between Switzerland and Italy.

Reservations: As well as compulsory reservations for international journeys mentioned above, optional seat reservations are also available on other *ICE*, *RJ*, *EC* and *IC* trains. Reservation is recommended for travel in first class panorama cars. Standard fares in Switzerland are generally calculated according to distance, although artificially inflated tariff-kilometres are used on certain routes. However, distances shown in our tables are always actual kilometres.

501 NYON - ST CERGUE - LA CURE
Narrow gauge 2nd class only NStCM

km		⑥⑦k	Ⓐj	⚒j	⚒j	j	⚒j							⚒		⚒		⚒		Ⓐj				
0	**Nyon** d.	0100	0522	0552	0622	0652	0722	0752	0822	and at the same	1452	1522	1552	1622	1652	1722	1752	1822	1852	1922	1952	2052	2200	2330
19	St Cergue d.	0131	0601	0631	0701	0731	0759	0831	0859	minutes past	1531	1559	1631	1659	1731	1759	1831	1859	1931	1959	2031	2131	2234	0004
27	**La Cure** a.	...	0614	0644	0714	0744	...	0844	...	each hour until	1544	...	1644	...	1744	...	1844	...	1944	...	2044	2144	...	...

		Ⓐj		Ⓐj	⚒j	⚒j	j	Ⓐj							⚒		⚒			⚒j			
La Cure d.	...	...	...	0616	0648	0716	0748	...	0848	...	and at the same	1548	...	1648	...	1748	...	1848	1948	...	2048	2148	...
St Cergue d.	0010	0533	0604	0633	0704	0733	0804	0833	0904	0933	minutes past	1604	1633	1704	1733	1804	1833	1904	2004	2033	2104	2202	2241
Nyon a.	0044	0608	0638	0708	0738	0808	0838	0908	0938	1008	each hour until	1638	1708	1738	1808	1838	1908	1938	2038	2108	2138	...	2316

j – Not Sept. 16.
k – Not Apr. 20.

502 MORGES - BIÈRE and L'ISLE MONT LA VILLE
Narrow gauge 2nd class only MBC

km			⑥⑦k	⚒	⚒		⚒		⚒				△				Ⓐ	Ⓐ	Ⓐ	Ⓐ	Ⓐ	Ⓐ	Ⓐ
0	**Morges** d.	0011	0116	0611	0641	0711	0741	0811	0841	0911	1011	and	2311	...	...	Additional	1141	1241	1641	1741	1841	1941	2041
12	Apples a.	0030	0134	0628	0658	0730	0800	0830	0900	0930	1030	hourly	2328	...	...	services	1200	1300	1700	1800	1900	2000	2100
19	**Bière** a.	0041	0145	0641	0711	0741	0811	0841	0911	0941	1041	until	2341	...	...	on Ⓐ	1211	1311	1711	1811	1911	2011	2111

	⑥⑦k			⚒	⚒		⚒		⚒							Ⓐ	Ⓐ	Ⓐ	Ⓐ	Ⓐ	Ⓐ	Ⓐ
Bière d.	0019	...	...	0519	0549	0619	0649	0719	0749	0819	0919	and	2319	...	Additional	1049	1149	1549	1649	1749	1849	1949
Apples d.	0030	...	...	0530	0600	0630	0700	0730	0800	0830	0930	hourly	2330	...	services	1100	1200	1600	1700	1800	1900	2000
Morges a.	0049	...	...	0549	0619	0649	0719	0749	0819	0849	0949	until	2349	...	on Ⓐ	1119	1219	1619	1719	1819	1919	2019

km		⑥⑦k	⑥⑦k			Ⓐ	Ⓒ	Ⓐ	Ⓐ	Ⓒ	Ⓐ		Ⓐ	Ⓒ	Ⓐ									△	
0	Apples d.	0030	0134	...	0556	0630	0630	0700	0730	0730	0800	0930	1130	1130	1200	1230	1430	1530	1630	1730	1830	1930	2030	2230	2330
11	L'Isle Mont la Ville d.	0044	0148	...	0610	0643	0644	0713	0743	0744	0813	0944	1143	1144	1213	1244	1444	1544	1644	1744	1844	1944	2044	2244	2344

	⑥⑦k	⑥⑦k			Ⓐ	Ⓒ	Ⓐ	Ⓐ	Ⓒ	Ⓐ		Ⓐ	Ⓒ	Ⓐ										
L'Isle Mont la Ville d.	0012	0112	...	0614	0645	0712	0715	0745	0812	0815	1012	1145	1212	1215	1312	1512	1612	1712	1812	1912	2012	2112	...	2312
Apples a.	0026	0126	...	0628	0658	0726	0728	0758	0826	0828	1026	1158	1226	1228	1326	1526	1626	1726	1826	1926	2026	2126	...	2326

k – Not Apr. 20.
△ – Runs 5 minutes later on ①②③④⑦.

503 YVERDON - FRIBOURG
SBB

Subject to alteration April 27 - May 19 and August 10–25 due to engineering work (🚌 replacement Yverdon - Estavayer-le-Lac with amended timings).

km		Ⓐ	Ⓐ	Ⓐ	Ⓐ		Ⓐ		Ⓐ		Ⓐ				Ⓐ		Ⓐ		Ⓐ				
0	**Yverdon** d.	0445	0548	0618	0648	0718	0748	0818	0848	0918	0948	1018	and	1518	1548	1618	1648	1718	1748	1818	and	2218	2318
18	Estavayer-le-Lac d.	0501	0604	0635	0704	0735	0804	0835	0904	0935	1004	1035	hourly	1535	1604	1635	1704	1735	1804	1835	hourly	2235	2335
28	Payerne d.	0516	0616	0646	0716	0746	0816	0846	0916	0946	1014	1046	until	1546	1616	1646	1716	1746	1816	1846	until	2246	2344
50	**Fribourg** a.	0543	0642	0712	0743	0812	0843	0912	0943	1012	...	1112		1612	1643	1712	1743	1812	1843	1912		2312	...

	Ⓐ	Ⓐ	Ⓐ	Ⓐ	Ⓐ		Ⓐ		Ⓐ				Ⓐ		Ⓐ		Ⓐ				A		
Fribourg d.	...	0517	0547	0615	0716	0747	0816	0847	0916	0947	and	1647	1716	1747	1816	1847	1916	1947	2047	2147	2247	...	2338
Payerne d.	0512	0545	0615	0645	0745	0815	0845	0915	0945	1015	hourly	1715	1745	1815	1845	1915	1945	2015	2115	2215	2315	...	0007
Estavayer-le-Lac d.	0521	0554	0624	0654	0754	0824	0854	0924	0954	1024	until	1724	1754	1824	1854	1924	1954	2024	2124	2224	2324	...	0016
Yverdon a.	0540	0613	0643	0713	0813	0843	0913	0943	1013	1043		1743	1813	1843	1913	1943	2013	2043	2143	2243	2343	...	0035

A – ①②③④⑦ (also Apr. 19).
☛ Additional trains run on Ⓐ.

504 LAUSANNE - PALÉZIEUX - PAYERNE
SBB

Service to May 22 and from September 16.

km								⑥⑦	⑥⑦	
0	**Lausanne** 505 d.	0513	0613	0713	and	2313	...	0100	0253	...
21	Palézieux 505 d.	0529	0629	0729	hourly	2329	...	0122	0315	...
38	Moudon d.	0552	0652	0752	until	2352	...	0140	...	...
58	**Payerne** a.	0613	0713	0813		0013	...	0159	...	...

			Ⓐ						
Payerne d.	0547	0647	0717	0747	and	2147	...	2247	2347
Moudon d.	0605	0705	0737	0805	hourly	2205	...	2305	0005
Palézieux 505 d.	0629	0729	0757	0829	until	2229	...	2329	0029
Lausanne 505 a.	0648	0748	...	0848		2248	...	2346	0046

Service May 23 - September 15. During this period all services are operated by 🚌 between Palézieux and Moudon (shaded timings).

km								⑥⑦		
0	**Lausanne** 505 d.	0513	0613	0713		2313	...	0003	...	...
21	Palézieux 505 a.	0529	0629	0729	and	2329	...	0025	...	...
21	Palézieux 🚌 d.	0539	0639	0739	hourly	2339	...	0105	...	...
38	Moudon 🚌 a.	0614	0714	0814	until	0014	...	0138	...	...
38	Moudon d.	0623	0723	0823		0023	...	0140	...	...
58	**Payerne** a.	0643	0743	0843		0043	...	0159	...	...

Payerne d.	...	0647	0717	0747		2147	...	2217	2317
Moudon a.	...	0705	0735	0805	and	2205	...	2235	2335
Moudon 🚌 d.	...	0716	0746	0816	hourly	2216	...	2246	2346
Palézieux 🚌 a.	...	0751	0821	0851	until	2251	..	2321	0021
Palézieux 505 d.	...	0800	...	0900		2300	...	2329	0029
Lausanne 505 a.	...	0816	...	0916		2316	....	2346	0046

SBB GENÈVE - LAUSANNE - BERN / BIEL - ZÜRICH 505

See panel on page 262 for other fast trains Bern - Zürich

km		IR 2155 ① z	IR 2155 ②–⑦ d	IR 2355 ① z	IR 2355 ②–⑦ d	IC 703	IC 1507 ✕	IR 2159	IC 507 ✕	IR 2357 Ⓐ §	IR 2505	IC 805 R✕	RE 4809	RE 2809	IC 705 ✕	IC 1509 ✕	RE 18403	IC 509 ✕	IR 2359	IR 2507	RE 18405	IC 1511 ✕	IC 707 ✕	IR 2163
0	Genève Aéroport ✈ 570 d.	...	...	...	...	...	...	...	...	...	...	...	...	...	...	...	...	...	...	...	0505b	...	...	...
6	**Genève** 570 d.	...	...	...	...	...	...	...	...	...	...	...	...	...	...	...	0413b	...	...	...	0513b	...	0542	...
27	Nyon 570 d.	...	...	...	...	...	...	...	...	...	...	...	...	...	...	...	0435	...	...	...	0535	...	|	...
53	Morges 570 d.	...	...	...	...	...	...	...	...	...	...	...	...	...	...	...	0456	...	...	...	0556	...	|	...
66	**Lausanne** 570 a.	...	...	...	...	...	...	...	...	...	...	...	...	...	...	...	0509	...	...	...	0609	...	0618	...
66	**Lausanne** d.	...	...	...	...	...	...	...	...	...	0444g	...	...	...	...	...	▬	0543	...	0544	▬	0615	0620	...
	Yverdon d.	...	...	...	...	...	...	...	...	...	|	...	...	...	...	...	...	0606	...	|	...	0639	|	...
	Neuchâtel d.	...	...	...	...	...	...	...	...	...	|	...	...	...	...	...	...	0626	...	|	...	0659	|	...
	Biel / Bienne a.	...	...	...	...	...	...	...	...	...	|	...	...	...	...	...	...	0642	...	|	...	0715	|	...
	Biel / Bienne d.	...	...	...	...	...	0516	...	0543	...	|	...	...	...	...	0616	...	0644	...	|	...	0717	|	...
	Solothurn d.	...	...	...	...	...	0533	...	0601	...	|	...	...	...	...	0633	...	0701	...	|	...	0734	|	...
87	Palézieux d.	...	...	...	...	...	|	...	|	...	0500g	...	...	...	...	|	...	|	...	0600	...	|	|	...
106	Romont 568 d.	...	...	...	...	...	|	...	|	...	0516g	...	...	...	...	|	IR	|	...	0616	RE	|	|	...
132	Fribourg 568 d.	...	...	...	...	...	|	...	|	...	0534	...	...	...	0604	|	**2161**	|	...	0634	**2811**	|	0704	...
163	**Bern** 568 a.	...	...	...	...	...	|	...	|	...	0556	...	...	...	0626	|		|	...	0656		|	0726	...
163	**Bern** d.	0402	0421e	0432	0440	0529f	|	...	|	0538	0600	0602	...	0606	0632	|	0634	|	0638	0700	0706	|	0732	0734
	Luzern 565 a.	|	|	|	|	|	|	...	|	|	0701	|	...	|	|	|	|	|	|	0801	|	|	|	|
186	Burgdorf d.	|	|	0454	0454	|	|	...	|	0553	...	|	...	0621	|	|	|	|	0653	▬	0721	|	|	|
210	Langenthal d.	|	|	0513	0513	|	|	...	|	0612	...	|	...	0641	|	|	|	|	0712	RE	0741	|	|	|
230	**Olten** a.	0446	0446	0525	0525	0555	0557	...	0618	0624	...	0628	...	0654	|	0657	0700	0718	0724	**4811**	0754	0757	|	0800
230	**Olten** d.	0448	0448	0530	0530	0557	0559	0602	0620	0626	...	0631	...	...	|	0659	0702	0720	0730		...	0759	|	0802
243	Aarau 510 d.	0459	0459	0542	0542	|	|	0615	0632	0642	...	|	0653	...	|	|	0715	0732	|	0753	...	|	|	0815
253	Lenzburg 510 d.	0506	0506	0549	0549	|	|	|	|	0649	...	|	0700	...	|	|	|	|	|	0800	...	|	|	|
	Brugg 510 d.	|	|	|	|	|	|	0630	|	|	...	|	|	...	|	|	0730	|	|	|	...	|	|	0830
	Baden 510 a.	|	|	|	|	|	|	0638	|	|	...	|	|	...	|	|	0738	|	|	|	...	|	|	0838
285	**Zürich** HB 510 a.	0527	0527	0615	0615	0628	0630	0654	0656	0713	...	0702	0722	...	0728	0730	0754	0756	0806	0822	...	0830	0828	0854
	Zürich Flughafen ✈ 530/5 a.	0539	0539	...	...	0642	0651	...	...	...	...	0714	...	...	0742	0751	...	...	...	...	...	0851	0842	...
	St Gallen 530 a.	...	...	...	...	0735	0752	...	...	...	...	...	...	...	0835	0852	...	...	...	...	...	0952	0935	...

km		IR 2361	IR 2509 🍷	IC 511 ✕	RE 4813	RE 18409	IC 1513 ✕	IC 709 ✕	IR 2165	IR 2363	IR 2511 🍷	IC 513 ✕	RE 4815	RE 18413	IC 1515 ✕	IC 711 ✕	IR 2167	IR 2365	IR 2513 🍷	IC 515 ✕	RE 4817	RE 18417	IC 1517 ✕	IC 713 ✕
	Genève Aéroport ✈ 570 d.	...	0549	0602	...	0609	...	0632	...	...	0649	0705	...		...	0732	...	...	0749	0805	...		...	0832
	Genève 570 d.	...	0600	0612	...	0619	...	0642	...	...	0700	0715	...	0719	...	0742	...	...	0800	0815	...	0819	...	0842
	Nyon 570 d.	...	0614	0625	...	0635	...	|	...	...	0714	|	...	0735	...	|	...	...	0814	|	...	0835	...	|
0	Morges 570 d.	...	0630	0642	...	0656	...	|	...	...	0730	0742	...	0756	...	|	...	...	0830	0842	...	0856	...	|
	Lausanne 570 a.	...	0642	|	...	0709	...	0718	...	...	0742	|	...	0809	...	0818	...	...	0842	|	...	0909	...	0918
0	**Lausanne** d.	...	0644	|	...	▬	0715	0720	...	...	0744	|	...	▬	0815	0820	...	...	0844	|	...	▬	0915	0920
39	Yverdon d.	...	|	0706	...	...	0739	|	...	...	|	0806	...	...	0839	|	...	...	|	0906	...	...	0939	|
75	Neuchâtel d.	...	|	0726	...	...	0759	|	...	...	|	0826	...	...	0859	|	...	...	|	0926	...	...	0959	|
105	**Biel / Bienne** a.	...	|	0743	...	...	0815	|	...	...	|	0843	...	...	0915	|	...	...	|	0943	...	...	1015	|
105	**Biel / Bienne** d.	...	|	0746	...	...	0817	|	...	...	|	0846	...	...	0917	|	...	...	|	0946	...	...	1017	|
130	Solothurn d.	...	|	0801	...	...	0834	|	...	...	|	0901	...	...	0934	|	...	...	|	1001	...	...	1034	|
	Palézieux d.	...	0700	|	...	...	|	|	...	...	0800	|	...	...	|	|	...	...	0900	|	...	...	|	|
	Romont 568 d.	...	0716	|	...	RE	|	|	...	...	0816	|	...	RE	|	|	...	...	0916	|	...	RE	|	|
	Fribourg 568 d.	...	0734	|	...	**2813**	|	0804	...	...	0834	|	...	**2815**	|	0904	...	...	0934	|	...	**2817**	|	1004
	Bern 568 a.	...	0756	|	...		|	0826	...	...	0856	|	...		|	0926	...	...	0956	|	...		|	1026
	Bern d.	0738	0800	|	...	0806	|	0832	0834	0838	0900	|	...	0906	|	0932	0934	0938	1000	|	...	1006	|	1032
	Luzern 565 a.	|	0901	|	...	|	|	|	|	|	1001	|	...	|	|	|	|	|	1101	|	...	|	|	|
	Burgdorf d.	0753	...	|	...	0821	|	|	|	0853	...	|	...	0921	|	|	|	0953	...	|	...	1021	|	|
	Langenthal d.	0812	...	|	...	0841	|	|	|	0912	...	|	...	0941	|	|	|	1012	...	|	...	1041	|	|
165	**Olten** a.	0824	...	0818	...	0854	0857	|	0900	0924	...	0918	...	0954	0957	|	1000	1024	...	1018	...	1054	1057	|
165	**Olten** d.	0830	...	0820	...	...	0859	|	0902	0930	...	0920	...	...	0959	|	1002	1030	...	1020	...	...	1059	|
178	Aarau 510 d.	|	...	0832	0853	...	|	|	0915	|	...	0932	0953	...	|	|	1015	|	...	1032	1053	...	|	|
	Lenzburg 510 d.	|	...	|	0900	...	|	|	|	|	...	|	1000	...	|	|	|	|	...	|	1100	...	|	|
196	Brugg 510 d.	|	...	|	|	...	|	|	0930	|	...	|	|	...	|	|	1030	|	...	|	|	...	|	|
205	Baden 510 a.	|	...	|	|	...	|	|	0938	|	...	|	|	...	|	|	1038	|	...	|	|	...	|	|
227	**Zürich** HB 510 a.	0906	...	0856	0922	...	0930	0928	0954	1006	...	0956	1022	...	1030	1028	1054	1106	...	1056	1122	...	1130	1128
	Zürich Flughafen ✈ 530/5 a.	...	...	...	...	...	0951	0942	...	...	...	...	...	...	1051	1042	...	...	...	...	...	...	1151	1142
	St Gallen 530 a.	...	...	...	...	...	1052	1035	...	...	...	...	...	...	1152	1135	...	...	...	...	...	...	1252	1235

	IR 2169	IR 2367	IR 2515 🍷	IC 517 ✕	RE 4819	RE 18421	IC 1519 ✕	IC 715 ✕	IR 2171	IR 2369	IR 2517 🍷	IC 519 ✕	RE 4821	RE 18425	IC 1521 ✕	IC 717 ✕	IR 2173	IR 2371	IR 2519 🍷	IC 521 ✕	RE 4823	RE 18429	IC 1523 ✕	IC 719 ✕
Genève Aéroport ✈ 570 d.	...	...	0849	0905	...	...	...	0932	...	...	0949	1005	...	...	...	1032	...	...	1049	1105	...	...	...	1132
Genève 570 d.	...	...	0900	0915	...	0919	...	0942	...	...	1000	1015	...	1019	...	1042	...	...	1100	1115	...	1119	...	1142
Nyon 570 d.	...	...	0914	|	...	0935	...	|	...	...	1014	|	...	1035	...	|	...	...	1114	|	...	1135	...	|
Morges 570 d.	...	...	0930	0942	...	0956	...	|	...	...	1030	1042	...	1056	...	|	...	...	1130	1142	...	1156	...	|
Lausanne 570 a.	...	...	0942	|	...	1009	...	1018	...	...	1042	|	...	1109	...	1118	...	...	1142	|	...	1209	...	1218
Lausanne d.	...	...	0944	|	...	▬	1015	1020	...	...	1044	|	...	▬	1115	1120	...	...	1144	|	...	▬	1215	1220
Yverdon d.	...	...	|	1006	...	...	1039	|	...	...	|	1106	...	...	1139	|	...	...	|	1206	...	...	1239	|
Neuchâtel d.	...	...	|	1026	...	...	1059	|	...	...	|	1126	...	...	1159	|	...	...	|	1226	...	...	1259	|
Biel / Bienne a.	...	...	|	1043	...	...	1115	|	...	...	|	1143	...	...	1215	|	...	...	|	1243	...	...	1315	|
Biel / Bienne d.	...	...	|	1046	...	...	1117	|	...	...	|	1146	...	...	1217	|	...	...	|	1246	...	...	1317	|
Solothurn d.	...	...	|	1101	...	...	1134	|	...	...	|	1201	...	...	1234	|	...	...	|	1301	...	...	1334	|
Palézieux d.	...	...	1000	|	...	...	|	|	...	...	1100	|	...	...	|	|	...	...	1200	|	...	...	|	|
Romont 568 d.	...	...	1016	|	...	RE	|	|	...	...	1116	|	...	RE	|	|	...	...	1216	|	...	RE	|	|
Fribourg 568 d.	...	...	1034	|	...	**2819**	|	1104	...	...	1134	|	...	**2821**	|	1204	...	...	1234	|	...	**2823**	|	1304
Bern 568 a.	...	...	1056	|	...		|	1126	...	...	1156	|	...		|	1226	...	...	1256	|	...		|	1326
Bern d.	1034	1038	1100	|	...	1106	|	1132	1134	1138	1200	|	...	1206	|	1232	1234	1238	1300	|	...	1306	|	1332
Luzern 565 a.	|	|	1201	|	...	|	|	|	|	|	1301	|	...	|	|	|	|	|	1401	|	...	|	|	|
Burgdorf d.	|	1053	...	|	...	1121	|	|	|	1153	...	|	...	1221	|	|	|	1253	...	|	...	1321	|	|
Langenthal d.	|	1112	...	|	...	1141	|	|	|	1212	...	|	...	1241	|	|	|	1312	...	|	...	1341	|	|
Olten a.	1100	1124	...	1118	...	1154	1157	|	1200	1224	...	1218	...	1254	1257	|	1300	1324	...	1318	...	1354	1357	|
Olten d.	1102	1130	...	1120	...	...	1159	|	1202	1230	...	1220	...	...	1259	|	1302	1330	...	1320	...	...	1359	|
Aarau 510 d.	1115	|	...	1132	1153	...	|	|	1215	|	...	1232	1253	...	|	|	1315	|	...	1332	1353	...	|	|
Lenzburg 510 d.	|	|	...	|	1200	...	|	|	|	|	...	|	1300	...	|	|	|	|	...	|	1400	...	|	|
Brugg 510 d.	1130	|	...	|	|	...	|	|	1230	|	...	|	|	...	|	|	1330	|	...	|	|	...	|	|
Baden 510 a.	1138	|	...	|	|	...	|	|	1238	|	...	|	|	...	|	|	1338	|	...	|	|	...	|	|
Zürich HB 510 a.	1154	1206	...	1156	1222	...	1230	1228	1254	1306	...	1256	1322	...	1330	1328	1354	1406	...	1356	1422	...	1430	1428
Zürich Flughafen ✈ 530/5 a.	...	...	...	...	...	...	1251	1242	...	...	...	...	...	...	1351	1342	...	...	...	...	...	...	1451	1442
St Gallen 530 a.	...	...	...	...	...	...	1352	1335	...	...	...	...	...	...	1452	1435	...	...	...	...	...	...	1552	1535

R – To Romanshorn (Table **535**).

b – 4–6 minutes later on ©.
d – Also Apr. 22, June 10.
e – 0407 on ②–⑤ May 14–24, Sept. 24 - Oct. 4 (also Mar. 23, 24, Oct. 26, 27).
f – 0513 on ①–⑤ May 13–27, Sept. 23 - Oct. 4 (also Feb. 4, 25, Mar. 23–25, May 6, July 29, Sept. 2, Oct. 26–28, Nov. 11, 25, Dec. 2).

g – ① (not Apr. 22, June 10).
z – ① (not Apr. 22, June 10). Change trains at Zollikofen (8 minutes from Bern).

§ – Runs as *RE* **4509** Olten - Zürich.

505 GENÈVE - LAUSANNE - BERN / BIEL - ZÜRICH SBB

See panel below main table for other fast trains Bern - Zürich

	IR 2175	IR 2373	IR 2521	IC 523	RE 4825	RE 18433	IC 1525	IC 721	IR 2177	IR 2375	IR 2523	IC 525	RE 4827	RE 18437	IC 1527	IC 723	IR 2179	IR 2377	IR 2525	IC 527	RE 4829	RE 18441	IC 1529	IC 725
			🍷	✕			✕	✕			🍷	✕			✕	✕				✕			✕	✕
Genève Aéroport ✈ 570 d.	...	...	1149	1205	...	...	...	1232	...	...	1249	1305	...	...	...	1332	...	...	1349	1405	...	...	...	1432
Genève 570 d.	...	...	1200	1215	...	1219	...	1242	...	...	1300	1315	...	1319	...	1342	...	...	1400	1415	...	1419	...	1442
Nyon 570 d.	...	...	1214	|	...	1235	...	|	...	...	1314	|	...	1335	...	|	...	...	1414	|	...	1435	...	|
Morges 570 d.	...	...	1230	1242	...	1256	...	|	...	...	1330	1342	...	1356	...	|	...	...	1430	1442	...	1456	...	|
Lausanne 570 a.	...	...	1242	|	...	1309	...	1318	...	...	1342	|	...	1409	...	1418	...	...	1442	|	...	1509	...	1518
Lausanne d.	...	...	1244	|	...	▬	1315	1320	...	...	1344	|	...	▬	1415	1420	...	...	1444	|	...	▬	1515	1520
Yverdon d.	...	...	|	1306	...	...	1339	|	...	...	|	1406	...	...	1439	|	...	...	|	1506	...	...	1539	|
Neuchâtel d.	...	...	|	1326	...	...	1359	|	...	...	|	1426	...	...	1459	|	...	...	|	1526	...	...	1559	|
Biel / Bienne a.	...	...	|	1343	...	...	1415	|	...	...	|	1443	...	...	1515	|	...	...	|	1543	...	...	1615	|
Biel / Bienne d.	...	...	|	1346	...	...	1417	|	...	...	|	1446	...	...	1517	|	...	...	|	1546	...	...	1617	|
Solothurn d.	...	...	|	1401	...	...	1434	|	...	...	|	1501	...	...	1534	|	...	...	|	1601	...	...	1634	|
Palézieux d.	...	...	1300	|	...	...	|	|	...	...	1400	|	...	...	|	|	...	...	1500	|	...	...	|	|
Romont 568 d.	...	...	1316	|	...	*RE*	|	|	...	...	1416	|	...	*RE*	|	|	...	...	1516	|	...	*RE*	|	|
Fribourg 568 d.	...	...	1334	|	...	**2825**	|	1404	...	...	1434	|	...	**2827**	|	1504	...	...	1534	|	...	**2829**	|	1604
Bern 568 a.	...	...	1356	|	...		|	1426	...	...	1456	|	...		|	1526	...	...	1556	|	...		|	1626
Bern d.	1334	1338	1400	|	...	1406	|	1432	1434	1438	1500	|	...	1506	|	1532	1534	1538	1600	|	...	1606	|	1632
Luzern 565 a.	|	|	1501	|	...	|	|	|	|	|	1601	|	...	|	|	|	|	|	1701	|	...	|	|	|
Burgdorf d.	|	1353	...	|	...	1421	|	|	|	1453	...	|	...	1521	|	|	|	1553	...	|	...	1621	|	|
Langenthal d.	|	1412	...	|	...	1441	|	|	|	1512	...	|	...	1541	|	|	|	1612	...	|	...	1641	|	|
Olten a.	1400	1424	...	1418	...	1454	1457	|	1500	1524	...	1518	...	1554	1557	|	1600	1624	...	1618	...	1654	1657	|
Olten d.	1402	1430	...	1420	...	...	1459	|	1502	1530	...	1520	...	...	1559	|	1602	1630	...	1620	...	...	1659	|
Aarau 510 d.	1415	|	...	1432	1453	...	|	|	1515	|	...	1532	1553	...	|	|	1615	|	...	1632	1653	...	|	|
Lenzburg 510 d.	|	|	...	|	1500	...	|	|	|	|	...	|	1600	...	|	|	|	|	...	|	1700	...	|	|
Brugg 510 d.	1430	|	...	|	|	...	|	|	1530	|	...	|	|	...	|	|	1630	|	...	|	|	...	|	|
Baden 510 a.	1438	|	...	|	|	...	|	|	1538	|	...	|	|	...	|	|	1638	|	...	|	|	...	|	|
Zürich HB 510 a.	1454	1506	...	1456	1522	...	1530	1528	1554	1606	...	1556	1622	...	1630	1628	1654	1706	...	1656	1722	...	1730	1728
Zürich Flughafen ✈ 530/5 a.	...	...	...	...	...	...	1551	1542	...	...	...	...	...	...	1651	1642	...	...	...	...	...	...	1751	1742
St Gallen 530 a.	...	...	...	...	...	...	1652	1635	...	...	...	...	...	...	1752	1735	...	...	...	...	...	...	1852	1835

	IR 2181	IR 2379	IR 2527	IC 529	RE 4831	RE 18445	IC 1531	IC 727	IR 2183	IR 2381	IR 2529	IC 531	RE 4833	RE 18449	IC 1533	IC 729	IR 2185	IR 2383	IR 2531	IC 533	RE 4835	RE 18453	IC 1535	IC 731
			🍷	✕			✕	✕			🍷	✕			✕	✕			🍷	✕			✕	✕
Genève Aéroport ✈ 570 d.	...	...	1449	1505	...	...	...	1532	...	...	1549	1605	...	...	...	1632	...	...	1649	1705	...	...	...	1732
Genève 570 d.	...	...	1500	1515	...	1519	...	1542	...	...	1600	1615	...	1619	...	1642	...	...	1700	1715	...	1719	...	1742
Nyon 570 d.	...	...	1514	|	...	1535	...	|	...	...	1614	|	...	1635	...	|	...	...	1714	|	...	1735	...	|
Morges 570 d.	...	...	1530	1542	...	1556	...	|	...	...	1630	1642	...	1656	...	|	...	...	1730	1742	...	1756	...	|
Lausanne 570 a.	...	...	1542	|	...	1609	...	1618	...	...	1642	|	...	1709	...	1718	...	...	1742	|	...	1809	...	1818
Lausanne d.	...	...	1544	|	...	▬	1615	1620	...	...	1644	|	...	▬	1715	1720	...	...	1744	|	...	▬	1815	1820
Yverdon d.	...	...	|	1606	...	...	1639	|	...	...	|	1706	...	...	1739	|	...	...	|	1806	...	...	1839	|
Neuchâtel d.	...	...	|	1626	...	...	1659	|	...	...	|	1726	...	...	1759	|	...	...	|	1826	...	...	1859	|
Biel / Bienne a.	...	...	|	1643	...	...	1715	|	...	...	|	1743	...	...	1815	|	...	...	|	1843	...	...	1915	|
Biel / Bienne d.	...	...	|	1646	...	...	1717	|	...	...	|	1746	...	...	1817	|	...	...	|	1846	...	...	1917	|
Solothurn d.	...	...	|	1701	...	...	1734	|	...	...	|	1801	...	...	1834	|	...	...	|	1901	...	...	1934	|
Palézieux d.	...	...	1600	|	...	...	|	|	...	...	1700	|	...	...	|	|	...	...	1800	|	...	...	|	|
Romont 568 d.	...	...	1616	|	...	*RE*	|	|	...	...	1716	|	...	*RE*	|	|	...	...	1816	|	...	*RE*	|	|
Fribourg 568 d.	...	...	1634	|	...	**2831**	|	1704	...	...	1734	|	...	**2833**	|	1804	...	...	1834	|	...	**2835**	|	1904
Bern 568 a.	...	...	1656	|	...		|	1726	...	...	1756	|	...		|	1826	...	...	1856	|	...		|	1926
Bern d.	1634	1638	1700	|	...	1706	|	1732	1734	1738	1800	|	...	1806	|	1832	1834	1838	1900	|	...	1906	|	1932
Luzern 565 a.	|	|	1801	|	...	|	|	|	|	|	1901	|	...	|	|	|	|	|	2001	|	...	|	|	|
Burgdorf d.	|	1653	...	|	...	1721	|	|	|	1753	...	|	...	1821	|	|	|	1853	...	|	...	1921	|	|
Langenthal d.	|	1712	...	|	...	1741	|	|	|	1812	...	|	...	1841	|	|	|	1912	...	|	...	1941	|	|
Olten a.	1700	1724	...	1718	...	1754	1757	|	1800	1824	...	1818	...	1854	1857	|	1900	1924	...	1918	...	1954	1957	|
Olten d.	1702	1730	...	1720	...	...	1759	|	1802	1830	...	1820	...	...	1859	|	1902	1930	...	1920	...	...	1959	|
Aarau 510 d.	1715	|	...	1732	1753	...	|	|	1815	|	...	1832	1853	...	|	|	1915	|	...	1932	1953	...	|	|
Lenzburg 510 d.	|	|	...	|	1800	...	|	|	|	|	...	|	1900	...	|	|	|	|	...	|	2000	...	|	|
Brugg 510 d.	1730	|	...	|	|	...	|	|	1830	|	...	|	|	...	|	|	1930	|	...	|	|	...	|	|
Baden 510 a.	1738	|	...	|	|	...	|	|	1838	|	...	|	|	...	|	|	1938	|	...	|	|	...	|	|
Zürich HB 510 a.	1754	1806	...	1756	1822	...	1830	1828	1854	1906	...	1856	1922	...	1930	1928	1954	2006	...	1956	2022	...	2030	2028
Zürich Flughafen ✈ 530/5 a.	...	...	...	...	...	...	1851	1842	...	...	...	...	...	...	1951	1942	...	...	...	...	...	...	2051	...
St Gallen 530 a.	...	...	...	...	...	...	1952	1935	...	...	...	...	...	...	2052	2035	...	...	...	...	...	...	2152	...

	IR 2187	IR 2385	IR 2533	IC 535	RE 4837	RE 18457	IC 1537	IC 733	IR 2189	IR 2387	IR 2535	IC 537	RE 4839	RE 18461	IC 1539	IC 735 ⑤⑥	IC 735	IR 2191	IR 2389	IR 2537	IC 539	RE 4841	RE 18471	IC 1541
			🍷	✕			✕	✕				✕				r✕	A✕				✕			
Genève Aéroport ✈ 570 d.	...	...	1749	1805	...	...	...	1832	...	...	1849	1905	...	...	...	1932	1932	...	...	1949	2005	...	...	...
Genève 570 d.	...	...	1800	1815	...	1819	...	1842	...	...	1900	1915	...	1919	...	1942	1942	...	...	2000	2015	...	2019	...
Nyon 570 d.	...	...	1814	|	...	1835	...	|	...	...	1914	|	...	1935	...	|	|	...	...	2014	|	...	2035	...
Morges 570 d.	...	...	1830	1842	...	1856	...	|	...	...	1930	1942	...	1956	...	|	|	...	...	2030	2042	...	2056	...
Lausanne 570 a.	...	...	1842	|	...	1909	...	1918	...	...	1942	|	...	2009	...	2018	2018	...	...	2042	|	...	2109	...
Lausanne d.	...	...	1844	|	...	▬	1915	1920	...	...	1944	|	...	▬	2015	2020	2020	...	...	2044	|	...	▬	2115
Yverdon d.	...	...	|	1906	...	...	1939	|	...	...	|	2006	...	...	2039	|	|	...	...	|	2106	...	...	2139
Neuchâtel d.	...	...	|	1926	...	...	1959	|	...	...	|	2026	...	...	2059	|	|	...	...	|	2126	...	...	2159
Biel / Bienne a.	...	...	|	1943	...	...	2015	|	...	...	|	2043	...	...	2115	|	|	...	...	|	2143	...	...	2215
Biel / Bienne d.	...	...	|	1946	...	...	2017	|	...	...	|	2046	...	...	2117	|	|	...	...	|	2146	...	...	2217
Solothurn d.	...	...	|	2001	...	...	2034	|	...	...	|	2101	...	...	2134	|	|	...	...	|	2201	...	...	2234
Palézieux d.	...	...	1900	|	...	...	|	|	...	...	2000	|	...	...	|	|	|	...	...	2100	|	...	...	|
Romont 568 d.	...	...	1916	|	...	*RE*	|	|	...	...	2016	|	...	*RE*	|	|	|	...	...	2116	|	...	*RE*	|
Fribourg 568 d.	...	...	1934	|	...	**2837**	|	2004	...	...	2034	|	...	**2839**	|	2104	2104	...	...	2134	|	...	**2841**	|
Bern 568 a.	...	...	1956	|	...		|	2026	...	...	2056	|	...		|	2126	2126	...	...	2156	|	...		|
Bern d.	1934	1938	2000	|	...	2006	|	2032	2034	2038	2100	|	...	2106	|	2132	2132	2134r	2138	2200	|	...	2206	|
Luzern 565 a.	|	|	2101	|	...	|	|	|	|	|	2201	|	...	|	|	|	|	|	|	2301	|	...	|	|
Burgdorf d.	|	1953	...	|	...	2021	|	|	|	2053	...	|	...	2121	|	|	|	|	2154	...	|	...	2223	|
Langenthal d.	|	2012	...	|	...	2041	|	|	|	2112	...	|	...	2141	|	|	|	|	2212	...	|	...	2242	|
Olten a.	2000	2024	...	2018	...	2054	2057	|	2100	2124	...	2118	...	2154	2157	|	2157	2200r	2225	...	2218	...	2254	2257
Olten d.	2002	2030	...	2020	...	...	2059	|	2102	...	...	2120	...	...	2159r	|	2200	2202	...	...	2220	...	...	▽
Aarau 510 d.	2015	|	...	2032	2053	...	|	|	2115	...	...	2132	2153	...	|	|	|	2215	...	...	2232	2253	...	...
Lenzburg 510 d.	|	|	...	|	2100	...	|	|	|	...	...	|	2200	...	|	|	|	|	...	...	|	2300	...	...
Brugg 510 d.	2030	|	...	|	|	...	|	|	2130	...	...	|	|	...	|	|	|	2230	...	...	|	|	...	...
Baden 510 a.	2038	|	...	|	|	...	|	|	2138	...	...	|	|	...	|	|	|	2238	...	...	|	|	...	...
Zürich HB 510 a.	2054	2106	...	2056	2122	...	2130	2128	2154	...	...	2156	2222	...	2230r	2228	2232	2254	...	...	2256	2322	...	...
Zürich Flughafen ✈ 530/5 a.	...	...	...	...	...	...	2151	...	...	...	...	...	...	...	2251r	...	...	...	...	...	...	...	...	...
St Gallen 530 a.	...	...	...	...	...	...	2252	...	...	...	...	...	...	...	2352r	...	...	...	...	...	...	...	...	...

OTHER NON-STOP TRAINS BERN - ZÜRICH. See Table **560** for origin and destination.

	IC 807	IC 1411	IC 809	IC 811	IC 813	IC 815	IC 817	IC 819	IC 821	IC 823	IC 825	IC 1429	IC 827	IC 1431	IC 829	IC 831	IC 833	IC 835	IC 837					
	✕	Ⓐ✕	✕	⊗	✕	⊗	✕	⊗	✕	✕	✕	Ⓐ	⊗	Ⓐ🍷	✕	⊗	✕	⊗						
Bern d.	0702	0710	0802	0902	1002	1102	1202	1302	1402	1502	1602	1610	1702	1710	1802	1902	2002	2102	2202	...	...	...	...	...
Zürich HB a.	0758	0810	0858	0958	1058	1158	1258	1358	1458	1558	1658	1710	1758	1810	1858	1958	2058	2158	2302	...	...	...	...	...

FOR NOTES SEE NEXT PAGE →

SBB GENÈVE - LAUSANNE - BERN / BIEL - ZÜRICH 505

See panel on page 264 for other fast trains Zürich - Bern

	IC 737	IR 2193	IR 2539	IC 839	IC 541	RE 4843	RE 4793	RE 18477	IC 1543	IC 739	IR 1839 ⑤⑥	IR 2541	IC 543	RE 18483 ⑤⑥	IC 1545	IR 1841 ⑤⑥	IR 2543	IR 2543 ⑤⑥	RE 2847 ⑥⑦	RE 18487 ⑤⑥	IC 1547	RE 18493 ⑥⑦	IR 2503 ⑥⑦	RE 18497 ⑥⑦
	✕										r	¶		r	D	r		r	k	r		k		k
Genève Aéroport ✈ 570 d.	2032	...	2049	...	2102	...	...	2109	...	...	2147	...	...	2211	...	2232	...	...	...	2312	...	0021	...	0107
Genève 570 d.	2042	...	2100	...	2112	...	...	2119	...	...	2157	...	...	2219	...	2243	...	...	...	2322	...	0031	...	0117
Nyon 570 d.	|	...	2114	...	2125	...	...	2135	...	...	2210	...	...	2234	...	2300	...	...	...	2338	...	0047	...	0135
Morges 570 d.	|	...	2130	...	2142	...	...	2156	...	...	2226	...	...	2257	...	2324	...	...	...	2359	...	0108	...	0156
Lausanne 570 a.	2118	...	2142	...	|	...	...	2209	...	...	2239	...	...	2310	...	2339	...	...	...	0012	...	0121	...	0209
Lausanne d.	2120	...	2144	...	|	...	...	▬	2215	2220	...	2244	...	▬	2315	...	2346	2346	...	...	0017	...	0130	...
Yverdon d.	|	...	|	...	2206	...	...	...	2239	|	...	|	...	...	2339	...	|	|	...	...	0041	...	|	...
Neuchâtel d.	|	...	|	...	2226	...	...	...	2259	|	...	|	...	...	2359	...	|	|	...	...	0100	...	|	...
Biel/Bienne a.	|	...	|	...	2243	...	...	...	2315	|	...	|	...	...	0015	...	|	|	...	...	0117	...	|	...
Biel/Bienne d.	|	...	|	...	2246	...	...	...	2317	|	...	|	2346	...	...	...	|	|	...	...	...	...	|	...
Solothurn d.	|	...	|	...	2305	...	...	...	2334	|	...	|	0005	...	...	...	|	|	...	...	...	...	|	...
Palézieux d.	|	...	2200	...	|	...	...	...	|	|	...	2300	|	...	...	...	0002	0002	...	...	...	...	0146	...
Romont 568 d.	|	...	2216	...	|	...	...	*RE*	|	|	...	2316	|	*RE*	...	...	0018	0018	...	...	...	...	0202	...
Fribourg 568 d.	2204	...	2234	...	|	...	...	**2843**	|	2304	...	2334	|	**2845**	...	...	0036	0036	...	...	...	...	0219	...
Bern 568 a.	2226	...	2256	...	|	...	...		|	2326	...	2356	|		...	...	0101	0101	...	...	...	...	...	...
Bern d.	2232	...	2300	2302	|	...	...	2306	|	2332	...	0002	|	0006	...	...	...	0104	0107	...	...	...	...	...
Luzern 565 a.	|	...	0001	|	|	...	...	|	|	|	...	|	|	|	...	...	...	|	|	...	...	...	...	...
Burgdorf d.	|	...	...	|	|	...	...	2323	|	|	...	|	|	0023	...	...	...	|	0123	...	...	...	...	...
Langenthal d.	|	...	...	|	|	...	...	2342	|	|	...	|	|	0042	...	...	...	|	0142	...	...	...	...	...
Olten a.	2257	...	...	2328	2330	...	...	2355	2357	2358	...	0028	0030	0055	...	...	...	0130	0155	...	...	...	...	...
Olten d.	2300	2302	...	2330	2335	...	2337	...	...	0002	...	0033	0035	...	...	...	...	0133	...	...	...	...	...	...
Aarau 510 d.	|	2315	...	|	2347	2353	2348	...	...	0014	...	|	0047	...	...	...	...	0145	...	...	...	...	...	...
Lenzburg 510 d.	|	|	...	|	|	0000	|	...	...	|	...	|	0053	...	...	...	...	|	...	...	...	...	...	...
Brugg 510 d.	|	2330	...	|	|	|	0003	...	...	|	...	|	|	...	...	...	...	|	...	...	...	...	...	...
Baden 510 a.	|	2338	...	|	|	|	0013	...	...	|	...	|	|	...	...	...	...	|	...	...	...	...	...	...
Zürich HB 510 a.	2331	2354	...	0001	0010	0022	0042	...	...	0037	...	0104	0112	...	...	...	...	0207	...	...	...	...	...	...
Zürich Flughafen ✈ 530/5 a.	...	...	...	...	...	...	...	...	...	...	...	...	...	...	...	...	...	...	...	...	...	...	...	...
St Gallen 530 a.	...	...	...	...	...	...	...	...	...	...	...	...	...	...	...	...	...	...	...	...	...	...	...	...

km ⊡		RE 18404	RE 18406	RE 18408	RE 18410	IC 504	IR 2504	IC 702	IC 1504	RE 18414	IC 1606	RE 2806 Ⓐ	IR 2506	IR 2354	IC 704	IC 1506	RE 18418	RE 2808	IR 2508	IR 2356	IC 508	IR 2158	IC 1508	IC 706
								✕	✕		D✕				✕	✕			🍸		✕		✕	✕
	St Gallen 530 d.	...	...	...	...	...	...	...	...	...	...	...	...	...	...	...	...	...	...	...	...	...	...	0504
	Zürich Flughafen ✈ 530/5 d.	...	...	...	...	...	...	...	...	...	...	...	...	...	...	...	...	...	...	...	...	...	...	0609
	Zürich HB 510 d.	...	...	...	...	...	...	...	...	...	...	...	...	...	0519	...	...	...	...	0553	0603	0606	0630	0632
	Baden 510 d.	...	...	...	...	...	...	...	...	...	...	...	...	...	|	...	...	...	...	|	|	0622	|	|
	Brugg 510 d.	...	...	...	...	...	...	...	...	...	...	...	...	...	|	...	...	...	...	|	|	0632	|	|
	Lenzburg 510 d.	...	...	...	...	...	...	...	...	...	...	...	...	...	0540	...	...	...	...	|	|	|	|	|
	Aarau 510 d.	...	...	...	...	...	...	...	...	...	...	...	...	...	0548	...	...	...	...	|	0629	0646	|	|
	Olten a.	...	...	...	...	...	...	...	...	...	...	...	...	...	0557	...	...	...	...	0627	0638	0657	0700	|
0	**Olten** d.	...	...	...	...	...	...	...	...	...	...	0506	...	0536	0602	0602	...	0606	...	0636	0640	0659	0702	|
	Langenthal d.	...	...	...	...	...	...	...	...	...	...	0518	...	0548	|	|	...	0618	...	0648	|	|	|	|
	Burgdorf d.	...	...	...	...	...	...	...	...	...	...	0538	...	0607	|	|	...	0638	...	0707	|	|	|	|
	Luzern 565 d.	...	...	...	...	...	...	...	...	...	...	|	...	|	|	|	...	|	0600	|	|	|	|	|
62	**Bern** a.	...	...	...	...	...	...	...	...	...	...	0553	...	0621	0628	|	...	0653	0700	0721	|	0726	|	0728
	Bern 568 d.	...	...	...	...	...	0504	0534	...	...	...	...	0604	...	0634	|	...	...	0704	...	|	...	|	0734
	Fribourg 568 d.	...	...	...	...	...	0526	0556	...	...	...	...	0626	...	0656	|	...	...	0726	...	|	...	|	0756
	Romont 568 d.	...	...	...	...	...	0544	|	...	...	...	...	0644	...	|	|	...	...	0744	...	|	...	|	|
	Palézieux d.	...	...	...	...	...	0600	|	...	...	...	...	0700	...	|	|	...	...	0800	...	|	...	|	|
	Solothurn d.	...	...	...	...	...	|	|	...	...	...	...	|	...	|	0626	...	...	|	...	0658	...	0726	|
	Biel/Bienne a.	...	...	...	...	...	|	|	...	...	...	...	|	...	|	0643	...	...	|	...	0713	...	0743	|
	Biel/Bienne d.	...	...	...	...	0516	|	|	0545	...	0616	...	|	...	|	0645	...	...	|	...	0716	...	0745	|
	Neuchâtel d.	...	...	...	...	0534	|	|	0603	...	0634	...	|	...	|	0703	...	...	|	...	0734	...	0803	|
	Yverdon d.	...	...	...	...	0553	|	|	0622	...	0653	...	|	...	|	0722	...	...	|	...	0753	...	0822	|
	Lausanne a.	...	...	...	...	|	0616	0640	0645	...	|	...	0716	...	0740	0745	...	...	0816	...	|	...	0845	0840
	Lausanne 570 d.	0351	0451	0521	0551	|	0618	0642	...	0651	|	...	0718	...	0742	...	0751	...	0818	...	|	...	...	0842
	Morges 570 d.	0404	0504	0534	0604	0617	0628	|	...	0704	0717	...	0728	...	|	...	0804	...	0828	...	0817	...	...	|
	Nyon 570 d.	0424	0524	0554	0624	|	0644	|	...	0724	|	...	0744	...	|	...	0824	...	0844	...	|	...	...	|
	Genève 570 a.	0442	0540	0610	0640	0645	0700	0718	...	0740	0745	...	0800	...	0818	...	0840	...	0900	...	0845	...	...	0918
	Genève Aéroport ✈ 570 a.	0451	0549	0619	...	0654	0711	0727	...	...	0754	...	0811	...	0827	...	...	...	0911	...	0854	...	...	0927

km ⊡		RE 18422	RE 2810	IR 2510	RE 4808	IR 2358	IC 510	IR 2160	IC 1510	IC 708	RE 2812	IR 2512	RE 4810	IR 2360	IC 512	IR 2162	IC 1512	IC 710	RE 2814	IR 2514	RE 4812	IR 2362	IC 514	IR 2164
				🍸			✕		✕	✕		🍸			✕		✕	✕		🍸			✕	
	St Gallen 530 d.	...	...	...	...	...	...	...	0607	0625	...	...	...	...	...	...	0707	0725	...	...	...	...	...	...
	Zürich Flughafen ✈ 530/5 d.	...	...	...	...	...	...	...	0709	0718	...	...	...	...	...	...	0809	0818	...	...	...	...	...	...
	Zürich HB 510 d.	...	...	...	0638	0653	0703	0706	0730	0732	...	...	0738	0753	0803	0806	0830	0832	...	...	0838	0853	0903	0906
	Baden 510 d.	...	...	...	|	|	|	0722	|	|	...	...	|	|	|	0822	|	|	...	...	|	|	|	0922
	Brugg 510 d.	...	...	...	|	|	|	0732	|	|	...	...	|	|	|	0832	|	|	...	...	|	|	|	0932
	Lenzburg 510 d.	...	...	...	0658	|	|	|	|	|	...	...	0758	|	|	|	|	|	...	...	0858	|	|	|
	Aarau 510 d.	...	...	...	0705	|	0729	0746	|	|	...	...	0805	|	0829	0846	|	|	...	...	0905	|	0929	0946
	Olten a.	...	...	...	...	0727	0738	0757	0800	|	...	...	...	0827	0838	0857	0900	|	...	...	...	0927	0938	0957
0	**Olten** d.	...	0706	...	...	0736	0740	0759	0802	|	0806	...	...	0836	0840	0859	0902	|	0906	...	...	0936	0940	0959
	Langenthal d.	...	0718	...	...	0748	|	|	|	|	0818	...	...	0848	|	|	|	|	0918	...	...	0948	|	|
	Burgdorf d.	...	0738	...	...	0807	|	|	|	|	0838	...	...	0907	|	|	|	|	0938	...	...	1007	|	|
	Luzern 565 d.	...	|	0700	...	|	|	|	|	|	|	0800	...	|	|	|	|	|	|	0900	...	|	|	|
	Bern a.	...	0753	0800	...	0821	|	0826	|	0828	0853	0900	...	0921	|	0926	|	0928	0953	1000	...	1021	|	1026
	Bern 568 d.	...	...	0804	...	...	|	...	|	0834	▬	0904	...	...	|	...	|	0934	▬	1004	...	...	|	...
	Fribourg 568 d.	...	...	0826	...	...	|	...	|	0856	...	0926	...	...	|	...	|	0956	...	1026	...	...	|	...
	Romont 568 d.	...	...	0844	...	...	|	...	|	|	...	0944	...	...	|	...	|	|	...	1044	...	...	|	...
	Palézieux d.	...	...	0900	...	...	|	...	|	|	...	1000	...	...	|	...	|	|	...	1100	...	...	|	...
36	Solothurn d.	...	...	|	...	...	0758	...	0826	|	...	|	...	...	0858	...	0926	|	...	|	...	...	0958	...
61	**Biel/Bienne** a.	...	...	|	...	...	0813	...	0843	|	...	|	...	...	0913	...	0943	|	...	|	...	...	1013	...
	Biel/Bienne d.	...	...	|	...	...	0816	...	0845	|	...	|	...	...	0916	...	0945	|	...	|	...	...	1016	...
	Neuchâtel d.	...	...	|	...	...	0834	...	0903	|	*RE*	|	...	...	0934	...	1003	|	*RE*	|	...	...	1034	...
	Yverdon d.	...	...	|	...	...	0853	...	0922	|	**18426**	|	...	...	0953	...	1022	|	**18430**	|	...	...	1053	...
	Lausanne a.	...	...	0916	...	...	|	...	0945	0940		1016	...	...	|	...	1045	1040		1116	...	...	|	...
	Lausanne 570 d.	0851	...	0918	...	...	|	...	...	0942	0951	1018	...	...	|	...	...	1042	1051	1118	...	...	|	...
	Morges 570 d.	0904	...	0928	...	...	0917	...	...	|	1004	1028	...	...	1017	...	...	|	1104	1128	...	...	1117	...
	Nyon 570 d.	0924	...	0944	...	...	|	...	...	|	1024	1044	...	...	|	...	...	|	1124	1144	...	...	|	...
	Genève 570 a.	0940	...	1000	...	...	0945	...	...	1018	1040	1100	...	...	1045	...	...	1118	1140	1200	...	...	1145	...
	Genève Aéroport ✈ 570 a.	...	...	1011	...	...	0954	...	...	1027	...	1111	...	...	1054	...	...	1127	...	1211	...	...	1154	...

A – ①②③④⑦ (also Apr. 19).
D – From/to Delémont (Table **505a**).

k – Not Apr. 20.
r – ⑤⑥ (not Apr. 19).

▽ – Continues as *IR* **2193** (2302 Olten - Zürich).
¶ – Runs as *IC* **841** Bern - Zürich.
⊡ – Kilometres via the high-speed line.

505 ZÜRICH - BIEL / BERN - LAUSANNE - GENÈVE SBB

See panel below main table for other fast trains Zürich - Bern

	IC 1514	IC 712	RE 2816	IR 2516	RE 4814	IR 2364	IC 516	IR 2166	IC 1516	IC 714	RE 2818	IR 2518	RE 4816	IR 2366	IC 518	IR 2168	IC 1518	IC 716	RE 2820	IR 2520	RE 4818	IR 2368	IC 520	IR 2170
	✕	✕		🍷			✕		✕	✕		🍷			✕		✕	✕		🍷			✕	
St Gallen **530** d.	0807	0825	...	...	...	...	...	...	0907	0925	...	...	...	...	...	...	1007	1025	...	...	...	...	...	...
Zürich Flughafen ✈ **530/5** d.	0909	0918	...	...	...	...	...	...	1009	1018	...	...	...	...	...	...	1109	1118	...	...	...	...	...	...
Zürich HB **510** d.	0930	0932	...	...	0938	0953	1003	1006	1030	1032	...	...	1038	1053	1103	1106	1130	1132	...	...	1138	1153	1203	1206
Baden **510** d.	|	|	...	...	|	|	|	1022	|	|	...	...	|	|	|	1122	|	|	...	...	|	|	|	1222
Brugg **510** d.	|	|	...	...	|	|	|	1032	|	|	...	...	|	|	|	1132	|	|	...	...	|	|	|	1232
Lenzburg **510** d.	|	|	...	...	0958	|	|	|	|	|	...	...	1058	|	|	|	|	|	...	...	1158	|	|	|
Aarau **510** d.	|	|	...	...	1005	|	1029	1046	|	|	...	...	1105	|	1129	1146	|	|	...	...	1205	|	1229	1246
Olten a.	1000	|	...	...	...	1027	1038	1057	1100	|	...	...	...	1127	1138	1157	1200	|	...	...	...	1227	1238	1257
Olten d.	1002	|	1006	...	...	1036	1040	1059	1102	|	1106	...	...	1136	1140	1159	1202	|	1206	...	...	1236	1240	1259
Langenthal d.	|	|	1018	...	...	1048	|	|	|	|	1118	...	...	1148	|	|	|	|	1218	...	...	1248	|	|
Burgdorf d.	|	|	1038	...	...	1107	|	|	|	|	1138	...	...	1207	|	|	|	|	1238	...	...	1307	|	|
Luzern **565** d.	|	|	|	1000	...	|	|	|	|	|	|	1100	...	|	|	|	|	|	|	1200	...	|	|	|
Bern a.	|	1028	1053	1100	...	1121	|	1126	|	1128	1153	1200	...	1221	|	1226	|	1228	1253	1300	...	1321	|	1326
Bern **568** d.	|	1034	▬	1104	...	...	|	...	|	1134	▬	1204	...	...	|	...	|	1234	▬	1304	...	...	|	...
Fribourg **568** d.	|	1056	...	1126	...	...	|	...	|	1156	...	1226	...	...	|	...	|	1256	...	1326	...	...	|	...
Romont **568** d.	|	|	...	1144	...	...	|	...	|	|	...	1244	...	...	|	...	|	|	...	1344	...	...	|	...
Palézieux d.	|	|	...	1200	...	...	|	...	|	|	...	1300	...	...	|	...	|	|	...	1400	...	...	|	...
Solothurn d.	1026	|	...	|	...	...	1058	...	1126	|	...	|	...	...	1158	...	1226	|	...	|	...	...	1258	...
Biel / Bienne a.	1043	|	...	|	...	...	1113	...	1143	|	...	|	...	...	1213	...	1243	|	...	|	...	...	1313	...
Biel / Bienne d.	1045	|	...	|	...	...	1116	...	1145	|	...	|	...	...	1216	...	1245	|	...	|	...	...	1316	...
Neuchâtel d.	1103	|	*RE*	|	...	...	1134	...	1203	|	*RE*	|	...	...	1234	...	1303	|	*RE*	|	...	...	1334	...
Yverdon d.	1122	|	**18434**	|	...	...	1153	...	1222	|	**18438**	|	...	...	1253	...	1322	|	**18442**	|	...	...	1353	...
Lausanne a.	1145	1140		1216	...	...	|	...	1245	1240		1316	...	...	|	...	1345	1340		1416	...	...	|	...
Lausanne **570** d.	...	1142	1151	1218	...	...	|	...	...	1242	1251	1318	...	...	|	...	...	1342	1351	1418	...	...	|	...
Morges **570** d.	...	|	1204	1228	...	...	1217	...	...	|	1304	1328	...	...	1317	...	...	|	1404	1428	...	...	1417	...
Nyon **570** d.	...	|	1224	1244	...	...	|	...	...	|	1324	1344	...	...	|	...	...	|	1424	1444	...	...	|	...
Genève **570** a.	...	1218	1240	1300	...	...	1245	...	...	1318	1340	1400	...	...	1347	...	...	1418	1440	1500	...	...	1445	...
Genève Aéroport ✈ **570** a.	...	1227	...	1311	...	...	1254	...	...	1327	...	1411	...	...	1356	...	...	1427	...	1511	...	...	1454	...

	IC 1520	IC 718	RE 2822	IR 2522	RE 4820	IR 2370	IC 522	IR 2172	IC 1522	IC 720	RE 2824	IR 2524	RE 4822	IR 2372	IC 524	IR 2174	IC 1524	IC 722	RE 2826	IR 2526	RE 4824	IR 2374	IC 526	IR 2176
	✕	✕		🍷			✕		✕	✕		🍷			✕		✕	✕		🍷			✕	
St Gallen **530** d.	1107	1125	...	...	...	...	...	...	1207	1225	...	...	...	...	...	...	1307	1325	...	...	...	...	...	...
Zürich Flughafen ✈ **530/5** d.	1209	1218	...	...	...	...	...	...	1309	1318	...	...	...	...	...	...	1409	1418	...	...	...	...	...	...
Zürich HB **510** d.	1230	1232	...	...	1238	1253	1303	1306	1330	1332	...	...	1338	1353	1403	1406	1430	1432	...	...	1438	1453	1503	1506
Baden **510** d.	|	|	...	...	|	|	|	1322	|	|	...	...	|	|	|	1422	|	|	...	...	|	|	|	1522
Brugg **510** d.	|	|	...	...	|	|	|	1332	|	|	...	...	|	|	|	1432	|	|	...	...	|	|	|	1532
Lenzburg **510** d.	|	|	...	...	1258	|	|	|	|	|	...	...	1358	|	|	|	|	|	...	...	1458	|	|	|
Aarau **510** d.	|	|	...	...	1305	|	1329	1346	|	|	...	...	1405	|	1429	1446	|	|	...	...	1505	|	1529	1546
Olten a.	1300	|	...	...	...	1327	1338	1357	1400	|	...	...	...	1427	1438	1457	1500	|	...	...	...	1527	1538	1557
Olten d.	1302	|	1306	...	...	1336	1340	1359	1402	|	1406	...	...	1436	1440	1459	1502	|	1506	...	...	1536	1540	1559
Langenthal d.	|	|	1318	...	...	1348	|	|	|	|	1418	...	...	1448	|	|	|	|	1518	...	...	1548	|	|
Burgdorf d.	|	|	1338	...	...	1407	|	|	|	|	1438	...	...	1507	|	|	|	|	1538	...	...	1607	|	|
Luzern **565** d.	|	|	|	1300	...	|	|	|	|	|	|	1400	...	|	|	|	|	|	|	1500	...	|	|	|
Bern a.	|	1328	1353	1400	...	1421	|	1426	|	1428	1453	1500	...	1521	|	1526	|	1528	1553	1600	...	1621	|	1626
Bern **568** d.	|	1334	▬	1404	...	...	|	...	|	1434	▬	1504	...	...	|	...	|	1534	▬	1604	...	...	|	...
Fribourg **568** d.	|	1356	...	1426	...	...	|	...	|	1456	...	1526	...	...	|	...	|	1556	...	1626	...	...	|	...
Romont **568** d.	|	|	...	1444	...	...	|	...	|	|	...	1544	...	...	|	...	|	|	...	1644	...	...	|	...
Palézieux d.	|	|	...	1500	...	...	|	...	|	|	...	1600	...	...	|	...	|	|	...	1700	...	...	|	...
Solothurn d.	1326	|	...	|	...	...	1358	...	1426	|	...	|	...	...	1458	...	1526	|	...	|	...	...	1558	...
Biel / Bienne a.	1343	|	...	|	...	...	1413	...	1443	|	...	|	...	...	1513	...	1543	|	...	|	...	...	1613	...
Biel / Bienne d.	1345	|	...	|	...	...	1416	...	1445	|	...	|	...	...	1516	...	1545	|	...	|	...	...	1616	...
Neuchâtel d.	1403	|	*RE*	|	...	...	1434	...	1503	|	*RE*	|	...	...	1534	...	1603	|	*RE*	|	...	...	1634	...
Yverdon d.	1422	|	**18446**	|	...	...	1453	...	1522	|	**18450**	|	...	...	1553	...	1622	|	**18454**	|	...	...	1653	...
Lausanne a.	1445	1440		1516	...	...	|	...	1545	1540		1616	...	...	|	...	1645	1640		1716	...	...	|	...
Lausanne **570** d.	...	1442	1451	1518	...	...	|	...	...	1542	1551	1618	...	...	|	...	...	1642	1651	1718	...	...	|	...
Morges **570** d.	...	|	1504	1528	...	...	1517	...	...	|	1604	1628	...	...	1617	...	...	|	1704	1728	...	...	1717	...
Nyon **570** d.	...	|	1524	1544	...	...	|	...	...	|	1624	1644	...	...	|	...	...	|	1724	1744	...	...	|	...
Genève **570** a.	...	1518	1540	1600	...	...	1545	...	...	1618	1640	1700	...	...	1645	...	...	1718	1740	1800	...	...	1745	...
Genève Aéroport ✈ **570** a.	...	1527	...	1611	...	...	1554	...	...	1627	...	1711	...	...	1654	...	...	1727	...	1811	...	...	1754	...

	IC 1526	IC 724	RE 2828	IR 2528	RE 4826	IR 2376	IC 528	IR 2178	IC 1528	IC 726	RE 2830	IR 2530	RE 4828	IR 2378	IC 530	IR 2180	IC 1530	IC 728	RE 2832	IR 2532	RE 4830	IR 2380	IC 532	IR 2182
	✕	✕		🍷			✕		✕	✕		🍷			✕		✕	✕					✕	
St Gallen **530** d.	1407	1425	...	...	...	...	...	...	1507	1525	...	...	...	...	...	...	1607	1625	...	...	...	...	...	...
Zürich Flughafen ✈ **530/5** d.	1509	1518	...	...	...	...	...	...	1609	1618	...	...	...	...	...	...	1709	1718	...	...	...	...	...	...
Zürich HB **510** d.	1530	1532	...	...	1538	1553	1603	1606	1630	1632	...	...	1638	1653	1703	1706	1730	1732	...	...	1738	1753	1803	1806
Baden **510** d.	|	|	...	...	|	|	|	1622	|	|	...	...	|	|	|	1722	|	|	...	...	|	|	|	1822
Brugg **510** d.	|	|	...	...	|	|	|	1632	|	|	...	...	|	|	|	1732	|	|	...	...	|	|	|	1832
Lenzburg **510** d.	|	|	...	...	1558	|	|	|	|	|	...	...	1658	|	|	|	|	|	...	...	1758	|	|	|
Aarau **510** d.	|	|	...	...	1605	|	1629	1646	|	|	...	...	1705	|	1729	1746	|	|	...	...	1805	|	1829	1846
Olten a.	1600	|	...	...	...	1627	1638	1657	1700	|	...	...	...	1727	1738	1757	1800	|	...	...	...	1827	1838	1857
Olten d.	1602	|	1606	...	...	1636	1640	1659	1702	|	1706	...	...	1736	1740	1759	1802	|	1806	...	...	1836	1840	1859
Langenthal d.	|	|	1618	...	...	1648	|	|	|	|	1718	...	...	1748	|	|	|	|	1818	...	...	1848	|	|
Burgdorf d.	|	|	1638	...	...	1707	|	|	|	|	1738	...	...	1807	|	|	|	|	1838	...	...	1907	|	|
Luzern **565** d.	|	|	|	1600	...	|	|	|	|	|	|	1700	...	|	|	|	|	|	|	1800	...	|	|	|
Bern a.	|	1628	1653	1700	...	1721	|	1726	|	1728	1753	1800	...	1821	|	1826	|	1828	1853	1900	...	1921	|	1926
Bern **568** d.	|	1634	▬	1704	...	...	|	...	|	1734	▬	1804	...	...	|	...	|	1834	▬	1904	...	...	|	...
Fribourg **568** d.	|	1656	...	1726	...	...	|	...	|	1756	...	1826	...	...	|	...	|	1856	...	1926	...	...	|	...
Romont **568** d.	|	|	...	1744	...	...	|	...	|	|	...	1844	...	...	|	...	|	|	...	1944	...	...	|	...
Palézieux d.	|	|	...	1800	...	...	|	...	|	|	...	1900	...	...	|	...	|	|	...	2000	...	...	|	...
Solothurn d.	1626	|	...	|	...	...	1658	...	1726	|	...	|	...	...	1758	...	1826	|	...	|	...	...	1858	...
Biel / Bienne a.	1643	|	...	|	...	...	1713	...	1743	|	...	|	...	...	1813	...	1843	|	...	|	...	...	1913	...
Biel / Bienne d.	1645	|	...	|	...	...	1716	...	1745	|	...	|	...	...	1816	...	1845	|	...	|	...	...	1916	...
Neuchâtel d.	1703	|	*RE*	|	...	...	1734	...	1803	|	*RE*	|	...	...	1834	...	1903	|	*RE*	|	...	...	1934	...
Yverdon d.	1722	|	**18458**	|	...	...	1753	...	1822	|	**18462**	|	...	...	1853	...	1922	|	**18466**	|	...	...	1953	...
Lausanne a.	1745	1740		1816	...	...	|	...	1845	1840		1916	...	...	|	...	1945	1940		2016	...	...	|	...
Lausanne **570** d.	...	1742	1751	1818	...	...	|	...	...	1842	1851	1918	...	...	|	...	...	1942	1951	2018	...	...	|	...
Morges **570** d.	...	|	1804	1828	...	...	1817	...	...	|	1904	1928	...	...	1917	...	...	|	2004	2028	...	...	2017	...
Nyon **570** d.	...	|	1824	1844	...	...	|	...	...	|	1924	1944	...	...	|	...	...	|	2024	2044	...	...	|	...
Genève **570** a.	...	1818	1840	1900	...	...	1845	...	...	1918	1940	2000	...	...	1945	...	...	2018	2040	2100	...	...	2045	...
Genève Aéroport ✈ **570** a.	...	1827	...	1911	...	...	1854	...	...	1927	...	2011	...	...	1954	...	...	2027	...	2111	...	...	2054	...

OTHER NON-STOP TRAINS ZÜRICH - BERN. See Table **560** for origin and destination.

	IC 804	IC 1408	IC 806	IC 1410	IC 808	IC 810	IC 812	IC 814	IC 816	IC 818	IC 820	IC 822	IC 824	IC 826	IC 828	IC 830	IC 832	IC 834						
	✕	Ⓐ	⊗	Ⓐ 🍷	✕	⊗	✕	✕	✕	⊗	✕	⊗	✕	⊗	✕	✕	✕	⊗						
Zürich HB d.	0602	0649	0702	0749	0802	0902	1002	1102	1202	1302	1402	1502	1602	1702	1802	1902	2002	2102	...	...	...	...	...	...
Bern a.	0658	0750	0758	0850	0858	0958	1058	1158	1258	1358	1458	1558	1658	1758	1858	1958	2058	2158	...	...	...	...	...	...

SBB ZÜRICH - BIEL / BERN - LAUSANNE - GENÈVE 505

See panel on page 264 for other fast trains Zürich - Bern

	IC 1532	IC 730	RE 2834	IR 2534	RE 4832	IR 2382	IC 534	IR 2184	IC 1534	IC 732	RE 4834	RE 2836	IR 2536	IR 2384	IC 536	IR 2186	IC 1536	IC 734	IC 734	IC 734	RE 4836	RE 2838	IR 2538	IR 2386
				⑤⑥															⑤⑥	†				
	✕	✕		r			✕		✕	✕					✕		✕	✕	r✕	✕				
St Gallen **530** d.	1707	1725	...	...	...	...	...	...	1807	1825	...	...	...	...	...	...	1907	1925	1925	1925	...	...	...	...
Zürich Flughafen ✈ **530/5** d.	1809	1818	...	...	...	...	...	...	1909	1918	...	...	...	...	...	...	2009	2018	2018	2018	...	...	...	...
Zürich HB **510** d.	1830	1832	...	...	1838	1853	1903	1906	1930	1932	1938	...	...	1953	2003	2006	2030	2032	2032	2032	2038	...	...	2053
Baden **510** d.	|	|	...	...	|	|	|	1922	|	|	|	...	...	|	|	2022	|	|	|	|	|	...	...	|
Brugg **510** d.	|	|	...	...	|	|	|	1932	|	|	|	...	...	|	|	2032	|	|	|	|	|	...	...	|
Lenzburg **510** d.	|	|	...	...	1858	|	|	|	|	|	1958	...	...	|	|	|	|	|	|	|	2058	...	...	|
Aarau **510** d.	|	|	...	...	1905	|	1929	1946	|	|	2005	...	...	|	2029	2046	|	|	|	|	2105	...	...	|
Olten a.	1900	|	...	...	▬	1927	1938	1957	2000	|	▬	...	...	2027	2038	2057	2100	|	|	|	▬	...	...	2127
Olten d.	1902	|	1906	...	*IR*	1936	1940	1959	2002	|	...	2006	...	2036	2040	2059	2102	|	|	|	...	2106	...	2136
Langenthal d.	|	|	1918	...	**2534**	1948	|	|	|	|	...	2018	...	2048	|	|	|	|	|	|	...	2118	...	2148
Burgdorf d.	|	|	1938	...	**A**	2007	|	|	|	|	...	2038	...	2107	|	|	|	|	|	|	...	2138	...	2209
Luzern **565** d.	|	|	|	1900	1900	|	|	|	|	|	...	|	2000	|	|	|	|	|	|	|	...	|	2100	|
Bern a.	|	1928	1953	2000	2000	2021	|	2026	|	2028	...	2053	2100	2121	|	2126	|	2128	2128	2128	...	2153	2200	2226
Bern **568** d.	|	1934	▬	2004	2004	...	|	...	|	2034	...	▬	2104	...	|	▬	|	2134	2134	2134	...	▬	2204	...
Fribourg **568** d.	|	1956	...	2026	2026	...	|	...	|	2056	...	...	2126	...	|	...	|	2156	2156	2156	...	...	2226	...
Romont **568** d.	|	|	...	2044	2044	...	|	...	|	|	...	...	2144	...	|	...	|	|	|	|	...	...	2244	...
Palézieux d.	|	|	...	2100	2100	...	|	...	|	|	...	...	2200	...	|	...	|	|	|	|	...	...	2300	...
Solothurn d.	1926	|	...	|	|	...	1958	...	2026	|	...	...	|	...	2058	...	2126	|	|	|	...	...	|	...
Biel / Bienne a.	1943	|	...	|	|	...	2013	...	2043	|	...	...	|	...	2113	...	2143	|	|	|	...	...	|	...
Biel / Bienne d.	1945	|	...	|	|	...	2016	...	2045	|	...	...	|	...	2116	*IR*	2145	|	|	|	...	...	|	...
Neuchâtel d.	2003	|	*RE*	|	|	...	2034	...	2103	|	*RE*	*RE*	|	...	2134	**1836**	2203	|	|	|	*EC*	*RE*	|	...
Yverdon d.	2022	|	**18474**	|	|	...	2053	...	2122	|	**18480**	**18480**	|	...	2153	⑤⑥	2222	|	|	|	**42**	**18484**	|	...
Lausanne a.	2045	2040		2116	2116	...	|	...	2145	2140	**H**	**J**	2216	...	|	**r**	2245	2240	2240	2240			2316	...
Lausanne **570** d.	...	2042	2051	2118	2118	...	|	...	...	...	2151	2158	...	...	|	2221	...	...	2242	2242	2245	2251	...	...
Morges **570** d.	...	|	2104	2128	2133	...	2117	...	...	...	2204	2211	...	...	2217	2234	...	...	|	|	|	2304	...	...
Nyon **570** d.	...	|	2124	2144	2158	...	|	...	...	...	2223	2231	...	...	2232	2256	...	...	|	|	|	2325	...	...
Genève **570** a.	...	2118	2140	2200	2216	...	2145	...	...	...	2239	2246	...	...	2251	2313	...	...	2318	2320	2324	2348	...	...
Genève Aéroport ✈ **570** a.	...	2127	...	2211	...	...	2154	...	...	...	2249	2254	...	...	2300	...	...	...	2327	...	...	2356	...	...

	IR 1838	IC 538	IR 2188	IC 1538	IC 736	RE 4838	IC 836	IR 2540	IR 2388	IC 540	IR 2190	IC 738	RE 4840	IC 838	IR 2502	IR 2390	IC 542	IC 542	IR 2192	IC 740	RE 4842	IR 2194	IR 2392	IC 844
															B			⑤⑥					⑥⑦	⑥⑦
				✕	✕		R							R				r					k	k
St Gallen **530** d.	...	...	...	2007	...	...	...	...	...	...	...	...	...	...	...	...	...	...	...	...	...	...	...	...
Zürich Flughafen ✈ **530/5** d.	...	...	...	2109	...	...	2146	...	...	...	...	...	...	2246	...	...	...	...	...	...	...	...	...	...
Zürich HB **510** d.	...	2103	2106	2130	2132	2138	2202	...	...	2203	2206	2232	2238	2302	...	...	2303	2303	2306	2332	2338	0006	...	0102
Baden **510** d.	...	|	2122	|	|	|	|	...	...	|	2222	|	|	|	...	...	|	|	2322	|	|	0022	...	|
Brugg **510** d.	...	|	2132	|	|	|	|	...	...	|	2232	|	|	|	...	...	|	|	2332	|	|	0030	...	|
Lenzburg **510** d.	...	|	|	|	|	2158	|	...	...	|	|	|	2258	|	...	...	|	|	|	|	2358	...	...	|
Aarau **510** d.	...	2129	2146	|	|	2205	|	...	...	2229	2246	|	2305	|	...	...	2329	2329	2346	|	0005	...	...	|
Olten a.	...	2138	2157	2200	|	...	2232	...	...	2238	2257	2302	...	2332	...	...	2338	2338	2357	0002	...	...	...	0132
Olten d.	...	2140	2159	2202	|	...	2235	...	2237	2240	▬	2304	...	2335	...	2337	2340	2340	▬	0004	...	...	0037	0135
Langenthal d.	...	|	|	|	|	...	|	...	2249	|	...	|	...	|	...	2349	|	|	...	|	...	...	0049	|
Burgdorf d.	...	|	|	|	|	...	|	...	2309	|	...	|	...	|	...	0009	|	|	...	|	...	...	0110	|
Luzern **565** d.	...	|	|	|	|	...	|	2200	|	|	...	|	...	|	...	|	|	|	...	|	...	...	|	|
Bern a.	...	|	2226	|	2228	...	2302	2300	2326	|	...	2331	...	0002	...	0023	|	|	...	0031	...	...	0124	0204
Bern **568** d.	...	|	...	|	2234	...	...	2308	...	|	...	▬	...	...	0008	...	|	|	...	▬	...	...	...	...
Fribourg **568** d.	...	|	...	|	2255	...	...	2330	...	|	...	...	...	...	0032	...	|	|	...	...	...	...	...	...
Romont **568** d.	...	|	...	|	▬	...	...	2348	...	|	...	...	...	...	0050	...	|	|	...	...	...	...	...	...
Palézieux d.	...	|	...	|	...	...	...	0004	...	|	...	...	...	...	0106	...	|	|	...	...	...	...	...	...
Solothurn d.	...	2158	...	2226	...	...	...	|	...	2257	...	...	...	...	|	...	0005	0005	...	...	...	...	...	...
Biel / Bienne a.	...	2213	...	2243	...	...	...	|	...	2314	...	...	...	...	|	...	0022	0022	...	...	...	...	...	...
Biel / Bienne d.	...	...	...	2245	*RE*	...	...	|	...	2316	*IR*	*RE*	...	...	|	...	...	0025	*RE*	*RE*	...	...	...	...
Neuchâtel d.	...	...	...	2303	**18490**	...	...	|	...	2334	**1840**	**18494**	...	...	|	...	...	0042	**18496**	**18498**	...	...	...	...
Yverdon d.	...	...	...	2322	⑤⑥	...	...	|	...	2353	⑥⑦	⑥⑦	...	...	|	...	...	0102	⑥⑦	⑥⑦	...	...	...	...
Lausanne a.	...	...	...	2345	**r**	...	...	0020	...	0016	**k**	**k**	...	...	0122	...	...	0125	**k**	**k**	...	...	...	...
Lausanne **570** d.	2321	...	...	...	2351	...	...	...	...	...	0025	0051	...	...	...	...	...	...	0131	0251	...	...	...	...
Morges **570** d.	2333	...	...	...	0004	...	...	...	...	...	0037	0104	...	...	...	...	...	...	0144	0304	...	...	...	...
Nyon **570** d.	2357	...	...	...	0024	...	...	...	...	...	0055	0124	...	...	...	...	...	...	0204	0324	...	...	...	...
Genève **570** a.	0016	...	...	...	0040	...	...	...	...	...	0111	0140	...	...	...	...	...	...	0220	0340	...	...	...	...
Genève Aéroport ✈ **570** a.	...	...	...	...	0049	...	...	...	...	...	...	...	...	...	...	...	...	...	...	...	...	...	...	...

A – ①②③④⑦ (also Apr. 19).
B – ①⑥⑦.
H – ⑤⑥ to Aug. 24 (not Apr. 19); daily from Aug. 30.
J – ①②③④⑦ to Aug. 29 (also Apr. 19).
R – From Romanshorn (Table **535**).

k – Not Apr. 20.
r – ⑤⑥ (not Apr. 19).

SBB BIEL - BASEL 505a

km		IC 1545	RE 4148			IC 1607		RE 18164	IC 1609		RE 18166	IC 1611			RE 18194	IC 1639		RE 18196	IC 1641		RE 18198			
			⑥⑦																					
		L	k					D	✕		D	✕	and at		D			D						
0	**Biel / Bienne** **515** d.	0019	0121	...	...	0549	...	0619	0649	...	0719	0749	the same	...	2119	2149	...	2219	2249	...	2319	...	...	...
24	Moutier **515** d.	0039	0138	...	...	0608	...	0638	0708	...	0738	0808	minutes	...	2138	2208	...	2238	2308	...	2338	...	...	...
	Porrentruy **515** d.	|	|	...	0508	|	0610	|	|	0710	|	|	past each	2110	|	|	2210	|	|	2310	|	...	...	...
35	Delémont **515** a.	0048	0148	...	0539	0618	0639	0648	0718	0739	0748	0818	hour until	2139	2148	2218	2239	2248	2318	2339	2348	...	...	...
	Delémont d.	...	...	...	0543	0623	0643	...	0723	0743	...	0823		2143	...	2223	2243	...	2323	2343	...	...	...	...
74	**Basel** a.	...	...	...	0623	0653	0723	...	0753	0823	...	0853		2223	...	2253	2323	...	2353	0028	...	...	...	...

			RE 18159		IC 1606	RE 18161		IC 1608	RE 18163		IC 1610	RE 18165			IC 1638	RE 18193		IC 1640			IC 1642	RE 4143		
																						⑤⑥		
					G	D		✕	D		✕	D		and at		D						r		
Basel d.	0042	...	...	0457	...	...	0537	0603	...	0637	0703	...	0737	the same	2103	...	2137	2203	...	2237	2303	...	...	2342
Delémont a.	0122	...	...	0537	...	...	0617	0637	...	0717	0737	...	0817	minutes	2137	...	2217	2237	...	2317	2337	...	...	0022
Delémont **515** d.	...	...	0512	...	0542	0612	0621	0642	0712	0721	0742	0812	0821	past each	2142	2212	2221	2242	...	2321	...	2342	...	0023
Porrentruy **515** a.	...	...	|	...	|	|	0650	|	|	0750	|	|	0850	hour until	|	|	2250	|	...	2350	...	|	...	0052
Moutier **515** d.	...	...	0522	...	0552	0622	...	0652	0722	...	0752	0822	...		2152	2222	...	2252	...	...	...	2354	...	...
Biel / Bienne **515** d.	...	...	0541	...	0610	0641	...	0710	0741	...	0810	0841	...		2210	2241	...	2310	...	...	...	0013	...	...

D – To / from Delle (Table **515**).
G – To Genève Aéroport (Table **505**).
L – From Lausanne (Table **505**).

k – Not Apr. 20.
r – Not Apr. 19.

506 SWISS LAKES

June 29 - September 1 — BRIENZERSEE — Operator: BLS

	⑦	T			T		A	⑥			⑦	T			T		A	⑥
0907	1007	1107	1207	1307	1407	1507	1607	1907	d. Interlaken Ost ... a.	1153	1253	1353	1453	1553	1653	1753	1835	2153
0925	1025	1125	1225	1325	1425	1525	|	1925	d. Bönigen ... d.	1135	1235	1335	1435	1535	1635	1735		2135
0954	1046	1154	1246	1354	1454	1546	1639	1954	d. Iseltwald ... d.	1117	1208	1308	1408	1517	1608	1708	1801	2108
1009	1109	1209	1309	1409	1509	1609	...	2009	d. Giessbach ... d.	1051	1151	1251	1351	1451	1551	1651	...	2051
1020	1120	1220	1320	1420	1520	1620	...	2020	a. Brienz ... d.	1040	1140	1240	1340	1440	1540	1640	...	2040

June 16 - September 1 — LAC LÉMAN — Operator: CGN

⚒					S	©S		S	S		S		S		⚒			S			©S	S	S			S	S	
...	...	...	...	...	1015	1225	...	1410	1510	...	1900	...	...	d. Genève ⊗ ... a.	...	...	...	1400	...	...	1500	1745	1830	...	...	...	2210	...
...	...	...	...	...	1101	|	...	1455	|	...	1935	...	...	d. Coppet ... d.	...	...	...	1310	...	...	|	1655	|	...	...	...	2110	...
...	...	...	...	...	1135	|	...	1525	|	...	|	...	...	d. Nyon ... d.	...	...	...	|	...	...	|	1625	1710	...	...	...	|	...
...	...	...	...	...	1205	1340	...	1605	1638	...	2032	...	2037	d. Yvoire ... d.	...	...	...	1240	...	...	1345	1555	1645	...	...	2025	2035	...
...	...	...	...	...	|	▬	...	|	▬	...	▬	...	|	d. Thonon-les-Bains ... d.	...	...	...	|	...	...	▬	|	▬	...	...	|	▬	2316
0700	0820	1005	1145	1315	|	1445	1615	|	1800	1900	2045	2200	|	d. Évian-les-Bains ... d.	0655	0815	1000	|	1135	1305	1435	|	1605	1750	1915	|	2035	2256
|	|	|	|	|	1320	|	|	1720	|	|	|	|	2153	d. Morges ... d.	|	|	|	1124	|	|	|	1439	|	|	|	1925	...	|
0735	0855	1040	1220	1350	1354	1520	1650	1757	1835	1955	2120	2220	2227	a. Lausanne-Ouchy ... d.	0620	0740	0925	1050	1100	1230	1400	1405	1530	1715	1840	1845	2000	2235

S		S	S	S	S	S	S	S	S		S	S		S	S	S	S	S	S	S
0920	0930	1100	1230	...	1420	1530	...	1805	...	d. Lausanne-Ouchy ... a.	1040	1220	1352	...	1520	...	1748	1833	...	2025
|	1032	1205	|	1405	1527	|	1605	1857	1900	d. Vevey-Marché ... d.	0955	1135	1251	1400	1435	1600	1645	1745	1850	|
|	1037	1210	|	1410	|	|	1610	|	|	d. Vevey-La Tour ... d.	|	|	|	|	|	|	|	|	|	|
|	1101	1240	|	1440	1550	|	1640	1917	|	d. Montreux ... d.	0933	1113	1229	|	1415	|	1620	1720	1830	1920
|	1108	1247	|	1447	|	|	1647	...	|	d. Territet ... d.	|	|	|	|	|	|	|	|	|	...
|	1116	1255	|	1455	1600	|	1655	...	|	d. Château-de-Chillon ... d.	|	1100	|	|	1403	|	1605	1705	1815	...
|	1124	1303	|	1503	...	|	1703	...	|	d. Villeneuve ... d.	|	1050	|	|	1355	|	...	1657	1806	...
1010	|	|	1320	|	...	1620	|	...	|	d. St Gingolph ... d.	|	|	|	1338	|	1538	...	|	1740	...
1025	1145	1325	1333	1525	...	1635	1725	...	1920	d. Bouveret ... d.	0910	1025	|	1325	1333	1525	...	1635	1725	...
...	1200	1338	...	1538	....	...	1738	...	...	a. St Gingolph ... d.	...	1010	1200	...	1320	...	...	1620	...	...

May 25 - September 8 — VIERWALDSTÄTTERSEE — Operator: SGV

		S				⚒S	S						N							S			⚒S	S				N
0812	...	0912	1012	1112	...	1212	1312	1412	1512	1612	1712	1812	1912	d. Luzern (Bahnhofquai) .. a.	1047	1147	1247	1347	...	1447	1547	1647	1747	1847	1903	1947	2047	2147
0822	...	0922	1022	1122	...	1222	1322	1422	1522	1622	1722	1822	1922	d. Verkehrshaus Lido .... d.	1035	|	1235	1333	...	1435	1535	1635	1735	1835	|	1935	2035	2135
|	...	|	|	|	...	|	|	|	|	|	|	|	|	d. Kehrsiten-Bürgenstock d.	|	1120	|	|	...	|	|	|	|	|	1834	|	|	2112
0843	...	0943	1043	1143	...	1243	1343	1443	1543	1643	1743	1843	1943	d. Hertenstein ... d.	1014	|	1214	1314	...	1414	1514	1614	1714	1814	|	1914	2014	|
0853	...	0953	1053	1153	...	1253	1353	1453	1553	1653	1753	1853	1953	d. Weggis ... d.	1005	1105	1205	1305	...	1405	1505	1605	1705	1805	|	1905	2005	2057
0910	...	1010	1110	1210	...	1310	1410	1510	1610	1710	1809	1910	2009	d. Vitznau ... d.	0949	1049	1149	1249	...	1349	1449	1549	1649	1749	1810	1849	1949	|
0927	...	1027	1127	1227	...	1327	1427	1527	1627	1800	...	1926	2031	d. Beckenried ... d.	...	1000	1132	1232	...	1332	1432	1532	1632	1732	...	1832	1932	2032
0945	...	1045	1145	1245	...	1345	1445	1545	1645	1817	...	...	...	d. Gersau ... d.	...	0942	1114	1214	...	1314	1414	1514	1614	1714	...	1814	...	...
1002	...	1102	1202	1302	...	1402	1502	1602	1702	1834	...	...	...	d. Treib ... d.	...	0927	1057	1157	...	1257	1357	1457	1557	1657	...	1757	...	...
1011	1020	1111	1211	1311	1320	1411	1511	1611	1711	1841	...	...	...	d. Brunnen ... d.	...	0919	1049	1149	1220	1249	1349	1449	1549	1649	...	1749	...	...
1021	1031	1121	1221	1321	1331	1421	1521	1621	1721	...	...	...	...	d. Rütli ... d.	...	...	1036	1136	|	1236	1336	1436	1536	1636	...	1736	...	...
1032	|	|	-|	1332	|	|	1532	|	1732	...	...	...	...	d. Sisikon ... d.	...	...	1024	|	1202	1224	|	|	|	|	...	|	...	...
|	|	|	|	|	|	|	|	|	|	...	...	...	...	d. Tellsplatte ... ▲d.	...	...	|	|	|	|	|	|	|	|	...	|	...	...
|	1047	1135	1235	|	1347	1435	|	1635	1744	...	...	...	...	d. Bauen ... d.	...	...	1006	1121	|	|	1321	1421	1521	1621	...	1724	...	...
|	1055	1143	1243	|	1355	1443	|	1643	1751	...	...	...	...	d. Isleten-Isenthal ... d.	...	...	0958	1112	1146	|	1312	1412	1512	1612	...	|	...	...
1055	1107	1155	1255	1355	1420	1455	1555	1655	1803	...	...	...	...	a. Flüelen ... d.	...	...	0946	1100	1119	1200	1300	1400	1500	1600	...	1700	...	...

					S				S								S					S		
0838	0938	1000	1038	1150	1200	1238	1338	1400	1438	1638	1600	d. Luzern (Bahnhofquai) ... a.	1153	1028	1245	1328	1345	1358	1503	1547	1625	1745	1802	1847
|	0948	1010	1048	1200	1210	1248	1348	1410	1448	1648	1610	d. Verkehrshaus Lido ... d.	|	1016	|	1316	1335	|	1451	|	1614	|	1750	|
|	|	1053	|	|	1253	|	|	1453	|	|	1704	a. Küssnacht am Rigi ... d.	1055	|	|	|	1255	|	|	1455	|	|	1706	|
|	|	...	1123	|	...	|	|	...	1513	|	...	d. Kehrsiten-Bürgenstock ... d.	...	|	1154	|	...	|	|	...	1551	|	...	|
|	|	...	1131	|	...	|	1409	...	1523	1709	...	d. Kehrsiten Dorf ... d.	...	|	1145	|	...	|	1430	...	1542	|	...	|
|	1016	...	1146	|	...	|	1424	...	1548	1724	...	d. Hergiswil ... d.	...	|	1130	1247	...	|	1415	...	|	1710	...	|
|	1025	...	|	1226	...	1314	1433	...	1558	1733	...	d. Stansstad ... d.	...	0951	1121	|	...	1326	1406	...	1531	1700	...	|
|	|	...	|	|	...	|	|	...	|	|	...	d. Hergiswil ... d.	...	|	|	|	...	|	|	...	|	|	...	|
0925	1046	...	1210	1250	...	1335	1455	...	1621	1754	...	a. Alpnachstad ... d.	...	0930	1100	1222	...	1305	1345	...	1510	1637	...	1757

June 1 - September 30 — ZÜRICHSEE — Operator: ZSG

	†																			
0930	1030	1115	1130	1230	1330	1430	1530	1630	1730	d. Zürich (Bürkliplatz) ... a.	1325	1425	1525	1625	1725	1825	1855	1925	2025	2155
|	1100	1146	|	1300	|	1500	|	1700	|	d. Erlenbach ... d.	1253	|	1453	|	1653	|	|	1853	|	|
1000	|	|	1200	|	1400	|	1600	|	1800	d. Thalwil ... d.	|	1355	|	1555	|	1755	1825	|	1955	2130
1007	|	|	1207	|	1407	|	1607	|	1807	d. Oberrieden ... d.	|	1346	|	1546	|	1746	1816	|	1946	|
|	1142	1227	|	1342	|	1542	|	1742	1859	d. Wädenswil ... d.	1212	|	1412	|	1612	|	|	1812	|	2034
1120	1225	1315	1315	1425	1520	1625	1720	1825	1946	a. Rapperswil ... d.	1130	1235	1330	1435	1530	1635	1700	1730	1835	1950

May 11 - October 13 — THUNERSEE — Operator: BLS

		⑦L			L			P			X			⑦L					L		P			X
0840	0940	1008	...	1140	1240	...	1340	1440	...	1540	1840	d. Thun ... a.	...	1220	1320	1420	1620	...	1720	...	1750	1820	2015	2120
0851	0951	|	...	1151	1251	...	1351	1451	...	1551	1851	d. Hünibach ... d.	...	1209	1309	1409	1609	...	1709	...	1739	1809	|	2109
|	1003	|	...	1203	1303	...	1403	|	...	1603	1903	d. Oberhofen ... d.	...	1157	1257	1357	1557	...	1657	...	|	1757	1957	2057
|	1016	|	...	1216	1316	...	1416	|	...	1616	1916	d. Gunten ... d.	...	1144	1244	1344	1544	...	1644	...	|	1744	1944	2044
0928	1028	1036	...	1228	1328	...	1428	1528	...	1628	1928	d. Spiez ... d.	...	1134	1234	1334	1534	...	1634	...	1704	1734	1934	2034
0940	1040	|	...	1240	1340	...	1440	1540	...	1640	1940	d. Faulensee ... d.	...	1120	1220	1320	1520	...	1620	...	1650	1720	1920	2020
0955	1055	|	...	1255	1355	...	1455	|	...	1655	1955	d. Merligen ... d.	...	1105	1205	1305	1505	...	1605	...	|	1705	1905	|
1002	1102	1055	...	1302	1402	...	1502	1602	...	1702	2002	d. Beatenbucht ... d.	...	1058	1158	1258	1458	...	1558	...	1633	1658	1858	2003
1049	1149	...	...	1349	1449	...	1549	...	...	1749	...	a. Interlaken West ... d.	...	...	1110	1210	1410	...	1510	...	...	1610	1810	...

A – Round trip to/from Interlaken Ost arrives 1715 / departs 1727.
N – Normally operated by historic steamship ①⑦.
S – Normally operated by historic steamship.
T – Daily. Normally operated by historic steamship from May 18.
U – June 29 - Sept 9.
X – ②–⑥ June 4 - Sept 21; not Aug. 1.
▲ – Landing stage currently closed for re-construction.
⊗ – Genève has landing stages at Mont-Blanc, Jardin-Anglais, Pâquis and Eaux-Vives. Services do not call at all landing stages.

Operators:

BLS – Schifffahrt Berner Oberland: ✆ +41 (0)58 327 48 11. (www.bls.ch)
CGN – Compagnie Générale de Navigation: ✆ +41 (0)848 811 848. (www.cgn.ch)
SGV – Schifffahrtsgesellschaft Vierwaldstättersee: ✆ +41 (0)41 367 67 67. (www.lakelucerne.ch)
ZSG – Zürichsee Schifffahrtsgesellschaft: ✆ +41 (0)44 487 13 33. (www.zsg.ch)

508 FRIBOURG - MURTEN - INS - NEUCHATEL — TPF

km		⚒	⚒			▲			⑤⑥		⑥⑦	⚒	⑦	⚒		▲		
0	**Fribourg** ... d.	0455	0532	0631	0732	and at the	2132	2232	2334	**Neuchâtel** ... **511** d.	...	...	...	0635	0735	and at the	2235	...
22	Murten ... d.	0527	0603	0703	0803	same minutes	2203	2303	0007	Ins ... **511** d.	0037	0547	0647	0647	0747	same minutes	2247	2320
32	Ins ... **511** a.	0538	0612	0712	0812	past each	2212	2312	0018	Murten ... d.	0050	0557	0657	0657	0757	past each	2257	2332
45	**Neuchâtel** ... **511** a.	...	0625	0725	0825	hour until	2225	...	...	**Fribourg** ... a.	0119	0627	0728	0728	0828	hour until	2328	0001

▲ – On Oct. 6 departures from Fribourg at 1032 / 1132 and from Neuchâtel at 0935 / 1035 do not operate Fribourg - Murten and v.v.

Via Lenzburg

km		*IC* 551	*EC* 191	*ICE* 1251	*IC* 559	*IR* 2259	*IR* 2259	*IC* 761	*IC* 1253	*IC* 1255	*IC* 561	*IR* 2261	*ICE* 3	*IC* 563	*IR* 2263	*ICE* 271	*IC* 565	*IR* 2265	*IC* 767	*TGV* 9203	*IC* 553	*IR* 2267	*IC* 769	*IC* 569	*IR* 2269	*IC* 771	*IC* 571
							Ⓐ	Ⓐ	Ⓒ	Ⓐ	Ⓒ									①–⑥	⑦						
			M					⊗	✕	✕	✕		A			B				♦	y						
0	**Basel** SBB d.	0533	0543	0607	0633	0643	0643	0707	0707	0733	0733	0743	0807	0833	0843	0907	0933	0943	1007	1033	1033	1043	1107	1133	1143	1207	1233
14	Liestal d.	|	0554	|	|	0654	0654	|	|	|	|	0754	|	|	0854	|	|	0954	|	|	|	1054	|	|	1154	|	|
50	Aarau **505** d.	|	0623	|	|	0723	0723	|	|	|	|	0823	|	|	0923	|	|	1023	|	|	|	1123	|	|	1223	|	|
59	Lenzburg **505** d.	|	0631	|	|	0731	0731	|	|	|	|	0831	|	|	0931	|	|	1031	|	|	|	1131	|	|	1231	|	|
91	**Zürich** HB **505** a.	0626	0652	0700	0726	0752	0752	0800	0800	0826	0826	0852	0900	0926	0952	1000	1026	1052	1100	1126	1126	1152	1200	1226	1252	1300	1326
	St Gallen **530** a.	...	0805	...	|	...	0905	|	|	|	|	...	...	|	...	|	|	...	...	...	...	...	...	|	...	...	|
	Chur **520** a.	...	...	...	0852	...	...	0922	0922	0952	0952	...	...	1052	...	1122	1152	...	...	...	...	...	...	1352	...	...	1452

	IR 2271	*ICE* 71	*TGV* 9211	*IR* 2273	*IC* 775	*IC* 575	*IR* 2275	*ICE* 73	*TGV* 9213	*IR* 2277	*IR* 2277	*EC* 9	*IC* 579	*IR* 2279	*ICE* 75	*ICE* 1175	*IC* 581	*IR* 2281	*IC* 783	*IC* 583	*IC* 583	*IR* 2283	*ICE* 77	*TGV* 9219	*IR* 2285	*IC* 787
											Ⓐ				①–⑥	⑦z					Ⓑ					
		H△	P					H△	P			H			vH△	H△							H△	P		
Basel SBB d.	1243	1307	1333	1343	1407	1433	1443	1507	1533	1543	1543	1607	1633	1643	1707	1707	1733	1743	1807	1833	1833	1843	1907	1933	1943	2007
Liestal d.	1254	|	|	1354	|	|	1454	|	|	1554	1554	|	|	1654	|	|	|	1754	|	|	|	1854	|	|	1954	|
Aarau **505** d.	1323	|	|	1423	|	|	1523	|	|	1623	1623	|	|	1723	|	|	|	1823	|	|	|	1923	|	|	2023	|
Lenzburg **505** d.	1331	|	|	1431	|	|	1531	|	|	1631	1631	|	|	1731	|	|	|	1831	|	|	|	1931	|	|	2031	|
Zürich HB **505** a.	1352	1400	1426	1452	1500	1526	1552	1600	1626	1652	1652	1700	1726	1752	1800	1800	1826	1852	1900	1926	1926	1952	2000	2026	2052	2100
St Gallen **530** a.	...	|	...	...	...	|	...	...	...	...	1805	...	|	...	|	...	|	2005a	...	...	|	...	...	...	...	...
Chur **520** a.	...	1522	...	...	...	1652	...	...	...	...	...	...	1852	...	1922	...	1952	...	...	...	2052	...	...	...	...	...

	IC 587	*IC* 587	*IC* 1261	*IR* 2287	*ICE* 79	*TGV* 9223	*IR* 2289	*IC* 791	*IR* 2291	*IC* 793	
	①–④	①–⑥	⑦					⑤⑥		⑤⑥	
	f				H△	P		g		g	
Basel SBB d.	2033	2033	2033	2043	2107	2133	2143	2207	2243	2307	...
Liestal d.	|	|	|	2054	|	|	2154	|	2254	|	...
Aarau **505** d.	|	|	|	2123	|	|	2223	|	2323	|	...
Lenzburg **505** d.	|	|	|	2131	|	|	2231	|	2331	|	...
Zürich HB **505** a.	2126	2126	2126	2152	2200	2226	2252	2300	2352	2400	...
St Gallen **530** a.	|	...	...	...	...	...	...	...	...	...	...
Chur **520** a.	2252	...	...	...	...	...	...	...	...	...	...

	IR 2292	*IR* 2296	*IR* 2252	*ICE* 78	*IR* 2254	*IC* 556	*IC* 556	*IC* 760	*IR* 2256	*TGV* 9206
		⑥⑦					⚒			
		n		H△						P
Chur **520** d.	...	...	...	...	...	...	0509	...	...	...
St Gallen **530** a.	...	...	...	...	...	...	|	...	...	...
Zürich HB **505** d.	0008	0108	0508	0600	0608	0634	0634	0700	0708	0734
Lenzburg **505** d.	0028	0128	0528	|	0628	|	|	|	0728	|
Aarau **505** d.	0036	0136	0536	|	0636	|	|	|	0736	|
Liestal d.	0101	0201	0601	|	0701	|	|	|	0801	|
Basel SBB a.	0113	0213	0613	0653	0713	0727	0727	0753	0813	0827

	ICE 76	*IR* 2258	*IR* 2258	*IC* 560	*IC* 764	*IR* 2260	*IR* 2260	*TGV* 9210	*ICE* 74	*IR* 2262	*IC* 564	*EC* 8	*IR* 2264	*IC* 596	*TGV* 9218	*ICE* 72	*IR* 2266	*IC* 568	*IC* 772	*IR* 2268	*TGV* 9222	*ICE* 70	*IR* 2270	*IC* 572	*IC* 776	*IR* 2272
			Ⓐ				Ⓐ																			
	H△							P	H△			H		h	Pj	H△					P	H△				
Chur **520** d.	...	...	...	0709	...	...	...	...	...	...	0909	...	...	...	...	1039	...	1109	...	...	...	1239	...	1309	...	...
St Gallen **530** a.	...	...	0655	|	...	...	0755	...	...	...	|	...	...	...	...	|	...	|	...	...	...	|	...	|	...	...
Zürich HB **505** d.	0800	0808	0808	0834	0900	0908	0908	0934	1000	1008	1034	1100	1108	1134	1134	1200	1208	1234	1300	1308	1334	1400	1408	1434	1500	1508
Lenzburg **505** d.	|	0828	0828	|	|	0928	0928	|	|	1028	|	|	1128	|	|	|	1228	|	|	1328	|	|	1428	|	|	1528
Aarau **505** d.	|	0836	0836	|	|	0936	0936	|	|	1036	|	|	1136	|	|	|	1236	|	|	1336	|	|	1436	|	|	1536
Liestal d.	|	0901	0901	|	|	1001	1001	|	|	1101	|	|	1201	|	|	|	1301	|	|	1401	|	|	1501	|	|	1601
Basel SBB a.	0853	0913	0913	0927	0953	1013	1013	1027	1053	1113	1127	1153	1213	1227	1227	1253	1313	1327	1353	1413	1427	1453	1513	1527	1553	1613

	TGV 9226	*IC* 590	*IC* 778	*IR* 2274	*IC* 576	*ICE* 272	*ICE* 1172	*ICE* 292	*IR* 2276	*IC* 578	*IC* 1256	*IC* 782	*IR* 2278	*IR* 2278	*IC* 580	*ICE* 4	*IR* 2280	*IC* 582	*IR* 2282	*IC* 584	*IC* 1260	*IR* 2284	*IC* 1258	*IC* 790	*IR* 2286	*IC* 792
	Ⓑ	⑥				Ⓐ	⑥	⑦			⑦	①–⑥		Ⓐ									⑤⑥	⑤⑥		⑤⑥
	♦	k				♦	♦	♦								F							g	g		g
Chur **520** d.	...	...	...	...	1509	...	...	...	...	1609	1639	...	...	...	1709	...	...	1809	...	1909	...	...	2009	...	...	...
St Gallen **530** a.	...	...	...	...	|	...	...	...	...	|	|	...	...	1655	|	...	...	|	...	|	...	...	|	...	...	...
Zürich HB **505** d.	1534	1534	1600	1608	1634	1700	1700	1700	1708	1734	1800	1800	1808	1808	1834	1900	1908	1934	2008	2034	2100	2108	2134	2200	2208	2300
Lenzburg **505** d.	|	|	|	1628	|	|	|	|	1728	|	|	|	1828	1828	|	|	1928	|	2028	|	|	2128	|	|	2228	|
Aarau **505** d.	|	|	|	1636	|	|	|	|	1736	|	|	|	1836	1836	|	|	1936	|	2036	|	|	2136	|	|	2236	|
Liestal d.	|	|	|	1701	|	|	|	|	1801	|	|	|	1901	1901	|	|	2001	|	2101	|	|	2201	|	|	2301	|
Basel SBB a.	1627	1627	1653	1713	1727	1753	1753	1753	1813	1827	1853	1853	1913	1913	1927	1953	2013	2027	2113	2127	2153	2213	2227	2253	2313	2353

Via Baden

km		*IR* 2055	*IR* 1957	*IR* 2057	*IR* 1959	*IR* 2059	*IR* 1961	*IR* 2061	*IR* 1963	*IR* 2063	*IR* 1965	*IR* 2065	*IR* 1967	*IR* 2067	*IR* 1969	*IR* 2069	*IR* 1971	*IR* 2071	*IR* 1973	*IR* 2073	*IR* 1975	*IR* 2075	*IR* 1977	*IR* 2077	*IR* 1979	*IR* 2079
0	**Basel** SBB d.	0437	0513	0537	0613	0637	0713	0737	0813	0837	0913	0937	1013	1037	1113	1137	1213	1237	1313	1337	1413	1437	1513	1537	1613	1637
17	Rheinfelden d.	0450	0526	0550	0626	0650	0726	0750	0826	0850	0926	0950	1026	1050	1126	1150	1226	1250	1326	1350	1426	1450	1526	1550	1626	1650
57	Brugg **505** d.	0520	0600	0620	0700	0720	0800	0820	0900	0920	1000	1020	1100	1120	1200	1220	1300	1320	1400	1420	1500	1520	1600	1620	1700	1720
66	Baden **505** d.	0529	0608	0629	0708	0729	0808	0829	0908	0929	1008	1029	1108	1129	1208	1229	1308	1329	1408	1429	1508	1529	1608	1629	1708	1729
88	**Zürich** HB **505** a.	0549	0624	0649	0724	0749	0824	0849	0924	0949	1024	1049	1124	1149	1224	1249	1324	1349	1424	1449	1524	1549	1624	1649	1724	1749
	Zürich Flug ✈ **530 535** a.	0604	...	0704	...	0804	...	0904	...	1004	...	1104	...	1204	...	1304	...	1404	...	1504	...	1604	...	1704	...	1804

	IR 1981	*IR* 2081	*IR* 1983	R 2083	*IR* 1985	*IR* 2085	*IR* 1987	*IR* 1989	*IR* 1991	*IR* 1993	*IR* 1995
Basel SBB d.	1713	1737	1813	1837	1913	1937	2013	2113	2213	2313	0013
Rheinfelden d.	1726	1750	1826	1850	1926	1950	2026	2126	2226	2326	0026
Brugg **505** d.	1800	1820	1900	1920	2000	2020	2100	2200	2300	0000	0100
Baden **505** d.	1808	1829	1908	1929	2008	2029	2108	2208	2308	0008	0108
Zürich HB **505** a.	1824	1849	1924	1949	2024	2049	2124	2224	2324	0024	0124
Zürich Flug ✈ **530 535** a.	...	1904	...	2004	...	2104	...	...	...	...	...

	IR 1956	*IR* 2058	*IR* 1958	*IR* 2060	*IR* 1960	*IR* 2062	*IR* 1962	*IR* 2064	*IR* 1964	*IR* 2066
Zürich Flug ✈ **530 535** d.	...	0556	...	0656	...	0756	...	0856	...	0956
Zürich HB **505** d.	0536	0610	0636	0710	0736	0810	0836	0910	0936	1010
Baden **505** d.	0552	0632	0652	0732	0752	0832	0852	0932	0952	1032
Brugg **505** d.	0601	0641	0702	0741	0802	0841	0902	0941	1002	1041
Rheinfelden d.	0635	0713	0734	0810	0834	0910	0934	1010	1034	1110
Basel SBB a.	0650	0731	0747	0824	0850	0924	0950	1024	1047	1124

	IR 1966	*IR* 2068	*IR* 1968	*IR* 2070	*IR* 1970	*IR* 2072	*IR* 1972	*IR* 2074	*IR* 1974	*IR* 2076	*IR* 1976	*IR* 2078	*IR* 1978	*IR* 2080	*IR* 1980	*IR* 2082	*IR* 1982	*IR* 2084	*IR* 1984	*IR* 2086	*IR* 1986	*IR* 2088	*IR* 1988	*IC* 1252	*IR* 1990	*IR* 1992
																							⑤⑥g	S		
Zürich Flug ✈ **530 535** d.	...	1056	...	1156	...	1256	...	1356	...	1456	...	1556	...	1656	...	1756	...	1856	...	1956	...	2056	...	...	...	...
Zürich HB **505** d.	1036	1110	1136	1210	1236	1310	1336	1410	1436	1510	1536	1610	1636	1710	1736	1810	1836	1910	1936	2010	2036	2110	2136	2136	2236	2336
Baden **505** d.	1052	1132	1152	1232	1252	1332	1352	1432	1452	1532	1552	1632	1652	1732	1752	1832	1852	1932	1952	2032	2052	2132	2152	2152	2252	2352
Brugg **505** d.	1102	1141	1202	1241	1302	1341	1402	1441	1502	1541	1602	1641	1702	1741	1802	1841	1902	1941	2002	2041	2102	2141	2202	2202	2302	0002
Rheinfelden d.	1134	1210	1234	1310	1334	1410	1434	1510	1534	1610	1634	1710	1734	1810	1834	1910	1934	2010	2034	2110	2134	2210	2234	2234	2334	0034
Basel SBB a.	1147	1224	1247	1324	1347	1424	1447	1524	1547	1624	1647	1724	1747	1824	1847	1924	1947	2024	2047	2124	2147	2224	2247	2247	2347	0047

♦ – **NOTES** (LISTED BY TRAIN NUMBER)

272 – Ⓐ (also May 30, Aug. 1): [12] and ✕ Zürich - Basel - Hamburg.
292 – ⑦ (also Apr. 22, June 10; not Apr. 21, June 9): [12] and ✕ Zürich - Basel - Berlin Ost.
1172 – ⑥ (also Apr. 19, 21, June 9): [12] and ✕ Zürich - Basel - Hamburg.
9203 – ①-⑥ (not Apr. 22, June 10, Nov. 11). [12] and ⊗ Paris - Basel - Zürich.
9226 – Ⓑ (not May 30, Aug. 15, Nov. 1): [12] and ⊗ Zürich - Basel - Paris Lyon.

A – [12] and ✕ (Karlsruhe Ⓐ -) Basel - Zürich.
B – From Hamburg on ① (running as *ICE* **1271**); from Frankfurt (Main) on ②-⑦.
F – [12] and ✕ Frankfurt (Main) - Basel - Zürich / Chur and v.v.
H – [12] and ✕ Kiel / Hamburg - Basel - Zürich / Chur and v.v.
M – [12] and ✕ München - St Gallen - Basel and v.v.
P – [12] and ⊗ Paris - Basel - Zürich and v.v.
S – ①②③④⑦ (also Apr. 19).

a – Ⓐ only.
d – Dec. 9 - Aug. 4 (also Apr. 22, June 10).
e – Aug. 11 - Dec. 8.
f – Not May 30, Aug. 1.
g – Not Apr. 19.
h – Dec. 9 - Mar. 31.
j – Apr. 1 - Dec. 14.
k – Also May 30, Aug. 15, Nov. 1.
n – Also Aug. 1; not Apr. 20.
v – Not Apr. 22, June 10.
y – Also Apr. 22, June 10, Nov. 11.
z – Also Apr. 22, June 10.

△ – Train number varies on certain dates.

02 ✕ – **Restaurant** ⊗ – **Bistro** (🍸) – **Bar coach** 🍸 – **Minibar**

511 BERN - PAYERNE and NEUCHÂTEL BLS

km																									
					⚒																				
0	**Bern** d.	0553	0608	...	...	...	0653	0708	...	...		2053	2108	...	...	2153	2208	...	...	2253	2308	...	2337	0008	...
22	Kerzers ▲ d.	0611	0631	0634	0634	0704	0711	0731	0734	0804	and at	2111	2131	2134	2204	2211	2231	2234	2303	2311	2331	2334	0003	0034	0036
	Murten d.	|	|	0643	0643	0721	|	|	0743	0815	the same	|	|	2143	2221	|	|	2243	2321	|	|	2343	|	|	0045
	Avenches d.	|	|	...	0649	0729	|	|	...	0829	minutes	|	|	...	2229	|	|	...	2329	|	|	2350	|	|	...
	Payerne a.	|	|	...	0657	0741	|	|	...	0841	past each	|	|	...	2241	|	|	...	2341	|	|	0002	|	|	...
30	Ins 508 d.	0617	0640	...	...	...	0717	0740	...	...	hour until	2117	2140	...	...	2217	2240	...	...	2317	2340	...	0013	0041	...
43	**Neuchâtel** 508 a.	0627	0656	...	...	...	0727	0756	...	...		2127	2156	...	...	2227	2256	...	...	2327	2356	...	0026	0056	...

km																										
	Neuchâtel 508 d.	0532	...	0601	0632	...	...	0701	0732	...	...	0801	0832		...	...	2201	2232	...	...	2301	2332	...	...	0009
	Ins 508 d.	0543	...	0617	0643	...	...	0717	0743	...	...	0817	0843	and at	...	...	2217	2243	...	...	2317	2343	...	...	0025
0	Payerne d.	|	0600d	|	|	0618	0700d	|	|	0718	...	|	|	the same	2118	...	|	|	2218	...	|	|	2318	0006	|
11	Avenches d.	|	0608d	|	|	0630	0708d	|	|	0730	...	|	|	minutes	2130	...	|	|	2230	...	|	|	2330	0017	|
18	Murten d.	|	0617	|	|	0647	0717	|	|	0747	0817	|	|	past each	2147	2217	|	|	2247	2317	|	|	2347	0025	|
26	Kerzers ▲ d.	0549	0626	0630	0649	0656	0726	0730	0749	0756	0826	0830	0849	hour until	2156	2226	2230	2249	2256	2326	2330	2349	2356	0034	0038
	Bern a.	0607	...	0652	0707	...	...	0752	0807	...	...	0852	0907		...	...	2252	2307	...	...	2352	0012	...	...	0103

d – ⚒ only.

▲ – Connecting services **KERZERS - LYSS** and v.v.: *17 km*, journey 20 minutes.
From **Kerzers**: 0606 and hourly until 2306. From **Lyss**: 0535 and hourly until 2335, then 0009.

512 BIEL and NEUCHÂTEL - LA CHAUX DE FONDS - LE LOCLE SBB

km																								
0	**Biel / Bienne** d.	0547	...	0647	...	...	0747	...	and at	1847	...	1920	1947	...	...	2047	...	...	2147	...	2247	...	...	2347	...
28	St Imier d.	0613	...	0713	...	...	0813	...	the same	1913	...	2000	2017	...	...	2117	...	...	2217	...	2317	...	...	0017	...
	Neuchâtel d.	|	0600	|	0700	...	|	0800	minutes	|	1900	|	|	2000	...	|	2100	...	|	2200	|	2300	...	|	0000
44	La Chaux de Fonds d.	0628	0631	0728	0731	...	0828	0831	past each	1928	1931	2017	2034	2037	...	2134	2135	...	2234	2237	2334	2337	...	0034	0037
52	**Le Locle** a.	...	0639	...	0739	...	...	0839	hour until	...	1939	...	...	2045	...	...	2143	...	...	2245	...	2345	...	...	0045

km																									
																								A	B
0	**Le Locle** d.	0521	...	0621	...	0721	...	...	0821	...	and at	1921	...	...	2021	...	...	2113	...	2221	...	...	2321	...	...
8	La Chaux de Fonds a.	0529	0532	0629	0632	0729	0732	...	0829	0832	the same	1929	1932	1943	2029	2043	...	2121	2143	2229	2243	...	2329	2343	2343
37	**Neuchâtel** a.	0600	|	0700	|	0800	|	...	0900	|	minutes	2000	|	|	2100	|	...	2200	|	2300	|	...	2400	|	|
	St Imier d.	...	0545	...	0645	...	0745	...	...	0845	past each	...	1945	2000	...	2100	...	...	2200	...	2300	...	...	0000	0000
	Biel / Bienne a.	...	0612	...	0712	...	0812	...	...	0912	hour until	...	2012	2040	...	2140	...	...	2240	...	2340	...	...	0040	0046

A – ①②③④⑦ (also Apr. 19). B – ⑤⑥ (not Apr. 19). ☛ Additional stopping services operate.

513 BERN - BIEL SBB

km																					
			⑥⑦k		Ⓐ																
0	**Bern** d.	0012	0112	...	0500	0530	0612	0642	and at the same	2012	2042	...	2112	2132	...	2212	2232	...	2312	2332	...	...
23	Lyss d.	0030	0135	...	0522	0552	0630	0700	minutes past	2030	2100	...	2130	2154	...	2230	2254	...	2330	2354	...	...
34	**Biel / Bienne** a.	0038	0143	...	0535	0605	0638	0708	each hour until	2038	2108	...	2138	2207	...	2238	2307	...	2338	0007	...	...

	⑥⑦k																			
Biel / Bienne d.	0026	...	...	0518	0552	0622	0652	and at the same	2022	2052	...	2122	2154	...	2222	2254	...	2322	2354	...	...
Lyss d.	0035	...	...	0531	0601	0631	0701	minutes past	2031	2101	...	2131	2207	...	2231	2307	...	2331	0007	...	...
Bern a.	0052	...	...	0554	0618	0648	0718	each hour until	2048	2118	...	2148	2230	...	2248	2330	...	2348	0030	...	...

k – Not Apr. 20. ☛ Additional stopping services operate.

514 BERN - LUZERN via Langnau BLS

For fast services via Zofingen see Table **565**

km												
0	**Bern** d.	0536a	0612	0636	0712	and at	2136	2212	2236	2312	2342	0012
21	Konolfingen d.	0552a	0634	0652	0734	the same	2152	2234	2252	2334	0005	0034
38	Langnau d.	0605	0652	0705	0752	minutes	2205	2252	2305	2352	0023	0052
75	Wolhusen d.	0645	...	0745	...	past each	2245	...	2345	...	...	...
96	**Luzern** a.	0703	...	0803	...	hour until	2303	...	0010	...	...	...

	Ⓐ									
Luzern d.	...	0557	...	and at	2057	...	2157	...	2216	...
Wolhusen d.	...	0615	...	the same	2115	...	2215	...	2244	...
Langnau d.	0553	0653	0707	minutes	2153	2207	2253	2307	2321	0008
Konolfingen d.	0607	0707	0726	past each	2207	2226	2307	2326	...	0026
Bern a.	0626	0726	0748	hour until	2226	2248	2326	2348	...	0049

a – Ⓐ only. ☛ Additional stopping services operate.

515 BIEL/BIENNE - DELÉMONT - DELLE - MEROUX SBB

km																								
0	**Biel / Bienne** 505a d.	...	...	...	...	0619	0719	0819	0919	1019	1119	1219	1319	1419	1519	1619	1719	1819	1919	2019	2119	2219	...	2319
24	Moutier 505a d.	...	...	...	...	0638	0738	0838	0938	1038	1138	1238	1338	1438	1538	1638	1738	1838	1938	2038	2138	2238	...	2338
35	Delémont 505a d.	0417	0449	...	0551	0651	0751	0851	0951	1051	1151	1251	1351	1451	1551	1651	1751	1851	1951	2051	2151	2251	...	2351
63	Porrentruy d.	0448	0520	...	0622	0722	0822	0922	1022	1122	1222	1322	1422	1522	1622	1722	1822	1922	2022	2122	2222	2322	...	0020
75	**Delle** 🏛 a.	0506	0536	...	0640	0738	0838	0938	1038	1138	1238	1338	1440	1540	1638	1738	1838	1938	2040	2138	2238	2340	...	...
75	**Delle** 🏛 370b d.	...	0538r	...	...	0740k	0840	0940	1040a	1140	1240	1340	...	...	1640v	1710t	1840	1940b	...	2140	2240v	...	...	...
89	Meroux TGV ⊡ 370b d.	...	0554r	...	...	0755k	0855	0955	1055a	1155	1255	1355	...	...	1655v	1755t	1855	1955b	...	2155	2255v	...	...	...

Meroux TGV ⊡ 370b d.	...	...	...	...	...	0602r	...	0803k	0903	1003	1103a	1203	1303	1403	...	...	1703v	1803t	1903	2003b	...	...	2203	2303v
Delle 🏛 370b a.	...	...	...	...	...	0618r	...	0818k	0918	1018	1118a	1218	1318	1418	...	...	1718v	1818t	1918	2018b	...	...	2218	2318v
Delle 🏛 d.	0022	...	...	0517	...	0620	0719	0820	0920	1020	1120	1220	1320	1420	1519	1619	1720	1820	1920	2020	2119	...	2220	2320
Porrentruy d.	0042	...	0436	0540	...	0640	0740	0840	0940	1040	1140	1240	1340	1440	1540	1640	1740	1840	1940	2040	2140	...	2240	2340
Delémont 505a d.	0110	...	0512	0612	...	0712	0812	0912	1012	1112	1212	1312	1412	1512	1612	1712	1812	1912	2012	2112	2212	...	2309	0009
Moutier 505a a.	...	...	0521	0621	...	0721	0821	0921	1021	1121	1221	1321	1421	1521	1621	1721	1821	1921	2021	2121	2221	...	...	...
Biel / Bienne 505a a.	...	...	0541	0641	...	0741	0841	0941	1041	1141	1241	1341	1441	1541	1641	1741	1841	1941	2041	2141	2241	...	...	...

a – ①–⑤ during the following periods: Dec. 10 – 21, Jan. 7 - Feb. 15, Mar. 4 - Apr. 12, Apr. 29, 30, May 2 – 7, 9 – 29, 31, June 3 – 7, June 11 - July 5, Sept. 2 - Oct. 18, Nov. 4 – 8, Nov. 12 - Dec. 13.
b – Not ⑥.
k – ⑥ (also Dec. 24, 26 – 28, 31, Jan. 2 – 4, ①–⑤ Feb. 18 - Mar. 1, Apr. 15 – 19, 23 – 26, ①–⑤ July 8 - Aug. 14, ①–⑤ Aug. 16 – 30, Oct. 21 – 25, 28 – 31).
r – ①–⑥ (not Dec. 25, Jan. 1, Apr. 22, May 1, 8, 30, June 10, Aug. 15, Nov. 1, 11).
t – ⑥ only.
v – ⑦ (also Dec. 25, Jan. 1, May 1, 8, 30, June 10, Aug. 15, Nov. 1, 11).
⊡ – Meroux station is a short walk to / from Belfort-Montbéliard TGV station.

516 BERN - SOLOTHURN Narrow gauge. RBS

km																					
		⚒	⚒																		
0	Bern RBS d.	0513	0550	...	0605	0635	and at the same	2005	2035	...	2105	...	2137	2207	2237	2308	2338	...	0011	...	...
14	Jegenstorf d.	0532	0603	...	0618	0648	minutes past	2018	2048	...	2118	...	2156	2226	2256	2326	2356	...	0029	...	...
34	**Solothurn** a.	0556	0627	...	0642	0712	each hour until	2042	2112	...	2142	...	2220	2250	2320	2350	0020	...	0053	...	...

Solothurn d.	...	0519	0549	...	0619	0649	and at the same	2019	2049	...	2119	...	2141	2211	2241	2311	2341	...	...	...	...
Jegenstorf d.	...	0542	0612	...	0642	0712	minutes past	2042	2112	...	2142	...	2204	2234	2304	2334	0004	...	...	...	...
Bern RBS a.	...	0556	0626	...	0656	0726	each hour until	2056	2126	...	2156	...	2223	2253	2323	2353	0023	...	...	...	...

☛ Additional services operate on Ⓐ.

BLS SOLOTHURN - BURGDORF - THUN 517

km		⚒																						
0	**Solothurn** d.	0518	0545	0615	0645		1915	1945	...	2015	...	...	2115	...	...	2215	...	...	2315	...	...	...	0009	...
5	Biberist Ost d.	0523	0550	0620	0650	and at	1920	1950	...	2020	...	...	2120	...	...	2220	...	...	2320	...	...	...	0014	...
21	**Burgdorf** a.	0545	0612	0645	0712	the same	1945	2012	...	2045	...	...	2145	...	...	2245	...	...	2345	...	...	...	0039	...
21	**Burgdorf** 505 d.	0551	0625	0651	0725		1951	2025	...	2051	2049	...	2151	2149	...	2251	2249	...	2351	2349	...	...	...	0049
28	Hasle-Rüegsau d.	|	0638	|	0738	minutes	|	2038	...	|	2057	2101	|	2157	2201	|	2257	2301	|	2357	0001	...	...	0057
46	Konolfingen a.	|	0700	|	0800		|	2100	...	|	...	2123	|	...	2223	|	...	2323	|	...	0023	...	...	...
46	Konolfingen d.	|	0701	|	0801	past each	|	2101	...	|	...	2136	|	...	2236	|	...	2336	|	...	0037	...	...	...
	Bern 505 a.	0610	|	0710	|	hour until	2010	|	...	2110	...	|	2210	...	|	2310	...	|	0010	...	|	...	...	...
61	**Thun** a.	0651	0719	0751	0819		2051	2119	...	2151	...	2157	2251	...	2257	2351	...	2357	0057	...	0058	...	...	...

			Ⓐ																						
Thun d.	0503	0532	...	0607	0639		1807	1839	1907	1939	2007	2039	2109	...	2107	2209	...	2207	2309	...	2307	...	0009	...
Bern 505 d.	0550	|	...	0650	|	and at	1850	|	1950	|	2050	|	|	...	2150	|	...	2250	|	...	2350	...	|	...
Konolfingen a.	|	0553	...	|	0658	the same	|	1858	|	1958	|	2058	2130	...	|	2230	...	|	2330	...	|	...	0030	...
Konolfingen d.	|	0600	...	|	0700		|	1900	|	2000	|	2100	2136	...	|	2236	...	|	2336	...	|	...	...	0037
Hasle-Rüegsau d.	|	0622	...	|	0722	minutes	|	1922	|	2022	|	2122	2157	2201	|	2257	2301	|	2357	0001	|	...	...	0058
Burgdorf 505 a.	0608	0632	...	0708	0732	past each	1908	1932	2008	2032	2108	2132	...	2211	2208	...	2311	2308	...	0011	0008	...	...	0107
Burgdorf d.	0615	0647	0647	0715	0747		1915	1947	2015	...	2115	...	...	...	2215	...	...	2315	...	...	0015	...	...	...
Biberist Ost a.	0637	0706	0706	0737	0806	hour until	1937	2006	2037	...	2137	...	...	...	2237	...	...	2337	...	...	0037	...	...	...
Solothurn a.	0643	0713	0713	0743	0813		1943	2013	2043	...	2143	...	...	...	2243	...	...	2343	...	...	0043	...	...	...

SBB ZÜRICH - SARGANS - CHUR 520

km		RE 3495			RE 3459	IC 557	RJX 161	IC 911	RE 3461	IC 559	IC 913	IC 1253	RE 3463	IC 1255	IC 561	EC 163	RE 3465	IC 563	ICE 271	RE 3467	IC 565	RJX 165	IC 919	RE 3469	IC 567
		⑥⑦ k				✕	W✕	✕		✕	Ⓐ ⊗	Ⓒ ✕		Ⓐ ✕	Ⓒ ⊗	T✕		⊗	H✕		✕	B✕	⑥Y		⊗
	Basel SBB 510 d.	...	...	...	...	...	...	...	...	0633	0707	0707	...	0733	0733	...	...	0833	0907	...	0933	...	...	...	...
0	**Zürich** HB 522 555 d.	0020	...	...	0612	0637	0640	0707	0712	0737	0807	0807	0812	0837	0837	0840	0912	0937	1007	1012	1037	1040	1107	1112	1137
12	Thalwil 555 d.	0028	...	...	0621	|	|	|	0721	|	|	|	0821	|	|	|	0921	|	|	1021	|	|	|	1121	|
24	Wädenswil 522 d.	0037	...	...	0631	|	|	|	0731	|	|	|	0831	|	|	|	0931	|	|	1031	|	|	|	1131	|
33	Pfäffikon 522 d.	0045	...	...	0641	|	|	|	0741	|	|	|	0841	|	|	|	0941	|	|	1041	|	|	|	1141	|
57	Ziegelbrücke 522 d.	0100	...	...	0659	|	|	|	0759	|	|	|	0859	|	|	|	0959	|	|	1059	|	|	|	1159	|
90	**Sargans** 534 d.	0119	...	...	0723	0733	0737	0803	0823	0833	0903	0903	0923	0933	0933	0937	1023	1033	1103	1123	1133	1137	1203	1223	1233
106	Buchs 534 a.	|	...	...	|	|	0748	|	|	|	|	|	|	|	|	0948	|	|	|	|	|	1148	|	|	|
103	Landquart 534 545 d.	0130	...	...	0734	0743	...	0812	0834	0843	0912	0912	0934	0943	0943	...	1034	1043	1112	1134	1143	...	1212	1234	1243
116	**Chur** 534 545 a.	0137	...	...	0743	0752	...	0822	0843	0852	0922	0922	0943	0952	0952	...	1043	1052	1122	1143	1152	...	1222	1243	1252

	IC 921	RE 3471	IC 569	RJX 167	RE 3473	IC 571	ICE 71	RE 3475	IC 573	RJX 169	RE 3477	IC 575	IC 929	RE 3479	IC 577	RJX 367	IC 931	RE 3481	IC 579	ICE 75	IC 933	RE 3483	IC 581	RJX 369	RE 3485
	🍸		✕	W✕		✕	H✕		✕	W✕		⊗	🍸		✕	W✕	Ⓐ		⊗	①–⑥ H✕	⑦		✕	N✕	
Basel SBB 510 d.	...	...	1133	...	...	1233	1307	...	...	...	...	1433	...	...	...	...	...	...	1633	1707	...	...	1733	...	...
Zürich HB 522 555 d.	1207	1212	1237	1240	1312	1337	1407	1412	1437	1440	1512	1537	1607	1612	1637	1640	1707	1712	1737	1807	1807	1812	1837	1840	1912
Thalwil 555 d.	|	1221	|	|	1321	|	|	1421	|	|	1521	|	|	1621	|	|	|	1721	|	|	|	1821	|	|	1921
Wädenswil 522 d.	|	1231	|	|	1331	|	|	1431	|	|	1531	|	|	1631	|	|	|	1731	|	|	|	1831	|	|	1931
Pfäffikon 522 d.	|	1241	|	|	1341	|	|	1441	|	|	1541	|	|	1641	|	|	|	1741	|	|	|	1841	|	|	1941
Ziegelbrücke 522 d.	|	1259	|	|	1359	|	|	1459	|	|	1559	|	|	1659	|	|	|	1759	|	|	|	1859	|	|	1959
Sargans 534 d.	1303	1323	1333	1337	1423	1433	1503	1523	1533	1537	1623	1633	1703	1723	1733	1737	1803	1823	1833	1903	1903	1923	1933	1937	2023
Buchs 534 a.	|	|	|	1348	|	|	|	|	|	1548	|	|	|	|	|	1748	|	|	|	|	|	|	|	1948	|
Landquart 534 545 d.	1312	1334	1343	...	1434	1443	1512	1534	1543	...	1634	1643	1712	1734	1743	...	1812	1834	1843	1912	1912	1934	1943	...	2034
Chur 534 545 a.	1322	1343	1352	...	1443	1452	1522	1543	1552	...	1643	1652	1722	1743	1752	...	1822	1843	1852	1922	1922	1943	1952	...	2043

	IC 583	IC 593	RE 3487	IC 585	RE 3489	IC 597	IC 587	RE 3491		RE 3493	
	Ⓑ ✕	⑥				m	n				
Basel SBB 510 d.	1833	...	...	...	...	...	2033	...	...	...	...
Zürich HB 522 555 d.	1937	1937	2012	2037	2112	2137	2137	2212	...	2312	...
Thalwil 555 d.	|	|	2021	|	2121	|	|	2221	...	2321	...
Wädenswil 522 d.	|	|	2031	|	2131	|	|	2231	...	2331	...
Pfäffikon 522 d.	|	|	2041	|	2141	|	|	2241	...	2341	...
Ziegelbrücke 522 d.	|	|	2059	|	2159	|	|	2259	...	0000	...
Sargans 534 d.	2033	2033	2124	2133	2224	2233	2233	2328	...	0028	...
Buchs 534 a.	|	|	|	|	|	|	|	|	...	|	...
Landquart 534 545 d.	2043	2043	2135	2143	2235	2243	2243	2338	...	0038	...
Chur 534 545 a.	2052	2052	2143	2152	2243	2252	2252	2347	...	0047	...

	IC 556	RE 3456		IC 558	RE 3458	IC 912	IC 560	RE 3460	IC 562
	⚒ ✕			✕		Ⓐ 🍸	✕		✕
Chur 534 545 d.	0509	0516	...	0609	0616	0639	0709	0716	0809
Landquart 534 545 d.	0519	0525	...	0619	0625	0649	0719	0725	0819
Buchs 534 d.	|	|	...	|	|	|	|	|	|
Sargans 534 d.	0528	0537	...	0628	0637	0658	0728	0737	0828
Ziegelbrücke 522 d.	|	0600	...	|	0700	|	|	0800	|
Pfäffikon 522 d.	|	0619	...	|	0719	|	|	0819	|
Wädenswil 522 d.	|	0629	...	|	0729	|	|	0829	|
Thalwil 555 d.	|	0639	...	|	0739	|	|	0839	|
Zürich HB 522 555 a.	0623	0648	...	0723	0748	0753	0823	0848	0923
Basel SBB 510 a.	0727	...	...	...	...	...	0927	...	...

	RE 3462	IC 916	IC 564	RE 3464		RJX 360	IC 566	RE 3466	ICE 72	IC 568	RE 3468		RJX 368	IC 570	RE 3470	ICE 70	IC 572	RE 3472		RJX 160	IC 574	RE 3474	IC 928	IC 576	RE 3476
		✕	✕			N✕	⊗		H✕	⊗			W✕	✕		H✕	⊗			W✕	✕		🍸	✕	
Chur 534 545 d.	0816	0839	0909	0916	...	...	1009	1016	1039	1109	1116	...	...	1209	1216	1239	1309	1316	...	...	1409	1416	1439	1509	1516
Landquart 534 545 d.	0825	0849	0919	0925	...	...	1019	1025	1049	1119	1125	...	...	1219	1225	1249	1319	1325	...	...	1419	1425	1449	1519	1525
Buchs 534 d.	|	|	|	|	...	1012	|	|	|	|	|	...	1212	|	|	|	|	|	...	1412	|	|	|	|	|
Sargans 534 d.	0837	0858	0928	0937	...	1025	1028	1037	1058	1128	1137	...	1225	1228	1237	1258	1328	1337	...	1425	1428	1437	1458	1528	1537
Ziegelbrücke 522 d.	0900	|	|	1000	...	|	|	1100	|	|	1200	...	|	|	1300	|	|	1400	...	|	|	1500	|	|	1600
Pfäffikon 522 d.	0919	|	|	1019	...	|	|	1119	|	|	1219	...	|	|	1319	|	|	1419	...	|	|	1519	|	|	1619
Wädenswil 522 d.	0929	|	|	1029	...	|	|	1129	|	|	1229	...	|	|	1329	|	|	1429	...	|	|	1529	|	|	1629
Thalwil 555 d.	0939	|	|	1039	...	|	|	1139	|	|	1239	...	|	|	1339	|	|	1439	...	|	|	1539	|	|	1639
Zürich HB 522 555 a.	0948	0953	1023	1048	...	1120	1123	1148	1153	1223	1248	...	1320	1323	1348	1353	1423	1448	...	1520	1523	1548	1553	1623	1648
Basel SBB 510 a.	...	...	1127	...	...	...	...	...	1253	1327	...	...	...	...	...	1453	1527	...	...	...	...	...	...	1727	...

	RJX 162	IC 578	RE 3478	IC 1256	IC 580	RE 3480	IC 934	EC 164	IC 582	RE 3482	IC 936	IC 584	RE 3484		RJX 166	IC 1258	IC 1252	IC 586	RE 3486	IC 588	RE 3488	RJX 168	RE 3490		RE 3492
	B✕	✕		✕	⊗		Z	T✕	✕		🍸	⊗			W✕	⑤⑥ r	p	⑦		†		W✕			⑤⑥ r
Chur 534 545 d.	...	1609	1616	1639	1709	1716	1739	...	1809	1816	1839	1909	1916	...	...	2009	2009	2009	2016	2109	2114	...	2214	...	2314
Landquart 534 545 d.	...	1619	1625	1649	1719	1725	1749	...	1819	1825	1849	1919	1925	...	...	2019	2019	2019	2025	2119	2122	...	2222	...	2322
Buchs 534 d.	1612	|	|	|	|	|	|	1812	|	|	|	|	|	...	2012	|	|	|	|	|	|	2212	|	...	|
Sargans 534 d.	1625	1628	1637	1658	1728	1737	1758	1825	1828	1837	1858	1928	1937	...	2025	2028	2028	2028	2037	2128	2137	2225	2237	...	2337
Ziegelbrücke 522 d.	|	|	1700	|	|	1800	|	|	|	1900	|	|	2000	...	|	|	|	|	2100	|	2200	|	2300	...	0000
Pfäffikon 522 d.	|	|	1719	|	|	1819	|	|	|	1919	|	|	2019	...	|	|	|	|	2119	|	2219	|	2319	...	0019
Wädenswil 522 d.	|	|	1729	|	|	1829	|	|	|	1929	|	|	2029	...	|	|	|	|	2129	|	2229	|	2329	...	0029
Thalwil 555 d.	|	|	1739	|	|	1839	|	|	|	1939	|	|	2039	...	|	|	|	|	2139	|	2239	|	2339	...	0039
Zürich HB 522 555 a.	1720	1723	1748	1753	1823	1848	1853	1920	1923	1948	1953	2023	2048	...	2120	2123	2123	2123	2148	2223	2248	2320	2348	...	0048
Basel SBB 510 a.	...	1827	...	...	1927	...	...	...	2027	...	...	2127	...	...	...	2227	2247	...	...	...	...	...	...	...	...

Other services **SARGANS - BUCHS**

Sargans d.	0500	0536	and at the same minutes past	2300	2336	...	0000	...
Buchs a.	0512	0545	each hour until	2312	2345	...	0012	...

	⚒							
Buchs d.	0512	0615	0647	and at the same minutes past	2315	2347	0015	0047
Sargans a.	0525	0625	0700	each hour until	2325	0000	0025	0100

B – 1 2 and ✕ Budapest - Wien - Zürich and v.v.
H – 1 2 and ✕ Kiel / Hamburg / Frankfurt - Basel - Zürich - Chur and v.v. Train number may vary on certain dates.
N – 1 2 and ✕ Innsbruck - Zürich and v.v.

T – TRANSALPIN – 1 2 and ✕ Zürich - Graz and v.v.
W – 1 2 and ✕ Bratislava/Wien - Salzburg - Zürich and v.v.
Y – ⑥ Dec. 22 - Mar. 9.
Z – ⑦ Dec. 23 - Feb. 3; ⑥⑦ Feb. 9 - Mar. 3 (also Mar. 10).

k – Not Apr. 20.
m – ⑤–⑦ (also May 30, Aug. 1).
n – ①–④ (not May 30, Aug. 1).
p – ①–④ (also Apr. 19).
r – Not Apr. 19.

✕ – Restaurant ⊗ – Bistro (🍸) – Bar coach 🍸 – Minibar

522 (ZÜRICH -) ZIEGELBRÜCKE - LINTHAL SBB

km												
	Zürich HB .... **520** d.	...	...	...	0643		1743	...	1843	...		...
	Wädenswil .... **520** d.	...	...	...	0700	and	1800	...	1901	...	and	...
	Pfäffikon .... **520** d.	...	...	...	0708		1808	...	1909	...		...
0	**Ziegelbrücke** .. **520** d.	0430	0530	0630	0730	hourly	1830	1903	1930	2003	hourly	2303
11	Glarus .... d.	0444	0544	0644	0744		1844	1917	1944	2017		2317
16	Schwanden .... d.	0500	0600	0700	0800	until	1900	1929	1952	2029	until	2329
27	**Linthal** .... ▲ a.	0517	0617	0717	0817		1917	1946	...	2046		2346

	Ⓐ								
Linthal .... ▲ d.	0443	0543		1843	...	1946	2011		0011
Schwanden .... d.	0504	0607	and	1907	...	2007	2033	and	0033
Glarus .... d.	0513	0616		1916	...	2016	2042		0042
Ziegelbrücke .... **520** a.	0526	0629	hourly	1929	...	2029	2056	hourly	0056
Pfäffikon .... **520** a.	0551	0651		1951	...	...	...		...
Wädenswil .... **520** a.	0600	0700	until	2000	...	...	...	until	...
Zürich HB .... **520** a.	0617	0717		2017	...	...	...		...

h – Also Aug. 15.
x – Change required at either Balm (Klausen) or Klausen Passhöhe; 68/70 minutes respectively.

▲ – 🚌 service **Linthal - Flüelen** Bahnhof and v.v. operates **June 22 - September 22, 2019** via the Klausenpass. Ⓡ. Journey time: ± 2 hours 15 minutes. **NO WINTER SERVICE**.
From **Linthal** at 0827Ⓒ **h**, 0927, 1027, 1227 **x**, 1527 and 1727Ⓒ **h**.
From **Flüelen** at 0600Ⓒ **h**, 0735 **x**, 0935 **x**, 1205 **x**, 1505Ⓒ **h** and 1545.
Operator: PostAuto Zentralschweiz, Luzern. ✆ (Luzern) 058 448 06 22, fax: 058 667 34 33.

525 ARTH GOLDAU - ST GALLEN - ROMANSHORN SBB, SOB*

km				2561 S		Ⓐ	Ⓒ	2563 S			2565 S		2567 S			2589 S		2591 S		2593 S		2595 S		
	Luzern **550** .... d.	...	...	...	...	...	...	...	...	...	...	...	0739	...		1839	...	1939	...	...	...	...	...	...
0	**Arth Goldau** .... d.	...	...	...	...	*0519*	...	...	...	*0619*	...	...	0814	...	and at	1914	...	2014	...	*2114*	...	*2214*	...	2313
20	Biberbrugg ◐ .... ● d.	...	...	...	...	0550	0552	...	...	0652	...	...	0837	...		1937	...	2037	...	*2137*	...	*2237*	...	2337
26	Samstagern ◐ .... ● d.	...	...	...	...	0601	0601	...	...	0701	...	...	|	...	the same	|	...	|	...	*2145*	...	*2245*	...	2345
34	Pfäffikon .... ● d.	...	...	...	...	0617	0617	...	...	0717	...	...	0854	...		1954	...	2054	...	*2157*	...	*2257*	...	2357
38	Rapperswil .... ● a.	...	...	...	...	0622	0622	...	...	0722	...	...	0859	...	minutes	1959	...	2102	...	*2202*	...	*2302*	...	0002
38	Rapperswil .... d.	...	...	0603	...	...	...	0703	...	...	0803	...	0903	...		2003	...	2103	...	2203	...	2303	...	...
66	Wattwil .... d.	0459	0559	0628	...	...	...	0728	...	...	0828	...	0928	...	past each	2028	...	2128	...	2228	...	2328	...	...
89	Herisau .... d.	0524	0624	0647	0705	...	...	0747	0805	...	0847	0905	0947	1005		2047	2105	2147	2205	2247	2305	2349	0005	...
97	**St Gallen** .... a.	0533	0633	0656	0714	...	...	0756	0814	...	0856	0914	0955	1014	hour until	2056	2114	2156	2215	2256	2315	2357	0015	...
97	**St Gallen** .... **538** d.	*0549*	*0649*	...	0715	...	...	...	0815	...	...	0915	...	1015		...	*2119*	...	*2219*	...	*2319*	...	...	...
119	**Romanshorn** ...... **538** a.	*0616*	*0716*	...	0733	...	...	...	0833	...	...	0933	...	1033		...	*2146*	...	*2246*	...	*2346*	...	...	...

		2560 S	Ⓒ	Ⓐ		2562 S			2564 S			2588 S		2590 S			2592 S		2594 S		2596 S		2598 S
Romanshorn .... **538** d.	...	...	...	...	*0514*	...	...	0626	...		1826	...	1926	...	...	2026	...	2114	...	2214	...	2314	...
St Gallen .... **538** a.	...	...	...	...	*0541*	...	...	0644	...	and at	1844	...	1944	...	...	2044	...	2141	...	2241	...	2341	...
St Gallen .... d.	...	...	...	...	0556	0603	...	0645	0703		1845	1903	1945	2003	...	2045	2103	▬	2203	▬	2303	▬	0003
Herisau .... d.	...	0513	...	...	0605	0613	...	0654	0713	the same	1854	1913	1954	2013	...	2054	2113	...	2213	...	2313	...	0013
Wattwil .... d.	...	0533	...	...	0630	0633	...	...	0733		...	1933	...	2033	...	...	2133	...	2233	...	2333	...	0033
Rapperswil .... a.	...	0557	...	...	...	0657	...	...	0757	minutes	...	1957	...	2057	...	...	2157	...	2257	...	2357	...	0057t
Rapperswil .... ● d.	0544	...	0636	0636	...	...	0659	...	0759		...	1959	...	...	2057	...	...	2157	...	2257	...	0003	...
Pfäffikon .... ● d.	0549	...	0641	0641	...	...	0704	...	0803	past each	...	2003	...	...	2102	...	...	2202	...	2302	...	0007	...
Samstagern ◐ .... ● d.	0559	...	0655	0658	...	...	0714	...	|		...	|	...	...	2113	...	...	2213	...	2313	...	0019	...
Biberbrugg ◐ .... ● d.	0616	...	0702	0705	...	...	0721	...	0820	hour until	...	2020	...	...	2121	...	...	2221	...	2321	...	...	...
Arth Goldau .... a.	0641	...	...	...	...	...	0744	...	0844		...	2044	...	...	2146	...	...	2246	...	2346	...	...	...
Luzern **550** .... a.	...	...	...	...	...	...	...	...	0921		...	2121	...	...	...	...	...	...	...	...	...	...	...

km		Ⓐ			and at						v
0	**Wädenswil** .... d.	0541	0610	0634	the same	2210	2234	2310	2334	0015	0050
6	Samstagern ..... ● d.	0549	0617	0641	minutes	2217	2241	2317	2341	0023	0058
11	Biberbrugg .... ● d.	0558	0625	0651	past each	2225	2251	2325	2351	0031	0106
17	**Einsiedeln** ...... ● a.	0605	0633	0658	hour until	2233	2258	2333	2358	0038	0114

	Ⓐ			and at					w
Einsiedeln .... ● d.	0454	0525	0558	the same	2225	2258	2325	...	2358
Biberbrugg .... ● d.	0501	0532	0607	minutes	2232	2307	2332	...	0004
Samstagern .... ● d.	0509	0541	0617	past each	2241	2317	2341	...	0012
Wädenswil .... a.	0518	0550	0626	hour until	2250	2326	2350	...	0023

S – VORALPEN EXPRESS – 🅁 Luzern / Arth Goldau / Rapperswil - St Gallen and v.v. Most services convey (🍷).

t – ⑥⑦ (also Apr. 19, 22, May 1, 30, 31, June 10, Aug. 1, Nov. 1).
v – ⑥⑦ (also Apr. 19, 22, May. 1, 30, 31, June 10, Aug. 1).
w – ⑤⑥ (also Apr. 18, 21, 30, May 29, 30, June 9, July 31).

◐ – For service to Einsiedeln – see panel.
● – Additional services run Einsiedeln - Biberbrugg - Samstagern - Pfäffikon - Rapperswil and v.v.
* – Operated by SOB, except Rapperswil - Wattwil (SBB)

526 GOSSAU - APPENZELL - WASSERAUEN Narrow gauge. AB

km		⚒	Ⓐ																				🚌 j			
0	**Gossau** .... d.	0551	...	0651	0751	0851	0951	1051	1121	1151	1221	1251	1321	1421	1521	1551	1621	1721	1751	1851	1951	2051	...	2151	2251	2351
5	Herisau .... d.	0558	0558	0658	0758	0858	0958	1058	1128	1158	1228	1258	1328	1428	1528	1558	1628	1728	1758	1858	1958	2058	...	2158	2258	2358
15	Urnäsch .... d.	...	0613	0713	0813	0913	1013	1113	1143	1213	1243	1313	1343	1443	1543	1613	1643	1743	1813	1913	2013	2113	...	2213	2313	0013
26	**Appenzell** .... d.	...	0632	0731	0831	0931	1031	1131	1201	1231	1301	1330	1401	1501	1601	1631	1701	1801	1831	1930	2030	2130	2132	2230	2330	0030
32	**Wasserauen** .... a.	...	0643	0743	0842	0942	1042	1142	1212	1242	1312	...	1412	1512	1612	1642	1712	1812	1842	*1942*y	*2042*y	...	2142	...	...	...

	Ⓑ																					🚌 j		
Wasserauen .... d.	...	...	0648a	0748	0848	0948	1048	1148	1218	1248	1318	...	1418	1518	1618	1648	1718	1818	1848	...	*1942*y	*2042*y	2142	...	...
Appenzell .... d.	0530	0630	0700	0800	0900	1000	1100	1200	1230	1300	1330	1400	1430	1530	1630	1700	1730	1830	1900	1930	2000	2100	2153	2200	2300
Urnäsch .... d.	0545	0645	0715	0815	0915	1015	1115	1215	1245	1315	1345	1415	1445	1545	1645	1715	1745	1845	1915	1945	2015	2115	...	2215	2315
Herisau .... d.	0602	0702	0732	0832	0932	1032	1132	1232	1302	1332	1402	1432	1502	1602	1702	1732	1802	1902	1932	2002	2032	2132	...	2232	2332
Gossau .... a.	0608	0708	0738	0838	0938	1038	1138	1238	1308	1338	1408	1438	1508	1608	1708	1738	1808	1908	1938	2008	2038	2138	...	2238	2338

a – Ⓐ only.
j – Apr. 28 - Nov. 3.
y – Connection by 🚌.
☛ Additional services operate Apr. 28 - Nov. 3.

527 ST GALLEN - APPENZELL Narrow gauge rack railway. AB

km		⚒			⑥	Ⓐ										⑥⑦y	🚌 y	🚌 y					
0	**St Gallen** .... d.	0520	0550	0620	0650	0650	0720	0750	0826	0856	and every	2226	2256	...	2326	0026	0137	0243	...	...	...	...	...
7	Teufen .... d.	0535	0605	0635	0705	0705	0735	0805	0841	0911	30 minutes	2241	2311	...	2341	0038	0149	0255	...	...	...	...	...
14	Gais ▲ .... d.	0548	0618	0648	0718	0720	0748	0818	0854	0924	until	2254	2324	...	2354	0048	0159	0305	...	...	...	...	...
20	**Appenzell** .... a.	0558	0630	0658	0728	0730	0758	0828	0904	0934		2304	2334	...	0004	0058	0209	0315	...	...	...	...	...

	⚒	⚒																				
Appenzell .... d.	0509	0609	0639	0709	0739	0815	0845	and every	1815	1845	1915	1945	2015	2045	2115	2145	2215	2245	2315	...	...	...
Gais ▲ .... d.	0522	0622	0652	0722	0752	0828	0858	30 minutes	1824	1858	1928	1958	2028	2058	2128	2158	2228	2258	2328	...	...	...
Teufen .... d.	0535	0635	0705	0735	0805	0841	0911	until	1841	1911	1941	2011	2041	2111	2141	2211	2241	2311	2341	...	...	...
St Gallen .... a.	0550	0650	0720	0750	0820	0856	0926		1856	1926	1956	2026	2056	2126	2156	2226	2256	2326	2356	...	...	...

y – ⑥⑦ (also Apr. 19, 22, May 1, 30, 31, June 10, Aug. 1, Nov. 1).

▲ – Rail service **Gais - Altstätten Stadt** and v.v. *8 km*. Journey time: 19–22 minutes. **Operator**: AB.
From **Gais**: 0622Ⓐ, 0722, 0825 and hourly until 1825, then 1925🚌, 2025🚌.
From **Altstätten Stadt**: 0652Ⓐ, 0752 and hourly until 1852, then 1952🚌, 2052🚌.
A bus connects Altstätten Stadt with Altstätten SBB station (Table **534**). Journey time: 6 minutes.

529 ZÜRICH - ZÜRICH FLUGHAFEN ✈ SBB

Journey time: 9–13 minutes

From **Zürich** HB:
0502, 0514, 0529, 0539, 0544, 0546, 0552, 0601, 0605, 0609, 0614, 0616, 0633, 0635, 0639, 0644, 0646, 0652, 0705, 0709, 0714, 0716, 0733, 0735, 0739, 0744, 0746, 0752, then 10–13 trains per hour until 2052, then 2105, 2109, 2114, 2116, 2135, 2139, 2144, 2146, 2205, 2209, 2214, 2216, 2235, 2239, 2244, 2246, 2305, 2309, 2314, 2316, 2339, 2344, 2346, 0014, 0017.

From **Zürich** Flughafen:
0500, 0534, 0538, 0556, 0601, 0604, 0606, 0609, 0615, 0631, 0634, 0636, 0638, 0646, 0648Ⓐ, 0656, 0701, 0704, 0706, 0709, 0715, 0718, 0731, 0734, 0736, 0738, 0746, 0756, then 10–13 trains per hour until 2056, then 2101, 2104, 2106, 2109, 2115, 2131, 2134, 2136, 2138, 2146, 2201, 2204, 2209, 2215, 2231, 2234, 2236, 2238, 2246, 2301, 2304, 2315, 2331, 2334, 2336, 2338, 2346, 0004, 0005, 0013, 0034, 0038.

SBB — ZÜRICH - ST GALLEN — 530

km		IC 701	IR 3255	IC 703	IC 1507	EC 191	IR 3257	IC 705	IC 1509	IR 3259	IC 707	IC 1511	IR 3261	IC 709	IC 1513	IR 3263	IC 711	IC 1515	IR 3265	IC 713	IC 1517	IR 3267	IC 715	IC 1519
						M		F																
		✕		✕	✕	✕		✕	✕		✕	✕		✕	✕		✕	✕		✕	✕		✕	✕
	Genève Aéroport + **505** d.	...	...	...	...	...	...	...	...	...	...	...	...	0632	...	...	0732	...	...	0832	...	...	0932	...
	Genève **505** d.	...	...	...	...	...	...	...	...	...	0542	...	...	0642	...	...	0742	...	...	0842	...	...	0942	...
	Lausanne **505** d.	...	...	...	...	...	...	...	...	...	0620	0615	...	0720	0715	...	0820	0815	...	0920	0915	...	1020	1015
	Biel/Bienne **505** d.	...	...	...	0516	...	...	...	0616	...	|	0717	...	|	0817	...	|	0917	...	|	1017	...	|	1117
	Bern **505** d.	...	...	0513	|	...	...	0632	|	...	0732	|	...	0832	|	...	0932	|	...	1032	|	...	1132	|
	Basel **510** d.	...	...	|	|	0543	...	|	|	...	|	|	...	|	|	...	|	|	...	|	|	...	|	|
0	**Zürich** HB **535** d.	0539	0609	0633	0639	0702	0709	0733	0739	0809	0833	0839	0909	0933	0939	1009	1033	1039	1109	1133	1139	1209	1233	1239
10	**Zürich** Flughafen + **535** d.	0553	0623	0644	0653	0714	0723	0744	0753	0823	0844	0853	0923	0944	0953	1023	1044	1053	1123	1144	1153	1223	1244	1253
30	Winterthur **535** d.	0608	0638	0659	0708	0729	0738	0759	0808	0838	0859	0908	0938	0959	1008	1038	1059	1108	1138	1159	1208	1238	1259	1308
57	Wil **534** d.	0626	0656	|	0726	|	0756	|	0826	0856	|	0926	0956	|	1026	1056	|	1126	1156	|	1226	1256	|	1326
78	Gossau **534** d.	0645	0715	|	0745	|	0815	|	0845	0915	|	0945	1015	|	1045	1115	|	1145	1215	|	1245	1315	|	1345
87	**St Gallen** **534** a.	0653	0722	0735	0752	0805	0822	0835	0852	0922	0935	0952	1022	1035	1052	1122	1135	1152	1222	1235	1252	1322	1335	1352
	Chur **534** a.	...	0848	...	...	...	0948	...	...	1048	...	...	1148	...	...	1248	...	...	1348	...	...	1448	...	...

	EC 195	IR 3269	IC 717	IC 1521	IR 3271	IC 719	IC 1523	IR 3273	IC 721	IC 1525	IR 3275	IC 723	IC 1527	IR 3277	IC 725	IC 1529	EC 197	IR 3279	IC 727	IC 1531	IR 3281	IC 729	IC 1533	IR 3283
	M																M				S			S
	d✕		✕	✕		✕	✕		✕	✕		✕	✕		✕	✕	✕		✕	✕		✕	✕	
Genève Aéroport + **505** d.	...	...	1032	...	...	1132	...	...	1232	...	...	1332	...	...	1432	...	...	...	1532	...	...	1632	...	...
Genève **505** d.	...	...	1042	...	...	1142	...	...	1242	...	...	1342	...	...	1442	...	...	...	1542	...	...	1642	...	...
Lausanne **505** d.	...	...	1120	1115	...	1220	1215	...	1320	1315	...	1420	1415	...	1520	1515	...	...	1620	1615	...	1720	1715	...
Biel/Bienne **505** d.	...	...	|	1217	...	|	1317	...	|	1417	...	|	1517	...	|	1617	...	...	|	1717	...	|	1817	...
Bern **505** d.	...	...	1232	|	...	1332	|	...	1432	|	...	1532	|	...	1632	|	...	...	1732	|	...	1832	|	...
Basel **510** d.	...	...	|	|	...	|	|	...	|	|	...	|	|	...	|	|	...	...	|	|	...	|	|	...
ürich HB **535** d.	1302	1309	1333	1339	1409	1433	1439	1509	1533	1539	1609	1633	1639	1709	1733	1739	1802	1809	1833	1839	1909	1933	1939	2009
ürich Flughafen + **535** d.	1314	1323	1344	1353	1423	1444	1453	1523	1544	1553	1623	1644	1653	1723	1744	1753	1814	1823	1844	1853	1923	1944	1953	2023
/interthur **535** d.	1329	1338	1359	1408	1438	1459	1508	1538	1559	1608	1638	1659	1708	1738	1759	1808	1829	1838	1859	1908	1938	1959	2008	2038
/il **534** d.	|	1356	|	1426	1456	|	1526	1556	|	1626	1656	|	1726	1756	|	1826	|	1856	|	1926	1956	|	2026	2056
ossau **534** d.	|	1415	|	1445	1515	|	1545	1615	|	1645	1715	|	1745	1815	|	1845	|	1915	|	1945	2015	|	2045	2115
t Gallen **534** a.	1405	1422	1435	1452	1522	1535	1552	1622	1635	1652	1722	1735	1752	1822	1835	1852	1905	1922	1935	1952	2022	2035	2052	2122
Chur **534** a.	...	1548	...	...	1648	...	...	1748	...	...	1848	...	...	1948	...	...	...	2048	...	...	...	...	...	...

	IC 1535	IR 3285	IR 2137	IC 1537	IR 3287	IC 1549	IC 1539	IR 3289	RE 11095	IR 3293
		S			S	e	⑤⑥ r			
	✕									
Genève Aéroport + **505** d.	...	...	...	...	...	1932	...	...	...	...
Genève **505** d.	...	...	...	...	...	1942	...	...	...	...
Lausanne **505** d.	1815	...	...	1915	...	2020	2015	...	...	...
Biel/Bienne **505** d.	1917	...	...	2017	...	|	2117	...	...	...
Bern **505** d.	|	...	...	|	...	2132	|	...	...	...
Basel **510** d.	|	...	...	|	...	|	|	...	...	...
ürich HB **535** d.	2039	2109	2135	2139	2209	2239	2239	2309	2339	0017
ürich Flughafen + **535** d.	2053	2123	2146	2153	2223	2253	2253	2323	2353	0030
/interthur **535** d.	2108	2138	2159	2208	2238	2308	2308	2338	0009	0045
/il **534** d.	2126	2156	...	2226	2256	2326	2326	2356	0030	0103
ossau **534** d.	2145	2215	...	2245	2315	2345	2345	0015	0047	0120
t Gallen **534** a.	2152	2222	...	2252	2322	2352	2352	0022	0054	0128
Chur **534** a.	...	...	...	...	...	...	...	...	...	...

	IR 3252	IC 706	IR 3254	IC 1510	IC 708	IR 3256	IC 1512	IC 710	IR 3258
						S			
		✕		✕	✕		✕	✕	
Chur **534** d.	...	...	...	...	...	...	...	...	0612
St Gallen **534** d.	0437	0504	0537	0607	0625	0637	0707	0725	0737
Gossau **534** d.	0446	0512	0546	0616	|	0646	0716	|	0746
Wil **534** d.	0504	0533	0604	0634	|	0704	0734	|	0804
Winterthur **535** d.	0524	0554	0624	0654	0703	0724	0754	0803	0824
Zürich Flughafen + **535** d.	0538	0609	0638	0709	0718	0738	0809	0818	0838
Zürich HB **535** a.	0551	0621	0651	0721	0727	0751	0821	0827	0851
Basel **510** a.	...	|	...	|	|	...	|	|	...
Bern **505** a.	...	0728	...	|	0828	...	|	0928	...
Biel/Bienne **505** a.	...	|	...	0843	|	...	0943	|	...
Lausanne **505** a.	...	0840	...	0945	0940	...	1045	1040	...
Genève **505** a.	...	0918	...	...	1018	...	...	1118	...
Genève Aéroport + **505** a.	...	0927	...	...	1027	...	...	1127	...

	IC 1514	IC 712	IR 3260	IC 1516	IC 714	IR 3262	IC 1518	IC 716	IR 3264	EC 196	IC 1520	IC 718	IR 3266	IC 1522	IC 720	IR 3268	IC 1524	IC 722	IR 3270	IC 1526	IC 724	IR 3272	IC 1528	IC 726
										M														
	✕	✕		✕	✕		✕	✕		✕	✕	✕		✕	✕		✕	✕		✕	✕		✕	✕
Chur **534** d.	...	...	0712	...	...	0812	...	...	0912	...	...	...	1012	...	...	1112	...	...	1212	...	...	1312	...	...
t Gallen **534** d.	0807	0825	0837	0907	0925	0937	1007	1025	1037	1055	1107	1125	1137	1207	1225	1237	1307	1325	1337	1407	1425	1437	1507	1525
ossau **534** d.	0816	|	0846	0916	|	0946	1016	|	1046	|	1116	|	1146	1216	|	1246	1316	|	1346	1416	|	1446	1516	|
/il **534** d.	0834	|	0904	0934	|	1004	1034	|	1104	|	1134	|	1204	1234	|	1304	1334	|	1404	1434	|	1504	1534	|
/interthur **535** d.	0854	0903	0924	0954	1003	1024	1054	1103	1124	1133	1154	1203	1224	1254	1303	1324	1354	1403	1424	1454	1503	1524	1554	1603
ürich Flughafen + **535** d.	0909	0918	0938	1009	1018	1038	1109	1118	1138	1148	1209	1218	1238	1309	1318	1338	1409	1418	1438	1509	1518	1538	1609	1618
ürich HB **535** a.	0921	0927	0951	1021	1027	1051	1121	1127	1151	1158	1221	1227	1251	1321	1327	1351	1421	1427	1451	1521	1527	1551	1621	1627
Basel **510** a.	|	|	...	|	|	...	|	|	...	...	|	|	...	|	|	...	|	|	...	|	|	...	|	|
Bern **505** a.	|	1028	...	|	1128	...	|	1228	...	...	|	1328	...	|	1428	...	|	1528	...	|	1628	...	|	1728
Biel/Bienne **505** a.	1043	|	...	1143	|	...	1243	|	...	...	1343	|	...	1443	|	...	1543	|	...	1643	|	...	1743	|
Lausanne **505** a.	1145	1140	...	1245	1240	...	1345	1340	...	...	1445	1440	...	1545	1540	...	1645	1640	...	1745	1740	...	1845	1840
Genève **505** a.	...	1218	...	...	1318	...	...	1418	...	...	...	1518	...	...	1618	...	...	1718	...	...	1818	...	...	1918
Genève Aéroport + **505** a.	...	1227	...	...	1327	...	...	1427	...	...	...	1527	...	...	1627	...	...	1727	...	...	1827	...	...	1927

	IR 3274	EC 194	IC 1530	IC 728	IR 3276	IC 1532	IC 730	IR 3278	IC 1534	IC 732	IR 3280	IC 1536	IC 734	IC 734	IR 3282	IC 1538	IR 3284	IC 1540	IR 3286	EC 190	RE 11094	IR 3288	IR 3290	IR 3292
		M d											⚒	†						M				
		✕	✕	✕		✕	✕		✕	✕		✕	✕	✕		✕		✕		✕				
Chur **534** d.	1412	...	...	...	1512	...	...	1612	...	...	1712	...	...	...	1812	...	1912	...	2012	...	...	...	...	...
t Gallen **534** d.	1537	1555	1607	1625	1637	1707	1725	1737	1807	1825	1837	1907	1925	1925	1937	2007	2037	2107	2137	2155	2213	2238	2338	0038
ossau **534** d.	1546	|	1616	|	1646	1716	|	1746	1816	|	1846	1916	|	|	1946	2016	2046	2116	2146	|	2222	2246	2346	0045
/il **534** d.	1604	|	1634	|	1704	1734	|	1804	1834	|	1904	1934	|	|	2004	2034	2104	2134	2204	|	2239	2304	0004	0102
/interthur **535** d.	1624	1633	1654	1703	1724	1754	1803	1824	1854	1903	1924	1954	2003	2003	2024	2054	2124	2154	2224	2233	2301	2324	0028	...
ürich Flughafen + **535** d.	1638	1648	1709	1718	1738	1809	1818	1838	1909	1918	1938	2009	2018	2018	2038	2109	2138	2209	2238	2248	2315	2338	0042	...
ürich HB **535** a.	1651	1658	1721	1727	1751	1821	1827	1851	1921	1927	1951	2021	2027	2027	2051	2121	2151	2221	2151	2258	2325	2351	0053	...
Basel **510** a.	...	...	|	|	...	|	|	...	|	|	...	|	|	|	...	|	...	...	...	0013	...	...	...	...
Bern **505** a.	...	...	|	1828	...	|	1928	...	|	2028	...	|	2128	2128	...	|	...	...	...	...	...	...	...	...
Biel/Bienne **505** a.	...	...	1843	|	...	1943	|	...	2043	|	...	2143	|	|	...	2243	...	...	...	...	...	...	...	...
Lausanne **505** a.	...	...	1945	1940	...	2045	2040	...	2145	2140	...	2245	2240	2240	...	2345	...	...	...	...	...	...	...	...
Genève **505** a.	...	...	...	2018	...	...	2118	...	...	...	...	...	2318r	2320	...	...	...	...	...	...	...	...	...	...
Genève Aéroport + **505** a.	...	...	...	2027	...	...	2127	...	...	...	...	...	2327r	...	...	...	...	...	...	...	...	...	...	...

– From/to Fribourg (Table **505**).
– From/to München (Table **75**).
– From/to Sargans (Table **534**).

d – Dec. 9 - July 21 and Sept. 9 - Dec. 14.
e – ①②③④⑦ (also Apr. 19).
r – ⑤⑥ (not Apr. 19).

SBB — WINTERTHUR - SCHAFFHAUSEN — 531

km																								
0	**Winterthur** d.	0542	0606	0619	0642	and at the same minutes past each hour until	1806	1819	1842	1906	1919	1942	2006	2019	2042	...	2106	2119	2142	2206	2242	2306	2342	...	0012
30	**Schaffhausen** a.	0613	0638	0646	0713		1838	1846	1913	1938	1946	2013	2038	2046	2113	...	2138	2146	2213	2238	2313	2338	0013	...	0041

								Ⓐj																
chaffhausen d.	0515	0521	0546	0615	0621	...	0646	0653	0715	0721	0746	0815	0821	0846	and at the same minutes past each hour until	2015	2021	2046	2121	2146	2221	2246	...	2321	2346
/interthur a.	0542	0554	0619	0642	0654	...	0719	0733	0742	0754	0819	0842	0854	0919		2042	2054	2119	2154	2219	2254	2319	...	2354	0023

– Not May 1.

533 SCHAFFHAUSEN - KREUZLINGEN — URh

	✕A		✕C		✕A		✕A		
Schaffhausen d.	0910	...	1110	...	1318	...	1518	...	...
Stein am Rhein d.	1115	...	1315	...	1523	...	1723	...	...
Kreuzlingen Hafen a.	1355	...	1555	...	1805	...	2005d	...	...

	✕A		✕B		✕A		✕D		
Kreuzlingen Hafen d.	0900	...	1100	...	1427	...	1627	...	...
Stein am Rhein d.	1130	...	1330	...	1657	...	1857	...	...
Schaffhausen a.	1245	...	1445	...	1815	...	2015d	...	...

A – Apr. 13 - Sept. 29 (not Apr. 15, 16, 17, 23, 24).
B – Apr. 13 - Oct. 13 (not Apr. 15, 16, 17, 23, 24).
C – ⑦ Apr. 14 - June 16 (also Apr. 19, 22, May 1, 30, June 10, 20); daily June 22 - Sept. 8 (also Sept. 15, 22); daily Sept. 29 - Oct. 13.
D – ⑦ Apr. 21 - June 16 (also Apr. 19, 22, May 1, 30, June 10, 20); daily June 22 - Sept. 8 (also Sept. 15, 22, 29).
d – Not Aug. 10.

534 WIL - ST GALLEN - BUCHS - CHUR — SBB

km		IR 3251	IR 3253	IR 3255 Z	EC 191 M	IR 3257 Z	IR 3259 Z	IR 3261 Z	IR 3263 Z	IR 3265 Z	IR 3267 Z	EC 195 Me	IR 3269 Z	IR 3271 Z	IR 3273 Z	IR 3275 Z	IR 3277 Z	EC 197 M	IR 3279 Z	IR 3281 Z	IC 585				RE 3493	
	Wil 530 d.	0456	0556	0656	...	0756	0856	0956	1056	1156	1256	...	1356	1456	1556	1656	1756	...	1856	1956	...	*2056*	*2156*	*2256*	...	2356
	Gossau 530 d.	0515	0615	0715	...	0815	0915	1015	1115	1215	1315	...	1415	1515	1615	1715	1815	...	1915	2015	...	*2115*	*2215*	*2315*	...	0015
0	**St Gallen** 530 d.	0525	0625	0725	0807	0825	0925	1025	1125	1225	1325	1407	1425	1525	1625	1725	1825	1907	1925	2025	...	2125	2225	2325	...	0022
16	Rorschach d.	0539	0639	0739	|	0839	0939	1039	1139	1239	1339	|	1439	1539	1639	1739	1839	|	1939	2039	...	2139	2239	2339	...	...
27	**St Margrethen** d.	0547	0647	0747	0830	0847	0947	1047	1147	1247	1347	1442	1447	1547	1647	1747	1847	1930	1947	2047	...	2147	2247	2347	...	...
39	Altstätten d.	0600	0700	0800	...	0900	1000	1100	1200	1300	1400	...	1500	1600	1700	1800	1900	...	2000	2100	...	2200	2300	0000	...	...
65	**Buchs** ⊖ 520 d.	0615	0715	0815	...	0915	1015	1115	1215	1315	1415	...	1515	1615	1715	1815	1915	...	2015	2115	...	2215	2315	0015	...	...
81	Sargans ⊖ 520 d.	0627	0727	0827	...	0927	1027	1127	1227	1327	1427	...	1527	1627	1727	1827	1927	...	2027	2125	2133	2225	2325	0025	0028	...
93	Landquart 520 a.	0638	0736	0836	...	0936	1036	1136	1236	1336	1436	...	1536	1636	1736	1836	1936	...	2036	...	2141	*2241*	*0016*	...	0037	...
107	**Chur** 520 a.	0649	0748	0848	...	0948	1048	1148	1248	1348	1448	...	1548	1648	1748	1848	1948	...	2048	...	2152	*2252*	*0026*	...	0047	...

	IC 556 ⚒	IR 3256 Z	IR 3258 Z	IR 3260 Z	IR 3262 Z	IR 3264 Z	EC 196 M	IR 3266 Z	IR 3268 Z	IR 3270 Z	IR 3272 Z	IR 3274 Z	EC 194 Me	IR 3276 Z	IR 3278 Z	IR 3280 Z	IR 3282 Z	IR 3284 Z	IR 3286 Z	EC 190 M	RE 3488		RE 3490			
Chur 520 d.	0509	...	0612	0712	0812	0912	...	1012	1112	1212	1312	1412	...	1512	1612	1712	1812	1912	2012	...	2114	...	2214	...	*2231*	*2301*
Landquart 520 d.	0519	...	0622	0722	0822	0922	...	1022	1122	1222	1322	1422	...	1522	1622	1722	1822	1922	2022	...	2122	...	2222	...	*2239*	*2309*
Sargans ⊖ 520 d.	0527	0536	0636	0736	0836	0936	...	1036	1136	1236	1336	1436	...	1536	1636	1736	1836	1936	2036	...	2132	2136	2232	2236	2300	2336
Buchs ⊖ 520 d.	...	0545	0645	0745	0845	0945	...	1045	1145	1245	1345	1445	...	1545	1645	1745	1845	1945	2045	...	...	2145	...	2245	2315	2345
Altstätten d.	...	0601	0701	0801	0901	1001	...	1101	1201	1301	1401	1501	...	1601	1701	1801	1901	2001	2101	...	...	2201	...	2301	2338	0001
St Margrethen d.	...	0613	0713	0813	0913	1013	1029	1113	1213	1313	1413	1513	1529	1613	1713	1813	1913	2013	2113	2129	...	2213	...	2313	2352	0013
Rorschach d.	...	0621	0721	0821	0921	1021	|	1121	1221	1321	1421	1521	|	1621	1721	1821	1921	2021	2121	|	...	2221	...	2321	0002	0021
St Gallen 530 a.	...	0635	0735	0835	0935	1035	1053	1135	1235	1335	1435	1535	1553	1635	1735	1835	1935	2035	2135	2153	...	2235	...	2335	0020	0035
Gossau 530 a.	...	0646	0746	0846	0946	1046	...	1146	1246	1346	1446	1546	...	1646	1746	1846	1946	2046	2146	...	...	*2246*	...	*2346*	...	...
Wil 530 a.	...	0703	0803	0903	1003	1103	...	1203	1303	1403	1503	1603	...	1703	1803	1903	2003	2103	2203	...	...	*2303*	...	*0003*	...	...

VADUZ (LIECHTENSTEIN) 🚌 services

[line 11]	Ⓐ	⚒	Ⓐ	⑥						and at the same minutes past each hour until												
Feldkirch (Bahnhof) d.	...	...	...	...	...	0624	0654	0724	0754		1724	1754	1824	1854	1924	1954	2024	2054	2124	2154	2254	...
Schaan (Bahnhof) d.	0515	0530a	0600	0600	0630	0700	0730	0800	0830		1800	1830	1900	1930	2000	2030	2100	2130	2200	2230	2330	...
Vaduz Post d.	0526	0541	0611	0608	0641	0711	0741	0811	0841		1811	1841	1908	1941	2008	2041	2108	2141	2208	2238	2338	...
Sargans (Bahnhof) a.	0557	0612	0642	...	0712	0742	0812	0842	0912		1842	1912	...	2012	...	2112	...	2212	...	...	...	...

[line 11]	Ⓐ	①–⑥							and at the same minutes past each hour until													
Sargans (Bahnhof) d.	...	...	0544a	0614a	0644	0714a	0744	0814		1844	1914	1944	...	...	2044	...	...	2144	...	...	2244	...
Vaduz Post d.	0522	0548	0618	0648	0718	0748	0818	0848		1918	1948	2018	2048	...	2118	2148	...	2218	2248	...	2318	...
Schaan (Bahnhof) d.	0530	0600	0630	0700	0730	0800	0830	0900		1930	2000	2030	2100	...	2130	2200	...	2230	2300	...	2326	...
Feldkirch (Bahnhof) a.	0606	0636	0706	0736	0806	0836	0906	0936		2006	2036	2106	2136	...	2206	2236	...	2306	2336	...	...	...

🚌 [line 12] **Buchs** (Rheinau) - **Vaduz** (Post). Journey time: ± 15 minutes. **Runs on Ⓐ only**. Operator: LIEmobil, Postplatz 7, FL-9494 Schaan. ✆ +423 237 94 94 (www.liemobil.li).
From Buchs at 0630, 0700, 0730, 1200, 1230, 1300, 1630, 1700, 1730, 1800.
From Vaduz at 0639, 0709, 0739, 1209, 1239, 1309, 1639, 1709, 1739, 1809, 1839.

M – 🚃12 and ✕ Zürich - München and v.v.
Z – From / to Zürich (Table **530**).
a – Ⓐ only.
e – Dec. 9 - July 21 and Sept. 9 - Dec. 14.
⊖ – See panel below main table for 🚌 links to / from Vaduz (Liechtenstein).

535 ZÜRICH - KONSTANZ and ROMANSHORN — SBB

km		IC 803 ⊗	IR 2107	IC 805 ✕	IR 2109	IC 807 ✕	IR 2111	IC 809 ✕	IR 2113	IC 811 ⊗	IR 2115	IC 813 ✕	IR 2117	IC 815 ⊗	IR 2119	IC 817 ✕	IR 2121	IC 819 ⊗	IR 2123	IC 821 ✕	IR 2125	IC 823 ✕	IR 2127	IC 825 ✕	IR 2129	IC 827 ⊗	IR 2131
	Brig 560 d.	...	...	...	...	0546	...	0648	...	0748	...	0848	...	0948	...	1048	...	1148	...	1248	...	1348	...	1448	...	1548	...
	Bern 505 560 d.	...	...	0602	...	0702	...	0802	...	0902	...	1002	...	1102	...	1202	...	1302	...	1402	...	1502	...	1602	...	1702	...
0	**Zürich** HB 530 d.	0605	0635	0705	0735	0805	0835	0905	0935	1005	1035	1105	1135	1205	1235	1305	1335	1405	1435	1505	1535	1605	1635	1705	1735	1805	1835
10	**Zürich** Flug ✈ 530 d.	0616	0646	0716	0746	0816	0846	0916	0946	1016	1046	1116	1146	1216	1246	1316	1346	1416	1446	1516	1546	1616	1646	1716	1746	1816	1846
30	Winterthur 530 d.	0631	0701	0731	0801	0831	0901	0931	1001	1031	1101	1131	1201	1231	1301	1331	1401	1431	1501	1531	1601	1631	1701	1731	1801	1831	1901
46	Frauenfeld d.	0642	0712	0742	0812	0842	0912	0942	1012	1042	1112	1142	1212	1242	1312	1342	1412	1442	1512	1542	1612	1642	1712	1742	1812	1842	1912
64	Weinfelden ▲ d.	0655	0725	0755	0825	0855	0925	0955	1025	1055	1125	1155	1225	1255	1325	1355	1425	1455	1525	1555	1625	1655	1725	1755	1825	1855	1925
	Kreuzlingen ▲ a.	|	0743	|	0843	|	0943	|	1043	|	1143	|	1243	|	1343	|	1443	|	1543	|	1643	|	1743	|	1843	|	1943
	Konstanz ▲ a.	|	0750	|	0850	|	0950	|	1050	|	1150	|	1250	|	1350	|	1450	|	1550	|	1650	|	1750	|	1850	|	1950
86	**Romanshorn** a.	0712	...	0812	...	0912	...	1012	...	1112	...	1212	...	1312	...	1412	...	1512	...	1612	...	1712	...	1812	...	1912	...

	IC 829 ✕	IR 2133	IC 831 ⊗	IR 2135	IC 833 ✕	IR 2137	IC 835	IR 2139 §	IC 837	RE 2143	IC 845
Brig 560 d.	1648	...	1748	...	1848	...	1948	...	...	...	...
Bern 505 560 d.	1802	...	1902	...	2002	...	2102	...	2202	...	...
Zürich HB 530 d.	1905	1935	2005	2035	2105	2135	2205	2235	2305	2339	0005
Zürich Flug ✈ 530 d.	1916	1946	2016	2046	2116	2146	2216	2246	2316	2353	0016
Winterthur 530 d.	1931	2001	2031	2101	2131	2201	2231	2301	2331	0008	0031
Frauenfeld d.	1942	2012	2042	2112	2142	2212	2242	2312	2342	0018	0042
Weinfelden ▲ d.	1955	2025	2055	2125	2155	2225	2255	2325	2355	0030	0055
Kreuzlingen ▲ a.	|	2043	|	2143	|	2243	|	2343	|	0048	|
Konstanz ▲ a.	|	2050	|	2150	|	2250	|	2350	|	0051	|
Romanshorn a.	2012	...	2112	...	2212	...	2312	...	0012	...	0112

	IR 2106	IC 806 ⊗	IR 2108	IC 808 ✕	IR 2110	IC 810 ⊗	IR 2112	IC 812 ✕	IR 2114	IC 814 ✕	IR 2116
Romanshorn d.	...	0548	...	0648	...	0748	...	0848	...	0948	...
Konstanz ▲ d.	0509	|	0609	|	0709	|	0809	|	0909	|	1009
Kreuzlingen ▲ d.	0516	|	0616	|	0716	|	0816	|	0916	|	1016
Weinfelden ▲ d.	0536	0606	0636	0706	0736	0806	0836	0906	0936	1006	1036
Frauenfeld d.	0548	0618	0648	0718	0748	0818	0848	0918	0948	1018	1048
Winterthur 530 d.	0601	0631	0701	0731	0801	0831	0901	0931	1001	1031	1101
Zürich Flughafen ✈ 530 a.	0613	0644	0713	0744	0813	0844	0913	0944	1013	1044	1113
Zürich HB 530 a.	0625	0655	0725	0755	0825	0855	0925	0955	1025	1055	1125
Bern 505 560 a.	...	0758	...	0858	...	0958	...	1058	...	1158	...
Brig 560 a.	...	0911	...	1011	...	1111	...	1211	...	1311	...

km		IC 816 ✕	IR 2118	IC 818 ⊗	IR 2120	IC 820 ✕	IR 2122	IC 822 ⊗	IR 2124	IC 824 ✕	IR 2126	IC 826 ⊗	IR 2128	IC 828 ✕	IR 2130	IC 830 ✕	IR 2132	IC 832 ✕	IR 2134	IC 834 ⊗	IR 2136	IC 836 ✕	IR 2138 §	IC 838	RE 2142	IC 840	RE 2146
	Romanshorn d.	1048	...	1148	...	1248	...	1348	...	1448	...	1548	...	1648	...	1748	...	1848	...	1948	...	2048	...	2148	...	2248	...
0	**Konstanz** ▲ d.	|	1109	|	1209	|	1309	|	1409	|	1509	|	1609	|	1709	|	1809	|	1909	|	2009	|	2109	|	2209	|	2309
1	Kreuzlingen ▲ d.	|	1116	|	1216	|	1316	|	1416	|	1516	|	1616	|	1716	|	1816	|	1916	|	2016	|	2116	|	2216	|	2316
24	Weinfelden ▲ d.	1106	1136	1206	1236	1306	1336	1406	1436	1506	1536	1606	1636	1706	1736	1806	1836	1906	1936	2006	2036	2106	2136	2206	2236	2306	2336
	Frauenfeld d.	1118	1148	1218	1248	1318	1348	1418	1448	1518	1548	1618	1648	1718	1748	1818	1848	1918	1948	2018	2048	2118	2148	2218	2248	2318	2348
	Winterthur 530 d.	1131	1201	1231	1301	1331	1401	1431	1501	1531	1601	1631	1701	1731	1801	1831	1901	1931	2001	2031	2101	2131	2201	2231	2259	2331	2359
	Zürich Flug ✈ 530 a.	1144	1213	1244	1313	1344	1413	1444	1513	1544	1613	1644	1713	1744	1813	1844	1913	1944	2013	2044	2113	2144	2213	2244	*2313*	2344	*0040*
	Zürich HB 530 a.	1155	1225	1255	1325	1355	1425	1455	1525	1555	1625	1655	1725	1755	1825	1855	1925	1955	2025	2055	2125	2155	2225	2255	*2325*	2355	*0053*
	Bern 505 560 a.	1258	...	1358	...	1458	...	1558	...	1658	...	1758	...	1858	...	1958	...	2058	...	2158	...	2302	...	0002	...	...	...
	Brig 560 a.	1411	...	1511	...	1611	...	1711	...	1811	...	1911	...	2011	...	2111	...	...	...	...	...	...	...	...	...	...	...

§ – Runs as *RE* train on ①②③④⑦ (also Apr. 19).

▲ – Additional services operate **Weinfelden - Konstanz and v.v.** journey time: 30 – 36 minutes.
From Weinfelden at 0606, 0706 and hourly until 2306, 0006.
From Konstanz at 0523, 0623 and hourly until 2123, 2223.

BSB/SBS ROMANSHORN - FRIEDRICHSHAFEN car ferry service 536

	d	d	e	e		and		f	f
Romanshorn ⊡ d.	0522	0622	0722	0822	0922	hourly	1622	1722 1822	1922 2022
Friedrichshafen ⊡ a.	0603	0703	0803	0903	1003	until	1703	1803 1903	2003 2103

	d	d	e	e		and				f	f
Friedrichshafen ⊡ d.	0527	0627	0727	0827	0927	hourly	1627	1727	1827	1927	2027
Romanshorn ⊡ a.	0608	0708	0808	0908	1008	until	1708	1808	1908	2008	2108

d – ①–⑤ (not Apr. 19, 22, May 1, 30, June 10, 20, Aug. 1, Oct. 3).
e – ①–⑥ to Mar. 16; daily Mar. 18 - Nov. 9; ①–⑥ Nov. 11 - Dec. 14.
f – ①–⑤ Jan. 7 - Mar. 15; daily Mar. 18 - Nov. 8; ①–⑤ Nov. 11 - Dec. 13.

⊡ – Autoquai.

Operator: BSB / SBS ✆ 071 466 78 88.

SBB, THURBO* SCHAFFHAUSEN - ROMANSHORN - RORSCHACH 538

km																								
0	**Schaffhausen** d.	...	...	...	0519	...	0549	...	0619	...		2049	...	2119	...	2149	...	2219	...	2249	...	2319	2349	...	...
20	Stein am Rhein d.	...	0513	...	0543	...	0613	...	0643	...		2113	...	2143	...	2213	...	2243	...	2313	...	2343	0013	...	...
46	**Kreuzlingen** d.	...	0545	...	0615	...	0645	...	0715	...	and at	2145	...	2215	...	2245	...	2315	...	2345	...	0015	0043	...	...
47	Kreuzlingen Hafen d.	...	0547	...	0617	...	0647	...	0717	...	the same	2147	...	2217	...	2247	...	2317	...	2347	...	0017	...	...	...
65	**Romanshorn** a.	...	0612	...	0642	...	0712	...	0742	...	minutes	2212	...	2242	...	2312	...	2342	...	0012	...	0042	...	...	...
65	**Romanshorn** d.	0516	0613	0616	0643	0646	0713	0716	0743	0746	past each	2213	2216	2243	2246	2313	2316	2343	2346	0013	0017	...	...	...	...
	St Gallen **525** a.	|	0641	|	0711	|	0741	|	0811	|	hour	2241	|	2311	|	2341	|	0011	|	0041	|	...	...	...	...
73	Arbon a.	0525	...	0625	...	0655	...	0725	...	0755	until	...	2225	...	2255	...	2325	...	2355	...	0025	...	...	...	...
79	Rorschach Hafen a.	0533	...	0633	...	0703	...	0733	...	0803		...	2233	...	2303	...	2333	...	0003	...	0033	...	...	...	...
80	**Rorschach** a.	0536	...	0636	...	0706	...	0736	...	0806		...	2236	...	2306	...	2336	...	0006	...	0036	...	...	...	...

Rorschach d.	...	...	0524	...	0554	...	0624	...	0654	...		2124	...	2154	...	2224	...	2254	...	2324	...	2354	...	...	...
Rorschach Hafen d.	...	...	0526	...	0556	...	0626	...	0656	...		2126	...	2156	...	2226	...	2256	...	2326	...	2356	...	...	...
Arbon d.	...	...	0534	...	0604	...	0634	...	0704	...	and at	2134	...	2204	...	2234	...	2304	...	2334	...	0004	...	...	...
St Gallen **525** d.	...	...	|	0519	|	0549	|	0619	|	0649	the same	|	2119	|	2149	|	2219	|	2249	|	2319	|	2349	...	...
Romanshorn a.	...	...	0542	0546	0613	0616	0643	0646	0713	0716	minutes	2143	2146	2213	2216	2243	2246	2313	2316	2343	2346	0013	0016	...	...
Romanshorn d.	...	0518	...	0548	...	0618	...	0648	...	0718	past each	...	2148	...	2218	...	2248	...	2318	...	2348	...	0018	...	...
Kreuzlingen Hafen d.	...	0540	...	0610	...	0640	...	0710	...	0740	hour	...	2210	...	2240	...	2310	...	2340	...	0010	...	0040	...	...
Kreuzlingen d.	0516	0546	...	0616	...	0646	...	0716	...	0746	until	...	2216	...	2246	...	2316	...	2346	...	0013	...	0043	...	...
Stein am Rhein d.	0546	0616	...	0646	...	0716	...	0746	...	0816		...	2246	...	2316	...	2346	...	0016	...	...	...	...	...	...
Schaffhausen a.	0613	0643	...	0713	...	0743	...	0813	...	0843		...	2313	...	2343	...	0013	...	0043	...	...	...	...	...	...

* – SBB Romanshorn - Rorschach; THURBO Schaffhausen - Romanshorn.

THURBO WEINFELDEN - WIL 539

km			Ⓐ			Ⓐ					
0	Weinfelden d.	0502	0532	and at the same minutes past	1902	1932	2002	2102	2202	2302	0002
19	Wil a.	0527	0557	each hour until	1927	1957	2027	2127	2227	2327	0027

	Ⓐ			Ⓐ					
Wil d.	0502	0532	and at the same minutes past	2002	2032	2132	2232	2332
Weinfelden a.	0530	0600	each hour until	2030	2100	2200	2300	2400

PA CHUR - FLIMS 542

Chur (Postautostation) - **Flims** Dorf (Post), ± 35 minutes, and **Flims** Waldhaus (Caumasee), ± 40 minutes.

From **Chur**:
0603 ⚒, 0638 Ⓐ, 0658, 0728 Ⓐ, 0758, 0828, 0858, 0928, 0958, 1028, 1058, 1128, 1158, 1228, 1245 Ⓐ, 1258, 1328, 1358, 1428, 1458, 1528, 1558, 1628, 1658, 1728, 1758, 1828 Ⓐ, 1858, 1928 Ⓐ, 2000, 2100, 2200, 2300.

From **Flims** Waldhaus (± 5 minutes later from Flims Dorf):
0516 ⚒, 0613, 0700 Ⓐ, 0714, 0744, 0814, 0844 Ⓐ, 0914, 0944, 1014, 1044, 1114, 1149, 1214, 1229, 1259 Ⓐ, 1314, 1344, 1414, 1444, 1514, 1544, 1614, 1644, 1714, 1744, 1814, 1844, 1914, 1944 Ⓐ, 2013, 2113, 2213, 2313.

PA, RhB* ST MORITZ and TIRANO - CHIAVENNA - LUGANO 543

			P🅁		B🅁					
St Moritz, Bahnhof § d.	0720	0915	1025	1115	...	1315	1415	1515	1715	1915
Silvaplana § d.	0732	0923	1035**u**	1123	...	1323	1423	1523	1723	1927
Sils / Segl Maria, Posta § d.	0739	0931	1041**u**	1131	...	1331	1431	1531	1731	1934
Maloja, Posta § d.	0751	0946	1052**u**	1146	...	1346	1446	1554	1746	1946
Castasegna 🏛 § d.	0830	1030	1122**u**	1230	...	1430	1530	1638	1830	2025
Tirano, Stazione d.	|	|	|	|	1420	|	|	|	|	|
Chiavenna, Stazione § a.	0853	1053	1137	1253	|	1453	1553	1701	1853	2048
Chiavenna, Stazione d.	...	...	1150	...	|	...	...	...	...	...
Menaggio d.	...	...	1245**x**	...	|	...	...	...	...	...
Lugano, Stazione ◐ a.	...	...	1350**s**	...	1730	...	...	...	...	...
Lugano, Autosilo Balestra a.	...	...	1400	...	...	...	...	...	...	...

					B🅁				P🅁	
Lugano, Autosilo Balestra d.	...	...	...	...	...	...	...	...	1513	...
Lugano, Stazione ◐ d.	...	...	...	...	1000	...	...	...	1531**u**	...
Menaggio d.	...	...	...	...	|	...	...	...	1621**x**	...
Chiavenna, Stazione a.	...	...	...	...	|	...	...	...	1726	...
Chiavenna, Stazione § d.	0715	0906	1106	1306	|	1506	1606	1706	1739	1915
Tirano, Stazione d.	|	|	|	|	1300	|	|	|	|	|
Castasegna 🏛 § d.	0733	0926	1126	1326	...	1526	1626	1726	1754**s**	1933
Maloja, Posta § d.	0812	1012	1212	1412	...	1612	1712	1814	1826**s**	2014
Sils / Segl Maria, Posta § d.	0825	1025	1225	1425	...	1625	1725	1827	1837**s**	2027
Silvaplana § d.	0833	1033	1233	1433	...	1633	1733	1836	1843**s**	2036
St Moritz, Bahnhof § a.	0842	1042	1242	1442	...	1642	1742	1851	1856	2051

B – Bernina Express: ④⑤⑥⑦ Feb. 21 - Apr. 21; daily Apr. 23 - Oct. 27; ④⑤⑥⑦ Oct. 31 - Nov. 24.
P – Palm Express: ⑤⑥⑦ (daily June 7 - Oct. 20).
s – Stops to set down only.
u – Stops to pick up only.
x – Calls only if advance reservation is made.

§ – Additional services operate St Moritz - Chiavenna and v.v.
◐ – 🏛 is at Gandria.
* – Operators:
Tirano - Lugano: RhB. Reservation: ✆ (081) 288 65 65;
St Moritz - Chiavenna - Lugano: PA.
Reservation: ✆ St Moritz (058) 341 34 92; fax (058) 667 49 81.

PA CHUR - BELLINZONA and CHIAVENNA 544

km			S	Bh	Bj	B		S	B	Bj		B	Bj		B	B		B	S	Bj		B		🅁✗g	🅁✗g
0	**Chur** Postautostation d.	0655	...	0808	0813	0913	...	...	1008	1113	...	1208	1313	...	1408	1513	...	1608	...	1713	...	1808	...	...	...
40	Thusis Bahnhof ⊡ d.	0720	...	0835	0840	0940	0935	...	1035	1140	1135	1235	1340	1335	1435	1540	1535	1635	...	1740	1735	1835	1935	2135	2355
64	Splügen Dorf d.	0744	0820	0904	0904	1004	1009	1020	1104	1204	1209	1304	1404	1409	1504	1604	1609	1704	1715	1804	1809	1904	2009	2202	0022
	San Bernardino Posta a.	0803	|	0923	0923	1023	1029	|	1123	1223	1229	1323	1423	1429	1523	1623	1629	1723	|	1823	1829	1923	2029	...	...
	Chiavenna Stazione ◐ a.	|	1020	|	|	|	|	1220	|	|	|	|	|	|	|	|	|	|	1915	|	|	|	|	...	...
179	**Bellinzona** Stazione a.	0850	...	1020	1013	1113	1151	...	1220	1313	1351	1420	1513	1551	1620	1713	1751	1820	...	1913	1952	2020	2152	...	...

	Ⓐ		S		B	B		Bj	B		Bj	B		B	S	B		Bj	S	B		B	B	🅁✗g	🅁✗g
Bellinzona Stazione d.	...	0707	...	0807	0845	0941	1007	1045	1141	1207	1245	1341	1407	1445	...	1541	1607	1645	...	1741	1807	1845	2045	...	...
Chiavenna Stazione ◐ d.	...	|	0750	|	|	|	|	|	|	|	|	|	|	|	1440	|	|	|	1640	|	|	|	|	...	...
San Bernardino Posta d.	0600	0823	|	0923	0935	1032	1123	1135	1232	1323	1335	1432	1523	1535	|	1632	1723	1735	|	1832	1923	1935	2135	...	...
Splügen Dorf d.	0622	0845	0945	0945	0953	1051	1145	1153	1252	1345	1353	1452	1545	1553	1635	1652	1745	1753	1835	1852	1945	1953	2153	2217	0037
Thusis Bahnhof ⊙ d.	0704	0924	...	1024	1020	1126	1224	1220	1326	1424	1420	1526	1624	1620	...	1726	1824	1820	...	1926	2024	2020	2220	2245	0105
Chur Postautostation a.	...	...	...	...	1045	1151	...	1245	1351	...	1445	1551	...	1645	...	1751	...	1845	...	1951	...	2050	2245	...	...

B – San Bernardino Route Express. 🅁.
S – Splügen Pass service. Runs June 8 - Oct. 20. Supplement payable.

g – Operated by Bustaxi. ✆ (081) 651 55 77.
h – Dec. 9 - June 7 and Oct. 21 - Dec. 14.
j – June 8 - Oct. 20.

⊙ – Stops to set down only.
⊡ – Stops to pick up only.
◐ – 🏛 is at Splügen Pass.
✗ – Supplement payable.

Reservations:
✆ Chur (058) 386 31 66; Thusis (058) 341 34 89.

545 RHÄTISCHE BAHN (RhB) services — Narrow gauge

For *Glacier Express* services see Table **575**

DISENTIS / MUSTÉR - CHUR - LANDQUART - KLOSTERS - SCUOL TARASP *Service to March 10 and from September 8 – see note ⊠*

km		Ⓐ M	⚒ D	⚒	⚒	Ⓐ D			D		⚒	M	D			❖ M	D			❖ M	D		Ⓐ M	D	
0	**Disentis / Mustér** d.	...	...	...	...	...	...	0544	...	...	0615	...	...	0644	...	...	...	0744		...	...	1544	...	...	1644
12	Trun d.	...	...	...	...	...	...	0602	...	...	0631	...	...	0702	...	...	...	0802		...	...	1602	...	...	1702
30	Ilanz d.	...	...	...	...	...	...	0624	...	...	0653	...	...	0724	...	...	...	0824	and at	...	...	1624	...	...	1724
49	Reichenau-Tamins d.	...	...	...	0534	...	...	0649	...	...	0718	...	...	0750	...	...	...	0849		...	...	1649	...	...	1749
59	**Chur** a.	...	...	...	0548	...	...	0703	...	...	0733	...	...	0803	...	...	...	0901	the same	...	...	1701	...	...	1801
59	**Chur** 520 534 d.	...	...	...	0550	...	...	0721	...	...	...	...	...	0821	...	...	...	0921		...	...	1721	...	...	1821
73	**Landquart** 520 534 a.	...	...	...	0610	...	...	0741	...	...	...	...	...	0841	...	...	...	0942	minutes	...	...	1742	...	...	1842
73	**Landquart** d.	0455	0512	0534	...	0620	0647	...	0747	0750	...	0820	0847	...	0850	0920	0947	0950		1720	1747	1750	1820	1847	1850
94	Küblis d.	0515	0538	0608	...	0646	0714	...	0810	0814	...	0844	0910	...	0914	0944	1010	1014	past each	1744	1810	1814	1844	1910	1914
103	Klosters Dorf d.	│	0554	0623	...	0659	0727	...	0823	│	...	│	0923	...	│	│	1023	│		│	1823	│	│	1923	│
105	**Klosters** Platz 🚗 d.	0529	0557	0630	...	0702	0733	...	0826	0833	...	0859	0926	...	0933	0959	1026	1033	hour until	1759	1826	1833	1859	1926	1933
127	Sagliains 🚗 § ⊠ a.	...	...	0652	...	...	0750	...	...	0852	...	...	...	...	0952	...	...	1052		...	...	1852	...	...	1952
136	Ardez ⊠ a.	...	...	0709	...	...	0809	...	...	0907	...	...	...	...	1007	...	...	1107		...	...	1907	...	...	2007
144	**Scuol-Tarasp** ⊠ a.	...	...	0718	...	...	0819	...	...	0915	...	...	...	...	1015	...	...	1115		...	...	1915	...	...	2015

	D		D		D		D		D		⑤⑥
Disentis / Mustér d.	...	1744	...	1844	...	1944	...	2044	...	2221	...
Trun d.	...	1802	...	1902	...	2002	...	2102	...	2237	...
Ilanz d.	...	1824	...	1924	...	2024	...	2123	...	2257	...
Reichenau-Tamins d.	...	1849	...	1949	...	2049	...	2149	...	2323	...
Chur a.	...	1901	...	2001	...	2101	...	2202	...	2333	...
Chur 520 534 d.	...	1921	...	—	...	—	...	—	...	...	...
Landquart 520 534 a.	...	1941	...	...	...	...	...	...	...	...	...
Landquart d.	1920	...	1947	1950f	2047	...	2147	...	2247	...	...
Küblis d.	1944	...	2013	2017f	2113	...	2213	...	2313	...	...
Klosters Dorf d.	│	...	2027	2031f	2127	...	2227	...	2327	...	...
Klosters Platz 🚗 d.	2000	...	2029	2035	2129	2135	2229	2235	2329	...	2332
Sagliains 🚗 § ⊠ a.	...	...	...	2053	...	2153	...	2252	...	...	│
Ardez ⊠ a.	...	...	...	2109	...	2209	...	2309	...	...	2359
Scuol-Tarasp ⊠ a.	...	...	...	2118	...	2218	...	2318	...	...	0008

	⚒	⚒ D	⚒	⚒	D		Ⓐ D	⚒	D		D
Scuol-Tarasp ⊠ d.	...	...	...	0541	...	...	...	0641	...	...	...
Ardez ⊠ d.	...	...	...	0550	...	...	...	0649	...	...	...
Sagliains 🚗 § ⊠ d.	...	...	...	0603	...	...	...	0703	...	...	...
Klosters Platz 🚗 d.	...	0529	...	0622	0628	...	0655	0723	0728	...	0758
Klosters Dorf d.	...	0532	...	—	0631	...	0659	...	0731	...	│
Küblis d.	...	0545	...	...	0645	...	0714	...	0745	...	0815
Landquart a.	...	0613	...	...	0713	...	0739	...	0813	...	0836
Landquart 520 534 d.	...	...	0617	...	...	0717	...	...	...	0817	...
Chur 520 534 a.	...	...	0637	...	...	0736	...	...	...	0836	...
Chur d.	0609	...	0653	0653	...	0756	...	...	...	0856	...
Reichenau-Tamins d.	0623	...	0703	0703	...	0805	...	...	...	0905	...
Ilanz d.	0654	...	0733	0733	...	0833	...	...	...	0933	...
Trun d.	0715	...	0754	0754	...	0854	...	...	...	0954	...
Disentis / Mustér a.	0731	...	0811	0811	...	0911	...	...	...	1011	...

		D		D	❖ M			D	❖ M		D	M		D	M		D		D			D			⑤⑥
Scuol-Tarasp ⊠ d.	0741	...	0841	...	...		1441	...	...	1541	...	...	1641	...	...	1741	...	1841	...	1941	2041	...	2141	...	2241
Ardez ⊠ d.	0749	...	0849	...	...		1449	...	...	1549	...	...	1649	...	...	1749	...	1849	...	1949	2050	...	2150	...	2250
Sagliains 🚗 § ⊠ d.	0803	...	0903	...	...	and at	1503	...	...	1603	...	...	1703	...	...	1803	...	1903	...	2003	2103	...	2202	2203	2303
Klosters Platz 🚗 d.	0825	0831	0925	0931	0957		1525	1531	1557	1625	1631	1657	1725	1731	1757	1825	1831	1925	1931	2029	2123	2129	—	2222	2321
Klosters Dorf d.	│	0835	│	0935	│	the same	│	1535	│	│	1635	│	│	1735	│	│	1835	│	1935	2032	—	2132	...	2226	...
Küblis d.	0844	0850	0944	0950	1016		1544	1550	1616	1644	1650	1715	1744	1750	1816	1844	1850	1944	1950	2046	...	2146	...	2239	...
Landquart a.	0910	0913	1010	1013	1036	minutes	1610	1613	1636	1710	1713	1736	1810	1813	1836	1910	1913	2010	2013	2113	...	2213	...	2305	...
Landquart 520 534 d.	...	0917	1017	...	...		1617	...	...	1717	...	—	1817	...	...	1917	...	...	—	...	...	...	...	...	...
Chur 520 534 a.	...	0936	1036	...	...	past each	1636	...	...	1736	...	...	1836	...	...	1936	...	...	...	...	...	...	...	...	...
Chur d.	...	0956	1056	...	...		1656	...	...	1756	...	1825	1856	...	...	1956	...	...	2059	...	2159	...	2259	...	...
Reichenau-Tamins d.	...	1005	1105	...	...	hour until	1705	...	...	1805	...	│	1905	...	...	2005	...	...	2113	...	2211	...	2311	...	...
Ilanz d.	...	1033	1133	...	...		1733	...	...	1833	...	1902	1933	...	...	2033	...	...	2140	...	2234	...	2334	...	...
Trun d.	...	1054	1154	...	...		1754	...	...	1854	...	1924	1954	...	...	2054	...	...	2200	...	...	...	...	...	...
Disentis / Mustér a.	...	1111	1211	...	...		1811	...	...	1911	...	1940	2011	...	...	2111	...	...	2215	...	...	...	...	...	...

KLOSTERS - DAVOS

km		⚒	⚒	Ⓐ													Ⓐ						
	Landquart d.	0512	...	0620	...	0747	0847	...	and in the same	1347	1447	...	1547	1647	...	1747	...	1847	1920	1947	2047	2147	2247
0	**Klosters** Platz d.	0558	0627	0703	0732	0829	0929	1002	pattern every	1429	1529	1602	1629	1729	1802	1829	1902	1929	2001	2030	2130	2230	2330
18	**Davos** Platz a.	0633	0657	0729	0757	0857	0957	1032	**two** hours until	1457	1557	1632	1657	1757	1829	1857	1930	1957	2030	2058	2158	2258	2358

	⚒		Ⓐ																			
Davos Platz d.	0500	0600	0626	0700	...	0730	0802	0902	...	0926	1002	1102	and in the same	1726	1802	1902	...	2000	2100	...	2150	...
Klosters Platz a.	0527	0627	0653	0727	...	0757	0828	0929	...	0954	1028	1129	pattern every	1754	1828	1929	...	2027	2127	...	2217	...
Landquart a.	0613	0713	0739	0813	...	0836	0913	1013	...	...	1113	1213	**two** hours until	...	1913	2013	...	...	2213	...	...	...

DAVOS - FILISUR

km		⚒				961 ♦			♣		
0	**Davos** Platz d.	0605	0731	0831	0931	0951	...	1031	and hourly	1931	2031
16	**Filisur** a.	0630	0756	0856	0956	1017	...	1056	until	1956	2056

	⚒		♣		960 ♦					
Filisur d.	0634	0804	and hourly	1804	1818	1904	2004	...	2104	...
Davos Platz a.	0658	0829	until	1829	1847	1929	2029	...	2129	...

SCUOL TARASP and KLOSTERS - ST MORITZ and PONTRESINA *Service to March 10 and from September 8 – see note ⊠*

km		⚒	†	Ⓐ	⚒		⚒	†							❖			❖		Ⓐ					⑤⑥	
0	**Scuol-Tarasp** ⊠ d.	...	...	...	0541	...	0601	0641	...	0741	...	0834	...	0934	...	1034	and at	...	1834	...	1934	2041	...	2141	2241	...
	Landquart d.	...	...	0455	│	...	│	│	...	│	...	│	0820	│	0920	│		1720	│	1820	│	│	...	│	│	...
	Klosters Platz d.	...	...	0530	│	...	│	│	...	│	...	│	0901	│	1001	│	the same	1801	│	1901	│	│	...	│	│	...
17	Sagliains § ⊠ d.	...	...	│	0600	...	│	0703	...	0801	0803	0856	│	0956	│	1056		│	1856	│	1956	2102	2103	2203	2301	2303
19	Susch ⊠ d.	...	...	0554	...	...	0625	0705	...	...	0806	0859	0921	0959	1019	1059	minutes	1819	1859	1919	1959	...	2106	2206	...	2305
25	Zernez ⊖ d.	...	...	0603	...	...	0632	0713	...	...	0813	0907	0930	1007	1026	1107		1826	1907	1926	2007	...	2113	2213	...	2313
42	Zuoz d.	...	...	0623	...	0633**d**	0654	0733	0757**d**	...	0834	0928	0954	1028	1046	1128	past each	1846	1928	1946	2028	...	2133	2233	...	2332
52	Samedan a.	...	...	0634	...	0646**d**	0708	0746	0811**d**	...	0848	0942	1008	1042	1057	1142		1857	1942	2000	2042	...	2146	2246	...	2345
52	Samedan d.	0530	0545	0636	...	0648	0710	0748	0812	...	0849	0948	1009	1048	1100	1148	hour until	1900	1948	2001	2048	...	2150	2250	...	2346
	St Moritz a.	│	│	0644	...	│	0717	│	0819	...	│	│	1016	│	1109	│		1909	│	2009	│	...	│	│	...	2354
57	**Pontresina** a.	0536	0551	...	...	0655	...	0755	...	...	0856	0955	...	1055	...	1155		...	1955	...	2055	...	2156	2256	...	...

	Ⓐ	⚒	⚒	⚒	†	†				❖			❖												
Pontresina d.	...	...	...	0542	...	0558	0702	...	0802	...	and at	1402	...	1502	...	1602	...	1702	1802	1902	2002	...	2102	...	2202	2302
St Moritz d.	...	0445	0541	│	0558	│	│	...	│	0847		│	1447	│	1538	│	1647	│	│	│	│	...	│	...	│	│
Samedan a.	...	0451	0548	0548	0605	0605	0708	...	0808	0855	the same	1408	1455	1508	1545	1608	1655	1708	1808	1908	2008	...	2108	...	2208	2309
Samedan d.	0453	0513	—	0553	...	0608	0713	...	0813	0858		1413	1458	1513	1545	1613	1658	1713	1813	1913	2013	...	2113	...	2213	—
Zuoz d.	0506	0526	...	0607	...	0622	0727	...	0827	0910	minutes	1427	1510	1527	1559	1627	1710	1727	1827	1927	2027	...	2127	...	2227	...
Zernez ⊖ d.	0526	0547	...	...	...	0646	0747	...	0849	0930		1449	1530	1549	1628	1649	1730	1749	1849	1949	2047	...	2147	...	2247	...
Susch ⊠ d.	0533	0554	⚒	...	...	0653	0754	...	0858	0937	past each	1458	1537	1558	1635	1658	1737	1758	1858	1958	2054	...	2154	...	2254	...
Sagliains § ⊠ a.	│	0557	0656	...	...	0655	0756	0758	0901	│		1501	│	1601	│	1701	│	1801	1901	2001	2056	2058	2156	2158	2256	2258
Klosters Platz a.	0551	│	│	...	...	...	...	│	│	0956	hour until	│	1556	│	1654	│	1756	│	│	│	...	│	...	│	...	│
Landquart a.	0643	│	│	...	...	...	...	│	│	1036		│	1636	│	1736	│	1836	│	│	│	...	│	...	│	...	│
Scuol-Tarasp ⊠ a.	...	0623	0718	...	...	...	...	0819	0923	...		1523	...	1623	...	1723	...	1823	1923	2023	...	2118	...	2218	...	2318

FOR NOTES SEE NEXT PAGE

For *Glacier Express* services see Table 575

CHUR - ST MORITZ

km																								
											951		961											
			⚒	2⚒		⚒					◆R✓		◆R✓									k		
0	**Chur**	d.	0428	0510	...	0604	...	0658	0758	...	0832	0858	...	...	0958		1558	1658	1758	1858	1958	2056	2156	2315
10	Reichenau-Tamins	d.	0440	|	...	0617	...	0709	0809	...	|	0909	...	...	1009	and at	1609	1709	1809	1909	2009	2108	2209	2328
27	Thusis	d.	0502	0542	...	0640	...	0730	0830	...	|	0930	...	...	1030		1630	1730	1830	1930	2030	2133	2231	2350
41	Tiefencastel	d.	▬	0558	...	...	...	0747	0847	...	0918u	0947	...	...	1047	the same	1647	1747	1847	1947	2047	2149	...	...
	Davos Platz	d.	...	|	...	...	...	|	|	...	|	|	0951	...	|		|	|	|	|	|	|	...	...
51	**Filisur**	d.	...	0614	...	...	...	0802	0902	...	0933u	1002	1017u	...	1102	minutes	1702	1802	1902	2002	2102	2205	...	...
59	Bergün / Bravuogn	d.	...	0630	...	...	...	0815	0914	...	0947u	1014	1030u	...	1114		1714	1814	1914	2014	2115	2217	...	...
72	Preda	d.	...	0647	...	...	...	0832	0932	...	|	1032	|	...	1132	past each	1732	1832	1932	2032	2132	2234	...	...
84	**Samedan**	a.	...	0700	...	...	...	0847	0945	...	|	1045	1109u	...	1145		1745	1845	1945	2045	2148	2248	...	...
84	**Samedan**	d.	0556	...	0702	...	0749	0849	0949	...	|	1049	...	...	1149	hour until	1749	1849	1949	2049	2149	2251	...	...
	Pontresina	a.	|	...	|	...	|	|	|	...	1018	|	...	...	|		|	|	|	|	|	|	...	...
87	Celerina	d.	0601	...	0706	...	0753	0853	0953	...	...	1053	...	...	1153		1753	1853	1953	2053	2153	2255	...	...
89	**St Moritz**	a.	0606	...	0710	...	0757	0858	0958	...	...	1058	...	...	1158		1758	1858	1958	2058	2158	2258	...	...

												950		960									
		⚒	Ⓐ	Ⓐ	⚒	†						◆R✓		◆R✓			k						
St Moritz	d.	...	...	...	0541	0558	0702	0802		1602	...	...	1702	...	1802	1902	2002	2102	...	2202	...	2224	2320	2359
Celerina	d.	...	...	...	0545	0601	0706	0805	and at	1605	...	...	1705	...	1805	1905	2005	2105	...	2205	...	2228	2324	0002
Pontresina	d.	...	...	...	|	|	|	|		|	...	1624s	|	1724s	|	|	|	|	...	|	...	|	|	|
Samedan	a.	...	...	...	0548	0605	0709	0809	the same	1609	...	|	1709	1729s	1809	1909	2009	2109	...	2209	...	2231	2327	0005
Samedan	d.	...	...	0511	0550	0607	0716	0816		1616	...	|	1716	|	1816	1916	2016	...	...	...	...	...	...	...
Preda	d.	...	...	|	0603	0619	0730	0830	minutes	1630	...	|	1730	|	1830	1931	2031	...	...	...	...	...	...	...
Bergün / Bravuogn	d.	...	...	0539	0620	0637	0747	0847		1647	...	1704s	1747	1803s	1847	1948	2048	...	...	...	...	...	...	...
Filisur	d.	...	...	0554	0635	0652	0801	0901	past each	1701	...	1718s	1801	1819s	1901	2001	2101	...	...	...	...	...	...	...
Davos Platz	a.	...	...	|	|	|	|	|		|	...	|	|	1847	|	|	|	...	...	...	...	...	...	...
Tiefencastel	d.	...	...	0611	0651	0707	0815	0915	hour until	1715	...	1732s	1815	...	1915	2015	2116	...	...	...	...	...	...	...
Thusis	d.	0509	0544	0627	0709	0728	0833	0933		1733	...	1750s	1833	...	1933	2033	2133	...	2236	...	2354	...	...	...
Reichenau-Tamins	d.	0534	0608	0653	|	0753	0854	0954		1754	...	|	1854	...	1954	2053	2157	...	2257	...	0015	...	...	...
Chur	a.	0548	0623	0705	0742	0805	0903	1003		1803	...	1819	1903	...	2003	2103	2209	...	2310	...	0028	...	...	...

ST MORITZ - TIRANO

km																									
									973		951			961					975						
					⚒			△	◆R✓	▷	◆R✓		△	◆R✓			◇	▽▷	◆R✓	△	▷			Ⓐ	
0	**St Moritz**	d.	...	...	...	...	0748	0848	0939	0948	...	...	1048	...	1148	1248	1348	1448	1511	1548	1648	1748	1848	1948	2020
2	Celerina Staz	⊡ d.	...	...	...	...	0751	0851	|	0951	...	...	1051	...	1151	1251	1351	1451	|	1551	1651	1751	1851	1951	2023
6	**Pontresina**	a.	...	...	...	...	0757	0857	0947	0957	...	...	1057	...	1157	1257	1357	1457	|	1557	1657	1757	1857	1957	2029
6	**Pontresina**	d.	...	...	0702	...	0808	0904	0952	1008	1022e	...	1104	1117u	1208	1304	1408	1504	1520u	1608	1704	1808	1904	2004	...
12	Morteratsch	⊡ d.	...	...	0711	...	0818	0913	|	1018	|	...	1113	|	1218	1313	1418	1513	|	1619	1713	1818	1914	2014	...
17	Bernina Diavolezza	⊡ d.	...	...	0720	...	0829	0923	|	1029	1039c	...	1123	1134s	1229	1323	1429	1523	|	1629	1723	1828	1923	2023	...
18	Bernina Lagalb	⊡ d.	...	...	0724	...	0833	0925	|	1033	|	...	1125	|	1233	1325	1433	1525	|	1633	1725	1831	1926	2026	...
22	Ospizio Bernina	d.	...	...	0731	...	0840	0933	|	1040	|	...	1133	|	1240	1333	1440	1533	1552	1640	1733	1839	1934	2034	...
27	Alp Grüm	d.	...	...	0744	...	0853	0944	1028s	1053	1115	...	1144	1158s	1253	1344	1453	1544	1610	1653	1744	1853	1946	2045	...
44	**Poschiavo**	a.	...	...	0830	...	0941	1022	1114s	1141	1201	...	1222	1254s	1341	1422	1541	1622	1653s	1741	1822	1932	2023	2123	...
44	**Poschiavo**	d.	0620	0742	0834	0834	0942	1023	1123s	1142	1210	...	1223	|	1342	1423	1542	1623	|	1742	1823	...	...	...	...
48	Le Prese	d.	0627	0749	0841	0841	0949	1030	1132s	1149	1220s	...	1230	1303s	1349	1430	1549	1630	1702s	1749	1830	...	...	...	...
51	Miralago	⊡ d.	0633	0755	0847	0847	0955	1035	|	1155	|	...	1235	|	1355	1435	1555	1635	|	1755	1835	...	...	...	...
54	Brusio	⊡ d.	0642	0803	0857	0857	1003	1043	|	1203	|	...	1243	|	1403	1443	1603	1643	|	1803	1843	...	...	...	...
58	Campocologno ▦	d.	0654	0814	0908	0908	1014	1052	|	1214	|	...	1252	|	1414	1452	1614	1652	|	1814	1852	...	...	...	...
61	**Tirano**	a.	0703	0823	0917	0917	1023	1100	1200	1223	1249	...	1300	1333	1423	1500	1623	1700	1732	1823	1900	...	...	...	...

									976						974	950			960					
			⚒				◇	▽▷	◆R✓	△	▷	▷			◆R✓	◆R✓		△	◆R✓		△			
Tirano	d.	...	...	...	...	0741	0900	0941	1007	1100	1141	1300	1341	...	1407	1425	...	1500	1513	...	1541	1700	1741	1900	1941
Campocologno ▦	d.	...	...	...	...	0752	0908	0952	|	1108	1152	1308	1352	...	|	|	...	1508	|	...	1552	1708	1752	1910	1952
Brusio	⊡ d.	...	...	...	...	0803	0916	1003	|	1116	1203	1316	1403	...	|	|	...	1516	|	...	1603	1716	1803	1920	2003
Miralago	⊡ d.	...	...	...	...	0811	0923	1011	|	1123	1211	1323	1411	...	|	|	...	1523	|	...	1611	1723	1811	1927	2011
Le Prese	d.	...	...	...	...	0816	0928	1016	1041u	1128	1216	1328	1416	...	1441u	1454u	...	1528	1542u	...	1616	1728	1816	1932	2016
Poschiavo	a.	...	...	...	...	0825	0936	1025	1047	1136	1225	1336	1425	...	|	1502	...	1536	1553	...	1625	1736	1825	1940	2025
Poschiavo	d.	...	0628	...	0732	0828	0937	1028	1048	1137	1228	1337	1428	...	1449u	1509	...	1537	1556	...	1628	1737	1828	...	...
Alp Grüm	d.	...	0707	...	0813	0908	1012	1108	1126s	1212	1308	1412	1508	...	|	1545u	...	1612	1634	...	1708	1812	1908	...	...
Ospizio Bernina	d.	...	0714	...	0821	0916	1020	1116	1149s	1220	1316	1420	1516	...	|		...	1620	1651u	...	1716	1820	1916	...	...
Bernina Lagalb	⊡ d.	...	0724	...	0831	0926	1031	1126	|	1231	1326	1431	1526	...	|		...	1631	|	...	1726	1831	1926	...	...
Bernina Diavolezza	⊡ d.	...	0727	...	0834	0929	1034	1129	|	1234	1329	1434	1529	...	|		...	1634	|	...	1729	1834	1929	...	...
Morteratsch	⊡ d.	...	0738	...	0845	0940	1044	1140	|	1244	1340	1444	1540	...	|		...	1644	|	...	1740	1844	1940	...	...
Pontresina	a.	...	0748	...	0856	0951	1053	1151	1225s	1253	1351	1453	1551	...	1604s	1615	...	1653	1721s	...	1751	1853	1951	...	...
Pontresina	d.	...	0801	0801	0901	1001	1101	1201	1227s	1301	1401	1501	1601	...	|	...	...	1701	|	...	1801	1901	2001	...	...
Celerina Staz	⊡ d.	...	0806	0806	0906	1006	1106	1206	|	1306	1406	1506	1606	...	|	...	...	1706	|	...	1806	1906	2006	...	...
St Moritz	a.	...	0811	0811	0911	1011	1111	1211	1236	1311	1411	1511	1611	...	1619	...	...	1711	...	...	1811	1911	2011	...	...

CHUR - AROSA

km													
			⚒									p	h
0	**Chur**	d.	0508	0620	0708	0808	and	1908	2006	2100	2155	2300
8	Langwies	d.	0552	0704	0749	0850	hourly	1950	2048	2141	2232	2341
6	**Arosa**	a.	0609	0721	0809	0909	until	2009	2104	2158	2248	2358

		⚒	Ⓐ	Ⓒ						p	h
Arosa	d.	0548	0625	0648	0748	0848	and	1948	2109	2203	2300
Langwies	d.	0605	0640	0704	0805	0905	hourly	2005	2125	2219	2315
Chur	a.	0651	0721	0751	0851	0951	until	2051	2205	2259	2356

NOTES (LISTED BY TRAIN NUMBER)

1 – BERNINA EXPRESS – (12) [panorama car] and 🍸 Tirano - Chur and v.v.
1 – BERNINA EXPRESS – May 11 - Oct. 27: (12) [panorama car] and 🍸 Tirano - Davos and v.v.
4 – BERNINA EXPRESS – May 11 - Oct. 27: (12) [panorama car] and 🍸 Tirano - St Moritz and v.v.
6 – BERNINA EXPRESS – Apr. 19 - Nov. 3: (12) [panorama car] and 🍸 Tirano - St Moritz and v.v.

(12) Davos - Landquart and v.v.
(12) St Moritz - Landquart and v.v.

Dec. 9 - Mar. 3 (stops to set down only).
⚒ only.
Dec. 9 - May 10 and Oct. 28 - Dec. 14. Stops to pick up only.
⑤ only.
Daily Dec. 9 - Apr. 22; ⑤–⑦ Apr. 26 - Nov. 17 (also May 29, 30, June 10, July 31, Aug. 1); daily Nov. 18 - Dec. 14.
By 🚌 Thusis - Tiefencastel and v.v. Feb. 11 - Oct. 27 (in similar timings).
⑤⑥ Dec. 22 - Mar. 9.
Dec. 9 - May 10 and Oct. 28 - Dec. 14.
Stops to set down only.
Stops to pick up only.
Stops only on request.
May 11 - Oct. 27.

All services Scuol-Tarasp - Susch and v.v. are subject to alteration Mar. 11 - Sept. 7 with a 🚌 replacement service in operation. See page 562 for revised timings during this period.

△ – Conveys (12) [panorama car] Dec. 9 - Mar. 31, R, ✓.
▽ – Conveys (12) [panorama car] Dec. 9 - Mar. 31, Oct. 28 - Dec. 14, R, ✓.
▷ – Conveys open panorama car July 1 - Aug. 31, R, ✓. Subject to good weather.
◇ – Conveys (12) [panorama car] Jan. 7 - Mar. 31, R, ✓.
✣ – Runs every **two** hours.
♣ – Variations May 11 - Oct. 27: 10xx and 16xx departures from Davos depart 1018, 1618 (Filisur a. 1053, 1653); 11xx and 17xx from Filisur depart 1106, 1706 (Davos a. 1150, 1750). Operated with historic rolling stock.
§ – Sagliains station can only be used for changing trains.
⊡ – Request stop.
✓ – Supplement payable.
🚗 – Car-carrying shuttle available Klosters Selfranga - Sagliains and v.v. ✆ +41 (0)81 288 37 37. www.rhb.ch/en/car-transporter

⊖ – 🚌 service **Zernez - Malles and v.v.** Journey ±1 h 30 minutes.
From Zernez at 0715, 0815, 0915, 1015 **y**, 1032, 1115, 1215 **y**, 1315, 1415 **y**, 1515, 1615, 1715.
From Malles / Mals bahnhof at 0610 **y**, 0657⚒, 0803, 0903, 1003 **y**, 1103, 1203 **y**, 1303, 1403 **y**, 1503, 1545 **y**, 1603, 1703, 1803, 1903.
Operator: AutoDaPosta (PA); ✆ +41 (0)81 856 10 90.

550 LUZERN and ZÜRICH - ERSTFELD, LUGANO and MILANO

SBB, F

km		RE 25509 B	RE 25511 A	EC 11 ◧ ✕	IR 2309	RE 4313	EC 13 ◧ ✕	IR 2311	2567 S	IC 861 🍷	IC 663 ✕	IC 1463 ✕	RE 4317 P	IR 2313 N	IR 3091 H	2569 S	IC 865 ⑥⑦ d🍷	IC 665	EC 15 ◧ V✕	IR 2315	2571 S	IC 867 ✕	IC 667 ✕	RE 4321 P	IR 24
	Basel SBB **565** d.	...	...	...	0504	...	...	0604	...	...	0704	...	...	...	...	...	...	0804	...	...	...	...	0904	...	..
	Luzern d.	...	...	...	0618	...	...	0718	0739	...	0818	...	...	0820	...	0839	...	0918	...	0920	0939	...	1018	...	..
	Küssnacht am Rigi d.	...	...	...	|	...	...	|	0758	...	|	...	...	|	...	0858	...	|	...	|	0958	...	|	...	..
0	**Zürich** HB d.	...	...	0610	|	...	0710	|	|	0732	|	0810	...	|	0757	|	0832	|	0910	|	|	0932	|	...	10
29	Zug d.	...	...	0631	|	...	0731	|	|	0800	|	0831	...	|	|	|	0900	|	0931	|	|	1000	|	...	10
45	**Arth-Goldau** a.	...	...	0647	0646k	...	0747	0746	0811	0815	0846	0847	...	0848	0908	0911	0915	0946	0947	0948	1011	1015	1046	...	104
45	**Arth-Goldau** d.	...	...	0650	0653	...	0750	0753	...	0818	0848	0850	...	0853	0911	...	0918	0948	0950	0953	...	1018	1050	...	10
53	Schwyz d.	...	...	|	0701	...	|	0801	...	|	|	|	...	0901	0919	...	|	|	|	1001	...	|	|	...	11
56	Brunnen d.	...	...	|	0705	...	|	0805	...	|	|	|	...	0905	|	...	|	|	|	1005	...	|	|	...	11
68	Flüelen d.	...	...	0708	0716	...	0808	0816	...	|	|	|	...	0916	0933	...	|	|	|	1016	...	|	|	...	11
77	**Erstfeld** 550a d.	...	...	|	0723	...	|	0823	...	|	|	|	0837	0923	0943	...	|	|	|	1023	...	|	|	1037	11
165	Bellinzona ▲ 550a a.	...	...	0747	...	...	0847	...	...	0917	0945	0947	1009	...	1120	...	1017	1045	1047	...	...	1117	1147	1209	..
165	Bellinzona 550a ‡ d.	0613	0713	0751	...	0813	0851	...	...	0921	...	0951	1013	...	...	...	1021	...	1051	...	...	1121	1151	1213	..
194	**Lugano** 550a ‡ d.	0642	0742	0822	...	0842	0922	...	...	0948	...	1018	1041	...	...	...	1048	...	1122	...	...	1148	1218	1242	..
213	Mendrisio 592 ‡ d.	0657	0758	|	...	0857	|	...	...	...	...	...	...	...	...	...	...	...	|	...	...	...	...	1257	..
220	**Chiasso** 592 ‡ a.	0704	0804	0846	...	0904	0946	...	...	...	...	...	...	...	...	...	...	...	1146	...	...	...	...	1304	..
220	**Chiasso** 🛃 § d.	0707	0807	0851	...	0907	0951	...	...	...	...	...	...	...	...	...	...	...	1151	...	...	...	...	1307	..
224	Como San Giovanni § a.	0713	0813	|	...	0912	0955	...	...	...	...	...	...	...	...	...	...	...	|	...	...	...	...	1312	..
271	**Milano** Centrale § a.	0750	0850	0935	...	0950	1035	...	...	...	...	...	...	...	...	...	...	...	1235	...	...	...	...	1350	..

km		2573 S	IC 869 Ⓒ ✕	EC 17 ◧ ✕	RE 25523	IR 2319	2575 S	IC 871 Ⓒ 🍷	EC 151 ◧ F✕	RE 4325 P	IR 2421	2577 S	EC 19 ◧ ✕	RE 25527	IR 2323	2579 S	IC 875 Ⓒ 🍷	IC 675 ✕	RE 4329 P	IR 2425	2581 S	IC 877 ⑦ 🍷	EC 21 ◧ ✕	RE 4331 P	IR 23
	Basel SBB **565** d.	...	...	...	...	1004	...	...	1104	...	...	...	...	...	1204	...	...	1304	...	...	...	...	...	...	14
0	**Luzern** d.	1039	...	...	...	1118	1139	...	1218	...	...	1239	...	...	1318	1339	...	1418	...	...	1439	...	...	...	15
16	Küssnacht am Rigi d.	1058	...	...	...	|	1158	...	|	...	...	1258	...	...	|	1358	...	|	...	...	1458	...	...	...	
	Zürich HB d.	|	1032	1110	...	|	|	1132	|	...	1210	|	1310	...	|	|	1332	|	...	1410	|	1432	1510	...	|
	Zug d.	|	1100	1131	...	|	|	1200	|	...	1231	|	1331	...	|	|	1400	|	...	1431	|	1500	1531	...	
28	**Arth-Goldau** a.	1111	1115	1147	...	1146k	1211	1215	1246	...	1246k	1311	1347	...	1346k	1411	1415	1446	...	1446k	1511	1515	1547	...	154
	Arth-Goldau d.	...	1118	1150	...	1153	...	1218	1250	...	1253	...	1350	...	1353	...	1418	1450	...	1453	...	1518	1550	...	15
	Schwyz d.	...	|	|	...	1201	...	|	|	...	1301	...	|	...	1401	...	|	|	...	1501	...	|	|	...	16
	Brunnen d.	...	|	|	...	1205	...	|	|	...	1305	...	|	...	1405	...	|	|	...	1505	...	|	|	...	16
	Flüelen d.	...	|	|	...	1216	...	|	|	...	1316	...	|	...	1416	...	|	|	...	1516	...	|	|	...	16
	Erstfeld 550a d.	...	|	|	...	1223	...	|	|	1237	1323	...	|	...	1423	...	|	|	1437	1523	...	|	|	1537	16
	Bellinzona ▲ 550a a.	...	1217	1247	...	...	...	1317	1347	1409	...	...	1447	...	...	...	1517	1547	1609	...	...	1617	1647	1709	..
	Bellinzona 550a ‡ d.	...	1221	1251	...	...	...	1321	1351	1413	...	...	1451	...	...	...	1521	1551	1613	...	...	1621	1651	1713	..
	Lugano 550a ‡ d.	...	1248	1322	1342	...	...	1348	1422	1442	...	...	1522	1542	...	...	1548	1618	1642	...	...	1648	1722	1742	..
	Mendrisio 592 ‡ d.	...	...	|	1358	...	...	...	|	1457	...	...	|	1558	...	...	...	...	1657	...	...	...	|	1757	..
	Chiasso 592 ‡ a.	...	...	1346	1404	...	...	...	1446	1504	...	...	1546	1604	...	...	...	...	1704	...	...	...	1746	1804	..
	Chiasso 🛃 § d.	...	...	1351	1407	...	...	...	1451	1507	...	...	1551	1607	...	...	...	...	1707	...	...	...	1751	1807	..
	Como San Giovanni § a.	...	...	1355	1413	...	...	...	1455	1512	...	...	|	1613	...	...	...	...	1712	...	...	...	1755	1812	..
	Milano Centrale § a.	...	...	1435	1450	...	...	...	1535	1550	...	...	1635	1650	...	...	...	...	1750	...	...	...	1835	1850	..

	2583 S	IC 879 ✕	IC 679 ✕	RE 4333 P	IR 2429 N	2585 S	EC 23 ◧ ✕	IR 2331	2587 S	IC 883 🍷	IC 683 ✕	IR 2433	2589 S	EC 25 ◧ ✕	IR 2335	2591 S	IC 887	IC 687 ✕	IR 2437	IC 1489 ①–⑤ ✕	IR 2339	IC 1489 ⑥⑦ ✕	IC 691	IR 2441	R 24
Basel SBB **565** d.	...	...	1504	...	...	...	...	1604	...	...	1704	...	...	...	1804	...	...	1904	...	...	2004	...	2104	...	
Luzern d.	1539	...	1618	...	...	1639	...	1718	1739	...	1818	...	1839	...	1918	1939	...	2018	...	...	2118	...	2218	...	
Küssnacht am Rigi d.	1558	...	|	...	...	1658	...	|	1758	...	|	...	1858	...	|	1958	...	|	...	...	|	...	|	...	
Zürich HB d.	|	1532	|	...	1610	|	1710	|	|	1732	|	1810	|	1910	|	|	1932	|	2010	2110	|	2132	|	2210	23
Zug d.	|	1600	|	...	1631	|	1731	|	|	1800	|	1831	|	1931	|	|	2000	|	2031	2131	|	2200	|	2231	23
Arth-Goldau a.	1611	1615	1646	...	1646k	1711	1747	1746k	1811	1815	1846	1846k	1911	1947	1946k	2011	2015	2046	2046k	2147	2146k	2215	2246	2246k	23
Arth-Goldau d.	...	1618	1650	...	1653	...	1750	1753	▬	1818	1850	1853	...	1950	1953	...	2018	2050	2053	2150	2153	2218	2250	2253	.
Schwyz d.	...	|	|	...	1701	...	|	1801	...	|	|	1901	...	|	2001	...	|	|	2101	|	2201	|	|	2301	.
Brunnen d.	...	|	|	...	1705	...	|	1805	...	|	|	1905	...	|	2005	...	|	|	2105	|	2205	|	|	2305	.
Flüelen d.	...	|	1708	...	1716	...	|	1816	...	|	|	1916	...	|	2016	...	|	|	2116	|	2216	|	|	2316	.
Erstfeld 550a d.	...	|	|	1637	1723	...	|	1823	RE	|	|	1923	...	|	2023	...	|	|	2123	|	2226	|	|	2326	.
Bellinzona ▲ 550a a.	...	1717	1747	1809	...	...	1847	...	**25523**	1917	1947	...	...	2047	...	...	2117	2147	...	2247	...	2321	2351	...	.
Bellinzona 550a ‡ d.	...	1721	1751	1813	...	...	1851	...		1921	1951	...	...	2051	...	...	2121	2151	...	2251	...	2323	2353	...	.
Lugano 550a ‡ d.	...	1748	1818	1842	...	...	1922	...	1942	1948	2018	...	...	2122	...	...	2148	2220	...	2320	...	2352	0022	...	.
Mendrisio 592 ‡ d.	...	...	...	1857	...	...	|	...	1958	...	...	...	...	|	...	...	...	2235	...	2335	...	0008	0038	...	.
Chiasso 592 ‡ a.	...	...	...	1904	...	...	1946	...	2004	...	...	...	...	2146	...	...	...	2245	...	2345	...	0017	0047	...	.
Chiasso 🛃 § d.	...	...	...	1907	...	...	1951	...	2007	...	...	...	...	2151	...	...	...	...	...	...	...	...	...	...	.
Como San Giovanni § a.	...	...	...	1912	...	...	|	...	2013	...	...	...	...	2159	...	...	...	...	...	...	...	...	...	...	.
Milano Centrale § a.	...	...	...	1950	...	...	2032	...	2050	...	...	...	...	2250	...	...	...	...	...	...	...	...	...	...	.

	RE 2408	IR 2308	IR 2310	IC 1456 ✕	IR 2312	IC 1458 ✕	2564 S	IR 2412	RE 25504 P	IC 668 ✕	IC 866 🍷	2566 S	IR 2316	RE 25506 P	EC 12 ◧ ✕	2568 S	IR 2416 N	RE 25508 P	IC 672 ✕	IC 868 Ⓒ 🍷	RE 25510	2570 S	IR 2320	EC 14 ◧ ✕	8
Milano Centrale § d.	...	...	...	...	...	...	...	...	...	...	...	...	...	0710	0725	...	...	0810	...	...	0905	...	...	0925	.
Como San Giovanni § d.	...	...	...	...	...	...	...	...	...	...	...	...	...	0747	|	...	...	0847	...	...	0947	...	...	1003	.
Chiasso 🛃 § a.	...	...	...	...	...	...	...	...	...	...	...	...	...	0752	0810	...	...	0852	...	...	0952	...	...	1010	.
Chiasso 592 ‡ d.	...	...	...	0515	...	0615	...	...	0655	0712	0739	...	...	0755	0815	...	...	0855	...	...	0955	...	...	1015	.
Mendrisio 592 ‡ d.	...	...	...	0524	...	0624	...	...	0703	0724	0747	...	...	0803	|	...	...	0903	...	...	1003	...	...	|	.
Lugano 550a ‡ d.	...	...	...	0543	...	0643	...	...	0719	0743	0811	...	...	0819	0843	...	...	0919	0943	1011	1018	...	...	1043	11
Bellinzona 550a ‡ a.	...	...	...	0610	...	0710	...	...	0747	0810	0838	...	...	0847	0910	...	...	0947	1010	1038	...	...	...	1110	11
Bellinzona ▲ 550a d.	...	...	...	0613	...	0713	...	...	0751	0813	0841	...	...	0851	0913	...	...	0951	1013	1041	...	...	...	1113	11
Erstfeld 550a d.	...	...	0627	|	0734	|	...	0834	0924	|	|	...	0934	1024	|	...	1034	1124	|	|	...	...	1134	|	
Flüelen d.	...	...	0637	0650	0742	|	...	0842	...	0850	|	...	0942	...	|	...	1042	...	|	|	...	...	1142	|	
Brunnen d.	0555a	...	0651	|	0754	|	...	0854	...	|	|	...	0954	...	|	...	1054	...	|	|	...	...	1154	|	
Schwyz d.	0600a	...	0655	|	0758	|	...	0858	...	|	|	...	0958	...	|	...	1058	...	|	|	...	...	1158	|	
Arth-Goldau a.	0609a	...	0706	0709	0806	0809	...	0906	...	0909	0939	...	1006	...	1009k	...	1106	...	1109k	1139	...	...	1206	1209k	12
Arth-Goldau d.	0611	0614	0714	0713	0814	0813	0848	0913	...	0914	0945	0948	1014	...	1013	1048	1113	...	1114	1145	...	1148	1214	1213	12
Zug d.	0629	|	|	0729	|	0829	|	0929	...	|	1002	|	|	...	1029	|	1129	...	|	1202	...	|	|	1229	13
Zürich HB a.	0650	|	|	0750	|	0850	|	0950	...	|	1028	|	|	...	1050	|	1150	...	|	1228	...	|	|	1250	13
Küssnacht am Rigi d.	...	|	|	...	|	...	0900	...	...	|	...	1000	|	...	...	1100	...	...	|	...	...	1200	|	...	
Luzern a.	...	0641	0741	...	0841	...	0921	...	...	0941	...	1021	1041	...	...	1121	...	...	1141	...	...	1221	1241	...	.
Basel SBB **565** a.	...	0755	0855	...	0955	...	...	...	...	1055	...	...	1155	...	...	...	...	...	1255	...	...	...	1355	...	.

Local services **BELLINZONA - LOCARNO**

km				and at the same minutes past each hour until			R	R	R	R
0	Bellinzona d.	0458	0528		2128	2158	2228	2258	2328	2358
21	Locarno a.	0529	0559		2159	2229	2259	2329	2359	0029

			and at the same minutes past each hour until			R	R	R	
Locarno d.	0535	0605		2205	2235	2305	2335	0005	00
Bellinzona a.	0600	0630		2230	2300	2330	2400	0030	0

A – From Airolo (Table **550a**).
B – From Biasca (Table **550a**).
F – 🚃 and ✕ Frankfurt - Basel - Milano.
H – GOTTHARD WEEKENDER – Ⓒ Apr. 20 - June 8 (also Apr. 19): 🚃 Zürich - Bellinzona. Also conveys panorama car.
P – Via Gotthard pass (Table **550a**).
N – To/from Göschenen on Ⓒ.
R – By 🚌 Cadenazzo - Locarno on certain dates. Please check with operator.
S – VORALPEN EXPRESS – 🚃 and (🍷) Luzern - Arth Goldau - Rapperswil - St Gallen and v.v. (Table 525).

NOTES CONTINUE ON NEXT PAGE

MILANO, LUGANO and ERSTFELD - ZÜRICH and LUZERN — 550

SBB, FS

	2572	IR 2420	RE 4312	EC 158	IC 870	2574	IR 2324	EC 16	2576	IR 2424	RE 4316	IC 680	IC 878	IR 25518	2578	IR 2328	EC 18	IC 880	2580	RE 2428	RE 4320	RE 25520	IC 684	IC 882	RE 25522
				◧				◧					Ⓒ				◧	⑥⑦							
	S		P	✕	✕	S		✕	S		P	✕	🍸		S		✕	d✕	S		P		✕	🍸	
lano Centrale § d.	...	...	...	1015	...	...	...	1125	...	...	...	...	...	1310	...	...	1325	...	...	...	...	1410	...	...	1510
mo San Giovanni § d.	...	...	...	1101	...	...	...	1203	...	...	...	...	...	1347	...	...	|	...	...	...	...	1447	...	...	1547
hiasso 🛃 § a.	...	...	...	1110	...	...	...	1210	...	...	...	...	...	1352	...	...	1410	...	...	...	...	1452	...	...	1552
hiasso 592 ‡ d.	...	...	...	1115	...	...	...	1215	...	...	...	...	...	1355	...	...	1415	...	...	...	...	1455	...	...	1555
endrisio 592 ‡ d.	...	...	...	|	...	...	...	|	...	...	...	...	...	1403	...	...	|	...	...	...	...	1503	...	...	1603
ugano 550a ‡ d.	...	...	1119	1143	1211	...	...	1243	...	...	1319	1343	1411	1418	...	...	1443	1511	...	...	1519	1522	1543	1611	1618
ellinzona 550a ‡ a.	...	...	1147	1210	1238	...	...	1310	...	...	1347	1410	1438	...	...	...	1510	1538	...	...	1547	...	1610	1638	—
ellinzona ▲ 550a d.	...	...	1151	1213	1241	...	...	1313	...	...	1351	1413	1441	...	...	...	1513	1541	...	...	1551	...	1613	1641	...
rstfeld 550a d.	...	1234	1324	|	|	...	1334	|	...	1434	1524	|	|	...	...	1534	|	|	...	1634	1724	...	|	|	...
üelen d.	...	1242	...	|	|	...	1342	|	...	1442	...	|	|	...	...	1542	|	|	...	1642	...	...	1650	|	...
unnen d.	...	1254	...	|	|	...	1354	|	...	1454	...	|	|	...	...	1554	|	|	...	1654	...	...	|	|	2582
hwyz d.	...	1258	...	|	|	...	1358	|	...	1458	...	|	|	...	...	1558	|	|	...	1658	...	...	|	|	
th-Goldau a.	...	1306	...	1309k	1339	...	1406	1409k	...	1506	...	1509k	1539	...	...	1606	1609k	1639	...	1706	...	...	1709k	1739	S
th-Goldau d.	1248	1313	...	1314	1345	1348	1414	1413	1448	1513	...	1514	1545	...	1548	1614	1613	1645	1648	1713	...	...	1714	1745	1748
Zug d.	|	1329	...	|	1402	|	|	1429	|	1529	...	|	1602	...	|	|	1629	1702	|	1729	...	...	|	1802	|
Zürich HB a.	|	1350	...	|	1428	|	|	1450	|	1550	...	|	1628	...	|	|	1650	1728	|	1750	...	...	|	1828	|
ssnacht am Rigi d.	1300	...	...	|	...	1400	|	...	1500	...	...	|	...	...	1600	|	...	...	1700	...	...	...	|	...	1800
izern a.	1321	...	...	1341	...	1421	1441	...	1521	...	...	1541	...	...	1621	1641	...	...	1721	...	...	...	1741	...	1821
Basel SBB 565 a.	...	...	...	1455	...	...	1555	...	...	...	...	1655	...	...	...	1755	...	...	...	...	...	...	1855	...	...

	IR 2332	EC 20	IR 3094	IC 884	2584	IR 2432	RE 25524	IC 688	IC 886	2586	IR 2336	RE 25526	EC 22	IC 888	RE 25528	IR 2338	IC 692	EC 10	IC 890	IR 2340	RE 25530	EC 24	RE 25532	IR 2440	IC 696
		◧		Ⓒ									◧	†			†	◧				◧			
		✕	H	🍸	S	N	P	✕	✕	S		P	✕	✕				V✕				✕			
lano Centrale § d.	...	1525	...	...	...	...	1610	...	...	...	...	1710	1728	...	1810	...	...	1825	...	...	1910	1925	2010	...	...
mo San Giovanni § d.	...	1603	...	...	...	...	1647	...	...	...	...	1747	|	...	1847	...	...	|	...	...	1947	2003	2047	...	...
hiasso 🛃 § a.	...	1610	...	...	...	...	1652	...	...	...	...	1752	1810	...	1852	...	...	1910	...	...	1952	2010	2052	...	...
hiasso 592 ‡ d.	...	1615	...	...	...	...	1655	...	...	...	...	1755	1815	...	1855	...	...	1915	...	...	1955	2015	2055	...	...
endrisio 592 ‡ d.	...	|	...	...	...	...	1703	...	...	...	...	1803	|	...	1903	...	...	|	...	...	2003	|	2103	...	...
gano 550a ‡ d.	...	1643	...	1711	...	...	1719	1743	1811	...	...	1819	1843	1911	1918	...	1939	1943	2011	...	2018	2043	2118	...	2143
llinzona 550a ‡ a.	...	1710	...	1738	...	...	1747	1810	1838	...	...	1847	1910	1938	—	...	2007	2010	2038	...	...	2110	...	...	2210
llinzona ▲ 550a d.	...	1713	1618	1741	...	...	1751	1813	1841	...	...	1851	1913	1941	...	...	2010	2013	2041	...	...	2113	...	...	2213
stfeld 550a d.	1734	|	1755	|	...	1834	1924	|	|	...	1934	2024	|	|	...	2034	|	|	|	2134	...	|	...	2234	|
ielen d.	1742	|	1802	|	...	1842	...	|	|	...	1942	...	|	|	...	2042	|	|	|	2142	...	|	...	2242	|
unnen d.	1754	|	|	|	...	1854	...	|	|	...	1954	...	|	|	2588	2054	|	|	|	2154	...	|	...	2254	|
hwyz d.	1758	|	1816	|	...	1858	...	|	|	...	1958	...	|	|		2058	|	|	|	2158	...	|	...	2258	|
th-Goldau a.	1806	1809	1824	1839	...	1906	...	1909k	1939	...	2006	...	2009k	2039	S	2106	2109	2109k	2139	2206	...	2209k	...	2306	2309k
th-Goldau d.	1814	1813	1827	1845	1848	1913	...	1914	1945	1948	2014	...	2013	2045	2048	2114z	2114	2113	2145	2214	...	2213	...	2313	2314
Zug d.	|	1829	|	1902	|	1929	...	|	2002	|	|	...	2029	2102	|	|	|	2129	2202	|	...	2229	...	2329	|
Zürich HB a.	|	1850	1942	1928	|	1950	...	|	2028	|	|	...	2050	2128	|	|	|	2150	2228	|	...	2250	...	2350	|
ssnacht am Rigi d.	|	...	...	...	1900	...	...	|	...	2000	|	...	...	...	2100	|	|	...	...	...	...	...	...	...	...
zern a.	1841	...	...	...	1921	...	...	1941	...	2021	2041	...	...	...	2121	2141z	2141	...	...	2241	...	...	...	...	2341
Basel SBB 565 a.	1955	...	...	...	...	...	...	2055	...	...	2155	...	...	...	...	2259z	2259	...	...	2359	...	...	...	...	0102

TES (continued from previous page)

- Ⓐ only.
- Not Apr. 22.
- Connects with train in previous column(s).
- ⚒ only.

◧ – Supplement payable in Italy and for international journeys.
▲ – For local services Bellinzona - Locarno and v.v. see panel on page 276.
‡ – Local services operate Chiasso - Bellinzona (every 30 minutes, journey 1 hour).
§ – Local services operate Milano Porta Garibaldi - Chiasso (every 30 minutes, journey 68 minutes).

ERSTFELD - LUGANO (via Gotthard pass) — 550a

BB

km		RE 25509	RE 25511		RE 4313	RE 4315	RE 4317	IR 2313	RE 4319	IR 3091	RE 4321	RE 4323		RE 4325	RE 4327	3093	RE 4329	RE 4331	RE 4333	IR 2429	RE 4335	RE 4337	RE 4339	RE 4341	RE 4343
								Ⓒ		Ⓒ						②–⑦				Ⓒ					
		M	M		M			B		H	M					G	M	M	M	Z					
0	Erstfeld d.	...	...	...	...	0737	0837	0925	0937	0943	1037	1137	...	1237	1337	...	1437	1537	1637	1724	1737	1837	1937	2037	2137e
29	Göschenen d.	...	...	...	0655r	0802	0902	0949	1002	1012	1102	1202	...	1302	1402	1447	1502	1602	1702	1749	1802	1902	2002	2102	2202e
45	Airolo d.	...	0613	...	0713	0813	0913	...	1013	1023	1113	1213	...	1313	1413	1506	1513	1613	1713	...	1813	1913	2013	2113	2213
65	Faido d.	...	0631	...	0731	0831	0931	...	1031	1043	1131	1231	...	1331	1431	|	1531	1631	1731	...	1831	1931	2031	2131	2231
91	Biasca d.	0554	0654	...	0754	0854	0954	...	1054	1106	1154	1254	...	1354	1454	|	1554	1654	1754	...	1854	1954	2054	2154	2254
10	Bellinzona a.	0609	0709	...	0809	0909	1009	...	1109	1120	1209	1309	...	1409	1509	1603	1609	1709	1809	...	1909	2009	2109	2209	2309
10	Bellinzona d.	0613	0713	...	0813	...	1013	...	...	...	1213	...	...	1413	...	1608	1613	1713	1813	...	...	...	...	...	...
39	Lugano a.	0641	0741	...	0841	...	1041	...	...	...	1241	...	...	1441	...	1638	1641	1741	1841	...	...	...	...	...	...

	RE 4300	RE 4302	RE 25504	RE 25506	IR 2416	RE 25508	3092		RE 4310	RE 4312	RE 4314	RE 4316	RE 4318	RE 4320		IR 3094	RE 4322	IR 2432	RE 25524	RE 25526		RE 4328	RE 25540	
					Ⓒ		②–⑦									Ⓒ		Ⓒ						
				M	Z	M	G									H		Z	M	M				
gano d.	...	...	0719	0819	...	0919	0922	...	...	1119	...	1319	...	1519	...	...	...	...	1719	1819	...	...	...	...
linzona a.	...	...	0747	0847	...	0947	0950	...	...	1147	...	1347	...	1547	...	...	...	...	1747	1847	...	...	...	...
linzona d.	0551	0651	0751	0851	...	0951	0956	...	1051	1151	1251	1351	1451	1551	...	1618	1651	...	1751	1851	...	1951	2051	...
sca d.	0605	0705	0805	0905	...	1005	|	...	1105	1205	1305	1405	1505	1605	...	1633	1705	...	1805	1905	...	2005	2105	...
do d.	0628	0728	0828	0928	...	1028	|	...	1128	1228	1328	1428	1528	1628	...	1655	1728	...	1828	1928	...	2028	2128	...
olo d.	0646	0746	0846	0946	...	1046	1052	...	1146	1246	1346	1446	1546	1646	...	1716	1746	...	1846	1946	...	2046	2146	...
schenen d.	0658	0758	0858	0958	1006	1058	1110	...	1158	1258	1358	1458	1558	1658	...	1728	1758	1806	1858	1958	...	2058e	...	...
stfeld a.	0724	0824	0924	1024	1031	1124	...	...	1224	1324	1424	1524	1624	1724	...	1753	1824	1831	1924	2024	...	2124e	...	...

- From Luzern (Table 550).
- ②–⑦ Apr. 19 - June 8 (also Apr. 22). GOTTHARD PANORAMA EXPRESS – 🚃12 Flüelen - Göschenen - Lugano and v.v. Conveys panorama car. Supplement payable.
- Ⓒ Apr. 20 - June 8 (also Apr. 19). GOTTHARD WEEKENDER – 🚃12 Zürich - Bellinzona and v.v. Conveys panorama car.
- From/to Milano (Table 550).

Z – From/to Zürich (Table 550).

e – ⑤–⑦ only.
r – ⑤–⑦ Apr. 12 - June 8 (also May 30).

LOCARNO - DOMODOSSOLA — 551

ART

km		C	C	C	V	C	V	V		V	C		
				🍸	🍸	🍸	🍸	🍸	🍸m	🍸p	🍸		⑤⑦
0	Locarno d.	0649	0749	0850	1050	1150	1250	1450	1550	1550	1650	1747	1847
20	Camedo 🛃 d.	0724	0824	0924	1124u	1224	1324u	1524u	1624	1624	1724	1824	1924
26	Re d.	0740	0840x	0940x	1140x	1240x	1340x	1540x	1640	1640	1740x	1840x	1940x
34	S. M. Maggiore § d.	0753	0853x	0953x	1153x	1253x	1353x	1553x	1653	1653	1753x	1853x	1955x
53	Domodossola a.	0836	0936	1036	1236	1336	1436	1636	1736	1736	1836	1936	2036

		C	V	V		V		V	C	C	C	C
			🍸	🍸	🍸		🍸	🍸m	🍸p	🍸			⑤⑦
modossola d.	0530a	0825	0925	1025	1125	1225	1325	1525	1525	1625	1725	1900	2025
M. Maggiore § d.	0612a	0910x	1010x	1110x	1210x	1310	1410x	1610x	1610x	1710x	1810	1943	2109x
d.	0625	0922x	1022x	1122x	1222x	1322	1422x	1622x	1622x	1722x	1822	1955	2122x
nedo 🛃 d.	0639	0941	1041	1141	1241	1341	1441	1641	1641	1740	1840	2009s	2137s
carno a.	0720	1019	1119	1219	1319	1419	1519	1719	1719	1819	1919	2042	2215

C – CENTOVALLI EXPRESS.
V – TRENO PANORAMICO VIGEZZO VISION – Conveys panorama car. Supplement payable.

a – ①–⑤ (not Mar. 19, May 1, 31, Aug. 15, Nov. 1).
m – Dec. 9 - Apr. 13, Oct. 14 - Dec. 14.
p – Apr. 14 - Oct. 13.
s – Stops to set down only.
u – Stops to pick up only.
x – Stops only on request.

§ – Full name is Santa Maria Maggiore.

552 LUZERN - STANS - ENGELBERG

Narrow gauge rack railway. ZB

km		E		E				E			E		🚌			🚌			🚌					T	T
0	**Luzern** ...... 561 d.	0504	0527	0610	0627	0657	and at	2010	2027	2057	2110	2127	...	2157	2227	...	2257	2327	...	2357	0032	0102		0836	0936
9	Hergiswil ... 561 d.	0514	0540	|	0640	0710	the same	|	2040	2110	|	2140	...	2210	2240	...	2310	2340	...	0010	0045	0115	EXTRA	0847	0947
11	Stansstad .... d.	0518	0544	|	0644	0714	minutes	|	2044	2114	|	2144	...	2214	2244	...	2314	2344	...	0014	0050	0119	SERVICES	0851	0951
15	Stans .... d.	0523	0548	0624	0648	0718	past each	2024	2048	2118	2124	2148	...	2218	2248	...	2318	2348	...	0018	0054	0123	▶▶▶	0854	0954
19	Dallenwil .... d.	0528	0552	0629	0652	...	hour until	2029	2052	...	2129	2152	2155	2222	2252	2255	2322	2352	2355	0022	0059	...		|	|
34	**Engelberg** .. ⊡ a.	0552	...	0653	...	...		2053	...	...	2153	...	2216	...	...	2316	...	...	0016	...	...	...		0921	1021

		🚌			E				E			E		🚌			🚌			🚌			T	T
Engelberg .... ⊡ d.	...	0500	...	...	0602	...	...	and at	2102	...	...	2202	...	2230	...	...	2330	...	...	0018	...		1624	1724
Dallenwil .... d.	0455	0523	0527	0604	0629	...	0704	the same	2129	...	2204	2229	2234	2253	2304	2334	2353	...	0004	0038	0041	EXTRA	|	|
Stans .... d.	0501	...	0532	0610	0634	0640	0710	minutes	2134	2140	2210	2234	2240	...	2310	2340	...	...	0010	...	0047	SERVICES	1701	1801
Stansstad .... d.	0505	...	0535	0614	|	0644	0714	past each	|	2144	2214	|	2244	...	2314	2344	...	...	0014	...	0051	▶▶▶	1705	1805
Hergiswil .... 561 d.	0509	...	0540	0618	|	0648	0718	hour until	|	2148	2218	|	2248	...	2318	2348	...	...	0018	...	0055		1709	1809
Luzern .... 561 a.	0522	...	0549	0632	0649	0702	0732		2149	2202	2232	2249	2302	...	2332	0002	...	...	0032	...	0109		1720	1820

E – LUZERN - ENGELBERG EXPRESS. Conveys panorama car.
T – Ⓒ Dec. 9 - Mar. 31 and May 18 - Oct. 27.

⊡ – Station for Titlis, accessible by cable car system (including the world's first revolving cable car).

553 MOUNTAIN RAILWAYS IN CENTRAL SWITZERLAND

2nd class only. RB

km	Until June 8		p							p	q		
0	Arth-Goldau .... d.	0755	0908	1008	1108	1208	1307	1423	1623	1723	1823	...	...
9	Rigi Kulm .... a.	0840	0947	1047	1147	1247	1347	1502	1702	1802	1902	...	...

Until June 8		p								p	q	
Rigi Kulm .... d.	0858	1001	1101	1201	1316	1416	1516	1616	1716	1816	1916	...
Arth-Goldau. a.	0948	1048	1148	1248	1403	1503	1603	1703	1803	1903	2003	...

December 9 - April 18 and October 21 - December 14

km						k✗					
0	Rigi Kulm .... d.	0900	1000	and hourly	1400	1430	1500	1600	1700	...	...
7	Vitznau .... a.	0940	1040	until	1440	1539	1540	1640	1740	...	...

					k✗				n	x✿
Vitznau .... d.	0815	0915	1015	1115	1116	1215	and hourly	1615	1740	1915
Rigi Kulm .... a.	0947	0947	1047	1147	1234	1247	until	1647	1811	1947

April 19 - May 24 and September 9 - October 20

							j✗				⑤⑥
Rigi Kulm .... d.	0900	1000	1100	1200	1300	1400	1415	1500	and hourly	2000	2240
Vitznau .... a.	0940	1040	1140	1240	1340	1440	1506	1540	until	2040	2320

				j✗							⑤⑥
Vitznau .... d.	0815	0915	1015	1051	1115	1215	1315	and hourly	1815	1915	220
Rigi Kulm .... a.	0847	0947	1047	1218	1247	1247	1447	until	1847	1947	223

May 25 - September 8

							z✗				
Rigi Kulm .... d.	0900	1000	1100	1200	1300	1400	1415	1500	and hourly	2000	2240
Vitznau .... a.	0940	1040	1140	1240	1340	1440	1506	1540	until	2040	2320

				†	z✗						
Vitznau .... d.	0815	0915	1015	1050	1051	1115	1215	and hourly	1815	1915	220
Rigi Kulm .... a.	0847	0947	1047	1124	1218	1247	1247	until	1847	1947	223

ALPNACHSTAD - PILATUS KULM. Narrow gauge rack railway. *5 km*. Journey time: 30 minutes uphill, 40 minutes downhill. **Operator**: PB, ✆ 041 329 11 11.
Services run daily **early May - November 17** (weather permitting). **No winter service** (December - April).
From **Alpnachstad**: 0810 **r**, 0850, 0935, 1015, 1055, 1135, 1220, 1300, 1345, 1425, 1505, 1550, 1630 **r**, 1710 **r**, 1750 **s**.
From **Pilatus Kulm**: 0845 **r**, 0930, 1010, 1050, 1130, 1215, 1255, 1340, 1420, 1500, 154[illegible], 1625, 1705 **r**, 1745 **r**, 1845 **s**.

BRIENZ - BRIENZER ROTHORN. Narrow gauge rack railway. *8 km*. Most services operated by 🚂. Journey time: 55 – 60 minutes uphill, 60 – 70 minutes downhill.
Operator: BRB, ✆ 033 952 22 22. Service valid **June 1 - October 20**, and is subject to weather conditions on the mountain and demand. Extra trains may run at busy times. **No winter servic**
From **Brienz**: 0736 **t**, 0836, 0940, 1000③✗, 1045, 1145, 1258, 1358, 1458, 1636.
From **Brienzer Rothorn**: 0906 **t**, 0938, 1115, 1220, 1328, 1428, 1528, 1628, 1740.

j – Oct. 6. Operated by 🚂.
k – Jan. 27, Feb. 24. Operated by 🚂.
n – Dec. 26 - Mar. 10; Oct. 21 - Dec. 8.
p – Daily Dec. 15 - Mar. 10; Apr. 29 - June 8; Ⓒ Mar. 16 - Apr. 28 (also Dec. 9).
q – ⑤ Dec. 14 - Apr. 26; ⑤⑥⑦ Apr. 27 - June 8 (also Apr. 18, May 29, 30; not Apr. 19).
r – Until Oct. 26.
s – June 16 - Aug. 18.
t – ⑦ July 7 - Sept. 29.
x – ⑤⑥ Dec. 28 - Mar. 9, Oct. 25 - Dec. 7.
z – June 2, July 4, Aug. 18, Sept. 1, 8. Operated by 🚂. Reservations: ✆ 041 399 87 87.
✗ – Supplement payable.
✿ – Subject to favourable weather conditions.

554 🚌 MEIRINGEN - ANDERMATT

Service June 22 - Oct. 13 (no winter service) PA

							Ⓒ				
Meiringen Bahnhof .... d.	...	0850	...	0925	...	1050	1055	1325	1325	1520	...
Steingletscher, Susten .. d.	...	0944	1000	|	...	|	1149	|	1425	|	...
Susten Passhöhe .... d.	...	...	1010	|	...	|	...	|	1435	|	...
Göschenen Bahnhof .... d.	...	...	1049	|	...	|	...	|	1514	|	...
Grimsel Passhöhe .... d.	0912	...	|	1100	...	1204	...	1439	|	1634	...
Gletsch Post .... d.	0922	...	|	1110	...	1215	...	1450	|	1645	...
Oberwald Bahnhof .... a.	0937	...	|	1125	...	1230	...	1505	|	1700	...
Oberwald Bahnhof .... d.	...	...	|	...	1220	...	...	...	|	...	*1704*
Gletsch Post .... d.	...	...	|	...	1318	...	...	...	|	...	1720
Furka Passhöhe .... d.	...	...	|	...	1340	...	...	...	|	...	1740
Realp Post .... d.	...	...	|	...	1404	...	...	...	|	...	1804
Andermatt Bahnhof .... a.	...	...	1104	...	1423	...	...	...	1529	...	1823

						Ⓒ					
Andermatt Bahnhof ...... d.	...	...	...	0830	...	...	...	...	1534	1551	...
Realp Post .... d.	...	...	...	0842	...	...	...	...	1546	|	...
Furka Passhöhe .... d.	...	...	...	0906	...	...	...	...	1610	|	...
Gletsch Post .... d.	...	...	...	1005	...	...	...	...	1639	|	...
Oberwald Bahnhof .... a.	...	...	...	1020	...	...	...	...	*1700*	|	...
Oberwald Bahnhof .... d.	...	...	0845	...	1030	...	1250	1530	...	|	170
Gletsch Post ....) .... d.	...	...	0857	...	1046	...	1302	1542	...	|	171
Grimsel Passhöhe .... d.	...	...	0911	...	1131	...	1337	1617	...	|	173
Göschenen Bahnhof . d.	0911	...	...	...	|	...	|	|	...	1611	|
Susten Passhöhe .... d.	0946	...	...	...	|	...	|	|	...	1646	|
Steingletscher, Susten d.	0956	1000	...	...	|	1150	|	|	...	1720	|
Meiringen Bahnhof .... a.	...	1050	...	...	1225	1240	1434	1714	...	1810	183

Reservations: ✆ +41 (0)58 448 20 08.

555 ZÜRICH FLUGHAFEN ✈ - ZÜRICH - LUZERN

All trains *IR* SBB

km			C✗	C✗	C✗														Ⓐ			Ⓐ		
0	**Zürich** Flughafen ✈ .... ‡ d.	...	...	...	...	...	...	...	0615	...	0715	...	0815	...	0915	and at	...	1615	...	...	...	...	...	181
10	**Zürich** HB .... 520 ‡ d.	0008	0135	0235	0335	...	0535	0604	0635	0704	0735	0804	0835	0904	0935	the same	1604	1635	1639	1704	1735	1739	1804	183
22	Thalwil .... 520 d.	0017	|	|	|	...	0545	0614	0645	0714	0745	0814	0845	0914	0945	minutes	1614	1645	|	1714	1745	|	1814	184
39	Zug .... d.	0035	0155	0255	0355	...	0602	0628	0702	0728	0802	0828	0902	0928	1002	past each	1628	1702	1712	1728	1802	1812	1828	190
49	Rotkreuz .... d.	0046	0202	0302	0402	...	0610	|	0710	|	0810	|	0910	|	1010	hour until	|	1710	1721	|	1810	1821	|	191
67	**Luzern** .... a.	0107	0225	0325	0425	...	0625	0649	0725	0749	0825	0849	0925	0949	1025		1649	1725	1739	1749	1825	1839	1849	192

Zürich Flughafen ✈ .... ‡ d.	...	1915	...	2015	...	...	...	...	...	...
Zürich HB .... 520 ‡ d.	1904	1935	2004	2035	2104	2135	2204	2235	2304	2335
Thalwil .... 520 d.	1914	1945	2014	2045	2114	2145	2214	2245	2314	2345
Zug .... d.	1928	2002	2028	2102	2128	2202	2228	2302	2328	0002
Rotkreuz .... d.	|	2010	|	2110	|	2210	|	2310	|	0010
Luzern .... a.	1949	2025	2049	2125	2149	2225	2249	2325	2349	0025

	C	C✗	C✗					Ⓐ	
Luzern .... d.	0035	0135	0235	...	0455	0528	0610	0620	063
Rotkreuz .... d.	0049	0146	0246	...	0513	0548	|	0636	064
Zug .... d.	0058	0155	0255	...	0526	0558	0631	0648	065
Thalwil .... 520 d.	0115	0211	0311	...	0543	0615	0646	|	071
Zürich HB .... 520 ‡ a.	0125	0225	0325	...	0555	0625	0656	0720	072
Zürich Flughafen ✈ ...... ‡ a.	...	...	...	...	0611	0644	...	...	074

		Ⓐ																						
Luzern .... d.	0710	0720	0735	0810	0835	and at	1510	1535	1610	1635	1710	1735	1810	1835	1910	1935	2010	2035	2110	2135	2210	2235	2310	233
Rotkreuz .... d.	|	0736	0749	|	0849	the same	|	1549	|	1649	|	1749	|	1849	|	1949	|	2049	|	2149	|	2249	|	234
Zug .... d.	0731	0748	0757	0831	0857	minutes	1531	1557	1631	1657	1731	1757	1831	1857	1931	1957	2031	2057	2131	2157	2231	2257	2331	235
Thalwil .... 520 d.	0746	|	0815	0846	0915	past each	1546	1615	1646	1715	1746	1815	1846	1915	1946	2015	2046	2115	2146	2215	2246	2315	2346	001
Zürich HB .... 520 ‡ a.	0756	0820	0825	0856	0925	hour until	1556	1625	1656	1725	1756	1825	1856	1925	1956	2025	2056	2125	2156	2225	2256	2325	2356	002
Zürich Flughafen ✈ .... ‡ a.	...	...	0844	...	0944		...	1644	...	...	...	1844	...	1944	...	2044	...	...	...	...	...	...	...	...

C – ⑥⑦ (also Apr. 19, 22, May 30, 31).
✗ – Supplement payable.
‡ – See also Tables **529**, **530** and **535**.

BB BASEL - BERN - INTERLAKEN and BRIG 560

m		IC 955	IC 802	IC 1057	IC 957	IC 804	EC 51	IC 959	IC 806	IC 333	IC 961	IC 808	IC 1063	IC 963	IC 810	IC 1065	IC 965	IC 812	IC 1067	IC 967	IC 814	IC 1069	ICE 275	IC 816	EC 57
			⊗	✕	⊗	✕	◧ ✕	⊗	⊗		✕	✕	✕	✕	⊗	⊗	✕	✕	D✕	⊗	✕	✕	G✕	✕	◧ ✕
	Romanshorn **535** d.	...	...	...	...	...	...	...	0548	...	...	0648	...	...	0748	...	...	0848	...	...	0948	...	...	1048	...
	Zürich Flug ✈ **535** d.	...	...	...	...	...	...	...	0646	...	...	0746	...	...	0846	...	...	0946	...	...	1046	...	...	1146	...
	Zürich HB **505** d.	...	...	...	...	0602	...	...	0702	...	...	0802	...	...	0902	...	...	1002	...	...	1102	...	...	1202	...
0	**Basel** SBB **565** d.	...	...	0524	0559	|	0631	0659	|	0731	0759	|	0831	0859	|	0931	0959	|	1031	1059	|	1131	1159	|	1231
39	Olten **505 565** d.	...	...	0557	0629	|	0657	0729	|	0757	0829	|	0857	0929	|	0957	1029	|	1057	1129	|	1157	1229	|	1257
01	**Bern** **505** a.	...	...	0624	0656	0658**k**	0724	0756	0758**k**	0824	0856	0858**k**	0924	0956	0958**k**	1024	1056	1058**k**	1124	1156	1158**k**	1224	1256	1258**k**	1324
01	**Bern** d.	0604	0606	0634	0704	0706	0734	0804	0806	0834	0904	0906	0934	1004	1006	1034	1104	1106	1134	1204	1206	1234	1304	1306	1334
32	Thun d.	0623	0625	0654	0723	0725	0754	0823	0825	0854	0923	0925	0954	1023	1025	1054	1123	1125	1154	1223	1225	1254	1323	1325	1354
42	**Spiez** a.	0632	0634	0702	0732	0734	0802	0832	0834	0902	0932	0934	1002	1032	1034	1102	1132	1134	1202	1232	1234	1302	1332	1334	1402
42	**Spiez** ▷ d.	0633	0636	0703	0733	0736	0805	0833	0836	0903	0933	0936	1005	1033	1036	1103	1133	1136	1205	1233	1236	1303	1333	1336	1405
	Interlaken West ▷ a.	0651	|	0722	0751	|	|	0851	|	0922	0951	|	|	1051	|	1122	1151	|	|	1251	|	1322	1351	|	|
	Interlaken Ost ▷ a.	0657	|	0728	0757	|	|	0857	|	0928	0957	|	|	1057	|	1128	1157	|	|	1257	|	1328	1357	|	|
97	Visp **570** d.	...	0703	...	...	0803	0832	...	0903	...	...	1003	1032	...	1103	...	...	1203	1232	...	1303	...	...	1403	1432
06	**Brig** **570** a.	...	0711	...	...	0811	0840	...	0911	...	...	1011	1040	...	1111	...	...	1211	1240	...	1311	...	...	1411	1440
	Milano C **590** a.	...	...	...	...	...	1037	...	...	...	...	...	...	...	...	...	...	...	...	...	...	...	...	...	1637

	IC 971	IC 818	IC 1073	EC 7	IC 820	IC 1075	IC 975	IC 822	IC 1077	IC 977	IC 824	IC 1079	IC 979	IC 826	EC 59	ICE 371	IC 828	IC 1083	IC 983	IC 830	IC 1085	ICE 373	IC 1087	IC 1089	IC 987
	⊗	⊗	✕	G✕	✕	✕	✕	⊗	⊗	⊗	✕	⊗	✕	⊗	◧ ✕	G✕	✕	⊗	✕	✕	✕	G✕	①–⑥ ✕	⑦ ✕	
Romanshorn **535** d.	...	1148	...	...	1248	...	...	1348	...	...	1448	...	...	1548	...	...	1648	...	...	1748	...	...	...	...	...
Zürich Flug ✈ **535** d.	...	1246	...	...	1346	...	...	1446	...	...	1546	...	...	1646	...	...	1746	...	...	1846	...	...	...	...	...
Zürich HB **505** d.	...	1302	...	...	1402	...	...	1502	...	...	1602	...	...	1702	...	...	1802	...	...	1902	...	...	...	...	...
sel SBB **565** d.	1259	|	1331	1359	|	1431	1459	|	1531	1559	|	1631	1659	|	1731	1759	|	1831	1859	|	1931	1959	2031	2031	2059
en **505 565** d.	1329	|	1357	1429	|	1457	1529	|	1557	1629	|	1657	1729	|	1757	1829	|	1857	1929	|	1957	2029	2057	2057	2129
rn **505** a.	1356	1358**k**	1424	1456	1458**k**	1524	1556	1558**k**	1624	1656	1658**k**	1724	1756	1758**k**	1824	1856	1858**k**	1924	1956	1958**k**	2024	2056	2124	2124	2156
rn d.	1404	1406	1434	1504	1506	1534	1604	1606	1634	1704	1706	1734	1804	1806	1834	1904	1906	1934	2004	2006	2034	2106	2134	2134	2206
un d.	1423	1425	1454	1523	1525	1554	1623	1625	1654	1723	1725	1754	1823	1825	1854	1923	1925	1954	2023	2025	2054	2126	2154	2154	2226
iez a.	1432	1434	1502	1532	1534	1602	1632	1634	1702	1732	1734	1802	1832	1834	1902	1932	1934	2002	2032	2034	2102	2135	2202	2202	2235
iez ▷ d.	1433	1436	1503	1533	1536	1605	1633	1636	1703	1733	1736	1805	1833	1836	1905	1933	1936	2003	2033	2036	2105	2136	2205	2205	2236
nterlaken West ▷ a.	1451	|	1522	1551	|	|	1651	|	1722	1751	|	|	1851	|	|	1951	|	2022	2049	|	|	2151	|	|	2251
nterlaken Ost ▷ a.	1457	|	1528	1557	|	|	1657	|	1728	1757	|	|	1857	|	|	1957	|	2028	2054	|	|	2157	|	|	2257
p **570** d.	...	1503	...	...	1603	1632	...	1703	...	...	1803	1832	...	1903	1932	...	2003	...	...	2103	2132	...	2232	|	...
g **570** a.	...	1511	...	...	1611	1640	...	1711	...	...	1811	1840	...	1911	1940	...	2011	...	...	2111	2140	...	2240	2309	...
Milano C **590** a.	...	...	...	...	...	...	...	...	...	...	...	...	...	...	2137	...	...	...	...	...	...	...	...	...	...

	IC 1091	TGV 9225	IC 1093	IC 1095	IC 989	IC 1097	RE 4293	IC 991	IC 993	
			①–⑥	⑦					⑥⑦	
		P⊗							z	
Romanshorn **535** d.	...	...	...	...	...	...	...	...	...	...
Zürich Flug ✈ **535** d.	...	...	...	...	...	...	...	...	...	...
Zürich HB **505** d.	...	...	...	...	...	...	...	...	...	...
sel SBB **565** d.	2131	2136	...	...	2159	2228	...	...	...	...
en **505 565** d.	2157	2202	...	...	2229	2257	...	...	...	...
rn **505** a.	2224	2251	...	...	2256	2326	...	...	...	...
rn d.	...	...	2234	2234	2308	2339	...	0008	0108	...
un d.	...	...	2254	2254	2327	0000	...	0029	0135	...
ez a.	...	...	2302	2302	2336	0009	...	0038	0144	...
ez ▷ d.	...	...	2305	2305	2337	0010	0013	0039	0145	...
nterlaken West ▷ a.	...	...	|	|	2355	0026	|	0055	0202	...
nterlaken Ost ▷ a.	...	...	f	f	0001	0032	f	0100	0207	...
p **570** d.	...	...	2336	|	...	...	|	...	...	...
g **570** a.	...	...	2344	0012	...	...	0123	...	...	...
Milano C **590** a.	...	...	...	...	...	...	...	...	...	...

	IC 956	IC 805	IC 1056	ICE 372	IC 807	IC 1058	IC 960	IC 809	IC 1060	IC 962
			✕	G✕	✕	⊗	⊗	✕	✕	✕
Milano C **590** d.	...	...	...	...	...	...	...	...	...	...
Brig **570** d.	...	...	...	...	0546	...	...	0648	0719	...
Visp **570** d.	...	...	...	...	0554	...	...	0657	0728	...
Interlaken Ost ▷ d.	0458	...	0521	0600	f	0627	0700	|	|	0800
Interlaken West ▷ d.	0503	...	0526	0605	|	0632	0705	|	|	0805
Spiez ▷ a.	0518	...	0548	0621	0624	0652	0721	0724	0753	0821
Spiez d.	0520	...	0550	0622	0625	0654	0722	0725	0754	0822
Thun d.	0530	...	0601	0633	0636	0704	0733	0736	0804	0833
Bern a.	0552	...	0624	0652	0654**k**	0724	0752	0754**k**	0824	0852
Bern **505** d.	0604	0602	0636	0704	0702	0736	0804	0802	0836	0904
Olten **505 565** a.	0630	0628	0703	0730	|	0803	0830	|	0903	0930
Basel SBB **565** a.	0659	|	0729	0759	|	0829	0859	|	0929	0959
Zürich HB **505** a.	...	0702	...	...	0758	...	...	0858	...	...
Zürich Flug ✈ **535** a.	...	0714	...	...	0814	...	...	0914	...	...
Romanshorn **535** a.	...	0812	...	...	0912	...	...	1012	...	...

m		IC 811	IC 1062	IC 964	IC 813	EC 50	ICE 278	IC 815	TGV 9216	IC 1066	IC 968	IC 817	IC 1068	EC 6	IC 819	IC 1070	IC 972	IC 821	EC 52	IC 974	IC 823	IC 1074	ICE 376	IC 825	IC 1076
		⊗	⊗	✕	✕	◧ ✕	G✕	⊗	P⊗	⊗	✕	✕	✕	G✕	⊗	✕	⊗	✕	◧ F✕	⊗	✕		G✕	✕	D✕
	Milano C **590** d.	...	...	...	...	0723	...	...	...	...	...	...	...	...	...	...	...	...	1123	...	...	...	...	...	...
	Brig **570** d.	0748	...	...	0848	0919	...	0948	...	...	...	1048	1120	...	1148	...	...	1248	1319	...	1348	...	...	1448	1519
	Visp **570** d.	0757	...	...	0857	0928	...	0957	...	...	...	1057	1128	...	1157	...	...	1257	1328	...	1357	...	...	1457	1528
0	**Interlaken** Ost ▷ d.	|	0830	0900	|	|	1000	|	...	1030	1100	|	|	1200	|	1230	1300	|	|	1400	|	1430	1500	|	|
2	Interlaken West ▷ d.	|	0835	0905	|	|	1005	|	...	1035	1105	|	|	1205	|	1235	1305	|	|	1405	|	1435	1505	|	|
8	**Spiez** ▷ a.	0824	0852	0921	0924	0953	1021	1024	...	1052	1121	1124	1153	1221	1224	1252	1321	1324	1353	1421	1424	1452	1521	1524	1553
	Spiez d.	0825	0854	0922	0925	0954	1022	1025	...	1054	1122	1125	1154	1222	1225	1254	1322	1325	1354	1422	1425	1454	1522	1525	1554
	Thun d.	0836	0904	0933	0936	1004	1033	1036	...	1104	1133	1136	1204	1233	1236	1304	1333	1336	1404	1433	1436	1504	1533	1536	1604
	Bern a.	0854**k**	0924	0952	0954**k**	1024	1052	1054**k**	...	1124	1152	1154**k**	1224	1252	1254**k**	1324	1352	1354**k**	1424	1452	1454**k**	1524	1552	1554**k**	1624
	Bern **505** d.	0902	0936	1004	1002	1036	1104	1102	1110	1136	1204	1202	1236	1304	1302	1336	1404	1402	1436	1504	1502	1536	1604	1602	1636
	Olten **505 565** a.	|	1003	1030	|	1103	1130	|	|	1203	1230	|	1303	1330	|	1403	1430	|	1503	1530	|	1603	1630	|	1703
	Basel SBB **565** a.	|	1029	1059	|	1129	1159	|	1224	1229	1259	|	1329	1359	|	1429	1459	|	1529	1559	|	1629	1659	|	1729
	Zürich HB **505** a.	0958	...	...	1058	...	...	1158	...	...	...	1258	...	...	1358	...	...	1458	...	...	1558	...	...	1658	...
	Zürich Flug ✈ **535** a.	1014	...	...	1114	...	...	1214	...	...	...	1314	...	...	1414	...	...	1514	...	...	1614	...	...	1714	...
	Romanshorn **535** a.	1112	...	...	1212	...	...	1312	...	...	...	1412	...	...	1512	...	...	1612	...	...	1712	...	...	1812	...

	IC 978	IC 827	IC 1078	IC 980	IC 829	IC 1080	IC 982	IC 831	IC 1082	IC 984	IC 833	IC 1084	IC 986	IC 835	EC 56	IC 336	IC 837	IC 1088	IC 338	IC 990	IC 1090	IC 1096	IC 992	IC 1092	IC 1094
															◧						①–⑥			⑦	⑤⑥
	⊗	⊗	✕	✕	✕	✕	✕	⊗	⊗	⊗	✕	⊗	✕	⊗	✕										r
Milano C **590** d.	...	...	...	...	...	...	...	...	...	...	...	...	...	...	1823	...	...	...	...	...	...	...	...	...	...
g **570** d.	...	1548	...	...	1648	1720	...	1748	...	...	1848	1920	...	1948	2020	...	...	2120	...	...	2219	...	...	2226	...
p **570** d.	...	1557	...	...	1657	1728	...	1757	...	...	1857	1928	...	1957	2028	...	...	2128	...	...	2228	...	...	|	...
nterlaken Ost ▷ d.	1600	|	1630	1700	|	|	1800	|	1830	1900	|	|	2000	|	|	2100	...	|	...	2200	|	...	2300	|	2333
nterlaken West ▷ d.	1605	|	1635	1705	|	|	1805	|	1835	1905	|	|	2005	|	|	2105	...	|	...	2205	|	...	2305	|	2338
ez ▷ a.	1621	1624	1652	1721	1724	1753	1821	1824	1852	1921	1924	1953	2021	2024	2053	2121	...	2153	...	2221	2253	...	2321	2322	2356
ez d.	1622	1625	1654	1722	1725	1754	1822	1825	1854	1922	1925	1954	2022	2025	2054	2122	...	2154	...	2222	2254	...	2322	2325	2357
un d.	1633	1636	1704	1733	1736	1804	1833	1836	1904	1933	1936	2004	2033	2036	2104	2133	...	2204	...	2233	2304	...	2333	2336	0007
rn a.	1652	1654**k**	1724	1752	1754**k**	1824	1852	1854**k**	1924	1952	1954**k**	2024	2052	2054**k**	2124	2152	...	2224	...	2252	2324	...	2352	2354	0027
rn **505** d.	1704	1702	1736	1804	1802	1836	1904	1902	1936	2004	2002	2036	2104	2102	2136	...	2202	...	2236	...	...	2336	...	...	...
en **505 565** a.	1730	|	1803	1830	|	1903	1930	|	2003	2030	|	2103	2130	|	2203	...	2228	...	2308	...	...	0008	...	...	...
sel SBB **565** a.	1759	|	1829	1859	|	1929	1959	|	2029	2059	|	2129	2159	|	2232	...	|	...	2335	...	...	0035	...	...	...
ürich HB **505** a.	...	1758	...	...	1858	...	...	1958	...	...	2058	...	...	2158	...	...	2302	...	...	...	...	...	...	...	...
ürich Flug ✈ **535** a.	...	1814	...	...	1914	...	...	2014	...	...	2114	...	...	2214	...	...	2314	...	...	...	...	...	...	...	...
Romanshorn **535** a.	...	1912	...	...	2012	...	...	2112	...	...	2212	...	...	2312	...	...	0012	...	...	...	...	...	...	...	...

[12] Basel - Brig - Domodossola and v.v.
[12] and ✕ Milano - Basel - Frankfurt.
[12] and ✕ Interlaken - Basel - Frankfurt / Berlin / Hamburg and v.v.
[12] and (🍸) Paris - Basel - Bern and v.v.

f – Via Frutigen.
k – Connects with train in previous column.
r – ⑤⑥ (not Apr. 19).
z – ⑥⑦ (not Apr. 20).

◧ – Supplement payable for journeys from / to Italy.
▷ – Other trains Spiez - Interlaken West - Interlaken Ost and v.v.:
From Spiez at 0556, 0709, 0805, 0909, 1005, 1109, 1205, 1309, 1405, 1509, 1605, 1709, 1805 and 1905.
From Interlaken Ost at 0729, 0820, 0929, 1020, 1129, 1220, 1329, 1420, 1529, 1620, 1729, 1820 and 1929.

561 LUZERN - INTERLAKEN

Narrow gauge rack railway. Z

From March 18 to April 14 trains are replaced by 🚌 between Luzern and Alpnachstad in similar timings (minor variations may occur).

km		Ⓐ	Ⓐ	L		L			L				L			L			L			L		
0	**Luzern** 552 d.	...	...	...	0542	0606	0612	0642	0706	0712	0742		1706	1712	1742	1806	1812	1842	1906	1912	1942	2006	2012	204
9	Hergiswil 552 d.	...	...	...	0554	|	0624	0654	|	0724	0754		|	1724	1754	|	1824	1854	|	1924	1954	|	2024	205
13	Alpnachstad d.	...	...	...	0559	|	0629	0659	|	0729	0759	and at	|	1729	1759	|	1829	1859	|	1929	1959	|	2029	205
15	Alpnach Dorf d.	...	...	...	0601	|	0631	0701	|	0731	0801		|	1731	1801	|	1831	1901	|	1931	2001	|	2031	210
21	Sarnen d.	...	...	...	0609	0624	0639	0709	0724	0739	0809	the same	1724	1739	1809	1824	1839	1909	1924	1939	2009	2024	2039	210
23	Sachseln d.	...	...	...	0613	0628	0643	0713	0728	0743	0813		1728	1743	1813	1828	1843	1913	1928	1943	2013	2028	2043	21
29	Giswil d.	...	...	...	0621	0638	0651	0721	0738	0751	0821	minutes	1738	1751	1821	1838	1851	1921	1938	1951	2021	2038	2051	212
36	Lungern d.	...	...	...	▬	0652	...	▬	0752	...	▬		1752	...	▬	1852	...	...	1952	▬	...	2052	▬	...
40	Brünig Hasliberg d.	...	...	...	...	0704	...	...	0804	...	...	past each	1804	...	...	1904	...	...	2004	...	...	2104	...	...
45	**Meiringen ●** a.	...	...	...	...	0716	...	...	0816	...	...		1816	...	...	1916	...	...	2016	...	...	2116	...	...
45	**Meiringen ●** d.	0515	0545	0614	0651	0722	...	0751	0822	...	0851	hour until	1822	...	1851	1922	...	...	...	2020	...	...	2120	...
58	**Brienz** d.	0527	0556	0628	0702	0733	...	0802	0837	...	0902		1837	...	1902	1935	...	...	...	2033	...	...	2132	...
65	Oberried d.	0537	0608	0639	0712	0744	...	0812	|	...	0912		|	...	1912	1944	...	...	...	2043	...	...	2142	...
74	**Interlaken Ost** a.	0550	0620	0651	0724	0754	...	0824	0855	...	0924		1855	...	1924	1955	...	...	...	2055	...	...	2155	...

	L		⑤⑥r								
Luzern 552 d.	2106	...	...	2112	2142	2212	2242	2312	2342	0012	0042
Hergiswil 552 d.	|	...	...	2124	2154	2224	2254	2324	2354	0024	0056
Alpnachstad d.	|	...	...	2129	2159	2229	2259	2329	2359	0029	0059
Alpnach Dorf d.	|	...	...	2131	2201	2231	2301	2331	0001	0031	0101
Sarnen d.	2124	...	...	2139	2209	2239	2309	2339	0009	0039	0109
Sachseln d.	2128	...	...	2143	2213	2243	2313	2343	0013	0043	0113
Giswil d.	2138	...	...	2151	2221	2251	2321	2351	0021	0051	0121
Lungern d.	2152	...	...	...	...	...	...	...	...	...	...
Brünig Hasliberg d.	2204	...	...	...	...	...	...	...	...	...	...
Meiringen ● a.	2216	...	...	...	...	...	...	...	...	...	...
Meiringen ● d.	...	2220	2320	...	...	...	...	...	...	...	...
Brienz d.	...	2232	2332	...	...	...	...	...	...	...	...
Oberried d.	...	2242	2342	...	...	...	...	...	...	...	...
Interlaken Ost a.	...	2255	2355	...	...	...	...	...	...	...	...

	⑥⑦z					L	Ⓐ			L
Interlaken Ost d.	0006	...	...	...	...	...	0557	...	...	..
Oberried d.	0017	...	...	...	...	...	0609	...	...	..
Brienz d.	0026	...	...	...	...	...	0618	...	...	..
Meiringen ● a.	0039	...	...	...	...	...	0631	...	...	..
Meiringen ● d.	...	...	...	...	...	0542	...	...	...	064
Brünig Hasliberg d.	...	...	...	...	...	0552	...	...	...	065
Lungern d.	...	...	...	...	...	0605	...	...	...	070
Giswil d.	...	...	0505	0535	0605	0622	...	0635	0705	072
Sachseln d.	...	...	0513	0543	0613	0629	...	0643	0713	072
Sarnen d.	...	...	0519	0549	0619	0635	...	0649	0719	073
Alpnach Dorf d.	...	...	0524	0554	0624	|	...	0654	0724	|
Alpnachstad d.	...	...	0529	0559	0629	|	...	0659	0729	|
Hergiswil 552 d.	...	...	0534	0603	0634	|	...	0703	0734	|
Luzern 552 a.	...	...	0547	0617	0647	0655	...	0717	0747	075

		Ⓐ		L			L				L			L			vL	wL						
Interlaken Ost d.	...	0627	...	0704	...	0733	0804	...	0833		1804	...	1833	1904	...	1933	2004	...	...	2104	...	2204	...	23
Oberried d.	...	0640	...	0714	...	0745	|	...	0844		|	...	1844	|	...	1946	2015	...	...	2115	...	2215	...	23
Brienz d.	...	0650	...	0725	...	0754	0825	...	0854	and at	1825	...	1854	1925	...	1956	2025	...	...	2124	...	2224	...	23
Meiringen ● a.	...	0703	...	0736	...	0807	0836	...	0907		1836	...	1907	1936	...	2009	2036	...	...	2137	...	2237	...	23
Meiringen ● d.	...	...	...	0742	...	▬	0842	...	▬	the same	1842	...	▬	1942	...	▬	2042	2042	...	▬	...	▬	...	▬
Brünig Hasliberg d.	...	...	...	0752	...	...	0852	...	...		1852	...	...	1952	...	...	2052	2052	...	...	...	...	...	...
Lungern d.	...	...	...	0805	...	...	0905	...	...	minutes	1905	...	...	2005	...	...	2105	2105	...	...	...	...	...	...
Giswil d.	0735	...	0805	0822	0835	0905	0922	0935	1005		1922	1935	2005	2022	2035	2105	2122	2122	2135	2205	2235	2305	2335	00
Sachseln d.	0743	...	0813	0829	0843	0913	0929	0943	1013	past each	1929	1943	2013	2029	2043	2113	2129	2129	2143	2213	2243	2313	2343	00
Sarnen d.	0749	...	0819	0835	0849	0919	0935	0949	1019		1935	1949	2019	2035	2049	2119	2135	2135	2149	2219	2249	2319	2349	00
Alpnach Dorf d.	0754	...	0824	|	0854	0924	|	0954	1024	hour until	|	1954	2024	|	2054	2124	|	|	2154	2224	2254	2324	2354	00
Alpnachstad d.	0759	...	0829	|	0859	0929	|	0959	1029		|	1959	2029	|	2059	2129	|	|	2159	2229	2259	2329	2359	00
Hergiswil 552 d.	0803	...	0834	|	0903	0934	|	1003	1034		|	2003	2034	|	2103	2134	|	|	2203	2234	2303	2334	0003	00
Luzern 552 a.	0817	...	0847	0855	0917	0947	0955	1017	1047		1955	2017	2047	2055	2117	2147	2155	2155	2217	2247	2317	2347	0017	00

L – LUZERN - INTERLAKEN EXPRESS. Conveys [12] [panorama car] (reservation recommended). Also conveys ✕ on most services.

r – ⑤⑥ (not Apr. 19).
v – ①②③⑤⑥⑦ (also May 30, Aug. 1).
w – ④ (not May 30, Aug. 1).
z – ⑥⑦ (not Apr. 20).

● – Rail service **Meiringen - Innertkirchen** and v.v. Narrow gauge. 2nd class only. *5 km.* Journey time: 11 minutes. **Operator:** MIB.

From Meiringen at 0612 Ⓐ, 0634 Ⓐ, 0656 Ⓐ, 0718 Ⓐ, 0745, 0818 Ⓐ, 0845, 0945, 1045, 1118 Ⓐ, 1145, 1218 Ⓐ, 1245, 1318 Ⓐ, 1345, 1445, 1545, 1618 Ⓐ, 1645, 1718 Ⓐ, 1745, 1818 Ⓐ, 184 1918 Ⓐ, 1945, 2045, 2145 and 2245 ⑤⑥ **r**.

From Innertkirchen at 0558 Ⓐ, 0623 Ⓐ, 0629 Ⓒ, 0645 Ⓐ, 0707, 0729 Ⓐ, 0802, 0829 Ⓐ, 090 1002, 1102, 1129 Ⓐ, 1202, 1229 Ⓐ, 1302, 1329 Ⓐ, 1402, 1502, 1602, 1629Ⓐ, 1702, 1729 1802, 1829 Ⓐ, 1902, 1929 Ⓐ, 2002, 2059 and 2202 ⑤⑥ **r**.

562 BERN - SPIEZ - BRIG (via Lötschberg pass)

BL

km														Ⓐ	Ⓒ					P	⑦Q		*IC* **1093** ①–⑥	*IC* **10** ⑦
0	**Bern** 560 d.	...	...	...	...	0739	0839	0939	1039	1139	1239	1339	1439	1539	1639	1639	1739	1839	1939	...	...	...	...	2234	22
31	Thun 560 d.	...	...	...	0701	0801	0901	1001	1101	1201	1301	1401	1501	1601	1701	1701	1801	1901	2001	...	...	...	...	2254	22
41	**Spiez** 560 d.	0013	...	0612	0712	0812	0912	1012	1112	1212	1312	1412	1512	1612	1712	1712	1812	1912	2012	2112	2212	2212	...	2305	23
55	Frutigen ● d.	0025	...	0625	0725	0825	0925	1025	1125	1225	1325	1425	1525	1625	1725	1725	1825	1925	2025	2125	2225	2225	...	2317	23
72	Kandersteg 🚗 d.	0042	...	0641	0741	0841	0941	1041	1141	1241	1341	1441	1541	1641	1741	1741	1841	1941	2041	2141	2241	2247	...	|	23
89	Goppenstein 🚗 d.	0055	...	0655	0755	0855	0955	1055	1155	1255	1355	1455	1555	1655	1755	1755	1855	1955	2055	2155	2255	2302	...	|	23
115	**Brig** 560 a.	0123	...	0720	0822	0920	1022	1120	1222	1320	1422	1520	1622	1720	1820	1822	1920	2022	2122	2220	2322	2329	...	2344	00
	Domodossola 590 a.	...	...	0754	...	0954	...	1154	...	1354	...	1554	...	1754	1854	...	1954	...	...	2254	...	...	...	...	.

		IC **807** **R**				Ⓒ	Ⓐ												Ⓒ	Ⓐ				
Domodossola 590 d.	0437	...	...	...	0558	...	0658	0758	...	0958	...	1158	...	1358	...	1558	...	1758	...	1858	...	1958	...	.
Brig 560 d.	0514	0546	...	...	0636	0734	0736	0836	0934	1036	1134	1236	1334	1436	1534	1636	1734	1836	1934	1936	...	2036	...	22
Goppenstein 🚗 d.	0538	|	...	...	0700	0800	0800	0900	1000	1100	1200	1300	1400	1500	1600	1700	1800	1900	2000	2000	...	2100	...	22
Kandersteg 🚗 d.	0553	|	←	...	0715	0815	0815	0915	1015	1115	1215	1315	1415	1515	1615	1715	1815	1915	2015	2015	...	2115	...	22
Frutigen ● d.	0609	0612	0632	...	0732	0832	0832	0932	1032	1132	1232	1332	1432	1532	1632	1732	1832	1932	2032	2032	...	2132	...	23
Spiez 560 a.	→	0624	0644	...	0744	0844	0844	0944	1044	1144	1244	1344	1444	1544	1644	1744	1844	1944	2044	2044	...	2144	...	23
Thun 560 a.	...	0634	0658	...	0758	0858	0858	0958	1058	1158	1258	1358	1458	1558	1658	1758	1858	...	...	...	...	...	...	.
Bern 560 a.	...	0654	0721	...	0821	0921	0920	1021	1121	1221	1321	1421	1521	1621	1721	1821	1921	...	...	...	...	...	...	.

P – ①–⑥ (daily Dec. 23 - Apr. 27).
Q – Apr. 28 - Dec. 8.
R – [12] Brig - Romanshorn.

🚗 – Car-carrying shuttle available. ✆ +41 (0) 58 327 41 14.
www.bls.ch/en/fahren/unterwegs-mit/autoverlad/kandersteg-goppenstein

● – 🚌 **SERVICE FRUTIGEN - ADELBODEN**. 20 km. Journey ±30 minutes.
Operator: AFA, 3715 Adelboden. ✆ +41 (0) 33 673 74 74, fax +41 (0) 33 673 74 70.

From Frutigen at 0615 Ⓐ, 0633, 0700 Ⓐ, 0733, 0800, 0833, 0900 Ⓒ, 0933, 1000 Ⓒ, 1033, 1133 and hourly until 1633, then 1700, 1733, 1800, 1833, 1900 Ⓐ, 1933, 2033, 2133, 2233 and 2325.

From Adelboden (Post) at 0537 Ⓐ, 0552, 0622 Ⓐ, 0652, 0725, 0752, 0825 Ⓒ, 0852, 0925 Ⓒ, 0952, 1052 and hourly until 1552, then 1625, 1652, 1725, 1752, 1825 Ⓐ, 1852 1952, 2052, 2152 and 2225.

INTERLAKEN - SPIEZ - ZWEISIMMEN 563

3LS

km				T			©																Ⓐ		
	Interlaken Ost ◇ .... 560 d.	...	...	...	...	...	...	...	0908	...	...	...	...	...	1308	...	...	...	...	1508	...	...	...	...
	Bern 560 .... d.	...	...	...	...	0739	...	0839	|	0939	1039	...	1139	1239	|	1339	...	1439	...	|	1539	...	1639	...
0	Spiez .... 560 d.	0612	...	0712	0738	0812	0838	0912	0938	1012	1112	1138	1212	1312	1338	1412	...	1512	...	1538	1612	1638	1712	...
11	Erlenbach im Simmental .... d.	0629	...	0729	0753	0829	0853	0929	0953	1029	1129	1153	1229	1329	1353	1429	...	1529	...	1553	1629	1653	1729	...
26	Boltigen .... d.	0650	...	0750	0811	0850	0911	0950	1011	1050	1150	1211	1250	1350	1411	1450	...	1550	...	1611	1650	1711	1750	...
35	Zweisimmen .... a.	0659	...	0759	0820	0859	0920	0959	1020	1059	1159	1220	1259	1359	1420	1459	...	1559	...	1620	1659	1720	1759	...

			Ⓐ						⑤⑥
terlaken Ost ◇ .... 560 d.	1708	...	...	...	...	...	...	...	...
Bern 560 .... d.	|	1739	...	1839	1939	...	...	...	...
piez .... 560 d.	1738	1812	1838	1912	2012	...	2106	2206	2306
rlenbach im Simmental .... d.	1753	1829	1853	1929	2029	...	2122	2222	2322
oltigen .... d.	1811	1850	1911	1950	2050	...	2141	2241	2341
weisimmen .... a.	1820	1859	1920	1959	2059	...	2152	2252	2352

	Ⓐ		Ⓐ		Ⓐ					
Zweisimmen .... d.	0539	0554	0639	0702	0739	0802	...	0902	0939	1002
Boltigen .... d.	0549	0603	0649	0711	0749	0811	...	0911	0949	1011
Erlenbach im Simmental .... d.	0605	0622	0705	0730	0805	0830	...	0930	1005	1030
Spiez .... 560 a.	0621	0639	0721	0747	0821	0847	...	0947	1021	1047
Bern 560 .... a.	...	0721	...	0821	...	0921	...	1021	...	1121
Interlaken Ost ◇ .... 560 a.	...	...	...	...	...	...	...	...	...	...

											©													⑥⑦
weisimmen .... d.	1102	1139	1202	1302	1339	1402	1502	...	1539	1602	1639	...	1702	1739	1802	...	...	1902	2002	2104	...	2204	2304	0010
oltigen .... d.	1111	1149	1211	1311	1349	1411	1511	...	1549	1611	1649	...	1711	1749	1811	...	...	1911	2012	2114	...	2214	2314	0020
rlenbach im Simmental .... d.	1130	1205	1230	1330	1405	1430	1530	...	1605	1630	1705	...	1730	1805	1830	...	...	1930	2031	2134	...	2234	2333	0042
piez .... 560 a.	1147	1221	1247	1347	1421	1447	1547	...	1621	1647	1721	...	1747	1821	1847	...	...	1947	2047	2150	...	2250	2353	0058
Bern 560 .... a.	1221	|	1321	1421	|	1521	1621	...	|	1721	...	...	1821	|	1921	...	...	...	...	...	...	...	...	...
terlaken Ost ◇ .... 560 a.	...	1250	...	...	1450	...	...	...	1650	...	...	...	...	1850	...	...	...	...	...	...	...	...	...	...

– From Thun (d. 0701).

◇ – Trains also call at Interlaken West.

INTERLAKEN - KLEINE SCHEIDEGG - JUNGFRAUJOCH 564

Narrow gauge rack railway. BOB, WAB, JB

km																											
0	Interlaken Ost .... d.	0635	0635	0705	0705	0735	0735	0805	0805	0835	0835	0905	0905	0935	0935	1005	1005	1035	1035	1105	1105	1135	1135	1205	1205	1235	1305
3	Wilderswil ▲ .... d.	0640	0640	0710	0710	0740	0740	0810	0810	0840	0840	0910	0910	0940	0940	1010	1010	1040	1040	1110	1110	1140	1140	1210	1210	1240	1310
8	Zweilütschinen .... d.	0646	0647	0716	0717	0746	0747	0816	0817	0846	0847	0916	0917	0946	0947	1016	1017	1046	1047	1116	1117	1146	1147	1216	1217	1246	1317
12	Lauterbrunnen ● .... a.	0655	|	0725	|	0755	|	0825	|	0855	|	0925	|	0955	|	1025	|	1055	|	1125	|	1155	|	1225	|	1255	|
	change trains	|	|	|	|	|	|	|	|	|	|	|	|	|	|	|	|	|	|	|	|	|	|	|	|	|	|
12	Lauterbrunnen .... d.	0707	|	0737	|	0807	|	0837	|	0907	|	0937	|	1007	|	1037	|	1107	|	1137	|	1207	|	1237	|	1307	|
16	Wengen .... a.	0719	|	0749	|	0819	|	0849	|	0919	|	0949	|	1019	|	1049	|	1119	|	1149	|	1219	|	1249	|	1319	|
16	Wengen .... d.	0724	|	0754	|	0824r	|	0854	|	0924r	|	0954	|	1024r	|	1054	|	1124r	|	1154	|	1224r	|	1254	|	1324r	|
19	Grindelwald .... a.	|	0708	|	0738	|	0808	|	0838	|	0908	|	0938	|	1008	|	1038	|	1108	|	1138	|	1208	|	1238	|	1338
	change trains	|	|	|	|	|	|	|	|	|	|	|	|	|	|	|	|	|	|	|	|	|	|	|	|	|	|
19	Grindelwald .... d.	|	0717	|	0747	|	0817	|	0847	|	0917	|	0947	|	1017	|	1047	|	1117	|	1147	|	1217	|	1247	|	1347
20	Grindelwald Grund . d.	|	0725	|	0755	|	0825	|	0855	|	0925	|	0955	|	1025	|	1055	|	1125	|	1155	|	1225	|	1255	|	1355
23*	Kleine Scheidegg .... a.	0749	0749	0819	0819	0849r	0849	0919	0919	0949r	0949	1019	1019	1049r	1049	1119	1119	1149r	1149	1219	1219	1249r	1249	1319	1319	1349r	1419

terlaken Ost .... d.	1305	1405	1405	1435	1505	1505	1535	1535	1605	1605	1635	1635	1705	1705	1735	1805	1805	1835	1835	1905	1905	2005	2005	2105	2105	2202	2205
ilderswil ▲ .... d.	1310	1410	1410	1440	1510	1510	1540	1540	1610	1610	1640	1640	1710	1710	1740	1810	1810	1840	1840	1910	1910	2010	2010	2110	2110	2207	2210
weilütschinen .... d.	1316	1417	1416	1447	1516	1517	1546	1547	1616	1617	1646	1647	1716	1717	1746	1816	1817	1846	1847	1916	1917	2016	2017	2116	2117	2213	2217
uterbrunnen ● .... a.	1325	|	1425	|	1525	|	1555	|	1625	|	1655	|	1725	|	1755	1825	|	1855	|	1925	|	2025	|	2125	|	2222	|
change trains	|	|	|	|	|	|	|	|	|	|	|	|	|	|	|	|	|	|	|	|	|	|	|	|	|	|	|
uterbrunnen .... d.	1337	|	1437	|	1537	|	1607	|	1637	|	1707	|	1737	|	1807	1837	|	1907	|	1937	|	2037	|	2130	|	2230	|
engen .... a.	1349	|	1449	|	1549	|	1619	|	1649	|	1719	|	1749	|	1819	1849	|	1919	|	1949	|	2049	|	2141	|	2241	|
engen .... d.	1354	|	1454	|	1554	|	1624r	|	1654	|	1724t	|	1754r	|	1824j	1854j	|	...	|	...	|	...	|	...	|	...	|
Grindelwald .... a.	|	1438	|	1508	|	1538	|	1608	|	1638	|	1708	|	1738	|	|	1838	...	1908	...	1938	...	2038	...	2138	...	2238
change trains	|	|	|	|	|	|	|	|	|	|	|	|	|	|	|	|	|	|	|	|	|	|	|	|	|	|	|
Grindelwald .... d.	|	1447	|	1517	|	1547	|	1617	|	1647	|	1717t	|	1747n	|	|	1847t	...	1917n	...	1947j	...	...	...	...	...	...
Grindelwald Grund .. d.	|	1455	|	1525	|	1555	|	1625	|	1655	|	1725t	|	1755n	|	|	1855j	...	1922n	...	1952j	...	...	...	...	...	...
eine Scheidegg .... a.	1419	1519	1519	1549	1619	1619	1649r	1649	1719	1719	1749t	1749t	1819r	1819n	1849j	1919j	1919j	...	...	...	...	...	...	...	...	...	...

eine Scheidegg .... d.	...	...	...	...	...	...	...	...	...	...	...	...	...	0801	0803	0831	0833	0901r	0903	0931	0933	1001r	1003	1031	1033	1101r	1103
Grindelwald Grund .. d.	...	...	...	...	...	...	0641d	...	0708	...	0738	...	0808	|	0838	|	0908	|	0938	|	1008	|	1038	|	1108	|	1138
Grindelwald .... a.	...	...	...	...	...	...	0645d	...	0712	...	0742	...	0812	|	0842	|	0912	|	0942	|	1012	|	1042	|	1112	|	1142
change trains														|	|	|	|	|	|	|	|	|	|	|	|	|	|	|
Grindelwald .... d.	0519	...	0547	...	0619	...	0649	...	0719	...	0749	...	0819	|	0849	|	0919	|	0949	|	1019	|	1049	|	1119	|	1149
engen .... a.	|	...	|	...	|	...	|	...	|	...	|	...	|	0829	|	0859	|	0929r	|	0959	|	1029r	|	1059	|	1129r	|
engen .... d.	|	0504	|	0603	|	0633	|	0703	|	0733	|	0803	|	0833	|	0903	|	0933	|	1003	|	1033	|	1103	|	1133	|
uterbrunnen .... a.	|	0519	|	0620	|	0650	|	0720	|	0750	|	0820	|	0850	|	0920	|	0950	|	1020	|	1050	|	1120	|	1150	|
change trains	|	|	|	|	|	|	|	|	|	|	|	|	|	|	|	|	|	|	|	|	|	|	|	|	|	|	|
uterbrunnen ● .... d.	|	0532	|	0632	|	0702	|	0732	|	0802	|	0832	|	0902	|	0932	|	1002	|	1032	|	1102	|	1132	|	1202	|
weilütschinen .... d.	0542	0542	0610	0642	0642	0712	0712	0742	0742	0812	0812	0842	0842	0912	0912	0942	0942	1012	1012	1042	1042	1112	1112	1142	1142	1212	1212
ilderswil ▲ .... d.	0548	0548	0616	0648	0648	0718	0718	0748	0748	0818	0818	0848	0848	0918	0918	0948	0948	1018	1018	1048	1048	1118	1118	1148	1148	1218	1218
terlaken Ost .... a.	0552	0552	0621	0653	0653	0723	0723	0753	0753	0823	0823	0853	0853	0923	0923	0953	0953	1023	1023	1053	1053	1123	1123	1153	1153	1223	1223

eine Scheidegg .... d.	1131	1133	1201r	1231	1233	1331	1333	1401r	1403	1431	1433	1501r	1503	1531	1533	1631	1633	1701r	1703	1731	1733	1833n	1831r	1933j	1931j	...	...
Grindelwald Grund .. d.	|	1208	|	|	1308	|	1408	|	1438	|	1508	|	1538	|	1608	|	1708	|	1738	|	1808	1908n	|	2008j	|	...	...
Grindelwald .... a.	|	1212	|	|	1312	|	1412	|	1442	|	1512	|	1542	|	1612	|	1712	|	1742	|	1812	1912n	|	2012j	|	...	...
change trains	|	|	|	|	|	|	|	|	|	|	|	|	|	|	|	|	|	|	|	|	|	|	|	|	|	|	...
Grindelwald .... d.	|	1219	|	|	1319	|	1419	|	1449	|	1519	|	1549	|	1619	|	1719	|	1749	|	1819	1919	|	2019	|	2119	...
engen .... a.	1159	|	1229r	1259	|	1359	|	1429r	|	1459	|	1529r	|	1559	|	1659	|	1729r	|	1759	|	|	1859r	|	1959j	|	...
engen .... d.	1203	|	1233	1303	|	1403	|	1433	|	1503	|	1533	|	1603	|	1703	|	1733	|	1803	|	|	1903	|	2003	|	2103
uterbrunnen .... a.	1220	|	1250	1320	|	1420	|	1450	|	1520	|	1550	|	1620	|	1720	|	1750	|	1820	|	|	1920	|	2020	|	2120
change trains	|	|	|	|	|	|	|	|	|	|	|	|	|	|	|	|	|	|	|	|	|	|	|	|	|	|	|
uterbrunnen ● .... d.	1232	|	1302	1332	|	1432	|	1502	|	1532	|	1602	|	1632	|	1732	|	1802	|	1832	|	|	1932	|	2032	|	2132
weilütschinen .... d.	1242	1242	1312	1342	1342	1442	1442	1512	1512	1542	1542	1612	1612	1642	1642	1742	1742	1812	1812	1842	1842	1942	1942	2042	2042	2138	2142
ilderswil ▲ .... d.	1248	1248	1318	1348	1348	1448	1448	1518	1518	1548	1548	1618	1618	1648	1648	1748	1748	1818	1818	1848	1848	1948	1948	2048	2048	2144	2148
terlaken Ost .... a.	1253	1253	1323	1353	1353	1453	1453	1523	1523	1553	1553	1623	1623	1653	1653	1753	1753	1823	1823	1853	1853	1953	1953	2053	2053	2149	2153

km																				t	t	j	j
0	Kleine Scheidegg .... d.	0800	0830	0900	0930	1000	1030	1100	1130	...	1200	1230	1300	1330	1400	1430	...	1500	1530	1600	1630	1700	1730	1800
2	Eigergletscher .... △ d.	0808	0838	0908	0938	1008	1038	1108	1138	...	1208	1238	1308	1338	1408	1438	...	1508	1538	1608	1638	1708	1738	1808
9	Jungfraujoch .... △ a.	0835	0905	0935	1005	1035	1105	1135	1205	...	1235	1305	1335	1405	1435	1505	...	1535	1605	1635	1705	1735	1805	1835

																		t	t	j	j	
ngfraujoch .... △ d.	0843	0913	0943	1013	1043	1113	1143	1213	1243	1313	...	1343	1413	1443	1513	1543	1613	1643	1713	1743	1813	1843	...
ergletscher .... △ d.	0910	0940	1010	1040	1110	1140	1210	1240	1310	1340	...	1410	1440	1510	1540	1610	1640	1710	1740	1810	1840	1910	...
eine Scheidegg .... a.	0918	0948	1018	1048	1118	1148	1218	1248	1318	1348	...	1418	1448	1518	1548	1618	1648	1718	1748	1818	1848	1918	...

- ⚒ only.
May 11 - Sept. 1.
- Dec. 22 - Mar. 17, Apr 19 - Oct. 20.
- June 29 - Oct. 27.
Dec. 22 - Oct. 20.
Apr. 19 - Oct. 20.

– Additional services operate Dec. 22 - Mar. 31 and May 25 - Oct. 20.
Via Wengen (*28 km* via Grindelwald).
– At times of heavy snowfall (November - April) the Eigergletscher - Jungfraujoch service is subject to cancellation.

● – Cableway operates **Lauterbrunnen - Grütschalp**, and narrow gauge railway **Grütschalp - Mürren**, *total: 5 km.*
Operator: BLM. Journey time: 20 minutes including connection.
From Lauterbrunnen at 0613, 0631, 0701, 0731, 0801, 0838, 0908 and every 30 minutes ◇ until 1938.
From Mürren at 0606, 0636, 0706, 0736, 0806, 0828, 0858 and every 30 minutes ◇ until 1858.
Cableway operates **Mürren - Schilthorn and v.v. Dec. 9 - Apr. 22, Apr. 28 - Nov. 11**.
From Mürren at 0810, 0840, 0910 and every 30 minutes until 1610. **From Schilthorn** at 0903, 0933 and every 30 minutes until 1633. Additional services available Mar. 31 - Nov. 10. Operator: Schilthornbahn, ✆ +41 33 826 00 07.

▲ – Narrow gauge rack railway operates **May 30 - Oct. 27 Wilderswil - Schynige Platte**.
7 km. Journey time: 52 minutes. **Operator**: BOB. Service may be reduced In bad weather.
From Wilderswil at 0725, 0805 **q**, 0845, 0925, 1005, 1045, 1125, 1205, 1245, 1325, 1405, 1445, 1525, 1605, 1645.
From Schynige Platte at 0821, 0901 **q**, 0941, 1021, 1101, 1141, 1221, 1301, 1341, 1421, 1501, 1541, 1621, 1701, 1753.

565 BASEL and BERN - LUZERN

SBB

km		IR	IR	RE	IR	IR	IR	RE	IR	IC	IR	RE	IR	IC	IR	RE	IR	IC	IR	RE	IR	IR	IR	RE	IR	EC
		2309	2457	4709	2505	2311	2459	4711	2507	663	2461	4713	2509	665	2463	4715	2511	667	2465	4717	2513	2319	2467	4719	2515	151
			Ⓐ																							◧
		E				E			🍷	L			🍷	L			🍷	G✕			🍷	E			🍷	F✕
0	**Basel** SBB 560 d.	0504	...	...	...	0604	0617	...	...	0704	0717	...	...	0804	0817	...	...	0904	0917	...	...	1004	1017	...	...	110
14	Liestal d.	|	...	...	...	|	0627	...	...	|	0727	...	...	|	0827	...	...	|	0927	...	...	|	1027	...	...	|
21	Sissach d.	|	...	...	...	|	0633	...	...	|	0733	...	...	|	0833	...	...	|	0933	...	...	|	1033	...	...	|
39	**Olten** 560 a.	0528	...	...	...	0628	0648	...	...	0728	0748	...	...	0828	0848	...	...	0928	0948	...	...	1028	1048	...	...	112
39	**Olten** d.	0530	0548	0606	...	0630	0649	0706	...	0730	0749	0806	...	0830	0849	0906	...	0930	0949	1006	...	1030	1049	1106	...	113
	Genève Aéroport + 505 d.	|	|	|	...	|	|	|	...	|	|	|	0549	|	|	|	0649	|	|	|	0749	|	|	|	0849	|
	Genève 505 d.	|	|	|	...	|	|	|	...	|	|	|	0600	|	|	|	0700	|	|	|	0800	|	|	|	0900	|
	Lausanne 505 d.	|	|	|	0444e	|	|	|	0544	|	|	|	0644	|	|	|	0744	|	|	|	0844	|	|	|	0944	|
	Bern d.	|	|	|	0600	|	|	|	0700	|	|	|	0800	|	|	|	0900	|	|	|	1000	|	|	|	1100	|
47	Zofingen d.	|	0558	0613	0628	|	0658	0713	0728	|	0758	0813	0828	|	0858	0913	0928	|	0958	1013	1028	|	1058	1113	1128	|
69	Sursee d.	|	0611	0632	0641	|	0711	0732	0741	|	0811	0832	0841	|	0911	0932	0941	|	1011	1032	1041	|	1111	1132	1141	|
95	**Luzern** a.	0605	0630	0655	0701	0705	0730	0755	0801	0805	0830	0855	0901	0905	0930	0955	1001	1005	1030	1055	1101	1105	1130	1155	1201	120

	IR	RE	IR	IR	IR	RE	IR	IC	IR	RE	IR	IR	IR	RE	IR	IC	IR	RE	IR	IR	IR	RE	IR	IC	IR	RE
	2469	4721	2517	2323	2471	4723	2519	675	2473	4725	2521	2327	2475	4727	2523	679	2477	4729	2525	2331	2479	4731	2527	683	2481	473
			🍷	E			🍷	G✕			🍷	E			🍷	G✕				E			🍷	G✕		
Basel SBB 560 d.	1117	...	...	1204	1217	...	...	1304	1317	...	...	1404	1417	...	...	1504	1517	...	...	1604	1617	...	...	1704	1717	...
Liestal d.	1127	...	...	|	1227	...	...	|	1327	...	...	|	1427	...	...	|	1527	...	...	|	1627	...	...	|	1727	...
Sissach d.	1133	...	...	|	1233	...	...	|	1333	...	...	|	1433	...	...	|	1533	...	...	|	1633	...	...	|	1733	...
Olten 560 a.	1148	...	...	1228	1248	...	...	1328	1348	...	...	1428	1448	...	...	1528	1548	...	...	1628	1648	...	...	1728	1748	...
Olten d.	1149	1206	...	1230	1249	1306	...	1330	1349	1406	...	1430	1449	1506	...	1530	1549	1606	...	1630	1649	1706	...	1730	1749	180
Genève Aéroport + 505 d.	|	|	0949	|	|	|	1049	|	|	|	1149	|	|	|	1249	|	|	|	1349	|	|	|	1449	|	|	|
Genève 505 d.	|	|	1000	|	|	|	1100	|	|	|	1200	|	|	|	1300	|	|	|	1400	|	|	|	1500	|	|	|
Lausanne 505 d.	|	|	1044	|	|	|	1144	|	|	|	1244	|	|	|	1344	|	|	|	1411	|	|	|	1544	|	|	|
Bern d.	|	|	1200	|	|	|	1300	|	|	|	1400	|	|	|	1500	|	|	|	1600	|	|	|	1700	|	|	|
Zofingen d.	1158	1213	1228	|	1258	1313	1328	|	1358	1413	1428	|	1458	1513	1528	|	1558	1613	1628	|	1658	1713	1728	|	1758	181
Sursee d.	1211	1232	1241	|	1311	1332	1341	|	1411	1432	1441	|	1511	1532	1541	|	1611	1632	1641	|	1711	1732	1741	|	1811	183
Luzern a.	1230	1255	1301	1305	1330	1355	1401	1405	1430	1455	1501	1505	1530	1555	1601	1605	1630	1655	1701	1705	1730	1755	1801	1805	1830	185

	IR	IR	IR	RE	IR	IC	IR	RE	IR	IR	IR	RE	IR	IC	IR	RE	IR	IR	IR	RE	IR	IR	IR	RE	IR	IR
	2529	2335	2483	4735	2531	687	2485	4737	2533	2339	2487	4739	2535	691	2489	4741	2537	2343	2491	4743	2539	2345	2493	4745	2347	234
																			⑤⑥				⑤⑥			⑥⑦
	🍷	E			🍷	C✕				E				C					r				r			z
Basel SBB 560 d.	...	1804	1817	...	...	1904	1917	...	...	2004	2017	...	...	2104	2117	...	...	2204	2217	...	...	2258	2317	...	0002	010
Liestal d.	...	|	1827	...	...	|	1927	...	...	|	2027	...	...	|	2127	...	...	|	2227	...	...	2308	2327	...	0012	011
Sissach d.	...	|	1833	...	...	|	1933	...	...	|	2033	...	...	|	2133	...	...	|	2233	...	...	|	2333	...	|	011
Olten 560 a.	...	1828	1848	...	...	1928	1948	...	...	2028	2048	...	...	2128	2148	...	...	2228	2248	...	...	2325	2348	...	0028	012
Olten d.	...	1830	1849	1906	...	1930	1949	2006	...	2030	2049	2106	...	2130	2149	2206	...	2230	2249	2307	...	2330	...	0007	0035	013
Genève Aéroport + 505 d.	1549	|	|	|	1649	|	|	|	1749	|	|	|	1849	|	|	|	1949	|	|	|	2049	|	...	|	|	|
Genève 505 d.	1600	|	|	|	1700	|	|	|	1800	|	|	|	1900	|	|	|	2000	|	|	|	2100	|	...	|	|	|
Lausanne 505 d.	1644	|	|	|	1744	|	|	|	1844	|	|	|	1944	|	|	|	2044	|	|	|	2144	|	...	|	|	|
Bern d.	1800	|	|	|	1900	|	|	|	2000	|	|	|	2100	|	|	|	2200	|	|	|	2300	|	...	|	|	|
Zofingen d.	1828	|	1858	1913	1928	|	1958	2013	2028	|	2058	2113	2128	|	2158	2213	2228	|	2256	2314	2328	|	...	0014	0042	014
Sursee d.	1841	|	1911	1932	1941	|	2011	2032	2041	|	2111	2132	2141	|	2211	2232	2241	|	...	2332	2341	|	...	0034	0056	015
Luzern a.	1901	1905	1930	1955	2001	2005	2030	2055	2101	2105	2130	2155	2201	2205	2230	2255	2301	2305	...	2355	0001	0005	...	0056	0116	021

km		RE	IR	IR	IR	IR	RE	IR	IR	IR	RE	IR	IR	IR	RE	IR	IR	IR	RE	IR	IC	IR	RE	IR	IR	IR
		4706	2456	2456	2306	2508	4708	2458	2308	2510	4710	2460	2310	2512	4712	2462	2312	2514	4714	2464	668	2516	4716	2466	2316	251
			Ⓐ																							
						🍷			A	🍷			E	🍷			E	🍷			C✕	🍷			E	🍷
	Luzern d.	0456	0530	...	0554	0600	0605	0630	0654	0700	0705	0730	0754	0800	0805	0830	0854	0900	0905	0930	0954	1000	1005	1030	1054	110
	Sursee d.	0521	0548	...	|	0618	0626	0648	|	0718	0726	0748	|	0818	0826	0848	|	0918	0926	0948	|	1018	1026	1048	|	111
0	Zofingen d.	0543	0602	...	|	0632	0643	0702	|	0732	0743	0802	|	0832	0843	0902	|	0932	0943	1002	|	1032	1043	1102	|	113
63	**Bern** a.	|	|	...	|	0700	|	|	|	0800	|	|	|	0900	|	|	|	1000	|	|	|	1100	|	|	|	120
	Lausanne 505 a.	|	|	...	|	0816	|	|	|	0916	|	|	|	1016	|	|	|	1116	|	|	|	1216	|	|	|	131
	Genève 505 a.	|	|	...	|	0900	|	|	|	1000	|	|	|	1100	|	|	|	1200	|	|	|	1300	|	|	|	140
	Genève Aéroport + 505 a.	|	|	...	|	0911	|	|	|	1011	|	|	|	1111	|	|	|	1211	|	|	|	1311	|	|	|	141
	Olten a.	0552	0610	...	0627	...	0652	0710	0727	...	0752	0810	0827	...	0852	0910	0927	...	0952	1010	1027	...	1052	1110	1127	...
	Olten 560 d.	...	0612	0612	0630	...	...	0712	0730	...	...	0812	0830	...	...	0912	0930	...	...	1012	1030	...	...	1112	1130	...
	Sissach d.	...	0627	0627	|	...	...	0727	|	...	...	0827	|	...	...	0927	|	...	...	1027	|	...	...	1127	|	...
	Liestal d.	...	0633	0633	|	...	...	0733	|	...	...	0833	|	...	...	0933	|	...	...	1033	|	...	...	1133	|	...
	Basel SBB 560 a.	...	0644	0644	0655	...	...	0744	0755	...	...	0847	0855	...	...	0947	0955	...	...	1044	1055	...	...	1144	1155	...

	RE	IR	IC	IR	RE	IR	IR	IR	RE	IR	EC	IR	RE	IR	IR	IR	RE	IR	IC	IR	RE	IR	IR	IR	RE	IR
	4718	2468	672	2520	4720	2470	2320	2522	4722	2472	158	2524	4724	2474	2324	2526	4726	2476	680	2528	4728	2478	2328	2530	4730	248
											◧															
			G✕	🍷			E	🍷			M✕	🍷			E	🍷			G✕	🍷			E	🍷		
Luzern d.	1105	1130	1154	1200	1205	1230	1254	1300	1305	1330	1354	1400	1405	1430	1454	1500	1505	1530	1554	1600	1605	1630	1654	1700	1705	173
Sursee d.	1126	1148	|	1218	1226	1248	|	1318	1326	1348	|	1418	1426	1448	|	1518	1526	1548	|	1618	1626	1648	|	1718	1726	174
Zofingen d.	1143	1202	|	1232	1243	1302	|	1332	1343	1402	|	1432	1443	1502	|	1532	1543	1602	|	1632	1643	1702	|	1732	1743	180
Bern a.	|	|	|	1300	|	|	|	1400	|	|	|	1500	|	|	|	1600	|	|	|	1700	|	|	|	1800	|	|
Lausanne 505 a.	|	|	|	1416	|	|	|	1516	|	|	|	1616	|	|	|	1716	|	|	|	1816	|	|	|	1916	|	|
Genève 505 a.	|	|	|	1500	|	|	|	1600	|	|	|	1700	|	|	|	1800	|	|	|	1900	|	|	|	2000	|	|
Genève Aéroport + 505 a.	|	|	|	1511	|	|	|	1611	|	|	|	1711	|	|	|	1811	|	|	|	1911	|	|	|	2011	|	|
Olten a.	1152	1210	1227	...	1252	1310	1327	...	1352	1410	1427	...	1452	1510	1527	...	1552	1610	1627	...	1652	1710	1727	...	1752	181
Olten 560 d.	...	1212	1230	...	...	1312	1330	...	...	1412	1430	...	...	1512	1530	...	...	1612	1630	...	...	1712	1730	...	...	181
Sissach d.	...	1227	|	...	...	1327	|	...	...	1427	|	...	...	1527	|	...	...	1627	|	...	...	1727	|	...	...	182
Liestal d.	...	1233	|	...	...	1333	|	...	...	1433	|	...	...	1533	|	...	...	1633	|	...	...	1733	|	...	...	183
Basel SBB 560 a.	...	1244	1255	...	...	1344	1355	...	...	1444	1455	...	...	1544	1555	...	...	1644	1655	...	...	1744	1755	...	...	184

	IC	IR	RE	IR	IR	IR	RE	IR	IC	IR	RE	IR	IR	IR	RE	IR	IR	IR	RE	IR	IR	IR	RE	IC	RE	IR
	684	2532	4732	2482	2332	2534	4734	2484	688	2536	4736	2486	2336	2538	4738	2488	2338	2540	4740	2490	2340	2542	4742	696	4744	234
																⑤⑥	◇			⑤⑥						⑥(
	G✕				E				G✕				E			r	E			r	E			G		
Luzern d.	1754	1800	1805	1830	1854	1900	1905	1930	1954	2000	2005	2030	2054	2100	2105	2130	2154	2200	2205	...	2254	2300	2305	2354	0005	004
Sursee d.	|	1818	1826	1848	|	1918	1926	1948	|	2018	2026	2048	|	2118	2126	2148	|	2218	2226	...	|	2318	2326	|	0026	010
Zofingen d.	|	1832	1843	1902	|	1932	1943	2002	|	2032	2043	2102	|	2132	2143	2202	|	2232	2243	2302	|	2332	2343	|	0043	012
Bern a.	|	1900	|	|	|	2000	|	|	|	2100	|	|	|	2200	|	|	|	2300	|	|	|	2400	|	|	|	|
Lausanne 505 a.	|	2016	|	|	|	2116	|	|	|	2216	|	|	|	2316	|	|	|	0020	|	|	|	...	|	|	|	|
Genève 505 a.	|	2100	|	|	|	2200t	|	|	|	...	|	|	|	...	|	|	|	...	|	|	|	...	|	|	|	|
Genève Aéroport + 505 a.	|	2111	|	|	|	2211r	|	|	|	...	|	|	|	...	|	|	|	...	|	|	|	...	|	|	|	|
Olten a.	1827	...	1852	1910	1927	...	1952	2010	2027	...	2052	2110	2127	...	2152	2210	2227	...	2252	2310	2327	...	2352	0027	0052	012
Olten 560 d.	1830	...	...	1912	1930	...	...	2012	2030	...	...	2112	2130	...	...	2212	2233	...	...	2312	2333	...	...	0035	...	013
Sissach d.	|	...	...	1927	|	...	...	2027	|	...	...	2127	|	...	...	2227	|	...	...	2327	|	...	...	|	...	|
Liestal d.	|	...	...	1933	|	...	...	2033	|	...	...	2133	|	...	...	2233	2249	...	...	2333	2349	...	...	0052	...	015
Basel SBB 560 a.	1855	...	...	1944	1955	...	...	2044	2055	...	...	2144	2155	...	...	2244	2259	...	...	2344	2359	...	...	0102	...	020

A – 🚃 Arth-Goldau - Basel and v.v.
C – 🚃 Basel - Chiasso and v.v.
E – 🚃 Basel - Erstfeld / Göschenen and v.v.
F – 🚃 Frankfurt - Basel - Luzern - Arth-Goldau - Milano.
G – 🚃 Basel - Lugano and v.v.
L – 🚃 Basel - Locarno and v.v.
M – 🚃 Milano - Arth-Goldau - Luzern - Basel.

e – ① (not Apr. 22, June 10).
r – ⑤⑥ (not Apr. 19).
t – 2216 on ①②③④⑦ (also Apr. 19).
z – Not Apr. 20.

◇ – Runs as *IC* **692** on †.
◧ – Supplement payable in Italy and for international journeys.

LENK - ZWEISIMMEN - MONTREUX 566

arrow gauge. MOB

km																											
		Ⓐ		Ⓐ				Ⓒ		Ⓒ										Ⓐ		Ⓐ					⑤⑥
0	**Lenk** d.	0611	0634	0703	0737	0837	0937	1003	1037	1103	1137	1237	1303	1337	1437	1537	1603	1637	1737	1803	1842	1903	1937	2037	2137	2237	2337
13	**Zweisimmen** a.	0629	0652	0721	0755	0855	0955	1021	1055	1121	1155	1255	1321	1355	1455	1555	1621	1655	1755	1821	1900	1921	1955	2055	2155	2255	2355

km																											
								2111			2115	2217		2119			2123			2127	2229		2131				
			Ⓐ	Ⓒ	Ⓐ	Ⓒ		P			P	B		P			P			B	P	Ⓐ	P				⑤⑥
0	**Zweisimmen** d.	0405	0505	0505	0605	0605	0705	0825	0905	1005	1025	1105	1205	1225	1305	1405	1425	1505	1605	1625	1705	1805	1825	1905	2005	2105	2200
9	Saanenmöser d.	0420	0520	0520	0622	0622	0720	0839	0920	1019	1039	1120	1219	1239	1320	1419	1439	1520	1619	1639	1720	1819	1840	1920	2019	2119	2214
11	Schönried d.	0424	0524	0524	0626	0626	0724	0844	0924	1024	1044	1124	1224	1244	1324	1424	1444	1524	1624	1644	1724	1824	1844	1924	2023	2123	2219
16	**Gstaad** d.	0439	0537	0537	0637	0637	0737	0853	0937	1034	1053	1137	1234	1253	1337	1434	1453	1537	1634	1653	1737	1834	1853	1937	2037	2137	2235
19	Saanen d.	0443	0542	0542	0642	0642	0742	0858	0942	1038	1058	1142	1238	1258	1342	1438	1458	1542	1638	1658	1742	1838	1858	1942	2042	2142	2239
23	Rougemont d.	0449	0547	0547	0647	0647	0747	0903	0947	1044	1103	1147	1244	1303	1347	1444	1503	1547	1644	1703	1747	...	1903	1947	2047	2147	2244
29	Château d'Oex d.	0502	0602	0602	0702	0702	0802	0913	1002	...	1113	1202	...	1313	1402	...	1513	1602	...	1713	1802	...	1913	2002	2101	2201	2254
40	**Montbovon** d.	0522	0622	0622	0722	0722	0828	0929	1026	...	1129	1226	...	1329	1426	...	1529	1626	...	1729	1828	...	1928	2028	2117	2217	2309
51	Les Avants § d.	0543	0643	0643	0742	0742	0849	0949	1047	...	1149	1247	...	1349	1447	...	1549	1647	...	1749	1849	...	1948	2049	2138	2238	2329
55	Chamby ⊙ § d.	0549	0649	0649	0748	0748	0855	0955	1053	...	1155	1253	...	1355	1453	...	1555	1653	...	1755	1855	...	1954	2055	2144	2244	2335
58	Chernex § d.	0600	0701	0701	0758	0757	0904	1004	1104	...	1204	1304	...	1404	1504	...	1604	1704	...	1804	1904	...	2004	2104	2153	2253	2341
62	**Montreux** § a.	0611	0710	0712	0807	0808	0913	1013	1113	...	1213	1313	...	1413	1513	...	1613	1713	...	1813	1913	...	2013	2113	2203	2303	2350

						2112	2214	2214	2118			2122			2126		2228	2130				2234					
	Ⓐ	Ⓐ	Ⓒ	Ⓐ		P	B	®T	P			P			B		P	P			Ⓐ	P					⑤⑥
ontreux § d.	...	...	...	0537	0638	0744	0844	0844	0944	...	1044	1144	...	1244	1344	...	1444	1544	...	1644	...	1744	1844	1944	2114	2214	2355
ernex § d.	...	...	...	0547	0647	0755	0853	0853	0953	...	1053	1153	...	1253	1353	...	1453	1553	...	1653	...	1753	1853	1953	2125	2225	0005
amby ⊙ § d.	...	...	...	0552	0652	0800	0857	0857	0958	...	1057	1158	...	1257	1358	...	1457	1558	...	1657	...	1757	1857	1957	2130	2230	0009
s Avants § d.	...	...	...	0601	0701	0808	0907	0907	1007	...	1107	1207	...	1307	1407	...	1507	1607	...	1707	...	1807	1907	2007	2138	2238	0017
ontbovon d.	...	0521	0546	0623	0723	0828	0929	0927**a**	1028	...	1129	1228	...	1329	1428	...	1529	1628	...	1729	...	1828	1929	2029	2159	2259	0037
âteaux d'Oex d.	...	0537	0602	0639	0740	0843	0945	...	1043	...	1145	1243	...	1345	1443	...	1545	1643	...	1745	...	1845	1945	2045	2215	2317	0051
ugemont d.	...	0548	0613	0654	0754	0853	1000	...	1053	1111	1200	1253	1311	1400	1453	1511	1600	1653	1711	1800	...	1903	2000	2100	2226	2328	0102
anen d.	0500	0553	0618	0659	0759	0859	1005	...	1059	1117	1205	1259	1317	1405	1459	1517	1605	1659	1717	1805	1847	1908	2005	2105	2231	2333	0107
taad d.	0505	0557	0626	0704	0804	0905	1023	...	1105	1124	1223	1305	1324	1423	1505	1524	1623	1705	1724	1823	1853	1923	2023	2123	2235	2337	0111
hönried d.	0513	0607	0635	0713	0814	0914	1032	...	1114	1133	1232	1314	1333	1432	1514	1533	1632	1714	1733	1832	1902	1933	2032	2132	2244	2346	0120
anenmöser d.	0519	0611	0639	0719	0818	0919	1038	...	1119	1139	1238	1319	1339	1438	1519	1539	1638	1719	1739	1839	1907	1938	2038	2138	2248	2350	0125
eisimmen a.	0535	0625	0653	0733	0833	0933	1052	...	1133	1153	1252	1333	1353	1452	1533	1553	1652	1733	1753	1853	1921	1952	2052	2152	2302	0004	0138

	Ⓐ		Ⓐ				Ⓒ		Ⓒ				Ⓐ							Ⓐ		Ⓐ					⑤⑥
eisimmen d.	0550	0611	0634	0703	0803	0903	0937	1003	1037	1103	1137	1203	1237	1303	1403	1503	1537	1603	1703	1737	1803	1824	1903	2003	2103	2203	2306
nk a.	0608	0629	0652	0721	0821	0921	0955	1021	1055	1121	1155	1221	1255	1321	1421	1521	1555	1621	1721	1755	1821	1842	1921	2021	2121	2221	2324

Other trains **LES AVANTS - MONTREUX** (2nd class only)

	Ⓐ	Ⓐ	Ⓐ	Ⓐ	Ⓐ	Ⓐ					
s Avants d.	0615	0718	0813	1319	1713	1813	2110	2320	...	...	...
amby ⊙ d.	0621	0724	0819	1325	1719	1819	2116	2326	...	...	...
ernex d.	0627	0731	0832	1332	1732	1832	2125	2332	...	...	...
ontreux a.	0637	0741	0841	1341	1741	1841	2135	2342	...	...	...

	Ⓐ	Ⓐ	Ⓐ	Ⓐ	Ⓐ	Ⓐ	Ⓐ				
Montreux d.	0528	0615	0715	1215	1615	1715	1815	2015	2145	2245	...
Chernex d.	0537	0627	0730	1224	1624	1724	1824	2024	2154	2254	...
Chamby ⊙ d.	0541	0631	0734	1228	1628	1728	1828	2028	2158	2258	...
Les Avants a.	0549	0639	0742	1236	1636	1736	1836	2036	2206	2306	...

- MOB BELLE EPOQUE – [12] and ⊗.
- MOB PANORAMIC – conveys [12] [panorama car].
- TRAIN DU CHOCOLAT – ①②③④ May 1 - June 27; daily July 1 - Aug. 31; ①④⑤ Sept. 2 - Oct 31. Conveys [12] and 🍸.

a – Arrival time.

⊙ – Chamby is a request stop.
§ – See panel below main table for other trains.

MONTBOVON - BULLE - PALÉZIEUX 568

arrow gauge. 2nd class only. TPF

Warning! Trains are replaced by 🚌 between Châtel-St Denis and Palézieux until Nov. 30.

km																								
		⚒	Ⓐ		⚒	Ⓐ	Ⓐ	Ⓒ															⑤⑥	
0	**Montbovon** d.	...	0539	...	0639	0723	...	0740	0840	0940	1040	1140	1240	1340	1440	1540	1640	1740	1840	1940	2040	...	...	...
13	Gruyères d.	...	0559	...	0659	0744	...	0800	0900	1000	1100	1200	1300	1400	1500	1600	1700	1800	1900	2000	2100	...	...	...
17	**Bulle** ▽ a.	...	0607	...	0707	0753	...	0808	0908	1008	1108	1208	1308	1408	1508	1608	1708	1808	1908	2008	2108	...	...	...
17	**Bulle** ▽ d.	0515	0615	0715	0715	...	0815	0815	0915	1015	1115	1215	1315	1415	1515	1615	1715	1815	1915	2015	2115	2215	2315	...
37	Châtel-St Denis a.	0540	0640	0740	0740	...	0840	0840	0940	1040	1140	1240	1340	1440	1540	1640	1740	1840	1940	2040	2140	2240	2340	...
37	Châtel-St Denis ▲ d.	0544	0644	0744	0744	...	0844	0844	0944	1044	1144	1244	1344	1444	1544	1644	1744	1844	1944	2044	2144	2244	2344	...
44	**Palézieux** ▲ a.	0556	0656	0756	0756	...	0856	0856	0956	1056	1156	1256	1356	1456	1556	1656	1756	1856	1956	2056	2156	2256	2356	...

	Ⓐ	⚒	⚒	Ⓐ														Ⓐ	Ⓐ	Ⓒ				
lézieux ▲ d.	...	...	0603	0633	0703	0803	0903	1003	1103	1203	1303	1403	1503	...	1603	1703	1803	1903	...	1903	2003	2103	2203	2303
âtel-St Denis ▲ a.	...	...	0614	0644	0714	0814	0914	1014	1114	1214	1314	1414	1514	...	1614	1714	1814	1914	...	1914	2014	2114	2214	2314
âtel-St Denis d.	...	...	0618	0648	0718	0818	0918	1018	1118	1218	1318	1418	1518	...	1618	1718	1818	1918	...	1918	2018	2118	2218	2318
lle ▽ a.	...	...	0644	0714	0744	0844	0944	1044	1144	1244	1344	1444	1544	...	1644	1744	1844	1944	...	1944	2044	2144	2244	2344
lle ▽ d.	0450	0550	0650	...	0753	0851	0951	1051	1151	1251	1351	1451	...	1551	1651	1751	1851	...	1952	1951	...	...	...	...
uyères d.	0458	0558	0658	...	0801	0859	0959	1059	1159	1259	1359	1459	...	1559	1659	1759	1859	...	1959	1959	...	...	...	...
ntbovon a.	0519	0619	0719	...	0822	0920	1020	1120	1220	1320	1420	1520	...	1620	1720	1820	1920	...	2020	2020	...	...	...	...

BULLE - FRIBOURG - BERN

Operator: TPF

m													
				and at					Ⓐ				
0	**Bulle** ▽ d.	0550	0620	the same	1850	1920	1950	2020	2050	2120	2220	2320	...
18	Romont d.	0609	0638	minutes	1909	1938	2009	2038	2109	2138	2238	2338	...
44	Fribourg **505** d.	0627	0655	past each	1927	1955	2026	2055	2126	2155	2255	2355	...
75	**Bern** **505** a.	0651	...	hour until	1951	...	...	...	...	...	...	...	...

				and at					
Bern **505** d.	...	...	0709	the same	...	2009	...	...	...
Fribourg. **505** d.	0604	0704	0734	minutes	2004	2034	2104	2204	2304
Romont d.	0623	0723	0753	past each	2023	2053	2123	2223	2323
Bulle ▽ a.	0641	0741	0811	hour until	2041	2111	2141	2241	2341

– **Local service Bulle - Broc and v.v.**: Journey 11 minutes.
From Bulle at 0617Ⓐ, 0717, 0817 and hourly until 1917.
From Broc Fabrique at 0632Ⓐ, 0732, 0832 and hourly until 1932.
All services call at Broc Village (2 minutes from Broc Fabrique).

▲ – A 🚌 replacement service operates Châtel-St Denis - Palézieux and v.v. until Nov. 30.

Operator: Transports Publics Fribourgeois (TPF), ✆ +41 26 351 02 00, fax +41 26 351 02 90.

MONTREUX - CAUX - ROCHERS DE NAYE 569

arrow gauge rack railway. 2nd class only. MVR

During bad weather, the service between Caux and Rochers de Naye may be suspended.

m																									
0	**Montreux** d.	0547	0644	0744	...	0817	0917	1017	1117	...	1217	1317	1417	1517	...	1617	1717	...	1817	...	1917	2017	2117	2217	...
3	Glion ▲ d.	0558	0655	0755	...	0829	0929	1029	1129	...	1229	1329	1429	1529	...	1629	1729	...	1829	...	1927	2027	2127	2227	...
5	Caux a.	0607	0704	0804	...	0839	0939	1039	1139	...	1239	1339	1439	1539	...	1639	1739	...	1839	...	1936	2036	2136	2236	...
10	**Rochers de Naye** a.	...	...	...	...	0906	1006	1106	1206	...	1306	1406	1506	1606	...	1706t	1806t	...	1906v	...	...	...	...	...	...

																						v		
chers de Naye d.	...	...	...	...	0911	1011	1111	1211	...	1311	1411	1511	1611	...	1711**t**	1811**t**	...	...	...	...	...	2213	...	...
ux d.	0612	0712	0812	...	0941	1041	1141	1241	...	1341	1441	1541	1641	...	1741	1841	...	1946	2046	2146	...	2242	...	2250
on ▲ d.	0625	0725	0829	...	0953	1053	1153	1253	...	1353	1453	1553	1653	...	1753	1853	...	1958	2058	2158	...	2253**s**	...	2302
ntreux a.	0637	0737	0841	...	1006	1106	1206	1306	...	1406	1506	1606	1706	...	1806	1906	...	2011	2111	2211	...	2307	...	2315

Stops to set down only.
May 9 - Oct. 20.
⑤ Aug. 9 - Oct. 18.

▲ – Funicular railway operates **Glion** - **Territet** and v.v. (no service Oct. 14 - 19): From **Glion** at 0512, 0527, 0542, 0557 and every 15 minutes until 2057; then 2112, 2142 and every 30 minutes until 0042. From **Territet** at 0512, 0527, 0542, 0557 and every 15 minutes until 2057; then 2112 and every 30 minutes until 0042. **Operator**: MVR, ✆ 021 989 81 90.

570 GENÈVE - LAUSANNE - SION - BRIG SB

km		IR 1705	IR 1805	EC 35 ▮ ✕	IR 1707	IR 1807	IR 1709	IR 1809	EC 37 ▮ V✕	IR 1711	IR 1811	IR 1713	IR 1813	IR 1715	IR 1815	IR 1717	IR 1817	IR 1719	IR 1819	IR 1721	IR 1821	EC 39 ▮ ✕	IR 1723	IR 1823	IR 17
0	**Genève** Aéroport ✈ 505 d.	...	...	...	0520	...	0620	0702	...	0720	0802	0820	0902	0920	1002	1020	1102	1120	1202	1220	1302	...	1320	1402	14
6	**Genève** 505 d.	...	0451	0539	0530	0609	0630	0712	0739	0730	0812	0830	0912	0930	1012	1030	1112	1130	1212	1230	1312	1339	1330	1412	14
27	Nyon 505 d.	...	0506	|	0544	|	0644	|	|	0744	|	0844	|	0944	|	1044	|	1144	|	1244	|	|	1344	|	14
53	Morges 505 d.	...	0524	|	0600	|	0700	|	|	0800	|	0900	|	1000	|	1100	|	1200	|	1300	|	|	1400	|	15
66	**Lausanne** 505 a.	...	0538	0615	0612k	0648	0712	0748	0815	0812k	0848	0912	0948	1012	1048	1112	1148	1212	1248	1312	1348	1415	1412k	1448	15
66	**Lausanne** ▲ d.	...	0545	0618	0621	0650	0717	0750	0818	0821	0850	0917	0950	1017	1050	1117	1150	1217	1250	1317	1350	1418	1421	1450	15
84	Vevey ▲ d.	...	0559	|	0635	0704	0731	0804	|	0835	0904	0931	1004	1031	1104	1131	1204	1231	1304	1331	1404	|	1435	1504	15
92	**Montreux** ▲ d.	...	0607	0637	0643	0712	0739	0812	0837	0843	0912	0939	1012	1039	1112	1139	1212	1239	1312	1339	1412	1437	1443	1512	15
105	Aigle d.	...	0618	|	0654	0723	0750	0823	|	0854	0923	0950	1023	1050	1123	1150	1223	1250	1323	1350	1423	|	1454	1523	15
114	Bex d.	...	0625	|	|	|	0757	|	|	|	|	0957	|	1057	|	1157	|	1257	|	1357	|	|	|	|	15
118	St Maurice d.	...	0630	|	|	0732	|	0832	|	|	0932	|	1032	|	1132	|	1232	|	1332	|	1432	|	|	1532	
133	Martigny d.	0610	0641	|	0713	0743	0810	0843	|	0913	0943	1010	1043	1110	1143	1210	1243	1310	1343	1410	1443	|	1513	1543	16
158	**Sion** d.	0625	0656	0713	0727	0759	0825	0859	0913	0927	0959	1025	1059	1125	1159	1225	1259	1325	1359	1425	1459	1513	1527	1559	16
174	Sierre d.	0635	0706	|	0737	0809	0835	0909	|	0937	1009	1035	1109	1135	1209	1235	1309	1335	1409	1435	1509	|	1537	1609	16
184	Leuk d.	0643	0714	|	|	|	0843	|	|	|	|	1043	|	1143	|	1243	|	1343	|	1443	|	|	|	|	16
203	Visp 560 d.	0655	0725	|	0755	0825	0855	0925	|	0955	1025	1055	1125	1155	1225	1255	1325	1355	1425	1455	1525	|	1555	1625	16
212	**Brig** 560 a.	0702	0732	0740	0802	0832	0902	0932	0940	1002	1032	1102	1132	1202	1232	1302	1332	1402	1432	1502	1532	1540	1602	1632	17
	Milano Centrale 590 a.	...	...	0937	...	...	...	...	1137	...	...	...	...	...	...	...	...	...	...	...	...	1737	...	...	

	IR 1825	IR 1727	IR 1827	IR 1729 Ⓐ	IR 1729 Ⓒ	IR 1927 Ⓐ	IR 1829	IR 1929 Ⓐ	IR 1731 Ⓐ	IR 1731 Ⓒ	IR 1931 Ⓐ	IR 1831	EC 41 ▮ ✕	IR 1733	IR 1833	IR 1735	IR 1835	IR 1737	IR 1837	IR 1739	IR 1839	IR 1741	IR 1841 ⑤⑥ r	RE 3591 ⑤⑥ r	IR 17
Genève Aéroport ✈ 505 d.	1502	1520	1602	1625	1620	1620	1702	1654	1725	1720	1720	1802	...	1820	1902	1920	2002r	2020	2059r	2120	2147r	...	2232	...	23
Genève 505 d.	1512	1530	1612	1635	1630	1630	1712	1705	1735	1730	1730	1812	1839	1830	1912	1930	2012r	2030	2109r	2130	2157r	...	2243	...	23
Nyon 505 d.	|	1544	|	|	1644	1644	|	|	|	1744	1744	|	|	1844	|	1944	|	2044	|	2144	2210r	...	2300	...	23
Morges 505 d.	|	1600	|	|	1700	1700	|	1735	|	1800	1800	|	|	1900	|	2000	|	2100	|	2200	2226r	...	2324	...	23
Lausanne 505 a.	1548	1612	1648	1715	1712	1712	1748	1751	1815	1812	1812	1848	1915	1912k	1948	2012	2048r	2112	2148r	2212	2239r	...	2339	...	00
Lausanne ▲ d.	1550	1617	1650	1717	1717	1721	1750	1756	1817	1817	1821	1850	1918	1921	1950	2021	2050	2121	2150	2221	2250	2321	...	2350	00
Vevey ▲ d.	1604	1631	1704	|	1731	1735	1804	1810	|	1831	1835	1904	|	1935	2004	2035	2104	2135	2204	2235	2304	2335	...	0004	00
Montreux ▲ d.	1612	1639	1712	1737	1739	1743	1812	1818	1837	1839	1843	1912	1937	1943	2012	2043	2112	2143	2212	2243	2312	2343	...	0012	00
Aigle d.	1623	1650	1723	1748	1750	1754	1823	1831	1848	1850	1854	1923	|	1954	2023	2053	2123	2154	2223	2254	2323	2354	...	0022	00
Bex d.	|	1657	|	|	1757	1802	|	1838	|	1857	1902	|	|	2001	|	2101	|	2201	|	2301	2330	0001	...	0029	01
St Maurice d.	1632	|	1732	|	|	1807	1832	1843	|	|	1907	1932	|	|	2032	|	2132	|	2232	2306	2335	0006	...	0033	01
Martigny d.	1643	1710	1743	1805	1810	1818	1843	...	1905	1910	1918	1943	|	2014	2043	2112	2143	2214	2244	2317	2346	0017	...	...	01
Sion d.	1659	1725	1759	1820	1825	1833	1859	...	1920	1925	1933	1959	2013	2029	2059	2127	2159	2227	2259	2330	0001	0032	...		01
Sierre d.	1709	1735	1809	1830	1835	...	1909	...	1932	1935	...	2009	|	2039	2109	2139r	2209	...	2309	...	0011	0042	...	...	...
Leuk d.	|	1743	|	1838	1843	...	|	...	1940	1943	...	|	|	2047	|	2147r	|	...	2316	...	0019	0050	...	...	...
Visp 560 d.	1725	1755	1825	1850	1855	...	1925	...	1952	1955	...	2025	|	2100	2125	2159r	2225	...	2327	...	0030	0101	...	...	...
Brig 560 a.	1732	1802	1832	1857	1902	...	1932	...	1959	2002	...	2032	2040	2107	2132	2206r	2232	...	2334	...	0036	0108	...	...	...
Milano Centrale 590 a.	...	...	...	...	...	...	...	...	...	...	...	...	2237	...	...	...	...	...	...	...	...	...	...	...	...

	IR 1702	IR 1804	IR 1704	IR 1904 Ⓐ	IR 1806	IR 1906 Ⓐ	IR 1706 Ⓐ	IR 1706 Ⓒ	IR 1908 Ⓐ	IR 1808	IR 1708	IR 1810	IR 1710	IR 1812	IR 1712	IR 1814	IR 1714 Ⓐ	IR 1714 Ⓒ	EC 32 ▮ ✕	IR 1816	IR 1716	IR 1818	IR 1718	IR 1820	IR 17
Milano Centrale 590 d.	...	...	...	...	...	...	...	...	...	...	...	...	...	...	...	...	...	...	0823	...	...	...	...	...	
Brig 560 d.	...	0421	...	...	0524	...	0551	0557	...	0624	0657	0726	0757	0826	0857	0926	0957	0957	1020	1026	1057	1126	1157	1226	12
Visp 560 d.	...	0429	...	...	0532	...	0559	0606	...	0632	0706	0735	0806	0835	0906	0935	1006	1006	|	1035	1106	1135	1206	1235	13
Leuk d.	...	0439	...	...	0542	...	0609	0616	...	0642	0716	|	0816	|	0916	|	|	1016	|	|	1116	|	1216	|	13
Sierre d.	...	0447	...	...	0550	...	0617	0624	...	0650	0724	0750	0824	0850	0924	0950	1021	1024	|	1050	1124	1150	1224	1250	13
Sion d.	0428	0459	0528	0551	0602	0638	0628	0635	...	0702	0735	0802	0835	0902	0935	1002	1032	1035	1047	1102	1135	1202	1235	1302	13
Martigny d.	0441	0513	0542	0606	0616	0653	0642	0649	...	0716	0749	0816	0849	0916	0949	1016	1046	1048	|	1116	1149	1216	1249	1316	13
St Maurice d.	0452	0524	0553	0617	0627	|	0653	|	0717	0727	|	0827	|	0927	|	1027	|	|	|	1127	|	1227	|	1327	|
Bex d.	0457	0529	0558	0623	|	|	0658	0702	0723	|	0802	|	0902	|	1002	|	|	|	|	|	1202	|	1302	|	14
Aigle d.	0504	0536	0605	0630	0636	0711	0705	0709	0730	0736	0809	0836	0909	0936	1009	1036	1104	1105	|	1136	1209	1236	1309	1336	14
Montreux ▲ d.	0515	0547	0616	0641	0647	0722	0716	0720	0741	0747	0820	0847	0920	0947	1020	1047	1115	1116	1121	1147	1220	1247	1320	1347	14
Vevey ▲ d.	0523	0555	0624	0649	0655	|	0724	0728	0749	0755	0828	0855	0928	0955	1028	1055	1123	1123	|	1155	1228	1255	1328	1355	14
Lausanne ▲ a.	0538	0610	0639	0704	0710	0742	0739	0743	0804	0810	0843	0910	0943	1010	1043	1110	1138	1138	1142k	1210	1243	1310	1343	1410	14
Lausanne 505 d.	0547	0612	0647	0708	0712	0745	0747	0747	0808	0812	0847	0912	0947	1012	1047	1112	1147	1147	1145	1212	1247	1312	1347	1412	14
Morges 505 d.	0558	|	0658	0721	|	|	0758	0758	0821	|	0858	|	0958	|	1058	|	1158	1158	|	|	1258	|	1358	|	14
Nyon 505 d.	0614	|	0714	|	|	|	0814	0814	|	|	0914	|	1014	|	1114	|	1214	1214	|	|	1314	|	1414	|	15
Genève 505 a.	0630	0648	0730	0753	0748	0821	0830	0830	0853	0848	0930	0948	1030	1048	1130	1148	1230	1230	1221	1248	1330	1350	1430	1448	15
Genève Aéroport ✈ 505 a.	0639	0657	0739	0802	0757	0830	0839	0839	0902	0857	0939	0957	1039	1057	1139	1157	1239	1239	...	1257	1339	1359	1439	1457	15

	IR 1822	IR 1722	EC 34 ▮ ✕	IR 1824	IR 1724	IR 1826	IR 1726	IR 1828	IR 1728	IR 1830	IR 1730	IR 1832	IR 1732	EC 36 ▮ ✕	IR 1834	IR 1734	IR 1836	IR 1736	EC 42 ▮ V✕	IR 1838	IR 1838 ⑤⑥ r	RE 3586 ⑤⑥ r	IR 1840	R 35 ⑥
Milano Centrale 590 d.	...	...	1223	...	...	...	...	...	...	...	...	...	...	1723	...	...	...	...	1923	...	...	...	...	
Brig 560 d.	1326	1357	1420	1426	1457	1526	1557	1626	1657	1726	1757	1826	1857	1918	1926	1957	2023	2057	2118	2126	2126	...	2226	...
Visp 560 d.	1335	1406	|	1435	1506	1535	1606	1635	1706	1735	1806	1835	1906	|	1935	2006	2030	2106	|	2135	2135	...	2235	...
Leuk d.	|	|	|	|	1516	|	1616	|	1716	|	1816	|	|	|	|	2016	2040	|	|	|	|	...	|	
Sierre d.	1350	1421	|	1450	1524	1550	1624	1650	1724	1750	1824	1850	1921	|	1950	2024	2048	2121	|	2150	2150	...	2250	...
Sion d.	1402	1432	1447	1502	1535	1602	1635	1702	1735	1802	1835	1902	1932	1947	2002	2035	2100	2132	2147	2202	2202	...	2302	...
Martigny d.	1416	1446	|	1516	1549	1616	1649	1716	1749	1816	1849	1916	1946	|	2016	2049	2114	2146	|	2216	2216	...	2316	...
St Maurice d.	1427	|	|	1527	|	1627	|	1727	|	1827	|	1927	|	|	2027	|	2125	|	|	2227	2227	2254	2327	00
Bex d.	|	|	|	|	1602	|	1702	|	1802	|	1902	|	|	|	|	2102	2129	2158	|	|	|	2258	|	00
Aigle d.	1436	1504	|	1536	1609	1636	1709	1736	1809	1836	1909	1936	2004	|	2036	2109	2136	2205	|	2236	2236	2305	2336	00
Montreux ▲ d.	1447	1515	1521	1547	1620	1647	1720	1747	1820	1847	1920	1947	2015	2021	2047	2120	2147	2216	2221	2247	2247	2316	2347	01
Vevey ▲ d.	1455	1523	|	1555	1628	1655	1728	1755	1828	1855	1928	1955	2023	|	2055	2128	2155	2223	|	2255	2255	2324	2355	01
Lausanne ▲ a.	1510	1538	1542k	1610	1643	1710	1743	1810	1843	1910	1943	2010	2038	2042k	2110	2143	2210	2239	2242	2310	2310	2339	0010	01
Lausanne 505 d.	1512	1547	1545	1612	1647	1712	1747	1812	1847	1912	1947	2012r	2047	2045	2112r	2148	2221r	...	2245	2321	2321	...	0025z	
Morges 505 d.	|	1558	|	|	1658	|	1758	|	1858	|	1958	|	2058	|	|	2158	2234r	...	|	2333	2333	...	0037z	
Nyon 505 d.	|	1614	|	|	1714	|	1814	|	1914	|	2014	|	2114	|	|	2214	2256r	...	|	2357	2357	...	0055z	
Genève 505 a.	1548	1630	1621	1648	1730	1748	1830	1848	1930	1948	2030	2048r	2130	2121	2148r	2230	2313r	...	2322	0016	0016	...	0111z	
Genève Aéroport ✈ 505 a.	1557	1639	...	1657	1739	1757	1839	1857	1941	1957	2039	2057r	2139	...	2157r	2239	...	...	...	...	0025	...		

Local services **LAUSANNE - MONTREUX - VILLENEUVE**

Lausanne d.	0600	0635	and at the same minutes past each hour until	2000	2035	2100	2200	2300	0000
Vevey d.	0622	0652		2022	2052	2122	2222	2322	0022
Montreux d.	0631	0702		2031	2102	2131	2231	2331	0031
Territet d.	0632	|		2032	|	2132	2232	2332	0032
Veytaux-Chillon d.	0634	|		2034	|	2134	2234	2334	0034
Villeneuve a.	0638	0707		2038	2107	2138	2238	2338	0038

Villeneuve d.	0519	0549	0619	0652	and at the same minutes past each hour until	2019	2052	2119	2219	23
Veytaux-Chillon d.	0521	|	0621	|		2021	|	2121	2221	23
Territet d.	0522	|	0623	|		2023	|	2123	2223	23
Montreux d.	0526	0553	0626	0656		2026	2056	2126	2226	23
Vevey d.	0537	0604	0637	0707		2037	2107	2137	2237	23
Lausanne a.	0558	0624	0658	0724		2058	2124	2158	2258	23

V – [12] Genève - Milano - Venezia and v.v.

k – Connects with train in previous column.
r – ⑤⑥ (not Apr. 19).
z – ⑥⑦ (not Apr. 20).

▲ – See also panel below main table.
▮ – Supplement payable for journeys from / to Italy.

nd class only — Local services from VEVEY, AIGLE and BEX — 571

EVEY - BLONAY: Narrow gauge. *6 km.* Journey time: 14 – 16 minutes. **Operator**: MVR.

om **Vevey**: 0610⚒, 0627Ⓐ, 0640Ⓒ, 0649Ⓐ, 0710⚒, 0727Ⓐ, 0740Ⓒ, 0747Ⓐ, 0810⚒, 0829Ⓐ, 0840Ⓒ, 0849Ⓐ, 0910⚒, 0940, 1010⚒, 1040, 1110⚒, 1140, 1210⚒, 1240, 1310⚒, 1340, 1410⚒, 1440, 1510⚒, 1540, 1610⚒, 1629Ⓐ, 1640Ⓒ, 1649Ⓐ, 1710⚒, 1729Ⓐ, 1740Ⓒ, 1749Ⓐ, 1810⚒, 1829Ⓐ, 1840Ⓒ, 1849Ⓐ, 1910⚒, 1940, 2010⚒, 2039, 2139, 2239, 2339, 0045**h**

From **Blonay**: 0531⚒, 0604, 0629Ⓐ, 0634⑥, 0651Ⓐ, 0704, 0729Ⓐ, 0734⑥, 0749Ⓐ, 0804, 0831Ⓐ, 0834⑥, 0852Ⓐ, 9004, 0934⚒, 1004, 1034⚒, 1104, 1134⚒, 1204, 1234⚒, 1304, 1334⚒, 1404, 1434⚒, 1504, 1534⚒, 1604, 1631Ⓐ, 1634⑥, 1651Ⓐ, 1704, 1731Ⓐ, 1734⑥, 1751Ⓐ, 1804, 1831Ⓐ, 1834⑥, 1851Ⓐ, 1904, 1934⚒, 2004, 2111, 2211, 2311, 0004**h**.

IGLE - LEYSIN: Narrow gauge rack railway. *6 km.* Journey time: 29 – 39 minutes. **Operator**: TPC.

om **Aigle**: 0547Ⓐ, 0608Ⓐ, 0623Ⓒ, 0656Ⓒ, 0725Ⓐ, 0757, 0856, 0957, 1055 and hourly until 1355, then 1456, 1555, 1655, 1756, 1856, 1956, 2056, 2156, 2256.

From **Leysin** Grand Hotel: 0522, 0619Ⓐ, 0639Ⓐ, 0656Ⓒ, 0757, 0853, 0954, 1052 and hourly until 1352, 1453, 1552, 1652, 1753, 1853, 1953, 2053, 2153, 2253, 2329.

IGLE - LES DIABLERETS: Narrow gauge. *23 km.* Journey time: 45 – 55 minutes. **Operator**: TPC.

om **Aigle**: 0557, 0705, 0827, 0926, 1056 and hourly until 2056; then 2200.

From **Les Diablerets**: 0609, 0710, 0807, 0935, 1136 and hourly until 2036; then 2104, 2236.

IGLE - CHAMPÉRY: Narrow gauge rack railway. 2nd class only. **Operator**: TPC. Additional services operate Aigle - Monthey Ville and v.v.

km																										
			⚒																							
0	**Aigle**	d.	0507	0620	0732	0828	0932	1028	...	1132	1228	1332	1428	1532	...	1628	1728	1828	1928	2033	...	2130	2233	2303	2358	...
11	Monthey Ville	a.	0526	0639	0752	0849	0952	1049	...	1152	1249	1352	1449	1552	...	1649	1749	1849	1949	2052	...	2149	2252	2322	0017	...
11	Monthey Ville	d.	0528	0641	0800	0851	1000	1100	...	1200	1251	1400	1451	1600	...	1700	1800	1900	1951	2100	...	2151	...	...	...	...
23	**Champéry**	a.	0601	0717	0833	0924	1033	1133	...	1233	1324	1433	1524	1633	...	1733	1833	1933	2024	2133	...	2224	...	...	...	...

		⚒		Ⓐ		Ⓐ	⚒	⚒																
hampéry	d.	...	...	...	0602	0628	...	0657	...	0757	0904	0957	1057	1157	1304	1357	1504	1557	1657	1757	1857	2004	2057	2204	2235
onthey Ville	a.	...	...	...	0635	0701	...	0730	...	0830	0937	1030	1130	1230	1337	1430	1537	1630	1730	1830	1930	2037	2130	2237	2308
onthey Ville	d.	0439	0540	0604	0643	0705	0705	0739	0739	0837	0940	1037	1140	1237	1340	1437	1540	1637	1737	1837	1937	2040	2137	2240	2310
igle	a.	0459	0600	0624	0706	0729	0729	0800	0800	0857	1000	1057	1200	1257	1400	1457	1600	1657	1757	1857	1957	2100	2157	2300	2330

EX - VILLARS-SUR-OLLON: *12 km.* Journey time: 40 – 46 minutes. All trains call at Bex (Place du Marché), and Bévieux (*3 km* and 4 minutes from Bex). **Operator**: TPC.

om **Bex**: 0629, 0715, 0804, 0911, 1004, 1116, 1204, 1304, 1404, 1511, 1604, 1704, 1804, 1904, 2016, 2104.

From **Villars**: 0533, 0621, 0709, 0813, 0903, 0956, 1108, 1213, 1313, 1356, 1503, 1556, 1713, 1813, 1856, 2008, 2056.

LLARS-SUR-OLLON - COL-DE-BRETAYE: *5 km.* Journey time: 18 – 20 minutes. **Operator**: TPC.

om **Villars**:
ec. 9 - 21, Apr. 23 - May 10, Oct. 28 - Dec. 14: 0900, 1000, 1100, 1200, 1300, 1500, 1600.
ec. 22 - Apr. 22: 0805, 0830, 0900, 0930 and every 30 minutes until 1730.
ay 11 - Oct. 27: 0805, 0900, 1000 and hourly until 1700.

From **Col-de-Bretaye**:
Dec. 9 - 21, Apr. 23 - May 10, Oct. 28 - Dec. 14: 0930, 1030, 1130, 1230, 1330, 1530, 1630.
Dec. 22 - Apr. 22: 0840, 0855, 0925, 0955 and every 30 minutes until 1725, then 1815.
May 11 - Oct. 27: 0830, 0930, 1030 and hourly until 1730.

– ⑥⑦ Dec. 9 - June 29.

nd class only. SNCF, TMR. Narrow gauge rack railway — MARTIGNY - CHAMONIX — 572

Vallorcine - Chamonix - St Gervais is valid April 1 to June 21 (during this period all services between Chamonix and St Gervais are operated by 🚌).

km																										
				Ⓐ	Ⓒ																			¶		♣
0	**Martigny**	d.	...	...	...	0600	0655	0746	0846	0946	1046	1146	1246	1346	1446	1546	...	1646	1746	1846	1946	2046	2146	2246	...	2348
7	Salvan	d.	...	...	...	0614	0709	0800	0900	1000	1100	1200	1300	1400	1500	1600	...	1700	1800	1900	2000	2100	2200	2300	...	0002
9	Les Marécottes	d.	...	...	...	0618	0713	0804	0904	1004	1104	1204	1304	1404	1504	1604	...	1704	1804	1904	2004	2104	2204	2304	...	0006
14	Finhaut	d.	...	...	...	0631	0726	0817	0917	1017	1117	1217	1317	1417	1517	1617	...	1717	1817	1917	2017	2117	2217	2317	...	0019
18	Le Châtelard Frontière 🛃	d.	...	...	...	0640	0735	0827	0927	1027	1127	1227	1327	1427	1527	1627	...	1727	1827	1927	2026	2126	2226	2326	...	0028
21	**Vallorcine**	a.	...	...	...	...	...	0833	0933	1033	1133	1233	1333	1433	1533	1633	...	1733	1833	1933	...	...	...	...	...	...
21	**Vallorcine**	d.	0638	0708	0738	...	...	0838	0938	1038	1138	1238	1338	...	1538	1638	...	1738	1838	1938	...	...	...	...	...	...
28	Argentière Haute Savoie	d.	0654	0724	0754	...	...	0854	0954	1054	1154	1254	1354	...	1554	1654	...	1754	1854	1954	...	...	...	...	...	...
32	Les Tines	d.	0705	0734	0805	...	...	0905	1005	1105	1205	1305	1405	...	1605	1705	...	1805	1905	2005	...	...	...	...	...	...
36	**Chamonix**	a.	0712	0742	0812	...	...	0912	1012	1112	1212	1312	1412	...	1612	1712	...	1812	1912	2012	...	...	...	...	...	...
	St Gervais **365a**	a.	*0755*	...	*0855*	...	...	*0955*	*1055*	...	*1255*	*1355*	*1455*	...	*1655*	*1755*	...	*1855*	*1955*	*2055*	...	...	...	...	...	...

		Ⓐ																			¶			
St Gervais **365a**	d.	...	...	...	...	*0706*	*0806*	*0906*	*1006*	...	*1206*	*1306*	*1406*	...	...	*1606*	*1706*	*1806*	*1906*	...	...	...	...	...	...
amonix	d.	...	...	...	...	0754	0854	0954	1054	...	1254	1354	1454	...	...	1654	1754	1854	1954	...	...	...	...	...	...
s Tines	d.	...	...	...	...	0804	0904	1004	1104	...	1304	1404	1504	...	...	1704	1804	1904	2004	...	...	...	...	...	...
gentière Haute Savoie	d.	...	...	...	...	0812	0912	1012	1112	...	1312	1412	1512	...	...	1712	1812	1912	2012	...	...	...	...	...	...
llorcine	a.	...	...	...	...	0831	0931	1031	1131	...	1331	1431	1531	...	...	1731	1831	1931	2031	...	...	...	...	...	...
llorcine	d.	...	...	...	...	0844	0944	1044	1144	1244	1344	1444	1544	1644	...	1744	1844	1944	2044	...	...	...	...	...	...
Châtelard Frontière 🛃	d.	0527	...	0651	0751	0851	0951	1051	1151	1251	1351	1451	1551	1651	...	1751	1851	1951	2051	2151	2251	2335	...	...	...
haut	d.	0537	...	0701	0801	0901	1001	1101	1201	1301	1401	1501	1601	1701	...	1801	1901	2001	2101	2201	2301	2345	...	...	...
s Marécottes	d.	0549	...	0713	0813	0913	1013	1113	1213	1313	1413	1513	1613	1713	...	1813	1913	2013	2113	2213	2313	2357	...	...	...
lvan	d.	0554	...	0718	0818	0918	1018	1118	1218	1318	1418	1518	1618	1718	...	1818	1918	2018	2118	2218	2318	0002	...	...	...
artigny	a.	0612	...	0736	0836	0936	1036	1136	1236	1336	1436	1536	1636	1736	...	1836	1936	2036	2136	2236	2336	0020	...	...	...

– Runs only by prior reservation before 2230. ✆ 027 764 12 71.

♣ – Runs ⑤⑥ only by prior reservation before 2230 (not Aug. 1).

SION VALLEY RESORTS — 573

ARTIGNY - ORSIÈRES▲ and LE CHÂBLE: *19 km.* Journey time: 26 minutes to both resorts. ▲ – A change of train is usually necessary at Sembrancher. **Operator**: RA.

om **Martigny**: 0607Ⓐ, 0717, 0751, 0817, 0851, 0917, 0951, 1051, 1151, 1251, 1351, 1451, 1551, 1651, 1751, 1851, 1951, 2051, 2152, 2319⑤⑥.

From **Orsières and Le Châble**: 0534Ⓐ, 0638, 0710, 0746, 0846, 0946, 1046, 1146, 1257, 1346, 1446, 1546, 1646, 1746, 1846, 1946, 2046, 2246⑤⑥.

CHÂBLE - VERBIER: 🚌 service. Journey time: ± 25 minutes. **Operator**: PA.

m **Le Châble** Gare: 0650⚒, 0753†, 0757⚒, 0850, 0950, 1121⑥†, 1221⚒, 1250†, 1350, 1450⚒, 1621⑥†, 1721, 1750⚒, 1821†, 1850⚒, 1921†, 1950, 2121.

From **Verbier** Post: 0610⚒, 0719⚒, 0819†, 0845⚒, 0919, 1019, 1219, 1319, 1419⚒, 1519, 1650, 1750, 1819⚒, 1850†, 1919⚒, 1950†, 2019, 2150.

ARTIGNY - AOSTA: 🚌 service via Grand St Bernard tunnel. Service runs daily throughout the year (**not Dec. 25**). Journey time: ± 1 hour 45 minutes. **Operator**: TMR / SAVDA.

m **Martigny** Gare: 0835②⑤, 1830②⑤⑦.

From **Aosta** Autostazione: 1100②⑤, 1600②⑤⑦.

ON - CRANS-SUR-SIERRE: 🚌 service. Journey time: ± 45 minutes. **Operator**: PA.

m **Sion** Gare: 0645⚒, 0745, 0840⚒, 1000, 1045⚒, 1145⑥†, 1150Ⓐ**z**, 1230⚒ 1345, 1510⑥†, 1540Ⓐ**z**, 1648⚒, 1710†, 1810, 1910, 2105⚒.

From **Crans-sur-Sierre** Post: 0643, 0740⚒, 0835, 0930⚒, 1050, 1135⚒, 1235⑥†, 1245Ⓐ**z**, 1335⚒, 1545, 1635, 1805, 1910, 2005⚒.

ERRE - CRANS-SUR-SIERRE - MONTANA: 🚌 service. Principal stop in **Crans-sur-Sierre** is Hotel Scandia (± 40 minutes from Sierre, ± 8 minutes from Montana). **Operator**: SMC.

m **Sierre** Gare: 0745, 0845, 0945⚒, 1045⚒, 1145, 1200⚒, 1231⚒, 1340, 1440⚒, 1546, 1715, 1745, 1840⚒, 1945, 2042, 2215, 0050⑥⑦**y**. *No service on April 19.*

From **Montana** Gare: 0557⚒, 0633, 0736†, 0839⚒, 0958, 1037⚒, 1133⚒, 1226, 1334⚒, 1435, 1558, 1646, 1733⚒, 1833, 1907, 2058, 0003⑥⑦**y**. *No service on April 19.*

IG - SAAS-FEE: 🚌 service. Journey time: 50 – 70 minutes. All services call at **Visp** (Bahnhof Süd) ± 20 minutes from Brig, and **Saas Grund** (Post) ± 10 minutes from Saas Fee.

m **Brig** (Bahnhof): 0420, 0545, 0615, 0645 and every 30 minutes until 1045, then 1115, 1140, 1215, 1247, 1315, 1345 and every 30 minutes until 1845, then 1945, 2045, 2215.

From **Saas-Fee** Busterminal: 0530, 0600, 0630, 0700, 0730, 0752, 0822, 0852, 0922, 0952 and every 30 minutes until 1852, then 1930, 1957.

erator: PA. Seat reservation recommended on Ⓒ from Saas Fee to Brig. ✆ 058 454 26 16.

Also Mar. 5, 6, 19, May 30, June 20; not Nov. 2.

z – Also Apr. 19; not Mar. 19, June 20, Aug. 15, Nov. 1.

575 GLACIER EXPRESS

MGB, RhB*

Glacier Express through services (compulsory reservation). **No service Oct. 14 - Dec. 14, 2019.** For local services see Tables **545** and **576**. Narrow gauge railway (part rack).

km		WINTER SERVICE ▶▶▶	902 Ⓡ ✕	904 Ⓡ C ✕	SUMMER SERVICE ▶▶▶	900 Ⓡ ✕	902 Ⓡ ✕	904 Ⓡ ✕	906 Ⓡ ✕
0	**Zermatt** d.		0852	0952		0752	0852	0952	...
21	St Niklaus △d.		|	|		|	|	|	...
36	Visp △d.		|	|		|	|	|	...
45	**Brig** △d.		1018	1118		0918	1018	1118	1410
62	Fiesch △d.		|	|		|	|	|	|
113	**Andermatt** a.	**Dec. 9**	1146	1246	**May 11**	1046	1146	1246	1546
113	**Andermatt** d.	**to**	1154	1254	**to**	1054	1154	1254	1554
142	**Disentis / Mustér** a.	**May 10**	1255	1355	**Oct. 13**	1155	1255	1355	1655
142	**Disentis / Mustér** d.		1311	1411	■	1211	1311	1411	1711
201	**Chur** ▽a.		1415	1515		1324	1415	1515	1824
228	Thusis ▽a.		|	|		...	|	|	1928
242	Tiefencastel ▽a.		1527	1627		...	1527	1627	1946
252	**Filisur** ▽a.		1541	1641		...	1541	1641	2000
260	Bergün / Bravuogn ▽a.		|	|		...	|	|	2014
285	**Samedan** ▽a.		1629	1729		...	1629	1729	2045
288	Celerina ▽a.		|	|		...	|	|	2052
290	**St Moritz** a.		1638	1738		...	1638	1738	2058

	WINTER SERVICE ▶▶▶	923 Ⓡ ✕	925 Ⓡ C ✕	SUMMER SERVICE ▶▶▶	901 Ⓡ ✕	903 Ⓡ ✕	905 Ⓡ ✕	907 Ⓡ ✕
St Moritz d.		0915	1020		0702	0915	1020	...
Celerina △d.		|	|		0706	|	|	...
Samedan △d.		0925	1028		0716	0925	1028	...
Bergün / Bravuogn. △d.		|	|		0747	|	|	...
Filisur △d.		1019	1119		0801	1019	1119	...
Tiefencastel △d.	**Dec. 9**	1033	1133	**May 11**	0815	1033	1133	...
Thusis △d.	**to**	|	|	**to**	0833	|	|	...
Chur △d.	**May 10**	1126	1226	**Oct. 13**	0926	1126	1226	1416
Disentis / Mustér a.		1227	1327	■	1027	1227	1327	1527
Disentis / Mustér d.		1237	1337		1037	1237	1337	1537
Andermatt a.		1352	1452		1152	1352	1452	1652
Andermatt d.		1354	1454		1208	1408	1508	1708
Fiesch ▽a.		|	|		|	|	|	|
Brig ▽a.		1540	1640		1340	1540	1640	1840
Visp ▽a.		|	|		...	|	|	|
St Niklaus ▽a.		|	|		...	|	|	|
Zermatt a.		1710	1810		...	1710	1810	2010

All Glacier Express trains convey (12) [panorama cars]. Reservations can be made at any Swiss station. Reservations for ✕ are obligatory in advance: RhB, ✆ 081 288 65 65. Meals are served between 1100 and 1330 at your seat.
Further information: www.glacierexpress.ch

C – Apr. 19 - May 10.
△ – Calls to pick up only.
▽ – Calls to set down only.
■ – Subject to Confirmation.

* – Operators:
MGB: Zermatt - Brig - Andermatt - Disentis;
RhB: Disentis - Chur - St Moritz.

576 ZERMATT - BRIG - ANDERMATT (- GÖSCHENEN) - DISENTIS local services

MGB

Narrow gauge railway (part rack). For *Glacier Express* through services see Table **575**

ZERMATT - VISP - BRIG

km														
0	**Zermatt** d.	0537	0613	0637	0813		1813	1837	1913	1937	2013	2113	2213
8	Täsch d.	0548	0625	0648	0825	and	1825	1848	1925	1948	2025	2125	2223
21	St Niklaus d.	0613	0650	0713	0850	every	1850	1913	1950	2013	2050	2150	2244
29	Stalden-Saas d.	0635	0710	0735	0910	hour	1910	1935	2010	2035	2110	2210	2305
36	Visp a.	0646	0722	0746	0922	until	1922	1946	2022	2046	2122	2222	2316
36	Visp d.	0650	0725	0750	0925	△	1925	1950	2025	2050	2125	2225	2318
45	**Brig** a.	0702	0737	0802	0937		1937	2002	2037	2102	2137	2237	2327

										①-⑥	⑦	
Brig d.	0520	0552	0627	0652	0727		1827	1952	2052	2227	2317	...
Visp a.	0531	0603	0638	0703	0738	and	1838	2003	2103	2238	2328	...
Visp d.	0533	0608	0641	0708	0741	every	1841	2008	2108	2241	2329	...
Stalden-Saas d.	0542	0618	0651	0718	0751	hour	1851	2018	2118	2249	2338	...
St Niklaus d.	0559	0636	0711	0736	0811	until	1911	2036	2136	2308	2355	...
Täsch d.	0621	0700	0736	0800	0836	▽	1936	2100	2200	2336	0017	...
Zermatt a.	0633	0714	0751	0814	0851		1951	2114	2214	2348	0028	...

VISP - BRIG - ANDERMATT

km										①-⑥		⑦
	Visp d.	...	0708	0808		1908	...	2008	2108	2238	...	2255
0	**Brig** d.	0623	0723	0823	and	1923	...	2023	2123	2250	...	2316
7	Mörel d.	0633	0733	0833	every	1933	...	2033	2133	2300	...	2325
10	Betten d.	0639	0739	0839	hour	1939	...	2039	2139	2306	...	2332
17	Fiesch d.	0656	0756	0856	until	1956	...	2056	2155	2322	...	2349
41	Oberwald 🚗 d.	0742	0842	0942		2042	...	2139	*2237*z	...	...	...
59	Realp ▲ 🚗 § d.	0805	0905	1005		2105	...	...	...	...	...	...
68	**Andermatt** a.	0820	0920	1020		2120	...	...	...	...	...	...

											①-⑥	⑦
Andermatt d.	...	...	0737	0837		1737	1837	1925	2025	...	...
Realp ▲ 🚗 § d.	...	...	0750	0850	and	1750	1850	1936	2036	...	...
Oberwald 🚗 d.	*0612*z	0712	0812	0912	every	1812	1912	1953	2056	*2250*z	*2250*
Fiesch d.	0656	0756	0856	0956	hour	1856	1956	2031	2131	2326	235
Betten d.	0715	0815	0915	1015	until	1915	2015	2047	2147	2344	001
Mörel d.	0722	0822	0922	1022		1922	2022	2057	2157	2351	001
Brig a.	0733	0833	0933	1033		1933	2033	2106	2206	0001	002
Visp a.	0750	0850	0950	1050		1950	2103	2138	2221	...	...

ANDERMATT - GÖSCHENEN

km												
0	**Andermatt** d.	0638	0725	0740	0829	and hourly	1740	1829	1937	2037	2153	2253
4	**Göschenen** a.	0651	0740	0755	0844	until	1755	1844	1951	2051	2208	2308

Göschenen d.	0704	0804	0811	and hourly	1804	1811	1911	2011	2111	2211	231
Andermatt a.	0714	0814	0821	until	1814	1821	1921	2021	2121	2221	232

ANDERMATT - DISENTIS

km		🚌Ⓐ	🚌																	🚌		🚌v	🚌	🚌x		
0	**Andermatt** 🚗 d.	...	...	0728	0828	...	0928	1028	1128	1228	...	1328	...	1428	1528	...	1628	1728	1828	...	...	...	2124p	...	...	...
10	Oberalppass d.	...	...	0750	0850	...	0950	1050	1150	1250	...	1350	...	1450	1550	...	1650	1750	1850	...	...	...	2139p	...	...	...
19	Sedrun 🚗 d.	0616	0705	0816	0916	...	1016	1116	1216	1316	...	1416	...	1516	1616	...	1716	1816	1916	2001	...	2101	2201	2308	...	...
29	**Disentis / Mustér** a.	0634	0725	0839	0939	...	1039	1139	1239	1339	...	1439	...	1539	1639	...	1739	1839	1939	2018	...	2118	2218	2320	...	...

	🚌	n	r															🚌	🚌		🚌v	🚌	🚌q		
Disentis / Mustér d.	0640	0708	0714	0814	...	0914	1014	1114	1214	...	1314	1414	1514	1614	...	1714	1814	1922	2022	...	2122	2222	0022	...	...
Sedrun 🚗 d.	0650	0731	0731	0831	...	0931	1031	1131	1231	...	1331	1431	1531	1631	...	1731	1831	1940	2040	...	2140	2240	0040	...	...
Oberalppass d.	...	0753	0753	0853	...	0953	1053	1153	1253	...	1353	1453	1553	1653	...	1753	1853	...	2102p	...	...	...	...	...	...
Andermatt 🚗 a.	...	0822	0822	0922	...	1022	1122	1222	1322	...	1422	1522	1622	1722	...	1822	1922	...	2117p	...	...	...	...	...	...

n – Dec. 9 - May 10, Oct. 14 - Dec. 14.
p – May 1 - Oct. 31.
q – ⑥⑦ Dec. 22 - Mar. 31.
r – May 11 - Oct. 13.
v – Dec. 9 - Apr. 30, Nov. 1 - Dec. 14.
x – ⑤⑥ Dec. 21 - Mar. 30.
z – Connection by 🚌.

◇ – Subject to favourable weather conditions.
§ – Realp is a request stop.
△ – Additional services Zermatt - Visp: 0737, 0837 and hourly until 1737.
▽ – Additional services Visp - Zermatt: 0808, 0908 and hourly until 1908.

▲ – 🚂 service (summer only, not daily) runs Realp - Furka - Gletsch - Oberwald and v.v. Operator: Dampfbahn Furka-Bergstrecke ✆ 0848 000 144.
🚗 – Car-carrying shuttle available. ✆ +41 (0) 848 642 442.
www.matterhorngotthardbahn.ch/de/winter/anreise/autoverlad/

578 ZERMATT - GORNERGRAT

Narrow gauge rack railway. GGB

Journey 33 minutes uphill, 44 minutes downhill, *9 km. Services are liable to be suspended in bad weather*

Dec. 9 - Apr. 23, June 15 - Oct. 13, Nov. 23 - Dec. 14:
From Zermatt: 0700**t**, 0800, 0824, 0848, 0912*, 0936*, 1000*, 1024*, 1048*, 1112*, 1136, 1200, 1224, 1248, 1312, 1336, 1400, 1424, 1448, 1512, 1536, 1600, 1624, 1724, 1824**m**, 1924**p**.
From Gornergrat: 0735, 0843, 0907, 0931, 0955, 1019, 1043, 1107, 1131, 1155, 1219, 1243, 1307, 1331, 1355, 1419, 1443, 1507, 1531, 1555, 1619, 1638, 1718, 1818, 1918**m**, 2007**p**.

Apr. 24 - June 14, Oct. 14 - Nov. 3:
From Zermatt: 0700, 0805, 0845, 0925, 1005, 1045, 1125, 1205, 1245, 1325, 1405, 1445, 1525, 1605, 1705, 1825.
From Gornergrat: 0741, 0842, 0922, 1002, 1042, 1122, 1202, 1242, 1322, 1402, 1442, 1522, 1602, 1642, 1742, 1922.

m – Dec. 13 - Apr. 23, June 15 - Oct. 13.
p – Dec. 13 - Apr. 23, June 27 - Sept. 22.
t – June 15 - Oct. 13.
* – Duplicated by non-stop journeys Dec. 22 - Apr. 23 (journey time 29 minutes).

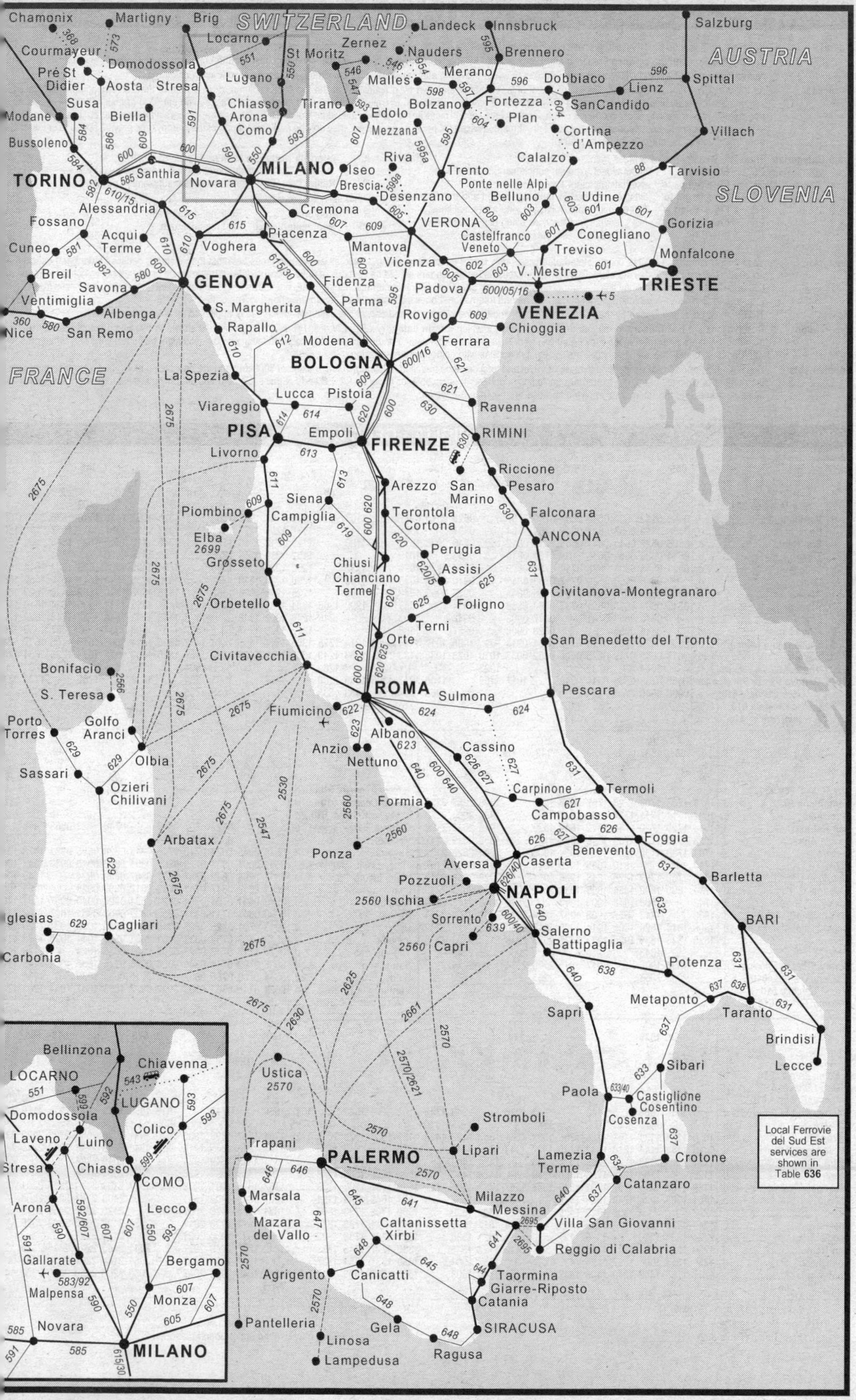
SWITZERLAND
AUSTRIA
SLOVENIA
FRANCE
Chamonix
Martigny
Brig
Locarno
Landeck
Innsbruck
Salzburg
Courmayeur
Domodossola
Zernez
St Moritz
Nauders
Brennero
Pré St Didier
Aosta
Stresa
Lugano
Malles
Merano
Dobbiaco
Lienz
Spittal
Susa
Biella
Chiasso
Arona
Como
Tirano
Edolo
Bolzano
Fortezza
SanCandido
Modane
Plan
Cortina d'Ampezzo
Villach
Bussoleno
Mezzana
Riva
Calalzo
Tarvisio
TORINO
Santhia
Novara
MILANO
Iseo
Brescia
Trento
Ponte nelle Alpi
Belluno
Udine
Desenzano
Alessandria
Cremona
VERONA
Gorizia
Fossano
Acqui Terme
Piacenza
Castelfranco Veneto
Conegliano
Cuneo
Voghera
Mantova
Treviso
Monfalcone
Vicenza
Breil
V. Mestre
Savona
GENOVA
Fidenza
Padova
TRIESTE
Ventimiglia
Parma
Albenga
S. Margherita
VENEZIA
Nice
San Remo
Rovigo
Chioggia
Rapallo
Modena
Ferrara
BOLOGNA
La Spezia
Lucca
Pistoia
Ravenna
Viareggio
PISA
Empoli
FIRENZE
RIMINI
Livorno
San Marino
Riccione
Pesaro
Arezzo
Siena
Falconara
Piombino
Campiglia
Terontola Cortona
ANCONA
Elba
Grosseto
Perugia
Chiusi Chianciano Terme
Assisi
Civitanova-Montegranaro
Orbetello
Foligno
Terni
Orte
San Benedetto del Tronto
Civitavecchia
Bonifacio
ROMA
Sulmona
Pescara
S. Teresa
Fiumicino
Porto Torres
Golfo Aranci
Albano
Olbia
Anzio
Nettuno
Cassino
Sassari
Ozieri Chilivani
Carpinone
Termoli
Formia
Campobasso
Arbatax
Ponza
Benevento
Foggia
Aversa
Caserta
Pozzuoli
NAPOLI
Barletta
Ischia
Sorrento
BARI
Iglesias
Cagliari
Salerno
Battipaglia
Capri
Carbonia
Potenza
Metaponto
Taranto
Sapri
Brindisi
Bellinzona
Chiavenna
Lecce
LOCARNO
Ustica
Sibari
LUGANO
Paola
Castiglione Cosentino
Domodossola
Cosenza
Colico
Stromboli
Laveno
Luino
Trapani
Lipari
Stresa
Chiasso
PALERMO
Lamezia Terme
Crotone
COMO
Catanzaro
Marsala
Milazzo
Arona
Lecco
Messina
Mazara del Vallo
Caltanissetta
Xirbi
Villa San Giovanni
Reggio di Calabria
Gallarate
Bergamo
Malpensa
Agrigento
Canicatti
Taormina Giarre-Riposto
Monza
Catania
Novara
Pantelleria
MILANO
Gela
SIRACUSA
Linosa
Ragusa
Lampedusa
Local Ferrovie del Sud Est services are shown in Table 636

ITALY

Operator: Services are operated by Trenitalia, a division of Ferrovie dello Stato Italiane S.p.a. (FS), unless otherwise noted: www.trenitalia.com.
Trenord is a joint venture between Trenitalia and Ferrovie Nord Milano (LeNord) that operates local services, mainly in the Lombardia region: www.trenord.it.
Nuovo Trasporto Viaggiatori (NTV) is an open-access operator providing alternative services over the high-speed network: www.italotreno.it.

Services: All trains convey First and Second classes of travel unless otherwise shown by a figure "2" at the top of the column, or in a note in the Table heading. Four classes c accommodation is available on Frecciarossa (*FR*) services: Executive, Business, Premium and Standard class. Overnight sleeping car (🛏) or couchette (🛏) trains do nc necessarily convey seating accommodation or may convey only second class seats - refer to individual footnotes. Excelsior sleeping cars offer en-suite facilities. Descriptions c sleeping and couchette cars appear on page 10. Refreshment services (✕ or 🍷) where known, may only be available for part of the journey, and may be added to or taken awa from trains during the currency of the timetable.

Train Categories: There are 9 categories of express train:

EC	**EuroCity**	international express; supplement payable.
EN	**EuroNight**	international night express.
FA	**Frecciargento**	tilting trains used on both high-speed and traditional lines.
FB	**Frecciabianca**	fast premium fare services using traditional lines.
FR	**Frecciarossa**	fast premium fare services using high-speed lines.
IC	**InterCity**	internal day express; supplement payable.
ICN	**InterCity Notte**	internal night express.
ITA	**.italo**	high-speed service (operated by NTV).
RJ	**Railjet**	Austrian express; supplement payable.

Other services are classified:

R	**Regionale**	Regional (local) train.
RV	**Regionale Veloce**	Fast regional train.

Timings: Valid until **December 14, 2019** unless stated otherwise - only partial information was available as we went to press but most long-distance services have been checked an updated. Only minor changes are expected to other services, although readers should be cautious of any exception dates if travelling on or around public holidays. Trains ma be cancelled or altered at holiday times – for public holiday dates see page 4. Some international trains are not shown in this section; these include night services from Austria France and Germany – see International pages. Trains and international buses operating via Tarvisio are shown in Table **88**.

Tickets: Tickets must be date-stamped by the holder before boarding the train using the self-service validating machines – this applies to all tickets except passes.

Reservations: Reservations are **compulsory** for all journeys by services for which a **train category** (*EC, EN, FA, FB, FR, IC, ICN, RJ*) is shown in the timing column and passenger boarding without a prior reservation may be surcharged. Reservations for sleeping and couchette car accommodation on domestic night trains are valid only when presente with personal identification. *ITA* services are 'global' price trains with compulsory reservation.

Supplements: Supplements are calculated according to class of travel and total distance travelled (minimum 10km, maximum 3000km), and are payable on all *EC* and *IC* trains, regardless c the number of changes of train. A higher fare (including supplement) is payable for travel by *FA*, *FB* and *FR* trains. Some trains are only available to passengers holding lon distance tickets and the restrictions applying to these are noted in the tables.

580 VENTIMIGLIA - GENOVA

km		*IC* 655 A		2 Ⓐ	2 Ⓐ	*IC* 505	2	2	2	2 Ⓐ	*EC* 139 🍷	2	2	*IC* 745	Ⓒ	2	2	2 Ⓐ	*IC* 1539 †	2 Ⓒa	2	2	2 Ⓐ	*EC* 145 🍷	2 Z	Ⓒ	2
	Nice Ville **360 361** d.	...	...	...	...	...	...	...	...	...	0801	...	...	...	...	...	...	...	...	...	...	...	...	1402	...	...	...
0	**Ventimiglia** 🏛 d.	0451	0512	0530	0555	0641	0700	0757	...	0828	0910	0957	...	1103	...	1128	1157	1228	1303	...	1328	1357	1428	1510	1528	...	155
5	Bordighera d.	0458	0519	0537	0603	0648	0709	0804	...	0837	|	1004	...	1111	...	1137	1204	1237	1311	...	1337	1404	1437	|	1537	...	160
16	**San Remo** d.	0508	0527	0545	0611	0658	0718	0812	...	0846	0923	1012	...	1120	...	1146	1212	1246	1320	...	1346	1412	1446	1523	1546	...	161
24	Taggia Arma d.	0514	0533	0551	0616	|	0724	0819	...	0853	|	1019	...	|	...	1152	1219	1253	1326	...	1353	1419	1453	|	1553	...	161
39	Imperia d.	0524	0543	0601	0625	0710	0734	0829	...	0904	0935	1029	...	1132	...	1202	1229	1304	1336	...	1404	1429	1504	1535	1604	1544	162
46	Diano d.	|	0548	0606	0630	0717	0739	0835	...	0910	0941	1035	...	1138	...	1208	1235	1310	|	...	1410	1435	1510	1541	1610	1550	163
61	Alassio d.	0537	0559	0622	0644	0730	0755	0848	...	0926	0952	1048	...	1152	...	1225	1248	1326	1352	...	1426	1448	1526	1552	1626	1609	164
67	**Albenga** d.	0545	0606	0630	0651	0737	0803	0855	...	0934	1000	1055	...	1200	1206	1234	1255	1334	1400	1418	1434	1455	1534	1600	1634	1616	165
76	Loano d.	|	0612	0651	0701	|	0817	0903	...	0948	|	1103	...	|	1216	1248	1303	1348	|	1428	1448	1503	1548	|	1648	1626	170
79	Pietra Ligure d.	|	0616	0655	|	|	0823	0908	...	0957	|	1108	...	|	1221	1257	1308	1357	|	1432	1457	1508	1557	|	1657	1630	170
85	Finale Ligure Marina d.	0600	0623	0701	0710	0752	0831	0914	...	1005	1017	1114	...	1214	1228	1305	1314	1405	1414	1438	1505	1514	1605	1617	1705	1637	171
108	**Savona** d.	0617	0645	0719	0726	0805	0852	0933	1010	1025	1033	1133	1201	1233	1249	1325	1333	1425	1432	1456	1525	1533	1625	1633	1725	1654	173
120	Varazze d.	|	0654	|	0734	|	...	|	1023	...	|	|	1215	|	1259	...	|	...	|	1504	...	|	...	|	...	1701	|
151	**Genova** Piazza Principe § a.	0655	0738	0805	0814	0848	...	1017	1108	...	1105	1217	1305	1305	1330	...	1417	...	1505	1534	...	1617	...	1705	...	1730	181
	Milano Centrale **610** a.	0900	0940	...	...	|	...	...	...	...	1253	...	...	1453	1535	...	...	...	1653	1735	...	...	...	1853	...	1937	...
	Pisa Centrale **610** a.	...	...	...	...	1101	...	...	...	...	...	...	...	...	...	...	...	...	...	...	...	...	...	...	...	...	...
	Roma Termini **610** a.	...	...	...	...	1433	...	...	...	...	...	...	...	...	...	...	...	...	...	...	...	...	...	...	...	...	...

	2 Ⓐ	*IC* 681 Ⓐ	*IC* 1537 Ⓒ	2 Z	2	2 Ⓐ	*EC* 147 🍷 M	2	2 Z	2	2
Nice Ville **360 361** d.	...	...	...	...	...	...	1808	...	...	...	...
Ventimiglia 🏛 d.	1628	1703	1703	1728	1757	1828	1910	...	1928	1957	2120
Bordighera d.	1637	1711	1711	1737	1804	1837	|	...	1937	2004	2128
San Remo d.	1646	1720	1720	1746	1812	1846	1923	...	1946	2012	2136
Taggia Arma d.	1653	1726	1726	1753	1819	1853	|	...	1953	2019	2142
Imperia d.	1704	1736	1736	1804	1829	1904	1935	...	2004	2029	2152
Diano d.	1710	|	|	1810	1835	1910	1941	...	2010	2035	2157
Alassio d.	1726	1752	1752	1826	1848	1926	1952	...	2026	2048	2212
Albenga d.	1734	1800	1800	1834	1855	1934	2000	2010	2034	2055	2219
Loano d.	1748	|	1808	1848	1903	1943	|	2019	2048	2103	2230
Pietra Ligure d.	1800	|	1813	1857	1908	1957	|	2023	2057	2108	2234
Finale Ligure Marina d.	1806	1814	1820	1905	1914	2005	2017	2030	2105	2114	2242
Savona d.	1825	1833	1835	1925	1933	2025	2033	2048	2125	2133	2305
Varazze d.	...	|	1843	...	|	...	|	2056	...	2146	...
Genova Piazza Principe § a.	...	1908	1908	...	2017	...	2105	2134	...	2224	...
Milano Centrale **610** a.	...	2053	2053	...	...	...	2253	...	...	...	...
Pisa Centrale **610** a.	...	...	...	...	...	...	...	...	...	...	...
Roma Termini **610** a.	...	...	...	...	...	...	...	...	...	...	...

	2 Ⓐ	2 Ⓐ	2	2	2 ⚒	2 †	2 Ⓐ	2 T	*EC* 142 🍷	2 Ⓐ	2 Ⓒ
Roma Termini **610** d.	...	...	...	...	...	...	...	...	...	...	...
Pisa Centrale **610** d.	...	...	...	...	...	...	...	...	...	...	...
Milano Centrale **610** d.	...	...	...	...	...	...	...	...	0710	...	...
Genova Piazza Principe § d.	...	...	0522	0607	0646	...	0746	...	0858	0943	...
Varazze d.	...	...	0605	0653	0729	...	|	...	|	|	...
Savona d.	0515	0545	0621	0710	0745	0745	0828	0855	0931	1028	102
Finale Ligure Marina d.	0531	0601	0636	0729	0801	0801	0843	0915	0943	1043	104
Pietra Ligure d.	0537	0608	0642	0737	0807	0807	0849	0924	|	1049	104
Loano d.	0541	0612	0647	0742	0812	0812	0853	0928	|	1053	105
Albenga d.	0549	0631	0704	0804	0824	0824	0901	0940	0957	1101	110
Alassio d.	0600	0645	0711	0811	0832	0832	0908	0951	1007	1108	110
Diano d.	0613	0701	0725	0825	0846	0846	0920	1008	1021	1120	112
Imperia d.	0618	0705	0732	0832	0851	0851	0928	1014	1028	1128	112
Taggia Arma d.	0629	0717	0742	0842	0901	0901	0938	1024	|	1138	113
San Remo d.	0635	0723	0748	0848	0906	0906	0945	1030	1042	1145	114
Bordighera d.	0644	0733	0756	0857	0915	0915	0954	1039	|	1154	115
Ventimiglia 🏛 a.	0654	0745	0803	0903	0922	0922	1003	1047	1054	1203	120
Nice Ville **360 361** a.	...	...	...	...	...	...	...	...	1200	...	...

	2 T	*IC* 660 Ⓐ	*IC* 1536 Ⓒ	2 Ⓐ	2	2	2 Ⓒ	*EC* 144 🍷	2 Ⓐ	2	2	2	2 Ⓐ	2	2 T	2	*EC* 160 🍷 M	2 Ⓐ	2	2	2	*IC* 676	2	2	*IC* 518	*IC* 690	
Roma Termini **610** d.	...	...	...	...	...	...	...	...	...	...	...	...	...	...	...	...	...	...	...	...	...	...	...	...	1557	...	...
Pisa Centrale **610** d.	...	...	...	...	...	...	...	...	...	...	...	...	...	...	...	...	...	...	...	...	...	...	...	...	1903	...	...
Milano Centrale **610** d.	...	0910	0910	...	...	...	...	1110	...	...	...	...	...	...	...	...	1505	...	...	...	...	1705	...	...	|	2000	202
Genova Piazza Principe § d.	...	1058	1058	...	1143	...	1203	1258	...	1343	1348	...	...	1543	...	1613	1658	...	1743	...	1813	1858	1943	...	2135	2158	222
Varazze d.	...	|	1123	...	|	...	1247	|	...	|	1435	...	...	|	...	1705	|	...	|	...	1905	|	|	...	|	|	230
Savona d.	1055	1131	1131	1157	1228	1255	1304	1331	1357	1428	1452	1455	1557	1628	1655	1720	1731	1757	1828	1855	1920	1931	2028	2055	2206	2232	231
Finale Ligure Marina d.	1115	1143	1144	1218	1243	1315	1327	1343	1418	1443	...	1515	1618	1643	1715	...	1743	1816	1843	1915	...	1943	2043	2116	2219	2245	233
Pietra Ligure d.	1124	|	1153	1224	1249	1324	1334	|	1424	1449	...	1524	1624	1649	1724	...	|	1822	1849	1924	...	|	2049	2124	|	|	233
Loano d.	1128	|	1159	1228	1253	1328	1339	|	1428	1453	...	1528	1628	1653	1728	...	|	1826	1853	1928	...	|	2053	2128	|	|	234
Albenga d.	1139	1157	1211	1237	1301	1339	1348	1357	1437	1501	...	1539	1637	1701	1739	...	1757	1838	1901	1939	...	1957	2101	2140	2235	2301	235
Alassio d.	1151	1208	1226	1249	1308	1349	...	1407	1449	1508	...	1551	1649	1708	1751	...	1807	1849	1908	1951	...	2008	2108	2151	2243	2308	...
Diano d.	1208	|	|	1306	1320	1406	...	1421	1506	1520	...	1609	1706	1720	1807	...	1821	1906	1920	2007	...	|	2120	2207	2255	2319	...
Imperia d.	1214	1223	1240	1311	1328	1411	...	1428	1511	1528	...	1614	1711	1728	1812	...	1828	1911	1928	2012	...	2024	2128	2212	2302	2326	...
Taggia Arma d.	1224	1234	1250	1321	1338	1421	...	|	1521	1538	...	1624	1721	1738	1822	...	|	1921	1938	2021	...	2034	2138	2221	|	|	...
San Remo d.	1230	1241	1257	1327	1345	1428	...	1442	1527	1545	...	1630	1727	1745	1828	...	1842	1927	1945	2027	...	2041	2145	2227	2315	2339	...
Bordighera d.	1239	1251	1306	1337	1354	1437	...	|	1537	1554	...	1639	1737	1754	1837	...	|	1937	1954	2037	...	2051	2154	2237	2324	2349	...
Ventimiglia 🏛 a.	1247	1258	1312	1349	1403	1447	...	1454	1549	1603	...	1650	1749	1803	1847	...	1854	1949	2003	2047	...	2058	2203	2250	2330	2356	...
Nice Ville **360 361** a.	...	...	...	...	...	...	...	1600	...	...	...	...	...	...	...	...	1959	...	...	...	...	...	...	...	...	...	...

A – ①–⑥ (not July 18, Aug. 15, Nov. 1).
M – To / from Marseille (Table **360**).
T – To / from Torino (Table **582**).
a – Until Aug. 31.
§ – Local services may use the underground platforms.

2nd class only — VENTIMIGLIA and NICE - CUNEO — 581

km																										
		⚒			Ⓐ												Ⓐ	⚒	Ⓒ				Ⓐ			
								b											a							
	Ventimiglia d.	...	...	...	...	...	...	...	...	...	1037	...	...	...	...	...	...	...	1730	...	...	1837	...	...	...	...
0	**Nice** Ville d.	...	...	...	0548	...	0730	0833	...	0917	|	...	1224	...	1455	...	1643	...	|	1713	...	|	1802	...	1859	1941
34	Sospel d.	...	...	...	0658	...	0825	0935	...	1012	|	...	1319	...	1551	...	1738	...	|	1812	...	|	1908	...	2008	2036
43	Breil sur Roya a.	...	...	...	0710	...	0837	0947	...	1024	1108	...	1332	...	1603	...	1750	...	1804	1824	...	1908	1920	...	2020	2049
	Breil sur Roya d.	...	...	...	...	...	...	...	...	1029	1109	...	1336	...	1608	...	...	...	1805	...	...	1917	...	...	...	...
	Tende d.	...	...	...	...	...	...	...	...	1124	1201	...	1431	...	1704	...	...	...	1854	...	...	2009	...	...	...	...
	Limone 🚡 d.	0640	0732	0932	...	...	...	...	1132	...	1232	1332	...	1532	...	1732	...	1840	1922	...	1932	2040	...	2132	...	...
	Cuneo a.	0719	0811	1011	...	...	...	...	1211	...	1311	1411	...	1611	...	1811	...	1919	1946	...	2011	2115	...	2211	...	...
	Fossano **582** a.	...	0835	1035	...	...	...	...	1235	...	...	1435	...	1635	...	1835	...	...	2010	...	2035	...	...	2235	...	...

km																										
		⚒	Ⓐ		⚒	Ⓐ	Ⓒ	Ⓑ																	⚒	
							a														c					
	Fossano **582** d.	...	...	...	...	...	...	...	...	0725	...	...	0925	...	1125	...	1325	...	...	...	...	1525	...	1725	...	1925
0	**Cuneo** d.	...	...	0550	...	0641	0641	...	...	0750	0841	...	0950	...	1150	...	1350	1441	...	...	...	1550	...	1750	1841	1950
29	Limone 🚡 d.	...	...	0628	...	0719	0720	...	...	0830	0919	...	1028	...	1228	...	1428	1517	...	...	...	1628	...	1828	1919	2028
47	Tende d.	...	...	...	...	...	0748	...	...	0859	...	...	...	1212	...	1447	...	1544	...	...	1733	...	...	...	...	...
75	Breil sur Roya a.	...	...	...	...	...	0837	...	...	0954	...	...	...	1302	...	1537	...	1638	...	...	1823	...	...	...	...	...
75	Breil sur Roya d.	0540	0611	...	0645	...	0840	0722	0922	0955	...	1101	...	1307	...	1539	...	1642	1725	...	1825	...	1924	...	...	...
	Sospel d.	0553	0625	...	0658	...	|	0734	0935	|	...	1114	...	1319	...	1551	...	|	1738	...	1838	...	1937	...	...	...
	Nice Ville a.	0645	0720	...	0802	...	|	0832	1038	|	...	1208	...	1414	...	1646	...	|	1837	...	1932	...	2041	...	...	...
96	**Ventimiglia** a.	...	...	...	...	...	0920	...	...	1027	...	...	...	...	...	...	...	1720	...	...	...	...	...	...	...	...

– Until Sept. 1. **b** – Daily until July 7; Ⓒ July 8 - Aug. 30; daily from Aug. 31. **c** – Ⓐ June 9 - Sept. 1; daily from Sept. 2.

Most trains 2nd class only — TORINO - CUNEO and SAVONA — 582

km																									
			†	⚒						⚒															
						V							V												
0	**Torino** Porta Nuova d.	0525	...	...	...	0625	...	...	0722	...	...	...	0825	...	0925	...	1025	...	1125	...	1225	...	...	1325	...
52	Savigliano d.	0603	...	...	...	0703	...	...	0803	...	...	...	0903	...	1003	...	1103	...	1203	...	1303	...	...	1403	...
64	Fossano d.	0612	0622	0622	...	0713	0725	...	0812	0822	...	...	0913	0925	1012	1022	1113	1125	1212	1222	1313	1325	...	1412	1422
90	**Cuneo** a.	0636	|	|	...	|	0749	...	0836	|	...	...	|	0949	1036	|	|	1149	1236	|	|	1349	...	1436	|
83	Mondovi d.	...	0640	0640	...	0728	...	...	...	0840	...	...	0928	...	...	1040	1128	...	...	1240	1328	...	...	...	1440
103	Ceva d.	...	0658	0700	...	0742	...	...	...	0858	...	...	0942	...	...	1058	1142	...	...	1258	1342	...	...	...	1458
153	**Savona** a.	...	...	0752	...	0836	...	...	...	...	...	...	1036	...	...	...	1236	...	...	...	1436	...	...	...	...

										Ⓐ	Ⓐ						⚒							
	V										b						b							
orino Porta Nuova d.	1425	...	1525	...	1625	...	1725	...	...	1750	...	1825	...	...	1855	1925	1955	2025	...	...	2125	...	2325	...
avigliano d.	1503	...	1603	...	1703	...	1803	...	...	1829	...	1903	...	...	1931	2003	2032	2103	...	...	2203	...	0014	...
ossano d.	1513	1525	1612	1622	1713	1725	1812	1822	...	1837	1845	1913	1925	...	1941	2012	2041	2113	2125	...	2212	2217	0022	...
Cuneo a.	|	1549	1636	|	|	1749	1836	|	...	1901	|	|	1949	...	|	2036	|	|	2150	...	2236	|	0046	...
ondovi d.	1528	...	...	1640	1728	...	...	1840	...	...	1858	1928	...	...	1956	...	2100	2128	...	...	...	2235	...	...
eva d.	1542	...	...	1658	1742	...	...	1858	...	...	1912	1942	...	...	2018	...	2120	2142	...	...	...	2253	...	...
avona a.	1636	...	...	...	1836	...	...	...	...	...	...	2036	...	...	2112	...	...	2236	...	...	...	...	...	...

	Ⓐ			†	⚒			⚒	⚒			⚒			⚒	†				⚒				
									b															
avona d.	...	...	...	...	...	...	0531	...	...	...	...	...	...	0731	0808	...	...	...	0931	...	...	...	1131	...
eva d.	...	...	...	0502	0520	...	0617	...	0650	0700	...	...	...	0817	0900	0900	...	...	1017	1100	...	...	1217	1300
ondovi d.	...	...	...	0522	0540	...	0632	...	0706	0720	...	...	...	0832	0920	0920	...	...	1032	1120	...	...	1232	1320
Cuneo d.	0421	...	0524	|	|	0612	|	0654	|	|	0724	0751	0812	|	|	|	0924	1012	|	|	1124	1212	|	|
ossano d.	0441	...	0544	0540	0558	0635	0644	0714	0722	0738	0744	0814	0835	0844	0938	0938	0944	1035	1044	1138	1144	1235	1244	1338
avigliano d.	0449	...	0552	...	...	...	0652	0722	0731	...	0752	0822	...	0852	...	...	0952	...	1052	...	1152	...	1252	...
orino Porta Nuova a.	0535	...	0635	...	...	...	0735	0805	0815	...	0835	0905	...	0935	...	...	1035	...	1135	...	1235	...	1335	...

														⚒	†		Ⓒ							
												V					a		V					V
avona d.	...	...	1330	...	...	...	...	1531	...	...	...	1731	...	1800	...	...	...	...	1931	...	...	...	...	2131
eva d.	...	...	1417	1500	...	...	...	1617	1700	...	...	1817	...	1900	1900	...	...	...	2017	2100	...	...	...	2217
ondovi d.	...	...	1432	1520	...	...	...	1632	1720	...	...	1832	...	1920	1920	...	...	...	2032	2120	...	...	...	2232
Cuneo d.	1324	1412	|	|	1524	1612	...	|	|	1724	1812	|	...	|	|	1924	1951	2012	|	|	2124	...	2212	|
ossano d.	1344	1435	1444	1538	1544	1635	...	1644	1738	1744	1835	1844	...	1938	1938	1944	2015	2035	2044	2138	2144	...	2235	2244
avigliano d.	1352	...	1452	...	1552	...	...	1652	...	1752	...	1852	...	...	...	1952	2028	...	2052	...	2152	...	...	2252
orino Porta Nuova a.	1435	...	1535	...	1635	...	...	1735	...	1835	...	1935	...	...	...	2035	2115	...	2135	...	2235	...	...	2340

– To/from Ventimiglia (**Table 580**). **a** – Until Sept. 1. **b** – Not Aug. 5–31.

.eNord Service until June 8, 2019 — MILANO MALPENSA AEROPORTO ✈ — 583

lano Centrale d.	0525	0555	and at	1925	1955	2025	2125	2225	2325
lano Porta Garibaldi d.	0535	0605	the same	1935	2005	2035	2135	2235	2335
lano Bovisa d.	0542	0612	minutes	1942	2012	2042	2142	2242	2342
alpensa Aeroporto ✈ T1 a.	0616	0646	past each	2016	2046	2116	2216	2316	0016
alpensa Aeroporto ✈ T2 a.	0622	0652	hour until	2022	2052	2122	2222	2322	0022

Malpensa Aeroporto ✈ T2 d.	0537	...	0607	0637	and at	2107	2137	2237
Malpensa Aeroporto ✈ T1 d.	0543	...	0613	0643	the same	2113	2143	2243
Milano Bovisa a.	0618	...	0648	0718	minutes	2148	2218	2318
Milano Porta Garibaldi a.	0624	...	0654	0724	past each	2154	2224	2324
Milano Centrale a.	0635	...	0705	0735	hour until	2205	2235	2335

All services below operate as *Malpensa Express*. Special fare payable.

lano Cadorna d.	0427	0457	...	0527	0557	and	2227	2257	2327
lano Bovisa d.	0433	0503	...	0533	0603	each hour	2233	2303	2333
alpensa Aeroporto ✈ T1 a.	0504	0534	...	0604	0634	until	2304	2334	0004
alpensa Aeroporto ✈ T2 a.	0510	0540	...	0610	0640		2310	2340	0010

Malpensa Aeroporto ✈ T2 d.	0520	0550	0620	0650	and	2320	2350	0020
Malpensa Aeroporto ✈ T1 d.	0526	0556	0626	0656	each hour	2326	2356	0026
Milano Bovisa a.	0556	0626	0656	0726	until	2356	0026	0056
Milano Cadorna a.	0603	0633	0703	0733		0003	0033	0103

perator: Ferrovie Nord Milano (LeNord), Piazzale Cadorna 14, 20123 Milano. ✆ + 39 02 85 111, fax: + 39 02 85 11 708, www.trenord.it

584 TORINO - OULX - BARDONECCHIA - MODANE

2nd class only

For Italy - France *TGV* services via Oulx and Modane – see Table **44**.

km		⚒	⚒	†	⚒	⚒		⑥	Ⓐ	†	⚒	⚒		⚒	†	⚒	⚒		⚒	†	⚒	⚒		⚒	†
0	**Torino** Porta Nuova d.	0445	0515	0545	0545	0615	0645	0710	0715	0745	0745	0815	0845	0915	0945	0945	1015	1045	1115	1145	1145	1215	1245	1315	1345
46	Bussoleno d.	0543	0559	0632	0643	0659	0743	0754	0759	0832	0843	0859	0943	0959	1032	1043	1059	1143	1159	1232	1243	1259	1343	1359	1432
54	Susa a.	0553	|	|	0653	|	0753	|	|	|	0853	|	0953	|	|	1053	|	1153	|	|	1253	|	1353	|	|
76	Oulx-Claviere-Sestriere ▲ d.	...	0628	0701	...	0728	...	0823	0828	0901	...	0928	...	1028	1101	...	1128	...	1228	1301	...	1328	...	1428	1501
87	Bardonecchia ♣ d.	...	0641	0714	...	0741	...	0837	0841	0915	...	0941	...	1042	1115	...	1141	...	1242	1315	...	1341	...	1442	1515
107	**Modane** 🚌 **367** ♣ a.	...	...	...	...	...	...	0855	...	0933	...	...	...	1100**d**	1133	...	...	...	1300**d**	1333	...	...	...	1500**d**	1533

	⚒	⚒		⚒	†		⚒	⚒		⚒	†	⚒	⚒		⚒	†	⚒	⚒			⚒	†	⚒	⚒	
Torino Porta Nuova d.	1345	1415	1445	1515	1545	...	1545	1615	1645	1715	1745	1745	1815	1845	1915	1945	1945	2015	2045	...	2115	2145	2145	2215	2245
Bussoleno d.	1443	1459	1543	1559	1632	...	1643	1659	1743	1759	1832	1843	1859	1943	1959	2032	2043	2059	2143	...	2159	2232	2243	2259	2342
Susa a.	1453	|	1553	|	|	...	1653	|	1753	|	|	1853	|	1953	|	|	2053	|	2153	...	|	|	2253	|	...
Oulx-Claviere-Sestriere ▲ d.	...	1528	...	1628	1701	...	...	1728	...	1828	1901	...	1928	...	2028	2101	...	2128	...	...	2228	2301	...	2328	...
Bardonecchia ♣ d.	...	1541	...	1642	1715	...	...	1741	...	1842	1914	...	1941	...	2041	2114	...	2141	...	...	2241	2314	...	2341	...
Modane 🚌 **367** ♣ a.	...	...	...	1700**d**	1733	...	...	...	...	1900**d**	...	...	...	...	...	...	...	...	...	...	...	...	...	...	...

	⚒	†	⚒	†	⚒	⚒	⚒	⚒	†	⚒		⚒	⚒	†		⚒		⚒	⚒	†	⚒		⚒	⚒	†
Modane 🚌 **367** ♣ d.	...	...	...	...	...	...	...	...	...	...	...	...	...	...	...	...	...	1002**d**	...	1029	...	...	1202**d**	...	1229
Bardonecchia ♣ d.	...	...	...	0509	0521	...	0621	...	0648	0721	...	0821	...	0848	...	0921	...	1021	...	1048	1121	...	1221	...	1248
Oulx-Claviere-Sestriere ▲ d.	...	...	...	0522	0534	...	0634	...	0701	0734	...	0834	...	0901	...	0934	...	1034	...	1101	1134	...	1234	...	1301
Susa d.	...	0439	0509	|	|	0609	|	0709	|	|	0809	|	0909	|	...	|	1009	|	1109	|	|	1209	|	1309	|
Bussoleno d.	0419	0449	0519	0549	0601	0619	0701	0719	0728	0801	0819	0901	0919	0928	...	1001	1019	1101	1119	1128	1201	1219	1301	1319	1328
Torino Porta Nuova a.	0515	0545	0615	0645	0645	0715	0745	0815	0815	0845	0915	0945	1015	1015	...	1045	1115	1145	1215	1215	1245	1315	1345	1415	1415

	⚒		⚒	⚒	†	⚒		⚒	⚒	†	⚒			⚒	⚒	†	⚒		⚒	⚒	†	⚒		⚒	
Modane 🚌 **367** ♣ d.	...	...	1402**d**	...	1429	...	...	1602**d**	...	1629	...	...	...	1802**d**	...	1829	...	...	2002**d**	...	...	...	...	...	...
Bardonecchia ♣ d.	1321	...	1421	...	1448	1521	...	1621	...	1648	1721	...	...	1821	...	1848	1921	...	2021	...	2048	2121	...	2221	...
Oulx-Claviere-Sestriere ▲ d.	1334	...	1434	...	1501	1534	...	1634	...	1701	1734	...	...	1834	...	1901	1934	...	2034	...	2101	2134	...	2234	...
Susa d.	|	1409	|	1509	|	|	1609	|	1709	|	|	...	1809	|	1909	|	|	2009	|	2109	|	|	2209	|	...
Bussoleno d.	1401	1419	1501	1519	1528	1601	1619	1701	1719	1728	1801	...	1819	1901	1919	1928	2001	2019	2101	2119	2128	2201	2219	2301	...
Torino Porta Nuova a.	1445	1515	1545	1615	1615	1645	1715	1745	1815	1815	1845	...	1915	1945	2015	2015	2045	2115	2145	2215	2215	2245	2317	2345	...

d – ⑥.

▲ – Station for the resorts of Cesana, Claviere and Sestriere.

♣ – A cross-border 🚌 service is available Bardonecchia - Modane and v.v.
From **Bardonecchia**: 0800Ⓐ, 1200Ⓐ, 1500Ⓐ, 1900Ⓐ.
From **Modane**: 0730Ⓐ, 0930Ⓐ, 1330Ⓐ, 1630Ⓐ.
Journey time 30 minutes. See www.bardonecchia.it

585 TORINO - MILANO

For high-speed services – see Table **600.** For Italy - France *TGV* services – see Table **44**.

km										*ICN* **1575** ♦							2 Ⓐ	*IC* **509**				*ICN* **793** ⊙♦	*ICN* **797** ⊙♦		
0	**Torino** Porta Nuova **586** d.	0454	0554	0654	0754	0854	1054	1154	1254	1335	1354	1454	...	1554	1654	1754	1820	1850	1854	1954	2054	2125	2125	2154	2254
6	**Torino** Porta Susa **586** d.	0505	0605	0705	0805	0905	1105	1205	1305	1345**u**	1405	1505	...	1605	1705	1805	1829	1858	1905	2005	2105	2140**u**	2140**u**	2205	2305
29	Chivasso **586** d.	0520	0620	0720	0820	0920	1120	1220	1320	|	1420	1520	...	1620	1720	1820	1842	|	1920	2020	2120	|	|	2220	2320
60	Santhià d.	0538	0638	0738	0838	0938	1138	1238	1338	|	1438	1538	...	1638	1738	1838	1904	|	1938	2038	2138	|	|	2238	2338
79	Vercelli d.	0549	0649	0749	0849	0949	1149	1249	1349	1425	1449	1549	...	1649	1749	1849	1916	1952	1949	2049	2149	2222	2222	2249	2349
101	Novara d.	0604	0704	0804	0904	1004	1204	1304	1404	1443	1504	1604	...	1704	1804	1904	1937	2009	2004	2104	2204	2238	2238	2304	0004
149	**Milano** Porta Garibaldi a.	|	|	|	|	|	|	|	|	1542	|	|	...	|	|	|	2020	|	|	|	|	2315	2315	|	|
153	**Milano** Centrale a.	0646	0746	0846	0946	1046	1246	1346	1446	...	1546	1646	...	1746	1846	1946	...	2055	2046	2146	2246	...	...	2346	0046

			2 Ⓐ	*ICN* **792** ⊙♦	*ICN* **798** ⊙♦		*IC* **508**			Ⓐ					*ICN* **794** ♦									⚒	①
Milano Centrale d.	0518	0618	...	...	...	0718	0738	0818	0918	...	1118	1218	1318	1418	...	1518	1618	1718	1818	1914	2018	2115	2218	2318	0018
Milano Porta Garibaldi d.	|	|	0640	0714	0714	|	|	|	|	1005	|	|	|	|	1444	|	|	|	|	|	|	|	|	|	|
Novara d.	0558	0658	0718	0805	0805	0758	0822	0858	0958	1050	1158	1258	1358	1458	1521	1558	1658	1758	1858	1954	2058	2155	2258	2358	0058
Vercelli d.	0612	0712	0735	0821	0821	0812	0838	0912	1012	1103	1212	1312	1412	1512	1536	1612	1712	1812	1912	2010	2112	2209	2312	0012	0112
Santhià d.	0624	0724	0747	|	|	0824	|	0924	1024	1115	1224	1324	1424	1524	|	1624	1724	1824	1924	2022	2124	2221	2324	0024	0126
Chivasso **586** d.	0643	0743	0812	|	|	0843	|	0943	1043	1138	1243	1343	1443	1543	|	1643	1743	1843	1943	2040	2143	2240	2343	0043	0147
Torino Porta Susa **586** a.	0658	0758	0829	0910**s**	0910**s**	0858	0918**s**	0958	1058	1152	1258	1358	1458	1558	1630**s**	1658	1758	1858	1958	2054	2158	2255	2358	0058	0203
Torino Porta Nuova **586** a.	0710	0810	0840	0922	0922	0910	0930	1010	1110	1205	1310	1410	1510	1610	1640	1710	1810	1910	2010	2106	2210	2307	0010	0110	0215

♦ – **NOTES** (LISTED BY TRAIN NUMBER)

794 – Not June 29, July 20: 1, 2 cl., 2 cl. (4 berth) and (2) Reggio di Calabria - Milano - Torino. Train **35394** Aug. 3–30 (Milano P. Garibaldi a. 1425 / d. 1427).
793 – 1, 2 cl., 2 cl. (4 berth) and (2) Torino - Milano - Napoli - Salerno.
792 – 1, 2 cl., 2 cl. (4 berth) and (2) Salerno - Napoli - Milano - Torino.
797 – 1, 2 cl., 2 cl. (4 berth) and (2) Torino - Milano - Napoli - Salerno.
798 – 1, 2 cl., 2 cl. (4 berth) and (2) Salerno - Napoli - Milano - Torino.
1575 – Not June 15, 16, July 6, 7: 1, 2 cl., 2 cl. (4 berth) and (2) Torino - Milano - Reggio di Calabria. Train **1597** on ① from Torino and Aug. 3–31.

s – Stops to set down only.
u – Stops to pick up only.
⊙ – Subject to confirmation.

586 TORINO - AOSTA

Most trains 2nd class only

km						†	q		⚒	⚒		q		⚒		⚒				⚒		†	†	⚒	⚒	
0	**Torino** Porta Nuova **585** d.	...	0530	0730	0830	0930	1130	...	*1130*	1230	1330	1430	...	*1430*	1630	...	1730	...	1830	...	1930	2030	...	...	...	223
6	**Torino** Porta Susa **585** d.	...	0539	0739	0839	0939	1139	...	*1139*	1239	1339	1439	...	*1439*	1639	...	1739	...	1839	...	1939	2039	...	...	...	223
29	Chivasso **585** d.	0525	0605	0805	0905	1005	1205	...	1225	1305	1405	1505	...	1525	1705	...	1805	1825	1905	...	2005	2105	...	2125	...	230
62	Ivrea a.	0607	0638	0831	0931	1031	1231	...	1307	1331	1431	1531	...	1607	1731	...	1831	1907	1931	...	2031	2131	...	2207	...	233
	Change trains						⚒	†		q		⚒	†	q												
62	Ivrea d.	0616	0646	0837	0937	1037	1237	1247	1312	1341	1446	1537	1547	1643	1747	1800	1847	1912	1947	2000	2047	...	2138	...	2212	233
79	Pont Saint Martin d.	0629	0659	0849	0949	1049	1249	1300	1332	1354	1459	1550	1600	1656	1800	1825	1900	1929	2000	2025	2100	...	2150	...	2229	235
91	Verrès d.	0644	0714	0900	1002	1101	1302	1315	1346	1415	1515	1600	1615	1715	1815	1844	1915	1944	2015	2044	2115	...	2200	...	2244	000
104	Chatillon-Saint Vincent d.	0703	0725	0912	1013	1113	1313	1326	1402	1426	1526	1611	1626	1726	1826	1903	1926	2003	2026	2103	2126	...	2212	...	2303	001
129	**Aosta** a.	0723	0748	0933	1041	1135	1335	1353	1423	1453	1553	1635	1653	1753	1853	1923	1953	2023	2053	2123	2153	...	2234	...	2323	003

		⚒						⚒	†		⚒			⚒		†	⚒				⚒					
Aosta d.	0518	0540	0628	0640	0728	0828	1028	1134	1140	1228	...	1340	1428	1503	1528	1628	1640	1705	1728	1828	1859	1928	2028	...	2128	...
Chatillon-Saint Vincent d.	0539	0603	0649	0703	0756	0849	1049	1155	1203	1249	...	1401	1449	1526	1549	1649	1701	1726	1749	1849	1926	1949	2049	...	2149	...
Verrès d.	0550	0615	0700	0714	0806	0900	1101	1206	1216	1302	...	1415	1500	1536	1600	1700	1715	1737	1800	1900	1944	2000	2100	...	2200	...
Pont Saint Martin d.	0601	0629	0713	0731	0816	0915	1111	1220	1232	1313	...	1429	1515	1550	1613	1713	1730	1801	1813	1913	2000	2013	2113	...	2213	...
Ivrea a.	0614	0644	0726	0745	0829	0928	1122	1235	1244	1326	...	1444	1528	1608	1626	1728	1744	1816	1826	1926	2014	2026	2126	...	2226	...
Change trains																										
Ivrea d.	0623	0650	0732	0750	0834	0934	1134	1250	1250	1334	1434	1450	1534	...	1634	1734	1750	...	1834	1934	...	2034	...	2134	...	223
Chivasso **585** a.	0656	0737	0756	0837	0856	0956	1156	1337	1337	1356	1456	1537	1556	...	1656	1756	1837	...	1856	1956	...	2056	...	2156	...	230
Torino Porta Susa **585** a.	0724	*0758*	0824	*0858*	0924	1024	1224	*1358*	*1358*	1424	1524	*1558*	1624	...	1724	1824	*1858*	...	1924	2024	...	2124	...	2224	...	*235*
Torino Porta Nuova **585** a.	0735	*0810*	0835	*0910*	0935	1035	1235	*1410*	*1410*	1435	1535	*1610*	1635	...	1735	1835	*1910*	...	1935	2035	...	2135	...	2235	...	*001*

q – Runs daily.

BRIG - STRESA - MILANO 590

km		♠	2 ⚒	2	♠	2 ⚒	2 †	EC 35 ✕ ◧	♠	EC 51 ✕ ◧	2	EC 37 ✕ ◧V	2	♠	2	♠	EC 57 ✕ ◧	2	EC 39 ✕ ◧	♠	2	♠	2	EC 59 ✕ ◧	2 ©	EC 41 ✕ ◧
	Genève 570 d.	...	...	...	...	...	...	0539	...	...	...	0739	...	...	...	...	...	...	1339	...	...	...	...	...	...	1839
	Lausanne 570 d.	...	...	...	...	...	...	0618	...	...	...	0818	...	...	...	...	...	...	1418	...	...	...	...	...	...	1918
	Basel 560 d.	...	...	...	...	...	...	|	...	0631	...	|	...	...	...	...	1231	...	|	...	...	...	...	1731	...	|
	Bern 560 d.	...	...	...	...	...	...	|	...	0734	...	|	...	...	...	...	1334	...	|	...	...	...	...	1834	...	|
0	**Brig** 🏛 d.	...	...	...	...	...	...	0744	...	0844	...	0944	...	...	...	...	1444	...	1544	...	...	...	...	1944	...	2044
2	**Domodossola** 🏛 § a.	...	...	...	...	...	...	0812	...	0912	...	1012	...	...	...	...	1512	...	1612	...	...	...	...	2012	...	2112
2	**Domodossola** d.	0453	0551	0603	0651	0720	0758	0817	0853	0917	0958	1017	1158	1253	1358	1453	1517	1558	1617	1653	1758	1853	1958	2017	2051	2117
2	Verbània-Pallanza d.	0513	0611	0629	0713	0743	0824	|	0913	|	1024	|	1224	1313	1424	1513	|	1624	|	1713	1824	1913	2024	|	2111	|
7	Baveno d.	|	|	0634	|	|	0829	|	|	|	1029	|	1229	|	1429	|	|	1629	|	|	1829	|	2029	|	|	|
1	Stresa d.	0521	0619	0639	0721	0751	0835	0840	0921	0940	1035	|	1235	1321	1435	1521	1540	1635	1640	1721	1835	1921	2035	|	2119	2140
8	Arona d.	0535	0635	0701	0735	0806	0906	|	0935	|	1106	|	1306	1335	1506	1535	|	1706	|	1735	1906	1935	2106	|	2135	|
4	Gallarate ▲ d.	0558	0658	0732	0758	0834	0934	|	0958	|	1134	1104	1334	1358	1534	1558	|	1734	|	1758	1934	1958	2134	2105	2158	|
0	Rho Fiera Milano d.	0619	0719	0800	0823	0900	1000	|	1019	|	1200	|	1400	1419	1600	1619	|	1800	|	1819	2000	2019	2200	|	2219	|
5	**Milano** Porta Garibaldi a.	|	|	0811	|	0911	1011	|	|	|	1211	|	1411	|	1611	|	|	1811	|	|	2011	|	2211	|	|	|
7	**Milano** Centrale a.	0631	0731	...	0835	...	...	0937	1031	1037	...	1137	...	1435	...	1631	1637	...	1737	1831	...	2035	...	2137	2231	2237

	2	EC 50 ✕ ◧	♠	2	EC 32 ✕ ◧	♠	2	EC 52 ✕ ◧F	2	EC 34 ✕ ◧	♠	2	♠	2	EC 36 ✕ ◧	♠	EC 56 ✕ ◧	2	⚒	EC 42 ✕ ◧V	2	2	♠ 2 ⚒	♠	♠ 2 ⚒	♠ 2
ano Centrale d.	...	0723	0729	...	0823	0829	0929	1123	...	1223	1329	...	1529	...	1723	1729	1823	...	1829	1923	1929	...	...	2129	...	...
ano Porta Garibaldi d.	0612	|	|	0749	|	|	|	|	1149	|	|	1349	|	1549	|	|	|	1749	|	|	|	1949	2049	|	2149	2249
Fiera Milano d.	0622	|	0740	0759	|	0840	0940	|	1159	|	1340	1359	1540	1559	|	1740	|	1759	1840	|	1940	1959	2059	2140	2159	2259
arate ▲ d.	0649	0757	0802	0826	|	0902	1002	|	1226	|	1402	1426	1602	1626	|	1802	|	1826	1902	1957	2002	2026	2126	2202	2226	2326
na d.	0721	|	0823	0855	|	0923	1023	|	1255	|	1423	1455	1623	1655	|	1823	|	1855	1923	|	2023	2055	2155	2223	2255	2355
esa d.	0742	|	0838	0916	0921	0938	1038	1221	1316	1321	1438	1516	1638	1716	1821	1838	1921	1916	1938	|	2038	2116	...	2238	...	...
eno d.	0746	|	|	0921	|	|	|	|	1321	|	|	1521	|	1721	|	|	|	1921	|	|	|	2121	...	|	...	...
bània-Pallanza d.	0751	|	0845	0926	|	0945	1045	|	1326	|	1445	1526	1645	1726	|	1845	|	1926	1945	|	2045	2126	...	2245	...	...
nodossola a.	0820	0843	0907	1002	0943	1007	1109	1243	1402	1343	1507	1602	1707	1802	1843	1907	1943	2002	2009	2043	2109	2202	...	2307	...	...
nodossola 🏛 § d.	...	0848	...	...	0948	...	...	1248	...	1348	...	...	...	...	1848	...	1948	...	...	2048	...	...	...	...	...	...
g 🏛 a.	...	0916	...	...	1016	...	...	1316	...	1416	...	...	...	...	1916	...	2016	...	...	2116	...	...	...	...	...	...
Bern 560 a.	...	1024	...	...	|	...	...	1424	...	|	...	...	...	...	|	...	2124	...	...	|	...	...	...	...	...	...
Basel 560 a.	...	1129	...	...	|	...	...	1529	...	|	...	...	...	...	|	...	2232	...	...	|	...	...	...	...	...	...
ausanne 570 a.	...	...	...	...	1142	...	...	...	...	1542	...	...	...	...	2042	...	...	...	...	2242	...	...	...	...	...	...
enève 570 a.	...	...	...	...	1221	...	...	...	...	1621	...	...	...	...	2121	...	...	...	...	2324	...	...	...	...	...	...

Other services BRIG - DOMODOSSOLA

km			Ⓐ			⑥									⑥		⑥						Ⓐ			
0	**Brig** 🚗 d.	0522	0622	...	0722	0840	...	0922	0940	...	1044	1122	...	1322	1344	...	1440	1522	...	1644	1722	...	1822	2222	...	0022
3	Iselle di Trasquera § 🚗 d.	0536	0636	...	0736	|	...	0936	|	...	|	1136	...	1336	|	...	|	1536	...	|	1736	...	1836	2236	...	0036
2	**Domodossola** a.	0554	0654	...	0754	0907	...	0954	1008	...	1112	1154	...	1354	1412	...	1507	1554	...	1712	1754	...	1854	2254	...	0054

				Ⓐ						⑥			⑥			⑥							Ⓐ	†		
nodossola d.	0437	0558	...	0658	0758	...	0958	1048	...	1148	1158	...	1344	1358	...	1548	1558	...	1648	1748	1758	...	1858	1941	1958	2258
e di Trasquera § 🚗 d.	0456	0616	...	0716	0816	...	1016	|	...	|	1216	...	|	1416	...	|	1616	...	|	|	1816	...	1916	|	2016	2316
g 🚗 a.	0511	0633	...	0733	0833	...	1033	1116	...	1216	1233	...	1412	1433	...	1616	1633	...	1716	1816	1833	...	1933	2011	2033	2333

To Frankfurt (Tables **560** and **912**).
To / from Venezia (Table **605**).

🅁 inclusive of supplement.
Operator: Trenord.
Ticket point is **Iselle**.

▲ – 🚌 service operates Gallarate - Milano Malpensa Aeroporto and v.v. Journey time 25 minutes; operator: S.A.C.O. ✆ 0331 25 84 11.

🚗 – Car-carrying shuttle available. ✆ +41 (0) 58 327 41 14. www.bls.ch/en/fahren/unterwegs-mit/autoverlad/brig-iselle

d class only DOMODOSSOLA and ARONA - NOVARA 591

km		⚒	⚒		⚒		⚒				
0	**Domodossola** d.	0520	0617	0648	0800	1245	1343	1545	...	1747	1848
3	Omegna d.	0614	0657	0752	0850	1337	1444	1641	...	1842	1940
4	Pettenasco d.	0621	0704	0759	0856	1343	1451	1648	...	1849	1947
7	Orta-Miasino d.	0626	0712	0804	0904	1351	1456	1653	...	1854	1952
0	Borgomanero d.	0641	0724	0815	0917	1406	1507	1704	...	1905	2004
0	**Novara** a.	0716	0754	0842	0945	1437	1541	1740	...	1943	2039

	⚒				⚒		Ⓐ		Ⓐ	
Novara d.	0546	0645	...	1223	1345	1515	1619	1734	1818	1915
Borgomanero d.	0621	0725	...	1249	1420	1550	1650	1811	1851	1950
Orta-Miasino d.	0645	0740	...	1306	1432	1608	1711	1826	1911	2006
Pettenasco d.	0649	0744	...	1311	1436	1613	1715	1831	1915	2011
Omegna d.	0656	0751	...	1318	1443	1619	1722	1843	1922	2018
Domodossola a.	0748	0849	...	1417	1542	1714	1804	1938	2004	2114

d class only

ARONA - NOVARA

	⚒	⚒	†	†	†	⚒	†	⚒	†	⚒	⚒	†	⚒	†
Arona d.	0648	0748	0915	1115	1315	1348	1515	1548	1715	1748	1848	1915	1948	2115
Oleggio d.	0712	0812	0932	1132	1332	1412	1532	1612	1732	1812	1912	1932	2012	2132
Novara a.	0732	0832	0948	1148	1348	1432	1548	1632	1748	1832	1932	1948	2032	2148

	⚒	⚒	†	†	†	†	⚒	⚒	†	⚒	†	⚒	⚒	†
Novara d.	0650	0750	0812	1012	1212	1412	1423	1523	1612	1723	1812	1823	1923	2012
Oleggio d.	0713	0813	0826	1026	1226	1426	1441	1541	1626	1741	1826	1841	1941	2026
Arona a.	0739	0839	0845	1045	1245	1445	1512	1612	1645	1812	1845	1912	2012	2045

d class only

NOVARA - ALESSANDRIA

		⚒		⚒	†	⚒	⚒	⚒	†	†
Novara ▲ d.	0608	0708	0808	0908	1408	1423	1608	1708	1908	2008
Alessandria ▲ a.	0715	0815	0915	1015	1515	1532	1715	1815	2015	2125

	♠†			⚒				♠⚒		⚒
Alessandria ▲ d.	0645	...	1245	1345	1645	1745	...	1845	1945	2045
Novara ▲ a.	0753	...	1353	1453	1753	1853	...	1957	2053	2153

Additional journeys available by changing trains at Mortara (*25 km* from Novara).

♠ – Operator: Trenord.

erator: TILO 2nd class only CHIASSO - STABIO - MILANO MALPENSA ✈ 592

Chiasso 550 d.	0520	0620	0720	0820	and	1920	2020	2120	2220	2320
Mendrisio 550 d.	0533	0633	0733	0833	each train	1933	2033	2133	2233	2333
Stabio 🏛 d.	0537	0637	0737	0837	every	1937	2037	2137	2237	2337
Varese 607 d.	0600	0654	0800	0854	two hours	2000	2054	2200	2254	2354
Gallarate 607 d.	0618	...	0818	...	until	2018	...	2218	...	...
Milano Malpensa ✈ ⊖ a.	0647	...	0847	...		2047	...	2247	...	...

Milano Malpensa ✈ ⊖ d.	...	...	0713	...	0913	...	and	2113	...	2313
Gallarate 607 d.	...	...	0746	...	0946	...	each train	2146	...	2346
Varese 607 d.	0606	0706	0806	0906	1006	1106	every	2206	2306	0006
Stabio 🏛 d.	0623	0723	0823	0923	1023	1123	two hours	2223	2323	0023
Mendrisio 550 d.	0632	0732	0832	0932	1032	1132	until	2232	2332	0027
Chiasso 550 a.	0640	0740	0840	0940	1040	1140		2240	2340	*0104*

BELLINZONA - CADENAZZO - GALLARATE

Bellinzona d.	0552	...	*0928*	*1128*	...	*1328*	*1528*	*1728*	*1928*	...
Cadenazzo d.	0607	0804	1004	1204	...	1404	1604	1804	2004	...
Pino-Tronzano 🏛 d.	0628	0828	1028	1228	...	1428	1628	1828	2028	...
Luino d.	0645	0845	1042	1241	...	1445	1645	1845	2042	...
Laveno Mombello d.	0706	0900	...	...	...	1500	1700	1900	...	...
Gallarate d.	0741	0941	...	...	...	1541	1741	1941	...	...

Gallarate d.	0608	...	0819	...	...	...	1419	1619	1819	2019
Laveno Mombello d.	0641	...	0901	...	...	...	1501	1701	1901	2101
Luino d.	0702	0710	0918	1118	1318	...	1518	1718	1918	2118
Pino-Tronzano 🏛 d.	...	0723	0930	1130	1330	...	1530	1730	1930	2130
Cadenazzo a.	...	0745	0954	1154	1354	...	1554	1754	1954	2154
Bellinzona a.	...	*0800*	*1030*	*1230*	*1430*	...	*1630*	*1816*f	*2030*	*2230*

Ⓐ.

⊖ – Services terminate / originate at Milano Malpensa Aeroporto ✈ Terminal 2. Trains also call at Terminal 1; journey 6 minutes.

593 MILANO - COLICO - TIRANO and COLICO - CHIAVENNA

Operator: Treno

km	Subject to confirmation																								
		2								2		2		2	2			2					2	2	2
					†Z		©										⚒								
0	**Milano** Centrale ▷ d.	...	0620	0720	0722**p**	0820	0920	1020	1220	1252**p**	1320	1352**p**	1420	1452**p**	1552**p**	1620	1720	1752**p**	1820	1920	2020	2120	2252	2322	23
12	Monza ▷ d.	...	0632	0732	0739	0832	0932	1032	1232	1309	1332	1409	1432	1509	1609	1632	1732	1809	1832	1932	2032	2132	2309	2339	00
50	Lecco ▷ d.	...	0702	0802	0815	0902	1002	1102	1302	1353	1402	1453	1502	1553	1653	1702	1802	1853	1902	2002	2102	2202	2353	0023	00
72	Varenna-Esino d.	...	0724	0824	0853	0924	1024	1124	1324	...	1424	...	1524	...	...	1724	1824	...	|	2024	2124	2236	...	...	
75	Bellano-Tartavalle Terme d.	...	0729	0829	0858	0929	1029	1129	1329	...	1429	...	1529	...	...	1729	1829	...	1929	2029	2129	2241	...	...	
89	**Colico** a.	...	0747	0847	0923	0947	1047	1147	1347	...	1447	...	1547	...	...	1747	1847	...	1947	2047	2147	2258	...	...	
130	Sondrio a.	0533	0820	0920	...	1020	1120	1220	1420	...	1520	...	1620	...	...	1820	1921	...	2020	2120	2221	2334	...	...	
156	**Tirano** ♣ a.	0607	0852	0952	...	1052	1205	1252	1452	...	1552	...	1652	...	...	1852	...	...	2052	2152	...	...	...	...	

Subject to confirmation																									
				2				2			2		2	2			2					2			2
	†	⚒									⚒		⚒				⚒		†Z	©		⚒			
Tirano ♣ d.	...	...	...	...	0612	0712	0908	...	1108	1208	...	1308	...	...	1508	1608	...	1708	...	1808	1908	...	2008	...	
Sondrio d.	0432	0441	0532	...	0641	0741	0941	...	1141	1241	...	1341	...	...	1541	1641	...	1741	...	1841	1941	...	2041	2122	
Colico d.	0503	0516	0603	...	0716	0816	1016	...	1216	1316	...	1416	...	...	1616	1716	...	1816	1837	1916	2016	...	2116	2200	
Bellano-Tartavalle Terme d.	0518	0532	0618	...	0732	0832	1032	...	1232	1332	...	1432	...	...	1632	1732	...	1832	1901	1932	2032	...	2132	2215	
Varenna-Esino d.	0523	0537	0623	...	0737	0837	1037	...	1237	1337	...	1437	...	...	1637	1737	...	1837	1906	1937	2037	...	2137	2220	
Lecco ▷ d.	0549	0601	0652	0707	0759	0901	1059	1207	1301	1401	1437	1501	1537	1607	1701	1801	1837	1901	1946	2001	2101	2137	2201	2243	23
Monza ▷ a.	0622	0626	0724	0749	0824	0926	1123	1249	1326	1426	1519	1526	1619	1649	1726	1826	1919	1926	2019	2026	2126	2219	2226	2315	23
Milano Centrale ▷ a.	0640	0640	0738	0808**p**	0838	0945	1138	1308**p**	1340	1440	1538**p**	1540	1638**p**	1708**p**	1740	1840	1938**p**	1940	2038**p**	2040	2140	2238**p**	2240	2330	000

COLICO - CHIAVENNA

2nd class or

km																						
			⚒	⚒	⚒		†Z		⚒		⚒		⚒			⚒	†		⚒		🚌†	⚒
0	Colico d.	0545	0706	0810	0845	...	0925	1004	1045	1204	1245	1404	1445	...	1604	1645	1730	1804	1852	2004	2100	2117
27	Chiavenna a.	0617	0737	0835	0917	...	0956	1035	1117	1235	1317	1435	1517	...	1635	1717	1756	1835	1923	2035	2135	2148

	🚌Ⓐ		⚒	⚒	⚒		⚒			⚒		⚒		†	⚒		†Z		⚒	†	⚒		
Chiavenna d.	0512	0625	0703	0745	0843	0925	1043	1125	...	1243	1325	1443	1525	1637	1643	1725	1804	...	1847	1925	1931	...	20
Colico a.	0548	0656	0735	0809	0915	0956	1115	1156	...	1315	1356	1515	1556	1703	1715	1756	1835	...	1919	1956	2002	...	21

Z – (12) Milano - Colico - Chiavenna and v.v.

p – Milano **Porta Garibaldi**.
q – ⑥ (also Ⓐ school holidays).
s – Schooldays only.

▷ – Additional local services operate (approximately hourly) Milano Porta Garibaldi - Lecco and v.v.
♣ – For 🚌 service Tirano - Edolo and v.v. see panel.

🚌 TIRANO - EDOLO (Subject to confirmation)

	⚒	⚒	⚒	⚒	⚒
Tirano Stazione d.	0840	1040	1245	1435	1635
Aprica S Pietro a.	0920	1120	1315	1515	1720
Edolo a.	0945	1145	...	1540	1745

	⚒	⚒	⚒	⚒	⚒
Edolo d.	0615	0915	1115	1515	17
Aprica S Pietro d.	0650	0940	1140	1540	17
Tirano Stazione a.	0730	1020	1220	1620	18

Operator: Automobilistica Perego (AP): ✆ +39 (0)342 70 12 00; fax +39 (0)342 70 44 00.

595 INNSBRUCK - BOLZANO / BOZEN - VERONA - BOLOGNA

km																										
			FA	*FR*			*FA*								*FA*				*EC*	*EC*					*FA*	*E*
			8503	**8505**			**8507**				§				**8511**				**1289**	**81**					**8517**	**8**
		2	🍷	🍷	2	2	🍷	2	2	2	2	2	2	2	🍷	2	2	2	✕	✕	2	2	2	2	🍷	
				♦	⚒	⚒	♦	⚒M		⚒M	M	Ⓐ	M	Ⓐ	♦	©	©M	©B	♠b	♠a			M	M		♠
	München Hbf **951** d.	...	...	...	...	...	...	...	...	...	...	...	...	...	...	...	...	...	0734	0734	...	...	...	...	...	09
0	**Innsbruck** Hbf ▲ d.	...	...	...	...	...	...	...	...	...	0622	...	...	...	...	...	...	...	0924	0924	...	...	...	...	...	11
37	**Brennero / Brenner** 🏛 ▲ a.	...	...	...	...	...	...	...	...	...	0659	...	...	...	...	...	...	...	1000	1000	...	...	...	...	...	12
37	**Brennero / Brenner** 🏛 d.	...	...	...	...	...	...	0536	0608	0638	0702	...	0738	0808	...	...	0838	0938	1010	1014	...	...	1038	1138	...	12
60	Vipiteno / Sterzing d.	...	...	...	...	...	...	0555	0627	0657	0723	...	0757	0827	...	...	0857	0957	|	|	...	...	1057	1157	...	
78	Fortezza / Franzensfeste d.	...	...	...	0536	...	...	0613	0645	0715	0739	0745	0815	0845	...	...	0915	1015	1041	1046	...	...	1115	1215	...	12
89	Bressanone / Brixen d.	...	...	...	0545	...	...	0623	0655	0725	0749	0755	0825	0855	...	...	0925	1025	1050	1056	...	...	1125	1225	...	12
99	Chiusa / Klausen d.	...	...	...	0553	...	...	0631	0703	0733	0758	0803	0833	0903	...	...	0933	1033	|	|	...	...	1133	1233	...	
127	**Bolzano / Bozen** a.	...	...	...	0617	...	...	0655	0729	0759	0823	0829	0859	0929	...	...	0959	1059	1115	1127	...	...	1159	1259	...	13
					|				|	2	2⑥	|		2©			2©	2	|	|			2			
127	**Bolzano / Bozen** d.	0500	0516	...	0620	0634	0716	...	0731	0736	0831	0831	...	...	...	0936	1031	...	1117	1131	...	1136	1231	...	1316	13
143	Ora / Auer d.	0512	|	...	0633	0651	|	...	0743	0755	0843	0843	...	...	...	0955	1043	...	|	|	...	1155	1243	...	|	
165	Mezzocorona d.	0525	|	...	0650	0712	|	...	0756	0816	0856	0856	...	...	...	1016	1056	...	|	|	...	1216	1256	...	|	
182	**Trento** d.	0537	0547	...	0705	0733	0747	...	0810	0833	0910	0910	...	...	...	1033	1110	...	1149	1204	...	1233	1310	...	1347	14
206	Rovereto d.	0551	0602	...	0720	0747	0802	...	0825	0847	0925	0925	...	...	...	1047	1125	...	|	1219	...	1247	1325	...	1402	14
274	**Verona** Porta Nuova a.	0640	0642	...	0814	0854	0842	...	0914	0951	1014	1014	...	...	...	1151	1214	...	1236	1256	...	1351	1414	...	1442	14
274	**Verona** Porta Nuova d.	0703	0652	0752	...	...	0852	...	...	...	...	...	...	1026	1152	...	...	1226	1238	1313	1326	...	1426	...	1452	15
388	**Bologna** Centrale a.	0838	0742	0842	...	...	0942	...	...	...	...	...	...	1155	1242	...	...	1355	|	1410	1455	...	1555	...	1542	16
	Milano Centrale **615** a.	...	|	|	...	...	|	...	...	...	...	...	...	...	|	...	...	...	|	...	...	...	...	...	|	
	Venezia Santa Lucia **605** a.	...	|	|	...	...	|	...	...	...	...	...	...	...	|	...	...	...	1355	...	...	...	...	...	|	
	Firenze Campo di Marte a.	...	0829	0929	...	...	1029	...	...	...	...	...	...	...	1329	...	...	...	...	...	...	...	...	...	1629	
	Roma Termini **600 620** a.	...	0953	1053	...	...	1153	...	...	...	...	...	...	...	1458	...	...	...	...	...	...	...	...	...	1753	

					FA	*EC*	*FA*					*FA*	*EC*						*EC*				*ICN*			
					8523	**87**	**8525**					**8527**	**89**						**83**				**763**	§		
	2	2	2	2	🍷	✕	🍷	2	2	2	2	🍷	✕	2	2	2	2	2	✕	2	2	2		2	2	
		M		M		♠	♦	M		Ⓐ	M	♦	♠		M		Ⓐ	M	♠	M		M	♦	A		
München Hbf **951** d.	...	...	...	...	...	1135	...	...	...	...	...	...	1335	...	...	...	...	...	1534	...	...	...	...	...	...	
Innsbruck Hbf ▲ d.	...	...	...	...	...	1324	...	...	...	...	...	...	1524	...	...	...	...	...	1724	...	...	...	...	...	...	2
Brennero / Brenner 🏛 ▲ a.	...	...	...	...	...	1400	...	...	...	...	...	...	1600	...	...	...	...	...	1800	...	...	...	...	...	...	2
Brennero / Brenner 🏛 d.	...	1238	1308	1338	...	1414	...	1438	1508	...	1538	...	1614	...	1638	1708	...	1738	1814	1838	1908	1938	...	...	...	2
Vipiteno / Sterzing d.	...	1257	1327	1357	...	|	...	1457	1527	...	1557	...	|	...	1657	1727	...	1757	|	1857	1927	1957	...	...	...	22
Fortezza / Franzensfeste d.	...	1315	1345	1415	...	1446	...	1515	1545	...	1615	...	1646	...	1715	1745	...	1815	1846	1915	1945	2015	...	2118	...	22
Bressanone / Brixen d.	...	1325	1355	1425	...	1456	...	1525	1555	...	1625	...	1656	...	1725	1755	...	1825	1856	1925	1955	2025	...	2127	...	22
Chiusa / Klausen d.	...	1333	1403	1433	...	|	...	1533	1603	...	1633	...	|	...	1733	1803	...	1833	|	1933	2003	2033	...	2135	...	22
Bolzano / Bozen a.	...	1359	1429	1459	...	1527	...	1559	1629	...	1659	...	1727	...	1759	1829	...	1859	1927	1959	2029	2059	...	2158	...	22
			|	2Ⓐ		|		2	|		2Ⓐ		|		2Ⓐ	|		2Ⓐ	|	2	|	2Ⓐ				
Bolzano / Bozen d.	1334	...	1431	1436	1516	1531	...	1536	1631	1636	1704	1713	1731	1736	1806	1831	1836	1906	1931	1936	2031	2040	2130	...	2136	2
Ora / Auer d.	1351	...	1443	1455	|	|	...	1555	1643	1655	1720	|	|	1755	1822	1843	1855	1922	|	1955	2043	2100	2144	...	2155	2
Mezzocorona d.	1412	...	1456	1516	|	|	...	1616	1656	1716	1740	|	|	1816	1842	1856	1916	1942	|	2016	2056	2122	2200	...	2216	2
Trento d.	1433	...	1510	1533	1547	1604	...	1633	1710	1733	1758	1747	1804	1833	1855	1910	1933	1955	2004	2033	2110	2139	2216	...	2233	2
Rovereto d.	1447	...	1525	1547	1602	1619	...	1647	1725	1747	1811	1802	1819	1847	1909	1925	1947	2010	2019	2047	2125	2154	2232	...	2247	
Verona Porta Nuova a.	1551	...	1614	1654	1642	1658	...	1751	1814	1854	...	1842	1858	1951	...	2014	2051	2108	2056	2151	2214	2300	2316	...	2348	
Verona Porta Nuova d.	...	...	1626	...	1652	1700	1752	...	1826	...	...	1852	1915	...	...	2104	...	...	...	...	...	...	2336	...	...	
Bologna Centrale a.	...	...	1755	...	1742	|	1842	...	1955	...	...	1942	2016	...	...	2230	...	...	...	...	...	...	|	...	...	
Milano Centrale **615** a.	...	...	...	...	|	|	|	...	...	...	...	|	...	...	...	...	...	...	...	...	...	...	|	...	...	
Venezia Santa Lucia **605** a.	...	...	...	...	|	1810	|	...	...	...	...	|	...	...	...	...	...	...	...	...	...	...	|	...	...	
Firenze Campo di Marte a.	...	...	...	...	1829	...	1929	...	...	...	...	2029	...	...	...	...	...	...	...	...	...	...	|	...	...	
Roma Termini **600 620** a.	...	...	...	...	1956	...	2053	...	...	...	...	2153	...	...	...	...	...	...	...	...	...	...	0600	...	...	

♦ – **NOTES** (LISTED BY TRAIN NUMBER)

84 – (12) and ✕ (⑤⑥⑦ Aug. 2 - Sept. 8: Rimini -) Bolgona - München.
85 – (12) and ✕ München - Bolgona (- Rimini: ④⑤⑥ Aug. 1 – Sept. 7).
763 – ⑥⑦: 🛏 1, 2 cl., 🛏 2 cl. (4 berth) and (2) Bolzano - Roma.
764 – ⑤⑥ from Roma: 🛏 1, 2 cl., 🛏 2 cl. (4 berth) and (2) Roma - Bolzano.
8338 – ⑥⑦ until Sept. 15: (12) and 🍷 Ancona - Bologna - Bolzano.
8505 – (12) and 🍷 Bergamo - Brescia - Verona - Roma.
8506 – (12) and 🍷 Napoli - Roma - Bologna - Bolzano.
8507 – (12) and 🍷 Bolzano - Bologna - Roma - Napoli.
8508 – (12) and 🍷 Roma - Verona - Brescia - Bergamo.
8511 – (12) and 🍷 Vicenza (**8510**) - Verona (**8511**) - Roma.
8524 – (12) and 🍷 Napoli - Roma - Bologna - Bolzano.
8525 – (12) and 🍷 Bergamo - Brescia - Verona - Roma.
8527 – (12) and 🍷 Bolzano - Bologna - Roma - Napoli.
8528 – (12) and 🍷 Roma - Verona - Brescia - Bergamo.

NOTES CONTINUE ON NEXT PAGE →

BOLOGNA - VERONA - BOLZANO / BOZEN - INNSBRUCK 595

						§	ICN 764								EC 88	FA 8504			EC 80	FA 8506					FA 8508	EC 84
	2	2	2	2	2	2		2	2	2	2	2	2	2	🍴	🍷	2	2	🍴	🍷	2	2	2	2	🍷	🍴
	⚒	Ⓐ	⚒	†	⚒		◆	⚒	⚒					Ⓐ	♠		ⒸM	†	♠	◆	†	⚒			◆	♠◆
Roma Termini **600 620** d.	...	...	...	...	...	...	2300	...	...	...	...	...	...	...	...	0645	...	...	...	0845	...	...	...	...	0945	...
Firenze Campo di Marte d.	...	...	...	...	...	...	|	...	...	...	...	...	...	...	...	0803	...	...	...	1003	...	...	...	...	1103	...
Venezia Santa Lucia **605** d.	...	...	...	...	...	...	|	...	...	...	...	...	...	...	...	|	...	...	...	|	...	...	...	...	|	...
Milano Centrale **615** d.	...	...	...	...	...	...	|	...	...	...	...	...	...	...	...	|	...	...	...	|	...	...	...	...	|	...
ologna Centrale d.	...	...	...	...	...	...	|	...	...	...	0603	...	0710	...	0745	0845	...	...	...	1045	...	...	1010f	...	1145	1152
rona Porta Nuova a.	...	...	...	...	...	...	0530	...	...	...	0743	...	0832	...	0847	0937	...	...	...	1137	...	...	1132f	...	1237	1247
rona Porta Nuova d.	...	...	...	...	0525	...	0600	0607	0707	0750	▬	0809	...	0850	0904	0947	...	0953	1102	1147	...	1109	1150	1209	▬	1304
vereto d.	...	...	...	...	0612	...	0701	0710	0810	0839	...	0912	...	0937	0943	1026	...	1042	1143	1226	...	1212	1239	1312	...	1343
ento d.	...	0530	0602	0632	0632	0640	0717	0730	0830	0854	...	0932	...	0952	0959	1040	...	1057	1159	1240	1225	1226	1254	1332	...	1359
ezzocorona d.	...	0544	0617	0646	0646	0653	0730	0744	0844	0905	...	0946	...	1005	|	|	...	1108	|	|	1239	1240	1305	1346	...	|
a / Auer d.	...	0603	0636	0706	0706	0711	0747	0804	0905	0919	...	1006	...	1020	|	|	...	1122	|	|	1300	1300	1319	1406	...	|
lzano / Bozen a.	...	0620	0652	0724	0724	0728	0805	0823	0923	0930	...	1022	...	1039	1031	1117	...	1133	1231	1314	1322	1322	1330	1422	...	1431
		|		▬		|	▬			|					|				|	▬			|		|
		|	2⚒M	2†		|	2M	2M		|	2M				|			2⑥C	|	2M			|	2M	|
lzano / Bozen d.	0602	0632	0702	0702	...	0732	0802	0902	...	0932	1002	...	...	...	1034	...	1102	1202	1234	1302	...	...	1332	...	1402	1434
iusa / Klausen d.	0625	0655	0725	0725	...	0755	0825	0925	...	0955	1025	...	...	...	|	...	1125	1225	|	1325	...	...	1355	...	1425	|
essanone / Brixen d.	0633	0703	0733	0733	...	0803	0833	0933	...	1003	1033	...	...	...	1104	...	1133	1233	1304	1333	...	...	1402	...	1433	1504
rtezza / Franzensfeste d.	0645	0715	0745	0745	...	0815	0845	0945	...	1015	1045	...	...	...	1115	...	1145	1245	1315	1345	...	...	1415	...	1445	1515
iteno / Sterzing d.	0703	0733	0803	0803	...	0833	0903	1003	...	1033	1103	...	...	...	|	...	1203	1303	|	1403	...	...	1433	...	1503	|
ennero / Brenner 🏛 a.	0722	0752	0822	0822	...	0852	0922	1022	...	1052	1122	...	...	...	1148	...	1222	1322	1348	1422	...	...	1452	...	1522	1548
ennero / Brenner 🏛 ▲ d.	...	...	...	...	...	0902	...	...	...	...	...	...	...	...	1200	...	...	...	1400	...	...	...	...	...	...	1600
sbruck Hbf ▲ a.	...	...	...	...	...	0938	...	...	...	...	...	...	...	...	1236	...	...	...	1436	...	...	...	...	...	...	1636
München Hbf **951** a.	...	...	...	...	...	...	...	...	...	...	...	...	...	...	1426	...	...	...	1625	...	...	...	...	...	...	1827

	FA 8512				EC 86					EC 82	EC 1288		FA 8518				FA 8338		FA 8524			FA 8526		FR 8528		
	🍷	2	2	2	🍴	2	2	2	2	🍴	🍴	2	🍷	2	2	2	🍷	2	🍷	2	2	🍷	2	🍷	2	2
		⚒			♠	Ⓐ		Ⓐ		a♠	b♠	Ⓐ					◆	Ⓐ	◆				Ⓐ	◆		
Roma Termini **600 620** d.	1045	...	...	...	...	...	...	...	...	...	...	...	1445	...	...	...	...	...	1645	...	...	1745	...	1845	...	...
Firenze Campo di Marte d.	1203	...	...	...	...	...	...	...	...	...	...	...	1603	...	...	...	...	...	1803	...	...	1903	...	2003	...	...
Venezia Santa Lucia **605** d.	|	...	...	...	1350	...	...	...	...	...	1535	...	|	...	...	...	...	...	|	...	...	|	...	|	...	...
Milano Centrale **615** d.	|	...	...	...	|	...	...	...	...	...	|	...	|	...	...	...	...	...	|	...	...	|	...	|	...	...
ologna Centrale d.	1245	...	1210	...	|	...	1410	...	...	1550	|	...	1645	1610	...	...	1803	...	1845	1810	...	1945	...	2045	2010	*2110*
rona Porta Nuova a.	1337	...	1332	...	1500	...	1535	...	...	1645	1651	...	1737	1732	...	...	1858	...	1937	1938	...	2037	...	2137	2132	*2242*
rona Porta Nuova d.	1347	1257	1350	1409	1502	...	1550	...	1609	1702	1702	1709	...	1750	...	1809	1908	1909	1947	1950	2009	2047	2109	...	2150	2250
vereto d.	1426	1409	1439	1512	1543	1550	1639	1650	1712	1743	1743	1812	...	1839	...	1912	1949	2012	2026	2039	2112	2126	2212	...	2239	2339
ento d.	1440	1424	1454	1532	1559	1605	1654	1705	1732	1759	1759	1832	...	1854	...	1932	2005	2032	2040	2054	2126	2140	2232	...	2254	2352
ezzocorona d.	|	1440	1505	1546	|	1616	1705	1716	1746	|	|	1846	...	1905	...	1946	|	2046	|	2105	2140	|	2246	...	2305	...
a / Auer d.	|	1500	1519	1606	|	1636	1719	1736	1806	|	|	1906	...	1919	...	2006	|	2106	|	2119	2200	|	2306	...	2319	...
lzano / Bozen a.	1514	1522	1530	1622	1631	1652	1730	1752	1822	1831	1831	1923	...	1930	...	2022	2040	2127	2114	2130	2222	2214	2322	...	2332	...
	▬		|	▬	|		|		|	|	|	▬		|						|		▬				
	2M		|	2M	|	2M	|	2M	|	|	|	2M		|		§2				|		§2				
lzano / Bozen d.	1502	...	1532	1602	1634	1701	1732	1802	1824e	1834	1834	1902	...	1932	2002	2032	...	...	...	2132	...	2232	...	...	...	...
iusa / Klausen d.	1525	...	1555	1625	|	1722	1755	1825	1847e	|	|	1925	...	1955	2025	2055	...	...	...	2157	...	2255	...	...	...	...
essanone / Brixen d.	1533	...	1603	1633	1704	1730	1803	1833	1856e	1904	1904	1933	...	2003	2033	2103	...	...	...	2207	...	2303	...	...	...	...
rtezza / Franzensfeste d.	1545	...	1615	1645	1715	1745	1815	1845	1905e	1915	1915	1945	...	2015	2045	2115	...	...	...	2216	...	2314	...	...	...	...
iteno / Sterzing d.	1603	...	1633	1703	|	1803	1833	1903	1923e	|	|	2003	...	2033	2103	2133	...	...	...	2234	...	...	...	...	...	...
ennero / Brenner 🏛 a.	1622	...	1652	1722	1748	1822	1852	1922	1944e	1948	1948	2022	...	2052	2122	2151	...	...	...	2252	...	...	...	...	...	...
ennero / Brenner 🏛 ▲ d.	...	...	...	...	1800	...	...	...	...	2000	2000	...	...	...	...	2154	...	...	...	...	...	...	...	...	...	...
sbruck Hbf ▲ a.	...	...	...	...	1836	...	...	...	...	2036	2036	...	...	...	...	2230	...	...	...	...	...	...	...	...	...	...
München Hbf **951** ■ a.	...	...	...	...	2025	...	...	...	...	2227	2227	...	...	...	...	...	...	...	...	...	...	...	...	...	...	...

Other stopping services **INNSBRUCK - BRENNERO / BRENNER** — 2nd class only

km		⚒						⚒															⚒		
0	**Innsbruck** Hbf d.	0522	0552	0622	0649	0749	...	0819	0849	0949	1049	1149	1249	1349	1449	1549	1649	1749	...	1849	1949	2100	2149	2253	2353
18	Matrei d.	0540	0610	0640	0706	0806	...	0836	0906	1006	1106	1206	1306	1406	1506	1606	1706	1806	...	1906	2006	2118	2206	2310	0010
23	Steinach in Tirol d.	0545	0615	0645	0711	0811	...	0841	0911	1011	1111	1211	1311	1411	1511	1611	1711	1811	...	1911	2011	2123	2211	2315	0015
37	**Brennero / Brenner** 🏛 a.	0602	0632	0659	0728	0828	...	0858	0928	1028	1128	1228	1328	1428	1528	1628	1728	1828	...	1928	2028	2137	2228	2332	0032

	⚒c	⚒c		⚒																				
ennero / Brenner 🏛 d.	0527	0558	0628	0658	0733	...	0833	0902	0933	1033	1133	...	1233	1333	1433	1533	1633	...	1733	1833	1933	2033	2154	2303
einach in Tirol d.	0546	0617	0647	0717	0750	...	0850	0917	0950	1050	1150	...	1250	1350	1450	1550	1650	...	1750	1850	1950	2050	2209	2320
trei d.	0550	0621	0651	0721	0754	...	0854	0921	0954	1054	1154	...	1254	1354	1454	1554	1654	...	1754	1854	1954	2054	2213	2324
sbruck Hbf a.	0607	0638	0708	0739	0811	...	0911	0938	1013	1111	1213	...	1311	1413	1511	1613	1711	...	1813	1911	2011	2111	2230	2341

NOTES CONTINUED FROM PREVIOUS PAGE.

- ⟨2⟩ Lienz - Fortezza - Bolzano - Merano.
- Also Ⓐ June 10 – 14, Sept. 2 - Dec. 13.
- Also Ⓐ June 10 – 14, Sept. 2 - Dec. 13. From Merano (Table **597**).
- To / from Merano (Table **597**).
- ①–⑤ only.
- ⑥⑦ only.
- Ⓐ only.
- Ⓒ only.

§ – Operated by *SAD* (for contact details see Table **598**).
♠ – Also available to passengers without reservation. Operator within Italy: LeNord.
▲ – For additional trains Brennero / Brenner - Innsbruck see panel belwo main table. Austrian holiday dates apply Brennero / Brenner - Innsbruck.

entino Trasporti

TRENTO - MALÉ - MEZZANA 595a

Service until June 21.

m		†	⚒	⚒	⚒	†	⚒	⚒	†	⚒	†	⚒	⚒	⚒	†	⚒	†	⚒	†	⚒	⚒	†	⚒			🚌⚒
0	**Trento** d.	0602	0611	0710	0810	0812	0931	1027	1030	1202	1233	1243	1326	1341	1343	1454	1456	1554	1625	1634	1718	1722	1727	1836	1932	2225
7	Mezzocorona Ferrovia ♠ d.	0628	0639	0742	0841	0838	0957	1054	1056	1230	1300	1311	1353	1408	1410	1521	1522	1620	1652	1700	1739	1749	1754	1903	1958	2252
2	Mezzolombardo d.	0635	0647	0756	0849	0845	1006	1102	1103	1238	1307	1319	1402	1416	1418	1529	1529	1631	1659	1708	1746	1756	1802	1911	2005	2300
5	Cles d.	0712	0727	0833	0927	0922	1042	1139	1140	1318	1344	1357	1435	1454	1453	1607	1606	1708	1736	1745	1819	1834	1840	1948	2041	2331
6	Malé d.	0738	0752	0859	0953	0947	1107	1205	1206	1347	1409	1421	1454	1522	1519	1638	1631	1736	1800	1810	1839	1858	1905	2013	2105	2355
6	**Mezzana** a.	0754	...	0915	1009	1003	1123	1221	1222	1406	1425	...	...	1540	1535	1654	1647	1752	...	...	1856	...	...	...	...	...

	⚒	†	⚒	⚒	⚒	⚒	†	⚒	⚒	†	⚒	⚒	†	⚒	⚒	†	⚒	⚒	†	⚒	†	⚒	⚒	†	⚒	†
zzana d.	...	...	0611	...	0656	...	0814	0925	1021	...	1136	1231	1245	1345	1423	1444	...	...	1614	1619	1713	1716	1806	...	1946	...
é d.	0528	0555	0630	0644	0716	0823	0832	0943	1039	1152	1154	1252	1303	1407	1441	1503	1509	1530	1633	1639	1731	1735	1825	1829	1958	2001
s d.	0551	0619	0649	0710	0756	0849	0856	1008	1105	1218	1223	1320	1327	1434	1509	1529	1530	1554	1658	1707	1757	1801	1852	1854	2023	2026
zzolombardo a.	0625	0655	0721	0747	0830	0926	0932	1043	1140	1252	1300	1359	1402	1512	1545	1604	1603	1630	1735	1745	1833	1839	1931	1930	2058	2101
zzocorona Ferrovia ♠ d.	0633	0703	0727	0757	0840	0935	0940	1053	1149	1301	1310	1409	1411	1522	1554	1612	1609	1639	1743	1755	1842	1849	1939	1938	2106	2109
nto a.	0700	0729	0749	0826	0906	1002	1006	1121	1216	1327	1338	1436	1437	1547	1620	1639	1630	1705	1810	1822	1908	1916	2005	2004	2132	2136

- Adjacent to Mezzocorona FS station.

Operator: Trentino Trasporti Esercizio S.p.a, Via Innsbruck 65, 38121 Trento.
✆ +39 0 461 821000, fax +39 0 461 031407.

596 FORTEZZA / FRANZENSFESTE - S. CANDIDO / INNICHEN - LIENZ

2nd class only

Subject to alteration Sillian - Lienz and v.v. on Ⓐ until July 6.

km																								
		Ⓐ																Ⓒ						
0	**Fortezza / Franzensfeste** △ d.	0547	0650	0750	...	0850	0950	1050	...	1150	1250	1350	...	1450	1550	1650	...	1750	1850	...	1950	2050	...	...
33	Brunico / Bruneck △ d.	0630	0730	0830	...	0930	1030	1130	...	1230	1330	1430	...	1530	1630	1730	...	1830	1930	...	2030	2130	...	...
61	Dobbiaco / Toblach △ d.	0706	0806	0906	...	1006	1106	1206	...	1306	1406	1506	...	1606	1706	1806	...	1906	2006	...	2106	2206	...	...
65	**S. Candido / Innichen** △ a.	0710	0810	0910	...	1010	1110	1210	...	1310	1410	1510	...	1610	1710	1810	...	1910	2010	...	2110	2210	...	...
65	**S. Candido / Innichen** 🏨 d.	0716	0816	0916	...	1016	1116	1216	...	1316	1416	1516	...	1616	1716	1816	...	1916	2016	...	...	...	...	...
78	Sillian 🏨 d.	0730	0830	0930	...	1030	1130	1230	...	1330	1430	1530	...	1630	1730	1830	...	1930	2030	...	...	...	...	...
108	**Lienz** a.	0809	0909	1009	...	1109	1209	1309	...	1409	1509	1609	...	1709	1809	1909	...	2009	2109	...	...	...	...	...

									Ⓐ	Ⓒ												
																			♡			
Lienz d.	0550	0650	0750	...	0850	0950	1050	...	...	1150	1250	...	1350	1450	1550	...	1650	1750	...	1850	1950	...	...
Sillian d.	0630	0730	0830	...	0930	1030	1130	...	...	1230	1330	...	1430	1530	1630	...	1730	1830	...	1930	2030	...	...
S. Candido / Innichen 🏨 a.	0643	0743	0843	...	0943	1043	1143	...	...	1243	1343	...	1443	1543	1643	...	1743	1843	...	1943	2043	...	...
S. Candido / Innichen 🏨 △ d.	0650	0750	0850	...	0950	1050	1150	...	1250	1250	1350	...	1450	1550	1650	...	1750	1850	...	1950	2050	...	...
Dobbiaco / Toblach △ d.	0655	0755	0855	...	0955	1055	1155	...	1255	1255	1355	...	1455	1555	1655	...	1755	1855	...	1955	2055	...	...
Brunico / Bruneck △ d.	0731	0831	0931	...	1031	1131	1231	...	1331	1331	1431	...	1531	1631	1731	...	1831	1931	...	2031	2131	...	...
Fortezza / Franzensfeste △ a.	0810	0910	1010	...	1110	1210	1310	...	1410	1410	1510	...	1610	1710	1810	...	1910	2010	...	2110	2210	...	...

△ – Additional services **Fortezza / Franzensfeste - S. Candido / Innichen** and v.v.:
From Fortezza / Franzensfeste at 0617 Ⓐ, 0720 Ⓐ 0820 Ⓐ, 1020 Ⓐ, 1120 Ⓐ, 1220 Ⓐ, 1320 Ⓐ, 1420 Ⓐ, 1520 Ⓐ, 1620 Ⓐ, 1720 Ⓐ, 1920 Ⓐ.
From S. Candido / Innichen at 0550 Ⓐ, 0620 Ⓐ, 0720 Ⓐ, 0820 Ⓐ, 0920 Ⓐ, 1020 Ⓐ, 1220 Ⓐ, 1320 Ⓐ, 1420 Ⓐ, 1520 Ⓐ, 1620 Ⓐ, 1720 Ⓐ.

♡ – 2 Lienz - Fortezza - Bolzano - Merano.

Operators: *SAD*: Fortezza - S. Candido; *ÖBB*: S. Candido - Lienz.

597 BOLZANO / BOZEN - MERANO / MERAN

2nd class only

km																									
		⚒	⚒	⚒		⚒	⚒	⚒§		⚒	Ⓐ§	Ⓒ	⚒§	ⒸA	⚒		⚒§		⚒				⚒§		⚒
	Brennero **595** d.	...	...	0536	...	...	0638	0702	0738	...	...	0838	...	0938	...	1038	...	1138	...	1238	...	1338	...	1438	..
0	**Bolzano / Bozen** d.	0547	0626	0657	0657	0735	0801	0835	0901	0935	1001	1001	1035	1101	1135	1201	1235	1301	1335	1401	...	1501	1535	1601	163
32	**Merano / Meran** a.	0633	0707	0743	0743	0815	0845	0915	0945	1015	1045	1045	1115	1145	1215	1245	1315	1345	1415	1445	...	1545	1615	1645	17

		⚒§		⚒§		⚒§			L§	
Brennero **595** d.	1538	...	1638	...	1738	...	1838	1938	...	...
Bolzano / Bozen d.	1701	1735	1801	1835	1901	1935	2001	2101	2203	...
Merano / Meran a.	1745	1815	1845	1914	1944	2014	2044	2144	2247	...

	⚒	⚒	Ⓐ§		⚒		⚒		⚒§	Ⓒ
Merano / Meran d.	0602	0635	0656	0713	0745	0816	0846	0916	0946	10
Bolzano / Bozen a.	0648	0720	0732	0759	0826	0859	0926	0959	1026	10
Brennero **595** a.	0822	...	...	0922	...	1022	...	1122	...	12

	⚒	⑥A	⚒§		⚒		⚒§		⚒		⚒§			⚒§		⚒§		⚒§		§		⚒§	†		
Merano / Meran d.	1046	1116	1146	1216	1246	1316	1346	1416	1446	1516	1546	...	1616	1646	1716	1746	1816	1846	1916	1946	...	2046	2046	2146	..
Bolzano / Bozen a.	1126	1159	1226	1259	1326	1359	1426	1459	1526	1559	1626	...	1659	1726	1759	1826	1859	1926	1957	2027	...	2126	2126	2227	..
Brennero **595** a.	...	1322	...	1422	...	1522	...	1622	...	1722	...	...	1822	...	1922	...	2022	...	...	2151	...	...	...	...	..

A – Also Ⓐ June 10 – 14, Sept. 2 - Dec. 13.

L – 2 Lienz - Fortezza - Bolzano - Merano.

§ – Operated by *SAD* (for contact details see Table 59

598 MERANO / MERAN - MALLES / MALS

2nd class only SA

km							
		⚒			and		
0	**Merano / Meran** d.	0538	0638	0716	hourly	1916	1946 2046 2146 2250 ...
60	**Malles / Mals** a.	0654	0754	0838	until	2038	2055 2155 2255 2358 ...

	⚒				and		
Malles / Mals d.	0520	0542	0616	0720	hourly	1820	1920 2020 2120 ..
Merano / Meran a.	0630	0654	0732	0843	until	1943	2039 2139 2239 ..

Additional services operate.

Trains call at Silandro / Schlanders 46 – 54 minutes after leaving Merano, 24–28 minutes after leaving Malles.

Ferrovia della Val Venosta Operator: Servizi Autobus Dolomiti (SAD), Via Conciapelli 60, I - 39100 Bolzan
✆ +39 0471 97 12 59, fax +39 0471 97 00 42.

599 ITALIAN LAKES (LAGO MAGGIORE, GARDA, COMO)

Lago Maggiore: ⛴ services link Arona, Stresa, Baveno, Laveno, Luino and Locarno throughout the year on an irregular schedule.
Operator: Navigazione sul Lago Maggiore, P. le Baracca 1, 28041 Arona, Italy. ✆ +39 (0)322 233 200, fax: +39 (0)322 249 530. www.navigazionelaghi.it

Lago di Garda: ⛴ services link Desenzano, Peschiera, Garda, Salo, Gardone and Riva, (April to October 7 only), on an irregular schedule with a very limited service at other times.
Operator: Navigazione sul Lago di Garda, Piazza Matteotti 1, 25015 Desenzano del Garda, Italy. ✆ +39 (0)30 914 9511, fax: +39 (0)30 914 9520. www.navigazionelaghi.it

Lago di Como: ⛴ services link Como, Bellagio, Menaggio, Varenna, Bellano and Colico (April to September only) on an irregular schedule.
Operator: Navigazione Lago di Como, Via Per Cernobbio 18, 22100 Como, Italy. ✆ +39 (0)31 579 211, fax: +39 (0)31 570 080. www.navigazionelaghi.it

Hydrofoil service: May 26 - Oct. 6, 2019

	⚒		†	⚒	⚒	†	⚒	†	⚒	⚒	
Como d.	0733	0900	1110	1215	1330	1400	1420	1615	1710	1810	1920
Tremezzo d.	0819r	0941	1153	1252	1419	1449	1457	1652	1746	1857	1957
Bellagio d.	0813r	0950	1200	1300	1439r	1459	1504	1658	1752	1904	2003
Menaggio d.	0808	0958	1207	1307	1430	1507	1511	1704	1758	1919	2009
Bellano d.	...	1008	1216	...	1455	1523	...	1713	1808	2018	2021
Colico a.	...	1038	1243	...	1528	1555	...	1740	...	2043	2044

	⚒	⚒	†	⚒		⚒	†	⚒		†	⚒
Colico d.	0606	...	0707	...	1039	...	1356	...	1558	1741	..
Bellano d.	0630	...	0738	...	1108	...	1424	...	1638	1806	18
Menaggio d.	0641	0703	0748	0808	1118	1307	1435	1511	1654	1814	18
Bellagio d.	0647	0712	0757	0814	1131	1323	1442	1525	1704	1820	18
Tremezzo d.	0653	0718	0803	0820	1138	1328	1448	1531	1710	1826	18
Como a.	0730	0805	0850	0857	1225	1406	1525	1607	1800	1905	19

r – Via Menaggio.

599a LAKE GARDA 🚌 services

Subject to confirmatio

Desenzano FS → Salo *+0h33* → Gardone *+0h38* → Maderno *+0h46* → Toscolano *+0h49* → Gargnano *+1h00* → Limone *+1h32* → **Riva** *+1h50*.
Route LN027. From Desenzano: 0600, 0810, 1135, 1330, 1620, 1830.

Riva → Limone *+0h18* → Gargnano *+0h50* → Toscolano *+1h01* → Maderno *+1h04* Gardone *+1h12* → Salo *+1h17* → **Desenzano** FS *+1h50*.
Route LN027. From Riva: 0540, 0810, 0910, 1245, 1510, 1710.

Verona P N → **Peschiera** FS *+0h53* → Lazise *+ 1h17* → Bardolino *+1h29* → **Garda** *+ 1h39*.
Route 164. From Verona: 0541, 0741, 0841 and hourly until 2041.

Garda → Bardolino *+0h10* → Lazise *+0h22* → **Peschiera** FS *+0h46* → **Verona P N** *+ 1h34*.
Route 164. From Garda: 0620, 0810, 0910 and hourly until 2010.

Verona P N → Lazise *+0h54* → Bardolino *+1h06* → **Garda** *+1h16*.
Route 163. From Verona: 0641, 0811, 1011, 1211, 1411, 1611, 1811, 2011.

Garda → Bardolino *+0h10* → Lazise *+0h22* → **Verona P N** *+1h16*.
Route 163. From Garda: 0615, 0645, 0840, 1040, 1240, 1440, 1640, 1840, 2040.

Garda → Torri del Benaco *+0h14* → Porto Brenzone *+0h35* → Malcesine *+ 0h46* → Torbole *+1h06* → **Riva** *+1h18*
Route 484. From Garda: 0625, 0725 and hourly until 2025.

Riva → Torbole *+0h15* → Malcesine *+ 0h35* → Porto Brenzone *+0h48* → Torri del Benaco *+1h09* → **Garda** *+1h22*.
Route 484. From Riva: 0510, 0616, 0746, 0843, 0943 and hourly until 1743, then 1913, 20

Services from Verona Porta Nuova bus station, and Peschiera and Desenzano railway stations (Table **605**).

Operator: Azienda Transporti Verona s.r.l., Lungadige Galtarossa 5, 37133 Verona.
✆ 045 8057811, fax 045 8057800.

Additional local services run serving the lakeside resorts.

Other operators: Brescia Transporti ✆ 030 44061, fax 030 3754505;
Trentino Transporti ✆ 0461 821000, fax 0461 031407.

HIGH-SPEED SERVICES 600

Operator: Nuovo Trasporto Viaggiatori (NTV)

ll trains Ⓡ Club Executive, Prima, Comfort and Smart class. *Trenitalia* tickets and passes not valid www.italotreno.it

TORINO - MILANO - ROMA - NAPOLI

	ITA 9901	*ITA* 9969 9971	*ITA* 9907	*ITA* 9973	*ITA* 8931	*ITA* 9911	*ITA* 9975	*ITA* 8933 A	*ITA* 8905	*ITA* 9915 9917	*ITA* 9977	*ITA* 9919	*ITA* 8909	*ITA* 9923 9925	*ITA* 9981	*ITA* 8911	*ITA* 9927	*ITA* 9931	*ITA* 9985	*ITA* 8915	*ITA* 9935	*ITA* 8939 ④–① C	*ITA* 8917	*ITA* 9939	*ITA* 9943	*ITA* 9991	*ITA* 8961 8963
rino Porta Nuova d.	...	...	...	0605	...	...	...	...	...	...	...	0810	...	0925	...	...	...	...	1205	...	...	...	...	...	1410	1450	...
rino Porta Susa d.	...	...	...	0615	...	...	...	...	...	...	...	0820	...	0935	...	...	...	...	1215	...	...	...	...	...	1420	1500	...
lano Centrale a.	...	...	...	0705	...	...	...	...	...	...	...	0910	...	1025	...	...	...	...	1305	...	...	...	...	...	1507	1550	...
lano Centrale d.	...	0600	0625	0715	...	0735	0815	...	...	0835	0910	0935	...	1035	1115	...	1135	1235	1315	...	1335	...	...	1435	1535	1610	...
lano Rogoredo d.	...	|	0637	0724	...	0745	0824	...	...	0845	0922	0945	...	1045	1124	...	1145	1248	1324	...	1345	...	...	1445	1545	1621	...
ggio Emilia ⊖ d.	...	0641	0712	|	...	0823	|	...	...	0923	|	1023	...	1123	|	...	1223	1323	|	...	1423	...	...	1523	1623	|	...
Venezia Santa Lucia d.	...	|	|	|	...	|	|	...	0800	|	|	|	1000	|	|	1100	|	|	|	1300	|	...	1400	|	|	|	1600
Venezia Mestre d.	...	|	|	|	...	|	|	...	0812	|	|	|	1012	|	|	1112	|	|	|	1312	|	...	1412	|	|	|	1612
Padova d.	...	|	|	|	...	|	|	...	0828	|	|	|	1028	|	|	1128	|	|	|	1328	|	...	1428	|	|	|	1628
Ferrara d.	...	|	|	|	...	|	|	...	|	|	|	|	1059	|	|	1159	|	|	|	|	|	...	1459	|	|	|	1659
Brescia d.	...	|	|	|	0627	|	|	...	|	|	|	|	|	|	|	|	|	|	|	|	|	...	|	|	|	|	|
Bolzano d.	...	|	|	|	|	|	|	0641	|	|	|	|	|	|	|	|	|	|	|	|	|	1241	|	|	|	|	|
Verona Porta Nuova d.	...	|	|	|	0717	|	|	0817	|	|	|	|	|	|	|	|	|	|	|	|	|	1417	|	|	|	|	|
logna Centrale ❖ d.	...	|	0740	|	0810	0850	|	0910	0930	0950	1015	1050	1130	1150	|	1230	1250	1350	|	1430	1450	1510	1530	1550	1650	1715	1730
enze SMN a.	...	|	0815	|	0844	0925	|	0944	1005	1025	|	1125	1205	1225	|	1305	1325	1425	|	1505	1525	1244	1605	1625	1725	|	1805
enze SMN d.	...	|	0823	|	0852	0933	|	0952	1013	1033	|	1133	1213	1233	|	1313	1333	1433	|	1513	1533	1552	1613	1633	1733	|	1813
ma Tiburtina a.	...	|	0943	1004	1017	1053	1104	|	1133	1153	|	1253	1333	1353	1404	1433	1453	1553	1604	1633	1653	1413	1733	1753	1853	|	1933
ma Termini a.	...	0859	0955	1014	1025	1105	1113	1125	1146	1205	1214	1305	1345	1405	1414	1445	1505	1605	1614	1645	1705	1725	1746	1805	1905	1914	1945
ma Termini d.	0740	0911	1004	...	1035	1115	...	...	1203	1215	...	1315	...	1415	...	1500	1518	...	...	...	1715	1735	...	...	1915	1925	1958
poli Afragola d.	0837	|	|	...	|	1212	...	...	|	1311	...	1412	...	|	...	|	1612	...	...	...	1812	|	...	...	|	|	|
poli Centrale a.	0850	1020	1110	...	1145	1227	...	...	1320	1327	...	1425	...	1523	...	1620	1630	...	...	...	1830	1850	...	...	2025	2035	2105
poli Centrale d.	...	1035	...	...	...	...	...	...	...	1337	...	...	...	1537	...	...	...	...	...	...	...	1913	...	...	...	...	2125
lerno a.	...	1116	...	...	...	...	...	...	...	1416	...	...	...	1616	...	...	...	...	...	...	...	2000	...	...	...	...	2209

	ITA 9947	*ITA* 9993	*ITA* 9951 9953	*ITA* 9995	*ITA* 8945 8947	*ITA* 8925	*ITA* 9955	*ITA* 9997	*ITA* 8927	*ITA* 9959	*ITA* 9963 Ⓑ
rino Porta Nuova d.	...	...	1625	...	...	...	...	1800	...	...	1925
rino Porta Susa d.	...	...	1635	...	...	...	...	1810	...	...	1935
ano Centrale a.	...	...	1725	...	...	...	...	1857	...	...	2025
ano Centrale d.	1635	1710	1735	1815	...	...	1837	1915	...	1955	2035
ano Rogoredo d.	1645	1723	1747	1824	...	...	1849	1924	...	2005	|
ggio Emilia ⊖ d.	1723	|	1826	|	...	...	1923	|	...	2040	|
Venezia Santa Lucia d.	|	|	|	|	...	1800	|	|	1900	|	|
Venezia Mestre d.	|	|	|	|	...	1812	|	|	1912	|	|
Padova d.	|	|	|	|	...	1828	|	|	1928	|	|
Ferrara d.	|	|	|	|	...	1859	|	|	|	|	|
Brescia d.	|	|	|	|	1727	|	|	|	|	|	|
Bolzano d.	|	|	|	|	|	|	|	|	|	|	|
Verona Porta Nuova d.	|	|	|	|	1817	|	|	|	|	|	|
logna Centrale ❖ d.	1750	1815	1850	|	1910	1930	1950	|	2030	2110	2140
enze SMN a.	1825	|	1925	|	1944	2005	2025	|	2105	2145	2215
enze SMN d.	1833	|	1933	|	1952	2013	2033	|	2113	2153	2223
ma Tiburtina a.	1953	|	2053	2104	2117	2133	2153	2204	2233	2316	2343
ma Termini a.	2005	2014	2105	2114	2125	2145	2205	2214	2245	2325	2355
ma Termini d.	2015	...	2115	2125	2135	2200	2215	...	...	...	...
poli Afragola d.	2112	...	2214	|	|	|	2312	...	...	...	...
poli Centrale a.	2125	...	2225	2235	2245	2310	2330	...	...	...	...
poli Centrale d.	...	...	2238	...	2255	...	...	...	...	...	...
erno a.	...	...	2315	...	2332	...	...	...	...	...	...

	ITA 9900	*ITA* 9902 ①–⑥	*ITA* 8902	*ITA* 9906	*ITA* 9972	*ITA* 8932 ④–① B	*ITA* 9910	*ITA* 9974	*ITA* 8906	*ITA* 9914 9916	*ITA* 9976
Salerno d.	...	...	...	...	...	...	...	...	...	0631	...
Napoli Centrale a.	...	...	...	...	...	...	...	...	...	0710	...
Napoli Centrale d.	...	...	...	...	...	0550	0615	0644	0655	0720	0745
Napoli Afragola d.	...	...	...	...	...	0603	|	0659	|	0734	|
Roma Termini a.	...	...	...	...	...	0705	0725	0755	0805	0830	0855
Roma Termini d.	...	0545	0615	0645	0710	0715	0745	0810	0815	0845	0910
Roma Tiburtina d.	...	0553	0625	0655	0719	0725	0755	0819	0825	0855	0919
Firenze SMN a.	...	0717	0746	0817	|	0846	0917	|	0946	1017	|
Firenze SMN d.	...	0725	0754	0825	|	0854	0925	|	0954	1025	|
Bologna Centrale ❖ d.	...	0803	0833	0903	|	0933	1003	|	1033	1103	|
Verona Porta Nuova a.	...	|	|	|	|	1024	|	|	|	|	|
Bolzano d.	...	|	|	|	|	1200	|	|	|	|	|
Brescia a.	...	|	|	|	|	...	|	|	|	|	|
Ferrara a.	...	|	0857	|	|	...	|	|	1057	|	|
Padova a.	...	|	0932	|	|	...	|	|	1133	|	|
Venezia Mestre a.	...	|	0948	|	|	...	|	|	1148	|	|
Venezia Santa Lucia a.	...	|	1000	|	|	...	|	|	1200	|	|
Reggio Emilia ⊖ d.	...	0824	...	0924	|	...	1024	|	...	1124	|
Milano Rogoredo a.	...	0905	...	1003	0957	...	1103	1057	...	1203	1157
Milano Centrale a.	...	0916	...	1015	1009	...	1115	1109	...	1215	1209
Milano Centrale d.	0755	0925	...	...	...	...	1127	...	...	1228	...
Torino Porta Susa a.	0843	1014	...	...	...	...	1215	...	...	1316	...
Torino Porta Nuova a.	0855	1026	...	...	...	...	1227	...	...	1328	...

	ITA 8908	*ITA* 9918 9920	*ITA* 9922	*ITA* 9980	*ITA* 8962 8964	*ITA* 9926	*ITA* 8938	*ITA* 9932	*ITA* 9984	*ITA* 9934	*ITA* 8918	*ITA* 9938	*ITA* 8920	*ITA* 9942 9944	*ITA* 9990	*ITA* 8948 D	*ITA* 9946	*ITA* 9992	*ITA* 8924	*ITA* 9950 9952	*ITA* 9994	*ITA* 8926	*ITA* 9954	*ITA* 9996	*ITA* 8952	*ITA* 9956 9958	*ITA* 9960 b
lerno d.	...	0737	...	...	0853	...	...	...	...	...	...	...	...	1330	...	...	...	...	...	1530	...	...	...	...	...	1730	...
poli Centrale a.	...	0815	...	...	0935	...	...	...	...	...	...	...	...	1410	...	...	...	...	...	1610	...	...	...	...	...	1805	...
poli Centrale d.	0750	0825	0925	...	0945	...	...	1125	...	1223	...	1323	1355	1420	...	...	...	1548	...	1625	...	...	1725	...	1748	1825	1918
poli Afragola d.	|	|	|	...	0958	...	...	|	...	|	...	1339	|	1434	...	...	...	|	...	|	...	...	1739	...	|	1839	1932
ma Termini a.	0900	0935	1035	...	1058	...	...	1235	...	1335	...	1435	1505	1530	...	...	...	1655	...	1735	...	...	1835	...	1858	1935	2028
ma Termini d.	0915	0945	1045	1110	1115	1145	1215	1245	1310	1345	1415	1445	1515	1545	1610	1615	1645	1710	1715	1745	1810	1815	1845	1910	1915	1950	2045
ma Tiburtina d.	0925	0955	1055	1118	1125	1155	1225	1255	1318	1355	1425	1455	1525	1555	1625	1625	1655	1718	|	1755	1819	1825	1855	1918	1925	|	2055
enze SMN a.	1046	1117	1217	|	1246	1317	1346	1417	|	1517	1546	1617	1646	1717	1619	1746	1817	|	1846	1917	|	1946	2017	|	2046	2117	2217
enze SMN d.	1054	1125	1225	|	1254	1325	1354	1425	|	1525	1554	1625	1654	1725	|	1754	1825	|	1854	1925	|	1954	2025	|	2054	2125	2225
logna Centrale ❖ d.	1133	1203	1303	|	1333	1403	1433	1503	|	1603	1633	1703	1733	1803	|	1833	1903	|	1933	2003	|	2033	2103	|	2133	2203	2303
Verona Porta Nuova a.	|	|	|	|	|	|	1526	|	|	|	|	|	|	|	|	1923	|	|	|	|	|	|	|	|	2223	|	|
Bolzano a.	|	|	|	|	|	|	|	|	|	|	|	|	|	|	|	2100	|	|	|	|	|	|	|	|	|	|	|
Brescia a.	|	|	|	|	|	|	1616	|	|	|	|	|	|	|	|	...	|	|	|	|	|	|	|	|	2316	|	|
Ferrara a.	|	|	|	|	1357	|	...	|	|	|	|	|	1757	|	|	...	|	|	|	|	|	2057	|	|	...	|	|
Padova a.	1232	|	|	|	1432	|	...	|	|	|	1733	|	1832	|	|	...	|	|	2027	|	|	2132	|	|	...	|	|
enezia Mestre a.	1248	|	|	|	1448	|	...	|	|	|	1748	|	1848	|	|	...	|	|	2042	|	|	2148	|	|	...	|	|
enezia Santa Lucia a.	1300	|	|	|	1500	|	...	|	|	|	1800	|	1900	|	|	...	|	|	2054	|	|	2200	|	|	...	|	|
ggio Emilia ⊖ d.	...	1224	1324	|	...	1424	...	1524	|	1624	...	|	...	1824	|	...	1924	|	...	2024	|	...	2124	|	...	2226	2324
ano Rogoredo a.	...	1303	1403	1357	...	1503	...	1603	1557	1703	...	1754	...	1903	1857	...	2003	1957	...	2103	2057	...	2203	2157	...	2303	0003
ano Centrale a.	...	1315	1415	1409	...	1515	...	1615	1609	1715	...	1807	...	1918	1909	...	2017	2009	...	2115	2109	...	2215	2209	...	2315	0015
ano Centrale d.	...	...	1428	...	...	1525	...	...	...	1740	...	...	...	...	...	...	2028	...	...	2124	...	...	...	2223	...	...	...
ino Porta Susa a.	...	...	1516	...	...	1614	...	...	...	1828	...	...	...	...	...	...	2116	...	...	2212	...	...	...	2311	...	...	...
ino Porta Nuova a.	...	...	1528	...	...	1625	...	...	...	1840	...	...	...	...	...	...	2128	...	...	2224	...	...	...	2323	...	...	...

TORINO - MILANO - VENEZIA

	ITA 8971	*ITA* 8973 8975	*ITA* 8981		*ITA* 8985		*ITA* 8987	*ITA* 8993 8991	*ITA* 8995	
ino Porta Nuova d.	...	0725	1020	...	1225	...	1325	...	...	...
ino Porta Susa d.	...	0735	1030	...	1235	...	1335	...	...	...
ano Centrale d.	0634	0834	1134	...	1334	...	1434	1634	1837	...
scia d.	0713	0913	1213	...	1413	...	1513	1713	1913	...
senzano-Sirmione d.	|	0937	|	...	1427	...	|	1727	|	...
schiera del Garda d.	0734	|	1234	...	|	...	1534	|	1934	...
rona Porta Nuova d.	0750	0950	1250	...	1450	...	1550	1750	1950	...
enza d.	0817	1017	1317	...	1517	...	1617	1820	2016	...
dova d.	0834	1034	1334	...	1534	...	1634	1840	2034	...
nezia Mestre a.	0847	1047	1347	...	1547	...	1647	1853	2051	...
nezia Santa Lucia a.	0859	1059	1359	...	1559	...	1659	1905	2103	...

	ITA 8970		*ITA* 8972		*ITA* 8976	*ITA* 8980 8982	*ITA* 8988		*ITA* 8992	*ITA* 8996 8998
Venezia Santa Lucia d.	0601	...	0701	...	0901	1201	1501	...	1701	2001
Venezia Mestre d.	0613	...	0713	...	0913	1213	1513	...	1713	2013
Padova d.	0628	...	0730	...	0928	1228	1528	...	1728	2028
Vicenza d.	0645	...	0745	...	0945	1245	1545	...	1745	2045
Verona Porta Nuova d.	0712	...	0812	...	1012	1312	1612	...	1812	2112
Peschiera del Garda d.	0726	...	|	...	1026	|	1626	...	|	2126
Desenzano-Sirmione d.	|	...	0833	...	|	1333	|	...	1833	|
Brescia a.	0747	...	0847	...	1047	1347	1647	...	1847	2147
Milano Centrale a.	0826	...	0927	...	1126	1425	1726	...	1930	2226
Torino Porta Susa a.	0928	...	1028	...	1228	...	...	...	2038a	...
Torino Porta Nuova a.	0940	...	1040	...	1240	...	...	...	2050a	...

- Also calls at Trento d. 0712 and Rovereto d. 0727.
- Also calls at Roverto a. 1112 and Trento a. 1126.
- Also calls at Trento d. 1312 and Rovereto d. 1327.
- Also calls at Roverto a. 2012 and Trento a. 2026.

a – From May 1.
b – Ⓑ from May 1.

⊖ – Reggio Emilia Mediopadana.
❖ – Most services use underground platforms 16–19; allow a minimum of 10 minutes for connecting services from/to the main station.

600 HIGH-SPEED SERVICES

All trains Ⓡ and 🍷 Operator: Trenitalia

km		FR	FR	FR	FR	FR	FR	FA	FR	FR	FR	FA	FA	FR	FR	FR	FR	FR	FR	FR	FR	FR	FR	FR	FR
		9681	9683	9685	9601	9503	9605	8551	9505	9505	9607	8503	9403	9609*	9509*	9613	9707	8505	9615	9301	9407	9521	9709	9305	961
				①–⑥	Ⓐ						Ⓐ		①–⑥			⚒				Ⓐ					Ⓐ
		a		a		M	Bc	M	b	c		Y	Za		d		ⒶT	E		h	Z	e	V		
0	**Torino** Porta Nuova d.	...	...	...	...	...	...	...	...	...	...	...	...	0550	...	...	0635	...	...	0620	...	0700	0705	0720	...
6	Torino Porta Susa d.	...	...	...	...	...	...	...	...	...	...	...	...	0600u	...	...	0645u	...	...	0630u	...	0710u	0715u	0730u	...
148	**Milano** Centrale a.	...	...	...	...	...	...	...	...	...	...	...	...	0650	...	...	0735	...	...	|	...	0800	0805	|	...
148	**Milano** Centrale d.	...	...	...	0520	0550	0608	...	0610	0615	0630	...	...	0700	0720	0730	...	...	0800	|	...	0820	...	|	083
	Milano Porta Garibaldi d.	...	...	...	|	|	|	...	|	|	|	...	...	|	|	|	...	...	|	0718	...	|	...	0818	|
158	Milano Rogoredo d.	...	...	...	0532	0601	|	...	0620	|	|	...	...	0709	|	|	...	...	|	0735	...	|	...	0835	|
299	Reggio Emilia AV d.	...	...	...	0609	|	0654	...	0701	0701	|	...	...	|	|	|	...	...	|	0811	...	|	...	0911	|
	Verona Porta Nuova d.	...	...	...	|	|	|	...	|	|	|	0652	...	|	|	|	...	0752	|	|	...	|	...	|	|
363	**Bologna** Centrale ✣ a.	...	...	...	0630	0802	|	...	0719	0719	0732	0742	...	|	0819	0832	...	0842	|	0837	...	0919	...	0937	093
363	**Bologna** Centrale ✣ d.	...	...	...	0633	0805	|	0710	0722	0722	0735	0745	0755	|	0822	0835	...	0845	|	0840	0855	0922	...	0940	093
455	**Firenze** SMN a.	...	...	...	|	0844	|	0750	0800	0800	|	|	0835	|	0900	|	...	|	|	0915	0935	1000	...	1020	|
455	**Firenze** SMN d.	...	...	0610	|	0853	|	0759	0813	0813	|	|	0844	|	0913	|	...	|	|	0924	0943	1013	...	1029	|
	Firenze Campo di Marte d.	...	...	|	|	|	|	|	|	|	|	0831	|	|	|	|	...	0931	|	|	|	|	...	|	|
	Arezzo d.	...	...	|	|	|	|	0834	|	|	|	|	|	|	|	|	...	|	|	|	|	|	...	|	|
	Roma Tiburtina a.	...	...	|	|	1016s	|	0941s	0936	0936	|	|	1008s	0956	1035	|	...	|	|	1043s	1108	1136	...	1151	|
716	**Roma** Termini a.	...	...	0740	0837	1027	0922	0953	0947	0947	0937	0953	1018	1007	1047	1037	...	1053	1103	1055	1117	1147	...	|	113
716	**Roma** Termini d.	0700	0735	0755	0848	...	0933	...	0958	0958	...	...	...	1018	1057	1048	...	...	...	...	1133	1158	...	|	114
	Napoli Afragola a.	|	|	0848	0940	...	|	...	1052	1052	...	...	...	|	1152s	1143s	...	...	...	...	|	1254	...	|	|
938	**Napoli** Centrale a.	0810	0845	0905	|	...	1043	...	1108	1108	...	...	...	1128	1208	1158	...	...	...	...	1243	1310	...	1300	125
938	**Napoli** Centrale d.	...	...	...	|	...	...	...	1118	1118	...	...	...	...	...	...	...	...	...	...	...	...	...	1311	...
988	Salerno a.	...	...	...	1013	...	...	...	1158	1158	...	...	...	...	...	...	...	...	...	...	...	...	...	1352	...

km		FA	FR	FA	FR	FR	FR	FR	FR	FR	FA	FR	FR	FR	FR	FR	FR	FR	FR	FR	FR	FA	FR	FA	FA
		8507	9619	8413	9409	9525	9713	9621	9309	9623	8419	9413	9529	9717	9591	9887*	9627	9419	9533	9629	9723	8511	9631	8427	842
								⚒				Ⓐ	Ⓐ	Ⓒ	Ⓒ					Ⓐ			⚒		
		Y		T	Uj		V				Z	Z	d	Te	e	Lq		Z			V	C		Z	Z
	Torino Porta Nuova d.	...	0750	...	...	0800	0805	...	0820	...	...	...	0905	0905	...	0920	0950	...	...	...	1033	...	...	...	...
	Torino Porta Susa d.	...	0800u	...	...	0810	0815u	...	0830u	...	...	...	0915	0915u	...	0930u	1000u	...	...	...	1043u	...	...	...	...
	Milano Centrale a.	...	0850	...	...	0900	0907	...	|	...	...	...	1005	1005	...	|	1050	...	...	...	1133	...	...	...	...
	Milano Centrale d.	...	0900	...	...	0920	...	0930	|	1000	...	...	1015	...	1020	|	1100	...	1120	1130	...	...	1200	...	...
	Milano Porta Garibaldi d.	...	|	...	...	|	...	|	0918	|	...	...	|	...	|	1020	|	...	|	|	...	...	|	...	...
	Milano Rogoredo d.	...	0909	...	...	|	...	|	0935	|	...	...	|	...	|	1038	1109	...	|	|	...	...	|	...	...
	Reggio Emilia AV d.	...	|	...	...	|	...	|	1011	|	...	...	1101	...	|	1116	|	...	|	|	...	...	|	...	...
0	**Verona** Porta Nuova d.	0852	|	...	...	|	...	|	|	|	...	...	|	...	|	|	|	...	|	|	...	1152	|	...	...
114	**Bologna** Centrale ✣ a.	0942	|	...	...	1019	...	1032	1037	|	...	...	1119	...	1119	1142	|	...	1219	1232	...	1242	|	...	...
—	**Bologna** Centrale ✣ d.	0945	|	0955	1005	1022	...	1035	1040	|	1055	1105	1122	...	1122	...	|	1155	1222	1235	...	1245	|	1255	130
	Firenze SMN a.	|	|	1035	1044	1100	...	|	1120	|	1130	1144	1200	...	1200	...	|	1235	1300	|	...	|	|	1335	134
0	**Firenze** SMN d.	|	|	1043	1052	1113	...	|	1129	|	1138	1152	1213	...	1213	...	|	1243	1313	|	...	|	|	1343	135
	Firenze Campo di Marte d.	1031	|	|	|	|	...	|	|	|	|	|	|	...	|	...	|	|	|	|	...	1331	|	|	|
	Arezzo d.	|	|	|	|	|	...	|	|	|	|	|	|	...	|	...	|	|	|	|	...	|	|	|	|
257	Roma Tiburtina a.	|	|	|	1216s	1236	...	|	1251s	|	1258	1316s	1336	...	1336	...	|	1408	1436	|	...	|	|	1508s	1516
261	**Roma** Termini a.	1153	1207	1218	1228	1247	...	1237	1303	1303	1310	1328	1347	...	1347	...	1407	1418	1447	1438	...	1458	1503	1518	152
	Roma Termini d.	1203	...	...	...	1303	...	...	...	1313	1320	...	1403	...	1403	...	...	1438	1458	1448	...	...	...	...	...
	Napoli Afragola a.	|	...	...	...	1358s	...	...	...	|	♣	...	1458	...	1458	...	...	1534s	|	1543s	...	...	...	...	...
	Napoli Centrale a.	1320	...	...	...	1415	...	...	...	1423	...	...	1515	...	1515	...	...	1552	1610	1558	...	...	...	...	...
	Napoli Centrale d.	...	...	...	...	...	...	...	...	...	...	...	1530	...	1530	...	...	...	...	...	...	...	...	...	...
	Salerno a.	...	...	...	...	...	...	...	...	...	...	...	1605	...	1605	...	...	...	...	...	...	...	...	...	...

	FR	FR	FR	FR	FR	FR	FR	FR	FR	FR	FA	FR	FA	FR	FR	FR	FR	FR	FR	FR	FR	FR	FR	FR	FA
	9535	9635	9427	9539*	9637	9639	9793	9329	9543	9641	8517	9643	9435	9737	9547	9645	9333	9809	9647	9439	9585	9551	9651	9743	852
		⚒			Ⓐ		Ⓑ			⚒						Ⓑ					⑤		Ⓑ		
	e		Z			m	V				Y		Z	T	Oe			Rq		Z	f			V	Y
Torino Porta Nuova d.	...	1150	...	...	...	...	1302	1320	...	...	...	...	...	1405	...	...	1420	...	...	...	...	1500	...	1505	...
Torino Porta Susa d.	...	1200u	...	...	...	...	1312u	1330u	...	...	...	...	...	1415u	...	...	1430u	...	...	...	...	1510	...	1515u	...
Milano Centrale a.	...	1250	...	...	...	...	1402	|	...	...	...	...	...	1502	...	...	|	...	...	...	...	1600	...	1607	...
Milano Centrale d.	1220	1300	...	1320	1330	1400	▬	|	1420	1430	...	1500	...	▬	1520	1530	|	1545	1600	...	1605	1615	1630	...	...
Milano Porta Garibaldi d.	|	|	...	|	|	|	...	1418	|	|	...	|	...	...	|	|	1518	|	|	...	|	|	|	...	...
Milano Rogoredo d.	|	|	...	|	|	1409	FA	1435	|	|	...	|	...	FR	|	|	1535	|	|	...	|	1628	|	...	...
Reggio Emilia AV d.	|	|	...	|	|	|	8435	1511	|	|	...	|	...	9433	|	|	1611	1632	|	...	|	|	|	...	...
Verona Porta Nuova d.	|	|	...	|	|	|		|	|	|	1452	|	...		|	|	|	|	|	...	|	|	|	...	165
Bologna Centrale ✣ a.	1319	|	...	1419	1432	|	Z	1537	1519	1532	1542	|	...	Z	1619	1632	1637	1659	|	...	1707	1719	1732	...	174
Bologna Centrale ✣ d.	1322	|	1355	1422	1435	|	1455	1540	1522	1535	1545	|	1555	1605	1622	1635	1640	...	|	1655	1710	1722	1735	...	174
Firenze SMN a.	1400	|	1435	1500	|	|	1535	1620	1600	|	|	|	1635	1644	1700	|	1720	...	|	1735	1750	1800	|	...	|
Firenze SMN d.	1413	|	1443	1513	|	|	1543	1629	1613	|	|	|	1643	1652	1713	|	1729	...	|	1743	1759	1813	|	...	|
Firenze Campo di Marte d.	|	|	|	|	|	|	|	|	|	|	1631	|	|	|	|	|	|	...	|	|	|	|	|	...	183
Arezzo d.	|	|	|	|	|	|	|	|	|	|	|	|	|	|	|	|	|	...	|	|	|	|	|	...	|
Roma Tiburtina a.	1536	|	1608	1636	|	|	1708s	1751	1736	|	|	|	1808s	1816	1836	|	1851s	...	|	1908	|	1936	|	...	|
Roma Termini a.	1547	1603	1618	1647	1637	1707	1718	|	1747	1737	1753	1803	1818	1828	1847	1837	1903	...	1903	1918	1933	1947	1938	...	195
Roma Termini d.	1558	1613	1633	1658	...	1718	...	|	1758	...	...	...	...	1838	1858	1848	...	...	1913n	1933	1943	1957	1948	...	...
Napoli Afragola a.	1653s	|	|	1753s	...	|	...	|	1853s	...	...	...	...	|	|	1943s	...	...	|	|	|	|	2045s	...	...
Napoli Centrale a.	1708	1723	1743	1810	...	1828	...	1900	1910	...	...	...	...	1948	2005	2000	...	...	2025n	2043	2053	2105	2058	...	...
Napoli Centrale d.	...	...	...	...	...	...	...	1912	...	...	...	...	...	...	2015	...	...	...	...	2053	...	2118	...	...	...
Salerno a.	...	...	...	...	...	...	...	1956	...	...	...	...	...	...	2050	...	...	...	...	2131	...	2154	...	...	...

	FR	FR	FR	FR	FR	FR	FA	FR	FR	FR	FR	FR	FA	FR	FR	FR	FR	FR	FR	FR	FR	FR	FR	FR	FR
	9653	9445	9747	9555	9655	9341	8525	9811	9657	9751	9559	9659	8527	9453	9563	9663	9587	9565	9665	9667	9757	9567	9589	9673	967
					Ⓑ	⑤–⑦						Ⓑ			Ⓑ		⑤		Ⓑ	Ⓑ			Ⓑ		†
		Z	T		f		E	S	m	V			Y	Z	P	p	f				T				
Torino Porta Nuova d.	1550	...	1605	...	...	1620	...	...	...	1705	...	...	...	...	...	1750	...	1810	...	...	1835	1910	...	...	195
Torino Porta Susa d.	1600u	...	1615u	...	...	1630u	...	...	...	1715u	...	...	...	...	...	1800u	...	1822u	...	...	1845u	1920u	...	...	20
Milano Centrale a.	1650	...	1705	...	...	|	...	...	...	1805	...	...	...	...	...	1850	...	1910	...	...	1935	2010	...	...	20
Milano Centrale d.	1700	...	▬	1720	1730	|	...	1740	1800	▬	1820	1830	...	...	1845	1900	1901	1920	1930	2000	▬	2020	2050	2100	21
Milano Porta Garibaldi d.	|	...	...	|	|	1718	...	|	|	...	|	|	...	...	|	|	|	|	|	|	...	|	|	|	|
Milano Rogoredo d.	1709	...	FR	|	|	1735	...	|	1810u	FA	|	|	...	...	1858	1909	|	|	|	|	FR	|	|	|	|
Reggio Emilia AV d.	|	...	8447	|	|	1813	...	1833	|	8451	|	|	...	...	1938	|	|	|	|	|	9457	|	2138	|	|
Verona Porta Nuova d.	|	...		|	|	|	1752	|	|		|	|	1852	...	|	|	|	|	|	|		|	|	|	|
Bologna Centrale ✣ a.	|	...	Z	1819	1832	1837	1842	1855	|	Z	1919	1932	1942	...	2002	|	2007	2019	2032	|	Z	2119	2205	2200	22
Bologna Centrale ✣ d.	|	1755	1805	1822	1835	1840	1845	...	|	1855	1922	1935	1945	1955	2005	|	2010	2022	2035	|	2055	2122	2208	2203	22
Firenze SMN a.	|	1835	1844	1900	|	1920	|	...	|	1935	2000	|	|	2035	2044	|	2050	2100	|	|	2135	2200	2248	|	|
Firenze SMN d.	|	1843	1852	1913	|	1929	|	...	|	1943	2013	|	|	2043	2053	|	2059	2113	|	|	2143	2213	...	|	|
Firenze Campo di Marte d.	|	|	|	|	|	|	1931	...	|	|	|	|	2031	|	|	|	|	|	|	|	|	|	...	|	|
Arezzo d.	|	|	|	|	|	|	|	...	|	|	|	|	|	|	2126	|	|	|	|	|	|	|	...	|	|
Roma Tiburtina a.	1956s	2008	2016s	2036	|	2051	|	...	|	2108s	2135	|	|	2208s	...	|	|	2236s	|	|	2308	2336s	...	|	|
Roma Termini a.	2007	2018	2028	2047	2037	2103	2053	...	2103	2118	2147	2137	2153	2218	...	2207	2228	2247	2237	2303	2318	2347	...	0007	000
Roma Termini d.	...	2033	...	2058	2048g	2118	...	...	2113	...	2158	2148	2203	...	...	2218	2238	...	2248	...	...	...	...	...	...
Napoli Afragola a.	...	|	...	2152	|	|	...	...	|	...	|	2243	|	...	...	|	2333s	...	2345s	...	...	...	...	...	...
Napoli Centrale a.	...	2145	...	2208	2158g	2228	...	...	2223	...	2308	|	2318	...	...	2328	2348	...	2358	...	...	...	...	...	...
Napoli Centrale d.	...	...	...	2218	...	...	...	...	...	...	...	|	...	...	...	...	...	...	...	...	...	...	...	...	...
Salerno a.	...	...	...	2255	...	...	...	...	...	...	...	2316	...	...	...	...	...	...	...	...	...	...	...	...	...

B – To/from Brescia (Table **605**).
C – To/from Vicenza (Table **605**).
E – To/from Bergamo (Table **605**).
L – To/from Lecce (Tables **630**/**631**).
M – From/via Modena (Table **615**).
O – To/from Taranto (Table **638**).
P – To/from Perugia (Table **620**).

R – To/from Bari (Tables **630**/**631**).
S – To/from Pescara (Tables **630**/**631**).
T – To/from Trieste (Table **601**).
U – To/from Udine (Table **601**).
V – To/from Venezia (Table **605**).
Y – To/from Bolzano (Table **595**).
Z – To/from Venezia (Table **616**).

a – Not Nov. 1.
b – July 28 - Dec. 14.
c – Until July 27.
d – June 10 - July 28.
e – June 9 - July 27.
f – Also Oct. 31; not Aug. 9, 16, Nov. 1.
g – Ⓐ only.

h – Not Aug. 7 – 16.
j – Not June 16, 23.
k – Also Oct. 31; not Aug. 9 – 18, Nov.
m – Not Aug. 7 – 18.
n – ⑤⑥⑦ only.

NOTES CONTINUE ON NEXT PAGE →

Operator: Trenitalia | All trains Ⓡ and 🍸 | **HIGH-SPEED SERVICES** | **600**

	FR 9790	FR 9580	FR 9500	FR 9582	FR 9400	FR 9502	FR 9600	FR 9802	FR 9504	FR 9602	FA 8504	FA 8408	FR 9606	FR 9306	FR 9508	FR 9668	FR 9608	FR 9406	FR 9610	FR 9512	FR 9612	FA 8416	FA 8506	FR 9412	FR 9614
		①–⑥	①–⑤	⑥	Ⓐ	①–⑥	①–⑥			Ⓐ						①–⑤	⑥				⚒				
		a	P	P	Z	a	a	S	e		Y	Z				r		Z				Z	Y	Z	
Salerno d.	...	...	...	...	...	...	...	...	...	...	...	...	0520	...	...	...	...	...	...	0611	...	...	...	0640	...
Napoli Centrale a.	...	...	...	...	...	...	...	...	...	...	...	...	|	...	...	...	...	...	...	0647	...	...	...	0717	...
Napoli Centrale d.	...	...	...	...	...	...	...	...	...	0510	...	...	|	...	...	0610	...	...	0639	0700	...	...	0708	0730	0740
Napoli Afragola d.	...	...	...	...	...	...	...	...	...	|	...	...	0550	...	...	|	...	...	|	0714	...	...	|	|	|
Roma Termini a.	...	...	...	...	...	...	...	...	...	0620	...	...	0650	...	...	0720	...	...	0750	0810	...	...	0823	0840	0850
Roma Termini d.	...	...	...	...	0535	0535	0600	...	0620	0630	0645	0650	0700	0705	0720	0730	0730	0750	0800	0820	0830	0835	0845	0850	0900
Roma Tiburtina d.	...	...	...	...	|	0545u	|	...	0629u	|	|	0700u	0707	0715u	0729u	|	|	0800u	|	0829	|	0845u	|	0900	|
Arezzo d.	...	...	0604	0604	|	|	|	...	|	|	|	|	|	|	|	|	|	|	|	|	|	|	|	|	|
Firenze Campo di Marte d.	...	...	|	|	|	|	|	...	|	|	0803	|	|	|	|	|	|	|	|	|	|	|	1003	|	|
Firenze SMN a.	...	...	0634	0634	0705	0710	|	...	0751	|	|	0822	|	0836	0851	|	|	0922	|	0951	|	1007	|	1022	|
Firenze SMN d.	...	0555	0643	0643	0715	0730	|	...	0800	|	|	0830	|	0845	0900	|	|	0930	|	1000	|	1015	|	1030	|
Bologna Centrale ❖ a.	...	0630	0718	0718	0750	0805	|	...	0835	0825	0842	0905	|	0920	0935	0925	0925	1005	|	1035	1025	1050	1042	1105	|
Bologna Centrale ❖ d.	...	0633	0721	0721	▬	0808	|	0813	0838	0828	0845	▬	|	0923	0938	0928	0928	▬	|	1038	1028	...	1045	...	|
Verona Porta Nuova a.	...	|	|	|	*FR*	|	|	|	|	|	0937	*FR*	|	|	|	|	|	*FR*	|	|	|	...	1137	...	|
Reggio Emilia AV d.	...	0654	0742	0742	**9702**	|	|	0844	|	|	...	**9710**	|	0944	|	|	|	**9714**	|	1059	|	...	...	...	|
Milano Rogoredo a.	...	0727	|	|		|	|	|	0930	|	...		0947s	1022	|	|	|		1048	|	|	...	...	...	1147s
Milano Porta Garibaldi a.	...	|	|	|	V	|	|	|	|	|	...	Ta	|	1042	|	|	|	V	|	|	|	...	...	...	|
Milano Centrale a.	...	0745	0830	0830	...	0910	0855	0935	0943	0929	...	...	0959	|	1040	1029	1029	...	1059	1145	1129	...	...	...	1159
Milano Centrale d.	0700	...	0848	...	0900	...	0908	...	0953	...	...	1000	...	|	...	...	...	1055	1108	...	...	...	...	...	...
Torino Porta Susa a.	0752s	...	0944s	...	0949s	...	0954s	...	1040s	...	...	1050s	...	1130s	...	...	...	1143s	1158s	...	...	...	...	...	...
Torino Porta Nuova a.	0805	...	0955	...	1000	...	1005	...	1055	...	...	1100	...	1140	...	...	...	1155	1210	...	...	...	...	...	...

	FR 9518	FR 9516	FR 9314	FR 9616	FA 8508	FR 9414	FR 9618*	FR 9806	FR 9318	FR 9520	FR 9620	FR 9416	FA 8512	FR 9420	FR 9622	FR 9524	FR 9624	FR 9422	FR 8432	FR 9626	FR 9734	FR 9528	FR 9628	FA 8434	FR 9630
	①–④	⑤–⑦	①–⑥	⚒					①–⑥		Ⓐ												Ⓐ		⚒
			a		E	Z	m	R	a			Z	Y	Z		O		Z	Z		V			Z	
Salerno d.	...	...	0717	...	...	...	...	...	...	...	...	...	...	0841	...	0914	...	...	...	...	...	...	...	...	...
Napoli Centrale a.	...	...	0752	...	...	...	...	...	...	...	...	...	...	0917	...	0950	...	...	...	...	...	...	...	...	...
Napoli Centrale d.	0800	0800	0805	0810	...	0830	0840	...	...	0900	...	0915	...	0930	0940	1000	1005	...	...	...	...	1100	...	...	...
Napoli Afragola d.	|	|	|	0824u	...	0844u	|	...	...	0914	...	|	...	|	|	|	|	...	♠	...	...	1114u	...	...	...
Roma Termini a.	0907	0907	|	0920	...	0940	0950	...	...	1010	...	1022	...	1040	1050	1109	1115	...	1140	...	...	1210	...	...	...
Roma Termini d.	0920	0920	|	0930	0945	0950	1000	...	1005	1020	1030	1035	1045	1050	1100	1120	1130	1135	1150	1200	...	1220	1230	1250	1300
Roma Tiburtina d.	0929	0929	0915	|	|	1000	|	...	1015u	1029	|	1045	|	1100	|	1129	|	1145u	1200	|	...	1229	|	1300u	|
Arezzo d.	|	|	|	|	|	|	|	...	|	|	|	|	|	|	|	|	|	|	|	|	...	|	|	|	|
Firenze Campo di Marte d.	|	|	|	|	1103	|	|	...	|	|	|	|	1203	|	|	|	|	|	|	|	...	|	|	|	|
Firenze SMN a.	1051	1051	1036	|	|	1122	|	...	1136	1151	|	1207	|	1222	|	1251	|	1307	1322	|	...	1351	|	1422	|
Firenze SMN d.	1100	1100	1045	|	|	1130	|	...	1145	1200	|	1215	|	1230	|	1300	|	1315	1330	|	...	1400	|	1430	|
Bologna Centrale ❖ a.	1135	1135	1120	1125	1142	1205	|	...	1220	1235	|	1250	1242	1305	|	1335	1325	1350	1405	|	...	1435	1425	1505	|
Bologna Centrale ❖ d.	1138	1138	1123	1128	1145	...	|	1215	1223	1238	1225	▬	1245	...	|	1338	1328	...	...	|	...	1438	1428	...	|
Verona Porta Nuova a.	|	|	|	|	1237	...	|	|	|	|	1228	*FR*	1337	...	|	|	|	...	...	|	...	|	|	...	|
Reggio Emilia AV d.	|	1159	1144	|	...	...	|	|	1244	|	|	**9726**	...	...	|	1359	|	...	...	|	...	1459	|	...	|
Milano Rogoredo a.	|	1238s	1222	|	...	...	1245s	|	1322	|	|		...	...	|	1438s	|	...	...	|	...	1538	|	...	1547
Milano Porta Garibaldi a.	|	|	1242	|	...	...	|	|	1342	|	|	Tq	...	...	|	|	|	...	...	|	...	|	|	...	|
Milano Centrale a.	1240	1250	|	1229	...	...	1259	1320	|	1340	1329	...	...	...	1355	1450	1429	...	...	1455	...	1550	1529	...	1559
Milano Centrale d.	...	...	|	...	...	...	...	...	|	...	...	1355	...	...	1405	...	...	...	...	...	1555	1600	...	...	...
Torino Porta Susa a.	...	...	1330s	...	...	...	...	...	1430s	...	...	1443s	...	...	1452s	...	...	...	...	...	1643s	1648s	...	...	...
Torino Porta Nuova a.	...	...	1340	...	...	...	...	...	1440	...	...	1455	...	...	1505	...	...	...	...	...	1655	1700	...	...	...

	FR 9532	FR 9632	FR 9430	FR 9634	FR 9536	FR 9636	FA 8518	FR 9434	FR 9638	FR 9742	FR 9338	FR 9544*	FR 9640	FA 8446	FR 9642	FR 9342	FR 9342	FR 9552*	FR 9644	FA 8448	FA 8524	FR 9440	FR 9646	FR 9808*	FR 9556
		Ⓐ				Ⓐ				Ⓑ	Ⓑ		Ⓑ				⑦		Ⓑ						
			Z					Z						Z					t	T	Y	U		L	
Salerno d.	...	...	...	...	...	...	...	...	...	...	1311	...	...	...	...	...	...	...	...	...	...	...	...	...	1508
Napoli Centrale a.	...	...	...	...	...	...	...	...	...	...	1347	...	...	...	...	...	...	...	...	...	...	...	...	...	1545
Napoli Centrale d.	1200	1205	1230	...	1257	...	...	...	...	...	1405	1400	1410	...	1440	...	1450	1500	1505	...	1525	...	1542	...	1600
Napoli Afragola d.	|	|	|	...	1311u	...	...	...	...	...	|	|	1425u	◧	|	...	|	|	1520u	...	|	...	|	...	|
Roma Termini a.	1307	1315	1340	...	1408	...	...	...	...	...	|	1510	1520	1540	1550	...	1555	1610	1615	...	1635	...	1650	...	1710
Roma Termini d.	1320	1330	1350	1400	1420	1430	1445	1450	1500	...	|	1522	1530	1550	1600	1605	1605	1620	1630	1635	1645	1650	1700	...	1720
Roma Tiburtina d.	1329	|	1400	|	1429	|	|	1500u	|	...	1515	1529	|	1600	|	1615u	1615u	1629	|	|	|	1700u	|	...	1729
Arezzo d.	|	|	|	|	|	|	|	|	|	...	|	|	|	|	|	|	|	|	|	|	|	|	|	...	|
Firenze Campo di Marte d.	|	|	|	|	|	|	1603	|	|	...	|	|	|	|	|	|	|	|	|	|	1803	|	|	...	|
Firenze SMN a.	1451	|	1522	|	1551	|	|	1622	|	...	1636	1651	|	1722	|	1736	1736	1751	|	1807	|	1822	|	...	1851
Firenze SMN d.	1500	|	1530	|	1600	|	|	1630	|	...	1645	1700	|	1730	|	1745	1745	1800	|	1815	|	1830	|	...	1900
Bologna Centrale ❖ a.	1535	1525	1605	|	1635	1625	1642	1705	|	...	1720	1735	1725	1805	|	1820	1820	1835	1825	1850	1842	1905	|	...	1935
Bologna Centrale ❖ d.	1538	1528	▬	|	1638	1628	1645	...	|	...	1723	1738	1728	...	|	1823	1823	1838	1828	...	1845	▬	|	1918	1938
Verona Porta Nuova a.	|	|	*FR*	|	|	|	1737	...	|	...	|	|	|	...	|	|	|	|	|	...	1937	*FR*	|	|	|
Reggio Emilia AV d.	|	|	**9738**	|	|	|	...	...	|	...	1744	|	|	...	|	1844	1844	|	|	...	...	**9750**	|	1944	1959
Milano Rogoredo a.	1631s	|		|	|	|	...	...	|	...	1822	|	|	...	1848s	1922	1922	|	|	...	...		1947	2022	|
Milano Porta Garibaldi a.	|	|	V	|	|	|	...	...	|	...	1842	|	|	...	|	1942	1942	|	|	...	...	V	|	2042	|
Milano Centrale a.	1645	1629	...	1655	1742	1729	...	...	1755	...	|	1842	1829	...	1859	|	|	1940	1929	...	...	...	1959	|	2045
Milano Centrale d.	...	...	1655	1705	...	...	...	...	1805	1810	|	1900	...	...	...	|	|	...	...	...	...	1955	2010	|	...
Torino Porta Susa a.	...	...	1745s	1752s	...	...	...	...	1852s	1908s	1930s	1948s	...	...	...	2030s	2030s	...	...	...	...	2045s	2059s	2130s	...
Torino Porta Nuova a.	...	...	1755	1805	...	...	...	...	1905	1920	1940	2000	...	...	...	2040	2040	...	...	...	...	2055	2110	2140	...

	FR 9648	FR 9446	FA 8526	FR 9444	FR 9650	FR 9350	FR 9350	FR 9560*	FR 9592	FA 8552	FR 9652	FR 8528	FA 9450	FR 9654	FR 9762	FR 9564	FR 9584	FR 9566	FR 8464	FR 9660	FR 9570	FR 9572	FR 9664	FR 9662	FR 9666
		Ⓑ				Ⓑ	⑥	①–⑤	⑥⑦		Ⓑ						⑤⑦			Ⓑ	Ⓑ	Ⓑ	†		†
		Z	Y	Z	Bm					M	t	E	Z		V		k	M	Z			t			
Salerno d.	...	...	...	...	...	...	...	...	1613	...	...	...	...	...	...	1710	...	...	...	1749	...	...	...	...	...
Napoli Centrale a.	...	...	...	...	...	...	...	...	1650	...	...	...	...	...	...	1748	...	...	...	1823	...	...	...	...	...
Napoli Centrale d.	1605	...	...	1630	1640	...	1650	1700	1700	...	1710	...	...	1740	...	1758	1810	...	...	1840	1900	1930	1940	...	2035
Napoli Afragola d.	|	...	...	|	|	...	|	1714u	1714	...	1724u	...	...	|	...	1811	|	...	...	|	|	1944	|	...	|
Roma Termini a.	1715	...	...	1740	1750	...	1755	1810	1810	...	1820	...	...	1850	...	1908	1920	...	...	1950	2010	2040	2050	...	2145
Roma Termini d.	1730	1735	1745	1750	1800	1805	1805	1820	1820	1829	1830	1845	1850	1900	...	1920	1930	1935	1950	2000	2020	2050	2100	2100	...
Roma Tiburtina d.	|	1744u	|	1800	|	1815u	1815	1829	1829	1839u	|	|	1900u	|	...	1929	1939	1945u	2000u	|	2029	2100	|	|	...
Arezzo d.	|	|	|	|	|	|	|	|	|	|	|	|	2002	|	...	|	|	|	|	|	|	2202	|	|	...
Firenze Campo di Marte d.	|	|	1903	|	|	|	|	|	|	|	|	2003	|	|	...	|	|	|	|	|	|	|	|	|	...
Firenze SMN a.	|	1907	|	1922	|	1936	1936	1951	1951	2002	|	|	2035	|	...	2051	2102	2107	2122	|	2151	2235	|	|	...
Firenze SMN d.	|	1915	|	1930	|	1945	1945	2000	2000	2011	|	|	2043	|	...	2100	2111	2116	2130	|	2200	...	|	|	...
Bologna Centrale ❖ a.	1925	1950	1942	2005	1955	2020	2020	2035	2035	2047	2025	2042	2120	|	...	2135	2145	2150	2205	|	2235	...	2255	2255	...
Bologna Centrale ❖ d.	1928	...	1945	...	1958	2023	2023	2038	2038	...	2028	2045	...	|	...	2138	2148	2153	...	|	2238	...	2258	2258	...
Verona Porta Nuova a.	|	...	2037	...	|	|	|	|	|	...	|	2137	...	|	...	|	|	|	...	|	|	...	|	|	...
Reggio Emilia AV d.	|	...	...	...	|	2044	2044	2059	2059	...	|	...	...	2116	...	2159	2214	|	...	|	2259	...	|	|	...
Milano Rogoredo a.	|	...	...	...	|	2122	2122	2138s	2138s	...	|	...	...	|	...	|	2253s	|	...	|	2335s	...	|	|	...
Milano Porta Garibaldi a.	|	...	...	...	|	2142	2142	|	|	...	|	...	...	|	...	|	|	|	...	|	|	...	|	|	...
Milano Centrale a.	2029	...	...	...	2059	|	|	2150	2150	...	2129	...	...	2202	...	2245	2305	2355	...	2255	2350	...	2359	2359	...
Milano Centrale d.	...	...	...	...	...	|	|	...	...	...	...	...	...	2212	2230	...	...	...	...	...	...	...	...	...	...
Torino Porta Susa a.	...	...	...	...	...	2230s	2230s	...	...	...	...	...	...	2302y	2319z	...	...	...	...	...	...	...	...	...	...
Torino Porta Nuova a.	...	...	...	...	...	2240	2240	...	...	...	...	...	...	2312y	2330z	...	...	...	...	...	...	...	...	...	...

– NOTES CONTINUED FROM PREVIOUS PAGE.

- – Not Oct. 18 – 22, Nov. 5 – 10.
- – June 9 - Sept. 15.
- – Not Aug. 6 – 14, 16, 19, Nov. 1.
- – Calls to set down only.
- – Not Aug. 6 – 19.

u – Calls to pick up only.

y – Arrives Torino P. Susa 2340**s** and P. Nuova 2350 on ⑥ June 1 - July 20, Aug. 31 - Sept. 28, Oct. 19, 26.

z – Arrives Torino P. Susa 0009**s** and P. Nuova 0020 on ⑥ June 1 - July 20, Aug. 31 - Sept. 28, Oct. 19, 26.

♣ – To Roma Fiumicino ✈ (a. 1352).

♠ – From Roma Fiumicino ✈ (d. 1108).

◧ – From Roma Fiumicino ✈ (d. 1508).

* – Uses a different train number on certain dates.

❖ – Most services use underground platforms 16 – 19; allow a minimum of 10 minutes for connecting services from / to the main station.

601 VENEZIA - TRIESTE

km		2				*FR* **9707** Ⓐ T		*FR* **9717** Ⓒ Ta					*IC* **589**		*FR* **9737** Tc			*FR* **9747** Td		*FA* **8449** e ♦	*FR* **9757** T	*IC* **593**	
	Roma Termini **616** d.	...	...	...	...	...	...	...	...	...	...	...	1030	...	...	...	...	...	...	1635	...	1540	...
0	**Venezia** Santa Lucia d.	...	0641	0741	0941	...	1041	...	1241	1341	1441	1541	|	1641	...	1741	1841	...	1941	|	...	|	2241
9	**Venezia** Mestre d.	0553	0653	0753	0953	1020	1053	1244	1253	1353	1453	1553	1643	1653	1746	1753	1853	1949	1953	2021	2155	2200	2253
42	S. Dona di Piave-Jesolo ◧ d.	0617	0717	0817	1017	1046	1117	1302	1317	1417	1517	1617	1708	1717	|	1817	1917	|	2017	|	|	2221	2317
69	Portogruaro-Caorle d.	0637	0737	0837	1037	1104	1137	1318	1337	1437	1537	1637	1731	1737	1829	1837	1937	2029	2037	|	|	2238	2337
83	Latisana-Lignano-Bibione d.	0648	0748	0848	1048	1114	1148	1327	1348	1448	1548	1648	1742	1748	1836	1848	1948	2037	2048	2105	2236	2249	2348
101	S. Giorgio di Nogaro d.	0700	0800	0900	1100	|	1200	|	1400	1500	1600	1700	|	1800	|	1900	2000	|	2101	|	|	|	0000
112	Cervignano-Aquileia-Grado d.	0709	0809	0909	1109	1131	1209	1343	1409	1509	1609	1709	1800	1809	1849	1909	2009	|	2110	|	2255	2307	0009
124	Trieste Airport ✈ d.	0717	0817	0917	1117	1140	1217	1352	1417	1517	1517	1717	1810	1817	1900	1917	2017	2059	2117	2126	2304	2317	0017
129	Monfalcone d.	0723	0823	0923	1123	1148	1223	1359	1423	1523	1623	1723	1816	1823	1906	1923	2023	2105	2123	|	2311	2324	0023
157	**Trieste** Centrale ⊗ a.	0746	0848	0946	1146	1211	1246	1422	1446	1546	1646	1746	1839	1846	1929	1946	2046	2128	2148	2154	2334	2347	0046

		FR **9710** Ta		*FA* **8412** ♦	*FR* **9716** Mc		*IC* **584**			*FR* **9726** Te		*IC* **594**					*FR* **9758** M				2 Ⓐ	2	2
Trieste Centrale ⊗ d.	0515	0602	0615	0644	0705	0715	0721	0815	0915	0938	1215	1302	1315	1415	1515	1615	1702	1715	1815	1915	2015	2115	2206
Monfalcone d.	0539	0626	0638	|	0730	0739	0746	0839	0939	1003	1239	1327	1339	1439	1539	1639	1727	1739	1839	1939	2039	2139	2229
Trieste Airport ✈ d.	0544	0632	0644	0709	0736	0744	0752	0844	0944	1009	1244	1333	1344	1444	1544	1644	1733	1744	1844	1944	2044	2144	2234
Cervignano-Aquileia-Grado d.	0551	0640	0651	|	|	0751	0801	0851	0951	1015	1251	1342	1351	1451	1551	1651	1740	1751	1851	1951	2051	2151	2242
S. Giorgio di Nogaro d.	0600	|	0700	|	|	0800	|	0900	1000	|	1300	|	1400	1500	1600	1700	|	1800	1900	2000	2100	2200	2249
Latisana-Lignano-Bibione d.	0613	|	0713	|	0756	0813	0821	0913	1013	1027	1313	1359	1413	1513	1613	1713	1754	1813	1913	2013	2113	2213	2300
Portogruaro-Caorle d.	0624	|	0724	|	0806	0824	0832	0924	1024	1037	1324	1410	1424	1524	1624	1724	1804	1824	1924	2024	2124	2224	2310
S. Dona di Piave-Jesolo ◧ d.	0642	|	0742	|	|	0842	0850	0942	1042	|	1342	1426	1442	1542	1642	1742	1820	1842	1942	2042	...	...	2329
Venezia Mestre a.	0708	0740	0808	0823	0851	0908	0912	1008	1108	1117	1408	1452	1508	1608	1708	1808	1842	1908	2008	2108	...	...	2351
Venezia Santa Lucia a.	0720	...	0820	|	...	0924	|	1020	1120	...	1424	|	1524	1620	1720	1820	...	1920	2020	2120	...	...	...
Roma Termini **616** a.	...	...	...	1218	...	...	1530	...	...	...	...	2049	...	...	...	...	...	...	...	...	...	...	...

Services via Udine

km		Ⓐ	2 Ⓐ	*ICN* **774** ♦	2 Ⓐ	2 ⚒	⚒	2 †	2 ⚒		2 ⚒	†		Ⓐ	*FR* **9704** ♦	2 †	■ Ⓒ		2 Ⓒ		2 ⚒	⚒	2		Ⓐ
0	**Venezia** Santa Lucia d.	0505	0515	0535	0602	0615	0705	0715	0715	...	0805	0805	0831	0905	0920	...	...	1005	1115	1205	1215	1305	1315	1405	1505
9	**Venezia** Mestre d.	0517	0529	|	0617	0629	0717	0729	0729	...	0817	0817	0843	0917	0932	...	...	1017	1129	1217	1229	1317	1329	1417	1517
30	Treviso Centrale d.	0536	0554	0605	0636	0654	0736	0754	0754	...	0836	0836	0907	0936	0949	...	...	1036	1154	1236	1254	1336	1354	1436	1536
57	Conegliano d.	0554	0621	0629	0654	0721	0754	0821	0821	...	0854	0854	0931	0954	1007	...	...	1054	1221	1254	1321	1354	1421	1454	1554
74	Sacile d.	0605	0636	0647	0705	0736	0805	0836	0836	...	0905	0905	0944	1005	|	...	...	1105	1236	1305	1336	1405	1436	1505	1605
87	Pordenone d.	0617	0650	0700	0717	0750	0817	0850	0850	...	0917	0917	...	1017	1028	...	...	1117	1250	1317	1350	1417	1450	1517	1617
136	**Udine** a.	0653	0730	0744	0753	0830	0853	0930	0930	...	0953	0953	...	1053	1059	...	...	1153	1330	1353	1430	1453	1530	1553	1653
136	**Udine** d.	0655	0736	0746	...	...	0855	...	0932	...	...	0955	...	...	...	1109	1134	1155	...	1355	...	...	...	1555	1655
169	Gorizia Centrale ♣ d.	0719	0807	0819	...	...	0919	...	1003	...	...	1019	...	...	...	1140	|	1219	...	1419	...	...	...	1619	1719
192	Monfalcone d.	0740	0831	0841	...	...	0940	...	1027	...	...	1040	...	...	...	1204	1230	1240	...	1440	...	...	...	1640	1740
219	**Trieste** Centrale ⊗ a.	0803	0900	0905	...	...	1003	...	1056	...	...	1103	...	...	...	1233	1253	1303	...	1503	...	...	...	1703	1803

	2	2			2 Ⓐ	2 Ⓐ	†	Ⓐ	■2 Ⓐx	2 †	2 ⚒	2		2 Ⓐ	Ⓐ	2 †	2 ⚒	■ Ⓒ	2		*FR* **9440** R	*FR* **9752** ♦	2		
Venezia Santa Lucia d.	...	1515	...	1605	...	1615	1705	1705	...	...	...	1715	1805	1815	1905	1905	...	...	1915	2005	...	...	2115	2205	2305
Venezia Mestre d.	...	1529	...	1617	...	1629	1717	1717	...	...	...	1729	1817	1829	1917	1917	...	...	1929	2017	2040	2110	2129	2217	2317
Treviso Centrale d.	...	1554	...	1636	...	1654	1736	1736	...	...	...	1754	1836	1854	1936	1936	...	...	1954	2036	2056	2130	2154	2236	2336
Conegliano d.	...	1621	...	1654	...	1721	1754	1754	...	...	...	1821	1854	1921	1954	1954	...	...	2021	2054	2115	2148	2221	2254	2354
Sacile d.	...	1636	...	1705	...	1736	1805	1805	...	...	...	1836	1905	1936	2005	2005	...	...	2036	2105	|	|	2236	2305	0005
Pordenone d.	...	1650	...	1717	...	1750	1817	1817	...	...	...	1850	1917	1950	2017	2017	...	...	2050	2117	2136	2208	2250	2317	0017
Udine a.	...	1730	...	1753	...	1830	1853	1853	...	...	...	1930	1953	2030	2053	2053	...	...	2130	2153	2205	2237	2330	2353	0053
Udine d.	1709	...	...	1755	1812	...	...	1855	1908	1909	1916	...	1955	...	...	2120	2120	2117	...	2155	...	...	...	2355	...
Gorizia Centrale ♣ d.	1740	...	...	1819	1843	...	...	1919	|	1931	1947	...	2019	...	...	2151	2151	|	...	2219	...	...	...	0026	...
Monfalcone d.	1804	...	...	1840	1907	...	...	1940	1941	1952	2011	...	2040	...	...	2215	2215	2210	...	2240	...	...	...	0049	...
Trieste Centrale ⊗ a.	1833	...	...	1903	1936	...	...	2003	2010	2015	2040	...	2103	...	...	2244	2244	2239	...	2303	...	...	...	0118	...

	Ⓐ		*FR* **9791** ♦	2	*FR* **9409** Rb	⚒	■ Ⓒ	2 ⚒	■2 ⚒		2 Ⓒ	2	2 †			2 †	Ⓐz		2	*FR* **9739** ♦	Ⓐ	2 †	⑥	2 ⚒	2 ⚒
Trieste Centrale ⊗ d.	...	...	...	...	...	0527	0545	0557	0620	0657	...	0727	...	...	0857	0927	...	1057	...	...	1127	1127	...	...	1227
Monfalcone d.	...	...	...	...	...	0557	0612	0627	0644	0721	...	0757	...	...	0921	0957	...	1121	...	...	1157	1157	...	...	1257
Gorizia Centrale ♣ d.	...	...	...	...	...	0619	|	0651	|	0742	...	0819	...	...	0942	1019	...	1142	...	...	1219	1219	...	...	1319
Udine a.	...	...	...	...	...	0651	0714	0721	0722	0805	...	0851	...	...	1005	1051	...	1205	...	...	1251	1251	...	...	1351
Udine d.	0507	0600	0615	0631	0655	0701	...	0731	...	0807	0831	...	0907	...	1007	...	1107	1207	1230	1300	1307	...	1307	1331	...
Pordenone d.	0542	0635	0644	0710	0729	0740	...	0810	...	0842	0910	...	0942	...	1042	...	1142	1242	1308	1327	1342	...	1342	1410	...
Sacile d.	0553	0646	|	0724	|	0753	...	0824	...	0853	0924	...	0953	...	1053	...	1153	1253	1321	|	1353	...	1353	1424	...
Conegliano d.	0605	0658	0705	0740	0752	0805	...	0840	...	0905	0940	...	1005	...	1105	...	1205	1305	1336	1344	1405	...	1405	1440	...
Treviso Centrale d.	0625	0723	0730	0807	0814	0825	...	0907	...	0925	1007	...	1025	...	1125	...	1225	1325	1408	1406	1425	...	1425	1507	...
Venezia Mestre a.	0643	0743	0749	0832	0837	0843	...	0932	...	0943	1032	...	1043	...	1143	...	1243	1343	1432	1418	1443	...	1443	1532	...
Venezia Santa Lucia a.	0655	0755	...	0846	...	0855	...	0946	...	0955	1046	...	1055	...	1155	...	1255	1355	1446	1430	1455	...	1455	1546	...

		2	Ⓐ	2 Ⓐ	2 Ⓐ		2 Ⓑ	2	2 Ⓒ	Ⓐ	■ Ⓒ	2 Ⓐ	2 Ⓐ		2	2	†		Ⓐz	2			*ICN* **770** ♦		2
Trieste Centrale ⊗ d.	1257	...	1327	...	1427	1457	...	...	1527	...	1550	...	1630	1657	...	1727	...	...	1757	...	1857	2031	2043	...	2217
Monfalcone d.	1321	...	1357	...	1457	1521	...	...	1557	...	1617	...	1700	1721	...	1757	...	...	1821	...	1921	2057	2109	...	2246
Gorizia Centrale ♣ d.	1342	...	1419	...	1519	1542	...	...	1619	...	|	...	1722	1742	...	1819	...	...	1842	...	1942	2119	2132	...	2308
Udine a.	1405	...	1451	...	1551	1605	...	...	1651	...	1716	...	1754	1805	...	1851	...	...	1905	...	2005	2151	2156	...	2340
Udine d.	1407	1431	1507	1531	...	1607	...	1631	...	1707	...	1731	...	1807	1831	...	1907	...	1907	1931	2007	2207	2158	...	...
Pordenone d.	1442	1510	1542	1610	...	1642	...	1710	...	1742	...	1810	...	1842	1910	...	1942	...	1942	2010	2042	2242	2232	...	...
Sacile d.	1453	1524	1553	1624	...	1653	...	1724	...	1753	...	1824	...	1853	1924	...	1953	...	1953	2024	2053	2252	2242	...	...
Conegliano d.	1505	1540	1605	1640	...	1705	1731	1740	...	1805	...	1840	...	1905	1940	...	2005	...	2005	2040	2105	2305	2255	...	...
Treviso Centrale d.	1525	1607	1625	1707	...	1725	1754	1807	...	1825	...	1907	...	1925	2007	...	2025	...	2025	2107	2125	2325	2314	...	...
Venezia Mestre a.	1543	1632	1643	1732	...	1743	1818	1832	...	1843	...	1932	...	1943	2032	...	2043	...	2043	2132	2143	2344	|	...	...
Venezia Santa Lucia a.	1555	1646	1655	1746	...	1755	1830	1846	...	1855	...	1946	...	1955	2046	...	2058	...	2058	2146	2155	2356	2340	...	...

♦ – **NOTES** (LISTED BY TRAIN NUMBER)

770 – 1, 2 cl., 2 cl. (4 berth) and (2) Trieste - Udine (**771**) - Venezia - Bologna - Roma.

774 – 1, 2 cl., 2 cl. (4 berth) and (2) Roma - Bologna - Venezia - Udine (**775**) - Trieste.

8412 – (12) and 🍸 Trieste - Venezia (**8413**) - Roma.

8449 – (12) and 🍸 Roma (**8448**) - Venezia - Trieste.

9704 – (12) and 🍸 Milano (**9703**) - Venezia - Udine.

9739 – (12) and 🍸 Udine - Venezia (**9740**) - Milano.

9752 – (12) and 🍸 Milano (**9753**) - Venezia - Udine.

9791 – (12) and 🍸 Udine - Venezia (**9712**) - Milano.

M – (12) and 🍸 Milano - Trieste and v.v.

R – (12) and 🍸 Roma - Venezia - Udine and v.v.

T – (12) and 🍸 Torino - Milano - Trieste and v.v.

a – June 9 - July 27.

b – Not June 16, 23.

c – June 10 - Sept. 16.

d – June 9 - Sept. 12 (not July 9 – 11).

e – June 9 - Sept. 15.

s – Stops to set down only.

u – Stops to pick up only.

■ – Service runs via Cervignano and Trieste Airport.

◧ – A frequent 🚌 service operates 0600 - 1930 to Lido di Jesolo; 1 – 2 per hour, journey time 35 minutes.

♣ – An international 🚌 service operates between Gorizia Centrale and Nova Gorica (Slovenia bus stop 100 metres from station on Italian side) stations. Total journey time ± 20 minutes

⊗ – 🚋 service **Trieste** (Piazza Oberdan) - **Villa Opicina** (Stazione Trenovia) and v.v. *Linea Tranviaria.* Operator: Trieste Trasporti S.p.A. *Service currently suspended, replacement* 🚌 (Line **2**).

From **Trieste**: 0711, 0731, 0751 and every 20 minutes until 2011.
From **Villa Opicina**: 0700, 0720, 0740 and every 20 minutes until 2000.
Walking times: Trieste Centrale railway station - Piazza Oberdan ± 10 minutes;

VICENZA - TREVISO 602

2nd class only

km			⚒		⚒		†		Ⓐ			⚒			⚒				⚒	⚒				
0	**Vicenza**	d.	0614	0714	0814	...	0914	...	1114	1214	...	1314	1414	...	1514	...	1614	...	1714	1814	...	1914	...	2014	...
24	Cittadella	d.	0639	0739	0839	...	0939	...	1139	1239	...	1339	1439	...	1539	...	1639	...	1739	1839	...	1939	...	2039	...
36	Castelfranco Veneto	d.	0655	0755	0855	...	0955	...	1155	1255	...	1355	1455	...	1555	...	1655	...	1755	1855	...	1955	...	2055	...
60	**Treviso** Centrale	a.	0722	0822	0922	...	1022	...	1222	1322	...	1422	1522	...	1622	...	1722	...	1822	1922	...	2022	...	2122	...

		⚒	⚒			⚒		†		Ⓑ		⚒				⚒			⚒				⚒		
'reviso Centrale	d.	0538	0638	...	0738	0838	...	0938	...	1138	...	1238	...	1338	...	1438	1538	...	1638	...	1738	...	1838	...	2038
:astelfranco Veneto	d.	0607	0707	...	0807	0907	...	1007	...	1207	...	1307	...	1407	...	1507	1607	...	1707	...	1807	...	1907	...	2107
:ittadella	d.	0621	0721	...	0821	0921	...	1021	...	1221	...	1321	...	1421	...	1521	1621	...	1721	...	1821	...	1921	...	2121
'icenza	a.	0646	0746	...	0846	0946	...	1046	...	1246	...	1346	...	1446	...	1546	1646	...	1746	...	1846	...	1946	...	2146

CONEGLIANO and PADOVA - BELLUNO and CALALZO 603

2nd class only

km			①–⑥				①–⑤ 🚌				①–⑥			①–⑤			①–⑥			Ⓑ			🚌				
0	**Conegliano**	d.	0641	0741	...	0841	...	...	0941	1241	1341	...	1441	1541	...	1641	1741	...	1841	1941	...	2041	2201	...	...	...	...
14	Vittorio Veneto	d.	0702	0802	...	0902	...	...	1002	1302	1402	...	1502	1602	...	1702	1802	...	1902	2002	...	2102	2225	...	...	...	...
41	Ponte nelle Alpi-Polpet	a.	0731	0831	...	0931	...	...	1031	1331	1431	...	1531	1631	...	1731	1831	...	1931	2031	...	2131	2259	...	...	...	...
41	Ponte nelle Alpi-Polpet	d.	0736*	0839*	...	...	0939	...	1039*	1339*	1439*	...	1539*	1639*	...	1739*	1839*	...	1939*	2039*	...	2139*	2300	...	...	...	...
78	**Belluno**	a.	0746*	0849*	...	...	0949	...	1049*	1349*	1449*	...	1549*	1649*	...	1749*	1849*	...	1949*	2049*	...	2149*	2312	...	...	...	...

		①–⑥			①–⑥				①–⑤				①–⑥		Ⓑ				🚌							
3elluno	d.	0530*	0610*	...	0710*	0810*	...	1010*	1210*	1310*	...	1410*	1510*	...	1610*	1810*	...	1910*	2020	...	...	...	...	...	...	...
⁾onte nelle Alpi-Polpet	a.	0540*	0620*	...	0720*	0820*	...	1020*	1220*	1320*	...	1420*	1520*	...	1620*	1820*	...	1920*	2032	...	...	...	...	...	...	...
⁾onte nelle Alpi-Polpet	d.	0549	0633	...	0733	0833	...	1033	1233	1333	...	1433	1533	...	1633	1833	...	1933	2303	...	...	...	...	...	...	...
/ittorio Veneto	d.	0615	0701	...	0801	0901	...	1101	1301	1401	...	1501	1601	...	1701	1901	...	2001	2107	...	...	...	...	...	...	...
:onegliano	a.	0632	0718	...	0818	0918	...	1118	1318	1418	...	1518	1618	...	1718	1918	...	2018	2131	...	...	...	...	...	...	...

km			①–⑥	⑥⑦	①–⑤	⑥	①–⑤	⑦		①–⑤ 🚌	⑥⑦ 🚌	⑥⑦	①–⑤		⑦	①–⑥	①–⑥		①–⑥		①–⑥	①–⑤		Ⓑ			
0	**Padova**	d.	...	0604	0607	0704	0707	0723	0804j	...	...	0904	0907	1104j	...	1125	1204j	1304j	1404j	1504j	1604j	1625	1704j	1804j	1904j	2004j	2125
31	Castelfranco Veneto	d.	...	0636	0636	0736	0736	0751	0836	...	...	0936	0936	1136	...	1152	1236	1336	1436	1536	1636	1652	1736	1836	1936	2036	2156
48	Montebelluna	d.	0600	0653	0653	0753	0753	0806	0853	...	...	0953	0953	1153	1200	1206	1253	1353	1453	1553	1653	1706	1753	1853	1953	2053	2210
83	Feltre	d.	0639	0739	...	0839	0839	0839	...	...	...	1039	1039	...	1239	1239	1339	1439	1539	1639	...	1739	1839	1939	2039	...	2249
114	**Belluno**	a.	0715	0815	...	0915	0915	0910	...	...	...	1115	1115	...	1315	1315	1415	1515	1615	1715	...	1815	1915	2015	2115	...	2325
114	**Belluno**	d.	0730*	0830*	...	...	0930*	0930*	...	1028	1030	...	1230*	...	...	1330*	1430*	1530*	...	1730*	...	1830*	1930*	2030*	...	...	...
121	Ponte nelle Alpi-Polpet	a.	0740*	0840*	...	...	0940*	0940*	...	1038	1040	...	1240*	...	...	1340*	1440*	1540*	...	1740*	...	1840*	1940*	2040*	...	...	...
121	Ponte nelle Alpi-Polpet	d.	0741*	0841*	...	...	0941*	0941*	...	1039	1041	...	1241*	...	...	1341*	1441*	1541*	...	1741*	...	1841*	1941*	2041*	...	...	...
158	**Calalzo** ▲	a.	0815*	0915*	...	...	1015*	1015*	...	1128	1115	...	1326*	...	...	1415*	1515*	1615*	...	1815*	...	1926*	2015*	2115*	...	...	...

		①–⑥	①–⑥			①–⑥ 🚌		⑦	①–⑥			①–⑥	①–⑤ 🚌		①–⑥	①–⑥		①–⑤ 🚌	①–⑥	Ⓑ	①–⑤ 🚌	⑥ 🚌		Ⓑ 🚌		
alalzo ▲	d.	...	...	...	...	0628	...	0728*	0728*	...	0928*	...	1203	...	1228*	...	1328*	1423	...	1528*	1613	1628	...	1728	...	1828*
onte nelle Alpi-Polpet	a.	...	...	...	...	0702	...	0802*	0802*	...	1002*	...	1202	...	1302*	...	1402*	1505	...	1602*	1655	1702	...	1802	...	1902*
onte nelle Alpi-Polpet	d.	...	...	...	...	0703	...	0803*	0803*	...	1003*	...	1203	...	1303*	...	1403*	1506	...	1603*	1656	1703	...	1803	...	1903*
elluno	a.	...	...	...	...	0713	...	0813*	0813*	...	1013*	...	1215	...	1313*	...	1413*	1518	...	1613*	1708	1712	...	1813	...	1913*
elluno	d.	0434	0534	...	0634	...	0734	0834	0844		1034	...	...	1234	1334	...	1434	...	1534	1634	...	...	1734	...	1834	1934
eltre	d.	0505	0613	...	0713	...	0813	0913	0923	...	1113	...	...	1313	1413	...	1513	...	1613	1713	...	...	1813	...	1913	2013
lontebelluna	d.	0541	0656	0707	0807	...	0907	0956	0957	1007	1207	1307	...	1407	1457	1507	1607	...	1707	1807	...	...	1907	...	2007	2107
astelfranco Veneto	d.	0554	...	0725	0825	...	0925	...	1010	1025	1225	1325	...	1425	1510	1525	1625	...	1725	1825	...	...	1925	...	2025	2125
adova	a.	0620	...	0756	0856	...	0956	...	1038	1056	1256	1356	...	1456	1534	1556	1656	...	1756	1856	...	...	1956	...	2056	2156

– 3 minutes later on ①–⑤. * – Connection by 🚌. ▲ – Full name of station is Calalzo-Pieve di Cadore-Cortina.

VAL GARDENA / GRÖDNERTAL and CORTINA 🚌 services 604

Service 445/446		⚒										
. Candido / Innichen	d.	...	0838	...	1038	...	1338	...	1538	...	1738	...
obbiaco / Toblach ♣	d.	0710	0846	0910	1046	1110	1346	1410	1546	1610	1746	1818
ortina	a.	0755	...	0955	...	1155	...	1455	...	1655	...	1855

Service 445/446		⚒										
Cortina	d.	0805	...	1005	...	1305	...	1505	...	1705	...	1905
Dobbiaco / Toblach ♣	d.	0845	0910	1045	1110	1345	1410	1545	1610	1745	1810	1945
S. Candido / Innichen	a.	...	0918	...	1118	...	1418	...	1618	...	1818	...

♣ – Dobbiaco bus station. Services also call at Dobbiaco railway station en route between Dobbiaco town and Cortina (5 minutes from town stop).

Service 350		⚒										
olzano / Bozen ♦	d.	0628	0828	...	1128	...	...	1528	...	1728	...	1930
onte Gardena / Waidbruck	d.	0657	0857	1057	1157	1257	1357	1557	1657	1757	1857	1959
rtisei / St Ulrich ▲	d.	0727	0927	1127	1227	1327	1427	1627	1727	1827	1927	2029
anta/St Cristina ▲	d.	0740	0940	1140	1240	1340	1440	1640	1740	1840	1940	2042
elva / Wolkenstein ▲	d.	0748	0948	1148	1248	1348	1448	1648	1748	1848	1948	2050
lan ▲	a.	0752	0952	1152	1252	1352	1452	1652	1752	1852	1952	2054

Service 350		⚒										
Plan ▲	d.	0604	0704	0804	0904	1004	1204	1404	1504	1704	1804	1904
Selva / Wolkenstein ▲	d.	0607	0707	0707	0907	1007	1207	1407	1507	1707	1807	1907
Santa/St Cristina ▲	d.	0616	0716	0816	0916	1016	1216	1416	1516	1716	1618	1916
Ortisei / St Ulrich ▲	d.	0631	0731	0831	0931	1031	1231	1431	1531	1731	1831	1931
Ponte Gardena / Waidbruck	a.	0659	0759	0859	0959	1059	1259	1459	1559	1759	1859	2001
Bolzano / Bozen ♦	a.	0728	...	0928	...	...	1328	...	1628	...	1928	...

– Bolzano / Bozen town. Services also call at railway station (2 minutes from town stop). ▲ – Extra buses run Ortisei/St Ulrich - Plan and v.v. in summer.

alid until December 14, 2019.
perator: Servizi Autobus Dolomiti, Via Conciapelli 60, 39100, Bolzano / Bozen. ✆ : + 39 0471 450111 Fax: + 39 0471 970042.

🚌 service **30 Cortina – Calalzo**. 35 km. Journey time: 55 minutes.
alid September 12, 2018 – June 9, 2019.

Operator: Dolomitibus, via Col Da Ren 14, 32100, Belluno, Italy.
✆ +39 00 437 217 111, fax +39 00 437 940 522.

'om **Cortina Autostazione** (Bus Station):
0535⚒, 0623, 0650⚒, 0820, 0930⚒, 1115, 1220⚒, 1240⚒, 1240†, 1315⚒, 1402, 1505, 1620⚒, 1705, 1755⚒, 1920⚒, 1940⚒, 1940†, 2010⚒, 2010†.

From **Calalzo Stazione** (FS rail station):
0622⚒, 0658, 0720†, 0740⚒, 0820, 0935, 1100⑥, 1110Ⓐ, 1215⚒, 1215†, 1310⚒, 1310†, 1400⚒, 1400†, 1450, 1635, 1740⚒, 1850†, 1900⚒, 2035.

605 MILANO - VERONA - VENEZIA

km				FR			FR	FR	FR		FR	FR		FR	FR		FR	FR	EC	FR	EC		FR	EC
				9701			8505	9703	9705		9707	9709		9711	9713		9715	9717	1289	9723	37		9727	315
		2	2	🍷	2	2	🍷	🍷	🍷	2	🍷	🍷	2	🍷	🍷	2	🍷	🍷	✕	🍷	✕	2	🍷	✕
		Ⓐ	⚒	①–⑥	⚒	†	♦				Ⓐ			♦				Ⓒ a	♦		♦			♦
	Torino Porta Nuova **600** ....d.	...	...	...	...	...	...	...	...	...	0635	0705	...	...	0805	...	...	0905	...	1033	...	...	...	...
0	**Milano** Centrale....d.	...	...	0615	...	...	...	0645	0715	...	0745	0815	...	0845	0915	...	0945	1015	...	1145	1205	...	1245	1305
83	Brescia....d.	...	...	0653	0631	...	0702	0723	0753	...	0823	0853	...	0923	0953	...	1023	1053	...	1223	1253	...	1323	1353
111	Desenzano-Sirmione....d.	...	...	|	0654	...	|	0738	|	...	|	0908	...	|	1008	...	|	|	...	1238	|	...	1338	|
125	Peschiera del Garda ‡....d.	...	...	0714	0703	...	|	|	0814	...	0844	|	...	0944	|	...	1044	1114	...	|	1314	...	|	1414
148	**Verona** Porta Nuova....a.	...	...	0728	0719	...	0741	0758	0828	...	0858	0928	...	0958	1028	...	1058	1128	...	1258	1328	...	1358	1428
148	**Verona** Porta Nuova....d.	0521	0621	0730	0721	0721	...	0800	0830	0821	0900	0930	0921	1000	1030	1021	1100	1130	1238	1300	1330	1321	1400	1430
200	Vicenza....d.	0602	0702	0756	0801	0801	...	0826	0856	0902	0926	0956	1002	1026	1056	1102	1126	1156	1306s	1326	1356	1402	1426	1456
230	Padova.... **616** d.	0621	0721	0814	0821	0821	...	0844	0914	0921	0944	1014	1021	1044	1114	1121	1144	1214	1324s	1344	1414	1421	1444	1514
258	**Venezia** Mestre.... **616** a.	0636	0736	0828s	0836	0836	...	0858	0928s	0936	0958	1028s	1036	1058s	1128s	1136	1158s	1228	1341s	1358s	1428s	1436	1458s	1528s
258	**Venezia** Mestre.... **616** d.	0638	0738	|	0838	0838	...	0900	|	0938	1020	|	1038	|	|	1138	|	1244	|	|	|	1438	|	|
267	**Venezia** Santa Lucia.... **616** a.	0648	0748	0840	0848	0848	...	0910	0940	0948	|	1040	1048	1110	1140	1148	1210	|	1355	1410	1440	1448	1510	1540
	Udine **601**....a.	...	...	...	...	...	...	1059	...	...	|	...	...	...	...	...	...	|	...	...	...	...	...	...
	Trieste Centrale **601**....a.	...	...	...	...	...	...	...	...	...	1211	...	...	...	...	...	...	1422	...	...	...	...	...	...

		FR		FR	FR	FR		EC	FR			FA	FR		FR	FR	FR	FR	FR	FR	FR	FR	FR	
		9731		9793	9733	9737		87	9743			8525	9745		9747	9749	9751	9753	9755	9757	9759	9649	9761	
	2	🍷	2	🍷	🍷	🍷	2	✕	🍷	2		🍷	🍷	2	🍷	🍷	🍷	🍷	🍷	🍷	🍷	🍷	🍷	2
								◧ ♦				♦										e ♦	Ⓑ	
Torino Porta Nuova **600**....d.	...	...	...	1302b	...	1405	...	...	1505	...	...	...	...	...	1605	...	1705	...	...	1835	...	...	...	...
Milano Centrale....d.	...	1345	...	1415	1445	1515	...	...	1615	...	...	...	1645	...	1715	1745	1815	1845	1915	1945	2015	2115	2045	...
Brescia....d.	...	1423	...	1453	1523	1553	...	...	1653	...	...	1700	1723	...	1753	1823	1853	1923	1953	2023	2053	2153	2123	...
Desenzano-Sirmione....d.	...	|	...	1508	1538	|	...	...	1708	...	...	|	1738	...	|	1838	1908	|	2008	|	|	...	2138	...
Peschiera del Garda ‡....d.	...	1444	...	|	|	1614	...	...	|	...	...	1725	|	...	1814	|	|	1944	|	|	2114	...	2147	...
Verona Porta Nuova....a.	...	1458	...	1528	1558	1628	...	...	1728	...	...	1741	1758	...	1828	1858	1928	1958	2028	2053	2128	...	2201	...
Verona Porta Nuova....d.	1421	1500	1521	1530	1600	1630	1621	1700	1730	1721	...	...	1800	1821	1830	1900	1930	2000	2030	2055	2130	...	2203	2221
Vicenza....d.	1502	1526	1602	1556	1626	1656	1702	1724s	1756	1802	...	...	1826	1902	1856	1926	1956	2026	2056	|	2156	...	2229	2302
Padova.... **616** d.	1521	1544	1621	1614	1644	1714	1721	1742s	1814	1821	...	...	1844	1921	1914	1944	2014	2044	2114	|	2214	...	2247	2321
Venezia Mestre.... **616** a.	1536	1558s	1636	1628s	1658s	1728	1736	1758s	1828s	1836	...	...	1858s	1936	1928	1958s	2028s	2058	2128s	2145	2228s	...	2301s	2336
Venezia Mestre.... **616** d.	1538	|	1638	|	|	1746	1738	|	|	1838	...	...	|	1938	1949	|	|	2110	|	2155	|	...	|	2338
Venezia Santa Lucia.... **616** a.	1548	1610	1648	1640	1710	|	1748	1810	1840	1848	...	...	1910	1948	|	2010	2040	|	2140	|	2240	...	2313	2348
Udine **601**....a.	...	...	...	...	...	|	...	...	...	...	...	...	...	...	|	...	...	2237	...	|	...	...	...	...
Trieste Centrale **601**....a.	...	...	...	...	...	1929	...	...	...	...	...	...	...	...	2128	...	...	...	...	2334	...	...	...	...

	FR	FR		FR	FR		FR	FR	FR		FR	FR	FA	FR	FR		FA	FR		FR	FR		FR	EC
	9604	9700		9702	9706		9708	9710	9712		9714	9716	8510	9724	9726		8508	9728		9730	9732		9734	86
	🍷	🍷	2	🍷	🍷	2	🍷	🍷	🍷	2	🍷	🍷	🍷	🍷	🍷	2	🍷	🍷	2	🍷	🍷	2	🍷	✕
	a ♦	①–⑥	⚒					a					♦		c		♦		Ⓐ					◧ ♦
Trieste Centrale **601**....d.	...	...	...	...	...	...	...	0602	...	...	...	0705	...	...	0938	...	...	...	...	...	...	...	...	...
Udine **601**....d.	...	...	...	...	...	...	...	|	0615	...	...	|	...	...	|	...	...	...	...	...	...	...	...	...
Venezia Santa Lucia.... **616** d.	...	0540	0612	0620	0650	0712	0720	|	|	0812	0820	|	...	1050	|	1112	...	1150	1212	1220	1250	1312	1320	1350
Venezia Mestre.... **616** a.	...	|	0622	|	|	0722	|	0740	0749	0822	|	0851	...	|	1117	1122	...	|	1222	|	|	1322	|	|
Venezia Mestre.... **616** d.	...	0552u	0624	0632u	0702u	0724	0732u	0750	0802	0824	0832u	0902	...	1102u	1132	1124	...	1202u	1224	1232u	1302u	1324	1332u	1402u
Padova.... **616** d.	...	0607	0640	0648	0718	0740	0748	|	0818	0840	0848	0918	...	1118	1148	1140	...	1218	1240	1248	1318	1340	1348	1418
Vicenza....d.	...	0623	0659	0705	0735	0759	0805	|	0835	0859	0905	0935	1124	1135	1205	1159	...	1235	1259	1305	1335	1359	1405	1435
Verona Porta Nuova....a.	...	0650	0739	0730	0800	0840	0830	0844	0900	0939	0930	1000	1150	1200	1230	1239	...	1300	1339	1330	1400	1439	1430	1500
Verona Porta Nuova....d.	...	0652	...	0732	0802	...	0832	0846	0902	...	0932	1002	...	1202	1232	...	1251	1302	...	1332	1402	...	1432	...
Peschiera del Garda ‡....d.	...	0707	...	0748	|	...	0848	|	|	...	0947	|	...	|	|	...	1306	1318	...	1348	|	...	1448	...
Desenzano-Sirmione....d.	...	0716	...	|	0823	...	|	|	0923	...	|	1023	...	1223	1253	...	|	|	...	|	1423	...	|	...
Brescia....d.	0517	0734	...	0809	0839	...	0909	|	0939	...	1009	1039	...	1239	1309	...	1332	1339	...	1409	1439	...	1509	...
Milano Centrale....a.	0555	0812	...	0845	0915	...	0945	0950	1017	...	1045	1115	...	1315	1345	...	...	1415	...	1445	1515	...	1545	...
Torino Porta Nuova **600**....a.	...	...	...	1000	...	...	...	1100	...	...	1155	...	...	...	1455	...	...	...	...	...	...	...	1655	...

		FR	FR		EC	EC	FR			EC	FR		FR	FR		FR	FR		FR		FR	FR		
		9738	9740		310	1288	9744			42	9748		9750	9754		9756	9758		9762		8528	9764		
	2	🍷	🍷	2	✕	✕	🍷	2	2	🍷	🍷	2	🍷	🍷	2	🍷	🍷	2	🍷	2	🍷	🍷	2	2
					♦	♦	♦	†	⚒	♦											♦	Ⓑ		Ⓒ
Trieste Centrale **601**....d.	...	...	...	...	...	...	...	...	...	...	...	...	...	...	...	...	1702	...	...	...	...	...	...	...
Udine **601**....d.	...	...	1300	...	...	...	...	...	...	...	...	...	...	...	...	...	|	...	...	...	...	...	...	...
Venezia Santa Lucia.... **616** d.	1412	1420	1450	1512	1520	1535	1550	1612	1612	1620	1650	1712	1720	1750	1812	1820	|	1912	1950	2012	...	2050	2112	2135
Venezia Mestre.... **616** a.	1422	|	1500	1522	|	|	|	1622	1622	|	|	1722	|	|	1822	|	1842	1922	|	2022	...	|	2122	2147
Venezia Mestre.... **616** d.	1424	1432u	1502	1524	1532u	1547u	1602u	1624	1624	1632u	1702u	1724	1732u	1802u	1824	1832u	1902	1924	2002u	2024	...	2102u	2124	2149
Padova.... **616** d.	1440	1448	1518	1540	1548	1606u	1618	1640	1640	1648	1718	1740	1748	1818	1840	1848	1918	1940	2018	2040	...	2118	2140	2226
Vicenza....d.	1459	1505	1535	1559	1605	1622u	1635	1659	1659	1705	1735	1759	1805	1835	1859	1905	1935	1959	2035	2059	...	2135	2159	2253
Verona Porta Nuova....a.	1539	1530	1600	1639	1630	1651	1700	1739	1739	1730	1800	1839	1830	1900	1939	1930	2000	2039	2100	2139	...	2200	2239	2336
Verona Porta Nuova....d.	...	1532	1602	...	1632	...	1702	...	1749	1732	1802	...	1832	1902	...	1932	2002	...	2102	...	2151	2202	...	...
Peschiera del Garda ‡....d.	...	|	|	...	1648	...	|	...	1807	1748	|	...	1848	1918	...	|	2018	...	|	...	|	2218	...	...
Desenzano-Sirmione....d.	...	1553	1623	...	|	...	1723	...	1816	|	1823	...	|	|	...	1953	|	...	2123	...	|	|	...	...
Brescia....d.	...	1609	1639	...	1709	...	1739	...	1842	1809	1839	...	1909	1939	...	2009	2039	...	2139	...	2232	2239	...	...
Milano Centrale....a.	...	1645	1715	...	1755	...	1815	...	...	1855	1915	...	1945	2015	...	2045	2115	...	2215	...	...	2315	...	...
Torino Porta Nuova **600**....a.	...	1755	...	...	...	...	...	...	...	...	...	...	2055	...	...	...	...	...	2330d	...	...	...	...	...

Other local services **MILANO - VERONA** — Operator: Trenord

					†																			🚌
Milano Centrale....d.	0625	0725	0825	...	0925	...	1125	1225	1325	1425	...	1525	1625	...	1725	1825	...	1925	2025	2125	2225	2325	0015	...
Milano Lambrate....d.	0633	0733	0833	...	0933	...	1133	1233	1333	1433	...	1533	1633	...	1733	1833	...	1933	2033	2133	2233	2333	0022	...
Treviglio....d.	0656	0756	0856	...	0956	...	1156	1256	1356	1456	...	1556	1656	...	1756	1856	...	1956	2056	2156	2256	2356	0048	...
Brescia....d.	0732	0832	0932	...	1032	...	1232	1332	1432	1532	...	1632	1732	...	1832	1932	...	2032	2132	2232	2332	0032	0135	0140
Desenzano-Sirmione....d.	0748	0848	0948	...	1048	...	1248	1348	1448	1548	...	1648	1748	...	1848	1948	...	2048	2148	2248	2348	0048	...	0210
Peschiera del Garda ‡....d.	0758	0858	0958	...	1058	...	1258	1358	1458	1558	...	1658	1758	...	1858	1958	...	2058	2158	2258	2358	0058	...	0230
Verona Porta Nuova....a.	0815	0915	1015	...	1115	...	1315	1415	1515	1615	...	1715	1815	...	1915	2015	...	2115	2215	2315	0015	0115	...	0300

			Ⓐ					2									†							
Verona Porta Nuova....d.	0545	0645	0655	0745	...	0840	0945	...	1245	1345	1445	1545	...	1645	1745	...	1817	1845	...	1945	2045	...	2145	...
Peschiera del Garda ‡....d.	0559	0659	0712	0759	...	0859	0959	...	1259	1359	1459	1559	...	1659	1759	...	1832	1859	...	1959	2059	...	2159	...
Desenzano-Sirmione....d.	0609	0709	0722	0809	...	0909	1009	...	1309	1409	1509	1609	...	1709	1809	...	1842	1909	...	2009	2109	...	2209	...
Brescia....d.	0628	0728	0740	0828	...	0928	1028	1248	1328	1428	1528	1628	...	1728	1828	...	1900	1928	...	2028	2128	...	2228	...
Treviglio....d.	0705	0805	0813	0905	...	1005	1105	1335	1405	1505	1605	1705	...	1805	1905	...	1935	2005	...	2105	2205	...	2305	...
Milano Lambrate....d.	0728	0828	0837	0928	...	1028	1128	1402	1428	1528	1628	1728	...	1828	1928	...	1958	2028	...	2128	2228	...	2328	...
Milano Centrale....a.	0735	0835	0845	0935	...	1035	1135	1410	1435	1535	1635	1735	...	1835	1935	...	2005	2035	...	2135	2235	...	2335	...

♦ – **NOTES** (LISTED BY TRAIN NUMBER)

37/42 – (12) and 🍷 Genève - Milano - Venezia and v.v. Ⓡ inclusive of supplement.
86/87 – (12) and ✕ Venezia - Verona - München and v.v.
310/15 – (12) and ✕ Zürich - Milano - Venezia and v.v. Ⓡ inclusive of supplement.
1288/9 – ⑥⑦: (12) and ✕ Venezia - Verona - München and v.v. Operated within Italy by LeNord.
8505 – (12) and 🍷 Bergamo (d. 0612) - Brescia - Verona - Roma.
8508 – (12) and 🍷 Roma - Verona - Brescia - Bergamo (a. 1420).
8510 – (12) and 🍷 Vicenza (**8510**) - Verona (**8511**) - Roma.
8525 – (12) and 🍷 Bergamo (d. 1600) - Brescia - Verona - Roma.
8528 – (12) and 🍷 Roma - Verona - Brescia - Bergamo (a. 2310).
9604 – (12) and 🍷 Brescia (**9604**) - Milano (**9605**) - Napoli.
9649 – (12) and 🍷 Napoli (**9650**) - Roma - Bologna - Milano (**9649**) - Brescia.
9711 – (12) and 🍷 Genova (**9796**) - Milano (**9711**) - Venezia.
9744 – (12) and 🍷 Venezia (**9744**) - Milano (**9795**) - Genova.

a – June 9 - July 27.
b – Ⓑ only.
c – June 9 - Sept. 15.
d – Arrives 0020 on certain dates (see Table **600**).
e – Not Aug. 7 – 18.
s – Stops to set down only.
u – Stops to pick up only.
♠ – Operator: Trenord.
◧ – Also available to passengers without reservation. Operated within Italy by LeNord.
‡ – Station for Gardaland Park. Free shuttle bus available.

MILANO LOCAL SERVICES 607

Operator: Trenord

MILANO - BERGAMO

Some services 2nd class only

km							Ⓐ	Ⓒ		Ⓐ	Ⓒ	
0	**Milano** Centrale d.	0535	0605	0705	0805	0905	1005	1005	...	1105	1105	1205
56	**Bergamo** a.	0623	0653	0753	0853	0953	1055	1100	...	1153	1158	1253

Milano Centrale d.	1305	1405	1505	1605	1705	1805	1905	2005	2105	2205	2340
Bergamo a.	1353	1453	1553	1653	1753	1853	1953	2053	2153	2255	0050

				Ⓐ			Ⓒ	Ⓐ	Ⓒ	Ⓐ	
Bergamo d.	0500	0602	0702	0735	0802	0902	0957	1002	1057	1102	1202
Milano Centrale a.	0550	0650	0750	0830	0850	0950	1050	1050	1150	1150	1250

Bergamo d.	1302	1402	1502	1602	1702	1802	1902	2002	2102	2202	2300
Milano Centrale a.	1350	1450	1550	1650	1750	1850	1950	2050	2150	2250	2350

Additional trains run approximately hourly Milano Porta Garibaldi - Bergamo via Monza, journey 54 minutes, *43 km*.

BRESCIA - EDOLO

2nd class only

km		⚒	†						Ⓐ		
0	**Brescia** d.	0555	0707	0907	1107	1307	1507	1707	1758	1907	...
103	**Edolo** a.	0834	0907	1107	1307	1507	1707	1907	2018	2107	...

	⚒	⚒							†	
Edolo d.	0554	0647	0754	0954	1154	1354	1554	1754	1954	...
Brescia a.	0754	0903	0954	1154	1354	1554	1754	1954	2200	...

For 🚌 Edolo - Tirano see Table **593**.

MILANO - COMO LAGO

46 km Journey: 52 – 65 minutes 2nd class only

From **Milano** Cadorna: 0613 ⚒, 0643, 0713 Ⓐ, 0743, 0800 Ⓐ, 0813 Ⓐ, 0843, 0900, 0943, 1043, 1143, 1213 ⚒, 1243, 1313 Ⓐ, 1343, 1400 †, 1413 Ⓐ, 1443, 1513 Ⓐ, 1543, 1613 Ⓐ, 1643, 1700 Ⓐ, 1713 ⚒, 1743, 1800 Ⓐ, 1813, 1843, 1900 Ⓐ, 1913 ⚒, 1943, 2013 ⚒, 2043, 2113 Ⓐ, 2143, 2243.

From **Como Nord Lago**: 0546 ⚒, 0616, 0635 Ⓐ, 0646 ⚒, 0716, 0735 Ⓐ, 0746 ⚒, 0816, 0835 ⚒, 0916, 0946 Ⓐ, 1016, 1116, 1216, 1246 Ⓐ, 1316, 1346 ⚒, 1416, 1446 Ⓐ, 1516, 1546 Ⓐ, 1616, 1646 Ⓐ, 1716, 1746 Ⓐ, 1816, 1835 †, 1846 ⚒, 1916, 1946, 2016, 2046 ⚒, 2116.

A reduced service operates in peak summer.

MILANO - VARESE - LAVENO

72 km Journey: 87 – 107 mins 2nd class only

From **Milano** Cadorna: 0609 ⚒, 0639, 0709 Ⓐ, 0752, 0852, 0939, 1039, 1139, 1209 ⚒, 1252, 1352, 1439 Ⓒ, 1452 Ⓐ, 1539, 1609 Ⓐ, 1652, 1722 Ⓐ, 1752, 1822 Ⓐ, 1852, 1922 Ⓐ, 1939 Ⓒ, 2022 Ⓐ, 2039 Ⓒ.

From **Laveno-Mombello** FN: 0538 Ⓐ, 0608 ⚒, 0638, 0708 Ⓐ, 0738, 0808 Ⓐ, 0838, 0938, 1038, 1138, 1238, 1308 ⚒, 1338, 1438, 1538, 1638, 1738, 1808 Ⓐ, 1838, 1938, 2038.

A reduced service operates in peak summer.

MILANO - LUINO

2nd class only

km			Ⓐ		†				Ⓐ		Ⓐ	
0	**Milano** P Garibaldi d.	...	...	0806	...	...	...	...	1806	...	1906	...
	Gallarate d.	0608	0719	0842	1019	1319	1519	1719	1842	1919	1942	2119
	Laveno-Mombello d.	0641	0801	0927	1101	1401	1601	1801	1922	2001	2022	2201
91	**Luino** a.	0702	0816	0941	1116	1416	1616	1816	1941	2016	2041	2216

	Ⓒ	Ⓐ	Ⓐ	⚒	†						Ⓐ	Ⓒ
Luino d.	0604	0619	0720	1000	1044	1344	1544	1744	1944	2045	2144	2152
Laveno-Mombello d.	0620	0642	0736	1032	1100	1400	1600	1800	2000	2100	2200	2216
Gallarate d.	0653	0719	0806	1146	1141	1441	1641	1841	2041	2141	2241	2325
Milano P Garibaldi a.	0728	0757	0844	...	...	...	...	...	...	...	...	...

MILANO - CREMONA - MANTOVA

km											
0	**Milano** Centrale d.	0620	0820	1020	1220	1420	1620	1715	1820	1915	2020
60	Codogno d.	0702	0902	1102	1302	1502	1702	1758	1902	1958	2102
88	Cremona d.	0732	0930	1130	1330	1530	1730	1820	1930	2020	2130
151	**Mantova** a.	0825	1019	1210	1410	1619	1821	1919	2019	2110	2210

Mantova d.	0518	0610	0641	0841	1041	1241	1441	1641	1841	2050
Cremona d.	0617	0656	0732	0930	1130	1330	1530	1730	1930	2130
Codogno a.	0638	0717	0752	0952	1152	1352	1552	1752	1952	2152
Milano Centrale a.	0730	0810	0842	1040	1240	1440	1640	1840	2040	2240

MILANO - PORTO CERESIO

km										
0	**Milano** P Garibaldi d.	0632	0732	0832	0932		1732	1832	1932	2032
13	Rho Fiera Milano d.	0645	0745	0845	0945	and	1745	1845	1945	2045
44	Gallarate **592** d.	0707	0807	0907	1007	hourly	1807	1907	2007	2107
63	Varese **592** d.	0725	0825	0925	1025	until	1825	1925	2025	2125
77	**Porto Ceresio** a.	0745	0845	0945	1045		1845	1945	2045	2145

Porto Ceresio d.	0516	0616	0716	0816		1816	1916	2016	2116
Verese **592** d.	0536	0636	0736	0836	and	1836	1936	2036	2136
Gallarate **592** d.	0552	0702	0752	0852	hourly	1852	1952	2052	...
Rho Fiera Milano d.	0615	0733	0815	0915	until	1915	2015	2115	...
Milano P Garibaldi a.	0628	0746	0828	0928		1928	2028	2128	...

☛ Minor alterations are possible, especially around holiday dates. Operator: Trenord. ✆ 800 500 005. www.trenord.it

Local services in NORTHERN and CENTRAL ITALY 609

2nd class only

ALESSANDRIA - ACQUI TERME

34 km Journey 28 – 38 minutes

From **Alessandria**: 0640, 0740, 0935, 1040 ⚒, 1140, 1340, 1540, 1740, 1940.

From **Acqui Terme**: 0645 ⚒, 0737, 0942, 1137, 1337, 1437 ⚒, 1537, 1737, 1937.

BOLOGNA - PORRETTA TERME

59 km Journey 60 – 72 minutes

From **Bologna** Centrale: 0552 ⚒§, 0630 ⚒, 0704, 0804 ⚒, 0904 ⚒§, 0904 †, 1004 ⚒, 1104, 1204 ⚒§, 1204 †, 1304, 1404, 1504, 1604 §, 1704, 1734, 1804, 1834 Ⓐ, 1904 Ⓐ, 1904 Ⓒ§, 1934 Ⓐ§, 2004, 2104, 2204.

From **Porretta Terme**: 0500 ⚒, 0550, 0608, 0640, 0718 ⚒§, 0718 †, 0750 ⚒, 0822, 0922 ⚒, 1022 ⚒§, 1022 †, 1122 ⚒, 1222, 1322, 1422 ⚒§, 1422 †, 1522, 1622, 1722 §, 1821, 1921, 2021 Ⓐ, 2021 Ⓒ§, 2050 Ⓐ, 2122 Ⓐ§.

CAMPIGLIA - PIOMBINO

16 km Journey 22 – 30 minutes

From **Campiglia Marittima**: 0556 ⚒, 1003 ⑥, 1336 ⚒, 1533, 1640, 1736 Ⓐ, 1806.

From **Piombino Marittima**: 0632 ⚒, 0920, 1053 ⑥†, 1527 ⚒, 1608, 1724, 1812 Ⓐ, 1845.

GENOVA - ACQUI TERME

58 km Journey 65 – 81 minutes

From **Genova** Piazza Principe: 0612 Ⓐ, 0713, 0917, 1020 ⚒, 1120, 1220 Ⓐ, 1320, 1420 Ⓐ, 1620, 1721 Ⓐ, 1820, 1920, 2043.

From **Acqui Terme**: 0520 Ⓐ, 0604, 0703 ⚒, 0740 Ⓐ, 0917, 1117, 1217, 1317, 1417 Ⓐ, 1617, 1717 Ⓐ, 1817, 2040.

MANTOVA - MODENA

61 km Journey 60 – 90 minutes

From **Mantova**: 0535 ⚒, 0629, 0729 ⚒§, 0829, 0929, 1129, 1229 ⚒§, 1329, 1429 ⚒, 1529 ⚒§, 1529 †, 1629 ⚒, 1729, 1829 ⚒§, 1929, 2029 ⚒, 2129 ⚒§, 2129 †.

From **Modena**: 0549 ⚒§, 0630 ⚒, 0707 †, 0709 ⚒, 0809 ⚒, 0907 †, 0909 ⚒, 1107 †, 1209 ⚒, 1307 †, 1309 ⚒, 1409 ⚒§, 1507 †, 1509 ⚒, 1609 ⚒, 1707 †, 1709 ⚒§, 1809 ⚒, 1907 †, 1909 ⚒, 2007 †, 2009 ⚒§, 2131 ⚒, 2207 †, 2209 ⚒.

PORRETTA TERME - PISTOIA

40 km Journey 60 – 75 minutes

From **Porretta Terme**: 0655 ⚒, 0717, 0926 ⚒, 1322, 1524, 1824.

From **Pistoia**: 0600, 0823 ⚒, 1220, 1420, 1721, 1926.

ROVIGO - CHIOGGIA

km		⚒		⚒	Ⓑ	†	⚒	⚒	†	⚒	Ⓑ	Ⓐ	
0	**Rovigo** d.	0615	0715	0815	0915	1115	1315	1415	1515	1615	1715	1815	1915
25	Adria d.	0642	0742	0842	0942	1142	1342	1442	1542	1642	1742	1842	1942
57	**Chioggia** a.	0725	0825	0925	1025	1225	1425	1525	1625	1725	1825	1925	2025

	⚒	⚒		Ⓑ		⚒	†	⚒	Ⓐ		Ⓐ	Ⓑ	⑥
Chioggia d.	0535	0635	0735	0935	...	1235	1335	1435	1535	1735	1835	1935	2035
Adria d.	0614	0714	0814	1014	...	1314	1414	1514	1614	1814	1914	2014	2114
Rovigo a.	0645	0745	0845	1045	...	1345	1445	1545	1645	1845	1945	2045	2145

SANTHIÀ - BIELLA S. PAOLO

27 km Journey 20 – 35 minutes

From **Santhià**: 0550 ⚒, 0650 ⚒, 0750, 0850 ⚒, 0950, 1150, 1250 ⚒, 1350, 1450 ⚒, 1550, 1650 ⚒, 1750, 1850 ⚒, 1915 Ⓐ, 1950, 2050, 2150.

From **Biella S. Paolo**: 0551 ⚒, 0648 †, 0651 ⚒, 0720 Ⓐ, 0751 ⚒, 0848 †, 0851 ⚒, 0951 ⚒, 1048 †, 1151 ⚒, 1248 †, 1251 ⚒, 1351 ⚒, 1448 †, 1451 ⚒, 1551 ⚒, 1648 †, 1651 ⚒, 1751 ⚒, 1848 †, 1951 ⚒, 1943 †, 1951 ⚒, 2048 †, 2051 ⚒, 2151 ⚒.

SIENA - GROSSETO

km		⚒	†	⚒	†	⚒	†	⚒	⚒	†	†	⚒		
0	**Siena** d.	0545	0748	0810	0943	1209	1243	1322	1542	1544	1738	1745	1846	1943
29	Buonconvento d.	0623	0819	0845	1012	1238	1312	1351	1610	1613	1815	1816	1934	2013
102	**Grosseto** a.	0735	0920	0948	1123	1342	1419	1502	1724	1715	1923	1924	2045	2118

	⚒	†	⚒		⚒		†	⚒	⚒	†	⚒		
Grosseto d.	0500	0500	0601	0716	0958	1004	1323	1330	1500	1617	1632	1755	1952
Buonconvento d.	0554	0559	0718	0818	1102	1107	1435	1441	1611	1732	1732	1906	2100
Siena a.	0623	0629	0748	0846	1140	1137	1508	1513	1643	1805	1810	1940	2130

TRENTO - BASSANO DEL GRAPPA

97 km Journey 120 – 130 minutes

From **Trento**: 0505 ⚒, 0605, 0700 ⚒‡**n**, 0800 ⚒‡**n**, 0805 †‡, 0905, 1005 ⚒‡, 1105 ⚒, 1105 †‡, 1205 ⚒, 1305, 1405 ⚒‡, 1505 ‡, 1605 ⚒, 1705, 1805 ⚒, 1905, 2005 ⚒‡.

From **Bassano del Grappa**: 0500 ⚒, 0621 ⚒‡, 0725 ⚒, 0725 †‡, 0825 ⚒, 0925 ⚒‡**n**, 0925 †, 1025 ⚒**n**, 1125 ⚒, 1125 †‡, 1225 ⚒‡, 1325, 1425 ⚒, 1525, 1625 ⚒‡, 1725 †‡, 1825 ⚒‡, 1925, 2025 ⚒, 2125.

All services call at Levico Terme and Borgo Valsugana Centro (*31/44 km*, ± 50/65 minutes from Trento, respectively).

VENEZIA - BASSANO DEL GRAPPA

km		⚒	⚒	⚒						
0	**Venezia** Santa Lucia d.	0526	0556	0626	0656	0756	0856	and	2056	2156
9	Venezia Mestre d.	0540	0608	0640	0708	0808	0908	hourly	2108	2210
45	Castelfranco Veneto d.	0628	0646	0728	0746	0846	0946	until	2146	2252
64	**Bassano del Grappa** a.	0644	0707	0744	0807	0907	1007		2207	2313

	⚒	⚒		⚒					
Bassano del Grappa d.	0523	0546	0623	0646	0723	0823	and	2023	2123
Castelfranco Veneto d.	0546	0604	0646	0704	0746	0846	hourly	2046	2146
Venezia Mestre a.	0622	0650	0722	0750	0822	0922	until	2122	2226
Venezia Santa Lucia a.	0634	0704	0734	0804	0834	0934		2134	2240

Additional services operate on ⚒.

VERONA - MANTOVA

37 km Journey 45 – 50 minutes

From **Verona** Porta Nuova: 0632 ⚒, 0732 ⚒, 0832 ⚒, 0932, 1232 ⚒, 1332, 1432 ⚒, 1532, 1632 ⚒, 1732, 1832 ⚒, 1932, 2032 ⚒, 2132 †.

From **Mantova**: 0629 ⚒, 0729 ⚒, 0829, 0929 ⚒, 1229, 1329 ⚒, 1429, 1529 ⚒, 1629, 1729 ⚒, 1829, 1929 ⚒, 2029.

– By 🚌. ‡ – Operator: *TTE* ✆ contact centre 0461 821000; www.ttesercizio.it § – Operator: *TPER*. Trenitalia tickets valid.

610 TORINO and MILANO - GENOVA - PISA

Subject to alteration August 15 – 29.

km		2⚒	IC 501 ♦	2	FB 8601 🍷	FA 8583 ①–⑥ ♦	2⚒	2	FB 8605 🍷	2	2	IC 651	IC 503 2	⚒	2	EC 141 🍷 N	IC 505 ♦		2	IC 657 Ⓐ ♦	IC 1533 Ⓒ ♦	2	2⚒	2	IC 659 Ⓐ V
0	**Torino** Porta Nuova 615 d.	...	...	...	...	...	...	...	...	...	0530	...	0605	...	0630	...	...	...	0730	...	...	...	...	0820	...
56	Asti 615 d.	...	...	...	...	...	...	...	...	...	0607	...	0641	...	0707	...	...	...	0807	...	...	...	...	0904	...
91	Alessandria 615 d.	...	...	...	...	...	...	...	...	...	0631	...	0702	...	0731	...	...	...	0831	...	...	...	...	0931	...
112	Novi Ligure d.	...	...	...	...	...	...	...	...	...	0644	...	0716	...	0744	...	...	...	0844	...	...	...	...	0944	...
	Milano Centrale d.	...	...	...	...	...	...	...	...	...	|	0610	|	0625	|	0710	...	0725	|	0810	0810	...	...	|	0910
	Milano Rogoredo d.	...	...	...	...	...	...	...	...	...	|	|	|	0638	|	|	...	0738	|	|	|	...	...	|	|
	Pavia d.	...	...	...	...	...	...	...	...	...	|	0635	|	0700	|	0735	...	0800	|	0835	0835	...	...	|	0935
	Voghera 615 d.	...	...	...	...	...	...	...	...	...	|	|	|	0715	|	0751	...	0815	|	0851	0851	...	...	|	|
	Tortona 615 d.	...	...	...	...	...	...	...	...	...	|	0659	|	0725	|	|	...	0825	|	|	|	...	...	|	0959
166	**Genova** Piazza Principe a.	...	...	...	...	...	...	...	...	...	0730	0744	0803	0818	0830	0844	...	0908	0928	0944	0944	...	...	1030	1044
166	**Genova** Piazza Principe d.	...	...	...	0515	0610	...	...	0705	0711	0732	0747	...	0818	...	...	0851	0911	0930	0947	0947	...	...	1032	...
169	**Genova** Brignole d.	...	...	0500	0522u	0617u	...	0600	0712u	0720	0739	0756	...	0826	...	...	0900	0920	0939	0956	0956	1045	...	1039	...
194	S. Margherita-Portofino d.	...	...	0528	|	|	...	0632	|	0759	▬	0820	...	...	...	...	|	1002	▬	1016	1016	1115	...	...	...
196	Rapallo d.	...	...	0532	|	|	...	0636	0737	0803	...	0825	...	...	...	...	0922	1007	...	1021	1021	1119	...	...	...
205	Chiavari d.	...	...	0540	0548	|	...	0650	0746	0811	...	0834	...	...	...	...	0931	1016	...	1030	1030	1127	...	...	...
212	Sestri Levante d.	...	0505	0550	|	|	...	0700	|	0820	...	0842	...	...	...	...	0938	1028	...	1038	1038	1135	...	...	...
235	Levanto d.	...	0522	0617	|	|	...	0720	|	0844	...	0901	...	...	...	...	|	...	...	1100	1100	1150	...	...	...
240	Monterosso d.	...	0528	0622	|	|	...	0725	|	0849	2	0907	...	...	...	...	|	...	2	1107	1107	|	...	...	...
249	Riomaggiore d.	...	|	0638	|	|	...	|	|	0903	†	|	...	...	...	...	|	...		|	|	1203	...	...	...
256	**La Spezia** Centrale d.	0443	0544	0650	0618	0709	0739	0740	0816	0913	0915	0923	...	...	...	...	1011	...	1020	1123	1123	1210	1215	...	...
272	Sarzana d.	0459	0557	...	|	|	0758	...	|	...	0931	|	...	...	...	...	|	...	1035	|	|	...	1228	...	...
282	Carrara-Avenza d.	0507	0606	...	|	|	0805	...	|	...	0939	|	...	...	...	...	|	...	1043	|	1141	...	1236	...	...
289	Massa Centro d.	0513	0614	...	0638	|	0812	...	0836	...	0946	0945	...	...	...	...	1033	...	1049	1145	1148	...	1242	...	...
310	Viareggio d.	0530	0628	...	0650	|	0830	...	0848	...	1011	1000	...	...	...	...	1046	...	1109	1200	1209	...	1259	...	...
331	**Pisa** Centrale a.	0551	0644	...	0704	0747	0849	...	0904	...	1038	1017	...	...	...	...	1101	...	1139	1217	1223	...	1322	...	...
	Livorno Centrale 611 a.	...	0701	...	0720	|	...	...	0920	...	...	1035	...	...	...	...	1124	...	...	1235	1240	...	...	...	...
	Roma Termini 611 a.	...	1015o	...	1003	1001t	...	...	1203	...	...	...	...	...	...	...	1433	...	...	...	...	...	...	...	...

	IC 1535 Ⓒ V	FB 8613 🍷	2	2	2	EC 143 🍷 N	IC 511 ♦	2	2Ⓐ	2	IC 665		2	2	FB 8619 🍷 c	2	IC 669	2	2		EC 159 🍷 M		FB 8623 🍷 b	2
Torino Porta Nuova 615 d.	...	...	...	...	1030	...	1040	...	...	1130	...	...	1230	...	...	1330	...	1430	...	...	...	...	1520	1530
Asti 615 d.	...	...	...	...	1107	...	1113	...	...	1207	...	...	1307	...	...	1407	...	1507	...	...	...	...	1600	1607
Alessandria 615 d.	...	...	...	...	1131	...	1136	...	...	1231	...	...	1331	...	...	1431	...	1531	...	...	...	...	1616	1631
Novi Ligure d.	...	...	...	...	1144	...	|	...	...	1244	...	...	1344	...	...	1444	...	1544	...	...	...	...	|	1644
Milano Centrale d.	0910	...	...	...	|	1110	|	...	...	|	1210	1225	|	...	1310	|	1405	|	...	1425	1505	...	|	|
Milano Rogoredo d.	|	...	...	...	|	|	|	...	...	|	|	1238	|	...	|	|	1416u	|	...	1438	|	...	|	|
Pavia d.	0935	...	...	...	|	1135	|	...	...	|	1235	1300	|	...	1335	|	1435	|	...	1500	1535	...	|	|
Voghera 615 d.	|	...	...	...	|	1151	|	...	...	|	|	1315	|	...	|	|	1451	|	...	1515	1551	...	|	|
Tortona 615 d.	0959	...	...	...	|	|	|	...	...	|	1259	1325	|	...	|	|	|	|	...	1525	|	...	|	|
Genova Piazza Principe a.	1044	...	...	...	1235	1244	1221	...	...	1330	1344	1418	1430	...	1437	1530	1544	1630	...	1618	1644	...	1700	1730
Genova Piazza Principe d.	...	1210	...	...	1237	...	1224	...	...	1332	1347	1418	1432	...	1502	1532	1547	1632	...	...	...	...	1705	1732
Genova Brignole d.	...	1217u	...	1245	1243	...	1233	...	1320	1339	1356	1427	1439	1445	1512	1539	1556	1639	1645	...	...	...	1712	1739
S. Margherita-Portofino d.	...	|	...	1315	...	...	|	...	1402	▬	1416	▬	...	1515	|	▬	|	▬	1715	...	...	...	|	...
Rapallo d.	...	|	...	1319	...	...	1304	...	1407	...	1421	...	...	1519	1537	...	1621	...	1719	...	...	...	1737	...
Chiavari d.	...	1246	...	1327	...	...	1313	...	1417	...	1430	...	...	1527	1546	...	1630	...	1727	...	...	...	1746	...
Sestri Levante d.	...	|	...	1335	...	...	1321	...	1429	...	1438	...	...	1535	|	...	1638	...	1735	...	...	...	|	...
Levanto d.	...	|	...	1350	...	...	|	...	1510	...	1500	...	...	1550	|	...	1700	...	1750	...	...	...	|	...
Monterosso d.	...	|	...	1355	...	...	|	...	1516	2	1507	2	...	1555	|	2	1707	2	1755	...	...	...	|	...
Riomaggiore d.	...	|	...	|	...	...	|	...	|	†	|		...	1604	|	†	|		|	...	...	...	|	...
La Spezia Centrale d.	...	1316	1319	1410	...	...	1352	1414	1540	1441	1521	1540	...	1610	1616	1641	1721	1740	1810	...	...	...	1816	...
Sarzana d.	...	|	1334	...	...	...	|	1429	...	1500	...	1600	...	...	|	1700	...	1800	...	...	...	...	|	...
Carrara-Avenza d.	...	|	1342	...	...	...	1411	1439	...	1508	...	1608	...	...	|	1708	...	1808	...	...	...	...	|	...
Massa Centro d.	...	1336	1348	...	...	...	1419	1445	...	1514	...	1614	...	...	1636	1714	...	1814	...	...	...	...	1836	...
Viareggio d.	...	1348	1406	...	...	...	1434	1502	...	1533	...	1633	...	...	1648	1733	...	1834	...	...	...	...	1848	...
Pisa Centrale a.	...	1404	1427	...	...	...	1447	1526	...	1551	...	1651	...	...	1704	1751	...	1851	...	...	...	...	1904	...
Livorno Centrale 611 a.	...	1420	...	...	...	...	1502	...	...	...	...	...	...	...	1720	...	...	...	...	...	...	...	1920	...
Roma Termini 611 a.	...	1703	...	...	...	...	1803	...	...	...	...	...	...	...	2003	...	...	...	...	...	...	...	2203	...

	IC 673	Ⓒ	Ⓐ	2	IC 675 V	FB 8627 🍷 ⊙♦	2	2	IC 679	FR 9795 🍷 ♦	IC 519 2	2	2	IC 685	2	IC 689 V	ICN 1963 ⊙♦	IC 687 d	IC 687 e	2	A	2	ICN 799 ♦	♠
Torino Porta Nuova 615 d.	...	...	...	...	...	...	...	1730	...	...	1805	1830	...	...	1930	...	...	...	...	...	...	2130	2155	...
Asti 615 d.	...	...	...	...	...	...	...	1807	...	...	1843	1907	...	...	2007	...	...	...	...	...	...	2207	2236	...
Alessandria 615 d.	...	...	...	...	...	...	...	1831	...	...	1902	1931	...	...	2031	...	...	...	...	...	...	2231	2259	...
Novi Ligure d.	...	...	...	...	...	...	...	1844	...	...	1916	1944	...	...	2044	...	...	...	...	...	...	2244	|	...
Milano Centrale d.	1605	1625	1625	...	1705	...	...	|	1805	1825	|	|	...	1905	|	2000	2010	2110	2110	...	2025	|	|	2325
Milano Rogoredo d.	1616u	1638	1638	...	1716u	...	...	|	1816u	1837	|	|	...	1916u	|	2012u	|	|	|	...	2038	|	|	2338
Pavia d.	1635	1700	1700	...	1735	...	...	|	1835	|	|	|	...	1935	|	2032	2038	2135	2135	...	2100	|	|	2359
Voghera 615 d.	1651	1715	1715	...	1751	...	...	|	1851	|	|	|	...	1951	|	2049	2056	2151	2151	...	2115	|	|	0023
Tortona 615 d.	|	1725	1725	...	|	...	...	|	1901	|	|	|	...	|	|	|	2108	|	|	...	2125	|	|	0033
Genova Piazza Principe a.	1744	1814	1818	...	1844	...	...	1930	1944	1955	2002s	2030	...	2044	2130	2144	2154	2240	2245	...	2214	2330	2350	...
Genova Piazza Principe d.	1747	...	1818	...	...	1852	...	1932	1947	...	|	2032	...	2047	2132	...	2156	2243	2247	...	...	2332	2353	...
Genova Brignole d.	1756	...	1827	1845	...	1859u	1930	1939	1956	...	2020	2039	2045	2056	2139	...	2205	2252	2255	2256	...	2339	0002	...
S. Margherita-Portofino d.	1816	...	...	1915	...	|	2009	...	2016	...	...	...	2115	|	▬	...	|	2315	2318	2332	...	...	|	...
Rapallo d.	1821	...	...	1919	...	|	2014	...	2021	...	...	...	2119	2126	...	...	|	2320	2323	2336	...	...	0028	...
Chiavari d.	1830	...	...	1927	...	|	2023	...	2030	...	...	...	2127	2135	...	...	|	2329	2332	2344	...	...	0038	...
Sestri Levante d.	1838	...	...	1935	...	|	2032	...	2038	...	...	...	2135	2142	...	...	|	2341	2344	2355	...	...	|	...
Levanto d.	1900	...	...	1955	...	|	2052	...	2100	...	...	...	2150	|	...	...	|	2357	0001	0017	...	...	|	...
Monterosso d.	1907	...	...	2000	...	|	2057	...	2107	...	...	...	2155	|	2	...	|	0003	0007	0022	...	...	|	...
Riomaggiore d.	|	...	...	2008	...	|	2106	...	|	...	...	...	2203	|		...	|	|	|	0037	...	...	|	...
La Spezia Centrale d.	1923	...	...	2015	...	2003	2112	...	2123	...	...	...	2210	2223	2226	...	2309	0018	0022	0051	...	...	0127	...
Sarzana d.	|	...	...	...	...	|	...	...	|	...	...	...	...	2235	2241	...	|	...	...	...	...	...	|	...
Carrara-Avenza d.	1941	...	...	...	...	|	...	...	|	...	...	...	...	2243	2249	...	|	...	...	...	...	...	|	...
Massa Centro d.	1949	...	...	...	...	2023	...	...	2145	...	...	...	...	2250	2256	...	|	...	...	...	...	...	|	...
Viareggio d.	2002	...	...	...	...	|	...	...	2200	...	...	...	...	2303	2317	...	2343	...	...	...	...	...	|	...
Pisa Centrale a.	2017	...	...	...	...	2046	...	...	2217	...	...	...	...	2317	2342	...	2359	...	...	...	...	...	0216	...
Livorno Centrale 611 a.	2035	...	...	...	...	|	...	...	2235	...	...	...	...	2335	...	...	0015	...	...	...	...	...	0237	...
Roma Termini 611 a.	...	...	...	...	...	2259	...	...	...	...	...	...	...	...	...	...	...	...	...	...	...	...	0543o	...

♦ – NOTES (LISTED BY TRAIN NUMBER)

501 – [12] Sestri Levante - Napoli.
505 – [12] Ventimiglia - Genova - Roma.
511 – [12] Torino - Salerno.
657 – [12] Milano - Grosseto.
799 – 🛏 1,2 cl., ▬ 2 cl. (4 berth) and [2] Torino - Napoli - Salerno. Train 35299 Aug. 15 – 29.
1533 – [12] Milano - Grosseto.
1963 – 🛏 1,2 cl., 🛏 1,2 cl. (T2) and ▬ 2 cl. (4 berth) Milano - Genova - Siracusa;
🛏 1,2 cl. and ▬ 2 cl. (4 berth) Milano - Messina (1967) - Palermo.
8583 – [12] and 🍷 Genova - Pisa (8584) - Roma.
8627 – [12] and 🍷 Genova - Pisa (8628) - Firenze (8629) - Roma.
9795 – [12] and 🍷 Venezia (9744) - Milano (9795) - Genova.

A – To Albenga (Table 580).
M – To Marseille (Tables 360 / 580).
N – To Nice (Table 580).
V – To Ventimiglia (Table 580).

b – June 9 - Aug. 11.
c – Not Aug. 16 – 29.
d – June 9 - July 14.

e – July 15 - Dec. 14.
o – Roma **Ostiense**.
s – Stops to set down only.
t – Roma **Tiburtina**.
u – Stops to pick up only.

⊙ – Subject to confirmation.
♠ – Operator: Trenord.

PISA - GENOVA - MILANO and TORINO 610

Subject to alteration August 15 – 29.

km		2		*ICN* **796** ◆	2⚒	2	*IC* **652** e	*IC* **652** d	*FR* **9796** 🍷 ◆	*IC* **500** 2	*IC* **656** ①-⑥ Vf	2	V	2Ⓐ	2†	2Ⓐ	*IC* **658**	2	*ICN* **1552** ⊙◆	*IC* **662**	2	2	*IC* **504** 2	2	*FB* **8604** 🍷 ◆
	Roma Termini **611** d.	...	...	0011**o**	...	...	...	...	...	...	...	...	...	...	...	...	...	...	...	...	...	...	...	...	0605
	Livorno Centrale **611** d.	...	...	0309	...	...	...	...	...	...	...	...	...	...	...	...	0525	...	0540**s**	0625	...	...	...	...	|
	Pisa Centrale d.	...	...	0326	...	...	...	...	...	...	...	...	...	...	...	...	0542	...	0557**s**	0642	...	0702	...	...	0828
	Viareggio d.	...	...	|	...	...	...	...	...	...	...	...	...	...	...	...	0557	...	0617**s**	0657	...	0724	...	...	|
	Massa Centro d.	...	...	|	...	...	...	...	...	...	...	...	...	...	...	...	0612	...	|	0709	...	0745	...	...	0851
	Carrara-Avenza d.	...	...	|	...	...	...	...	...	...	...	...	...	...	...	...	|	...	|	0716	...	0751	...	...	|
	Sarzana d.	...	...	|	...	...	...	...	...	...	...	...	...	...	...	...	|	...	|	0724	...	0802	...	...	|
	La Spezia Centrale d.	...	...	0425	0430	...	0455	0459	...	...	...	...	...	0540	0600	0625	0638	...	0654**s**	0738	0750	0826	...	...	0913
	Riomaggiore d.	...	...	|	0439	...	|	|	...	...	...	...	...	0549	0608	|	|	...	|	|	|	...	...	...	|
	Monterosso d.	...	...	|	0455	...	0511	0517	...	...	...	...	...	0604	0623	|	0654	...	|	|	|	...	...	...	|
	Levanto d.	...	...	|	0500	...	0517	0524	...	...	...	...	...	0609	0628	0641	0700	...	|	0757	0811	...	...	...	|
	Sestri Levante d.	...	0432	|	0526	...	0533	0540	...	...	...	...	...	0636	0657	0657	0716	...	|	0814	0826	...	...	...	|
	Chiavari d.	...	0443	0512	0535	...	0545	0552	...	...	...	...	...	0645	0707	0706	0724	...	|	0824	0833	...	...	...	|
	Rapallo d.	...	0451	0521	0547	...	0554	0601	...	...	...	...	...	0656	0716	|	0733	...	|	0833	0841	...	...	...	|
	S. Margherita-Portofino d.	...	0455	|	0552	...	0600	0607	...	...	...	...	...	0700	0720	|	0739	...	|	|	0845	...	...	...	|
	Genova Brignole d.	0521	0536	0555	0638	0621	0630	0635	...	0648	...	0721	...	0756	0756	0745	0809	0821	0830**s**	0910	0915	...	...	...	1013**s**
	Genova Piazza Principe a.	0530	0542	0601	0644	0630	0636	0641	...	|	...	0730	...	0802	0802	0749	0816	0830	0839**s**	0915	...	...	...	...	1021
0	**Genova** Piazza Principe d.	0530	0544	0606	...	0630	0639	0644	0705	0656**u**	0719	0730	0750	...	...	...	0819	0830	|	0918	...	...	0924	0930	...
72	Tortona **615** d.	|	0632	|	...	|	|	|	|	|	|	|	0832	...	...	...	0900	|	0922**s**	|	...	...	|	|	...
89	Voghera **615** d.	|	0643	|	...	|	0730	0734	|	|	0808	|	0843	...	...	...	0911	|	0935**s**	1008	...	...	|	|	...
115	Pavia d.	|	0701	|	...	|	0751	0751	|	|	0825	|	0901	...	...	...	0927	|	0954**s**	1025	...	...	|	|	...
144	**Milano** Rogoredo a.	|	0720	|	...	|	0810**s**	0810**s**	0824	|	0846**s**	|	0920	...	...	...	|	|	|	|	...	...	|	|	...
154	**Milano** Centrale a.	|	0735	|	...	|	0823	0823	0835	|	0900	|	0940	...	...	...	0958	|	1050	1055	...	...	|	|	...
	Novi Ligure d.	0614	...	|	...	0714	...	...	...	0734	...	0814	...	...	...	...	...	0914	...	...	...	...	|	1014	...
	Alessandria **615** d.	0631	...	0657	...	0731	...	...	...	0748	...	0831	...	...	...	...	...	0931	...	...	...	...	1010	1031	...
	Asti **615** d.	0654	...	0723	...	0754	...	...	...	0807	...	0854	...	...	...	...	...	0954	...	...	...	...	1029	1054	...
	Torino Porta Nuova **615** a.	0730	...	0810	...	0830	...	...	...	0845	...	0930	...	...	...	...	...	1030	...	...	...	...	1110	1130	...

	2⚒	2	2	*EC* **140** 🍷 N	*FB* **8606** 🍷 c	*IC* **666**	2	*IC* **746** V	2	2	Ⓐ	2	*IC* **670**	2†	*IC* **1540** † V	2	*IC* **510** g◆	2©	*IC* **674**	2⚒	2†	*FB* **8616** 🍷	*EC* **146** 🍷 N	2
Roma Termini **611** d.	...	...	...	...	0657	...	...	...	...	...	...	...	...	...	...	...	0957	...	...	...	...	1157	...	...
Livorno Centrale **611** d.	0801	...	...	...	0941	...	...	...	...	...	...	...	1124	...	...	...	1245	...	1324	...	1417	1440	...	...
Pisa Centrale d.	0819	...	...	...	0956	...	...	...	...	...	...	1105	1142	1205	...	...	1302	...	1342	1354	1433	1456	...	...
Viareggio d.	0837	...	...	...	1012	...	...	...	...	...	...	1122	1200	1223	...	...	1317	...	1402	1415	1452	1512	...	...
Massa Centro d.	0858	...	...	...	1025	...	...	...	...	...	...	1143	1212	1243	...	...	1330	...	1414	1433	1510	1525	...	...
Carrara-Avenza d.	0906	...	...	...	|	...	...	...	...	...	...	1149	1219	1249	...	...	1339	...	|	1439	1516	|	...	...
Sarzana d.	0913	...	...	...	|	...	...	...	...	...	...	1156	|	1257	...	...	|	...	|	1449	1525	|	...	...
La Spezia Centrale d.	0937	...	0950	...	1046	1035	...	...	1150	...	...	1220	1238	1322	...	1350	1405	...	1438	1509	1539	1546	...	1550
Riomaggiore d.	...	...	|	...	|	|	...	...	|	...	...	▬	|	▬	...	1358	|	...	|	...	▬	|	...	1558
Monterosso d.	...	...	|	...	|	1055	...	...	|	...	...	...	1255	...	...	1406	|	...	1455	...	...	|	...	1606
Levanto d.	...	...	1011	...	|	1102	...	...	1211	...	...	...	1302	...	...	1411	|	...	1502	...	...	|	...	1611
Sestri Levante d.	...	...	1026	...	|	1124	...	...	1226	...	...	...	1324	...	...	1426	1443	...	1524	...	...	|	...	1626
Chiavari d.	...	...	1034	...	1116	1132	...	...	1234	...	...	...	1332	...	...	1434	1451	...	1532	...	...	1616	...	1634
Rapallo d.	...	...	1042	...	|	1141	...	...	1242	...	...	...	1341	2	...	1442	1500	...	1541	...	2	1625	...	1642
S. Margherita-Portofino d.	...	...	1046	...	|	|	...	...	1246	...	...	...	1346		...	1446	|	...	1546	...		|	...	1646
Genova Brignole d.	...	1021	1115	...	1145	1210	1221	...	1315	1321	1336	©	1410	1421	...	1515	1530	...	1608	...	1621	1651**s**	...	1715
Genova Piazza Principe a.	...	1030	...	...	1150	1216	1230	...	...	1330	1344		1416	1430	...	...	1536	...	1614	...	1630	1658	...	...
Genova Piazza Principe d.	...	1030	...	1119	1159	1219	1230	1319	...	1330	1344	1344	1419	1430	1519	...	1539	1546	1616	...	1630	...	1719	...
Tortona **615** d.	...	|	...	|	|	|	|	|	...	|	1432	1432	|	|	|	...	|	1632	1700	...	|	...	|	...
Voghera **615** d.	...	|	...	1208	|	1308	|	1408	...	|	1443	1443	1508	|	1608	...	|	1643	|	...	|	...	1808	...
Pavia d.	...	|	...	1225	|	1325	|	1425	...	|	1501	1501	1525	|	1625	...	|	1701	1725	...	|	...	1825	...
Milano Rogoredo a.	...	|	...	|	|	|	|	|	...	|	1520	1520	|	|	|	...	|	1720	|	...	|	...	|	...
Milano Centrale a.	...	|	...	1253	|	1353	|	1453	...	|	1535	1535	1559	|	1653	...	|	1735	1800	...	|	...	1853	...
Novi Ligure d.	...	1114	...	...	|	...	1314	...	...	1414	...	...	...	1514	...	...	|	...	...	...	1714	...	...	...
Alessandria **615** d.	...	1131	...	...	1244	...	1331	...	...	1431	...	...	...	1531	...	...	1636	...	...	...	1731	...	...	...
Asti **615** d.	...	1154	...	...	1302	...	1354	...	...	1454	...	...	...	1554	...	...	1700	...	...	...	1754	...	...	...
Torino Porta Nuova **615** a.	...	1230	...	...	1340	...	1430	...	...	1530	...	...	...	1630	...	...	1740	...	...	...	1830	...	...	...

	2	2	*IC* **680**	2	*FB* **8620** 🍷 c	*IC* **682** Ⓐ V	*IC* **1538** © V	2	*IC* **1534** © ◆	*IC* **684** Ⓐ ◆	2Ⓐ	*EC* **148** 🍷 M	2	2	*IC* **518** ◆	2	*FB* **8626** 🍷	2	2©	*FB* **8630** 🍷	2⚒	*FA* **8590** 🍷Ⓑ ◆	2	*IC* **522** ◆
Roma Termini **611** d.	...	...	...	...	1357	...	...	...	...	...	...	...	...	...	1557	...	1657	...	...	1827	...	1950**t**	...	1943**o**
Livorno Centrale **611** d.	...	...	...	...	1640	...	...	...	1718	1724	...	...	...	...	1846	...	1940	...	...	2107	...	|	...	2236
Pisa Centrale d.	...	1505	...	...	1656	...	...	...	1736	1742	1758	...	...	...	1903	1935	1956	2035	...	2123	2136	2153	...	2253
Viareggio d.	...	1523	...	...	1712	...	...	...	1753	1800	1817	...	...	...	1919	1955	2012	2055	...	2140	2156	|	...	2310
Massa Centro d.	...	1543	...	...	1725	...	...	...	1814	1814	1835	...	...	...	1932	2012	2025	2111	...	2154	2216	|	...	2323
Carrara-Avenza d.	...	1549	...	...	|	...	...	...	1821	|	1841	...	...	...	|	2019	|	2120	...	|	2228	|	...	2331
Sarzana d.	...	1557	...	...	|	...	...	...	|	|	1851	...	...	...	|	2028	|	2128	...	|	2236	|	...	2340
La Spezia Centrale d.	...	1625	1638	...	1746	...	...	1750	1838	1838	1914	...	...	1945	1953	2050	2046	2144	2145	2216	2254	2237	2310	0008
Riomaggiore d.	...	▬	|	...	|	...	...	1758	|	|	▬	...	...	1953	|	▬	|	...	2153	|	...	|	2319	|
Monterosso d.	...	...	1655	...	|	...	...	|	1855	1855	...	...	...	2005	|	...	|	...	2201	|	...	|	2335	0024
Levanto d.	...	...	1702	...	|	...	...	1811	1902	1902	...	...	...	2010	2025	...	|	...	2206	|	...	|	2340	0031
Sestri Levante d.	...	...	1724	...	|	...	...	1826	1924	1924	...	...	...	2027	|	...	|	...	2224	|	...	|	0005	0049
Chiavari d.	...	...	1732	...	1816	...	...	1834	1932	1932	...	...	...	2036	2033	...	|	...	2231	2246	...	|	0014	...
Rapallo d.	...	...	1741	...	|	...	...	1842	1941	1941	2	...	...	2047	2042	...	2123	...	2239	|	...	|	0025	...
S. Margherita-Portofino d.	...	..	1746	...	|	...	...	1846	1946	1946		...	...	2052	|	...	|	...	2243	|	...	|	0029	...
Genova Brignole d.	1721	©	1809	1821	1845	...	...	1915	2010	2010	2021	...	2121	2138	2126	Ⓑ	2143**s**	...	2309	2313**s**	...	2332**s**	0123	...
Genova Piazza Principe a.	1730		1816	1830	1850	...	...	...	2016	2016	2030	...	2130	...	2132		2150	...	...	2320	...	2340	...	...
Genova Piazza Principe d.	1730	1744	1818	1830	1852	1919	1919	...	2019	2019	2030	2119	2130	...	...	2146	...	...	...	...	...	...	...	...
Tortona **615** d.	|	1832	1900	|	|	2000	2000	...	|	|	|	|	|	...	...	2232	...	...	...	...	...	...	...	...
Voghera **615** d.	|	1843	|	|	|	|	|	...	2108	2108	|	2208	|	...	...	2243	...	...	...	...	...	...	...	...
Pavia d.	|	1901	1925	|	2006	2025	2025	...	2125	2125	|	2225	|	...	...	2301	...	...	...	...	...	...	...	...
Milano Rogoredo a.	|	1920	1943**s**	|	|	|	|	...	|	|	|	|	|	...	...	2320	...	...	...	...	...	...	...	...
Milano Centrale a.	|	1937	2000	|	2040	2053	2053	...	2153	2153	|	2253	|	...	...	2335	...	...	...	...	...	...	...	...
Novi Ligure d.	1814	...	...	1914	...	...	...	...	...	...	2114	...	2214	...	...	...	...	...	...	...	...	...	...	...
Alessandria **615** d.	1831	...	...	1931	...	...	...	...	...	...	2131	...	2231	...	...	...	...	...	...	...	...	...	...	...
Asti **615** d.	1854	...	...	1954	...	...	...	...	...	...	2154	...	2254	...	...	...	...	...	...	...	...	...	...	...
Torino Porta Nuova **615** a.	1930	...	...	2030	...	...	...	...	...	...	2230	...	2340	...	...	...	...	...	...	...	...	...	...	...

◆ – **NOTES** (LISTED BY TRAIN NUMBER)

10 – [12] Salerno - Torino.
18 – [12] Roma - Genova - Ventimiglia.
22 – [12] Napoli - Sestri Levante.
84 – [12] Grosseto - Milano.
96 – Not June 29, 30, July 20 from Salerno: 🛏 1, 2 cl., ▬ 2 cl. (4 berth) and [2] Salerno - Napoli - Torino. Train **1596** on ① from Salerno.
534 – [12] Grosseto - Milano.
552 – 🛏 1,2 cl., 🛏 1,2 cl. (T2) and ▬ 2 cl. (4 berth) Siracusa - Genova - Milano (Train **1556** on ①); 🛏 1,2 cl. and ▬ 2 cl. (4 berth) Palermo (**1964**) - Messina - Milano.
590 – [12] and 🍷 Roma (**8588**) - Firenze - Pisa - Genova.
604 – [12] and 🍷 Roma (**8602**) - Firenze - Pisa - Genova.
796 – [12] and 🍷 Genova - Milano (**9711**) - Venezia.

M – From Marseille (Tables **360** / **580**).
N – From Nice (Table **580**).
V – From Ventimiglia (Table **580**).

c – Not Aug. 16 – 29.
d – June 9 - July 14.
e – July 15 - Dec. 14.

f – Not July 18, Aug. 15, Nov. 1.
g – Not June 30.
o – Roma **Ostiense**.
s – Stops to set down only.
u – Stops to pick up only.

⊙ – Subject to confirmation.

611 PISA - ROMA

km		2 ⚒	2 ⚒		IC 501 ♦	FB 8601 🍷		FB 8605 🍷	IC 505 ♦		IC 1533 Ⓒ♦	IC 657 Ⓐ♦	FB 8613 🍷		IC 511 ♦	2		FB 8619 🍷 a			FB 8623 🍷 b	2	2 Ⓑ	ICN 1963 ⊙♦	ICN 799 ♦	
	Torino P. Nuova **610** d.	...	...	...	...	...	...	...	...	...	...	...	...	...	1040	...	...	...	...	...	1520	...	...	...	2155	...
	Milano Centrale **610** d.	...	...	...	...	...	...	...	...	...	0810	0810	...	...	|	...	...	1310	...	...	|	...	...	2010	|	...
	Genova P. Principe **610** d.	...	...	...	...	0515	...	0705	0851	...	0947	0947	1210	...	1224	...	...	1502	...	...	1705	...	...	2156	2353	...
0	**Pisa** Centrale d.	...	...	0545	0647	0707	0745	0907	1111	1145	1226	1220	1407	1343	1450	...	1545	1707	1745	...	1907	1945	2150	0002	0221	...
20	**Livorno** Centrale d.	...	...	0603	0703	0722	0803	0922	1126	1203	1255	1255	1422	1400	1504	...	1603	1722	1803	...	1922	2003	2209	0015	0240	...
43	Rosignano d.	...	...	0620	|	|	0820	|	|	1220	|	|	|	1416	|	...	1620	|	1820	...	|	2020	2230	...	|	...
54	Cecina d.	...	...	0629	0728	|	0829	|	1150	1229	1323	1326	|	1424	|	...	1629	|	1829	...	1944	2029	2238	...	|	...
89	Campiglia Marittima d.	...	...	0650	0747	0757	0851	0957	|	1251	1341	1350	1457	1444	1540	...	1651	1757	1851	...	2002	2051	2306	...	|	...
106	Follonica d.	...	...	0700	0758	|	0902	|	1215	1302	1352	1401	|	1455	1552	...	1702	|	1902	...	|	2102	2318	...	|	...
148	Grosseto d.	0419	0523	0728	0819	0824	0930	1024	1235	1330	1425	1433	1524	1530	1614	1629	1730	1824	1930	...	2028	2130	2343	...	0357	...
186	Orbetello-Monte Argentario d.	0444	0549	0751	0838	|	0953	|	|	1353	...	...	|	1553	|	1655	1753	|	1953	...	2043	2153	...	...	|	...
225	Tarquinia d.	0518	0622	0827	|	|	1029	|	|	1429	...	...	|	1629	|	1729	1829	|	2029	...	|	2229	...	...	|	...
255	**Civitavecchia** d.	0532	0636	0842	0924	0916	1044	1116	1326	1444	...	...	1616	1644	1708	1743	1844	1916	2044	...	2117	2244	...	...	0500	...
264	S. Marinella d.	0539	0643	0849	|	|	1051	|	|	1451	...	...	|	1651	|	1750	1851	|	2051	...	|	2251	...	...	|	...
286	Ladispoli-Cerveteri d.	0555	0700	0905	|	|	1105	|	|	1505	...	...	|	1705	|	1806	1905	|	2105	...	|	2305	...	...	|	...
329	**Roma** Ostiense a.	0633	0739	0936	1015	|	1139	|	1420**s**	1536	...	...	|	1736	1752	1838	1936	|	2136	...	|	2336	...	...	0543	...
336	**Roma** Termini a.	0648	0750	0948	|	1003	1150	1203	1433	1548	...	...	1703	1747	1803	1848	1948	2003	2148	...	2203	2348	...	...	|	...
	Napoli Centrale **640** a.	...	...	...	1229	...	...	...	...	...	...	...	...	...	2029	...	...	...	...	...	...	...	...	...	0817	...

	ICN 796 ♦	ICN 1552 ⊙♦	2 ⚒	2 †	2	FB 8606 🍷 a	IC 510 c♦		FB 8616 🍷		FB 8620 🍷 a	IC 1534 Ⓒ♦	IC 684 Ⓐ♦		IC 518 ♦		FB 8626 🍷	FB 8630 🍷		IC 522 d♦		2	2 †	2 ⚒	2
Napoli Centrale **640** d.	2146	...	...	...	...	...	0731	...	...	...	...	...	...	...	...	...	...	...	...	1731	...	...	...	...	...
Roma Termini d.	|	...	...	...	0612	0657	0957	1012	1157	1212	1357	...	...	1412	1557	1612	1657	1827	1812	|	2012	2112	2212	2212	2327
Roma Ostiense d.	0011	...	...	...	0623	|	1007	1023	|	1223	|	...	...	1423	1607**u**	1623	|	|	1823	1943	2023	2121	2223	2223	2338
Ladispoli-Cerveteri d.	|	...	...	...	0651	|	|	1051	|	1251	|	...	...	1451	|	1651	|	|	1855	|	2051	2155	2301	2300	0016
S. Marinella d.	|	...	...	...	0706	|	|	1107	|	1307	|	...	...	1506	|	1706	|	|	1910	|	2106	2211	2317	2322	0035
Civitavecchia d.	0053	...	...	...	0715	0746	1047	1115	1246	1315	1446	...	...	1515	1647	1715	1746	1916	1924	2023	2115	2220	2324	2330	0044
Tarquinia d.	|	...	...	...	0728	|	|	1129	|	1328	|	...	...	1528	|	1728	|	|	1937	|	2128	2233	2336	...	...
Orbetello-Monte Argentario d.	|	...	0602	...	0800	|	|	1202	|	1400	|	...	...	1600	|	1800	|	|	2009	2102	2200	2306	0009	...	...
Grosseto d.	0153	...	0628	0647	0823	0839	1139	1227	1339	1427	1539	1604	1610	1625	1739	1825	1839	2007	2033	2121	2227	2330	0034	...	...
Follonica d.	|	...	0652	0710	0845	|	1158	1254	|	1453	|	1624	1631	1653	1759	1849	|	|	2057	2141	2253	...	...	...	...
Campiglia Marittima d.	|	...	0704	0722	0854	0905	1209	1305	1405	1504	1605	1636	1642	1704	|	1858	1905	2032	2108	2151	2304	...	...	...	...
Cecina d.	|	...	0729	0746	0916	0920	|	1327	|	1527	|	1655	1700	1727	1823	1922	|	|	2128	2210	2327	...	...	...	...
Rosignano d.	|	...	0737	0754	0927	|	|	1336	|	1536	|	|	|	1736	|	1930	|	|	2136	|	2336	...	...	...	...
Livorno Centrale d.	0309	0540**s**	0755	0812	0955	0941	1245	1358	1440	1558	1640	1718	1724	1758	1846	1956	1940	2107	2158	2236	2358	...	...	...	...
Pisa Centrale a.	0323	0557**s**	0811	0829	1018	0953	1259	1415	1453	1615	1653	1733	1739	1815	1900	2015	1953	2120	2215	2250	0015	...	...	...	...
Genova P. Principe **610** a.	0601	0839	...	...	...	1150	1536	...	1658	...	1850	2016	2016	...	2132	...	2150	2320	...	...	...	...	...	...	...
Milano Centrale **610** a.	|	1050	...	...	...	|	|	...	...	...	2040	2153	2153	...	...	...	...	...	...	...	...	...	...	...	...
Torino P. Nuova **610** a.	0810	...	...	...	...	1340	1740	...	...	...	...	...	...	...	...	...	...	...	...	...	...	...	...	...	...

♦ – **NOTES** (LISTED BY TRAIN NUMBER)

501 – 🚃(12) Sestri Levante - Napoli.
505 – 🚃(12) Ventimiglia - Genova - Roma.
510 – 🚃(12) Salerno - Torino.
511 – 🚃(12) Torino - Salerno.
518 – 🚃(12) Roma - Genova - Ventimiglia.
522 – 🚃(12) Napoli - Sestri Levante.
657 – 🚃(12) Milano - Grosseto.
684 – 🚃(12) Grosseto - Milano.
796 – Not June 29, 30, July 20 from Salerno: 🛏 1,2 cl., ▬ 2 cl. (4 berth) and 🚃(2) Salerno - Napoli - Torino. Train **1596** on ① from Salerno.
799 – 🛏 1,2 cl., ▬ 2 cl. (4 berth) and 🚃(2) Torino - Napoli - Salerno. Train **35299** Aug. 15–29.
1533 – 🚃(12) Milano - Grosseto.
1534 – 🚃(12) Grosseto - Milano.
1552 – 🛏 1,2 cl., 🛏 1,2 cl. (T2) and ▬ 2 cl. (4 berth) Siracusa - Genova - Milano (Train **1556** on ①); 🛏 1,2 cl. and ▬ 2 cl. (4 berth) Palermo (**1964**) - Messina - Milano.
1963 – 🛏 1,2 cl., 🛏 1,2 cl. (T2) and ▬ 2 cl. (4 berth) Milano - Genova - Siracusa; 🛏 1,2 cl. and ▬ 2 cl. (4 berth) Milano - Messina (**1967**) - Palermo.

a – Not Aug. 16–29.
b – June 9 - Aug 11.
c – Not June 30.
d – Not June 29, 30.
s – Stops to set down only.
u – Stops to pick up only.

⊙ – Subject to confirmation.

612 PARMA and FIDENZA - SARZANA and LA SPEZIA

Most services 2nd class only

km		⚒							B		⚒			⚒							⚒	⑤		⚒	⚒	†
	Milano Centrale **615** d.	...	...	...	...	...	...	0645	...	...	...	...	...	...	...	...	...	...	...	1705	...	1857**g**	...	...	...	...
0	**Parma** d.	...	...	...	0514	0625	0750	|	...	...	1226	1256	1344	...	1448	1553	1648	...	1747	|	1944	|	2057	2150	2240	2240
*	**Fidenza** d.	...	...	...	|	|	|	0824	0918	...	|	|	|	...	|	|	|	...	|	1830	|	2030	|	|	|	|
23	Fornovo d.	...	...	...	0532	0648	0816	0842	0935	...	1247	1322	1407	...	1518	1622	1718	...	1814	1848	2014	2049	2124	2218	2308	2308
61	Borgo Val di Taro d.	...	0544	...	0605	0728	0849	0933	1002	...	1323	1401	1444	...	1554	1656	1751	...	1849	1932	2045	2145	2202	2252	2344	2344
79	Pontremoli d.	0545	0601	...	0627	0743	0905	0951	1018	1221	1342	1418	1503	1542	1610	1711	1810	1821	1904	1952	2103	2201	2218	2308	2357	2359
100	Aulla Lunigiana d.	0607	0623	...	0652	0813	0923	1021	1035	1243	1410	...	1523	1610	...	1735	...	1843	1922	2026	2124	2220	2236	...	...	0019
108	S. Stefano di Magra d.	0614	0631	...	0659	0820	0931	1028	1042	1251	1416	...	1532	1616	...	1742	...	1851	1929	2034	2131	2230	2242	...	...	0026
116	**Sarzana** a.	|	0638	...	|	|	|	1042	1057	1300	|	...	|	|	...	|	...	1900	|	2042	|	2248	|	...	...	|
	Pisa Centrale **611** a.	|	0736	...	|	|	|	1145	1200	1351	|	...	|	|	...	|	...	1951	|	2138	|	2343	|	...	...	|
	Livorno Centrale **611** a.	|	...	...	|	|	|	...	...	...	|	...	|	|	...	|	...	...	|	2155	|	2359	|	...	...	|
120	**La Spezia** Centrale a.	0631	...	...	0722	0838	0944	...	...	...	1432	...	1556	1633	...	1800	...	...	1947	...	2151	...	2300	...	...	0042

		⚒				⚒	⚒			⚒				⚒		⚒	⚒	⚒	⑦		B	⚒				G
La Spezia Centrale d.	...	...	0540	0611	...	0810	0927	1015	1226	...	1325	1419	...	1527	1607	...	...	1727	...	1809	...	1927	...	2009	...	2114
Livorno Centrale **611** d.	...	...	|	|	0552	|	|	|	|	...	|	|	...	|	|	...	...	|	1658	|	...	|	...	|	...	|
Pisa Centrale **611** a.	...	...	|	|	0610	|	|	|	|	...	|	|	...	|	|	1605	...	|	1712	|	1822	|	1909	|	2006	|
Sarzana d.	...	...	|	|	0700	|	|	|	|	...	|	|	...	|	|	1657	...	|	1802	|	1915	|	1959	|	2058	|
S. Stefano di Magra d.	...	...	0551	0629	0711	0829	0945	1031	1242	...	1343	1434	...	1545	1626	1707	...	1745	1809	1826	1926	1943	2015	2028	2109	2125
Aulla Lunigiana d.	...	...	0558	0638	0718	0838	0952	1038	1249	...	1351	1442	...	1552	1635	1718	...	1752	1816	1835	1932	1950	2025	2037	2116	2132
Pontremoli d.	0410	0556	0626	0658	0741	0859	1015	1058	1308	1350	1413	1459	1550	1613	1657	1739	1750	1815	1837	1856	1952	2015	2042	2057	2139	2151
Borgo Val di Taro d.	0426	0612	0642	0714	0800	0915	...	1114	1323	1406	...	1515	1606	...	1713	...	1808	...	1852	1912	2008	...	2102	2113	...	2207
Fornovo d.	0502	0649	0717	0749	0843	0952	...	1149	1407	1443	...	1552	1643	...	1746	...	1843	...	1928	1946	2048	...	2136	2145	...	2244
Fidenza a.	|	|	|	|	0903	|	...	|	|	|	...	|	|	...	|	...	|	...	2000	|	2103	...	2156	|	...	|
Parma a.	0530	0713	0739	0810	|	1011	...	1209	1431	1508	...	1614	1708	...	1809	...	1908	...	|	2010	...	...	|	2211	...	2310
Milano Centrale **615** a.	...	...	...	...	1020	...	...	...	...	...	...	...	...	...	...	...	...	...	2133**g**	...	...	...	2320	...	...	...

B – 🚃(2) Fidenza - Pisa and v.v. From Bergamo (d. 0645) / to Bergamo (a. 2304).
G – 🚃(2) Genova - La Spezia - Parma.
g – Milano **Porta Garibaldi**.
* – Fidenza - Fornovo is *25 km*.

FIRENZE - SIENA, PISA and LIVORNO — 613

Most services 2nd class only

km		⚒		⚒				⚒	⚒		⚒	*FB* **8602** ◆				f	⚒		⚒	⚒					
0	**Firenze** SMN .... **614** d.	0430	0535	...	0620	0653	0700	...	0728	...	0738	0728	0753	0810	0828	0853	0910	0928	0953	1010	1028	1053	1100	1110	1128
34	Empoli ....d.	0506	0601	0621	0650	0730	0722	0726	0758	0806	0813	|	0827	0840	0858	0927	0940	0958	1027	1040	1058	1127	|	1140	1157
72	Poggibonsi ▲........d.	|	|	0702	0724j	|	|	0811	|	0848	|	|	|	0915	|	|	1015	|	|	1115	|	|	|	1215	|
97	**Siena** ....a.	|	|	0731	0747j	|	|	0840	|	0915	|	|	|	0938	|	|	1038	|	|	1138	|	|	|	1238	|
81	**Pisa** Centrale ...... **614** d.	0555	0637	...	...	0809	0752	...	0837	...	0857	0826	0903	...	0932	1010	...	1032	1103	...	1132	1203	1153	...	1227
101	**Livorno** Centrale ....a.	0616	0651	...	...	0821	0808	...	0851	...	...	...	...	...	0948	...	...	1048	...	...	1148	...	1208	...	1244

	⚒						⚒	⚒	⚒						⚒			⚒		Ⓑ	⚒	⚒	⚒		⚒
Firenze SMN .... **614** d.	...	1138	1210	1228	...	1253	1300	1310	1328	...	1338	1353	1410	1428	...	1453	1500	1510	...	1538	1610	1628	...	1653	1700
Empoli ....d.	1208	1213	1240	1258	1308	1327	|	1340	1358	1408	1413	1427	1440	1458	1508	1527	|	1540	1608	1613	1640	1658	1708	1727	|
Poggibonsi ▲........d.	1249	|	1315	|	1349	|	|	1415	|	1449	|	|	1514	|	1549	|	|	1615	1649	|	1715	|	1749	|	|
Siena ....a.	1314	|	1338	|	1414	|	|	1438	|	1517f	|	|	1537	|	1614	|	|	1638	1714	|	1738	|	1814	|	|
Pisa Centrale .... **614** d.	...	1302	...	1332	...	1403	1355	...	1432	...	1509	1503	...	1532	...	1603	1553	...	...	1659	...	1732	...	1803	1753
Livorno Centrale ....a.	...	1320	...	1348	...	...	1412	...	1448	...	1526h	...	...	1548	...	...	1612	...	...	...	...	1748	...	...	1808

			⚒		Ⓐ									⚒			⚒	⚒			*FA* **8588** Ⓑ ◆				
Firenze SMN .... **614** d.	1710	1728	...	1738	1753	1810	1828	...	1853	1900	1910	...	1928	...	1953	2010	2028	...	2038	2058	2104c	2128	2138k	2157	2307
Empoli ....d.	1740	1758	1808	1813	1827	1840	1858	1908	1927	|	1940	...	1958	2008	2027	2040	2058	2108	2113	2132	|	2158	2208	2233	2343
Poggibonsi ▲........d.	1815	|	1849	|	|	1915	|	1949	|	|	2015	...	|	2049	|	2115	|	2150	|	|	|	|	2250	|	|
Siena ....a.	1838	|	1914	|	|	1938	|	2014	|	|	2038	...	|	2114	|	2135	|	2211	|	|	|	|	2314	|	|
Pisa Centrale .... **614** d.	...	1832	...	1858	1904	...	1933	...	2003	1949	...	...	2032	...	2103	...	2128	...	2204	2210	2150	2232j	...	2327	0035
Livorno Centrale ....a.	...	1846	...	1912	...	...	1948	...	...	...	...	...	2048	...	...	...	...	...	...	2229	...	2248j	...	2344	0050

		⚒	⚒	⚒		⚒	†		⚒	⚒	†	*FA* **8584** ◆	⚒	†			⚒					⚒	†	⚒	⚒
Livorno Centrale ....d.	...	...	0500	...	0612	...	...	...	...	0710	...	...	...	...	0730	0743	...	0812	...	0852	...	0912	0912	...	1012
Pisa Centrale .... **614** d.	0415	...	0519	...	0629	...	...	0654	...	0732	0732	0750	...	...	0754	0801	...	0832	...	0912	...	0932	0932	...	1032
Siena ....d.	|	0500	|	0543	|	0625	0636	|	0636	|	|	|	0702	0715	|	|	0733	|	0818	|	0848	|	|	0918	|
Poggibonsi ▲........d.	|	0522	|	0606	|	|	0658	|	0659	|	|	|	0728	0745	|	|	0805	|	0846	|	0909	|	|	0946	|
Empoli ....d.	0453	0556	0602	0645	0659	0709	0735	0730	0750	0804	0804	|	0820	0820	0832	0847	0852	0904	0921	|	0940	1004	1017	1021	1104
Firenze SMN .... **614** a.	0527	...	0638	0721	0727	0734	0802	0807	0827	0832	0832	0844c	0857	0857	0907	0922	...	0932	0950	1000	1007	1032	1046	1050	1132

		⚒	⚒		⚒	⚒				⚒		A ⚒						⚒		⚒	⚒		†	⚒	
Livorno Centrale ....d.	...	...	...	1112	...	...	...	1212	...	...	1252	...	1312	...	...	1343	1412	...	...	1452	1512	...	1540	...	1612
Pisa Centrale .... **614** d.	1054	1112	...	1132	...	1154	...	1232	...	1254	1312	...	1332	...	1354	1401	1432	...	1454	1512	1532	...	1601	...	1632
Siena ....d.	|	|	1041	|	1118	|	1145	|	1218	|	|	1241	|	1318	|	|	|	1418	|	|	|	1518	|	1541	|
Poggibonsi ▲........d.	|	|	1112	|	1146	|	1212	|	1246	|	|	1312	|	1346	|	|	|	1446	|	|	|	1546	|	1612	|
Empoli ....d.	1132	|	1152	1204	1221	1232	1252	1304	1321	1332	|	1352	1404	1421	1432	1447	1504	1521	1532	|	1604	1621	1647	1652	1704
Firenze SMN .... **614** a.	1207	1200	...	1232	1250	1307	...	1332	1350	1407	1400	...	1432	1450	1507	1524	1532	1550	1607	1600	1632	1650	1724	...	1732

	⚒						Ⓐ	⑥						⚒		⚒	Ⓐ			*FB* **8628** ⊙ ◆					
Livorno Centrale ....d.	...	...	1652	...	1712	...	...	...	...	1812	...	...	1852	...	...	...	...	...	2012	...	...	...	2112	...	...
Pisa Centrale .... **614** d.	...	1654	1712	...	1732	...	1754	1754	...	1832	...	1854	1912	...	1932	...	2001	...	2032	2048	...	2101	2132	...	2230
Siena ....d.	1618	|	|	1641	|	1719	|	|	1741	|	1818	|	|	1841	|	1918	|	1941	|	|	2018	|	|	2140	|
Poggibonsi ▲........d.	1646	|	|	1712	|	1746	|	|	1812	|	1846	|	|	1912	|	1946	|	2012	|	|	2046	|	|	2211	|
Empoli ....d.	1721	1732	1737	1752	1804	1821	1832	1836	1852	1904	1921	1932	|	1952	2004	2021	2047	2052	2104	|	2121	2147	2204	2241	2315
Firenze SMN .... **614** a.	1750	1807	1801	...	1832	1850	1907	1918	...	1932	1950	2007	2000	...	2032	2050	2122	...	2132	2140c	2150	2225	2232	2313	2350

◆ – **NOTES** (LISTED BY TRAIN NUMBER)

8584 – [12] and 🍸 Genova (**8583**) - Pisa - Firenze (**8585**) - Roma.
8588 – [12] and 🍸 Roma - Firenze - Pisa - Genova.
8602 – [12] and 🍸 Roma - Firenze - Pisa (**8604**) - Genova.
8628 – [12] and 🍸 Genova (**8627**) - Pisa - Firenze (**8629**) - Roma.

A – Also departures at 1341, 1441, 1541.
c – Firenze **Campo di Marte**.
f – Runs 3 minutes earlier on †.
h – † only.

j – 5–7 minutes later on ⚒.
k – ⚒ only.
▲ – Poggibonsi-S. Gimignano.
⊙ – Subject to confirmation.

FIRENZE - LUCCA - VIAREGGIO and PISA — 614

Most services 2nd class only

km		⚒	⚒	⚒	⚒				†	⚒							†	Ⓐ	⚒					
0	**Firenze** SMN .... **613** d.	...	0510	...	...	...	0603	0710	...	...	0738	0810	...	...	0910	...	1010	...	1138	1210	...	and at	1610	...
17	Prato Centrale ....d.	...	0533	...	...	...	0623	0729	...	...	0759	0831	...	...	0931	...	1031	...	1159	1231	...	the same	1631	...
34	Pistoia ....d.	...	0551	...	...	...	0640	0745	...	...	0816	0844	...	...	0944	...	1044	...	1216	1244	...	minutes	1644	...
47	Montecatini Centro ......d.	...	0604	...	...	...	0658	0801	...	...	0832	0901	...	...	1001	...	1101	...	1232	1301	...	past each	1701	...
78	Lucca .... ⊡ d.	0537	0645	0652	0708	0740	0755	0830	0842	0910	0923	0930	0942	...	1049	1042	1134	1242	1323	1329	1342	hour	1729	1742
101	**Viareggio** ....a.	|	...	|	|	|	|	0913	|	|	...	*1015*b	|	...	1129	|	*1215*b	|	...	...	|	until	...	|
102	**Pisa** Centrale . ⊡ **613** a.	0602	...	0717	0741	0813	0825	...	0913	0945	...	...	1013	...	...	1111	...	1313	...	...	1413		...	1813

		⚒	⚒		†	⚒					⚒	
Firenze SMN .... **613** d.	1710	...	...	1810	...	...	1910	...	2010	...	2110	2210
Prato Centrale ....d.	1731	...	...	1831	...	...	1931	...	2031	...	2131	2231
Pistoia ....d.	1744	...	...	1844	...	...	1944	...	2044	...	2144	2246
Montecatini Centro.................d.	1801	...	...	1901	...	...	2001	...	2101	...	2200	2301
Lucca .... ⊡ d.	1850	1842	1912	1933	1941	1944	2029	2042	2150	2142	2253	2334
Viareggio..........................a.	1931	|	|	...	|	|	...	|	2235	|	*2330*b	*0015*b
Pisa Centrale............ **613** ⊡ a.	...	1913	1943	...	2013	2015	...	2113	...	2213	...	...

	⚒		⚒	⚒			
Pisa Centrale.......... **613** ⊡ d.	...	0525	...	0613	...	...	0704
Viareggio.........................d.	...	|	...	|	...	0638	|
Lucca .... ⊡ d.	0505	0559	0609	0640	0648	0727	0736
Montecatini Centro.............d.	0533	...	0641	...	0715	0753	...
Pistoia ....d.	0551	...	0708	...	0732	0812	...
Prato Centrale ....d.	0611	...	0727	...	0747	0827	...
Firenze SMN............. **613** a.	0637	...	0750	...	0806	0850	...

	⚒							⚒												⚒			
Pisa Centrale............ **613** ⊡ d.	...	0750	...	0850	...	0950	...	1020	...	1250	...	1343	...	1450	...	and at	1950	...	2050	...	2150	...	...
Viareggio.........................d.	...	|	...	|	*0850*b	|	0949	|	1152	|	...	|	1339	|	...	the same	|	1953	|	...	|	2152	...
Lucca .... ⊡ d.	0740	0823	0831	0920	0931	1018	1031	1048	1231	1317	1331	1409	1431	1517	1531	minutes	2017	2031	2118	2131	2217	2231	...
Montecatini Centro...............d.	0821	...	0857	...	0957	...	1057	...	1257	...	1357	...	1457	...	1557	past each	...	2057	...	2157	...	2257	...
Pistoia ....d.	0841	...	0912	...	1012	...	1112	...	1312	...	1412	...	1512	...	1612	hour	...	2112	...	2212	...	2312	...
Prato Centrale ....d.	0900	...	0929	...	1029	...	1129	...	1329	...	1429	...	1529	...	1629	until	...	2129	...	2229	...	2329	...
Firenze SMN.................. **613** a.	0922	...	0950	...	1050	...	1150	...	1350	...	1450	...	1550	...	1650		...	2150	...	2250	...	2350	...

b – By 🚌.

⊡ – Additional services operate Lucca - Pisa Centrale and v.v. on ⚒.

615 MILANO and TORINO - BOLOGNA

For high-speed services see Table **600**.

km																										
		FA		*FR*		*IC*	*IC*		*IC*		*FB*					*IC*		*FB*		*FB*		*FB*			*FB*	
		8551		**9503**		**1589**	**583**		**605**		**8803**					**1545**		**8809**		**8811**		**8891**			**8813**	
		🍷		🍷		⑥					🍷	Ⓒ	Ⓐ			⑥		🍷		🍷		🍷			🍷	
						◆			**T**		**Ba**					**L**		**T**		**L**		**L**			**Lb**	
0	**Milano** Centrale d.	...	0515	0550	...	0640	0650	...	0705	0715	0735	...	...	...	0920	1000	...	1035	1120	1135	...	1235	...	1320	1335	...
10	**Milano** Rogoredo d.	...	0527	0601	...	0653**u**	0703**u**	...	0717**u**	0727	|	...	...	...	0932	1012**u**	...	|	1132	|	...	|	...	1332	|	...
72	Piacenza d.	...	0609	0635	0649	0734	0740	0749	0810	0814	0820	0849	0849	0949	1014	1048	1049	1120	1214	1220	1249	1320	1345	1414	1420	1449
107	Fidenza d.	...	0632	|	0714	0805	0758	0814	0827	0843	|	0911	0911	1014	1043	1105	1114	|	1243	|	1311	|	1412	1443	|	1511
129	Parma d.	...	0647	0705	0727	0819	0811	0827	0840	0859	0847	0927	0927	1027	1059	1118	1127	1147	1259	1247	1327	1347	1427	1459	1447	1527
157	Reggio Emilia d.	...	0703	0723	0744	0835	0830	0830	0855	0919	0902	0944	0944	1044	1119	1133	1144	1202	1319	1302	1344	1402	1444	1519	1502	1544
182	Modena d.	0647	0724	0741	0758	0853	0848	0848	0926	0938	0918	0958	0958	1058	1138	1149	1158	1218	1338	1318	1358	1418	1458	1538	1518	1558
219	**Bologna** Centrale a.	0707	0805	0802	0825	0933	0914	0925	0954	1010	0942	1025	1025	1125	1210	1219	1225	1242	1410	1342	1425	1442	1525	1610	1542	1625
	Roma Tiburtina **600 620** a.	0941	...	1016	|	1314	1321	|	|	...	|	|	|	|	...	|	|	|	...	|	|	|	|	...	|	|
	Napoli Centrale **640** a.	...	...	...	|	1547	1529	|	|	...	|	|	|	|	...	|	|	|	...	|	|	|	|	...	|	|
	Rimini **630** a.	...	...	...	1003	...	...	1102	1113	...	1038	1203	1227	1319	...	1348	1405	1338	...	1438	1605	1538	1736	...	1638	1807
	Ancona **630** a.	...	...	...	1120	...	...	...	1225	...	1130	1320	1358	1449	...	1458	1520	1433	...	1533	1720	1633	...	...	1733	1923

	IC			*IC*	*FB*	*ICN*				*FB*	*IC*				*FB*			*FB*	*ICN*		*ICN*				*ICN*	*ICN*
	1577			**613**	**8819**	**1575**				**8823**	**599**				**8825**			**8829**	**765**		**755**				**797**	**793**
					🍷					🍷					🍷			🍷		2		2		2	⑤–⑦	①–④
	Fc			**P**	**Bd**	◆				**Pe**	◆								⊙ ◆		⊙ ◆			§	⊙ ◆	⊙ ◆
Milano Centrale d.	1448	...	1520	1510	1535	1544**g**	...	...	1720	1735	1740	...	...	1815	1835	...	1920	1935	1950	...	2050	...	2120	2215	2317**g**	2317**g**
Milano Rogoredo d.	1501**u**	...	1532	1521**u**	|	1630	...	...	1732	|	1801**u**	...	...	1827	|	...	1932	|	|	...	|	...	2132	2227	|	|
Piacenza d.	1545	1549	1614	1610	1620	|	1649	1749	1814	1820	1845	...	1849	1909	1922	1949	2014	2020	|	2055	2135	2148	2214	2305	0011	0011
Fidenza d.	1603	1614	1643	1627	|	|	1714	1814	1843	|	1903	...	1914	1933	|	2014	2043	|	|	2118	|	2213	2242	|	|	|
Parma d.	1616	1627	1659	1640	1647	1705	1727	1827	1859	1847	1916	...	1927	1957	1947	2027	2059	2047	|	2133	2206	2226	2257	2334	0101	0044
Reggio Emilia d.	1633	1644	1719	1655	1702	1725	1744	1844	1919	1902	1933	...	1941	2017	2002	2044	2118	2102	|	2149	2224	2243	...	2349	|	|
Modena d.	1650	1705	1738	1724	1718	1744	1801	1858	1938	1918	1950	...	1958	2034	2018	2058	2144	2118	|	2204	2240	2257	...	0005	|	|
Bologna Centrale a.	1714	1725	1810	1750	1742	1814	1825	1925	2010	1942	2014	...	2025	2108	2042	2125	2215	2142	2156	2233	2305	2324	...	0030	|	|
Roma Tiburtina **600 620** a.	2118	|	...	|	|	2317	|	|	...	|	...	...	|	...	|	|	...	|	|	...	...	...	...	...	0717	0820
Napoli Centrale **640** a.	2350	|	...	|	|	...	|	|	...	|	...	...	|	...	|	|	...	|	|	...	...	...	...	...	...	...
Rimini **630** a.	...	1907	...	1913	1850	...	2005	2112	...	2050	...	...	2205	...	2150	2322	...	2238	2328	...	...	...	...	...	...	...
Ancona **630** a.	...	2035	...	2025	1944	...	2120	...	...	2144	...	...	2322	...	2244	...	...	2333	0048	...	...	...	...	...	...	...

	ICN	*ICN*	*ICN*	*ICN*					*FA*			*FA*		*FB*		*IC*			*IC*	*FB*		*ICN*			*FB*	
	752	**758**	**792**	**798**					**8802**			**8804**		**8806**		**580**			**604**	**8810**		**794**			**8814**	
					2			2	🍷			🍷		🍷						🍷					🍷	
	⊙ ◆	⊙ ◆	⊙ ◆	⊙ ◆				§						**Pe**		◆			**P**	**Bd**		⊙ ◆			**L**	
Ancona **630** d.	0213	0236	...	...	...	...	...	...	0500	0435	...	0620	0535	0716	0635	...	...	0742	0838	0929	0842	...	...	...	1129	1042
Rimini **630** d.	0311	0333	...	...	...	...	...	...	0550	0600	...	0709	0646	0806	0757	...	...	0900	0947	1020	0957	...	...	1041	1220	1157
Napoli Centrale **640** d.	|	|	...	...	...	...	...	...	|	|	...	|	|	|	|	...	...	|	|	|	|	...	...	|	|	|
Roma Tiburtina **600 620** d.	|	|	2355	2355	...	...	...	...	|	|	...	|	|	|	|	...	...	|	|	|	|	0639	...	|	|	|
Bologna Centrale d.	0415	0441	|	|	0500	0528	0550	0700	0705	0733	0750	0818	0833	0918	0933	0946	0950	1033	1105	1118	1133	1142	1150	1233	1318	1333
Modena d.	0440	|	|	|	0526	0555	0624	0737	0725	0802	0824	0840	0902	0940	1002	1010	1024	1102	1136	1140	1202	1213	1224	1302	1340	1402
Reggio Emilia d.	0456	|	|	|	0541	0610	0642	0757	0738	0817	0842	0854	0917	0954	1017	1024	1042	1117	1204	1154	1211	1232	1242	1307	1354	1417
Parma d.	0516	|	0524	0524	0557	0627	0705	0820	0753	0833	0905	0910	0933	1011	1033	1039	1105	1133	1220	1211	1233	1254	1305	1333	1411	1433
Fidenza d.	|	|	|	|	0610	0639	0726	0833	|	0845	0926	|	0947	|	1045	1054	1126	1145	1232	|	1245	|	1326	1345	|	1445
Piacenza d.	0551	|	0602	0602	0634	0706	0755	0858	0824	0910	0950	0941	1010	1041	1110	1119	1150	1210	1252	1241	1310	1328	1350	1410	1441	1510
Milano Rogoredo a.	|	|	|	|	*0733*	0747	0837	0936	0856**s**	*1008*	1033	1012**s**	...	|	...	1204**s**	1233	...	1333**s**	|	...	|	1433	...	|	...
Milano Centrale a.	0640	0712	0712**g**	0712**g**	*0745*	0800	0850	0950	0910	*1020*	1045	1025	...	1125	...	1215	1245	...	1345	1325	...	1442**g**	1445	...	1525	...

			FB				*IC*	*FB*			*FB*		*IC*	*IC*				*IC*		*FA*			*IC*	*FR*	*FB*	
			8818				**590**	**8882**			**8884**		**1546**	**612**				**596**		**8552**			**1590**	**9566**	**8830**	
			🍷					🍷			🍷		⑦						2	🍷	⑥⑦		⑦	🍷	🍷	
			L				**Fc**	**Tf**			**Lf**		**L**	**T**				**Fh**					**j** ◆		**B**	
Ancona **630** d.	...	1142	1325	1242	...	...	...	1525	1442	...	1631	...	1617	1638	1642	...	...	...	...	...	...	1842	...	...	2025	...
Rimini **630** d.	...	1257	1420	1400	...	1442	...	1622	1557	...	1723	...	1729	1747	1757	...	...	...	...	...	...	2000	...	...	2120	2050
Napoli Centrale **640** d.	...	|	|	|	...	|	1031	|	|	...	|	...	|	|	|	...	...	1431	...	...	...	|	1452	...	|	|
Roma Tiburtina **600 620** d.	...	|	|	|	...	|	1240	|	|	...	|	...	|	|	|	...	...	1639	...	1839	...	|	1709	1945	|	|
Bologna Centrale d.	1350	1433	1518	1533	1550	1633	1645	1718	1733	1750	1818	...	1845	1905	1933	1950	2033	2046	...	2050	2050	2133	2139	2153	2218	2229
Modena d.	1421	1502	1540	1602	1624	1702	1708	1740	1802	1824	1840	...	1913	1936	2002	2024	2102	2110	...	2113	2120	2202	2209	2217	2240	2255
Reggio Emilia d.	1442	1517	1554	1617	1642	1717	1724	1754	1817	1842	1854	...	1926	2003	2017	2042	2117	2124	...	...	2136	2217	2225	2231	2254	2310
Parma d.	1505	1533	1611	1633	1705	1733	1741	1811	1833	1905	1911	...	1941	2018	2033	2105	2133	2140	...	...	2152	2233	2243	2247	2311	2325
Fidenza d.	1524	1545	|	1645	1726	1745	1755	|	1845	1926	|	...	1954	2030	2045	2126	2145	2154	2158	...	2206	2245	2304	|	|	...
Piacenza d.	1550	1610	1641	1707	1750	1810	1819	1841	1912	1950	1941	...	2019	2051	2110	2150	2210	2219	2226	...	2233	2310	2322	2316	2341	...
Milano Rogoredo a.	1633	...	|	...	1833	...	1904**s**	|	...	2033	|	...	2104**s**	2130**s**	...	2233	...	2306**s**	2309	...	...	...	2356**s**	|	|	...
Milano Centrale a.	1645	...	1725	...	1845	...	1917	1925	...	2045	2025	...	2115	2145	...	2245	...	2320	2320	...	...	...	0010	2355	0025	...

km										
					ICN					
					757					
		2	2	2						
					⊙ ◆					
0	**Torino** Porta Nuova **610** d.	...	...	...	2020	...	...	...	...	...
56	Asti **610** d.	...	...	...	2101	...	...	...	...	...
91	Alessandria **610** d.	...	...	...	2122	...	...	...	...	...
	Genova Brignole d.	...	1156	1757	|	...	...	...	...	...
	Genova Piazza Principe d.	...	1204	1805	|	...	...	...	...	...
113	Tortona **610** d.	...	1250	1850	2139	...	...	...	...	...
130	Voghera d.	0701	1301	1901	2153	...	...	...	...	...
188	Piacenza d.	0749	1346	1949	2230	...	...	...	...	...
335	**Bologna** Centrale a.	0925	*1610*	2125	2347	...	...	...	...	...

	ICN		*ICN*						
	1580		**754**						
	①	2	②–⑦	2	2				
	⊙ ◆		⊙ ◆						
Bologna Centrale d.	0400	0500	0510	0633	*1233*	...	...	...	...
Piacenza d.	0520	0634	0657	0810	1418	...	...	...	...
Voghera d.	0553	0719	0745	0857	1505	...	...	...	...
Tortona **610** d.	0605	...	0757	0908	1516	...	...	...	...
Genova Piazza Principe a.	|	...	|	0958	1605	...	...	...	...
Genova Brignole a.	|	...	|	1009	1613	...	...	...	...
Alessandria **610** d.	0624	...	0814	...	...	...	...	...	...
Asti **610** d.	0646	...	0841	...	...	...	...	...	...
Torino Porta Nuova **610** a.	0740	...	0920	...	...	...	...	...	...

◆ – **NOTES** (LISTED BY TRAIN NUMBER)

580/99 – (12) Terni - Milano and v.v.
752 – 🛏 1, 2 cl., ▬ 2 cl. (4 berth) and (2) Lecce - Bologna - Milano.
754 – 🛏 1, 2 cl., ▬ 2 cl. (4 berth) and (2) Lecce - Bologna - Torino.
755 – 🛏 1, 2 cl., ▬ 2 cl. (4 berth) and (2) Milano - Bologna - Lecce.
757 – 🛏 1, 2 cl., ▬ 2 cl. (4 berth) and (2) Torino - Bologna - Lecce.
758 – 🛏 1, 2 cl., ▬ 2 cl. (4 berth) and (2) Lecce - Bologna - Milano.
765 – 🛏 1, 2 cl., ▬ 2 cl. (4 berth) and (2) Milano - Bologna - Lecce.
793 – 🛏 1, 2 cl., ▬ 2 cl. (4 berth) and (2) Torino - Milano - Napoli - Salerno.
792/8 – 🛏 1, 2 cl., ▬ 2 cl. (4 berth) and (2) Salerno - Napoli - Milano - Torino.
794 – 🛏 1, 2 cl., ▬ 2 cl. (4 berth) and (2) Reggio di Calabria - Milano - Torino.
795 – 🛏 1, 2 cl., ▬ 2 cl. (4 berth) and (2) Torino - Milano - Reggio di Calabria.
797 – 🛏 1, 2 cl., ▬ 2 cl. (4 berth) and (2) Torino - Milano - Napoli - Salerno.
798 – 🛏 1, 2 cl., ▬ 2 cl. (4 berth) and (2) Salerno - Napoli - Milano - Torino.
1575 – Not June 15, 16, July 6, 7: 🛏 1, 2 cl., ▬ 2 cl. (4 berth) and (2) Torino - Milano - Reggio di Calabria. Train **1597** on ① from Torino and Aug. 3 – 31.
1580 – 🛏 1, 2 cl., ▬ 2 cl. (4 berth) and (2) Lecce - Bologna - Torino.
1589 – (12) Milano - Reggio di Calabria. Train **1591** until Sept. 21.
1590 – (12) Reggio di Calabria - Milano. Train **1568** from Sept. 22.

B – From/to Bari (Tables **630**/**631**).
F – Via Firenze (Table **620**).
L – From/to Lecce (Tables **630**/**631**).
P – From/to Pescara (Tables **630**/**631**).
T – From/to Taranto (Tables **630**/**631**).

a – June 9 - Sept. 28.
b – June 9 - Nov. 23.
c – Not June 15, 16, 30, July 6, 7.
d – June 9 - Oct. 26.
e – June 9 - July 27.
f – June 9 - Sept. 15.
g – Milano **Porta Garibaldi**.
h – Not June 29, 30.
s – Stops to set down only.
u – Stops to pick up only.

§ – Operated by *TPER*. Trenitalia tickets valid.
⊙ – Subject to confirmation.

VENEZIA - BOLOGNA 616

Local services 2nd class only

km		ICN 771			FA 9403		FB 8881		FR 9407		FA 8413	FR 9409		FR 8419	FR 9413	IC 585	FR 9419			FA 8427	FA 8429	FR 9421		FR 9427
		♦		⚒	①–⑥ a		c♦				T	U b		♦	Ⓐ	♦					Ⓐ	Ⓒ		
0	**Venezia** Santa Lucia ..... **605** d.	0003	...	...	0625	0642	0655	...	0725	0742	...	...	0842	0925	0935	...	1025	...	1042	1125	1135	1135	1142	1225
9	**Venezia** Mestre .... **605** d.	0015	...	0554	0637**u**	0654	0707**u**	...	0737**u**	0754	0837	0847	0854	0937**u**	0947**u**	0929	1037**u**	...	1054	1137**u**	1147**u**	1147**u**	1154	1237**u**
37	Padova .... **605** d.	0035	...	0610	0653	0710	0724	...	0753	0810	0853	0903	0910	0953	1003	0945	1053	...	1110	1153	1203	1203	1210	1253
81	Rovigo .... d.	0115	0557	0650	|	0753	0748	...	|	0851	|	|	0951	|	|	1022	|	...	1151	|	|	|	1251	|
113	Ferrara .... d.	0141	0617	0712	|	0817	0808	...	|	0913	0925	|	1012	|	|	1046	|	...	1213	|	|	|	1313	|
160	**Bologna** Centrale .... a.	0212	0700	0743	0752	0848	0842	...	0852	0945	0952	1002	1045	1052	1102	1112	1152	...	1245	1252	1302	1302	1345	1352
	Roma Termini **600 620** ...... a.	0635	...	...	1018	...	...	...	1117	...	1218	1228	...	1310	1328	1530	1418	...	...	1518	1528	1528	...	1618
	Napoli Centrale **600** .... a.	...	...	...	...	...	...	...	1243	...	...	...	...	...	...	...	1552	...	...	...	...	...	...	1743

		FA 8435		FA 9435	FR 9433		FB 8815	IC 595	FR 9439		FR 9445	FR 8447		FA 8451			FR 9453		FR 9457				
							♦	♦	♦														
Venezia Santa Lucia .... **605** d.	1242	1325	1342	1425	1435	1442	1455	...	1525	1542	1625	1635	1642	1725	1742	...	1825	1842	1925	1942	2142	...	...
Venezia Mestre .... **605** d.	1254	1337**u**	1354	1437**u**	1447**u**	1454	1507**u**	1517	1537**u**	1554	1637**u**	1647**u**	1654	1737**u**	1754	...	1837**u**	1854	1937**u**	1954	2154	...	...
Padova .... **605** d.	1310	1353	1410	1453	1503	1510	1524	1533	1553	1610	1653	1703	1710	1753	1810	...	1853	1910	1953	2010	2210	...	...
Rovigo .... d.	1351	|	1451	|	|	1551	1546	1601	|	1651	|	1725	1751	|	1851	...	|	1954	|	2051	2248	...	...
Ferrara .... d.	1413	|	1514	|	|	1613	1603	1621	|	1715	|	|	1812	1825	1913	...	|	2015	2025	2112	...	...	...
Bologna Centrale .... a.	1445	1452	1548	1552	1602	1643	1637	1647	1652	1747	1752	1802	1845	1852	1947	...	1952	2047	2052	2145	...	...	...
Roma Termini **600 620** .... a.	...	1718	...	1818	1828	...	...	2049	1918	...	2018	2028	...	2118	...	...	2218	...	2318	...	...	...	...
Napoli Centrale **600** .... a.	...	...	...	...	1948	...	...	...	2043	...	2145	...	...	...	...	...	...	...	...	...	...	...	...

	ICN 774				FA 9400		FA 8408		FR 9406		FA 8416	FR 9412		FR 9414		FR 9416	FR 9420		FR 9422		FR 8432	FB 8816	
	♦		⚒		Ⓐ							♦					♦				♦	♦	
Napoli Centrale **600** .... d.	...	...	...	...	...	...	...	...	...	...	...	...	...	0830	...	0915	0930	...	...	...	...	...	...
Roma Termini **600 620** .... d.	2235	...	...	...	0535	...	0650	...	0750	...	0835	0850	...	0950	...	1035	1050	...	1135	...	1150	...	...
Bologna Centrale .... d.	0318	...	0615	0715	0753	0815	0908	0915	1008	1015	1053	1108	...	1208	1215	1253	1308	1315	1353	...	1408	1418	1424
Ferrara .... d.	0349	...	0648	0748	|	0848	0932	0948	|	1048	|	|	...	|	1248	1319	|	1348	|	...	|	1443	1457
Rovigo .... d.	0411	...	0708	0808	|	0908	|	1008	|	1108	1132	|	...	|	1308	|	|	1408	|	...	|	1500	1515
Padova .... **605** d.	0450	...	0751	0847	0854	0951	1009	1051	1109	1147	1154	1209	...	1309	1347	1354	1409	1447	1454	...	1509	1530	1551
Venezia Mestre .... **605** a.	0508	...	0806	0903	0908**s**	1006	1023**s**	1106	1123**s**	1203	1208**s**	1223**s**	...	1323**s**	1403	1408**s**	1423**s**	1503	1508**s**	...	1523**s**	1553**s**	1606
Venezia Santa Lucia .... **605** a.	0519	...	0818	0918	0920	1018	1035	1118	1135	1218	1220	1235	...	1335	1418	1420	1435	1518	1520	...	1535	1605	1618

	IC 588	FA 8434		FR 9430		FR 9434		FR 8446			FA 8448	FR 9440				IC 592	FA 9446	FR 9444	FB 8888			FA 9450	FR 8464
	♦							♦			♦	U				♦	Ⓑ		c♦				
Napoli Centrale **600** .... d.	...	...	...	1230	...	...	...	...	...	...	...	...	...	...	...	...	...	1630	...	...	...	...	...
Roma Termini **600 620** .... d.	1030	1250	...	1350	...	1450	...	1550	...	...	1635	1650	...	...	...	1540	1735	1750	...	...	...	1850	1950
Bologna Centrale .... d.	1447	1508	1515	1608	1615	1708	1715	1808	1815	...	1853	1908	...	1915	...	1952	1953	2008	2018	2115	...	2123	2208
Ferrara .... d.	1515	|	1548	|	1648	|	1748	|	1848	...	|	|	...	1948	...	2030	|	|	2043	2155	...	|	2232
Rovigo .... d.	1532	|	1608	|	1708	|	1807	|	1908	...	|	1946	...	2008	...	2053	|	|	2102	2214	...	|	|
Padova .... **605** d.	1600	1609	1651	1709	1751	1809	1851	1909	2000	...	1954	2009	...	2051	...	2122	2054	2109	2140	2251	...	2224	2309
Venezia Mestre .... **605** a.	1616	1623**s**	1706	1723**s**	1806	1823**s**	1906	1923**s**	2016	...	2008	2021	...	2106	...	2136	2108**s**	2123**s**	2153**s**	2306	...	2238**s**	2323**s**
Venezia Santa Lucia .... **605** a.	...	1635	1718	1735	1818	1835	1918	1935	2030	...	...	...	...	2118	...	...	2120	2135	2205	2318	...	2250	2335

♦ – **NOTES** (LISTED BY TRAIN NUMBER)

85 – [12] Trieste (**584**) - Venezia Mestre - Roma.
88 – [12] Roma - Venezia Mestre (**589**) - Trieste.
92 – [12] Roma - Venezia Mestre (**593**) - Trieste.
95 – [12] Trieste (**594**) - Venezia Mestre - Roma.
71 – 🛏 1, 2 cl., ▬ 2 cl. (4 berth) and [2] Trieste (**770**) - Udine - Venezia - Roma.
74 – 🛏 1, 2 cl., ▬ 2 cl. (4 berth) and [2] Roma - Bologna - Venezia - Udine (**775**) - Trieste.
419 – [12] and 🍷 Venezia - Roma Termini (**8420**) - Roma Fiumicino Aeroporto ✈.
432 – [12] and 🍷 Roma Fiumicino Aeroporto ✈ (**8431**) - Roma Termini - Venezia.
446 – [12] and 🍷 Roma Fiumicino Aeroporto ✈ (**8445**) - Roma Termini - Venezia.
448 – [12] and 🍷 Roma - Venezia (**8449**) - Trieste.
315 – [12] and 🍷 Venezia - Bologna - Lecce.
316 – [12] and 🍷 Lecce - Bologna - Venezia.
381 – [12] and 🍷 Venezia - Bologna - Lecce.
388 – [12] and 🍷 Lecce - Bologna - Venezia.

9412 – [12] and 🍷 Salerno (**9410**) - Napoli - Roma - Venezia.
9420 – [12] and 🍷 Salerno (**9418**) - Napoli - Roma - Venezia.
9439 – [12] and 🍷 Venezia - Roma - Napoli (**9441**) - Salerno.

T – To / from Trieste (Table **601**).
U – To / from Udine (Table **601**).

a – Not Nov. 1.
b – Not June 16, 23.
c – June 9 - Sept. 15.
s – Stops to set down only.
u – Stops to pick up only.

SIENA - CHIUSI-CHIANCIANO TERME 619

2nd class only

km																									
		⚒	†	†	⚒	†		⚒	⚒	⚒	†	⚒		†	⚒	⚒		⚒	†	⚒		⚒	†	⚒	
0	Siena .... d.	0554	0600	0802	0804	1002	...	1215	1328	1357	1402	1443	...	1602	1604	1655	...	1743	1802	1816	...	1927	2002	2023	...
89	Chiusi-Chianciano Terme .... a.	0717	0721	0927	0923	1127	...	1332	1448	1523	1523	1615	...	1727	1721	1822	...	1851	1927	1940	...	2055	2127	2142	...

	⚒	⚒	†		⚒	⚒	†		⚒	†	⚒		†	⚒	⚒		†	⚒		†	⚒	⚒		†	⚒
Chiusi-Chianciano Terme .... d.	0428	0602	0627	...	0647	0707	0830	...	0914	1030	1046	...	1230	1348	1510	...	1630	1714	...	1830	1840	1955	...	2030	2151
Siena .... a.	0546	0725	0746	...	0756	0826	0950	...	1035	1150	1159	...	1350	1519	1632	...	1750	1840	...	1950	2003	2122	...	2150	2305

620 BOLOGNA - FIRENZE (- PERUGIA - FOLIGNO) - ROMA

For high-speed services see Table **600**.

km		*ICN* 763 ♦	*ICN* 793 ⊙♦	*ICN* 797 ⊙♦	*ICN* 771 ⊙♦	⚒	*IC* 581 ①–⑥	2	2 ⚒		2	*IC* 583	*IC* 1589 ⑥♦	2		*IC* 585 ♦	2	2	2	2	2	*IC* 595 ♦	2	2	*IC* 1577 b
	Milano Centrale **600 615** d.	...	2317g	2317g	...	...	...	...	...	...	...	0650	0640	...	...	...	...	...	...	...	...	...	...	...	1448
0	**Bologna** Centrale d.	...	|	|	0217	...	...	...	...	...	...	0918	0937	...	...	1118	...	...	...	...	...	1650	...	...	1718
81	Prato Centrale d.	...	|	|	|	...	..	...	...	...	...	1004	1044	...	...	1210	...	...	...	...	...	1737	...	...	1811
97	**Firenze** S M Novella a.	...	|	|	|	...	...	...	...	...	...	1013r	1052r	...	...	1219r	...	...	...	...	...	1752r	...	...	1822
97	**Firenze** S M Novella d.	...	|	|	|	...	0545	0640	0734	0802	0904	1016r	1055r	1113	1213	1222r	1313	1413	1513	1613	1713	1755r	...	1813	1825
185	Arezzo d.	...	|	|	0425	...	0625	0743	0855	0913	1007	1113	|	1216	1316	1302	1416	1516	1616	1716	1815	1835	...	1916	1907
203	Castiglion Fiorentino d.	...	|	|	|	...	|	0755	0907	0924	1020	|	|	1227	1327	|	1427	1527	1627	1727	1827	|	...	1927	|
219	Terontola-Cortona d.	...	|	|	0445s	0600	0645	0808	0921	0941	1035	1134	|	1240	1341	1326	1440	1541	1640	1741	1841	1854	...	1941	1929
231	Passignano sul Trasimeno d.	...	|	|	|	|	|	|	|	0950	|	|	|	|	1349	|	|	1550	|	1750	|	|	...	1950	|
262	**Perugia** 625 d.	...	|	|	|	|	|	|	|	1021	|	|	|	|	1424	|	|	1624	|	1825	|	|	...	2031	|
	Assisi 625 d.	...	|	|	|	|	|	|	|	1050	|	|	|	|	1447	|	|	1649	|	1846	|	|	...	2051	|
	Foligno 625 a.	...	|	|	|	|	|	|	|	1106	|	|	|	|	1501	|	|	1703	|	1901	|	|	...	2110	|
230	Castiglione del Lago d.	...	|	|	|	0610	|	0815	0930	...	1042	|	|	1247	...	|	1447	...	1647	...	1847	|	...	...	|
248	Chiusi-Chianciano Terme d.	...	|	|	0507	0622	0704	0831	0943	...	1054	1152	1207	1259	...	1345	1459	...	1659	...	1859	1911	1910	...	1950
288	Orvieto d.	0500	0613	0613	|	0650	0725	0859	...	...	1120	1217	|	1325	...	1410	1525	...	1725	...	...	1934	1938	...	2015
330	Orte 625 d.	|	0644	0644	|	0724	|	0943	...	...	1155	1249	|	1400	...	1449	1600	...	1800	...	...	2008	2016	...	2051
408	**Roma** Tiburtina 625 a.	|	0717	0717	|	0803	|	1049	...	...	1237	1321	1314	1438	...	|	1642	...	1833	...	...	|	2113	...	2118
413	**Roma** Termini 625 a.	0600	|	|	0635	0811	0820	...	...	...	1248	|	|	1450	...	1530	1656	...	1850	...	...	2049	2125	...	|
	Napoli Centrale **640** a.	...	0938	0938	...	...	...	...	...	...	...	1529	1547	...	...	...	...	...	...	...	...	...	...	...	2350

	2	*ICN* 1575 ♦	*FR* 9563 Ⓑ	⑥	Ⓑ	2	*IC* 599 ♦		
Milano Centrale **600 615** d.	...	1544g	1845	...	...	...	1740	...	...
Bologna Centrale d.	...	1818	2005	...	...	...	2018	...	...
Prato Centrale d.	...	1910	|	...	...	...	2108	...	...
Firenze S M Novella a.	...	1933c	2044	...	...	...	2120	...	...
Firenze S M Novella d.	1913	1936c	2053	2013	2013	2113	2144	...	...
Arezzo d.	2016	|	2128	2116	2116	2216	2225	...	...
Castiglion Fiorentino d.	2027	|	|	2127	2127	2227	|	...	...
Terontola-Cortona d.	2040	|	|	2141	2153	2240	2249	...	...
Passignano sul Trasimeno d.	|	|	|	2150	2204	|	|	...	...
Perugia 625 d.	|	|	2220	2221	2246	|	2318	...	...
Assisi 625 d.	|	|	...	2242	2258	|	2339	...	...
Foligno 625 a.	|	|	...	2257	2315	|	2350	...	...
Castiglione del Lago d.	2047	|	...	...	...	2247	...	...	...
Chiusi-Chianciano Terme d.	2059	|	...	...	...	2259	...	...	...
Orvieto d.	2125	|	...	...	...	2325	...	...	...
Orte 625 d.	2205	|	...	...	...	2358	...	...	...
Roma Tiburtina 625 a.	2245	2317	...	...	...	0032	...	...	...
Roma Termini 625 a.	2256	...	...	...	...	0045	...	...	...
Napoli Centrale **640** a.	...	...	...	...	...	...	...	...	...

	2 ⚒	*FR* 9500 A	2 ⚒	*IC* 580 ♦	2	*ICN* 794 ⊙♦	2		2
Napoli Centrale **640** d.	...	...	...	...	...	0421	...	...	...
Roma Termini 625 d.	...	...	...	...	0602	|	0728	...	0900
Roma Tiburtina 625 d.	...	...	...	...	0611	0639	0737	...	0908
Orte 625 d.	...	...	...	...	0647	|	0811	...	0942
Orvieto d.	...	...	...	...	0721	|	0844	...	1015
Chiusi-Chianciano Terme d.	0545	...	...	...	0758	|	0909	...	1058
Castiglione del Lago d.	0558	...	...	...	0809	|	0920	...	1109
Foligno 625 d.	|	...	0516	0555	|	|	|	0912	|
Assisi 625 d.	|	...	0530	0608	|	|	|	0925	|
Perugia 625 d.	|	0513	0600	0635	|	|	|	0952	|
Passignano sul Trasimeno d.	|	|	0636	|	|	|	|	1022	|
Terontola-Cortona d.	0604	|	0656	0710	0819	|	0927	1036	1119
Castiglion Fiorentino d.	0618	|	0710	|	0831	|	0940	|	1131
Arezzo d.	0632	0604	0725	0732	0844	|	0953	1100	1145
Firenze S M Novella a.	0738	0634	0835	0806	0948	1005c	1100	1157	1248
Firenze S M Novella d.	...	0643	...	0821	...	1007c	...	...	...
Prato Centrale d.	...	|	...	0837	...	1030	...	...	...
Bologna Centrale a.	...	0718	...	0942	...	1138	...	...	...
Milano Centrale **600 615** a.	...	0830	...	1215	...	1442g	...	...	...

	IC 588 ♦		2	*IC* 590 b		2 †	2 ⚒		2	*IC* 592 ♦			*IC* 596 b		*IC* 1590 B♦	2	*IC* 598 Ⓑ		2	⚒	*ICN* 774 ⊙♦	*ICN* 764 ♦	*ICN* 792 ⊙♦	*ICN* 798 ⊙♦
Napoli Centrale **640** d.	...	...	...	1031	...	...	...	...	...	...	...	...	1431	...	1452	...	...	...	...	...	...	...	2131	213
Roma Termini 625 d.	1030	...	...	|	...	1300	1300	...	1502	1540	...	...	|	...	|	1712	1812	...	2005	...	2235	2300	|	|
Roma Tiburtina 625 d.	|	...	1109	1240	...	1309	1309	...	1510	|	...	...	1639	...	1709	1722	|	...	2015	...	|	|	2355	235
Orte 625 d.	1110	...	1147	1314	...	1347	1347	...	1552	1617	...	...	1715	...	|	1756	1854	...	2045	...	|	2341	0027	0027
Orvieto d.	1145	...	1221	1345	...	1421	1421	...	1626	1645	...	...	1744	...	1817	1829	1923	...	2119	...	|	0011	0103	010
Chiusi-Chianciano Terme d.	1210	...	1258	1410	...	1517	1520	...	1658	1710	...	...	1810	...	1847	1858	1946	...	2147	...	0007	...	|	|
Castiglione del Lago d.	|	...	1309	|	...	1529	1531	...	1709	|	...	...	|	...	|	1909	|	...	2158	...	|	...	|	|
Foligno 625 d.	|	1108	|	|	1303	|	|	1503	|	|	1706	...	|	...	|	|	|	1903	|	2053	|	...	|	|
Assisi 625 d.	|	1122	|	|	1317	|	|	1517	|	|	1721	...	|	...	|	|	|	1917	|	2110	|	...	|	|
Perugia 625 d.	|	1144	|	|	1339	|	|	1539	|	|	1744	...	|	...	|	|	|	1941	|	2134	|	...	|	|
Passignano sul Trasimeno d.	|	1212	|	|	1408	|	|	1610	|	|	1810	...	|	...	|	|	|	2009	|	2207	|	...	|	|
Terontola-Cortona d.	1230	1221	1319	1427	1419	1536	1540	1619	1719	1730	1819	...	1830	...	1909	1919	2004	2019	2205	2218	0025	...	|	|
Castiglion Fiorentino d.	|	1234	1331	|	1431	1549	...	1631	1731	|	1831	...	|	...	|	1931	|	2031	2218	...	|	...	|	|
Arezzo d.	1255	1245	1344	1455	1444	1603	...	1644	1744	1755	1844	...	1855	...	1936	1944	2026	2044	2231	...	0047	...	|	|
Firenze S M Novella a.	1336r	1351	1448	1536r	1548	...	...	1757	1848	1836r	1954	...	1936r	...	2020r	2048	2120	2148	2340	...	0144c	...	|	|
Firenze S M Novella d.	1339r	...	...	1539r	...	...	...	...	...	1839r	...	...	1939r	...	2023r	...	...	...	...	...	0147c	...	|	|
Prato Centrale d.	1352	...	...	1552	...	...	...	...	...	1852	...	...	1952	...	2038	...	...	...	...	...	|	...	|	|
Bologna Centrale a.	1443	...	...	1641	...	...	...	...	...	1948	...	...	2038	...	2130	...	...	...	...	...	0313	...	|	|
Milano Centrale **600 615** a.	...	...	...	1917	...	...	...	...	...	...	...	...	2320	...	0010	...	...	...	...	...	...	...	0712g	0712

♦ – **NOTES** (LISTED BY TRAIN NUMBER)

580/99 – (12) Terni - Milano and v.v.
585 – (12) Trieste (**584**) - Venezia Mestre - Roma.
588 – (12) Roma - Venezia Mestre (**589**) - Trieste.
592 – (12) Roma - Venezia Mestre (**593**) - Trieste.
595 – (12) Trieste (**594**) - Venezia Mestre - Roma.
763 – ⑥⑦ from Bolzano, ①⑦ from Orvieto: 🛏 1, 2 cl., ▬ 2 cl. (4 berth) and (2) Bolzano - Roma.
764 – ⑤⑥: 🛏 1, 2 cl., ▬ 2 cl. (4 berth) and (2) Roma - Bolzano.
771 – 🛏 1, 2 cl., ▬ 2 cl. (4 berth) and (2) Trieste (**770**) - Udine - Venezia - Bologna - Roma.
774 – 🛏 1, 2 cl., ▬ 2 cl. (4 berth) and (2) Roma - Bologna - Venezia - Udine (**775**) - Trieste.
794 – 🛏 1, 2 cl., ▬ 2 cl. (4 berth) and (2) Reggio di Calabria - Milano - Torino.
795 – 🛏 1, 2 cl., ▬ 2 cl. (4 berth) and (2) Torino - Milano - Reggio di Calabria.
797/3 – 🛏 1, 2 cl., ▬ 2 cl. (4 berth) and (2) Torino - Milano - Napoli - Salerno.
798/2 – 🛏 1, 2 cl., ▬ 2 cl. (4 berth) and (2) Salerno - Napoli - Torino.
1575 – Not June 15, 16, July 6, 7: 🛏 1, 2 cl., ▬ 2 cl. (4 berth) and (2) Torino - Milano - Reggio di Calabria. Train **1597** on ① from Torino and Aug. 3–31.
1589 – (12) Milano - Reggio di Calabria. Train **1591** until Sept. 21.
1590 – (12) Reggio di Calabria - Milano. Train **1568** from Sept. 22.

A – ①–⑥. To Torino on ①–⑤. Runs as train *FR* **9582** on ⑥.
B – ⑦ (not June 16, 30, July 7).

b – Not June 15, 16, 30, July 6, 7.
c – Firenze **Campo di Marte**.
g – Milano **Porta Garibaldi**.
r – Firenze **Rifredi**.

⊙ – Subject to confirmation.

621 FERRARA and BOLOGNA - RAVENNA - RIMINI

2nd class only except where shown

See Table **630** for fast services Bologna - Rimini via Faenza.

km		⚒	8851 R	⊙	⊙	⊙	⊙ ⚒		⚒	⊙ ⚒		8881 Vz			⊙ †	⊙ ⚒			†	⊙ ⚒	†			⚒	⚒	⊙
0	**Ferrara** d.	...	...	0513	...	0551	0631	...	...	0710	...	0808	...	...	0827	0827	...	...	...	0915	1003	...	...	1137	...	123
	Bologna Centrale d.	...	...	|	...	|	|	...	0650	|	...	|	0806	...	|	|	...	0906	...	|	|	1006	1106	|	1206	|
	Imola d.	...	...	|	...	|	|	...	0712	|	...	|	0827	...	|	|	...	0927	...	|	|	1027	1127	|	1227	|
	Castelbolognese ★ d.	...	...	|	...	|	|	...	0719	|	...	|	0831	...	|	|	...	0934	...	|	|	1034	1134	|	1234	|
	Lugo d.	...	...	|	...	|	|	...	0734	|	...	|	0848	...	|	|	...	0948	...	|	|	1048	1148	|	1128	|
74	**Ravenna** a.	...	...	0617	...	0702	0741	...	0805	0825	...	|	0915	...	0942	0942	...	1015	...	1025	1111	1115	1215	1248	1315	134
74	**Ravenna** d.	0529	0600	...	0626	...	...	0747	...	...	...	|	0919	...	...	0947	...	...	1020	...	1119	...	1219	...	1319	...
95	Cervia-Milano Marittima d.	0541	|	...	0647	...	...	0808	...	...	...	|	0938	...	...	1008	...	...	1038	...	1138	...	1238	...	1338	...
103	Cesenatico d.	0550	|	...	0653	...	...	0815	...	...	...	|	0946	...	...	1016	...	...	1046	...	1146	...	1246	...	1346	...
124	**Rimini** a.	0610	0634	...	0723	...	...	0842	...	...	...	0938	1017	...	...	1041	...	...	1117	...	1217	...	1317	...	1417	...

FOR NOTES SEE NEXT PAGE →

FERRARA and BOLOGNA - RAVENNA - RIMINI — 621

2nd class only except where shown

See Table **630** for fast services Bologna - Rimini and v.v. via Faenza.

			⊙ ⚒	⊙				**8815** V	Ⓐ			⚒	⊙ ⚒			⊙				⊙			
Ferrara d.	...	...	1337	1435	...	...	...	1603	1630	1637	...	...	1737	...	...	1835	...	...	...	2037	...	...	...
Bologna Centrale d.	1306	...	|	|	1406	1506	...	|	|	|	1606	1632	|	1706	...	|	1806	1906	2006	|	2112	...	2206
Imola d.	1327	...	|	|	1427	1527	...	|	|	|	1627	1655	|	1727	...	|	1827	1927	2027	|	2133	...	2239
Castelbolognese ★ d.	1334	...	|	|	1434	1534	...	|	|	|	1634	1702	|	1734	...	|	1834	1934	2034	|	2110	...	2245
Lugo d.	1348	...	|	|	1418	1548	...	|	|	|	1648	|	|	1748	...	|	1848	1948	2048	|	2154	...	2259
Ravenna a.	1415	...	1448	1548	1515	1615	...	|	|	1748	1715	|	1848	1815	...	1948	1915	2015	2115	2148	2220	...	2325
Ravenna d.	1419	...	...	...	1519	1619	...	|	|	...	1719	|	...	1819	...	...	1919	2019	2119	...	2224	...	...
Cervia-Milano Marittima d.	1438	...	...	...	1538	1638	...	|	|	...	1738	|	...	1838	...	...	1938	2038	2137	...	2241	...	...
Cesenatico d.	1446	...	...	...	1546	1646	...	|	|	...	1746	|	...	1846	...	...	1946	2046	2143	...	2247	...	...
Rimini a.	1517	...	...	...	1617	1717	...	1738	1845	...	1817	1805	...	1917	...	...	2017	2117	2217	...	2318	...	...

km																								
				⚒			⊙		⊙ ⚒	⚒		⊙ ⚒		⊙ †	⊙		⊙ ⚒		†	†	⊙ ⚒			
	Rimini d.	...	0525	...	...	0612	...	0654	...	0748	...	...	0843	...	0918	...	...	...	1043	...	...	...	...	1243
	Cesenatico d.	...	0550	...	...	0641	...	0721	...	0816	...	...	0916	...	0946	...	...	...	1116	...	...	...	...	1316
	Cervia-Milano Marittima d.	...	0557	...	...	0647	...	0727	...	0822	...	...	0922	...	0952	...	...	...	1122	...	...	...	...	1322
	Ravenna a.	...	0622	...	...	0707	...	0746	...	0839	...	...	0941	...	1014	...	...	...	1140	...	...	...	...	1341
0	**Ravenna** d.	0503	...	0629	0628	...	0712	0755	0752	...	0845	0847	0945	0953	...	1045	1038	1145	...	1147	1210	1245	1310	1345
28	Lugo d.	0528	...	|	0657	...	|	0815	|	...	0912	|	1012	|	...	1112	|	1212	...	|	|	1312	|	1412
42	Castelbolognese ★ d.	0546	...	|	0714	...	|	|	|	...	0928	|	1028	|	...	1128	|	1228	...	|	|	1328	|	1428
50	Imola d.	0555	...	|	0721	...	|	|	|	...	0934	|	1034	|	...	1134	|	1234	...	|	|	1334	|	1434
84	**Bologna** Centrale a.	0626	...	|	0743	...	|	0854	|	...	0954	|	1054	|	...	1154	|	1254	...	|	|	1354	|	1454
	Ferrara a.	...	...	0731	...	...	0819	...	0901	...	...	0951	...	1105	...	...	1200	...	...	1259	1324	...	1424	...

	8816 V	⊙			⊙ ⚒		⊙			⊙				⊙ ⚒		**8888** V y	⊙			**8852** R	⊙	⊙	⊙
Rimini d.	1320	...	...	1343	...	1443	1520	1543	1643	...	...	...	1743	...	1843	1920	...	1943	2043	2129	...	2143	2243
Cesenatico d.	|	...	...	1416	...	1516	1546	1616	1716	...	...	...	1816	...	1916	|	...	2016	2116	|	...	2217	2315
Cervia-Milano Marittima d.	|	...	...	1422	...	1522	1552	1622	1722	...	...	...	1822	...	1922	|	...	2022	2122	|	...	2223	2321
Ravenna a.	|	...	...	1441	...	1541	1612	1641	1741	...	...	...	1841	...	1941	|	...	2074	2141	2200	...	2245	2340
Ravenna d.	|	1412	...	1445	1512	1545	1616	1645	1745	1712	...	...	1845	1912	1945	|	2012	2045	2145	...	2212	...	...
Lugo d.	|	|	...	1512	|	1613	|	1712	1812	|	...	...	1912	|	2012	|	|	2112	2220	...	|	...	...
Castelbolognese ★ d.	|	|	...	1528	|	1628	|	1728	1828	|	...	...	1928	|	2028	|	|	2128	2234	...	|	...	...
Imola d.	|	|	...	1534	|	1634	|	1734	1834	|	...	...	1934	|	2034	|	|	2134	2240	...	|	...	...
Bologna Centrale a.	|	|	...	1554	|	1654	|	1754	1854	|	...	...	1954	|	2054	|	|	2154	2300	...	|	...	...
Ferrara a.	1441	1524	...	...	1624	...	1724	...	...	1824	...	...	...	2024	...	2041	2124	...	...	...	2322	...	...

R – *FB* train. (12) and 🍷 Roma - Falconara - Rimini - Ravenna and v.v.
V – *FB* train. (12) and 🍷 Venezia - Rimini - Lecce and v.v.
y – Train **8828** from Sept. 16.
z – Train **8801** from Sept. 16.
⊙ – Operated by *TPER*. Trenitalia tickets valid.
★ – Full name: Castelbolognese-Riolo Terme.

ROMA AIRPORTS ✈ — 622

OMA FIUMICINO AIRPORT ✈

eonardo Express rail service Roma Termini - Roma Fiumicino ✈. *31 km* Journey time: 32 minutes. Special fare payable.

rom **Roma** Termini: 0520, 0535, 0550, 0605, 0620, 0635, 0650, 0705, 0735, 0750, 0805, 820, 0835, 0850, 0905, 0935, 0950, 1035, 1050, 1105, 1120, 1135, 1150, 1205, 1220, 1235, 250, 1305, 1335, 1350, 1405, 1435, 1450, 1505, 1520, 1535, 1550, 1605, 1620, 1635, 1650, 705, 1720, 1735, 1750, 1805, 1835, 1850, 1905, 1920, 1935, 1950, 2005, 2020, 2035, 2050, 105, 2120, 2135, 2150, 2205, 2220, 2235.

From **Roma Fiumicino**: 0608, 0623, 0638, 0653, 0708, 0723, 0738, 0753, 0823, 0838, 0853, 0908, 0923, 0938, 0953, 1023, 1053, 1123, 1138, 1153, 1208, 1223, 1238, 1253, 1308, 1323, 1338, 1353, 1423, 1438, 1453, 1523, 1538, 1553, 1608, 1623, 1638, 1653, 1708, 1723, 1738, 1753, 1808, 1823, 1838, 1853, 1923, 1938, 1953, 2008, 2023, 2038, 2053, 2108, 2123, 2138, 2153, 2208, 2223, 2253, 2308, 2323.

dditional rail service (2nd class only) operates from Roma Tiburtina **and** Roma Ostiense - Roma Fiumicino ✈. *39 km* Journey times: Tiburtina - ✈ ± 45 minutes; Ostiense - ✈ ± 30 minutes.

rom **Roma** Tiburtina (Ostiense 15 minutes later):
501, 0546⚒, 0601, 0616Ⓐ, 0631, 0646Ⓐ, 0701, 0716Ⓐ, 0731, 0746⚒, 0801, 0816⚒, 831, 0846Ⓐ, 0901, 0916⚒, 0931, 0946Ⓐ, 1001, 1016Ⓐ, 1031, 1046Ⓐ, 1101, 1116Ⓐ, 131⚒, 1146Ⓐ, 1201⚒, 1216Ⓐ, 1231⚒, 1246Ⓐ, 1301, 1316Ⓐ, 1331, 1346⚒, 1401, 416Ⓐ, 1431, 1446Ⓐ, 1501, 1516Ⓐ, 1531, 1546Ⓐ, 1601, 1616⚒, 1631, 1646⚒, 1701, 716⚒, 1731, 1746Ⓐ, 1801, 1816Ⓐ, 1831, 1846Ⓐ, 1901, 1916Ⓐ, 1931, 2001, 2031, 2101, 146, 2201.

From **Roma Fiumicino** ✈:
0557, 0627, 0642⚒, 0657, 0712Ⓐ, 0727, 0742Ⓐ, 0757, 0812Ⓐ, 0827, 0842Ⓐ, 0857⚒, 0912⚒, 0927⚒, 0942Ⓐ, 0957⚒, 1012⚒, 1027, 1042Ⓐ, 1057, 1112Ⓐ, 1127, 1142Ⓐ, 1157, 1212Ⓐ, 1227, 1242Ⓐ, 1257, 1312Ⓐ, 1327, 1342Ⓐ, 1357, 1412⚒, 1427, 1442⚒, 1457, 1512Ⓐ, 1527, 1542Ⓐ, 1557, 1612Ⓐ, 1627, 1642Ⓐ, 1657, 1712Ⓐ, 1727, 1742⚒, 1757, 1812⚒, 1827, 1842Ⓐ, 1857, 1912Ⓐ, 1927, 1942Ⓐ, 1957, 2012Ⓐ, 2042, 2112, 2142, 2212, 2242.

A reduced service operates in summer.

OMA CIAMPINO AIRPORT ✈

requent rail services operate Roma Termini - Ciampino and v.v. There is a 🚌 service, *Ciampino Airlink*, between Ciampino station and the airport. Overall journey time: 30 – 35 minutes.

ROMA - ANZIO and ALBANO LAZIALE — 623

OMA - ANZIO *57 km* Journey time: 56 – 68 minutes. 2nd class only. All services continue to Nettuno (*3 km* and 4 – 6 minutes from Anzio).

rom **Roma** Termini:
⚒: 0506, 0640, 0742, 0812, 0942, 1042, 1142, 1242, 1342, 1412Ⓐ, 1442, 1542, 1642, 1742, 1812Ⓐ, 1842, 1912Ⓐ, 1942, 2042, 2142.
: 0640, 0812, 0942, 1142, 1342, 1442, 1642, 1842, 1942, 2142.

From **Anzio**:
⚒: 0455, 0559, 0635, 0703Ⓐ, 0733, 0816, 0912, 1012, 1112, 1212, 1312, 1412, 1512, 1612, 1630Ⓐ, 1712, 1812, 1912, 2012, 2112Ⓐ, 2201.
†: 0635, 0731, 0912, 1012, 1310, 1510, 1705, 1810, 2010, 2201.

OMA - ALBANO LAZIALE *29 km* Journey time: 40 – 58 minutes. 2nd class only.

rom **Roma** Termini: 0542⚒, 0721, 0821, 0900⚒, 1221, 1321⚒, 1421, 1521⚒, 1621, 1721⚒, 1821, 1921⚒, 2021, 2121⚒.

From **Albano Laziale**: 0629⚒, 0700⚒, 0743⚒, 0838, 1023, 1144⚒, 1343, 1443⚒, 1543, 1643⚒, 1743, 1843⚒, 1943, 2043⚒, 2140⚒, 2145†.

ll trains call at Marino Laziale and Castel Gandolfo approximately 35 and 40 minutes from Roma, 7 and 15 minutes from Albano Laziale respectively.

ROMA - PESCARA — 624

2nd class only

km																												
		⚒		⚒		†	⚒	⚒	⚒		⚒		⚒		⚒			†	⚒	⚒				⚒			⚒	⚒
0	**Roma** Termini ▲ d.	...	...	...	...	0710	0715	...	0810t	0857	...	...	...	1110t	...	...	1310	1430	1430	...	...	...	1645	...	...	1845	...	1915t
40	Tivoli ▲ d.	...	...	...	...	0812	0828	...	0901	0952	...	...	...	1211	...	...	1405	1504	1504	...	...	...	1720	...	...	1919	...	1959
108	Avezzano d.	...	...	...	0713	0920	0947	...	1023	1106	...	...	1255	1319	1355	...	1517	1602	1603	...	1611	...	1819	1840	...	2019	...	2110
172	Sulmona d.	0523	0635	0715	0840	1020	...	1027	...	...	1130	1400	1406	...	1518	1557	...	...	1656	1702	1730	1753	1912	1955	2000	2112	2130	...
226	Chieti a.	0617	0729	0813	0932	1058	...	1119	...	...	1222	1457	...	...	...	1647	...	...	1736	1757	...	1844	1951	...	2053	2151	2229	...
240	**Pescara** Centrale a.	0640	0755	0840	1000	1115	...	1145	...	...	1239	1521	...	...	...	1709	...	...	1752	1820	...	1903	2007	...	2112	2207	2252	...

	⚒		⚒	†	⚒		†	⚒		⚒	⚒			⚒	⚒	⚒	⚒	†	⚒		⚒	†	⚒	†	⚒			
Pescara Centrale d.	...	...	0523	...	0656	0730	...	0923	...	...	1119	...	1215	...	1310	1410	...	1446	1510	...	...	1613	1615	1627	1715	...	2017	2115
Chieti d.	...	...	0536	...	0714	0744	...	0936	...	...	1138	...	1241	...	1331	1431	...	1501	1532	...	...	1631	1635	1648	1738	...	2038	2134
Sulmona d.	...	...	0619	0619	0815	0826	...	1019	...	...	1232	...	1340j	1416	1435	1530	...	1545	1630	1700	...	1727	1735	1736	1845	...	2145	2230
Avezzano d.	0508	0545	0712	0712	...	0919	1112	1112	1145	1320	1345	1408	...	1530	...	...	1604	1638	...	1815	1835	...	...	1840	2010	2112	...	...
Tivoli ▲ d.	0610	0700	0812	0812	...	1023	1211	1211	1259	1436	...	1533	...	1642	...	...	1721	1749	...	...	2000	...	...	1950	...	2232	...	...
Roma Termini ▲ a.	0700t	0806t	0844	0845	...	1055t	1245	1245	1350	1536t	...	1625	...	1736t	...	...	1828	1828	...	...	2053t	...	...	2035t	...	2315	...	...

– Arrives 1325 on †.
– Roma Tiburtina **Piazzale Est**.
▲ – Additional services operate Roma Tiburtina (Piazzale Est) - Tivoli and v.v., journey 60 – 75 minutes.

625 ROMA - PERUGIA and ANCONA

km		2 Ⓐ	2 ⚒	2 ⚒	*IC* 580 T	2 †	2 ⚒		⚒	*IC* 534		⚒	2 ⚒			*IC* 540		⚒	*FB* 8852 R	2 Ⓐ	Ⓑ		⚒	*IC* 546 Ⓑ		
0	**Roma** Termini ... 620 d.	...	...	...	...	...	...	0545	0653	0740	0758	0928	1158	1328	1428	1535	1558	1658	1730	...	1758	1836	1904	1958	2106	2240
5	**Roma** Tiburtina ... 620 d.	...	...	...	...	...	...	0555	0702	|	0807	0938	1208	1337	1439	|	1607	1709	|	...	1807	1845	1913	2008	2115	2249
83	Orte ... 620 d.	...	...	...	...	...	...	0634	0739	0817	0840	1013	1240	1410	1511	1609	1640	|	|	...	1840	1917	1945	2037	2148	2321
112	Terni ... d.	...	...	...	0505	...	...	0654	0800	0843	0901	1037	1305	1432	1531	1630	1704	1802	1823	...	1902	1943	2008	2054	2212	2339
141	Spoleto ... d.	...	...	...	0532	...	...	0718	0835	0913	0932	1108	1329	1458	1555	1656	1731	1825	1845	...	1932	2008	2032	2121	2235	...
167	**Foligno** ... a.	...	...	...	0553	...	...	0740	0853	0930	0949	1131	1350	1516	1612	1712	1751	1844	1858	...	1953	2029	2051	2136	2252	...
167	**Foligno** ... 620 d.	...	...	0545	0555	0615	0640	0742	...	0932	0953	1133	*1416*	1518	1614	1714	1753	...	1900	...	1955	2031	2053	2138	2254	...
172	Spello ... d.	...	...	|	|	|	|	|	...	|	|	|	|	|	1619	|	|	...	|	...	2001	|	2059	|	|	...
183	Assisi ... 620 d.	...	...	|	0608	|	|	|	...	|	1008	|	|	|	1628	|	|	...	|	...	2010	|	2110	2151	|	...
196	Perugia Ponte SG ▲ ... d.	...	...	|	0623	|	|	|	...	|	1018	|	|	|	1646	|	|	...	|	...	2021	|	2124	2202	|	...
207	**Perugia** ... 620 a.	...	...	|	0633	|	|	|	...	|	1028	|	|	|	1659	|	|	...	|	...	2032	|	2132	2213	|	...
224	Fabriano ... d.	0500	0600	0646	...	0714	0736	0846	...	1030	...	1226	*1523*	1620	...	1805	1846	...	1942	1948	...	2123	...	...	2346	...
268	Jesi ... d.	0537	0641	0733	...	0756	0820	0923	...	1100	...	1310	*1605*	1704	...	1840	1922	...	2015	2030	...	2200	...	...	0023	...
286	Falconara Marittima ... 630 d.	0551	0658	0748	...	0813	0837	0940	...	1115	...	1330	*1626*	1722	...	1855	1940	...	2028	2046	...	2213	...	...	0039	...
295	**Ancona** ... 630 a.	0605	0710	0803	...	0828	0852	0955	...	1125	...	1345	*1637*	1738	...	1909	1956	...	...	2057	...	2225	...	...	0055	...

	⚒		⚒	2 ⚒	*IC* 531 ①–⑥	†	*IC* 533	2 Ⓐ	*FB* 8851 R			⚒	2 ⚒		2 Ⓐ	⚒	*IC* 541	2 ⚒		2			2 Ⓐ	2	*IC* 599 T
Ancona ... 630 d.	...	0350	...	0505	...	...	0547	0650	...	0847	...	...	1250	1340	...	...	1530	1540	...	1735	1830	1950	2030	2130	...
Falconara Marittima ... 630 d.	...	0401	...	0513	...	...	0600	0701	0730	0857	...	...	1305	1351	...	...	1541	1550	...	1746	1842	2001	2040	2139	...
Jesi ... d.	...	0415	...	0526	...	...	0614	0720	0742	0912	...	...	1323	1407	...	...	1554	1606	...	1802	1856	2016	2056	2153	...
Fabriano ... d.	...	0451	...	0604	...	...	0651	0808	0818	0949	...	...	1412	1450	...	...	1629	1657	...	1852	1941	2052	2143	2235	...
Perugia ... 620 d.	...	|	0554	|	0640	0712	|	...	|	|	1105	1343	|	|	1517	1556	|	...	1805	...	|	|	...	|	2318
Perugia Ponte SG ▲ ... d.	...	|	0603	|	0651	0721	|	...	|	|	1114	1353	|	|	1526	1605	|	...	1815	...	|	|	...	|	2328
Assisi ... 620 d.	...	|	0618	|	0703	0732	|	...	|	|	1129	1410	|	|	1546	1625	|	...	1827	...	|	|	...	|	2339
Spello ... d.	...	|	0628	|	|	0741	|	...	|	|	1139	1424	|	|	1555	1636	|	...	1836	...	|	|	...	|	|
Foligno ... 620 a.	...	0537	0634	0700	0715	0748	0739	...	0858	1039	1146	1434	1512	1543	1605	1640	1733	...	1843	...	2029	2145	...	2334	2350
Foligno ... d.	...	0539	0636	...	0717	0749	0741	...	0900	1041	1148	1436	1514	1545	...	1642	1735	...	1846	...	2031	2147	...	...	2354
Spoleto ... d.	...	0555	0653	...	0734	0809	0756	...	0914	1057	1206	1455	1532	1607	...	1658	1752	...	1902	...	2048	2203	...	...	0011
Terni ... d.	0540	0625	0732	...	0758	0833	0826	...	0936	1122	1235	1524	1609	1630	...	1728	1823	...	1925	...	2118	2234	...	...	0035
Orte ... 620 d.	0600	0651	0801	...	0816	0854	0947	...	|	1149	1305	1547	1632	1657	...	1749	1848	...	1949	...	2140	2252	...	...	...
Roma Tiburtina ... 620 a.	0630	0723	0836	...	0847	0923	|	...	|	1219	1340	1618	...	1724	...	1817	|	...	2020	...	2212	2323	...	...	...
Roma Termini ... 620 a.	0640	0737	0850	...	0858	0935	0927	...	1027	1235	1356	1633	...	1741	...	1835	1928	...	2032	...	2225	2335	...	...	...

R – (12) and 🍷 Ravenna - Rimini - Falconara - Roma and v.v.
T – (12) Terni - Perugia - Milano and v.v.
▲ – Perugia Ponte San Giovanni.

626 ROMA - CASERTA - NAPOLI and FOGGIA

km		2 ⚒	2 ⚒	2 ⚒	*FA* 8305 🍷	2 ⚒	*IC* 703 a	*IC* 35129 b	2 †	2 ⚒	2 ⚒	*FA* 8315 🍷	2 ⚒	*FA* 8317 🍷 ⑤⑦	*FA* 8319 🍷 Ⓑ	*IC* 705 ⑤	2 Ⓐ	*FA* 8323 🍷	2	*FA* 8325 🍷 Ⓑ	2 ⚒	2 †	2	2 Ⓐ	*ICN* 789 ⊙♦
0	**Roma** Termini ... 627 d.	...	...	...	0805	*0621*	0728	0756	*1014*	1235	...	1508	*1307*	1603	1656	1601	*1442*	1803	*1542*	1903	1642	1655	1807	*1907*	2358
138	Cassino ... 627 d.	0505	0550	0705	|	0840	0912	|	1305	1406	1435	|	1510	|	|	|	1705	|	1805	|	1858	1857	1946	2055	|
170	Vairano-Caianello ... d.	0538	0623	0738	|	0913	0935	|	1338	1430	1508	|	1543	|	|	|	1738	|	1838	|	1928	1930	2008	2120	|
216	Caserta ... d.	0622	0707	0822	0915	0957	1011	1011	1422	1512	1552	1625	1630	|	1805	1812	1823	1915	1925	2013	2018	2013	2045	2158	0236
250	**Napoli** Centrale ... a.	0705	0746	0905	|	1040	|	|	1505	|	1635	|	...	|	|	|	1905	|	...	|	*2103*	*2103*	...	...	|
279	Benevento ... d.	...	...	...	0952	...	1059	1059	...	1615	...	1704	...	|	1844	1906	...	1953	...	2058	...	...	...	...	0324
380	**Foggia** ... a.	...	...	...	1056	...	1226	1226	...	...	...	1759	...	|	1945	2034	...	2051	...	|	...	...	...	...	0449
	Bari Centrale **631** ... a.	...	...	...	1204	...	1400	1400	...	...	...	1909	...	1940	...	2212	...	2159	...	2249	...	...	...	...	0627
	Taranto **631** ... a.	...	...	...	|	...	...	...	...	...	...	|	...	...	...	2332	...	|	...	...	...	...	...	...	|
	Lecce **631** ... a.	...	...	...	1336**c**	...	...	...	...	...	...	2035	...	...	...	...	...	2323	...	...	...	...	...	...	0809

	ICN 788 ⊙♦	2 ⚒	*FA* 8300 🍷 ①–⑥	2 ⚒	2	*FA* 8348 🍷 ①–⑥	2 ⚒	*FA* 8302 🍷	2 ⚒	*FA* 8306 🍷 ①⑥		2 ⚒	*FA* 8314 🍷	2 ⚒	2 ⚒	2 ⚒	2 †	2 Ⓐ	*IC* 704 b	*IC* 704 a	*FA* 8324 🍷	2 ⚒	2 Ⓐ	*IC* 710 ⑦
Lecce **631** ... d.	2230	...	...	...	...	...	...	0555	...	...	...	...	1150	...	...	...	...	...	...	...	1647**f**	...	...	...
Taranto **631** ... d.	|	...	...	...	...	...	...	|	...	...	...	...	|	...	...	...	...	...	...	...	|	...	...	1540
Bari Centrale **631** ... d.	0015	...	...	...	...	0623	...	0717	...	0855	...	...	1314	...	...	...	...	...	1555	1555	1817	...	...	1714
Foggia ... d.	0200	...	0500	...	...	|	...	0827	...	|	...	...	1422	...	...	...	...	...	1741	1741	1927	...	...	1839
Benevento ... d.	0321	...	0555	0520	...	0813	0632	0925	...	|	...	...	1525	...	...	...	...	...	1900	1900	2031	...	...	2002
Napoli Centrale ... d.	|	...	|	|	*0510*e	|	|	|	0755	|	...	1155	|	...	...	...	1550	1713	|	|	|	1755	1955	|
Caserta ... d.	0407	0410	0632	0609	0610	0851	0730	1010	0736	|	...	1236	1602	1330	1530	1620	1631	1754	1958	1958	2110	1836	2036	2053
Vairano-Caianello ... d.	|	0455	|	|	0646	|	0808	|	0918	|	...	1317	|	1413	1613	1704	1713	1836	|	2026	|	1918	2118	|
Cassino ... 627 d.	|	0530	|	|	0711	|	0837	|	0955	|	...	1355	|	1447	1650	1740	1750	1913	|	2048	|	1955	2145	|
Roma Termini ... 627 a.	0610	*0748*	0742	0827	0848	0958	1013	1123	*1147*	1230	...	*1620*	1720	*1720*	*1920*	...	*1934*	*2148*	2154	2220	2220	*2241*	...	2311

♦ – **NOTES** (LISTED BY TRAIN NUMBER)

788 – ⑦ from Lecce: 🛏 1, 2 cl., ▬ 2 cl. (4 berth) and (2) Lecce - Roma.
789 – ⑤ from Roma: 🛏 1, 2 cl., ▬ 2 cl. (4 berth) and (2) Roma - Lecce.

a – Not Aug. 3 - Sept. 1.
b – Aug. 3 - Sept. 1.
c – Arrives 1328 from Sept. 16 (Train **8303**).

e – Connection on ⚒ only.
f – Departs 1655 from Sept. 16 (Train **8326**).
⊙ – Subject to confirmation.

627 ROMA and NAPOLI - CAMPOBASSO - TERMOLI

2nd class only

km		🚌	⚒		⚒	†		🚌 ⚒	⚒	⚒	†	⚒	🚌 ⚒	†	⚒	🚌		†	🚌		⚒	†	Ⓐ	⑥
0	**Roma** Termini ... ● d.	...	...	0615	...	...	0907	...	...	1307	...	...	...	1435	1435	...	...	1740	...	...	1935	2014	2035	2042
138	Cassino ... ● d.	...	...	0742	...	...	1033	...	...	1445	...	...	...	1602	1603	...	...	|	...	...	|	|	|	|
	Napoli Centrale ... d.	...	...	|	...	...	|	...	1206	|	1400	1400	...	|	|	...	1706	|	...	1930	|	|	|	|
	Caserta ... d.	...	...	|	0805	0842	|	...	1242	|	1440	1440	...	|	|	...	1742	|	...	2004	|	|	|	|
	Vairano-Caianello ... d.	...	...	|	0850	0926	|	...	1322	|	1516	1516	...	|	|	...	1823	|	...	2040	|	|	|	|
187	Isernia ... d.	...	0645	0828	0935	1012	1118	...	1408	1528	1600	1557	...	1640	1650	...	1903	1948	...	2126	2148	2226	2238	2245
198	Carpinone ... ♣ d.	...	0657	0840	|	|	1130	...	1420	1540	1612	1610	...	|	|	...	1915	2000	...	2138	|	|	|	|
246	**Campobasso** ... ▲ a.	0646	0755	0924	1036	1110	1219	1414	1518	1633	1708	1714	1720	1742	1749	1828	2008	2052	2100	2227	2242	2325	2338	2345
333	Termoli ... a.	0830	...	...	...	...	...	1600	...	...	...	...	1905	...	...	2010	...	...	2245	...	...	...	...	...

km		⚒		⚒	⚒	†	🚌 ⚒	🚌 †		⚒	†		⚒	†	🚌 ⚒	⚒	†	🚌 ⚒	Ⓐ	⑥		🚌		🚌
	Termoli ... d.	...	...	...	...	...	0548	0630	...	...	...	...	...	...	1325	...	...	1450	...	...	...	1728	...	2045
	Campobasso ... ▲ d.	0513	0545	0628	0653	0727	0735	0815	0836	1232	1232	1314	1415	1421	1510	1542	1621	1635	1645	1715	1758	1915	1938	2230
	Carpinone ... ♣ d.	0553	|	0716	|	0811	...	...	0926	1315	1317	1359	|	|	...	1635	1712	...	1736	1803	1846	...	|	...
0	Isernia ... d.	0606	0640	0728	0745	0825	...	...	0938	1328	1330	1411	1509	1515	...	1651	1724	...	1749	1814	1904	...	2033	...
46	Vairano-Caianello ... d.	0649	|	0809	|	0910	...	...	|	|	1412	1459	|	|	...	1731	|	...	|	|	1949	...	|	...
92	Caserta ... a.	0718	|	0849	|	0944	...	...	|	|	1449	1533	|	|	...	1811	|	...	|	|	2025	...	|	...
126	**Napoli** Centrale ... a.	0752	|	0926	|	1020	...	...	|	|	...	1609	|	|	...	...	|	...	|	|	2103	...	|	...
	Cassino ... ● a.	...	0723	...	|	...	...	...	1017	1416	...	...	1549	1557	...	...	1804	...	1829	1854	...	...	2115	...
	Roma Termini ... ● a.	...	0853	...	0959	...	...	...	1147	...	...	...	1727	1727	...	...	1934	...	1953	2026	...	...	2254	...

● – See panel on next page for additional services Roma - Cassino and v.v.
♣ – See panel on next page for 🚌 services Sulmona - Castel di Sangro - Carpinone and v.v.
▲ – See panel on next page for 🚌 services Campobasso - Benevento and v.v.

2nd class only

ROMA and NAPOLI - CAMPOBASSO - TERMOLI 627

ROMA - CASSINO

	⚒		†	⚒	⚒	†	⚒		†	⚒	⚒	⚒				⚒	†	Ⓐ				⚒		Ⓐ	⑥	
Roma Termini ... d.	0535	0615	0707	0742	0800	0800	0835	0907	1014	1014	1235	1307	1342	1435	1542	1642	1655	1707	1742	1807	1842	1907	1942	2042	2049	2128
Cassino ... a.	0736	0742	0857	0942	0947	1014	1058	1033	1227	1245	1406	1445	1544	1603	1742	1858	1857	1844	1940	1946	2040	2045	2142	2245	2305	2340

		⚒	†	⚒	†	⚒		⚒	†		⚒	†	⚒	⚒	†		†	⚒	†	Ⓐ	⑥	Ⓐ	†			Ⓐ
Cassino ... d.	0607	0618	0627	0805	0850	0913	1017	1218	1231	1318	1422	1458	1515	1549	1557	1620	1715	1720	1804	1829	1854	1932	1934	2018	2115	2120
Roma Termini ... a.	0748	0820	0834	0948	1107	1107	1147	1448	1448	1520	1620	1720	1720	1727	1727	1820	1920	1920	1934	1953	2026	2148	2148	2241	2254	2334

🚌 SULMONA - CASTEL DI SANGRO - CARPINONE

	⚒	⚒		⚒		⚒	⚒
Sulmona ... d.	...	...	1030	...	...	...	1950
Castel di Sangro . d.	0615	0805	1130	1240	...	1830	2050
Carpinone ... a.	0718	0908	...	1343	...	1933	...

	⚒	⚒	⚒	⚒	†	⚒	⚒
Carpinone ... d.	...	0653	0853	1433	...	...	2015
Castel di Sangro .. d.	0555	0758	0958	1538	1615	1640	2120
Sulmona ... a.	0705	...	...	...	1725	1750	...

🚌 **CAMPOBASSO - BENEVENTO and v.v.**
(*67 km*, journey time 70 minutes).
From Campobasso: 0620⚒, 1305⚒, 1416⚒, 1750⚒.
From Benevento: 0640⚒, 0740⚒, 1420⚒, 1740⚒.

Some trains 2nd class only

SARDINIA 629

km																											
		⚒		⚒	⚒	†	†	†	†	⚒	⚒	†	⚒	⚒	†	†	⚒	†	⚒	†	⚒	⚒	⚒	†	⚒	†	†
0	**Cagliari** ... d.	...	...	...	...	...	...	...	0624	0630	...	...	0722	0835	...	...	...	0930	0925	1010	1040	...	1112	1112	...	1222	...
17	Decimomannu ... d.	...	...	...	...	...	...	...	0638	0641	...	...	0737	|	...	...	...	0944	0939	1028	|	...	1131	1129	...	1238	...
95	**Oristano** ... d.	...	...	...	...	...	...	...	0730	0730	...	...	0830	0931	...	...	...	1043	1048	1132	1134	...	1232	1225	...	1331	...
154	Macomer ... d.	...	...	...	...	...	...	...	0821	0824	...	...	...	1025	...	...	...	1139	1144	...	1227	...	...	▬	...	1431	...
214	Ozieri-Chilivani ... a.	...	...	...	...	...	...	...	0904	0903	...	...	...	1104	...	...	...	▬	▬	...	|	...	...	⚒	...	1516	...
214	Ozieri-Chilivani ... d.	...	...	0645	0645	0746	0747	...	0912	0906	0910	0912	...	1107	1102	1105	1109	...	...	...	|	...	...	1441	...	1521	1521
	Sassari ... d.	...	0650	|	0738	0824	|	0835	0950	|	0950	|	...	|	1142	|	1148	...	...	...	1339	1344	...	1525	1530	|	1600
	Porto Torres ... a.	...	0705	|	0753	...	|	0848	...	|	...	|	...	|	...	|	▬	...	...	...	...	1359	...	...	1545	|	...
	Porto Torres Marittima ... a.	...	0708	|	0756	...	|	0852	...	|	...	|	...	|	...	|	†	⚒	⚒	...	...	1403	...	...	1549	|	...
285	Olbia ... a.	0645	...	0746	...	...	0848	...	...	0958	...	1012	...	1202	...	1208	1313	1315	1430	...	...	...	...	...	...	1620	...
306	Golfo Aranci ... a.	0708	...	...	...	...	...	...	...	...	...	...	...	...	...	...	1338	1340	1455	...	...	...	...	...	...	...	...

km																											
		⚒	⚒	⚒	†	†	⚒	⚒	🚌	⚒	⚒	⚒	†	†	†	†	⚒	†	⚒	†	⚒	†	⚒	⚒	⚒	⚒	†
	Cagliari ... d.	1222	...	1325	1413	...	1430	...	...	1522	1630	...	1640	...	...	1713	1720	1820	1830	...	...	1915	...	1920	🚌	2035	2040
	Decimomannu ... d.	1237	...	1341	1428	...	|	...	...	1537	|	...	|	...	...	1732	1739	1834	|	...	...	1934	...	1940	...	2050	2055
	Oristano ... d.	1330	...	1437	1531	...	1534	...	...	1632	1731	...	1742	...	...	1829	1841	1926	1936	...	...	2034	...	2050	2056	2154	2201
	Macomer ... d.	1431	...	1535	1629	...	1631	...	...	...	1819	...	1830	...	...	...	...	2027	2024	...	...	...	2036	...	2216	...	...
	Ozieri-Chilivani ... a.	1516	...	▬	1712	...	1709	...	...	...	1858	...	1908	...	...	...	...	2115	|	...	...	...	2121	...	...	...	...
0	Ozieri-Chilivani ... d.	1524	1522	...	1719	1717	1717	1711	...	...	1901	1903	1915	1913	1954	...	...	2118	|	2120	2126	...	2123	...	...	...	...
47	**Sassari** ... d.	|	1601	...	1758	|	1756	|	...	...	|	1947	1954	|	2030	...	...	|	2134	2200	2206	...	|	...	...	...	...
66	Porto Torres ... a.	|	...	...	1810	|	1811	|	...	...	|	...	...	|	...	...	...	|	...	...	...	...	|	...	...	...	...
67	Porto Torres Marittima ... a.	|	...	...	1814	|	1816	|	...	...	|	...	...	|	...	...	...	|	...	...	...	...	|	...	...	...	...
	Olbia ... a.	1631	...	1636	...	1820	...	1822	1826	...	1956	...	...	2013	...	...	...	2216	...	...	...	...	2223	...	...	...	...
	Golfo Aranci ... a.	...	...	1702	...	...	...	...	1858	...	...	...	...	...	...	...	...	...	...	...	...	...	...	...	...	...	...

		⚒	⚒	⚒	⚒	⚒	⚒	⚒	†	†	⚒		⚒	⚒	†	†	†	⚒		⚒	†	⚒	⚒	⚒	⚒	†	⚒
Golfo Aranci ... d.	...	🚌	...	🚌	...	...	...	...	...	...	...	...	0715	...	...	...	...	...	...	...	...	...	...	...	...	1345	1347
Olbia ... d.	...	...	...	...	...	...	0546	...	0640	...	...	...	0738	0806	...	0802	...	...	1006	...	...	...	...	...	1337	1405	1410
Porto Torres Marittima ... d.	...	...	...	...	...	...	|	...	|	...	...	0718	▬	|	...	|	...	0952	|	...	1005	...	...	...	|	▬	▬
Porto Torres ... d.	...	...	...	...	...	...	|	...	|	...	...	0721	⚒	|	...	|	...	0955	|	...	1008	...	...	...	|	...	...
Sassari ... d.	...	...	...	...	...	0601	|	0630	|	0704	...	0736	0820	|	0826	|	0922	1010	|	1023	1022	...	1120	...	|	...	...
Ozieri-Chilivani ... a.	...	...	...	...	...	0640	0640	|	0740	0742	...	...	0859	0902	0905	0907	1009	...	1102	1100	1100	...	1207	...	1436	...	...
Ozieri-Chilivani ... d.	...	...	...	...	...	▬	0645	|	...	0750	...	...	...	0905	...	0910	...	...	...	1107	1108	...	...	...	...	...	...
Macomer ... d.	...	0510	...	0605	...	†	0730	0743	...	0839	...	...	...	0945	...	0954	...	...	...	1146	1151	...	...	1341	...	†	†
Oristano ... d.	0530	0620	0630	0725	0730	0730	...	0831	...	0925	0930	...	...	1031	...	1042	...	...	...	1233	1237	1330	...	1437	...	1430	1530
Decimomannu ... d.	0629	...	0721	...	0821	0828	...	|	...	1015	1027	...	...	|	...	1139	...	...	...	|	1343	1422	...	1538	...	1530	1629
Cagliari ... a.	0643	...	0737	...	0837	0841	...	0928	...	1029	1048	...	...	1125	...	1155	...	...	...	1327	1358	1438	...	1554	...	1552	1650

	†	†	⚒	⚒	⚒	⚒	⚒	†	⚒		⚒	†		†	⚒	⚒	⚒		⚒	†	⚒	†	†	⚒	†	†	⚒
Golfo Aranci ... d.	...	...	...	...	...	...	...	...	1525	...	...	...	1731	...	...	...	...	...	...	...	...	...	...	...	...	...	...
Olbia ... d.	1413	...	...	1415	...	...	...	...	1550	...	1611	1557	1755	...	...	...	1800	...	...	...	...	1841	...	...	...	2015	2018
Porto Torres Marittima ... d.	|	...	1416	|	...	...	1606	...	...	...	|	|	...	...	...	...	|	...	1830	1840	...	|	...	...	...	|	|
Porto Torres ... d.	|	...	1419	|	...	...	1609	...	...	...	|	|	...	...	...	...	|	...	1833	1843	...	|	...	...	...	|	|
Sassari ... d.	|	1433	1434	|	1439	...	1624	...	...	1629	|	|	...	...	...	1815	|	...	1848	1858	1900	|	1904	2031	2032	|	|
Ozieri-Chilivani ... a.	1514	1511	...	1517	1518	...	...	...	...	1708	1707	1708	...	...	...	1853	1855	...	...	...	|	1949	1949	2118	2111	2116	2121
Ozieri-Chilivani ... d.	...	1519	...	...	1525	...	...	...	...	...	1712	...	...	...	...	...	1900	...	...	...	|	...	1956	...	...	...	...
Macomer ... d.	...	1558	...	...	1605	1632	...	1729	...	...	1752	...	...	...	...	...	1940	...	...	...	2024	...	2047	...	...	...	...
Oristano ... d.	...	1654	...	...	1649	1731	...	1830	...	...	1848	...	...	1930	1936	...	2032	...	...	...	2116	...	2137	...	...	...	...
Decimomannu ... d.	...	1745	...	...	|	1830	...	1936	...	...	|	...	...	2029	2036	...	|	...	...	...	2216	...	2235	...	...	...	...
Cagliari ... a.	...	1800	...	...	1744	1847	...	1951	...	...	1943	...	...	2050	2049	...	2128	...	...	...	2232	...	2249	...	...	...	...

km																											
		⚒	⚒	⚒	Ⓐ					⚒	⚒	Ⓑ	Ⓑ	⚒	⚒	Ⓑ	Ⓑ		⚒	⚒			⚒	⚒	⚒	⚒	
0	**Cagliari** ... d.	0526	0545	...	0614	0644	...	0744	...	0844	...	0944	...	1044	...	1145	...	...	1244	...	1344	...	1418	🚌	1444	...	1544
17	Decimomannu ... d.	0541	0604	...	0635	0704	...	0803	...	0903	...	1003	...	1103	...	1203	...	...	1304	...	1403	...	1432	...	1503	...	1603
46	Villamassargia ... a.	0601	0629	0635	0701	0729	0734	0829	0834	0929	0934	1029	1034	1129	1134	1229	1234	...	1329	1334	1429	1434	1459	1504	1529	1534	1629
	Carbonia Serbariu ... a.	|	0651	|	|	|	0751	0847	|	|	0951	1047	|	|	1150	1247	|	...	|	1350	1447	|	|	1527	|	1550	1647
55	**Iglesias** ... a.	0611	...	0644	0712	0741	...	...	0843	0940	...	...	1043	1140	...	...	1243	...	1340	...	...	1443	1509	...	1540	...	...

	Ⓑ	Ⓑ			Ⓐ	Ⓐ				🚌	
Cagliari ... d.	1644	...	1744	...	1844	...	1944	...	2044	...	...
Decimomannu ... d.	1703	...	1803	...	1903	...	2004	...	2103	...	...
Villamassargia ... a.	1729	1734	1829	1834	1929	1934	2029	2034	2129	2135	...
Carbonia Serbariu ... a.	|	1750	1847	|	|	1950	2047	|	|	2158	...
Iglesias ... a.	1740	...	...	1843	1940	...	...	2043	2140	...	...

	⚒	⚒	⚒	†	⚒			Ⓐ			⚒
Iglesias ... d.	0553	0623	...	0627	0653	...	0721	0754	0818	...	...
Carbonia Serbariu ... d.	|	|	0613	|	|	0710	|	|	|	0810	0910
Villamassargia ... d.	0603	0630	0635	0636	0703	0726	0731	0803	0826	0831	0926
Decimomannu ... d.	0633	...	0702	0703	0732	...	0756	0831	...	0856	...
Cagliari ... a.	0652	...	0724	0723	0750	...	0815	0850	...	0915	...

km																												
		⚒	Ⓑ	†	Ⓐ	⚒	⚒	Ⓑ	†	Ⓐ	⚒	⚒		†	⚒	⚒	⚒	⚒			Ⓑ	Ⓑ			Ⓐ	Ⓐ		
	Iglesias ... d.	0921	1018	...	...	...	1121	1218	...	...	...	1321	1418	...	...	...	1521	1552	1618	...	...	1721	1818	...	...	1921	2018	...
0	**Carbonia** Serbariu d.	|	|	1010	1010	1110	|	|	1210	1210	1310	|	|	1410	1410	1510	|	|	|	1610	1710	|	|	1810	1910	|	|	2010
23	Villamassargia ... d.	0931	1026	1031	1031	1126	1131	1226	1231	1231	1326	1331	1426	1431	1431	1526	1531	1601	1626	1631	1726	1731	1826	1831	1926	1931	2026	2031
	Decimomannu ... d.	0956	...	1057	1058	...	1156	...	1257	1258	...	1356	...	1456	1500	...	1556	1631	...	1656	...	1756	...	1857	...	1956	...	2101
	Cagliari ... a.	1015	...	1116	1117	...	1215	...	1317	1317	...	1415	...	1515	1520	...	1614	1645	...	1717	...	1814	...	1920	...	2015	...	2122

Narrow gauge services on Sardinia are operated by ARST Gestione FdS, Via Zagabria 54, 09129 Cagliari. ✆ +39 070 4098 1, fax +39 070 4098 220, www.arst.sardegna.it.

Regular services operate on the following routes to differing frequencies: Monserrato Gottardo - Isili (*71 km*); Macomer - Nuoro (*61 km*); Sassari - Alghero (*30 km*); Sassari - Sorso (*11 km*). Tram connections are available at Monserrato Gottardo to / from Cagliari (Repubblica).

Additionally, summer only tourist services operate on the following routes: Sassari - Tempio (*91 km*); Tempio - Palau Marina (*59 km*); Macomer - Bosa Marina (*46 km*); Mandas - Arbatax (*159 km*); Isili - Sorgono (*83 km*).
See www.treninoverde.com.

630 MILANO - BOLOGNA - RIMINI - ANCONA

km		2 ⚒	2	2 †	FB 8851 🍸 ♦		Ⓐ	Ⓒ	IC 603 Ⓐ	IC 623 Ⓒ	FR 9803 A	FB 8881 🍸 Va		2 ⑥⑦	FB 8803 🍸 b	2	IC 605 T	Ⓒ	Ⓐ	FR 9887 🍸 a		IC 607	FB 8809 🍸 T	IC 1545 ⑥		FB 8811 🍸
	Torino Porta Nuova **600 615** . d.	...	...	...	...	...	...	...	...	...	...	...	...	...	...	...	...	...	...	0920	...	...	...	...	...	...
0	**Milano** Centrale d.	...	...	...	...	...	...	...	...	...	0705	...	...	...	0735	...	0705	...	...	1020g	...	...	1035	1000	...	1135
219	**Bologna** Centrale d.	...	0500	...	...	0632	0732	0732	0800	0800	0815	0845	0832	0912	0945	0932	0958	1031	1032	1145	1132	1200	1245	1225	1232	1345
254	Imola d.	...	0527	...	...	0655	0800	0800	|	|	|	|	0846	0944	|	0955	|	1058	1058	|	1155	|	|	|	1255	|
261	Castelbolognese-Riolo Terme d.	...	0533	...	...	0701	0806	0806	|	|	|	|	0902	|	|	1002	|	1104	1104	|	1202	|	|	|	1302	|
269	Faenza d.	...	0539	...	...	0717	0817	0817	0828	0828	|	|	0917	0954	|	1017	1028	1117	1120	|	1217	1228	|	1256	1317	|
284	Forlì d.	...	0548	...	...	0728	0828	0828	0838	0838	|	|	0928	1003	|	1028	1038	1128	1138	|	1228	1238	|	1306	1328	|
302	Cesena d.	...	0603	...	...	0742	0842	0842	0851	0851	|	|	0942	1014	|	1045	1052	1142	1202	|	1244	1251	|	1319	1342	|
331	**Rimini** ● ⊖ d.	0545	0630	0647	0636	0805	0905	0905	0915	0919	0917	0940	1005	1044	1040	1102	1115	1203	1227	1240	1319	1315	1340	1352	1405	1440
340	Riccione d.	0555	...	0655	|	0815	0912	0912	0925	0930	0925	|	1015	1054	|	...	1124	1216	1236	1248	1330	1325	|	1400	1415	|
349	Cattolica-Gabicce d.	0603	...	0701	|	0824	0919	0919	|	|	|	|	1024	1102	|	...	|	1224	1246	|	1340	|	|	|	1424	|
364	Pesaro d.	0614	...	0712	0656	0835	0930	0930	0942	0947	|	1003	1035	1114	1059	...	1142	1235	1304	1303	1352	1342	1359	1418	1435	1459
376	Fano d.	0622	...	0720	|	0843	0938	0938	0951	0956	|	|	1043	|	|	...	1151	1242	1316	|	1403	1351	|	1427	1443	|
398	Senigallia d.	0636	...	0735	|	0858	0953	0954	1005	1010	|	|	1058	1133	|	...	1205	1258	1330	|	1418	1405	|	1439	1458	|
415	Falconara Marittima **625** d.	0652	...	0747	0721	0909	1003	1011	|	|	|	|	1109	|	|	...	|	1309	1346	|	1437	|	|	|	1509	|
423	**Ancona** **625** a.	0705	...	0800	...	0922	1016	1023	1021	1038	1013	1033	1120	1154	1130	...	1225	1320	1358	1333	1449	1425	1433	1458	1520	1533
	Pescara Centrale **631** a.	...	...	...	...	...	...	...	1159	1206	...	1144	...	1410	1247	...	1359	...	...	1444	...	1559	1547	1631	...	1644
	Bari Centrale **631** a.	...	...	...	...	...	...	...	1505	1507	...	1425	...	...	1527	...	1705	...	...	1725	...	1905	1825	2018	...	1925
	Lecce **631** a.	...	...	...	...	...	...	...	1700	1700	...	1601	...	...	...	...	...	...	...	1852	...	...	...	2208	...	2058

		IC 609		FB 8891 🍸	FB 8813 🍸 c		IC 611	EC 85 ♦	FB 8815 🍸 V		FR 9809 🍸 a	FB 8819 🍸 d		IC 613		FR 9811 🍸	FB 8823 🍸 e		FB 8825 🍸		FB 8829 🍸		ICN 765 ⊙♦	ICN 755 ⊙♦	ICN 757 ⊙♦
Torino Porta Nuova **600 615** d.	...	...	...	...	...	...	...	...	...	...	...	...	...	...	...	...	...	...	...	...	...	...	...	...	2020
Milano Centrale d.	...	...	...	1235	1335	...	...	...	...	...	1545	1535	...	1510	...	1740	1735	...	1835	...	1935	...	1950	2050	|
Bologna Centrale d.	1332	1400	1432	1445	1545	1532	1600	1623	1645	1632	1702	1745	1732	1758	1832	1858	1945	1932	2045	2035	2146	2131	2200	2310	2352
Imola d.	1355	|	1455	|	|	1555	|	|	|	1655	|	|	1755	|	1858	|	|	1955	|	2055	|	2155	|	|	|
Castelbolognese-Riolo Terme d.	1402	|	1502	|	|	1602	|	|	|	1702	|	|	1802	|	1905	|	|	2002	|	2102	|	2202	|	|	|
Faenza d.	1417	1428	1517	|	|	1617	1628	|	|	1717	|	1811	1817	1828	1912	|	2011	2017	2111	2119	|	2217	2234	2337	|
Forlì d.	1428	1438	1528	|	|	1628	1638	|	|	1728	|	1822	1828	1838	1923	1931	2021	2029	2121	2130	|	2228	2246	2348	|
Cesena d.	1442	1451	1542	|	|	1642	1651	1712	|	1742	|	1835	1845	1851	1937	|	2033	2046	2133	2143	|	2245	2300	0002	|
Rimini 621 ● ⊖ d.	1505	1515	1605	1540	1640	1702	1715	1733	1740	1807	1801	1852	1907	1915	2005	1956	2052	2112	2152	2205	2240	2322	2330	0025	0058
Riccione d.	1512	1525	1615	|	|	1715	1725	...	|	1816	|	|	1916	1925	2015	|	|	...	|	2215	|	...	|	|	|
Cattolica-Gabicce d.	1519	|	1621	|	|	1724	|	...	|	1824	|	|	1925	|	2024	|	|	...	|	2224	|	...	|	|	|
Pesaro d.	1530	1542	1635	1559	1659	1736	1742	....	1759	1835	|	1910	1936	1942	2035	2016	2110	...	2210	2235	2259	...	2358	|	|
Fano d.	1538	1551	1643	|	|	...	1751	...	|	1843	|	|	1944	1951	2043	|	|	...	|	2243	|	...	|	|	|
Senigallia d.	1553	1605	1658	|	|	...	1805	...	|	1857	|	|	1958	2005	2058	|	|	...	|	2258	|	...	|	|	|
Falconara Marittima **625** d.	1603	|	1709	|	|	...	|	...	|	1910	|	|	2019	|	2109	|	|	...	|	2312	|	...	|	|	|
Ancona **625** a.	1613	1625	1720	1633	1733	...	1825	...	1833	1923	1847	1944	2035	2025	2120	2046	2144	...	2244	2322	2333	...	0048	0130	0206
Pescara Centrale **631** a.	...	1759	...	1744	1844	...	2005	...	1944	...	1956	2100	...	2155	...	2200	2306	...	...	...	...	...	0234	0313	0338
Bari Centrale **631** a.	...	2105	...	2025	2125	...	2307	...	2225	...	2230	2340	...	...	...	...	...	...	...	...	...	...	0611	0644	0654
Lecce **631** a.	...	2258	...	2152	2252	...	...	...	2350	...	...	...	...	...	...	...	...	...	...	...	...	...	0924	0830	0852

	ICN 1580 ⑦ ⊙♦	ICN 752 ⊙♦	ICN 758 ⊙♦	ICN 754 ⊙♦			FA 8802 🍸		FR 9802 🍸	FA 8804 🍸		FB 8806 🍸 e		IC 604		FB 8810 🍸 d	EC 84 ♦		FR 9806 🍸 a	IC 606		FB 8814 🍸		FB 8816 🍸 V	IC 608
Lecce **631** d.	1855	1920	1831	2020	...	...	...	...	...	...	...	...	...	...	...	...	...	...	...	...	...	0606	...	0706	0625
Bari Centrale **631** d.	2050	2114	2138	2209	...	...	...	...	...	...	...	...	...	...	...	0532	...	...	0635	0551	...	0732	...	0832	0806
Pescara Centrale **631** d.	0026	0041	0106	0118	...	...	...	...	0500	...	...	0555	...	0705	...	0814	...	...	0914	0902	...	1014	...	1114	1102
Ancona **625** d.	0201	0213	0236	0246	...	0435	0500	0535	0610	0620	0635	0716	0742	0838	0842	0929	...	...	1029	1038	1042	1129	1142	1225	1238
Falconara Marittima **625** d.	|	|	|	|	...	0444	|	0545	|	|	0648	|	0754	|	0852	|	...	...	|	|	1052	|	1152	|	|
Senigallia d.	|	|	|	|	...	0457	|	0555	|	|	0701	|	0807	0856	0902	|	...	...	|	1056	1102	|	1202	|	1256
Fano d.	|	|	|	|	...	0512	|	0610	|	|	0716	|	0823	0909	0917	|	...	...	|	1109	1117	|	1217	|	1309
Pesaro d.	|	|	|	0321	...	0520	0528	0619	0638	0649	0724	0745	0831	0919	0925	0956	...	...	|	1119	1125	1156	1225	1256	1319
Cattolica-Gabicce d.	|	|	|	|	...	0539	|	0630	|	|	0735	|	0842	|	0936	|	...	...	|	|	1136	|	1236	|	|
Riccione d.	|	|	|	|	...	0549	|	0637	|	|	0740	|	0851	0938	0948	|	...	...	|	1138	1148	|	1246	|	1338
Rimini ● ⊖ d.	0259	0311	0333	0348	...	0600	0550	0646	0700	0709	0757	0806	0900	0947	0957	1020	1035	1041	1120	1147	1157	1220	1257	1320	1347
Cesena d.	|	|	|	0406	...	0618	0607	0705	|	0725	0819	0825	0919	1009	1019	|	1054	1110	|	1207	1219	|	1319	|	1407
Forlì d.	|	|	|	0419	...	0631	0620	0718	0725	0738	0832	0838	0931	1021	1032	|	|	1127	|	1219	1231	|	1331	|	1419
Faenza d.	|	|	|	0429	...	0642	0629	0729	|	0749	0841	0849	0941	1031	1042	|	|	1140	|	1229	1241	|	1341	|	1429
Castelbolognese-Riolo Terme d.	|	|	|	|	...	0648	|	0743	|	|	0847	|	0947	|	1048	|	|	1147	|	|	1247	|	1347	|	|
Imola d.	|	|	|	|	...	0700	|	0800	|	|	0900	|	1000	|	1059	|	|	1200	|	|	1300	|	1400	|	|
Bologna Centrale a.	0355	0410	0436	0505	...	0726	0701	0826	0810	0815	0926	0915	1026	1101	1121	1115	1148	1225	1212	1300	1326	1315	1426	1415	1500
Milano Centrale a.	|	0640	0712	|	...	...	0910	...	0935	1025	...	1125	...	1345	...	1325	...	...	1320	...	...	1525	...	...	...
Torino Porta Nuova **600 615** a.	0740	...	...	0920	...	...	...	...	...	...	...	...	...	...	...	...	...	...	...	...	...	...	...	...	...

		FB 8818 🍸		IC 610 f		FB 8882 🍸 Ta	FA 8338 🍸 ♦	FB 8884 🍸 a	IC 1546 ⑦	IC 612 T		FR 9808 🍸		FB 8888 🍸 Va		2 ⑥	2 ⑦	IC 614		FB 8830 🍸 b		FB 8852 🍸 ♦			
Lecce **631** d.	...	0806	...	0820	...	...	...	1058	1005	...	...	1206	...	1255	...	...	...	...	...	...	...	...	...	...	...
Bari Centrale **631** d.	...	0932	...	0955	...	1132	...	1232	1142	1155	...	1332	...	1432	...	...	...	1355	...	1632	...	...	...	...	...
Pescara Centrale **631** d.	...	1214	...	1302	...	1414	...	1516	1448	1502	...	1614	...	1714	...	1555	1622	1702	...	1914	...	...	...	...	...
Ancona **625** d.	1242	1325	...	1438	1442	1525	1600	1631	1617	1638	1642	1725	...	1825	...	1800	1806	1838	1842	2025	...	...	2042	2241	...
Falconara Marittima **625** d.	1254	|	...	|	1452	|	|	|	|	|	1652	|	...	|	...	1809	1816	|	1854	|	...	2042	2054	2251	...
Senigallia d.	1304	|	...	1456	1502	|	1617	|	1632	1656	1702	|	...	|	...	1822	1827	1856	1904	|	...	|	2106	2303	...
Fano d.	1319	|	...	1509	1517	|	|	|	1646	1709	1717	|	...	|	...	1837	1840	1909	1919	|	...	|	2121	2317	...
Pesaro d.	1327	1356	...	1519	1525	1556	1633	1701	1658	1719	1725	1756	1817	1856	...	1847	1849	1919	1927	2056	...	2105	2129	2325	...
Cattolica-Gabicce d.	1338	|	...	|	1536	1608	1644	|	|	|	1736	|	1828	|	...	1907	1907	|	1938	|	...	|	2140	2335	...
Riccione d.	1348	|	...	1538	1546	|	1652	|	1719	1738	1746	|	1838	1912	...	1917	1917	1938	1948	|	...	|	2149	2341	...
Rimini ● ⊖ d.	1400	1420	1441	1547	1557	1622	1704	1723	1729	1747	1757	1820	1847	1922	...	1927	1927	1947	2000	2120	2050	2127	2204	2350	...
Cesena d.	1419	|	1510	1607	1619	|	|	|	1746	1807	1819	|	1913	|	...	1944	1944	2007	2019	|	2113	...	2222	...	...
Forlì d.	1431	|	1528	1619	1631	|	|	|	1758	1819	1831	|	1931	|	...	1956	1956	2019	2031	|	2127	...	2236	...	...
Faenza d.	1441	|	1540	1629	1641	|	|	|	1808	1829	1841	|	1941	|	...	2007	2007	2029	2041	|	2139	...	2247	...	...
Castelbolognese-Riolo Terme d.	1447	|	1548	|	1647	|	|	|	|	|	1847	|	1947	|	...	|	|	|	2047	|	2146	...	2253	...	...
Imola d.	1500	|	1600	|	1700	|	|	|	|	|	1900	|	2000	|	...	2017	2017	|	2100	|	2200	...	2300	...	...
Bologna Centrale a.	1523	1515	1626	1700	1726	1715	1800	1815	1840	1901	1926	1915	2026	2015	...	2046	2046	2100	2126	2218	2224	...	2321	...	...
Milano Centrale a.	...	1725	...	...	...	1925	...	2025	2115	2145	...	2042g	...	...	...	...	...	...	...	0025	...	...	...	...	...
Torino Porta Nuova **600 615** a.	...	...	...	...	...	...	...	...	...	...	...	2140	...	...	...	...	...	...	...	...	...	...	...	...	...

♦ – **NOTES** (LISTED BY TRAIN NUMBER)

- **84** – (12) and ✕ (⑤⑥⑦ Aug. 2 - Sept. 8: Rimini -) Bolgona - München.
- **85** – (12) and ✕ München - Bolgona (- Rimini: ④⑤⑥ Aug. 1 - Sept. 7).
- **752** – 🛏 1,2 cl., ▬ 2 cl. (4 berth) and (2) Lecce - Bologna - Milano.
- **754** – ①-⑥: 🛏 1,2 cl., ▬ 2 cl. (4 berth) and (2) Lecce - Bologna - Torino.
- **755** – 🛏 1,2 cl., ▬ 2 cl. (4 berth) and (2) Milano - Bologna - Lecce.
- **757** – 🛏 1,2 cl., ▬ 2 cl. (4 berth) and (2) Torino - Bologna - Lecce.
- **758** – 🛏 1,2 cl., ▬ 2 cl. (4 berth) and (2) Lecce - Bologna - Milano.
- **765** – 🛏 1,2 cl., ▬ 2 cl. (4 berth) and (2) Milano - Bologna - Lecce.
- **1580** – 🛏 1,2 cl., ▬ 2 cl. (4 berth) and (2) Lecce - Bologna - Torino.
- **8338** – ⑥⑦ until Sept. 15: (12) and 🍸 Ancona - Bologna - Bolzano.
- **8851** – (12) and 🍸 Ravenna - Rimini - Falconara - Roma.
- **8852** – (12) and 🍸 Roma - Falconara - Rimini - Ravenna.

- **A** – ⑥⑦ until Sept. 15 (also Aug. 15).
- **T** – From / to Taranto.
- **V** – From / to Venezia.
- **a** – June 9 - Sept. 15.
- **b** – June 9 - Sept. 28.
- **c** – June 9 - Nov. 23.
- **d** – June 9 - Oct. 26.
- **e** – June 9 - July 27.
- **f** – Not June 15 - Sept. 15.
- **g** – Milano **Porta Garibaldi**.

- ⊙ – Subject to confirmation.
- ⊖ – Connections may be available to service(s) in previous columns.
- ● – See shaded panel on page 313 for 🚌 service Rimini - San Marino and v.v.

ANCONA - BARI - LECCE 631

km		2 Ⓒ	2 Ⓐ	*ICN* 789 ⑤ ⊙♦	2 Ⓐ	*ICN* 765 ⊙♦	*ICN* 755 ⊙♦	*ICN* 757 ⊙♦	2 Ⓐ	2 Ⓐ	2 Ⓒ	2 Ⓐ	2 Ⓒ	*FA* 8303 🍷 c	*FA* 8305 🍷 a	2 Ⓒ	2 Ⓐ	*IC* 703	2 Ⓐ	2 Ⓒ	*FB* 8881 🍷 Va	2 Ⓐ	*IC* 603 Ⓐ	*IC* 623 Ⓒ	*FB* 8803 🍷 b	2 Ⓐ
	Torino Porta Nuova **615** d.	...	...	...	...	...	...	2020	...	...	...	...	...	...	...	...	...	...	...	...	...	...	...	...	...	...
	Milano Centrale **615 630** d.	...	...	...	...	1950	2050	|	...	...	...	...	...	...	...	...	...	...	...	...	...	...	...	...	0735	...
	Bologna Centrale **615 630** d.	...	...	...	...	2200	2310	2352	...	...	...	...	...	...	...	...	...	...	...	...	0845	...	0800	0800	0945	...
0	**Ancona** d.	...	...	...	...	0051	0134	0209	...	...	...	...	...	...	...	...	...	...	...	...	1036	...	1024	1041	1133	...
43	Civitanova Marche-Montegranaro d.	...	...	...	...	|	|	|	...	...	...	...	...	...	...	...	...	...	...	...	|	...	1050	1103	1155	...
85	S. Benedetto del Tronto d.	...	...	...	...	|	|	|	...	...	...	...	...	...	...	...	...	...	...	...	|	...	1121	1128	1215	...
146	**Pescara** Centrale a.	...	...	...	...	0234	0313	0338	...	...	...	...	...	...	...	...	...	...	...	...	1144	...	1159	1206	1247	...
146	**Pescara** Centrale d.	...	...	...	...	0239	0315	0340	...	...	...	...	...	...	...	...	...	...	...	...	1147	...	1201	1208	1250	...
236	Termoli d.	...	...	...	...	|	|	|	...	...	...	...	...	...	...	...	...	...	...	...	1235	...	1252	1259	1338	...
	Roma Termini **626** d.	...	...	2358	...	|	|	|	...	...	...	...	...	0805	0805	...	...	0728j	...	...	|	...	|	|	|	...
323	**Foggia** a.	...	...	0449	...	0451	0515	0535	...	...	...	...	...	1056	1056	...	...	1226	...	...	1319	...	1348	1353	1420	...
323	**Foggia** d.	...	...	0504	...	0454	0519	0539	...	...	...	...	...	1105	1105	...	...	1241	...	...	1322	...	1351	1356	1424	...
391	Barletta d.	...	...	0537	...	0529	0556	0615	...	...	...	...	...	1136	1136	...	...	1310	...	...	1351	...	1420	1425	1453	...
446	**Bari** Centrale a.	...	...	0627	...	0611	0644	0654	...	...	...	...	...	1204	1204	...	...	1400	...	...	1425	...	1505	1507	1527	...
446	**Bari** Centrale ▲ d.	0520	0601	0631	0631	0641	0648	0658	0731	0801	0801	1001	1015	1208	1208	1215	1231	...	1401	1435	1429	1501	1509	1511	...	1701
	Gioia del Colle ▲ d.	|	|	|	|	0717	|	|	|	|	|	|	|	|	|	|	|	...	|	|	|	|	|	|	...	|
	Taranto ▲ a.	|	|	|	|	0753	|	|	|	|	|	|	|	|	|	|	|	...	|	|	|	|	|	|	...	|
487	Monopoli d.	0555	0626	0655	0656	|	0715	0727	0756	0828	0837	1026	1051	|	1230	1253	1256	...	1426	1512	1452	1526	1537	1537	...	1726
501	Fasano d.	0604	0635	0705	0705	|	0726	0740	0805	0837	0846	1035	1059	|	|	1301	1308	...	1435	1521	1502	1535	1549	1549	...	1735
521	Ostuni d.	0618	0646	0718	0716	|	0740	0754	0819	0852	0900	1046	1115	|	1249	1315	1316	...	1448	1534	1514	1549	1604	1604	...	1746
557	**Brindisi** ♣ d.	0642	0709	0741	0741	0857	0801	0820	0842	0914	0924	1112	1138	1304	1311	1338	1342	...	1514	1558	1538	1614	1627	1627	...	1812
596	**Lecce** a.	0712	0739	0809	0812	0924	0830	0852	0912	0944	0955	1142	1209	1328	1336	1409	1411	...	1541	1628	1601	1644	1700	1700	...	1842

	IC 605	*FR* 9887 🍷 a	2 Ⓒ	*FB* 8809 🍷	2 Ⓐ	*IC* 607	*FA* 8315 🍷	*FB* 8811 🍷 c	*FB* 8811 🍷 a	2 Ⓐ	2 Ⓒ	*IC* 1545 ⑥	*FB* 8891 🍷	*IC* 609	*FB* 8813 🍷 d	*IC* 705 ⑤	*FA* 8323 🍷	*FB* 8815 🍷 V	*FA* 8325 🍷 Ⓑ	2	*IC* 611	*FR* 9809 🍷 a	*FB* 8819 🍷 e	*IC* 613	*FR* 9811 🍷	*FB* 8823 🍷 f
Torino Porta Nuova **615** d.	...	0920	...	...	...	...	...	...	...	...	...	...	...	...	...	...	...	...	...	...	...	...	...	...	...	...
Milano Centrale **615 630** d.	0705	1020g	...	1035	...	...	...	1135	1135	...	...	1000	1235	...	1335	...	...	...	...	...	...	1545	1535	1510	1740	1735
Bologna Centrale **615 630** d.	0958	1145	...	1245	...	1200	...	1345	1345	...	...	1225	1445	1400	1545	...	...	1645	...	...	1600	1702	1745	1758	1858	1945
Ancona d.	1228	1336	...	1436	...	1428	...	1536	1536	...	...	1500	1636	1628	1736	...	...	1836	...	...	1828	1850	1947	2028	2049	2147
Civitanova Marche-Montegranaro d.	1250	|	...	|	...	1450	...	|	|	...	...	1523	|	1650	|	...	...	|	...	...	1850	|	|	2050	|	|
S. Benedetto del Tronto d.	1321	|	...	|	...	1521	...	|	|	...	...	1548	|	1721	|	...	...	|	...	...	1921	|	2027	2117	|	2227
Pescara Centrale a.	1359	1444	...	1547	...	1559	...	1644	1644	...	...	1631	1744	1759	1844	...	...	1944	...	...	2005	1956	2100	2155	2200	2306
Pescara Centrale d.	1401	1447	...	1547	...	1601	...	1647	1647	...	...	1635	1747	1801	1847	...	...	1947	...	...	2007	1959	2103	...	...	...
Termoli d.	1452	1535	...	1635	...	1652	...	1735	1739	...	...	1749	1835	1852	1935	...	...	2035	...	...	2059	2048	2151	...	...	...
Roma Termini **626** d.	|	|	...	|	...	|	1508	|	|	...	...	|	|	|	|	1601	1803	|	1903	...	|	|	|	...	...	...
Foggia a.	1548	1619	...	1721	...	1746	1759	1819	1822	...	...	1849	1919	1948	2019	2034	2051	2119	|	...	2152	2130	2235	...	...	...
Foggia d.	1551	1622	...	1722	...	1749	1808	1822	1825	...	...	1852	1922	1951	2022	2049	2100	2122	|	...	2155	2133	2238	...	...	...
Barletta d.	1620	1651	...	1751	...	1820	1836	1851	1853	...	...	1933	1951	2020	2051	2123	2131	2151	2219	...	2226	|	2307	...	...	...
Bari Centrale a.	1705	1725	...	1825	...	1905	1909	1925	1925	...	...	2018	2025	2105	2125	2212	2159	2225	2249	...	2307	2230	2340	...	...	...
Bari Centrale ▲ d.	1720	1729	1818	1840	1831	...	1913	1929	1929	2006	2017	2034	2029	2109	2129	2227	2203	2229	...	2301	...	...	...	...	...	...
Gioia del Colle ▲ d.	1754	|	|	1912	|	...	|	|	|	|	|	|	|	|	|	2259	|	|	...	|	...	...	...	...	...	...
Taranto ▲ a.	1826	|	|	1946	|	...	|	|	|	|	|	|	|	|	|	2332	|	|	...	|	...	...	...	...	...	...
Monopoli d.	...	|	1854	...	1856	...	|	|	1952	2032	2103	2100	|	2133	|	...	|	|	...	2338	...	...	...	...	...	...
Fasano d.	...	|	1902	...	1905	...	|	|	|	2041	2111	2110	|	2146	|	...	|	|	...	2346	...	...	...	...	...	...
Ostuni d.	...	|	1917	...	1916	...	|	|	2014	2055	2125	2123	|	2201	|	...	|	|	...	0000	...	...	...	...	...	...
Brindisi ♣ d.	...	1823	1941	...	1942	...	2014	2023	2035	2120	2155	2144	2129	2235	2223	...	2259	2323	...	0024	...	...	...	...	...	...
Lecce a.	...	1852	2012	...	2011	...	2035	2052	2058	2148	2225	2208	2152	2258	2252	...	2323	2350	...	0054	...	...	...	...	...	...

	FR 9802 🍷	*FB* 8806 🍷 f	2 ⚒	*FB* 8810 🍷 e	*IC* 606	*FR* 9806 🍷 a	2	*FA* 8302 🍷	*FB* 8814 🍷	2 Ⓐ	*IC* 608	2 Ⓒ	2 Ⓐ	*FB* 8816 🍷 V	2 Ⓐ	2 Ⓒ	*FB* 8818 🍷	*IC* 610 k	*FB* 8882 🍷 a	*IC* 1546 🍷 ⑦	*IC* 612	2 Ⓒ	*FB* 8884 🍷 a	*FA* 8314 🍷	*FR* 9808 🍷	*IC* 614
Lecce d.	...	...	...	...	...	...	0450	0555	0606	0611	0625	0630	0643	0706	0713	0725	0806	0820	...	1005	...	1010	1058	1150	1206	...
Brindisi ♣ d.	...	...	0400	...	...	...	0518	0616	0629	0639	0649	0701	0711	0729	0741	0756	0829	0842	...	1029	...	1040	1122	1211	1229	...
Ostuni d.	...	...	0422	...	...	...	0542	|	|	0659	0712	0723	0733	|	0804	0819	|	0904	...	1050	...	1104	1143	|	|	...
Fasano d.	...	...	0433	...	...	...	0557	|	|	0713	0725	0737	0744	|	0818	0833	|	0917	...	1103	...	1118	|	|	|	...
Monopoli d.	...	...	0441	...	...	...	0605	|	|	0722	0735	0746	0753	|	0826	0841	|	0927	...	1114	...	1126	1202	|	|	...
Taranto ▲ d.	...	...	|	...	...	...	|	|	|	|	|	|	|	|	|	|	|	|	1019	|	1027	|	|	|	|	...
Gioia del Colle ▲ d.	...	...	|	...	...	...	|	|	|	|	|	|	|	|	|	|	|	|	1053	|	1102	|	|	|	|	...
Bari Centrale ▲ a.	...	...	0515	...	...	...	0644	0713	0728	0758	0802	0824	0834	0828	0854	0921	0928	0951	1123	1139	1135	1204	1228	1310	1328	...
Bari Centrale d.	...	...	▬	0532	0551	0635	...	0717	0732	...	0806	...	...	0832	...	...	0932	0955	1132	1142	1155	...	1232	1314	1332	1355
Barletta d.	...	...	...	0606	0636	|	...	0749	0806	...	0850	...	...	0906	...	...	1006	1039	1206	1224	1239	...	1306	1345	1406	1439
Foggia a.	...	...	...	0636	0708	0736	...	0818	0836	...	0920	...	...	0936	...	...	1036	1110	1236	1252	1310	...	1336	1413	1436	1510
Foggia d.	...	...	*IC*	0639	0715	0739	...	0827	0839	...	0923	...	...	0939	...	...	1039	1113	1239	1254	1313	...	1339	1422	1439	1513
Roma Termini **626** a.	...	...	**604**	|	|	|	...	1123	|	...	|	...	...	|	...	...	|	|	|	|	|	...	|	1720	|	|
Termoli d.	...	...		0725	0806	0825	...	...	0925	...	1010	...	...	1025	...	...	1125	1210	1325	1354	1410	...	1425	...	1525	1610
Pescara Centrale a.	...	...		0811	0900	0911	...	...	1011	...	1100	...	...	1111	...	...	1211	1300	1411	1446	1500	...	1513	...	1611	1700
Pescara Centrale d.	0500	0555	0705	0814	0902	0914	...	...	1014	...	1102	...	...	1114	...	...	1214	1302	1414	1448	1502	...	1516	...	1614	1702
S. Benedetto del Tronto d.	|	0630	0739	0848	0939	|	...	...	|	...	1139	...	...	|	...	...	|	1339	|	1523	1539	...	1548	...	|	1739
Civitanova Marche-Montegranaro d.	|	|	0810	|	1010	|	...	...	1105	...	1210	...	...	|	...	...	|	1410	|	1548	1610	...	|	...	|	1810
Ancona a.	0607	0713	0835	0926	1035	1026	...	...	1126	...	1235	...	...	1222	...	...	1322	1435	1522	1614	1635	...	1628	...	1722	1835
Bologna Centrale **615 630** a.	0810	0915	1101	1115	1300	1212	...	...	1315	...	1500	...	...	1415	...	...	1515	1700	1715	1840	1901	...	1815	...	1915	2100
Milano Centrale **615 630** a.	0935	1125	1345	1325	...	1320	...	...	1525	...	...	...	...	...	...	...	1725	...	1925	2115	2145	...	2025	...	2042g	...
Torino Porta Nuova **615** a.	...	...	...	...	...	...	...	...	...	...	...	...	...	...	...	...	...	...	...	...	...	...	...	...	2140	...

♦ – **NOTES** (LISTED BY TRAIN NUMBER)

752 – 🛏 1, 2 cl., ▬ 2 cl. (4 berth) and 2 Lecce - Bologna - Milano.
754 – ①–⑥: 🛏 1, 2 cl., ▬ 2 cl. (4 berth) and 2 Lecce - Bologna - Torino.
755 – 🛏 1, 2 cl., ▬ 2 cl. (4 berth) and 2 Milano - Bologna - Lecce.
757 – 🛏 1, 2 cl., ▬ 2 cl. (4 berth) and 2 Torino - Bologna - Lecce.
758 – 🛏 1, 2 cl., ▬ 2 cl. (4 berth) and 2 Lecce - Bologna - Milano.
765 – 🛏 1, 2 cl., ▬ 2 cl. (4 berth) and 2 Milano - Bologna - Lecce.
788 – 🛏 1, 2 cl., ▬ 2 cl. (4 berth) and 2 Lecce - Roma.
789 – 🛏 1, 2 cl., ▬ 2 cl. (4 berth) and 2 Roma - Lecce.
1580 – 🛏 1, 2 cl., ▬ 2 cl. (4 berth) and 2 Lecce - Bologna - Torino.

V – From / to Venezia.

a – June 9 - Sept. 15.
b – June 9 - Sept. 28.
c – Sept. 16 - Dec. 14.
d – June 9 - Nov. 23.
e – June 9 - Oct. 26.
f – June 9 - July 27.
g – Milano **Porta Garibaldi**.
h – Arrives 2154 Aug. 3 - Sept. 1.
j – Departs 0756 Aug. 3 - Sept. 1.
k – Not June 15 - Sept. 15.

⊙ – Subject to confirmation.
▲ – See panel below main table on page 314 for other local services Bari - Taranto and v.v.
♣ – See panel below main table for direct services Brindisi - Taranto and v.v.

BRINDISI - TARANTO
No service on †

	⚒	⚒	⚒		⚒	⚒	⚒		⚒	⚒
Brindisi d.	0647	0754	1100	...	1401	1519	1647	...	1809	2011
Francavilla Fontana d.	0724	0841	1138	...	1440	1553	1725	...	1846	2046
Taranto a.	0751	0918	1206	...	1513	1625	1758	...	1922	2116

	⚒	⚒	⚒		⚒	⚒	⚒		⚒	⚒
Taranto d.	0535	0610	0853	...	1244	1402	1523	...	1645	1849
Francavilla Fontana d.	0602	0639	0921	...	1312	1429	1551	...	1713	1915
Brindisi a.	0637	0721	1002	...	1350	1506	1634	...	1752	2001

● – 🚌 service **RIMINI - SAN MARINO**. **Valid until June 7, 2019.**
27 km, journey 50 – 55 minutes.
From Rimini (FS railway station) at 0810, 0925, 1040, 1155⚒, 1310⚒, 1425, 1540, 1655, 1810, 1925⚒.
From San Marino at 0645⚒, 0800, 0915, 1030, 1145⚒, 1300⚒, 1415, 1530, 1645, 1800, 1915⚒.
Operator: BonelliBus s.a.s., Via Murano 47838, Riccione ✆ +39 0541 662 069.

631 LECCE - BARI - ANCONA

			FB		*FB*	*IC*				*IC*			*FA*	*FA*						*ICN*	*ICN*	*ICN*		*ICN*		*ICN*
			8888		**8830**	**704**				**710**			**8324**	**8326**						**1580**	**752**	**758**		**754**		**788**
	2	2	🍷	2	🍷		2		2		2	2	🍷	🍷	2	2	2	2		⑦		⑦	2		2	
	Ⓐ	Ⓒ	V a	Ⓐ	b		Ⓒ		Ⓐ	⑦	⑥	Ⓐ	a	c	Ⓐ	Ⓒ	Ⓒ	Ⓐ		⊙♦	⊙♦	⊙♦	Ⓐ	⊙♦	Ⓐ	⊙♦
Lecce d.	1213	1219	1255	1313	...	...	1419	...	1430	...	1600	1613	1647	1655	1713	1723	1801	1813	...	1855	1920	1831	2013	2020	2113	2230
Brindisi ♣ d.	1242	1250	1320	1340	...	...	1450	...	1501	...	1631	1640	1709	1716	1740	1750	1830	1840	...	1924	1949	1901	2040	2048	2142	2255
Ostuni d.	1303	1313	1340	1403	...	...	1513	...	|	...	1654	1703	1730	|	1803	1813	1855	1903	...	1948	2013	|	2103	2111	2203	2317
Fasano d.	1320	1327	1352	1420	...	...	1527	...	1532	...	1708	1720	|	|	1820	1830	1909	1920	...	2003	2028	|	2120	2126	2214	2330
Monopoli d.	1328	1335	1402	1428	...	...	1535	...	1540	...	1716	1728	1748	|	1828	1838	1918	1928	...	2015	2039	|	2128	2137	2223	2341
Taranto ▲ d.	|	|	|	|	...	...	|	...	|	1540	|	|	|	|	|	|	|	|	...	|	|	2001	|	|	|	|
Gioia del Colle ▲ d.	|	|	|	|	...	...	|	...	|	1612	|	|	|	|	|	|	|	|	...	|	|	2034	|	|	|	|
Bari Centrale ▲ a.	1354	1413	1428	1454	...	...	1613	...	1611	1649	1754	1754	1813	1813	1854	1916	1955	1954	...	2046	2110	2117	2154	2205	2304	0010
Bari Centrale d.	...	...	1432	...	1632	1555	...	...	...	1714	...	...	1817	1817	...	...	...	...	...	2050	2114	2138	...	2209	...	0015
Barletta d.	...	...	1506	...	1706	1643	...	...	...	1746	...	...	1847	1847	...	...	...	...	...	2141	2202	2234	...	2246	...	0103
Foggia a.	...	...	1536	...	1736	1715	...	...	...	1819	...	...	1918	1918	...	...	...	...	...	2220	2238	2311	...	2321	...	0145
Foggia d.	...	...	1539	...	1739	1741	...	...	...	1839	...	...	1927	1927	...	...	...	...	...	2223	2242	2314	...	2325	...	0200
Roma Termini **626** a.	...	...	|	...	|	2220h	...	...	...	2311	...	...	2220	2220	...	...	...	...	...	|	|	|	...	|	...	0610
Termoli d.	...	...	1625	...	1825	...	...	...	...	...	...	...	...	...	...	...	...	...	...	2324	|	|	...	|	...	...
Pescara Centrale a.	...	...	1711	...	1911	...	...	...	...	...	...	...	...	...	...	...	...	...	...	0023	0039	0104	...	0115	...	...
Pescara Centrale d.	...	...	1714	...	1914	...	...	...	...	...	...	...	...	...	...	...	...	...	...	0026	0041	0106	...	0118	...	...
S. Benedetto del Tronto d.	...	...	|	...	|	...	...	...	...	...	...	...	...	...	...	...	...	...	...	|	|	|	...	|	...	...
Civitanova Marche-Montegranaro d.	...	...	|	...	|	...	...	...	...	...	...	...	...	...	...	...	...	...	...	|	|	|	...	|	...	...
Ancona a.	...	...	1822	...	2022	...	...	...	...	...	...	...	...	...	...	...	...	...	...	0155	0209	0232	...	0243	...	...
Bologna Centrale **615 630** a.	...	...	2015	...	2215	...	...	...	...	...	...	...	...	...	...	...	...	...	...	0355	0410	0436	...	0505	...	...
Milano Centrale **615 630** a.	...	...	...	...	0025	...	...	...	...	...	...	...	...	...	...	...	...	...	...	|	0640	0712	...	|	...	...
Torino Porta Nuova **615** a.	...	...	...	...	...	...	...	...	...	...	...	...	...	...	...	...	...	...	...	0740	...	...	...	0920	...	...

Local services **BARI - TARANTO** — 2nd class only

km																										
		⚒		⚒	⚒		†	⚒		⚒		⚒	⚒		†	⚒		†	⚒		⚒			⚒		⚒
0	**Bari** d.	0530	...	0625	0720	...	0815	1000	...	1040	...	1310	1335	...	1443	1524	...	1600	1624	...	1800	1822	...	1939	2100	2350
54	Gioia del Colle d.	0610	...	0705	0805	...	0856	1041	...	1121	...	1343	1417	...	1524	1555	...	1640	1703	...	1832	1902	...	2020	2141	0033
115	**Taranto** a.	0650	...	0746	0847	...	0938	1116	...	1202	...	1416	1458	...	1605	1635	...	1723	1745	...	1914	1957	...	2103	2221	0113

	⚒	⚒			⚒	⚒		†	⚒		⚒		⚒	†		⚒		⚒		⚒		†	⚒		⚒
Taranto d.	0500	0557	0625	...	0705	0756	...	1040	1147	...	1220	...	1345	1352	...	1441	...	1539	1645	1803	...	1910	1927	...	2016
Gioia del Colle d.	0534	0636	0706	...	0745	0835	...	1120	1219	...	1301	...	1425	1431	...	1520	...	1621	1723	1835	...	1950	1958	...	2034
Bari a.	0612	0716	0745	...	0826	0916	...	1201	1302	...	1351	...	1506	1519	...	1602	...	1653	1756	1908	...	2033	2041	...	2127

← FOR NOTES SEE PREVIOUS PAGE.

632 FOGGIA - POTENZA

2nd class only

km																								
				⚒	⚒	†	⚒			†	†	⚒	⚒			⚒				⚒			🚌	
0	**Foggia** d.	0506	0534	0620	0645	0645	...	0842	...	1029	1137	...	*1305**	1429	...	*1630**	1752	...	...	1830	2036	...	2250	...
67	Melfi d.	0555	0633	0723	0757	0748	0859	0942	...	1124	1232	1238	1420	1532	1608	1729	1849	...	...	1930	2140	...	2340	...
119	**Potenza** Centrale a.	0705	0758	0837	0917	0919	1013	1101	...	1237	1347	1347	1551	1644	1723	1850	2000	...	...	2048	2238	...	0033	...

		⚒	†	⚒	⚒	†		⚒		⚒		†	⚒		⚒							🚌
Potenza Centrale d.	0528	0618	0715	0715	0840	0842	...	0936	1128	1234	...	1330	1330	1410	1605	...	1704	1816	2010	...	2111	...	2235
Melfi d.	0636	0726	0826	0846	0945	0945	...	1055	1229	1350	...	1450	1452	1521	1718	...	1815	1933	2119	...	2225	...	2346
Foggia a.	0746	0823	0935	*0946**	1040	1040	...	*1200**	1329	*1500**	...	1603	1603	...	...	...	1931	2032	2217	...	2321	...	0040

* – Connection by 🚌.

633 PAOLA - COSENZA - SIBARI

2nd class only

km																								
		⚒	⚒	⚒	⚒		Ⓒ	Ⓐ				⚒	⚒	†	⚒			⚒	⚒	†			r	
	Napoli Centrale **640** d.	...	...	...	...	...	0632	...	...	...	0850	...	...	...	...	1244	...	...	...	...	...	...	...	1925
0	**Paola 640** d.	0524	0657	0727	0827	0927	1027	1045	...	1227	1300	1402	1427	1530	1544	1627	...	1727	1827	1827	1937	2050	2127	2302
21	Castiglione Cosentino a.	0537	0710	0740	0840	0940	1040	1058	...	1240	1313	1415	1440	1543	1557	1640	...	1740	1840	1840	1950	2103	2141	2316
21	Castiglione Cosentino d.	0538	0711	0742	0842	0942	1041	1059	...	1241	1314	1416	1442	1544	1559	1641	...	1741	1842	1841	1951	2105	|	2317
26	**Cosenza** a.	0546	0719	0750	0850	0950	1049	1107	...	1249	1322	1424	1450	1558	1607	1649	...	1729	1850	1849	1959	2113	2159	2325

	⚒		⚒		r		Ⓐ		†	⚒	⚒	Ⓒ		⚒			⚒	⚒	⚒		⚒	†	⚒ 🚌
Cosenza d.	0536	0605	0625	0631	0725	0737	0837	0936	1052	1137	1236	1325	1336	1436	1502	1636	1700	1736	1836	1857	2020	2100	2115
Castiglione Cosentino a.	0542	0610	0630	0637	|	0741	0841	0941	1057	1141	1241	1331	1341	1441	1507	1641	1705	1741	1841	1902	2025	2106	2125
Castiglione Cosentino d.	0543	0611	0631	0638	0743	0743	0843	0943	1058	1143	1243	1331	1343	1443	1508	1643	1706	1743	1843	1903	2026	2106	2125
Paola 640 a.	0559	0627	0647	0654	0759	0759	0859	0959	1114	1159	1259	1347	1359	1459	1524	1658	1722	1759	1859	1921	2042	2121	2200
Napoli Centrale **640** a.	...	1010	...	...	...	...	...	...	...	...	...	1740	...	...	1910	...	...	...	...	2255	...	...	...

km										
			⚒	⚒	Ⓐ	⚒	†	⚒		p
0	**Cosenza** d.	0545	0722	1345	1430	1745	1845	1912	...	2159
5	Castiglione Cosentino d.	0551	0728	1351	1436	1751	1856	1923	...	2205
65	**Sibari** a.	0654	0815	1440	1526	1841	1946	2030	...	2254

	⚒	p		⚒	Ⓐ	⚒		⚒	†
Sibari d.	0540	0630	...	0843	1243	1534	1643	1915	1920
Castiglione Coséntino d.	0625	0719	...	0932	1331	1624	1731	2002	2010
Cosenza a.	0636	0725	...	0938	1338	1630	1738	2035	2016

p – To/from Paola.

r – To/from Sibari.

634 CATANZARO LIDO - LAMEZIA TERME

2nd class only

km																								
		⚒			⚒				†		⚒ 🚌	⚒		⚒	⚒		†	†		⚒			🚌	
0	Catanzaro Lido d.	0547	0640	...	0747	0825	...	0947	1040	...	1147	1245	...	1340	1440	...	1450	1547	...	1547	1623	...	1950	...
9	Catanzaro d.	0555	0648	...	0755	0837	...	0955	1048	...	1156	1254	...	1348	1448	...	1458	1555	...	1555	1636	...	1959	...
47	**Lamezia Terme** Centrale a.	0630	0730	...	0830	0918	...	1030	1130	...	1243	1330	...	1427	1530	...	1533	1630	...	1629	1710	...	2030	...

	⚒	⚒	†		⚒		†		⚒ 🚌	†	⚒		⚒	⚒	†		⚒		†			🚌	
Lamezia Terme Centrale d.	0655	0747	0757	...	0851	1105	1155	...	1243	1405	1405	...	1455	1551	1606	...	1714	1755	1910	...	1914	2125	...
Catanzaro d.	0729	0836	0836	...	0927	1139	1229	...	1329	1440	1449	...	1529	1635	1656	...	1747	1829	1944	...	1949	2205	...
Catanzaro Lido a.	0737	0844	0844	...	0937	1147	1237	...	1337	1448	1457	...	1537	1643	1704	...	1755	1837	1952	...	1956	2215	...

No service on †. Valid until June 1, 2019 **SUD EST services** **636**

ine 1: BARI - TARANTO

km																									
		🚌														🚌			🚌						
0	Bari Centrale .... d.	0504	0529	0547	0554	0624	0630	0650	0701	0729	0754	0813	0829	0936	1009	...	1029	1121	...	1129	1158	1203	1233	1241	1254
1	Bari Sud Est .... d.	0507	0532	0550	0557	0628	0634	0653	0704	0732	0757	0816	0832	0939	1012	...	1032	1124	...	1132	1201	1207	1236	1244	1257
4	Mungivacca .... d.	|	0538	0556	0606	0641	0642	0709	0714	0738	0806	0822	0843	0946	1018	...	1040	1132	...	1138	1207	1213	1243	1250	1309
	Casamassima .... d.	|	0620	|	*0635***a**	|	0723	*0751***a**	|	0820	*0848***a**	|	0923	|	|	...	1120	|	...	1220	*1249***a**	|	1320	|	*1351***a**
43	Putignano .... d.	0648	0705	0712	*0725***a**	0749	0806	*0828***a**	0825	0906	*0925***a**	0940	1006	1058	1133	...	1205	1245	...	1305	*1326***a**	1322	1406	1357	*1425***a**
78	Martina Franca **2** .... d.	0744	...	*0817***b**	...	*0852***b**	...	...	...	...	...	...	...	...	*1229***b**	1312	...	*1356***b**	1411	...	...	...	...	*1457***b**	...
113	Taranto .... a.	...	...	...	...	...	...	...	...	...	...	...	...	...	...	1406	...	...	1504	...	...	...	...	...	...

km																									
				🚌					🚌																
	Bari Centrale .... d.	1329	1345	...	1354	1421	1429	1457	...	1537	1629	1647	1729	1723	1750	1757	1837	1831	1854	1909	1929	1955	2029	2021	2059
	Bari Sud Est .... d.	1332	1348	...	1357	1425	1432	1500	...	1540	1632	1650	1732	1726	1753	1800	1840	1834	1857	1912	1932	1958	2032	2024	2102
0	Mungivacca .... d.	1338	1354	...	1406	1434	1438	1509	...	1546	1640	1656	1741	1739	1812	1810	1849	1846	1913	1918	1941	2007	2038	2034	2109
20	Casamassima .... d.	1420	|	...	...	|	1520	|	...	|	1720	|	1820	|	...	|	|	1924	...	|	2020	...	2120	|	|
44	Putignano .... d.	1506	1511	...	...	1547	1602	1624	...	1659	1805	1810	1906	1845	...	1921	1958	2007	...	2035	2105	...	2204	2145	2221
	Martina Franca **2** .... d.	...	*1626***b**	1628	...	...	...	*1724***b**	1725	...	...	...	...	*1942***b**	...	*2017***b**	...	...	...	*2144***b**	...	–	...	*2245***b**	...
	Taranto .... a.	...	...	1720	...	...	...	...	1820	...	...	...	...	...	...	...	...	...	...	...	...	...	...	...	...

										🚌					🚌			🚌						
aranto .... d.	...	...	...	...	...	...	...	...	...	0520	...	...	...	...	0638	...	...	0847	...	...	...	...	...	...
artina Franca **2** .... d.	...	...	*0448***b**	...	...	*0521***b**	...	...	...	0615	*0623***b**	...	*0655***b**	...	0732	*0828***b**	...	0937	*0938***b**	...	...	...	...	...
utignano .... d.	0508	0510	0544	*0547***a**	0609	0616	*0647***a**	0650	0709	...	0727	*0742***a**	0802	0810	...	0924	1010	...	1035	1109	1111	*1147***a**	1148	1209
Casamassima .... d.	|	0552	|	*0625***a**	0652	|	*0725***a**	|	0752	...	|	*0820***a**	|	0852	...	|	1052	...	|	1152	|	*1225***a**	|	1252
ungivacca .... d.	0619	0634	0655	0709	0736	0729	0807	0812	0834	...	0843	0910	0916	0931	...	1038	1130	...	1152	1234	1237	1309	1302	1336
ari Sud Est .... a.	0627	0640	0703	0716	0742	0736	0815	0521	0840	...	0849	0916	0924	0938	...	1046	1136	...	1200	1243	1135	1315	1310	1342
ari Centrale .... a.	0630	0643	0706	0719	0745	0739	0818	0824	0843	...	0852	0919	0927	0941	...	1049	1139	...	1203	1246	1138	1319	1313	1345

							🚌		🚌					🚌						🚌			🚌	
aranto .... d.	...	...	...	...	...	...	1314	...	1412	...	...	...	...	1511	...	...	...	...	...	1730	...	...	1901	...
artina Franca **2** .... d.	...	...	*1238***b**	...	...	...	1407	*1410***b**	1506	*1507***b**	...	...	...	1603	*1605***b**	...	*1730***b**	...	...	1823	*1824***b**	...	1953	*1954***b**
utignano .... d.	1259	1309	1336	*1347***a**	1410	1412	...	1523	...	1602	1609	1635	1708	...	1711	1809	1824	1859	1910	...	1935	2010	...	2048
Casamassima .... d.	|	1352	|	*1425***a**	1452	|	...	|	...	|	1652	|	1752	...	|	1852	|	|	1852	...	|	2052	...	|
ungivacca .... d.	1416	1434	1449	1507	1535	1531	...	1641	...	1717	1732	1751	1839	...	1825	1941	1946	2014	2034	...	2053	2130	...	2202
ari Sud Est .... a.	1424	1440	1459	1513	1545	1539	...	1649	...	1725	1738	1759	1845	...	1834	1947	1953	2023	2041	...	2101	2136	...	2210
ari Centrale .... a.	1427	1443	1502	1516	1548	1542	...	1652	...	1728	1741	1802	1849	...	1837	1950	1956	2026	2041	...	2104	2139	...	2213

ine 2: MARTINA FRANCA - LECCE

km																									
0	Martina Franca **1** .... d.	0506	0554	...	...	0716	...	...	...	0940	...	1200	1237	...	...	...	...	1521	...	1653	...	...	1833	...	...
41	Francavilla Fontana .... d.	0601	0652	...	...	0814	...	...	...	1036	...	1256	1334	...	1414	...	...	1618	...	1749	...	...	1929	...	...
92	Novoli **3** .... d.	0725	0814	...	0856	0933	...	1022	1148	1204	1315	1419	...	1453	1533	1609	1737	1753	...	1911	1945	...	2054	2110	...
103	Lecce **5** .... a.	0740	0829	...	0911	0948	...	1037	1203	1219	1330	1434	...	1508	1550	1624	1752	1808	...	1926	2000	...	2109	2125	...

	🚌																						🚌	🚌
ecce **5** .... d.	...	0426	0600	0628	0705	0839	0950	1005	...	1132	...	1235	1258	1350	...	1438	1510	1640	1655	1842	...	1930	2017	2040
ovoli **3** .... d.	...	0441	0614	0643	0735	0853	1005	1019	...	1146	...	1250	1312	1405	...	1457	1524	1654	1710	1857	...	1944	2037	2101
ancavilla Fontana .... d.	0541	0602	...	0813	0906	...	1126	...	...	...	1340	1409	...	1528	...	1619	...	...	1840	2019	...	...	...	...
artina Franca **1** .... a.	0630	0710	...	0918	1012	...	1234	...	...	...	1442	...	...	1635	...	1727	...	...	1948	2124	...	...	...	...

ine 3: NOVOLI - GAGLIANO

km												
												🚌
0	Novoli **2** .... d.	0515	0615	0731	0857	1024	1151	1318	1526	1655	1946	2038
25	Nardò Centrale **5** .... d.	0556	0703	0814	0940	1106	1233	1401	1607	1737	2030	2120
49	Casarano **4** .... d.	0643	0749	0859	1024	1151	1317	1445	1652	1821	2113	...
74	Gagliano Leuca **6** .... a.	0725	0831	0940	1105	1232	1358	1526	1733	1902	2154	...

agliano Leuca **6** .... d.	...	0648	0812	0942	...	1106	1235	1401	1530	1739	1903
asarano **4** .... d.	0600	0731	0857	1024	...	1150	1318	1444	1613	1822	1945
ardò Centrale **5** .... d.	0643	0816	0940	1109	...	1235	1404	1528	1657	1905	2029
ovoli **2** .... a.	0725	0854	1018	1147	...	1313	1442	1607	1736	1943	2107

ine 4: CASARANO - GALLIPOLI

km												
			🚌				🚌					🚌
0	Casarano **3** .... d.	0730	0810	1149	...	1311	1350	1446	...	1642	1825	2000
22	Gallipoli **5** .... a.	0808	0851	1227	...	1349	1431	1524	...	1720	1903	2039

				🚌			🚌				🚌
allipoli **5** .... d.	0520	...	0649	0724	0810	1230	1305	1351	1533	1731	1910
asarano **3** .... a.	0559	...	0728	0806	0849	1309	1347	1430	1612	1810	1949

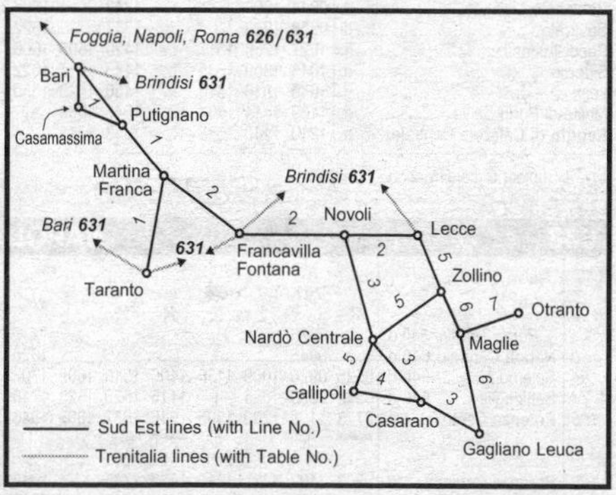

ine 5: LECCE - GALLIPOLI

km																									
0	Lecce **2** .... d.	0546	0559	...	0655	...	0839	...	0935	...	1045	...	1259	...	1352	...	1430	...	1653	...	1755	...	1923	...	2049
19	Zollino **6** .... d.	0618	0632	...	0737	...	0909	...	1012	...	1121	...	1334	...	1432	...	1507	...	1728	...	1835	...	1958	...	2123
36	Nardò Centrale **3** .... d.	...	0701	...	0816	...	0939	...	1040	...	1148	...	1402	...	1503	...	1537	...	1757	...	1904	...	2028	...	2150
53	Gallipoli **4** .... a.	...	0729	...	0844	...	1007	...	1108	...	1217	...	1430	...	1531	...	1606	...	1826	...	1932	...	2056	...	2218

allipoli **4** .... d.	0557	0629	0738	...	...	0906	1008	...	...	1141	...	1228	1327	...	...	1431	1532	...	1728	...	...	...	1952	...
ardò Centrale **3** .... d.	0629	0703	0815	...	...	0941	1045	...	...	1214	...	1301	1400	...	...	1504	1608	...	1757	...	...	...	2027	...
llino **6** .... d.	0701	0735	0843	...	0808	1010	1118	...	1135	1243	...	1336	1436	...	...	1534	1636	1702	1830	...	1845	...	2057	...
cce **2** .... a.	0734	0808	0916	...	0837	1042	1150	...	1207	1316	...	1409	1509	...	...	1606	1709	1735	1902	...	1917	...	2129	...

ine 6: ZOLLINO - GAGLIANO

km																									
																								🚌	
0	Zollino **5** .... d.	0621	...	0734	...	0914	...	1013	...	1119	...	1342	...	1432	...	1505	...	1728	...	1829	...	1957	...	2130	...
10	Maglie **7** .... d.	0637	...	0802	...	0938	...	1034	...	1137	...	1403	...	1447	...	1520	...	1750	...	1851	...	2015	...	2147	...
47	Gagliano Leuca **3** .... a.	...	...	0910	...	1045	...	1142	...	1245	...	1503	...	1549	...	1622	...	1858	...	1958	...	2122	...	...	...

gliano Leuca **3** .... d.	0546	...	0610	...	0646	...	0833	...	1007	...	1106	...	1207	...	1255	...	1547	...	1722	...	1921	...	...	...
aglie **7** .... d.	0643	...	0714	...	0752	...	0948	...	1117	...	1221	...	1314	...	1407	...	1647	...	1827	...	2032	...	...	...
llino **5** .... d.	0658	...	0731	...	0807	...	1004	...	1134	...	1237	...	1330	...	1424	...	1701	...	1844	...	2049	...	...	...

ne 7: MAGLIE - OTRANTO

m														
0	Maglie **6** .... d.	0647	0757	...	0942	...	...	1138	1310	1405	1523	1649	1751	1854
8	Otranto .... a.	0715	0826	...	1011	...	...	1206	1335	1430	1548	1715	1817	1922

Otranto .... d.	0720	...	...	0903	1043	...	1223	1337	1452	1616	1720	1822	1940
Maglie **6** .... a.	0746	...	...	0932	1112	...	1249	1402	1517	1642	1746	1849	2008

🚌 connection at Adelfia.

b – Connection by 🚌.

637 REGGIO DI CALABRIA - SIBARI - TARANTO

2nd class only

km											*IC* 564/5								*IC* 562/3						
		🚌 ⚒	⚒	🚌 ⚒	⚒	⚒		⚒	†		⊙	Ⓐ		🚌 ⚒	⚒	Ⓑ	†	🚌 ⚒	⊙	⚒		†	⚒	⚒	🚌 ⚒
0	**Reggio di Calabria** Centrale d.	...	...	...	...	0500	...	0540	...	0718	0735	...	0918	...	...	1010	...	...	1155	...	1318	...	...	1410	...
30	Melito di Porto Salvo d.	...	...	...	...	0524	...	0609	...	0743	0759	...	0943	...	...	1042	...	...	1219	...	1343	...	...	1442	...
96	Locri d.	...	...	...	...	0614	0635	0725	...	0836	0854	...	1035	...	...	1153	...	...	1316	1330	1435	...	...	1553	...
101	Siderno d.	...	...	...	...	0619	0646	0730	...	0844	0901	...	1044	...	...	1201	...	...	1323	1338	1444	...	...	1601	...
112	Roccella Jonica d.	...	...	...	...	0633	0658	0742	...	0856	0921	...	1056	...	...	1215	...	...	1340	1358	1456	...	...	1620	...
160	Soverato d.	...	...	...	...	0714	0759	0827	...	0927	0959	...	1127	...	...	▬	...	...	1425	1455	1527	...	...	...	...
178	Catanzaro Lido a.	...	...	...	...	0731	0815	0842	...	0942	1011	...	1142	...	...	⚒	...	...	1439	1520	1542	...	...	...	...
178	Catanzaro Lido d.	...	0520	...	0645	...	...	...	0850	...	1013	1050	...	...	1239	1345	1345	...	1441	...	...	1555	1555	...	...
238	**Crotone** d.	...	0615	...	0746	...	...	...	0939	...	1114	1147	...	...	1327	1433	1433	...	1551	...	...	1648	1646	...	...
325	Rossano d.	...	0752	...	0906	...	...	...	1107	...	1216	1258	...	...	1457	1548	1551	...	1706	...	...	1801	1801	...	...
336	Corigliano Calabro d.	...	0801	...	0915	...	...	...	1116	...	1226	1313	...	...	1517	1556	1601	...	1716	...	...	1809	1815	...	...
351	**Sibari** a.	...	0815	...	0930	...	...	...	1130	...	1240	1327	...	...	1528	1610	1616	...	1729	...	...	1827	1828	...	...
351	**Sibari** d.	0440	...	0835	...	...	...	...	...	...	1243	...	...	1403	...	...	...	1635	1731	...	...	...	...	...	190
366	Trebisacce d.	0454	...	0849	...	...	...	...	...	...	1255	...	...	1417	...	...	...	1649	1743	...	...	...	...	...	191
430	Metaponto 638 d.	0610	...	1007	...	...	...	...	...	...	1339	...	...	1530	...	...	...	1807	1835	...	...	...	...	...	203
473	**Taranto** 638 a.	0705	...	1117	...	...	...	...	...	...	1410	...	...	1640	...	...	...	1902	1907	...	...	...	...	...	212

	⚒	⚒	⚒	⚒	⚒		⚒	⚒	⚒
Reggio di Calabria Centrale d.	...	1518	...	...	...	1718	1810	1918	2038
Melito di Porto Salvo d.	...	1543	...	...	...	1742	1843	1942	2109
Locri d.	...	1635	...	1655	...	1834	1955	2041	2213
Siderno d.	...	1644	...	1702	...	1841	2002	2055	2219
Roccella Jonica d.	...	1656	...	1721	...	1857	2015	2107	2232
Soverato d.	...	1728	...	1820	...	1929	▬	2138	...
Catanzaro Lido a.	...	1745	...	1840	...	1945	🚌	2153	...
Catanzaro Lido d.	1653	...	1758	...	1852	...	⚒	...	...
Crotone d.	1756	...	1849	...	1945	...	2110	...	...
Rossano d.	1923	...	2016	...	2103	...	2238	...	...
Corigliano Calabro d.	1936	...	2025	...	2112	...	2256	...	...
Sibari a.	1950	...	2038	...	2125	...	2315	...	...
Sibari d.	...	...	...	...	...	...	2315	...	...
Trebisacce d.	...	...	...	...	...	...	2340	...	...
Metaponto 638 d.	...	...	...	...	...	...	...	...	...
Taranto 638 a.	...	...	...	...	...	...	...	...	...

	⚒	⚒	⚒	†	⚒	⚒		⚒		🚌 ⚒
Taranto 638 d.	...	...	...	...	...	...	...	...	...	051
Metaponto 638 d.	...	...	...	...	...	...	...	...	...	061
Trebisacce d.	...	...	...	...	...	...	...	...	...	073
Sibari a.	...	...	...	...	...	...	...	...	...	075
Sibari d.	...	...	...	...	...	0508	...	0608	0708	...
Corigliano Calabro d.	...	...	...	...	...	0520	...	0621	0720	...
Rossano d.	...	...	...	...	...	0529	...	0630	0729	...
Crotone d.	...	...	...	...	...	0643	...	0745	0844	...
Catanzaro Lido a.	...	...	...	...	...	0735	...	0845	0935	...
Catanzaro Lido d.	...	0544	...	...	0630	...	0744	...	...	...
Soverato d.	...	0557	...	...	0645	...	0757	...	...	...
Roccella Jonica d.	0530	0633	0705	0705	0726	...	0829	...	...	...
Siderno d.	0542	0645	0716	0717	0743	...	0843	...	...	...
Locri d.	0548	0650	0726	0725	0750	...	0853	...	...	...
Melito di Porto Salvo d.	0652	0739	0839	0839	...	...	0939	...	...	...
Reggio di Calabria Centrale a.	0727	0810	0915	0918	...	...	1015	...	...	...

		IC 558/9										*IC* 566/7													
		⊙	⚒	🚌 ⚒		Ⓐ	⚒	⚒	⚒		⚒	⊙	⚒	†		⚒	🚌 ⚒	⚒	⚒	🚌 ⚒	Ⓐ			🚌 ⚒	🚌 ⚒
Taranto 638 d.	...	0811	...	0920	...	...	...	...	...	...	...	1307	...	...	...	...	1425	...	...	...	...	...	...	1800	192
Metaponto 638 d.	...	0844	...	1017	...	...	...	...	...	...	...	1339	...	...	...	...	1517	...	...	1605	...	...	...	1857	202
Trebisacce d.	...	0931	...	1136	...	...	...	...	...	...	...	1423	...	...	...	...	1625	...	...	1724	...	...	...	2013	213
Sibari a.	...	0946	...	1155	...	...	...	...	...	...	...	1432	...	...	...	...	1640	...	...	1745	...	...	...	2027	215
Sibari d.	...	0948	...	...	...	...	...	1300	...	...	...	1434	1503	1528	...	1613	...	...	1658	...	1758	1920	...	...	...
Corigliano Calabro d.	...	1003	...	...	...	...	...	1313	...	...	...	1447	1514	1540	...	1624	...	...	1715	...	1814	1934	...	...	...
Rossano d.	...	1013	...	...	...	...	...	1323	...	...	...	1456	1523	1550	...	1636	...	...	1724	...	1824	1943	...	...	...
Crotone d.	...	1115	...	...	...	...	...	1447	...	...	...	1610	1641	1712	...	1757	...	...	1848	...	1944	2107	...	...	...
Catanzaro Lido a.	...	1207	...	...	...	...	...	1538	...	...	...	1710	1736	1755	...	1847	...	...	1939	...	2035	2155	...	...	...
Catanzaro Lido d.	0944	1209	...	...	1342	...	1507	...	1544	...	1652	1712	...	...	1805	...	...	2001	...	...	...	...	...	...	...
Soverato d.	0958	1223	...	...	1357	...	1527	...	1557	...	1709	1729	...	...	1819	...	...	2014	...	...	...	...	...	...	...
Roccella Jonica d.	1027	1255	1317	...	1429	1505	1606	...	1627	1705	1758	1822	...	...	1857	...	...	2044	...	...	...	...	...	...	...
Siderno d.	1043	1309	1335	...	1443	1517	1622	...	1643	1717	1816	1840	...	...	1912	...	...	2055	...	...	...	...	...	...	...
Locri d.	1049	1316	1340	...	1450	1523	1630	...	1649	1723	1825	1847	...	...	1919	...	...	2101	...	...	...	...	...	...	...
Melito di Porto Salvo d.	1139	1414	1504	...	1545	1639	...	...	1739	1841	...	1937	...	...	2018	...	...	2203	...	...	...	...	...	...	...
Reggio di Calabria Centrale a.	1210	1440	1535	...	1613	1715	...	...	1810	1918	...	2005	...	...	2046	...	...	2237	...	...	...	...	...	...	...

⊙ – Subject to confirmation.

638 NAPOLI - POTENZA - TARANTO

2nd class on

km			*IC* 701							*IC* 707		*FR* 9549
		⚒		†	🚌 ⚒	⚒	⚒					A
	Roma Termini 640 d.	...	0626	...	...	...	...	...	...	1526	...	1858
0	**Napoli** Centrale 640 d.	...	0845	...	...	...	...	...	1620	1753	...	2015
54	Salerno 640 d.	0526	0926	1009	1135	1400	1510	1609	1703	1827	1954	2052
74	Battipaglia 640 d.	0542	0939	1025	|	1415	1525	1623	1718	1840	2010	|
166	**Potenza** Centrale a.	0723	1100	1202	1305	1546	1657	1805	1846	2002	2154	2216
		▬	|		|	▬ ⚒	🚌 ⚒		|	|		|
166	**Potenza** Centrale d.	0802	1102	...	1310	1428	1735	...	1848	2004	...	2218
273	Metaponto 637 d.	0933	1223	...	1443	1604	1908	...	2007	2124	...	2332
317	**Taranto** 637 a.	1007	1255	...	1523	1640	1950	...	2045	2156	...	0001

		FR 9522	*IC* 700				*IC* 702				
		B			⚒	🚌 ⚒		⚒	⚒	†	⚒
Taranto 637 d.	...	0550	0803	1010	1101	1235	1356	...	...	...	182
Metaponto 637 d.	...	0620	0837	1047	1136	1315	1430	...	...	...	190
Potenza Centrale a.	...	0736	0956	1215	1311	1445	1546	...	...	...	204
		|	|	|		|	|				
Potenza Centrale	0700	0738	0958	1217	1325	1450	1548	1729	1858	1928	210
Battipaglia 640 d.	0837	|	1127	1346	1502	|	1715	1912	2028	2102	224
Salerno 640 d.	0853	0914	1140	1401	1520	|	1730	1931	2045	2119	230
Napoli C 640 a.	...	0950	1215	1440	...	1650	1805	...	...	...	...
Roma T 640 a.	...	1109	1434	...	...	...	2034	...	...	...	...

A – June 9 - July 27: (12) and 🍸 Milano (**9547**) - Napoli - Salerno - Taranto.

B – (12) and 🍸 Taranto - Salerno - Napoli (**9524**) - Milano.

639 NAPOLI - SORRENTO, BAIANO and SARNO

2nd class only — Circumvesuviana Ferrovi

km																											
0	**Napoli** P. Garibaldi ▲ d.	0611	0642	0711	0741	0813	0841	0911	and	1311	1343	1411	1441	1513	1541	1611	1641	1711	1743	1811	1834	1913	1941	2011	and	2111	21
10	Ercolano Scavi d.	0628	0652	0728	0758	0823	0858	0928	every	1328	1353	1428	1458	1523	1558	1628	1658	1728	1753	1828	1858	1923	1958	2028	every	2128	22
23	Pompei S. Villa Misteri d.	0647	0705	0747	0817	0836	0917	0947	30	1347	1406	1447	1517	1536	1617	1647	1717	1747	1806	1847	1917	1936	2017	2047	30	2147	22
29	Castellammare d.	0657	0715	0757	0827	0846	0927	0957	minutes	1357	1416	1457	1527	1546	1627	1657	1727	1757	1816	1857	1927	1946	2027	2057	minutes	2157	22
42	**Sorrento** a.	0717	0732	0817	0847	0903	0947	1017	until	1417	1433	1517	1547	1603	1647	1717	1747	1817	1833	1917	1947	2003	2047	2117	until	2217	22

Sorrento d.	0601	0625	0722	0755	0826	0907	0937	1037	1107	and	1307	1325	1356	1422	1455	1526	1607	1637	1707	1725	1756	1822	1855	1926	2007	2037	2107	21
Castellammare d.	0621	0645	0739	0815	0845	0927	0957	1057	1127	every	1327	1345	1415	1439	1515	1545	1627	1657	1727	1745	1815	1839	1915	1945	2027	2057	2127	22
Pompei S. Villa Misteri d.	0631	0655	0748	0825	0853	0937	1007	1107	1137	30	1337	1356	1423	1448	1525	1553	1637	1707	1737	1755	1823	1848	1925	1953	2037	2107	2137	22
Ercolano Scavi d.	0649	0713	0807	0843	0906	0955	1025	1125	1155	minutes	1355	1414	1436	1507	1543	1606	1655	1725	1755	1813	1836	1907	1943	2006	2055	2125	2155	22
Napoli P. Garibaldi ▲ a.	0707	0731	0826	0901	0916	1013	1043	1143	1213	until	1413	1431	1446	1526	1601	1616	1713	1743	1813	1831	1846	1926	2001	2016	2113	2143	2213	22

NAPOLI (Porta Nolana) **- BAIANO and v.v.** Journey 60 minutes.

From **Napoli:** 0618, 0648⚒, 0718, 0748, 0818, 0918, 1018, 1118, 1148, 1218, 1318, 1418, 1448⚒, 1518, 1618, 1648⚒, 1718, 1748Ⓐ, 1818, 1848, 1918, 1948.

From **Baiano:** 0602, 0632⚒, 0700, 0730, 0802, 0832, 0902, 0932, 1002, 1102, 1202, 13 1332⚒, 1402, 1502, 1602, 1632⚒, 1702, 1802, 1832⚒, 1902, 1932Ⓐ, 2002.

NAPOLI (Porta Nolana) **- SARNO and v.v.** Journey 65 minutes. All services call at Poggiomarino (49 minutes from Napoli, 12 minutes from Sarno).

From **Napoli:** 0632, 0651 **p**, 0722, 0802, 0902, 1002, 1102, 1132⚒, 1202, 1302, 1402, 1432⚒, 1502, 1602, 1702, 1732Ⓐ, 1802, 1832, 1932, 2002 **p**.

From **Sarno:** 0619, 0649, 0719, 0759, 0819, 0849, 0949, 1049, 1149, 1249, 1334Ⓐ **p**, 13 1449, 1549, 1619⚒, 1649, 1749, 1849, 1919Ⓐ, 1949.

p – To/from Poggiomarino only.

▲ – Services originate / terminate at Napoli Porta Nolana station (journey time: 1 – 2 minutes).

Operator: Circumvesuviana Ferrovia ✆ +39 081 77 22 444, fax +39 081 77 22 450.

A reduced service operates in peak summer.

ROMA - NAPOLI - COSENZA and REGGIO DI CALABRIA 640

For high-speed services see Table **600**.

km		*ICN* 1575	*ICN* 789		*ICN* 1963	*ICN* 1967							*ICN* 799	*IC* 701			*FA* 8345	*IC* 1523	*IC* 721	*ICN* 797	*ICN* 793			
				2			2	2	2	2	2	2			2	2	🍷					2	2	2
		◆	⊙◆		⊙◆	A⊙							◆	T		⚒		Rp	Rp	⊙◆	⊙◆	⚒	†	
	Torino Porta Nuova **610** d.	1335	...	...	...	...	...	...	...	...	...	...	2155	...	...	...	...	...	...	2125	2125	...	...	...
	Milano Centrale **615** d.	1544g	...	...	2010	2010	...	...	...	...	...	...	|	...	...	...	...	...	...	2317g	2317g	...	...	...
	Venezia Santa Lucia **616** d.	|	...	...	|	|	...	...	...	...	...	...	|	...	...	...	...	...	...	|	|	...	...	...
	Bologna Centrale **620** d.	1818	...	...	|	|	...	...	...	...	...	...	|	...	...	...	...	...	...	|	|	...	...	...
0	**Roma** Termini d.	2320t	2358	...	|	|	...	...	...	...	...	0531	0546o	0626	...	0656	0858	0726	0726	0722t	0825t	...	0736	0736
62	Latina d.	|	|	...	|	|	...	...	...	...	...	0608	0637	0700	...	0731	|	0800	0800	|	|	...	0818	0818
129	Formia-Gaeta d.	|	|	...	|	|	...	...	...	...	...	0657	0717	0735	...	0821	|	0835	0835	|	|	...	0906	0912
195	Aversa d.	|	|	...	|	|	...	...	...	...	...	0746	0758	0811	...	0914	|	0911	0911	|	|	...	1006	1013
	Caserta **626** d.	|	0232	...	|	|	...	...	...	...	...	|	|	|	...	|	|	|	|	|	|	...	|	|
214	**Napoli** Centrale **626** a.	|	▬	...	|	|	...	...	...	...	...	0812	0817	0829	...	0950	0959f	0929	0929	0938	1048	...	1038	1036
214	**Napoli** Centrale **638** d.	|	...	...	|	|	...	0540	...	0650	0755	...	0835	0845	0850	...	1001f	0950	0950	0955	1105	...	▬	▬
268	Salerno **638** d.	0221	...	...	0556s	0556s	0551	0637	...	0736	0841	...	0912	0926	0933	...	1031	1039	1029	1050	1145	...	...	...
288	Battipaglia **638** d.	|	...	...	0616s	0616s	0610	0652	...	0750	0856	...	...	0937	0947	...	|	|	|	...	...	...	...	...
318	Agropoli-Castellabate d.	|	...	...	0637s	0637s	0632	0715	...	0812	0921	...	...	...	1009	...	|	|	|	...	...	...	2	...
349	Ascea d.	|	...	...	0703s	0703s	0656	0741	...	0836	0950	...	...	...	1033	...	|	|	|	...	...	...	⚒	...
395	Sapri d.	0343	...	...	0735s	0735s	0745	0825	...	0912	1030	...	...	...	1127	...	|	1144	1144	...	...	...	1250	...
407	Maratea d.	|	2	...	0746s	0746s	0754	...	...	0922	...	...	...	...	1136	...	|	|	|	...	...	...	1303	2
455	Belvedere Marittimo d.	|	⚒	...	|	|	0832	...	...	0956	...	...	...	...	1218	...	|	|	|	...	...	...	1344	
	Cosenza **633** d.	|	0533	0631	|	|	|	...	0936	|	...	...	...	...	|	...	|	|	|	...	...	1236	|	1336
489	Paola **633** d.	0442	0609	0707	0837s	0837s	0907	...	1009	1027	...	...	...	...	1244	...	1212	1234	1234	...	...	1309	1402	1409
	Cosenza **633** a.	|	|	|	|	|	...	...	|	1049k	...	...	...	...	1322	...	|	|	|	...	...	|	1424	|
546	**Lamezia Terme** Centrale a.	0518	0640	0737	0916s	0916s	...	...	1040	...	...	...	...	...	...	...	1240	1302	1302	...	...	1340	...	1442
546	**Lamezia Terme** Centrale d.	0520	0642	0739	|	|	...	...	1042	...	...	...	...	...	...	...	1240	1304	1304	...	...	1342	...	1444
616	Gioia Tauro d.	0700	0720	0820	1006s	1004s	...	...	1120	...	...	...	...	...	...	...	|	1339	1339	...	...	1420	...	1522
652	Villa S. Giovanni a.	0735	0751	0851	1040s	1040s	...	...	1151	...	...	...	...	...	...	...	1339	1410	1410	...	...	1451	...	1553
652	Villa S. Giovanni d.	0738	0753	0853	|	|	...	...	1153	...	...	...	...	...	...	...	1340	1430	1430	...	...	1453	...	1555
667	**Reggio di Calabria** Centrale a.	0805	0810	0910	|	|	...	...	1210	...	...	...	...	...	...	...	1357	|	|	...	...	1510	...	1612
	Siracusa **641** a.	...	...	...	1548	|	...	...	...	...	...	...	...	...	...	...	...	|	1833	...	...	...	...	...
	Palermo Centrale **641** a.	...	...	...	...	1656	...	...	...	...	...	...	...	...	...	...	...	1925	...	...	...	...	...	...

	FB 8863	*IC* 1551	*IC* 1551			*IC* 501			*IC* 1527	*IC* 729				*IC* 1553		*IC* 583	*FB* 8867		*IC* 1589	*IC* 1591		*IC* 1525	*IC* 1525	
	🍷			2	2		2	2				2	2		2		🍷	2			2			2
	a	aq	r	⚒		◆	†	⚒	Ra	Ra		†	⚒	a	†			⚒	⑥d	⑥c	⚒	bq	r	
Torino Porta Nuova **610** d.	...	...	...	...	...	...	...	...	...	...	...	...	...	...	...	...	...	...	...	...	...	...	...	...
Milano Centrale **615** d.	...	...	...	...	...	...	...	...	...	...	...	...	...	...	...	0650	...	...	0640	0640	...	...	...	...
Venezia Santa Lucia **616** d.	...	...	...	...	...	...	...	...	...	...	...	...	...	...	...	|	...	...	|	|	...	...	...	...
Bologna Centrale **620** d.	...	...	...	...	...	...	...	...	...	...	...	...	...	...	...	0918	...	...	0937	0937	...	...	...	...
Roma Termini d.	1010	0926	0926	...	...	1018o	1036	1036	1126	1126	...	1136	1156	1226	1236	1324t	1356	...	1317t	1317t	...	1426	1426	...
Latina d.	|	1000	1000	...	...	1057	1118	1118	1200	1200	...	1218	1231	1300	1318	1400	|	...	1406	1406	...	1500	1500	...
Formia-Gaeta d.	|	1035	1035	...	...	1134	1207	1212	1235	1235	...	1307	1321	1335	1406	1435	|	...	1444	1444	...	1535	1535	...
Aversa d.	|	1111	1111	...	...	1209	1302	1314	1311	1311	...	1402	1414	1411	1506	1511	|	...	1523	1523	...	1611	1611	...
Caserta **626** d.	|	|	|	...	...	|	|	|	|	|	...	|	|	|	|	|	|	...	|	|	...	|	|	...
Napoli Centrale **626** a.	1157	1129	1129	...	...	1229	1323	1340	1329	1329	...	1423	1440	1429	1535	1529	1541	...	1547	1547	...	1629	1629	...
Napoli Centrale **638** d.	1210	1145	1145	...	1244	...	...	...	1345	1345	...	▬	...	1445	▬	...	1553	1520	1610	1610	...	1645	1645	1720
Salerno **638** d.	1244	1222	1222	...	1330	...	...	...	1424	1424	...	...	...	1526	...	...	1628	1603	1653	1653	...	1729	1729	1803
Battipaglia **638** d.	|	1236	1236	...	1347	...	...	...	|	|	...	...	...	1540	...	...	1641	1618	|	|	...	1743	1743	1821
Agropoli-Castellabate d.	|	1257	1257	...	1407	...	...	...	|	|	...	...	...	1600	...	...	|	1642	|	|	...	1804	1804	1843
Ascea d.	|	|	|	...	1431	...	...	...	|	|	...	...	...	|	...	...	|	1712	1739	1739	...	1830	1830	1907
Sapri d.	1356	1347	1347	...	1509	...	...	...	1533	1533	...	...	...	1646	...	...	1741	1757	1813	1813	...	1905	1905	1947
Maratea d.	|	1357	1357	...	1518	...	...	...	|	|	...	2	...	|	2	...	|	...	|	|	...	|	|	...
Belvedere Marittimo d.	|	|	|	...	1553	...	...	...	|	|	...	⚒	...	|	⚒	...	|	...	|	|	...	|	|	...
Cosenza **633** d.	|	|	|	1436	|	...	...	...	|	|	...	1636	...	|	1736	...	|	...	|	|	1836	|	|	...
Paola **633** d.	1449	1457	1458	1509	1627	...	...	...	1629	1629	...	1709	...	1743	1809	...	1827	...	1915	1915	1909	2003	2005	...
Cosenza **633** a.	|	|	|	|	1649	...	...	...	|	|	...	|	...	|	|	...	|	...	|	|	|	|	|	...
Lamezia Terme Centrale a.	1516	1528	1535	1540	...	...	...	...	1658	1658	...	1740	...	1816	1841	...	1854	...	1946	1946	1940	2034	2039	...
Lamezia Terme Centrale d.	1517	1531	1538	1542	...	...	...	...	1658	1658	...	1742	...	1817	1843	...	1854	...	1949	1949	1942	2037	2042	...
Gioia Tauro d.	1559	1621	1618	1622	...	...	...	...	1733	1733	...	1822	...	1900	1921	...	1937	...	2036	2143	2020	2119	2122	...
Villa S. Giovanni a.	1625	1646	1643	1653	...	...	...	...	1805	1805	...	1855	...	1926	1952	...	2002	...	2058	2208	2051	2143	2146	...
Villa S. Giovanni d.	1628	1649	1646	1655	...	...	...	...	1825	1825	...	1855	...	1926	1954	...	2005	...	2101	2211	2053	2146	2149	...
Reggio di Calabria Centrale a.	1647	1705	1703	1712	...	...	...	...	|	|	...	1912	...	1948	2012	...	2020	...	2120	2229	2110	2203	2206	...
Siracusa **641** a.	...	...	...	...	...	...	...	...	2250	|	...	...	...	...	...	...	...	...	...	...	...	...	...	...
Palermo Centrale **641** a.	...	...	...	...	...	...	...	...	...	2305	...	...	...	...	...	...	...	...	...	...	...	...	...	...

km			*IC* 707	*FA* 8343		*IC* 705	*IC* 1521				*IC* 591				*IC* 511				*IC* 1577	*ICN* 1593	*ICN* 1957	*ICN* 1559	*ICN* 1959	*ICN* 1961
		2		🍷	2			2	2	2		2	2	2		2	2	2						
		⚒	T		†	⑤◆	b	†	⚒		b		†	⚒	◆	⚒	Ⓑ		h◆	⊙◆	D⊙	⊙◆	⊙◆	C⊙
	Torino Porta Nuova **610** d.	...	...	...	...	...	...	...	...	...	...	...	...	...	1040	...	...	...	...	...	...	...	...	...
	Milano Centrale **615** d.	...	...	...	...	...	...	...	...	...	...	...	...	...	|	...	...	...	1448	...	...	...	...	...
	Venezia Santa Lucia **616** d.	...	...	...	...	...	...	...	...	...	...	...	...	...	|	...	...	...	|	...	...	...	...	...
	Bologna Centrale **620** d.	...	...	...	...	...	...	...	...	...	...	...	...	...	|	...	...	...	1718	...	...	...	...	...
0	**Roma** Termini d.	1453	1526	1728	1536	1601	1626	1636	1656	...	1726	...	1736	1756	1826	1856	...	1956	2120t	2131	2131	2300	2300	2300
	Latina d.	1530	1600	|	1618	|	1700	1718	1731	...	1800	...	1818	1832	1900	1931	...	2032	2152	2207	2207	2335	|	|
	Formia-Gaeta d.	1610	1635	|	1707	|	1735	1807	1821	...	1835	...	1907	1921	1935	2021	...	2110	2226	2244	2244	0014	|	|
	Aversa d.	|	1711	|	1806	|	1811	1902	1857	...	1911	...	2006	2014	2011	2119	...	|	2310	|	|	|	|	|
216	Caserta **626** d.	1710	|	|	|	1809	|	|	|	...	|	...	|	|	|	|	...	2207	|	|	|	|	|	|
	Napoli Centrale **626** a.	...	1729	1830f	1843	...	1829	1923	1940	...	1929	...	2043	2040	2029	2140	...	2252	2350	2359	2359	|	|	|
	Napoli Centrale **638** d.	...	1753	1832f	...	...	1845	...	...	1925	1950	2023	...	...	2045	...	2120	...	...	0015	0015	|	|	|
287	Salerno **638** d.	...	1827	1900	...	...	1924	...	...	2008	2030	2106	...	...	2124	...	2203	...	...	0047	0047	|	|	|
—	Battipaglia **638** d.	...	1838	|	...	...	1938	...	...	2023	...	2123	...	...	...	...	2221	...	...	|	|	|	|	|
	Agropoli-Castellabate d.	...	...	|	...	...	|	...	...	2043	...	2147	...	...	...	...	2241	...	...	|	|	|	|	|
	Ascea d.	...	...	|	...	...	|	...	...	2107	...	2211	...	...	...	...	2303	...	...	|	|	|	|	|
	Sapri d.	...	...	|	...	...	2047	...	...	2146	...	2248	...	...	...	...	2340	...	...	|	|	|	|	|
	Maratea d.	...	...	|	...	...	2058	...	...	2155	...	...	...	...	...	...	...	...	...	|	|	|	|	|
	Belvedere Marittimo d.	...	...	|	...	...	|	...	...	2229	...	...	...	...	...	...	...	...	...	|	|	|	|	|
	Cosenza **633** d.	...	...	|	...	...	|	...	...	|	...	...	...	...	...	...	...	...	...	|	|	|	|	|
0	Paola **633** d.	...	...	2035	...	...	2147	...	...	2302	...	...	...	...	...	...	...	...	...	|	|	|	|	|
26	Cosenza **633** a.	...	...	|	...	...	|	...	...	2325	...	...	...	...	...	...	...	...	...	|	|	|	|	|
	Lamezia Terme Centrale a.	...	...	2104	...	...	2220	...	...	...	...	...	...	...	...	...	...	...	...	|	|	|	|	|
	Lamezia Terme Centrale d.	...	...	2104	...	...	2221	...	...	...	...	...	...	...	...	...	...	...	...	|	|	|	|	|
	Gioia Tauro d.	...	...	|	...	...	2304	...	...	...	...	...	...	...	...	...	...	...	...	|	|	|	|	|
	Villa S. Giovanni a.	...	...	2203	...	...	2330	...	...	...	...	...	...	...	...	...	...	...	...	0425s	0425s	0610s	0610s	0610s
	Villa S. Giovanni d.	...	...	2205	...	...	2333	...	...	...	...	...	...	...	...	...	...	...	...	|	0445s	0635s	0635s	0635s
	Reggio di Calabria Centrale a.	...	...	2221	...	...	2347	...	...	...	...	...	...	...	...	...	...	...	...	|	|	|	|	|
	Siracusa **641** a.	...	...	...	...	...	...	...	...	...	...	...	...	...	...	...	...	...	...	0936	|	1123	1123	|
	Palermo Centrale **641** a.	...	...	...	...	...	...	...	...	...	...	...	...	...	...	...	...	...	...	...	1005	...	...	1157

OR THROUGH TRAINS AND CARS SEE PAGE 319

640 REGGIO DI CALABRIA and COSENZA - NAPOLI - ROMA

For high-speed services, see Table **600**.

	ICN 788	2	*ICN* 794	*ICN* 1956	*ICN* 1954	2	2	2	*IC* 582	2	2	*IC* 510	*ICN* 1960	*ICN* 1958		2	2	2	2	2	*FA* 8340	*IC* 590	2	2
	⊙♦	⚒	⊙♦	⊙♦	X⊙	⚒	†	⚒	a	†	①–⑥	a♦	⊙♦	W⊙			⚒	†			🍷	h	⚒	⚒
Palermo Centrale **641** d.	...	...	...	...	1848	...	...	...	...	...	...	...	...	2055	...	...	...	...	...	...	...	...	...	...
Siracusa **641** d.	...	...	...	1910	|	...	...	...	...	...	...	...	2145	|	...	...	...	...	...	...	...	...	...	...
Reggio di Calabria Centrale d.	...	...	2135	|	|	...	...	...	...	...	...	...	|	|	...	...	...	...	...	...	0643	...	...	0510
Villa S. Giovanni a.	...	...	2152	2335	2335	...	...	...	...	...	...	...	|	|	...	...	...	...	...	...	0655	...	...	0525
Villa S. Giovanni d.	...	...	2155	0005	0005	...	...	...	...	...	...	...	|	|	...	...	...	...	...	...	0658	...	...	0527
Gioia Tauro d.	...	...	2237	|	|	...	...	...	...	...	...	...	|	|	...	...	...	...	...	...	|	...	...	0559
Lamezia Terme Centrale a.	...	...	0009	|	|	...	...	...	...	...	...	...	|	|	...	...	...	...	...	...	0753	...	...	0637
Lamezia Terme Centrale d.	...	...	0012	|	|	...	...	...	...	...	...	...	|	|	...	...	...	...	...	...	0756	...	...	0639
Cosenza **633** d.	...	...	|	|	|	...	...	...	...	...	...	...	|	|	...	...	...	...	...	0605	|	...	0625	|
Paola **633** d.	...	...	0052	|	|	...	...	...	...	...	...	...	|	|	...	...	...	...	...	0629	0826	...	0650	0727
Cosenza **633** a.	...	...	|	|	|	...	...	...	...	...	...	...	|	|	...	...	...	...	...	|	|	...	|	0750
Belvedere Marittimo d.	...	...	|	|	|	...	...	...	...	...	...	...	|	|	...	...	...	...	...	0655	|	...	0721	...
Maratea d.	...	...	|	|	|	...	...	...	...	...	...	...	|	|	...	...	...	...	...	0729	|	...	0803	...
Sapri d.	...	...	0153	|	|	...	...	...	...	...	0435	...	|	|	...	0540	...	...	0645	0740	|	...	0817	...
Ascea d.	...	...	|	|	|	...	...	...	...	...	0512	...	|	|	...	0617	...	...	0718	0817	|	...	...	...
Agropoli-Castellabate d.	...	...	|	|	|	...	...	...	...	...	0538	...	|	|	...	0643	...	...	0744	0843	|	...	...	...
Battipaglia **638** d.	...	...	|	|	|	...	...	...	...	...	0600	...	|	|	...	0706	...	...	0810	0910	|	...	...	...
Salerno **638** d.	...	...	0325	|	|	...	...	...	0528	...	0618	0625	0646s	0646s	...	0725	...	...	0831	0931	1002	...	...	...
Napoli Centrale **638** a.	...	...	0405	|	|	...	...	...	0605	...	0700	0705	0725s	0725s	...	0805	...	...	0910	1010	1031f	...	...	...
Napoli Centrale **626** d.	...	0404	0421	|	|	0500	0510	...	0631	0637	...	0731	0741s	0741s	...	...	0820	0830	...	...	1033f	1031	...	...
Caserta **626** d.	0407	|	|	|	|	|	|	0609	|	|	...	|	|	|	...	...	|	|	...	...	|	|	...	...
Aversa d.	|	0426	0440	|	|	0525	0528	|	0648	0659	...	0749	|	|	...	...	0838	0856	...	...	|	1049	...	...
Formia-Gaeta d.	|	0510	0518	0551s	0551s	0611	0614	0705	0722	0752	...	0822	0833s	0833s	...	...	0938	0949	...	...	|	1122	...	...
Latina d.	|	0548	0555	0632s	0632s	0656	0710	0743	0800	0842	...	0900	0912s	0912s	...	...	1028	1041	...	...	|	1200	...	...
Roma Termini a.	0610	0627	0634t	0713	0713	0734	0754	0827	0834	0924	...	0934	0951	0951	...	...	1104	1124	...	...	1135	1237t	...	...
Bologna Centrale **620** a.	...	...	1138	...	...	...	...	...	...	...	...	|	...	...	...	...	...	...	...	...	...	1641	...	...
Venezia Santa Lucia **616** a.	...	...	|	...	...	...	...	...	...	...	...	|	...	...	...	...	...	...	...	...	...	|	...	...
Milano Centrale **615** a.	...	...	1442g	...	...	...	...	...	...	...	...	|	...	...	...	...	...	...	...	...	...	1917	...	...
Torino Porta Nuova **610** a.	...	...	1640	...	...	...	...	...	...	...	...	1740	...	...	...	...	...	...	...	...	...	...	...	...

	IC 1504	2	*IC* 700	2	*FB* 8862	*IC* 1502	2	*IC* 596	2	2	*IC* 1590	*IC* 1568	2	*IC* 1506	2	2	2	*IC* 1528	*IC* 722	2	*FA* 8866	2	*IC* 522	2
	b	⚒	T		🍷	b	⚒	h	†	⚒	⑦ j♦	⑦ ♦		b	†	⚒		R	R	†	🍷	⚒	b♦	
Palermo Centrale **641** d.	...	...	...	...	...	...	...	...	...	...	...	...	...	...	...	...	...	0700	...	...	...	...	...	...
Siracusa **641** d.	...	...	...	...	...	...	...	...	...	...	...	...	...	...	...	...	...	|	0732	...	...	...	...	...
Reggio di Calabria Centrale d.	0610	0615	...	0715	0835	0810	...	...	...	...	0900	0925	...	1010	...	...	...	|	|	...	1250	...	...	...
Villa S. Giovanni a.	0626	0632	...	0730	0847	0825	...	...	...	...	0916	0938	...	1025	...	...	...	1120	1120	...	1303	...	...	...
Villa S. Giovanni d.	0629	0634	...	0732	0850	0828	...	...	...	...	0918	0941	...	1028	...	...	...	1150	1155	...	1306	...	...	...
Gioia Tauro d.	0652	0704	...	0804	0914	0852	...	...	...	...	0941	1009	...	1052	...	...	...	|	|	...	1329	...	...	...
Lamezia Terme Centrale a.	0734	0742	...	0844	0955	0935	...	...	...	...	1101	1100	...	1136	...	...	...	1253	1253	...	1407	...	...	...
Lamezia Terme Centrale d.	0737	0742	...	0846	0958	0938	...	...	...	...	1103	1103	...	1138	...	...	...	1256	1256	...	1410	...	...	...
Cosenza **633** d.	|	|	...	|	|	|	...	...	...	...	|	|	...	|	...	...	...	|	|	...	|	...	...	1325k
Paola **633** d.	0810	0827	...	0927	1025	1013	...	...	...	...	1136	1136	...	1213	...	...	1223	1330	1330	...	1438	...	...	1349
Cosenza **633** a.	|	0850	...	0950	|	|	...	...	...	...	|	|	...	|	...	...	|	|	|	...	|	...	...	|
Belvedere Marittimo d.	|	...	...	...	|	|	...	...	...	...	|	|	...	|	...	...	1249	|	|	...	|	...	...	1420
Maratea d.	0900	...	...	...	|	|	...	...	...	...	|	|	...	|	...	...	1328	|	|	...	|	...	...	1456
Sapri d.	0914	...	...	...	1112	1118	...	...	...	...	1229	1229	1300	1310	...	...	1400	1420	1420	...	1528	...	...	1507
Ascea d.	|	...	...	...	|	|	...	...	...	...	1259	1259	1342	1341	...	...	1441	|	|	...	|	...	...	1545
Agropoli-Castellabate d.	|	...	...	...	|	1203	...	...	...	...	|	|	1411	1404	...	...	1512	|	|	...	|	...	...	1615
Battipaglia **638** d.	1014	...	1127	...	1214	1222	...	...	...	...	|	|	1440	1424	...	...	1540	|	|	...	|	...	...	1644
Salerno **638** d.	1037	...	1140	...	1229	1237	...	...	...	...	1347	1347	1501	1437	...	...	1601	1537	1537	...	1644	...	...	1702
Napoli Centrale **638** a.	1115	...	1215	...	1305	1315	...	...	...	...	1428	1428	1540	1510	...	...	1640	1615	1615	...	1717	...	...	1740
Napoli Centrale **626** d.	1131	...	1231	...	1319	1331	1325	1431	1417	1420	1452	1452	...	1531	1540	1620	...	1631	1631	1617	1736	1720	1731	...
Caserta **626** d.	|	...	|	...	|	|	|	|	|	|	|	|	...	|	|	|	...	|	|	|	|	|	|	...
Aversa d.	1149	...	1249	...	|	1349	1345	1449	1445	1438	1510	1510	...	1549	1559	1638	...	1649	1649	1645	|	1738	1753	...
Formia-Gaeta d.	1222	...	1322	...	|	1422	1443	1522	1551	1538	1548	1548	...	1622	1652	1738	...	1722	1722	1752	|	1838	1828	...
Latina d.	1300	...	1400	...	|	1500	1528	1600	1641	1628	1625	1625	...	1700	1742	1828	...	1800	1800	1842	|	1937	1903	...
Roma Termini a.	1334	...	1434	...	1504	1534	1611	1637t	1724	1712	1705t	1705t	...	1734	1824	1904	...	1834	1834	1924	1930	2024	1941o	...
Bologna Centrale **620** a.	...	...	...	...	...	...	...	2038	...	...	2130	2130	...	...	...	...	...	...	...	...	...	...	...	...
Venezia Santa Lucia **616** a.	...	...	...	...	...	...	...	|	...	...	|	|	...	...	...	...	...	...	...	...	...	...	...	...
Milano Centrale **615** a.	...	...	...	...	...	...	...	2320	...	...	0010	0010	...	...	...	...	...	...	...	...	...	...	...	...
Torino Porta Nuova **610** a.	...	...	...	...	...	...	...	...	...	...	...	...	...	...	...	...	...	...	...	...	...	...	...	...

	2	*FA* 8344	*IC* 702	2	*IC* 1524	*IC* 730	*IC* 1560	*IC* 1570		*IC* 710	2	*ICN* 798	*ICN* 796		2		2	2	*ICN* 1552	*ICN* 1964	2			2
	⚒	🍷	T		R	R	bv	w		⑦♦	†	⊙♦	♦		⚒				⊙♦	B⊙	⚒			
Palermo Centrale **641** d.	...	...	...	...	...	1000	...	...	...	...	...	...	...	...	...	...	...	...	...	1235	...	...	...	...
Siracusa **641** d.	...	...	...	...	1020	|	...	...	...	...	...	...	...	...	...	...	...	...	1335	|	...	...	...	...
Reggio di Calabria Centrale d.	1215	1520	...	...	|	|	1510	1510	...	...	...	...	...	...	1618	...	1715	...	|	|	...	...	...	1815
Villa S. Giovanni a.	1230	1534	...	...	1420	1420	1525	1525	...	...	...	...	...	...	1633	...	1730	...	1815	1815	...	...	...	1834
Villa S. Giovanni d.	1232	1537	...	...	1450	1450	1528	1528	...	...	...	...	...	...	1635	...	1732	...	1845	1845	...	...	...	1836
Gioia Tauro d.	1304	|	...	...	1518	1518	1552	1552	...	...	...	...	...	...	1707	...	1804	...	1921	1921	...	...	...	1906
Lamezia Terme Centrale a.	1342	1635	...	...	1607	1607	1645	1643	...	...	...	...	...	...	1745	...	1842	...	2007	2007	...	...	...	1944
Lamezia Terme Centrale d.	1344	1638	...	...	1609	1609	1646	1646	...	...	...	...	...	...	1747	...	1844	...	2010	2010	...	...	...	1946
Cosenza **633** d.	|	|	...	1502	|	|	|	|	...	...	...	...	...	...	|	...	|	1857	|	|	2020	...	...	|
Paola **633** d.	1427	1708	...	1528	1639	1639	1717	1718	...	...	1729	...	...	...	1827	...	1915	1921	2047	2047	2050	...	...	2050
Cosenza **633** a.	1450	|	...	|	|	|	|	|	...	...	|	...	...	...	1850	...	...	|	|	|	|	...	...	2113
Belvedere Marittimo d.	...	|	...	1556	|	|	|	|	...	...	1756	...	...	...	...	...	...	1947	|	|	2119	...	...	...
Maratea d.	...	|	...	1634	|	|	1807	1802	...	...	1833	...	...	...	...	...	...	2020	2143	2143	2201	...	...	...
Sapri d.	...	|	...	1645	1729	1729	1816	1813	...	...	1845	...	...	...	...	...	...	2031	2156	2156	2211	...	...	...
Ascea d.	...	|	...	1720	|	|	|	|	...	...	1919	...	...	...	...	...	...	2105	2228	2226	...	...	...	...
Agropoli-Castellabate d.	...	|	...	1747	|	|	1904	1859	...	...	1943	...	...	...	...	...	...	2129	2254	2254	...	...	...	...
Battipaglia **638** d.	...	|	1715	1812	|	|	1924	1923	...	...	2009	...	...	...	...	...	...	2154	2313	2315	...	...	...	...
Salerno **638** d.	...	1848	1730	1831	1839	1839	1937	1937	...	...	2031	2038	2052	...	...	...	...	2212	2333	2333	...	...	...	...
Napoli Centrale **638** a.	...	1917f	1805	1910	1915	1915	2012	2012	...	...	2110	2115	2128	...	...	...	...	2255	|	|	...	...	...	...
Napoli Centrale **626** d.	...	1919f	1831	...	1931	1931	2031	2031	...	...	...	2131	2146	...	...	...	...	...	|	|	...	...	...	...
Caserta **626** d.	...	|	|	...	|	|	|	|	...	2053	...	|	|	...	...	...	...	...	|	|	...	...	...	...
Aversa d.	...	|	1849	...	1949	1949	2049	2049	...	|	...	|	2205	...	...	...	...	...	|	|	...	...	...	...
Formia-Gaeta d.	...	|	1922	...	2028	2028	2122	2122	...	|	...	|	2243	...	...	...	...	...	|	|	...	...	...	...
Latina d.	...	|	2000	...	2105	2105	2200	2200	...	|	...	|	2321	...	...	...	...	...	|	|	...	...	...	...
Roma Termini a.	...	2023	2034	...	2138	2138	2234	2234	...	2311	...	2349t	0011o	...	...	...	...	...	|	|	...	...	...	...
Bologna Centrale **620** a.	...	...	...	...	...	...	...	...	...	...	...	|	|	...	...	...	...	...	|	|	...	...	...	...
Venezia Santa Lucia **616** a.	...	...	...	...	...	...	...	...	...	...	...	|	|	...	...	...	...	...	|	|	...	...	...	...
Milano Centrale **615** a.	...	...	...	...	...	...	...	...	...	...	...	0712g	|	...	...	...	...	...	1050	1050	...	...	...	...
Torino Porta Nuova **610** a.	...	...	...	...	...	...	...	...	...	...	...	0922	0810	...	...	...	...	...	...	...	...	...	...	...

FOR THROUGH TRAINS AND CARS SEE PAGE 319

VILLA SAN GIOVANNI - MESSINA - SIRACUSA and PALERMO 641

km				*ICN* **1593**	*ICN* **1957**						*ICN* **1961**	*ICN* **1959**	*ICN* **1559**							*ICN* **1963**	*ICN* **1967**				*IC* **721**
		2 ⚒	2 ⚒	⊙♦	D⊙	2 †	2 ⚒	2 ⚒	2 †	2 ⚒	C⊙	⊙♦	⊙♦	2	2 Z	2 ⚒	2 ⚒	2 ⚒	2 Ⓐ	⊙♦	A⊙	2 ⚒	2	2	Rp
0	**Villa S. Giovanni** ▲ d.	...	...	0425s	0445s	...	...	...	...	...	0635s	0635s	0635s	...	...	...	...	...	...	1105s	1105s	...	...	...	1430
9	**Messina** Centrale ▲ a.	...	...	0610s	0610s	...	...	...	...	...	0805s	0805s	0805s	...	...	...	...	...	...	1245s	1245s	...	...	...	1535
9	**Messina** Centrale d.	0450	0513	0640s	0655s	0652	0652	0726	0749	0753	0837s	0840s	0840s	0918	...	1040	1115	1220	1230	│	│	1318	1435	1440	1600
	Taormina-Giardini d.	│	0552	0731s	│	0756	0756	0806	│	│	│	0932s	0932s	1001	...	│	1154	1319	│	1354s	│	1405	1539	│	1642
	Giarre-Riposto d.	│	0610	0748s	│	0814	0823	0820	│	│	│	0948s	0948s	1016	...	│	1216	1339	│	1408s	│	1422	1603	│	1658
	Catania Centrale a.	│	0630	0817s	│	0852	0901	0840	│	│	│	1011s	1011s	1036	...	│	1236	1411	│	1432s	│	1443	1633	│	1725
	Catania Centrale d.	│	0632	│	│	...	...	0850	│	│	│	1014s	1014s	...	1045	│	1238	...	│	│	│	1456	...	│	1728
	Augusta d.	│	0730	0913s	│	...	...	0933	│	│	│	1103s	1103s	...	1144	│	1320	...	│	1524s	│	1547	...	│	1814
	Siracusa a.	│	0755	0936	│	...	...	0952	│	│	│	1123	1123	...	1208	│	1345	...	│	1548	│	1610	...	│	1833
45	Milazzo d.	0508	...	...	0721s	...	...	...	0808	0813	0859s	...	...	...	...	1058	...	...	1249	...	1341s	...	...	1458	...
174	Cefalù d.	0658	...	...	0904s	...	...	...	1005	1005	1056s	...	...	...	...	1239	...	...	1438	...	1551s	...	...	1638	...
204	Termini Imerese **645 647** d.	0720	...	...	0923s	...	...	...	1024	1024	1118s	...	...	...	...	1300	...	...	1500	...	1614s	...	...	1700	...
241	**Palermo** Centrale **645 647** a.	0747	...	...	1005	...	...	...	1058	1058	1157	...	...	...	...	1329	...	...	1529	...	1655	...	...	1729	...

	IC **1523**						*IC* **729**	*IC* **1527**		
	Rp	2	2	2 ⚒	2 Z	2 ⚒	Ra	Ra	2	2
Villa S. Giovanni ▲ d.	1430	...	...	...	...	...	1825	1825	...	...
Messina Centrale ▲ a.	1535	...	...	...	...	...	1935	1935	...	...
Messina Centrale d.	1610	1714	1715	1745	...	1927	2000	2010	2018	2120
Taormina-Giardini d.	│	│	1758	1850	...	2031	│	2057	2123	2228
Giarre-Riposto d.	│	│	1813	1909	...	2052	│	2114	2146	2251
Catania Centrale a.	│	│	1832	1934	...	2117	│	2137	2220	2327
Catania Centrale d.	│	│	1834	...	2042	...	│	2140	...	...
Augusta d.	│	│	1931	...	2126	...	│	2225	...	...
Siracusa a.	│	│	1958	...	2145	...	│	2250	...	...
Milazzo d.	1632	1731	...	...	...	...	2022	...	...	...
Cefalù d.	1836	1913	...	...	...	...	2214	...	...	...
Termini Imerese **645 647** d.	1857	1933	...	...	...	...	2238	...	...	...
Palermo Centrale **645 647** a.	1925	2002	...	...	...	...	2305	...	...	...

								IC **722**	*IC* **1528**	
	2 ⚒	2 Ⓐ	2 ⚒	2	2 Z	2 ⚒	2 ⚒	R	R	2
Palermo C **645 647** d.	...	...	0508	...	...	0616	...	...	0700	0833
Termini Imerese **645 647** d.	...	...	0534	...	...	0645	...	...	0728	0859
Cefalù d.	...	...	0555	...	...	0705	...	...	0751	0919
Milazzo d.	...	...	0739	...	...	0846	...	...	0934	1055
Siracusa d.	...	0512	│	...	0555	│	0640	0732	│	│
Augusta d.	...	0532	│	...	0616	│	0706	0753	│	│
Catania Centrale a.	...	0615	│	...	0713	│	0801	0838	│	│
Catania Centrale d.	0501	0617	│	0626	...	│	0803	0841	│	│
Giarre-Riposto d.	0530	0640	│	0653	...	│	0827	0904	│	│
Taormina-Giardini d.	0552	0659	│	0715	...	│	0849	0918	│	│
Messina Centrale a.	0655	0751	0800	0833	...	0910	0942	0953	0955	1115
Messina Centrale ▲ d.	...	...	...	...	...	...	...	1010	1010	...
Villa S. Giovanni ▲ a.	...	...	...	...	...	...	...	1120	1120	...

km				*IC* **1524**	*IC* **730**			*ICN* **1964**	*ICN* **1552**									*ICN* **1956**	*ICN* **1954**				*ICN* **1960**	*ICN* **1958**
		2	2	R	R	2 ⚒	2 ⚒	B⊙	⊙♦	2 ⚒	2	2 Z	2	2 ⚒	2 ⚒	2	2	⊙♦	X⊙	2 ⚒	2 ⚒	2	⊙♦	W⊙
	Palermo Centrale **645 647** d.	...	...	...	1000	...	...	1235	...	...	1427	...	...	1633	...	...	1833	...	1848	...	...	2033	...	2055
	Termini Imerese **645 647** d.	...	...	...	1035	...	...	1305u	...	...	1458	...	...	1658	...	...	1858	...	1917u	...	...	2058	...	2122u
	Cefalù d.	...	...	...	1059	...	...	1335u	...	...	1522	...	...	1716	...	...	1919	...	1936u	...	...	2117	...	2143u
	Milazzo d.	...	...	...	1236	...	...	1558u	...	...	1704	...	...	1900	...	...	2053	...	2125u	...	...	2259	...	2350u
0	**Siracusa** d.	0844	...	1020	│	...	1253	│	1335	1406	│	1605	...	│	1712	1820	│	1910	│	1930	...	│	2145	│
31	Augusta d.	0912	...	1041	│	...	1321	│	1400	1426	│	1624	...	│	1733	1841	│	1932	│	1954	...	│	2206	│
87	**Catania** Centrale a.	1011	...	1130	│	...	1408	│	1451	1513	│	1711		│	1826	1925	│	2019	│	2040	...	│	2251	│
87	**Catania** Centrale d.	1015	1104	1133	│	1221	1410	│	1454	1523	│	...	1721	│	1836	1927	│	2026	│	...	2051	│	2254	│
117	Giarre-Riposto d.	1037	1131	1157	│	1253	1432	│	1522	1547	│	...	1743	│	1900	1948	│	2051	│	...	2116	│	2318	│
135	Taormina-Giardini d.	1103	1154	1212	│	1319	1448	│	1539	1606	│	...	1758	│	1919	2000	│	2107	│	...	2135	│	2333	│
182	**Messina** Centrale a.	1200	1253	1255	1258	1430	1541	1620	1625	1652	1726	...	1840	1920	2000	2045	2113	2150	2155	...	2225	2320	0015	0020
182	**Messina** Centrale ▲ d.	...	...	1310	1310	...	...	1640	1640	...	...	...	...	...	...	...	...	2210	2210	...	...	...	0035	0035
191	**Villa S. Giovanni** ▲ a.	...	...	1420	1420	...	...	1815	1815	...	...	...	...	...	...	...	...	2335	2335	...	...	...	...	...

♦ – **NOTES FOR TABLES 640 / 641**

501 – [12] Sestri Levante - Napoli.
510 – [12] Salerno - Torino.
511 – [12] Torino - Salerno.
522 – [12] Napoli - Sestri Levante.
705 – [12] Roma - Taranto.
710 – [12] Taranto - Roma.
788 – ⑦ from Lecce : 🛏 1, 2 cl., ▬ 2 cl. (4 berth) and [2] Lecce - Roma.
789 – ⑤ from Roma : 🛏 1, 2 cl., ▬ 2 cl. (4 berth) and [2] Roma - Lecce.
793 – ①–④ : 🛏 1, 2 cl., ▬ 2 cl. (4 berth) and [2] Torino - Milano - Napoli - Salerno.
794 – 🛏 1, 2 cl., ▬ 2 cl. (4 berth) and [2] Reggio di Calabria - Milano - Torino.
795 – 🛏 1, 2 cl., ▬ 2 cl. (4 berth) and [2] Torino - Milano - Reggio di Calabria.
796 – Not June 29, 30, July 20 from Salerno : 🛏 1, 2 cl., ▬ 2 cl. (4 berth) and [2] Salerno - Napoli - Torino. Train **1596** on ① from Salerno.
797 – 🛏 1, 2 cl., ▬ 2 cl. (4 berth) and [2] Torino - Milano - Napoli - Salerno.
798 – 🛏 1, 2 cl., ▬ 2 cl. (4 berth) and [2] Salerno - Napoli - Torino.
799 – 🛏 1, 2 cl., ▬ 2 cl. (4 berth) and [2] Torino - Napoli - Salerno. Train **35299** Aug. 15 – 29.
1552 – 🛏 1,2 cl., 🛏 1,2 cl. (T2) and ▬ 2 cl. (4 berth) Siracusa - Genova - Milano (Train **1556** on ①); 🛏 1,2 cl. and ▬ 2 cl. (4 berth) Palermo (**1964**) - Messina - Milano.
1559 – ① from Roma : 🛏 1,2 cl. and ▬ 2 cl. (4 berth) Roma - Siracusa; 🛏 1,2 cl. and ▬ 2 cl. (4 berth) Roma - Messina (**1961**) - Palermo.
1568 – See train **1590.**
1575 – Not June 15, 16, July 6, 7 : 🛏 1, 2 cl., ▬ 2 cl. (4 berth) and [2] Torino - Milano - Reggio di Calabria. Train **1597** on ① from Torino and Aug. 3 – 31.
1577 – [12] Milano - Firenze - Napoli.
1584 – See train **1552**.
1589 – [12] Milano - Reggio di Calabria. Train **1591** until Sept. 21.
1590 – [12] Reggio di Calabria - Milano. Train **1568** from Sept. 22.
1593 – 🛏 1,2 cl. and ▬ 2 cl. (4 berth) Roma - Siracusa; 🛏 1,2 cl. and ▬ 2 cl. (4 berth) Roma - Messina (**1957**) - Palermo.
1956 – 🛏 1,2 cl. and ▬ 2 cl. (4 berth) Siracusa - Roma; 🛏 1,2 cl. and ▬ 2 cl. (4 berth) Palermo (**1954**) - Messina - Roma.
1959 – ②–⑦ from Roma : 🛏: 1,2 cl. and ▬ 2 cl. (4 berth) Roma - Siracusa; 🛏 1,2 cl. and ▬ 2 cl. (4 berth) Roma - Messina (**1961**) - Palermo.
1960 – 🛏 1,2 cl. and ▬ 2 cl. (4 berth) Siracusa - Roma; 🛏 1,2 cl. and ▬ 2 cl. (4 berth) Palermo (**1958**) - Messina - Roma.
1963 – 🛏 1,2 cl., 🛏 1,2 cl. (T2) and ▬ 2 cl. (4 berth) Milano - Genova - Siracusa; 🛏 1,2 cl. and ▬ 2 cl. (4 berth) Milano - Messina (**1967**) - Palermo.

A – 🛏 1,2 cl. and ▬ 2 cl. (4 berth) Milano (**1963**) - Genova - Messina - Palermo.
B – 🛏 1,2 cl. and ▬ 2 cl. (4 berth) Palermo - Messina (**1552**) - Genova - Milano.
C – 🛏 1,2 cl. and ▬ 2 cl. (4 berth) Roma (**1559 / 1959**) - Messina - Palermo.
D – 🛏 1,2 cl. and ▬ 2 cl. (4 berth) Roma (**1593**) - Messina - Palermo.
R – [12] Roma - Siracusa and v.v. ; [12] Roma - Palermo and v.v.
T – [12] Taranto - Napoli - Roma and v.v.
W – 🛏 1,2 cl. and ▬ 2 cl. (4 berth) Palermo - Messina (**1960**) - Roma.
X – 🛏 1,2 cl. and ▬ 2 cl. (4 berth) Palermo - Messina (**1956**) - Roma.
Z – To / From Palermo Table **645**.

a – Not June 30.
b – Not June 29, 30.
c – June 15 - Sept. 21.
d – Sept. 28 - Dec. 14.
f – Napoli **Afragola**.
g – Milano **Porta Garibaldi**.
h – Not June 15, 16, 30, July 6, 7.
j – Not June 16, 30, July 7.
k – Ⓒ only.
o – Roma **Ostiense**.
p – Not June 30, July 21.
q – June 9 - July 9.
r – July 10 - Dec. 14.
s – Stops to set down only.
t – Roma **Tiburtina**.
u – Stops to pick up only.
v – June 9 - Sept. 15.
w – Sept. 16 - Dec. 14.

▲ – Through trains are conveyed by ⛴ Villa S. Giovanni - Messina and v.v. See Table **2695** for other available sailings.

Ferrovia Circumetnea

CATANIA - RANDAZZO - RIPOSTO 644

Winter service valid from September 10, 2018. No service on †.

km		⚒	⚒	⚒	⚒	⚒	⚒	⚒	⚒	⚒	⚒	⚒	⚒	Ⓐ	⚒
0	**Catania** ♥ d.	...	0536	0641	0801	0943	1135	1235	1348	1512	1642	1732	1844	1940	2008
20	Paternò d.	...	0608	0718	0835	1016	1212	1311	1423	1545	1716	1805	1919	2013	2041
36	Adrano N. d.	...	0636	0755	0902	1040	1240	1341	1452	1612	1745	1833	1946	2042	...
52	Bronte d.	...	0701	0818	0924	1100	1303	1404	1512	1635	1810	1858	2009	...	...
71	Randazzo a.	...	0732	0846	0950	1126	1331	1431	1537	1701	1836	1927	2037	...	...
71	Randazzo d.	0632	0750	...	0955	...	1333	...	...	1715	...	...	...	...	...
109	Giarre a.	0746	0854	...	1059	...	1439	...	...	1819	...	...	...	...	...
111	**Riposto** a.	0750	0858	...	1103	...	1443	...	...	1823	...	...	...	...	...

	⚒	⚒	⚒	⚒	⚒	⚒	⚒	⚒	⚒	⚒	⚒	⚒	Ⓐ	⑥
Riposto d.	...	...	...	0636	0915	1115	...	1252	1350	1455	...	...	...	...
Giarre d.	...	...	...	0641	0919	1120	...	1257	1357	1500	...	...	...	...
Randazzo a.	...	...	...	0744	1024	1225	...	1403	1508	1603	...	...	...	...
Randazzo d.	0525	0603	0701	0816	1033	1233	1335	1443	...	...	1742	1851	...	...
Bronte d.	0550	0629	0730	0848	1101	1303	1403	1513	...	...	1810	1920	...	...
Adrano N. d.	0610	0651	0753	0916	1125	1326	1426	1537	...	...	1834	1946	2050	...
Paternò d.	0638	0719	0821	0939	1153	1354	1455	1600	...	...	1902	2014	2119	2050
Catania ♥ a.	0711	0752	0853	1012	1227	1427	1528	1632	...	...	1935	2048	2151	2124

♥ – Catania Borgo station.

Metropolitana di Catania operates a metro service Nesima - San Nullo - Milo - Borgo ♥ - Giuffrida - Galatea - Giovanni XXIII - Stesicoro (- Galatea - Porto) and v.v. *(8.8 km). The Galatea - Porto section is currently closed for maintenance.* Weekdays only: **From Nesima** every 10 minutes 0640 – 1500, every 15 minutes 1515 - 2045; **from Stesicoro** every 10 minutes 0700 - 1510, every 15 mimutes 1525 - 2110.

645 PALERMO and AGRIGENTO - CATANIA

2nd class only except where shown

km																									
		⚒	⚒	⚒		⚒			⚒	⚒	⚒	⚒	⚒	⚒	⚒						†	⚒	⚒		⚒
							A													A					
0	**Palermo** Centrale .... **641 647** d.	...	...	...	...	...	0731	...	0931	...	...	1331	...	...	...	...	1531	...	...	1731	...	...	...	...	1931
37	Termini Imerese ..... **641 647** d.	...	...	...	...	...	0756	...	0956	...	...	1356	...	...	...	...	1556	...	...	1756	...	...	...	...	1956
70	Roccapalumba-Alia .... **647** d.	...	...	0620	...	0730	|	...	|	...	...	|	...	1519	1553	...	|	...	...	|	...	...	1954	...	|
	Agrigento Centrale ... **647** d.	...	...	|	...	|	|	...	|	...	1250	|	1350	|	|	...	|	...	...	|	1910	1912	|	...	|
	Aragona-Caldare .... **647** d.	...	...	|	...	|	|	...	|	...	1306	|	1406	|	|	...	|	...	...	|	1928	1928	|	...	|
	Canicattì .... **648** d.	...	...	|	...	|	|	...	|	...	1347	|	1443	|	|	...	|	...	...	|	2007	2007	|	...	|
	Caltanissetta Xirbi .... a.	...	...	0718	...	0821	0900	...	1100	...	|	1500	|	1616	1642	...	1700	...	...	1900	|	|	2048	...	2100
	Caltanissetta C .... **648** d.	0530	0614	0737	0800	0838	|	...	|	1357	1415	|	1512	1634	1705	...	|	1757	...	|	2036	2035	2105	...	|
127	Caltanissetta Xirbi .... d.	0539	0627	...	0808	...	0901	...	1101	1406	...	1501	...	...	...	...	1701	1805	...	1901	...	2043	...	...	2101
154	Enna .... d.	0606	0650	...	0836	...	0924	...	1124	1438	...	1524	...	...	...	...	1724	1838	...	1924	...	...	...	...	2124
243	**Catania** Centrale .... a.	0733	0755	...	1005	...	1030	...	1230	1602	...	1630	...	...	...	...	1831	2009	...	2030	...	...	...	...	2230

km																									
		⚒	⚒	⚒	⚒				⚒	⚒	⚒	⚒		⚒			⚒	⚒	⚒				†	⚒	⚒
						A														A					
	Catania Centrale .... d.	...	...	0500	...	0723	...	0845	0923	...	...	1329	...	1439	1523	...	...	...	1645	1728	...	...	1842	1847	1932
	Enna .... d.	...	...	0606	...	0837	...	1010	1037	...	...	1437	...	1613	1637	...	...	...	1811	1837	...	...	2012	2013	2055
0	Caltanissetta Xirbi .... a.	...	...	0626	...	0900	...	1033	1100	...	...	1500	...	1635	1700	...	...	...	1834	1900	...	...	2040	2040	2124
6	Caltanissetta C .... **648** d.	0502	0558	|	0645	|	...	1042	|	1256	1345	|	...	1645	|	...	1727	1746	1842	|	...	1935	2055	2054	2132
	Caltanissetta Xirbi .... d.	0517	|	0627	|	0901	...	...	1101	1311	1404	1501	...	...	1701	...	|	1822	...	1901	...	|	...	...	...
35	Canicattì .... **648** d.	|	0635	|	0722	|	...	...	|	|	|	|	...	...	|	...	1806	|	...	|	...	2015	...	...	...
65	Aragona-Caldare .... **647** d.	|	0705	|	0755	|	...	...	|	|	|	|	...	...	|	...	1843	|	...	|	...	2052	...	...	...
78	**Agrigento** Centrale ... **647** a.	|	0730	|	0812	|	...	...	|	|	|	|	...	...	|	...	1900	|	...	|	...	2109	...	...	...
	Roccapalumba-Alia .... **647** d.	0609	...	|	...	|	...	...	|	1405	1505	|	...	...	|	...	...	1904	...	|	...	...	...	...	...
	Termini Imerese ..... **641 647** d.	...	...	0732	...	1005	...	...	1205	...	...	1604	...	...	1805	...	...	...	...	2005	...	...	...	...	...
	Palermo Centrale .... **641 647** a.	...	...	0755	...	1029	...	...	1229	...	...	1629	...	...	1829	...	...	...	...	2029	...	...	...	...	...

A – To / from Siracusa Table **641**.

646 PALERMO - TRAPANI

2nd class only

km																									
		⚒	⚒	⚒	⚒	†		⚒	b	⚒	b	†	b	⚒	b	†	⚒	⚒	⚒	b		b		b	
0	**Palermo** Centrale .... d.	...	...	...	...	...	...	...	0605	...	0705	...	1005	...	1105	...	...	...	...	1605	...	1805	...	2005	...
	Fiera .... d.	...	...	...	...	...	...	...	|	...	|	...	|	...	|	...	...	...	...	|	...	|	...	|	...
32	Piraineto .... d.	...	...	...	...	...	...	0646	0716	...	0816	0911	1116	1125	1216	1221	...	...	...	1716	1717	1716	1925	2116	2130
73	Castellammare del Golfo ..... d.	...	...	...	...	...	...	0725	...	...	...	0951	...	1205	...	1303	...	...	...	...	1758	...	2013	...	2209
79	Alcamo Diramazione .... d.	...	...	...	...	...	...	0734	...	...	...	0958	...	1212	...	1310	...	1458	...	...	1806	...	2027	...	2216
121	Castelvetrano .... d.	0520	0609	0629	0725	0830	...	0811	...	0942	...	1038	...	1251	...	1350	1403	1549	1714	...	1846	...	2105	...	2253
144	Mazara del Vallo .... d.	0540	0631	0654	0745	0851	...	0830	...	1005	...	1057	...	1320	...	...	1422	1609	1736	...	1906	...	2125	...	...
165	Marsala .... d.	0621	0716	0722	0805	0909	...	0856	...	1025	...	1015	...	1341	...	...	1446	1630	1801	...	1925	...	2145	...	...
196	**Trapani** .... a.	0635	0733	0752	0846	0938	...	0919	...	1055	...	1144	...	1421	...	...	1523	1658	1831	...	1952	...	2219	...	...

km																									
		⚒	⚒	⚒	†	⚒	†	⚒	c	⚒	†	c	⚒	⚒	⚒		⚒	c		c	Ⓐz		c	⚒	
0	**Trapani** .... d.	...	...	0555	0555	...	...	0646	...	0804	0830	...	1200	1240	1338	...	1439	...	1601	...	1728	1834	...	1957	2045
	Marsala .... d.	...	...	0623	0623	...	...	0701	...	0836	0910	...	1234	1314	1411	...	1519	...	1631	...	1800	1902	...	2028	2117
	Mazara del Vallo .... d.	...	...	0653	0653	...	...	0746	...	0859	0935	...	1253	1340	1441	...	1542	...	1650	...	1820	1926	...	2053	2147
	Castelvetrano .... d.	0500	...	0713	0714	...	...	0812	...	0922	1000	...	1315	1402	1502	1512	1610	...	1710	...	1841	1947	...	2126	2210
47	Alcamo Diramazione .... d.	0542	...	...	0752	...	...	0852	...	...	1048	...	...	1445	...	1553	...	...	1807	...	...	2026	...	...	...
53	Castellammare del Golfo ..... d.	0550	...	...	0759	...	...	0859	...	...	1056	...	...	...	...	1600	...	...	1816	...	...	2035	...	...	...
94	Piraineto .... d.	0632	0644	...	0841	0846	0856	0940	0946	...	1136	1146	...	...	...	1639	...	1646	1902	1946	...	2120	2146	...	...
	Fiera .... a.	...	|	...	...	|	|	...	|	...	...	|	...	...	...	...	...	|	...	|	...	...	|	...	...
126	**Palermo** Centrale .... a.	...	0753	...	...	0953	0947	...	1053	...	...	1253	...	...	...	...	...	1753	...	2053	...	...	2153	...	...

b – Arrives 10 – 14 minutes earlier on †.
c – Departs 10 minutes later on †.
z – Not days before holidays.

647 PALERMO - AGRIGENTO

2nd class only

See also Table **645**.

km		⚒	⚒	a	⚒	Ⓐa			Ⓐ	⚒			
0	**Palermo** Centrale ... d.	0542	0743	0843	1143	1243	1343	1443	1543	1643	1743	1843	2043
37	Termini Imerese ...... d.	0610	0812	0912	1212	1312	1412	1512	1612	1712	1812	1911	2112
70	Roccapalumba-Alia . d.	0640	0841	0945	1241	1341	1443	1544	1643	1744	1843	1944	2139
125	Aragona-Caldare ..... d.	0732	0932	1032	1339	1432	1532	1632	1732	1832	1932	2032	2222
139	**Agrigento** Centrale .. a.	0747	0947	1047	1347	1447	1547	1647	1747	1847	1947	2047	2238

	⚒	⚒	⚒			Ⓐb	⚒	⚒	Ⓐ			⚒
Agrigento Centrale . d.	0445	0522	0619	0818	1018	1218	1315	1415	1515	1715	1815	2015
Aragona-Caldare .... d.	0459	0536	0633	0832	1032	1232	1332	1432	1532	1732	1832	2029
Roccapalumba-Alia .. d.	0543	0618	0722	0917	1117	1317	1420	1516	1620	1820	1915	2127
Termini Imerese ...... d.	0613	0651	0748	0949	1149	1349	1449	1549	1649	1849	1949	2151
Palermo Centrale .... a.	0642	0717	0821	1017	1217	1417	1517	1617	1717	1917	2017	2219

a – Additional trip: 1043Ⓐ.
b – Additional trips: 0715Ⓐ, 1615†.

648 SIRACUSA - GELA - CALTANISSETTA

2nd class only

km		⚒	⚒	Ⓐ	⚒	⚒	⚒	⚒	⚒	⚒
			z							
0	**Siracusa** .... d.	...	...	0536	1030	...	1410	1535	1741	2019
62	Pozzallo .... d.	...	...	0654	1135	...	1527	1653	1850	2133
92	Modica .... d.	0531	0734	0749	1211	1344	1601	1733	1926	2209
112	Ragusa .... d.	0553	0801	0822	1233	1406	1627	1800	1955	...
153	Vittoria .... d.	0633	0846	0902	1321	1444	1718	1842	...	...
183	**Gela** .... d.	0657	0910	0931	1350	1507	1745	...	...	...
218	Licata .... d.	0725	0937	...	...	1534	...	...	...	...
264	Canicattì .... **645** d.	0806	1018	...	...	1615	...	...	...	...
293	**Caltanissetta** Centrale .. **645** a.	0841	1044	...	...	1646	...	...	...	...

	⚒	⚒	⚒	⚒	⚒	⚒	⚒	⚒	Ⓐ
									z
Caltanissetta Centrale **645** d.	...	...	0518	...	...	...	1516	...	1916
Canicattì .... **645** d.	...	...	0545	...	...	...	1541	...	1942
Licata .... d.	...	...	0623	...	...	...	1620	...	2021
Gela .... d.	...	...	0658	...	1250	1513	1650	1805	2049
Vittoria .... d.	...	...	0721	...	1320	1542	1719	1843	2114
Ragusa .... d.	...	...	0800	...	1407	1626	1759	1930	2157
Modica .... d.	0503	0557	0823	0834	1432	1647	1820	1954	2220
Pozzallo .... d.	0537	0632	...	0906	1506	1720	...	2025	...
Siracusa .... a.	0650	0740	...	1012	1618	1836	...	2130	...

z – Not days before holidays.

MALTA

Frequent bus services throughout Malta and Gozo are operated by Malta Public Transport www.publictransport.com.mt. Travellers will also find useful information on the unofficial website www maltabybus.com.

649 PRINCIPAL BUS SERVICES

Routes from Valletta: **X4** Airport - Hal Far, **1** L'Isla (Senglea), **2/4** Birgu (Vittoriosa), **3** Birgu - Smart City - Rinella - Kalkara, **13-15** Sliema - San Giljan (St Julian's), **13** Bahar ic-Caghaq, **31/45/4** Mosta - Bugibba (**45** via Qawra seafront), **31/43/45** Naxxar, **41/42** Mosta - St Paul's Bay - Mellieha - Ghadira - Cirkewwa (for Gozo ferry), **44** Ghajn Tuffieha (Golden Bay), **49** Armier Bay (summer) **51-53** Rabat / Mdina, **52/56** Dingli, **61** Zebbug, **62** Siggiewi, **71/73** Zurrieq, **72** Qrendi, **74** Hagar Qim - Blue Grotto, **80/82/X4** Birzebbuga, **81/85** Marsaxlokk, **91-93** Marsaskala, **94** Xghajra.

Other routes: **X1** Airport - Cirkewwa, **X2** Airport - Sliema, **X3** Airport - Rabat - Bugibba, **186** Bugibba - Ta' Qali - Rabat, **202** Sliema - Naxxar - Mosta - Rabat, **203** Sliema - Naxxar - Mosta - Bugibba **212** Sliema - San Giljan - Bugibba, **221** Bugibba - Mellieha - Cirkewwa, **222** Sliema - St Paul's Bay - Mellieha - Cirkewwa, **223** Bugibba - Ghajn Tuffieha, **225** Sliema - St Paul's Bay - Ghajn Tuffieha

Gozo: routes from Rabat (Victoria): **301/303** Mgarr (for Cirkewwa ferry), **302** Ramla, **305** Sannat, **306/330** Xlendi, **307** Xaghra, **308** Ta' Pinu - Ghasri, **309** Zebbug, **310** Marsalforn, **311** Dwejra

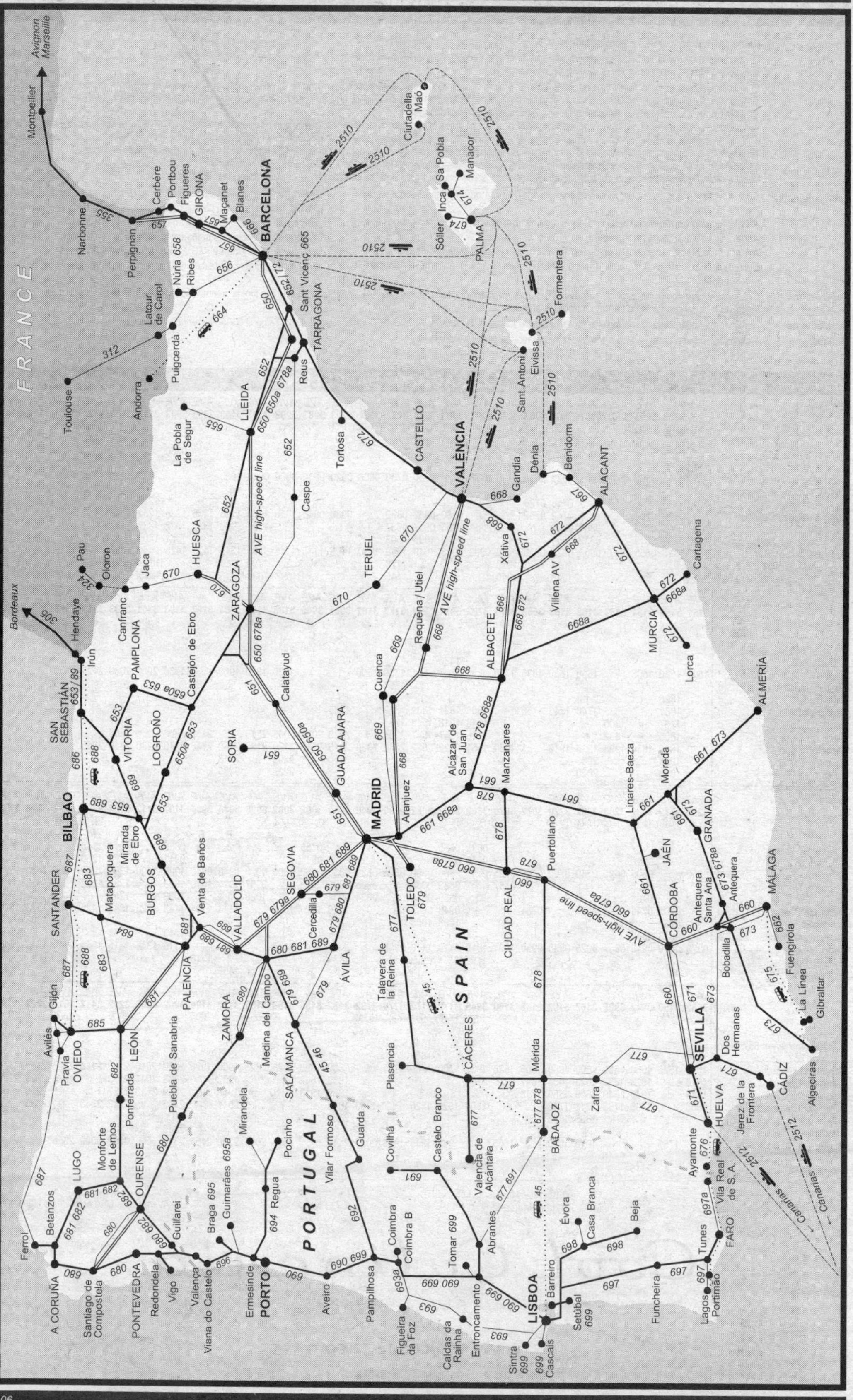
FRANCE
SPAIN
PORTUGAL
BARCELONA
MADRID
VALÈNCIA
SEVILLA
BILBAO
LISBOA
PORTO
ZARAGOZA
MÁLAGA
CÓRDOBA
GRANADA
ALACANT
MURCIA
ALMERÍA
SAN SEBASTIÁN
SANTANDER
OVIEDO
A CORUÑA
VALLADOLID
SALAMANCA
TOLEDO
CÁCERES
BADAJOZ
HUELVA
CÁDIZ
FARO
AVE high-speed line
Montpellier
Toulouse
Bordeaux
Avignon Marseille
PALMA
Eivissa
Formentera

SPAIN

Operator: **Renfe Operadora** – unless otherwise indicated. www.renfe.es

Services: On long-distance trains first class is known as *Preferente* and second class as *Turista*. Unless otherwise indicated (by '2' in the train column or [2] in the notes), all trains convey both first- and second-class seating accommodation.

🍸 indicates a buffet car (*cafetería*) or a mobile trolley service. ✕ indicates a full restaurant car service or the availability of hot meals served from the buffet car. Meals are served free of extra charge, on Mondays to Fridays, to holders of *Preferente* tickets on all *AVE* and *Euromed* trains. Note that catering services may not be available throughout a train's journey, particularly in the case of trains with multiple origins / destinations.

▬ indicates coaches equipped with couchettes: for occupancy of these a standard supplement is payable in addition to the normal *Turista* fare. 🛏 indicates sleeping-cars with single, double, and 3- or 4-berth compartments. The *Turista* fare is payable plus a sleeping-car supplement corresponding to the type and standard of accommodation. *Trenhotel* services additionally convey *Gran Clase* accommodation: *de luxe* single- and double-occupancy compartments with *en suite* shower and toilet. *Preferente* fare is payable for travel in *Gran Clase* plus a sleeping-car supplement corresponding to the type and standard of accommodation.

Local (*Media Distancia*) and suburban (*Cercanías*) trains are shown without an indication of category except for some fast **Media Distancia** (*MD*).

Train categories:

- ***Altaria*** (*Alta*): Talgo trains which can change gauge and run on the high-speed lines as well as the broad-gauge system.
- ***Alta Velocidad Española*** (*AVE*): High-speed trains running on the standard-gauge lines.
- ***Alvia***: High-speed gauge-changing trains.
- ***Avant*** (*Av*): Medium-distance high-speed trains on the standard-gauge lines.
- ***Euromed*** (*Em*): *AVE*-like trains running on the broad-gauge Barcelona - València - Alacant route.
- ***Intercity*** (*IC*): *Alvia*-like trains offering *Turista* class only.
- ***Media Distancia*** (*MD*): Medium distance regional trains.
- ***Regional Exprés*** (*RE*): Medium distance regional trains.
- ***Talgo***: Quality express trains using light, articulated stock.
- ***Train à Grande Vitesse*** (*TGV*): French High-speed trains.
- ***Trenhotel*** (*Hotel*): Quality night express trains (see Services, above).

Reservations: Reservations are compulsory for all journeys by services for which a train category (e.g. *AVE*, *RE*) is shown in the timing column. Advance purchase of tickets is also available for travel by services for which a train number is shown.

Supplements: Higher fares, incorporating a supplement, are payable for travel by *Altaria, Alvia, AVE, Euromed, InterCity, Talgo, TGV* and *Trenhotel* services.

Timings: Timings have been compiled from the latest information supplied by operators.

650 MADRID - ZARAGOZA - BARCELONA — High-speed services

km		*AVE*	*AVE*	*AVE*	*Av*	*AVE*	*AVE*	*AVE*	*AVE*	*AVE*	*AVE*	*AVE*	*AVE*	*AVE*	*AVE*	*AVE*	*AVE*	*AVE*	*AVE*	*AVE*	*AVE*	*AVE*	*AVE*	*AVE*	*Av*	*AVE*
		3263	**3053**	**3061**	**8087**	**3463**	**3063**	**3071**	**3271**	**3483**	**3073**	**3073**	**3081**	**3283**	**3083**	**3293**	**3093**	**3103**	**3993**	**3943**	**3113**	**3123**	**9724** **19725** **M**	**3141**	**8167**	**3143**
		①–⑤	①④⑤	①–④		⑥⑦	①–⑤	①–⑤	①–④	⑥⑦	①–⑤	⑥⑦	①–⑤	①–④		②③								Ⓑ	Ⓑ	Ⓑ
	Sevilla **660** d.	...	...	...	...	...	...	...	...	...	...	...	...	...	...	...	...	...	...	0850	...	...	...	...	...	...
	Málaga **660** d.	...	...	...	...	...	...	...	...	...	...	...	...	...	...	...	...	...	0840	|	...	...	...	...	...	...
0	**Madrid** Puerta de Atocha d.	...	0550	0610	...	0620	0630	0700	0720	...	0730	0730	0800	0820	0830	0900	0930	1030	|	|	1130	1230	1325	1400	...	1430
64	Guadalajara - Yebes d.	...	|	|	...	|	|	|	|	...	0754	0754	|	|	|	|	|	|	|	|	|	|	1350	|	...	|
221	Calatayud d.	...	|	|	...	0716	0726	|	|	...	|	|	|	|	|	|	|	|	|	|	1226	|	|	|	...	1526
307	**Zaragoza** Delicias d.	0620	0706	|	...	0742	0752	|	|	0800	0852	0852	|	0936	0946	1016	1046	1146	1236	1236	1252	1346	1452	|	...	1552
447	Lleida d.	0705	0750	|	0800	0826	|	|	|	0855	0937	0937	|	|	|	|	1131	|	1322	1322	1337	1431	|	|	1600	|
526	Camp de Tarragona d.	0735	0819	|	0832	0854	|	|	|	0923	1005	1005	|	|	|	|	1159	|	1351	1351	1405	|	1547	|	1632	|
621	**Barcelona** Sants a.	0810	0855	0840	0908	0929	0920	0930	0950	0958	1040	1040	1030	1105	1115	1145	1234	1315	1425	1425	1440	1530	1624	1630	1708	1721
	Girona **657** a.	...	...	...	...	1023	...	1023	...	...	...	1128	...	...	...	...	1322	...	...	...	1529f	1618v	1723	...	...	1815
	Figueres Vilafant **657** a.	...	...	...	...	1040	...	1040	...	...	...	1145	...	...	...	...	1339	...	...	...	1545f	1635v	1740	...	...	1832

	AVE	*AVE*	*AVE*	*Av*	*AVE*	*AVE*	*Av*	*AVE*	*Av*	*AVE*	*AVE*	*AVE*	*AVE*	*AVE*	*AVE*	*AVE*	*AVE*	*AVE*	*Av*	*AVE*	*AVE*	*AVE*	*AVE*	*AVE*		
	3151	**3153**	**3161**	**8187**	**3163**	**3163**	**3563**	**3171**	**3793**	**3991**	**3941**	**3173**	**3181**	**3995**	**3945**	**3183**	**3183**	**3191**	**8207**	**3193**	**3201**	**3203**	**3211**	**3593**		
	①–⑤		Ⓑ		①–⑤	⑥⑦	④⑤⑦	Ⓑ	⑤⑦				Ⓑ	⑦ **C**	⑦ **C**	⑥	Ⓑ	Ⓑ			Ⓑ		Ⓑ	Ⓑ		
Sevilla **660** d.	...	...	...	...	...	...	...	...	...	...	1450	...	...	...	1555	...	...	...	...	...	...	...	...	...	...	...
Málaga **660** d.	...	...	...	...	...	...	...	...	...	1435	|	...	...	1535	|	...	...	...	...	...	...	...	...	...	...	...
Madrid Puerta de Atocha d.	1500	1530	1600	...	1630	1630	1635	1700	...	|	|	1730	1800	|	|	1830	1830	1900	...	1930	2000	2030	2125	2130	...	...
Guadalajara - Yebes d.	|	|	|	...	|	|	|	|	...	|	|	1754	|	|	|	|	|	|	...	|	|	2054	|	2155	...	...
Calatayud d.	|	1626	|	...	|	|	|	|	...	|	|	|	|	|	|	|	|	|	...	|	|	|	|	2235	...	...
Zaragoza Delicias d.	|	1652	|	...	1746	1746	1756	|	1805	1831	1831	1852	|	1935	1935	1946	1946	|	...	2046	|	2152	|	2300	...	...
Lleida d.	|	1737	|	1800	|	|	...	|	1848	1918	1918	1937	|	|	|	|	|	|	2040	2131	|	2237	|	...	...	...
Camp de Tarragona d.	|	1805	|	1832	|	|	...	|	1916	1947	1947	2005	|	2039	2039	2045	2045	|	2112	2206	|	2305	|	...	...	...
Barcelona Sants a.	1730	1840	1830	1908	1915	1915	...	1930	1951	2022	2022	2040	2030	2115	2115	2120	2120	2130	2148	2240	2230	2340	2355	...	...	...
Girona **657** a.	...	1928	...	...	2003	...	...	...	...	...	...	...	...	...	...	2208	...	2218	...	...	...	...	...	...	...	...
Figueres Vilafant **657** a.	...	1945	...	...	2020	...	...	...	...	...	...	...	...	...	...	2225	...	2235	...	...	...	...	...	...	...	...

	AVE	*AVE*	*AVE*	*AVE*	*AVE*	*AVE*	*AVE*	*AVE*	*AVE*	*AVE*	*AVE*	*AVE*	*AVE*	*AVE*	*AVE*	*AVE*	*Av*	*AVE*	*AVE*	*AVE*	*AVE*	*AVE*	*AVE*	*AVE*	*AVE*	*AVE*
	3252	**3772**	**3062**	**3260**	**3462**	**3270**	**3072**	**3070**	**3662**	**3082**	**3082**	**3080**	**3940**	**3990**	**3092**	**3092**	**8096**	**3944**	**3994**	**3102**	**3112**	**3122**	**9731** **19730** **M**	**3132**	**3142**	**3152**
	①–④	①–⑥	①–⑥	①–⑤	①–④	①–④		①–④	①–⑤	①–⑤	⑥⑦	①–⑥			①–⑥	⑦		⑥ **B**	⑥ **B**					①–⑥		
Figueres Vilafant **657** d.	...	...	...	...	...	...	...	...	0630	0655	...	...	...	...	0755	...	...	...	...	0855	...	...	1143	...	...	...
Girona **657** d.	...	...	...	...	...	...	...	...	0646	0711	...	...	...	...	0811	...	...	...	...	0911	...	...	1200	...	...	...
Barcelona Sants d.	0550	...	0605	0625	0640	0700	0705	0725	0740	0800	0800	0825	0830	0830	0900	0900	0920	0940	0940	1000	1100	1200	1250	1325	1400	1500
Camp de Tarragona d.	|	...	0638	|	|	|	|	0757	|	0833	0833	|	0905	0905	|	|	0957	1015	1015	1033	|	1233	1322	|	1433	|
Lleida d.	|	...	0704	|	|	|	|	|	|	0859	0859	|	0934	0934	|	|	1028	|	|	1059	|	1259	|	|	1459	|
Zaragoza Delicias d.	|	0705	0748	|	0806	|	0831	|	|	0943	0943	|	1020	1020	1026	1026	...	1114	1114	1143	1226	1343	1425	1451	1543	1626
Calatayud d.	|	0732	|	|	|	|	|	|	|	1008	1008	|	|	|	|	|	...	|	|	|	|	|	|	|	1608	|
Guadalajara - Yebes d.	|	0813	0845	|	|	|	|	|	|	|	|	|	|	|	|	|	...	|	|	1243	|	1443	|	|	|	|
Madrid Puerta de Atocha a.	0820	0840	0915	0855	0925	0930	0950	1001	1010	1110	1110	1055	|	|	1145	1145	...	|	|	1310	1345	1510	1545	1610	1710	1745
Málaga **660** a.	...	...	...	...	...	...	...	...	...	...	...	...	|	1424	...	...	...	|	1516	...	...	...	...	...	...	...
Sevilla **660** a.	...	...	...	...	...	...	...	...	...	...	...	...	1402	...	...	...	...	1455	...	...	...	...	...	...	...	...

	Av	*AVE*	*AVE*	*AVE*	*AVE*	*AVE*	*Av*	*AVE*	*AVE*	*AVE*	*AVE*	*AVE*	*Av*	*AVE*	*Av*	*AVE*	*AVE*	*AVE*	*AVE*	*AVE*	*Av*	*AVE*	*AVE*	*AVE*	*AVE*	
	3562	**3150**	**3942**	**3992**	**3162**	**3162**	**8166**	**3160**	**3946**	**3172**	**3172**	**3170**	**3792** **10792**	**3182**	**8186**	**3180**	**3180**	**3192**	**3190**	**3202**	**8206**	**3212**	**3412**	**3610**	**3222**	
	⑤⑦	①–⑤			①–⑥	⑦	Ⓑ	Ⓑ	⑤	①–⑥	⑦	Ⓑ	④⑤⑦			①–⑤	⑦		Ⓑ			⑤⑦	**A**	⑤⑦		
Figueres Vilafant **657** d.	...	...	...	...	1455	...	...	...	...	...	1545	...		1655	...	...	1720	1755	...	...	...	...	...	...	...	...
Girona **657** d.	...	...	...	...	1511	...	...	...	...	...	1601	...	...	1711	...	...	1736	1811	...	...	...	...	...	...	...	...
Barcelona Sants d.	1515	1525	1550	1550	1600	1600	1605	1625	1632	1700	1700	1725	...	1800	1805	1825	1825	1900	1925	2000	2010	2100	2115	2125	2150	...
Camp de Tarragona d.	1548	|	1623	1623	1633	1633	1642	|	1705	|	|	|	...	1833	1842	|	|	1932	|	2033	2047	2133	|	|	2223	...
Lleida d.	1614	|	1649	1649	1659	1659	1713	|	|	|	|	|	...	1859	1913	|	|	1958	|	2059	2118	2159	|	|	2250	...
Zaragoza Delicias d.	1655	|	1733	1733	1743	1743	...	|	1804	1826	1826	|	1900	1943	...	|	|	2041	|	2143	...	2243	2243	|	2335	...
Calatayud d.	...	|	|	|	1808	1808	...	|	|	|	|	|	|	2008	...	|	|	|	|	|	...	|	|	|	...	...
Guadalajara - Yebes d.	...	|	|	|	|	|	...	|	|	|	|	|	|	|	...	|	|	|	|	2243	...	|	|	|	...	...
Madrid Puerta de Atocha a.	...	1755	|	|	1910	1910	...	1855	|	1945	1945	1955	2030	2110	...	2055	2055	2200	2155	2310	...	0002	0002	2355	...	...
Málaga **660** a.	...	...	|	2140	...	...	...	...	|	...	...	...	...	...	...	...	...	...	...	...	...	...	...	...	...	...
Sevilla **660** a.	...	...	2115	...	...	...	...	...	2143	...	...	...	...	...	...	...	...	...	...	...	...	...	...	...	...	...

A – ①②③④⑥.
B – ⑥ (①–⑥ July 17 - Sept. 17).
C – ⑦ (Ⓑ July 10 - Sept. 17).
M – To / from Marseille (Table **13**).
f – ①–⑤.
v – Not ⑥.
☛ *AVE* trains convey ✕ and 🍸. *Avant* trains (*Av*) are *Turista* class only.

MADRID – LOGROÑO, PAMPLONA / IRUÑA, HUESCA – BARCELONA 650a

	Hotel 921 🍷 A	IC 635 ①–⑤	IC 10655 ⑥ y	Alvia 533 K	Alvia 433 F	Alvia 601 ①–⑤	IC 631 ①–⑥ B	Alvia 603 ⑥	Alvia 605 Ⓑ	IC 633 ⑦ B	Alvia 661 ①–⑥ G	AVE 3363 ⑤⑦	IC 10657 ⑦ b	Alvia 621 625 J	Alvia 537 K	Alvia 437 Ⓑ F	Alvia 609	Alvia 613 ⑤	Alvia 613 ④⑦ b	Alvia 701 Ⓑ	AVE 3393	Alvia 801 Ⓑ	
Madrid Puerta de Atocha d.	...	...	...	...	...	0735	...	0940	1135	...	...	1605	...	...	...	...	1505	1735	1735	1835	1905	1935	...
Guadalajara - Yebes d.	...	...	...	...	...	|	...	1007	1202	...	...	|	...	...	...	...	1532	|	|	1901	1928	|	...
Calatayud d.	...	...	...	...	...	|	...	1055	1250	...	...	|	...	...	...	...	1620	|	|	1948	2007	|	...
Logroño **653** a.	0403	...	...	...	0904	|	1021	|	|	1434	...	|	...	...	...	1753	|	|	|	2158	|	|	...
Pamplona / Iruña **653** a.	|	0625	0812	0913	|	1038	|	1252	1440	|	1508	|	1625	1724	1754	|	1826	2043	2043	...	|	2240	...
Zaragoza Delicias d.	0632	0810	1003	1113	1113	...	1215	...	...	1628	1701	1727	1811	1918	1952	1952	...	...	...	...	2034	...	...
Huesca **670** a.	|	|	|	|	|	...	|	...	...	|	|	1810	|	|	|	|	...	...	...	...	2118	...	...
Lleida d.	0730	0900	1056	1203	1203	...	1313	...	...	1722	1754	...	|	2013	2051	2051	...	...	...	...	...	...	...
Camp de Tarragona d.	0804	0930	1127	1238	1238	...	1343	...	...	1753	1827	...	1924	2050	2128	2128	...	...	...	...	...	...	...
Barcelona Sants a.	0849	1010	1205	1320	1320	...	1420	...	...	1835	1903	...	2000	2133	2209	2209	...	...	...	...	...	...	...

	Alvia 802 ①–⑤	AVE 3272	Alvia 702 ①–⑥	Alvia 800 ① b	Alvia 600 ⑥	Alvia 534 K	Alvia 434 ①–⑥ F	Alvia 602 Ⓑ	Alvia 622 626 J	IC 10560 ⑥ b	Alvia 606	Alvia 664 G	IC 632 B	Alvia 612 ⑦	Alvia 612 ⑤ b	Alvia 530 K	Alvia 430 F	AVE 3592 ⑤⑦	Alvia 610 Ⓑ	IC 562 ①–⑤ w	IC 562 ⑦	Hotel 922 🍷 A	
Barcelona Sants d.	...	...	...	...	...	0730	0730	...	0930	1005	...	1210	1410	...	...	1530	1530	...	...	1840	1930	2020	...
Camp de Tarragona d.	...	...	...	...	...	0808	0808	...	1007	1043	...	1248	1447	...	...	1608	1608	...	...	1918	2008	2103	...
Lleida d.	...	...	...	...	...	0844	0844	...	1037	1115	...	1322	1517	...	...	1639	1639	...	...	1950	2041	2142	...
Huesca **670** d.	...	0815	...	...	...	|	|	...	|	|	...	|	|	...	...	|	|	1935	...	|	|	|	...
Zaragoza Delicias d.	...	0900	...	...	...	0934	0934	...	1128	1204	...	1414	1608	...	...	1729	1729	2020	...	2102	2134	2250	...
Pamplona / Iruña **653** d.	0635	|	...	0810	0900	1117	|	1130	1315	1354	1535	1606	|	1807	1807	1922	|	|	1935	2244	2328	|	...
Logroño **653** d.	|	|	0735	|	|	...	1123	|	...	...	|	...	1750	|	|	...	1936	|	|	...	...	0102	...
Calatayud d.	|	0925	0936	|	1101	...	...	1324	...	...	|	...	...	|	|	...	...	|	2134	...	...	...	...
Guadalajara - Yebes d.	|	1005	1022	|	1150	...	...	1412	...	...	|	...	...	|	|	...	...	|	2224	...	...	...	...
Madrid Puerta de Atocha a.	0945	1035	1050	1120	1218	...	...	1440	...	...	1838	...	...	2125	2125	...	...	2140	2253	...	...	...	...

A – Ⓑ (daily June 17 - Sept. 16): GALICIA *Trenhotel* – 🛏, [1] (reclining) Barcelona - Logroño - A Coruña and Vigo and v.v.

B – [12] Salamanca - Valladolid - Barcelona and v.v. (Tables **653**, **689**).

F – [12] Bilbao - Barcelona and v.v. (Table **653**).

G – [12] Gijón - Barcelona and v.v. (Table **685**).

J – [12] Vigo / A Coruña - Barcelona and v.v. (Table **680**).

K – [12] Irún - Barcelona and v.v. (Table **653**).

b – From / to Irún (Table **653**).

w – To Vitoria / Gasteiz on ⑤ (Table **653**).

y – From Vitoria / Gasteiz (Table **653**).

MADRID - SORIA and ZARAGOZA 651

km	For high-speed trains see Tables **650** and **650a**	2 Ⓐ		2 Ⓒ		2 Ⓐ H	2 Ⓐ	2 Ⓒ	2 Ⓒ		2 Ⓐ		2 ⑤	2 ⑤	2 w		2 ⑦	2	2 Ⓐ	2 ⑦			
0	**Madrid** Chamartín d.	...	...	...	...	0715	0745	0814	0915	...	...	...	1432	1540	1545	...	...	1900	1943	2002	...	...	...
55	Guadalajara d.	...	...	...	...	0756	0823	0854	0959	...	...	...	1509	1624	1638	...	...	1940	2031	2038	...	...	...
138	Sigüenza d.	...	...	...	...	0858	0915	0944	1102	...	...	...	1612	1713	1740	...	...	2032	2134	2142	...	...	...
248	**Soria** a.	...	...	...	...	|	1042	1110	|	...	...	...	...	1840	|	...	...	2158	...	...	...	...	...
178	Arcos de Jalón d.	0650	...	0850	...	0936	...	...	1140	...	...	...	...	...	1814	...	...	...	...	...	...	...	...
241	Calatayud d.	0736	...	0936	...	1016	...	...	1221	...	1321	...	...	...	1859	...	2116	...	...	...	...	...	...
339	**Zaragoza** Delicias ♣ a.	0855	...	1101	...	1114	...	...	1325	...	1438	...	...	...	2011	...	2238	...	...	...	...	...	...

For high-speed trains see Tables **650** and **650a**	2 Ⓐ		2 Ⓐ		2 Ⓒ		2 f		2 H	2 ⑤	2 Ⓑ	2 ⑦		2		2 ⑦		2					
Zaragoza Delicias ♥ d.	...	...	...	...	...	...	0857	...	1407	...	1620	...	...	...	...	...	...	2036	...	...	...	...	...
Calatayud d.	...	...	...	...	...	...	1018	...	1506	...	1742	...	...	...	...	...	...	2157	...	...	...	...	...
Arcos de Jalón d.	...	...	...	...	...	...	1104	...	1543	...	...	...	...	...	...	...	...	2244	...	...	...	...	...
Soria d.	...	...	0750	...	0845	...	|	...	|	...	...	1657	...	1906	...	...	...	...	...	...	...	...	...
Sigüenza d.	0650	...	0914	...	1009	...	1140	...	1619	1700	...	1817	...	2033	...	2150	...	...	...	...	...	...	...
Guadalajara d.	0800	...	1006	...	1057	...	1244	...	1723	1758	...	1908	...	2126	...	2248	...	...	...	...	...	...	...
Madrid Chamartín a.	0913	...	1045	...	1136	...	1329	...	1807	1837	...	1948	...	2206	...	2327	...	...	...	...	...	...	...

H – To / from Barcelona (Table **652**).

f – From Lleida on Ⓐ (Table **652**).

w – To Lleida (Table **652**).

♥ – All services call 7 – 8 minutes earlier at Zaragoza **Goya** and 5 minutes earlier at Zaragoza **Portillo**.

♣ – All services call 4 – 5 minutes later at Zaragoza **Portillo** and 6 – 8 minutes later at Zaragoza **Goya**.

ZARAGOZA - BARCELONA 652

km	For high-speed trains see Tables **650** and **650a**	2 ⚒	2	2	2	Hotel 921¶ G 🍷	2	2 Ⓐ	2	2	2	2 ⑥	2 ⑦	2	2 Ⓐ	2 Ⓒ	2	2	2 Ⓐ	2 ⚒	2 ⑦	2	2	2
	Madrid Chamartín **651** d.	...	...	...	...	...	...	...	...	...	...	...	...	...	0715	...	...	...	...	...	...	...	...	1545
0	**Zaragoza** Delicias ♣ d.	...	...	...	...	0632	...	0610	...	...	...	0857	1027	...	1116	1116	...	...	1515	...	...	1630	2015	2012
114	Caspe d.	...	...	...	...	|	0705	|	...	...	...	|	|	...	1252	1252	...	...	|	...	...	1800	2155	|
★	Lleida d.	...	...	...	0715	0730	|	0820	...	...	...	1121	1237	1310	|	|	1545	...	1727	1748	1748	|	...	2240
239	Reus d.	0537	0641	0734	|	|	0906	...	1107	1206	1308	...	...	1437	1454	1454	1714	1837	...	|	|	2005	...	...
257	Tarragona **672** d.	0555	0659	0749	|	0804t	0926	...	1125	1225	1326	...	...	1455	1512	1512	1730	1859	...	|	|	2027	...	...
282	Sant Vicenç de Calders **672** d.	0616	0719	0810	0847	|	0948	...	1145	1246	1347	...	...	1517	1536	1536	1750	1920	...	1913	1923	2046	...	...
342	**Barcelona** Sants **672** a.	0718	0807	0907	0939	0849	1037	...	1237	1337	1437	...	...	1610	1637	1637	1840	2010	...	2010	2019	2137	...	...
345	Barcelona Pass. de Gràcia a.	0724	0813	0913	0944		1044	...	1244	1346	1444	...	...	1615	1644	1644	1845	2017	...	2015	2024	2143	...	...
350	**Barcelona** França a.	0735	0824	0925	0954	...	1055	...	1255	1357	1455	...	...	1625	1655	1655	1855	2028	...	2025	2034	2154	...	...

For high-speed trains see Tables **650** and **650a**	2 Ⓐ	2 Ⓐ	2	2 Ⓒ	2 ⑥	2	2	2	2	2	2	2	2	2 ⑦	2 Ⓐ	2	2	2	2	2	2 Ⓑ	2	Hotel 922¶ G 🍷	2
Barcelona França d.	...	...	0610	...	...	0647	0713	0843	0943	1143	...	1313	1343	...	...	1543	1643	1713	1843	1847	1943	2013	...	2113
Barcelona Pass. de Gràcia d.	...	...	0621	...	...	0658	0724	0853	0954	1154	...	1323	1354	...	...	1554	1654	1724	1854	1859	1954	2024	...	2124
Barcelona Sants **672** d.	...	...	0630	...	...	0706	0733	0903	1003	1203	...	1333	1403	...	...	1603	1703	1733	1903	1906	2003	2033	2020	2133
Sant Vicenç de Calders **672** d.	...	...	0719	...	...	0807	0822	0950	1046	1248	...	1419	1449	...	...	1649	1747	1820	1948	2005	2049	2119	|	2222
Tarragona **672** d.	...	...	0741	...	...	|	0844	1011	1108	1308	...	1442	1511	...	...	1710	1809	1841	|	2037	2110	2140	2103t	2243
Reus d.	...	...	0757	...	...	|	0900	1028	1124	1326	...	1459	1531	...	...	1727	1827	1858	|	2052	2126	2156	|	2259
Lleida d.	...	0625	...	...	1025	0956	...	|	...	1455	1515	...	1650	1803	1836	|	1955	|	2112	...	...	...	2142	...
Caspe d.	0651	|	...	1040	|	...	...	1229	...	...	|	...	...	|	|	1944	...	2108	...	...	...	...	|	...
Zaragoza Delicias ♥ a.	0823	0856	...	1212	1253	...	...	1405	...	...	1729	...	...	2023	2044	2119	...	...	...	...	...	...	2238	...
Madrid Chamartín **651** a.	...	1329	...	...	...	...	...	1807	...	...	...	...	...	...	...	...	...	...	...	...	...	...	...	...

G – Ⓑ (daily June 17 - Sept. 16): GALICIA *Trenhotel* – 🛏, [1] (reclining) Barcelona - A Coruña and Vigo and v.v.

t – **Camp** de Tarragona.

¶ – Via high speed line.

★ – Leida - Reus: *90 km.* Zaragoza - Lleida: *189 km.* Lleida - Sant Vicenç: *106 km.*

♥ – All trains (except *Hotel* **922**) call 5 – 8 minutes earlier at Zaragoza **Goya** and 3 – 5 minutes earlier at Zaragoza **Portillo**.

♣ – All trains (except *Hotel* **921**) call 4 – 5 minutes later at Zaragoza **Portillo** and 6 – 8 minutes later at Zaragoza **Goya**.

653 ZARAGOZA - IRÚN and BILBAO

km				Alvia	Alvia	Alvia	Alvia	Alvia	Alvia	IC		Alvia			IC	Alvia		Alvia		Alvia	Alvia				IC	Alvia	Alvia		Hotel
		18071	16071	601	603	534	434	622	605	10560	18021	664	18073	16015	632	609	18023	530	16017	430	613	18075	16027	18077	562	701	801	18079	922
		2	2					626			2		2	2			2		2			2	2	2	S			2	G🍷
		①-⑥	①-⑤	①-⑤	⑥		B	J	Ⓑ	⑥		A			C		⑤		①-⑥		D		⑦		Ⓑ	Ⓑ	Ⓑ	⑤⑥⑦	¶
	Barcelona Sants **652** d.	...	...	...	...	0730	0730	0930	...	1005	...	1210	...	...	1410	...	...	1530	...	1530	...	...	...	...	1840	...	...	...	2020
	Madrid PA ‡ **650a** d.	...	...	0735	0940	|	|	|	1135	|	...	|	...	...	|	1505	...	|	...	|	1735	...	...	...	|	1835	1935	...	|
0	**Zaragoza** Delicias d.	0625	...	|	|	0934	0934	1128	|	1204	1309	1414	1435	...	1608	|	1652	1729	...	1729	|	1742	...	1921	2102	|	|	2109	2250
94	Castejón de Ebro ★ d.	0729	0730	0945	1159	1028	1031	1224	|	1259	1417	|	1540	...	1702	|	1748	1833	...	1845	|	1849	1852	2031	|	|	|	2215	0014
182	**Pamplona / Iruña** d.	0837	|	1038	1252	1119	|	1317	1440	1356	1526	1608	|	1642	|	1826	1859	1924	1958	|	2044	|	2005	2138	2244a	|	2240	|	|
234	Altsasu **689** d.	0918t	|	...	...	1150	|	|	...	|	...	|	|	1718t	|	...	...	1953	2034t	|	|	|	2046t	...	|	|	...	|	|
275	Vitoria / Gasteiz **689** d.	0950	|	...	...	|	|	1410	...	|	...	1702	|	1753	|	...	...	|	2107	|	|	|	2118	...	2337r	|	...	|	|
321	San Seb / Don ❖ d.	|	|	...	...	1303	|	|	...	1550	...	|	|	|	|	...	...	2110	...	|	2227x	|	|	...	...	|	...	|	|
337	**Irún** **689** a.	|	|	...	...	...	|	|	...	...	...	|	|	|	|	...	...	...	...	|	...	|	|	...	...	|	...	|	|
171	**Logroño 650a** d.	|	0829	...	...	...	1125	|	...	...	...	|	1635	|	1751	...	...	...	...	1938	...	1945	|	...	...	2158	...	2312	0102
242	Miranda de Ebro **689** d.	1016	...	...	...	...	1225	1431	...	...	...	1722	...	1820	1851	...	...	...	...	2032	...	...	2143	...	...	...	...	...	...
347	**Bilbao** Abando **689** a.	...	...	...	...	...	1404	...	...	...	...	...	...	...	...	...	...	...	...	2209	...	...	...	...	...	...	...	...	...

		IC		Alvia	Alvia	Alvia		IC	Alvia	Alvia	Alvia		Alvia	IC		Alvia	Alvia	IC			Alvia	Alvia	Alvia	Alvia	Alvia				Hotel
	18068	635	18072	802	800	702	18074	10655	600	533	433	16019	602	631	18076	661	606	10657	18070	18029	621	537	437	612	610	16111	16011	18078	921
	2		2		E		2					2			2	A			2	2	625					2	2	2	G🍷
	①-⑤	①-⑤	①-⑤	①-⑤	①	①-⑥		⑥	⑥				Ⓑ	C		①-⑥		⑦	⑤⑥⑦	b	J		P	⑤⑦	Ⓑ	①-⑥	⑦	❦	¶
Bilbao Abando **689** d.	...	...	...	...	...	...	...	...	...	...	0630	...	...	...	...	...	...	...	...	...	...	...	1520	...	...	...	...	...	...
Miranda de Ebro **689** d.	...	...	...	...	...	...	...	...	...	...	0805	0940	...	0921	...	1347	...	...	...	1501	1605	...	1652	...	...	...	...	...	...
Logroño 650a d.	...	...	0615	...	...	0735	...	...	...	...	0904	|	...	1021	1415	|	...	...	1642	|	|	...	1753	...	...	...	...	2018	0403
Irún **689** d.	...	...	|	...	...	|	...	...	...	...	|	|	...	|	|	|	...	...	|	|	|	...	|	...	...	...	...	|	|
San Seb / Don ❖ d.	...	...	|	...	0624	|	...	...	...	0728	|	|	...	|	|	|	...	1437	|	|	|	1610	|	1619r	...	...	...	|	|
Vitoria / Gasteiz **689** d.	...	...	|	...	|	|	...	0718	...	|	|	1005	...	|	|	1411	...	|	|	1530	1627	|	|	|	...	1900	1921	|	|
Altsasu **689** d.	...	...	|	...	|	|	...	|	...	0842	|	1038t	...	|	|	|	...	|	|	1601t	|	1722	|	|	...	1931t	1952t	|	|
Pamplona / Iruña d.	...	0625	|	0635	0810	|	0743z	0812	0900	0913	|	1110	1130	|	|	1508	1535	1625	|	1638	1724	1754	|	1807	1935	2015	2026	|	|
Castejón de Ebro d.	0605	0717	0720e	0725	|	|	0850	|	0952	1010	1010	...	|	1114	1510	1602	|	|	1741	1744	1818	1854	1854	|	|	2111	2123	2121	0456
Zaragoza Delicias a.	0715	0807	0836	|	|	|	0956	1000	|	1110	1110	...	|	1212	1611	1659	|	1808	...	1851	1916	1950	1950	|	|	...	2217	2229	0629
Madrid PA ‡ **650a** a.	...	|	...	0945	1120	1050	...	|	1218	|	|	...	1440	|	...	|	1838	|	...	...	|	|	|	2125	2253	...	...	...	|
Barcelona Sants **652** a.	...	1010	...	...	...	...	...	1205	...	1320	1320	...	...	1420	...	1903	...	2000	...	...	2133	2209	2209	...	...	...	...	...	0849

A – [12] Barcelona - Gijón and v.v. (Table **685**).

B – ①-⑥ (daily June 18 - Sept. 9).

C – [12] Barcelona - Valladolid - Salamanca and v.v. (Tables **650a, 689**). On ⑦ *IC* **631** runs as *IC* **633**, departs Miranda de Ebro 1337, Logroño 1434, Castejón de Ebro 1527, arrives Zaragoza 1626, Barcelona 1835.

D – ④⑤⑦ (not July 23 - Aug. 27).

E – ① (not July 23 - Aug. 27).

G – Ⓑ (daily June 17 - Sept. 16): GALICIA *Trenhotel* – 🛏, [1] (reclining) Barcelona - A Coruña and Vigo and v.v.

J – [12] 🍷 Barcelona - Vigo / A Coruña and v.v. (Table **680**).

P – Ⓑ (daily June 17 - Sept. 8).

S – On ⑦ departs Barcelona 1930, Zaragoza 2134, arrives Pamplona 2328.

a – Arrival time.

b – From Burgos Rosa de Lima on ①-⑥ (Table **689**).

e – Arrive 0709.

r – ⑤ (not July 23 - Aug. 27).

t – Altsasu Pueblo (*230 km*).

x – ④⑦ (not July 23 - Aug. 27).

z – ①-⑤.

❦ – On ⑦ runs 13 - 18 minutes earlier.

¶ – Via high speed line.

★ – Calatayud - Castejón : *140 km.*

‡ – Full name is Madrid Puerta de Atocha.

❖ – Full name is San Sebastián / Donostia.

655 LLEIDA - LA POBLA DE SEGUR

FGC 2nd class

km		Ⓐ				A	Ⓑ		⑥	†	①-④	⑤	
0	**Lleida** d.	0525	0620	0747	0905	1040	1047	1330	1505	1705	1730	1925	...
27	Balaguer d.	0552	0646	0815	0931	1110	1115	1356	1531	1731	1756	1951	...
77	Tremp d.	0647	...	0909	...	|	1209	...	1625	1825	1850	2045	...
90	**La Pobla de Segur** a.	0700	...	0922	...	1235	1222	...	1638	1838	1903	2058	...

	Ⓐ	Ⓑ	⑥	Ⓑ	⑦	⑥	①-⑤	A	Ⓒ	①-④	B	⑤
La Pobla de Segur d.	0708	1008	1300	...	1515	...	1530	1700	1900	1930	...	2122
Tremp d.	0719	1019	1311	...	1526	...	1541	|	1911	1941	...	2133
Balaguer d.	0815	1115	1407	1408	1622	1623	1637	1830f	2007	2037	2202	2229
Lleida a.	0841	1141	1433	1434	1648	1649	1703	1900	2033	2103	2228	2255

A – Tren dels Llacs: ⑥ Apr. 13 - July 13, ⑥ Aug. 17 - Nov. 2 (Subject to confirmation).

B – Runs 19 minutes earlier on ⑥.

f – Arrive 1815.

656 BARCELONA - PUIGCERDÀ - LATOUR DE CAROL

2nd class

km		Ⓐ ❖	Ⓐ	Ⓐ	Ⓐ	Ⓒ	Ⓐ	Ⓒ	Ⓐ	Ⓒ	Ⓐ	Ⓐ	Ⓒ	Ⓐ	Ⓒ	Ⓐ	Ⓐ	Ⓒ	Ⓐ	Ⓒ	Ⓐ	Ⓒ	Ⓐ	Ⓒ	Ⓐ	Ⓒ	Ⓐ
0	**Barcelona** Sants d.	...	0511	0602	0622	0701	0701	0749	0752	0936	0951	1022	1109	1122	1207	1233	1303	1317	1402	1408	1501	1510	1549	1623	1702	1717	1732
	La Sagrera-Meridiana d.	...	0524	0615	0636	0714	0714	0802	0805	0949	1004	1035	1122	1135	1220	1246	1316	1330	1415	1421	1514	1523	1602	1637	1715	1730	1745
	Sant Andreu Arenal d.	...	0526	0617	0639	0717	0716	0804	0807	0951	1006	1037	1124	1137	1222	1248	1318	1332	1417	1423	1516	1525	1604	1639	1717	1732	1747
33	Granollers - Canovelles d.	...	0556	0645	0706	0743	0744	0833	0837	1017	1033	1108	1153	1209	1248	1315	1347	1406	1444	1450	1542	1550	1633	1708	1741	1759	1817
74	Vic d.	...	0638	0722	0743	0816	0824	0914	0924	1051	1115	1147	1232	1252	1326	1353	1426	1445	1519	1521	1617	1623	1714	1755	1813	1832	1900
90	Torelló d.	...	...	0736	0805	0831	...	0927	0938	1105	1129	1202	1246	1305	1340	1408	1441	1501	1535	1536	1632	1636	1730	1809	1827	1847	1916
110	Ripoll d.	...	...	0801	0829	0856	...	0953	1006	1130	1156	1228	1313	1330	1404	1436	1513	1531	1559	1600	1658	1700	1757	1835	1856	1914	1942
124	Ribes de Freser **658** a.	...	...	...	0847	0914	...	1013	1023	1147	1214	...	...	...	1421	1458	...	1548	...	...	1715	1718	...	...	1916	1931	...
145	La Molina a.	...	...	...	0912	0947	...	...	...	1212	1240	...	...	...	1448	1523	...	...	...	...	1740	1751	...	...	1949	1958	...
159	Puigcerdà a.	0801	...	...	0934	1007	...	...	...	1232	1259	...	...	...	1508	1542	...	...	...	...	1800	1811	...	...	2007	2017	...
163	**Latour de Carol** 🏛 **312** a.	0807	...	...	0940	1013	...	...	...	1238	1305	...	...	...	1514	1548	...	...	...	...	1806	1817	...	...	...	...	...

	Ⓐ	Ⓐ	Ⓒ	Ⓐ	Ⓒ	Ⓐ	Ⓐ	Ⓐ	Ⓒ	Ⓐ	
Barcelona Sants d.	1827	1857	1857	2012	2015	2054	2102	2132	2207	2230	...
La Sagrera-Meridiana d.	1840	1910	1910	2025	2028	2107	2115	2145	2220	2243	...
Sant Andreu Arenal d.	1842	1912	1912	2027	2030	2109	2117	2147	2222	2245	...
Granollers - Canovelles d.	|	1939	1941	2054	2055	2139	2145	2217	2251	2312	...
Vic d.	1935	2017	2019	2128	2131	2218	2223	2256	2328	2349	...
Torelló d.	|	2036	2033	2143	2145	...	...	...	...	...	...
Ripoll d.	2010	2102	2059	2208	2210	...	...	...	...	...	...
Ribes de Freser **658** a.	|	2119	2116	...	...	...	...	...	...	...	...
La Molina a.	|	2143	2141	...	...	...	...	...	...	...	...
Puigcerdà a.	2106	2201	2200	...	...	...	...	...	...	...	...
Latour de Carol 🏛 **312** a.	...	...	...	...	...	...	...	...	...	...	...

		Ⓐ		Ⓐ	Ⓒ	Ⓐ	Ⓐ	Ⓒ	Ⓐ	Ⓒ	Ⓐ
Latour de Carol 🏛 **312** d.	...	...	...	...	...	...	...	...	...	...	...
Puigcerdà d.	...	...	...	...	...	...	0617	0652	0729	...	...
La Molina d.	...	...	...	...	...	...	|	0710	0747	...	...
Ribes de Freser **658** d.	...	...	...	...	...	...	|	0735	0812	...	...
Ripoll d.	...	0530	...	0625	...	...	0713	0753	0830	...	0913
Torelló d.	...	0555	...	0651	...	...	|	0817	0854	...	0940
Vic d.	0548	0611	0641	0705	0723	0726	0750	0831	0908	0917	0955
Granollers - Canovelles d.	0625	0652	0720	0744	0801	0803	|	0902	0942	0956	1034
Sant Andreu Arenal a.	0651	0719	0750	0809	0830	0832	0843	0930	1010	1024	1059
La Sagrera-Meridiana a.	0654	0722	0753	0812	0833	0835	0847	0933	1013	1027	1102
Barcelona Sants a.	0707	0734	0806	0825	0846	0850	0902	0946	1026	1040	1115

	Ⓒ	Ⓒ	Ⓐ	Ⓐ	Ⓒ	Ⓐ	Ⓒ	Ⓐ	Ⓒ	Ⓒ	Ⓐ	Ⓐ	Ⓒ	Ⓐ	Ⓐ	Ⓒ	Ⓒ	Ⓐ	Ⓒ	Ⓐ	Ⓒ	Ⓐ		Ⓒ	Ⓐ	Ⓐ	Ⓒ
Latour de Carol 🏛 **312** d.	...	0848	0850	...	...	...	...	1048	1113	...	...	1334	1347	...	...	...	...	...	...	...	1652	1713	...	1859	1852	...	...
Puigcerdà d.	...	0855	0856	...	...	...	...	1055	1120	...	...	1341	1354	...	...	...	...	...	...	...	1659	1720	...	1906	1859	...	...
La Molina d.	...	0913	0915	...	...	...	...	1113	1138	...	...	1359	1412	...	...	...	...	...	...	...	1717	1739	...	1924	1917	...	...
Ribes de Freser **658** d.	...	0938	0944	...	...	1103	1111	1137	1205	...	...	1423	1439	...	...	...	1640	...	...	...	1744	1805	...	1951	1943	...	...
Ripoll d.	0919	0956	1004	1036	...	1121	1129	1155	1223	1407	1342	1441	1457	...	1604	...	1658	1705	...	...	1802	1823	1906	2009	2004	2104	...
Torelló d.	0946	1020	1028	1102	...	1149	1156	1222	1247	1431	1410	1507	1522	...	1631	...	1724	1732	...	...	1828	1848	1933	2035	2035	2130	...
Vic d.	1001	1034	1041	1117	1121	1203	1211	1236	1301	1446	1425	1521	1536	1601	1646	1650	1739	1746	1806	1823	1846	1902	1949	2051	2049	2145	2140
Granollers - Canovelles d.	1044	1110	1115	1155	1201	1243	1256	1312	1332	1529	1505	1558	1608	1640	1727	1728	1817	1826	1850	1904	1918	1938	2033	2123	2124	2227	2219
Sant Andreu Arenal a.	1112	1135	1141	1221	1230	1310	1328	1339	1357	1557	1536	1627	1635	1708	1754	1757	1851	1851	1918	1937	1942	2009	2058	2150	2151	2253	2247
La Sagrera-Meridiana a.	1115	1137	1143	1223	1233	1312	1331	1341	1359	1600	1538	1629	1637	1711	1756	1800	1854	1853	1921	1940	1944	2011	2101	2152	2153	2256	2250
Barcelona Sants a.	1128	1149	1156	1236	1246	1325	1344	1354	1411	1613	1551	1643	1649	1724	1809	1813	1907	1906	1934	1954	1957	2024	2114	2205	2206	2309	2303

❖ – Timing subject to confirmation. Please check locally.

BARCELONA - GIRONA - FIGUERES - PORTBOU / PERPIGNAN 657

Reservations are not compulsory on *Media Distancia* (*MD*) services on the Barcelona - Girona - Portbou - Cebère route. All stopping services convey 2nd class only.

km	km		MD 15900 Ⓐ	Ⓐ	⑥	TGV 9708 10709* AP	Ⓐ	MD 15056 Ⓒ	MD 15076 Ⓐ	AVE 9736 34737* L	Ⓒ	Ⓐ	TGV 9702 34703* P	AVE 3071 34071*	MD 15908 Ⓒ	MD 15094 Ⓐ	Ⓒ	AVE 3073 34073* ⑥⑦	Ⓐ	MD 15078 Ⓐ	MD 15078 Ⓒ	AVE 3093 34093*	MD 15004 Ⓐ	Ⓒ	Ⓐ	TGV 9704 34705* P
		Madrid ⊠ **660** d.	...	...	...	...	...	...	...	...	...	...	...	0700x	...	...	...	0730	...	...	...	0930	...	...	...	...
0	0	**Barcelona** Sants **666** d.	0556	0616	0646	0705	0716	0746	0816	0825	0846	0916	0925	0945	0946	1016	1046	1050	1116	1146	1146	1244	1246	1246	1316	1320
3		Barcelona P de G ¶ d.	0601	0621	0651	|	0721	0751	0821	|	0851	0921	|	|	0951	1021	1051	|	1121	1151	1151	|	1251	1251	1321	|
31		Granollers Centre d.	|	0648	0718	|	0753	|	|	|	0918	0948	|	|	|	|	1118	|	1148	|	|	|	|	1318	1348	|
72		Maçanet - Massanes **666** d.	0651	0721	0751	|	0831	0843	0913	|	0950	1021	|	|	1043	1113	1151	|	1221	1243	1243	|	1343	1351	1421	|
86		Caldes de Malavella d.	0702	0741	0811	|	0851	0854	0924	|	1008	1041	|	|	1054	1124	1218	|	1241	1254	1253	|	1353	1411	1441	|
102	95	**Girona** d.	0713	0756	0826	0746	0906	0905	0935	0906	1023	1056	1006	1026	1105	1135	1233	1130	1256	1305	1305	1324	1404	1426	1456	1401
118		Flaçà d.	0726	0811	0841	|	0921	0915	0948	|	1038	1111	|	|	1118	1148	1248	|	1311	1318	1318	|	1417	1441	1511	|
143		Figueres § d.	0744	0834	0904	|	0943	0937	1007	|	1101	1134	|	|	1137	1207	1311	|	1334	1336	1337	|	1437	1504	1534	|
	129	Figueres Vilafant § d.	...	|	|	0803	|	|	|	0923	|	|	1023	1040	|	|	|	1145	|	...	|	1339	...	|	|	1418
162		Llançà d.	...	0849	0919	|	0958	0950	1020	|	1116	1149	|	...	1150	1220	1326	...	1349	...	1350	...	...	1519	1549	|
169		**Portbou** 🏢 **355** a.	...	0900	0930	|	1009	0957	1027	|	1127	1200	|	...	1157	1227	1337	...	1400	...	1357	...	...	1530	1600	|
171		**Cerbère** 🏢 **355** a.	...	0904	0934	|	1013	...	...	|	1131	1204	|	...	...	...	1341	...	1404	...	...	...	...	1534	1604	|
	177	**Perpignan** **355** a.	...	...	...	0831	...	...	...	0946	...	...	1046	...	...	...	...	...	...	...	...	...	...	...	...	1442

	MD 15910 ⑤⑦	MD 15096 ①–⑥	AVE 3113 34113* ①–⑤		AVE 3123 34123* Ⓑ	MD 15098	TGV 9706 34607* CP❖		AVE 9724 19725* M	TGV 3143 34143 Ⓑ	MD 15080 Ⓐ	MD 15082 Ⓐ	MD 15922 Ⓒ	AVE 9726 31727* ET❖	MD 15084 Ⓐ	AVE 3153 34153*		AVE 3163 31163* ①–⑤	AVE 31399* ⑦	MD 15086 Ⓐ	MD 15088 Ⓒ	MD 15006 Ⓑ	AVE 3183 31183* ⑥	AVE 3191 31191* Ⓑ	MD 15916	
Madrid ⊠ **660** d.	...	...	1130	...	1230	...	...	...	1325	1430	...	...	...	...	...	1530	...	1630	...	...	...	...	1830	1900	...	...
Barcelona Sants **666** d.	1346	1416	1450	1516	1540	1616	1620	1716	1645	1737	1746	1816	1819	1830	1846	1850	1916	1925z	1945	1946	2016	2046	2130	2140	2146	...
Barcelona P de G ¶ d.	1351	1421	|	1521	|	1621	|	1721	|	|	1751	1821	1824	|	1851	|	1920	|	|	1951	2021	2051	|	|	2151	...
Granollers Centre d.	|	|	|	1548	|	|	|	1748	|	|	|	|	|	|	|	|	1947	|	|	|	|	|	|	|	|	...
Maçanet - Massanes **666** d.	1443	1513	|	1621	|	1713	|	1821	|	|	1843	1913	1920	|	1945	|	2026	|	|	2043	2113	2157	|	|	2250	...
Caldes de Malavella d.	1454	1524	|	1641	|	1724	|	1841	|	|	1854	1924	1931	|	1956	|	2037	|	|	2054	2124	2206	|	|	2301	...
Girona d.	1505	1535	1531	1656	1620	1735	1701	1856	1726	1817	1905	1935	1942	1911	2007	1930	2054	2005z	2025	2105	2135	2217	2210	2220	2311	...
Flaçà d.	1518t	1548	|	1711	|	1748	|	1911	|	|	1918	1948	1955	|	2020	|	2108	|	|	2118	2148	2229	|	|	2323	...
Figueres § d.	1537t	1607	|	1734	|	1806	|	1934	|	|	1937	2006	2013	|	2038	|	2130	|	|	2138	2206	2246	|	|	2341	...
Figueres Vilafant § d.	|	|	1545	|	1635	...	1718	|	1743	1832	|	...	...	1928	...	1945	|	2020z	2040	...	...	...	2225	2235	...	...
Llançà d.	1550t	1620f	...	1749	...	...	|	1949	|	...	1950	...	...	|	...	...	2145	...	...	...	...	...	...	...	...	...
Portbou 🏢 **355** a.	1557t	1627f	...	1800	...	...	|	2000	|	...	1957	...	...	|	...	...	2155	...	...	...	...	...	...	...	...	...
Cerbère 🏢 **355** a.	...	...	...	1804	...	...	|	2004	|	...	...	...	...	|	...	...	...	...	...	...	...	...	...	...	...	...
Perpignan **355** a.	...	...	...	...	...	...	1742	...	1804	...	...	...	...	1952	...	...	...	...	...	...	...	...	...	...	...	...

	MD 15010 Ⓐ	MD 15046 ①–⑥	AVE 3662 34662* ①–⑤	AVE 3082 31082* ①–⑤	MD 15060 Ⓐ	MD 15060 Ⓒ	Av 31472* ①–⑤	①–⑥	AVE 3092 31092* ①–⑥	MD 15064 ⑦	MD 15066 ①–⑥	AVE 3102 31102*		MD 15068	AVE 9729 31628* BT❖	Ⓒ	Ⓐ	AVE 9731 34730* M	MD 15070	TGV 9711 34610* CP❖	Ⓒ	Ⓐ	MD 15090	AVE 3162 31162* ①–⑥	Ⓒ	Ⓐ
Perpignan **355** d.	...	...	...	...	...	...	...	...	...	...	...	...	...	...	1000	...	...	1117	...	1212	...	...	...	...	...	...
Portbou 🏢 **355** d.	...	...	...	...	0623	...	...	0703	...	...	...	...	0833	...	|	1020	1027	|	1127	|	1210	1227	1327	...	1417	1427
Llançà d.	...	...	...	...	0630	...	...	0712	...	...	...	...	0842	...	|	1030	1037	|	1135	|	1220	1237	1335	...	1427	1437
Figueres Vilafant § d.	...	...	0630	0655	|	...	0720	|	0755	...	...	0855	|	...	1026	|	|	1143	|	1239	|	|	|	1455	|	|
Figueres § d.	0544	0555	|	|	0643	0643	|	0728	|	0749	0819	|	0858	0949	|	1047	1054	|	1149	|	1237	1254	1349	|	1444	1454
Flaçà d.	0600	0615	|	|	0659	0659	|	0750	|	0805	0835	|	0920	1005	|	1107	1114	|	1205	|	1257	1314	1405	|	1504	1514
Girona d.	0614	0629	0646	0711	0713	0713	0736	0806	0811	0819	0849	0911	0936	1019	1043	1123	1130	1200	1219	1256	1313	1330	1419	1511	1520	1530
Caldes de Malavella d.	0624	0640	|	|	0724	0724	|	0820	|	0829	0859	|	0950	1029	|	1138	1145	|	1229	|	1328	1345	1429	|	1535	1545
Maçanet - Massanes **666** d.	0635	0651	|	|	0735	0735	|	0831	|	0839	0909	|	1001	1039	|	1157	1204	|	1239	|	1347	1404	1439	|	1554	1604
Granollers Centre d.	|	|	|	|	|	|	|	0905	|	|	|	|	1035	|	|	1238	1238	|	|	|	1421	1438	|	|	1635	1638
Barcelona P de G ¶ a.	0735	0749	|	|	0835	0835	|	0934	|	0935	1005	|	1105	1135	|	1305	1305	|	1335	|	1448	1505	1535	|	1705	1705
Barcelona Sants **666** a.	0739	0753	0725	0750	0839	0839	0815	0939	0850	0939	1009	0950	1109	1139	1121	1309	1309	1238	1339	1334	1452	1509	1539	1550	1709	1709
Madrid ⊠ **660** a.	...	...	1010	1110	...	...	...	...	1145	...	...	1310	...	...	...	...	...	1545	...	...	...	...	...	1910	...	...

	TGV 9713 34712* P	AVE 3172 34172* ⑦	MD 15072	Ⓒ	Ⓐ	AVE 3182 34182*	AVE 3180 ⑦	⑥	MD 15018 Ⓐ	MD 15018 ⑦	AVE 3192 34192*	MD 15092 Ⓐ	MD 15092 Ⓒ	Ⓐ	MD 15918 ⑦	AVE 9743 34742* L	MD 15074 Ⓑ	MD 15920 ⑥	Ⓒ	TGV 9715 34714* P	Ⓐ	Ⓒ	AVE 34222*	TGV 9717 AP	Ⓐ	Ⓒ
Perpignan **355** d.	1513	...	...	...	...	...	...	...	...	...	...	...	...	...	...	1810	...	...	...	1913	...	...	...	2125	...	...
Portbou 🏢 **355** d.	|	...	1527j	1547	1557	...	...	1633	...	...	...	...	1727	1727	1757	|	...	...	1841	|	1857	1935	...	|	2019	2024
Llançà d.	|	...	1535j	1556	1607	...	...	1642	...	...	...	...	1735	1737	1805	|	...	...	1851	|	1907	1945	...	|	2027	2033
Figueres Vilafant § d.	1539	1545	|	|	|	1655	1720	|	...	...	1755	...	|	|	|	1836	...	...	|	1939	|	|	2045	2150	|	|
Figueres § d.	|	|	1549	1612	1624	|	|	1658	1719	...	|	...	1749	1754	1819	|	1849	1856	1906	|	1924	2002	|	|	2042	2048
Flaçà d.	|	|	1605	1628	1644	|	|	1720	1735	...	|	...	1805	1814	1835	|	1905	1912	1926	|	1944	2023	|	|	2058	2106
Girona d.	1556	1601	1619	1642	1700	1711	1736	1736	1749	1749	1811	1819	1819	1830	1849	1853	1919	1926	1942	1956	2000	2039	2101	2207	2112	2120
Caldes de Malavella d.	|	|	1629	1652	1715	|	|	1750	1759	1759	|	1829	1829	1845	1859	|	1929	1936	1956	|	2015	2054	|	|	2122	2133
Maçanet - Massanes **666** d.	|	|	1639	1711	1734	|	|	1801	1809	1809	|	1839	1839	1904	1909	|	1939	1946	2015	|	2034	2113	|	|	2141	2152
Granollers Centre d.	|	|	|	|	1808	|	|	1835	|	|	|	|	|	1938	|	|	|	|	|	|	2108	2147	|	|	|	2225
Barcelona P de G ¶ a.	|	|	1735	1805	1835	|	|	1905	1905	1905	|	1935	1935	2005	2005	|	2035	2042	2105	|	2135	2215	|	|	2235	2252
Barcelona Sants **666** a.	1634	1640	1739	1809	1839	1750	1815	1909	1909	1909	1850	1939	1939	2009	2009	1931	2039	2046	2109	2034	2139	2219	2140	2244	2239	2255
Madrid ⊠ **660** a.	...	1945	...	...	...	2110	2055	...	...	...	2200	...	...	...	...	...	...	...	...	...	...	...	...	...	...	...

		J				Ⓐ					
Portbou 🏢 d.	...	1216	...	1416	...	1616	...	...	1916	...	...
Cerbère 🏢 a.	...	1222	...	1422	...	1622	...	...	1922	...	...

	Ⓐ	Ⓒ	Ⓐ	J	Ⓐ		Ⓐ	Ⓐ	Ⓒ	Ⓐ				
Cerbère 🏢 d.	0912	0942	1021	1132	1212	1332	1412	1532	1542	1612	1755	1812	1927	2012
Portbou 🏢 a.	0916	0946	1025	1136	1216	1336	1416	1536	1546	1616	1759	1816	1931	2016

A – June 30 - Aug. 26.
B – Apr. 3 - Sept. 25.
C – June 2 - Aug. 27.
E – Mar. 23 - Sept. 24.
J – Not Feb. 18 - Mar. 23.

L – To/from Lyon (Table **13**).
M – To/from Marseille (Table **13**).
P – To/from Paris (Table **13**).
T – To/from Toulouse (Table **13**).

f – ⑥ only.
j – Ⓒ only.
t – ⑦ only.
x – 0620 on ⑥⑦.

⊠ – Madrid Puerta de Atocha.
* – Train number for *Turista class (classified Av)*.
¶ – Barcelona Passeig de Gràcia.

❖ – Service runs Barcelona - Girona - Figueres and v.v. when International service does not run.

§ – **FIGUERES VILAFANT - FIGUERES BUS STATION (150m from Figueres)**. *5 km*. By 🚌. Journey time: 15 - 20 minutes.

From **Figueres Vilafant**: 0835 Ⓐ, 1020, 1050, 1125, 1150, 1255, 1345, 1550 Ⓐ, 1645 Ⓑ, 1725, 1830, 1935, 1955, 2035 Ⓐ, 2240.

From **Figueres Bus Station**: 0600 Ⓐ, 0625 Ⓐ, 0725 ⚒, 0815, 0945, 1030, 1105, 1215, 1425 ⚒, 1515 ⑦, 1625, 1740, 1810, 1845, 1915, 2015, 2205.

2nd class VALL DE NÚRIA 658

Ribes Enllaç - **Ribes** Vila - **Queralbs** - **Núria** rack railway

HIGH SEASON:

⑥⑦ (daily July 15 - Sept. 11), also Apr. 1, May 1, 20, June 24, Nov. 1:
From **Ribes** Enllaç: 0735 **v**, 0830 **n**, 0920 and hourly until 1730, also 1840 **c**.
From **Núria**: 0830, 0920 **n**, 1020 and hourly until 1820, also 1930 **c**.

LOW SEASON:

①–⑤ (except dates above). No service from Nov. 4 (resumes early December)
From **Ribes** Enllaç: 0730 **v**, 0910, 1110, 1250, 1440, 1630, 1820 ⑤
From **Núria**: 0820, 1000, 1200, 1345, 1530, 1720, 1910 ⑤.

Journey times **Ribes** – **Queralbs** (*6 km*) 24 minutes, **Ribes** – **Núria** (*12 km*) 44 minutes.

Ferrocarrils de la Generalitat de Catalunya (FGC) ✆ +34 972 73 20 20. www.valldenuria.cat

c – ⑤ (also July 27, Aug. 3 - 31, Sept. 1, 7, 11).
n – Ski season only, also ⑥⑦ in June and July (daily July 29 - Sept. 1).
v – From Ribes Vila.

2nd class AEROPORT BARCELONA 659

Local rail service *Cercanías* (suburban) line **R2 Nord**. *14km*

Aeroport - Barcelona Sants – Barcelona Passeig de Gràcia

Journey time: 19 minutes Sants, 26 minutes Passeig de Gràcia

From Aeroport del Prat:

0542, 0608, 0638, 0708, 0738 and every 30 minutes until 2208, 2238, 2308, 2338.

From Barcelona Sants:

0513, 0535, 0609, 0639, 0709 and every 30 minutes until 2139, 2209, 2239, 2314.

660 MADRID - CÓRDOBA - SEVILLA and MÁLAGA — High-speed services

Buses replace trains between Antequera - Santa Ana and Granada until Summer 2019. See Table 678a for provisional timetable Madrid - Granada from June 24.

km		Av 2260	AVE 2070	AVE 2072	AVE 2072	AVE 2080	AVE 2082	Alvia 2084	Alta 9366	AVE 2090	AVE 3982	AVE 2092	Alvia 2294	IC 2494	Alvia 2094	AVE 2100	Alvia 2294	IC 2494	AVE 2102	AVE 2110	Alvia 2114	AVE 3940	AVE 3990	AVE 2112	AVE 2120	AVE 3944	AVE 3994	AVE 2130	AVE 2122
		①-⑤	①-⑤	①-⑤	⑥⑦	①-⑥	①-④				①-⑥		⑦			①-⑥	⑦	①-⑥	①-⑥									Ⓑ	
		D ⋙	D								V		J	L	N		N	N			G					B	B		
	Barcelona Sants **650** . d.	...	...	...	...	...	...	...	...	...	...	...	...	...	...	...	...	...	...	...	...	0830	0830	...	...	0940	0940	...	...
0	**Madrid** Puerta de Atocha d.	0620	0700	0720	0735	0800	0825	0830	0835	0900	...	0935	0945	0945	0945	1000	1025	1025	1035	1100	1105	│	│	1135	1200	│	│	1300	1300
171	Ciudad Real d.	0720	│	│	│	│	│	0924	0937	0951	1021	1026	│	│	│	│	│	│	│	│	│	1213	1213	│	│	│	│	1351	1351
210	Puertollano d.	0738	│	│	│	│	│	0941	0953	1007	1037	1044	│	│	│	│	│	│	│	│	│	1229	1229	│	│	│	│	1407	1407
345	**Córdoba** d.	0830	0845	0902	0917	0945	│	1026	1039	1054	1121	1127	1132	1132	1133	1145	1222	1222	│	1245	│	1319	1330	1324	1345	1406	1416	1452	1505j
470	**Sevilla** a.	0916	0932	│	│	1032	│	1114	│	1138	1205	│	│	1225	1225	1232	│	1314	│	1332	│	1402	│	│	1432	1455	│	1540	│
	Cádiz **671** a.	...	...	│	│	...	│	1248	│	...	...	│	│	│	1400	...	│	│	│	...	1513	...	│	│	...	...	│	...	│
	Huelva **671** a.	...	...	│	│	...	│	...	│	...	...	│	1320	1352	...	...	1415	1450	│	...	...	...	│	│	...	...	│	...	│
419	Puente Genil - Herrera ¶ a.	...	...	0923	0938	...	│	...	│	...	...	│	...	...	...	...	...	...	│	...	...	...	1350	│	...	...	1438	...	1526j
455	Antequera - Santa Ana § a.	...	...	0937	0952	...	│	...	1117	...	...	1155	...	...	...	...	...	...	│	...	...	...	1402	1352	...	...	1452	...	1539j
	Algeciras **673** a.	...	...	│	│	...	│	...	1348	...	...	│	...	...	...	...	...	...	│	...	...	...	│	│	...	...	│	...	│
	Granada **673** a.	...	...	*1130*¦	*1130*¦	...	│	...	...	...	...	*1330*¦	...	...	...	...	...	...	│	...	...	...	*1610*¦	│	...	...	*1630*¦	...	│
513	**Málaga** María Zambrano . a.	...	...	1005	1020	...	1049	...	...	...	...	1222	...	...	...	...	...	...	1259	...	...	...	1424	1417	...	...	1516	...	1605j

	Alvia 2134	AVE 2140	AVE 2142	AVE 2142	AVE 2150	Alta 9330	AVE 2152	AVE 2160	Alvia 2164	IC 2364	AVE 2360	AVE 2162	AVE 2170	AVE 2172	AVE 2180	Alvia 2384	AVE 2182	AVE 3942	AVE 3992	AVE 3974	Alvia 2184	AVE 2190	AVE 3946	AVE 2390	AVE 2192	AVE 2200	AVE 2202	Av 2410	AVE 2212
			Ⓑ	⑥	Ⓑ		Ⓑ			⑤	Ⓑ					Ⓑ	Ⓑ			①⑤⑦			⑤						⑤⑦
					D	◐				R	D									E	S		K	H				⋙	
Barcelona Sants **650** .. d.	...	...	...	...	...	...	...	...	...	...	...	...	...	...	...	...	...	1550	1550	...	...	...	1632	...	...	...	...	...	...
Madrid Puerta de Atocha d.	1330	1400	1435	1435	1500	1505	1535	1600	1615	1620	1630	1635	1700	1735	1800	1805	1830	│	│	...	1835	1900	│	1930	1930	2035	2035	2125	2120
Ciudad Real d.	1421	│	│	│	│	│	│	│	│	│	│	│	1752	1826	│	│	│	1936	1936	1942	│	1951	│	│	│	2126	2126	2219	│
Puertollano d.	1435	│	│	│	│	│	│	│	│	│	│	│	1807	1842	│	│	│	│	│	1957	│	2007	│	│	│	2142	2142	2234	│
Córdoba d.	1517	1545	1619	1619	│	1708	1725	1744	│	│	│	1819	1854	1925	1945	1952	│	2030	2040	2045	2016	2054	2056	2114	2132	2227	2240	2324	│
Sevilla a.	1605	1632	│	│	1721	│	│	1830	│	1852	1851	│	1938	│	2032	│	│	2115	│	│	2106	2138	2143	2205	│	2315	│	0010	│
Cádiz **671** a.	1740	...	│	│	...	│	│	...	2015	│	...	│	...	│	...	│	│	...	│	│	2239	...	...	...	│	...	│	...	│
Huelva **671** a.	...	...	│	│	...	│	│	...	...	2026	...	│	...	│	...	2155	│	...	│	│	...	...	...	...	│	...	│	...	│
Puente Genil - Herrera ¶. a.	...	...	│	│	...	│	│	...	...	...	...	│	...	1946	...	...	│	...	2103	2110	...	...	...	...	│	...	2302	...	│
Antequera - Santa Ana §. a.	...	...	1654	1654	...	1753	1757	...	...	...	...	│	...	1959	...	...	│	...	2117	2125	...	...	...	...	│	...	2315	...	│
Algeciras **673** a.	...	...	│	│	...	2030	│	...	...	...	...	│	...	│	...	...	│	...	│	│	...	...	...	...	│	...	│	...	│
Granada **673** a.	...	...	*1820*¦	│	...	...	│	...	...	...	...	│	...	*2130*¦	...	...	│	...	*2300*¦	*2300*¦	...	...	...	...	│	...	│	...	│
Málaga María Zambrano . a.	...	...	1718	1718	...	...	1820	...	...	...	...	1908	...	2025	...	...	2054	...	2140	2151	...	...	...	...	2220	...	2340	...	2345

	Av 2261	AVE 2063	AVE 2061	AVE 2073	AVE 2471	AVE 2271	AVE 2071	AVE 2083	AVE 2081	AVE 3993	AVE 3943	Alvia 2285	AVE 2093	AVE 2091	Alvia 2085	AVE 3971	AVE 2101	AVE 2113	Alta 9367	Alvia 2205	AVE 2111	AVE 2123	Alvia 2105	AVE 2121	AVE 2131	AVE 2143	AVE 2141	AVE 3991	AVE 3941
	①-⑤	①-④	①-⑤	①-④	⑥⑦	①-④	①-⑥					①-⑤		①-⑥		⑤⑥								Ⓑ			Ⓑ		
	D★	D	D	D	P	D						D				U				T			G						
Málaga María Zambrano . d.	...	0620	...	0710	...	...	...	0800	...	0840	...	...	0900	...	...	0945	...	1055	...	...	...	1205	...	...	...	1405	...	1435	...
Granada **673** d.	...	│	...	│	...	...	...	*0655*¦	...	*0645*¦	...	...	│	...	...	*0830*¦	...	*1000*¦	...	...	...	│	...	...	...	│	...	*1245*¦	...
Algeciras **673** d.	...	│	...	│	...	...	...	│	...	│	...	...	│	...	...	│	...	│	0843	...	...	│	...	...	...	│	...	│	...
Antequera - Santa Ana §. d.	...	0644	...	│	...	...	...	0823	...	0902	...	...	0926	...	...	1008	...	1123	│	...	...	│	...	...	...	1429	...	1500	...
Puente Genil - Herrera ¶. d.	...	0657	...	│	...	...	...	│	...	0916	...	...	│	...	...	1021	...	│	│	...	...	│	...	...	...	1442	...	1513	...
Huelva **671** d.	...	│	...	│	...	...	...	│	...	│	...	0800	│	...	...	│	...	│	│	1025	...	│	...	...	...	│	...	│	...
Cádiz **671** d.	...	│	...	│	...	...	...	│	...	│	...	│	│	...	0815	│	...	│	│	│	...	│	1050	...	...	│	...	│	...
Sevilla d.	0610	│	0645	│	0700	0715	0745	│	0845	│	0850	│	│	0945	0950	│	1045	│	│	│	1145	│	│	1245	1340	│	1445	│	1450
Córdoba d.	0653	0722	0729	│	0750	0803	│	0856	0929	0943	0943	0950	0959	1028	1042	1051	1129	1156	1202	1218	1229	1301	│	1328	│	1506	1529	1542	1542
Puertollano d.	0744	│	│	│	0841	0845	│	│	│	│	│	│	1041	1111	1125	1135	│	│	│	│	│	│	│	1411	│	1548	│	1625	1625
Ciudad Real d.	0759	│	│	│	0858	0859	│	│	│	1039	1039	│	1057	1126	1140	1148	│	│	│	│	│	│	│	1426	│	1603	│	1641	1641
Madrid Puerta de Atocha a.	0858	0908	0915	0938	1002	0955	1006	1040	1115	│	│	1141	1150	1223	1236	...	1317	1340	1405	1410	1417	1445	1458	1523	1610	1655	1715	│	│
Barcelona Sants **650** .. a.	...	...	...	...	...	...	...	...	...	1425	1425	...	...	...	...	...	...	...	...	...	...	...	...	...	...	...	...	2022	2022

	AVE 2153	Alvia 2135	AVE 2151	AVE 3995	AVE 3945	AVE 2163	AVE 2163	AVE 2361	AVE 2161	Alvia 2155	AVE 3973	AVE 2173	Alvia 2365	AVE 2171	Alta 9331	AVE 2183	AVE 3981	AVE 2181	IC 2375	Alvia 2175	AVE 2391	AVE 2193	AVE 2191	AVE 2391	AVE 2203	Alvia 2195	Av 2411	AVE 2213	
	Ⓑ					Ⓑ	⑥	Ⓑ			⑦		⑦				Ⓑ							④⑤⑦				⑤⑦	
				A	A			D		N	F				★		V		Q			H				S	★	X	
Málaga María Zambrano . d.	1500	...	...	1535	...	1555	1555	...	...	...	1638	1700	...	...	...	1810	...	...	...	...	...	1905	...	...	2005	...	...	2120	...
Granada **673** d.	│	...	...	*1400*¦	...	*1500*¦	│	...	...	...	*1520*¦	│	...	...	...	│	...	...	...	...	...	│	...	...	*1900*¦	...	...	│	...
Algeciras **673** d.	│	...	...	│	...	│	│	...	...	...	│	│	...	...	1503	│	...	...	...	...	...	│	...	...	│	...	...	│	...
Antequera - Santa Ana §. d.	│	...	...	1557	...	1623	1623	...	...	...	1701	1724	...	...	1733	│	...	...	...	...	...	1929	...	...	2030	...	...	│	...
Puente Genil - Herrera ¶. d.	│	...	...	1611	...	│	│	...	...	...	1714	1737	...	...	│	│	...	...	...	...	...	│	...	...	2044	...	...	│	...
Huelva **671** d.	│	...	...	│	...	│	│	...	...	...	│	│	1620	...	│	│	...	...	1750	...	...	│	...	...	│	...	...	│	...
Cádiz **671** d.	│	1333	...	│	...	│	│	...	...	1505	│	│	│	...	│	│	...	...	│	1728	...	│	...	...	│	1855	...	│	...
Sevilla d.	│	1458	1545	│	1555	│	│	1615	1645	1643	│	│	│	1745	│	│	1825	1845	│	│	1915	│	1945	2015	│	2036	2100	│	...
Córdoba d.	│	1554	1629	1641	1641	1656	1656	1700	1729	1731	1743	1802	1810	1829	1815	1900	1909	1929	1919	│	│	2001	2029	│	2110	2127	2148	2208	...
Puertollano d.	│	1637	│	│	│	│	│	1742	│	│	1827	│	│	│	1919	│	1952	│	│	│	│	│	│	│	2153	│	2238	│	...
Ciudad Real d.	│	1652	│	│	│	│	│	1756	│	│	1843	│	│	│	1936	│	2005	│	│	│	│	│	│	│	2208	│	2255	│	...
Madrid Puerta de Atocha a.	1742	1750	1815	│	│	1841	1841	1854	1917	1920	...	1945	2003	2017	2035	2045	...	2117	2159	2127	2135	2145	2217	2236	2302	2314	2352	2356	...
Barcelona Sants **650** .. a.	...	...	...	2115	2115	...	...	...	...	...	...	...	...	...	...	...	...	...	...	...	...	...	...	...	...	...	...	...	...

A – Ⓑ Apr. 7 - May 31.
B – ①-⑥ Apr. 7 - May 31.
D – Not July 24 - Sept. 3.
E – ①⑤⑦ (Ⓑ July 14 - Sept. 10). From València (Table **668**).
F – ⑦. To València (Table **668**).
G – ①②③⑥ July 4 - Sept. 30.
H – ③④⑤⑦.
J – July 9-23.
K – Not July 8 - Sept 9.
L – ①-⑥ Mar. 17 - July 21, Sept. 3 - Oct. 13.
N – July 24 - Sept. 3.
P – ⑥⑦ (daily July 25 - Sept. 4).
Q – ⑦ (Ⓑ Mar. 21 - Oct. 15).
R – Until Mar. 20 and from Oct. 16.
S – ⑤⑦ (Ⓑ Mar. 21 - Oct. 15).
T – ⑥ (daily July 24 - Sept. 3).
U – ⑤⑥ (②③④⑤⑥ July 14 - Sept. 15). To València (Table **668**).
V – From/to València (Table **668**).
X – ⑤⑦ (Ⓑ July 25 - Sept. 4).
j – 15 minutes earlier on ⑥.
t – By 🚌.
¶ – ± *8 km* from Puente Genil.
§ – ± *17 km* from Antequera.
‡ – Antequera - Ciudad.

★ – Also calls at Villanueva de CLP (⊠), 23-24 mins. after departing Córdoba.
◐ – Also calls at Villanueva de CLP (⊠), 100 mins. after departing Madrid.
⋙ – Also calls at Villanueva de CLP (⊠), 25-28 mins. after departing Puertollano.
⊠ – Full name: Villanueva de Córdoba-Los Pedroches.
¦ – 🚌 Antequera-Santa Ana - Granada and v.v. Until Summer 2019.
☛ All trains convey 🍸. *AVE* trains also convey ✕.

Avant high-speed shuttle services — Málaga – Córdoba – Sevilla — *Turista* class; 🍸

	8654	8664	8664	8694	8714	8744	8764	8784	8804
	①-⑤	①-⑤			①-⑤		①-⑤		
Málaga María Zambrano d.	...	0645	...	0910	...	1415	1615	1820	2015
Antequera - Santa Ana § d.	...	0711	...	0936	...	1441	1641	1844	2041
Puente Genil - Herrera ¶ d.	...	0725	...	0950	...	1455	1655	1858	2055
Córdoba a.	...	0750	...	1015	...	1520	1720	1922	2120
Córdoba d.	0650	0755	0755	1020	1300	1525	1725	1930	2125
Sevilla a.	0735	0840	0840	1105	1345	1610	1810	2015	2210

	8075	8085	8095	8095	8125	8155	8175	8195	8215	
	①-⑤	①-⑤	⑥⑦				①-⑤			
Sevilla d.	0650	0800	0920	0920	1250	1540	1755	1935	2135	...
Córdoba a.	0735	0845	1005	1005	1335	1625	1840	2020	2220	...
Córdoba d.	0740	0855	1010	...	1340	1630	1845	2025	...	...
Puente Genil - Herrera ¶ d.	0803	0918	1033	...	1403	1653	1908	2048	...	...
Antequera - Santa Ana § d.	0817	0932	1047	...	1417	1707	1922	2102	...	...
Málaga María Zambrano a.	0845	1000	1115	...	1445	1735	1950	2130	...	...

§ – ± *17 km* from Antequera. ¶ – ± *8 km* from Puente Genil.

Avant high-speed shuttle services — Madrid – Puertollano — *Turista* class; 🍸

		8260		8080		8100			8130	8140		8150		8170	8180	8190	8200		8220					
		①-⑤		①-⑥						①-⑤		①-⑥			①-⑤		Ⓑ							
Madrid Puerta de Atocha d.	...	0640	...	0805	...	1015	...	...	1315	1415	...	1545	...	1715	1815	1915	2015	...	2215	...	...	...	...	...
Ciudad Real d.	...	0736	...	0901	...	1111	...	...	1411	1511	...	1641	...	1812	1911	2011	2111	...	2311	...	...	...	...	...
Puertollano a.	...	0753	...	0918	...	1128	...	...	1428	1528	...	1658	...	1828	1928	2028	2128	...	2328	...	...	...	...	...

		8261		8271	8471	8081	8081		8101		8121			8151	8161	8171	8181	8191		8211				
		①-⑤		①-⑤	①-⑤	①-⑤	⑥							①-⑥	①-⑤		⑦							
Puertollano d.	...	0625	...	0700	0750	0815	0815	...	1015	...	1215	...	...	1515	1615	1715	1820	1915	...	2115	...	...	...	...
Ciudad Real d.	...	0642	...	0717	0807	0832	0832	...	1032	...	1232	...	...	1532	1632	1732	1837	1932	...	2132	...	...	...	...
Madrid Puerta de Atocha a.	...	0742	...	0813	0903	0928	0939	...	1128	...	1329	...	...	1628	1728	1828	1932	2028	...	2228	...	...	...	...

MADRID - ALMERÍA and JAÉN 661

For other trains Madrid – Córdoba – Granada / Málaga and v.v. via the AVE high-speed line, see Table 660

km		MD 17008 2 ①–⑤	MD 13079 2 E		Talgo 276 🍷	MD 18030 2		MD 18170 2 C	MD 13083 2 E	MD 13035 2 E	Talgo 697 🍷 N	MD 13073 2 E		Talgo 278 🍷	MD 18032 2 ①–⑤		Talgo 230 🍷 ❦	MD 18034 2 Ⓑ		MD 18036 2		MD 17000 2	
0	**Madrid** Chamartín ... **668a 669** d.	...	...	...	0800	0916	...	1258	...	...	...	...	...	1456	1545	...	1658	1720	...	1918	...	2114	...
8	**Madrid** Atocha Cercanías **668a 669** d.	0713	...	...	0819	0929	...	1310	...	...	...	...	...	1513	1559	...	1718	1734	...	1932	...	2128	...
57	Aranjuez ... **668a 669** d.	0751	...	...	|	1004	...	1342	...	...	...	...	...	|	1634	...	|	|	...	2010	...	2207	...
	Barcelona Sants **672** ... d.	|	...	...	|	|	...	|	...	...	0930	...	...	|	|	...	|	|	...	|	...	|	...
	València Nord **668** ... d.	|	...	...	|	|	...	|	...	...	1300	...	...	|	|	...	|	|	...	|	...	|	...
157	Alcázar de San Juan ... **678** d.	0840	...	...	0937	1101	...	1435	...	...	1603	...	...	1634	1723	...	|	1854	...	2101	...	2301	...
206	Manzanares ... **678** d.	...	...	...	|	1125	...	1459	...	...	1626	...	...	1657	1747	...	|	1918	...	2124	...	...	...
323	Linares - Baeza ... a.	...	...	...	1117	1249	...	...	...	...	1745	...	...	1811	1911	...	2020	2039	...	2241	...	...	...
323	Linares - Baeza ... d.	...	...	...	1119	1250	...	...	...	...	1747	...	...	1813	1912	...	2022	2040	...	2242	...	...	...
441	Moreda ... d.	...	...	...	|	|	...	...	...	...	|	...	...	1951	|	...	|	|	...	|	...	...	...
499	**Granada** ... **673** a.	...	...	...	|	|	...	...	...	...	|	...	...	|	|	...	2233	|	...	|	...	...	...
466	Guadix ... **673** d.	...	...	...	1304	|	...	...	...	...	|	...	...	2013	|	...	...	|	...	|	...	...	...
565	**Almería** ... **673** a.	...	...	...	1417	|	...	...	...	...	|	...	...	2129	|	...	...	|	...	|	...	...	...
¶	**Jaén** ... d.	...	0637	...	...	1333	...	...	1430	1650	|	1830	...	...	1955	...	...	2125	...	2325	...	...	...
371	Andújar ... d.	...	0720	...	...	...	...	...	1514	1737	1831	1913	...	...	...	...	...	...	...	...	...	...	...
450	**Córdoba** ... a.	...	0810	...	...	...	...	...	1610	1828	1926	2007	...	...	...	...	...	...	...	...	...	...	...

	MD 18047 2 ①–⑤		MD 18031 2 ①–⑤		MD 18033 2	Talgo 231 🍷 ❦	Talgo 277 🍷		MD 13001 2 ①–⑤ E	Talgo 694 🍷 N	MD 18171 2		MD 13003 2 ⑥⑦ E	MD 17041 2 C		MD 18035 2	MD 13009 2 E	MD 18037 2	MD 13011 2 T	Talgo 279 🍷		MD 13017 🍷 E	
Córdoba ... d.	...	...	...	...	...	...	...	...	0906	0950	...	...	1002	...	...	...	1451	...	1626	...	...	2105	...
Andújar ... d.	...	...	...	...	...	...	...	...	0959	1040	...	...	1056	...	...	...	1544	...	1720	...	...	2157	...
Jaén ... d.	...	...	0610	...	0830	...	...	...	1049	|	...	...	1143	...	...	1520	1629	1718	1811	...	...	2245	...
Almería ... **673** d.	...	...	|	...	|	...	0735	...	...	|	...	...	...	...	...	|	...	|	...	1605	...	...	...
Guadix ... **673** d.	...	...	|	...	|	...	0852	...	...	|	...	...	...	...	...	|	...	|	...	1719	...	...	...
Granada ... **673** d.	...	...	|	...	|	0735	|	...	...	|	...	...	...	...	...	|	...	|	...	|	...	...	...
Moreda ... d.	...	...	|	...	|	|	0913	...	...	|	...	...	...	...	...	|	...	|	...	|	...	...	...
Linares - Baeza ... a.	...	...	0650	...	0912	0942	1044	...	...	1117	...	...	...	...	...	1602	...	1800	...	1914	...	...	...
Linares - Baeza ... d.	...	...	0651	...	0913	0944	1046	...	...	1120	...	...	...	...	...	1603	...	1801	...	1916	...	...	...
Manzanares ... **678** d.	...	...	0807	...	1032	|	|	...	...	1237	...	...	...	1520	...	1723	...	1921	...	2035	...	...	...
Alcázar de San Juan ... **678** d.	0527	...	0832	...	1055	|	1223	...	...	1315	1355	...	...	1546	...	1745	...	1946	...	2059	...	...	...
València Nord **668** ... a.	|	...	|	...	|	|	|	...	...	1605	|	...	...	|	...	|	...	|	...	|	...	...	...
Barcelona Sants **672** ... a.	|	...	|	...	|	|	|	...	...	2000	|	...	...	|	...	|	...	|	...	|	...	...	...
Aranjuez ... **668a 669** d.	0621	...	0918	...	1143	|	|	...	...	...	1447	...	...	1643	...	1830	...	2032	...	|	...	...	...
Madrid Atocha Cercanías **668a 669** a.	0656	...	0959	...	1214	1243	1343	...	...	...	1526	...	...	1717	...	1905	...	2109	...	2219	...	...	...
Madrid Chamartín ... **668a 669** a.	...	...	1013	...	1228	1259	1358	...	...	...	1541	...	...	1731	...	1919	...	2122	...	2233	...	...	...

C – To / from Ciudad Real (Table **678**).
E – To / from Cádiz (Table **671**).
N – TORRE DEL ORO – (12) 🍷 Barcelona - Córdoba - Sevilla and v.v. (Tables **671**, **672**, **678**).
T – Daily from Sevilla. From Cádiz on ①–⑤. Table **671**.
¶ – Linares - Jaen: *59 km*. Jaen - Andújar: *54 km*.
❦ – May not run from June 24.

2nd class MÁLAGA - TORREMOLINOS - FUENGIROLA 662

km					❦							
0	**Málaga** María Zambrano d.	0523	0558	0633	0653	and	2133	2203	2233	2303	2333	...
8	Málaga Aeropuerto ✈ d.	0532	0607	0642	0702	every	2142	2212	2242	2312	2342	...
16	**Torremolinos** d.	0543	0618	0653	0713	20	2153	2223	2253	2323	2353	...
20	Benalmádena d.	0554	0629	0704	0724	mins.	2204	2234	2304	2334	0004	...
31	**Fuengirola** a.	0606	0641	0716	0736	until	2216	2246	2316	2346	0016	...

				❦							
Fuengirola d.	0610	0645	0720	0740	and	2220	2250	2320	2350	0020	...
Benalmádena d.	0624	0659	0734	0754	every	2234	2304	2334	0004	0034	...
Torremolinos d.	0633	0708	0743	0803	20	2243	2313	2343	0013	0043	...
Málaga Aeropuerto ✈ d.	0644	0719	0754	0814	mins.	2254	2324	2354	0024	0054	...
Málaga María Zambrano a.	0652	0727	0802	0822	until	2302	2332	0002	0032	0102	...

❦ – 0653, 0733, 0813 from Málaga and 0740, 0820, 0900 from Fuengirola do not run on ⑥⑦.

🚌 BARCELONA - ANDORRA 664

From **Barcelona** Nord bus station: 0630*, 0700, 0730*, 1030, 1500, 1700*, 1900.
From **Andorra la Vella** bus station: 0600, 0815*, 1100, 1500, 1700*, 1915.
Journey 3 hr 15 min (* 4 hours). Operator: Alsina Graells, Barcelona (ALSA) ✆ (+34) 91 327 05 40.

From **Barcelona Airport** ✈ (T1 and T2): 0730, 0930, 1100, 1300, 1500, 1730, 2000, 2130, 2300.
From **Barcelona** Sants railway station: 0615, 0815, 1015, 1145, 1345, 1545, 1815, 2045, 2215, 2345.
From **Andorra la Vella** bus station: 0330, 0615, 0815, 1115, 1315, 1515, 1630, 1815, 2015, 2215.
Journey 3 hours (3 hrs 30 mins to / from Barcelona ✈). Operator: Autocars Nadal ✆ +376 805 151.

2nd class BARCELONA - SITGES - SANT V de CALDERS 665

Local rail service **Barcelona** - **Sitges** - **Sant Vicenç de Calders**.
From Barcelona Sants: 0606, 0636 and every 30 minutes until 2206; then 2306.
From Sant Vicenç: 0601, 0616 ⚒, 0631 Ⓐ, 0659, 0729, 0751, 0831, 0902, 0932 and every 30 minutes until 2102, 2132 Ⓐ, then 2200.

Additional trains operate **Barcelona** - **Sitges** and v.v.
Journey times: **Barcelona** – **Sitges** (*34 km*) 30 minutes,
Barcelona – **Sant Vicenç** (*60 km*) 57 minutes.

2nd class BARCELONA - MATARÓ, BLANES and MAÇANET 666

Cercanías (suburban) line **R1**. For faster services Barcelona - Maçanet via Granollers, see Table **657**.
Approximate journey times (in mins) to / from **Barcelona** Sants: Mataró (46), Arenys de Mar (57), Calella (69), Pineda de Mar (73), Malgrat de Mar (79), Blanes (84), Maçanet - Massanes (97).

Barcelona Sants – **Mataró** and v.v. *35 km*
Ⓐ: 4 – 6 trains per hour.
From Barcelona 0546 – 2354; from Mataró 0450 – 2313.
Ⓒ: 2 – 4 trains per hour.
From Barcelona 0612 – 0010; from Mataró 0457 – 2220.

Barcelona Sants – **Blanes** *67 km*
0612, 0642 and every 30 mins. until 2042, then 2112 Ⓒ, 2124 Ⓐ, 2142 Ⓒ, 2154 Ⓐ, 2213 Ⓒ, 2224 Ⓐ.
Blanes - **Barcelona** Sants
Ⓐ: 2 trains per hour, 0617 – 2115, 2155
Ⓒ: 2 trains per hour; 0603 – 2103, 2144.

Barcelona Sants – Blanes – **Maçanet - Massanes** *82 km*
Ⓐ: 0546 and hourly until 2045, 2124, 2154.
Ⓒ: 0612 and hourly until 2012, then 2042, 2142.
Maçanet - Massanes – Blanes – **Barcelona** Sants
Ⓐ: 0605, 0636, 0704, 0734, 0804 and hourly until 2103
Ⓒ: 0620, 0650, 0720 and hourly until 2020, then 2130.

2nd class ALACANT - BENIDORM - DÉNIA 667

◐ *By tram (route L1)*	①–⑤								
Alacant Luceros ⊙ d.	...	0541	0611	0711	every	1911	2011	2111	2211
El Campello d.	...	0609	0639	0739	hour	1939	2039	2139	2239
La Vila Joiosa d.	0612	0635	0705	0805	◐	2005	2105	2205	2305
Benidorm a.	0630	0653	0723	0823	until	2023	2123	2223	2323

✣ *By tram (route L1)*	①–⑤								
Benidorm d.	0635	0705	0805	every	1905	2005	2105	2205	2235
La Vila Joiosa d.	0653	0723	0823	hour	1923	2023	2123	2223	2253
El Campello d.	0723	0753	0853	✣	1953	2053	2153	2253	...
Alacant Luceros ⊙ a.	0751	0821	0921	until	2021	2121	2221	2321	...

By train (route L9)									
Benidorm d.	0601	0701	0801	0901		1901	2001	2101	2201
Altea d.	0615	0715	0815	0915	every	1915	2015	2115	2215
Calpe a.	0636	0736	0836	0936	hour	1936	2036	2136	...
Calpe 🚌 d.	0641	0741	0841	0941	◐	1941	2041	2141	...
Gata 🚌 d.	0714	0814	0914	1014	until	2014	2114	2214	...
Dénia 🚌 a.	0741	0841	0941	1041		2041	2141	2241	...

By train (route L9)									
Dénia 🚌 d.	0545	0645	0745	0845		1845	1945	2045	...
Gata 🚌 d.	0612	0712	0812	0912	every	1912	2012	2112	...
Calpe 🚌 a.	0645	0745	0845	0945	hour	1945	2045	2145	...
Calpe d.	0652	0752	0852	0952	◐	1952	2052	2152	...
Altea d.	0714	0814	0914	1014	until	2014	2114	2214	2228
Benidorm a.	0727	0827	0927	1027		2027	2127	2227	2241

◐ – Alacant - Benidorm runs every 30 minutes 0641 - 2141 (also 0025, 0155 night of ⑤⑥ June 30 - Aug. 26).
✣ – Benidorm - Alacant runs every 30 minutes 0635 - 2205 (also 0211, 0441 night of ⑤⑥ June 30 - Aug. 26).
⊙ – ± 400 m from Alacant Renfe station.
Operator: Tram Metropolitano / FGV ✆ 900 72 04 72 www.fgvalicante.com

668 MADRID - ALBACETE, ALACANT and VALÈNCIA

km		AVE			AVE	AVE	AVE	AVE	AVE	AVE	AVE	AVE	MD	AVE	MD	IC	AVE	Alvia	AVE	AVE	AVE	Talgo	AVE	Alvia	AVE
		5270	**18024**	**18018**	**5072**	**5070**	**5070**	**5080**	**5080**	**5290**	**5092**	**5098**	**14404**	**5102**	**18081**	**5710**	**5110**	**4072**	**5122**	**3971**	**5120**	**694**	**5340**	**4092**	**5142**
		①–⑤	①–⑤	⑥⑦	①–⑥	①–④	①–⑤	①–⑥	⑦	①–⑤			①–⑥		2			①–⑤	⑥⑦	⑤⑥	①–⑤	🍷		⑥⑦	①–⑤
		c	B	CC		c	D								h		L	S		M	c	T		S	
0	**Madrid** Puerta de Atocha ... d.	0645	...	...	0745	0740	0740	0840	0840	0910	0925	0940	...	1045	...	1110	1155	1215	1230	...	1240	...	1410	1420	1445
189	Cuenca Fernando Zóbel ... d.	0737	...	...	0846	|	0836	0936	0936	1006	|	|	...	1146	...	1220	|	1325	|	1319	|	...	1506	1526	1546
321	Requena / Utiel ... d.	0811	...	...	|	|	0910	|	1010	|	|	|	...	|	...	1259	|	|	|	|	|	...	1540	|	|
322*	**Albacete** ... d.	|	0806	0918	0924	|	|	|	|	|	1057	|	1100	1224	1229	|	|	1405	1402	|	|	1420	|	1605	1624
436	Villena AV ... d.	|	|	|	0959	|	|	|	|	|	|	|	|	1259	|	|	|	1449	1437	|	|	|	|	1652	1659
486	**Alacant** Terminal ... a.	|	|	|	1020	|	|	|	|	|	1147	|	|	1320	1400	|	|	1512	1458	|	|	|	|	1715	1720
477	Xátiva ... d.	|	0931	1042	...	|	|	|	|	|	...	|	1206	...	...	|	|	...	...	|	|	1524	|	...	...
391	**València** Joaquín Sorolla ... § a.	0839	|	|	...	0922	0934	1029	1034	1059	...	1124	|	...	...	1325	1337	...	...	1418	1422	|	1604	...	...
	València Nord ... § a.	...	1014	1118	...	...	...	...	...	...	...	|	1245	...	...	|	...	...	...	...	...	1602	...	...	...
	Sagunt ... a.	...	...	...	...	...	...	...	...	...	...	|	...	...	...	1357	...	...	...	...	...	|	...	...	...
	Castelló de la Plana **672** ... a.	...	...	...	...	...	...	...	...	...	...	1212	...	...	...	1431	...	...	...	...	...	1703	...	...	...

	IC	IC	AVE	AVE	AVE	MD	Alvia	AVE	AVE	Alvia	MD	AVE	AVE	IC	AVE	AVE	AVE	AVE	AVE	Alvia	AVE	AVE	AVE	AVE	
	5750	**5850**	**5352**	**5152**	**5150**	**14406**	**4584**	**5162**	**5362**	**4110**	**18181**	**5370**	**5170**	**5036**	**5380**	**5180**	**3973**	**5392**	**5198**	**4140**	**3981**	**5200**	**5212**	**5410**	
	⑤		①–④	⑤			⑥	⑤⑦		Ⓑ	2	⑤		Ⓑ	⑤		⑦				Ⓑ	Ⓑ	Ⓑ		
	Z	H					W			G	h	c			c	J	K			G	P				
Madrid Puerta de Atocha ... d.	1510	1510	1525	1530	1540	...	1555	1625	1655	1645	...	1710	1740	1748	1810	1840	...	1920	1940	2010	...	2040	2115	2110	...
Cuenca Fernando Zóbel ... d.	1618	1618	1626	|	|	...	1701	|	1756	|	...	|	|	|	|	|	2012	|	2036	2117	2125	|	2216	2203	...
Requena / Utiel ... d.	|	|	|	|	|	...	|	|	|	|	...	|	|	|	|	|	|	|	|	|	|	|	|	2238	...
Albacete ... d.	|	|	1704	|	|	1650	1741	|	1834	|	1849	|	|	2014	|	|	|	2052	|	2156	|	|	2254	|	...
Villena AV ... d.	|	|	|	|	|	|	1828	|	1909	|	|	|	|	|	|	|	|	|	|	2239	|	|	2329	|	...
Alacant Terminal ... a.	|	|	1758	1748	|	|	1850	1843	1930	|	2032	|	|	|	|	|	|	2142	|	2301	|	|	2350	|	...
Xátiva ... d.	|	|	...	...	|	1800	...	...	...	|	...	|	|	2119	|	|	|	...	|	...	|	|	...	|	...
València Joaquín Sorolla ... § a.	1720	1720	...	...	1724	|	...	...	...	1850	...	1854	1922	|	1952	2022	2118	...	2129	...	2219	2230	...	2304	...
València Nord ... § a.	|	...	...	...	...	1840	...	...	...	|	...	...	...	2158	...	...	...	...	|	...	...	...	...	...	...
Sagunt ... a.	1753	...	...	...	...	...	...	...	...	1929	...	...	...	...	...	...	...	...	|	...	...	...	...	...	...
Castelló de la Plana **672** ... a.	1819	...	...	...	...	...	...	...	...	1955	...	...	...	...	...	...	...	...	2225	...	...	...	...	...	...

	AVE	AVE	IC	AVE	AVE	AVE	AVE	AVE	AVE	AVE	Alvia	AVE	AVE	AVE	AVE	IC	MD	Alvia	Alvia	Alvia	AVE	AVE	Talgo	MD	
	5261	**5063**	**5035**	**5069**	**5081**	**5081**	**5081**	**3982**	**5073**	**5281**	**4111**	**5091**	**5083**	**5093**	**5301**	**5801**	**18183**	**4143**	**4345**	**4143**	**5321**	**5123**	**697**	**14405**	
	①–⑤	①–⑤	①–⑤	①–⑤	①–⑤	①–⑤	⑥⑦	①–⑥	①–⑥	①–④	①–⑥	①–⑥		①–⑤	⑦	①–⑥	2	⑦	⑦	①–⑥			🍷		
	c				c	D		P			G					AA	h	S	F	S			T		
Castelló de la Plana **672** ... d.	...	...	...	0615	...	...	...	...	...	...	0752	...	...	...	...	...	...	...	...	...	...	...	1158	...	...
Sagunt ... d.	...	...	...	|	...	...	...	...	...	...	0819	...	...	...	...	...	...	...	...	...	...	...	|	...	...
València Nord ... § d.	...	...	...	|	...	...	...	...	...	...	|	...	...	...	...	...	...	...	...	...	...	...	1255	1345	...
València Joaquín Sorolla ... § d.	0645	...	0620	0710	0800	0800	0800	0807	...	0840	0900	0940	...	...	1040	1040	...	...	...	...	1240	...	|	|	...
Xátiva ... d.	|	...	0659	|	|	|	|	|	...	|	|	|	...	...	|	|	...	...	...	...	|	...	1337	1426	...
Alacant Terminal ... d.	|	0608	|	|	|	|	|	|	0714	|	|	|	0834	0940	|	|	1012	1020	1020	1030	|	1240	|	|	...
Villena AV ... d.	|	0629	|	|	|	|	|	|	|	|	|	|	0855	1001	|	|	|	1043	1043	1053	|	1301	|	|	...
Albacete ... d.	|	0707	0803	|	|	|	|	|	0805	|	|	|	0932	1038	|	|	1146	1125	1125	1135	|	1338	1439	1537	...
Requena / Utiel ... d.	0708	|	|	|	|	0823	0823	|	|	|	|	|	|	|	|	1111	...	|	|	|	|	|	...	...	...
Cuenca Fernando Zóbel ... d.	0743	0745	|	|	0855	0858	0858	0902	|	|	|	|	1010	|	1135	1151	...	1204	1204	1213	|	1416	...	...	...
Madrid Puerta de Atocha ... a.	0838	0845	1020	0851	0948	0953	0953	...	0935	1021	1103	1121	1110	1211	1228	1305	...	1310	1310	1320	1421	1516	...	...	...

	AVE	Alvia	AVE	AVE	AVE	AVE	AVE	MD		IC	AVE	AVE	AVE	AVE	AVE	AVE	IC	Alvia	AVE	MD	AVE				
	5141	**4181**	**5149**	**5161**	**5153**	**5171**	**3974**	**18083**	**18027**	**5771**	**5181**	**5183**	**5191**	**5193**	**5391**	**5201**	**5811**	**5203**	**5221**	**14407**	**5213**				
		4381		Ⓑ			①⑤⑦	2		⑦	Ⓑ			⑤⑦	⑤⑦				⑦	Ⓑ	⑦				
		G		c			C	h	A	DD			N		c				Q						
Castelló de la Plana **672** ... d.	...	...	1415	...	...	...	...	...	...	1625	...	...	...	...	...	...	2007	...	...	...	...	...	...	...	...
Sagunt ... d.	...	...	|	...	...	...	...	...	...	1651	...	...	...	...	...	...	|	...	...	...	...	...	...	...	...
València Nord ... § d.	...	...	|	...	...	...	...	...	1730	|	...	...	...	...	...	...	|	...	...	2050	...	...	...	...	...
València Joaquín Sorolla ... § d.	1410	...	1510	1615	...	1710	1712	...	|	1730	1810	...	1910	...	1940	2015	2105	...	2205	|	...	...	...	...	...
Xátiva ... d.	|	...	|	|	...	|	|	...	1806	|	|	...	|	...	|	|	|	...	|	2129	...	...	...	...	...
Alacant Terminal ... d.	|	1445	|	|	1545	|	|	1705	|	|	|	1810	|	1855	|	|	|	2010	|	|	2118	...	...	...	...
Villena AV ... d.	|	1508	|	|	1606	|	|	|	|	|	|	|	|	|	|	|	|	2031	|	|	|	...	...	...	...
Albacete ... d.	|	1553	|	|	1643	|	|	1840	1927	|	|	1901	|	|	|	|	|	2109	|	2237	|	...	...	...	...
Requena / Utiel ... d.	|	|	1533	|	|	|	|	...	...	|	|	|	|	|	|	|	2137	|	|	...	|	...	...	...	...
Cuenca Fernando Zóbel ... d.	|	1630	1607	|	1721	|	1812	...	...	1834	1904	|	|	|	|	|	2217	2147	|	...	|	...	...	...	...
Madrid Puerta de Atocha ... a.	1548	1735	1703	1756	1821	1851	...	...	...	1943	1958	2032	2051	2111	2124	2156	2332	2247	2352	...	2334	...	...	...	...

A – To Alcázar de San Juan on ①–⑥, arrive 2050. To Ciudad Real on ⑦ (Table **678**).
B – From Alcázar de San Juan on ①–⑤, dep. 0645. From Ciudad Real on ① (Table **678**).
C – ①⑤⑦ (Ⓑ July 14 - Sept. 10). To Málaga (Table **660**).
D – ①–⑤ July 17 - Sept. 10.
E – ①–⑥ (daily July 4 - Sept. 10).
F – To Ferrol (Table **682**).
G – From / to Gijón (Table **685**).
H – ⑤ (Ⓑ June 24 - Sept. 10). To / from Gandia, arrive 1422.
J – Daily (not ⑥ July 4 - Sept. 10).
K – ⑦. From Málaga (Table **660**).
L – ①②③④⑥⑦ July 4 - Sept. 10.
M – ⑤⑥ (②③④⑤⑥ July 14 - Sept. 15). From Málaga (Table **660**).
N – ①②③④⑥⑦.
P – From / to Sevilla (Table **660**).
R – ⑤⑦ (Ⓑ June 19 - Sept. 10).
S – From / to Santander (Table **684**).
T – TORRE DEL ORO – 12 🍷 Barcelona - Sevilla and v.v. (Table **672**).
U – ①–⑤ (daily June 1 - Sept. 30).
W – From Pontevedra (Table **680**).
Z – ⑤. To Vinaròs (Table **672**).
AA – July 4 - Sept. 10. From Gandia.
BB – ⑦ (daily July 4 - Sept. 10). From Gandia.
CC – From Alcázar de San Juan, dep. 0800.
DD – ⑦. From Vinaròs (Table **672**).

c – Not July 17 - Sept. 10.
e – Not ⑥⑦.
h – From/to Ciudad Real (Table **678**).
y – ⑥ only.

§ – Free 🚌 between València Joaquín Sorolla and València Nord, 0615 - 2330, every ± 10 minutes.
* – Albacete - Xátiva - València: *203 km*.

△ – *Cercanías* (suburban) line **C1**: **València** - **Gandia** and v.v. *62 km* 2nd class. Journey time: 54 - 60 minutes.

From **València** Nord
Ⓐ: 0611, 0641 and every 30 minutes until 1941; then 1956, 2033, 2041, 2111, 2141, 2211, 2241.
Ⓒ: 0641, 0741 and hourly until 2241.

From **Gandia**
Ⓐ: 0605, 0640, 0655, 0710, 0725, 0740, 0755, 0825, 0840, 0855, 0915, 0925, 0955 and every 30 minutes until 2225.
Ⓒ: 0655, 0755 and hourly until 2055; then 2225.

668a MADRID - CARTAGENA

km		Alvia	Alta	Alta	MD	IC	Alta	Alvia	MD	Alta	
		5576	**220**	**228**	**18040**	**10146**	**224**	**5676**	**18042**	**226**	
		①–⑥	⑦	Ⓑ		⑤	⑥	Ⓑ	Ⓑ	Ⓑ	
						2					
0	**Madrid** Chamartín ... ‡ d.	...	0734	1234	1419	1540	1629	...	1818	1833	...
8	**Madrid** Atocha C ◧ .. ‡ d.	0655	0750	1251	1432	1602	1648	1720	1832	1853	...
57	Aranjuez ... ‡ d.	|	|	|	1509	1639	|	|	1908	|	...
157	Alcázar de San Juan ‡ d.	|	|	1404	1604	|	|	|	2000	2015	...
288	**Albacete** ... d.	0835	1010	1502	1715	1821	1857	1900	2106	2117	...
354	Hellín ... d.	0919	|	|	...	|	|	|	...	2159	...
450	Murcia ... **672** ¦ d.	1022	1151	1633	...	2003	2034	2045	...	2257	...
	Lorca Sutullena ... ¦ a.	|	|	|	...	2105	|	|	...	|	...
562	Aguilas ... ¦ a.	|	|	|	...	2200	|	|	...	|	...
515	**Cartagena** ... **672** ¦ a.	1112	1244	1718	...	...	2122	2136	...	2345	...

	MD	MD	MD	Alvia	Alta	Alvia	Alta	MD	Alvia	Alta	IC	Alta
	18047	**18041**	**18049**	**5567**	**223**	**5597**	**229**	**18043**	**5667**	**225**	**10418**	**227**
	①–⑤	①–⑤	⑥⑦	①–⑤	Ⓑ	⑥	Ⓑ		Ⓑ	⑥	⑦	Ⓑ
											2	
Cartagena ... **672** ¦ d.	...	...	...	0456	0818	0824	1338t	...	1555	1555	...	1843
Aguilas ... ¦ d.	...	...	...	|	|	|	|	...	|	|	1550	|
Lorca Sutullena ¦ d.	...	...	...	|	|	|	|	...	|	|	1639	|
Murcia ... **672** ¦ d.	...	...	...	0545	0908	0916	1423	...	1646	1645	1732	1930
Hellín ... d.	...	...	...	|	1015	1013	|	...	1743	|	|	2041
Albacete ... d.	0412f	0605	0730c	0735	1055	1104	1601	1740	1834	1820	1905	2125
Alcázar de San Juan ‡ d.	0527	0711	0837	|	1200	|	1655	1851	|	1926	|	2222
Aranjuez ... ‡ d.	0621	0807	0933	|	|	|	|	1948	|	|	2049	|
Madrid Atocha C ◧ ‡ a.	0656	0844	1008	0911	1324	1240	1820	2022	2010	2045	2127	2345
Madrid Chamartín . ‡ a.	...	0858	1022	...	1340	...	1839	2036	...	2100	2149	2359

c – ⑥ only. f – ① only. t – ⑦ only. ‡ – See also Table **661**. ◧ – Madrid **Atocha Cercanías**. ¦ – Additional local trains operate between these stations.

MADRID - CUENCA - VALÈNCIA 669

2nd class

km		18160 ①–⑤	18160 ⑦	18160 ⑥	18162 ①–⑤	18162 ⑦	14162 ⑦	18164 ①–④	18164 ⑤⑥⑦	18768 ⑤
0	**Madrid** Chamartín d.	*0554*	...	...	*1207*	...	...	*1607*	...	...
8	**Madrid** Atocha Cercanías d.	*0607*	0620	0800	*1221*	1242	...	*1621*	1630	1754
16	Villaverde Bajo **677** d.	*0616*	0630	0808	*1229*	1250	...	*1629*	1640	1803
57	Aranjuez **661 668a** a.	*0652*	0700	0836	*1305*	1318	...	*1705*	1708	1832
	change trains on certain services	|	|		|			|	|	
57	Aranjuez **661 668a** d.	0702	0702	0837	1322	1322	...	1709	1709	1833
209	**Cuenca** d.	0918	0918	1044	1537	1537	1740	1921	1921	2055
335	Requena d.	1152	1152	1303	1756	1756	2010	2145	2145	...
407	**València** Nord a.	1317	1317	1436	1925	1925	2143	2307	2307	...

	18161 ⑥⑦	18161 ①–⑤	18163 ⑤⑦	18163 ①–④	18765 ⑦	18165 ⑤	18165 ①–④	18165 ⑥⑦	14163 ⑤
València Nord d.	0638	0638	0950	0950	...	1450	1450	1450	1641
Requena d.	0818	0818	1126	1126	...	1638	1638	1639	1814
Cuenca d.	1045	1045	1405	1405	1745	1914	1914	1914	2045
Aranjuez **661 668a** a.	1254	1254	1618	1618	1954	2123	2123	2126	...
change trains on certain services	|	|	|	|	|	|	|	|	
Aranjuez **661 668a** d.	1255	*1312*	1619	*1630*	1955	2125	*2132*	2128	...
Villaverde Bajo **677** a.	1328	*1348*	1649	*1706*	2027	2156	*2208*	2209	...
Madrid Atocha Cercanías a.	1337	*1357*	1657	*1715*	2035	2204	*2216*	2217	...
Madrid Chamartín a.	...	*1410*	...	*1728*	...	...	*2230*	...	...

VALÈNCIA - TERUEL - ZARAGOZA - HUESCA - CANFRANC 670

2nd class (except *AVE* trains)

km		©	Ⓐ	©	18500	*MD* 18502 15750		*MD* 18504 C	*AVE* 3363 ⑤⑦	*AVE* 3393		*MD* 18506	14530 A
0	**València** Nord d.	...	...	...	...	0935	...	1215	...	...	...	1617	1908
34	Sagunt d.	...	...	...	...	1005	...	1248	...	...	...	1649	1946
65	Segorbe d.	...	...	...	...	1033	...	1316	...	...	...	1716	2022
171	**Teruel** d.	...	...	...	0625	1202	...	1451	...	...	...	1845	2218
242	Calamocha d.	...	...	...	0716	|	...	1538	...	...	...	1931	...
305	Cariñena d.	...	...	...	0814	1347	...	1630	...	...	...	2025	...
	Madrid ◇ **650** d.	...	...	...	|	|	...	|	1605	1905	...	|	...
359	**Zaragoza** Delicias d.	0640	0843	0847	0901	1428	1542	1709	1727	2033	2140	2109	...
361	**Zaragoza** Portillo d.	0643	0848	0852	0905	1433	1546	1712	|	|	2143	2114	...
363	**Zaragoza** Goya d.	0645	0851	0854	0913	1435	1549	1714	|	|	2145	2117	...
417	Tardienta d.	0731	0935	0938	▬	1511f	1632	...	|	2103	2228	...	...
439	**Huesca** d.	0752	0956	1001	...	1526f	1654	...	1810	2118	2244	...	...
474	Ayerbe d.	0831	1035	1046	...	...	1734	...	...	...	...	...	...
533	Sabiñánigo d.	0938	1142	1157	🚌	...	1844	...	...	...	...	...	...
549	Jaca d.	0955	1159	1212	1450	...	1903	...	...	...	...	...	...
574	**Canfranc 324** a.	1030	1234	...	1515	...	1942	...	...	...	...	...	...

	Ⓐ	*MD* 18511	*AVE* 3272	©	Ⓐ	*MD* 18523 w	©	*MD* 18515	🚌	©	*AVE* 3592 ⑤⑦	
Canfranc 324 d.	...	...	...	...	0600	...	0845	...	1310	...	...	1753
Jaca d.	...	...	...	...	0635	...	0920	...	1340	1611	...	1828
Sabiñánigo d.	...	...	...	...	0650	...	0935	...	▬	1626	...	1843
Ayerbe d.	...	...	...	...	0757	...	1047	...	...	1735	...	1952
Huesca d.	0639	...	0815	0829	0845	...	1136	1558	...	1825	1935	2038
Tardienta d.	0655	...	0827	0846	0901	...	1153	1615	**18517**	1841	|	2055
Zaragoza Goya d.	0739	0807	|	0933	0949	1109	1236	1702	1923	1936	|	2139
Zaragoza Portillo d.	0742	0810	|	0936	0952	1112	1239	1706	1926	1939	|	2143
Zaragoza Delicias d.	0744	0814	0900	0939	0955	1120	1243	1720	1931	1943	2020	2148
Madrid ◇ **650** a.	▬	|	1035	...	...	|	...	|	|	...	2140	...
Cariñena d.	**14531**	0857	...	...	...	1204	...	1809	2023	...	...	...
Calamocha d.	**B**	0950	...	...	...	1258	...	1915	2127	...	...	...
Teruel d.	0733	1041	...	...	...	1346	...	2004	2219	...	...	...
Segorbe d.	0914	1213	...	...	...	1512	...	2131	...	...	...	...
Sagunt d.	0950	1241	...	...	...	1543	...	2202	...	...	...	...
València Nord a.	1026	1315	...	...	...	1615	...	2231	...	...	...	...

A – ②④⑥⑦.
B – ①③⑤⑦.
C – From Cartagena on ①–⑤. From Murcia on ⑥ (Table **672**).
f – ①–⑤.
w – To Cartagena (Table **672**).
◇ – Madrid Puerta de Atocha.
🚌 Jaca - Canfranc (- Astun). See Table **324** for 🚌 Canfranc - Bedous.

CÓRDOBA - SEVILLA - HUELVA and CÁDIZ 671

km		*MD* 13000 2 ①–⑤	*MD* 13002 2 ①–⑥	*MD* 13030 2 ①–⑤	*MD* 13030 2 ⑥⑦	*MD* 13099 2 ⑥⑦		*MD* 13079 2 J	*MD* 13037 2 ①–⑤	*MD* 13020 2	*Alvia* 2084	*Alvia* 2294 C	*IC* 2494 D	*Alvia* 2094 N	*MD* 13008 2 ①–⑤	*Alvia* 2294 N ⑦	*IC* 2494 N ①–⑥	*Alvia* 2114 A	*MD* 13010 2	*MD* 13032 2 ⑥⑦	*MD* 13032 2 ①–⑤	*Alvia* 2134	*MD* 13014 2	*MD* 13039 2	*MD* 13083 2 J
	Madrid PA ❖ **660** d.	...	...	...	...	...	...	...	...	...	0830	0945	0945	0945	...	1025	1025	1105	...	...	...	1330	...	...	...
0	**Córdoba 660** d.	...	...	0700	...	...	...	0812	...	0908	1026	1133	1132	1133	...	1222	1222	|	...	1400	1400	1517	...	...	1612
51	Palma del Río d.	...	...	0729	...	...	...	0845	...	0940	|	|	|	|	...	|	|	|	...	1431	1431	|	...	...	1643
129	**Sevilla 660** a.	...	...	0821	...	...	...	0937	...	1029	1114	|	1225	1225	...	|	1314	|	...	1520	1520	1605	...	...	1730
129	**Sevilla 673** § d.	0640	0745	0830	0830	0845	...	0945	1000	1045	1116	|	1230	1228	1245	|	1324	|	1445	...	1545	1608	1645	1700	1745
204	La Palma del Condado d.	|	|	|	|	0949	...	|	1108	|	|	1256	1325	|	|	1349	1425	|	|	...	|	|	|	1758	|
244	**Huelva** a.	|	|	|	|	1020	...	|	1138	|	|	1323	1352	|	|	1415	1450	|	|	...	|	|	|	1834	|
145	Dos Hermanas **673** § d.	0654	0758	0843	0843	...	...	0958	...	1058	|	...	...	|	1258	...	...	|	1500	...	1559	|	1658	...	1758
162	Utrera § d.	0705	|	0854	0854	...	...	|	...	1108	|	...	...	|	1308	...	...	|	|	...	1609	|	|	...	1808
224	Aeropuerto de Jerez ▲ d.	0739	|	0929	0929	...	...	|	...	1143	|	...	...	|	1345	...	...	|	1540	...	|	|	1741	...	1844
236	Jerez de la Frontera ▲ d.	0746	0846	0936	0936	...	...	1047	...	1151	1212	...	...	1322	1353	...	...	1435	1548	...	1651	1705	1749	...	1852
251	Puerto de Santa María d.	0756	0855	0946	0946	...	...	1057	...	1200	1222	...	...	1332	1402	...	...	1445	1558	...	1700	1714	1758	...	1901
270	San Fernando - Bahía Sur d.	0809	0911	1002	1002	...	...	1112	...	1214	1237	...	...	1349	1418	...	...	1503	1615	...	1714	1729	1813	...	1917
285	**Cádiz** a.	0826	0923	1013	1013	...	...	1126	...	1226	1248	...	...	1400	1430	...	...	1515	1627	...	1726	1740	1825	...	1930

	Alvia 2164	*IC* 2364 B ⑤	*MD* 13035 2 J	*MD* 13394 2	*Talgo* 697 T	*Alvia* 2384 Ⓑ	*MD* 13095 2	*MD* 13073 2 J	*Alvia* 2184 F		
Madrid PA ❖ **660** d.	1615	1620	...	...	...	1805	...	...	1835	...	...
Córdoba 660 d.	|	|	1830	...	1931	1952	...	2010	2019	...	...
Palma del Río d.	|	|	1905	...	|	|	...	2042	|	...	...
Sevilla 660 a.	|	1852	1956	...	2051	|	...	2128	2108	...	...
Sevilla 673 § d.	|	1902	2010	2045	...	|	2050	2150	2112	...	...
La Palma del Condado d.	|	2000	|	|	...	2130	2149	|	|	...	...
Huelva a.	|	2026	|	|	...	2155	2218	|	|	...	...
Dos Hermanas **673** § d.	|	...	2023	2058	...	...	...	2203	|	...	...
Utrera § d.	|	...	|	2109	...	...	...	2213	|	...	...
Aeropuerto de Jerez ▲ d.	|	...	|	|	...	...	...	2248	|	...	...
Jerez de la Frontera ▲ d.	1938	...	2113	2148	...	...	...	2256	2209	...	...
Puerto de Santa María d.	1948	...	2122	2157	...	...	...	2305	2219	...	...
San Fernando - Bahía Sur d.	2003	...	2137	2212	...	...	...	2321	2234	...	...
Cádiz a.	2015	...	2150	2223	...	...	...	2335	2245	...	...

	MD 13001 2J ①–⑤	*MD* 13041 2	*Talgo* 694 T	*Alvia* 2285 P ①–⑤	*MD* 13003 2 M		*Alvia* 2085	*MD* 13005 2	*MD* 13007 2 ①–⑤
Cádiz d.	0540	...	...	...	0630	...	0815	0840	0940
San Fernando - Bahía Sur d.	0553	...	...	...	0641	...	0827	0851	0951
Puerto de Santa María d.	0608	...	...	...	0656	...	0840	0905	1006
Jerez de la Frontera ▲ d.	0617	...	...	...	0705	...	0850	0914	1015
Aeropuerto de Jerez ▲ d.	0624	...	...	...	0713	...	|	|	1023
Utrera § d.	0702	...	...	...	0751	...	|	|	|
Dos Hermanas **673** § d.	0712	...	...	...	0801	...	|	1005	1107
Huelva d.	|	0655	...	0800	|	...	|	|	|
La Palma del Condado d.	|	0725	...	0824	|	...	|	|	|
Sevilla 673 § a.	0728	0825	...	|	0816	...	0947	1020	1120
Sevilla 660 d.	0740	...	0835	|	0838	...	0950	...	...
Palma del Río d.	0828	...	|	|	0926	...	|	...	...
Córdoba 660 a.	0904	...	0945	0948	1000	...	1040	...	...
Madrid PA ❖ **660** a.	...	...	...	1141	...	...	1236	...	...

	Alvia 2205 H	*Alvia* 2105 A	*MD* 13009 2 J	*MD* 13011 2J ①–⑤	*MD* 13011 2J ⑥⑦	*Alvia* 2135	*MD* 13393 2	*MD* 13013 2 ①–⑤	*MD* 13043 2	*Alvia* 2155 N	*Alvia* 2365 ⑦	*MD* 13015 2		*Alvia* 2175	*IC* 2375 E	*MD* 13017 2 J	*MD* 13031 2	*MD* 13049 2	*Alvia* 2195 F	*MD* 13019 2	*MD* 13021 2				
Cádiz d.	...	1050	1140	1240	...	1333	1412	1440	...	1505	...	1540	...	1728	...	1740	1840	...	1855	1940	2040	...	...	...	...
San Fernando - Bahía Sur d.	...	1102	1151	1251	...	1344	1423	1451	...	1518	...	1551	...	1740	...	1751	1851	...	1907	1951	2052	...	...	...	...
Puerto de Santa María d.	...	1116	1206	1306	...	1357	1436	1506	...	1535	...	1606	...	1754	...	1805	1905	...	1921	2006	2106	...	...	...	...
Jerez de la Frontera ▲ d.	...	1126	1215	1315	...	1406	1445	1515	...	1546	...	1615	...	1805	...	1814	1914	...	1931	2015	2115	...	...	...	...
Aeropuerto de Jerez ▲ d.	...	|	1223	|	...	|	|	1523	...	|	...	1623	...	|	...	1822	1921	...	|	|	|	...	...	...	...
Utrera § d.	...	|	|	1356	...	|	1525	|	...	|	...	1700	...	|	...	|	|	...	|	2102	2156	...	...	...	...
Dos Hermanas **673** § d.	...	|	1306	1406	...	|	1535	1606	...	|	...	1710	...	|	...	1906	2005	...	|	2112	2206	...	...	...	...
Huelva d.	1025	|	|	|	...	|	|	|	1500	|	1620	|	...	|	1750	|	|	1900	|	|	|	...	...	...	...
La Palma del Condado d.	1047	|	|	|	...	|	|	|	1530	|	1647	|	...	|	1817	|	|	1930	|	|	|	...	...	...	...
Sevilla 673 § a.	|	|	1320	1420	...	1456	1549	1620	1627	1640	|	1725	...	|	1914	1920	2017	2030	2033	2128	2220	...	...	...	...
Sevilla 660 d.	|	|	1330	1503	1503	1458	...	...	...	1643	|	1735	...	|	1919	1940	2030	...	2036	...	...	...	...	...	...
Palma del Río d.	|	|	1415	1551	1551	|	...	...	...	|	|	1824	...	|	|	2027	2117	...	|	...	...	...	...	...	...
Córdoba 660 a.	1216	|	1449	1624	1624	1552	...	...	...	1729	1808	1857	...	|	|	2102	2148	...	2125	...	...	...	...	...	...
Madrid PA ❖ **660** a.	1410	1458	...	...	...	1750	...	...	...	1920	2003	...	...	2127	2159	...	...	...	2314	...	...	...	...	...	...

A – Mar. 17 - Sept. 9.
B – Until Mar. 9 and from Oct. 19.
C – July 8, 15, 22.
D – ①–⑥ Mar. 17 - July 21, Sept. 3 - Oct. 13.
E – ⑦ (Ⓑ Mar. 17 - Sept. 7).
F – ⑤⑦ (④⑤⑦ Mar. 14 - Apr. 15, Ⓑ Apr. 16 - Nov. 8).
H – ⑥ (daily July 23 - Sept. 3, also July 8, 15, 22).
J – From / to Jaén (Table **661**).
M – To Jaén on ⑥⑦ (Table **661**).
N – July 22 - Sept. 3.
P – Not July 22 - Aug. 31.
T – TORRE DEL ORO – 12 🍸 Barcelona - València - Córdoba - Sevilla and v.v. (Tables **661**, **672**, **678**).
t – ①–⑤.
❖ – Madrid Puerta de Atocha.
§ – Frequent suburban services operate Sevilla - Utrera and v.v.
▲ – Additional suburban services operate Jerez de la Frontera - Aeropuerto de Jerez and v.v.: depart Aeropuerto 0720 Ⓐ, 0820 ©, 1325, 1920; depart Jerez 0657 Ⓐ, 0757 ©, 1257, 1857.

672 BARCELONA - VALÈNCIA - ALACANT - CARTAGENA

km		MD 14123 2	AVE 5069 ①-⑤	Alvia 4111 ①-⑥ G	①-⑤ 2	⑥ 2	①-⑥ 2	Em 1071 ①-⑥	Em 1081 ①-④	2	Em 1091 ⑤⑥⑦	Talgo 697 A	Em 1101	2	Talgo 1111	Ⓑ 2	AVE 5149	①-⑤ 2	⑥⑦ 2	Talgo 463 🍷	2	2
0	**Barcelona** França d.	...	...	...	...	...	0543	0634t	0734	0743	0833	0904	0933	0913	...	...	...	1043	1043	...	...	1243
5	Barcelona Passeig de Gràcia d.	...	...	...	...	...	0556	|	|	0756	|	|	|	0926	...	...	...	1054	1054	...	...	1256
8	**Barcelona** Sants 652 d.	...	...	...	...	...	0603	0700	0800	0803	0900	0930	1000	0933	1100	...	...	1103	1103	1200	...	1303
68	Sant Vicenç de Calders 652 d.	...	...	...	...	...	0649	|	|	0848	|	|	|	1019	|	...	...	|	1149	|	...	1347
82	Altafulla - Tamarit d.	...	...	...	...	...	0700	|	|	0901	|	|	|	1030	|	...	...	|	1202	|	...	1400
93	**Tarragona** 652 d.	...	...	...	...	...	0710	0754	0854	0911	0956	1029	1054	1041	1155	...	...	1201	1211	1254	...	1410
103	Port Aventura d.	...	...	...	...	...	0719	|	|	0920	|	|	|	1051	|	...	...	1215	1224	|	...	1420
105	Salou d.	...	...	...	...	...	0724	|	|	0924	|	1046	|	1055	1210	...	...	1218	1228	1312	...	1424
	Tortosa d.	...	...	...	0635	0758	|	|	|	|	|	|	|	|	|	...	...	|	|	|	1338	|
163	L'Aldea - Amposta d.	...	...	...	0648	0811	0815	|	0937	1019	1040	1118	|	1147	1247	...	...	1309	1313	1344	1353	1514
176	Tortosa a.	...	...	...	|	|	0826	|	|	1029	|	|	|	1156	|	...	...	1320	1323	|	|	1524
202	Vinaròs ¦ d.	...	...	...	0710	0833	...	|	|	...	|	1133	|	1241	1304	...	...	...	...	1359	1415	...
208	Benicarló - Peñíscola ¦ d.	...	...	...	0716	0839	...	|	|	...	|	1140	|	1247	1309	...	...	...	...	1404	1421	...
268	Benicàssim ¦ d.	...	...	0722	0754	0917	...	|	|	...	|	|	|	1324	1340	...	...	...	...	1427	1458	...
280	Castelló de la Plana ¦ d.	...	0615	0732	0805	0934	...	0928	1024	...	1124	1208	1220	1333	1350	...	1415	...	...	1435	1507	...
353	**València** Nord ¦ a.	...	|	|	0905	1038	...	|	|	...	|	1255	|	1434	1438	...	|	...	...	1525	1610	...
353	**València** Nord 668 d.	0708	|	|	...	...	...	|	|	...	|	1300	|	...	1448	1502	|	...	...	1538	...	...
	València Joaquín Sorolla a.	|	0703	0830	...	...	...	1012	1112	...	1214	|	1306	...	|	|	1500	...	...	|	...	...
	València Joaquín Sorolla 668 d.	|	0710	0845	...	...	...	1020	...	...	...	|	1314	...	|	|	1510	...	...	|	...	...
409	Xátiva 668 d.	0744	|	|	...	...	...	|	...	...	...	1342	|	...	1529	1539	|	...	...	1616	...	...
	Madrid P de Atocha 668 a.	|	0851	1045	...	...	...	|	...	...	...	|	|	...	|	|	1703	...	...	|	...	...
	Sevilla 671 a.	|	...	...	...	...	...	|	...	...	...	2051	|	...	|	|	...	...	...	|	...	...
495	Elda - Petrer d.	0840	...	...	...	...	...	|	...	...	...	...	|	...	1623	1632	...	...	...	1658	...	...
536	**Alacant** a.	0908	...	...	...	...	...	1156	...	...	...	...	1455	...	1658	1704	...	...	...	1727	...	...
536	**Alacant** ¦ d.	0916	...	...	...	...	...	...	...	...	...	...	...	...	...	...	...	...	...	1745	...	...
614	Murcia 668a ¦ a.	1043	...	...	...	...	...	...	...	...	...	...	...	...	...	...	...	...	...	1859	...	...
677	**Lorca** Sutullena ¦ a.	...	...	...	...	...	...	...	...	...	...	...	...	...	...	...	...	...	...	2007	...	...
679	**Cartagena** 668a ¦ a.	...	...	...	...	...	...	...	...	...	...	...	...	...	...	...	...	...	...	...	...	...

	MD 18523 🅁2 p	⑤ 2	IC 5771 ⑦ B	Em 1341	Talgo 165	2	Talgo 10541 ⑤	Em 1161 Ⓑ	Em 1161 ⑥	①-⑤ 2	⑥⑦ 2	Talgo 1171	IC 5811	2	Em 1571 Ⓑ	Em 1181 Ⓑ	Em 1181 ⑥	2	Talgo 1391	2	Em 1401 Ⓑ	2
Barcelona França d.	...	...	...	1403	...	1443	...	1533	1533	1613	1613	...	...	...	...	1734	1734	1743	...	1913	2004	2043
Barcelona Passeig de Gràcia d.	...	...	...	|	...	1456	...	|	|	1625	1625	...	...	...	...	|	|	1755	...	1925	|	2056
Barcelona Sants 652 d.	...	...	...	1430	1500	1503	1530	1600	1600	1633	1633	1700	...	...	1730	1800	1800	1803	1930	1933	2030	2103
Sant Vicenç de Calders 652 d.	...	...	...	|	|	1547	|	|	|	|	1713	|	...	...	|	|	|	1847	|	2017	|	2148
Altafulla - Tamarit d.	...	...	...	|	|	1558	|	|	|	|	1725	|	...	...	|	|	|	1859	|	2030	|	2201
Tarragona 652 d.	...	...	...	1524	1555	1607	1629	1654	1654	1727	1735	1754	...	...	1824	1854	1854	1909	2024	2041	2125	2211
Port Aventura d.	...	...	...	|	|	1616	|	|	|	1735	1744	|	...	...	|	|	|	1917	|	2051	|	2222
Salou d.	...	...	...	|	1608	1620	|	|	|	1740	1748	1807	...	...	|	|	|	1921	2037	2055	|	2226
Tortosa d.	...	...	...	|	|	|	|	|	|	|	|	|	...	1902	|	|	|	|	|	|	|	|
L'Aldea - Amposta d.	...	...	...	1606	1647	1718	|	|	1739	1825	1845	1849	...	1919	1905	|	1947	2023	2113	2147	2215	2319
Tortosa a.	...	...	...	|	|	1730	|	|	|	1835	1859	|	...	|	|	|	|	2034	|	2158	|	2330
Vinaròs ¦ d.	...	...	1543	|	1704	...	|	|	|	...	...	1904	...	1942	|	|	|	...	2129	...	|	...
Benicarló - Peñíscola ¦ d.	...	...	1548	|	1710	...	|	|	|	...	...	1909	...	1947	|	|	|	...	2135	...	|	...
Benicàssim ¦ d.	...	...	1616	|	1736	...	|	|	|	...	...	1937	...	2032	|	|	|	...	2203	...	|	...
Castelló de la Plana ¦ d.	...	...	1625	1650	1745	...	|	1819	1824	...	...	1946	2007	2042	1956	2029	2033	...	2212	...	2300	...
València Nord ¦ a.	...	...	|	|	1830	...	1855	|	|	...	...	2034	|	2155	|	|	|	...	2305	...	|	...
València Nord 668 d.	1635	1705	|	|	1840	...	1905	|	|	...	...	2046	|	...	|	|	|	...	...	...	|	...
València Joaquín Sorolla a.	|	|	1722	1740	|	...	|	1907	1910	...	...	|	2055	...	2042	2116	2120	...	...	...	2345	...
València Joaquín Sorolla 668 d.	|	|	1730	...	|	...	|	1920	1920	...	...	|	2105	...	...	2126	2130	...	...	...	...	...
Xátiva 668 d.	1711	1744	|	...	1914	...	1946	|	|	...	...	2123	|	...	...	|	|	...	...	...	...	...
Madrid P de Atocha 668 a.	|	|	1943	...	|	...	|	|	|	...	...	|	2332	...	...	|	|	...	...	...	...	...
Sevilla 671 a.	|	|	...	...	|	...	|	|	|	...	...	|	...	...	...	|	|	...	...	...	...	...
Elda - Petrer d.	1757	1839	...	...	1954	...	|	|	|	...	...	2207	...	...	...	|	|	...	...	...	...	...
Alacant a.	1823	1914	...	...	2020	...	2100	2055	2055	...	...	2235	...	...	...	2303	2307	...	...	...	...	...
Alacant ¦ d.	1830	...	...	...	2035	...	...	...	...	...	...	2250	...	...	...	...	...	...	...	...	...	...
Murcia 668a ¦ a.	1947	...	...	...	2150	...	...	...	...	...	...	2355	...	...	...	...	...	...	...	...	...	...
Lorca Sutullena ¦ a.	|	...	...	...	|	...	...	...	...	...	...	...	...	...	...	...	...	...	...	...	...	...
Cartagena 668a ¦ a.	2036	...	...	...	2255	...	...	...	...	...	...	...	...	...	...	...	...	...	...	...	...	...

	①-⑤ 2	⑥ 2	Em 1262 ①-⑤	2	Em 1472 ①-⑥	2	Em 1282 ⑥⑦	Em 1282 ①-⑤	2	2	Talgo 1102	Em 1112 ⑦	Em 1112 ①-⑥	AVE 5098	①-⑤ 2	⑥⑦ 2	MD 18504 ①-⑥ 2 f	Talgo 460 🍷	2	IC 5710	Talgo 1142 🍷	2
Cartagena 668a ¦ d.	...	...	...	...	...	...	...	...	...	...	...	...	...	...	...	...	0740z	...	...	...	...	...
Lorca Sutullena ¦ d.	...	...	...	...	...	...	...	...	...	...	...	...	...	...	...	...	|	0828	...	...	...	...
Murcia 668a ¦ d.	...	...	...	...	...	...	...	...	...	...	0630k	...	...	...	...	...	0838	0934	...	...	...	...
Alacant ¦ a.	...	...	...	...	...	...	...	...	...	...	0744k	...	...	...	...	...	0955	1052	...	...	...	...
Alacant d.	...	...	...	...	...	...	0645	0650	...	...	0800	0910	0915	...	...	...	1003	1108	...	...	...	...
Elda - Petrer d.	...	...	...	...	...	...	|	|	...	...	0828	|	|	...	...	...	1032	1137	...	...	...	...
Sevilla 671 d.	...	...	...	...	...	...	|	|	...	...	|	|	|	...	...	...	|	|	...	...	...	...
Madrid P de Atocha 668 d.	...	...	...	...	...	...	|	|	...	...	|	|	|	0940	...	...	|	|	...	1110	...	...
Xátiva 668 d.	...	...	...	...	...	...	|	|	...	...	0917	|	|	|	...	...	1120	1216	...	|	...	...
València Joaquín Sorolla 668 a.	...	...	...	...	...	...	0818	0822	...	...	|	1042	1047	1124	...	...	|	|	...	1325	...	...
València Joaquín Sorolla d.	...	...	0620	...	0725	...	0826	0830	...	...	|	1050	1055	1130	...	...	|	|	...	1331	...	...
València Nord 668 a.	...	...	|	...	|	...	|	|	...	...	0954	|	|	|	...	...	1156	1253	...	|	...	...
València Nord ¦ d.	...	...	|	...	|	...	|	|	0805	...	1005	|	|	|	...	...	...	1305	...	|	1350	1427
Castelló de la Plana ¦ d.	...	...	0701	...	0805	...	0906	0910	0917	...	1050	1130	1135	1212	...	...	...	1344	...	1431	1442	1536
Benicàssim ¦ d.	...	...	|	...	|	...	|	|	0930	...	1100	|	|	...	...	...	...	1354	...	...	1450	1547
Benicarló - Peñíscola ¦ d.	...	...	|	...	|	...	|	|	1007	...	1133	|	|	...	...	...	...	1422	...	...	1519	1629
Vinaròs ¦ d.	...	...	|	...	|	...	|	|	1013	...	1139	|	|	...	...	...	...	1427	...	...	1524	1634
Tortosa d.	0556	0601	|	0743	|	0900	|	|	|	1107	|	|	|	...	1333	1344	...	|	1543	...	|	|
L'Aldea - Amposta d.	0608	0614	0746	0754	0849	0913	0952	|	1039	1118	1156	1218	|	...	1344	1355	...	1445	1554	...	1540	1701
Tortosa a.	|	|	|	|	|	|	|	|	1050	|	|	|	|	...	|	|	...	|	|	...	|	1720
Salou d.	0657	0707	|	0841	|	1004	|	|	...	1204	1228	|	|	...	1428	1446	...	1524	1644	...	1619	...
Port Aventura d.	0700	0710	|	0844	|	1009	|	|	...	1207	1231	|	|	...	1431	1449	...	|	1648	...	|	...
Tarragona 652 d.	0711	0725	0837	0855	0936	1021	1037	1037	...	1218	1241	1311	1311	...	1442	1459	...	1539	1658	...	1636	...
Altafulla - Tamarit d.	|	0732	|	0904	|	1029	|	|	...	1227	|	|	|	...	|	1506	...	|	1706	...	|	...
Sant Vicenç de Calders 652 d.	|	0746	|	0918	|	1043	|	|	...	1241	|	|	|	...	|	1520	...	|	1719	...	|	...
Barcelona Sants 652 a.	0810	0835	0939	1009	1040	1136	1141	1141	...	1337	1341	1408	1408	...	1540	1609	...	1640	1807	...	1740	...
Barcelona Passeig de Gràcia a.	0816	0841	|	1015	...	1142	|	|	...	1343	...	|	|	...	1546	1616	...	...	1814	...	...	...
Barcelona França a.	0827	0852	1005	1027	...	1155	1205	1205	...	1354	...	1434	1434	...	1557	1627	...	...	1825	...	...	...

A – TORRE DEL ORO – (12) 🍷 Barcelona - Sevilla. (Tables **661**, **671**).
B – ⑦ Jan. 23 - June 22, Sept. 11 - Dec. 10.
G – To/from Gijón (Tables **681**, **685**).
J – Ⓑ (daily July 31 - Aug. 31).

f – To Zaragoza (Table **670**).
k – ①-⑥.
p – From Zaragoza.
t – Not ①.

z – ①-⑤.
¦ – Additional local trains operate between these stations.

CARTAGENA - ALACANT - VALÈNCIA - BARCELONA 672

	Em 1162 ⑥	Em 1162 Ⓑ	2	Talgo 694 A	Talgo 264	2	2	IC 5750 ⑤ K	Em 1182 ⑥	Em 1182 Ⓑ	Talgo 10458 ⑦	Em 1192 ①-④	Alvia 4140 Ⓑ G	Em 1392 ⑤⑦	2	Ⓑ 2	Talgo 1202 ①-⑥	Talgo 1202 ⑦	MD 14202 2	Ⓑ 2	AVE 5198	
Cartagena 668a ¦ d.	...	...	...	...	1248	...	...	...	...	...	...	...	...	...	...	...	...	...	1638	...	...	...
Lorca Sutullena ¦ d.	...	...	...	...	|	...	...	...	...	...	...	...	...	...	...	...	...	...	|	...	...	...
Murcia 668a ¦ d.	...	...	...	...	1348	...	...	...	...	...	...	...	...	...	...	...	...	1651	1735	...	...	...
Alacant ¦ a.	...	...	...	...	1455	...	...	...	...	...	...	...	...	...	...	...	...	1804	1846	...	...	...
Alacant d.	1352	1357	...	...	1510	...	...	...	1605	1610	1625	...	...	...	...	...	1838	1838	1856	1930	...	...
Elda - Petrer d.	|	|	...	...	1540	...	...	...	|	|	|	...	...	...	...	...	1905	1905	1925	2004	...	...
Sevilla **671** d.	|	|	...	0835	|	...	...	...	|	|	|	...	...	...	...	...	|	|	|	|	...	...
Madrid P de Atocha **668** d.	|	|	...	|	|	...	...	1510	|	|	|	...	1645	...	...	...	|	|	|	|	1940	...
Xàtiva **668** d.	|	|	...	1524	1620	...	...	|	|	|	1747	...	|	...	...	...	1945	1945	2017	2103	|	...
València Joaquín Sorolla **668** a.	1533	1540	...	|	|	...	...	1720	1744	1749	|	...	1850	...	...	...	|	|	|	|	2129	...
València Joaquín Sorolla d.	1543	1550	...	|	|	...	...	1728	1754	1800	|	1850	1900	1920	...	...	|	|	|	|	2135	...
València Nord **668** a.	|	|	...	1602	1658	...	...	|	|	|	1833	|	|	|	...	...	2021	2021	2051	2143	|	...
València Nord ¦ d.	|	|	...	1610	1710	...	1635	|	|	|	1842	|	|	|	...	2005	2031	2031	...	...	|	...
Castelló de la Plana ¦ d.	1624	1630	...	1649	1750	...	1747	1821	1834	1840	|	1930	1955	2000	...	2107	2116	2116	...	...	2225	...
Benicàssim ¦ d.	|	|	...	|	1757	...	1755	1828	|	|	|	|	2011	|	...	2115	2126	2126	...	...	...	...
Benicarló - Peñíscola ¦ d.	|	|	...	1721	1823	...	1834	1855	|	|	|	|	...	|	...	2151	2158	2158	...	...	...	...
Vinaròs ¦ d.	|	|	...	1727	1829	...	1840	1900	|	|	|	|	...	|	...	2157	2204	2204	...	...	...	...
Tortosa d.	|	|	1708	|	|	1836	1931	...	|	|	|	|	...	|	2052	|	|	|	...	...	...	...
L'Aldea - Amposta d.	1710	|	1720	1743	1844	1848	1943	...	1918	|	|	2015	...	2046	2106	2219	2222	2222	...	...	...	...
Tortosa a.	|	|	|	|	|	|	|	...	|	|	|	|	...	|	|	2233	|	|	...	...	...	...
Salou d.	|	|	1811	1832	1919	1945	2036	...	|	|	|	|	...	|	2159	...	2258	2258	...	...	...	...
Port Aventura d.	|	|	1815	|	|	1948	2041	...	|	|	|	|	...	|	2203	...	|	|	...	...	...	...
Tarragona **652** d.	1800	1800	1825	1842	1933	1959	2057	...	2007	2007	2105	2106	...	2132	2215	...	2310	2310	...	...	...	...
Altafulla - Tamarit d.	|	|	1834	|	|	2006	2105	...	|	|	|	|	...	|	|	...	|	|	...	...	...	...
Sant Vicenç de Calders **652** d.	|	|	1848	|	|	2019	2117	...	|	|	|	|	...	|	2235	...	|	|	...	...	...	...
Barcelona Sants **652** a.	1909	1909	1937	2000	2040	2107	2207	...	2110	2110	2210	2210	...	2237	2322	...	2359	2359	...	...	...	...
Barcelona Passeig de Gràcia a.	|	|	1944	|	...	2114	2214	...	|	|	...	|	...	|	2328	...	...	...	...	...	...	...
Barcelona França a.	1935	1935	1955	2034	...	2125	2225	...	2137	2137	...	2237	...	2306j	2341	...	...	...	...	...	...	...

Murcia – Cartagena

	Ⓐ 2	Ⓐ 2	2	Alta 222 m	Ⓐ 2	Alta 228 Jm	Ⓐ 2	MD 18523 p2	Alta 224 m	Talgo 165	Alta 226 Ⓑm	
Murcia d.	0745	0950	1150	1326	1443	1645	1745	1948	2050	2202	2331	...
Cartagena a.	0834	1040	1240	1412	1536	1728	1840	2033	2138	2245	0017	...

	Alta 221 Ⓐm	MD 18504 Ⓐf	Alta 223 m	2	Alta 229 ⑦m	Talgo 264	Ⓐ 2	Alta 225 m	MD 14202 2	Alta 227 Ⓑm	Ⓐ 2	Ⓐ 2	Ⓒ 2
Cartagena d.	0530	0740	0850	1050	1215	1248	1438	1600	1638	1820	1938	2110	2205
Murcia a.	0608	0830	0934	1140	1256	1340	1528	1645	1726	1902	2030	2205	2257

A – TORRE DEL ORO – (12) 🍷 Sevilla - Barcelona. (Tables **661**, **668a**, **671**).

G – To / from Gijón (Tables **681**, **685**).

J – Ⓑ (daily July 31 - Aug. 31).

K – ⑤ Jan. 23 - June 22, Sept. 11 - Dec. 10.

f – To Zaragoza (Table **670**).

j – ⑤ only.

m – From / to Madrid (Table **668a**).

p – From Zaragoza (Table **670**).

¦ – Additional local trains operate between these stations.

2nd class

SEVILLA and ALGECIRAS - MÁLAGA, GRANADA and ALMERÍA 673

For trains **Sevilla** – **Málaga** and v.v. via **Córdoba**, see Table **660**. **Buses replace trains between Antequera - Santa Ana and Granada until Summer 2019**

km		MD 13920	MD 13063	MD 13900		Alta 9367		MD 13902	MD 13922	MD 13065	MD 13904	MD 13906 ⑤⑦		MD 13061 🚌	Alta 9331	MD 13077	MD 13924	MD 13908	MD 13926		MD 13910	
0	**Sevilla** ¶ d.	0635	...	0740	...	...	...	1038	1145	...	1308	1510	...	...	...	...	1556	1720	1756	...	2002	...
15	Dos Hermanas ¶ d.	0650u	...	0754u	...	...	...	1053u	1200u	...	1323u	1525u	...	...	...	...	1613u	1735u	1812u	...	2017u	...
	Algeciras d.	|	0615	|	...	0843	...	|	|	1145	|	|	...	...	1503	1530	|	|	|	...	|	...
	San Roque - La Línea d.	|	0630	|	...	0858	...	|	|	1201	|	|	...	...	1518	1546	|	|	|	...	|	...
	Ronda d.	|	0753	|	...	1009	...	|	|	1336	|	|	...	1610	1631	1713	|	|	|	...	|	...
167	Bobadilla **661** d.	|	0846	1000	...	|	...	1309	|	1429	1534	1733	...	1739	|	1801	|	1939	|	...	2229	...
236	**Málaga** M. Zambrano **661** a.	|	|	1106	...	|	...	1415	|	|	1635	1827	...	1853	|	|	|	2037	|	...	2325	...
	Antequera - Santa Ana § a.	0844	0851	...	...	|	...	...	1357	1435	...	...	...	...	1732	1806	1809	...	2009	...	...	...
	Madrid Pta de Atocha **660** a.	|	|	...	...	1405	...	...	|	|	...	...	...	...	2035	|	|	...	|	...	...	...
183	Antequera - Ciudad d.	*0904*¦	*0915*¦	...	...	...	...	...	*1417*¦	*1459*¦	...	...	...	...	...	*1828*¦	*1830*¦	...	*2029*¦	...	...	...
290	**Granada** **661** a.	*1049*¦	*1055*¦	...	...	...	...	...	*1544*¦	*1610*¦	...	...	...	...	...	*1945*¦	*1957*¦	...	*2148*¦	...	...	...
372	Guadix **661** d.	1153	...	...	...	...	...	...	1652	...	...	...	...	...	...	...	2108	...	2308	...	...	...
471	**Almería** **661** a.	1331	...	...	...	...	...	...	1847	...	...	...	...	...	...	...	2249	...	0052	...	...	...

km		MD 13901	MD 13062	MD 13941	MD 13057 🚌	Alta 9366		MD 13903	MD 13943		MD 13905	MD 13064		MD 13907	Alta 9330		MD 13076	MD 13945	MD 13909 ⑤⑦	MD 13911	MD 13947	
0	**Almería** **661** d.	...	...	0508	...	...	...	...	0800	...	...	...	...	...	...	...	...	1400	...	...	1800	...
99	Guadix **661** d.	...	...	0658	...	...	...	...	0944	...	...	...	...	...	...	...	...	1546	...	...	1953	...
181	**Granada** d.	...	*0645*¦	*0813*¦	...	...	...	...	*1053*¦	...	...	*1245*¦	...	...	...	...	*1700*¦	*1703*¦	...	...	*2115*¦	...
288	Antequera - Ciudad d.	...	*0750*¦	*0925*¦	...	...	...	...	*1205*¦	...	...	*1402*¦	...	...	...	...	*1807*¦	*1815*¦	...	...	*2227*¦	...
	Madrid Pta de Atocha **660** d.	...	|	|	...	0835	...	...	|	...	...	|	...	...	1503	...	|	|	...	...	|	...
	Antequera - Santa Ana § d.	...	0818	0948	...	1118	...	...	1228	...	...	1440	...	...	1754	...	1853	1838	...	...	2250	...
	Málaga M. Zambrano **661** d.	0708	|	|	0940	|	...	1006	|	...	1322	|	...	1604	|	...	|	|	1822	1950	|	...
304	Bobadilla **661** d.	0801	0826	|	1105	|	...	1103	|	...	1416	1452	...	1714	|	...	1900	|	1918	2054	|	...
376	Ronda d.	|	0918	|	1208	1221	...	|	|	...	|	1546	...	|	1858	...	1954	|	|	|	|	...
468	San Roque - La Línea d.	|	1045	|	...	1335	...	|	|	...	|	1725	...	|	2016	...	2117	|	|	|	|	...
480	**Algeciras** a.	|	1100	|	...	1348	...	|	|	...	|	1740	...	|	2030	...	2132	|	|	|	|	...
456	Dos Hermanas ¶ a.	1010s	...	1147s	...	...	...	1310s	1428s	...	1629s	...	...	1919s	...	...	...	2033s	2125s	2246s	0049s	...
471	**Sevilla** ¶ a.	1030	...	1204	...	...	...	1328	1448	...	1645	...	...	1935	...	...	...	2048	2144	2302	0110	...

s – Calls to set down only.

u – Calls to pick up only.

§ – ± *17 km* from Antequera.

¦ – 🚌 Antequera-Santa Ana - Antequera-Ciudad - Granada and v.v. Until Summer 2019.

¶ – Frequent suburban services run Sevilla - Dos Hermanas and v.v.

674 PALMA DE MALLORCA - INCA - SA POBLA and MANACOR — SFM 2nd class

km			Ⓐ	Ⓐ ◧	Ⓐ	Ⓐ	Ⓐ	Ⓐ	Ⓐ ◧	Ⓐ	Ⓐ	Ⓐ	and at the same	Ⓐ	Ⓐ	Ⓐ	Ⓐ	Ⓐ		Ⓒ	Ⓒ	and at the same	Ⓒ	Ⓒ	
0	**Palma** d.	Ⓐ	0546	0607	0617	0638	0717	0738	0745	0817	0838	0850	minutes	2038	2050	2117	2132	2220	Ⓒ	0610	0640	minutes	2140	2210	...
7	Marratxi d.		0600	0615	0625	0646	0725	0746	0753	0825	0846	0904	past	2046	2104	2125	2146	2235		0624	0654	past	2154	2225	...
29	**Inca** d.		0620	0632	0645	0707	0745	0806	0810	0845	0907	0924	each	2107	2124	2145	2207	2255		0645	0715	each	2215	2250	...
***	sa Pobla a.		0637	...	|	0724	|	0824	...	|	0924	...	hour	2124	...	|	2224	|		|	0732	hour	2232	|	...
64	**Manacor** a.		...	...	0718	...	0816	...	...	0916	...	...	until	...	...	2216	...	2325		0715	...	until	...	2315	...

		Ⓐ	Ⓐ ◧	Ⓐ	Ⓐ	Ⓐ	Ⓐ ◧	Ⓐ	Ⓐ	Ⓐ ◧	Ⓐ	Ⓐ	Ⓐ	and at the same	Ⓐ	Ⓐ	Ⓐ	Ⓐ		Ⓒ	Ⓒ	Ⓒ	and at the same	Ⓒ	Ⓒ
Manacor d.	Ⓐ	...	...	0625	...	0659	...	0725	...	...	0825	...	...	minutes	...	2125	...	2228	Ⓒ	0624	0724	...	minutes	...	2224
sa Pobla d.		0605	...	|	0700	|	...	|	0800	...	|	0900	...	past	...	|	2200	|		|	|	0807	past	2207	|
Inca d.		0621	0650	0656	0716	0729	0733	0756	0816	0833	0856	0916	0936	each	2136	2156	2216	2258		0655	0755	0824	each	2224	2255
Marratxi d.		0641	0707	0716	0736	...	0750	0816	0836	0850	0916	0936	0956	hour	2156	2216	2236	2318		0715	0815	0844	hour	2244	2315
Palma a.		0655	0715	0724	0744	...	0758	0824	0844	0858	0924	0944	1010	until	2210	2230	2250	2333		0729	0829	0858	until	2258	2329

◧ – Incaexprés. *** – *19 km* Inca - sa Pobla. **Operator**: Serveis Ferroviaris de Mallorca (SFM) ✆ +34 971 752 245.

PALMA DE MALLORCA - SÓLLER *28 km* Journey time: 55 minutes. **Operator**: Ferrocarril de Sóller (FS) ✆ +34 971 752 051.

Nov. - Mar.: 1030, 1250, 1510, 1800. Apr. - Oct.: 1010, 1050, 1215, 1330, 1510, 1940.

SÓLLER - PALMA DE MALLORCA

Nov. - Mar.: 0900, 1140, 1400, 1700. Apr. - Oct.: 0900, 1050, 1215, 1400, 1830.

A connecting tram service operates **Sóller** - **Port de Sóller**. *5 km*. Journey time: 15–20 minutes. Not all services shown.

From Sóller: 0800, 0900, 1000, 1100, 1200, 1300, 1400, 1500, 1600, 1700, 1800, 1900.
From Port de Sóller: 0830, 0930, 1030, 1130, 1230, 1330, 1430, 1530, 1630, 1730, 1830, 1930.

675 🚌 MÁLAGA and ALGECIRAS - LA LÍNEA (for Gibraltar)

There are no cross-border 🚌 services: passengers to/from Gibraltar must cross the frontier on foot (walking-time about 5 minutes) and transfer to/from Gibraltar local 🚌 services

🚌 **MÁLAGA** bus stn – **LA LÍNEA** bus station (for **Gibraltar**)

From Málaga: 0700, 1130▽, 1400, 1630, 1915⑦.
From La Línea: 0850, 1030, 1630▽, 1900, 2045⑦.
Journey time: 3 hours. Operator: Automóviles Portillo, Málaga ✆ (+34) 902 020 052.
▽ – Journey operated by Alsina Graells (see Table **664** for contact details).

🚌 **ALGECIRAS** bus station - **LA LÍNEA** bus station (for **Gibraltar**) Route M-120

From Algeciras: Ⓐ: 0700 and every 30 minutes until 2130, also 2230.
⑥: every 45 mins 0700–2115, also 2230. †: every 45 mins 0800–2130, also 2230.
From La Línea: Ⓐ: 0700, 0745 and every 30 minutes until 2215, also 2315.
⑥: every 45 mins 0700–2200, also 2315. †: 0700, 0845 then every 45 mins until 2215, also 2315
Journey time: 45 mins. Operator: Transportes Generales Comes SA, Algeciras ✆ (+34) 902 450 550

676 🚌 SEVILLA - AYAMONTE - FARO - LAGOS — DAMAS ☆

					Ⓐ	Ⓒ		Ⓐ	†	⑥	Ⓐ			⚒		Ⓐ	⑥	⑦	Ⓐ		Ⓑ	⑥	†	⚒
Sevilla ⊖ d.	**Summer** July 1 -	0730	0930	1130	*1230*	*1330*	1530	1800	1900	2000	2030	**Winter** Sept. 4 -	0730	0930	1130	...	1300	...	...	1530	...	1730	1900	1930
Huelva d.	Sept. 3	0900	1100	1300	1400	1500	1700	1930	2030	2130	2200	June 30,	0900	1100	1300	1400	1430	1430	1530	1700	1900	1900	2030	2100
Ayamonte a.		1015	1215	1415	1500	1600	1815	2045	2145	2245	2315	2018	1015j	1215	1415f	1500	1545	1555	1630	1815z	2000x	2015	2145	2215

		⚒	Ⓑ		⚒	Ⓐ	⑥	†	Ⓐ	⑦			⚒	Ⓐ			Ⓐ	⑥	†	Ⓐ	⑥	⑥	Ⓑ	
Ayamonte d.	**Summer** July 1 -	0640	0830	0930	1145	1400	1515	1615	1715	1730	1945	**Winter** Sept. 4 -	0640	0830	0930	1145	1400	1500	1515	1545	1615	1715	1730	1930
Huelva d.	Sept. 3	0740	0930	1030z	1245	1500	1645	1715	1815	1830	2045	June 30,	0740x	0930	1030j	1245j	1500	1600	1615	1645	1715	1830	1845	2045j
Sevilla ⊖ a.		0910	*1115*	1215z	*1515*	1645	1815	1845	1945	*2015*	2215	2018	0910	...	1215	...	...	1715	1745	1815	1845	1945	...	2230

⛴ **Ayamonte - Vila Real de Santo António Guadiana** Journey time: 10 minutes. ✆ (+34) 959 470 617. Sept. 16 - Mar. 31: hourly (from Ayamonte 1000-1900⚒, 1100-1700, 1815†). Apr. 1 - June 30: hourly (from Ayamonte 1000-2000⚒, 1100-1700, 1815†). July 1 - Sept. 15: every 30 mins (from Ayamonte 0930-2100⚒, 1000-1900, 2015†).

INTERNATIONAL 🚌 SERVICE Joint EVA △/DAMAS ☆ service *for international journeys only* No service Dec. 25, Jan. 1

Sevilla, Plaza de Armas ⊖ d.		0730	1615		0730	0930	1445	1615
Huelva d.	→	0845	1730	→	0845	1100	1600	1730
Ayamonte 🏛 ES d.	**Winter**	0930	|	**Summer**	|	1200	|	|
Vila Real de Santo António 🏛 PT a.		0855	1720		|	|	|	1720
Faro, Av. da República a.	Sept. 11 -	1020	1835	July 1 -	0920	1240	1605	1835
Albufeira, Alto dos Caliços a.	June 30,	1120	1940	Sept. 10	1015	1340	1705	1940
Portimão, Largo do Dique a.	2019	1150	2010		|	1410	|	2010
Lagos, Rossio de S. João a.		1215	2035		1100	1435	1750	2035

Lagos, Rossio de S. João d.		0620	1345		0620	0800	1230	1515
Portimão, Largo do Dique d.	→	0645	1410	→	0645	|	|	1540
Albufeira, Alto dos Caliços d.	**Winter**	0720	1440	**Summer**	0720	0845	1315	1610
Faro, Av. da República d.		0805	1525		0805	0930	1355	1655
Vila Real de Santo António 🏛 PT d.	Sept. 11 -	0935	1655	July 1 -	0935	|	|	|
Ayamonte 🏛 ES a.	June 30,	|	1820	Sept. 10	|	|	|	1950
Huelva a.	2019	1125	1920		1125	1150	1645	2105
Sevilla, Plaza de Armas ⊖ a.		1240	2035		1240	1305	1800	2220

☆ – DAMAS, Huelva ✆ +34 959 256 900. www.damas-sa.es
△ – EVA, Faro ✆ +351 289 899 700. www.eva-bus.com
⊖ – Sevilla Plaza de Armas bus station (± 2 km from Santa Justa rail station).
ES – Spain (Central European Time).
PT – Portugal (West European Time).
Huelva bus station is ± 1.7 km from the rail station.
Ayamonte bus station is ± 1.5 km from the ferry terminal.

MADRID - CÁCERES - BADAJOZ 677

km																								
										MD	*MD*				*AP*					*MD*	*Talgo*	*MD*		
		13084					**17905**	**17014**	**17028**	**17900**	**17902**		**5500**	**4432**	**126**	**17702**				**17012**	**194**	**18330**	**17018**	**17706**
		2	2	2	2	2	2	2	2	2	2	2	2	2		2	2	2	2	2		2	2	2
		①–⑥	Ⓐ	Ⓐ	Ⓒ		Ⓐ	①–⑥	**T**	⑤⑥⑦	①–④				Ⓑ		⑦	Ⓐ	Ⓑ				Ⓑ	
0	**Madrid** Chamartín d.	...	...	...	...	...	...	...	...	...	...	...	...	...	...	...	...	...	...	...	1548	...	...	...
8	**Madrid** Atocha Cercanías d.	...	...	...	...	...	...	0804	...	1025	1025	...	...	...	...	1228	...	...	...	1448	1608	...	1847	2110
16	Villaverde Bajo **669** d.	...	...	...	...	...	...	|	...	|	|	...	...	...	...	1236	...	...	...	|	|	...	|	2118
146	Talavera de la Reina d.	...	...	...	...	...	...	0938	...	1157	1157	...	...	...	...	1410	...	...	...	1622	1736	...	2023	2242
	Navalmoral de La Mata d.	...	...	...	...	...	...	1017	...	1233	1233	...	...	...	...	...	...	...	...	1705	1813	...	2100	...
278	Plasencia a.	...	...	...	...	...	...	1110	...	1313	1313	...	...	...	...	...	...	...	...	1801	|	...	2149	...
278	Plasencia d.	...	...	...	...	...	0704	1114	...	1316	1316	...	...	...	...	...	...	...	...	1805**z**	|	...	2152	...
*343**	**Cáceres** d.	...	0646	...	0805	...	0822	1224	1225	1422	1422	...	...	...	...	...	1645	1645	...	1908**z**	1937	...	2300	...
	San Vicente de Alcántara d.	...	|	...	|	...	|	|	1338	|	|	...	...	...	...	...	|	|	...	...	|	...	...	...
430	Valencia de Alcántara d.	...	|	...	|	...	|	|	1353	|	|	...	...	...	...	...	|	|	...	...	|	...	...	...
409	Mérida a.	...	0744	...	0901	...	0930	1322	...	1524	1524	...	...	...	...	...	1747	1747	...	...	2038	...	...	...
409	Mérida **678** d.	...	0754	0754	0910	0910	...	1325	...	1529	1529	1530	❋	...	...	...	...	1758	1758	...	2048	2145	...	...
469	**Badajoz** 🏛 **678** ES a.	...	|	0841	|	1011	...	1408	...	|	|	1611	1624	...	...	...	...	|	1846	...	2126	2232	...	...
	Elvas 🏛 PT a.	...	|	...	|	...	...	...	...	|	|	❋	1548	...	...	...	...	|	...	...	...	...	...	...
	Abrantes **691** a.	...	|	...	|	...	...	...	...	|	|	...	1751	...	...	...	...	|	...	...	...	...	...	...
	Entroncamento **691** a.	...	|	...	|	...	...	...	...	|	|	...	1825	1844	1942	...	...	|	...	...	...	...	...	...
	Lisboa Oriente **691** a.	...	|	...	|	...	...	...	...	|	|	...	...	2012	2032	...	...	|	...	...	...	...	...	...
742	**Lisboa** S Apolónia **691** a.	...	|	...	|	...	...	...	...	|	|	...	...	2020	2040	...	...	|	...	...	...	...	...	...
475	Zafra d.	...	0843	...	0959	...	...	...	...	1621	1621	...	...	...	...	...	...	1851	...	...	...	...	...	...
649	Sevilla a.	...	1133	...	1247	...	...	...	...	|	...	...	...	...	...	...	...	...	...	...	...	...	...	...
521	Fregenal de la Sierra d.	...	...	...	...	...	...	...	...	1701	...	...	...	...	...	...	...	...	...	...	...	...	...	...
	Jabugo-Galaroza d.	0735	...	...	...	...	...	...	...	1744	...	...	...	...	...	...	...	...	...	...	...	...	...	...
660	Huelva a.	0932	...	...	...	...	...	...	...	1935	...	...	...	...	...	...	...	...	...	...	...	...	...	...

					MD	*Talgo*	*Talgo*						*IC*			*MD*	*MD*		*MD*			*MD*		
	17703	**17705**	**17021**		**18331**	**197**	**199**	**17707**		**17026**	**17709**	**17029**	**541**	**5501**		**17907**	**17907**		**17025**			**13089**		
	2	2	2	2	2	Ⓐ	Ⓒ	2	2	2	2	2		2	2	2	2		2	2	2	2		
	Ⓐ	Ⓒ	①–⑥	Ⓐ				Ⓐ	Ⓐ		Ⓒ	**T**				⑤⑥⑦	①–④		Ⓑ			Ⓑ		
Huelva d.	...	...	...	...	...	...	...	...	...	...	...	...	...	...	...	1100	...	...	...	...	...	1940	...	...
Jabugo-Galaroza d.	...	...	...	...	...	...	...	...	...	...	...	...	...	...	...	1257	...	...	...	...	...	2133	...	...
Fregenal de la Sierra d.	...	...	...	...	...	...	...	...	...	...	...	...	...	...	...	1340	...	...	...	...	...	...	...	...
Sevilla d.	...	...	...	...	...	...	...	...	...	...	...	...	...	...	...	|	...	...	...	...	1712	...	...	...
Zafra d.	...	...	...	0655	...	...	...	...	...	...	...	...	...	...	...	1423	1423	...	...	...	1958	...	...	...
Lisboa S Apolónia **691** d.	...	...	...	|	...	...	...	...	...	...	...	...	0815	...	...	|	|	...	...	...	|	...	...	...
Lisboa Oriente **691** d.	...	...	...	|	...	...	...	...	...	...	...	...	0823	...	...	|	|	...	...	...	|	...	...	...
Entroncamento **691** d.	...	...	...	|	...	...	...	...	...	...	...	...	0923	1010	...	|	|	...	...	...	|	...	...	...
Abrantes **691** d.	...	...	...	|	...	...	...	...	...	...	...	...	...	1054	...	|	|	...	...	...	|	...	...	...
Elvas 🏛 PT d.	...	...	...	|	...	...	...	...	...	...	...	...	...	1253	❋	|	|	...	...	...	|	...	...	...
Badajoz 🏛 **678** ES d.	...	...	...	|	0652	0717	0845	...	1230	...	...	...	...	1416	1430	|	|	...	1718	2004	|	...	...	...
Mérida **678** a.	...	...	...	0742	0737	0753	0923	...	1316	...	...	...	...	❋	1528	1512	1512	...	1756	2049	2046	...	...	...
Mérida d.	...	...	...	...	...	0803	0933	...	...	1325	...	...	...	...	...	1525	1525	...	1806	...	2055	...	...	...
Valencia de Alcántara d.	...	...	...	...	...	|	|	...	...	|	...	1435	...	...	...	|	|	...	|	...	|	...	...	...
San Vicente de Alcántara d.	...	...	...	...	...	|	|	...	...	|	...	1449	...	...	...	|	|	...	|	...	|	...	...	...
Cáceres d.	...	...	0712	...	...	0903	1035	...	...	1427	...	1607	...	...	...	1622	1622	...	1909	...	2159	...	...	...
Plasencia a.	...	...	0820	...	...	|	|	...	...	1541	...	...	...	...	...	1723	1723	...	2020	...	...	...	...	...
Plasencia d.	...	...	0824	...	...	|	|	...	...	1545	...	...	...	...	...	1726	1726	...	2023	...	...	...	...	...
Navalmoral de La Mata d.	...	...	0907	...	...	1022	1157	...	...	1631	...	...	...	...	...	1807	1807	...	2105	...	...	...	...	...
Talavera de la Reina d.	0650	0836	0941	...	...	1059	1239	1518	...	1708	1752	...	...	...	...	1852	1852	...	2140	...	...	...	...	...
Villaverde Bajo **669** a.	0810**j**	1008	|	...	...	|	|	1647	...	|	1917	...	...	...	...	|	|	...	|	...	...	...	...	...
Madrid Atocha Cercanías a.	0823	1018	1108	...	...	1226	1353	1656	...	1852	1926	...	...	...	...	2016	2016	...	2312	...	...	...	...	...
Madrid Chamartín a.	...	...	...	...	...	1242	1411	...	...	...	...	...	...	...	...	...	...	...	...	...	...	...	...	...

T – Not ②.
j – Villaverde Alto.
z – ⑤ only.
❋ – Connection not guaranteed.
* – Madrid - Cáceres via Plasencia *363 km*.
ES – Spain (Central European Time).
PT – Portugal (West European Time).

ALCÁZAR DE SAN JUAN - BADAJOZ 678

km											
		MD				*MD*	*MD*	*Talgo*	*MD*	*MD*	**18027**
		17042				**18183**	**18170**	**697**	**18330**	**18083**	**A**
		2	2	2	2	2	2		2	2	2
					Ⓑ	**h**	**f**	**T**		**h**	⑦
	Madrid AC § **661 668** d.	...	...	...	...	...	1310	...	...	...	...
	Albacete **668a** d.	...	...	...	...	1148	|	1450	...	1842	1929
0	**Alcázar de San Juan 661** d.	0715	...	...	...	1300	1435	1603	1620	1954	2053
50	Manzanares **661** d.	0740	...	...	...	1325	1500	1625	1643	2021	2120
114	Ciudad Real **660** d.	0820	...	...	...	1406	1546	...	1730	2102	2200
153	Puertollano **660** d.	...	...	1145	...	...	...	...	1801	...	...
265	Cabeza del Buey d.	...	0720**x**	1328	1552**z**	...	...	...	1954	...	...
392	Mérida **677** d.	...	0910	1530	1758	...	...	...	2145	...	...
451	**Badajoz** **677** a.	...	1011	1611	1846	...	...	...	2232	...	...

	18024	*MD*	*Talgo*	*MD*	*MD*	*MD*				*MD*
	B	**18081**	**694**	**18331**	**17041**	**18181**				**17043**
	2	2		2	2	2	2		2	2
	①	**h**	**T**		**f**	**h**				
Badajoz **677** d.	...	...	...	0652	...	...	1430	...	2004	...
Mérida **677** d.	...	...	...	0750	...	...	1528	...	2104	...
Cabeza del Buey d.	...	...	...	0935	...	...	1715	...	2256	...
Puertollano **660** d.	...	...	...	1118	...	...	1902	...	...	...
Ciudad Real **660** d.	0536	1012	...	1158	1440	1625	...	...	...	2222
Manzanares **661** d.	0614	1052	1237	1243	1520	1712	...	...	...	2300
Alcázar de San Juan 661 a.	0642	1117	1300	1309	1545	1735	...	...	...	2327
Albacete **668a** a.	0805	1227	1418	...	|	1847	...	...	...	...
Madrid AC § **661 668** a.	...	...	...	...	1717	...	...	...	...	...

A – ⑦: 2 València - Albacete - Ciudad Real (Table **668**).
B – ①: 2 Ciudad Real - Albacete - València (Table **668**).
T – TORRE DEL ORO – 12 🍸 Barcelona - València - Córdoba - Sevilla and v.v. (Tables **661**, **671**, **672**).
f – From/to Madrid **Chamartin** (Table **661**).
h – From/to Alacant (Table **668**).
x – ①–⑥.
z – ⑦ only.
§ – Madrid Atocha Cercanías.

BARCELONA / MADRID - GRANADA 678a

Provisional service from June 24. Subject to confirmation.

train type		*AVE*		*AVE*		*AVE*		*AVE*	
train number				**3930**					
notes									
Barcelona Sants d.	...	...	...	0650	...	...	...	...	...
Madrid Puerta de Atocha d.	...	0720	...	|	...	1400	...	1930	...
Córdoba a.	...	0902	...	1137	...	1542	...	2112	...
Puente Genil - Herrera ¶ a.	...	0923	...	1201	...	1603	...	2133	...
Antequera - Santa Ana § a.	...	0937	...	1217	...	1617	...	2147	...
Granada a.	...	1025	...	1315	...	1705	...	2235	...

train type		*AVE*		*AVE*		*AVE*		*AVE*	
train number						**3931**			
notes									
Granada d.	...	0659	...	1000	...	1535	...	1859	...
Antequera - Santa Ana § d.	...	0747	...	1047	...	1633	...	1947	...
Puente Genil - Herrera ¶ d.	...	0801	...	1101	...	1648	...	2001	...
Córdoba d.	...	0822	...	1122	...	1715	...	2022	...
Madrid Puerta de Atocha a.	...	1005	...	1305	...	|	...	2205	...
Barcelona Sants a.	...	...	...	...	...	2200	...	...	...

¶ – ± *8 km* from Puente Genil.
§ – ± *17 km* from Antequera.

679 MADRID - TOLEDO, SEGOVIA, VALLADOLID, SALAMANCA and EL ESCORIAL — 2nd class

km		*Av*	*Av*	*Av*	*Av*	*Av*	*Av*	*Av*		*Av*	*Av*	*Av*	*Av*	*Av*	*Av*	*Av*		*Av*					
		8062	**8072**	**8082**	**8292**	**8102**	**8312**	**8322**		**8132**	**8142**	**8152**	**8162**	**8172**	**8182**	**8192**		**8212**					
		①–⑤	①–⑤								①–⑤		①–⑤		①–⑤								
0	**Madrid** Puerta de Atocha d.	0650	0750	0850	0920	1020	1120	1220	...	1350	1450	1550	1650	1750	1850	1950	...	2150	...	...	...	...	...
75	**Toledo** a.	0723	0823	0923	0953	1051	1153	1253	...	1423	1523	1623	1723	1823	1923	2023	...	2223	...	...	...	...	...

	Av	*Av*	*Av*	*Av*		*Av*	*Av*		*Av*	*Av*		*Av*	*Av*	*Av*	*Av*	*Av*	*Av*	*Av*					
	8063	**8273**	**8073**	**8283**		**8093**	**8103**		**8123**	**8133**		**8153**	**8163**	**8173**	**8183**	**8193**	**8203**	**8213**					
	①–⑤	①–⑤	①–⑤	①–⑤									①–⑤										
Toledo d.	0625	0650	0725	0755	...	0925	1025	...	1225	1325	...	1525	1618	1725	1825	1920	2025	2130	...	...	...	...	...
Madrid Puerta de Atocha a.	0658	0723	0758	0828	...	0958	1058	...	1258	1358	...	1558	1651	1758	1858	1953	2058	2203	...	...	...	...	...

km	km		*Av*	*Av*	*Alvia*	*Av*		*Av*	*Alvia*	*Av*	*Av*	*Av*	*Av*	*Alvia*	*IC*	*Av*	*Av*	*Av*	*Av*	*Av*	*Av*	*Av*	*Alvia*	*Av*	
			8069	**8079**	**4899**	**8109**		**8129**	**4929**	**8139**	**34149**	**8159**	**8359**	**4969**	**10167**	**8169**	**8179**	**8389**	**8189**	**8199**	**8209**	**34209**	**4909**	**8219**	
			①–⑤	①–⑤					①–⑤	⑤	Ⓑ	⑤				①–⑤		Ⓑ	**A**	①–⑤		Ⓑ			
0	*0*	**Madrid** Chamartín d.	0640	0730	0855	1015	...	1200	1240	1340	1440	1510	1540	1555	1605	1635	1700	1810	1840	1925	2000	2025	2040	2130	...
68	*68*	**Segovia** AV d.	0708	0758	0923	1043	...	1228	1308	1408	1508	1538	1608	1623	1635	1703	1728	1838	1908	1952	2028	|	2108	2158	...
		Medina del Campo AV d.	|	|	|	|	...	|	1336	|	|	|	|	|	|	|	|	|	|	|	|	|	2137	|	...
180		**Valladolid** ⊠ a.	0745	0835	|	1120	...	1305	|	1445	1541	1615	1645	|	1721	1740	1805	1915	1945	2031**x**	2105	2119	|	2235	...
	230	**Salamanca** a.	...	...	1031	...	...	...	1421	...	...	...	...	1731	...	...	...	...	...	...	...	...	2221	...	...

	Av	*Av*	*Alvia*	*Av*	*Av*	*Av*	*Av*	*Alvia*	*Av*	*Alvia*	*Av*	*IC*	*Av*	*Av*	*Alvia*		*Av*	*Av*	*Alvia*	*Av*	*Av*				
	8058	**8068**	**4868**	**8078**	**8278**	**34078**	**8088**	**4898**	**8098**	**4918**	**8108**	**10086**	**8148**	**8158**	**4958**		**8178**	**34178**	**4988**	**8198**	**8208**				
	①–⑤	①–⑤	①–⑤	①–⑤		①–⑤	①–⑤	⑥⑦	⑥⑦	①–⑤	①–⑤							Ⓑ							
Salamanca d.	...	...	0625	...	...	...	...	0840	...	1050	...	...	...	...	1530	...	...	...	1820	...	...	...	...	...	...
Valladolid ⊠ d.	0623**x**	0645	|	0715	0750	0811	0845	|	0935	|	1130	1311	1410	1520	|	...	1745	1836	|	1946	2035	...	...	...	...
Medina del Campo AV d.	|	|	|	|	|	|	|	0924	|	|	|	|	|	|	1614	...	|	|	|	|	|	...	...	...	...
Segovia AV d.	0700	0722	0736	0752	0827	|	0922	0954	1012	1159	1207	1359	1447	1557	1644	...	1822	1912	1929	2023	2112	...	...	...	...
Madrid Chamartín a.	0728	0750	0803	0820	0855	0907	0950	1021	1040	1226	1235	1428	1515	1625	1711	...	1850	1939	1956	2051	2140	...	...	...	...

km		①–⑤	⑥⑦	⑥⑦	①–⑤	⑥⑦		⑤	⑥⑦	①–⑤	⑥⑦
0	**Madrid** Chamartín d.	...	0845	*1015*	*1116*	*1216*	...	*1547*	*1616*	*1846*	*1916*
58	Cercedilla d.	0700	0947	1132	1230	1332	...	1700	1732	2000	2032
100	**Segovia** a.	0737	1024	1208	1307	1409	...	1736	1808	2039	2110

	①–⑤	⑥⑦	⑥⑦			⑤	⑥⑦	①–⑤	⑥⑦	
Segovia d.	0750	1050	1250	1450	...	1750	1850	2050	2120	...
Cercedilla a.	0828	1128	1326	1527	...	1826	1926	2127	2157	...
Madrid Chamartín a.	*0935*	*1234*	*1435*	*1635*	...	*1935*	*2036*	*2235*	2254	...

km		*MD*	*MD*	*MD*	*MD*	*MD*	*MD*	*MD*	*MD*	*MD*	
		18001	**18901**	**18921**	**18903**	**18905**	**18907**	**18913**	**18909**	**18911**	
		①–⑤	①–⑤	⑥⑦		①–⑤				Ⓑ	
0	**Madrid** Chamartín ◧ d.	0633	0740**p**	0828**p**	1110**p**	1340**p**	1528**p**	1757**p**	1937**p**	2112**p**	...
122	Ávila ◧ d.	0807	0908	0958	1239	1506	1714	1930	2109	2240	...
233	**Salamanca** a.	...	1036	1120	1353	1614	1825	2043	2217	2346	...

	MD	*MD*	*MD*	*MD*	*MD*	*MD*	*MD*	*MD*	*MD*	
	18920	**18910**	**18900**	**18912**	**18902**	**18904**	**18906**	**18006**	**18908**	
	①–⑤	①–⑥					Ⓑ			
Salamanca d.	...	0548	0737	0945	1228	1644	1738	...	1958	...
Ávila ◧ d.	0555	0655	0845	1055	1339	1812	1849	1900	2106	...
Madrid Chamartín ◧ a.	0739**p**	0826**p**	1011**p**	1225**p**	1512**p**	1948**p**	...	2052	2241**p**	...

MADRID ATOCHA CERCANÍAS - VILLALBA - EL ESCORIAL. *45 km*. Line C8. Journey time: Villalba, 53 minutes; El Escorial, 66-67 minutes. Depart 14 minutes later from Madrid Chamartín; arrive 15 minutes earlier at Madrid Charmartín. Additional services operate.

From **Madrid Atocha Cercanías**: 0621 Ⓐ, 0635 Ⓒ, 0651 Ⓐ, 0709 Ⓐ, 0723 Ⓐ, 0737 Ⓒ, 0750 Ⓐ, 0835 Ⓒ, 0839 Ⓐ, 0935 Ⓒ, 0941 Ⓐ, 1036, 1135, 1235, 1335, 1407 Ⓐ, 1436 Ⓒ, 1450 Ⓐ, 1521 Ⓐ, 1536 Ⓒ, 1547 Ⓐ, 1635, 1715 Ⓐ, 1736 Ⓒ, 1745 Ⓐ, 1827 Ⓐ, 1836 Ⓒ, 1847 Ⓐ, 1920, 1936, Ⓒ, 1944 Ⓐ, 2036 Ⓐ, 2042 Ⓒ, 2139, 2236, 2334.

From **El Escorial**: 0548, 0616 Ⓒ, 0631 Ⓐ, 0658 Ⓐ, 0706 Ⓐ, 0716 Ⓒ, 0736 Ⓐ, 0802 Ⓐ, 0817 Ⓒ, 0831 Ⓐ, 0915, 1015, 1115, 1215, 1315, 1414, 1515, 1601 Ⓐ, 1615 Ⓒ, 1624 Ⓐ, 1713, 1815, 1858 Ⓐ, 1912 Ⓐ, 1915 Ⓒ, 1930 Ⓐ, 1959 Ⓐ, 2013 Ⓒ, 2029 Ⓐ, 2115, 2215.

A – ①②③④⑥.
x – From September 10.
p – Madrid **Principe Pio**.
MD – Medium Distance Plus.
Av – ***Avant*** high-speed services. Single class.
⊠ – Full name is Valladolid Campo Grande.
◧ – See also Tables **680**, **681**, **689**.

679a MADRID - VALLADOLID

High-speed services. For Avant high-speed services, see Table **679**.

		Alvia	*Alvia*	*Alvia*	*Alvia*	*Alvia*	*AVE*		*Alvia*		*Alvia*	*Alvia*	*Alvia*	*Alvia*	*Alvia*	*Alvia*	*Alvia*	*Alvia*	*Alvia*		*Alvia*	*IC*	*Alvia*		
		4071	**4275**	**4073**	**4087**	**4187**	**4099**		**4111**		**4143**	**4149**	**4541**	**4141**	**4345**	**4145**	**4143**	**4167**	**4267**		**4179**	**4177**	**4377**		
		①–⑥	①–⑤	①–⑥		①–⑥	**4299**					Ⓑ	⑥	Ⓑ	⑦	①–⑤	⑤		Ⓑ		Ⓑ	⑤	⑦		
							L		**V**			**LS**	**U**	**S**	**F**	**F**	2				2 **P**	2 **Q**	2 **Q**		
	Alacant Terminal **668** d.	...	...	...	...	...	...	...	...	...	1030**c**	...	...	...	1020	...	...	...	...	...	...	...	...	...	...
0	**Madrid** Chamartín d.	0705	0720	0745	0800	0800	0935	...	1148	...	1410	1440	1440	1450	1500	1500	1525	1605	1605	...	1730	1740	1740	...	...
68	Segovia AV d.	|	0750	|	0830	0830	1003	...	1220	...	1440	1508	|	|	1531	1531	|	1635	1635	...	1758	|	|	...	...
	A Coruña **680** a.	|	|	|	|	|	|	...	|	...	|	|	|	|	2052	2052	|	|	|	...	|	|	|	...	...
	Pontevedra **680** a.	|	1353	|	|	|	|	...	|	...	|	|	|	|	...	...	|	|	|	...	|	|	|	...	...
180	**Valladolid** ⊠ a.	0808	...	0843	0916	0916	1036	...	1257	...	1515	1541	1539	1549	...	...	1626	1721	1721	...	1833	1848	1848	...	...
	Gijón Cercanías **681** a.	1217	...	|	|	|	...	...	1721	...	|	...	1943	1939	...	...	|	|	|	...	...	...	...	...	...
	Santander **681** a.	...	...	1150	|	|	...	...	...	...	1815	...	...	...	...	...	1947	|	|	...	...	...	...	...	...
	Bilbao Abando **689** a.	...	...	...	|	1304	...	...	...	...	...	...	...	...	...	...	...	|	2116	...	...	...	...	...	...
	Hendaye **689** a.	...	...	...	1355	...	...	...	...	...	...	...	...	...	...	...	...	2158	...	...	...	...	...	...	...

		Alvia	*Alvia*	*Alvia*	*AVE*				
		4181	**4193**	**4197**	**4209**				
		4381		①–④					
				T	**L**				
Alacant Terminal **668** d.	...	1445	...	...	...	...	...	...	...
Madrid Chamartín d.	...	1830	1905	1915	2025	...	...	...	...
Segovia AV d.	...	|	|	|	|	...	...	...	...
A Coruña **680** a.	...	|	|	|	|	...	...	...	...
Pontevedra **680** a.	...	|	|	|	|	...	...	...	...
Valladolid ⊠ a.	...	1930	2005	2023	2119	...	...	...	...
Gijón Cercanías **681** a.	...	2338**r**	|	...	...	...	...	...	...
Santander **681** a.	...	...	2312	...	...	...	...	...	...
Bilbao Abando **689** a.	...	...	...	...	...	...	...	...	...
Hendaye **689** a.	...	...	...	...	...	...	...	...	...

	AVE	*Alvia*	*Alvia*	*Alvia*	*Alvia*	*Alvia*	*Alvia*	*Alvia*	*Alvia*	*Alvia*	
	4078	**4088**	**4076**	**4072**	**4070**	**4270**	**4064**	**4092**	**4086**	**4186**	
	①–⑤	①–⑤	①–⑤	①–⑤	①–⑥	⑦	①–⑤	⑥⑦		①–⑥	
	LS	2 **P**	**T**				**F**				
Irún **689** d.	...	...	...	...	...	...	...	...	0840	...	...
Bilbao Abando **689** d.	...	...	...	...	...	...	...	...	|	0920	...
Santander **681** d.	...	...	...	0705	...	...	...	0910	|	|	...
Gijón Cercanías **681** d.	...	...	...	|	0700	0700	...	|	|	|	...
Valladolid ⊠ d.	0811	0910	0916	1011	1047	1105	...	1216	1311	1311	...
Pontevedra **680** d.	|	|	|	|	|	|	...	|	|	|	...
A Coruña **680** d.	|	|	|	|	|	|	0715	|	|	|	...
Segovia AV d.	|	0947	|	1051	|	|	1237	1256	1359	1359	...
Madrid Chamartín a.	0910	1015	1030	1121	1150	1208	1306	1326	1428	1428	...
Alacant Terminal **668** a.	...	...	...	1512	...	...	...	1715	...	...	...

		AVE	*Alvia*	*Alvia*	*Alvia*		*Alvia*	*Alvia*	*AVE*	*AVE*	*IC*	*Alvia*	*AVE*	*Alvia*	*Alvia*	*AVE*	*Alvia*	*Alvia*	*Alvia*	*Alvia*	*Alvia*				
		4128	**4084**	**4584**	**4110**		**4142**	**4140**	**4178**	**4188**	**4176**	**4162**	**4198**	**4166**	**4266**	**4398**	**4354**	**4180**	**4380**	**4208**	**4192**				
		①–⑤	①–⑤	⑥					Ⓑ	⑥	⑦	⑦	⑥		Ⓑ	⑦	Ⓑ	①–⑤	⑦	⑦	Ⓑ				
		2 **L**			**V**				**LS**	2 **L**	2 **Q**		**L**			**L**				2 **P**					
Irún **689** d.	...	...	...	...	...	...	...	...	...	...	...	...	...	1615	...	...	...	...	...	...	...	...	...	...	...
Bilbao Abando **689** d.	...	...	...	...	...	...	...	...	...	...	...	...	...	|	1700	...	...	...	...	...	...	...	...	...	...
Santander **681** d.	...	...	...	...	...	...	1400	...	...	...	...	1610	...	|	|	...	...	...	...	...	1900	...	...	...	...
Gijón Cercanías **681** d.	...	...	...	...	1050	...	|	1412	...	...	...	|	...	|	|	...	...	1751	1800	...	|	...	...	...	...
Valladolid ⊠ d.	...	1331	...	...	1450	...	1704	1813	1836	1901	1914	1930	2005	2050	2050	2106	...	2145	2145	2156	2207	...	...	...	...
Pontevedra **680** d.	...	|	0818	0818	|	...	|	|	|	|	|	|	|	|	|	|	1546	|	|	|	|	...	...	...	...
A Coruña **680** d.	...	|	|	|	|	...	|	|	|	|	|	|	|	|	|	|	|	|	|	|	|	...	...	...	...
Segovia AV d.	...	1414	|	|	|	...	|	|	1915	1941	|	|	2042	2137	2137	2145	2216	|	|	|	|	...	...	...	...
Madrid Chamartín a.	...	1441	1504	1506	1600	...	1807	1921	1942	2008	2027	2040	2110	2206	2206	2214	2245	2255	2255	2303	2310	...	...	...	...
Alacant Terminal **668** a.	...	...	...	1846	...	...	...	2301	...	...	...	...	...	...	...	...	...	...	...	...	...	...	...	...	...

F – To / from Ferrol (Table **682**).
L – To / from Leon (Table **681**).
P – To / from Ponferrada (Tables **681**, **682**).
Q – To / from Irún (Table **689**).
S – Ⓑ (⑤⑦ July 30 - Aug. 23).
T – To and from Vitoria / Gasteiz (Table **689**).
U – ⑥ (①②③④⑥ July 30 - Aug. 23).
V – From / to Castelló de la Plana and València on dates shown in Table **668**.
c – 1020 on ⑦.
r – 2320 on ⑤.
⊠ – Full name is Valladolid Campo Grande.
☛ All trains convey 🍸. *AVE* trains also convey ✕.

MADRID - ZAMORA - VIGO, PONTEVEDRA and A CORUÑA 680

For services to / from A Coruña via León, see Table **682**

Additional connections between Vigo and Ourense can be made by changing trains at Santiago de Compostela

km			Av	MD		Av		MD		MD	Hotel			Alvia		Av	MD		Alvia	MD	Av		MD	MD	
		12512	**9470**	**9072**	**12480**	**9480**	**12584**	**9082**	**12526**	**9112**	**922**	**12586**	**12528**	**4275**		**9520**	**9132**	**12960**	**4095**	**9142**	**9550**	**12538**	**9162**	**9172**	
		🅁	2	🅁	🅁	2	2	🅁	🅁	🅁	🍷	🅁	🅁		2	2	🅁	🅁		🅁	2	🅁	🅁	🅁	
		①–⑤	①–⑤	2	2		①–⑤	2	2	2	**G**	①–⑤	2	①–⑤	**h**		2	2	①–⑥	①–⑤	①–⑤	2	2	2	
		2										2							**b**	2					
0	**Madrid** Chamartín. **681 689** d.	...	...	...	...	...	...	...	...	...	...	...	...	0715	...	...	...	...	0915	...	...	...	...	...	...
68	Segovia AV......... **679 679a** d.	...	...	...	...	...	...	...	...	...	...	...	...	0745	...	...	...	...	|	...	...	...	...	...	...
	Irún **689**........................ d.	...	...	...	...	...	...	...	...	...	...	...	...	|	...	...	...	...	|	...	...	...	...	...	...
	Barcelona Sants **652**......... d.	...	...	...	...	...	...	...	...	...	2020	...	...	◧	...	...	...	...	◧	...	...	...	...	...	...
	Miranda de Ebro **681 689** .d.	...	...	...	...	...	...	...	...	...	|	...	...	|	...	...	...	...	|	...	...	...	...	...	...
07*	Medina AV............ **681 689** d.	...	...	...	...	...	...	...	...	...	|	...	...	0815	...	...	...	...	|	...	...	...	...	...	...
297	**Zamora** .... d.	...	...	...	...	...	...	...	...	...	|	...	...	0851	...	...	...	...	1044	...	...	...	...	...	...
404	Puebla de Sanabria............ d.	...	...	...	...	...	...	...	...	...	|	...	...	1007	...	...	...	...	|	...	...	...	...	...	...
547	**Ourense**........................ d.	...	0650	...	...	0755	...	...	...	...	0938	...	...	1151	1208	1210	...	1330	1336	...	1530	...	...	...	...
641	Guillarei.......................... d.	...	|	...	...	|	...	...	...	...	1109	...	...	1254	1333	|	...	|	|	...	|	...	...	...	...
	Vigo Urzáiz.................... d.	0513**c**	|	0640	0658**c**	|	0725**c**	0850	0945**c**	1115	|	1210**c**	1230**c**	|	|	|	1340	|	|	1435	|	1510**c**	1635	1715	...
666	Redondela AV .... d.	0526**r**	|	0648	0711**r**	|	0737**r**	|	0958**r**	|	1130	1222**r**	1243**r**	1313**r**	1357**r**	|	1348	|	|	|	|	1521**r**	|	|	...
678	**Vigo** Guixar.................... a.	|	◧	|	|	◧	|	|	|	|	1141	|	|	1323	1412	◧	|	|	◧	|	◧	|	|	|	...
684	**Pontevedra**.................... d.	0544	|	0659	0729	|	0758	0905	1017	1130	...	1243	1302	1356	...	|	1401	|	|	1450	|	1542	1650	1730	...
717	Vilagarcía de Arousa......... d.	0602	|	0716	0747	|	...	0920	1035	1145	...	...	1320	...	...	|	1418	|	|	1505	|	1600	1705	1745	...
77§	Santiago de Compostela ..... d.	0648	0730	0742	0828	0835	...	0942	1122	1207	...	...	1405	...	...	1250	1444	1515	1417	1527	1610	1644	1727	1807	...
51§	**A Coruña** .... a.	0727	0758	0813	...	0903	...	1010	1158	1235	...	...	1442	...	...	1318	1512	...	1448	1555	1638	1721	1755	1835	...

	Alvia	Av		MD		IC	IC	Alvia	MD	Av		Alvia	Alvia		Alvia	Alvia	MD		RE	Alvia	Av	Hotel	Hotel		
	4325	**9570**	**12588**	**9182**	**12488**	**283**	**283**	**4145**	**9192**	**9590**	**12554**	**4165**	**4165**		**622**	**626**	**9212**	**12560**	**18322**	**4185**	**4195**	**751**	**851**		
		🅁	2	🅁	🅁	2	2 🍷	**4345**	🅁	2	🅁			2	🍷	🍷	🅁	2	2			🍴	🍴		
	q	2	①–⑤	2	2	**B**	**A**	Ⓑ	2		2	①–⑤	⑥⑦	**h**	**P**	**Q**	2	Ⓑ	**J**		①–⑤	**C**	**D**		
								b d							❖	❖						Ⓑ	Ⓑ		
adrid Chamartín ..**681 689** d.	1305	...	...	...	...	...	...	1500	...	...	...	1625	1625	...	...	...	...	...	...	1850	1940	2214	2214	...	...
egovia AV...........**679 679a** d.	1337	...	...	...	...	...	...	1531	...	...	...	|	|	...	...	...	...	...	...	|	2010	|	|	...	...
Irún **689**........................ d.	|	...	...	...	...	...	0910	|	...	...	...	|	|	...	...	...	...	...	...	|	|	|	|	...	...
Barcelona Sants **652** .... d.	◧	...	...	...	...	...	|	◧	...	...	...	◧	◧	...	0930	0930	...	...	...	◧	◧	|	|	...	...
Miranda de Ebro **681 689** .. d.	|	...	...	...	...	1140	1140	|	...	...	...	|	|	...	1432	1432	...	...	...	|	|	|	|	...	...
'edina AV..............**681 689** d.	1408	...	...	...	...	|	|	1602	...	...	...	|	|	...	|	|	...	...	1805**x**	|	2041	0030**x**	0030**x**	...	...
amora .... d.	1441	...	...	...	...	|	|	1636	...	...	...	1752	1752	...	|	|	...	...	1858	2019	2114	|	|	...	...
uebla de Sanabria .... d.	1556	...	...	...	...	|	|	1755	...	...	...	|	|	...	|	|	...	...	2024	2135	...	|	|	...	...
urense............................ d.	1742	1800	...	...	...	1913	1918	1939	...	2010	...	2045	2045	2100	2125	2120	...	...	...	2319	...	|	0655	...	...
Guillarei............................ d.	...	|	...	...	...	2027	|	|	...	|	...	|	2148	2218	|	|	...	...	...	|	...	|	0808	...	...
Vigo Urzáiz..................... d.	...	|	1725**c**	1815	1820**c**	|	|	|	1935	|	2030**c**	|	|	|	|	|	2135	...		|	...	|	|	...	...
Redondela AV .... d.	...	|	1739**r**	|	1833**r**	2051**r**	|	|	|	|	2043**r**	|	2207**r**	2239**r**	2252	|	2143	...	...	|	...	|	0834**r**	...	...
Vigo Guixar .... a.	...	◧	|	|	|	2104	◧	◧	|	◧	|	2214	2219	2249	2303	◧	|	...	...	◧	...	|	0846	...	...
Pontevedra...................... d.	...	|	1801	1830	1852	...	|	|	1950	|	2102	2246	2302	...	...	|	2156	...	...	|	...	|	0933	...	...
Vilagarcía de Arousa .... d.	...	|	...	1845	1914	...	|	|	2005	|	2122	...	...	...	...	|	2213	...	...	|	...	|	...	...	...
antiago de Compostela...... d.	...	1840	...	1907	1956	...	2001	2021	2027	2050	2207	...	...	...	...	2200	2239	2255	...	2359	...	|	...	...	...
Coruña........................... a.	...	1908	...	1935	...	...	2033	2052	2055	2118	2243	...	...	...	...	2230	2307	2331	...	...	...	0841	...	...	...

km		Av	RE	Alvia	Alvia		Av		MD	Alvia		Alvia	Alvia	Alvia	MD	MD	Av	IC	IC		MD	Av	Alvia	MD	MD
		4194	**18321**	**4344**	**4254**	**12411**	**9071**	**12585**	**9073**	**4064**		**621**	**625**	**4484**	**9083**	**9093**	**9581**	**280**	**280**	**12421**	**9113**	**9111**	**4114**	**9123**	**12587**
			2			🅁	2	2	🅁		2	🍷	🍷	**4584**	🅁	🅁	2	2 🍷	2	🅁	🅁	2		🅁	2
		①–⑤	**J**	①–⑤	⑥⑦	①–⑤	①–⑤	①–⑤	2	①–⑤	**h**	**R**	**S**	①–⑥	2	2		**A**	**B**	2	①–⑤			2	①–⑤
						2				**b**		❖	❖	**y**							2		**q**		
0	**A Coruña** .... d.	...	...	...	...	0538	0630	...	0700	0715	...	...	0805	...	0800	0900	0910	0930	...	1000	1100	1140	...	1200	...
74	Santiago de Compostela ..... d.	...	...	0515	0600	0617	0700	...	0730	0748	...	...	0834	...	0830	0930	0939	1006	...	1042	1130	1210	...	1230	...
116	Vilagarcía de Arousa .... d.	...	...	|	|	0654	|	...	0756	|	...	...	|	...	0850	0950	|	|	...	1120	1150	|	...	1250	...
149	**Pontevedra**.................... d.	...	...	|	|	0714	|	0805	0813	|	...	...	|	0818	0906	1006	|	|	...	1138	1206	|	...	1306	1350
	Vigo Guixar .... d.	...	...	|	|	|	◧	|	|	◧	0705	0745	◧	0849	|	|	◧	◧	0916	|	|	◧	...	|	|
167	Redondela AV .... d.	...	...	|	|	0733**r**	|	0823**r**	|	|	0716**r**	0756	|	0901**r**	|	|	|	|	0927	1156**r**	|	|	...	|	1408**r**
179	**Vigo** Urzáiz.................. d.	...	...	|	|	0744**c**	|	0835**c**	0833	|	|	|	|	|	0920	1020	|	|	|	1209**c**	1220	|	...	1320	1420**c**
192	Guillarei......................... d.	...	...	|	|	...	|	...	...	|	0735	|	|	0920	...	...	|	|	0947	...	...	|	...	...	...
	Ourense........................ d.	...	...	0555	0640	...	0738	...	...	0829	0855	0916	0916	1027	...	...	1016	1113	1113	...	...	1248	1303	...	...
	Puebla de Sanabria........... d.	...	0702	0733	0818	...	...	...	...	1007	...	|	|	|	...	...	...	|	|	...	...	...	1451	...	...
	Zamora .... d.	0705	0826	0850	0940	...	...	...	...	1130	...	|	|	1333	...	...	...	|	|	...	...	...	1616	...	...
	Medina AV............ **681 689** d.	0737	0919**x**	|	|	...	...	...	...	1205	...	|	|	|	...	...	...	|	|	...	...	...	1655	...	...
	Miranda de Ebro **681 689** a.	|	...	|	|	...	...	...	...	|	...	1603	1603	|	...	...	...	1842	1842	...	...	...	|	...	...
	Barcelona Sants **652** .... a.	◧	...	◧	◧	...	...	...	...	◧	...	2125	2125	◧	...	...	...	|	...	...	...	...	◧	...	...
	Hendaye **689**................... a.	|	...	|	|	...	...	...	...	|	...	...	...	|	...	...	...	2121	...	...	...	...	|	...	...
	Segovia AV......... **679 679a** d.	0809	...	|	|	...	...	...	...	1237	...	...	...	|	...	...	...	...	...	...	...	...	1725	...	...
	Madrid Chamartín. **681 689** a.	0837	...	1023	1109	...	...	...	...	1306	...	...	...	1504	...	...	...	...	...	...	...	...	1754	...	...

	MD		Av		Alvia	MD		Av	Alvia	MD		Hotel	MD		MD		Av	Hotel		MD		Hotel	MD		
	9133	**12453**	**9141**	**12455**	**4134**	**9153**		**9161**	**4354**	**12431**	**12967**	**921**	**9173**	**12589**	**9183**	**12441**	**9201**	**852**	**12459**	**9213**	**12461**	**752**	**12561**		
	🅁	🅁	2	🅁	🍷	🅁	2	2	🍷	🅁	🅁	🍷	🅁	2	🅁	🅁	2	🍴	🅁	🅁	🅁	🍴	🅁		
	2	2	①–⑤	2	**b**	2	**h**		Ⓑ	2	2	**G**	2	①–⑤	2	2		Ⓑ	2	2	2	Ⓑ	Ⓑ		
																		D				**C**	2		
Coruña........................... d.	1300	1315	1400	...	1440	1500	...	1630	...	1545	...	...	1700	...	1800	1908	2000	...	...	2105	...	2225	2210	...	...
antiago de Compostela...... d.	1330	1357	1430	1435	1512	1530	...	1700	...	1627	1725	...	1730	...	1830	1950	2030	...	2040	2137	2200	|	2248	...	...
Vilagarcía de Arousa .... d.	1355	1433	|	1516	|	1550	...	|	...	1704	|	...	1750	...	1850	2033	|	...	2118	2203	2241	|	...	...	...
Pontevedra...................... d.	1412	...	|	1534	|	1606	...	|	1546	1722	|	...	1806	1840	1906	2054	|	2128	2136	2221	2259	|	...	...	...
Vigo Guixar .... d.	|	...	◧	|	◧	|	1430	◧	1619	|	|	1755	|	|	|	|	◧	2215	|	|	|	|	...	...	...
Redondela AV .... d.	1422	...	|	1554**r**	|	|	1443**r**	|	1630**r**	1740**r**	|	1805	|	1858**r**	|	2115**r**	|	2226**r**	2156**r**	2233	2319**r**	|	...	...	...
Vigo Urzáiz..................... d.	1429	...	|	1607**c**	|	1620	|	|	|	1753**c**	|	|	1820	1910**c**	1920	2126**c**	|	|	2209**c**	2241	2332**c**	|	...	...	...
Guillarei............................ d.	...	...	|	...	|	...	1504	|	1647	...	|	1825	...	...	...	...	|	2251	...	...	...	|	...	...	...
urense............................ d.	...	...	1508	...	1550	...	1629	1738	1753	...	1911	1933	...	...	...	...	2108	2359	...	...	...	|	...	...	...
uebla de Sanabria .... d.	...	...	...	...	|	...	...	...	1947	...	...	|	...	...	...	...	...	|	...	...	...	|	...	...	...
amora .... d.	...	...	...	...	1844	...	...	...	2108	...	...	|	...	...	...	...	...	|	...	...	...	|	...	...	...
edina AV..............**681 689** d.	...	...	...	...	|	...	...	...	2144	...	...	|	...	...	...	...	...	0650**x**	...	...	...	0650**x**	...	...	...
Miranda de Ebro **681 689**. a.	...	...	...	...	|	...	...	...	|	...	...	|	...	...	...	...	...	|	...	...	...	|	...	...	...
Barcelona Sants **652** .... a.	...	...	...	...	◧	...	...	...	◧	...	...	0849	...	...	...	...	...	|	...	...	...	|	...	...	...
Hendaye **689**................... a.	...	...	...	...	|	...	...	...	|	...	...	...	...	...	...	...	...	|	...	...	...	|	...	...	...
egovia AV...........**679 679a** d.	...	...	...	...	|	...	...	...	2216	...	...	...	...	...	...	...	...	|	...	...	...	|	...	...	...
adrid Chamartín ..**681 689** a.	...	...	...	...	2017	...	...	...	2245	...	...	...	...	...	...	...	...	0931	...	...	...	0931	...	...	...

– CAMINO DE SANTIAGO – [2] 🍷 Irún / Hendaye - Miranda de Ebro - A Coruña and v.v.
– CAMINO DE SANTIAGO – [2] Bilbao - Miranda de Ebro - Ourense - Vigo and v.v.
– Ⓑ: ATLÁNTICO *Trenhotel* – 🛏, [2] Madrid - A Coruña - Ferrol and v.v.
– Ⓑ: RÍAS GALLEGAS *Trenhotel* – 🛏, [2] Madrid - Pontevedra and v.v.
– Ⓑ (daily June 17 - Sept. 16): GALICIA *Trenhotel* – 🛏, [1] (reclining) Barcelona - Vigo and v.v.
– [2] Valladolid - Medina del Campo - Puebla de Sanabria and v.v. (Table **689**).
– ③⑤⑦ [12] 🍷 Barcelona - Ourense - Vigo ❖.
– ①②④⑥ [12] 🍷 Barcelona - Ourense - A Coruña ❖.
– ①④⑥ [12] 🍷 Vigo - Ourense - Barcelona ❖.
– ②③⑤⑦ [12] 🍷 A Coruña - Ourense - Barcelona ❖.

b – To / from Ferrol (Table **682**).
c – Vigo **Guixar**.
d – From Alacant on ⑦ (Table **668**).
h – To / from León (Table **682**).
q – To / from Lugo (Table **682**).
r – Redondela **de Galica**.
x – Medina del Campo.
y – To Alacant on ⑥ (Table **668**).
◐ – Via Lugo (Table **682**).

◧ – Via high-speed line.
* – *153 km* Madrid - Medina del Campo via high-speed line.
§ – *636 km* Madrid - Santiago de Compostela via high-speed line. *697 km* Madrid - A Coruña via high-speed line.
❖ – On days of indirect service, connections are available between Ourense and Vigo / A Coruña and v.v. in the same timings.

681 MADRID - LEÓN

km	km via HSL		Ⓐ 2	Ⓒ 2	Alvia 4071 ①–⑥	Alvia 4073 ①–⑥	18101 2	AVE 4099 4299	Alvia 4111 P	IC 283 2🍷 B	IC 283 2 K	Alvia 4143 E	Alvia 622 626 L	AVE 4149 Ⓑ	Alvia 4541 ⑥	Alvia 4141 Ⓑ	Alvia 664	MD 18003 2	Alvia 4179 Ⓑ 2	Alvia 4181 4381 m	MD 18005 2	Alvia 4193	AVE 4209	Hotel 751 Ⓑ C	Hotel 922 G	
0	0	**Madrid** Chamartín **680 689** d.	...	...	0705	0745	...	0935	1148	...	...	1410	...	1440	1440	1450	...	1628**p**	1730	1830	1827**p**	1905	2025	2214	...	...
121		Ávila **680 689** d.	...	...	◧	◧	...	◧	◧	...	...	◧	...	◧	◧	◧	...	1759	◧	◧	2009	◧	◧	2344	...	...
207		Medina del Campo **680 689** d.	...	...	|	|	...	|	|	...	...	|	...	|	|	|	...	1845	|	|	2057	|	|	0030	...	...
249	180	**Valladolid** C. Grande **689** d.	0700	0720	0810	0845	0955	1040	1259	...	...	1518	...	1543	1541	1551	...	1913	1835	1932	2210	2007	2121	0058	...	...
286		Venta de Baños **689** d.	0732	0752	|	|	1027	|	|	...	...	|	...	|	|	|	...	1938	|	|	2147	|	|	0126	...	...
		Barcelona Sants **652** d.	|	|	|	|	|	|	|	...	...	|	0930	|	|	|	1210	|	|	|	|	|	|	|	2020	...
		Irún **689** d.	|	|	|	|	|	|	|	0910	...	|	|	|	|	|	|	|	|	|	|	|	|	|	|	...
		Bilbao Abando **689** d.	|	|	|	|	|	|	|	|	0942	|	|	|	|	|	|	|	|	|	|	|	|	|	|	...
		Miranda de Ebro **689** d.	|	|	|	|	|	|	|	1140	1140	|	1432	|	|	|	1723	|	|	|	|	|	|	|	|	...
		Burgos Rosa de Lima **689** d.	|	|	|	|	|	|	|	1233	1233	|	1525	|	|	|	1816	|	|	|	|	|	|	|	0249	...
297	233	Palencia **689** d.	0746	0806	0838	0917	1038	1107	1326	1323	1323	1550	1613	1610	|	|	1906	1949	1902	1959	2158	2039	2148	0139	0342	...
		Santander **684** a.	|	|	|	1150	1341	|	|	|	|	1815	|	|	|	|	|	|	|	|	|	2312	|	|	|	...
420	345	**León** a.	0913	0931	0921	...	...	1150	1415	1428	1428	...	1721	1653	1655	|	2014	2102	1945	2043**e**	2307	...	2231	0246	0450	...
		Gijón Sanz Crespo **685** a.	1228	1243	1217	...	...	...	1721	|	|	...	|	...	1943	1939	2312**x**	...	|	2338**z**	...	...	...	|	|	...
		Ponferrada **682** a.	...	...	...	...	...	...	...	1612	1612	...	1852	...	...	...	...	...	2133	...	...	...	...	0431	0649	...
		Vigo Guixar **682** a.	...	...	...	...	...	...	...	|	2104	...	2303	...	...	...	...	...	...	...	...	...	...	|	1141	...
		A Coruña **682** a.	...	...	...	...	...	...	...	2033	...	...	2230	...	...	...	...	...	...	...	...	...	...	0841	1114	...
		Ferrol **682** a.	...	...	...	...	...	...	...	...	...	...	...	...	...	...	...	...	...	...	...	...	...	1025	...	...

	MD 18002 2 w	AVE 4078 ①–⑤	Alvia 4088 ①–⑤ 2	Alvia 4072 ①–⑤ E	AVE 4288 ⑥⑦	Alvia 4070 4270	Alvia 4092 ⑥⑦ E	Alvia 661 ①–⑥	AVE 4128 ①–⑤	Alvia 4110 P	Alvia 625 621 L	IC 280 2🍷 B	IC 280 2 K	Alvia 4142	MD 18006 2	Alvia 4140 m	AVE 4178 Ⓑ	18104 2	AVE 4198 ⑥	⑦ 2	✣ 2	Alvia 4180 ①–⑤	Alvia 4380 ⑦	Alvia 4192 Ⓑ	Hotel 921 G	Hotel 752 Ⓑ C
Ferrol **682** d.	...	...	...	...	...	...	...	...	...	...	...	...	...	...	...	...	...	...	...	...	...	...	...	...	...	2040
A Coruña **682** d.	...	...	...	...	...	...	...	...	...	...	0805	0930	...	...	...	...	...	...	...	...	...	...	...	...	1749	2225
Vigo Guixar **682** d.	...	...	...	...	...	...	...	...	...	...	0745	|	0916	...	...	...	...	...	...	...	...	...	...	...	1755	|
Ponferrada **682** d.	...	...	0611	...	...	...	...	...	...	...	1128	1344	1344	...	...	...	...	...	...	1715	...	...	...	...	2222	0236
Gijón Sanz Crespo **685** d.	...	...	|	...	...	0700	...	0757	...	1050	|	|	|	...	...	1412	...	...	...	|	1627**t**	1751	1800	...	|	|
León d.	0640	0700	0750	...	0840	0941**j**	...	1044	1220	1336	1310	1544	1544	...	1550	1659	1725	...	1850	1935	1947	2031	|	...	0012	0425
Santander **684** d.	|	|	|	0705	|	|	0910	|	|	|	|	|	|	1400	|	|	|	1538	|	|	|	|	|	1900	|	|
Palencia **689** d.	0750	0744	0834	0935	0924	|	1140	1157	1304	1420	1419	1655	1655	1628	1702	1743	1809	1844	1935	2103	2111	2115	2115	2131	0124	0536
Burgos Rosa de Lima **689** d.	|	|	|	|	|	|	|	1252	|	|	1508	1746	1746	|	|	|	|	|	|	|	|	|	|	|	0217	|
Miranda de Ebro **689** a.	|	|	|	|	|	|	|	1345	|	|	1603	1842	1842	|	|	|	|	|	|	|	|	|	|	|	|	|
Bilbao Abando **689** a.	|	|	|	|	|	|	|	|	|	|	|	|	2032	|	|	|	|	|	|	|	|	|	|	|	|	|
Hendaye **689** a.	|	|	|	|	|	|	|	|	|	|	|	2121	...	|	|	|	|	|	|	|	|	|	|	|	|	|
Barcelona Sants **652** a.	|	|	|	|	|	|	|	1903	|	|	2125	...	...	|	|	|	|	|	|	|	|	|	|	|	0849	|
Venta de Baños **689** d.	0803	|	|	|	|	|	|	...	|	|	...	...	...	|	1717	|	|	1855	|	2116	2123	|	|	|	...	0548
Valladolid C. Grande **689** d.	0833	0811	0910	1011	0951	1047**v**	1216	...	1331	1450	...	...	...	1704	1747	1813	1836	1927	2005	2149	2154	2145	2145	2207	...	0618
Medina del Campo **680 689** a.	0859	|	|	|	|	|	|	...	|	|	...	...	...	|	1813	|	|	...	|	...	...	|	|	|	...	0648
Ávila **680 689** a.	0943	◧	◧	◧	◧	◧	◧	...	◧	◧	...	...	...	◧	1900	◧	◧	...	◧	...	...	◧	◧	◧	...	0738
Madrid Chamartín **680 689** a.	1126**p**	0910	1015	1121	1050	1150**v**	1326	...	1441	1600	...	...	...	1807	2048**p**	1921	1942	...	2110	...	...	2255	2255	2310	...	0931

☛ **FOR NOTES**, SEE TABLE **682** BELOW.

682 LEÓN - VIGO, FERROL and A CORUÑA

km		MD 37064 2 ①–⑤	MD 12641 2 ①–⑤	Hotel 922 🍷 G	Hotel 922 G	MD 12741 2 ⑥⑦	2	Alvia 4134 A	Alvia 4095 ①–⑥ A	MD 12685 2	MD 12687 2	IC 283 2🍷 B	IC 283 2 K	Alvia 4325 M	MD 12691 2	Alvia 4145 4345 Ⓑ A g	2	MD 37752 2 Ⓑ	Alvia 626 L	Alvia 622 L	MD 12647 2 R	Alvia 4179 2 Ⓑ	Hotel 751 Ⓑ C	Hotel 851 Ⓑ D	
	Madrid Chamartín ‡ d.	...	...	...	...	...	...	...	0915	...	...	...	...	1305	...	1500	...	...	...	...	...	1730	2214	2214	...
	Barcelona Sants ‡ d.	...	...	2020	2020	...	...	...	|	...	...	...	...	|	...	|	...	...	0930	0930	...	|	|	|	...
	Irún ‡ d.	...	...	|	|	...	...	...	|	...	...	0910	...	|	...	|	...	...	|	|	...	|	|	|	...
	Bilbao Abando ‡ d.	...	...	|	|	...	...	...	|	...	...	|	0942	|	...	|	...	...	|	|	...	|	|	|	...
0	**León** d.	...	...	0505	0505	...	0625**h**	...	|	...	...	1443	1443	|	...	|	1700	...	1726	1726	...	1950	0301	0301	...
52	Astorga d.	...	...	0541	0541	...	0707**h**	...	|	...	...	1515	1515	|	...	|	1733	...	1756	1756	...	2026	0335	0335	...
128	**Ponferrada** d.	...	...	0651	0651	...	0910	...	|	...	...	1614	1614	|	...	|	1834	...	1853	1853	...	2133	0432	0432	...
238	Monforte de Lemos a.	...	...	0822	0822	...	1104	...	|	...	...	1749	1749	1831	...	|	2016	...	2022	2022	...	...	0559	0559	...
238	Monforte de Lemos d.	...	0730	0835	0842	0900	1108	...	|	...	...	1805	1805	1833	...	|	2021	...	2027	2027	2042	...	0614	0615	...
285	Ourense **680** d.	...	|	|	0938	|	1208	...	1336	...	...	1918	1913	1752	...	1939	2100	...	2120	2125	1950	...	|	0655	...
416	**Vigo** Guixar **680** a.	...	|	|	1141	|	1412	...	|	...	...	|	2104	|	...	|	2249	...	|	2303	|	...	|	0846	...
309	Lugo d.	...	0824	0935	...	0956	...	...	|	...	...	|	...	1926	1945	|	...	...	|	...	2134	...	0710	...	...
445	**Ferrol** d.	0555	|	|	...	|	...	1325	|	1718	1915	▲	...	...	|	|	...	2040	▲	...	|	...	|	...	...
402	Betanzos - Infesta d.	0641	0950	1052	...	1127	...	1408	1526	1811	2004	|	...	...	2056	2127	...	2225**f**	|	...	2246	...	0818	...	...
428	**A Coruña** **680** a.	0705	1016	1114	...	1151	...	1430	1448	1835	2030	2033	...	...	2125	2052	...	2207	2230	...	2315	...	0841	...	...
445	**Ferrol** a.	...	...	...	...	...	...	...	1604	...	...	...	...	...	...	2209	...	...	...	...	...	...	1025	...	...

	Alvia 4088 2 ①–⑤	2	MD 12644 2 R	MD 12680 2 ①–⑥	Alvia 4064 A ①–⑤	Alvia 621 L	Alvia 625 L	MD 37751 2 ①–⑥	MD 12686 2	Alvia 4114 M	IC 280 2🍷 B	IC 280 2 K	MD 12682 2 ⑥⑦	Alvia 4134 A	MD 12684 2	Alvia 4208 2 ⑦	2	Alvia 4095 A ①–⑥	MD 12696 2	Hotel 921 G	Hotel 921 🍷 G	MD 12642 2	MD 37145 12692 2	Hotel 752 Ⓑ C	Hotel 852 Ⓑ D
Ferrol d.	...	...	...	...	0555	...	...	...	...	...	...	...	...	1325	...	...	...	...	...	...	...	...	...	2040	...
A Coruña **680** d.	...	...	0638	0706	0715	...	0805	0845	0920	...	0930	...	1050	1440	1431	...	...	1458	1720	...	1749	1930	2059	2225	...
Betanzos - Infesta d.	...	...	0708	0738	0641	...	|	0947**f**	0949	...	|	...	1123	1408	1459	...	...	1526	1751	...	1811	2001	2127	2249	...
Ferrol a.	...	...	|	0820	|	...	▲	1025	|	...	▲	...	1207	|	1545	...	...	1604	1838	...	|	|	2209	|	...
Lugo d.	...	...	0826	...	|	...		...	1056	1110	|	...	▬	|	▬	...	...	...	...	...	1924	2135	...	2356	...
Vigo Guixar **680** d.	...	0705	|	...	|	0745	|	...	...	|	|	0916	...	|	...	...	1435	...	...	1755	|	|	...	|	2215
Ourense **680** d.	...	0858	1020	...	0829	0916	0916	...	...	1303	1113	1113	...	1550	...	...	1635	...	...	1933	|	|	...	|	2359
Monforte de Lemos a.	...	0946	0929	...	|	0953	0953	...	...	1203	1150	1150	⑦**y**	|	①–⑥	...	1731	...	...	2013	2021	2228	...	0048	0038
Monforte de Lemos d.	...	0951	...	...	|	0958	0958	...	...	1206	1208	1208	2	|	2	...	1735	...	...	2041	2041	...	...	0108	0108
Ponferrada d.	0611	1144	...	...	|	1128	1128	...	...	|	1344	1344	1715	|	1755	1855	1941	...	...	2222	2222	...	...	0236	0236
Astorga d.	0708	1247	...	...	|	1228	1228	...	...	|	1453	1453	1846	|	1920	1957	...	...	...	2325	2325	...	...	0332	0332
León a.	0745	1323	...	...	|	1302	1302	...	...	|	1528	1528	1930	|	2017	2035	...	...	...	2357	2357	...	...	0410	0410
Bilbao Abando ‡ a.	|	...	...	...	|	|	|	...	...	|	|	2032	...	|	...	|	...	...	...	|	|	...	...	|	|
Hendaye ‡ a.	|	...	...	...	|	|	|	...	...	|	2121	...	...	|	...	|	...	...	...	|	|	...	...	|	|
Barcelona Sants ‡ a.	|	...	...	...	|	2133	2133	...	...	|	...	...	...	|	...	|	...	...	...	0849	0849	...	...	|	|
Madrid Chamartín ‡ a.	1015	...	...	...	1306	...	...	...	...	1754	...	...	...	2017	...	2303	...	...	...	...	...	...	...	0931	0931

A – 🚃12 Madrid - Zamora - Ourense - A Coruña - Betanzos - Ferrol and v.v. (Table **680**).
B – CAMINO DE SANTIAGO – 🚃2 🍷 Irún / Hendaye - Monforte de Lemos - Santiago - A Coruña and v.v.
C – Ⓑ: ATLÁNTICO *Trenhotel* – 🛏, 🚃1 (reclining) Madrid - A Coruña - Ferrol and v.v.
D – Ⓑ: RÍAS GALLEGAS *Trenhotel* – 🛏, 🚃2 Madrid - Vigo - Pontevedra and v.v.
E – 🚃12 Alacant - Madrid - Santander and v.v.
G – Ⓑ (daily June 17 - Sept. 16): GALICIA *Trenhotel* – 🛏, 🚃1 (reclining) Barcelona - A Coruña and Vigo and v.v.
K – CAMINO DE SANTIAGO – 🚃2 Bilbao - Monforte de Lemos - Vigo and v.v.
L – 🚃12 🍷 Barcelona - A Coruña and Vigo and v.v. For days of running see Table **680**.
M – 🚃12 Madrid - Zamora - Ourense - Monforte de Lemos - Lugo and v.v. (Table **680**).
P – From / to Castelló de la Plana and València on dates shown in Table **668**.

R – Routeing is A Coruña - Lugo - Monforte de Lemos - Ourense and v.v., with connections at Ourense to and from Madrid (Table **680**).

e – Not ⑤.
f – Betanzos - **Cidade**.
g – From Alicant on ⑦ (Table **668**).
h – On ⑥ depart León 0705, Astorga 0752.
j – ⑦ only.
m – From / to Alacant (Table **668**).
p – Madrid **Principe Pio**.
t – ①–⑥.

v – 18 minutes later on ⑦.
w – Runs 10 minutes later on Ⓒ.
x – Not ⑥.
y – To Valladolid (Table **681**).
z – 2320 on ⑤.

▲ – Via Santiago (Table **680**).
‡ – See Table **681**.
◧ – Via high-speed line (Table **663**).
✣ – On ⑦ runs 4 - 11 minutes later.

683 LEÓN - BILBAO

FEVE narrow-gauge

1350 ✣ →	1410 →	1445 →	1535 →	1636 →	1715 →	1801 →	1935 →	2044 →	2134
León	San Feliz	La Vecilla	Cistierna	Guardo	Vado Cervera	Mataporquera	Espinosa	Balmaseda	**Bilbao** Concordia
2203 ✣	← 2138	← 2059	← 2018	← 1921	← 1841	← 1800	← 1623	← 1520	← 1430

✣ – Journey may be by 🚌 between León and Asunción-Universidad y León, due to construction of a new tunnel.

PALENCIA - SANTANDER 684

km		Alvia 4073			Alvia 4143	Alvia 4153			Alvia 4193	
		①-⑥				⑤	2	⑤		
			2		A	2	C	2		
	Madrid Chamartín **681 689** d.	0745	...	...	1410	1525	...	...	1905	...
	Valladolid C G **681 689** d.	0845	0955	...	1518	1628	1654	1829	2007	...
0	**Palencia** d.	0917	1038	...	1550	1706	1736	1915	2039	...
98	Aguilar de Campoo d.	1012	1152	...	|	1805	1750	2028	2132	...
110	Mataporquera **683** ‡ d.	|	1201	...	|	1815	1901	2042	|	...
129	Reinosa § d.	1035	1216	...	|	1831	1917	2058	2157	...
188	Torrelavega § d.	1124	1312	...	1751	1921	2020	2153	2246	...
218	**Santander** § a.	1150	1341	...	1815	1947	2102	2222	2312	...

		Alvia 4072	Alvia 4092		Alvia 4142		Alvia 4162	Alvia 4192	
	⑥⑦	①-⑤	⑥⑦	①-⑤			⑦	Ⓑ	
	2	A	A	2		2	2		
Santander § d.	0700	0705	0910	0919	1400	1538	1610	1900	...
Torrelavega § d.	0729	0729	0934	0953	1424	1609	1633	1923	...
Reinosa § d.	0823	0816	1021	1056	|	1702	1729	2010	...
Mataporquera **683** ‡ d.	0839	|	|	1112	|	1723	1745	|	...
Aguilar de Campoo d.	0849	0838	1047	1122	|	1733	1754	2032	...
Palencia a.	1004	0933	1138	1234	1626	1843	1854	2129	...
Valladolid C G **681 689** a.	1050	1006	1211	1320	1659	1927	1928	2202	...
Madrid Chamartín **681 689** a.	...	1121	1326	...	1807	...	2040	2310	...

A – From/to Alacant (Table **668**). **C** – ①②③④⑥⑦. ‡ – Narrow gauge station is 600 metres. § – Additional local services operate between these stations.

LEÓN - OVIEDO - GIJÓN 685

km				Alvia 4071	Alvia 4111	Alvia 4541	Alvia 4141	Alvia 4171	Alvia 664	Alvia 4381	Alvia 4181
		Ⓐ 2	Ⓒ 2	①-⑥		⑥	Ⓑ	⑤		⑤	
		Y	Y		V	U	S	2	A	C	CZ
	Barcelona Sants **681** d.	...	...	...	...	...	...	...	1210	...	...
	Madrid Chamartín **681** d.	...	...	0705	1148	1440	1450	1715	|	1830	1830
0	**León** d.	0918	0936	0926	1427	1700	|	|	2019	|	2048
109	Pola de Lena § a.	1122	1137	|	1617	|	|	|	2202x	|	|
140	**Oviedo** ▽ § a.	1155	1210	1144	1648	1910	1905	2139	2236x	2244	2306
172	**Gijón** Sanz Crespo § a.	1228	1243	1217	1721	1943	1939	2212	2312x	2320	2338

	Alvia 4070	Alvia 661	Alvia 4110	Alvia 4140	Alvia 4160	2	Alvia 4180	Alvia 4380		
		①-⑥			⑦	①-⑥	①-⑤	⑦	⑦	
		A	W	C	2	Y				
Gijón Sanz Crespo § d.	0700	0757	1050	1412	1620	1627	1751	1800	2025	...
Oviedo ▽ § d.	0730	0826	1120	1441	1650	1658	1821	1831	2055	...
Pola de Lena § d.	|	0855	1151	1510	|	1735	|	|	2127	...
León a.	|	1039	1331	1654	|	1942	2026	|	2350	...
Madrid Chamartín **681** a.	1150f	|	1600	1921	2111	...	2255	2255	...	...
Barcelona Sants **681** a.	...	1903	...	...	...	...	...	...	...	...

A – (12) Gijón - Barcelona and v.v. (Table **681**).
C – From/to Alacant (Table **668**).
S – Ⓑ (⑤⑦ July 30 - Aug. 23).
U – ⑥ (①②③④⑥ July 30 - Aug. 23).
V – From Castelló de la Plana and València on ①-⑥ (Table **668**).
W – To València and Castelló de la Plana on Ⓑ (Table **668**).
Y – From/to Valladolid (Table **681**).
Z – ①②③④⑥⑦.
f – 1208 on ⑦.
x – Not ⑥.

▽ – **OVIEDO – AVILÉS** and v.v. ***Renfe Cercanías*** (suburban) service. *31 km.* Journey time: ± 38 minutes. **Additional services on Ⓐ.**
From Oviedo: Approximately 1 train each hour 0550 Ⓐ, 0616 Ⓐ, then 0716 until 2216. **From Avilés**: Approximately 1 train each hour 0641 Ⓐ, 0741 Ⓐ, then 0841 until 2311.

§ – **GIJÓN – OVIEDO – POLA de LENA** and v.v. ***Renfe Cercanías*** (suburban) service. *63 km.* Journey time: ± 78 minutes.
From Pola de Lena: Approximately 1–2 trains each hour from 0630 until 2200. **From Gijón**: Approximately 1–2 trains each hour from 0600 until 2230.

Euskotren (narrow gauge) SAN SEBASTIÁN - BILBAO 686

	Ⓐ	Ⓐ	Ⓒ					
San Sebastián ⊡ Amara d.	0550	0650	...	0750	0850		1950	2050
Zarautz d.	0620	0720	...	0820	0920		2020	2120
Zumaia d.	0629	0729	...	0829	0929	and	2029	2129
Eibar d.	0711	0811	0811	0911	1011	hourly	2111	2211
Durango d.	0741	0841	0841	0941	1041	until	2141	2241
Bilbao Casco Viejo § ⊖ a.	0821	0921	0921	1021	1121		2221	...
Bilbao Matiko a.	0825	0925	0924	1024	1124		2225	...

	Ⓐ	Ⓐ	Ⓒ					Ⓐ
Bilbao Matiko d.	...	0555	...	0655x	0755x		1955x	2055
Bilbao Casco Viejo § ⊖ d.	...	0558	...	0658x	0758x		1958x	2058
Durango d.	0539	0639	...	0739	0839	and	2039	2139
Eibar d.	0614	0714	...	0814	0914	hourly	2114	2214
Zumaia d.	0700	0800	0800	0900	1000	until	2200	...
Zarautz d.	0708	0808	0808	0908	1008		2208	...
San Sebastián ⊡ Amara a.	0738	0838	0838	0938	1038		2238	...

x – 3 minutes earlier on Ⓒ. ⊡ – San Sebastián/Donostia. ⊖ – Metro interchange.
§ – Bilbao Casco Viejo ⇆ Bilbao Abando (*Renfe*): ± *400 m.* Linked by tram approx every 3-5 minutes, journey 2 minutes.
Operator: Euskotren. 2nd class, narrow gauge. Distance: San Sebastian - Bilbao *108* km.

FEVE (narrow gauge) BILBAO - SANTANDER - OVIEDO - FERROL 687

		Ⓐ			Ⓐ					
Bilbao Concordia § d.	...	...	...	0800	...	1300	...	...	1932	...
Marrón d.	...	0715	...	0944	...	1440	...	...	2114	...
Treto d.	...	0726	...	0956	...	1451	...	...	2125	...
Santander a.	...	0825	...	1101	...	1600	...	...	2225	...
Santander ▽ d.	...	...	0910	...	...	...	1610	...	...	...
Torrelavega ▽ d.	...	...	0937	...	...	...	1637	...	...	...
Cabezón de la Sal ▽ d.	...	...	1007	...	...	...	1707	...	...	...
Unquera d.	...	...	1049	...	...	...	1749	...	...	...
Llanes d.	0740	...	1121	...	1442	...	1826	...	...	...
Ribadesella d.	0822	...	1200	...	1521	...	1905	...	...	...
Oviedo a.	1039	...	1400	...	1742	...	2110	...	...	...

					Ⓐ			Ⓐ		
Oviedo d.	...	...	0835	...	1045	...	1535	...	1855	...
Ribadesella d.	...	...	1041	...	1256	...	1746	...	2105	...
Llanes d.	...	...	1121	...	1333	...	1826	...	2141	...
Unquera d.	...	...	1151	...	...	...	1855	...	...	...
Cabezón de la Sal ▽ d.	...	...	1233	...	...	...	1936	...	...	...
Torrelavega ▽ d.	...	...	1303	...	...	...	2005	...	...	...
Santander ▽ a.	...	...	1333	...	...	...	2033	...	...	...
Santander d.	0758	...	...	1400	...	1900	...	2042	...	...
Treto d.	0901	...	...	1507	...	2001	...	2144	...	...
Marrón d.	0913	...	...	1519	...	2013	...	2155	...	...
Bilbao Concordia § a.	1057	...	...	1658	...	2133	...	...	...	...

					Ⓐ					
Oviedo △ d.	...	...	0730	...	...	...	...	...	1430	...
Gijón Sanz Crespo △ d.	...	0701	|	0931	...	...	1131	1421	|	1831
Avilés △ d.	...	0740	|	1018	...	...	1218	1500	|	1918
Pravia △ d.	...	0812	0833	1048	...	...	1248	1529	1534	1948
Luarca d.	...	...	1004	...	...	...	...	...	1708	...
Navia d.	...	...	1034	...	...	...	...	...	1739	...
Ribadeo d.	0655	...	1134	...	...	1500	...	...	1840	...
Viveiro d.	0803	...	1244	...	...	1609	...	...	1948	...
Ortigueira d.	0843	...	1324	...	1505	1650	...	...	2028	...
Ferrol a.	1000	...	1444	...	1624	1810	...	...	2144	...

							Ⓐ			
Ferrol d.	...	...	0820	...	1045	...	1300	1530	...	1905
Ortigueira d.	...	...	0938	...	1204	...	1420	1649	...	2027
Viveiro d.	...	...	1018	...	1245	...	...	1729	...	2106
Ribadeo d.	...	...	1130	...	1353	...	...	1841	...	2215
Navia d.	...	...	1226	...	...	...	...	1939	...	...
Luarca d.	...	...	1256	...	...	...	...	2011	...	...
Pravia △ d.	0848	1148	1429	1448	...	1648	...	2151	2155	...
Avilés △ d.	0926	1226	|	1526	...	1726	...	|	2229	...
Gijón Sanz Crespo △ a.	1008	1308	|	1608	...	1808	...	|	2309	...
Oviedo △ a.	...	...	1530	...	...	...	...	2253	...	...

▽ – Additional trains run Santander - Cabezón de al Sal and v.v.
△ – Additional trains run Oviedo/Gijón - Pravia and v.v.
§ – Bilbao Concordia is adjacent to Bilbao Abando (*Renfe*).
Operator: FEVE. 2nd class, narrow gauge.

ALSA ★ IRÚN - BILBAO - SANTANDER - GIJÓN 688

	▽ ①-⑥			♡ Ⓑ	♡ ⑥	①-⑥	⑦				♡ Ⓑ	⑥		♡ Ⓑ		♡	⑤⑦					⊖ ⑤⑦		⑦	
Irún RENFE rail station d.	...	...	...	0645	...	0745	...	...	0845	...	...	...	1100	...	1345	1445	...	...	1615	...	1830	...	2045	2115	2355
San Sebastián/Donostia d.	...	...	...	0710	...	0810	...	...	0910	...	...	...	1125	...	1410	1510	...	...	1640	...	1855	...	2110	2140	0020
Bilbao TermiBus d.	0600	...	0700	0830	0830	0930	0930	1000	1030	1130	1230	1230	1330	1430	1530	1630	1730	1730	1800	1845	2030	2115	2230	2300	0145
Santander d.	0715	0830	0830	0950	0950	1100	1115	1130	1215	1300	1350	1400	1530	1550	1700	1750	1900	1900	1930	2015	2200	2235	2350	0020	0330
Oviedo a.	1000*	1145	...	1205	1205	...	...	...	1530	...	1605	...	1845	1805	...	2005	2145	...	2230	2230	...	0050	...	...	0600
Gijón a.	0930	1215	...	1230	1230	...	...	...	1600	...	1635	...	1915	1835	...	2030	2215	...	2300	2300	...	0120	...	...	0700

		①-⑥			①-⑥	♡	♡ ①-⑥	⑤	⑦	①-⑥	♡ ①-⑥		⑤⑦	♡			⑥	♡ Ⓑ				▽ Ⓑ	⑤⑦	▽ ⑤	▽ ⑦
Gijón d.	0014	...	...	...	...	0715	...	...	0815	0815	0915	1130	...	1315	...	1515	1545	1630	...	1715	...	1915	2015	2115	2115
Oviedo d.	0100	...	...	...	...	0745	...	...	0845	0845	0945	|	...	1345	...	|	1615	1700	...	1745	...	1945	2045	2145	2145
Santander d.	0345	0600	0700	0800	0930	1005	1200	...	1200	1230	1200	1400	1545	1605	1700	1900	1900	1920	...	2030	2100	2205	2340	0005	2359
Bilbao TermiBus d.	0515	0730	0840	0930	1100	1120	1315	1400	1400	1415	1315	1530	1745	1720	1830	2045	2030	2035	2045	2200	2230	2320	...	0120	0115
San Sebastián/Donostia a.	0640	0845	1000	...	1210	1230	...	1510	1600	1615	...	...	1855	1830z	1940	2155	...	2145r	2155	2310	...	...	...	...	0225
Irún RENFE rail station a.	0700	0915	1030	...	1240	1305	...	1545	1630	1645	...	...	1925	1905z	2010	2225	...	2220r	2225	2340	...	...	...	...	0300

♡ – *Clase Supra+* luxury coach.
▽ – *Clase Supra Economy* luxury coach.
⊖ – *Supra+ on* ⑤, *Supra Economy* on ⑦.
r – ①-④ only.
z – ⑥ only.
* – Calls after Gijon.
★ – ALSA: ✆ +34 913 270540 www.alsa.es
Frequent services operate Bilbao - Santander and Oviedo - Gijon.

689 MADRID and SALAMANCA - BILBAO and IRÚN

km		RE	RE	Hotel	IC	RE			RE	Alvia	Alvia	MD	RE	RE	IC	Alvia	MD			Alvia	MD		
△		16207	16001	310	631	16019	17227	17201	18302	4087	4187	18001	17203	18321	633	661	18061	18029		621	18011		
		2	2	✕		2	2	2	2			2	2	2		A	2	2	2	625	2		
		①–⑤		B	①–⑥	N		①–⑤			①–⑥	①–⑤	⑥⑦	Y	⑦	①–⑥		Z		Q	⑥⑦		
0	**Madrid** Chamartín ... **680 681** d.	...	...	...	...	...	...	...	...	0800	0800	0628**p**	...	...	...	...	0907**p**	...	...	...	0940**p**	...	...
121	Ávila ... **680 681** d.	...	...	...	...	...	...	0645	...	|	|	0808	0812	...	...	...	1038	...	...	...	1118	...	...
	Salamanca ... d.	...	...	0456	0605	...	...	|	0712	◧	◧	|	|	...	1015	...	|	...	...	...	|	...	...
207	Medina del Campo ... **680 681** d.	...	...	0600	0645	...	0655	0733	0802	|	|	0856	0902	0920	1057	...	1125	...	...	...	1206	...	...
250	**Valladolid** Campo Grande ... **681** d.	...	...	0635	0716	...	0730	0807	0830	0918	0918	0934	0937	0955	1123	...	1150	...	1225	...	1235	...	...
286	Venta de Baños ... **681** d.	...	...	|	|	...	...	...	...	|	|	...	...	...	|	...	1215	...	1300	...	...	...	...
298	Palencia ... **681** d.	...	...	|	|	...	...	...	...	|	|	...	...	...	|	1157	1229	...	1313	1419	...	...	...
371	**Burgos** Rosa de Lima ... **681** d.	...	...	0748	0821	...	...	...	...	1028	1028	...	...	...	1231	1252	1320	1405**j**	...	1508	...	...	...
460	Miranda de Ebro ... **653** d.	0720	0825	0848	0921	0940	...	...	...	1128	1135	...	...	...	1337	1347	1419	1501	...	1605	...	...	...
565	**Bilbao** Abando ... **653** a.	|	|	|	|	|	...	...	...	|	1304	...	...	...	|	|	|	|	...	|	...	...	...
494	Vitoria / Gasteiz ... **653** d.	0747	0857	0912	|	1005	...	...	...	1151	...	...	...	...	|	1411	1442	1530	...	1627	...	...	...
	Barcelona Sants **653** ... a.	...	|	|	1420	|	...	...	...	|	...	...	...	...	1835	1903	|	|	...	2125	...	...	...
537	Altsasu ... **653** d.	...	0929	|	...	1038**n**	...	...	...	|	...	...	...	...	...	...	1511	1601**n**	...	...	...	...	...
624	**San Sebastián / Donostia** ... ▲ **653** d.	...	1048	1055	...	...	...	...	...	1324	...	...	...	...	...	...	1634	...	...	...	...	...	...
641	**Irún** ... ▲ **653** a.	...	...	1122**s**	...	...	...	...	...	...	...	...	...	...	...	...	...	...	...	...	...	...	...
643	Hendaye ... ▲ **653** a.	...	...	1133	...	...	...	...	...	...	...	...	...	...	...	...	...	...	...	...	...	...	...

	MD	MD	MD	IC	IC	MD		MD			RE	Alvia	Alvia	IC	Alvia	Alvia	MD	RE	MD	Hotel			
	18063	18063	18306	280	280	18905	17221	18314	16111	16011	18009	4167	4267	4177	4377	4197	18065	18312	18007	921			
	2	2	2	2	2	2	2	2	**Z** 2	**Z** 2	2		g	2			2	2	2	🍸			
	Ⓑ	⑥		D	E				①–⑥	⑦	⑤		Ⓑ	⑤	⑦	①–④	Ⓑ		Ⓑ	G			
Madrid Chamartín ... **680 681** d.	1226**p**	1220**p**	...	...	...	1335	...	...	...	...	1455**p**	1605	1605	1740	1740	1915	1712**p**	...	2028**p**	...	...	...	...
Ávila ... **680 681** d.	1405	1405	...	...	...	1506	1510	...	...	...	1641	|	|	|	|	|	1850	...	2209	...	...	...	...
Salamanca ... d.	|	|	1400	...	...	...	|	1555	...	...	|	◧	◧	◧	◧	◧	|	2053	|	...	...	...	...
Medina del Campo ... **680 681** d.	1452	1452	1504	...	...	...	1559	1635	...	...	1734	|	|	|	|	|	1938	2148	2256	...	...	...	...
Valladolid Campo Grande ... **681** d.	1517	1517	1529	...	...	...	1632	1703	...	...	1806	1723	1723	1850	1850	2025	2006	2223	2321	...	...	...	...
Venta de Baños ... **681** d.	1542	1542	1605	...	...	...	...	...	...	...	1834	|	|	|	|	|	2034	...	2347	...	...	...	...
Palencia ... **681** d.	1557	1557	1617	1655	1655	...	...	...	...	...	|	|	|	|	|	|	2050	...	2358	0124	...	...	...
Burgos Rosa de Lima ... **681** d.	1645	1652	...	1745	1745	...	...	...	...	...	1927	1833	1833	2006	2006	2134	2143	...	...	0217	...	...	...
Miranda de Ebro ... **653** d.	1741	1759	...	1850	1858	...	...	...	...	...	2027	1935	1948	2101	2101	2230	2239	...	...	|	...	...	...
Bilbao Abando ... **653** a.	|	|	...	|	2032	...	...	...	...	...	|	|	2116	|	|	|	|	...	...	|	...	...	...
Vitoria / Gasteiz ... **653** d.	1802	1819	...	1911	...	...	...	...	1900	1921	2050	1956	...	2124	2124	2252	2300	...	...	|	...	...	...
Barcelona Sants **653** ... a.	|	|	...	|	...	...	...	...	|	|	...	|	...	|	|	...	...	...	...	0849	...	...	...
Altsasu ... **653** d.	1829	1848	...	1934	...	...	...	...	1931**n**	1952**n**	...	|	...	|	|	...	...	...	...	...	...	...	...
San Sebastián / Donostia ... ▲ **653** d.	1948	2011	...	2049	...	...	...	...	...	...	...	2128	...	2257	2257	...	...	...	...	...	...	...	...
Irún ... ▲ **653** a.	...	...	...	2116**s**	...	...	...	...	...	...	...	...	...	...	...	...	...	...	...	...	...	...	...
Hendaye ... ▲ **653** a.	...	...	...	2121	...	...	...	...	...	...	...	...	...	...	...	...	...	...	...	...	...	...	...

km		MD	RE	Alvia	Alvia	MD	MD		RE	RE	Alvia	Alvia	IC	IC	MD	MD	RE	MD	MD	Alvia	RE		RE
		18066	18300	4056	4076	18304	18010	17218	16000	18071	4086	4186	283	283	18308	18004	18070	18012	18012	622	16204		18322
		2	2	K	J	2	2	2	2	**Z** 2		g	2	2	2	2	2	2	2		2	2	2
		①–⑥	①–⑤	①	②–⑤		①–⑥		①–⑥	①–⑥		①–⑥	E	D			①–⑥	①–⑥	⑦	Q	①–⑤		Y
0	**Irún** ... ▲ **653** d.	...	...	...	...	...	...	...	...	...	...	...	...	0910	...	...	...	...	...	...	...	...	...
17	**San Sebastián / Donostia** ... ▲ **653** d.	...	...	0510	...	...	...	...	0618	...	0857	...	...	0933	...	...	...	1114	1114	...	...	...	...
104	Altsasu ... **653** d.	...	...	|	...	...	...	...	0736	0918**n**	|	...	...	1046	...	...	...	1237	1237	...	...	...	...
	Barcelona Sants **653** ... d.	...	...	|	...	...	...	...	|	|	|	...	...	|	...	...	...	|	|	0930	...	...	...
147	Vitoria / Gasteiz ... **653** d.	...	...	0645	0645	...	0745	...	0808	0950	1033	...	...	1108	...	...	...	1307	1307	1410	1430	...	...
	Bilbao Abando ... **653** d.	...	...	|	|	...	|	...	...	|	|	0920	0942	|	...	...	...	|	|	|	|	...	...
180	Miranda de Ebro ... **681** d.	...	...	0706	0706	...	0806	...	...	1016	1058	1058	1140	1140	...	...	1245	1327	1327	1432	1457	...	...
270	**Burgos** Rosa de Lima ... **681** d.	...	...	0800	0800	...	0903	...	...	...	1156	1156	1233	1233	...	...	1347	1424	1435	1525	...	...	...
353	Palencia ... **681** d.	0550	...	|	|	...	1002	...	...	...	|	|	1323	1323	1335	...	...	1516	1533	1611	...	1633	...
355	Venta de Baños ... **681** d.	0603	...	|	|	...	1013	...	...	...	|	|	...	...	1348	...	...	1527	1544	...	...	1646	...
391	**Valladolid** Campo Grande ... **681** d.	0636	0735	0916	0916	0940	1039	1205	...	...	1311	1311	...	...	1419	1424	...	1554	1610	...	...	1720	1740
434	Medina del Campo ... **680 681** d.	0702	0816	|	|	1007	1105	1243	...	...	|	|	...	...	1448	1511	...	1620	1635	...	...	...	1804
511	**Salamanca** ... a.	|	0913	◧	◧	1046	|	|	...	...	◧	◧	...	...	1548	|	...	|	|	...	...	...	...
	Ávila ... **680 681** d.	0750	...	|	|	...	1155	1334	...	...	|	|	...	...	...	1600	...	1710	1721	...	...	...	...
	Madrid Chamartín ... **680 681** a.	0941**p**	...	1030	1030	...	1325**p**	...	...	...	1428	1428	...	...	...	1731**p**	...	1842**p**	1909**p**	...	...	...	...

	MD	RE	IC	Alvia		RE		Alvia	Alvia	IC		Hotel			RE	RE	Hotel						
	18014	18318	4176	664	17200	18008	16015	4166	4266	632	17226	313	16017	16027	16004	16004	922						
	2	2	2		2	2	2				2	✕	2 **N**	2 **b**	2	2	G						
			⑦	A		⑦	N		Ⓑ			C	①–⑥	⑦	Ⓑ	⑥	🍸						
Irún ... ▲ **653** d.	...	...	...	...	...	...	...	...	...	...	...	1845	...	...	...	...	...	...	...	...	...	...	...
San Sebastián / Donostia ... ▲ **653** d.	1404**p**	...	1509	...	...	...	...	1633	...	...	...	1910	...	...	1957	2040	...	...	...	...	...	...	...
Altsasu ... **653** d.	1524	...	|	...	...	...	1718**n**	|	...	...	...	|	2004**n**	2046**n**	2116	2200	...	...	...	...	...	...	...
Barcelona Sants **653** ... d.	|	...	|	1210	...	...	|	|	...	1410	...	|	|	|	|	|	2020	...	...	...	...	...	...
Vitoria / Gasteiz ... **653** d.	1554	...	1644	1702	...	1720	1753	1809	...	|	...	2046	2037	2118	2150	2234	|	...	...	...	...	...	...
Bilbao Abando ... **653** d.	|	...	|	|	...	|	|	|	1700	|	...	|	...	|	|	|	|	...	...	...	...	...	...
Miranda de Ebro ... **681** d.	1614	...	1705	1723	...	1744	1820	1835	1835	1856	...	2108	...	2143	2215	2229	|	...	...	...	...	...	...
Burgos Rosa de Lima ... **681** d.	1713	...	1759	1816	...	1843	...	1933	1933	1948	...	2200	...	...	...	...	0249	...	...	...	...	...	...
Palencia ... **681** d.	1802	...	|	1904	...	|	...	|	|	|	...	|	...	...	...	...	0339	...	...	...	...	...	...
Venta de Baños ... **681** d.	1814	...	|	...	...	1933	...	|	|	|	...	|	...	...	...	...	...	...	...	...	...	...	...
Valladolid Campo Grande ... **681** d.	1845	1912	1914	...	2030	2005	...	2050	2050	2100	2240	2310	...	...	...	...	...	...	...	...	...	...	...
Medina del Campo ... **680 681** d.	1916	1940	|	...	2107	2040	...	|	|	2131	2313	0011	...	...	...	...	...	...	...	...	...	...	...
Salamanca ... a.	|	2028	◧	...	|	|	...	◧	◧	2212	...	0057	...	...	...	...	...	...	...	...	...	...	...
Ávila ... **680 681** d.	2003	...	|	...	2157	2137	...	|	|	...	...	...	...	...	...	...	...	...	...	...	...	...	...
Madrid Chamartín ... **680 681** a.	2148	...	2027	...	...	2340**p**	...	2206	2206	...	...	...	...	...	...	...	...	...	...	...	...	...	...

A – [12] Gijón - Barcelona and v.v. (Table **685**).
B – SUD EXPRESSO / SUREX *Trenhotel* – 🛏 *Gran Clase / Gran Classe* (1, 2 berths), 🛏 *Preferente* (1, 2 berths), 🛏 *Turista* (4 berths), [2] ✕ Lisboa (**310**) - Vilar Formoso (**311**) - Salamanca - Hendaye (Table **45**).
C – SUREX / SUD EXPRESSO *Trenhotel* – 🛏 *Gran Clase / Gran Classe* (1, 2 berths), 🛏 *Preferente* (1, 2 berths), 🛏 *Turista* (4 berths), [2] ✕ Hendaye (**312**) - Salamanca - Vilar Formoso (**313**) - Lisboa (Table **45**).
D – CAMINO DE SANTIAGO – [2] A Coruña - Palencia - Miranda de Ebro - Irún / Hendaye and v.v.
E – CAMINO DE SANTIAGO – [2] Vigo - Palencia - Miranda de Ebro - Bilbao and v.v.
G – Ⓑ (daily June 17 - Sept. 16): GALICIA *Trenhotel* – 🛏, [1] (reclining) 🍸 Barcelona - A Coruña and Vigo and v.v.
J – ②–⑤ (not July 31 - Aug. 28).
K – ① June 19 - Aug. 28 (also July 26, Aug. 16; not July 24, Aug. 14).
N – To / from Pamplona (Table **653**).
Q – [12] Vigo / A Coruña - Palencia - Barcelona and v.v. (Table **680**).
Y – [2] Puebla de Sanabria - Medina del Campo - Valladolid and v.v. (Table **680**).
Z – To / from Pamplona and Zaragoza (Table **653**).

b – From / to Castejón de Ebro and Pamplona / Iruña (Table **653**).
g – Daily June 18 - Oct. 16.
j – ①–⑥.
n – Altsasu Pueblo.
p – Madrid **Principe Pio**.
s – Calls to set down only.
x – Not Apr. 19 - July 10.

◧ – Via high-speed line (Table **679a**).
△ – Via Ávila.

▲ – **SAN SEBASTIÁN - IRÚN** and v.v. ***Renfe Cercanías*** (suburban) service. Additional journeys can be made by changing trains at Pasaia. *17 km.* Journey time: ± 27 minutes
From San Sebastián: 0626⑦, 0701⚒, 0726Ⓒ, 0751Ⓐ, 0816⑥, 0838Ⓐ, 0946⑦, 0951⚒, 1036⚒, 1100⑦, 1116⑥, 1126⑦, 1146Ⓐ, 1218⑦, 1226⚒, 1346, 1421⚒, 1516⚒, 1546 1639Ⓑ, 1648⑥, 1743, 1816⑦, 1931⚒, 1954⑦, 2001⚒, 2046⚒, 2144.
From Irún: 0648⚒, 0738Ⓐ, 0810⑥, 0828Ⓑ, 0928Ⓑ, 1028⚒, 1042⑦, 1128Ⓐ, 1158Ⓒ, 1218Ⓐ, 1258Ⓒ, 1333, 1453, 1535⑦, 1618, 1713⑦, 1723⑥, 1727Ⓐ, 1733⑦, 1813⑥ 1858Ⓑ, 1918, 2033, 2128, 2215.

▲ – **SAN SEBASTIÁN / DONOSTIA** (Amara) - **IRÚN** (Colón, near Renfe station) - **HENDAYE** (SNCF station) and v.v. ***EuskoTren*** (narrow-gauge) service. *22 km.* Journey time: ± 37 minutes
From San Sebastián: 0615Ⓐ, 0645Ⓐ, 0715, 0745 and every 30 mins until 2215, 2245. **From Hendaye (A)**: 0533Ⓐ, 0603Ⓐ, 0633Ⓐ, 0703, 0733 and every 30 mins until 2233.
A – 4 minutes later from Irún.

PORTUGAL

SEE MAP PAGE 321

rator: CP – Comboios de Portugal (www.cp.pt).

n categories: ***Alfa Pendular*** – *AP* – high-quality tilting express trains. ***Intercidades*** – *IC* – high-quality express trains linking the main cities. ***Interregional*** – *IR* – 'semi-fast' links usually calling at principal stations only. ***Celta*** – International services between Porto and Vigo. ***Regional*** and ***Suburbano*** – local stopping trains (shown without train numbers). Higher fares are payable for travel by *AP* and *IC* trains, also the international **Sud Expresso** service (Lisboa - Hendaye and v.v.), and there is an additional supplement for travel by *AP* trains. The **Lusitania** *Hotel Train* service (Lisboa - Madrid and v.v.) is shown in Table **45**, special fares apply.

vices: All services shown with a train number convey first and second class accommodation (on *Alfa Pendular* trains termed, respectively, *Conforto* and *Turística*) unless otherwise indicated. *Regional* and *Suburbano* trains convey second-class seating only. *AP*, *IC*, *IR* and international trains convey a buffet car (*carruagem-bar*) and there is an at-seat service of meals to passengers in 1st class on *AP* and certain *IC* trains.

ervations: Reservations are **compulsory** for travel by *AP*, *IC* and international trains. Seat reservation is not normally available on other services.

ngs: Timings are the latest received. Amendments to timetables may come into effect at short notice, especially during the Christmas and New Year period.

LISBOA - COIMBRA - PORTO 690

eservations compulsory on *AP* and *IC* trains. For local trains Entroncamento - Coimbra / Coimbra - Aveiro see Table **699**. Local trains Aveiro - Porto run approx hourly.

	IR 823	*IC* 521	*AP* 131	*IC* 511	*AP* 121	*AP* 123	*IC* 721	*AP* 182	*IC* 621	*AP* 125	*IC* 513*	*AP* 133	*IC* 523	*AP* 135	*AP* 127	*IC* 527	*AP* 137	*IC* 515*	*AP* 186	*IC* 723	*AP* 141		310 335	*IC* 529
		①–⑥				Ⓐ				⚒				Ⓑ§							Ⓑ	Ⓑ	S	
		n	△	◇			△		☆		◇	△		△			△	◇		△	☆		🅁	
Faro **697** d.	...	...	...	...	...	...	...	0700	...	...	...	...	...	...	...	...	...	...	1600	...	...	...	...	...
Lisboa S Apolónia ▷ d.	...	0630	0700	0730	0800	0900	0930	|	1130	1200	1330	1400	1530	1600	1700	1730	1800	1830	|	1930	2000	...	2125	2130
Lisboa Oriente ▷ d.	...	0639	0709	0739	0809	0909	0939	1009	1139	1209	1339	1409	1539	1609	1709	1739	1809	1839	1909	1939	2009	...	2134	2139
Vila Franca de Xira ▷ d.	...	0652	|	0752	|	|	0952	|	1152	|	1352	|	1552	|	|	1752	|	1852	|	1952	|	...	|	2153
Santarém ▷ d.	...	0713	|	0813	0839	|	1013	|	1213	|	1413	|	1613	|	|	1813	|	1913	|	2013	2039	...	|	2216
Entroncamento ▷ d.	...	0730	|	0830	0855	|	1030	|	1230	|	1430	|	1630	|	|	1830	|	1930	|	2030	2055	2127	2229	2235
Fátima ⊙ d.	...	|	|	0844	|	|	|	|	|	|	1444	|	|	|	|	|	|	1944	|	|	|	2148	|	|
Caxarias ⊖ d.	...	|	|	0851	|	|	1049	|	|	|	1451	|	|	|	|	1849	|	1951	|	|	|	2157	2247	2254
Pombal d.	...	0805	|	0909	0926	|	1107	|	1305	|	1509	|	1705	|	|	1907	|	2009	|	2105	2126	2222	2306	2313
Alfarelos d.	...	|	|	0923	|	|	|	|	1319	|	1523	|	1719	|	|	|	|	2023	|	|	|	2245	|	|
Coimbra B ▶ d.	0510	0831	0845	0938	0951	1045	1134	1145	1333	1345	1538	1545	1733	1745	1845	1934	1945	2038	2045	2131	2151	2309	2332	2339
Pampilhosa d.	0524	|	|	0950	|	|	|	|	1345	|	1550	|	1745	|	|	|	|	2050	|	|	|	2322	...	|
Aveiro d.	0554	0906	0915	...	1020	1115	1206	1215	1406	1415	...	1615	1806	1815	1915	2006	2015	...	2115	2206	2220	2356	...	0011
Espinho d.	0627	0930	|	...	1041	|	1230	|	1428	|	...	|	1828	|	|	2030	|	...	|	2230	2241	0026	...	0035
Vila Nova de Gaia d.	0641	0939	0945	...	1051	1144	1240	1244	1440	1444	...	1645	1839	1845	1944	2039	2045	...	2144	2240	2252	0038	...	0046
Porto Campanhã ▽ a.	0646	0946	0950	...	1057	1150	1246	1250	1446	1450	...	1650	1846	1850	1950	2046	2050	...	2150	2246	2257	0044	...	0051

	3400	313 332	*AP* 180	*AP* 130	*IC* 520	*AP* 140	*IC* 510	*IC* 522	*AP* 120	*IC* 720	*AP* 122	*IC* 524	*AP* 132	*IC* 512*	*AP* 184	*IC* 722	*AP* 124	*AP* 126	*IC* 620	*AP* 134	*IC* 514*	*IC* 528	*AP* 136	*IC* 21530	*IR* 822
	①–⑥	S			①–⑥	①–⑥			⚒		Ⓑ							Ⓑ					Ⓑ§	⑥	
		🅁		△	n	☆	◇			△	b		△	◇		△	❋		☆	△	◇		△	E	
o Campanhã ▽ d.	0055	...	0540	0640	0645	0740	...	0845	0940	1045	1140	1245	1340	...	1440	1445	1640	1740	1745	1840	...	1945	2040	2045	2150
Nova de Gaia d.	0101	...	0545	0645	0650	0745	...	0850	0945	1050	1145	1250	1345	...	1445	1450	1645	1745	1750	1845	...	1950	2045	2050	2156
nho d.	0123	...	|	|	0700	0754	...	0901	|	1100	|	1300	|	...	|	1500	|	1754	1801	|	...	2000	|	|	2207
ro d.	0200	...	0615	0715	0726	0816	...	0926	1015	1125	1215	1326	1415	...	1515	1525	1715	1816	1826	1915	...	2026	2115	2122	2242
pilhosa d.	0231	...	|	|	|	|	0908	|	|	1144	|	|	|	1438	|	1544	|	|	|	|	2008	|	|	|	2312
nbra B ▶ d.	0243	0447	0644	0744	0759	0844	0922	0957	1044	1157	1244	1357	1444	1452	1544	1557	1744	1844	1857	1944	2022	2057	2144	2150	2326
elos d.	0258	|	|	|	|	|	0936	|	|	1211	|	|	|	1506	|	1611	|	|	|	|	2036	|	|	|	...
bal d.	0319	0522	|	|	0827	0910	0952	1024	|	1227	|	1424	|	1522	|	1627	|	1910	1924	|	2052	2124	|	|	...
arias ⊖ d.	0340	0543	|	|	|	|	1009	1041	|	|	|	1441	|	1539	|	|	|	|	1941	|	2109	2141	|	|	...
na ⊙ d.	0349	|	|	|	|	|	1017	|	|	|	|	|	|	1547	|	|	|	|	|	|	2117	|	|	|	...
oncamento ▷ d.	0416	0606	|	|	0901	0941	1031	1100	|	1301	|	1501	|	1601	|	1701	|	1942	2001	|	2131	2201	|	|	...
arém ▷ d.	0442	|	|	|	0919	0957	1048	1118	|	1319	|	1519	|	1618	|	1719	|	1958	2019	|	2148	2219	|	|	...
Franca de Xira ▷ d.	0524	|	|	|	0939	|	1109	1139	|	1339	|	1539	|	1639	|	1739	|	|	2040	|	2209	2239	|	|	...
oa Oriente ▷ a.	0550	0720	0822	0922	0952	1033	1122	1152	1222	1352	1422	1552	1622	1652	1722	1752	1922	2032	2052	2122	2222	2252	2322	2343	...
oa S Apolónia ▷ a.	0559	0730	|	0930	1000	1040	1130	1200	1230	1400	1430	1600	1630	1700	|	1800	1930	2040	2100	2130	2230	2300	2330	2350	...
ro **697** a.	...	...	1123	...	...	...	...	...	...	...	...	...	...	...	2023	...	...	...	...	...	...	...	...	...	...

⑥ June 1 - Oct. 26.
SUD EXPRESSO / LUSITANIA – see Tables **45** / **692**. International journeys only.
Not public holidays.
If the following day is a public holiday runs on ① instead.
Not ① if it is a public holiday. Not ⑥ if the day before is a public holiday.
Lisboa - Guarda and v.v. (Table **692**).
Lisboa - Porto - Guimarães and v.v. (Table **695a**).
Lisboa - Porto - Braga and v.v. (Table **695**).

▷ – For other fast trains see Table **691**, for local trains see Table **699**.
▽ – Local services run Porto Campanhã - Porto São Bento.
▶ – Local trains run Coimbra B - Coimbra and v.v.
❋ – On ⑦ additional train *IC* **526** runs at 1645 (same station stops as *IC* **620** at 1745).
⊙ – *20 km* from Fátima (full name of station is Chão de Maçãs - Fátima).
⊖ – 🚌 available Caxarias - Fátima. See www.rodotejo.pt for details.
§ – Not on ⑦ if the following day is a public holiday. Not on ⑤ if it is a public holiday.
* – A different train number applies on ⑤ from Lisboa and ⑦ towards Lisboa.

LISBOA - ENTRONCAMENTO - COVILHÃ 691

a da Beira Baixa

			IC 541			*IC* 543			*IC* 545	
	Ⓐ									
Lisboa Sta Apolónia ▷ d.	0550	...	0815	*0945*	...	1315	1615	...	1915	1945
Lisboa Oriente ▷ d.	0558	...	0823	*0953*	...	1323	1623	...	1923	1953
Vila Franca de Xira ▷ d.	0616	...	0838	*1011*	...	1338	1639	...	1938	2011
Santarém ▷ d.	0655	...	0904	*1055*	...	1404	1706	...	2004	2055
Entroncamento ▷ a.	0718	...	0923	*1119*	...	1423	1725	...	2023	2119
Entroncamento d.	▬	0746	0924	1128	...	1424	1726	1933	2024	*2154*
Abrantes d.	...	0817	0946	1204	...	1446	1802	2008	2046	*2230*
Ródão d.	⚒	0921	1043	1304	...	1536	1901	2111	2143	...
Castelo Branco d.	0625	0954	1107	1332	1414	1607	1945	2140	2207	...
Fundaõ d.	0713	1042	1142	...	1507	1642	2033	...	2242	...
Covilhã a.	0729	1058	1155	...	1524	1655	2049	...	2255	...

		IC 540					*IC* 542			*IC* 544
	①–⑥			Ⓐ						
Covilhã d.	...	0753	0850	...	1256	...	1453	...	1825	1853
Fundaõ d.	...	0807	0906	...	1312	...	1507	...	1841	1907
Castelo Branco d.	0556	0843	1010	...	1403	...	1543	*1814*	1929	1943
Ródão d.	0624	0907	1043	...	1431	...	1607	*1843*	...	2007
Abrantes d.	0721	1002	1141	...	1535	...	1702	*1948*	...	2102
Entroncamento a.	0800	1023	1217	...	1606	...	1723	*2019*	...	2123
Entroncamento ▷ d.	0808	1024	...	1237	...	1639	1724	2044	...	2124
Santarém ▷ d.	0827	1041	...	1301	...	1703	1741	2107	...	2141
Vila Franca de Xira ▷ d.	0856	1101	...	1347	...	1747	1801	2147	...	2201
Lisboa Oriente ▷ a.	0911	1113	...	1405	...	1805	1813	2205	...	2213
Lisboa Sta Apolónia ▷ a.	0920	1120	...	1413	...	1813	1820	2213	...	2220

		b	
Entroncamento d.	...	1010	...
Abrantes d.	...	1054	...
Portalegre d.	...	1209	...
Elvas 🏛 d.	...	1253	...
Badajoz 🏛 ⊙ a.	...	1416	...

		d	
Badajoz 🏛 ⊙ d.	...	1624	...
Elvas 🏛 d.	...	1548	...
Portalegre d.	...	1633	...
Abrantes d.	...	1751	...
Entroncamento a.	...	1825	...

b – For connection from Lisboa Sta Apolónia (*IC* train depart 0815) see panel above.
d – For connection to Lisboa Sta Apolónia see Table **690** (*IC* train arrive 2000 on ⑦) or Table **699** (local train arrives 2020 daily).
▷ – For other fast trains see Table **690**, for local trains see Table **699**.
⊙ – Spanish time (one hour ahead of Portugal).

(LISBOA -) COIMBRA - GUARDA - VILAR FORMOSO 692

a da Beira Alta

	IC 511			*IC* 513					*IC* 515	310
				◇		Ⓑ		Ⓑ	◇	S 🅁
Lisboa Sta Apolónia **690** d.	0730	...	...	1330	...	...	...	...	1830	2125
Lisboa Oriente **690** d.	0739	...	...	1339	...	...	...	...	1839	2134
Coimbra ▶ d.	|	...	1220	|	...	1624	1824	2014	|	|
Coimbra B d.	0938	...	1225	1538	...	1630	1828	2017	2038	2333
Pampilhosa d.	0950	...	1237	1550	...	1644	1850	...	2050	|
Santa Comba Dão d.	1022	...	1313	1622	...	1723	1935	...	2122	0016
Nelas d.	1044	...	1344	1644	...	1800	2006	...	2144	|
Mangualde d.	1052	...	1353	1652	...	1810	2016	...	2152	0046
Guarda a.	1151	1306	1458	1751	1806	1919	2121	...	2251	0144
Vilar Formoso 🏛 a.	...	1346	...	...	1846	...	...	...	...	0220

	313		*IC* 510			*IC* 512				*IC* 514
	S 🅁	⚒		⑦h		◇	⚒b	⑦z	⚒b	◇
Vilar Formoso 🏛 d.	0150	0618	...	0920	...	...	...	*1533*	1715	...
Guarda d.	0223	0658	0707	1000	1014	1237	1625	1625	1755	1807
Mangualde d.	0324	...	0806	▬	1121	1336	1733	1733	...	1906
Nelas d.	|	...	0814	...	1131	1344	1744	1744	...	1914
Santa Comba Dão d.	0355	...	0835	...	1200	1405	1812	1812	...	1935
Pampilhosa d.	|	...	0908	Ⓒ	1237	1438	1848	1850	...	2008
Coimbra B a.	0445	...	0921	0929	1251	1451	1900	1904	...	2021
Coimbra ▶ a.	|	...	|	0933	1256	*1511*r	1904	*1913*r	...	|
Lisboa Oriente **690** a.	0720	...	1123	...	...	1653	...	2143	...	2223
Lisboa Sta Apolónia **690** a.	0730	...	1130	...	...	1700	...	2150	...	2230

SUD EXPRESSO / LUSITANIA – see Tables **45** / **690**. Not Dec. 24, 31 from Lisboa or from Hendaye / Madrid.
①–⑥ (if ① is a public holiday runs previous day instead).

h – Also public holidays unless it is a ⑤.
r – Change at Coimbra B.
z – If the following day is a public holiday runs ① instead.

▶ – Local trains run Coimbra B - Coimbra and v.v.
◇ – A different train number applies on ⑤ from Lisboa and ⑦ towards Lisboa.

693 LISBOA - CALDAS DA RAINHA - FIGUEIRA DA FOZ / COIMBRA *Linha do Oest*

km			b		Ⓐ	Ⓒ		Ⓒ	Ⓐ	b
	Lisboa Santa Apolónia	d.	0541	...	1150	...	...	1625	...	...	...
0	**Lisboa** Rossio	▷ d.	|	0831	|	1321	1331	|	1731	1801	1831
7	Entrecampos	▷ d.	0555	|	1201	|	|	1641	|	|	|
9	Sete Rios	▷ d.	0558	|	1204	|	|	1644	|	|	|
22	Agualva - Cacém ⊙	▷ d.	0613	0857	1221	1347	1357	1700	1757	1827	1857
26	Mira Sintra - Meleças	▷ a.	0617	0900	1226	1350	1400	1704	1800	1830	1900
26	Mira Sintra - Meleças	d.	0618	0925	1227	1409	1409	1705	1835	1835	1930
72	Torres Vedras	d.	0716	1023	1326	1509	1509	1813	1936	1936	2030
95	Bombarral	d.	0746	1047	1354	1531	1531	1836	2001	2001	...
114	**Caldas da Rainha**	a.	0808	1109	1416	1553	1553	1858	2023	2023	...

							Ⓐ	Ⓒ			
Caldas da Rainha	d.	0606	0726	1116	1316	1616	1616	1730	1923	..
Bombarral	d.	0627	0747	1137	1337	1637	1637	1750	1945	..
Torres Vedras	d.	0651	0809	1159	1400	1659	1659	1814	2009	..
Mira Sintra - Meleças	a.	0753	0915	1301	1501	1758	1758	1913	2108	..
Mira Sintra - Meleças	▷ d.	0754	0930	1330	1502	1810	1830	1930	2109	..
Agualva - Cacém ⊙	▷ a.	0757	0933	1333	1506	1813	1833	1933	2113	..
Sete Rios	▷ a.	0813	|	|	1523	|	|	|	2128	..
Entrecampos	▷ a.	0816	|	|	1527	|	|	|	2132	..
Lisboa Rossio	▷ a.	|	0959	1359	|	1839	1859	1959	|	..
Lisboa Santa Apolónia	a.	0830	...	...	1541	...	...	...	2142	..

km			△			△			△		
0	**Caldas da Rainha**	d.	0615	...	0830	1115	...	1430	1615	...	1930
12	São Martinho do Porto	d.	0623	...	0841	1123	...	1441	1623	...	1941
46	Marinha Grande	d.	0652	...	0920	1152	...	1520	1652	...	2020
56	Leiria	d.	0700	...	0928	1200	...	1528	1700	...	2028
109	Verride	a.	0745	...	...	1245	...	...	1745	...	...
109	Verride	d.	0748	0756	...	1248	1349	...	1748	1749	...
123	Bifurcação de Lares	a.	|	0803	...	|	1356	...	|	1756	...
129	**Figueira da Foz**	a.	|	0815	...	|	1409	...	|	1809	...
117	Alfarelos	d.	0756	...	...	1256	...	...	1756	...	...
136	**Coimbra** B	a.	0812	...	...	1312	...	...	1812	...	...

				△			△			⊿
Coimbra B	d.	...	...	0850	...	...	1350	...	...	18
Alfarelos	d.	...	...	0906	...	...	1406	...	...	19
Figueira da Foz	d.	...	0858	|	...	1358	|	...	1858	
Bifurcação de Lares	d.	...	0911	|	...	1411	|	...	1911	
Verride	a.	...	0918	0915	...	1418	1415	...	1918	19
Verride	d.	...	...	0921	...	...	1421	...	...	19
Leiria	d.	0625	...	1009	1213	...	1509	1813	...	20
Marinha Grande	d.	0636	...	1019	1224	...	1519	1824	...	20
São Martinho do Porto	d.	0713	...	1046	1256	...	1546	1856	...	20
Caldas da Rainha	a.	0725	...	1055	1308	...	1555	1908	...	20

b – On Ⓐ an additional train runs 20 mins later Lisboa Rossio - Mira Sintra - Meleças.
▷ – For suburban services see Table **699** (including connections from / to Oriente).
⊙ – Connections from / to Lisboa Rossio and Lisboa Oriente run every 20 - 30 minutes (see Table **699**).
△ – *IR* train.

693a FIGUEIRA DA FOZ - COIMBRA

km			⚒	Ⓐ	⚒	Ⓐ	Ⓐ																			
0	**Figueira da Foz**	d.	0558	0633	0658	0740	...	0858	...	0958	1058	...	1158	1258	...	1358	1458	1558	...	1658	1758	...	1858	1958	...	21
8	Bifurcação de Lares	d.	0611	0642	0711	0750	...	0911	...	1014	1111	...	1211	1311	...	1411	1511	1611	...	1711	1811	...	1911	2011	...	22
20	Verride	d.	0620	0650	0720	0757	...	0920	...	1022	1120	...	1220	1320	...	1420	1520	1620	...	1720	1820	...	1920	2020	...	22
28	Alfarelos	d.	0633	0701	0733	0806	0902	0938	1004	1036	1133	1202	1231	1333	1402	1433	1533	1633	1655	1733	1835	1902	1933	2033	2102	22
47	**Coimbra** B	a.	0702	0719	0802	0825	0924	1007	1026	1105	1202	1224	1300	1402	1424	1502	1602	1702	1717	1802	1904	1924	2002	2101	2124	23
49	**Coimbra**	a.	0711	0728	0811	0838	0933	1016	1035	1114	1211	1233	1309	1411	1433	1511	1611	1711	1727	1811	1913	1937	2011	2111	2137	23

			⚒		Ⓐ	Ⓐ										Ⓐ			Ⓐ	Ⓑ		Ⓐ			Ⓑ	
Coimbra	d.	0016	0552	0658	0714	0753	0814	0852	0952	1016	1158	1258	1320	1358	1452	1558	1620	1658	1714	1758	1814	1905	1914	1952	2014	22
Coimbra B	d.	0025	0600	0706	0722	0801	0822	0900	1000	1024	1206	1306	1328	1406	1501	1606	1631	1706	1722	1806	1822	1913	1922	2000	2024	22
Alfarelos	d.	0055	0636	0736	0745	0833	0845	0931	1036	1046	1236	1336	1351	1436	1538	1636	1653	1736	1745	1836	1845	1933	1945	2038	2046	23
Verride	d.	0106	0649	0756	...	0849	...	0946	1049	...	1248	1349	...	1449	1551	1649	...	1749	...	1849	...	1942	...	2050	...	23
Bifurcação de Lares	d.	0114	0656	0803	...	0856	...	0953	1056	...	1255	1356	...	1456	1559	1656	...	1756	...	1856	...	|	...	2057	...	23
Figueira da Foz	a.	0126	0709	0815	...	0909	...	1009	1109	...	1309	1409	...	1509	1613	1709	...	1809	...	1909	...	1956	...	2109	...	23

For main line trains calling at Alfarelos see Table **690**. Other trains: Coimbra - Alfarelos Table **699**, Figueira da Foz - Bifurcação de Lares Table **693**.

694 PORTO - RÉGUA - TUA - POCINHO *Linha do Do*

km			Ⓒ	Ⓐ	⚒	*IR* 861	*IR* 863	21811 M			*IR* 865	*IR* 867	🚂 H	Ⓐ	Ⓒb		*IR* 869	*IR* 873	*IR* 871 Ⓐ	Ⓒ	*IR* 875	Ⓐ		
0	**Porto** São Bento	d.	0625	0630	...	...	0910	0925	0930	...	...	...	...	1330	1400	1510	...	...	1740	1830	1925	1930	...	2
3	**Porto** Campanhã	d.	0630	0635	...	0714	0915	0931	0935	...	1115	1314	...	1335	1405	1515	...	1715	1745	1835	1930	1935	2156	2
12	Ermesinde	d.	0642	0647	...	0727	0927	0942	0947	...	1127	1327	...	1347	1417	1527	...	1727	1757	1847	1941	1947	2205	2
50	Caide	d.	0728	0723	0729	0807	1007	1017	1033r	1042	1207	1407	...	1442	1512	1607	...	1807	1845	1927	2014	2040	2237	0
59	Livração	d.	...	...	0743	0816	1016	|	...	1055	1216	1416	...	1455	1526	1616	...	1816	1859	1941	2022	2053	2251	0
64	Marco de Canaveses	d.	...	...	0751	0824	1024	|	...	1105	1224	1424	...	1505	1535	1624	...	1824	1907	1949	2030	2101	2259	0
107	**Régua**	a.	...	...	0846	0909	1109	1138	...	1203	1309	1509	...	1603	1629	1709	...	1909	2004	2045	2116	2201	2355	
107	**Régua**	d.	...	...	...	0910	1110	...	...	...	...	1510	1523	...	...	...	1718	1910	...	...	...	...	...	
130	Pinhão	d.	...	...	...	0937	1137	...	...	...	...	1537	|	...	...	...	1745	1937	...	...	...	...	...	
143	Tua	d.	...	...	...	0953	1154	...	...	...	...	1553	1634	...	...	...	1803	1953	...	...	...	...	...	
175	**Pocinho**	a.	...	...	...	1035	1236	...	...	...	...	1635	...	...	...	...	1846	2035	...	...	...	...	...	

		⚒	*IR* 860	*IR* 862	*IR* 864		Ⓒ	Ⓒ	*IR* 868	*IR* 870	Ⓒd	*IR* 872 Ⓐ	*IR* 874 Ⓒ	*IR* 876 Ⓒ	*IR* 878		Ⓐ	Ⓒ	🚂 H	*IR* 960	20824 M		ⒸS	
Pocinho	d.	...	...	...	0717	...	...	...	...	1111	...	1321	...	1508	...	...	...	...	...	1721	...	1907	...	
Tua	d.	...	...	...	0759	...	...	...	...	1155	...	1404	...	1552	...	...	...	...	1710	1804	...	1952	...	
Pinhão	d.	...	...	...	0814	...	...	...	...	1211	...	1420	...	1608	...	...	...	...	|	1820	...	2007	...	
Régua	a.	...	...	...	0840	...	...	...	...	1238	...	1447	...	1635	...	...	...	...	1832	1846	...	2034	...	
Régua	d.	0511	0610	0649	...	0848	0913	...	1048	1248	1312	1448	1448	...	1648	1754	...	...	...	1848	1911	...	2050	2
Marco de Canaveses	d.	0609	0705	0736	...	0936	1011	...	1136	1336	1411	1536	1536	...	1736	1853	...	...	...	1936	|	...	2152	2
Livração	d.	0615	0710	0742	...	0942	1017	...	1142	1342	1418	1542	1542	...	1742	1900	...	...	...	1942	|	...	2158	2
Caide	d.	0638	0731	0755	...	0955	1034	1058	1155	1355	1436	1555	1555	...	1755	1917	1938	1958	...	1955	2030	...	2216	2
Ermesinde	d.	0714	0809	0826	...	1026	...	1144	1226	1426	1544	1626	1626	...	1826	...	2014	2044	...	2026	2100	...	2247	2
Porto Campanhã	a.	0725	0821	0835	...	1035	...	1155	1235	1435	1555	1635	1635	...	1834	...	2025	2055	...	2035	2108	...	2254	2
Porto São Bento	a.	0730	...	0850	...	...	...	1200	...	1450	1600	...	...	...	1850	...	2030	2100	...	...	2115	...	2300	2

H – COMBOIO HISTORICO – ⑥ June 1 - Oct. 26 (also Aug. 15). Steam-hauled tourist train, 🅁, special fares.
J – By 🚌 from Caide (a. 0048) Apr. 23 - May 19.
M – MIRADOURO, July 13 - Sept. 30, 2018 🅁. Rail passes not accepted. 2019 dates and times to follow.
S – Ⓒ May 1 - Oct. 27.
b – Change at Penafiel (a. 1453 / d. 150
d – Change at Penafiel (a. 1446 / d. 150
r – 1023 on Ⓐ.

695 PORTO - BRAGA

km						*AP* 131				*IC* 721					*AP* 133			Ⓐ	*AP* 135 Ⓑh				*AP* 137		Ⓐ	*IC* 723	
	Lisboa Sta Ap. **690**	d.	...	...	...	0700	...	...	...	0930	...	...	...	...	1400	...	...	...	1600	...	...	...	1800	...	...	1930	
0	**Porto** São Bento	△ d.	0645	0745	0845	|	0950	1045	1145	|	1245	1345	1445	1545	|	1650	1745	1815	|	1840	1915	1945	|	2050	2145	|	2
3	**Porto** Campanhã	△ d.	0650	0750	0850	0951	0955	1050	1150	1248	1250	1350	1450	1550	1651	1655	1750	1820	1851	1845	1920	1950	2051	2055	2150	2248	2
12	Ermesinde	△ d.	0702	0802	0902	|	1008	1102	1202	|	1304	1402	1504	1602	|	1708	1802	1832	|	1901	1932	2002	|	2108	2202	|	2
26	Trofa	△ d.	0716	0816	0916	|	1022	1116	1216	|	1318	1416	1518	1616	|	1722	1816	1844	|	1917	1944	2016	|	2122	2216	|	2
35	Famalicão	△ d.	0727	0827	0927	1013	1033	1127	1227	1310	1329	1427	1529	1627	1713	1733	1827	1852	1913	1928	1952	2027	2113	2133	2227	2310	2
42	Nine	△ d.	0735	0835	0935	1019	1041	1135	1235	1316	1337	1435	1537	1635	1719	1741	1835	1857	1919	1936	1957	2035	2119	2141	2235	2316	2
57	**Braga**	△ a.	0756	0856	0956	1030	1102	1156	1256	1326	1358	1456	1558	1656	1730	1802	1856	1909	1930	1956	2009	2056	2130	2202	2256	2326	2

		⚒	*AP* 130		Ⓐ	Ⓒ				*IC* 720				*AP* 132		*IC* 722				Ⓐ		*AP* 134	Ⓐ			*AP* 136 Ⓑh	
Braga	▽ d.	0529	0601	0629	0721	0734	0804	0834	0934	1005	1039	1134	1229	1301	1334	1405	1439	1534	1634	1721	1737	1801	1821	1834	1937	2001	2
Nine	▽ d.	0549	0612	0649	0733	0754	0824	0854	0954	1016	1059	1154	1249	1312	1354	1416	1459	1554	1654	1733	1757	1812	1833	1854	1957	2012	2
Famalicão	▽ d.	0557	0617	0657	0738	0802	0832	0902	1002	1021	1107	1202	1257	1317	1402	1421	1507	1602	1702	1738	1805	1817	1838	1902	2005	2017	2
Trofa	▽ d.	0608	|	0708	0746	0813	0843	0913	1013	|	1118	1213	1308	|	1413	|	1518	1613	1713	1746	1816	|	1846	1913	2016	|	2
Ermesinde	▽ d.	0623	|	0723	0759	0829	0859	0929	1029	|	1134	1229	1323	|	1429	|	1533	1629	1729	1759	1838	|	1859	1929	2038	|	2
Porto Campanhã	▽ a.	0635	0640	0735	0811	0841	0911	0941	1041	1045	1146	1241	1335	1340	1441	1445	1545	1641	1741	1811	1850	1840	1911	1941	2050	2040	2
Porto São Bento	▽ a.	0640	|	0740	0815	0845	0915	0945	1045	|	1150	1245	1340	|	1445	|	1550	1645	1745	1815	1855	|	1915	1945	2055	|	2
Lisboa Sta Ap. **690**	a.	...	0930	...	...	...	...	...	...	1400	...	...	...	1630	...	1800	...	...	...	...	...	2130	...	...	...	2330	

d – Journey 55 minutes.
h – Not ⑦ if ① is public holiday. Not ⑤ if a public holiday.
△ – Additional journeys: 0100, 0615Ⓐ**d**, 0715Ⓐ, 0815Ⓐ**d**, 1215Ⓐ**d**, 1615Ⓐ**d**, 1715Ⓐ**d**. Porto - Nine see also Table
▽ – Additional journeys: 0434, 0621Ⓐ**d**, 0745Ⓐ**d**, 1321Ⓐ**d**, 2139Ⓒ, 2239Ⓐ, 2332. Nine - Porto see also Table **696**.

PORTO - GUIMARÃES 695a

60 km

							IC 621					*AP* 141
			Ⓐ							Ⓐ		Ⓑ
Lisboa Sta Ap. **690** ..d.	...	...	...	...	...	...	1130	...	...	...	...	2000
orto São Bento ....▷ d.	0720	0820	0920	1020	1220	1420	|	1620	1820	1855	2020	|
orto Campanhã ....▷ d.	0725	0825	0925	1025	1225	1425	1448	1625	1825	1900	2025	2300
rmesinde ....▷ d.	0737	0837	0935	1037	1237	1437	|	1637	1837	1910	2037	|
rofa......................▷ d.	0752	0852	0946	1052	1252	1452	1506	1652	1852	1921	2052	2317
uimarães ....a.	0836	0936	1022	1133	1336	1533	1539	1736	1937	1954	2133	2349

		AP 140							*IC* 620			
	Ⓐ	⚒	Ⓐ							Ⓐ	Ⓐ	
Guimarães ....d.	0548	0643	0706	0848	0948	1159	1348	1548	1650	1812	2012	2148
Trofa........................▷ d.	0633	0721	0739	0933	1033	1243	1433	1633	1723	1901	2104	2233
Ermesinde..................▷ d.	0649	|	0751	0949	1049	1259	1449	1649	|	1919	2119	2249
Porto Campanhã ....▷ a.	0701	0738	0801	1001	1101	1311	1501	1701	1743	1931	2131	2301
Porto São Bento.....▷ a.	0705	|	0805	1005	1105	1315	1505	1705	|	1935	2135	2305
Lisboa Sta Ap. **690** ..a.	...	1040	...	...	...	...	...	...	2100	...	...	...

.SO: **Porto - Guimarães** 0620Ⓐ, 1120Ⓐ, 1720Ⓐ, 1920Ⓐ, 2120Ⓒ, 2220Ⓐ, 2320; **Guimarães - Porto** 0648Ⓒ, 0804Ⓐ, 1248Ⓐ, 1712Ⓐ, 1748Ⓒ, 1916Ⓐ, 1948Ⓒ, 2248. ▷ – **695, 696**.

PORTO - VIANA DO CASTELO - VALENÇA - VIGO 696

Linha do Minho

km																								
		IR 851				421*						*IR* 853				*IR* 855			*IR* 857			423*	*IR* 859	
		Ⓐ	Ⓐ		⚒	[R]		Ⓐ						Ⓐ								[R]	Ⓐ	
0	**Porto** Campanhã.............▷ d.	0610	0620	...	*0650*	0813	...	0820	...	0955	...	1300	1250	...	*1350*	1615	...	...	1815	1845	...	1910	2015	2210
12	Ermesinde ....▷ d.	0619	0632	...	*0702*	|	...	0832	...	1008	...	1311	1304	...	*1402*	1625	...	...	1826	1901	...	|	2026	2221
23	Trofa ....▷ d.	0630	0644	...	*0716*	|	...	0844	...	1022	...	1324	1318	...	*1416*	1636	...	...	1837	1917	...	|	2037	2232
32	Famalicão.........................▷ d.	0638	0652	...	*0727*	|	...	0852	...	1033	...	1334	1329	...	*1427*	1644	...	...	1845	1928	...	|	2047	2241
39	**Nine** ....▷ a.	0644	0656	...	*0735*	0841	...	0856	...	1041	...	1341	1337	...	*1435*	1650	...	...	1851	1935	...	1939	2053	2247
39	**Nine** ....d.	0644	...	0701	0747	0842	...	...	0904	...	1105	1342	...	1357	1505	1651	...	1736	1852	...	2001	1940	2054	2248
51	Barcelos ....d.	0654	...	0716	0803	|	...	...	0917	...	1118	1352	...	1410	1518	1702	...	1749	1902	...	2014	|	2105	2302
82	**Viana do Castelo**.................a.	0733	...	0800	0849	0914	...	...	1006	...	1201	1423	...	1452	1600	1733	...	1832	1934	...	2102	2012	2137	2343
82	**Viana do Castelo**.................d.	0735	...	0822	...	0915	...	...	1014	...	...	1425	...	...	1620	1734	...	1836	1935	...	...	2013	2138	...
16	Vila Nova de Cerveira...........d.	0804	...	0911	...	|	...	...	1058	...	...	1458	...	...	1703	1803	...	1919	2007	...	...	|	2207	...
30	**Valença**....................🏛 PT d.	0818	...	0934	...	0957	1005	...	1115	...	...	1511	...	...	1720	1816	1944	1943	2020	...	...	2050	2220	...
34	Tui...............................🏛 ES d.	...	...	...	...	|	1112	...	...	...	...	...	...	...	...	...	2051	...	...	...	...	|	...	...
62	Redondela **680** ....d.	...	...	...	...	|	1144	...	...	...	...	...	...	...	...	...	2124	...	...	...	...	|	...	...
74	**Vigo** Guixar ◐ **680** ....a.	...	...	...	...	1135	1155	...	...	...	...	...	...	...	...	...	2135	...	...	...	...	2234	...	...

					IR 850	420*				*IR* 852					*IR* 854					*IR* 856			422*	
		Ⓐ	Ⓐ	Ⓐ		[R]						Ⓐ	Ⓐ				Ⓐ						[R]	
go Guixar ◐ **680**...............d.	...	...	...	...	...	0858	...	...	0920	...	...	...	...	...	...	...	...	...	...	...	1812	...	1956	...
edondela **680** ....d.	...	...	...	...	...	|	...	...	0931	...	...	...	...	...	...	...	...	...	...	...	1824	...	|	...
i...............................🏛 ES d.	...	...	...	...	...	|	...	...	1003	...	...	...	...	...	...	...	...	...	...	...	1858	...	|	...
lença.........................🏛 PT d.	...	...	0537	0614	0733	0836	...	...	0911	0923	1121	...	...	...	1425	1517	...	...	...	1749	1806	1829	1933	...
a Nova de Cerveira............d.	...	...	0551	0630	0745	|	...	...	...	0939	1137	...	...	...	1436	1533	...	...	...	1802	...	1845	|	...
ana do Castelo.................a.	...	...	0630	0715	0814	0911	...	...	...	1013	1221	...	...	...	1508	1617	...	...	...	1835	...	1931	2009	...
ana do Castelo.................d.	0511	...	0632	0718	0816	0916	0946	...	...	1015	1222	...	1347	...	1509	1618	...	1750	...	1838	...	...	2014	2022
rcelos ....d.	0553	...	0717	0802	0851	|	1029	...	...	1044	1303	...	1434	...	1540	1703	...	1835	...	1920	...	...	|	2104
ne ....a.	0605	...	0732	0817	0901	0950	1043	...	...	1053	1318	...	1449	...	1549	1717	...	1849	...	1930	...	...	2048	2118
ne ....▷ d.	...	0633	0735	*0824*	0902	0951	...	1059	...	1054	...	1333	...	1459	1550	...	1733	...	1854	1931	...	...	2048	2119
malicão...........................▷ d.	...	0638	0743	*0832*	0911	|	...	1107	...	1102	...	1338	...	1507	1557	...	1738	...	1902	1938	...	...	|	2126
ofa.....................................▷ d.	...	0646	0751	*0843*	0919	|	...	1118	...	1109	...	1346	...	1518	1605	...	1746	...	1913	1946	...	...	|	2133
mesinde ....▷ d.	...	0659	0807	*0859*	0935	|	...	1134	...	1121	...	1359	...	1533	1620	...	1759	...	1929	2000	...	...	|	2146
rto Campanhã..............▷ a.	...	0710	0819	*0910*	0945	1020	...	1145	...	1130	...	1410	...	1544	1630	...	1810	...	1940	2010	...	...	2118	2155

– New terminus (1 km from Vigo Urzaiz).
– See also Table **695**.

* – Trains **420 - 423** are branded *Celta*. 2nd class.

ES – Spain (Central European Time).
PT – Portugal (West European Time).

LISBOA - PINHAL NOVO - TUNES - FARO 697

km		*AP* 180	*IC* 21180	*IC* 570		*IC* 572		*AP* 184	*IC* 574	
			⑥S							
	Porto Campanhã **690** ....d.	0540	...	...	...	...	...	1440	...	...
	Coimbra B **690** ....d.	0644	...	...	...	...	...	1544	...	...
0	**Lisboa** Oriente ....⊙ d.	0823	0830	1002	...	1402	...	1723	1822	...
7	Entrecampos ....⊙ d.	0831	0840	1010	...	1410	...	1731	1830	...
9	Sete Rios ....⊙ d.	|	|	1014	...	1414	...	|	1834	...
18	Pragal.................................⊙ d.	|	|	1026	...	1426	...	|	1846	...
47	Pinhal Novo ....⊙ d.	0906	0917	1048	...	1448	...	1806	1906	...
18	Grândola ....d.	|	|	1119	...	1516	...	|	1934	...
80	Funcheira ....d.	|	|	1155	...	1552	...	|	2012	...
64	**Tunes** ....▷ d.	1054	1122	1302	...	1707	...	1955	2122	...
69	Albufeira ....▷ d.	1101	1129	1307	...	1712	...	2002	2127	...
86	Loulé ....▷ d.	1113	1141	1319	...	1724	...	2014	2139	...
02	**Faro** ....▷ a.	1123	1150	1330	...	1735	...	2023	2150	...

	AP 182	*IC* 670		*IC* 672	*IC* 21184	*AP* 186		*IC* 674	
					⑥S				
Faro ....▷ d.	0700	0822	...	1354	1515	1600	...	1756	...
Loulé ....▷ d.	0710	0833	...	1405	1525	1611	...	1806	...
Albufeira ....▷ d.	0723	0845	...	1417	1544	1624	...	1818	...
Tunes....................................▷ d.	0729	0851	...	1423	1550	1630	...	1825	...
Funcheira...............................d.	0823	1000	...	1526	|	|	...	1935	...
Grândola................................d.	0854	1037	...	1604	|	|	...	2010	...
Pinhal Novo ....⊙ d.	0923	1107	...	1637	1744	1823	...	2040	...
Pragal..................................⊙ a.	|	1130	...	1704	|	|	...	2104	...
Sete Rios ....⊙ a.	|	1143	...	1714	|	|	...	2114	...
Entrecampos........................⊙ a.	0957	1146	...	1717	1817	1857	...	2117	...
Lisboa Oriente ....⊙ a.	1005	1156	...	1726	1826	1905	...	2126	...
Coimbra B **690** ....a.	1145	...	...	...	...	2045	...	...	...
Porto Campanhã **690**.........a.	1250	...	...	...	...	2150	...	...	...

LOCAL TRAINS LAGOS - TUNES - FARO

			⚒		Ⓐ					Ⓐ		
0	**Lagos** ....d.	0616	0658	0746	0903	1114	1310	1513	1705	1815	2000	...
18	Portimão...........d.	0634	0717	0805	0922	1133	1329	1532	1724	1834	2019	...
29	Silves ....d.	0650	0733	0821	...	1150	1350	1549	1745	1851	2036	...
42	Algoz.................d.	0705	0748	0837	...	1206	1409	1605	1801	1913	2051	...
46	**Tunes** ....▷ d.	0711	0754	0851	...	1212	1423	1611	1807	1919	2058	...
52	Albufeira ......▷ d.	0722	0800	0858	...	1218	1429	1623	1818	1926	2111	...
69	Loulé ....▷ d.	0743	0815	0919	...	1239	1444	1638	1834	1941	2126	...
85	**Faro** ....▷ a.	0759	0835	0934	...	1254	1459	1654	1849	1956	2142	...

	⚒	Ⓐ		R	S				Ⓐ		
Faro ....▷ d.	0711	...	0902	1023	1023	1222	1617	1718	1812	1919	2038
Loulé ....▷ d.	0728	...	0919	1039	1039	1239	1638	1740	1834	1941	2055
Albufeira ...▷ d.	0743	...	0935	1100	1100	1307	1655	1756	1851	2001	2111
Tunes.......▷ d.	0754	...	0942	1106	1124r	1313	1708	1807	1857	2008	2124
Algoz ....d.	0800	...	0947	1112	1130	1319	1714	1813	1903	2014	2129
Silves.............d.	0821	...	1003	1130	1150	1335	1730	1830	1919	2036	2144
Portimão ....d.	0834	0931	1018	1150	1205	1350	1745	1851	1933	2051	2158
Lagos............a.	0853	0950	1036	1208	1223	1408	1803	1910	1952	2108	2216

- Not dates in note **S**.
- ⑥ June 30 - Sept. 1 (2018 dates).

r – Arrives 1106.
▷ – Also see other section of table above or below.

⊙ – See Table **698** for other fast trains, Table **699** for local services, including connections Barreiro - Pinhal Novo.

FARO - VILA REAL DE SANTO ANTÓNIO 697a

				R	S							
0	**Faro** ....d.	0750	0955	1134	1155	1355	1500	1706	1751	1922	2036	2206
10	Olhão ....d.	0805	1006	1145	1206	1406	1511	1721	1802	1933	2047	2218
32	Tavira ....d.	0830	1031	1210	1231	1432	1536	1746	1827	2003	2112	2243
56	**Vila Real** §........a.	0858	1100	1238	1307	1501	1605	1822	1855	2031	2141	2308

								Ⓐ			
Vila Real §.....d.	0548	0642	0711	0908	1113	1239	1429	1533	1627	1754	2044
Tavira ....d.	0617	0711	0740	0938	1139	1308	1503	1607	1657	1827	2112
Olhão..................d.	0643	0736	0805	1006	1206	1332	1533	1631	1721	1856	2136
Faro ....a.	0653	0747	0815	1017	1217	1343	1544	1642	1731	1907	2146

- Not dates in note **S**.
- ⑥ June 30 - Sept. 1 (also Aug. 15).

§ – Vila Real de Santo António (± *1500m* from bus station / ferry terminal).

ADDITIONAL JOURNEYS:
Faro - Villa Real 0857Ⓐ, 1255Ⓐ, 1823Ⓐ. Villa Real - Faro 1905Ⓐ.

LISBOA - PINHAL NOVO - ÉVORA and BEJA 698

nha do Alentejo

m		*IC* 590	*IC* 581	*IC* 592	*IC* 583	*IC* 594	*IC* 585	*IC* 596	*IC* 587	*IC* 598	*IC* 589
		Ⓐ	Ⓐ	Ⓐ	Ⓐ	Ⓒ	Ⓒ				
0	**Lisboa** Oriente ...▷ d.	0702	...	0902	...	0952	...	1702	...	1902	...
7	Entrecampos.......▷ d.	0710	...	0910	...	1000	...	1710	...	1910	...
9	Sete Rios............▷ d.	0714	...	0914	...	1004	...	1714	...	1914	...
8	Pragal..................▷ d.	0726	...	0926	...	1015	...	1726	...	1926	...
7	**Pinhal Novo**.......▷ d.	0748	...	0948	...	1032	...	1748	...	1948	...
8	Vendas Novas ....d.	0818	...	1010	...	1102	...	1810	...	2010	...
2	Casa Branca ....a.	0831	...	1023	...	1115	...	1823	...	2023	...
2	Casa Branca ....d.	0832	0835	1024	1030	1116	1119	1824	1829	2024	2025
8	Évora ....a.	0842	|	1035	|	1126	|	1835	|	2035	|
5	**Beja**..........................a.	...	0926	...	1121	...	1210	...	1920	...	2115

	IC 580	*IC* 690		*IC* 582	*IC* 692		*IC* 584	*IC* 694		*IC* 586	*IC* 696
	Ⓐ	Ⓐ									
Beja ....d.	0623	...	...	0822	...	...	1611	...	...	1815	...
Évora ....d.	|	0706	...	|	0906	...	|	1657	...	|	1906
Casa Branca...............a.	0711	0716	...	0914	0916	...	1700	1707	...	1908	1916
Casa Branca...............d.	...	0717	...	...	0917	...	...	1708	...	...	1917
Vendas Novas ....d.	...	0731	...	...	0931	...	...	1722	...	...	1931
Pinhal Novo..........▷ d.	...	0753	...	...	0953	...	...	1751	...	...	1953
Pragal.....................▷ a.	...	0814	...	...	1014	...	...	1814	...	...	2014
Sete Rios.................▷ a.	...	0824	...	...	1024	...	...	1824	...	...	2024
Entrecampos............▷ a.	...	0828	...	...	1028	...	...	1828	...	...	2028
Lisboa Oriente ......▷ a.	...	0836	...	...	1036	...	...	1836	...	...	2036

- See Table **697** for other fast trains and Table **699** for local services, including connections Barreiro - Pinhal Novo.

699 OTHER LOCAL SERVICES

LISBOA - ESTORIL - CASCAIS

km																										
0	**Lisboa** Cais do Sodre . d.	Ⓐ	0530	every	0700	every	1000	every	1700	every	2024	2030	every	2130	2200	every	0130	Ⓒ	0530	every	0800	every	1900	every	0130
24	Estoril d.		0606	30	0729	12	1036	20	1729	12	2053	2106	20	2206	2236	30	0206		0606	30	0836	20	1936	30	0206
26	**Cascais** a.		0610	mins	0733	mins	1040	mins	1733	mins	2057	2110	mins	2210	2240	mins	0210		0610	mins	0840	mins	1940	mins	0210

															⊡										
Cascais d.	Ⓐ	0530	0600	0630	0652	every	2016	2028	2040	2100	every	0130	Ⓒ	0600	0630	0704	every	1904	1934	every	2104	2130	every	0130
Estoril d.		0534	0604	0634	0656	12-20 ◧	2020	2032	2044	2104	30	0134		0604	0634	0708	20	1908	1938	30	2108	2134	30	0134
Lisboa Cais do Sodre . a.		0610	0640	0710	0725	mins	2049	2108	2120	2140	mins	0210		0640	0710	0744	mins	1944	2014	mins	2144	2210	mins	0210

◧ – Every 12 minutes 0704 - 1004, every 20 minutes 1004 - 1704, every 12 minutes 1704 - 2016. ⊡ – Also at 0530.

LISBOA ORIENTE - SINTRA

		Ⓐ		Ⓐ		Ⓒ			Ⓒ
Lisboa Oriente d.	Ⓐ	0558		0108	Ⓒ	0608			0108
Roma Areeiro d.		0605	See	0115		0615	every		0115
Entrecampos d.		0607	note	0117		0617	30		0117
Sete Rios d.		0610	△	0120		0620	mins		0120
Monte Abraão d.		0625		0135		0635	until		0135
Agualva - Cacém d.		0631		0141		0641			0141
Sintra a.		0645		0155		0655			0155

		Ⓐ		Ⓐ		Ⓒ		Ⓒ
Sintra d.	Ⓐ	0506		0006	Ⓒ	0506		0006
Agualva - Cacém d.		0519	See	0019		0519	every	0019
Monte Abraão d.		0524	note	0024		0524	30	0024
Sete Rios d.		0539	▽	0039		0539	mins	0039
Entrecampos d.		0542		0042		0542	until	0042
Roma Areeiro d.		0544		0044		0544		0044
Lisboa Oriente a.		0552		0052		0552		0052

△ – 0558, 0618, every 10 mins 0638 - 0938, every 20 mins 0958 - 1638, every 10 mins 1648 - 1958, 2018, every 30 mins 2038 - 0108.

▽ – 0506, 0536, 0606, every 10 mins 0626 - 0936, every 20 mins 0956 - 1556, every 10 mins 1616 - 1936, 1956, 2016, every 30 mins 2036 - 0006.

LISBOA ROSSIO - SINTRA and MIRA SINTRA-MELEÇAS

	Ⓐ	Ⓒ			n		n
Lisboa Rossio d.	0541	0601		0101	0621	and	2021
Monte Abraão d.	0601	0621	See	0121	0641	hourly	2041
Agualva - Cacém d.	0607	0627	note	0127	0647	until	2047
Mira Sintra - Meleças a.	|	|	△	|	0650	⊡	2050
Sintra a.	0621	0641		0141	...		...

Sintra d.	0520		0020	...		...	...
Mira Sintra - Meleças d.	|	See	|	0730	and	2030	...
Agualva - Cacém d.	0533	note	0033	0733	hourly	2033	...
Monte Abraão d.	0539	▽	0039	0739	until	2039	...
Lisboa Rossio a.	0559		0059	0759	⊡	2059	...

n – On Ⓒ runs 10 minutes later.

△ – Ⓐ: every 30 mins 0541 - 2041 (◧) and 2101 - 0101.
Ⓒ: hourly 0601 - 2001, every 30 mins 2101 - 0101.

▽ – Ⓐ: every 30 mins 0520 - 0620, 0640 - 2010 (◐), 2050 - 0020.
Ⓒ: every 30 mins 0520 - 0650, hourly 0650 - 2050, every 30 mins 2050 - 0020.

⊡ – Additional services operate during peak hours on Ⓐ

◧ – Between 0941Ⓐ and 1641Ⓐ runs at xx41, xx01.

◐ – Between 0940Ⓐ and 1640Ⓐ runs at xx40, xx00.

LISBOA - PINHAL NOVO - SETÚBAL

Operator: Fertagus. CP tickets not valid.

Roma Areeiro d.	Ⓐ	0043	0543		2243	2358	Ⓒ	0643		2343
Entrecampos d.		0045	0545	and	2245	0000		0645	and	2345
Sete Rios d.		0049	0549	every	2249	0004		0649	every	2349
Pragal d.		0100	0600	hour	2300	0015		0700	hour	0000
Pinhal Novo d.		0128	0628	until	2328	0043		0728	until	0028
Setúbal a.		0141	0641		2341	0056		0741		0041

Setúbal d.	Ⓐ	0548	0658		1858	1928	2018		0018	Ⓒ	0558		225
Pinhal Novo d.		0602	0712	and	1912	1942	2032	and	0032		0612	and	231
Pragal d.		0629	0739	every	1939	2009	2059	every	0059		0639	every	233
Sete Rios d.		0640	0750	hour	1950	2020	2110	hour	0110		0650	hour	235
Entrecampos d.		0644	0754	until	1954	2024	2114	until	0114		0654	until	235
Roma Areeiro a.		0646	0756		1956	2026	2116		0116		0656		235

Additional journeys on Ⓐ: from Roma Areeiro 1813, 1913, 2013, from Setúbal 0628, 0728, 0828. Trains run every 10 – 20 minutes (every 30 mins evenings and Ⓒ) Roma Areeiro - Pragal - Coir

Catamaran LISBOA - BARREIRO

Transtejo — *Certain Ⓐ peak journeys do not run in July / Augus*

From Lisboa Terreiro do Paço: By ⛴ journey time 20 - 25 minutes. *10* km

Ⓐ: 0545, 0610, 0640, 0700 and approx every 10 minutes until 0920, 0940, 0955 and every 30 minutes until 1555, 1615, 1630, 1650 and approx every 10 minutes 2010, 2030, 2050, 2110, 2125, 2155, 2225, 2255, 2330, 0000, 0100, 0200.

Ⓒ: 0545, 0615, 0647, 0715, 0755, 0825⑥, 0855, 0925⑥, 0955, 1025⑥, 1055, 1155, 1255, 1355, 1455, 1525, 1555, 1625, 1655, 1725, 1755, 1825, 1855, 1925, 1955, 2055, 2125, 2155, 2255, 0000, 0100, 0200.

From Barreiro Barcos: By ⛴ journey time 20 - 25 minutes. *10* km

Ⓐ: 0515, 0545, 0615, 0635 and approx every 10 minutes until 0855, 0910, 0925, 0940, 095 1025 and every 30 minutes until 1525, 1545, 1600, 1620 and approx every 10 minute until 1940, 2005, 2020, 2040, 2100, 2125, 2200, 2225, 2300, 2330, 0030, 0130.

Ⓒ: 0515, 0545, 0622, 0650, 0725, 0755⑥, 0825, 0855⑥, 0925, 0955⑥, 1025, 1125, 122 1325, 1425, 1455, 1525, 1555, 1625, 1655, 1725, 1755, 1825, 1855, 1925, 2025, 205 2125, 2225, 2330, 0030, 0130.

BARREIRO - SETÚBAL

km								
		Ⓐ						
0	**Barreiro** d.	0555	0625	every 30 mins	2125	2232	2325	0029
15	Pinhal Novo d.	0614	0644	(hourly on Ⓒ)	2144	2251	2344	0048
28	**Setúbal** a.	0626	0656	until	2156	2303	2356	0100

	Ⓐ	Ⓒ	Ⓐ			Ⓐ				
Setúbal d.	0508	0548	0618	0648	every 30 mins	2048	2122	2151	2248	234
Pinhal Novo d.	0520	0600	0630	0700	(hourly on Ⓒ)	2100	2136	2202	2300	00(
Barreiro a.	0538	0618	0648	0718	until	2118	2154	2220	2318	00

Most journeys continue to / from Praias do Sado A (8 minutes from Setúbal).

LISBOA - ENTRONCAMENTO - TOMAR

km																								
			Ⓐ	⚒		Ⓐ		Ⓐ	Ⓐ		Ⓐ		Ⓐ			Ⓐ§		Ⓐ§				Ⓐ		
0	**Lisboa** Santa Apolónia ▷ d.	0015	0550	0645	0745	0845	0945	1045	1145	1245	1345	1445	1545	1615	1645	1715	1745	1815	1845	1945	2045	2145	2245	..
7	**Lisboa** Oriente ▷ d.	0025	0558	0653	0753	0853	0953	1053	1153	1253	1353	1453	1553	1623	1653	1723	1753	1823	1853	1953	2053	2153	2253	..
31	Vila Franca de Xira d.	0051	0616	0711	0811	0911	1011	1111	1211	1311	1411	1511	1611	1639	1711	1739	1811	1838	1911	2011	2111	2211	2311	..
75	Santarém d.	0135	0655	0755	0855	0957	1055	1148	1255	1348	1455	1549	1655	1706	1756	1806	1855	1907	1955	2055	2149	2249	2349	..
107	Entroncamento a.	0159	0718	0819	0919	1021	1119	1212	1319	1412	1519	1615	1719	1725	1820	1825	1919	1926	2019	2119	2214	2312	0012	..
130	**Tomar** a.	...	0751	0847	0947	...	1151	1242	...	1440	1551	1647	1751	...	1853	1900	1951	2000	2051	2149	2251	2340	0040	..

	①–⑥	Ⓐ	Ⓐ§		Ⓐ§		①–⑥		Ⓐ			Ⓐ		Ⓐ					Ⓐ	⑦d		Ⓐ	⑦d	
Tomar d.	...	0515	0605	0615r	0650	0711r	...	0802	...	1011	1111r	...	1315	...	1511	1606	1711	1811	1910	...	2011	...	...	22
Entroncamento d.	0416	0544	0626	0644	0711	0744	0808	0839	0944	1039	1144	1237	1344	1439	1544	1639	1744	1844	1944	2039	2044	2145	2227	224
Santarém d.	0442	0607	0645	0707	0731	0807	0827	0903	1008	1103	1207	1301	1408	1503	1607	1703	1807	1907	2009	2059	2107	2205	2246	230
Vila Franca de Xira d.	0524	0647	0717	0747	0800	0847	0856	0947	1047	1147	1247	1347	1447	1547	1654	1747	1847	1955	2055	2126	2147	2247	2326	234
Lisboa Oriente ▷ d.	0550	0705	0733	0805	0815	0905	0911	1005	1105	1205	1305	1405	1505	1605	1712	1805	1905	2012	2113	2142	2205	2305	2342	000
Lisboa Santa Apolónia ▷ a.	0559	0713	0741	0813	0828	0913	0920	1013	1113	1213	1313	1413	1513	1613	1720	1813	1913	2020	2120	2150	2213	2313	2350	00

▷ – Additional local trains are available. d – If ⑦ is a public holiday runs next day instead. r – ⚒ only. § – *IR* train.

ENTRONCAMENTO - COIMBRA

Local trains — For fast trains see Table 69

km												
		†	Ⓐ		Ⓐ						Ⓐ		Ⓑ
0	**Entroncamento** d.	...	0603	0642	0738	0840	1038	1238	1538	1738	1838	1938	2127
24	Fátima ⊙ d.	...	0624	0702	0804	0907	1104	1304	1558	1804	1904	2004	2148
64	Pombal d.	...	0658	0736	0839	0941	1139	1339	1632	1839	1939	2039	2222
91	Alfarelos d.	0719	0721	0800	0902	1004	1202	1402	1655	1902	2002	2102	2245
111	**Coimbra B** a.	0743	0743	0821	0924	1026	1224	1424	1717	1924	2024	2124	2307
111	**Coimbra B** d.	0748	0748	0830	0929	1031	1229	1429	1722	1933	2029	2133	...
113	**Coimbra** a.	0752	0752	0834	0933	1035	1233	1433	1727	1937	2033	2137	...

	⚒	Ⓐ					Ⓐ			Ⓑ
Coimbra d.	0603	0714	0814	1016	1320	1620	1714	1814	1914	20
Coimbra B a.	0606	0717	0817	1019	1323	1624	1717	1817	1917	20
Coimbra B d.	0611	0722	0822	1024	1328	1631	1722	1822	1922	20
Alfarelos d.	0634	0745	0845	1047	1351	1654	1745	1845	1945	20
Pombal d.	0710	0819	0919	1119	1417	1719	1819	1918	2019	21
Fátima ⊙ d.	0745	0904	0953	1153	1501	1753	1853	2002	2053	21
Entroncamento a.	0805	0924	1013	1213	1521	1813	1913	2022	2113	22

r – Ⓐ only. ⊙ – Station is *20 km* from Fátima (full name of station is Chão de Maçãs - Fátima). *For fast trains Entroncamento - Coimbra B see Table* **690**.

AVEIRO - COIMBRA

Local trains — For fast trains see Table 69

km													
					Ⓐ		Ⓐ		Ⓐ				
0	**Aveiro** d.	0644	0746	0946	1046	1140	1224	1346	1446	1534	1746	1946	2152
41	Pampilhosa d.	0721	0822	1023	1123	1217	1301	1422	1522	1611	1822	2023	2228
55	**Coimbra B** a.	0738	0838	1038	1140	1234	1318	1438	1538	1628	1836	2039	2244
57	**Coimbra** a.	0743	0851	1044	1151	1239	1329	1444	1551	1634	1843	2051	2252

		⚒								
Coimbra d.	0630	0744	0842	1053	1343	1448	1643	1829	1941	22
Coimbra B d.	0635	0748	0850	1058	1348	1453	1648	1837	1950	22
Pampilhosa d.	0653	0805	0909	1116	1405	1511	1705	1900	2012	22
Aveiro a.	0732	0844	0946	1155	1444	1550	1744	1939	2051	23

Additional trains: **Aveiro - Coimbra**: 0544⚒, 0729Ⓐ, 0846Ⓐ, 1644Ⓐ, 1846Ⓐ, 2046Ⓐ. **Coimbra - Aveiro**: 0533Ⓐ, 1005Ⓐ, 1143Ⓐ, 1243Ⓐ, 1542Ⓐ, 1743Ⓐ, 2042Ⓐ.

 Reservations are compulsory for travel by AP and IC trains (also Sud Expresso and Lusitania)

FINLAND
For routes north of Narvik, see page 365.
For to / from Svolvær see note ♣ in Table 787.
KØBENHAVN
Aarhus
Ebeltoft
Helsingborg
Sj. Odde
Helsingør
Samsø
Vejle
Lund
Malmö
Kalundborg
Fredericia
Roskilde
Odense
Ringsted
Trelleborg
Korsør
Nyborg
Vordingborg
Bøjden
Fynshav
Nakskov
Nykøbing
Rødby
Sønderborg
Gedser
Kirkenes
Narvik
Svolvær
Kiruna
Moskenes
Bodø
Fauske
Gällivare
Mo i Rana
Boden
Haparanda
Kemi
Luleå
Arvidsjaur
Sandnessjøen
Mosjøen
Skellefteå
Brønnøysund
Bastuträsk
Storuman
Rørvik
Vännäs
Umeå
SWEDEN
Steinkjer
Örnsköldsvik
TRONDHEIM
Åre
Hell
Storlien
Östersund
Kristiansund
Støren
Bräcke
Härnösand
Molde
Røros
Ånge
Sundsvall
Oppdal
Sveg
Ålesund
Åndalsnes
Hudiksvall
Orsa
Bollnäs
Geiranger
Dombås
Mora
Söderhamn
Eckerö
Måløy
NORWAY
Rättvik
Mariehamn
Sogndal
Lillehammer
Falun
Gävle
Balestrand
Lærdal
Elverum
Borlänge
Grisslehamn
Hamar
Flåm
Gjøvik
Avesta
Eidsvoll
Ludvika
Voss
Myrdal
Gol
Oslo
Kongsvinger
Uppsala
Kapellskär
Roa
Fagersta
Arlanda
Västerås
BERGEN
Geilo
Charlottenberg
STOCKHOLM
Hønefoss
Nykroppa
Frövi
Odda
Lillestrøm
Eskilstuna
Södertälje
Drammen
OSLO
Kil
Örebro
Notodden
Karlstad
Nynäshamn
Kristinehamn
Hallsberg
Katrineholm
Nordagutu
Skien
Fredrikstad
Laxå
Larvik
Mariestad
Norrköping
Strömstad
Motala
Linköping
Stavanger
Nelaug
Uddevalla
Öxnered
Mjölby
Trollhättan
Falköping
Västervik
Arendal
Egersund
Moi
Kristiansand
Herrljunga
Visby
Jönköping
Nässjö
Hirtshals
Skagen
Hjørring
Borås
Berga
Oskarshamn
GÖTEBORG
Frederikshavn
Hanstholm
Aalborg
Varberg
Alvesta
Växjö
Kalmar
Thisted
Emmaboda
Randers
Halmstad
Karlskrona
Struer
Langå
Karlshamn
Holstebro
Kristianstad
see inset above
Skjern
Herning
Hässleholm
DENMARK
Esbjerg
Simrishamn
Ystad
Fanø
Ribe
Rønne
Tønder
Niebüll
Padborg
Flensburg
Puttgarden
Sassnitz Fährhafen
GERMANY
Kiel
Rostock

DENMARK

Operators: The principal operator is Danske Statsbaner (*DSB*): www.dsb.dk. Arriva Tog (*AT*) operate many local services in Jutland: www.arriva.dk. Local trains over the Øresund bridge marketed as Øresundståg (*Øtåg*).

Services: InterCity (*IC*) and InterCityLyn (*Lyn*) trains offer *Business* (1st class), *Standard* (2nd class), and on some services *Hvilepladser* ('quiet' seats) and *Familiepladser* ('family' sea These services often consist of two or more portions for different destinations and care should be taken to join the correct portion. Other trains convey 1st and 2nd (standa classes of accommodation unless otherwise shown.

Timings: Valid until **December 14, 2019** unless otherwise stated. Readers should note, however, that minor amendments may be made at any time, especially on and around the dates public holidays (Dec. 25, 26, Jan. 1, Apr. 18, 19, 22, May 17, 30, June 10). Engineering work often affects schedules (particularly late evening / early morning services and a during the summer months) and readers are advised to check locally.

Reservations: Seat reservations (currently 30 DKK) are recommended for travel on *IC* and *Lyn* trains (especially at peak times) and may be purchased a maximum of two months an minimum of 15 minutes before departure of the train from its *originating* station. Passengers may board the train without a reservation but are not guaranteed a seat. Reservatic are also available on EuroCity (*EC*) trains. It is not possible to reserve seats on other types of train. Special reservation rules may apply during holiday periods.

700 KØBENHAVN - ODENSE - FREDERICIA - AARHUS

Subject to alteration until August

Most Aarhus services run to / from Aalborg (Table **701**). Services København - Middelfart and v.v. run to / from Esbjerg (Table **705**). For other through cars see Tables **710**, **712** and **715**

km		IC 1601		IC 1609 Ⓒ	IC 1611 Ⓐ	IC 111 Ⓐ	IC 113 Ⓐ	Lyn 17 Ⓐ	IC 117 Ⓐ	IC 117	IC 821 Ⓐ	Lyn 21 Ⓐ	IC 121	IC 821 Ⓐ	Lyn 25	IC 125	IC 829	Lyn 29	IC 129	IC 5729 N	IC 833	Lyn 41	IC 133	IC 837
	København Lufthavn ✈ d.	0010	...	0213	0213	...	...	...	0438	...	...	0530	0538	...	...	0638	...	0730	0738	...	...	...	0838	...
0	**København** H ... § 720 d.	0036	...	0236	0236	...	...	...	0500	...	0530	0552	0600	0630	0652	0700	0730	0752	0800	...	0830	0852	0900	0930
20	Høje Taastrup .... § 720 d.	0052	...	0252	0252	...	...	...	0515	...	0545	0605	0615	0645	0705	0715	0745	0805	0815	...	0845	0905	0915	0945
31	Roskilde .... § 720 d.	0100	...	0300	0300	...	...	...	0523	...	0553	|	0623	0653	|	0723	0753	|	0823	...	0853	|	0923	0953
64	Ringsted .... 720 d.	0125	...	0325	0321	...	...	...	0539	...	0609	|	0639	0709	|	0739	0809	|	0839	...	0909	|	0939	1009
93	Slagelse .... d.	0144	...	0344	0343	...	...	...	0557	...	0627	|	0657	0727	|	0757	0827	|	0857	...	0927	|	0957	1027
108	Korsør .... d.	0153	...	0353	0353	...	...	...	0607	...	0637	|	0707	0737	|	0807	0837	|	0907	...	0937	|	1007	1037
132	Nyborg .... d.	0207	...	0408	0408	...	0515	...	0620	...	0650	|	0720	0750	|	0820	0850	|	0920	...	0950	|	1020	1050
160	**Odense** .... a.	0227	...	0425	0425	...	0531	...	0636	...	0704	0708**k**	0736	0804	0808**k**	0836	0904	0908**k**	0936	...	1004	1008**k**	1036	1104
160	**Odense** .... d.	0229	...	0427	0427	...	0533	0604	0638	0638	0713	0710	0738	0813	0810	0838	0913	0910	0938	...	1013	1010	1038	1113
210	Middelfart .... d.	0252	...	0450	0450	...	0556	|	0701	0701	0736	|	0801	0836	|	0901	0936	|	1001	...	1036	|	1101	1136
220	**Fredericia** .... a.	0304	...	0459	0506	...	0603	0633	0708	0708	...	0738	0808	...	0838	0908	...	0938	1008	...	...	1038	1108	...
220	**Fredericia** .... 705 715 d.	0306	...	0501	...	0514	0614	0641	0714	0714	...	0741	0814	...	0841	0914	...	0941	1014	1021	...	1041	1114	...
246	Vejle .... 705 715 d.	0322	...	0517	...	0529	0629	0657	0729	0729	...	0757	0829	...	0857	0929	...	0957	1029	1036	...	1057	1129	...
277	Horsens .... 705 d.	0339	...	0534	...	0545	0645	0714	0745	0745	...	0814	0845	...	0914	0945	...	1014	1045	1055	...	1114	1145	...
306	Skanderborg . 705 713 d.	0355	...	0550	...	0601	0701	0730	0801	0801	...	0830	0901	...	0930	1001	...	1030	1101	1111	...	1130	1201	...
329	**Aarhus** .... 705 713 a.	0414	...	0603	...	0613	0713	0743	0813	0813	...	0843	0913	...	0943	1013	...	1043	1113	1125	...	1143	1213	...

	IC 137	IC 841	Lyn 45	IC 141	IC 845	Lyn 47	IC 145	IC 386 H	IC 849	Lyn 49	IC 149	IC 853	Lyn 53	IC 153	IC 857	Lyn 57	IC 157	Lyn 259 Ⓐw	IC 861	Lyn 61	IC 161	IC 384 H	Lyn 263 Ⓐw	IC 865
København Lufthavn ✈ d.	0938	...	...	1038	...	1130	1138	...	...	...	1238	...	1330	1338	...	...	1438	1458	...	1530	1538	...	1558	...
København H ... § 720 d.	1000	1030	1052	1100	1130	1152	1200	...	1230	1252	1300	1330	1352	1400	1430	1452	1500	1521	1530	1552	1600	...	1621	1630
Høje Taastrup .... § 720 d.	1015	1045	1105	1115	1145	1205	1215	...	1245	1305	1315	1345	1405	1415	1445	1505	1515	1534	1545	1605	1615	...	1634	1645
Roskilde .... § 720 d.	1023	1053	|	1123	1153	|	1223	...	1253	|	1323	1353	|	1423	1453	|	1523	|	1553	|	1623	...	|	1653
Ringsted .... 720 d.	1039	1109	|	1139	1209	|	1239	...	1309	|	1339	1409	|	1439	1509	|	1539	|	1609	|	1639	...	|	1709
Slagelse .... d.	1057	1127	|	1157	1227	|	1257	...	1327	|	1357	1427	|	1457	1527	|	1557	1614	1627	|	1657	...	1714	1727
Korsør .... d.	1107	1137	|	1207	1237	|	1307	...	1337	|	1407	1437	|	1507	1537	|	1607	|	1637	|	1707	...	|	1737
Nyborg .... d.	1120	1150	|	1220	1250	|	1320	...	1350	|	1420	1450	|	1520	1550	|	1620	1636	1650	|	1720	...	1736	1750
Odense .... a.	1136	1204	1208**k**	1236	1304	1308**k**	1336	...	1404	1408**k**	1436	1504	1508**k**	1536	1604	1608**k**	1636	1650	1704	1708**k**	1736	...	1750	1804
Odense .... d.	1138	1213	1210	1238	1313	1310	1338	...	1413	1410	1438	1513	1510	1538	1613	1610	1638	1700	1713	1710	1738	...	...	1813
Middelfart .... d.	1201	1236	|	1301	1336	|	1401	...	1436	|	1501	1536	|	1601	1636	|	1701	1727	1736	|	1801	...	...	1836
Fredericia .... a.	1208	...	1238	1308	...	1338	1408	...	...	1438	1508	...	1538	1608	...	1638	1708	1734	...	1738	1808	...	...	...
Fredericia ..... 705 715 d.	1214	...	1241	1314	...	1341	1414	1418	...	1441	1514	...	1541	1614	...	1641	1714	1736	...	1741	1814	1818	...	...
Vejle .... 705 715 d.	1229	...	1257	1329	...	1357	1429	1434	...	1457	1529	...	1557	1629	...	1657	1729	|	...	1757	1829	1834	...	...
Horsens .... 705 d.	1245	...	1314	1345	...	1414	1445	1451	...	1514	1545	...	1614	1645	...	1714	1745	|	...	1814	1845	1851	...	...
Skanderborg .. 705 713 d.	1301	...	1330	1401	...	1430	1501	1506	...	1530	1601	...	1630	1701	...	1730	1801	|	...	1830	1901	1906	...	...
Aarhus .... 705 713 a.	1313	...	1343	1413	...	1443	1513	1519	...	1543	1613	...	1643	1713	...	1743	1813	1830	...	1843	1913	1918	...	...

	IC 165	Lyn 267 Ⓐw	IC 869	Lyn 69	IC 169	IC 873	Lyn 73	IC 173	IC 877	Lyn 77	IC 177	IC 5727 zN	IC 382 SH		IC 881	Lyn 81	IC 181 ⑤⑥t	IC 1681 A	IC 885	IC 185 ⑤⑥t	IC 1685 A		IC 430 BJ	IC 189 E
København Lufthavn ✈ d.	1638	...	...	1730	1738	...	...	1838	...	1930	1938	...	...	...	...	...	2038	2038	...	2138	2138	...	2238	2238
København H ... § 720 d.	1700	1721	1730	1752	1800	1830	1852	1900	1930	1952	2000	...	...	...	2030	2052	2100	2100	2130	2200	2200	...	2300	2300
Høje Taastrup .... § 720 d.	1715	1734	1745	1805	1815	1845	1905	1915	1945	2005	2015	...	...	...	2045	2105	2115	2115	2145	2215	2215	...	2315	2315
Roskilde .... § 720 d.	1723	|	1753	|	1823	1853	|	1923	1953	|	2023	...	...	...	2053	|	2123	2123	2153	2223	2223	...	2323	2323
Ringsted .... 720 d.	1739	|	1809	|	1839	1909	|	1939	2009	|	2039	...	...	...	2109	|	2139	2139	2209	2239	2247	...	2347	2347
Slagelse .... d.	1757	1814	1827	|	1857	1927	|	1957	2027	|	2057	...	...	...	2127	|	2157	2157	2227	2257	2309	...	0009	0009
Korsør .... d.	1807	|	1837	|	1907	1937	|	2007	2037	|	2107	...	...	...	2137	|	2207	2207	2237	2307	2318	...	0018	0018
Nyborg .... d.	1820	1836	1850	|	1920	1950	|	2020	2050	|	2120	...	...	...	2150	|	2220	2220	2250	2320	2333	...	0033	0033
Odense .... a.	1836	1850	1904	1908**k**	1936	2004	2008**k**	2036	2104	2108**k**	2136	...	...	...	2204	2208**k**	2236	2236	2310	2336	2355	...	0055	0055
Odense .... d.	1838	...	1913	1910	1938	2013	2010	2038	2113	2110	2138	...	...	...	...	2210	2238	2238	...	2338	...	...	0057	0057
Middelfart .... d.	1901	...	1936	|	2001	2036	|	2101	2136	|	2201	...	...	...	...	|	2301	2301	...	0001	...	...	0120	0120
Fredericia .... a.	1908	...	...	1938	2008	...	2038	2108	...	2138	2208	...	...	...	...	2240	2308	2314	...	0008	...	...	0128	0128
Fredericia ..... 705 715 d.	1914	...	...	1941	2014	...	2041	2114	...	2141	2214	2218	2218	...	...	...	2318	2318	...	...	...	...	...	0132
Vejle .... 705 715 d.	1929	...	...	1957	2029	...	2057	2129	...	2157	2229	2234	2234	...	...	...	2333	2337	...	...	...	...	...	0147
Horsens .... 705 d.	1945	...	...	2014	2045	...	2114	2145	...	2214	2245	2253	2253	...	...	...	2349	2357	...	...	...	...	...	0204
Skanderborg .. 705 713 d.	2001	...	...	2030	2101	...	2130	2201	...	2230	2301	2308	2308	...	...	...	0005	0012	...	...	...	...	...	0219
Aarhus .... 705 713 a.	2013	...	...	2043	2113	...	2143	2213	...	2248	2318	2325	2325	...	...	...	0017	0030	...	...	...	...	...	0238

	IC 190		1600 Ⓐ	IC 1602 Ⓒ	IC 1131 GJ	IC 431 MJ	IC 1604 ⒶL	IC 104	Lyn 6 Ⓐ	IC 808 Ⓐ	Lyn 206 Ⓐw	IC 108	Lyn 10 Ⓐ	IC 812 Ⓐ	Lyn 210 Ⓐw	IC 5722 ⒶN	IC 112 Ⓐ	IC 112	Lyn 14	IC 816	IC 116	Lyn 18	IC 820	IC 5720 ⒸN
Aarhus .... 705 713 d.	0047	...	...	0242	...	...	...	...	0409	...	...	...	0512	...	0519	0526	0542	...	0614	...	0642	0714	...	0735
Skanderborg .. 705 713 d.	0101	...	...	0255	...	...	...	...	0423	...	...	...	0526	...	0533	0542	0556	...	0628	...	0656	0728	...	0749
Horsens .... 705 d.	0117	...	...	0310	...	...	...	...	0438	...	...	...	0541	...	0548	0558	0611	...	0643	...	0711	0743	...	0805
Vejle .... 705 715 d.	0137	...	...	0328	...	...	...	...	0500	...	...	...	0600	...	0607	0616	0628	...	0700	...	0728	0800	...	0822
Fredericia ..... 705 715 a.	0154	...	...	0343	...	...	...	...	0516	...	...	...	0616	...	0623	0631	0643	...	0716	...	0743	0816	...	0836
Fredericia .... d.	0158	...	...	0348	0348	0356	...	...	0521	...	...	0548	0621	...	0625	...	0648	...	0721	...	0748	0821	...	...
Middelfart .... d.	0206	...	...	0356	0356	|	...	...	|	0520	...	0556	|	0620	0632	...	0656	...	|	0720	0756	|	0820	...
Odense .... a.	0235	...	...	0419	0419	0436	...	...	0549	0545**k**	...	0619	0649	0645**k**	0659	...	0719	...	0749	0745**k**	0819	0849	0845**k**	...
Odense .... d.	0237	...	0345	0421	0421	0445	0445	0521	0551	0554	0611	0621	0651	0654	0711	...	0721	0721	0751	0754	0821	0851	0854	...
Nyborg .... d.	0254	...	0402	0438	0438	0459	0459	0538	|	0608	0626	0638	|	0708	0726	...	0738	0738	|	0808	0838	|	0908	...
Korsør .... d.	0308	...	0416	0451	0451	0513	0513	0551	|	0621	|	0651	|	0721	|	...	0751	0751	|	0821	0851	|	0921	...
Slagelse .... d.	0318	...	0427	0501	0501	0522	0522	0601	|	0631	0646	0701	|	0731	0746	...	0801	0801	|	0831	0901	|	0931	...
Ringsted .... 720 a.	0335	...	0449	0518	0518	0540	0540	0618	|	0647	|	0718	|	0747	|	...	0818	0818	|	0847	0918	|	0947	...
Roskilde .... § 720 a.	0353	...	0512	0535	0535	0604	0604	0635	|	0705	|	0735	|	0805	|	...	0835	0835	|	0905	0935	|	1005	...
Høje Taastrup .... § 720 a.	0402	...	0527	0545	0545	0613	0613	0644	0653	0714	0724	0744	0753	0814	0824	...	0844	0844	0853	0914	0944	0953	1014	...
København H ... § 720 a.	0423	...	0544	0601	0601	0629	0629	0701	0708	0731	0739	0801	0808	0831	0839	...	0901	0901	0908	0931	1001	1008	1031	...
København Lufthavn ✈ a.	0442	...	...	0624	0624	...	...	...	0733	...	0804	0825	...	...	0904	...	0925	0925	0933	...	1025	...	...	...

A – ①②③④⑦ (not Apr. 17, 18, 21, May 16, 29, 30, June 9).
B – Mar. 30 - Sept. 16. Train number **1130** on ⑥.
D – To Mar. 29 and from Sept. 17.
E – Mar. 31 - Sept. 17.
G – Ⓒ Mar. 31 - Sept. 15.
H – [12] and 🍸 Hamburg - Aarhus (Table **710**).

J – [12] København - Hamburg and v.v. Ⓡ for international journeys.
L – To Mar. 29 and from Sept. 18.
M – Ⓐ Apr. 1 - Sept. 17.
N – From / to Flensburg (Table **710**).
S – June 22 - Aug. 18.

k – Connects with train in previous column.
t – Also Apr. 17, 18, 21, May 16, 29, 30, June 9.
w – Not Apr. 15, 16, 17, May 31, July 1 - Aug. 9.
z – Not June 22 - Aug. 18.

§ – *IC* and *Lyn* trains are not available for local journeys. Frequent local trains run between Roskilde and Københa

ubject to alteration until August 4

AARHUS - FREDERICIA - ODENSE - KØBENHAVN 700

Most services from Aarhus start from Aalborg (Table **701**). Services Middelfart - København start from Esbjerg (Table **705**). For other through cars see Tables **710**, **712** and **715**.

	Lyn 22	*IC* 824	*IC* 124	*Lyn* 26	*IC* 828	*IC* 383 ⒶH	*IC* 1183 ©H	*IC* 128	*Lyn* 40	*IC* 832	*IC* 132	*Lyn* 42	*IC* 836	*IC* 136	*Lyn* 44	*IC* 840	*IC* 140	*Lyn* 46	*IC* 844	*IC* 385 ⒶH	*IC* 1185 ©H	*IC* 144	*Lyn* 48	*IC* 848	*IC* 148
rhus .... **705 713** d.	0814	...	0842	0914	...	0926	0933	0942	1014	...	1042	1114	...	1142	1214	...	1242	1314	...	1326	1332	1342	1414	...	1442
anderborg .. **705 713** d.	0828	...	0856	0928	...	0942	0949	0956	1028	...	1056	1128	...	1156	1228	...	1256	1328	...	1342	1349	1356	1428	...	1456
rsens .... **705** d.	0843	...	0911	0943	...	0958	1005	1011	1043	...	1111	1143	...	1211	1243	...	1311	1343	...	1358	1405	1411	1443	...	1511
jle .... **705 715** d.	0900	...	0928	1000	...	1016	1022	1028	1100	...	1128	1200	...	1228	1300	...	1328	1400	...	1416	1422	1428	1500	...	1528
edericia ..... **705 715** a.	0916	...	0943	1016	...	1031	1038	1043	1116	...	1143	1216	...	1243	1316	...	1343	1416	...	1431	1438	1443	1516	...	1543
edericia .... d.	0921	...	0948	1021	...	...	...	1048	1121	...	1148	1221	...	1248	1321	...	1348	1421	...	...	...	1448	1521	...	1548
ddelfart .... d.	|	0920	0956	|	1020	...	...	1056	|	1120	1156	|	1220	1256	|	1320	1356	|	1420	...	...	1456	|	1520	1556
lense .... a.	0949	0945**k**	1019	1049	1045**k**	...	...	1119	1149	1145**k**	1219	1249	1245**k**	1319	1349	1345**k**	1419	1449	1445**k**	...	...	1519	1549	1545**k**	1619
lense .... d.	0951	0954	1021	1051	1054	...	...	1121	1151	1154	1221	1251	1254	1321	1351	1354	1421	1451	1454	...	...	1521	1551	1554	1621
borg .... d.	|	1008	1038	|	1108	...	...	1138	|	1208	1238	|	1308	1338	|	1408	1438	|	1508	...	...	1538	|	1608	1638
rsør .... d.	|	1021	1051	|	1121	...	...	1151	|	1221	1251	|	1321	1351	|	1421	1451	|	1521	...	...	1551	|	1621	1651
igelse .... d.	|	1031	1101	|	1131	...	...	1201	|	1231	1301	|	1331	1401	|	1431	1501	|	1531	...	...	1601	|	1631	1701
igsted .... **720** a.	|	1047	1118	|	1147	...	...	1218	|	1247	1318	|	1347	1418	|	1447	1518	|	1547	...	...	1618	|	1647	1718
skilde .... § **720** a.	|	1105	1135	|	1205	...	...	1235	|	1305	1335	|	1405	1435	|	1505	1535	|	1605	...	...	1635	|	1705	1735
je Taastrup .... § **720** a.	1053	1114	1144	1153	1214	...	...	1244	1253	1314	1344	1353	1414	1444	1453	1514	1544	1553	1614	...	...	1644	1653	1714	1744
benhavn H ... § **720** a.	1108	1131	1201	1208	1231	...	...	1301	1308	1331	1401	1408	1431	1501	1508	1531	1601	1608	1631	...	...	1701	1708	1731	1801
benhavn Lufthavn ✈ a.	1133	...	1225	...	...	...	...	1325	1333	...	1425	...	...	1525	1533	...	1625	...	...	...	...	1725	1733	...	1825

	Lyn 50	*IC* 852	*IC* 152	*Lyn* 54	*IC* 856	*IC* 156	*Lyn* 58	*IC* 860	*IC* 387 PH	*IC* 5760 ⒶrN	*IC* 1187 ©F	*IC* 160	*Lyn* 62	*IC* 864	*IC* 164	*Lyn* 66	*IC* 868	*IC* 1668 ◧	*Lyn* 70	*IC* 172 ⑤⑥t	*IC* 1672 A	*IC* 176 ⑤⑥t	*IC* 1676 A	*IC* 1680	*IC* 1680 ⑤⑥v
rhus .... **705 713** d.	1514	...	1542	1614	...	1642	1714	...	1726	1726	1732	1742	1814	...	1842	1914	...	1942	2014	2042	2042	2142	2142	2247	2247
anderborg .. **705 713** d.	1528	...	1556	1628	...	1656	1728	...	1742	1742	1749	1756	1828	...	1856	1928	...	1956	2028	2056	2056	2156	2156	2301	2301
rsens .... **705** d.	1543	...	1611	1643	...	1711	1743	...	1758	1758	1805	1811	1843	...	1911	1943	...	2011	2043	2111	2111	2211	2211	2317	2317
le .... **705 715** d.	1600	...	1628	1700	...	1728	1800	...	1816	1816	1822	1828	1900	...	1928	2000	...	2028	2100	2128	2128	2230	2230	2337	2337
edericia ..... **705 715** a.	1616	...	1643	1716	...	1743	1816	...	1831	1831	1838	1843	1916	...	1943	2016	...	2043	2116	2146	2146	2246	2246	2356	2356
edericia .... d.	1621	...	1648	1721	...	1748	1821	...	...	...	...	1848	1921	...	1948	2021	...	2048	2121	2151	2151	2251	2251	2358	2358
ddelfart .... d.	|	1620	1656	|	1720	1756	|	1820	...	...	...	1856	|	1920	1956	|	2020	2056	|	2158	2158	2258	2258	0006	0006
lense .... a.	1649	1645**k**	1719	1749	1745**k**	1819	1849	1845**k**	...	...	...	1919	1949	1945**k**	2019	2049	2045**k**	2119	2149	2220	2220	2320	2326	0035	0035
lense .... d.	1651	1654	1721	1751	1754	1821	1851	1854	...	...	...	1921	1951	1954	2021	2051	2054	2121	2151	2222	2222	2322	2328	...	0037
borg .... d.	|	1708	1738	|	1808	1838	|	1908	...	...	...	1938	|	2008	2038	|	2108	2138	|	2239	2239	2339	2345	...	0054
rsør .... d.	|	1721	1751	|	1821	1851	|	1921	...	...	...	1951	|	2021	2051	|	2121	2151	|	2252	2252	2352	2358	...	0108
igelse .... d.	|	1731	1801	|	1831	1901	|	1931	...	...	...	2001	|	2031	2101	|	2131	2201	|	2301	2301	0001	0007	...	0118
igsted .... **720** a.	|	1747	1818	|	1847	1918	|	1947	...	...	...	2018	|	2047	2118	|	2147	2220**z**	|	2318	2320	0018	0026	...	0135
skilde .... § **720** a.	|	1805	1835	|	1905	1935	|	2005	...	...	...	2035	|	2105	2135	|	2205	2240**z**	|	2335	2346	0035	0052	...	0153
je Taastrup .... § **720** a.	1753	1814	1844	1853	1914	1944	1953	2014	...	...	...	2044	2053	2114	2144	2153	2214	2249**z**	2253	2344	2355	0044	0100	...	0202
benhavn H ... § **720** a.	1808	1831	1901	1908	1931	2001	2008	2031	...	...	...	2101	2108	2131	2201	2208	2231	2309**z**	2313	0001	0015	0101	0124	...	0223
benhavn Lufthavn ✈ a.	...	...	1925	1933	...	2025	...	...	...	...	...	2125	2133	...	2225	2233	...	2325**t**	2339	0024	0037	0128	0144	...	0242

- ①②③④⑦ (not Apr. 17, 18, 21, May 16, 29, 30, June 9).
To Flensburg (also Hamburg June 22 - Aug. 18). See Table **710**.
- 12 and 🍷 Aarhus - Hamburg (Table **710**).
- To Flensburg (Table **710**).
- Ⓐ June 24 - Aug. 16.

k – Connects with train in previous column.
r – Not June 24 - Aug. 16.
t – ⑤⑥ (also Apr. 17, 18, 21, May 16, 29, 30, June 9).
v – Also Apr. 17, May 16, 29; not Apr. 19, May 17.
z – 2–8 minutes earlier on ⑤⑥.

◧ – Train number **168** on ⑤⑥**t**.
§ – *IC* and *Lyn* trains are not available for local journeys. Frequent local trains run between Roskilde and København.

ubject to alteration until August 11

AARHUS - AALBORG 701

m		*IC* 195 ©		*IC* 1601 ©	Ⓐ		Ⓐ	Ⓐ	*IC* 1609 ©	*IC* 111 Ⓐ	Ⓐ	*IC* 113 Ⓐ	*IC* 113	*Lyn* 17 Ⓐ	*IC* 117	*Lyn* 21 Ⓐ	*Lyn* 21	*IC* 121	*Lyn* 25	*IC* 125	*Lyn* 29	*IC* 129	*Lyn* 41	*IC* 133	*Lyn* 43
	København H **700** ... d.	...	...	0036	...	...	...	...	0236	...	...	...	...	...	0500**a**	0552	...	0600	0652	0700	0752	0800	0852	0900	0952
	Odense **700** .... d.	...	...	0229	...	...	...	...	0427	...	...	0533	...	0604	0638	0710	...	0738	0810	0838	0910	0938	1010	1038	1110
	Fredericia **700** .... d.	...	...	0306	...	...	...	...	0501	0514	...	0614	...	0641	0714	0741	...	0814	0841	0914	0941	1014	1041	1114	1141
0	**Aarhus** .... **712** d.	0246	...	0422	0422	...	0520	0548	0610	0621	0649	0721	0721	0750	0821	0850	0850	0921	0950	1021	1050	1121	1150	1221	1250
46	Langå .... **712** d.	0311	...	0448	0448	...	0547	|	0637	0647	|	0747	0747	|	0847	|	|	0947	|	1047	|	1147	|	1247	|
59	Randers .... d.	0321	...	0458	0458	...	0556	0620	0647	0657	0720	0757	0757	0822	0857	0922	0922	0957	1022	1057	1122	1157	1222	1257	1322
91	Hobro .... d.	0336	...	0514	0514	...	0612	0636	0704	0712	0736	0812	0812	0838	0912	0938	0938	1012	1038	1112	1138	1212	1238	1312	1338
40	**Aalborg** .... a.	0415	...	0554	0554	...	0651	0708	0745	0751	0808	0851	0851	0907	0951	1007	1007	1051	1107	1151	1207	1251	1307	1351	1407

	IC 137	*Lyn* 45	*IC* 141	*Lyn* 47	*IC* 145	*Lyn* 49	*IC* 149	*Lyn* 53	*IC* 153	*Lyn* 57	*IC* 157	*Lyn* 61	*IC* 161	*Lyn* 65	*IC* 165	*Lyn* 69	*IC* 169		*IC* 173		*IC* 177				
øbenhavn H **700** .... d.	1000	1052	1100	1152	1200	1252	1300	1352	1400	1452	1500	1552	1600	1652	1700	1752	1800	...	1900	...	2000	...	...	...	...
dense **700** .... d.	1138	1210	1238	1310	1338	1410	1438	1510	1538	1610	1638	1710	1738	1810	1838	1910	1938	...	2038	...	2138	...	...	...	...
redericia **700** .... d.	1214	1241	1314	1341	1414	1441	1514	1541	1614	1641	1714	1741	1814	1841	1914	1941	2014	...	2114	...	2214	...	...	...	...
hus .... **712** d.	1321	1350	1421	1450	1521	1550	1621	1650	1721	1750	1821	1850	1921	1950	2021	2050	2121	...	2221	...	2337	...	...	...	...
gå .... **712** d.	1347	|	1447	|	1547	|	1647	|	1747	|	1847	|	1947	|	2047	|	2147	...	2247	...	0003	...	...	...	...
nders .... d.	1357	1422	1457	1522	1557	1622	1657	1722	1757	1822	1857	1922	1957	2022	2057	2122	2157	...	2257	...	0013	...	...	...	...
oro .... d.	1412	1438	1512	1538	1612	1638	1712	1738	1812	1838	1912	1938	2012	2038	2112	2148	2212	...	2312	...	0029	...	...	...	...
borg .... a.	1451	1507	1551	1607	1651	1707	1751	1807	1851	1907	1951	2007	2051	2107	2151	2207	2258	...	2358	...	0112	...	...	...	...

	IC 192		*IC* 102 ©		*Lyn* 14 Ⓐ	*IC* 116 Ⓐ	*Lyn* 18 Ⓐ	*IC* 120	*Lyn* 22	*IC* 124	*Lyn* 26	*IC* 128	*Lyn* 40	*IC* 132	*Lyn* 42	*IC* 136	*Lyn* 44	*IC* 140	*Lyn* 46	*IC* 144	*Lyn* 48	*IC* 148	*Lyn* 50	*IC* 152	*Lyn* 54
borg .... d.	0014	...	0205	...	0444	0501	0547	0603	0647	0703	0747	0803	0847	0903	0947	1003	1047	1103	1147	1203	1247	1303	1347	1403	1447
ro .... d.	0053	...	0244	...	0515	0541	0617	0642	0717	0742	0817	0842	0917	0942	1017	1042	1117	1142	1217	1242	1317	1342	1417	1442	1517
ders .... d.	0109	...	0300	...	0532	0558	0633	0658	0733	0758	0833	0858	0933	0958	1033	1058	1133	1158	1233	1258	1333	1358	1433	1458	1533
gå .... **712** d.	0118	...	0309	...	|	0607	|	0707	|	0807	|	0907	|	1007	|	1107	|	1207	|	1307	|	1407	|	1507	|
hus .... **712** a.	0152	...	0336	...	0606	0635	0706	0735	0806	0835	0906	0935	1006	1035	1106	1135	1206	1235	1306	1335	1406	1435	1506	1535	1606
redericia **700** .... a.	...	...	...	...	0716	0743	0816	0843	0916	0943	1016	1043	1116	1143	1216	1243	1316	1343	1416	1443	1516	1543	1616	1643	1716
dense **700** .... a.	...	...	...	...	0749	0819	0849	0919	0949	1019	1049	1119	1149	1219	1249	1319	1349	1419	1449	1519	1549	1619	1649	1719	1749
øbenhavn H **700** .... a.	...	...	...	...	0908	1001	1008	1101	1108	1201	1208	1301	1308	1401	1408	1501	1508	1601	1608	1701	1708	1801	1808	1901	1908

	IC 156	*Lyn* 58	*IC* 160	*Lyn* 62	*IC* 164	*Lyn* 66	*IC* 168 ⑤⑥t	*IC* 1668 A	*Lyn* 70	*IC* 172 ⑤⑥t	*IC* 1672 A	*Lyn* 74	*IC* 176 ⑤⑥t	*IC* 1676 A		*IC* 1680	*IC* 1680 ⑤⑥v		*IC* 184		*IC* 188				
borg .... d.	1503	1547	1603	1647	1703	1747	1803	1803	1847	1903	1903	1947	2003	2003	...	2103	2103	...	2203	...	2303	...	...	...	...
ro .... d.	1542	1617	1642	1717	1742	1817	1842	1842	1917	1942	1942	2017	2042	2042	...	2142	2142	...	2242	...	2342	...	...	...	...
ders .... d.	1558	1633	1658	1733	1758	1833	1858	1858	1933	1958	1958	2033	2058	2058	...	2158	2158	...	2258	...	2358	...	...	...	...
gå .... **712** d.	1607	|	1707	|	1807	|	1907	1907	|	2007	2007	|	2107	2107	...	2207	2207	...	2307	...	0007	...	...	...	...
hus .... **712** a.	1635	1706	1735	1806	1835	1906	1935	1935	2006	2035	2035	2106	2135	2135	...	2238	2238	...	2343	...	0041	...	...	...	...
redericia **700** .... a.	1743	1816	1843	1916	1943	2016	2043	2043	2116	2146	2146	...	2246	2246	...	2356	2356	...	...	...	...	...	...	...	...
dense **700** .... a.	1819	1849	1919	1949	2019	2049	2119	2119	2149	2220	2220	...	2320	2326	...	0035	0035	...	...	...	...	...	...	...	...
øbenhavn H **700** .... a.	2001	2008	2101	2108	2201	2208	2301	2309	2313	0001	0015	...	0101	0124	...	...	0223	...	...	...	...	...	...	...	...

①②③④⑦ (not Apr. 17, 18, 21, May 16, 29, 30, June 9). **a** – Ⓐ only. **t** – Also Apr. 17, 18, 21, May 16, 29, 30, June 9. **v** – Also Apr. 17, May 16, 29; not Apr. 19, May 17.

rdjyske Jernbaner A/S

AALBORG - FREDERIKSHAVN 702

n			Ⓐ							
0	**Aalborg** .... d.	0420	0512	0612	and	2212	2312	...	...	...
8	Hjørring .... d.	0459	0558	0658	hourly	2258	2358	...	...	...
5	**Frederikshavn** .... a.	0525	0624	0724	until	2324	0024	...	...	...

	Ⓐ								
Frederikshavn .... d.	0450	0532	0632	and	2232	2332	...	...	...
Hjørring .... d.	0537**r**	0606	0706	hourly	2306	0006	...	...	...
Aalborg .... a.	0613	0643	0743	until	2343	0043	...	...	...

Arrives 0516.

703 HELSINGØR - KØBENHAVN - KØBENHAVN LUFTHAVN ✈ - MALMÖ

EASTBOUND

Services operate every 20 minutes (less frequent 0000 - 0400 hours) **Helsingør** - Østerport - København H - København Lufthavn ✈ - **Malmö C**.

Journey times:
Helsingør - København H: 46 minutes;
København H - København Lufthavn ✈: 12 minutes;
København Lufthavn ✈ - Malmö C: 27 minutes.

København H - København Lufthavn ✈ services operate every 10 minutes.

WESTBOUND

Services operate every 20 minutes (less frequent 0000 - 0400 hours) **Malmö C** - Københa[vn] Lufthavn ✈ - København H - Østerport - **Helsingør**.

Journey times:
Malmö C - København Lufthavn ✈: 21 minutes;
København Lufthavn ✈ - København H: 14 minutes;
København H - Helsingør: 45 minutes.

København Lufthavn ✈ - København H services operate every 10 minutes.

704 KØBENHAVN - KALUNDBORG

km																							
			©		Ⓐ	Ⓐ		Ⓐ		Ⓐ							⑤⑥v					Ⓐw	Ⓐw	Ⓐ
0	**København** H ...... ▷ d.	0026	0226	...	0452	0543	0626	0643	0726	0743	0826	0843	and at	2026	2043	2126	2143	2226	2326	...		1512	1612	17
20	Høje Taastrup .... ▷ d.	0042	0242	...	0508	0556	0642	0656	0742	0756	0842	0856	the same	2042	2056	2142	2156	2242	2342	...	A	1528	1628	172
31	**Roskilde** .... ▷ d.	0056	0256	...	0521	0606	0653	0706	0753	0806	0853	0906	minutes	2053	2106	2153	2206	2256	2356	...	L	1536	1636	173
67	Holbæk .... ▷ a.	0130	0327	...	0553	0628	0725	0728	0825	0828	0925	0928	past each	2125	2128	2225	2228	2329	0030	...	S	1558	1658	175
67	Holbæk ....d.	0131**c**	...	...	0554	0629	0729**c**	0729	0829**c**	0829	...	0929	hour until	...	2129	2229**r**	2229	2330	0031	...	O	1559	1659	175
111	**Kalundborg** ....a.	0212**c**	...	...	0643	0712	0812**c**	0812	0912**c**	0912	...	1012		...	2212	2312**r**	2312	0012	0112	...		1636	1736	183

	©		Ⓐ		Ⓐw	Ⓐ	©		Ⓐw	Ⓐ	©		Ⓐw	Ⓐ	©								⑤⑥v		
Kalundborg ....d.	...	...	...	0445	0519	0545	0545	...	0619	0644	0644	...	0719	0744	0744	...	0844	...	and at	2044	...	2144	2144**r**	224
Holbæk ....a.	...	...	...	0528	0553	0628	0628	...	0656	0728	0728	...	0756	0828	0828	...	0927	...	the same	2127	...	2227	2228**r**	232
Holbæk .... ▷ d.	0335	...	0503	0529	0559	0629	0635	0635	0659	0729	0735	0735	0759	0829	0835	0835	0928	0935	minutes	2128	2135	2228	2235	233
Roskilde .... ▷ d.	0407	...	0538	0604	0623	0651	0708	0708	0723	0751	0808	0808	0823	0851	0908	0908	0951	1008	past each	2151	2208	2251	2307	000
Høje Taastrup .... ▷ d.	0421	...	0549	0618	0634	0701	0719	0719	0734	0801	0819	0819	0834	0901	0919	0919	1001	1019	hour until	2201	2219	2301	2321	002
København H .... ▷ a.	0438	...	0605	0635	0648	0715	0735	0735	0748	0815	0835	0835	0848	0915	0935	0935	1015	1035		2215	2235	2319	2340	003

c – © only.
r – ①②③④⑦ (also Apr. 19, May 17; not Apr. 17, May 16, 29).
v – Also Apr. 17, May 16, 29; not Apr. 19, May 17.
w – Not Apr. 15, 16, 17, May 31, July 1 - Aug. 9.
▷ – Additional trains run København - Holbæk and v.v. on Ⓐ.

705 AARHUS - FREDERICIA - ESBJERG

km																										
						IC		*IC*		*IC*		*IC*		*IC*		*IC*		*IC*		*IC*		*IC*		*IC*		*IC*
				615		**821**		**825**		**829**		**833**		**837**		**841**		**845**		**849**		**853**		**857**		**86**
		Ⓐ2	2	Ⓐ	2	Ⓐ	2		2		2		2		2		2		2		2		2		2	
	Aarhus .... **700 713** d.	...	...	...	0554**a**	...	0654	...	0754	...	0854	...	0954	...	1054	...	1154	...	1254	...	1356	...	1454	...	1554	..
	Skanderborg **700 713** d.	...	...	...	0610**a**	...	0710	...	0810	...	0910	...	1010	...	1110	...	1210	...	1310	...	1412	...	1510	...	1610	..
	Horsens .... **700** d.	...	...	...	0625**a**	...	0725	...	0825	...	0925	...	1025	...	1125	...	1225	...	1325	...	1427	...	1525	...	1625	..
	Vejle .... **700 715** d.	...	...	...	0646**a**	...	0746	...	0846	...	0946	...	1046	...	1146	...	1246	...	1346	...	1446	...	1546	...	1646	..
	København H **700**.. d.	...	...	...	|	0530	|	0630‡	|	0730	|	0830	|	0930	|	1030	|	1130	|	1230	|	1330	|	1430	|	15
	Odense .... **700** d.	...	...	0607	|	0713	|	0813	|	0913	|	1013	|	1113	|	1213	|	1313	|	1413	|	1513	|	1613	|	17
0	Middelfart .... **700** d.	...	...	0631	|	0737	|	0837	|	0937	|	1037	|	1137	|	1237	|	1337	|	1437	|	1537	|	1637	|	17
	Fredericia 700 710/5 d.	0511	0614	|	0714	|	0814	|	0914	|	1014	|	1114	|	1214	|	1314	|	1414	|	1514	|	1614	|	1714	|
23	Kolding .... **710** d.	0525	0628	0646	0728	0751	0828	0851	0928	0951	1028	1051	1128	1151	1228	1251	1328	1351	1428	1451	1528	1551	1628	1651	1728	175
36	Lunderskov .... **710** d.	0533	0636	0654	0736	0759	0836	0859	0936	0959	1036	1059	1136	1159	1236	1259	1336	1359	1436	1459	1536	1559	1636	1659	1736	175
47	Vejen .... d.	0541	0644	0702	0744	0807	0844	0907	0944	1007	1044	1107	1144	1207	1244	1307	1344	1407	1444	1507	1544	1607	1644	1707	1744	18
75	Bramming .... **709** d.	0603	0705	0723	0805	0821	0905	0921	1005	1021	1105	1121	1205	1221	1305	1321	1405	1421	1505	1521	1605	1621	1705	1721	1805	18
91	**Esbjerg** .... **709** a.	0614	0717	0734	0817	0832	0917	0932	1017	1032	1117	1132	1217	1232	1317	1332	1417	1432	1517	1532	1617	1632	1717	1732	1817	18

		IC		*IC*		*IC*		*IC*		
		865		**869**		**873**		**877**	**677**	**681**
	2		2		2		2			
Aarhus .... **700 713** d.	1654	...	1754	...	1856	...	1954	...	...	...
Skanderborg . **700 713** d.	1710	...	1810	...	1912	...	2010	...	...	...
Horsens .... **700** d.	1725	...	1825	...	1927	...	2025	...	...	...
Vejle .... **700 715** d.	1746	...	1846	...	1946	...	2046	...	...	...
København H **700** .. d.	|	1630	|	1730	|	1830	|	1930	2000	2100
Odense .... **700** d.	|	1813	|	1913	|	2013	|	2113	2138	2238
Middelfart .... **700** d.	|	1837	|	1937	|	2037	|	2137	2201	2301
Fredericia . **700 710/5** d.	1814	|	1914	|	2014	|	2114	|	2214	2325
Kolding .... **710** d.	1828	1851	1928	1951	2028	2051	2128	2151	2227	2339
Lunderskov .... **710** d.	1836	1859	1936	1959	2036	2059	2136	2159	2236	2347
Vejen .... d.	1844	1907	1944	2007	2044	2107	2144	2207	2244	2354
Bramming .... **709** d.	1905	1921	2005	2021	2105	2121	2205	2221	2306	0016
Esbjerg .... **709** a.	1917	1932	2017	2032	2117	2132	2217	2232	2322	0032

	IC	*IC*		*IC*			*IC*		*IC*		*IC*
	808	**812**		**816**	**616**		**820**		**824**		**82**
	Ⓐ	Ⓐ	Ⓐ2		©	Ⓐ2		2		2	
Esbjerg .... **709** d.	...	0524	0538	0625**a**	0636	0637	0725	0736	0825	0837	09
Bramming .... **709** d.	...	0536	0549	0636**a**	0647	0649	0736	0749	0836	0849	09
Vejen .... d.	...	0550	0611	0650**a**	0708	0711	0750	0811	0850	0911	09
Lunderskov .... **710** d.	...	0558	0619	0658**a**	0716	0719	0758	0819	0858	0919	09
Kolding .... **710** d.	0506	0606	0628	0706	0725	0728	0806	0828	0906	0928	10
Fredericia ... **700 710 715** a.	|	|	0642	|	0739	0742	|	0842	|	0942	
Middelfart .... **700** a.	0519	0619	|	0719	0755	|	0819	|	0919	|	10
Odense .... **700** a.	0545	0645	|	0745	0819	|	0845	|	0945	|	10
København H **700** .... a.	0731	0831	|	0931	1001	|	1031	|	1131	|	12
Vejle .... **700 715** a.	...	...	0709	...	...	0809	...	0909	...	1009	..
Horsens .... **700** a.	...	...	0730	...	...	0830	...	0930	...	1030	..
Skanderborg .... **700 713** a.	...	...	0746	...	...	0846	...	0946	...	1046	..
Aarhus .... **700 713** a.	...	...	0804	...	...	0904	...	1004	...	1104	..

		IC		*IC*		*IC*		*IC*		*IC*		*IC*		*IC*		*IC*		*IC*		*IC*		*IC*				
		832		**836**		**840**		**844**		**848**		**852**		**856**		**860**		**864**		**868**		**872**	**672**	**676**		
	2		2		2		2		2		2		2		2		2		2		2	◇		△	♣2	2
Esbjerg .... **709** d.	0938	1025	1038	1125	1138	1225	1238	1325	1338	1425	1438	1525	1538	1625	1638	1725	1738	1825	1838	1925	1938	2025**k**	2038	2138	2238	23
Bramming .... **709** d.	0949	1036	1049	1136	1149	1236	1249	1336	1349	1436	1449	1536	1549	1636	1649	1736	1749	1836	1849	1936	1949	2036	2049	2149	2249	23
Vejen .... d.	1011	1050	1111	1150	1211	1250	1311	1350	1411	1450	1511	1550	1611	1650	1711	1750	1811	1850	1911	1950	2011	2050	2111	2211	2311	00
Lunderskov .... **710** d.	1019	1058	1119	1158	1219	1258	1319	1358	1419	1458	1519	1558	1619	1658	1719	1758	1819	1858	1919	1958	2019	2058	2119	2219	2319	00
Kolding .... **710** d.	1028	1106	1128	1206	1228	1306	1328	1406	1428	1506	1528	1606	1628	1706	1728	1806	1828	1906	1928	2006	2028	2107	2128	2228	2328	00
Fredericia . **700 710/5** a.	1042	|	1142	|	1242	|	1342	|	1442	|	1542	|	1642	|	1742	|	1842	|	1942	|	2042	|	2142	2242	2342	00
Middelfart .... **700** a.	|	1119	|	1219	|	1319	|	1419	|	1519	|	1619	|	1719	|	1819	|	1919	|	2019	|	2121	2157	2257	...	.
Odense .... **700** a.	|	1145	|	1245	|	1345	|	1445	|	1545	|	1645	|	1745	|	1845	|	1945	|	2045	|	2145	2220	2326	...	.
København H **700** .. a.	|	1331	|	1431	|	1531	|	1631	|	1731	|	1831	|	1931	|	2031	|	2131	|	2231	|	...	0015**r**	0124	...	.
Vejle .... **700 715** a.	1109	...	1209	...	1309	...	1409	...	1509	...	1609	...	1709	...	1809	...	1909	...	2009	...	2109	...	...	...	...	.
Horsens .... **700** a.	1130	...	1230	...	1330	...	1430	...	1530	...	1630	...	1730	...	1830	...	1930	...	2030	...	2130	...	...	...	...	.
Skanderborg . **700 713** a.	1146	...	1246	...	1346	...	1446	...	1546	...	1646	...	1746	...	1846	...	1946	...	2046	...	2146	...	...	...	...	.
Aarhus .... **700 713** a.	1204	...	1304	...	1404	...	1504	...	1604	...	1704	...	1804	...	1904	...	2004	...	2104	...	2204	...	...	...	...	.

a – Ⓐ only.
k – 2022 on ©.
r – 0001 on the mornings of ⑥⑦ (also Apr. 18, 19, 22, May 17, 30, 31, June 10).
♣ – On Ⓐ Esbjerg d. 2243, Bramming d. 2254, Vejen d. 2315, Lunderskov d. 2323, Kolding d. 2335, Fredericia a. 23
△ – On ⑤⑥ (also Apr. 17, 18, 21, May 16, 29, 30, June 9) arrives Odense 2320, København 0101.
◇ – Train number **870** on ©.
‡ – On © departs 0652 (train number **25** København - Odense).

707 ESBJERG - SKJERN

Operator: *AT*; 2nd class or

km																												
			Ⓐ	Ⓐ	Ⓐ	Ⓐ	Ⓐ	Ⓐ		Ⓐ	Ⓐ	Ⓐ	Ⓐ	Ⓐ	Ⓐ	Ⓐ			⑥	⑥	†	©	©		©	(
0	**Esbjerg** ...... ▷ d.	Ⓐ	0458	0548	0647	0805	0830	0929	and	1529	1636	1736	1936	2136	2236	2336	...	©	0452	0543	0644	0752	0952	and every	2152	22
17	Varde .... ▷ d.		0516	0611	0707	0824	0856	0956	hourly	1556	1700	1800	2000	2200	2254	2354	...		0511	0602	0703	0813	1013	**two** hours	2213	23
60	**Skjern** .... a.		0553	0651	0748	0901	0935	1035	until	1635	1739	1839	2037	2237	...	...	...		0543	0640	0739	0849	1049	until	2249	.

		Ⓐ	Ⓐ	Ⓐ	Ⓐ	Ⓐ		Ⓐ	Ⓐ	Ⓐ	Ⓐ	Ⓐ	Ⓐ	Ⓐ	Ⓐ	Ⓐ			⑥	⑥	†	©	©		©	(
Skjern .... d.	Ⓐ	0503	0603	0700	0810	0948	and	1448	1548	1652	1752	1852	...	2052	...	2252	...	©	0612	0717	0801	0917	1117	and every	2117	23
Varde .... ▷ d.		0551	0650	0739	0853	1028	hourly	1528	1633	1733	1833	1933	2033	2133	2233	2333	...		0653	0755	0855	0955	1155	**two** hours	2155	23
Esbjerg ...... ▷ a.		0609	0708	0800	0914	1049	until	1549	1654	1754	1854	1954	2054	2154	2254	2354	...		0711	0813	0913	1013	1213	until	2213	00

▷ – Additional services operate Esbjerg - Varde and v.v.

SKJERN - STRUER 708

Operator: *AT* 2nd class only

km			Ⓐ	Ⓐ	Ⓐ	Ⓐ	Ⓐ	Ⓐ	Ⓐ		Ⓐ	Ⓐ	Ⓐ	Ⓐ	Ⓐ	
0	**Skjern** d.	Ⓐ	0502	0616	0713	0802	0902	0944	1046	and hourly until	1546	1646	1851	2056	2256	...
3	Ringkøbing a.		0520	0638	0731	0820	0920	1002	1104		1604	1704	1909	2114	2314	...
3	Ringkøbing d.		0523	0640	0734	0827	0921	1003	1105		1605	1705	1910	2115	2315	...
1	Holstebro a.		0603	0722	0814	0910	0959	1044	1144		1644	1744	1948	2156	2356	...
1	Holstebro 715 d.		0604	0723	0824	0919	1002	1045	1145		1645	1749	1950	2157	2357	...
6	**Struer** 715 a.		0619	0736	0837	0932	1019	1058	1158		1658	1802	2003	2210	0010	...

		⑥	⑥	†	Ⓒ	Ⓒ		Ⓒ	Ⓒ
Skjern d.	Ⓒ	0549	0653	0740	0853	1053	and every two hours until	2053	2253
Ringkøbing a.		0610	0711	0801	0911	1111		2111	2311
Ringkøbing d.		0611	0712	0802	0912	1112		2112	2312
Holstebro a.		0650	0750	0848	0950	1150		2150	2350
Holstebro 715 d.		0652	0751	0849	0951	1151		2151	2353
Struer 715 a.		0704	0805	0902	1005	1205		2205	0006

		Ⓐ	Ⓐ	Ⓐ	Ⓐ	Ⓐ	Ⓐ	Ⓐ		Ⓐ	Ⓐ	Ⓐ	Ⓐ		Ⓐ	
Struer 715 d.	Ⓐ	0431	0518	0633	0723	0824	0948	1059	and hourly until	1559	1733	1933	2059	...	2259	...
Holstebro 715 a.		0443	0530	0648	0736	0837	1000	1111		1611	1748	1948	2111	...	2311	...
Holstebro d.		0444	0532	0651	0739	0839	1002	1112		1612	1749	1949	2112	...	2312	...
Ringkøbing a.		0523	0614	0733	0823	0918	1041	1156		1656	1827	2027	2151	...	2351	...
Ringkøbing d.		0523	0616	0733	0824	0922	1042	1207		1707	1828	2028	2152	...	2352	...
Skjern a.		0542	0634	0752	0843	0941	1104	1226		1726	1847	2048	2211	...	0011	...

		⑥	⑥	†	Ⓒ	Ⓒ		Ⓒ	Ⓒ
Struer 715 d.	Ⓒ	0456	0551	0647	0752	0952	and every two hours until	1952	2152
Holstebro 715 a.		0508	0603	0659	0805	1005		2005	2205
Holstebro d.		0509	0604	0701	0806	1007		2007	2207
Ringkøbing a.		0548	0646	0740	0845	1046		2046	2246
Ringkøbing d.		0549	0648	0740	0847	1047		2047	2247
Skjern a.		0607	0712	0759	0912	1112		2112	2312

ESBJERG - TØNDER - NIEBÜLL 709

Operator: *AT* 2nd class only

km			Ⓐ	Ⓐ	Ⓐ	Ⓐ	Ⓐ	Ⓐ	Ⓐ	Ⓐ	Ⓐ	Ⓐ	Ⓐ	Ⓐ	Ⓐ	Ⓐ	Ⓐ	Ⓐ
0	**Esbjerg** ▷ d.	Ⓐ	0459	0614	0758	0858	0958	1058	1158	1258	1358	1458	1558	1659	1759	1859	1959	2159
6	Bramming ▷ d.		0512	0627	0811	0911	1011	1111	1211	1311	1411	1511	1611	1712	1812	1912	2012	2212
3	Ribe ▷ d.		0537	0645	0831	0931	1031	1131	1231	1331	1431	1531	1631	1732	1832	1932	2032	2232
0	**Tønder** a.		0628	0734	0922	1022	1122	1222	1322	1422	1522	1622	1722	1823	1923	2023	2123	2323
			Ⓐy	Ⓐ		|		|	Ⓐ	|	|	|		|		|	⑤F	
0	**Tønder** d.		0706	0832	...	1032	...	1232	1340	1432	1532	1632	...	1832	...	2032	2232	...
7	Niebüll a.		0725	0851	...	1051	...	1251	1402	1451	1551	1651	...	1851	...	2051	2251	...

		⑥	⑥	Ⓒ	Ⓒ		Ⓒ	Ⓒ	Ⓒ
Esbjerg ▷ d.	Ⓒ	0531	0731	0731	0931	and every two hours until	1931	2130	2230
Bramming ▷ d.		0545	0745	0745	0945		1945	2145	2244
Ribe ▷ d.		0605	0805	0805	1005		2005	2205	2303
Tønder a.		0653	0852	0852	1052		2052	2252	2353
			|		|		|	|	
Tønder d.		...	0906	...	1106		2106	2256t	...
Niebüll a.		...	0925	...	1125		2125	2315t	...

			Ⓐy	Ⓐ		Ⓐ		Ⓐ	Ⓐ	Ⓐ	Ⓐ	Ⓐ		Ⓐ		Ⓐ		⑤F
Niebüll ★ d.	Ⓐ	...	0639	0733	...	1007	...	1207	1320	1407	1507	1607	...	1807	...	2007	...	2207
Tønder a.		...	0656	0750	...	1024	...	1224	1337	1424	1524	1624	...	1824	...	2024	...	2224
		Ⓐ	Ⓐ	Ⓐ	Ⓐ	|	Ⓐ	|	Ⓐ	|	|	|	Ⓐ	|	Ⓐ	|	Ⓐ	|
Tønder d.		0556	0636	0827	0927	1027	1127	1227	1327	1427	1527	1627	1728	1828	1928	2028	2228	2228
Ribe ▷ d.		0650	0728	0914	1014	1114	1214	1314	1414	1514	1614	1714	1815	1915	2015	2115	2315	2315
Bramming ▷ a.		0707	0746	0931	1031	1131	1231	1331	1431	1531	1631	1731	1832	1932	2032	2132	2332	2332
Esbjerg ▷ a.		0724	0800	0945	1045	1145	1245	1345	1445	1545	1645	1745	1849	1949	2049	2149	2349	2349

		⑥	Ⓒ	Ⓒ	⑥	Ⓒ		Ⓒ	Ⓒ
Niebüll ★ d.	Ⓒ	...	...	...	0837	1037	and every two hours until	2037	2207t
Tønder a.		...	...	...	0855	1055		2055	2224t
					|	|		|	|
Tønder d.		0513	0713	0913	0913	1113		2113	2258
Ribe ▷ d.		0611	0811	1011	1011	1211		2211	2346
Bramming ▷ a.		0629	0829	1029	1029	1229		2229	0004
Esbjerg ▷ a.		0643	0843	1043	1043	1243		2243	0018

⑤ Apr. 5 - Oct. 25.

t – Apr. 6 - Oct. 27.
y – Also Apr. 18, May 17.

▷ – Additional services operate Esbjerg - Ribe and v.v. See Table **705** for other services Esbjerg - Bramming and v.v.
★ – Danish public holiday dates apply.

FREDERICIA - SØNDERBORG and FLENSBURG 710

See Table **705** for other *IC* services København - Odense - Kolding - Lunderskov and v.v.

km		*IC* 5744 ⚒	Ⓐ2	*IC* 5722 ⚒	*IC* 5722		Ⓒ2	*Lyn* 921 Ⓐ	*IC* 5720	*Lyn* 929	*IC* 383 ⒶH	*IC* 1183 ⒸH	*Lyn* 943	*IC* 5736	*Lyn* 947	*IC* 385 ⒶH	*IC* 1185 ⒸH	*Lyn* 953	*IC* 5752	*Lyn* 961	*IC* 5760 Ⓐz	*IC* 387 AH	*IC* 1187 Ⓒ	*IC* 1187 ⒸS
	København H 700 d.	...	...	...	...	...	...	0552	...	0752	...	...	0952	...	1152	...	...	1352	...	1552	...	...	...	...
	Odense 700 d.	...	0510	...	...	...	0641	0710	...	0910	...	...	1110	...	1310	...	...	1510	...	1710	...	...	...	...
	Aarhus 700 d.	...	|	0526a	...	...	|	|	0735c	|	0926	0933	|	...	|	1326	1332	|	...	|	1726	1726	1732	1732
0	**Fredericia** 705 d.	...	0549	0646	...	...	0749	0749	0846	0949	1046	1046	1149	1246	1349	1446	1446	1549	1646	1749	1846	1846	1846	1846
0	Kolding 705 d.	...	0601	0658	...	...	0801	0801	0858	1001	1058	1058	1201	1258	1401	1458	1458	1601	1658	1801	1858	1858	1858	1858
3	Lunderskov 705 d.	...	0609	0706	...	...	0809	0809	0906	1009	1106	1106	1209	1306	1409	1506	1506	1609	1706	1809	1906	1906	1906	1906
0	Vojens d.	...	0626	0722	...	...	0826	0826	0922	1026	1122	1122	1226	1322	1426	1522	1522	1626	1722	1826	1922	1922	1922	1922
5	Tinglev d.	0610	0647	0744	0744	...	0847	0847	0944	1047	1144	1144	1247	1344	1447	1544	1544	1647	1744	1847	1944	1944	1944	1944
6	**Sønderborg** a.	|	0721	|	|	...	0921	0921	|	1121	|	|	1321	|	1521	|	|	1721	|	1921	|	|	|	|
0	Padborg 🏛 a.	0620	...	0754	0754	...	...	...	0954	...	1154	1154	...	1354	...	1554	1554	...	1754	...	1954	1954	1954	1954
2	**Flensburg** 🏛 a.	0635	...	0807	0807	...	...	...	1007	...	1207	1207	...	1407	...	1607	1607	...	1807	...	2007	2007	2007	2007
2	*Hamburg Hbf 823* a.	...	...	...	...	...	...	...	...	...	1402	1402	...	...	...	1802	1802	...	...	...	...	2159	...	2158

	Lyn 969	*IC* 5768	*Lyn* 977		2	2		*IC* 430 BK	*IC* 1130 DK	
København H 700 d.	1752	...	1952	...	...	...	...	2300	2300	...
Odense 700 d.	1910	...	2110	...	...	...	...	0057	0057	...
Aarhus 700 d.	|	...	|	...	...	...	...	|	|	...
Fredericia 705 d.	1949	2046	2152	...	2321	0014	...	0135	0135	...
Kolding 705 d.	2001	2058	2204	...	2333	0026	...	|	|	...
Lunderskov 705 d.	2009	2106	2212	...	2341	0034	...	|	|	...
Vojens d.	2026	2122	2229	...	2357	0050	...	|	|	...
Tinglev d.	2047	2144	2250	...	0022	0117	...	|	|	...
Sønderborg a.	2121	|	2324	...	...	0151	...	|	|	...
Padborg 🏛 a.	...	2154	...	...	...	...	...	|	|	...
Flensburg 🏛 a.	...	2207	...	...	...	...	...	|	|	...
Hamburg Hbf 823 a.	...	...	...	...	...	...	...	0540	0553	...

	Ⓐ2		*Lyn* 914 Ⓐ		*IC* 5721 ⚒	†2	*Lyn* 922		*IC* 5729
Hamburg Hbf 823 d.	...	...	...	...	...	...	...	...	...
Flensburg 🏛 ★ d.	...	...	...	...	0648	...	...	...	0848
Padborg 🏛 d.	...	...	...	...	0704	...	...	...	0904
Sønderborg d.	...	...	0533	...	|	...	0735	...	|
Tinglev d.	0511	...	0611	...	0715	0715	0811	...	0915
Vojens d.	0531	...	0631	...	0735	0735	0831	...	0935
Lunderskov 705 d.	0547	...	0647	...	0751	0751	0847	...	0951
Kolding 705 d.	0556	...	0656	...	0801	0801	0856	...	1001
Fredericia 705 a.	0608	...	0708	...	0814	0814	0908	...	1014
Aarhus 700 a.	...	...	|	...	...	...	|	...	1125
Odense 700 a.	...	...	0749	...	...	...	0949	...	...
København H 700 a.	...	...	0908	...	...	...	1108	...	...

	Lyn 940		*IC* 5737	*Lyn* 944		*IC* 386 H	*Lyn* 948		*IC* 5753	*Lyn* 954		*IC* 384 H	*Lyn* 962		*IC* 5769	*Lyn* 970		*IC* 5727 z	*IC* 382 SH	2	*IC* 5745		*IC* 1131 GK	*IC* 431 EK
Hamburg Hbf 823 d.	...	...	...	...	...	1053	...	...	...	...	...	1452	...	...	...	...	...	...	1901	...	...	...	2342	2342
Flensburg 🏛 ★ d.	...	...	1048	...	...	1250	...	...	1448	...	...	1650	...	...	1848	...	...	2048	2050	...	2248	...	|	|
Padborg 🏛 d.	...	...	1104	...	...	1305	...	...	1504	...	...	1705	...	...	1904	...	...	2105	2105	...	2304	...	|	|
Sønderborg d.	0935	...	|	1135	...	|	1335	...	|	1535	...	|	1735	...	|	1935	...	|	|	2135	|	...	|	|
Tinglev d.	1011	...	1115	1211	...	1315	1411	...	1515	1611	...	1715	1811	...	1915	2011	...	2115	2115	2211	2315	...	|	|
Vojens d.	1031	...	1135	1231	...	1335	1431	...	1535	1631	...	1735	1831	...	1935	2031	...	2135	2135	2231	2335	...	|	|
Lunderskov 705 d.	1047	...	1151	1247	...	1351	1447	...	1551	1647	...	1751	1847	...	1951	2047	...	2151	2151	2247	2351	...	|	|
Kolding 705 d.	1056	...	1201	1256	...	1401	1456	...	1601	1656	...	1801	1856	...	2001	2056	...	2201	2201	2256	0001	...	|	|
Fredericia 705 a.	1108	...	1214	1308	...	1414	1508	...	1614	1708	...	1814	1908	...	2014	2108	...	2214	2214	2308	0014	...	0336	0336
Aarhus 700 a.	|	...	...	|	...	1519	|	...	...	|	...	1918	|	...	...	|	...	2325	2325	|	...	...	|	|
Odense 700 a.	1149	...	...	1349	...	...	1549	...	...	1749	...	...	1949	...	...	2149	...	...	...	2356	...	...	0419	0436
København H 700 a.	1308	...	...	1508	...	...	1708	...	...	1908	...	...	2108	...	...	2313	...	...	...	...	...	...	0601	0629

Ⓐ June 24 - Aug. 16.
Ⓑ Mar. 31 - Sept. 16.
⑥ Mar. 30 - Sept. 14.
From Hamburg on ①②③④⑦ Mar. 31 - Sept. 16 (not Apr. 17, 18, 21, May 16, 29, June 9).
From Hamburg on ⑤⑥ Mar. 30 - Sept. 14 (also Apr. 17, 18, 21, May 16, 29, June 9).
(12) and 🍷 Aarhus - Hamburg and v.v.
(12) København - Hamburg and v.v. Ⓡ for international journeys.
June 22 - Aug. 18.

a – Ⓐ only.
c – Ⓒ only.
z – Not June 22 - Aug. 18.

★ – Danish public holiday dates apply.

712 AARHUS - VIBORG - STRUER

Operator: *AT* (except trains marked ♣); 2nd class or

See Table **715** for direct services København - Herning - Struer and v.v.

km									629								663						
	Ⓐ								♣								♣						
		Ⓐ	Ⓐ	Ⓐ	Ⓐ	Ⓐ	Ⓐ	Ⓐ	Ⓐ	Ⓐ	Ⓐ	Ⓐ	Ⓐ	Ⓐ	Ⓐ	Ⓐ	Ⓐ	Ⓐ	Ⓐ	Ⓐ		Ⓐ	
	København H **700** ... d.	...	...	...	...	...	...	...	0752	...	...	...	...	...	...	...	1552	...	...	...	...	...	...
0	**Aarhus** .... **701** ▷ d.	0439	0525	0625	0654	0754	0854	0954	1053	1154	1254	1354	1454	1554	1654	1754	1853	1954	2054	2154	...	2329	...
46	Langå .... **701** ▷ a.	0509	0555	0655	0724	0824	0924	1024	1121	1224	1324	1424	1524	1624	1724	1824	1921	2024	2124	2224	...	2359	...
46	Langå .... ▷ d.	0514	0600	0700	0729	0829	0929	1029	1129	1229	1329	1429	1529	1629	1729	1829	1929	2029	2129	2229	...	0004	...
86	Viborg .... ▷ d.	0547	0649j	0732	0807	0907	1006	1106	1206	1306	1406	1506	1606	1706	1806	1906	2006	2106	2206	2306	...	0034	...
116	Skive .... d.	0615	0715	0755	0829	0929	1030	1130	1230	1330	1430	1530	1630	1730	1830	1930	2030	2127	2230	2330	...	...	...
148	**Struer** .... a.	0637	0739	0819	0856	0956	1053	1153	1253	1353	1453	1553	1653	1753	1853	1953	2053	...	2253	2353	...	...	...

									643		645							661					
Ⓒ									♣		♣							♣					
	⑥	Ⓒ	Ⓒ	Ⓒ	Ⓒ	⑥	Ⓒ	Ⓒ	⑥	†	†	⑥	Ⓒ	Ⓒ	†	Ⓒ	Ⓒ	Ⓒ	Ⓒ	Ⓒ	Ⓒ	Ⓒ	⑥
København H **700** .... d.	...	...	...	...	...	...	...	...	0952	...	1052	...	...	...	...	...	...	1552	...	...	...	...	...
Aarhus .... **701** ▷ d.	0553	0653	0753	0853	0953	0953	1053	1153	1253	1253	1353	1353	1453	1553	1553	1653	1753	1853	1953	2053	2153	2253	2253
Langå .... **701** ▷ a.	0623	0723	0823	0923	1023	1023	1123	1223	1321	1323	1421	1423	1523	1623	1623	1723	1823	1921	2023	2123	2223	2323	2323
Langå .... ▷ d.	0628	0728	0828	0928	1028	1028	1128	1228	1328	1328	1428	1428	1528	1628	1628	1728	1828	1928	2028	2128	2228	2328	2328
Viborg .... ▷ d.	0659	0759	0859	0959	1059	1059	1159	1259	1359	1359	1459	1459	1559	1659	1659	1759	1859	1959	2059	2159	2259	2358	2359
Skive .... d.	0722	0822	0922	1022	1120	1122	1222	1322	1422	1422	1522	1522	1622	1720	1722	1822	1922	2022	2122	2222	2322	...	0022
Struer .... a.	0745	0845	0945	1045	...	1145	1245	1345	1445	1445	1545	1545	1645	...	1745	1845	1945	2045	2145	2245	2345	...	0045

						626						652											
Ⓐ						♣						♣											
	Ⓐ	Ⓐ	Ⓐ	Ⓐ	Ⓐ	Ⓐ	Ⓐ	Ⓐ	Ⓐ	Ⓐ	Ⓐ	Ⓐ	Ⓐ	Ⓐ	Ⓐ	Ⓐ	Ⓐ	Ⓐ	Ⓐ	Ⓐ	Ⓐ		
Struer .... d.	...	0447	0514	0552	0642	0719	0820	0920	1015	1115	1215	1315	1415	1515	1615	1715	1815	1915	2015	...	2215	...	...
Skive .... d.	...	0510	0537	0615	0704	0742	0843	0943	1042	1142	1242	1342	1442	1542	1642	1742	1842	1942	2042	2142	2242	...	...
Viborg .... ▷ d.	0455	0534	0609	0639	0738k	0809	0909	1009	1109	1209	1309	1409	1509	1609	1709	1809	1909	2009	2109	2209	2309	...	...
Langå .... ▷ a.	0526	0612	0642	0712	0812	0842	0942	1041	1141	1241	1341	1442	1541	1641	1741	1841	1941	2041	2141	2241	2341	...	...
Langå .... **701** ▷ d.	0531	0617	0648	0717	0817	0848	0948	1048	1148	1248	1348	1448	1548	1648	1748	1848	1948	2048	2148	2248	2348	...	...
Aarhus .... **701** ▷ a.	0603	0649	0720	0749	0849	0919	1020	1120	1220	1320	1420	1520	1620	1720	1820	1920	2020	2120	2220	2320	0020	...	...
København H **700** .... a.	...	...	...	...	...	1301	...	...	...	...	...	1901	...	...	...	...	...	...	...	...	...	...	...

					628										660		664						
Ⓒ					♣										♣		♣						
	⑥	⑥	⑥	Ⓒ	Ⓒ	Ⓒ	Ⓒ	Ⓒ	⑥	Ⓒ	Ⓒ	Ⓒ	Ⓒ	†	⑥	⑥	†	†	Ⓒ	Ⓒ	Ⓒ	Ⓒ	Ⓒ
Struer .... d.	...	0523	0623	...	0723	0823	0923	1023	1123	...	1223	1323	1423	1523	1523	1623	1623	1723	...	1823	1923	2023	2123
Skive .... d.	...	0555	0655	...	0755	0855	0955	1055	1155	1155	1255	1355	1455	1555	1555	1655	1655	1755	1755	1855	1955	2055	2155
Viborg .... ▷ d.	0523	0623	0723	0723	0823	0923	1023	1123	1223	1223	1323	1423	1523	1623	1623	1723	1723	1823	1823	1923	2023	2123	2223
Langå .... ▷ a.	0554	0654	0754	0754	0854	0954	1054	1154	1254	1254	1354	1454	1554	1654	1654	1754	1754	1854	1854	1954	2054	2154	2254
Langå .... **701** ▷ d.	0559	0659	0759	0759	0900	0959	1059	1159	1259	1259	1359	1459	1559	1659	1700	1759	1800	1859	1859	1959	2059	2159	2259
Aarhus .... **701** ▷ a.	0631	0731	0831	0831	0931	1031	1131	1231	1331	1331	1431	1531	1631	1731	1731	1831	1831	1931	1931	2031	2131	2231	2331
København H **700** .... a.	...	...	...	...	1301	...	...	...	...	...	...	...	...	...	2101	...	2201	...	...	...	...	...	...

j – Arrives 0630.
k – Arrives 0727.

♣ – *Lyn* or *IC* service operated by DSB. Also conveys 1st class.
▷ – Additional services operate Aarhus - Viborg and v.v.

713 AARHUS - HERNING - SKJERN

Operator: *AT*; 2nd class or

km																						
	Ⓐ			Ⓐ	Ⓐ	Ⓐ	Ⓐ	Ⓐ	Ⓐ	Ⓐ	Ⓐ	Ⓐ	Ⓐ	Ⓐ	Ⓐ	Ⓐ	Ⓐ	Ⓐ	Ⓐ	Ⓐ	Ⓐ	Ⓐ
0	**Aarhus** .... **700 705** ▷ d.	...	...	0530	0633	0730	0800	0830	0930	1030	1130	1230	1330	1430	1530	1630	1730	1818	1918	2018	2118	2218
23	Skanderborg .... **700 705** ▷ d.	...	...	0551	0655	0751	0820	0851	0951	1051	1151	1251	1351	1451	1551	1651	1751	1839	1939	2039	2139	2239
53	Silkeborg .... ▷ d.	...	...	0616	0722	0813	0849	0912	1012	1112	1212	1312	1412	1512	1612	1712	1817	1908	2008	2108	2208	2305
94	**Herning** .... ▷ a.	...	...	0646	0754	0847	0931	0946	1046	1146	1246	1346	1446	1546	1646	1746	1848	1948	2048	2148	2248	2341
	change trains	Ⓐ	Ⓐ	Ⓐ	Ⓐ		Ⓐ		Ⓐ	Ⓐ	Ⓐ	Ⓐ	Ⓐ	Ⓐ	Ⓐ	Ⓐ		Ⓐ		Ⓐ	Ⓐ	
94	**Herning** .... d.	0523	0615	0707	0822	...	0938	...	1107	1207	1307	1407	1507	1607	1708	1808	...	2006	...	2206	2323	...
136	**Skjern** .... a.	0558	0650	0743	0856	...	1013	...	1142	1242	1342	1442	1542	1642	1743	1845	...	2041	...	2241	2358	...

Ⓒ	⑥	⑥	Ⓒ	Ⓒ		Ⓒ	Ⓒ	Ⓒ	Ⓒ	Ⓒ
Aarhus .... **700 705** d.	...	0625	0725	0825	and hourly	1925	2025	2125	2225	2340
Skanderborg .... **700 705** d.	...	0645	0745	0845	Aarhus -	1945	2045	2145	2245	2359
Silkeborg .... d.	...	0712	0812	0912	Herning,	2012	2112	2212	2311	0026
Herning .... a.	...	0748	0848	0948	every	2048	2148	2248	2349	0102
change trains		Ⓒ		Ⓒ	**two** hours		Ⓒ	Ⓒ		
Herning .... d.	0609	0806	...	1006	Herning -	...	2206	2326	...	...
Skjern .... a.	0644	0841	...	1041	Skjern	...	2241	0001	...	...

Ⓐ		Ⓐ	Ⓐ	Ⓐ	Ⓐ
Skjern .... d.	...	0513	0605	0657	0812
Herning .... a.	...	0553	0642	0734	0850
change trains	Ⓐ	Ⓐ	Ⓐ	Ⓐ	Ⓐ
Herning .... ▷ d.	0513	0554	0647	0755	0854
Silkeborg .... ▷ d.	0551	0629	0728	0828	0929
Skanderborg .... **700 705** ▷ a.	0620	0650	0749	0849	0950
Aarhus .... **700 705** ▷ a.	0640	0710	0809	0909	1010

	Ⓐ	Ⓐ	Ⓐ	Ⓐ	Ⓐ	Ⓐ	Ⓐ	Ⓐ		Ⓐ	Ⓐ		Ⓐ	Ⓐ
Skjern .... d.	0954	1056	1156	1256	1356	1456	1556	1657	...	1757	1917	...	2117	2247
Herning .... a.	1033	1135	1235	1335	1435	1535	1635	1736	...	1836	1952	...	2152	2322
change trains	Ⓐ	Ⓐ	Ⓐ	Ⓐ	Ⓐ	Ⓐ	Ⓐ	Ⓐ	Ⓐ	Ⓐ	Ⓐ	Ⓐ	Ⓐ	Ⓐ
Herning .... ▷ d.	1054	1154	1254	1354	1454	1554	1654	1746	1809	1911	2011	2111	2211	2325
Silkeborg .... ▷ d.	1129	1229	1329	1429	1529	1629	1729	1818	1951	1951	2051	2151	2251	0005
Skanderborg .... **700 705** ▷ a.	1150	1250	1350	1450	1550	1650	1750	1839	1920	2020	2120	2220	2320	0035
Aarhus .... **700 705** ▷ a.	1210	1310	1410	1510	1610	1710	1810	1900	1940	2040	2140	2240	2340	0055

Ⓒ		⑥		Ⓒ			Ⓒ
Skjern d.	...	0517	...	0717	and every	...	2117
Herning a.	...	0552	...	0752	**two** hours	...	2152
change trains	⑥	⑥	Ⓒ	Ⓒ	Skjern -	Ⓒ	Ⓒ
Herning ▷ d.	0508	0608	0708	0808	Herning,	2108	2208
Silkeborg ▷ d.	0547	0647	0747	0847	hourly	2147	2247
Skanderborg 700 705 ▷ a.	0615	0715	0815	0915	Herning -	2215	2315
Aarhus 700 705 ▷ a.	0635	0735	0835	0935	Aarhus	2235	2335

▷ – Additional services operate Aarhus - Herning and v.v. on Ⓐ.

715 FREDERICIA - HERNING - STRUER

km						*Lyn*	◧		*Lyn*	*Lyn*		*Lyn*		*Lyn*		*Lyn*	*Lyn*		*Lyn*	*Lyn*		*Lyn*		
						725	**3729**		**741**	**741**		**745**		**749**		**757**	**761**		**765**	**765**		**773**		
		Ⓐ2	Ⓐ2	2	2		Ⓐ	Ⓒ2		Ⓒ	2		2		2		Ⓐ	Ⓒ2	Ⓒ	Ⓐ	2		B2	A2
	København H **700** ... d.	...	...	...	...	0652	0752	...	0852	0852	...	1052	...	1252	...	1452	1552	...	1652	1652	...	1852	...	...
	Odense **700** .... d.	...	...	...	...	0810	0910	...	1010	1010	...	1210	...	1410	...	1610	1710	...	1810	1810	...	2010	...	...
0	**Fredericia** .... **700 705** d.	0445	0545	0647	0747	0847	0947	0947	1047	1047	1147	1247	1347	1447	1547	1647	1747	1747	1847	1847	1947	2047	2147	2153
26	Vejle .... **700 705** d.	0502	0602	0702	0802	0902	1002	1002	1102	1102	1202	1302	1402	1502	1602	1702	1802	1802	1902	1902	2002	2102	2202	2212
99	Herning .... a.	0558	0658	0758	0858	0958	1058	1058	1158	1158	1258	1358	1458	1558	1658	1758	1858	1858	1958	1958	2058	2158	2259	2312
99	Herning .... d.	0600	0700	0806	0900	1000	1100	1100	1200	1200	1300	1400	1500	1600	1700	1800	1900	1900	2000	2000	2100	2200	2301	2313
140	Holstebro .... **708** d.	0636	0737	0841	0936	1036	1136	1136	1236	1236	1336	1436	1536	1636	1736	1836	1936	1936	2036	2036	2136	2232	2336	2347
155	**Struer** .... **708** a.	0647	0749	0852	0947	1047	1147	1147	1247	1247	1347	1447	1547	1647	1747	1847	1947	1947	2047	2047	2147	2243	2347	2358
	Thisted **716** .... a.	...	...	...	...	...	1322	...	...	1412	...	...	...	...	...	...	...	...	2212	2217	...	...	...	...

	Lyn	*Lyn*		*Lyn*			*Lyn*		*Lyn*		*Lyn*	*Lyn*		*Lyn*	◐		*Lyn*	*Lyn*		*Lyn*				
	710	**714**		**718**			**726**		**742**		**746**	**748**		**750**	**3752**		**758**	**758**		**766**				
	Ⓐ	D	⑤f2		2			2		2		Ⓐ	Ⓒ2		Ⓐ	Ⓒ2		Ⓒ	2		2	2	2	
Thisted **716** .... d.	...	...	...	...	...	...	0650	...	...	...	...	...	...	...	1328	...	...	1421	...	...	...	...	...	...
Struer .... **708** d.	0412	0511	0511	0607	0705	...	0812	0907	1007	1107	1207	1307	1307	1407	1507	1507	1607	1607	1707	1807	1907	2007	2107	...
Holstebro .... **708** d.	0424	0524	0524	0620	0720	...	0825	0920	1020	1120	1220	1320	1320	1420	1520	1520	1620	1620	1720	1820	1920	2020	2120	...
Herning .... a.	0456	0556	0556	0649	0750	...	0855	0949	1049	1149	1249	1349	1349	1449	1549	1549	1649	1649	1749	1849	1949	2049	2149	...
Herning .... d.	0458	0558	0558	0658	0758	...	0858	0958	1058	1158	1258	1358	1358	1458	1558	1558	1658	1658	1758	1858	1958	2058	2158	...
Vejle .... **700 705** d.	0556	0656	0656	0756	0856	...	0956	1056	1156	1256	1356	1456	1456	1556	1656	1656	1756	1756	1856	1956	2056	2156	2256	...
Fredericia ..... **700 705** a.	0612	0712	0712	0812	0912	...	1012	1112	1212	1312	1412	1512	1512	1612	1712	1712	1812	1812	1912	2012	2112	2212	2318	...
Odense **700** .... a.	0649	0749	...	0849	...	...	1049	...	1249	...	1449	1549	...	1649	1749	...	1849	1849	...	2049	...	...	...	...
København H **700** .... a.	0808	0908	...	1008	...	...	1208	...	1408	...	1608	1708	...	1808	1908	...	2008	2008	...	2208	...	...	...	...

A – ①②③④⑦ (not Apr. 17, 18, 21, May 16, 29, 30, June 9).
B – ⑤⑥ (also Apr. 17, 18, 21, May 16, 29, 30, June 9).
D – ①-④ (not Apr. 17, 18, 22, May 16, 29, 30, June 10).
f – Also Apr. 17, May 16, 29; not Apr. 19, May 17.
◧ – Train *Lyn* **29** København - Fredericia.
◐ – Train *Lyn* **54** Fredericia - København.

STRUER - THISTED 716

)perator: *AT* (except trains marked ♣); 2nd class only

km																									
		Ⓐ					3729 K♣							3765 K♣		Ⓒ	♣				741 K♣				3767 K♣	
			Ⓐ	Ⓐ	Ⓐ	Ⓐ	Ⓐ	Ⓐ	Ⓐ	Ⓐ	Ⓐ	Ⓐ	Ⓐ	Ⓐ	Ⓐ		⑥	Ⓒ	Ⓒ	Ⓒ	Ⓒ	Ⓒ	Ⓒ	Ⓒ	Ⓒ	Ⓒ
0	Struer ....d.		0427	0544	0722	1005	1205	1305	1405	1505	1605	1705	1905	2100	2300		0516	0646	0854	1054	1254	1454	1654	1854	2054	2254
74	Thisted ....a.		0600	0721	0912	1122	1322	1423	1523	1623	1723	1823	2022	2217	0017		0634	0805	1012	1212	1412	1612	1812	2012	2212	0012

	Ⓐ		726 K♣				3752 K♣							♣	Ⓒ		726 K♣				758 K♣				♣
		Ⓐ	Ⓐ	Ⓐ	Ⓐ	Ⓐ	Ⓐ	Ⓐ	Ⓐ	Ⓐ	Ⓐ	Ⓐ	Ⓐ	Ⓐ		⑥	Ⓒ	Ⓒ	Ⓒ	Ⓒ	Ⓒ	Ⓒ	Ⓒ	Ⓒ	Ⓒ
ısted ....d.		0605	0650	0744	0931	1131	1328	1428	1528	1628	1728	1828	2027	2227		0521	0650	0821	1021	1221	1421	1621	1821	2021	2221
ruer ....a.		0721	0810	0901	1053	1253	1453	1552	1652	1752	1852	1952	2147	2347		0641	0810	0941	1141	1341	1541	1741	1941	2141	2341

– (12) København - Struer - Thisted and v.v. InterCityLyn (*Lyn*) service (see Table **715**).

♣ – Operated by *DSB*.

KØBENHAVN - RØDBY - PUTTGARDEN (- HAMBURG) 720

/ARNING! Subject to alteration until September 29. All services are replaced wholly or partially by 🚌 between Ringsted and Nykøbing in amended timings (please confirm timings locally). International *EC* services to / from Germany are replaced by 🚌 between København and Rødby - please refer to Table **50** for amended international timings during this period.

km																							
												EC 38				*EC* 36					*EC* 34		
		①-⑤	⑥⑦		①-⑤	①-⑤	①-⑤			①-⑤						A	B						
0	København H........ **700 704** d.	0000	0009	...	...	0505	0535	...	0609	0635	0709	0735	0809	0835	0909	0935	0935	1009	1035	1109	1135	1209	1235
20	Høje Taastrup........ **700 704** d.	0015	0024	...	...	0520	0549	...	0624	0649	0724	0749	0824	0849	0924	0949	0949	1024	1049	1124	1149	1224	1249
31	Roskilde................ **700 704** d.	0023	0034	...	...	0529	0559	...	0633	0659	0733	0759	0833	0859	0933	0959	0959	1033	1059	1133	1159	1233	1259
64	Ringsted....................... **700** d.	0051	0058	...	...	0547	|	...	0651	|	0751	|	0851	|	0951	|	|	1051	|	1151	|	1251	|
91	Næstved...............................d.	0110	0117	...	...	0606	0630	...	0710	0732	0810	0830	0910	0930	1010	1030	1030	1110	1130	1210	1230	1310	1330
'18	Vordingborg.........................d.	0135	0138	...	...	0626	0648	...	0731	0750	0831	0849	0931	0949	1031	1049	1049	1131	1149	1231	1249	1331	1349
'47	Nykøbing (Falster)........... ⊙ d.	0202	0205	...	0645	0703	0717	0753	0759	0815	0859	0916	0959	1015	1059	1116	1116	1159	1215	1259	1316	1359	1415
'83	**Rødby** .... ⛴ ▲ a.	...	...	...	0707	...	...	0815	...	...	...	0937	...	...	...	1137	1137	...	...	...	1337	...	...
'02	**Puttgarden** .... ⛴ ▲ a.	...	...	...	...	...	...	...	...	...	...	1036	...	...	...	1236	...	...	...	...	1436	...	...
'91	*Lübeck* **825**........................a.	...	...	...	...	...	...	...	...	...	...	1137	...	...	...	1337	...	...	...	...	1537	...	...
'53	*Hamburg Hbf* **825** ....a.	...	...	...	...	...	...	...	...	...	...	1216	...	...	...	1416	...	...	...	...	1616	...	...

						EC 32																	
																			⑦-④	⑤⑥		⑦-④	⑤⑥
›benhavn H .... **700 704** d.	1309	1335	1409	1435	1509	1535	1609	1635	1709	1735	1809	1835	1909	1935	2009	...	2109	...	2200	2209	...	2300	2309
ıje Taastrup........... **700 704** d.	1324	1349	1424	1449	1524	1549	1624	1649	1724	1749	1824	1849	1924	1949	2024	...	2124	...	2215	2224	...	2315	2324
skilde .... **700 704** d.	1333	1359	1433	1459	1533	1559	1633	1659	1733	1759	1833	1859	1933	1959	2033	...	2133	...	2223	2233	...	2323	2333
ıgsted.............................**700** d.	1351	|	1451	|	1551	|	1651	|	1751	|	1851	|	1951	|	2051	...	2151	...	2251	2251	...	2351	2351
ɘstved....................................d.	1410	1430	1510	1530	1610	1630	1710	1730	1810	1830	1910	1930	2010	2030	2110	...	2210	...	2310	2310	...	0010	0010
rdingborg................................d.	1431	1449	1531	1549	1631	1649	1731	1749	1831	1849	1931	1949	2031	2049	2131	...	2234	...	2335	2335	...	0035	0035
›øbing (Falster) .... ⊙ d.	1459	1516	1559	1615	1659	1716	1759	1815	1859	1916	1959	2010	2059	2115	2200	...	2302	...	0002	0002	...	0102	0102
dby .... ⛴ ▲ a.	...	1537	...	...	...	1737	...	...	...	1937	...	...	...	...	2223	...	...	...	...	...	...	...	...
ttgarden .... ⛴ ▲ a.	...	...	...	...	...	1836	...	...	...	...	...	...	...	...	...	...	...	...	...	...	...	...	...
Lübeck **825**..............................a.	...	...	...	...	...	1937	...	...	...	...	...	...	...	...	...	...	...	...	...	...	...	...	...
Hamburg Hbf **825**...................a.	...	...	...	...	...	2016	...	...	...	...	...	...	...	...	...	...	...	...	...	...	...	...	...

																			EC 33				
	①-⑤	①-⑤		①-⑤		①-⑤		①-⑤															
Hamburg Hbf **825**..................d.	...	...	...	...	...	...	...	...	...	...	...	...	...	...	...	...	...	...	0928	...	...	...	...
Lübeck **825**.............................d.	...	...	...	...	...	...	...	...	...	...	...	...	...	...	...	...	...	...	1006	...	...	...	...
ttgarden .... ⛴ ▲ d.	...	...	...	...	...	...	...	...	...	...	...	...	...	...	...	...	...	...	1108	...	...	...	...
dby .... ⛴ ▲ d.	...	...	...	...	...	...	...	0720	...	0822	...	...	...	1020	...	...	...	...	1220	...	...	...	1420
›øbing (Falster) .... ⊙ d.	0423	0455	0523	0556	0618	0653	0719	0747	0747	0819	0847	0919	0947	1019	1047	1119	1147	1219	1247	1319	1347	1419	1447
rdingborg................................d.	0450	0522	0550	0622	0650	0722	0750	0811	0811	0850	0911	0950	1011	1050	1111	1150	1211	1250	1311	1350	1411	1450	1511
ɘstved....................................d.	0512	0544	0612	0644	0712	0744	0812	0829	0829	0912	0929	1012	1029	1112	1129	1212	1229	1312	1329	1412	1429	1512	1529
ıgsted.............................**700** a.	0530	0602	0630	0702	0730	0803	0830	|	|	0930	|	1030	|	1130	|	1230	|	1330	|	1430	|	1530	|
skilde .... **700 704** a.	0553	0623	0653	0723	0753	0823	0853	0859	0859	0953	0959	1053	1059	1153	1159	1253	1259	1353	1359	1453	1459	1553	1559
je Taastrup........... **700 704** a.	0604	0636	0704	0736	0803	0836	0904	0908	0908	1004	1008	1104	1108	1204	1208	1304	1308	1404	1408	1504	1508	1604	1608
benhavn H .... **700 704** a.	0621	0654	0721	0754	0820	0854	0921	0926	0926	1021	1026	1121	1126	1221	1226	1321	1326	1421	1426	1521	1526	1621	1626

				EC 35					*EC* 37				*EC* 39										
								B	A					⑤⑥	⑦-④		⑦-④	⑤⑥					
Hamburg Hbf **825**..................d.	...	...	...	1328	...	...	...	...	1528	...	...	...	1728	...	...	...	...	...	...	...	...	...	...
Lübeck **825**.............................d.	...	...	...	1406	...	...	...	...	1606	...	...	...	1806	...	...	...	...	...	...	...	...	...	...
ttgarden .... ⛴ ▲ d.	...	...	...	1508	...	...	...	...	1708	...	...	...	1908	...	...	...	...	...	...	...	...	...	...
dby .... ⛴ ▲ d.	...	...	...	1620	...	...	...	1820	1820	...	...	...	2020	...	...	...	...	...	...	...	...	...	...
›øbing (Falster) .... ⊙ d.	1519	1547	1619	1647	1719	1747	1819	1847	1847	1919	...	2019	2047	2119	2119	...	2210	2219	...	...	...	...	...
rdingborg................................d.	1550	1611	1650	1711	1750	1811	1850	1911	1911	1950	...	2050	2111	2150	2150	...	2235	2252	...	...	...	...	...
ɘstved....................................d.	1612	1629	1712	1729	1812	1829	1912	1929	1929	2012	...	2112	2129	2212	2212	...	2257	2314	...	...	...	...	...
ıgsted.............................**700** a.	1630	|	1730	|	1830	|	1930	|	|	2030	...	2130	|	2230	2230	...	2315	2332	...	...	...	...	...
skilde .... **700 704** a.	1653	1659	1753	1759	1853	1859	1953	1959	1959	2053	...	2153	2159	2253	2258	...	2346	2353	...	...	...	...	...
je Taastrup........... **700 704** a.	1704	1708	1804	1808	1904	1908	2004	2008	2008	2104	...	2204	2208	2304	2307	...	2355	0004	...	...	...	...	...
benhavn H .... **700 704** a.	1721	1726	1821	1826	1921	1926	2021	2026	2026	2121	...	2221	2226	2323	2331	...	0015	0021	...	...	...	...	...

- Dec. 20 - Jan. 6.
- From Jan. 7.

⊙ – Trains run approximately hourly (more frequent on Ⓐ) Nykøbing (Falster) - Nakskov and v.v. Journey time: 45 minutes. Operator: Lokaltog A/S.

▲ – Through trains are conveyed by ⛴ Rødby - Puttgarden and v.v. ✕ on board ship. Passengers to/from Rødby or Puttgarden may be required to leave or join the train on board the train-ferry. See Table **2375** for other available sailings.

FREDRIKSHAVN - SKAGEN and HJØRRING - HIRTSHALS 728

›rdjyske Jernbaner (2nd class only)

›m Frederikshavn to Skagen:
Ⓐ at 0458, 0528, 0558, 0628, 0658, 0742, 0838, 0938, 1038, 1138, 1238, 1315, 1345, ›5, 1445, 1515, 1545, 1615, 1645, 1715, 1745, 1838, 1938, 2038, 2138, 2238 and 2338.
⑥ at 0603, 0703, 0738, 0838 and hourly until 2338.
† at 0603, 0658, 0735, 0835 and hourly until 2335.

›m Hjørring to Hirtshals:
Ⓐ at 0500, 0525, 0600, 0630, 0700, 0730, 0800, 0902, 1002, 1102, 1202, 1302, 1330, ›0, 1430, 1500, 1530, 1600, 1630, 1700, 1730, 1800, 1902, 2002, 2102, 2202 and 2302.
Ⓒ at 0002, 0602 ⑥, 0702, 0802 and hourly until 2302.

From Skagen to Frederikshavn: *40 km* Journey 36 – 40 minutes
On Ⓐ at 0022, 0545, 0615, 0645, 0715, 0745, 0852, 0952, 1052, 1152, 1252, 1332, 1402, 1432, 1502, 1532, 1602, 1632, 1702, 1732, 1802, 1852, 1952, 2052, 2152, 2252 and 2352.
On ⑥ at 0022, 0652, 0752 and hourly until 2352.
On † at 0022, 0648, 0748 and hourly until 2348.

From **Hirtshals to Hjørring**: *18 km* Journey 22 – 23 minutes
On Ⓐ at 0527, 0602, 0632, 0702, 0732, 0802, 0831, 0931, 1031, 1131, 1231, 1332, 1402, 1432, 1502, 1532, 1602, 1632, 1702, 1732, 1802, 1831, 1931, 2031, 2131, 2231 and 2331.
On Ⓒ at 0031, 0631 ⑥, 0731, 0831 and hourly until 2331.

ICELAND

There are no railways in Iceland but bus services serve most major settlements. Principal services enabling a circuit of the country (along road number 1) and some other important routes ar shown below. Additional information may be obtained from the websites of operators. For a complete listing of all routes, including local services and ferries, see www.publictransport.is. Buses hav scheduled stops in all settlements (often at N1 filling stations) but stops at other points along the route are possible after prior agreement with the operator.

Winter: Only the public operators *STR*, *SVA*, *FAS* and services to Keflavík airport operate. There are no long-distance *STR* services on Dec. 24, 25, 31, Jan. 1.

Summer: In addition to *STR*, further routes are run by private operators. Please note that several routes have been withdrawn recently and services may be reduced further. Travelling a full circle around the country by bus is only possible in summer and involves use of local buses in the east.

All schedules may change at short notice – confirm all timings with the operators. In winter buses are frequently cancelled, delayed, advanced or diverted due to adverse weather conditions.

Reservations: On public services operated by *STR*, *SVA* and *FAS*, reservations are not possible; tickets can be bought from the driver or obtained beforehand. All private services operated b *RE*, *SBA*, *STA*, *THU* and *TRX* must be pre-booked for guaranteed transportation, although tickets can also be obtained from the driver if space is available. Additional day tours and touris excursions are available throughout the year.

Public holidays in 2019: Jan. 1, Apr. 18, 19, 21, 22, 25, May 1, 30, June 9, 10, 17, Aug. 5, Dec. 25, 26.

729 PRINCIPAL BUS SERVICES

REYKJAVÍK - AKUREYRI - EGILSSTADIR

km	*STR Route 57*		④‡V	xV	⑥‡V	†V	ⒶV	†V		⚒E	†E	ⒶE	†E
0	Reykjavík (BSÍ terminal). ■ d.		*0832***c**	*0832***c**	*0832***c**	0840	*1658***c**	*1704***c**		*0832***c**	0840	*1658***c**	*1704***c**
7	Reykjavík (Mjódd) .... ■ d.	W	0900	0900	0900	0900	1730	1730	S	0900	0900	1730	1730
89	Borgarnes (N1) .... a.	I	1023	1023	1023**b**	1023	1853	1853	U	1023	1023	1853	1853
89	Borgarnes (N1) .... d.	N	...	1028	1028	1028	1858	1858	M	1028	1028	1858	1858
426	Akureyri (Hof) .... a.	T	...	1529**b**	1529	1529**b**	2359	2359	M	1529**b**	1529**b**	2359	2359
		E							E				
	STR Route 56	R				Y			R	E			
426	Akureyri (Hof) .... d.		...	...	...	1550	...	...		0800	...	...	...
513	Reykjahlíd (Mývatn) .... (N1) d.		...	...	...	1705	...	...		0915	...	...	...
676	Egilsstadir (Campsite) .... d.		...	...	...	1906	...	...		1116	...	...	...

STR Route 56				Y			E
Egilsstadir (Campsite).......d.		...	...	0909		...	1215
Reykjahlíd (Mývatn) .. (N1) d.	W	...	...	1110	S	...	1416
Akureyri (Hof) .... a.	I	...	...	1225	U	...	1531
	N				M		
STR Route 57	T	ⒷV	④‡V	yV	M	ⒷE	E
Akureyri (Hof) .... d.	E	1015	...	1620	E	1015	1620
Borgarnes (N1) .... a.	R	1518	...	2123	R	1518	2123
Borgarnes (N1) .... d.		1523	2128	2128		1523	2128
Reykjavík (Mjódd)......... ■ a.		1644	2249	2249		1644	2249
Reykjavík (BSÍ terminal) ■ a.		*1702***c**	*2301***c**	*2301***c**		*1702***c**	*2301*

Additional *STR* services operate Reykjavík (Mjódd) - Borgarnes (N1) and v.v. 3 – 8 services per day; no services on Dec. 25, Jan. 1. Very limited service on Dec. 24, 31.

EGILSSTADIR - HÖFN *Timings for summer 2019 are subject to confirmation*

km	*SVA Route 1*	Ⓐ	⑥B	⑥‡T		Ⓐ		
0	Egilsstadir (Campsite)............ d.	0902	0942	1022	1455**r**	1620	...	2255**r**
33	Reydarfjördur (Orkan)............ a.	0930	1010	1050	1525	1650	...	2325
km	*SVA Route 2*							
0	Reydarfjördur (Orkan)............ d.	0826	...	1626	...	0026	...	...
66	Breiddalsvík (Kaupfjelagid) ..... a.	0930	...	1730	...	0130	...	...
km	*SVA Route 4*	zB	zT		⑦B	⑦T	zB	⑦B
0	Breiddalsvík (Kaupfjelagid) ..... d.	...	...	...	...	...	1320	1815
65	Djúpivogur (Hótel Framtíd)...... d.	0810	0810	...	1400	1400	1415	1910
168	Höfn í Hornafirdi (N1) .... a.	0930**u**	1012**t**	...	1520**u**	1545**t**	1540**u**	2035**u**

SVA Route 1	ⒶT	ⒶB	⑥B		⑥‡T	ⒶB	ⒶT		①–④	
Reydarfjördur (Orkan).......... d.	0735	0741	0821	0826	0851	1501	1503	1626	1811	002
Egilsstadir (Campsite).......... a.	0806	0809	0849	0858**r**	0919	1530	1534	1658**r**	1843**r**	005
SVA Route 2										
Breiddalsvík (Kaupfjelagid)... d.	0620	...	1420	...	2220	...	...	...	...	...
Reydarfjördur (Orkan).......... a.	0725	...	1525	...	2325	...	...	...	...	...
SVA Route 4	zT	zB		zB	⑦T	⑦B		⑦B		
Höfn í Hornafirdi (N1) .... d.	1012**t**	1015**u**	...	1540**u**	1545**t**	1555**u**	...	2035**u**	...	...
Djúpivogur (Hótel Framtíd)... d.	1130	1220	...	1800	1710	1730	...	2200	...	...
Breiddalsvík (Kaupfjelagid)... a.	...	1320	...	...	...	1815	...	...	...	...

HÖFN - REYKJAVÍK

km	*operator*		*STR*	*STR*	*STR*		*STR*	*STA*	*STR*	
	route number		51	51	51		51	SC	51	
			⑥‡V	†V	ⒶV		E	D§	E	
0	Höfn í Hornafirdi (N1)............. d.	W	...	1025**s**	1155**s**	S	0740**s**	...	1610**s**	...
79	Jökulsárlón glacier lagoon .... d.	I	...	1125	1255	U	0840	1700	1710	...
135	Skaftafell .... d.	N	...	1220	1350	M	0935	1800	1805	...
275	Vík í Mýrdal (N1)..................... a.	T	...	1415**b**	1545**b**	M	1130**b**	2000	2000**b**	...
275	Vík í Mýrdal (N1)..................... d.	E	1442	1442	1600	E	1200	2030	2030	...
403	Selfoss (N1)............................ a.	R	1627	1627	1745	R	1345**b**	|	2215**b**	...
403	Selfoss (N1)............................ d.		1629	1629	1750		1350	|	2220**f**	...
456	Reykjavík (Mjódd) .... ■ a.		1724	1724	1845		1445	|	2315**f**	...
461	Reykjavík (BSÍ) .... ■ a.		*1802***c**	*1801***c**	*1902***c**		*1502***c**	2330**h**	*2331***c**	...

operator		*STR*	*STR*	*STR*		*STA*	*STR*	*STR*	*STR*	*STR*
route number		51	51	51		SC	51	51	51	51
		⑥‡V	†V	ⒶV		D§	⚒E	†E	ⒶE	ⒸE
Reykjavík (BSÍ) .... ■ d.	W	*1102***c**	*1104***c**	*1232***c**	S	0745**h**	*0832***c**	*0840***a**	*1558***c**	*1702*
Reykjavík (Mjódd)....... ■ d.	I	1130	1130	1300	U	|	0900	0900	1630	172
Selfoss (N1)..................... a.	N	1224	1224	1354	M	|	0954**b**	0954**b**	1724**b**	1819
Selfoss (N1)..................... d.	T	1227	1227	1357	M	|	0957	0957	1827	182
Vík í Mýrdal (N1)............. a.	E	1412	1412**b**	1542**b**	E	1130	1142**b**	1142**b**	2012**b**	2012
Vík í Mýrdal (N1)............. d.	R	...	1445	1615	R	1230	1200	1200	2030	203
Skaftafell .... d.		...	1650	1820		1430	1405	1405	2235	223
Jökulsárlón glacier lagoon . d.		...	1735	1905		1530	1450	1450	2320	232
Höfn í Hornafirdi (N1) ...... a.		...	1835**s**	2005**s**		...	1550**s**	1550**s**	0020**s**	0020

Additional *STR* services operate (Hvolsvöllur (N1) -) Selfoss (N1) - Reykjavík (Mjódd) and v.v., *100 km*, journey ± 1h 40 m, 3 – 8 services per day. No services on Dec. 25, Jan. 1. On Dec. 24, 31 only first morning services operate. Reservations possible and recommended on *STA* services.

OTHER SERVICES

Reykjavík - Keflavík Airport: *50 km*, journey ± 50 minutes. From BSÍ terminal ■: *flybus*, operator *RE*. From Klettagardar 4 terminal ■: *airportexpress*, reservation recommended, operator G From Reykjavík Terminal (Skógarhlíd 10) ■: *Airport direct*, Ⓡ, operator *AD*. *RE* and *GL* both offer departures in connection with all flights. *AD* operate to a fixed schedule, at least every hou All offer optional hotel transfer. Additional stopping services: *STR* route 55, BSÍ (Umferdarmidstödin ■) - KEF Airport and v.v. on Ⓐ peak hours only. During off-peak hours and on Ⓒ route 55 o operates Hafnarfjördur (Fjördur) – KEF Airport and v.v. From Reykjavík, use STR city route 1 from Hlemmur via BSÍ/Landspítalinn ■ direction Hfj. Vellir and change to route 55 at Hafnarfjörc (Fjördur). 7 – 13 services per day with a total journey time of 75 – 90 minutes.

Reykjavík - Blue Lagoon: 48 *km*, journey ± 45 minutes. From BSÍ terminal ■: operator *RE*. From Reykjavík Terminal (Skógarhlíd 10) ■: 'Destination Blue Lagoon', operator *AD*. Both operat offer departures every hour, also infrequent departures from Keflavík airport.

Egilsstadir - Seydisfjördur: 27 *km*, journey ± 35 minutes, *SVA* route 3, operated by *FAS*. Services connect with Smyril Line ferry (Table **2285**). Confirm departure point with operator. Summer (June 1 - Aug. 25, 2018): From **Egilsstadir** (Campsite) 0900Ⓐ, 1045④, 1300⑥⑦, 1615Ⓐ. From **Seydisfjördur** (Herdubreid, Austurvegur 4) 0750Ⓐ, 1000④**m**, 1215⑥⑦, 1515 Winter (Aug. 26, 2018 - May 31, 2019): From **Egilsstadir** (Campsite) 0900Ⓐ, 1005⑥, 1050② **U**, 1615Ⓐ. From **Seydisfjördur** (Herdubreid, Austurvegur 4) 0745Ⓐ, 0920⑥, 1015② **U m**, 1515

Reykjavík - Thingvellir - Geysir - Gullfoss (Golden Circle): Only available as a day excursion (daily all year by different operators). Geysir / Gullfoss also served by SBA route 610 (see belo

KJÖLUR HIGHLAND ROUTE: Reykjavík - Akureyri via Selfoss - Geysir§ - Gulfoss§ - Kerlingarfjöll§ - Hveravellir§ (448 *km*). Operator: *SBA* route 610/610a. Reservation possible. Reykjavík BSÍ terminal ■ d. 0800 → Geysir a. 0955, d. 1025 → Gullfoss a. 1040, d. 1110 → Akureyri Oddeyrarbót 2 (adjacent to Hof) a. 1830. ①③⑤⑦ June 19 - Sept. 6, 2019 ⊖. Akureyri Oddeyrarbót 2 d. 0800 → Gullfoss a. 1520, d. 1550 → Geysir a. 1605, d. 1635 → Reykjavík BSÍ terminal ■ a. 1830. ②④⑥⑦ June 18 - Sept. 5, 2019 ⊖.

LAUGAVEGUR HIKING TRAIL: Reykjavík - Landmannalaugar, *215 km*, journey ± 4 h 15 m, 1 – 10 services per day. Reykjavík - Thórsmörk, *158 km*, journey ± 4 h 30 m, 1 – 8 services per da Landmannalaugar service operated daily in 2019 (⊖) by *RE* June 14 - Sept. 15, *TRX* June 21 - Sept. 8, *THU* June 15 - Sept. 15, *STA* June 15 - Sept. 15. Thórsmörk operated daily in 2019 (by *RE* June 1 - Sept. 20, *TRX* June 14 - Sept. 8, *THU* June 15 - Sept. 15, *STA* June 15 - Sept. 15. Both services are dependent on road opening dates. Reservation recommended.

- **B** – June 1 - Aug. 31, 2019 (subject to confirmation).
- **D** – July 1 - Aug. 31, 2019.
- **E** – May 26 - ca. Sept. 7, 2019.
- **T** – Sept. 1, 2018 - May 31, 2019.
- **U** – ② Aug. 28 - Oct. 23, 2018, Apr. 2 - May 29, 2019.
- **V** – Sept. 9, 2018 - May 25, 2019.
- **Y** – ①②⑤† Sept. 9, 2018 - May 25, 2019.
- **a** – *STR* route 57 from BSÍ terminal, change in Mjódd.
- **b** – Change buses. Passengers travelling onwards should inform operator / bus driver.
- **c** – Connection with *STR* city route 3 from/to BSÍ/Landspítalinn, change in Mjódd (see ■).
- **f** – *STR* route 52 on Ⓐ; *STR* route 51 on Ⓒ.
- **h** – Reykjavík Harpa concert hall. Also serves Reykjavík campsite (Laugardalur).
- **m** – Seydisfjördur Smyril Line terminal.
- **r** – Egilsst. Hamragerdi, 250 metres south of campsite.
- **s** – Höfn *STR* bus stop at Vikurbraut / swimming pool (600 metres south of N1).
- **t** – Höfn campsite (opposite of N1).
- **u** – Höfn tourist information, 1 km south of N1.
- **x** – ①②③⑤ (not holidays).
- **y** – ①②③⑤⑥⑦ (also holidays).
- **z** – ①③④⑤.
- ⊖ – Dependent on highland road opening dates.

- ‡ – Not holidays.
- § – With sightseeing stops.

N1 – Bus stop is at N1 filling station.
SC – *STA* South Coast route.

Operators:

AD	Airport Direct ✆ +354 497 8000 www.airportdirect.is and www.destinationbluelagoon.is
FAS	Ferdathjónusta Austurlands ✆ +354 472 1515 www.visitseydisfjordur.com
GL	Gray Line Iceland ✆ +354 540 1313 www.airportexpress.is
RE	Reykjavik Excursions ✆ +354 580 5400 www.re.is or www.ioyo.is
SBA	SBA - Nordurleid ✆ +354 550 0700 www.sba.is
STA	Sterna ✆ +354 551 1166 www.icelandbybus.is
STR	Straetó ✆ +354 540 2700 www.straeto.is
SVA	Straetisvagnar Austurlands ✆ +354 471 2320 www.svaust.is
THU	Thule Travel ✆ +354 519 3399 www.thuletravel.is
TRX	TREX ✆ +354 587 6000 www.trex.is

■ – Reykjavík terminals

Terminal (and Operator)	*Location*
BSÍ bus terminal	city centre (south)
○ terminal (*RE*, *SBA*, also certain *STR* services on routes 52 and 57)	
○ bus stop "Umferdarmidstödin" 50 m north of BSÍ terminal (STR route 5	
○ bus stop "BSÍ/Landspítalinn" 100 m north of BSÍ terminal (STR city buse	
Reykjavík Terminal, Skógarhlíd 10 (*AD*)	1 km east of BSÍ
Harpa concert hall (*STA*)	city centre (old harbour)
Hlemmur (*STR* city services)	city centre (east)
Klettagardar 4 terminal (*GL*)	5 km east of city centre
Mjódd bus terminal (*STR*)	7 km southeast of city centre

Connections from city centre:

To BSÍ: optional hotel transfer by *RE* or *STR* city services 1, 3, 5, 6, 14, 15.
To Skógarhlíd 10: optional hotel transfer by *AD* (*Smartbus*); *STR* city service 1, 3, 6 (nearest bus stop is Klambratún).
To Klettagardar: optional hotel transfer by *GL* or *STR* city service 16.
To Mjódd: *STR* city services 3, 11, 12, 17. City service 3 runs at least every mins from Hlemmur to Sel/Fell via Harpa, BSÍ/Landspítalinn, Klambratún a Mjódd. Journey to Mjódd 25 – 32 minutes from Hlemmur, 14 – 21 minutes fro BSÍ/Landspítalinn. From Mjódd to city centre: *STR* city service 3 directi Hlemmur, departs at least xx21 and xx51 past each hour. Note: no city servic on † mornings before 0950. Tickets valid on connecting *STR* services.

SWEDEN

SEE MAP PAGE 343

erators: Most services are operated by **SJ AB** (*SJ*) - Swedish State Railways - formerly part of Statens Järnvägar: www.sj.se. There is, however, a number of other operators that run services shown within the European Rail Timetable; these are indicated by their initials in the relevant table heading, or at the top of each train column where more than one operator runs services on the same route.

AEX – Arlanda Express (A-Train AB) · *IB* – Inlandsbanan AB · *MTR* – MTR Express · *NSB* – Norges Statsbaner
NT – Norrtåg · *Øtåg* – Øresundståg · *SKJB* – Skandinaviska Jernbanor · *ST* – Snälltåget
Tågab – Tågåkeriet i Bergslagen AB · *Vy* – Vy Tåg AB

The Regional Public Transport Authority is responsible for many local services, known collectively as Länstrafik (*LT*). Those shown within these pages are abbreviated as follows:
JLT – Jönköpings Länstrafik · *KLT/ÖT* – Kalmar Läns Trafik / ÖstgötaTrafiken · *Skåne* – Skånetrafiken
V – Västtrafik · *VTAB* – Värmlandstrafik · *XT* – X-Trafik

rvices: Trains convey first and second classes of accommodation, unless otherwise shown. The fastest trains are classified *Snabbtåg (Sn)* and *InterCity (IC)*. On *SJ* night trains, sleeping cars (🛏) offer the following accommodation: 1st class compartments (one or two berths) with shower and WC. These can only be booked as a private compartment. A hotel breakfast is usually included if arriving between 0630 and 0900. 2nd class compartments (three berths) with shower and WC available in the car. These can be booked as a private compartment for one, two or three persons, or as a single berth in a shared compartment (male or female). Couchette cars (▬) have six berths; these can be booked as a single berth in a shared compartment or as a private compartment when four or more passengers are travelling together. Refreshment services (✕, 🍸 or Shop) may be available for part of the journey only. Snälltåget (*ST*) night trains offer different sleeping and couchette options - contact operator for details.

nings: **Valid until December 14, 2019** except where shown otherwise. Services may be amended or cancelled on and around the dates of public holidays.
WARNING! From June 24 to August 18 engineering work will disrupt services in the Stockholm area, particularly affecting trains to and from the south of the country (Tables 730, 732, 733, 740, 750, 755 and 756). Affected trains will instead serve either Stockholm Södra or Flemingsberg stations (as indicated in the individual table headers) and passengers wishing to travel from or to the city centre should use alternative suburban services.

servations: Seat reservation is compulsory on all *Snabbtåg* and night trains, and for through journeys to København (excluding local and *Skåne* services). Reserved seats are not labelled and, if occupied, must be claimed by presenting the seat ticket on the train.

pplements: Special supplements are payable for travel on *Snabbtåg* high-speed trains.

kets: Travellers should ensure they are in possession of a valid ticket before joining a train as penalties can be severe (1200 SEK on *SJ* services, for example). Local operators issue tickets onboard the train where stations have no ticket machines.

STOCKHOLM - MALMÖ - KØBENHAVN 730

Service valid from August 19 (subject to alteration on and around public holidays). From June 24 to August 18 services operate from / to Stockholm Södra (not Central) in revised timings. For other regional and *IC* services Stockholm - Norrköping - Linköping, see next page.
Trains in this table are not available for local journeys Stockholm - Södertälje Syd and v.v.

m			Sn 517 🅁✕ ①	Sn 519 🅁✕ Ⓐ	Sn 501 🅁✕ ⑥	Sn 521 🅁✕ Ⓐ	Sn 523 🅁✕ Ⓐ	Sn 525 🅁✕ C	Sn 527 🅁✕ C	ST 3941 ✕ △	Sn 529 🅁✕ C	Sn 531 🅁✕ Ⓑ	Sn 533 🅁✕	ST 3931 ✕ D△	Sn 535 🅁✕ Ⓑ	Sn 507 🅁✕ ⑥	Sn 537 🅁✕ ⒷE	Sn 539 🅁✕ ⒷE	Sn 541 🅁✕ Ⓑ	Sn 541 🅁✕ ⑥	ST 3943 ✕△ ①–⑥	Sn 513 🅁✕ ⒶJ	ST 3943 ✕ △⑦	Sn 10513 🅁✕ ⑦J	Sn 505 🅁✕ ⑦E
0	**Stockholm** Central	‡ d.	0425	0525	0622	0625	0722	0825	0925	0933	1025	1125	1225	1229	1325	1422	1425	1524	1624	1624	1628	1630	1635	1637	1705
36	Södertälje Syd	‡ d.	0444	0544	0640	|	0741	|	0944	0951	|	1144	|	1253	1344	1440	|	1544	|	|	1645	1648	1652	1656	|
62	**Norrköping**	754 d.	0541	0641	0737	0739	0838	0937	1041	1057	1137	1241	1337	1359	1441	1537	1537	1641	1737	1737	1750	1757	1755	1803	|
09	Linköping	754 d.	0605	0705	0801	0803	0902	1002	1105	1124	1201	1305	1401	1425	1505	1601	1601	1706	1801	1801	1819	1826	1821	1831	|
41	**Mjölby**	d.	|	|	0817	0819	|	1017	|	|	1217	|	1417	|	|	1617	1617	|	1817	1817	|	1841	|	1852	|
77	Tranås	d.	|	|	|	|	0931	|	|	|	|	|	|	|	|	|	|	|	|	|	|	1908	|	1912	|
29	**Nässjö**	d.	0655	0755	0855	0856	0956	1055	1155	1219	1254	1355	1455	1522	1555	1655	1655	1757	1855	1855	1917	1933	1917	1943	|
76	Alvesta	746 d.	0729	0829	0929	0929	1030	1129	1229	1256	1329	1429	1529	1606	1629	1729	1729	1831	1929	1929	1954	...	1954	...	2000
53	Älmhult	746 d.	|	0848	|	|	|	|	|	|	|	|	|	|	1648	|	|	1850	|	|	|	...	|	...	|
4	Hässleholm	745 746 a.	0809	0909	1009	1009	1109	1209	1309	1335s	1409	1509	1609	1655s	1709	1809	1809	1910	2009	2009	2035s	...	2035s	...	2038
31	Lund	745 746 ● a.	0838s	0938s	1038	1038	1138	1238	1338s	1415s	1438	1538s	1638	1725s	1740s	1838	1838	1939s	2039	2039s	2110s	...	2110s	...	2113s
97	**Malmö** C	● a.	0854	0954	1054	1054	1154	1254	1354	1430	1454	1554	1654	1745	1754	1854	1854	1954	2054	2054	2125	...	2125	...	2125
97	**Malmö** C	● d.	...	...	1059	1059	1159	1259	...	...	1459	...	1658	...	...	1858	1858	...	2058	...	...	...	...	...	...
96	København Lufthavn ✈	● a.	...	...	1117s	1117s	1217s	1317s	...	...	1517s	...	1717s	...	...	1917s	1917s	...	2117s	...	...	...	...	...	...
4	**København** H	● a.	...	...	1131	1131	1231	1332	...	...	1531	...	1731	...	...	1931	1931	...	2131	...	...	...	...	...	...

		Sn 505 🅁✕ ⑦	Sn 543 🅁✕ Ⓑ	Sn 555 🅁✕ ⑥	Sn 545 🅁✕ ⒷE	Sn 547 🅁✕ ⒷE	Sn 549 🅁✕ ⑦	1 🅁 ⒷA	ST 3921 🅁 T
ckholm Central	‡ d.	1705	1725	1820	1823	1925	2025	2309	2325
lertälje Syd	‡ d.	|	1744	1838	|	1944	|	|	|
rköping	754 d.	|	1841	1936	1936	2041	2137	0102	0135s
köping	754 d.	|	1905	2000	2000	2105	2201	0138	0215s
lby	d.	|	|	2016	2016	|	2217	|	|
nås	d.	|	|	|	|	|	|	|	|
ssjö	d.	|	1955	2054	2054	2155	2255	0341e	0335s
esta	746 d.	2000	2029	2128	2128	2229	2329	0444	0455s
hult	746 d.	|	|	|	|	2248	|	|	|
sleholm	745 746 a.	2038	2109	2209	2209	2310	0008	0553s	0600s
d	745 746 ● a.	2113s	2138s	2238s	2238s	2339s	0037s	0636s	0645s
mö C	● a.	2125	2154	2254	2254	2354	0051	0655	0705
mö C	● d.	...	...	...	...	...	...	...	...
enhavn Lufthavn ✈	● a.	...	...	...	...	...	...	...	...
enhavn H	● a.	...	...	...	...	...	...	...	...

		Sn 520 🅁✕ Ⓐ	Sn 512 🅁✕ ⒶJ	Sn 522 🅁✕ Ⓐ	Sn 516 🅁✕ ⑥J	Sn 524 🅁✕ Ⓐ		Sn 526 🅁✕	Sn 528 🅁✕ ①–⑥	Sn 530 🅁✕ F	ST 3940 ✕ △
København H	● d.	...	...	...	...	...	...	...	...	0823	...
København Lufthavn ✈	● d.	...	...	...	...	...	...	...	...	0836u	...
Malmö C	● a.	...	...	...	...	...	...	...	...	0859	...
Malmö C	● d.	0404	...	0510	...	0604	...	0710	0810	0910	0918
Lund	745 746 ● d.	0415u	...	0524u	...	0617u	...	0724u	0824u	0924	0930u
Hässleholm	745 746 d.	0444	...	0552	...	0647	...	0752	0852	0952	1005u
Älmhult	746 d.	0505	...	|	...	0710	...	|	|	|	|
Alvesta	746 d.	0525	...	0631	...	0729	...	0831	0931	1031	1045
Nässjö	d.	0559	0637	0705	0736	0803	...	0905	1005	1105	1123
Tranås	d.	0623	0702	|	0802	|	...	|	|	|	|
Mjölby	a.	|	|	0741	|	|	...	0941	|	1141	|
Linköping	754 a.	0652	0735	0757	0836	0853	...	0957	1053	1157	1221
Norrköping	754 a.	0718	0802	0821	0903	0918	...	1021	1118	1221	1247
Södertälje Syd	‡ a.	0816	0908	|	1009	1015	...	|	1215	|	1352
Stockholm Central	‡ a.	0835	0928	0934	1031	1034	...	1134	1234	1336	1410

		Sn 532 🅁✕ Ⓑ	Sn 534 🅁✕	Sn 502 🅁✕ ⑦		Sn 536 🅁✕ Ⓐ	Sn 10536 🅁✕ ⑦	ST 3930 ✕ △		Sn 538 🅁✕ G	Sn 540 🅁✕ Ⓑ	Sn 542 🅁✕		Sn 544 🅁✕ Ⓑ	ST 3942 ✕ △	Sn 546 🅁✕		Sn 548 🅁✕ Ⓑ	ST 3920 🅁 S	Sn 506 🅁✕ ⑦		Sn 550 🅁✕ Ⓑ	Sn 508 🅁✕ ⑦	2 🅁 ⒷA	
enhavn H	● d.	...	1023	...	...	...	...	...	...	1223	1323	1423	...	...	...	1623	...	...	...	...	...	1823	...	...	...
enhavn Lufthavn ✈	● d.	...	1036u	...	...	...	...	...	...	1236u	1337u	1436u	...	...	...	1636u	...	...	...	...	...	1836u	...	...	...
mö C	● a.	...	1059	...	...	...	...	...	...	1259	1359	1459	...	...	...	1659	...	...	...	...	...	1859	...	...	...
mö C	● d.	1010	1110	1119	...	1210	1210	1220	...	1310	1410	1510	...	1604	1615	1710	...	1810	1630	1834	...	1910	2036	2232	...
d	745 746 ● d.	1026u	1125	1132u	...	1224u	1224u	1230u	...	1324	1426	1523	...	1617u	1628u	1724	...	1824u	1650u	1847u	...	1924	2049u	2246u	...
sleholm	745 746 d.	1054	1152	1201	...	1252	1252	1309u	...	1352	1453	1553	...	1648	1700u	1752	...	1852	1735u	1917	...	1952	2119	2332u	...
hult	746 d.	|	|	|	...	|	|	|	...	|	|	|	...	1709	|	|	...	|	|	|	...	|	|	|	...
esta	746 d.	1132	1230	1239	...	1331	1331	1353	...	1431	1531	1631	...	1731	1738	1831	...	1931	1820u	1955	...	2031	2156	0032	...
sjö	d.	1205	1304	1313	...	1405	1405	1433	...	1505	1605	1705	...	1805	1817	1905	...	2005	1915u	2029	...	2105	2229	0126	...
nås	d.	|	|	|	...	|	|	|	...	|	1630	|	...	|	|	|	...	|	|	|	...	2128	|	|	...
by	a.	|	1341	|	...	|	|	|	...	1541	|	1741	...	|	|	1941	...	|	|	|	...	|	|	|	...
öping	754 a.	1253	1357	1401	...	1453	1453	1533	...	1557	1658	1757	...	1853	1918	1957	...	2053	2025u	2120	...	2157	2317	0248	...
rköping	754 a.	1318	1421	1426	...	1518	1518	1602	...	1624	1722	1821	...	1918	1946	2021	...	2118	2100u	2145	...	2221	2342	0320	...
ertälje Syd	‡ a.	1416	|	|	...	1618	1618	1715	...	|	1820	|	...	2015	2050	|	...	2215	|	|	...	2318	0039	|	...
ckholm Central	‡ a.	1435	1535	1545	...	1637	1640	1745	...	1736	1839	1935	...	2034	2110	2136	...	2234	2300	2258	...	2337	0058	0555	...

Conveys 🛏, ▬ and 2.
Daily from Aug. 31 (also Aug. 24, 25).
⑦ until June 23 (also June 3–8).
From Sept. 1.
Ⓐ Aug. 19–30 (runs as **10530**); daily from Aug. 31 (also Aug. 24, 25).
Ⓑ Aug. 19–30 (not Aug. 24); daily from Aug. 31.
To / from Jönköping (Table **733**).
③⑥ Aug 28 - Sept 21: 🛏, ▬ and ✕ / 🍸 Malmö - Stockholm - Storlien / Duved (Table **767**).
⑦ Aug. 29 - Sept. 19: 🛏, ▬ and ✕ / 🍸 Storlien / Duved - Stockholm - Malmö (Table **767**).

e – Arrives 0301.
s – Stops to set down only.
u – Stops to pick up only.

‡ – Trains in this table are not available for local journeys Stockholm - Södertälje Syd and v.v. Frequent local trains operate.
● – See also Tables **735**, **737**, **745** and **746** for other trains Lund - Malmö - København and v.v.
△ – Subject to confirmation.

Sn – High-speed train. 🅁 and ✕. Supplement payable.

730 STOCKHOLM - MALMÖ - KØBENHAVN

Service valid from August 19 (subject to alteration on and around public holidays).
From June 24 to August 18 services operate from / to Stockholm Södra (not Central) in revised timings.
Other regional and *IC* services STOCKHOLM - NORRKÖPING - LINKÖPING

			IC		*IC*		*IC*		*IC*	*Sn*		*IC*		*IC*		*IC*	*IC*	*IC*			*IC*		*IC*	*IC*	
			267		**259**		**261**		**265**	**565**		**269**		**273**		**275**	**297**	**277**			**281**		**285**	**287**	
	Ⓐ	Ⓐ	Ⓐ	Ⓐ	Ⓐ	Ⓐ	⑥	Ⓒ	Ⓒ	🅁A	B			⑤-⑦	Ⓑc	Ⓐ	⑦	☆	①-⑥	Ⓑ	d		⑦	Ⓐ	
Gävle C **761** d.	...	...	...	...	0613	...	0712	...	0916	0916	...	1103	...	1313	...	1403	1503	1513	...	...	1713	...	1903	2013	
Stockholm Central d.	0456	0557	0638	0647	0745	0754	0845	0935	1045	1103	1136	1245	1333	1445	1535	1546	1648	1642	1647	1734	1845	1935	2045	2145	21
Flemingsberg d.	0507	0608	|	0658	|	0805	|	0946	|	|	1147	|	1350	|	1546	|	|	|	1658	1745	|	1946	|	|	22
Södertälje Syd d.	0519	0620	0657	0710	0804	0817	0904	0957	1105	1123	1158	1305	1401	1505	1557	1606	1707	1701	1712	1757	1904	1957	2104	2204	22
Nyköping d.	0603	0706	|	0800	|	0900	|	1036	|	|	1235	|	1445	|	1645	|	|	|	1752	1840	|	2037	|	|	22
Norrköping **754** a.	0646	0750	0800	0840	0908	0940	1007	1116	1209	1228	1324	1409	1524	1608	1724	1709	1810	1821	1832	1925	2009	2129e	2210	2309	23
Linköping **754** a.	...	...	0833	...	0934	...	1033	...	1235	1255	...	1435	...	1634	...	1736	1851	1852	...	...	2036	...	2236	2335	

		IC		*IC*				*IC*	*IC*	*IC*			*IC*	*IC*		*IC*		*IC*	*Sn*			*IC*		*IC*	
		262		**264**				**266**	**298**	**268**			**270**	**272**		**274**		**278**	**580**			**282**		**284**	
	Ⓐ	Ⓐ	Ⓐ	Ⓐ	ⒶF	①-③	⑥	⑥	†	Ⓐ	ⒶA	Ⓒ	⑥	Ⓐ	Ⓒ	Ⓒ★		Ⓒ	🅁Ⓐ		ⒶA			¶	
Linköping **754** d.	...	0520	...	0621	0610	...	...	0722	0820	0820	...	0812	0920	1020	...	1120	...	1320	1422	...	...	1520	...	1725	
Norrköping **754** d.	0510	0548	0552	0648	0639	0715	0739	0749	0847	0847	0831	0840	0947	1047	1043	1147	1230	1347	1449	1430	1530	1548	1628	1752	21
Nyköping d.	0551	|	0634	|	0720	0758	0820	|	|	|	0916	0921	|	|	1125	|	1317	|	|	1517	1617	|	1715	|	22
Södertälje Syd d.	0631	0652	0715	0752	0803	0840	0903	0853	0951	0951	0954	1001	1051	1151	1204	1251	1400	1450	1552	1556	1658	1654	1802	1855	23
Flemingsberg d.	0643	|	0727	|	0815	0852	0915	|	|	|	1005	1013	|	|	1216	|	1412	|	|	1611	1710	|	1814	|	23
Stockholm Central a.	0656	0714	0740	0813	0842	0908	0928	0915	1013	1013	1017	1025	1113	1213	1229	1313	1428	1511	1613	1624	1723	1714	1827	1914	23
Gävle C **761** a.	...	0856	...	0943	...	...	...	1046	1143	1146	...	...	1246	1346	...	1443	...	1656	1743	...	...	1856	...	2046	

A – Ⓐ from Sept. 2.
B – From Aug. 30.
F – Until Aug. 30.
c – Not Aug. 25.

d – *IC* **291** on ⑦.
e – 2116 on ⑥.

★ – *IC* **20274** on ⑦.
¶ – *IC* **286** on ⑤⑥⑦.

☆ – ①-⑥. Runs as *IC* **10297** on ⑥ (Linköping a. 1838).

☛ Additional trains **Stockholm Central - Norrköping** at 0731⑥, 1025Ⓐ A, 1435Ⓐ;
Norrköping - Stockholm Central at 0931Ⓐ, 1130Ⓐ, 1727Ⓐ, 1830Ⓑ, 2030Ⓒ.

731 MALMÖ - YSTAD - SIMRISHAMN and TRELLEBORG

Operator: *Skå*

km		⚒	Ⓐ	Ⓐ	⑥	Ⓐ		Ⓐ		⚒							⚒		⚒	⚒		⚒	⚒		⑤⑥	
0	**Malmö** C d.	0007	...	0507	...	0537	0607	0637	0707	0737	0807	0837	and at the same	1907	1937	2007	2037	2107	2137	2207	2207	2237	2307	2307	2337a	23
70	Ystad a.	0056	0458	0556	0558	0628	0656	0728	0756	0828	0856	0928	minutes past	1956	2028	2056	2128	2156	2228	2256	2256	2328	2356	2356	0028a	00
116	Simrishamn a.	...	0538	0638	0638	...	0738	...	0838	...	0938	...	each hour until	2038	...	2138	...	2238	...	2338	...	...	0038	...	...	

	Ⓐ	Ⓐ		Ⓐ	Ⓐ	Ⓒ	Ⓐ	⚒		Ⓐ							⚒		⚒	G	⑤⑥	⚒		⚒	⚒	⑤
Simrishamn d.	...	...	...	...	0547	...	...	0647	...	...	0747	...	and at the same	1847	...	1947	...	2047	...	2147	2147	...	2247	2247	2347	23
Ystad d.	0430	0500	0530	0600	0630	0630	0700	0730	0730	0800	0830	0900	minutes past	1930	2000	2030	2100	2130	2200	2230	2230	2300	2326	2330	0026	00
Malmö C a.	0521	0551	0621	0651	0721	0721	0751	0821	0821	0851	0921	0951	each hour until	2021	2051	2121	2151	2221	2251	2315	2321	2351	...	0021	|	01

km		⑥⑦	⑥⑦						⑤⑥	G	
0	**Malmö** C d.	0020	0050	...	0550	0620	and every 30 minutes	2250	2320	2326	2350
44	Trelleborg C a.	0052	0122	...	0622	0652	until	2322	2352	2352	0022

	H								G	⑤
Trelleborg C d.	0005	...	0505	0535	and every 30 minutes	2205	2235	2305	2335	23
Malmö C a.	0032r	...	0539	0612	until	2239	2301j	2332j	0001	00

G – ①②③④† only.
H – ②-⑦ only.

a – Not June 26, Nov. 11.
j – 8 – 12 minutes later on ⑤⑥.
r – 0039 on Ⓒ.

732 STOCKHOLM - ESKILSTUNA - ARBOGA - ÖREBRO

Service valid from August 19 (subject to alteration on and around public holidays).
From June 24 to August 18 services operate from / to Stockholm Södra (not Central) in revised timings.

km		Ⓐ	Ⓐ			Ⓐ		Ⓐ		Ⓐ		Ⓐ	Ⓐ	Ⓒ	Ⓐ	Ⓐ		Ⓐ	Ⓐ	ⒶH		Ⓐ		G	⑤
0	**Stockholm** Central d.	...	0531	0629	...	0748	0848	0948	1048	1148	1248	1348	1449	1449	1550	1612	1653	1653	1718	1748	1850	1947	2048	2250	23
36	Södertälje Syd d.	...	0553	0651	...	0810	0910	1010	1110	1210	1310	1410	1511	1511	1612	1635	1716	1716	1740	1810	1912	2009	2110	2312	23
67	Läggesta ● d.	...	0612	0709	...	0828	0928	1028	1128	1228	1328	1428	1528	1528	1630	1654	1734	1734	1758	1828	1929	2028	2128	2330	00
83	Strängnäs d.	0511	0624	0722	...	0838	0938	1038	1138	1238	1338	1438	1538	1538	1640	1704	1744	1747	1808	1838	1939	2038	2138	2340	00
115	Eskilstuna a.	0531	0643	0743	...	0855	0955	1055	1155	1255	1355	1455	1555	1555	1657	1724	1801	1801	1826	1855	1955	2055	2154	2357	00
115	Eskilstuna d.	0535	0647	0800	...	...	1000	...	1200	...	1400	1500	1600	1600	1701	...	1803	1803	...	1900	2000	...	2200	...	
141	Kungsör d.	0558	0702	0815	...	...	1015	...	1215	...	1415	1515	1615	1615	1721	...	1818	1818	...	1915	2015	...	2215	...	
159	Arboga **756** a.	0606	0713	0826	...	...	1026	...	1226	...	1426	1526	1626	1626	1731	...	1829	1829	...	1926	2026	...	2226	...	
205	**Örebro** C **756** a.	0638	0738	*0903*	...	...	*1104*	...	*1306*	...	*1503*	1550	1652	*1704*	1753	...	...	1852	...	1953	...	...	...	...	

	Ⓐ	Ⓐ	Ⓐ	ⒶH		Ⓐ	⑦	Ⓐ	⑥	Ⓐ		Ⓐ		Ⓐ		Ⓐ		Ⓐ	Ⓒ	Ⓐ	Ⓐ			
Örebro C **756** d.	...	0503	...	0600	...	...	*0643*	0703	*0757*	0807	*0857*	...	*1057*	...	*1257*	...	*1456*	1606	*1657*	1705	1806	*1857*	*2057*	
Arboga **756** d.	...	0526	...	0624	...	...	0726	0726	0830	0830	0930	...	1130	...	1330	...	1530	1629	1728	1728	1829	1930	2130	22
Kungsör d.	...	0537	...	0635	...	...	0737	0737	0841	0841	0941	...	1141	...	1341	...	1540	1640	1743	1743	1840	1941	2141	22
Eskilstuna a.	...	0553	...	0652	...	...	0753	0753	0858	0858	0957	...	1158	...	1357	...	1557	1656	1758	1758	1856	1957	2157	23
Eskilstuna d.	0511	0556	0623	0654	0654	0717	0755	0755	0902	0902	0959	1102	1202	1300	1400	1500	1600	1658	1800	1800	1900	2000	2200	
Strängnäs d.	0527	0612	0640	0710	0710	0733	0811	0811	0918	0918	1015	1118	1218	1316	1416	1516	1616	1714	1816	1816	1916	2016	2216	
Läggesta ● d.	0536	0621	0650	0719	0719	0742	0820	0820	0927	0927	1024	1127	1227	1325	1425	1524	1625	1723	1825	1825	1925	2025	2225	
Södertälje Syd a.	0554	0639	0708	0736	0736	0800	0837	0837	0945	0945	1042	1145	1245	1343	1443	1543	1648	1741	1843	1843	1943	2043	2243	
Stockholm Central a.	0618	0703	0735	0801	0801	0824	0900	0900	1009	1009	1106	1209	1310	1407	1507	1610	1712	1805	1906	1906	2007	2107	2307	

G – ①②③④⑦.
H – From / to Hallsberg (Table **756**).

● – Summer only narrow gauge service operates Mariefred - Läggesta (nedre) - Taxinge-Näsby and v.v.
Operator: Östra Södermanlands Järnväg, Box 53, SE - 647 22 Mariefred. ✆ +46 (0) 159 210 00, fax +46 (0) 159 211

733 SKÖVDE - JÖNKÖPING - NÄSSJÖ

2nd class only — Operator: *V* (except *Sn* trai

Valid until June 22

km			*Sn*	*Sn*																					
			512	**516**																					
		Ⓐ	Ⓐ	⑥	Ⓐ	Ⓐ	Ⓐ		⑥	Ⓐ		Ⓐ				⑥	Ⓐ	Ⓑ		Ⓐ	⑦		Ⓐ	Ⓐ	⑥
	Skövde **740** d.	0437	...	...	0549	0655	0757	0856	*0926*	0956	1056	*1124*	1256	*1326*	1456	1556	1552	...	1652	*1739*	...	1856	1942	2057	2
0	Falköping **740** d.	0457	...	...	0609	0715	0821	0916	1016	1016	1116	1216	1316	1414	1516	1616	1610	1617	1715	1804	1816	1917	2015	2119	2
30	Jönköping a.	0540	...	...	0655	0800	0902	1001	1101	1101	1201	1301	1400	1459	1603	1702	...	1702	1801	1849	1902	2001	2100	2203	2
100	Jönköping d.	0543	0600	0659	0702	0805	0903	1006	1103	1103	1205	1303	1405	1501	1605	1706	...	1705	1808	1852	1905	2003	2106	2209	2
100	**Nässjö** a.	0616	0631	0728	0738	0842	0940	1041	1139	1139	1242	1343	1439	1541	1640	1741	...	1741	1842	1925	1938	2037	2140	2240	2
143	*Stockholm C* **730** a.	...	0928	1031	...	...	...	...	...	...	...	...	...	...	...	...	...	...	...	...	...	...	...	...	

																				Sn	*Sn*		
																				513	**513**		
	Ⓐ	Ⓐ	Ⓐ	⑥	①-⑥		Ⓐ		⑥	Ⓐ		⑦	Ⓐ		⑥	Ⓑ		Ⓑ	Ⓒ	Ⓐ	Ⓐ	⑦	Ⓐ
Stockholm C **930** d.	...	...	...	...	...	...	...	...	...	...	...	...	...	...	...	...	...	...	...	...	1630	1637	...
Nässjö d.	0436	0551	0714	0729	0816	0919	1020	1115	1219	1219	1316	1416	1416	1528	1620	1620	1717	1818	1916	1925	1943	1943	2021
Jönköping a.	0507	0627	0750	0801	0851	0958	1056	1152	1252	1252	1349	1448	1448	1601	1653	1654	1755	1851	1956	1957	2015	2015	2058
Jönköping d.	0509	0629	0800	0803	0902	1002	1101	1202	1254	1301	1400	1501	1501	1604	1702	1702	1803	1902	2002	2002	...	...	2100
Falköping **740** a.	0554	0713	0845	0847	0945	1047	1145	1245	1342	1344	1443	1545	1545	1647	1746	1744	1845	1942	2045	2045	...	...	2146
Skövde **740** a.	0629	*0741*	0906	0908	*1017*	1107	*1248*d	1306	*1438*	1406	1503	1606	*1619*	1707	1806	*1823*e	1909	*2028*	2110f	2110	...	...	*2224*

A – Until June 21.
d – 1239 on ⑤.
e – 1809 on Ⓐ.
f – ⑦ only.
Sn – High-speed train. 🅁 and ✕. Supplement payable.

KRISTIANSTAD - HÄSSLEHOLM - HELSINGBORG 734

Operator: *Skåne* 2nd class only

km		Ⓒ		Ⓐ	Ⓐ	Ⓐ		⚒	Ⓐ		Ⓐ		Ⓐ				Ⓐ				Ⓐ						
0	**Kristianstad** 745 d.	0003	...	...	...	0538	0603	...	0638	0703	0738	0803	0838	0903	and at	1403	1438	1503	and at	1738	1803	1903	2003	2103	2138	2303
30	Hässleholm 745 a.	0024	...	...	...	0559	0624	...	0659	0724	0759	0824	0859	0924	the same	1424	1459	1524	the same	1759	1824	1924	2024	2124	2159	2324
30	Hässleholm d.	0031	...	0501	0531	0601	...	0631	0701	0731	0801	0831	0901	0931	minutes	1431	1501	1531	minutes	1801	1831	1931	2031	2131	2231	2331
83	Åstorp d.	0112	...	0540	0612	0640	...	0712	0740	0812	0840	0912	0940	1012	past each	1512	1540	1612	past each	1840	1912	2012	2112	2212	2312	0012
107	**Helsingborg** a.	0135	...	0603	0635	0703	...	0735	0803	0835	0903	0935	1003	1035	hour until	1535	1603	1635	hour until	1903	1935	2035	2135	2235	2335	0035

	Ⓒ		Ⓐ	Ⓐ	Ⓐ	⚒	Ⓐ	Ⓐ		Ⓐ		Ⓐ				Ⓐ			Ⓐ							⚒
Helsingborg d.	0017	...	0417	...	0447	0517	...	0547	0617	0647	0717	0747	0817	and at	1317	1347	1417	and at	1647	1717	1817	1917	2017	2117	2217	2317
Åstorp d.	0040	...	0440	...	0511	0540	...	0611	0640	0711	0740	0811	0840	the same	1340	1411	1440	the same	1711	1740	1840	1940	2040	2140	2240	2340
Hässleholm a.	0118	...	0518	...	0548	0618	...	0648	0718	0748	0818	0848	0918	minutes	1418	1448	1518	minutes	1748	1818	1918	2018	2118	2218	2318	0018
Hässleholm 745 d.	0200	...	...	0531	0550	...	0631	0650	0731	0750	0831	0850	0931	past each	1431	1450	1531	past each	1750	1831	1932	2031	2132	2231	2331	0031
Kristianstad 745 a.	0221	...	...	0552	0611	...	0652	0711	0752	0811	0852	0911	0952	hour until	1452	1511	1552	hour until	1811	1852	1952	2052	2152	2252	2352	0052

GÖTEBORG - MALMÖ - KØBENHAVN 735

Operator: *Øtåg* (except *Sn* trains)

Subject to alteration on and around public holidays.

km				*Sn* 10481		*Sn* 483		*Sn* 485		*Sn* 469			*Sn* 487		*Sn* 477			*Sn* 479		*Sn* 491		*Sn* 497		*Sn* 493	
		Ⓐ	Ⓐ	Ⓐc	①-⑥	Ⓐc		⑥e		a			f		b			b		f		b		Ⓑf	
0	**Göteborg** C ▲ d.	...	...	0530	0555k	0639	0655	0734	0755	0834	0855	0955	1009	1055	1139	1155	1255	1339	1355	1409	1455	1539	1555	1609	1655
28	Kungsbacka ▲ d.	...	...	0547	0613k	|	0713	|	0813	|	0913	1013	|	1113	|	1213	1313	|	1413	|	1513	|	1613	|	1713
76	Varberg ▲ d.	...	...	0608	0634k	|	0734	|	0834	0911	0934	1034	|	1134	1211	1234	1334	1411	1434	|	1534	1611	1634	|	1734
106	Falkenberg ▲ d.	...	...	0622	0648k	|	0748	|	0848	|	0948	1048	|	1148	|	1248	1348	|	1448	|	1548	|	1648	|	1748
150	**Halmstad** ▲ d.	0512	0612	0641	0712	0740	0812	0833	0912	0940	1012	1112	1110	1212	1240	1312	1412	1440	1512	1511	1612	1640	1712	1710	1812
173	Laholm d.	0522	0622	|	0722	|	0822	|	0922	|	1022	1122	|	1222	|	1322	1422	|	1526	|	1622	|	1722	|	1822
185	Båstad d.	0528	0628	|	0728	|	0828	|	0928	|	1028	1128	|	1228	|	1328	1428	|	1528	|	1628	|	1728	|	1828
210	Ängelholm d.	0541	0641	|	0741	|	0841	|	0941	|	1041	1141	|	1241	|	1341	1441	|	1541	|	1641	|	1741	|	1841
237	**Helsingborg** a.	0608	0708	0718	0808	0818	0908	0911	1008	1008	1108	1208	1147	1308	1318	1408	1508	1518	1608	1549	1708	1718	1808	1755	1908
237	**Helsingborg** 737 d.	0611	0711	0720	0811	0819	0911	0912	1011	1019	1111	1211	1148	1311	1319	1411	1511	1519	1611	1550	1711	1719	1811	1757	1911
259	Landskrona 737 d.	0622	0722	|	0822	|	0922	|	1022	|	1122	1222	|	1322	|	1422	1522	|	1622	|	1722	|	1822	|	1922
290	Lund 737 ● d.	0640	0740	0748s	0840	0848s	0940	0940s	1040	1048s	1140	1240	1210s	1340	1343	1440	1540	1546	1640	1613s	1740	|	1840	1825s	1940
306	**Malmö** C ● a.	0651	0751	0801	0851	0901	0951	0954	1051	1102	1151	1251	1222	1351	1357	1451	1551	1557	1651	1628	1751	1757	1851	1839	1951
306	**Malmö** C ● d.	0653	0753	0813	0853	0913	0953	1013	1053	...	1153	1253	...	1353	1400	1453	1553	...	1653	...	1753	1759	1853	...	1953
335	København Lufthavn ✈ ● a.	0713	0813	0833	0913	0933	1013	1033	1113	...	1213	1313	...	1413	1417s	1513	1613	...	1713	...	1813	1817s	1913	...	2013
353	**København** H ● a.	0728	0828	0848	0928	0948	1028	1048	1128	...	1228	1328	...	1428	1431	1528	1628	...	1728	...	1828	1831	1928	...	2028

	Sn 495		*Sn* 439						
	f		Sg						
Göteborg C ▲ d.	1739	1755	1838	1855	1955	2055	2155	2255	2355
Kungsbacka ▲ d.	|	1813	|	1913	2013	2113	2213	2313	0013
Varberg ▲ d.	|	1834	|	1934	2034	2134	2235	2335	0035
Falkenberg ▲ d.	|	1848	|	1948	2048	2148	2249	2349	0049
Halmstad ▲ d.	1840	1912	1940	2012	2112	2212	2312	0007	0107
Laholm d.	|	1922	|	2022	2122	2222	2322	...	...
Båstad d.	|	1928	|	2028	2128	2228	2328	...	...
Ängelholm d.	|	1941	|	2041	2141	2241	2341	...	...
Helsingborg a.	1918	2008	2018	2108	2208	2308	0004	...	...
Helsingborg 737 d.	1919	2011	2019	2111	2211	2311	...	...	...
Landskrona 737 d.	|	2022	|	2122	2222	2322	...	...	...
Lund 737 ● d.	1942s	2040	2042s	2140	2240	2340	...	...	...
Malmö C ● a.	1957	2051	2057	2151	2251	2351	...	...	...
Malmö C ● d.	2013	2053	2112	2153	2253	...	...	...	...
København Lufthavn ✈ ● a.	2033	2113	2133	2213	2313	...	...	...	...
København H ● a.	2048	2128	2148	2228	2328	...	...	...	...

					Sn 426		*Sn* 482		
	Ⓐ	Ⓐ	Ⓒ	Ⓐ	ⒶS	⚒	Ⓐ		
København H ● d.	...	...	...	...	0507	0527	0607	0627	0727
København Lufthavn ✈ ● d.	...	...	...	...	0522	0542	0622	0642	0742
Malmö C ● a.	...	...	...	...	0546	0606	0646	0706	0806
Malmö C ● d.	...	...	...	0508	0601g	0608	0657	0708	0808
Lund 737 ● d.	...	...	...	0521	0614u	0621	0710u	0721	0821
Landskrona 737 d.	...	...	...	0536	|	0636	|	0736	0836
Helsingborg 737 a.	...	...	...	0548	0640g	0648	0740	0748	0848
Helsingborg d.	...	0453	...	0553	0641g	0653	0741	0753	0853
Ängelholm d.	...	0516	...	0616	|	0716	|	0816	0916
Båstad d.	...	0527	...	0627	|	0727	|	0827	0927
Laholm d.	...	0533	...	0633	|	0733	|	0833	0933
Halmstad ▲ d.	0451	0551	0651	0652	0717g	0752	0816	0852	0952
Falkenberg ▲ d.	0508	0608	0708	0709	|	0809	|	0909	1011
Varberg ▲ d.	0522	0623	0722	0724	|	0824	|	0924	1025
Kungsbacka ▲ d.	0545	0645	0745	0745	|	0845	|	0945	1045
Göteborg C ▲ a.	0605	0705	0805	0805	0820g	0905	0920	1005	1105

	Sn 484			*Sn* 486		*Sn* 478		*Sn* 488		*Sn* 470		*Sn* 490		*Sn* 496		*Sn* 492			*Sn* 494			*Sn* 480		
	h			f		f		f		b		Ⓑf		b		f			Ⓑf			b		
København H ● d.	...	0827	0927	1007	1027	1123	1127	1207	1227	1307	1327	...	1427	1524	1527	1607	1627	1727	1807	1827	1927	2023	2027	2227
København Lufthavn ✈ ● d.	...	0842	0942	1022	1042	1136u	1142	1222	1242	1322	1342	...	1442	1537u	1542	1622	1642	1742	1822	1842	1942	2038u	2042	2242
Malmö C ● a.	...	0906	1006	1046	1106	1159	1206	1246	1306	1346	1406	...	1506	1557	1606	1646	1706	1806	1846	1906	2006	2058	2106	2306
Malmö C ● d.	0834	0908	1008	1101	1108	1202	1208	1301	1308	1401	1408	1434	1508	1558	1608	1657	1708	1808	1901	1908	2008	2100	2108	2308
Lund 737 ● d.	0847u	0921	1021	1115u	1121	1215	1221	1315u	1321	1415u	1421	1447u	1521	1610	1621	1710u	1721	1821	1914u	1921	2021	2116	2121	2319
Landskrona 737 d.	|	0936	1036	|	1136	|	1236	|	1336	|	1436	|	1536	|	1636	|	1736	1836	|	1936	2036	|	2136	2336
Helsingborg 737 a.	0913	0948	1048	1141	1148	1141	1248	1340	1348	1440	1448	1511	1548	1640	1648	1740	1748	1848	1939	1948	2048	2140	2148	2352
Helsingborg d.	0914	0953	1053	1146	1153	1146	1253	1341	1353	1441	1453	1512	1553	1641	1653	1741	1753	1853	1941	1953	2053	2141	2153	2353
Ängelholm d.	|	1016	1116	|	1216	|	1316	|	1416	|	1516	|	1616	|	1716	|	1816	1916	|	2016	2116	|	2216	0016
Båstad d.	|	1027	1127	|	1227	|	1327	|	1427	|	1527	|	1627	|	1727	|	1827	1927	|	2027	2127	|	2227	0027
Laholm d.	|	1033	1133	|	1233	|	1333	|	1433	|	1533	|	1633	|	1733	|	1833	1933	|	2033	2133	|	2233	0033
Halmstad ▲ d.	0949	1052	1152	1223	1252	1223	1352	1415	1452	1516	1552	1547	1652	1716	1752	1816	1852	1952	2017	2052	2152	2218	2252	0046
Falkenberg ▲ d.	|	1109	1208	|	1309	|	1409	|	1509	|	1609	|	1709	|	1809	|	1909	2009	|	2109	2209	|	2309	...
Varberg ▲ d.	|	1124	1224	|	1324	|	1424	|	1524	1546	1624	|	1724	1746	1824	|	1924	2024	|	2124	2224	2250	2324	...
Kungsbacka ▲ d.	|	1145	1245	|	1345	|	1445	|	1545	|	1645	|	1745	|	1845	|	1945	2045	|	2145	2245	|	2345	...
Göteborg C ▲ a.	1050	1205	1305	1325	1405	1325	1505	1520	1605	1620	1710	1650	1805	1820	1905	1920	2005	2105	2120	2205	2305	2330	0005	...

– To/from Stockholm, Table **740**.
– June 1 - Aug. 18.
– June 24 - Aug. 18.
– Not June 21 - Aug. 18.

e – Not June 22 - Aug. 23.
f – Not June 24 - Aug. 18.
g – Ⓑ (not June 30 - Aug. 9).
h – ①-⑥ (not June 22 - Aug. 18).

k – Ⓐ only.
s – Stops to set down only.
u – Stops to pick up only.

▲ – Additional services operate Göteborg - Halmstad and v.v. on Ⓐ.
● – See also Tables **737**, **745** and **746**.
Sn – High-speed train. 🅁 and ✕. Supplement payable.

ÖREBRO - HALLSBERG - LIDKÖPING - HERRLJUNGA - GÖTEBORG 736

Operator: *V* 2nd class

km		Ⓐ	Ⓐ	⑥	Ⓐ	Ⓐa	⑥	†	Ⓐ	Ⓐb	†	⑥	Ⓐ	†	†	⑥d	⑥m	Ⓐb	Ⓐ	⑥	†	Ⓐ	⑥	Ⓐ	Ⓐb	†
	Örebro C 755 756 d.	...	...	...	...	...	...	...	0749	...	...	...	1109	1204c	...	1214	1214	...	...	1512	...	1627	...	...	1818	1818k
0	**Hallsberg** 740 755 756 d.	...	...	...	...	...	...	...	0810	...	...	...	1132	1237	...	1250	1255	...	...	1606	...	1649	...	...	1859	1908
30	Laxå 756 d.	...	...	...	...	...	...	...	0832	...	...	...	1209	1256	...	1309	1314	...	...	1625	...	1709	...	...	1918	1927
92	Mariestad d.	...	0520	...	0656	0800	0818	0825	0920	1019	...	1227	1313	1342	1420	1420g	1612n	1432	1625	1709	1716	1812f	1814	...	2010	2012
146	Lidköping a.	...	0603	...	0747	0857	0908	0909	1011	1109	...	1317	1405	...	1501	1511	1702	1523	1715	...	1806	1855	1904	...	2058	2102
146	Lidköping d.	0518	0612	0713	0800	0903	0918	0918	1018	1111	1134	1322	1409	...	1503	1518	1718	1528	1718	...	1809	...	1918	2010	...	...
201	**Herrljunga** 740 756 a.	0608	0659	0801	0849	0953	1001	1001	1105	1159	1223	1410	1457	...	1603	1602	1802	1613	1800	...	1856	...	2005	2057	...	...
	Göteborg C 740 756 a.	0710	0755	0900	0940	1105	1055	1055	1200z	1300	1330	1500	1600	...	1700	1655	1855	1725	1905	...	1950	...	2100e	2200	...	...

	Ⓐ	Ⓐa	Ⓐ	Ⓐ	⑥r	†	Ⓐ	⑥	Ⓐb	Ⓐ	†	⑥	Ⓐ	Ⓐ	B	†	†	⑥	Ⓐb	Ⓐ	⑥t	†	Ⓐ	†	Ⓐy	⑥
Göteborg C 740 756 d.	...	...	...	0604p	...	...	0825	0900	1035	1055s	1125	1135	1159s	1325	...	1435	...	1535	1535	1700	1730	1735	1759	2000	2000	2055
Herrljunga 740 756 d.	...	...	...	0700	...	...	0921	1004	1125	1216s	1223	1223	1310s	1419	...	1521	...	1632	1632	1800	1816	1831	1857r	2049	2106	2156
Lidköping a.	...	...	...	0750	...	...	1006	1051	1213	1302s	1306	1307	1357s	1510	...	1607	...	1716	1717	1848	1902	1915	1942r	2133	2152	2242
Lidköping d.	...	0508	0606	0758	0920	0957	1013	1054	1216	1306	1310	1320	1423	1530	...	1610	...	1719	1720	1859	1907	1917	...	...	...	...
Mariestad d.	0555	0604	0652	0851	1013	1050	1110	1145	1300	1403	1357	1424h	1518	1620	1645	1659	1708	1808	1810	1943	1952	2003	...	...	...	...
Laxå 756 d.	0641	...	...	...	1100	1137	1156	...	...	1452	...	1510	...	...	1734	...	1755	...	...	...	...	...	...	...	...	...
Hallsberg 740 755 756 a.	0659	...	...	...	1118	1155	1225	...	...	1510	...	1528	...	...	1753	...	1813	...	...	...	...	...	...	...	...	...
Örebro C 755 756 a.	0722	...	...	...	1155	1248	1248	...	...	1533	...	1643	...	...	1848	...	1848	...	...	...	...	...	...	...	...	...

Ⓐ until June 28; ①②④⑤ from Aug 19.
Not June 15 - Aug. 18.
Not June 29 - Aug. 18.
Not June 24 - Aug. 10.
Not June 16 - Aug. 23.

e – Arrives 2110 June 29 - Aug. 17.
f – Arrives 1751.
g – Arrives 1353.
h – Arrives 1411.
k – 11 minutes earlier Aug. 7 - Aug. 28.

m – June 21 - Aug. 17.
n – Arrives 1358.
p – 5 minutes earlier June 24 - Aug. 16.
r – 10 minutes earlier June 24 - Aug. 16.
s – Not June 29 - Aug. 18.

t – Not June 16 - Aug. 23.
y – Not Oct. 31, Nov. 1.
z – 1155 on ①-③.

737 KØBENHAVN - MALMÖ - HELSINGBORG

Operator: *Skåne* (Ø – *Øtåg*)

For other trains København - Helsingborg and v.v. see also Tables **735**. For other trains København - Lund and v.v. see Tables **745** and **746**.

km			M	Ø	Ø	ØⒶ	Ⓐ2	2	Ø	Ø	Ⓐ2	2	Ø	Ⓐ2	2	Ø	Ⓐ2	2	Ø	Ⓐ2	2	Ø	Ⓐ2	2	Ø	2	2
0	**København** H	d.	...	0207	0307	...	...	...	0507	0527	...	...	0627	...	...	0727	...	...	0827	...	...	0927	...	...	1027	...	...
12	København Lufthavn ✈	d.	...	0222	0322	...	...	...	0522	0542	...	...	0642	...	...	0742	...	...	0842	...	...	0942	...	...	1042	...	...
47	**Malmö** C	d.	0041	0248	0348	0508	0514	0541	0548	0608	0614	0641	0708	0714	0741	0808	0814	0841	0908	0914	0941	1008	1014	1041	1108	1123	114
63	Lund	d.	0055	0259	0359	0521	0528	0555	0559	0621	0628	0655	0721	0728	0755	0821	0828	0855	0921	0928	0955	1021	1028	1055	1121	1137	115
95	Landskrona	d.	0120	...	...	0536	0552	0620	...	0636	0652	0720	0736	0752	0820	0836	0852	0920	0936	0952	1020	1036	1052	1120	1136	|	122
116	**Helsingborg**	a.	0138	...	...	0548	0609	0638	...	0648	0709	0738	0748	0809	0838	0848	0909	0938	0948	1009	1038	1048	1109	1138	1148	1227	123

		Ø	2	2	Ø	2	2	Ø	Ⓐ2	2	Ø	Ⓐ2	2	Ø	Ⓐ2	2	Ø	Ⓐ2	2	Ø	Ⓐ2	2	Ø	Ⓐ2	2	Ø
København H	d.	1127	...	...	1227	...	...	1327	...	...	1427	...	...	1527	...	...	1627	...	...	1727	...	...	1827	...	...	192
København Lufthavn ✈	d.	1142	...	...	1242	...	...	1342	...	...	1442	...	...	1542	...	...	1642	...	...	1742	...	...	1842	...	...	194
Malmö C	d.	1208	1223	1241	1308	1323	1341	1408	1414	1441	1508	1514	1541	1608	1614	1641	1708	1714	1741	1808	1814	1841	1908	1914	1941	200
Lund	d.	1221	1237	1255	1321	1337	1355	1421	1428	1455	1521	1528	1555	1621	1628	1655	1721	1728	1755	1821	1828	1855	1921	1928	1955	202
Landskrona	d.	1236	|	1320	1336	|	1420	1436	1452	1520	1536	1552	1620	1636	1652	1720	1736	1752	1820	1836	1852	1920	1936	1952	2020	203
Helsingborg	a.	1248	1327	1338	1348	1427	1438	1448	1509	1538	1548	1609	1638	1648	1709	1738	1748	1809	1838	1848	1909	1938	1948	2009	2038	204

		2	Ø	2	Ø	2	Ø	⚒2	Ø	
København H	d.	...	2027	...	2127	...	2227	...	2327	...
København Lufthavn ✈	d.	...	2042	...	2142	...	2242	...	2342	...
Malmö C	d.	2041	2108	2143	2208	2243	2308	2341	0008	...
Lund	d.	2055	2121	2157	2219	2257	2319	2355	0021	...
Landskrona	d.	2120	2136	2222	2236	2322	2336	0020	0036	...
Helsingborg	a.	2138	2148	2240	2252	2340	2352	0038	0048	...

		Ⓒ2	Ø	Ⓒ2	Ø	Ø	Ⓐ2	Ø	ØⒶ	Ⓐ2	2
Helsingborg	d.	0054	...	0154	...	...	0454	...	0511	0524	055
Landskrona	d.	0111	...	0211	...	...	0511	...	0522	0541	061
Lund	d.	0135	0220	0235	0320	0440	0535	0540	0540	0605	063
Malmö C	a.	0148	0231	0248	0331	0451	0548	0551	0551	0618	064
København Lufthavn ✈	a.	...	0253	...	0353	0513	...	0613	0613	...	...
København H	a.	...	0308	...	0408	0528	...	0628	0628	...	...

		Ø	Ⓐ2	2	Ø	Ⓐ2	2	Ø	Ⓐ2	2	Ø	Ⓐ2	2	Ø	Ⓐ2	2	Ø	2	2	Ø	2	2	Ø	2	2	Ø
Helsingborg	d.	0611	0624	0654	0711	0724	0754	0811	0824	0854	0911	0924	0954	1011	1024	1054	1111	1131	1154	1211	1231	1254	1311	1331	1354	141
Landskrona	d.	0622	0641	0711	0722	0741	0811	0822	0841	0911	0922	0941	1011	1022	1041	1111	1122	|	1211	1222	|	1311	1322	|	1411	142
Lund	d.	0640	0705	0735	0740	0805	0835	0840	0905	0935	0940	1005	1035	1040	1105	1135	1140	1223	1235	1240	1323	1335	1340	1423	1435	144
Malmö C	a.	0651	0718	0748	0751	0818	0848	0851	0918	0948	0951	1018	1048	1051	1118	1148	1151	1235	1248	1251	1335	1348	1351	1435	1448	145
København Lufthavn ✈	a.	0713	...	...	0813	...	...	0913	...	...	1013	...	...	1113	...	...	1213	...	...	1313	...	...	1413	...	...	151
København H	a.	0728	...	...	0828	...	...	0928	...	...	1028	...	...	1128	...	...	1228	...	...	1328	...	...	1428	...	...	152

		Ⓐ2	2	Ø	Ⓐ2	2	Ø	Ⓐ2	2	Ø	Ⓐ2	2	Ø	Ⓐ2	2	Ø	Ⓐ2	2	Ø	2	Ø	2	Ø	2	Ø	⚒2
Helsingborg	d.	1424	1454	1511	1524	1554	1611	1624	1654	1711	1724	1749	1811	1824	1854	1911	1924	1954	2011	2054	2111	2155	2211	2255	2311	235
Landskrona	d.	1441	1511	1522	1541	1611	1622	1641	1711	1722	1741	1811	1822	1841	1911	1922	1941	2011	2022	2111	2122	2212	2222	2312	2322	001
Lund	d.	1505	1535	1540	1605	1635	1640	1705	1735	1740	1805	1835	1840	1905	1935	1940	2005	2035	2040	2135	2140	2235	2240	2335	2340	003
Malmö C	a.	1518	1548	1551	1618	1648	1651	1718	1748	1751	1818	1848	1851	1918	1948	1951	2018	2048	2051	2148	2151	2248	2251	2348	2351	004
København Lufthavn ✈	a.	...	...	1613	...	...	1713	...	...	1813	...	...	1913	...	...	2013	...	...	2113	...	2213	...	2313	...	...	...
København H	a.	...	...	1628	...	...	1728	...	...	1828	...	...	1928	...	...	2028	...	...	2128	...	2228	...	2328	...	...	...

M – Daily **except** ①.

Ø – Operated by *Øtåg*.

738 South-eastern SECONDARY LINES

Operator: *KLT*/*Ö*

km			Ⓐ									Ⓑ
0	Västervik	d.	0541	0736	...	1007	1207	...	1409	1607	1807	2008
77	Åtvidaberg	d.	0647	0842	...	1113	1313	...	1515	1715	1914	2114
116	Linköping	a.	0727	0920	...	1151	1351	...	1551	1751	1951	2151

		Ⓐ										Ⓑ
Linköping	d.	0540	...	0805	1010	1210	...	1410	1610	1810	...	200
Åtvidaberg	d.	0615	...	0842	1042	1242	...	1444	1645	1844	...	204
Västervik	a.	0725	...	0949	1149	1349	...	1550	1750	1950	...	215

km			Ⓐ	Ⓐ	⑥						Ⓑ	Ⓑ
0	Linköping	d.	...	0532	...	0824	1026	1225	1426	1625	1825	2025
41	Rimforsa	d.	...	0605	...	0902	1101	1301	1501	1701	1901	2101
123	Hultsfred	d.	0606	0707	0710	1005	1205	1405	1604	1805	2006	2204
159	Berga	a.	0631	0733	0736	1033	1233	1433	1632	1833	2034	2228
159	Berga ▷	d.	0636	0739	0741	1038	1238	1438	1638	1838	2039	2228
188	Oskarshamn ▷	a.	|	|	|	|	|	|	|	|	|	2249
235	Kalmar **746**	a.	0738	0838	0840	1138	1338	1538	1738	1936	2138	...

		Ⓐ	Ⓐ	⑥	Ⓐ						Ⓑ	Ⓐ
Kalmar **746**	d.	...	0538	...	0634	0830	1036	1236	1436	1636	1836	193
Oskarshamn ▷	a.	0449	|	0624	|	|	|	|	|	|	|	|
Berga ▷	a.	0509	0635	0644	0731	0933	1133	1333	1533	1733	1933	203
Berga	d.	0509	0642	0644	0736	0938	1138	1338	1538	1738	1938	203
Hultsfred	d.	0534	0708	0711	0800	1004	1205	1405	1605	1805	2005	210
Rimforsa	d.	0638	0807	0810	...	1103	1303	1503	1703	1903	2103	...
Linköping	a.	0720	0842	0851	...	1138	1338	1539	1742	1938	2138	...

▷ – Additional services operate on Ⓐ **Berga - Oskarshamn** and v.v. (journey 20 minutes): From **Berga**: 0834; from **Oskarshamn**: 1612.

739 VARBERG - UDDEVALLA

2nd class only — Operator: *V* (except *Sn* trains

Subject to alteration on and around public holidays.

km			Ⓐ	Ⓐ	Ⓐ	⑥G	⑦C	Ⓒ	Ⓐ	ⒶH	*Sn* **463** B¶	Ⓐ	Ⓒ	Ⓐ	⑥	†	Ⓐ	Ⓐ	Ⓒ	ⒶH	⑥	†	①–⑤	†
0	**Varberg**	d.	...	...	0608	...	...	...	0706	0811	...	1035	1043	...	...	...	1338	1439	1439	1537	...	...	1741	...
84	Borås	a.	...	...	0726	...	...	...	0829	0939	...	1157	1200	...	...	...	1454	1556	1557	1658	...	...	1902	...
84	Borås	d.	0545	0654	0730	0702	0749	0945	0915	1041	...	1214	1214	1354	1355	1355	1502**g**	1615	1614	1742	1744	1745	1930	194
127	Herrljunga	a.	0632	0739	0816	0745	0831	1031	0956	1129	...	1256	1254	1437	1437	1437	1548**g**	1658	1654	1829	1831	1831	2017	203
127	Herrljunga	d.	0642	0805	0903	0930	0930	1129	1132**c**	...	1255	1328	1329	1534	1531	1532	1614**g**	1731	1731	1836	1907	1934	2120**j**	212
191	Vänersborg	d.	0732	0856	0951	1022	1022	1217	1222**c**	...	1238	1419	1421	1624	1622	1621	1724**g**	1828	1828	1928	1955	2020	2215**j**	220
195	Öxnered	d.	0739	0902	0958	1028	1028	1223	1228**c**	...	|	1425	1427	1630	1629	1627	1729**g**	1834	1834	1934	2002	2026	2221**j**	221
217	**Uddevalla** C	a.	0755	0918	1013	1043	1043	1240	1246**c**	...	1400	1441	1443	1646	1645	1644	1751**g**	1850	1849	1949	2016	2040	2236**j**	222

		ⒶH	Ⓐ	*Sn* **462** ⒶF¶	Ⓐ	Ⓐ	Ⓒ	Ⓐ	Ⓒ	Ⓒ	Ⓐ	ⒶH	Ⓒ	Ⓐ	Ⓐ	Ⓒ	ⒶE	Ⓐ	⑥	†	*Sn* **466** B¶	L	†	①–
Uddevalla C	d.	...	0508	0527	0617	0724	0726	0817	0920	1137	1141	...	1317	1317	...	1517	1613	...	1718	1718	1754	1917	1920	...
Öxnered	d.	...	0524	|	0633	0744	0743	0833	0936	1153	1157	...	1332	1333	...	1533	1629	...	1734	1734	|	1934	1936	...
Vänersborg	d.	...	0530	0549	0649	0750	0749	0840	0942	1159	1208	...	1342	1340	...	1539	1635	...	1740	1740	1816	1940	1942	...
Herrljunga	a.	...	0622	0636	0740	0838	0838	0937	1034	1252	1257	...	1429	1433	...	1631	1726	...	1834	1831	1906	2030	2031	...
Herrljunga	d.	0534	0642	...	0753	0858	0933	1030	1130	1307	1308	1337	1531	1526	1603**c**	1733	1732	1920	1900	1928	...	2120	2120	212
Borås	a.	0617	0725	...	0836	0944	1014	1111	1211	1348	1349	1423	1612	1608	1645**c**	1814	1813	2001	1942	2013	...	2202	2202	220
Borås	d.	0625	0727	...	0839	0959	...	1204	*1300*	...	...	1456	...	...	1700	...	...	2006	...	...	...	...	...	...
Varberg	a.	0746	0852	...	0959	1116	...	1322	*1417*	...	...	1616	...	...	1819	...	...	2123	...	...	...	...	...	...

GÖTEBORG - UDDEVALLA - STRÖMSTAD

km			ⒶC	①–⑥			①–⑥	⑦				
0	**Göteborg** C ▲	d.	0640	0740	0840	1040	1240	1240	1440	1640	...	1840
89	Uddevalla C ▲	a.	0753	0853	0953	1153	1353	1353	1553	1753	...	1953
89	Uddevalla C	d.	0804	0856**h**	1007**b**	1202	1358**d**	1405**f**	1557**k**	1800**a**	...	2000
173	Skee	d.	0916	1008**h**	1133**b**	1314	1514**d**	1522**f**	1713**k**	1932**a**	...	2112
180	**Strömstad**	a.	0923	1015**h**	1140**b**	1322	1524**d**	1532**f**	1721**k**	1939**a**	...	2120

		①–⑥	⚒A	†B			K	†D	ⒶF	Ⓒ	
Strömstad	d.	0641	0820	0837	1039	1219**b**	1422	1429	1622	1631**e**	184
Skee	d.	0649	0828	0845	1047	1227**b**	1430	1437	1630	1639**e**	184
Uddevalla C	a.	0800	0950	0956	1200	1355**b**	1543	1550	1744	1752	195
Uddevalla C ▲	d.	0807	1007	1007	1207	1407	1607	1607	1754	1807	200
Göteborg C ▲	a.	0920	1120	1120	1320	1520	1720	1720	1915	1920	212

A – June 17 - Aug. 17.
B – June 22 - Aug. 18.
C – Also ⑥ June 22 - Aug 17.
D – Runs daily June 22 - Aug. 18.
E – Not June 17 - Aug. 16.
F – Not June 21 - Aug. 18.
G – Not June 22 - Aug. 17.
H – Not July 1 - Aug. 16.
K – ①-⑥ (not June 22 - Aug. 17).
L – ⑤ June 1 – 14; ⑤ Aug. 23 - Sept. 13; ④⑤ from Sept. 20.

a – June 16 - Aug.18.
b – June 17 - Aug. 18.
c – July 1 - Aug. 16.
d – Not June 22 - Aug. 17.
e – Not June 24 - Aug. 23.
f – Not June 30 - Aug. 18.
g – Not July 17 - Aug. 16.
h – Not ⑥ June 22 - Aug. 17.
j – ⑤ (also ④ from Sept. 26).
k – 8–9 minutes later on Ⓒ to June 23/from Aug. 24; 3–4 minutes later June 24 - Aug. 18.

¶ – (12) and ✕ Stockholm - Herrljunga - Uddevalla and v.v. Ⓡ.
▲ – Additional services Göteborg - Uddevalla and v.v.:
From Göteborg C at 0040 Ⓒ, 0525 Ⓐ, 0740 Ⓐ, 0840, 0940⚒, 1140⚒, 1340⚒, 1540, 1710 Ⓐ, 1740, 1940, 2040, 2140, 2240 and 2340 Ⓑ.
From Uddevalla C at 0007 Ⓒ, 0534 Ⓐ, 0607 Ⓐ, 0637 Ⓐ, 0707⚒, 0807 0907⚒, 1107⚒, 1307⚒, 1507, 1707, 1907, 2107, 2107, 2207 and 2307

Sn – High-speed train. Ⓡ and ✕. Supplement payable.

STOCKHOLM - HALLSBERG - GÖTEBORG 740

Services valid from August 19 (subject to alteration on and around public holidays).
From June 24 to August 18 services operate from / to Stockholm Södra (not Central) in revised timings.
See Table **756** for slower regional services via Västerås and Örebro. See Table **767** for long distance sleeper trains.

	Sn	MTR	Sn		Sn	MTR	Sn	MTR	MTR	Sn	MTR	MTR	Sn	Sn	MTR	Sn	MTR	Sn	Sn	MTR	Sn	Sn	MTR
	401	**2021**	**421**		**423**	**12003**	**425**	**2081**	**2025**	**427**	**2049**	**12049**	**419**	**429**	**12009**	**431**	**12011**	**413**	**433**	**12005**	**435**	**415**	**2013**
	R ✕	🍷	R ✕		R ✕	🍷★	R ✕	🍷▲	🍷▲	R ✕	🍷★	🍷★	R ✕	R ✕	🍷★	R ✕	🍷★	R ✕	R ✕	🍷★	R ✕	R ✕	🍷★
	Ⓐ	A	Ⓐ B		Ⓐ B	Ⓐ		⑥⑦	④⑤	C	Ⓐ	⑥	⑥⑦	Ⓐ B	⑥	Ⓑ E	Ⓑ c	⑤⑦	E	⑦	Ⓐ	⑦	⚒
Stockholm C ..... **750/6** d.	0553	0606	0610	...	0733	0744**a**	0833	0843	0845	0929	0939**a**	0944**a**	1029	1032	1041**a**	1133	1120**a**	1212	1233	1245**a**	1329	1329	1344**a**
Södertälje Syd △ ..... **750** d.	|	0624	0629	...	|	0800	|	|	0903	0948	1000	1000	|	|	1057	|	1136	|	|	1301	1348	1348	1400
Katrineholm ..... **750** d.	|	|	0709	...	0825	|	0926	|	|	1026	|	|	1122	1125	|	1226	|	|	1326	|	1426	1426	|
Hallsberg ..... **750** a.	|	|	0734	...	|	|	|	|	|	|	|	|	|	|	|	|	|	|	|	|	|	|	|
Hallsberg ..... **756** d.	|	|	0735	...	|	|	|	|	|	|	|	|	|	|	|	|	|	|	|	|	|	|	|
Töreboda ..... **756** d.	|	|	|	...	|	|	|	|	|	|	|	|	|	|	|	|	|	|	|	|	|	|	|
Skövde ..... **756** d.	|	0809	0819	...	0932	0954	1033	1045	1049	1132	1150	1158	1229	|	|	1333	1331	1407	1433	1452	|	1532	1600
Falköping ..... **756** d.	|	|	|	...	|	|	|	|	|	|	|	|	|	|	|	|	|	|	|	|	|	|	|
Herrljunga ..... **756** d.	|	0837	0846	...	|	1029	|	1113	|	|	|	1230	1257	1255	1321	|	1404	|	|	1542	1555	|	1633
Uddevalla C **739** ..... a.	|	|	|	...	|	|	|	|	|	|	|	|	|	|	|	|	|	|	|	|	|	|	|
Alingsås ▽ ..... **756** a.	|	0853	0901	...	|	1045	|	|	1129	|	|	1245	|	|	1339	|	1420	|	|	1558	|	|	1648
Göteborg C ..... **756** a.	0850	0925	0930	...	1035	1125	1135	1155	1155	1235	1240	1315	1335	1335	1410	1435	1455	1510	1535	1625	1635	1635	1725

	Sn	MTR	MTR	SKJB	Sn	IC	Sn	Sn	MTR	Sn	Sn	Sn	MTR	Sn	MTR	MTR	Sn	MTR	SKJB	Sn	Sn	MTR		Sn
	437	**2065**	**2037**	**7075**	**439**	**109**	**405**	**10405**	**12035**	**451**	**10441**	**441**	**2067**	**467**	**2077**	**2051**	**407**	**2035**	**7073**	**453**	**443**	**12027**		**445**
	R ✕	🍷▲	🍷▲	▲	R ✕		R ✕	R ✕	🍷★	R ✕	R ✕	R ✕	🍷▲	R ✕	🍷▲	🍷▲	R ✕	🍷★	▲	R ✕	R ✕	🍷★		R ✕
	d	⑥⑦	⑤	⑥	Ⓑ	⑥ G	B	⑦	⑦	⑥	⑦	Ⓐ B	⑥	Ⓐ B	⑦	⑤	Ⓑ E	Ⓐ	⑥	⑥	Ⓑ d	⑥		Ⓑ
Stockholm C ..... **750/6** d.	1432	1442	1444	1400	1519	1414	1603	1606	1544**a**	1619	1619	1619	1647	1607	1645	1651	1705	1640**a**	1530	1713	1729	1738**a**	...	1828
Södertälje Syd △ ..... **750** d.	|	1500	|	|	1538	1434	|	|	1600	|	|	|	|	|	1703	|	|	1657	|	1732	1748	1800	...	|
Katrineholm ..... **750** d.	1526	|	|	|	|	|	|	|	|	1712	1712	1712	|	|	|	|	|	|	|	1813	1826	|	...	1922
Hallsberg ..... **750** a.	|	|	|	1606	1636	1610	|	|	|	|	|	|	|	|	|	|	|	|	1750	|	|	|	...	|
Hallsberg ..... **756** d.	|	|	|	1608	1637	1619	|	|	|	|	|	|	|	|	|	|	|	|	1752	|	|	|	...	|
Töreboda ..... **756** d.	|	|	|	|	|	|	|	|	|	|	|	|	|	1814	|	|	|	|	|	|	|	|	...	|
Skövde ..... **756** d.	1633	1646	1646	1709	1722	1712	|	|	1749	1818	1818	1821	1848	1829	1849	1852	|	1854	1900	1925	1933	1951	...	2029
Falköping ..... **756** d.	|	|	|	|	|	|	|	|	|	|	|	|	|	1847	|	|	|	|	|	|	|	|	...	|
Herrljunga ..... **756** d.	|	1713	1713	|	|	1750	|	|	1825	1846	|	|	|	1903	1918	1920	|	1935	|	|	|	|	...	2056
Uddevalla C **739** ..... a.	|	|	|	|	|	|	|	|	|	|	|	|	|	2016	|	|	|	|	|	|	|	|	...	|
Alingsås ▽ ..... **756** a.	|	1728	|	1755	|	|	|	|	1841	|	1857	1900	1927	...	1932	1935	|	1950	1955	|	|	2036	...	|
Göteborg C ..... **756** a.	1735	1755	1755	1830	1825	1835	1900	1900	1910	1925	1925	1930	1955	...	2000	2000	2005	2025	2030	2035	2035	2105	...	2135

	MTR	MTR	SKJB		Sn	MTR	Sn		
	2027	**2089**	**7077**		**447**	**2047**	**449**		
	🍷★	🍷▲	▲		R ✕	🍷▲	R ✕		
	⑦	⑥⑦	⑦		Ⓑ	Ⓑ	Ⓑ		
Stockholm C ..... **750/6** d.	1744**a**	1842	1741	...	1932	1945	2033	...	...
Södertälje Syd △ ..... **750** d.	1800	1900	|	...	1952	|	|	...	...
Katrineholm ..... **750** d.	|	|	|	...	|	|	2125	...	...
Hallsberg ..... **750** a.	|	|	1945	...	|	|	|	...	...
Hallsberg ..... **756** d.	|	|	1950	...	|	|	|	...	...
Töreboda ..... **756** d.	|	|	|	...	|	|	|	...	...
Skövde ..... **756** d.	1957	2046	2051	...	2132	2146	2232	...	...
Falköping ..... **756** d.	|	|	|	...	|	|	|	...	...
Herrljunga ..... **756** d.	|	|	|	...	|	2214**s**	|	...	...
Uddevalla C **739** ..... a.	|	|	|	...	|	|	|	...	...
Alingsås ▽ ..... **756** a.	2054	2126	2150	...	|	2229	|	...	...
Göteborg C ..... **756** a.	2155	2155	2230	...	2235	2255	2335	...	...

	Sn	Sn	Sn	MTR		MTR	Sn	Sn	MTR
	420	**400**	**402**	**2000**		**2022**	**462**	**422**	**12004**
	R ✕	R ✕	R ✕	🍷▲		🍷▲	R ✕	R ✕	🍷★
	Ⓐ	H	Ⓐ	K		Ⓐ	Ⓐ	①–⑥	Ⓐ
Göteborg C ..... **756** d.	0504	0544	0549	0555	...	0600	...	0629	0655
Alingsås △ ..... **756** d.	0530	|	|	0621	...	0626	...	0655	0722
Uddevalla C **739** ..... d.	|	|	|	|	...	|	0527	|	|
Herrljunga ..... **756** d.	0546	|	|	|	...	0641	0646	|	0737
Falköping ..... **756** d.	0601	|	|	|	...	|	0701	|	|
Skövde ..... **756** d.	0619	|	|	0700	...	0708	0719	0734	0808
Töreboda ..... **756** d.	0635	|	|	|	...	|	|	|	|
Hallsberg ..... **756** a.	0707	|	|	|	...	|	0804	|	|
Hallsberg ..... **750** d.	0708	|	|	|	...	|	0805	|	|
Katrineholm ..... **750** d.	0734	|	|	|	...	|	|	0847	|
Södertälje Syd ▽ ..... **750** a.	0811	|	|	|	...	0855	|	|	1000
Stockholm C ..... **750/6** a.	0831	0839	0845	0904	...	0914	0931	0943	1018**a**

	Sn	Sn	MTR	MTR	Sn	Sn		SKJB	MTR	Sn	Sn		MTR	Sn	SKJB	MTR	Sn		Sn	Sn	MTR	Sn	Sn	SKJB
	460	**424**	**2026**	**2060**	**10426**	**416**		**7074**	**12008**	**428**	**418**		**2030**	**430**	**7070**	**12010**	**432**		**10406**	**406**	**12002**	**434**	**414**	**7076**
	R ✕	R ✕	🍷▲	🍷▲	R ✕	R ✕		▲	🍷★	R ✕	R ✕		🍷▲	R ✕	▲	🍷★	R ✕		R ✕	R ✕	🍷★	R ✕	R ✕	▲
	⑥	Ⓐ	④⑤	⑥⑦	L	⑥⑦		⑥	①⑥	L	⑥⑦		⑤		N	Ⓐ	Ⓑ d		⑦ E	⑤ G	⑦	Ⓐ	⑥⑦	⑦
Göteborg C ..... **756** d.	...	0734	0805	0805	0834	0834	...	0740	0855	0929	0934	...	1005	1029	0900	1155	1129	...	1154	1154	1055	1229	1229	1100
Alingsås △ ..... **756** d.	...	|	0831	0831	|	|	...	0812	0922	|	1000	...	1031	|	0942	1223	|	...	|	|	1123	|	|	1142
Uddevalla C **739** ..... d.	0637	|	|	|	|	|	...	|	|	|	|	...	|	|	|	|	|	...	|	|	|	|	|	|
Herrljunga ..... **756** d.	0753	|	0847	0847	|	0910	...	|	|	1006	|	...	|	|	|	1238	|	...	|	|	|	1306	1306	|
Falköping ..... **756** d.	0808	|	|	|	|	|	...	|	|	|	|	...	|	|	|	|	|	...	|	|	|	|	|	|
Skövde ..... **756** d.	0825	0835	0913	0913	0935	0939	...	0858	1006	|	1040	...	1110	1130	1037	1311	1230	...	1259	1259	1214	|	1334	1238
Töreboda ..... **756** d.	|	|	|	|	|	|	...	|	|	|	|	...	|	|	|	|	|	...	|	|	|	|	|	|
Hallsberg ..... **756** a.	0912	|	|	|	1020	|	...	0950	|	|	1125	...	|	|	1128	|	|	...	|	1346	|	|	|	1333
Hallsberg ..... **750** d.	0913	|	|	|	1021	|	...	0952	|	|	1126	...	|	|	1130	|	|	...	|	1347	|	|	|	1337
Katrineholm ..... **750** d.	|	0944	|	|	1047	1048	...	|	|	1143	|	...	|	1239	|	|	|	...	|	|	|	1438	1447	|
Södertälje Syd ▽ ..... **750** a.	1020	|	|	1100	|	|	...	|	1200	|	|	...	|	|	|	1502	1411	...	|	|	1402	|	|	|
Stockholm C ..... **750/6** a.	1042	1037	1117	1119	1145	1141	...	1202	1225**a**	1237	1241	...	1314	1332	1401	1522**a**	1431	...	1457	1506	1412**b**	1531	1541	1601

	Sn	MTR	Sn	MTR	Sn		MTR	MTR	Sn	Sn	MTR		MTR	IC	Sn	Sn	MTR	MTR	Sn	MTR	Sn	MTR	MTR	Sn
	412	**12006**	**436**	**2062**	**438**		**2074**	**12072**	**440**	**454**	**12034**		**2042**	**108**	**442**	**408**	**2016**	**2034**	**444**	**2088**	**446**	**2028**	**12018**	**450**
	R ✕	🍷★	R ✕	🍷	R ✕		🍷▲	🍷★	R ✕	R ✕	🍷★		🍷▲		R ✕	R ✕	🍷★	🍷★	R ✕	🍷▲	R ✕	🍷★	🍷★	R ✕
	P	⑥⑦	Ⓑ E	⑥	2		⑦	Ⓐ	Ⓑ E	⑥	⑥		R	⑦	2	E	Ⓐ	⑦	Ⓑ	S		⑦	Ⓐ	Ⓑ
Göteborg C ..... **756** d.	1254	1305	1329	1455	1429	...	1505	1500	1529	1529	1700	...	1605	1534	1629	1654	1650	1700	1729	1805	1829	1900	2005	2034
Alingsås △ ..... **756** d.	|	1331	|	1523	|	...	1531	1526	|	1556	1726	...	1631	|	|	|	1722	1726	1755	|	|	1926	2031	|
Uddevalla C **739** ..... d.	|	|	|	|	|	...	|	|	|	|	1741	...	|	|	|	|	1737	|	|	|	|	|	|	|
Herrljunga ..... **756** d.	|	1346	|	|	|	...	|	|	|	|	|	...	|	1616	1706	|	1746	|	|	1846	|	1941	2046	|
Falköping ..... **756** d.	|	|	|	|	|	...	|	|	|	|	|	...	|	|	|	|	|	|	|	|	|	|	|	|
Skövde ..... **756** d.	1359	1418	1430	1606	1530	...	1610	1614	1630	1640	1813	...	1710	1648	1734	|	1810	1809	1835	1913	1930	2013	2113	2135
Töreboda ..... **756** d.	|	|	|	|	|	...	|	|	|	|	|	...	|	|	|	|	|	|	|	|	|	|	|	|
Hallsberg ..... **756** a.	|	|	|	|	|	...	|	|	|	|	|	...	|	1742	|	|	|	|	1919	|	|	|	|	2220
Hallsberg ..... **750** d.	|	|	|	|	|	...	|	|	|	|	|	...	|	1743	|	|	|	|	1920	|	|	|	|	2221
Katrineholm ..... **750** d.	|	|	|	|	1639	...	|	|	1739	|	|	...	|	|	1847	|	|	|	1946	|	2039	|	|	2247
Södertälje Syd ▽ ..... **750** a.	1544	1605	1613	1757	|	...	1757	1810	1815	1830	2001	...	|	1901	|	|	2001	2001	2023	2100	|	2201	2207	|
Stockholm C ..... **750/6** a.	1604	1621**a**	1633	1813**a**	1732	...	1816	1826**a**	1835	1850	2017**a**	...	1919	1922	1939	1951	2017**a**	2017**a**	2043	2119	2132	2217**a**	2223**a**	2341

Ⓐ until June 20.
From Sept. 2.
Daily from Aug. 31 (also Aug. 24, 25).
Daily from Aug. 31 (also Aug. 24).
From Sept. 1.
From Sept. 6.
①–④ from Sept. 2.
①–③ until June 19.
Ⓐ Aug. 19–30.
①④⑤ until June 7. Train **7072** on ⑤.
⑤⑦ from Aug. 25.
②③④ June 11–19.
⑥⑥⑦ until June 23.

a – Departs / arrives Stockholm Södra.
b – Arrives Flemingsberg.
c – Train **12031** on ⑦.
d – Not Aug. 25.

★ – June 24 - Aug. 18.
▲ – Subject to confirmation.
△ – Trains call to pick up only.
▽ – Trains call to set down only.

Sn – High-speed train. R and ✕. Supplement payable.

745 KØBENHAVN - MALMÖ - KRISTIANSTAD - KARLSKRONA

Operator: Øt

For other trains København - Lund and v.v. see Tables 735 and 737. For other trains København - Hässleholm and v.v see Tables 730 and 746.

km		Ⓐ	Ⓐ	⚒	†		Ⓐ			⚒									Ⓑ			Ⓑ				
0	**København** H ... d.	...	0507	0547	0547	0647	0747	0747	0847	0947	0947	1047	1147	1247	1347	1447	1547	1647	1747	1747	1847	1947	1947	2047	2147	[illegible]
12	København Lufthavn ✈ . d.	...	0522	0602	0602	0702	0802	0802	0902	1002	1002	1102	1202	1302	1402	1502	1602	1702	1802	1802	1902	2002	2002	2102	2202	[illegible]
47	**Malmö** C ... a.	...	0546	0626	0626	0726	0826	0826	0926	1026	1026	1126	1226	1326	1426	1526	1626	1726	1826	1826	1926	2026	2026	2126	2226	[illegible]
47	**Malmö** C ... d.	0528	0548	0628	0628	0728	0828	0828	0928	1028	1028	1128	1228	1328	1428	1528	1628	1728	1828	1828	1928	2028	2028	2128	2228	[illegible]
63	Lund ... d.	0541	0601	0641	0641	0741	0841	0841	0941	1041	1041	1141	1241	1341	1441	1541	1641	1741	1841	1841	1941	2041	2041	2141	2241	[illegible]
130	Hässleholm ... **734** d.	0612	0637	0712	0712	0812	0912	0912	1012	1112	1112	1212	1312	1412	1512	1612	1712	1812	1912	1912	2012	2112	2112	2212	2312	[illegible]
160	**Kristianstad** ... **734** a.	0632	...	0732	0732	0832	0932	0932	1032	1132	1132	1232	1332	1432	1532	1632	1732	1832	1932	1932	2032	2132	2132	2232	2332	[illegible]
160	**Kristianstad** ... d.	0638	...	0738	...	0838	0938	...	1038	1138	...	1238	1338	1438	1538	1638	1738	1838	1938	...	2038	2138	...	2238	...	[illegible]
191	Sölvesborg ... d.	0658	...	0758	...	0858	0958	...	1058	1158	...	1258	1358	1458	1558	1658	1758	1858	1958	...	2058	2158	...	2258	...	[illegible]
222	**Karlshamn** ... d.	0719	...	0819	...	0919	1019	...	1119	1219	...	1319	1419	1519	1619	1719	1819	1919	2019	...	2119	2219	...	2319	...	[illegible]
260	Ronneby ... d.	0746	...	0846	...	0946	1046	...	1146	1246	...	1346	1446	1546	1646	1746	1846	1946	2046	...	2146	2246	...	2346	...	[illegible]
290	**Karlskrona** ... a.	0812	...	0912	...	1012	1112	...	1212	1312	...	1412	1512	1612	1712	1812	1912	2012	2112	...	2212	2312	...	0012	...	[illegible]

		Ⓐ	⚒	†	Ⓐ	†		⚒	†		⚒	†						Ⓑ			Ⓑ			Ⓑ		
Karlskrona ... d.	...	0447	0547	...	0647	...	0747	0847	...	0947	1047	...	1147	1247	1347	1447	1547	1647	...	1747	1847	...	1947	2047	...	[illegible]
Ronneby ... d.	...	0507	0607	...	0707	...	0807	0907	...	1007	1107	...	1207	1307	1407	1507	1607	1707	...	1807	1907	...	2007	2107	...	[illegible]
Karlshamn ... d.	...	0535	0635	...	0735	...	0835	0935	...	1035	1135	...	1235	1335	1435	1535	1635	1735	...	1835	1935	...	2035	2135	...	[illegible]
Sölvesborg ... d.	...	0557	0657	...	0757	...	0857	0957	...	1057	1157	...	1257	1357	1457	1557	1657	1757	...	1857	1957	...	2057	2157	...	[illegible]
Kristianstad ... a.	...	0618	0718	...	0818	...	0918	1018	...	1118	1218	...	1318	1418	1518	1618	1718	1818	...	1918	2018	...	2118	2218	...	[illegible]
Kristianstad ... **734** d.	0524	0624	0724	0724	0824	0824	0924	1024	1024	1124	1224	1224	1324	1424	1524	1624	1724	1824	1824	1924	2024	2024	2124	2224	2224	[illegible]
Hässleholm ... **734** d.	0544	0644	0744	0744	0844	0844	0944	1044	1044	1144	1244	1244	1344	1444	1544	1644	1744	1844	1844	1944	2044	2044	2144	2244	2244	[illegible]
Lund ... d.	0620	0720	0820	0820	0920	0920	1020	1120	1120	1220	1320	1320	1420	1520	1620	1720	1820	1920	1920	2020	2120	2120	2220	2320	2320	[illegible]
Malmö C ... a.	0631	0731	0831	0831	0931	0931	1031	1131	1131	1231	1331	1331	1431	1531	1631	1731	1831	1931	1931	2031	2131	2131	2231	2331	2331	[illegible]
Malmö C ... d.	0633	0733	0833	0833	0933	0933	1033	1133	1133	1233	1333	1333	1433	1533	1633	1733	1833	1933	1933	2033	2133	2133	2233	2333	2333	[illegible]
København Lufthavn ✈ ... a.	0653	0753	0853	0853	0953	0953	1053	1153	1153	1253	1353	1353	1453	1553	1653	1753	1853	1953	1853	2053	2153	2153	2253	2353	2353	[illegible]
København H ... a.	0708	0808	0908	0908	1008	1008	1108	1208	1208	1308	1408	1408	1508	1608	1708	1808	1908	2008	2008	2108	2208	2208	2308	0008	0008	[illegible]

746 KØBENHAVN, MALMÖ and GÖTEBORG - KALMAR

Other trains: København - Lund see Tables 735 and 737; København - Lund - Hässleholm see Table 745; København - Lund - Hässleholm - Alvesta see Table 730.

km		Øtåg Ⓐ	Øtåg Ⓐ	Øtåg	Øtåg Ⓐ	Ⓐ	Øtåg	Øtåg	Øtåg Ⓐ	⑥	Øtåg	Øtåg	Øtåg Ⓐ		①–⑥	Øtåg	Øtåg	Øtåg Ⓐ	⑦	Øtåg	Øtåg Ⓒ	Øtåg Ⓐ	Øtåg	Øtåg	Øtåg †	Øtåg Ⓐ	
0	**København** H ... d.	...	0507	0607	0607	...	0707	0807	0807	...	0907	1007	1007	...	...	1107	1207	1207	...	1307	1407	1407	1507	1607	1607	1607	
12	København Lufthavn ✈ d.	...	0522	0622	0622	...	0722	0822	0822	...	0922	1022	1022	...	...	1122	1222	1222	...	1322	1422	1422	1522	1622	1622	1622	
47	**Malmö** C ... a.	...	0546	0646	0646	...	0746	0846	0846	...	0946	1046	1046	...	...	1146	1246	1246	...	1346	1446	1446	1546	1646	1646	1646	
47	**Malmö** C ... d.	...	0548	0648	0648	...	0748	0848	0848	...	0948	1048	1048	...	...	1148	1248	1248	...	1348	1448	1448	1548	1648	1648	1648	
63	Lund ... d.	...	0601	0701	0701	...	0801	0901	0901	...	1001	1101	1101	...	...	1201	1301	1301	...	1401	1501	1501	1601	1701	1701	1701	
80	Eslöv ... d.	...	0611	0711	0711	...	0811	0911	0911	...	1011	1111	1111	...	...	1211	1311	1311	...	1411	1511	1511	1611	1711	1711	1711	
130	Hässleholm ... d.	...	0640	0737	0740	...	0840	0937	0940	...	1040	1137	1140	...	...	1240	1337	1340	...	1440	1540	1540	1640	1737	1740	1740	
181	Älmhult ... d.	...	0703	...	0803	...	0903	...	1003	...	1103	...	1203	...	...	1303	...	1403	...	1503	1603	1603	1703	...	1803	1803	
	Göteborg C ... ▲ d.	...	|	...	|	0604	|	...	|	0804	|	...	|	...	1004	|	...	|	1159	|	|	|	|	...	|	|	[illegible]
	Borås ... ▲ d.	...	|	...	|	0658	|	...	|	0858	|	...	|	...	1059	|	...	|	1254	|	|	|	|	...	|	|	[illegible]
	Limmared ... d.	...	|	...	|	0728	|	...	|	0927	|	...	|	...	1129	|	...	|	1325	|	|	|	|	...	|	|	[illegible]
	Värnamo ... d.	...	|	...	|	0808	|	...	|	1010	|	...	|	...	1209	|	...	|	1410	|	|	|	|	...	|	|	[illegible]
228	Alvesta ... a.	...	0725	...	0825	0835	0925	...	1025	1035	1125	...	1225	...	1234	1325	...	1425	1436	1525	1625	1625	1725	...	1825	1825	[illegible]
228	Alvesta ... ▲ d.	0632	0726	...	0834	0836	0937	...	1038	1035	1138	...	1226	...	1234	1337	...	1438	1437	1538	1632	1638	1738	...	1827	1836	[illegible]
245	**Växjö** ... ▲ d.	0648	0748	...	0844	0851	0947	...	1048	1049	1148	...	1237	...	1249	1347	...	1448	1450	1548	1643	1648	1748	...	1837	1846	[illegible]
302	Emmaboda ... a.	0725	0825	...	...	0927	1025	...	1125	1126	1225	...	...	...	1326	1425	...	1525	1526	1627	...	1725	1825	...	...	...	[illegible]
302	Emmaboda ... ▽ d.	0730	0830	...	...	0928	1030	...	1130	1128	1230	...	...	...	1328	1430	...	1530	1527	1632	...	1730	1830	...	...	...	[illegible]
330	Nybro ... d.	0743	0843	...	...	0943	1043	...	1143	1143	1243	...	...	...	1344	1443	...	1549	1543	1645	...	1743	1843	...	...	...	[illegible]
359	**Kalmar** ... a.	0759	0859	...	...	1001	1059	...	1159	1200	1259	...	...	...	1404	1459	...	1604	1600	1700	...	1759	1859	...	...	...	[illegible]

	Øtåg	Øtåg	Øtåg Ⓑ	Ⓑ	Øtåg	Øtåg	Øtåg Ⓑ	Øtåg	Øtåg	
København H ... d.	1707	1807	1807	...	1907	2007	2007	2107	2147	...
København Lufthavn ✈ d.	1722	1822	1822	...	1922	2022	2022	2122	2202	...
Malmö C ... a.	1746	1846	1846	...	1946	2046	2046	2146	2226	...
Malmö C ... d.	1748	1848	1848	...	1948	2048	2048	2148	2228	...
Lund ... d.	1801	1901	1901	...	2001	2101	2101	2201	2241	...
Eslöv ... d.	1812	1911	1911	...	2013	2111	2111	2211	|	...
Hässleholm ... d.	1840	1937	1940	...	2040	2137	2140	2243	2312	...
Älmhult ... d.	1903	...	2003	...	2103	...	2203	2306	...	...
Göteborg C ... ▲ d.	|	...	|	1804	|	...	|	|	...	...
Borås ... ▲ d.	|	...	|	1858	|	...	|	|	...	...
Limmared ... d.	|	...	|	1928	|	...	|	|	...	...
Värnamo ... d.	|	...	|	2013	|	...	|	|	...	...
Alvesta ... a.	1925	...	2025	2039	2125	...	2225	2325	...	...
Alvesta ... ▲ d.	1938	...	2026	2041	2138	...	2232	2327	...	...
Växjö ... ▲ d.	1948	...	2039	2053	2149	...	2242	2338	...	...
Emmaboda ... a.	2028	...	...	2130	2225	...	...	...	...	...
Emmaboda ... ▽ d.	2035	...	...	2131	2230	...	...	...	...	...
Nybro ... d.	2048	...	...	2146	2243	...	...	...	...	...
Kalmar ... a.	2104	...	...	2203	2259	...	...	...	...	...

km		Øtåg Ⓐ	Øtåg	Ⓐ	Øtåg Ⓐ	Øtåg	Øtåg Ⓐ	Øtåg ⑥	Øtåg	Øtåg	⑥	Øtåg Ⓐ	Ø
	Kalmar ... d.	...	...	0459	...	...	0600	...	...	0700	0754	0800	
	Nybro ... d.	...	...	0516	...	...	0614	...	...	0714	0811	0814	
	Emmaboda ... ▽ a.	...	...	0531	...	...	0629	...	...	0729	0827	0829	
	Emmaboda ... d.	...	...	0532	...	...	0630	...	...	0730	0828	0830	
	Växjö ... ▲ d.	0510	...	0608	0618	...	0710	0710	...	0810	0904	0910	[illegible]
	Alvesta ... ▲ a.	0520	...	0620	0628	...	0720	0720	...	0820	0916	0920	[illegible]
0	Alvesta ... d.	0524	...	0621	0630	...	0722	0722	...	0822	0919	0922	[illegible]
49	Värnamo ... d.	|	...	0647	|	...	|	|	...	|	0945	|	
110	Limmared ... d.	|	...	0728	|	...	|	|	...	|	1026	|	
149	Borås ... ▲ a.	|	...	0758	|	...	|	|	...	|	1058	|	
222	**Göteborg** C ... ▲ a.	|	...	0855	|	...	|	|	...	|	1155	|	
	Älmhult ... d.	0543	...	...	0649	...	0741	0741	...	0841	...	0941	[illegible]
	Hässleholm ... d.	0622	0622	...	0722	0722	0822	0822	0822	0922	...	1022	[illegible]
	Eslöv ... d.	0645	0645	...	0745	0745	0845	0845	0845	0945	...	1045	[illegible]
	Lund ... d.	0700	0700	...	0800	0800	0900	0900	0900	1000	...	1100	[illegible]
	Malmö C ... a.	0711	0711	...	0811	0811	0911	0911	0911	1011	...	1111	[illegible]
	Malmö C ... d.	0713	0713	...	0813	0813	0913	0913	0913	1013	...	1113	[illegible]
	København Lufthavn ✈ a.	0733	0733	...	0833	0833	0933	0933	0933	1033	...	1133	[illegible]
	København H ... a.	0748	0748	...	0848	0848	0948	0948	0948	1048	...	1148	[illegible]

	Øtåg	Øtåg		Øtåg Ⓐ	Øtåg	Øtåg	Ⓑ	Øtåg Ⓐ	Øtåg	Øtåg	Øtåg Ⓐ	Øtåg †	Øtåg		Øtåg	①–⑥	Øtåg Ⓐ	Øtåg	Øtåg	⑦	Øtåg Ⓐ	Øtåg Ⓑ	Øtåg	Øtåg	Øtåg Ⓐ	Øtåg Ⓑ	Ø
Kalmar ... d.	...	0900	0954	...	...	1100	1152	...	...	1300	1400	...	...	...	1500	1556	...	...	1655	1755	1800	...	...	1906	2001	...	[illegible]
Nybro ... d.	...	0914	1011	...	...	1114	1211	...	...	1314	1414	...	...	...	1514	1617	...	...	1712	1812	1814	...	...	1920	2018	...	[illegible]
Emmaboda ... ▽ a.	...	0929	1026	...	...	1129	1226	...	...	1329	1429	...	...	...	1529	1632	...	...	1729	1827	1829	...	...	1936	2035	...	[illegible]
Emmaboda ... d.	...	0930	1027	...	...	1130	1227	...	...	1332	1430	...	...	...	1530	1632	...	...	1730	1828	1830	...	...	1937	2035	...	[illegible]
Växjö ... ▲ d.	...	1010	1106	1110	...	1210	1305	1311	...	1410	1510	1510	...	...	1610	1707	1712	...	1810	1903	1910	1910	...	2010	2110	2110	[illegible]
Alvesta ... ▲ a.	...	1020	1118	1121	...	1220	1317	1321	...	1420	1520	1520	...	...	1620	1719	1722	...	1820	1915	1920	1920	...	2020	2120	2120	
Alvesta ... d.	...	1022	1119	1122	...	1222	1318	1322	...	1422	1522	1522	...	...	1622	1720	1723	...	1822	1920	1922	1922	...	2022	2122	2122	
Värnamo ... d.	...	|	1145	|	...	|	1343	|	...	|	|	|	...	...	|	1748	|	...	|	1948	|	|	...	|	|	|	
Limmared ... d.	...	|	1226	|	...	|	1423	|	...	|	|	|	...	...	|	1828	|	...	|	2030	|	|	...	|	|	|	
Borås ... ▲ a.	...	|	1256	|	...	|	1453	|	...	|	|	|	...	...	|	1858	|	...	|	2106	|	|	...	|	|	|	
Göteborg C ... ▲ a.	...	|	1350	|	...	|	1550	|	...	|	|	|	...	...	|	1950	|	...	|	2200	|	|	...	|	|	|	
Älmhult ... d.	...	1041	...	1141	...	1241	...	1341	...	1441	1541	1541	...	...	1641	...	1741	...	1841	...	1941	1941	...	2041	2141	2141	
Hässleholm ... d.	1022	1122	...	1222	1222	1322	...	1422	1422	1522	1622	1622	1622	...	1722	...	1822	1822	1922	...	2022	2022	2022	2122	2222	2222	
Eslöv ... d.	1045	1145	...	1245	1245	1345	...	1445	1445	1545	1645	1645	1645	...	1745	...	1845	1845	1946	...	2045	2045	2045	2145	2245	2245	
Lund ... d.	1100	1200	...	1300	1300	1400	...	1500	1500	1600	1700	1700	1700	...	1800	...	1900	1900	2000	...	2100	2100	2100	2200	2300	2300	
Malmö C ... a.	1111	1211	...	1311	1311	1411	...	1511	1511	1611	1711	1711	1711	...	1811	...	1911	1911	2011	...	2111	2111	2110	2211	2311	2311	
Malmö C ... d.	1113	1213	...	1313	1313	1413	...	1513	1513	1613	1713	1713	1713	...	1813	...	1913	1913	2013	...	2113	2113	2112	2213	2313	2313	
København Lufthavn ✈ a.	1133	1233	...	1333	1333	1433	...	1533	1533	1633	1733	1733	1733	...	1833	...	1933	1933	2033	...	2133	2133	2133	2233	2333	2333	
København H ... a.	1148	1248	...	1348	1348	1448	...	1548	1548	1648	1748	1748	1748	...	1848	...	1948	1948	2048	...	2148	2148	2148	2248	2348	2348	

EMMABODA - KARLSKRONA (2nd class only)

Operator: *LT*

km		Ⓐ	①–⑥	①–⑥	①–⑥		①–⑥				Ⓑ		Ⓑ		Ⓑ		Ⓑ
0	Emmaboda ... d.	0634	0734	0834	0934	1034	1146	1234	1334	1434	1534	1636	1734	1834	1943	2040	2135
57	Karlskrona ... a.	0716	0816	0916	1016	1116	1228	1316	1416	1516	1616	1719	1816	1916	2025	2122	2217

	Ⓐ	①–⑥	①–⑥	①–⑥		①–⑥				Ⓑ		Ⓑ		Ⓑ		Ⓑ
Karlskrona ... a.	0542	0642	0742	0842	0942	1042	1135	1242	1342	1442	1542	1640	1742	1842	1932	2032
Emmaboda ... d.	0624	0724	0824	0924	1024	1124	1217	1324	1424	1524	1624	1726	1824	1924	2014	2113

▲ – Additional trains run Göteborg - Borås and v.v and Alvesta - Växjö and v.v.

▽ – See panel below main table for connecting tra Emmaboda - Karlskrona and v.v.

perator: A-Train AB (*AEX*) Arlanda Express — STOCKHOLM - STOCKHOLM ARLANDA ✈ 747

urney time: 20 minutes. All services stop at Arlanda Södra (17 minutes from Stockholm, 2 minutes from Arlanda Norra). Södra serves terminals 2, 3 and 4; Norra serves terminal 5.

om **Stockholm** Central: 0420, 0435, 0450, 0505, 0520, 0535, 0550, 0605, 0620, 0635, 0650 and at the same minutes past each hour until 2205, then 2220, 2235, 2305, 2335, 0005, 0035.

From **Arlanda** Norra: 0450, 0505, 0520, 0535, 0550, 0605, 0620, 0635, 0650 and at the same minutes past each hour until 2205, then 2220, 2235, 2250, 2305, 2335, 0005, 0035, 0105.

Minor alterations to schedules are possible at peak times

STOCKHOLM - HALLSBERG - KARLSTAD - OSLO 750

Service valid from August 19 (subject to alteration on and around public holidays).
From June 24 to August 18 services operate from / to Stockholm Södra (not Central) in revised timings.

km		VTAB	VTAB	VTAB	Sn	VTAB		Vy	VTAB	IC	VTAB	IC	VTAB	VTAB	Sn	SN	VTAB	IC	Vy		VTAB	Sn	IC	Tågab	VTAB	VTAB	IC
		★	★	★	**621**	★			★	**611**	★	**613**	★	★	**10629**	**661**	★	**603**			★	**635**	**605**	**7061**	★	★	**615**
		2	2	2	🅁✕	2			2	🅁	2	🅁	2	2	🅁✕	🅁✕	2	🅁			2	🅁✕	🅁	☆	2	2	🅁
		Ⓐ	Ⓐ	Ⓐ	ⒶA	Ⓒ		Ⓒ	Ⓐ	Ⓒ	Ⓐ	ⒶH	Ⓐ	Ⓒ	⑥	Ⓐ	Ⓐ	B	⑦		Ⓐ	Ⓐ	⑥	†	⑥	Ⓐ	Ⓐ
0	**Stockholm** C △ d.	...	...	...	0616	...	...	...	...	0807	...	0910	...	...	1008	1013	...	1141	...	...	...	1358	1404	1444	...	...	1508
36	Södertälje Syd △ d.	...	...	...	0634**u**	...	...	...	...	0827**u**	...	0930**u**	...	...	1027**u**	1032**u**	...	1201**u**	...	...	...	1417**u**	1424**u**	|	...	...	1528**u**
31	Katrineholm △ d.	...	...	...	0716	...	...	...	...	0911	...	1017	...	...	1109	1111	...	1245	...	...	...	1500	1508	|	...	...	1614
97	**Hallsberg** △ d.	...	...	0611	0745	...	...	0901**d**	...	0942	1009	1100	...	...	1138	1137	1306	1316	...	...	...	1529	1539	|	...	...	1655
61	Degerfors d.	...	...	0647	0817	...	...	0933**d**	...	1016	1041	1135	...	...	1210	1208	1341	1350	...	...	...	1602	1613	1726	...	...	1737
87	Kristinehamn d.	...	0606	0706	0832	...	...	0949**d**	1012	1040	1106	1149	1206	...	1224	1223	1402	1406	...	...	1604	1619	1628	1739	...	1701	1757
27	**Karlstad** a.	...	0644	0737	0904	...	...	1018**d**	1044	1104	1134	1214	1235	...	1248	1246	1427	1433	...	...	1632	1649	1653	1800	...	1734	1822
27	**Karlstad** **751** d.	0534	0651	0740	...	0910	...	*1021*	1045	1106	1137	1217	1238	1242	...	...	1429	...	1525	...	1634	...	...	1841	1725	1749	1824
47	Kil **751** d.	0549	0704	0753	...	0922	...	*1035*	1058	|	1150	|	1258	1254	...	...	1442	...	1537	...	1649	...	...	1853	1741	1821	|
95	Arvika d.	0622	0747	0828	...	0957	...	*1109*	1132	1145	1226	1302	1333	1329	...	...	1514	...	1615	...	1728	...	...	...	1828	1853	1913
30	Charlottenberg 🛃 a.	0648	0810	0850	...	1021	...	*1133*	1154	|	1248	|	1356	1352	...	...	1538	...	1639	...	1750	...	...	...	1851	1915	|
72	Kongsvinger a.	...	...	...	...	...	...	...	...	1231	...	1350	...	...	...	...	...	...	1704	...	...	...	...	...	...	...	1959
72	**Oslo** Sentral a.	...	...	...	...	...	...	...	...	1409	...	1509	...	...	...	...	...	...	1844	...	...	...	...	...	...	...	2124

	IC	VTAB	Tågab		Tågab	Sn	VTAB	Sn	VTAB	Tågab	IC	Tågab
	617	★	**7041**		**7061**	**643**	★	**645**	★	**7039**	**607**	**7053**
	🅁	2	☆		☆	🅁✕	2	🅁✕	2	☆	🅁	☆
	⑦	Ⓐ	⑦		⑥	Ⓑ	⑦	⑥	Ⓐ	†	ⒶC	①–④
ockholm C △ d.	1529	...	1545	...	1633	1713	...	1810	...	1831	1856	2046
ödertälje Syd △ d.	1549**u**	...	|	...	|	1731**u**	...	1829**u**	...	|	1925**u**	|
atrineholm △ d.	1634	...	|	...	1731	1808**u**	...	1911	...	1932	2009	2146
allsberg △ d.	1705	1722	1723	...	1801	1836	...	1940	...	2022	2040	2217
egerfors d.	1739	1755	1757	...	1840	1906	...	2011	...	2055	2116	2252
istinehamn d.	1756	1829	1813	...	1855	1919	...	2032	2045	2110	2130	2307
arlstad a.	1821	1903	1836	...	1924	1942	...	2056	2112	2133	2155	2332
arlstad **751** d.	1826	1908	1841	...	...	...	2011	...	2114	...	...	...
l **751** d.	|	1924	1852	...	...	...	2023	...	2139	...	...	...
vika d.	1913	2000	*2000*	...	...	...	2058	...	2218	...	...	...
harlottenberg 🛃 a.	|	...	*2023*	...	...	...	...	...	2254	...	...	...
ongsvinger a.	1959	...	...	...	...	...	...	...	...	...	...	...
slo Sentral a.	2124	...	...	...	...	...	...	...	...	...	...	...

	Sn	Tågab	VTAB	Sn	IC	VTAB	Tågab	IC	IC	VTAB	VTAB	IC
	620	**7021**	★	**622**	**602**	★	**7060**	**604**	**612**	★	★	**606**
	🅁✕	☆	2	🅁✕	🅁	2	☆	🅁	🅁	2	2	🅁
	Ⓐ	Ⓐ	Ⓐ	⑥	Ⓐ	Ⓐ	⑥	⑦	ⒶA	Ⓒ	Ⓐ	⑥
Oslo Sentral d.	...	...	...	...	...	...	...	...	0556	...	...	...
Kongsvinger d.	...	...	...	...	...	...	...	...	0704	...	...	...
Charlottenberg 🛃 d.	...	...	0538	...	...	0712	...	...	|	0744	0830	...
Arvika d.	*0500*	...	0600	...	...	0806	...	...	0748	0806	0854	...
Kil **751** d.	*0533*	...	0637	...	...	0842	...	...	|	0842	0929	...
Karlstad **751** a.	*0546*	...	0650	...	...	0855	...	...	0829	0856	0942	...
Karlstad d.	0556	0607	0652	0719	0736	0902	0748	0757	0831	...	0944	1001
Kristinehamn d.	0617	0631	0720	0740	0759	0934	0812	0820	0854	...	1012	1024
Degerfors d.	0632	0646	0735	0754	0816	...	0826	0836	0913	...	...	1039
Hallsberg △ d.	|	...	0809	0826	0850	...	0901	0911	0950	...	...	1113
Katrineholm △ a.	|	...	...	0851	0920	...	0929	0941	1025	...	...	1144
Södertälje Syd △ a.	|	...	...	0929**s**	1008**s**	...	|	1025**s**	|	...	...	1236**s**
Stockholm C. △ a.	0816	...	...	0949	1029	...	1034	1046	1129	...	...	1257

	Sn	Sn	VTAB	Tågab	Sn	Sn	IC	VTAB		Tågab	Sn	VTAB		IC	VTAB	Tågab	Vy	VTAB	Sn	VTAB		IC	IC	IC	VTAB	VTAB	Vy
	628	**10628**		**7040**	**10634**	**634**	**600**	★		**7034**	**614**			**608**		**7052**		★	**644**	★		**636**	**616**	**626**	★	★	
	🅁✕	🅁✕	2	☆	🅁✕	🅁✕	🅁	2		☆	🅁✕	2		🅁	2	☆	2	2	🅁✕	2		🅁	🅁	🅁	2	2	2
	Ⓐ	⑦	Ⓐ	†E	⑥	Ⓐ	⑦	Ⓐ		†	⑥	Ⓒ		ⒷH	Ⓐ	Ⓐ	Ⓒ	Ⓐ	Ⓑ	Ⓐ		⑦	Ⓐ	⑥	Ⓒ	Ⓐ	⑦
slo Sentral d.	...	...	...	...	...	...	...	...	...	...	1156	...	...	...	...	...	1346	...	...	...	...	1656	1656	1656	...	...	1936
ongsvinger d.	...	...	...	...	...	...	...	...	...	...	1311	...	...	...	...	...	1504	...	...	...	...	1805	1805	1805	...	...	2055
harlottenberg 🛃 d.	...	...	0925	...	...	...	...	1204	...	...	|	1404	...	...	1409	...	1533	1548	...	1640	...	|	|	|	1915	2019	2120
vika d.	...	...	0947	...	...	...	...	1225	...	...	1354	1426	...	...	1431	...	1555	1614	...	1704	...	1849	1850	1853	1941	2041	2143
l **751** d.	...	...	1023	1018	...	...	...	1300	...	1420	|	1500	...	...	1506	1554	1627	1657	...	1737	...	|	|	|	2019	2116	2226
arlstad **751** a.	...	...	1036	1033	...	...	...	1315	...	1434	1435	1514	...	...	1525	1612	1641	1710	...	1750	...	1938	1939	1938	2032	2129	2240
arlstad d.	1010	1017	1043	1049	1310	1313	1314	1318	...	1437	1437	...	...	1523	1527	1617	1643**f**	...	1717	1752	...	1941	1941	1941	...	...	...
istinehamn d.	1033	1041	1106	1117	1333	1334	1337	1346	...	1501	1500	...	...	1547	1552	1645	1709**f**	...	1739	1819	...	2005	2010	2005	...	...	...
egerfors d.	1047	1056	1120	1131	1350	1349	1357	1409	...	1515	1516	...	...	1602	...	1658	1724**f**	...	1804	...	...	2021	2026	2021	...	...	...
allsberg △ d.	1122	1132	1201	1218	1430	1421	1432	1444	...	1549	1551	...	...	1638	...	1733	1805**f**	...	1847	...	...	2111	2103	2103	...	...	...
atrineholm △ a.	1151	1201	...	|	1459	1446	1503	...	...	|	1621	...	...	1708	...	|	...	...	1916	...	...	2141	2143	2133	...	...	...
ödertälje Syd △ a.	1236**s**	1244**s**	...	|	1542**s**	1524**s**	1553**s**	...	...	|	1728**s**	...	...	1752**s**	...	|	...	...	1959**s**	...	...	2226**s**	2226**s**	2226**s**	...	...	...
ockholm C △ a.	1256	1305	...	1350	1603	1544	1614	...	...	1718	1749	...	...	1813	...	1909	...	...	2020	...	...	2247	2247	2247	...	...	...

Other regional services **STOCKHOLM** - **HALLSBERG** (2nd class only)

	Ⓐ	Ⓐ	①–⑥	†	Ⓐ		Ⓑ	A	⑥	A		Ⓐ	F	⑤	①–④	⑤⑥
ockholm C d.	0641	0751	0851	0946	1051	1251	1452	1529	1548	1635	1751	1855	1950	2051	2200	2333**j**
emingsberg d.	0652	0802	0902	0957	1102	1302	1503	1540	1559	1646	1802	1906	2001	2102	2211	2344
ödertälje Syd d.	0703	0814	0914	1009	1114	1313	1515	1550	1611	1658	1814	1917	2012	2114	2223	2356
en **754** d.	0738	0850	0950	1045	1150	1350	1551	1624	1647	1742	1850	1952	2047	2151	2259	0034
atrineholm **754** d.	0751	0903	1003	1059	1203	1403	1606	1642	1700	1754	1903	2005	2059	2204	2312	0047
allsberg a.	0823	0936	1037	1133	1237	1437	1644	1712	1732	1831	1934	2044	2132	2236	2345	0120

	Ⓐ	Ⓐ	Ⓐ	⑥		Ⓐ	⑦		①–⑥	Ⓑ	①–⑥	Ⓐ	⑥	Ⓑ	Ⓐ	Ⓑ
allsberg d.	0521	0623	0712	0726	0923	1127	1224	...	1317	1519	1618	1718	1821	1821	1910	2018
atrineholm d.	0555	0657	0756	0800	0957	1159	1256	...	1350	1553	1650	1752	1853	1853	1949	2052
en **754** d.	0608	0709	0808	0812	1009	1211	1308	...	1402	1605	1702	1804	1905	1909	2002	2004
ödertälje Syd **754** d.	0644	0745	0844	0848	1045	1248	1344	...	1438	1641	1738	1840	1941	1947	2037	2140
emingsberg a.	0656	0757	0855	0859	1057	1259	1355	...	1450	1653	1749	1851	1952	1958	2048	2151
ockholm C a.	0709	0810	0908	0911	1110	1311	1407	...	1503	1706	1801	1903	2004	2010	2100	2202

A – Ⓐ from Sept. 2.
B – Ⓑ from Sept. 1 (also Aug. 25; not Sept. 9 – 13).
C – Until Aug. 30.
E – Until June 16.
F – ①②③④⑦.
H – Not Sept. 9 – 13.
d – ⑥ only.
f – ⑦ only.
j – 2330 on Aug. 23, 30.
s – Calls to sets down only.
u – Calls to picks up only.
★ – Services until Aug. 11.
☆ – Subject to confirmation.
△ – For other regional services see panel below main table. For other fast services see Table **740**.

KARLSTAD - GÖTEBORG 751

km					Tågab					Tågab	Tågab		
		Ⓐ	Ⓐ		⑦	①–⑥			Ⓑ	⑥☆	Ⓐ☆		Ⓑ
0	**Karlstad** **750** d.	0614	0809	...	1005	1017	1213	1415	1612	1613	1639	1809	2222
19	Kil **750** d.	0627	0828	...	1020	1030	1226	1428	1625	1625	1700	1828	2236
70	Säffle d.	0700	0901	...	1052	1102	1300	1500	1659	1659	1738	1901	2308
87	Åmål d.	0710	0911	...	1110	1112	1311	1510	1709	1708	1751	1912	2318
28	Mellerud d.	0741	0936	...	1133	1137	1335	1536	1736	|	1819	1938	2342
69	Öxnered a.	0802	0956	...	1153	1157	1359	1557	1759	1756	1839	1958	0002
79	Trollhättan a.	0808	1003	...	1201	1205	1405	1603	1806	1802	1845	2006	0008
51	**Göteborg** C a.	0845	1035	...	1235	1240	1440	1645	1845	1840	1930	2040	0040

		Tågab		Tågab				Tågab	Tågab				Tågab
	Ⓐ	Ⓐ☆	Ⓐ	⑥☆		①–⑥		⑦☆	Ⓐ☆		Ⓑ		⑦☆
Göteborg C. d.	0514	0610	0714	0715	0914	1114	1314	1340	1340	1514	1714	1914	2040
Trollhättan d.	0551	0645	0753	0752	0953	1153	1352	1414	1414	1553	1752	1952	2114
Öxnered d.	0601	0653	0800	0800	1000	1159	1359	1421	1421	1600	1759	1959	2121
Mellerud d.	0622	0715	0821	0822	1022	1220	1420	1443	1443	1620	1819	2019	2141
Åmål d.	0646	0739	0847	0847	1048	1245	1446	1510	1510	1644	1846	2043	2205
Säffle d.	0659	0750	0900	0900	1101	1259	1459	1521	1521	1659	1859	2055	2215
Kil **750** a.	0730	0821	0932	0932	1132	1330	1531	1548	1552	1731	1933	2127	2250
Karlstad **750** a.	0751	0834	0953	0945	1148	1346	1544	1601	1612	1745	1945	2141	2304

– Subject to confirmation.

nd class only — VÄSTERÅS - LUDVIKA 752

km		Ⓐ	⑥	Ⓐ	Ⓐ	Ⓒ	Ⓐ	Ⓐ	Ⓒ	Ⓐ	Ⓐ	Ⓒ	Ⓐ	Ⓐ	⑦	Ⓐ	⑥	Ⓐ	⑦	Ⓐ	Ⓐ	Ⓒ	Ⓐ	Ⓐ	Ⓐ
0	**Västerås** d.	0541	0723	0742	0844	0928	0943	1044	1128	1144	1242	1328	1344	1444	1528	1544	1628	1644	1728	1741	1843	1928	1944	2044	2219
80	Fagersta C d.	0641	0827	0841	0942	1027	1044	1144	1227	1247	1341	1427	1441	1541	1627	1642	1734	1742	1827	1841	1942	2026	2042	2144	2318
129	**Ludvika** a.	0725	0917	0926	...	1115	1129	...	1318	...	1426	1517	...	1625	1718	...	1819	1826	1918	...	2026	2111	...	2228	...

	Ⓐ	Ⓐ	Ⓐ	⑥	Ⓐ	Ⓐ	Ⓒ	Ⓐ	Ⓐ	Ⓒ	Ⓐ	Ⓐ	Ⓒ	Ⓐ	Ⓐ	Ⓒ	Ⓐ	Ⓐ	Ⓒ	Ⓐ	Ⓐ	⑦	Ⓐ	Ⓐ
udvika d.	...	0530	...	0655	0733	...	0846	0935	...	1046	...	1232	1246	...	1433	1446	...	1633	1646	...	1834	1846	...	2037
agersta C d.	0532	0618	0717	0743	0820	0918	0934	1022	1118	1134	1209	1319	1334	1418	1520	1534	1618	1718	1734	1818	1919	1933	2018	2122
ästerås a.	0630	0715	0815	0842	0917	1016	1032	1119	1218	1232	1312	1416	1432	1516	1617	1632	1716	1815	1832	1915	2016	2032	2116	2222

754 LINKÖPING - NORRKÖPING - VÄSTERÅS - SALA

2nd class only

Subject to alteration until August 11

km		Ⓐ	Ⓐ	Ⓐ	Ⓒ						Ⓒ	Ⓐ
	Linköping ...... **730** d.	0508	0604	...	0808	1007	1207	1407	1607	1807	2010	2010
0	**Norrköping** .... **730** d.	0535	0632	0827	0835	1035	1235	1435	1635	1835	2037	2043
48	Katrineholm .... **750** d.	0601	0703	0854	0902	1101	1301	1502	1700	1902	2107	2114
71	Flen .... **750** d.	0613	0716	0914	0915	1113	1313	1515	1714	1915	2120	2126
112	Eskilstuna .... a.	0647	0750	0948	0948	1148	1348	1549	1748	1949	2154	2207
112	Eskilstuna .... d.	0652	0752	0952	0952	1151	1351	1551	1751	1951	2156	2209
160	**Västerås** .... a.	0725	0825	1025	1025	1225	1425	1625	1825	2025	2228	2240
160	**Västerås** .... d.	0728	0828	1028	1027	1228	1428	1627	1827	2027	...	...
199	Sala .... a.	0756	0853	1053	1054	1253	1454	1654	1854	2054	...	...

	Ⓐ		Ⓐ							
Sala .... d.	...	0704	0804	0904	1104	1305	1504	1704	1904	210
Västerås .... a.	...	0730	0830	0930	1130	1330	1530	1730	1930	213
Västerås .... d.	0528	0733	0833	0933	1133	1335	1533	1733	1933	213
Eskilstuna .... a.	0601	0807	0907	1007	1207	1407	1607	1807	2007	220
Eskilstuna .... d.	0603	0808	0908	1008	1208	1409	1608	1808	2008	2207
Flen .... **750** d.	0639	0842	0942	1042	1242	1442	1642	1842	2042	2240
Katrineholm . **750** d.	0652	0856	0955	1056	1256	1457	1656	1855	2055	2258
Norrköping . **730** a.	0717	0921	1020	1121	1320	1521	1720	1920	2119	2323
Linköping ... **730** a.	0749	0949	1049	1148	1348	1548	1748	1948	2154	235

a – Ⓐ only.

☛ **Additional journeys** Linköping - Sala and v.v. on Ⓐ: **From Linköping** at 0702, 0908, 1108, 1308, 1508, 1708 and 1907 (also Eskilstuna - Sala at 0546). **From Sala** at 0551, 1004, 1204, 1404, 1604, 1804 and 2004.

755 MJÖLBY - HALLSBERG - ÖREBRO - GÄVLE

Subject to alteration July 8 - August 11

km		Ⓐ	Ⓐ	Ⓐ	①–⑥	Ⓐ	Ⓐ	Ⓐ	Ⓐ	⑥	Ⓐ	①–⑥			Ⓐ	⑥	Ⓐ	⑦	Ⓐ		Ⓐ	Ⓐ	Ⓒ	Ⓐ	Ⓑ	⑦	Ⓐ	Ⓑ
0	**Mjölby** .... d.	...	...	...	...	...	0550	...	...	...	...	0801	...	1001	...	...	...	1201	...	1401	...	...	1601	1601	1801	...	...	200
27	Motala .... d.	...	...	...	...	...	0606	...	...	...	...	0820	...	1020	...	...	...	1220	...	1420	...	...	1620	1620	1820	...	...	202
96	**Hallsberg** .... a.	...	...	...	...	...	0646	...	...	...	...	0906	...	1106	...	...	...	1306	...	1506	...	...	1706	1706	1906	...	...	210
	Hallsberg .... **756** d.	...	...	...	0528	0635	0656	0729	0814	...	...	0920	1032**a**	1117	...	...	1247	1317	...	1516	1649	...	1728	1728	1927	1941	1941	211
121	**Örebro** C .... **756** a.	...	...	...	0548	0656	0716	0749	0834	...	...	0940	1052**a**	1137	...	...	1307	1337	...	1538	1709	...	1748	1748	1947	2001	2001	213
	Örebro C .... d.	...	...	...	0550	0658	0720	0751	0849	0852	0853	0953	1053	1153	1253	1309	1309	1353	1452	1553	1710	1653	1753	1753	1958	2003	2003	215
146	Frövi .... d.	...	...	...	0605	0713	0735	0808	0904	0907	0908	1008	1108	1209	1307	1324	1324	1408	1507	1608	1725	1708	1808	1808	2013	2018	2018	220
204	Kopparberg .... d.	...	...	...	0654	0757	|	0853	|	|	0954	1054	1202	1259	1354	|	|	1457	1555	1655	|	1758	1856	1856	|	|	|	224
232	Grängesberg ...... d.	...	...	...	0722	0822	|	0917	|	|	1018	1125	1222	1320	1421	|	|	1518	1620	1721	|	1822	1924	1924	|	|	|	|
247	Ludvika .... d.	...	...	0628	0734	0837	|	0935	|	|	1030	1140	1239	1331	1438	|	|	1531	1632	1732	|	1836	1935	1940	2138	|	|	232
295	**Borlänge** .... a.	...	...	0702	0809	0906	|	1009	|	|	1111	1208	1310	1406	1508	|	|	1559	1700	1801	|	1907	2004	2013	2208	|	|	235
	Borlänge .... **758** d.	0557	...	0705	0813	0910	|	1010	|	|	1112	1210**d**	1311**b**	1410	1512	|	|	1608	1711	1804	|	1908	2011	2027	2209	|	|	...
317	Falun .... **758** d.	0616	...	0722	0830	0928	|	1028	|	|	1128	1228**d**	1329**b**	1427	1530	|	|	1627	1729	1822	|	1926	2029	2045	2225	|	|	...
	Fagersta .... d.	|	0600	|	|	|	0820	|	0953	0953	|	|	|	|	|	1409	1409	|	|	|	1813	|	|	|	...	2102	2120	...
	Avesta Krylbo.. d.	|	0626	|	|	|	0845	|	1023	1018	|	|	|	|	|	1434	1434	|	|	|	1837	|	|	|	...	2127	2147	...
371	Storvik .... d.	0657	0704	0802	0906	1006	0926	1106	1059	1055	1211	1308**d**	1405**b**	1504	1605	1513	1521	1705	1806	1904	1913	2003	2110	2125	...	2205	2231	...
385	Sandviken .... d.	0708	0715	0813	0917	1018	0937	1117	1109	1106	1222	1319**d**	1415**b**	1514	1615	1524	1532	1722	1817	1915	1923	2014	2121	2135	...	2216	2244	...
408	**Gävle** .... a.	0724	0738	0829	0933	1038	0955	1136	1126	1122	1238	1335**d**	1436**b**	1531	1636	1540	1550	1740	1837	1933	1940	2030	2136	2151	...	2232	2300	...

km		Ⓐ	Ⓐ	①–⑥	Ⓐ	①–⑥	①–⑥	Ⓐ	Ⓐ	⑥	⑦	Ⓐ	⚒	⑦	Ⓐ	Ⓐ		Ⓐ	Ⓐ			Ⓑ	Ⓑ	Ⓐ	Ⓑ	⑦	Ⓐ	Ⓑ
0	**Gävle** .... d.	...	0415	0422**a**	0512	0615	0824	0715	0819	...	1028	0924	1023	1023	1121	1235	1221	1309	1431	1421	...	1635	1620	1708	1822	1828	1858	202
23	Sandviken .... d.	...	0431	0438**a**	0528	0631	0840	0732	0835	...	1044	0940	1039	1039	1137	1251	1241	1331	1447	1437	...	1651	1636	1725	1838	1844	1920	230
37	Storvik .... d.	...	0443	0450**a**	0540	0643	0852	0746	0847	...	1056	0952	1049	1049	1149	1303	1253	1344	1459	1447	...	1703	1648	1737	1849	1856	1934	204
95	Avesta Krylbo.. d.	...	0521	|	|	|	0930	|	|	...	1134	|	|	|	|	1341	|	|	1538	|	...	1741	|	|	|	1933	2011	|
130	Fagersta .... d.	...	0553	|	|	|	0955	|	|	...	1159	|	|	|	|	1407	|	|	1603	|	...	1810	|	|	|	1956	2040	|
	Falun .... **758** d.	...	|	0535**a**	0620	0724	|	0828	0930	...	|	1031	1130	1126	1226	|	1331	1429	|	1528	...	|	1728	1825	1928	...	...	212
	Borlänge .... **758** a.	...	|	0552**a**	0642	0741	|	0844	0947	...	|	1048	1147	1143	1243	|	1348	1446	|	1546	...	|	1745	1841	1953	...	...	214
	Borlänge .... d.	...	|	0558	0648	0755	|	0846	...	0955	|	1057	1150	1150	1250	|	1352	1450	|	1558	...	|	1801	1848	1954	...	...	...
	Ludvika .... d.	...	|	0628	0718	0824	|	0921	...	1028	|	1126	1225	1225	1328	|	1422	1529	|	1630	...	|	1832	1926	2032	...	...	...
	Grängesberg ...... d.	...	|	0639	0732	0834	|	0934	...	1040	|	1138	1235	1235	1341	|	1433	1540	|	1641	...	|	1844	1937	2044	...	...	...
	Kopparberg .... d.	...	|	0659	0758	0856	|	0958	...	1100	|	1159	1255	1255	1401	|	1459	1600	|	1700	...	|	1904	1859**c**	2104**f**	...	...	...
202	Frövi .... d.	...	0638	0745	0842	0942	1039	1043	...	1143	1243	1246	1343	1343	1444	1451	1543	1643	1647	1746	...	1854	1947	2047**c**	2146**f**	...	...	...
228	**Örebro** C .... a.	...	0654	0800	0858	0958	1055	1100	...	1158	1259	1301	1359	1359	1459	1507	1558	1658	1078	1801	...	1910	2009	2108**c**	2201**f**	...	...	...
	Örebro C .... **756** d.	0617	0656	0811	0959	1014	1056	...	...	1214	...	...	1414	1414	...	1508	1612	...	1709	1807	...	1912	2014	...	2203**f**	...	...	...
252	**Hallsberg** .... **756** a.	0637	0716	0832	0919	1034	1116	...	...	1234	...	...	1434	1434	...	1528	1632	...	1729	1828	...	1932	2034	...	2223**f**	...	...	...
	Hallsberg .... d.	0646	...	0846	...	1046	...	...	...	1246	...	...	1446	1446	...	...	1646	...	...	1846**b**	...	...	2046	...	...	...	...	...
	Motala .... d.	0727	...	0926	...	1126	...	...	...	1326	...	...	1526	1526	...	...	1726	...	...	1926**b**	...	...	2128	...	...	...	...	...
	Mjölby .... a.	0745	...	0945	...	1145	...	...	...	1345	...	...	1545	1545	...	...	1745	...	...	1945**b**	...	...	2145	...	...	...	...	...

a – Ⓒ only. b – Ⓐ only. c – Ⓐ from Aug. 12. d – Runs daily. f – Ⓑ from Aug. 12.

756 STOCKHOLM - VÄSTERÅS - ÖREBRO - HALLSBERG - GÖTEBORG

Service valid from August 19 (subject to alteration on and around public holidays). From June 24 to August 18 services operate from / to Stockholm Södra (not Central) in revised timings. See Table **740** for fast services Stockholm - Hallsberg - Skövde - Göteborg and v.v.

km		Ⓐ	Ⓐ	⑥	①–⑥	①–⑥	①–⑥	①–⑥							Ⓑ	⑥		Ⓐ		Ⓐ	Ⓑ		①–⑥	⑦	Ⓑ
0	**Stockholm** C .... ‡ d.	...	...	...	0613	0713	...	0813	0913	1013	1113	1213	1313	1413	1513	1513	1613	1643	1713	1748	1813	1913	2013	2013	221
72	Enköping .... ‡ d.	...	...	...	0654	0754	...	0854	0954	1054	1154	1254	1354	1454	1554	1554	1657	1727	1754	|	1854	1954	2054	2057	225
107	**Västerås** .... ‡ d.	0511	0610	...	0712	0812	0812	0912	1012	1112	1212	1313	1412	1512	1612	1612	1718	1747	1812	**e**	1912	2012	2112	2119	231
141	Köping .... ‡ d.	0528	0629	...	0730	0830	0830	0930	1030	1130	1230	1330	1430	1530	1630	1630	1741	1806	1830	|	1930	2030	2131	2143	233
159	Arboga .... ‡ d.	0541	0640	...	0741	0841	0841	0941	1041	1141	1241	1341	1441	1541	1641	1641	1752	1818	1841	1926	1941	2041	2146	2205	234
205	**Örebro** C .... ‡ a.	0605	0713	...	0804	0903	0903	1003	1104	1203	1306	1403	1503	1603	1704	1704	1816	1842	1903	1953	2003	2103	2215	2231	000
205	**Örebro** C .... **755** ‡ d.	0609	0714	0719	0805	0912	0912	1004	1109	1204	1312	1404	1512	1604	1719	1719	1818	1843	1907	1953	2004	2104	2217	2233	000
230	**Hallsberg** .. **736 755** ‡ d.	0632	0738	0743	0828	0935	0935	1025	1132	1225	1335	1427	1535	1626	1743	1743	1839	1904	1933	2018	2027	2124	2238	2254	002
260	Laxå .... **736** d.	0649	0756	0800	...	0952	0952	...	1149	...	1352	...	1552	...	1801	1801	...	...	1949	...	...	...	...	...	...
305	Töreboda .... d.	0708	0815	0819	...	1011	1011	...	1208	...	1411	...	1611	...	1820	1820	...	...	2008	...	...	...	...	...	...
344	**Skövde** .... d.	0724	0831	0835	...	1027	1038	...	1235	...	1438	...	1639	...	1836	1836	...	...	2035	...	...	...	...	...	...
374	Falköping .... a.	0742	0848	0853	...	1101	1055	...	1252	...	1454	...	1656	...	1852	1852	...	...	2052	...	...	...	...	...	...
408	Herrljunga .... **736** a.	0759	0912	0910	...	1119	1121	...	1309	...	1511	...	1718	...	1909	1909	...	...	2109	...	...	...	...	...	...
443	Alingsås .... a.	0820	0932	0930	...	1138	1140	...	1339	...	1536	...	1732	...	1928	1936	...	...	2144**f**	...	...	...	...	...	...
488	**Göteborg** C .... a.	0855	1000	1000	...	1210	1210	...	1410	...	1605	...	1805	...	1955	2005	...	...	2215**f**	...	...	...	...	...	...

	Ⓐ	Ⓐ	Ⓒ	Ⓐ		⑥	Ⓐ	⑦	①–⑥	Ⓒ	Ⓐ						Ⓐ	Ⓒ			⑦		Ⓒ	Ⓐ	K
Göteborg C .... d.	...	...	...	...	...	0559	0604	...	...	0759	0759	...	0959	...	1159	...	1359	1359	...	1559	...	...	1754	1759	185
Alingsås .... d.	...	...	...	...	...	0627	0632	...	...	0826	0826	...	1026	...	1226	...	1426	1426	...	1626	...	...	1822	1826	192
Herrljunga .... **736** d.	...	...	...	...	...	0646	0651	...	...	0851	0851	...	1051	...	1251	...	1445	1451	...	1651	...	...	1841	1845	194
Falköping .... d.	...	...	...	...	...	0702	0707	...	...	0907	0907	...	1107	...	1307	...	1501	1507	...	1707	...	...	1901	1901	200
Skövde .... d.	...	...	...	...	...	0719	0724	...	...	0924	0924	...	1124	...	1324	...	1518	1524	...	1724	...	...	1918	1918	202
Töreboda .... d.	...	...	...	...	...	0736	0741	...	...	0941	0941	...	1141	...	1341	...	1535	1541	...	1741	...	...	1935	1935	204
Laxå .... **736** d.	...	...	...	...	...	0755	0800	...	...	1001	1001	...	1208	...	1401	...	1555	1608	...	1801	...	...	1955	1955	210
Hallsberg ... **736 755** ‡ d.	...	0533	0538	0620	0734	0814	0827	0827	0934	1020	1028	1134	1227	1334	1426	1534	1622	1627	1723	1827	1931	...	2023	2023	212
Örebro C .... **755** ‡ a.	...	0554	0559	0641	0755	0835	0848	0848	0955	1041	1049	1155	1248	1355	1447	1555	1643	1648	1744	1848	1952	...	2044	2044	214
Örebro C .... ‡ d.	0503	0555	0600	0643	0757	0857	0857	0857	0957	1057	1057	1157	1257	1357	1456	1557	1657	1657	1746	1857	1954	...	2057	2057	214
Arboga .... ‡ d.	0526	0617	0624	0706	0818	0918	0918	0918	1018	1118	1118	1218	1318	1418	1518	1618	1718	1718	1819	1918	2015	...	2119	2119	220
Köping .... ‡ d.	|	0628	|	0717	0829	0929	0929	0929	1029	1129	1129	1229	1329	1429	1529	1629	1729	1729	1830	1929	2029	...	2129	2129	221
Västerås .... ‡ d.	**e**	0648	**e**	0744	0848	0948	0948	0948	1048	1148	1148	1248	1348	1448	1548	1648	1748	1748	1848	1949	2048	...	2149	2149	223
Enköping .... ‡ d.	|	0704	|	0802	0904	1004	1004	1004	1104	1205	1205	1305	1404	1504	1604	1704	1804	1804	1904	2005	2104	...	2205	2205	225
Stockholm C .... ‡ a.	0703	0747	0847	0847	0946	1046	1046	1046	1146	1246	1246	1346	1447	1547	1647	1747	1847	1847	1946	2046	2146	...	2246	2246	233

K – ①②③④⑦.

e – Via Eskilstuna (Table **732**).
f – 15 minutes earlier on Ⓐ; 10 minutes earlier on ⑥.

‡ – Additional services operate Stockholm - Västerås - Hallsberg and v
See Table **732** for Stockholm - Örebro via Eskilstuna.

STOCKHOLM - BORLÄNGE - FALUN and MORA 758

Subject to alteration on and around public holidays.

km			IC 12		IC 14	IC 32	IC 42	IC 16		IC 56		IC 18	IC 36	IC 20*	IC 46	IC 62*	IC 62	IC 64*	IC 48*			IC 26	IC 26	
		Ⓐ	Ⓐ		①–⑥	①–⑥			Ⓐ	Ⓐ		Ⓒ		①–⑥	⑦	Ⓑ	⑥	Ⓐ		Ⓒ	Ⓐ	†	Ⓐ	Ⓐ
		2v	v		v	a	w	b	2v	v	2	w	b				b	v	x	2	2		v	2t
0	**Stockholm** C ♠ d.	...	0614	...	0744g	0744	0944	0944	...	1114	...	1144	1144	1344	1344	1544g	1544	1646d	1744	...	...	1944	1944	2214
39	Arlanda C ✈ ◧ ♠ d.	...	0636	...	0808	0808	1007	1007	...	1136§	...	1207	1207	1407§	1407	1608§	1608	1707§	1807§	...	...	2007	2007	2234§
69	Uppsala ♠ d.	...	0655	...	0825	0825	1025	1025	...	1155§	...	1225	1225	1425§	1425	1625§	1625	1725§	1825	...	...	2025	2025	2253
31	Sala d.	0609	0739	...	0859	0900	1100	1059	...	1230	...	1300	1300	1500	1500	1700	1700	1805	1900	...	...	2100	2100	2332
54	Avesta Krylbo d.	0635	0758	...	0920	0920	1120	1119	...	1257	...	1320	1320	1520	1520	1719	1719	1823	1920	...	...	2120	2120	2353
29	**Borlänge** 755 d.	0725	0843	...	1014	1012	1215	1213	1311	1338	1410	1413	1412	1612	1612	1808	1808	1900	2004	2011	2027	2203	2203	0034
53	Falun 755 a.	0747e	0900	...	1032	|	|	1232	1327	...	1426	1430	|	1629	|	1826	1826	1918	|	2028	2044	2220	2220	0052
	Leksand d.	...	...	...	...	1050	1252	...	...	...	...	...	1450	...	1650	...	...	...	2042	...	...	...	...	...
	Rättvik d.	...	...	...	...	1109	1311	...	...	...	...	...	1509	...	1709	...	...	...	2101	...	...	...	...	...
	Mora a.	...	...	...	...	1134	1336	...	...	...	...	...	1533	...	1734	...	...	...	2125	...	...	...	...	...

	IC 13*	IC 51*		IC 41	IC 15		IC 43	IC 17*		IC 19*	IC 65		IC 31	IC 57	IC 57	IC 21		IC 47			IC 25	IC 27	IC 49
	Ⓐ	Ⓐ	①–⑥	Ⓐ	⑥	①–⑥	⑥	Ⓑ	⑦	①–⑥	⑦			①–⑥	⑥	⑦			Ⓐ			Ⓐ	⑦
	v	v	2			2			2c		w	2	b	v	u	w	2	w	2v	2	w	w	
ra d.	...	...	...	0625	...	...	0830	...	...	...	1033	...	1229	...	...	...	...	1433	...	...	...	...	1821
ttvik d.	...	...	...	0649	...	...	0854	...	...	...	1057	...	1253	...	...	...	...	1457	...	...	...	...	1845
ksand d.	...	...	...	0708	...	...	0913	...	...	...	1116	...	1312	...	...	...	...	1516	...	...	...	...	1906
Falun 755 d.	0530	0613	0724	|	0738	0930	|	0937	1126	1135	|	1331	|	...	1337	1337	1528	|	1629	1728	1733	1923	|
rlänge 755 d.	0549	0632	0741	0751	0757	0947	0956	0956	1143	1156	1156	1348	1356	1356	1356	1356	1546	1556	1650	1745	1752	1947	1949
esta Krylbo d.	0633	0708	...	0839	0840	...	1039	1039	...	1239	1239	...	1439	1439	1439	1439	...	1639	1742	...	1840	2039	2039
a d.	0653	|	...	0900	0900	...	1100	1100	...	1300	1300	...	1500	1500	1500	1500	...	1700	1809	...	1900	2100	2100
psala ♠ d.	0731	0801‡	...	0935	0935	...	1135	1134‡	...	1335	1334‡	...	1535	1534‡	1534	1535	...	1735	1903	...	1935	2135	2135
anda C ✈ ◐ ♠ a.	0748	0822‡	...	0952	0952	...	1152	1152‡	...	1352	1352‡	...	1152	1552‡	1552	1552	...	1752	1922‡	...	1952	2152	2152
ckholm C ♠ a.	0810	0842h	...	1015	1015	...	1215	1215	...	1415	1415	...	1615	1615	1615	1615	...	1815	1943	...	2015	2215	2215

Other local services **BORLÄNGE - MORA** (2nd class only)

km		Ⓐ	①–⑥	①–⑥	⑦			①–⑥		Ⓑ
			f	w	w	b	w			
0	**Borlänge** d.	0632	0850	1019	1024	1220	1424	1618	1818	2212
43	Leksand d.	0705	0926	1052	1057	1253	1457	1652	1851	2245
63	Rättvik d.	0723	0941	1107	1115	1313	1515	1707	1906	2300
03	**Mora** ♣ a.	0746	1004	1130	1138	1336	1538	1730	1929	2323
04	Morastrand ♣ a.	0750	1008	1134	1142	1340	1542	1734	1933	2327

	Ⓐ	⑥	Ⓑ	①–⑥				①–⑥	Ⓑ
					w	b	w		
Morastrand ♣ d.	0502	0626	0830	1019	1221	1419	1619	1818	2029
Mora ♣ d.	0507	0631	0835	1024	1226	1424	1624	1823	2034
Rättvik d.	0531	0655	0859	1048	1250	1448	1648	1847	2058
Leksand d.	0546	0710	0914	1106	1308	1506	1706	1905	2116
Borlänge 755 a.	0618	0742	0946	1138	1340	1538	1738	1937	2148

- July 1 - Aug. 10.
- June 30 - Aug. 10.
- June 24 - Aug. 11.
- Departs 10 minutes earlier June 24 – 28 and Aug. 12 – 16.
- Change at Borlänge Aug. 12 - Dec. 12.
- Daily June 24 - Aug. 10.
- Departs 3 minutes later on Ⓐ June 1 – 20 / from Aug. 12.
- Arrives 0853 June 24 - Aug. 16.

t – Not June 29 - Aug. 8.
u – Not June 22, July 6 - Aug. 10.
v – Not July 1 - Aug. 9.
w – Not June 30 - Aug. 10.
x – Not June 24 - Aug. 4.

‡ – Arrival Time. Some services call to set down only.
§ – Stops to pick up only.
* – Train Number may vary.
◧ – Northbound trains call at Arlanda to pick up only.
◐ – Southbound trains call at Arlanda to set down only.
♠ – See also Table **761**. Frequent local services operate Stockholm - Uppsala and v.v.
♣ – Local journeys are not permitted Mora - Morastrand and v.v.

STOCKHOLM - SUNDSVALL - UMEÅ 760

Subject to alteration on and around public holidays.
For additional services Stockholm - Gävle and v.v. see Table **761**. For sleeper services see Table **767**.

km		NT	Sn 590	NT	NT	Sn 560	NT	Sn 562	Sn 564	Sn 566	Sn 568	IC 298	NT	Sn 10570	Sn 570	Sn 572	NT	Sn 574	Sn 576	NT	Sn 578	Sn 580	Sn 580	Sn 582	Sn 584	Sn 588
		2	R ✕	2	2	R ✕	2	R ✕	R ✕	R ✕	R ✕	R	2	R ✕	R ✕	R ✕	2	R ✕	R ✕	2	R ✕	R ✕	R ✕	R ✕	R ✕	R ✕
		Ⓐ	Ⓐ	①–⑥	⑦	E	⑥	Ⓐ J	Ⓒ K	Ⓑ D	⑥	⑦	Ⓐ	⑦ L	Ⓐ N	Ⓒ	Ⓐ	Ⓐ		Ⓒ	Ⓑ P	Ⓑ F	⑥	Ⓑ R		⑦ L
0	**Stockholm** C d.	...	0336	...	...	0621	...	0721	0821	0921	1021	1021	...	1121	1121	1221	...	1321	1421	...	1521	1621	1621	1721	1821	2021
39	Arlanda C ✈ ◧ d.	...	0356	...	...	0642	...	0742	0842	0942	1042	1042	...	1142	1142	1242	...	1342	1441	...	1542	1642	1642	1742	1842	2042
69	Uppsala ◧ d.	...	0414	...	...	0700	...	0800	0900	1000	1100	1100	...	1200	1200	1300	...	1400	1500	...	1600	1700	1700	1800	1900	2100
82	**Gävle** C d.	...	0459	...	...	0745	...	0845	0945	1045	1145	1145	...	1245	1245	1345	...	1445	1545	...	1645	1745	1745	1845	1945	2145
60	Söderhamn d.	...	0546	...	...	0830	...	0930	1030	1130	1230	1230	...	1330	1330	1430	...	1530	1630	...	1730	1830	1830	1930	2030	2230
14	Hudiksvall d.	...	0634	...	...	0858	...	0958	1058	1158	1258	1300e	...	1358	1358	1458	...	1558	1658	...	1758	1858	1858	2000	2100	2258
02	**Sundsvall** a.	...	0739	...	...	0953	...	1058	1157	1257	1353	1403f	...	1457	1505	1553	...	1657	1757	...	1853	1953	1953	2055	2155	2353
02	**Sundsvall** d.	0539	...	0824	0904	1002	1030	*1209*	*1203*d	...	*1424*	*1419*	1425	*1512*	*1514*	1559	1635	1702	...	1807	1859	*2018*a	2002	2059	...	...
70	Härnösand d.	0641	...	0926	1002	1050	1126	*1305*	*1251*d	...	*1520*	*1514*	1521	*1609*	*1606*	1649	1730	1752	...	1859	1949	*2114*a	2056	2149	...	...
16	Kramfors d.	0707	...	0951	1027	1115	1151	*1332*	*1317*d	...	*1546*	*1546*	1554	*1635*	*1632*	1714	1755	1817	...	1925	2014	*2140*a	2121	2214	...	...
03	Örnsköldsvik C d.	0751	...	1038	1117	1151	1233	*1417*	*1357*d	...	*1634*	*1624*	1637	*1720*	*1722*	1752	1832	1855	...	2007	2049	*2223*a	2156	2250	...	...
13	**Umeå** Östra ◐ a.	0852	...	1142	1219	1234	1336	*1515*	*1442*d	...	*1735*	*1730*	1745	*1817*	*1824*	1836	1931	1939	...	2110	2134	*2320*a	2240	2334	...	...
15	**Umeå** C a.	0856	...	1146	1223	1238	1341	*1519*	*1446*d	...	*1740*	*1735*	1750	*1822*	*1828*	1840	1935	1943	...	2114	2138	*2324*a	2244	2338	...	...

	Sn 561	Sn 563	Sn 565	Sn 567	NT	Sn 569	NT	Sn 571	Sn 573	Sn 10573	NT	Sn 575	Sn 575	NT	NT	NT	Sn 579	Sn 583	Sn 10585	NT	Sn 585	Sn 587	Sn 589	NT	NT	Sn 599
	R ✕	R ✕	R ✕	R ✕	2	R ✕	2	R ✕	R ✕	R ✕	2	R ✕	R ✕	2	2	2	R ✕	R ✕	R ✕	2	R ✕	R ✕	R ✕	2	2	R ✕
	Ⓐ G	Ⓐ M	Ⓐ H		Ⓐ	Ⓐ A	Ⓐ	Ⓒ	Ⓐ B	⑦ C	⑥	Ⓒ	Ⓐ J	⑦	⑥	Ⓑ	D	K b	⑦ L	⑥	Ⓐ	⑥	Ⓑ	Ⓐ	⑥	⑦
eå C d.	...	...	0419	*0434*a	0546	0613	0640	0719	0802	...	0759	0914	...	0950	1029	1041	...	*1245*	1404	1416	1421	1519	1615c	1626	1647	*1730*
eå Östra ◧ d.	...	...	0423	*0446*a	0548	0617	0642	0723	0806	...	0801	0918	...	0952	1031	1043	...	*1247*	1408	1418	1425	1523	1819c	1628	1649	*1732*
sköldsvik C d.	...	...	0506	*0539*a	0648	0702	0740	0807	0851	...	0858	1002	...	1049	1131	1139	...	*1344*	1452	1517	1508	1607	1703c	1724	1750	*1838*
mfors d.	...	...	0542	*0616*a	0730	0738	0824	0843	0927	...	0939	1038	...	1130	1215	1221	...	*1430*	1528	1557	1544	1642	1741c	1805	1831	*1920*
nösand d.	...	...	0605	*0641*a	0755	0803	0847	0908	0952	...	1008	1108	...	1155	1240	1246	...	*1455*	1551	1622	1607	1708	1804c	1835	1856	*1945*
ndsvall a.	...	...	0657	*0736*a	0850	0855	0947	1000	1049	...	1109	1157	...	1252	1335	1346	...	*1551*	1646	1721	1657	1800	1858c	1933	1952	*2042*
ndsvall d.	0459	0606	0703	0806	...	0901	...	1006	1106	1106	...	1206	1206	...	...	...	1406	1606	1706	...	1706	1806	1904	...	...	2057
diksvall d.	0553	0700	0757	0900	...	1000	...	1100	1200	1200	...	1300	1300	...	...	...	1500	1700	1800	...	1800	1900	2002	...	...	2201
derhamn d.	0621	0728	0828	0928	...	1028	...	1128	1228	1228	...	1328	1328	...	...	...	1528	1728	1828	...	1828	1928	2030	...	...	2230
vle C d.	0706	0816	0916	1016	...	1116	...	1216	1316	1316	...	1416	1416	...	...	...	1616	1816	1916	...	1916	2016	2116	...	...	2318
psala ◐ a.	0749	0859	0959	1059	...	1159	...	1259	1359	1359	...	1459	1459	...	...	...	1659	1859	1959	...	1959	2059	2203	...	...	0005
anda C ✈ ◐ a.	0807	0917	1017	1117	...	1217	...	1317	1417	1417	...	1517	1517	...	...	...	1717	1917	2017	...	2017	2117	2221	...	...	0024
ckholm C a.	0828	0938	1038	1138	...	1238	...	1338	1438	1438	...	1538	1538	...	...	...	1738	1938	2038	...	2038	2138	2243	...	...	0045

Other local services **GÄVLE - SUNDSVALL** (operated by *XT*, 2nd class only)

	Ⓐ	⑦	⑥	Ⓐ	⑥		Ⓐ	⑦	Ⓐ	⑥	Ⓐ	
vle C d.	0612	0745	0850	1142	1300	...	1333	1455	1604	1700	1710	2115
derhamn d.	0701	0829	0942	1230	1346	...	1426	1546	1652	1758	1802	2159
diksvall d.	0737	0900	1012	1300	1415	...	1500	1616	1729	1827	1838	2228
ndsvall a.	0741	0954	1115	1356	1516	...	1556	1723	1830	1925	1940	2322

	Ⓐ	Ⓒ	Ⓐ	⑦	⑥	Ⓐ	⑥	Ⓐ	⑦	Ⓐ	⑥	Ⓐ
Sundsvall d.	0538	0843	0935	1032	1309	1436	1535	1626	1804	1957	2003	2137
Hudiksvall d.	0634	0943	1035	1132	1414	1532	1635	1731	1901	2100	2100	2245
Söderhamn d.	0702	1014	1106	1203	1447	1604	1704	1803	1929	2129	2128	2313
Gävle C a.	0745	1111	1200	1249	1530	1652	1746	1850	2014	2219	2217	2359

- Not June 11 – 13.
- Not June 3 – 16, 18 – 19, Sept. 9 – 25.
- Also June 10, 14 – 16, 18 – 20, Ⓐ Sept. 9 - Oct. 25.
- Not June 3 – 7, 11, 12, July 3 - Aug. 4.
- ①–⑥ (not June 3 – 7, 10 – 14, 18 – 20, July 6, 13, 20, 27, Aug. 4, 11).
  Not Aug. 11, 18, 25, Sept. 1, 8, 15, 22.
- Not June 7, July 7 - Aug. 9.
- Not June 21, July 1 - Aug. 9.
  June 10 - Dec. 13 (not June 11 – 16).

K – Until June 29.
L – Not June 30 - Aug. 4.
M – Also ⑥ June 1 – 29, Aug. 17 - Dec. 14.
N – Not June 3 – 7.
P – Not June 29 - Aug. 9.
R – Not ⑦ June 30 - Aug. 4.

a – Ⓐ (not June 21 - Aug. 9).
b – Not June 8.

c – † June 30 - Aug. 4.
d – ⑥ July 7 - Aug. 10; ⑦ June 30 - Aug. 4.
e – Departs 2 minutes earlier June 29 - Aug. 10.
f – Arrives 10 minutes earlier June 29 - Aug. 10.

◧ – Stops to pick up only.
◐ – Stops to set down only.

Sn – High-speed train. R and ✕. Supplement payable.

761 STOCKHOLM and SUNDSVALL - ÖSTERSUND - TRONDHEIM

Subject to alteration on and around public holidays.
See Table **760** for other fast services Stockholm - Gävle and v.v. For sleeper services see Table **767**.

km		NT	NSB	NT	NT	NT	NT	IC	IC	NT	NT	NT	NSB	NT	NT	IC	IC	IC	NT	Sn	Sn	Sn	Sn	Sn	NT
								80	80							84	84	84		574	580	598	598	598	
		2	2	2Ⓐ	2ⒶB	2⑥	2	⚒	†F	2	2Ⓐ	2Ⓒ	2	2⑦	2⑥	⑥G	⑥D	⑦H	2Ⓐ	⑥	Ⓐ	ⒶA	⑦	M	2E
0	**Stockholm** C ▲ d.	...	...	...	...	...	...	0749	0749	...	...	...	...	...	...	1414	1414	1414	...	1421	1621	1701	1701	1701	...
39	Arlanda C ✈ ▲ d.	...	...	...	...	...	...	0813	0813	...	...	...	...	...	...	1437	1437	1437	...	1441u	1641	1722u	1722u	1722u	...
69	Uppsala ▲ d.	...	...	...	...	...	...	0832	0832	...	...	...	...	...	...	1504	1504	1504	...	1500u	1659	1740u	1740u	1740u	...
182	**Gävle** C ▲ d.	...	...	...	...	...	...	0928	0928	...	...	...	...	...	...	1556	1556	1556	...	1545	1743	1828	1828	1828	...
281	Bollnäs d.	...	...	...	...	...	...	1025	1025	...	...	...	...	...	...	1655	1655	1655	...	|	...	1924	1924	1924	...
344	Ljusdal d.	...	...	...	...	...	...	1107	1107	...	...	...	...	...	...	1741	1741	1741	...	|	...	1958	1958	1958	...
	Sundsvall d.	0500a	...	0605	0800	0803	1013	|	|	1215	1405	1405	...	1609	1618	|	|	|	1808	1810	...	|	|	|	200
450	Ånge d.	0617a	...	0723	0919	0921	1131	1213	1213	1337	1523	1526	...	1726	1743	1841	1841	1841	1931	1919	...	2056	2056	2056	212
480	Bräcke d.	0634a	...	0740	0936	0938	1148	1233	1233	1354	1540	1543	...	1743	1800	1900	1900	1900	1948	1938	...	2114	2114	...	214
551	**Östersund** C a.	0724a	...	0832	1027	1036	1239	1317	1317	1450	1630	1632	...	1837	1852	1948	1948	1948	2037	2021	...	2201	2201	...	223
551	**Östersund** C d.	0724	...	...	1028	...	1240a	1322	1322c	...	1631	1635	...	1838	...	1950	...	...	2041	...	...	...	...	...	...
656	Åre d.	0838	...	...	1144	...	1400a	1442	1442c	...	1747	1749	...	1947	...	2132	...	...	2159	...	...	...	...	...	...
665	Duved d.	0845	...	...	...	...	1408a	...	...	...	1754	1756	...	1955	...	2150	...	...	2207	...	...	...	...	...	...
713	Storlien 🏛 a.	0920	0936	...	...	...	...	...	...	...	1829	1830	1836	...	...	...	...	...	...	...	...	...	...	...	...
819	**Trondheim** a.	...	1109	...	...	...	...	...	...	...	...	...	2014	...	...	...	...	...	...	...	...	...	...	...	...

km		NT	Sn	Sn	NT	Sn	IC	Sn	NT	NT	NSB	NT	NT	NT	NT	NT	NT	NT	NT	IC		NT	NSB	NT	NT
			591	565		597	81	10573												85					
		2Ⓐ	ⒶJ	ⒶL	2Ⓐ	⑥	①K	⑦	2⑥	2Ⓑ	2	2	2Ⓒ	2E	2Ⓐ	2⑥	2†	2Ⓐ	2⑥			2E	2	2Ⓑ	2⑥
	Trondheim d.	...	...	...	...	...	...	...	...	...	0750	...	...	...	...	...	...	...	...	...	...	...	1650	...	...
	Storlien 🏛 d.	...	...	...	...	...	...	...	...	...	0930	0938	...	...	...	...	...	...	...	...	...	...	1830	1844	184
	Duved d.	...	...	...	0600	...	...	...	0745	...	...	1013	...	...	...	...	...	1506	...	...	...	...	...	1919	192
	Åre d.	...	...	...	0608	...	...	...	0754	...	...	1021	...	1210	1521	...	...	1514	...	1550	...	...	...	1928	192
	Östersund C a.	...	...	...	0722	...	...	...	0911	...	...	1134	...	1324	1613	...	...	1628	...	1715	...	...	...	2042	204
	Östersund C d.	0512	0539	...	0723	0746	0748	0839	0918	0919	...	1135	1317	1325	1631	1523	1612	1629	1703	1719	...	1927	...	2043	...
	Bräcke d.	0601	0621	...	0815	0827	|	0919	1011	1011	...	1222	1410	1414	1751	1615	1703	1718	1754	1801	...	2021	...	2133	...
0	Ånge d.	0619	0638	...	0833	0845	|	0936	1029	1029	...	1240	1427	1432	...	1633	1721	1736	1812	1821	...	2038	...	2151	...
94	**Sundsvall** a.	0742	|	...	0954	|	|	1056	1153	1153	...	1357	1548	1555	...	1752	1847	1857	1942	|	...	2200	...	2313	...
	Ljusdal d.	...	0735	...	...	0943	0943	|	...	...	...	...	...	...	...	...	...	...	...	1920	...	...	...	...	...
	Bollnäs a.	...	0810	...	...	1019	1024	|	...	...	...	...	...	...	...	...	...	...	...	2006	...	...	...	...	...
	Gävle C ▲ d.	...	0906	0916	...	1116	1133	1316	...	...	...	...	...	...	...	...	...	...	...	2107	...	...	...	...	...
	Uppsala ▲ a.	...	0950s	1000	...	1159s	1228s	1359s	...	...	...	...	...	...	...	...	...	...	...	2200	...	...	...	...	...
	Arlanda C ✈ ▲ a.	...	1007s	1018	...	1217s	1251s	1417s	...	...	...	...	...	...	...	...	...	...	...	2227	...	...	...	...	...
	Stockholm C ▲ a.	...	1028	1038	...	1238	1314	1438	...	...	...	...	...	...	...	...	...	...	...	2249	...	...	...	...	...

Other *IC* services **STOCKHOLM - GÄVLE**

km		IC 262	IC 264	IC 266	IC 298	IC 268	IC 270	IC 272	IC 274	IC 278	IC 282	IC 284
		ⒶP	Ⓐ	⑥	⑦H	Ⓐ	⑥	Ⓐ	Ⓒ			
0	**Stockholm** C d.	0731	0821	0921	1021	1021	1121	1221	1321	1531	1731	1921
39	Arlanda C ✈ ◧ d.	0752	0842	0942	1042	1042	1142	1242	1342	1553	1753	1942
69	Uppsala d.	0810	0859	1000	1100	1059	1200	1300	1400	1610	1810	2000
182	**Gävle** C a.	0856	0943	1046	1143	1146	1246	1346	1443	1656	1856	2046

	IC 259	IC 263	IC 265	IC 269	IC 273	IC 275	IC 297	IC 277	IC 281	IC 285	IC 2
	ⒶB	⚒B	ⒸN	B	⑥	ⒶP	⑦	①-⑥		⑦	Ⓐ
Gävle C d.	0613	0712	0916	1103	1313	1403	1503	1513	1713	1903	201
Uppsala d.	0701	0800	0956	1150	1400	1450	1550	1600	1800	1950	210
Arlanda C ✈ ◐ a.	0718	0817	1017	1208	1417	1507	1608	1617	1817	2007	21
Stockholm C a.	0738	0838	1038	1228	1438	1528	1628	1638	1838	2028	21

A – June 17 - Dec. 13.
B – Not July 1 - Aug. 9.
D – Sept. 15 - Dec. 13.
E – Ⓐ (not June 21 - Aug. 9).
F – June 30 - Aug. 11.
G – Aug. 16 - Sept. 13.
H – Not June 29 - Aug. 4.
J – Not June 24 - Aug. 16.
K – Not July 1 - Aug. 5.
L – To / from Linköping (Table **730**).
M – ①②③⑤ June 3 – 14.
N – Ⓐ June 29 - Aug. 11.
P – Not June 29 - Aug. 11.
a – Ⓐ only.
c – June 2 – 23 and Aug. 18 - Dec. 8.
s – Stops to set down only.
u – Stops to pick up only.
◧ – Trains call to pick up only.
◐ – Trains call to set down only.
▲ – For other *IC* trains Stockholm - Gävle and v.v. see panel below main table.
Sn – High-speed train. [R] and ✕. Supplement payable.

763 UMEÅ - LULEÅ

Operator: *NT (2nd class only)*

km		Ⓐ	Ⓐa	Ⓐa	Ⓐ	Ⓒ	Ⓐ	Ⓐa	Ⓐ	Ⓐ	⑦	Ⓐa	Ⓐ
0	**Umeå Östra** ♣ d.	0633	...	0902	1213	1327	1336	1428	1614	1728	1750	1842	2100
2	**Umeå C** ♣ d.	0636	0734	0905	1216	1330	1339	1431	1617	1731	1753	1845	2103
33	Vännäs ♣ d.	0700	|	0929	1240	1359	|	1455	1641	1755	1823	1909	2127
142	Bastuträsk d.	...	0907	...	...	1508	1508	...	...	...	1931	...	...
269	Älvsbyn d.	...	1019	...	...	1620	1620	...	...	...	2048	...	...
315	Boden 765 d.	...	1045	...	...	1646	1646	...	...	...	2114	...	...
351	**Luleå** 765 a.	...	1120	...	...	1723	1723	...	...	...	2147	...	...

	Ⓐ	Ⓐa	Ⓐ	Ⓐ	⑥	Ⓐa	⑦	Ⓐ	Ⓐa	Ⓐ	Ⓑ	⑦
Luleå 765 d.	...	...	0615	...	0843	...	1037	...	1320	...	...	185
Boden 765 d.	...	...	0647	...	0921	...	1107	...	1353	...	...	192
Älvsbyn d.	...	...	0712	...	0946	...	1133	...	1418	...	...	195
Bastuträsk d.	...	...	0825	...	1057	...	1245	...	1535	...	...	210
Vännäs ♣ d.	0708	0824	|	1133	1217	1344	1404	1532	|	1805	2018	222
Umeå C ♣ a.	0731	0847	0952	1156	1238	1409	1426	1555	1705	1828	2040	224
Umeå Östra ♣ a.	0736	0852	0957	1201	1243	1414	1431	1600	...	1833	2045	224

a – Not June 24 - Aug. 9.

♣ – Other journeys Umeå Östra - Umeå C - Vännäs and v.v.:
From Umeå Östra at 0522Ⓐ, 0746Ⓐ, 1015⑦, 1136⑥, 1535⑥, 1632⑦ and 2155⑦.
From Vännäs at 0558Ⓐ, 0957⑥, 1213⑦, 1333⑥, 1649Ⓐ, 1728⑥ and 1919Ⓐ**a**.

765 LULEÅ - NARVIK

km		IC			NT	IC	NT	NT	NT	IC
		90		94		96				98
		2		[R]	2	2	2	2	2	
		P			①-⑥		Ⓐ	⑦		H
0	**Luleå** 763 d.	...	...	0509	0602	1003	1023	1150	1629	...
36	Boden 763 d.	...	...	0600	0632	1034	1057	1216	1658	...
204	Gällivare d.	...	...	0801	0839	1317	1254	1423	1854	...
304	**Kiruna** a.	...	...	0912	0942	1429	1406	1526	2036	...
304	**Kiruna** d.	0659	...	0929	...	1449	...	...	...	2204
397	Abisko Östra d.	0758	...	1105	...	1554	...	...	...	2302
406	Björkliden d.	|	...	1124§	...	1608¶	...	...	...	|
426	Vassijaure ◇ d.	0837	...	|	...	1632	...	...	...	2341
433	Riksgränsen 🏛 d.	0847	...	1206	...	1646	...	...	...	2351
473	**Narvik** a.	0955	...	1254	...	1737	...	...	...	0117

	NT	NT	NT	IC	NT	NT			IC
				95			93	10093	9
	2	2	2	2	2	2	[R]	[R]	2
	①-⑥	⑦	①-⑥		⑦	Ⓐ	J	S	R
Narvik d.	...	...	...	1052	...	...	1515	1515	181
Riksgränsen 🏛 d.	...	...	...	1143	...	...	1600	1600	192
Vassijaure ◇ d.	...	...	...	1154	...	...	|	|	194
Björkliden d.	...	...	...	1212¶	...	...	1628¶	|	|
Abisko Östra d.	...	...	...	1228	...	...	1644	1644	201
Kiruna a.	...	...	...	1330	...	...	1802	1802	213
Kiruna d.	0557	0748	1041	1347	1613	1650	1832	1832	...
Gällivare d.	0711	0904	1149	1522	1719	1756	1951	1951	...
Boden 763 d.	0906	1102	1343	1728	1916	2000	2157	2157	...
Luleå 763 a.	0932	1128	1410	1756	1946	2029	2224	2224	...

FOR NOTES SEE TABLE 767

766 KRISTINEHAMN - MORA - ÖSTERSUND - GÄLLIVARE

INLANDSBANAN

km		♠■		
		ⒶW	H	C
0	**Kristinehamn 750** d.	0904	1031	...
40	Nykroppa d.	0941	1106	...
131	Grängesberg d.	1050	1209	...
146	Ludvika d.	1107	1219	...
192	Borlänge d.	*1215*	1254	...
296	**Mora 758** ◇ d.	*1336*	1405	1452
310	Orsa ◇ d.	...	...	1504
433	Sveg d.	...	...	1701
617	**Östersund C 761** a.	...	...	2030

			♥■	♥■
	C	ⒶW	ⒷH	⑥H
Östersund C 761 d.	0817	...	...	...
Sveg d.	1110	...	...	...
Orsa ◇ d.	1328	...	...	...
Mora 758 ◇ d.	1346	*0507*	1444	1444
Borlänge d.	...	0628	1606	1606
Ludvika d.	...	0702	1642	1642
Grängesberg d.	...	0713	1652	1652
Nykroppa d.	...	0818	1800	1800
Kristinehamn 750 a.	...	0850	1835	1839

km		D	
0	**Östersund C 761** d.	0735	...
115	Ulriksfors d.	0927	...
244	Vilhelmina d.	1137	...
312	Storuman d.	1330	...
384	Sorsele d.	1452	...
420	Slagnäs 🚂 d.	1519	...
473	Arvidsjaur 🚂 d.	1617	...
646	Jokkmokk d.	1950	...
746	**Gällivare 765** a.	2131	...

	E
Gällivare 765 d.	0748
Jokkmokk d.	0921
Arvidsjaur 🚂 d.	1311
Slagnäs 🚂 d.	1350
Sorsele d.	1440
Storuman d.	1539
Vilhelmina d.	1720
Ulriksfors d.	1930
Östersund C 761 a.	2124

C – June 6 - Aug. 18.
D – June 6 - Aug. 17.
E – June 7 - Aug. 18.
H – June 30 - Aug. 11‡.
W – Aug. 12 - Dec. 13‡.
‡ – Operated by *Tågab.*
■ – Different timetables operates on Jul. 7 and Aug. 11 Kristinehamn - Mora and v.v.
♠ – 🚌12 Göteborg (d. 0740 **H**; 0610 **W**) - Kristinehamn - Mora.
♥ – 🚌12 Mora - Kristinehamn - Göteborg (a. 2130 **H**; 1140 **W**).
◇ – Additional local services operate on Ⓐ Mora - Orsa and v.v.
🚂 – Steam train normally operates ⑤⑥ July 19 - Aug. 3, Arvidsjaur - Slagnäs and v.v. (*53 km*); depart 1745, arrive back 2140 (approximate timings). Contact: Arvidsjaur Järnvägsförening ✆ +46 (0)730 81 93 69.
Operator: Inlandsbanan AB, Box 561, 831 27, Östersund. ✆ +46 (0)771 53 53 5

LONG DISTANCE SLEEPER TRAINS 767

WARNING! Subject to alteration July 28 - August 3 (trains may be retimed and diverted).

						ST			
	94	94	92	92		3920	72	72	
	Ⓡ	Ⓡ	Ⓡ	Ⓡ		Ⓡ	Ⓡ	Ⓡ	
	G●	G	D	D		C	L	L	
Malmö C **730** ..... d.	...	...	...	...	...	1630	...	...	...
Göteborg ..... d.	...	...	...	...	...	|	1834	1834	...
Herrljunga ..... d.	...	...	...	...	...	|	|	|	...
Skövde ..... d.	...	...	...	...	...	|	1952**u**	1952**u**	...
Hallsberg ..... d.	...	...	...	...	...	|	|	|	...
Stockholm C ..... a.	...	...	...	...	...	2230	|	|	...
Stockholm C ..... d.	1811	1811	2112	2112	...	2300	|	|	...
Arlanda C ✈ ..... d.	1833**u**	1833**u**	2135	2135	...	|	|	|	...
Uppsala ..... d.	1903**u**	1903**u**	2156	2156	...	2340	|	|	...
Gävle ..... a.	1955	1955	2255	2255	...	|	|	|	...
Gävle ..... d.	2002	2002	2300	2300	...	|	|	|	...
Söderhamn ..... d.	2057	2057	|	2355	...	|	|	|	...
Hudiksvall ..... d.	2135	2135	|	0030	...	|	|	|	...
Sundsvall ..... a.	2232	2232	0158	0158	...	|	0220	0220	...
Sundsvall ..... d.	2246	2246	0335	0245	...	|	0335	0245	...
Härnösand ..... d.	2339	2339	|	0341	...	|	|	0341	...
Kramfors ..... d.	0009	0009	|	0414	...	|	|	0414	...
Ånge ..... d.	|	|	|	|	...	|	|	|	...
Bräcke ..... d.	|	|	|	|	...	|	|	|	...
Östersund C ..... a.	|	|	0622	|	...	0615**s**	0622	|	...
Östersund C ..... d.	|	|	0633	|	...	|	0633	|	...
Åre ..... a.	|	|	0817**s**	|	...	0735**s**	0817**s**	|	...
Duved ..... a.	|	|	0836	|	...	0755**s**	0836	|	...
Storlien 🏛 ..... a.	|	|	...	|	...	0855	...	|	...
Örnsköldsvik ..... d.	0056	0056	...	0503	...	...	...	0503	...
Umeå C ..... a.	0214	0214	...	0613	...	...	...	0613	...
Umeå C ..... d.	0218	0218	...	0617	...	...	...	0617	...
Bastuträsk ..... d.	0347	0347	...	0819	...	...	...	0819	...
Älvsbyn ..... d.	0511	0511	...	0938	...	...	...	0938	...
Boden ..... a.	0540	0540	...	1012	...	...	...	1012	...
Luleå ..... a.	|	0635	...	1103	...	...	...	1103	...
Narvik **765** ..... a.	1254	...	...	...	...	...	...	...	...

	ST	*ST*							
	3921	3921	71	71	91	91	3962	93	
	Ⓡ	Ⓡ	Ⓡ	Ⓡ	Ⓡ	Ⓡ	Ⓡ	Ⓡ	
	A	B	M	N⊠	N⊠	M	F	F▲	
Narvik **765** ..... d.	...	...	...	...	...	...	...	1515	...
Luleå ..... d.	...	...	...	...	1658	1658	2114	|	...
Boden ..... d.	...	...	...	...	1744	1744	2209	2209	...
Älvsbyn ..... d.	...	...	...	...	1814	1814	2237	2237	...
Bastuträsk ..... d.	...	...	...	...	1932	1932	0002	0002	...
Umeå C ..... a.	...	...	...	...	2103	2103	0138	0138	...
Umeå C ..... d.	...	...	...	...	2113	2113	0142	0142	...
Örnsköldsvik ..... d.	...	...	...	...	2225	2225	0237	0237	...
Storlien 🏛 ..... d.	1500	1520	...	...	|	|	|	|	...
Duved ..... d.	1550**u**	1610**u**	1927	1927	|	|	|	|	...
Åre ..... d.	1615**u**	1635**u**	2000**u**	2000**u**	|	|	|	|	...
Östersund C ..... a.	|	|	2131	2131	|	|	|	|	...
Östersund C ..... d.	1740**u**	1802**u**	2137	2137	|	|	|	|	...
Bräcke ..... d.	|	|	2238	2238	|	|	|	|	...
Ånge ..... d.	|	|	2259	2259	|	|	|	|	...
Kramfors ..... d.	|	|	|	|	2319	2319	0324	0324	...
Härnösand ..... d.	|	|	|	|	2357	2357	0358	0358	...
Sundsvall ..... a.	|	|	0011	0011	0110	0110	0457	0457	...
Sundsvall ..... d.	|	|	0135	0157	0157	0135	0504	0504	...
Hudiksvall ..... d.	|	|	|	|	0302	|	0608	0608	...
Söderhamn ..... d.	|	|	|	|	0344	|	0641	0641	...
Gävle ..... a.	|	|	|	0439**s**	0439**s**	|	0735	0735	...
Gävle ..... d.	|	|	|	|	|	|	0745	0745	...
Uppsala ..... d.	2250	2255	|	0552**s**	0552**s**	|	0855**s**	0855**s**	...
Arlanda C ✈ ..... d.	|	|	|	0615**s**	0615**s**	|	0922**s**	0922**s**	...
Stockholm C ..... a.	2325	2335	|	0638	0638	|	0945	0945	...
Stockholm C ..... d.	2335	2335	|	...	...	|	...	...	...
Hallsberg ..... d.	|	|	0750	...	...	0750	...	...	...
Skövde ..... d.	|	|	0859**s**	...	...	0859**s**	...	...	...
Herrljunga ..... a.	|	|	|	...	...	|	...	...	...
Göteborg ..... a.	|	|	1025	...	...	1025	...	...	...
Malmö C **730** ..... a.	0640	0705	...	...	...	...	...	...	...

A – ④ Aug. 29 - Sept. 19: 🛏, 🛌 and ✕/🍸 Storlien - Stockholm - Malmö.
B – ⑦ Sept. 1 - Sept. 22: 🛏, 🛌 and ✕/🍸 Storlien - Stockholm - Malmö.
C – ③④ Aug. 29 - Sept. 19: 🛏, 🛌, 2 and ✕/🍸 Malmö - Stockholm - Storlien.
D – Daily (not July 29 - Aug. 4). Conveys 🛏 and 🛌 and ✕/🍸.
F – 🛏, 🛌, 2 and ✕/🍸 Luleå (**3962**) - Boden (**93**) - Stockholm.
🛏, 🛌, 2 and ✕/🍸 Narvik (**93**) - Boden - Stockholm.
G – Daily (not June 2–6, July 29 - Aug. 4). 🛏, 🛌, 2 and ✕/🍸 Stockholm (**94**) - Boden - Narvik; 🛏, 🛌, 2 and ✕/🍸 Stockholm (**94**) - Boden (**3965**) - Luleå.
L – 🛏 and 🛌, 2 and ✕ Göteborg (**72**) - Sundsvall (**92**) - Luleå.
🛏 and 🛌, 2 and ✕ Göteborg (**92**) - Sundsvall - Duved.
M – 🛏 and 🛌, 2 and ✕ Duved (**71**) - Sundsvall - Göteborg.
🛏 and 🛌, 2 and ✕ Luleå (**91**) - Sundsvall (**71**) - Göteborg.
N – Daily to July 6 and from Sept. 13; ⑤⑥ July 12 - Sept. 7.
🛏 and 🛌, 2 and ✕ Duved (**71**) - Sundsvall (**91**) - Stockholm.
🛏 and 🛌, 2 and ✕ Luleå (**91**) - Sundsvall - Stockholm.

s – Stops to set down only.
u – Stops to pick up only.

● – Not June 2–6.
▲ – Not June 3–8.
¶ – Not June 10 - Sept. 8.
§ – Not June 2–5, June 8 - Sept. 7.
⊠ – Subject to alteration Sundsvall - Stockholm July 7 - Sept. 12.
◇ – Ticket point.

🚌 UMEÅ - LULEÅ - HAPARANDA-TORNIO - KEMI 768

UMEÅ - LULEÅ - HAPARANDA-TORNIO — Länstrafiken Norrbotten, routes 20/100; valid until Dec. 14, 2019

	Ⓐ			Ⓐ		Ⓐ	Ⓒ		Ⓒ	Ⓐ		†	Ⓐ	⚒			Ⓒ	†	Ⓐ		Ⓐ			
Umeå ..... d.	...	...	...	...	...	0515	0545	...	0730	0730	...	0900	0900	...	...	1315	1430	...	1525	1630	1725	1930	2000	2100
Skellefteå ..... d.	...	...	0535	0635	...	0740	0800	...	0950	0955	...	1115	1125	...	...	1520	1635	...	1755	1835	1955	2135	2205	2300
Piteå ..... d.	...	...	0700	0805	...	0910	0925	...	1115	1125	...	1240	1250	...	...	1635	1750	...	1925	1950	2120	2250	2320	...
Luleå ..... a.	...	...	0800	0905	...	1010	1025	...	1210	1220	...	1335	1345	...	...	1725	1840	...	2015	2040	2215	2340	0010	...
Luleå ..... d.	0515	...	0820	0950	...	1050	1050	...	1230	1245	...	1350	1400	1510	...	1735	...	1855	...	2050	...	...	...	...
Haparanda-Tornio 🏛 ..... § d.	0755	...	1035	1215	...	1320	1315	...	1500	1520	...	1635	1645	1745	...	1950	...	2110	...	2305	...	...	...	...

			Ⓐ			Ⓐ	⑥			Ⓐ	Ⓒ			†	Ⓐ	Ⓒ		Ⓐ	Ⓐ	Ⓐ	Ⓒ	Ⓐ	†	Ⓐ
Haparanda-Tornio 🏛 ..... § d.	...	...	0530	...	...	0645	0725	...	0810	0955	1050	...	1230	...	1340	1345	...	1510	...	1610	1710	1720	1810	2020
Luleå ..... a.	...	...	0750	...	...	0940	0950	...	1030	1235	1310	...	1450	...	1605	1610	...	1750	...	1845	1945	1955	2045	2235
Luleå ..... d.	0540	...	0800	0800	...	0955	...	...	1040	1300	1320	...	1500	...	1635	1635	...	1810	...	1910	2005	2010	2055	...
Piteå ..... d.	0635	...	0855	0855	...	1100	...	...	1135	1405	1415	...	1555	...	1750	1750	...	1915	...	2010	2105	2110	2150	...
Skellefteå ..... d.	0750	...	1015	1015	...	1225	...	...	1250	1535	1530	...	1715	1830	1925	1925	...	2025	2030	2130	2225	2230	2300	...
Umeå ..... a.	0945	...	1210	1210	...	1435	...	...	1445	1740	1725	...	1910	2035	2130	2130	...	...	2235	2340	0030	...	...	...

HAPARANDA-TORNIO - KEMI — Valid until August 9, 2019

		①–⑤		①–⑤ A		①–⑤		⑦		⑦		①–⑤		⑦		①–⑤ B		⑦		⑦	①–⑤	①–⑤		①–⑤
Haparanda-Tornio 🏛 ..... § ⊡ d.	...	0638	...	1045	...	1100	...	1205	...	1245	...	1300	...	1405	...	1450	...	1505	...	1545	1600	1655	...	1915
Kemi ..... ⊡ a.	...	0720	...	1130	...	1150	...	1245	...	1320	...	1350	...	1445	...	1525	...	1545	...	1625	1630	1730	...	1955

	①–⑤			①–⑤		⑥ C		①–⑤		⑦		①–⑤		⑦	⑦		①–⑤	①–⑤		⑦		⑦		①–⑤
Kemi ..... ⊡ d.	0655	...	...	0925	...	1045	...	1135	...	1300	...	1425	...	1500	1630	...	1730	1805	...	1830	...	2005	...	2040
Haparanda-Tornio 🏛 ..... § ⊡ a.	0720	...	...	1000	...	1120	...	1225	...	1340	...	1455	...	1540	1710	...	1800	1845	...	1855	...	2035	...	2106

From Kemi services call at Kemi railway station 1 minute later; from Haparanda-Tornio services run via Kemi railway station upon request.

All stops refer to bus stations except where shown otherwise.

A – Change at Keminmaa Tupasvilla.
B – Until Aug. 6.
C – Not June 22.

⊡ – Finnish time, one hour later than Swedish time.
§ – Swedish name: Haparanda-Tornio.
Finnish name: Tornio-Haaparanta.

Haparanda-Tornio bus station is located on the Swedish side of the border (distance to border approximately 100 metres).

Operators:
LN – Länstrafiken Norrbotten: www.ltnbd.se
NET – NET-Matkat: www.netmatkat.com
J M Eskelisen Lapin Linjat: www.eskelisen.fi
NorthBus: www.northbus.fi
Orajärven Bussit: www.orajarvenbussit.fi
Ketosen Liikenne: www.ketosenliikenne.fi
Kemin Taksipalvelu: www.kemintaksi.fi

See also www.matkahuolto.fi

NORWAY

SEE MAP PAGE 343

Operator: Vy www.vy.no

Services: All trains convey second class seating accommodation. Many services, as identified in the notes, also convey *Vy Komfort* accommodation (see below). Sleeping-cars (🛏) have one and two-berth compartments; the sleeper supplement is 950 NOK per compartment (for two people travelling together, or sole use for single travellers). Most long distance express trains convey a bistro car (✗) serving hot and cold meals, drinks and snacks. 🍸 indicates that drinks and light refreshments are available from automatic vending machines.

Timings: Vy services are valid **until December 14**, 2019 (unless otherwise stated). Dec. 25, 26, Jan. 1, Apr. 18, 19, 21, 22, May 1, 17, 30, June 9, 10 are Norwegian public holidays and services are subject to alteration on and around these dates. Alterations to internal Norwegian services during holiday periods are not always shown in the tables and readers are advised to confirm timings before travelling (✆ +47 61 05 19 10).

Reservations: Seat reservation is highly recommended on long-distance routes Oslo - Kristiansand - Stavanger (Table **775**), Oslo - Bergen (Table **780**), Oslo - Trondheim / Åndalsnes (Table **785**) and Trondheim - Bodø (Table **787**).

NSB Komfort: Vy Komfort is a dedicated area provided on many trains with complimentary tea / coffee and newspapers; a supplement of 100 NOK is payable per single journey.

770 OSLO - HALDEN - GÖTEBORG

All trains convey Vy Komfort and 🍸

Warning! Journeys between Oslo and Rygge are replaced by 🚌 June 22 - August 4 in amended timings (earlier departures from Oslo / Moss).

km	Norwegian train number	139		103	105	107	109	111	113	115	117	119	121	141	123	383	143	125	127	129	131	133	135		137
	Swedish train number				391						395								399						
		C		Ⓐ	B		⚒		⚒					ⒶC		A	ⒶC			ⒷC		ⒷC			ⒷC
0	**Oslo** Sentral d.	0001	...	0601	0701	0802	0901	1001	1101	1201	1301	1401	1501	1528	1601	...	1628	1702	1802	1901	2001	2101	2201	...	2301
60	Moss d.	0052	...	0644	0745	0844	0944	1044	1144	1244	1344	1444	1546	1614	1645	...	1713	1746	1844	1944	2044	2144	2244	...	2344
69	Rygge ✈ d.	0059	...	0651	0752	0851	0951	1051	1151	1251	1351	1451	1553	1621	1652	...	1720	1753	1851	1951	2051	2151	2251	...	2351
94	Fredrikstad d.	0119	...	0710	0812	0911	1016	1112	1211	1311	1411	1511	1616	1642	1713	...	1741	1813	1911	2011	2112	2211	2311	...	0011
109	Sarpsborg d.	0133	...	0729	0825	0929	1033	1126	1225	1325	1425	1529	1633	1656	1727	...	1755	1827	1925	2028	2126	2225	2325	...	0025
137	**Halden** ★ d.	0152	...	0748	0846	0948	1052	1145	1244	1344	1446	1548	1652	1720	1746	1753	1820	1846	2002**z**	2047	2145	2244	2344	...	0044
268	Öxnered **751** d.	...	...	...	1001	...	...	...	...	...	1601	...	...	...	...	1920	...	...	2116	...	...	...	...	...	...
278	Trollhättan **751** d.	...	...	...	1008	...	...	...	...	...	1608	...	...	...	...	1927	...	...	2122	...	...	...	...	...	...
350	**Göteborg 751** a.	...	...	...	1040	...	...	...	...	...	1650	...	...	...	...	2005	...	...	2200	...	...	...	...	...	...

Swedish train number										390						394		382				398		
Norwegian train number	102	154	104	142	156	106	144	108	110		112	114	116	118	120	122	124	126		128	130	132	134	136	138
	Ⓐ	⑥	Ⓐ	ⒶC	†	⚒	ⒶC	⚒			B△		⚒						A			ⒷC		ⒷC	
Göteborg 751 d.	...	...	...	...	...	...	...	...	...	...	0655	...	...	...	...	...	1300	...	1445	...	...	...	1755	...	...
Trollhättan **751** d.	...	...	...	...	...	...	...	...	...	...	0735	...	...	...	...	...	1335	...	1519	...	...	...	1837	...	...
Öxnered **751** d.	...	...	...	...	...	...	...	...	...	...	0741	...	...	...	...	...	1341	...	1526	...	...	...	1843	...	...
Halden ★ d.	0401	0500	0503	0532	0600	0603	0632	0700	0802	...	0910	1005	1103	1202	1302	1402	1510	1605	1649	1703	1802	1902	2005	2102	2202
Sarpsborg d.	0422	0520	0524	0552	0620	0624	0653	0721	0824	...	0930	1026	1125	1224	1324	1424	1530	1626	...	1725	1825	1924	2026	2124	2224
Fredrikstad d.	0436	0534	0538	0607	0634	0638	0708	0736	0838	...	0944	1040	1139	1238	1338	1438	1544	1640	...	1739	1839	1938	2040	2138	2238
Rygge ✈ d.	0454	0552	0556	0626	0652	0656	0727	0756	0856	...	1002	1058	1157	1256	1356	1456	1602	1658	...	1757	1857	1956	2058	2156	2256
Moss d.	0503	0601	0608	0635	0701	0708	0736	0808	0908	...	1012	1108	1208	1308	1408	1508	1612	1711	...	1808	1908	2008	2108	2208	2308
Oslo Sentral a.	0552	0651	0651	0722	0751	0751	0822	0851	0949	...	1052	1149	1249	1349	1449	1549	1652	1751	...	1849	1949	2049	2149	2249	2349

A – Ⓐ (not June 14 - Aug. 18).
B – ①–⑥ (not June 10).
C – Not June 22 - Aug. 4.
z – Arrives 1944.
△ – Subject to alteration June 25 - July 1.
★ – 🛃 at Kornsjø (*km169*).

771 OSLO - OSLO LUFTHAVN GARDERMOEN ✈

See also Tables 783 and 785

Operated by Flytoget AS.
Special fares apply.
✆ +47 23 15 90 00
www.flytoget.no

Daily services (journey time: 19 – 22 minutes)
Non-stop services
From Oslo Sentral 0440 - 0000 (0440 - 2340 on ⑥).
From Gardermoen 0530 - 0050 (0530 - 0000 on ⑥).
①–⑤: Services every 10 minutes 0630 - 2240, other times every 20 minutes.
⑥: Services every 20 minutes
†: Services every 10 minutes 1150 - 2320, other times every 20 minutes.

Additional Services (journey time: 23 – 25 minutes)
Trains call at Lillestrøm 10 minutes from Oslo
From Oslo Sentral service 0654 - 0044 at 24, 34 and 54 past the hour.
From Gardermoen service 0643 - 2343 at 03, 13 and 43 past the hour.
Reduced frequency on ⑥⑦.

773 OSLO - GJØVIK

All trains convey 🍸

km		Ⓐ	Ⓐ					Ⓐ	Ⓒ			Ⓐ▲
0	**Oslo** S d.	0002	0702	0902	1102	1302	1502	1612	1702	1902	2102	2302
56	Roa d.	0103	0800	0959	1158	1358	1600	1705	1803	1959	2158	0003
70	Jaren d.	0119	0816	1015	1214	1414	1616	1722	1819	2015	2214	0019
99	Eina d.	0142**x**	0840	1039	1238	1437	1639	1750	1842	2039	2238	0042
110	Raufoss d.	0152	0850	1049	1248	1447	1649	1801	1852	2049	2248	0052
122	**Gjøvik** a.	0202	0900	1059	1258	1457	1659	1811	1902	2059	2258	0102

	Ⓐ	Ⓒr	Ⓐ⊠	Ⓐ◇								
Gjøvik d.	0431	0528	0541	0629	0733	0932	1131	1327	1530	1729	1932	2131
Raufoss d.	0442	0539	0552	0639	0744	0943	1142	1338	1541	1740	1943	2142
Eina d.	0452**x**	0549	0602	0649	0754	0953	1152	1348	1551	1751	1953	2152
Jaren d.	0515	0612	0625	0713	0817	1016	1215	1412	1615	1818	2016	2215
Roa d.	0531	0628	0643	0730	0833	1032	1231	1429	1631	1834	2032	2231
Oslo S a.	0628	0728	0744	0830	0930	1128	1330	1530	1730	1930	2130	2328

r – Not June 29 - Aug. 4.
x – Request stop.
▲ – June 25 - Aug 4 departs Oslo 2226, Roa 2334, Jaren 2350, Elna 0013, Raufoss 0023, arrives Gjøvik 0033.
⊠ – June 24 - Aug. 4 departs Gjøvik 0547, Raufoss 0558, Elna 0608, Jaren 0639, Roa 0656, arrives Oslo 0804.
◇ – June 24 - Aug. 4 departs Gjøvik 0639, Raufoss 0649, Elna 0658, Jaren 0721, Roa 0738, arrives Oslo 0848.

775 OSLO - KRISTIANSAND - STAVANGER

Long distance services are not available for local journeys Oslo - Drammen and v.v. or Sandnes - Stavanger and v.v.

Warning! Journeys between Oslo and Kongsberg are replaced by 🚌 June 22 - August 4 in amended timings (earlier departures from Oslo / Drammen).

km		701	709	709	715	719	719	723	729	733	733	737	745
		Ⓐ	Ⓒ	Ⓐ		⑦	Ⓐ			Ⓑ	⑥	Ⓑ	Ⓑ
		⊡	✗⊡	✗⊡	✗⊡	✗⊡	✗⊡	✗⊡	✗⊡	✗⊡	✗⊡	✗⊡	♣✗
0	**Oslo** Sentral § d.	...	...	0419	0725	...	0925	1125	1425	1625	1625	1825	2225
41	Drammen § d.	...	...	0454**u**	0800**u**	...	1000**u**	1200**u**	1500**u**	1700**u**	1700**u**	1900**u**	2300**u**
87	Kongsberg § d.	...	...	0530	0836	...	1036	1236	1547	1747	1747	1946	2344
134	Nordagutu d.	...	...	0604	0911	...	1114	|	1620	1823	1823	2022	0020**x**
151	Bø d.	...	...	0619	0925	...	1128	1327	1638	1841	1841	2037	0036
209	Neslandsvatn d.	...	...	0712	1010	...	1212	1412	1720	1924	1924	2124	0125**x**
270	Nelaug d.	...	...	0800	1055	...	1257	1459	1806	2012	2012	2209	0218**x**
353	**Kristiansand** a.	...	...	0856	1153	...	1358	1601	1903	2108	2108	2307	0330
353	**Kristiansand** d.	0502	0906	0906	1202	1408	1408	1615	1910	2115	...	...	0346
457	Sira d.	0622	1025	1025	1326	1526	1526	1743	2027	2236	...	...	0512**x**
465	Moi d.	0629**x**	1032**x**	1032**x**	1333	1533**x**	1533**x**	1751**x**	2034**x**	2243**x**	...	...	0520**x**
514	Egersund ◇ d.	0705	1108	1108	1407	1607	1607	1830	2113	2318	...	...	0605
573	Sandnes S ◇ a.	0752**v**	1152**v**	1152**v**	1452	1705**v**	1705**v**	1922**v**	2151**v**	2358**v**	...	...	0702**v**
587	**Stavanger** ◇ a.	0805	1205	1205	1505	1719	1719	1936	2204	0011	...	...	0720

	702	708	712	716	720	724	730	730	734	744
	Ⓐ	A				Ⓑ	Ⓑ	⑥	Ⓑ	Ⓑ
	⊡	✗⊡	✗⊡	✗⊡	✗⊡	✗⊡	✗⊡	✗⊡	✗⊡	♣✗
Stavanger ◐ d.	...	0430	0647	0847	1016	1248	1533	1533	1748	2217
Sandnes S ◐ d.	...	0444**v**	0701**v**	0901**v**	1031**v**	1302**v**	1550**v**	1550**v**	1802**v**	2232**v**
Egersund ◐ d.	...	0532	0744	0941	1120	1343	1646	1646	1844	2318
Moi d.	...	0616**x**	0820**x**	1018**x**	1200**x**	1424**x**	1723**x**	1723**x**	1921**x**	0004**x**
Sira d.	...	0623	0827	1026	1208	1431	1730	1730	1928	0012**x**
Kristiansand a.	...	0742	0945	1145	1333	1548	1846	1846	2047	0153
Kristiansand d.	0445	0754	0956	1155	1350	1603	1853	...	...	0215
Nelaug d.	0545	0858	1056	1256	1457	1702	1957	...	...	0331**x**
Neslandsvatn d.	0631	0943	1143	1343	|	|	2043	...	...	0423**x**
Bø d.	0714	1027	1227	1429	1625	1827	2125	...	...	0509
Nordagutu d.	0728	1041	1241	1444	1641	1842	2141	...	...	0524**x**
Kongsberg ‡ d.	0802	1117	1317	1519	1717	1917	2217	...	...	0608
Drammen ‡ a.	0851**a**	1151**a**	1350**a**	1551**a**	1751**a**	1951**a**	2251**a**	...	...	0650**a**
Oslo S ‡ a.	0925	1225	1425	1625	1825	2025	2325	...	...	0725

Nelaug - Arendal

km		Ⓐ		⚒								†	
0	Nelaug d.	0700	...	0905	1104	1304	1505	...	1815	2020	...	2218	...
36	Arendal a.	0737	...	0942	1141	1341	1542	...	1852	2057	...	2255	...

	Ⓐ		⚒				Ⓑ	⑥		†
Arendal d.	0503	...	0811	1008	1209	1408	1615	1720	1911	2123
Nelaug a.	0540	...	0848	1045	1246	1445	1652	1757	1948	2200

A – Ⓐ Stavanger - Oslo; ⑥ Kristiansand - Oslo.

u – Calls to pick up only.
v – Calls on request to set down only.
x – Request stop.

♣ – Conveys 🛏 and 🛋2. Reservation recommended.
⊡ – Reservation recommended. Conveys *Vy Komfort*.

§ – Other local trains **Oslo** S - **Drammen** (35 minutes) - **Kongsberg** (75 – 81 minutes): 0009, 0609 Ⓐ, 0709, 0809, 0909, 1009, 1109, 1209, 1309, 1409, 1509, 1609, 1709, 1809, 1909, 2009, 2109, 2209 and 2309. ***Subject to alteration June 22 - August 4.***

‡ – Other local trains **Kongsberg** - **Drammen** (43 – 44 minutes) - **Oslo** S (77 – 78 minutes): 0434 Ⓐ, 0534, 0634, 0734, 0834, 0934, 1034, 1134, 1234, 1334, 1434, 1534, 1633, 1734, 1834, 1934, 2033, 2134 and 2234. ***Subject to alteration June 22 - August 4.***

◇ – Other local trains **Egersund** - **Sandnes** S (51 – 58 minutes) - **Stavanger** (67 – 74 minutes): 0453 Ⓐ, 0518 Ⓐ, 0551 Ⓐ, 0621 ⚒, 0650 Ⓐ, 0718 ⚒, 0818 ⚒, 0916, 1019, 1119, 1221, 1316, 1419, 1450 Ⓐ, 1520, 1550 Ⓐ, 1620, 1650 Ⓐ, 1721, 1818, 1920, 2020, 2123, 2220 and 2321.

◐ – Other local trains **Stavanger** - **Sandnes** S (16 minutes) - **Egersund** (69 – 78 minutes): 0449 Ⓐ, 0524 Ⓐ, 0554 ⚒, 0654 ⚒, 0754 ⚒, 0854, 0954, 1054, 1154, 1254, 1324 Ⓐ, 1354, 1424 Ⓐ, 1454, 1524 Ⓐ, 1554, 1624 Ⓐ, 1654, 1754, 1854, 1954, 2054, 2154, 2254 and 2354.

PORSGRUNN - NOTODDEN 779

No service on Ⓒ

km		Ⓐ	Ⓐa	Ⓐ	Ⓐ	Ⓐa	Ⓐ	Ⓐa	Ⓐ
0	**Porsgrunn** 783 d.	...	0640	0749	1151	1339	1441	1605	1752
9	Skien 783 d.	0530	0649	0758	1200	1350	1455	1617	1801
43	Nordagutu a.	0600	0719	0828	1230	1420	1528	1650	1831
43	Nordagutu d.	0606	0720	0829	1231	1421	1529	1651	1832
62	**Notodden** a.	0625	0739	0848	1250	1440	1548	1710	1851

	Ⓐ	Ⓐa	Ⓐ	Ⓐ	Ⓐa	Ⓐ	Ⓐa	Ⓐ
Notodden d.	0637	0807	0913	1301	1450	1610	1810	2010
Nordagutu a.	0655	0825	0931	1319	1508	1628	1828	2028
Nordagutu d.	0656	0828	0932	1320	1509	1630	1831	2029
Skien 783 a.	0730	0858	1002	1350	1539	1701	1901	2059
Porsgrunn 783 a.	0739	0907	1011	1401	1551	1710	1910	...

a – Not June 24 - Aug. 2.

OSLO - BERGEN 780

WARNING! June 22 - August 4 services are diverted between Oslo and Hønefoss, not calling at Drammen (Oslo departures may vary by up to 11 minutes, arrivals by up to 33 minutes). Passengers travelling from / to Drammen are conveyed by 🚌 to / from Hønefoss).

km		603 A 🍸	609 B ✕⊡	61 ✕⊡		601 ✕⊡	607 ⑦D ✕⊡	63 ✕⊡		605 Ⓑ ♥✕
0	**Oslo** Sentral 783 d.	...	0625	0825	...	1203	...	1543	...	2325
41	Drammen 783 d.	...	0700u	0900u	...	1238u	...	1618u	...	0003u
112	Hønefoss d.	...	0757	0954	...	1333	...	1712	...	0103
208	Nesbyen d.	...	0907	1102	...	1444	...	1821	...	0225
225	Gol d.	0724	0921	1115	...	1500	...	1835	...	0240
250	Ål d.	0743	0941	1135	...	1520	1542	1854	...	0301
275	Geilo d.	0804	1007	1156	...	1541	1603	1920	...	0324
286	Ustaoset d.	0816	1019	1207	...	1552	1616	1931	...	0335
324	Finse d.	0847	1106	1234	...	1622	1648	1959	...	0407
354	**Myrdal** 781 a.	0911	1137r	1258	...	1647	1715	2023	...	0434
403	**Voss** 781 a.	1000n	1300	1341	...	1736	1803	2108	...	0524
443	Dale 781 a.	1112	...	1414	...	1814	|	2139	...	0558
480	Arna 781 a.	1148	...	1448s	...	1844	1903s	2210	...	0636s
489	**Bergen** 781 a.	1156	...	1457	...	1855	1916	2219	...	0648

	62 ✕⊡		602 ✕⊡		64 ✕⊡	610 B ✕⊡	604 ⑤F ✕⊡	608 G 🍸	606 Ⓑ ♥✕
Bergen 781 d.	0757	...	1159	...	1557	...	1708	...	2259
Arna 781 d.	0807	...	1209	...	1607u	...	1720u	...	2310
Dale 781 d.	0839	...	1241	...	|	...	|	...	2345
Voss 781 d.	0907	...	1311	...	1710	1744	1828	1905	0019
Myrdal 781 d.	0949	...	1406	...	1753	1833	1910	2023	0104
Finse d.	1015	...	1434	...	1819	1912	1939	2056	0133
Ustaoset d.	1041	...	1503	...	1845	1952	2014	2125	0203
Geilo d.	1054	...	1516	...	1858	2006	2027	2138	0215
Ål d.	1114	...	1540	...	1918	2030	2046	2157	0238
Gol d.	1139	...	1600	...	1937	2053	...	...	0307
Nesbyen d.	1152	...	1613	...	1949	2105	...	...	0321
Hønefoss d.	1304	...	1732	...	2100	2227	...	...	0437
Drammen 783 a.	1410s	...	1828s	...	2154s	2325s	...	...	0533s
Oslo Sentral 783 a.	1445	...	1905	...	2227	0005	...	...	0613

– July 17 - Aug. 18.
– Until Sept. 29.
– Oct. 6 - Dec. 12.
F – Oct. 4 - Dec. 12.
G – July 14 - Aug.17.
n – Departs 1039.
r – Departs 1206.
s – Calls to set down only.
u – Calls to pick up only.
♥ – Conveys 🛏 and 🛌. Reservation recommended.
⊡ – Reservation recommended. Conveys *NSB Komfort*.

MYRDAL - VOSS - BERGEN and FLÅM 781

SERVICE APRIL 29 - SEPTEMBER 29. Oslo timings are subject to alteration June 22 - Aug. 4.

km		Ⓐ	605 ①–⑥ ✕◇		Ⓐ	Ⓐ	Ⓒ	Ⓐ	Ⓐ			Ⓐ		609 ✕◇	61 ✕◇		Ⓐ			601 ✕◇			63 ✕◇	⑤	⑥	Ⓑ
	Oslo Sentral **780** d.	...	2325p	...	...	...	...	...	...	...	...	...	...	0625	0825	...	...	...	...	1203	...	...	1543	...	...	...
0	**Myrdal** d.	...	0437	...	...	...	...	0816	...	*0914*b	0956	...	1111	1206	1300	1331	...	1436	1551	1649	1712	...	2024	2033	...	...
18	Mjølfjell d.	...	|	...	...	0740k	...	|	...	|	1014x	...	1129	|	|	1349	...	1454	|	|	1736	...	|	2052x	...	...
49	**Voss** a.	...	0524	...	...	0815k	...	0902	...	*1000*b	1054	...	1208	1300	1341	1429	...	1532	1632	1736	1814	...	2108	2132	...	...
49	**Voss** d.	0506	0529	0606	0720	0833	0833	...	0918	1039	...	1127	1236	...	1346	...	1437	1538	1635	1740	1839	1937	2112	...	2154	2238
89	Dale d.	0537	0558	0641	0751	0908	0908	...	0955	1112	...	1202	1311	...	1414	...	1513	1612	1713	1814	1912	2014	2139	...	2225	2315
104	Vaksdal d.	0553	|	0657	0806	0926	0926	...	1011	1129	...	1226	1327	...	|	...	1528	1628	1729	|	1928	2032	|	...	2244	2331
126	Arna ‡ d.	0612	0636s	0719	0828	0945	0945	...	1030	1148	...	1248	1348	...	1448s	...	1548	1648	1748	1844	1948	2051	2210	...	2303	2350
135	**Bergen** ‡ a.	0620	0648	0727	0836	0953	0953	...	1038	1156	...	1256	1356	...	1457	...	1556	1656	1756	1855	1956	2059	2219	...	2311	2358

	①–⑥	Ⓐ			62 ✕◇			Ⓐ	602 ✕◇			Ⓐ			64 ✕◇	Ⓐ	610 ✕◇		⑤	D	Ⓐ		Ⓐ		606 Ⓑ ✕◇	⑥
Bergen ‡ d.	0009	0541	...	0651	0757	0839	0959	1059	1159	...	1257	1359	...	1515	1557	1615	...	1659	...	...	1759	1859	2039	2158	2259	2321
Arna ‡ d.	0017	0549	...	0659	0807u	0847	1007	1107	1209	...	1305	1407	...	1524	1607s	1624	...	1707	...	...	1807	1907	2050	2209	2310u	2329
Vaksdal d.	0038	0612	...	0720	|	0905	1027	1128	|	...	1326	1428	...	1545	|	1645	...	1728	...	...	1828	1927	2108	2227	|	2347
Dale d.	0053	0627	...	0735	0839	0922	1042	1142	1241	...	1341	1443	...	1559	|	1659	...	1743	...	...	1843	1942	2122	2242	2345	0002
Voss a.	0124	0659	...	0809	0906	0953	1113	1216	1308	...	1415	1514	...	1630	1708	1730	...	1816	...	...	1914	2013	2156	2313	0016	0033
Voss d.	...	0701k	0724	0816	0907	1000	1120	...	1311	1341	1439	...	1548	...	1710	...	1744	...	1820	1905	...	...	...	...	0019	...
Mjølfjell d.	...	0734k	|	0850x	|	1033x	|	...	|	|	1513x	...	1620	...	|	...	|	...	1854x	1945	...	...	...	...	|	...
Myrdal a.	...	...	0810	0908	0947	1051	1206	...	1403	1427	1531	...	1639	...	1751	...	1826	...	1912	2000	...	...	...	...	0101	...
Oslo Sentral **780** a.	...	...	...	...	1445	...	...	...	1905	...	...	...	...	...	2227	...	0005	...	...	...	...	...	...	...	0613	...

MYRDAL - FLÅM ⊠

km											
0	Myrdal d.	0826	0940	1058	1213	1327	1442	1559	1715	1835	2005
20	Flåm a.	0920	1035	1155	1310	1425	1540	1655	1810	1930	2055

Flåm d.	0730	0835	0945	1105	1220	1335	1450	1605	1725	1840
Myrdal a.	0812	0928	1042	1201	1315	1430	1545	1702	1817	1936

– July 14 - Aug. 17.
– July 15 - Aug. 18.
– Not June 24 - Aug. 15.
p – Previous day.
s – Calls to set down only.
u – Calls to pick up only.
x – Request stop.
◇ – Reservation recommended.
‡ – Additional local services operate.
⊠ – Operator: **Flåm Utvikling AS.** ✆ + 47 57 63 21 00. 30% discount for rail pass holders.

May 1 - Sept. 30 ⛴ FLÅM - GUDVANGEN and 🚌 GUDVANGEN - VOSS 781a

	⛴	⛴	🚌	⛴	🚌		⛴	🚌	⛴		⛴	🚌	
Flåm d.	0800	0900	...	1100	...	...	1330	...	1400	...	1600	...	...
Gudvangen a.	1015	1100	...	1300	...	...	1530	...	1600	...	1800	...	...
Gudvangen d.	...	...	1140	...	1320	...	...	1540	...	...	...	1805	...
Voss a.	...	...	1255	...	1435	...	...	1655	...	...	...	1920	...

	⛴	⛴	🚌	⛴	⛴	🚌	⛴		⛴	🚌 Ⓐ	
Voss d.	...	...	1010	...	...	1430	...	...	...	1610	...
Gudvangen a.	...	...	1120	...	...	1535	...	...	...	1710	...
Gudvangen d.	0830	1030	...	1130	1330	...	1545	...	1630	...	...
Flåm a.	1030	1245	...	1330	1530	...	1800	...	1830	...	...

🚌 operators: Skyss ✆ +47 55 55 90 70. ⛴ operator: Fjord1 AS ✆ +47 57 75 70 00.

May 1 - Sept. 30 ⛴ / 🚌 LILLEHAMMER and GOL - FLÅM - BALESTRAND - BERGEN 782

	⛴ ①–⑥	🚌	⛴ ⑦	🚌 Ⓑ	🚌 Ⓐ‡	🚌 ⑥‡	⛴	🚌	🚌	🚌 Ⓑ	🚌 ⑦‡	🚌
Lillehammer skysst. d.	...	...	...	...	0915	0925	...	...	...	...	1335	...
Gjøvik skysstasjon d.	...	...	...	...	1005	1005	...	...	...	...	1420	...
Sogndal ⊕ d.	...	0755	...	1130	|	|	...	1430	...	1715	|	...
Kaupangsenteret d.	...	0810	...	1145	|	|	...	1445	...	1730	|	...
Gol Skysstasjon d.	...	|	...	|	|	|	...	|	1320	|	|	1900
Lærdal Rådhuset d.	...	0845	...	1225	|	|	...	1525	1525	1805	|	2105
Kaupangsenteret d.	...	|	...	|	|	|	...	|	1600	|	|	2140
Sogndal ⊕ a.	...	|	...	|	|	|	...	|	1615	|	|	2155
Sogndal ⊕ d.	0705	|	1040	|	|	|	...	|	*1620*	|	|	*2205*
Flåm d.	|	0930	|	1310	1500	1525	1530	1618	|	1850	1930	|
Leikanger d.	0730	|	1110	|	|	|	1630	|	*1645*	|	|	*2230*
Balestrand d.	0750	|	1130	|	|	|	1655	|	*1735*	|	|	*2315*
Voss a.	|	1035	|	1415	1610	1630	|	1720	...	2000	2035	...
Bergen ⊡ a.	1150	1225	1520	1605	1745	1810	2045	1910	...	2145	2210	...

	⛴	🚌	🚌	🚌 ‡	🚌	🚌 ⚒	🚌 Ⓐ	⛴ ⑥	🚌 ⑥⑦	⛴ Ⓑ	🚌 Ⓑ
Bergen ⊡ d.	0800	...	0845	0910	...	1115	1350	1415	1525	1630	1715
Voss d.	|	...	1035	1050	...	1300	1540	|	1720	|	1900
Balestrand d.	1155	*1005*a	|	|	*1310*	|	|	1820	|	2030	|
Leikanger d.	1220	*1055*a	|	|	*1355*	|	|	1835	|	2050	|
Flåm a.	1325	|	1145	1200	|	1415	1653	|	1830	|	2020
Sogndal ⊕ a.	...	*1125*a	|	|	*1425*	|	|	1900	|	2120	|
Sogndal ⊕ d.	...	1130	|	|	1430	|	|	...	|	...	|
Kaupangsenteret d.	...	1145	|	|	1445	|	|	...	|	...	|
Lærdal Rådhuset a.	...	1225	1245	|	1525	1505	1745	...	1920	...	2105
Gol skysstasjon a.	...	1415	|	|	1715	|	|	...	|	...	|
Kaupangsenteret a.	...	...	1320	|	...	1540	1820	...	2000	...	2140
Sogndal ⊕ a.	...	...	1335	|	...	1555	1835	...	2015	...	2155
Gjøvik skysstasjon a.	...	...	...	1715	...	...	...	...	...	...	...
Lillehammer skysst. a.	...	...	...	1800	...	...	...	...	...	...	...

– Ⓑ only.
– Subject to confirmation from mid-June.
⊕ – 🚌: Sogndal skysstasjon. ⛴: Sogndal kai.
⊡ – 🚌: Bus station. ⛴: Strandkaiterminal.
🚌 operators: Nettbuss express ✆ +47 4070 5070. NOR-WAY Bussekspress ✆ +47 2231 3150.
⛴ operator: Norled AS ✆ +47 5186 8700.

783 EIDSVOLL - OSLO - SKIEN

All trains convey *Vy Komfort* and 🍷

km		Ⓐ	⚒		⚒		⚒				ⒶB		Ⓐ	ⒶB		ⒶB	ⒶB			Ⓑ		Ⓑ		Ⓑ	
0	**Eidsvoll** 785 d.	0500	0600	0700	0800	0900	1000	1100	1200	1300	...	1400	...	...	1500	...	...	1600	1700	1800	1900	2000	2100	2200	2300
16	Oslo Lufthavn ✈ ¶ 785 d.	0513	0613	0713	0813	0913	1013	1113	1213	1313	...	1413	...	...	1513	...	...	1613	1713	1813	1913	2013	2113	2213	2313
47	Lillestrøm 785 d.	0526	0626	0726	0826	0926	1026	1126	1226	1326	...	1426	...	...	1526	...	...	1626	1726	1826	1926	2026	2126	2226	2326
68	**Oslo** S 785 a.	0536	0636	0736	0836	0936	1036	1136	1236	1336	...	1436	...	...	1536	...	...	1636	1736	1836	1936	2036	2136	2236	2336
68	**Oslo** S 785 d.	0539	0639	0739	0839	0939	1039	1139	1239	1339	1405	1439	1505	1533	1539	1605	1633	1639	1739	1839	1939	2039	2139	2239	2339
108	Drammen 785 d.	0614	0714	0814	0914	1014	1114	1214	1314	1414	1445	1514	1545	|	1614	1645	|	1714	1814	1914	2014	2114	2214	2314	0014
142	Holmestrand d.	0638	0733	0833	0933	1033	1133	1233	1333	1433	1506	1533	1606	|	1633	1706	|	1733	1833	1933	2033	2133	2233	2333	0033
156	Skoppum d.	0650	0741	0841	0941	1041	1141	1241	1341	1441	1518	1541	1618	|	1641	1718	|	1741	1841	1941	2041	2141	2241	2341	0041
172	Tønsberg d.	0703	0752	0852	0952	1052	1152	1252	1352	1452	1529	1552	1629	1643**z**	1652	1729	1743**z**	1752	1852	1952	2052	2152	2252	2352	0052
191	Torp ✈ d.	0721	0812	0912	1012	1112	1212	1312	1412	1512	|	1612	|	|	1712	|	|	1812	1912	2012	2112	2212	2312	0008	|
196	**Sandefjord** d.	0727	0818	0918	1018	1118	1218	1318	1418	1518	1548	1618	1648	1705	1718	1748	1805	1818	1918	2018	2118	2218	2318	0013	0111
215	Larvik d.	0746	0833	0933	1033	1133	1233	1333	1433	1533	1602	1633	1702	1719	1733	1802	1819	1833	1933	2033	2133	2233	2332	0027	0125
240	Porsgrunn 779 d.	0758	0845	0945	1045	1145	1245	1345	1445	1545	1618	1645	1718	1731	1745	1818	1831	1845	1945	2045	2145	2245	2344	0039	0137
249	**Skien** 779 a.	0806	0853	0953	1053	1153	1253	1353	1453	1553	1626	1653	1726	1739	1753	1826	1839	1853	1953	2053	2153	2253	2352	0047	0145

	Ⓐ	ⒶB	⚒	Ⓐ	ⒶB		ⒶB	ⒶB	⚒		⚒										Ⓑ		Ⓑ	
Skien 779 d.	0411	0431	0511	0527	0545	0608	0618	0630	0711	0809	0909	1009	1109	1209	1309	1409	1509	1607	1707	1807	1909	2009	2109	2209
Porsgrunn 779 d.	0419	0439	0519	0535	0553	0616	0626	0638	0719	0817	0917	1017	1117	1217	1317	1417	1517	1617	1717	1817	1917	2017	2117	2217
Larvik d.	0432	0453	0532	0549	0606	0629	0640	0652	0732	0832	0932	1032	1132	1232	1332	1432	1532	1632	1732	1832	1932	2032	2132	2232
Sandefjord d.	0447	0508	0547	0604	0621	0643	0654	0707	0747	0847	0947	1047	1147	1247	1347	1447	1547	1647	1747	1847	1947	2047	2147	2247
Torp ✈ d.	0451	0512	0551	0608	|	0647	|	0711	0751	0851	0951	1051	1151	1251	1351	1451	1551	1651	1751	1851	1951	2051	2151	2251
Tønsberg d.	0508	0529	0608	0626	0640	0708**z**	0719	0728	0808	0908	1008	1108	1208	1308	1408	1508	1608	1708	1808	1908	2008	2108	2208	2308
Skoppum d.	0518	0539	0618	0636	|	0718	|	0740	0818	0918	1018	1118	1218	1318	1418	1518	1618	1718	1818	1918	2018	2118	2218	2318
Holmestrand d.	0526	0548	0626	0645	|	0726	|	0749	0826	0926	1026	1126	1226	1326	1426	1526	1626	1726	1826	1926	2026	2126	2226	2326
Drammen 785 d.	0547	0610	0647	0710	|	0747	|	0812	0847	0947	1047	1147	1247	1347	1447	1547	1647	1747	1847	1947	2047	2147	2247	2347
Oslo S 785 a.	0621	0645	0721	0745	0749	0821	0825	0845	0921	1021	1121	1221	1321	1421	1521	1621	1721	1821	1921	2021	2121	2221	2321	0021
Oslo S 785 d.	0624	...	0724	...	0752	0824	...	...	0924	1024	1124	1224	1324	1424	1524	1624	1724	1824	1924	2024	2124	2224	2324	0024
Lillestrøm 785 d.	0635	...	0735	...	0802	0835	...	...	0935	1035	1135	1235	1335	1435	1535	1635	1735	1835	1935	2035	2135	2235	2335	0035
Oslo Lufthavn ✈ ¶ 785 d.	0649	...	0749	...	...	0849	...	...	0949	1049	1149	1249	1349	1449	1549	1649	1749	1849	1949	2049	2149	2249	2349	0049
Eidsvoll 785 a.	0700	...	0800	...	...	0900	...	...	1000	1100	1200	1300	1400	1500	1600	1700	1800	1900	2000	2100	2200	2300	2400	0100

B – Not June 24 - Aug. 2. z – Arrives 6–7 minutes earlier. ¶ – Oslo Lufthavn Gardermoen ✈.

784 HAMAR - RØROS - TRONDHEIM

km		Ⓐ	⑥	Ⓐ	⚒a	†	Ⓐ	Ⓒ		Ⓑb	Ⓑ	
0	**Hamar** d.	...	...	0810	1011	1210	1210	...	1607	1811	2017	...
32	Elverum d.	...	...	0833	1036	1235	1235	...	1633	1834	2042	...
64	Rena d.	...	...	0855	1059	1257	1257	...	1656	1859	2104	...
120	Koppang d.	...	...	0937	1141	1339	1339	...	1739	1941	2146	...
273	**Røros** d.	0505	0700	1130	1337	1531	1537	1630	1937	2133	2339	...
384	Støren 785 d.	0640	0830	...	...	...	1710	1802	2108	...	...	...
435	**Trondheim** S 785 a.	0735	0925	...	...	...	1802	1855	2200	...	...	...

	Ⓐ	⚒a	Ⓐ		Ⓑb	†	⚒	Ⓐ	†
Trondheim S 785 d.	...	...	0545	0945	...	1346	...	1615	2032
Støren 785 d.	...	...	0640	1040	...	1442	...	1712	2133
Røros d.	0419	0617	0818	1218	1410	1620	1620	1847	2305
Koppang d.	0611	0809	1015	1416	1605	1817	1817	...	...
Rena d.	0653	0854	1059	1458	1656	1859	1859	...	...
Elverum d.	0715	0916	1121	1520	1718	1921	1921	...	...
Hamar a.	0740	0941	1146	1545	1743	1946	1946	...	...

a – Not Ⓐ June 24 - Aug. 16. b – Not Ⓐ July 1 - Aug. 9.

785 OSLO - LILLEHAMMER - ÅNDALSNES and TRONDHEIM

km		407	41	2341	311	2343	45	2345	47	2347	329	405	
		Ⓐa			Ⓐ	Ⓐ			Ⓑ	Ⓑ	Ⓑ	Ⓑ	
		R	R	R		R	R	R	R	R		R	
		⊡	🍴⊡	🍷	🍷⊡	🍷	🍴⊡	🍷	🍴⊡	🍷	🍷⊡	🍴N	
0	**Oslo** Sentral ★ d.	...	0802	...	0934	...	1402	...	1602	...	1834	2306	...
21	Lillestrøm ★ d.	...	0813**u**	...	0945	...	1413**u**	...	1613**u**	...	1845	2321**u**	...
52	Oslo ✈ ⊖ ★ d.	...	0828**u**	...	0959	...	1429**u**	...	1629**u**	...	1859	2340**u**	...
127	**Hamar** ★ d.	...	0921	...	1052	...	1522	...	1722	...	1952	0031	...
185	**Lillehammer** ★ d.	...	1009	...	1140	1150	1611	...	1812	...	2048	0121	...
243	Ringebu d.	...	1052	...	...	1248	1654	...	1856	...	2129	0209	...
267	Vinstra d.	...	1108	...	...	1305	1712	...	1919	...	2144	0226	...
298	Otta d.	...	1131	...	...	1328	1736	...	1942	...	2207	0256	...
344	Dombås d.	...	1203	1205	...	1404	1809	1813	2013	2016	2238	0346	...
458	**Åndalsnes** a.	...	|	1323	...	1531	|	1932	|	2134	...	|	...
430	Oppdal d.	0645	1301	...	...	...	1907	...	2111	...	...	0447	...
502	Støren 784 d.	0735	1349	...	...	...	1957	...	2204	...	...	0541	...
553	**Trondheim** S 784 a.	0830	1431	...	...	...	2045	...	2249	...	...	0640	...

	308	2340	316	2342	42	2344	44	2346	46	406
	⚒	Ⓐ	Ⓐ			Ⓑ	Ⓑ			Ⓑ
		R		R	R	R	R	R	R	R
	🍷⊡	🍷	🍷⊡	🍷	🍴⊡	🍷	🍴⊡	🍷	🍴⊡	🍴N
Trondheim S 784 d.	...	...	...	...	0818	...	1320	...	1529	232
Støren 784 d.	...	...	...	...	0905	...	1409	...	1615	001
Oppdal d.	...	...	...	...	0958	...	1501	...	1706	011
Åndalsnes d.	...	0738	...	0930	|	1430	|	1630	|	|
Dombås d.	0517	0859	...	1050	1057	1551	1557	1750	1809	021
Otta d.	0549	0930	...	...	1129	...	1627	...	1838	025
Vinstra d.	0613	0953	...	...	1152	...	1649	...	1900	032
Ringebu d.	0629	1010	...	...	1209	...	1710	...	1916	033
Lillehammer ★ d.	0714	1055	1114	...	1250	...	1751	...	1958	042
Hamar ★ d.	0807	...	1208	...	1335	...	1840	...	2042	052
Oslo ✈ ⊖ ★ a.	0903	...	1303	...	1432**s**	...	1933**s**	...	2133**s**	0616
Lillestrøm ★ a.	0916	...	1316	...	1449**s**	...	1949**s**	...	2149**s**	0635
Oslo Sentral ★ a.	0926	...	1326	...	1503	...	2004	...	2204	065

🚌	Ⓐ	Ⓒ		Ⓐ			Ⓐ	⚒			⑦	Ⓐ
Åndalsnes d.	0610	0625	1000	1140	1335	1340	1545	1600	1945	1945	2135	2200
Molde a.	0740	0740	1125	1305	|	1510	|	1720	|	2107	2250	2320
Ålesund a.	...	...	...	...	1540	...	1740	...	2150	...	...	...

🚌	Ⓐ		Ⓑ	⚒	Ⓐ	Ⓑ		Ⓐ	Ⓒ	
Ålesund d.	...	...	0710	...	1210	...	1400	...	...	...
Molde d.	0610	0750	|	0955	|	1255	|	1430	1435	220
Åndalsnes a.	0720	0913	0915	1113	1415	1413	1605	1553	1553	231

🚌	⑥	Ⓐ		Ⓐ		Ⓑ		⑤⑦		Ⓑ		
Oppdal skysstasjon d.	0530	0530	...	1050	...	1315	...	1810	...	2120	...	...
Kristiansund a.	0845	0910	...	1425	...	1635	...	2125	...	0025	...	...

🚌	Ⓐ		Ⓐ	⑥		Ⓑ		⑤⑦		Ⓑ
Kristiansund d.	0630	...	1045	1125	...	1325	...	1635	...	212
Oppdal skysstasjon a.	0940	...	1445	1445	...	1645	...	2010	...	003

	Ⓐ	Ⓐ		⚒		⚒		⚒						Ⓑ		Ⓑ		Ⓑ	
Drammen 783 △ d.	...	0557	0657	0757	0857	0957	1057	1157	1257	1357	1457	1557	1657	1757	1857	1957	2057	2157	2257
Oslo Sentral 771 783 d.	...	0634	0734	0834	0934	1034	1134	1234	1334	1434	1534	1634	1734	1834	1934	2034	2134	2234	2334
Lillestrøm 783 d.	...	0645	0745	0845	0945	1045	1145	1245	1345	1445	1545	1645	1745	1845	1945	2045	2145	2245	2345
Oslo ✈ ⊖ ... 771 783 d.	...	0659	0759	0859	0959	1059	1159	1259	1359	1459	1559	1659	1759	1859	1959	2059	2159	2259	2359
Eidsvoll 783 d.	...	0710	0810	0910	1010	1110	1210	1310	1410	1510	1610	1710	1810	1910	2010	2110	2210	2310	0010
Hamar a.	...	0750	0850	0950	1050	1150	1250	1350	1450	1550	1650	1750	1852	1950	2053	2150	2251	2350	0050
Hamar d.	0652	0752	0852	0952	1052	1152	1252	1352	1452	1552	1652	1752	1853	1952	2054	2152	2253	2352	0052
Lillehammer a.	0740	0840	0937	1040	1140	1238	1347	1441	1537	1640	1737	1840	1940	2040	2141	2237	2338	0037	0137**v**

	Ⓐ			⚒		⚒		⚒							Ⓑ		Ⓑ	
Lillehammer d.	0414	...	0526	0615	0714	0814	0907	1014	1114	1208	1314	1415	1507	1614	1707	1810	1910	2007	2115
Hamar a.	0500	...	0611	0705	0805	0905	1005	1105	1205	1305	1405	1505	1605	1705	1805	1906	2005	2106	2205
Hamar d.	0502	...	0613	0708	0807	0907	1007	1107	1207	1307	1407	1507	1607	1707	1807	1908	2008	2108	2207
Eidsvoll 783 d.	0540	...	0651	0751	0851	0951	1051	1151	1251	1351	1451	1551	1651	1751	1851	1951	2051	2151	2251
Oslo ✈ ⊖ ... 771 783 d.	0603	...	0703	0803	0903	1003	1103	1203	1303	1403	1503	1603	1703	1803	1903	2003	2103	2203	2303
Lillestrøm 783 d.	0616	...	0716	0816	0916	1016	1116	1216	1316	1416	1516	1616	1716	1816	1916	2016	2116	2216	2316
Oslo Sentral 771 783 a.	0626	...	0726	0826	0926	1026	1126	1226	1326	1426	1526	1626	1726	1826	1926	2026	2126	2226	2326
Drammen 783 △ a.	0702	...	0802	0902	1002	1102	1202	1302	1402	1502	1602	1702	1802	1902	2002	2102	2202	2302	0002

N – Conveys 🛏 and 2nd class couchette.
R – Reservation recommended.

a – Not June 24 - Aug. 16.
s – Stops to set down only.
u – Stops to pick up only.
v – Arrives 0158 June 22 - Aug. 1.

⊡ – Conveys Vy Komfort.
⊖ – Oslo Lufthavn Gardermoen.
★ – See also panel below main table.
△ – Services from/to Drammen are subject to alteration June 22 - Aug. 4.

786 SOUTHWEST NORWAY 🚌 LINKS

BERGEN - TRONDHEIM (Operator: NOR-WAY Bussekspress ✆ +47 2231 3150)
Bergen ⊡ d. 1630 → Oppdal a. 0440 → Trondheim a. 0642.
Trondheim d. 2230 → Oppdal d. 0032 → Bergen ⊡ a. 1220.

BERGEN - ÅLESUND (Operator: Nettbuss express ✆ +47 4070 5070)
Bergen ⊡ d. 0800 → Ålesund a. 1715 ⑥ / 1745 Ⓑ. Ålesund d. 1110 → Bergen ⊡ a. 2025.

BERGEN - STAVANGER (Operator: NOR-WAY Bussekspress ✆ +47 2231 3150)
Journey time: 4½ – 5½ hours. From Bergen ⊡ at 0600 Ⓐ, 0730 ⑥, 0900, 1000 Ⓐ, 1040 ⑦, 1100 Ⓐ, 1130 ⑥, 1200 Ⓑ, 1300, 1430 ⑥, 1445 Ⓐ, 1500 ⑦, 1600 Ⓒ, 1615 Ⓐ, 1700 Ⓑ, 1900.
From Stavanger ⊙ at 0545 Ⓐ, 0715 Ⓐ, 0745 ⑥, 0815 Ⓐ, 0845 ⑥, 0915 Ⓑ, 1015 Ⓐ, 1045 ⑦, 1115 ⚒, 1245 ⑥, 1315 Ⓑ, 1415 Ⓑ, 1510 Ⓐ, 1515 Ⓒ, 1615 Ⓒ, 1715 Ⓑ, 1835 ⑦, 1845 ⚒.

BERGEN - ODDA ★ 🚌/⛴ *Journey time: 2 hrs 45 m – 3 hrs.*
From Bergen ⊡ at 0820, 1145 Ⓑ and 2050 Ⓑ. From Odda ⊡ at 0530 ⚒, 1710 and 2040 Ⓑ.

VOSS - ODDA ★ *Journey time: 1 hr 55 m – 2 hrs 10 m.*
From Voss at 0920, 1125 ⚒, 1250, 1550 ⚒, 1745 and 2205 Ⓑ.
From Odda ⊡ at 0620 ⚒, 0720, 1225, 1410 ◇⚒, 1700 and 2030 Ⓑ.

¶ – On ①–⑤ change at Arna, for onward rail connection to Bergen.
◇ – Departs 1405 on schooldays.
⊡ – Bus station.
⊙ – Stavanger Byterminalen.
★ – Operator: Tide Buss AS / Skyss ✆ +47 55 55 90 70.

TRONDHEIM - BODØ and NARVIK 787

km		1793	1781	1783	475		473	1785	471	1791		479	477
		⑥⑦	Ⓐ	Ⓐ		🚌	Ⓐ	Ⓐ T		Ⓐ	🚌	Ⓑ T	Ⓑ
		🍷	🍷	🍷	R N	◇	🍷 R	🍷	✕ R	🍷	◇	🍷 R	🍷 R
0	**Trondheim** S ... d.	...	...	...	2340	...	...	...	0738	...	...	...	1600
33	Værnes ✈ ‡ ..... d.	...	...	...	0006	...	...	...	0811	...	...	...	1630u
34	Stjørdal .... d.	...	...	...	0011	...	...	...	0817	...	...	...	1636u
126	Steinkjer .... d.	...	...	...	0129	...	...	...	0947	...	...	...	1801u
220	Grong .... d.	...	...	...	0240	...	...	...	1055	...	...	...	1909
406	Mosjøen .... d.	...	...	...	0458	...	0655	...	1314	...	...	1655	2133
498	Mo i Rana......... d.	...	...	...	0610	...	0800	...	1424	...	...	1757	2241
648	Rognan............ d.	0105	0542	0642	0800	...	0953	1125	1616	1750	...	1943	...
	Bodø ⊖ .... d.	|	|	|	|	0715	|	|	|	|	1645	|	...
674	Fauske .... a.	0124	0601	0701	0820	0820	1012	1144	1637	1809	1750	2001	...
674	Fauske .... d.	0125	0602	0702	0831	0850	1014	1145	1647	1817	1809	2002	...
	Narvik ⊡ ♣ .. a.	|	|	|	|	1330	|	|	|	|	2300	|	...
729	**Bodø** .... a.	0206	0643	0743	0916	...	1055	1226	1732	1857	...	2043	...

	478	470	1784		472	1790	474		476	1792
		Ⓐ T	Ⓐ T	🚌		Ⓐ	Ⓑ	🚌		⚒
	🍷 R	🍷 R	🍷	◇	✕ R	🍷	🍷 R	◇	R N	△🍷
Bodø .... d.	...	0745	1010	...	1228	1605	1734	...	2110	2355
Narvik ⊡ ♣ d.	...	|	|	0700	|	|	|	1610	|	|
Fauske .... a.	...	0826	1058	1145	1314	1645	1814	2110	2156	0035
Fauske .... d.	...	0830	1059	1210	1316	1647	1815	2125	2200	0037
Bodø ⊖ ..... a.	...	|	|	1320	|	|	|	2230	|	|
Rognan........... d.	...	0848	1117	...	1336	1707	1838	...	2221	0056
Mo i Rana .... d.	0815	1032	...	...	1535	...	2024	...	0020	...
Mosjøen.......... d.	0927	1135	...	...	1645	...	2128	...	0150	...
Grong .... d.	1149	...	...	...	1907	...	...	...	0426	...
Steinkjer .... d.	1252s	...	...	...	2016	...	...	...	0540	...
Stjørdal.......... d.	1404s	...	...	...	2134	...	...	...	0705	...
Værnes ✈ ‡ .. d.	1406s	...	...	...	2136	...	...	...	0707	...
Trondheim .... a.	1437	...	...	...	2205	...	...	...	0747	...

Local services Trondheim - Steinkjer and v.v.

km	▶	Ⓐ	⚒					Ⓐ		Ⓐ			Ⓑ
0	**Trondheim** S ... d.	0610	0710	0910	1110	1310	1510	1610	1710	1810	1910	2110	2310
31	Hell ● .... d.	0643	0743	0942	1141	1341	1541	1641	1741	1841	1941	2141	2341
33	Værnes ✈ ‡ ...... d.	0645	0745	0944	1143	1343	1543	1643	1743	1843	1943	2143	2343
34	Stjørdal............ d.	0652	0752	0952	1152	1352	1552	1652	1752	1852	1952	2152	2347
126	**Steinkjer** .... a.	0819	0916	1116	1321	1516	1716	1816	1916	2016	2116	2313	0105

▶	Ⓐ			Y					Ⓐ T	
Steinkjer .... d.	0528	0728	0928	1128	1328	1528	1728	1925	2028	2128
Stjørdal.......... d.	0652	0852	1052	1252	1452	1652	1852	2052	2152	2252
Værnes ✈ ‡ .. d.	0654	0854	1054	1254	1454	1654	1854	2054	2154	2254
Hell ● .... d.	0657	0857	1057	1257	1457	1657	1857	2057	2157	2257
Trondheim S. a.	0732	0932	1132	1332	1532	1732	1932	2132	2227	2332

N – Conveys 🛏, 🛌2 and ✕.
R – Reservation recommended.
T – Not June 24 - Aug. 16.
V – Not July 1 - Aug. 2.
Y – Not ①–⑤ June 24 - Aug. 16.

s – Calls to set down only.
u – Calls to pick up only.

x – June 21 - Aug. 18.
z – 0950 until June 21 and from Aug. 19.

● – Trains stop on request.
⊡ – Bus station.
⊖ – Bodø Sentrumsterminalen.
‡ – Station for Trondheim Airport.
◇ – Operator: Saltens Bilruter Nordlandsbuss.

△ – Runs 1 hour later on ⑤⑥ June 28 - Aug. 17 (departing Bodø on the mornings of ⑥⑦ June 29 - Aug. 18).

▶ – Additional services on Ⓐ Trondheim - Stjørdal - Steinkjer and v.v.:
From Trondheim at 0515 **T**, 0810, 1010 **T**, 1210, 1410 **T**, 1445 **T** and 1545.
From Steinkjer at 0500 **V**, 0600 **T**, 0628, 0828, 1028, 1228, 1428, 1628 **T** and 1828.

♣ – 🚌 **Narvik - Svolvær** (Lofoten). *253 km*. Journey time: 3 hrs 50 m - 4 hrs 15 m.
From Narvik bussterminal at 0955, 1550, 1920 **x** and 2145 Ⓑ **x**.
From Svolvær sentrum at 0625 Ⓑ **x**, 0940 **z**, 1345 **x** and 1515.

LAPLAND 🚌 LINKS 789

Subject to alteration on and around public holiday dates

Narvik – Tromsø – Alta

Operator: Torghatten www.tromskortet.no

km		①–⑤	①–⑥			Ⓑ				⑦	
0	**Narvik** bus station ...... d.	0535	...	...	1305	...	...	←	1545	1900	...
181	Nordkjosbotn .... d.	0825	0825	...	1615	1620	...	1620	1845	2200	...
252	**Tromsø** Prostneset . d.	0930	0930	...	→	|	1600	1725	1950	2305	...
241	Lyngseidet.............. d.	...	...	...	...	1731	1900	...	...	...	...
465	**Alta** .... a.	...	...	...	...	...	2215	...	...	...	...

km		①–⑤			①–⑥	①–⑤		⑦	⑦	⑦
0	**Alta** .... d.	...	...	...	1055	...	...	1415	...	...
224	Lyngseidet.............. d.	...	...	...	1545	1545	...	1915	1915	...
293	**Tromsø** Prostneset . d.	0610	1030	...	1725	|	1600	2055	|	1920
	Nordkjosbotn .... d.	0725	1135	...	...	1653	1705	...	2023	2025
	Narvik bus station ...... a.	1005	1420	...	...	...	1950	...	...	2310

Alta – Hammerfest – Karasjok – Kirkenes

Operator: Snelandia www.snelandia.no

km		①–⑤	①–⑤	⑦	⑦	⑦	①–⑤	①–⑤	Ⓑ		⑤⑦	Ⓑ ◧
0	**Alta** .... d.	0640	...	0900	...	...	...	1145	...	1430	1605	1700
	Hammerfest .... d.	|	0720	|	...	1200	1225	|	1515	|	|	|
87	Skaidi .... d.	0819	0820	1045	1145	1300	1325	1330	1615	1615	|	1830
144	Hammerfest .... a.	|	|	|	1245	|	|	|	|	|	|	1930
112	Olderfjord .... d.	0845	0845	1115	...	1325	1400	1400	1655	1655	|	...
212	Honningsvåg ★ a.	1030	|	1300	...	|	|	1545	|	1835	|	...
	Nordkapp .... a.	1120k	|	1350k	...	|	|	...	|	...	|	...
174	Lakselv .... d.	...	0945	...	...	1440	1515	...	1755	...	|	...
248	Karasjok .... d.	...	|	...	...	|	1620	...	1900	...	1917	...
429	Tanabru.............. d.	...	1400	...	...	1845	...	...	...	...	...	...
571	**Kirkenes** AMFI ♠ a.	...	1646	...	...	2103	...	...	...	...	...	...

	①–⑤	①–⑤	⑦	⑦	①–⑤	①–⑤	①–⑤	⑦	Ⓑ	Ⓑ	⑦	⑤⑦
Kirkenes AMFI ♠ d.	...	...	...	...	...	0605	...	...	...	...	1120	...
Tanabru .... d.	...	...	...	...	...	0915	...	...	...	...	1415	...
Karasjok.............. d.	...	0615	...	...	...	|	...	...	...	1430	|	1928
Lakselv .... d.	...	0730	...	...	...	1305	...	...	...	1545	1755	|
Nordkapp .... d.	...	|	...	...	...	|	...	...	1420k	|	|	|
Honningsvåg ★ d.	0655	|	...	0920	...	|	1220	...	1510	|	|	|
Olderfjord .... d.	0845	0845	...	1115	...	1400	1400	...	1655	1655	1855	|
Hammerfest...... d.	|	|	1040	|	1120	|	|	1400	|	|	|	|
Skaidi.................. d.	0910	0915	1140	1145	1219	1425	1430	1459	1725	1725	1915	|
Hammerfest...... a.	|	1015	...	|	|	1525	|	|	|	1825	2015	|
Alta..................... a.	1037	...	...	1312	1340	...	1557	1620	1852	...	...	2240

Rovaniemi – Muonio – Tromsø

www.matkahuolto.fi

km	Operator:	G	E	G
0	**Rovaniemi** bus station d.	0800	1140	1720
	Rovaniemi rail station d.	0820	1120	1730
157	Kittilä .... d.	1030	1335	1935
238	Muonio .... d.	1300z	1505	2045
327	Karesuvanto .... d.	1435	1625b	...
440	Kilpisjärvi ⊡ .... FI d.	1625	1810b	...
535	Nordkjosbotn ⊕ .... NO d.	...	1825b	...
608	**Tromsø** Prostneset .... a.	...	1925b	...

	G	E	G
Tromsø Prostneset .. d.	...	0725e	...
Nordkjosbotn ⊕ . NO d.	...	0820e	...
Kilpisjärvi ⊡ .... FI d.	...	1100e	1315
Karesuvanto .... d.	...	1240e	1515
Muonio..................... d.	0840	1405	1700f
Kittilä....................... d.	1000	1530	1835
Rovaniemi rail station a.	1200x	1725	2035x
Rovaniemi bus station a.	1205	1735	2040

Rovaniemi – Karasjok, Nordkapp and Tanabru

www.matkahuolto.fi

km	Operator:	G		E	E		E		E		G/L
					D		①–⑤				Ⓑ
0	**Rovaniemi** bus station d.	0800	...	1145	1145	...	1520	...	1720	...	2100
	Rovaniemi rail station d.	0820	...	1120	1120	...	1525	...	1725	...	2115
130	Sodankylä.................. d.	1020	...	1345	1345	...	1710	...	1910	...	2305
305	Ivalo .... FI d.	1250	...	1625f	1625f	...	...	...	2115	...	0115
345	Inari..................... FI d.	...	...	1655	1655	...	...	...	2150	...	...
461	Karasjok ⊖.......... NO a.	...	...	1740	1740	...	...	...	|	...	...
536	Lakselv, Circle K......... a.	...	...	...	1855	...	...	...	|	...	...
	Honningsvåg ◇ .... a.	...	...	...	2135x	...	...	...	|	...	...
735	**Nordkapp** .... a.	...	...	...	2215	...	...	...	|	...	...
	Tanabru ⊙........ NO a.	...	...	...	...	...	...	...	2340r	...	...

Operator:	E		E		G/L		E	E		G
			①–⑤		①–⑥		H			
Tanabru ⊙ .... NO d.	0320t	...	...	...	...	...	...	...	...	...
Nordkapp......................... d.	|	...	...	...	...	...	0100	...	...	...
Honningsvåg ◇ .... d.	|	...	...	...	...	...	0510g	...	...	...
Lakselv, Circle K.................. d.	|	...	...	...	...	...	0810	...	...	...
Karasjok ⊖...................... NO d.	|	...	...	...	...	...	0915	0915	...	...
Inari.................................. FI d.	0705	...	...	...	...	...	1210	1210	...	...
Ivalo .... FI d.	0750	...	...	...	1215	...	1315f	1315f	...	1615
Sodankylä.......................... d.	1000	...	1230	...	1500	...	1545	1545	...	1845
Rovaniemi rail station .... a.	1140	...	1425	...	1715	...	1725	1725	...	2030
Rovaniemi bus station .... a.	1150	...	1430	...	1710	...	1730	1730	...	2035

Operator codes:

E – Eskelisen Lapin Linjat.
G – Gold Line.
L – Liikenne O. Niemelä.

Time Zones:

FI – Finland (East European Time).
NO – Norway (Central European Time).
RU – Russia (Moskva Time).

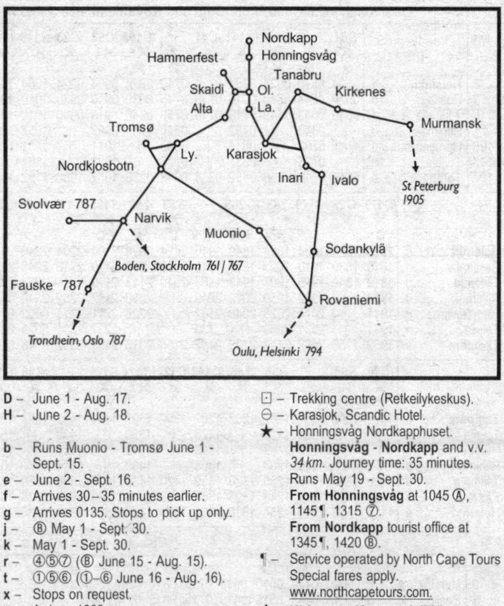

D – June 1 - Aug. 17.
H – June 2 - Aug. 18.

b – Runs Muonio - Tromsø June 1 - Sept. 15.
e – June 2 - Sept. 16.
f – Arrives 30–35 minutes earlier.
g – Arrives 0135. Stops to pick up only.
j – Ⓑ May 1 - Sept. 30.
k – May 1 - Sept. 30.
r – ④⑤⑦ (Ⓑ June 15 - Aug. 15).
t – ①⑤⑥ (①-⑥ June 16 - Aug. 16).
x – Stops on request.
z – Arrives 1200.

◧ – Runs 45 minutes later on ⑦.
◇ – Honningsvåg, Scandic Hotel.
⊙ – Tanabru, Elva hotell og camping.
⊕ – Nordkjosbotn Gjestgiveri.

⊡ – Trekking centre (Retkeilykeskus).
⊖ – Karasjok, Scandic Hotel.
★ – Honningsvåg Nordkapphuset.
Honningsvåg - Nordkapp and v.v. *34 km*. Journey time: 35 minutes. Runs May 19 - Sept. 30.
From Honningsvåg at 1045 Ⓐ, 1145 ¶, 1315 ⑦.
From Nordkapp tourist office at 1345 ¶, 1420 Ⓑ.
¶ – Service operated by North Cape Tours. Special fares apply. www.northcapetours.com.
♠ – **Kirkenes - Murmansk** (RU) and v.v. Journey time: 4 hours. Operated by Pasvikturist AS. www.pasvikturist.no Please check visa requirements. From Kirkenes at 1500 (1400 during winter time). From Murmansk at 0700.

FINLAND

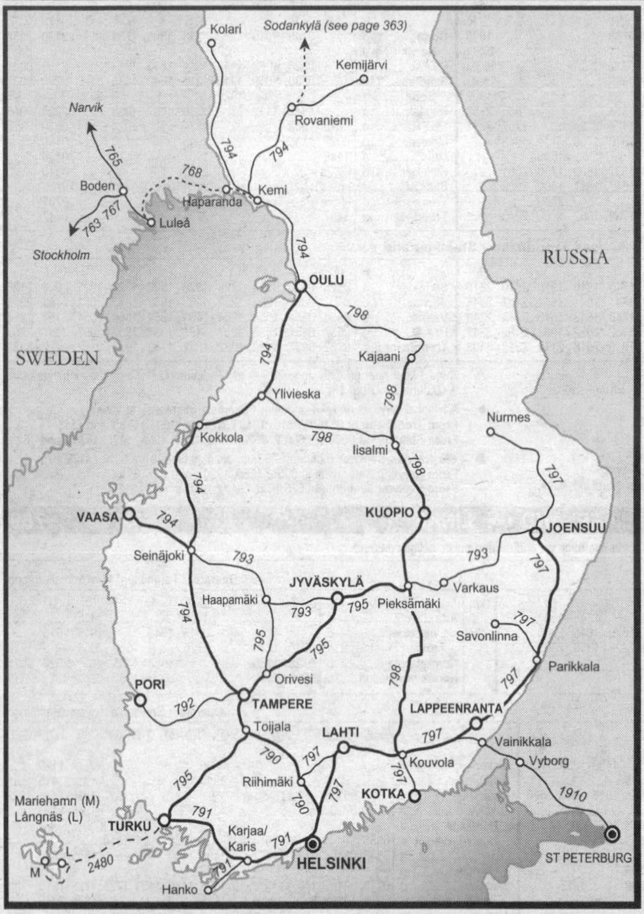

Operator: **VR** – VR-Yhtymä Oy www.vr.fi

Tickets and train types: Travel classes in Finland are referred to as *Extra* (1st) and *Eco* (2nd). For all except purely local journeys, tickets are always sold for travel by a specific train or combination of trains with seat reservations included. Standard *Eco* fares are referred to as 'Basic', whilst cheaper advance puchase 'Saver' fares are also available in limited numbers. In both cases tickets can be changed to a different date / departure time for a €5 fee (plus any price difference). Both ticket types can be upgraded to a seat in *Extra* class for a variable fee (€4 – 17, dependent on the length of journey). Tickets may be purchased on board long-distance trains (also regional trains outside of the Helsinki area), although an additional charge of €3 (for short journeys up to 76km) or €6 (for journeys over 76km) will be added to the 'Basic' fare. Please note, on board ticket purchase is **not** permitted on local trains (shown as 2nd class only in tables) Helsinki - Riihimäki - Tampere (Table **790**), Helsinki - Karjaa (Table **791**) Helsinki - Lahti - Kouvola (Table **797**) and Riihimäki - Lahti (Table **797**).

- ▶ **S Pendolino** (e.g. *S* **123**) – high-speed tilting trains, with *Extra* and *Eco* class seats, all reservable.
- ▶ **InterCity** (e.g. *IC* **124**) – quality fast trains between major centres, with *Eco* class seats (most also convey *Extra* class seats), all reservable.
- ▶ **Express**, *pikajunat* (train number only shown, e.g. **128**) – other fast trains, with *Eco* class seats, all reservable. Night expresses convey sleeping-cars and *Eco* class seats only (marked ★ in the tables).
- ▶ **Regional**, *taajamajunat* (no train number shown) – stopping-trains, normally with *Eco* class seats only. Regional fares apply.

Rail tickets are **not** valid on 🚌 services (except Seinäjoki - Vaasa and Kemi - Haparanda-Tornio).

Services: ✕ indicates a train with a restaurant car. Trains marked 🍸 convey a *MiniBistro* trolley. A variable supplement is payable for travel in sleeping-cars (🛏) in addition to the relevant *Eco* class fare – the price to be paid depends on the date of travel and the type of accommodation required. A higher supplement is charged for occupancy of a single-berth cabin.

Timings: Timings are valid, unless otherwise indicated, **June 17 - December 14, 2019.**
In these tables Ⓐ = ①-⑤, ⚒ = ①-⑥, Ⓑ = ①-⑤ and ⑦.
Changes to the normal service pattern are likely to occur on and around the dates of public holidays (see page 4).

790 HELSINKI - TAMPERE

For through journeys to / from **Oulu** and **Rovaniemi**, see Table **794**. For through journeys to / from **Jyväskylä** and **Pieksämäki**, see Table **795**.

km		*S* 81		*IC* 121	*IC* 141	*IC* 41		*IC* 163	*IC* 93	*IC* 23	*S* 143	*IC* 43	*S* 169		*IC* 125
		✕	2	✕	✕	✕	2	✕¶	✕¶	✕	✕‡	✕	✕	2	✕
		Ⓐ	Ⓐ	⚒		Ⓐ	⚒	⚒							
0	**Helsinki** .... d.	0524	*0540*	0624	0704	0724	0740	0824	0904	0924	1004	1024	1104	1140	1224
3	Pasila .... d.	0530	*0545*	0630	0710	0730	0745	0830	0910	0930	1010	1030	1110	1145	1230
16	Tikkurila .... d.	0540	*0553*	0640	0719	0740	0753	0840	0919	0940	1019	1040	1119	1153	1240
71	Riihimäki .... d.	|	0640	|	0752	|	0840	|	0952	|	1052	|	1152	1240	|
108	Hämeenlinna .. d.	|	0702	|	0811	|	0902	|	1011	|	1111	|	1211	1302	|
147	Toijala .... d.	|	0725	|	0831	|	0925	|	1031	|	1131	|	1231	1325	|
187	**Tampere** .... a.	0656	0748	0756	0852	0856	0948	0956	1052	1056	1152	1156	1252	1348	1356

km		*IC* 173	*S* 145		*IC* 175	*S* 45	*IC* 151		*IC* 27	*IC* 147	*S* 47	*IC* 177		*S* 49
		✕‡	✕‡	2	🍸	✕	✕	2	✕	✕	✕	✕	2	✕
					Ⓑ P		Ⓑ					Ⓑ		
0	**Helsinki** .... d.	1304	1324	1340	1404	1424	1504	1510	1524	1604	1624	1704	1710	1724
3	Pasila .... d.	1310	1330	1345	1410	1430	1510	1515	1530	1610	1630	1710	1715	1730
16	Tikkurila .... d.	1319	1340	1353	1419	1440	1519	1523	1540	1619	1640	1719	1723	1740
71	Riihimäki .... d.	1352	|	1440	1452	|	1552	1613	|	1652	|	1752	1811	|
108	Hämeenlinna .. d.	1411	|	1502	1511	|	1611	1635	|	1711	|	1811	1833	|
147	Toijala .... d.	1431	|	1525	1531	|	1631	1658	|	1731	|	1831	1856	|
187	**Tampere** .... a.	1452	1456	1548	1552	1556	1652	1721	1656	1752	1756	1852	1919	1856

	IC 179	*IC* 29	*IC* 149	263	*IC* 265		*S* 53	269	*S* 195	*IC* 187		*IC* 273
	✕	✕	✕			2	✕		✕‡	✕‡	2	
	Q			★	★A		L	★	LQ			★C
Helsinki .... d.	1804	1824	1904	1814	1849	1940	2024	2028	2104	2204	2240	2313
Pasila .... d.	1810	1830	1910	1821	1857	1945	2030	2035	2110	2210	2245	2320
Tikkurila .... d.	1819	1840	1919	1907	1943	1953	2040	2113	2119	2219	2253	2359
Riihimäki .... d.	1852	|	1952	1959	2022	2040	|	2200	2152	2252	2340	0044
Hämeenlinna .... d.	1911	|	2011	2025	2048	2102	|	2226	2211	2311	0002	0106
Toijala .... d.	1931	|	2031	2050	|	2130	|	|	2231	2331	0025	0130
Tampere .... a.	1952	1956	2052	2118	2138	2152	2156	2315	2252	2352	0048	0155

	IC 266	*IC* 160	270	*IC* 162	*IC* 274	272	*S* 40	*IC* 164	*S* 42	*IC* 150	*S* 44	*IC* 140
		✕		✕			✕	✕‡	✕	✕	✕	✕
	★B	Ⓐ	★	Ⓐ	★A	★	Ⓐ	P	⚒	⚒	⚒	
Tampere .... d.	0345	0515	0543	0604	0612	0622	0702	0707	0802	0807	0902	0907
Toijala .... d.	0412	0538	0610	0627	0639	0701	|	0728	|	0828	|	0928
Hämeenlinna .... d.	0438	0600	0637	0648	0706	0753	|	0749	|	0849	|	0949
Riihimäki .... d.	0503	0620	0702	0708	0739	0818	|	0808	|	0908	|	1008
Tikkurila .... a.	0545	0649	0746	0739	0829	0858	0820	0839	0920	0939	1020	1039
Pasila .... a.	0617	0658	0824	0748	0906	0938	0829	0848	0929	0948	1029	1048
Helsinki .... a.	0624	0704	0832	0754	0914	0945	0835	0854	0935	0954	1035	1054

	IC 20	*S* 54		*S* 94	*S* 46	*IC* 142	*IC* 122	*IC* 174	*S* 178		*IC* 48	*IC* 144	*IC* 24	
	✕	✕	2	✕	✕	✕	✕	✕¶	✕	2	✕	✕	✕	2
	⚒	⑦												
Tampere .... d.	1002	1002	1007	1107	1202	1207	1302	1307	1402	1407	1502	1507	1602	1611
Toijala .... d.	|	|	1030	1128	|	1228	|	1328	|	1430	|	1528	|	1634
Hämeenlinna .... d.	|	|	1053	1149	|	1249	|	1349	|	1453	|	1549	|	1657
Riihimäki .... d.	|	|	1126	1208	|	1308	|	1408	|	1526	|	1608	|	1726
Tikkurila .... a.	1120	1120	1205	1239	1320	1339	1420	1439	1520	1605	1620	1639	1720	1805
Pasila .... a.	1129	1129	1214	1248	1329	1348	1429	1448	1529	1614	1629	1648	1729	1814
Helsinki .... a.	1135	1135	1219	1254	1335	1354	1435	1454	1535	1619	1635	1654	1735	1819

	IC 86	*S* 84	*IC* 180		*IC* 50	*S* 146	*IC* 26	*S* 88	*IC* 186	*S* 56	*S* 148	*IC* 28		*S* 152
	✕	✕	🍸‡	2	✕	✕	✕	✕	✕	✕	✕‡	✕	2	✕
	Ⓑ	⑥	Ⓑ					⑤⑦	P	⑤⑦				⑦
Tampere .... d.	1702	1702	1707	1737	1802	1807	1902	2002	2007	2102	2107	2202	2237	2302
Toijala .... d.	|	|	1728	1800	|	1828	|	|	2028	|	2128	|	2300	|
Hämeenlinna .... d.	|	|	1749	1823	|	1849	|	|	2049	|	2149	|	2323	|
Riihimäki .... d.	|	|	1808	1856	|	1908	|	|	2108	|	2208	|	2356	|
Tikkurila .... a.	1820	1820	1839	1935	1920	1939	2020	2120	2139	2220	2239	2320	0035	0020
Pasila .... a.	1829	1829	1848	1944	1929	1948	2029	2129	2148	2229	2248	2329	0044	0029
Helsinki .... a.	1835	1835	1854	1949	1935	1954	2035	2135	2154	2235	2254	2335	0049	0035

Selected regional trains HELSINKI - RIIHIMÄKI (2nd class only)

km			Ⓐ	Ⓐ							
0	**Helsinki** .... d.	0040	0440	0510	0610	0710	0810	0910	0940		2340
3	Pasila .... d.	0045	0445	0515	0615	0715	0815	0915	0945	and	2345
16	Tikkurila .... d.	0053	0453	0523	0623	0723	0823	0923	0953	hourly	2353
37	Järvenpää .... d.	0108	0508	0538	0638	0738	0838	0938	1008		0008
59	Hyvinkää .... d.	0124	0524	0554	0654	0754	0854	0954	1024	until	0024
71	**Riihimäki** .... a.	0138	0533	0603	0703	0803	0903	1003	1033		0038

	Ⓐ		Ⓐ	⚒							
Riihimäki ...... d.	0526	0626	0656	0756	0826		1926	2056	2156	2256	2356
Hyvinkää .... d.	0534	0634	0704	0804	0834	and	1934	2104	2204	2304	0004
Järvenpää ..... d.	0549	0649	0719	0819	0849	hourly	1949	2119	2219	2319	0019
Tikkurila .... d.	0605	0705	0735	0835	0905		2005	2135	2235	2335	0035
Pasila .... a.	0614	0714	0744	0844	0914	until	2014	2144	2244	2344	0044
Helsinki .... a.	0619	0719	0749	0849	0919		2019	2149	2249	2349	0049

A – Significant alterations during June, July and August - please check locally.
B – Not Nov. 17, 18.
C – Not Nov. 15, 16.
L – ①②③④⑦
P – To / from Pori (Table **792**).
Q – To Pori on Ⓑ (Table **792**).
¶ – Different train number on ⑥.
‡ – Different train number on ⑦.
★ – Overnight train to / from northern Finland. Conveys 🛏, ▭2 and ✕. For through cars and days of running see Table **794**.

HELSINKI - KARJAA - TURKU and KARJAA - HANKO 791

Subject to alteration June 24 – 30, July 15 – 28.

km		IC 941	IC 943		IC 979	IC 945	S 987	IC 947	S 949	IC 951	IC 953	IC 955	S 997	IC 957	IC 959	IC 924	IC 961	IC 963	IC 965	IC 971	IC 977	S 967			
		✕	🍷		🍷	🍷	✕	🍷	✕	✕	🍷	🍷	🍷	🍷	🍷		🍷	✕	🍷	🍷	🍷	✕		2	
		Ⓐ	Ⓐ		⚒¶		①–④	⑤–⑦	⚒		⑤	⚒§	①–④	⑤⑦	⑥⑦		Ⓑ		Ⓑ	⑤⑥	A	B		D	
0	**Helsinki** d.	0528	0628	...	0737	0837	0937	0937	1037	1137	1237	1337	1437	1437	1537	...	1637	1737	1837	1937	2037	2037	...	2308	...
3	Pasila d.	0534	0634	...	0743	0843	0943	0943	1043	1143	1243	1343	1443	1443	1543	...	1643	1743	1843	1943	2042	2042	...	2312	...
87	Karjaa / Karis d.	0626	0726	...	0836	0932	1032	1032	1132	1232	1332	1432	1532	1532	1632	...	1732	1832	1932	2032	2131	2131	...	0023	...
138	Salo d.	0657**a**	0803	...	0904	1001	1101	1101	1201	1301	1401	1501	1601	1601	1701	...	1801	1901	2001	2101	2201	2201	...	...	...
194	**Turku** a.	0738**a**	0834	...	0934	1031	1134	1134	1234	1334	1434	1534	1634	1634	1734	1804	1834	1931	2036	2131	2231	2231	...	...	...
197	Turku satama a.	0747**a**	...	...	...	...	...	...	...	...	...	...	...	...	...	1811	...	1940	...	...	...	...	...	...	...

		IC 942	IC 944		IC 946	IC 948	S 978	IC 950	IC 954	S 996	IC 956	S 958	IC 960	IC 982	IC 962	IC 964	S 998	S 998	IC 966		IC 968		IC 972	IC 974	IC 980
	2	🍷	🍷		🍷	✕	✕	🍷	🍷	✕	🍷	✕	🍷	✕	✕	🍷	✕	✕	🍷		🍷		✕	🍷	🍷
	Ⓐ	Ⓐ	Ⓐ		⚒	Ⓑ	⑥	⚒		①–④	⑤⑦			Ⓐ	⑥⑦	‡	H	C	E		Ⓑ			⑦	⑤
Turku satama d.	...	...	...	...	...	0810	0810	...	...	...	...	...	...	...	...	...	...	...	...	...	...	...	2018	...	...
Turku d.	...	0525	0623	...	0729	0825	0825	0925	1125	1225	1225	1325	1425	1525	1525	1625	1718	1725	1725	...	1825	...	2027	2122	2150
Salo d.	...	0556	0656	...	0802	0903	0859	0959	1159	1259	1259	1359	1459	1559	1559	1659	1759	1759	1759	...	1859	...	2059	2159	2228
Karjaa / Karis d.	0543	0628	0728	...	0831	0931	0928	1028	1228	1328	1328	1428	1528	1628	1628	1728	1828	1828	1828	...	1928	...	2128	2228	2255
Pasila a.	0648	0717	0817	...	0919	1019	1017	1117	1317	1417	1417	1517	1617	1717	1717	1818	1920	1920	1920	...	2017	...	2220	2320	2347
Helsinki a.	0653	0723	0823	...	0925	1025	1023	1123	1323	1423	1423	1523	1623	1723	1723	1823	1926	1926	1926	...	2023	...	2226	2326	2356

KARJAA - HANKO

km		Ⓐ										
0	**Karjaa / Karis** d.	0733	0939	...	1239	1439	1639	1839	...	2139	...	...
16	Tammisaari d.	0746	0952	...	1252	1452	1652	1852	...	2152	...	...
49	**Hanko** a.	0813	1019	...	1319	1519	1719	1919	...	2219	...	...

	Ⓐ										
Hanko d.	0632	...	0840	...	1140	1340	1535	...	1740	...	2040
Tammisaari d.	0659	...	0907	...	1207	1407	1602	...	1807	...	2107
Karjaa / Karis a.	0712	...	0920	...	1220	1420	1615	...	1820	...	2120

A – ①②③④⑦ to Aug. 11; Ⓑ from Aug. 12.
B – ⑤⑥ to Aug. 10; ⑥ from Aug. 17.
C – ①②③④⑥⑦ to Aug. 11.
D – Runs 5 minutes later until Aug. 11.

E – ⑤ until Aug. 11 (as *IC* **986**); ⑥⑦ from Aug. 12.
H – Ⓐ from Aug. 12 (as *IC* **986** on ⑤).

a – Until Aug. 11: Salo d. 0653, Turku a. 0726, Turku satama a. 1733.

¶ – On ⑥ runs as *IC* **981**.
§ – On ⑥ runs as *S* **985** (✕).
‡ – On Ⓐ from Aug. 12 runs as *IC* **984**.

TAMPERE - PORI 792

Most trains convey ✕

km		IC 477	IC 461	IC 479	IC 465	IC 467	IC 469	IC 175	IC 471	IC 179	IC 475
		Ⓐ	⚒	Ⓐ			⑥	Ⓑ		Ⓑ	
	Helsinki **790** d.	...	...	...	...	...	...	1404	...	1804	...
0	**Tampere** d.	0603	0807	1007	1215	1415	1615	1615	1815	2007	2207
17	Nokia d.	0618	0822	1022	1230	1430	1630	1630	1830	2022	2222
59	Vammala d.	0701	0851	1053	1301	1501	1701	1701	1901	2051	2251
135	**Pori** a.	0748	0937	1139	1347	1547	1747	1747	1947	2137	2337

	IC 164	IC 462	IC 466	IC 476	IC 464	IC 478		IC 468	IC 470	IC 186
	⚒	⚒		Ⓐ		Ⓐ				
Pori d.	0520	0615	0715	0815	1005	1205	...	1415	1615	1815
Vammala d.	0607	0702	0803	0907	1054	1302	...	1502	1702	1902
Nokia d.	0636	0731	0836	0936	1123	1337	...	1531	1733	1931
Tampere a.	0650	0745	0850	0951	1137	1351	...	1545	1747	1945
Helsinki **790** a.	0854	...	...	...	...	...	...	...	...	2154

☛ Frequent 🚌 services operate Turku - Rauma - Pori and v.v. See www.matkahuolto.fi.

JOENSUU - PIEKSÄMÄKI - JYVÄSKYLÄ - SEINÄJOKI 793

km				IC 142		S 146			S 148		
		⚒2	2				2	2	§	⑦	Ⓑ2
0	**Joensuu** d.	...	0700	...	...	...	...	1550	...	...	...
134	Varkaus d.	...	0837	...	...	...	...	1727	...	...	...
183	**Pieksämäki** 795 d.	...	0912	0923	...	1525	...	1802	1816	2035	...
263	**Jyväskylä** 795 d.	0600	...	1009	...	1611	1625	...	1910	2126	...
	Tampere **795** d.	|	...	2007	...	1807	|	...	2050	2254	2019
341	Haapamäki d.	0707	...	...	...	...	1741	...	...	...	2139
414	Alavus d.	0813	...	...	...	...	1842	...	...	...	2240
459	**Seinäjoki** d.	0845	...	...	...	...	1913	...	...	...	2312

			IC 159	IC 141			S 143	S 145		IC 151		
	Ⓐ2	⑥2			2	2		‡	⑥2	Ⓑ	Ⓑ2	Ⓑ2
Seinäjoki d.	0440	0651	...	...	...	1034	...	...	...	...	...	1941
Alavus d.	0513	0724	...	...	...	1107	...	...	...	...	...	2014
Haapamäki d.	0619	0830	...	...	...	1217	...	...	...	...	...	2121
Tampere **795** a.	0740	0950	...	1105	...	|	1205	1505	...	1705	...	|
Jyväskylä 795 d.	...	...	0802	1039	...	1322	1339	1638	...	1837	...	2226
Pieksämäki 795 d.	...	...	0848	1125	1142	...	1425	1726	1817	1925	1938	...
Varkaus d.	...	...	...	...	1219	...	...	...	1854	...	2015	...
Joensuu a.	...	...	...	...	1353	...	...	...	2028	...	2149	...

‡ – Runs as *IC* **155** on ⑦.

§ – Runs as *IC* **158** on ⑦.

TAMPERE - VAASA, OULU, KOLARI and ROVANIEMI 794

km		IC 273	S 455	IC 403	IC 121		IC 41	IC 41	IC 23	IC 443	IC 43	IC 125	IC 445	IC 917	S 45	IC 27		S 47	S 51	IC 405	S 49	IC 29	S 457	S 53	263	IC 265	269
		★⊕	✕	2🍷	✕§	🚌	✕	✕	✕	2🍷	✕	✕§	2🍷	2🍷§	✕	✕	🚌	✕	✕	2🍷	✕	✕	✕	✕	★	★	★
		e	Ⓐ	⚒	⚒	Ⓐ		Ⓐ		Ⓑ			Ⓑ	Ⓑ T			Ⓐ		Ⓑ	⑥	Ⓑ		⑤⑥	G	F	J	B
	Helsinki **790** d.	2313	...	*0524***a**	0624	...	*0704*	0724	0924	...	1024	1224	...	...	1424	1524	...	1624	1624	...	1724	1824	...	2024	1814	1849	2028
0	**Tampere** d.	0230	...	0701	0800	...	0900	0900	1100	...	1200	1400	...	1508	1600	1700	...	1800	1800	...	1900	2000	...	2200	2134	2211	2359
75	Parkano d.	0318	...	0749	|	...	0942	0942	|	...	1242	|	...	1549	1636	|	...	1842	1842	...	|	|	...	2234	|	2303	|
159	Seinäjoki a.	0407	...	0829	0904	...	1016	1016	1204	...	1316	1504	...	1623	1717	1804	...	1916	1916	...	2004	2104	...	2308	2345	0008	0217
159	Seinäjoki d.	0410	0655	0831	0907	0915	1028	1028	1208	1214	1328	1508	1522	1626	1720	1808	1815	1920	1925	1929	2007	2108	2112	2317	2349	0012	0220
233	**Vaasa** a.	|	0751	|	|	1035	1118	1118	|	1311	1418	|	1619	|	1810	|	1935	2010	|	|	2057	|	2202	0007	|	|	|
292	Kokkola d.	0545	...	0934	1017	▬	...	...	1305	▬	...	1617	▬	1751	...	1905	...	...	2037	2049	...	2210	...	...	0135	0154	0352
371	Ylivieska d.	0637	...	1014	1104	*IC* **711**	...	...	1350	*IC* **413**	...	1703	*IC* **415**	1836	...	1945	...	...	2120	2142	...	2252	...	...	0229	0249	0439
493	**Oulu** a.	0810	...	1120	1218	✕K	...	...	1454	2🍷	...	1819	✕Ⓑ	1955	...	2048	...	...	2235**h**	2305	...	0003	...	...	0405	0444	0553
493	**Oulu** d.	0830**b**	...	...	...	1227	...	...	...	1503	...	...	1830	...	...	2053	...	...	...	...	...	...	...	...	0437	0450	0623
599	Kemi d.	0938**b**	...	...	...	1327	...	...	...	1603	...	...	1931	...	...	2155	...	...	...	...	...	...	...	...	0548	0556	0801
808	**Kolari** a.	|	...	...	...	|	...	...	...	|	...	...	|	...	...	|	...	...	...	...	...	...	...	...	0847	|	1100
713	**Rovaniemi** a.	1105**b**	...	...	...	1440	...	...	...	1717	...	...	2044	...	...	2318	...	...	...	...	...	...	...	...	...	0713	...
796	Kemijärvi a.	...	...	...	...	...	...	...	...	...	...	...	...	...	...	...	...	...	...	...	...	...	...	...	...	0845	...

	S 40	S 52	S 42	S 44	IC 20	S 54	IC 402	S 46	IC 122	IC 48	IC 414	IC 24	IC 406	IC 50	IC 416	IC 126	IC 442	S 456	S 56	IC 710	IC 28	IC 404	262	IC 266	270	272	IC 274
	✕	✕	✕	✕	✕	✕	2🍷	✕	✕§	✕	✕	✕	2	✕	2🍷	✕§	2🍷	✕△	✕	✕	✕	2🍷	★	★⊕	★	★	★
	Ⓐ	①–④	⚒	⚒	⚒	⑦	Ⓑ				⚒		⑥				Ⓑ	⑤⑦	⑤⑦	K		Ⓑ	E	d	⑥C	D	A
Kemijärvi d.	...	...	...	...	...	...	...	...	...	...	...	...	...	...	...	...	...	...	...	...	...	...	...	...	...	...	1935
Rovaniemi d.	...	...	...	...	...	...	...	...	0603**r**	...	0920	0920**v**	...	...	1206	...	...	...	...	1518	...	...	...	1800**b**	...	...	2115
Kolari d.	...	...	...	...	...	...	...	...	|	...	|	|	...	...	|	...	...	...	...	|	...	...	1500	|	1810	1810	|
Kemi d.	...	...	...	...	...	...	...	...	0725**r**	...	1043	1043**v**	...	...	1325	...	...	...	...	1639	...	...	1808	1929**b**	2116	2116	2233
Oulu a.	...	...	...	...	...	...	...	...	0823**r**	...	1151	1151**v**	...	...	1423	...	...	...	...	1736	...	...	1922	2032**b**	2234	2234	2335
Oulu d.	...	...	...	...	0553	...	0654	...	0835	...	▬	1155	1300	...	▬	1434	...	...	1604	▬	1755	1904	2000	2102	2305	2305	2342
Ylivieska d.	...	0441	...	...	0708	...	0813	...	0950	...	*IC* **444**	1307	1423	...	🚌	1552	...	...	1722	*S* **458**	1908	2024	2212	2238	0045	0045	0103
Kokkola d.	...	0522	...	...	0750	...	0858	...	1042	...	2Ⓑ	1353	1515	...	Ⓐ	1642	...	...	1812	✕H	1953	2113	2314	2332	0142	0142	0157
Vaasa d.	0453	|	0552	0648	|	0802	|	0938	|	1238	1342	|	|	1546	1620	|	1703	1828	|	1933	|	|	|	|	|	|	|
Seinäjoki a.	0542	0636	0641	0737	0848	0851	1023	1027	1149	1327	1438	1450	1632	1635	1740	1749	1758	1918	1925	2045	2048	2225	0114	0100	0320	0320	0340
Seinäjoki d.	0545	0649	0649	0739	0853	0853	...	1037	1153	1337	...	1453	...	1638	...	1753	1810	1934	1934	...	2053	2227	0120	0112	0353	0353	0402
Parkano d.	0620	0724	0724	0814	|	|	...	1112	|	1412	...	|	...	1713	...	|	1858	2014	2014	...	|	2312	|	0202	|	|	|
Tampere a.	0654	0758	0758	0855	0958	0958	...	1155	1258	1455	...	1558	...	1755	...	1858	1950	2055	2055	...	2158	2350	0346	0305	0535	0535	0540
Helsinki **790** a.	0835	0935	0935	1035	1135	1135	...	1335	1435	1635	...	1735	...	1935	...	2035	*2154***f**	2235	2235	...	2335	...	0655	0624	0832	0945	0914

A – Not June 21, 24 – 27, July 1 – 4, Aug. 19 – 22, 26 – 29, Sept. 16 – 18, Nov. 16, 17.
B – Runs on June 24, 26, July 3, Aug. 19, 21, 22, 26, 28, 29 only.
C – Also ⑤ Aug. 23 - Sept. 27.
D – ②④⑦ (not June 4, 9, 20, 25, 27, July 2, 4, Aug. 20, 22, 27, 29, Sept. 17, Nov. 17, Dec. 5).
E – Runs on June 25, 27, July 4, Aug. 20, 22, 27, 29 only.
F – ①③⑤⑥ (also June 20, Sept. 5, 12, 19, 26; not June 21, 24, 26, July 1, 3, Aug. 19, 21, 26, 28, Sept. 16, Nov. 15, 16).
G – ①②③④⑦.
H – ①②③④⑥. On ⑥ runs as *S* **454** (arriving Seinäjoki 2031).
J – Not June 21, 24 – 27, July 1 – 4, Aug. 19 – 22, 26 – 29, Sept. 15 – 17, Nov. 16, 17.
K – From / to Kuopio (Table **798**).
T – From Turku (Table **795**).

a – Ⓐ only.
b – Not July 2, 3, Sept. 16 – 18.
d – Not June 21, Nov. 16, 17.
e – Not June 21, Nov. 15, 16 (from Helsinki).
f – *2135* on ⑤⑦.
h – ④⑤ only.
r – Not ⑦.
v – ⑦ only.

§ – Train number varies from Aug. 12.
★ – Conveys 🛏, 2 and ✕.
⊕ – Conveys 🛏 Turku - Tampere - Rovaniemi and v.v. See Table **795**.
△ – Change trains at Seinäjoki on ⑤.

795 TURKU - TAMPERE - PIEKSÄMÄKI

km		S81	IC905	IC141	IC909	IC93	S143	IC917	S145	S87	IC921	IC151	IC923	IC147	S89	S89	IC927	IC149	IC931	IC933	S91
		✕	🍷	✕	🍷	✕	✕	2🍷	✕	✕	🍷	✕	🍷	✕	✕	✕	🍷	✕	🍷	🍷	✕
		Ⓐ	⚒			Ⓐ		P◐	¶	⑤⑦	⑤⑦	Ⓑ			Ⓑ	⑦K				R	⑦
	Turku satama ....d.	...	...	...	*0810*	...	...	...	...	...	...	...	...	...	...	...	...	...	1945	*2018*	...
0	**Turku** ....d.	...	0654	...	0905	...	...	1305	...	...	1505	...	1605	...	...	...	1805	...	2005	2125	...
66	Loimaa ....d.	...	0740	...	0944	...	...	1344	...	...	1544	...	1644	...	...	...	1844	...	2044	2212	...
86	Humppila ....d.	...	0753	...	0959	...	...	1359	...	...	1559	...	1659	...	...	...	1859	...	2059	2227	...
	Helsinki **790** ...d.	0524	|	0704	|	0904	1004	|	1324	1424	|	1504	|	1604	1724	1724	|	1904	|	|	2204
128	Toijala ....**790** d.	|	0819	0831	1025	1031	1131	1425	|	|	1625	1631	1725	1731	|	|	1925	2031	2125	2256	2331
168	**Tampere** ....**790** a.	0656	0842	0852	1047	1052	1152	1447	1456	1556	1647	1652	1747	1752	1856	1856	1947	2052	2147	2322	2352
168	**Tampere** ....d.	0709	...	0905	...	1105	1205	...	1505	1609	...	1705	...	1805	1909	1909	...	2105	...	...	2359
210	Orivesi ....d.	0733	...	0930	...	1130	1230	...	1530	1634	...	1730	...	1830	1934	1934	...	|	...	...	|
266	Jämsä ....d.	0813	...	1006	...	1205	1307	...	1610	1715	...	1805	...	1912	2014	2014	...	2200	...	...	0105
323	Jyväskylä ... **793** d.	0840	...	1039	...	1240	1339	...	1638	1745	...	1837	...	1939	2047	2051	...	2227	...	...	0140
403	**Pieksämäki 793** a.	...	...	1125	...	...	1425	...	1726	...	...	1925	...	*2032*a	...	2135	...	...	...	...	...

	IC904	S80	IC150	IC140	S94	IC910	IC142	IC916	IC144	IC922	IC924	IC86	S84	S146	IC928	IC930	IC154	S88	S148	IC934	S152
	🍷	✕	✕	✕	✕	2🍷	✕	🍷	✕	🍷	🍷	✕	✕	✕	🍷	🍷		✕	✕	🍷	✕
	T	Ⓐ	⚒	⚒	Ⓐ							Ⓑ	⑥			⑤⑦	Ⓐ	⑤⑦	‡	Ⓑ	⑦K
Pieksämäki 793 d.	...	...	...	0630	...	...	0923	...	1223	...	...	...	...	1525	...	...	1712	...	1816	...	2035
Jyväskylä.... **793** d.	...	0528	0620	0720	0911	...	1011	...	1313	...	...	1518	1518	1614	...	...	1801	1813	1917j	...	2126
Jämsä .... d.	...	0556	0651	0748	0939	...	1047	...	1351	...	...	1546	1546	1651	...	...	...	1848	1950	...	2159
Orivesi .... d.	...	|	0726	0825	1019	...	1122	...	1426	...	...	1626	1626	1726	...	...	...	|	2026	...	|
Tampere .... a.	...	0650	0750	0849	1043	...	1146	...	1450	...	...	1650	1650	1749	...	...	...	1944	2050	...	2254
Tampere ....**790** d.	0550	0702	0807	0907	1107	0911	1207	1211	1507	1511	1606	1702	1702	1807	1811	1911	...	2002	2107	2111	2302
Toijala....**790** d.	0614	|	0828	0928	1128	0935	1228	1235	1528	1535	1635	|	|	1828	1835	1935	...	|	2128	2135	|
Helsinki **790**.... a.	|	0835	0954	1054	1254	|	1354	|	1654	|	|	1835	1835	1954	|	|	...	2135	2254	|	0035
Humppila .... d.	0641	...	...	...	...	1000	...	1300	...	1600	1700	...	...	...	1900	2000	...	...	...	2200	...
Loimaa .... d.	0655	...	...	...	...	1013	...	1313	...	1613	1713	...	...	...	1915	2013	...	...	...	2213	...
Turku .... a.	0733	...	...	...	...	1050	...	1355	...	1655	1750	...	...	...	1955	2055	...	...	...	2250	...
Turku satama ... a.	0752	...	...	...	...	...	...	...	...	...	1811	...	...	...	2007	...	...	...	...	...	...

TAMPERE - HAAPAMÄKI

km		2	2	Ⓑs2
	Tampere .....d.	1005	1617	2019
0	Orivesi ....d.	1031	1643	2045
47	Vilppula ....d.	1106	1718	2120
72	**Haapamäki** .a.	1124	1736	2138

	Ⓐs2	⑥s2	2	2
Haapamäki d.	0619	0830	1224	1833
Vilppula ..... d.	0640	0850	1245	1854
Orivesi .... d.	0715	0925	1320	1929
Tampere ... a.	0740	0950	1345	1954

K – To / from Kuopio (Table **798**).
P – To Oulu on Ⓑ (Table **794**).
R – 12 Turku - Tampere; conveys 🛏 Turku - Tampere (**273**) - Rovaniemi.
T – 12 Tampere - Turku; conveys 🛏 Rovaniemi (**266**) - Tampere - Turku.

a – Ⓐ only.
j – Arrives 1910.
s – To / from Seinäjoki (Table **793**).

¶ – Runs as *IC* **155** on ⑦.
‡ – Runs as *IC* **158** on ⑦.
◐ – Runs as *IC* **917** from Aug. 12.

797 HELSINKI - KOUVOLA - JOENSUU - NURMES

km		IC61	IC71	IC1			IC63	S105	IC3	IC65	IC5			S109	S67	IC7	S9	S9	S69		IC111	IC11		IC73	IC115	S113
		✕	2	✕	2	2	✕	✕	✕	✕	✕	2	2	✕	✕	✕	✕	✕	✕	2	✕	✕	2	✕	✕	✕
		A K	⑥a				K	Ⓐ		K				Ⓑ	K	Ⓑ		Ⓑ	Ⓑ K		Ⓑ			K	Ⓑ	⑥
0	**Helsinki** .... ☐ d.	0557	0557	0657	...	...	0819	0919	1019	1119	1319	...	...	1357	1419	1519	1619	1619	1619	1635	1719	1829	...	1919	2019	2019
3	Pasila .... ☐ d.	0603	0603	0703	...	...	0825	0925	1025	1125	1325	...	...	1403	1425	1525	1625	1625	1625	1640	1725	1835	...	1925	2025	2025
16	Tikkurila .... ☐ d.	0613	0613	0713	...	...	0835	0935	1035	1135	1335	...	...	1413	1435	1535	1635	1635	1635	1649	1735	1845	...	1935	2035	2035
104	**Lahti** .... ☐ d.	0651	0651	0751	...	...	0913	1013	1113	1216	1413	...	...	1451	1513	1613	1713	1713	1713	1749b	1813	1923	...	2013	2113	2113
166	**Kouvola** ....a.	0719	0719	0819	...	...	0941	1041	1141	1245	1441	...	...	1519	1541	1641	1741	1741	1741	1832c	1841	1951	...	2041	2141	2141
166	**Kouvola** ....d.	...	▬	0823	...	...	...	1043	1143	▬	1443	...	...	1525	...	1643	1746	1746	▬	...	1843	1953	...	...	2143	2143
252	Lappeenranta ....d.	...	2	0911	...	...	...	1121	1223	2	1523	...	...	1605	...	1723	1826	1826	2	...	1923	2033	...	...	2223	2223
288	Imatra ....d.	...	⚒	0941	...	...	...	...	1254	...	1554	...	...	...	...	1750	1854	1858	Ⓑ	...	1951	2103	...	...	2251	2251
352	Parikkala ....d.	...	0730	1023	1030	...	...	...	1333	1337	1634	1637	...	...	...	|	...	1940	1944	...	...	2144	2149	...	...	...
411	Savonlinna ....a.	...	0823	|	1123	...	...	...	|	1430	|	1730	...	...	...	|	...	|	2037	...	...	|	2242	...	...	...
482	**Joensuu** ....d.	...	...	1140	...	1154	...	...	1449	...	1750	...	1800	...	...	1936	...	2056	...	...	...	2300	...	...	...	...
586	Lieksa ....d.	...	...	...	...	1315	...	...	...	...	...	...	1921	...	...	...	...	...	...	...	...	...	...	...	...	...
642	**Nurmes** ....a.	...	...	...	...	1400	...	...	...	...	...	...	2006	...	...	...	...	...	...	...	...	...	...	...	...	...

		IC102		IC104		S2	IC62	IC4	S100	S64			IC6	S106	S66		IC8	S114	IC68		IC10	IC72			IC12	
	2	✕	2	✕	2	✕	✕	✕	✕	✕	2	2	✕	✕	✕	2	✕	✕	✕	2	✕	✕	2	2	✕	2
	Ⓐ	⚒	Ⓐ	⚒	⚒	⚒	⚒K	⚒	⑦	⚒K				Ⓐ	K			Ⓑ	K			AK				Ⓑ
Nurmes ....d.	...	...	...	...	...	...	...	...	...	...	0635	...	...	...	...	...	...	...	...	...	...	...	1540	...	...	...
Lieksa ....d.	...	...	...	...	...	...	...	...	...	...	0722	...	...	...	...	...	...	...	...	...	...	...	1626	...	...	...
Joensuu ....d.	...	...	...	...	...	0512	...	0610	...	...	0850	...	0906	...	...	...	1213	...	...	...	1513	...	1745	...	1815	...
Savonlinna ....d.	...	...	...	...	0525	|	...	|	...	...	...	0923	|	...	...	1230	|	...	...	1530	|	...	...	1837	|	2050
Parikkala ....d.	...	...	...	...	0618	0624	...	0727	...	...	▬	1016	1026	...	...	1323	1331	...	...	1623	1631	...	▬	1930	1938	2138
Imatra ....d.	...	0508	...	0608	...	0702	...	0809	0809	...	IC74	...	1108	...	...	...	1409	...	...	...	1709	...	IC70	...	2020	...
Lappeenranta ....d.	...	0538	...	0638	...	0728	...	0838	0838	...	✕	...	1137	1238	...	...	1438	1627	...	...	1744	...	✕	...	2053	...
Kouvola ....a.	...	0617	...	0717	...	0807	...	0917	0917	...	⑦K	...	1216	1317	...	...	1517	1706	...	...	1822	...	K	...	2130	...
Kouvola ....d.	0528	0619	0628	0719	...	0809	0819	0919	0919	1119	1119	...	1219	1319	1419	...	1519	1708	1719	...	1824	1919	2015	...	2132	...
Lahti .... ☐ d.	0614	0649	0714	0749	...	0839	0849	0949	0949	1149	1149	...	1249	1349	1449	...	1549	1738	1749	...	1854	1949	2047	...	2207	...
Tikkurila .... ☐ a.	0711	0725	0811	0825	...	0915	0925	1025	1025	1225	1225	...	1325	1425	1525	...	1625	1814	1825	...	1930	2025	2131	...	2245	...
Pasila .... ☐ a.	0721	0734	0821	0834	...	0924	0934	1034	1034	1234	1234	...	1334	1434	1534	...	1634	1823	1834	...	1939	2034	2140	...	2254	...
Helsinki .... ☐ a.	0726	0740	0826	0840	...	0930	0940	1040	1040	1240	1240	...	1340	1440	1540	...	1640	1829	1840	...	1945	2040	2145	...	2259	...

Local trains **KOUVOLA - KOTKA** and v.v. 2nd class only.

km		⚒	Ⓐ	Ⓐ	⑥⑦			Ⓐ	
0	**Kouvola** .... d.	0600	0653	0800	0900	1253	1457	1557	1752
51	**Kotka** .... a.	0644	0737	0844	0944	1337	1544	1643	1836
52	**Kotka** satama a.	0647	0740	0847	0947	1340	1546	1645	1839

	⚒	Ⓐ				Ⓐ	
Kotka satama d.	0654	0800	1015	1425	1553	1651	1918
Kotka ....d.	0657	0803	1018	1428	1556	1654	1921
Kouvola ....a.	0742	0848	1103	1513	1639	1738	2006

Local trains **RIIHIMÄKI - LAHTI** and v.v. 2nd class only. *59 km.* Journey time: 42 minutes. **From Riihimäki** at 0613 ⚒, 0713 ⚒, 0813 and hourly until 1913; then 2113 and 2213. **From Lahti** at 0548 Ⓐ, 0616 ⑥ 0704 ⚒, 0804 and hourly until 2004; then 2204.

A – ①②③④⑥ June 17 - Aug. 10; ①–④ from Aug. 12.
K – To / from stations in Table **798**.

a – From Aug. 17.
b – Ⓐ only.
c – On ⑥⑦ arrives 1738.

☐ – Other local journeys Helsinki - Lahti and v.v. (2nd class only, journey 63 – 72 minutes): **From Helsinki** at 0630, 0730, 0835, 0935 and hourly until 1435; then 1530 Ⓐ, 1535 ⑥⑦, 1635, 1735 and hourly until 2135; then 2310. **From Lahti** at 0529 Ⓐ, 0620 ⑥⑦, 0720 ⑥⑦ 0758, 0914, 1020 and hourly until 2320.

798 KOUVOLA - KUOPIO - OULU

km		IC711	IC61	S71	IC63	IC713		IC65		S67	S67	S67	IC717	IC701	S69	S89		IC73	IC73
		✕	✕	✕	✕	2🍷		✕		✕	✕	✕	2🍷	2🍷	✕	✕		✕	✕
		R	A	⑥B							⚒	Ⓐ	⑦	Ⓑ	Ⓑ	⑦			①–④
	Helsinki **797** ...d.	...	0557	0557	0819	...	...	1119	...	1419	1419	1419	...	*1519*	1619	1724	...	1919	1919
0	**Kouvola** ....d.	...	0731	0731	0950	...	...	1301	...	1550	1550	1550	...	1648	1750	|	...	2051	2051
113	Mikkeli ....d.	...	0843	0843	1054	...	...	1410	...	1656	1656	1656	...	1752	1853	◇	...	2154	2154
184	Pieksämäki ....d.	...	0923	0923	1134	...	...	1449	...	1738	1738	1738	...	1837	1932	2137	...	2233	2233
273	**Kuopio** ....a.	...	1012	1012	1223	...	...	1539	...	1830	1830	1830	...	1927	2023	2225	...	2325	2325
273	**Kuopio** ....d.	0753	...	...	...	1239	...	1543	...	...	1838	1838	1838	...	2027	...	...	...	2329
358	Iisalmi ....d.	0857	...	...	...	1340	...	1643	...	...	1937	1937	1937	...	2131	...	...	...	0033
441	**Kajaani** ....a.	0952	...	...	...	1428	...	1731	...	...	2032	2032	2032	...	2220	...	...	...	0122
441	**Kajaani** ....d.	0956	...	...	...	1430	...	1748	...	...	...	2110	2110	...	...	...	...	...	...
484	Paltamo ....d.	1027	...	...	...	1459	...	1819	...	...	...	2144	2144	...	...	...	...	...	...
633	**Oulu** ....a.	1209	...	...	...	1637	...	1959	...	...	...	2326	2326	...	...	...	...	...	...

	IC700	IC62	IC62		S64	IC74		IC714	S66	S66	S66	IC716	IC68	IC72	S76	IC70	S152		IC710
	2🍷	✕	✕		✕	✕		2🍷	✕	✕	✕	2🍷	✕	✕	✕	✕	✕		✕
	⚒	⚒	②–⑤		⚒	⑦		①	②–⑥	②–⑦				A	⑥B		⑦		R
Oulu ....d.	...	...	...	...	...	...	...	0710	0710	...	...	1000	...	...	...	1247	...	...	1746
Paltamo ....d.	...	...	...	...	...	...	...	0850	0850	...	...	1143	...	...	...	1427	...	...	1928
Kajaani ....a.	...	...	...	...	...	...	...	0920	0920	...	...	1213	...	...	...	1502	...	...	2000
Kajaani ....d.	...	...	0340	...	0633	...	...	0927	0927	0927	...	1217	...	...	...	1517	...	...	2006
Iisalmi ....d.	...	...	0433	...	0725	...	...	1018	1018	1018	...	1308	...	...	...	1611	...	...	2057
Kuopio ....a.	...	...	0530	...	0821	...	...	1115	1115	1115	...	1407	...	...	...	1708	...	...	2153
Kuopio ....d.	0435	0535	0535	...	0826	0826	...	...	1126	1126	1126	...	1424	1614	1614	1712	1938	...	...
Pieksämäki ....d.	0528	0629	0629	...	0920	0920	...	...	1222	1222	1222	...	1523	1709	1709	1813	2035	...	...
Mikkeli ....d.	0608	0709	0709	...	1000	1000	...	...	1302	1302	1302	...	1603	1755	1755	1852	◇	...	...
Kouvola ....a.	0710	0811	0811	...	1106	1106	...	...	1403	1403	1403	...	1711	1903	1903	1954	|	...	...
Helsinki **797** ...a.	*0840*	0940	0940	...	1240	1240	...	...	1540	1540	1540	...	1840	2040	2040	2145	0035	...	...

IISALMI - YLIVIESKA

km		⚒2	2
0	**Iisalmi** .... d.	0737	1647
99	Haapajärvi .... d.	0847	1753
154	**Ylivieska** .... a.	0923	1829

	2		Ⓑ2
Ylivieska .... d.	1414	...	2030
Haapajärvi .... d.	1450	...	2106
Iisalmi .... a.	1600	...	2213

A – ①②③④⑥ June 17 - Aug. 10; ①–④ from Aug. 12.
B – From Aug. 17.
R – To / from Rovaniemi (Table **794**).
◇ – Via Tampere (Table **795**).

GERMANY

Operator: Principal operator is Deutsche Bahn AG (DB) www.bahn.de
Many regional services are run by private operators – these are specified in the table heading (or by footnotes for individual trains).

Services: Trains convey first- and second-class seating accommodation unless otherwise shown (by '2' in the column heading, a footnote or a general note in the table heading). Overnight sleeping car (🛏) and couchette (▬) trains do not necessarily convey seating accommodation - refer to individual footnotes for details. Descriptions of sleeping and couchette cars appear on page 10.

There are various categories of trains in Germany. The type of train is indicated by the following letter codes above each column (or by a general note in the table heading):

ICE	**InterCity Express**	German high-speed (230–320 km/h) train.
EC	**EuroCity**	International express train.
IC	**InterCity**	Internal express train.
ALX	**alex**	Regional express train operated by *Vogtlandbahn*.
FLX	**Flixtrain**	Independent long-distance operator – see special table below.
RJX/RJ	**Railjet**	Austrian express train. Conveys first and economy (2nd) class. *Business class* also available to first class ticket holders (supplement payable).
TGV	**Train à Grande Vitesse**	French high-speed (320 km/h) train. Reservation compulsory for all international journeys.
IRE	**InterRegio Express**	Regional express train.
RE	**Regional Express**	Regional semi-fast train.
RB	**Regional Bahn**	Regional stopping train.
S-Bahn		Suburban stopping train.

Overnight services:

NJ	**ÖBB nightjet**	Quality overnight express train operated by Austrian Railways. All services convey *Deluxe* sleeping cars (1/2/3 berth) with en-suite shower and WC, standard sleeping cars (1/2/3 berth), couchettes (4/6 berth) and 2nd class seats (in a compartment). **Reservation compulsory.** For further details see pages 10 and 35.
EN	**EuroNight**	Other international overnight express train. See also pages 10 and 35.
D	**Durchgangszug**	Or **Schnellzug** – other express train (day or night); rarely used nowadays.

Timings: Valid **June 11 - December 14**, 2019 (except where shown otherwise).

Many long distance trains operate on selected days only for part of the journey. These are often indicated in the train composition footnote by showing the dated journey segment within brackets. For example '(12) Leipzig - Hannover (- Dortmund ⑦)' means that the train runs daily (or as shown in the column heading) between Leipzig and Hannover, but only continues to Dortmund on Sundays. Additional footnotes/symbols are often used to show more complex running dates, e.g. '(12) (München ◻ -) Nürnberg - Hamburg' means that the train runs only on dates in note ◻ between München and Nürnberg, but runs daily (or as shown in the column heading) between Nürnberg and Hamburg. Please note that international overnight trains that are not intended for internal German journeys are not usually shown in the German section (refer to the International section).

Engineering work may occasionally disrupt services at short notice (especially at weekends and during holiday periods), so it is advisable to check timings locally before travelling. Please see panel below for information regarding major engineering work alterations affecting long-distance services during this timetable period.

Tickets: There are three standard levels of fares, corresponding to travel by (in ascending order of price): ○ Regional trains. ○ *IC/EC* trains. ○ High-speed *ICE* (also *TGV/RJ*) trains. A variable supplement is payable for sleeping car and couchette accommodation (and sometimes seating) on overnight *EN/NJ* trains, the cost of which depends on the type required. Please note that Interrail and Eurail pass holders may have to pay a special fare on overnight trains.

Catering: Two types of catering are indicated in the tables: 🍷 Bordbistro – hot and cold drinks, snacks and light meals (at-seat service on certain trains); ✕ Bordrestaurant – full restaurant car service (bordbistro also available). First class passengers on *ICE* and *IC* trains benefit from an at-seat service. On overnight trains 🍷 indicates that drinks and light snacks are available, usually from the sleeping or couchette car attendant (the refreshment service may only be available to sleeping and couchette car passengers).

Reservations: Reservation compulsory for travel in sleeping car and couchette accommodation on overnight *EN* trains (also in the seating accommodation of *ÖBB nightjet* services). Optional reservations are available on *ICE/EC/IC* trains (€ 4,50 in second class, € 5,90 in first class).

Holidays: Dec. 25, 26, Jan. 1, Apr. 19, 22, May 1, 30, June 10 and Oct. 3 are German national public holidays (trains marked ⚒ or Ⓐ do not run). In addition there are other regional holidays as follows: Jan. 6 – Heilige Drei Könige (Epiphany), June 20 – Fronleichnam (Corpus Christi), Aug. 15 – Mariä Himmelfahrt (Assumption), Oct. 31 – Reformationstag (Reformation Day), Nov. 1 – Allerheiligen (All Saints Day) and Nov. 20 – Buß und Bettag. On these days the regional service is usually that applicable on ⑦ (please refer to individual footnotes).

MAJOR ENGINEERING WORK ALTERATIONS AFFECTING LONG DISTANCE SERVICES

- ◻ June 9 – 16: Services via Aschaffenburg (Table **920**) are subject to extended journey times (earlier departures München - Nürnberg - Aschaffenburg) and trains may not call at Hanau.
- ◻ Until June 23: Services between Würzburg/Nürnberg and München via Augsburg are re-timed (on ⑥⑦, also late evening on the previous ⑤, services are also subject to diversion, not calling at intermediate stations via Augsburg).
- ◻ Until October 11: Most services via Bielefeld are retimed by a few minutes in the Bielefeld area (certain station calls may be omitted, particularly at Hamm, Gütersloh and Herford). The service until October 11 is shown on pages 384 and 385 whilst the service from October 12 is shown on pages 564 and 565.
- ◻ July 13 - August 25: Services in the Rhein-Ruhr region are subject to considerable alteration, particularly those which normally operate via Essen. Many services are retimed with diversions in operation. It is not possible for us to show amended timings for this period and so please confirm your travel arrangements locally if travelling to and from stations in Table **800**.
- ◻ June 11 - July 28: Hamburg area alterations - services between Hannover/Bremen and Schwerin are diverted, not calling at Hamburg Hbf (calling additionally at Hamburg Harburg and/or Hamburg Bergedorf). Affected services are indicated in our tables.
- ◻ From June 11: Services between Magdeburg and Halle via Köthen are amended with all *IC* services diverted via Dessau. Timings shown in our tables are valid from June 11.
- ◻ From June 11: The high-speed line between Hannover and Göttingen is temporarily closed meaning all services are re-timed and diverted via Elze. Fewer services operate north of Kassel as a result. Our tables show revised timings valid from June 11.
- ◻ July 19 - September 8: Many services do not serve Heidelberg Hbf, particularly those running to/from/via Stuttgart. See also following entry.
- ◻ July 19 - September 8, October 7 – 20 (also ⑥⑦ September 14 – 29): Services between Frankfurt and Karlsruhe via Heidelberg are subject to alteration. July 20 - September 8 and October 5 – 20 most services do not run Heidelberg - Karlsruhe and v.v. (on ⑥⑦ July 20 - September 8 and ⑥⑦ October 5 – 20 *ICE* **1671/2** and *IC* **2370** continue to run to/from Karlsruhe but are diverted, not calling at Heidelberg or Bruchsal; the same applies to train *IC* **2371** on ⑥ July 20 - Sept. 7 and ⑥ Oct. 5 – 19 and train *ICE* **1675** on ⑤ July 19 - Sept. 6 and ⑤ Oct. 4 – 18). See also Frankfurt entry below when services are diverted via Frankfurt Süd (not calling at Frankfurt Hbf). Timings may vary by a few minutes and different train numbers may apply during these changes.
- ◻ ⑥⑦ August 10 - October 20 (daily Sept. 14 - Oct. 20): Many services via Frankfurt are diverted, not calling at Frankfurt (Main) Hbf. As Frankfurt is a major hub of the German network, we have indicated in our tables the services which are diverted. Please note that different train numbers may also apply (not shown in our tables).
- ◻ ⑥⑦ August 10 - September 29: *EC/IC* services between Frankfurt and Stuttgart via Darmstadt/Heidelberg (Tables **912/930**) are subject to alteration (services may be diverted and/or retimed; certain services do not run between Frankfurt and Darmstadt). Readers are strongly advised to check timings locally if using services via this route on these dates. See also the Heidelberg entry (July 19 - September 8) above.
- ◻ August 10 - October 27: Most services between Eisenach and Fulda are subject to revised timings with some trains diverted via Kassel. A special version of Table **850** has been included and will be found on pages 566 and 567.
- ◻ September 14 - October 20: Timings of long-distance services Mannheim - Karlsruhe - Basel and v.v. may vary by up to 12 minutes (earlier departures possible).
- ◻ From October 26: Alterations to services in the Frankfurt area. Many services are diverted, not calling at Frankfurt Flughafen (timings at Frankfurt Hbf may also vary by up to 13 minutes with some earlier departures). In addition, certain northbound services from Frankfurt via Koblenz do not call at Mainz Hbf. Affected services may also run with a different train number.

FLX FLIXTRAIN service summary 800/810/902/912

Special fares payable (**DB tickets not valid**). Engineering work may affect timings; subject to alteration on and around public holidays (please check when booking). Website: www.flixtrain.de

		1803 J	1803 E	1805 F	1807 Ⓑ
Hamburg Hbf ★	d.	0849	0849	1249	1649
Osnabrück Hbf	d.	1044	1044	1444	1844
Münster (Westf) Hbf	d.	1109	1109	1509	1909
Gelsenkirchen Hbf	d.	1151	1158	1550	1950
Essen Hbf	d.	1204	|	1605	2004
Duisburg Hbf	d.	1218	1225	1618	2018
Düsseldorf Hbf	d.	1233	1250	1633	2033
Köln Hbf	a.	1257	1316	1657	2059

		1800 B	1802 G	1804 H	1806 ⑦
Köln Hbf	d.	0701	1101	1501	1901
Düsseldorf Hbf	d.	0727	1127	1527	1927
Duisburg Hbf	d.	0742	1142	1542	1942
Essen Hbf	d.	0756	1156	1556	1956
Gelsenkirchen Hbf	d.	0806	1206	1606	2006
Münster (Westf) Hbf	d.	0847	1249	1647	2046
Osnabrück Hbf	d.	0914	1316	1714	2114
Hamburg Hbf ★	a.	1111	1508	1909	2309

		27802 n		27800 A	
Berlin Hbf ●	d.	0820	...	1620	...
Wolfsburg	d.	0935	...	1736	...
Hannover Hbf	d.	1024	...	|	...
Bielefeld Hbf	d.	1141	...	1942	...
Dortmund Hbf	d.	1233	...	2033	...
Essen Hbf	d.	1305	...	|	...
Duisburg Hbf	d.	1318	...	|	...
Düsseldorf Hbf	d.	1333	...	2122k	...
Köln Hbf	a.	1357	...	2146	...

		27805 D		27803 m	
Köln Hbf	d.	0645	...	1601	...
Düsseldorf Hbf	d.	0714	...	1628	...
Duisburg Hbf	d.	0730	...	1643	...
Essen Hbf	d.	0743	...	1656	...
Dortmund Hbf	d.	0806	...	1732	...
Bielefeld Hbf	d.	0905r	...	1816v	...
Hannover Hbf	d.	1004	...	1944	...
Wolfsburg	d.	1038	...	2023	...
Berlin Hbf ●	a.	1205	...	2145	...

		32622 w	32620 C w
Stuttgart Hbf	d.	0621t	1412
Vaihingen	d.	0640t	1430
Heidelberg Hbf	d.	0717t	1516
Weinheim (Bergstr)	d.	0733t	1533
Darmstadt Hbf	d.	0804	1555
Frankfurt (Main) Süd	d.	0828	1614
Hanau	d.	0841	1635
Fulda	d.	0923	1719
Kassel Wilhelmshöhe	d.	0958	1754
Göttingen	d.	|	|
Hannover Messe/L	d.	1108	1908
Wolfsburg Hbf	d.	1149	1949
Berlin Zoo	a.	1258	2057
Berlin Hbf	a.	1304	2104
Berlin Ostbahnhof	a.	1315	2116
Berlin Ostkreuz	a.	1322	2123
Berlin Lichtenberg	a.	1333	2135

		32621 C w	32623 w
Berlin Lichtenberg	d.	0629	1428
Berlin Ostkreuz	d.	0639	1438
Berlin Ostbahnhof	d.	0644	1443
Berlin Hbf	d.	0654	1454
Berlin Zoo	d.	0701	1501
Wolfsburg Hbf	d.	0808	1609
Hannover Messe/L	d.	0850	1651
Göttingen	d.	|	|
Kassel Wilhelmshöhe	d.	1001	1804
Fulda	d.	1037	1838
Hanau	d.	1118	1916
Frankfurt (Main) Süd	d.	1134	1937
Darmstadt Hbf	d.	1154	1954
Weinheim (Bergstr)	d.	1217	2017
Heidelberg Hbf	d.	1246	2045
Vaihingen	d.	1316	2116
Stuttgart Hbf	a.	1332	2132

A – ④⑤⑦.
B – ①③⑥.
C – ①④⑤⑥⑦.
D – ①⑤⑥.
E – ①–⑥ from July 13.
F – ⑦ to July 7; ⑤–⑦ from July 12.
G – ②④⑤⑦ (also ⑥ from July 13).
H – ①⑤ to July 8; Ⓑ from July 12.
J – ①⑤⑥ to July 12.
k – ⑤ (also ④ from Oct. 17).
m – Not ② June 4 - July 9.
n – Not ③ June 5 - July 10.
r – From Oct. 12.
t – On Ⓒ Stuttgart d. 0639, Vaihingen d. 0657, Heidelberg d. 0728, Weinheim d. 0744.
v – July 13 - Aug. 25 and from Oct. 12.
w – July 20 - Sept. 8 does not call at Heidelberg and timings at Stuttgart and Vaihingen may vary by up to 9 minutes.
★ – Trains also serve Hamburg Altona.
● – Trains also serve Berlin Südkreuz and Berlin Spandau.

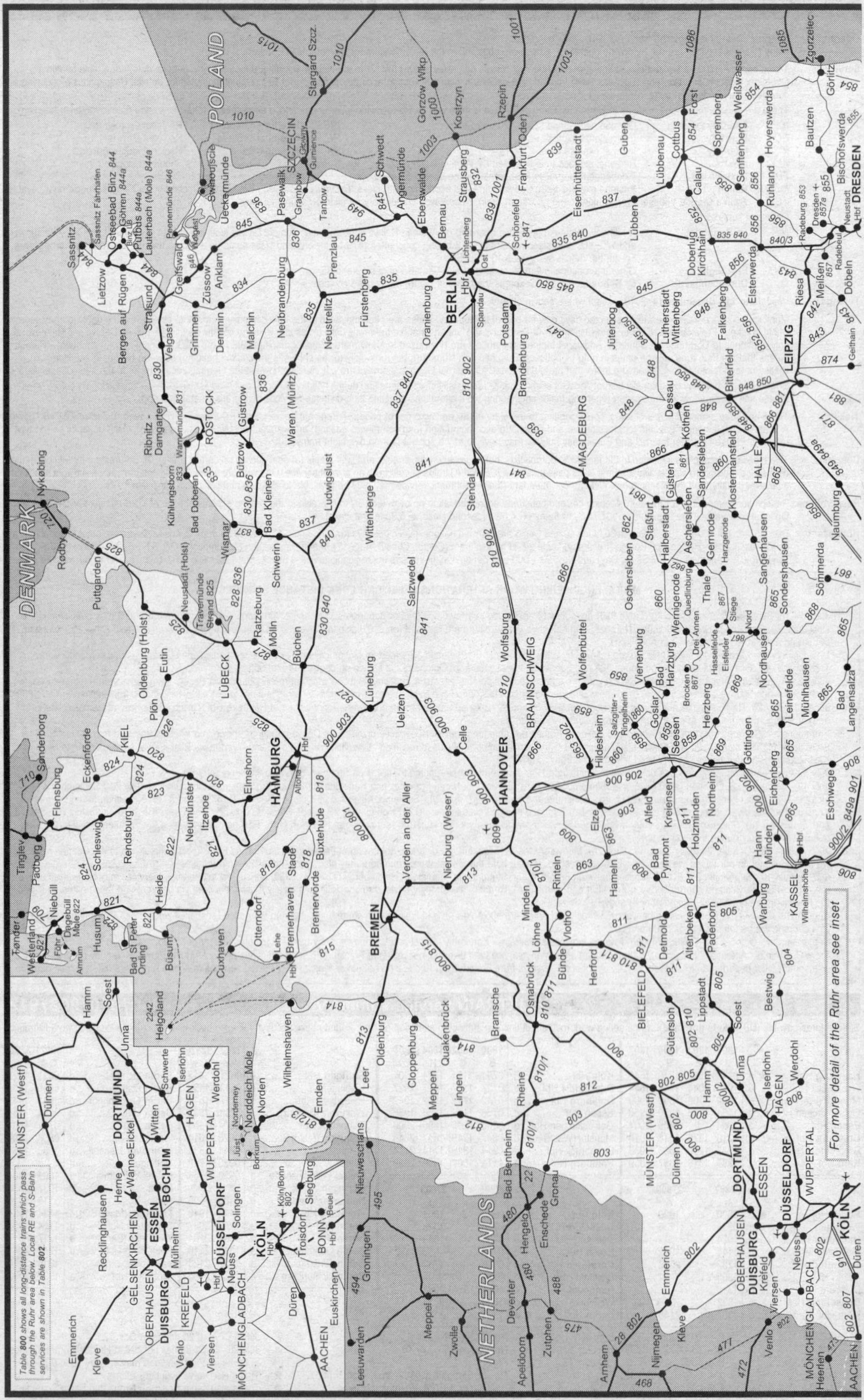
DENMARK
POLAND
NETHERLANDS
BERLIN
HAMBURG
HANNOVER
BREMEN
LEIPZIG
DRESDEN
MAGDEBURG
HALLE
BRAUNSCHWEIG
LÜBECK
KIEL
ROSTOCK
SZCZECIN
BIELEFELD
KASSEL
DORTMUND
DÜSSELDORF
KÖLN
ESSEN
DUISBURG
BOCHUM
WUPPERTAL
HAGEN
AACHEN
MÜNSTER (Westf)
Table 800 shows all long-distance trains which pass through the Ruhr area below. Local RE and S-Bahn services are shown in Table 802
For more detail of the Ruhr area see inset

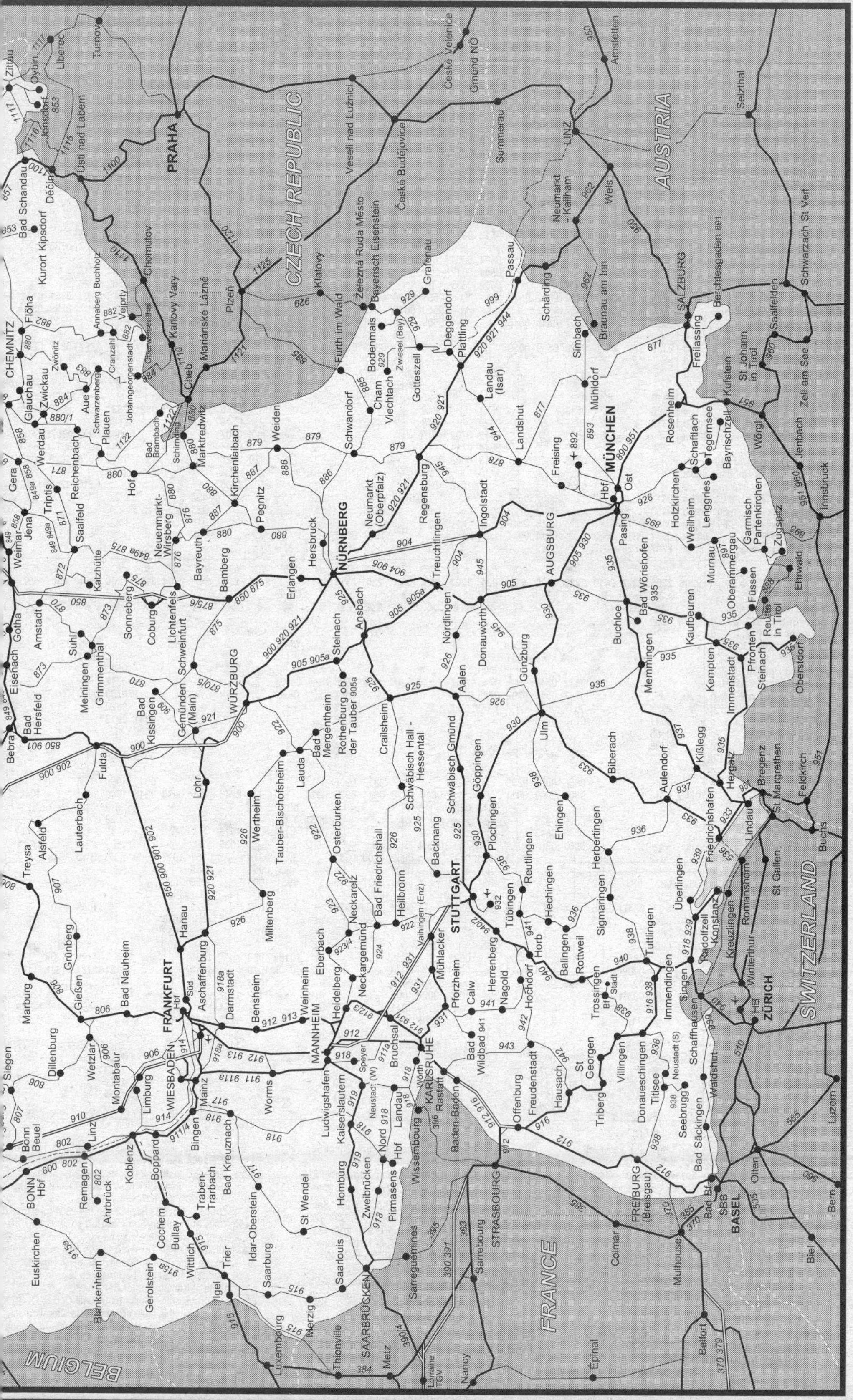
CZECH REPUBLIC
AUSTRIA
SWITZERLAND
FRANCE
BELGIUM
PRAHA
FRANKFURT
MÜNCHEN
NÜRNBERG
STUTTGART
WÜRZBURG
AUGSBURG
MANNHEIM
KARLSRUHE
WIESBADEN
SAARBRÜCKEN
STRASBOURG
BASEL
ZÜRICH
SALZBURG
LINZ
CHEMNITZ
BONN
FREIBURG (Breisgau)
Regensburg
Ingolstadt
Passau
Ulm
Heidelberg
Koblenz
Mainz
Trier
Luxembourg
Innsbruck
Bregenz
Lindau
Konstanz
Kempten
Würzburg
Bamberg
Hof
Cheb
Plzeň
České Budějovice
Karlovy Vary
Dresden

800 KOBLENZ - KÖLN - DORTMUND - HAMBURG

km	SEE NOTE ❖	IC 2020	ICE 928	IC 1028	ICE 541	IC 2214	IC 2314	IC 2445	ICE 853	ICE 843	IC 2208	IC 208	IC 1098	ICE 222	ICE 222	ICE 553	ICE 543	IC 2212	ICE 618	ICE 1018	IC 2443	ICE 855	ICE 845	ICE 1045	IC 24
			Ⓐ	①–⑤	①–⑥	T		①–⑥	①–⑥		⑥B		①–④		①–⑤	①–⑥	t		①–⑥	⑦	①–⑥	t	①–⑤	⑥⑦	⑥
		▲	✕	✕	△✕	🍷	🍷♦	D🍷	t✕	△✕	N	🍷♦	⊙🍷	A✕	A✕	¶✕	✕	🍷♦	✕	✕	D🍷	✕	△✕	△✕	F
	Basel SBB 🚌 **912** d.	...	...	...	...	...	...	...	...	...	...	2313	...	...	...	...	...	...	...	...	...	...	...	...	..
	Karlsruhe Hbf **912** d.	...	...	...	...	...	...	...	...	...	...	0130	...	...	...	...	...	...	0349*	0349*	...	...	...	...	..
	München Hbf **904 930** d.	...	...	...	...	...	...	...	...	...	...	|	...	...	...	...	...	...	0001◊	0001◊	...	...	...	...	..
	Stuttgart Hbf **912** d.	...	...	...	...	...	...	...	...	...	...	|	...	...	...	...	...	...	0228	0228	...	...	...	...	..
	Nürnberg Hbf **920** d.	...	...	...	...	...	...	...	...	...	...	|	...	...	...	...	...	...	|	|	...	...	...	...	..
	Frankfurt (Main) Hbf **910/1** d.	2322	...	...	...	...	...	...	...	...	...	0308	...	...	0529	...	...	...	0544	0544	...	...	...	...	..
	Frankfurt Flughafen ✈ § d.	2339	...	...	...	...	...	...	...	...	...	0323	...	...	0543	...	...	...	0601	0601	...	...	...	...	..
	Mainz Hbf **911** d.	0001	...	...	...	...	...	...	...	...	...	0403	...	...	|	...	...	...	|	|	...	...	...	...	..
0	**Koblenz** Hbf d.	0058	...	...	...	...	...	...	...	...	...	0507	...	...	|	0545	...	0605	|	|	...	...	...	...	..
18	Andernach d.	0110	...	...	...	...	...	...	...	...	...	0519	...	...	|	0558	...	0618	|	|	...	...	...	...	..
39	Remagen d.	0122	...	...	...	...	...	...	...	...	...	0531	...	...	|	|	...	0631	|	|	...	...	...	...	..
59	**Bonn** Hbf d.	0137	...	...	...	...	...	...	...	...	...	0546	...	...	|	0623	...	0646	|	|	...	...	...	...	..
	Köln/Bonn Flughafen ✈ d.	|	...	...	...	...	...	...	...	...	...	|	...	...	|	|	...	|	|	|	...	...	0712	...	..
93	**Köln** Hbf a.	0157	...	...	...	...	...	...	...	...	...	0606	...	...	0633	0643	...	0705	0705	0705	...	...	|	...	..
93	**Köln** Hbf d.	0210	...	0400	0425	0509	0509	0513	0544	0528	0541	0609	0614	0641	0641	0648	0626	0709	0713	0711	0712	0748	|	0727	072
94	**Köln** Messe/Deutz d.	|	...	0405	|	|	|	|	|	|	|	|	|	|	|	|	|	|	|	|	|	|	0729	|	|
	Solingen Hbf d.	|	...	|	|	|	|	0531	0604	|	|	|	|	|	|	|	|	|	|	0729	0731	|	|	|	|
	Wuppertal Hbf d.	|	...	|	|	|	|	0544	0617	|	|	|	|	|	|	0716	|	|	|	0743	0744	0816	|	|	|
	Hagen Hbf d.	|	...	|	|	|	|	0602	0635	|	|	|	|	|	|	0735t	|	|	|	0801	0802	0835	|	|	|
133	**Düsseldorf** Hbf d.	0233	...	0427	0449	0532	0532	|	|	0551	0608	0632	0637	0709	0709	|	0652	0732	0737	|	|	|	0751	0752	075
140	Düsseldorf Flughafen ✈ d.	0240h	...	0435	0457	|	|	|	|	0559	0615	|	|	|	|	|	0700	|	|	|	|	|	0759	0800	|
157	**Duisburg** Hbf d.	0250	...	0444	0507	0546	0546	|	|	0609	0626	0646	0651	0727	0727	|	0710	0746	0751	|	|	|	0809	0810	08
165	Oberhausen Hbf d.	|	...	|	|	|	|	|	|	|	0633	|	|	0732	0732	|	|	|	|	|	|	|	|	|	|
176	**Essen** Hbf d.	0306	...	0500	0520	0559	0559	|	|	0623	|	0659	0703	...	...	|	0723	0759	0804	|	|	|	0823	0823	|
	Gelsenkirchen Hbf d.	|	...	|	|	|	|	|	|	|	0645	|	|	...	...	|	|	|	|	|	|	|	|	|	08
	Wanne-Eickel Hbf d.	|	...	|	|	|	|	|	|	|	0651	|	|	...	...	|	|	|	|	|	|	|	|	|	08
	Recklinghausen Hbf d.	|	...	|	|	|	|	|	|	|	0659	|	|	...	...	|	|	|	|	|	|	|	|	|	08
192	Bochum Hbf d.	0316	...	0511	0532	|	|	|	|	0635	|	0710	|	...	...	|	0735	|	0814k	|	|	|	0835	0835	|
210	**Dortmund** Hbf a.	0326	...	0521	0543	|	|	0621	|	0646	|	0721	|	...	...	|	0746	|	0827k	0821	0821	|	0846	0846	|
210	**Dortmund** Hbf **805** d.	0332	...	0524	0545	|	|	0628	|	0648	|	0725	|	...	...	|	0748	|	...	...	0828	|	0848	0848	|
	Hamm (Westf) **805** a.	0350	...	|	0601	|	|	0642	0702	0707t	|	|	|	...	...	0800v	0807	|	...	...	0842	0902	0907t	0907t	|
	Hamm (Westf) d.	0352	...	|	0603	|	|	0644	0711	0711t	|	|	|	...	...	0802v	0811	|	...	...	0844	0911	0911t	0911t	|
	Hannover Hbf **810** a.	|	...	|	0728	|	|	0818	0828	0828	|	|	|	...	...	0928	0928	|	...	...	1018	1028	1028	1028	|
	Leipzig Hbf **849a 866** a.	|	...	|	|	|	|	1115	|	|	|	|	|	...	...	|	|	|	...	...	1315	|	|	|	|
	Berlin Hbf **810** a.	|	...	|	0906	|	|	...	1010	1010	|	|	|	...	...	1105	1105	|	...	...	...	1210	1210	1210	|
266	Münster (Westf) Hbf **801** d.	0415	...	0557	...	0657	0657	...	...	...	0728	0757	|	...	...	...	...	0857	...	...	...	...	...	...	09
316	Osnabrück Hbf **801 815** d.	0450	...	0623	...	0723	0723	...	...	...	...	0823	|	...	...	...	...	0923	...	...	...	...	...	...	09
438	**Bremen** Hbf **801 815** d.	0555	0717	0727	...	0819	0819	...	...	...	...	0919	|	...	...	...	...	1018	...	...	...	...	...	...	10
553	**Hamburg** Hbf **801** a.	0651	0812	0833	...	0914	0914	...	...	...	...	1014	0948	...	...	...	...	1114‡	...	...	...	...	...	...	114
560	**Hamburg** Altona a.	0707	0828	0847	...	0929	...	...	...	...	...	...	1003	...	...	...	...	...	...	...	...	...	...	...	...

SEE NOTE ❖	IC 2206	IC 2206	IC 2222	IC 2410	IC 2220	IC 2320	ICE 616	ICE 824	ICE 1223	ICE 555	ICE 545	ICE 220	IC 2310	IC 2441	ICE 822	IC 2155	ICE 857	ICE 847	IC 2204	IC 5107	IC 2028	ICE 614	ICE 820	ICE 557	IC 54
	Y	①–⑥	①–⑤	R		⊡		①–⑤			t				①–⑥		t						①–⑥		t
	N	N	G	F	🍷♦	🍷	✕	✕	✕♦	✕	✕	A✕	🍷♦	D🍷	✕	♦	✕	△✕	E	X	🍷	✕	✕	✕	✕
Basel SBB 🚌 **912** d.	...	...	...	...	...	...	...	...	...	...	...	...	...	...	...	...	...	...	...	...	...	...	...	...	...
Karlsruhe Hbf **912** d.	...	...	...	...	...	...	...	...	...	...	...	...	...	...	...	...	...	...	...	...	...	...	...	...	...
München Hbf **904 930** d.	...	...	...	...	...	...	0324b	...	...	...	...	...	...	...	0448	...	...	...	...	...	...	0522	0547f	...	..
Stuttgart Hbf **912** d.	...	...	...	...	...	...	0551	...	...	...	...	...	...	...	|	...	...	...	...	...	...	0751	|	...	..
Nürnberg Hbf **920** d.	...	...	...	...	...	...	|	0500	...	...	...	...	...	...	0600	...	...	...	...	...	0526	|	0657	...	..
Frankfurt (Main) Hbf **910/1** d.	...	...	...	...	0542	0542	|	0710	...	...	...	0725	0638	...	0810•	...	...	...	...	...	0742	|	0909•	...	..
Frankfurt Flughafen ✈ § d.	...	...	...	...	0557	0557	0709	0725	0714r	...	...	0743	0657	...	0825	...	...	...	...	...	0758	0909	0923	...	..
Mainz Hbf **911** d.	...	...	...	...	0617	0617	|	|	|	...	...	|	0717	...	|	...	...	...	...	...	0820	|	|	...	..
Koblenz Hbf d.	...	0641	...	...	0713	0713	|	|	|	...	...	|	0813	...	|	...	...	...	...	0841	0913	|	|	...	..
Andernach d.	...	0656	...	...	|	|	|	|	|	...	...	|	|	...	|	...	...	...	...	0856	|	|	|	...	..
Remagen d.	...	0708	...	...	|	|	|	|	|	...	...	|	|	...	|	...	...	...	...	0908	|	|	|	...	..
Bonn Hbf d.	...	0723	...	...	0746	0746	|	|	|	...	...	|	0846	...	|	...	...	...	...	0923	0946	|	|	...	..
Köln/Bonn Flughafen ✈ d.	...	|	...	...	|	|	|	|	|	...	...	|	|	...	|	...	...	...	...	|	|	|	|	...	..
Köln Hbf a.	...	0743	...	...	0805	0805	0805	|	|	...	...	0833	0905	...	|	...	...	...	...	0943	1005	1005	|	...	..
Köln Hbf d.	0746	0746	...	...	0809	0809	0811	|	|	0848	0828	0841	0909	0913	|	0901	0948	0928c	0938	0946	1009	1011	|	1048	..
Köln Messe/Deutz d.	|	|	...	0804	|	|	|	0817	0825	|	|	|	|	|	0917	|	|	|	|	|	|	|	1027	|	..
Solingen Hbf d.	|	|	...	|	0829	0829	|	|	|	|	|	|	|	0931	|	|	|	|	|	|	1029	|	|	|	..
Wuppertal Hbf d.	|	|	...	|	0843	0843	|	|	|	0916	|	|	|	0944	|	|	1016	|	|	|	1043	|	|	1116	..
Hagen Hbf d.	|	|	...	|	0901	0901	|	|	|	0935t	|	|	|	1002	|	|	1035	|	|	|	1101	|	|	1135t	..
Düsseldorf Hbf d.	0812	0812	...	0827	|	|	0833	0838	0847	|	0852	0909	0932	|	0938	0946	|	0951	1012	1009	|	1033	1048	|	10
Düsseldorf Flughafen ✈ d.	|	|	...	|	|	|	|	|	|	|	0900	|	|	|	|	0953	|	0959	|	...	|	|	|	|	11
Duisburg Hbf d.	0827	0827	0831	0842	|	|	0847	0851	0902	|	0910	0927	0946	|	0951	1003	|	1009	1027	...	|	1047	1101	|	11
Oberhausen Hbf d.	0834	0834	|	|	|	|	|	|	|	|	|	0932	|	|	|	|	|	|	1034	...	|	|	|	|	|
Essen Hbf d.	|	|	0847t	0855	|	|	0859	0902	0917	|	0923	...	0959	|	1004	1017	|	1023	|	...	|	1059	1116	|	11
Gelsenkirchen Hbf d.	0846	0846	|	0905	|	|	|	...	|	|	|	...	|	|	|	|	|	|	1046	...	|	|	|	|	|
Wanne-Eickel Hbf d.	0852	0852	|	|	|	|	|	...	|	|	|	...	|	|	|	|	|	|	1052	...	|	|	|	|	|
Recklinghausen Hbf d.	0900	0900	|	|	|	|	|	...	|	|	|	...	|	|	|	|	|	|	1100	...	|	|	|	|	|
Bochum Hbf d.	|	|	0858t	|	|	|	0909	...	0929	|	0935	...	|	|	1016k	1030	|	1035	|	...	|	1109	1128k	|	11
Dortmund Hbf a.	|	|	0909t	|	0921	0921	0921	...	0940	|	0946	...	|	1021	1030k	1040	|	1046	|	...	1121	1121	1141k	|	11
Dortmund Hbf **805** d.	|	|	0912t	|	0925	0925	...	...	0942	|	0948	...	|	1028	...	1043	|	1048	|	...	1125	...	...	|	11
Hamm (Westf) **805** a.	|	|	0932t	|	|	|	...	...	1002	1002v	1007	...	|	1042	...	1102	1102	1107t	|	...	|	...	...	1202v	12
Hamm (Westf) d.	|	|	0934t	|	|	|	...	...	...	1011v	1011	...	|	1044	...	...	1111	1111t	|	...	|	...	...	1211v	12
Hannover Hbf **810** a.	|	|	1101	|	|	|	...	...	...	1128	1128	...	|	1218	...	...	1228	1228	|	...	|	...	...	1328	13
Leipzig Hbf **849a 866** a.	|	|	|	|	|	|	...	...	...	|	|	...	|	1515	...	...	|	|	|	...	|	...	...	|	|
Berlin Hbf **810** a.	|	|	1252	|	|	|	...	...	...	1306	1306	...	|	...	...	...	1410	1410	|	...	|	...	...	1505	15
Münster (Westf) Hbf **801** d.	0930	0930	...	|	0957	0957	...	...	...	...	...	...	1057	...	...	...	...	...	1128	...	1157	...	...	...	..
Osnabrück Hbf **801 815** d.	...	...	...	|	1023	1023	...	...	...	...	...	...	1123	...	...	...	...	...	...	...	1223	...	...	...	..
Bremen Hbf **801 815** d.	...	...	...	|	1118	1118	...	...	...	...	...	...	1219	...	...	...	...	...	...	...	1319	...	...	...	..
Hamburg Hbf **801** a.	...	...	...	1147z	1213	1213	...	...	...	...	...	...	1314	...	...	...	...	...	...	...	1414	...	...	...	..
Hamburg Altona a.	...	...	...	...	...	1229	...	...	...	...	...	...	...	...	...	...	...	...	...	...	1429	...	...	...	..

♦ – **NOTES** (LISTED BY TRAIN NUMBER)

208 – [12] Basel - Frankfurt - Köln - Kiel; 🍷 Köln - Kiel.
1223 – [12] and ✕ (Darmstadt Hbf, d. 0648 Ⓐ **r** -) Köln - Kassel - München.
2155 – [12] Köln - Paderborn - Kassel - Weimar - Gera.
2212 – RÜGEN – [12] and 🍷 Koblenz - Stralsund - Ostseebad Binz.
2220 – ②–④ to June 27; ②–④ Sept. 18 - Oct. 30 (not Oct. 2, 3); ⑤⑦ from Nov. 8. [12] and 🍷 Frankfurt - Köln - Lübeck Hbf (a. 1301).
2310 – NORDFRIESLAND – [12] and 🍷 Frankfurt - Köln - Westerland.
2314 – Until Nov. 3. DEICHGRAF – [12] and 🍷 Köln - Westerland.

A – To Amsterdam (Table **28**). Diversions / retimings are scheduled June 27 – 30, Aug. 2 – 11, Sept. 28, 29, Nov. 16, 17 (different train numbers may apply).
B – ⑥ to Aug. 24 (also June 20; not June 22); ④–⑦ Aug. 29 - Nov. 3 (not Oct. 5).
D – To Dresden (Table **842**).
E – To Emden (Table **812**).
F – FEHMARN – To Lübeck Hbf (a. 1253) and Fehmarn-Burg (Table **825**).
G – KAROLINGER – From Aachen Hbf (d. 0707), Rheydt Hbf (d. 0748), Mönchengladbach Hbf (d. 0755), Viersen (d. 0803), Krefeld Hbf (d. 0816).
N – To Norddeich Mole (Table **812**).
R – Ⓑ to Sept. 17 (also June 15, 22; not June 12, 13, 19, 25, 26, 27); ①⑤⑦ Sept. 20 - Nov. 3 (also Sept. 21, Oct. 2, 3).

S – ⑥ June 29 - Nov. 2 (not Sept. 21).
T – From Nov. 4.
X – From Luxembourg (Table **915**).
Y – Daily to Nov. 9; ①–⑥ from Nov. 11.

b – 0315 on ①⑦ July 28 - Sept. 2.
c – Daily to Aug. 29; ①②③④⑥⑦ Aug. 31 - Oct. 10; ⑥⑦ from Oct. 12.
f – ①–⑤ to July 12 (not June 20); ①–⑤ Aug. 15 - Sept. 27; ⚒ Sept. 30 - Nov. 2.
h – ①–⑤ (also ⑥ from Nov. 9).
k – ⑥ only.
r – Ⓐ to Oct. 25 (not June 20).
t – From Oct. 12.
v – Until Oct. 11 arrives Hamm 2 minutes earlier, departs 9 minutes earlier.
z – Hamburg **Harburg**.
‡ – June 11 - July 28 calls at Hamburg Harburg (not Hamburg Hbf).

⊙ – ①–④ (not July 15 - Aug. 22, Oct. 2, 3). Runs as *ICE* **1098** and conveys ✕ from Oct. 14.
⊡ – ①⑤⑥⑦ to June 24; daily June 28 - Sept. 17; ①⑤⑥⑦ Sept. 20 - Nov. 3 (also Oct. 2, 3, 31); ①②③④⑥ from Nov. 4.
◊ – On ①⑦ July 28 - Sept. 2 departs 2354 (previous da
• – Calls at Frankfurt Süd (not Hbf) on ⑥⑦ Aug. 10 - Sept. 29 (departure may be up to 3 minutes earlie
▲ – Timings Bonn - Duisburg are up to 8 minutes later on the mornings of © (also June 20, Nov. 1).
△ – Certain timings are 1 – 3 minutes later from Oct. 12
* – Calls at Karlsruhe after Stuttgart.
¶ – Also runs Köln - Berlin on ⑦ until Oct. 6.
❖ – Services in this table are subject to alteration July 1 August 25, particularly those via Duisburg / Essen. See the engineering work panel on page 369 for furt details and also for other alterations affecting servi in this table.
§ – Frankfurt Flughafen Fernbahnhof (Tables **910** / **911**

 *See Table **802** for Rhein-Ruhr regional services. FlixTrain also run fast services between Köln and Hamburg (see page 369).*

KOBLENZ - KÖLN - DORTMUND - HAMBURG 800

SEE NOTE ❖	ICE 128 A✕	ICE 916 Q ✕	IC 1955/9 ⑤⑦ n♦	IC 2010 ①–⑤ T🍸	IC 2018 ⑥ 🍸♦	IC 2216 🍸♦	IC 2049 D🍸	ICE 728 ✕	ICE 859 t ✕	ICE 849 △✕	IC 2202 N	IC 2226 🍸♦	ICE 612 ✕	ICE 726 ①–⑥ ✕	ICE 559 ✕	ICE 549 t ✕	ICE 126 A✕	ICE 914 ①–⑥ n✕	IC 2218 🍸	ICE 200 ⑥f ✕	IC 2047 Ⓑg D🍸	ICE 724 ✕	ICE 1051 t ✕	ICE 941 △✕	IC 2000 ⑤⑦ rN
Basel SBB 🚌 **912** d.	...	...	...	...	...	...	...	...	...	...	...	...	...	...	...	...	...	...	...	0913	...	...	...	...	...
Karlsruhe Hbf **912** d.	...	...	...	...	...	...	...	...	...	...	...	...	...	...	...	...	...	...	...	1059	...	...	...	...	...
München Hbf **904 930** d.	...	...	...	...	...	...	...	0648	...	...	...	...	0728	0752	...	...	...	...	...	|	...	0848	...	...	...
Stuttgart Hbf **912** d.	...	0833	...	0714	0714n	0737	...	|	...	...	...	...	0951	|	...	...	...	1041	0937	|	...	|	...	...	...
Nürnberg Hbf **920** d.	...	|	...	|	|	|	...	0800	...	...	...	0729e	|	0902	...	...	...	|	|	|	...	1000	...	...	...
Frankfurt (Main) Hbf **910/1** d.	0929	|	...	|	|	|	...	1010•	...	...	...	0942	|	1110•	...	...	1129	|	|	|	...	1210•	...	...	...
Frankfurt Flughafen ✈ § d.	0943	0955	...	|	|	|	...	1025	...	...	...	0958	1109	1122	...	...	1143	1155	|	1209	...	1225	...	...	...
Mainz Hbf **911** d.	|	|	...	0849	0849n	0920	...	|	...	...	...	1020	|	|	...	...	|	|	1120	|	...	|	...	...	...
oblenz Hbf d.	|	|	...	0944	0944n	1013	...	|	...	...	1044a	1113	|	|	...	...	|	|	1213	|	...	|	...	...	...
ndernach d.	|	|	...	0956	0956n	|	...	|	...	...	1056a	|	|	|	...	...	|	|	|	|	...	|	...	...	...
emagen d.	|	|	...	1008	1008n	|	...	|	...	...	1108a	|	|	|	...	...	|	|	|	|	...	|	...	...	...
onn Hbf d.	|	|	...	1023	1023n	1046	...	|	...	...	1123a	1146	|	|	1222j	...	|	|	1246	|	...	|	...	...	...
Köln/Bonn Flughafen ✈ d.	|	|	...	|	|	|	...	|	...	...	|	|	|	|	|	...	|	|	|	|	...	1313	...	...	...
öln Hbf a.	1033	|	...	1043	1043n	1105	...	|	...	...	1143a	1205	1205	|	1243j	...	1233	|	1305	1305	...	|	...	...	...
öln Hbf d.	1041	|	...	...	1046	1109	1113	|	1148	...	1146	1209	1211	|	1248	...	1241	|	1309	1311	1313	|	1348	...	1338
öln Messe/Deutz d.	|	1046	...	...	|	|	|	1117	|	...	|	|	|	1227	|	...	|	1246	|	|	|	1326	|	...	|
Solingen Hbf d.	|	|	...	...	|	|	1131	|	|	...	|	1229	|	|	|	...	|	|	|	1329	1331	|	|	...	|
Wuppertal Hbf d.	|	|	...	...	|	|	1144	|	1216	...	|	1243	|	|	1316	...	|	|	|	1342	1344	|	1416	...	|
Hagen Hbf d.	|	|	...	...	|	|	1202	|	1235	...	|	1301	|	|	1335t	...	|	|	|	1401	1402	|	1435	...	|
üsseldorf Hbf d.	1109	1113	1113	...	1118	1132	|	1138	|	1151	1212	|	1233	1248	|	1252	1309	1313	1332	|	|	1348	|	1351	1409
üsseldorf Flughafen ✈ d.	|	|	|	...	|	|	|	|	|	1159	|	|	|	|	|	1300	|	|	|	|	|	|	|	1359	|
uisburg Hbf d.	1126	1129	1129	...	|	1146	|	1151	|	1209	1226	|	1247	1302	|	1310	1326	1328	1346	|	|	1402	|	1409	1427
Oberhausen Hbf d.	1132	|	|	...	|	|	|	|	|	|	1234	|	|	|	|	|	1332	|	|	|	|	|	|	|	1434
ssen Hbf d.	...	1141	1141	...	|	1159	|	1204	|	1223	|	|	1259	1318	|	1323	...	1341	1359	|	|	1417	|	1423	|
Gelsenkirchen Hbf d.	...	|	|	...	1148	|	|	|	|	|	1246	|	|	|	|	|	...	|	|	|	|	|	|	|	1446
Wanne-Eickel Hbf d.	...	|	|	...	|	|	|	|	|	|	1252	|	|	|	|	|	...	|	|	|	|	|	|	|	1452
Recklinghausen Hbf d.	...	|	|	...	1159	|	|	|	|	|	1300	|	|	|	|	|	...	|	|	|	|	|	|	|	1500
ochum Hbf d.	...	1152	1154	...	|	|	|	1215c	|	1235	|	|	1309	1329k	|	1335	...	1352	|	|	|	1429k	|	1435	|
ortmund Hbf a.	...	1203	1205	...	|	|	1221	1230c	|	1246	|	1321	1321	1343k	|	1346	...	1403	|	1421	1421	1442k	|	1446	|
ortmund Hbf **805** d.	...	...	1208	...	|	|	1228	...	|	1248	|	1325	...	...	|	1348	...	...	|	...	1428	...	|	1448	|
Hamm (Westf) **805** a.	...	...	1227	...	|	|	1242	...	1302	1307t	|	|	...	...	1402v	1407	...	...	|	...	1442	...	1502	1507t	|
Hamm (Westf) d.	...	...	1234	...	|	|	1244	...	1311	1311t	|	|	...	...	1411v	1411	...	...	|	...	1444	...	1511	1511t	|
Hannover Hbf **810** a.	...	...	|	...	|	|	1418	...	1428	1428	|	|	...	...	1528	1528	...	...	|	...	1618	...	1628	1628	|
Leipzig Hbf **849a 866** a.	...	...	1726	...	|	|	1722	...	|	|	|	|	...	...	|	|	...	...	|	...	1915	...	|	|	|
Berlin Hbf **810** a.	...	...	...	...	|	|	...	...	1610	1610	|	|	...	...	1706	1706	...	...	|	...	...	...	1810	1810	|
ünster (Westf) Hbf **801** d.	...	...	...	...	1228	1257	...	...	...	...	1328	1357	...	...	...	...	...	...	1457	...	...	...	...	...	1528
snabrück Hbf **801 815** d.	...	...	...	...	...	1323	...	...	...	...	...	1423	...	...	...	...	...	...	1523	...	...	...	...	...	...
remen Hbf **801 815** d.	...	...	...	...	...	1418	...	...	...	...	...	1519	...	...	...	...	...	...	1619	...	...	...	...	...	...
amburg Hbf **801** a.	...	...	...	...	...	1512‡	...	...	...	...	...	1614	...	...	...	...	...	...	1714	...	...	...	...	...	...
amburg Altona a.	...	...	...	...	...	...	...	...	...	...	...	...	...	...	...	...	...	...	1729	...	...	...	...	...	...

SEE NOTE ❖	IC 2200 R N	IC 1922 ⑤⑦ Z🍸	IC 1922 ⑤⑦ Y🍸	IC 2024 P🍸	ICE 610 ✕	ICE 722 Ⓐd ✕	ICE 1122 Ⓒs ✕	ICE 651 ✕	ICE 641 t ✕	IC 1926 Ⓑ B🍸	ICE 124 A✕	ICE 1014 n ✕	IC 2312 🍸	ICE 108 ⑥ ✕	IC 2045 Ⓑ D🍸	ICE 720 ✕	IC 2157 ♦	ICE 1053 Ⓑt ✕	ICE 943 △✕	IC 2006 ⑥ 🍸♦	IC 2004 🍸♦	IC 2014 ⑤ 🍸♦	IC 2026 ⊙ 🍸	ICE 518 ✕	IC 2196 Ⓑ m🍸
Basel SBB 🚌 **912** d.	...	...	...	...	...	...	...	...	...	...	...	...	...	1113	...	...	...	...	...	...	...	...	...	...	...
Karlsruhe Hbf **912** d.	...	...	...	...	...	...	...	...	...	...	...	...	...	1300	...	...	...	...	...	1221	1221w	...	...	...	...
München Hbf **904 930** d.	...	...	...	...	0928	0951	0951	...	...	...	...	...	...	|	...	1055	...	...	...	|	|	...	...	1128	...
Stuttgart Hbf **912** d.	...	1009	1009	...	1151	|	|	...	...	...	...	1237	1137	|	...	|	...	...	...	|	|	1208	...	1351	...
Nürnberg Hbf **920** d.	...	|	|	0929	|	1100	1100	...	...	...	...	|	|	|	...	1200	...	...	...	|	|	|	...	|	...
Frankfurt (Main) Hbf **910/1** d.	...	|	|	1142	|	1310	1310•	...	...	...	1329	|	|	|	...	1410•	...	...	...	|	|	|	1344	|	...
Frankfurt Flughafen ✈ § d.	...	|	|	1158	1309	1325	1322	...	...	...	1343	1355	|	1409	...	1425	...	...	...	|	|	|	1358	1509	...
Mainz Hbf **911** d.	...	1144	1144	1220	|	|	|	...	...	...	|	|	1320	|	...	|	...	...	...	1344	1344w	1344	1420	|	...
oblenz Hbf d.	...	1244	1244	1313	|	|	|	...	...	...	|	|	1413	|	...	|	...	...	...	1444	1444	1444	1513	|	...
ndernach d.	...	1256	1256	|	|	|	|	...	...	...	|	|	|	|	...	|	...	...	...	1456	1456	1456	|	|	...
emagen d.	...	1308	1308	|	|	|	|	...	...	...	|	|	|	|	...	|	...	...	...	1508	1508	1508	|	|	...
onn Hbf d.	...	1323	1323	1346	|	|	|	...	...	...	|	|	1446	|	...	|	...	...	...	1523	1523	1523	1546	|	...
Köln/Bonn Flughafen ✈ d.	...	|	|	|	|	|	|	...	...	...	|	|	|	|	...	|	...	...	...	|	|	|	|	|	...
öln Hbf a.	...	1343	1343	1405	1405	|	|	...	...	...	1433	|	1505	1505	...	|	...	...	...	1543	1543	1543	1605	1605	...
öln Hbf d.	1346	1346	1348	1409	1411	|	|	1448	...	1438	1444	|	1510	1511	1513	|	1520	1548	...	1546	1546	1546	1609	1611	1614
öln Messe/Deutz d.	|	|	|	|	|	1417	1427	|	...	|	|	1449	|	|	|	1517	|	|	...	|	|	|	|	|	|
Solingen Hbf d.	|	|	|	1429	|	|	|	|	...	|	|	|	|	1529	1531	|	|	|	...	|	|	|	1629	|	|
Wuppertal Hbf d.	|	|	1416	1443	|	|	|	1516	...	|	|	|	|	1542	1544	|	|	1616	...	|	|	|	1643	|	|
Hagen Hbf d.	|	|	1435	1501	|	|	|	1535t	...	|	|	|	|	1601	1602	|	|	1635	...	|	|	|	1701	|	|
üsseldorf Hbf d.	1412	1414	|	|	1433	1438	1448	|	1452	1509	1513	1517	1533	|	|	1538	1545	|	1551	1611	1612	1612	|	1633	1637
üsseldorf Flughafen ✈ d.	|	|	|	|	|	|	|	|	1500	|	|	|	|	|	|	|	1552	|	1559	|	|	|	|	|	|
uisburg Hbf d.	1427	1430	|	|	1447	1453	1502	|	1510	1524	1529	1533	1546	|	|	1551	1602	|	1609	1624	1626	1626	|	1647	1650
Oberhausen Hbf d.	1434	|	|	|	|	|	|	|	|	|	1534	|	|	|	|	|	|	|	|	|	1633	1633	|	|	|
ssen Hbf d.	|	1446	|	|	1459	1504	1517	|	1523	1537	...	1546	1559	|	|	1604	1616	|	1623	1640	|	|	|	1700	1702
Gelsenkirchen Hbf d.	1446	|	|	|	|	...	|	|	|	1548	...	|	|	|	|	|	|	|	|	|	1645	1646	|	|	|
Wanne-Eickel Hbf d.	1452	|	|	|	|	...	|	|	|	|	...	|	|	|	|	|	|	|	|	|	1651	1652	|	|	|
Recklinghausen Hbf d.	1500	|	|	|	|	...	|	|	|	1559	...	|	|	|	|	|	|	|	|	|	1700	1700	|	|	|
ochum Hbf d.	|	1457	|	|	1509	...	1528k	|	1535	|	...	|	|	|	|	1615k	1629	|	1635	1654	|	|	|	1710	|
ortmund Hbf a.	|	1508	|	1521	1521	...	1542k	|	1546	|	...	1607	|	1621	1621	1627k	1640	|	1646	1704	|	|	|	1721	|
ortmund Hbf **805** d.	|	1512	|	1525	...	...	...	|	1548	|	...	...	|	...	1628	...	1643	|	1648	...	|	|	|	...	|
Hamm (Westf) **805** a.	|	1532	1502	|	...	...	...	1602v	1607	|	...	...	|	...	1642	...	1702	1702	1707t	...	|	|	|	...	|
Hamm (Westf) d.	|	1534	1511	|	...	...	...	1611v	1611	|	...	...	|	...	1644	...	...	1711	1711t	...	|	|	|	...	|
Hannover Hbf **810** a.	|	1701	1701	|	...	...	...	1728	1728	|	...	...	|	...	1818	...	...	1828	1828	...	|	|	|	...	|
Leipzig Hbf **849a 866** a.	|	|	|	|	...	...	...	|	|	|	...	...	|	...	2115	...	...	|	|	...	|	|	|	...	|
Berlin Hbf **810** a.	|	1854	1854	|	...	...	...	1905	1905	|	...	...	|	...	...	...	...	2010	2010	...	|	|	|	...	|
ünster (Westf) Hbf **801** d.	1528	...	...	1557	...	...	...	...	...	1630	...	...	1657	...	...	...	...	...	...	...	1728	1728	1757	...	|
snabrück Hbf **801 815** d.	...	...	...	1623	...	...	...	...	...	1655t	...	...	1723	...	...	...	...	...	...	...	...	...	1823	...	|
remen Hbf **801 815** d.	...	...	...	1719	...	...	...	...	...	...	...	...	1819	...	...	...	...	...	...	...	...	...	1919	...	|
amburg Hbf **801** a.	...	...	...	1814	...	...	...	...	...	...	...	...	1914	...	...	...	...	...	...	...	...	...	2014	...	1946
amburg Altona a.	...	...	...	1829	...	...	...	...	...	...	...	...	1929	...	...	...	...	...	...	...	...	...	2029	...	2002

♦ – **NOTES** (LISTED BY TRAIN NUMBER)

955/9 – ⑤⑦ (also June 19, Oct. 2, 31; not June 21, Oct. 4, Nov. 1). 🚃 Düsseldorf - Kassel - Erfurt - Leipzig.
004 – ①②③④⑦ (also Nov. 1; not June 19, Oct. 2, 31). 🚃 (Konstanz - Karlsruhe ⑦ **w** -) Koblenz - Emden.
006 – 🚃 and 🍸 Konstanz - Karlsruhe - Mannheim - Dortmund.
014 – ⑤ (also June 19, Oct. 2, 31; not Nov. 1). 🚃 and 🍸 Stuttgart - Mannheim - Münster - Emden.
018 – ⑥ to Nov. 2 (also June 20, Oct. 3). 🚃 and 🍸 Stuttgart - Münster - Emden - Norddeich Mole.
157 – 🚃 Köln - Paderborn - Kassel - Erfurt (- Gera Ⓑ).
216 – GREIFSWALDER BODDEN – 🚃 and 🍸 Stuttgart - Köln - Hamburg - Stralsund (- Greifswald Ⓑ).
226 – 🚃 and 🍸 (Passau ⑤⑥ **u** -) (Regensburg ①–⑥ **e** -) Frankfurt - Köln - Hamburg - Kiel.

– To Amsterdam (Table **28**). Diversions / retimings are scheduled June 27 – 30, Aug. 2 – 11, Sept. 28, 29, Nov. 16, 17 (different train numbers may apply).
– To Berlin (Table **810**). On ⑦ runs with train number **2326** and continues to Rostock (Table **835**).
– To Dresden (Table **842**).
– To Norddeich Mole (Table **812**).
– From Passau (Table **920**).
– ①②③④⑥ (not June 19, July 13 - Aug. 24, Oct. 2, 31).
– ①②③④⑥ (also June 9, 21, Oct. 4, Nov. 1; not June 10, 19, Oct. 2, 31).

T – ①–⑤ (not June 10, 20, 21, Oct. 3, 4, Nov. 1). From Tübingen (Table **930**).
Y – ⑤⑦ until Oct. 11 (also June 19, Oct. 2; not June 21, Oct. 4).
Z – ⑤⑦ from Oct. 13 (also Oct. 31; not Nov. 1).

a – Ⓐ (not June 20, Nov. 1).
c – ⑥⑦ only.
d – Not June 20.
e – ①–⑥ only.
f – Not July 13 - Aug. 24, Oct. 26, Nov. 2.
g – Also July 13, 20, 27, Aug. 3, 10, 17, 24, Oct. 26, Nov. 2.
j – ①–⑥ from Oct. 12.
k – ⑥ only.
m – Not July 14 - Aug. 25, Oct. 3.
n – Not July 13 - Aug. 25.
r – Also June 10, 19, Oct. 2, 31; not June 9, 21, Oct. 4, Nov. 1.
s – Also June 20.
t – From Oct. 12.
u – Also June 19, 20.
v – Until Oct. 11 arrives Hamm 2 minutes earlier, departs 9 minutes earlier.
w – ⑦ (also June 20, Oct. 3, Nov. 1).

• – Calls at Frankfurt (Main) Süd (not Hbf) on ⑥⑦ Aug. 10 - Sept. 29 (departure may be up to 3 minutes earlier).
△ – Düsseldorf Hbf, Düsseldorf Flughafen and Duisburg departures are 1 minute later from Oct. 12.
⊙ – Runs as *ICE* **926** and conveys ✕ on ⑥.
❖ – Services in this table are subject to alteration July 13 - August 25, particularly those via Duisburg / Essen. See the engineering work panel on page 369 for further details and also for other alterations affecting services in this table.
‡ – June 11 - July 28 calls at Hamburg Harburg (not Hamburg Hbf).
§ – Frankfurt Flughafen Fernbahnhof (Tables **910** and **911**).

800 KOBLENZ - KÖLN - DORTMUND - HAMBURG

SEE NOTE ❖	ICE 628	ICE 653	ICE 643	IC 2012	EC 8	IC 2043	ICE 626	ICE 122	ICE 1055	ICE 945	IC 2002	ICE 922	ICE 516	ICE 624	ICE 1124	ICE 655	ICE 645	ICE 1010	IC 1918	EC 6	EC 6	ICE 204	ICE 104	IC 2041	ICE 622
			t						t	Ⓑ				⚒d	†s		t			Ⓑ	⑥	①–⑤		⑦	
	✕	✕	✕	🍷♦	✕♦	🍷♦	✕	A✕	✕	△✕	♦	✕	✕	✕	✕	✕	✕	✕	♦	D✕	D✕	✕	A✕	🍷	✕
Basel SBB 🚌 **912** d.	...	...	...	...	1220	...	...	...	...	...	...	...	...	...	...	...	...	...	...	1427	1427	1513	1513	...	...
Karlsruhe Hbf **912** d.	...	...	...	...	1412	...	...	...	...	...	...	...	...	...	...	...	...	...	...	1612	1612	1700	1700	...	...
München Hbf **904 930** d.	1151	...	...	...	│	...	1250	...	...	...	...	...	1328	1351	1351	...	...	...	...	│	│	│	│	...	1451
Stuttgart Hbf **912** d.	│	...	...	1312	│	...	│	...	...	...	...	...	1551	│	│	...	...	1637	1512	│	│	│	│	...	│
Nürnberg Hbf **920** d.	1257	...	...	│	│	...	1400	...	...	...	...	...	│	1500	1500	...	...	│	│	│	│	│	│	...	1600
Frankfurt (Main) Hbf **910/1** d.	1510•	...	...	│	│	...	1609•	1627	...	...	...	1544	│	1710•	1710•	...	...	│	│	│	│	│	│	...	1810•
Frankfurt Flughafen ✈ § d.	1525	...	...	│	│	...	1626	1643	...	...	...	1558	1709	1725	1722	...	...	1755	│	│	│	1809	1809	...	1825
Mainz Hbf **911** d.	│	...	...	1449	1520	...	│	│	...	...	...	1620	│	│	│	...	...	│	1649	1720	1720	│	│	...	│
Koblenz Hbf d.	│	...	...	1544	1613	...	│	│	...	...	...	1713	│	│	│	...	...	│	1744	1813	1813	│	│	...	│
Andernach d.	│	...	...	1556	│	...	│	│	...	...	...	│	│	│	│	...	...	│	1756	│	│	│	│	...	│
Remagen d.	│	...	...	1608	│	...	│	│	...	...	...	│	│	│	│	...	...	│	1808	│	│	│	│	...	│
Bonn Hbf d.	│	...	...	1623	1646	...	│	│	...	...	1723h	1746	│	│	│	...	...	│	1823	1846	1846	│	│	...	│
Köln/Bonn Flughafen ✈ d.	│	...	...	│	│	...	│	│	...	...	│	│	│	│	│	...	...	│	│	│	│	│	│	...	│
Köln Hbf a.	│	...	...	1643	1705	...	│	1739	...	...	1742h	1805	1805	│	│	...	...	│	1843	1905	1905	1905	1905	...	│
Köln Hbf d.	│	1648	...	1646	1709	1713	│	1746	1748	...	1745	1809	1811	│	│	1848	...	│	1846	1909	1909	1911	1914	1913	│
Köln Messe/Deutz d.	1619	│	...	│	│	│	1717	│	│	...	│	│	│	1817	1828	│	...	1843	│	│	│	│	│	│	1924
Solingen Hbf d.	│	│	...	│	│	1731	│	│	│	...	│	1829	│	│	│	│	...	│	│	│	│	1929	│	1931	│
Wuppertal Hbf d.	│	1716	...	│	│	1744	│	│	1816	...	│	1843	│	│	│	1916	...	│	│	│	│	1942	│	1944	│
Hagen Hbf d.	│	1735t	...	│	│	1802	│	│	1835	...	│	1901	│	│	│	1935t	...	│	│	│	│	2001	│	2002	│
Düsseldorf Hbf d.	1641	│	1652	1714	1732	│	1738	1813	│	1751	1817z	│	1833	1838	1848	│	1852	1907	1913	1932	1932	│	1938	│	1946
Düsseldorf Flughafen ✈ d.	│	│	1700	│	│	│	│	│	│	1759	│	│	│	│	│	│	1900	│	│	│	│	│	│	│	│
Duisburg Hbf d.	1654	│	1710	1732	1747	│	1751	1827	│	1809	1830	│	1847	1851	1902	│	1910	1924	1932	1946	1946	│	1951	│	2003
Oberhausen Hbf d.	│	│	│	│	│	│	│	1832	│	│	1837	│	│	│	│	│	│	│	│	│	│	│	1957	│	│
Essen Hbf d.	1717z	│	1723	1745	1800	│	1804	...	│	1823	│	│	1859	1904	1917	│	1923	1936	1946	1959	1959	│	...	│	2017
Gelsenkirchen Hbf d.	│	│	│	│	│	│	│	...	│	│	1849	│	│	│	│	│	│	1946	│	│	│	│	...	│	│
Wanne-Eickel Hbf d.	│	│	│	│	│	│	│	...	│	│	│	│	│	│	│	│	│	1952	│	│	│	│	...	│	│
Recklinghausen Hbf d.	│	│	│	│	│	│	│	...	│	│	1900	│	│	│	│	│	│	2000	│	│	│	│	...	│	│
Bochum Hbf d.	1729k	│	1735	1756	│	│	1815k	...	│	1835	│	│	1910	1915	1929	│	1935	│	1957	│	2010	│	...	│	2029
Dortmund Hbf a.	1742k	│	1746	1807	│	1821	1830k	...	│	1846	│	1921	1921	1930	1942	│	1946	│	2007	│	2021	2021	...	2021	2042
Dortmund Hbf **805** d.	...	│	1748	...	│	1828	...	...	│	1848	│	1924	...	...	...	│	1948	│	...	│	...	...	...	2028	...
Hamm (Westf) **805** a.	...	1802v	1807	...	│	1842	...	...	1902	1907t	│	│	...	...	...	2002v	2007	│	...	│	...	...	...	2042	...
Hamm (Westf) d.	...	1811v	1811	...	│	1844	...	...	1911	1911t	│	│	...	...	...	2011v	2011	│	...	│	...	...	...	2044	...
Hannover Hbf **810** a.	...	1928	1928	...	│	2018	...	...	2028	2028	│	│	...	...	...	2128	2128	│	...	│	...	...	...	2218	...
Leipzig Hbf **849a 866** a.	...	│	│	...	│	2318w	...	...	│	│	│	│	...	...	...	│	│	│	...	│	...	...	...	...	...
Berlin Hbf **810** a.	...	2105	2105	...	│	...	...	...	2218	2218	│	│	...	...	...	2306	2306	│	...	│	...	...	...	...	...
Münster (Westf) Hbf **801** d.	...	...	...	...	1857	...	...	...	...	...	1928	1959	...	...	...	...	...	2028	...	2057	...	...	...	...	...
Osnabrück Hbf **801 815** d.	...	...	...	...	1924	...	...	...	...	...	...	2025	...	...	...	...	...	...	...	2123	...	...	...	...	...
Bremen Hbf **801 815** d.	...	...	...	...	2019	...	...	...	...	...	...	2119	...	...	...	...	...	...	...	2220	...	...	...	...	...
Hamburg Hbf **801** a.	...	...	...	...	2114	...	...	...	...	...	...	2214	...	...	...	...	...	...	...	2316	...	...	...	...	...
Hamburg Altona a.	...	...	...	...	2129	...	...	...	...	...	...	2229	...	...	...	...	...	...	...	2331	...	...	...	...	...

SEE NOTE ❖	ICE 828	ICE 1057	ICE 947	EC 114	ICE 26	ICE 1212	ICE 620	ICE 120	ICE 912	ICE 657	IC 2318	IC 2318	ICE 1102	ICE 102	ICE 528	ICE 1622	ICE 512	ICE 526	IC 1910	IC 2210	ICE 100	ICE 949	ICE 524	ICE 22	ICE 522
	①–④	⑤⑦				¶		Ⓑ	Ⓑn	⑦		Ⓑ	⑥	Ⓑ					⑦	Ⓑ					
	j✕	t✕	△✕	🍷♦	B✕	✕	✕	A✕	✕	✕	🍷	🍷	✕	✕	✕	H✕			🍷	🍷		♥		B✕	
Basel SBB 🚌 **912** d.	...	...	...	...	...	...	...	...	...	...	...	...	1713	1713	...	...	...	...	...	...	1913	...	...	...	...
Karlsruhe Hbf **912** d.	...	...	...	...	...	...	...	...	...	...	...	...	1900	1900	...	...	...	...	...	...	2101	...	...	...	...
München Hbf **904 930** d.	...	...	...	1347x	...	1528	1551	...	...	...	...	...	│	│	1649	1618	1728	1751	1618c	...	│	...	1851	...	1948
Stuttgart Hbf **912** d.	...	...	...	1608	...	1751	│	...	1837	...	1737	1737	│	│	│	│	1951	│	1914	1918‡	│	...	│	...	│
Nürnberg Hbf **920** d.	...	...	...	│	1530o	│	1657	...	│	...	│	│	│	│	1800	1736	│	1857	│	│	│	...	2000	1930	2100
Frankfurt (Main) Hbf **910/1** d.	1816*	...	...	│	1742	│	1910•	1929	│	...	│	│	│	│	2010•	1940	│	2110•	│	│	│	...	2210•	2146	2310◊
Frankfurt Flughafen ✈ § d.	1831*	...	...	│	1758	1909	1922	1943	1955	...	│	│	2009	2009	2025	1958	2109	2125	│	│	2209	...	2225	2159	2325
Mainz Hbf **911** d.	│	...	...	1744	1820	│	│	│	│	...	1920	1920	│	│	│	2020f	│	│	2049	2120	│	...	│	2220	│
Koblenz Hbf d.	│	...	...	1844	1913	│	│	│	│	...	2013	2013	│	│	│	2113	│	│	2144	2213	│	...	│	2313	│
Andernach d.	│	...	...	1856	│	│	│	│	│	...	│	│	│	│	│	│	│	│	2156	│	│	...	│	│	│
Remagen d.	│	...	...	1908	│	│	│	│	│	...	│	│	│	│	│	│	│	│	2208	│	│	...	│	│	│
Bonn Hbf d.	│	...	...	1923	1946	│	│	│	│	2024t	2046	2046	│	│	│	2146	│	│	2223	2246	│	...	│	2346	│
Köln/Bonn Flughafen ✈ d.	1939	...	...	│	│	│	│	│	│	│	│	│	│	│	│	│	│	│	│	│	│	...	2328	│	│
Köln Hbf a.	│	...	...	1943	2005	2005r	│	2033	│	2044t	2105	2105	2105	2105	│	2205	2205	│	2243	2305	2305	...	│	0005	0039
Köln Hbf d.	│	1948	1927b	1946	2009	2011r	│	2042	│	2048	...	2109	2111	2111	│	2210	2211	│	2246	...	2311	2245	│	0009	0042
Köln Messe/Deutz d.	1951	│	│	│	│	2008q	2027	│	2047	│	...	│	│	│	2117	│	│	2217	│	...	│	│	2339	│	│
Solingen Hbf d.	│	│	│	│	2029	│	│	│	│	│	...	│	│	2129	│	2230	│	│	│	...	│	│	│	│	│
Wuppertal Hbf d.	2017	2016	│	│	2043	│	│	│	│	2116	...	│	│	2142	│	2243	│	│	│	...	│	│	│	│	│
Hagen Hbf d.	2035	2035	│	│	2101	│	│	│	│	2135t	...	│	│	2201	│	2301	│	│	│	...	│	│	│	│	│
Düsseldorf Hbf d.	│	│	1951	2010	│	2032	2048	2109	2113	│	...	2132	2133	│	2138	│	2233	2238	2309	...	2333	2341	0000	0032	0105
Düsseldorf Flughafen ✈ d.	│	│	1959	│	│	│	│	│	│	│	...	│	│	│	│	│	│	│	│	...	2341	│	│	│	0113
Duisburg Hbf d.	│	│	2009	2024	│	2047	2102	2126	2129	│	...	2146	2146	│	2151	│	2246	2251	2323	...	2351	2356	0013	0046	0123
Oberhausen Hbf d.	│	│	│	│	│	│	│	2132	│	│	...	│	│	│	│	│	│	│	│	...	│	│	│	│	│
Essen Hbf d.	│	│	2023	2040	│	2059	2117	...	2142	│	...	2159	2200	│	2204	│	2307z	2304	2340	...	0004	0008	0027	0058	0136
Gelsenkirchen Hbf d.	│	│	│	│	│	│	│	...	│	│	...	│	│	│	│	│	2317	│	│	...	│	│	│	│	│
Wanne-Eickel Hbf d.	│	│	│	│	│	│	│	...	│	│	...	│	│	│	│	│	│	│	│	...	│	│	│	│	│
Recklinghausen Hbf d.	│	│	│	│	│	│	│	...	│	│	...	│	│	│	│	│	2328	│	│	...	│	│	│	│	│
Bochum Hbf d.	│	│	2035	2052	│	2109	2129	...	2152	│	...	2210	2211	│	2215	│	│	2315	2351	...	0015	0019	0037	0109	0145
Dortmund Hbf a.	│	│	2046	2103	2120	2121	2142	...	2203	│	...	2221	2222	2221	2228	2320	│	2326	0002	...	0026	0030	0050	0121	0156
Dortmund Hbf **805** d.	│	│	2048	...	...	2124	...	...	...	│	...	2232w	2228	2228	...	...	│	...	...	...	...	0032	...	...	...
Hamm (Westf) **805** a.	2104	2102	2107t	...	...	│	...	...	...	2202	...	│	2247	2247	...	...	│	...	...	...	...	0047	...	...	...
Hamm (Westf) d.	...	2111	2111t	...	...	│	...	...	...	2210e	...	│	2249	2249	...	...	│	...	...	...	...	0049	...	...	...
Hannover Hbf **810** a.	...	2228	2228	...	...	│	...	...	...	2328	...	│	0018	0018	...	...	│	...	...	...	...	0223	...	...	...
Leipzig Hbf **849a 866** a.	...	│	│	...	...	│	...	...	...	│	...	│	...	...	...	...	│	...	...	...	...	...	...	...	...
Berlin Hbf **810** a.	...	0010	0010	...	...	│	...	...	...	0110	...	│	...	...	...	...	│	...	...	...	...	0536	...	...	...
Münster (Westf) Hbf **801** d.	...	...	...	...	...	2156	...	...	...	...	...	2316w	...	...	...	...	2358	...	...	...	...	...	...	...	...
Osnabrück Hbf **801 815** d.	...	...	...	...	...	2224	...	...	...	...	...	...	...	...	...	...	...	...	...	...	...	...	...	...	...
Bremen Hbf **801 815** d.	...	...	...	...	...	2320	...	...	...	...	...	...	...	...	...	...	...	...	...	...	...	...	...	...	...
Hamburg Hbf **801** a.	...	...	...	...	...	0016	...	...	...	...	...	...	...	...	...	...	...	...	...	...	...	...	...	...	...
Hamburg Altona a.	...	...	...	...	...	0033	...	...	...	...	...	...	...	...	...	...	...	...	...	...	...	...	...	...	...

♦ – **NOTES** (LISTED BY TRAIN NUMBER)

8 – [12] and ✕ Zürich - Basel - Hamburg.
114 – WÖRTHERSEE – [12] and 🍷 Klagenfurt - Salzburg - München - Dortmund.
1918 – [12] (June 25 - Sept. 9 and Nov. 10 - Dec. 14: Berchtesgaden -) Stuttgart - Dortmund.
2002 – [12] Bonn - Köln - Münster (- Emden on dates in Table **812**).
2012 – ALLGÄU – [12] and 🍷 Oberstdorf - Ulm - Stuttgart - Dortmund.
2043 – [12] Köln - Hannover (- Magdeburg Ⓑ) (- Leipzig ⑦).

A – To Amsterdam (Table **28**). Diversions/retimings are scheduled June 27 – 30, Aug. 2 – 11, Sept. 28, 29, Nov. 16, 17 (different train numbers may apply; also applies to train *ICE* **120** on June 26, Aug. 1, Sept. 27 and Nov. 15).
B – From Wien (Tables **950**/**920**).
D – From Interlaken via Bern (Table **560**).
H – From Innsbruck via Garmisch (Table **895**) on ©. Train number **1222** on ©.

b – Daily to Oct. 12; ①②③④⑥ from Oct. 14.
c – 1614 until July 28.
d – Not June 20.
e – 2203 until Oct. 6.
f – Until Oct. 25.
h – Ⓑ to Nov. 1 (not June 20, Oct. 3); daily from Nov. 3.
j – Not Oct. 2.
k – ⑥ only.
n – Not July 14 - Aug. 25.
o – 1 – 2 minutes later on ⑦.
q – Until Sept. 1.
r – From Sept. 2.
s – Also June 20.
t – From Oct. 12.
v – Until Oct. 11 arrives Hamm 2 minutes earlier, departs 9 minutes earlier.
w – ⑦ only.
x – Until July 28 serves München Pasing (not Hbf).
z – Arrives 8 – 11 minutes earlier.

* – 19 minutes earlier from Oct. 28.
‡ – 1937 on ⑤⑦ to July 14 (also June 19; not June 21), Ⓑ Jul 19 - Sept. 8, ⑤⑦ from Sept. 13 (also Oct. 31; not Nov. 1
• – Calls at Frankfurt (Main) Süd (not Hbf) on ⑥⑦ Aug. 10 - Sept. 29 (departure may be up to 3 minutes earlier).
◊ – Calls at Frankfurt Süd (not Hbf) on ⑤–⑦ Aug. 9 - Sept. 2 (d. 2307).
¶ – Train number **1210** from Sept. 2.
△ – Düsseldorf Hbf, Düsseldorf Flughafen and Duisburg departures are 1 minute later from Oct. 12.
♥ – On ⑤ June 28 - Sept. 13 runs as *IC* **1049**, departs Köln 2317, arrives Berlin Hbf 0531 and continues to Ostseebac Binz via Rostock and Stralsund (Tables **830**, **835** and **844**)
❖ – Services in this table are subject to alteration July 13 - August 25, particularly those via Duisburg/Essen. See the engineering work panel on page 369 for further details and also for other alterations affecting services in this table.
§ – Frankfurt Flughafen Fernbahnhof (Tables **910**/**911**).

HAMBURG - DORTMUND - KÖLN - KOBLENZ 800

km	SEE NOTE ❖	ICE 523	ICE 511	ICE 23	ICE 1125	ICE 525	ICE 101	IC 2319	ICE 948	ICE 913	IC 2003	ICE 813	ICE 1127	ICE 527	ICE 1221	ICE 513	ICE 815	EC 115	ICE 529	ICE 103	EC 7	EC 7	ICE 121	ICE 1011	IC 1919
		①-⑥	①		⑦p	①-⑥	①-⑥	①-⑥		①-⑥	Ⓐ	①-⑤	⑥	①-⑤			①-⑤				①-⑥	⑦	①-⑥		
		✕	g	✕♦	✕	d✕	✕	🍷	♥	n✕	a		✕	✕	T✕	✕	✕	🍷♦	✕	✕	D✕	D✕	A✕	✕	♦
	Hamburg Altona d.	...	...	...	...	...	...	...	...	...	...	...	...	...	...	...	...	...	...	...	0423	...	...	...	...
	Hamburg Hbf 801 d.	...	...	...	...	...	...	...	...	...	...	...	...	...	...	...	...	...	...	...	0438	...	...	...	...
	Bremen Hbf 801 815 d.	...	...	...	...	...	...	...	...	...	...	...	...	...	...	...	...	...	...	...	0540	...	...	...	...
	Osnabrück Hbf 801 815 d.	...	...	...	...	...	...	...	...	...	...	...	...	...	...	...	...	...	...	...	0637	...	...	...	...
	Münster (Westf) Hbf 801 d.	...	...	...	...	...	...	0446g	...	...	...	...	...	...	...	0601	...	0631	...	...	0703	...	...	0727	...
	Berlin Hbf 810 d.	...	...	...	...	...	...	|	2352	...	...	...	...	...	...	|	...	|	...	...	|	...	...	|	...
	Leipzig Hbf 849a 866 d.	...	...	...	...	...	...	|	|	...	...	...	...	...	...	|	...	|	...	...	|	...	...	|	...
	Hannover Hbf 810 d.	...	...	...	...	...	...	|	0340	...	...	...	...	...	...	|	...	|	...	0540	|	...	...	|	...
	Hamm (Westf) a.	...	...	...	...	...	...	|	0509	...	...	...	...	...	...	|	...	|	...	0713	|	...	...	|	...
0	Hamm (Westf) 805 d.	...	...	...	...	...	...	|	0511	...	...	...	...	...	...	|	...	|	...	0715	|	...	...	|	...
	Dortmund Hbf 805 a.	...	...	...	...	...	...	0521g	0530	...	...	...	...	...	...	0634	...	|	...	0732	|	...	...	|	...
	Dortmund Hbf d.	0404	0435	0435	0512	0523	0535	0537	0533	0550	0548	0558	0612	0623	0635	0637	0650	|	0723	0737	|	0737	...	|	0724
	Bochum Hbf d.	0417	|	0449	0525	0537	|	0550	|	0604	|	|	0625	0637	|	0648	0703	|	0737	|	|	0750	...	|	|
	Recklinghausen Hbf d.	|	|	|	|	|	|	|	|	|	|	|	|	|	|	|	|	0700	|	|	|	|	...	0758	|
	Wanne-Eickel Hbf d.	|	|	|	|	|	|	|	|	|	0608	|	|	|	|	|	|	0708	|	|	|	|	...	0806	|
	Gelsenkirchen Hbf d.	|	|	|	|	|	|	|	|	|	0614	|	|	|	|	|	|	0714	|	|	|	|	...	0812	|
	Essen Hbf d.	0430	|	0500	0537	0554	|	0600	0604	0615	|	|	0637	0653	|	0700	0715	|	0753	|	0800	0800	...	0823	|
	Oberhausen Hbf d.	|	|	|	|	|	|	|	|	|	0627	|	|	|	|	|	|	0726	|	|	|	|	0826	|	|
	Duisburg Hbf d.	0444	|	0513	0551	0607	|	0613	0618	0628	0634	|	0651	0707	|	0713	0729	0734	0807	|	0813	0813	0834	0838	|
	Düsseldorf Flughafen ✈ d.	|	|	|	|	|	|	|	|	|	|	|	|	|	|	|	|	|	|	|	|	|	|	|	|
	Düsseldorf Hbf d.	0458	|	0527	0606	0621	|	0627	0633	0648	0652	|	0706	0721	|	0727	0745	0751	0821	|	0827	0827	0847	0852	|
48	**Hagen** Hbf d.	|	0457	|	|	|	0557	|	|	|	|	0621	|	|	0657	|	|	|	|	0757	|	|	|	|	0753
75	Wuppertal Hbf d.	|	0515	|	|	|	0614	|	|	|	|	0637	|	|	0714	|	|	|	|	0814	|	|	|	|	0830
93	Solingen Hbf d.	|	0526	|	|	|	0627	|	|	|	|	0649	|	|	0727	|	|	|	|	0827	|	|	|	|	|
120	**Köln** Messe/Deutz a.	0518	|	|	0627	0642	|	|	|	0710	|	|	0728	0742	|	|	0809	|	0842	|	|	|	|	0915	|
121	**Köln** Hbf a.	|	0546	0550	|	|	0646	0650	0657	|	0715	0709	|	|	0746	0749	|	0815	|	0846	0850	0850	0915	|	0912
	Köln Hbf d.	|	0555	0553	|	|	0655	0653	...	|	0718	0720	|	|	0753	0755	|	0818	|	0855	0853	0853	0928	|	0917
	Köln/Bonn Flughafen ✈ a.	0529	|	|	|	|	|	|	...	|	|	|	|	|	|	|	0820	|	|	|	|	|	|	|	|
	Bonn Hbf d.	|	|	0614	|	|	|	0714	...	|	0738	|	|	|	0814	|	|	0838	|	|	0914	0914	|	|	0938
	Remagen d.	|	|	|	|	|	|	|	...	|	0751	|	|	|	|	|	|	0851	|	|	|	|	|	|	0951
	Andernach d.	|	|	|	|	|	|	|	...	|	0804	|	|	|	|	|	|	0904	|	|	|	|	|	|	1004
	Koblenz Hbf a.	|	|	0646	|	|	|	0746	...	|	0816	|	|	|	0846	|	|	0916	|	|	0946	0946	|	|	1016
	Mainz Hbf 911 a.	|	|	0738	|	|	|	0839	...	|	...	|	|	|	0939	|	|	1015	|	|	1039	1039	|	|	1110
	Frankfurt Flughafen ✈ § a.	0633	0649	0759	0733	0733	0749	|	...	0807	...	0826	0833	0833	0959	0849	0926	|	0933	0949	|	|	1016	1007	|
	Frankfurt (Main) Hbf 910/1 a.	0648•	|	0813	0748•	0748•	|	|	...	|	...	0841	0848•	0848	1013	|	0941	|	0948•	|	|	|	1031	|	|
	Nürnberg Hbf 920 a.	0901	|	1027	0958	0958	|	|	...	|	...	...	1100	1100	1224	|	...	|	1159	|	|	|	...	|	|
	Stuttgart Hbf 912 a.	|	0808	...	|	|	|	1024	...	0924	...	...	|	|	|	1008	...	1153	|	|	|	|	...	1122	1246
	München Hbf 904 930 a.	1006	1027	...	1108	1108	|	...	...	...	...	...	1207	1207	1338	1227	...	1411x	1306	|	|	|	...	...	...
	Karlsruhe Hbf 912 a.	...	...	...	...	...	0858	...	...	...	...	...	...	...	...	...	...	...	...	1058	1147	1147	...	...	...
	Basel SBB 🏛 912 a.	...	...	...	...	...	1047	...	...	...	...	...	...	...	...	...	...	...	...	1247	1330	1330	...	...	...

SEE NOTE ❖	ICE 646	ICE 656	ICE 621	IC 1099	IC 2401	ICE 27	ICE 1113	IC 2005	ICE 946	ICE 1056	ICE 623	ICE 105	IC 2042	EC 9	IC 2013	ICE 644	ICE 654	ICE 625	ICE 923	ICE 517	IC 2009	ICE 944	ICE 1054	IC 2156	ICE 627
	Ⓐt	Ⓐ		①-④	⑤f		¶	①-⑥	①-⑥	①-⑥						①-⑥							①-⑥		
	✕	✕	✕	◇🍷	🍷	✕♦	✕	🍷♦	✕	t✕	✕	A✕	🍷♦	Z✕	🍷♦	t✕	✕	✕	✕	✕	♦	✕	t✕	♦	✕
amburg Altona d.	...	...	...	0556	0558	...	0520	...	...	...	...	...	...	0631	...	...	...	...	0730	...	...	...	...	...	...
amburg Hbf 801 d.	...	...	...	0610	0612	...	0546	...	...	...	...	...	...	0646	...	...	...	...	0746	...	...	...	...	...	...
remen Hbf 801 815 d.	...	...	...	|	|	...	0644	...	...	...	...	...	...	0744	...	...	...	...	0844	...	...	...	...	...	...
snabrück Hbf 801 815 d.	...	...	...	|	|	...	0737	...	...	...	...	...	...	0837	...	...	...	...	0937	...	...	...	...	...	...
inster (Westf) Hbf 801 d.	...	...	...	|	|	...	0802	0832	...	...	...	...	...	0903	...	...	...	...	1003	...	1032	...	...	...	...
Berlin Hbf 810 d.	0430	0430	...	|	|	...	|	|	0540	0540	...	...	...	|	...	0650	0650	...	|	...	|	0749	0749	...	...
Leipzig Hbf 849a 866 d.	|	|	...	|	|	...	|	|	|	|	...	...	0439g	|	...	|	|	...	|	...	|	|	|	...	...
Hannover Hbf 810 d.	0621	0621	...	|	|	...	|	|	0731	0731	...	...	0740	|	...	0831	0831	...	|	...	|	0931	0931	...	...
Hamm (Westf) a.	0748	0748v	...	|	|	...	|	|	0848t	0848	...	...	0914	|	...	0948	0948v	...	|	...	|	1048t	1048	...	...
Hamm (Westf) 805 d.	0752	0754v	...	|	|	...	|	|	0852t	0854	...	...	0916	|	...	0952	0954v	...	|	...	|	1052t	1054	1056	...
ortmund Hbf 805 a.	0809	|	...	|	|	...	0833	|	0910	|	...	...	0932	|	...	1009	|	...	1033	...	|	1110	|	1114	...
ortmund Hbf d.	0812	|	0813c	|	|	0834	0837	|	0912	|	0915c	...	0937	|	0950	1012	|	1014c	1036	1035	|	1112	|	1116	1123j
chum Hbf d.	0824	|	0827c	|	|	|	0848	|	0924	|	0928c	...	|	|	1003	1024	|	1028c	|	1048	|	1124	|	1129	1137j
Recklinghausen Hbf d.	|	|	|	|	|	|	|	0900	|	|	|	...	|	|	|	|	|	|	|	|	1100	|	|	|	|
Wanne-Eickel Hbf d.	|	|	|	|	|	|	|	0909	|	|	|	...	|	|	|	|	|	|	|	|	1109	|	|	|	|
Gelsenkirchen Hbf d.	|	|	|	|	|	|	|	0915	|	|	|	...	|	|	|	|	|	|	|	|	1115	|	|	|	|
ssen Hbf d.	0836	|	0840	0854	0854	|	0900	|	0936	|	0941	...	|	1000	1014	1036	|	1041	|	1100	|	1136	|	1140	1154
Oberhausen Hbf d.	|	|	|	|	|	|	|	0927	|	|	|	0959	|	|	|	|	|	|	|	|	1127	|	|	|	|
uisburg Hbf d.	0849	|	0855	0907	0907	|	0913	0934	0949	|	0955	1008	|	1013	1029	1049	|	1055	|	1113	1134	1149	|	1155	1207
isseldorf Flughafen ✈ d.	0857s	|	|	|	|	|	|	|	0957s	|	|	|	|	|	|	1057s	|	|	|	|	|	1157s	|	1205	|
isseldorf Hbf d.	0906	|	0913	0921	0921	|	0927	0949	1006	|	1012	1022	|	1027	1048	1110	|	1108	|	1127	1149	1206	|	1214	1221
Hagen Hbf d.	...	0823t	|	|	|	0857	|	|	...	0923	|	|	0958	|	|	...	1023t	|	|	|	|	...	1123	|	|
Wuppertal Hbf d.	...	0840	|	|	|	0914	|	|	...	0940	|	|	1014	|	|	...	1040	|	1114	|	|	...	1140	|	|
Solingen Hbf d.	...	|	|	|	|	0925	|	|	...	|	|	|	1027	|	|	...	|	|	1128	|	|	...	|	|	|
öln Messe/Deutz a.	...	|	0934	|	|	|	0947h	|	...	|	1032	|	|	|	|	...	|	1128	|	|	|	...	|	|	1242
öln Hbf a.	...	0909	|	0945	0945	0946	0949q	1015	...	1009	|	1046	1046	1050	1113	...	1109	|	1146	1149	1215	...	1209	1239	|
öln Hbf d.	...	...	|	...	...	0953	0955q	1018	...	...	|	1055	...	1053	1117	...	...	|	1153	1155	...	...	...	...	|
Köln/Bonn Flughafen ✈ a.	...	...	|	...	...	|	|	|	...	...	1043	|	...	|	|	...	...	|	|	|	...	...	...	...	|
onn Hbf d.	...	...	|	...	...	1014	|	1038	...	...	|	|	...	1114	1137	...	...	|	1214	|	...	...	...	...	|
emagen d.	...	...	|	...	...	|	|	1051	...	...	|	|	...	|	1151	...	...	|	|	|	...	...	...	...	|
dernach d.	...	...	|	...	...	|	|	1104	...	...	|	|	...	|	1204	...	...	|	|	|	...	...	...	...	|
oblenz Hbf a.	...	...	|	...	...	1046	|	1116	...	...	|	|	...	1146	1216	...	...	|	1246	|	...	...	...	...	|
Mainz Hbf 911 a.	...	...	|	...	...	1139	|	1215r	...	...	|	|	...	1239	1310	...	...	|	1339	|	...	...	...	...	|
Frankfurt Flughafen ✈ § a.	...	...	1033	...	...	1159	1050	|	...	...	1133	1149	...	|	|	...	...	1233	1401	1249	...	...	...	...	1333
Frankfurt (Main) Hbf 910/1 a.	...	...	1048•	...	...	1213	|	|	...	...	1148•	|	...	|	|	...	...	1248•	1413	|	...	...	...	...	1348•
Nürnberg Hbf 920 a.	...	...	1259	...	...	1427	|	|	...	...	1404	|	...	|	|	...	...	1500	...	|	...	...	...	...	1559
Stuttgart Hbf 912 a.	...	...	|	...	...	...	1208	|	...	...	|	|	...	|	1446	...	...	|	...	1408	...	...	...	...	|
München Hbf 904 930 a.	...	...	1406	...	...	...	1427	|	...	...	1509	|	...	|	...	...	...	1606	...	1627	...	...	...	...	1704
Karlsruhe Hbf 912 a.	...	...	...	...	...	...	...	1334r	...	...	...	1258	...	1347	...	...	...	...	...	...	...	...	...	...	...
Basel SBB 🏛 912 a.	...	...	...	...	...	...	...	...	...	...	...	1447	...	1535	...	...	...	...	...	...	...	...	...	...	...

– **NOTES** (LISTED BY TRAIN NUMBER)

7 – [12] and ✕ Dortmund - Regensburg - Passau - Linz - Wien.
5 – WÖRTHERSEE – [12] and 🍷 Münster - München - Salzburg - Klagenfurt.
19 – [12] Dortmund - Stuttgart (- Berchtesgaden June 24 - Sept. 8 and Nov. 9 - Dec. 14).
05 – [12] and 🍷 Emden - Münster - Koblenz (- Karlsruhe - Konstanz ⑤⑥ **r**).
09 – [12] (Emden on dates in Table **812** -) Münster - Köln.
13 – ALLGÄU – [12] and 🍷 Dortmund - Mainz - Mannheim - Stuttgart - Oberstdorf.
42 – [12] (Leipzig ① **g** -) (Magdeburg ①-⑥ -) Hannover - Köln.
56 – [12] (Gera ①-⑥ -) Erfurt - Kassel - Paderborn - Köln.

- From Amsterdam (Table **28**). Diversions / retimings are scheduled June 27 – 30, Aug. 2 – 11, Sept. 28, 29, Nov. 16, 17 (different train numbers may apply).
- To Interlaken via Bern (Table **560**).
- Continues to Seefeld (Table **895**) on ⑤⑥ (also Oct. 2).
- To Zürich (Tables **510**).

- Not June 20, Nov. 1.

c – ⑥⑦ only.
d – Not June 20, Oct. 3.
f – Also Oct. 2; not June 21, July 19 - Aug. 23, Oct. 4, Nov. 1.
g – ① (also June 11).
h – Until Sept. 1.
j – ⑤-⑦ (also Oct. 2; not Oct. 4).
n – Not July 13 - Aug. 25.
p – Also June 20, Oct. 3.
q – From Sept. 2.
r – ⑤⑥ (also June 19, Oct. 2, 31).
s – Stops to set down only.
t – From Oct. 12.
v – Until Oct. 11 arrives Hamm 6 minutes later, departs 2 minutes later.
x – Until July 28 serves München Pasing (not München Hbf).

◇ – ①-④ (not July 15 - Aug. 22, Oct. 2, 3). Runs as *ICE* **1099** and conveys ✕ from Oct. 14.
¶ – Train number **1211** from Sept. 2.
• – Calls at Frankfurt (Main) Süd (not Hbf) on ⑥⑦ Aug. 10 - Sept. 29.
♥ – On ⑥ June 29 - Sept. 14 (from Berlin) departs Berlin Hbf 2343 and runs as *IC* **1048** from Ostseebad Binz via Stralsund and Rostock (Tables **830**, **835** and **844**).
❖ – Services in this table are subject to alteration July 13 - August 25, particularly those via Duisburg / Essen. See engineering work panel on page 369 for further details and also for other alterations affecting services in this table.
§ – Frankfurt Flughafen Fernbahnhof (Tables **910** and **911**).

800 HAMBURG - DORTMUND - KÖLN - KOBLENZ

	ICE	IC	IC	IC	ICE	IC	ICE	ICE	ICE	ICE	ICE	IC	IC	ICE	ICE	ICE	ICE	IC	IC	IC	ICE	IC		ICE	ICE
SEE NOTE ❖	**107**	**2044**	**2313**	**1911**	**123**	**1929**	**642**	**652**	**629**	**925**	**519**	**5106**	**2001** **2201**	**942**	**1052**	**721**	**109**	**2046**	**2217**	**2417**	**915**	**2011**		**640**	**650**
	⑦	①–⑥		⑤⑦		①–⑤	t			▽					t		⑦	①–⑥			⊡	Ⓑ		t	
	✕	D	🍷	u 🍷	A ✕	B 🍷	✕	✕	✕	✕	✕	L	N	✕	✕	✕	✕	D 🍷	🍷 ♦	♦	✕	U 🍷		✕	✕
Hamburg Altona d.	...	...	0829	...	...	...	...	...	...	0930	...	...	...	...	...	...	...	...	...	...	...	...	...	...	...
Hamburg Hbf 801 d.	...	...	0846	...	...	...	...	...	...	0946	...	...	...	...	...	...	...	...	1046‡	1117x	...	...	...	...	...
Bremen Hbf 801 815 d.	...	...	0944	...	...	...	...	...	...	1044	...	...	...	...	...	...	...	...	1144	|	...	...	...	...	...
Osnabrück Hbf 801 815 d.	...	...	1037	...	...	1108	...	...	...	1137	...	...	...	...	...	...	...	...	1237	|	...	...	...	...	...
Münster (Westf) Hbf 801 d.	...	...	1103	...	...	1132	...	...	...	1203	...	...	1232	...	...	...	...	...	1303	|	...	...	...	...	...
Berlin Hbf 810 d.	...	...	|	...	...	|	0850	0850	...	|	...	...	|	0950	0950	...	...	...	|	|	...	...	...	1050	1050
Leipzig Hbf 849a 866 d.	...	0636	|	...	...	|	|	|	...	|	...	...	|	|	|	...	...	0836	|	|	...	...	...	|	|
Hannover Hbf 810 d.	...	0940	|	...	...	|	1031	1031	...	|	...	...	|	1131	1131	...	...	1140	|	|	...	...	...	1231	1231
Hamm (Westf) a.	...	1114	|	...	...	|	1148	1148v	...	|	...	...	|	1248t	1248	...	...	1314	|	|	...	...	...	1348	1348
Hamm (Westf) 805 d.	...	1116	|	...	...	|	1152	1154v	...	|	...	...	|	1252t	1254	...	...	1316	|	|	...	...	...	1352	1354
Dortmund Hbf 805 a.	...	1132	|	...	...	|	1209	|	...	|	...	...	|	1310	|	...	...	1332	|	|	...	...	...	1409	|
Dortmund Hbf d.	1135	1137	|	1150	...	|	1212	|	1214k	|	1235	...	|	1312	|	1323c	1335	1337	|	|	1350	...	...	1412	|
Bochum Hbf d.	|	|	|	1203	...	|	1224	|	1228k	|	1248	...	|	1324	|	1337c	|	|	|	|	1404	...	...	1424	|
Recklinghausen Hbf d.	|	|	|	|	...	1203	|	|	|	|	|	...	1300	|	|	|	|	|	|	1338	|	...	...	|	|
Wanne-Eickel Hbf d.	|	|	|	|	...	|	|	|	|	|	|	...	1309	|	|	|	|	|	|	1346	|	...	...	|	|
Gelsenkirchen Hbf d.	|	|	|	|	...	|	|	|	|	|	|	...	1315	|	|	|	|	|	|	1352	|	...	...	|	|
Essen Hbf d.	|	|	1200	1214	...	1225f	1236	|	1241	|	1300	...	|	1336	|	1354	|	|	1400	1404	1415	...	...	1436	|
Oberhausen Hbf d.	|	|	|	|	1226	|	|	|	|	|	|	...	1327	|	|	|	|	|	|	|	|	...	...	|	|
Duisburg Hbf d.	|	|	1213	1230	1234	1238	1249	|	1255	|	1313	...	1334	1349	|	1407	|	|	1413	1418	1438o	...	...	1449	|
Düsseldorf Flughafen ✈ d.	|	|	|	|	|	|	1257s	|	|	|	|	...	|	1357s	|	|	|	|	|	|	|	...	...	1457s	|
Düsseldorf Hbf d.	|	|	1227	1244	1248	1252	1311	|	1308	|	1327	1350	1353	1406	|	1421	|	|	1427	1433	1454	...	...	1506	|
Hagen Hbf d.	1157	1158	|	|	|	|	...	1223t	|	|	|	|	|	...	1323	|	1357	1358	|	|	|	...	...	...	1423
Wuppertal Hbf d.	1214	1214	|	|	|	|	...	1240	|	1314	|	|	|	...	1340	|	1414	1414	|	|	|	...	...	...	1440
Solingen Hbf d.	1227	1227	|	|	|	|	...	|	|	1328	|	|	|	...	|	|	1427	1427	|	|	|	...	...	...	|
Köln Messe/Deutz a.	|	|	|	|	|	|	...	|	1329	|	|	|	|	...	|	1442	|	|	|	|	1518	...	...	...	|
Köln Hbf a.	1246	1246	1250	1312	1315	1318	...	1309	|	1346	1349	1415	1418	...	1409	|	1446	1446	1450	1459	|	...	...	...	1509
Köln Hbf d.	1255	...	1253	1317	1328	...	...	...	|	1353	1355	1418	...	...	...	|	1455	...	1453	...	|	1517	...	...	...
Köln/Bonn Flughafen ✈ a.	|	...	|	|	|	...	...	...	|	|	|	|	...	...	...	|	|	...	|	...	|	|	...	...	...
Bonn Hbf d.	|	...	1314	1337	|	...	...	...	|	1414	|	1438	...	...	...	|	|	...	1514	...	|	1537	...	...	...
Remagen d.	|	...	|	1351	|	...	...	...	|	|	|	1451	...	...	...	|	|	...	|	...	|	1551	...	...	...
Andernach d.	|	...	|	1404	|	...	...	...	|	|	|	1503	...	...	...	|	|	...	|	...	|	1604	...	...	...
Koblenz Hbf a.	|	...	1346	1416	|	...	...	...	|	1446	|	1514	...	...	...	|	|	...	1546	...	|	1616	...	...	...
Mainz Hbf 911 a.	|	...	1439	1510	|	...	...	...	|	1539	|	...	...	...	...	|	|	...	1639	...	|	1710	...	...	...
Frankfurt Flughafen ✈ § a.	1349	...	|	|	1416	...	...	...	1436	1559	1449	...	...	...	...	1533	1549	...	|	...	1607	|	...	...	...
Frankfurt (Main) Hbf 910/1 a.	|	...	|	|	1431	...	...	...	1449•	1613	|	...	...	...	...	1548•	|	...	|	...	|	|	...	...	...
Nürnberg Hbf 920 a.	|	...	|	|	...	...	...	...	1658	...	|	...	...	...	...	1759	|	...	|	...	|	|	...	...	...
Stuttgart Hbf 912 a.	|	...	1622	1646	...	...	...	...	|	...	1608	...	...	...	...	|	|	...	1829	...	1720	1846	...	...	...
München Hbf 904 930 a.	|	...	...	...	...	...	...	...	1804	...	1827	...	...	...	...	1911	|	...	...	...	...	...	...	...	...
Karlsruhe Hbf 912 a.	1456	...	...	...	...	...	...	...	...	...	...	...	...	...	...	...	1658	...	...	...	...	...	...	...	...
Basel SBB 🚌 912 a.	1647	...	...	...	...	...	...	...	...	...	...	...	...	...	...	...	1847	...	...	...	...	...	...	...	...

	ICE	ICE	IC	ICE	IC	IC	IC	ICE	ICE	ICE	IC	IC	IC	ICE	ICE	ICE	ICE	ICE	ICE	ICE	IC	ICE	IC	ICE	ICE
SEE NOTE ❖	**125**	**723**	**2027**	**611**	**2413**	**2019**	**2203**	**940**	**1050**	**725**	**2048**	**2311**	**1915**	**917**	**127**	**548**	**558**	**1228**	**1224**	**727**	**2229**	**613**	**2205**	**848**	**858**
						⑥H	J		t				⑤⑦	Ⓑn		t		Ⓐa	Ⓒb	Ⓑ					t
	A ✕	✕	P 🍷	✕	♦	🍷 N	N	✕	✕	✕	D 🍷	🍷 ♦	r T 🍷	✕	A ✕	✕	✕	★ ✕	★ ✕	✕	🍷 ♦	✕	N	✕	✕
Hamburg Altona d.	...	...	1130	...	...	...	...	...	...	...	...	...	...	...	...	...	...	...	...	...	...	...	...	...	...
Hamburg Hbf 801 d.	...	...	1146	...	1202x	...	...	...	...	...	...	1246	...	...	...	...	...	...	...	...	1346	...	...	...	...
Bremen Hbf 801 815 d.	...	...	1244	...	1252	...	...	...	...	...	...	1344	...	...	...	...	...	...	...	...	1444	...	...	...	...
Osnabrück Hbf 801 815 d.	...	...	1337	...	|	...	...	...	...	...	...	1437	...	...	...	...	...	...	...	...	1537	...	...	...	...
Münster (Westf) Hbf 801 d.	...	...	1403	...	1409	1432	1432	...	...	...	...	1503	...	...	...	...	...	...	...	...	1603	...	1632	...	...
Berlin Hbf 810 d.	...	...	|	...	|	|	|	1149	1149	...	...	|	1201	...	...	1250	1250	...	...	...	|	...	|	1349	1349
Leipzig Hbf 849a 866 d.	...	...	|	...	|	|	|	|	|	...	1036	|	|	...	...	|	|	...	...	...	|	...	|	|	|
Hannover Hbf 810 d.	...	...	|	...	|	|	|	1331	1331	...	1340	|	1356	...	...	1431	1431	...	...	...	|	...	|	1531	1531
Hamm (Westf) a.	...	...	|	...	|	|	|	1448t	1448	...	1514	|	1524	...	...	1548	1548v	...	...	...	|	...	|	1648t	1648
Hamm (Westf) 805 d.	...	...	|	...	|	|	|	1452t	1454	...	1516	|	1533	...	...	1552	1554v	1556	1556	...	|	...	|	1652t	1654
Dortmund Hbf 805 a.	...	...	1433	...	|	|	|	1510	|	...	1532	|	|	...	...	1609	|	1614	1614	...	1633	...	|	1710	|
Dortmund Hbf d.	...	1414c	1436	1435	|	|	|	1512	|	1523k	1537	|	|	1551	...	1612	|	1616	1616	...	1636	1635	|	1712	|
Bochum Hbf d.	...	1428c	|	1448	|	|	|	1524	|	1537k	|	|	|	1604	...	1624	|	1628	1628	...	|	1648	|	1724	|
Recklinghausen Hbf d.	...	|	|	|	1438	1500	1500	|	|	|	|	|	|	|	...	|	|	|	|	...	|	|	1700	|	|
Wanne-Eickel Hbf d.	...	|	|	|	1446	1509	1509	|	|	|	|	|	|	|	...	|	|	|	|	...	|	|	1709	|	|
Gelsenkirchen Hbf d.	...	|	|	|	1452	1515	1515	|	|	|	|	|	|	|	...	|	|	|	|	...	|	|	1715	|	|
Essen Hbf d.	...	1440	|	1500	1504	|	|	1536	|	1555	|	|	|	1615	...	1636	|	1640	1640	1653	|	1700	|	1736	|
Oberhausen Hbf d.	1426	|	|	|	|	1527	1527	|	|	|	|	|	|	|	1626	|	|	|	|	|	|	|	1727	|	|
Duisburg Hbf d.	1434	1455	|	1513	1518	1534	1534	1549	|	1608	|	1613	|	1630	1634	1649	|	1655	1655	1707	|	1713	1734	1749	|
Düsseldorf Flughafen ✈ d.	|	|	|	|	|	|	|	1557s	|	|	|	|	|	|	|	1657s	|	|	|	|	|	|	|	1759	|
Düsseldorf Hbf d.	1450	1513	|	1527	1532	1549	1549	1606	|	1622	|	1627	|	1645	1651j	1711	|	1708	1708	1721	|	1727	1749	1808	|
Hagen Hbf d.	|	|	|	|	|	|	|	...	1523	|	1558	|	1608t	|	|	...	1623t	|	|	|	|	|	|	|	1723
Wuppertal Hbf d.	|	|	1514	|	|	|	|	...	1540	|	1614	|	1631	|	|	...	1640	|	|	|	1714	|	|	|	1740
Solingen Hbf d.	|	|	1528	|	|	|	|	...	|	|	1627	|	|	|	|	...	|	|	|	|	1728	|	|	|	|
Köln Messe/Deutz a.	|	1533	|	|	|	|	|	...	|	1642	|	|	|	1710	|	...	|	1729	|	1742	|	|	|	|	|
Köln Hbf a.	1519	|	1546	1549	1557	1613	1614	...	1609	|	1646	1650	1712	|	1718j	...	1709	|	1733	|	1746	1749	1814	1832z	1809
Köln Hbf d.	1529	|	1553	1555	...	1617	1617	...	...	|	...	1653	1717	|	1728	...	...	|	...	|	1753	1755	1817q	...	...
Köln/Bonn Flughafen ✈ a.	|	|	|	|	...	|	|	...	...	|	...	|	|	|	|	...	...	|	...	|	|	|	|	...	...
Bonn Hbf d.	|	|	1614	|	...	1637	1635	...	...	|	...	1714	1737	|	|	...	...	|	...	|	1814	|	1837q	...	...
Remagen d.	|	|	|	|	...	1651	...	...	...	|	...	|	1751	|	|	...	...	|	...	|	|	|	1851q	...	...
Andernach d.	|	|	|	|	...	1704	...	...	...	|	...	|	1804	|	|	...	...	|	...	|	|	|	1904q	...	...
Koblenz Hbf a.	|	|	1646	|	...	1716	...	...	...	|	...	1746	1816	|	|	...	...	|	...	|	1846	|	1916q	...	...
Mainz Hbf 911 a.	|	|	1739	|	...	1815	...	...	...	|	...	1839	1910	|	|	...	...	1855	...	|	1939	|	...	...	...
Frankfurt Flughafen ✈ § a.	1618	1633	1759	1650	...	|	...	...	...	1733	...	|	|	1807	1816	...	...	1915	...	1833	1959	1850	...	...	...
Frankfurt (Main) Hbf 910/1 a.	1631	1648•	1813	|	...	|	...	...	...	1748•	...	|	|	|	1831	...	...	1933	...	1848•	2013	|	...	...	...
Nürnberg Hbf 920 a.	...	1900	2027	|	...	|	...	...	...	1959	...	|	|	|	...	...	...	...	...	2100	2227q	|	...	...	...
Stuttgart Hbf 912 a.	...	|	...	1808	...	1958	...	...	...	|	...	2024	2046	1924	...	...	...	...	...	|	...	2008	...	...	...
München Hbf 904 930 a.	...	2007	...	2028	...	...	...	...	...	2109	...	...	...	...	...	...	...	...	...	2206	...	2226	...	...	...
Karlsruhe Hbf 912 a.	...	...	...	...	...	...	...	...	...	...	...	...	...	...	...	...	...	...	...	...	...	...	...	...	...
Basel SBB 🚌 912 a.	...	...	...	...	...	...	...	...	...	...	...	...	...	...	...	...	...	...	...	...	...	...	...	...	...

♦ – **NOTES** (LISTED BY TRAIN NUMBER)

2217 – GREIFSWALDER BODDEN – [12] and 🍷 (Greifswald on dates in Table **845** -) Stralsund - Hamburg - Stuttgart.
2229 – [12] and 🍷 Kiel - Köln - Frankfurt (- Nürnberg Ⓑ) (- Regensburg - Passau ⊖).
2311 – NORDFRIESLAND – [12] and 🍷 Westerland - Stuttgart.
2413 – ⑥⑦ to Nov. 3. FEHMARN – [12] Fehmarn-Burg - Lübeck Hbf (d. 1103) - Köln.
2417 – ⑤ to Nov. 1 (also June 19, Oct. 2; not June 21, July 19 - Aug. 23, Oct. 4). FEHMARN – [12] Fehmarn-Burg - Lübeck Hbf (d. 1019) - Köln.

A – From Amsterdam (Table **28**). Diversions/retimings are scheduled June 27–30, Aug. 2–11, Sept. 28, 29, Nov. 16, 17 (different train numbers may apply).
B – From Berlin (Table **810**).
D – From Dresden (Table **841**).
H – ⑥ to Nov. 2 (also June 20, Oct. 3).
J – Ⓑ to Nov. 1 (not June 20, Oct. 3); daily from Nov. 3.
L – To Luxembourg (Table **915**).
N – From Norddeich Mole (Table **812**).

P – To Passau (Table **920**).
T – To Tübingen (Table **930**) on ⑦. Until Oct. 11 Hamm a. 1546, d. 1549, Wuppertal d. 1634.
U – Ⓑ (not June 20, 21, Oct. 3, 4, Nov. 1). To Tübingen (Table **930**) on ①–④ (not June 19, 20, Oct. 2, 3).

a – Not June 20.
b – Also June 20.
c – ⑥⑦ only.
f – Not June 20, Oct. 3, Nov. 1.
j – On Aug. 31, Oct. 5, 12, 19, 26, Nov. 2 Düsseldorf d. 1648, Köln a. 1712.
k – ⑥ only.
n – Not July 14 - Aug. 25.
o – Arrives 1427.
q – Not ⑥.
r – Also June 19, Oct. 2, 31; not June 21, July 12, 19, 26, Aug. 2, 9, 16, 23, Oct. 4, Nov. 1.
s – Stops to set down only.
t – From Oct. 12.
u – Also June 19, Oct. 2, 31; not June 21, Oct. 4, Nov. 1.
v – Until Oct. 11 arrives Hamm 6 minutes later, departs 2 minutes later.
x – Hamburg **Harburg**.
z – Daily to Oct. 12; ⑥ from Oct. 19 (not Oct. 26).

⊡ – ①②③④⑥ (not June 19, July 13, Aug. 24, Oct. 2, 31).
★ – From München via Kassel and Paderborn (Tables **805**/**900**).
▽ – Runs as *IC* **2025** on ⑥ (conveys 🍷
• – Calls at Frankfurt (Main) Süd (not Hbf) on ⑥⑦ Aug. 10 - Sept. 29.
‡ – June 11 - July 28 calls at Hambu Harburg (not Hamburg Hbf).
⊖ – See Table **920**.
❖ – Services in this table are subject to alteration July 13 - August 25, particularly those via Duisburg/Essen. See the engineering work panel on page 369 for further deta and also for other alterations affecting services in this table.
§ – Frankfurt Flughafen ✈ Fernbahnh (Tables **910** and **911**).

HAMBURG - DORTMUND - KÖLN - KOBLENZ — 800

SEE NOTE ✣		IC 2152	ICE 729	IC 2440	IC 2213	IC 1917	IC 1917	IC 2223	ICE 129	ICE 919	ICE 821	ICE 546	ICE 556	ICE 556	IC 2029	IC 2195	ICE 615	IC 2207	ICE 846	ICE 1046	ICE 856	ICE 605	IC 2442	IC 2215	IC 2315	ICE 221
						⑦J	⑦t	①-⑤		Ⓑn	Ⓑ	t	⑥⑦	①-⑤		①-⑤		E	Q	⑤t	t		Ⓑ	T		
		◆	✕	D🍷	🍷◆	🍷	🍷	G	A✕	✕	✕	✕	✕	✕	🍷	z🍷	✕		✕	B✕	✕	✕	D🍷	🍷	🍷◆	A✕
Hamburg Altona	d.	...	...	...	...	...	...	...	...	...	...	...	...	...	1530	1555	...	...	...	...	...	...	...	1630	...	...
Hamburg Hbf **801**	d.	...	...	...	1446‡	...	...	...	...	...	...	...	...	...	1546	1609	...	...	...	...	...	...	...	1646	1646	...
Bremen Hbf **801 815**	d.	...	...	...	1544	...	...	...	...	...	...	...	...	...	1644	|	...	...	...	...	...	...	...	1744	1744	...
Osnabrück Hbf **801 815**	d.	...	...	...	1637	...	...	...	...	...	...	...	...	...	1737	|	...	...	...	...	...	...	...	1837	1837	...
Münster (Westf) Hbf **801**	d.	...	...	...	1703	...	...	...	...	...	...	...	...	...	1803	|	...	1832	...	...	...	...	...	1903	1903	...
Berlin Hbf **810**	d.	...	...	...	|	1355	1355	1355	...	...	...	1451	1451	1451	|	|	...	|	1549	1549	1549	...	...	|	|	...
Leipzig Hbf **849a 866**	d.	...	...	1236	|	|	|	|	...	...	...	|	|	|	|	|	...	|	|	|	|	...	1436	|	|	...
Hannover Hbf **810**	d.	...	...	1540	|	1556	1556	1556	...	...	...	1631	1631	1631	|	|	...	|	1731	1731	1731	...	1740	|	|	...
Hamm (Westf)	a.	...	...	1714	|	|	1724	1724	...	...	...	1748	1748v	1748v	|	|	...	|	1848t	1848	1848	...	1914	|	|	...
Hamm (Westf) **805**	d.	1656	...	1716	|	|	1733	1726	...	...	...	1752	1754v	1754v	|	|	...	|	1852t	1852	1854	...	1916	|	|	...
Dortmund Hbf **805**	a.	1714	...	1732	|	|	|	1748	...	...	...	1809	|	|	1833	|	...	|	1910	1909	|	...	1932	|	|	...
Dortmund Hbf	d.	1716	1723h	1737	|	|	|	1752	...	1756	...	1812	|	|	1836	|	1835	|	1912	1912	|	1923h	1937	|	|	...
Bochum Hbf	d.	1729	1737h	|	|	|	|	1803	...	|	...	1824	|	|	|	|	1848	|	1924	1924	|	1938h	|	|	|	...
Recklinghausen Hbf	d.	|	|	|	|	|	|	|	...	|	...	|	|	|	|	|	|	1900	|	|	|	|	|	|	|	...
Wanne-Eickel Hbf	d.	|	|	|	|	|	|	|	...	|	...	|	|	|	|	|	|	1909	|	|	|	|	|	|	|	...
Gelsenkirchen Hbf	d.	|	|	|	|	|	|	|	...	|	...	|	|	|	|	|	|	1915	|	|	|	|	|	|	|	...
Essen Hbf	d.	1740	1754	|	|	|	|	1814	...	1825	1841	1836	|	|	|	1854	1900	|	1936	1936	|	1950	|	2000	2000	...
Oberhausen Hbf	d.	|	|	|	|	|	|	|	1826	|	|	|	|	|	|	|	|	1927	|	|	|	|	|	|	|	2026
Duisburg Hbf	d.	1755	1808	|	1813	|	|	1828	1834	1839	1855	1849	|	|	|	1907	1913	1934	1949	1951	|	2004	|	2013	2013	2034
Düsseldorf Flughafen ✈	d.	1805	|	|	|	|	|	...	|	|	|	1857s	|	|	|	|	|	|	1959	|	|	|	|	|	|	|
Düsseldorf Hbf	d.	1811	1822	|	1827	|	|	...	1848	1852	1908	1910	|	|	|	1921	1927	1949	2008	2016	|	2018	|	2027	2027	2048
Hagen Hbf	d.	...	|	1758	|	1816	1809	...	|	|	|	...	1823t	1823t	|	|	|	|	|	...	1923	|	1958	|	|	|
Wuppertal Hbf	d.	...	|	1814	|	1832	1830	...	|	|	|	...	1840	1840	1914	|	|	|	|	...	1940	|	2014	|	|	|
Solingen Hbf	d.	...	|	1827	|	1847	|	...	|	|	|	...	|	|	1928	|	|	|	|	...	|	|	2027	|	|	|
Köln Messe/Deutz	a.	...	1842	|	|	|	|	...	|	1918	1928	...	|	|	|	|	|	|	|	...	|	|	|	|	|	|
Köln Hbf	a.	...	|	1846	1850	1909	1912	...	1915	|	|	...	1909f	1909	1946	1945	1949	2013	2036	...	2009	2040	2046	2050	2050	2112
Köln Hbf	d.	...	|	...	1853	1912	1917	...	1921	|	|	...	...	1912	1953	...	1955	...	...	...	...	2046	...	2053	2053	2128
Köln/Bonn Flughafen ✈	a.	...	|	...	|	|	|	...	|	|	|	...	...	|	|	...	|	...	...	...	...	|	...	|	|	|
Bonn Hbf	d.	...	|	...	1914	1935	1937	...	|	|	|	...	...	1934	2014	...	|	...	...	...	...	|	...	2114	2114	|
Remagen	d.	...	|	...	|	1951	1951	...	|	|	|	...	...	|	|	...	|	...	...	...	...	|	...	|	|	|
Andernach	d.	...	|	...	|	2004	2004	...	|	|	|	...	...	2001	|	...	|	...	...	...	...	|	...	|	|	|
Koblenz Hbf	a.	...	|	...	1946	2016	2016	...	|	|	|	...	...	2013	2046	...	|	...	...	...	...	|	...	2146	2146	|
Mainz Hbf **911**	a.	...	|	...	2039	2110	2110	...	|	|	|	...	...	...	2142	...	|	...	...	...	...	|	...	2239	2239	|
Frankfurt Flughafen ✈ §	a.	...	1933	...	|	|	|	...	2010	2007	2033	...	...	...	2159	...	2049	...	...	...	...	2152	...	2302	2302	2216
Frankfurt (Main) Hbf **910/1**	a.	...	1948•	...	|	|	|	...	2026	|	2048•	...	...	...	2213	...	|	...	...	...	...	|	...	2315	2315	2231
Nürnberg Hbf **920**	a.	...	2159	...	|	|	|	...	...	|	2259	...	...	...	0044	...	|	...	...	...	...	|	...	...	...	...
Stuttgart Hbf **912**	a.	...	|	...	2224	|	|	...	...	2123	|	...	...	...	...	...	2208	...	...	...	...	|	...	...	...	...
München Hbf **904 930**	a.	...	2310	...	...	|	|	...	...	...	0007c	...	...	...	...	...	0027	...	...	...	...	|	...	...	...	...
Karlsruhe Hbf **912**	a.	...	...	...	...	2221	2224	...	...	...	...	...	...	...	...	...	...	...	...	...	...	2300	...	...	...	...
Basel SBB 🏛 **912**	a.	...	...	...	...	...	...	...	...	...	...	...	...	...	...	...	...	...	...	...	...	0052r	...	...	...	...

SEE NOTE ✣		ICE 544	ICE 554	IC 2197	IC 2321	IC 2221	IC 2411	IC 2209	ICE 619	ICE 844	ICE 854	ICE 854	IC 2307	IC 2444	IC 1952	ICE 542	ICE 552	ICE 552	IC 209	ICE 842	ICE 852	IC 2446	ICE 609	IC 2419	ICE 840	IC 2021
		t		⑦z	H			R			Ⓑt	⑦t		Ⓑ	⑤⑦	t	t	F			⑦t	⑦		①g	⑤-⑦	
		✕	✕	🍷	🍷	🍷◆	◆	N	✕	✕	✕	✕	🍷	D🍷	◆	✕	✕	✕	K🍷	△✕	✕	D🍷	P		b	
Hamburg Altona	d.	...	...	1754	1730	...	...	...	...	...	...	...	1830	...	...	...	...	...	...	...	...	...	2030	...	...	2230
Hamburg Hbf **801**	d.	...	...	1810	1746	1746	1753x	...	...	...	...	...	1846	...	...	...	...	...	1946	...	...	...	2046	...	...	2246
Bremen Hbf **801 815**	d.	...	...	|	1844	1844	1852	...	...	...	...	...	1944	...	...	...	...	...	2044	...	...	...	2144	...	...	2344
Osnabrück Hbf **801 815**	d.	...	...	|	1937	1937	|	...	...	...	...	...	2037	...	...	...	...	...	2137	...	...	...	2238	...	...	0037
Münster (Westf) Hbf **801**	d.	...	...	|	2003	2003	|	2032	...	...	...	...	2103	...	...	...	...	...	2203	...	...	...	2303	...	...	0105
Berlin Hbf **810**	d.	1650	1650	|	|	|	|	|	...	1749	1749	1749	|	...	...	1850	1850	1850	|	1949	1949	...	|	...	2122	|
Leipzig Hbf **849a 866**	d.	|	|	|	|	|	|	|	...	|	|	|	|	1636	1637	|	|	|	|	|	|	1836	|	...	|	|
Hannover Hbf **810**	d.	1831	1831	|	|	|	|	|	...	1931	1931	1931	|	1940	|	2031	2031	2031	|	2131	2131	2140	|	...	2331	|
Hamm (Westf)	a.	1948	1948v	|	|	|	|	|	...	2048t	2048	2048	|	2113	2134	2148	2148	2154	|	2248	2248	2312	|	...	0058	0123
Hamm (Westf) **805**	d.	1952	1954v	|	|	|	|	|	...	2052t	2054	2054	|	2114	2140	2152	2154	2156	|	2252	2254	2313	|	...	0100	0125
Dortmund Hbf **805**	a.	2009	|	|	|	|	|	|	...	2110	|	|	|	2132	2157	2209	|	|	2233	2309	|	2332	|	...	0119	0141
Dortmund Hbf	d.	2012	|	|	|	|	|	|	2056	2112	|	|	|	2137	2200	2212	|	|	2237	2312	|	2337	|	...	0121	0144
Bochum Hbf	d.	2024	|	|	|	|	|	|	2109	2124	|	|	|	|	2212	2224	|	|	|	2324	|	|	|	...	0133	0156
Recklinghausen Hbf	d.	|	|	|	|	|	2038	2100	|	|	|	|	|	|	|	|	|	|	|	|	|	|	|	...	|	|
Wanne-Eickel Hbf	d.	|	|	|	|	|	2047	2108	|	|	|	|	|	|	|	|	|	|	|	|	|	|	|	...	|	|
Gelsenkirchen Hbf	d.	|	|	|	|	|	2054	2114	|	|	|	|	|	|	|	|	|	|	|	|	|	|	|	...	|	|
Essen Hbf	d.	2036	|	2054	2100	2100	2105	|	2125	2136	|	|	2200	|	2225	2236	|	|	2300	2336	|	|	0001	...	0145	0207
Oberhausen Hbf	d.	|	|	|	|	|	|	2127	|	|	|	|	|	|	|	|	|	|	|	|	|	|	|	...	|	|
Duisburg Hbf	d.	2049	|	2107	2113	2113	2118	2134	2139	2149	|	|	2213	|	2241	2249	|	|	2313	2349	|	|	0014	...	0158	0220
Düsseldorf Flughafen ✈	d.	2059	|	|	|	|	|	|	|	2159	|	|	|	|	|	2259	|	|	|	2359	|	|	|	...	0208	0230
Düsseldorf Hbf	d.	2109	|	2121	2127	2127	2132	2148	2155	2208	|	|	2227	|	2300	2308	|	|	2327	0008	|	|	0028	...	0217	0239
Hagen Hbf	d.	|	2023t	|	|	|	|	|	|	|	2123	2123	|	2158	|	|	2223	2225	|	|	2323	2358	|	...	|	|
Wuppertal Hbf	d.	|	2040	|	|	|	|	|	|	|	2140	2140	|	2214	|	|	2240	2243	|	|	2340	0014	|	...	|	|
Solingen Hbf	d.	|	|	|	|	|	|	|	|	|	|	|	|	2227	|	|	2253	|	|	|	|	0027	|	...	|	|
Köln Messe/Deutz	a.	2136	|	|	|	|	|	|	|	|	|	|	|	|	|	|	|	|	|	|	|	|	|	...	|	|
Köln Hbf	a.	2141	2109	2145	2150	2150	2158	2213	2219	2231	2209	2209	2250	2246	2326	2330	2313	2312	2350	0030	0009	0046	0050	...	0242	0301
Köln Hbf	d.	...	...	...	2153	2153	...	...	2230	...	...	2217	2253	...	...	...	...	2317	2353	...	...	...	...	0206	...	0349
Köln/Bonn Flughafen ✈	a.	...	...	...	|	|	...	...	2241	...	...	|	|	...	...	...	...	|	|	...	...	...	...	|	...	|
Bonn Hbf	d.	...	...	...	2214	2214	...	...	|	...	...	2237	2314	...	...	...	...	2340	0014	...	...	...	...	0229	...	0414
Remagen	d.	...	...	...	|	|	...	...	|	...	...	|	2328	...	...	...	...	|	|	...	...	...	...	0243	...	0431
Andernach	d.	...	...	...	|	|	...	...	|	...	...	2301	2341	...	...	...	...	0004	|	...	...	...	...	0255	...	0445
Koblenz Hbf	a.	...	...	...	2246	2246	...	...	|	...	...	2313	2354	...	...	...	...	0017	0046	...	...	...	...	0308	...	0458
Mainz Hbf **911**	a.	...	...	...	2339	2339	...	...	|	...	...	...	...	...	...	...	...	...	0139	...	...	...	...	0409	...	0627
Frankfurt Flughafen ✈ §	a.	...	...	...	2359	2359	...	...	2343	...	...	...	...	...	...	...	...	...	0159	...	...	...	...	0438	...	0645
Frankfurt (Main) Hbf **910/1**	a.	...	...	...	0013	0013	...	...	2359	...	...	...	...	...	...	...	...	...	0232	...	...	...	...	0454	...	0702
Nürnberg Hbf **920**	a.	...	...	...	...	...	...	...	|	...	...	...	...	...	...	...	...	...	|	...	...	...	...	|	...	...
Stuttgart Hbf **912**	a.	...	...	...	...	...	...	...	0320	...	...	...	...	...	...	...	...	...	|	...	...	...	...	0700	...	...
München Hbf **904 930**	a.	...	...	...	...	...	...	...	0602	...	...	...	...	...	...	...	...	...	|	...	...	...	...	...	...	...
Karlsruhe Hbf **912**	a.	...	...	...	...	...	...	...	0156a	...	...	...	...	...	...	...	...	...	0401	...	...	...	...	...	...	...
Basel SBB 🏛 **912**	a.	...	...	...	...	...	...	...	...	...	...	...	...	...	...	...	...	...	0622	...	...	...	...	...	...	...

◆ – **NOTES** (LISTED BY TRAIN NUMBER)

952 – ⑤⑦ (also June 19, Oct. 2, 31; not June 21, July 14 - Aug. 25, Oct. 4, Nov. 1). 🚌12 Leipzig - Kassel - Paderborn - Köln.
152 – 🚌12 Gera - Weimar - Kassel - Paderborn - Düsseldorf.
213 – RÜGEN – 🚌12 and 🍷 Ostseebad Binz - Stralsund - Köln - Stuttgart.
221 – ②-④ to June 27; ②-④ Sept. 18 - Oct. 30 (not Oct. 2, 3); ⑤⑦ from Nov. 8. 🚌12 and 🍷 Lübeck Hbf (d. 1637) - Hamburg - Frankfurt.
315 – Until Nov. 3. DEICHGRAF – 🚌12 and 🍷 Westerland - Frankfurt.
411 – ①-④ July 1 - Sept. 17 (also June 11, 17, 18, 20, 24); ① Sept. 23 - Oct. 28 (also Oct. 3). FEHMARN – 🚌12 Fehmarn-Burg - Lübeck Hbf (d. 1703) - Köln.

– From Amsterdam (Table **28**). Diversions / retimings are scheduled June 27 – 30, Aug. 2 – 11, Sept. 28, 29, Nov. 16, 17 (different train numbers may apply).
– To Neuss Hbf (a. 2029) and Mönchengladbach Hbf (a. 2043).
– From Dresden (Table **842**).
– Daily to Nov. 8; Ⓑ from Nov. 10. From Emden (Table **812**).
– Daily until Oct. 11 Berlin - Köln; ⑦ until Oct. 6 Köln - Koblenz.
– ①-⑤ from Oct. 14. KAROLINGER – To Krefeld Hbf (a. 1844), Viersen (a. 1856), Mönchengladbach Hbf (a. 1905), Rheydt Hbf (a. 1910), Aachen Hbf (a. 1950).
– ①⑤⑥⑦ to June 24; daily June 28 - Sept. 17; ①⑤⑥⑦ Sept. 20 - Nov. 3 (also Oct. 2, 3, 31); ①②③④⑥ from Nov. 4.

J – Until Oct. 6.
K – From Kiel (Table **820**). 🍷 Kiel - Köln.
N – From Norddeich Mole (Table **912**).
P – Daily to Nov. 8; Ⓑ from Nov. 10. Runs as *IC* **2309** on ⑤⑥. ✕ on ①②③④⑦.
Q – Daily to Oct. 17; ①②③④⑥⑦ from Oct. 19.
R – ⑤-⑦ to Aug. 25 (also June 10, 19; not June 9); ③-⑦ Aug. 28 - Nov. 3; ⑦ from Nov. 10.
T – From Nov. 4.

a – Calls at Karlsruhe before Stuttgart.
c – Nürnberg - München on ④⑤⑦ (also June 19).
f – 1912 on ⑦ to Oct. 6.
g – Also June 11; not July 8 - Aug. 26.
h – ⑥ only.
n – Not July 14 - Aug. 25.
r – Basel **Badischer Bf**. Runs Karlsruhe - Basel on ①②③④⑦.
s – Stops to set down only.
t – From Oct. 12.

v – Until Oct. 11 arrives Hamm 6 minutes later, departs 2 minutes later.
x – Hamburg **Harburg**.
z – Not July 14 - Aug. 25.

• – Calls at Frankfurt (Main) Süd (not Hbf) on ⑥⑦ Aug. 10 - Sept. 29.
△ – Runs 4 – 7 minutes later Hamm - Köln until Oct. 10.
‡ – June 11 - July 28 calls at Hamburg Harburg (not Hamburg Hbf).
✣ – Services in this table are subject to alteration July 13 - Aug. 25, particularly those via Duisburg / Essen. See the engineering work panel on page 369 for further details and also for other alterations affecting services in this table.
§ – Frankfurt Flughafen Fernbahnhof (Tables **910** and **911**).

801 Local services MÜNSTER - OSNABRÜCK and BREMEN - HAMBURG

See Table **800** for fast trains

MÜNSTER - OSNABRÜCK and v.v. Operated by *eurobahn*. Journey time: 36 minutes. Trains call at **Lengerich** (Westf), 21 minutes from Münster, 14 minutes from Osnabrück.
From Münster (Westf) Hbf at 0003 Ⓒ **z**, 0103 Ⓒ **z**, 0503 Ⓐ, 0603 ⚒, 0633 Ⓐ, 0703, 0733 Ⓐ, 0803, 0833 Ⓐ, 0903, 1003, 1103, 1203, 1303, 1333 Ⓐ, 1403, 1503, 1533 Ⓐ, 1603, 1633 Ⓐ, 1703, 1733 Ⓐ, 1803, 1833 Ⓐ, 1903, 2003, 2103, 2203 and 2303. **From Osnabrück** Hbf at 0019 Ⓒ **z**, 0119 Ⓒ **z**, 0519 Ⓐ, 0549 Ⓐ, 0619 ⚒, 0649 Ⓐ, 0719, 0749 Ⓐ, 0819, 0849 Ⓐ, 0919, 1019, 1119, 1219, 1319, 1419, 1447 Ⓐ, 1519, 1549 Ⓐ, 1619, 1649 Ⓐ, 1719, 1749 Ⓐ, 1819, 1919, 2016, 2119, 2219 and 2319.

BREMEN - HAMBURG and v.v. Operated by *metronom*. Journey time: 69 – 90 minutes. Trains call at **Rotenburg** (Wümme), 21 – 30 minutes from Bremen, 47 – 56 minutes from Hamburg.
From Bremen Hbf at 0015 Ⓒ, 0115 Ⓒ, 0432 Ⓐ, 0458, 0528 Ⓐ, 0559, 0626 Ⓐ, 0633 Ⓒ, 0658, 0733, 0758, 0833, 0858, 0933, 0958, 1033, 1059, 1133, 1159, 1233 1258 and at 33 and 58 minutes past each hour until 2033, 2058; then 2133 ⑤⑥ **v**, 2158 and 2315. **From Hamburg** Hbf (◇) at 0057 Ⓒ, 0256 Ⓒ, 0457, 0537 ⚒, 0558 Ⓐ, 0615 Ⓒ, 0637, 0715, 0737, 0815, 0837 and at 15 and 37 minutes past each hour until 2115, 2137; then 2237 and 2337.

v – Also June 9, Oct. 2. **z** – Also June 20, Nov. 1. ◇ – Certain services depart Hamburg 1 minute later until July 28.

802 RHEIN – RUHR LOCAL SERVICES

RE / RB services

Services in this table (pages 376 – 378) are shown route by route. Sub-headings indicate the route number and principal stations served. **WARNING! Subject to alteration July 13 - August 25.**

RE1 / RE11 Aachen - Köln - Düsseldorf - Dortmund - Hamm (- Kassel: Table 805) ⊡ ⊕ *RE6* Köln - Neuss - Düsseldorf - Bielefeld (- Minden) ⊡

km		m	Ⓐek	Ⓐe		k	Ⓐe		k	⚒r			m				m							
0	**Aachen** Hbf .... **807** d.	...	...	⊖	0451e	...	⊖	0551	...	⊖	0651	...	...	❖	1851	...	...	1951	...	2051	...	2151	...	2251
31	Düren .... **807** d.	...	...	...	0517e	...	...	0617	...	...	0717	...	...		1917	...	...	2017	...	2117	...	2217	...	2317
	Köln/Bonn Flugh ✈ .d.	...	...	0448	|	...	0548	|	...	0648	|	...	0748		|	...	1948	|	2048	|	2148	|	2248	|
70	**Köln** Hbf .... **807** a.	...	...	0501	0544e	...	0601	0644	...	0701	0744	...	0801		1944	...	2001	2044	2101	2144	2201	2244	2301	2344
70	**Köln** Hbf .... d.	...	...	0507b	0549	...	0607	0649	...	0707	0749	...	0807	and at	1949	...	2007	2049	2107	2149	2207	2249	2307	2349
71	**Köln** Messe/Deutz ......d.	...	...	|	0552	...	|	0652	...	|	0752	...	|		1952	...	|	2052	|	2152	|	2252	|	2352
83	Leverkusen Mitte ....d.	...	...	|	0604	...	|	0704	...	|	0804	...	|	the same	2004	...	|	2104	|	2204	|	2304	|	0004
	Neuss Hbf .... d.	...	...	0537	|	...	0637	|	...	0737	|	...	0837		|	...	2037	|	2137	|	2237	|	2337	|
110	**Düsseldorf** Hbf .... d.	...	0536	0554j	0621	0636	0654j	0721	0736	0754j	0821	0836	0854j	minutes	2021	2036	2054j	2121	2154j	2221	2254j	2321	2354j	0021
117	Düsseldorf Flughafen ✈ d.	...	0542	0602	0628	0642	0702	0728	0742	0802	0828	0842	0902		2028	2042	2102	2128	2202	2228	2302	2328	0002	0028
134	**Duisburg** Hbf .... d.	...	0557	0615	0638	0657	0715	0738	0757	0815	0838	0857	0915	past each	2038	2057	2115	2138	2215	2238	2315	2338	0017	0038
144	Mülheim (Ruhr) Hbf ...... d.	...	0604	0621	0644	0704	0721	0744	0804	0821	0844	0904	0921		2044	2104	2121	2144	2221	2244	2321	2344	0023	0044
153	**Essen** Hbf .... d.	...	0613	0629	0652	0713	0729	0752	0813	0829	0852	0913	0929	hour until	2052	2113	2129	2152	2229	2252	2329	2352	0031	0052
169	Bochum Hbf .... d.	...	0626	0642	0703	0726	0742	0803	0826	0842	0903	0926	0942		2103	2126	2142	2203	2242	2303	2342	0003	0044	0103
187	**Dortmund** Hbf ...... ☆ d.	0555	0639	0655	0716	0739	0755	0816	0839	0855	0916	0939	0955		2116	2139	2155	2216	2255	2316	2353	0016	0055	0116
218	**Hamm** (Westf) **810** ☆ d.	0615	0702	0715	0739	0802	0815	0839	0902	0915	0939	0959	1015		2145	2202	2215	2244	2315	2344	...	0044	...	0144
268	Gütersloh Hbf ...... **810** d.	0648	...	0748	...	...	0848	...	...	0948	...	...	1048		...	...	2248	...	2348	...	...	...	...	...
285	**Bielefeld** Hbf ...... **810** a.	0659	...	0759	...	...	0859	...	...	0959	...	...	1059		...	...	2259	...	0004	...	...	...	...	...

				Ⓐe				m	⚒m	k		m▲		k		m	k		m		m		⑤⑥v	m
Bielefeld Hbf .... **810** d.	...	...	...	0458*	...	...	...	0558*	0558*	...	...	0658*	▲	...	...	1958*	...	...	2058*	...	2158*	...	...	2258*
Gütersloh Hbf .... **810** d.	...	...	...	0508*	...	...	...	0608*	0608*	...	...	0708*		...	...	2008*	...	...	2108*	...	2208*	...	...	2308*
Hamm (Westf).. **810** ☆ d.	0416	...	0516	0544	...	0557e	0620	0644	0644	0657	0720	0744		1957	2020	2044	2057	2116	2144	2216	2244	2316	2316	2344
Dortmund Hbf .... ☆ d.	0445	...	0545	0606	...	0621	0645	0704	0706	0721	0745	0806		2021	2045	2106	2121	2145	2206	2245	2306	2345	2345	0006
Bochum Hbf .... d.	0455	...	0555	0619	...	0633	0655	▬	0719	0733	0755	0819	and at	2033	2055	2119	2133	2155	2219	2255	2319	2355	2355	0019
Essen Hbf .... d.	0509	...	0609	0632	...	0647	0709	...	0732	0747	0809	0832		2047	2109	2132	2147	2209	2232	2309	2332	0009	0009	0032
Mülheim (Ruhr) Hbf ...... d.	0515	...	0615	0638	...	0655	0715	...	0738	0753	0815	0838	the same	2055	2115	2138	2155	2215	2238	2315	2338	0015	0015	0038
Duisburg Hbf .... d.	0522	...	0622	0648	...	0707	0722	...	0748	0807	0822	0848		2107	2122	2148	2207	2222	2248	2322	2348	0022	0022	0048
Düsseldorf Flughafen ✈ d.	0532	...	0632	0657	...	0716	0732	...	0757	0816	0832	0857	minutes	2116	2132	2157	2216	2232	2257	2332	2357	0032	0032	0057
Düsseldorf Hbf .... d.	0539	0614	0639	0714j	0714	0724	0739	0814	0814j	0824	0839	0914j		2124	2139	2214j	2224	2239	2314j	2339	0004	0038	0039	0104
Neuss Hbf .... d.	|	0624	|	0724	0724	...	|	0824	0824	...	|	0924	past each	...	|	2224	...	|	2324	|	...	...	|	...
Leverkusen Mitte .... d.	0555	|	0655	|	|	...	0755	|	|	...	0855	|		...	2155	|	...	2255	|	2355	...	...	0055	...
Köln Messe/Deutz ...... d.	0608	|	0708	|	|	...	0808	|	|	...	0908	|	hour until	...	2208	|	...	2308	|	0008	...	...	0108	...
Köln Hbf .... a.	0612	0651	0712	0752	0752	...	0812	0851	0851	...	0912	0953		...	2212	2251	...	2312	2351	0012	...	...	0112	...
Köln Hbf .... **807** d.	0615	0658	0715	0758	0758	...	0815	0858	0858	...	0915	0958		...	2215	2256	...	2315	2356	0015	...	...	0115	...
Köln/Bonn Flugh ✈ ..a.	|	0711	|	0811	0811	...	|	0911	0911	...	|	1011		...	|	2311	...	|	0011	|	...	...	|	...
Düren .... **807** d.	0639	...	0739	...	...	...	0839	...	...	...	0939	...		...	2239	...	...	2339	...	0039	...	...	0139	...
Aachen Hbf .... **807** a.	0707	...	0807	...	...	...	0907	...	...	...	1007	...		...	2307	...	...	0008	...	0108	...	...	0207	...

RE2 Düsseldorf - Essen - Gelsenkirchen - Münster ⊡ *RE42* Mönchengladbach - Essen - Münster

km			⚒r	⚒r	⚒r							●												¶
0	**Düsseldorf** Hbf .... d.	0006	...	0506	...	0606r	...	0706	...	0806	...		1806	...	1906	...	2006	...	2106	...	2206	...	2306	...
7	Düsseldorf Flughafen ✈ d.	0013	...	0513	...	0613r	...	0713	...	0813	...		1813	...	1913	...	2013	...	2113	...	2213	...	2313	...
	Mönchengladbach . d.	|	...	|	0522	|	0622	|	0722	|	0822	and at	|	1822	|	1922	|	2022	|	2122	|	2222	|	2337
	Viersen .... d.	|	...	|	0531	|	0631	|	0731	|	0831		|	1831	|	1931	|	2031	|	2131	|	2231	|	2345
	Krefeld Hbf .... d.	|	...	|	0542	|	0642	|	0742	|	0842	the same	|	1842	|	1942	|	2042	|	2142	|	2242	|	2359
24	**Duisburg** Hbf .... d.	0024	...	0524	0602	0624r	0702	0724	0802	0824	0902	minutes	1824	1902	1927	2002	2027	2102	2124	2202	2224	2302	2324‡	0024
34	Mülheim (Ruhr) Hbf ...... d.	0030	...	0530	0610	0630r	0710	0730	0810	0830	0910		1830	1910	1934	2010	2036	2110	2130	2210	2230	2310	2330‡	...
43	**Essen** Hbf .... d.	0044	0444	0544	0618	0644	0718	0744	0818	0844	0918	past each	1844	1918	1944	2018	2044	2118	2144	2218	2244	2318	2344	...
53	Gelsenkirchen Hbf ...... d.	0053	0453	0553	0626	0653	0726	0753	0826	0853	0926	hour until	1853	1926	1953	2026	2053	2126	2153	2226	2253	2326	2353	...
58	Wanne-Eickel Hbf ...... d.	0058	0458	0558	0631	0658	0731	0758	0833	0858	0931		1858	1931	1958	2031	2058	2131	2158	2231	2258	2331	2358	...
68	Recklinghausen Hbf .... d.	0107	0507	0605	0639	0705	0739	0805	0841	0905	0939		1905	1939	2005	2039	2105	2139	2205	2239	2305	2339	0007	...
84	Haltern am See .... d.	0118	0518	0616	0650	0716	0750	0816	0852	0916	0950		1916	1950	2016	2050	2116	2150	2216	2250	2316	2350	0018	...
97	Dülmen .... d.	0127	0527	0625	0659	0725	0759	0825	0901	0925	0959		1925	1959	2025	2059	2125	...	2225	...	2326	...	0027	...
126	**Münster** (Westf) Hbf .... a.	0152	0552	0650	0722	0750	0822	0852	0924	0950	1022		1950	2022	2052	2122	2150	...	2250	...	2351	...	0052	...

		Ⓒz		Ⓐe	⚒r	⚒r	⚒r								♥									⑤⑥v
Münster (Westf) Hbf ..... d.	0008	0108	0208	...	0408	...	0508	0536e	0610	0636r	0709	0736r	0810	0836		2010	2036	2110	...	...	2212	...	2308	2308
Dülmen .... d.	0032	0132	0232	...	0432	...	0532	0558e	0633	0658r	0732	0758r	0833	0858		2033	2058	2133	...	...	2235	...	2332	2332
Haltern am See .... d.	0042	0142	0242	...	0442	0507	0542	0607	0643	0707	0742	0807	0843	0907		2043	2107	2143	2207	...	2245	...	2342	2342
Recklinghausen Hbf ..... d.	0054	0154	0254	...	0454	0518	0554	0618	0654	0718	0753	0818	0854	0918	and at	2054	2118	2154	2218	...	2257	...	2354	2354
Wanne-Eickel Hbf .... d.	0103	0203	0303	...	0502	0527	0602	0627	0702	0727	0801	0827	0902	0927	the same	2102	2127	2202	2227	...	2306	...	0003	0003
Gelsenkirchen Hbf .... d.	0109	0209	0309	...	0508	0532	0608	0632	0708	0732	0807	0832	0908	0932		2108	2132	2208	2232	...	2311	...	0009	0009
Essen Hbf .... d.	0119	0219	0321	...	0521	0544	0621	0644	0721	0744	0820	0844	0921	0944	minutes	2121	2144	2221	2244	...	2322	...	0019	0021
Mülheim (Ruhr) Hbf ...... d.	...	...	0327	...	0527	0551	0627	0651	0727	0751	0826	0851	0927	0951	past each	2127	2151	2227	2251	...	2330	...	...	0027
Duisburg Hbf .... d.	...	...	0336	0505	0536	0600	0636	0700	0736	0800	0836	0900	0936	1000	hour until	2136	2200	2237	2300	2335	2338	0035	...	0036
Krefeld Hbf .... d.	...	...	|	0530	|	0618	|	0718	|	0818	|	0918	|	1018		|	2218	|	2318	0000	|	0100	...	|
Viersen .... d.	...	...	|	0543	|	0632	|	0732	|	0832	|	0932	|	1032		|	2232	|	2332	0013	|	0113	...	|
Mönchengladbach . a.	...	...	|	0551	|	0642	|	0742	|	0842	|	0942	|	1042		|	2242	|	2342	0020	|	0120	...	|
Düsseldorf Flughafen ✈ . d.	...	...	0346	...	0546	...	0646	...	0746	...	0846	...	0946	...		2146	...	2246	...	...	2347	...	...	0046
Düsseldorf Hbf .... a.	...	...	0353	...	0553	...	0653	...	0753	...	0853	...	0953	...		2153	...	2253	...	...	2354	...	...	0053

RE3 Düsseldorf - Duisburg - Gelsenkirchen - Dortmund - Hamm ⊡ ◇

km		Ⓐe									
0	**Düsseldorf** Hbf .... d.	0445	0545	0645		1845	1945	2045	2145	2245	2345
7	Düsseldorf Flughafen ✈ .. d.	0453	0553	0653		1853	1953	2053	2153	2253	2353
24	**Duisburg** Hbf .... d.	0510	0610	0710	and	1910	2010	2110	2210	2310	0010
32	Oberhausen Hbf .... d.	0516	0616	0716	hourly	1916	2016	2116	2216	2316	0016
48	Gelsenkirchen Hbf .... d.	0529	0629	0729		1929	2029	2129	2229	2329	0029
53	Wanne-Eickel Hbf .... d.	0534	0634	0734	until	1934	2034	2134	2234	2334	0034
57	Herne .... d.	0538	0638	0738		1938	2038	2138	2238	2338	0038
78	**Dortmund** Hbf .... a.	0557	0657	0757		1957	2057	2157	2257	2357	0057
109	**Hamm** (Westf) .... a.	0629	0729r	0829		2029	*2145*	*2244*	*2344*	*0044*	*0144*

Hamm (Westf) .... d.	...	0530e	0630e	0730r	0830		2030	*2116*	*2216*
Dortmund Hbf .... d.	0303	0603	0703	0803	0903		2103	2203	2303
Herne .... d.	0320	0620	0720	0820	0920	and	2120	2220	2320
Wanne-Eickel Hbf .... d.	0324	0624	0724	0824	0924	hourly	2124	2224	2324
Gelsenkirchen Hbf .... d.	0329	0629	0729	0829	0929		2129	2229	2329
Oberhausen Hbf .... d.	0343	0643	0743	0843	0943	until	2143	2243	2343
Duisburg Hbf .... d.	0353	0653	0753	0853	0953		2153	2253	2353
Düsseldorf Flughafen ..... d.	0404	0704	0804	0904	1004		2204	2304	0004
Düsseldorf Hbf .... a.	0412	0712	0812	0912	1012		2212	2312	0012

b – 0504 on Ⓒ **z**.
e – Ⓐ (not June 20, Nov. 1).
j – Arrives 7 – 10 minutes earlier.
k – To / from stations in Table **805**.
m – To / from Minden (Table **811**).
r – ⚒ (not June 20, Nov. 1).
v – Also June 9, 19, Oct. 2, 31.
z – Also June 20, Nov. 1.

* – 1 – 2 minutes later until Oct. 12.
¶ – From Aachen (see next page).
‡ – On ⑦ (also June 10; not June 9) departs Duisburg 2327, Mülheim 2336.
⊖ – To Minden (Table **811**). Runs daily Köln/Bonn Flughafen ✈ - Düsseldorf and Dortmund - Bielefeld - Minden.
❖ – Certain Hamm arrival times may vary by a few minutes. On Ⓐ (not June 20) Köln/Bonn Flughafen d. 1740 (not 1748).
▲ – The 1158 (daily), 1258 (on Ⓐ **e**) and 1358 (on Ⓐ **e**) from Bielefeld arrive Köln Hbf 3 minutes earlier and then run 6 minutes earlier Köln Hbf - Köln/Bonn Flughafen.

● – Trains may depart Duisburg / Mülheim up to 6 minutes later. Certain Münster arrivals are 2 minutes later.
♥ – Certain trains run 2 minutes later Münster - Essen.
◇ – Operated by **eurobahn** Keolis Deutschland.
⊕ – *RE11* operated by Abellio Rail NRW. *RE1* trains from / to Aachen are diverted in the Köln area on June 22, 23.
⊡ – See note and shaded panel on page 379. Many services are subject to alteration July 13 - August 25.

RE4 Aachen - Mönchengladbach - Düsseldorf - Wuppertal - Dortmund *RE13* Venlo - Mönchengladbach - Düsseldorf - Wuppertal - Hamm ◇

km			⚒r	Ⓐe	⚒r	⚒r		⚒r																
0	**Aachen** Hbf 473 d.	0253	0413	...	...	0513	0513	...	0613	...	0713	...		1713	...	1813	...	1913	...	2013	...	2113	...	2237
14	Herzogenrath 473 d.	0307	0427	...	...	0527	0527	...	0628	...	0727	...		1727	...	1827	...	1927	...	2027	...	2127	...	2252
58	Rheydt Hbf d.	0341	0503	...	...	0603	0603	...	0703	...	0803	...		1803	...	1903	...	2003	...	2103	...	2203	...	2330
	Venlo 🏛 d.	|	|	0505	0505	|	|	0605	|	0705	|	0805	and at	|	1805	|	1905	|	2005	|	2105	|	2205	|
	Kaldenkirchen d.	|	|	0510	0510	|	|	0610	|	0710	|	0810		|	1810	|	1910	|	2010	|	2110	|	2210	|
	Viersen d.	|	|	0527	0527	|	|	0627	|	0727	|	0827	the same	|	1827	|	1927	|	2027	|	2127	|	2227	|
62	**Mönchengladbach** Hbf d.	0349	0510	0545j	0545j	0610	0610	0645j	0710	0745j	0810	0845j		1810	1845j	1910	1945j	2010	2045j	2110	2145j	2210	2236	2336
79	Neuss Hbf d.	0403	0524	0557	0557	0624	0624	0657	0724	0757	0824	0857	minutes	1824	1857	1924	1957	2024	2057	2124	2157	2224	...	s
90	**Düsseldorf** Hbf a.	0413	0534	0608	0608	0634	0634	0708	0735	0808	0834	0908		1834	1908	1934	2008	2034	2108	2134	2208	2234	...	...
90	**Düsseldorf** Hbf d.	d	0540e	0612	...	0640	...	0712	0740	0812	0840	0912	past each	1840	1912	1940	2012	2040	...	2140	...	2240	...	...
117	**Wuppertal** Hbf d.	...	0602e	0632	...	0702	...	0732	0802	0832	0902	0932		1902	1932	2002	2032	2102	...	2202	...	2302	...	...
144	**Hagen** Hbf 804 d.	...	0629e	0658	...	0729	...	0758	0829	0858	0929	0958	hour until	1929	1958	2029	2055	2129	...	2229	...	2329	...	...
159	Witten d.	...	0640e	|	...	0740	...	|	0840	|	0940	|		1940	|	2040	...	2140	...	2240	...	2340	...	...
175	**Dortmund** Hbf d.	...	0650e	|	...	0750	...	|	0850	|	0950	|		1950	|	2050	...	2150	...	2250	...	2350	...	...
	Schwerte 804 d.	...	...	0708	...	...	...	0808e	...	0908r	...	1008		...	2008	...	...	...	...	...	...	...	...	...
	Unna d.	...	...	0720	...	...	...	0820e	...	0920r	...	1020		...	2020	...	...	...	...	...	...	...	...	...
	Hamm (Westf) d.	...	...	0734	...	...	...	0834e	...	0934r	...	1034		...	2034	...	...	...	...	...	...	...	...	...

km		⚒r	⚒r	⚒r		Ⓐe		⚒r		⚒r														
0	**Hamm** (Westf) d.	...	...	...	...	...	...	0625e	...	...	...	0725e	...	0825e	...	0925r	...	1025		1925	...	...	...	...
19	Unna d.	...	...	...	...	...	...	0637e	...	...	...	0737e	...	0837e	...	0937r	...	1037		1937	...	...	...	...
35	Schwerte 804 d.	...	...	...	...	...	...	0649e	...	...	...	0749e	...	0849e	...	0949r	...	1049		1949	...	...	...	...
	Dortmund Hbf d.	...	...	...	...	0609	...	|	...	0709	...	|	0809	|	0909	|	1009	|	and at	|	2009	...	2109	2209
	Witten d.	...	...	...	...	0619	...	|	...	0719	...	|	0819	|	0919	|	1019	|		|	2019	...	2119	2219
48	**Hagen** Hbf 804 d.	...	...	0602e	...	0632	...	0702	...	0732	...	0802	0832	0902	0932	1002	1032	1102	the same	2002	2032	...	2132	2232
75	**Wuppertal** Hbf d.	...	...	0625e	...	0658	...	0725	...	0758	...	0825	0858	0925	0958	1025	1058	1125		2025	2058	...	2158	2258
102	**Düsseldorf** Hbf a.	...	...	0646e	...	0719	...	0746	...	0819	...	0846	0919	0946	1019	1046	1119	1146	minutes	2046	2119	...	2219	2319
102	**Düsseldorf** Hbf d.	0549	0622	0649	...	0722	0722	0749	0749	0822	0822	0849	0922	0949	1022	1049	1122	1149		2049	2122	2149	2222	2322
113	Neuss Hbf d.	0601	0636	0701	...	0736	0736	0801	0801	0836	0836	0901	0936	1001	1036	1101	1136	1201	past each	2101	2136	2201	2236	2336
130	**Mönchengladbach** Hbf d.	0625j	0649	0725j	0725	0749	0749	0825j	0825j	0849	0849	0925j	0949	1025j	1049	1125j	1149	1225j		2125j	2149	2225j	2249	2349
139	Viersen d.	0633	|	0733	0733	|	|	0833	0833	|	|	0933	|	1033	|	1133	|	1233	hour until	2133	|	2233	|	|
157	Kaldenkirchen a.	0650	|	0750	0750	|	|	0850	0850	|	|	0950	|	1050	|	1150	|	1250		2150	|	2250	|	|
167	**Venlo** 🏛 a.	0656	|	0756	0756	|	|	0856	0856	|	|	0956	|	1056	|	1156	|	1256		2156	|	2256	|	|
	Rheydt Hbf d.	...	0654	...	...	0754	0754	...	...	0854	0854	...	0954	...	1054	...	1154	...		...	2154	...	2254	2354
	Herzogenrath 473 d.	...	0729	...	...	0829	0829	...	...	0929	0929	...	1029	...	1129	...	1229	...		...	2229	...	2329	0029
	Aachen Hbf 473 a.	...	0745	...	...	0845	0845	...	...	0945	0945	...	1045	...	1145	...	1245	...		...	2245	...	2345	0045

RE5 Koblenz - Bonn - Köln - Düsseldorf - Duisburg - Wesel ❦ *RE19* Düsseldorf - Emmerich - Arnhem ⊙ ❦

km			⚒r ◐	Ⓐe	⚒r		◐	⚒r		◐△				◐			◐			◐			◐	◐
0	**Koblenz** Hbf d.	...	0426	0517	...	...	0526	0612	...	0626	0717		...	1930	2017	...	2030	2117	...	2130	2217	...	2230	2326
18	Andernach d.	...	0444	0528	...	...	0544	0624	...	0644	0728		...	1945	2028	...	2045	2128	...	2145	2228	...	2245	2344
29	Bad Breisig d.	...	0454	0535	...	...	0554	0631	...	0654	0735	and at	...	1955	2035	...	2055	2135	...	2155	2235	...	2255	2354
39	Remagen d.	...	0511j	0546	...	...	0611j	0644	...	0711j	0746		...	2011j	2046	...	2111j	2146	...	2211j	2246	...	2311j	0011j
59	**Bonn** Hbf d.	...	0533	0604	...	...	0632	0704	...	0732	0804	the same	...	2033	2104	...	2133	2204	...	2233	2304	...	2333	0033
93	**Köln** Hbf ♥ d.	*0549*	0602	0631	0631	*0649*	0702	0731	*0749*	0802	0831		*2049*	2102	2131	*2149*	2202	2228	*2249*	2302	2328	2349	0002	0102
106	Leverkusen Mitte d.	*0604*	...	0645	0645	*0704*	...	0745	*0804*	...	0845	minutes	*2104*	...	2145	*2204*	...	...	*2304*	...	...	0004	▬	...
133	**Düsseldorf** Hbf d.	0626	...	0703	0703	0726	...	0803	0826	...	0903		2126	...	2203	2226	...	...	2326	...	...	0021	...	...
140	Düsseldorf Flughafen ✈ d.	0633	...	0709	0709	0733	...	0809	0833	...	0909	past each	2133	...	2209	2233	...	...	2334	...	...	0028	...	...
157	**Duisburg** Hbf d.	0644	...	0720	0720	0744	...	0820	0844	...	0920		2144	...	2220	2244	...	...	2344	...	...	0036	0044	...
165	Oberhausen Hbf d.	0650	...	0727	0727	0750	...	0827	0850	...	0927	hour until	2150	...	2227	2250	...	...	2350	...	...	...	0050	...
192	Wesel d.	0717	...	0755	0755	0817	...	0853	0917	...	0955		2217	...	2253	2317	...	...	0017	...	...	...	0117	...
226	**Emmerich** 🏛 d.	0745	...	...	...	0845	...	...	0945	...	...		2245	...	...	2345	...	...	0046	...	...	...	0145	...
256	**Arnhem** a.	0815	...	...	...	0915	...	...	1015	...	...		2315	...	...	0015	...	...	...	...	...	...	...	...

	Ⓐe	◐	⚒r	◐			◐		▽	◐				◐			◐			◐				
rnhem d.	...	...	...	...	...	...	...	0544t	...	...	0644		...	...	1844	...	...	1944	...	...	2044	2144	...	2244
mmerich 🏛 d.	...	...	...	...	0508	0539e	...	0608	...	...	0708		...	...	1908	...	...	2008	...	...	2108	2208	...	2308
/esel d.	...	...	0506e	...	0543	0606r	...	0643	0706	...	0743	and at	1906	...	1943	2011	...	2043	2106	...	2143	2243	...	2343
berhausen Hbf d.	...	...	0534e	...	0608	0634r	...	0708	0734	...	0808		1934	...	2008	2034	...	2108	2133	...	2208	2308	...	0008
uisburg Hbf d.	...	...	0542	...	0616	0642r	...	0716	0742	...	0816	the same	1942	...	2016	2042	...	2116	2144	...	2216	2315	2322	0015
isseldorf Flughafen ✈ d.	...	...	0550	...	0625	0650r	...	0725	0750	...	0825		1950	...	2025	2050	...	2025	2152	...	2225	▬	2332	▬
üsseldorf Hbf d.	...	...	0558	...	0633	0658r	...	0733	0758	...	0833	minutes	1958	...	2033	2058	...	2133	2159	...	2233	...	2339	...
everkusen Mitte d.	...	...	0614	...	*0655*	0714r	...	*0755*	0814	...	*0855*		2014	...	*2055*	2114	...	*2155*	2213	...	*2255*	◐	2355	◐
öln Hbf ★ d.	0532	0556	0632	0656	*0712*	0732	0756	*0812*	0832	0856	*0912*	past each	2032	2056	*2112*	2132	2156	*2212*	2232	2256	*2312*	2356	0012	0056
onn Hbf d.	0556	0627	0656	0727	...	0756	0827	...	0856	0927	...		2056	2127	...	2156	2227	...	2257	2327	...	0027	...	0126
emagen d.	0615	0654j	0716	0754j	...	0816	0854j	...	0916	0954j	...	hour until	2116	2157j	...	2216	2254j	...	2316	2354j	...	0054j	...	0154j
ad Breisig d.	0622	0702	0723	0802	...	0823	0902	...	0923	1002	...		2123	2205	...	2223	2302	...	2323	0002	...	0102	...	0202z
ndernach d.	0629	0712	0730	0813	...	0830	0912	...	0930	1012	...		2130	2215	...	2230	2312	...	2330	0012	...	0112	...	0212z
oblenz Hbf a.	0642	0727	0742	0828	...	0842	0927	...	0942	1027	...		2142	2236	...	2242	2332	...	2344	0030	...	0132	...	0232z

RE7 Köln - Wuppertal - Hagen - Hamm - Münster (- Rheine: Table 812)

km		Ⓐe									
0	**Köln** Hbf ♥ d.	...	0521e	0621r	0721		1921	2021	2121	2221	2352
28	Solingen Hbf d.	...	0543e	0643r	0743	and	1943	2043	2143	2243	0020
46	**Wuppertal** Hbf d.	...	0556e	0656r	0756		1956	2056	2156	2256	0036
73	**Hagen** Hbf d.	0522	0622	0722	0822	hourly	2022	2122	2222	2322	▬
86	Schwerte (Ruhr) d.	0533	0633	0733	0833		2033	2133	2233	2333	...
102	Unna d.	0544	0644	0744	0844	until	2044	2144	2244	2344	...
121	**Hamm** (Westf) d.	0559	0659	0759	0859		2059	2159	2259	2357	0010
157	**Münster** (Westf) Hbf a.	0622	0722	0822	0922		2122	2229	2329	...	0040

	Ⓐe	⚒r								⑤⑥v
Münster (Westf) d.	...	...	0529e	0634		2034	...	2134	2234	2234
Hamm (Westf) d.	...	0500	0600	0700	and	2100	...	2200	2300	2300
Unna d.	...	0513	0613	0713		2113	...	2213	2313	2313
Schwerte (Ruhr) d.	...	0525	0625	0725	hourly	2125	...	2225	2325	2325
Hagen Hbf d.	0439	0539	0639	0739		2139	2232	2236	2336	2339
Wuppertal Hbf d.	0504	0604	0704	0804	until	2204	2320	...	...	0005
Solingen Hbf d.	0515	0615	0715	0815		2215	2337	...	...	...
Köln Hbf ★ a.	0538	0638	0738	0839		2238	0005	...	...	...

Düsseldorf and Köln - Krefeld - Kleve ⊖

km	km		⚒r	⚒r						n	
0		**Düsseldorf** Hbf d.	...	0609	...	0709		...	2209	...	2309
	0	**Köln** Hbf d.	0542	|	0642	|	and at	2142	|	2242	|
	36	Neuss Hbf d.	0607	|	0707	|	the same	2207	|	2307	|
27	54	**Krefeld** Hbf d.	0624	0636	0724	0736		2224	2236	2324	2336
57		Geldern d.	...	0702	...	0802	minutes	...	2302	...	0002
66		Kevelaer d.	...	0708	...	0808	past each	...	2308	...	0008
72		Weeze d.	...	0717	...	0817		...	2317	...	0017
79		Goch d.	...	0723	...	0823	hour until	...	2323	...	0023
92		**Kleve** a.	...	0735	...	0835		...	2335	...	0035

	⚒r								
Kleve d.	0525	...	0625	...	0721	...		2221	...
Goch d.	0538	...	0638	...	0738	...	and at	2238	...
Weeze d.	0545	...	0645	...	0745	...	the same	2245	...
Kevelaer d.	0551	...	0651	...	0751	...		2251	...
Geldern d.	0558	...	0658	...	0758	...	minutes	2258	...
Krefeld Hbf d.	0626	0635	0726	0735	0826	0835	past each	2326	2335
Neuss Hbf d.	|	0653	|	0753	|	0853		|	2353
Köln Hbf a.	|	0718	|	0819	|	0919	hour until	|	0018
Düsseldorf Hbf a.	0652	...	0752	...	0852	...		2352	...

– To Düsseldorf Flughafen Terminal (a. 0425).
– Ⓐ (not June 20, Nov. 1).
– Arrives 7 – 11 minutes earlier.
– Not Sept. 22 – 26, 29.
– ⚒ (not June 20, Nov. 1).
– To Duisburg (see previous page).
– ①–⑥ (not June 10).
– Also June 9, 19, Oct. 2, 31.
– © (also June 20, Nov. 1).
– Stopping train operated by Mittelrheinbahn.
– Subsequent trains depart Koblenz at 0726, 0830 and then at 30 minutes past the hour.

▽ – Certain services depart Wesel at xx11.
♥ – Trains also call at Köln Messe/Deutz (3 minutes after Köln Hbf).
★ – Trains also call at Köln Messe/Deutz (3 – 6 minutes before Köln Hbf).
◇ – *RE13* operated by eurobahn.
⊙ – *RE19* operated by Abellio Rail NRW.
⊖ – Düsseldorf - Kleve is operated by Nord West Bahn (additional services run on Ⓐe).
❦ – Timings north of Köln are subject to alteration July 13 - Aug. 25.

	RE1	*RE2*	*RE3*	*RE4*	*RE5*	*RE6*	*RE7*	*RE11*	*RE13*	*RE42*
Aachen Hbf	●	...	...	●	...	...	...	...	...	...
Köln Hbf	●	...	...	|	●	●	●	...	...	...
Mönchengladbach Hbf	|	...	...	●	|	|	|	...	●	●
Düsseldorf Hbf	●	●	●	●	●	●	|	●	●	|
Duisburg Hbf	●	●	●	|	●	●	|	●	|	●
Essen Hbf	●	●	|	|	...	●	|	●	|	●
via Gelsenkirchen	|	●	●	|	...	|	|	|	|	●
via Wuppertal and Hagen	|	|	|	●	...	|	●	|	●	|
Dortmund Hbf	●	|	●	●	...	●	|	●	|	|
Hamm (Westf)	●	|	●	...	...	●	●	●	●	|
Münster (Westf) Hbf	...	●	...	...	...	...	●	...	...	●

802 RHEIN – RUHR LOCAL SERVICES *RE / RB services*

RE8 / RB27 Mönchengladbach - Köln - Königswinter - Koblenz

km		Ⓐe	⑥	Ⓐe	⚒r	Ⓒz	Ⓐe	⚒r	Ⓒz	Ⓐe		†z	⚒r			†z	⚒r	Ⓑ	†z	⚒r				
0	**Mönchengladbach** .. ⊖ d.	0440	...	0503	0540	...	0603	0640	...	0703	0740	...	0803	▲	1740	...	1803	1840	...	1903	1940	2003r	*2040*	*214*
3	Rheydt Hbf ⊖ d.	0444	...	0507	0544	...	0607	0644	...	0707	0744	...	0807		1744	...	1808	1844	...	1908	1944	2007r	*2044*	*214*
22	Grevenbroich ⊖ d.	0502	...	0528	0602	...	0628	0702	...	0728	0802	...	0828	and at	1802	...	1828	1902	...	1928	2002	2028r	*2102*	*220*
56	**Köln** Hbf ⊖ a.	0535	...	0600	0635	...	0700	0735	...	0800	0835	...	0900		1835	...	1900	1935	...	2000	2035	2058r	*2135*	*223*
56	**Köln** Hbf 807 d.	0538	0601	0603	0638	0701	0703	0738	0801	0803	0838	0901	0903	the same	1838	1901	1903	1938	2001	2003	|	2101	2201	230
57	**Köln** Messe/Deutz d.	0541	0604	0607	0641	0704	0707	0741	0804	0807	0841	0904	0907		1841	1904	1907	1941	2004	2007	2040	2104	2204	230
71	Köln/Bonn Flughafen ✈ d.	0551	|	|	0651	|	|	0751	|	|	0851•	|	|	minutes	1851	|	|	1951	|	|	...	|	|	|
83	Troisdorf 807 d.	0601	0623	0623	0701	0723	0723	0801	0823	0823	0901	0923	0923		1901	1923	1923	2001	2023	2023	...	2123	2223	232
92	**Bonn** Beuel d.	0611	0633	0633	0711	0733	0733	0811	0833	0833	0911	0933	0933	past each	1911	1933	1933	2011	2033	2033	...	2133	2233	233
100	Königswinter d.	0620	0643	0643	0720	0743	0743	0820	0843	0843	0920	0943	0943		1920	1943	1943	2020	2043	2043	...	2143	2243	234
105	Bad Honnef d.	0626	0649	0649	0726	0749	0749	0826	0849	0849	0926	0949	0949	hour until	1926	1949	1949	2026	2049	2049	...	2149	2249	234
115	Linz (Rhein) d.	0637	0702	0702	0735t	0802	0802	0835	0902	0902	0935	1002	1002		1935	2002	2002	2035	2102	2102	...	2202	2302	000
122	Bad Hönningen d.	0642	0709	0709	0740t	0809	0809	0840	0909	0909	0940	1009	1009		1940	2009	2009	2040	2109	2109	...	2209	2309	...
138	Neuwied 914 d.	0654	0724	0724	0751t	0824	0824	0851	0924	0924	0951	1024	1024		1951	2024	2024	2051	2124	2124	...	2224	2324	...
◊153	**Koblenz** Hbf 914 a.	0715	0740	0740	0815	0840	0840	0914	0940	0940	1014	1040	1040		2014	2040	2040	2114	2140	2140	...	2240	2340	...

	⚒r	⚒r				Ⓐe		⚒r	Ⓐe	⑥		⚒r							⑥	Ⓑ			⑤⑥v	
Koblenz Hbf 914 d.	...	...	...	0518r	...	0537	...	0618	0637	0645	0718	0745	0818	0845	△	1818	1845	1918	...	1945	2018	2118	2218	221
Neuwied 914 d.	...	...	...	0533r	...	0557	...	0633	0657	0708	0733	0808	0833	0908		1833	1908	1933	...	2008	2033	2133	2233	223
Bad Hönningen d.	...	...	...	0546r	...	0611	...	0646	0711	0719	0746	0819	0846	0919	and at	1846	1919	1946	...	2019	2046	2146	2246	224
Linz (Rhein) d.	...	0453	...	0553	...	0618	0653	0653	0718	0724	0753	0824	0853	0924		1853	1924	1953	...	2024	2053	2153	2253	225
Bad Honnef d.	...	0503	...	0603	...	0629	0703	0703	0729	0733	0803	0833	0903	0933	the same	1903	1933	2003	...	2033	2103	2203	2303	
Königswinter d.	...	0509	...	0609	...	0635	0709	0709	0735	0739	0809	0839	0909	0939		1909	1939	2009	...	2039	2109	2209	2309	...
Bonn Beuel d.	...	0518	...	0618	...	0646	0718	0718	0746	0749	0818	0849	0918	0949	minutes	1918	1949	2018	...	2049	2118	2218	2318	...
Troisdorf 807 d.	...	0528	...	0628	...	0659	0728	0728	0759	0759	0828	0859	0928	0959		1928	1959	2028	...	2059	2128	2228	2328	...
Köln/Bonn Flughafen ✈ d.	...	|	...	|	...	0708	|—	|	0808	0808	|	0908	|	1008	past each	|	2008	|	...	2108	|	|	|	...
Köln Messe/Deutz a.	0519	0550	0619	0650	0719	0719	0750	0750	0819	0819	0850	0919	0950	1019		1950	2019	2050	2119	2119	2150	2250	2350	001
Köln Hbf 807 a.	0522	0553	0622	0653	0722	0722	0753	0753	0822	0822	0853	0921	0953	1022	hour until	1953	2022	2053	2122	2122	2153	2252	2353	002
Köln Hbf ⊖ d.	0525	0559e	0625	0659e	0725	0725	...	0759	0825	0825	0859k	0925	0959r	1025		1959r	2025	...	2125	2125	*2225*	*2325*	...	002
Grevenbroich ⊖ d.	0555	0630e	0655	0730e	0755	0755	...	0830	0855	0855	0930k	0955	1030r	1055		2030r	2055	...	2155	2155	*2255*	*2355*	...	005
Rheydt Hbf ⊖ d.	0615	0651e	0715	0751e	0815	0815	...	0851	0915	0915	0951k	1015	1051r	1115		2051r	2115	...	2215	2216	*2315*	*0015*	...	011
Mönchengladbach ⊖ a.	0620	0656e	0720	0756e	0820	0820	...	0856	0920	0920	0956k	1020	1056r	1120		2056r	2120	...	2220	2221	*2320*	*0020*	...	012

S-Bahn 13 Köln - Köln/Bonn Flughafen ✈ - Troisdorf

		Ⓐe		Ⓐe		⑥		⑥	⑥		⑥		†z		†z					
Köln Hbf d.	Ⓐ	0401	and every 20 minutes until	2041	⑥	0441	and every 30 minutes until	0811	0821	and every 20 minutes until	2041	†	0441	and every 30 minutes until	2041	DAILY	2111	and every 30 minutes until	0041	014
Köln Messe/Deutz d.		0403		2043		0443		0813	0823		2043		0443		2043		2113		0043	014
Köln/Bonn Flughafen ✈ d.		0416		2056		0456		0826	0836		2056		0456		2056		2126		0056	015
Troisdorf a.		0427		2107		0507		0836	0847		2107		0507		2107		2136		0107	020

		Ⓐe		Ⓐe		⑥		⑥	⑥		⑥		†z		†z					
Troisdorf d.	Ⓐ	0413	and every 20 minutes until	2113	⑥	0513	and every 30 minutes until	0713	0753	and every 20 minutes until	2113	†	0513	and every 30 minutes until	2113	DAILY	2143	and every 30 minutes until	0113	021
Köln/Bonn Flughafen ✈ d.		0424		2124		0524		0724	0804		2124		0524		2124		2154		0124	022
Köln Messe/Deutz a.		0436		2136		0536		0736	0816		2136		0536		2136		2206		0136	023
Köln Hbf a.		0439		2139		0539		0739	0819		2139		0539		2139		2209		0139	023

Dortmund - Unna - Soest ❖ ⊙

km			Ⓒz		⚒r	⚒r							Ⓒz		⚒r	⚒r				
0	**Dortmund** Hbf 805 d.	0007	0107	...	0507	0607	0707	and hourly until	2307	...	**Soest** 805 d.	0003	0103	...	0503	0603	0703	and hourly until	2303	...
23	Unna d.	0032	0132	...	0532	0632	0732		2332	...	Unna d.	0027	0127	...	0527	0627	0727		2327	...
53	**Soest** 805 a.	0054	0154	...	0554	0654	0754		2354	...	**Dortmund** Hbf 805 a.	0051	0151	...	0551	0651	0751		2351	...

RB 53 Dortmund - Schwerte - Iserlohn ⊡

km		Ⓒz	Ⓒz		Ⓐe		⚒r						Ⓒz		Ⓐe	Ⓐe					⑤⑥
0	**Dortmund** Hbf d.	0023	0123	...	0523	0623	0623	0723	and hourly until	2323	...	**Iserlohn** d.	0051	...	0521	0621	0651r	0751	and hourly until	2251	235
18	Schwerte (Ruhr) d.	0045	0145	...	0545	0642	0645	0745		2345	...	Schwerte (Ruhr) d.	0120	...	0550	0650	0720	0820		2320	002
38	**Iserlohn** a.	0111	0209	...	0609	...	0709	0809		0009	...	**Dortmund** Hbf a.	0138	...	0608	0708	0738	0838		2338	003

Bonn - Remagen - Ahrbrück

km		⚒r		⚒r						⑤⑥v		Ⓐe	⚒r	⚒r						
0	**Bonn** Hbf 800 d.	...	...	0747	...	0847	and hourly until	2047	2147	2147	**Ahrbrück** d.	0603	...	0703	...	0803	and hourly until	2003	2103	220
20	Remagen 800 d.	0611	0711	0811	0811	0911		2111	2211	2211	Ahrweiler d.	0631	0631	0731	0731	0831		2031	2131	223
33	Ahrweiler d.	0628	0728	0828	0828	0928		2128	2227	2228	Remagen 800 a.	0647	0647	0747	0747	0847		2047	2147	224
49	**Ahrbrück** a.	0656	0756	0856	0856	0956		2156	...	2256	**Bonn** Hbf 800 a.	0712	0712	0812	0812	0912		2112	...	...

OTHER USEFUL S-BAHN LINKS

Services operate every 20 minutes (every 30 minutes evenings and weekends)

Service	Route (*journey time in minutes*)
S 1	Solingen Hbf - Düsseldorf Hbf (22) - Düsseldorf Flughafen ✈ (35) - Duisburg Hbf (53) - Essen Hbf (72) - Bochum Hbf (90) - Dortmund Hbf (113).
S 3	Oberhausen Hbf - Mülheim Hbf (8) - Essen Hbf (17).
S 9	Essen Hbf - Wuppertal Hbf (46).
S 11	Düsseldorf Flughafen Terminal ✈ - Düsseldorf Hbf (12) - Neuss Hbf (31) - Köln Hbf (82).

e – Ⓐ (not June 20, Nov. 1).
k – ⚒ (not June 20, 27 – 29, Aug. 2 – 10, Sept. 28, Nov. 1, 16).
r – ⚒ (not June 20, Nov. 1).
t – 2 – 3 minutes later on Ⓐ (not June 2… Nov. 1).
v – Also June 9, 19, Oct. 2, 31.
z – Also June 20, Nov. 1.

▲ – On Ⓐe the 1040, 1140, 1240, 1340 and 1440 from Mönchengladbach run up to 5 minutes later Linz (Rhein) - Koblenz Hbf. The 1003 from Mönchengladbach does no… run Mönchengladbach - Köln on June 27 – 29, Aug. 2 – 10, Sept. 28, Nov. 16.
△ – On Ⓐe the 1245 from Koblenz departs Neuwied, Bad Hönningen and Linz (Rhein) 2 minutes earlier.
◊ – Via Koblenz-Lützel (*159 km* via Ehrenbreitstein).
❖ – Operated by **eurobahn** Keolis Deutschland (2nd class only).
⊙ – Additional trains run on ⚒ (not June 20, Nov. 1).
⊡ – Additional trains run on Ⓐ (not June 20, Nov. 1).
⊖ – Additional journeys Mönchengladbach - Köln and v.v.: **From Mönchengladbach Hbf** at 0040 Ⓒz, 0440 ⑥, 0540 †z, 0627 Ⓐe, 0640 † … 1840 ⑥, 2240 and 2338. **From Köln Hbf** at 0125 Ⓒz, 0459 Ⓐe, 0825 †z and 0925 †z.

803 DORTMUND and MÜNSTER - ENSCHEDE *2nd class only*

km	△	Ⓐe	⚒r		⚒r						△	Ⓐe	⚒r	⚒r		Ⓐe	⑥			
0	**Dortmund** Hbf d.	0552	0652	...	0752	0852	and hourly until	2052	2152	2252	**Enschede** d.	...	...	0556e	...	0656	0702	0802	and hourly until	210
44	Dülmen d.	0640	0740	...	0840	0940		2140	2240	2340	Gronau (Westf) 🛃 a.	...	...	0607e	...	0707	0713	0813		211
61	Coesfeld (Westf) a.	0653	0753	...	0853	0953		2153	2253	2353	Gronau (Westf) d.	...	0524e	0620	...	0708	0720	0820		212
61	Coesfeld (Westf) d.	0705	0800	0900	0900	1000		2200	...	...	Coesfeld (Westf) a.	...	0557e	0657	...	0757	0757	0857		215
96	Gronau (Westf) a.	0738	0833	0933	0933	1033		2233	...	...	Coesfeld (Westf) d.	0506	0603	0703	0803	0803	0803	0903		220
96	Gronau (Westf) 🛃 d.	0745	0845	0945	0945	1045		2245	...	...	Dülmen d.	0520	0617	0717	0817	0817	0817	0917		221
103	**Enschede** a.	0756	0856	0956	0956	1056		2256	...	...	**Dortmund** Hbf a.	0607	0707	0807	0907	0907	0907	1007		230

km	△		Ⓒz		Ⓐe	Ⓐe	⚒r				△	Ⓐe	⚒r	⚒r						⑤⑥
0	**Münster** (Westf) Hbf d.	0008	0008	...	0508	0608	0708	0808	and hourly until	2308	**Enschede** d.	...	...	0626	0732r	0832	and hourly until	2232	2332	233
56	Gronau (Westf) a.	0105	0105	...	0605	0705	0805	0905		0005	Gronau (Westf) 🛃 a.	...	...	0637	0743r	0843		2243	2343	234
56	Gronau (Westf) 🛃 d.	...	0115	...	0609	0715	0815	0915		0015	Gronau (Westf) d.	0445	0545	0645	0745	0845		2245	...	234
63	**Enschede** a.	...	0126	...	0620	0726	0826	0926		0026	**Münster** (Westf) Hbf a.	0544	0644	0744	0844	0944		2344	...	004

e – Ⓐ (not June 20, Nov. 1).
r – ⚒ (not June 20, Nov. 1).
v – Also June 9, 19, Oct. 2, 31.
z – Also June 20, Nov. 1.
△ – German holiday dates apply.

HAGEN - KASSEL — 804

RE services

km		Ⓐe	⑥		⚒e																	d	d	d
0	**Hagen** Hbf ... 802 d.	0503	...	...	0603	...	0717	0817	0917	1017	1117	1217	1317	1417	1517	1617	1717	1817	1917	2017	...	*2122*	*2222*	*2322*
14	Schwerte (Ruhr) ... 802 d.	0513	...	...	0613	...	0728	0828	0928	1028	1128	1228	1328	1428	1528	1628	1728	1828	1928	2028	...	2149	2249	2349
57	Arnsberg (Westf) ... d.	0542	...	...	0642	...	0758	0858	0958	1058	1158	1258	1358	1458	1558	1658	1758	1858	1958	2058	...	2221	2321	0021
77	Meschede ... d.	0600	...	...	0700	...	0816	0916	1016	1116	1216	1316	1416	1516	1616	1716	1816	1916	2016	2116	...	2239	2339	0039
85	Bestwig ... d.	0608	0616	...	0708	...	0823	0923	1023	1123	1223	1323	1423	1523	1623	1723	1823	1923	2022	2123	...	2246	2345	0045
100	Brilon Wald ... d.	0622	0629	...	0732j	...	0837	0937	1037	1137	1237	1337	1437	1537	1637	1737	1837	1937	...	2137	...	2259	...	...
126	Marsberg ... d.	0650	0700	...	0800	...	0900	1000	1100	1200	1300	1400	1500	1600	1700	1800	1900	2000	...	2200	...	...	...	...
151	Warburg (Westf) ... a.	0709	0719	...	0819	...	0919	1019	1119	1219	1319	1419	1519	1619	1719	1819	1919	2019	...	2219	...	...	...	...
151	Warburg (Westf) ... 805 d.	0723	0723	...	...	...	0923	...	...	...	1323	...	1523	...	1723	...	1923	...	...	...	...	...	...	...
177	Hofgeismar ... 805 d.	0739	0739	...	...	...	0939	...	...	...	1339	...	1539	...	1739	...	1939	...	...	...	...	...	...	...
202	**Kassel** Wilhelmshöhe ... 805 a.	0758	0758	...	...	...	0958	...	...	...	1400	...	1558	...	1757	...	1957	...	...	...	...	...	...	...

	⚒e	⚒e	⚒e		Ⓐe	⑥																		
Kassel Wilhelmshöhe ... 805 d.	...	...	...	...	...	...	...	...	0802	...	1002	...	1202	...	...	...	1602	...	1802	...	...	2002	...	...
Hofgeismar ... 805 d.	...	...	...	...	...	...	...	...	0820	...	1020	...	1220	...	...	...	1620	...	1820	...	...	2020	...	...
Warburg (Westf) ... 805 a.	...	...	...	...	...	...	...	...	0836	...	1036	...	1236	...	...	...	1636	...	1836	...	...	2036	...	...
Warburg (Westf) ... d.	...	...	0535	...	0630	0635	...	0738	0838	0938	1038	1138	1238	1338	1438	1538	1638	1738	1838	1938	...	2038	...	2138
Marsberg ... d.	...	...	0555	...	0650	0655	...	0758	0859	0958	1059	1158	1259	1358	1459	1558	1659	1758	1859	1958	...	2059	...	2159
Brilon Wald ... d.	...	...	0621	...	0718	0721	...	0821	0921	1021	1121	1221	1321	1421	1521	1621	1721	1821	1921	2021	...	2125	2149	2225
Bestwig ... d.	0434	0534	0634	0634	0734	0734	0734	0834	0934	1034	1134	1234	1334	1434	1534	1634	1734	1834	1934	2034	...	2138	2210	2238
Meschede ... d.	0441	0541	0641	0641	0741	0741	0741	0841	0941	1041	1141	1241	1341	1441	1541	1641	1741	1841	1941	2041	...	2145	2217	2245
Arnsberg (Westf) ... d.	0459	0559	0659	0659	0759	0759	0759	0859	0959	1059	1159	1259	1359	1459	1559	1659	1759	1859	1959	2059	...	...	2234	...
Schwerte (Ruhr) ... 802 a.	0528	0628	0728	0728	0828	0828	0828	0928	1028	1128	1228	1328	1428	1528	1628	1728	1828	1928	2028	2128	...	...	2303	...
Hagen Hbf ... 802 a.	0542	0642	0742	0742	0842	0842	0842	0942	1042	1142	1242	1342	1442	1542	1642	1742	1842	1942	2042	2142	...	...	2313	...

– From Dortmund Hbf (departs 26 minutes before Schwerte departure time).
e – Not June 20, Nov. 1.
j – Arrives 0722.

DORTMUND and MÜNSTER - PADERBORN - KASSEL — 805

Warning! Services Köln - Düsseldorf - Dortmund - Hamm and v.v. are subject to alteration July 13 - August 25.

km		◇ Ⓒz		⊕ Ⓐe	◇ ⚒r	◇		⊕	◇	⊕	◇		⊕	◇		*ICE* **1223** N✕	◇		*IC* **2155** G	◇	⊕	*IC* **1955/9** ⑤⑦ bL	◇		⊕
	Köln Hbf **800 802** ... d.	...	...	...	...	...	...	...	...	...	...	...	...	...	...	0825‡	...	...	0901	...	...	...	...	...	...
	Düsseldorf Hbf **800 802** ... d.	...	...	...	...	...	...	0536e	...	0636	...	...	0736	...	...	0847	...	...	0946	...	1036	1113	...	...	1136
0	**Dortmund** Hbf ... 802 d.	...	...	0433	...	...	...	0639	...	0739	...	...	0839	...	...	0942	...	...	1043	...	1139	1208	...	...	1239
	Münster (Westf) Hbf .. 802 d.	0010	...	|	0510	0610	0634	|	*0710*	|	*0810*	0834	|	0910	0934	|	1010	1034	|	1110	|	|	1210	1234	|
31	Hamm (Westf) ... 802 a.	0037	...	0453	0537	0637	0657	0702	*0737*	0802	*0837*	0857	0902	0937	0957	1002	1037	1057	1102	1137	1202	1227	1237	1257	1302
31	Hamm (Westf) ... d.	0057	...	0501	0546	0646	...	0707	0746	0807	0846	...	0907	0946	...	1007	1046	...	1108	1146	1207	1234	1246	...	1307
57	Soest ... 802 d.	0113	...	0515	0602	0702	...	0721	0802	0821	0902	...	0921	1002	...	1022	1102	...	1123	1202	1221	1249	1302	...	1321
77	Lippstadt ... d.	0125	...	0526	0614	0714	...	0732	0814	0832	0914	...	0932	1014	...	1033	1114	...	1134	1214	1232	1300	1314	...	1332
109	**Paderborn** Hbf ... 809 811 d.	0150	...	0542	0642	0739	...	0748	0842	0847	0939	...	0948	1042	...	1049	1139	...	1150	1238	1247	1317	1339	...	1348
126	Altenbeken ... 809 811 d.	...	...	0556	0654	...	...	0802	0854	...	...	...	1002	1054	...	1104	...	...	1204	...	...	1330	...	...	1402
163	Warburg (Westf) ... 804 d.	...	...	0618	0716	...	...	0824	0916	...	...	...	1024	1116	...	1126	...	...	1226	...	...	|	...	...	1424
189	Hofgeismar ... 804 d.	...	...	0634	...	...	...	0839	...	...	...	...	1039	...	...	|	...	...	|	...	...	|	...	...	1439
214	**Kassel** Wilhelmshöhe .. 804 a.	...	...	0652	...	...	...	0857	...	...	...	...	1056	...	...	1156	...	...	1255	...	...	1417	...	...	1456

	◇	⊕	◇		⊕	◇	⊕	◇		*IC* **2157** G	◇	⊕	◇		⊕	◇	⊕	◇		⊕	◇	◇	◇ ⑤⑥f		◇
Köln Hbf **800 802** ... d.	...	...	...	...	...	...	...	...	...	1520	...	...	...	...	...	...	...	...	...	...	...	...	...	...	...
Düsseldorf Hbf **800 802** ... d.	...	1236	...	...	1336	...	1436	...	...	1545	...	1636	...	...	1736	...	1836	...	...	1936	...	...	...	...	...
Dortmund Hbf ... 802 d.	...	1339	...	...	1439	...	1539	...	...	1643	...	1739	...	...	1839	...	1939	...	...	2039	...	...	...	...	...
Münster (Westf) Hbf .. 802 d.	1310	|	*1410*	1434	|	1510	|	1610	1634	|	1710	|	1810	1834	|	1910	|	2010	2034	|	*2134*	*2234*	*2234*	...	2310
Hamm (Westf) ... 802 a.	1337	1402	*1437*	1457	1502	1537	1602	1637	1657	1702	1737	1802	1837	1857	1902	1937	2002	2037	2057	2102	*2157*	*2257*	*2257*	...	2337
Hamm (Westf) ... d.	1346	1407	1446	...	1507	1546	1607	1646	...	1708	1746	1807	1846	...	1907	1946	2007	2046	...	2107	2209	2304	2304	...	0004
Soest ... 802 d.	1402	1421	1502	...	1521	1602	1621	1702	...	1723	1802	1821	1902	...	1921	2002	2021	2102	...	2121	2225	2325	2325	...	0025
Lippstadt ... d.	1414	1432	1514	...	1532	1614	1632	1714	...	1733	1814	1832	1914	...	1932	2014	2032	2114	...	2132	2237	2337	2337	...	0037
Paderborn Hbf ... 809 811 d.	1442	1448	1539	...	1548	1642	1647	1739	...	1749	1842	1847	1939	...	1948	2039	2047	2139	...	2148	2302	0002	0002	...	0102
Altenbeken ... 809 811 d.	1454	...	...	...	1602	1654	...	...	...	1804	1854	...	...	...	2002	...	...	...	...	2202	...	...	0014	...	...
Warburg (Westf) ... 804 d.	1516	...	...	...	1624	1716	...	...	...	1826	1916	...	...	...	2024	...	...	...	...	2224	...	...	0037	...	...
Hofgeismar ... 804 d.	...	...	...	...	1639	...	...	...	...	|	...	...	...	...	2039	...	...	...	...	2239	...	...	...	...	...
Kassel Wilhelmshöhe ... 804 a.	...	...	...	...	1656	...	...	...	...	1857	...	...	...	...	2056	...	...	...	...	2257	...	...	...	...	...

	◇ ⚒r	⊕ Ⓐe		◇	⊕ Ⓐe	⊕ ⚒r		◇	⊕		◇	⊕	◇	*IC* **2156** G		◇	⊕	◇	⊕		◇	⊕	◇	⊕	
Kassel Wilhelmshöhe ... 804 d.	...	...	...	...	0555	...	...	...	0702	...	...	...	...	0902	...	...	...	...	1102	...	...	...	...	1303	...
Hofgeismar ... 804 d.	...	...	...	...	0611	...	...	...	0719	...	...	...	...	|	...	...	...	...	1119	...	...	...	...	1319	...
Warburg (Westf) ... 804 d.	...	0534	...	...	0634	...	...	...	0734	...	...	...	0839	0935	...	...	...	1039	1134	...	...	...	1239	1334	...
Altenbeken ... 809 811 d.	...	0559	...	...	0659	...	...	...	0759	...	...	...	0902	0956	...	...	...	1102	1159	...	...	...	1302	1359	...
Paderborn Hbf ... 809 811 d.	0521	0611	...	0621	0711	0711	...	0721	0811	...	0821	0911	0921j	1010	...	1021	1111	1121j	1211	...	1221	1311	1321j	1411	...
Lippstadt ... d.	0544	0626	...	0644	0726	0726	...	0744	0826	...	0844	0926	0944	1026	...	1044	1126	1144	1227	...	1244	1326	1344	1426	...
Soest ... 802 d.	0556	0637	...	0656	0737	0737	...	0756	0837	...	0856	0937	0956	1037	...	1056	1137	1156	1238	...	1256	1337	1356	1437	...
Hamm (Westf) ... a.	0614	0652	...	0714	0752	0752	...	0814	0852	...	0914	0952	1014	1050	...	1114	1152	1214	1252	...	1314	1352	1414	1452	...
Hamm (Westf) ... 802 d.	0620	0657	0659	0720	0757	0757	0759	0820	0857	0859	*0920*	0957	*1020*	1056	1059	*1120*	1157	1220	1257	1259	1320	1357	1420	1457	1459
Münster (Westf) Hbf ... 802 a.	0647	|	0722	0747	|	|	0822	0847	|	0922	*0947*	|	*1047*	|	1122	*1147*	|	1247	|	1322	1347	|	1447	|	1522
Dortmund Hbf ... 802 a.	...	0719	...	...	0819	0819	...	...	0919	...	...	1018	...	1114	...	...	1219	...	1317	...	...	1419	...	1519	...
Düsseldorf Hbf **800 802** ... a.	...	0824	...	...	0924	0924	...	...	1024	...	...	1124	...	1211	...	...	1324	...	1424	...	...	1524	...	1624	...
Köln Hbf **800 802** ... a.	...	...	...	...	...	...	...	...	...	...	...	...	...	1239	...	...	...	...	...	...	...	...	...	...	...

	◇	*ICE* **1224** Ⓒ M✕	*ICE* **1228** Ⓐ A✕		◇	*IC* **2152** G		◇	⊕	◇	⊕		◇	⊕	◇	⊕		◇	*IC* **1952** ⑤⑦ bL		◇	⊕		◇	◇
Kassel Wilhelmshöhe ... 804 d.	...	1403	1403	...	...	1502	...	...	...	...	1703	...	...	...	...	1903	...	...	1944	...	...	2102	...	...	...
Hofgeismar ... 804 d.	...	|	|	...	...	|	...	...	...	...	1719	...	...	...	...	1919	...	...	|	...	...	2119	...	...	...
Warburg (Westf) ... 804 d.	...	1433	1433	...	...	1535	...	...	...	1639	1734	...	...	...	1839	1934	...	...	2018	...	2039	2134	...	...	...
Altenbeken ... 809 811 d.	...	1456	1456	...	...	1556	...	...	...	1702	1759	...	...	...	1902	1959	...	...	2040	...	2102	2159	...	...	...
Paderborn Hbf ... 809 811 d.	1421	1510	1510	...	1521	1610	...	1621	1711	1721j	1811	...	1821	1911	1921j	2011	...	2015	2054	...	2115	2211	...	2215	2315
Lippstadt ... d.	1444	1526	1526	...	1544	1626	...	1644	1726	1744	1826	...	1844	1926	1944	2026	...	2038	2110	...	2138	2228	...	2238	2338
Soest ... 802 d.	1456	1537	1537	...	1556	1637	...	1656	1737	1756	1837	...	1856	1937	1956	2037	...	2050	2121	...	2150	2239	...	2250	2350
Hamm (Westf) ... a.	1514	1551	1551	...	1614	1650	...	1714	1752	1814	1852	...	1914	1952	2014	2052	...	2108	2134	...	2208	2254	...	2308	0008
Hamm (Westf) ... 802 d.	1520	1556	1556	1559	1620	1656	1659	*1720*	1757	1820	1857	1859	1920	1957	2020	2057	2059	2120	2140	2159	2220	2259	2259	2320	0010
Münster (Westf) Hbf .. 802 a.	1547	|	|	1622	1647	|	1722	*1747*	|	1847	|	1922	1947	|	2047	|	2122	2147	|	2229	2247	|	2329	2347	0040
Dortmund Hbf ... 802 a.	...	1614	1614	...	...	1714	...	...	1817	...	1919	...	...	2019	...	2119	...	...	2157	...	...	2319	...	...	...
Düsseldorf Hbf **800 802** ... a.	...	1706	1706	...	...	1811	...	...	1924	...	2024	...	...	2124	...	2224	...	...	2255	...	...	...	...	...	...
Köln Hbf **800 802** ... a.	...	1733	1729‡	...	...	...	...	...	...	...	...	...	...	...	...	...	...	...	2326	...	...	...	...	...	...

– Ⓐ (not June 20). 12 ✕ München - Nürnberg - Kassel - Düsseldorf - Wiesbaden - Frankfurt.
– To / from Gera via Weimar (Table **849a**).
– To / from Leipzig (Table **849a**).
– Ⓒ (also June 20). 12 ✕ München - Nürnberg - Kassel - Köln.
– 12 ✕ (Darmstadt / Wiesbaden Ⓐ **n** -) Köln - Kassel - Nürnberg - München.

– Also June 10, 19, Oct. 2, 31; not June 9, 21, July 14 - Aug. 25, Oct. 4, Nov. 1.

e – Ⓐ (not June 20, Nov. 1).
f – Also June 9, 19, Oct. 2, 31.
j – Arrives 6 minutes earlier.
n – Not June 20.
r – Not June 20, Nov. 1.
z – Also June 20, Nov. 1.

‡ – Köln **Messe/Deutz**.
◇ – Operated by **eurobahn** Keolis Deutschland (2nd class only).
⊕ – Operated by Abellio Rail NRW.

806 FRANKFURT - GIESSEN - KASSEL and SIEGEN

FRANKFURT - GIESSEN - KASSEL

ICE/IC trains	ICE 1674	ICE 1672	IC 2370	ICE 1578	ICE 1578	ICE 1576	ICE 1574	ICE 1572	ICE 1572	ICE 1570
SEE NOTE ✤	Ⓐ			E	⑤–⑦			⑦w	①–⑥	Ⓑq
	✕	✕		✕	v✕	✕	✕	✕	n✕	✕
Karlsruhe Hbf 912 d.	...	0702	0906	...	1110	1310	1510	1709	1709	1910
Heidelberg Hbf 912 d.	...	0746	0946	...	1146	1346	1546	1746	1746	1946
Frankfurt (Main) Hbf d.	0649	0851•	1051•	1251	1251•	1448•	1649•	1848•	1848•	2051•
Friedberg (Hess) d.	0716	0917	1117	1317	1317	1517	1717	1917	1917	2117
Gießen d.	0733	0934	1134	1334	1334	1534	1734	1934	1934	2134
Marburg (Lahn) d.	0749	0950	1151	1350	1350	1550	1750	1951	1951	2150
Stadtallendorf d.	0804	1005	|	1405	1405	|	1805	2005	2005	2205
Treysa d.	0816	1017	1215	1417	1417	1614	1817	2017	2018	2217
Wabern d.	0833	|	1232	|	|	1633	1834	|	2035	|
Kassel Wilhelmshöhe a.	0854	1054	1253	1454	1454	1654	1855	2053	2055	2255
Hannover Hbf 900 a.	...	...	...	...	...	...	...	...	...	...
Hamburg Hbf 900 a.	...	...	...	...	...	...	...	...	...	...
Stralsund Hbf 830 a.	...	...	...	...	...	...	...	...	...	...

ICE/IC trains	ICE 1571	ICE 1573	ICE 1575	ICE 1575		ICE 1577	ICE 1579	IC 2371	ICE 1673	ICE 1675	ICE 1675
SEE NOTE ✤	Ⓐ	⚒	E	⑤–⑦							⑤
	✕	✕	✕	v✕		✕	✕		✕	✕	✕
Stralsund Hbf 830 d.	...	...	...	...	...	...	...	...	...	...	...
Hamburg Hbf 900 d.	...	...	...	...	...	...	...	...	...	...	...
Hannover Hbf 900 d.	...	...	...	...	...	...	...	...	...	...	...
Kassel Wilhelmshöhe d.	0459	0700	0903	0903	...	1104	1303	1503	1703	1903	1903
Wabern d.	0519	0719	|	|	...	1123	|	1522	|	1923	1923
Treysa d.	0536	0736	0936	0936	...	1140	1336	1539	1736	1940	1940
Stadtallendorf d.	0550	0750	0950	0950	...	|	1350	|	1750	1954	1954
Marburg (Lahn) d.	0604	0804	1004	1004	...	1205	1404	1604	1804	2008	2008
Gießen d.	0622	0822	1022	1022	...	1223	1422	1622	1822	2026	2026
Friedberg (Hess) d.	0642	0842	1042	1042	...	1243	1442	1642	1842	2045	2045
Frankfurt (Main) Hbf a.	0709	0911•	1111	1111•	...	1310•	1509•	1709•	1909•	2111	2111
Heidelberg Hbf 912 a.	0812	1013	...	1213	...	1413	1613	1813	2013	...	2248
Karlsruhe Hbf 912 a.	0850	1050	...	1250	...	1450	1650	1851	2052	...	2327

km	Regional trains	RB 15036	RE 4170	RE 4150	◇	◇	RE 4152	◇	◇	RE 4154	◇	RE 4156	◇	RE 4158	◇	RE 4160	◇	RE 4162	RB 15024	◇	RE 4164	◇	RE 4166	◇	RE 4168	RE 4168
			†z	⚒r	Ⓐt	Ⓒz		Ⓐt	Ⓒz																	D
0	**Frankfurt (Main)** Hbf d.	0051	0508	0521	0616	0621	0719	0815	0821	0921	1021	1121	1221	1321	1421	1521	1620	1721	1751	1820	1921	2021	2121	2221	2324	2324
34	Friedberg (Hess) d.	0139	0533	0545	0645	0645	0745	0845	0845	0945	1045	1145	1245	1345	1445	1545	1645	1745	1815	1845	1945	2045	2145	2245	2346	2346
66	**Gießen** d.	0205	0604	0604	0705	0705	0804	0905	0905	1004	1105	1204	1305	1404	1505	1604	1705	1804	1839	1905	2004	2105	2204	2305	0007	0007
96	Marburg (Lahn) d.	0232	0620	0620	0721	0720	0820	0920	0920	1020	1120	1220	1320	1420	1520	1620	1720	1820	1905	1920	2020	2120	2220	2320	0031	0031
118	Stadtallendorf d.	...	0634	0634	0738	0738	0834	0938	0938	1034	1138	1234	1338	1434	1538	1634	1738	1834	1924	1938	2034	2138	2234	2340	0048	0048
138	Treysa d.	...	0649	0649	0755	0755	0849	0955	0955	1049	1155	1249	1355	1449	1555	1649	1755	1849	1939r	1955	2049	2155	2249	2356	0103	0104
166	Wabern d.	...	0707	0707	0817	0817	0907	1017	1017	1107	1217	1307	1417	1507	1617	1707	1817	1907	...	2017	2107	2217	2307	0019	...	0122
196	**Kassel** Wilhelmshöhe a.	...	0726	0726	0845	0845	0926	1045	1045	1126	1245	1326	1445	1526	1645	1726	1845	1926	...	2047	2126	2244	2326	0049	...	0142
200	**Kassel** Hbf a.	...	0734	0734	0854	0854	0934	1054	1054	1134	1251	1334	1454	1534	1654	1734	1854	1934	...	2052	2134	2252	2334	0055	...	0149

Regional trains	RB 15039	RE 4171	RE 4151	◇	RE 4177	RE 4173	RE 4153	◇	◇	RE 4155	◇	RE 4157	◇	RE 4159	◇	RE 4161	◇	RE 4163	◇	RE 4165	◇	RE 4167	◇	◇	◇	RE 4169
		Ⓐt	Ⓒz	⑥	Ⓐt	Ⓐt	Ⓒz	⑥	Ⓐt														Ⓑ	⑥		
Kassel Hbf d.	...	0400	0423	...	...	0611	0615	0704	0704	0823	0904	1023	1104	1223	1304	1423	1504	1623	1704	1823	1904	2023	2104	2104	...	2223
Kassel Wilhelmshöhe d.	...	0405	0429	...	...	0617	0621	0709	0709	0829	0909	1029	1109	1229	1309	1429	1508	1629	1709	1829	1909	2029	2109	2109	...	2229
Wabern d.	...	0423	0448	...	...	0639	0645	0738	0738	0848	0938	1048	1138	1248	1338	1448	1538	1648	1738	1848	1938	2048	2138	2138	...	2252
Treysa d.	...	0441	0506	0559	0600	0700	0703	0800	0803	0906	1005	1106	1205	1306	1405	1506	1605	1706	1805	1906	2005	2106	2205	2205	...	2310
Stadtallendorf d.	...	0455	0519	0614	0615	0716	0718	0815	0819	0919	1019	1119	1219	1319	1419	1519	1619	1719	1819	1919	2019	2119	2219	2219	...	2323
Marburg (Lahn) d.	0359	0512	0535	0635	0634	0734	0734	0835	0835	0935	1035	1135	1235	1335	1435	1535	1635	1735	1835	1935	2035	2135	2235	2235	...	2339
Gießen d.	0430	0536	0553	0654	0652	0753	0753	0854	0854	0953	1054	1153	1254	1353	1454	1553	1654	1753	1854	1953	2054	2153	2250	2254	2254	0008
Friedberg (Hess) d.	0458	0559	0612	0712	0712	0812	0812	0913	0913	1012	1113	1212	1313	1412	1512	1612	1713	1812	1913	2012	2112	2212	...	2313	2313	0038
Frankfurt (Main) Hbf a.	0527	0627	0635	0736	0740	0839	0837	0939	0939	1037	1137	1237	1337	1437	1537	1639	1737	1839	1937	2039	2135	2236	...	2335	2335	0112

FRANKFURT - GIESSEN - SIEGEN

km						◇		◇	◇		◇			◇	◇	◇		◇			◇		◇		◇	
			Ⓒz		†z	⚒r	Ⓐt	Ⓐt	Ⓒz	Ⓐt	⚒r		⚒r	Ⓐt	⑥	†z		⚒r		⚒r						
0	**Frankfurt** (Main) Hbf d.	0051	0208	...	0508	*0521*	0551	...	...	0631	*0719*	0745	0745	0815	0821	*0821*	0831	*0921*	0951	0951	1021	1031	*1121*	1151	1221	1231
34	Friedberg (Hess) d.	0139	0252	...	0533	*0545*	0615	...	...	0657	*0745*	0815	0815	0845	0845	*0845*	0859	*0945*	1015	1015	1045	1059	*1145*	1215	1245	1259
38	Bad Nauheim d.	0143	0256f	...	0537	|	0619	...	...	0701	|	0819	0819	|	|	|	0903	|	1020	1020	|	1103	|	1220	|	1303
66	**Gießen** a.	0204	0319f	...	0603	*0603*	0635	...	...	0724	*0803*	0835	0835	0902	0902	*0902*	0928	*1003*	1035	1035	1102	1128	*1203*	1235	1302	1328
66	**Gießen** 906 d.	...	...	...	...	0609	0640	0652	0709	0740	0809	0840	0840	0909	0909	0909	0940	1009	1040	1040	1109	1140	1209	1240	1309	1340
79	Wetzlar 906 d.	...	...	...	...	0618	0650	0703	0718	0750	0818	0849	0850	0918	0918	0918	0950	1018	1049	1050	1118	1150	1218	1250	1318	1350
101	Herborn d.	...	...	...	...	0633	0712	0730	0733	0812	0833	...	0912	0933	0933	0933	1012	1033	...	1112	1133	1212	1233	1312	1333	1412
107	Dillenburg d.	...	...	...	...	0638	0722	0738	0738	0822	0838	...	0922	0938	0938	0938	1022	1038	...	1122	1138	1222	1238	1322	1338	1422
139	**Siegen** Hbf a.	...	...	...	...	0705	...	0805	0805	...	0905	...	...	1005	1005	1005	...	1105	...	...	1205	...	1305	...	1405	...

	◇		◇		◇		◇			◇	◇		◇		◇		◇			◇		◇				◇
									Ⓐt	Ⓒz	Ⓐt								Ⓒz							
Frankfurt (Main) Hbf d.	*1321*	1351	1421	1431	*1521*	1551	1620	1631	1701	*1721*	1731	1751	1820	1831	*1921*	1951	2021	2031	2031	*2121*	2151	2221	2231	...	2324	...
Friedberg (Hess) d.	*1345*	1415	1445	1459	*1545*	1615	1645	1659	1726	*1745*	|	1815	1845	1859	*1945*	2015	2045	2059	2059	*2145*	2215	2245	2259	...	2346	...
Bad Nauheim d.	|	1420	|	1503	|	1620	|	1703	1730	|	1758	1819	|	1903	|	2019	|	2103	2103	|	2219	|	2303	...	|	...
Gießen a.	*1403*	1435	1502	1528	*1603*	1635	1702	1728	1748	*1803*	|	1835	1902	1928	*2003*	2035	2102	2128	2128	*2203*	2235	2302	2328	...	0005	...
Gießen 906 d.	1409	1440	1509	1540	1609	1640	1709	1740	...	1809	|	1840	1909	1940	2009	2040	2109	2140	2140	2209	2240	2309	2333	...	...	0011
Wetzlar 906 d.	1418	1450	1518	1550	1618	1650	1718	1750	...	1818	1820	1850	1918	1950	2018	2050	2118	2150	2150	2218	2250	2318	2343	...	...	0021
Herborn d.	1433	1512	1533	1612	1633	1712	1733	1812	...	1833	1835	1912	1933	2012	2033	2112	2133	2211	2212	2233	2312	2333	0005	...	...	0043
Dillenburg d.	1438	1522	1538	1622	1638	1722	1738	1822	...	1838	1840	1922	1938	2022	2038	2122	2138	...	2222	2238	2322	2338	0014	...	...	0050
Siegen Hbf a.	1505	...	1605	...	1705	...	1805	...	...	1905	1905	...	2005	...	2105	...	2205	...	...	2305	...	0005	...	...	...	0120

						◇				◇	◇		◇			◇	◇			◇		◇			◇	
		Ⓐt	Ⓐt	⑥	Ⓐt	Ⓐt	Ⓐt	Ⓐt	†z	⑥	Ⓐt	Ⓐt	⚒r	Ⓐt		⚒r	†z	⚒r		⚒r			⚒r			
Siegen Hbf d.	...	...	...	...	...	0457	...	...	...	0555	0600	...	0654	...	...	0754	0754	...	...	0854	...	0954	...	...	1054	...
Dillenburg d.	...	0424	...	0457	0510	0525	...	0533	0552	0618	0626	...	0728	...	0733	0817	0817	0833	...	0917	0933	1017	1033	...	1117	1133
Herborn d.	...	0432	...	0505	0518	0530	...	0540	0600	0622	0631	...	0734	...	0740	0822	0822	0840	...	0922	0940	1022	1040	...	1122	1140
Wetzlar 906 d.	...	0454	...	0527	0540	0547	...	0602	0621	0637	0649	...	0751	...	0802	0837	0837	0902	0902	0937	1002	1037	1102	1102	1137	1202
Gießen 906 a.	...	0505	...	0538	0551	|	...	0614	0632	0646	0659	...	0801	...	0814	0846	0846	0914	0914	0947	1014	1046	1114	1114	1147	1214
Gießen d.	0430	0514	0536	*0553*	...	|	0606	0628	0640	0654	0709	0736	...	0808	0828	0854	*0854*	0922	0922	*0953*	1028	1054	1122	1122	*1153*	1228
Bad Nauheim d.	0454	0538	0555	|	...	0611	0625	0653	0704	|	0728	0755	...	0826	0853	|	|	0939	0939	|	1053	|	1139	1139	|	1253
Friedberg (Hess) d.	0458	0542	0559	*0612*	...	|	0630	0658	0709	0712	0733	0759	...	0830	0858	0913	*0913*	0943	0943	*1012*	1058	1113	1143	1143	*1212*	1258
Frankfurt (Main) Hbf a.	0527	0608	0627	*0635*	...	0642	0657	0724	0734	0736	0802	0827	...	0857	0927	0939	*0938*	1009	1009	*1037*	1127	1137	1209	1209	*1237*	1327

	◇		◇		◇		◇		◇		◇		◇		◇		◇		◇	◇			◇			
																									⑤⑥	
Siegen Hbf d.	1154	...	1254	...	1354	...	1454	...	1554	...	1654	...	1754	...	1854	...	1954	...	2054	2154	...	...	2311	...	...	...
Dillenburg d.	1217	1233	1317	1333	1417	1433	1517	1533	1617	1633	1717	1733	1817	1833	1917	1933	2017	2033	2117	2217	...	...	2334	...	2338	2338
Herborn d.	1222	1240	1322	1340	1422	1440	1522	1540	1622	1640	1722	1740	1822	1840	1922	1940	2022	2040	2122	2222	...	...	2339	...	2346	2346
Wetzlar 906 d.	1237	1302	1337	1402	1437	1502	1537	1602	1637	1702	1737	1802	1837	1902	1937	2002	2037	2102	2137	2237	...	...	2352	...	0008	0008
Gießen 906 a.	1246	1314	1347	1414	1446	1514	1547	1614	1646	1714	1747	1814	1846	1914	1947	2014	2046	2114	2147	2246	...	...	0001	...	0019	0019
Gießen d.	1254	1322	*1353*	1428	1454	1522	*1553*	1628	1654	1722	*1753*	1828	1854	1922	*1953*	2031	2054	2122	*2153*	2254	2315	...	...	0008	0028	...
Bad Nauheim d.	|	1339	|	1453	|	1539	|	1653	|	1739	|	1853	|	1939	|	2055	|	2139	|	|	2338	...	...	0031	0051	...
Friedberg (Hess) d.	1313	1343	*1412*	1458	1512	1543	*1612*	1658	1713	1743	*1812*	1858	1913	1943	*2012*	2100	2112	2143	*2212*	2313	2342	...	...	0038	0055	...
Frankfurt (Main) Hbf a.	1337	1409	*1437*	1527	1537	1615	*1639*	1727	1737	1815	*1839*	1927	1937	2008	*2039*	2127	2135	2208	*2236*	2335	0038	...	...	0112	0141	...

D – ⑤–⑦ (also June 10, 20, Oct. 2, 3).
E – Daily to Aug. 9; ①–⑤ Aug. 12 - Sept. 27; daily from Sept. 30.

f – 6 minutes later June 29 - Oct. 27.
n – Not Oct. 4.
q – Not Oct. 2.
r – ⚒ (not June 20).
t – Ⓐ (not June 20).
v – Also Oct. 3.
w – Also Oct. 4.
z – Also June 20.

• – Calls at Frankfurt (Main) **Süd** (not Hbf) on ⑥⑦ Aug. 10 - Sept. 29 (departures from Frankfurt Süd are up to 9 minutes earlier, arrivals are up to 7 minutes later).
✤ – Service from June 11. During this timetable period services in this table do not run north of Kassel – see Table **900** for other connecting services. Services Karlsruhe - Frankfurt and v.v are subject to alteration July 20 - Sept. 8 and Oct. 7 – 20 (also ⑥⑦ Sept. 14 – 29); see the engineering work summary panel on page 369 for further details.
◇ – Operated by Hessische Landesbahn.

RE / RB services

AACHEN - KÖLN - SIEGEN 807

km		Ⓒz	2	Ⓐe¶	Ⓒz2	⑥¶	Ⓐe2	⑥¶	Ⓐt¶	⚒r							Ⓐe							
0	**Aachen** Hbf ... **802 910** d.	...	...	...	0237	...	...	...	...	0518e	0618e	0718e	0818r	0918		1518	...	1618	1718	1818	1918	2018r	...	...
31	Düren ... **802** d.	...	0003	...	0303	...	...	...	...	0545e	0645e	0745e	0845r	0945		1545	...	1645	1745	1845	1945	2045r	...	...
70	**Köln** Hbf ... **802 910** a.	...	0040	...	0340	...	...	...	...	0612e	0712e	0812e	0912r	1012		1612	...	1712	1812	1912	2012	2112r	...	...
70	**Köln** Hbf ... **802 910** d.	0022	0041	...	0341	...	0431	...	...	0623	0723	0823	0923	1023	and	1623	1659	1723	1823	1923	2023	2123	2223	2323
71	**Köln** Messe/Deutz **802 910** d.	0026	0043	...	0343	...	0433	...	...	0626	0726	0826	0926	1026		1626	1702	1726	1826	1926	2026	2126	2226	2326
91	Troisdorf ... **802** d.	0041	0108	...	0408	...	0454	...	...	0641	0741	0841	0941	1041	hourly	1641	1719	1741	1841	1941	2041	2141	2241	2341
95	Siegburg/Bonn ... **910** d.	0046	0112	...	0412	...	0500	...	...	0646	0746	0846	0946	1046		1646	1724	1746	1846	1946	2046	2146	2246	2346
102	Hennef (Sieg) ... d.	0050	0117	...	0417	...	0506	...	...	0651	0750	0850	0950	1050	until	1650	1729	1750	1850	1950	2050	2150	2250	2350
114	Eitorf ... d.	0059	0130	...	0430	...	0518	...	...	0700	0759	0859	0959	1059		1659	1738	1759	1859	1959	2059	2159	2259	2359
136	Au (Sieg) ... d.	0116	0151	0448	0455	0501	0541	0607	0610	0716	0816	0916	1016	1116		1716	1802	1816	1916	2016	2116	2216	2316	0016
142	Wissen (Sieg) ... d.	0124	...	0455	...	0508	...	0614	0616	0722	0821	0921	1021	1121		1721	1809	1821	1921	2021	2121	2224	2324	0024
154	Betzdorf (Sieg) ... d.	0138	...	0509	...	0522	...	0627	0628	0731	0830	0930	1030	1130		1730	1824	1830	1930	2030	2130	2238	2338	0038
171	**Siegen** Hbf ... a.	0200	...	0532	...	0545	...	0651	0652	0750	0850	0950	1050	1150		1750	1843	1850	1950	2050	2150	2300	2400	0100

	Ⓐe	Ⓐe	⑥	Ⓐe		Ⓐe										2	2	¶
Siegen Hbf ... d.	...	0454	0454	0526	0610	0623	0710	0810		1810	1910	2010	2110	2210	...	...	2311
Betzdorf (Sieg) ... d.	...	0515	0515	0546	0628	0643	0728	0828		1828	1928	2028	2128	2228	...	...	2335
Wissen (Sieg) ... d.	...	0528	0528	0558	0637	0655	0737	0837		1837	1937	2037	2137	2237	...	...	2347
Au (Sieg) ... d.	...	0537	0537	0605	0643	0701	0743	0843	and	1843	1943	2043	2143	2243	2320	...	2355
Eitorf ... d.	...	0557	0557	0624	0700	0724	0800	0900		1900	2000	2100	2200	2300	2339	...	...
Hennef (Sieg) ... d.	...	0609	0610	0637	0709	0737	0809	0909	hourly	1909	2009	2109	2209	2309	2353	...	...
Siegburg/Bonn ... **910** d.	...	0614	0614	0642	0714	0741	0814	0914		1914	2014	2114	2214	2314	2357	...	...
Troisdorf ... **802** d.	...	0618	0619	0647	0718	0747	0818	0918	until	1918	2018	2118	2218	2318	0003	0013	...
Köln Messe/Deutz ... **802 910** d.	0533	0633	0634	0709	0733	0809	0833	0933		1933	2036	2133	2233	2333	0027	0037	...
Köln Hbf ... **802 910** a.	0536	0636	0637	0712	0736	0812	0836	0936		1936	2039	2136	2236	2336	0029	0039	...
Köln Hbf ... **802 910** d.	0547	0648	...	...	0747e	...	0848r	0948	❖	1947	2043r	...	...	...	...	0040	...
Düren ... **802** d.	0614	0714	...	...	0814e	...	0914r	1014		2014	2114r	...	...	...	...	0118	...
Aachen Hbf ... **802 910** a.	0644	0744	...	...	0844e	...	0944r	1045		2045	2145r	...	...	...	...	0144	...

e – Ⓐ (not June 20, Nov. 1).
r – ⚒ (not June 20, Nov. 1).
t – Not June 20.
z – Also June 20, Nov. 1.
❖ – Certain services depart Köln Hbf at 47 minutes past the hour.
¶ – Operated by Hessische Landesbahn.

☛ **Warning!** On June 22, 23 most trains from / to Aachen are diverted in the Köln area, not calling at Köln Hbf or Köln Messe/Deutz.

ABELLIO Rail NRW

ESSEN - HAGEN - SIEGEN 808

km		Ⓒz	Ⓐe	Ⓐe	Ⓐe	Ⓐe	Ⓒz	Ⓐe		⚒r				⚒r		★	⚒r				⚒r				
0	**Essen** Hbf ... ⊡ d.	...	...	...	...	...	...	...	0634e	...	0734e	...	0834r	...	0934		...	1734	...	1834	...	1934	...	...	...
16	Bochum Hbf ... ⊡ d.	...	...	...	...	...	...	...	0647e	...	0747e	...	0847r	...	0947	and at	...	1747	...	1847	...	1947	...	...	...
30	Witten Hbf ... ⊡ d.	...	...	...	...	...	...	...	0657e	...	0757e	...	0857r	...	0957		...	1757	...	1857	...	1957	...	...	...
45	**Hagen** Hbf ... ⊡ a.	...	...	...	...	...	...	...	0710e	...	0810e	...	0910r	...	1009	the same	...	1809	...	1909	...	2009	...	...	...
45	**Hagen** Hbf ... d.	0033	...	...	0540	0610	0615	0640	0715	0740	0815	0840	0915	0940	1015		1740	1815	1840	1915	1940	2015	2115	2215	2315
75	Altena (Westf) ... d.	0058	...	...	0605	0636	0640	0705	0740	0805	0840	0905	0940	1005	1040	minutes	1805	1840	1905	1940	2005	2040	2140	2240	2340
84	Werdohl ... d.	0107	...	...	0614	0645	0649	0714	0749	0814	0849	0914	0949	1014	1049		1814	1849	1914	1949	2014	2049	2149	2249	2349
106	Finnentrop ... d.	0125	0500	0558	0631	0703	0707	0731	0807	0831	0907	0931	1007	1031	1107	past each	1831	1907	1931	2007	2031	2110	2207	2307	0007
119	Lennestadt ♥ ... d.	0138	0513	0610	0643	0715	0718	0743	0818	0843	0918	0943	1018	1043	1118		1843	1918	1943	2018	2043	2121	2219	2319	0019
141	Kreuztal ... d.	0201	0538	0633	0706	0738	0737	0806	0837	0906	0937	1006	1037	1106	1137	hour until	1906	1937	2006	2037	2106	2142	2242	2342	0042
152	**Siegen** Hbf ... a.	0213	0551	0644	0719	0750	0748	0819	0848	0919	0948	1019	1048	1119	1148		1919	1948	2020	2048	2121	2154	2254	2354	0054

	Ⓒz	⚒r	Ⓐe	⚒r		Ⓐe		Ⓐe		⚒r		♣	⚒r				⚒r							
Siegen Hbf ... d.	0111	...	0402	0503	...	0543	0612	0635	0712	0743	0812		1543	1612	1643	1712	1744	1812	1844	1912	2011	2111	2211	2311
Kreuztal ... d.	0122	...	0413	0514	...	0554	0622	0647	0722	0754	0822	and at	1554	1622	1654	1722	1755	1822	1855	1922	2022	2122	2222	2323
Lennestadt ♥ ... d.	0145	...	0436	0537	...	0617	0641	0710	0741	0817	0841		1617	1641	1717	1741	1818	1841	1919	1941	2045	2145	2245	2347
Finnentrop ... d.	0158	0453	0453	0553	0553	0630	0653	0730	0754	0830	0853	the same	1630	1653	1730	1753	1831	1853	1932	1953	2058	2158	2258	2400
Werdohl ... d.	...	0510	0510	0610	0610	0647	0710	0747	0810	0847	0910		1647	1710	1747	1810	1848	1910	1948	2010	2115	2215	2315	...
Altena (Westf) ... d.	...	0518	0518	0618	0618	0655	0718	0755	0818	0855	0918	minutes	1655	1718	1755	1818	1856	1918	1957	2018	2123	2223	2323	...
Hagen Hbf ... a.	...	0546	0546	0646	0646	0723	0746	0823	0846	0923	0946		1723	1746	1823	1846	1923	1946	2023	2046	2151	2251	2352	...
Hagen Hbf ... ⊡ d.	...	...	...	0651e	...	...	0751e	...	0851r	...	0951	past each	...	1751	...	1851	...	1951	...	...	...	...	...	...
Witten Hbf ... ⊡ d.	...	...	...	0702e	...	...	0802e	...	0902r	...	1002		...	1802	...	1902	...	2002	...	...	...	...	...	...
Bochum Hbf ... ⊡ d.	...	...	...	0714e	...	...	0814e	...	0914r	...	1014	hour until	...	1814	...	1914	...	2014	...	...	...	...	...	...
Essen Hbf ... ⊡ a.	...	...	...	0729e	...	...	0829e	...	0929r	...	1029		...	1829	...	1929	...	2029	...	...	...	...	...	...

		Ⓒz	Ⓒz						
Essen Hbf ... d.	0012	0107	0207	...	0507	and	2307	...	...
Bochum Hbf ... d.	0027	0122	0221	...	0522	hourly	2322	...	...
Witten Hbf ... d.	0038	0133	0234	...	0533	until	2333	...	...
Hagen Hbf ... a.	0052	0147	0248	...	0547		2347	...	...

		Ⓒz	Ⓒz						
Hagen Hbf ... d.	0016	0116	0216	...	0516	and	2216	2317	...
Witten Hbf ... d.	0030	0130	0230	...	0530	hourly	2230	2331	...
Bochum Hbf ... d.	0042	0142	0242	...	0542	until	2242	2342	...
Essen Hbf ... a.	0057	0157	0257	...	0557		2257	2357	...

e – Ⓐ (not June 20, Nov. 1).
r – ⚒ (not June 20, Nov. 1).
z – Also June 20, Nov. 1.
★ – The 1040, 1240, 1440 and 1640 from Hagen run daily.
♣ – The 0843, 1043, 1243 and 1443 from Siegen run daily.
⊡ – See also panel below main table.
♥ – Lennestadt - Altenhundem.

S-Bahn 5

PADERBORN - HAMELN - HANNOVER - HANNOVER FLUGHAFEN ✈ 809

km										Ⓐ	⑥			⚒	†										
0	**Paderborn** Hbf ... **805 811** d.	...	...	...	...	...	...	...	...	0512	...	...	...	0615	...	...	0715	...	0815	...	0915	...	1015	...	1115
17	Altenbeken ... **805 811** d.	...	...	...	...	...	...	...	...	0524	...	...	...	0627	...	...	0727	...	0827	...	0927	...	1027	...	1127
56	Bad Pyrmont ... d.	...	...	...	...	...	...	0505r	...	0602	0605	...	0635e	0702	0705	0735e	0802	...	0902	...	1002	...	1102	...	1202
75	Hameln ... a.	...	...	...	...	...	...	0519r	...	0616	0618	...	0649e	0716	0718	0749e	0816	...	0916	...	1016	...	1116	...	1216
75	Hameln ... d.	...	...	...	...	0420e	0450r	0520	0550r	0620	0620	0620	0650r	0720	0720	0750r	0820	0850r	0920	0950r	1020	1050r	1120	1150r	1220
133	**Hannover** Hbf ... a.	...	...	...	...	0503e	0533r	0603	0633r	0703	0703	0703	0733r	0803	0803	0833r	0903	0933r	1003	1033r	1103	1133r	1203	1233r	1303
133	**Hannover** Hbf ... d.	0335	...	0411	0435	0505	0535	0605	0635	0705	0705	0705	0735	0805	0805	0835	0905	0935	1005	1035	1105	1135	1205	1235	1305
148	**Hannover** Flughafen ✈ ... a.	0353	...	0429	0453	0523	0553	0623	0653	0723	0723	0723	0753	0823	0823	0853	0923	0953	1023	1053	1123	1153	1223	1253	1323

																							⑤⑥f	A
Paderborn Hbf ... **805 811** d.	...	1215	...	1313	...	1415	...	1515	...	1615	...	1715	...	1815	...	1915	...	2015	...	2115	...	2215	...	2310	...
Altenbeken ... **805 811** d.	...	1227	...	1327	...	1427	...	1527	...	1627	...	1727	...	1827	...	1927	...	2027	...	2127	...	2227	...	2322	...
Bad Pyrmont ... d.	...	1302	1335e	1402	...	1502	...	1602	1635e	1702	1735e	1802	1835e	1902	...	2002	...	2102	...	2202	...	2302	...	2357	0005
Hameln ... a.	...	1316	1349e	1416	...	1516	...	1616	1649e	1716	1749e	1816	1849e	1916	...	2016	...	2116	...	2216	...	2316	...	0011	0019
Hameln ... d.	1250r	1320	1350r	1420	1450r	1520	1550	1620	1650	1720	1750	1820	1850	1920	1950	2020	2050e	2120	...	2220	...	2320	...	0020	0020
Hannover Hbf ... a.	1333r	1403	1433r	1503	1533r	1603	1633	1703	1733	1803	1833	1903	1933	2003	2033	2103	2133e	2203	...	2303	...	0003	...	0103	0103
Hannover Hbf ... d.	1335	1405	1435	1505	1535	1605	1635	1705	1735	1805	1835	1905	1935	2005	2035	2105	2135	2205	2235	2305	2335	0005	0035	0105	0105
Hannover Flughafen ✈ ... a.	1353	1423	1453	1523	1553	1623	1653	1723	1753	1823	1853	1923	1953	2023	2053	2123	2153	2223	2253	2323	2353	0023	0053	0123	0123

			Ⓐe					⚒		Ⓐe		⚒													
Hannover Flughafen ✈ ... d.	0006	0036	0036	0106	0136	...	0406	0436	0436	0506	0506	0536	0536	0606	0636	0706	0736	0806	0836	0906	0936	1006	1036	1106	1136
Hannover Hbf ... a.	0024	0053	0053	0124	0154	...	0424	0453	0453	0523	0523	0553	0553	0623	0653	0723	0753	0823	0853	0923	0953	1023	1053	1123	1153
Hannover Hbf ... d.	...	...	0055	...	...	...	...	0455	...	0525	...	0555	...	0625r	0655	0725r	0755	0825r	0855	0925r	0955	1025r	1055	1125r	1155
Hameln ... a.	...	...	0140	...	...	...	...	0540	...	0610	...	0640	...	0710r	0740	0810r	0840	0910r	0940	1010r	1040	1110r	1140	1210r	1240
Hameln ... d.	...	...	...	...	...	...	...	0544	...	0611	...	0644	...	0711e	0744	...	0844	...	0944	...	1044	...	1144	...	1244
Bad Pyrmont ... d.	...	...	...	...	...	...	...	0600	...	0625	...	0700	...	0725e	0800	...	0900	...	1000	...	1100	...	1200	...	1300
Altenbeken ... **805 811** d.	...	...	...	...	...	...	...	0633	...	...	...	0733	...	...	0833	...	0933	...	1033	...	1133	...	1233	...	1333
Paderborn Hbf ... **805 811** a.	...	...	...	...	...	...	...	0646	...	...	...	0746	...	...	0846	...	0946	...	1046	...	1146	...	1246	...	1346

																						B	⑤⑥f		
Hannover Flughafen ✈ ... d.	1206	1236	1306	1336	1406	1436	1506	1536	1606	1636	1706	1736	1806	1836	1906	1936	2006	2036	2106	2136	2206	2236	2236	2306	2336
Hannover Hbf ... a.	1223	1253	1323	1353	1423	1453	1523	1553	1623	1653	1723	1753	1823	1853	1923	1953	2023	2053	2123	2153	2223	2253	2253	2323	2353
Hannover Hbf ... d.	1225r	1255	1325r	1355	1425r	1455	1525	1555	1625	1655	1725	1755	1825	1855	1925	1955	2025r	2055	2125e	2155	...	2255	2255	...	2355
Hameln ... a.	1310r	1340	1410r	1440	1510r	1540	1610	1640	1710	1740	1810	1840	1910	1940	2010	2040	2110r	2140	2210e	2240	...	2340	2340	...	0040
Hameln ... d.	1311e	1344	...	1444	...	1544	1611e	1644	1711e	1744	1811e	1844	...	1944	...	2044	...	2144	...	2244	...	2341	2344	...	...
Bad Pyrmont ... d.	1325e	1400	...	1500	...	1600	1625e	1700	1725e	1800	1825e	1900	...	2000	...	2100	...	2200	...	2300	...	2355	0000	...	...
Altenbeken ... **805 811** d.	...	1433	...	1533	...	1633	...	1733	...	1833	...	1933	...	2033	...	2133	...	2233	...	2333	...	...	0033	...	...
Paderborn Hbf ... **805 811** a.	...	1446	...	1546	...	1646	...	1746	...	1846	...	1946	...	2046	...	2146	...	2246	...	2346	...	...	0046	...	...

A – Mornings of ①–⑤ (not June 10, 20, Oct. 3, Nov. 1).
B – ①②③④⑦ (not June 9, 19, Oct. 2, 31).
e – Ⓐ (not Oct. 31).
f – Also June 9, 19, Oct. 2, 31.
r – ⚒ (not Oct. 31).

810 HAMM and BAD BENTHEIM - HANNOVER - BERLIN

SERVICE JUNE 11 - OCTOBER 11. Timings between Köln and Hamm are subject to alteration July 13 - August 25. See page 564 for service from October 12.

km		IC 1049 ⑤ Z	ICE 949 T	ICE 649 Ⓐ ✕	IC 2447 ①g D🍷	ICE 841 ①–⑥ L✕	IC 2241 ①–⑥ M🍷	ICE 541 ①–⑥ ✕	ICE 1041 ⑦ ✕	IC 2445 ①–⑥ D🍷	ICE 843 ✕	IC 2343 ⑦ N🍷	IC 245 ①–⑥ 🍷	ICE 553 K	IC 2443 ①–⑥ D🍷	ICE 845 ①–⑤ ✕	ICE 1045 ⑥⑦ ✕	IC 2222 ①–⑤ V
	Köln Hbf **800** d.	2317	2245	...	...	...	...	0425	...	0513	0528	...	...	0648	0712	...	0727	...
	Wuppertal Hbf **800** d.	|	|	...	...	...	...	|	...	0544	|	...	...	0716	0744	⊙	|	...
	Düsseldorf Hbf **800** d.	2341	2341	...	...	...	...	0449	...	|	0551	...	...	|	|	0751	0751	...
	Dortmund Hbf **800** d.	0032	0032	...	...	...	...	0545	...	0628	0648	...	...	|	0828	0848	0848	...
0	**Hamm** (Westf) **802** d.	0049	0049	...	...	...	...	0603	...	0644	|	...	...	0802	0844	|	|	...
50	Gütersloh Hbf **802** d.	|	|	...	...	...	...	|	...	|	|	...	...	|	|	|	|	...
67	**Bielefeld** Hbf **802 811** d.	0121	0121	...	0513	...	...	0634	...	0719	0734	...	...	0834	0919	0934	0934	...
81	Herford **811** d.	|	|	...	0528	...	...	|	...	|	|	...	...	|	|	|	|	...
	Amsterdam C **22** d.	|	|	...	|	...	...	|	...	|	|	...	0502a	|	|	|	|	...
	Bad Bentheim 🏛 **811** d.	|	|	...	|	...	...	|	...	|	|	...	0721	|	|	|	|	...
	Rheine **811** d.	|	|	...	|	...	...	|	...	|	|	...	0735	|	|	|	|	...
	Osnabrück Hbf **811** d.	|	|	...	|	...	0604	|	...	|	|	0804	0805	|	|	|	|	...
	Bünde (Westf) **811** d.	|	|	...	|	...	0627	|	...	|	|	0827	0826	|	|	|	|	...
97	Bad Oeynhausen **811** d.	|	|	...	|	...	0638	|	...	|	|	0839	0839	|	|	|	|	...
112	Minden (Westf) **811** d.	0151	0151	...	0547	...	0647	|	...	0746	|	0848	0848	|	0946	|	|	...
177	**Hannover** Hbf **811** a.	0223	0223	...	0619	...	0718	0728	...	0818	0828	0918	0918	0928	1018	1028	1028	...
177	**Hannover** Hbf d.	0240	0240	0527	0637	0631	0722	0731	0731	0837	0831	0922	0922	0931	1037	1031	1031	1104
	Magdeburg Hbf **866** a.	0401	0401	▽	0754	|	|	|	|	0954	|	|	|	|	1154	|	|	|
	Leipzig Hbf **866** a.	|	|	|	0915	|	|	|	|	1115	|	|	|	|	1315	|	|	|
252	Wolfsburg **902** d.	|	|	0620	...	0705	0754	|	0804	...	0905	0954	0954	|	...	1105	1105	1138
327	Stendal **838** d.	|	|	0646	...	0733	0826	|	0832	...	|	1026	1026	|	...	|	|	|
419	**Berlin** Spandau **838 902** a.	|	|	0722	...	0809	0904	0854	0906	...	0958	1104	1104	1054	...	1158	1158	1238
435	**Berlin** Hbf **838 902** a.	0531	0536	0732	...	0825	0922	0906	0917	...	1010	1122	1122	1105	...	1210	1210	1252
440	**Berlin** Ostbahnhof **838 902** a.	...	0547	...	...	...	0934	...	...	...	...	1134	1134	...	...	...	...	...

	IC 141 🍷	ICE 555 ✕	IC 2441 D🍷	ICE 847 ✕	IC 143 🍷	ICE 557 ✕	IC 2049 D🍷	ICE 849 ✕	IC 145 🍷	ICE 559 ✕	IC 2047 Ⓑb D🍷	ICE 941 ✕	IC 1922 ⑤⑦ S🍷	IC 147 🍷	ICE 651 ✕	IC 2326 ⑦ R🍷	IC 1926 ①–⑤ 🍷
Köln Hbf **800** d.	...	0848	0913	0928c	...	1048	1113	...	...	1248	1313	...	1348	...	1448	1438	1438
Wuppertal Hbf **800** d.	...	0916	0944	|	...	1116	1144	...	...	1316	1344	...	1416	...	1516	↓	|
Düsseldorf Hbf **800** d.	...	|	|	0951	...	|	|	1151	...	|	|	1351	|	...	|	1509	1509
Dortmund Hbf **800** d.	...	|	1028	1048	...	|	1228	1248	...	|	1428	1448	|	...	|	|	|
Hamm (Westf) **802** d.	...	1002	1044	|	...	1202	1244	|	...	1402	1444	|	1511	...	1602	|	|
Gütersloh Hbf **802** d.	...	|	|	|	...	|	|	|	...	|	|	|	|	...	|	|	|
Bielefeld Hbf **802 811** d.	...	1034	1119	1134	...	1234	1319	1334	...	1434	1519	1534	|	...	1634	|	|
Herford **811** d.	...	|	|	|	...	|	|	|	...	|	|	|	|	...	|	|	|
Amsterdam C **22** d.	0700	|	|	|	0900	|	|	|	1100	|	|	|	|	1300	|	|	|
Bad Bentheim 🏛 **811** d.	0928	|	|	|	1128	|	|	|	1328	|	|	|	|	1528	|	◧	◧
Rheine **811** d.	0942	|	|	|	1142	|	|	|	1342	|	|	|	|	1542	|	|	|
Osnabrück Hbf **811** d.	1008	|	|	|	1208	|	|	|	1408	|	|	|	|	1608	|	|	|
Bünde (Westf) **811** d.	|	|	|	|	1228	|	|	|	|	|	|	|	|	1628	|	|	|
Bad Oeynhausen **811** d.	1037	|	|	|	|	|	|	|	1437	|	|	|	|	|	|	|	|
Minden (Westf) **811** d.	1047	|	1146	|	1247	|	1346	|	1447	|	1546	|	|	1647	|	|	|
Hannover Hbf **811** a.	1118	1128	1218	1228	1318	1328	1418	1428	1518	1528	1618	1628	1701	1718	1728	1802	1802
Hannover Hbf d.	1122	1131	1237	1231	1322	1331	1437	1431	1522	1531	1637	1631	1704	1722	1731	1805	1805
Magdeburg Hbf **866** a.	|	|	1354	|	|	|	1554	|	|	|	1754	|	|	|	|	|	|
Leipzig Hbf **866** a.	|	|	1515	|	|	|	1722	|	|	|	1915	|	|	|	|	|	|
Wolfsburg **902** d.	1154	|	...	1305	1354	|	...	1505	1554	|	...	1705	1738	1754	|	1839	1839
Stendal **838** d.	1226	|	...	|	1426	|	...	|	1626	|	...	|	|	1826	|	|	|
Berlin Spandau **838 902** a.	1304	1255	...	1358	1504	1454	...	1558	1704	1654	...	1800	1838	1904	1854	1938	1938
Berlin Hbf **838 902** a.	1322	1305	...	1410	1522	1505	...	1610	1722	1706	...	1810	1854	1922	1905	1953	1955
Berlin Ostbahnhof **838 902** a.	1334	...	...	...	1534	...	...	...	1734	...	...	...	1905	1934	...	...	2008

	IC 2045 Ⓑ D🍷	ICE 943 ✕	IC 149 🍷	ICE 653 ✕	IC 2043 🍷	IC 2043 Ⓑ 🍷	IC 2043 ⑦ 🍷	ICE 945 Ⓑ ✕	IC 241 🍷	IC 241 ⑦ 🍷	ICE 655 ✕	IC 2041 ⑦ 🍷	ICE 947 ✕	IC 243 ⑦ 🍷	ICE 657 ⑦ ✕	ICE 102 Ⓑ Q	ICE 1102 ⑥ Q
Köln Hbf **800** d.	1513	...	...	1648	1713	1713	1713	...	...	...	1848	1913	1927	...	2048	2111	2111
Wuppertal Hbf **800** d.	1544	...	...	1716	1744	1744	1744	...	...	...	1916	1944	|	...	2116	2142	|
Düsseldorf Hbf **800** d.	|	1551	...	|	|	|	|	1751	...	...	|	|	1951	...	|	|	2133
Dortmund Hbf **800** d.	1628	1648	...	|	1828	1828	1828	1848	...	...	|	2028	2048	...	|	2228	2228
Hamm (Westf) **802** d.	1644	|	...	1802	1844	1844	1844	|	...	...	2002	2044	|	...	2203	2249	2249
Gütersloh Hbf **802** d.	|	|	...	|	|	|	|	|	...	...	|	|	|	...	|	2309	2309
Bielefeld Hbf **802 811** d.	1719	1734	...	1834	1919	1919	1919	1934	...	...	2034	2119	2134	...	2235	2322	2322
Herford **811** d.	|	|	...	|	|	|	|	|	...	...	|	|	|	...	|	|	|
Amsterdam C **22** d.	|	|	1500	|	|	|	|	|	1700	1700	|	|	|	1900	|	|	|
Bad Bentheim 🏛 **811** d.	|	|	1728	|	|	|	|	|	1928	1928	|	|	|	2128	|	|	|
Rheine **811** d.	|	|	1742	|	|	|	|	|	1942	1942	|	|	|	2142	|	|	|
Osnabrück Hbf **811** d.	|	|	1808	|	|	|	|	|	2008	2008	|	|	|	2208	|	|	|
Bünde (Westf) **811** d.	|	|	|	|	|	|	|	|	2028	2028	|	|	|	|	|	|	|
Bad Oeynhausen **811** d.	|	|	1837	|	|	|	|	|	|	|	|	|	|	2237	|	|	|
Minden (Westf) **811** d.	1746	|	1847	|	1946	1946	1946	|	2047	2047	|	2146	|	2247	|	2347	2347
Hannover Hbf **811** a.	1818	1828	1918	1928	2018	2018	2018	2028	2118	2118	2128	2218	2228	2321	2328	0018	0018
Hannover Hbf d.	1837	1831	1922	1931	...	2037	2037	2031	...	2122	2131	...	2231	...	2331	...	...
Magdeburg Hbf **866** a.	1954	|	|	|	...	2154	2154	|	...	|	|	...	|	...	|	...	...
Leipzig Hbf **866** a.	2115	|	|	|	...	...	2318	|	...	|	|	...	|	...	|	...	...
Wolfsburg **902** d.	...	1905	1954	|	...	...	...	2105	...	2154	|	...	2305	...	0004	...	...
Stendal **838** d.	...	|	2026	|	...	...	...	2132	...	2226	|	...	|	...	|	...	...
Berlin Spandau **838 902** a.	...	1958	2104	2054	...	...	...	2207	...	2304	2254	...	2358	...	0100	...	...
Berlin Hbf **838 902** a.	...	2010	2122	2105	...	...	...	2218	...	2322	2306	...	0010	...	0110	...	...
Berlin Ostbahnhof **838 902** a.	...	...	2134	...	...	...	...	...	...	2334	...	...	...	...	...	...	...

D – To Dresden (Table **842**).
K – From Koblenz on ①–⑥ (Table **800**).
L – 🚌12 and ✕ (Oldenburg - Bremen ①⑥ -) Hannover - Berlin.
M – From Münster (Westf) Hbf (d. 0538).
N – From Münster (Westf) Hbf (d. 0738).
Q – 🚌12 and 🍷 Basel - Karlsruhe - Köln - Hannover.
R – To Rostock (Table **835**).
S – ⑤⑦ (also June 19, Oct. 2; not June 21, Oct. 4). From Stuttgart (Tables **911** and **912**).
T – Daily to June 27; ①②③④⑥⑦ June 29 - Sept. 12; daily from Sept. 14. Also calls at Braunschweig Hbf (a. 0314), Brandenburg Hbf (a. 0444), Potsdam Hbf (a. 0504), Berlin Wannsee (a. 0513) and Berlin Zoo (a. 0529).
V – KAROLINGER – From Aachen Hbf (d. 0707), Rheydt Hbf (d. 0748), Mönchengladbach Hbf (d. 0755), Viersen (d. 0803), Krefeld Hbf (d. 0816) and Duisburg (d. 0831).
Z – ⑤ June 28 - Sept. 13. Continues to Ostseebad Binz via Rostock and Stralsund (Tables **830**, **835** and **844**). Also calls at Braunschweig Hbf (a. 0314) and Brandenburg Hbf (a. 0444).

a – Until Aug. 31.
b – Also July 13, 20, 27, Aug. 3, 10, 17, 24.
c – Daily to Aug. 29; ①②③④⑥⑦ Aug. 31 - Oct. 10.
g – Also June 11.

⊙ – From Köln/Bonn Flughafen (Table **800**).
◧ – Via Münster (Table **800**).
▽ – Via Braunschweig Hbf (d. 0601).

BERLIN - HANNOVER - HAMM and BAD BENTHEIM 810

SERVICE JUNE 11 - OCTOBER 11. Timings between Hamm and Köln are subject to alteration July 13 - August 25. See page 565 for service from October 12.

km		*ICE* 103	*ICE* 656	*IC* 242	*ICE* 946	*IC* 2042	*IC* 2042	*IC* 2042	*ICE* 654	*IC* 240	*IC* 240	*ICE* 944	*IC* 2044	*IC* 1929	*ICE* 652	*IC* 148	*ICE* 942	*IC* 2046
			Ⓐ	①–⑥	①–⑥		①–⑥	① g			①–⑥		①–⑥	①–⑤				①–⑥
		L ✕	✕	🍷	✕	🍷	🍷	🍷	✕	🍷	🍷	✕	D 🍷	🍷	✕	🍷	✕	D 🍷
0	**Berlin** Ostbahnhof . **838 902** d.	...	...	...	...	...	...	...	...	...	0622	...	...	0748	...	0822	...	...
5	**Berlin** Hbf **838 902** d.	...	0430	...	0540	...	...	...	0650	...	0634	0749	...	0759	0850	0834	0950	...
21	**Berlin** Spandau **838 902** d.	...	0442	...	0550	...	...	...	0702	...	0651	0800	...	0814	0902	0851	1000	...
113	Stendal **838** d.	...	0514	...	0625	...	...	...	|	...	0732	|	...	|	|	0932	|	...
188	Wolfsburg **902** d.	...	0548	...	0653	...	...	...	0753	...	0801	0853	...	0920	|	1001	1053	...
	Leipzig Hbf **866** d.	...	|	...	|	...	...	0439	|	...	|	|	0636	|	|	|	|	0836
	Magdeburg Hbf **866** d.	...	|	...	|	...	0601	0601	|	...	|	|	0803	|	|	|	|	1003
263	**Hannover** Hbf a.	...	0618	...	0728	...	0723	0723	0828	...	0836	0928	0923	0953	1028	1036	1128	1123
263	**Hannover** Hbf **811** d.	0540	0621	0640	0731	0740	0740	0740	0831	0840	0840	0931	0940	0956	1031	1040	1131	1140
328	Minden (Westf) **811** d.	0612	0650	0711	|	0814	0814	0814	|	0911	0911	|	1014	|	|	1111	|	1214
343	Bad Oeynhausen **811** d.	|	|	0722	|	|	|	|	|	|	|	|	|	|	|	1122	|	|
359	Bünde (Westf) **811** d.	|	|	|	|	|	|	|	|	0932	0932	|	|	|	|	|	|	|
396	**Osnabrück** Hbf **811** d.	|	|	0753	|	|	|	|	|	0953	0953	|	|	1108	|	1153	|	|
444	Rheine **811** d.	|	|	0821	|	|	|	|	|	1021	1021	|	|	|	|	1221	|	|
465	Bad Bentheim 🏛 **811** a.	|	|	0834	|	|	|	|	|	1034	1034	|	|	|	|	1234	|	|
647	*Amsterdam C* **22** a.	|	|	1100	|	|	|	|	|	1300	1300	|	|	|	|	1500	|	|
	Herford **811** d.	0632	0713	...	|	|	|	|	|	...	...	|	|	◧	|	...	|	|
	Bielefeld Hbf **802 811** d.	0643	0726	...	0826	0842	0842	0842	0926	...	...	1026	1042	|	1126	...	1226	1242
	Gütersloh Hbf **802** d.	|	|	...	|	|	|	|	|	...	...	|	|	|	|	...	|	|
	Hamm (Westf) **802** a.	0713	0754	...	|	0914	0914	0914	0954	...	...	|	1114	|	1154	...	|	1314
	Dortmund Hbf **800** a.	0732	|	...	0910	0932	0932	0932	|	...	...	1110	1132	|	|	...	1310	1332
	Düsseldorf Hbf **800** a.	|	|	...	1006	|	|	|	|	...	...	1206	|	1250	|	...	1406	|
	Wuppertal Hbf **800** a.	0813	0838	...	...	1012	1012	1012	1038	...	...	...	1212	|	1238	...	...	1412
	Köln Hbf **800** a.	0846	0909	...	...	1046	1046	1046	1109	...	...	...	1246	1318	1309	...	...	1446

	ICE 650	*IC* 146	*ICE* 940	*IC* 2048	*IC* 1915	*ICE* 558	*IC* 144	*ICE* 848	*IC* 2440	*IC* 1917	*IC* 2223	*ICE* 556	*IC* 142	*ICE* 846	*IC* 2442	*ICE* 554	*IC* 140
					⑤⑦					⑦	①–⑤				Ⓑ		
	✕	🍷	✕	D 🍷	S 🍷	✕	🍷	✕	D 🍷	K 🍷	⊖	T ✕	🍷	✕	D 🍷	✕	🍷
Berlin Ostbahnhof .. **838 902** d.	...	1022	...	...	1150	...	1222	...	...	...	...	...	1422	...	...	...	1622
Berlin Hbf **838 902** d.	1050	1034	1149	...	1201	1250	1234	1349	...	1355	1355	1451	1434	1549	...	1650	1634
Berlin Spandau **838 902** d.	1102	1051	1200	...	1216	1302	1251	1359	...	1405	1405	1502	1451	1600	...	1702	1651
Stendal **838** d.	|	1132	|	...	|	|	1332	|	...	1442	1446	|	1532	|	...	|	1732
Wolfsburg **902** d.	|	1201	1253	...	1321	|	1401	1453	...	1520	1520	|	1601	1653	...	|	1801
Leipzig Hbf **866** d.	|	|	|	1036	|	|	|	|	1236	|	|	|	|	|	1436	|	|
Magdeburg Hbf **866** d.	|	|	|	1203	|	|	|	|	1403	|	|	|	|	|	1603	|	|
Hannover Hbf a.	1228	1236	1328	1323	1353	1428	1436	1528	1523	1553	1553	1628	1636	1728	1723	1828	1836
Hannover Hbf **811** d.	1231	1240	1331	1340	1356	1431	1440	1531	1540	1556	...	1631	1640	1731	1740	1831	1840
Minden (Westf) **811** d.	|	1311	|	1414	|	|	1511	|	1614	|	...	|	1711	|	1814	|	1911
Bad Oeynhausen **811** d.	|	|	|	|	|	|	1522	|	|	|	...	|	|	|	|	|	1922
Bünde (Westf) **811** d.	|	1332	|	|	|	|	|	|	|	|	...	|	1732	|	|	|	|
Osnabrück Hbf **811** d.	|	1353	|	|	|	|	1553	|	|	|	...	|	1753	|	|	|	1953
Rheine **811** d.	|	1421	|	|	|	|	1621	|	|	|	...	|	1821	|	|	|	2021
Bad Bentheim 🏛 **811** a.	|	1434	|	|	|	|	1634	|	|	|	...	|	1834	|	|	|	2034
Amsterdam C **22** a.	|	1700	|	|	|	|	1900	|	|	|	...	|	2100	|	|	|	2300
Herford **811** d.	|	...	|	|	|	|	...	|	|	|	...	|	...	|	|	|	...
Bielefeld Hbf **802 811** d.	1326	...	1426	1442	|	1526	...	1626	1642	|	...	1726	...	1826	1842	1926	...
Gütersloh Hbf **802** d.	|	...	|	|	|	|	...	|	|	|	...	|	...	|	|	|	...
Hamm (Westf) **802** a.	1354	...	|	1514	1546	1554	...	|	1714	|	...	1754	...	|	1914	1954	...
Dortmund Hbf **800** a.	|	...	1510	1532	|	|	...	1710	1732	|	...	|	...	1910	1932	|	...
Düsseldorf Hbf **800** a.	|	...	1606	|	|	|	...	1806	|	|	...	|	...	2006	|	|	...
Wuppertal Hbf **800** a.	1438	...	...	1612	1632	1638	...	|	1812	1830	...	1838	...	|	2012	2038	...
Köln Hbf **800** a.	1509	...	...	1646	1712	1709	...	1832	1846	1909	...	1909f	...	2036	2046	2109	...

	ICE 844	*IC* 2444	*ICE* 552	*IC* 2242		*IC* 1932	*ICE* 842	*ICE* 832	*IC* 2446	*IC* 1932	*IC* 2240	*ICE* 540	*IC* 2240	*ICE* 840	*ICE* 840	*ICE* 1048	*ICE* 948
		Ⓑ				⑦		⑤	⑦	⑦	⑦	⑦	⑦		⑤–⑦	⑥	
	✕	D 🍷	U ✕	M		R	✕	O ✕	D 🍷	R	N 🍷	✕	N 🍷	✕	b	Y	W
Berlin Ostbahnhof .. **838 902** d.	...	...	...	1822	...	...	...	...	...	...	2022	...	...	...	...	...	2341
Berlin Hbf **838 902** d.	1749	...	1850	1834	...	...	1949	1949	...	...	2034	2050	...	2122	2122	2343	2352
Berlin Spandau **838 902** d.	1800	...	1902	1851	...	1954	2000	2000	...	←	2051	2102	←	2135	2135	|	|
Stendal **838** d.	|	...	|	1932	...	2030	|	|	...	2031	2131	|	2132	2217	2217	|	|
Wolfsburg **902** d.	1853	...	|	2001	...	→	2053	2053	...	2104	→	2155	2201	2249	2249	|	|
Leipzig Hbf **866** d.	|	1636	|	|	...	...	|	|	1836	|	...	|	|	|	|	|	|
Magdeburg Hbf **866** d.	|	1803	|	|	...	...	|	|	2003	|	...	|	|	|	|	0130	0149
Hannover Hbf a.	1928	1923	2028	2036	...	...	2128	2128	2123	2140	...	2225	2236	2322	2322	0303	0309
Hannover Hbf **811** d.	1931	1940	2031	2040	...	...	2131	...	2140	...	...	...	2240	...	2331	0340	0340
Minden (Westf) **811** d.	|	2014	|	2111	...	...	|	...	2214	...	...	...	2311	...	|	0411	0411
Bad Oeynhausen **811** d.	|	|	|	2122	...	...	|	...	|	...	...	...	2322	...	|	|	|
Bünde (Westf) **811** d.	|	|	|	2135	2146	...	|	...	|	...	...	...	2335	...	|	|	|
Osnabrück Hbf **811** d.	|	|	|	2159	2214	...	|	...	|	...	...	...	2357	...	|	|	|
Rheine **811** d.	|	|	|	...	2248	...	|	...	|	...	...	...	...	...	|	|	|
Bad Bentheim 🏛 **811** a.	|	|	|	...	2303	...	|	...	|	...	...	...	...	...	|	|	|
Amsterdam C **22** a.	|	|	|	...	...	...	|	...	|	...	...	...	...	...	|	|	|
Herford **811** d.	|	|	|	...	...	...	|	...	|	...	...	...	...	...	|	|	|
Bielefeld Hbf **802 811** d.	2026	2042	2126	...	...	...	2226	...	2242	...	...	...	...	...	0028	0438	0438
Gütersloh Hbf **802** d.	|	|	|	...	...	...	|	...	|	...	...	...	...	...	0041	|	|
Hamm (Westf) **802** a.	|	2113	2154	...	...	...	2254	...	2312	...	...	...	...	...	0100	0509	0509
Dortmund Hbf **800** a.	2110	2132	|	...	...	...	2315	...	2332	...	...	...	...	...	0119	0530	0530
Düsseldorf Hbf **800** a.	2206	|	|	...	...	...	0013	...	|	...	...	...	...	...	0215	0630	0630
Wuppertal Hbf **800** a.	|	2212	2241	...	...	...	|	...	0012	...	...	...	...	...	|	|	|
Köln Hbf **800** a.	2231	2246	2312	...	...	...	0037	...	0046	...	...	...	...	...	0241	0657	0657

D – From Dresden (Table **842**).
K – To Karlsruhe (Tables **911** and **912**).
L – To Basel (Table **912**).
M – To Münster (Westf) Hbf (a. 2225). Conveys 🍷 on Ⓑ.
N – To Münster (Westf) Hbf (a. 0025).
O – To Oldenburg via Bremen (Table **813**).
R – 12 Stralsund - Berlin Gesundbrunnen - Bremen - Oldenburg.
S – ⑤⑦ (also June 19, Oct. 2; not June 21, Oct. 4). To Stuttgart (Tables **911** and **912**).
T – To Koblenz on ①–⑤ (Table **800**).
U – To Koblenz on ⑦ (Table **800**).
W – Daily to June 28; Ⓑ June 30 - Sept. 13; daily from Sept. 15. Also calls at Berlin Zoo (d. 2359), Berlin Wannsee (d. 0039), Potsdam Hbf (d. 0047), Brandenburg Hbf (d. 0108) and Braunschweig Hbf (d. 0236).
Y – ⑥ June 29 - Sept. 14. From Ostseebad Binz via Stralsund and Rostock (Tables **830**, **835** and **844**). Also calls at Brandenburg Hbf (d. 0047) and Braunschweig Hbf (d. 0224).

b – Also Oct. 2, 3; not Oct. 4, 5.
f – 1912 on ⑦.
g – Also June 11.

⊖ – KAROLINGER – To Münster Hbf (a. 1742), Krefeld Hbf (a. 1941) and Aachen Hbf (a. 2049).
◧ – Via Münster (Table **800**).

811 Regional services BIELEFELD and HENGELO - HANNOVER and PADERBORN

See Table 22 for international *IC* services Amsterdam - Hengelo - Bad Bentheim - Hannover and v.v. See Table **810** for fast *ICE*/*IC* services Bielefeld/Bad Bentheim - Hannover and v.v.

SUBJECT TO ALTERATION FROM OCTOBER 12

km		¶	⚒‡	⚒¶	⚒‡	¶	⚒t	‡	¶		‡	¶		‡	¶	A	A‡	B¶	A	A‡	B¶			‡
0	**Hengelo** ▷ d.	...	...	...	...	...	...	...	...	...	0634e	...	...	0734r	...	...	0834	...	...	0934	...		...	1834
26	Bad Bentheim 🏛 d.	...	...	...	...	...	...	0557e	...	...	0657r	...	...	0757	...	...	0857	...	...	0957	...		...	1857
47	**Rheine** d.	...	...	...	0514	...	...	0614e	0638	...	0714r	...	...	0814	0838	...	0914	...	...	1014	1038	and in	...	1914
69	Ibbenbüren d.	...	...	...	0528	...	...	0628e	0654	...	0728r	...	...	0828	0854	...	0928	...	...	1028	1054		...	1928
95	**Osnabrück** Hbf d.	...	0447	0516	0547	...	...	0647	0716	...	0747	...	...	0847	0916	...	0947	...	...	1047	1116	the same	...	1947
132	Bünde (Westf) d.	...	0513	0539	0613	...	D	0713	0739	K	0813	...	K	0913	0939	K	1013	...	K	1113	1139		K	2013
	Bielefeld Hbf d.	0422	|	|	|	0622	0700	|	|	0800	|	0822	0900	|	|	1000	|	1022	1100	|	|	pattern	2000	|
146	Herford a.	0431	0526	|	0626	0631	0709	0726	|	0809	0826	0831	0909	0926	|	1009	1026	1031	1109	1126	|	every	2009	2026
146	Herford d.	0433	0537	|	0637	0633	0710	0737	|	0810	0837	0833	0910	0937	|	1010	1037	1033	1110	1137	|		2010	2037
160	**Bielefeld** Hbf a.	|	0548	|	0648	|	|	0748	|	|	0848	|	|	0948	|	|	1048	|	|	1148	|	**two** hours	|	2048
	Löhne d.	0440§	...	0551	—	0641	0716	...	0751	0816	...	0840	0916	...	0951	1016	...	1040	1116	...	1151	until	2016	...
	Bad Oeynhausen d.	0445§	...	0557	...	0646	0721	...	0757	0821	...	0845	0921	...	0957	1020	...	1045	1121	...	1157		2021	...
	Minden (Westf) a.	0457§	...	0607	...	0658	0732	...	0807	0832	...	0857	0932	...	1007	1032	...	1057	1132	...	1207		2032	...
	Minden (Westf) d.	0507	...	0608	0608	0707	*0735*	...	0808	*0835*	...	0907	*0935*	...	1008	*1035*	...	1107	*1135*	...	1208		*2035*	...
	Hannover Hbf a.	0550	...	0650	0650	0750	*0830*	...	0850	*0930*	...	0950	*1030*	...	1050	*1130*	...	1150	*1230*	...	1250		*2130*	...
	Braunschweig Hbf **866** a.	0641	...	0741	0741	0841	...	...	0941	...	...	1041	...	...	1140	...	...	1241	...	...	1341		...	...

	¶		‡	¶		‡	¶		‡	¶	‡
Hengelo ▷ d.	...	...	1934	...	...	2034	..	...	2134	...	2234
Bad Bentheim 🏛 d.	...	...	1957	...	...	2057	...	...	2157	...	2257
Rheine d.	...	...	2014	2038	...	2114	...	...	2214	2238	2314
Ibbenbüren d.	...	...	2028	2054	...	2128	...	...	2228	2254	2328
Osnabrück Hbf d.	...	...	2047	2116	...	2147	...	...	2247	2316	2345
Bünde (Westf) d.	...	K	2113	2139	K	2213	...	K	2313	2339	...
Bielefeld Hbf d.	2022	2100	|	|	2200	|	2222	2300	|	|	...
Herford a.	2031	2109	2126	|	2209	2226	2231	2309	2326	|	...
Herford d.	2033	2110	2137	|	2210	2237	2233	2310	2337	|	...
Bielefeld Hbf a.	|	|	2148	|	|	2248	|	|	2348	|	...
Löhne d.	2040	2116	...	2151	2216	...	2241	2316	...	0009j	...
Bad Oeynhausen d.	2045	2121	...	2157	2221	...	2246	2320	...	0015	...
Minden (Westf) a.	2057	2132	...	2207	2232	...	2257	2333	...	0026	...
Minden (Westf) d.	2107	*2135*	...	2208	*2235*	...	2307	...	...	...	...
Hannover Hbf a.	2150	*2230*	...	2250	*2330*	...	2350	...	...	...	...
Braunschweig Hbf **866** a.	2241	...	...	2340	...	...	0056	...	...	...	...

km		Ⓐ‡	Ⓐt	⚒‡	⚒¶	¶	⚒‡	⚒	
	Braunschweig Hbf **866** d.	...	...	...	0420	...	...	...	...
0	**Hannover** Hbf d.	...	...	...	0509	...	...	0528	...
65	Minden (Westf) a.	...	...	...	0553	...	...	0623	...
65	Minden (Westf) d.	...	0526	...	0555	...	...	...	0626
80	Bad Oeynhausen d.	...	0537	...	0605	...	...	...	0637
86	Löhne d.	...	0542	...	0611	...	..	...	0642
	Bielefeld Hbf d.	...	|	0508	|	...	0608	...	|
96	Herford a.	...	0548	0520	|	...	0620	...	0648
96	Herford d.	...	0548	0532	|	...	0632	...	0648
110	**Bielefeld** Hbf a.	...	0558	|	|	...	|	...	0658
	Bünde (Westf) d.	...	K	0546	0621	...	0646	...	K
	Osnabrück Hbf d.	0514	...	0614	0646	0646	0714	...	...
	Ibbenbüren d.	0530	...	0630	0703	0703	0730	...	...
	Rheine d.	0548	...	0648	0721	0721	0748	...	...
	Bad Bentheim 🏛 a.	0603	...	0703	...	...	0803	...	...
	Hengelo ▷ a.	0626	...	0726	...	...	0826	...	...

	¶	‡	⚒t	B¶	A‡	A	B¶	A‡	A		¶	‡		¶	‡		¶	‡		¶	‡	¶		¶
Braunschweig Hbf **866** d.	0520	...	...	0620	...	...	0720	...	...		1820	...	...	1920	...	...	2020	...	...	2120	...	2220	...	2320
Hannover Hbf d.	0609	...	*0628*	0709	...	*0728*	0809	...	*0828*		1909	...	*1928*	2009	...	*2028*	2109	...	*2128*	2209	...	2309	...	0009
Minden (Westf) a.	0659	...	*0723*	0751	...	*0823*	0853	...	*0923*		1951	...	*2023*	2053	...	*2123*	2151	...	*2223*	2253	...	2351	...	0051
Minden (Westf) d.	0702	...	0726	0752	...	0826	0902	...	0926	and in	1952	...	2026	2102	...	2126	2152	...	2226	2302	...	2352	...	...
Bad Oeynhausen d.	0714	...	0737	0804	...	0837	0914	...	0937	the same	2004	...	2037	2114	...	2137	2204	...	2237	2314	...	0004	...	...
Löhne d.	0719	...	0742	0809	...	0842	0919	...	0942	pattern	2009	...	2042	2119	...	2142	2209	...	2242	2319	...	0009	...	...
Bielefeld Hbf d.	|	0708	|	|	0808	|	|	0908	|		|	2008	|	|	2108	|	|	2208	|	|	2308	|	...	...
Herford a.	0724	0720	0748	|	0820	0848	0924	0920	0948	every	|	2020	2048	2124	2120	2148	|	2220	2248	2324	2320	|	...	...
Herford d.	0725	0732	0748	|	0832	0848	0925	0932	0948	**two** hours	|	2032	2048	2125	2132	2148	|	2232	2248	2325	2332	|	...	...
Bielefeld Hbf a.	0743	|	0758	|	|	0859	0943	|	0958		|	|	2058	2143	|	2158	|	|	2258	2336	|	|	...	...
Bünde (Westf) d.	...	0746	K	0820	0846	K	...	0946	K	until	2020	2046	K	...	2146	E	2220	2246	E	...	2346	0020	...	...
Osnabrück Hbf d.	...	0814	...	0846	0914	...	...	1014	...		2046	2114	...	...	2214	...	2246	2314	...	...	0012	0041	...	...
Ibbenbüren d.	...	0830	...	0903	0930	...	...	1030	...		2103	2130	...	...	2230	...	2303	2330	...	...	...	...	...	...
Rheine d.	...	0848	...	0921	0948	...	...	1048	...		2121	2148	...	...	2248	...	2321	2346	...	...	...	...	...	...
Bad Bentheim 🏛 a.	...	0903	...	...	1003	...	...	1103	...		...	2203	...	...	2303	...	...	...	...	...	...	...	...	...
Hengelo ▷ a.	...	0926	...	...	1026	...	...	1126	...		...	2226	...	...	...	...	...	...	...	...	...	...	...	...

BIELEFELD - PADERBORN - HOLZMINDEN - KREIENSEN ⊖ and OTTBERGEN - GÖTTINGEN ★ ⊖

km		Ⓒz				⚒t	⚒t	⚒t																	
0	**Bielefeld** Hbf d.	0034	...	...	...	0634	0734	0834	0934	1034	1134	1234	1334	1434	1534	...	1634	1734	1834	1934	...	2034	2134	2234	2334
44	**Paderborn** Hbf a.	0127	...	...	...	0727	0827	0927	1027	1127	1227	1327	1427	1527	1627	...	1727	1827	1927	2027	...	2127	2227	2327	0027
	Change trains		Ⓐ	⚒		⚒	d	d							Ⓐa	Ⓒb					†b		N		
44	**Paderborn** Hbf **805 809** d.	...	0453	0553	0653	0753	0853	0953	1053	1153	1253	1353	1453	1553	1653	1653	1753	1853	1953	2053	2053	2206	2315	...	...
61	Altenbeken **805 809** d.	...	0507	0607	0707	0807	0907	1007	1107	1207	1307	1407	1507	1607	1707	1707	1807	1907	2007	2107	2107	2219	2329	...	...
92	Ottbergen ★ d.	...	0536	0636	0736	0836	0936	1036	1136	1236	1336	1436	1536	1636	1736	1736	1836	1936	2036	2136	2136	2245	2355	...	...
102	Höxter Rathaus d.	...	0545	0645	0745	0845	0945	1045	1145	1245	1345	1445	1545	1645	1745	1745	1845	1945	2045	2145	2145	2253	0003	...	...
110	Holzminden a.	...	0554	0654	0754	0854	0954	1054	1154	1254	1354	1454	1554	1654	1754	1754	1854	1954	2054	2154	2154	2302	0012	...	...
110	Holzminden d.	...	*0629*a	*0711*a	0758	...	0958	...	1158	...	1358	...	1558	1654a	1754	1758	...	1958	...	...	2158	...	...	...	...
154	**Kreiensen** a.	...	*0703*a	*0745*a	0832	...	1032	...	1232	...	1432	...	1632	1728a	1828	1832	...	2032	...	...	2232	...	...	...	...

		Ⓐ	⚒	⚒	Ⓐa	⑥											Ⓐa	Ⓒb		Ⓐa					†
Kreiensen d.	...	...	...	0627e	0709	0723	...	0754a	0923	...	1123	...	1323	...	1523	...	1652	1723	...	1828	...	1923	...	2125	2241
Holzminden a.	...	...	...	0700e	0742	0756	...	0827a	0956	...	1156	...	1356	...	1556	...	1725	1756	...	1900	...	1956	...	2158	2314
Holzminden d.	...	0501	0601	0701	0801	0801	0801	0901	1001	1101	1201	1301	1401	1501	1601	1701	...	1801	1801	1901	1901	2001	2101	2201	2316
Höxter Rathaus d.	...	0510	0610	0710	0810	0810	0810	0910	1010	1110	1210	1310	1410	1510	1610	1710	...	1810	1810	1910	1910	2010	2110	2210	2325
Ottbergen ★ d.	...	0526	0626	0726	0826	0826	0826	0926	1026	1126	1226	1326	1426	1526	1626	1726	...	1826	1826	1926	1926	2026	2126	2226	2335
Altenbeken **805 809** d.	...	0552	0652	0752	0852	0852	0852	0952	1052	1152	1252	1352	1452	1552	1652	1752	...	1852	1852	1952	1952	2052	2152	2252	0001
Paderborn Hbf **805 809** a.	...	0605	0705	0805	0905	0905	0905	1005	1105	1205	1305	1405	1505	1605	1705	1805	...	1905	1905	2005	2005	2105	2205	2305	0015
Change trains	⚒t	⚒t	⚒t	d																					
Paderborn Hbf d.	0513	0613	0713	0813	...	...	0913	1013	1113	1213	1313	1413	1513	1613	1713	1813	...	...	1913	...	2013	2113	2213	2313	...
Bielefeld Hbf a.	0610	0710	0810	0910	...	...	1010	1110	1210	1310	1410	1510	1610	1710	1810	1910	...	...	2010	...	2110	2210	2310	0010	...

BIELEFELD - DETMOLD - ALTENBEKEN ‡

km		⚒t		⚒t			⚒t				
0	**Bielefeld** Hbf d.	0749	0849	0949	1049	1249	1349	1449	1649	1849	2049
11	Oerlinghausen d.	0803	0903	1003	1103	1303	1403	1503	1703	1903	2103
22	Lage (Lippe) d.	0813	0913	1013	1113	1313	1413	1513	1713	1913	2113
31	Detmold a.	0820	0920	1020	1120	1320	1420	1520	1720	1920	2120
60	**Altenbeken** a.	...	0947	1047	1147	1347	1447	1547	1747	1947	2147r

	⚒t			⚒t			⚒t				⚒t
Altenbeken d.	...	...	1013	1113	1213	1413	1513	1613	1813	2013	2213
Detmold d.	0740	0840	1040	1140	1240	1440	1540	1640	1840	2040	2240
Lage (Lippe) d.	0750	0850	1050	1150	1250	1450	1550	1650	1850	2050	2250
Oerlinghausen d.	0800	0900	1100	1200	1300	1500	1600	1700	1900	2100	2300
Bielefeld Hbf a.	0811	0911	1111	1211	1311	1511	1611	1711	1911	2111	2311

HERFORD - PADERBORN ‡

km		Ⓐt		⚒t					P
0	**Herford** d.	0530	...	0633	0733	and	2133	2233	2233
8	Bad Salzuflen d.	0537	...	0640	0740		2140	2240	2240
19	Lage (Lippe) d.	0549	...	0652	0752	hourly	2152	2252	2252
28	Detmold d.	0559	...	0702	0802	until	2202	2258	2302
57	Altenbeken **805 809** d.	0625	...	0727	0827		2227	...	2327
74	**Paderborn** Hbf **805 809** a.	0638	...	0741	0841		2241	...	2341

	Ⓐt	⚒t							
Paderborn Hbf **805 809** d.	...	0518	...	0621	and	2121	...	...	...
Altenbeken **805 809** d.	...	0530	...	0633		2133	...	...	...
Detmold d.	0458	0558	...	0701	hourly	2201	...	...	...
Lage (Lippe) d.	0506	0606	...	0709	until	2209	...	...	...
Bad Salzuflen d.	0517	0617	...	0720		2220	...	...	...
Herford a.	0524	0624	...	0727		2227	...	...	...

A – Train runs hourly.
B – Train runs every **two** hours.
D – From Dortmund (Table **802**).
E – To Düsseldorf (Table **802**).
K – From/to Köln/Bonn Flughafen via Dortmund (Table **802**).
N – ⑤-⑦ (also June 10, Oct. 3).
P – ⑤-⑦ (also June 10, 20, Oct. 3).

a – Ⓐ (not Oct. 31).
b – Also Oct. 31.
d – Daily.
e – Ⓐ only.
j – Arrives 2349.
r – ⚒ only.
t – Not June 20, Nov. 1.
z – Also June 20, Nov. 1.

¶ – Operated by WestfalenBahn.
‡ – Operated by **eurobahn** Keolis Deutschland.
⊖ – Operated by NordWestBahn. 2nd class only.
§ – 8–9 minutes later on Ⓐ Aug. 19 - Oct. 11.

▷ – All trains from/to Hengelo also call at Oldenzaal (7–9 minutes from Hengelo). German holiday dates apply.
★ – **OTTBERGEN - GÖTTINGEN** ⊖. *63 km.* Journey: 72–83 minutes (103–113 minutes for trains marked ◇). Most trains run from/to Paderborn, attached to Holzminden trains shown in the main table above. **From Ottbergen** at 0534 ⚒, 0634 ⚒, 0734, 0834 ⚒, 0934, 1034 ⚒, 1134, 1234 ⑥ **b**, 1234 Ⓐ **a**◇, 1334 Ⓒ **b** 1534, 1634 Ⓐ, 1734, 1834 Ⓐ, 1934 and 2034. **From Göttingen** at 0601 ⚒, 0710, 0801 ⚒, 0910, 1001 ⚒ 1110, 1201 ⚒, 1310 Ⓒ **b**, 1331 Ⓐ **a**◇, 1401 ⑥, 1510, 1601 Ⓐ, 1710, 1801 Ⓐ, 1910, 2001 Ⓐ and 2110.

MÜNSTER - EMDEN - NORDDEICH 812

RE services except where shown

Warning! Timings at Düsseldorf may vary by up to 6 minutes July 13 - August 25.

km			IC					IC					IC					IC	IC				IC			
		◇	2438	◇		◇		2208	◇		◇		2206	◇		◇		2204	2432	◇	◇		2018		◇	
		⚒	①–⑥	⚒	Ⓐd		Ⓐd	C				Ⓐd	Q				Ⓐd			Ⓒ	Ⓐ		⑥			Ⓐd
			e																				🍷♦			
	Koblenz Hbf **800** .... d.	...	...	...	...	...	...	...	...	...	...	...	0641e	...	...	...	...	...	...	...	...	...	0944x	...	...	...
	Köln Hbf **800 802** ... d.	...	...	...	...	...	0521	0541	...	0621v	...	0721	0746	...	0821	...	0921	0938	...	...	...	1021	1046	...	...	1121
	Düsseldorf Hbf **800** d.	...	...	...	...	...	|	0608	...	|	...	|	0812	...	|	...	|	1012	...	...	...	|	1118	...	...	|
	Hagen Hbf **802** ... d.	...	...	...	0522	...	0622	|	...	0722	...	0822	|	...	0922	...	1022	|	...	...	...	1122	|	...	...	1222
0	**Münster** (Westf) Hbf .. d.	0502a	...	0602	0624	0702	0724	0731	0805	0824	0905	0924	0932	1005	1024	1105	1124	1131	...	1205	1205	1224	1231	...	1305	1324
15	Greven .... d.	0513a	...	0613	0637	0713	0733	|	0814	0833	0914	0933	|	1014	1033	1114	1133	|	...	1214	1214	1233	|	...	1314	1333
26	Emsdetten .... d.	0522a	...	0622	0646	0722	0740	|	0822	0840	0922	0940	|	1022	1040	1122	1140	|	...	1222	1222	1240	|	...	1322	1340
39	**Rheine** .... d.	0534	...	0634	0658	0734	0751	0756	0834	0851	0934	0951	0956	1034	1051	1134	1151	1156	...	1234	1234	1251	1256	...	1334	1351
70	Lingen (Ems) .... d.	0555	...	0655	▬	0755	...	0815	0855	▬	0955	...	1015	1055	▬	1155	...	1215	...	1255	1255	...	|	...	1355	...
90	Meppen .... d.	0609	...	0709	...	0809	...	0829	0909	...	1009	...	1029	1109	...	1209	...	1229	...	1309	1328z	...	|	...	1409	...
136	Papenburg (Ems) .... d.	0642	...	0742	...	0842	...	0856	0942	...	1042	...	1056	1142	...	1242	...	1256	...	1342	1404	...	|	...	1442	...
153	Leer (Ostfriesl) ..... **813** d.	0653	0715	0753	0824	0853	...	0909	0953	1024	1053	...	1109	1153	1224	1253	...	1309	1322	1353	1417	...	|	1424	1453	...
180	**Emden** Hbf ◧ ..... **813** a.	0709	0731	0809	0841	0909	...	0925	1009	1041	1109	...	1125	1209	1241	1309	...	1325	1338	1409	1432	...	1416	1441	1509	...
180	**Emden** Hbf .... **813** d.	...	0742	...	0842	...	...	0942	...	1042	...	...	1142	...	1242	...	...	...	1342	...	...	...	1421	1442	...	...
209	Norden .... **813** d.	...	0808	...	0906	...	...	1005	...	1106	...	...	1205	...	1306	...	...	...	1408	...	...	...	1447	1506	...	...
215	**Norddeich** .... **813** a.	...	0814	...	0912	...	...	1011	...	1112	...	...	1211	...	1312	...	...	...	1414	...	...	...	1453	1512	...	...
	Norddeich Mole ‡ **813** a.	...	0819	...	0916	...	...	1016	...	1116	...	...	1216	...	1316	...	...	...	1420	...	...	...	1500	1516	...	...

	IC					IC					IC	IC	IC						IC	IC						
	2202	◇		◇		2000	◇		◇		2014	2004	2036	◇			◇		2002	2034	◇		◇	◇	⊙	⊙
					Ⓐd	2200				Ⓐd	⑤		Ⓑb					Ⓐd	N							
											🍷♦	🍷♦							B							
Koblenz Hbf **800** ..... d.	1044d	...	...	...	...	...	...	...	...	...	1444	1444	...	...	...	...	...	...	...	...	...	...	...	...	...	...
Köln Hbf **800 802** ... d.	1146	...	1221	...	1321	1346n	...	1421	...	1521	1546	1546	...	...	...	1621	...	1721	1745	...	...	1821	...	...	...	...
Düsseldorf Hbf **800** . d.	1212	...	|	...	|	1412n	...	|	...	|	1612	1612	...	...	...	|	...	|	1817	...	...	|	...	...	...	...
Hagen Hbf **802** ... d.	|	...	1322	...	1422	|	...	1522	...	1622	|	|	...	...	...	1722	...	1822	|	...	...	1922	...	...	...	...
Münster (Westf) Hbf ... d.	1331	1405	1424	1505	1524	1531	1605	1624	1705	1724	1731	1731	...	1805	...	1824	1905	1924	1931	...	2005	2024	2105	2211	2313	0013
Greven .... d.	|	1414	1433	1514	1533	|	1614	1633	1714	1733	|	|	...	1814	...	1833	1914	1933	|	...	2014	2033	2114	2222	2325	0025
Emsdetten .... d.	|	1422	1440	1522	1540	|	1622	1640	1722	1740	|	|	...	1822	...	1840	1922	1940	|	...	2022	2040	2122	2231	2334	0034
Rheine .... d.	1356	1434	1451	1534	1551	1556	1634	1651	1734	1751	1756	1756	...	1834	...	1851	1934	1951	1956	...	2034	2051	2134	2252j	2345	0045
Lingen (Ems) .... d.	1415	1455	▬	1555	...	1615	1655	▬	1755	...	1815	1815	...	1855	...	...	1955	...	2015	...	2055	▬	2155	2313	...	...
Meppen .... d.	1429	1509	...	1609	...	1629	1709	...	1809	...	1829	1829	...	1909	...	...	2009	...	2029	...	2109	...	2209	2327	...	...
Papenburg (Ems) .... d.	1456	1542	...	1642	...	1656	1742	...	1842	...	1856	1856	...	1942	...	...	2042	...	2056	...	2142	...	2242	0000	...	...
Leer (Ostfriesl) ..... **813** d.	1509	1553	1624	1653	...	1709	1753	1824	1853	...	1909	1909	1922	1953	2024	...	2053	...	2109	2122	2153	2224	2253	0012	...	...
Emden Hbf ◧ ...... **813** a.	1525	1609	1641	1709	...	1725	1809	1841	1909	...	1925	1925	1938	2009	2041	...	2109	...	2125	2138	2209	2241	2309	0028	...	...
Emden Hbf .... **813** d.	1542	...	1642	...	...	1728	...	1842	...	...	...	...	1942	...	2042	...	...	...	...	2142	...	2242	...	...	...	...
Norden .... **813** d.	1605	...	1706	...	...	1751	...	1906	...	...	...	...	2008	...	2106	...	...	...	...	2208	...	2306	...	...	...	...
Norddeich .... **813** a.	1611	...	1712	...	...	1757	...	1912	...	...	...	...	2014	...	2112	...	...	...	...	2214	...	2312	...	...	...	...
Norddeich Mole ‡ **813** a.	1616	...	1716	...	...	1804	...	1916	...	...	...	...	2020	...	2116	...	...	...	...	...	...	...	...	...	...	...

						IC	IC						IC	IC					IC							IC
	⊙		◇		◇	2035	2005		◇	◇		◇	2037	2009		◇		◇	2001		◇		◇	◇	◇	2019
	⚒v	Ⓐd	⚒	⚒t		①–⑥	①–⑥	Ⓐd	Ⓐ	Ⓒ			①–⑥	Q	Ⓐd				2201	Ⓐd			Ⓐ	Ⓒ	Ⓐ	⑥
						e	🍷♦						e													🍷♦
Norddeich Mole ‡ **813** d.	...	...	...	...	...	...	...	...	...	...	...	...	0736	...	...	...	0839	...	0952	...	...	1039	...	...	...	1136
Norddeich .... **813** d.	...	...	...	0445	...	0536		...	...	...	0641	...	0739	...	...	...	0841	...	0955	...	...	1041	...	...	...	1139
Norden .... **813** d.	...	...	...	0451	...	0543		...	...	...	0647	...	0746	...	...	...	0847	...	1004	...	...	1047	...	...	...	1146
Emden Hbf .... **813** a.	...	...	...	0517	...	0607	...	...	...	...	0717	...	0814	...	...	...	0917	...	1026	...	...	1117	...	...	...	1214
Emden Hbf ◧ ...... **813** d.	...	...	0452	0517	0552r	0609	0634	...	0642	0652	0717	0752	0816	0833	...	0852	0917	0952	1034	...	1052	1117	1152	1152	1224	1234
Leer (Ostfriesland) **813** d.	...	...	0509	0534	0609r	0626	0653	...	0659	0709	0734	0809	0833	0853	...	0909	0934	1009	1053	...	1109	1134	1209	1209	1241	1253
Papenburg (Ems) .... d.	...	...	0519	▬	0619r	...	0704	...	0709	0719	▬	0819	...	0904	...	0919	▬	1019	1104	...	1119	▬	1219	1219	1251	1304
Meppen .... d.	...	...	0550	...	0650	...	0731	...	0750j	0750	...	0850	...	0931	...	0950	...	1050	1131	...	1150	...	1250	1250	1325	1331
Lingen (Ems) .... d.	...	...	0604	...	0704	...	0744	...	0804	0804	...	0904	...	0944	...	1004	...	1104	1144	...	1204	...	1304	1304	→	1344
Rheine .... d.	0453	0608	0628	0708	0729	...	0804	0808	0829	0829	0908	0929	...	1004	1008	1029	1108	1129	1204	1208	1229	1308	1327	1329	...	1404
Emsdetten .... d.	0502	0616	0636	0716	0737	...	|	0816	0837	0837	0916	0937	...	|	1016	1037	1116	1137	|	1216	1237	1316	1337	1337	...	|
Greven .... d.	0511	0623	0644	0723	0745	...	|	0823	0845	0845	0923	0945	...	|	1023	1045	1123	1145	|	1223	1245	1323	1346	1345	...	|
Münster (Westf) Hbf ... a.	0525	0633	0654	0733	0756	...	0829	0833	0856	0856	0933	0956	...	1029	1033	1056	1133	1156	1229	1233	1256	1333	1356	1356	...	1429
Hagen Hbf **802** ... a.	...	0736	...	0836	...	...	|	0936	...	...	1036	...	...	|	1136	...	1236	...	|	1336	...	1436	...	...	...	|
Düsseldorf Hbf **800** . a.	...	|	...	|	...	...	0946	|	...	...	|	...	...	1147	|	...	|	...	1346f	|	...	|	...	...	...	1546
Köln Hbf **800 802** ... a.	...	0839	...	0938	...	...	1015	1038	...	...	1138	...	...	1215	1238	...	1338	...	1418	1438	...	1538	...	...	...	1613
Koblenz Hbf **800** ..... a.	...	...	...	...	...	...	1116	...	...	...	...	...	...	...	...	...	...	...	...	...	...	...	...	...	...	1716

	IC						IC					IC	IC					IC								
	2203		◇	◇		◇	2205		◇		◇	2435	2207		◇		◇	2209		◇		◇	◇		◇	⊙
	E	Ⓐd	Ⓐ	Ⓒ				Ⓐd					N	Ⓐd				D	Ⓐd							
	B																									
Norddeich Mole ‡ **813** d.	1136	...	...	...	1239	...	1351k	...	...	1439	...	1537	...	...	...	1639	...	1758	...	...	1839	...	...	2039	...	...
Norddeich .... **813** d.	1139	...	...	...	1241	...	1357k	...	...	1441	...	1540	...	...	...	1641	...	1801	...	...	1841	...	...	2041	...	...
Norden .... **813** d.	1146	...	...	...	1247	...	1407k	...	...	1447	...	1547	...	...	...	1647	...	1808	...	...	1847	...	...	2047	...	...
Emden Hbf .... **813** a.	1214	...	...	...	1317	...	1429k	...	...	1517	...	1614	...	...	...	1717	...	1830	...	...	1917	...	...	2117	...	...
Emden Hbf ◧ ...... **813** d.	1234	...	...	1252	1317	1352	1434	...	1452	1517	1552	1616	1634	...	1652	1717	1752	1834	...	1852	1917	1952	2052	2117	2214	...
Leer (Ostfriesland) **813** d.	1253	...	...	1309	1334	1409	1453	...	1509	1534	1609	1633	1653	...	1709	1734	1809	1853	...	1909	1934	2009	2109	2134	2231	...
Papenburg (Ems) .... d.	1304	...	←	1319	▬	1419	1504	...	1519	▬	1619	...	1704	...	1719	▬	1819	1904	...	1919	...	2019	2119	▬	2240	...
Meppen .... d.	1331	...	1337	1350	...	1450	1531	...	1550	...	1650	...	1731	...	1750	...	1850	1931	...	1950	...	2050	2150	...	2313	...
Lingen (Ems) .... d.	1344	...	1351	1404	...	1504	1544	...	1604	...	1704	...	1744	...	1804	...	1904	1944	...	2004	...	2104	2204	⊙	2327	...
Rheine .... d.	1404	1408	1429j	1429	1508	1529	1604	1608	1629	1708	1729	...	1804	1808	1829	1908	1929	2004	2008	2029	...	2129	2229	2253	2349	2353
Emsdetten .... d.	|	1416	1437	1437	1516	1537	|	1616	1637	1716	1737	...	|	1816	1837	1916	1937	|	2016	2037	...	2137	2237	2302	...	0003
Greven .... d.	|	1423	1445	1445	1523	1545	|	1623	1645	1723	1745	...	|	1823	1845	1923	1945	|	2023	2046	...	2146	2245	2311	...	0011
Münster (Westf) Hbf ... a.	1429	1433	1456	1456	1533	1556	1629	1633	1656	1733	1756	...	1829	1833	1856	1933	1956	2029	2033	2056	...	2156	2256	2325	...	0025
Hagen Hbf **802** ... a.	|	1536	...	...	1636	...	|	1736	...	1836	...	...	|	1936	...	2036	...	|	2136	...	...	...	...	...	...	...
Düsseldorf Hbf **800** . a.	1546	|	...	...	|	...	1747	|	...	|	...	...	1946	|	...	|	...	2146	|	...	...	...	...	...	...	...
Köln Hbf **800 802** ... a.	1614	1638	...	...	1738	...	1814	1838	...	1938	...	...	2013	2038	...	2138	...	2213	2238	...	...	...	...	...	...	...
Koblenz Hbf **800** ..... a.	...	...	...	...	...	...	1916b	...	...	...	...	...	...	...	...	...	...	...	...	...	...	...	...	...	...	...

♦ – **NOTES** (LISTED BY TRAIN NUMBER)

2004 – ①②③④⑦ (also Nov. 1; not June 9, 19, Oct. 2, 31). [12] and 🍷 (Konstanz - Karlsruhe ⑦**w** -) Koblenz - Emden.

2005 – ①–⑥ (not June 10). [12] and 🍷 Emden - Koblenz (- Karlsruhe - Konstanz ⑤⑥**p**).

2014 – ⑤ (also June 19, Oct. 2, 31; not Nov. 1). [12] and 🍷 Stuttgart - Mannheim - Münster - Emden.

2018 – ⑥ to Nov. 2 (also June 20, Oct. 3). [12] and 🍷 Stuttgart - Mannheim - Münster - Norddeich Mole.

2019 – ⑥ to Nov. 2 (also June 20, Oct. 3). [12] and 🍷 Norddeich Mole - Münster - Mannheim - Stuttgart.

B – From / to Bonn on dates in Table **800**.
C – ⑥ to Aug. 24 (also June 20; not June 22); ④–⑦ Aug. 29 - Nov. 3 (not Oct. 5).
D – ⑤–⑦ to Aug. 25 (also June 10, 19; not June 9); ③–⑦ Aug. 28 - Nov. 3; ⑦ from Nov. 10.
E – Ⓑ to Nov. 1 (not June 20, Oct. 3); daily from Nov. 3.
N – Daily to Nov. 8; Ⓑ from Nov. 10.
Q – Daily to Nov. 9; ①–⑥ from Nov. 11.

a – Ⓐ only.
b – Ⓑ (not June 9).
d – Ⓐ (not June 20, Nov. 1).
e – ①–⑥ (not June 10).
f – 1349 on ① (also June 11; not June 10).
– Arrives 9–11 minutes earlier.

k – On ⑥ (also June 20, Oct. 3) Norddeich Mole d. 1337, Norddeich d. 1340, Norden d. 1347, Emden a. 1413.
n – On ⑤⑦ (also June 10, 19, Oct. 2, 31; not June 9, 21, Oct. 4, Nov. 1) Köln d. 1338, Düsseldorf d. 1409.
p – Also June 19, Oct. 2, 31.
r – ⚒ only.
t – Not Oct. 31.
v – ⚒ (not June 20, Nov. 1).
w – Also June 10, 20, Oct. 3, Nov. 1.
x – Not July 13 - Aug. 24.
z – Arrives 1307.

◇ – Operated by WestfalenBahn.
⊙ – Operated by Eurobahn.
‡ – For ⛴ to / from Juist and Norderney. See www.reederei-frisia.de for latest timings.
◧ – For train / 🚌 / ⛴ connections to / from Borkum via Emden Außenhafen (certain Emden trains may be extended to / from Emden Außenhafen to connect with sailings). See www.ag-ems.de for latest timings.

813 NORDDEICH - EMDEN - BREMEN - HANNOVER

SERVICE FROM JUNE 11

km		RE 4441	ICE 841	IC 2249	RE 4443	IC 2033	IC 2033	RE 4405	RE 4407	IC 2253	RE 4407	IC 2035	IC 2035	RE 4409	RE 4411	IC 2255	IC 2255	RE 4411	IC 2037	RE 4413	RE 4415	IC 2257	IC 2257	RE 4415	IC 2039
			①⑥	①–⑤		①–⑥				①–⑥		①–⑥				⑥⑦						⑦			
			✕			🍷	🍷	B				🍷		B					🍷	B					🍷
	Norddeich Mole ‡ **812** d.	...	...	...	...	...	...	...	...	...	...	...	...	...	...	...	...	...	0736e	...	0839	...	...	...	0936
0	**Norddeich** **812** d.	...	...	...	...	...	...	...	0445t	...	...	0536	...	...	0641	...	...	...	0739e	...	0841	...	...	...	0939
6	Norden **812** d.	...	...	...	...	...	...	...	0451t	...	...	0543	...	...	0647	...	...	...	0746e	...	0847	...	...	...	0946
35	**Emden** Hbf ◧ **812** d.	...	...	...	...	0416	...	...	0517	...	...	0609	...	...	0717	...	...	...	0816	...	0917	...	...	...	1016
62	Leer (Ostfriesland) **812** a.	...	...	...	...	0433	...	...	0534	...	...	0626	...	...	0734	...	...	...	0833	...	0934	...	...	...	1033
62	Leer (Ostfriesland) d.	...	...	...	...	0441	...	...	0541	...	...	0634	...	...	0741	...	...	...	0841	...	0941	...	...	...	1041
101	Bad Zwischenahn d.	...	...	...	...	0513	...	...	0612	...	...	0712	...	...	0812	...	...	...	0913	...	1012	...	...	...	1113
116	**Oldenburg** (Oldb) a.	...	...	...	...	0523	...	...	0623	...	...	0723	...	...	0823	...	...	...	0923	...	1023	...	...	...	1123
116	**Oldenburg** (Oldb) d.	...	0440	0440	...	0535	...	...	0635	0641	...	0735	0735	...	0835	0841	...	...	0935	...	1035	1041	...	...	1135
147	Delmenhorst d.	...	0458	0458	...	0554	...	...	0654	0659	...	0754	0754	...	0854	0859	...	...	0954	...	1054	1059	...	...	1154
161	**Bremen** Hbf a.	...	0508	0508	...	0605	...	...	0705	0709	←	0805	0805	...	0905	0909	...	←	1005	...	1105	1109	...	←	1205
161	**Bremen** Hbf d.	0408	0512	0512	0517	0609	0609	0617	0717	0715	0717	0809	0809	0817	0917	0915	0915	0917	1009	1017	1117	1115	1115	1117	1209
196	Verden (Aller) d.	0441	0533	0533	0541	0630	0630	0641	→	|	0741	0830	0830	0841	→	|	|	0941	1030	1041	→	|	|	1141	1230
227	Nienburg (Weser) d.	0503	|	|	0603	0646	0646	0703	...	|	0803	0846	0846	0903	...	|	|	1003	1046	1103	...	|	|	1203	1246
283	**Hannover** Hbf a.	0538	0614	0614	0638	0713	0713	0738	...	0814	0838	0913	0913	0938	...	1014	1014	1038	1113	1138	...	1214	1214	1238	1313
	Magdeburg Hbf **866** a.	...	|	...	...	0857	0857	...	...	...	...	1057	...	...	...	...	...	...	1257	...	...	...	...	...	1457
	Berlin Hbf **810** a.	...	0825	...	...	|	|	...	...	...	...	|	...	...	...	...	...	...	|	...	...	...	...	...	|
	Leipzig Hbf **866** a.	...	...	...	...	1049	1049	...	...	...	...	1249	...	...	...	...	...	...	1449	...	...	...	...	...	1649
	Nürnberg Hbf **900** a.	...	...	...	...	...	...	...	...	...	...	...	...	...	...	...	...	...	...	...	...	...	...	...	...
	München Hbf **900** a.	...	...	...	...	...	...	...	...	...	...	...	...	...	...	...	...	...	...	...	...	...	...	...	...

	RE 4417	IC 1933	IC 2259	RE 4419	IC 2431	RE 4421	IC 2251	RE 4423	IC 2433	RE 4425	IC 2243	RE 4427	IC 2435	RE 4429	IC 2245	RE 4431	IC 2437	IC 2437	RE 4433	RE 4435	IC 2439	RE 4437	RE 4439	RE 4445	♣
		⑤f																Ⓑ							
	B				C 🍷	B			🍷	B			D 🍷	B					B			B			
Norddeich Mole ‡ **812** d.	...	...	...	1039	...	...	...	1239	...	...	...	1439	1537	...	...	1639	...	...	...	1839	...	...	2039	...	...
Norddeich **812** d.	...	...	...	1041	...	...	...	1241	...	...	...	1441	1540	...	...	1641	...	...	...	1841	...	...	2041	...	...
Norden **812** d.	...	...	...	1047	...	...	...	1247	...	...	...	1447	1547	...	...	1647	...	...	...	1847	...	...	2047	...	...
Emden Hbf ◧ **812** d.	...	...	...	1117	1218	...	...	1317	1416	...	...	1517	1616	...	...	1717	1816	1816	...	1917	2016	...	2117	...	...
Leer (Ostfriesland) **812** a.	...	...	...	1134	1235	...	...	1334	1433	...	...	1534	1633	...	...	1734	1833	1833	...	1934	2033	...	2134	...	...
Leer (Ostfriesland) d.	...	...	...	1141	1241	...	...	1341	1441	...	...	1541	1641	...	...	1741	1841	1841	...	1941	2041	...	2141	...	...
Bad Zwischenahn d.	...	...	...	1212	1313	...	...	1412	1513	...	...	1612	1713	...	...	1812	1913	1913	...	2012	2113	...	2212	...	2345
Oldenburg (Oldb) a.	...	...	...	1223	1323	...	...	1423	1523	...	...	1623	1723	...	...	1823	1923	1923	...	2023	2123	...	2223	...	2357
Oldenburg (Oldb) d.	...	1230	...	1235	1335	...	...	1435	1535	...	...	1635	1735	...	...	1835	1935	1935	...	2035	2135	...	2235	...	0006
Delmenhorst d.	...	1247	...	1254	1354	...	...	1454	1554	...	...	1654	1754	...	...	1854	1954	1954	...	2054	2154	...	2254	...	0031
Bremen Hbf a.	...	1300	...	1305*	1405	...	...	1505*	1605	...	...	1705*	1805	...	...	1905*	2005	2005	...	2105	2205	...	2305	...	0044
Bremen Hbf d.	1217	1305	1315	1317	1409	1417	1515	1517	1609	1617	1715	1717	1809	1817	1915	1917	...	2009	2017	2117	...	2217	2313	0013	...
Verden (Aller) d.	1241	|	|	1341	1430	1441	|	1541	1630	1641	|	1741	1830	1841	|	1941	...	2030	2041	2141	...	2241	2346	0046	...
Nienburg (Weser) d.	1303	|	|	1403	1446	1503	|	1603	1646	1703	|	1803	1846	1903	|	2003	...	2046	2103	2203	...	2303	0008	0108	...
Hannover Hbf a.	1338	1407	1413	1438	1513	1538	1613	1638	1713	1738	1813	1838	1913	1938	2013	2038	...	2113	2138	2238	...	2338	0040	0140	...
Magdeburg Hbf **866** a.	...	1532	...	...	1658	...	...	...	1857	...	...	...	2057	...	...	...	...	2302	...	...	...	...	...	...	...
Berlin Hbf **810** a.	...	|	...	...	1822	...	...	...	|	...	...	...	|	...	...	...	...	...	...	...	...	...	...	...	...
Leipzig Hbf **866** a.	...	1714	...	...	...	...	...	...	2049	...	...	...	2245	...	...	...	...	...	...	...	...	...	...	...	...
Nürnberg Hbf **900** a.	...	...	...	...	...	...	...	...	...	...	...	...	...	...	...	...	...	...	...	...	...	...	...	...	...
München Hbf **900** a.	...	...	...	...	...	...	...	...	...	...	...	...	...	...	...	...	...	...	...	...	...	...	...	...	...

	RE 4440		♣	RE 4438	RE 4400	IC 2438	RE 4402	RE 4404	IC 2436	IC 2436	RE 4406	IC 2246	RE 4408	IC 2434	RE 4410	IC 2244	RE 4412	IC 2432	RE 4414	IC 2252	RE 4416	IC 2430	RE 4418	IC 2250	RE 4420
			Ⓐh	⚒t		①–⑥				①–⑥		①–⑤				①–⑥									
					B			B					B	🍷			B	C 🍷			B	🍷			B
München Hbf **900** d.	...	...	...	...	...	...	...	...	...	...	...	...	...	...	...	...	...	...	...	...	...	...	...	...	...
Nürnberg Hbf **900** d.	...	...	...	...	...	...	...	...	...	...	...	...	...	...	...	...	...	...	...	...	...	...	...	...	...
Leipzig Hbf **866** d.	...	...	...	...	...	...	...	...	...	...	...	...	...	0511e	...	...	...	...	...	...	...	0912	...	...	...
Berlin Hbf **810** d.	...	...	...	...	...	...	...	...	...	...	...	...	...	|	...	...	...	0730	...	...	...	|	...	...	...
Magdeburg Hbf **866** d.	...	...	...	...	...	...	...	...	...	0500	...	...	...	0700e	...	...	...	0900	...	...	...	1100	...	...	...
Hannover Hbf d.	0020	...	...	...	0420	...	0520	0618r	...	0645	0720	0745	0820	0845	0920	0945	1020	1045	1120	1145	1220	1245	1320	1345	1420
Nienburg (Weser) d.	0054	...	...	...	0454	...	0554	0654	...	0713	0754	|	0854	0913	0954	|	1054	1113	1154	|	1254	1313	1354	|	1454
Verden (Aller) d.	0116	...	...	...	0516	...	0616	0716	...	0730	0816	|	0916	0930	1016	|	1116	1130	1216	|	1316	1330	1416	|	1516
Bremen Hbf a.	0147	...	...	...	0539	...	0639	0739	...	0750	0839	0844*	0939	0950	1039	1044*	1139	1150	1239	1244*	1339	1350	1439	1444*	1539
Bremen Hbf d.	...	...	0415	...	...	0553	0653	...	0753	0753	0853	...	...	0953	1053	...	...	1153	1253	...	...	1353	1453	...	...
Delmenhorst d.	...	...	0428	...	...	0604	0703	...	0804	0804	0903	...	...	1004	1103	...	...	1204	1303	...	...	1404	1503	...	...
Oldenburg (Oldb) a.	...	...	0453	...	...	0623	0723	...	0823	0823	0923	...	...	1023	1123	...	...	1223	1323	...	...	1423	1523	...	...
Oldenburg (Oldb) d.	...	...	0458	0533	...	0626	0733	...	0833	0833	0933	...	...	1033	1133	...	...	1233	1333	...	...	1433	1533	...	...
Bad Zwischenahn d.	...	...	0510	0544	...	0637	0744	...	0844	0844	0944	...	...	1044	1144	...	...	1244	1344	...	...	1444	1544	...	...
Leer (Ostfriesland) a.	...	...	...	0613	...	0707	0813	...	0914	0914	1013	...	...	1114	1213	...	...	1314	1413	...	...	1514	1613	...	...
Leer (Ostfriesland) **812** d.	...	...	...	0624	...	0715	0824	...	0922	0922	1024	...	...	1122	1224	...	...	1322	1424	...	...	1522	1624	...	...
Emden Hbf ◧ **812** d.	...	...	...	0642	...	0742k	0842	...	0938	0938	1042	...	...	1138	1242	...	...	1342	1442	...	...	1538	1642	...	...
Norden **812** d.	...	...	...	0706	...	0808	0906	...	...	...	1106	...	...	...	1306	...	...	1408	1506	...	...	...	1706	...	...
Norddeich **812** a.	...	...	...	0712	...	0814	0912	...	...	...	1112	...	...	...	1312	...	...	1414	1512	...	...	...	1712	...	...
Norddeich Mole ‡ **812** a.	...	...	...	0716	...	0819	0916	...	...	...	1116	...	...	...	1316	...	...	1420	1516	...	...	...	1716	...	...

	IC 2038	RE 4422	IC 2258	RE 4424	IC 2036	IC 2036	RE 4426	IC 2256	RE 4428	IC 2034	IC 1934	RE 4430	ICE 776	RE 4432	IC 2032	IC 2032	RE 4434	IC 2248	ICE 832	IC 1932	RE 4434	RE 4434	RE 4442	IC 2342	RE 4444
						Ⓑ					⑦		Ⓑ		Ⓑ				⑤	⑦		⑥			
	🍷			B	🍷	🍷			B	🍷	D 🍷		F ✕	B				T	✕	S					
München Hbf **900** d.	...	...	...	...	...	...	...	...	...	...	...	...	...	...	...	...	...	...	...	...	...	...	...	...	...
Nürnberg Hbf **900** d.	...	...	...	...	...	...	...	...	...	...	...	...	...	...	...	...	...	...	...	...	...	...	...	...	...
Leipzig Hbf **866** d.	1112	...	...	...	...	1312	...	...	...	1512b	1604	...	...	...	1712	...	...	...	...	...	...	...	...	...	...
Berlin Hbf **810** d.	|	...	...	...	...	|	...	...	...	|	|	...	...	...	|	...	...	...	1949	1954z	...	...	...	...	...
Magdeburg Hbf **866** d.	1300	...	...	...	...	1500	...	...	...	1700b	1728	...	...	...	1900	...	...	...	|	|	...	...	...	...	...
Hannover Hbf d.	1445	1520	1545	1620	1645	1645	1720	1745	1820	1845	1901	1920	2001	2020	2045	2045	2120	2140	2140	2143	...	...	2220	2245	2320
Nienburg (Weser) d.	1513	1554	|	1654	1713	1713	1754	|	1854	1913	1929	1954	|	2054	2113	2113	2154	2208	2208	2211	...	...	2254	2318	2354
Verden (Aller) d.	1530	1616	|	1716	1730	1730	1816	|	1916	1930	1948	2016	|	2116	2130	2130	2216	2228	2228	2229	...	...	2316	2337	0016
Bremen Hbf a.	1550	1639	1644*	1739	1750	1750	1839	1844*	1939	1950	2009	2039	2103	2139	2150	2150	2239	2247	2247	2247	←	←	2347	2356	0047
Bremen Hbf d.	1553	1653	...	...	1753	1753	1853	...	...	1953	2013	2054	2106	...	2153	2153	→	2249	2249	2249	2253	2253	...	2359	...
Delmenhorst d.	1604	1703	...	...	1804	1804	1903	...	...	2004	2024	2104	|	...	2204	2204	...	2300	2300	2300	2304	2304	...	0010	...
Oldenburg (Oldb) a.	1623	1723	...	...	1823	1823	1923	...	...	2023	2040	2123	2134	...	2223	2223	...	2318	2318	2318	2323	2323	...	0025	...
Oldenburg (Oldb) d.	1633	1733	...	...	1833	1833	1933	...	...	2033	2042	2133	...	...	2233	...	...	...	...	...	...	2333	...	...	...
Bad Zwischenahn d.	1644	1744	...	...	1844	1844	1944	...	...	2044	2055	2144	...	...	2244	...	...	...	...	...	...	2344	...	...	...
Leer (Ostfriesland) a.	1714	1813	...	...	1914	1914	2013	...	...	2114	2128	2213	...	...	2314	...	...	...	...	...	...	0013	...	...	...
Leer (Ostfriesland) **812** d.	1722	1824	...	...	1922	1922	2024	...	...	2122	2136	2224	...	...	2322	...	...	...	...	...	...	0024	...	...	...
Emden Hbf ◧ **812** d.	1738	1842	...	...	1938	1942	2042	...	...	2142	2152	2242	...	...	2338	...	...	...	...	...	...	0041	...	...	...
Norden **812** d.	...	1906	...	...	...	2008	2106	...	...	2208	...	2306	...	...	...	...	...	...	...	...	...	...	...	...	...
Norddeich **812** a.	...	1912	...	...	...	2014	2112	...	...	2214	...	2312	...	...	...	...	...	...	...	...	...	...	...	...	...
Norddeich Mole ‡ **812** a.	...	1916	...	...	...	2020	2116	...	...	...	...	...	...	...	...	...	...	...	...	...	...	...	...	...	...

B – To / from Bremerhaven (Table **815**).
C – To / from Cottbus on dates in Table **838**.
D – From / to Dresden (Table **842**).
F – From Frankfurt (Table **900**).
S – From Stralsund (Table **845**).
T – ①②③④⑥.

b – Not ⑥.
e – Not ⑦.
f – Also Oct. 2; not Oct. 4.
h – Not Oct. 31.
k – Arrives 0731.
r – 0620 on Ⓒ.
t – ⚒ (not Oct. 31).

z – Berlin **Spandau**.

♣ – Operated by Nord West Bahn (2nd class only).
‡ – For sailings from / to Juist and Norderney. See www.reederei-frisia.de for latest timings.
◧ – For train / 🚌 / ⛴ connections from / to Borkum via Emden Außenhafen. See www.ag-ems.de for latest timings.
* – Connects with train in previous column.

Nord West Bahn — OSNABRÜCK - OLDENBURG - WILHELMSHAVEN — 814

WARNING! All journeys Varel - Wilhelmshaven and v.v. are operated by 🚌 on ⑥⑦ (also applies to the 2101 and 2201 departures from Osnabrück on ⑤).
When 🚌 replacements are in operation journey times to / from Wilhelmshaven are extended by up to 40 minutes (earlier southbound departures from Wilhelmshaven and Varel).

km		⚒t	Ⓐt				
0	**Osnabrück** Hbf......... d.	...	0459	0601		2201	2301
20	Bramsche .... d.	...	0518	0619	and	2219	2319
50	Quakenbrück.............. d.	...	0540	0640		2240	2340
72	Cloppenburg .... d.	...	0556	0656	hourly	2256	2356
113	**Oldenburg** (Oldb) ..... a.	...	0629	0729		2329	0029
113	**Oldenburg** (Oldb) ..... d.	0536	0636	0736	until	2336	...
143	Varel (Oldb)............... d.	0559	0659	0759		2359	...
165	**Wilhelmshaven** Hbf . a.	0619	0719	0819		0019	...

	Ⓐt	⚒t		⚒t	Ⓐt			
Wilhelmshaven Hbf......... d.	...	0440v	...	0540	0609	0640		2140
Varel (Oldb)...................... d.	...	0500	...	0600	0629	0700	and	2200
Oldenburg (Oldb)............ a.	...	0521	...	0621	0650	0721		2221
Oldenburg (Oldb)............ d.	0406	0529	0629	0629	0659	0729	hourly	2229
Cloppenburg .... d.	0438	0606	0706	0706	0736	0806		2306
Quakenbrück...................... d.	0453	0621	0721	0721	0751	0821	until	2321
Bramsche........................... d.	0516	0642	0741	0741	0812	0841		2341
Osnabrück Hbf................ a.	0534	0658	0758	0758	0830	0858		2358

t – Not Oct. 31.
v – *0420* on ① until Aug. 26, also on June 11 (by 🚌 to Varel).

RE services — OSNABRÜCK - BREMEN - BREMERHAVEN - CUXHAVEN — 815

Services Bremen - Bremerhaven-Lehe and v.v. are subject to alteration on Ⓒ June 1 - July 14 (also applies to certain late evening services on ⑤ June 7 - July 12).

km		⚒t¶	⚒t	ⒶtH	⚒t	H		H		H		H		H		H		H		H		¶	Ⓒz	Ⓐt	w¶	
0	**Osnabrück** Hbf.. **800** d.	...	0417	...	0534	*0634*	0734	*0834*	0934	*1034*	1134	*1234*	1334	*1434*	1534	*1634*	1734	*1834*	1934	*2034*	2134	...	2234	2252	...	2352
53	Diepholz.................... d.	...	0450	...	0604	*0704*	0804	*0904*	1004	*1104*	1204	*1304*	1404	*1504*	1604	*1704*	1804	*1904*	2004	*2104*	2204	...	2304	2321	...	0021
122	**Bremen** Hbf....... **800** a.	...	0546	...	0651	*0751*	0851	*0951*	1051	*1151*	1251	*1351*	1451	*1551*	1651	*1751*	1851	*1951*	2051	*2151*	2251	...	2351	0007	...	0107
122	**Bremen** Hbf.............. d.	0540	...	0556	0656	0756	0856	0956	1056	1156	1256	1356	1456	1556	1656	1756	1856	1956	2056	2156	...	2312	...	...	0012	...
143	Osterholz-Scharmbeck d.	0556	...	0610	0710	0810	0910	1010	1110	1210	1310	1410	1510	1610	1710	1810	1910	2010	2110	2210	...	2328	...	...	0028	...
185	**Bremerhaven** Hbf..... a.	0625	...	0631	0731	0831	0931	1031	1131	1231	1331	1431	1531	1631	1731	1831	1931	2031	2131	2231	...	2357	...	...	0057	...
188	**Bremerhaven**-Lehe .. a.	0630	...	0635	0735	0835	0935	1035	1135	1235	1335	1435	1535	1635	1735	1835	1945j	2035	2135	2235	...	0002	...	...	0102	...

	Ⓒz¶	⚒t	⚒t	⚒t¶	ⒶtH		⚒t		H		H		H		H		H		H		H		H	¶		¶
Bremerhaven-Lehe ... d.	0008	...	...	0407	0523	...	0623	...	0723	0823	0923	1023	1123	1223	1323	1423	1523	1623	1723	1823	1923	2023	2123	2158	...	2258
Bremerhaven Hbf ..... d.	0013	...	...	0412	0528	...	0628	...	0728	0828	0928	1028	1128	1228	1328	1428	1528	1628	1728	1828	1928	2028	2128	2203	...	2303
Osterholz-Scharmbeck. d.	0043	...	...	0444	0550	...	0650	...	0750	0850	0950	1050	1150	1250	1350	1450	1550	1650	1750	1850	1950	2050	2150	2233	...	2333
Bremen Hbf .... a.	0100	...	...	0504	0603	...	0703	...	0803	0903	1003	1103	1203	1303	1403	1503	1603	1703	1803	1903	2003	2103	2203	2253	...	2350
Bremen Hbf ....**800** d.	...	0407	0507	...	...	0607	0707	0707	*0807*	0907	*1007*	1107	*1207*	1307	*1407*	1507	*1607*	1707	*1807*	1907	*2007*	2107	*2207*	...	2313	...
Diepholz .... d.	...	0452	0552	...	...	0652	0752	0752	*0852*	0952	*1052*	1152	*1252*	1352	*1452*	1553	*1653*	1752	*1852*	1952	*2052*	2152	*2255*	...	0002	...
Osnabrück Hbf ...**800** a.	...	0523	0623	...	...	0723	0823	0823	*0923*	1023	*1123*	1223	*1323*	1423	*1523*	1623	*1723*	1823	*1923*	2023	*2123*	2223	*2327*	...	0034	...

BREMERHAVEN - CUXHAVEN

km	⊡	Ⓒz		Ⓐt	⚒t					
0	**Bremerhaven** Hbf..... d.	0003	...	0506	0636	0736	0836	and	2236	...
3	Bremerhaven-Lehe.... d.	0008	...	0511	0641	0741	0841	hourly	2241	...
43	**Cuxhaven** .... a.	0050	...	0557	0727	0827	0927	until	2327	...

⊡	Ⓐt		⚒t						
Cuxhaven .... d.	0509	...	0639	0739	0839	and	2239	...	...
Bremerhaven-Lehe........... d.	0549	...	0719	0819	0919	hourly	2319	...	...
Bremerhaven Hbf............ a.	0553	...	0723	0823	0923	until	2323	...	...

H – From / to Hannover (Table **813**).
j – 1935 on ⑥⑦.
t – Not Oct. 31.
w – Not June 17, 24, July 1, 8, 15.
z – Also Oct. 31.
⊡ – Operated by Elbe-Weser.
¶ – Operated by Nord West Bahn (2nd class only).

Regionalverkehre Start Deutschland; Elbe-Weser — HAMBURG - CUXHAVEN and BREMERHAVEN — *Service from June 12* — 818

km	❖	⑥	Ⓐt	‡	⑥	Ⓐt	‡	†z	⚒t																	‡
0	**Hamburg** Hbf ....¶ ⊖ d.	...	...	0528	...	*0602*	0628	...	*0702*n	*0758*	*0858*	*0958*	*1058*	*1158*	*1258*	*1358*	*1458*	*1558*	*1658*	*1758*	*1858*	*1958*	*2058*	*2158*	*2258*	0028
12	**Hamburg** Harburg ⊖ d.	...	...	0543	...	0624	0643	...	0724	0824	0924	1024	1124	1224	1324	1424	1524	1624	1724	1824	1924	2024	2124	2224	2324	0043
33	**Buxtehude** ....⊖ d.	...	...	0607	...	0641	0707	...	0741	0841	0941	1041	1141	1241	1341	1441	1541	1641	1741	1841	1941	2041	2141	2241	2341	0107
54	Stade.....................⊖ d.	0540	0553	0629	0640	0657	0729	0740	0757	0857	0957	1057	1157	1257	1357	1457	1557	1657	1757	1857	1957	2057	2157	2257	2357	0129
102	Otterndorf .... d.	0622	0635	...	0722	0737	...	0822	0837	0937	1037	1137	1237	1337	1437	1537	1637	1737	1837	1937	2037	2137	2237	2337	0037	...
116	**Cuxhaven** .... a.	0635	0648	...	0735	0750	...	0835	0850	0950	1050	1150	1250	1350	1450	1550	1650	1750	1850	1950	2050	2150	2250	2350	0050	...

❖	Ⓐt	⚒t	Ⓐt		Ⓐt	Ⓒz						Ⓐt	Ⓒz										⑤⑥k	‡	★
Cuxhaven .... d.	0430	0509	0549	0609	0650	0709	0809	0909	1009	1109	1209	1309	1309	1409	1509	1609	1709	1809	1909	2009	2109	...	2209	...	2237
Otterndorf .... d.	0442	0521	0601	0621	0701	0721	0821	0921	1021	1121	1221	1321	1321	1421	1521	1621	1721	1821	1921	2021	2121	...	2221	...	2250
Stade..............................⊖ d.	0524	0603	0643	0703	0743	0803	0903	1003	1103	1203	1303	1403	1403	1503	1603	1703	1803	1903	2003	2103	2203	...	2303	2334	2332
Buxtehude ....⊖ d.	0541	0621	0701	0721	0801	0821	0921	1021	1121	1221	1321	1421	1421	1521	1621	1721	1821	1921	2021	2121	2221	...	2321	2354	...
Hamburg Harburg ....⊖ a.	0556	0638	0717	0738	0817	0838	0938	1038	1138	1238	1338	1436	1438	1538	1638	1738	1838	1938	2038	2138	2236	...	2336	0020	...
Hamburg Hbf..............¶ ⊖ a.	*0619*	*0705*	*0739*	*0805*	*0839*	*0905*	*1005*	*1105*	*1205*	*1305*	*1405*	*1459*	*1505*	*1605*	*1705*	*1805*	*1905*	*2005*	*2105*	*2205*	*2305*	...	*0015*	0035	...

km	△		Ⓐt	Ⓐt	Ⓐt	Ⓐt	Ⓐt		Ⓐt	Ⓐt		Ⓐt	Ⓐt	Ⓐt	Ⓐt		⑥	Ⓒz	Ⓒz	Ⓒz	Ⓒz		Ⓒz		Ⓒz	†z
	Hamburg Hbf ....¶ d.	Ⓐ	...	*0448*	*0548*	*0628*	*0748*		*1248*	*1408*		*1908*	*2008*	*2108*	*2208*	Ⓒ	...	...	...	*0648*	*0758*		*1958*	...	*2058*	*2128*
0	**Buxtehude** .... d.		...	0537	0637	0717	0837	and	1337	1453	and	1953	2053	2153	2253		...	...	...	0745	0845	and	2045	...	2145	2245
39	Bremervörde .... a.		...	0623	0723	0823	0923	hourly	1423	1536	hourly	2036	2136	2236	2336		...	...	...	0828	0928	hourly	2128	...	2228	2328
39	Bremervörde .... d.		0538	0638	0738	0838	0938	until	1438	1538	until	2038	...	...	...		0538	0638	0738	0838	0938	until	2138	...	...	...
78	**Bremerhaven** Hbf..... a.		0620	0720	0820	0920	1020		1520	1620		2120	...	...	...		0620	0720	0820	0920	1020		2220	...	...	...

△		Ⓐt	Ⓐt		Ⓐt	Ⓐt		Ⓐt	Ⓐt	⑤k	Ⓐt		Ⓐt			Ⓒz	⑥	Ⓒz		Ⓒz	Ⓒ	⑥	Ⓒz	Ⓒz	Ⓒz
Bremerhaven Hbf .... d.	Ⓐ	...	0536		1236	1336		1936	2036	2136	2136	...	2354	...	Ⓒ	...	0636	0736		1936	2036	2136	2136	2236	2354
Bremervörde........................ a.		...	0620	and	1320	1420	and	2020	2120	2220	2220	...	0037	...		...	0720	0820	and	2020	2120	2221	2221	2320	0037
Bremervörde........................ d.		0525	0625	hourly	1325	1438	hourly	2038	2138	2238	...	...	...	...		0732	0732	0832	hourly	2032	...	2232	...	...	...
Buxtehude........................... a.		0609	0709	until	1409	1526	until	2126	2226	2326	...	...	...	...		0816	0816	0916	until	2116	...	2316	...	...	...
Hamburg Hbf.....................¶ a.		*0655*	*0755*		*1455*	*1615*		*2215*	*2315*	*0015*	...	...	...	...		*0905*	*0905*	*1005*		*2205*	...	*0035*	...	...	...

k – Also Oct. 2, 30.
n – *0648* on ⑥.
t – Not Oct. 31.
z – Also Oct. 31.
★ – ①②③④⑦ (not Oct. 2, 30).
‡ – Hamburg S-Bahn (2nd class only).
⊖ – Additional S-Bahn trains operate.
❖ – Hamburg - Cuxhaven operated by Regionalverkehre Start Deutschland.
△ – Buxtehude - Bremerhaven operated by Elbe-Weser.
¶ – Connections shown are Hamburg S-Bahn services.

RE services except where shown — HAMBURG - KIEL — *Service from June 11* — 820

km				Ⓒ	Ⓐ	⚒ ⊡	†	⚒	⊡			⊡		⊡				*IC* 478 ⑥ T	*IC* 208 B	*ICE* 674 D	*ICE* 696 A	*IC* 2226 F	*ICE* 74 Z	*EC* 378 L	*ICE* 974 ①–⑤ S
0	**Hamburg** Hbf **823** d.	0043	0437j	0537	0637	0640	0719	0737	0740	0822	0843	and at the same	2022	2043	2122	2222	2324	A	0802	1017	1159	1225t	1617	1757	1914	2101
37	Elmshorn....... **823** d.	0111	0505j	0605	0705	0709	0747	0805	0809	0847	0909	minutes	2047	2109	2147	2248	2349	L	|	|	|	|	|	|	|	|
73	Neumünster .. **823** d.	0135k	0532	0632	0732	0732	0813	0832	0832	0913	0932	past each	2113	2132	2213	2318	0015	S	0903	1106	1252	1325	1706	1858	2001	2153
111	**Kiel** Hbf ....a.	0158k	0555	0655	0755	0755	0832	0855	0855	0932	0955	hour until	2132	2155	2232	2338	0034	O	0920	1122	1309	1343	1723	1916	2018	2214

		Ⓐ	Ⓒ	⚒ ⊡		⊡	❖		⊡								*ICE* 973 ①–⑥ S	*ICE* 73 ①–⑥ Z	*EC* 379 L	*ICE* 1175 ⑦ Z	*ICE* 1177 ⑥⑦ Z	*IC* 2229 F	*ICE* 801 K	*ICE* 1171 D	*IC* 209 Y B	*IC* 479 T
Kiel Hbf................. d.	0403	0447	0502	0527	0602	0627	and at the same	1902	1927	2002	2027	2102	2127	2205	2305	A	0546	0645	0742	0832	1020r	1237	1413	1439	1838	2014
Neumünster... **823** d.	0430	0514	0528	0546	0628	0646	minutes	1928	1946	2028	2046	2128	2146	2232	2332	L	0604	0704	0759	0850	1042r	1256	1432	1457	1857	2035
Elmshorn .... **823** d.	0454	0536	0549	0612	0649	0712	past each	1949	2012	2049	2112	2149	2212	2258	2358	S	|	|	|	|	|	|	|	|	|	|
Hamburg Hbf **823** a.	0521	0601	0615	0637	0715	0737	hour until	2016	2037	2116	2137	2216	2237	2325	0025	O	0658	0800	0848	0950	1157	1342	1532v	1551	1942	2142

A – [12] and ✕ (Frankfurt ①–⑥ -) Erfurt - Leipzig - Berlin - Kiel.
B – [12] and 🍷 Basel - Frankfurt - Köln - Kiel and v.v.
D – [12] and ✕ Karlsruhe - Frankfurt - Kiel and v.v.
F – [12] and 🍷 Kiel - Köln - Frankfurt and v.v.
K – [12] and ✕ Kiel - Berlin - Erfurt - München.
L – [12] and ✕ Praha - Dresden - Berlin - Kiel and v.v.
S – [12] and ✕ Kiel - Frankfurt - Stuttgart and v.v.
T – [12] Basel - Frankfurt - Hannover - Kiel and v.v.
Y – ⑥ to Nov. 30 (also ⑤ June 28 - Sept. 13).
Z – [12] and ✕ Kiel - Frankfurt - Basel - Zürich and v.v.
j – 3 minutes later on †.
k – 7 minutes later on Ⓒ.
r – On ⑦ departs Kiel 1046, Neumünster 1106.
t – Also calls at Hamburg Altona (d. 1246).
v – Also calls at Hamburg Altona (a. 1511).
⊡ – June 11 - July 27 diverted to run from / to Hamburg **Altona** (not serving Hamburg Hbf).
❖ – On ⑦ (not June 23, 30) the 0702 from Kiel runs 7 – 12 minutes later Neumünster - Hamburg.
☛ Train numbers of long-distance *ICE* / *IC* services may differ during certain periods.

821 HAMBURG - WESTERLAND

See Tables **820** and **823** for connecting *RE* services Hamburg Hbf - Elmshorn and v.v. Frequent S-Bahn services operate Hamburg Hbf - Altona and v.v.

km														*IC*• 2314					*IC*• 2072			*IC*• 2310			
		X	Ⓐe	Ⓒz	⚒		Ⓐe		Ⓒz	Ⓐe	Ⓒ T		Ⓒ V		S 🍷	W	S	① M		D 🍷			F 🍷		⑤–⑦ U	
	Köln Hbf **800** d.	...	...	...	...	...	...	...	...	...	...	...	...	...	0509	...	...	...	...	...	...	...	0909	...	...	...
	Berlin Hbf **840** d.	...	...	...	...	...	...	...	...	...	...	...	...	...	|	...	...	...	...	0906	...	...	|	...	...	...
	Hamburg Hbf . **820** d.	...	...	...	...	...	...	...	...	...	...	...	...	...	0917	...	...	...	...	1116	...	...	1317	...	1402	...
0	**Hamburg** Altona d.	...	...	...	...	...	0529	...	0629	0640	0729	0740	0829	0840	|	0940	0940	1005	1040	|	1140	1240	|	1340	|	1440
30	Elmshorn **820** d.	...	...	...	...	...	0549	...	0649	0701	|	0801	|	0901	|	1001	1001	1033u	1101	|	1201	1301	|	1401	|	1501
64	Itzehoe d.	...	...	...	0508	...	0612	...	0714	0724	|	0824	|	0924	1015t	1024	1024	1058u	1124	1214t	1224	1324	1415t	1424	|	1524
123	Heide (Holst) a.	...	...	...	0530	...	0656	...	0758	0758	|	0858	|	0958	1050	1058	1058	|	1158	1250	1258	1358	1450	1458	1522	1558
123	Heide (Holst) d.	...	...	...	0531	...	0701	...	0801	0801	|	0901	|	1001	1052	1101	1101	|	1201	1252	1301	1401	1452	1501	1524	1601
157	Husum d.	0458	0558	0600	0614	0630	0730	0730	0830	0830	0905	0930	1005	1030	1119	1130	1130	1200	1230	1319	1330	1430	1519	1530	1553	1630
197	Niebüll a.	0526	0626	0628	...	0658	0758	0758	0858	0858	0929	0958	1029	1058	1146	1158	1206	1226	1258	1345	1406	1458	1546	1606	1624	1658
197	Niebüll d.	0531	0631	0631	...	0701	0801	0801	0901	0901	0931	1001	1031	1101	1201	1201	1216	1231	1301	1401	1431	1501	1601	1616	1631	1701
237	**Westerland** (Sylt) a.	0605	0705	0705	...	0735	0835	0835	0937	0937	1005	1035	1107	1135	1234	1235	1251	1305	1337	1434	1505	1537	1634	1651	1705	1735

		IC 2374	*IC* 2374									
		P K 🍷	Q 🍷						⑥h	Ⓑd		⑤–⑦ r
Köln Hbf **800** d.	...	...	...	...	...	...	...	...	...	...	...	...
Berlin Hbf **840** d.	...	...	...	...	...	...	...	...	...	...	...	...
Hamburg Hbf... **820** d.	...	1532	...	...	...	...	...	...	...	...	...	...
Hamburg Altona d.	1540	|	1609	1640	1740	1840	1940	2040	2140	2140	2245	2345
Elmshorn **820** d.	1601	|	|	1701	1801	1901	2001	2101	2201	2201	2306	0006
Itzehoe d.	1624	1642t	1655	1724	1824	1926	2026	2126	2226	2226	2331	0031
Heide (Holst) a.	1658	1717	1720	1758	1858	2000	2100	2200	2310	2310	0015	0115
Heide (Holst) d.	1701	1719	1732	1801	1901	2001	2101	2201	2311	2311	0016	0116
Husum d.	1730	1743	1801	1830	1930	2030	2130	2230	2340	2340	0044	0144
Niebüll a.	1758	1808	1826	1858	1958	2058	2158	2258	0008	0008	...	...
Niebüll d.	1801	1830	1830	1901	2001	2101	2201	2301	0010	0010	...	...
Westerland (Sylt) a.	1835	1904	1904	1935	2035	2135	2235	2335	0043	0050	...	...

										IC• 2311
	Ⓐe	Ⓐe			†z	⚒e				H 🍷
Westerland (Sylt) d.	...	0422	...	0522	0622	0622	0722	0822	0910	0926
Niebüll a.	...	0453	...	0559	0659	0659	0759	0859	0944	0959
Niebüll d.	...	0454	...	0601	0701	0701	0801	0901	1000	1013
Husum d.	0424	0524	0524	0631	0729	0731	0831	0931	1031	1042
Heide (Holst) a.	0449	0549	0549	0657	0752	0757	0857	0957	1057	1106
Heide (Holst) d.	0450	0550	0550	0658	0753	0802	0902	1002	1102	1108
Itzehoe d.	0534	0634	0634	0734	0837	0837	0937	1037	1137	1155t
Elmshorn **820** d.	0600	0700	0700	0800	0900	0900	1000	1100	1200	|
Hamburg Altona a.	0621	0721	0721	0821	0921	0921	1021	1121	1221	|
Hamburg Hbf **820** a.	...	...	...	...	...	...	...	...	...	1242
Berlin Hbf **840** a.	...	...	...	...	...	...	...	...	...	|
Köln Hbf **800** a.	...	...	...	...	...	...	...	...	...	1650

			IC 2375	*IC* 2375					*IC*• 2315				*IC*• 2073													
	⑤–⑦ U		R 🍷	P K 🍷			S	W	S G 🍷		Ⓒz	Ⓐe	D 🍷		⑦ Y		L		⑥ T				⑤⑥ h	N		
Westerland (Sylt) d.	0952	1022	1056	1056	1122	1222	1310	1322	1326	1422	1452	1507	1526	1622	1652	1722	1752	1822	1852	1922	2022	2122	2122	...	2222	2322
Niebüll a.	1029	1059	1129	1129	1159	1259	1344	1359	1359	1459	1529	1543	1559	1659	1729	1759	1829	1859	1929	1959	2059	2159	2159	...	2255	2355
Niebüll d.	1034	1101	1131	1145	1201	1301	1355	1401	1413	1501	1555	1546	1613	1701	1731	1801	1831	1901	1931	2001	2101	2201	2201	...	2301	0001
Husum d.	1104	1131	1158	1212	1231	1331	1431	1431	1442	1531	1631	1631b	1642	1731	1756	1831	1856	1931	1956	2031	2131	2229	2231	2248	2329	0029
Heide (Holst) a.	1126	1157	1221	1233	1257	1357	1457	1457	1506	1557	1657	1657	1706	1757	|	1857	|	1957	|	2057	2157	...	2257	2313	▬	...
Heide (Holst) d.	1128	1202	1223	1235	1302	1402	1502	1502	1508	1602	1702	1702	1708	1802	|	1902	|	2002	|	2104	2204	...	2304	2314	△	...
Itzehoe d.	|	1237	1302	1326t	1337	1437	1537	1537	1555t	1637	1737	1737	1758t	1837	|	1937	|	2037	|	2139	2248	...	2348	2354	*0002*	...
Elmshorn **820** d.	|	1300	|	|	1400	1500	1600	1600	|	1700	1800	1800	|	1900	|	2000	|	2100	|	2202	2313	...	0011	...	0033	...
Hamburg Altona a.	|	1321	1354	|	1421	1521	1621	1621	|	1721	1821	1821	|	1921	1928	2021	2028	2121	2128	2223	2334	...	0032	...	0057	...
Hamburg Hbf... **820** a.	1302	...	...	1424	...	...	...	...	1642	...	...	...	1848	...	...	...	...	...	...	...	...	...	...	...	...	...
Berlin Hbf **840** a.	...	...	...	...	...	...	...	...	|	...	...	...	2055	...	...	...	...	...	...	...	...	...	...	...	...	...
Köln Hbf **800** a.	...	...	...	...	...	...	...	...	2050	...	...	...	...	...	...	...	...	...	...	...	...	...	...	...	...	...

D – UTHLANDE – From / to Dresden on dates in Table **840**.
F – NORDFRIESLAND – (12) and 🍷 Frankfurt - Köln - Westerland.
G – DEICHGRAF – (12) and 🍷 Westerland - Köln - Frankfurt.
H – NORDFRIESLAND – (12) and 🍷 Westerland - Köln - Stuttgart.
K – WATTENMEER – (12) and 🍷 Karlsruhe - Frankfurt - Hamburg - Westerland and v.v.
L – Ⓒ to Sept. 22; ⑥ Sept. 28 - Nov. 2.
M – ① until Sept. 23 (also June 11; not June 10).
N – ①②③④⑦ (not June 9, Oct. 2, 30).
P – Until June 10.
Q – Daily June 11 - Nov. 3; ④–⑦ Nov. 7 - Dec. 1; ⑤–⑦ from Dec. 6.
R – Daily June 11 - Nov. 4; ①⑤⑥⑦ from Nov. 8.
S – Until Nov. 3.
T – Until Sept. 22.
U – ⑤–⑦ until Sept. 22 (also June 10).
V – Ⓒ until Nov. 3 (also Oct. 31).
W – From Nov. 4.
Y – ⑦ until Nov. 3 (also June 10, Oct. 3, 31; not June 9).
X – Daily to Nov. 8; ①–⑤ from Nov. 11.

b – Arrives 1619.
d – Not June 9, Oct. 2, 30.
e – Not Oct. 31.
h – Also June 9, Oct. 2, 30.
r – Also June 10, Oct. 3, 31.
t – Arrives 12 – 16 minutes earlier.
u – Calls to pick up only.
z – Also Oct. 31.

• – Conveys (2) to / from Dagebüll Mole on dates in Table **822**.
△ – Operated by *nordbahn*.

822 SCHLESWIG-HOLSTEIN BRANCH LINES

NEUMÜNSTER - HEIDE - BÜSUM (Operated by *nordbahn*)

km		⚒e	⚒e	†z	⚒e	⑥	Ⓐe																		
0	Neumünster d.	...	...	...	...	0535	0535	...	0735	...	0935	...	1135	...	1335	...	1535	...	1735	...	1935	...	...	...	2135
63	Heide a.	...	...	...	...	0645	0710	...	0845	...	1045	...	1245	...	1445	...	1645	...	1845	...	2045	...	...	...	2245
63	Heide d.	0449	0556	0652	0701	0701	...	0801	0901	1001	1101	1201	1301	1401	1501	1601	1701	1801	1901	2003	...	2103	2203	...	...
87	Büsum a.	0515	0622	0718	0727	0727	...	0827	0927	1027	1127	1227	1327	1427	1527	1627	1727	1827	1927	2029	...	2129	2229	...	...

	⚒e	⚒e	⚒e	⑥		†z	⚒e																		
Büsum d.	...	0519	0626	0626	...	0722	0731	0831	0931	1031	1131	1231	1331	1431	1531	1631	1731	1831	1931	2033	...	...	2133	...	2233
Heide a.	...	0545	0652	0652	...	0748	0757	0857	0957	1057	1157	1257	1357	1457	1557	1657	1757	1857	1957	2059	...	...	2159	...	2259
Heide d.	0517	...	...	0717	0717	...	...	0917	...	1117	...	1317	...	1517	...	1717	...	1917	...	...	2117	...	...	...	2317
Neumünster a.	0625	...	...	0825	0825	...	...	1025	...	1225	...	1425	...	1625	...	1825	...	2025	...	...	2225	...	...	...	0025

HUSUM - BAD ST PETER ORDING

km		Ⓐe								
0	Husum d.	0436	0536	0636	and	1836	1936	2036	2136	2236
21	Tönning d.	0501	0601	0701	hourly	1901	2001	2101	2201	2301
43	Bad St Peter Ording a.	0527	0627	0727	until	1927	2027	2127	2227	2327

	Ⓐe								
Bad St Peter Ording d.	0533	0633	0733	and	1933	2033	2133	2233	2333
Tönning d.	0604	0704	0804	hourly	2004	2104	2204	2304	0004
Husum a.	0625	0725	0825	until	2025	2125	2225	2325	0025

NIEBÜLL - DAGEBÜLL MOLE *See note* ⊡

km	*June 24 - Oct. 27*					★	d	★	★			d
	Hamburg Hbf a.	...	...	...	...	0917	...	1116	1317r	...	...	...
	Niebüll a.	...	...	...	...	1146	...	1345	1546r	...	...	...
0	Niebüll neg d.	0735	0905	1010	1135	1212	1335	1440	1605	1710	1815	1910
14	Dagebüll Mole a.	0753	0923	1028	1153	1230	1353	1458	1623	1728	1832	1928

June 24 - Oct. 27		★				★	★			d	d
Dagebüll Mole d.	0815	0930	1035	1210	1245	1340	1505k	1635	1735	1835	1935
Niebüll neg a.	0833	0948	1053	1235	1303	1357	1523k	1653	1753	1853	1953
Niebüll d.	...	1013	...	...	...	1413	1613	...	...	...	...
Hamburg Hbf a.	...	1242	...	...	...	1642	1848	...	...	...	...

km	*From Oct. 28*			①–⑤		①–⑤						
0	Niebüll neg d.	0635	0905	1010	1125	1235	1335	1440	1605	1815	1910	2010
14	Dagebüll Mole a.	0653	0923	1029	1143	1253	1353	1458	1621	1832	1928	2028

From Oct. 28			①–⑤		①–⑤						
Dagebüll Mole d.	0700	0930	1035	1150	1305	1415	1505	1625	1835	1935	2035
Niebüll neg a.	0718	0948	1053	1208	1323	1433	1523	1643	1853	1953	2053

C – ⑥⑦ June 29 - Sept. 15.
F – ⑤ June 28 - Sept. 20.
H – ⑤–⑦ June 28 - Sept. 20.

d – Not ⑥⑦ June 29 - Sept. 15.
e – Not Oct. 31.
k – On ⑥⑦ June 29 - Sept. 15 departs Dagebüll Mole 1510, arrives Niebüll neg 1529.

r – Until Sept. 20.
z – Also Oct. 31.

★ – Conveys (2) (*IC*) from / to Hamburg and beyond (Table **821**).

⊡ – **Operator**: Norddeutsche Eisenbahngesellschaft Niebüll GmbH. ✆ +49 (0) 4661 980 880. Niebüll neg station is situated a short distance from the Niebüll DB station forecourt. Subject to alteration until June 23 when most services use the platform at Dagebüll Hafen instead of Dagebüll Mole (approx. 250 metres from the ferry terminal). Dagebüll Mole is the station for ferries to / from the islands of Föhr and Amrum (see www.faehre.de).
Additional journeys June 24 - Oct. 27: Niebüll neg → Dagebüll Mole at 0635, 1025 **H**, 1310, 1410 **C**, 1935 **C**, 2010 **d** and 2035 **C**. Dagebüll Mole → Niebüll neg at 0700, 1055 **C** 1110 **F**, 1400 **d**, 1440 **C**, 1900 **C**, 2000 **C** and 2035 **d**.
Additional journeys from Oct. 28: Niebüll neg → Dagebüll Mole at 0735 Ⓐ**e**. Dagebüll Mole → Niebüll neg at 0815 Ⓐ**e**.

HAMBURG - NEUMÜNSTER - FLENSBURG — 823

RE / RB services except where shown

km		n	B		⚒r m	①–⑥ d						*IC* 386 A					*IC* 384 A					*IC* 382 E A				△
0	**Hamburg** Hbf .... **820** d.	...	...	...	...	...	0637k	0740r	0843	0943	1043	1053	1143	1243	1343	1443	1452	1543	1643	1743	1843	1901	1943	2043	2146	2243
37	Elmshorn .... **820** d.	...	...	...	...	...	0705k	0809r	0909	1009	1109	|	1209	1309	1409	1509	|	1609	1709	1809	1909	|	2009	2109	2214	2311
73	Neumünster .... **820** d.	0040	*0042*b	...	0534	0646	0734	0834	0934	1034	1134	|	1234	1334	1434	1534	|	1634	1734	1834	1934	|	2034	2134	2239	2334
112	Rendsburg .... **824** d.	0107	0134	...	0601	0715	0801	0901	1001	1101	1201	1213	1301	1401	1501	1601	1617	1701	1801	1901	2001	2013	2101	2201	2306	0001
136	Schleswig .... **824** d.	0123	0150	...	0617	0731	0817	0917	1017	1117	1217	|	1317	1417	1517	1617	|	1717	1817	1917	2017	|	2117	2217	2322	0017
174	**Flensburg** .... a.	0148	0215	...	0642	0756	0842	0942	1042	1142	1242	1248	1342	1442	1542	1642	1648	1742	1842	1942	2042	2048	2142	2242	2347	0042

	①–⑥ d	①–⑥ d	⑦ w						*IC* 383 1183 A					*IC* 385 1185 A					*IC* 1187 ⑥⑦ EA	*IC* 387 ①–⑤ EA		† z			D	p
Flensburg .... d.	0515	0615	0623	0715	0815	0915	1015	1115	1209	1215	1315	1415	1515	1609	1615	1715	1815	1915	2009	2009	2015	2015	2115	2215	2250	2315
Schleswig .... **824** d.	0539	0639	0647	0739	0839	0939	1039	1139	|	1239	1339	1439	1539	|	1639	1739	1839	1939	|	|	2039	2039	2139	2239	2314	2339
Rendsburg .... **824** d.	0557	0657	0705	0757	0857	0957	1057	1157	1243	1257	1357	1457	1557	1643	1657	1757	1857	1957	2043	2043	2057	2057	2157	2257	2332	2357
Neumünster .... **820** a.	0622	0722	0731	0822	0922	1022	1122	1222	|	1322	1422	1522	1622	|	1722	1822	1922	2022	|	|	2122	2122	2222	2322	*0024*b	0022
Elmshorn .... **820** a.	0648	0748	0755	0848	0948	1048	1148	1248	|	1348	1448	1548	1648	|	1748	1848	1948	2048	|	|	...	2148	...	...	...	...
Hamburg Hbf ...... **820** a.	0715	0815	0827	0915	1015	1115	1215	1315	1402	1415	1515	1615	1716	1802	1816	1916	2016	2116	2158	2159	...	2216	...	...	...	...

A – To/from Aarhus (Table **710**).
B – ②–⑥ Aug. 8 - Sept. 14.
D – ①–⑤ Aug. 7 - Sept. 13.
E – June 22 - Aug. 18.
b – By 🚌 to/from Rendsburg.
d – Also June 23, 30.
k – ⑥ only.
m – Not ③–⑤ Aug. 8 - Sept. 13.
n – Not ②–⑥ Aug. 8 - Sept. 14.
p – Not ①–⑤ Aug. 7 - Sept. 13.
r – ⚒ (not Oct. 31).
w – Not June 23, 30.
z – Also Oct. 31; not Apr. 21, June 9.
△ – Subject to alteration on June 21, 22, 28, 29 (by 🚌 Neumünster - Rendsburg with extended journey time).

KIEL - HUSUM and FLENSBURG — 824

RB services

km				⚒r¶							
0	**Kiel** Hbf .... d.	0003	...	0348	0503h	0603h	0703j	and	2103j	2203j	2303j
40	Rendsburg . **823** d.	0043	...	0435b	0535	0635	0735	hourly	2135	2235	2343
65	Schleswig .. **823** d.	0101y	...	0453	0553	0653	0753	until	2153	2253	0001
102	**Husum** .... a.	0133y	...	0525	0625	0725	0825		2225	2325	0033

	⚒r								
Husum .... d.	0430	0535	...	0635	and	2035	2135	2235	2335
Schleswig .... **823** d.	0502	0607	...	0707	hourly	2107	2207	2307	0007
Rendsburg .... **823** d.	0521	0626	...	0726	until	2126	2226	2329v	0031
Kiel Hbf .... a.	0557t	0657e	...	0757t		2157t	2257t	2400v	0113

km		Ⓐr	⚒r	Ⓐr	Ⓒz						
0	**Kiel** Hbf .... d.	0414	0518	0618	0641	0743	and	2043	2143	2248	2348
29	Eckernförde ...... d.	0449	0549	0649	0711	0811	hourly	2111	2216	2321	0021
50	Süderbrarup ...... d.	0507	0607	0707	0731	0831	until	2131	2240	2340	0040
81	**Flensburg** .... a.	0537	0637	0737	0757	0857		2157	2306	0006	0107

	⚒r								
Flensburg .... d.	0504	0604	0704	0804	and	2004	2104	2213	2313
Süderbrarup .... d.	0530	0630	0730	0830	hourly	2030	2130	2240	2340
Eckernförde .... d.	0550	0650	0750	0850	until	2050	2155	2300	0000
Kiel Hbf .... a.	0617	0717	0817	0917		2117	2225	2330	0030

– Arrives 0419.
– ①–⑥ (also June 23, 30). Arrives 0704 from Aug. 3.
– ①–⑥ (also June 23, 30). Departs 7 minutes earlier until Aug. 3.
– 7 minutes **earlier** until Aug. 3.
r – Not Oct. 31.
t – 7 minutes later until Aug. 3.
v – Until Aug. 3 Rendsburg d. 2326, Kiel a. 0013.
y – Not June 22, 23, 29, 30.
z – Also Oct. 31.
¶ – On June 22, 29 departs Kiel 0403, arrives Rendsburg 0434 and then as shown.

HAMBURG - LÜBECK - PUTTGARDEN and TRAVEMÜNDE — 825

RB / RE services

HAMBURG - LÜBECK

km				Ⓒd		⚒e		Ⓐe			Ⓐe									F	B		ⒷH
0	**Hamburg** Hbf .... d.	0024	0055	0255	...	0504	0604	0634	and at the same	2004	2034	...	2108	2208	...	2323	...	...	also	1219	1300	...	2103
40	Bad Oldesloe .... d.	0050	0137	0337	...	0530	0630	0702	minutes past	2030	2102	...	2132	2232	...	2347	...	...		|	|	...	|
63	**Lübeck** Hbf .... a.	0108	0155	0355	...	0548	0648	0720	each hour until	2048	2120	...	2150	2250	...	0005	...	...		1301	1339	...	2142

		Ⓒd		⚒e	Ⓐe		Ⓐe		Ⓐe										J		B	F
Lübeck Hbf .... d.	0016	0213	...	0413	0508	0543	0608	0643	and at the same	1908	1943	2008	...	2108	2208	2308	...	...	also	0816	...	1415	1637
Bad Oldesloe .... d.	0033	0230	...	0430	0525	0600	0625	0700	minutes past	1925	2000	2025	...	2125	2225	2325	...	...		|	...	|	|
Hamburg Hbf .... a.	0108	0313	...	0513	0551	0626	0651	0726	each hour until	1951	2026	2051	...	2151	2251	2351	...	...		0856	...	1456	1732

LÜBECK - TRAVEMÜNDE STRAND *SEE NOTE* ⊠

km		Ⓐe	⚒e								
0	**Lübeck** Hbf .... d.	0503	0603	0703	0803r	and	2003r	2103	2203t	2303
18	Travemünde Skandinavienkai a.	0519	0619	0719	0819	hourly	2019	2119	2219	2319
21	**Travemünde** Strand .... a.	0525	0625	0725	0825	until	2025	2125	2225	2325

	Ⓐe	⚒e						
Travemünde Strand .... d.	0534	0634	0734	0834	and	2134	2234	2334
Travemünde Skandinavienkai .... d.	0539	0639	0739	0839	hourly	2139	2239	2339
Lübeck Hbf .... a.	0556	0656	0756	0858	until	2158	2258	2356

HAMBURG - LÜBECK - PUTTGARDEN (- KØBENHAVN)

km		Ⓐ e			*EC* 231 R	T	Ⓒ v	*EC* 33	T	*EC* 235 Y	z	W	*IC* 2410 L	*EC* 35	T	Ⓒ v	*EC* 37 K		*EC* 39						
0	**Hamburg** Hbf .... d.	...	...	...	0726	...	0827	0928	...	1128	...	...	1151h	1328	...	1427	1528	...	1728	...	...	...	...	...	...
63	**Lübeck** Hbf .... ⊡ d.	0512	...	0712	0806	0912	0915	1006	1112	1206	1308	1312	1314	1406	1512	1515	1606	1712	1806	...	1912	...	2112	...	2312
93	Neustadt (Holst) .. ⊡ a.	|	...	|	|	|	|	|	|	|	|	|	|	|	|	|	|	|	|	...	|	...	|	...	2345
115	Oldenburg (Holst) .... d.	0616	...	0816	0839	1016	1016	1039	1216	1239	1405	1416	1417	1439	1616	1616	1639	1816	1839	...	2016	...	2216	...	0017
144	Fehmarn-Burg .... a.	0643	...	0840	|	1040	1042	|	1240	|	1428	1440	1442	|	1640	1642	|	1840	|	...	2040	...	2240	...	0040
151	**Puttgarden** ⛴ .... a.	0656	...	0855j	0905	1055g	1058	1105	1255z	1305	1440	...	...	1505	1655z	1658	1705	1855	1905	...	2055z	...	2255	...	0055
	København H **50 720** a.	...	...	...	*1240**	...	...	1426b	...	*1640**	...	...	...	1826b	...	...	*2040**	...	2226b	...	...	...	...	...	...

	Ⓐ e			*IC* 2417 N	*IC* 2413 M			*EC* 38/438	Ⓒ v	T	*EC* 436 K	z	W	*EC* 34/434	*IC* 2415 A	*IC* 2411 P		*EC* 232 Y	Ⓒ v	T	*EC* 32/432			*EC* 230 Q	
København H **50 720** a.	...	...	...	...	...	...	...	0735c	...	...	*0910**	...	...	1135c	...	...	...	*1310**	...	...	1535c	...	...	*1710**	...
Puttgarden ⛴ .... d.	0519	0620	0720	...	...	0915j	...	1042	1110	1115g	1242	1310	...	1442	...	...	1515z	1642	1710	1715z	1842	1915	...	2042	2115z
Fehmarn-Burg .... d.	0530	0631	0731	0824	0908	0931	...	|	1125	1131	|	1321	1331	|	1510	1510	1531	|	1725	1731	|	1931	...	|	2131
Oldenburg (Holst) .... d.	0553	0654	0754	0912	0932	0954	...	1107	1151	1154	1307	1344	1354	1507	1534	1534	1554	1707	1751	1754	1907	1954	...	2107	2154
Neustadt (Holst) ... ⊡ d.	0623	|	|	|	|	|	...	|	|	|	|	|	|	|	|	|	|	|	|	|	|	|	...	|	|
Lübeck Hbf .... ⊡ a.	0654	0754	0854	1004	1035	1054	...	1137	1242	1254	1337	1454	1454	1537	1636	1636	1654	1737	1842	1854	1937	2054	...	2137	2254
Hamburg Hbf .... a.	...	...	...	1114h	1153h	...	...	1216	1334	...	1416	...	...	1616	1732	1750h	...	1816	1936	....	2016	...	...	2217	...

– ⑤–⑦ to Nov. 3 (also June 10, Oct. 2).
– Until June 10. *ICE* **1681/2**. To/from München (Table **900**).
– ①–④ to Oct. 30 (also June 21, July 19, 26, Aug. 2, 9, 16, 23, Oct. 4; not June 10, 19, Oct. 2, 3); daily from Nov. 4
– ⑤–⑦ to Nov. 3 (also June 10, 12, 19, Oct. 2, 3, 31; not June 21, July 12, 19, 26, Aug. 2, 9, 16, 23, Oct. 4).
– ②–④ to June 27; ②–④ Sept. 18 - Oct. 30 (not Oct. 2, 3); ⑤⑦ from Nov. 8. *IC* **2220/1**. From/to Frankfurt via Köln (Tables **800/911**).
– Ⓑ to June 10 (not June 9). *ICE* **584**. From München (Table **900**).
– ①–⑥ to June 8. *ICE* **585**. To München (Table **900**).
– ⑤–⑦ to June 16 (also June 10); daily June 21 - Aug. 18; ⑤–⑦ Aug. 23 - Sept. 15.
– Daily to Sept. 17 (not June 12, 13, 19, 25–27); ①⑤⑥⑦ from Sept. 20 (also Oct. 2, 3). FEHMARN – 🚃12 Köln - Düsseldorf - Fehmarn-Burg. Train number **2418** on ⑥ June 29 - Sept. 14 and ⑥ Sept. 28 - Nov. 2. Train number **2302** on Ⓑ July 14 - Aug. 25.
– ⑥⑦ to Nov. 3 (also June 10). FEHMARN – 🚃12 Fehmarn-Burg - Köln.
– ⑤ to Nov. 1 (also June 19, Oct. 2; not June 21, July 19 - Aug. 23, Oct. 4). FEHMARN – 🚃12 Fehmarn-Burg - Köln.
– ①–④ July 1 - Sept. 17 (also June 11, 17, 18, 20, 24); ① Sept. 23 - Oct. 28 (also Oct. 3). FEHMARN – 🚃12 Fehmarn-Burg - Köln.
– June 21 - Aug. 18.

R – June 22 - Aug. 19.
T – Ⓐ to Nov. 1 (not Oct. 31); daily from Nov. 4.
W – From Nov. 4.
Y – Until Sept. 16.
b – 14 minutes later until Sept. 29 (by 🚌 from Rødby).
c – 25 minutes **earlier** until Sept. 29 (by 🚌 to Rødby).
d – Also Oct. 31.
e – Not Oct. 31.
g – Ⓐ to Nov. 1; ⑥⑦ from Nov. 9.
h – Hamburg **Harburg**.
j – Daily to Nov. 8; ①–⑤ from Nov. 11.
r – 2 minutes **earlier** on Ⓒ until Nov. 3.
t – 2201 on ⑥ until Nov. 2.
v – Ⓒ to Nov. 3 (also Oct. 31).
z – Until Nov. 3.

* – By 🚌 from/to Rødby.
⊠ – Evening services (from approximately 1900) are subject to alteration July 19 – 28.
⊡ – Full service **Lübeck - Neustadt** (Holst) and v.v. (journey time 31 – 51 minutes):
From Lübeck Hbf at 0442 Ⓐ**e**, 0512 Ⓐ**e**, 0612, 0712, 0812, 0912 **T**, 0919 Ⓒ**v**, 1012, 1112, 1212, 1308 **z**, 1312 **W**, 1412, 1508 Ⓒ**v**, 1512 **T**, 1612, 1712, 1812, 1912, 2012, 2112, 2212 and 2312.
From Neustadt (Holst) at 0523 Ⓐ**e**, 0623, 0653 Ⓐ**e**, 0717 Ⓐ**e**, 0723 Ⓒ**d**, 0817, 0919 **E**, 0923 **D**, 1017, 1114 Ⓒ**v**, 1123 **T**, 1217 **T**, 1223 Ⓒ**v**, 1314 **z**, 1323 **W**, 1417, 1514 Ⓒ**v**, 1523 **T**, 1617, 1714 Ⓒ**v**, 1723 **T**, 1817 **T**, 1823 Ⓒ**v**, 1923, 2017, 2123, 2217 and 2317.

826 KIEL - LÜBECK *RE/RB services*

On Oct. 31 services run as on ⑦.

km		Ⓐ	Ⓒ	Ⓒ	Ⓐ							
0	**Kiel** Hbf.......d.	0543	0543	0643	0643	0743	and	1943	2043	2143	2243	2343
33	Plön.......d.	0615	0615	0713	0715	0815	hourly	2015	2115	2215	2315	0015
47	Eutin.......d.	0629	0629	0727	0729	0829	until	2029	2131	2229	2329	0029
80	**Lübeck** Hbf......a.	0653	0658	0752	0752	0852		2052	2153	2258	2358	0058

	⑥	Ⓐ	Ⓒ	Ⓐ							
Lübeck Hbf ...d.	0501	0504	0601	0606	0704	0806	and	2006	2106	2201	2301
Eutin.......d.	0529	0529	0629	0630	0729	0829	hourly	2029	2131	2229	2329
Plön.......d.	0544	0544	0643	0645	0745	0845	until	2045	2145	2244	2344
Kiel Hbf.......a.	0617	0616	0716	0716	0816	0916		2116	2216	2317	0017

Other stopping trains Kiel - Lübeck and v.v. (journey 87–88 minutes): **From Kiel** Hbf at 0436 Ⓐ, 0443 Ⓒ, 0515 Ⓐ, 0604 Ⓐ, 0704 and hourly until 2004.
From Lübeck Hbf at 0017, 0356 Ⓐ, 0401 Ⓒ, 0528 Ⓐ, 0628 Ⓐ, 0728 and hourly until 2028.

827 LÜBECK - BÜCHEN - LÜNEBURG *RB services*

km		Ⓐe	Ⓐe	Ⓒz	Ⓐe	Ⓒz															
0	**Lübeck** Hbf.......d.	0505	0605	0609	0707	0709	0809	0909	1009	1109	1209	1309	1409	1509	1609	1709	1809	1909	2009	2109	2209	2329
9	Lübeck Flughafen ✈ ▷ d.	0514	0614	0619	0716	0719	0819	0919	1019	1119	1219	1319	1419	1519	1619	1719	1819	1919	2019	2119	2219	2339
22	Ratzeburg.......d.	0526	0627	0630	0730	0730	0830	0930	1030	1130	1230	1330	1430	1530	1630	1730	1830	1930	2030	2130	2230	2352
31	Mölln (Lauenburg)......d.	0533	0634	0637	0737	0737	0837	0937	1037	1137	1237	1337	1437	1537	1637	1737	1837	1937	2037	2137	2237	2359
50	Büchen.......a.	0545	0646	0649	0749	0749	0849	0949	1049	1149	1249	1349	1449	1549	1649	1749	1849	1949	2049	2149	2249	0013
50	Büchen.......d.	0555	0655	0655	0759	0750	0859	0950	1107	1150	1307	1350	1507	1550	1707	1750	1907	1950	2107	2202	2250	...
79	**Lüneburg**.......a.	0618	0718	0718	0822	0815	0922	1015	1130	1215	1330	1415	1530	1615	1730	1815	1930	2015	2130	2225	2315	...

	Ⓐe	Ⓐe	⑥	Ⓐe		Ⓐe	Ⓒz														Ⓒd	
Lüneburg.......d.	0420	0526	0545	0628	0630z	0742	0745	0830	0945	1030	1145	1230	1345	1430	1545	1630	1745	1830	1945	2030	2138k	2245
Büchen.......a.	0442	0547	0608	0650	0652z	0808	0808	0852	1008	1052	1208	1252	1408	1452	1608	1652	1808	1852	2008	2052	2200k	2309
Büchen.......d.	0455	0555	0609	0657	0709	0809	0809	0909	1009	1109	1209	1309	1409	1509	1609	1709	1809	1909	2009	2109	2209	2333
Mölln (Lauenburg)......d.	0509	0609	0622	0709	0722	0822	0822	0922	1022	1122	1222	1322	1422	1522	1622	1722	1822	1922	2022	2122	2222	2345
Ratzeburg.......d.	0517	0617	0632	0717	0732	0832	0832	0932	1032	1132	1232	1332	1432	1532	1632	1732	1832	1932	2032	2132	2232	2352
Lübeck Flughafen ✈ ▷ d.	0525	0625	0640	0726	0740	0840	0840	0940	1040	1140	1240	1340	1440	1540	1640	1740	1840	1940	2040	2140	2240	0001
Lübeck Hbf.......a.	0536	0636	0652	0737	0752	0852	0852	0952	1052	1152	1252	1352	1452	1552	1652	1752	1852	1952	2052	2154	2252	0011

d – Also Oct. 2, 30, 31.
e – Not Oct. 31.
k – ⑥ (also June 9, Oct. 2, 30).
z – Ⓒ (also Oct. 31).

▷ – Trains call at Lübeck Flughafen on request only.

828 LÜBECK - BAD KLEINEN *RE/RB services*

km			ⒶeT		T		T		T		T		T		T		T		T	R
0	**Lübeck** Hbf.... d.	0502	0602	0703	0802	0903	1002	1103	1202	1303	1402	1503	1602	1703	1802	1903	2002	2103	2206	2307
39	Grevesmühlen. d.	0537	0637	0737	0837	0937	1037	1137	1237	1337	1437	1537	1637	1737	1837	1937	2037	2137	2242	2340
62	**Bad Kleinen**... a.	0552	0656	0752	0854	0952	1054	1152	1254	1352	1454	1552	1656	1752	1854	1952	2054	2152	2259	2354

	ⒶeS		ⒶeT		T		T		T		T		T		T		T		T	
Bad Kleinen.....d.	0434	...	0518	0603	0700	0803	0900	1003	1100	1203	1300	1403	1500	1603	1700	1803	1900	2003	2100	2204
Grevesmühlen ..d.	0448	...	0539	0617	0716	0817	0916	1017	1116	1217	1316	1417	1516	1617	1716	1817	1916	2017	2116	2221
Lübeck Hbf......a.	0525	...	0624	0656	0756	0856	0956	1056	1156	1256	1356	1456	1556	1656	1756	1856	1956	2056	2156	2300

R – To Schwerin Hbf (a. 0017).
S – From Schwerin Hbf (d. 0415).
T – To/from stations in Table **836**.

e – Not Oct. 31.

830 *Service from June 11* HAMBURG - ROSTOCK - STRALSUND *RE services except where shown*

km								IC			ICE			ICE	IC			IC	IC			ICE			IC	IC
								1049			1678			1676	2238			2212	2212			1748			2216	2174
			Ⓐe			Ⓐe	Ⓐe	⑥			①–⑥							⑥h	Ⓑj							⑤f
			S		S			♦		S	✕♦		S	✕	♦		S	🍷♦	🍷♦		S	✕		S	🍷♦	
0	**Hamburg** Hbf.......d.	0030	...	...	...	...	0509	...	0621	...	0743§	0822	...	0943	...	1021	...	1118‡	1142	1221	...	1343	1420	...	1517‡	1541
47	Büchen.......d.	0107	...	0458a	...	...	0552r	...	0658t	...	|	0858t	...	|	...	1058t	...	|	|	1258t	...	|	1458t	...	|	|
123	**Schwerin** Hbf.....**837** d.	0156	...	0548	...	0642	0648	...	0748	...	0837	0948	...	1037	1056	1148	...	1237c	1237	1348	...	1437	1548	...	1614	1637
140	Bad Kleinen . **836 837** d.	▬	...	0603	...	0659	...	...	0803	...	|	1003	...	|	1109	1203	...	|	|	1403	...	|	1603	...	|	1649
181	Bützow.......**836** d.	...	...	0629	...	0723	...	...	0829	...	0910	1029	...	1110	1136	1229	...	1310	1310	1429	...	1510	1629	...	1646b	1713
211	**Rostock** Hbf.......a.	S	...	0650	...	0750	...	...	0850	...	0932	1050	...	1132	1156	1253	...	1332	1332	1450	...	1532	1650	...	1706	1733
211	**Rostock** Hbf.......d.	0454	0554	...	0700	...	...	0837	...	0901	0938	...	1101	1138	...	...	1301	1338	1338	...	1501	1538	...	1701	1717*	1745
240	Ribnitz-D'garten West . d.	0515	0616	...	0724	...	...	0904	...	0922	1002o	...	1122	1200	...	...	1322	1400	1400	...	1522	1600	...	1722	1739*	1807
265	Velgast.......d.	0539	0640	...	0741	...	...	|	...	0940	1016	...	1140	1216	...	...	1340	1416	1416	...	1540	1616	...	1740	1754*	1828
283	**Stralsund** Hbf.......a.	0554	0655	...	0757	...	...	0926	...	0955	1029	...	1155	1229	...	...	1355	1430	1430	...	1555	1629	...	1755	1812*	1841
	Ostseebad Binz **844** a.	...	...	...	...	...	...	1040	...	...	1120v	...	...	...	...	...	...	1530	1530	...	...	1719k	...	...	...	...

			ICE			IC	ICE	IC			
			1744			2404	1596	2188			
						⑤g	⑦	①–④			
		S	✕♦		S		✕	m		B	
Hamburg Hbf.......d.	1622	...	1742‡	1818	...	1943	1942	1944	2017	...	2254
Büchen.......d.	1658t	...	|	1858t	...	|	|	|	2058t	...	2328
Schwerin Hbf......**837** d.	1748	...	1837	1948	...	2037	2037	2037	2148	...	0019
Bad Kleinen..**836 837** d.	1803	...	1849	2003	...	2049	2049	2049	2203	...	0029
Bützow.......**836** d.	1829	...	1913	2029	...	2113	2113	2113	2229	...	0055
Rostock Hbf.......a.	1850	...	1933	2050	...	2133	2133	2133	2250	...	0118
Rostock Hbf.......d.	...	1901	1938	...	2101	2138	2138	...	...	2301	...
Ribnitz-Damgarten West d.	...	1922	2000	...	2122	2200	2200	...	...	2322	...
Velgast.......d.	...	1940	2016	...	2140	2216	2216	...	...	2340	...
Stralsund Hbf.......a.	...	1955	2029	...	2155	2229	2229	...	...	2355	...
Ostseebad Binz **844** a.	...	...	...	...	...	...	...	...	...	...	...

				IC		ICE			IC
				2189		1745			2217
	Ⓐe	Ⓒd	Ⓐe	Ⓐn		Ⓐ	①–⑥			
						S	H✕	S		🍷♦
Ostseebad Binz **844**.....d.	...	...	...	...	...	...	...	...	...	...
Stralsund Hbf.......d.	...	...	...	...	...	0454	0522	0600	...	0727
Velgast.......d.	...	...	...	...	...	0509	0536	0614	...	0741
Ribnitz-Damgarten West .. d.	...	...	...	...	...	0526	0551	0632	...	0756
Rostock Hbf.......a.	...	...	...	...	...	0548	0616	0654	...	0816
Rostock Hbf.......d.	...	...	...	0458	0507	...	0625	...	0707	0825
Bützow.......**836** d.	...	...	...	0519	0529	...	0645	...	0729	0846
Bad Kleinen.......**836 837** d.	...	...	...	0543	0558	...	0709	...	0758	|
Schwerin Hbf.......**837** d.	0350	0442	0449	0557	0611	...	0721	...	0811	0921
Büchen.......d.	0448	0540	0553	0634	0707t	...	|	...	0907t	|
Hamburg Hbf.......a.	0518	0611	0629	0703	0738	...	0817‡	...	0938	1015‡

			ICE			IC			IC	ICE			ICE						ICE			IC				
			1671			2213			2239	1749			1677						1679			1049				
														Ⓐe			Ⓐe	E	⑦			⑥				
	S		H✕	S		🍷♦	S		♦	H✕	S		✕♦		S				H✕			♦	S		S	
Ostseebad Binz **844** d.	...	...	...	...	...	1028	...	...	...	1227z	...	...	...	...	...	...	...	...	...	1704	...	1818	...	...	...	...
Stralsund Hbf.......d.	0800	...	0927	1000	...	1126	1200	...	...	1327	1400	...	1527	...	1600	...	1701	...	1727	1800	...	1925	2000	...	2200	...
Velgast.......d.	0815	...	0941	1015	...	1140	1215	...	...	1341	1415	...	1541	...	1615	...	1712	...	1741	1815	...	1941	2015	...	2215	...
Ribnitz-Damgarten West d.	0833	...	0959	1033	...	1155	1233	...	...	1354o	1433	...	1554o	...	1633	...	1738t	...	1800	1833	...	1955	2033	...	2233	...
Rostock Hbf.......a.	0855	...	1019	1055	...	1219	1255	...	...	1419	1455	...	1619	...	1655	...	1801	...	1820	1855	...	2019	2055	...	2255	...
Rostock Hbf.......d.	...	0907	1025	...	1107	1244	...	1307	1405	1425	...	1507	1625	...	...	1707	...	1808	1825	...	1907	...	...	2107	...	2307
Bützow.......**836** d.	...	0929	1046	...	1129	1304	...	1329	1427	1446	...	1529	1646	...	...	1729	...	1830	1846	...	1929	...	...	2129	...	2329
Bad Kleinen..**836 837** d.	...	0958	|	...	1158	|	...	1358	1450	|	...	1558	|	...	...	1758	...	1903t	|	...	1958	...	...	2158	...	2355
Schwerin Hbf......**837** d.	...	1011	1121	...	1211	1339	...	1411	1500	1521	...	1611	1721	1724	...	1811	...	1915	1921	...	2011	...	...	2211	...	0005
Büchen.......d.	...	1107t	|	...	1307t	|	...	1507t	...	|	...	1707t	|	1822	...	1907t	...	...	|	...	2107t	...	...	2303	...	...
Hamburg Hbf.......a.	...	1138	1216‡	...	1338	1432‡	...	1537	...	1615‡	...	1738	1816‡	1857	...	1939	...	...	2019‡	...	2138	...	...	2338	...	...

♦ – **NOTES** (LISTED BY TRAIN NUMBER)

1048/9 – ⑥ June 29 - Sept. 14. 🚃 Köln (see Tables **800/810**) - Berlin - Rostock - Stralsund - Ostseebad Binz and v.v.
1677 – 🚃 and ✕ Stralsund - Hamburg (- Hannover Ⓑ).
1678 – 🚃 and ✕ Hannover - Hamburg - Stralsund (- Ostseebad Binz until Oct. 5).
1744 – 🚃 and ✕ Hannover - Hamburg - Stralsund. Continues to Greifswald (a. 2050) on ⑦.
2212 – RÜGEN – 🚃 and 🍷 Koblenz - Köln - Hamburg - Ostseebad Binz.
2213 – RÜGEN – 🚃 and 🍷 Ostseebad Binz - Hamburg - Köln - Stuttgart.
2216/7 – GREIFSWALDER BODDEN – 🚃 and 🍷 Stuttgart - Koblenz - Köln - Hamburg - Stralsund (- Greifswald ♥).
2238/9 – ⑤–⑦ to June 23 (also June 10); daily June 28 - Sept. 17; ⑤–⑦ Sept. 20 - Nov. 3 (also Oct. 2, 3, 29, 30, 31); ⑤ from Nov. 8. WARNOW – 🚃 Leipzig - Magdeburg - Stendal - Schwerin - Rostock (- Warnemünde ●) and v.v.

B – To Bergen auf Rügen on ①②③④⑦ (Table **844**).
E – ①②③④⑥ (not June 10, Oct. 3, 31).
H – To Hannover (Table **900**).

S – To/from Sassnitz (Table **844**).

a – Ⓐ only.
b – Not ⑥.
c – Arrives 1210.
d – Also Oct. 31.
e – Not Oct. 31.
f – Also Oct. 2; not Oct. 4.
g – Also June 19, Oct. 2, 31; not June 21, Oct. 4, Nov. 1.
h – Runs daily June 11 - July 28.
j – Not June 11 - July 28.
k – ⑥ only.
m – Not June 19, Oct. 2, 3, 31.
n – Not Oct. 4.
o – Ribnitz-Damgarten **Ost**.

r – Arrives 0542.
t – Arrives 6–7 minutes earlier.
v – Until Oct. 5.
z – Daily to Oct. 6; ⑦ from Oct. 13.

‡ – June 11 - July 28 calls at Hamburg Bergedo (not Hamburg Hbf).
§ – On ①–⑤ June 11 - July 26 calls at Hambur Bergedorf (not Hamburg Hbf).
* – 16–21 minutes later on ⑥ June 15 - July 2
♥ – See Table **845** for running dates to/from Greifswald.
● – To/from Warnemünde until Nov. 3. **2238** arrives Warnemünde 1214. **2239** departs Warnemünde 1343.

S-Bahn — ROSTOCK - WARNEMÜNDE — 831

ROSTOCK - WARNEMÜNDE and v.v. *13 km*. Journey time: 21 minutes. Additional services run at peak times on Ⓐ. On Oct. 31 services run as on ⑦.

From Rostock Hbf at 0003 **A**, 0433, 0448 Ⓐ, 0503, 0518 Ⓐ, 0533, 0548 Ⓐ, 0603, 0618 Ⓐ, 0633, 0648 Ⓐ, 0703, 0718 Ⓐ, 0733, 0748 Ⓐ, 0803, 0818, 0833, 0848, 0903, 0918, 0933, 0948 and at 03, 18, 33 and 48 minutes past each hour until 2103, 2118, 2133, 2148; then 2203, 2233 **B**, 2237 ①–④ **C**, 2303 **B**, 2307 ①–④ **C**, 2333 **B** and 2337 ①–④ **C**.

From Warnemünde at 0003 **A**, 0403, 0430, 0448 Ⓐ, 0503, 0518 Ⓐ, 0533, 0548 Ⓐ, 0603, 0618 Ⓐ, 0633, 0648 Ⓐ, 0703, 0718 Ⓐ, 0733, 0748 Ⓐ, 0803, 0818 Ⓐ, 0833, 0848, 0903, 0918, 0933, 0948 and at 03, 18, 33 and 48 minutes past each hour until 2103, 2118, 2133, 2148; then 2203, 2229 ①–④ **C**, 2233 **B**, 2259 ①–④ **C**, 2303 **B**, 2329 ①–④ **C** and 2333 **B**.

A – ①⑥⑦ (daily from Sept. 28). **B** – ⑤–⑦ (daily from Sept. 27). **C** – ①–④ to Sept. 26.

Niederbarnimer Eisenbahn (2nd class only) — BERLIN - KOSTRZYN — 832

km																								
			Ⓒ	Ⓐ								Ⓒ	Ⓐ				G							
0	**Berlin** Ostkreuz ★ d.	0533	0633	0633	0733	0833	0933	1033	1133	1233	1333	1433	1433	1533	1633	1733	1833	1933	2033	2133	...	2333	...	...
25	Strausberg d.	0558	0658	0658	0758	0858	0958	1058	1158	1258	1358	1458	1458	1558	1658	1758	1858	1958	2058	2158	...	2358	...	...
49	Müncheberg (Mark) ¶ d.	0614	0714	0721	0814	0914	1014	1114	1214	1314	1414	1514	1517	1614	1717	1814	1914	2014	2114	2214	...	0014	...	...
82	**Kostrzyn** 🏨 a.	0657	0747	0754	0857	0947	1057	1147	1257	1347	1457	1547	1550	1657	1750	1857	1947	2057	2147	2257	...	0057	...	...

				ⒶG	Ⓐ	Ⓒ		Ⓐ	ⒸG						Ⓐ	Ⓒ								
Kostrzyn 🏨 d.	0402	0502	0602	0615	0702	0709	0802	0909	0909	1002	1109	1202	1309	1402	1505	1509	1602	1705	1802	1909	2002	...	2202	...
Müncheberg (Mark) ¶ d.	0449	0549	0649	0659	0749	0749	0849	0949	0949	1049	1149	1249	1349	1449	1549	1549	1649	1749	1849	1949	2049	...	2249	...
Strausberg d.	0505	0605	0705	0714	0805	0805	0905	1005	1005	1105	1205	1305	1405	1505	1605	1605	1705	1805	1905	2005	2105	...	2305	...
Berlin Ostkreuz ★ a.	0528	0628	0728	0733**h**	0828	0828	0928	1028	1028	1128	1228	1328	1428	1528	1628	1628	1728	1828	1928	2028	2128	...	2328	...

G – To / from Gorzów (Table **1000**). **h** – Berlin **Lichtenberg**. ★ – Trains call at Berlin Lichtenberg (4–5 minutes from Ostkreuz). ¶ – Station for Buckower Kleinbahn.

RE services — WISMAR - ROSTOCK — 833

km		⚒r	Ⓐr				
0	**Wismar** d.	0442	0542	0642	and	2042	2142
22	Neubukow d.	0511	0611	0711	hourly	2111	2211
41	Bad Doberan ▲ d.	0530	0630	0730	until	2130	2230
57	**Rostock** Hbf a.	0551	0651	0751		2151	2251

	Ⓐr		⚒r				
Rostock Hbf d.	0412	0506	0606	0706	and	2006	2106
Bad Doberan ▲ d.	0432	0532	0632	0732	hourly	2032	2132
Neubukow d.	0451	0551	0651	0751	until	2051	2151
Wismar a.	0515	0615	0715	0815		2115	2215

r – Not Oct. 31.

▲ – **BAD DOBERAN - OSTSEEBAD KÜHLUNGSBORN WEST**. All services worked by steam locomotive. 2nd class only. Journey time: 39–47 minutes.
Operator: Mecklenburgische Bäderbahn Molli GmbH, Am Bahnhof, 18209 Bad Doberan. ✆ +49 (0) 38293 431331, Fax +49 (0) 38293 431332. **Service until Nov. 3**.
From **Bad Doberan** at 0835 Ⓐ **r**, 0936, 1036 and hourly until 1636; then 1745 and 1845. From **Kühlungsborn West** at 0640 Ⓐ **r**, 0828, 0935, 1035 and hourly until 1735.

Service June 11 - September 6 — STRALSUND - NEUBRANDENBURG - NEUSTRELITZ — 834

km																										
					Ⓐ			①–⑥			①–⑥			①–⑥			Ⓑ			Ⓑ			Ⓑ			
0	**Stralsund** Hbf d.	...	0502	...	0604	0702	...	0804	0902	...	1004	1102	...	1204	1302	...	1404	1502	...	1604	1702	...	1804	1902	...	2106
23	Grimmen d.	...	0523	...	0624	0723	...	0824	0923	...	1024	1123	...	1224	1323	...	1424	1523	...	1624	1723	...	1824	1923	...	2128
47	Demmin d.	...	0546	...	0646	0746	...	0846	0946	...	1046	1146	...	1246	1346	...	1446	1546	...	1646	1746	...	1846	1946	...	2146
89	**Neubrandenburg** a.	...	0629	...	0729	0829	...	0929	1029	...	1129	1229	...	1329	1429	...	1529	1629	...	1729	1829	...	1929	2029	...	2229
89	**Neubrandenburg** d.	0511	0630	0711	...	0830	0911	...	1030	1111	...	1230	1311	...	1430	1511	...	1630	1711	...	1830	1911	...	2030	2111	2230
124	**Neustrelitz** Hbf a.	0545	0659	0743	...	0859	0943	...	1059	1143	...	1259	1343	...	1459	1543	...	1659	1743	...	1859	1943	...	2059	2143	2259
	Berlin Hbf **835** a.	...	0815	...	...	1014	...	...	1214	...	...	1414	...	...	1616	...	...	1814	...	...	2015	...	...	2216	...	0035**v**

		Ⓐ			①–⑥			①–⑥			①–⑥			Ⓑ			Ⓑ			Ⓑ						
Berlin Hbf **835** d.	...	...	...	0543	...	...	0742	...	...	0942	...	...	1142	...	...	1342	...	...	1541	...	...	1742	...	1942	...	2142
Neustrelitz Hbf d.	0501**a**	...	0613	0701	...	0816	0901	...	1014	1101	...	1214	1301	...	1414	1501	...	1614	1701	...	1814	1901	2014	2101	2214	2301
Neubrandenburg a.	0528**a**	...	0646	0729	...	0846	0929	...	1046	1129	...	1246	1329	...	1446	1529	...	1646	1729	...	1846	1929	2046	2129	2246	2329
Neubrandenburg d.	0531	0631	...	0731	0831	...	0931	1031	...	1131	1231	...	1331	1431	...	1531	1631	...	1731	1831	...	1931	...	2131	...	...
Demmin d.	0609	0710	...	0810	0910	...	1010	1110	...	1210	1310	...	1410	1510	...	1610	1710	...	1810	1910	...	2010	...	2210	...	...
Grimmen d.	0629	0729	...	0829	0929	...	1029	1129	...	1229	1329	...	1429	1529	...	1629	1729	...	1829	1929	...	2029	...	2229	...	...
Stralsund Hbf a.	0651	0750	...	0851	0950	...	1051	1150	...	1251	1350	...	1451	1550	...	1651	1750	...	1851	1950	...	2051	...	2251	...	...

a – Ⓐ only. **v** – Neustrelitz - Berlin on ⑤⑥ only.

Service June 11 - September 6 — ROSTOCK - BERLIN - ELSTERWERDA — 835

km		RE 3503	RE 4353	RE 3505	RE 4355	IC 2355	RE 3507	RE 4357	RE 3509	RE 4359	ICE 1727	RE 3511	RE 4361	RE 3513	ICE 1736	RE 4363	RE 3515	RE 4365	RE 3517	RE 18491	RE 4367	RE 3519	IC 1048	RE 4369	RE 3521	RE 3525
						Ⓐ 🍷					⑥⑦r M✕				⑥d F✕					Ⓒ			⑥ ★🍷		⑤⑥ v	
	Warnemünde **831** d.	...	...	...	...	...	...	...	...	...	1114	...	...	...	1406	...	...	...	...	1806	...	...	...	...	...	...
0	**Rostock** Hbf **831** d.	...	0434**e**	...	0634	0723	...	0834	...	1034	1133	...	1234	...	1433	1434	...	1634	...	1831	1834	...	2033	2034	...	2334
34	Güstrow d.	...	0456**e**	...	0656**c**	|	...	0856	...	1056	|	...	1256	...	|	1456	...	1656	...	|	1856	...	|	2056	...	0000
85‡	Waren (Müritz) d.	...	0529**e**	...	0729	0804	...	0929	...	1129	1214	...	1329	...	1514	1529	...	1729	...	1918	1929	...	2114	2129	...	0033
	Stralsund Hbf **834** d.	...	|	0502	|	|	0702	|	0902	|	|	1102	|	1302	|	|	1502	|	1702	|	|	1902	|	|	2106	|
	Neubrandenburg **834** d.	0429**z**	|	0630	|	|	0830	|	1030	|	|	1230	|	1430	|	|	1630	|	1830	|	|	2030	|	|	2230	|
120	**Neustrelitz** Hbf a.	0458**z**	0550**e**	0659	0750	0821	0859	0950	1059	1150	1232	1259	1350	1459	1532	1550	1659	1750	1859	1940	1950	2059	2132	2150	2259	0054
120	**Neustrelitz** Hbf d.	0459	0552	0700	0752	0823	0900	0952	1100	1152	1234	1300	1352	1500	1534	1552	1700	1752	1900	1943	1952	2100	2134	2152	2320	...
141	Fürstenberg (Havel) d.	0510	0603	0711	0803	|	0911	1003	1111	1203	|	1311	1403	1511	|	1603	1711	1803	1911	1956	2003	2111	|	2203	2331	...
162	Gransee d.	0524	0617	0723	0817	|	0923	1017	1123	1217	|	1323	1417	1523	|	1617	1723	1817	1923	|	2017	2123	|	2217	2343	...
191	Oranienburg d.	0545	0644**j**	0744	0844**j**	|	0944	1044**j**	1144	1244**j**	|	1344	1444**j**	1544	|	1644**j**	1744	1844**j**	1944	2033	2044**j**	2144	|	2244**j**	0004	...
223	**Berlin** Gesundbrunnen d.	0611	0711	0810	0911	0926**s**	1010	1110	1210	1310	1343	1410	1510	1611	1641	1710	1810	1911	2010	2058	2111	2211	2243	2312	0030	...
227	**Berlin** Hbf a.	0615	0716	0815	0915	0933	1014	1114	1214	1314	1348	1414	1514	1616	1648	1715	1814	1916	2015	2107	2116	2216	2248	2316	0035	...
227	**Berlin** Hbf d.	0619**e**	0718	0818	0918	...	1018	1118	1218	1318	1405	1418	1518	1618	1704	1718	1818	1918	2018	...	2118	2218	2343	2318	...	...
233	**Berlin** Südkreuz d.	0627**e**	0727	0824	0927	...	1024	1127	1224	1327	1409	1426	1527	1626	1709	1727	1826	1927	2024	...	2127	2224	2348	2325	...	...
347	Doberlug-Kirchhain d.	0754**e**	0905	...	1105	...	...	1305	...	1504	...	1554**e**	1705	1754**e**	...	1905	1954**e**	2105	...	...	2305	...	...	...	...	...
367	**Elsterwerda** a.	0804**e**	0919	...	1119	...	...	1319	...	1518	...	1604**e**	1719	1804**e**	...	1920	2004**e**	2119	...	...	2319	...	...	...	...	...

	RE 4350	RE 3504	IC 1049	RE 4352	RE 3506	RE 18490	RE 4354	ICE 1531	RE 3508	RE 4356	RE 3510	RE 4358	RE 3512	ICE 1724	RE 4360	RE 3514	RE 4362	RE 3516	IC 2356	ICE 92	RE 4364	RE 3518	IC 2326	RE 4366	RE 3520	RE 4368
	Ⓐ		⑥ ★🍷			Ⓒ		⑥d E✕						⑥b M✕					①–④ m	⑤f A✕			⑦w K🍷			
Elsterwerda d.	...	...	...	0440	0555**e**	...	0641	...	0755**e**	0840	...	1040	...	...	1240	...	1440	1555**e**	...	...	1640	1755**e**	...	1840	1955**e**	2040
Doberlug-Kirchhain d.	...	...	...	0456	0606**e**	...	0657	...	0806**e**	0856	...	1056	...	...	1256	...	1456	1606**e**	...	...	1656	1806**e**	...	1856	2006**e**	2056
Berlin Südkreuz d.	...	0533**e**	0526	0633	0733	...	0833	0853	0933	1033	1133	1233	1333	1350	1434	1533	1633	1733	1802	1753	1833	1933	...	2033	2133	2233
Berlin Hbf a.	...	0540**e**	0531	0640	0740	...	0840	0858	0940	1040	1140	1240	1340	1355	1441	1539	1640	1740	|	1758	1840	1940	...	2040	2140	2240
Berlin Hbf d.	0441	0543	0619	0642	0742	0811	0842	0913	0942	1042	1142	1242	1342	1413	1443	1541	1642	1742	1813	1813	1842	1942	2011	2042	2142	2242
Berlin Gesundbrunnen d.	0447	0549	0626	0647	0749	0818	0849	0921	0949	1049	1149	1249	1349	1421	1449	1549	1649	1749	1821	1821	1849	1949	2018	2049	2149	2249
Oranienburg d.	0511	0611	|	0711	0811	0841	0911	|	1011	1111	1211	1311	1411	|	1511	1611	1711	1811	|	|	1911	2011	|	2111	2211	2311
Gransee d.	0542	0635	|	0741	0835	|	0941	|	1035	1141	1235	1341	1435	|	1541	1635	1741	1835	|	|	1941	2035	|	2142	2235	2330
Fürstenberg (Havel) d.	0556	0648	|	0756	0848	0913	0956	|	1048	1156	1248	1356	1448	|	1556	1648	1756	1848	|	|	1956	2048	|	2157	2248	2345
Neustrelitz Hbf a.	0607	0659	0725	0807	0859	0926	1007	1019	1059	1207	1259	1407	1459	1519	1607	1659	1807	1859	1919	1919	2007	2059	2116	2207	2259	2355
Neustrelitz Hbf d.	0608	0701	0727	0808	0901	0928	1008	1021	1101	1208	1301	1408	1501	1521	1608	1701	1808	1901	1921	1921	2008	2101	2118	2208	2301	2356
Neubrandenburg **834** a.	|	0729	|	|	0929	|	|	|	1129	|	1329	|	1529	|	|	1729	|	1929	|	|	|	2129	|	|	2329	|
Stralsund Hbf **834** a.	|	0851	|	|	1051	|	|	|	1251	|	1451	|	1651	|	|	1851	|	2051	|	|	|	2251	|	|	...	|
Waren (Müritz) d.	0630	...	0747	0830	...	0951	1030	1043	...	1230	...	1430	...	1543	1630	...	1830	...	1943	1943	2030	...	2142	2230	...	0018
Güstrow d.	0701	...	|	|	...	|	|	|	...	|	...	|	...	|	|	...	|	...	|	|	|	...	|	2301	...	0050
Rostock Hbf **831** a.	0723	...	0828	0923	...	1037	1123	1123	...	1323	...	1523	...	1622	1723	...	1923	...	2023	2023	2123	...	2223	2323	...	0112
Warnemünde **831** a.	...	...	...	...	...	1057	...	1143	...	...	...	...	...	1651	...	...	...	...	...	...	...	...	...	...	...	...

A – From Wien via Nürnberg (Tables **850**/**920**).
E – From Eisenach (Table **850**).
F – To Frankfurt (Table **850**).
K – From Köln (Tables **800**/**810**).
M – To / from München (Table **850**).

b – Also Apr. 19, 21, May 30, June 20; not Apr. 20.
c – Ⓒ only.
d – Also Apr. 19.
e – Ⓐ only.
f – Also Apr. 18, May 29; not Apr. 19, May 31.
j – Arrives 9 minutes earlier.
m – Not Apr. 18, 22, May 29, June 10.
r – Also Apr. 19, 22, May 30, June 10; not Apr. 21, June 1, 9.
s – Calls to set down only.
v – ⑤⑥ (also Apr. 18, 21, 30, May 29, June 9).
w – Also Apr. 22, June 10; not Apr. 21, June 9.
z – ①–⑥ (also June 2, 9, 30; not Apr. 22).

‡ – Rostock to Waren is 78 km direct.
★ – ⑥ June 29 - Sept. 14. 🚌12 Köln (Tables **800**/**810**) - Berlin - Rostock - Stralsund - Ostseebad Binz (Table **844**) and v.v.

836 (LÜBECK -) BAD KLEINEN - PASEWALK - SZCZECIN

RE services

SERVICE UNTIL SEPTEMBER 6

km		Ⓐ	Ⓑ	Ⓐ																B	⑤				
	Lübeck Hbf **828** d.	...	...	...	...	...	0602t	...	0802	...	1002	...	1202	...	1402	...	1602	...	1802	...	...	...	2002	...	2206
0	**Bad Kleinen** **830** d.	...	...	...	...	*0603*	0705	*0803*	0904	*1003*	1102	*1203*	1304	*1403*	1504	*1603*	1705	*1803*	1904	*2003*	*2003*	*2003*	2104	*2203*	2304
41	Bützow **830** d.	...	...	...	0533	0633	0733	0833	0933	1033	1137	1233	1333	1433	1533	1633	1733	1833	1933	2033	2033	2033	2133	2233	2333
55	Güstrow a.	...	...	...	0542	0642	0742	0842	0942	1042	1146	1242	1342	1442	1542	1642	1742	1842	1942	2042	2042	2042	2142	2242	2342
55	Güstrow d.	...	...	...	0605	0705	0805	0905	1005	1105	1205	1305	1405	1505	1605	1705	1805	1905	2005	2105	2105	2105	2205	2305	...
84	Teterow d.	...	...	...	0633	0733	0833	0933	1033	1133	1233	1333	1433	1533	1633	1733	1833	1933	2033	2133	2133	2133	2233	2328	...
98	Malchin d.	...	...	0529	0644	0744	0844	0944	1044	1144	1244	1344	1444	1544	1644	1744	1844	1944	2044	2144	2144	2144	2243	2338	...
142	**Neubrandenburg** a.	...	...	0601	0725	0825	0925	1025	1125	1225	1325	1425	1525	1625	1725	1825	1925	2025	2125	2225	2225	2225	2315	0010	...
142	**Neubrandenburg** d.	0513	...	0606	0733	0833r	0933	1033	1133	1233	1333	1433	1533	1633	1733	1833	1933	2033	2133	...	2233	2233	...	...	...
195	**Pasewalk** a.	0559	...	0654	0814	0914r	1014	1114	1214	1314	1414	1514	1614	1714	1814	1914	2014	2114	2214	...	2314	2314	...	...	...
195	**Pasewalk** ▷ d.	0615	0615	0700	0815	...	1015	...	1215	...	1415	1525t	1615	...	1815	...	2015	...	...	...	...	2315	...	...	...
	Ueckermünde S ¶ ▷ a.	|	|	0731	|	...	|	...	|	...	|	1556t	|	...	|	...	|	...	...	...	...	|	...	...	...
222	Grambow d.	0637	0637	...	0837	...	1037	...	1237	...	1437	...	1637	...	1837	...	2037	...	...	...	...	2337	...	...	...
232	Szczecin Gumience 🏛 d.	0648	0648	...	0848	...	1048	...	1248	...	1448	...	1648	...	1848	...	2048	...	...	...	...	2348	...	...	...
237	**Szczecin** Głowny a.	0654	0654	...	0854	...	1054	...	1254	...	1454	...	1654	...	1854	...	2054	...	...	...	...	2354	...	...	...

	① g				Ⓐ		Ⓐ												A		⑦ w				
Szczecin Głowny d.	0226	...	...	...	0500	...	...	...	0700	...	0900	...	1100	...	1300	...	1500	...	1700	...	1730	...	1900	...	2100
Szczecin Gumience 🏛 d.	0232	...	...	...	0506	...	...	...	0706	...	0906	...	1106	...	1306	...	1506	...	1706	...	1736	...	1906	...	2106
Grambow d.	|	...	...	...	0517	...	...	...	0717	...	0917	...	1117	...	1317	...	1517	...	1717	...	1747	...	1917	...	2117
Ueckermünde S ¶ ▷ d.	|	...	...	...	|	...	0600	...	|	0738t	|	...	|	...	|	...	|	1601t	|	...	|	...	|	...	|
Pasewalk ⊙ ▷ a.	0300	...	...	...	0539	...	0632	...	0739	0810t	0939	...	1139	...	1339	...	1539	1632t	1739	...	1809	...	1939	...	2139
Pasewalk ⊙ d.	0301	...	...	...	0541	0541	0638	...	0743	0843r	0943	1043	1143	1243	1343	1443	1543	1643	1743	1743	1843	1843	1943	2043	2143
Neubrandenburg a.	0338	...	...	...	0623	0623	0723	...	0826	0926r	1026	1126	1226	1326	1426	1526	1626	1726	1826	1826	1926	1926	2026	2126	2226
Neubrandenburg d.	0340	...	0447	0544	0633	0633	0733	0733	0833	0933	1033	1133	1233	1333	1433	1533	1633	1733	1833	1833	1933	1933	2033	2133	...
Malchin d.	0410	...	0531j	0620	0710	0710	0813	0813	0913	1013	1113	1213	1313	1413	1513	1613	1713	1813	1913	1913	2013	2013	2113	2213	...
Teterow d.	0421	...	0541	0631	0731j	0731j	0830	0830	0930	1030	1130	1230	1330	1430	1530	1630	1730	1830	1930	1930	2030	2030	2130	2230	...
Güstrow a.	0439	...	0603	0653	0754	0754	0853	0853	0953	1053	1153	1253	1353	1453	1553	1653	1753	1853	1953	1953	2053	2053	2153	2253	...
Güstrow d.	0440	0501	0608	0708	0808	0808	0908	0908	1008	1108	1208	1308	1405	1508	1608	1708	1808	1908	2008	2008	2108	2108	2208	2308	...
Bützow **830** a.	0450	0511	0618	0718	0818	0818	0918	0918	1018	1118	1218	1318	1415	1518	1618	1718	1818	1918	2018	2018	2118	2118	2218	2318	...
Bad Kleinen **830** a.	0517	*0554*	0646	*0754*	0846	0846	*0954*	*0954*	1046	*1154*	1246	*1354*	1442	*1554*	1646	*1754*	1846	*1954*	2046	2046	*2154*	*2154*	2246	*2354*	...
Lübeck Hbf **828** a.	0624	...	0756	...	0956	0956	...	...	1156	...	1356	...	1556	...	1756	...	1956	...	2156	2156	...	...	...	...	...

A – ①–⑥ (also June 9; not June 10).
B – ⑤–⑦ (also June 10).

g – Also June 11; not June 10.
j – Arrives 11–13 minutes earlier.
m – Not ⑤.

r – ⚒ only.
t – Ⓐ only.
w – Also June 10; not June 9.

¶ – Ueckermünde Stadthafen.
‡ – Journey time 45 minutes.

▷ – Full service **PASEWALK - UECKERMÜNDE** (30 km, journey 31–35 minutes).
From Pasewalk at 0518 Ⓐ, 0610 ⚒, 0700 Ⓐ, 0822, 1022, 1222, 1422 **m**, 1428 ⑤, 1525 Ⓐ, 1608 ‡, 1822 and 2022.
From Ueckermünde Stadthafen at 0600 Ⓐ, 0700 ⚒, 0738 Ⓐ, 0900, 1100, 1300, 1500 **m**, 1522 ⑤, 1601 Ⓐ, 1700, 1900 and 2100.

837 WISMAR - BERLIN - COTTBUS

DB; Ostdeutsche Eisenbahn

km			⚒		Ⓐ		⚒														Ⓐ		2239 L		2431 Ⓑ E
0	**Wismar** d.	...	...	...	0417	...	0522	...	...	0624	0734	...	0824	0924	...	1024	1124	...	1224	1324	...	1424	...	...	...
16	Bad Kleinen **830** d.	...	...	...	0431	...	0536	...	...	0639	0748	...	0839	0938	...	1039	1142	...	1239	1339	...	1439	1450	...	...
32	**Schwerin** Hbf **830** a.	...	...	...	0443	...	0548	...	...	0651	0759	...	0851	0950	...	1051	1153	...	1251	1351	...	1451	1500	...	...
32	**Schwerin** Hbf d.	...	...	...	0500	0500	0600	...	...	0700	0801	...	0900	1000	...	1100	1200	...	1300	1400	...	1500	1502	...	...
72	Ludwigslust **840** d.	...	...	...	0534	0534	0634	...	...	0734	0835	...	0934	1034	...	1134	1234	...	1334	1435	...	1534	1524	...	...
116	Wittenberge **840** d.	0406	0506	...	0606j	0606j	0704	0704	0806	...	0904	1006	...	1104	1206	...	1304	1406	...	1504	...	...	1545	1606	...
207	Nauen d.	0501	0601	...	0701	0701	0801	0801	0901	...	1001	1101	...	1201	1301	...	1401	1501	...	1601	...	...	...	1701	...
229	**Berlin** Spandau **840** d.	0517	0617	...	0721	0721	0821	0821	0921	...	1021	1121	...	1221	1321	...	1421	1521	...	1621	...	...	...	1721	...
241	**Berlin** Zoo d.	0526	0626	0626	0730	0730	0830	0830	0930	...	1030	1130	...	1230	1330	...	1430	1530	...	1630	1700	...	...	1730	...
245	**Berlin** Hbf **840** d.	0532	0632	0632	0735	0735	0835	0835	0935	...	1035	1135	...	1235	1335	...	1435	1535	...	1635	1705	...	...	1735	1826
250	**Berlin** Ostbahnhof d.	|	|	|	|	|	|	|	|	...	|	|	...	|	|	...	|	|	...	|	1716	...	...	|	1840
252	**Berlin** Ostkreuz d.	0546	0646	0646	0751	0751	0851	0851	0951	...	1051	1151	...	1251	1351	...	1451	1551	...	1651	1721	...	...	1751	|
283	Königs Wusterhausen d.	0608	0708	0708	0811	0811	0911	0911	1011	...	1111	1211	...	1311	1411	...	1511	1611	...	1711	1743	...	...	1811	1903
329	Lübben (Spreewald) d.	0631	0731	0731	0834	0834	0934	0934	1034	...	1134	1234	...	1334	1434	...	1534	1634	...	1734	1809	...	...	1834	1925
340	Lübbenau (Spreew) d.	0638	0737	0737	0841	0841	0941	0941	1041	...	1141	1241	...	1341	1441	...	1541	1641	...	1741	1820	...	...	1841	1934
370	**Cottbus** a.	0700	0759	0759	0859	0859	0959	0959	1059	...	1159	1259	...	1359	1459	...	1559	1659	...	1759	1845	...	...	1859	1950

Wismar d.	1524	...	1624	1724	...	1824	1924	2024	2124	2244
Bad Kleinen **830** d.	1539	...	1639	1738	...	1839	1938	2039	2138	2306
Schwerin Hbf **830** a.	1551	...	1651	1750	...	1851	1950	2051	2150	2318
Schwerin Hbf d.	1600	...	1700	1800	...	1900	2000	2100	2200	...
Ludwigslust **840** d.	1634	...	1734	1834	...	1934	2034	2134	2234	...
Wittenberge **840** d.	1704	1806	...	1904	2006	...	2104	▬	2307j	...
Nauen d.	1801	1901	...	2001	2101	...	2201	...	0003	...
Berlin Spandau **840** d.	1821	1921	...	2021	2121	...	2221	...	0021	...
Berlin Zoo d.	1830	1930	...	2030	2130	...	2230	...	0031	...
Berlin Hbf **840** d.	1835	1935	...	2035	2135	...	2235	...	0036z	...
Berlin Ostbahnhof d.	|	|	...	|	|	...	2246	2345x	0058	...
Berlin Ostkreuz d.	1851	1951	...	2051	2151	...	2251	2349	0102	...
Königs Wusterhausen d.	1911	2011	...	2111	2211	...	2311	0012	0123	...
Lübben (Spreewald) d.	1934	2034	...	2134	2234	...	2346	0048	0158	...
Lübbenau (Spreew) d.	1941	2041	...	2141	2241	...	2353	0055	0205	...
Cottbus a.	1959	2059	...	2159	2300	...	0016	0117	0227	...

				⚒			D	⑦ w	2432 D G	
Cottbus d.	...	...	0356	0356	...	0456	0532	0556	0603	0701
Lübbenau (Spreew) d.	...	...	0419	0419	...	0520	0555	0619	0619	0719
Lübben (Spreewald) d.	...	...	0426	0426	...	0527	0602	0626	0627	0726
Königs Wusterhausen d.	...	...	0450	0450	...	0551	0628	0650	0649	0750
Berlin Ostkreuz d.	...	0402	0510	0510	...	0610	0648	0710	0709	0810
Berlin Ostbahnhof d.	...	0406	|	|	...	|	0653	|	0719	|
Berlin Hbf **840** d.	...	0421	0525	0525	...	0625	0704	0725	0726	0825
Berlin Zoo d.	...	0426	0531	0532	...	0631	0731v	0731	...	0831
Berlin Spandau **840** d.	...	0435	▬	0541	...	0640	0740	0740	...	0840
Nauen d.	...	0459	...	0600	...	0656	0756	0756	...	0856
Wittenberge **840** d.	...	0603	Ⓐ a	0701	...	0757	0901	0901	...	0957
Ludwigslust **840** d.	0506a	0628	0648	0726	0826	...	0926	0926	...	...
Schwerin Hbf a.	0538a	0658	0720	0757	0858	...	0957	0957	...	...
Schwerin Hbf **830** d.	0539	0659	0739	0805	0904	...	1005	1005	...	...
Bad Kleinen **830** d.	0601j	0711	0801j	0818	0917	...	1018	1018	...	...
Wismar a.	0616	0726	0816	0837	0937	...	1037	1037	...	...

	2238 L																				Ⓑ			③–⑦	①②
Cottbus d.	...	...	0801	...	0901	1001	...	1101	1201	...	1301	1401	...	1501	1601	1701	...	1801	1901	2001	2001	2101	2201	2301	2301
Lübbenau (Spreew) d.	...	...	0819	...	0919	1019	...	1119	1219	...	1319	1419	...	1519	1619	1719	...	1819	1919	2019	2019	2119	2224	2324	2324
Lübben (Spreewald) d.	...	...	0826	...	0926	1026	...	1126	1226	...	1326	1426	...	1526	1626	1726	...	1826	1926	2026	2026	2126	2230	2330	2330
Königs Wusterhausen d.	...	...	0850	...	0950	1050	...	1150	1250	...	1350	1450	...	1550	1650	1750	...	1850	1950	2050	2050	2150	2258	0007	0007
Berlin Ostkreuz d.	...	...	0910	...	1010	1110	...	1210	1310	...	1410	1510	...	1610	1710	1810	...	1910	2010	2110	2110	2210	2319	0029	0029
Berlin Ostbahnhof d.	...	...	|	...	|	|	...	|	|	...	|	|	...	|	|	|	...	|	|	|	|	|	2323x	0034	0034
Berlin Hbf **840** d.	...	...	0925	...	1025	1125	...	1225	1325	...	1425	1525	...	1625	1725	1825	...	1925	2025	2125	2125	2225	...	0046	0058
Berlin Zoo d.	...	...	0931	...	1031	1131	...	1231	1331	...	1431	1531	...	1631	1731	1831	...	1931	2031	2131	2131	2231	...	0052	0103
Berlin Spandau **840** d.	...	...	0940	...	1040	1140	...	1240	1340	...	1440	1540	...	1640	1740	1840	...	1940	2040	2140	2140	2240	...	0100	0111
Nauen d.	...	...	0956	...	1056	1156	...	1256	1356	...	1456	1556	...	1656	1756	1856	...	1956	2056	2156	2156	2256	...	...	...
Wittenberge **840** d.	1011	...	1101	...	1157	1301	...	1357	1501	...	1557	1701	...	1757	1901	1957	...	2101	2157	2301	2301	2357	...	...	...
Ludwigslust **840** d.	1032	1036	1126	1226	...	1326	1426	...	1526	1626	...	1726	1826	...	1926	...	2026	2126	...	2326	2326	...	...	...	...
Schwerin Hbf a.	1054	1108	1157	1258	...	1357	1458	...	1557	1658	...	1757	1858	...	1957	...	2058	2157	...	2357	2357	...	...	...	...
Schwerin Hbf **830** d.	1056	1109	1205	1304	...	1405	1504	...	1605	1704	...	1805	1904	...	2005	...	2104	2205	...	...	0005	...	...	...	...
Bad Kleinen **830** d.	1106	1122	1218	1317	...	1419	1517	...	1618	1717	...	1818	1917	...	2018	...	2117	2218	...	...	0032n	...	...	...	...
Wismar a.	...	1138	1237	1337	...	1437	1537	...	1637	1737	...	1837	1937	...	2037	...	2137	2232	...	...	0046	...	...	...	...

D – ①–⑥ (not June 10).
E – Ⓑ (not June 9). *IC* **2431**. 🅧12 Emden - Bremen - Hannover - Magdeburg - Berlin - Cottbus.
G – *IC* **2432**. 🅧12 Cottbus - Berlin - Magdeburg - Hannover - Bremen - Norddeich.
L – ⑤–⑦ to June 23 (also June 10); daily June 28 - Sept. 17; ⑤–⑦ Sept. 20 - Nov. 3 (also Oct. 2, 3, 29, 30, 31); ⑤ from Nov. 8. *IC* **2238/9**. WARNOW – 🅧12 Leipzig - Magdeburg - Stendal - Rostock (- Warnemünde until Nov. 3) and v.v.

a – Ⓐ (not Oct. 31).
j – Arrives 8–10 minutes earlier.
n – Arrives 0017.
v – Arrives 0709.
w – Also June 10.
x – Berlin **Lichtenberg**.
z – 0040 on the mornings of ①④⑤⑥⑦.

MAGDEBURG - BERLIN - FRANKFURT (ODER) - COTTBUS — 839

RE services; valid from June 11

km		©										P				B	w♣						
0	**Magdeburg** Hbf ..... d.	0042	...	...	0427a	...	0527	0604	...	and at the same minutes past each hour until	1604	...	1701	1706	...	1804	...	1855	1904	...	2004	2104	2204	2323
79	**Brandenburg** Hbf ..... d.	0139	0425	0500	0526	0600	0626	0700	0725		1700	1725	1740	1802	1825	1900	1925	|	2000	2025	2100	2159	2259	0019
114	Potsdam Hbf ..... d.	0206	0455	0525	0555	0625	0655	0725	0755		1725	1755	1800	1825	1855	1925	1955	2009	2025	2055	2125	2225	2325	0048
123	Berlin Wannsee ..... d.	0213	0502	0532	0602	0632	0702	0732	0802		1732	1802	1809	1832	1902	1932	2002	2020	2032	2102	2132	2232	2332	0055
138	**Berlin** Zoo ..... d.	0226	0515	0545	0615	0645	0715	0745	0815		1745	1815	|	1845	1915	1945	2015	2032z	2045	2115	2145	2245	2345	0109
142	**Berlin** Hbf ..... **1001** d.	0232	0521	0551	0621	0651	0721	0751	0821		1751	1821	1826	1851	1921	1951	2021	2038z	2051	2121	2151	2251	2351	...
147	**Berlin** Ostbahnhof ..... d.	0245	0534	0604	0634	0704	0734	0804	0834		1804	1834	1835	1904	1934	2004	2034	2051z	2104	2134	2204	2307	0004	...
149	**Berlin** Ostkreuz ..... d.	0250	0539	0609	0639	0709	0739	0809	0839		1809	1839	...	1909	1939	2009	2039	...	2109	2137	2209	2312	0009	...
194	Fürstenwalde (Spree) ..... d.	0321	0610	0637	0710	0737	0810	0837	0910		1837	1910	...	1937	2010	2037	2110	...	2140	...	2240	2343	0040	...
228	**Frankfurt (Oder)** ..... **1001** a.	0348	0628	0704	0728	0804	0828	0904	0928		1904	1928	...	2004	2028	2104	2128	...	2207	...	2307	0010	0107	...

	©	©						D		©♣	N		D									⊡B	⊖B	
rankfurt (Oder) ..... **1001** d.	0028	0028	...	...	0355	...	0455	0535	0559	...	...	0635	0659	0735	0759	and at the same minutes past each hour until	1835	1859	1935	2035	2128	2230	2230	2325
ürstenwalde (Spree) ..... d.	0054	0054	...	...	0421	...	0521	0552	0626	...	...	0652	0726	0752	0826		1852	1926	1952	2052	2154	2257	2257	2352
erlin Ostkreuz ..... d.	0126	0126	...	...	0454	0524	0554	0624	0654	...	0709	0724	0754	0824	0854		1924	1954	2024	2124	2226	2329	2329	0024
erlin Ostbahnhof ..... d.	0131	0131	...	...	0459	0529	0559	0629	0659	0709	0719	0729	0759	0829	0859		1929	1959	2029	2129	2231	2333	2346r	0029
erlin Hbf ..... **1001** d.	0143	0143	0244	...	0511	0541	0611	0641	0711	0720	0730	0741	0811	0841	0911		1941	2011	2041	2141	2243	2345	2358	0043
erlin Zoo ..... d.	0148	0149	0250	...	0517	0547	0617	0647	0717	0727	|	0747	0817	0847	0917		1947	2017	2047	2147	2249	2351	0004	0049
erlin Wannsee ..... d.	...	0202	0303	...	0530	0600	0630	0700	0730	0739	0746	0800	0830	0900	0930		2000	2030	2100	2200	2302	0004	0017	0101
otsdam Hbf ..... d.	...	0210	0311	...	0538	0608	0638	0708	0738	0749	0755	0808	0838	0908	0938		2008	2038	2108	2208	2310	0012	0025	0109
randenburg Hbf ..... d.	...	0239	0340	0420	0559	0637	0659	0740	0757	|	0814	0840	0857	0940	0957		2040	2057	2138	2237	2340	0041	0053	0137
agdeburg Hbf ..... a.	...	...	...	0518	0654	...	0754	0839	...	0900	0856	0939	...	1039	...		2139	...	2235	...	0031	...	...	...

FRANKFURT (ODER) - COTTBUS

km		Ⓐ		Ⓐ				B		
0	**Frankfurt (Oder)** ..... d.	0411	0537	0604	0636	0737	and hourly until	2037	2130	2315
23	Eisenhüttenstadt ..... d.	0431	0558	0619	0657	0758		2058	2150	2336
48	Guben ..... d.	0452	0618	0636	0718	0818		2118	2210	2356
86	**Cottbus** ..... a.	0530	0656	0700	0756	0856		2156	2247	0033

	⚒D		ⒶD						B	
Cottbus ..... d.	0414	0506	0550	0606	0706	and hourly until	1906	2006	2109	2306
Guben ..... d.	0450	0544	0615	0644	0744		1944	2043	2146	2343
Eisenhüttenstadt ..... d.	0510	0605	0635	0704	0804		2004	2104	2205	0004
Frankfurt (Oder) ..... a.	0532	0626	0656	0726	0826		2026	2124	2227	0024

– [12] Brandenburg - Berlin - Frankfurt (Oder) - Cottbus and v.v.
– [12] Cottbus - Frankfurt (Oder) - Berlin - Magdeburg.
– *IC* **2432**. [12] (Cottbus ①–⑥ -) Berlin - Hannover - Bremen - Emden - Norddeich Mole.
– *IC* **2431**. [12] Emden - Bremen - Hannover - Berlin (- Cottbus Ⓑ).

a – Ⓐ only.
r – Arrives 2331.
w – ⑤–⑦ (also Oct. 2, 3, 31).
z – Not Sept. 10 - Oct. 14 (diverted to Berlin Gesundbrunnen, a. 2041).

⊖ – ①② only.
⊡ – ③–⑦ only.
♣ – *HARZ-BERLIN-EXPRESS*. [2] Berlin - Halberstadt - Thale (Table **862**) / Goslar (Table **860**) and v.v. Operated by Abellio Rail Mitteldeutschland. Not available for local journeys Berlin - Potsdam and v.v. **DB tickets not valid**.

HAMBURG - BERLIN - DRESDEN — 840

Service from June 11

km		*EC* 171	*ICE* 701	*ICE* 505	*EC* 173	*ICE* 903	*ICE* 703	*ICE* 507	*EC* 379	*ICE* 599	*ICE* 705	*EC* 175	*ICE* 707	*ICE* 1601	*EC* 177	*ICE* 709	*ICE* 803	*ICE* 603	*EC* 179	*ICE* 801	*ICE* 1605	*ICE* 1605	*ICE* 1705	*IC* 2071	*IC* 2079
			①–⑤	①–⑥		①–⑤	⑥⑦										⑤f				⑥	Ⓑ	Ⓑd		
		P✕	M✕	M✕	H✕	✕	M✕	M✕	L✕	F✕	✕	P✕	M✕	M✕	P✕	M✕	✕	M✕	P✕	B✕	✕	M✕	J✕	✕	✕
0	**Hamburg** Altona ..... d.	...	0512	0618	0636	0721	0721	0819	...	0921	1019	...	1121	1218	1238	1321	1333	1419	1437	1518	1618	1618	1618	1638	...
7	**Hamburg** Hbf ..... **830** d.	...	0527	0635	0648	0738	0738	0835	0851	0936	1035	...	1136	1235	1251	1338	1349	1435	1451	1537	1635	1635	1635	1651	...
54	Büchen ..... **830** d.	...	|	|	0714	|	|	|	0914	|	|	...	|	|	1314	|	|	|	1514	|	|	|	|	1714	...
122	Ludwigslust ..... **837** d.	...	0613	|	0741	|	|	|	0941	|	|	...	|	|	1341	|	|	|	1541	|	|	|	|	1741	...
167	Wittenberge ..... **837** d.	...	0631	|	0802	|	|	|	1002	|	|	...	|	|	1402	|	|	|	1602	|	|	|	|	1802	...
280	**Berlin** Spandau ..... **837** d.	...	0712	0810	0846	0912	0912	1010	1046	1112	1210	...	1312	1410	1446	1512	1527s	1610	1646	1712	1810	1810	1810	1846	...
293	**Berlin** Hbf ..... **837** a.	...	0722	0820	0855	0922	0922	1020	1055	1122	1220	...	1322	1420	1455	1522	1540	1620	1655	1722	1820	1820	1820	1855	...
293	**Berlin** Hbf ..... **835** d.	0659	0737	0830	0859	|	0937	1030	1059	1128	|	1259	1337	1430	1459	1537	|	1630	1659	1737	|	1830	1830	|	1859
299	**Berlin** Südkreuz ..... **835** d.	0705	0742	0837	0905	0930	0942	1037	1105	1135	1229	1305	1342	1437	1505	1542	1549t	1637	1705	1742	1831	1837	1837	1903t	1905
	Leipzig Hbf **850** ..... a.	|	...	0942	|	...	...	1142	|	1242	...	|	...	1542	|	...	...	1742	|	...	...	1942	1942	...	|
433	Elsterwerda ..... **843 835** d.	|	...	...	|	...	...	...	|	...	...	|	...	...	|	...	...	...	1826	...	...	...	...	...	2026
486	**Dresden** Neustadt ..... a.	0900	...	...	1100	...	...	...	1300	...	...	1500	...	...	1700	...	...	...	1900	...	...	...	...	...	2100
490	**Dresden** Hbf ..... **843** a.	0907	...	...	1107	...	...	...	1307	...	...	1507	...	...	1707	...	...	...	1907	...	...	...	...	...	2107

	ICE 697	*ICE* 1607	*IC* 2073	*IC* 2073	*IC* 1912	*ICE* 993	*ICE* 907	*ICE* 905	*ICE* 909	*ICE* 809	
		Ⓑ		⊡	②y		Ⓑ		⑤f	⑦	
	✕	D✕	U🍷	U🍷	🍷	G✕	✕	✕	✕		
amburg Altona ..... d.	1720	1819	...	...	...	1921	2017	2136	2237	2237	...
amburg Hbf ..... **830** d.	1735	1835	1851	1851	...	1936	2034	2151	2251	2251	...
ichen ..... **830** d.	|	|	1914	1914	...	|	|	2215	2315	2315	...
idwigslust ..... **837** d.	1819	|	1941	1941	...	|	2119	2242	2342	2342	...
ittenberge ..... **837** d.	|	|	2002	2002	...	|	|	2303	0002	0002	...
erlin Spandau ..... **837** d.	1910s	2010	2046	2046	2040	2112	2211s	2343s	0042s	0042s	...
erlin Hbf ..... **837** a.	1922	2020	2055	2055	2051	2122	2223	2355	0053	0053	...
erlin Hbf ..... **835** d.	|	2030	...	2058	2059	2128	|	|	|	|	...
erlin Südkreuz ..... **835** d.	1930	2037	...	2105	2105	2135	2231	0003	0101	0101	...
Leipzig Hbf **850** ..... a.	...	2142	...	|	|	2247k	...	...	...	...	...
sterwerda ..... **843 835** d.	...	...	...	|	|	...	...	...	...	...	...
esden Neustadt ..... a.	...	...	...	2300	2259	...	...	...	...	...	...
esden Hbf ..... **843** a.	...	...	...	2307	2306	...	...	...	...	...	...

	IC 1978	*ICE* 908	*ICE* 808	*IC* 2070	*ICE* 1606	*IC* 2078	*ICE* 806	*IC* 2076	*IC* 2072
	①g	Ⓐ	①–⑥		①–⑥	①–⑥		③⑦	⊖
	🍷	✕	✕	✕	✕	✕	E✕	z🍷	U🍷
Dresden Hbf ..... **843** d.	...	...	...	...	...	0544	...	0644	0644
Dresden Neustadt ..... d.	...	...	...	...	...	0551	...	0651	0651
Elsterwerda ..... **843 835** d.	...	...	...	...	...	0626	...	0726	0726
Leipzig Hbf **850** ..... d.	...	...	...	...	0616	|	0716	|	|
Berlin Südkreuz ..... **835** d.	0458	0519	0629	0658	0724	0735s	0827	0834s	0836
Berlin Hbf ..... **835** a.	|	|	|	|	0729	0741	0832	0841	0844
Berlin Hbf ..... **837** d.	0506	0528	0638	0706	0740	...	0838	...	0906
Berlin Spandau ..... **837** d.	0517	0538	0648	0717	0750	...	0848	...	0917
Wittenberge ..... **837** d.	0601	0621	|	0802	|	...	|	...	1002
Ludwigslust ..... **837** d.	0620	0641	0742	0820	|	...	|	...	1020
Büchen ..... **830** d.	0648	|	|	0848	|	...	|	...	1048
Hamburg Hbf ..... **830** a.	0712	0725	0824	0911	0924	...	1021	...	1112
Hamburg Altona ..... a.	0724	0742	0839	0923	0939	...	1038	...	...

	IC 2072	*ICE* 1604	*ICE* 1704	*ICE* 1604	*ICE* 696	*EC* 178	*IC* 2322	*ICE* 602	*ICE* 802	*EC* 176	*ICE* 1600	*ICE* 800	*EC* 174	*ICE* 508	*ICE* 690	*EC* 378	*ICE* 506	*ICE* 706	*EC* 172	*ICE* 504	*ICE* 704	*EC* 170	*ICE* 502	*ICE* 702	*ICE* 898
		Ⓑ	①–⑤	⑥			⑥														Ⓑv		♠	⑤⑦r	♣
	U 🍷	N✕	hJ ✕	✕	A✕	P✕	O	M✕	M✕	P✕	M✕	M✕	P✕	M✕	F✕	L✕	M✕	M✕	H✕	M✕	M✕	P✕	M✕	M✕	✕
esden Hbf ..... **843** d.		...		...	...	0846	0922	...	...	1046	...	...	1246	...	...	1446	...	...	1646	...	...	1846	...	...	...
esden Neustadt ..... d.	...	...	...	...	...	0852	|	...	...	1052	...	...	1252	...	...	1452	...	...	1652	...	...	1852	...	...	...
sterwerda ..... **843 835** d.	...	...	...	...	...	|	0959	...	...	|	...	...	|	...	...	|	...	...	|	...	...	|	...	...	...
Leipzig Hbf **850** ..... d.	...	0818	0818	...	0916	|	|	1016	...	|	1216	...	|	1416	1516	|	1616	...	|	1816	...	|	2016	...	...
erlin Südkreuz ..... **835** d.	0836	0925	0925	0931t	1024	1034s	1120	1124	1219	1236	1324	1419	1438	1524	1624	1636	1724	1820	1836	1924	2019	2034s	2124	2219	2228
erlin Hbf ..... **835** a.	0844	0930	0930	|	1029	1041	1125	1129	1224	1241	1329	1424	1443	1529	1629	1641	1729	1826	1841	1929	2026	2041	2129	2224	|
erlin Hbf ..... **837** d.	0906	0940	0940	0940	1038	...	...	1140	1238	1306	1340	1438	1506	1540	1638	1706	1740	1838	1906	1940	2038	...	2138	2238	2238
erlin Spandau ..... **837** d.	0917	0950	0950	0950	1048	...	...	1150	1248	1317	1350	1448	1517	1550	1648	1717	1750	1848	1917	1950	2048	...	2148	2248	2248
ttenberge ..... **837** d.	1002	|	|	|	|	...	...	|	|	1402	|	|	1602	|	|	1802	|	|	2002	|	|	...	2229	2330	2330
dwigslust ..... **837** d.	1020	|	|	|	|	...	...	|	|	1420	|	|	1621	|	|	1820	|	|	2020	|	|	...	2249	2348	2348
ichen ..... **830** d.	1048	|	|	|	|	...	...	|	|	1448	|	|	1648	|	|	1848	|	|	2048	|	|	...	|	|	|
amburg Hbf ..... **830** a.	1112	1124	1124	1124	1221	...	...	1324	1421	1511	1525	1621	1711	1724	1822	1911	1924	2023	2115	2124	2221	...	2333	0033	0033
amburg Altona ..... a.	...	1139x	1139x	1139	1238	...	...	1339	1438	1527	1539	1638	1724	1741	1838	...	1938	2038	2136	2140	2238	...	2350b	...	0048

– [12] and ✕ (Karlsruhe ①g -) (Frankfurt ①–⑥ -) Erfurt - Berlin - Kiel.
– [12] and ✕ Kiel - Hamburg - Berlin - Erfurt (- München ♥).
– To Erfurt (Table **850**).
– From Eisenach on ①–⑤ (Table **850**).
– [12] and ✕ Hamburg - Berlin - Leipzig - Erfurt - Frankfurt - München and v.v.
– [12] and ✕ Hamburg - Berlin (- Leipzig on dates in note **b**). Continues to München via Erfurt and Frankfurt daily to Sept. 1, ⑤⑦ from Sept. 6 (see Tables **850** and **930**).
– HUNGARIA – [12] and ✕ Budapest - Bratislava - Praha - Dresden - Hamburg and v.v.
– From / to Jena (Table **849a**).
– [12] and ✕ Praha - Dresden - Hamburg - Kiel and v.v.
– [12] and ✕ Hamburg - Berlin - Erfurt - Nürnberg - München and v.v.
– [12] and ✕ (Nürnberg Ⓐ **h** -) (Leipzig Ⓑ -) Berlin - Hamburg.
– To Ostseebad Binz (Tables **844** and **845**).

P – To / from Praha (Tables **60**/**1100**).
U – UTHLANDE – To / from Westerland (Table **821**).

b – Not ⑥.
d – Not June 9, Oct. 30.
f – Also Oct. 2; not Oct. 4.
g – Also June 11.
h – Not Oct. 31.
k – Daily to Sept. 6; Ⓑ from Sept. 8.
r – Also Oct. 2; not Oct. 4.
s – Arrival time. Calls to set down only.
t – From Sept. 7.

v – Not Oct. 3.
x – Not June 14, 21, 28, July 5, 12, 19, 26.
y – Also June 12; not June 11.
z – Also June 13; not June 12.

⊡ – ①③④⑤⑦ (also June 11; not June 12).
⊖ – ①②④⑤⑥ (also June 12; not June 13).
♥ – Daily to Sept. 6 (not June 15, July 6); Ⓑ from Sept. 8 (also Oct. 5).
♠ – ⑤–⑦ to Aug. 25; daily from Aug. 30.
♣ – ①②③④⑥ (also Oct. 4; not Oct. 2).

841 MAGDEBURG - STENDAL - UELZEN and WITTENBERGE

RE / S-Bahn services (except train R)

km		Ⓐe	⚒t	Ⓐe	Ⓐe				Ⓐe	†z			R													
0	**Magdeburg** Hbf .... d.	...	0351	...	0445	0508	0552	0608	0638	0703	0708	0808	0858	0903	0908	1008	1103	1108	1208	1303	1308	1408	1503	1508	1603	1608
58	Stendal .... a.	...	0437	...	0527	0556	0633	0656	0727	0743	0756	0856	0932	0943	0956	1056	1143	1156	1256	1343	1356	1456	1543	1556	1643	1656
58	Stendal .... d.	0410	0441	0500	0528	0600	0634	0700**e**	0730	0744	0800	0900**r**	0933	0944	1000	1100**e**	1144	1200	1300**e**	1344	1400	1500**e**	1544	1600	1644	1700
113	**Wittenberge** .... a.	0452	|	0542	0610	0642**j**	|	0742**e**	|	|	0842	0942**r**	1009	|	1042	1142**e**	|	1242	1342**e**	|	1442	1542**e**	|	1642	|	1742
116	Salzwedel .... d.	...	0519	...	...	...	0714	...	0806	0814	...	...	...	1014	...	...	1214	...	...	1414	...	...	1614	...	1714	...
167	**Uelzen** .... a.	...	0550	...	...	...	0746	...	...	0846	...	...	...	1046	...	...	1246	...	...	1446	...	...	1646	...	1747	...

							B				
Magdeburg Hbf .... d.	1703	1708	1808	1903	1908	2008	2104	2108	2140	2212	2314
Stendal .... a.	1743	1756	1856	1943	1956	2056	2144	2156	2219	2300	2400
Stendal .... d.	1744	1803	1900**e**	1944	2000	2100**b**	2145	2200	2232**b**	...	...
Wittenberge .... a.	|	1845	1942**e**	|	2042	2142**b**	|	2242	|	...	...
Salzwedel .... d.	1814	...	...	2014	...	...	2216	...	2310**b**	...	...
Uelzen .... a.	1847	...	...	2046	...	...	2246	...	...	...	...

					Ⓐe	⚒t		⚒t		†z	
Uelzen .... d.	...	...	...	...	...	0619	...	0700	...	0802	...
Salzwedel .... d.	...	...	0556	...	...	0652	...	0737	...	0839	...
Wittenberge .... d.	...	0501**e**	|	0611**e**	0637	|	0711	|	0807**e**	|	091
Stendal .... a.	...	0541**e**	0634	0652**e**	0712	0721	0751	0816	0846**e**	0906	095
Stendal .... d.	0456	0556	0640	0657	0717	0725**e**	0756	...	0856	0910	095
Magdeburg Hbf .... a.	0543	0643	0724	0743	0757	0813**e**	0843	...	0943	0950	104

		⚒										R								Ⓐe				Ⓑb		B
Uelzen .... d.	0902	...	...	...	1102	...	...	1302	...	...	1502	...	...	...	1702	...	1802	...	1902	...	...	...	2102	...	...	2302
Salzwedel .... d.	0935	...	1004	...	1135	...	...	1335	...	...	1535	...	...	...	1735	...	1836	...	1935	...	2004	...	2135	...	...	2336
Wittenberge .... d.	|	1011	|	1111	|	1211**e**	1311	|	1411**e**	1511	|	1547	1611**e**	1711	|	1811**e**	|	1911	|	2011	|	2111	|	2211	2307	|
Stendal .... a.	1007	1051	1043	1151	1207	1251**e**	1351	1407	1451**e**	1551	1607	1622	1651**e**	1751	1807	1851**e**	1913	1951	2007	2051	2043	2151	2212	2251	2346	0004
Stendal .... d.	1010	...	1056	1156	1210	1256	1356	1410	1456	1556	1610	1624	1656	1756	1810	1856	...	1956	2010	...	2056	2156	2221	...	2347	000
Magdeburg Hbf .... a.	1050	...	1143	1243	1250	1343	1443	1450	1543	1643	1651	1658	1743	1843	1850	1943	...	2043	2051	...	2144	2243	2303	...	0032	004

Regional service **BERLIN - SALZWEDEL - HAMBURG** (2nd class only)

	IRE **4276** ④–⑥	*IRE* **4278** ⑦v	*IRE* **4272**	
Berlin Ostbahnhof ...... d.	0752	1311	1651	...
Berlin Hbf .... △ d.	0802	1320	1702	...
Berlin Zoo .... △ d.	0809	1327	1709	...
Berlin Spandau ...... △ d.	0819	1337	1719	...
Stendal .... d.	0906	1416	1807**f**	...
Salzwedel .... d.	0934	1454	1838	...
Uelzen .... ▽ a.	1003	1529	1903	...
Lüneburg .... ▽ a.	1029	1548	1930	...
Hamburg Hbf .... a.	1104	1622**n**	2004	...

	IRE **4273** ⚒t	*IRE* **4275** †z	*IRE* **4277** ④⑤	*IRE* **4279** ⑥⑦v
Hamburg Hbf .... d.	0655**k**	1241	1642	1931
Lüneburg .... △ d.	0735	1313	1715	2005
Uelzen .... △ d.	0756	1331	1733	2025
Salzwedel .... d.	0822	1356	1808	2057
Stendal .... d.	0851	1437*	1844	2126
Berlin Spandau .. ▽ a.	0925	1521*	1924	2202
Berlin Zoo .... ▽ a.	0935	1532*	1935	2213
Berlin Hbf .... ▽ a.	0941	1540*	1941	2219
Berlin Ostbahnhof .. a.	0950	1550*	1951	2228

△ – Trains call to pick up only.
▽ – Trains call to set down only.

* – 5 – 11 minutes **earlier** on Oct. 31.

B – ⑤–⑦ (also June 10, Oct. 3, 31).
R – ⑤–⑦ to June 23 (also June 10); daily June 28 - Sept. 17; ⑤–⑦ Sept. 20 - Nov. 3 (also Oct. 2, 3, 29, 30, 31); ⑤ from Nov. 8. *IC* **2238/9**. 12 Leipzig - Schwerin - Rostock (- Warnemünde until Nov. 3) and v.v.

b – Ⓑ (not June 9).
e – Ⓐ (not Oct. 31).
f – Arrives 1755.
j – 0651 on Ⓐ to Oct. 29.
k – 0658 June 11 - July 27.
n – 1630 June 16 - July 21.
r – ⚒ only.
t – ⚒ (not Oct. 31).
v – Also June 10.
z – Also Oct. 31.

842 LEIPZIG - DRESDEN

Warning! Frankfurt timings are subject to alteration Aug. 10 - Oct. 27 (departures are 14 – 18 minutes **earlier**, arrivals 20 minutes later; see special version of Table **850** on pages 566 and 567).

km		*RE* **16501** ⚒r		*RE* **16503**	*EC* **259** ①–⑥ T	*RE* **16505** ⚒r		*RE* **16507** V	*RE* **16547** Ⓐ X	*RE* **16507** Ⓒ Z	*IC* **2449** Ⓐr M🍷	*RE* **16509**	*ICE* **1553** ①–⑥ eE	*RE* **16511**	*IC* **2447** D🍷	*RE* **16513**	*ICE* **1555** 🍴	*RE* **16515**	*IC* **2445** ①–⑥ eK 🍷	*IC* **1945** ⑦w L🍷	*RE* **16517**	*ICE* **1557** ¶🍴	*RE* **16519**	*IC* **244** K🍷
	Frankfurt (Main) Hbf **850** .... d.	...	...	...	...	...	...	...	...	...	...	...	...	...	...	...	0716	...		...	...	0920	...	...
0	**Leipzig** Hbf .... d.	0400	...	0500	0554	0600	...	0700	0700	0700	0730	0800	0831	0900	0930	1000	1031	1100	1130	1138	1200	1231	1300	133
26	Wurzen .... d.	0418	...	0518	|	0618	...	0718	0718	0718	|	0818	|	0918	|	1018	|	1118	|	|	1218	|	1318	|
53	Oschatz .... d.	0436	...	0536	|	0636	...	0736	0736	0736	|	0836	|	0936	|	1036	|	1136	|	|	1236	|	1336	|
66	Riesa .... d.	0445	...	0545	0632	0645	...	0745	0745	0745	0803	0845	0903	0945	1003	1045	1103	1145	1203	1210	1245	1303	1345	140
102	Coswig .... **843 856 857** d.	0513	...	0613	|	0713	...	0813	0813	0813	|	0913	|	1013	|	1113	|	1213	|	|	1313	|	1413	|
110	Radebeul Ost .... **857** d.	0519	...	0619	|	0719	...	0819	|	0819	|	0919	|	1019	|	1119	|	1219	|	|	1319	|	1419	|
116	**Dresden** Neustadt ...... **856/7** a.	0526	...	0626	0700	0726	...	0824	0824	0826	0833	0926	0933	1026	1033	1126	1133	1226	1233	1244	1326	1333	1426	143
120	**Dresden** Hbf ... **843 856 857** a.	0532	...	0632	0707	0732	...	0832	0832	0832	0839	0932	0939	1032	1039	1132	1139	1232	1239	1250	1332	1339	1432	143

	RE **16521** V	*RE* **16541** Ⓐ X	*RE* **16521** Ⓒ Z		*ICE* **1559** ¶🍴	*RE* **16523**	*IC* **2441** K🍷	*RE* **16525**	*ICE* **1651** ¶ 🍴	*RE* **16527**	*IC* **2049** K🍷	*RE* **16529**	*ICE* **1653** ¶ 🍴	*RE* **16531**	*IC* **2047** Ⓑb K🍷	*RE* **16533**	*ICE* **1655** ¶ 🍷	*RE* **16535**	*IC* **2045** Ⓑb K🍷	*RE* **16537**		*ICE* **1657** Ⓑb ¶	*IC* **2435** ⑥ B	*RE* **1653**
Frankfurt (Main) Hbf **850** ...... d.	...	...	...	...	1119	...	...	...	1319	...	...	...	1520	...	...	...	1716**h**	...	...	...	...	1919	...	...
Leipzig Hbf .... d.	1400	1400	1400	...	1431	1500	1530	1600	1631	1700	1730	1800	1831	1900	1930	2000	2031	2100	2130	2200	...	2231	2252	230
Wurzen .... d.	1418	1418	1418	...	|	1518	|	1618	|	1718	|	1818	|	1918	|	2018	|	2118	|	2218	...	|	|	231
Oschatz .... d.	1436	1436	1436	...	|	1536	|	1636	|	1736	|	1836	|	1936	|	2036	|	2136	|	2236	...	|	|	233
Riesa .... d.	1445	1445	1445	...	1503	1545	1603	1645	1703	1745	1803	1845	1903	1945	2002	2045	2103	2145	2202	2245	...	2303	2324	234
Coswig .... **843 856 857** d.	1513	1513	1513	...	|	1613	|	1713	|	1813	|	1913	|	2013	|	2113	|	2213	|	2313	...	|	|	001
Radebeul Ost .... **857** d.	1519	|	1519	...	|	1619	|	1719	|	1819	|	1919	|	2019	|	2119	|	2219	|	2319	...	|	|	001
Dresden Neustadt ...... **856/7** a.	1524	1524	1526	...	1533	1626	1633	1726	1733	1826	1833	1926	1933	2026	2033	2126	2131	2226	2233	2326	...	2331	2352	002
Dresden Hbf .... **843 856 857** a.	1532	1532	1532	...	1539	1632	1639	1732	1739	1832	1839	1932	1939	2032	2039	2132	2138	2232	2239	2332	...	2338	2358	003

	RE **16500** ⚒r		*IC* **2044** Ⓐr K🍷	*RE* **16502**	*ICE* **1654** ①–⑥ e¶🍴	*RE* **16504** ⚒r	*IC* **2046** ①–⑥ eK🍷	*RE* **16506**	*ICE* **1652** ¶🍴	*RE* **16508**	*IC* **2048** K🍷	*RE* **16510**	*ICE* **1650** ¶🍷	*RE* **16512**	*IC* **2440** K🍷	*RE* **16514**	*ICE* **1558** ¶🍴	*RE* **16516**	*IC* **2442** K🍷	*RE* **16518**	*ICE* **1556** ¶🍴	*RE* **16520**	*IC* **1934** ⑦w G🍷	*IC* **244** K🍷
Dresden Hbf .... **843 856 857** d.	0414	...	0510	0514	0610	0614	0710	0714	0810	0814	0910	0914	1010	1014	1110	1114	1210	1214	1310	1314	1410	1414	1452	151
Dresden Neustadt ...... **856/7** d.	0424	...	0516	0524	0616	0624	0716	0724	0816	0824	0916	0924	1016	1024	1116	1124	1216	1224	1316	1324	1416	1424	|	151
Radebeul Ost .... **857** d.	0431	...	|	0531	|	0631	|	0731	|	0831	|	0931	|	1031	|	1131	|	1231	|	1331	|	1431	|	|
Coswig .... **843 856 857** d.	0437	...	|	0537	|	0637	|	0737	|	0837	|	0937	|	1037	|	1137	|	1237	|	1337	|	1437	|	|
Riesa .... d.	0505	...	0548	0605	0648	0705	0748	0805	0848	0905	0948	1005	1048	1105	1148	1205	1248	1305	1348	1405	1448	1505	|	154
Oschatz .... d.	0514	...	|	0614	|	0714	|	0814	|	0914	|	1014	|	1114	|	1214	|	1314	|	1414	|	1514	|	|
Wurzen .... d.	0531	...	|	0631	|	0731	|	0831	|	0931	|	1031	|	1131	|	1231	|	1331	|	1431	|	1531	|	|
Leipzig Hbf .... a.	0550	...	0619	0650	0718	0750	0819	0850	0920	0950	1019	1050	1120	1150	1219	1250	1320	1350	1419	1450	1524	1550	1554	161
Frankfurt (Main) Hbf **850** ...... a.	...	...	...	...	1036	...	...	...	1236	...	...	...	1436	...	...	...	1636	...	...	...	1836	...	...	...

	RE **16522**	*ICE* **1554** ‡🍴	*RE* **16524**	*IC* **2446** K🍷	*RE* **16526**	*ICE* **1552** 🍴	*RE* **16528**	*IC* **2448** Ⓑb H	*RE* **16530**		*RE* **16532**	*EC* **258** Ⓑ T🍴	*RE* **16534**		*RE* **16536**		*RE* **16538**							
Dresden Hbf .... **843 856 857** d.	1514	1610	1614	1710	1714	1810	1814	1910	1914	...	2014	2046	2114	...	2214	...	2314	...	...	...	...	...	...	...
Dresden Neustadt ...... **856/7** d.	1524	1616	1624	1716	1724	1816	1824	1916	1924	...	2024	2052	2124	...	2224	...	2324	...	...	...	...	...	...	...
Radebeul Ost .... **857** d.	1531	|	1631	|	1731	|	1831	|	1931	...	2031	|	2131	...	2231	...	2331	...	...	...	...	...	...	...
Coswig .... **843 856 857** d.	1537	|	1637	|	1737	|	1837	|	1937	...	2037	|	2137	...	2237	...	2337	...	...	...	...	...	...	...
Riesa .... d.	1605	1648	1705	1748	1805	1848	1905	1948	2005	...	2105	2123	2205	...	2305	...	0005	...	...	...	...	...	...	...
Oschatz .... d.	1614	|	1714	|	1814	|	1914	|	2014	...	2114	|	2214	...	2314	...	0014	...	...	...	...	...	...	...
Wurzen .... d.	1631	|	1731	|	1831	|	1931	|	2031	...	2131	|	2231	...	2331	...	0031	...	...	...	...	...	...	...
Leipzig Hbf .... a.	1650	1724**y**	1750	1819	1850	1920	1950	2019	2050	...	2150	2202	2250	...	2350	...	0050	...	...	...	...	...	...	...
Frankfurt (Main) Hbf **850** ...... a.	...	2036	...	...	...	2236	...	...	...	...	...	...	...	...	...	...	...	...	...	...	...	...	...	...

B – 12 Norddeich Mole - Bremen - Hannover - Magdeburg - Dresden.
D – 12 (Bielefeld ①**g** -) Hannover - Leipzig - Dresden.
E – From Erfurt (Table **850**) on ⑥ (also Oct. 3; not Oct. 5).
G – 12 Dresden - Leipzig - Magdeburg - Hannover - Emden.
H – To Hannover (Table **866**).
K – 12 Köln - Dortmund - Hannover - Magdeburg - Dresden and v.v.
L – From Halle (Table **866**).
M – From Magdeburg (Table **866**).
T – 12 and 🍴 Praha - Dresden - Leipzig and v.v.

V – From Nov. 1.
X – Ⓐ to Oct. 30.
Z – Ⓒ to Oct. 27 (also Oct. 31).

b – Not June 9.
e – Not June 10.
g – Also June 11; not June 10.
h – 1720 on ⑥ (also June 9, 10).
r – Not Oct. 31, Nov. 20.

w – Also June 10; not June 9.
y – 4 – 6 minutes earlier from Aug. 10.

¶ – To / from Wiesbaden via Frankfurt Flughafen ✈ (Table **911**). Does not run Frankfurt - Wiesbaden and v.v. Aug. 10 - Oct. 27
‡ – To Wiesbaden until Aug. 8 (Table **911**). To Saarbrücken Aug. 9 - Oct. 27 (Table **919**).

843 ELSTERWERDA - CHEMNITZ and DRESDEN; DÖBELN - LEIPZIG

RE / RB services

ELSTERWERDA - CHEMNITZ *Operated by Mitteldeutsche Regiobahn* **WARNING!** SEE NOTE ▲

km																									
		Ⓐd	Ⓐe		Ⓐe		Ⓐe		Ⓐd		Ⓐd		Ⓐd		Ⓐe		Ⓐe			Ⓐe		†z	Ⓑ	⚒e	
0	**Elsterwerda** ▲ d.	...	0508	...	0608	...	0708	0814	...	1014	...	1214	...	1408	1508	1608	1708	...	1808	1908	2008	2124	...	2214	...
24	Riesa ▲ a.	...	0533	...	0637	...	0733	0839	...	1039	...	1239	...	1433	1533	1633	1733	...	1833	1933	2033	2149	...	2239	...
24	Riesa ▲ d.	0449	0549	0549	0649	0649	0749	0849	0949	1049	1149	1249	1349	1449	1549	1649	1749	1749	1849	1949	2049	2153	2153	2253	2253
50	Döbeln Hbf ▲ d.	0511	0611	0611	0711	0711	0811	0911	1011	1111	1211	1311	1411	1511	1611	1711	1811	1811	1911	2011	2111	2217	2217	2317	2317
91	**Chemnitz** Hbf ▲ a.	0549	0649	0649	0749	0749	0849	0949	1049	1149	1249	1349	1449	1549	1649	1749	1849	1849	1949	2049	2149	2258	2258	2358	2358

	Ⓐe		Ⓐe		Ⓐd		Ⓐd		Ⓐd		Ⓐe			Ⓐe		Ⓐe		Ⓑ		⑥		Ⓐe		
hemnitz Hbf d.	0409	0509	0509	0609	0707	0809	0909	1009	1109	1209	1309	1409	1509	1509	1609	1709	1809	1909	2009	2009	...	2136	...	2236
öbeln Hbf d.	0447	0547	0547	0647	0747	0847	0947	1047	1147	1247	1347	1447	1547	1547	1647	1747	1847	1947	2047	2047	...	2218	...	2318
esa a.	0510	0610	0610	0710	0810	0910	1010	1110	1210	1310	1410	1510	1610	1610	1710	1810	1910	2010	2110	2110	...	2240	...	2340
esa d.	0521	...	0621	0721	...	0915	...	1115	...	1315	1421	1521	...	1621	1721	1821	1921	2021k	...	2115	...	2252	...	...
sterwerda a.	0544	...	0644	0744	...	0938	...	1138	...	1338	1444	1544	...	1644	1744	1844	1944	2044k	...	2138	...	2315	...	...

ELSTERWERDA - DRESDEN

km		Ⓐ		Ⓐ				
0	**Elsterwerda-Biehla** d.	0439	0539a	0637	0739	and every	2139	*2328*
2	Elsterwerda d.	0443	0543	0643	0743	**two** hours	2143	2343
41	Coswig ▷ d.	0522	0622	0722	0822	until	2222	0022
59	**Dresden** Hbf ▷ a.	0544	0644	0744	0844		2244	0044

	Ⓐ							Ⓐ				
Dresden Hbf ▷ d.	0508	0608	0708	0908	1108	1308	1508	1608j	1708	1908	2108	2308
Coswig ▷ d.	0531	0631	0731	0931	1131	1331	1531	1631	1731	1931	2131	2331
Elsterwerda d.	0610	0710	0812	1010	1210	1410	1612	1710	1812	2012	2209	0009
Esterwerda-Biehla a.	0613	0713	0815	1013	1213	1413	1615	1713	1815	2015	...	...

DÖBELN - LEIPZIG *Operated by Mitteldeutsche Regiobahn*

km		Ⓐe	Ⓐe		Ⓐe			Ⓐe		
0	**Döbeln** Hbf d.	0450	0550	0650	0750	and hourly	1850	1950	2050	...
13	Leisnig d.	0502	0602	0702	0802	on Ⓐ,	1902	2002	2102	...
28	Großbothen d.	0517	0617	0717	0817	every **two**	1917	2017	2117	...
35	Grimma ob Bf d.	0526	0626	0726	0826	hours on	1926	2026	2126	2210
66	**Leipzig** Hbf a.	0600	0700	0800	0900	Ⓒ until	2000	2100	2200	2243

	Ⓐe		Ⓐe			Ⓐe			
Leipzig Hbf d.	0506	0606	0706	and hourly	1806	1906	2006	2106	2206
Grimma ob Bf d.	0541	0641	0741	on Ⓐ,	1841	1941	2041	2139	2240
Großbothen d.	0547	0647	0747	every **two**	1847	1947	2047	...	2246
Leisnig d.	0604	0704	0804	hours on	1904	2004	2104	...	2300
Döbeln Hbf a.	0617	0717	0817	Ⓒ until	1917	2017	2117	...	2213

– Ⓐ only.
– Not Oct. 31, Nov. 20.
– Not Oct. 31.

j – 1607 June 11 - Sept. 30.
k – 6 minutes earlier from Oct. 20.
z – Also Oct. 31.

▷ – See also Tables **842**, **856**, **857**.
▲ – From Oct. 19 southbound timings Elsterwerda - Riesa - Chemnitz may vary by up to 16 minutes (earlier departures possible).

844 STRALSUND - OSTSEEBAD BINZ / SASSNITZ

RE / RB services except where shown — *Service from June 11*

km														*IC*			*ICE*					*ICE*	
														1049			**1678**					**1714**	
		①–⑥	C		Ⓐ e		Ⓐ e	Ⓐ e	Ad	A			Ad	A	⑥ B			✕♦	Ad	A		⑥ ♦	Ad
	Rostock Hbf **830** d.	...	2301	...	...	0454	...	0554	...	...	0700	...	...	...	0837	0901	...	0938	...	...	1101	...	...	...
0	**Stralsund** Hbf d.	0000	0000	...	0501	0600	...	0700	0700	...	0800	...	0901	...	0935	1000	...	1031	1101	...	1200	...	1239	1301
29	Bergen auf Rügen d.	0028	0028	...	0530	0630	...	0730	0730	...	0830	...	0930	...	1000	1030	...	1056	1130	...	1230	...	1306	1330
39	Lietzow (Rügen) d.	...	...	...	0538	0639	0641	0739	0739	0741	0839	0841	0938	0941	|	1040	1043	|	1138	1141	1239	1241	|	1338
	Ostseebad Binz a.	...	...	...	|	|	0654	|	|	0754	|	0854	0951	|	1040	|	1056	1120	1151	|	|	1254	1329	1351
51	**Sassnitz** a.	...	...	...	0552	0652	...	0753	0753	...	0853	...	...	0954	...	1054	...	...	...	1154	1253	...	...	...

				IC	*IC*					*ICE*	*ICE*					*IC*								
				2212	**2322**					**1748**	**1710**					**2424**								
	A			♦	⑥ ♦	Ad	A			⑥ H✕	M	Ad	A			♦	Ad	A			Ad	A		
Rostock Hbf **830** d.	...	1301	...	1338	...	...	...	1501	...	1538	...	...	...	1701	...	...	...	...	1901	...	...	...	2101	...
ralsund Hbf d.	...	1400	...	1439	1449	1501	...	1600	...	1631	1646	1701	...	1800	...	1839	1901	...	2000	...	2102	...	2201	...
ergen auf Rügen d.	...	1430	...	1504	1516	1530	...	1630	...	1655	1714	1730	...	1830	...	1906	1930	...	2030	...	2131	...	2230	...
etzow (Rügen) d.	1341	1439	1441	|	|	1538	1541	1639	1641	|	|	1738	1741	1839	1841	|	1938	1941	2039	2041	2139	2142	2239	2241
Ostseebad Binz a.	|	|	1454	1530	1539	1551	|	|	1654	1719	1736	1751	|	|	1854	1929	1951	|	|	2054	2152	|	|	2254
ssnitz a.	1354	1453	...	...	...	...	1554	1653	...	...	...	...	1754	1853	...	...	...	1954	2053	...	...	2155	2253	...

km															*ICE*	*IC*						*IC*	*ICE*
															1711	**2213**						**2421**	**1749**
		Ⓐ e				Ⓐ e	⚒ e			A	Ad			A	Ad	M	♦			A	Ad		⑦ ♦	♦
	Sassnitz d.	0400	...	0504	...	...	0604	...	0704	...	0804	...	0904	1000	...	...	...	...	1104	1200	...	...	...	...
0	**Ostseebad Binz** d.	|	...	|	...	0602	|	0702	|	0802	|	0902	|	|	1004	1021	1028	1102	|	|	1204	...	1220	1227
12	Lietzow (Rügen) d.	0414	...	0518	...	0614	0618	0714	0718	0814	0818	0914	0918	1014	1018	|	|	1117	1120	1214	1218	...	|	|
22	Bergen auf Rügen d.	0423	...	0527	...	...	0627	...	0727	...	0827	...	0927	...	1027	1042	1054	...	1129	...	1227	...	1242	1255
51	**Stralsund** Hbf a.	0451	...	0555	...	...	0655	...	0755	...	0855	...	0955	...	1055	1106	1118	...	1157	...	1255	...	1306	1319
	Rostock Hbf **830** a.	0548	...	0654	...	...	...	...	0855	...	...	...	1055	...	...	...	1219	...	1255	...	...	...	...	1419

					ICE									*IC*										
					1715									**1048**										
			A	Ad	⑥ M			A	Ad			A	Ad	⑥ B			A	Ad			A	Ad		
ssnitz d.	...	1304	1400	...	...	...	1504	1600	...	1700	...	1800	...	...	...	1904	2000	...	...	2104	2201	...	...	...
Ostseebad Binz d.	1302	|	|	1404	1421	1502	|	|	1604	|	1704	|	1804	1818	1902	|	|	2004	2102	|	|	2204	...	...
etzow (Rügen) d.	1314	1318	1414	1418	|	1514	1520	1614	1618	1714	1718	1814	1818	|	1914	1918	2014	2018	2114	2118	2215	2218	...	...
rgen auf Rügen d.	...	1327	...	1427	1442	...	1529	...	1627	...	1727	...	1827	1841	...	1927	...	2027	...	2127	...	2227	...	...
ralsund Hbf a.	...	1355	...	1455	1506	...	1557	...	1655	...	1755	...	1855	1907	...	1955	...	2055	...	2155	...	2255	...	...
Rostock Hbf **830** a.	...	1455	...	...	...	...	1655	...	...	...	1855	...	...	2019	...	2055	...	...	...	2255	...	...	...	...

– **NOTES** (LISTED BY TRAIN NUMBER)

78 – ①–⑥ until Oct. 5. [12] ✕ Hannover - Hamburg - Ostseebad Binz.
14 – [12] ✕ Jena - Leipzig - Berlin - Ostseebad Binz.
49 – Daily to Oct. 6; ⑦ from Oct. 13. [12] ✕ Ostseebad Binz - Hamburg - Hannover.
12 – RÜGEN – [12] 🍷 Koblenz - Köln - Hamburg - Ostseebad Binz.
13 – RÜGEN – [12] 🍷 Ostseebad Binz - Hamburg - Köln - Stuttgart.
22 – [12] Dresden - Berlin - Ostseebad Binz.
21 – ⑥⑦ to Sept. 1; ⑦ from Sept. 8. To Berlin (Table **830**).
24 – Until Sept. 1. From Berlin (Table **830**).

A – Daily to Oct. 11; Ⓐ from Oct. 14 (not Oct. 31).
B – ⑥ June 29 - Sept. 14. [12] Köln (see Tables **800**/**810**) - Berlin - Ostseebad Binz and v.v.
C – From Rostock on ①②③④⑦.
H – From / to Hamburg (Table **830**).
M – [12] ✕ Ostseebad Binz - Berlin - Nürnberg - München and v.v.
d – Runs daily Stralsund - Bergen auf Rügen and v.v.
e – Not Oct. 31.

844a BERGEN AUF RÜGEN - PUTBUS - LAUTERBACH and RÜGENSCHE BÄDERBAHN

reßnitztalbahn

km		Ⓐe	Ⓐe	Ⓐe	Ⓒz						
0	**Bergen** auf Rügen d.	0640	0740	0840	0940	1040	1240	1340	and	1840	2040
10	**Putbus** a.	0649	0749	0849	0949	1049	1249	1349	hourly	1849	2049
12	**Lauterbach** Mole a.	0654	...	0854	0954	1054	1254	1354	until	1854	...

	Ⓐe	Ⓐe	Ⓐe		Ⓒz					
Lauterbach Mole d.	0600	0700	...	0900	1000	1100	1300	1400	and	1900
Putbus d.	0611	0711	0811	0911	1011	1111	1311	1411	hourly	1911
Bergen auf Rügen a.	0620	0720	0820	0920	1020	1120	1320	1420	until	1920

GENSCHE BÄDERBAHN **SUMMER SERVICE UNTIL OCTOBER 3.** Steam train service. Please note that Binz Lokalbahn station is situated 2½ km from Ostseebad Binz DB station.

km											b
0	**Lauterbach** Mole d.	...	...	...	1122	1322	1522	...	1722	1922	...
2	**Putbus** a.	...	...	...	1129	1329	1529	...	1729	1929	...
2	**Putbus** d.	0808	...	1008	1208	1408	1608	...	1808	2008	...
14	Binz Lokalbahn ♥ d.	0840	0944	1040	1240	1440	1640	1744	1840	2040	2244
22	Sellin (Rügen) Ost ♥ d.	0909	1013	1109	1309	1509	1709	1813	1909	2109	2313
27	**Göhren** (Rügen) ♥ a.	0923	1027	1123	1323	1523	1723	1827	1923	2123	2327

										b
Göhren (Rügen) ♥ d.	0849	0953	1153	1353	1553	1649	1753	1849	1953	2149
Sellin (Rügen) Ost. ♥ d.	0907	1011	1211	1411	1611	1707	1811	1907	2011	2207
Binz Lokalbahn ♥ d.	0933	1040	1240	1440	1640	1733	1840	1936	2040	2233
Putbus a.	...	1106	1306	1506	1706	...	1906	2002	2106	...
Putbus d.	...	1111	1311	1511	1711	...	1911	...	...	...
Lauterbach Mole a.	...	1117	1317	1517	1717	...	1917	...	...	...

- Until Sept. 8.
e – Not Oct. 31.
z – Also Oct. 31.
♥ – Additional journeys Binz Lokalbahn - Göhren: **From Binz** at 1144, 1344 and 1544. **From Göhren** at 1049, 1249 and 1449.

845 LUTHERSTADT WITTENBERG - BERLIN - STRALSUND

RE services except where shown

km			©		⚒	*IC* 2217 W N			*IC* 1049 ⑥ E🍷			S	H		*ICE* 1714 ⑥ B✕			*IC* 2322 ⑥ R			*ICE* 1710 J✕		S	
0	**Lutherstadt Wittenberg** .. 850 d.	...	0025	...	...	...	...	...	...	0503	...	...	0702	...	0848	0902	...	...	1102	...	1248	1302	...	...
	Falkenberg (Elster) d.	...	|	...	...	...	...	...	...	|	0548	...	|	0753	|	|	0951	...	|	1151	|	|	...	1351
32	Jüterbog d.	...	0053	...	...	...	...	0430	...	0532	0632	...	0734	0834	|	0934	1032	...	1134	1232	|	1334	...	1432
45	Luckenwalde d.	...	0101	...	...	...	...	0438	...	0540	0640	...	0742	0842	|	0942	1040	...	1142	1240	|	1342	...	1440
91	**Berlin** Südkreuz 850 d.	...	0147	...	...	...	...	0521	0526	0616	0716	...	0819	0918	0925	1016	1116	1120	1216	1316	1324	1416	...	1516
97	**Berlin** Hbf 850 a.	...	0153	...	...	...	...	0529	0531	0623	0723	...	0825	0925	0930	1023	1123	1125	1223	1323	1329	1423	...	1523
97	**Berlin** Hbf d.	0100	*0158*	...	...	...	0421	0531	0619	0632	0733	...	0832	0932	0946	1032	1132	1145	1232	1332	1346	1432	...	1532
101	**Berlin** Gesundbrunnen d.	0106	*0204*	...	...	...	0427	0537	0626	0639	0739	0804	0839	0939	0953	1039	1138	1153	1239	1338	1352	1439	1453	1539
122	Bernau (b. Berlin) d.	0121	*0219*	...	...	...	0441	0552	|	0654	0754	0821	0854	0954	|	1054	1154	|	1254	1354	|	1454	1511	1554
144	Eberswalde Hbf d.	0139	*0239*	...	...	...	0507	0607	|	0709	0809	0838	0909	1009	1022	1109	1209	1222	1309	1409	1419	1509	1527	1609
170	Angermünde a.	...	...	...	...	...	0526	0626	|	0728	0828	0853	0928	1028	1037	1128	1228	1238	1328	1428	1434	1528	1543	1628
170	Angermünde d.	...	...	...	...	...	0533	0634	|	0733	0834	...	0933	1034	1039	1133	1234	1240	1333	1434	1436	1533	...	1634
193	**Schwedt** (Oder) a.	...	...	...	...	...	|	0657	◧	|	0857	...	|	1057	|	|	1257	|	|	1457	|	|	...	1657
	Prenzlau d.	...	...	...	...	...	0601	...	|	0801	...	...	1001	...	1103	1201	...	1304	1401	...	1501	1601	...	...
	Pasewalk d.	...	...	...	0418	...	0620	...	|	0818	...	...	1018	...	1119	1218	...	1320	1418	...	1517	1618	...	...
	Anklam d.	...	...	...	0451	...	0651	...	|	0851	...	...	1051	...	1146	1251	...	1347	1451	...	1546	1651	...	...
	Züssow 846 d.	...	...	...	0505	0651c	0705	...	|	0905	...	...	1105	...	1158	1305	...	1359	1505	...	1558	1705	...	...
	Greifswald 846 d.	...	...	...	0521	0704	0721	...	|	0921	...	...	1121	...	1212	1321	...	1412	1521	...	1612	1721	...	...
	Stralsund Hbf 846 a.	...	...	...	0543	0725	0744	...	0926	0943	...	...	1143	...	1233	1343	...	1433	1543	...	1638	1743	...	...

	IC 2424 U		S		*IC* 2428 Ⓐ	*IC* 1924 ⑦ w				⑤–⑦	①–④	⑤ S		⑥	Ⓑ		⑤ h	⑦ q	⑥ d	①–④ x		⑦ k		⑤⑥ t
Lutherstadt Wittenberg ... 850 d.	...	1502	...	...	...	...	1702	...	1902	1902	...	...	...	...	...	2102	2102	2102	2102	...	...	...	...	...
Falkenberg (Elster) d.	...	|	...	1551	...	...	|	1751	|	|	...	...	1951	1951	...	|	|	|	|	...	...	...	2151	2151
Jüterbog d.	...	1534	...	1632	...	...	1734	1832	1934	1934	...	...	2032	2032	...	2134	2134	2134	2134	...	...	...	2232	2232
Luckenwalde d.	...	1542	...	1640	...	...	1742	1840	1942	1942	...	...	2040	2040	...	2142	2142	2142	2142	...	...	...	2240	2240
Berlin Südkreuz 850 d.	1536r	1616	...	1716	1813r	...	1816	1916	2016	2016	...	...	2116	2116	...	2217	2217	2217	2217	...	...	...	2321	2321
Berlin Hbf 850 a.	|	1623	...	1723	|	...	1823	1923	2023	2023	...	...	2123	2123	...	2224	2224	2224	2224	...	...	...	2330	2330
Berlin Hbf d.	1546	1632	...	1732	1821	1821	1832	1932	...	2032	2033	...	...	2132	2135	...	2232	2232	2234	2234	...	...	2332	2332
Berlin Gesundbrunnen d.	1552	1639	1719	1739	1827	1827	1839	1939	...	2039	2039	2104	...	2138	2141	...	2240	2240	2240	2240	...	...	2338	2338
Bernau (b. Berlin) d.	|	1654	1737	1754	|	|	1854	1954	...	2054	2054	2122	...	2153	2155	...	2256	2256	2256	2256	...	...	2352	2352
Eberswalde Hbf d.	1619	1709	1752	1809	1854	1854	1909	2009	...	2109	2109	2137	...	2212	2215	...	2315	2315	2315	2315	...	...	0012	0014
Angermünde a.	1634	1728	1806	1828	|	|	1928	2028	...	2128	2128	2153	...	2232	2235	...	2337	2337	2337	2337	...	...	...	0033
Angermünde d.	1636	1733	...	1834	|	|	1933	2034	...	2133	2133	...	...	2234	2237	...	2342	2338	2342	2338	2342	2342	...	0034
Schwedt (Oder) a.	|	|	...	1857	|	|	|	2057	...	|	|	...	...	2257	2259	...	|	2400	|	2400	|	|	...	0057
Prenzlau d.	1700	1801	...	...	1933	1933	2001	...	...	2201	2201	...	...	...	...	...	0011	...	0011	...	0011	0011	...	...
Pasewalk d.	1718	1818	...	...	1950	1950	2018	...	...	2218	2218	...	...	...	...	...	0026	...	0026	...	0026	0028	...	...
Anklam d.	1746	1851	...	...	2018	2018	2051	...	...	2251	2251	...	...	...	...	...	...	...	...	...	...	0059	...	...
Züssow 846 d.	1758	1905	...	...	|	|	2105	...	...	2305	2305	...	...	...	...	...	...	...	...	...	...	0113	...	...
Greifswald 846 d.	1812	1921	...	...	2040	2040	2121	...	...	2321	2321	...	...	...	...	...	...	...	...	...	...	0128	...	...
Stralsund Hbf 846 a.	1833	1943	...	...	2059	2059	2143	...	...	2343	2343	...	...	...	...	...	...	...	...	...	...	0149	...	...

km		Ⓐ				① g	Ⓐ	⚒		S			*IC* 2429 ①–④ m			S	*IC* 2425			*ICE* 1711 J✕			*IC* 2421 Y O	
0	**Stralsund** Hbf 846 d.	...	...	...	...	0405	...	0417	...	...	...	0617	0712	...	0817	...	0912	...	1017	1112	...	1217	1312	...
31	Greifswald 846 d.	...	...	...	...	0424	...	0439	...	...	...	0639	0736	...	0839	...	0936	...	1039	1136	...	1239	1336	...
49	Züssow 846 d.	...	...	...	...	0438	...	0455	...	...	...	0655	0752	...	0855	...	0952	...	1055	1152	...	1255	1352	...
66	Anklam d.	...	...	...	...	0449	...	0508	...	...	...	0708	0808	...	0908	...	1008	...	1108	1208	...	1308	1408	...
109	**Pasewalk** d.	...	...	...	...	0518	0518	0544j	0544	...	...	0744j	0838	...	0944j	...	1038	...	1144j	1238	...	1344j	1438	...
133	Prenzlau d.	...	...	...	...	0535	0535	0601	0601	...	...	0801	0853	...	1001	...	1053	...	1201	1254	...	1401	1453	...
.	**Schwedt** (Oder) d.	...	...	...	0506	|	|	|	|	...	0706	|	|	0906	|	...	|	1106	|	|	1306	|	|	1506
170	Angermünde a.	...	...	...	0528	0603	0603	0628	0628	...	0728	0828	0916	0928	1028	...	1116	1128	1228	1316	1328	1428	1516	1528
170	Angermünde d.	0427	...	...	0533	0605	0605	0633	0633	0707	0733	0833	0918	0933	1033	1106	1118	1133	1233	1318	1333	1433	1518	1533
196	Eberswalde Hbf d.	0448	0448	...	0553	0627	0627	0652	0652	0724	0753	0852	0934	0953	1052	1124	1134	1153	1252	1335	1353	1452	1534	1553
218	Bernau (b. Berlin) d.	0509	0509	...	0607	0644	0644	0707	0707	0741	0807	0907	|	1007	1107	1140	|	1207	1307	|	1407	1507	|	1607
239	**Berlin** Gesundbrunnen d.	0524	0524	...	0625	0700	0700	0725	0725	0755	0825	0925	1000a	1025	1125	1153	1159a	1225	1325	1401	1425	1525	1559a	1625
243	**Berlin** Hbf a.	0529	0529	...	0629	0705	0705	0729	0729	...	0830	0929	1007	1030	1129	...	1206	1230	1329	1407	1430	1529	1606	1630
243	**Berlin** Hbf 850 d.	0531	0531	...	0632	...	...	0731	0731	...	0832	0931	|	1032	1131	...	|	1232	1331	1430	1432	1536	|	1632
249	**Berlin** Südkreuz 850 d.	0544j	0544j	...	0641	...	...	0747j	0747j	...	0841	0947j	1017r	1041	1147j	...	1216r	1241	1347j	1437	1441	1547	1617r	1641
295	Luckenwalde d.	0618	0618	...	0715	...	...	0821	0821	...	0912	1021	...	1112	1221	...	...	1312	1421	|	1512	1621	...	1712
308	Jüterbog d.	0627	0627	...	0723	...	...	0833	0833	...	0921	1031	...	1121	1231	...	...	1321	1431	|	1521	1631	...	1721
357	**Falkenberg** (Elster) a.	0706	0706	...	|	...	...	0912	0912	...	|	1110	...	|	1310	...	...	|	1510	|	|	1710	...	|
	Lutherstadt Wittenberg .. 850 a.	...	...	...	0756	...	...	...	...	...	0956	...	...	1156	...	...	...	1356	...	1510	1556	...	...	1756

		ICE 1715 ⑥ D✕		⑤ S		*IC* 1932 ⑦ w A		⑤–⑦	①–④	Ⓑ q	⑥ h		*IC* 2216 Ⓑ q N	S		⑤–⑦ v		*IC* 1048 ⑥ E🍷			⑤⑥ t H	①–⑥ h	⑤⑥ t	⑦ q
Stralsund Hbf 846 d.	1417	1511	...	...	1617	1705	...	...	...	1804	1817	...	1816	...	...	...	...	1925	2017	...	...	2217	2217	223[illegible]
Greifswald 846 d.	1439	1535	...	...	1639	1725	...	...	...	1838p	1839	...	1836	...	...	...	...	|	2039	...	...	2239	2239	2259
Züssow 846 d.	1455	1552	...	...	1655	|	...	...	...	1855	1855	...	...	...	...	...	...	|	2055	...	...	2255	2255	231[illegible]
Anklam d.	1508	1604	...	...	1708	1746	...	...	...	1908	1908	...	...	...	...	...	...	|	2108	...	...	2308	2308	232[illegible]
Pasewalk d.	1544j	1630	...	...	1744j	1812	...	...	...	1944j	1944j	...	...	...	...	...	...	|	2144j	...	...	2337	2344	2357
Prenzlau d.	1601	1647	...	...	1801	1828	...	...	...	2001	2001	...	...	...	...	...	...	|	2201	...	...	...	0001	...
Schwedt (Oder) d.	|	|	1706	...	|	|	1906	1906	...	|	|	...	...	...	2106	2106	...	◧	|	2306	2306	...	|	...
Angermünde a.	1628	1709	1728	...	1828	|	1928	1928	...	2028	2028	...	...	...	2128	2128	...	|	2228	2328	2328	...	0028	...
Angermünde d.	1633	1711	1733	1808	1833	|	1933	1933	...	2033	2033	...	...	2046	2133	2133	...	|	2233	2333	2333	...	0033	...
Eberswalde Hbf d.	1652	1728	1753	1825	1852	1906	1953	1953	...	2052	2052	...	...	2104	2153	2153	...	|	2252	2353	2353	...	0052	...
Bernau (b. Berlin) d.	1707	1744	1807	1841	1907	|	2007	2007	...	2107	2107	...	...	2119	2207	2207	...	|	2312	0007	0007	...	0112	...
Berlin Gesundbrunnen d.	1725	1800	1825	1856	1925	1934	2022	2022	...	2124	2124	...	...	2138	2223	2223	...	2243	2329	0023	0023	...	0129	...
Berlin Hbf a.	1729	1805	1830	...	1929	...	2026	2026	...	2128	2128	...	...	...	2228	2228	...	2248	2334	0028	0028	...	0134	...
Berlin Hbf 850 d.	1731	1830	1832	...	1931	...	...	2032	2032	...	2135q	2135	...	...	...	2233	2233	2343	...	0042	0042	...	...	...
Berlin Südkreuz 850 d.	1747j	1837	1841	...	1947j	...	...	2041	2041	...	2147q	2147	...	...	...	2242	2242	2348	...	0051	0051	...	...	...
Luckenwalde d.	1821	|	1912	...	2021	...	...	2112	2112	...	2221q	2221	...	...	...	2322	2322	...	...	0134	0134	...	...	...
Jüterbog d.	1831	|	1921	...	2031	...	...	2121	2121	...	2231q	2231	...	...	...	2332	2332	...	...	0141	0142	...	...	...
Falkenberg (Elster) a.	1910	|	|	...	2110	...	...	|	|	...	2310q	2310	...	...	...	|	|	...	...	...	|	...	...	...
Lutherstadt Wittenberg .. 850 a.	...	1910	1948	...	...	...	...	2148	2156	...	...	...	...	...	...	2359	2359	...	...	...	0158	...	...	...

A – [12] Stralsund - Berlin Spandau - Hannover - Bremen - Oldenburg.
B – [12] and ✕ Jena - Leipzig - Berlin - Ostseebad Binz.
D – [12] and ✕ Ostseebad Binz - Berlin - Leipzig - München.
E – ⑥ June 29 - Sept. 14. [12] Köln (Tables **800**/**810**) - Hannover - Berlin - Rostock - Ostseebad Binz (Table **844**) and v.v.
H – From/to Halle on © (Table **848**).
J – [12] and ✕ Ostseebad Binz - Stralsund - Berlin - Leipzig - München and v.v.
N – GREIFSWALDER BODDEN – [12] Greifswald - Hamburg - Köln - Stuttgart and v.v.
O – From Ostseebad Binz (Table **844**).
R – [12] Dresden - Berlin - Ostseebad Binz.
S – To/from Szczecin (Table **949**).
U – Daily until Sept. 6; Ⓑ from Sept. 8. To Ostseebad Binz until Sept. 1 (Table **844**).
W – ①–⑥ to Nov. 2 (not June 10, Oct. 5); ①–⑤ from Nov. 4.

Y – ⑥⑦ to Sept. 1 (also June 10; not June 9); ⑦ from Sept. 8.

a – Arrival time.
c – ①⑥ to Nov. 2 (also June 11, Oct. 3; not June 10, Oct. 5).
d – Also Oct. 2.
g – Also June 11, Oct. 4; not June 10.
h – Also June 9.
j – Arrives 6–8 minutes earlier.
k – Also June 10, Oct. 3; not June 9.
m – Not June 10, Oct. 2.
p – Arrives 1825.

q – Not June 9.
r – From Sept. 7.
t – Also June 9, Oct. 2.
v – Also June 10, Oct. 3.
w – Also June 10; not June 9.
x – Not Oct. 2.

◧ – Via Rostock (Table **835**).

Jsedomer Bäderbahn (2nd class only) — STRALSUND - ZÜSSOW - ŚWINOUJŚCIE — 846

km												⊕						
0	**Stralsund** Hbf ..... 845 d.	0524	0617	0724	0817	0924	1017	1124	1217	1324	1417	1524	1617	1724	1804t	1924	2017	2124
31	Greifswald .... 845 d.	0549	0639	0749	0839	0949	1039	1149	1239	1349	1439	1549	1639	1749	1838	1949	2039	2149
49	Züssow .... 845 d.	0608	0708	0808	0908	1008	1108	1208	1308	1408	1508	1608	1708	1808	1908	2008	2108	2208
67	Wolgast ....d.	0631	0731	0831	0931	1031	1131	1231	1331	1431	1531	1631	1731	1831	1931	2031	2131	2231
77	Zinnowitz ▲ ....d.	0650	0750	0850	0950	1050	1150	1250	1350	1450	1550	1650	1750	1850	1950	2050	2150	2250
04	Seebad Heringsdorf ....a.	0725	0825	0925	1025	1125	1225	1325	1425	1525	1625	1725	1825	1925	2025	2125	2225	2325
06	Seebad Ahlbeck ....a.	0734	0834	0934	1034	1134	1234	1334	1434	1534	1634	1734	1834	1934	2034	2134	2234	...
10	**Świnoujście** Centrum a.	0741	0841	0941	1041	1141	1241	1341	1441	1541	1641	1741	1841	1941	2041	2141	2241	...

		Ⓐy	Ⓒz															
vinoujście Centrum..d.	...	0517	0555	0617	0717	0817	0917	1017	1117	1217	1317	1417	1517	1617	1717	1817	1917	2117
eebad Ahlbeck.........d.	...	0523	0601	0623	0723	0823	0923	1023	1123	1223	1323	1423	1523	1623	1723	1823	1923	2123
eebad Heringsdorf.......d.	0432	0532	0611	0632	0732	0832	0932	1032	1132	1232	1332	1432	1532	1632	1732	1832	1932	2132
nnowitz ▲..................d.	0511	0611	0650	0711	0811	0911	1011	1111	1211	1311	1411	1511	1611	1711	1811	1911	2011	2211
olgast ....d.	0530	0630	0730j	0730	0830	0930	1030	1130	1230	1330	1430	1530	1630	1730	1830	1930	2030	2230
ssow................ 845 a.	0548	0648	0748	0748	0848	0948	1048	1148	1248	1348	1448	1548	1648	1748	1848	1948	2048	2248
eifswald .... 845 a.	0622	0720	0822	0822	0920	1022	1120	1222	1320	1422	1520	1622	1720	1822	1920	2022	2120	2320
ralsund Hbf ...... 845 a.	0647	0744	0847	0847	0943	1047	1143	1247	1343	1447	1543	1647	1743	1847	1943	2047	2143	2343

j – Arrives 0705.
t – *1817* on ⑥ (also June 9).
y – Not Oct. 31.
z – Also Oct. 31.

⊕ – Change trains at Seebad Heringsdorf until Oct. 6.
▲ – **Zinnowitz - Peenemünde** and v.v. (*12 km*, journey 14 minutes).
From Zinnowitz at 0434 Ⓐy, 0514 Ⓐy, 0614, 0659 Ⓐy, 0714 Ⓒz, 0814, 0914 and hourly until 2114.
From Peenemünde at 0452 Ⓐy, 0532 Ⓐy, 0632, 0717 Ⓐy, 0732 Ⓒz, 0832, 0932 and hourly until 2132.

RE services — BERLIN SCHÖNEFELD ✈ - BERLIN - DESSAU — 847

km			Ⓐ			and in the same pattern every two hours until							A				
0	**Berlin** Schönefeld ✈...d.	0445	0545	0645	0745		1745	1845	1945	2045	2145	2245	2245	also	0503	and hourly until	2303
17	**Berlin** Ostkreuz...........d.	0459	0559	0659	0759		1759	1859	1959	2059	2159	2259	2259		0518		2318
19	**Berlin** Ostbahnhof.........d.	0503	0603	0703	0803		1803	1903	2003	2103	2203	2303	2303		0526		2326
24	**Berlin** Hbf ....d.	0515	0615	0715	0815		1815	1915	2015	2115	2215	2315	2315		0537		2337
28	**Berlin** Zoo....................d.	0521	0621	0721	0821		1821	1921	2021	2121	2221	2321	2321		0543		2345
	Berlin Spandau........a.	|	|	|	|		|	|	|	|	|	|	|		0554		2354
43	Berlin Wannsee ....d.	0534	0634	0734	0834		1834	1934	2034	2134	2234	2334	2334		...		...
95	Bad Belzig ....a.	0616	0716	0816	0916		1916	2016	2116	2216	2316	0016	0016		...		...
39	Roßlau (Elbe)........ 848 a.	0648	0749	0848	0949e		1949e	2048	2147e	2248	2347v	...	0048		...		...
44	**Dessau** Hbf......... 848 a.	0653	0754	0854	0954e		1954e	2053	2153e	2253	2353v	...	0053		...		...

						△ and in the same pattern every two hours until				B	D	Ⓒ				
essau Hbf........... 848 d.	...	0405e	0503h	0605e	0705	0806e		1905	2006e	2105	2217	2217	2317	also	...	and hourly until	...
ßlau (Elbe)......... 848 d.	...	0410e	0510h	0610e	0710	0811e		1910	2011e	2110	2222	2222	2322		...		...
d Belzig ....d.	0343e	0443	0543	0643	0743	0843		1943	2043	2143	2254	2254	2354		...		...
rlin Wannsee ....d.	0427e	0527	0627	0727	0827	0927		2027	2127	2227	2338	2339	0038		...		...
Berlin Spandau.........d.	|	|	|	|	|	|		|	|	|	|	|	|		0559		2059
erlin Zoo ....d.	0440	0540	0640	0740	0840	0940		2040	2140	2240	2353	0004k	0054		0610		2110
erlin Hbf ....d.	0446	0546	0646	0746	0846	0946		2046	2146	2246	2359	0008	0100		0616		2116
erlin Ostbahnhof ....d.	0457	0557	0657	0757	0857	0957		2057	2157	2257	0009	...	0109		0628		2128
erlin Ostkreuz ....d.	0502	0602	0702	0802	0902	1002		2102	2202	2300r	...	...	...		0632		2132
erlin Schönefeld ✈.....a.	0514	0614	0714	0814	0914	1014		2114	2214	...	...	...	...		0644		2144

A – ①②③④⑦ (not June 9, Oct. 2).
B – ③–⑤ (not Oct. 3).
D – ①② (not June 10).

e – Ⓐ only.
h – ①–⑥ only.
k – Arrives 2353.
r – ①–⑥ (also June 9; not June 10, Oct. 3).
v – † only.

△ – Dessau d. 1503 (not 1505).

RE / RB / S-Bahn services — MAGDEBURG - DESSAU - LEIPZIG and HALLE (SAALE) — *Service from June 11* — 848

km		ⒸA	Ⓒz		Ⓐe	Ⓐe			Ⓐe	Ⓐe				Ⓐe	Ⓒz		Ⓐe	Ⓐe							and in the same pattern every two hours until
0	**Magdeburg** Hbf........ d.	...	...	...	...	...	...	...	0432	...	...	...	0514	...	...	...	...	...	0614	...	...	0714	...	...	
56	Roßlau (Elbe) ..... 847 d.	...	...	...	...	...	0441	...	0516	...	...	0541e	0605	...	...	...	0627	...	0705	...	...	0805	...	...	
61	**Dessau** Hbf .... 847 a.	...	...	...	...	...	0445	...	0520	...	...	0545e	0609	...	...	...	0631	...	0713	...	...	0813	...	...	
61	**Dessau** Hbf .... d.	0224	...	...	0414	...	0448	...	0522	...	...	0547	0610	...	...	...	0633	0646	0714	0719	...	0814	...	0819	
	Lutherstadt W ⊡.. d.	|	...	...	|	...	|	0440	|	...	0541	|	|	...	0604	0604e	|	|	|	|	0704	|	0804	|	
87	Bitterfeld .... a.	0240	...	...	0439	...	0511	0508	0540	...	0610	0610	0629	...	0639	0643e	0656	0710	0729	0742	0739	0830	0843	0842	
87	Bitterfeld .... d.	0240	0245	...	0440	0444	0512	0516	0545	0545	0613	0615	0631	0638	0640	0645	0700	0712	0730	0745	0747	0831	0845	0847	
	Halle (Saale) Hbf.... a.	0257	|	...	0503	|	|	0540	|	0608	|	0639	|	0702	0703	|	0717	|	0749	|	0809	|	|	0909	
20	**Leipzig** Hbf.............. a.	...	0311	...	...	0513	0543‡	...	0613‡	...	0643‡	...	0659	...	...	0713‡	...	0743‡	...	0813‡	...	0859	0913‡	...	

							Ⓐe																			
agdeburg Hbf......... d.	1414	...	...	1514	...	...	...	1614	...	...	1714	...	...	1814	...	...	1914	...	...	2014	...	...	2105	...	2159j	2311
ßlau (Elbe)....... 847 d.	1505	...	...	1605	...	...	...	1705	...	...	1805	...	...	1905	...	...	2005	...	...	2105	...	...	2152	...	2252	0003
essau Hbf......... 847 a.	1513	...	...	1613	...	...	...	1713	...	...	1813	...	...	1913	...	...	2013	...	...	2113	...	...	2156	...	2256	0008
essau Hbf.................. d.	1514	1519	...	1614	...	1619	1646	1714	1719	...	1814	...	1819	1914	1919	...	2014	...	2019	2114	...	2119	2158	...	2258	▬
Lutherstadt W ⊡ .. d.	|	|	1504	|	1604	|	|	|	|	1707	|	1804	|	|	|	1907	|	2015	|	|	2104	|	|	2217	|	...
terfeld .... a.	1529	1542	1539	1630	1643	1642	1710	1729	1742	1742	1830	1843	1842	1929	1942	1942	2030	2043	2042	2129	2139	2142	2221	2245	2318	...
terfeld .... d.	1530	1545	1547	1631	1645	1647	1712	1730	1745	1747	1831	1845	1847	1930	1945	1947	2031	2045	2047	2130	2145	2147	2222	2246	2319	2325
Halle (Saale) Hbf..... a.	1549	|	1609	|	|	1709	|	1749	|	1809	|	|	1909	1949	|	2009	|	|	2109	2149	|	2209	|	2309	|	2349
ipzig Hbf .... a.	...	1613‡	...	1659	1713‡	...	1743‡	...	1813‡	...	1859	1913‡	...	...	2013‡	...	2059	2113‡	...	...	2213‡	...	2242	...	2346‡	...

	Ⓒz	Ⓒz	Ⓐe¶	Ⓐe			Ⓒz¶	Ⓐe	Ⓐe	B														and in the same pattern every two hours until	
ipzig Hbf .... d.	...	0020‡	...	...	...	0448‡	0501	...	0544	...	0548‡	...	...	0648‡	0701	...	0748‡	...	...	0848‡	0901	...	0948‡		...
Halle (Saale) Hbf..... d.	0023	|	0356	0356	0450	|	|	0542	|	0550	|	0611	0651	|	|	0750	|	0811	0851	|	|	0950	|		1411
terfeld .... a.	0044	0047	0418	0418	0512	0515	0524	0604	0607	0614	0615	0629	0713	0715	0724	0813	0815	0829	0913	0915	0924	1013	1015		1429
terfeld .... d.	0050	0050	0420	0427	0518	0516	0527	...	0609	0620k	0618	0630	0718	0717	0727	0820	0818	0830	0918	0917	0927	1020	1018		1430
Lutherstadt W ⊡ .. a.	0119	|	|	0457	|	0551	|	...	|	0658	|	|	|	0757	|	0857	|	|	|	0957	|	1057	|		|
essau Hbf.................. a.	...	0114	0443	...	0542	...	0547	...	0627	...	0642	0647	0742	...	0747	...	0842	0847	0942	...	0947	...	1042		1447
essau Hbf......... 847 d.	...	...	0451	...	...	...	0549	...	0629	...	...	0649	...	...	0749	...	...	0849	...	...	0949	...	...		1449
ßlau (Elbe)....... 847 d.	...	...	0455	...	...	...	0554	...	0634	...	...	0654	...	...	0755	...	...	0854	...	...	0954	...	...		1454
agdeburg Hbf......... a.	...	...	0544	...	...	...	0646	...	0724	...	...	0747	...	...	0847	...	...	0947	...	...	1047	...	...		1547

						◇																				
ipzig Hbf .... d.	...	1448‡	1501	...	1548‡	...	...	1648‡	1701	...	1748‡	...	...	1848‡	1901	...	1948‡	...	...	2048‡	2118‡	...	2218‡	2218‡	...	2320‡
Halle (Saale) Hbf..... d.	1451	|	|	1550	|	1611	1651	|	|	1751	|	1811	1851	|	|	1950	|	2011	2051	|	|	2204	|	|	2323	|
terfeld .... a.	1513	1515	1524	1613	1615	1629	1713	1715	1724	1813	1815	1829	1913	1915	1924	2013	2015	2029	2113	2115	2147	2228	2247	2247	2344	2347
terfeld .... d.	1518	1517	1527	1620	1618	1630	1718	1717	1727	1820	1818	1830	1918	1917	1927	2020	2018	2030	2118	2117	2148	...	2249	2252	2351	2348
Lutherstadt W ⊡ .. a.	|	1546	|	1657	|	|	|	1756	|	1857	|	|	|	1956	|	2057	|	|	|	2157	|	...	|	2321	|	0018
ssau Hbf.................. a.	1542	...	1547	...	1642	1647	1742	...	1747	...	1842	1847	1942	...	1947	...	2042	2047	2141	...	2211	...	2312	...	0014	...
ssau Hbf......... 847 d.	...	...	1549	...	...	1649	...	...	1749	...	...	1849	...	...	1949	...	...	2049	...	...	2213	...	2314	...	...	...
ßlau (Elbe)....... 847 d.	...	...	1554	...	...	1654	...	...	1754	...	...	1854	...	...	1954	...	...	2054	...	...	2217	...	2318	...	...	...
gdeburg Hbf......... a.	...	...	1647	...	...	1747	...	...	1847	...	...	1947	...	...	2047	...	...	2147	...	...	2259	...	0008	...	...	...

FALKENBERG - LUTHERSTADT WITTENBERG - DESSAU

km		ⒸA		Ⓐe	Ⓐe	⚒r	Ⓐe								Ⓒz		Ⓐe			Ⓐe					
0	**Falkenberg** (Elster)............d.	...	...	...	...	0527e	0606	...	0717	...	0917	...	1117	...	1317	1329e	...	...	1517	1609	...	1717	1809e	1917	2117
54	**Lutherstadt Wittenberg**.....d.	0158	0410	0502	0556	0615	0651	0715	0815	0915	1015	1115	1215	1315	1401	1415	1453	1515	1615	1653	1715	1815	1915	2015	2205
86	Roßlau (Elbe) ....d.	|	0441	0533	0627	0644	0721	0744	0844	0944	1044	1144	1244	1344	...	1444	1521	1544	1644	1721	1744	1844	1944	2044	2234
91	**Dessau** Hbf ....a.	0224	0445	0538	0631	0650	0725	0749	0849	0949	1049	1149	1249	1349	...	1450	1525	1549	1650	1725	1749	1849	1949	2049	2238

	Ⓐe		Ⓐe	Ⓐe	Ⓒz	⚒r				Ⓐe	Ⓒz			Ⓐe		Ⓐe		Ⓐe		Ⓐe					
ssau Hbf.......................... d.	0423	0521	0623	0709	0709	0809	0909	1009	1109	1209	1209	1309	1409	1435	1509	1535	1609	1635	1709	1735	1809	1909	2009	2109	2248
3lau (Elbe)......................... d.	0428	0526	0628	0714	0714	0815	0914	1015	1114	1215	1215	1314	1415	1440	1514	1540	1615	1640	1714	1740	1815	1914	2015	2114	2256
therstadt Wittenberg...... a.	0457	0555	0657	0742	0742t	0843	0942	1043	1142	1240	1243	1342	1443	1505	1542	1605	1643	1705	1742	1805	1843	1942	2043	2142	2324
kenberg (Elster)............. a.	0546	0646r	...	0828	0846	...	1046	...	1246z	1323	...	1446	...	1555	1646z	1650	...	1755	1846z	1850	...	2046	...	2246	...

- [12] Berlin - Lutherstadt - Dessau - Halle (Table **845**).
- To Berlin and Stralsund on Ⓒ (Table **845**).

- Ⓐ (not Oct. 31).
2155 on ⑦.

k – 0618 on ⑤.
r – ⚒ (not Oct. 31).
t – Departs 0803.
z – Ⓒ (also Oct. 31).

‡ – Runs to / from Leipzig-Stötteritz via the Leipzig City Tunnel.
¶ – Runs daily Dessau - Magdeburg.
◇ – On ⑦ Bitterfeld a. 1632, d. 1635, Dessau a. 1651, d. 1652, Roßlau d. 1657.
⊡ – Lutherstadt Wittenberg.

849 Local services HALLE and LEIPZIG - EISENACH and SAALFELD

Operated by ABELLIO Rail Mitteldeutschland. See Tables **849a** and **850** for faster *ICE* and *IC* trains.

HALLE / LEIPZIG - ERFURT - EISENACH *See lower panel for other connecting services Halle - Naumburg and v.v.*

km		△		Ⓐe	Ⓐe		Ⓐe				Ⓐe													Ⓒc	
0	**Halle** (Saale) Hbf d.	...	0055	...	0419	0423c	0459	...	0559	...	...	...	0807	...	and in	...	1807	...	...	2007	...	...	...	...	...
	Leipzig Hbf d.	0022	|	...	|	|	|	0519f	|	0619	0645	0719	|	0819		1719	|	1819	1919	|	2019	2119	2219	...	231
32	Weißenfels d.	0101	0123	...	0449	0451c	0521	0558	0620	0659	0722	0758	0828	0859	the same	1758	1828	1859	1958	2028	2059	2158	2259	...	235
46	Naumburg (Saale) Hbf a.	0111	0134	...	0459	0502c	0530	0607	0630	0707	0730	0807	0837	0907		1807	1837	1907	2007	2037	2107	2207	2307	...	000
46	Naumburg (Saale) Hbf d.	...	...	...	...	0504	0532	0608	0640	0708	0735	0808	0838	0908	pattern	1808	1838	1908	2008	2038	2108	2208	2308	...	000
72	Apolda d.	...	...	...	...	0526	0552	0630	0700	0730	0756	0830	0857	0930	every	1830	1857	1930	2030	2057	2129	2230	2329	...	003
87	Weimar **858** d.	...	...	...	...	0538	0603	0642	0713	0742	0806	0842	0909	0942	**two** hours	1842	1909	1942	2042	2109	2142	2242	2342	...	004
108	**Erfurt** Hbf **858** a.	...	...	...	...	0553	0620	0658	0729	0758	0821	0858	0922	0958		1858	1922	1958	2058	2122	2158	2258	2358	...	005
108	**Erfurt** Hbf d.	...	...	0507	...	0555	0625	0703	...	0800	...	0903	...	1000	until	1903	...	2000	*2104*	...	*2207*	*2310*	...	0007	...
136	Gotha d.	...	...	0535	...	0616	0643	0726	...	0822	...	0926	...	1022		1926	...	2022	*2126*	...	*2229*	*2333*	...	0029	...
165	**Eisenach** a.	...	...	0558	...	0637	0706	0748	...	0843	...	0948	...	1043		1948	...	2043	*2148*	...	*2251*	*2356*	...	0051	...

			Ⓐe		Ⓐe				⚒e																
Eisenach d.	...	...	0411	...	...	0458	...	0606	0643	...	0713	...	0806	0913	...	and in	1606	1713	...	1806	...	1913	2006	2113	221
Gotha d.	...	...	0434	...	...	0522	...	0630	0705	...	0736	...	0830	0936	...		1630	1736	...	1830	...	1936	2030	2136	224
Erfurt Hbf a.	...	...	0455	...	...	0542	...	0653	0728	...	0758	...	0853	0958	...	the same	1653	1758	...	1853	...	1958	2053	2157	230
Erfurt Hbf **858** d.	...	...	0458	0458	0530	0557	0630	0701	0736	0736	0801	0836	0901	1001	1036		1701	1801	1836	1901	1936	2001	2101	2200	231
Weimar **858** d.	...	...	0518	0518	0545	0615	0642	0718	0752	0752	0818	0852	0918	1018	1052	pattern	1718	1818	1852	1918	1952	2018	2118	2218	233
Apolda d.	...	...	0529	0529	0555	0629	0652	0729	0802	0802	0829	0902	0929	1029	1102	every	1729	1829	1902	1929	2002	2029	2129	2229	234
Naumburg (Saale) Hbf a.	...	...	0551	0551	0614	0651	0712	0751	0821	0821	0851	0919	0951	1051	1121		1751	1851	1921	1951	2022	2051	2151	2251	000
Naumburg (Saale) Hbf d.	0444	0444	0552	0552	0615	0652	0713	0752	0822	0822	0852	0920	0952	1052	1122	**two** hours	1752	1952	1922	1952	...	2052	2152	2252	000
Weißenfels d.	0456	0456	0602	0602	0625	0702	0722	0802	0832	0832	0902	0929	1002	1102	1132	until	1802	1902	1932	2002	...	2102	2202	2302	002
Leipzig Hbf a.	|	0539h	0639	0639	0703	0740	|	0840	|	|	0940	|	1040	1140	|		1840	1940	|	2040	...	2140	2240v	2340x	|
Halle (Saale) Hbf a.	0525	...	...	...	...	...	0747	...	0853	0853	...	0953	...	...	1154		...	...	1954	...	...	...	...	...	004

HALLE / LEIPZIG - JENA - SAALFELD *See upper panel for other connecting services Leipzig - Naumburg and v.v.*

km		Ⓐ	Ⓒ																		B				
	Halle (Saale) Hbf d.	...	...	0522	...	0622	0707	0722	...	0822	and in	1522	...	1622	1707	1722	...	1822	1907	1922	...	2022	2122	2222	232
0	**Leipzig** Hbf d.	...	...	|	0558	|	|	|	0808	|		|	1608	|	|	|	1808	|	|	|	2008	|	|	|	|
40	Weißenfels d.	...	...	0550	0625	0650	0730	0750	0837	0850	the same	1550	1637	1650	1730	1750	1837	1850	1930	1950	2037	2050	2150	2250	235
56	Naumburg (Saale) Hbf a.	...	...	0601	0635	0701	0739	0801	0846	0901	pattern	1601	1646	1701	1739	1801	1846	1901	1939	2001	2046	2101	2201	2301	000
56	Naumburg (Saale) Hbf d.	...	...	0613	0636	0713	0740	0813	0848	0913		1613	1648	1713	1740	1813	1848	1913	1940	2013	2048	2113	2213	2313	001
95	**Jena** Paradies d.	0509	0616	0646	0708	0746	0807	0846	0915	0946	every	1646	1715	1746	1807	1846	1915	1946	2007	2046	2115	2146	2246	2346	004
100	Jena-Göschwitz d.	0513	0621	0650	0713	0750	0814	0850	0919	0950	**two** hours	1650	1719	1750	1814	1850	1919	1950	2014	2050	2119	2150	2250	2350	005
132	Rudolstadt (Thür) d.	0540	0642	0715	0740	0816	...	0915	0941	1016	until	1715	1741	1816	...	1915	1941	2016	*2040*	2116	2141	2216	2316	0016	...
142	**Saalfeld** (Saale) a.	0549	0650	0724	0750	0825	...	0924	0950	1025		1724	1750	1825	...	1924	1950	2025	*2049*	2125	2150	2225	2325	0025	...
	Nürnberg Hbf **875** a.	0848t	0919	...	1019	...	...	...	1219	...		...	2019	...	...	...	2219z	...	...	...	...	...	...	...	...

		Ⓐe																							⑤⑥
Nürnberg Hbf **875** d.	...	...	...	...	...	...	0529	...	...	...	0738	and in	...	...	...	1538	...	...	...	1740	...	...	...	1938	...
Saalfeld (Saale) d.	0430	...	0523	...	0633	0733	0810	0834	...	0933	1008		1634	...	1733	1808	1834	*1907*	1933	2008	2033	...	2133	2208	223
Rudolstadt (Thür) d.	0439	...	0531	...	0642	0742	0820	0843	...	0942	1018	the same	1643	...	1742	1818	1843	*1916*	1942	2018	2042	...	2142	2217	224
Jena-Göschwitz d.	0504	0547	0558	0606	0707	0807	0843	0907	0944	1007	1041	pattern	1707	1744	1807	1841	1907	1944	2007	2041	2107	2144	2207	2240	230
Jena Paradies d.	0510	0553	0603	0614	0714	0814	0849	0914	0950	1014	1049		1714	1750	1814	1849	1914	1950	2014	2049	2114	2150	2214	2244	231
Naumburg (Saale) Hbf a.	0543	0624	0629	0646	0747	0846	0914	0946	1015	1046	1114	every	1746	1815	1846	1914	1946	2015	2046	2114	2146	2215	2246	...	234
Naumburg (Saale) Hbf d.	0556	0625	0630	0656	0756	0856	0915	0956	1016	1056	1115	**two** hours	1756	1816	1856	1915	1956	2016	2056	2115	2156	2216	2256	...	234
Weißenfels d.	0607	0635	0640	0707	0807	0907	0924	1007	1027	1107	1124		1807	1827	1907	1924	2007	2027	2107	2124	2207	2227	2307	...	235
Leipzig Hbf a.	|	|	0710	|	|	|	0953	|	|	|	1153	until	|	|	|	1953	|	|	|	2153	|	|	|	...	003
Halle (Saale) Hbf a.	0635	0658	...	0734	0835	0935	...	1035	1050	1135	...		1835	1850	1935	...	2035	2050	2135	...	2233	2250	2335	...	...

EISENACH - BEBRA *45km.* Journey time: 34 – 48 minutes. Operated by CANTUS Verkehrsgesellschaft (2nd class only).

From Eisenach at 0436 Ⓐ, 0530 Ⓐ **k**, 0613 ⚒, 0713 ⚒, 0813 **k**, 0902 ⚒, 1014, 1103 Ⓐ, 1214, 1303 Ⓐ, 1414, 1503 Ⓐ, 1613, 1703 Ⓐ, 1814, 1903 Ⓐ, 2014, 2114 Ⓐ **n** and 2214 Ⓒ.
From Bebra at 0504 Ⓐ, 0600 ⚒, 0659 Ⓐ, 0704 Ⓒ, 0719 Ⓐ, 0804 ⑥, 0904, 1004 Ⓐ, 1104, 1204 Ⓐ, 1304 Ⓒ, 1315 Ⓐ, 1404 Ⓐ, 1507, 1604 Ⓐ, 1704, 1804 Ⓐ, 1904, 2004 Ⓐ and 2104.

B – To Bamberg (Table **875**).
c – Ⓒ (also Oct. 31).
e – Not Oct. 31.
f – 0507 on ⑥⑦ June 29 - Aug. 31.
h – 0547 on ⑥⑦ June 29 - Aug. 31.
j – 0043 on the mornings June 29 - Aug. 31.
k – 5 – 6 minutes earlier Aug. 12 - Oct. 27.
n – 2111 Sept. 30 - Oct. 25.
t – Not June 20, Nov. 1.
v – 2251 on ①②③④⑦ June 24 - Aug. 29.
x – 2350 June 24 - Aug. 30.
z – Ⓒ (also June 20, Nov. 1).
△ – 13 – 19 minutes **earlier** June 25 - Aug. 3

849a LEIPZIG - NAUMBURG - WEIMAR - ERFURT - KASSEL and LEIPZIG - JENA - SAALFELD - NÜRNBERG

	IC	*IC*	*IC*	*IC*	*IC*	*IC*	*IC*	*IC*	*ICE*
	2156	**2156**	**2068**	**2152**	**1956**	**2060**	**1952**	**2150**	**1705**
	①–⑥	⑦	⑥		⑦	**A**	⑤⑦	Ⓑ	Ⓑ **b**
	e	**p**	**t**		**w**		**v**	**q**	**H**
			S		**L**	**S**			✕
Berlin Hbf **850** d.	...	...	...	...	...	...	...	...	1830
Halle (Saale) Hbf **849 850** d.	...	...	...	...	...	...	...	...	|
Leipzig Hbf **849 850** d.	...	...	0749	...	1344	1549	1637	...	1952
Weißenfels **849** d.	...	...	0819	...	1421	1619	1707	...	2022
Naumburg (Saale) Hbf **849** d.	...	...	0831	...	1432	1632	1719	...	2033
Jena Paradies **849 875** d.	...	...	0900	...	|	1700	|	...	2059
Jena Göschwitz **849 875** d.	...	...	0907	...	|	1707	|	...	...
Saalfeld (Saale) **849 875** d.	...	...	0936	...	|	1736	|	...	...
Kronach **875** d.	...	...	1026	...	|	1826	|	...	...
Lichtenfels **875** d.	...	...	1041	...	|	1840	|	...	...
Bamberg **850 875** d.	...	...	1058	...	|	1857	|	...	...
Erlangen **850 875** d.	...	...	1119	...	|	1917	|	...	...
Nürnberg Hbf **850 875** a.	...	...	1133	...	|	1933	|	...	...
Apolda **849** d.	...	...	...	...	1451	...	1736	...	...
Gera Hbf **858** d.	0603	...	...	1203	|	...	|	1803	...
Jena Göschwitz **858** d.	0638	...	...	1238	|	...	|	1838	...
Jena West **858** d.	0644	...	...	1244	|	...	|	1844	...
Weimar **849 858** d.	0702	...	...	1302	1503	...	1747	1902	...
Erfurt Hbf **849 850 858** a.	0716	...	...	1316	1516	...	1759	1916	...
Erfurt Hbf **849 850** d.	0718	0718	...	1318	1519	...	1801	1918	...
Gotha **849 850** a.	0735	0741	...	1335	1534	...	1815	1935	...
Gotha **849 850** d.	0748	0748	...	1348	1536	...	1817	1948	...
Eisenach **849 850** d.	0804	0804	...	1404	1600h	...	1835	2004	...
Frankfurt (Main) Hbf **850** a.	|	|	...	|	1758z	...	|	|	...
Bebra **849 901** d.	|	|	...	|	...	...	1902	2029	...
Kassel Wilhelmshöhe **901** a.	0900	0900	...	1500	...	...	1940	2106	...
Dortmund Hbf **800 805** ▲ a.	1114	1114	...	1714	...	...	2157	...	...
Düsseldorf Hbf **800** ▲ a.	1211	1211	...	1811	...	...	2255	...	...
Köln Hbf **800** ▲ a.	1239	1239	...	...	...	...	2326	...	...

	ICE	*ICE*	*ICE*	*IC*	*IC*	*IC*	*IC*	*IC*	*IC*	*IC*
	992	**992**	**1704**	**2151**	**2063**	**2155**	**1955/9**	**1957**	**2157**	**215**
			①–⑤	①–⑥	**B**		⑤⑦	⑤	⑥	Ⓑ
	D	**C**	**a H**	**e**			**v**	**f**	**k**	**q**
	M ✕	**M** ✕	✕		**S**					
Köln Hbf **800** ▲ d.	...	...	...	...	...	0901	...	...	1520	152
Düsseldorf Hbf **800** ▲ d.	...	...	...	...	...	0946	1113	...	1545	154
Dortmund Hbf **800 805** ▲ d.	...	...	...	...	...	1043	1208	...	1643	164
Kassel Wilhelmshöhe **901** d.	...	...	...	0650	...	1257	1420	...	1859	185
Bebra **849 901** d.	...	...	...	0728	...	|	1503	...	|	|
Frankfurt (Main) Hbf **850** d.	0247	0249	...	|	...	|	|	1546j	|	|
Eisenach **849 850** d.	|	0447	...	0752	...	1356	1528	1752	1956	195
Gotha **849 850** a.	|	0459	...	0810	...	1410	1541	1805	2010	201
Gotha **849 850** d.	|	0501	...	0825	...	1425	1543	1807	2017	202
Erfurt Hbf **849 850** a.	0605	0521	...	0842	...	1442	1558	1838	2041	204
Erfurt Hbf **849 850 858** d.	0607	0523	...	0844	...	1444	1600	1842	▬	204
Weimar **849 858** d.	|	0538	...	0859	...	1459	1613	1858	*IC*	205
Jena West **858** a.	|	|	...	0913	...	1513	|	|	**2361**	211
Jena Göschwitz **858** a.	|	|	...	0919	...	1519	|	|	⑤	211
Gera Hbf **858** a.	|	|	...	0955	...	1555	|	|	**f**	215
Apolda **849** d.	|	|	...	▬	...	...	1624	1910	**S**	...
Nürnberg Hbf **850 875** d.	|	|	...	...	1024	...	|	|	1824	...
Erlangen **850 875** d.	|	|	...	...	1040	...	|	|	1840	...
Bamberg **850 875** d.	|	|	...	*ICE*	1100	...	|	|	1900	...
Lichtenfels **875** d.	|	|	...	**1714**	1117	...	|	|	1917	...
Kronach **875** d.	|	|	...	⑥	1133	...	|	|	1933	...
Saalfeld (Saale) **849 875** d.	|	|	...	**O**	1225	...	|	|	2025	...
Jena Göschwitz **849 875** d.	|	|	...	✕	1255	...	|	|	2055	...
Jena Paradies **849 875** d.	|	|	0652	0652	1301	...	|	|	2101	...
Naumburg (Saale) Hbf **849** d.	|	0605	0719	0719	1329	...	1641	1929	2129	...
Weißenfels **849** d.	|	|	0729	0729	|	...	1653	1939	2139	...
Leipzig Hbf **849 850** a.	|	|	0802	0802	1410	...	1726	2016	2210	...
Halle (Saale) Hbf **849 850** a.	0638	0638	|	|	...	...	...	...	...	...
Berlin Hbf **850** a.	0758	0758	0930	0930	...	...	...	...	...	...

A – ①②③④⑦.
B – ①②③④⑥ (also Oct. 4, Nov. 1; not Oct. 2, 31).
C – Daily to Aug. 11; ①⑥ from Nov. 2.
D – Daily Aug. 12 - Sept. 2; ①⑥ Sept. 7 - Oct. 28.
H – To / from Hamburg (Table **840**).
L – To Karlsruhe (Table **912**).
M – From München (d. 2151 previous day; see Table **930**).
O – To Ostseebad Binz (Tables **844** and **845**).
S – To / from Karlsruhe via Stuttgart (Tables **925**/**931**).

a – Not June 10, Oct. 31.
b – Not June 9, Oct. 30.
e – Not June 10.
f – Also June 19, Oct. 2, 31; not June 21, Oct. 4, Nov. 1.
h – Arrives 1551.
j – 1520 Aug. 16 - Oct. 25.
k – Also June 9.
p – Also June 10.
q – Not June 9.

t – Also Oct. 3, 4, Nov. 1.
v – Also June 10, 19, Oct. 2, 31; not June 9, 2 July 14 - Aug. 25, Oct. 4, Nov. 1.
w – Also June 10; not June 9.
z – Frankfurt (Main) **Süd**. 1752 Oct. 6 – 27.

▲ – Timings at Dortmund, Düsseldorf and Köln are subject to alteration July 13 - Aug. 25.

 German national public holidays are on Jan. 1, Apr. 19, 22, May 1, 30, June 10, Oct. 3, Dec. 25, 26

BERLIN - HALLE / LEIPZIG - ERFURT - FRANKFURT / NÜRNBERG 850

SERVICE TO AUGUST 9 AND FROM OCTOBER 28 (see page 566 for service August 10 - October 27). See Table **902** for other services Berlin - Frankfurt via Braunschweig.

Other regional services: Table **845** Berlin - Lutherstadt Wittenberg. Table **848** Lutherstadt Wittenberg - Bitterfeld - Leipzig / Halle. Table **849** Leipzig / Halle - Weimar - Erfurt - Eisenach.

km		IC 1950	IC 1950		ICE 1646		ICE 1501	ICE 1656	ICE 501		ICE 593	ICE 1701	ICE 1001	ICE 1638	ICE 1654	ICE 503	ICE 1636	ICE 595	ICE 701	ICE 1003	ICE 1652	ICE 505	ICE 1634
		①	Ⓐ		Ⓐ		Ⓐ	①–⑥	①–⑥			Ⓐ	①–⑥	①–⑤	①–⑥		①–⑤						
		g	m				L	e	e		M		e	n	e		a	M					
		⊙			✕		✕	✕	✕		✕	✕	✕	✕	✕	✕	✕	✕	✕	✕	✕	✕	✕
	Hamburg Hbf **840** d.	...	...	...	...	...	...	...	...	...	...	...	...	...	...	...	...	...	0527**a**	...	...	0635**e**	...
0	**Berlin** Hbf d.	0026	...	...	...	...	...	...	0428	...	0528	0534	0601	0601	...	0630	0704	0728	0737	0805	...	0830	0904
6	**Berlin** Südkreuz d.	0033	...	...	...	...	...	...	0435	...	0535	0541	0607	0607	...	0637	0711	0735	0744	0811	...	0837	0911
97	Lutherstadt Wittenberg d.	0113	...	...	...	...	...	...	0512	...	0611	|	|	|	...	0712	|	0811	|	|	...	0912	|
134	Bitterfeld d.	0130	...	...	...	...	...	...	|	...	|	0634	|	|	...	|	|	|	0834	|	...	|	|
	Halle (Saale) Hbf d.	0151	...	...	...	...	...	...	|	...	|	0652	0712	0712	...	|	0815	|	0852	0918	...	|	1015
	Dresden Hbf **842** d.	|	...	...	...	...	...	...	|	...	|	|	|	|	0610	|	|	|	|	|	0810	|	|
167	**Leipzig** Hbf a.	0215	...	...	...	...	...	...	0542	...	0642	|	|	|	0718	0742	|	0842	|	|	0920	0942	|
167	**Leipzig** Hbf d.	0230	...	...	...	...	...	0533	0548	...	0648	|	|	|	0733	0748	|	0848	|	|	0933	0948	|
287	**Erfurt** Hbf a.	0351	...	...	...	...	...	0615	0628	...	0728	0724**p**	0740	0740	0815	0829	0848	0928	0924**p**	0945	1015	1029	1048
287	**Erfurt** Hbf **849a** d.	0400	0400	...	0514	...	...	0617	0630	...	0730	0732	0745	0751	0817	0831	0850	0930	0932	0947	1017	1031	1050
	Coburg **875** d.	|	|	...	|	...	...	|	0704	...	|	|	|	|	|	|	|	|	|	|	|	|	|
	Bamberg **875** d.	|	|	...	|	...	0642	|	0728	...	|	0818	|	|	|	0917	|	|	1017	|	|	1117	|
	Erlangen **875** d.	|	|	...	|	...	0708	|	0753	...	|	|	|	|	|	0937	|	|	|	|	|	1137	|
	Nürnberg Hbf **875** a.	|	|	...	|	...	0725	|	0808	...	|	0852	0856	|	|	0952	|	|	1052	1056	|	1152	|
	München Hbf **904 905** a.	|	|	...	|	...	0839	|	0917	...	|	1043‡	1001	|	|	1100	|	|	1242‡	1203	|	1302	|
315	Gotha **849a** d.	0416	0416	...	0531	...	...	0633	...	...	|	...	...	|	0833	...	|	|	...	...	1033	...	|
344	**Eisenach** **849a** d.	0432	0432	...	0547	...	...	0648	...	...	0756	...	...	|	0848	...	|	0956	...	...	1048	...	|
401	Bad Hersfeld d.	0508	0508	...	0617	...	...	0716	...	...	|	...	...	|	0916	...	|	|	...	...	1116	...	|
443	Fulda **900/1/2** d.	0540	0540	...	0644	...	...	0743	...	...	0850	...	...	|	0943	...	|	1050	...	...	1143	...	|
543	**Frankfurt** (Main) Süd **901** a.	|	|	...	0739	...	...	|	...	...	|	...	...	|	|	...	|	|	...	...	|	...	|
547	**Frankfurt** (Main) Hbf **900/1/2** a.	0640	0640	...	|	...	...	0836	...	...	0944	...	...	0956	1036	...	1056	1144	...	...	1236	...	1256
	Frankfurt Flughafen ✈ § a.	...	...	...	0751**j**	...	...	0855	...	...	|	...	...	...	1055	...	...	|	...	...	1255	...	...
	Wiesbaden Hbf **911** a.	...	...	...	...	...	...	0933	...	...	|	...	...	...	1133	...	...	|	...	...	1333	...	...
	Stuttgart Hbf **912** a.	...	...	...	...	...	...	...	...	...	1108	...	...	...	...	...	...	1308	...	...	...	...	...

	ICE 597	ICE 703	ICE 93	ICE 1650	ICE 507	ICE 1632	ICE 599	ICE 1005	ICE 1558	ICE 509	ICE 1630	IC 1956	ICE 691	IC 1956	ICE 707	ICE 1727	ICE 1556	ICE 1601	ICE 1711	ICE 1538	ICE 693	ICE 709	ICE 1007
												⑦ u		⑦		⑥⑦							
	M		A				M				q	G	M	G		uR			O		M		q
	✕	✕	✕	🍷	✕	✕	✕	✕	✕	✕	✕	♣	✕		✕	✕	✕	✕	✕	✕	✕	✕	✕
Hamburg Hbf **840** d.	...	0738**c**	...	...	0835	...	0936	...	...	...	...	...	...	...	1136	...	...	1235	...	...	...	1338	...
Berlin Hbf d.	0928	0937	1005	...	1030	1104	1128	1205	...	1230	1304	...	1328	...	1337	1405	...	1430	1430	1504	1527	1537	1605
Berlin Südkreuz d.	0935	0944	1011	...	1037	1111	1135	1211	...	1237	1311	...	1335	...	1344	1411	...	1437	1437	1511	1534	1544	1611
Lutherstadt Wittenberg d.	1011	|	|	...	1112	|	|	|	...	1312	|	...	1411	...	|	|	...	1512	1512	|	1611	|	|
Bitterfeld d.	|	1034	|	...	|	|	1225	|	...	|	|	...	|	...	1434	|	...	|	|	|	|	1634	|
Halle (Saale) Hbf d.	|	1052	1118	...	|	1215	|	1318	...	|	1415	...	|	...	1452	1518	...	|	|	1615	|	1652	1718
Dresden Hbf **842** d.	|	|	|	1010	|	|	|	|	1210	|	|	...	|	...	|	|	1410	|	|	|	|	|	|
Leipzig Hbf a.	1042	|	|	1120	1142	|	1242	|	1320	1342	|	...	1442	...	|	|	1524	1542	1542	|	1642	|	|
Leipzig Hbf d.	1048	|	|	1133	1148	|	1248	|	1333	1348	|	1344	1448	...	|	|	1533	1548	1548	|	1648	|	|
Erfurt Hbf a.	1128	1124**p**	1152	1215	1229	1248	1328	1345	1415	1428	1448	1516	1528	...	1524**p**	1552	1615	1629	1629	1648	1728	1724**p**	1745
Erfurt Hbf **849a** d.	1130	1132	1154	1217	1231	1250	1330	1347	1417	1431	1450	1519	1530	...	1532	1554	1617	1631	1631	1650	1730	1732	1747
Coburg **875** d.	|	|	1229	|	|	|	|	|	|	|	|	|	|	...	|	|	|	|	|	|	|	|	|
Bamberg **875** d.	|	1217	|	|	1317	|	|	|	|	1517	|	|	|	...	1617	1643	|	|	|	|	|	1817	|
Erlangen **875** d.	|	|	|	|	1337	|	|	|	|	1537	|	|	|	...	|	1708	|	1737	1737	|	|	|	|
Nürnberg Hbf **875** a.	|	1250	1324	|	1352	|	|	1456	|	1551	|	|	|	...	1652	1724	|	1753	1753	|	|	1852	1856
München Hbf **904 905** a.	|	1402	...	|	1543‡	|	|	1602	|	1700	|	|	|	...	1843‡	1837**x**	|	1906	1906	|	|	2042‡	2001
Gotha **849a** d.	|	...	...	1233	...	|	|	...	1433	...	|	1536	|	←	...	...	1633	...	...	|	|	...	...
Eisenach **849a** d.	1156	...	...	1248	...	|	1356	...	1448	...	|	1551	1556	1600	...	...	1648	...	...	|	1756	...	...
Bad Hersfeld d.	|	...	...	1316	...	|	|	...	1516	...	|	→	|	1632	...	...	1716	...	...	|	|	...	...
Fulda **900/1/2** d.	1250	...	...	1343	...	|	1450	...	1543	...	|	...	1648	1700	...	...	1743	...	...	|	1850	...	...
Frankfurt (Main) Süd **901** a.	|	...	...	|	...	|	|	...	|	...	|	...	|	1758	...	...	|	...	...	|	|	...	...
Frankfurt (Main) Hbf **900/1/2** a.	1344	...	...	1436	...	1456	1544	...	1636	...	1656	...	1744	...	...	...	1836	...	...	1856	1944	...	...
Frankfurt Flughafen ✈ § a.	|	...	...	1455	...	...	|	...	1655	...	...	...	|	...	...	...	1855	...	...	...	|	...	...
Wiesbaden Hbf **911** a.	|	..	...	1533	...	...	|	...	1733	...	...	...	|	...	...	...	1933	...	...	...	|	...	...
Stuttgart Hbf **912** a.	1508	...	...	...	...	...	1708	...	...	...	...	...	1907	...	...	...	...	...	...	...	2108	...	...

	ICE 1554	ICE 603	ICE 1536	ICE 1736	ICE 695	ICE 801	ICE 801	ICE 1009		ICE 1552	ICE 1715	ICE 1605	ICE 1705		ICE 1617	ICE 1627		ICE 1607		EN 452		ICE 993	ICE 993
			Ⓑ q	⑥ k			B	Ⓑ q			⑥	Ⓑ	Ⓑ t					Ⓑ q		③		E	D
	¶		S	R		K	K				O		J			◇				★		M	
	✕	✕	✕	✕	✕	✕	✕	✕		✕	✕	✕	✕		✕	✕		✕		Ⓡ			✕
Hamburg Hbf **840** d.	...	1435	...	...	...	1537	1537	...	...	...	...	1635	1635	...	...	...	...	1835	...	...	...	1936	1936
Berlin Hbf d.	...	1630	1704	1704	1728	1737	1737	1805	...	...	1830	1830	1830	...	1928	1928	...	2030	...	2103	...	2128	2128
Berlin Südkreuz d.	...	1637	1711	1711	1735	1744	1744	1811	...	...	1837	1837	1837	...	1935	1935	...	2037	...	|	...	2135	2135
Lutherstadt Wittenberg d.	...	1712	|	|	1811	|	|	|	...	...	1912	1912	1912	...	|	|	...	2112	...	|	...	2211	2211
Bitterfeld d.	...	|	|	|	|	1834	1834	|	...	...	|	|	|	...	2025	2030	...	|	...	|	...	2229	2229
Halle (Saale) Hbf d.	...	|	1815	1815	|	1852	1852	1918	...	...	|	|	|	...	|	2052	...	|	...	|	...	|	|
Dresden Hbf **842** d.	1610	|	|	|	|	|	|	|	...	1810	|	|	|	...	|	|	...	|	...	|	...	|	|
Leipzig Hbf a.	1724**z**	1742	|	|	1842	|	|	|	...	1920	1942	1942	1942	...	2042	|	...	2142	...	|	...	2247	2247
Leipzig Hbf d.	1733	1748	|	|	1848	|	|	|	...	1933	1948	1948	...	...	2048	|	...	2148	...	|	...	2253	...
Erfurt Hbf a.	1815	1828	1848	1848	1928	1924**p**	1924	1945	...	2015	2029	2029	...	...	2129	2125**p**	...	2232	...	2327	...	2333	...
Erfurt Hbf **849a** d.	1817	1831	1850	1850	1930	...	1932	1947	...	2017	2031	2031	...	...	2131	2133	...	...	...	2329	...	2341	...
Coburg **875** d.	|	|	|	|	|	...	|	|	...	|	|	|	...	...	2206	|	...	...	...	|	...	|	...
Bamberg **875** d.	|	1917	|	|	|	...	2017	|	...	|	|	|	...	...	2229	|	...	...	...	|	...	|	...
Erlangen **875** d.	|	1937	|	|	|	...	|	|	...	|	2137	2137	...	...	2251	|	...	...	...	|	...	|	...
Nürnberg Hbf **875** a.	|	1952	|	|	|	...	2052	2056	...	|	2152	2152	...	...	2308	|	...	...	...	|	...	|	...
München Hbf **904 905** a.	|	2105	|	|	|	...	2243‡	2201	...	|	2302**f**	2302**f**	...	...	0022**v**	|	...	...	...	|	...	|	...
Gotha **849a** d.	1833	...	|	|	|	...	...	...	...	2033	...	...	...	...	...	2149	...	...	...	|	...	2357	...
Eisenach **849a** d.	1848	...	|	|	1956	...	...	...	...	2048	...	...	...	...	...	2203	...	...	...	|	...	0012	...
Bad Hersfeld d.	1916	...	|	|	|	...	...	...	...	2116	...	...	...	...	...	2233	...	...	...	|	...	|	...
Fulda **900/1/2** d.	1943	...	|	|	2050	...	...	...	...	2143	...	...	...	...	...	2300	...	...	...	|	...	|	...
Frankfurt (Main) Süd **901** a.	|	...	|	|	|	...	...	...	...	|	...	...	...	...	...	|	...	...	...	0138	...	|	...
Frankfurt (Main) Hbf **900/1/2** a.	2036	...	2056	2056	2144	...	...	...	...	2236	...	...	...	...	...	2358	...	...	...	...	...	0215	...
Frankfurt Flughafen ✈ § a.	2057**h**	...	...	...	|	...	...	...	...	...	...	...	...	...	...	...	...	...	...	...	...	0238	...
Wiesbaden Hbf **911** a.	2133**h**	...	...	...	|	...	...	...	...	...	...	...	...	...	...	...	...	...	...	...	...	|	...
Stuttgart Hbf **912** a.	...	...	...	...	2308	...	...	...	...	...	...	...	...	...	...	...	...	...	...	...	...	0444	...

– BEROLINA – To Wien via Passau (Tables **920** and **950**).
– Daily to Aug. 9 (not June 9, 15, July 6); Ⓑ from Oct. 28.
– Daily to Aug. 9; Ⓑ from Oct. 28.
– Daily to Aug. 9; ⑤⑦ from Nov. 1.
– To Karlsruhe (Table **912**).
– To Jena (Table **849a**).
– From Kiel (Table **820**).
– Ⓐ (not June 20, Nov. 1). From Lichtenfels (d. 0624).
– To München via Ulm (Table **930**).
– From Ostseebad Binz (Tables **844**/**845**).
– From Warnemünde via Rostock (Table **835**).
– PFÄLZER WALD. To Saarbrücken (Table **919**).
– ①–⑤ (not June 10).

c – ⑥⑦ (also June 10).
e – ①–⑥ (not June 10).
f – 2328 on July 27, Aug. 3 (train **1715**), July 28, Aug. 4 (train **1605**).
g – Also June 11; not June 10, Oct. 28.
h – Until Aug. 8.
j – Until Aug. 9.
k – Also June 9.
m – Not June 20, 21.
n – Not June 10, 20.
p – Connects with train in previous column.
q – Not June 9.
t – Not June 9, Oct. 30.
u – Also June 10; not June 9.

v – 0051 on the mornings of July 28, 29, Aug. 4, 5.
x – Until July 28 diverted to München Ost (a. 1843).
z – 4–6 minutes earlier from Aug. 10.

¶ – To Saarbrücken on Aug. 9 (Table **919**).
⊙ – Also calls at Weimar (d. 0337).
◇ – Also calls at Hanau Hbf (a. 2338).
♣ – Via Weimar (see Table **849a**).
★ – 🛏 1, 2 cl. Moskva - Warszawa - Berlin - Strasbourg - Paris. See Table **24**. Operated by Russian Railways. Special fares.
‡ – Timings between Nürnberg and München via Augsburg are subject to alteration until June 23.

850 FRANKFURT and NÜRNBERG - ERFURT - LEIPZIG / HALLE - BERLIN

SERVICE TO AUGUST 9 AND FROM OCTOBER 28 (see page 567 for service August 10 - October 27). See Table **902** for other services Frankfurt - Berlin via Braunschweig.

Other regional services: Table **845** Lutherstadt Wittenberg - Berlin. Table **848** Leipzig / Halle - Bitterfeld - Lutherstadt Wittenberg. Table **849** Eisenach - Erfurt - Weimar - Leipzig / Halle.

km		ICE 1618	EN 453	ICE 1606	ICE 992	ICE 892	ICE 806	ICE 806	ICE 1531	ICE 1604	ICE 1604	ICE 1704	ICE 1714	ICE 1553	ICE 1008	ICE 804	ICE 696	ICE 696	ICE 1533	ICE 602	ICE 1555	ICE 1006	ICE 802
		①-⑤	⑤	①-⑥		②-⑤	①-⑤		①-⑥	Ⓐ	Ⓑ	①-⑤	⑥	⑥	Ⓐ	⑥	①-⑥		①-⑤				
		r	★	e	E	◇	e		eR	d		aJ	JO	u	t	k	eH	H	D				
		🍷	Ⓡ	✕	✕	✕	✕	✕	✕	✕	✕	✕	✕	🍷	✕	✕	✕	✕	✕	✕	✕	✕	✕
	Stuttgart Hbf **912** d.	...	...	...	0012	...	...	...	...	...	...	...	...	...	...	...	...	...	...	...	...	...	...
	Wiesbaden Hbf **911** d.	...	...	...	|	...	...	...	...	...	...	...	...	...	...	...	...	...	...	...	...	...	...
	Frankfurt Flughafen ✈ § d.	...	...	...	0230	...	...	...	...	...	...	...	...	...	...	...	...	...	...	...	...	...	...
	Frankfurt (Main) Hbf **900/1/2** d.	...	...	...	0249	...	...	...	...	...	...	...	...	...	...	...	0614	...	0702	...	0716	...	...
	Frankfurt (Main) Süd **901** d.	...	0158	...	|	...	...	...	...	...	...	...	...	...	...	...	|	...	|	...	|	...	...
	Fulda **900/1/2** d.	...	|	...	|	...	...	...	...	...	...	...	...	...	...	...	0709	...	|	...	0814	...	...
	Bad Hersfeld d.	...	|	...	|	...	...	...	...	...	...	...	...	...	...	...	|	...	|	...	0840	...	...
	Eisenach **849a** d.	...	|	...	0447	...	0553	...	0638	...	...	...	...	...	...	...	0803	...	|	...	0909	...	...
	Gotha **849a** d.	...	|	...	0501	...	0611	...	0653	...	...	...	...	...	...	...	|	...	|	...	0923	...	...
	München Hbf **904 905** d.	...	|	...	|	...	|	...	|	...	...	...	...	...	0557	0547	|	...	|	0657	|	0752	0713‡
0	**Nürnberg** Hbf **875** d.	...	|	...	|	...	|	...	|	0545	...	...	...	...	0701	0703	|	...	|	0804	|	0858	0905
24	Erlangen **875** d.	...	|	...	|	...	|	...	|	0600	...	...	...	...	|	0718	|	...	|	0819	|	|	|
62	**Bamberg** **875** d.	...	|	...	|	...	|	...	|	0622	...	...	...	...	|	0740	|	...	|	0842	|	|	0940
	Coburg **875** d.	...	|	...	|	...	|	...	|	0644	...	...	...	...	|	|	|	...	|	|	|	|	|
190	**Erfurt** Hbf **849a** a.	...	0438	...	0521	...	0626	...	0708	0724	...	...	...	...	0809	0824	0826p	...	0907	0926	0938	1009	1024
190	**Erfurt** Hbf d.	...	0443	...	0523	...	0628	...	0710	0727	...	...	...	0741	0811	0832	0828	0828	0909	0928	0940	1011	1032
	Leipzig Hbf a.	...	|	...	|	...	0710	...	|	0810	...	...	...	0825	|	|	0910	0910	|	1010	1024	|	|
	Leipzig Hbf d.	0508	|	0616	|	...	0716	0716	|	0818	0818	0818	0818	0831	|	|	0916	0916	|	1016	1031	|	|
	Dresden Hbf **842** a.	|	|	|	|	...	|	|	|	|	|	|	|	0939	|	|	|	|	|	|	1139	|	|
284	**Halle** (Saale) Hbf d.	|	|	|	0640	0640	|	|	0745	|	|	|	|	...	0840	0906	|	|	0945	|	...	1040	1106
314	Bitterfeld d.	0530	|	|	0658	0658	|	|	0803	|	|	|	|	...	|	0924	|	|	|	|	...	|	1124
351	Lutherstadt Wittenberg d.	0547	|	0648	|	|	0748	0748	|	0848	0848	0848	0848	...	|	|	0948	0948	|	1048	...	|	|
442	**Berlin** Südkreuz a.	0622	|	0722	0751	0751	0825	0825	0851	0923	0923	0923	0923	...	0944	1017	1022	1022	1048	1122	...	1144	1217
448	**Berlin** Hbf a.	0629	0721	0729	0758	0758	0832	0832	0858	0930	0930	0930	0930	...	0951	1024	1029	1029	1055	1129	...	1151	1224
	Hamburg Hbf **840** a.	...	...	0924	...	...	1021	1021	...	1124	1124	1124	...	...	...	...	1221	1221	...	1324	...	...	1421

	ICE 694	ICE 1535	ICE 1600	ICE 1710	ICE 1557	ICE 1724	ICE 1584	ICE 800	ICE 692	ICE 1537	ICE 508	ICE 1559	ICE 1004	ICE 690	ICE 1539	ICE 506	ICE 1651	ICE 92	ICE 706	ICE 598	ICE 1631	ICE 504	ICE 1653
						⑥	⑦																
		S		O		yR	q		M					M				A		M			
	✕	✕	✕	✕	✕	✕	✕	✕	✕	✕	✕	✕	✕	✕	✕	✕	✕	✕	✕	✕	✕	✕	✕
Stuttgart Hbf **912** d.	0651	...	...	...	...	...	...	...	0851	0903c	...	...	...	1051	...	...	...	...	...	1251	...	...	...
Wiesbaden Hbf **911** d.	|	...	...	...	0826	...	...	...	|	|	...	1026	...	|	...	...	1226	...	...	|	...	...	1426
Frankfurt Flughafen ✈ § d.	|	...	...	...	0902	...	...	...	|	|	...	1102	...	|	...	...	1302	...	...	|	...	...	1502
Frankfurt (Main) Hbf **900/1/2** d.	0814	0902	...	...	0920	...	...	...	1014	1102	...	1119	...	1214	1302	...	1319	...	...	1413	1502	...	1520
Frankfurt (Main) Süd **901** d.	|	|	...	...	|	...	...	...	|	|	...	|	...	|	|	...	|	...	...	|	|	...	|
Fulda **900/1/2** d.	0909	|	...	...	1014	...	...	...	1109	|	...	1214	...	1309	|	...	1414	...	...	1509	|	...	1614
Bad Hersfeld d.	|	|	...	...	1040	...	...	...	|	|	...	1240	...	|	|	...	1440	...	...	|	|	...	1640
Eisenach **849a** d.	1002	|	...	...	1109	...	...	...	1202	|	...	1309	...	1402	|	...	1509	...	...	1602	|	...	1709
Gotha **849a** d.	|	|	...	...	1123	...	...	...	|	|	...	1323	...	|	|	...	1523	...	...	|	|	...	1723
München Hbf **904 905** d.	|	|	0856	0856	|	0919	0921	0954	|	|	1013‡	|	1157	|	|	1255	|	...	1355	|	|	1456	|
Nürnberg Hbf **875** d.	|	|	1005	1005	|	1036	1036	1106	|	|	1204	|	1301	|	|	1404	|	1437	1506	|	|	1604	|
Erlangen **875** d.	|	|	1019	1019	|	|	|	|	|	|	1219	|	|	|	|	1419	|	|	|	|	|	1619	|
Bamberg **875** d.	|	|	|	|	|	|	|	1140	|	|	1242	|	|	|	|	1442	|	|	1540	|	|	1642	|
Coburg **875** d.	|	|	|	|	|	1129	1129	|	|	|	|	|	|	|	|	|	|	1529	|	|	|	|	|
Erfurt Hbf **849a** a.	1026p	1107	1126	1126	1138	1202	1202	1224	1226p	1307	1326	1338	1409	1426	1507	1526	1538	1602	1624	1626p	1707	1726	1738
Erfurt Hbf d.	1028	1109	1128	1128	1140	1204	1204	1232	1228	1309	1328	1340	1411	1428	1509	1528	1540	1604	1632	1628	1709	1728	1740
Leipzig Hbf a.	1110	|	1210	1210	1224	|	|	|	1310	|	1410	1424	|	1510	|	1610	1624	|	|	1710	|	1810	1824
Leipzig Hbf d.	1116	|	1216	1216	1231	|	|	|	1316	|	1416	1431	|	1516	|	1616	1631	|	|	1716	|	1816	1831
Dresden Hbf **842** a.	|	|	|	|	1339	|	|	|	|	|	|	1539	|	|	|	|	1739	|	|	|	|	|	1939
Halle (Saale) Hbf d.	|	1145	|	|	...	1240	1240	1306	|	1345	|	...	1440	|	1545	|	...	1640	1706	|	1745	|	...
Bitterfeld d.	|	|	|	|	...	|	|	1324	|	|	|	...	|	1535	|	|	...	|	1724	|	|	|	...
Lutherstadt Wittenberg d.	1148	|	1248	1248	...	|	|	|	1348	|	1448	...	|	|	|	1648	...	|	|	1748	|	1848	...
Berlin Südkreuz a.	1222	1248	1322	1322	...	1348	1348	1417	1422	1448	1522	...	1544	1622	1651	1722	...	1751	1817	1822	1851	1922	...
Berlin Hbf a.	1229	1255	1329	1329	...	1355	1355	1424	1429	1455	1529	...	1551	1629	1659	1729	...	1758	1826	1829	1858	1929	...
Hamburg Hbf **840** a.	...	...	1525	...	...	...	...	1621	...	...	1724	...	...	1822	...	1924	...	...	2023	...	...	2124	...

	ICE 1002	ICE 704	IC 1957	ICE 596	IC 1957	EC 218	ICE 1633	ICE 502	ICE 1655	ICE 1655	ICE 1000	ICE 702	ICE 594	ICE 1635	ICE 500	ICE 1657	ICE 592	ICE 1700	ICE 1500	ICE 1510	ICE 592	ICE 1659	ICE 1659
			⑤f		⑤f	①-④	Ⓑ		Ⓑ	⑥	Ⓑ	B				Ⓑ				①-④	⑤⑥	Ⓑ	⑤†
				M			b		h	z	b		M	q			M		T	Y	jM	b	q
	✕	✕		✕	♣	G 🍷	✕	✕	🍷	🍷	✕	✕	✕	✕	✕	✕	✕	✕			✕	✕§	✕§
Stuttgart Hbf **912** d.	...	...	...	1451	...	1404	...	...	...	...	...	...	1651	...	...	...	1851	...	...	...	...	...	...
Wiesbaden Hbf **911** d.	...	...	...	|	...	|	...	...	1626	1626	...	...	|	...	...	1826	|	...	...	...	...	2026	2026
Frankfurt Flughafen ✈ § d.	...	...	...	|	...	|	...	...	|	1702	...	...	|	...	...	1902	|	...	...	...	...	2102	2102
Frankfurt (Main) Hbf **900/1/2** d.	...	...	1546	1613		1614	1702	...	1716	1720	...	...	1814	1902	...	1919	2014	...	...	...	...	2119	2119
Frankfurt (Main) Süd **901** d.	...	...	|	|	...	|	|	...	|	|	...	...	|	|	...	|	|	...	...	...	...	|	|
Fulda **900/1/2** d.	...	...	1655	1709	...	1724	|	...	1816	1814	...	...	1909	|	...	2014	2109	...	...	...	...	2214	2214
Bad Hersfeld d.	...	...	1722	|	...	1753	|	...	1840	1840	...	...	|	|	...	2040	2136	...	...	...	...	2240	2240
Eisenach **849a** d.	...	...	1752	1802	←	1828	|	...	1909	1909	...	...	2002	|	...	2109	2207	...	...	...	...	2309	2309
Gotha **849a** d.	...	...	1805	|	1807	1844	|	...	1923	1923	...	...	|	|	...	2123	2221	...	...	...	...	2323	2323
München Hbf **904 905** d.	1556	1514‡	→	|	|	|	|	1655	|	|	1757	1705‡	|	|	1856	|	|	1955	1955	1955	...	|	|
Nürnberg Hbf **875** d.	1701	1705	...	|	|	|	|	1804	|	|	1901	1905	|	|	2004	|	|	2105	2105	2105	...	|	|
Erlangen **875** d.	|	|	...	|	|	|	|	1819	|	|	|	|	|	|	2019	|	|	2120	2120	2120	...	|	|
Bamberg **875** d.	|	1740	...	|	|	|	|	1842	|	|	|	1940	|	|	2042	|	|	2143	2143	2143	...	|	|
Coburg **875** d.	|	|	...	|	|	|	|	|	|	|	|	|	|	|	|	|	|	2206	2206	2206	←	|	|
Erfurt Hbf **849a** a.	1809	1824	...	1826p	1838	1859	1907	1926	1938	1938	2009	2024	2026p	2107	2126	2138	2236	2238	2238	2238	2236	2338	2338
Erfurt Hbf d.	1811	1832	...	1828	1842	...	1909	1928	1940	1940	2011	2032	2028	2109	2128	2140•	→	2242	2246	2246	2246	...	2340
Leipzig Hbf a.	|	|	...	1910	2016	...	|	2010	2024	2024	|	|	2110	|	2210	2225	...	|	2329	2336	2329	...	0024
Leipzig Hbf d.	|	|	...	1916	...	...	|	2016	2031	2031	|	|	2116	|	2216	2231	...	|	...	...	...	...	...
Dresden Hbf **842** a.	|	|	...	|	...	...	|	|	2138	2138	|	|	|	|	|	2338	...	|	...	...	...	...	...
Halle (Saale) Hbf d.	1840	1906	...	|	...	...	1945	|	...	...	2040	2106	|	2145	|	...	...	2317	...	...	...	...	...
Bitterfeld d.	|	1924	...	|	...	...	|	|	...	...	|	2124	|	|	2234	...	...	|	...	...	...	...	...
Lutherstadt Wittenberg d.	|	|	...	1948	...	...	|	2048	...	...	|	|	2148	|	2251	...	...	2347	...	...	...	...	...
Berlin Südkreuz a.	1944	2017	...	2022	...	...	2048	2122	...	...	2144	2217	2222	2250	2326	...	...	0023	...	...	...	...	...
Berlin Hbf a.	1951	2026	...	2029	...	...	2055	2129	...	...	2151	2224	2229	2258	2335	...	...	0031	...	...	...	...	...
Hamburg Hbf **840** a.	...	2221b	...	...	...	...	...	2333x	...	...	...	0033v	...	...	...	...	...	...	...	...	...	...	...

A – BEROLINA – From Wien (Tables **950** and **920**). To Rostock (Table **835**) on ⑤.
B – Daily to Aug. 9 (not June 9, 15, July 6); Ⓑ from Oct. 28.
D – ①-⑤ (not June 10, 20). From Darmstadt Hbf (d. 0637).
E – Daily to Aug. 9; ①⑥ from Oct. 28. [12] München (d. 2151 previous day) - Stuttgart - Frankfurt - Berlin. Via Weimar (see Table **849a**). ✕ Erfurt - Berlin.
G – ①-④ (not June 10, 19, 20). CHIEMGAU – [12] and 🍷 Graz - München - Frankfurt - Erfurt.
H – [12] and ✕ (Karlsruhe ① g -) (Frankfurt ①-⑥ e -) Erfurt - Leipzig - Kiel.
J – From Jena (Table **849a**).
M – From München via Ulm (Table **930**).
O – To Ostseebad Binz (Tables **844/845**).
R – To Warnemünde via Rostock on dates in Table **835**.
S – PFÄLZER WALD. From Saarbrücken (Table **919**) on ①-⑥ (not Oct. 28).
T – ⑦ to Nov. 3 (not June 9); ①②③④⑦ from Nov. 10.
Y – ①-④ to Nov. 7.

a – Not June 10, Oct. 31.
b – Ⓑ (not June 9).
c – Ⓒ only. 0911 on † (also July 20, 27, Aug. 3).
d – Not Oct. 31.
e – Not June 10.
f – Also June 19, Oct. 31; not June 21, Nov. 1.
g – Also June 11; not June 10.
h – Not June 9, 10.
j – Also June 9.
k – Also June 20.
p – Connects with train in previous column.
q – Not June 9.
r – Not Oct. 31.
t – Not June 20.
u – Also Oct. 3; not Oct. 5.

v – Berlin - Hamburg on ⑤⑦ only.
x – ⑤-⑦ to Aug. 9; daily from Oct. 28.
y – Also June 20, Nov. 1; not Nov. 2.
z – Also June 9, 10.
◇ – From Oct. 29.
• – 2142 on ⑤.
‡ – Services between München and Nürnberg via Augsburg are subject to alteration until June 23.
§ – ✕ Wiesbaden - Fulda.
♣ – Via Weimar (see Table **849a**).
★ – 🛏 1, 2 cl. Paris - Berlin - Warszawa Moskva. See Table **24**. Operated by Russian Railways. Special fares.

COTTBUS - LEIPZIG — 852

/ RB services — *Subject to alteration Sept. 2 - Oct. 28*

	⚒									
Cottbus d.	0505	0705	0905	1105	1305	1505	1705	1905	2048	2305
Calau (Niederl) d.	0522	0722	0922	1122	1322	1522	1722	1922	2106	2324
Finsterwalde d.	0536	0736	0936	1136	1336	1536	1736	1936	2120	2340
Doberlug-Kirchhain d.	0543	0743	0943	1143	1343	1543	1743	1943	2127	2349
Falkenberg 856 d.	0600	0800	1000	1200	1400	1600	1800	2000	2147	0016
Torgau 856 d.	0612	0812	1012	1212	1412	1612	1812	2012	2159	...
Eilenburg 856 d.	0635	0835	1035	1235	1435	1635	1835	2035	2223	...
Leipzig Hbf 856 a.	0657	0857	1057	1257	1457	1657	1857	2057	2247	...

		⚒								
Leipzig Hbf 856 d.	...	0704	0904	1104	1304	1504	1704	1904	2104	2333
Eilenburg 856 d.	...	0724	0924	1124	1324	1524	1724	1924	2124	2351
Torgau 856 d.	...	0746	0946	1146	1346	1546	1746	1946	2146	0012
Falkenberg 856 d.	0652	0801	1001	1201	1401	1601	1801	2001	2201	0026
Doberlug-Kirchhain d.	0714	0814	1014	1214	1414	1614	1814	2014	2214	0040
Finsterwalde d.	0722	0822	1022	1222	1422	1622	1822	2022	2222	0048
Calau (Niederl) d.	0736	0836	1036	1236	1436	1636	1836	2036	2236	0101
Cottbus a.	0754	0854	1054	1254	1454	1654	1854	2054	2254	0118

er stopping trains: Cottbus → Falkenberg at 0604 Ⓐ, 0804, 1204, 1404, 1604, 1804, 2004, 2104. Falkenberg → Cottbus at 0443, 0552 Ⓐ, 0852 Ⓒ, 0855 Ⓐ, 1255, 1452, 1652, 1852.

STEAM TRAINS IN SACHSEN — 853

Lößnitzgrundbahn. SDG Sächsische Dampfeisenbahngesellschaft mbH, Am Bahnhof 1, 01468 Moritzburg. ✆ +49 (0) 35207 89290. SEE NOTE ⊠. www.loessnitzgrundbahn.de

	Ⓐe							A		
Radebeul Ost 842 857 d.	0515	...	0826	0956	1256	1426	...	1726	1856	...
Moritzburg d.	0541	...	0854	1027	1324	1457	...	1754	1924	...
Radeburg a.	0603	...	...	1050	...	1520	...	...	...	...

	Ⓐe								A
Radeburg d.	0625	...	...	1108	...	1538	...	...	...
Moritzburg d.	0648	...	0903	1135	1333	1605	1803	...	1933
Radebeul Ost 842 857 a.	0715	...	0930	1202	1400	1632	1830	...	2000

Weißeritztalbahn. SDG Sächsische Dampfeisenbahngesellschaft mbH, Am Bahnhof 1, 01468 Moritzburg. ✆ +49 (0) 35207 89290. SEE NOTE ❖. www.weisseritztalbahn.com

		B🚌		B	n	B	B🚌	n	B	
Dresden Hbf ▷ d.	*0906*	...	...	*1106*	*1234*	*1406*	...	*1506*	*1634*	...
Freital-Hainsberg ▷ a.	*0918*	...	...	*1118*	*1247*	*1418*	...	*1518*	*1647*	...
Freital-Hainsberg d.	0925	...	...	1141	1322	1425	...	1542	1700	...
Dippoldiswalde d.	1018	1022	...	1231	1407	1515	1522	1635	1750	...
Kurort Kipsdorf a.	1051n	1040	...	...	...	...	1540	1708	...	...

	B	n	B🚌	B	n	B	n	B🚌	B
Kurort Kipsdorf d.	...	1111	1210	...	...	...	1728	1730	...
Dippoldiswalde d.	1028	1145	1228	1244	1420	1528	1802	1748	1803
Freital-Hainsberg a.	1116	1230	...	1332	1505	1616	1847	...	1851
Freital-Hainsberg ▷ d.	*1138*	*1238*	...	*1338*	*1508*	*1638*	*1908*	...	*1908*
Dresden Hbf ▷ a.	*1150*	*1250*	...	*1350*	*1522*	*1650*	*1922*	...	*1922*

Zittauer Schmalspurbahn. SOEG - Sächisch Oberlausitzer Eisenbahngesellschaft mbH, Bahnhofstraße 41, 02763 Zittau. ✆ +49 (0) 3583 540540. www.soeg-zittau.de

			🍷	C d		🍷		C d		🍷		C d		🍷		C d		C d
Zittau d.	High	0850	0907	1002	...	1107	...	1202	...	1311	...	1402	...	1507	...	1602	...	...
Bertsdorf d.	season	0945r	0945t	1033	1034	1145t	1145	1233	1234	1348t	1348	1433	1434	1545t	1545	1634	1634	1723
Kurort Oybin a.	♥	|	0956	|	1045	1156	|	|	1245	1358	|	|	1445	1556	|	1645	|	1733
Kurort Jonsdorf a.	→	0956	...	1047	...	...	1156	1247	...	...	1359	1447	...	...	1556	...	1646	...

		🍷	🍷	🍷	🍷	🍷	🍷
Zittau d.	Low	0907	...	...	1307	...	...
Bertsdorf d.	season	0938	1035	1133	1338	1435	1533
Kurort Oybin a.	♣	0949	|	1145	1349	|	1545
Kurort Jonsdorf a.	→	...	1046	...	...	1446	...

			🍷		C d		🍷		C d		🍷		C d		🍷	C d		C d
rt Jonsdorf d.	High	1006	...	...	1057	1206	...	...	1257	1408	...	...	1457	1606	...	...	1710	...
urort Oybin d.	season	|	1007	1056	|	|	1207	1256	|	|	1408	1456	|	|	1607	1705	|	1743
sdorf d.	♥	1017	1020	1106	1110	1217	1220	1306	1310	1419	1420	1506	1510	1617	1620	1716	1723	1754
u a.	→	...	1054	...	1138	...	1251	...	1341	...	1451	...	1538	...	1651	...	1754	1825

		🍷	🍷	🍷	🍷	🍷	🍷
rt Jonsdorf d.	Low	...	1056	...	...	1456	...
urort Oybin d.	season	0959	|	1156	1359	|	1556
sdorf d.	♣	1010	1107	1208	1410	1507	1608
u a.	→	...	...	1237	...	...	1637

Until Oct. 31.
July 17 - Nov. 3.
⑥⑦ (also June 10, Oct. 3, 4, 31, Nov. 1).
Diesel train.

e – Not July 8 - Aug. 16, Oct. 14 – 25, 31, Nov. 1 – 20.
n – Not July 17 - Nov. 3.
r – Arrives 0922.
t – Arrives 6 minutes earlier.

▷ – Suggested main line connecting service operated by Mitteldeutsche Regiobahn.
⊠ – A special service operates Sept. 13 – 15. No service Nov. 1 – 19.
❖ – No service Nov. 4 – 15. An enhanced operates on ⑥⑦ from Nov. 30.
♥ – Apr. 6 - Nov. 3.
♣ – From Nov. 30 (no service Nov. 4 – 29).

FORST - COTTBUS - GÖRLITZ - ZITTAU — 854

EG ★ 2nd class only

	Ⓐt		Ⓐ	⚒t		⚒			⚒															
Cottbus d.	...	...	0504	...	...	0604	...	0704	0804	0904	1004	1104	1204	1304	1404	1504	1604	1704	1804	1904	2004	2104	2204	2305
Spremberg d.	...	...	0522	...	...	0622	...	0722	0822	0922	1022	1122	1222	1322	1422	1522	1622	1722	1822	1922	2022	2122	2222	2322
Weißwasser d.	...	...	0535	...	...	0635	...	0735	0835	0935	1035	1135	1235	1335	1435	1535	1635	1735	1835	1935	2035	2135	2235	2335
Horka d.	...	...	0559	...	...	0659	...	0759	0859	0959	1059	1159	1259	1359	1459	1559	1659	1759	1859	1959	2059	2159	2259	2359
Görlitz a.	...	...	0614	...	...	0714	...	0814	0914	1014	1114	1214	1314	1414	1514	1614	1714	1814	1914	2014	2114	2214	2314	0014
Görlitz d.	0515	...	0616t	0616	...	0719	0719	0817	0917t	1017	1117	1217	1317	1417	1517	1617	1717	1817	1917	2017	...	2217	...	...
Zittau a.	0554	...	0655t	0655	...	0756	0756	0856	0956t	1056	1156	1256	1356	1456	1556	1656	1756	1856	1956	2056	...	2256	...	...

	Ⓐ	⚒		⚒t	⚒	Ⓐt						⚒t													
u d.	...	...	...	0458	...	0559	...	0700	0800	0900	...	1000	1100	1200	1300	1400	1500	1600	1700	1800	1900	2000	...	...	2200
itz a.	...	...	...	0534	...	0635	...	0738	0836	0936	...	1036	1136	1236	1336	1436	1536	1636	1736	1836	1936	2036	...	...	2236
itz d.	0343	0443	0543	0543	0643	0643	...	0743	0843	0943	1043	1043	1143	1243	1343	1443	1543	1643	1743	1843	1943	2043	2143	...	...
a d.	0359	0459	0559	0559	0659	0659	...	0759	0859	0959	1059	1059	1159	1259	1359	1459	1559	1659	1759	1859	1959	2059	2159	...	...
wasser d.	0420	0520	0620	0620	0720	0720	...	0820	0920	1020	1120	1120	1220	1320	1420	1520	1620	1720	1820	1920	2020	2120	2220	...	...
mberg d.	0435	0538	0638	0638	0738	0738	...	0838	0938	1038	1138	1138	1238	1338	1438	1538	1638	1738	1838	1938	2038	2138	2238	...	...
ous a.	0453	0556	0656	0656	0756	0756	...	0856	0956	1056	1156	1156	1256	1356	1456	1556	1656	1756	1856	1956	2056	2156	2256	...	...

ST (Lausitz) - **COTTBUS** and v.v. *22 km*. Journey time: 18 – 19 minutes.
n Forst at 0431 Ⓐ, 0533, 0633 and hourly until 2133. **From Cottbus** at 0507 Ⓐ, 0607, 0707 and hourly until 2107; then 2309.

Not Oct. 31, Nov. 20.

★ – Ostdeutsche Eisenbahn. ✆ +49 (0) 30 514 88 88 88. www.odeg.de

DRESDEN - BISCHOFSWERDA - GÖRLITZ and ZITTAU — 855

ex (2nd class only)

	Ⓒz		Ⓐt		⚒tw						w				Ⓐt			Ⓐt	w					
Dresden Hbf d.	0048	...	0408	0535	0608	0635	0808	0835	1008	1035	1208	1235	1408	1435	1508	1608	1635	1708	1808	1835	2008	2035	2235	2334
Dresden Neustadt d.	0055	...	0415	0542	0615	0642	0815	0842	1015	1042	1215	1242	1415	1442	1515	1615	1642	1715	1815	1842	2015	2042	2242	2341
Bischofswerda d.	0131	...	0500	0621	0643	0717	0843	0917	1043	1117	1243	1317	1443	1517	1547	1643	1717	1747	1843	1917	2043	2117	2324	0021
Bautzen d.	0146	...	0514	0636	0656	0732	0856	0932	1056	1132	1256	1332	1456	1532	1559	1656	1732	1759	1856	1932	2056	2132	2338	0035
Löbau (Sachs) d.	0203	...	0533	0655	0710	0751	0910	0951	1110	1151	1310	1351	1510	1551	1614	1710	1751	1814	1910	1951	2110	2151	2357	0054
Görlitz a.	0222	...	0553	0714	0725	0812	0925	1012	1125	1212	1325	1412	1525	1612	1628	1725	1812	1828	1925	2012	2125	2212	0017	0114

				⚒t		w						w						w						
tz d.	0443	0539	0606	0640	0743	0841	0943	1041	1143	1241	1343	1441	1543	1641	1743	1841	1943	2041	...	2243	...	...	...	...
u (Sachs) d.	0504	0554	0627	0655	0804	0856	1004	1056	1204	1256	1404	1456	1604	1656	1804	1856	2004	2056	...	2304	...	...	...	...
zen d.	0522	0608	0645	0710	0822	0910	1022	1110	1222	1310	1422	1510	1622	1710	1822	1910	2022	2110	...	2322	...	...	...	...
ofswerda d.	0538	0620	0701	0722	0838	0922	1038	1122	1238	1322	1438	1522	1638	1722	1838	1922	2038	2122	...	2343	...	...	...	...
den Neustadt a.	0611	0647	0735	0749	0911	0949	1111	1149	1311	1349	1511	1549	1711	1749	1911	1949	2111	2149	...	0015	...	...	...	...
den Hbf a.	0620	0656	0742	0756	0920	0956	1120	1156	1320	1356	1520	1556	1720	1756	1920	1956	2120	2156	...	0021	...	...	...	...

	Ⓐt																							
Dresden Hbf d.	0408	0535	0708	0735	0908	0935	1108	1135	1308	1335	1508	1535	1708	1735	1908	1935	2134	2235	2334	...	...	...	...	...
Dresden Neustadt d.	0415	0542	0715	0742	0915	0942	1115	1142	1315	1342	1515	1542	1715	1742	1915	1942	2141	2242	2341	...	...	...	...	...
Bischofswerda d.	0454	0618	0743	0818	0943	1018	1143	1218	1343	1418	1545	1618	1745	1818	1943	2018	2215	2322	0018	...	...	...	...	...
Ebersbach (Sachs) d.	0530	0701	0815	0901	1015	1101	1215	1301	1415	1501	1615	1701	1815	1901	2015	2101	2245	2359	0048	...	...	...	...	...
Neugersdorf d.	0534	0705	0819	0905	1019	1105	1219	1305	1419	1505	1619	1705	1819	1905	2019	2105	2249	0003	0052	...	...	...	...	...
Zittau a.	0556	0727	0837	0927	1037	1127	1237	1327	1437	1527	1638	1727	1838	1927	2037	2127	2308	0025	0110	...	...	...	...	...
Liberec **1117** a.	...	...	0919	...	1124	...	...	...	1524	...	1715	...	1915	...	...	...	...	...	...	...	...	...	...	...

	⚒t		Ⓐt																					
erec **1117** d.	...	...	...	...	...	...	0838	...	1038	...	...	...	1433	...	1633	...	1833	...	...	...	...	...	...	...
u d.	0351	0505	0541	0633	0721	0832	0921	1032	1121	1232	1321	1432	1521	1632	1721	1832	1921	2032	2121	2215	...	...	...	...
ersdorf d.	0413	0523	0559	0656	0739	0855	0939	1055	1139	1255	1339	1455	1539	1655	1739	1855	1939	2055	2139	2237	...	...	...	...
sbach (Sachs) d.	0417	0531	0603	0701	0744	0900	0944	1100	1144	1300	1344	1500	1544	1700	1744	1900	1944	2100	2144	2245	...	...	...	...
ofswerda d.	0454	0605	0639	0738	0814	0938	1014	1138	1214	1338	1414	1538	1619	1738	1819	1938	2014	2138	2214	2321	2343	...	...	...
den Neustadt a.	0526	0633	0711	0811	0841	1011	1041	1211	1241	1411	1441	1611	1646	1811	1846	2011	2041	2211	2242	...	0015	...	...	...
den Hbf a.	0539	0640	0720	0820	0848	1020	1048	1220	1248	1420	1448	1620	1656	1820	1856	2020	2048	2220	2248	...	0021	...	...	...

Not Oct. 31, Nov. 20.

w – To / from Wrocław (Table **1085**).

z – Also Oct. 31, Nov. 20.

856 DRESDEN and LEIPZIG - RUHLAND - COTTBUS and HOYERSWERDA *RE* | *RB* servic

See Tables **842**, **843** and **857** for other services Dresden - Coswig. See Table **852** for other direct services Leipzig - Falkenberg - Cottbus.

km			Ⓐ	E		Ⓐ	Ⓒ																
0	**Dresden** Hbf d.	...	...	...	0551	...	...	0651	...	0751	...		1651	...	1751	...	1851	...	1951	...	2051	...	2151
4	**Dresden** Neustadt d.	...	...	...	0558	...	...	0658	...	0758	...		1658	...	1758	...	1858	...	1958	...	2058	...	2158
18	Coswig d.	...	...	...	0609	...	...	0709	...	0809	...		1709	...	1809	...	1909	...	2009	...	2109	...	2209
	Leipzig-Stötteritz ★ d.	...	...	...	|	...	...	|	0545	|	...	and in	|	1545	|	...	|	1745	|	...	|	1945	|
	Leipzig Hbf ★ d.	...	...	...	|	...	...	|	0558	|	...	the same	|	1558	|	...	|	1758	|	...	|	1958	|
	Eilenburg d.	...	...	...	|	...	...	|	0628	|	...		|	1628	|	...	|	1828	|	...	|	2028	|
	Torgau d.	...	...	...	|	...	...	|	0649	|	...	pattern	|	1649	|	...	|	1849	|	...	|	2049	|
	Falkenberg (Elster) a.	...	...	...	|	...	...	|	0709	|	...	every **two**	|	1709	|	...	|	1909	|	...	|	2109	|
	Falkenberg (Elster) d.	...	0413	...	|	0613	...	|	0717	|	0813		|	1717	|	1813	|	1917	|	2013	|	2117	|
	Elsterwerda-Biehla d.	...	0432	0522	|	0632	...	|	0735	|	0832	hours until	|	1735	|	1832	|	1935	|	2032	|	2135	|
73	Ruhland a.	...	0453	0554	0655	0653	...	0755	0756	0855	0853		1755	1756	1855	1853	1955	1956	2055	2053	2155	2156	2255
73	Ruhland d.	0458	0458	0559	0702	0658	0659	0800	0802	0902	0858		1800	1802	1902	1858	2000	2002	2102	2058	2200	2202	2302
	Hoyerswerda a.	|	|	|	0723	|	|	|	0824	0923	|		|	1824	1923	|	|	2024	2125	|	|	2224	2325
86	Senftenberg d.	0509	0509	0610	...	0709	0709	0810	...	...	0909		1810	...	...	1909	2010	...	...	2109	2210	...	...
120	**Cottbus** a.	0541	0541	0641	...	0741	0741	0839	...	...	0941		1839	...	...	1941	2039	...	...	2141	2239	...	...

km		Ⓐ				Ⓒ	Ⓐ															D	
	Cottbus d.	0415	...	...	0516	0615	0615	...	...	0716	0815	...		...	1716	1815	...	...	1916	2015	...	2215	...
	Senftenberg d.	0446	...	...	0544	0645	0646	...	...	0744	0846	...		...	1744	1846	...	...	1944	2046	...	2246	...
0	**Hoyerswerda** d.	|	0429	0534	|	|	|	0629	0734	|	|	0830		1734	|	|	1830	1934	|	|	2029	|	...
25	Ruhland a.	0456	0451	0555	0553	0655	0656	0651	0755	0753	0856	0851	and in	1755	1753	1856	1851	1955	1953	2056	2051	2256	...
25	Ruhland d.	0505	0502	0602	0602	...	0705	0702	0802	0802	0905	0902	the same	1802	1802	1905	1902	2002	2002	2105	2102	2305	...
51	Elsterwerda-Biehla d.	0528	|	0624	|	...	0728	|	0824	|	0928	|		1824	|	1928	|	2024	|	2128	|	2327	...
75	Falkenberg (Elster) a.	0547	|	0646	|	...	0747	|	0846	|	0947	|	pattern	1846	|	1947	|	2046	|	2147	|	...	...
75	Falkenberg (Elster) d.	...	|	0657	|	...	...	|	0857	|	...	|	every **two**	1857	|	...	|	2057	|	...	|	...	...
93	Torgau d.	...	|	0713	|	...	...	|	0913	|	...	|		1913	|	...	|	2113	|	...	|	...	...
120	Eilenburg d.	...	|	0735	|	...	...	|	0935	|	...	|	hours until	1935	|	...	|	2135	|	...	|	...	...
145	**Leipzig** Hbf ★ a.	...	|	0803	|	...	...	|	1003	|	...	|		2003	|	...	|	2203	|	...	|	...	...
152	Leipzig-Stötteritz ★ a.	...	|	0816	|	...	...	|	1016	|	...	|		2016	|	...	|	2216	|	...	|	...	...
	Coswig d.	...	0547	...	0647	...	...	0747	...	0847	...	0947		...	1847	...	1947	...	2047	...	2147	...	...
	Dresden Neustadt d.	...	0556	...	0656	...	...	0756	...	0856	...	0956		...	1856	...	1956	...	2056	...	2156	...	...
	Dresden Hbf a.	...	0601	...	0701	...	...	0801	...	0901	...	1001		...	1901	...	2001	...	2101	...	2201	...	...

D – To Elsterwerda (a. 2331).
E – From Elsterwerda (d. 0519).

★ – Trains also call City Tunnel stations Leipzig MDR, Bayerischer Bahnhof, Wilhelm-Leuschner-Platz and Markt.

857 BAD SCHANDAU - DRESDEN - MEISSEN *S-B*

km							Ⓐr			⚒r		✣									
0	**Bad Schandau** ⊡ 1100 d.	...	0015	...	...	...	0445	...	0515	0545	...	0615	0645		2011	2045	2115	2145	2215	2245	2315
23	Pirna d.	0007	0037	...	...	0437	0507	0507	0537	0607	0607	0637	0707	and every	2037	2107	2137	2207	2237	2307	2337
40	**Dresden** Hbf 842/3 856 1100 d.	0028	0058	...	0430	0500	0530	0530	0600	0630	0630	0700	0730	30 minutes	2100	2130	2200	2230	2300	2330	0000
44	**Dresden** Neustadt 842 856 d.	...	...	...	0437	0507	0537	0537	0607	0637	0637	0707	0737		2107	2137	2207	2237	2307	2337	0007
50	Radebeul Ost d.	...	...	...	0446	0516	0546	0546	0616	0646	0646	0716	0746	until	2116	2146	2216	2246	2316	2346	0016
58	Coswig 842/3 856 d.	...	...	...	0456	0526	0556	0556	0626	0656	0656	0726	0756		2126	2156	2226	2256	2326	2356	0026
68	**Meißen** a.	...	...	...	0504	0534	0604	0604	0634	0704	0704	0734	0804		2134	2204	2234	2304	2334	0004	0034

					Ⓐr			⚒r													
Meißen d.	0021	...	...	...	...	0421	0451	0451	0521	0551		2021	2051	2121	2151	2221	2251	2321	...	...	...
Coswig 842/3 856 d.	0030	...	...	...	...	0430	0500	0500	0530	0600	and every	2030	2100	2130	2200	2230	2300	2330	...	...	...
Radebeul Ost d.	0040	...	...	...	...	0440	0510	0510	0540	0610		2040	2110	2140	2210	2240	2310	2340	...	...	...
Dresden Neustadt 842 856 d.	0050	...	...	...	...	0450	0520	0520	0550	0620	30 minutes	2050	2120	2150	2220	2250	2320	2350	...	...	...
Dresden Hbf 842/3 856 1100 d.	0057	0100	...	0429	0429	0459	0529	0529	0559	0629	until	2059	2129	2159	2229	2259	2329	0012f	...	...	...
Pirna d.	...	0121	...	0450	0451	0521	0550	0551	0621	0651		2121	2151	2221	2251	2321	2350	0034	...	...	...
Bad Schandau ⊡ 1100 a.	...	...	...	...	0513	0543	...	0613	0643	0713		2143	2213	2243	2313	2343	...	0056	...	...	...

f – Arrives 2357.
r – Not Oct. 31, Nov. 20.

✣ – Subsequent trains depart Bad Schandau 0715, 0811, 0915, 1011, 1115, 1211, 1315, 1411, 1515, 1611, 1715, 1811 and 1915 (other timings follow the same pattern).

⊡ – A frequent ferry services links the railway station with Bad Schandau town centre. **Operator**: Oberelbische Verkehrsgesellschaft Pirna - Sebnitz mbH. www.ovps.de ✆ +49 (0) 3501 7920.

857a DRESDEN - DRESDEN FLUGHAFEN ✈ *S-B*

km									
0	**Dresden** Hbf d.	0418	0448	and every	2218	2248	2318	...	...
4	**Dresden** Neustadt d.	0425	0455	30 minutes	2225	2255	2325	...	...
15	**Dresden** Flughafen ✈ a.	0439	0509	until	2239	2309	2339	...	...

Dresden Flughafen ✈ d.	0448	0518	and every	2248	2318	2348	...
Dresden Neustadt a.	0500	0530	30 minutes	2300	2330	2400	...
Dresden Hbf a.	0509	0539	until	2309	2339	0009	...

858 GLAUCHAU and ALTENBURG - GERA - ERFURT *RE* servi

km		Ⓐe‡	Ⓒz‡	⚒r		G★	⑦h						★						⑥k	B★				‡	‡
0	**Glauchau** (Sachs) d.	...	...	...	...	...	...	0607r	...	0807	...	1007	...	1207	...	1407	...	1607	...	...	1807	...	2007	...	...
16	Gößnitz a.	...	...	...	...	...	...	0620r	...	0820	...	1020	...	1220	...	1420	...	1620	...	...	1820	...	2020	...	...
16	Gößnitz d.	...	...	...	...	...	...	0628	...	0828	...	1028	...	1228	...	1428	...	1628	...	...	1828	...	2028	...	...
	Altenburg d.	...	...	*0418*e	0507r	...	...	|	0725	|	0925	|	*1125*	|	1325	|	1525	|	1725	*1725*	|	1925	|	*2125*	*2302*
51	**Gera** Hbf a.	...	...	*0455*e	0545r	...	...	0659	0800	0859	1000	1059	*1200*	1259	1400	1459	1600	1659	1800	*1800*	1859	2000	2059	*2200*	*2338*
51	**Gera** Hbf d.	...	...	0503	0555	0603	0619	0705	0805	0905	1005	1105	1203	1305	1405	1505	1605	1705	1805	1803	1905	2005	2105	2210	2342
91	Jena-Göschwitz d.	0411	0416	0532	0624	0638	0647	0732	0832	0932	1032	1132	1238	1332	1432	1532	1632	1732	1832	1838	1932	2032	2132	2240	0015
96	**Jena** West d.	0416	0421	0538	0630	0644	0653	0738	0838	0938	1038	1138	1244	1338	1438	1538	1638	1738	1838	1844	1938	2038	2138	2245	0020
119	Weimar 849 850 d.	0438	0438	0554	0646	0702	0708	0755	0855	0955	1055	1155	1302	1355	1455	1555	1655	1755	1855	1902	1955	2055	2155	2302	0038
140	**Erfurt** Hbf 849 850 a.	0455	0452	0607	0702	0716	0721	0807	0909	1007	1109	1207	1316	1407	1509	1607	1709	1807	1910	1916	2007	2108	2207	2316	...
	Göttingen **865** a.	...	...	0751	...	...	...	0951	...	1151	...	1351	...	1551	...	1751	...	1951	...	...	2150	2256	...	...	...

km		‡		Ⓐe				G★	⑦h						★						Ⓑ	B★	⑥k		
	Göttingen **865** d.	...	...	...	...	...	0604	...	...	0808	...	1008	...	1208	...	1408	...	1608	...	1808	1808	...	...	2008	2108
	Erfurt Hbf 849 850 d.	0031	0439	0544	...	0650	0750	0844	0850	0952	1050	1150	1250	1352	1444	1550	1650	1752	1850	1952	1952	2044	2050	2150	2302
	Weimar 849 850 d.	0051	0453	0557	...	0705	0805	0859	0904	1006	1104	1204	1304	1406	1459	1605	1704	1806	1904	2007	2007	2059	2104	2204	2314
	Jena West d.	0110	0507	0612	...	0719	0820	0915	0919	1022	1119	1220	1319	1422	1515	1620	1719	1822	1919	2022	2022	2115	2119	2220	2329
	Jena-Göschwitz d.	0116	0516	0625	...	0724	0825	0921	0924	1027	1124	1225	1324	1427	1521	1625	1724	1827	1924	2027	2027	2121	2124	2225	2334
	Gera Hbf a.	0147z	0544	0654	...	0753	0853	0955	0953	1055	1153	1253	1353	1455	1555	1654	1753	1855	1953	2056	2056	2155	2153	2253	0002
0	**Gera** Hbf d.	...	0547	0658	0658	0758	0858	*0958*	0958	1058	1158	1258	1358	1458	*1558*	1658	1758	1858	1958	...	2058	...	...	2304	...
50	**Altenburg** a.	...	0624	|	|	0832	|	*1032*	1032	|	1232	|	1432	|	*1632*	|	1832	|	2032	...	|	...	...	2343	...
	Gößnitz a.	...	...	0728	0728	...	0928	...	...	1128	...	1328	...	1528	...	1728	...	1928	...	...	2128	...	...	...	...
	Gößnitz d.	...	...	0737	0737	...	0937	...	...	1137	...	1337	...	1537	...	1737	...	1937	...	...	2137	...	...	...	...
	Glauchau (Sachs) a.	...	...	0750	0750	...	0950	...	...	1150	...	1350	...	1550	...	1750	...	1950	...	...	2150	...	...	...	...

B – Ⓑ (not June 9).
G – ①–⑥ (not June 10).
e – Ⓐ (not Oct. 31).

h – Also June 10.
k – Also June 9.
r – ⚒ (not Oct. 31).
z – Ⓒ (also Oct. 31).

★ – *IC* service (see Table **849a**). Regional tickets valid Gera - Erfurt and v.v. (also for connectin regional services from / to Altenburg).
‡ – Operated by Erfurter Bahn.

BRAUNSCHWEIG - BAD HARZBURG, GOSLAR and HERZBERG — 859

)B (*RB* services); *erixx*

BRAUNSCHWEIG - GOSLAR and BAD HARZBURG ⊠

km		⚒	Ⓐ	⚒	⚒																		
0	**Braunschweig** Hbf d.	0524	0524	0624	0624	0724	0724	and	2124	2124	2224	2224	2324	2324	...	...	...	...	...	...	...	...	...
12	Wolfenbüttel d.	0533	0533	0633	0633	0733	0733	hourly	2133	2133	2233	2233	2333	2333	...	...	...	...	...	...	...	...	...
39	Vienenburg 860 d.	0601	0602	0700	0702	0800	0802		2200	2202	2300	2302	0000	0002	...	...	...	...	...	...	...	...	...
47	**Bad Harzburg** 860 a.	|	0611	|	0711	|	0811	until	|	2211	|	2311	|	0011	...	...	...	...	...	...	...	...	...
	Goslar 860 a.	0616	...	0712	...	0812	...		2212	...	2312	...	0012	...	...	...	...	...	...	...	...	...	...

km		⚒	⚒	⚒	Ⓐ	Ⓐ	Ⓒ	Ⓒ																
0	**Goslar** 860 d.	0445	...	0545	...	0645	...	0645	...	0745	and	...	2145	...	2245	...	...	...	...	...	...	...	...
	Bad Harzburg 860 d.	|	0545	|	0626	|	0645	|	0745	|		2145	|	2245	|	...	...	...	...	...	...	...	...
13	Vienenburg 860 d.	0503	0603	0603	0635	0700	0703	0703	0803	0803	hourly	2203	2203	2303	2303	...	...	...	...	...	...	...	...
40	Wolfenbüttel d.	0526	0626	0626	0659	0723	0726	0726	0826	0826	until	2226	2226	2326	2326	...	...	...	...	...	...	...	...
52	**Braunschweig** Hbf a.	0535	0635	0635	0709	0732	0735	0735	0835	0835		2235	2235	2335	2335	...	...	...	...	...	...	...	...

BRAUNSCHWEIG - HERZBERG

km		ⒸB		Ⓐ	Ⓐd		⚒d		⚒d		⚒d		⚒d		⚒d		⚒d		⚒d			HB	⑤⑥j		
0	**Braunschweig** Hbf d.	0005	...	0505	0605	0705	0805	0905	1005	1105	1205	1305	1405	1505	1605	1705	1805	1905	2005	2105	2205	2205	2305	...	...
31	Salzgitter-Ringelheim d.	0029	...	0529	0629	0729	0829	0929	1029	1129	1229	1329	1429	1529	1629	1729	1829	1929	2029	2129	2229	2229	2329	...	...
52	Seesen d.	0044	...	0545	0645	0745	0845	0945	1045	1145	1245	1345	1445	1545	1645	1745	1845	1945	2045	2145	2243	2243	2344	...	...
71	Osterode (Harz) Mitte d.	...	...	0607	0707	0807	0907	1007	1107	1207	1307	1407	1507	1607	1707	1807	1907	2007	2107	2207	...	...	...	...	...
83	**Herzberg** (Harz) a.	...	...	0621	0721	0821	0921	1021	1121	1221	1321	1421	1521	1621	1721	1821	1921	2021	2121	2221	...	...	...	...	...

	ⒶB	Ⓐ	⑥B	Ⓐd		⚒d		⚒d		⚒d		⚒d		⚒d		⚒d		⚒d							
rzberg (Harz) d.	...	0534	...	0634	0734	0834	0934	1034	1134	1234	1334	1434	1534	1634	1734	1834	1934	2034	2134	...	...	...	...	...	...
terode (Harz) Mitte d.	...	0547	...	0647	0747	0847	0947	1047	1147	1247	1347	1447	1547	1647	1747	1847	1947	2047	2147	...	...	...	...	...	...
esen d.	0513	0613	0613	0713	0813	0913	1013	1113	1213	1313	1413	1513	1613	1713	1813	1913	2013	2113	2213	2313	...	...	...	...	...
lzgitter-Ringelheim d.	0529	0629	0629	0729	0829	0929	1029	1129	1229	1329	1429	1529	1629	1729	1829	1929	2029	2129	2229	2329	...	...	...	...	...
aunschweig Hbf a.	0551	0651	0651	0751	0851	0951	1051	1151	1251	1351	1451	1551	1651	1751	1851	1951	2051	2151	2251	2351	...	...	...	...	...

BAD HARZBURG - KREIENSEN - GÖTTINGEN *Service from June 11*

km		ⒸB		Ⓐ	Ⓒ	Ⓐ																	HB			
0	**Bad Harzburg** 860 d.	...	...	...	...	0630	0711	0811	0911	1011	1111	1211	1311	1411	1511	1611	1711	1811	1911	2011	2111	...	2211	...	...
11	Goslar 860 d.	...	...	0544	0636	0643	0736	0836	0936	1036	1136	1236	1336	1436	1536	1636	1736	1836	1936	2036	2136	...	2236	...	...
34	Seesen d.	0045	...	0603	0654	0702	0755	0855	0955	1055	1155	1255	1355	1455	1555	1655	1755	1855	1955	2055	2155	2244	2255	...	...
48	Bad Gandersheim d.	0055	...	0613	0705	0713	0806	0906	1006	1106	1206	1306	1406	1506	1606	1706	1806	1906	2006	2106	2206	2254	2306	...	...
54	**Kreiensen** a.	0100	...	0618	0711	0718	0812	0912	1012	1112	1212	1312	1412	1512	1612	1712	1812	1912	2012	2112	2212	2259	2312	...	...
54	**Kreiensen** 903 d.	...	...	*0623*t	*0719*	*0723*t	*0823*	*0923*	*1023*	*1119*	*1223*	*1319*	*1423*	*1519*	*1623*	*1722*	*1823*	*1919*	*2023*	*2119*	*2223*	...	*2319*	...	...
73	Northeim (Han) 903 d.	...	...	*0636*t	*0733*	*0736*t	*0836*	*0937*	*1036*	*1133*	*1236*	*1333*	*1436*	*1533*	*1636*	*1736*	*1836*	*1933*	*2036*	*2133*	*2236*	...	*2333*	...	...
93	**Göttingen** 903 a.	...	...	*0649*t	*0747*	*0749*t	*0849*	*0950*n	*1049*	*1146*	*1249*	*1346*	*1449*	*1546*	*1649*	*1750*	*1849*	*1946*	*2049*	*2146*	*2249*	...	*2346*	...	...

	ⒶB			Ⓐ	⑥B		Ⓐ	Ⓒ																	
ttingen 903 d.	*0409*	...	0504	...	...	0607	...	...	*0707*	*0809*	*0907*	*1005*	*1107*	*1209*	*1307*	*1409*	*1507*	*1609*	*1707*	*1805*	*1907*	*2009*	*2107*	*2209*	...
rtheim (Han) 903 d.	*0422*	...	0517	...	...	0620	...	...	*0720*	*0823*	*0920*	*1018*	*1120*	*1223*	*1320*	*1423*	*1520*	*1623*	*1720*	*1818*	*1920*	*2023*	*2120*	*2223*	...
eiensen 903 a.	*0436*	...	0530	...	...	0633	...	...	*0733*	*0836*	*0933*	*1032*	*1133*	*1236*	*1333*	*1436*	*1533*	*1636*	*1733*	*1832*	*1933*	*2036*	*2133*	*2236*	...
eiensen d.	0456	...	...	0535	0556	...	0640	0642	0742	0842	0942	1042	1142	1242	1342	1442	1542	1642	1742	1842	1942	2042	2142	2242	...
d Gandersheim d.	0501	...	...	0540	0601	...	0645	0647	0747	0847	0947	1047	1147	1247	1347	1447	1547	1647	1747	1847	1947	2047	2147	2247	...
esen d.	0511	...	...	0551	0611	...	0656	0658	0758	0858	0958	1058	1158	1258	1358	1458	1558	1658	1758	1858	1958	2058	2158	2258	...
slar 860 d.	...	...	...	0611	...	...	0718	0716	0819	0918	1018	1118	1218	1318	1418	1518	1618	1718	1818	1918	2018	2118	2218	2316	2356
d Harzburg 860 a.	...	...	...	0623	...	...	0731	*0806*	0831	0930	1031	1130	1230	1330	1430	1530	1630	1730	1830	1930	2030	2130	2230	...	0006

– 12 Braunschweig - Seesen - Kreiensen and v.v.
– ①–④ (not June 10, Oct. 3).
d – Runs daily Braunschweig - Seesen and v.v.
j – Also June 9, Oct. 2, 30.
n – *0952* from Oct. 15.
t – Not Oct. 31.
⊠ – Operated by *erixx*.

HANNOVER - BAD HARZBURG and GOSLAR - HALLE — 860

rixx; *Abellio*

HANNOVER - BAD HARZBURG ⊠

km		⚒								
0	**Hannover** Hbf d.	0548	0648		1848	1948	2048	2148	2248	...
36	**Hildesheim** Hbf d.	0614	0714	and	1914	2014	2114	2214	2314	...
70	Salzgitter-Ringelheim d.	0641	0741	hourly	1941	2041	2141	2241	2341	...
89	Goslar 859 d.	0656	0756	until	1956	2056	2156	2256	2356	...
00	**Bad Harzburg 859** a.	0706	0806		2006	2106	2206	2306	0006	...

	⚒	⚒		Ⓐ				
Bad Harzburg 859 d.	...	0548	...	...	0648		2048	2148
Goslar 859 d.	0503	0603	0603	0635	0703	and	2103	2203
Salzgitter-Ringelheim d.	0516	0616	0616	0648	0716	hourly	2116	2216
Hildesheim Hbf d.	0544	0644	0644	0717	0744	until	2144	2244
Hannover Hbf a.	0610	0710	0710	0744	0810		2210	2310

GOSLAR - HALBERSTADT - HALLE ◇

km		t	Ⓐt	Ⓐt	Ⓒz	Ⓐt			Ⓐt	⑥	Ⓒz														
0	**Goslar 859** d.	...	...	...	...	...	...	...	0606	0606	...	0705	...	0806	0904	...	1006	1105	...	1206	1305	...	1406	1505	...
13	Vienenburg 859 d.	...	...	...	...	...	...	...	0616	0616	...	0715	...	0816	0915	...	1016	1115	...	1216	1315	...	1416	1515	...
29	Ilsenburg d.	...	0411	...	...	...	0529	...	0629	0630	0630	0731	...	0831	0931	...	1031	1131	...	1231	1331	...	1431	1531	...
38	Wernigerode d.	...	0422	...	...	...	0540	...	0640	0641	0641	0742	...	0840	0942	...	1040	1142	...	1240	1342	...	1440	1542	...
62	**Halberstadt** a.	...	0438	...	...	...	0556	...	0656	0656	0656	0756	...	0856	0956	...	1056	1156	...	1256	1356	...	1456	1556	...
62	**Halberstadt** d.	0334	...	0446	0446	0528	0601	0607	0701	0657	0657	0801	0802	0901	1001	1002	1101	1201	1202	1301	1401	1402	1501	1601	1602
	Magdeburg Hbf 862 a.	|	...	|	|	|	0645	|	|	|	|	0845	|	|	1046	|	|	1245	|	|	1445	|	|	1645	|
94	Aschersleben d.	0400	...	0521	0521	0557	...	0641	0726	0726	0726	...	0824	0926	...	1024	1126	...	1224	1326	...	1424	1526	...	1624
05	Sandersleben (Anh) d.	0419	...	0537	0537	0606	...	0656	0737	0737	0737	...	0837	0937	...	1037	1137	...	1237	1337	...	1437	1537	...	1637
22	Könnern d.	0432	...	0550	0550	0620	...	0710	0750	0750	0750	...	0850	0950	...	1050	1150	...	1250	1350	...	1450	1550	...	1650
52	**Halle** (Saale) Hbf a.	0500	...	0609	0619	0639	...	0741	0809	0809	0809	...	0909	1009	...	1109	1209	...	1309	1409	...	1509	1609	...	1709

		A										
slar 859 d.	1606	1705	...	1806	1905	...	2006	2105	2206	...	2305	...
nenburg 859 d.	1616	1715	...	1816	1915	...	2016	2115	2216	...	2315	...
nburg d.	1631	1731	...	1831	1931	...	2031	2131	2232	...	2331	...
rnigerode d.	1640	1742	...	1840	1942	...	2040	2142	2243	...	2342	...
lberstadt a.	1656	1756	...	1856	1956	...	2056	2156	2258	...	2356	...
lberstadt d.	1701	1801	1802	1901	2001	2002	2101	2202	2305	...	...	...
agdeburg Hbf 862 a.	|	1845	|	|	2056	|	|	2257	|	...	...	...
chersleben d.	1726	...	1824	1926	...	2024	2126	...	2333	...	...	...
ndersleben (Anh) d.	1737	...	1837	1937	...	2037	2137	...	2347	...	...	...
nern d.	1750	...	1850	1950	...	2050	2150	...	0000	...	...	...
le (Saale) Hbf a.	1809	...	1909	2011	...	2109	2209	...	0028	...	...	...

	⚒	Ⓐ						
Halle (Saale) Hbf d.	...	0345	...	...	...	0526	0633	...
Könnern d.	...	0405	...	...	...	0551	0710	...
Sandersleben (Anh) d.	...	0418	...	...	...	0606	0724	...
Aschersleben d.	...	0429	...	...	...	0627j	0737	...
Magdeburg Hbf 862 d.	...	|	...	...	...	|	|	0708
Halberstadt a.	...	0458	...	...	...	0656	0757	0758
Halberstadt d.	0459	0459	...	0559	...	0702	...	0804
Wernigerode d.	0516	0516	...	0616	...	0719	...	0818
Ilsenburg d.	0530	0530	...	0630	...	0730	...	0829
Vienenburg 859 d.	0541	0541	...	0643	...	0741	...	0842
Goslar 859 a.	0552	0552	...	0654	...	0752	...	0853

			B																						
le (Saale) Hbf d.	0746	0846	...	0946	1046	...	1146	1246	...	1346	1446	...	1546	1646	...	1746	1846	...	1949	...	2046	...	...	2309	...
nern d.	0810	0910	...	1010	1110	...	1210	1310	...	1410	1510	...	1610	1710	...	1810	1910	...	2010	...	2110	...	...	2329	...
ndersleben (Anh) d.	0823	0923	...	1023	1123	...	1223	1323	...	1423	1523	...	1623	1723	...	1823	1923	...	2023	...	2123	...	...	2347	...
chersleben d.	0835	0937	...	1035	1137	...	1235	1337	...	1435	1537	...	1635	1737	...	1835	1937	...	2035	...	2137	...	...	0006	...
agdeburg Hbf 862 d.	|	|	0908	|	|	1104	|	|	1308	|	|	1508	|	|	1708	|	|	1908	|	...	|	2109	...	|	2319
berstadt a.	0859	0957	0958	1059	1157	1159	1259	1357	1358	1459	1557	1558	1659	1757	1758	1859	1957	1958	2104	...	2157	2159	...	0034	0011
berstadt d.	0904	...	1004	1104	...	1204	1304	...	1404	1504	...	1604	1704	...	1804	1904	...	2004	2105	...	...	2204	...	...	0038
rnigerode d.	0921	...	1018	1121	...	1218	1321	...	1418	1521	...	1618	1721	...	1818	1921	...	2018	2121	...	...	2218	...	...	0055
nburg d.	0930	...	1029	1130	...	1229	1330	...	1429	1530	...	1629	1730	...	1829	1930	...	2029	2130	...	...	2229	...	...	0106
nenburg 859 d.	0941	...	1042	1141	...	1242	1341	...	1442	1541	...	1642	1741	...	1842	1941	...	2042	2141	...	...	2242	...	...	...
slar 859 a.	0952	...	1053	1152	...	1253	1352	...	1453	1552	...	1653	1752	...	1853	1952	...	2053	2152	...	...	2253	...	...	...

To Berlin via Magdeburg on ⑤–⑦ (also June 10, Oct. 2, 3, 31). See Tables **862**/**839**.
From Berlin via Magdeburg on Ⓒ. See Tables **839**/**862**.

j – Arrives 0618.
t – Not Oct. 31.
z – Also Oct. 31.
⊠ – Operated by *erixx*.
◇ – Operated by Abellio Rail Mitteldeutschland.

861 MAGDEBURG - SANGERHAUSEN - ERFURT and DESSAU - ASCHERSLEBEN

Operated by Abellio Rail Mitteldeutschland

Magdeburg - Erfurt and Aschersleben

km																										
		©z	Ⓐe	Ⓐe										Ⓐe	©z	Ⓐe			Ⓐe							
0	**Magdeburg** Hbf d.	0051	0437	0511	0608	0711	0826	0911	1026	1111	1226	1311	1426	1458	1511	1530	1626	1711	1711	...	1826	1911	2026	2111	2217	225
17	Schönebeck (Elbe) d.	0102	0450	0526	0623	0726	0838	0926	1038	1126	1238	1326	1438	1509	1526	1544	1638	1726	1726	...	1838	1926	2038	2126	2231	231
37	Staßfurt d.	0125	0509	0550	0651	0750	0852	0950	1052	1150	1252	1350	1452	1533	1550	1608	1652	1750	1750	...	1852	1950	2052	2150	2246	233
44	Güsten d.	0133	0515	0558	0658	0758	0858	0958	1058	1158	1258	1358	1458	1541	1558	1615	1658	1758	1803	...	1858	1958	2058	2158	2251	234
	Aschersleben a.	0145	|	0610	|	0810h	|	1010	|	1210	|	1410	|	|	1610	1627	|	1811	|	...	|	2010	|	2210	|	235
60	Sandersleben d.	▬	0546k	▬	0711	▬	0911	▬	1111	▬	1311	▬	1511	1554	▬	...	1711	...	1816	...	1911	▬	2111	...	2305	...
66	Hettstedt d.	...	0554	...	0718	...	0918	...	1118	...	1318	...	1518	1601	...	...	1718	...	1823	...	1918	...	2118	...	2312	...
75	Klostermansfeld d.	...	0603	...	0728	...	0928	...	1128	...	1328	...	1528	1611	...	...	1728	...	1832	...	1928	...	2128	...	2321	...
97	**Sangerhausen** d.	0547	0623	0641	0748	0852	0948	1052	1148	1252	1348	1452	1548	1629	1652	...	1748	...	1856	1905	1956j	2051	2158j	...	2339	...
142	Sömmerda d.	0633	0701	0731	0829	0931	1029	1131	1229	1331	1429	1531	1629	...	1731	...	1829	...	...	1953	2037	2139	2245	...	...	...
167	**Erfurt** Hbf a.	0654	0720	0751	0850	0951	1050	1151	1250	1351	1451	1551	1650	...	1751	...	1850	...	...	2014	2057	2200	2305	...	...	...

	Ⓐe	Ⓐe	©	Ⓐe	Ⓐe			Ⓐe																	
Erfurt Hbf d.	...	...	...	...	...	0506	...	0613	0704	0809	0910	1009	1110	1209	1310	1409	1509	1609	1710	...	1809	1906	...	2018	2136	23
Sömmerda d.	...	...	...	...	...	0523	...	0633	0730	0829	0932	1029	1132	1229	1332	1429	1532	1629	1732	...	1829	1928	...	2038	2155	233
Sangerhausen d.	...	...	...	0510	...	0618j	...	0723	0818	0909	1018	1109	1218	1309	1418	1509	1618	1709	1818	...	1909	2018	...	2123	2242	002
Klostermansfeld d.	...	...	...	0529	...	0637	...	...	0837	▬	1037	▬	1237	▬	1437	▬	1637	▬	1837	...	...	2037	...	...	...	
Hettstedt d.	...	...	...	0538	...	0646	...	...	0846	...	1046	...	1246	...	1446	...	1646	...	1846	...	...	2046	...	...	...	
Sandersleben d.	...	...	...	0546	...	0653	...	...	0853	...	1053	...	1253	...	1453	...	1653	...	1853	...	...	2053	...	...	...	
Aschersleben d.	0448	0530	0544	|	0623	|	0746	...	|	0946	|	1146	|	1346	|	1546	|	1746	|	1946	...	|	2146	...	...	
Güsten d.	0501	0541	0556	0559	0635	0707	0758	...	0907	0958	1107	1158	1307	1358	1507	1558	1707	1758	1907	1958	...	2107	2158	...	...	
Staßfurt d.	0509	0553	0604	0612	0644	0714	0808	...	0914	1008	1114	1208	1314	1408	1514	1608	1714	1808	1914	2008	...	2114	2208	...	...	
Schönebeck (Elbe) d.	0529	0614	0626	0627	0704	0729	0829	...	0929	1029	1129	1229	1329	1429	1529	1629	1729	1829	1929	2029	...	2129	2230	...	...	
Magdeburg Hbf a.	0542	0626	0641	0641	0716	0742	0841	...	0941	1043	1145	1241	1342	1441	1540	1641	1741	1841	1941	2041	...	2141	2247	...	...	

Dessau - Aschersleben *Shaded timings are operated by 🚌 (all services are operated by 🚌 between Köthen and Bernburg).*

km																										
		Ⓐ🚌	Ⓐe			Ⓐe	©z									Ⓐe	©z						🚌			🚌
0	**Dessau** Hbf d.	0438	...	0549	0648	...	...	0749	0848	0949	1048	1149	1248	1318	1448	...	...	1549	1648	1749	1848	1949	2142	...	...	23
21	Köthen a.	0519	...	0607	0706	...	...	0807	0906	1007	1106	1207	1306	1340	1506	...	...	1607	1706	1807	1906	2007	2223	...	...	23
21	Köthen 🚌 d.	0520	...	0612	0711	...	...	0812	0911	1012	1111	1212	1311	1345	1511	...	...	1612	1711	1812	1911	2012	2224	...	...	235
42	Bernburg 🚌 a.	0552	...	0647	0738	...	...	0839	0938	1039	1138	1239	1338	1420	1538	...	...	1639	1738	1839	1938	2039	2256	...	...	00
42	Bernburg d.	...	0557	0653	...	*0743*	0754	0853	0943	1053	1143	1253	1343	1453	...	1543	1543	1653	1743	1853	1943	2053	...	2301	0023	...
54	Güsten d.	...	0609	0704	...	0758	0805	0904	0954	1104	1154	1304	1354	1504	...	1554	1554	1704	1754	1904	1954	2104	...	2312	0034	...
66	**Aschersleben** a.	...	0620	0715	...	0810	0816	0915	*1010*	1115	*1210*	1315	*1410*	1515	...	1605	*1610*	1715	*1811*	1915	*2010*	2115	...	2323	0046	...

			Ⓐe											Ⓐe	©z						🚌				🚌
Aschersleben d.	...	0431	0516	0553	0649	*0746*	0849	*0946*	1049	*1146*	1249	*1346*	1449	1536	*1546*	1649	*1746*	1849	*1946*	2042	...	...	2146	...	...
Güsten d.	...	0442	0527	0604	0702	0801	0902	1001	1102	1201	1302	1401	1502	1549	1601	1702	1801	1902	2001	2053	2111	...	2157	2202	...
Bernburg a.	...	0453	0538	0613	0712	0812	0912	1012	1112	1212	1312	1412	1512	1600	1612	1712	1812	1912	2012	...	2128	...	...	2212	...
Bernburg 🚌 d.	0448	0509	0543	0617	0717	0841	0917	1017	1117	1217	1317	1417	1517	1610	1617	1717	1817	1917	2023	...	2129	...	...	...	22
Köthen 🚌 a.	0515	0543	0610	0644	0744	0915	0944	1044	1144	1244	1344	1444	1544	1644	1644	1744	1844	1944	2057	...	2203	...	...	...	22
Köthen d.	0520	0548	0615	0649	0750	0920	0950	1049	1150	1249	1350	1449	1550	1649	1649	1750	1849	1950	2102	...	2204	...	...	...	22
Dessau Hbf a.	0544	0610	0635	0709	0810	0944	1010	1109	1210	1309	1410	1509	1610	1709	1709	1810	1909	2010	2127	...	2238	...	...	...	23

e – Not Oct. 31. **h** – *0816* on © **z** (change trains at Güsten, d. *0805*). **j** – Arrives 10–12 minutes earlier. **k** – Arrives 0528. **z** – Also Oct. 31.

862 MAGDEBURG - HALBERSTADT - THALE

Abellio Rail Mitteldeutschlan

km																									
		Ⓐ				◧		◧	Ⓒ ▲		◧		◧		◧		◧			◧		◧			◐
	Berlin Hbf **839** d.	...	...	...	...	...	...	...	0720	...	...	...	...	...	...	...	...	...	...	...	...	...	...	...	...
0	**Magdeburg** Hbf d.	0429	...	...	0544	0708	0808	0908	0908	1008	1104	1208	1308	1408	1508	1608	1708	1808	1844	1908	2007	2109	2207	...	23
39	Oschersleben (Bode) d.	0507	...	...	0625	0742	0842	0942	0942	1042	1144	1242	1342	1442	1542	1642	1742	1842	1926	1942	2045	2144	2246	...	235
59	**Halberstadt** a.	0524	...	...	0641	0758	0858	0958	0958	1058	1159	1258	1358	1458	1558	1658	1758	1858	1942	1958	2101	2159	2302	...	00
59	**Halberstadt** d.	0540	0540	0610	0708	0808	0908	1008	1008	1108	1208	1308	1408	1508	1608	1708	1808	1908	...	2008	2108	2201	...	...	00
77	Quedlinburg a.	0556	0556	0626	0723	0823	0923	1023	1023	1123	1223	1323	1423	1523	1623	1723	1823	1923	...	2023	2123	2216	...	...	004
77	Quedlinburg d.	0557	0557	0630	0730	0830	0930	1030	1030	1130	1230	1330	1430	1530	1630	1730	1830	1930	...	2030	2130	2217	...	...	004
87	**Thale** Hbf a.	0609	0609	0642	0742	0842	0942	1042	1042	1142	1242	1342	1442	1542	1642	1742	1842	1942	...	2042	2142	2228	...	...	005

	Ⓐ		◐	Ⓐ		◧		◧		◧		◧		◧		◧	⑤–⑦ h▲		◧			◧			
Thale Hbf d.	...	...	0521	...	0617	0717	0817	0917	1017	1117	1217	1317	1417	1517	1617	1717	1717	1817	1917	2017	2117	...	2230	...	234
Quedlinburg a.	...	...	0531	...	0628	0728	0828	0928	1028	1128	1228	1328	1428	1528	1628	1728	1728	1828	1928	2028	2128	...	2240	...	23
Quedlinburg d.	...	...	0533	...	0633	0733	0833	0933	1033	1133	1233	1333	1433	1533	1633	1733	1733	1833	1933	2033	2133	...	2241	...	23
Halberstadt a.	...	...	0549	...	0649	0749	0849	0949	1049	1149	1249	1349	1449	1549	1649	1749	1749	1849	1949	2049	2149	...	2258	...	00
Halberstadt d.	0328	0443	0601	0618	0701	0801	0901	1001	1101	1201	1301	1401	1501	1601	1701	1801	1801	1901	2001	2103	...	2202	...	...	...
Oschersleben (Bode) d.	0344	0459	0617	0635	0717	0817	0917	1017	1117	1217	1317	1417	1517	1617	1717	1817	1817	1917	2017	2119	...	2218	...	...	...
Magdeburg Hbf a.	0420	0537	0645	0715	0745	0845	0945	1046	1152	1245	1345	1445	1545	1645	1745	1845	1845	1945	2056	2148	...	2257	...	...	...
Berlin Hbf **839** a.	...	...	...	...	...	...	...	...	...	...	...	...	...	...	...	...	2038	...	...	...	...	...	...	...	...

h – Also June 10, Oct. 2, 3, 31.
◧ – Conveys (12) Magdeburg - Halberstadt - Goslar and v.v. (Table **860**).
◐ – Conveys (12) Magdeburg - Halberstadt - Ilsenburg and v.v. (Table **860**).
▲ – *HARZ-BERLIN-EXPRESS*. DB tickets not valid for journeys from/to Ber Also conveys (2) Berlin - Halberstadt - Goslar and v.v. (Table **860**).

863 BRAUNSCHWEIG - HILDESHEIM - HAMELN - BÜNDE

Nord West Bahn

km																									
		Ⓐ	Ⓐ	⑥	Ⓐ																				
0	**Hildesheim** Hbf d.	...	0537	0634	0637t	0737	0834	0937	1034	1137	1234	1337	1434	1537	1634	1737	1834	1937	2034	2137	2234	...	...	...	...
18	Elze a.	...	0553	0650	0653t	0753	0850	0953	1050	1153	1250	1353	1450	1553	1650	1753	1850	1953	2050	2153	2250	...	...	...	...
18	Elze d.	...	0602	0702	0702t	0802	0902	1002	1102	1202	1302	1402	1502	1602	1702	1802	1902	2002	2102	2202	2307	...	...	...	...
47	**Hameln** d.	0529	0629	0727	0729	0829	0929	1029	1129	1229	1329	1429	1529	1629	1729	1829	1929	2029	2127	2227	2332	...	...	...	...
71	Rinteln d.	0546	0646	...	0746	0846	0946	1046	1146	1246	1346	1446	1546	1646	1746	1846	1946	2046	...	...	...	...	...	...	...
88	Vlotho d.	0601	0701	...	0801	0901	1001	1101	1201	1301	1401	1501	1601	1701	1801	1901	2001	2101	...	...	...	...	...	...	...
100	Löhne (Westf) **811** a.	0614	0714	...	0814	0914	1014	1114	1214	1314	1414	1514	1614	1714	1814	1914	2014	2114	...	...	...	...	...	...	...
110	**Bünde** (Westf) **811** a.	0625	0725	...	0825	...	1025t	...	1225e	1325e	1425e	...	1625e	1725e	1825e	...	...	...	...	...	...	...	...	...	...

	⚒v	Ⓐt	⚒v	⚒		Ⓐ						C	Ⓐh											
Bünde (Westf) **811** d.	...	...	...	0632e	...	0732	...	0832e	...	1032e	...	1232r	1232	1332e	1432e	...	1632e	1732e	1832e	...	...	...	...	...
Löhne (Westf) **811** d.	...	0545	...	0645	...	0745	...	0845	0945	1045	1145	1245	1245	1345	1445	1545	1645	1745	1845	1945	2045	...	...	...
Vlotho d.	...	0559	...	0659	...	0759	...	0859	0959	1059	1159	1259	1259	1359	1459	1559	1659	1759	1859	1959	2059	...	...	...
Rinteln d.	...	0610	...	0710	...	0810	...	0910	1010	1110	1210	1310	1310	1410	1510	1610	1710	1810	1910	2010	2110	...	...	...
Hameln d.	0528	0628	0628	0728	0728	0828	0828	0928	1028	1128	1228	1328	1335	1428	1528	1628	1728	1828	1928	2028	2128	2228	...	...
Elze a.	0553	0652	0652	0753	0753	0852	0852	0953	1052	1153	1252	1353	1401	1452	1553	1652	1753	1852	1953	2052	2153	2252	...	...
Elze d.	0602	0702	0702	0802	0802	0907	0907	1002	1107	1202	1307	1402	1402	1507	1602	1707	1802	1907	2002	2107	2202	2307	...	...
Hildesheim Hbf a.	0620	0720	0720	0820	0820	0925	0925	1020	1125	1220	1325	1420	1423	1525	1620	1725	1820	1925	2020	2125	2220	2325	...	...

Regional trains **WOLFSBURG - BRAUNSCHWEIG - HILDESHEIM** ⊠

km									
				Ⓐ	⚒				
0	**Wolfsburg** Hbf d.	0014	...	0514	0614	0714	and	2314	...
32	**Braunschweig** Hbf d.	0033	...	0535	0635	0735	hourly	2335	...
75	**Hildesheim** Hbf a.	...	...	0602	0702	0802	until	0002	...

			Ⓐ	⚒	⚒					
Hildesheim Hbf d.	...	...	0455	...	0555	...	...	0655	and	22
Braunschweig Hbf d.	0046	...	0526	0526	0626	0626	...	0726	hourly	23
Wolfsburg Hbf a.	0107	...	0545	0545	0645	0645		0745	until	23

C – © (also June 11, Oct. 31; runs daily July 4 - Aug. 14 and Oct. 3 - 20).
e – Ⓐ only.
h – Not June 11, July 4 - Aug. 14, Oct. 4 - 18, 31.
r – ①–⑤ July 4 - Aug. 14 (also June 11, Oct. 4, 7 - 11, 14 - 18, 31).
t – Ⓐ (not Oct. 31).
v – Not Oct. 31.
★ – Bünde - Hildesheim operated by Nord West Ba
⊠ – Operated by *enno*. See Table **902** for faster IC trains operated by DB.

864 GÖTTINGEN - KASSEL local services

;ANTUS Verkehrsgesellschaft (2nd class only)

km		Ⓐ	⑥	⑥	Ⓐ							Ⓒ	Ⓐ									Ⓑ	⑥		D
0	**Göttingen** .... **908** d.	0442	0444	0543	0600	0718	0814**f**	0914	1018	1114	1218	1314	1326	1418	1514	1614**v**	1714	1814**v**	1914	2014	2115	2214	2219	2314	2359
20	Eichenberg .... **908** a.	0456	0458	0557	0613	0732	0828**f**	0928	1032	1128	1232	1328	1341	1432	1528	1628**v**	1728	1828**v**	1928	2028	2129	2228	2234	2328	0013
20	Eichenberg .... **865** d.	0508	0502	0603	0623	0733	0833	0933	1033	1133	1233	1333	1342	1433	1533	1633	1733	1833	1933	2033	2133	2234	2239	2336	0014
43	Hann Münden...... **865** d.	0528	0523	0623	0644	0753	0853	0953	1053	1153	1253	1353	1403	1453	1553	1653	1753	1853	1953	2053	2152	2255	2301	2356	0033
67	**Kassel** Hbf ⊡ ..... **865** a.	0549	0543	0643	0703	0813	0913	1013	1113	1213	1313	1413	1428	1513	1614	1713	1813	1913	2013	2113	2213	2316	2324	0016	0054

	Ⓒ		Ⓐ	Ⓐ	⑥	Ⓐ	Ⓒ				Ⓐ	Ⓒ													
ıssel Hbf ⊡....... **865** d.	0046	...	0415	0534	0546	0625	0636	0746	0846	0946	1046	1046	1146	1246	1346	1446	1546	1646	1746	1846	1946	2046	2146	2246	2346
ınn Münden....... **865** d.	0106	...	0435	0554	0606	0645	0656	0806	0906	1006	1106	1106	1206	1306	1406	1506	1606	1706	1806	1906	2006	2106	2206	2306	0006
:henberg .... **865** a.	0126	...	0455	0614	0626	0705	0715	0826	0926	1026	1126	1126	1226	1326	1426	1526	1626	1726	1825	1926	2026	2126	2226	2326	0026
:henberg .... **908** d.	0127	...	0502	0624	0627	0707	0722	0832	0932	1032	1127	1132	1232	1327	1432	1527	1632	1727	1832	1927	2032	2127	2227	2327	0027
››ttingen .... **908** a.	0141	...	0515	0638	0641	0721	0736	0846	0946	1046	1142	1145	1246	1342	1446	1542	1646	1741	1846	1940	2046	2142	2242	2341	0041

– ⑤–⑦ (also June 10, Oct. 3).

f – 4 minutes later on †.

v – 4 minutes later on Ⓒ.

⊡ – See Tables **806** and **901** for connecting trains to / from Kassel Wilhelmshöhe.

865 ERFURT and HALLE - LEINEFELDE - KASSEL and GÖTTINGEN

)B (*RE* / *RB* services); Abellio

km		Ⓐt △	Ⓐt △	Ⓐ		Ⓐt	△	G	Ⓐt △			△	A	⚒r △			△	A	△			△	A	△	
0	**Erfurt** Hbf .... **849 850** d.	...	...	...	0423	0502	...	0611	...	0622	0707	...	0810	...	0833	0907	...	1010	...	1033	1107	...	1210	...	1233
27	Gotha .... **849 850** d.	...	...	...	0458	◇	...	0637	...	|	◇	...	0837	...	|	◇	...	1037	...	|	◇	...	1237	...	|
48	Bad Langensalza ....d.	...	...	0449	0510	0555	...	0648	...	0710	0800	...	0848	...	0914	1000	...	1048	...	1114	1200	...	1248	...	1314
67	Mühlhausen (Thür) ....d.	...	...	0506	0523	0611	...	0700	...	0726	0815	...	0900	...	0926	1015	...	1100	...	1126	1215	...	1300	...	1326
	Halle (Saale) Hbf.............d.	...	...	|	|	|	0455	|	0534	|	|	0703	|	0802	|	|	0857	|	1002	|	|	1057	|	1202	|
	Lutherstadt Eisleben ....d.	...	...	|	|	|	0526	|	0615	|	|	0734	|	0831	|	|	0934	|	1031	|	|	1134	|	1231	|
	Sangerhausen ....d.	...	0415	|	|	|	0545	|	0634	|	|	0752	|	0849	|	|	0952	|	1049	|	|	1152	|	1249	|
	Nordhausen ....d.	...	0448	|	|	|	0619	|	0707	|	|	0825	|	0916	|	|	1025	|	1116	|	|	1225	|	1316	|
94	**Leinefelde**.......................a.	...	0528	0532	0542	0634	0651	0717	0747	0750	0840	0856	0917	0948	0951	1040	1056	1117	1148	1151	1240	1256	1317	1348	1351
94	**Leinefelde**.......................d.	0425	...	0533	0544	*0638*	0654	0718	...	0751	*0844*	0857	0918	...	0954	*1044*	1057	1118	...	1154	*1244*	1257	1318	...	1354
10	Heilbad Heiligenstadt..........d.	0439	...	0547	0556	*0652*	0705	0729	...	0801	*0857*	0907	0929	...	1005	*1057*	1107	1129	...	1205	*1257*	1307	1329	...	1405
44	**Göttingen** ....a.	|	...	|	0625	...	|	0751	...	|	...	|	0951	...	|	...	|	1151	...	|	...	|	1351	...	|
25	Eichenberg................... **864** d.	0452	...	0602	...	...	0719	...	...	0816	...	0919	...	...	1019	...	1119	...	...	1219	...	1319	...	...	1419
48	Hann Münden .... **864** d.	*0528*	...	0622	...	...	0736	...	...	0833	...	0936	...	...	1036	...	1136	...	...	1236	...	1336	...	...	1436
72	**Kassel** Hbf .... **864** a.	*0549*	...	0643	...	...	|	...	...	|	...	|	...	...	|	...	|	...	...	|	...	|	...	...	|
76	**Kassel** Wilhelmshöhe ....a.	...	...	0656	...	...	0754	...	...	0852	...	0954	...	...	1055	...	1153	...	...	1256	...	1356	...	...	1455

		△	A	△			△	A	△			△	A	△			△	A		△	⑥	L		△	△
ʼurt Hbf..............**849 850** d.	1307	...	1410	...	1433	1507	...	1609	...	1633	1707	...	1810	...	1833	1907	...	2010	2033	...	...	2112	2249	...	...
Gotha..................**849 850** d.	◇	...	1436	...	|	◇	...	1637	...	|	◇	...	1837	...	|	◇	...	2037	|	...	...	2139	2314	...	...
d Langensalza ....d.	1400	...	1448	...	1514	1600	...	1648	...	1714	1800	...	1848	...	1914	2000	...	2048	2113	...	...	2150	2328	...	...
ʼhlhausen (Thür) ....d.	1415	...	1500	...	1526	1615	...	1700	...	1726	1815	...	1900	...	1926	2017	...	2100	2127	...	...	2200	2340	...	...
Halle (Saale) Hbf..............d.	|	1257	|	1402	|	|	1457	|	1602	|	|	1657	|	1802	|	...	1857	|	|	2002	...	|	|	2106	2320
Lutherstadt Eisleben.........d.	|	1334	|	1431	|	|	1534	|	1631	|	|	1734	|	1832	|	...	1934	|	|	2031	...	|	|	2136	2349
Sangerhausen.................d.	|	1352	|	1449	|	|	1552	|	1649	|	|	1752	|	1849	|	...	1952	|	|	2049	...	|	|	2155	0008
Nordhausen..................d.	|	1425	|	1516	|	|	1625	|	1716	|	|	1825	|	1916	|	...	2025	|	|	2123**k**	...	|	|	2227	0041
ınefelde.........................a.	1440	1456	1517	1548	1551	1640	1656	1717	1748	1751	1840	1856	1917	1948	1951	...	2056	2117	2146	2204	...	2218	2357	...	...
ınefelde.........................d.	*1444*	1457	1518	...	1554	*1644*	1657	1718	...	1754	*1844*	1857	1918	...	1954	...	2057	2118	2148	▬	...	2219	...	...	...
ılbad Heiligenstadt ....d.	*1457*	1507	1529	...	1605	*1657*	1707	1729	...	1805	*1857*	1907	1929	...	2005	...	2107	2129	2158	...	...	2230	...	...	...
Göttingen........................a.	...	|	1551	...	|	...	|	1751	...	|	...	|	1951	...	|	...	|	2150	|	Ⓑ	...	2256	...	...	...
henberg .... **864** d.	...	1519	...	...	1619	...	1719	...	...	1819	...	1919	...	...	2019	...	2119	...	2212	2234	2239	...	...	...	...
ın Münden.............. **864** d.	...	1536	...	...	1636	...	1736	...	...	1836	...	1936	...	...	2036	...	2136	...	...	2255	2301	...	...	...	...
ssel Hbf .... **864** a.	...	|	...	...	|	...	|	...	...	|	...	|	...	...	|	...	2154	...	...	2316	2324	...	...	...	...
ssel Wilhelmshöhe..........a.	...	1553	...	...	1656	...	1753	...	...	1856	...	1954	...	...	2055	...	...	...	...	...	...	...	...	...	...

km		△		Ⓐt △	Ⓐt	⚒r △	A	Ⓐt △	Ⓒz △		Ⓐ		△	A	△			△	A	△			△	A	△
0	**Kassel** Wilhelmshöhe ....d.	...	...	...	...	...	...	...	...	...	0704	...	...	...	0806	...	0906	...	...	1006	...	1106	...	...	1206
	Kassel Hbf .... **864** d.	...	...	*0415*	...	...	...	0559	0606	...	|	...	...	...	|	...	|	...	...	|	...	|	...	...	|
23	Hann Münden .... **864** d.	...	...	*0435*	...	...	...	0615	0623	...	0724	...	...	...	0823	...	0922	...	...	1023	...	1122	...	...	1223
46	Eichenberg................... **864** d.	...	...	0501	...	...	...	0633	0640	...	0744	...	...	...	0840	...	0940	...	...	1040	...	1140	...	...	1240
	Göttingen ....d.	...	...	|	...	...	0604	|	|	...	|	...	...	0808	|	...	|	...	1008	|	...	|	...	1208	|
61	Heilbad Heiligenstadt...........d.	...	0444**t**	0514	...	...	0628	0647	0652	...	0757	...	...	0831	0852	...	0955	...	1031	1052	...	1155	...	1231	1252
77	**Leinefelde**.........................a.	...	0459**t**	0527	...	...	0638	0701	0702	...	0807	...	...	0841	0902	...	1005	...	1041	1102	...	1205	...	1241	1302
77	**Leinefelde**.........................d.	0440**t**	0501	0527	0547	0549**h**	0640	0702	0703	0719**t**	0808	0808	0811**t**	0843	0903	0919	1007	1010**r**	1043	1103	1119	1207	1210	1243	1303
19	**Nordhausen** ....d.	0533	|	0601	|	0632	|	0734	0734	|	|	|	0844**t**	|	0934	|	|	1044**r**	|	1134	|	|	1244	|	1337
57	Sangerhausen ....d.	0611	|	0633	|	0709	|	0808	0808	|	|	|	0912	|	1008	|	|	1112	|	1208	|	|	1312	|	1409
79	Lutherstadt Eisleben ....d.	0631	|	0651	|	0727	|	0826	0826	|	|	|	0928	|	1026	|	|	1128	|	1226	|	|	1328	|	1427
17	**Halle** (Saale) Hbf..............a.	0701	|	0728	|	0801	|	0857	0857	|	|	|	1003	|	1057	|	|	1203	|	1257	|	|	1403	|	1458
—	Mühlhausen (Thür) ....d.	...	0524	...	0612	...	0658	...	...	0742	0832	0832	...	0859	...	0942	1032	...	1059	...	1142	1232	...	1259	...
0	Bad Langensalza ....d.	...	0536	...	0630	...	0709	...	...	0759	0844	0844	...	0909	...	0959	1044	...	1109	...	1159	1244	...	1309	...
	Gotha .... **849 850** a.	...	0551	...	⊙	...	0720	...	...	⊙	|	|	...	0921	...	⊙	|	...	1121	...	⊙	|	...	1321	...
88	**Erfurt** Hbf .... **849 850** a.	...	0617**v**	...	0720	...	0746	...	...	0846	0921	0921	...	0946	...	1046	1121	...	1146	...	1246	1321	...	1346	...

			△	A	△			△	A	△			△	A	△			△	L	△	G		△		
ssel Wilhelmshöhe.........d.	...	1306	...	...	1406	...	1506	...	...	1606	...	1706	...	...	1805	...	1906	...	...	2006	...	2106	...	...	...
ssel Hbf .... **864** d.	...	|	...	...	|	...	|	...	...	|	...	|	...	...	|	...	|	...	...	|	...	|	...	*2146*	...
ın Münden.............. **864** d.	...	1322	...	...	1423	...	1522	...	...	1623	...	1722	...	...	1823	...	1922	...	...	2023	...	2122	...	*2206*	...
henberg .... **864** d.	...	1340	...	...	1440	...	1540	...	...	1640	...	1740	...	...	1840	...	1940	...	...	2040	...	2141	...	*2241*	...
Göttingen..........................d.	...	|	...	1408	|	...	|	...	1608	|	...	|	...	1808	|	...	|	...	2008	|	2108	|	...	|	2308
ıbad Heiligenstadt ....d.	...	1355	...	1431	1452	...	1555	...	1631	1652	...	1755	...	1831	1852	...	1955	...	2031	2052	2132	2155	...	2253	2332
nefelde...........................a.	...	1405	...	1441	1502	...	1605	...	1641	1702	...	1805	...	1841	1902	...	2005	...	2041	2102	2142	2206	...	2303	2343
nefelde...........................d.	1319	1407	1410	1443	1503	1519	1607	1610	1643	1703	1719	1807	1810	1843	1903	1919	2007	2013	2043	2103	2149	2220	2226	...	...
Nordhausen......................d.	|	|	1444	|	1534	|	|	1644	|	1734	|	|	1844	|	1934	|	|	2056**k**	|	2136	|	|	2306	...	...
Sangerhausen....................d.	|	|	1512	|	1608	|	|	1712	|	1808	|	|	1912	|	2008	|	|	2130	|	2210	|	|	2337	...	...
ıtherstadt Eisleben..........d.	|	|	1528	|	1626	|	|	1728	|	1826	|	|	1928	|	2026	|	|	2149	|	2229	|	|	2356	...	...
alle (Saale) Hbf...............a.	|	|	1603	|	1657	|	|	1803	|	1857	|	|	2003	|	2059	|	|	2228	|	2301	|	|	0034	...	...
ıhlhausen (Thür) ....d.	1342	1432	...	1459	...	1542	1632	...	1659	...	1742	1832	...	1859	...	1942	2028	...	2059	...	2214	2239	...	...	...
Langensalza.....................d.	1359	1444	...	1509	...	1559	1644	...	1709	...	1759	1844	...	1909	...	1959	2043	...	2109	...	2223	2256	...	...	...
›otha.....................**849 850** a.	⊙	|	...	1521	...	⊙	|	...	1721	...	⊙	|	...	1921	...	⊙	|	...	2121	...	2235	|	...	...	...
ırt Hbf....................**849 850** a.	1446	1521	...	1546	...	1646	1721	...	1746	...	1846	1921	...	1947	...	2051	2121	...	2146	...	2259	2335	...	...	...

From / to Glauchau (Table **858**).
From / to Gera (Table **858**).
From / to Altenburg (Table **858**).

0558 on ⑥.
Arrives 6 – 8 minutes earlier.
⚒ (not Oct. 31).
Ⓐ (not Oct. 31).
Not June 10, Oct. 3, 31.
Also Oct. 31.

◇ – Connecting trains Gotha - Bad Langensalza (journey time: 18 minutes).
From Gotha at 0531 Ⓐ**t**, 0737, 0937, 1137, 1337, 1537, 1737 and 1937.

⊙ – Connecting trains Bad Langensalza - Gotha (journey time: 19 minutes).
From Bad Langensalza at 0650 Ⓐ**t**, 0801, 1001, 1201, 1401, 1601, 1801 and 2001.

△ – Operated by Abellio Rail Mitteldeutschland.

866 HANNOVER - MAGDEBURG - LEIPZIG

SERVICE FROM JUNE 11. See panels below main table for regional / S-Bahn trains. Please note that *IC* trains between Magdeburg and Leipzig are diverted via Dessau until December 1
Dortmund tmings may may by 2 – 3 minutes July 13 - August 25. See Table **848** for other regional trains between Magdeburg and Leipzig via Dessau.

km		*IC* 2449		*IC* 2031	*IC* 2447	*IC* 2033	*IC* 2445	*IC* 1945	*IC* 2035	*IC* 2443	*IC* 2037	*IC* 2441	*IC* 2039	*IC* 1933	*IC* 2049	*IC* 2431	*IC* 2239	*IC* 2047	*IC* 2433	*IC* 2045	*IC* 2435	*IC* 2043	*IC* 2043		*IC* 243
		Ⓐ t 🍷		Ⓐ	①–⑥ 🍷	🍷	①–⑥ 🍷	⑦ 🍷	①–⑥ 🍷	🍷	🍷	🍷	🍷	⑤ f	🍷	C 🍷	B	Ⓑ d 🍷	🍷	Ⓑ 🍷	🍷	Ⓑ	⑦		Ⓑ
	Köln Hbf **800** d.	...	...	...	...	...	0513	...	...	0712e	...	0913	...	...	1113	...	...	1313	...	1513	...	1713	1713	...	...
	Dortmund Hbf **800** d.	...	...	...	...	...	0628	...	...	0828e	...	1028	...	...	1228	...	...	1428	...	1628	...	1828	1828	...	...
	Bielefeld Hbf **810** d.	...	...	...	0513g	...	0719	...	...	0919e	...	1119	...	...	1319	...	...	1519	...	1719	...	1919	1919	...	...
	Norddeich **813** d.	...	...	...	|	...	|	...	0536	|	0739e	|	0939	...	|	...	...	|	...	|	1540	|	|	...	...
	Emden Hbf **813** d.	...	...	...	|	0416e	|	...	0609	|	0816	|	1016	...	|	1218	...	|	1416	|	1616	|	|	...	181
	Oldenburg (Oldb) **813** d.	...	...	...	|	0535e	|	...	0735	|	0935	|	1135	1230	|	1335	...	|	1535	|	1735	|	|	...	193
	Bremen Hbf **813** d.	...	...	...	|	0609	|	...	0809	|	1009	|	1209	1305	|	1409	...	|	1609	|	1809	|	|	...	200
0	**Hannover** Hbf d.	...	...	0534	0637	0737	0837	...	0937	1037	1137	1237	1337	1411	1437	1537	...	1637	1737	1837	1937	2037	2037	...	213
35	Peine d.	...	...	0555	|	|	|	...	|	|	|	|	|	|	|	|	...	|	|	|	|	|	|	...	215
61	**Braunschweig** Hbf d.	...	...	0610	0710	0810	0910	...	1010	1110	1210	1310	1410	1448	1510	1610	...	1710	1810	1910	2010	2110	2110	...	221
97	Helmstedt d.	...	...	0632	|	0832	|	...	1032	|	1232	|	1432	|	|	1632	...	|	1832	|	2032	|	|	...	223
145	**Magdeburg** Hbf a.	...	...	0657	0754	0857	0954	...	1057	1154	1257	1354	1457	1532	1554	1658	...	1754	1857	1954	2057	2154	2154	...	230
145	**Magdeburg** Hbf **848** d.	0559	...	0700	0757	0900	0957	...	1100	1157	1300	1357	1500	1536	1557	1701	1704	1757	1900	1957	2100	...	2200	...	...
	Berlin Hbf **839** a.	|	...	|	|	|	|	...	|	|	|	|	|	|	|	1822	|	|	|	|	|	...	|	...	...
195	Köthen d.	|	...	|	|	|	|	...	|	|	|	|	|	|	|	...	|	|	|	|	|	...	|	...	...
	Dessau Hbf **848** d.	0642	...	0745	0842	0945	1042	...	1145	1242	1345	1442	1545	1627	1642	...	1743	1842	1945	2042	2146	...	2243	...	...
	Bitterfeld **848** d.	0700	...	0803	0859	1003	1059	...	1203	1259	1403	1459	1603	1652	1659	...	1802	1859	2003	2059	2203	...	2301	...	...
231	**Halle** (Saale) Hbf **848** a.	|	...	0820	|	1020	|	...	1220	|	1420	|	1620	|	|	...	1820	|	2020	|	2219	...	|	...	...
231	**Halle** (Saale) Hbf ⊡ d.	|	...	0822	|	1022	|	1103	1222	|	1422	|	1622	|	|	...	1822	|	2022	|	2221	...	|	...	...
249	Leipzig/Halle Flughafen ✈ ⊡ a.	|	...	0832	|	1032	|	1114	1232	|	1432	|	1632	|	|	...	1832	|	2032	|	2230	...	|	...	...
268	**Leipzig** Hbf ⊡ a.	0716	...	0849	0915	1049	1115	1131	1249	1315	1449	1515	1649	1714	1722	...	1849	1915	2049	2115	2245	...	2318	...	...
	Dresden Hbf **842** a.	0839n	...	...	1039	...	1239	1250	...	1439	...	1639	...	...	1839	...	...	2039	...	2239	2358k	...	...	......	...

	IC 2436		*IC* 2042	*IC* 2042		*IC* 2434	*IC* 2044	*IC* 2238	*IC* 2432	*IC* 2046	*IC* 2430	*IC* 2048	*IC* 2038	*IC* 2440	*IC* 2036	*IC* 2442	*IC* 2034	*IC* 1934	*IC* 2444	*IC* 2032	*IC* 2446	*IC* 2446		*IC* 2030	*IC* 244
	①–⑥		① m	①–⑥		①–⑥ 🍷	①–⑥ e 🍷	A	C 🍷	①–⑥ 🍷	🍷	🍷	🍷	🍷	Ⓑ 🍷	🍷	Ⓑ 🍷	⑦ 🍷	🍷	Ⓑ 🍷	🍷	⑦ 🍷		D	Ⓑ
Dresden Hbf **842** d.	...	...	...	...	...	...	0510a	...	...	0710	...	0910	...	1110	...	1310		1452	1510	...	1710	1710		...	19
Leipzig Hbf ⊡ d.	...	...	0439	...	...	0511	0636	0712	...	0836	0912	1036	1112	1236	1312	1436	1512	1604	1636	1712	1836	1836	...	1912	203
Leipzig/Halle Flughafen ✈ ⊡ d.	...	...	|	...	...	0524	|	0724	...	|	0924	|	1124	|	1324	|	1524	|	|	1724	|	|	...	1924	|
Halle (Saale) Hbf ⊡ a.	...	...	|	...	...	0534	|	0734	...	|	0934	|	1134	|	1334	|	1534	|	|	1734	|	|	...	1934	|
Halle (Saale) Hbf **848** d.	...	...	|	...	...	0536	|	0736	...	|	0936	|	1136	|	1336	|	1536	|	|	1736	|	|	...	1936	|
Bitterfeld **848** d.	...	...	0457	...	...	0555	0700	0757	...	0857	0957	1057	1157	1257	1357	1457	1557	1626	1657	1757	1857	1857	...	1957	205
Dessau Hbf **848** d.	...	...	0514	...	...	0615	0717	0815	...	0914	1015	1114	1215	1314	1415	1514	1615	1646	1714	1815	1914	1914	...	2015	211
Köthen d.	...	...	|	...	...	|	|	|	...	|	|	|	|	|	|	|	|	|	|	|	|	|	...	|	|
Berlin Hbf **839** d.	...	...	|	...	...	|	|	|	0730	|	|	|	|	|	|	|	|	|	|	|	|	|	...	|	|
Magdeburg Hbf **848** a.	...	...	0553	...	...	0657	0801	0852	0856	0954	1057	1154	1257	1354	1457	1554	1657	1726	1754	1857	1954	1954	...	2058	215
Magdeburg Hbf d.	0500	...	0601	0601	...	0700	0803	...	0900	1003	1100	1203	1300	1403	1500	1603	1700	1728	1803	1900	2003	2003	...	...	220
Helmstedt d.	0526	...	0628	0628	...	0726	|	...	0929	|	1126	|	1326	|	1526	|	1726	|	|	1926	|	|	...	...	223
Braunschweig Hbf d.	0549	...	0651	0651	...	0749	0849	...	0951	1049	1149	1249	1349	1449	1549	1649	1749	1816	1849	1949	2049	2049	...	...	225
Peine d.	0606	...	|	|	...	|	|	...	|	|	|	|	|	|	|	|	|	|	|	|	|	|	...	...	|
Hannover Hbf a.	0626	...	0723	0723	...	0823	0923	...	1025	1123	1223	1323	1423	1523	1623	1723	1823	1851	1923	2023	2123	2123	...	...	232
Bremen Hbf **813** a.	0750	...	|	|	...	0950	|	...	1150	|	1350	|	1550	|	1750	|	1950	2009	|	2150	...	|	...	...	...
Oldenburg (Oldb) **813** a.	0823	...	|	|	...	1023	|	...	1223	|	1423	|	1623	|	1823	|	2023	2040	|	2223	...	|	...	...	...
Emden Hbf **813** a.	0938	...	|	|	...	1138	|	...	1338	|	1538	|	1738	|	1938	|	2138	2152	|	2338	...	|	...	...	...
Norddeich **813** a.	...	...	|	|	...	...	|	...	1414	|	...	|	...	|	2014	|	2214	...	|	...	...	|	...	...	...
Bielefeld Hbf **810** a.	...	...	0840	0840	...	...	1040	...	...	1240	...	1440	...	1640	...	1840b	...	...	2040b	...	...	2240	...	...	...
Dortmund Hbf **800** a.	...	...	0932	0932	...	...	1132	...	...	1332	...	1532	...	1732	...	1932b	...	...	2132b	...	...	2332	...	...	...
Köln Hbf **800** a.	...	...	1046	1046	...	...	1246	...	...	1446	...	1646	...	1846	...	2046b	...	...	2246b	...	...	0046	...	...	...

Other regional trains **HANNOVER - BRAUNSCHWEIG** (operated by WestfalenBahn; most trains start from / continue to Bielefeld or Rheine – see Table **811**)

				Ⓒ	⚒					
Hannover Hbf d.	0013	0113	...	0314	0455	0555	and	2155	2255	...
Peine d.	0039	0139	...	0340	0524	0624	hourly	2224	2324	...
Braunschweig Hbf a.	0056	0156	...	0356	0541	0641	until	2241	2340	...

			Ⓒ		⚒			
Braunschweig Hbf d.	0020	...	0213	...	0420	0520	and	23
Peine d.	0038	...	0230	...	0438	0538	hourly	23
Hannover Hbf a.	0105	...	0254	...	0505	0605	until	00

Other regional stopping trains **BRAUNSCHWEIG - MAGDEBURG**

	⑦		Ⓐ t	Ⓒ z	⑥	Ⓐ t		Ⓐ t		Ⓐ t		Ⓐ t	Ⓒ z	Ⓐ t	Ⓐ t		Ⓐ t		Ⓐ t			Ⓑ	⑥	Ⓑ	
Braunschweig Hbf d.	0107	...	...	0542	...	0617	0717	0817	0917	1017	1117	1217	1317	1320	1417	1517	1617	1717	1817	1917	2017	2117	2147	2217	23
Helmstedt d.	0136	0435	0606	0610	0645	0646	0746	0846	0946	1046	1146	1246	1346	1348	1446	1546	1646	1746	1846	1946	2046	2146	2216	2246	00
Magdeburg Hbf a.	0219	0519	0652	0652	0729	0729	0829	0929	1029	1129	1229	1329	1429	1429	1529	1629	1729	1829	1929	2029	2129	2229	2259	2329	..

	⑥	Ⓐ t	Ⓒ z	Ⓐ				Ⓐ t			Ⓐ t		Ⓐ t		Ⓐ t			Ⓐ t			Ⓐ t				
Magdeburg Hbf d.	0253	0433	0533	*0530*t	0633	0733	...	0833	0933	...	1033	1133	1233	1333	1433	1533	...	1633	1733	...	1833	1933	2033	2205	23
Helmstedt d.	0333	0513	0613	0615	0713	0813	0913	0913	1013	1113	1113	1213	1313	1413	1513	1613	1713	1713	1813	1913	1913	2013	2113	2245	23
Braunschweig Hbf a.	0402	0541	0641	0645	0741	0841	0941	0941	1041	1141	1141	1241	1341	1441	1541	1641	1741	1741	1841	1941	1941	2041	2141	2313	..

Other regional trains **MAGDEBURG - HALLE** (all services are operated by 🚌 between Sachsendorf and Halle)

Magdeburg Hbf d.	0415	0503	0537		1737	1837	1937	2037	2208	2307
Schönebeck (Elbe) d.	0424	0514	0551	and	1751	1851	1951	2051	2221	2321
Sachsendorf a.	0437	0532	0604	hourly	1804	1904	2004	2104	2234	2334
Sachsendorf 🚌 d.	*0443*	*0542*	*0614*	until	*1814*	*1910*	*2010*	*2110*	*2244*	*2344*
Köthen 🚌 d.	*0512*	*0611*	*0643*		*1843*	*1939*	*2039*	*2139*	*2313*	*0013*
Halle (Saale) Hbf 🚌 a.	*0602*	*0659*	*0733*		*1933*	*2029*	*2129*	*2229*	*0003*	*0103*

	⑥⑦			Ⓐ t						Ⓑ
Halle (Saale) Hbf 🚌 d.	*0012*	...	*0451*	*0524*	*0624*		*1924*	*2038*	*2138*	*22*
Köthen 🚌 d.	*0102*	...	*0541*	*0614*	*0714*	and	*2014*	*2128*	*2228*	*23*
Sachsendorf 🚌 a.	*0131*	...	*0610*	*0643*	*0743*	hourly	*2043*	*2157*	*2257*	*00*
Sachsendorf d.	0136	...	0620	0653	0753	until	2053	2203	2303	00
Schönebeck (Elbe) d.	0150	...	0634	0709	0808		2108	2218	2318	00
Magdeburg Hbf a.	0205	...	0650	0722	0822		2122	2232	2332	00

A – Runs daily Leipzig - Magdeburg. Continues to Rostock / Warnemünde via Schwerin on ⑤–⑦ to June 23 (also June 10), daily June 28 - Sept. 17, ⑤–⑦ Sept. 20 - Nov. 3 (also Oct. 2, 3, 29, 30, 31) and ⑤ from Nov. 8. See also Tables **830**, **837** and **841**.
B – Runs daily Magdeburg - Leipzig. From Warnemünde / Rostock via Schwerin on ⑤–⑦ to June 23 (also June 10), daily June 28 - Sept. 17, ⑤–⑦ Sept. 20 - Nov. 3 (also Oct. 2, 3, 29, 30, 31) and ⑤ from Nov. 8. See also Tables **830**, **837** and **841**.
C – To / from Cottbus on dates in Table **838**.
D – ①②③④⑦ (not Oct. 2, 3).

a – Ⓐ (not Oct. 31, Nov. 20).
b – Not ⑥.
d – Also runs Köln - Leipzig on July 13, 20, 27, Aug. 3, 10, 17, 24, Oct. 26, Nov. 2.

e – ①–⑥ only.
f – Also Oct. 2; not Oct. 4.
g – ① (also June 11). 0519 from Oct. 14.
k – ⑥ only.
m – Also June 11.
n – Not Nov. 20.
t – Not Oct. 31.
z – Also Oct. 31.

⊡ – See Table **881** for other S-Bahn services

2nd class only

HARZER SCHMALSPURBAHNEN 867

Nordhausen - Wernigerode: *Die Harzquerbahn*; Eisfelder Talmühle - Stiege - Alexisbad - Quedlinburg: *Die Selketalbahn*; Drei Annen Hohne - Brocken: *Die Brockenbahn*

Summer service: April 27 - October 26, 2019

km			🚂	🚂	🚂	🚂	🚂 B	🚂	🚂	🚂 B	🚂	
0	**Wernigerode** § d.	0725	0855	0940	1025	1155	...	1325	1455	...	1625	1625
15	Drei Annen Hohne a.	0802	0932	1017	1102	1232	...	1402	1532	...	1702	1702
15	Drei Annen Hohne ◇ d.	0810	0945	1030	1115	1240	1245	1415	1546	1540	1716	1718
20	Schierke ◇ a.	|	0957	1042	1127	|	1257	1427	1558	|	1728	|
20	Schierke ◇ d.	|	1005	1050	1135	|	1313	1440	1621	|	1748	|
34	**Brocken** ◇ a.	|	1036	1121	1206	|	1344	1530	1652	|	1819	|
19	Elend d.	0822	—	...	...	1252	—	...	...	1552	...	1730
28	Sorge d.	0841	...	...	...	1311	...	...	...	1611	...	1749
31	Benneckenstein d.	0850	...	...	...	1320	...	...	...	1620	...	1758
44	Eisfelder Talmühle a.	0918	⊕	...	...	1348	...	...	...	1649	...	1826
44	Eisfelder Talmühle d.	...	0943	...	...	...	1402	...	...	1702	...	*1833*
50	Ilfeld d.	...	0959	...	...	...	1417	...	...	1717	...	*1850*
61	**Nordhausen** Nord § a.	...	1023*	...	...	...	1439*	...	...	1739	...	*1913*

		🚂 B	🚂	🚂		🚂	🚂	🚂	🚂		
Nordhausen Nord § d.	*0854**	1024	...	...	1325	...	...	...	...	*1754**	...
Ilfeld d.	*0917*	1047	...	...	1346	...	...	...	...	1817	...
Eisfelder Talmühle a.	*0931*	1101	...	...	1400	...	...	...	...	1831	...
Eisfelder Talmühle d.	0938	1108	...	...	—	1408	...	...	...	—	1838
Benneckenstein d.	1007	1137	...	...	...	1437	...	...	...	...	1907
Sorge d.	1015	1145	...	...	...	1445	...	...	...	...	1915
Elend d.	1035	1205	...	...	🚂 B	1505	...	...	...	🚂	1935
Brocken ◇ d.	|	|	1136	1314	1451	|	1622	1707	1749	1831	|
Schierke a.	|	|	1216	1354	1521	|	1702	1746	1829	1901	|
Schierke ◇ d.	|	|	1224	1355	1522	|	1703	1747	1830	1902	|
Drei Annen Hohne ◇ a.	1046	1216	1236	1406	1533	1516	1714	1759	1841	1913	1946
Drei Annen Hohne d.	1108	...	1253	1423	...	1553	1723	1808	1853	1923	1954
Wernigerode § a.	1145	...	1333	1503	...	1633	1800	1845	1930	2000	2030

km		🚂	◧	🚂	◧	🚂	◧				◧	🚂
0	**Quedlinburg** § d.	...	0830	1030	1338	...	...	...	1530	...	1753	1942
8	**Gernrode** a.	...	0845	1045	1353	...	...	...	1545	...	1808	1957
8	**Gernrode** d.	0734	0846	1046	—	1357	1502	...	1546	...	1809	—
18	Mägdesprung d.	0804	0918	1117	...	1428	1532	...	1618	...	1842	...
	Harzgerode d.	|	|	|	1210	|	|	1620	|	...	|	1840
23	Alexisbad a.	0818	0932	1131	1220	1442	1546	1630	1632	...	1856	1850
23	Alexisbad d.	0825	0939	*1133*	1229	1456	—	—	1633	1634	1903	1858
26	**Harzgerode** a.	0835	|	*1143*	|	|	...	...	|	1643	1913	|
26	Silberhütte d.	—	0949	—	1239	1506	...	...	1644	—	—	1909
30	Straßberg (Harz) d.	...	1001	...	1251	1520	...	...	1655	...	...	1920
35	Güntersberge d.	...	1010	...	1300	1530	🚂	...	1704	...	...	1930
	Hasselfelde d.	1012	|	...	|	|	1610	...	|	1758	...	|
44	Stiege a.	1025	1026	...	1316	1546	1623	...	1720	1811	...	1946
44	Stiege d.	...	1027	...	1326	1547	1624	...	1734	1812	...	1947
48	**Hasselfelde** a.	...	|	...	|	1600	|	🚂 B	1747	|	...	|
53	Eisfelder Talmühle d.	...	1050	1103	1402r	...	1644	1702	...	1833	1915	2015
59	Ilfeld d.	...	...	1118	1417	...	...	1717	...	1850	1929	2029
70	**Nordhausen** Nord § a.	...	...	1139	1439*	...	...	1739	...	1913	1952	2053*

		⊕		🚂 B	◧					🚂	
Nordhausen Nord § d.	0825	0854*	...	1024	...	1225	1325	...	1625	...	...
Ilfeld d.	0849	0917	...	1047	...	1246	1346	...	1646	...	...
Eisfelder Talmühle d.	0903	0932	...	1101	1105	1301	1401	...	1700	1702	...
Hasselfelde d.	—	|	1012	—	|	|	|	1439	—	|	...
Stiege a.	...	0952	1025	...	1125	1321	1421	1452	...	1722	...
Stiege d.	...	0953	1031	...	1126	1322	1422	1453	...	1732	1734
Hasselfelde a.	...	1006	|	...	|	|	1435	|	...	|	1747
Güntersberge d.	...	—	1047	...	1144	1340	...	1509	...	1748	—
Straßberg (Harz) d.	...	...	1057	...	1154	1350	...	1519	...	1758	...
Silberhütte d.	...	🚂	1108	...	1205	1401	...	1531	...	1809	◧
Harzgerode d.	...	0845	|	...	|	|	...	|	...	⊙	1923
Alexisbad a.	...	0855	1119	🚂	1216	1412	...	1541	◧	1820	1933
Alexisbad d.	...	0902	1133	1146	1223	1413	...	1548	1602	1827	1940
Harzgerode a.	...	|	1143	|	|	|	...	1558	|	⊙	|
Mägdesprung d.	...	0919	...	1201	1237	1429	...	...	1619	1841	1954
Gernrode a.	◧	0949	...	1230	1306	1459	...	...	1649	1911	2024
Gernrode d.	0800	0959	...	...	1307	1500	...	...	1659	1912	...
Quedlinburg § a.	0815	1015	...	...	1323	1515	...	...	1715	1927	...

– [2] Brocken - Nordhausen and v.v.

– Arrives 1348.

– Nordhausen **Bahnhofsplatz**.

– Adjacent to DB station.

–Steam train.

◧ – 🚂 on ④⑤⑥ (also June 9). Diesel train on other dates.

⊙ – Connecting trains: Harzgerode d. 1811 → Alexisbad a. 1821. Alexisbad d. 1825 → Harzgerode a. 1835.

⊕ – Change trains at Ilfeld on Ⓐ (through train on Ⓒ).

◇ – Additional journeys (🚂) Drei Annen Hohne - Brocken and v.v.: From Drei Annen Hohne at 1200, 1339, 1506 and 1647. From Brocken at 1051, 1221, 1359 and 1540.

Operator: Harzer Schmalspurbahnen GmbH. Friedrichstraße 151, 38855 Wernigerode. ✆ + 49 (0) 3943 558 0. Fax + 49 (0) 3943 558 148.

RE / *RB* services

ERFURT - NORDHAUSEN 868

km		Ⓐe																	
0	**Erfurt** Hbf d.	0448	0559	0700	0802	0902	1002	1102	1202	1302	1402	1502	1602	1702	1802	1902	2016	...	2218
27	Straußfurt d.	0514	0624	0725	0829	0924	1029	1124	1229	1324	1429	1524	1629	1724	1829	1924	2045	...	2245
60	Sondershausen d.	0547	0657	0757	0857	0957	1057	1157	1257	1357	1457	1557	1657	1757	1857	1957	2113	...	2317
80	**Nordhausen** a.	0610	0715	0820	0915	1020	1115	1220	1315	1420	1515	1620	1715	1820	1915	2020	2130	...	2338

	Ⓐe	Ⓐe																	
ordhausen d.	0420	0521	...	0623	0729	0834	0929	1034	1129	1234	1329	1434	1529	1634	1729	1834	1929	...	2137
ndershausen d.	0443	0550	...	0640	0757	0857	0957	1057	1157	1257	1357	1457	1557	1657	1757	1857	1957	...	2158
raußfurt d.	0515	0626	...	0710	0830	0924	1030	1124	1230	1324	1430	1524	1630	1724	1830	1924	2031	...	2230
furt Hbf a.	0541	0651	...	0738	0856	0950	1056	1150	1256	1350	1456	1550	1656	1750	1856	1950	2057	...	2258

e – Not Oct. 31.

RB services

NORDHAUSEN - GÖTTINGEN 869

km		Ⓐ	⚒																	
0	**Nordhausen** d.	...	0539	0639	0739	0839	0939	1039	1139	1239	1339	1439	1539	1639	1739	1839	1939	2039	2139
20	Walkenried d.	0503	0603	0703	0803	0903	1003	1103	1203	1303	1403	1503	1603	1703	1803	1903	2003	2103	2203
23	Bad Sachsa d.	0508	0608	0708	0808	0908	1008	1108	1208	1308	1408	1508	1608	1708	1808	1908	2008	2108	2208
37	Bad Lauterberg ⊡ d.	0519	0619	0719	0819	0919	1019	1119	1219	1319	1419	1519	1619	1719	1819	1919	2019	2119	2219
43	Herzberg (Harz) d.	0526	0626	0726	0826	0926	1026	1126	1226	1326	1426	1526	1626	1726	1826	1926	2026	2126	2226
70	Northeim (Han) 903 a.	0550	0650	0750	0850	0950	1050	1150	1250	1350	1450	1550	1650	1750	1850	1950	2050	2150	2250
90	**Göttingen** 903 a.	0609	0710	0808	*0950*r	1008	*1146*	1208	*1346*	1408	*1546*	1608	*1750*	1808	*1946*	2008	*2146*	2209	*2346*

	Ⓐ	⚒	Ⓒ	Ⓐ															⑤⑥f
ttingen 903 d.	*0409*	0549	*0607*	0649	0749	*0809*	0949	*1005*	1149	*1209*	1349	*1409*	1549	*1609*	1749	*1805*	1949	*2009*	2149
rtheim (Han) 903 d.	0506	0606	0706	0706	0806	0906	1006	1106	1206	1306	1406	1506	1606	1706	1806	1906	2006	2106	2206
rzberg (Harz) d.	0530	0630	0730	0730	0830	0930	1030	1130	1230	1330	1430	1530	1630	1730	1830	1930	2030	2130	2230
d Lauterberg ⊡ d.	0536	0636	0736	0736	0836	0936	1036	1136	1236	1336	1436	1536	1636	1736	1836	1936	2036	2136	2236
d Sachsa d.	0547	0647	0747	0747	0847	0947	1047	1147	1247	1347	1447	1547	1647	1747	1847	1947	2047	2147	2247
lkenried d.	0552	0652	0752	0752	0852	0952	1052	1152	1252	1352	1452	1552	1652	1752	1852	1952	2052	2152	2252
rdhausen a.	0615	0715	0815	0815	0915	1015	1115	1215	1315	1415	1515	1615	1715	1815	1915	2015	2115	2215	2315

f – ⑤⑥ (also Oct. 2; runs daily Göttingen - Herzberg).

r – *0952* from Oct. 15.

⊡ – Bad Lauterberg im Harz Barbis.

☛ Timings for connecting trains Northeim - Göttingen and v.v. are valid from June 11.

B (*RE* services); *STB*; *EB*

ERFURT - MEININGEN - SCHWEINFURT - WÜRZBURG 870

km				▽	▽◇ Ⓐe	▽		▽		▽		▽		▽		▽		▽		▽ Ⓐe	▽ g		▽	▽
0	**Erfurt** Hbf 872 d.	...	0459	...	0601	0700	0735	0902	0935	1102	1135	1301	1335	1502	1535	1702	1735	1901	1935	2010	2116	...	2246	2349
23	Arnstadt Hbf 872 d.	...	0516	...	0620	0719	0751	0919	0951	1119	1151	1319	1351	1519	1551	1719	1751	1919	1951	2028	2138	...	2303	0011
31	Plaue (Thür) d.	...	0523	...	0627	0727	0759	0927	0959	1127	1159	1327	1359	1527	1559	1727	1759	1927	1959	2035	2146	...	2312	0023
37	Gräfenroda d.	...	0528	...	0632	0732	|	0932	|	1132	|	1332	|	1532	|	1732	|	1932	2004	2040	2155	...	2317	0028
58	Zella-Mehlis d.	...	0543	0557e	0652	0751	0816	0951	1016	1151	1216	1351	1416	1551	1616	1751	1816	1951	2019	2058	2214	...	2334	0047
64	Suhl d.	...	0550	0603e	0658	0758	0822	0958	1022	1158	1222	1358	1422	1558	1622	1758	1822	1958	2025	2104	2220	...	2341	0053
84	Grimmenthal 873 a.	...	0601	0623	0714	0813	0832	1013	1032	1213	1232	1413	1432	1613	1632	1813	1832	2013	2035	2117	2236g	...	2353	0109
92	**Meiningen** 873 a.	...	*0611*e	0629	*0724*	0821	*0847*	1021	*1047*	1221	*1247*	1421	*1447*	1621	*1647*	1821	*1847*	2021	*2047*	2131	2249	...	2400	0117
			|		|	—	|	—	|	—	|	—	|	—	|	—	|	—	|	—	—		—	
		◇	|	◇	|	◇	|	◇	|	◇	|	◇	|	◇	|	◇	|	◇	|	◇	▽	◇		
				Ⓐt		Ⓒv																		
	Meiningen 873 d.	0524	*0550*	0642	*0710*	0720	*0822*	0924	*1022*	1124	*1222*	1324	*1422*	1539	*1622*	1724	*1822*	1924	*2022*	2124	2230	...	...	...
34	Grimmenthal 873 d.	|	0604	|	0725	|	0835	|	1035	|	1235	|	1435	|	1635	|	1835	|	2036	|	2236	2240	...	...
10	Mellrichstadt d.	0548	0623	0709	0749	0749	0849	0948	1049	1148	1250	1348	1449	1603	1649	1748	1849	1948	2049	2148	...	2258	...	...
24	Bad Neustadt (Saale) d.	0600	0635	0718	0801	0801	0857	0959	1057	1159	1258	1359	1457	1612	1657	1759	1857	1959	2057	2159	...	2307	...	...
34	Münnerstadt d.	0608	0643	0727	0809	0809	0903	1007	1103	1207	1305	1407	1504	1623	1703	1807	1903	2007	2104	2207	...	2315	...	...
49	Ebenhausen (Unterfr) a.	0619	0654	0737	0819	0819	0912	1018	1112	1217	1313	1418	1512	1633	1712	1818	1912	2018	2112	2217	...	2326	...	...
49	Ebenhausen (Unterfr) d.	0625	0659	0742	0827	0827	0918	1026	1118	1227	1319	1426	1518	1640	1718	1826	1918	2027	2118	2229	...	2329	...	...
63	**Schweinfurt** Hbf 875 a.	0638	0714	0754	0842	0842	0926	1042	1126	1242	1327	1440	1526	1652	1726	1842	1926	2042	2126	2240	...	2341	2344	...
06	**Würzburg** Hbf 875 a.	*0722*	0746	*0820*	*0922*	*0922*	0955	*1121*	1155	*1320*	1355	*1522*	1555	*1722*	1755	*1922*	1955	*2122*	2157	...	...	...	0016	...

Ⓐ (not Oct. 31).

Connects with train in the following column at Grimmenthal.

t – Not June 20, Aug. 15, Nov. 1.

v – Also Oct. 31.

▽ – Operated by Süd Thüringen Bahn (2nd class only).

◇ – Operated by Erfurter Bahn (2nd class only).

870 WÜRZBURG - SCHWEINFURT - MEININGEN - ERFURT

DB (RE services); STB; EB

				◇	◇	◇	◇		◇		◇		◇	◇		◇		◇		◇		◇	◇	◇
				⚒r	Ⓐt	Ⓐt	Ⓒz						Ⓐt	Ⓒz										
Würzburg Hbf ... 876 d.	...	...	0454r	...	...	0621	0604	0801	0835	1001	1035	1201	1207	1235	1401	1435	1601	1636	1801	1836	2001	2035	2139	2307
Schweinfurt Hbf ... 876 d.	...	...	0530	0610	0610	0702	0718	0830	0913	1030	1113	1230	1243	1311	1430	1513	1631	1713	1831	1913	2030	2113	2214	2347
Ebenhausen (Unterf) ... a.	...	...	0539	0623	0623	0713	0731	0838	0929	1038	1129	1238	1253	1329	1439	1529	1639	1730	1839	1929	2039	2129	2226	2359
Ebenhausen (Unterf) ... d.	...	...	0541	0629	0629	0715	0741	0840	0932	1040	1132	1240	1253	1332	1441	1532	1641	1735	1841	1932	2040	2132	2230	0001
Münnerstadt ... d.	...	...	0550	0646	0646	0729	0752	0849	0944	1049	1144	1249	1308	1344	1450	1543	1650	1747	1850	1944	2049	2144	2241	0012
Bad Neustadt (Saale) ... d.	...	...	0557	0654	0654	0737	0800	0857	0958	1057	1158	1257	1319	1358	1457	1555	1657	1757	1857	1958	2057	2157	2249	0020
Mellrichstadt ... d.	...	...	0605	0703	0707	0746	0809	0906	1007	1106	1207	1306	1328	1407	1506	1606	1706	1806	1906	2007	2106	2206	2258	...
Grimmenthal ... 873 a.	...	...	0619					0919		1119		1319			1519		1719		1919		2120	2224		...
Meiningen ... 873 a.	...	...	0629	...	0731*	0810	0833	0934	1031	1134	1231	1334	1358	1431	1534	1631	1734	1831	1934	2031	2131	2249	2322	...

	▽	▽		▽	▽	▽			▽		▽		▽	▽		▽		▽		▽		▽	▽	
	Ⓐe			⚒eE		Ⓐe								Ⓐe									⑤⑥f	
Meiningen ... 873 d.	0504	0526	0611	0710	0735	0822	...	0901	0935	1101	1135	1301	1335	1422	1501	1535	1701	1735	1901	1935	2101	2132	2327	...
Grimmenthal ... 873 d.	0511	0533	0621	0717	0741	0834	...	0919	0941	1119	1141	1319	1341	1434	1519	1541	1719	1741	1919	1941	2121	2142	2333	...
Suhl ... d.	0524	0550	0633	0730	0759	0848	...	0932	0959	1132	1159	1332	1359	1448	1532	1559	1732	1759	1932	1959	2133	2158	2353	...
Zella-Mehlis ... d.	0532	0556	0639	0737	0805	0855	...	0938	1005	1138	1205	1338	1405	1455	1538	1605	1738	1805	1938	2005	2139	2214v	2359	...
Gräfenroda ... d.	0548	0615	0655	0753	0824	0912	...		1024		1224		1424	1512		1624		1824		2024	2153	2232	0016x	...
Plaue (Thür) ... d.	0553	0627v	0700		0829	0917	...	0957	1029	1157	1229	1357	1429	1517	1557	1629	1757	1829	1957	2029	2158	2245v	0025	...
Arnstadt Hbf ... 872 d.	0604	0635	0707	0805	0839	0925	...	1005	1039	1205	1239	1405	1439	1525	1605	1639	1805	1839	2005	2039	2205	2253	0033	...
Erfurt Hbf ... 872 a.	0620	0654	0725	0821	0856	0943	...	1021	1056	1221	1256	1421	1456	1543	1621	1656	1821	1855	2021	2057	2221	2313	0055	...

E – From Eisenach (Table **873**).
e – Not Oct. 31.
f – Also June 9, Oct. 2, 30.
r – ⚒ (not June 20, Aug. 15, Nov. 1).
t – Not June 20, Aug. 15, Nov. 1.
v – Arrives 7–10 minutes earlier.
x – Calls on request only.
z – Also June 20, Aug. 15, Nov. 1.
* – 0735 on Oct. 31.
▽ – Operated by Süd Thüringen Bahn (2nd class only).
◇ – Operated by Erfurter Bahn (2nd class only).

871 *Service June 16 - November 16* LEIPZIG - GERA - SAALFELD

Erfurter Bahn; 2nd class only

km																									
		Ⓐe	Ⓐe	Ⓒv	Ⓐe	Ⓐe		Ⓐe◧	Ⓒv		◧		◧		◧		◧		◧						‡
0	**Leipzig** Hbf ... d.	...	...	...	0459	...	0608	0655	0655k	0754	0854	0954	1054	1154	1254	1354	1454	1554	1656	1754	1856	1956	2058	2200	2308
45	Zeitz ... d.	0429	...	...	0545	...	0703	0737	0737k	0835	0935	1035	1135	1235	1335	1435	1535	1635	1736	1835	1936	2042	2139	2240	2348
72	**Gera** Hbf ... a.	0452	...	...	0616	...	0736	0800	0800k	0858	0958	1058	1158	1258	1358	1458	1558	1658	1800	1858	1959	2105	2204	2304	0013
72	**Gera** Hbf ... d.	0453	0530	0548	0628	0730	...	0801	0801	0901	1001	1101	1201	1301	1401	1501	1601	1701	1801	1901	2001	2113	2209	2313	...
84	Weida ... d.	0504	0543	0608	0642	0745	...	0812	0814	0913	1014	1113	1214	1313	1414	1514	1614	1713	1814	1913	2014	2125	2221	2325	...
99	Triptis ... d.	0516	0557	0620	0654	0757	...	...	0827	0931	1027	1131	1227	1331	1427	1531	1627	1731	1827	1931	2026	2141	...	2338	...
108	Neustadt (Orla) ... d.	0522	0603	0627	0701	0804	...	...	0833	0938	1033	1138	1233	1338	1433	1538	1633	1738	1833	1938	2037	2147	...	2344	...
139	**Saalfeld** (Saale) ... a.	0552	0637	0653	0728	0835	...	...	0900	1000	1100	1200	1300	1400	1500	1600	1700	1801	1900	2000	2105	2215	...	0012	...

	Ⓐe		⚒e	⚒e		Ⓐe		Ⓒv	Ⓐe		◧		◧		◧		◧		◧		◧				⑤⑥
Saalfeld (Saale) ... d.	...	...	...	0511	...	0553	...	0652	0652	0758	0857	0958	1057	1158	1257	1358	1457	1557	1657	1758	1857	2009	2059	2209	220
Neustadt (Orla) ... d.	...	...	...	0538	...	0619	...	0722	0725	0819	0924	1019	1124	1219	1324	1419	1524	1619	1724	1819	1924	2036	2122	2235	223
Triptis ... d.	...	...	...	0545	...	0626	...	0729	0732	0827	0931	1027	1131	1227	1331	1427	1531	1627	1731	1827	1931	2043	2128	2241	224
Weida ... d.	...	...	...	0601	...	0641	...	0745	0745	0843	0946	1040	1146	1240	1346	1440	1546	1640	1746	1840	1946	2055	2140	2254	225
Gera Hbf ... a.	...	...	...	0612	...	0653	...	0756	0756	0855	0957	1053	1157	1253	1357	1453	1557	1653	1757	1853	1957	2109	2150	2307	230
Gera Hbf ... d.	0346	0458	0540	0616	0616	0659	0659	0801	0801	0901	1001	1101	1201	1301	1401	1500	1601	1700	1801	1901	2001	...	2151	...	231
Zeitz ... d.	0410	0523	0605	0640	0640	0724	0724	0825	0825	0925	1025	1125	1225	1325	1425	1525	1625	1725	1825	1925	2025	...	2214	...	233
Leipzig Hbf ... a.	0452	0603	0650	0721	0721	0808	0808	0908	0908	1008	1108	1208	1308	1408	1508	1608	1709	1808	1909	2008	2105	...	2300‡	...	002

(LEIPZIG -) GERA - HOF

km									
			⚒e						
	Leipzig Hbf ... d.	...	0655	...	0854	1054	1254	1454	1656
0	**Gera** Hbf ... d.	0548	0801	0801	1001	1201	1401	1601	1801
12	Weida ... d.	0611	0816	0816	1016	1216	1416	1616	1816
84	**Hof** Hbf ... a.	0725	0925	0925	1125	1325	1525	1725	1925

Hof Hbf ... d.	0833	1033	1233	1433	1633	1833	2034
Weida ... a.	0939	1139	1339	1539	1739	1939	2137
Gera Hbf ... a.	0957	1157	1357	1557	1757	1957	2157
Leipzig Hbf ... a.	1108	1308	1508	1709	1909	2105	...

e – Not Oct. 31.
r – Also Oct. 2, 30.
k – ⑥ only.
v – Also Oct. 31.
‡ – Subject to alteration on ①②③④⑦ June 24 - Aug. 29.
§ – Subject to alteration June 28 - Aug. 3
◧ – Conveys (12) Leipzig - Weida - Ho and v.v. (see panel below main table

872 ERFURT - SAALFELD and ROTTENBACH - KATZHÜTTE

DB; Erfurter Bahn★; 2nd class only

km										
		Ⓐe	Ⓐe							
0	**Erfurt** Hbf ... 870 d.	0428	0523	0638	and at the same minutes past each hour until	1938	2038	2145	2246	...
23	Arnstadt Hbf ... 870 d.	0453	0548	0700		2000	2100	2214	2313	...
38	Stadtilm ... d.	0506	0601	0713		2013	2113	2227	2326	...
54	Rottenbach ... d.	0520	0613	0727		2027	2127	2245	2340	...
62	Bad Blankenburg ... d.	0528	0621	0734		2034	2134	2252	2347	...
70	**Saalfeld** (Saale) ... a.	0535	0629	0742		2042	2042	2300	2355	...

	Ⓐe							
Saalfeld (Saale) ... d.	0504	0612	0711	and at the same minutes past each hour until	2011	...	2111	...	222
Bad Blankenburg ... d.	0511	0622	0718		2018	...	2118	...	223
Rottenbach ... d.	0519	0629	0727		2027	...	2127	...	224
Stadtilm ... d.	0533	0643	0740		2040	...	2140	...	225
Arnstadt Hbf ... 870 d.	0550	0658	0756		2056	...	2153	...	230
Erfurt Hbf ... 870 a.	0610	0717	0817		2117	...	2221	...	232

km										
		Ⓐe					⑤⑦f			
0	Rottenbach ... d.	0535	0641	0741	and hourly until	1941	2041	...	...	...
15	Obstfelderschmiede ... a.	0558	0705	0805		2005	2105	...	...	...
25	Katzhütte ... a.	0614	0722	0822		2022	2122	...	...	...

	Ⓐe					⑤⑦f			
Katzhütte ... d.	0529	0636	0736	and hourly until	1936	2036	...	...	...
Obstfelderschmiede ... d.	0546	0653	0753		1953	2053	...	...	...
Rottenbach ... a.	0608	0715	0815		2015	2115	...	...	...

e – Not Oct. 31.
f – Also June 10; not June 9.
★ – Erfurt - Saalfeld operated by Erfurter Bahn. Rottenbach - Katzhütte operated by DB.

☛ **Oberweißbacher Bergbahn**. Obstfelderschmiede - Lichtenhain - Cursdorf. Journey: 28–44 minute **From Obstfelderschmiede** at 0630, 0700, 0730 and every 30 minutes until 1730; then 1808, 1830, 1908, 1930. **From Cursdorf** at 0614, 0640, 0706, 0734, 0814, 0844 and every 30 minutes until 194

873 EISENACH - MEININGEN - SONNEBERG

Süd Thüringen Bahn (2nd class); SEE NOTE ✣

km																										
		Ⓐt	Ⓐt	Ⓐt	Ⓐt		E						Ⓒz	Ⓐt		Ⓒz	Ⓐt									
0	**Eisenach** ... ✣ d.	...	...	0418	0500	...	0603	...	0716	0816	0916	1016	1116	1116	1216	1316	1316	1416	1516	1616	1716	1816	1916	2016	2121	221
27	Bad Salzungen ... d.	...	...	0444	0531	...	0632	...	0742	0842	0942	1042	1142	1142	1242	1342	1342	1442	1542	1642	1742	1842	1942	2042	2152	224
41	Wernshausen ... d.	...	...	0500	0547	...	0649	...	0759	0859	0959	1059	1159	1159	1259	1359	1359	1459	1559	1659	1759	1859	1959	2059	2209	230
61	**Meiningen** ... a.	...	...	0517	0604	...	0706	...	0816	0916	1016	1116	1216	1216	1316	1416	1416	1516	1616	1716	1816	1916	2016	2116	2226	232
61	**Meiningen** ... 870 d.	0403	0455	...	0611	0611	0710r	0725	0822	0920	1022	1120	1222	1222	1320	1422	1422	1520	1622	1720	1822	1920	2022	...	2230	...
68	Grimmenthal ... 870 d.	0412	0507	...	0623j	0623j	0716r	0733	0841f	0930	1041f	1130	1241f	1241f	1330	1441f	1441f	1530	1641f	1730	1841f	1930	2041f	...	2240	...
82	Themar ... d.	0425	0520	...	0636	0636	...	0746	0859j	0943	1059j	1143	1259j	1259j	1343	1459j	1459j	1543	1659j	1743	1859j	1943	2055	...	2253	...
94	Hildburghausen ... d.	0437	0537j	...	0652j	0652j	...	0801	0911	1001j	1111	1201j	1311	1320f	1401j	1511	1528k	1601j	1711	1801j	1911	2004f	2116f	...	2304	...
109	**Eisfeld** ... d.	0452	0552	...	0706	0706	...	0816	0926	1016	1126	1216	1326	1335	1416	1526	1543	1616	1726	1816	1926	2019	2131	...	2319	...
141	**Sonneberg** (Thür) Hbf a.	0536	0639	...	...	...	...	0900	...	1100	...	1300	...	...	1500	...	...	1700	...	1900	...	2103	...	...	...	...

	Ⓐt	Ⓐt		Ⓐt																
Sonneberg (Thür) Hbf d.	...	...	...	...	...	0548t	0702	...	0902	...	1102	...	1302	...	1502	...	1702	...	1902	2012
Eisfeld ... d.	...	0420	...	0520	...	0634	0746	0831	0946	1031	1146	1231	1346	1431	1546	1631	1746	1831	1949	2059
Hildburghausen ... d.	...	0441j	...	0535	...	0650	0801	0846	1001	1046	1201	1246	1401	1446	1601	1646	1801	1846	2004	2114
Themar ... d.	...	0452	...	0547	...	0701	0812	0857	1012	1057	1212	1257	1412	1457	1612	1657	1812	1857	2015	2126
Grimmenthal ... 870 d.	...	0513j	...	0605j	0623	0718	0830j	0928k	1030j	1128k	1230j	1328k	1430j	1528k	1630j	1728k	1830j	1928k	2030	2139
Meiningen ... 870 a.	...	0519	...	0611	0629	0724	0836	0934	1036	1134	1236	1334	1436	1534	1636	1734	1836	1934	2036	2145
Meiningen ... d.	0441	0526	0526	...	0630	0739	0839	0939	1039	1139	1239	1339	1439	1539	1639	1739	1839	1939	2039	2149
Wernshausen ... d.	0500	0548j	0548j	...	0650	0758	0858	0958	1058	1158	1258	1358	1458	1558	1658	1758	1858	1958	2058	2209
Bad Salzungen ... d.	0514	0602	0602	...	0712j	0812	0912	1012	1112	1212	1312	1412	1512	1612	1712	1812	1912	2012	2112	2224
Eisenach ... ✣ a.	0542	0630	0630	...	0743	0843	0943	1043	1143	1243	1343	1443	1543	1643	1743	1843	1943	2043	2138	2255

E – To Erfurt on ⚒r (Table **870**
f – Arrives 10–12 minutes earli
j – Arrives 6–9 minutes earlier
k – Arrives 18–19 minutes earli
r – ⚒ (not Oct. 31).
t – Ⓐ (not Oct. 31).
z – Also Oct. 31.

✣ – Eisenach - Bad Salzungen and v.v. is operated by 🚌 June 15 - Aug. 31 with most journey times extended by up to 16 minutes (earlier departures from Eisenach; please check locall

874 LEIPZIG - CHEMNITZ

Mitteldeutsche Regiobahn; SEE NOTE ⊠

km							
			⚒r				△
0	**Leipzig** Hbf ... d.	0518	0620	0720	and hourly until	2220	2337
33	Bad Lausick ... d.	0547	0647	0747		2247	0000
44	Geithain ... d.	0556	0656	0756		2256	0009
66	Burgstädt ... d.	0613	0713	0813		2313	0026
81	**Chemnitz** Hbf ... a.	0625	0725	0825		2325	0039

		⚒r				
Chemnitz Hbf ... d.	0421	0531	0631	and hourly until	2131	2231
Burgstädt ... d.	0433	0543	0643		2143	2243
Geithain ... d.	0451	0600	0700		2200	2300
Bad Lausick ... d.	0500	0609	0709		2209	2309
Leipzig Hbf ... a.	0525	0629	0729		2229	2333

r – Not Oct. 31, Nov. 20.
△ – 6–7 minutes later on ①–④ (not Oct. 2, 30, Nov. 19).
⊠ – Subject to alteration until Sept. 19 (see page 568).

 German national public holidays are on Jan. 1, Apr. 19, 22, May 1, 30, June 10, Oct. 3, Dec. 25, 26

E / RB services

NÜRNBERG - BAMBERG - SONNEBERG, SAALFELD and WÜRZBURG 875

m																										
			Ⓐt	Ⓒz	Ⓐt				Ⓒz		Ⓐt			⊖		Ⓐt	Ⓐt	⊖				Ⓐt				
0	**Nürnberg** Hbf .... **850** d.	0607	...	0638	0710	0810	0838	0938	1010	1038y	1110	1210	1238	1410	1441	1510	...	1610	1638	1810	1838	1910	1938	...	2138	2247
8	Fürth (Bay) Hbf .... d.	0613	...	0644	0716	0816	0844	0944	1016	1044y	1116	1216	1244	1416	1447	1516	...	1616	1644	1816	1844	1916	1944	...	2145	2253
24	Erlangen .... **850** d.	0623	...	0654	0728	0828	0854	0954	1028	1054	1128	1228	1254	1428	1457	1528	...	1628	1654	1828	1854	1928	1954	...	2155	2302
39	Forchheim (Oberfr) .... d.	0632	...	0704	0737	0837	0904	1004	1037	1104	1137	1237	1303	1437	1506	1537	...	1637	1704	1837	1904	1937	2004	...	2204	2311
62	**Bamberg** .... **850** a.	0652	...	0720	0753	0852	0920	1021	1052	1120	1152	1252	1320	1452	1520	1552	...	1654	1720	1852	1920	1952	2020	...	2221	2328
62	**Bamberg** .... **876** d.	0654	...	0723	0805	0854	0923	1023	1054	1123	1154	1254	1322	1454	1523	1555	1606	1656	1722	1854	1922	1954	2022	...	2238	2346
94	Lichtenfels .... **876** a.	|	...	0741	|	|	0941	1044	|	1141	|	|	1340	|	1541	1623	|	|	1742	|	1945	|	2044	...	2303	0010
94	Lichtenfels .... d.	|	0701	0745	|	|	0945	1102	|	1200	|	|	1402	|	1545	1624	|	|	1802	|	2001	|	2050	2103z	2316	0011
114	**Coburg** .... **850** a.	0720	0725	0801	0828	0920	1002	1122	1118	1225	1217p	1318	1425	1518	1601	1644	1629	1720	1824	1918	2025	2018	2109	2124z	2335	0030
114	**Coburg** .... d.	0731z	0729	0831	0831	0931	1031	1131t	1133	1231	...	1331	1431	1533	1633	1708	1633	1731	1831	1931	2031z	2039	...	2126	2336	...
135	**Sonneberg** (Thür) Hbf a.	0753z	0754	0853	0853	0953	1053	1153t	1153	1253	...	1353	1453	1556	1655	1735	1655	1753	1853	1954	2053z	2101	...	2148	2358	...

		Ⓐt		Ⓐr	Ⓐt	Ⓐt	Ⓒz	Ⓒz	Ⓐt	Ⓐt				⊖			Ⓐt			Ⓐt		Ⓒz	Ⓐt		Ⓐt	Ⓒz
nneberg (Thür) Hbf d.	...	0445	0541	0610	...	0705	0705	0806	0806	0906	0906z	1006	1104	1203	1306	1406	...	1503	1606	...	1706	1807	1807	1906	2006	2006
burg .... a.	...	0507	0603	0631	...	0727p	0728	0828	0828	0928	0928z	1028	1126	1224	1328	1428	...	1525p	1628	...	1729p	1829	1829	1928	2027	2027
burg ....**850** d.	0449	0508	0611	0635	0732	0728	0753	0838	0833	0938	0955	1038	1155	1238	1332	1436	1529	1554	1639	1737	1731	1838	1833	1935	2031	2031
ntenfels .... a.	0508	0529	|	0655	|	0759	0812	|	0855	|	1012	|	1212	|	1355	|	|	1612	|	|	1753	|	1855	1953	2049	2049
htenfels ....**876** d.	0509	0530	|	0709	|	0819	0819	|	0912	|	1019	|	1219	|	1419	|	|	1619	|	|	1819	|	1912	2019	2114	2112
mberg ....**876** a.	0535	0557	0635	0736	0755	0837	0837	0903	0935	1002	1037	1102	1237	1302	1437	1502	1553	1637	1702	1802	1837	1903	1935	2037	2137	2136
mberg ....**850** d.	0538	0604	0638	0739	0804	0838	0838	0905	0938	1004	1038	1104	1238	1304	1438	1504	1603	1638	1704	1804	1838	1905	1938	2038	2139	2139
chheim (Oberfr) ..... d.	0553	0619	0653	0753	0819	0853	0853	0919	0953	1019	1053	1119	1253	1320	1453	1519	1619	1653	1719	1819	1853	1921	1953	2053	2153	2153
angen ....**850** d.	0602	0629	0702	0802	0829	0902	0902	0929	1002	1029	1102	1129	1302	1329	1502	1529	1629	1702	1729	1829	1902	1930	2002	2102	2202	2202
th (Bay) Hbf .... d.	0612	0641	0712	0812	0841	0912	0912	0941	1012	1041	1112	1141	1312	1341	1513	1541	1642	1712	1743	1841	1912	1942	2012	2112	2212	2212
rnberg Hbf ......**850** a.	0619	0648	0719	0819	0848	0919	0919	0948	1019	1048	1119	1148	1319	1349	1519	1549	1649	1722	1749	1848	1919	1948	2019	2119	2219	2219

m																									
				Ⓐt		Ⓐt	Ⓒz	Ⓐt						Ⓒz	Ⓐt										
0	**Nürnberg** Hbf ..... **849a 850** d.	0049	...	...	0529	0629	0638	0710	0738	0838	0938	1038y	1138	1238	1238	1338	1441	1538	1638	1740	1838	1938	2038	2138	2347
8	Fürth (Bay) Hbf .... d.	0057	...	...	0537	0637	0644	0716	0744	0844	0944	1044y	1144	1244	1244	1344	1447	1544	1644	1746	1844	1944	2044	2145	2353
24	Erlangen .... **849a 850** d.	0114	...	...	0547	0649	0654	0728	0754	0854	0954	1054	1154	1254	1254	1354	1457	1554	1654	1756	1854	1954	2054	2155	0003
39	Forchheim (Oberfr) .... d.	0129	...	...	0557	0659	0704	0737	0803	0904	1004	1104	1204	1303	1303	1404	1506	1604	1704	1805	1904	2004	2104	2204	0011
62	**Bamberg** .... **849a 850** d.	0149	...	0507	0627f	0723	0723	0755	0823	0923	1023	1123	1223	1322	1322	1423	1523	1623	1722	1823	1922	2022	2136j	2238j	0034
94	Lichtenfels .... **849a** d.	...	...	0535	0653	0741	0743	0821	0845	0943	1045	1143	1245	1342	1345	1445	1543	1645	1744	1845	1947	2045	2203	2309	0100
8	Kronach .... **849a** d.	...	...	0557	0713	0758	0757	...	0905	0957	1105	1157	1306	1356	1359	1505	1557	1705	1758	1905	2007	2107	2223	2329	...
31	**Saalfeld** (Saale) .... **849a** a.	...	...	0654	0809	0852	0851	...	1005	1051	1205	1251	1405	1452	1453	1605	1651	1805	1853	2005	2101	2206	...	...	...
	Jena Paradies **849** .... a.	...	...	...	0847	...	...	...	1045	...	1245	...	1445	...	...	1645	...	1845	...	2045	...	2244	...	...	...
	Leipzig Hbf **849** .... a.	...	...	...	0953	...	...	...	1153	...	1353	...	1553	...	...	1753	...	1953	...	2153	...	...	...	...	...

	Ⓐr	Ⓐt	Ⓐr	Ⓒw	Ⓐt	Ⓒz	Ⓐt														Ⓒz	Ⓐt			
eipzig Hbf **849** .... d.	◇	...	...	...	...	...	...	0558	...	0808	...	1008	...	1208	...	1408	...	1608	...	1808	1808	...	...	2008	...
ena Paradies **849** .... d.	...	...	...	...	0509	0616k	...	0708	...	0915	...	1115	...	1315	...	1515	...	1715	...	1915	1915	...	...	2115	...
alfeld (Saale) .... **849a** d.	...	...	...	...	0610	0658	0704	0751	0906	0951	1106	1151	1306	1351	1506	1551	1706	1751	1906	1951	1951	...	...	2151	...
nach .... **849a** d.	...	0611	0647	0647	0715	0758	0800	0852	1001	1052	1201	1252	1401	1452	1601	1652	1801	1852	2001	2052	2052	...	...	2252	...
ntenfels .... **849a** d.	0624	0637	0709	0709	0735	0819	0819	0912	1019	1112	1219	1312	1419	1512	1619	1712	1819	1912	2019	2111	2112	2114	2213	2316	...
mberg .... **849a 850** d.	0642	0706f	0739	0739	0804	0838	0838	0938	1038	1138	1238	1338	1438	1538	1638	1738	1838	1938	2038	...	2139	2139	2239	2341	0034
chheim (Oberfr) .... d.	|	0720	0753	0753	0819	0853	0853	0953	1053	1153	1253	1353	1453	1553	1653	1753	1853	1953	2053	...	2153	2153	2253	...	0053
angen .... **849a 850** d.	0708	0729	0802	0802	0829	0902	0902	1002	1102	1202	1302	1402	1502	1602	1702	1803	1902	2002	2102	...	2202	2202	2302	...	0107
th (Bay) Hbf .... d.	|	0741	0812	0812	0841	0912	0912	1012	1112	1212	1312	1412	1513	1612	1712	1812	1912	2012	2112	...	2212	2212	2312	...	0125
rnberg Hbf .... **849a 850** a.	0725	0749	0819	0822	0848	0919	0919	1019	1119	1219	1319	1419	1519	1619	1722	1819	1919	2019	2119	...	2219	2219	2319	...	0133

m																									
		Ⓐr	Ⓒw		Ⓐr	Ⓒw	Ⓐr		⊙		⊙		⊙		⊙		⊙		⊙		⊙				
	Nürnberg Hbf ..... **849a 850** d.	...	...	...	...	...	...	0529	...	0738	...	0938	...	1138	...	1338	...	1538	...	1740	...	1938	...	...	...
	Fürth (Bay) Hbf .... d.	...	...	...	...	...	...	0537	...	0744	...	0944	...	1144	...	1344	...	1544	...	1746	...	1944	...	...	...
	Erlangen .... **849a 850** d.	...	...	...	...	...	...	0547	...	0754	...	0954	...	1154	...	1354	...	1554	...	1756	...	1954	...	...	...
	Forchheim (Oberfr) .... d.	...	...	...	...	...	...	0557	...	0803	...	1004	...	1204	...	1404	...	1604	...	1805	...	2004	...	...	...
0	**Bamberg** .... **849a 850** d.	0034	0037	...	0445	0445	0526	0625f	0726	0827f	0926	1025	1126	1225	1326	1425	1526	1625	1726	1825	1926	2025	2041	2141	2304
2	Haßfurt .... d.	0055	0059	...	0506	0506	0549	0641	0742	0843	0942	1041	1142	1241	1342	1441	1542	1641	1742	1841	1942	2041	2102	2202	2326
7	Schweinfurt Hbf .... **870** d.	0113	0117	...	0526	0526	0610	0656	0757	0856	0956	1056	1156	1256	1356	1456	1556	1656	1756	1856	1956	2056	2119	2220	2344
0	**Würzburg** Hbf .... **870** a.	...	0148	...	0548	0557	0648	0722	0820	0922	1020	1121	1220	1320	1420	1522	1620	1722	1820	1922	2020	2122	2150	2251	0016

		Ⓒw		Ⓐr	⚒r		Ⓐr	⊙		⊙		⊙		⊙		⊙		⊙		⊙		⊙			Ⓒw
rzburg Hbf .... **870** d.	0036	0036	...	...	0454	0604	0635	0738	0835	0935	1035	1135	1235	1338	1435	1538	1636	1738	1836	1938	2035	2139	2236	2307	2307
weinfurt Hbf .... **870** d.	0106	0107	...	0434	0543j	0636	0702	0803	0902	1003	1102	1203	1302	1403	1502	1603	1702	1803	1902	2003	2102	2203	2300	2340	2344
furt .... d.	...	0126	...	0453	0601	0654	0715	0816	0915	1016	1115	1216	1315	1416	1515	1616	1715	1816	1915	2016	2115	2216	2317	...	0003
nberg .... **849a 850** a.	...	0147	...	0518	0621	0717	0733	0832	0930	1032	1130	1232	1330	1432	1530	1632	1730	1832	1930	2032	2130	2232	2340	...	0027
chheim (Oberfr) .... a.	...	...	...	...	...	...	0752	...	0952	...	1152	...	1352	...	1552	...	1752	...	1952	...	2152z	...	...	...	...
ngen .... **849a 850** a.	...	...	...	...	...	...	0800	...	1000	...	1200	...	1400	...	1600	...	1801	...	2000	...	2200z	...	...	...	...
h (Bay) Hbf .... a.	...	...	...	...	...	...	0811	...	1011	...	1211	...	1411	...	1611	...	1811	...	2011	...	2211z	...	...	...	...
nberg Hbf .... **849a 850** a.	...	...	...	...	...	...	0819	...	1019	...	1219	...	1419	...	1619	...	1819	...	2019	...	2219z	...	...	...	...

Arrives 7 – 11 minutes earlier.
Arrives 15 – 18 minutes earlier.
0615 on June 20, Nov. 1 (change at Saalfeld).

p – Connects with train in previous column.
r – Not June 20, Aug. 15, Nov. 1.
t – Not June 20, Nov. 1.

w – Also June 20, Aug. 15, Nov. 1.
y – 2 minutes later on Ⓒ**z**.
z – Ⓒ (also June 20, Nov. 1).

◇ – *ICE* **1501**. To München (Table **904**).
⊙ – From / to Frankfurt (Table **921**).
⊖ – Change trains at Coburg on Ⓐ**t**.

E / RB services

BAMBERG - HOF and BAYREUTH 876

m																										
				Ⓒz	Ⓐe									N				N				N				N
0	**Bamberg** .... **875** d.	...	...	...	...	...	...	...	0838	0838	...	...	1046	1046	...	...	1246	1246	...	...	1446	1446	...	...	1646	1646
2	Lichtenfels .... **875** d.	0549e	0549z	0658	0658	0658z	0802v	0802v	0859	0859	1003	1003	1104	1104	1203	1203	1304	1304	1403	1403	1504	1504	1603	1603	1704	1704
2	Kulmbach .... d.	0613e	0611z	0717	0721	0717z	0822	0822	0917	0917	1022	1022	1123	1123	1222	1222	1323	1323	1422	1422	1523	1523	1622	1622	1723	1723
4	Neuenmarkt-Wirsberg a.	0624e	0622z	0727	0729	0727z	0830	0830	0927	0927	1032	1032	1131	1131	1232	1232	1331	1331	1432	1432	1531	1531	1632	1632	1731	1731
4	Neuenmarkt-Wirsberg d.	0625	0634	0729	0730	0732	0832	0835	0929	0932	1033	1035	1132	1135	1233	1235	1332	1335	1433	1435	1532	1535	1633	1635	1732	1735
6	**Bayreuth** Hbf .... a.	|	0658	|	|	0757	|	0857	|	0956	|	1057	|	1156	|	1257	|	1356	|	1457	|	1557	|	1657	|	1757
3	Münchberg .... **880** d.	0649	...	0755	0755	...	0859	...	0955	...	1100	...	1155	...	1300	...	1356	...	1500	...	1556	...	1700	...	1755	...
6	Schwarzenbach .... d.	0704	...	0806	0806	...	0911	...	1007	...	1112	...	1206	...	1312	...	1406	...	1512	...	1606	...	1711	...	1806	...
7	**Hof** Hbf .... **880** a.	0716	...	0818	0818	...	0921	...	1019	...	1123	...	1217	...	1323	...	1417	...	1523	...	1617	...	1724	...	1817	...

				N					◐	◐		T
nberg ....**875** d.	...	...	1846	1846	...	...	2046	2046	...	...	2242h	2242h
tenfels ....**875** d.	1803	1803	1904	1904	2003	2003	2106	2106	2236	...	2313	2313
nbach .... d.	1823	1823	1923	1923	2022	2022	2128	2128	2300	...	2337	2337
enmarkt-Wirsberg a.	1833	1833	1931	1931	2032	2032	2138	2138	2311	...	2349	2349
enmarkt-Wirsberg d.	1834	1837	1932	1935	2033	2036	2139	2141	2312	2314	2350	2350
ayreuth Hbf .... a.	|	1857	|	1957	|	2058	|	2200	2332	|	0016	|
chberg ....**880** d.	1902	...	1955	...	2100	...	2206	...	...	2341	...	0037
warzenbach .... d.	1916	...	2006	...	2112	...	2217	...	...	2354	...	0046
Hbf ....**880** a.	1928	...	2019	...	2122	...	2230	...	...	0006	...	0058

		Ⓒz	Ⓐe			N			
Hof Hbf .... **880** d.	...	0523	0526	...	0635	...	0744	...	0835
Schwarzenbach .... d.	...	0534	0536	...	0645	...	0752	...	0845
Münchberg .... **880** d.	...	0545	0545	...	0657	...	0802	...	0856
Bayreuth Hbf .... d.	0545	|	|	0701	|	0802	|	0902	|
Neuenmarkt-Wirsberg .... a.	0608	0613	0615	0720	0725	0820	0824	0920	0925
Neuenmarkt-Wirsberg .... d.	0615z	0615	0616	0727	0727	0827	0827	0927	0927
Kulmbach .... d.	0625z	0625	0626	0737	0737	0835	0835	0937	0937
Lichtenfels .... **875** a.	0648z	0648	0647	0756	0756	0853	0853	0957	0957
Bamberg .... **875** a.	...	...	...	0819	0819	0912	0912	...	...

	N				N				N				N												R	
Hbf ....**880** d.	...	0944	...	1036	...	1144	...	1236	...	1344	...	1436	...	1544	...	1636	...	1743	...	1836	1936	...	...	2035	2134	...
warzenbach .... d.	...	0952	...	1045	...	1152	...	1245	...	1352	...	1445	...	1552	...	1645	...	1753	...	1845	|	...	...	2046	2143	...
chberg ....**880** d.	...	1002	...	1056	...	1202	...	1256	...	1402	...	1456	...	1602	...	1656	...	1804	...	1856	1954	...	...	2058	2154	...
ayreuth Hbf .... d.	1002	|	1102	|	1202	|	1301	|	1402	|	1502	|	1602	|	1702	|	1803	|	1902	|	|	2003	2103	|	|	2205
enmarkt-Wirsberg a.	1020	1024	1120	1125	1221	1225	1321	1325	1421	1425	1520	1525	1621	1625	1720	1725	1825	1830	1920	1925	2022	2026	2121	2126	2231	2231
enmarkt-Wirsberg d.	1027	1027	1127	1127	1227	1227	1328	1328	1427	1427	1527	1527	1627	1627	1727	1727	1832	1832	1927	1927	...	2027	2128	2128	2232	2232
nbach .... d.	1035	1035	1137	1137	1235	1235	1337	1337	1435	1435	1537	1537	1635	1635	1737	1737	1841	1841	1936	1936	...	2036	2138	2138	2244	2244
tenfels ....**875** a.	1053	1053	1156	1156	1254	1254	1358	1358	1453	1453	1557	1557	1653	1653	1756	1756	1901	1901	1956	1956	...	2056	2200	2200	2307	2307
nberg ....**875** a.	1112	1112	...	...	1312	1312	...	...	1512	1512	...	...	1712	1712	...	...	1922	1922	...	...	...	2120h	...	...	...	...

To / from Nürnberg via Pegnitz (Table **880**).
Change trains at Trebgast (a. 2215, d. 2225).
Change trains at Trebgast (a. 2355, d. 0011).

e – Ⓐ (not June 20, Nov. 1).
h – ⑤–⑦ (also June 10, 20, Oct. 3).

v – 0801 on † (also June 20, Nov. 1).
z – Ⓒ (also June 20, Nov. 1).

◐ – Operated by *agilis* (2nd class only).

877 LANDSHUT - MÜHLDORF - SALZBURG
RB servic

km				Ⓒz	Ⓐe						
0	**Landshut** (Bay) Hbf ..... d.	0608r	0837	1037	1037	1237	1437	1637	1837	2037	2145
55	Mühldorf (Oberbay) ..... a.	0712r	0928	1128	1128	1328	1528	1728	1928	2128	2239
55	Mühldorf (Oberbay) ..... d.	0741	0943	1143	1143	1343	1544	1743	1943	2146	2250
120	Freilassing .... 890/1 a.	0834	1044	1243	1243	1443	1643	1843	2043	2239	2344
126	**Salzburg** Hbf..... 890/1 a.	0854	1054	1254	1313	1454	1654	1854	2054	2254	0019

Salzburg Hbf. 890/1 d.	0615	...	0704b	0908	1108	1313	1508	1708	1908	21
Freilassing ...... 890/1 d.	0628	...	0718	0924	1124	1324	1524	1724	1924	21
Mühldorf (Oberbay) ... a.	0723	...	0814	1015	1215	1415	1615	1815	2015	22
Mühldorf (Oberbay) ... d.	...	0730	0830	1030	1230	1430	1630	1830	2032	22
Landshut (Bay) Hbf .. a.	...	0821	0921	1121	1321	1521	1721	1921	2121	23

b – 0650 on ⑥ (not Oct. 26); 0642 on ⑦ (also June 10, 20, Aug. 15, Oct. 26, Nov. 1). Change trains at Freilassing on Ⓒ.
e – Not June 20, Aug. 15, Nov. 1.
r – ⚒ (not June 20, Aug. 15, Nov. 1).
z – Also June 20, Aug. 15, Nov. 1.
☛ Additional services opera

878 MÜNCHEN - REGENSBURG
DB (RE services); A

See Table 892 for services Regensburg - Landshut - Freising - München Flughafen ✈ and v.v.

km		ALX ⚒rP	N	ALX P	ALX	N	ALX P	N	ALX P	N	ALX P	N	ALX P	N	ALX ⑦w	ALX D	ALX P	N	ALX	N	ALX	ALX ⑦w		ALX △	A
0	**München** Hbf ...... 944 d.	0444	0544	0643	0643	0744	0843	0944	1043	1144	1243	1344	1443	1543	1602	1603x	1643	1744	1843	1944	2043	2043	2144	2243	00
42	Freising .... 944 d.	0508	0608	0708	0708	0808	0908	1008	1108	1208	1308	1408	1508	1608	1628	1628	1708	1808	1908	2008	2108	2108	2208	2308	00
76	Landshut (Bay) Hbf 944 d.	0529	0631	0729	0729	0830	0929	1030	1129	1230	1329	1430	1529	1630	1649	1649	1729	1830	1929	2030	2129	2129	2230	2335	00
99	Neufahrn (Niederbay) .. d.	0543	0648	0743	0743	0848	0943	1048	1143	1248	1343	1448	1543	1648	|	|	1743	1848	1946	2048	2146	2146	2248	2352	01
138	**Regensburg** Hbf .... a.	0607	0717	0806	0806	0915	1006	1115	1206	1315	1406	1515	1606	1715	1724	1725	1806	1915	2010	2115	2208	2208	2320	0017	01
	Schwandorf 879 885 a.	0646	...	0842	0842	...	1042	...	1242	...	1442	...	1642	...	1758	1802	1842	...	2102	...	2253	2253	...	0120	
	Hof Hbf 879 .... a.	...	...	...	1018j	...	1218	...	1418	...	1618	...	1818	...	m	1933	2018	...	m	...	...	0028	...	...	

	ALX ⚒r		ALX	Ⓐe	ALX Ⓒz	ALX Ⓐe	ⒶeN	ALX	N	ALX P	N	ALX P	N	ALX P	N	ALX P	N	ALX P	N	ALX P	N	ALX ⑦w	ALX	ALX P△	N
Hof Hbf 879 .... d.	...	...	...	...	m	m	...	0531r	...	0740	...	0940	...	1140	...	1340	...	1540	...	1740	...	m	...	1940v	
Schwandorf 879 885. d.	0400e	...	0502r	...	0603	0609	...	0707	...	0917	...	1117	...	1317	...	1517	...	1717	...	1917	...	2013	...	2117	
Regensburg Hbf .... d.	0442	...	0547	0622	0646	0649	0702	0753	0846	0953	1046	1153	1246	1353	1446	1553	1646	1753	1846	1953	2040	2053	2053	2157	22
Neufahrn (Niederbay) ... d.	0508	...	0610	0649	0711	|	0728	0816	0912	1016	1112	1216	1312	1416	1512	1616	1712	1816	1912	2016	|	2116	2116	2222	23
Landshut (Bay) Hbf 944 d.	0527	...	0628	0709	0729	0733	0747	0832	0929	1032	1129	1232	1329	1432	1529	1632	1729	1832	1929	2032	2126	2132	2132	2237	23
Freising .... 944 d.	0549	...	0649	0732	0751	|	0810	0852	0951	1052	1151	1252	1351	1452	1551	1652	1751	1852	1951	2052	...	2152	2152	2257	23
München Hbf .... 944 a.	0616	...	0716	0757	0817	0821	0836	0919	1018	1118	1216	1318	1416	1518	1616	1718	1816	1918	2018	2118	...	2217	2217	2321	00

D – ①-⑥ (also June 9; not June 10).
N – To / from Nürnberg (Table 921).
P – Conveys [12] München - Schwandorf - Praha and v.v. See Tables 57 and 885.
e – Ⓐ (not June 20, Aug. 15, Nov. 1).
j – Change trains at Schwandorf on †z.
m – To Marktredwitz (Table 879).
r – ⚒ (not June 20, Aug. 15, Nov. 1).
v – Change trains at Schwandorf on ①-⑤ (not June 10, 19, Aug. 14, Oct. 2, 31).
w – Also June 10; not June 9.
x – 1602 on ⑥ until Aug. 24 (also June 9).
z – Also June 20, Aug. 15, Nov. 1.
△ – München timing is subject to altera on ⑥⑦ July 27 - Sept. 1.
ALX – Operated by Vogtlandbahn. 🍸.

879 REGENSBURG - HOF
ALX; Oberpfalzba

km		2 Ⓐe	ALX ⚒r	2	2 Ⓒz	ALX ⊕	2	ALX	2	ALX	2	ALX	2	ALX	2	ALX ⑦w	ALX D	ALX	2	2	ALX	2	ALX	ALX ⑦w	2	
	München Hbf 878 .. d.	...	0444	...		0643	...	0843	...	1043	...	1243	...	1443	...	1602	1603x	1643	...	...	1843	...	2043	2043	...	
0	**Regensburg** Hbf 885 d.	0512	0615	0707	0707	0814	0857	1014	1057	1214	1256	1414	1457	1614	1658	1732	1733	1814	1857	1957	2033	2138	2216	2216	...	23
42	Schwandorf .... 885 a.	0541	0646	0734	0734	0842	0925	1042	1125	1242	1325	1442	1525	1642	1727	1758	1802	1842	1925	2026	2102	2207	2253	2253	...	00
42	Schwandorf .... d.	0552	0651	0735	0735	0846	0926	1046	1126	1246	1326	1446	1526	1646	1728	1759	1803	1846	1926	2027	2106	2209	...	2255	2315	00
86	Weiden (Oberpf) .... d.	0630	0717	0813	0814	0914	1002	1114	1202	1314	1402	1514	1602	1714	1803	1825	1830	1916	2002	2101	2130	2248	...	2321	2350	00
137	Marktredwitz .... 880 a.	0711	0753	...	0855	0949	1044	1149	1244	1350	1442	1549	1644	1749	1844	1859	1906	1950	2044	...	2211	2327	...	2400	...	
179	**Hof** Hbf .... 880 a.	0754	0820	...	0924	1018	1115	1218	1315	1418	1517	1618	1715	1818	1915v	1924	1933	2018	2126	...	2242	0004	...	0028	...	

	ALX ⚒r	ALX ⑥	ALX Ⓒz	ALX Ⓐe	ALX	2 Ⓒz	2 Ⓐe	ALX	2	ALX	2	ALX	2	ALX	2	ALX	2	2 ⑦k	2	ALX	2	ALX ⑦w	ALX ⊙	2	2	
Hof Hbf .... 880 d.	...	...	...	0432	0531r	0629	0629	0740	0843	0940	1043	1140	1243	1340	1443	1540	...	1643	1643h	1740	...	1843	1940	...	2043	2
Marktredwitz .... 880 d.	...	0502	...	0508	0559	0704	0704	0806	0915	1006	1115	1206	1315	1406	1515	1606	1615	1707	1715h	1806	1815	1912	2006	...	2115	2
Weiden (Oberpf) .... d.	0414e	0539	...	0545	0639	0742	0744	0841	0955	1041	1155	1241	1356	1441	1555	1641	1656	1744	1755	1841	1856	1946	2041	2116	2222j	00
Schwandorf .... a.	0451e	0602	...	0608	0703	0807	0809	0906	1030	1106	1230	1306	1431	1506	1630	1706	1731	1809	1830	1906	1931	2010	2106	2152	2257	
Schwandorf .... 885 d.	0502	0603	0603	0609	0707	0808	0810	0917	1032	1117	1232	1317	1432	1517	1632	1717	1732	1810	1832	1917	1932	2013	2117	2207	2313	
Regensburg Hbf . 885 a.	0537	0636	0636	0640	0741	0837	0837	0945	1104	1145	1304	1345	1504	1545	1704	1744	1804	1836	1904	1945	2004	2045	2149	2238	2341	
München Hbf 878 ... a.	0716	0817	0817	0821	0919	...	...	1118	...	1318	...	1518		1718	...	1918	...	...	...	2118	...	2217	2321y	...	...	

D – ①-⑥ (also June 9; not June 10).
e – Ⓐ (not June 20, Aug. 15, Nov. 1).
h – ①-⑥ (not June 10).
j – Arrives 2154.
k – Also June 10.
r – ⚒ (not June 20, Aug. 15, Nov. 1).
v – ⚒ (not June 20, Nov. 1).
w – Also June 10; not June 9.
x – 1602 on ⑥ until Aug. 24 (also June 9).
y – Subject to alteration on ⑥⑦ July 27 - Sept. 1.
z – Also June 20, Aug. 15, Nov. 1.
⊙ – Change trains at Schwandorf on ① (not June 10, 19, Aug. 14, Oct. 2,
⊕ – Change trains at Schwandorf on †
ALX – Operated by Vogtlandbahn. 🍸.

880 NÜRNBERG - HOF - DRESDEN
RE / RB servic

NÜRNBERG - HOF

km				Ⓒz	Ⓒz	Ⓐe	Ⓐe	B			Ⓐe		B			Ⓐe			B			Ⓐe			
0	**Nürnberg** Hbf .... ● d.	0538	0538	0631	0631	0637	0637	0656	0738	0738	0758	0837	0905	0938	0938	1005	1037	1037	1105	1138	1138	1205	1237	1237	1
28	Hersbruck (r Pegnitz) .... ● d.	0556	0556	0652	0652	|	|	0715	0754	0754	0815	|	0920	|	|	1019	|	|	1120	|	|	1219	|	|	1
67	Pegnitz .... ● a.	0617	0617	0713	0713	0714	0714	0738	0822	0822	0839	0914	0942	1015	1015	1042	1114	1114	1142	1215	1215	1242	1314	1314	1
67	Pegnitz .... d.	0628	0619	0715	0720	0715	0720	0739	0824	0828	0841	0916	0943	1017	1021	1043	1116	1120	1143	1217	1221	1243	1316	1320	1
	Bayreuth Hbf .... d.	|	0641	0732	|	0732	|	0758	0847	|	0855	0932	1000	1042	|	1058	1132	|	1200	1242	|	1257	1332	|	1
	Münchberg .... 876 d.	|	▬	0805	|	0805	|	...	...	|	▬	1004	...	...	|	▬	1205	|	...	...	|	▬	1405	|	
94	Kirchenlaibach .... d.	0643	⊖	|	0734	|	0734	...	...	0845	⊖	|	...	...	1035	⊖	|	1134	...	...	1235	⊖	|	1334	
125	Marktredwitz .... 879 d.	0700	0712	|	0759r	|	0759r	...	...	0901	0908	|	...	...	1053	1108	|	1159r	...	...	1253	1308	|	1359r	
	Cheb .... a.	|	0737	|	0822	|	0822	...	...	|	0933	|	...	...	|	1133	|	1222	...	...	|	1333	|	1422	
167	**Hof** Hbf .... 876 879 a.	0723	...	0823	...	0823	...	...	...	0924	...	1022	...	...	1115	...	1222	...	...	...	1315	...	1422	...	

			Ⓐe			B			Ⓐe						Ⓐe										
Nürnberg Hbf .... ● d.	1338	1338	1405	1437	1437	1505	1537	1537	1605	1637	1637	1705	1738	1738	1805	1837	1837	1905	1938	1938	2055	2055	2206	2206	2
Hersbruck (r Pegnitz) .... ● d.	|	|	1420	|	|	1520	|	|	1620	|	|	1720	|	|	1820	|	|	1920	1954	1954	2112	2112	2223	2223	2
Pegnitz .... ● a.	1415	1415	1442	1514	1514	1542	1615	1615	1642	1714	1714	1742	1815	1815	1842	1914	1914	1942	2021	2021	2137	2137	2248	2248	2
Pegnitz .... d.	1417	1421	1443	1516	1520	1543	1617	1621	1643	1716	1720	1743	1817	1821	1843	1916	1920	1943	2023	2027	2139	2144	2250	2255	2
Bayreuth Hbf .... d.	1442	|	1458	1532	|	1600	1642	|	1658	1732	|	1800	1842	|	1858	1932	|	2000	2048	|	2158	|	2310	|	2
Münchberg .... 876 d.	...	|	▬	1605	|	...	...	|	▬	1805	|	...	...	|	▬	2005	|	...	...	|	...	|	▬	|	0
Kirchenlaibach .... d.	...	1435	⊖	|	1534	...	...	1635	⊖	|	1734	...	...	1835	⊖	|	1935	...	...	2044	...	2158	⊖	2309	
Marktredwitz .... 879 d.	...	1455	1508	|	1559r	...	...	1653	1708	|	1759r	...	...	1853t	1911	|	2001	...	...	2101	...	2216	2218	2333	
Cheb .... a.	...	|	1533	|	1622	...	...	|	1733	|	1822	...	...	|	1936	|	...	...	...	|	...	|	2243	|	
Hof Hbf .... 876 879 a.	...	1517	...	1622	...	...	...	1715	...	1822	...	...	...	1915t	...	2022	...	...	...	2126	...	2242	...	0004	0

HOF - DRESDEN ⊠

km			Ⓒw																						
0	**Hof** Hbf .... 881 d.	...	...	...	...	0427	...	0527	...	and at the same minutes past each hour until	1727	...	1827	...	1937	...	2029	...	...	...	...	...	...	2
48	Plauen (Vogtl) ob Bf ..... 881 d.	...	...	...	...	0459	...	0559	...		1759	...	1859	...	2008	...	2101	...	...	...	...	...	...	2
73	Reichenbach (Vogtl) ob Bf 881 d.	...	...	...	...	0515	...	0615	...		1815	...	1915	...	2024	...	2117	...	...	...	...	...	...	2
96	**Zwickau** (Sachs) Hbf .... 881 d.	...	0343	...	0439	0531	0539	0631	0639		1831	1839	1931	1939	2040	...	2133	2139	...	2243	...	2343	...	0
112	Glauchau (Sachs) .... 858 d.	...	0359	...	0455	0540	0555	0640	0655		1840	1855	1940	1955	2050	2055	2142	2155	...	2258	...	2358	...	
144	**Chemnitz** Hbf .... 858 d.	0430	0430	0503	0530	0603	0630	0703	0730		1903	1930	2003	2030	2112	2130	2204	2230	...	2330	...	0029	...	
157	Flöha .... d.	0443	0443	0513	0543	0613	0643	0713	0743		1913	1943	2013	2043	2122	2143	...	2243	...	2343	...	...	...	
183	Freiberg (Sachs) .... d.	0508	0508	0531	0608	0631	0708	0731	0808		1931	2008	2031	2108	2139	2208	...	2308	...	0008	...	...	...	
223	**Dresden** Hbf .... a.	0550	0550	0603	0650	0703	0750	0803	0850		2003	2050	2104	2150	2211	2250	...	2350	...	0050	...	...	...	

B – To Bamberg (Table 876).
e – Not June 20, Nov. 1
r – Arrives 5–6 minutes earlier.
t – On † (also June 20, Nov. 1) Marktredwitz a. 1852, d. 1902, Hof a. 1924.
w – Also Oct. 31, Nov. 20.
z – Also June 20, Nov. 1
⊖ – Operated by Oberpfalzbahn.
◇ – Operated by Vogtlandbahn.
⊠ – Operated by Mitteldeutsche Regiobahn (2nd class only).
● – Certain trains between Nürnberg and Pegnitz convey por for two separate destinations. Passengers should take ca join the correct portion for their destination.

DRESDEN - HOF - NÜRNBERG 880

RE / RB services

DRESDEN - HOF ⊠

	Ⓐj◇																			◇				Ⓒw
resden Hbf ... d.	...	...	...	0452	0506	0552	0606	0652	0706	0752	and at the same minutes past each hour until	1706	1752	1806	1852	1906	1952	2006	2052	...	2106	2206	2306	...
eiberg (Sachs) ... d.	...	...	...	0525	0550	0625	0650	0725	0750	0825		1750	1825	1850	1925	1950	2025	2050	2125	...	2150	2250	2350	...
öha ... d.	...	...	...	0543	0613	0643	0713	0743	0813	0843		1813	1843	1913	1943	2013	2043	2113	2143	...	2213	2313	0013	...
hemnitz Hbf ... 858 d.	...	...	0410	0554	0631	0654	0731	0754	0831	0854		1831	1854	1931	1954	2031	2054	2131	2155	...	2231	2331	0025	0050
auchau (Sachs) ... 858 d.	...	...	0441	0616	0702	0716	0802	0816	0902	0916		1902	1916	2002	2016	2102	2116	2202	2218	...	2302	0002	...	0121
wickau (Sachs) Hbf ... 881 d.	0400	...	0512c	0627	0718	0727	0818	0827	0918	0927		1918	1927	2018	2027	2118	2128	2218	2229	2236	2318	0018	...	0137
eichenbach (Vogtl) ob Bf. 881 d.	0418	...	0528	0642	...	0742	...	0842	...	0942		...	1942	...	2042	...	2143	...	...	2307	...	...	...	...
auen (Vogtl) ob Bf ... 881 d.	0442	...	0546	0659	...	0759	...	0900	...	0959		...	1959	...	2059	...	2200	...	...	2331	...	...	...	...
of Hbf ... 881 a.	0521	...	0618	0731	...	0831	...	0931	...	1031		...	2031	...	2131	...	2231	...	...	...	...	...	...	...

HOF - NÜRNBERG

km			Ⓐe	Ⓐe	Ⓒz	Ⓒz	Ⓐe	Ⓐe	⊖				⚒e	⊖						⊖			B		⊖
0	Hof Hbf ... 876 879 d.	...	0420	...	...	*0517*k	...	0526	...	0629	...	...	0736	...	0843	...	...	...	0936	...	1043	...	...	1136	...
	Cheb ... d.	...	|	...	...	|	...	|	0629	|	...	...	|	0829	|	...	...	0936	|	1025	|	...	...	|	1225
	Marktredwitz ... 879 d.	...	0442	...	...	0601	0601	|	0654	0657	...	...	|	0855	0905	...	...	1005t	|	1050	1105	...	...	|	1250
	Kirchenlaibach ... d.	...	0507	...	...	0616	0620	|	▬	0713	...	...	|	▬	0923	...	...	1024	|	▬	1123	...	...	|	▬
24	Münchberg ... 876 d.	...	|	...	...	|	|	0545	Ⓐe	|	...	...	0752	Ⓐe	|	...	...	|	0952	Ⓐe	|	...	...	1152	Ⓐe
72	Bayreuth Hbf ... d.	0500	|	0551	0605	|	|	0624	0703	|	0712	0800	0829	0903	|	0915	1001	|	1029	1103	|	1115	1201	1229	1303
99	Pegnitz ... a.	0521	0525	0611	0626	0631	0633	0639	0717	0731	0735	0817	0844	0918	0937	0941	1018	1038	1044	1118	1137	1141	1219	1244	1318
99	Pegnitz ... d.	0529	0529	0612	0633	0633	0641	0641	0718	0738	0738	0818	0845	0919	0944	0944	1019	1046	1046	1119	1144	1144	1219	1245	1319
138	Hersbruck (r Pegnitz) ... d.	0552	0552	0634	0656	0656	0702	0702	0742	0802	0802	0841	|	0939	|	|	1039	|	|	1139	|	|	1241	|	|
166	Nürnberg Hbf ... a.	0607	0607	0651	0712	0712	0719	0719	0757	0819	0819	0857	0922	0955	1020	1020	1056	1122	1122	1155	1220	1220	1256	1322	1355

			B			⊖			B			⊖			B			⊖		B			⊖		
of Hbf ... 876 879 d.	1243	...	...	...	1336	...	1443	...	...	...	1536	...	1643	...	...	...	1736	...	1843	...	...	1936	...	2043	2134
Cheb ... d.	|	...	...	1336	|	1425	|	...	...	1536	|	1625	|	...	...	1736	|	1825	|	...	1937	|	2025	|	|
arktredwitz ... 879 d.	1306	...	...	1405t	|	1450	1506	...	...	1605t	|	1650	1705	...	...	1805t	|	1850	1906	...	2009v	|	2050	2105	|
rchenlaibach ... d.	1323	...	...	1424	|	▬	1523	...	...	1624	|	▬	1723	...	...	1824	|	▬	1923	...	2025	|	▬	2121	|
Münchberg ... 876 d.	|	...	...	|	1352	Ⓐe	|	...	...	|	1552	Ⓐe	|	...	...	|	1754	...	|	...	|	1954	...	|	2154
Bayreuth Hbf ... d.	|	1315	1401	|	1429	1503	|	1515	1601	|	1629	1703	|	1715	1801	|	1829	1915	|	2001	|	2029	2113	|	2227
egnitz ... a.	1337	1341	1419	1438	1444	1518	1537	1541	1619	1638	1644	1718	1737	1741	1819	1838	1844	1941	1937	2019	2039	2044	2133	2138	2246
egnitz ... d.	1344	1344	1419	1446	1446	1519	1544	1544	1619	1646	1646	1719	1744	1744	1819	1846	1846	1944	1944	2019	2047	2047	2141	2141	2247
ersbruck (r Pegnitz) ... d.	1405	1405	1440	|	|	1539	|	|	1640	|	|	1739	|	|	1840	|	|	2007	2007	2040	|	|	2207	2207	2314
ürnberg Hbf ... a.	1420	1420	1456	1522	1522	1555	1620	1620	1656	1722	1722	1755	1820	1820	1856	1922	1922	2022	2022	2056	2122	2122	2222	2222	2329

– From Bamberg (Table **876**).
– Arrives 0457.
– Not June 20, Nov. 1.
Not Oct. 31, Nov. 20.

k – *0531* on ⑥.
t – Arrives 6 minutes earlier.
v – Arrives 1959.
w – Also Oct. 31, Nov. 20.
z – Also June 20, Nov. 1.

⊖ – Operated by Oberpfalzbahn.
◇ – Operated by Vogtlandbahn.
⊠ – Operated by Mitteldeutsche Regiobahn (2nd class only).

ZWICKAU - LEIPZIG - HALLE 881

S-Bahn 5

km																						
0	Zwickau (Sachs) Hbf ... 858 d.	0350	...	0504e	0520	0604	...	0704e	0720	0804	...	0904	and in the same pattern every **two** hours until	1720	1804	...	1904	1920	2004	...	2104e	2122	2232
9	Werdau ... 858 d.	0401	...	0512e	0532	0612	...	0712e	0732	0812	...	0912		1732	1812	...	1912	1932	2012	...	2112e	2134	2244
29	Gößnitz ... 858 d.	0419	...	0527e	0550	0627	...	0727e	0750	0827	...	0927		1750	1827	...	1927	1950	2027	...	2127e	2152	2302
44	Altenburg ... d.	0434t	0504	0538	0604	0638	0704	0738	0804	0838	0904	0938		1804	1838	1904	1938	2004	2038	2104	2138	2204	2314
80	Leipzig-Connewitz ★ ... d.	0512	0542	0612	0642	0712	0742	0812	0842	0912	0942	1012		1842	1912	1942	2012	2042	2112	2142	2212	2242	2352
85	Leipzig Hbf ★ ... 866 d.	0523	0553	0623	0653	0723	0753	0823	0853	0923	0953	1023		1853	1923	1953	2023	2053	2123	2153	2223	2251	0010
04	Leipzig/Halle Flughafen ✈ ... 866 d.	0538	0608	0638	0708	0738	0808	0838	0908	0938	1008	1038		1908	1938	2008	2038	2107	2138	2207	2238	...	|
22	Halle (Saale) Hbf ... 866 a.	0549	0619e	0649	0719	0749	0819	0849	0919	0949	1019	1049		1919	1949	2019	2049	...	2149	...	2249	...	0050

	Ⓒz	Ⓒz	Ⓐe			Ⓐe																	
alle (Saale) Hbf ... 866 d.	0056	0247	0414	...	0514	0514	0541e	0614	0639e	0714	0741	0814	0841	and in the same pattern every **two** hours until	1914	1941	2014	2041	2114	...	2214	...	2321
ipzig/Halle Flughafen ✈ ... 866 d.	0108	|	0425	0452	0525	0525	0552	0625	0652	0725	0752	0825	0852		1925	1952	2025	2052	2125	2152	2225	2241	|
ipzig Hbf ★ ... 866 d.	0123	0338r	0439	0509	0539	0539	0609	0639	0709	0739	0809	0839	0909		1939	2009	2039	2109	2139	2209	2239	2308r	0008f
ipzig-Connewitz ★ ... d.	0133	0348	0449	0519	0549	0549	0619	0649	0719	0749	0819	0849	0919		1949	2019	2049	2119	2149	2219	2249	2318	0018
enburg ... d.	...	0436	0520	0601	0619	0620	0656	0720	0801	0820	0856	0920	1001		2020	2056	2120	2201	2220	2256	...	2356	0105
ößnitz ... 858 d.	...	0449	0533	0614	...	0633	...	0733	0814	0833	...	0933	1014		2033	...	2133	2214	2233	...	...	0009	...
erdau ... 858 d.	...	0508	0549	0633	...	0649	...	0749	0833	0849	...	0949	1033		2049	...	2149	2233	2251	...	...	0028	...
ickau (Sachs) Hbf ... 858 a.	...	0520	0558	0645	...	0658	...	0758	0845	0858	...	0958	1045		2058	...	2158	2245	2259	...	...	0040	...

PLAUEN - WERDAU ◇

km		Ⓐj	Ⓐj	Ⓐj			Ⓐj		
	Plauen (Vogt) ob Bf ... 880 d.	0432	0529	0623	0729	and hourly until	1929	2029	2202
0	Reichenbach (Vogt) ob Bf ... 880 d.	0454	0551	0648	0751		1951	2051	2224
17	Werdau ... a.	0507	0603	0700	0803		2003	2103	2239
	Zwickau (Sachs) Hbf ... 880 a.	0523	0616	0714	0816		2016	2116	2252

	Ⓐj	Ⓐj					
Zwickau (Sachs) Hbf ... 880 d.	0537	0637	0737	and hourly until	1937	2040	2236
Werdau ... d.	0553	0653	0753		1953	2053	2254
Reichenbach (Vogt) ob Bf ... 880 d.	0605	0705	0805		2005	2105	2307
Plauen (Vogt) ob Bf ... 880 a.	0628	0728	0828		2028	2128	2331

– Ⓐ (not Oct. 31).
– Arrives 2358.
Not Oct. 31, Nov. 20.

r – Arrives 14 minutes earlier.
t – 0431 on Ⓒ (also Oct. 31).
z – Also Oct. 31.

◇ – Operated by Vogtlandbahn (2nd class only). Certain services run from / to Cheb (see Table **1122**).
★ – All trains also call at Leipzig MDR, Leipzig Bayerischer Bahnhof, Leipzig Wilhelm-Leuschner-Platz and Leipzig Markt.

CHEMNITZ - CRANZAHL - VEJPRTY - CHOMUTOV 882

DB (*RB* services); ČD

km												
0	Chemnitz Hbf ... 880 d.	0636	0836	0936	1136	1236	1336	1436	1636	1836	2036	2236
13	Flöha ... 880 d.	0647	0847	0947	1147	1247	1347	1447	1647	1847	2047	2247
31	Zschopau ... d.	0708	0908	1008	1208	1308	1410	1508	1708	1910	2108	2308
57	Annaberg-Buchholz ¶ d.	0743	0943	1048	1243	1348	1445	1543	1743	1945	2143	2343
64	Cranzahl ⊖ ... d.	...	0955	1100	1255	1400	1501	1555z	1755	...	...	...
			C						C			
64	Cranzahl ... d.	...	1007	...	...	...	...	...	1812	...	...	...
75	Vejprty 🚌 ... d.	...	1025	...	...	...	...	...	1830	...	...	...
133	Chomutov ... a.	...	1147	...	...	...	...	...	1949	...	...	...

			C						C	
Chomutov ... d.	...	...	0752	...	...	...	...	...	1610	...
Vejprty 🚌 ... d.	...	...	0925	...	...	...	...	...	1734	...
Cranzahl ... a.	...	...	0941	...	...	...	...	...	1750	...
			d						d	
Cranzahl ⊖ ... d.	...	...	1001	1155	1301	1445	1557	1655z	1801	...
Annaberg-Buchholz ¶ d.	0607	0807	1013	1207	1313	1507	1609	1707	1813	2007
Zschopau ... d.	0644	0844	1047	1244	1347	1544	1644	1744	1847	2044
Flöha ... 880 a.	0708	0908	1108	1308	1408	1608	1708	1808	1908	2108
Chemnitz Hbf . 880 a.	0720	0920	1120	1320	1420	1620	1720	1820	1920	2120

– **Cranzahl - Kurort Oberwiesenthal** *Fichtelbergbahn* (17 km, narrow gauge steam). Journey: 57 – 64 minutes. **No service Nov. 4 – 27.**
Operator: SDG Sächsische Dampfeisenbahngesellschaft GmbH, Bahnhofstraße 7, 09484 Kurort Oberwiesenthal. ✆ + 49 (0) 37348 151 0.
From Cranzahl at 0959, 1137, 1315, 1504, 1640 ⊡ and 1813. **From Kurort Oberwiesenthal** at 0820, 1014, 1152, 1330, 1519 ⊡ and 1655.

– ⑥⑦ Apr. 27 - Sept. 29 (also May 1).
d – Daily from Cranzahl.
z – Ⓒ (also Oct. 31, Nov. 20).
⊡ – Ⓒ (also Oct. 31); runs daily June 29 - Oct. 27.
¶ – Annaberg-Buchholz unterer Bf.

CHEMNITZ - AUE 883

RB services

RAIL SERVICE SUSPENDED UNTIL DECEMBER 2019 DURING ROUTE UPGRADE WORK

km												
0	Chemnitz Hbf ... d.	...	...	...	...	...	...	...	...	...	...	...
27	Thalheim ... d.	...	...	...	...	...	...	...	...	...	...	...
36	Zwönitz ... d.	...	...	...	...	...	...	...	...	...	...	...
51	Aue (Sachs) ... a.	...	...	...	...	...	...	...	...	...	...	...

Aue (Sachs) ... d.	...	...	...	...	...	...	...	...	...	...	...
Zwönitz ... d.	...	...	...	...	...	...	...	...	...	...	...
Thalheim ... d.	...	...	...	...	...	...	...	...	...	...	...
Chemnitz Hbf .. a.	...	...	...	...	...	...	...	...	...	...	...

884 ZWICKAU - JOHANNGEORGENSTADT - KARLOVY VARY

DB; ČD (2nd class only)

km		Ⓐd							⑤⑥v	
0	**Zwickau** (Sachs) Hbf . d.	0509	...	0609	and	2009	2109	2209	2309	...
27	Aue (Sachs) d.	0541	0541	0641	hourly	2041	2141	2241	2342	...
37	Schwarzenberg (Erzg) . d.	0556	0556	0656	until	2056	2154	...	2355	...
56	**Johanngeorgenstadt** . a.	0621	0621	0721		2121	...	...	...	...

	Ⓐd	Ⓐd							⑤⑥
Johanngeorgenstadt d.	...	0430	...	0530	0630	and	2030	...	...
Schwarzenberg (Erzg) d.	0354	0456	0456	0556	0656	hourly	2056	...	220
Aue (Sachs) d.	0409	0509	0509	0609	0709	until	2109	...	221
Zwickau (Sachs) Hbf a.	0441	0541	0541	0641	0741		2141	...	224

km	SEE NOTE ▶		Ⓐ	⊗						Ⓒ	
0	**Johanngeorgenstadt** . d.	...	...	0728	0931	1233	1450	1631	2054	2054	...
1	Potučky ⊞ d.	0442	0600	0731	0934	1236	1453	1634	2057	2057	...
28	Nejdek d.	0527	0700	0817	1017	1317	1542	1717	2136	2138	2226
44	**Karlovy Vary** a.	0552	0726	0841	1041	1341	1605	1741	...	2201	2251
47	**Karlovy Vary** dolní ... a.	0559	*0734*	0850	1050	1347	1616	1750	...	2207	...

SEE NOTE ▶					Ⓐ	Ⓒ	Ⓐ	Ⓒ		
Karlovy Vary dolní d.	0547e	0747	0947	1305	1405	1435	1705	1811	2105	...
Karlovy Vary d.	0554	0753	0953	1317	1411	1447	1717	1817	2111	...
Nejdek d.	0620	0817	1017	1341	1438	1511	1741	1841	2136	222
Potučky ⊞ d.	0707	0858	1058	1420	1524	1553	1820	1920	...	230
Johanngeorgenstadt a.	0709	0900	1100	1422	1526	1555	1822	1922	...	...

d – Not Oct. 31, Nov. 20. **e** – Ⓐ only. **v** – Also June 9. ⊗ – Change trains at Nejdek on Ⓐ. ▶ – Czech holiday dates apply (see page 4).

885 REGENSBURG - SCHWANDORF - FURTH IM WALD - PLZEŇ

km	SEE NOTE ❦	◇ Ⓐt	◇	351 ‡🍷	◇	353 ‡🍷	◇	355 ‡🍷	◇	357 ‡🍷	◇ Ⓒz	◇	359 ‡🍷	◇	◇	◇ D	361 ‡🍷	◇	◇ C	AN	363 ‡🍷	◇	N	◇
	München Hbf **878** d.	...	...	0444r	...	0643	...	0843	...	1043	...	...	1243	...	...	...	1443	...	...	...	1643	...	...	...
0	**Regensburg** Hbf **879** d.	...	...	0615	...	0814	...	1014	...	1214	...	...	1414	...	...	...	1614	...	...	...	1814	...	...	...
42	**Schwandorf** **879** d.	0544	0623r	0654	0801	0852	1001	1052	1202	1252	1309	1403	1452	1509	1601	1601	1652	1709	1709	1737	1852	2003	2109	2317
90	Cham (Oberpf) d.	0621	0707	0724	0839	0924	1040	1124	1237	1324	1346	1437	1524	1546	1641	1641	1724	1743	1743	1815	1924	2037	2143	2351
109	**Furth im Wald** ⊞ d.	0637	0724	0740	0900	0940	1056	1140	1254	1340	1402	1454	1540	1602	1658	1700	1740	1759	1800	1832	1940	2053	2159	0008
131	Domažlice ⊠ d.	...	...	0801	0922	1001	...	1201	...	1401	...	...	1601	...	...	1722	1801	...	1823	...	2001	...	...	...
190	**Plzeň** Hlavni ⊠ a.	...	...	0849	...	1049	...	1249	...	1449	...	...	1649	...	...	...	1849	...	...	...	2049	...	...	...
	Praha hl.n. **1120** a.	...	...	1019	...	1219	...	1419	...	1619	...	...	1819	...	...	...	2016	...	...	...	2216	...	...	...

SEE NOTE ❦	ⒶeN	N	◇	◇	362 ‡🍷	◇	360 ‡🍷	◇	◇ Ⓐt	358 ‡🍷	◇	◇	356 ‡🍷	◇	354 ‡🍷	◇	◇	352 ‡🍷		350 ‡🍷	◇	Ⓒ		
Praha hl.n. **1120** d.	...	...	...	...	0545	...	0745	...	...	0945	...	...	1145	...	1345	...	...	1545	...	1745	...	...	...	...
Plzeň Hlavni ⊠ d.	...	...	...	...	0710	...	0910	...	...	1110	...	...	1310	...	1510	...	...	1710	...	1910	...	2018	2118	2247
Domažlice ⊠ d.	...	...	...	...	0801	...	1001	1035	...	1201	...	...	1401	...	1601	...	...	1801	1835	2001	...	2124	2223	2347
Furth im Wald ⊞ d.	0445	0558	0659	0752	0823	0904	1022	1104	1150	1222	1304	1350	1422	1502	1622	1704	1748	1822	1904	2022	2103	...	...	...
Cham (Oberpf) d.	0501	0618	0724	0813	0837	0924	1037	1124	1213	1237	1324	1413	1437	1524	1637	1724	1814	1837	1924	2037	2122	...	...	...
Schwandorf **879** a.	0533	0653	0756	0851	0904	0956	1104	1155	1249	1304	1356	1449	1504	1556	1704	1756	1849	1904	1956	2105	2155	...	...	...
Regensburg Hbf **879** a.	...	...	...	...	0945	...	1145	...	...	1345	...	...	1545	...	1744	...	...	1945	...	2149b	...	...	...	...
München Hbf **878** a.	...	...	...	...	1118	...	1318	...	...	1518	...	...	1718	...	1918	...	...	2118	...	2321b	...	...	...	...

A – ①–④ (not June 10, 20, Oct. 3).
C – ⑥⑦ (also July 5, Oct. 28).
D – ①–⑤ (not July 5, Oct. 28).
N – From / to Nürnberg (Table **886**).
b – Ⓑ (not June 9, 19, Aug. 14, Oct. 2, 31).
e – Not June 20, Nov. 1.
r – ⚒ (not June 20, Aug. 15, Nov. 1).
t – Not June 20, Aug. 15, Nov. 1.
z – Also June 20, Aug. 15, Nov. 1.
◇ – Operated by Oberpfalzbahn (2nd class).
❦ – Services Furth - Praha - Plzeň and v.v. are subject to alteration June 14–21.
‡ – Train category *ALX* in Germany (operated by Vogtlandbahn).
⊠ – Other local trains Domažlice - Plzeň and v.v. (journey 63–78 minutes):
From Domažlice at 0345, 0430 Ⓐ, 0530, 0611 Ⓐ, 0634 Ⓒ, 0651 Ⓐ, 0725 Ⓐ, 0834, 1034, 1234, 1325 Ⓐ, 1434, 1527 Ⓐ, 1634 Ⓒ, 1636 Ⓐ, 1834 Ⓒ, 1925 Ⓐ and 2034 Ⓒ.
From Plzeň hl.n. at 0505 Ⓐ, 0601 Ⓐ, 0618 Ⓒ, 0818, 1018, 1218, 1318 Ⓐ, 1418, 1518 Ⓐ, 1618, 1718 Ⓐ, 1818 and 1918 Ⓐ.

886 NÜRNBERG - SCHWANDORF and WEIDEN

RE services

km		Ⓐe		Ⓐe											Ⓐe¶		⊖		⊖		¶					Ⓒz
0	**Nürnberg** Hbf ◧ d.	0430	0535	0559	0631	0738	0843	0943	1043	1143	1243	1343	1443	1543	1605	1643	1705	1743	1805	1843	1938	2055	2206	2257	0022	002
28	Hersbruck (r Pegnitz) ◧ d.	0445	0551	0621	0648	0757	0858	0958	1058	1158	1258	1358	1458	1558	1625	1658	1725	1758	1825	1858	1958	2117	2227	2316	0038	003
56	Sulzbach-Rosenberg . d.	0508	0619	0647	0728	0826	0925	1025	1126	1225	1326	1425	1525	1625	1649	1726	1751	1825	1852	1926	2026	2142	2251	2341	0104	010
68	Amberg d.	0519	0627	0704	0736	0833	0935	1033	1133	1233	1333	1433	1533	1632	1701	1736	1803	1833	1901	1933	2036	2150	2259	2348	0111	011
94	**Schwandorf** a.	0533	0643	0727	0757	0847	0948	1046	1148	1246	1350	1446	1548	1647	1724	1751	1824	1846	1926	1947	2051	2204	2312	0002	...	012

	Ⓐe	⚒e	†z	Ⓐe	Ⓐe¶	Ⓒz	Ⓐe	¶	Ⓐe																
Schwandorf d.	0407	0458	0516	0544	0607	0609	0644	0707	0740	0808	0907	1007	1107	1207	1307	1407	1507	1607	1707	1807	1908	2007	2110	2212	001
Amberg d.	0423	0526	0532	0559	0624	0626	0700	0725	0756	0822	0921	1021	1121	1221	1321	1421	1521	1621	1721	1821	1922	2021	2124	2226	002
Sulzbach-Rosenberg d.	0432	0535	0541	0607	0635	0634	0707	0732	0807	0829	0928	1029	1129	1229	1329	1429	1529	1629	1729	1829	1929	2029	2132	2234	...
Hersbruck (r pegnitz) d.	0503	0607	0607	|	0707	0707	|	0757	0841j	0900	0959	1100	1159	1300	1359	1500	1600	1700	1759	1900	1959	2100	2207j	2314j	...
Nürnberg Hbf a.	0518	0621	0622	0651	0723	0723	0751	0814	0857	0915	1014	1115	1214	1315	1414	1515	1615	1715	1814	1916	2014	2115	2222	2329	...

km	SEE NOTE △											
0	**Nürnberg** Hbf ◧ d.	0535	0631	0738	0843	and	1743	1843	1938	2055	2206	2257
28	Hersbruck (r Pegnitz) ◧ d.	0551	0648	0757	0858	hourly	1758	1858	1958	2117	2227	2316
97	**Weiden** (Oberpf) a.	0646	0748	0852	0950	until	1850	1952	2051	2214	2321	0008

SEE NOTE △			✣							
Weiden (Oberpf) ⇆ d.	0610	0657	0806	and	1603	1703	1803	1906	2003	221
Hersbruck (r Pegnitz) a.	0706	0756	0859	hourly	1659	1758	1859	1958	2059	230
Nürnberg Hbf a.	0723	0814	0915	until	1715	1814	1916	2014	2115	232

e – Not June 20, Nov. 1.
j – Arrives 8–10 minutes earlier.
z – Also June 20, Nov. 1.
⊖ – ①–④ (not June 10, 20, Oct. 3).
¶ – To / from Furth im Wald (Table **885**).
△ – Subject to alteration until July 7.
✣ – Weiden d. 1403 (not 1406).
◧ – Certain trains from Nürnberg and Hersbruck convey portions for two separate destinations. Passengers should take care to join the correct portion for their destination.

887 BAYREUTH - WEIDEN

Operated by *agilis* (2nd class only)

km				Ⓐe					Ⓒz	Ⓐe											
0	**Bayreuth** Hbf d.	0002	...	0442	0617	0718	0805	0901	1001	1004	1101	1201	1300	1401	1501	1601	1701	1801	1901	2023	2203
19	Kirchenlaibach a.	0018	...	0503	0638	0740	0826	0916	1016	1019	1115	1216	1315	1416	1515	1615	1715	1816	1915	2039	2223
19	Kirchenlaibach d.	...	...	0504	0652	...	0826	0920	1020	1020	1120	1220	1320	1420	1520	1620	1720	1820	1920	2048	2224
59	**Weiden** a.	...	...	0532	0726	...	0855	0950	1050	1050	1150	1249	1352	1449	1549	1649	1749	1849	1948	2117	2252

	Ⓐe	Ⓐe									Ⓒz	Ⓐe									
Weiden d.	...	0549	...	0638e	*0734*	...	0907	1007	1107	1207	1307	1323	1407	1507	1607	1707	1807	1907	2007	2134	...
Kirchenlaibach a.	...	0617	...	0707e	*0803*	...	0941	1041	1141	1241	1341	1354	1441	1541	1641	1741	1841	1940	2041	2204	...
Kirchenlaibach d.	0509	0618	0657	0720	0807	0840	0942	1042	1142	1242	1342	1355	1442	1542	1642	1742	1842	1941	2045	2204	2337
Bayreuth Hbf a.	0525	0634	0716	0735	0823	0856	0956	1056	1157	1256	1357	1415	1457	1557	1657	1757	1856	1957	2100	2220	2353

e – Ⓐ (not June 20, Nov. 1).
z – Also June 20, Nov. 1.

888 KEMPTEN - REUTTE IN TIROL - GARMISCH-PARTENKIRCHEN

RB services

km											
0	**Kempten** (Allgäu) Hbf d.	0733	0934	1134	1334	1534	1634	1734	1934	2033	2258
18	Oy-Mittelberg d.	0800	1002	1201	1401	1601	1702	1802	2001	2100	2327
24	Nesselwang d.	0812	1013	1213	1412	1613	1713	1813	2013	2111	2338
31	Pfronten-Ried d.	0821	1023	1222	1422	1622	1723	1823	2022	2120	2348
33	**Pfronten-Steinach** ⊞ d.	0827	1031	1227	1427	1627	1731	1831	2031	2125	2353
38	Vils Stadt ⊞ d.	0836	1039	1235	1435	1635	1739	1839	|	...	...
48	**Reutte in Tirol** a.	0851	1054	1250	1450	1650	1754	1854	2053	...	...

Reutte in Tirol d.	0709a	0803c	0907	1107	1307	1507	1707	1807	1903	211
Vils Stadt ⊞ d.	0725a	0818c	0922	1122	1322	1522	1722	1822	1918	212
Pfronten-Steinach ⊞ d.	0734	0834	0934	1134	1334	1534	1734	1834	1934	213
Pfronten-Ried d.	0738	0838	0938	1138	1338	1538	1738	1838	1938	214
Nesselwang d.	0747	0847	0947	1147	1347	1547	1747	1847	1947	215
Oy-Mittelberg d.	0801	0901	1001	1201	1401	1601	1801	1901	2001	220
Kempten (Allgäu) Hbf a.	0828	0928	1028	1228	1428	1628	1828	1928	2027	223

km			h			a			a	c		a	c		
0	**Reutte in Tirol** d.	0657	0757	0853	1057	1154	1252f	1457	1557	1625	1657	1757	1823	1857	2104
20	Lermoos d.	0724	0824	0920	1124	1224	1319f	1524	1624	1652	1724	1823	1851	1924	2130
23	Ehrwald Zugspitzbahn ⊞ d.	0730	0830	0926	1130	1230	1325f	1530	1630	1658	1730	1830	1857	1930	2136
45	**Garmisch**-Partenkirchen a.	0757	0857e	0957	1157	1257	1357	1557	1657	1729	1757	1857	1929	1957	2203
	München Hbf **895** a.	0926z	1026t	1126t	1326z	1426	1526	1726z	1826	1847	1926	2026t	2047	2126k	2326v

	h			a	a	c	y	a			c	a		Ⓑj	
München Hbf **895** d.	0453g	0532c	0713c	0732	0832	0913	1032c	1132	1232c	1432c	1532	1532	1632	1732	1813d
Garmisch-Partenkirchen d.	0633	0721	0828y	0921	1029	1032	1232	1321	1421x	1631r	1657	1720	1820	1920	2004
Ehrwald Zugspitzbahn ⊞ d.	0659	0753	0854y	0949	1059	1059	1259	1359	1452x	1659	1731	1753	1859	1953	2032
Lermoos d.	0703	0757	0859y	0953	1103	1103	1303	1403	1456x	1703	1735	1757	1903	1957	2036
Reutte in Tirol a.	0735	0831	0928	1022	1132	1132	1332	1431	1532	1732	1802	1832	1931	2024	2103

a – ①–⑤ (not June 10, 20, Aug. 15, Nov. 1). **c** – ⑥⑦ (also June 10, 20, Aug. 15, Nov. 1). **d** – 1832 on Ⓒ z.
e – 0901 on ⑥.
f – 5 minutes later on ⑥⑦ **c**.
g – ① (not June 10).
h – ①–⑥ (not June 10, 20, Aug. 15, Oct. 26, Nov. 1).
j – Ⓑ (not June 9, 19, Aug. 14, Oct. 25, 31). Runs 22–24 minutes **earlier** Garmisch - Reutte on ⑦ (also June 10, Aug. 15, Nov. 1).
k – Not ⑤.
r – 1621 on ①–⑤ **a**.
t – Ⓐ (not June 20, Aug. 15, Nov. 1).
v – ⑤ only.
x – 7–11 minutes later on ①–⑤ **a**.
y – 2–11 minutes **earlier** on ①–⑤ **a**.
z – Ⓒ (also June 20, Aug. 15, Nov. 1).

MÜNCHEN - SALZBURG 890

ayerische Oberlandbahn; DB

km		◇ Ⓐt		◇ Ⓒz	◇ Ⓐt	RJX 265 ✕	◇	79007 ⊡ 🍷	RJX 61 B✕	◇	RJ 111 ✕♦	◇	RJX 63 ⑥⑦j B✕	RJX 63 B✕	◇	EC 217 🍷♦	◇	RJX 65 B✕	◇	79019 ⊡ 🍷	EC 113 ✕♦	◇	RJX 67 B✕	◇
	Frankfurt (Main) Hbf **912** d.	...	...	...	...	...	...	...	...	...	...	...	0517y	...	...	...	...	...	...	...	0820	...	...	...
	Stuttgart Hbf **930** d.	...	...	...	...	...	...	...	...	...	...	...	0658	...	...	0758	...	...	...	...	0958	...	...	...
0	**München** Hbf **951** d.	...	...	0548	0552	0623	0655	0655	0723	0756	0817	0856	0930	0930	0955	1017c	1055	1130b	1155	1155	1217c	1255	1330	1355
10	München Ost **951** d.	...	...	0557	0601	0633	0704	0704	|	0805	0827	0905	|	|	1004	1027	1104	|	1204	1204	1227	1304	|	1404
65	Rosenheim **951** d.	0532	...	0635	0639	0703	0735	0735	0803	0835	0857	0935	|	|	1035	1057	1135	|	1235	1235	1257	1335	|	1435
82	Bad Endorf d.	0543	...	0646	0651	|	0746	0746	|	0846	|	0946	|	|	1046	|	1146	|	1246	1246	|	1346	|	1446
90	Prien am Chiemsee d.	0549	...	0652	0659	|	0752	0752	|	0852	0913	0952	|	|	1052	1113	1152	|	1252	1252	1313	1352	|	1452
18	Traunstein d.	0612	...	0716	0722	|	0816	0816	|	0916	0933	1016	|	|	1116	1133	1216	|	1316	1316	1333	1416	|	1516
47	Freilassing **891** d.	0633	...	0735	0742	|	0835	0835	|	0935	0951	1035	|	|	1135	1151	1235	|	1335	1335	1351	1435	|	1535
53	**Salzburg** Hbf 🏢 **891** a.	0640	...	0742	0752	0758	0842	0842	0858	0942	0959	1042	1058	1058	1142	1159	1242	1258	1342	1342	1359	1442	1458	1542
	Wien Hbf **950** a.	...	...	...	...	1030	...	1117w	1130	...	...	...	1330	1330	...	...	...	1530	...	1617w	...	...	1730	...

	EC 115 🍷♦	◇	RJX 69 ✕	IC 1919 ♦	◇	EC 219 🍷♦	◇	79033 ⊡ 🍷	RJX 261 ✕	◇	EC 117 🍷♦	◇	IC 1269 Ⓑq K🍷	◇	NJ 295 [R] △♦	EC 391 Ⓑq 🍷	◇		◇		◇	EN 463 [R] 🍷♦	EN 50463 [R] 🍷♦	◇
rankfurt (Main) Hbf **912** d.	...	...	...	...	...	1220	...	...	...	...	1420	...	...	...	...	1620	...	...	...	...	...	...	...	...
Stuttgart Hbf **930** d.	1158	...	...	1257	...	1359	...	...	...	...	1558	...	1654	...	...	1758	...	...	...	...	...	...	...	...
nchen Hbf **951** d.	1417c	1455	1530	|	1555	1617c	1655	1655	1730	1755	1817c	1856	1916	1955	2010	2017c	2043	...	2143	...	2244	2320n	2320n	2350
nchen Ost **951** d.	1427	1504	|	1547	1604	1627	1704	1704	|	1804	1827	1905	1926	2004	2020u	2029	2052	...	2152	...	2252	2331u	2331u	2359
senheim **951** d.	1457	1535	|	1620	1635	1657	1735	1735	|	1835	1857	1935	1956	2035	2050u	2058	2131	...	2231	...	2331	0003u	0003u	0035
d Endorf d.	|	1546	|	1632	1646	|	1746	1746	|	1846	|	1946	2008	2046	|	2110	2142	...	2242	...	2342	|	|	0046
en am Chiemsee d.	1513	1552	|	1642	1652	1713	1752	1752	|	1852	1913	1952	2015	2052	|	2117	2148	...	2248	...	2348	|	|	0052
unstein d.	1533	1616	|	1702	1716	1733	1816	1816	|	1916	1933	2016	2034	2116	|	2135	2211	...	2311	...	0011	|	|	0116
ilassing **891** d.	1551	1635	|	1721	1735	1751	1835	1835	|	1935	1951	2035	2053	2135	|	2155	2230	...	2330	...	0030	|	|	0135
zburg Hbf 🏢 **891** a.	1559	1642	1658	...	1742	1759	1842	1842	1858	1942	1959	2042	2100	2142	2152	2202	2237	...	2337	...	0037	0104	0104	0142
Wien Hbf **950** a.	...	...	1930	...	...	...	...	2117w	2130	...	...	...	...	...	...	...	...	...	...	...	...	0635	...	...

	◇ Ⓐt	EN 462 [R] 🍷♦	EN 498 [R] 🍷♦	◇	IC 1296 ①–⑥ e	◇ Ⓐt	◇	NJ 294 [R] ▽♦	IC 1268 ①–⑥ e K 🍷	◇ Ⓐt	①–⑤ n	◇	◇ Ⓒz	EC 390 🍷	◇	RJX 260 ✕	◇	79020 ⊡ 🍷	EC 218 🍷♦	IC 1918 ♦	◇	RJX 262 ¶ ✕	◇	EC 114 🍷♦
Wien Hbf **950** d.	...	2325	...	...	...	...	...	...		...	...	...	...	...	...	0630	...	0643w	...	...	...	0830	...	...
zburg Hbf 🏢 **891** d.	0400	0427	0427	0515	0545	0600	0615	0627	0642	0646	0704	...	0715	0800	0815	0900	0915	0915	1000	...	1015	1100	1115	1200
ilassing **891** d.	0408	|	|	0524	0553	0608	0624	|	0650	0654	0714	0724	0724	0808	0824	|	0924	0924	1008	1013	1024	|	1124	1208
unstein d.	0426	|	|	0544	0611	0627	0644	|	0707	0722	...	0744	0744	0825	0844	|	0944	0944	1025	1033	1044	|	1144	1225
en am Chiemsee d.	0448	|	|	0606	0629	0650	0706	|	0727	0744	...	0806	0806	0844	0906	|	1006	1006	1044	1051	1106	|	1206	1244
d Endorf d.	0455	|	|	0613	0637	0656	0713	|	0735	0751	...	0813	0813	|	0913	|	1013	1013	|	1059	1113	|	1213	|
senheim **951** d.	0508	0525s	0525s	0629	0652	0712	0729	0731s	0751	0803	...	0829	0829	0903	0929	|	1029	1029	1103	1113	1129	|	1229	1303
nchen Ost **951** a.	0535	0557s	0557s	0656	0719	0739	0756	|	0820	...	...	0856	0856	0931	0956	|	1056	1056	1131	1151	1156	|	1256	1331
nchen Hbf **951** a.	0545	0610	0610	0706	0731c	0749	0806	0819	0831f	...	...	0906	0906	0941c	1006	1030	1106	1106	1141c	|	1206	1230	1306	1341c
Stuttgart Hbf **930** a.	...	...	...	...	0959	...	...	...	1106	...	...	...	...	1159	...	...	...	...	1359	1500	...	...	...	1600
rankfurt (Main) Hbf **912** a.	...	...	...	...	1140	...	...	...	...	...	...	...	...	1340	...	...	...	...	1555v	...	...	...	...	...

	◇	RJX 60 B✕	◇	EC 112 ✕♦	◇	79032 ⊡ 🍷	RJX 62 B✕	◇	EC 216 🍷♦	◇	RJX 64 B✕	◇		◇	RJX 66 B✕	RJX 66 ⑤⑥r B✕	◇	79042 ⊡ 🍷	RJ 110 x ✕♦	◇	RJX 68 B✕	◇	◇ ⑤–⑦ p	◇
ien Hbf **950** d.	...	1030	...	...	...	1143w	1230	...	...	...	1430	...	...	...	1630	1630	...	1643w	...	...	1830	...	...	...
zburg Hbf 🏢 **891** d.	1215	1300	1313	1400	1415	1415	1500	1515	1600	1615	1700	1715	...	1815	1856	1856	1915	1915	2000	2015	2100	2115	2215	2300
lassing **891** d.	1224	|	1324	1408	1424	1424	|	1524	1608	1624	|	1724	...	1824	|	|	1929	1929	2008	2029	|	2129	2224	2310
unstein d.	1244	|	1344	1425	1444	1444	|	1544	1625	1644	|	1744	...	1844	|	|	1949	1949	2025	2049	|	2149	2244	2329
en am Chiemsee d.	1306	|	1406	1444	1506	1506	|	1606	1644	1706	|	1806	...	1906	|	|	2011	2011	2044	2111	|	2211	2306	2351
d Endorf d.	1313	|	1413	|	1513	1513	|	1613	|	1713	|	1813	...	1913	|	|	2018	2018	|	2118	|	2218	2313	2357
senheim **951** d.	1329	|	1429	1503	1529	1529	|	1629	1703	1729	|	1829	...	1929	|	|	2032	2032	2103	2132	2156	2232	2332	0012
nchen Ost **951** a.	1356	|	1456	1531	1556	1556	|	1656	1731	1756	|	1856	...	1956	|	|	2105	2105	2131	2205	|	2305	0005	0046
nchen Hbf **951** a.	1406	1434	1505	1541c	1606	1606	1632	1706	1741c	1806	1831	1906	...	2006	2032	2032	2115	2115	2142	2215	2231	2315	0015	0057
tuttgart Hbf **930** a.	...	...	...	1759	...	...	...	...	1959	...	...	...	...	...	...	2259	...	...	...	...	...	...	...	...
rankfurt (Main) Hbf **912** a.	...	...	...	1940	...	...	...	...	...	...	...	...	...	...	...	0044	...	...	...	...	...	...	...	...

NOTES (LISTED BY TRAIN NUMBER)

/1 – HOHE TAUERN – [12] and ✕ Klagenfurt - Villach - München and v.v.
/3 – BLAUER ENZIAN – [12] and ✕ Klagenfurt - Villach - München - Frankfurt and v.v.; [12] Zagreb (**212/3**) - Ljubljana - Jesenice 🏢 - Villach - München - Frankfurt and v.v.
– WÖRTHERSEE – [12] and 🍷 Klagenfurt - München - Mannheim - Dortmund.
– WÖRTHERSEE – [12] and 🍷 Münster - Köln - Mannheim - München - Klagenfurt.
– SALZACH – [12] and 🍷 Frankfurt - Villach - Klagenfurt. Until June 12 service is diverted between Rosenheim and Schwarzach (not calling at intermediate stations; see Table **970**).
7 – DACHSTEIN – [12] and 🍷 Graz - Salzburg - Mannheim - Saarbrücken and v.v.
– CHIEMGAU – [12] and 🍷 Graz - Salzburg - Frankfurt (- Erfurt ①–④ **m**)
– CHIEMGAU – [12] and 🍷 Frankfurt - Salzburg - Bischofshofen - Graz.
/5 – 🛏 1, 2 cl., ▬ 2 cl. and [2] Roma - Firenze - Bologna - München and v.v. Conveys 🛏 1, 2 cl., ▬ 2 cl. and [2] Milano (**40235/40295**) - Verona - München and v.v.
/3 – KÁLMÁN IMRE – 🛏 1, 2 cl., ▬ 2 cl., [2] and 🍷 Budapest - München and v.v.
– LISINSKI – 🛏 1, 2 cl., ▬ 2 cl. and [2] Zagreb - Ljubljana - Jesenice 🏢 - Villach - München; 🛏 1, 2 cl. and [2] (**480**) Rijeka - Ljubljana - München; 🛏 1, 2 cl., ▬ 2 cl. and [2] (*NJ* **40236**) Venezia - Villach - München.
8 – June 25 - Sept. 9 and Nov. 10 - Dec. 14. [12] Berchtesgaden - München Ost - Dortmund.
9 – June 24 - Sept. 8 and Nov. 9 - Dec. 14. [12] Dortmund - München Ost - Berchtesgaden.
63 – LISINSKI – 🛏 1, 2 cl., ▬ 2 cl. and [2] München - Villach - Jesenice 🏢 - Ljubljana - Zagreb; 🛏 1, 2 cl. and [2] (**60463**) München - Ljubljana - Rijeka; 🛏 1, 2 cl., ▬ 2 cl. and [2] (*NJ* **40463**) München - Villach - Venezia.

B – To / from Budapest (Table **1250**).
K – To / from Karlsruhe (Table **931**).

b – 1128 on ⑥ June 29 - July 27.
c – From July 29.
e – Not June 10.
f – 0833 on ⑥ until Aug. 31.
j – Also June 10.
m – Not June 10, 19, 20, Aug. 12 - Oct. 24.
n – Not June 10, 20, Aug. 15, Nov. 1.
p – Also June 10, 20, Aug. 15, Oct. 3.

q – Not June 9.
r – Also June 9.
s – Calls to set down only.
t – Not June 20, Aug. 15, Nov. 1.
u – Calls to pick up only.
v – 1540 on ⑤–⑦ (also June 10, 19, 20; daily Aug. 9 - Oct. 27).
w – Wien **Westbahnhof**.
y – 0531 from Oct. 26.
z – Also June 20, Aug. 15, Nov. 1.

⊡ – From Autumn 2019 (awaiting confirmation of start date). Service jointly operated by *Meridian* / *Westbahn*. Special fares payable for journeys to / from Wien.
¶ – On ⑥⑦ until Aug. 25 (also June 10, 20, Aug. 15) runs with train number **1162** and arrives München 1233.
△ – On Ⓒ to July 28 (also June 20) departs München Hbf 2008; on Ⓐ to July 26 (not June 20) starts from München Ost (d. 2017).
▽ – On Ⓒ to July 28 (also June 20) arrives München Hbf 0824; on Ⓐ to July 26 (not June 20) terminates at München Ost (a. 0813).
◇ – *Meridian* regional service (operated by Bayerische Oberlandbahn; German holiday dates apply).

SALZBURG - FREILASSING - BERCHTESGADEN 891

rchtesgadener Land Bahn *

			Ⓐt	Ⓒz				⊙									A	D							
0	**Salzburg** Hbf **890** d.	*0615*	*0704*	*0715*	0752a	*0823*	0842	and at	*1323*	1342	*1415*	1442	1523	*1542*	*1623*	1642	*1723*	*1723*	1742	*1823*	1842	*1923*	*2042*	*2142*	2229
6	Freilassing **890** a.	*0622*	*0714*	*0722*	0802a	*0834*	0854	the same	*1334*	1354	*1422*	1454	1534	*1554*	*1634*	1654	*1734*	*1734*	1754	*1834*	1854	*1934*	*2054*	*2154*	2241
6	Freilassing d.	0634	0718	0740	0804	0840	0859	minutes	1340	1359	1440	1459	1540	1604	1640	1659	1738	1740	1759	1840	1859	1940	2100	2200	2246
	Bad Reichenhall d.	0655	0741	0759	0821	0901	0920	past each	1401	1420	1501	1520	1558	1626	1701	1720	1801	1801	1820	1901	1920	2001	2122	2217	2306
	Berchtesgaden Hbf a.	0726	0810	0827	...	0928	...	hour until	1428	...	1528	...	...	1658	1728	...	1831	1828	...	1928	...	2028	2150	2245	2334

	Ⓐt	①g	Ⓐt						B	G													E	D		
chtesgaden Hbf d.	...	0530	...	0621	0706	...	0828	...	0852	...	0932	...	and at	1532	...	1619	...	1729	...	1832	...	1929	1932	2032	2210
Reichenhall d.	0528	0600	0600	0654	0740	0838	0900	...	0937	0938	1000	1038	the same	1600	1638	1700	1738	1800	1838	1900	1938	2000	2000	2100	2243
assing a.	0545	0617	0617	0711	0757	0858	0918	...	0958	0958	1018	1058	minutes	1618	1658	1718	1758	1818	1858	1918	1958	2018	2018	2117	2303
assing **890** d.	0547	0620	0620	*0719*	*0807*	*0903*	*0924*e	0935	*1007*	1007	*1024*	1107	past each	*1624*	1707	*1724*	1807	*1824*	1907	*1924*	2007	*2024*	*2024*	*2135*	*2307*
burg Hbf **890** a.	0558	0631	0631	*0731*	*0819*	*0913*	*0936*e	0942	*1019*	1019	*1036*	1119	hour until	*1636*	1719	*1736*	1819	*1836*	1919	*1936*	2019	*2036*	*2036*	*2142*	*2319*

June 24 - Sept. 8 and Nov. 9 - Dec. 14. *IC* **1919** – [12] Dortmund - München Ost - Berchtesgaden.
June 25 - Sept. 9 and Nov. 10 - Dec. 14. *IC* **1918** – [12] Berchtesgaden - München Ost - Dortmund.
Until June 23 and Sept. 9 - Nov. 8.
June 24 - Sept. 8 and Nov. 9 - Dec. 14
Until June 24 and Sept. 10 - Nov. 9

a – ①–⑤ (not June 10, 20, Aug. 15, Nov. 1).
e – ①–⑥ (not June 10, 20, Aug. 15, Oct. 26, Nov. 1).
g – Also Oct. 3; not June 10.
t – Not June 20, Aug. 15, Nov. 1.
z – Also June 20, Aug. 15, Nov. 1.

⊙ – The 0940 from Freilassing runs as a through train from Salzburg (d. 0923).
* – Services to / from Bad Reichenhall or Berchtesgaden are operated by Berchtesgadener Land Bahn GmbH. 2nd class only. Other trains are operated by either DB or ÖBB. German holiday dates apply.

892 MÜNCHEN FLUGHAFEN ✈

S-Bahn services S1, S8 from / to München (2nd class only)

S1 München Hbf (low level) - Freising - München Flughafen Terminal ✈ (41 km). Services run every 20 minutes. **From München Hbf** 0503 to 2323. **From München Flughafen** 0551 to 233 Journey: ± 45 minutes. **S1** trains from München Hbf are often combined with a Freising service - travel in the rear portion for the Airport.

S8 München Pasing - München Hbf (low level) - München Ost - München Flughafen Terminal ✈ (44 km). Services run every 20 minutes. **From München Pasing** 0305 to 0005 (10 minutes late from München Hbf, 19 minutes later from München Ost). **From München Flughafen** 0404 to 0004. Journey: 50 minutes from / to Pasing, 40 minutes from / to Hbf, 31 minutes from / to Ost.

Direct *RE* services Regensburg - Landshut - Freising - München Flughafen (on June 20, Aug. 15, Nov. 1 services run as on ⑦).

From Regensburg Hbf at 0318, 0417, 0512, 0613, 0713, 0814 and hourly until 2014; then 2214. Regensburg - München Flughafen journey time: 74 – 80 minutes (♣).

From München Flughafen Terminal at 0028, 0528, 0608 Ⓐ, 0628 Ⓒ, 0708 Ⓐ, 0728 Ⓒ, 0828 and hourly until 2228. München Flughafen - Regensburg journey time: 77 – 93 minutes (★).

♣ – Trains call at Landshut 39 – 45 minutes later, Freising 61 – 67 minutes later.

★ – Trains call at Freising 10 – 11 minutes later, Landshut 33 – 36 minutes later.

893 MÜNCHEN - MÜHLDORF - SIMBACH

On June 20, Aug. 15, Nov. 1 services run as on ⑦

km			⊗	⚒								Ⓐ		Ⓐ	Ⓒ	Ⓐ	Ⓒ	Ⓐ		Ⓐ		Ⓐ		⊙		
0	**München** Hbf ... d.	...	0607b	0706c	0807z	0907	1007	1107	1207	1307r	1407	1427	1506r	1522	1607	1626	1707	1726	1807	1831	1907r	1948	2027r	2128	2228	232
10	**München** Ost ... d.	...	0616	0716	0816	0917	1017	1117	1217	1317	1417	1439	1515	1532	1617	1638	1717	1738	1818	1840	1917	1957	2038	2138	2238	233
85	**Mühldorf** (Oberbay) .. a.	...	0722	0818	0919	1017	1116	1216	1316	1416	1516	1535	1619	1630	1717	1731	1816	1830	1919	1931	2020	2101	2140	2236	2336	003
		⚒	|	d							Ⓒ	|	Ⓒ	|		d	Ⓒ	|		d				|		
85	**Mühldorf** (Oberbay) .. d.	0639	0737	0837	0937	1037	1137	1227‡	1337	1437	1538	1538	1637	1634	...	1737	1837	1834	...	1937	2037	...	2147	2247	2342	...
124	**Simbach** (Inn) .... **962** a.	0713	0813	0913	1013	1113	1213	1258‡	1413	1513	1613	1613	1713	1708	...	1813	1913	1908	...	2013	2113	...	2219	2319	0014	...

			Ⓐ	⑥	Ⓐ	Ⓐ	Ⓒ											Ⓐ	Ⓒ		Ⓐ	Ⓒ	⊙			
Simbach (Inn) ...... **962** d.	...	...	0507	0540	0554	0648	0648	0749	0849	0949	1049	1149	1249•	1349	1449	1549	...	1641	1649	1749	1841	1849	1949	2049	2154	225
Mühldorf (Oberbay) ... a.	...	...	0540	0611	0628	0722	0722	0822	0922	1022	1122	1222	1322•	1422	1523	1622	...	1718	1722	1822	1917	1922	2022	2125	2229	232
	⚒	⚒	Ⓐ	Ⓒ	|	|	Ⓒ									Ⓒ	Ⓐ		d			d	|	|	|	
Mühldorf (Oberbay) ... d.	0429	0522	0546	0623	0637	0732	0731	0830	0937	1030	1138	1231	1340	1430	1538	1630	1634	...	1737	1842	...	1940	2034	2146	2245	...
München Ost ... a.	0524	0625	0640	0724	0722	0822	0826	0926	1045	1127	1245	1326	1443	1525	1645	1725	1745	...	1845	1945	...	2043	2142	2247	2352	...
München Hbf ... a.	0533	0637	0650	0736	0734	0834	0837	0935	1056	1138	1254r	1337	1454r	1535	1656	1737	1754	...	1855r	1955r	...	2055v	2153x	2300	0003	...

b – 0601 on Ⓒ to Aug. 25; 0608 on Ⓒ from Aug. 31.
c – 0659 on ⑥ to Aug. 24.
d – Daily from Mühldorf.
r – Ⓐ to Aug. 23; daily from Aug. 26.
v – 2057 on Ⓒ to Aug. 25.
x – 2204 on Ⓒ to Aug. 25.
z – Ⓒ only.
• – 10 minutes later on Ⓐ.
‡ – On Ⓒ Mühldorf d. 1237, Simbach a. 1313
⊙ – Change trains at Mühldorf on †.
⊗ – Change trains at Mühldorf on Ⓐ.

895 MÜNCHEN - GARMISCH - INNSBRUCK

DB; ÖBB (2nd class only in Austria

km		◧ Ⓐ e		◧ Ⓒ z			◧ Ⓒ z	◧	Ⓒ z	◧	◧ Ⓒ z		◧		◧	◧			*ICE* **1221** ⑤⑥ E	◧		• ◧	Ⓐ e	◧	Ⓐ e	◧
0	**München** Hbf ... d.	0453	...	0532	0632	...	0713	0732	0813	0832	0913	0932	1032	...	1132	1232	1332	...	1359	1432	...	1532	1613	1632	1709	173
7	München Pasing ... d.	0500	...	0538	0638	...	0720	0738	0820	0838	0920	0938	1038	...	1138	1238	1338	...	|	1438	...	1538	1620	1638	1715	173
40	Tutzing ... d.	0528	...	0601	0701	...	|	0801	|	0901	|	1001	1101	...	1201	1301	1401	...	1440	1501	...	1601	|	1700	|	180
54	Weilheim (Oberbay) ... d.	0545	...	0612	0712	...	0748	0812	0848	0912	0948	1012	1112	...	1212	1312	1412	...	1451	1512	...	1612	1648	1712	1749	181
75	Murnau ... d.	0604	...	0628	0728	...	0801	0828	0901	0928	1001	1028	1128	...	1228	1328	1428	...	1506	1528	...	1628	1701	1728	1801	182
101	**Garmisch**-Partenk. ... a.	0630	...	0654	0754	...	0824	0854	0924	0954	1024	1054	1154	...	1254	1354	1454	...	1536	1554	...	1654	1724	1754	1824	185
101	**Garmisch**-Partenk. ... d.	0632	0632	...	...	0802	0826	0906	0926	1002	1026	1102	...	1202	1302	1402	1502	...	1538	...	1602	1702	1726	1802	1826	190
118	**Mittenwald** ... a.	0653	0653	...	...	0823	0853	0927	0953	1023	1053	1123	...	1223	1323	1423	1523	...	1603	...	1623	1723	1753	1823	1853	192
118	**Mittenwald** 🏛 ... d.	0655	0655	...	...	0826	...	0936	▬	1026	...	1136c	...	1226	1336c	1426	1536	...	1605	...	1626	1736c	...	1826	...	193
125	Scharnitz 🏛 ... d.	0703	0703	...	...	0834	...	0944	...	1034	...	1144c	...	1234	1344c	1434	1544	...	|	...	1634	1744c	...	1834	...	194
135	Seefeld in Tirol ... d.	0716	0716	...	...	0846	...	0956	1016	1046	...	1156c	...	1246	1356c	1446	1556	1616	1627	...	1646	1756c	...	1846	...	195
160	**Innsbruck** Hbf ... a.	0753	0753	...	...	0923	...	...	1053	1123	...	...	...	1323	...	1523	...	1653	...	...	1723	...	...	1923	...	...

	◧ Ⓐ e	◧									Ⓒ
München Hbf ... d.	1813	1832	...	...	1932	2032	2132	2232	...	2332	2332
München Pasing ... d.	1820	1838	...	...	1938	2038	2138	2238	...	2338	2338
Tutzing ... d.	|	1901	...	...	2001	2101	2201	2301	...	0001	0001
Weilheim (Oberbay) ... d.	1849	1912	...	...	2012	2112	2212	2312	...	0012	0012
Murnau ... d.	1901	1928	...	...	2028	2128	2228	2328	...	0028	0028
Garmisch-Partenk. ... a.	1924	1954	...	...	2054	2154	2254	2354	...	0054	0054
Garmisch-Partenk. ... d.	1926	...	2002	...	2102	2202	2302	0005	...	...	0102
Mittenwald ... a.	1953	...	2023	...	2123	2223	2323	0026	...	...	0123
Mittenwald 🏛 ... d.	▬	...	2026	...	...	...	...	...	...	...	...
Scharnitz 🏛 ... d.	...	...	2034	2133	...	...	...	...	0003	...	...
Seefeld in Tirol ... d.	2016	...	2046	2146	...	...	...	...	0016	...	...
Innsbruck Hbf ... a.	2053	...	2123	2223	...	...	...	...	0053	...	...

	⚒ e	Ⓐ e	Ⓐ e	Ⓒ z	Ⓐ e	Ⓐ e	Ⓒ z	Ⓐ e		
Innsbruck Hbf ... d.	...	...	...	...	...	...	...	...	0638	070
Seefeld in Tirol ... d.	...	...	...	...	...	...	...	...	0715	074
Scharnitz 🏛 ... d.	...	...	...	...	...	...	...	...	0728	075
Mittenwald 🏛 ... a.	...	...	...	...	...	...	...	...	0735	▬
Mittenwald ... d.	...	0507	0530	0536	0603	0634	0634	...	0736	..
Garmisch-Partenkirchen .. a.	...	0528	0551	0557	0630	0700	0700	...	0757	◧
Garmisch-Partenkirchen .. d.	0500	0535	0559	0607	0635	0702	0707	0735	...	080
Murnau ... d.	0524	0554	0626	0632	0654	0728	0732	0758	...	083
Weilheim (Oberbay) ... d.	0541	0610	0646	0649	0711	0746	0749	0812	...	084
Tutzing ... d.	0555	|	0700	0700	|	0800	0800	|	...	090
München Pasing ... a.	0614	0638	0719	0719	0741	0819	0819	0839	...	091
München Hbf ... a.	0621	0646	0726	0726	0748	0826	0826	0846	...	092

	Ⓒ z	◧ Ⓐ e	◧				◧	◧	◧	*ICE* **1222** Ⓒ G				◧	◧ Ⓒ z	◧	Ⓒ z	◧	◧ Ⓒ z					◧		
Innsbruck Hbf ... d.	...	...	0838	0908	...	1038	...	...	1238	1254	...	1438	1508	...	...	1638	...	...	...	1838	1908	...	2008	2038	...	23
Seefeld in Tirol ... d.	...	...	0915	0944	1004	1115	...	1204c	1315	1333	1404c	1515	1544	1604	...	1715	...	1804c	...	1915	1944	2004	2045	2115	...	23
Scharnitz 🏛 ... d.	...	...	0928	...	1016	1128	...	1216c	1328	|	1416c	1528	▬	1616	...	1728	...	1816c	...	1928	▬	2016	2057	2128	...	23
Mittenwald 🏛 ... a.	...	...	0935	...	1025	1135	...	1225c	1335	1353	1425c	1535	...	1625	...	1735	...	1825c	...	1935	...	2025	...	2135	...	..
Mittenwald ... d.	0836	0836	0936	...	1036	1136	...	1236	1336	1403	1436	1536	...	1636	1704	1736	1804	1836	1904	1936	...	2036	...	2136	2236	..
Garmisch-Partenk. ... a.	0857	0900	1000	...	1057	1157	...	1300	1400	1430	1500	1557	◧	1700	1732	1800	1830	1900	1932	1957	◧	2057	...	2157	2257	..
Garmisch-Partenk. ... d.	0905	0907	1005b	...	1107	...	1207	1307	1407	1432	1507	...	1607	1705	1735	1805	1835	1905h	1936	...	2005	2107	...	2207	2307	..
Murnau ... d.	0932	0932	1032	...	1132	...	1231	1332	1432	1509	1532	...	1632	1732	1758	1832	1858	1932	1958	...	2031	2132	...	2232	2332	..
Weilheim (Oberbay) ... d.	0949	0949	1049	...	1149	...	1249	1349	1449	1526	1549	...	1649	1749	1812	1849	1912	1949	2012	...	2049	2149	...	2249	2349	..
Tutzing ... d.	1000	1000	1100	...	1200	...	1300	1400	1500	|	1600	...	1700	1800	|	1900	|	2000	|	...	2100	2200	...	2300	0000	.
München Pasing ... a.	1019	1019	1119	...	1219	...	1318	1419	1519	|	1619	...	1719	1819	1840	1919	1940	2019	2040	...	2119	2219	...	2319	0019	.
München Hbf ... a.	1026	1026	1126	...	1226	...	1326	1426	1526	1611	1626	...	1726	1826	1847	1926	1947	2026	2047	...	2126	2226	...	2326	0026	..

E – ⑤⑥ (also Oct. 2). 🚃12 ✕ Dortmund - Frankfurt - Nürnberg - Seefeld.
G – Ⓒ (not June 9). 🚃12 ✕ Innsbruck - Nürnberg - Frankfurt - Dortmund.
b – 2 minutes later on Ⓐ **e**.
c – ⑥⑦ (also June 10, 20, Aug. 15, Nov. 1).
e – Not June 20, Aug. 15, Nov. 1.
h – 1907 on Ⓒ (also June 20, Aug. 15, Nov. 1).
z – Also June 20, Aug. 15, Nov. 1.
◧ – Conveys on dates in Table **888** 🚃12 Müncher Garmisch - Reutte in Tirol and v.v.

A rack railway operates between Garmisch-Partenkirchen and the Zugspitz mountain: departures at 0815 and hourly to 1415, returning from Bf Zugspitzplatt at 0930 and hourly to 1630. All trains call at Eibsee (30 minutes from Garmisch, 45 minutes from Zugspitzplatt). Service may be suspended in bad weather conditions – please check locally before travelling. Cable cars between Eibsee and Zugspitzgipfel (Eibsee-Seilbahn) and between Zugspitzplatt and Zugspitzgipfel summit (Gletscherbahn). **Operator**: Bayerische Zugspitzbahn AG ✆ + 49 (0) 88 21 79

897 MURNAU - OBERAMMERGAU

RB servic

km		Ⓐ e	⑥	Ⓐ e													
0	**Murnau** ... d.	0512	0548	0600	0648	0742	0842	0942	1042	1142	1234	1334	1442	and	2242	...	2334
12	Bad Kohlgrub ... d.	0530	0606	0619	0706	0800	0900	1000	1100	1200	1252	1352	1500	hourly	2300	...	2352
24	**Oberammergau** ... ♥ a.	0550	0626	0638	0726	0821	0921	1021	1121	1221	1312	1412	1521	until	2321	...	0012

	Ⓐ e	⑥	Ⓐ e													
Oberammergau ... ♥ d.	0507	0543	0556	0643	0738	0838	0938	1038	1138	1229	1329	1438	and	2238	...	2329
Bad Kohlgrub ... d.	0529	0605	0618	0705	0800	0900	1000	1100	1200	1252	1352	1500	hourly	2300	...	2352
Murnau ... a.	0547	0623	0636	0723	0819	0919	1019	1119	1219	1310	1410	1519	until	2319	...	0010

e – Not June 20, Aug. 15, Nov. 1.
♥ – All trains call at Unterammergau (*km* 2 4 – 7 minutes from Oberammergau.

NÜRNBERG and FRANKFURT - HAMBURG 900

km	IMPORTANT: SEE NOTE ✣	ICE	ICE		ICE	ICE		NJ	IC	IC	IC	IC		ICE	NJ	NJ		ICE	ICE	ICE	ICE		ICE
		990	990		1688	1678		40470	478	468	478	468		1686	40420	490		1088	988	672	888		774
		①	①		Ⓐ	①–⑥		🅁	⑥♠	⑦♠	⑥♣	⑦♣		Ⓐ	🅁	🅁		①–⑤	①–⑥		①–⑤		①–⑥
		♥	★		✕	✕♦		♦	K	L	K	L		✕	⊖B	⊖♦		✕	✕	Y✕	⊗✕		✕
	Basel SBB **912** d.	...	...	...	...	...	...	2113	▽	▽	▽	▽	...	...	...	...	...	...	...	...	...	...	...
	Karlsruhe Hbf **912** d.	...	...	...	...	...	...	2304	0021	0021	0021e	0021v	...	...	...	...	...	...	...	...	...	...	...
	Stuttgart Hbf **912** d.	2305p	2305p	...	...	...	...	|	|	|	|	|	...	...	...	...	...	...	...	...	...	...	0502
	Mannheim Hbf **912** d.	2351p	2351p	...	...	...	...	2359	0119	0119	0119	0119	...	...	...	...	...	...	...	...	...	...	0605
	Frankfurt Flughafen Fernbf ✈ **912** d.	0031	0030	...	...	...	...	|	|	|	|	|	...	...	...	...	...	...	...	0534	...	...	0642
	Frankfurt (Main) Hbf ... **850 901 902** d.	0055	0048	...	...	...	...	0054x	0213	0213	0213	0213	...	...	...	...	...	...	0506	0550•	...	...	0658•
	Hanau Hbf **850 901 902** d.	0113	0106	...	...	...	...	|	0239	0239	|	0237z	...	...	...	...	...	...	0521	0607	...	...	|
	München Hbf **904 905** d.	|	|	...	...	...	...	|	|	|	|	|	...	...	2252	...	...	...	|	|	0413	...	|
	Augsburg Hbf **905** d.	|	|	...	...	...	...	|	|	|	|	|	...	...	2335	...	...	...	|	|	|	...	|
0	**Nürnberg** Hbf **920 921** d.	|	|	...	...	...	...	|	|	|	|	|	...	...	0200	0200	...	...	|	|	0532	...	|
102	**Würzburg** Hbf **920 921** d.	|	|	...	...	...	...	|	|	|	|	|	...	...	0300	0300	...	...	|	|	0628	...	|
195	Fulda **850 901 902** d.	0158	|	...	...	...	...	0148	0328	0333	|	|	...	...	|	|	...	...	0604	0647	0704	...	|
285	**Kassel** Wilhelmshöhe **901 902** d.	|	0256	...	...	...	...	|	|	|	0419	0419	...	...	|	|	...	...	0636	0721	0736	...	0821
330	Göttingen **902 903** d.	0325	0348	...	...	...	...	0316	0507	0507	0507	0507	...	0546	0553	0553	...	...	0656	0741	0756	...	0841
430	**Hannover** Hbf **903** a.	0421	0446	...	...	...	...	0604	0614	0614	0614	0614	...	0657	0649	0649	...	...	0754	0834	0856	...	0934
430	**Hannover** Hbf **903** d.	0424	0449	...	0512	0554	...	0607	0617	0617	0617	0617	...	0701	0705	0705	...	0736	0759	0837	0859	...	0937
	Bremen Hbf **813** a.	|	|	...	|	|	...	|	|	|	|	|	...	|	|	|	...	|	|	|	|	...	|
471	Celle **903** d.	|	|	...	0531	0617	...	|	0638	0638	0638	0638	...	0720	|	|	...	|	0820	|	0920	...	|
523	Uelzen **903** d.	|	|	...	0556	0642	...	|	0701	0701	0701	0701	...	0742	|	|	...	|	0842	|	0942	...	|
559	Lüneburg **903** d.	0515	0541	...	0613	0659	...	0717y	0718	0718	0718	0718	...	0758	|	|	...	|	0902	|	0958	...	|
608	**Hamburg** Hbf **903** a.	0551	0615	...	0644	0730h	...	0753	0751	0751	0751	0751	...	0829	0847	0847	...	0858	0934	0954	1030	...	1055
615	**Hamburg** Altona a.	0614	0633	...	0659	...	...	0808	...	...	...	...	...	0844	0904	0904	...	0912	0951	1010	1045	...	1110

IMPORTANT: SEE NOTE ✣	ICE	ICE		ICE	ICE		ICE	ICE		ICE	ICE		ICE	ICE	ICE		ICE	ICE		ICE	ICE	ICE	ICE
	784	784		674	886		772	1682		78	882		770	680	980		76	880		1224	1228	578	588
		①–⑥												⑤–⑦	①–④					Ⓒn	Ⓐt		
	✕	✕		K✕	✕		✕	✕		Z✕	✕		✕	r✕	s✕		Z✕	✕		H✕	H✕	✕	✕
Basel SBB **912** d.	...	...	...	0511b	...	...	...	...	...	0706	...	...	...	...	...	...	0906	...	...	...	...	...	...
Karlsruhe Hbf **912** d.	...	...	...	0651	...	...	...	...	...	0851	...	...	...	...	...	...	1051	...	...	...	...	...	...
Stuttgart Hbf **912** d.	...	...	...	|	...	...	0724	...	...	|	...	...	0924	...	...	...	|	...	...	...	...	1124	...
Mannheim Hbf **912** d.	...	...	...	0716	...	...	0805	...	...	0916	...	...	1005	...	...	...	1116	...	...	...	...	1205	...
Frankfurt Flughafen Fernbf ✈ **912** d.	...	...	...	|	...	...	0842	...	...	|	...	...	1042	...	...	...	|	...	...	...	...	1242	...
Frankfurt (Main) Hbf ... **850 901 902** d.	...	...	...	0758‡	...	...	0858•	...	...	0958‡	...	...	1058•	...	...	...	1158‡	...	...	...	...	1258•	...
Hanau Hbf **850 901 902** d.	...	...	...	|	...	...	|	...	...	|	...	...	|	...	...	...	|	...	...	...	...	|	...
München Hbf **904 905** d.	...	0516	...	|	0616	...	|	0719	...	|	0820	...	|	0840	0919	...	|	1021	...	1055	1055	|	1120
Augsburg Hbf **905** d.	...	|	...	|	|	...	|	|	...	|	|	...	|	0914	|	...	|	|	...	|	|	|	|
Nürnberg Hbf **920 921** d.	0633	0633	...	|	0733	...	|	0832	...	|	0933	...	|	1032	1032	...	|	1133	...	1200	1200	|	1233
Würzburg Hbf **920 921** d.	0728	0728	...	|	0828	...	|	0927	...	|	1028	...	|	1127	1127	...	|	1228	...	1301	1301	|	1328
Fulda **850 901 902** d.	0804	0804	...	|	0904	...	|	1004	...	|	1104	...	|	1204	1204	...	|	1304	...	1333	1333	|	1404
Kassel Wilhelmshöhe **901 902** d.	0836	0836	...	0921	0936	...	1021	1036	...	1121	1136	...	1221	1236	1236	...	1321	1336	...	1401	1401	1421	1436
Göttingen **902 903** d.	0856	0856	...	0941	0956	...	1041	1056	...	1141	1155	...	1241	1256	1256	...	1341	1356	...	...	...	1441	1456
Hannover Hbf **903** a.	0954	0954	...	1034	1056	...	1134	1154	...	1234	1255	...	1334	1354	1354	...	1434	1456	...	...	...	1534	1554
Hannover Hbf **903** d.	0959	0959	...	1037	1059	...	1137	1159	...	1237	1258	...	1337	1359	1359	...	1437	1459	...	...	...	1537	1559
Bremen Hbf **813** a.	|	|	...	|	|	...	|	|	...	|	|	...	|	|	|	...	|	|	...	...	...	|	|
Celle **903** d.	1020	1020	...	|	1120	...	|	1220	...	|	1319	...	|	1420	1420	...	|	1520	...	...	...	|	1620
Uelzen **903** d.	1042	1042	...	|	1143	...	|	1242	...	|	1342	...	|	1442	1442	...	|	1543	...	...	...	|	1642
Lüneburg **903** d.	1058	1058	...	1128	1159	...	|	1259	...	|	1358	...	|	1501	1501	...	|	1600	...	...	...	|	1701
Hamburg Hbf **903** a.	1131	1131	...	1156	1232f	...	1254	1330	...	1354	1429	...	1454	1530	1530	...	1554	1630	...	...	...	1653	1733
Hamburg Altona a.	1146	1146	...	...	1250f	...	1310	1345	...	1409	1445	...	1510	1546	1546	...	1610	1645	...	...	...	1709	1750

IMPORTANT: SEE NOTE ✣	ICE	ICE		ICE	ICE	ICE	ICE	IC	ICE		ICE	ICE	ICE	ICE	ICE		ICE	ICE		ICE	ICE		ICE
	1744	74		788	1742	576	586	2170	72		786	1086	1740	1740	1746		974	574		1084	776		70
					Ⓑ			①–④			A	⑤⑦	⑤G	⑤J	⑦		①–⑤	⑥⑦			Ⓑ		
	T✕	✕♦		✕	✕	✕	✕	m🍷	✕♦		✕	d✕	✕	✕			K✕	✕		✕	N✕		✕♦
Basel SBB **912** d.	...	1106	...	...	...	...	...	...	1306	...	...	...	...	...	...	...	...	...	...	...	...	...	1506
Karlsruhe Hbf **912** d.	...	1251	...	...	...	...	...	...	1451	...	...	...	...	...	...	...	...	...	...	...	...	...	1651
Stuttgart Hbf **912** d.	...	|	...	...	...	1324	...	...	|	...	...	...	...	...	...	...	1524	1524	...	...	...	...	|
Mannheim Hbf **912** d.	...	1316	...	...	...	1405	...	...	1516	...	...	...	...	...	...	...	1605	1605	...	...	...	...	1716
Frankfurt Flughafen Fernbf ✈ **912** d.	...	|	...	...	...	1442	...	...	|	...	...	...	...	...	...	...	1642	1642	...	...	...	...	|
Frankfurt (Main) Hbf ... **850 901 902** d.	...	1358‡	...	...	...	1458•	...	...	1558‡	...	...	...	...	...	...	...	1658	1658•	...	...	1714	...	1758‡
Hanau Hbf **850 901 902** d.	...	|	...	...	...	|	...	...	|	...	...	...	...	...	...	...	|	|	...	...	|	...	|
München Hbf **904 905** d.	...	|	...	1221	...	|	1318c	...	|	...	1338	1421	...	...	...	...	|	|	...	1521	|	...	|
Augsburg Hbf **905** d.	...	|	...	|	...	|	|	...	|	...	1413	|	...	...	...	...	|	|	...	|	|	...	|
Nürnberg Hbf **920 921** d.	...	|	...	1333	...	|	1434	...	|	...	1534	1534	...	...	...	...	|	|	...	1633	|	...	|
Würzburg Hbf **920 921** d.	...	|	...	1428	...	|	1528	...	|	...	1628	1628	...	...	...	...	|	|	...	1728	|	...	|
Fulda **850 901 902** d.	...	|	...	1504	...	|	1604	...	|	...	1704	1704	...	...	...	...	|	|	...	1804	|	...	|
Kassel Wilhelmshöhe **901 902** d.	...	1521	...	1536	...	1621	1636	...	1721	...	1736	1736	...	...	...	...	1821	1821	...	1836	|	...	1921
Göttingen **902 903** d.	...	1541	...	1556	...	1641	1656	...	1741	...	1756	1756	...	...	...	...	1841	1841	...	1856	1901	...	1941
Hannover Hbf **903** a.	...	1634	...	1656	...	1734	1754	...	1834	...	1856	1856	...	...	...	...	1934	1934	...	1954	1959	...	2034
Hannover Hbf **903** d.	1620	1637	...	1659	1720	1737	1759	1820	1837	...	1859	1859	1908	1908	1908	...	1937	1937	...	1959	2001	...	2037
Bremen Hbf **813** a.	|	|	...	|	|	|	|	|	|	...	|	|	|	|	|	...	|	|	...	|	2103	...	|
Celle **903** d.	|	|	...	1720	|	|	1820	|	|	...	1920	1920	1935	1935	1935	...	|	|	...	2020	...	...	|
Uelzen **903** d.	|	|	...	1742	|	|	1842	|	|	...	1942	1942	|	|	|	...	|	|	...	2042	...	...	|
Lüneburg **903** d.	|	|	...	1758	|	|	1859	|	|	...	1958	1958	|	2013	2013	...	2028	2028	...	2059	...	...	|
Hamburg Hbf **903** a.	1737j	1753	...	1829	1836	1853	1930	1935	1954	...	2030	2030	2039	2047	2049	...	2057	2057	...	2130	...	...	2154
Hamburg Altona a.	...	...	...	1845	1851	1909	1946	1951	2010	...	2045	2046	2101	2104	2109	...	...	2114	...	2145	...	...	2211

– NOTES (LISTED BY TRAIN NUMBER)

2 – [12] and ✕ Chur - Zürich - Basel - Hamburg.
– [12] and ✕ Zürich - Basel - Hamburg - Kiel.
0 – 1, 2 cl., 2 cl. and [2] Wien - Passau - Nürnberg - Hamburg. Journeys from Wien via Passau are subject to alteration July 15–24.
78 – [12] and ✕ Hannover - Hamburg - Stralsund (- Ostseebad Binz until Oct. 5).
470 – 1, 2 cl., 2 cl. and [2] Zürich (d. 2000) - Basel - Frankfurt - Hamburg. On the mornings June 29 - Oct. 27 departs Frankfurt Süd 0047, does not call at Fulda, departs Göttingen 0337 and then as shown.

- ①②③④⑥ (not June 15, 22). On June 20 departs München 1420, not calling at Augsburg.
- 1, 2 cl., 2 cl. and [2] Innsbruck - München - Hamburg. Does not call at Augsburg June 14–16, 21–23. On ⑥⑦ July 27 - Sept. 1 departs München 2307, Augsburg 2357.
- ⑤ from Aug. 2 (also Oct. 2).
- To Köln via Paderborn (Table **805**).
- Until July 26.
- To Kiel (Table **820**).
- Continues to Flensburg (a. 1000).
- To Oldenburg (Table **813**).
- To Stralsund (Table **830**).
- From Wiesbaden (Table **911**).
- From Zürich (Table **510**).

- ⑥⑦ only. Basel **Badischer Bf**.
- 1316 until June 23.
- Also June 15, 22.
- 0027 July 20 - Aug. 10; 0044 Aug. 17 - Sept. 7.
- On ⑤ (also Oct. 2; not Oct. 4) terminates at Hamburg **Harburg** (a. 1221).

h – On ①–⑤ June 11 - July 26 calls at Hamburg Harburg (not Hamburg Hbf).
j – June 11 - July 28 calls at Hamburg Bergedorf (not Hamburg Hbf).
m – Not Oct. 2, 3.
n – Also June 20.
p – Previous day.
r – Also June 20, Oct. 3.
s – Not June 20, Oct. 3.
t – Not June 20.
v – 0044 July 21 - Sept. 8.
x – Frankfurt (Main) **Süd**.
y – 3–4 minutes later on ⑥⑦.
z – From Aug. 11.

♥ – ① Nov. 4 - Dec. 9 (also June 11, 17, 24).
★ – ① July 1 - Oct. 28.
♠ – To June 23 and from Nov. 2.
♣ – June 29 - Oct. 27.
• – On ⑥⑦ Aug. 10 - Sept. 29 calls at Frankfurt (Main) **Süd** (not Hbf).
‡ – On ⑥⑦ Aug. 10 - Sept. 8, daily Sept. 14 - Oct. 20, calls at Frankfurt (Main) **Süd** (not Hbf).
⊗ – Departs München 0407 on ① July 29 - Sept. 2; departs Nürnberg 0525 on ① Aug. 19 - Sept. 2, Oct. 3, 31.
⊖ – On the mornings of June 29 - Aug. 11 departs Göttingen 0604, arrives Hannover 0702. On the mornings of ⑥⑦ Aug. 17 - Oct. 27 Göttingen d. 0634, Hannover a. 0749, d. 0755, Hamburg Hbf a. 1006, Altona a. 1026.
▽ – Starts from Basel Badischer Bahnhof (d. 2217 the previous day, Table **912**).
✣ – Please refer to the shaded engineering work panel on page 369 for details of various alterations affecting services in this table.

900 NÜRNBERG and FRANKFURT - HAMBURG

IMPORTANT: SEE NOTE ✣	ICE 90 ✕♦		ICE 572 ✕	ICE 582 ✕		ICE 376 ⑤⑦ ✕♦	ICE 782 ⑦ ✕	ICE 592 ✕	ICE 782 ①-⑥ ✕		ICE 570 ⑦ ✕		ICE 580 Ⓑ ✕	ICE 580 ⑦ ✕	ICE 292 ⑦ ✕♦	ICE 580 ⑦	ICE 1172 ⑥ Z✕	ICE 272 ①-⑤ Z✕		ICE 780 ⑦ ✕	ICE 590 ⑦ ✕		
Basel SBB **912** 🚌 d.	...	...	...	...	...	1706	...	...	...	...	...	...	...	...	1813	...	1813	1813	...	...	...	...	...
Karlsruhe Hbf **912** d.	...	...	...	...	...	1851	...	...	...	...	...	...	...	...	2000	...	2000	2000	...	...	...	...	...
Stuttgart Hbf **912** d.	...	...	1724	...	...	|	...	1851	...	...	1924	...	...	...	|	...	|	|	...	...	2051	...	...
Mannheim Hbf **912** d.	...	...	1805	...	...	1916	...	1932	...	...	2005	...	...	...	2032	...	2032	2032	...	...	2132	...	...
Frankfurt Flughafen Fernbf ✈ **912** d.	...	...	1842	...	...	|	...	|	...	...	2042	...	...	...	|	...	|	|	...	...	|	...	...
Frankfurt (Main) Hbf ... **850 901 902** d.	...	...	1858•	...	...	1958◊	...	2014	...	...	2058•	...	...	...	2114	...	2114	2114	...	...	2217	...	...
Hanau Hbf **850 901 902** d.	...	...	|	...	...	|	...	|	...	...	|	...	...	...	2130	...	2130	2130	...	...	2234	...	...
München Hbf **904 905** d.	...	...	|	1719	...	|	1819	|	1819	...	|	...	1853	1853	|	...	|	|	...	2021	|	...	...
Augsburg Hbf **905** d.	...	...	|	|	...	|	|	|	|	...	|	...	1930	1930	|	...	|	|	...	|	|	...	...
Nürnberg Hbf **920 921** d.	1732	...	|	1833	...	|	1933	|	1933	...	|	...	|	|	|	...	|	|	...	2134	|	...	...
Würzburg Hbf **920 921** d.	1826	...	|	1928	...	|	2028	|	2028	...	|	...	2130	2130	|	...	|	|	...	2228	|	...	...
Fulda **850 901 902** d.	1904	...	|	2004	...	|	2105	2107	2111	...	|	...	2204	2204	2212	←	2212	2212	...	2304	2319	...	...
Kassel Wilhelmshöhe **901 902** d.	1939	...	2021	2036	...	2121	2137	...	2144	...	2221	...	2235	2235	2245	2248	2245	2245	...	2339	2353	...	...
Göttingen **902 903** d.	|	...	2041	2056	...	2141	2204	...	2204	...	2241	...	...	→	2304	2313	2306	2306	...	...	0047	...	...
Hannover Hbf **903** a.	2055	...	2134	2154	...	2234	2304	...	2304	...	2334	...	...	...	...	0014	0002	0002	...	...	0146	...	...
Hannover Hbf **903** d.	2058	...	2137	2159	...	2237	2308	...	2308	...	2337	...	...	...	...	0018	0005	0005	...	...	0149	...	...
Bremen Hbf **813** a.	|	...	|	|	...	|	|	...	|	...	|	...	...	...	...	|	|	|	...	...	|	...	...
Celle **903** d.	2119	...	|	2220	...	2257	2328	...	2328	...	|	...	...	...	...	0038	|	0026	...	...	|	...	...
Uelzen **903** d.	2142	...	|	2242	...	2320	2352	...	2352	...	|	...	...	...	...	0102	0050	0050	...	...	|	...	...
Lüneburg **903** d.	2158	...	|	2259	...	2338	0010	...	0010	...	0029	...	...	...	...	0119	0106	0106	...	...	|	...	...
Hamburg Hbf **903** a.	2229	...	2254	2331	...	0011	0041	...	0041	...	0100	...	...	...	...	0151	0136	0138	...	...	0311	...	...
Hamburg Altona a.	2245	...	2310	2345	...	0026	...	...	...	...	0117	...	...	...	...	0206	0151	0200	...	...	0327	...	...

IMPORTANT: SEE NOTE ✣	ICE 591 ①-⑤ ✕	ICE 591 ①-⑥ ✕	ICE 781 ①g B✕	ICE 781 ①-⑥ ✕		ICE 581 ✕		ICE 571 ①-⑥ ✕		ICE 1097 ①-⑤ D✕	ICE 783 ①-⑥ ✕		ICE 71 ✕♦	IC 2175 Ⓐt 🍷	ICE 583 ✕		ICE 973 ①-⑥ K✕	ICE 573 ⑦ ✕	ICE 1743 ①-⑤ ✕	ICE 91 ✕♦		ICE 1173 ⑦ Z✕	ICE 73 ①- ✕♦
Hamburg Altona d.	0304	...	...	...	...	0412	...	0440	...	0500	0505	...	0546	0603	0609	...	...	0646	0706	0713	...	0747	...
Hamburg Hbf **903** d.	0320	...	...	...	...	0428	...	0455	...	0516	0524	...	0601	0618	0625	...	0701	0701	0722	0729	...	0802	080
Lüneburg **903** d.	0351	...	...	...	...	0459	...	0526	...	0548	0555	...	|	0648	0655	...	|	|	|	0801	...	|	|
Uelzen **903** d.	0408	...	...	...	...	0515	...	0542	...	|	0615	...	|	|	0715	...	|	|	|	0817	...	|	|
Celle **903** d.	0437	...	...	...	...	0539	...	|	...	|	0638	...	|	|	0738	...	|	|	|	0840	...	|	|
Bremen Hbf **813** d.	|	...	...	...	...	|	...	|	...	|	|	...	|	|	|	...	|	|	|	|	...	|	|
Hannover Hbf **903** a.	0456	...	...	...	...	0558	...	0621	...	0646	0658	...	0721	0736	0757	...	0821	0821	0838	0859	...	0921	092
Hannover Hbf **903** d.	0459	0459	...	...	...	0601	...	0624	...	0652	0701	...	0724	...	0804	...	0824	0824	...	0902	...	0924	092
Göttingen **902 903** d.	0555	0555	0545	...	...	0702	...	0718	...	0752	0802	...	0818	...	0902	...	0918	0918	...	1003	...	1018	101
Kassel Wilhelmshöhe **901 902** d.	0616	0616	0622	0622	...	0723	...	0739	...	|	0823	...	0839	...	0923	...	0939	0939	...	1025	...	1039	103
Fulda **850 901 902** d.	0648	0648	0656	0656	...	0756	...	|	...	|	0856	...	|	...	0956	...	|	|	...	1057	...	|	|
Würzburg Hbf **920 921** d.	|	|	0730	0730	...	0832	...	|	...	|	0931	...	|	...	1032	...	|	|	...	1135	...	|	|
Nürnberg Hbf **920 921** a.	|	|	0824	0824	...	0925	...	|	...	|	1023	...	|	...	1125	...	|	|	...	1227	...	|	|
Augsburg Hbf **905** a.	|	|	|	|	...	|	...	|	...	|	|	...	|	...	|	...	|	|	...	...	...	|	|
München Hbf **904 905** a.	|	|	0938	0938	...	1038	...	|	...	|	1138	...	|	...	1238	...	|	|	...	...	...	|	|
Hanau Hbf **850 901 902** d.	0728	0728	...	...	...	...	...	|	...	|	...	...	|	...	...	...	|	|	...	...	...	|	|
Frankfurt (Main) Hbf ... **850 901 902** a.	0744	0744	...	...	...	...	...	0900•	...	0928c	...	...	1000‡	...	...	...	1100•	1100•	...	...	...	1200‡	1200
Frankfurt Flughafen Fernbf ✈ **912** a.	|	|	...	...	...	...	...	0917	...	...	...	...	|	...	...	...	1117	1117	...	...	...	|	|
Mannheim Hbf **912** a.	0827	0827	...	...	...	...	...	0954	...	...	...	...	1044	...	...	...	1154	1154	...	...	...	1244	124
Stuttgart Hbf **912** a.	0908	0908	...	...	...	...	...	1035	...	...	...	...	|	...	...	...	1235	1235	...	...	...	|	|
Karlsruhe Hbf **912** a.	...	...	...	...	...	...	...	...	...	...	...	...	1108	...	...	...	...	...	...	...	...	1308	130
Basel SBB **912** a.	...	...	...	...	...	...	...	...	...	...	...	...	1256	...	...	...	...	...	...	...	...	1456	145

IMPORTANT: SEE NOTE ✣	ICE 1745 ①-⑥ T✕		ICE 1085 ⑥⑦ ✕	ICE 585 ①-⑤ ✕	ICE 575 ✕	ICE 1223 ✕♦		ICE 787 ✕		ICE 75 ①-⑥ ✕♦	ICE 1175 ⑦ ✕♦		ICE 587 ✕	ICE 577 ✕		ICE 789 ✕	ICE 77 ①-⑤ Z✕	ICE 1177 ⑥⑦ K✕		ICE 1671 T✕	ICE 1689 ✕		ICE 579 ✕
Hamburg Altona d.	...	...	0807	0807	0846	...	...	0910	...	0946	...	...	1012	1046	...	1113	1146	...	...	...	1212	...	124
Hamburg Hbf **903** d.	0824h	...	0828	0828	0901	...	...	0928	...	1001	1001	...	1028	1101	...	1128	1201	1201	...	1224h	1228	...	130
Lüneburg **903** d.	|	...	0859	0859	|	...	...	0959	...	|	|	...	1059	|	...	1159	|	|	...	|	1259	...	|
Uelzen **903** d.	|	...	0916	0916	|	...	...	1015	...	|	|	...	1115	|	...	1215	|	|	...	|	1315	...	|
Celle **903** d.	|	...	0939	0939	|	...	...	1038	...	|	|	...	1138	|	...	1238	|	|	...	|	1338	...	|
Bremen Hbf **813** d.	|	...	|	|	|	...	...	|	...	|	|	...	|	|	...	|	|	|	...	|	|	...	|
Hannover Hbf **903** a.	0939	...	0958	0958	1021	...	...	1058	...	1121	1121	...	1157	1221	...	1258	1321	1321	...	1338	1357	...	142
Hannover Hbf **903** d.	...	...	1004	1004	1024	...	...	1101	...	1124	1124	...	1204	1224	...	1301	1324	1324	...	...	1404	...	142
Göttingen **902 903** d.	...	...	1102	1102	1118	...	...	1202	...	1218	1218	...	1302	1318	...	1402	1418	1418	...	...	1502	...	151
Kassel Wilhelmshöhe **901 902** d.	...	...	1123	1123	1139	1158	...	1223	...	1239	1239	...	1323	1339	...	1424	1439	1439	...	...	1524	...	153
Fulda **850 901 902** d.	...	...	1156	1156	|	1228	...	1256	...	|	|	...	1356	|	...	1456	|	|	...	...	1557	...	|
Würzburg Hbf **920 921** d.	...	...	1232	1232	|	1313	...	1331	...	|	|	...	1432	|	...	1531	|	|	...	...	1634	...	|
Nürnberg Hbf **920 921** a.	...	...	1325	1325	|	1404	...	1424	...	|	|	...	1525	|	...	1624	|	|	...	...	1728	...	|
Augsburg Hbf **905** a.	...	...	|	|	|	|	...	|	...	|	|	...	1641	|	...	|	|	|	...	...	|	...	|
München Hbf **904 905** a.	...	...	1438	1441	|	1509	...	1539	...	|	|	...	1715	|	...	1741	|	|	...	...	1842	...	|
Hanau Hbf **850 901 902** d.	...	...	...	...	|	...	...	...	...	|	|	...	...	|	...	...	|	|	...	...	...	...	|
Frankfurt (Main) Hbf ... **850 901 902** a.	...	...	...	...	1300•	...	...	...	...	1400‡	1400‡	...	...	1500•	...	...	1600‡	1600‡	...	...	...	...	170
Frankfurt Flughafen Fernbf ✈ **912** a.	...	...	...	...	1317	...	...	...	...	|	|	...	...	1517	...	...	|	|	...	...	...	...	171
Mannheim Hbf **912** a.	...	...	...	...	1354	...	...	...	...	1444	1444	...	...	1554	...	...	1644	1644	...	...	...	...	175
Stuttgart Hbf **912** a.	...	...	...	...	1435	...	...	...	...	|	|	...	...	1635	...	...	|	|	...	...	...	...	183
Karlsruhe Hbf **912** a.	...	...	...	...	...	...	...	...	...	1508	1508	...	...	...	...	...	1708	1708	...	...	...	...	...
Basel SBB **912** a.	...	...	...	...	...	...	...	...	...	1656	1656	...	...	...	...	...	1856	1856	...	...	...	...	...

♦ – **NOTES** (LISTED BY TRAIN NUMBER)

71/5 – 🚃12 and ✕ Hamburg - Basel - Zürich - Chur.
73 – 🚃12 and ✕ Kiel - Hamburg - Basel - Zürich.
90 – 🚃12 and ✕ Wien - Linz - Passau - Regensburg - Hamburg.
91 – 🚃12 and ✕ Hamburg - Regensburg - Passau - Linz - Wien.
292 – 🚃12 and ✕ Zürich - Basel - Berlin.
376 – ⑤⑦ (also Oct. 2; not Oct. 4). 🚃12 and ✕ Interlaken - Basel - Hamburg.
1175 – 🚃12 and ✕ Kiel - Hamburg - Basel - Zürich.
1223 – 🚃12 and ✕ Köln - Paderborn - Kassel - München.

B – From Berlin (Table 902).
D – Continues to Darmstadt Hbf until Oct. 25 (a. 0952).
K – From Kiel (Table 820).
T – From Stralsund (Table 830).
Z – From / to Zürich (Table 510).

c – 0936 from Oct. 28.
g – Also June 11.
h – June 11 - July 28 calls at Hamburg Harburg (not Hamburg Hbf).
t – Not Oct. 4.

• – On ⑥⑦ Aug. 10 - Sept. 29 calls at Frankfurt (Main) **Süd** (not Hbf).
‡ – On ⑥⑦ Aug. 10 - Sept. 8 (daily Sept. 14 - Oct. 20) calls at Frankfurt (Main) **Süd** (not Hbf).
◊ – On ⑦ Aug. 11 - Oct. 20 (also Sept. 20, 27, Oct. 2, 11, 18) calls at Frankfurt (Main) **Süd** (not Hbf).
✣ – Please refer to the shaded engineering work panel on page 369 for details of various alterations affecting services in this table.

vice from June 11 — HAMBURG - FRANKFURT and NÜRNBERG — 900

IMPORTANT: SEE NOTE ❖	ICE 881	ICE 79		ICE 681	ICE 771		ICE 1585 Ⓑ	ICE 1585 Y		ICE 883	ICE 1171		ICE 1749	ICE 683	ICE 773		ICE 1657 ①–⑤	ICE 885		ICE 273	ICE 273 ⑤⑥		ICE 1677 Ⓑ
	✕	Z✕		✕	✕		✕	✕		✕	K✕		O✕	✕	✕		✕	✕		✕	✕		T✕
burg Altona d.	1313	1346	...	1413	1446	...	1506	1506	...	1513	...	...	...	1612	1645	...	1705	1712	...	1746	1746	...	...
burg Hbf 903 d.	1328	1401	...	1428	1501	...	1524	1524	...	1528	1601	...	1624h	1628	1701	...	1724	1728	...	1801	1801	...	1824g
burg 903 d.	1359	1429	...	1459	|	...	|	|	...	1558	|	...	|	1659	|	...	|	1759	...	|	|	...	|
en 903 d.	1415	|	...	1515	|	...	|	|	...	1617	|	...	|	1715	|	...	|	1818	...	|	|	...	|
903 d.	1438	|	...	|	|	...	|	|	...	1640	|	...	|	1738	|	...	|	1840	...	|	|	...	|
emen Hbf 813 d.	|	|	...	|	|	...	|	|	...	|	|	...	|	|	|	...	|	|	...	|	|	...	|
nover Hbf 903 a.	1458	1521	...	1558	1621	...	1638	1638	...	1659	1721	...	1738	1757	1821	...	1838	1859	...	1921	1921	...	1938
nover Hbf 903 d.	1501	1524	...	1604	1624	...	...	1653	...	1702	1724	...	...	1804	1824	...	...	1902	...	1924	1924	...	...
ngen 902 903 d.	1602	1618	...	1702	1718	...	...	1814	...	1802	1818	...	...	1902	1918	...	...	2002	...	2018	2018	...	...
sel Wilhelmshöhe 901 902 d.	1623	1639	...	1724	1739	...	...	...	...	1823	1839	...	...	1923	1939	...	...	2023	...	2039	2039	...	...
a 850 901 902 d.	1656	|	...	1757	|	...	...	...	...	1856	|	...	...	1956	|	...	...	2056	...	|	|	...	...
ürzburg Hbf 920 921 d.	1731	|	...	1835	|	...	...	...	...	1931	|	...	...	2032	|	...	...	2131	...	|	|	...	...
rnberg Hbf 920 921 a.	1824	|	...	1928	|	...	...	...	...	2024	|	...	...	2125	|	...	...	2224	...	|	|	...	...
Augsburg Hbf 905 a.	|	|	...	|	|	...	...	...	...	|	|	...	...	|	|	...	...	|	...	|	|	...	...
ünchen Hbf 904 905 a.	1942	|	...	2042	|	...	...	...	...	2141	|	...	...	2238	|	...	...	2340t	...	|	|	...	...
au Hbf 850 901 902 d.	...	|	...	...	|	...	...	...	...	...	|	...	...	...	|	...	...	...	...	|	|	...	...
kfurt (Main) Hbf ... 850 901 902 a.	...	1800‡	...	...	1900•	...	...	...	...	...	2000‡	...	...	...	2100•	...	...	...	...	2200‡	2200‡	...	...
ankfurt Flughafen Fernbf ✈ 912 a.	...	|	...	...	1917	...	...	...	...	...	|	...	...	...	2117	...	...	...	...	|	|	...	...
annheim Hbf 912 a.	...	1844	...	...	1954	...	...	...	...	...	2044	...	...	...	2154	...	...	...	...	2244	2244	...	...
Stuttgart Hbf 912 a.	...	|	...	...	2035	...	...	...	...	...	|	...	...	...	2250	...	...	...	...	|	|	...	...
rlsruhe Hbf 912 a.	...	1908	...	...	...	...	...	...	...	...	2109	...	...	...	...	...	...	...	...	2309	2309	...	...
sel SBB 912 a.	...	2056	...	...	...	...	...	...	...	...	2302c	...	...	...	...	...	...	...	...	...	0102	...	...

IMPORTANT: SEE NOTE ❖	ICE 685	ICE 685 W		ICE 775 ⑤⑦		ICE 887		ICE 1679 ⑦	NJ 491 Ⓡ G	NJ 40491 Ⓡ G	NJ 491 Ⓡ F	NJ 40491 Ⓡ F	ICE 1679 ⑦		NJ 401 Ⓡ J	NJ 401 Ⓡ H	IC 479 ⑥ S	IC 479 P	IC 469 ⑤ S	IC 469 ⑤ R		ICE 1271 ⑦★	ICE 1271 ①♥
	✕	✕		d✕		N✕		T✕	B	A	B	A	T✕		D	D	e⊡	⊡	⊙	⊙		C	C
burg Altona d.	1811	1811	...	1846	...	1906	...	...	2014	2014	2014	2014	...	...	2045	2045	...	...	...	...	...	2328	0030
burg Hbf 903 d.	1828	1828	...	1901	...	1927	...	2024h	2029	2029	2029	2029	...	...	2102	2102	2148	2148	2159	2159	...	2345	0045
burg 903 d.	1859	1859	...	|	...	1958	...	2051	|	|	|	|	...	...	2150	2150	2224	2224	2224	2224	...	|	|
en 903 d.	1915	1915	...	|	...	2016	...	2107	|	|	|	|	←	...	|	|	2247	2247	2247	2247	...	|	|
903 d.	1938	1938	...	|	...	2038	...	2132	|	|	|	|	2137	...	|	|	2330	2330	2330	2330	...	|	|
emen Hbf 813 d.	|	|	...	|	...	|	...	→	|	|	|	|	|	...	|	|	|	|	|	|	...	|	|
nover Hbf 903 a.	1957	1957	...	2021	...	2058	...	...	2154	2154	2154	2154	2159	...	2318	2318	2353	2353	2350	2350	...	0111	0207
nover Hbf 903 d.	2004	2004	...	2024	...	2101	...	...	2157	2157	2157	2157	...	...	2326	2326	0004	0004	0004	0004	...	0114	0210
ngen 902 903 d.	2102	2102	...	2118	...	2202	...	...	2259	2259	2259	2259	...	...	0126	0126	0120	0108	0120	0111	...	|	0307
sel Wilhelmshöhe 901 902 d.	2123	2123	...	2139	...	2223	...	...	|	|	|	|	...	...	|	|	|	0159	|	|	...	0333	|
a 850 901 902 d.	2156	2156	...	|	...	2256	...	...	|	|	|	|	...	...	0256	|	0249	|	0249	|	...	|	0433
ürzburg Hbf 920 921 d.	2231	2231	...	|	...	|	...	...	0134	0134	0255	0255	...	...	|	|	|	|	|	|	...	|	|
rnberg Hbf 920 921 a.	2326	2326	...	|	...	|	...	...	0232	0232	0351	0351	...	...	|	|	|	|	|	|	...	|	|
Augsburg Hbf 905 a.	...	|	...	|	...	|	...	...	...	0626	...	0626	...	...	|	|	|	|	|	|	...	|	|
ünchen Hbf 904 905 a.	...	0043v	...	|	...	|	...	...	...	0709	...	0709	...	...	|	|	|	|	|	|	...	|	|
au Hbf 850 901 902 d.	...	...	...	|	...	|	...	...	...	...	...	...	...	...	|	|	0333	0350	0333	0350	...	|	0520
kfurt (Main) Hbf ... 850 901 902 a.	...	...	...	2300	...	2352	...	...	...	...	...	...	...	...	0359x	0419x	0400	0406	0400	0406	...	0540	0537
ankfurt Flughafen Fernbf ✈ 912 a.	...	...	...	...	...	0024	...	...	...	...	...	...	...	...	|	|	|	|	|	|	...	|	|
annheim Hbf 912 a.	...	...	...	...	...	...	...	...	...	...	...	...	...	...	0440	0458	0507	0507	0507	0507	...	0625	0625
Stuttgart Hbf 912 a.	...	...	...	...	...	...	...	...	...	...	...	...	...	...	|	|	|	|	|	|	...	|	|
rlsruhe Hbf 912 a.	...	...	...	...	...	...	...	...	...	...	...	...	...	...	0507	0530	0549	0549	0549	0549	...	0656	0656
sel SBB 912 a.	...	...	...	...	...	...	...	...	...	...	...	...	...	...	0720	0752	0738b	0738b	0738b	0738b	...	0847	0847

🛏 1, 2 cl., ▬ 2 cl. and (2) Hamburg - München - Innsbruck. On the mornings ①–⑤ to July 26 calls at München **Ost** (a. 0720; not calling at München Hbf). On the mornings of ⑥⑦ to June 23 does not call at Augsburg.
🛏 1, 2 cl., ▬ 2 cl. and (2) Hamburg - Passau - Wien.
(12) Hamburg - Basel - Zürich - Chur. ✕ Frankfurt - Chur.
🛏 1, 2 cl., ▬ 2 cl. and (2) Hamburg - Basel - Zürich.
Aug. 11 - Oct. 27.
To Aug. 10 and from Oct. 28.
June 28 - Oct. 26.
To June 27 and from Oct. 27.
From Kiel (Table **820**).
To Wiesbaden (Table **911**).
From Stralsund (Table **830**), also Ostseebad Binz on dates in Table **845**.
⑤⑥ June 28 - Sept. 14; ⑥ Sept. 21 - Oct. 26.
⑤ Sept. 20 - Oct. 25.

S – To June 22 and from Nov. 1.
T – From Stralsund (Table **830**).
W – ④⑤⑦ (also June 19, Oct. 2; not Sept. 8, 15, 22, 29, Oct. 6, 13, 20, 27).
Y – ①②③④⑦ (not Oct. 2).
Z – To Zürich (Table **510**).

b – Basel **Badischer Bahnhof**.
c – ⑥⑦ only.
d – Also Oct. 2; not Oct. 4.
e – Not Dec. 7, 14.
g – June 11 - July 28 calls at Hamburg Bergedorf (d. 1807; not Hamburg Hbf).
h – June 11 - July 28 calls at Hamburg Harburg (not Hamburg Hbf).
t – 30 minutes later on ⑥⑦ July 27 - Sept. 1.
v – 0111 on the mornings of ① July 29 - Sept. 2.

x – Frankfurt (Main) **Süd**.

★ – ⑦ June 30 - Oct. 20.
♥ – ① from Oct. 28 (also June 11, 17, 24).
⊡ – From Kiel Hbf (d. 2014).
⊙ – From Flensburg (d. 2003).
• – On ⑥⑦ Aug. 10 - Sept. 29 calls at Frankfurt (Main) **Süd** (not Hbf), departing up to 6 minutes earlier.
‡ – On ⑥⑦ Aug. 10 - Sept. 8 (daily Sept. 14 - Oct. 20) calls at Frankfurt (Main) **Süd** (not Hbf), departing up to 8 minutes earlier.
❖ – Please refer to the shaded engineering work panel on page 369 for details of various alterations affecting services in this table.

/RB services — Local services FRANKFURT - FULDA - KASSEL — *Service from June 11* — 901

r *ICE / IC* services: Table **850** for Bebra - Kassel Wilhelmshöhe and v.v., also Frankfurt - Fulda - Bad Hersfeld and v.v. Tables **900 / 902** for Frankfurt - Fulda - Kassel Wilhelmshöhe and v.v.

							A	
Frankfurt (Main) Hbf. 921 ⊗ d.	0520	0626	0726		2126	2226	2326v
Frankfurt (Main) Süd ... 921 d.	0525	0633	0733	and	2133	2233	2333
Offenbach (Main) Hbf .... 921 d.	0530	0638	0738	hourly	2138	2238	2338
Hanau Hbf 921 d.	0540	0647	0748	until	2148	2248	2348
Fulda a.	0641	0749	0849		2249	2349	0049

		ⒶrB	†z	⚒r	ⒶrB							
Fulda d.	0401	0436	0507	0515	0600	0607	0707	0804	0904		2204	2311
Hanau Hbf 921 d.	0500	0539	0609	0616	0655	0709	0809	0909	1009	and	2309	0012
Offenbach (Main) Hbf . 921 d.	0509	0548	0617	0624	|	0717	0817	0921t	1017	hourly	2317	0020
Frankfurt Main) Süd .. 921 d.	0515	0553	0623	0630	0710	0723	0823	0927t	1023	until	2323	0026
Frankfurt (Main) Hbf .. 921 a.	0520	0558	0628	0636	0716	0728	0828	0932t	1028		2328	0031

FULDA - KASSEL. Operated by CANTUS Verkehrsgesellschaft (except trains marked with note **B**). 2nd class only. **WARNING!** Timings may vary Aug. 12 - Oct. 27 (see note △).

	Ⓐrn	Ⓐr		Ⓐr	Ⓒzg												D	⑤⑦j				g	h	ⒶfB
Fulda d.	...	0548	0616x	0644	0655	0719x	0819	0919	1020	1119	1219	1319	1419	1519	1619	1719	1819	1819	1919	2019	2122	2221	2301p	2356
Bad Hersfeld d.	0505	0616	0644	0714	0721	0747	0847	0947	1048	1147	1247	1347	1447	1547	1647	1747	1847	1847	1947	2047	2150	2250	2329	0027
Bebra d.	0520	0627	0657	0727	0731	0758	0858	0958	1058	1158	1258	1358	1458	1558	1658	1758	1857	1906k	1958	2058	2201	2301	2342	0041
Rotenburg (Fulda) d.	0526	0633	0703	0733	...	0804	0904	1004	1104	1204	1304	1404	1504	1604	1704	1804	1903	1912	2004	2104	2206	...	2348	...
Melsungen d.	0545	0653	0723	0753	...	0824	0924	1024	1124	1224	1324	1424	1524	1624	1724	1824	1923	1930	2024	2124	2225	...	0006	...
Kassel Wilhelmshöhe 804/6 d.	0611	0712	0742	0813	...	0843	0942	1042	1142	1242	1342	1442	1542	1642	1742	1842	1942	1949	2042	2146	2251	...	0033	...
Kassel Hbf 804/6 a.	0616	0718	0748	0818	...	0849y	0948	1048y	1148	1248y	1348	1448y	1548	1648y	1748	1848y	1948	1954	2048y	2150	2256	...	0037	...

	p	ⒶfB	ⒶrB	⚒r	Ⓒz	Ⓐr		g	†z	⚒r															
sel Hbf 804/6 d.	...	...	...	0506	0605	0626	0709	...	0806	0810	0910y	1010	1110y	1210	1310y	1410	1510y	1610	1710y	1810	1910y	2010	2110y	2210	2310
sel Wilhelmshöhe 804/6 d.	...	...	...	0510	0614	0630	0714	...	0814	0814	0914	1014	1115	1214	1314	1414	1514	1614	1715	1814	1914	2014	2115	2214	2316
ungen d.	...	...	...	0529	0634	0648	0733	...	0834	0834	0934	1034	1134	1234	1334	1434	1534	1634	1734	1834	1933	2034	2133	2233	2336
nburg (Fulda) d.	...	...	...	0549	0652	0708	0752	...	0853	0853	0952	1052	1152	1252	1352	1453	1552	1652	1752	1852	1951	2052	2151	2252	2355
a d.	0315	0359	0522	0558	0658	0716	0800	0820	0859	0859	0958	1058	1158	1258	1358	1459	1558	1658	1758	1859	1958	2058	2159	2303	0002
Hersfeld d.	0325	0408	0531	0608	0709	0725	0811	0829	0909	0909	1009	1109	1209	1309	1408	1509	1609	1709	1808	1909	2008	2109	2209	2315	0012
a a.	0354	0435	0558	0637e	0737	0753	...	0857	0937	0937	1037	1137	1237	1337	1438	1537	1637	1737	1838	1937	2037	2137	2237	...	...

To Bebra on Ⓐ (not June 20, Aug. 5 - Oct. 25).
(12) Bebra - Fulda - Frankfurt and v.v.
①②③④⑥ (not June 10, 19, 20, Oct. 2, 3, 31).
Not ⑥ Aug. 17 - Oct. 26.
Not June 20, Aug. 5 - Oct. 25.
To / from Göttingen (Table **908**).

h – Runs 8 minutes later on † (also June 20).
j – Also June 10, 19, 20, Oct. 2, 3, 31.
k – Arrives 1855.
n – Not July 1 - Aug. 9.
p – Not Aug. 12 - Oct. 27.
r – Not June 20.

t – 4 minutes earlier on Ⓒ (daily from Oct. 26).
v – 2324 July 29 - Oct. 17.
x – Not Ⓒ Aug. 17 - Oct. 27.
y – Not Sept. 28 - Oct. 27.
z – Also June 20.

⊗ – Frankfurt departures 0926 - 2126 are 2 minutes **earlier** on ⑥⑦ Aug. 10 - Sept. 29.
△ – Aug. 12 - Oct. 27 certain timings Fulda - Kassel vary by up to 10 minutes, Kassel - Fulda by up to 27 minutes (please check if travelling during this period).

902 FRANKFURT - BRAUNSCHWEIG - BERLIN

SERVICE FROM JUNE 11. See Table **850** for other fast services via Erfurt.
Independent operator **FlixTrain** also run fast services Stuttgart - Berlin and v.v. (see page 369).

km		*ICE* 649 Ⓐ ✕	*ICE* 988 ①–⑥ ✕	*ICE* 876 ①–⑥ ✕	*ICE* 998 ①g ✕	*ICE* 874 ✕	*ICE* 374 ✕		*ICE* 372 T✕		*ICE* 370 ✕		*ICE* 278 T✕		*ICE* 276 ⑥ ✕	*ICE* 276 Ⓑ ✕	*ICE* 1692 ⒷD ✕	*ICE* 1635 ⒷE ✕	*ICE* 274 ✕	*ICE* 292 ⑦ Z✕		*NJ* 470 A[R] N
	Basel SBB **912** d.	...	...	...	...	0412b	0606	...	0813	...	1013	...	1213	...	1413	1413	...	...	1613	1813	...	2113
	Karlsruhe Hbf **912** d.	...	...	...	...	0558	0800	...	1000	...	1200	...	1400	...	1601	1601	...	...	1801	2000	...	2304
	Stuttgart Hbf **912** d.	...	...	...	...	|	|	...	|	...	|	...	|	...	|	|	...	...	|	|	...	|
	Mannheim Hbf **912** d.	...	...	...	...	0632	0832	...	1032	...	1232	...	1432	...	1632	1632	...	...	1832	2032	...	2359
	Frankfurt Flughafen Fernbf ✈ d.	...	...	...	...	|	|	...	|	...	|	...	|	...	|	|	1809v	1809z	|	|	...	|
0	**Frankfurt** (Main) Hbf **850 900** d.	...	0506	...	...	0714	0914	...	1114	...	1314	...	1514	...	1714	1719	|	|	1914	2114	...	|
4	**Frankfurt** (Main) Süd d.	...	|	...	...	|	|	...	|	...	|	...	|	...	|	|	1820	1820	|	|	...	0054
23	Hanau Hbf **850 900** d.	...	0521	...	...	0730	0930	...	1130	...	1330	...	1530	...	1730	|	|	|	1930	2130	...	|
104	Fulda **850 900** d.	...	0604	...	...	0812	1012	...	1212	...	1412	...	1612	...	1812	1815	1913	|	2012	2212	...	0148
194	**Kassel** Wilhelmshöhe **900** d.	...	0636	0643	0744	0845	1045	...	1245	...	1445	...	1645	...	1845	1848	1946	1948	2045	2245	...	|
239	Göttingen **900** d.	...	0655	0704	0806	0904	1104	...	1304	...	1504	...	1704	...	1904	|	2006	|	2104	2305	...	0316
317	Hildesheim Hbf **863** d.	...	...	0806	0909	1006	1206	...	1406	...	1606	...	1806	...	2006	2006	2109	|	2206	0002	...	|
360	**Braunschweig** Hbf **863** d.	0601	...	0829	0932	1029	1229	...	1429	...	1629	...	1829	...	2029	2029	2132	◧	2229	0030	...	0459
392	Wolfsburg **810 863** d.	0620	...	0848	|	1048	1248	...	1448	...	1648	...	1848	...	2048	2048	|	|	2248	0049	...	|
559	**Berlin** Spandau **810** a.	0722	...	0943	1101	1143	1346	...	1547	...	1746	...	1942	...	2142	2142	2242	|	2353	0144	...	|
575	**Berlin** Hbf **850 810** a.	0732	...	0958	1126	1158	1400	...	1601	...	1801	...	1959	...	2157	2157	2257	2258	0014	0159	...	0754
580	**Berlin** Ostbahnhof **810** a.	...	...	1009	1138	1210	1411	...	1612	...	1812	...	2011	...	2209	2209	2309	...	0026	0211	...	0810

	ICE 781 ① M		*ICE* 275 ①–⑤ T✕		*ICE* 277 ✕	*ICE* 1091 ①–⑥ G✕	*ICE* 1091 ①–⑥ H✕	*ICE* 279 ✕		*ICE* 371 T✕		*ICE* 373 T✕		*ICE* 375 ✕		*ICE* 377 ✕	*ICE* 995 ✕	*ICE* 877 ✕		*ICE* 879 ⑦ ✕		*NJ* 471 A[R] Q
Berlin Ostbahnhof **810** d.	0152	...	0346	...	0546	0638	0638	0745	...	0946	...	1146	...	1346	...	1548	1646	1748	...	1946	...	2056
Berlin Hbf **850 810** d.	0204	...	0357	...	0557	0650	0650	0756	...	0957	...	1157	...	1357	...	1559	1658	1759	...	1957	...	2107
Berlin Spandau **810** d.	|	...	0412	...	0612	0705	0705	|	...	1012	...	1212	...	1412	...	1615	1714	1814	...	2012	...	|
Wolfsburg **810 863** d.	|	...	0509	...	0709	|	|	0909	...	1109	...	1309	...	1509	...	1709	1810	1909	...	2109	...	|
Braunschweig Hbf **863** d.	0414	...	0527	...	0728	0828	0828	0927	...	1128	...	1327	...	1528	...	1728	1830	1927	...	2128	...	2347
Hildesheim Hbf **863** d.	0438	...	0554	...	0754	0856	0856	0954	...	1154	...	1354	...	1554	...	1754	1857	1954	...	2154	...	|
Göttingen **900** d.	0545	...	0654	...	0854	|	|	1054	...	1254	...	1454	...	1654	...	1854	1953	2054	...	2254	...	0126
Kassel Wilhelmshöhe **900** d.	0622h	...	0715	...	0915	1016v	1016	1115	...	1315	...	1515	...	1715	...	1915	2015	2116	...	2315	...	|
Fulda **850 900** d.	0654	...	0747	...	0947x	|	|	1147	...	1347	...	1547	...	1747	...	1947	2047	2158r	...	2347	...	0256
Hanau Hbf **850 900** d.	...	...	0827	...	1027y	|	|	1227	...	1427	...	1627	...	1827	...	2027	|	2237t	...	0027	...	|
Frankfurt (Main) Süd a.	...	...	|	...	|	1139	|	|	...	|	...	|	...	|	...	|	|	|	...	|	...	0359
Frankfurt (Main) Hbf **850 900** a.	...	...	0844	...	1044y	|	1140	1244	...	1444	...	1644	...	1844	...	2044	2140	2254t	...	0044	...	|
Frankfurt Flughafen Fernbf ✈ a.	...	...	|	...	|	1151c	...	|	...	|	...	|	...	|	...	|	...	2312z	...	|	...	|
Mannheim Hbf **912** a.	...	...	0927	...	1127	...	...	1327	...	1527	...	1727	...	1927	...	2127	...	2353	...	0127	...	0440
Stuttgart Hbf **912** a.	...	...	|	...	|	...	...	|	...	|	...	|	...	|	...	|	...	|	...	|	...	|
Karlsruhe Hbf **912** a.	...	...	0958	...	1158	...	...	1358	...	1558	...	1758	...	1958	...	2158	...	0022	...	0154	...	0507
Basel SBB **912** a.	...	...	1147	...	1347	...	...	1547	...	1747	...	1947	...	2147	...	2354	...	...	...	...	...	0720

A – To June 27 and from Oct. 27.
B – June 28 - Oct. 26.
D – To Aug. 9 and from Oct. 28.
E – Aug. 11 - Oct. 27.
G – Until Oct. 26.
H – From Oct. 28.
M – To München (Table **900**). Also calls at Potsdam Hbf (d. 0226), Brandenburg Hbf (d. 0245) and Magdeburg Hbf (d. 0326).
N – 1, 2 cl., 2 cl. and (2) Zürich - Basel - Berlin. Also calls at Magdeburg Hbf (a. 0556*), Potsdam Hbf (a. 0706*), Berlin Wannsee (a. 0736) and Berlin Zoo (a. 0748).

Q – 1, 2 cl., 2 cl. and (2) Berlin - Basel - Zürich. Also calls at Berlin Zoo (d. 2116), Berlin Wannsee (d. 2128), Potsdam Hbf (d. 2140), Brandenburg Hbf (d. 2207) and Magdeburg Hbf (d. 2258).
T – From / to Interlaken via Bern (Table **560**).
Z – From Zürich HB (d. 1700).

b – ① (also June 11). Basel **Badischer Bahnhof**.
c – Not Oct. 26.
g – Also June 11.
h – Arrives 0609.

r – Arrives 2150. Departs 2152 Aug. 10 - Oct. 27.
t – 6 minutes earlier Aug. 10 - Oct. 27.
v – Until Aug. 9.
x – Does not call Aug. 10 – 14, Ⓐ Sept. 16 - Oct. 2
y – 4 minutes earlier Aug. 10 – 14, Ⓐ Sept. 16 - Oct
z – Until Oct. 25.

* – On mornings June 29 - Oct. 27 arrives Magdeb 0627, Potsdam 0727.
◧ – Via Erfurt (Table **850**).

903 Local services GÖTTINGEN - HANNOVER - UELZEN - HAMBURG

metron

SERVICE FROM JUNE 11. Services below are operated by ***metronom*** (except trains **A** and **D**). For faster *ICE* and *IC* services see Table **900**.

km																										
			⚒			Ⓐ A✕																				
0	**Göttingen** d.	...	0409	...	0504	0546	...	0607	...	0707	0809	0907	1005	1107	1209	1307	1409	1507	1609	1707	1805	1907	...	2009	2107	2209
20	Northeim (Han) d.	...	0422	...	0517	0600	...	0620	...	0720	0823	0920	1018	1120	1223	1320	1423	1520	1623	1720	1818	1920	...	2023	2120	2223
39	Kreiensen d.	...	0437	...	0533	0616	...	0633	...	0733	0837	0933	1037	1133	1237	1333	1437	1533	1637	1733	1837	1933	...	2037	2133	2237
58	Alfeld (Leine) d.	...	0450	...	0546	0629	...	0646	...	0746	0850	0946	1050	1146	1250	1346	1450	1546	1650	1746	1850	1946	...	2050	2146	2250
75	Elze (Han) d.	...	0503	...	0558	0640	...	0658	...	0758	0903	0958	1103	1158	1303	1358	1503	1558	1703	1758	1903	1958	...	2103	2158	2303
108	**Hannover** Hbf. a.	...	0527	...	0625r	0657	...	0723	...	0827r	0928r	1027r	1128r	1227r	1328r	1427r	1528r	1627r	1728r	1827r	1928r	2028r	...	2128r	2227r	2328r
			⚒h	Ⓐh				Ⓐh	Ⓒw																	d
108	**Hannover** Hbf. d.	...	0540	0540	0640	0701	...	0740	0740	0840	0940	1040	1140	1240	1340	1440	1540	1640	1740	1840	1940	2040	...	2140	2248	2340
149	Celle d.	...	0608	0608	0708	0720	...	0808	0808	0908	1008	1108	1208	1308	1408	1508	1608	1708	1808	1908	2008	2108	...	2208	2316	0008
201	**Uelzen** a.	...	0639	0639	0739	0740	...	0839	0839	0938	1039	1138	1239	1338	1439	1538	1639	1738	1839	1938	2039	2138	...	2239	2347	0039
								Ⓐh														⚒h	†w		⚒h	
201	**Uelzen** d.	0501	0605	0647	0704	0742	0801	0901	0901	1001	1101	1201	1301	1401	1501	1601	1701	1801	1902	2001	2101	2201	2201	2306	2356	...
214	Bad Bevensen d.	0509	0614	0655	0713	|	0810	0910	0910	1010	1109	1209	1309	1409	1509	1609	1709	1809	1910	2009	2110	2209	2209	2314	0004	...
237	Lüneburg d.	0524	0629	0709	0728	0758	0828	0928	0928	1028	1131j	1228	1328	1428	1528	1628	1728	1828	1929	2031j	2128	2228	2232j	2328	0020	...
256	Winsen (Luhe) d.	0535	0640	0720	0740	|	0839	0939	0939	1039	1142	1239	1339	1439	1539	1639	1739	1839	1940	2042	2139	2239	2248	2344	0035	...
286	**Hamburg** Hbf. a.	0557	0703	0741	0804	0829	0903	1003	1003	1102	1206	1303	1403	1503	1602	1703	1804	1903	2002	2104	2203	2302	2321	0020	0109	...

	Ⓒ						Ⓐ h	Ⓒ w									D✕									
Hamburg Hbf d.	0033	0033	...	...	...	...	0542	0558	0651	0757	0857	0957	1057	1157	1257	1357	1524	1457	1557	1657	1757	1857	1957	2057	2157	2233
Winsen (Luhe) d.	0106	0106	...	...	...	...	0604	0624	0713	0819	0919	1019	1119	1219	1319	1419	|	1519	1619	1719	1819	1919	2019	2119	2223	2307
Lüneburg d.	0122	0122	...	...	...	...	0615	0635	0724	0834	0934	1034	1134	1234	1332	1434	|	1534	1634	1734	1834	1934	2034	2130	2234	2323
Bad Bevensen d.	0137	0137	...	...	...	...	0630	0649	0742	0848	0948	1048	1148	1248	1348	1448	|	1548	1648	1751	1848	1948	2048	2145	2249	2337
Uelzen a.	0146	0146	...	...	...	...	0638	0657	0750	0856	0956	1056	1156	1256	1356	1456	|	1556	1656	1758	1856	1956	2056	2153	2256	2347
			⚒h	Ⓒ	Ⓐ		F	G																		
Uelzen d.	0151	...	0412	0509	0509	0609	0651	0709	0809	0909	1009	1109	1209	1309	1409	1509	|	1609	1709	1809	1909	2009	2114	2209	2309	2351f
Celle d.	0224	...	0446	0547	0547	0647	0747v	0747	0848	0947	1048	1147	1247	1347	1447	1547	|	1647	1747	1847	1947	2048	2147	2247	2347	0028f
Hannover Hbf a.	0252	...	0515	0616	0616	0716	0815	0815	0916	1015	1116	1215	1316	1415	1516	1615	1638	1716	1815	1916	2015	2115	2215	2316	0016	0056f
		Ⓐ	⚒																							
Hannover Hbf d.	...	0433	0536	0633	0636	0736	0819t	0819t	0936	1019t	1136	1219t	1336	1419t	1536	1619t	1653	1736	1819t	1936	2019t	2134k	2221z	2336	...	...
Elze (Han) d.	...	0456	0558	0655	0658	0758	0855	0855	0958	1055	1158	1255	1358	1455	1558	1655	1721	1758	1855	1958	2055	2158	2255	2358	...	...
Alfeld (Leine) d.	...	0508	0610	0706	0710	0810	0906	0906	1010	1106	1210	1306	1410	1506	1610	1706	1733	1810	1906	2010	2106	2210	2306	0010	...	...
Kreiensen d.	...	0521	0623	0719	0723	0823	0923	0923	1023	1119	1223	1319	1423	1519	1623	1722	1746	1823	1919	2023	2119	2223	2319	0023	...	...
Northeim (Han) d.	...	0534	0636	0733	0736	0836	0937	0937	1036	1133	1236	1333	1436	1533	1636	1736	1759	1836	1933	2036	2133	2236	2333	0036	...	...
Göttingen a.	...	0549	0649	0747	0749	0849	0950	0950	1049	1146	1249	1346	1449	1546	1649	1750	1814	1849	1946	2049	2146	2249	2346	0049	...	...

A – *ICE* **1686**. Operated by DB.
D – ①②③④⑦ (not Oct. 2). *ICE* **1585**. Operated by DB.
F – Ⓑ to Oct. 18; Ⓐ from Oct. 21 (not Oct. 31).
G – ⑥ to Oct. 12; Ⓒ from Oct. 19 (also Oct. 31).

d – Runs 8 minutes later on Ⓒ.
f – Uelzen - Hannover on ⑤⑥ only.
h – Not Oct. 31.
j – Arrives 7 – 9 minutes earlier.
k – 2136 on Ⓐ.

r – 2 – 4 minutes earlier from Oct. 15.
t – 14 minutes later from Oct. 15.
v – Arrives 0728.
w – Also Oct. 31.
z – 2233 from Oct. 15.

MÜNCHEN - INGOLSTADT - NÜRNBERG 904

m	Most *ICE* trains convey ✕	*ICE* 888	*ICE* 822	*ICE* 784	*ICE* 804	*ICE* 820	*ICE* 1008	*ICE* 886	*ICE* 728	*ICE* 602	*ICE* 1682	*ICE* 1006	*ICE* 726	*ICE* 882	*ICE* 724	*ICE* 1600	*ICE* 980	*ICE* 1724	*ICE* 722	*ICE* 800	*ICE* 880	*ICE* 720	*ICE* 588	*ICE* 628	*ICE* 1004	*ICE* 788
		①-⑤	①-⑥	①-⑥	⑥	D	Ⓐm						①-⑥				①-④	◊	1122							
			K		w	K			K				K		K		s	⊡	K			K♠		K		
0	**München** Hbf d.	0413a	0448	0516	0547	0547	0557	0616	0648	0657	0719	0752	0752	0820	0848	0856	0919	0919	0951	0954	1021	1055	1120	1151	1157	1221
81	**Ingolstadt** Hbf d.	0451	0525	0558	0624	0624	|	0654	0725	|	0757	|	|	0900	0925	|	0957	0957	|	1031	1100	|	1159	|	|	1300
171	**Nürnberg** Hbf a.	0521	0555	0630	0653	0654	0658	0725	0754	0801	0829	0854	0854	0930	0955	1002	1029	1029	1055	1103	1130	1157	1230	1254	1258	1330
	Würzburg Hbf **900 920** a.	0626	0652	0725	|	0752	|	0826	0852	|	0924	|	0952	1026	1052	|	1124	|	1152	|	1225	1252	1325	1352	|	1425
	Frankfurt (Main) Hbf **920** a.	|	0804x	|	|	0904	|	|	1004x	|	|	|	1104x	|	1204x	|	|	|	1304x	|	|	1404x	|	1504x	|	|
	Leipzig Hbf **850** a.	|	...	|	|	...	|	|	...	1010	|	|	...	|	...	1210	|	|	...	|	|	...	|	...	|	|
	Berlin Hbf **850** a.	|	...	|	1024	...	0951	|	...	1129	|	1151	...	|	...	1329	|	1355	...	1424	|	...	|	...	1551	|
	Hamburg Hbf **900** a.	1030	...	1131	...	...	...	1232•	...	...	1330	...	...	1429	...	...	1530	...	...	...	1630	...	1733	...	...	1829

Most *ICE* trains convey ✕	*ICE* 626	*ICE* 506	*ICE* 586	*ICE* 624	*ICE* 706	*ICE* 1086	*ICE* 622	*ICE* 504	*ICE* 1084	*ICE* 620	*ICE* 1002	*ICE* 1222	*ICE* 528	*ICE* 502	*ICE* 582	*ICE* 526	*ICE* 1000	*ICE* 782	*ICE* 524	*ICE* 500	*ICE* 522	*ICE* 1700	*ICE* 780	*ICE* 1620	*ICE* 520	*ICE* 1020
				1124		⑤⑦						1622					Ⓑ						⑦	⑥	920	1520
	K			K		v	K			K		JK	K			K			K		K		A		Ⓑ	Ⓑ⊖
nchen Hbf d.	1250	1255	1318b	1351	1355	1421	1451	1456	1521	1551	1556	1618	1649	1655	1719	1751	1757	1819	1851	1856	1948	1955	2021	2052	2054	2300
olstadt Hbf d.	|	|	1359	|	1431	1500	|	|	1600	|	|	1700	1726	|	1757	|	|	1900	|	|	2025	|	2100	2129	2131	2337
rnberg Hbf a.	1353	1400	1431	1454	1503	1531	1554	1601	1630	1654	1658	1733	1756	1801	1828	1854	1858	1930	1954	2001	2054	2102	2131	2201	2200n	0011
Würzburg Hbf **900 920** a.	1452	|	1525	1552	|	1626	1652	|	1725	1752	|	1827	1852	|	1925	1952	|	2025	2052	|	2152	|	2226	2255	2255n	...
rankfurt (Main) Hbf **920** a.	1604x	|	|	1704x	|	|	1804x	|	|	1904x	|	1936	2004x	|	|	2104x	|	|	2204x	|	2304y	|	...	0003	0004n	...
Leipzig Hbf **850** a.	...	1610	|	...	|	|	...	1810	|	...	|	...	...	2010	|	...	|	|	...	2210	...	|	...	...	...	...
Berlin Hbf **850** a.	...	1729	|	...	1826	|	...	1929	|	...	1951	...	...	2129	|	...	2151	|	...	2335	...	0031	...	...	...	...
amburg Hbf **900** a.	...	...	1930	...	...	2030	...	...	2130	...	...	...	...	...	2331	...	...	0041	...	...	...	...	...	...	...	...

Most *ICE* trains convey ✕	*ICE* 823	*ICE* 985	*ICE* 827	*ICE* 1501	*ICE* 521	*ICE* 501	*ICE* 781	*ICE* 1001	*ICE* 523	*ICE* 581	*ICE* 503	*ICE* 525	*ICE* 783	*ICE* 1003	*ICE* 527	*ICE* 1127	*ICE* 583	*ICE* 505	*ICE* 529	*ICE* 1221	*ICE* 703	*ICE* 621	*ICE* 1085	*ICE* 623	*ICE* 787	*ICE* 1005
	Ⓐt	Ⓐt	①-⑤	Ⓐh		①-⑥	①-⑥	①-⑥	①-⑥			1125	①-⑥		①-⑤	⑥										
			K	E	K		N		K			K			K	K			K	KH		K		K♠		
amburg Hbf **900** d.	...	...	...	...	...	...	...	...	...	0428	...	...	0524	...	...	...	0625	...	...	...	...	...	0828	...	0928	...
Berlin Hbf **850** d.	...	...	...	...	...	0428	...	0601	...	|	0630	...	|	0805	...	...	|	0830	...	...	0937	...	|	...	|	1205
Leipzig Hbf **850** d.	...	...	...	...	...	0548	...	|	...	|	0748	...	|	|	...	...	|	0948	...	...	|	...	|	...	|	|
rankfurt (Main) Hbf **920** d.	...	...	0454	...	0554x	|	...	|	0654x	|	|	0754x	|	|	0854	0854x	|	|	0954x	1021	|	1054x	|	1154x	|	|
Vürzburg Hbf **900 920** d.	...	...	0604	...	0704	|	0730	|	0804	0832	|	0904	0931	|	1004	1004	1032	|	1104	1131	|	1204	1232	1313	1331	|
rnberg Hbf d.	0557	0629	0702	0728	0802	0812	0827	0859	0904	0928	0955	1002	1027	1059	1104	1104	1128	1155	1202	1227	1253	1302	1328	1407	1427	1459
olstadt Hbf d.	0626	0702	0730	0802	|	|	0901	|	|	1001	|	1031	1101	|	|	|	1201	|	|	1301	1324	|	1401	|	1501	|
nchen Hbf a.	0704	0740	0807	0839	0904	0917	0938	1001	1006	1038	1100	1108	1138	1203	1207	1207	1238	1302	1306	1338	1402	1406	1441c	1509	1539	1602

Most *ICE* trains convey ✕	*ICE* 625	*ICE* 509	*ICE* 627	*ICE* 789	*ICE* 629	*ICE* 1727	*ICE* 1689	*ICE* 1601	*ICE* 721	*ICE* 881	*ICE* 1007	*ICE* 723	*ICE* 681	*ICE* 603	*ICE* 725	*ICE* 883	*ICE* 1009	*ICE* 727	*ICE* 683	*ICE* 1605	*ICE* 729	*ICE* 885	*ICE* 821	*ICE* 1617	*ICE* 685	*ICE* 1625
						⑥⑦											Ⓑ	Ⓑ		1715			Q			⑥
	K		K		K	R			K			K			K			K			K		K		T	B
amburg Hbf **900** d.	...	...	...	1128	...	...	1228	...	...	1328	...	...	1428	...	...	1528	...	...	1628	...	...	1728	...	...	1828	...
Berlin Hbf **850** d.	...	1230	...	|	...	1405	|	1430	...	|	1605	...	|	1630	...	|	1805	...	|	1830	...	|	...	1928	|	...
Leipzig Hbf **850** d.	...	1348	...	|	...	|	|	1548	...	|	|	...	|	1748	...	|	|	...	|	1948	...	|	...	2048	|	...
rankfurt (Main) Hbf **920** d.	1254x	|	1354x	|	1454x	|	|	|	1554x	|	|	1654x	|	|	1754x	|	|	1854	|	|	1954x	|	2054x	|	|	2119
Vürzburg Hbf **900 920** d.	1404	|	1504	1531	1604	|	1634	|	1704	1731	|	1804	1835	|	1904	1931	|	2004	2032	|	2104	2131	2204	|	2231	2235
rnberg Hbf d.	1504	1555	1602	1627	1702	1727	1731	1757	1802	1827	1859	1903	1932	1955	2002	2027	2059	2104	2128	2155	2202	2228	2302	2311	2330	2331
olstadt Hbf d.	|	|	|	1701	|	|	1805	|	1833	1901	|	|	2005	|	2032	2101	|	|	2201	|	2233	2301	2330	2345	0003	0005
nchen Hbf a.	1606	1700	1704	1741	1804	1837g	1842	1906	1911	1942	2001	2007	2042	2105	2109	2141	2201	2206	2238	2302r	2310	2340r	0007	0022q	0043	0043

RE services via the high-speed line (SEE NOTE ❖)

m																											
		⚒t	Ⓐt	†j	⚒t	Ⓐt	Ⓒz¶	⑥			◧		†p	⚒t	⑤		⑥	†j	Ⓐt	Ⓒz	Ⓐt	Ⓒz	Ⓐt			U	Y
0	**München** Hbf d.	0454	0602	0603	0705	0902	0905	1005	1005	1105	1204	1304	1402	1403	...	1503	1601	1602	1603	1705	1711	1805	1805	1905	2005	2101	2105
50	Pfaffenhofen (Ilm) d.	0525	0629	0630	0732	0932	0932	1032	1032	1132	1233	1331	1429	1433	...	1530	1629	1629	1632	1732	1742	1830	1832	1932	2034	2132	2133
81	**Ingolstadt** Hbf a.	0544	0648	0649	0751	0952	0952	1052	1052	1152	1253	1352	1448	1452	...	1551	1648	1649	1654	1752	1802	1848	1852	1951	2054	2153	2152
81	**Ingolstadt** Hbf d.	0546	...	0703	0803	*1004*	1004	1104	...	1203	...	1403	1504	...	1504	1604	1704	*1704*	...	1803	1803	*1904*	...	2001	...	*2207*	2200
171	**Nürnberg Hbf** a.	0635	...	0748	0848	*1049*	1049	1149	...	1248	...	1448	1550	...	1550	1649	1752	*1752*	...	1848	1848	*1949*	...	2046	...	*2252*	2248

	Ⓐt	Ⓐt	Ⓒz	Ⓐt	⑥	Ⓐ	⑥	†j	⚒t	Ⓑ		⑥	Ⓑ				⑤†‡	⚒t	†j		Ⓐt	Ⓒz			Y	U	⑤⑥k
rnberg Hbf d.	0508	...	0608	*0608*	...	0755	0816	0909	*0909*	...	1108	1208	...	1308	...	1509	1606	...	...	1708	...	*1806*	1908	...	2108	*2108*	2336
olstadt Hbf a.	0555	...	0658	*0657*	...	0851	0908	0956	*0956*	...	1155	1255	...	1355	...	1556	1656	...	...	1756	...	*1856*	1955	...	2155	*2155*	0021
olstadt Hbf d.	0600	0656	0700	0706	0805	0905	0910	1005	1006	1105	1205	1305	1305	1405	1505	1603	...	1705	1717	1809	1905	1909	2008	2105	2205	2205	0022
ffenhofen (Ilm) d.	0619	0711	0718	0728	0826	0926	0929	1025	1027	1125	1225	1325	1326	1425	1526	1623	...	1726	1738	1829	1925	1929	2029	2126	2225	2226	0038
nchen Hbf a.	0646	0736	0750	0758	0856	0953	0952	1052	1057	1154	1253	1352	1353	1453	1555	1653	...	1756	1813	1858	1953	1954	2057	2156	2252r	2257	0106◊

RE services via EICHSTÄTT and TREUCHTLINGEN

m																											
		⊕			Ⓐt																Ⓐ	Ⓒ			⑥		⊗
0	**München** Hbf d.	0031	...	...	0520	...	0620	0725	0825	0927	1027	1127	1227	1323	1427	1527	1627	1727	1827	1924	2022	2027	...	2131	2226	2226	2330
50	Pfaffenhofen (Ilm) d.	0106	...	...	0554	...	0655	0800	0900	1002	1102	1202	1302	1358	1502	1602	1702	1802	1902	1959	2101	2102	...	2206	2302	2302	0006
81	**Ingolstadt** Hbf a.	0126	...	...	0616	...	0718	0823	0921	1024	1126	1224	1324	1420	1524	1624	1723	1824	1924	2020	2124	2124	...	2227	2323	2323	0027
81	**Ingolstadt** Hbf d.	...	...	0528	0629	0629	0730	0831	0930	1026	1129	1226	1326	1430e	1526	1630f	1730	1827	1926	2030e	2131	2130	...	2232	2324	...	...
98	Eichstätt Bahnhof ♥ d.	...	...	0556	0656	0656	0757	0856	0956	1056	1156	1256	1356	1456	1556	1656	1756	1856	1956	2056	2156	2156	...	2257	2358	...	...
37	Treuchtlingen a.	...	...	0620	0719	0719	0820	0919	1020	1120	1220	1319	1419	1519	1620	1720	1821	1919	2020	2119	2220	2220	...	2320	0021	...	...
37	Treuchtlingen **905** d.	...	...	0625j	0725	0725	0828j	0925	1025j	1128	1225j	1325	1425j	1525	1628z	1728	1826z	1925	2025z	2125	...	2225	2225	2325	0022	...	...
46	Weißenburg **905** d.	...	...	0631j	0731	0731	0834j	0931	1031j	1134	1231j	1331	1431j	1531	1634z	1734	1832z	1931	2031z	2131	...	2231	2231	2331	0027	...	...
99	**Nürnberg** Hbf **905** a.	...	...	0715j	0815	0815	0917j	1015	1115j	1217	1315j	1415	1515j	1615	1717z	1817	1915z	2015	2115z	2215	...	2315	2315	0015	0109	...	...

	Ⓐt	Ⓒz		Ⓐt	Ⓒz	⑦	Ⓐt	⚒t	①-⑥					Ⓒz	Ⓐt						Ⓒz	Ⓐt					
rnberg Hbf **905** d.	...	...	0439j	0526	0539	0639	0630	...	...	0739	0839j	0939	1039j	1139	1139	1239j	1339	1439z	1539	1639z	1739	1739	1839z	1939	2039z	2139	2344
ißenburg **905** d.	...	...	0521j	0607	0621	0721	0712	...	...	0821	0921j	1021	1121j	1221	1221	1321j	1421	1521z	1621	1721z	1821	1821	1921z	2021	2121z	2221	0025
uchtlingen **905** a.	...	...	0527j	0615	0628	0728	0720	...	...	0827	0930j	1027	1130j	1227	1227	1330j	1429	1530z	1627	1730z	1828	1831	1930z	2030	2130z	2230	0032
uchtlingen d.	0450	...	0532	0632	0632	0735	0735	0735	...	0835	0935	1035	1135	1235	1240	1336	1435	1535	1635	1735	1835	1835	1935	2035	2135	2235	...
hstätt Bahnhof ♥ d.	0514	...	0556	0655	0655	0759	0759	0759	...	0900	0959	1058	1159	1258	1303	1400	1458	1559	1658	1759	1858	1858	1959	2058	2159	2258	...
olstadt Hbf a.	0531	...	0620	0719	0719	0823	0823	0823	...	0935	1033	1135	1223	1328	1336	1424	1535	1634	1725	1825	1922d	1922	2023	2122	2223	2323	...
olstadt Hbf d.	0534	0537	0631	0734	0734	0831	0831	0831	0831	0937	1035	1137	1233	1334	1339	1436	1537	1636	1731	1837	1935d	1935	2039	2134	2237	2334	...
ffenhofen (Ilm) d.	0555	0559	0654	0757	0757	0854	0900	0900	0900	0958	1058	1158	1256	1357	1401	1459	1600	1659	1754	1900	1958d	1958	2102	2157	2300	0003	...
nchen Hbf a.	0630	0634	0731	0833	0833	0933	0934	0934	0934	1034	1134	1234	1332	1434	1437	1535	1636	1735	1833	1938	2034d	2034	2138	2234	2336r	0039q	...

- To Kassel (Table **900**).
- From Wiesbaden (Table **911**). Arrives München 0111 on the mornings of July 28, Aug. 4, 11, 18, 25, Sept. 1.
- ①-⑤ to July 12 (not June 20) and Aug. 15 - Sept. 27; ⚒ Sept. 30 - Nov. 2.
- From Lichtenfels (Table **850**/**875**).
- Continues to Seefeld (Table **895**) on ⑤⑥ (also Oct. 2).
- From Innsbruck via Garmisch (Table **895**) on Ⓒ.
- To / from Köln, Essen or Dortmund (Table **910**).
- From Kassel (also Berlin on ①). See Tables **900**/**902**.
- ④⑤⑦ (also June 19).
- ⑥⑦ (also Oct. 3; not Oct. 5). From Warnemünde via Rostock (Table **835**).
- ④⑤⑦ (also June 19, Oct. 2; not Sept. 8, 15, 22, 29, Oct. 6, 13, 20, 27). Arrives München 0111 on the mornings of of ① July 29 - Sept. 2.
- ①-④ (not June 20, Aug. 15, Oct. 3).
- ⑤-⑦ (also June 20, Aug. 15, Oct. 3).

0407 on ① July 29 - Sept. 2.
1316 until June 23.

c – 1438 on ⑥⑦.
d – 3 – 8 minutes later on ⑦ to June 23 (also June 20).
e – 5 – 7 minutes earlier on ⑥⑦ to June 23 (also June 20).
f – 1625 on ⑦ to June 23 (also June 20).
g – Until July 28 diverted to München Ost (a. 1843).
h – Not June 20, Nov. 1.
j – † (also June 20, Aug. 15, Nov. 1).
k – Also June 19, Aug. 14, Oct. 2, 31.
m – Not June 20.
n – 1 – 2 minutes later on ⑤⑦ (also Oct. 2; not Oct. 4).
p – Also June 20, Nov. 1.
q – 22 – 29 minutes later on the mornings of ①⑦ July 28 - Sept. 2.
r – 24 – 30 minutes later on ⑥⑦ July 27 - Sept. 1.
s – Not June 20, Oct. 3.
t – Not June 20, Aug. 15, Nov. 1.
v – Also June 15, 22.
w – Also June 20, Oct. 3.
x – Calls at Frankfurt (Main) Süd (not Hbf) on ⑥⑦ Aug. 10 - Sept. 29.
y – Calls at Frankfurt (Main) Süd (not Hbf) on ⑤-⑦ Aug. 9 - Sept. 29.
z – Ⓒ (also June 20, Aug. 15, Nov. 1).

‡ – Also June 20, Aug. 15.
◊ – Not the mornings of ⑦ July 28 - Sept. 1.
⊖ – Not Oct. 4. Runs 38 minutes **earlier** on July 28, Aug. 4, 11, 18, 25, Sept. 1 (train number **1524**).
⊗ – 7 – 10 minutes later on ⑥⑦ July 27 - Sept. 1.
⊕ – 9 – 13 minutes later on ①⑦ July 28 - Sept. 2.
◧ – 4 minutes earlier on ⑥.
⊡ – ⑥ (also June 20, Oct. 3, Nov. 1; not Nov. 2). To Warnemünde (Table **835**). Does not call at Ingolstadt on June 15.
¶ – Change trains at Ingolstadt on ⑥.
• – On ⑤ (also Oct. 2; not Oct. 4) terminates at Hamburg **Harburg** (a. 1221).
♠ – Conveys 12 Köln - Paderborn - Kassel - Würzburg - München and v.v. (Tables **805**/**900**).
♥ – Connecting trains run Eichstätt Bahnhof - Eichstätt Stadt (*5 km*; Bayerische Regiobahn).
❖ – *RE* services via the high-speed line call at Kinding and Allersberg (112 and 146 km from München respectively).

*See Table **905** for services via Augsburg*

905 MÜNCHEN - AUGSBURG - NÜRNBERG and WÜRZBURG

SERVICE FROM JUNE 24. *ICE/IC* services. See Table **904** for services via Ingolstadt. See Table **905a** for local trains Treuchtlingen - Würzburg.

	ICE	*IC*		*ICE*		*IC*	*ICE*		*ICE*		*ICE*		*IC*	*ICE*	*IC*	*ICE*		*ICE*		*ICE*	*ICE*				
	985	**2162**		**802**		**2086**	**680**		**508**		**786**		**2224**	**704**	**2080**	**1502**		**702**		**580**	**580**				
	Ⓐ	Ⓐ				①–④	⑤–⑦						⑤e		⑤e	①–④		Y		①–⑤	⑦				
	t	r				w	d				G		F			w				S					
				✕		🍷	✕		✕		✕			✕	🍷	✕		✕		✕	✕				
München Ost d.	...	...	...	...	...	...	...	...	...	...	...	...	...	...	...	...	...	...	...	...	...	...	...	...	...
München Hbf **930** d.	...	0534	...	0713	...	0819	0840	...	1013	...	1338	...	1440	1514	1603	1609	...	1705	...	1853	1853	...	...	...	...
München Pasing **930** d.	0443	0542	...	0722	...	|	0849	...	1022	...	|	...	|	1523	1611	1618	...	1714	...	1902	1902	...	...	...	...
Augsburg Hbf **930** d.	0508	0609	...	0748	...	0854	0914	...	1047	...	1413	...	1516	1547	1640	1643	...	1739	...	1930	1930	...	...	...	...
Donauwörth d.	0529	0630	...	0808	...	0921	0935	...	1108	...	1437	...	1539	1608	1704	1704	...	1804**c**	...	1951	1951	...	...	...	...
Treuchtlingen d.	0549	0651	...	|	...	|	|	...	|	...	|	...	1605	|	1725	1725	...	1825**c**	...	2011	2011	...	...	...	...
Nürnberg Hbf **900 920** a.	0624	0725	...	0858	...	1020	1025	...	1158	...	1528	...	|	1658	1759	1759	...	1859	...	|	|	...	...	...	...
Leipzig Hbf **850** a.	...	...	...	|	...	...	|	...	1410	...	|	...	|	|	...	...	...	|	...	|	|	...	...	...	...
Berlin Hbf **850** a.	...	...	...	1224	...	...	|	...	1529	...	|	...	|	2026	...	...	...	2224	...	|	|	...	...	...	...
Würzburg Hbf **900 920** a.	...	...	...	...	...	...	1124	...	...	...	1626	...	1740	...	...	...	...	...	...	2128	2128	...	...	...	...
Hamburg Hbf **900** a.	...	...	...	...	...	...	1530	...	...	...	2030	...	...	...	...	...	...	...	...	...	0151	...	...	...	...

	ICE	*IC*	*ICE*		*ICE*		*ICE*		*ICE*		*ICE*	*ICE*		*IC*	*ICE*		*ICE*								
	981	**2087**	**989**		**1701**		**701**		**507**		**587**	**707**		**2161**	**709**		**801**								
	Ⓐ	Ⓐ	Ⓐ		Ⓐ									Z			Y								
	t	u	t																						
	✕	🍷	✕		✕		✕		✕		✕	✕			✕		✕								
Hamburg Hbf **900** d.	...	...	...	...	...	...	...	...	...	...	1028	...	...	...	...	...	...	...	...	...	...	...	...	...	...
Würzburg Hbf **900 920** d.	...	...	...	...	...	...	...	...	...	...	1432	...	...	...	...	...	...	...	...	...	...	...	...	...	...
Berlin Hbf **850** d.	...	...	...	...	0534	...	0737	...	1030	...	|	1337	...	...	1537	...	1737	...	...	...	...	...	...	...	...
Leipzig Hbf **850** d.	...	...	...	...	|	...	|	...	1148	...	|	|	...	...	|	...	|	...	...	...	...	...	...	...	...
Nürnberg Hbf **900 920** d.	...	0547	0615	...	0859	...	1058	...	1358	...	1530	1659	...	1831**y**	1859	...	2058	...	...	...	...	...	...	...	...
Treuchtlingen d.	...	0622	0651	...	|	...	|	...	|	...	|	|	...	1905	|	...	|	...	...	...	...	...	...	...	...
Donauwörth d.	0557	0643	0711	...	0950	...	1150	...	1450	...	1621	1750	...	1925	1950	...	2150	...	...	...	...	...	...	...	...
Augsburg Hbf **930** a.	0618	0705	0731	...	1009	...	1209	...	1509	...	1641	1809	...	1945	2009	...	2209	...	...	...	...	...	...	...	...
München Pasing **930** a.	0645	0734	0756	...	1033	...	1233	...	1533	...	1706	1833	...	|	2033	...	2233	...	...	...	...	...	...	...	...
München Hbf **930** a.	0655	0743	0806	...	1043	...	1242	...	1543	...	1715	1843	...	2018	2042	...	2243	...	...	...	...	...	...	...	...
München Ost a.	...	...	...	...	...	...	...	...	...	...	...	...	...	...	...	...	...	...	...	...	...	...	...	...	...

RE services. See Table **930** for other connecting trains München - Augsburg and v.v.

km		Ⓒ	⚒		⚒			⚒		⑥	Ⓐ			⚒		Ⓐ		Ⓐ		Ⓐ		Ⓐ				
		z	t		t		H	t			t		H	t		t		t		t	H	t				
0	**München** Hbf **930** d.	*0159*v	...	0529	...	0735**f**	...	...	0935	...	...	1135	...	...	1335	...	1534	...	1735	...	...	1935	...	2100	2200**g**	230
7	München Pasing **930** d.	*0206*	...	0536	...	0743	...	...	0943	...	...	1143	...	...	1343	...	1542	...	1743	...	...	1943	...	2107	2207	23
62	**Augsburg** Hbf **930** a.	*0246*	...	0619	...	0819	...	...	1019	...	...	1219	...	...	1419	...	1619	...	1819	...	...	2019	...	2148	2248	23
62	**Augsburg** Hbf d.	0319	0519	0628	0720	0828	0932	0923	1028	1127	1127	1229	1332	1322	1428	1527	1628	1726	1828	1920	1938	2028	2127	2154	2254	000
103	Donauwörth d.	0359	0559**k**	0659	0758	0858	0955	1000	1059	1158	1158	1259	1353	1359	1459	1558	1659	1758	1859	1958	2003	2059	2158	2233	2332	00
137	Treuchtlingen a.	0417	0620	0720	0820	0920	|	1020	1120	1220	1220	1320	|	1419	1520	1620	1720	1818	1920	2020	|	2120	2220	2253	...	..
137	Treuchtlingen **904** d.	0418	0623	*0725*	0828	*0925*	|	1028	*1128*	1228	1238	*1325*	|	1424	*1525*	1628	*1728*	1829	*1925*	2025	|	*2125*	2225	*2325*	...	..
146	Weißenburg (Bay) **904** d.	0424	0630	*0731*	0834	*0931*	|	1034	*1134*	1234	1245	*1331*	|	1431	*1531*	1634	*1734*	1835	*1931*	2031	|	*2131*	2231	*2331*	...	..
199	**Nürnberg** Hbf **904** a.	0506	0715	*0815*	0917	*1015*	1044	1117	*1217*	1317	1329	*1415*	1446	1515	*1615*	1718	*1817*	1917	*2015*	2115	2057	*2215*	2315	*0015*	...	..

	Ⓒ	Ⓒ	⑥	Ⓐ		⑥	Ⓐ			⚒		⚒		⚒			Ⓐ		Ⓐ			Ⓐ		Ⓐ	Ⓒ	Ⓐ
	z	z		t			t	H		t		t		t	H		t		t	H		t		t	a	t
Nürnberg Hbf **904** d.	0053	...	0439	0439	*0526*b	0636	0649	0716	*0739*	0839	*0939*	1039	*1139*	1239	1313	*1339*	1439	*1539*	1639	1732	*1739*	1839	*1939*	2039	*2139*	*21*
Weißenburg (Bay) **904** d.	0132	...	0521	0521	*0607*b	0718	0724	|	*0821*	0921	*1021*	1121	*1221*	1321	|	*1421*	1521	*1621*	1721	|	*1821*	1921	*2021*	2121	*2221*	22
Treuchtlingen **904** a.	0139	...	0527	0527	*0615*b	0723	0730	0748	*0827*	0930	*1027*	1130	*1227*	1330	|	*1429*	1530	*1627*	1730	|	*1831*	1930	*2030*	2130	*2230*	22
Treuchtlingen d.	0143	...	0528	0528	0633	0725	0731	0749	0834	0935	1034	1135	1234	1335	|	1435	1535	1634	1735	|	1834	1935	2034	2135	2235	22
Donauwörth d.	0204	0520	0549	0604**j**	0658	0754**n**	0754	0807	0858	0958	1058	1158	1258	1358	1405	1458	1558	1658	1758	1818	1858	1958	2058	2158	2258	22
Augsburg Hbf a.	0226	0558	0620	0635	0728	0825	0825	0828	0928	1028	1128	1230	1328	1434	1427	1528	1628	1728	1828	1840	1928	2028	2128	2228	2328	23
Augsburg Hbf **930** d.	...	0605	...	*0649*	0739	...	...	...	0939	...	1139	...	1339	...	...	1539	...	1739	...	...	1939	...	2139	...	2341	..
München Pasing **930** a.	...	0645	...	*0729*	0813	...	...	...	1013	...	1213	...	1413	...	...	1613	...	1813	...	...	2014	...	2222	...	0024	..
München Hbf **930** a.	...	0652	...	*0738*	0821	...	...	...	1022	...	1221	...	1421	...	...	1622	...	1822	...	...	2022	...	2231	...	0032**x**	..

F – To Frankfurt (Main) Hbf (a. 1852).
G – ①②③④⑥.
H – From/to Lindau and Oberstdorf (Table **935**).
S – To Kassel (Table **900**).
Y – Daily to Sept. 6 (not July 6); Ⓑ from Sept. 8 (also Oct. 5).
Z – ①②③④⑦ (not Oct. 31).

a – Change trains at Augsburg on † (also Aug. 15, Nov. 1).
b – 13–14 minutes later on Ⓒ (also Aug. 15, Nov. 1).
c – 3 minutes **earlier** on ⑦ (also June 29, July 13, 20, 27, Aug. 3, 10, 15, 17, 24, 31, Oct. 3, 5, Nov. 1).
d – Also Oct. 3.
e – Also Oct. 2, 31; not Oct. 4, Nov. 1.
f – 0733 until July 28.
g – 2157 on ⑥⑦ to July 28.
h – 2254 on ⑥⑦ July 27 - Sept. 1.
j – Arrives 0550.
k – Arrives 0548.
n – Arrives 0746.
r – Not Nov. 1.
t – Not Aug. 15, Nov. 1.
u – Not Aug. 15, Oct. 4, Nov. 1.
v – *0153* on ⑦ July 28 - Sept. 1.
w – Not Aug. 15, Oct. 2, 3, 31.
x – 0039 on the mornings ①⑦ July 28 - Sept.
y – 1829 Aug. 15 - Oct. 30.
z – Also Aug. 15, Nov. 1.

905a TREUCHTLINGEN - WÜRZBURG

RB services (except train

km		⚒r	Ⓒz	Ⓐt	Ⓐt	Ⓐt	Ⓒz		⑥						Ⓐt	Ⓒz			⑤F							
0	**Treuchtlingen** d.	...	0502	0512	0535	0613	0626	*0705*t	0725	0825	0925	1025	1125	1225	1306	1325	1424	1525	1605	1625	1725	1826	1925	2025	2125	22
24	Gunzenhausen d.	...	0515	0527	0550	0626	0639	*0719*t	0739	0839	0939	1039	1139	1239	1319	1339	1439	1539	1621	1639	1739	1839	1939	2039	2139	22
51	Ansbach a.	...	0535	0547	0611	0645	0659	*0739*t	0759	0859	0959	1059	1159	1259	1339	1359	1459	1559	1635	1659	1759	1859	1959	2059	2159	23
51	Ansbach d.	0441	0536	0606	0629	0701	0710	0810	0810	0910	1010	1110	1210	1311	1410	1410	1510	1610	1637	1710	1810	1910	2010	2110	...	23
83	Steinach (b Rothenb) ◐ d.	0504	0600	0628	0652	0724	0733	0833	0833	0933	1033	1133	1233	1333	1433	1433	1533	1633	1658	1733	1833	1933	2033	2133	...	23
140	**Würzburg** Hbf a.	0547	0645	0713	0736	0805	0816	0918	0918	1016	1118	1216	1318	1416	1516	1516	1616	1718	1740	1816	1916	2016	2116	2216	...	00

	⚒r	Ⓐt	Ⓒz	Ⓐt	Ⓐt	Ⓒz					Ⓒz	Ⓐt				Ⓐt								†z	⚒
Würzburg Hbf d.	0430	...	0531	0531	0632	0641	0738	0841	0941	1041	1141	1141	1241	1341	1441	...	1541	1641	1741	1841	1941	2041	2141	2241	23
Steinach (b Rothenb) ◐ d.	0513	...	0614	0614	0716	0724	0824	0924	1024	1124	1224	1224	1326	1424	1524	...	1624	1724	1824	1924	2024	2124	2224	2326	23
Ansbach a.	0535	...	0636	0636	0737	0746	0846	0946	1046	1146	1246	1246	1347	1446	1546	...	1646	1746	1846	1946	2046	2146	2246	2349	00
Ansbach d.	0537	0610	0644	0711	0754	0754	0854	0954	1054	1154	1254	1316	1354	1454	1554	1628	1654	1754	1854	1954	2054	2154	2247	...	00
Gunzenhausen d.	0556	0629	0705	0730	0815	0815	0915	1015	1115	1215	1315	1336	1415	1515	1615	1647	1715	1815	1915	2015	2115	2215	2306	...	00
Treuchtlingen a.	0609	0643	0720	0744	0830	0830	0930	1030	1130	1230	1330	1350	1429	1530	1630	1702	1730	1830	1929	2030	2130	2230	2321	...	00

◐ – Local trains **STEINACH** (b Rothenb) - **ROTHENBURG OB DER TAUBER** and v.v. 2nd class only *12 km* Journey time: 14 minutes

From Steinach at 0424 ⚒r, 0517 ⚒r, 0617 Ⓒz, 0631 Ⓐt, 0726 Ⓐt, 0736 Ⓒz, 0836, 0936, 1036, 1136, 1236, 1336, 1436, 1536, 1636, 1736, 1836 Ⓒz, 1845 Ⓐt, 1936, 2036 and 2236.

From Rothenburg ob der Tauber at 0445 ⚒r, 0541 Ⓒz, 0556 Ⓐt, 0657 Ⓐt, 0706 Ⓒz, 0806, 0906, 1006, 1106, 1206, 1309, 1406, 1506, 1606, 1706, 1806, 1906, 2006 and 2206 and 23

F – ⑤ (also Oct. 2, 31; not Oct. 4, Nov. 1). *IC* **2224**. [12] München - Frankfurt (Main) Hbf (a. 1852).

r – ⚒ (not June 20, Nov. 1).
t – Ⓐ (not June 20, Nov. 1).
z – Also June 20, Nov. 1.

B (*RE* services); HLB★ GIESSEN - KOBLENZ; LIMBURG - FRANKFURT and WIESBADEN 906

On June 20 services run as on ⑦.

m	⊠		◇	⚒									
0	**Gießen**........ **807** d.	...	0618	0716	0916	1116	1316	1516	1716	1916	2116	...	2248
3	Wetzlar........ **807** d.	...	0630	0726	0926	1126	1326	1526	1726	1926	2126	...	2300
6	Weilburg............. d.	...	0656	0742	0942	1142	1342	1542	1742	1942	2142	...	2325
5	**Limburg** (Lahn) .. a.	...	0733	0807	1007	1207	1407	1607	1807	2007	2207	...	0002
			◧	|	|	|	|	|	|	|	|		
5	**Limburg** (Lahn) .. d.	0645	0745	0808	1008	1208	1408	1608	1808	2008	2208	2245	...
8	Diez .... d.	0649	0749	0812	1012	1212	1412	1612	1812	2012	2212	2249	...
1	Nassau (Lahn) .... d.	0714	0814	0832	1032	1232	1432	1632	1832	2032	2232	2314	...
9	Bad Ems .... d.	0723	0823	0839	1039	1239	1439	1639	1839	2039	2239	2323	...
2	Niederlahnstein... d.	0741	0841	0852	1052	1252	1452	1652	1852	2052	2252	2341	...
7	**Koblenz** Hbf ...... a.	0749	0849	0858	1058	1258	1458	1658	1858	2058	2258	2349	...

⊠	Ⓐ										
Koblenz Hbf........ d.	0509	0657	0858	1058	1258	1458	1658	1858	1909	2109	2209
Niederlahnstein .... d.	0516	0704	0904	1104	1304	1504	1704	1904	1916	2116	2216
Bad Ems............. d.	0533	0718	0918	1118	1318	1518	1718	1918	1933	2133	2233
Nassau (Lahn)...... d.	0543	0726	0926	1126	1326	1526	1726	1926	1943	2143	2243
Diez.................... d.	0609	0746	0946	1146	1346	1546	1746	1946	2009	2209	2309
Limburg (Lahn).... a.	0613	0749	0949	1149	1349	1549	1749	1949	2013	2213	2313
	◧	|	|	|	|	|	|	|	|	◧	◧
	Ⓐ	|	|	|	|	|	|	|	|		
Limburg (Lahn).... d.	0618	0750	0950	1150	1350	1550	1750	1950	2023	2223	...
Weilburg............... d.	0655	0816	1016	1216	1416	1616	1816	2016	2101	2301	...
Wetzlar ....**807** d.	0720	0833	1033	1233	1433	1633	1833	2033	2126	2326	...
Gießen ....**807** a.	0731	0842	1042	1242	1442	1642	1842	2042	2138	2337	...

LIMBURG - NIEDERNHAUSEN - FRANKFURT and WIESBADEN

m			Ⓐ	Ⓐ	⑥	Ⓐ	Ⓒ	Ⓐ	Ⓐ	Ⓐ	⚒	†	Ⓐ		⚒	†		⚒	†		⚒	†	Ⓐ		⚒	†
0	**Limburg** (Lahn)......... d.	0418	0448	0518	0518	0555	0618	0625	0638	0655	0718	0718	0755	0818	0918	0918	1018	1118	1118	1218	1318	1318	1355	1418	1518	1518
21	Bad Camberg............ d.	0442	0512	0542	0542	0614	0642	0644	0703	0714	0742	0742	0814	0842	0942	0942	1042	1142	1142	1242	1342	1342	1414	1442	1542	1542
30	Idstein........................ d.	0452	0522	0552	0551	0622	0652	0652	0713	0722	0752	0751	0822	0852	0952	0951	1052	1152	1151	1252	1352	1351	1422	1452	1552	1551
38	Niedernhausen........‡ a.	0458	0528	0558	0559	0628	0658	0658	0722	0728	0758	0759	0828	0858	0958	0959	1058	1158	1159	1258	1358	1359	1428	1458	1558	1559
58	**Wiesbaden** Hbf..... a.	|	0556	0626	0626	0656	0726	|	0744	|	0827	0826	0857	0926	1026	1026	1126	1227	1226	1327	1427	1426	1457	1527	1627	1626
70	**Frankfurt** (Main) Hbf ‡ a.	0528	0557	0628	...	0658	0728	0728	...	0758	0828	...	0858	0928	1028	...	1128	1228	...	1328	1428	...	1458	1528	1628	...

	Ⓐ		Ⓐ	⚒	†	Ⓐ		⚒	†			
ıburg (Lahn) .... d.	1555	1618	1655	1718	1718	1755	1818	1918	1918	2018	2118	2218
ı Camberg .... d.	1614	1642	1714	1742	1742	1814	1842	1942	1942	2042	2142	2242
ein .... d.	1622	1652	1722	1752	1751	1822	1852	1952	1951	2052	2151	2251
dernhausen .... ‡ a.	1628	1658	1728	1758	1759	1828	1858	1958	1959	2058	2159	2258
Viesbaden Hbf...... a.	1657	1727	1757	1827	1826	1857	1927	2027	2026	2126	2226	2326
ınkfurt (Main) Hbf ‡ a.	1658	1728	1758	1828	...	1903	1928	2028	...	2128	...	2333

			Ⓐ	Ⓒ	Ⓐ	Ⓐ	Ⓒ	Ⓐ		⚒
Frankfurt (M) Hbf . ‡ d.	0028	...	0601	0631	0643	0731	...	...	0831	0931
Wiesbaden Hbf .. d.	0036**z**	0534**v**	0604	0636**k**	0650	0720	0736	0806	0836	0936
Niedernhausen ..... ‡ d.	0101	0601	0631	0701	0718	0801	0801	0831	0901	1001
Idstein .... d.	0108	0608	0638	0708	0725	0808	0808	0838	0908	1008
Bad Camberg......... d.	0117	0617	0647	0717	0734	0817	0817	0847	0917	1017
Limburg (Lahn)...... a.	0141	0641	0711	0741	0801	0841	0841	0911	0941	1041

	†		⚒	†		⚒	†		Ⓐ		Ⓐ	Ⓒ	Ⓐ	Ⓐ	⚒	†	Ⓐ		Ⓐ	⚒	†		⚒	†		
ınkfurt (Main) Hbf ‡ d.	...	1031	1131	...	1231	1331	...	1431	1501	1531**k**	1601	1631	...	1701	1730	...	1801	1831	1901	1931	...	2031	2131	...	2231	...
Viesbaden Hbf...... d.	0936	1036	1136	1136	1236	1336	1336	1436	1506	1536**b**	1606	1636	1636	1706	1736	1736	1806	1833**r**	1906	1936	1936	2036	2136	2136	2236	2336
dernhausen .... ‡ d.	1001	1101	1201	1201	1301	1401	1401	1501	1531	1601	1631	1701	1701	1731	1801	1801	1831	1901	1931	2001	2001	2101	2201	2201	2301	0001
ein .... d.	1008	1108	1208	1208	1308	1408	1408	1508	1538	1608	1638	1708	1708	1738	1808	1808	1838	1908	1938	2008	2008	2108	2208	2208	2308	0008
ı Camberg .... d.	1017	1117	1217	1217	1317	1417	1417	1517	1545	1617	1645	1717	1717	1745	1817	1817	1845	1917	1945	2017	2017	2117	2217	2217	2317	0017
ıburg (Lahn) .... a.	1041	1141	1241	1241	1341	1441	1441	1541	1604	1641	1704	1741	1741	1804	1841	1841	1904	1941	2004	2041	2041	2141	2241	2241	2341	0041

Change trains at Niedernhausen on ⑥.
⑥ only.
1836 on Ⓒ.
⚒ only. 0536 on ⑥.
Ⓒ only.

◧ – Change trains at Limburg.
◇ – Runs up to 3 minutes later Gießen - Limburg on †.
★ – Hessische Landesbahn.
⊠ – Additional stopping trains operate.

‡ – **Additional S-Bahn** *S2* **services** Frankfurt - Niedernhausen and v.v. Journey: 35 minutes.
From Frankfurt (Main) Hbf: On ⚒ every 30 minutes 0452 – 2352; on † at 0452, 0521, 0552, 0621, 0652, 0721, 0752, 0822, 0852 and every 30 minutes 2352.
From Niedernhausen: On ⚒ every 30 minutes 0403 – 2303; on † at 0433, 0533, 0603, 0633 and every 30 minutes until 2303.

essische Landesbahn GIESSEN - FULDA 907

On June 20 services run as on ⑦

m		Ⓐ	Ⓐ	⑥	⚒	Ⓒ	Ⓐ						Ⓐ	Ⓒ						Ⓒ	Ⓐ	Ⓒ	Ⓐ	Ⓐ	Ⓒ	
0	**Gießen** .... d.	...	0524	...	0617**e**	0744**k**	0747	0844	0947	1044	1147	1241	1346	1347	1444**t**	1547	1644**t**	1747	1844**t**	1947	1947	2055	2055	2208	2209	2309
23	Grünberg (Oberhess). d.	...	0549	...	0709**e**	0811**k**	0816	0911	1013	1111	1213	1311	1411	1413	1511	1611**v**	1711	1811**v**	1911	2015	2015	2119	2119	2236	2234	2340
60	Alsfeld (Oberhess)..... d.	0515	0633	0649	0749	0849	0849	0949	1049	1149	1249	1349	1449	1449	1549	1649	1749	1849	1949	2050	2054	2154	2210	2312	2310	0014
79	Lauterbach (Hess) ..... d.	0529	0649	0703	0803	0903	0903	1003	1103	1203	1303	1403	1503	1503	1603	1703	1803	1903	2003	2103	2107	...	...	...	...	...
06	**Fulda**........................ a.	0602	0719	0730	0830	0930	0930	1030	1130	1230	1330	1430	1530	1530	1630	1730	1830	1930	2030	2130	2137	...	...	...	...	...

	Ⓐ	Ⓐ	Ⓐ	⑥	Ⓐ	⑥	Ⓐ	Ⓐ	†	⑥													Ⓒ	Ⓐ		
da .... d.	...	...	...	...	0535	...	0610	0653	...	0735	0835	0935	1034	1134	1234	1334	1434	1534	1634	1734	1834	1934	2034	2059	2200	2308
terbach (Hess) ...... d.	...	...	...	...	0612**j**	...	0654**j**	0723	...	0805	0905	1005	1105	1205	1305	1405	1505	1605	1705	1805	1905	2005	2105	2124	2225	2333
feld (Oberhess)....... d.	0415	0532	0556	0612	0631	0712	0719**j**	0757**j**	0814	0819	0919	1019	1119	1219	1319	1419	1519	1619	1719	1819	1919	2019	2122	2137	2239	2347
nberg (Oberhess).. d.	0456	0614	0639	0647	0705	0747	0753	0838	0848	0850	0953	1050	1153	1250**t**	1353	1450**t**	1553	1650**t**	1753	1850**t**	1953	2056	2202	2215	2316**n**	...
ßen .... a.	0521	0640	0704	0711	0729	0816	0818	0906	0915	0915	1018	1115	1218	1315	1416**v**	1515	1616**v**	1715	1816**v**	1915	2018	2124	2232	2239	2339**n**	...

Ⓐ only.
Arrives 10 – 12 minutes earlier.
k – ⑥ only.
n – ⑤⑥ (also June 9, 19, Oct. 2).
t – 3 minutes later on Ⓐ.
v – 2 minutes later on Ⓒ.

ANTUS Verkehrsgesellschaft (2nd class only) GÖTTINGEN - BEBRA 908

Services Eschwege and Bebra and v.v are subject to alteration June 29 - Aug. 11. Certain timings vary by up to 3 minutes Sept. 28 - Oct. 27.

m		Ⓐ¶	⑥	Ⓐ	ⒶF‡	ⒸF	⚒	†								Ⓐ	Ⓒ	Ⓐ	Ⓒ	ⒶH	Ⓒ	Ⓐ	Ⓒ			L
0	**Göttingen**.......... **864** d.	0442	0543	0600	0658	0701	0814	0840	0914	1040	1114	1240	1314	1440	1514	1614	1640	1714	1714	1814	1840	1914	1914	2014	2115	2214
20	Eichenberg......... **864** d.	0458	0558	0618	0713	0719	0830	0854	0930	1054	1130	1254	1330	1454	1530	1630	1654	1730	1730	1830	1854	1930	1930	2030	2130	2230
35	Bad Sooden-Allendorf . d.	0509	0608	0628	0724	0729	0840	0905	0940	1105	1140	1305	1340	1505	1540	1640	1705	1740	1740	1840	1905	1940	1940	2040	2141	2239
49	Eschwege .... a.	0520	0619	0639	0735	0741	0852	0916	0952	1116	1152	1316	1352	1516	1552	1651	1716	1751	1751	1851	1916	1952	1952	2051	2154	2250
49	Eschwege .... d.	0525	0624	0644	0741	0746	0921	0921	1018	1121	1218	1321	1418	1521	1618	1656	1721	1756	1818	1856	1921	1957	2018	2056	2200	2256
87	**Bebra** .... a.	0553	0652	0711	0809	0814	0949	0949	1047	1149	1247	1349	1447	1549	1647	1724	1749	1828	1847	1924	1951	2027	2047	2124	2227	2324

	Ⓐ		Ⓐ	⑥	Ⓐ	G		Ⓐ	Ⓒ	Ⓐ	Ⓒ							Ⓐ	Ⓒ							F
bra........................ d.	0403	...	0518	0622	0633	0731	0832	0905	0932	1003	1032	1105	1203	1305	1403	1505	1603	1705	1705	...	1803	1905	2003	2103	2205	2303
hwege.................... a.	0432	...	0548	0650	0700	0800	0900	0934	1000	1031	1100	1134	1231	1334	1431	1534	1631	1734	1734	...	1831	1934	2031	2131	2233	2331
hwege.................... d.	0437	...	0555	0655	0705	0805	0905	1005	1005	1036	1105	1205	1236	1405	1436	1605	1636	1739	1805	1805	1836	2005	2036	2136	2238	2336
Sooden-Allendorf d.	0449	...	0606	0707	0716	0816	0916	1016	1016	1047	1116	1216	1247	1416	1447	1616	1647	1750	1816	1816	1847	2016	2047	2147	2249	2347
enberg ....**864** d.	0502	...	0624	0722	0732	0832	0932	1032	1032	1100	1132	1232	1301	1432	1500	1632	1700	1806	1832	1832	1900	2032	2100	2200	2300	0003
ttingen ....**864** a.	0515	...	0638	0736	0746	0846	0946	1046	1046	1113	1145	1246	1314	1446	1513	1646	1713	1820	1846	1846	1913	2046	2113	2215	2315	0017

To / from Fulda (Table **901**).
From Fulda (Table **901**) on Ⓒ (also June 20).
H – To Bad Hersfeld (a. 1937).
L – Runs 4 – 5 minutes later on ⑥.
¶ – Runs 3 – 4 minutes **earlier** Eichenberg - Bebra Aug. 12 - Oct. 25.
‡ – 4 – 5 minutes later until Aug. 9.

B (*RE* services); EB★ WÜRZBURG - BAD KISSINGEN - GEMÜNDEN 909

m								Ⓒz	Ⓐe		Ⓐe														
0	**Würzburg** Hbf .... **870 876** ‡ d.	0454**r**	0738	0801	0835	0935	1001	1135	1135	1201	1207	1338	1401	1435	1538	1601	1636	1738	1801	1836	1938	2001	2035	2139	2307
43	**Schweinfurt** Hbf. **870 876** ‡ d.	0610	0811	0830	0913	1011	1030	1205	1205	1230	1302	1411	1430	1513	1613	1631	1713	1811	1831	1913	2012	2030	2113	2214	2347
57	Ebenhausen (Unterf)... **870** ‡ d.	0625	0825	0843	0930	1025	1043	1224	1224	1243	1316	1425	1443	1530	1625	1643	1731	1825	1843	1930	2025	2043	2130	2228	0003
66	**Bad Kissingen**.................. a.	0633	0834	0853	0939	1034	1053	1233	1233	1253	1325	1434	1453	1539	1634	1653	1739	1834	1853	1939	2034	2053	2139	2237	0012
66	**Bad Kissingen**.................. d.	0636	0839	...	...	1039	...	1239	1239	...	1342	1439	...	1544**e**	1639	...	1743**e**	1839	...	1944	2044	...	2144	...	...
85	Hammelburg .... d.	0659	0908	...	...	1106	...	1308	1313	...	1405	1506	...	1608**e**	1706	...	1808**e**	1908	...	2007	2107	...	2212	...	...
73	**Gemünden** (Main).............. a.	0736	0941	...	...	1141	...	1341	1350	...	1441	1541	...	1641**e**	1741	...	1841**e**	1941	...	2039	2144	...	...	...	...

	Ⓐe		Ⓒz	Ⓐe	Ⓐe							Ⓒz	Ⓐe												
münden (Main) .... d.	...	...	...	0617	...	0707**r**	...	0812	...	1012	...	1212	1212	1320**e**	1412	1508**e**	...	1609	1709**e**	...	1809	1909**e**	...	2114	2211
nmelburg .... d.	0545	0612**e**	0636	0700	...	0748**r**	...	0844	...	1044	...	1244	1244	1407**e**	1444	1543**e**	...	1644	1744**e**	...	1844	1945**e**	...	2147	2248
Kissingen.................... a.	0608	0636**e**	0702	0721	...	0810**r**	...	0907	...	1107	...	1307	1307	1429**e**	1507	1609**e**	...	1706	1809**e**	...	1906	2010**e**	...	2210	2309
Kissingen.................... d.	0612	0644	0706	...	0730	0814	0900	0919	1100	1117	1300	1318	1327	1500	1517	1613	1700	1717	1813	1900	1917	2014	2100	2214	2313
nhausen (Unterf) ..... **870** a.	0621	0653	0715	...	0739	0823	0909	0928	1109	1126	1309	1327	1336	1509	1527	1622	1709	1727	1822	1909	1926	2023	2109	2224	2322
weinfurt Hbf ....**870 876** a.	0638	0714	0730	...	0754	0842	0926	0944	1126	1143	1327	1342	1357	1526	1543	1642	1726	1743	1842	1926	1944**v**	2042	2126	2240	2341
rzburg Hbf........**870 876** a.	0718	0746	0820	...	0820	0922	0955	1020	1155	1220	1355	1420	1451	1555	1620	1722	1755	1820	1922	1955	2020	2122	2157	...	0016

Ⓐ (not June 20, Aug. 15, Nov. 1).
⚒ (not June 20, Aug. 15, Nov. 1).
Change trains at Ebenhausen on Ⓒ**z**.
z – Also June 20, Aug. 15, Nov. 1.
‡ – Trains between Würzburg, Schweinfurt and Ebenhausen are often combined with a service to Meiningen or Erfurt. Passengers should take care to join the correct portion for their destination.
★ – Erfurter Bahn (2nd class only).

910 AACHEN - KÖLN - FRANKFURT via high-speed line

SERVICE FROM JUNE 11. See Tables **800**/**911** for services via Bonn and Koblenz. See Table **20** for *Thalys* services Paris - Brussels - Aachen - Köln.

km	km	SEE NOTES ⊠ AND ❖	ICE 827	ICE 827	ICE 521	ICE 523	ICE 511	ICE 711	ICE 811	ICE 1125	ICE 525	ICE 101	ICE 913	ICE 813	ICE 1127	ICE 527	ICE 513	ICE 11	ICE 815	ICE 529	ICE 103	ICE 1011	ICE 121	IC 62
				①–⑤		①–⑥		Ⓐs	①–⑤	⑦m	①–⑥		①–⑥	①–⑤	⑥	①–⑤		①–⑥	①–⑤				①–⑥	
						✕	✕	T✕	✕	✕	t✕	✕	⊗✕	✕	✕	✕	M✕	✕	✕	✕	H✕	M✕	⊠✕	✕
		Dortmund Hbf **800** d.	...	...	...	0404	0435g	...	...	0512	0523	0535e	0550	0558	0612	0623	0637	...	0650	0723	0737	...	...	081
		Essen Hbf **800** d.	...	...	...	0430	|	...	...	0537	0554	|	0615	|	0637	0653	0700	...	0715	0753	|	0823	...	084
		Amsterdam Centraal **28** ⊠ d.	...	...	...	|	|	...	...	|	|	|	|	|	|	|	|	...	|	|	|	|	0638	|
		Düsseldorf Hbf **800** d.	...	...	...	0458	◐	...	...	0606	0621	◐	0648	◐	0706	0721	0727	...	0745	0821	◐	0852	0847	09
		Brussels Midi/Zuid **21** d.	...	...	...	|	|	...	...	|	|	|	|	|	|	|	|	0625	|	|	|	|	|	|
		Aachen Hbf **802 807** d.	...	...	...	|	|	...	...	|	|	|	|	|	|	|	|	0739	|	|	|	|	|	|
		Köln Hbf **800 802 807** a.	...	...	...	|	0546g	...	...	|	|	0646e	|	0709	|	|	0749	0815	|	|	0846	|	0915	|
0	0	**Köln** Hbf **802 807** d.	0319	0319	0422	|	0555	0611	0620	|	|	0655	|	0720	|	|	0755	0827	|	|	0855	|	0928	|
1	1	**Köln** Messe/Deutz **802** d.	|	|	|	0520	|	|	|	0629	0644	|	0712	|	0730	0744	|	|	0811	0844	|	0917	|	09
	15	Köln/Bonn Flughafen ✈ **802** d.	0332	0332	|	0531	|	|	|	|	|	|	|	|	|	|	|	|	0822	|	|	|	|	|
25	31	Siegburg/Bonn 🚋 **807** d.	0342	0342	0436	0541	0609	0626	0635	0643	|	0709	|	0735	0743	|	0809	|	0831	|	0909	|	|	|
88	94	Montabaur d.	0403	0403	0456	0603	|	0645	0655	0703	|	|	|	0755	0803	|	|	|	0857	|	|	|	|	10
110	116	Limburg Süd d.	0414	0414	0507	0614	|	0655	0706	0714	|	|	|	0806	0814	|	|	|	0907	|	|	|	|	10
	171	**Wiesbaden** Hbf a.	|	|	|	|	|	0719	|	|	|	|	|	|	|	|	|	|	|	|	|	|	|	|
	181	**Mainz** Hbf a.	|	|	|	|	|	0744	|	|	|	|	|	|	|	|	|	|	|	|	|	|	|	|
169		**Frankfurt** Flughafen Fernbf ✈ a.	0433	0433	0526	0633	0649	|	0726	0733	0733	0749	0807	0826	0833	0833	0849	0916	0926	0933	0949	1007	1016	10
180		**Frankfurt** (Main) Hbf a.	0448	0448	0540•	0648•	|	|	0741	0748•	0748•	|	|	0841	0848•	0848	|	0931	0941	0948•	|	|	1031	104
		Nürnberg Hbf **920** a.	...	0659	0759	0901	|	|	...	0958	0958	|	|	...	1100	1100	|	...	...	1159	|	|	...	12
		Mannheim Hbf **912** a.	...	|	|	|	0723	0824	...	|	|	0823	0840	...	|	|	0923	...	...	|	1023	1039	...	
		Karlsruhe Hbf **912** a.	...	|	|	|	|	|	...	|	|	0858	|	...	|	|	|	...	...	|	1058	|	...	
		Basel SBB **912** a.	...	|	|	|	|	|	...	|	|	1047	|	...	|	|	|	...	...	|	1247	|	...	
		Stuttgart Hbf **912** a.	...	|	|	|	0808	0921	...	|	|	...	0924	...	|	|	1008	...	...	|	...	1122	...	
		München Hbf **904 930** a.	...	0807	0904	1006	1027	...	...	1108	1108	...	...	...	1207	1207	1227	...	...	1306	...	...	...	14

SEE NOTES ⊠ AND ❖	ICE 1113	ICE 13	ICE 623	ICE 105	ICE 1013	ICE 625	ICE 517	ICE 15	ICE 627	ICE 107	ICE 123	ICE 629	ICE 519	ICE 211	ICE 721	ICE 109	ICE 915	ICE 915	ICE 817	ICE 817	ICE 125	ICE 723	ICE 611	IC 1
				⊠	⊗						⊠						Q⊗	⊗	Ⓒp	Ⓐq	⊠			①–
	J✕	✕	✕	✕	✕	✕	✕	✕	✕	✕	✕	✕	✕	✕	✕	✕	✕	✕	✕	✕	✕	✕	✕	✕
Dortmund Hbf **800** d.	0837	...	0915c	...	...	1014c	1035	...	1123r	1135w	...	1214k	1235	...	1323c	1337w	1350	...	...	...	...	1414c	1435	...
Essen Hbf **800** d.	0900	...	0941	...	...	1041	1100	...	1154	|	...	1241	1300	...	1354	|	1415	...	...	...	...	1440	1500	...
Amsterdam Centraal **28** ⊠ d.	|	...	|	0808	...	|	|	...	|	|	1038	|	|	...	|	|	|	...	...	...	1238	|	|	...
Düsseldorf Hbf **800** d.	0927	...	1012	1022	1052	1108	1127	...	1221	◐	1248	1308	1327	...	1421	◐	1454	1454	...	...	1450	1513	1527	...
Brussels Midi/Zuid **21** d.	|	0823	|	|	|	|	|	1025	|	|	|	|	|	1225	|	|	|	|	...	...	|	|	|	14
Aachen Hbf **802 807** d.	|	0939	|	|	|	|	|	1139	|	|	|	|	|	1339	|	|	|	|	...	...	|	|	|	15
Köln Hbf **800 802 807** a.	0949h	1015	|	1046	|	|	1149	1215	|	1246w	1315	|	1349	1415	|	1446w	|	|	...	...	1519	|	1549	16
Köln Hbf **802 807** d.	0955h	1028	|	1055	|	|	1155	1218v	|	1255	1328	|	1355	1428	|	1455	|	|	1458	1500	1529	|	1555	16
Köln Messe/Deutz **802** d.	0949y	|	1034	|	1116	1130	|	|	1244	|	|	1333	|	|	1444	|	1520	1520	|	|	|	1536	|	|
Köln/Bonn Flughafen ✈ **802** d.	|	|	1045	|	|	|	|	1231v	|	|	|	|	|	|	|	|	|	|	|	|	|	|	|	|
Siegburg/Bonn 🚋 **807** d.	|	|	|	1109	|	1143	1209	|	|	1309	|	1346	1409n	|	|	1509	|	|	1516	1516	|	1552	|	|
Montabaur d.	|	|	|	|	|	1203	|	|	|	|	|	1406	|	|	|	|	|	|	1536	1536	|	|	|	|
Limburg Süd d.	|	|	|	|	|	1214	|	|	|	|	|	1417	|	|	|	|	|	|	1552	1552	|	|	|	|
Wiesbaden Hbf a.	|	|	|	|	|	|	|	|	|	|	|	|	|	|	|	|	|	|	|	|	|	|	|	|
Mainz Hbf a.	|	|	|	|	|	|	|	|	|	|	|	|	|	|	|	|	|	|	|	|	|	|	|	|
Frankfurt Flughafen Fernbf ✈ a.	1050	1116	1133	1149	1207	1233	1249	1316	1333	1349	1416	1436	1449	1516	1533	1549	1607	1607	1611	1611	1618	1633	1650	170
Frankfurt (Main) Hbf a.	|	1131	1148•	|	|	1248•	|	1331	1348•	|	1431	1449•	|	1531	1548•	|	|	|	1626	1626	1631	1648•	|	172
Nürnberg Hbf **920** a.	|	...	1404	|	|	1500	|	...	1559	|	...	1658	|	...	1759	|	|	|	...	...	...	1900	|	...
Mannheim Hbf **912** a.	1123	...	|	1223	1240	|	1323	...	|	1423	...	|	1523	...	|	1623	1639	1639	...	...	...	|	1723	...
Karlsruhe Hbf **912** a.	|	...	|	1258	|	|	|	...	|	1456	...	|	|	...	|	1658	|	|	...	...	...	|	|	...
Basel SBB **912** a.	|	...	|	1447	|	|	|	...	|	1647	...	|	|	...	|	1847	|	|	...	...	...	|	|	...
Stuttgart Hbf **912** a.	1208	...	|	...	1324	|	1408	...	|	...	...	|	1608	...	|	...	1720	1720	...	...	...	|	1808	...
München Hbf **904 930** a.	1427	...	1509	...	...	1606	1627	...	1704	...	...	1804	1827	...	1911	...	...	...	...	...	...	2007	2028	...

SEE NOTES ⊠ AND ❖	ICE 17	ICE 725	ICE 819	ICE 201	ICE 917	ICE 127	ICE 1228	ICE 727	ICE 613	ICE 215	ICE 729	ICE 911	ICE 1103	ICE 203	ICE 919	ICE 129	ICE 821	ICE 821	ICE 615	ICE 19	ICE 605	ICE 605	ICE 221	IC 6
	⑥⑦		Ⓐs		Ⓑ	⊠	Ⓐs	Ⓑ		Ⓑ			⑦	①–⑥	Ⓑ	⊠	Ⓑ	N				R	⊠	
	✕	✕	✕	✕	⊗✕	✕	L✕	✕	✕	✕	✕	✕	✕	✕	⊗✕	✕	✕	✕	✕	✕	✕	✕	✕	✕
Dortmund Hbf **800** d.	...	1523k	...	...	1551	...	1616	...	1635	...	1723k	...	...	...	1756	...	...	...	1835	...	1923k	...	...	20
Essen Hbf **800** d.	...	1555	...	...	1615	...	1640	1653	1700	...	1754	...	...	...	1825	...	1841	1841	1900	...	1950	1950	...	21
Amsterdam Centraal **28** ⊠ d.	...	|	...	...	|	1438	|	|	|	...	|	...	...	...	|	1638	|	|	|	...	|	|	1838	|
Düsseldorf Hbf **800** d.	...	1622	...	...	1645	1651z	1708	1721	1727	...	1822	...	...	...	1852	1848	1908	1908	1927	...	2018	2018	2048	21
Brussels Midi/Zuid **21** d.	1425	|	...	...	|	|	|	|	|	1622u	|	...	...	...	|	|	|	|	|	1825	|	|	|	|
Aachen Hbf **802 807** d.	1539	|	...	...	|	|	|	|	|	1739	|	...	...	...	|	|	|	|	|	1939	|	|	|	|
Köln Hbf **800 802 807** a.	1615	|	...	...	|	1718z	|	|	1749	1815	|	...	...	...	|	1915	|	|	1949	2015	2040	2040	2112	22
Köln Hbf **802 807** d.	1620	|	1628	1655	|	1728	|	|	1755	1819	|	1826	1854	1854	|	1921	|	|	1955	2027	2046	2046	2128	22
Köln Messe/Deutz **802** d.	|	1644	|	|	1713	|	1733	1744	|	|	1844	|	|	|	1920	|	1930	1930	|	|	|	|	|	|
Köln/Bonn Flughafen ✈ **802** d.	|	|	|	|	|	|	|	|	|	|	|	|	|	|	|	|	|	|	|	|	|	|	|	22
Siegburg/Bonn 🚋 **807** d.	1636	|	1643	1709	1726	|	1746	|	|	|	|	1843	1909	1909	|	|	1943	1943	2009	|	2100	2100	|	22
Montabaur d.	1656	|	1703	|	|	|	1806	|	|	|	|	1903	|	|	|	|	2003	2003	|	|	2121	2121	|	23
Limburg Süd d.	1707	|	1718	|	|	|	1820	|	|	|	|	1918	|	|	|	|	2014	2014	|	|	2132	2132	|	23
Wiesbaden Hbf a.	|	|	|	|	|	|	1840	|	|	|	|	|	|	|	|	|	|	|	|	|	|	|	|	|
Mainz Hbf a.	|	|	|	|	|	|	1855	|	|	|	|	|	|	|	|	|	|	|	|	|	|	|	|	|
Frankfurt Flughafen Fernbf ✈ a.	1726	1733	1740	1749	1807	1816	1915	1833	1850	1909	1933	1940	1949	1949	2007	2010	2033	2033	2049	2116	2152	2152	2216	23
Frankfurt (Main) Hbf a.	1741	1748•	1756	|	|	1831	1933	1848•	|	1925	1948•	1957	|	|	|	2026	2048•	2048•	|	2131	|	|	2231	23
Nürnberg Hbf **920** a.	...	1959	...	|	|	...	...	2100	|	...	2159	...	|	|	|	...	2259	2259	|	...	|	|	...	
Mannheim Hbf **912** a.	...	|	...	1823	1839	...	...	|	1923	...	|	...	2023	2023	2039	...	...	|	2123	...	2224	2224	...	01
Karlsruhe Hbf **912** a.	...	|	...	1858	|	...	...	|	|	...	|	...	2100	2100	|	...	...	|	|	...	2300	2300	...	01
Basel SBB **912** a.	...	|	...	2047	|	...	...	|	|	...	|	...	2250	2300a	|	...	...	|	|	...	...	0052b	...	|
Stuttgart Hbf **912** a.	...	|	...	...	1924	...	...	|	2008	...	|	...	...	...	2123	...	...	|	2208	...	...	...	...	03
München Hbf **904 930** a.	...	2109	...	...	...	...	...	2206	2226	...	2310	...	...	...	...	...	...	0007	0027	...	...	...	...	06

H – From Hannover (Table **810**).
J – From Hamburg (Table **800**). Train number **1211** from Sept. 2.
L – 🚃12 and ✕ Kassel - Paderborn - Dortmund - Mainz - Frankfurt.
M – From Münster (Table **800**).
N – ④⑤⑦ (also June 19).
Q – ①②③④⑥ (not June 19, Oct. 2, 31).
R – ①②③④⑦.
T – Until Oct. 4 runs as *ICE* 715 and arrives Stuttgart 1019.

a – ①–⑤ only.
b – Basel **Badischer Bahnhof**.
c – ⑥⑦ only.
e – ①–⑥ only.
g – ① (also June 11).
h – From Sept. 2.
k – ⑥ only.
m – Also June 20, Oct. 3.
n – From July 13.
p – Also June 20, Nov. 1.
q – Not June 20, Nov. 1.
r – ⑤–⑦ (also Oct. 2; not Oct. 4).

s – Not June 20.
t – Not June 20, Oct. 3.
u – 1625 on ⑦ (also June 10, Aug. 15, Nov. 1).
v – On June 27 – 30, Aug. 2 – 11, Sept. 28, 29, Nov. 16, 17 departs Köln Hbf 1228 and does not call at Köln/Bonn Flughafen.
w – ⑦ only.
y – Until Sept. 1.
z – On Aug. 31, Oct. 5, 12, 19, 26, Nov. 2 Düsseldorf d. 1648, Köln a. 1712.

⊗ – Not July 13 - Aug. 25.
• – Calls at Frankfurt (Main) Süd (not Hbf) on ⑥⑦ Aug. 10 - Sept. 29.
◐ – Via Wuppertal (Table **800**).
⊠ – Amsterdam services are subject to alteration June 27 – 30, Aug. 2 – 11, Sept. 28, 29, Nov. 16, (diversions and / or retimings are scheduled; different train numbers apply). Amsterdam servic are also affected by the alterations outlined in note ❖.
❖ – Timings of services from Amsterdam, Dortmund, Essen and Düsseldorf are subject to alterat July 13 - Aug. 25. From Oct. 26 certain services do not call at Frankfurt Flughafen and timi at Frankfurt Hbf / Flughafen may vary by up to 13 minutes. See the engineering work panel page 369 for further details and also for other alterations affecting services in this table
🚋 – Frequent light-rail services operate from / to Bonn Hbf.

FRANKFURT - KÖLN - AACHEN via high-speed line 910

SERVICE FROM JUNE 11. See Tables **800**/**911** for services via Koblenz and Bonn. See Table **20** for *Thalys* services Köln - Aachen - Brussels - Paris.

SEE NOTES ⊠ AND ❖	ICE 222	ICE 1018	ICE 618	ICE 712	ICE 18	ICE 616	ICE 824	ICE 1223	ICE 220	ICE 918	ICE 604	ICE 822	ICE 214	ICE 614	ICE 820	ICE 128	ICE 916	ICE 202	ICE 728	ICE 16	ICE 16	ICE 612	ICE 726	ICE 126
	①-⑤	⑦	①-⑥	Ⓐs	①-⑥		①-⑤	Ⓐs	⊠	①-⑥		①-⑥	△		①-⑥	⊠	①-⑥			⑦	①-⑥		①-⑥	⊠
	⊠✕	✕	✕		✕	✕	✕	D✕	✕	⊗✕	✕	✕	✕	✕	✕	✕	⊗✕	✕	✕	✕	✕	✕	✕	✕
München Hbf **904 930** d.	...	0001z	0001z	...	...	0324x	...	...	...	...	...	0448	...	0522	0547f	...	...	...	0648	...	...	0728	0752	...
Stuttgart Hbf **912** d.	...	0228	0228	...	...	0551	...	...	...	0640j	...	|	...	0751	|	...	0833	...	|	...	...	0951	|	...
Basel SBB **912** d.	...	|	|	...	...	|	...	...	...	|	0514b	|	...	|	|	...	|	0713e	|	...	...	|	|	...
Karlsruhe Hbf **912** d.	...	0349	0349	...	...	|	...	...	...	|	0700	|	...	|	|	...	|	0900	|	...	...	|	|	...
Mannheim Hbf **912** d.	...	0440	0440	...	...	0636	...	...	...	0721	0735	|	...	0836	|	...	0921	0935	|	...	...	1036	|	...
Nürnberg Hbf **920** d.	...	|	|	...	...	|	0500	...	...	|	|	0600	...	|	0657	...	|	|	0800	...	...	|	0902	...
Frankfurt (Main) Hbf d.	0529	0544	0544	...	0627	|	0710	...	0725	|	|	0810•	0814	|	0909•	0929	|	|	1010•	1016v	1029	|	1110•	1129
Frankfurt Flughafen Fernbf ✈ d.	0543	0601	0601	...	0643	0709	0725	0714	0743	0755	0809	0825	0831	0909	0923	0943	0955	1009	1025	1031v	1043	1109	1122	1143
Mainz Hbf d.	|	|	|	0607	|	|	|	|	|	|	|	|	|	|	|	|	|	|	|	|	|	|	|	|
Wiesbaden Hbf d.	|	|	|	0623	|	|	|	|	|	|	|	|	|	|	|	|	|	|	|	|	|	|	|	|
Limburg Süd d.	|	0620	0620	0643	|	|	|	0733	|	|	|	|	0850	|	0941	|	|	|	|	1050v	|	|	1140	|
Montabaur d.	|	0630	0630	0654	|	|	|	0748	|	|	|	|	0901	|	0951	|	|	|	|	1101v	|	|	1151	|
Siegburg/Bonn 🚋 **807** d.	|	0650	0650	|	|	0747	|	0807	|	|	0847	|	0921	0947n	1011	|	|	1047	|	|	|	|	1211	|
Köln/Bonn Flughafen ✈ **802** a.	|	|	|	|	0726‡	|	|	|	|	|	|	|	|	|	|	|	|	|	|	|	|	|	|	|
Köln Messe/Deutz **802** a.	|	|	|	|	|	|	0814	0822	|	0841	|	0914	|	|	1025	|	1041	|	1114	|	|	|	1225	|
Köln Hbf **802 807** a.	0633	0705	0705	0727	0740‡	0805	|	|	0833	|	0905	|	0939	1005	|	1033	|	1105	|	1133	1133	1205	|	1233
Köln Hbf **800 802 807** d.	0641	0711	0713	...	0742	0811	|	|	0841	|	...	|	0943	1011	|	1041	|	...	|	1143	1143	1211	|	1241
Aachen Hbf **802 807** a.	|	|	|	...	0816	|	|	|	|	|	...	|	1016	|	|	|	|	...	|	1216	1216	|	|	|
Brussels Midi/Zuid **21** a.	|	|	|	...	0935	|	|	|	|	|	...	|	1135	|	|	|	|	...	|	1335	1335	|	|	|
Düsseldorf Hbf **800** a.	0706	◐	0735	...	...	0831	0836	0845	0906	0911	...	0936	...	1031	1046	1105	1110	...	1136	...	...	1231	1246	1306
Amsterdam Centraal **28** ⊠ a.	0928	|	|	...	...	|	|	|	1128	...	...	|	...	|	|	1328	|	...	|	...	...	|	|	1528
Essen Hbf **800** a.	...	|	0802	...	...	0857	0902	0915	...	...	...	1002	...	1057	1114	...	1139y	...	1202	...	...	1257	1313	...
Dortmund Hbf **800** a.	...	0821	0827k	...	...	0921	...	0940	...	...	...	1030k	...	1121	1141k	...	1203y	...	1230p	...	...	1321	1343k	...

SEE NOTES ⊠ AND ❖	ICE 914	ICE 200	ICE 724	ICE 210	ICE 610	ICE 722	ICE 1122	ICE 124	ICE 818	ICE 1014	ICE 108	ICE 720	ICE 14	ICE 518	ICE 628	ICE 816	ICE 106	ICE 626	ICE 826	ICE 12	ICE 122	ICE 710	ICE 516	ICE 624
	⊗					Ⓐs	Ⓒm	⊠	Ⓐs	⊗						▲			Ⓐs	Ⓑ		Ⓐs		⚒s
	✕	✕	✕	✕	✕	✕	✕	✕	✕	✕	✕	✕	✕	✕	✕	✕	✕	✕	✕	✕	✕	T✕	✕	✕
München Hbf **904 930** d.	...	...	0848	...	0928	0951	0951	...	...	...	...	1055	...	1128	1151	...	...	1250	1250	...	...	...	1328	1351
Stuttgart Hbf **912** d.	1041	...	|	...	1151	|	|	...	...	1237	...	|	...	1351	|	...	...	|	|	...	...	1433	1551	|
Basel SBB **912** d.	|	0913	|	...	|	|	|	...	...	|	1113	|	...	|	|	...	1313	|	|	...	...	|	|	|
Karlsruhe Hbf **912** d.	|	1059	|	...	|	|	|	...	...	|	1300	|	...	|	|	...	1500	|	|	...	...	|	|	|
Mannheim Hbf **912** d.	1121	1135	|	...	1236	|	|	...	...	1321	1335	|	...	1436	|	...	1535	|	|	...	...	1533	1636	|
Nürnberg Hbf **920** d.	|	|	1000	...	|	1100	1100	...	...	|	|	1200	...	|	1257	...	|	1400	1400	...	...	|	|	1500
Frankfurt (Main) Hbf d.	|	|	1210•	1229	|	1310	1310•	1329	1335	|	|	1410•	1429	|	1510•	1516	|	1609•	1609	1627	1627	|	|	1710•
Frankfurt Flughafen Fernbf ✈ d.	1155	1209	1225	1243	1309	1325	1322	1343	1349	1355	1409	1425	1443	1509	1525	1531	1609	1626	1633	1643	1643	|	1709	1725
Mainz Hbf d.	|	|	|	|	|	|	|	|	|	|	|	|	|	|	|	|	|	|	|	|	|	1622	|	|
Wiesbaden Hbf d.	|	|	|	|	|	|	|	|	|	|	|	|	|	|	|	|	|	|	|	|	|	1645	|	|
Limburg Süd d.	|	|	|	|	|	|	1340	|	1412	|	|	|	|	|	|	1549	|	|	|	1701r	1701r	1708	|	|
Montabaur d.	|	|	|	|	|	|	1351	|	1422	|	|	|	|	|	|	1600	|	|	1656	|	|	1718	|	|
Siegburg/Bonn 🚋 **807** d.	|	1247	1303	|	|	1402	1411	|	|	|	1447	|	|	1547	|	1620	1647	|	1728a	|	|	1739	1747	|
Köln/Bonn Flughafen ✈ **802** a.	|	|	1311	|	|	|	|	|	|	|	|	|	|	|	|	|	|	|	|	|	|	1747	|	|
Köln Messe/Deutz **802** a.	1241	|	1324	|	|	1415	1425	|	|	1441	|	1514	|	|	1614	|	|	1713	1741	|	|	|	|	1814
Köln Hbf **802 807** a.	|	1305	|	1333	1405	|	|	1433	1456	|	1505	|	1533	1605	|	1639	1705	|	...	1739	1739	1801	1805	|
Köln Hbf **800 802 807** d.	|	1311h	|	1343	1411	|	|	1444	...	|	1511k	|	1543	1611	|	...	...	|	...	1743	1746	...	1811	|
Aachen Hbf **802 807** a.	|	|	|	1416	|	|	|	|	...	|	|	|	1616	|	|	...	...	|	...	1816	|	...	|	|
Brussels Midi/Zuid **21** a.	|	|	|	1535	|	|	|	|	...	|	|	|	1735	|	|	...	...	|	...	1935	|	...	|	|
Düsseldorf Hbf **800** a.	1310	◐	1345	...	1431	1436	1446	1510	...	1515	◐	1536	...	1631	1639	...	...	1736	...	...	1811	...	1831	1836
Amsterdam Centraal **28** ⊠ a.	|	|	|	...	|	|	|	1728	...	|	|	|	...	|	|	...	...	|	...	...	2028	...	|	|
Essen Hbf **800** a.	1339e	|	1415	...	1457	1504	1513	...	...	1544	|	1602	...	1658	1706	...	...	1802	...	...	...	...	1857	1902
Dortmund Hbf **800** a.	1403e	1421h	1442k	...	1521	...	1542k	...	...	1607	1621k	1627k	...	1721	1742k	...	...	1830k	...	...	...	...	1921	1930

SEE NOTES ⊠ AND ❖	ICE 1124	ICE 814	ICE 1010	ICE 204	ICE 104	ICE 622	ICE 10	ICE 828	ICE 812	ICE 1212	ICE 620	ICE 120	ICE 912	ICE 102	ICE 1102	ICE 528	ICE 1118	ICE 810	ICE 512	ICE 526	ICE 100	ICE 524	ICE 1110	ICE 522
	†m	①-⑥		①-⑤	⊠			①-④	⑤⑦			Ⓑ	Ⓑ	Ⓑ	⑥		⑦S	A					⑤-⑦	
	✕	✕	M✕	✕	✕	✕	✕	R✕	Q✕	J✕	✕	⊠✕	⊗✕	H✕	H✕	✕	✕	✕	M✕	✕	✕	✕		✕
München Hbf **904 930** d.	1351	...	...	...	...	1451	...	...	...	1528	1551	...	...	...	...	1649	...	...	1728	1751	...	1851	1928	1948
Stuttgart Hbf **912** d.	|	...	1637	...	...	|	...	...	...	1751	|	...	1837	...	...	|	...	...	1951	|	...	|	2151	|
Basel SBB **912** d.	|	...	|	1513	1513	|	...	...	...	|	|	...	|	1713	1713	|	...	...	|	|	1913	|	|	|
Karlsruhe Hbf **912** d.	|	...	|	1700	1700	|	...	...	...	|	|	...	|	1900	1900	|	...	...	|	|	2101	|	|	|
Mannheim Hbf **912** d.	|	...	1721	1735	1735	|	...	...	...	1836	|	...	1921	1935	1935	|	...	...	2036	|	2135	|	2236	|
Nürnberg Hbf **920** d.	1500	...	|	|	|	1600	...	...	...	|	1657	...	|	|	|	1800	...	...	|	1857	|	2000	|	2100
Frankfurt (Main) Hbf d.	1710•	1716	|	|	|	1810•	1827	1816	1816	|	1910•	1929	|	|	|	2010•	2016	2031	|	2110•	|	2210•	|	2310◊
Frankfurt Flughafen Fernbf ✈ d.	1722	1731	1755	1809	1809	1825	1843	1831	1831	1909	1922	1943	1955	2009	2009	2025	2031	2044	2109	2125	2209	2225	2311	2325
Mainz Hbf d.	|	|	|	|	|	|	|	|	|	|	|	|	|	|	|	|	|	|	|	|	|	|	|	|
Wiesbaden Hbf d.	|	|	|	|	|	|	|	|	|	|	|	|	|	|	|	|	|	|	|	|	|	|	|	|
Limburg Süd d.	1740	1749	|	|	|	|	|	1849	1849	|	1940	|	|	|	|	|	2050	2102	|	|	|	2243	|	2343
Montabaur d.	1751	1800	|	|	|	|	|	1906	1906	|	1951	|	|	|	|	|	2101	2113	|	|	|	2254	|	2354
Siegburg/Bonn 🚋 **807** d.	1811	1821c	|	1847	1847	|	1921	1927	1927	|	2011	|	|	2047	2047	|	2121	2134	2147	|	2247	2314	2347	0014
Köln/Bonn Flughafen ✈ **802** a.	|	|	|	|	|	|	|	1937	1937	|	|	|	|	|	|	|	|	2142t	|	|	|	2326	|	|
Köln Messe/Deutz **802** a.	1826	1845k	1841	|	|	1914	|	1949	|	2005d	2025	|	2042	|	|	2113	|	|	|	2214	|	2337	|	|
Köln Hbf **802 807** a.	|	...	|	1905	1905	|	1939	...	1955	2005g	|	2033	|	2105	2105	|	2140	2157	2205	|	2305	|	0005	0039
Köln Hbf **800 802 807** d.	|	...	|	1911	1914	|	1943	...	...	2011g	|	2042	|	2111	2111	|	2143	...	2211	|	2311	|	...	0042
Aachen Hbf **802 807** a.	|	...	|	|	|	|	2016	...	...	|	|	|	|	|	|	|	2216	...	|	|	|	|	...	|
Brussels Midi/Zuid **21** a.	|	...	|	|	|	|	2135	...	...	|	|	|	|	|	|	|	2335	...	|	|	|	|	...	|
Düsseldorf Hbf **800** a.	1846	...	1905	◐	1936	1944	...	...	...	2027	2046	2106	2110	◐	2131	2136	...	...	2231	2236	2331	2358	...	0103
Amsterdam Centraal **28** ⊠ a.	|	...	|	|	2158	|	...	...	...	|	|	2328	|	|	|	|	...	...	|	|	|	|	...	|
Essen Hbf **800** a.	1914	...	1934	|	...	2015	...	...	...	2058	2114	...	2140	|	2157	2202	...	...	2259	2302	0002	0025	...	0134
Dortmund Hbf **800** a.	1942	...	...	2021	...	2042	...	...	...	2121	2142	...	2203	2221	2222	2228	...	...	...	2326	0026	0050	...	0156

A – ①-⑥ to Nov. 2; daily from Nov. 4.
D – (12) and ✕ Darmstadt Hbf (d. 0648) - Dortmund - Paderborn - Kassel. From Oct. 28 starts from Wiesbaden Hbf (d. 0708), not calling at Darmstadt or Frankfurt Flughafen.
H – To Hannover (Table **810**).
J – To Hamburg (Table **800**). Train number **1210** from Sept. 2. Arrives Düsseldorf 2031 from Sept. 2.
M – To Münster (Table **800**).
Q – ⑤⑦ (also Oct. 2). Runs 17–25 minutes **earlier** from Oct. 27.
R – ①-④ (not Oct. 2). To Hamm via Wuppertal (Table **800**). From Oct. 28 runs 18–20 minutes **earlier** Frankfurt - Köln/Bonn Flughafen.
S – ⑦ to Nov. 3. Departures Frankfurt - Montabaur are 13–19 minutes **earlier** on Oct. 27, Nov. 3.
T – Until Oct. 4 runs as *ICE* **714** (departs Stuttgart 1335).

a – Arrives 1715.
b – ①-⑤ only. Basel **Badischer Bahnhof**.
c – Not ⑥ Oct. 26 - Dec. 14.
d – Until Sept. 1.
e – ①-⑥ only.
f – ①-⑤ to July 12 (not June 20); ①-⑤ Aug. 15 - Sept. 27; ⚒ Sept. 30 - Nov. 2.
g – From Sept. 2.
h – ⑥ (not July 13 - Aug. 24, Oct. 26, Nov. 2).
j – 0621 on ⑥.
k – ⑥ only.
m – Also June 20.
n – From July 13.
p – ⑥⑦ only.
r – Ⓐ (not July 15 - Aug. 23).
s – Not June 20.
t – Until Oct. 25.
v – 13–19 minutes earlier from Oct. 26.
x – 0315 on ①⑦ July 28 - Sept. 2.
y – ①②③④⑥ (not June 19, Oct. 2, 31).
z – On ①⑦ July 28 - Sept. 2 departs 2354 (the previous day).

⊗ – Not July 13 - Aug. 25.
‡ – Does not call at Köln/Bonn Flughafen, arrives Köln Hbf 0733 June 27–29, Aug. 2–10, Sept. 28, Nov. 16.
• – Calls at Frankfurt (Main) Süd (not Hbf) on ⑥⑦ Aug. 10 - Sept. 29 (may depart up to 3 minutes earlier).
◊ – Calls at Frankfurt Süd (not Hbf) on ⑤-⑦ Aug. 9 - Sept. 29 (d. 2307).
▲ – From Oct. 26 Frankfurt (Main) Hbf d. 1457, Frankfurt Flughafen d. 1512, Limburg Süd d. 1531, Montabaur d. 1548, Siegburg/Bonn a. 1606, d. 1620, Köln Hbf a. 1639.
△ – On June 27–30, Aug. 2–11, Sept. 28, 29 departs Frankfurt (Main) Hbf 0826, Frankfurt Flughafen 0843, arrives Köln 0932 and then as shown (not calling at Limburg, Montabaur or Siegburg/Bonn). From Oct. 26 Frankfurt (Main) Hbf d. 0754, Frankfurt Flughafen d. 0812, Limburg Süd d. 0832, Montabaur d. 0848, Siegburg/Bonn a. 0906, d. 0921 and then as shown.
⊠ – Amsterdam services are subject to alteration June 27–30, Aug. 2–11, Sept. 28, 29, Nov. 16, 17 (diversions and/or retimings are scheduled; different train numbers apply; also applies to train *ICE* **120** on June 26, Aug. 1, Sept. 27 and Nov. 15). Amsterdam services are also affected by the alterations outlined in note ❖.
❖ – Timings of services to Düsseldorf, Essen, Dortmund and Amsterdam are subject to alteration July 13 - Aug. 25. From Oct. 26 certain services do not call at Frankfurt Flughafen and timings at Frankfurt Hbf/Flughafen may vary by up to 13 minutes (earlier departures possible). See the engineering work panel on page 369 for further details and also for other alterations affecting services in this table.
◐ – Via Wuppertal (Table **800**).
🚋 – Frequent light-rail services operate from/to Bonn Hbf.

911 KOBLENZ - MAINZ - MANNHEIM and FRANKFURT

km	SEE NOTE ❖	IC 209		IC 2419	ICE 672	ICE 991	IC 2021	ICE 23	ICE 711	IC 2317	IC 2319	ICE 1557	ICE 1221	EC 115	EC 7	EC 7	ICE 1559	IC 1919	ICE 27	IC 2005	EC 9	ICE 1651	IC 2013	ICE 923
				①g		①–⑤			ⒶX	⑥F	①–⑥	⊠			①–⑥	⑦	⊠			⑤⑥		⊠		
		K			H ❦		◇	✕♦	✕		🍷	D	S✕	🍷♦	J✕	J✕	D✕	♦	✕♦	🍷♦	Z✕	D✕	🍷♦	✕
	Hamburg Hbf **800** d.	1946	...	...	...	...	2246	...	...	...	...	...	...	...	0438	...	...	...	...	...	0646	...	...	0746
	Dortmund Hbf **800** d.	2237	...	...	...	...	0144	0435	...	...	0537	...	0635	...	|	0737	...	0724	0834	...	|	...	0950	1036
	Köln Hbf **800** d.	2353	...	0206	...	...	0349	0553	0611	...	0653	...	0753	0818	0853	0853	...	0917	0953	1018	1053	...	1117	1153
	Bonn Hbf **800** d.	0014	...	0229	...	...	0414	0614	|	...	0714	...	0814	0838	0914	0914	...	0938	1014	1038	1114	...	1137	1214
0	**Koblenz** Hbf **914** d.	0048	...	0310	...	...	0531	0648	|	...	0748	...	0848	0918	0948	0948	...	1018	1048	1118	1148	...	1218	1248
61	Bingen (Rhein) Hbf **914** d.	|	...	0347	...	...	0610	|	|	...	|	...	|	0953	|	|	...	1053	|	1153	|	...	1253	|
	Wiesbaden Hbf **917a** d.	|	...	|	0500	0526	|	|	0732	...	|	0826	|	|	|	|	1026	|	|	|	|	1226	|	|
91	**Mainz** Hbf **914 917a** a.	0139	...	0409	0510	0536	0627	0738	0744	...	0839	0836	0939	1015	1039	1039	1036	1110	1139	1215	1239	1236	1310	1339
91	**Mainz** Hbf **911a 917a** d.	0142	...	0412	0512	0540	0629	0740	0746	0746	0842	0843	0942	1017	1042	1042	1043	1112	1142	1217	1242	1243	1312	1342
117	**Frankfurt** Flughafen ✈ ◧ **917a** a.	0159	...	0438	0530	|	0645	0759	|	|	|	0900	0959	|	|	|	1100	|	1159	|	|	1300	|	1401
128	**Frankfurt** (Main) Hbf **917a** a.	0232	...	0454	0544	|	0702	0813	|	|	|	0912	1013	|	|	|	1113	|	1213	|	|	1313	|	1413
	Nürnberg Hbf **920** a.	|	...	|	...	|	...	1027	|	|	|	...	1224	|	|	|	...	|	1427	|	|	...	|	...
	Worms Hbf **911a** d.	|	...	|	...	0608	...	...	|	|	|	...	|	1045	|	|	...	|	...	1245	|	...	|	...
	Mannheim Hbf **911a** a.	0331	...	|	...	0623	...	...	0824	0824	0921	...	|	1100	1121	1121	...	1152	...	1307	1321	...	1352	...
	Stuttgart Hbf **912** a.	|	...	0700	...	0707	...	...	0921	0928	1024	...	|	1153	|	|	...	1246	...	|	|	...	1446	...
	München Hbf **930** a.	|	...	...	...	0927	...	...	...	...	...	...	1338	1411h	|	|	...	...	...	|	|	...	...	...
	Karlsruhe Hbf **912** a.	0401	...	...	...	...	...	...	...	...	...	...	...	...	1147	1147	...	...	...	1334	1347	...	...	...
	Basel SBB **912** a.	0622	...	...	...	...	...	...	...	...	...	...	...	...	1330	1330	...	...	...	...	1535	...	...	...

SEE NOTE ❖	IC 2313	ICE 1653	IC 1911	ICE 925	IC 2217	ICE 1655	ICE 1655	IC 2011	IC 2027	IC 2019	IC 2311	ICE 1657	ICE 1228	IC 1915	IC 2229	IC 2213	ICE 1659	ICE 1625	IC 1917	IC 2029	IC 2215	IC 2315	IC 2221	IC 2321
		⊠	⑤⑦	▽		Ⓑj	⑥k	Ⓑ		⑥		Ⓑ⊠	Ⓐt	⑤⑦			Ⓑ	⑥	⑦		T	L		★
	🍷	D✕	v🍷	✕	🍷♦	D🍷	D🍷	U🍷	P🍷	🍷♦	G🍷	D✕	✕	🍷♦	🍷♦	🍷♦	⊠♦	✕	B🍷	🍷	🍷	G🍷	🍷♦	🍷
Hamburg Hbf **800** d.	0846	...	...	0946	1046	...	...	...	1146	...	1246	...	...	...	1346	1446	...	...	...	1546	1646	1646	1746	1746
Dortmund Hbf **800** d.	|	...	1150	|	|	...	...	...	1436	...	|	...	1616	...	1636	|	...	...	...	1836	|	|	|	|
Köln Hbf **800** d.	1253	...	1317	1353	1453	...	...	1517	1553	1617	1653	...	|	1717	1753	1853	...	...	1912b	1953	2053	2053	2153	2153
Bonn Hbf **800** d.	1314	...	1337	1414	1514	...	...	1537	1614	1637	1714	...	|	1737	1814	1914	...	...	1935b	2014	2114	2114	2214	2214
Koblenz Hbf **914** d.	1348	...	1418	1448	1548	...	...	1618	1648	1718	1748	...	|	1818	1848	1948	...	...	2018	2048	2148	2148	2248	2248
Bingen (Rhein) Hbf **914** d.	|	...	1453	|	|	...	...	1653	|	1753	|	...	|	1853	|	|	...	...	2053	2123	|	|	|	|
Wiesbaden Hbf **917a** d.	|	1426	|	|	|	1626	1626	|	|	|	|	1826	1846	|	|	|	2026	2026	|	|	|	|	|	|
Mainz Hbf **914 917a** a.	1439	1436	1510	1539	1639	1636	1636	1710	1739	1815	1839	1836	1855	1910	1939	2039	2036	2036	2110	2142	2239	2239	2339	2339
Mainz Hbf **911a 917a** d.	1442	1443	1512	1542	1642	1643	1643	1712	1742	1817	1842	1843	1857	1912	1942	2042	2043	2043	2112	2144	2242	2242	2342	2342
Frankfurt Flughafen ✈ ◧ **917a** a.	|	1500	|	1559	|	|	1700	|	1759	|	|	1900	1915	|	1959	|	2100	2100	|	2159	2302	2302	2359	2359
Frankfurt (Main) Hbf **917a** a.	|	1515	|	1613	|	1709	1715	|	1813	|	|	1913	1933	|	2013	|	2113	2113	|	2213	2315	2315	0013	0013
Nürnberg Hbf **920** a.	|	...	|	...	|	...	...	|	2027	|	|	...	...	|	2227q	|	...	2328	|	0044	...	...	...	...
Worms Hbf **911a** d.	|	...	|	...	|	...	...	|	...	1845	|	...	...	|	...	|	...	|	|	...	...	...	...	...
Mannheim Hbf **911a** a.	1521	...	1552	...	1721	...	...	1752	...	1901	1921	...	...	1952	...	2121	...	|	2152	...	...	...	...	...
Stuttgart Hbf **912** a.	1622	...	1646	...	1829	...	...	1846	...	1958	2024	...	...	2046	...	2224	...	|	|	...	...	...	...	...
München Hbf **930** a.	...	...	...	...	...	...	...	...	...	...	...	...	...	...	...	...	...	0043	|	...	...	...	...	...
Karlsruhe Hbf **912** a.	...	...	...	...	...	...	...	...	...	...	...	...	...	...	...	...	...	...	2221b	...	...	...	...	...
Basel SBB **912** a.	...	...	...	...	...	...	...	...	...	...	...	...	...	...	...	...	...	...	...	...	...	...	...	...

km	SEE NOTE ❖	ICE 887		IC 208		IC 2220	IC 2320		IC 2310	IC 2028	IC 2018	IC 2010	ICE 1656	IC 2216	IC 2226	ICE 1654	IC 2218	IC 1922	IC 2024	ICE 1652	IC 2312	IC 2006	IC 2004	IC 2014
							★		⊖		⑥	①–⑤	⊠			⊠		⑤⑦		⊠		⑥	⑦	⑤
		H		K		🍷♦	🍷		G🍷	🍷	🍷♦	E🍷	✕♦	🍷♦	🍷♦	D✕	🍷	vB 🍷	P🍷	D✕	🍷	🍷♦	🍷♦	🍷♦
	Basel SBB **912** d.	...	...	2313	...	...	...	...	...	...	...	...	...	...	...	...	...	...	...	...	...	...	...	...
	Karlsruhe Hbf **912** d.	...	...	0130	...	...	...	...	...	...	...	...	...	...	...	...	...	...	...	...	...	1221	1221	...
	München Hbf **930** d.	...	...	|	...	...	...	...	...	...	...	...	...	...	...	...	...	...	...	...	...	|	|	...
	Stuttgart Hbf **912** d.	...	...	|	...	...	...	...	...	...	0714	0714	...	0737	...	...	0937	1009	...	...	1137	|	|	1208
0	**Mannheim** Hbf **911a** d.	...	...	0216	...	...	...	...	...	...	0808	0808	...	0839	...	...	1039	1052	...	...	1239	1258	1258	1258
24	Worms Hbf **911a** d.	...	...	|	...	...	...	...	...	...	|	|	...	|	...	...	|	1115	...	...	|	1315	1315	1315
	Nürnberg Hbf **920** d.	...	...	|	...	...	...	...	...	0526	|	|	...	|	0729e	...	|	|	0929	...	|	|	|	|
	Frankfurt (Main) Hbf **917a** d.	0013	...	0308	...	0542	0542	...	0638	0742	|	|	0842	|	0942	1042	|	|	1142	1242	|	|	|	|
	Frankfurt Flughafen ✈ ◧ **917a** d.	0027	...	0323	...	0557	0557	...	0657	0758	|	|	0858z	|	0958	1058z	|	|	1158	1258z	|	|	|	|
70	**Mainz** Hbf **911a 917a** a.	0044	...	0345	...	0615	0615	...	0715	0818	0847	0847	0915	0918	1018	1115	1118	1142	1218	1315	1318	1342	1342	1342
70	**Mainz** Hbf **914 917a** d.	0046	...	0403	...	0617	0617	...	0717	0820	0849	0849	0922	0920	1020	1122	1120	1144	1220	1322	1320	1344	1344	1344
80	**Wiesbaden** Hbf **917a** a.	0058	...	|	...	|	|	...	|	|	|	|	0933	|	|	1133	|	|	|	1333	|	|	|	|
	Bingen (Rhein) Hbf **914 917a** d.	...	...	0425	...	0635	0635	...	|	|	0907	0907	...	|	|	...	|	1207	|	...	|	1407	1407	1407
	Koblenz Hbf **914 917a** a.	...	...	0505	...	0711	0711	...	0811	0911	0942	0942	...	1011	1111	...	1211	1242	1311	...	1411	1442	1442	1442
	Bonn Hbf **800** a.	...	...	0544	...	0744	0744	...	0844	0944	1021	1021	...	1044	1144	...	1244	1321	1344	...	1444	1521	1521	1521
	Köln Hbf **800** a.	...	...	0606	...	0805	0805	...	0905	1005	1043	1043	...	1105	1205	...	1305	1343	1405	...	1505	1543	1543	1543
	Dortmund Hbf **800** a.	...	...	0721	...	0921	0921	...	|	1121	...	...	...	|	1321	...	|	1508f	1521	...	|	1704	...	...
	Hamburg Hbf **800** a.	...	...	1014	...	1213	1213	...	1314	1414	...	...	...	1512	1614	...	1714	...	1814	...	1914	...	...	...

♦ – **NOTES** (LISTED BY TRAIN NUMBER)

22/3 – 🚃12 and ✕ Wien - Linz - Passau - Regensburg - Dortmund and v.v.
26/7 – 🚃12 and ✕ Wien - Linz - Passau - Regensburg - Dortmund and v.v.
114 – WÖRTHERSEE – 🚃12 and 🍷 Klagenfurt - Salzburg - München - Dortmund.
115 – WÖRTHERSEE – 🚃12 and 🍷 Münster - München - Salzburg - Klagenfurt.
1656 – 🚃12 and ✕ (Leipzig ①–⑥ -) Frankfurt - Wiesbaden.
1659 – 🚃12 and ✕ Wiesbaden - Frankfurt - Erfurt (- Leipzig on dates in Table **850**).
1915 – ⑤⑦ (also June 19, Oct. 2, 31; not June 21, July 12, 19, 26, Aug. 2, 9, 16, 23, Oct. 4, Nov. 1). 🚃12 Berlin - Köln - Stuttgart (- Tübingen ⑦).
1918 – 🚃12 (June 25 - Sept. 9 and Nov. 10 - Dec. 14: Berchtesgaden -) Stuttgart - Dortmund.
1919 – 🚃12 Dortmund - Stuttgart (- Berchtesgaden: June 24 - Sept. 8 and Nov. 9 - Dec. 14).
2004 – ⑦ (also June 20, Oct. 3, Nov. 1). 🚃12 and 🍷 Konstanz - Karlsruhe - Münster - Emden.
2005 – ⑤⑥ (also June 19, Oct. 2, 31). 🚃12 and 🍷 Emden - Münster - Karlsruhe - Konstanz.
2006 – 🚃12 and 🍷 Konstanz - Karlsruhe - Dortmund.
2012/3 – ALLGÄU – 🚃12 and 🍷 Oberstdorf - Ulm - Stuttgart - Dortmund and v.v.
2014 – ⑤ (also June 19, Oct. 2, 31; not Nov. 1). 🚃12 and 🍷 Stuttgart - Münster - Emden.
2018 – ⑥ to Nov. 2 (also June 20, Oct. 3; not July 13 - Aug. 24). 🚃12 and 🍷 Stuttgart - Münster - Norddeich Mole.
2019 – ⑥ to Nov. 2 (also June 20, Oct. 3). 🚃12 and 🍷 Norddeich Mole - Münster - Stuttgart.
2213 – RÜGEN – 🚃12 and 🍷 Ostseebad Binz - Stralsund - Rostock - Hamburg - Stuttgart. June 11 - July 28 calls at Hamburg Harburg (not Hamburg Hbf).
2216/7 – GREIFSWALDER BODDEN – 🚃12 and 🍷 Stuttgart - Hamburg - Rostock - Stralsund (- Greifswald ♥) and v.v. June 11 - July 28 calls at Hamburg Harburg (not Hamburg Hbf).
2220 – ②–④ to June 27; ②–④ Sept. 18 - Oct. 30 (not Oct. 2, 3); ⑤⑦ from Nov. 8. 🚃12 Frankfurt - Köln - Lübeck Hbf (a. 1301).
2221 – ②–④ to June 27; ②–④ Sept. 18 - Oct. 30 (not Oct. 2, 3); ⑤⑦ from Nov. 8. 🚃12 Lübeck Hbf (d. 1637) - Köln - Frankfurt.
2226 – 🚃12 and 🍷 (Passau ⑤⑥c -) (Regensburg ①–⑥ -) Frankfurt - Köln - Hamburg - Kiel.
2229 – 🚃12 and 🍷 Kiel - Köln - Frankfurt (- Nürnberg Ⓑ) (- Regensburg - Passau ♣).
2318 – 🚃12 and 🍷 Stuttgart - Köln (- Dortmund Ⓑ) (- Münster ⑦).

A – From Innsbruck via Garmisch (Table **895**) on Ⓒ. Train number **1222** on Ⓒ.
B – From / to Berlin (Table **810**).
D – To / from Dresden via Leipzig (Table **850**).
E – ①–⑤ (not June 20, 21, Oct. 3, 4, Nov. 1). From Tübingen (Table **930**).
F – From Oct. 12.
G – From / to Westerland (Table **821**).
H – To / from Hamburg (Table **900**).
J – From / to Interlaken via Bern (Table **560**).
K – From / to Kiel (Table **820**).
L – Until Nov. 3.
M – Ⓐ to Oct. 4 (not June 20); Ⓑ from Oct. 7.
P – From / to Passau (Table **920**).
Q – Until Aug. 8.
S – Continues to Seefeld (Table **895**) on ⑤⑥ (also Oct. 2).
T – From Nov. 4.
U – Ⓑ (not June 20, 21, Oct. 3, 4, Nov. 1). To Tübingen (Table **930**) on ①–④ (not June 19, 20, Oct. 2, 3).
W – Ⓐ (not June 20). Until Oct. 4 runs as *ICE* **714** (departs Stuttgart 1335).
X – Ⓐ (not June 20). Until Oct. 4 runs as *ICE* **715** (arrives Stuttgart 1019).
Z – To / from Zürich (Tables **510**).

b – From Oct. 13 departs Köln 1917, Bonn 1937, arrives Karlsruhe 2224.
c – Also June 19, 20.
e – ①–⑥ only.
f – From Oct. 13.
g – Also June 11; not July 8 - Aug. 26.
h – Until July 28 serves München Pasing (not München Hbf).
j – Not Aug. 11 - Oct. 27.
k – Not Aug. 10 - Oct. 26.
q – Ⓑ only.
r – 1–2 minutes later on ⑦.
t – Not June 20.
v – Also June 19, Oct. 2, 31; not June 21, Oct. 4, Nov. 1.
y – 1614 until July 28.
z – 2 minutes earlier from Oct. 28

⊠ – Not Aug. 10 - Oct. 27.
❦ – On ⑥⑦ Aug. 10 - Sept. 29 calls at Frankfurt (Main) **Süd** (not Frankfurt Hbf).
★ – ①⑤⑥⑦ to June 24; daily June 28 - Sept. 17; ①⑤⑥⑦ Sept. 20 - Nov. 3 (also Oct. 2, 3, 31); ①②③④⑥ from Nov. 4.
♠ – ⑤⑦ to July 14 (also June 19; not June 21); Ⓑ July 19 - Sept. 8; ⑤⑦ from Sept. 13 (also Oct. 31; not Nov. 1).
⊗ – ①–④ to July 18 (not June 19, 20); ①–④ from Sept. 9 (also Nov. 1; not Oct. 31
⊕ – ①②③④⑦. Train number **1190** on ⑦ (also June 10).
◇ – Also calls at Boppard Hbf (d. 0544).
⊖ – Also calls at Boppard Hbf (d. 0800).
⊙ – Also calls at Boppard Hbf (d. 0044). Arrives Bonn 0137, Köln 0205 on the mornings of Ⓒ (also June 20, Nov. 1).
△ – Runs as *ICE* **926** and conveys ✕ on ⑥.
▽ – Runs as *IC* **2025** on ⑥ (conveys 🍷).
♥ – See Table **845** for days of running to / from Greifswald.
♣ – See Table **920** for running dates to Regensburg and Passau.
◧ – Frankfurt Flughafen Fernbahnhof.
❖ – Services via Dortmund are subject to alteration July 13 - Aug. 25. Many service do not call at Frankfurt Flughafen from Oct. 26 (in addition, certain northboun services from Frankfurt via Koblenz do not call at Mainz Hbf). See the engineering work panel on page 369 for further details and also for other alterations affecting services in this table.

MANNHEIM and FRANKFURT - MAINZ - KOBLENZ 911

SEE NOTE ✣	IC 2026	IC 2012	ICE 1650	EC 8	ICE 922	ICE 710	IC 1918	ICE 1558	EC 6	EC 6	EC 114	IC 2316	ICE 26	ICE 1556	IC 2318	ICE 1622	IC 1910	ICE 1554	IC 2210	IC 2210	ICE 22		ICE 510	IC 2020
	△		⚛			Ⓐ W		⚛	Ⓑ	⑥		M		⚛			⑦	Q	①–④	♠			⊕	
	🍷	🍷♦	D 🍷	Z ✕	✕	✕	♦	D ✕	J ✕	J ✕	🍷♦		✕♦	D ✕	🍷♦	A ✕	🍷	D	⊗ 🍷	🍷	✕♦			⊙
Basel SBB **912** d.	...	...	...	1220	...	...	...	...	1427	1427	...	...	...	...	...	...	...	...	...	...	...	...	...	...
Karlsruhe Hbf **912** d.	...	...	...	1412	...	...	...	...	1612	1612	...	...	...	...	...	...	...	...	...	...	...	...	...	...
München Hbf **930** d.	...	...	...	|	...	...	...	...	|	|	1347**h**	...	...	...	...	1618	1618**y**	...	...	...	...	...	1928	...
Stuttgart Hbf **912** d.	...	1312	...	|	...	1433	1512	...	|	|	1608	1624	...	...	1737	|	1914	...	1918	1937	...	...	2151	...
annheim Hbf **911a** d.	...	1408	...	1439	...	1533	1608	...	1639	1639	1658	1738	...	...	1839	|	2008	...	2039	2039	...	...	2236	...
orms Hbf **911a** d.	...	|	...	|	...	|	|	...	|	|	1714	|	...	...	|	|	|	...	|	|	...	...	|	...
Nürnberg Hbf **920** d.	...	|	...	|	...	|	|	...	|	|	|	|	1530**r**	...	|	1736	|	...	|	|	1930	...	|	...
Frankfurt (Main) Hbf **917a** d.	1344	|	1442	|	1544	|	|	1642	|	|	|	|	1742	1842	|	1940	|	2042	|	|	2146	...	|	2322
Frankfurt Flughafen ✈ ◧ **917a** d.	1358	|	1458**z**	|	1558	|	|	1658**z**	|	|	|	|	1758	1858	|	1958	|	2059	|	|	2159	...	2313	2339
ainz Hbf **911a 917a** a.	1418	1447	1515	1518	1618	1615	1647	1715	1718	1718	1740	1815	1818	1915	1918	2018	2047	2115	2118	2118	2218	...	2329	2359
ainz Hbf **914 917a** d.	1420	1449	1522	1520	1620	1622	1649	1722	1720	1720	1744	1822	1820	1922	1920	2020	2049	2122	2120	2120	2220	...	2331	0001
Wiesbaden Hbf **917a** a.	|	|	1533	|	|	1633	|	1733	|	|	|	1833	|	1933	|	|	|	2133	|	|	|	...	2344	|
ngen (Rhein) Hbf **914 917a** d.	|	1507	...	|	|	|	1707	...	|	|	1807	...	|	...	|	|	2107	...	|	|	|	...	...	0018
oblenz Hbf **914 917a** a.	1511	1542	...	1611	1711	|	1742	...	1811	1811	1842	...	1911	...	2011	2111	2142	...	2211	2211	2311	...	...	0056
Bonn Hbf **800** a.	1544	1621	...	1644	1744	|	1821	...	1844	1844	1921	...	1944	...	2044	2144	2221	...	2244	2244	2344	...	...	0135
Köln Hbf **800** a.	1605	1643	...	1705	1805	1801	1843	...	1905	1905	1943	...	2005	...	2105	2205	2243	...	2305	2305	0005	...	...	0157
Dortmund Hbf **800** a.	|	1807	...	|	1921	...	2007	...	|	2021	2103	...	2120	...	2221**q**	2320	0002	...	...	...	0121	...	...	0326
Hamburg Hbf **800** a.	2014	...	...	2114	2214	...	...	...	2316	...	...	...	...	...	...	...	...	...	...	...	...	...	...	0651

✣ - FOR NOTES SEE PREVIOUS PAGE

RE / S-Bahn services — Local services MAINZ - MANNHEIM and MAINZ - SPEYER - KARLSUHE 911a

km																										
			Ⓐe	⚒r	Ⓐe	Ⓐe		⚒r	Ⓐd															Ⓒz		Ⓐe
0	**Mainz** Hbf **911** d.	0008	0456	0515	0545	...	0552**b**	0622	0652	0656	0722**r**	0752	0813	0913	0952	1013	1117	1152	1213	1317	1352	1413	1517	1552	1613	1617
46	Worms Hbf **911** a.	0051	0540	0556	0614	...	0634**b**	0706	0719	0739	0806**r**	0836	0839	0940	1036	1039	1144	1236	1239	1344	1436	1439	1544	1636	1639	1652
46	Worms Hbf **911** d.	...	0541	0556	0615	...	0635	0712	0720	0746	0816	0848	0840	0941	1048	1040	1145	1249	1240	1345	1448	1440	1545	1648	1640	1653
67	Ludwigshafen Hbf **918** d.	...	0558	0616	0637	0654	0653	0731	0736	0804	0837	0909	0857	0958**t**	1109	1057	1204**t**	1309	1257	1404**t**	1508	1457	1604**t**	1709	1655	1708
87	Speyer Hbf **918** d.	...	|	|	|	0713	|	|	|	|	|	|	0914	|	|	1114	|	|	1314	|	|	1514	|	|	1713	|
01	Germersheim **918** a.	...	|	|	|	0722	|	|	|	|	|	|	0922	|	|	1122	|	|	1322	|	|	1522	|	|	1721	|
38	**Karlsruhe** Hbf a.	...	|	|	|	0753	|	|	|	|	|	|	0952	|	|	1152	|	|	1352	|	|	1552	|	|	1753	|
70	**Mannheim** Hbf **911** a.	...	0603	0621	0641	...	0658	0736	0742	0811	0842	0915	...	1001	1115	...	1207	1314	...	1407	1514	...	1606	1714	...	1715

		Ⓒz	Ⓐe									
ainz Hbf **911** d.	1652	1717	1717	1752	1813	1917	1925	1952	2013	2117	2208	2308
orms Hbf **911** a.	1736	1744	1744	1836	1839	1944	2008	2036	2039	2155	2251	2351
orms Hbf **911** d.	1749	1745	1745	1848	1840	1945	2018	2048	2040	2156	2251	2351
dwigshafen Hbf **918** d.	1809	1806**t**	1800	1909	1857	2004**t**	2037	2109	2057**f**	2215	2309	0009
Speyer Hbf **918** d.	|	|	1819	|	1914	|	|	|	2114**f**	|	|	|
Germersheim **918** a.	|	|	1828	|	1922	|	|	|	2122**f**	|	|	|
Karlsruhe Hbf a.	|	|	...	|	1952	|	|	|	2152**f**	|	|	|
annheim Hbf **911** a.	1814	1810	...	1914	...	2007	2043	2114	...	2221	2314	0014

		⚒r	Ⓐe	⚒r	Ⓐe		Ⓐd		Ⓐe
Mannheim Hbf **911** d.	0015	0430	0500	0530	0550	...	...	0650	...
Karlsruhe Hbf d.	|	|	|	|	|	...	...	|	...
Germersheim **918** d.	|	|	|	|	|	...	0619	|	0719
Speyer Hbf **918** d.	|	|	|	|	|	...	0632	|	0728
Ludwigshafen Hbf **918** d.	0020	0436	0505	0535	0558	...	0656	0659	0750
Worms Hbf **911** a.	0038	0454	0524	0553	0615	...	0712	0718	0804
Worms Hbf **911** d.	...	0455	0525	0555	0622	0622	0713	0725	0805
Mainz Hbf **911** a.	...	0538	0608	0638	0708	0708	0747	0808	0836

	Ⓐe	Ⓒz																								⑥
annheim Hbf **911** d.	0748	0751	0844	...	0915	0958	1044	...	1149	1244	...	1349	1444	...	1549	1644	...	1752	1844	...	1951	2044	...	2144	2247	2330
Karlsruhe Hbf d.	|	|	|	0808	|	|	|	1008**v**	|	|	1208**v**	|	|	1408**v**	|	|	1608**v**	|	|	1808**v**	|	|	2008**v**	|	|	|
Germersheim **918** d.	|	|	|	0838	|	|	|	1038	|	|	1238**v**	|	|	1438**v**	|	|	1638**v**	|	|	1838**v**	|	|	2038**v**	|	|	|
Speyer Hbf **918** d.	|	|	|	0847	|	|	|	1047	|	|	1247**v**	|	|	1447**v**	|	|	1647**v**	|	|	1847**v**	|	|	2047**v**	|	|	|
dwigshafen Hbf **918** d.	0755	0753**t**	0850	0904	0920	1000**t**	1050	1104	1152**t**	1250	1304	1352**t**	1450	1504	1552**t**	1650	1704	1754**t**	1850	1904	1954**t**	2050	2104	2150	2253	2335
orms Hbf **911** a.	0814	0816	0914	0919	0938	1019	1111	1119	1216	1311	1319	1416	1514	1519	1616	1714	1719	1816	1913	1919	2016	2114	2119	2213	2312	2354
orms Hbf **911** d.	0825	0817	0925	0920	0955	1020	1125	1120	1217	1325	1320	1417	1525	1520	1617	1725	1720	1817	1925	1920	2017	2125	2120	2218	2315**b**	2355
ainz Hbf **911** a.	0908	0843	1008	0947	1036	1046	1208	1147	1243	1408	1347	1443	1608	1547	1652	1808	1747	1843	2008	1947	2043	2208	2147	2301	2359**b**	0038

- – Not ⑥.
- – Not June 20.
- **e** – Not June 20, Nov. 1.
- **f** – 1–2 minutes earlier Sept. 14 - Oct. 27.
- **r** – ⚒ (not June 20, Nov. 1).
- **t** – Ludwigshafen (Rhein) **Mitte**.
- **v** – 1–2 minutes later Sept. 14 - Oct. 27.
- **z** – Also June 20, Nov. 1.

;ervice from June 11 — FRANKFURT - BASEL and STUTTGART 912

km	km	IMPORTANT: SEE NOTE ✣	ICE 619	ICE 879	EN 452	ICE 993	IC 209	NJ 401	NJ 471	IC 2097	ICE 3	IC 479			RJX 63	IC 2419	ICE 991	ICE 271		TGV 9578	IC 1991	EC 217	ICE 511	ICE 5	ICE 9568
				①	③			🅁△	🅁△	①g	①–⑤	⑥⑦		①–⑤	⑥⑦	Ⓐm	①–⑤			①–⑥	Ⓐn			①–⑥	Ⓑ
					🅁♦	♦	K	♦	♦		✕	⊡	◐2	◐2	✕♦		✕♦	H ✕	◐2	♦🅁		🍷♦	✕	✕	🅁♦
		Hamburg Hbf **800 900** d.	...	...	...	...	1946	2102	...	...	...	2148**r**	...	...	...	...	...	⊙	...	...	...	...	...	...	✕
		Berlin Hbf **810 850 902** d.	...	1957**p**	2103	2128**p**	|	|	2107	...	...	|	...	...	...	...	...	|	...	...	...	...	...	...	...
		Hannover Hbf **810 900** d.	...	|	|	|	|	2326	|	...	...	0004	...	...	...	...	...	⊙	...	...	...	...	...	...	...
		Dortmund Hbf **800** d.	2056	|	|	|	2237	|	|	...	...	|	...	...	...	...	...	|	...	...	...	...	0435**g**	...	...
		Köln Hbf **800 910** d.	2230	|	|	|	2353	|	|	...	...	|	...	...	...	0206**h**	...	|	...	...	...	...	0555	...	...
		Koblenz Hbf **911** d.	|	|	|	|	0048	|	|	...	...	|	...	...	...	0310**h**	...	|	...	...	...	...	|	...	...
		Mainz Hbf **911** d.	|	|	|	|	0142	|	|	...	...	|	...	...	...	0412**h**	0540	|	...	...	...	...	|	...	...
0	0	**Frankfurt** (Main) Hbf **913** d.	0007	0050	0140•	0225	0248	0402•	0402•	0405	...	0420	...	...	0517	0520	|	0550	...	...	0554	...	|	0648	0658
		Frankfurt Flughafen ✈ ◧ d.	0028	|	|	0244	0215	|	|	|	...	|	...	...	0539	|	|	|	...	...	|	...	0652	|	|
78		**Mannheim** Hbf **913** a.	0104	0127	|	0326	0331	0440	0440	0445	...	0507	...	...	0610	|	0623	0625	...	...	|	...	0723	0727	0737
78		**Mannheim** Hbf **913** d.	0106	0130	|	0328	0333	0442	0442	0447	...	0509	...	...	0612	|	0629	0633	...	...	|	0711	0731	0736	0739
	28	Darmstadt Hbf **913** d.	|	|	|	|	|	|	|	|	...	|	...	...	|	0537	|	|	...	...	0613	|	|	|	|
	50	Bensheim **913** d.	|	|	|	|	|	|	|	|	...	|	...	...	|	0550	|	|	...	...	0625	|	|	|	|
	64	Weinheim **913** d.	|	|	|	|	|	|	|	|	...	|	...	...	|	0600	|	|	...	...	0636	|	|	|	|
	87	**Heidelberg** Hbf **913 931** d.	0119	|	|	|	|	|	|	0500	...	0523	...	...	|	0615	|	|	...	...	0652	|	|	|	|
	120	Bruchsal **913 931** d.	0138	|	|	|	|	|	|	|	...	|	...	...	|	|	|	|	...	...	|	|	|	|	|
		Vaihingen (Enz) **931** d.	0247	|	|	|	|	|	|	|	...	|	...	...	|	|	|	|	...	...	|	|	|	|	|
		Stuttgart Hbf **931** a.	0320	|	|	0444	|	|	|	0553	...	|	...	...	0652	0700	0707	|	...	...	0737	0753	0808	|	|
		München Hbf **930** a.	0602	|	|	0732	|	|	|	0844	...	|	...	...	0910	...	0927	|	...	...	▬	1011**x**	1027	|	|
38	141	**Karlsruhe** Hbf **913 916** d.	0156**a**	0154	0310	...	0403	0509	0509	...	0555	0553	...	...	...	...	...	0659	...	0732	①–⑤	...	...	0800	0807
67	172	Baden-Baden **916** d.	...	...	|	...	0426	0529	0529	...	0612	0613	...	...	...	...	...	0716	...	|	◐2	...	...	|	|
07		Offenburg **916** ☆ d.	...	...	0451	...	0450	0547	0547	...	0629	0630	0632	0705	...	...	...	0733	0735	|	0805	...	...	0829	|
	217	Kehl 🏛 d.	...	...	|	...	|	|	|	...	|	|	0654	0724	...	...	...	|	0754	|	0827	...	...	|	|
	225	**Strasbourg** a.	...	...	0514	...	|	|	|	...	|	|	0706	0735	...	...	...	|	0807	0813	0837	...	...	|	0846
70		**Freiburg** (Brsg) Hbf ☆ d.	...	...	...	...	0530	0622	0622	...	0702	0704	...	...	...	...	...	0804	...	...	...	...	...	0901	...
27		**Basel** Bad Bf 🏛 ☆ a.	...	...	...	...	0610	0706	0706	...	0736	0738	...	...	...	...	...	0835	...	...	...	...	...	0934	...
32		**Basel** SBB ☆ a.	...	...	...	...	0622	0720	0720	...	0747	...	...	...	...	...	...	0847	...	...	...	...	...	0947	...
		Zürich HB **510** a.	...	...	...	...	...	0905	0905	...	0900	...	...	...	...	...	...	1000	...	...	...	...	...	...	...

– **NOTES** (LISTED BY TRAIN NUMBER)

– [12] and ✕ Frankfurt - Salzburg - Wien - Budapest. From Oct. 26 departs Frankfurt Hbf 0531 and does not call at Frankfurt Flughafen.

7 – DACHSTEIN – [12] and 🍷 Saarbrücken - München - Salzburg - Graz.

1 – 🛏 1, 2 cl., ▬ 2 cl. and [2] Hamburg - Hannover - Basel - Zürich.

2 – From Berlin on ③, Frankfurt on ④. 🛏 1, 2 cl. Moskva - Warszawa - Berlin - Paris. See Table **24**. Operated by Russian Railways. Special fares payable. 🅁. Timings vary Aug. 14 - Oct. 23.

1 – 🛏 1, 2 cl., ▬ 2 cl. and [2] Berlin - Braunschweig - Basel - Zürich.

1 – [12] and ✕ Wiesbaden Hbf (d. 0526) - München.

3 – From Frankfurt daily to Sept. 2, ①⑥ from Sept. 7. [12] Berlin (previous day) - Leipzig - Frankfurt - München. Aug. 11 - Oct. 28 Frankfurt Hbf d. 0250, Mannheim a. 0335, d. 0337, not calling at Frankfurt Flughafen. From Nov. 2 departs Frankfurt Hbf 0222.

68 – [12] and ✕ Frankfurt - Paris (Table **30**).

78 – [12] and 🍷 Stuttgart - Paris (Table **32**).

H – To Chur (Table **520**). Train number **1271** on ① (also June 11).

K – From Kiel (Table **820**).

a – Arrival time (calls before Vaihingen).

g – ① (also June 11).

h – ① (also June 11; not July 8 - Aug. 26).

m – Not June 20.

n – Not June 20, 21, Oct. 4, Nov. 1.

p – Previous day.

r – Previous day. 2159 on ⑤ to June 21 and from Sept. 20.

x – Until July 28 serves München Pasing (not Hbf).

• – Frankfurt (Main) **Süd**.

⊡ – From Hannover on ⑥⑦ (not Dec. 8; from Hamburg previous day). Train number **469** on ⑥ to June 22 and from Sept. 21.

⊙ – From Hamburg / Hannover on dates in Table **900** (see train **1271** on page 419).

△ – Runs 18–37 minutes later Frankfurt - Zürich on the mornings June 29 - Oct. 27.

☆ – See also panel on page 428.

◐ – Operated by Südwestdeutsche Verkehrs. On June 10, Nov. 1 services run as on ⑦.

✣ – Please refer to the shaded engineering work panel on page 369 for details of various alterations affecting services in this table.

◧ – Frankfurt Flughafen Fernbahnhof.

912 FRANKFURT - BASEL and STUTTGART

IMPORTANT: SEE NOTE ❖			*ICE* 1571	*ICE* 676	*ICE* 711	*IC* 2317	*ICE* 591	*ICE* 101	*ICE* 913	*EC* 151	*TGV* 9596		*TGV* 9576	*EC* 113	*IC* 2319	*ICE* 513	*ICE* 275	*ICE* 9566	*ICE* 571	*ICE* 1573	*ICE* 593	*ICE* 103	*ICE* 1011	*ICE* 71	*ICE* 9574
		①–⑤	Ⓐ	①–⑤	ⒶR	⑥F			①–⑥		⑦	⑥⑦	①–⑥		①–⑥			⑥	①–⑥	⚒					P
	◐2	◐2	Q✕	✕	✕		✕	✕	n✕	✕♦	H🅁	◐2	H🅁	✕♦	🍷	M✕	N✕	E🅁	✕	Q✕	✕	✕	M✕	C✕	🅁✕
Hamburg Hbf **800 900** d.	...	...	...	...	...	...	0320a	...	...	...	...	...	...	...	...	...	...	✕	0455	...	...	...	...	0601	...
Berlin Hbf **810 850 902** d.	...	...	...	...	...	...	|	...	...	...	...	...	...	...	...	...	0357a	...	|	...	0528	...	...	|	...
Hannover Hbf **810 900** d.	...	...	...	...	...	...	0459e	...	...	...	...	...	...	...	...	...	|	...	0624	...	|	0540	...	0724	...
Dortmund Hbf **800** d.	...	...	...	...	...	...	|	0535e	0550	...	...	...	...	...	0537	0637	|	...	|	...	|	0737	...	|	...
Köln Hbf **800 910** d.	...	...	...	...	0611	...	|	0655	0712d	...	...	...	...	...	0653	0755	|	...	|	...	|	0855	0917d	|	...
Koblenz Hbf **911** d.	...	...	...	...	|	...	|	|	|	...	...	...	...	...	0748	|	|	...	|	...	|	|	|	|	...
Mainz Hbf **911** d.	...	...	...	...	0746	0746	|	|	|	...	...	...	...	...	0842	|	|	...	|	...	|	|	|	|	...
Frankfurt (Main) Hbf **913** d.	...	...	0714	...	|	|	0750	|	|	0801	...	...	...	0820	|	|	0850	0856	0906z	0920z	0950	|	|	1006y	...
Frankfurt Flughafen ✈ ◧ d.	...	...	|	...	|	|	|	0752	0809	|	...	...	...	|	|	0852	|	|	0923	|	|	0952	1009	|	...
Mannheim Hbf **913** a.	...	...	|	...	0824	0824	0827	0823	0840	0844	...	...	...	|	0921	0923	0927	0936	0954	|	1027	1023	1039	1044	...
Mannheim Hbf **913** d.	...	...	|	0818	0826	0826	0830	0836	0842	0846	...	...	...	|	0923	0931	0936	0940	0956	|	1030	1036	1041	1046	...
Darmstadt Hbf **913** d.	...	...	0731	|	|	|	|	|	|	|	...	...	...	0838	|	|	|	|	|	0937	|	|	|	|	...
Bensheim **913** d.	...	...	0746	|	|	|	|	|	|	|	...	...	...	0850	|	|	|	|	|	0950	|	|	|	|	...
Weinheim **913** d.	...	...	0758	|	|	|	|	|	|	|	...	...	...	0900	|	|	|	|	|	1000	|	|	|	|	...
Heidelberg Hbf **913 931** d.	...	...	0814	|	0838	0839	|	|	|	|	...	...	...	0914	0936	|	|	|	|	1015	|	|	|	|	...
Bruchsal **913 931** d.	...	...	0835	|	|	|	|	|	|	|	...	...	...	|	|	|	|	|	|	1036	|	|	|	|	...
Vaihingen (Enz) **931** d.	...	...	|	0848	|	0910	|	|	|	|	...	...	...	|	1006	|	|	|	|	|	|	|	|	|	...
Stuttgart Hbf **931** a.	...	...	|	0905	0921	0928	0908	|	0924	|	...	...	...	0953	1024	1008	|	|	1035	|	1108	|	1122	|	...
München Hbf **930** a.	...	...	|	...	...	▬	1127	|	...	|	...	...	...	1210x	...	1227	|	|	▬	|	1327	|	...	|	...
Karlsruhe Hbf **913 916** d.	...	...	0850	...	...	①–⑤	...	0900	...	0910	0932	...	0953	...	...	...	1000	1006	①–⑤	1050	...	1100	...	1110	1132
Baden-Baden **916** d.	...	...	...	...	...	◐2	...	0916	...	0926	|	...	|	...	...	...	|	|	◐2	...	...	|	...	1127	|
Offenburg **916** ☆ d.	0842	0905	...	...	...	0935	...	0935	...	|	|	1005	|	...	...	...	1029	|	1035	...	...	1128	...	|	|
Kehl 🏛 d.	0900	0924	...	...	...	0954	...	|	...	|	|	1022	|	...	...	...	|	|	1054	...	...	|	...	|	|
Strasbourg a.	0910	0936	...	...	...	1006	...	|	...	|	1012	1034	1037	...	...	...	|	1046	1106	...	...	|	...	|	1213
Freiburg (Brsg) Hbf ☆ d.	...	...	...	...	...	...	...	1006	...	1015	...	...	...	...	...	...	1101	...	...	...	...	1200	...	1212	...
Basel Bad Bf 🏛 ☆ a.	...	...	...	...	...	...	...	1038	...	1045	...	...	...	...	...	...	1135	...	...	...	...	1234	...	1247	...
Basel SBB ☆ a.	...	...	...	...	...	...	...	1047	...	1054	...	...	...	...	...	...	1147	...	...	...	...	1247	...	1256	...
Zürich HB **510** a.	...	...	...	...	...	...	...	...	...	...	...	...	...	...	...	...	...	...	...	...	...	...	...	1400	...

IMPORTANT: SEE NOTE ❖		*IC* 2293	*EC* 115	*EC* 7	*ICE* 1113		*ICE* 277		*IC* 1919	*ICE* 973	*ICE* 1575	*ICE* 595	*ICE* 105		*ICE* 1013	*ICE* 73		*EC* 219	*IC* 2005	*EC* 9	*ICE* 517	*ICE* 279		*IC* 2013	*ICE* 575
	⑥⑦				¶			①–⑤		⊖	⑤–⑦			①–⑤	n	□	⑥⑦		⑤⑥				①–⑤		
	◐2		🍷♦	N✕	✕	◐2	✕	◐2	♦	K✕	sQ	✕	✕♦	◐2	D✕	K✕	◐2	🍷♦	🍷♦	✕	✕	✕	◐2	🍷♦	✕
Hamburg Hbf **800 900** d.	...	...	...	0438e	0546	...	...	...	...	0701	✕	...	...	...	...	0803	...	...	...	0646	...	...	...	...	0901
Berlin Hbf **810 850 902** d.	...	...	...	|	|	...	0557	...	...	|	...	0728	...	...	...	|	...	...	...	|	...	0756	...	...	|
Hannover Hbf **810 900** d.	...	...	...	|	|	...	|	...	...	0824	...	|	...	...	...	0924	...	...	...	|	...	|	...	...	1024
Dortmund Hbf **800** d.	...	...	...	0737w	0837	...	|	...	0724	|	...	|	...	...	...	|	...	...	...	|	1035	|	...	0950	|
Köln Hbf **800 910** d.	...	...	0818	0853	0949c	...	|	...	0917	|	...	|	1055	...	1116d	|	...	...	1018	1053	1155	|	...	1117	|
Koblenz Hbf **911** d.	...	...	0918	0948	|	...	|	...	1018	|	...	|	|	...	|	|	...	...	1118	1148	|	|	...	1218	|
Mainz Hbf **911** d.	...	...	1017	1042	|	...	|	...	1112	|	...	|	|	...	|	|	...	...	1217	1242	|	|	...	1312	|
Frankfurt (Main) Hbf **913** d.	...	1020	|	|	|	...	1050	...	|	1106z	1120z	1150	|	...	|	1206y	...	1220	|	|	|	1250	...	|	1306
Frankfurt Flughafen ✈ ◧ d.	...	|	|	|	1052	...	|	...	|	1123	|	|	1152	...	1209	|	...	|	|	|	1252	|	...	|	1323
Mannheim Hbf **913** a.	...	|	1100	1121	1123	...	1127	...	1152	1154	|	1227	1223	...	1240	1244	...	|	1307	1321	1323	1327	...	1352	1354
Mannheim Hbf **913** d.	...	|	1102	1123	1131	...	1136	...	1154	1156	|	1230	1236	...	1242	1246	...	|	1309	1323	1331	1335	...	1354	1356
Darmstadt Hbf **913** d.	...	1037	|	|	|	...	|	...	|	|	1137	|	|	...	|	|	...	1237	|	|	|	|	...	|	|
Bensheim **913** d.	...	|	|	|	|	...	|	...	|	|	1150	|	|	...	|	|	...	1250	|	|	|	|	...	|	|
Weinheim **913** d.	...	1056	|	|	|	...	|	...	|	|	1200	|	|	...	|	|	...	1300	|	|	|	|	...	|	|
Heidelberg Hbf **913 931** d.	...	1110	|	|	|	...	|	...	1206	|	1215	|	|	...	|	|	...	1314	|	|	|	|	...	1406	|
Bruchsal **913 931** d.	...	|	|	|	|	...	|	...	|	|	1236	|	|	...	|	|	...	|	|	|	|	|	...	|	|
Vaihingen (Enz) **931** d.	...	|	1137	|	|	...	|	...	|	|	|	|	|	...	|	|	...	|	|	|	|	|	...	|	|
Stuttgart Hbf **931** a.	...	1150	1153	|	1208	...	|	...	1246	1235	|	1308	|	...	1324	|	...	1354	|	|	1408	|	...	1446	143
München Hbf **930** a.	...	...	1411x	|	1427	...	|	...	...	...	|	1528	|	...	...	|	...	1611x	|	|	1627	|	...	▬	...
Karlsruhe Hbf **913 916** d.	...	...	...	1149	...	...	1200	...	...	...	1250	...	1300	...	...	1310	...	...	1336	1349	...	1400	...	...	...
Baden-Baden **916** d.	...	...	...	|	...	...	1217	...	...	...	...	...	|	...	...	1327	...	...	1356	1407	...	|	...	◐2	...
Offenburg **916** ☆ d.	1205	...	...	|	...	1235	1234	1305	...	...	...	...	1328	1336	...	|	1405	...	1415	|	...	1429	1435	1505	...
Kehl 🏛 d.	1224	...	...	|	...	1254	|	1324	...	...	...	...	|	1354	...	|	1423	...	...	|	...	|	1454	1524	...
Strasbourg a.	1236	...	...	|	...	1306	|	1336	...	...	...	...	|	1406	...	|	1434	...	...	|	...	|	1506	1536	...
Freiburg (Brsg) Hbf ☆ d.	...	...	...	1251	...	...	1306	...	...	...	...	...	1400	...	...	1412	...	...	...	1455	...	1501	...	...	...
Basel Bad Bf 🏛 ☆ a.	...	...	...	1322	...	...	1338	...	...	...	...	...	1434	...	...	1447	...	...	...	1527	...	1534	...	...	...
Basel SBB ☆ a.	...	...	...	1330	...	...	1347	...	...	...	...	...	1447	...	...	1456	...	...	...	1535	...	1547	...	...	...
Zürich HB **510** a.	...	...	...	...	...	...	...	...	...	...	...	...	...	...	...	1600	...	...	...	1700	...	...	...	...	...

IMPORTANT: SEE NOTE ❖	*ICE* 1577	*ICE* 597	*ICE* 107	*TGV* 9580	*ICE* 75	*TGV* 9580	*ICE* 9572		*EC* 117	*IC* 2313	*ICE* 519	*ICE* 371		*ICE* 577	*IC* 1911	*ICE* 1579	*ICE* 599	*ICE* 109	*ICE* 915		*ICE* 77	*EC* 391	*IC* 2217	*ICE* 611	*ICE* 373
				🅁		🅁	G P						①–⑤		⑤⑦				n	①–⑤	⊡				
	Q✕	✕	✕	🍷♦	✕♦	🍷♦	🅁	◐2	🍷♦	🍷	✕	N✕	◐2	✕	v🍷	Q✕	✕	✕	✕	◐2	✕	🍷♦	🍷♦	✕	N✕
Hamburg Hbf **800 900** d.	...	...	...	...	1001	...	...	...	...	0846	...	...	...	1101	...	...	...	...	...	...	1201	...	1046	...	...
Berlin Hbf **810 850 902** d.	...	0928	...	...	|	...	...	...	...	|	...	0957	...	|	...	...	1128	...	...	...	|	...	|	...	115
Hannover Hbf **810 900** d.	...	|	...	...	1124	...	...	...	...	|	...	|	...	1224	...	...	|	...	...	...	1324	...	|	...	|
Dortmund Hbf **800** d.	...	|	1135w	...	|	...	...	...	...	|	1235	|	...	|	1150	...	|	1335w	1350j	...	|	...	|	1435	|
Köln Hbf **800 910** d.	...	|	1255	...	|	...	...	...	...	1253	1355	|	...	|	1317	...	|	1455	1520d	...	|	...	1453	1555	|
Koblenz Hbf **911** d.	...	|	|	...	|	...	...	...	...	1348	|	|	...	|	1418	...	|	|	|	...	|	...	1548	|	|
Mainz Hbf **911** d.	...	|	|	...	|	...	...	...	...	1442	|	|	...	|	1512	...	|	|	|	...	|	...	1642	|	|
Frankfurt (Main) Hbf **913** d.	1320z	1350	|	1358	1406y	...	...	...	1420	|	|	1450	...	1506z	|	1520z	1550	|	|	...	1606y	1620	|	|	165
Frankfurt Flughafen ✈ ◧ d.	|	|	1352	|	|	...	...	...	|	|	1452	|	...	1523	|	|	|	1552	1609	...	|	|	|	1652	|
Mannheim Hbf **913** a.	|	1427	1423	1437	1444	...	...	...	|	1521	1523	1527	...	1554	1552	|	1627	1623	1639	...	1644	|	1721	1723	172
Mannheim Hbf **913** d.	|	1430	1434	1439	1446	...	...	...	|	1523	1531	1536	...	1556	1554	|	1630	1636	1641	...	1646	|	1723	1731	173
Darmstadt Hbf **913** d.	1337	|	|	|	|	...	...	...	1437	|	|	|	...	|	|	1537	|	|	|	...	|	1637	|	|	|
Bensheim **913** d.	1350	|	|	|	|	...	...	...	1450	|	|	|	...	|	|	1550	|	|	|	...	|	1650	|	|	|
Weinheim **913** d.	1400	|	|	|	|	...	...	...	1500	|	|	|	...	|	|	1600	|	|	|	...	|	1700	|	|	|
Heidelberg Hbf **913 931** d.	1415	|	|	|	|	...	...	...	1514	1536	|	|	...	|	1606	1615	|	|	|	...	|	1714	1736	|	|
Bruchsal **913 931** d.	1435	|	|	|	|	...	...	...	|	|	|	|	...	|	|	1637	|	|	|	...	|	|	|	|	|
Vaihingen (Enz) **931** d.	|	|	|	|	|	...	...	...	|	1605	|	|	...	|	|	|	|	|	|	...	|	|	1808	|	|
Stuttgart Hbf **931** a.	|	1508	|	|	|	...	...	...	1553	1622	1608	|	...	1635	1646	|	1708	|	1720	...	|	1753	1829	1808	|
München Hbf **930** a.	|	1727	|	|	|	←	...	...	1811x	...	1827	|	...	▬	...	|	1927	|	▬	...	|	2011x	...	2028	|
Karlsruhe Hbf **913 916** d.	1450	...	1458	1504	1510	1512	1532	...	...	...	...	1600	...	...	...	1650	...	1700	①–⑤	...	1710	...	...	...	180
Baden-Baden **916** d.	...	...	|	→	1527	1534	|	...	...	...	...	|	...	◐2	...	...	...	|	◐2	...	1727	...	...	...	|
Offenburg **916** ☆ d.	...	...	1528	...	|	|	|	1605	...	...	...	1629	1635	1705	...	...	...	1728	1735	1805	|	...	...	...	183
Kehl 🏛 d.	...	...	|	...	|	|	|	1624	...	...	...	|	1654	1724	...	...	...	|	1754	1824	|	...	...	...	|
Strasbourg a.	...	...	|	...	|	1601	1612	1636	...	...	...	|	1706	1736	...	...	...	|	1806	1836	|	...	...	...	|
Freiburg (Brsg) Hbf ☆ d.	...	...	1600	...	1612	...	...	...	...	...	...	1701	...	...	...	...	...	1800	...	...	1812	...	...	...	190
Basel Bad Bf 🏛 ☆ a.	...	...	1634	...	1647	...	...	...	...	...	...	1736	...	...	...	...	...	1834	...	...	1847	...	...	...	193
Basel SBB ☆ a.	...	...	1647	...	1656	...	...	...	...	...	...	1747	...	...	...	...	...	1847	...	...	1856	...	...	...	194
Zürich HB **510** a.	...	...	...	...	1800	...	...	...	...	...	...	...	...	...	...	...	...	...	...	...	2000a	...	...	...	...

Regional trains **OFFENBURG - BASEL** (German holiday dates apply). On June 20, Nov. 1 regional services between Offenburg and Basel Bad Bf run as on ⑦.

	†	Ⓐ		⚒	⚒	Ⓐ		⚒																†		
Offenburg d.	0049	0425	0519g	...	0551	0632	...	0706	...	0807	0907	1007	1107	1204	1307	1404	1507	1607	1707	1807	1907	2007	...	2043	2107	224
Freiburg (Brsg) Hbf a.	0131	0525	0618g	...	0649	0727	...	0756	...	0855	0955	1055	1155	1257	1355	1450	1555	1656	1756	1856	1955	2055	...	2135	2202	234
Freiburg (Brsg) Hbf d.	0132	0526	0628	...	0710	0732	...	0815	0815	0915	1011	1115	1215	1315	1415	1515	1615	1715	1815	1915	2015	...	2145	2145	▬	234
Müllheim (Baden) d.	0152	0547	0655	...	0731	0749	...	0836	0836	0936	1036	1136	1236	1337	1436	1536	1636	1736	1836	1936	2036	...	2212	2212	...	001
Basel Bad Bf 🏛 a.	0220	0625	0732	0745	0806	0812	0819	0912	0912	1012	1112	1212	1312	1412	1512	1612	1712	1812	1912	2012	2112	...	2249	2249	2319	004
Basel SBB a.	...	*0650*	...	0750	...	0820t	0825	*0925*	*0925*	*1025*	*1125*	*1225*	*1325*	*1425*	*1525*	1622§	1721§	1820§	*1925*	*2025*	*2125*	...	...	...	2325	...

FOR NOTES SEE NEXT PAGE →

FRANKFURT - BASEL and STUTTGART 912

IMPORTANT: SEE NOTE ❖	*TGV* 9560		*ICE* 579	*IC* 2011	*IC* 2371	*IC* 2183	*ICE* 691	*ICE* 201	*ICE* 917	*ICE* 79	*TGV* 9570		*IC* 1956	*IC* 2295	*IC* 2019	*IC* 2311	*ICE* 613	*IC* 2262	*ICE* 375	*IC* 2262		*IC* 1915	*ICE* 771	*ICE* 1673	*ICE* 693
	E			Ⓑ		①–④			Ⓑ n		P		⑦ w	Ⓑ	⑥			Ⓑ		Ⓑ		⑤⑦			
	🅁 🍷	◐2	✕	U 🍷	Q	m	✕	✕	✕	✕	🅁 🍷	◐2	B	🍷	🍷♦	J 🍷	✕	🍷♦	✕	♦	◐2	T 🍷	✕	Q ✕	✕
Hamburg Hbf **800 900** ...... d.	...	...	1301	...	...	...	...	...	...	1401	...	...	...	...	...	1246	...	...	...	...	...	...	1501	...	...
Berlin Hbf **810 850 902** . d.	...	...	|	...	...	...	1328	...	...	|	...	...	...	...	...	|	...	...	1357	...	...	1201	|	...	1527
Hannover Hbf **810 900** ..... d.	...	...	1424	...	...	...	|	...	...	1524	...	...	...	...	...	|	...	...	|	...	...	1356	1624	...	|
Dortmund Hbf **800** .... d.	...	...	|	...	...	...	|	...	1551	|	...	...	...	...	...	|	1635	...	|	...	...	|	|	...	|
Köln Hbf **800 910** .... d.	...	...	|	1517	...	...	|	1655	1713**d**	|	...	...	...	...	1617	1653	1755	...	|	...	...	1717	|	...	|
Koblenz Hbf **911** .... d.	...	...	|	1618	...	...	|	|	|	|	...	...	...	...	1718	1748	|	...	|	...	...	1818	|	...	|
Mainz Hbf **911** .... d.	...	...	|	1712	...	...	|	|	|	|	...	...	...	...	1817	1842	|	...	|	...	...	1912	|	...	|
rankfurt (Main) Hbf ..... **913** d.	1658	...	1706**z**	|	1720**z**	1746	1750	|	|	1806**y**	...	...	1801•	1819	|	|	|	...	1850	...	...	|	1906**z**	1920**z**	1950
Frankfurt Flughafen ✈ ◧. d.	|	...	1723	|	|	|	|	1752	1809	|	...	...	|	|	|	|	1853	...	|	...	...	|	1923	|	|
lannheim Hbf .... **913** a.	1737	...	1754	1752	|	|	1827	1823	1839	1844	...	...	|	|	1901	1921	1923	...	1927	...	...	1952	1954	|	2027
lannheim Hbf .... **913** d.	1740	...	1756	1754	|	|	1830	1836	1841	1846	...	...	|	|	1903	1923	1931	...	1936	...	...	1954	1956	|	2030
Darmstadt Hbf........... **913** d.	|	...	|	|	1737	1804	|	|	|	|	...	...	1821	1837	|	|	|	...	|	...	...	|	|	1937	|
Bensheim................. **913** d.	|	...	|	|	1750	1817	|	|	|	|	...	...	1835	1850	|	|	|	...	|	...	...	|	|	1950	|
Weinheim................. **913** d.	|	...	|	|	1800	1828	|	|	|	|	...	...	1848	1900	|	|	|	...	|	...	...	|	|	2000	|
Heidelberg Hbf ...**913 931** d.	|	...	|	1806	1815	1843	|	|	|	|	...	...	1902	1914	1916	1936	|	...	|	...	...	2006	|	2015	|
Bruchsal ....**913 931** d.	|	...	|	|	1835	1902	|	|	|	|	...	...	|	|	|	|	|	...	|	...	...	|	|	2037	|
Vaihingen (Enz) .... **931** d.	|	...	|	|	|	|	|	|	|	|	...	...	|	|	|	2005	|	...	|	...	...	|	|	|	|
Stuttgart Hbf .... **931** a.	|	...	1835	1846	|	|	1907	|	1924	|	...	...	|	1954	1958	2024	2008	...	|	...	...	2046	2035	|	2108
München Hbf **930** .... a.	|	...	▬	...	|	|	2126	|	...	|	...	...	|	2215	...	...	2226	...	|	...	...	...	2319**f**	|	2329**q**
arlsruhe Hbf ....**913 916** d.	1807	...	①–⑤	...	1851	1916	...	1900	...	1910	1932	...	1942	...	...	...	...	1955	2000	...	...	...	...	2052	...
aden-Baden................ **916** d.	|	...	◐2	...	...	...	...	|	...	1927	|	...	...	...	...	...	...	|	2017	...	...	...	...	...	...
ffenburg ....**916** ☆ d.	|	1835	1905	...	...	...	...	1928	...	|	|	2005	...	...	...	...	...	2025	2034	...	2105	...	...	...	...
Kehl 🏛........................ d.	|	1854	1924	...	...	...	...	|	...	|	|	2024	...	...	...	...	...	|	|	...	2124	...	...	...	...
Strasbourg..................... a.	1847	1906	1936	...	...	...	...	|	...	|	2013	2036	...	...	...	...	...	|	|	←	2136	...	...	...	...
reiburg (Brsg) Hbf .... ☆ d.	...	...	...	...	...	...	...	2000	...	2012	...	...	...	...	...	...	...	2100	2106	2112	...	...	...	...	...
asel Bad Bf 🏛 ....☆ a.	...	...	...	...	...	...	...	2034	...	2047	...	...	...	...	...	...	...	→	2138	2155	...	...	...	...	...
asel SBB ....☆ a.	...	...	...	...	...	...	...	2047	...	2056	...	...	...	...	...	...	...	...	2147	...	...	...	...	...	...
Zürich HB **510** .... a.	...	...	...	...	...	...	...	...	...	2200	...	...	...	...	...	...	...	...	...	...	...	...	...	...	...

IMPORTANT: SEE NOTE ❖	*ICE* 203	*ICE* 1103	*ICE* 919	*ICE* 1171	*ICE* 1171	*ICE* 203		*IC* 2397	*IC* 2297	*IC* 2213	*ICE* 615	*ICE* 377	♣	*IC* 1917	*ICE* 773	*ICE* 695	*ICE* 605	*ICE* 1675	*IC* 1973	*ICE* 273	*ICE* 273	*ICE* 605	*ICE* 877	*ICE* 1595	*ICE* 1593
	①–⑥	⑦	Ⓑ n		⑥⑦	①–⑤		①–④	⑤–⑦				①–⑥	⑦				⑤	⑦		⑤⑥	⊙		Y	A
	✕	✕	✕	K ✕	K	✕	◐2	b ✕		🍷♦	✕	✕	◐2	🍷	✕	✕	✕♦	Q	✕	✕	✕	♦		△	△
Hamburg Hbf **800 900** ...... d.	...	...	...	1601	1601	...	...	...	...	1446	...	...	...	...	1701	...	...	...	...	1801	1801	...	...	...	...
Berlin Hbf **810 850 902** . d.	...	...	...	|	|	...	...	...	...	|	...	1559	...	1355	|	1728	...	...	...	|	|	...	1759	...	...
Hannover Hbf **810 900** ..... d.	...	...	...	1724	1724	...	...	...	...	|	...	|	...	1556	1824	|	...	...	...	1924	1924	...	|	...	...
Dortmund Hbf **800** .... d.	...	...	1756	|	|	...	...	...	...	|	1835	|	...	|	|	|	1923**h**	...	...	|	|	...	|	...	...
Köln Hbf **800 910** .... d.	1854	1854	1920**d**	|	|	...	...	...	...	1853	1955	|	...	1912**r**	|	|	2046	...	...	|	|	...	|	...	...
Koblenz Hbf **911** .... d.	|	|	|	|	|	...	...	...	...	1948	|	|	...	2018	|	|	|	...	...	|	|	...	|	...	...
Mainz Hbf **911** .... d.	|	|	|	|	|	...	...	...	...	2042	|	|	...	2112	|	|	|	...	...	|	|	...	|	...	...
rankfurt (Main) Hbf ..... **913** d.	|	|	|	2006**y**	2006**y**	...	...	2020	2020	|	|	2050	...	|	2106**z**	2151	|	2155	2155	2206**y**	2206**y**	...	2300	2308	2308
Frankfurt Flughafen ✈ ◧. d.	1952	1952	2009	|	|	...	...	|	|	|	2052	|	...	|	2123	|	2154	|	|	|	|	...	2318¦	|	|
lannheim Hbf .... **913** a.	2023	2023	2039	2044	2044	...	...	|	|	2121	2123	2127	...	2152	2154	2228	2224	|	|	2244	2244	...	2353	|	|
lannheim Hbf .... **913** d.	2036	2036	2041	2046	2046	...	...	|	|	2123	2131	2136	...	2156**r**	2156	2231	2236	|	|	2246	2246	...	2357	|	|
Darmstadt Hbf........... **913** d.	|	|	|	|	|	...	...	2037	2037	|	|	|	...	|	|	|	|	2212	2212	|	|	...	|	2327	2327
Bensheim................. **913** d.	|	|	|	|	|	...	...	2050	2050	|	|	|	...	|	|	|	|	2224	2224	|	|	...	|	2341	2341
Weinheim................. **913** d.	|	|	|	|	|	...	...	2100	2100	|	|	|	...	|	|	|	|	2234	2234	|	|	...	|	|	|
Heidelberg Hbf ...**913 931** d.	|	|	|	|	|	...	...	2114	2114	2136	|	|	...	|	2210	|	|	2250	2249	|	|	...	|	0004	0004
Bruchsal ....**913 931** d.	|	|	|	|	|	...	...	|	|	|	|	|	...	|	|	|	|	2310	|	|	|	...	|	|	|
Vaihingen (Enz) .... **931** d.	|	|	|	|	|	...	...	|	|	2205	|	|	...	|	|	|	|	|	2321	|	|	...	|	0033	0033
Stuttgart Hbf .... **931** a.	|	|	2123	|	|	...	...	2154	2154	2224	2208	|	...	|	2250	2308	|	|	2338	|	|	...	|	0050	0100
München Hbf **930** .... a.	|	|	...	|	|	←	...	...	...	...	0027	|	...	|	...	...	|	|	...	|	|	←	|	...	...
arlsruhe Hbf ....**913 916** d.	2100	2102	...	2109	2113	2113	...	...	...	...	...	2200	...	2221**r**	...	...	2300	2327	...	2309	2313	2313	0022	...	...
aden-Baden................ **916** d.	→	2118	...	...	2130	2129	...	...	...	...	...	2217	...	...	...	...	→	...	...	...	2330	2329	...	...	...
ffenburg ....**916** ☆ d.	...	2134	...	...	2145	2145	2205	...	...	...	...	2237	2325	...	...	...	...	...	...	...	2345	2345	...	...	...
Kehl 🏛........................ d.	...	|	...	...	|	|	2224	...	...	...	...	|	2346	...	...	...	...	...	...	...	|	|	...	...	...
Strasbourg..................... a.	...	|	...	...	|	|	2236	...	...	...	...	|	2358	...	...	...	...	...	...	...	|	|	...	...	...
reiburg (Brsg) Hbf .... ☆ d.	...	2207	...	...	2218	2217	...	...	...	...	...	2311	...	...	...	...	...	...	...	...	0018	0017	...	...	...
asel Bad Bf 🏛 ....☆ a.	...	2242	...	...	2254	2252	...	...	...	...	...	2346	...	...	...	...	...	...	...	...	0054	0052	...	...	...
asel SBB ....☆ a.	...	2250	...	...	2302	2300	...	...	...	...	...	2354	...	...	...	...	...	...	...	...	0102	...	...	...	...
Zürich HB **510** .... a.	...	...	...	...	...	...	...	...	...	...	...	...	...	...	...	...	...	...	...	...	...	...	...	...	...

♦ – **NOTES** (LISTED BY TRAIN NUMBER)

5 – 🚃12 and ✕ Hamburg - Zürich (- Chur ①–⑥). On ⑦ runs with train number **1175** and starts from Kiel (Table **820**).

05 – 🚃12 and ✕ Amsterdam - Köln - Basel. Subject to alteration June 27–30, Aug. 2–11, Sept. 28, 29, Nov. 16, 17.

13 – BLAUER ENZIAN – 🚃12 and ✕ Frankfurt - Salzburg - Villach - Klagenfurt; conveys 🚃12 Frankfurt - Villach (**213**) - Ljubljana - Zagreb.

15 – WÖRTHERSEE – 🚃12 and 🍷 Münster - München - Salzburg - Villach - Klagenfurt.

17 – SALZACH – 🚃12 and 🍷 Frankfurt - München - Salzburg - Klagenfurt.

51 – 🚃12 and ✕ Frankfurt - Basel - Luzern - Chiasso - Milano. Sept. 14 - Oct. 20 runs with train number **451** and departs Frankfurt 0754, Mannheim 0834, Karlsruhe 0908, Freiburg 1008 (not calling at Baden-Baden).

19 – CHIEMGAU – 🚃12 and 🍷 Frankfurt - München - Salzburg - Bischofshofen - Graz.

91 – 🚃12 and 🍷 Frankfurt - München (- Salzburg Ⓑ).

05 – 🚃12 (Dortmund ⑥ -) Essen - Karlsuhe (- Basel Bad Bf ①②③④⑦). ✕ to Karlsruhe.

919 – 🚃12 Dortmund - Stuttgart (- Berchtesgaden June 24 - Sept. 8 and Nov. 9 - Dec. 14).

005 – ⑤⑥ (also June 19, Oct. 2, 31). 🚃12 and 🍷 Emden - Münster - Konstanz.

013 – ALLGÄU – 🚃12 and 🍷 Dortmund - Stuttgart - Ulm - Oberstdorf.

019 – ⑥ to Nov. 2 (also June 20, Oct. 3). 🚃12 and 🍷 Norddeich Mole - Münster - Stuttgart.

213 – RÜGEN – 🚃12 and 🍷 Ostseebad Binz - Stralsund - Rostock - Hamburg - Stuttgart. June 11 - July 28 calls at Hamburg Harburg (not Hamburg Hbf).

217 – GREIFSWALDER BODDEN – 🚃12 and 🍷 (Greifswald on dates in Table **845** -) Stralsund - Hamburg - Köln - Stuttgart. June 11 - July 28 calls at Hamburg Harburg (not Hamburg Hbf).

262 – 🚃12 and 🍷 München - Stuttgart - Basel. Runs up to 17 minutes later July 21 - Aug. 4 and Sept. 15 - Oct. 20.

580 – 🚃12 and 🍷 Frankfurt - Strasbourg - Mulhouse - Lyon - Marseille.

– ①–⑤ to Aug. 8; ①–④ Aug. 12 - Oct. 30 (not Oct. 2); ①–⑤ from Nov. 1.
– From Leipzig (Tables **849a**/**850**). Departs Frankfurt Süd 1754 Oct. 6–27.
– To Chur (Table **520**).
– From Düsseldorf (Table **910**).
– 🚃12 Frankfurt - Strasbourg - Paris.
– From Oct. 12.
– Runs as *TGV* **9592** on ⑥ (also Apr. 21). *ICE* ✕, *TGV* 🍷.
– 🚃12 and 🍷 München - Stuttgart - Paris.
– From Westerland (Table **821**).
– From Kiel (Table **820**).
– From Münster (Table **800**).
– To Interlaken via Bern (Table **560**).
– 🚃12 Stuttgart - Paris (Table **32**).

Q – From Kassel via Gießen (Table **806**). Subject to alteration July 20 - Sept. 8 and Oct. 7–20 (also ⑥⑦ Sept. 14–29); see engineering work summary panel on page 369.

R – Ⓐ (not June 20). Until Oct. 4 runs as *ICE* **715** and is diverted between Heidelberg and Stuttgart via Heilbronn (a. 0941), Stuttgart a. 1019.

T – ⑤⑦ (also June 19, Oct. 2, 31; not June 21, July 12, 19, 26, Aug. 2, 9, 16, 23, Oct. 4, Nov. 1). To Tübingen (Table **930**) on ⑦.

U – Ⓑ (not June 20, 21, Oct. 3, 4, Nov. 1). To Tübingen (Table **930**) on ①–④ (not June 19, 20, Oct. 2, 3).

Y – ⑥⑦ to Aug. 4; ⑦ Aug. 11 - Oct. 20; ⑥⑦ from Oct. 27.

a – ①–⑤ only.
b – Not June 19, Oct. 2.
c – Until Sept. 1 calls at Köln Messe/Deutz (not Köln Hbf); from Sept. 2 calls at Köln Hbf, d. 0955.
d – Köln **Messe/Deutz**.
e – ①–⑥ only.
f – ⑤ (also Oct. 2; not Oct. 4).
g – Ⓐ only.
h – ⑥ only.
j – ①②③④⑥ (not June 19, Oct. 2, 31).
m – Not June 20, Oct. 3.
n – Not July 13 - Aug. 25.
q – Not ⑥. 2348 on ⑦ July 28 - Sept. 1.
r – From Oct. 13 Köln d. 1917, Mannheim d. 2158, Karlsruhe a. 2224.

s – Also Oct. 3.
t – Not Aug. 1.
v – Also June 19, Oct. 2, 31; not June 21, Oct. 4, Nov. 1.
w – ⑦ only.
x – Until July 28 serves München Pasing (not München Hbf).
y – On ⑥⑦ Aug. 10 - Sept. 8 (daily Sept. 14 - Oct. 20) calls at Frankfurt (Main) **Süd** (not Hbf), departing up to 8 minutes earlier.
z – On ⑥⑦ Aug. 10 - Sept. 29 calls at Frankfurt (Main) **Süd** (not Hbf), departing up to 6 minutes earlier.

¦ – Until Oct. 25.
⊙ – ①②③④⑦.

⊖ – Train number **573** on ⑦.
□ – Train number **1173** on ⑦ (departs Hamburg Hbf 0802).
⊡ – On ⑥⑦ runs with train number **1177** and starts from Kiel (Table **820**).
¶ – Train number **1211** from Sept. 2.
△ – Runs 8–38 minutes later July 29 - Oct. 17.
♣ – Oct. 14–18 operated by 🚌 Kehl - Strasbourg (a. 0018).
• – Frankfurt (Main) **Süd**.
❖ – Please refer to the shaded engineering work panel on page 369 for details of various alterations affecting services in this table.
§ – On ⑥⑦ (also June 10, Aug. 1) change trains at Basel Badischer Bahnhof (connection arrives Basel SBB 3–5 minutes later).
☆ – See panel on page 428 for other local services.
◐ – Operated by Südwestdeutsche Verkehrs. On June 10, Nov. 1 services run as on ⑦.
◧ – Frankfurt Flughafen Fernbahnhof.

912 BASEL and STUTTGART - FRANKFURT

km	km	IMPORTANT: SEE NOTE ❖	ICE 618 1018	ICE 696 ①g ✕	ICE 774 ①–⑥ ✕	ICE 874 ①g ✕	ICE 874 ✕	ICE 616 ✕	IC 2278 Ⓐm	ICE 674 ⑥⑦ K✕	ICE 674 ①–⑤ K✕	IC 2396 Ⓐu ✕	ICE 918 ①–⑥ nD ✕	ICE 604 ✕	ICE 604 ①–⑤ ✕	ICE 694 ✕	ICE 1672 Q✕	◐2	ICE 676 ①–⑤ ✕	ICE 772 ✕	IC 2018 ⑥ 🍷♦	IC 2010 ①–⑤ F🍷	IC 2261 ①–⑥ 🍷♦	ICE 374 ✕	ICE 614 ✕
		Zürich HB **510** d.	...	...	...	...	...	...	...	...	...	...	...	...	...	...	...	...	...	...	...	...	...	...	...
		Basel SBB ☆ d.	...	...	...	...	...	...	...	...	...	...	...	...	...	...	...	...	...	...	...	...	...	0606	...
		Basel Bad Bf ⊞ ☆ d.	...	...	...	0412	...	...	...	0511	...	...	...	...	0514	...	...	...	0547	...	...	...	0600	0618	...
		Freiburg (Brsg) Hbf ☆ d.	...	...	...	0447	...	...	...	0546	...	...	...	...	0551	...	...	...	0620	...	...	...	0646	0652	...
	0	**Strasbourg** d.	...	...	...	|	...	...	...	|	...	...	...	...	|	...	...	0620	|	...	...	...	|	|	...
	8	Kehl ⊞ d.	...	...	...	|	...	...	...	|	...	...	...	...	|	...	...	0633	|	...	...	...	|	|	...
	29	Offenburg **916** ☆ d.	...	...	...	0520	...	...	...	0618	...	...	...	...	0625	...	...	0652	0656	...	...	...	0731	0724	...
	—	Baden-Baden **916** d.	...	...	...	0535	...	...	...	0634	...	...	...	...	0640	...	...	...	0714	...	...	...	0748	0740	...
		Karlsruhe Hbf **913 916** d.	0349*	0500o	...	0558	0558	...	0615	0651	0651	...	...	0700	0700	...	0702	...	0736	...	...	...	0804	0800	...
		München Hbf **930** d.	0001‡	|	...	|	|	0324b	|	|	|	...	...	|	|	...	|	...	|	...	...	...	...	|	0522
0	0	**Stuttgart** Hbf **931** d.	0228	|	0502	|	|	0551	|	|	|	0602	0640◊	|	|	0651	|	...	|	0724	0714	0714	...	|	0751
29	29	Vaihingen (Enz) **931** d.	0255	|	0519	|	|	|	|	|	|	0620	|	|	|	|	|	...	|	|	|	|	...	|	|
		Bruchsal **913 931** d.	0405	|	|	|	|	|	0632	|	|	|	|	|	|	|	0722	...	|	|	|	|	...	|	|
	92	**Heidelberg** Hbf **913 931** d.	0428	|	0547	|	|	|	0654	|	|	0658	|	|	|	|	0746	...	|	|	0755	0755	...	|	|
		Weinheim **913** d.	|	|	|	|	|	|	|	|	|	0714	|	|	|	|	0800	...	|	|	|	|	...	|	|
		Bensheim **913** d.	|	|	|	|	|	|	|	|	|	0728	|	|	|	|	0809	...	|	|	|	|	...	|	|
		Darmstadt Hbf **913** d.	|	|	|	|	|	|	|	|	|	0742	|	|	|	|	0824	...	|	|	|	|	...	|	|
107	109	**Mannheim** Hbf **913** a.	0438	0526	0559	0623	0623	0628	0709	0714	0714	|	0719◊	0724	0724	0729	|	...	0800	0803	0806	0806	...	0824	0828
107		**Mannheim** Hbf **913** d.	0440	0528	0605	0632	0632	0636	0711	0716	0716	|	0721	0735	0735	0732	|	...	...	0805	0808	0808	...	0832	0836
179		**Frankfurt** Flughafen ✈ a.	0512	|	0636	|	|	0706	|	|	|	|	0753	0806	0806	|	|	...	...	0836	|	|	...	|	0906
		Frankfurt (Main) Hbf **913** a.	0533	0608	0652z	0708	0708	|	0752	0752y	0752	0802	|	|	|	0808	0840z	...	...	0852z	|	|	...	0908	|
		Mainz Hbf **911** a.	|	|	|	|	|	|	...	|	|	...	|	|	|	|	...	...	...	|	0847	0847	...	|	|
		Koblenz Hbf **911** a.	|	|	|	|	|	|	...	|	|	...	|	|	|	|	...	...	...	|	0942	0942	...	|	|
		Köln Hbf **800 910** a.	0705	|	|	|	|	0805	...	|	|	...	0841d	0905	0905	|	...	...	...	|	1043	1043	...	|	1005
		Dortmund Hbf **800** a.	0827‡	|	|	|	|	0921	...	|	|	...	...	...	...	|	...	...	...	|	...	...	...	|	1121
		Hannover Hbf **810 900** a.	...	|	0934	|	|	...	...	1034	1034	...	...	...	...	|	...	...	...	1134	...	...	...	|	...
		Berlin Hbf **810 850 902** a.	...	1029	|	1158	1158	...	...	|	|	...	...	...	...	1229	...	...	...	|	...	...	...	1400	...
		Hamburg Hbf **800 900** a.	...	...	1055	...	...	...	...	1156	1156	...	...	...	...	...	...	...	...	1254	...	...	...	...	...

IMPORTANT: SEE NOTE ❖	IC 2392 ①	IC 2216 🍷♦	IC 2294 ①–⑥ 🍷	ICE 78 ✕	ICE 916 ①–⑥ n✕	①–⑤ ◐2	◐2	ICE 202 ①–⑥ ✕	ICE 202 ✕	ICE 692 ✕	IC 2370 Q	ICE 770 ✕	ICE 1537 Ⓒ ✕♦	ICE 9571 P 🅁✕	①–⑤ ◐2	TGV 9561 ①–⑥ E🅁 🍷	ICE 372 N✕	ICE 612 ✕	IC 2218 🍷	IC 1296 ①–⑥ G🍷	IC 1296 🍷	IC 1922 ⑤⑦ v🍷	ICE 76 ✕	ICE 914 n ✕	◐2
Zürich HB **510** d.	...	...	...	0600	...	...	...	...	...	...	...	...	...	...	...	...	...	...	...	...	...	...	0800	...	...
Basel SBB ☆ d.	...	...	...	0706	...	...	...	0713	...	...	...	...	...	...	...	...	0813	...	...	...	...	...	0906	...	...
Basel Bad Bf ⊞ ☆ d.	...	...	...	0715	...	...	...	0722	...	...	...	...	...	...	...	...	0823	...	...	...	...	...	0915	...	...
Freiburg (Brsg) Hbf ☆ d.	...	...	...	0749	...	...	...	0754	...	...	...	...	...	...	...	...	0857	...	...	...	...	...	0949	...	...
Strasbourg d.	...	...	...	|	...	0720	0750	|	...	...	...	...	...	0831	0852	0911	|	...	...	...	...	...	|	...	0920
Kehl ⊞ d.	...	...	...	|	...	0733	0803	|	...	...	...	...	...	|	0903	|	|	...	...	...	...	...	|	...	0933
Offenburg **916** ☆ d.	...	...	...	|	...	0752	0822	0826	...	...	...	...	...	|	0922	|	0930	...	...	...	...	...	|	...	0952
Baden-Baden **916** d.	...	...	...	0834	...	...	...	0842	...	...	...	...	...	|	...	|	|	...	...	...	...	...	1034	...	...
Karlsruhe Hbf **913 916** d.	...	...	...	0851	...	...	...	0900	0900	...	0906	...	...	0908	...	0955	1000	...	...	...	...	...	1051	...	...
München Hbf **930** d.	...	...	0541a	|	...	...	...	|	|	0629e	|	...	...	...	...	|	|	0728	...	0746x	...	...	|	...	...
Stuttgart Hbf **931** d.	0718	0737	0805	|	0833	...	...	|	|	0851	|	0924	0903	...	...	|	|	0951	0937	1004	1004	1009	|	1041	...
Vaihingen (Enz) **931** d.	|	0755	|	|	|	...	...	|	|	|	|	|	0927	...	...	|	|	|	0955	|	|	|	|	|	...
Bruchsal **913 931** d.	|	|	|	|	|	...	...	|	|	|	0923	|	|	...	...	|	|	|	|	|	|	|	|	|	...
Heidelberg Hbf **913 931** d.	0800	0825	0846	|	|	...	...	|	|	|	0946	|	|	...	...	|	|	|	1025	1046	1046	|	|	|	...
Weinheim **913** d.	0823	|	0900	|	|	...	...	|	|	|	1000	|	1011	...	...	|	|	|	|	1100	1100	|	|	|	...
Bensheim **913** d.	0833	|	0909	|	|	...	...	|	|	|	1009	|	1022	...	...	|	|	|	|	1109	1109	|	|	|	...
Darmstadt Hbf **913** d.	0847	|	0924	|	|	...	...	|	|	|	1024	|	1039	...	...	|	|	|	|	1124	1124	|	|	|	...
Mannheim Hbf **913** a.	|	0837	|	0914	0919	...	...	0924	0924	0929	|	1003	|	...	...	1018	1023	1028	1037	|	|	1050	1114	1119	...
Mannheim Hbf **913** d.	|	0839	|	0916	0921	...	...	0935	0935	0932	|	1005	|	...	...	1021	1032	1036	1039	|	|	1052	1116	1121	...
Frankfurt Flughafen ✈ a.	|	|	|	|	0953	...	...	1006	1006	|	|	1036	|	...	...	|	|	1106	|	|	|	|	|	1153	...
Frankfurt (Main) Hbf **913** a.	0910w	|	0940	0952y	|	...	...	|	|	1008	1040z	1052z	1056	...	...	1058	1108	|	|	1140	1140	|	1152y	|	...
Mainz Hbf **911** a.	...	0918	...	|	|	...	...	|	|	|	...	|	|	...	...	...	|	|	1118	...	...	1142	|	|	...
Koblenz Hbf **911** a.	...	1011	...	|	|	...	...	|	|	|	...	|	|	...	...	...	|	|	1211	...	...	1242	|	|	...
Köln Hbf **800 910** a.	...	1105	...	|	1041d	...	...	1105	1105	|	...	|	|	...	...	...	|	1205	1305	...	...	1343	|	1241d	...
Dortmund Hbf **800** a.	...	|	...	|	1203j	...	...	...	...	|	...	|	|	...	...	...	|	1321	|	...	...	1508¶	|	1403e	...
Hannover Hbf **810 900** a.	...	|	...	1234	...	...	...	...	...	|	...	1334	|	...	...	...	|	...	|	...	...	1701	1434	...	...
Berlin Hbf **810 850 902** a.	...	|	...	|	...	...	...	...	...	1429	...	|	1455	...	...	...	1601	...	|	...	...	1854	|	...	...
Hamburg Hbf **800 900** a.	...	1512	...	1354	...	...	...	...	...	...	...	1454	...	...	...	...	...	...	1714	...	...	...	1554	...	...

IMPORTANT: SEE NOTE ❖	①–⑤ ◐2	ICE 200 ✕	ICE 690 ✕	ICE 1578 ⑤–⑦ sQ ✕	ICE 578 ✕	◐2	ICE 370 ✕	ICE 610 ✕	IC 2312 🍷	EC 390 G🍷	IC 2006 ⑥ 🍷♦	IC 2004 ⑦ 🍷♦	IC 2014 ⑤ 🍷♦	ICE 74 K✕	ICE 1014 n ✕	ICE 108 ✕	ICE 598 ✕	ICE 1576 Q✕	IC 2012 🍷♦	ICE 576 ✕	ICE 9573 TP 🅁	◐2	ICE 278 N✕	ICE 518 ✕	EC 8 ✕
Zürich HB **510** d.	...	...	...	...	...	...	...	...	...	...	...	...	...	1000	...	...	...	...	...	...	...	...	...	...	1100
Basel SBB ☆ d.	...	0913	...	...	...	...	1013	...	...	...	...	...	...	1106	...	1113	...	...	...	...	...	...	1213	...	1220
Basel Bad Bf ⊞ ☆ d.	...	0923	...	...	...	...	1023	...	...	...	...	...	...	1115	...	1123	...	...	...	...	...	...	1223	...	1229
Freiburg (Brsg) Hbf ☆ d.	...	0956	...	...	...	...	1057	...	...	...	...	...	...	1148	...	1156	...	...	...	...	...	...	1257	...	1304
Strasbourg d.	0950	|	...	...	...	1050	|	...	...	...	...	...	...	|	...	|	...	...	...	...	1246	1250	|	...	|
Kehl ⊞ d.	1003	|	...	...	...	1103	|	...	...	...	...	...	...	|	...	|	...	...	...	...	|	1303	|	...	|
Offenburg **916** ☆ d.	1022	1029	...	...	...	1122	1130	...	...	...	1139	1139	...	|	...	1229	...	...	...	...	|	1322	1330	...	|
Baden-Baden **916** d.	...	|	...	...	...	...	|	...	...	...	1202	1202	...	1233	...	|	...	...	...	...	|	...	|	...	1352
Karlsruhe Hbf **913 916** d.	...	1059	...	1110	...	...	1200	...	...	...	1221	1221	...	1251	...	1300	...	1310	...	...	1325	...	1400	...	1412
München Hbf **930** d.	...	|	0828	|	...	...	|	0928	...	0947x	|	|	...	|	...	|	1028	|	...	...	...	...	|	1128	|
Stuttgart Hbf **931** d.	...	|	1051	|	1124	...	|	1151	1137	1204	|	|	1208	|	1237	|	1251	|	1312	1324	...	...	|	1351	|
Vaihingen (Enz) **931** d.	...	|	|	|	|	...	|	|	1156	|	|	|	1226	|	|	|	|	|	|	|	...	...	|	|	|
Bruchsal **913 931** d.	...	|	|	1123	|	...	|	|	|	|	|	|	|	|	|	|	|	1323	|	|	...	...	|	|	|
Heidelberg Hbf **913 931** d.	...	|	|	1146	|	...	|	|	1225	1246	|	|	|	|	|	|	|	1346	1355	|	...	...	|	|	|
Weinheim **913** d.	...	|	|	1200	|	...	|	|	|	1300	|	|	|	|	|	|	|	1400	|	|	...	...	|	|	|
Bensheim **913** d.	...	|	|	1209	|	...	|	|	|	1309	|	|	|	|	|	|	|	1409	|	|	...	...	|	|	|
Darmstadt Hbf **913** d.	...	|	|	1224	|	...	|	|	|	1324	|	|	|	|	|	|	|	1424	|	|	...	...	|	|	|
Mannheim Hbf **913** a.	...	1123	1129	|	1203	...	1224	1228	1237	|	1250	1250	1256	1314	1319	1323	1329	|	1406	1403	...	...	1423	1428	1437
Mannheim Hbf **913** d.	...	1135	1132	|	1205	...	1232	1236	1239	|	1258	1258	1258	1316	1321	1335	1332	|	1408	1405	...	...	1432	1436	1439
Frankfurt Flughafen ✈ a.	...	1206	|	|	1236	...	|	1306	|	|	|	|	|	|	1353	1406	|	|	|	1436	...	...	|	1506	|
Frankfurt (Main) Hbf **913** a.	...	|	1208	1240	1252z	...	1308	|	|	1340	|	|	|	1352y	|	|	1408	1440z	|	1452z	...	...	1508	|	|
Mainz Hbf **911** a.	...	|	|	...	|	...	|	|	1318	...	1342	1342	1342	|	|	|	|	...	1447	|	...	...	|	|	1518
Koblenz Hbf **911** a.	...	|	|	...	|	...	|	|	1411	...	1442	1442	1442	|	|	|	|	...	1542	|	...	...	|	|	1611
Köln Hbf **800 910** a.	...	1305	|	...	|	...	|	1405	1505	...	1543	1543	1543	|	1441d	1505	|	...	1643	|	...	...	|	1605	1705
Dortmund Hbf **800** a.	...	1421k	|	...	|	...	|	1521	|	...	1704	...	...	|	1607	1621h	|	...	1807	|	...	...	|	1721	|
Hannover Hbf **810 900** a.	...	...	|	...	1534	...	|	...	|	...	...	...	...	1634	...	...	|	...	...	1734	...	...	|	...	|
Berlin Hbf **810 850 902** a.	...	...	1629	...	|	...	1801	...	|	...	...	...	...	|	...	...	1829	...	...	|	...	...	1959	...	|
Hamburg Hbf **800 900** a.	...	...	...	...	1653	...	...	...	1914	...	...	...	...	1753	...	...	...	...	...	1853	...	...	...	...	2114

Regional trains **BASEL - OFFENBURG** (German holiday dates apply). On June 20, Nov. 1 regional services between Basel Bad Bf and Offenburg run as on ⑦.

km		⚒		Ⓐ													Ⓐ			Ⓒ	⑥				⚒		
0	**Basel** SBB d.	0532	...	0603	...	0736§	0836§	0934	1034	1134	1234	1334	1434	1534	1636§	1736§	1804	1836§	...	1904	...	1934	...	2104	...	2240
5	**Basel** Bad Bf ⊞ d.	0538	0542	0625	0634	0748	0848	0948	1048	1148	1248	1348	1448	1546	1648	1748	1826	1848	1848	1926	...	1948	...	2110	2126	2258
37	Müllheim (Baden) d.	▬	0615	0650	0707	0823	0923	1023	1123	1223	1323	1423	1523	1622	1723	1823	1856	1923	1923	1955	1955	2023	2053	...	2159	2333
66	**Freiburg** (Brsg) Hbf a.	...	0641	0718	0736	0847	0944	1044	1144	1244	1344	1444	1544	1643	1744	1844	1923	1944	1944	2021	2021	2044	2122	...	2220	0001
66	**Freiburg** (Brsg) Hbf d.	0555	0656	0722	0803	0903	1003	1103	1203	1307	1403	1500	1603	1705	1803	1903	1925	...	2003	2025	2025	...	2125	...	2225	0018
129	**Offenburg** a.	0645	0745	0814	0851	0953	1053	1153	1253	1353	1450	1553	1650	1753	1850	1950	2021	...	2050	2122	2122	...	2221	...	2318	0112

FOR NOTES SEE NEXT PAGE →

BASEL and STUTTGART - FRANKFURT 912

IMPORTANT: SEE NOTE ❖	*EC* 218		*TGV* 9583	*ICE* 72	*TGV* 9583	*ICE* 106	*ICE* 596	*ICE* 710	*ICE* 1574	*IC* 1918	*ICE* 974	*ICE* 574		*ICE* 276	*ICE* 516	*EC* 6	*IC* 2292	*EC* 114		*TGV* 9575	*ICE* 70	*ICE* 1010	*ICE* 104	*ICE* 204	*ICE* 594
			Ⓡ		Ⓡ			Ⓐ R			①–⑤	⑥⑦							①–⑤	P				①–⑤	
	🍷♦	◐2	🍷♦	H✕	🍷♦	✕	✕	✕	Q✕	♦	K✕	✕	◐2	✕	✕	N✕		🍷♦	◐2	Ⓡ🍷	H✕	M✕	✕♦	✕	✕
Zürich HB **510** d.	...	...	...	1200	...	...	...	...	...	...	...	...	...	...	...	...	...	...	...	...	1400	...	...	...	...
asel SBB ☆ d.	...	...	...	1306	...	1313	...	...	...	...	...	...	...	1413	...	1427	...	...	...	...	1506	...	1513	1513	...
asel Bad Bf 🏛 ☆ d.	...	...	...	1315	...	1323	...	...	...	...	...	...	...	1423	...	1435	...	...	...	...	1515	...	1523	1523	...
reiburg (Brsg) Hbf ☆ d.	...	...	...	1349	...	1356	...	...	...	...	...	...	...	1455	...	1507	...	...	...	...	1549	...	1556	1556	...
Strasbourg d.	...	1320	1355	|	...	|	...	...	...	...	...	...	1450	|	...	|	...	...	1520	1546	|	...	|	|	...
Kehl 🏛 d.	...	1335	|	|	...	|	...	...	...	...	...	...	1503	|	...	|	...	...	1533	|	|	...	|	|	...
)ffenburg **916** ☆ d.	...	1352	|	|	...	1429	...	...	...	...	...	...	1522	1527	...	|	...	...	1552	|	|	...	1629	1629	...
aden-Baden **916** d.	...	...	1425	1434	←	|	...	...	...	...	...	...	...	1542	...	|	...	...	...	|	1634	...	|	|	...
arlsruhe Hbf **913 916** d.	...	...	1446	1451	1454	1500	...	...	1510	...	...	...	...	1601	...	1612	...	...	...	1625	1651	...	1700	1700	...
München Hbf **930** d.	1147f	...	→	|	|	|	1228	...	|	...	...	...	...	|	1328	|	...	1347x	...	...	|	...	|	|	1428
Stuttgart Hbf **931** d.	1404	...	...	|	|	|	1451	1433	|	1512	1524	1524	...	|	1551	|	1604	1608	...	...	|	1637	|	|	1651
Vaihingen (Enz) **931** d.	|	...	...	|	|	|	|	1454	|	|	|	|	...	|	|	|	|	1625	...	...	|	|	|	|	|
Bruchsal **913 931** d.	|	...	...	|	|	|	|	|	1523	|	|	|	...	|	|	|	|	|	...	...	|	|	|	|	|
Heidelberg Hbf **913 931** d.	1446	...	...	|	|	|	|	1520	1546	1555	|	|	...	|	|	|	1646	|	...	...	|	|	|	|	|
Weinheim **913** d.	1500	...	...	|	|	|	|	|	1600	|	|	|	...	|	|	|	1700	|	...	...	|	|	|	|	|
Bensheim **913** d.	1509	...	...	|	|	|	|	|	1609	|	|	|	...	|	|	|	1709	|	...	...	|	|	|	|	|
Darmstadt Hbf **913** d.	1524	...	...	|	|	|	|	|	1624	|	|	|	...	|	|	|	1724	|	...	...	|	|	|	|	|
annheim Hbf **913** a.	|	...	...	1514	1518	1523	1529	1531	|	1606	1603	1603	...	1624	1628	1637	|	1656	...	...	1714	1719	1723	1723	1729
annheim Hbf **913** d.	|	...	...	1516	1521	1535	1532	1533	|	1608	1605	1605	...	1632	1636	1639	|	1658	...	...	1716	1721	1735	1735	1732
Frankfurt Flughafen ✈ ◧ a.	|	...	...	|	|	1606	|	|	|	|	1636	1636	...	|	1706	|	|	|	...	...	|	1753	1806	1806	|
rankfurt (Main) Hbf **913** a.	1540	...	...	1552y	1558	|	1608	|	1640z	|	1652	1652z	...	1708	|	|	1740	|	...	...	1752y	|	|	|	1808
Mainz Hbf **911** a.	...	...	...	|	...	|	|	1615	...	1647	|	|	...	|	|	1718	...	1740	...	...	|	|	|	|	|
Koblenz Hbf **911** a.	...	...	...	|	...	|	|	|	...	1742	|	|	...	|	|	1811	...	1842	...	...	|	|	|	|	|
Köln Hbf **800 910** a.	...	...	...	|	...	1705	|	1801	...	1843	|	|	...	|	1805	1905	...	1943	...	...	|	1841d	1905	1905	|
Dortmund Hbf **800** a.	...	...	...	|	...	...	|	...	...	2007	|	|	...	|	1921	2021h	...	2103	...	...	|	...	...	2021	|
Hannover Hbf **810 900** a.	...	...	...	1834	...	...	|	...	...	...	1934	1934	...	|	...	|	...	...	...	...	2034	...	...	...	|
Berlin Hbf **810 850 902** a.	...	...	...	|	...	...	2029	...	...	...	|	|	...	2157	...	|	...	...	...	...	|	...	...	...	2229
Hamburg Hbf **800 900** a.	...	...	...	1954	...	...	...	...	...	...	2057	2057	...	...	...	2316p	...	...	...	...	2154	...	...	...	...

IMPORTANT: SEE NOTE ❖	*IC* 2316	*ICE* 1572	*ICE* 572	*EC* 52			*ICE* 9563	*ICE* 274	*ICE* 1212	*IC* 2318	*EC* 112	*ICE* 912		*TGV* 9577	*ICE* 376		*ICE* 102	*ICE* 592	*ICE* 1570	*ICE* 570	*IC* 1910		*ICE* 1172	*ICE* 272	*ICE* 292
	Ⓑ					①–⑤	E		♥			Ⓑ n		Ⓑ			⊙		Ⓑ ⊗	⑦	⑦	①–⑤	⑥	①–⑤	⑦
	B	Q✕	✕	✕♦	◐2	◐2	Ⓡ✕	✕	✕	🍷♦	✕♦	✕	◐2	Ⓡ♦ 🍷	N✕	◐2	✕	L✕	Q✕	✕	🍷	◐2	✕	✕	✕
Zürich HB **510** d.	...	...	...	...	...	...	...	...	...	...	...	...	...	...	...	...	...	...	...	...	...	...	1700	1700	1700
asel SBB ☆ d.	...	...	...	1538	...	...	...	1613	...	...	...	...	...	...	1706	...	1713	...	...	...	...	...	1813	1813	1813
asel Bad Bf 🏛 ☆ d.	...	...	...	1552	...	...	...	1623	...	...	...	...	...	...	1715	...	1723	...	...	...	...	...	1823	1823	1823
reiburg (Brsg) Hbf ☆ d.	...	...	...	1622	...	...	...	1655	...	...	...	...	...	...	1749	...	1755	...	...	...	...	...	1857	1857	1857
Strasbourg d.	...	...	...	|	1620	1650	1713	|	...	...	...	...	1721	1746	|	1750	|	...	...	...	...	1850	|	|	|
Kehl 🏛 d.	...	...	...	|	1633	1703	|	|	...	...	...	...	1733	|	|	1803	|	...	...	...	...	1903	|	|	|
)ffenburg **916** ☆ d.	...	...	...	|	1652	1722	|	1727	...	...	...	...	1752	|	|	1822	1826	...	...	...	...	1922	1930	1930	1930
aden-Baden **916** d.	...	...	...	|	...	...	|	1742	...	...	...	...	...	|	1834	...	1842	...	...	...	...	...	|	|	|
arlsruhe Hbf **913 916** d.	...	1709	...	1731	...	...	1755	1801	...	...	...	...	...	1825	1851	...	1900	...	1910	...	...	...	2000	2000	2000
München Hbf **930** d.	...	|	...	|	...	...	|	|	1528	...	1548x	...	...	...	|	...	|	1628	|	...	1618•	...	|	|	|
Stuttgart Hbf **931** d.	1624	|	1724	|	...	...	|	|	1751	1737	1804	1837	...	...	|	...	|	1851	|	1924	1914	...	|	|	|
Vaihingen (Enz) **931** d.	|	|	|	|	...	...	|	|	|	1755	|	|	...	...	|	...	|	|	|	|	|	...	|	|	|
Bruchsal **913 931** d.	|	1723	|	|	...	...	|	|	|	|	|	|	...	...	|	...	|	|	1923	|	|	...	|	|	|
Heidelberg Hbf **913 931** d.	1721	1746	|	|	...	...	|	|	|	1825	1846	|	...	...	|	...	|	|	1946	|	1955	...	|	|	|
Weinheim **913** d.	|	1800	|	|	...	...	|	|	|	|	1900	|	...	...	|	...	|	|	2000	|	|	...	|	|	|
Bensheim **913** d.	|	1809	|	|	...	...	|	|	|	|	1909	|	...	...	|	...	|	|	2009	|	|	...	|	|	|
Darmstadt Hbf **913** d.	|	1824	|	|	...	...	|	|	|	|	1924	|	...	...	|	...	|	|	2024	|	|	...	|	|	|
annheim Hbf **913** a.	1736	|	1803	1810	...	...	1818	1824	1828	1837	|	1919	...	...	1914	...	1924	1929	|	2003	2006	...	2024	2024	2024
annheim Hbf **913** d.	1738	|	1805	1812	...	...	1821	1832	1836	1839	|	1921	...	...	1916	...	1935	1932	|	2005	2008	...	2032	2032	2032
Frankfurt Flughafen ✈ ◧ a.	|	|	1836	|	...	...	|	|	1906	|	|	1953	...	...	|	...	2006	|	|	2036	|	...	|	|	|
rankfurt (Main) Hbf **913** a.	|	1840z	1852z	1859	...	...	1858	1908	|	|	1940	|	...	...	1952q	...	|	2008	2040z	2052z	|	...	2108	2108	2108
Mainz Hbf **911** a.	1815	...	|	...	...	...	...	|	|	1918	...	|	...	...	|	...	|	...	...	|	2047	...	|	|	|
Koblenz Hbf **911** a.	...	...	|	...	...	...	...	|	|	2011	...	|	...	...	|	...	|	...	...	|	2142	...	|	|	|
Köln Hbf **800 910** a.	...	...	|	...	...	...	...	|	2005c	2105	...	2042d	...	...	|	...	2105	...	...	|	2243	...	|	|	|
Dortmund Hbf **800** a.	...	...	|	...	...	...	...	|	2121	2221t	...	2203	...	...	|	...	2221	...	...	|	0002	...	|	|	|
Hannover Hbf **810 900** a.	...	...	2134	...	...	...	...	|	|	...	...	...	...	...	2234r	...	0018	...	...	2334	...	...	0002	0002	|
Berlin Hbf **810 850 902** a.	...	...	|	...	...	...	...	0014	|	...	...	...	...	...	|	...	...	...	...	|	...	...	|	|	0159
Hamburg Hbf **800 900** a.	...	...	2254	...	...	...	...	...	0016	...	...	...	...	...	0011r	...	...	...	...	0100	...	...	0136	0138	...

– **NOTES** (LISTED BY TRAIN NUMBER)

2 – [12] and ✕ Milano - Brig - Bern - Basel - Frankfurt. Arrives Frankfurt 1915 on ⑥⑦ Aug. 10 - Sept. 29.
04 – [12] and ✕ Basel - Köln - Amsterdam. Subject to alteration June 27 – 30, Aug. 2 – 11, Sept. 28, 29, Nov. 16, 17
12 – BLAUER ENZIAN – [12] and ✕ Klagenfurt - Villach - Salzburg - Frankfurt; [12] Zagreb (**212**) - Ljubljana - Villach (**112**) - Frankfurt.
14 – WÖRTHERSEE – [12] and 🍷 Klagenfurt - Villach - Salzburg - München - Dortmund.
18 – CHIEMGAU – [12] and 🍷 Graz - Bischofshofen - Salzburg - München - Frankfurt (- Erfurt ♣). Arrives Frankfurt 1555 on dates in note ♣.
537 – © (not Aug. 10 - Oct. 27). [12] and ✕ Stuttgart - Frankfurt - Erfurt - Berlin. On ⑦ (also June 10, July 20, 27, Aug. 3) departs Stuttgart 0911.
918 – [12] (June 25 - Sept. 9 and Nov. 10 - Dec. 14: Berchtesgaden -) Stuttgart - Dortmund.
004 – ⑦ (also June 20, Oct. 3, Nov. 1). [12] and 🍷 Konstanz - Karlsruhe - Münster - Emden.
006 – [12] and 🍷 Konstanz - Karlsruhe - Dortmund.
012 – ALLGÄU – [12] and 🍷 Oberstdorf - Ulm - Stuttgart - Dortmund.
014 – ⑤ (also June 19, Oct. 2, 31; not Nov. 1). [12] and 🍷 Stuttgart - Münster - Emden.
018 – ⑥ to Nov. 2 (also June 20, Oct. 3; not July 13 - Aug. 24). [12] and 🍷 Stuttgart - Münster - Norddeich Mole.
216 – GREIFSWALDER BODDEN – [12] and 🍷 Stuttgart - Hamburg - Rostock - Stralsund (- Greifswald Ⓑ). June 11 - July 28 calls at Hamburg Harburg (not Hamburg Hbf).
261 – [12] Basel - Stuttgart - München. July 20 - Aug. 3 and Sept. 14 - Oct. 19 departs Basel Bad Bf 0528, Freiburg 0609, Offenburg 0718, Baden Baden 0734, arrives Karlsruhe 0749.
318 – [12] and 🍷 Stuttgart - Köln (- Dortmund Ⓑ) (- Münster ⑦).
577 – [12] and 🍷 Paris - Strasbourg - München.
583 – [12] and 🍷 Marseille - Lyon - Mulhouse - Strasbourg - Frankfurt.

– Ⓐ to Oct. 4 (not June 20); Ⓑ from Oct. 7. To Wiesbaden Hbf (a. 1833).
– To Düsseldorf (Table **910**).
– [12] Paris - Strasbourg - Frankfurt.
– ①–⑤ (not June 10, 20, 21, Oct. 3, 4, Nov. 1). From Tübingen (Table **930**).
– From Salzburg (Table **890**).
– From Chur (Table **520**).
– To Kiel (Table **820**).
– To Leipzig (Table **850**).
– To Münster (Table **800**).
– From Interlaken via Bern (Table **560**).
– [12] Paris - Stuttgart (Table **32**).
– To Kassel via Gießen (Table **806**). Subject to alteration July 20 - Sept. 8 and Oct. 7 – 20 (also ⑥⑦ Sept. 14 – 29); see engineering work summary panel on page 369.

R – Ⓐ (not June 20) Until Oct. 4 runs as *ICE* **714**, departs Stuttgart 1335, does not call at Vaihingen and runs via Heilbronn (d. 1410), Heidelberg d. 1518.
T – Runs as *TGV* **9593** on ⑥. *ICE* ✕, *TGV* 🍷.

a – Ⓐ (not Nov. 1).
b – 0315 on ①⑦ July 28 - Sept. 2.
c – Until Sept. 1 calls at Köln **Messe/Deutz** (not Hbf); calls at Köln Hbf from Sept. 2.
d – Köln **Messe/Deutz**.
e – ①–⑥ only.
f – From July 29.
g – Also June 11.
h – ⑥ only.
j – ①②③④⑥ (not June 19, Oct. 2, 31).
k – ⑥ (not July 13 - Aug. 24, Oct. 26, Nov. 2).
m – Not June 20, 21, Oct. 4.
n – Not July 13 - Aug. 25.
o – 0455 Aug. 12 - Oct. 21.
p – Not ⑥.
q – On ⑦ Aug. 11 - Oct. 20 (also Sept. 20, 27, Oct. 2, 11, 18) calls at Frankfurt (Main) **Süd** (not Hbf).
r – Frankfurt - Hamburg on ⑤⑦ (also Oct. 2; not Oct. 4).
s – Also Oct. 3.
t – Ⓑ only.
u – Not June 20.
v – ⑤⑦ (also June 19, Oct. 2, 31; not June 21, Oct. 4, Nov. 1).
w – 0920 Aug. 12 - Oct. 21.
x – Until July 28 serves München Pasing (not München Hbf).
y – On ⑥⑦ Aug. 10 - Sept. 8 (daily Sept. 14 - Oct. 20) calls at Frankfurt (Main) **Süd** (not Hbf).
z – On ⑥⑦ Aug. 10 - Sept. 29 calls at Frankfurt (Main) **Süd** (not Hbf).

⊗ – Not Oct. 2.
¶ – From Oct. 13.

* – Calls at Karlsruhe after Vaihingen.
• – 1614 until July 28.
‡ – ⑥⑦ only. Arrives 0821 on ⑦.
⁝ – On ①⑦ July 28 - Sept. 2 departs 2354 (the previous day).
♣ – ①–④ to Aug. 8 (not June 10, 19, 20); ①–④ from Oct. 28,
◊ – On ⑥ departs Stuttgart 0621, arrives Mannheim 0706.
♥ – Train number **1210** from Sept. 2.
⊙ – Train number **1102** on ⑥.
❖ – Please refer to the shaded engineering work panel on page 369 for details of various alterations affecting services in this table.
§ – On ⑥⑦ (also June 10, Aug. 1) depart Basel SBB 2 minutes earlier and change trains at Basel Bad Bf.
☆ – See panel on page 430 for other local services.
◐ – Operated by Südwestdeutsche Verkehrs. On June 10, Nov. 1 services run as on ⑦.
◧ – Frankfurt Flughafen Fernbahnhof.

912 BASEL and STUTTGART - FRANKFURT

Service from June 11

IMPORTANT: SEE NOTE ✣	ICE	IC	IC	EC	IC		TGV	ICE	ICE		ICE	ICE	ICE	IC	ICE	RJX		NJ	NJ		IC	EN	ICE		IC
	512	2210	2210	216	1976		9579	100	590		4	1110	510	1990	990	66		40470	470		468‡	453	992		208
		①–④	Q				P					⑤–⑦		Ⓐm	A	⑤⑥		🅁	🅁		478‡	④			♣
	M✕	R🍷	🍷	🍷♦		◐2	🅁🍷	✕	✕	◐2	✕	✕	✕♦		✕	✕♦	◐2	♦	♦	◐2	⑤⑥	🅁♦	♦	◐2	K
Zürich HB 510 d.	...	...	...	...	...	...	...	...	...	...	1900	...	...	...	...	...	...	2000	2000	...	...	...	...	...	...
Basel SBB ☆ d.	...	...	...	...	...	...	...	1913	...	...	2013	...	...	...	...	...	...	2113	2113	...	...	...	...	...	2313
Basel Bad Bf 🏛 ☆ d.	...	...	...	...	...	...	...	1923	...	...	2023	...	...	...	...	...	...	2122	2122	...	2217	...	...	...	2323
Freiburg (Brsg) Hbf ☆ d.	...	...	...	...	...	...	...	1954	...	...	2055	...	...	...	...	...	...	2158	2158	...	2252	...	...	...	0005
Strasbourg d.	...	...	...	...	...	1922	1946	|	...	2021	|	...	...	...	...	...	2150	|	|	2250	|	2340	...	0005	|
Kehl 🏛 d.	...	...	...	...	...	1933	|	|	...	2033	|	...	...	...	...	...	2203	|	|	2303	|	|	...	0016	|
Offenburg 916 ☆ d.	...	...	...	...	...	1952	|	2027	...	2052	2127	...	...	...	...	...	2222	2230	2230	2322	2334	0018	...	0034	0044
Baden-Baden 916 d.	...	...	...	...	...	...	|	2043	...	...	2142	...	...	...	...	...	...	|	|	...	0002	|	...	...	0108
Karlsruhe Hbf 913 916 d.	...	...	...	...	...	...	2025	2101	...	...	2201	...	...	...	...	...	...	2304	2304	...	0021p	0052	...	...	0130
München Hbf 930 d.	1728	...	...	1747x	...	...	...	|	1828	...	|	1928	1928	...	2044	2044	...	|	|	...	|	|	2151	...	|
Stuttgart Hbf 931 d.	1951	1918	1937	2004	2009	...	...	|	2051	...	|	2151	2151	2204	2305	2305	...	|	|	...	|	|	0012	...	|
Vaihingen (Enz) 931 d.	|	|	1955	|	|	...	...	|	|	...	|	|	|	|	|	|	...	|	|	...	|	|	|	...	|
Bruchsal 913 931 d.	|	|	|	|	|	...	...	|	|	...	|	|	|	|	|	|	...	|	|	...	0036p	|	|	...	0143
Heidelberg Hbf 913 931 d.	|	2025t	2025	|	2054	...	...	|	|	...	|	|	|	2248	|	|	...	2333	2333	...	0100p	|	|	...	0202
Weinheim 913 d.	|	|	|	|	2109	...	...	|	|	...	|	|	|	2302	|	|	...	|	|	...	|	|	|	...	|
Bensheim 913 d.	|	|	|	|	2119	...	...	|	|	...	|	|	|	2313	|	|	...	|	|	...	|	|	|	...	|
Darmstadt Hbf 913 d.	|	|	|	|	2132	...	...	|	|	...	|	|	|	2327z	|	|	...	|	|	...	|	|	|	...	|
Mannheim Hbf 913 a.	2028	2037	2037	2048	|	...	...	2124	2129	...	2224	2229	2229	|	2345	2345	...	2348	2348	...	0117	|	0141	...	0214
Mannheim Hbf 913 d.	2036	2039	2039	...	|	...	...	2135	2132	...	2233	2236	2236	|	2351	2351	...	2359	2359	...	0119	|	0143	...	0216
Frankfurt Flughafen + ◧ a.	2106	|	|	...	|	...	...	2206	|	...	|	2307	2307	|	0023	0023	...	|	|	...	|	|	0224	...	0321
Frankfurt (Main) Hbf 913 a.	|	|	|	...	2152	...	...	|	2208	...	2316	|	|	2343z	0044	0044	...	0050r	0050r	...	0200	0154	0240	...	0302
Mainz Hbf 911 a.	|	2118	2118	...	...	...	...	|	|	...	...	|	2329	...	...	...	...	|	|	...	|	|	|	...	0345
Koblenz Hbf 911 a.	|	2211	2211	...	...	...	...	|	|	...	...	|	...	...	...	...	...	|	|	...	|	|	|	...	0505
Köln Hbf 800 910 a.	2205	2305	2305	...	...	...	...	2305	|	...	...	0005	...	...	...	...	...	|	|	...	|	|	|	...	0606
Dortmund Hbf 800 a.	...	...	...	...	...	...	...	0026	|	...	...	...	...	...	...	...	...	|	|	...	|	|	|	...	0721
Hannover Hbf 810 900 a.	...	...	...	...	...	...	...	...	0146h	...	...	...	...	...	0446g	...	...	0604	|	...	0614	|	|	...	|
Berlin Hbf 810 850 902 a.	...	...	...	...	...	...	...	...	|	...	...	...	...	...	|	...	...	|	0754	...	|	0721	0758	...	|
Hamburg Hbf 800 900 a.	...	...	...	...	...	...	...	...	0311h	...	...	...	...	...	0615g	...	...	0753	...	...	0751	...	...	...	1014

♦ – **NOTES** (LISTED BY TRAIN NUMBER)

- **66** – (12) and ✕ Budapest - Wien - Salzburg - Frankfurt.
- **216** – DACHSTEIN – (12) and 🍷 Graz - Bischofshofen - Salzburg - München - Saarbrücken.
- **453** – 🛏 1, 2 cl. Paris - Berlin - Warszawa - Moskva. See Table **24**. Operated by Russian Railways. Special fares payable. 🅁. Timings vary Aug. 15 - Oct. 24.
- **470** – 🛏 1, 2 cl., ▬ 2 cl. and (2) Zürich - Basel - Braunschweig - Berlin.
- **510** – ①②③④⑦. (12) and ✕ München - Wiesbaden Hbf (a. 2344). Train number **1190** on ⑦.
- **992** – From München daily to Sept. 1, ⑤⑦ from Sept. 6. (12) München - Frankfurt - Erfurt - Berlin.
- **40470** – 🛏 1, 2 cl., ▬ 2 cl. and (2) Zürich - Basel - Hannover - Hamburg.

- **A** – ①②③④⑦.
- **K** – To Kiel (Table **820**).
- **M** – To Münster (Table **800**).
- **P** – (12) and 🍷 Paris - Strasbourg - Stuttgart (- München ⑥).
- **Q** – ⑤⑦ to July 14 (also June 19; not June 21); Ⓑ July 19 - Sept. 8; ⑤⑦ from Sept. 13 (also Oct. 31; not Nov. 1).
- **R** – ①-④ to July 18 / from Sept. 9 (also Nov. 1; not June 19, 20, Oct. 31).

- **g** – Mornings of ① only. 24–25 minutes earlier to June 24 and from Nov. 4.
- **h** – Mornings of ① only.
- **m** – Not June 20, 21, Oct. 4.
- **p** – On the mornings of ⑦ July 21 - Sept. 8 (also ⑥ Aug. 17 - Sept. 7) departs Karlsruhe 0044 and does not call at Bruchsal or Heidelberg. On the mornings of ⑥ July 20 - Aug. 10 departs Karlsruhe 0027 and does not call at Bruchsal or Heidelberg.
- **r** – Frankfurt (Main) **Süd**. Arrives 0044 on the mornings June 29 - Oct. 27.
- **t** – Arrives 2002.
- **x** – Until July 28 serves München Pasing (not München Hbf).
- **z** – July 29 - Oct. 17 departs Darmstadt 2333, arrives Frankfurt 2356.
- **‡** – Train number **468** on ⑥, **478** on ⑤.
- **♣** – Subject to alteration on the mornings Oct. 15 – 19 (operated by 🚌 Strasbourg - Kehl, departing Strasbourg 2341 the previous day)
- **✣** – Please refer to the shaded engineering work panel on page 369 for details of various alterations affecting services in this table.
- **☆** – See panel on page 430 for other local services.
- **◐** – Operated by Südwestdeutsche Verkehrs-AG.
- **◧** – Frankfurt Flughafen Fernbahnhof.

913 Local trains FRANKFURT - HEIDELBERG - KARLSRUHE

RE / RB / S-Bahn services

FRANKFURT - DARMSTADT - HEIDELBERG and MANNHEIM (*SEE NOTE* ❦)

	Ⓒs		Ⓐr									Ⓐr			Ⓐr							Ⓒs	D	E	G
Frankfurt (Main) Hbf d.	0404	0506	0633	0834	1034	1206	1234	1306	1406	1434	1506	1534	1634	1706	1734	1834	1906	2006	2034	2106	2206	2234	2306	2312	2312
Darmstadt Hbf d.	0433	0530	0653	0853	1053	1230	1253	1330	1430	1453	1530	1553	1653	1730	1757	1853	1930	2030	2053	2130	2230	2253	2333	2333	2333
Bensheim d.	0458	0557	0710	0910	1110	1258	1310	1358	1458	1510	1558	1611	1710	1758	1825	1910	1958	2058	2110	2155	2255	2310	2355	2355	2355
Weinheim (Bergstr) d.	0514	0612	0722	0922	1122	1313	1322	1413	1513	1522	1613	1624	1722	1813	1842	1922	2012	2113	2122	2210	2310	2322	0013	0010	0012
Neu-Edingen / Friedrichsfeld a.	0527	0625	|	|	|	1325	|	1425	1525	|	1625	|	|	1825	1856	|	2024	2125	|	2224	2324	|	0027	0024	0027
Mannheim Hbf a.	|	|	0741	0940	1141	|	1340	|	|	1541	|	1642	1741	|	1911	1941	|	|	2142	|	|	2342	|	|	|
Heidelberg Hbf a.	0538	0635	...	...	...	1340	...	1439	1540	...	1636	...	...	1836	...	...	2039	2141	...	2238	2339	...	0037	0034	0038

	Ⓐr		Ⓐr							Ⓒs	Ⓐr						H	Ⓒs	H	H					
Heidelberg Hbf d.	0423	0520	...	0622	0723	0820	and hourly until	1320	1420	1520	1523	1620	1717	1820	1920	2020	2120	...	2220	2320	...	ALSO	...	and every two hours until	...
Mannheim Hbf d.	|	|	0606	|	|	|		|	|	|	|	|	|	|	|	|	|	2220	|	|	...		0820		2020
Neu-Edingen / Friedrichsfeld d.	0433	0535	|	0637	0736	0835		1335	1436	1535	1536	1635	1735	1835	1935	2035	2135	|	2235	2335	...		|		|
Weinheim (Bergstr) d.	0453	0549	0626	0650	0748	0848		1348	1448	1548	1548	1648	1748	1848	1948	2048	2149	2239	2248	2349	...		0839		2039
Bensheim d.	0506	0604	0640	0704	0801	0901		1401	1501	1601	1601	1701	1801	1901	2001	2102	2203	2251	2301	0003	...		0851		2051
Darmstadt Hbf d.	0530	0630	0658	0730	0830	0930		1430	1530	1630	1630	1730	1830	1930	2030	2130	2230	2307	2330	0030	...		0907		2107
Frankfurt (Main) Hbf a.	0548	0648	0716	0748	0848	0948		1448	1548	1648	1648	1748	1848	1948	2048	2148	2248	2324	2348	0048	...		0924		2124

FRANKFURT - BIBLIS - WORMS and MANNHEIM

km		Ⓐr	Ⓐr		⚒r			⊠			†B	A				†B	A				Ⓑ	⑥		
0	**Frankfurt** (Main) Hbf d.	...	...	0612	...	0712	...	and at the same minutes past each hour until	1712	...	1812	1812	...	1912	...	2012	2012	...	2112	...	2212	2212	...	2315
53	Biblis d.	0504	0607	0658	0658	0759	0804		1759	1804	1854	1859	1904	1959	2004	2054	2059	2104	2159	2204	2259	2259	2304	2359
	Worms Hbf a.	0514	0617	|	0708	|	0814		|	1814	|	|	1913	|	2014	|	|	2114	|	2214	|	|	2314	|
78	**Mannheim** Hbf a.	...	...	0719	...	0819	...		1819	...	1914	1919	...	2019	...	2113	2119	...	2219	...	2319	2321	...	0020

km				Ⓐr	Ⓐ	Ⓐr		⑥	Ⓐr															
	Mannheim Hbf d.	0009	...	...	0430	...	0532	...	...	0639	...	0739	and at the same minutes past each hour until	...	2139	...	...	2240	...	...	...	...	...	...
0	**Worms** Hbf d.	|	...	0443	|	0540	|	0640	0642	|	0743	|		2143	|	...	2243	|	...	...	...	...	...	...
10	Biblis d.	0035	...	0453	0501	0550	0559	0650	0653	0659	0753	0759		2153	2159	...	2253	2301	...	...	...	...	...	...
63	**Frankfurt** (Main) Hbf a.	0125	...	...	0545	...	0645	...	...	0745	...	0845		...	2245	...	...	2345	...	...	...	...	...	...

MANNHEIM - HEIDELBERG - KARLSUHE *Subject to alteration July 20 - September 8*

S-Bahn		Ⓐt	Ⓒz	Ⓐt		Ⓐt	Ⓒz	Ⓐt		Ⓐd	Ⓒw		◇				Ⓒz	Ⓐt								
Mannheim Hbf ⊡ d.	0008	...	0436	0457	0535k	0612	*0630*	0646	0729	0830	0830	0930	and hourly until	1330	1430	1530	1630	1630	1730	1759	1830	1930	2030	2137	2237	2304
Heidelberg Hbf ⊡ d.	0029	0407	0455	0516	0559	0633	0706	0706	0748	0848	0856	0948		1348	1448	1548	1648	1648	1748	1818	1848	1948	2057f	2155	2255	2328
Bruchsal d.	0057	0435	0528	0544	0626	0700	0732	0733	0817	0917	0924	1015		1415	1515	1615	1715	1716	1815	1844	1915	2015	2123	2223	2333f	2356
Karlsruhe Hbf a.	0118	0452	0544	0559	0644	0718	0752	0750	0833	0936	0938	1032		1431	1536	1632	1732	1736	1832n	1859n	1932	2032	2136	2237	2351	0016

S-Bahn		Ⓒz				Ⓐt	Ⓐt	Ⓒz	Ⓐt	Ⓒz	Ⓒz	Ⓐt	Ⓐt	Ⓒz	Ⓐt	Ⓐt			✣							
Karlsruhe Hbf d.	0013	0148	...	0328	...	0419	0445	0445	0516	0520	0610	0620	0647	0725	0728	0755	...	0828	and hourly until	1828	1858p	1928	2028	2128	2228	2328
Bruchsal d.	0027	0204	...	0345	...	0437	0503	0503	0534	0538	0629	0638	0703	0744	0744	0814	...	0844		1844	1914	1944	2044	2144	2244	2344
Heidelberg Hbf ⊡ d.	0055	0232	...	0413	...	0505	0536	0533	0602	0608	0702	0709	0731	0813	0813	0843	...	0913		1913	1943	2013	2114	2214	2314	0014
Mannheim Hbf ⊡ a.	0114	0248	...	0429	...	0522	0552	0553	0621	0625	0719	0726	0746	0829	0829	0901	...	0929		1929	2001	2029	2130	2230	2330	0030

- **A** – ⚒ to Oct. 19 (not June 20); daily from Oct. 21.
- **B** – † to Oct. 20 (also June 20).
- **D** – July 29 - Oct. 17.
- **E** – ①-⑥ to July 27 / from Oct. 18.
- **G** – ⑦ to July 28 / from Oct. 20.
- **H** – To July 28 and from Oct. 18.
- **d** – Not June 20, Nov. 1. Runs daily Sept. 9 - Oct. 25. Departs Bruchsal 0915 Sept. 14 - Oct. 20.
- **f** – Arrives 10 – 12 minutes earlier.
- **k** – Change trains at Heidelberg on Ⓒz.
- **n** – 5 minutes later Sept. 14 - Oct. 20.
- **p** – 1847 Sept. 14 - Oct. 20.
- **r** – Not June 20.
- **s** – Also June 20.
- **t** – Not June 20, Nov. 1.
- **w** – Also June 20, Nov. 1; not Sept. 14 - Oct. 20.
- **z** – Also June 20, Nov. 1.
- **⊠** – On ⑥⑦ Aug. 10 - Sept. 29 Frankfurt d. 0808 (not 0812).
- **◇** – Timings may vary by 1 – 2 minutes.
- **✣** – Sept. 14 - Oct. 20 departs Karlsruhe 1420, 1524, 1725 (not 1428, 1528, 1728).
- **❦** – Southbound service from Frankfurt is subject to confirmation. Subject to alteration on ⑥⑦ Aug. 10 - Sept. 29.
- **⊡** – See also Tables **918**, **919**, **923**, **924**.

Local trains KOBLENZ - WIESBADEN - FRANKFURT and KOBLENZ - MAINZ - FRANKFURT 914

Neuwied - Koblenz - St Goarshausen - Wiesbaden - Frankfurt *(Rechte Rheinstrecke; operated by VIAS)*

km		Ⓐe	Ⓐe								Ⓐe		Ⓐe			Ⓐe							Ⓒz	Ⓐe	v	
0	**Neuwied** .... 802 d.	0437	0537	...	0637z	0737	0837	0937	1037	1137	...	1237	...	1337	1437	...	1537	1637	1737	1837	1937	2037	2137	2137	...	2237
15	**Koblenz** Hbf .802 906 d.	0453	0553	...	0653	0753	0853	0953	1053	1153	1223	1253	1323	1353	1453	...	1553	1653	1753	1853	1953	2053	2153	2153	...	2253
20	Niederlahnstein .. 906 d.	0459	0559	...	0659	0759	0859	0959	1059	1159	1229	1259	1329	1359	1459	...	1559	1659	1759	1859	1959	2059	2159	2159	...	2259
26	Braubach .... d.	0506	0606	...	0706	0806	0906	1006	1106	1206	1236	1306	1336	1406	1506	...	1606	1706	1806	1906	2006	2106	2206	2206	...	2306
38	Kamp-Bornhofen .... d.	0516	0616	...	0716	0816	0916	1016	1116	1216	1246	1316	1346	1416	1516	...	1616	1716	1816	1916	2016	2116	2216	2216	...	2316
50	St Goarshausen .... d.	0526	0626	...	0726	0826	0926	1026	1126	1226	1256	1326	1356	1426	1526	...	1626	1726	1826	1926	2026	2126	2226	2226	...	2326
61	Kaub .... d.	0536	0636	0636	0736	0836	0936	1036	1136	1236	1306*	1336	1406	1436	1536	1606	1636	1736	1836	1936	2036	2136	2236	2236	...	2335
67	Lorch (Rhein) .... d.	0542	0642	0642	0742	0842	0942	1042	1142	1242	1312	1342	1412	1442	1542	1612	1642	1742	1842	1942	2042	2142	2242	2242	...	▬
79	Rüdesheim (Rhein) .... d.	0553	0653	0653	0753	0853	0953	1053	1153	1253	1323	1353	1423	1453	1553	1623	1653	1753	1853	1953	2053	2153	2253	2253	...	...
109	**Wiesbaden** Hbf .... a.	0625	0725	0725	0825	0925	1025	1125	1225	1325	1355	1425	1455	1525	1625	1655	1725	1825	1925	2025	2125	2225	2325	2325	...	②
109	**Wiesbaden** Hbf .... d.	0632	0732	0732	0832	0932	1032	1132	1232	1332	...	1432	...	1532	1632	1702	1732	1832	1932	2032	2132	2232	2332	...	2335	2335
150	**Frankfurt** (Main) Hbf .. a.	0705	0805	0805	0905	1005	1105	1205	1305	1405	...	1505	...	1605	1705	1735	1805	1905	2005	2105	2205	2305	0005	...	0018	0022

	Ⓐe	Ⓐe		⚒r										Ⓐe		Ⓐe		Ⓐe		Ⓐe						T
Frankfurt (Main) Hbf .. d.	...	...	...	0553e	0653	0753	0853	0953	1053	1153	1253	1353	1453	1523	1553	1623	1653	1723	1753	1823	1853	1953	2053	2153	2253	2253
Wiesbaden Hbf .... a.	...	...	...	0628e	0728	0828	0928	1028	1128	1228	1328	1428	1528	1558	1628	1658	1728	1758	1828	1858	1928	2028	2128	2228	2328	2328
Wiesbaden Hbf .... d.	...	...	0533e	0633	0733	0833	0933	1033	1133	1233	1333	1433	1533	1603	1633	1703	1733	1803	1833	1903	1933	2033	2133	2233	2333	2333
Rüdesheim (Rhein) ..... d.	...	0532	0606e	0706	0806	0906	1006	1106	1206	1306	1406	1506	1606	1636	1706	1736	1806	1836	1906	1936	2006	2106	2206	2306	0004	0006
Lorch (Rhein) .... d.	...	0541	0615e	0715	0815	0915	1015	1115	1215	1315	1415	1515	1615	1645	1715	1745	1815	1845	1915	1945	2015	2115	2215	2315	...	0015
Kaub .... d.	0450	0550	0623	0723	0823	0923	1023	1123	1223	1323	1423	1523	1623	1653	1724	1753	1823	1854	1924	1954	2023	2123	2223	2323	...	0023
St Goarshausen .... d.	0459	0559	0632	0732	0832	0932	1032	1132	1232	1332	1432	1532	1632	1702	1732	1802	1832	1902	1932	2002	2032	2132	2232	...	...	...
Kamp-Bornhofen .... d.	0510	0610	0643	0743	0843	0943	1043	1143	1243	1343	1443	1543	1643	1713	1743	1813	1843	1913	1943	2013	2043	2143	2243	...	...	...
Braubach .... d.	0521	0621	0654	0754	0854	0954	1054	1154	1254	1354	1454	1554	1654	1724	1754	1824	1854	1924	1954	2024	2054	2154	2254	...	...	...
Niederlahnstein .... 906 d.	0527	0627	0700	0800	0900	1000	1100	1200	1300	1400	1500	1600	1700	1730	1800	1830	1900	1930	2000	2030	2100	2200	2300	...	...	...
Koblenz Hbf. 802 906 a.	0533	0633	0706	0806	0906	1006	1106	1206	1306	1406	1506	1606	1706	1736	1806	1836	1906	1937	2006	2037	2106	2206	2306	...	...	...
Neuwied .... 802 a.	0556	...	0726	0826	0926	1026	1126	1226	1326	1426	1526	1626	1726	...	1826	...	1926	...	2026	...	2126	2226	2326	...	...	...

Koblenz - Bingen - Mainz - Frankfurt *(Linke Rheinstrecke)* ⊠

km			Ⓐe	Ⓐe		K		K		K		K		K		K				Ⓐd¶	⚒d¶					
0	**Koblenz** Hbf .... d.	0507	0606	0617	0707	0803	0904	1003	1104	1203	1304	1403	1504	1603	1704	1803	1902	2104		0450	0552	0730		2030	2152	2303
19	Boppard Hbf .... d.	0519	0618	0632	0719	0815	0916	1015	1116	1215	1316	1415	1516	1615	1716	1815	1916	2116		0505	0607	0744		2044	2207	2318
24	Boppard-Bad Salzig .. d.	|	|	0636	|	|	|	|	|	|	|	|	|	|	|	|	|	|		0509	0611	0748		2048	2211	2322
34	St Goar .... d.	|	|	0645	|	|	|	|	|	|	|	|	|	|	|	|	|	|	A	0517	0619	0756	and	2056	2219	2330
41	Oberwesel .... d.	0533	0633	0651	0733	0829	0930	1029	1130	1229	1330	1429	1530	1629	1730	1829	1930	2130	L	0523	0625	0801		2101	2225	2336
47	Bacharach .... d.	0537	|	0656	0737	|	0936	|	1136	|	1336	|	1536	|	1736	|	1936	2136	S	0527	0629	0806	hourly	2106	2229	2340
61	Bingen (Rhein) Hbf ..... a.	0546	0646	0709	0746	0842	0946	1042	1146	1242	1346	1442	1546	1642	1746	1842	1946	2146	O	0541	0643	0819		2119	2243	2356
61	Bingen (Rhein) Hbf ..... d.	0547	0647	0713	0747	...	0947	...	1147	...	1347	...	1547	...	1747	...	1947	2147		0552	0654	0824	until	2127	2254	...
62	Bingen (Rhein) Stadt .. d.	|	|	0716	|	...	|	...	|	...	|	...	|	...	|	...	|	|	⊡	0555	0657	0827		2129	2257	...
73	Ingelheim .... d.	0556	0655	0722	0755	...	0955	...	1155	...	1355	...	1555	...	1755	...	1955	2155		0605	0707	0837		2139	2307	...
91	**Mainz** Hbf .... a.	0608	0708	0736	0808	...	1008	...	1208	...	1408	...	1608	...	1808	...	2008	2208		0623	0726	0855		2156	2325	...
119	Frankfurt Flughafen ◧ a.	0634t	0733t	0805t	0835t	...	1035t	...	1235t	...	1435t	...	1635t	...	1833t	...	2033t	2236*		...	...	...		...	...	...
130	**Frankfurt** (Main) Hbf .. a.	0647	0751	0822	0849	...	1049	...	1249	...	1449	...	1648	...	1851	...	2051	2249		...	...	...		...	...	...

	Ⓐd		K		K		K		K		K	Ⓐe	S	ⒸzK	Ⓐe				Ⓐd							J
Frankfurt (Main) Hbf .. d.	0508b	0707b	...	0908	...	1108	...	1308	...	1508	...	1608	1708	...	1808	1908	2108		...	...	...	...		...	...	...
Frankfurt Flughafen ◧ d.	0521t	0720t	...	0923t	...	1123t	...	1323t	...	1523t	...	1623t	1723t	...	1823t	1923t	2123t		...	...	...	...		...	...	...
Mainz Hbf .... d.	0544	0751	...	0951	...	1151	...	1351	...	1551	...	1651	1751	...	1851	1951	2151		...	0547	0701	0803		2103	2203	2303
Ingelheim .... d.	0556	0802	...	1002	...	1202	...	1402	...	1602	...	1703	1802	...	1903	2002	2202	A	...	0604	0719	0821	and	2121	2221	2321
Bingen (Rhein) Stadt ... d.	|	|	...	|	...	|	...	|	...	|	...	|	|	...	|	|	|	L	...	0614	0735	0831		2131	2231	2331
Bingen (Rhein) Hbf ..... a.	0606	0811	...	1011	...	1211	...	1411	...	1611	...	1714	1811	...	1911	2011	2211	S	...	0618	0738	0834	hourly	2134	2234	2334
Bingen (Rhein) Hbf ..... d.	0607	0813	0913	1013	1113	1213	1313	1413	1513	1613	1713	1717	1813	1913	1913	2013	2216	O	0523	0626	0739	0839		2139	...	2335
Bacharach .... d.	0615	0821	|	1021	|	1221	|	1421	|	1621	|	1730	1821	|	1922	2021	2228		0535	0638	0750	0850	until	2150	...	2346
Oberwesel .... d.	0620	0826	0925	1026	1125	1226	1325	1426	1525	1626	1725	1735	1826	1925	1927	2026	2232	⊡	0539	0649	0754	0854		2154	...	2350
St Goar .... d.	|	|	|	|	|	|	|	|	|	|	|	1741	|	|	|	|	2238		0545	0656	0800	0900		2200	...	2356
Boppard-Bad Salzig ... d.	|	|	|	|	|	|	|	|	|	|	|	1748	|	|	|	|	2247		0553	0704	0808	0908		2208	...	0004
Boppard Hbf .... d.	0635	0840	0939	1040	1139	1240	1339	1440	1539	1640	1739	1752	1840	1939	1942	2040	2251		0557	0708	0812	0912		2212	...	0008
Koblenz Hbf .... a.	0651	0854	0953	1054	1153	1254	1353	1454	1553	1654	1753	1809	1856	1953	1958	2054	2309		0616	0723	0827	0927		2227	...	0022

J – Runs daily Mainz - Bingen (Rhein) Hbf; ⑤⑥ (also June 9, 19, Oct. 2, 31) Bingen (Rhein) Hbf - Koblenz.
K – To / from Kaiserslautern (Table **918**).
S – To Saarbrücken (Table **915**).
T – ⑤⑥† (also June 19, 20, Oct. 2).
b – 1–2 minutes earlier from Oct. 28.

d – Not June 20, Nov. 1.
e – Ⓐ (not June 20).
r – Not June 20.
t – Until Oct. 25.
v – Not ②.
z – Ⓒ (also June 20).

¶ – Runs daily Bingen (Rhein) Hbf - Mainz.
◧ – Frankfurt Flughafen Regionalbahnhof ✈.
* – Calls at Frankfurt Flughafen Fernbf from Oct. 26.
⊠ – See Table **911** for long-distance *ICE / IC* services. See Table **917a** for S-Bahn service Mainz - Frankfurt Flughafen ✈ - Frankfurt (Main) Hbf and v.v.
⊡ – Other stopping services (operated by Mittelrheinbahn).

Köln Düsseldorfer Deutsche Rheinschiffahrt — KÖLN - KOBLENZ - MAINZ — *2019 service* — 914a

◐		A	A⛴	K◇	D	A	E⊠	F⊠	Q⊠	Q	Q⊠
750	**Köln** (Rheingarten) ..... d.	...	...	...	...	...	...	...	...	0930	...
1600	**Bonn** .... d.	...	...	...	...	...	0730	0730	1030	1230	1430
1300	Bad Godesberg .... d.	...	...	...	...	...	0800	0800	1110	1300	1510
900	Königswinter Fähre ..... d.	...	...	...	...	...	0815	0815	1130	1330	1530
750	Bad Honnef (Rhein) ..... d.	...	...	...	...	...	0835	0835	1150	1350	1550
400	Remagen .... d.	...	...	...	...	...	0910	0910	1220	1420	1620
750	Linz am Rhein .... d.	...	...	...	...	...	0930	0930	1250	1450	1650
1500	Bad Breisig .... d.	...	...	...	...	...	1000	1000	▬	▬	...
400	Bad Hönningen .... d.	...	...	...	...	...	1005	1005	...	...	...
1200	Andernach .... d.	...	...	...	...	...	1050	1050	**A**	**Dw**	...
2200	**Koblenz** ⊙ .... d.	...	0900	0945	...	...	1300	1300	1400	1810	...
600	Winningen (Mosel) ... a.	...	|	1055	...	...	1430	|	|	|	...
800	Cochem (Mosel) ...... a.	...	|	1500	...	...	...	|	|	|	...
150	Oberlahnstein .... d.	...	0940	...	...	...	...	|	1440	1845	...
450	Braubach .... d.	...	1005	...	...	...	...	1345	1505	1910	...
400	**Boppard** .... d.	0900	1100	...	1300	1400	...	1430	1600	2000	...
400	Kamp-Bornhofen .... d.	0910	1110	...	1310	1410	...	...	1610	...	...
300	Bad Salzig .... d.	0925	1125	...	1325	1425	...	...	1625	...	...
450	**St Goarshausen** ... ★ d.	1010	1210	...	1410	1510	...	...	1710	...	...
250	**St Goar** .... ★ d.	1020	1220	...	1420	1520	...	...	1720	...	...
450	Oberwesel .... d.	1050	1250	...	1450	1550	...	...	1750	...	...
900	Kaub .... d.	1105	1305	...	1505	1605	...	...	1805	...	...
600	Bacharach .... d.	1130	1330	...	1530	1630	...	...	1830	...	...
400	**Bingen** (Rhein) ...... ♥ d.	1300	1500	...	1700	1800	...	...	2000	...	...
900	**Rüdesheim** (Rhein) ♥ d.	1315	1515	...	1715	1815	...	...	2015	...	...
1500	Wiesbaden-Biebrich .... d.	...	...	...	1900	2000t	...	...	...	...	...
1600	**Mainz** .... a.	...	...	...	1930	2030t	...	...	...	...	...

	Q⊠	A	D	A	F⊠	E⊠	A	K◇	D⛴	G
Mainz .... d.	...	...	0830	0930v	...	...	...	...	...	...
Wiesbaden-Biebrich . d.	...	...	0845	0945v	...	...	...	...	...	...
Rüdesheim .... ♥ d.	...	0915	1015	1115	...	...	1415	...	1615	1615
Bingen (Rhein) ... ♥ d.	...	0930	1030	1130	...	...	1430	...	1630	1630
Bacharach .... d.	...	1015	1115	1215	...	...	1515	...	1715	1715
Kaub .... d.	...	1025	1125	1225	...	...	1525	...	1725	1725
Oberwesel .... d.	...	1035	1135	1235	...	...	1535	...	1735	1735
St Goar .... ★ d.	...	1055	1155	1255	...	...	1555	...	1755	1755
St Goarshausen ★ d.	...	1105	1205	1305	...	...	1605	...	1805	1805
Bad Salzig .... d.	...	1130	|	|	...	...	1630	...	1830	1830
Kamp-Bornhofen ...... d.	...	1140	1240	1340	...	...	1640	...	1840	1840
Boppard .... d.	...	1150	1250	1350	1600	...	1650	...	1850	1850
Braubach .... d.	...	1220	▬	▬	1630	...	1720	...	1920	1920z
Oberlahnstein .... d.	...	1235	...	...	|	...	1735	...	1935	1935z
Cochem (Mosel) .... d.	...	|	...	...	|	...	|	1540	|	|
Winningen (Mosel) d.	...	|	...	...	|	1540	|	1845	|	|
Koblenz ⊙ .... d.	...	1310	...	...	1700	1700	1810	2000	2010	2010z
Andernach .... d.	...	▬	...	...	1805s	1805s	...	...	...	...
Bad Hönningen .... d.	...	...	...	...	1830s	1830s	...	...	...	...
Bad Breisig .... d.	...	**L**	**R**	**Q⊠**	1840s	1840s	...	...	...	...
Linz am Rhein .... d.	1250	1450	1550	1650	1905s	1905s	...	...	...	...
Remagen .... d.	1300	1500	1600	1700	1915s	1915s	...	...	...	...
Bad Honnef (Rhein) .. d.	1325	1525	1625	1725	1940s	1940s	...	...	...	...
Königswinter Fähre .. d.	1340	1540	1640	1740	2000	2000	...	...	...	...
Bad Godesberg .... d.	1345	1545	1645	1745	2010	2010	...	...	...	...
Bonn .... d.	1415	1615	1715	1815	2030	2030	...	...	...	...
Köln (Rheingarten) ... a.	...	1800	1900	...	....	...	...	...	...	...

A – Apr. 13 - Oct. 20.
D – Apr. 19 - Oct. 13.
E – ① July 22 - Aug. 19.
F – ③ July 17 - Aug. 21.
G – Apr. 13–18 and Oct. 14–20.
K – ⑤–⑦ May 10 - Oct. 13 (not May 24–26, July 6, 13, Aug. 10, 25, Sept. 14, 21).
L – ⑤⑥ Apr. 19 - Oct. 5 (also Oct. 11–13, 18–20).
Q – Apr. 19 - Oct. 6 (also Oct. 11–13, 18–20).
R – ①②③④⑦ Apr. 21 - Oct. 6.

s – Sets down only.
t – Daily July 1 - Sept. 1; ④–⑦ Sept. 5 - Oct. 20.
v – Daily July 1 - Sept. 2; ⑤–① Sept. 6 - Oct. 20.
w – Also Apr. 13, 14, Oct. 18–20.
z – ⑤–⑦ only.

⊠ – Operated by Personenschifffahrt Siebengebirge.
◇ – Operated by Personenschifffahrt Gilles.
⊙ – Koblenz (Konrad-Adenauer-Ufer).
◐ – Distance in metres from rail station to river landing stage.

⛴ – Operated by paddlesteamer *Goethe* Apr. 19 - Oct. 13.
★ – A frequent ferry service sails between St Goar and St Goarshausen operated by Rheinschifffahrt Goar. ✆ + 49 (0) 6771 26 20. www.faehre-loreley.de
♥ – A frequent ferry service sails between Bingen and Rüdesheim operated by Bingen-Rüdesheimer Fähr- und Schiffahrtsgesellschaft. ✆ + 49 (0) 6721 30808. www.bingen-ruedesheimer.de

Operator: Köln Düsseldorfer Deutsche Rheinschiffahrt, Frankenwerft 35, D-50667 Köln. ✆ +49 (0) 221 20 88 318, Fax +49 (0) 221 20 88 345. A special service operates on "Rhein in Flammen" days May 4, 25, July 6, 13, Aug. 10, Sept. 14, 21.

915 KOBLENZ - TRIER - LUXEMBOURG and SAARBRÜCKEN

RE services except where shown

Many Saarbrücken services continue to / start from Mannheim (see Table 919).

km		①–⑤ a	⑦ w	Ⓒ z				①–⑥ d	Ⓐ t			⑥				⊠					D				
0	**Koblenz** Hbf ... d.	...	...	...	...	...	...	0602	0602	...	0704	0704	...	0806	0806	and at	1406	1406	1503	1503	1519	1606	1606	1706	1706
47	Cochem (Mosel) ... d.	...	...	...	...	...	...	0637	0637	...	0739	0739	...	0841	0841		1441	1441	1538	1538	1554	1641	1641	1741	1741
59	Bullay ... d.	...	...	...	...	...	...	0648	0648	...	0748	0748	...	0851	0851		1451	1451	1548	1548	1603	1651	1651	1751	1751
76	Wittlich Hbf ... d.	...	...	...	0550a	...	...	0700	0700	...	0803	0803	...	0903	0903	the same	1503	1503	1602	1602	1616	1703	1703	1803	1803
112	**Trier** Hbf ... a.	...	...	...	0627a	...	...	0731	0731	...	0830	0830	...	0930	0930		1530	1530	1630	1630	1642	1730	1730	1830	1830
112	**Trier** Hbf ... ▷ d.	0456	0533	0551	0637	0633	0733	0733	0737	0737	0833*	0837	0837	0933	0937	minutes	1533	1537	1633	1637	1644	1733	1737	1833	1837
163	**Luxembourg** ... ▷ a.	|	|	|	0727	|	|	|	0825	0825	|	0925	0925	|	1025		|	1625	|	1725	1733	|	1825	|	1925
135	Saarburg ... d.	0514	0551	0618	...	0651	0751	0751	...	...	0851	...	...	0951	...	past each	1551	...	1651	...	...	1751	...	1851	...
161	Merzig (Saar) ... d.	0534	0610	0645	...	0710	0810	0810	...	...	0910	...	...	1010	...		1610	...	1710	...	...	1810	...	1910	...
173	Dillingen (Saar) ... d.	0543	0619	0656	...	0720	0820	0820	...	...	0920	...	...	1020	...	hour until	1620	...	1720	...	...	1820	...	1920	...
177	Saarlouis Hbf ... d.	0547	0623	0659	...	0724	0824	0824	...	...	0924	...	...	1024	...		1624	...	1724	...	...	1824	...	1924	...
190	Völklingen ... d.	0557	0632	0710	...	0732	0832	0832	...	...	0932	...	...	1032	...		1632	...	1732	...	...	1832	...	1932	...
200	**Saarbrücken** Hbf ... a.	0606	0641	0724	...	0741	0841	0841	...	...	0941	...	...	1041	...		1641	...	1741	...	...	1841	...	1941	...

			F					Ⓒ z		Ⓐ e	Ⓒ z		
Koblenz Hbf ... d.	1806	1806	1900	1919	2019	2019	2119	2119	...	2219	2219	2219	2319
Cochem (Mosel) ... d.	1841	1841	1938	1954	2054	2054	2154	2154	...	2254	2254	2254	2354
Bullay ... d.	1851	1851	1948	2003	2103	2103	2203	2203	...	2303	2303	2303	0003
Wittlich Hbf ... d.	1903	1903	2001	2015	2115	2115	2215	2215	...	2315	2315	2315	0015
Trier Hbf ... a.	1930	1930	2030	2041	2141	2141	2241	2241	...	2341	2341	2341	0041
Trier Hbf ... d.	1933	1937	2033	2042	2143	2149	2249	2244	2244	2345	2345	2349	...
Luxembourg ... a.	|	2025	|	2135	2235	|	|	2335	2335	|	|	0037	
Saarburg ... d.	1951	...	2051	...	...	2210	2310	...	...	0010	0010	...	
Merzig (Saar) ... d.	2010	...	2110	...	...	2230	2330	...	...	0033	0034	...	
Dillingen (Saar) ... d.	2020	...	2120	...	...	2240	2340	...	...	0041	0045	...	
Saarlouis Hbf ... d.	2024	...	2124	...	...	2244	2344	...	...	0045	0049	...	
Völklingen ... d.	2032	...	2132	...	...	2252	2352	...	...	0054	0100	...	
Saarbrücken Hbf ... a.	2041	...	2141	...	...	2301	0001	...	...	0103	0113	...	

	Ⓐ e	Ⓐ e	Ⓒ z	† z	①–⑤ a	Ⓐ e	①–⑥ d	Ⓐ e	Ⓒ z
Saarbrücken Hbf ... d.	...	...	...	...	...	0458	...	0516	0520
Völklingen ... d.	...	...	...	...	...	0506	...	0527	0531
Saarlouis Hbf ... d.	...	...	...	...	...	0514	...	0538	0541
Dillingen (Saar) ... d.	...	...	...	...	...	0518	...	0541	0545
Merzig (Saar) ... d.	...	...	...	...	...	0527	...	0552	0555
Saarburg ... d.	...	...	...	...	...	0547	...	0618	0622
Luxembourg ... d.	...	...	...	...	0519	|	...	|	|
Trier Hbf ... a.	...	...	...	...	0603	0606	...	0646	0649
Trier Hbf ... d.	0410	0510	...	0525	0610	0610	0610	...	...
Wittlich Hbf ... d.	0436	0536	...	0551	0636	0636	0636	...	...
Bullay ... d.	0449	0549	...	0605	0649	0649	0649	...	...
Cochem (Mosel) ... d.	0500	0600	0627	0627j	0700	0700	0700	...	...
Koblenz Hbf ... a.	0536	0636	0718	0718	0737	0737	0737	...	...

	D		①–⑤ a			✤						Ⓒ z									⑤	⑥ k			
Saarbrücken Hbf ... d.	...	0619	...	...	0719		...	1619	...	1719	...	...	1819	...	1919	...	2019	...	2119	...	...	2222	2222	...	2335
Völklingen ... d.	...	0627	...	...	0727	and at	...	1627	...	1727	...	...	1827	...	1927	...	2027	...	2127	...	...	2231	2231	...	2343
Saarlouis Hbf ... d.	...	0636	...	...	0736		...	1636	...	1736	...	...	1836	...	1936	...	2036	...	2136	...	...	2239	2239	...	2350
Dillingen (Saar) ... d.	...	0640	...	...	0740	the same	...	1640	...	1740	...	...	1840	...	1940	...	2040	...	2140	...	...	2242	2242	...	2354
Merzig (Saar) ... d.	...	0648	...	...	0748		...	1648	...	1748	...	...	1848	...	1948	...	2048	...	2148	...	...	2250	2250	...	0003
Saarburg ... d.	...	0708	...	...	0808	minutes	...	1708	...	1807	...	...	1908	...	2008	...	2108	...	2208	...	...	2309	2309	...	0023
Luxembourg ... ▷ d.	0605	|	0655	0733	|		1633	|	1733	|	1833	1833	|	1933	|	2033	|	2133	|	2233	2233	|	|	2333	|
Trier Hbf ... ▷ a.	0706	0727	0806	0824	0827	past each	1724	1727	1823	1827	1924	1924	1927	2024	2027	2124	2127	2224	2227	2324	2324	2328	2328	0024	0043
Trier Hbf ... d.	0710	0731	...	0831	0831		1731	1731	1831	1831	...	1931	1931	2031	2031	2131	2131	...	2231	...	2331	2331	...	...	...
Wittlich Hbf ... d.	0735	0756	...	0856	0856	hour until	1756	1756	1856	1856	...	1956	1956	2056	2056	2156	2156	...	2256	...	2356	2356	...	...	...
Bullay ... d.	0748	0809	...	0909	0909		1809	1809	1909	1909	...	2009	2009	2109	2109	2209	2209	...	2309	...	0010	0010	...	...	...
Cochem (Mosel) ... d.	0759	0819	...	0919	0919		1819	1819	1919	1919	...	2019	2019	2119	2119	2219	2219	...	2319	...	0020	0020	...	...	...
Koblenz Hbf ... a.	0836	0856	...	0956	0956		1856	1856	1956	1956	...	2056	2056	2156	2156	2256	2256	...	2356	...	0057	0057	...	...	...

C – ⑥⑦ (also June 10, Nov. 1).
D – To / from Düsseldorf via Köln (Table **800**). Train classification is *IC* Koblenz - Düsseldorf and v.v.
F – From Frankfurt (Table **914**).

a – ①–⑤ (not June 10, Nov. 1).
d – Not June 10, Nov. 1.
e – Not June 20, Nov. 1.
j – Arrives 0614.
k – Also June 9, Oct. 2.
t – Not Nov. 1.
w – Also June 10, Nov. 1.
z – Also June 20, Nov. 1.

⊠ – The 0906 from Koblenz to Luxembourg requires a change of trains at Trier.
✤ – The 0833 from Luxembourg to Koblenz requires a change of trains at Trier on Ⓒ z.
▷ – **Additional journeys** Trier - Luxembourg and v.v. on ①–⑤ (not June 10, Nov. 1): **From Trier** at 0534, 0607, 0714 and 0750. **From Luxembourg** at 1657, 1757 and 1857.

BULLAY - TRABEN-TRARBACH

13 km Journey time: 18 minutes

Operated by Rhenus Veniro.

From Bullay at 0600 ⚒, 0658, 0838, 0938 and hourly until 2138.

From Traben-Trarbach at 0625 ⚒, 0741, 0901, 1001 and hourly until 2201.

TRIER - PERL - METZ

km		C		C			C		C	
0	**Trier** Hbf ... d.	1042	...	1942	...	**Metz** ... d.	0842	...	1742	...
49	Perl 🏛 ... d.	1115	...	2015	...	Thionville ... d.	0908	...	1808	...
70	Thionville ... a.	1153	...	2053	...	Perl 🏛 ... d.	0945	...	1845	...
100	**Metz** ... a.	1213	...	2117	...	**Trier** Hbf ... a.	1018	...	1918	...

Other local *RB* services **Trier** - **Perl** and v.v. Journey time: 49 – 56 minutes.

From Trier Hbf at 0506 Ⓐ **e**, 0623 Ⓐ **e**, 0704 ⚒ **e**, 0746, 0846, 0946, 1046, 1146, 1246, 1323 Ⓐ **e**, 1346 Ⓒ **z**, 1446, 1605, 1705, 1746, 1850, 1946, 2107 and 2221.

From Perl at 0505 Ⓐ **e**, 0625 ⚒ **e**, 0649 Ⓐ **e**, 0725 ⚒ **e**, 0825, 0925, 1025, 1125, 1225, 1325, 1425, 1525, 1625, 1725, 1825, 1925, 2025 and 2125.

915a KÖLN - GEROLSTEIN - TRIER

RE / *RB* services

On June 20, Nov. 1 services run as on ⑦

km		Ⓐ	⑥	Ⓐ	⑥	†	Ⓐ	Ⓒ	Ⓐ		†	⚒	†	⚒	Ⓒ		Ⓒ	Ⓐ			Ⓐ		Ⓒ		Ⓒ
0	**Köln** Messe/Deutz ... d.	...	...	...	...	...	...	...	...	0605	0705	0715	0805	0815	0856	0915	1015	1015	1115	1215	1256	1315	1356	1415	1513
1	**Köln** Hbf ... d.	...	...	...	...	...	...	...	...	0611	0711	0721	0811	0821	0905	0921	1021	1021	1121	1221	1305	1321	1405	1421	1521
41	Euskirchen ... d.	...	...	...	...	...	...	...	...	0656	0756	0800	0900	0900	0943	1000	1100	1100	1200	1300	1343	1400	1443	1500	1600
56	Mechernich ... d.	...	...	...	...	...	...	...	...	0707	0807	0809	0909	0909	0953	1009	1109	1109	1209	1309	1352	1409	1452	1509	1609
65	Kall ... d.	...	...	...	...	...	...	...	...	0717	0817	0817	0917	0917	1000	1017	1117	1117	1217	1317	1400	1417	1500	1517	1617
81	Blankenheim ... d.	...	...	...	...	...	...	...	...	0732	0832	0832	0932	0932	|	1032	1132	1132	1232	1332	|	1432	|	1532	1632
94	Jünkerath ... d.	...	...	0514	0546	...	0604	...	0646	0746	0846	0846	0946	0946	1022	1046	1146	1146	1246	1346	1422	1446	1522	1546	1646
113	**Gerolstein** ... d.	0507	0508	0531	0603	0611	0622	0658	0703	0803	0903	0903	1003	1003	1035	1103	1203	1203	1303	1403	1435	1503	1535	1603	1703
143	Bitburg-Erdorf ... d.	0533	0540	0604	0640	0644	0657	0733	0740	0840	0940	0940	1040	1040	1100	1140	1233	1240	1340	1440	1500	1540	1600	1640	1733
182	**Trier** Hbf ... a.	0621	0627	0652	0727	0727	0739	0827	0827	0927	1027	1027	1127	1127	1140	1227	1327	1327	1427	1527	1540	1627	1638	1727	1827

	Ⓐ										⑤⑥ f
Köln Messe/Deutz ... d.	1513	1615	1713	1815	1856	1915	2006	2105	2205	2305	2305
Köln Hbf ... d.	1521	1621	1721	1821	1905	1921	2011	2111	2211	2311	2311
Euskirchen ... d.	1600	1700	1800	1900	1943	2000	2056	2156	2256	2353	2356
Mechernich ... d.	1609	1709	1809	1909	1952	2009	2107	2207	2307	...	0007
Kall ... d.	1617	1717	1817	1917	2000	2017	2117	2217	2317	...	0017
Blankenheim ... d.	1632	1732	1832	1932	|	2032	2132	2232	2332	...	0032
Jünkerath ... d.	1646	1746	1846	1946	2022	2046	2146	2246	2346	...	0046
Gerolstein ... d.	1703	1803	1903	2003	2035	2103	2203	2302	0002	...	0102
Bitburg-Erdorf ... d.	1740	1840	1940	2040	2100	2140	2240	...	...	...	...
Trier Hbf ... a.	1827	1927	2027	2127	2138	2227	2327	...	...	...	...

	⚒	Ⓐ	⑥	Ⓐ	Ⓐ	⑥	Ⓐ	†	⚒	⑥
Trier Hbf ... d.	...	...	...	...	0506	...	...	...	...	0529
Bitburg-Erdorf ... d.	...	...	...	...	0550	...	...	...	...	0619
Gerolstein ... d.	0441	0524	0542	0544	0618	0618	0629	0652	0656	0656
Jünkerath ... d.	0500	0543	0605	0601	0631	0635	0645	0709	0713	0713
Blankenheim ... d.	0514	0557	0619	0615	0645	0649	|	0723	0727	0727
Kall ... d.	0531	0613	0634	0632	0702	0705	0710	0738	0742	0742
Mechernich ... d.	0540	0622	0643	0641	0711	0714	0717	0745	0749	0749
Euskirchen ... d.	0556	0639	0656	0656	0723	0729	0729	0756	0803	0803
Köln Hbf ... a.	0639	0715	0739	0739	0758	0812	0812	0839	0839	0839
Köln Messe/Deutz ... a.	0645	0721	0745	0745	0804	0818	0818	0845	0845	0845

	†	⑥	Ⓐ							Ⓒ						Ⓒ		Ⓐ	Ⓒ						
Trier Hbf ... d.	...	0635	0635	0725	0735	0835	0935	1035	1135	1225	1235	1335	1435	1535	1635	1725	1735	1835	1835	...	1935	2035	2135	2235	2335
Bitburg-Erdorf ... d.	...	0719	0724	0759	0819	0919	1019	1119	1219	1259	1319	1419	1519	1619	1719	1759	1819	1919	1919	...	2019	2119	2219	2319	0019
Gerolstein ... d.	0756	0756	0756	0824	0856	0956	1056	1156	1256	1324	1356	1456	1556	1656	1756	1824	1856	1956	1956	...	2053	2156	2253	2353	0053
Jünkerath ... d.	0813	0813	0813	0837	0913	1013	1113	1213	1313	1337	1413	1513	1613	1713	1813	1837	1913	2013	2013	...	...	2213	...	...	...
Blankenheim ... d.	0827	0827	0827	|	0927	1027	1127	1227	1327	|	1427	1527	1627	1727	1827	|	1927	2027	2027	...	...	2227	...	...	...
Kall ... d.	0842	0842	0842	0859	0942	1042	1142	1242	1342	1359	1442	1542	1642	1742	1842	1859	1942	2042	2042	...	...	2242	...	...	...
Mechernich ... d.	0849	0849	0849	0906	0949	1049	1149	1249	1349	1406	1449	1549	1649	1749	1849	1906	1949	2049	2049	...	...	2249	...	...	...
Euskirchen ... d.	0900	0903	0903	0917	1003	1103	1203	1302	1402	1417	1503	1603	1703	1803	1903	1917	2003	2103	2102	...	...	2302	...	...	...
Köln Hbf ... a.	0939	0939	0939	0952	1039	1139	1239	1339	1439	1452	1539	1639	1739	1839	1939	1952	2039	2139	2144	...	...	2344	...	...	...
Köln Messe/Deutz ... a.	0945	0945	0945	0958	1045	1145	1245	1345	1445	1458	1545	1645	1745	1845	1945	1958	2045	2145	2150	...	...	2350	...	...	...

f – Also June 9, 19, Oct. 2, 31.

KARLSRUHE - OFFENBURG - KONSTANZ 916

RE services except where shown

Warning! Subject to alteration between Immendingen and Konstanz July 19 - September 8.

km			Ⓐ t	Ⓒ z									*IC* 2005 ⑤⑥ F 🍷					*IC* 2313 Ⓐ S				*IC* 2285 U	G	H	Ⓐ t
0	**Karlsruhe** Hbf 912 943 d.	...	*0403**	0455	0607	0704	0809h	0909	1009	1109	1209	1309	1336	1409	1509	1609	1709	1733	1809	1909	2009	...	2116	2209	*2209*
21	Rastatt 943 d.	...	|	0508	0619	0718	0823	0923	1023	1123	1223	1323	|	1423	1523	1623	1723	1746	1823	1923	2023	...	2129	2228	*2228*
29	Baden-Baden 912 d.	...	*0426**	0515	0625	0726	0830	0930	1030	1130	1230	1330	1356	1430	1530	1630	1730	1754	1830	1930	2030	...	2136	2235	*2235*
69	**Offenburg** 912 942 d.	...	0523	0554	0658	0759	0859	0959	1059	1159	1259	1359	1418	1459	1559	1659	1759	1814	1859	1959	2059	...	2205	2323	2323
102	Hausach 942 d.	...	0548	0619	0722	0821	0921	1021	1121	1221	1321	1421	1439	1521	1621	1721	1821	...	1921	2021	2124	...	2229	2348	2348
112	Hornberg (Schwarzw) d.	...	0556	0627	0730	0829	0929	1029	1129	1229	1329	1429	1448	1529	1629	1729	1829	...	1929	2029	2132	...	2237	2356	2356
125	Triberg d.	...	0609	0640	0743	0843	0943	1043	1143	1243	1343	1443	1503	1543	1643	1743	1843	...	1943	2043	2146	...	2250	0010	0010
140	St Georgen (Schwarzw) d.	...	0625	0655	0757	0857	0957	1057	1157	1257	1357	1457	1520	1557	1657	1757	1857	...	1957	2057	2201	...	2305	0024	0024
155	Villingen (Schwarzw) 938 d.	0551	0639	0705	0806	0906	1006	1106	1206	1306	1406	1506	1531	1606	1706	1806	1906	...	2006	2106	2210	...	2313	0032	0032
169	Donaueschingen 938 d.	0602	0654	0714	0816	0916	1016	1116	1216	1316	1416	1516	1542	1616	1716	1816	1916	...	2016	2116	2219	...	2323	...	...
188	Immendingen 938 d.	0619	0706	0726	0828	0928	1028	1128	1228	1328	1428	1528	1554	1628	1728	1828	1928	...	2028	2128	2235	...	2336	...	...
204	Engen 940 d.	0633	0719	0738	0840	0940	1040	1140	1240	1340	1440	1540	|	1640	1740	1840	1940	...	2040	2140	2247	2313	|	...	...
218	**Singen** 939 940 d.	0652j	0735	0752	0852	0952	1052	1152	1252	1352	1452	1552	1618	1652	1752	1852	1952	...	2052	2152	2303	2327	2357	...	...
228	Radolfzell 939 d.	0703	0746	0800	0900	1000	1100	1200	1300	1400	1500	1600	1628	1700	1800	1900	2000	...	2100	2200	2311	2335	0004	...	...
248	**Konstanz** a.	0725	0810	0816	0916	1016	1116	1216	1316	1416	1516	1616	1645	1716	1816	1916	2016	...	2116	2216	2331	2351	0019	...	...

	IC 2216 Ⓐ S		Ⓐ t	⑥ k		*IC* 2284 T				*IC* 2004 ⑦E 🍷	*IC* 2006 ⑥D 🍷							⊕							
onstanz d.	...	...	0451	0502	0522	0603	0640	0735	0840	0907	0907	0940	1040	1140	1240	1340	1440	1540	1640	1740	1840	1940	2040	2158	2323
adolfzell 939 d.	...	...	0505	0516	0537	0620	0656	0758j	0857	0921	0921	0957	1057	1157	1257	1357	1457	1557	1657	1757	1857	1957	2058	2222	2346
ngen 939 940 d.	...	...	0512	0530j	0546	0629	0706	0807	0907	0930	0930	1007	1107	1207	1307	1407	1507	1607	1707	1807	1907	2007	2106	2234	2358
ngen 940 d.	...	...	0523	0539	0555	0637	0715	0816	0916	|	|	1016	1116	1216	1316	1416	1516	1616	1716	1816	1916	2016	2115	2250	0010
nmendingen 938 d.	...	...	0536	0552	0612	...	0728	0830	0930	0951	0951	1030	1130	1230	1330	1430	1530	1630	1730	1830	1930	2030	2128	2307	...
onaueschingen 938 d.	...	*0506*r	0551	0603	0624	...	0740	0840	0940	1005	1005	1040	1140	1240	1340	1440	1540	1640	1740	1840	1940	2040	2140	2319	...
llingen (Schwarzw) 938 d.	...	0535	0600	0612	0635	...	0750	0850	0950	1016	1016	1050	1150	1250	1350	1450	1550	1650	1750	1850	1950	2050	2150	2328	...
Georgen (Schwarzw) d.	...	0544	0610	0621	0644	...	0759	0859	0959	1026	1026	1059	1159	1259	1359	1459	1559	1659	1759	1859	1959	2059	2159	▬	...
iberg d.	...	0558	0625	0635	0659	...	0814	0914	1014	1042	1042	1114	1214	1314	1414	1514	1614	1714	1814	1914	2014	2114	2213	...	...
ornberg (Schwarzw) d.	...	0612	0639	0649	0712	...	0826	0926	1026	1056	1056	1128	1226	1326	1426	1526	1626	1726	1826	1926	2026	2128	2227	...	...
ausach 942 d.	...	0621	0649	0657	0720	...	0837	0937	1037	1105	1105	1137	1237	1337	1437	1537	1637	1737	1837	1937	2037	2137	2235	...	...
ffenburg 912 942 a.	0557	0647	0721	0719	0744	...	0859	0959	1059	1125	1125	1159	1259	1359	1459	1559	1659	1759	1859	1959	2059	2159	2300	2323	...
aden-Baden 912 a.	0615	0724	*0801*	...	0819	...	0926	1027	1127	1200	1200	1227	1327	1427	1527	1627	1727	1827	1927	2027	2127	2227	...	2347	...
astatt 943 a.	0623	0731	*0807*	...	0825	...	0933	1033	1133	|	|	1233	1333	1433	1533	1633	1733	1833	1933	2033	2133	2233	...	2354	...
arlsruhe Hbf 912 943 a.	0635	0750	*0822*	...	0839	...	0949	1049	1149	1219	1219	1249	1349	1449	1549	1649	1749	1849	1949	2049	2149	2249	...	0007	...

– [12] and 🍷 Konstanz - Mannheim - Köln - Dortmund.
– ⑦ (also June 10, 20, Oct. 3, Nov. 1; not June 9). [12] and 🍷 Konstanz - Mannheim - Köln - Emden.
– ⑤⑥ (also June 19, Oct. 2, 31). [12] and 🍷 Emden - Köln - Mannheim - Konstanz.
– Runs daily Karlsruhe - Villingen, Ⓑ Villingen - Konstanz.
– Runs on Ⓒ (also June 20, Nov. 1) Karlsruhe - Hausach, † (also June 20, Nov. 1) Hausach - Villingen.
– Ⓐ (not June 20, 21, Oct. 4, Nov. 1). From/to Stuttgart (Table **931**).
– Not June 10, Oct. 26 - Nov. 3. To Stuttgart (Table **940**). Runs as *RE* **4774** on ⑦.
– Not June 9, Oct. 26 - Nov. 3. From Stuttgart (Table **940**). Runs as *RE* **4779** on ⑥.

h – 0811 on † (also June 20, Nov. 1).
j – Arrives 7 – 10 minutes earlier.
k – Also June 10, 20, Oct. 3, Nov. 1.
r – ⚒ (not June 20, Nov. 1).
t – Not June 20, Nov. 1.
z – Also June 20, Nov. 1.
* – Connection by *IC* train.
⊕ – Change trains at Offenburg on Ⓐ (not June 20, Nov. 1).

FRANKFURT - MAINZ - IDAR OBERSTEIN - SAARBRÜCKEN 917

Vlexx

km		⚒ r	⚒ r		Ⓐ t		⚒ t												Ⓒ c	Ⓐ d					
0	**Frankfurt** (Main) Hbf ‡ d.	...	...	...	...	...	...	...	0725	0825	...	1025	...	1225	...	1425	1525e	1625	...	1725	1825	1925e	2025	...	2225
11	Frankfurt Flughafen ✈ § ‡ d.	...	...	...	...	...	...	...	0737k	0837k	...	1037k	...	1237k	...	1437k	1537e	1637k	...	1737k	1837k	1937e	2037k	...	2237k
39	**Mainz** Hbf ‡ d.	...	...	...	...	...	0556	0655	0800	0900	0956	1100	1156	1300	1356	1500	1600	1700	1800	1800	1900	2000	2100	2158	2300
80	Bad Kreuznach d.	...	...	...	0513	...	0624	0724	0826	0926	1024	1126	1224	1326	1424	1526	1626	1726	1826	1829	1926	2026	2126	2226	2326
102	Bad Sobernheim d.	...	...	...	0535	...	0644	0744	0846	0946	1044	1146	1244	1346	1444	1546	1646	1746	1846	1849	1946	2046	2146	2246	2346
117	Kirn d.	...	...	...	0550	...	0654	0754	0856	0956	1054	1156	1254	1356	1454	1556	1656	1756	1856	1859	1956	2056	2156	2256	2356
131	Idar-Oberstein d.	...	...	...	0605	...	0705	0807	0907	1007	1107	1207	1307	1407	1507	1607	1707	1807	1907	1910	2007	2107	2207	2307	0007
155	Türkismühle d.	0409	0440	0541	0632	0642	0726	0826	0926	1026	1126	1226	1326	1426	1526	1626	1726	1826	1926	1929	2026	2126	2226	2326	0026
170	St Wendel d.	0425	0457	0557	0651	0659	0739	0837	0937	1037	1137	1237	1337	1437	1537	1637	1737	1837	1937	1940	2037	2137	2237	2337	0037
179	Ottweiler (Saar) d.	0434	0506	0606	0658	0708	0746	0844	0944	1044	1144	1244	1344	1444	1544	1644	1744	1844	1944	1947	2044	2144	2244	2344	0044
184	Neunkirchen (Saar) d.	0445	0513	0613	0705	0717	0753	0852	0952	1052	1152	1252	1352	1452	1552	1652	1752	1852	1952	1953	2052	2152	2252	2352	0052
205	**Saarbrücken** Hbf a.	0510	0540	0638	0723	0743	0812	0912	1012	1112	1212	1312	1412	1512	1612	1712	1812	1912	2012	2013	2111	2212	2312	0012	0112

										Ⓐ t	Ⓒ z		Ⓐ d	Ⓒ c											
arbrücken Hbf d.	0122	0346	0446	0541	0651	0751	0851	0951	1051	1151	1151	1251	1351	1351	1451	1549	1651	1751	1851	1951	2035	2112	2135	2235	2351
eunkirchen (Saar) d.	0148	0404	0504	0559	0710	0810	0910	1010	1110	1210	1210	1310	1410	1410	1510	1608	1710	1810	1910	2010	2100	2130	2214f	2323j	0016
ttweiler (Saar) d.	0155	0410	0510	0605	0715	0815	0915	1015	1115	1215	1215	1315	1415	1415	1515	1613	1715	1815	1915	2015	2107	2135	2221	2330	0023
Wendel d.	0204	0417	0517	0612	0722	0822	0922	1022	1122	1222	1222	1322	1422	1422	1522	1620	1722	1822	1922	2022	2127	2143	2231	2340	0033
irkismühle d.	...	0428	0528	0623	0732	0832	0932	1032	1132	1232	1232	1332	1432	1432	1532	1632	1732	1832	1932	2032	2142	2154	2247	2355	...
ar-Oberstein d.	...	0449	0549	0644	0752	0852	0952	1052	1152	1252	1252	1352	1452	1452	1552	1652	1752	1852	1952	2052	...	2219	...	...	...
n d.	...	0500	0600	0655	0803	0903	1003	1103	1203	1303	1303	1403	1503	1503	1603	1703	1803	1903	2003	2103	...	2230	...	...	...
ad Sobernheim d.	...	0510	0610	0705	0812	0912	1012	1112	1212	1312	1312	1412	1512	1512	1612	1712	1812	1912	2012	2112	...	2239	...	...	...
ad Kreuznach d.	...	0530	0630	0730	0832	0932	1032	1132	1232	1330	1332	1432	1530	1532	1632	1732	1832	1932	2032	2132	...	2300	...	...	...
ainz Hbf ‡ a.	...	0558	0658	0758	0858	0959	1058	1159	1258	1359	1359	1458	1558	1559	1658	1758	1858	1959	2058	2159	...	2328	...	...	...
ankfurt Flughafen ✈ § ‡ a.	...	0621k	0721k	0821e	0921k	...	1121k	...	1321k	...	...	1521k	1621k	...	1721k	1821e	1921k	...	2121k	...	...	...	...	...	...
ankfurt (Main) Hbf ‡ a.	...	0636	0736	0836e	0936	...	1136	...	1336	...	...	1536	1636	...	1736	1836e	1936	...	2136	...	...	...	...	...	...

– Also June 20.
– Not June 20.
– Ⓐ (not June 20). Does not call at Frankfurt Flughafen from Oct. 28.
– Arrives 2159.

j – Arrives 2259.
k – Until Oct. 25.
r – Not June 20, Aug. 15, Nov. 1.
t – Not June 20, Nov. 1.
z – Also June 20, Nov. 1.

‡ – See also Tables **911** / **914** / **917a**.
§ – Frankfurt Flughafen Regionalbahnhof.

Operator: Vlexx (except for local trains Türkismühle - St Wendel - Saarbrücken and v.v. which are operated by DB).

FRANKFURT - FRANKFURT FLUGHAFEN ✈ - MAINZ - WIESBADEN 917a

S-Bahn 8/9

Warning! From October 26 all services call at Frankfurt Flughafen Fernbahnhof (not Regionalbahnhof) with minor timing variations.

			w	w																					
ankfurt (Main) Hbf ▽ d.	0002	0017	0047	0117	0217	0317	0417	0447	0502	0517	0532	0547	and at	2102	2117	2132	2147	2202	2217	2232	2247	2302	2317	2332	2347
ankfurt Flughafen ★ d.	0015	0030	0100‡	0130‡	0230‡	0330‡	0430	0500	0514	0529	0544	0559	the same	2114	2129	2144	2200	2215	2230	2245	2300	2315	2330	2345	0000
ainz Hbf d.	|	0057	0127	0157	0257	0357	0457	0527	|	0557	|	0627	minutes	|	2157	|	2227	|	2257	|	2327	|	2357	|	0027
Mainz-Kastel d.	0039v	|	|	|	|	|	|	|	0539	|	0609	|	past each	2139	|	2209	|	2239	|	2309	|	2339	|	0009	|
iesbaden Hbf a.	0048v	0110	0140	0210	0310	0410	0510	0540	0548	0610	0618	0640	hour until	2148	2210	2218	2240	2248	2310	2318	2340	2348	0010	0018	0040

esbaden Hbf d.	0019	0049	0149	0249	0349	0411	0419	0441	0449	0511	0519	0541	0549	and at	2111	2119	2141	2149	2211	2219	2241	2249	2311	2319	2349
Mainz-Kastel d.	|	|	|	|	|	0419	|	0449	|	0519	|	0549	|	the same	2119	|	2149	|	2219	|	2249	|	2319	|	|
ainz Hbf d.	0033	0103	0203	0303	0403	|	0433	|	0503	|	0533	|	0603	minutes	|	2133	|	2203	|	2233	|	2303	|	2333	0003
ankfurt Flughafen ★ d.	0058‡	0128‡	0228‡	0328‡	0431	0446	0501	0517	0532	0547	0602	0617	0632	past each	2147	2201	2216	2231	2246	2301	2316	2331	2346	0001x	0031z
ankfurt (Main) Hbf a.	0113	0143	0243	0343	0443	0458	0513	0528	0543	0558	0613	0628	0643	hour until	2158	2213	2228	2243	2258	2313	2328	2343	2358	0013x	0043z

– Not ②.
– 3 – 8 minutes later on ① (not June 10).
– 4 – 5 minutes later on the mornings of ① (not June 10).
– On the mornings of ① (not June 10) Frankfurt Flughafen d. 0030, Frankfurt Hbf a. 0046.

▽ – From the low-level platforms.
★ – Frankfurt Flughafen Regionalbahnhof ✈.
‡ – Frankfurt Flughafen **Fernbahnhof** (not Regionalbahnhof).

918 RHEINLAND-PFALZ LOCAL SERVICES

RB / S-Bahn services

PIRMASENS - SAARBRÜCKEN

km		Ⓐe	⚒r	Ⓐe	⚒r					
0	**Pirmasens** Hbf d.	0515	0552	0622	*0732*	0832	and	1932	2032	...
7	Pirmasens Nord d.	0522	0559	0641	0743	0843	hourly	1943	2043	...
31	Zweibrücken Hbf d.	0552	0640	0713	0813	0913	until	2013	2113	...
67	**Saarbrücken** Hbf a.	0631	0723	0751	0851	0951		2051	2151	...

	⚒r	⑥	Ⓐe						
Saarbrücken Hbf d.	0602	...	0633	0705	0807	and	1907	2007	210
Zweibrücken Hbf d.	0643	...	0713	0745	0845	hourly	1945	2045	214
Pirmasens Nord a.	0715	0750	0741	0815	0915	until	2015	2115	221
Pirmasens Hbf a.	*0728e*	0757	0753	0826	0926		2026	2126	222

PIRMASENS - LANDAU (Pfalz)

km		Ⓐe	⑥	Ⓐe	Ⓐe					
0	**Pirmasens** Hbf d.	0440	0542	0544	*0622*	0702‡	0802	and	2002	...
7	Pirmasens Nord d.	0452	0555	0609	0636	0718	0818	hourly	2018	...
55	**Landau** (Pfalz) Hbf a.	0548	0658	0708	0734	0818	0918	until	2118	...

	Ⓐe	Ⓐe	⑥						
Landau (Pfalz) Hbf d.	0529	0608	0641	...	0741	and	1841	1941	204
Pirmasens Nord a.	0632	0715	0740	...	0840	hourly	1940	2040	214
Pirmasens Hbf a.	0657	0728	0757	...	0857	until	1957	2057	215

BINGEN - KAISERSLAUTERN - PIRMASENS

km			Ⓐe	⚒r		⚒r	†v								Ⓒz	Ⓐe			⊕	Ⓑ	⑤⑥				
	Koblenz Hbf **914** d.	...	...	...	...	...	...	0803	...		...	1603	...	...	...	1803	...	...	...	...		1003	1203	140
0	**Bingen** (Rhein) Hbf d.	...	...	0546e	0651r	0756	0800	0843	0856	and at	1556	1643	1656	1756	1756	1843	1856	1956	2056	2256	A	1043	1243	144
16	Bad Kreuznach a.	...	...	0606e	0711r	0816	0820	0855	0916	the same	1616	1655	1716	1816	1816	1855	1916	2016	2116	2316	L	1055	1255	145
16	Bad Kreuznach d.	...	0508	0607	0712	0817	0821	0856	0917	minutes	1617	1656	1717	1817	1834	1856	1917	2031	2131	2331	S	1056	1256	145
43	Rockenhausen d.	...	0536	0635	0743	0855	0857	0919	0955	past each	1655	1719	1755	1855	1902	1929	1955	2059	2159	2358	O	1119	1319	151
79	**Kaiserslautern** Hbf a.	...	0611	0712	0814	0926	0929	0952	1026	hour until	1726	1749	1826	1926	1938	1959	2026	2130	2232	0029		1152	1352	155
	Change trains	Ⓐe	⚒r	d			d							d					d	|				
79	**Kaiserslautern** Hbf d.	0516	0616	0735	0835	...	0935	...	1035		1735	...	1835	1935	...	...	2035	...	2300	0034		...	...	...
108	Pirmasens Nord a.	0554	0702	0809	0909	...	1009	...	1109		1809	...	1909	2009	...	...	2109	...	2332	0106		...	...	...
115	**Pirmasens** Hbf a.	0608	0719	0818	0918	...	1018	...	1118		1818	...	1918	2018	...	...	2118	...	2341	0115		...	...	...

			Ⓐe	⚒r	†v																				
Pirmasens Hbf d.	...	...	0531	0637	0641	...	0732t	0841		1341	1441	...	1541	1641	...	...	1741	1841	1941	2041		...	...	...
Pirmasens Nord d.	...	...	0538	0645	0652	...	0750	0850	and at	1350	1450	...	1550	1650	...	...	1750	1850	1950	2050		...	...	...
Kaiserslautern Hbf a.	...	...	0610	0722	0724	...	0826	0926	the same	1426	1526	...	1626	1726	...	...	1826	1926	2026	2126		...	...	...
Change trains	⚒r	⑥	Ⓐe		d				minutes						Ⓐe	Ⓒh								
Kaiserslautern Hbf d.	0514	*0620*	0637	...	0735	0754	0832	0932	past each	1432	1532	1601	1636	1736	1801	1801	1836	1932	2032	2148		1001	1201	140
Rockenhausen d.	0549	*0651*	0711	...	0810	0828	0902	1002	hour until	1502	1602	1628	1710	1810	1828	1828	1910	2002	2102	2222	A	1028	1228	142
Bad Kreuznach a.	0620	*0720*	0742	...	0839	0851	0939	1039		1539	1639	1651	1740	1840	1851	1851	1940	2039	2139	2251	L	1051	1251	145
Bad Kreuznach d.	0621n	0743	0743	...	0841	0900	0941	1041		1541	1641z	1652k	1741	1841	1856	1900	1941	2041	2141	...	S	1100	1300	150
Bingen (Rhein) Hbf a.	0641n	0803	0803	...	0902	0912	1002	1102		1602	1702z	1704k	1802	1902	1908	1912	2002	2102	2202	...	O	1112	1312	151
Koblenz Hbf **914** a.	...	...	...	...	...	0953	...	...		...	...	1753	...	...	...	1953	...	...	...	...		1153	1353	155

NEUSTADT (Weinstr) - KARLSRUHE and WISSEMBOURG

km		Ⓐe	Ⓐe	Ⓐe	Ⓐe	⚒r	⚒r	Ⓐe	Ⓐe	†v	⑥		⑥	Ⓑ					D	†E		D	†E	
	Kaiserslautern Hbf **919** d.	...	...	...	...	...	...	...	0629	...	0629	...	...	...	...	0841v	...	0941	...	...	...	...	...	114
0	**Neustadt** (Weinstr) Hbf **919** d.	0427	...	0506	...	0529	0608	0636	0659	0700	0709	0736	0805	0809	0836	0909	0936	1009	1036	1045	1109	1136	1145	120
18	Landau (Pfalz) Hbf d.	0449	...	0535	...	0555	0634	0658	0713	0722	0722	0758	0822	0822	0858	0922	0958	1022	1058	1058	1122	1158	1158	122
31	Winden (Pfalz) d.	0503	0505	0550	0555	0603	0650	0708	0722	0731	0731	0809	0831	0831	0909	0931	1009	1031	1109	1109	1131	1209	1209	123
47	**Wissembourg** 🏛 ◐ a.	|	0521	|	0615	|	|	0726	|	|	|	0827	|	|	0927	|	1028	|	1127	1127	|	1227	1227	|
44	Wörth (Rhein) d.	0520	...	0607	...	0617	0708	...	0735	0744	0744	...	0844	0844	...	0944j	...	1044	...	...	1144j	...	...	124
58	**Karlsruhe** Hbf a.	0534	...	0619	...	0636	0725	...	0753	0754	0754	...	0854	0854	...	0954j	...	1054	...	...	1154j	...	...	125

		Ⓐe	Ⓒz																					⑥
Kaiserslautern Hbf **919** d.	...	...	...	...	...	...	...	...	1541z	...	...	...	...	...	...	...	...	...	...	...	...	...	...	...
Neustadt (Weinstr) Hbf **919** d.	1236	1305	1309	1336	1409	1436	1509	1536	1609	1636	1709	1736	1809	1836	1909	1936	2009	2104	2136	...	2230	...	2336	233
Landau (Pfalz) Hbf d.	1258	1319	1322	1358	1422	1458	1522	1558	1622	1658	1722	1758	1822	1858	1922	1958	2022	2122	2158	...	2252	...	2357	235
Winden (Pfalz) d.	1309	1331	1331	1409	1431	1509	1531	1609	1631	1709	1731	1809	1831	1909	1931	2009	2031	2131	2213	2231	2306	...	...	001
Wissembourg 🏛 ◐ a.	1327	|	|	1427	|	1527	|	1627	|	1727	|	1829	|	1928	|	2027	|	|	...	|	|	...	...	|
Wörth (Rhein) d.	...	1344j	1344j	...	1444	...	1544j	...	1644	...	1744j	...	1844	...	1944j	...	2044	2144	...	2244	2320	...	...	002
Karlsruhe Hbf a.	...	1354j	1354j	...	1454	...	1554j	...	1654	...	1754j	...	1854	...	1954j	...	2054	2154	...	2254	2337	...	...	003

	Ⓐe	Ⓐe	Ⓐe	Ⓐe	⑥	Ⓐe	Ⓒz	Ⓐe	Ⓐe		Ⓐe	Ⓒz										Ⓒz	Ⓐe	
Karlsruhe Hbf d.	0430	...	0600	...	0611	0641	0705	0717	...	...	0805	0806	...	0906	...	1006	...	1106	...	1206	...	1306	1306	...
Wörth (Rhein) d.	0447	...	0617	...	0628	0653	0715	0736	...	...	0816	0816	...	0916	...	1016	...	1116	...	1216	...	1316	1316	...
Wissembourg 🏛 ◐ d.	|	0526	|	0626	|	|	|	|	0733	...	|	|	0833	|	0933	|	1033	|	1133	|	1233	|	|	133
Winden (Pfalz) d.	0502	0553	0631	0647	0641	0706	0727	0748	0757	...	0829	0829	0853	0929	0953	1029	1053	1129	1153	1229	1253	1329	1330	135
Landau (Pfalz) Hbf d.	0518	0607	0645	0701	0703	0721	0736	0757	0807	0807	0838	0838	0903	0938	1003	1038	1103	1138	1203	1238	1303	1338	1339	140
Neustadt (Weinstr) Hbf **919** a.	0540	0628	0704	0722	0724	0744	0751	0811	0826	0826	0851	0851	0924	0951	1024	1051	1124	1151	1224	1251	1324	1351	1351	142
Kaiserslautern Hbf **919** a.	...	...	...	...	...	0816	0816	...	...	...	...	...	...	1016	...	...	...	...	...	...	...	1416	...	...

					Ⓐe	Ⓒz	†E	D	Ⓐe	Ⓒz	†E	D							Ⓑ	⑥				
Karlsruhe Hbf d.	1406	...	1506	...	1602	1606	...	...	1705	1706	...	...	1806	...	1906	...	2006	...	...	...	2106	2206	...	231
Wörth (Rhein) d.	1416	...	1516	...	1616	1616	...	...	1716	1716	...	...	1816	...	1916	...	2016	...	...	...	2116	2216	...	232
Wissembourg 🏛 ◐ d.	|	1433	|	1533	|	|	1633	1633	|	|	1733	1733	|	1833	|	1933	|	...	2033	2103	|	|	...	|
Winden (Pfalz) d.	1429	1453	1529	1553	1629	1629	1653	1653	1729	1729	1753	1753	1829	1853	1929	1953	2029	...	2053	2123	2131	2229	...	233
Landau (Pfalz) Hbf d.	1438	1503	1538	1603	1638	1638	1701	1703	1738	1738	1801	1803	1838	1903	1938	2003	2038	2103	2103	2131	2140	2237	...	234
Neustadt (Weinstr) Hbf **919** a.	1451	1524	1551	1624	1651	1651	1712	1724	1751	1751	1816	1824	1851	1924	1951	2024	2051	2124	2124	...	2201	2256	...	000
Kaiserslautern Hbf **919** a.	...	...	...	...	...	...	...	...	...	...	...	...	1919	...	...	...	...	...	...	...	2226b	...	...	...

GERMERSHEIM - SPEYER - MANNHEIM - HEIDELBERG *See note* ⊠

km		Ⓐe	Ⓒz	Ⓐe	Ⓐe	Ⓐe	⑥	Ⓐe	Ⓒz														
0	**Germersheim** 911a d.	0415	0417	0520	...	0557	0622	0704	0703	0749	0810	0849	0912	0949	▲	1912	1949	2014	2049	2114	2158	2257	232
14	Speyer Hbf 911a d.	0429	0431	0533	...	0610	0635	0713	0716	0802	0823	0902	0925	1002	and at	1925	2002	2027	2102	2127	2211	2310	233
23	Schifferstadt 911a d.	0439	0441	0548	0608	0627	0647	|	0729	0811	0835	0911	0935	1011	the same	1935	2011	2046	2119	2148	2229	2320	235
34	Ludwigshafen Hbf . 911a 919 d.	0450	0452	0605	0621	0640	0659	0727	0742	0821	0848	0921	0948	1021	minutes	1948	2021	2057	2131	2201	2241	2332	000
35	Ludwigshafen Mitte 919 d.	0453	*0532*	...	0623	0643	0702	0730	0744	0823	0851	0923	0950	1023	past each	1950	2023	2059	2133	2203	2247	2334	000
37	**Mannheim** Hbf 919 ⊡ a.	0455	*0534*	...	0626	0645	0705	0732	0747	0825	0854	0926	0953	1026	hour until	1953	2026	2102	2136	2205	2251	2337	000
54	**Heidelberg** Hbf 919 ⊡ a.	0515	*0552*	...	0653	0704	0723	0754	*0823*	0845	0916	0944	1016	1044		2016	2047	2123	2153	2223	2322	2355	002

	Ⓐe	Ⓒz	Ⓐe	Ⓐe	Ⓒz	Ⓐe	⚒r																
Heidelberg Hbf 919 ⊡ d.	0505	*0533*	*0536*	0602	*0608*	0644	0709e	0742e	0813	0843e	0913	0943	1013	1043	▲	1913	1943	2013	*2033*	2114	2214	2244	231
Mannheim Hbf 919 ⊡ d.	0526	*0554*	*0554*	0622	0656	0705	0731	0804	0830	0904	0931	1004	1031	1104	and at	1931	2004	2031	2056	2137	2242	2315	233
Ludwigshafen Mitte 919 d.	0528	*0556*	*0556*	0625	0658	0707	0733	0806	0833	0907	0934	1007	1034	1107	the same	1934	2007	2034	2058	2139	2245	2318	234
Ludwigshafen Hbf .. 911a 919 d.	0530	0612	0612	0637	0702	0711	0736	0810	0836	0910	0936	1009	1036	1110	minutes	1936	2010	2036	2103	2142	2248	2320	234
Schifferstadt 911a d.	0545	0625	0626	0650	0717	0723	0755	0824	0847	0924	0947	1024	1047	1123	past each	1947	2023	2047	2120	2158	2305	2332	000
Speyer Hbf 911a d.	0555	0634	0635	0659	0726	0732	0805	0833	0856	0932	0956	1033	1056	1132	hour until	1957	2032	2057	2129	2208	2314	2342	001
Germersheim 911a a.	0610	0647	0648	0712	0740	0746	0818	0845	0909	0945	1009	1045	1109	1145		2009	2045	2109	2142	2221	2327	2356	002

D – ⚒ to Oct. 26 (not June 20); daily from Oct. 28.
E – † to Oct. 27 (also June 20).

b – Not ⑥.
d – Daily.
e – Ⓐ (not June 20, Nov. 1).
h – Also June 20.
j – 2–3 minutes later Sept. 14 - Oct. 27.
k – On Ⓒ (also June 20, Nov. 1) Bad Kreuznach d. 1701, Bingen a. 1712.
n – On ⑥ Bad Kreuznach d. 0641, Bingen a. 0702.
r – ⚒ (not June 20, Nov. 1).

t – 0741 on † (also June 20, Nov. 1).
v – † (also June 20, Nov. 1).
z – Ⓒ (also June 20, Nov. 1).

‡ – Change trains at Pirmasens Nord on Ⓐ (not June 20, Nov. 1).
⊕ – Change trains at Bad Kreuznach on Ⓐ (not June 20, Nov. 1).
⊠ – Subject to alteration Sept. 14 - Oct. 20.
▲ – Timings may vary by 1–2 minutes.
◐ – For Strasbourg connections see Table **396**.
⊡ – See also Tables **913**, **923** and **924**.

WIESBADEN - MAINZ - DARMSTADT - ASCHAFFENBURG — 918a

Hessische Landesbahn

km		⚒ r	Ⓐ t						⑤⑥ f	
0	**Wiesbaden** Hbf .... d.	...	0438	0538	0638		2138	2238	2238	2338
10	**Mainz** Hbf .... d.	...	0449	0549	0649	and	2149	2249	2249	2349
43	Darmstadt Hbf .... a.	...	0520	0620	0720	hourly	2220	2320	2320	0020
43	Darmstadt Hbf .... d.	0532	0532	0632r	0732	until	2232	...	2332	...
87	**Aschaffenburg** Hbf .... a.	0615	0615	0712r	0812		2312	...	0012	...

	Ⓐ t								⑤⑥ f
Aschaffenburg Hbf . d.	...	...	0540r	0643r	0747		2147	2247	2347
Darmstadt Hbf .... a.	...	...	0627r	0726r	0827	and	2227	2327	0027
Darmstadt Hbf .... d.	0440	0540	0640	0740	0840	hourly	2240	2340	0040
Mainz Hbf .... d.	0513	0613	0713	0813	0913	until	2313	0013	0113
Wiesbaden Hbf .... a.	0525	0625	0725	0825	0925		2325	0025	0125

f – Also June 9, 19, Oct. 2.
r – ⚒ (not June 20).
t – Not June 20.

☛ Additional services run Wiesbaden - Darmstadt and v.v. on ⚒, Darmstadt - Aschaffenburg and v.v. on Ⓐ.

SAARBRÜCKEN - MANNHEIM - FRANKFURT and STUTTGART — 919

RE services except where shown

Additional S-Bahn services run Kaiserslautern - Mannheim - Heidelberg and v.v.

km					*EC*				*ICE*						*IC*				*TGV*					*ICE*	
					217				**1535** ‡						**2059**				**9551**					**9553**	
			Ⓒ	Ⓐ			①–⑤	⑥	①–⑥	⑦			①–⑥	⑦	①–⑥										
			z	t	G 🍷		e		d E	k			d	u	d				P 🍷					P ✕	
	Trier Hbf **915** .... d.	...	...	...	...	...	0456	...	...	0533	...	0633	0733	0733	...	...	0833	0933	...	...	1033	1133	1233	...	...
0	**Saarbrücken** Hbf .... d.	...	...	0444	0537	0552	0608	...	0629	0647	0700	0747	0847	0847	0851	0902	0947	1047	1058	1102	1147	1247	1347	1459	1503
31	Homburg (Saar) Hbf .... d.	...	...	0505	0558	0623	0632	...	0650	0709	0727	0809	0909	0909	0916	0927	1009	1109	|	1127	1209	1309	1409	|	1527
67	**Kaiserslautern** Hbf .... a.	...	...	0527	0621	0650	0653	...	0712	0729	0754	0829	0929	0936	0935	0954	1029	1129	1134	1154	1229	1329	1429	1535	1554
67	**Kaiserslautern** Hbf .... d.	0409	0511	0528	0623	...	0654	0702	0714	0730	0758	0834	...	0937	0937	0958	1034	...	1136	1158	1234	1334	1434	1537	1558
100	Neustadt (Weinstr) Hbf .... d.	0437	0544	0551	0647	...	0717	0733	0740	0759	0830j	0859	...	1000	1001	1031j	1059	...	|	1230j	1259	1359	1459	|	1630j
128	Ludwigshafen Hbf .... **918** d.	0457	0612	0609	0705	...	0737	0800	|	|	0857	|	...	|	|	1057	|	...	|	1257	|	|	|	|	1657
129	Ludwigshafen Mitte .... **918** d.	0459	0614	|	|	...	|	0802	|	0817	0900	0917	...	1017	|	1100	1117	...	|	1300	1317	1417	1517	|	1700
131	**Mannheim** Hbf .... **918** a.	0503	0617	0616	0709	...	0745	0805	0800	0821	0903	0921	...	1021	1021	1102	1121	...	1216	1303	1321	1421	1521	1617	1703
131	**Mannheim** Hbf . **912 918** ▽ d.	0535	0630	0631	0711	...	0748f	0807	0802	0830	0907	0930	...	1030	1023	1107	1130	...	1219	1307	1330	1430	1530	1619	1707
	Heidelberg Hbf.. **912 918** d.	0552	0646	0644	|	...	0801f	0823	|	0845	0923	0944	...	1044	|	1123	1144	...	|	1323	1344	1444	1544	|	1723
	Stuttgart Hbf .... **912** a.	...	...	...	0753	...	...	...	|	...	...	...	...	...	1118	...	...	...	|	...	...	...	...	|	...
191	Darmstadt Hbf .... ▽ a.	...	...	...	...	...	...	...	0838	...	...	...	...	...	...	...	...	...	|	...	...	...	...	|	...
219▲	**Frankfurt** (Main) Hbf .... ▽ a.	...	...	...	...	...	...	...	0856	...	...	...	...	...	...	...	...	...	1258	...	...	...	...	1658	...

					ICE		*ICE*			
					9555		**9557**			
				⑥	Ⓑ q		⊡			
				h	P ✕		P ✕			
Trier Hbf **915** .... d.	1433	1533	1633	1733	...	1833	...	...	2033	...
Saarbrücken Hbf .... d.	1547	1647	1747	1847	1859	1947	2059	...	2147	2202
Homburg (Saar) Hbf .... d.	1609	1709	1809	1909	|	2009	|	...	2209	2227
Kaiserslautern Hbf .... a.	1629	1729	1829	1929	1935	2029	2135	...	2229	2257
Kaiserslautern Hbf .... d.	1634	1734	1834	1934	1937	2034	2137	2141	2230	2302
Neustadt (Weinstr) Hbf .... d.	1659	1759	1859	1959	|	2059	|	2210	2302j	2330
Ludwigshafen Hbf .... **918** d.	|	|	|	|	|	|	|	2241	|	0002
Ludwigshafen Mitte .... **918** d.	1717	1817	1917	2017	|	2117	|	2247	2326	0005
Mannheim Hbf .... **918** a.	1721	1821	1921	2021	2017	2121	2217	2251	2330	0007
Mannheim Hbf ... **912 918** ▽ d.	1730	1830	1930	2030	2019	2137	2219	2304	2338	0008
Heidelberg Hbf ... **912 918** d.	1745	1845	1945	2047	|	2153	|	2322	2355	0025
Stuttgart Hbf .... **912** a.	...	...	...	...	|	...	|	...	...	...
Darmstadt Hbf .... ▽ a.	...	...	...	...	|	...	|	...	...	...
Frankfurt (Main) Hbf .... ▽ a.	...	...	...	...	2058	...	2258	...	...	...

					ICE					*ICE*
					9558					**9586**
	⚒		Ⓒ	Ⓐ	A			⑥	Ⓑ	⑥
	r		z	t	P ✕					P ✕
Frankfurt (Main) Hbf ..... ▽ d.	...	...	...	...	0558	...	...	...	...	0658
Darmstadt Hbf .... ▽ d.	...	...	...	...	|	...	...	...	...	|
Stuttgart Hbf .... **912** d.	...	...	...	...	|	...	...	...	...	|
Heidelberg Hbf **912 918** d.	0413	...	0554	0602	|	...	0630t	0656	0713v	|
Mannheim Hbf. **912 918** ▽ a.	0429	...	0611	0621	0638	...	0650t	0712	0730v	0738
Mannheim Hbf .... **918** d.	0430	...	0612	0628	0639	...	0656	0718	0736	0739
Ludwigshafen Mitte ... **918** d.	0433	...	0615	0631	|	...	0658	0721	0739	|
Ludwigshafen Hbf ..... **918** d.	0436	...	0617	|	|	...	0702	|	0743	|
Neustadt (Weinstr) Hbf ...... d.	0505	...	0701n	0648	|	←	0731	0739	0800	|
Kaiserslautern Hbf .... a.	0533	...	0729	0716	0721	0716t	0759	0802	0824	0821
Kaiserslautern Hbf .... d.	0534	0623	...	→	0722	0731	...	0803	0831	0822
Homburg (Saar) Hbf .... d.	0606	0653	...	...	|	0752	...	0831	0852	|
Saarbrücken Hbf .... a.	0645	0716	...	...	0759	0816	...	0857	0915	0901
Trier Hbf **915** .... a.	...	0827	...	...	...	0927	...	1027	1027	...

			ICE				*ICE*			*TGV*						*IC*			*ICE*			*EC*		*ICE*	
			9556				**9554**			**9552**						**2058**			**9550**			**216**		**1536** §	
		⑥⑦	A			①–⑤	C									Ⓑ			Ⓑ q	⑥				Ⓑ q	
		u	P ✕			d	P ✕			P 🍷						q			P ✕	h		G 🍷		E	
Frankfurt (Main) Hbf .... ▽ d.	...	...	0856	...	...	...	1058	...	...	1258	...	...	...	...	...	...	...	...	1858	...	...	...	...	2102	...
Darmstadt Hbf .... ▽ d.	...	...	|	...	...	...	|	...	...	|	...	...	...	...	...	...	...	...	|	...	...	...	...	2119x	...
Stuttgart Hbf .... **912** d.	...	...	|	...	...	...	|	...	...	|	...	...	...	...	...	1655	...	...	|	...	...	2004	...	|	...
Heidelberg Hbf ... **912 918** d.	0817t	0913	|	0933	1013	1113	|	1133	1213	|	1335	1413	1513	1613	1713	|	1813	1833	|	1913	1933	|	2033	|	2214
Mannheim Hbf ... **912 918** ▽ a.	0836t	0929	0939	0951	1029	1129	1141	1151	1229	1338	1353	1429	1529	1629	1729	1745	1829	1851	1938	1929	1951	2048	2051	2155	2230
Mannheim Hbf .... **918** d.	0839	0939	0940	0954	1039	1139	1142	1156	1239	1340	1356	1439	1539	1639	1735	1747	1835	1856	1939	1939	1956	2050	2056	2157	2239
Ludwigshafen Mitte .... **918** d.	0842	0942	|	0956	1042	1142	|	1158	1242	|	1358	1442	|	|	1739	|	1839	1858	|	1942	1958	|	2058	|	2242
Ludwigshafen Hbf .... **918** d.	|	|	|	1002	|	|	|	1203	|	|	1403	|	1544	1644	|	|	|	1903	|	|	2001	|	2103	|	|
Neustadt (Weinstr) Hbf .... d.	0900	1000	|	1032	1100	1200	|	1232	1300	|	1432	1500	1600	1700	1800	1811	1900	1932	|	2000	2032	2112	2132	2219	2302
Kaiserslautern Hbf .... a.	0924	1024	1021	1059	1124	1224	1223	1258	1324	1421	1459	1524	1624	1724	1824	1834	1924	2000	2021	2024	2059	2133	2159	2243	2327
Kaiserslautern Hbf .... d.	0931	1031	1022	1103	1131	1231	1224	1303	1331	1422	1503	1531	1631	1731	1830	1836	1931	2003	2022	2031	2103	2135	2205	2245	2329
Homburg (Saar) Hbf .... d.	0952	1052	|	1130	1152	1252	|	1330	1352	|	1530	1552	1652	1752	1850	1856	1952	2030	|	2052	2132	2157	2233	2305	2356
Saarbrücken Hbf .... a.	1015	1115	1100	1156	1215	1315	1302	1356	1415	1500	1557	1615	1715	1815	1912	1918	2015	2056	2100	2115	2158	2218	2259	2329	0019
Trier Hbf **915** .... a.	1127	1227	...	...	1327	1427	...	...	1527	...	...	1727	1827	1927	2027	...	2127	...	...	2227	...	...	...	...	...

A – ①–⑤ (not June 10).
C – ⑥⑦ (also June 10).
E – PFÄLZER WALD – 🚃12 and ✕ Saarbrücken - Frankfurt - Erfurt - Berlin and v.v.
G – DACHSTEIN – 🚃12 and 🍷 Graz - Salzburg - München - Stuttgart - Saarbrücken and v.v.
P – From / to Paris (Table **390**). 🅁 for international journeys.

– Not June 10.
– Not June 10, Nov. 1.
– Not June 20, Oct. 3.
– Also June 9.
– Arrives 5–6 minutes earlier.
– Also June 10, Nov. 1.
– Arrives 0643.
– Not June 9.
– Not June 20, Nov. 1.

t – Ⓐ (not June 20, Nov. 1).
u – Also June 10.
v – On † (also June 20, Nov. 1) Heidelberg d. *0702*, Mannheim a. *0719*.
x – Not ⑦ Aug. 11 - Sept. 29.
z – Also June 20, Nov. 1.

‡ – Aug. 10 - Oct. 28 runs with train number **1551** and terminates at Frankfurt. On ⑥ Aug. 10 - Sept. 28 departs Mannheim 0805, arrives Frankfurt 0850 (not calling at Darmstadt).
§ – Aug. 9 - Oct. 27 runs with train number **1550** and starts from Dresden (not Berlin); see Table **850**.
⊡ – On ⑥ (also June 9) runs as *TGV* **9559** (conveys 🍷, not ✕).
▽ – See also Table **912** (*ICE* trains) and Table **913** (local trains).
▲ – *209 km* for trains running non-stop Mannheim - Frankfurt.

920 FRANKFURT - NÜRNBERG - PASSAU (- WIEN)

See Table 921 for other regional trains

km	SEE NOTE ❖						RE	RE	ICE	ICE	ICE	ICE	ICE	ICE	ICE	ICE	ICE	ICE	ICE	ICE	ICE	ICE	ICE	ICE
							59493	59275	827	521	21	523	1125	525	23	1127	527	529	1221	91	621	93	623	27
		⚒d	Ⓐr	Ⓐd		Ⓒv	Ⓐr	ⒸH	①–⑤			①–⑥	⑦m	①–⑥		⑥	①–⑤							
		◐		◐		◐			✕	✕	✕	✕	✕	s✕	✕	✕	✕	✕	T✕	✕	✕	B✕	✕	✕
	Hamburg Hbf **800 900** d.	...	...	...	...	...	...	...	...	...	...	...	...	...	...	...	...	...	...	0729	...	...	...	...
	Dortmund Hbf **800** d.	...	...	...	...	...	...	...	...	...	...	0404	0512	0523	0435	0612	0623	0723	0635	|	0813c	...	0915c	0834
	Essen Hbf **800** d.	...	...	...	...	...	...	...	...	...	...	0430	0537	0554	0500	0637	0653	0753	|	|	0840	...	0941	|
	Düsseldorf Hbf **800** d.	...	...	...	...	...	...	...	...	...	...	0458	0606	0621	0527	0706	0721	0821	|	|	0913	...	1012	|
	Köln Hbf **800 910** d.	...	...	...	...	...	...	...	0319	0422	...	|	|	|	0553	|	|	|	0753	|	|	...	|	0953
	Köln Messe/Deutz **910** d.	...	...	...	...	...	...	...	|	|	...	0520	0629	0644	|	0730	0744	0844	|	|	0936	...	1034	|
	Bonn Hbf **800** d.	...	...	...	...	...	...	...	|	|	...	|	|	|	0614	|	|	|	0814	|	|	...	|	1014
	Koblenz Hbf **911** d.	...	...	...	...	...	...	...	|	|	...	|	|	|	0648	|	|	|	0848	|	|	...	|	1048
	Mainz Hbf **911** d.	...	...	...	...	...	...	...	|	|	...	|	|	|	0740	|	|	|	0942	|	|	...	|	1142
0	**Frankfurt** Flughafen ✈ § d.	...	...	...	...	...	...	...	0436	0530	...	0636	0736	0736	0802	0836	0836	0936	1002	|	1036	...	1136	1202
11	**Frankfurt** (Main) Hbf d.	...	...	...	...	...	...	...	0454	0554•	0621	0654•	0754•	0754•	0819y	0854•	0854	0954•	1021	|	1054•	...	1154•	1221
35	Hanau Hbf d.	...	...	...	...	...	...	...	|	0610	0637	|	|	|	0837	|	|	|	1037	|	|	...	|	1236
57	Aschaffenburg Hbf d.	...	...	...	...	...	...	...	0523	0624	0651	0723	0823	0823	|	0923	0923	1023	|	|	1123	...	1223	|
136	**Würzburg** Hbf **900** d.	...	...	...	...	...	...	...	0604	0704	0734	0804	0904	0904	0935	1004	1004	1104	1131	1135	1204	...	1313	1335
238	**Nürnberg** Hbf **900** a.	...	...	...	...	...	...	...	0659	0759	0827	0901	0958	0958	1027	1100	1100	1159	1224	1227	1259	...	1404	1427
238	**Nürnberg** Hbf d.	...	0501	...	0521	...	0615	0705	0702	0802	0830	0904	1002	1002	1030	1104	1104	1202	1227	1230	1302	1332	1407	1430
	München Hbf **904** a.	...	|	...	|	...	|	|	0807	0904	|	1006	1108	1108	|	1207	1207	1306	1338	|	1406	|	1509	|
271	Neumarkt (Oberpf) d.	0445k	0534	0551	0555	0610	0638	0726	...	...	|	...	...	...	|	...	...	...	...	|	...	|	...	|
335	**Regensburg** Hbf d.	0540	...	0653	...	0709	0726	0818	...	...	0926	...	...	...	1126	...	...	...	...	1326	...	1426	...	1526
375	Straubing d.	0607	...	0722	...	0736	...	0844	...	...	|	...	...	...	|	...	...	...	...	|	...	1449z	...	|
400	Plattling **944** d.	0623	...	0738	...	0750	...	0858	...	...	0958	...	...	...	1159	...	...	...	...	1359	...	|	...	1559
452	**Passau** Hbf 🏛 **944** a.	*0718*	...	*0835*	...	*0837*	...	0930	...	...	1023	...	...	...	1225	...	...	...	...	1425	...	1526	...	1626
	Linz Hbf **950** a.	...	...	...	...	...	...	...	...	...	1124	...	...	...	1324	...	...	...	...	1524	...	1624	...	1724
	Wien Hbf **950** a.	...	...	...	...	...	...	...	...	...	1245	...	...	...	1445	...	...	...	...	1645	...	1745	...	1845

SEE NOTE ❖	ICE	ICE	ICE	RE	ICE	ICE	ICE	ICE	ICE	IC	ICE	ICE	IC	IC	IC		ICE	RE	ICE	IC	NJ	NJ	NJ	NJ
	625	627	29	59495	629	721	229	723	725	2027	727	729	2229	2229	2229		821	59499	1625	2029	491	40491	421	40421
			△	Ⓐr							Ⓑ		Ⓑ	④⑤⑦	④⑤		Ⓑ		⑥D		🅁	🅁	🅁	🅁
	✕	✕	✕		✕	✕	✕	✕	✕	❦🍷	✕	✕	🍷	◇🍷	◇🍷	◐	✕		✕		N⊗	AN	AN	N⊗
Hamburg Hbf **800 900** d.	...	...	...	...	...	...	...	...	...	1146	...	...	1346	1346	1346	...	...	...	...	1546	2029	2029	...	...
Dortmund Hbf **800** d.	1014c	1123j	...	...	1214k	1323c	...	1414c	1523k	1436	...	1723k	1636	1636	1636	...	...	...	...	1836	|	|	...	...
Essen Hbf **800** d.	1041	1154	...	...	1241	1354	...	1440	1555	|	1653	1754	|	|	|	...	1841	...	...	|	|	|	...	...
Düsseldorf Hbf **800** d.	1108	1221	...	...	1308	1421	...	1513	1622	|	1721	1822	|	|	|	...	1908	...	...	|	|	|	2054	2054
Köln Hbf **800 910** d.	|	|	...	...	|	|	...	|	|	1553	|	|	1753	1753	1753	...	|	...	...	1953	|	|	2121	2121
Köln Messe/Deutz **910** d.	1130	1244	...	...	1333	1444	...	1536	1644	|	1744	1844	|	|	|	...	1930	...	...	|	|	|	|	|
Bonn Hbf **800** d.	|	|	...	...	|	|	...	|	|	1614	|	|	1814	1814	1814	...	|	...	...	2014	|	|	2143	2143
Koblenz Hbf **911** d.	|	|	...	...	|	|	...	|	|	1648	|	|	1848	1848	1848	...	|	...	...	2048	|	|	2218	2218
Mainz Hbf **911** d.	|	|	...	...	|	|	...	|	|	1742	|	|	1942	1942	1942	...	|	...	2043	2144	|	|	2312	2312
Frankfurt Flughafen ✈ § d.	1236	1336	...	...	1438	1536	...	1636	1736	1802	1836	1936	2002	2002	2002	...	2036	...	2102	2202	|	|	2354	2354
Frankfurt (Main) Hbf d.	1254•	1354•	1421e	...	1454•	1554•	1621	1654•	1754•	1822	1854•	1954•	2022	2022	2022	...	2054•	...	2119	2221	|	|	0008f	0008f
Hanau Hbf d.	|	|	1437	...	|	|	1637	|	|	1838	|	|	2038	2038	2038	...	|	...	2134	2238	|	|	|	|
Aschaffenburg Hbf d.	1323	1423	|	...	1523	1623	1651	1723	1823	1851	1923	2023	2052	2052	2052	...	2123	...	2149	2252	|	|	|	|
Würzburg Hbf **900** d.	1404	1504	1535	...	1604	1704	1735	1804	1904	1935	2004	2104	2135	2135	2135	...	2204	...	2235	2346	0134	0134	0137	0137
Nürnberg Hbf **900** a.	1500	1559	1627	...	1658	1759	1827	1900	1959	2027	2100	2159	2227	2227	2227	...	2259	...	2328	0044	0232	0232	0237	0237
Nürnberg Hbf d.	1504	1602	1630	1636	1702	1802	1830	1903	2002	2030	2104	2202	...	2237	2237	...	2302p	2316	2331	...	0307	0342	0342	0307
München Hbf **904** a.	1606	1704	|	|	1804	1911	|	2007	2109	|	2206	2310	...	|	|	...	0007p	|	0043	...	|	0709	0709	|
Neumarkt (Oberpf) d.	...	...	|	1657	...	...	|	...	...	|	...	...	...	|	|	...	...	2338	...	...	|	...	...	|
Regensburg Hbf d.	...	...	1726	1747	...	...	1926	...	...	2133	...	...	...	2338	2340	0009	...	0028	...	...	0413	...	...	0413
Straubing d.	...	...	|	...	...	...	|	...	...	2154	...	...	...	...	0002	0036	...	...	...	...	|	...	...	|
Plattling **944** d.	...	...	1759	...	...	...	1959	...	...	2208	...	...	...	...	0017	0051	...	...	...	...	|	...	...	|
Passau Hbf 🏛 **944** a.	...	...	1826	...	...	...	2026	...	...	2241	...	...	...	...	0050	*0132*	...	...	...	...	0518	...	...	0518
Linz Hbf **950** a.	...	...	1924	...	...	...	2143	...	...	...	...	...	...	...	...	...	...	...	...	...	0643	...	...	0643
Wien Hbf **950** a.	...	...	2045	...	...	...	2309	...	...	...	...	...	...	...	...	...	...	...	...	...	0827	...	...	0827

A – To Innsbruck (Table **951**). Also calls at Augsburg Hbf (not the mornings of ⑥⑦ to June 23), a. 0626. On the mornings ①–⑤ to July 26 calls at München **Ost** (a. 0720; not München Hbf). Later timings at Würzburg / Nürnberg Aug. 12 - Oct. 28.
B – BEROLINA – From Berlin (Table **850**).
D – From Wiesbaden Hbf (d. 2026). Arrives München 0111 on the mornings of July 28, Aug. 4, 11, 18, 25, Sept. 1.
H – Ⓒ until Oct. 13 (also June 20).
N – Conveys 🛏 1, 2 cl., 🛏 2 cl. and 🚃(2).
T – Continues to Seefeld (Table **895**) on ⑤⑥ (also Oct. 2).

c – ⑥⑦ only.
d – Not June 20, Aug. 15, Nov. 1.
e – 1413 on ⑥⑦ Aug. 10 - Sept. 8.
f – Frankfurt (Main) **Süd**.
j – ⑤–⑦ (also Oct. 2; not Oct. 4).
k – ⑥ only.
m – Also June 20, Oct. 3.
p – Nürnberg - München on ④⑤⑦ (also June 19).
r – Not June 20, Nov. 1.
s – Not June 20, Oct. 3.
v – Also June 20, Aug. 15, Nov. 1.
y – 0821 on ⑦.
z – From Sept. 12.

• – Calls at Frankfurt Süd (not Hbf) on ⑥⑦ Aug. 10 - Sept. 29.
❦ – Terminates at Nürnberg Sept. 11 - Nov. 22.

△ – Does not run Frankfurt - Regensburg Sept. 12 - Nov. 21.
◇ – Also June 18, 19. Terminates at Nürnberg Sept. 11 - Nov. 21.
⊗ – Timings Passau - Wien are subject to alteration on the mornings June 29 - Oct. 28 (later arrivals; from Aug. 12 train **491** runs later Würzburg - Wien). On mornings July 16 – 24 service is diverted, not calling at Regensburg or Passau.
❖ – Timings at Dortmund, Essen and Düsseldorf are subject to alteration July 13 - Aug. 25. Certain services do not call at Frankfurt Flughafen from Oct. 26. See the engineering work panel on page 369 for further details and also for other work affecting services in this table.
◐ – Operated by *agilis*.
§ – Frankfurt Flughafen Fernbahnhof.

921 Regional trains FRANKFURT - WÜRZBURG - NÜRNBERG - REGENSBURG - PASSAU

RE services

See Table **920** for faster *ICE* / *IC* trains. Neumarkt - Regensburg - Plattling trains are operated by *agilis*.

km			Ⓒz	Ⓐt		△		△		△		△	Ⓒz	Ⓐt	△	Ⓒz	Ⓐt	△		△				⑤⑥f	
0	**Frankfurt** (Main) Hbf d.	...	0450k	0513	0634	0730	0834	0930	1034	1130	1234	1330	1434	1530	1534	1634	1730	1734	1834	1930	2034	2130	2230	2330	2330	0030
4	**Frankfurt** (Main) Süd d.	...	0458k	0519	0640	0736	0840	0936	1040	1136	1240	1336	1440	1536	1540	1640	1736	1740	1840	1936	2040	2136	2236	2336	2336	0036
10	Offenbach (Main) Hbf d.	...	|	0524	0645	|	0845	|	1045	|	1245	|	1445	|	1545	1645	|	1745	1845	|	2045	|	|	|	|	|
24	Hanau Hbf d.	...	0521k	0540	0657	0758	0857	0958	1057	1158	1257	1358	1457	1558	1558	1657	1758	1757	1857	1958	2057	2158	2259	2359	2359	0059
46	Aschaffenburg Hbf d.	0501	0612	0612	0717	0817	0917	1017	1117	1217	1317	1417	1517	1617	1617	1717	1817	1817	1917	2017	2117	2218	2322	0022	0022	0122
84	Lohr Bahnhof d.	0530	0640	0640	0742	0842	0942	1042	1142	1242	1342	1442	1542	1642	1642	1742	1842	1842	1942	2042	2142	2247	2350	0051	0051	...
96	Gemünden (Main) d.	0543	0656	0656	0756	0856	0956	1056	1156	1256	1356	1456	1556	1656	1656	1756	1856	1856	1956	2056	2156	2300	0003	0102	0103	...
109	Karlstadt (Main) d.	0554	0705	0705	0805	0905	1005	1105	1205	1305	1405	1505	1605	1705	1705	1805	1905	1905	2005	2105	2205	2310	0012	...	0112	...
134	**Würzburg** Hbf a.	0617	0721	0721	0821	0921	1021	1121	1221	1321	1421	1521	1621	1721	1721	1821	1921	1921	2021	2121	2221	2332	0027	...	0127	...
	Bamberg **875** a.	...	0832	0832	...	1032	...	1232	...	1432	...	1632	...	1832	1832	...	2032	2032	...	2232	...	...	...	...	...	...

km				⚒r		⚒r	Ⓒw	Ⓐr	Ⓒw	Ⓐr																
0	**Würzburg** Hbf d.	0038	...	0438	...	0536	...	0607	0637	0637	0741	0842	0942	1042	1142	1242	1342	1442	1542	1640	1742	1842	1942	2042	2148	2304
23	Kitzingen d.	0059	...	0456	...	0554	...	0623	0655	0655	0801	0901	1001	1101	1201	1301	1401	1501	1601	1701	1801	1901	2001	2101	2208	2323
61	Neustadt (Aisch) Bf d.	...	...	0519	0546	0616	0648	0648	0717	0717	0826	0926	1026	1126	1226	1324	1426	1526	1626	1726	1826	1926	2026	2126	2239	2346
94	Fürth (Bay) Hbf d.	...	...	0547	0614	0644	0712	0714	0738	0740	0847	0947	1047	1147	1247	1347	1447	1547	1647	1747	1847	1947	2047	2147	2309	0015
102	**Nürnberg** Hbf a.	...	...	0553	0621	0652	0719	0721	0745	0749	0853	0954	1054	1154	1254	1354	1454	1554	1654	1754	1853	1954	2054	2154	2316	0024

	Ⓐd	⊕			Ⓐd	Ⓒv			⊕						⊕			⊕			⊕	◇				
Nürnberg Hbf d.	0551	...	0735	...	...	...	0934	...	...	1136	...	...	1336	...	...	1536	...	...	1736	...	...	1936	...	...	2134	...
Neumarkt (Oberpf) d.	0619	0706	0759	0810	*0910*	*0910*	0959	1010	1110	1159	1210	1310j	1359	1410	1510	1559	1610	1710	1759	1810	1910	1959	2010	2110	2159	2210
Regensburg Hbf a.	0700	0758	0840	0903	*1003*	*1005*	1038	1103	1203	1238	1303	1403j	1438	1503	1603	1638	1703	1803	1838	1903	2003	2038	2103	2203	2238	2303
Regensburg Hbf d.	0702	0809	0846	0909	1009	1009	1046	1109	1209	1246	1309	1409	1446	1509	1609	1646	1709	1809	1846	1909	2009	...	2109	2209	2247	2309
München Hbf **878** a.	0836	|	1018	|	|	|	1216	|	|	1416	|	|	1616	|	|	1816	|	|	2018	|	|	...	|	|	0016	|
Straubing d.	...	0836	...	0936	1036	1036	▬	1136	1236	...	1336	1436	...	1536	1636	...	1736	1836	...	1936	2036	...	2136	2236	...	2336
Plattling a.	...	0851	...	0951	1051	1051	...	1151	1251	...	1351	1451	...	1551	1651	...	1751	1851	...	1951	2051	...	2151	2251	...	2351
Plattling **944** d.	...	*0902*	...	*1004*	...	1054p	1102	*1204*	*1302*	...	*1404*	*1504*	...	*1604*	*1702*	...	*1804*	*1902*	...	*2004*	*2102*	...	*2202*	*2306*	...	...
Passau Hbf **944** a.	...	*0937*	...	*1039*	...	1129p	1137	*1239*	*1337*	...	*1439*	*1539*	...	*1639*	*1737*	...	*1839*	*1937*	...	*2039*	*2139*	...	*2237*	*2341*	...	...

d – Not June 20, Aug. 15, Nov. 1.
f – Also June 9, 19, Aug. 14, Oct. 2, 31.
j – Ⓒ (daily June 8 – 23, July 27 - Sept. 9, Oct. 26 - Nov. 3).
k – ⑥ only.
p – Until Oct. 13.
r – Not June 20, Nov. 1.
t – Not June 20.
v – Also June 20, Aug. 15, Nov. 1.
w – Also June 20, Nov. 1.
z – Also June 20.
◇ – To Landshut (Table **878**).
⊕ – Change trains at Regensburg on Ⓐ **d**.
△ – On ⑥⑦ Aug. 10 - Sept. 29 departs Frankfurt Hbf / Süd 4 minutes **earlier** and does not call at Offenbach.

*See Table **921** for other regional trains*

(WIEN -) PASSAU - NÜRNBERG - FRANKFURT 920

SEE NOTE ❖	ICE 824 ①–⑤ ✖	IC 2028	ICE 822 ①–⑥ ✖	RE 59496 Ⓒw	RE 59492 Ⓐr	ICE 820 ①–⑥ ✖	IC 2226 ⑤⑥ g≋	IC 2226 ①–⑥ ≋🍷	ICE 728 ✖	◐	Ⓐd ◐	RE 4850	ICE 726 ①–⑥ ✖	IC 2024 ▲🍷	ICE 724 ✖	ICE 722 Ⓐm ✖	ICE 1122 Ⓒs ✖	ICE 228 ✖	ICE 720 ✖	ICE 628 ✖	ICE 28 △ ✖	ICE 626 ✖	ICE 826 Ⓐm ✖	ICE 92 B✖
Wien Hbf **950** d.	...	...	...	...	...	...	...	...	...	...	...	...	...	...	...	...	...	0650	...	...	0915	...	...	1015
Linz Hbf **950** d.	...	...	...	...	...	...	...	...	...	...	...	...	...	...	...	...	...	0817	...	...	1036	...	...	1136
Passau Hbf 🚉 **944** d.	...	...	...	...	...	...	0511	...	...	*0523*	...	...	...	0717	...	...	...	0934	...	...	1134	...	...	1234
Plattling **944** d.	...	...	...	...	...	...	0543	...	...	0609	0629	...	...	0751	...	...	...	1001	...	...	1201	...	...	|
Straubing d.	...	...	...	...	...	...	0557	...	...	0625	0645	...	...	0805	...	...	...	|	...	...	|	...	...	1312z
Regensburg Hbf d.	...	...	...	0530	0530	...	0622	0622	...	0658	0711	0719	...	0827	...	...	...	1032	...	...	1232	...	...	1332
Neumarkt (Oberpf) d.	...	...	...	0618	0620	...	0700	0700	...	0751	...	0800	...	|	...	...	...	|	...	...	|	...	...	|
München Hbf **904** d.	...	...	0448	|	|	0547n	|	|	0648	...	...	|	0752	|	0848	0951	0951	|	1055	1151	|	1250	1250	|
Nürnberg Hbf a.	...	...	0555	0640	0642	0654n	0722	0722	0754	...	...	0823	0854	0926	0955	1055	1055	1127	1157	1254	1327	1353	1353	1427
Nürnberg Hbf **900** d.	0500	0526	0600	...	...	0657	0729	0729	0800	...	...	...	0902	0929	1000	1100	1100	1130	1200	1257	1330	1400	1400	...
Würzburg Hbf **900** d.	0555	0624	0655	...	...	0755	0824	0824	0855	...	...	...	0955	1024	1055	1155	1155	1224	1256	1355	1424	1455	1455	...
Aschaffenburg Hbf d.	0633	0705	0733	...	...	0833	|	|	0933	...	...	...	1033	|	1133	1233	1233	|	1333	1433	|	1533	1533	...
Hanau Hbf d.	|	|	|	...	...	|	0917	0917	|	...	...	...	|	1117	|	|	|	1318	|	|	1518	|	|	...
Frankfurt (Main) Hbf a.	0704	0736	0804•	...	...	0904•	0932	0932	1004•	...	...	...	1104•	1136	1204•	1304	1304•	1336e	1404•	1504•	1536	1604•	1604	...
Frankfurt Flughafen ✈ § a.	0722	0755	0822	...	...	0921	0955	0955	1022	...	...	...	1120	1155	1222	1322	1320	...	1422	1522	...	1622	1622	...
Mainz Hbf **911** a.	|	0818	|	...	...	|	1018	1018	|	...	...	...	|	1218	|	|	|	...	|	|	...	|	|	...
Koblenz Hbf **911** a.	|	0911	|	...	...	|	1111	1111	|	...	...	...	|	1311	|	|	|	...	|	|	...	|	|	...
Bonn Hbf **800** a.	|	0944	|	...	...	|	1144	1144	|	...	...	...	|	1344	|	|	|	...	|	|	...	|	|	...
Köln Messe/Deutz **910** a.	0814	|	0914	...	...	1025	|	|	1114	...	...	...	1225	|	1324	1415	1425	...	1514	1614	...	1713	1741	...
Köln Hbf **800 910** a.	|	1005	|	...	...	|	1205	1205	|	...	...	...	|	1405	|	|	|	...	|	|	...	|	...	...
Düsseldorf Hbf **800** a.	0836	|	0936	...	...	1046	|	|	1136	...	...	...	1246	|	1345	1436	1446	...	1536	1639	...	1736	...	...
Essen Hbf **800** a.	0902	|	1002	...	...	1114	|	|	1202	...	...	...	1313	|	1415	1504	1513	...	1602	1706	...	1802	...	...
Dortmund Hbf **800** a.	...	1121	1030k	...	...	1141k	1321	1321	1230c	...	...	...	1343k	1521	1442k	...	1542k	...	1627k	1742k	...	1830k	...	...
Hamburg Hbf **800 900** a.	...	1414	...	...	...	...	1614	1614	...	...	...	...	...	1814	...	...	...	...	...	...	...	...	...	...

SEE NOTE ❖	ICE 624 ⚒m ✖	ICE 1124 †s ✖	ICE 26 ✖	ICE 622 ✖	ICE 620 ✖	ICE 90 ✖	ICE 1622 T✖	ICE 528 ✖	ICE 526 ✖	ICE 22 ✖	ICE 524 ✖	ICE 522 ✖	RE 59272 ⒸH	ICE 20 ✖	ICE 1620 ⑥	ICE 520 ①–④ y	ICE 920 ⑤⑦ h✖	◐	RB 59494	◐	NJ 490 Ⓡ N⊗	NJ 40420 Ⓡ AN	NJ 420 Ⓡ AN	NJ 40490 Ⓡ N⊗
Wien Hbf **950** d.	...	...	1115	...	...	1315	...	...	...	1515	...	...	...	1715	...	...	...	...	...	...	2041	...	...	2041
Linz Hbf **950** d.	...	...	1236	...	...	1436	...	...	...	1636	...	...	...	1836	...	...	...	...	...	...	2216	...	...	2216
Passau Hbf 🚉 **944** d.	...	...	1334v	...	...	1537	...	...	...	1734	...	...	1832	1937	...	...	...	*2126*	...	...	2322	...	...	2322
Plattling **944** d.	...	...	1401v	...	...	1604	...	...	...	1801	...	...	1903	2004	...	...	...	2207	...	2307	|	...	...	|
Straubing d.	...	...	|	...	...	|	...	...	...	|	...	...	1916	|	...	...	...	2223	...	2323	|	...	...	|
Regensburg Hbf d.	...	...	1432v	...	...	1635	...	...	...	1832	...	...	1944	2035	...	...	...	2252	2324	2351	0027	...	...	0027
Neumarkt (Oberpf) d.	...	...	|	...	...	|	...	...	...	|	...	...	2032	|	...	...	...	...	0021	...	|	...	...	|
München Hbf **904** d.	1351	1351	|	1451	1551	|	1618	1649	1751	|	1851	1948	|	|	2052	2054	2054	...	|	...	|	2252	2252	|
Nürnberg Hbf a.	1454	1454	1527v	1554	1654	1729	1733	1756	1854	1927	1954	2054	2057	2128	2201	2200	2202	...	0044	...	0127	0116	0116	0127
Nürnberg Hbf **900** d.	1500	1500	1530v	1600	1657	1732	1736	1800	1857	1930	2000	2100	...	2131	2204	2204	2205	...	...	...	0200	0200	0246	0246
Würzburg Hbf **900** d.	1555	1555	1624	1655	1755	1826	1830	1855	1955	2024	2055	2155	...	2224	2257	2257	2258	...	...	...	0300	0300	|	|
Aschaffenburg Hbf d.	1633	1633	|	1733	1833	|	|	1933	2033	|	2133	2233	...	2305	2335	2335	2336	...	...	...	|	|	|	|
Hanau Hbf d.	|	|	1716t	|	|	|	1920	|	|	2116	|	2247	...	2321	|	|	|	...	...	...	|	|	|	|
Frankfurt (Main) Hbf a.	1704•	1704•	1736	1804•	1904•	|	1936	2004•	2104•	2136	2204•	2304◊	...	2340	0003	0004	0006	...	...	...	|	|	0523f	0523f
Frankfurt Flughafen ✈ § a.	1722	1720	1755	1822	1920	|	1955	2022	2122	2157	2222	2322	...	...	...	...	...	...	...	...	|	|	0535j	0535j
Mainz Hbf **911** a.	|	|	1818	|	|	|	2018	|	|	2218	|	|	...	...	...	...	...	...	...	...	|	|	0602	0602
Koblenz Hbf **911** a.	|	|	1911	|	|	|	2111	|	|	2311	|	|	...	...	...	...	...	...	...	...	|	|	0704	0704
Bonn Hbf **800** a.	|	|	1944	|	|	|	2144	|	|	2344	|	|	...	...	...	...	...	...	...	...	|	|	|	|
Köln Messe/Deutz **910** a.	1814	1826	|	1914	2025	|	|	2113	2214	|	2337	|	...	...	...	...	...	...	...	...	|	|	|	|
Köln Hbf **800 910** a.	|	|	2005	|	|	|	2205	|	|	0005	|	0039	...	...	...	...	...	...	...	...	|	|	0815	0815
Düsseldorf Hbf **800** a.	1836	1846	|	1944	2046	|	|	2136	2236	0030	2358	0103	...	...	...	...	...	...	...	...	|	|	0842	0842
Essen Hbf **800** a.	1902	1914	|	2015	2114	|	|	2202	2302	0056	0025	0134	...	...	...	...	...	...	...	...	|	|	...	...
Dortmund Hbf **800** a.	1930	1942	2120	2042	2142	|	2320	2228	2326	0121	0050	0156	...	...	...	...	...	...	...	...	|	|	...	...
Hamburg Hbf **800 900** a.	...	...	...	...	...	2229	...	...	...	...	...	...	...	...	...	...	...	...	...	...	0847q	0847q	...	...

A – From Innsbruck (Table **951**). Also calls at Augsburg Hbf (d. 2335; does not call ⑤–⑦ to June 23).
B – BEROLINA – To Berlin (Table **850**). Continues to Rostock (Table **835**) on ⑤ (also Oct. 2; not Oct. 4).
H – Ⓒ until Oct. 13 (also June 20, Aug. 15).
N – Conveys 🛏 1, 2 cl., 🛌 2 cl. and 💺.
T – From Innsbruck (Table **895**) on Ⓒ (train number **1222**).
c – ⑥⑦ only.
d – Not June 20, Aug. 15, Nov. 1.
e – 1343 on ⑥⑦ Aug. 10 - Sept. 8.
f – Frankfurt (Main) **Süd**.
g – Also June 19, 20.
h – Also Oct. 2; not Oct. 4.

j – Frankfurt Flughafen **Regionalbahnhof** (Fernbahnhof from Oct. 26).
k – ⑥ only.
m – Not June 20.
n – ①–⑤ to July 12 (not June 20); ①–⑤ Aug. 15 - Sept. 27; ⚒ Sept. 30 - Nov. 2.
q – 1006 on ⑥⑦ Aug. 17 - Oct. 27.
r – Not June 20, Nov. 1.
s – Also June 20.
t – Until Oct. 25.
v – 1–3 minutes later on ⑦.
w – Also June 20, Nov. 1.
y – Also Oct. 4; not Oct. 2.
z – From Sept. 12.

• – Calls at Frankfurt Süd (not Hbf) on ⑥⑦ Aug. 10 - Sept. 29.
◊ – Calls at Frankfurt Süd (not Hbf) on ⑤–⑦ Aug. 9 - Sept. 29.
≋ – Service starts from Nürnberg Sept. 12 - Nov. 23.
▲ – Service starts from Nürnberg Sept. 12 - Nov. 22.
△ – Does not run Regensburg - Frankfurt Sept. 12 - Nov. 21.
⊗ – Subject to alteration July 15 – 24 (Wien d. 1835, Linz d. 2014 and does not call at Passau or Regensburg).
❖ – Timings at Düsseldorf, Essen and Dortmund are subject to alteration July 13 - Aug. 25. Certain services do not call at Frankfurt Flughafen from Oct. 26 (some northbound services do not call at Mainz Hbf). See the engineering work panel on page 369 for further details and also for other work affecting services in this table.
§ – Frankfurt Flughafen Fernbahnhof ✈.
◐ – Operated by *agilis*.

RE services

Regional trains PASSAU - REGENSBURG - NÜRNBERG - WÜRZBURG - FRANKFURT 921

See Table **920** for faster *ICE / IC* trains. Plattling - Regensburg - Neumarkt trains are operated by *agilis*.

	Ⓐd	Ⓒv				⊕			⊕			⊕			⊕				Ⓐd	Ⓒv			⊕			
Passau Hbf **944** d.	0604	0627	...	*0725*	...	*0826*	*0919*	...	*1026*	*1119*	...	*1219*	*1319*	...	*1426*	*1519*	...	1625	...	1620p	*1719*	...	*1822*	*1919*	...	*2026*
Plattling **944** a.	0640	0701	...	*0759*	...	*0900*	*0953*	...	*1100*	*1153*	...	*1253*	*1353*	...	*1500*	*1553*	...	1659	...	1655p	*1753*	...	*1856*	*1953*	...	*2100*
Plattling d.	▬	...	0707	0807	...	0907	1007	...	1107	1207	...	1307	1409	...	1507	1609	...	...	1707	1707	1807	...	1907	2009	...	2107
Straubing d.	...	...	0723	0823	...	0923	1023	...	1123	1223	...	1323	1424	...	1523	1624	...	...	1723	1723	1823	...	1923	2024	...	2123
München Hbf **878** d.	0544	...	|	|	0744	|	|	0944	|	|	1144	|	|	1344	|	|	1543	...	|	|	|	1744	|	|	1944	|
Regensburg Hbf a.	0717	...	0752	0850	0915	0950	1050	1115	1150	1250	1315	1350	1452	1515	1550	1652	1715	...	1750	1750	1850	1915	1950	2052	2115	2152
Regensburg Hbf d.	0719	...	0756	0856	0918	0957	1056	1118	1157	1256	1318	1357	1456	1518	1557	1656	1717	...	*1757*	*1757*	1856	1918	1957	2056	2118	...
Neumarkt (Oberpf) d.	0800	...	0852	0949	1000	1052	1149	1200	1252	1352	1400	1452	1549	1600	1652	1749	1800	...	*1852*	*1852*	1949	2000	2050	2149	2200	...
Nürnberg Hbf a.	0823	...	...	...	1023	...	...	1223	...	...	1423	...	...	1623	...	...	1824	...	...	...	...	2024	...	...	2223	...

				⚒r													Ⓐr									
Nürnberg Hbf d.	0101	...	...	0428	...	0604	0705	0805	0905	1005	1105	1205	1305	1405	1505	1605	1624	1705	1805	1905	2005	2105	2206	2238	...	2335
Fürth (Bay) Hbf d.	0109	...	...	0436	...	0611	0711	0811	0911	1011	1111	1211	1311	1411	1511	1611	1632	1712	1811	1911	2011	2111	2212	2247	...	2344
Neustadt (Aisch) Bf d.	0137	...	...	0506	...	0634	0734	0834	0934	1034	1134	1234	1334	1434	1534	1634	1700	1734	1834	1934	2034	2134	2234	2316	...	0013
Kitzingen d.	...	...	...	0528	...	0657	0757	0857	0957	1057	1157	1257	1357	1457	1557	1657	1725	1757	1857	1957	2057	2157	2257	...	...	0034
Würzburg Hbf a.	...	...	...	0548	...	0714	0817	0916	1016	1116	1216	1316	1416	1516	1616	1716	1749	1816	1916	2016	2116	2219	2315	...	...	0053

		Ⓒc			Ⓐt		△	Ⓐt	Ⓒz	△		△		△		△		△		△		△			
Bamberg **875** d.	...	...	...	...	...	...	...	..	...	...	0726	...	0926	...	1126	...	1326	...	1526	...	1726	...	1926	...	...	...
Würzburg Hbf d.	0045	0045	...	...	0419	...	0515	0637	0637	0737	0837	0937	1037	1137	1237	1337	1437	1537	1637	1737	1837	1937	2037	2135	2236	2339
Karlstadt (Main) d.	0108	0108	...	...	0443	...	0538	0653	0653	0753	0853	0953	1053	1153	1253	1353	1453	1553	1653	1753	1853	1953	2053	2157	2258	0003
Gemünden (Main) d.	0118	0120	...	...	0453	...	0549	0704	0704	0804	0904	1004	1104	1204	1304	1404	1504	1604	1704	1804	1904	2004	2104	2208	2309	0013
Lohr Bahnhof d.	...	0128	...	...	0504	...	0559	0715	0715	0815	0915	1015	1115	1215	1315	1415	1515	1615	1715	1815	1915	2015	2115	2218	2319	0023
Aschaffenburg Hbf d.	...	0154	...	0428	0538	0538	0637j	0743	0743	0843	0943	1043	1143	1243	1343	1443	1543	1643	1743	1843	1943	2043	2143	2251	2352	0054
Hanau Hbf d.	...	...	...	0454	0600	0600	0702	0802	0803	0902	1003	1102	1203	1302	1403	1502	1603	1702	1803	1902	2003	2102	2209	2316	0017	...
Offenbach (Main) Hbf d.	...	...	...	|	0610	0610	0712	0812	|	0912	|	1112	|	1312	|	1512	|	1712	|	1912	|	2112	|	|	|	...
Frankfurt (Main) Süd a.	...	...	...	0516	0615	0615	0716	0816	0825	0916	1025	1116	1225	1316	1425	1516	1625	1716	1825	1916	2025	2116	2231	2339	0040	...
Frankfurt (Main) Hbf a.	...	...	...	0524	0624	0624	0724	0824	0832	0924	1032	1124	1232	1324	1432	1524	1632	1724	1832b	1924	2032e	2124	2240	2347	0048	...

b – 1843 on ⑦ to Aug. 4 (also June 10, 20).
d – Not June 20, Aug. 15, Nov. 1.
e – 2040 on ⑤⑦ (also June 10, 19, 20, Oct. 2, 3, 31).
j – Arrives 0628.
p – Until Oct. 13.
r – Not June 20, Nov. 1.
t – Not June 20.
v – Also June 20, Aug. 15, Nov. 1.
z – Also June 20.
⊕ – Change trains at Regensburg on Ⓐd.
△ – On ⑥⑦ Aug. 10 - Sept. 29 does not call at Offenbach and arrives Frankfurt Süd / Hbf 8 – 9 minutes later.

922 WÜRZBURG - HEILBRONN - STUTTGART *RE services*

km		Ⓒz	Ⓐe	Ⓐe	Ⓐe	Ⓐe			Ⓐe			Ⓐe		Ⓐe		Ⓐe		⑤†v	Ⓐe			Ⓐe				
0	**Würzburg** Hbf ... d.	...	...	...	...	...	0636r	...	...	...	0837r	0937r	1037r	...	1237r	...	1438r	1537r	...	1637r	1737r	...	1837r	1937r	2037r	2137r
43	Lauda ... d.	...	...	...	0525	...	0707	...	...	...	0910	1008	1110	...	1310	...	1510	1608	...	1710	1807	...	1910	2007	2110	2207
78	Osterburken ... d.	...	0502	0521	0553	0614	0733	...	0836	...	0933	1032	1133	1236	1333	1436	1533	1631	1636	1733	1830	1836	1933	2030	2133	2230
94	Möckmühl ... d.	...	0519	0538	...	0630	0745	...	0851	...	0945	1043	1145	1251	1345	1451	1545	1643	1651	1745	1841	1851	1945	2042	2145	2242
116	Bad Friedrichshall Hbf d.	...	0544	0601	...	0658	0801	...	0915	...	1001	1101	1201	1315	1401	1515	1601	1700	1715	1801	1858	1915	2001	2058	2202	2258
127	**Heilbronn** Hbf ... ★d.	0554	0559	0615	...	0712	0812	0926	0926	...	1012	1111	1212	1326	1412	1527	1612	1713	1726	1812	1909	1928	2012	2108	2211	2309
140	Lauffen (Neckar) ... ★d.	0604	0610	0626	...	|	|	0937	0937	...	|	|	|	1337	|	1537	|	|	1737	|	|	1938	|	2117	2219	2318
157	Bietigheim-Bissingen ★d.	0625	0628	0646	...	|	0831	0956	0956	...	1031	1130	1231	1356	1431	1556	1631	1739	1756	1831	1929	1956	2031	2134	2235	2335
180	**Stuttgart** Hbf ... ★a.	0643	0651	0711	...	0747	0853	1015	1015	...	1053	1146	1253	1415	1453	1616	1653	1758	1815	1853	1950	2015	2053	2158	2254	2356

	Ⓐe	Ⓒz	Ⓒz	Ⓐe		Ⓐe				Ⓐe		⑤†v			Ⓐe	Ⓒz	Ⓐe	Ⓒz	Ⓐe			E	A			D
Stuttgart Hbf ... ★d.	0450	0456	...	0558	0702	0743	0907	...	1107	1143	1307	1409	1504	1555	1628	1704	1704	1808	1809	1907	1943	1943	1943	2104	2316	2316
Bietigheim-Bissingen ★d.	0508	0515	...	0619	0723	0800	0925	...	1125	1200	1325	1426	1525	1624	|	1725	1725	1825	|	1925	2000	2000	2000	2121	2334	2334
Lauffen (Neckar) ... ★d.	0525	0531	...	|	0739	0817	|	...	|	1217	|	|	|	|	|	|	|	|	|	|	2017	2017	2017	2137	2351	2351
Heilbronn Hbf ... ★d.	0536	0541	0544	0641	0749	0829	0945	...	1145	1229	1345	1446	1545	1645	1710	1745	1745	1845	1844	1945	2027	2027	2027	2150	2400	0002
Bad Friedrichshall Hbf d.	0549	...	0554	0650	0800	0841	0955	...	1155	1241	1355	1456	1555	1655	1723	1755	1757	1855	1854	1955	2036	2037	2037	2201	...	0022
Möckmühl ... d.	0606	...	0611	0713	0817	0906	1012	...	1213	1306	1413	1513	1612	1713	1755	1812	1814	1913	1918	2012	...	2100	2100	2218	...	0050
Osterburken ... d.	0617	...	0622	0727	0828	0922	1027	...	1227	1322	1427	1527	1627	1727	1813	1827	1827	1927	1930	2027	...	2116	2127	2230	...	0108
Lauda ... d.	0643	...	0650	0750	0851	...	1050	...	1250	...	1450	1550	1650	1750	...	1850	1850	1953	1953	2050	...	...	2156	2254	...	...
Würzburg Hbf ... a.	0724t	...	0720t	0820t	0921t	...	1121t	...	1321t	...	1521t	1621t	1721t	1821t	...	1921t	1921t	2024t	2024t	2121t	...	...	...	2326t	...	...

OTHER TRAINS HEILBRONN - STUTTGART

	Ⓐe	Ⓒz	Ⓐe		Ⓐe				Ⓐe	Ⓒz	Ⓐe			Ⓐe			✣		Ⓐe			Ⓒz		
Heilbronn Hbf ... d.	0435	0446	0627	0650	0725	0758	0826	0856	0956	1026	1029	1057	1126	1156	1227	1257	and in the same	1726	1754	1826	1857	1926	2026	2126
Lauffen (Neckar) ... d.	0445	0456	0637	0701	0736	0806	0837	0904	1004	1037	1039	1105	1137	1204	1237	1305	pattern every	1737	1802	1837	1905	1937	2037	2137
Bietigheim-Bissingen ... d.	0504	0515	0657	0719	0756	0825	0856	0925	1025	1056	1056	1125	1156	1225	1256	1325	**two** hours until	1756	1818	1856	1925	1956	2056	2156
Stuttgart Hbf ... a.	0523	0535	0718	0741	0815	0843	0915	0943	1045	1115	1115	1146	1215	1243	1315	1343		1815	1839	1915	1945	2015	2115	2215

			Ⓒz	Ⓐe	Ⓐe				Ⓐe				✣	Ⓐe				Ⓐe				Ⓐe		
Stuttgart Hbf ... d.	0020	...	0543	0543	0636	0743	0815	0845	0915	0943	1015	1045	and in the same	1515	1543	1616	1645	1715	1743	1813	1843	1914	2013	2215
Bietigheim-Bissingen ... d.	0037	...	0603	0604	0655	0800	0833	0903	0935	1000	1033	1103	pattern every	1535	1600	1634	1703	1735	1800	1833	1900	1935	2034	2234
Lauffen (Neckar) ... d.	0054	...	0620	0622	0712	0817	0850	0920	0953	1017	1050	1120	**two** hours until	1553	1617	1651	1720	1752	1817	1850	1917	1953	2051	2251
Heilbronn Hbf ... a.	0104	...	0629	0632	0722	0827	0901	0929	1001	1027	1101	1129		1601	1627	1701	1729	1801	1826	1901	1926	2001	2101	2301

A – ①–④ (not June 10, 19, 20, Oct. 2, 3, 31).
D – ⑤–⑦ (also June 10, 19, 20, Oct. 2, 3, 31).
E – ①–⑥ (also June 9; not June 10, 20, Oct. 3).

e – Not June 20, Nov. 1.
r – 31–33 minutes **earlier** until Aug. 18 (by 🚌 to Lauda).
t – 36–40 minutes later until Aug. 18 (by 🚌 from Lauda).
v – Also June 20.

z – Also June 20, Nov. 1.

✣ – Timings may vary by up to 3 minutes.
★ – See also panel below main table.

923 MANNHEIM - EBERBACH - OSTERBURKEN *S-Bahn*

On June 20, Nov. 1 services run as on ⑦. **Warning!** Services Mosbach-Neckarelz - Mosbach - Osterburken and v.v. are subject to alteration July 27 - Sept. 10.

km			Ⓒ	Ⓐ		Ⓐ	Ⓒ	Ⓐ		Ⓐ														
0	**Mannheim** Hbf ... **924** ▷ d.	0008	0210	0421	0535	0601	0630	0634	0738	0807	0838	0907	and at	1838	1907	1938	2007	2038	2107	2142	...	2137e	2207	2304
17	**Heidelberg** Hbf ... **924** ▷ d.	0026	0233	0442	0555	0625	0655	0655	0755	0825	0855	0925		1855	1925	1955	2025	2055	2127	2158	...	2201	2235	2325
28	Neckargemünd ... d.	0040	0247	0456	0609	0640	0709	0709	0809	0839	0909	0939	the same	1909	1939	2009	2039	2109	2141	|	...	2216	2249	2340
34	Neckarsteinach ... d.	0046	0254	0502	0616	0646	0715	0715	0815	0845	0915	0945		1915	1945	2015	2045	2115	2147	|	...	2222	2255	2346
41	Hirschhorn (Neckar) ... d.	0053	0301	0509	0622	0653	0722	0722	0822	0852	0922	0952	minutes	1922	1952	2022	2052	2122	2154	|	...	2229	2302	2353
50	Eberbach ... **924** d.	0100	0307	0516	0629	0713c	0729	0729	0829	0859	0929	0959	past each	1929	1959	2029	2059	2129	2201	2221	...	2235	2309	0000
69	Mosbach-Neckarelz ... **924** d.	0119	0326	0535	0648	0735	0748	0748	0848	0918	0948	1018	hour until	1948	2018	2048	2118	2148	2219	2234	2244	2254	2329	0020
72	Mosbach (Baden) ... d.	0124	0330	0540	0652	0740	0752	0752	0852	0923	0952	1023		1952	2023	2052	2123	2152	...	...	2249	...	2333	0025
101	**Osterburken** ... a.	...	...	0610	0723	...	0823	0823	0923	...	1023	...		2023	...	2123	...	2223	...	...	2320	...	...	0055

	Ⓐ	Ⓒ	Ⓐ	Ⓐ	Ⓒ	Ⓐ	Ⓐ	Ⓐ	Ⓒ			Ⓐ				✣							
Osterburken ... d.	...	...	...	0510	0529	0536	0557	...	0636	...	*0640*e	0702	0733	...	0836	and at	...	1836	...	1938	2036	2138	2238
Mosbach (Baden) ... d.	0432	0456	0504	0539	0558	0605	0627	...	0705	0705	*0718*e	0731	0802	0835	0905		1835	1905	1935	2007	2105	2207	2307
Mosbach-Neckarelz ... **924** d.	0437	0501	0521	0548	0603	0610	0633	0638	0710	0710	0729	0740	0810	0840	0910	the same	1840	1910	1940	2013	2110	2212	2312
Eberbach ... **924** d.	0456	0520	0541	0607	0622	0629	0647	0656	0729	0729	0743	0759	0829	0859	0929		1859	1929	1959	2032	2129	2231	2331
Hirschhorn (Neckar) ... d.	0503	0527	0548	0614	0629	0636	|	0703	0736	0736	|	0806	0836	0906	0936	minutes	1906	1936	2006	2039	2136	2238	2338
Neckarsteinach ... d.	0509	0534	0555	0620	0635	0642	|	0711	0742	0742	|	0812	0842	0912	0942	past each	1912	1942	2012	2045	2142	2244	2344
Neckargemünd ... d.	0516	0540	0601	0627	0642	0649	0703	0717	0749	0749	|	0819	0849	0919	0949		1919	1949	2019	2051	2149	2251	2351
Heidelberg Hbf ... **924** ▷ a.	0530	0553	0614	0641	0655	0702	0716	0732	0802	0802	0809	0832	0902	0932	1002	hour until	1932	2002	2032	2105	2203	2305	0005
Mannheim Hbf ... **924** ▷ a.	0552	0611	0635	0701	0712	0719	*0746*	0753	0819	0819	0824	0851	0920	0951	1019		1951	2020	2051	2130	2230	2330	0030

c – Arrives 0700. **e** – Ⓐ only. ✣ – On † Mosbach d. 1233 (not 1235) and then runs 2–4 minutes later from Mosbach-Neckarez. ▷ – See also Tables **913**, **918**, **919**.

924 MANNHEIM - HEIDELBERG - HEILBRONN *RE / RB services*

Additional S-Bahn trains run Heidelberg - Sinsheim - Heilbronn and Mosbach-Neckarelz - Heilbronn. See Table **923** for other S-Bahn services Mannheim - Mosbach-Neckarelz.
On June 20, Nov. 1 services run as on ⑦.

km		Ⓐ2	Ⓐ	Ⓒ2	Ⓒ2	Ⓐ	Ⓒ	Ⓐ	Ⓒ	Ⓒ2	Ⓐ	Ⓐ	2		Ⓐ	Ⓒ		Ⓐ	Ⓒ		Ⓐ	Ⓒ		Ⓐ	Ⓒ
0	**Mannheim** Hbf ... ▷ d.	...	...	...	...	...	*0535*	0631	...	...	...	0735	...	0835	0935	0935	1035	1135	1135	1235	1335	1335	1435	1535	1535
17	**Heidelberg** Hbf ... ▷ d.	...	...	...	...	...	0631	0645	...	...	...	0749	...	0849	0949	0949	1049	1149	1149	1249	1349	1349	1449	1549	1549
50	Eberbach ... d.	...	...	...	...	...	|	|	...	...	...	0814	...	|	1014	1018	|	1214	1218	|	1414	1418	|	1614	1618
69	Mosbach-Neckarelz ... d.	...	0613	...	0650	0652	|	|	...	0750	0752	0829	0850	|	1029	1032	|	1229	1232	|	1429	1432	|	1629	1632
	Sinsheim (Elsenz) Hbf ... d.	0540	|	0611	|	|	0708	0710	0711	|	|	|	|	0913	|	|	1113	|	|	1313	|	|	1513	|	|
	Bad Rappenau ... d.	0603	|	0630	|	|	...	0727	0727	|	|	|	|	0927	|	|	1127	|	|	1327	|	|	1527	|	|
	Bad Wimpfen ... d.	0612	|	0638	|	|	...	0732	0732	|	|	|	|	0932	|	|	1132	|	|	1332	|	|	1532	|	|
87	Bad Friedrichshall Hbf .. **922** d.	0618	0634	0648	0708	0712	...	0741	0743	0808	0812	0842	0908	0938	1042	1045	1138	1242	1245	1338	1442	1445	1538	1642	1645
98	**Heilbronn** Hbf ... **922** a.	0647	0648	0717	0737	0724	...	0751	0755	*0824*n	0824	0851	*0925*r	0951	1051	1054	1151	1251	1254	1351	1451	1454	1551	1651	1654
	Stuttgart Hbf **922** ... a.	...	0741	...	...	0815	...	...	...	*0915*n	0915	...	*1015*r	...	...	1146	...	...	1343v	...	...	...	...	...	1743

		Ⓐ	Ⓒ		Ⓐ	Ⓒ					2
Mannheim Hbf ... ▷ d.	1635	1735	1735	1835	1935	1935	2044	2142	*2207*	...	*2313*
Heidelberg Hbf ... ▷ d.	1649	1749	1749	1849	1949	1949	2059	2158	2231	...	*2331*
Eberbach ... d.	|	1814	1818	|	2014	2018	|	2221	|	...	|
Mosbach-Neckarelz ... d.	|	1829	1832	|	2029	2032	|	2235	|	...	|
Sinsheim (Elsenz) Hbf ... d.	1713	|	|	1913	|	|	2126	|	2308	2312	0012
Bad Rappenau ... d.	1727	|	|	1927	|	|	2140	|	...	2336	0031
Bad Wimpfen ... d.	1732	|	|	1932	|	|	2145	|	...	2342	0039
Bad Friedrichshall Hbf ... **922** d.	1738	1842	1845	1938	2042	2045	2149	2248	...	2346	0044
Heilbronn Hbf ... **922** a.	1751	1851	1854	1951	2052	2054	2201	2259	...	2400	0058
Stuttgart Hbf **922** ... a.	...	...	...	...	...	...	...	...	...	...	...

km		Ⓐ	Ⓐ	Ⓒ	Ⓐ	Ⓒ	Ⓒ2	Ⓐ2	
	Stuttgart Hbf **922** ... d.	...	...	...	0543	*0543*k	...	...	...
	Heilbronn Hbf ... **922** d.	0452	0542	...	0634	*0630*k	0636	0638	...
0	Bad Friedrichshall Hbf ... **922** d.	0502	0553	...	0645	0648	0712	0710	...
3	Bad Wimpfen ... d.	|	0556	...	|	|	0718	0718	...
9	Bad Rappenau ... d.	|	0604	...	|	|	0727	0726	...
26	Sinsheim (Elsenz) Hbf ... d.	|	0620	0649	|	|	0745	0745	0749
	Mosbach-Neckarelz ... d.	0515	|	|	0703	0707	...	...	|
	Eberbach ... d.	0529	|	|	...	...	...	...	|
58	**Heidelberg** Hbf ... ▷ a.	0553	0648	0725	...	...	...	...	0828
75	**Mannheim** Hbf ... ▷ a.	0606	0706	*0753*	...	...	...	...	*0851*

			Ⓒ	Ⓐ		Ⓒ	Ⓐ		Ⓒ	Ⓐ		Ⓒ	Ⓐ		Ⓒ	Ⓐ							2	2	2
Stuttgart Hbf **922** ... d.	...	...	0815	...	...	...	...	...	1215	...	...	1415v	...	...	...	...	...	1813j	...	...	...	...	...	...	...
Heilbronn Hbf ... **922** d.	0700	0806	0904	0906	1006	1104	1106	1206	1304	1306	1406	1504	1505	1605	1704	1705	1805	1906	2006	2105	2206	...	2218	2318	2348
Bad Friedrichshall Hbf ... **922** d.	0710	0818	0914	0916	1018	1114	1116	1218	1314	1316	1418	1514	1516	1618	1714	1716	1818	1916	2018	2116	2218	...	2248	2348	0019
Bad Wimpfen ... d.	|	0822	|	|	1022	|	|	1222	|	|	1422	|	|	1622	|	|	1822	|	2022	|	2222	...	|	|	0023
Bad Rappenau ... d.	|	0830	|	|	1030	|	|	1230	|	|	1430	|	|	1630	|	|	1830	|	2030	|	2230	...	|	|	0032
Sinsheim (Elsenz) Hbf ... d.	|	0844	|	|	1044	|	|	1244	|	|	1444	|	|	1644	|	|	1844	|	2044	|	2245	2249	|	|	0049
Mosbach-Neckarelz ... d.	0729	|	0929	0929	|	1129	1129	|	1329	1329	|	1529	1529	|	1729	1729	|	1929	|	2129	...	|	2307	0007	...
Eberbach ... d.	0743	|	0943	0943	|	1143	1143	|	1343	1343	|	1543	1543	|	1743	1743	|	1943	|	2143	...	|	...	...	...
Heidelberg Hbf ... ▷ a.	0809	0909	1009	1009	1109	1209	1209	1309	1409	1409	1509	1609	1609	1709	1809	1809	1909	2009	2109	2208	...	2326	...	...	...
Mannheim Hbf ... ▷ a.	0824	0924	1024	1024	1124	1224	1224	1324	1424	1424	1524	1624	1624	1724	1824	1824	1924	2024	2124	2224	...	*2400*	...	...	...

j – ⑥ only.
k – Change trains at Neckarsulm (a. *0635*, d. 0639).
n – Change trains at Neckarsulm (a. 0816, d. *0820*).
r – Change trains at Neckarsulm (a. 0916, d. *0920*).
v – † only.
▷ – See also Tables **913**, **918**, **919** and **923**.

RE services except where shown — STUTTGART - BACKNANG / AALEN - NÜRNBERG — 925

km						*IC* 2061				*IC* 2063				*IC* 2065			*IC* 2067			*IC* 2069			*IC* 2161				*IC* 2163
		Ⓐt	Ⓒz		Ⓐt	Ⓐt		Ⓐt	Ⓒz														¶			⚒r	
							◇			A	◇			◇			◇			◇			A	◇			
	Karlsruhe Hbf **931** .. d.	...	...	...	...	...	...	...	...	0706**e**	...	...	0906	...	...	1106	...	...	1306	...	...	1506	...	...	...	1706
0	**Stuttgart** Hbf .... ‡ d.	0425	0446	...	0539	0606	0620	0643	0652	0807	0820	0856	1007	1020	1056	1207	1220	1257	1407	1420	1456	1607	1620	1656	1726	1807
31	Backnang .... d.	0451	0511	...	0604	│	│	0721**k**	0722	│	│	0921	│	│	1124	│	│	1324	│	│	1524	│	│	1724	1754	│
73	Schwäbisch H-H ⊡ a.	0536	0546	...	0649	│	│	0758	0758	│	│	0959	│	│	1159	│	│	1359	│	│	1559	│	│	1759	1837	│
73	Schwäbisch H-H ⊡ d.	0537	0547	...	0655	│	│	0759	0800	│	│	1000	│	│	1200	│	│	1400	│	│	1600	│	│	1800	1839	│
	Schwäbisch Gmünd ‡ d.	│	│	...	│	0642	0702	│	│	0842	0902	│	1040	1102	│	1239	1302	│	1439	1502	│	1640	1702	│	│	1840
	Aalen Hbf .... ‡ a.	│	│	...	│	0657	0721	│	│	0857	0920	│	1056	1120	│	1255	1320	│	1455	1520	│	1656	1720	│	│	1855
	Aalen Hbf .... d.	│	│	...	│	0659	0729	│	│	0859	0929	│	1057	1129	│	1257	1329	│	1457	1529	│	1657	1729	│	│	1857
	Ellwangen .... d.	│	│	...	│	0710	0748	│	│	0910	0948	│	1108	1148	│	1308	1348	│	1508	1548	│	1708	1748	│	│	1908
100	Crailsheim .... d.	0555	0606	0606	0714	0726	0813	0818	0818	0926	1013	1018	1125	1213	1218	1325	1413	1418	1525	1613	1618	1725	1813	1818	1856	1925
146	Ansbach .... d.	...	0641	0641	0745	0750	...	0850	0850	0950	...	1050	1150	...	1250	1350	...	1450	1550	...	1650	1750	...	1850	...	1950
190	**Nürnberg** Hbf .... a.	...	0717	0717	...	0818	...	0920	0920	1018	...	1120	1218	...	1320	1418	...	1520	1618	...	1720	1818	...	1920	...	2018

					IC 2165						
				Ⓒz	Ⓑq						
	◇					◇			◇	◇	
Karlsruhe Hbf **931** .. d.	...	...	...	...	1906	...	...	...	...	...	...
Stuttgart Hbf .... ‡ d.	1820	1856	1953	...	2007	2020	2058	2156	2220	2320	2328
Backnang .... d.	│	1925**f**	2026	...	│	│	2126	2224	│	│	2355
Schwäbisch H-H ⊡. a.	│	1958**f**	2056	...	│	│	2204	2259	│	│	0031
Schwäbisch H-H ⊡. d.	│	1959**f**	2100**t**	2059	│	│	2205	*2304*	│	│	0032
Schwäbisch Gmünd .‡ d.	1902	│	│	│	2040	2102	│	│	2302	0002	│
Aalen Hbf .... ‡ a.	1920	│	│	│	2055	2121	│	│	2321	0021	│
Aalen Hbf .... d.	1929	│	│	│	2057	2132	│	│	2332	...	│
Ellwangen .... d.	1948	│	│	│	2108	2150	│	│	2350	...	│
Crailsheim .... d.	2013	2018	2118**t**	2121	2125	2213	2224	*2325*	0008	...	0049
Ansbach .... d.	...	2050	...	...	2150	...	...	...	...	...	...
Nürnberg Hbf .... a.	...	2120	...	...	2218	...	...	...	...	...	...

km								*IC* 2164			
		Ⓐt	Ⓒz	Ⓐt	Ⓐt	Ⓐt	Ⓒz	Ⓐt	Ⓐt		
					◇					◇	
0	**Nürnberg** Hbf .... d.	...	...	...	...	...	...	0537	...	...	0636
44	Ansbach .... d.	...	...	...	...	...	...	0603	...	...	0707
90	Crailsheim .... d.	0434	0506	0540	0512	0605	0628	0631	0638	0648	0742
111	Ellwangen .... d.	│	│	│	0530	│	│	0647	│	0711	│
127	**Aalen** Hbf .... a.	│	│	│	0549	│	│	0657	│	0729	│
127	**Aalen** Hbf .... ‡ d.	│	│	│	0605	│	│	0659	│	0735	│
152	Schwäbisch Gmünd ‡ d.	│	│	│	0624	│	│	0717	│	0754	│
	Schwäbisch H-H ⊡ a.	0452	0522	0559	│	0622	0645	│	0655	│	0759**j**
	Schwäbisch H-H ⊡ d.	0518	0523	0600	│	0623	0653	│	0659	│	0801**j**
	Backnang .... d.	0605	0605	0636	│	0706	0736	│	0736	│	0838**j**
203	**Stuttgart** Hbf .... ‡ a.	0633	0633	0702	0713	0733	0802	0753	0802	0843	0904**j**
	Karlsruhe Hbf **931** .. a.	...	...	...	...	...	...	0853	...	...	...

		IC 2162				*IC* 2160			*IC* 2068			*IC* 2066				*IC* 2064			*IC* 2062			*IC* 2060				
			Ⓐt	Ⓒz									⚒r	†z								Ⓑq				
	◇				◇			◇	A		◇				◇			◇			◇	A	◇		◇	◇
Nürnberg Hbf .... d.	...	0740	0830	0836	...	0940	1036	...	1140	1236	...	1340	1436	1436	...	1540	1636	...	1740	1836	...	1940	...	2036	...	...
Ansbach .... d.	...	0807	0907	0907	...	1007	1107	...	1207	1310**j**	...	1407	1507	1507	...	1607	1707	...	1807	1907	...	2007	...	2107	...	...
Crailsheim .... d.	0752	0835	0942	0942	0952	1035	1142	1152	1235	1342	1352	1435	1542	1542	1552	1635	1742	1752	1835	1942	1952	2035	...	2142	2152	...
Ellwangen .... d.	0811	0851	│	│	1011	1051	│	1211	1251	│	1411	1451	│	│	1611	1651	│	1811	1851	│	2011	2051	2111	│	2211	2311
Aalen Hbf .... a.	0831	0901	│	│	1031	1101	│	1231	1301	│	1431	1501	│	│	1631	1701	│	1831	1901	│	2031	2101	2131	│	2231	2331
Aalen Hbf .... ‡ d.	0837	0903	│	│	1037	1103	│	1237	1303	│	1437	1503	│	│	1637	1703	│	1837	1903	│	2037	2103	2137	│	2237	2337
Schwäbisch Gmünd .‡ d.	0855	0919	│	│	1055	1119	│	1255	1319	│	1455	1519	│	│	1655	1719	│	1855	1919	│	2055	2119	2155	│	2255	2355
Schwäbisch H-H ⊡. a.	│	│	0959	0959**j**	│	│	1159**j**	│	│	1359**j**	│	│	1559	1558	│	│	1759**j**	│	│	1958	│	│	│	2159	│	│
Schwäbisch H-H ⊡. d.	│	│	1001	1001**j**	│	│	1201**j**	│	│	1400**j**	│	│	1601	1559	│	│	1801**j**	│	│	1959	│	│	│	2207	│	│
Backnang .... d.	│	│	1036	1036	│	│	1236	│	│	1437**j**	│	│	1636	1635	│	│	1836	│	│	2036	│	│	│	2253	│	│
Stuttgart Hbf .... ‡ a.	0940	0953	1103	1103	1140	1153	1301	1340	1353	1507	1540	1553	1701	1702	1740	1753	1902	1940	1953	2102	2140	2153	2240	2319	2340	0040
Karlsruhe Hbf **931** .. a.	...	1053	...	...	...	1253	...	...	1453	...	...	1653	...	...	...	1853	...	...	2053	...	...	2259	...	...	...	...

A – To / from Leipzig on dates in Table **849a**.

e – ①–⑥ (not June 10).
f – On † (also June 20, Nov. 1) Backnang d. 1924, Schwäbisch Hall-Hessental a. 1959, d. 2000.
j – 1–3 minutes **earlier** on † (also June 20, Nov. 1).
k – Arrives 0709.
q – Ⓑ (not June 9).

r – Not June 20, Nov. 1.
t – Ⓐ (not June 20, Nov. 1).
z – Also June 20, Nov. 1.

⊡ – Schwäbisch Hall-Hessental.
◇ – Operated by Go-Ahead Verkehrsgesellschaft.

¶ – Train number **2361** on ⑤ (also June 19, Oct. 2, 31; not June 21, Oct. 4, Nov. 1).
‡ – Other regional services (◇) Stuttgart - Schwäbisch Gmünd - Aalen and v.v.
From Stuttgart Hbf at 0020, 0450 Ⓐ**t**, 0550 Ⓐ**t**, 0708 Ⓐ**t**, 0720, 0750 Ⓐ**t**, 0908, 0920, 0950 ⚒**r**, 1108, 1120, 1150 ⚒**r**, 1308, 1320, 1350 ⚒**r**, 1508, 1520, 1550 ⚒**r**, 1708, 1720, 1750 ⚒**r**, 1908, 1919, 1950 Ⓐ**t**, 2108, 2120 and 2238.
From Aalen at 0435 Ⓐ**t**, 0505 Ⓐ**t**, 0535, 0635, 0705 Ⓐ**t**, 0802, 0837, 0908 ⚒**r**, 0937, 1002, 1107 ⚒**r**, 1137, 1202, 1307 ⚒**r**, 1337, 1402, 1507 ⚒**r**, 1537, 1602, 1707 ⚒**r**, 1737, 1802, 1907 Ⓐ**t**, 1937, 2002 and 2202.

RE / *RB* services — HEILBRONN / ASCHAFFENBURG - CRAILSHEIM and AALEN - DONAUWÖRTH / ULM — 926

ASCHAFFENBURG - LAUDA - CRAILSHEIM ⊠

km		Ⓐe	Ⓒz	⊕							
0	**Aschaffenburg** Hbf .. d.	...	...	0639**f**	0923	1123	1323	1523	1723	1923**g**	...
38	Miltenberg .... d.	...	...	0750	0959	1159	1359	1559	1759	1959	...
69	Wertheim .... d.	...	*0626*	0828**j**	1035	1235	1435	1635	1835	2035	*2039**
93	Tauberbischofsheim .. d.	0545	*0653*	0900	1100	1300	1500	1700	1900	...	2129
100	**Lauda** .... a.	0555	*0702*	0906	1106	1306	1506	1706	1906	...	2134
100	**Lauda** .... d.	0608	0713	0913	1113	1313	1513	1713	1913	...	2135
110	Bad Mergentheim ...... d.	0620	0725	0925	1125	1325	1525	1725	1925	...	2146
169	**Crailsheim** .... a.	0726	0830	1028	1228	1429	1628	1828	2028	...	...

	Ⓐe	Ⓒz	Ⓐe							
Crailsheim .... d.	...	...	*0520*	0731	0931	1131	1328**s**	1531	1731	1931
Bad Mergentheim ... d.	...	0557	*0636*	0833**f**	1033	1233	1433	1633	1833	2033
Lauda .... a.	...	0608	*0647*	0843**f**	1043	1243	1443	1643	1843	2043
Lauda .... d.	...	0614	0702	0853	1053	1253	1453	1653	1853	2053
Tauberbischofsheim. d.	...	0624	0712	0859	1059	1259	1459	1659	1859	2059
Wertheim .... d.	0600	0700	0800**p**	0921	1121	1321	1521	1721	1921	...
Miltenberg .... d.	0636	0740	0837	0959	1159	1359	1559	1759	1959	...
Aschaffenburg Hbf. a.	0712	0829	0921	1037	1237	1437	1637	1838	2034**v**	...

(last column continued) Crailsheim d. ...; Bad Mergentheim d. ...; Lauda a. ...; Lauda d. ...; Tauberbischofsheim d. *2103**; Wertheim d. 2152; Miltenberg d. 2227; Aschaffenburg Hbf a. 2315.

HEILBRONN - CRAILSHEIM ⊠

km		Ⓐe		Ⓒz	Ⓐe		Ⓒz	Ⓐe	Ⓒz	Ⓐe
0	**Heilbronn** Hbf .... d.	*0546*	0803	1003	1005	and every	1803	1805	2003	2005
27	Öhringen .... d.	0618	0825	1025	1027	two hours	1825	1827	2025	2027
54	Schwäbisch Hall .... d.	0642	0851	1051	1051		1851	1851	2051	2051
61	Schwäbisch Hall-H ⊡ a.	0649	0858	1058	1058	until	1858	1858	2058	2058
88	**Crailsheim** .... a.	*0713*	0921	1121	1121		1921	1921	2121	*2118*

	Ⓒz	Ⓐe	Ⓐe	Ⓒz		Ⓐe	Ⓒz	Ⓒz	Ⓐe
Crailsheim .... d.	0634	*0638*	0838	0838	and every	1838	1838	2038	2038
Schwäbisch Hall-H ⊡ .... d.	0658	0658	0900	0900	two hours	1900	1900	2103	2106
Schwäbisch Hall .... d.	0704	0705	0906	0906		1906	1906	2110	2112
Öhringen .... a.	0729	0729	0929	0930	until	1929	1930	2136	2136
Heilbronn Hbf .... a.	0752	0752	0951	0952		1951	1952	*2221*	*2221*

AALEN - DONAUWÖRTH

km		Ⓐe	Ⓐe	Ⓒz	Ⓐe	Ⓐe	Ⓒz	Ⓐe	Ⓐe	Ⓐe	Ⓒz	Ⓐe	Ⓒz	Ⓐe	Ⓐe		Ⓐe	Ⓒz	Ⓐe	Ⓐe	Ⓒz	Ⓐe	Ⓐe	Ⓐe	Ⓒz		
0	**Aalen** Hbf .... d.	...	...	0531	0603	0625	0735	0735	0833	0933	0933	1033	1135	1135	1233	1333	1433	1535	1535	1635	1735	1735	1833	1933	1933	2035	2237
39	Nördlingen ...... a.	...	...	0613	0638	0706	0813	0813	0913	1013	1013	1112	1213	1219	1313	1413	1513	1613	1613	1713	1813	1813	1913	2013	2013	2113	2314
39	Nördlingen ...... d.	0518	0558	0622	0639	0707	0821	0821	0914	1015	1021	1113	1216	1222	1315	1414**k**	1515	1621	1621	1721	1821	1821	1915	2015	2021	2114	...
68	**Donauwörth** ... a.	0546	0631	0650	0706	0734	0848	0853	0945	1046	1048	1140	1244	1249	1347	1445	1547	1648	1653	1753	1848	1853	1946	2047	2048	2145	...

		Ⓐe		Ⓐe	Ⓒz	Ⓐe	Ⓐe		Ⓐe	Ⓒz	Ⓐe	Ⓐe		Ⓐe		Ⓐe	Ⓐe		Ⓐe	Ⓐe	Ⓐe		Ⓐe			Ⓐe	Ⓒz
Donauwörth ..... d.	...	...	...	0606	0706	0707	0811	0904	1005	1111	1111	1206	1305	1404	1505	1611	1625	1711	1737	1811	1837	1905	2005	2104	...	2205	2237
Nördlingen .... a.	...	...	...	0636	0734	0739	0839	0932	1033	1139	1143	1238	1333	1432	1533	1639	1657	1739	1809	1839	1909	1933	2033	2132	...	2233	2303
Nördlingen .... d.	0442	0531	0641	0641	0742	0742	0842	0942	1042	1144	1144	1242	1342	1442	1542	1644	...	1742	...	1842	...	1942	...	2134	...	...	...
Aalen Hbf .... a.	0524	0613	0721	0721	0824	0824	0924	1024	1124	1226	1226	1324	1424	1524	1624	1726	...	1824	...	1924	...	2024	...	2215	...	...	...

AALEN - ULM ◇

km		Ⓐe	2	Ⓐe	2	2		2	2		2	2		2	2		2	2		2	2		2	2		2	2
0	**Aalen** Hbf .... d.	0553	0623**b**	0703	0734	0834	0907	0934	1034	1107	1134	1234	1307	1334	1434	1507	1534	1634	1707	1732	1834	1907	1934	2034	2107	2134	2234
23	Heidenheim ..... d.	0612	0646**b**	0726	0800	0900	0924	1000	1100	1124	1200	1300	1324	1400	1500	1524	1600	1700	1724	1800	1900	1924	2000	2100	2124	2156	2302
73	**Ulm** Hbf .... a.	0658	0742	0758	0847	0947	0956	1047	1147	1156	1247	1347	1356	1447	1547	1556	1647	1747	1756	1847	1947	1956	2047	2144	2156	2248	2352

	Ⓐe	Ⓐe	2	Ⓐe 2	Ⓒz 2		2	2		2	2		2	2		2	2		2	2		2	2		2	2	2
Ulm Hbf .... d.	0427	0539	0556**c**	0645	0705	0804	0811	0911	1002	1011	1111	1202	1211	1311	1402	1411	1511	1602	1611	1711	1802	1811	1911	2002	2011	2117	2213
Heidenheim .... d.	0516	0626	0658	0800	0800	0835	0900	1000	1034	1100	1200	1234	1300	1400	1434	1500	1600	1634	1700	1800	1834	1900	2000	2034	2100	2206	2302
Aalen Hbf .... a.	0545	0649	0724	0824	0824	0853	0924	1024	1051	1124	1224	1251	1324	1424	1451	1524	1626	1651	1724	1824	1851	1924	2024	2051	2124	2227	2324

b – On Ⓒ (also June 20, Nov. 1) Aalen d. 0632, Heidenheim d. 0656.
c – 0606 on Ⓒ (also June 20, Nov. 1).
e – Not June 20, Nov. 1.
f – 2–3 minutes later on Ⓐ (not June 20, Nov. 1).
g – 1928 on Ⓒ (also June 20, Nov. 1).
j – 0835 on Ⓐ (not June 20, Nov. 1).

k – 1418 on Ⓒ (also June 20, Nov. 1).
p – Change trains (arrives 0738).
s – 1331 on Ⓒ (also June 20, Nov. 1); 1334 June 11–14, 17–19, 21, ①–⑤ July 29 - Sept. 6, Oct. 28–31.
v – *2121* on Ⓐ (not June 20, Nov. 1).
z – Ⓒ (also June 20, Nov. 1).

* – By 🚌.
⊕ – Change trains at Miltenberg on Ⓐ**e**.
⊠ – 2nd class only.
⊡ – Schwäbisch Hall-Hessental.
◇ – Operated by Hohenzollerische Landesbahn (trains shown as 2nd class only) or DB.

928 MÜNCHEN - BAYRISCHZELL, LENGGRIES and TEGERNSEE

Bayerische Oberlandbahn

Most trains run combined from München (please make sure you join the correct portion for your journey). On June 20, Aug. 15, Nov. 1 services run as on ⑦.
Warning! Timings may vary by a few minutes on © until Aug. 25.

km																											
			©	Ⓐ	Ⓐ	©		©							Ⓐ				Ⓐ								♥
0	**München** Hbf	d.	0004	0604	0629	0703	0704	0804	0827	0904	0924	1004	1104	...	1204	1229	1304	1404	1504	1527	1604	1704	1804	1904	2004	2104	2204	2304
37	Holzkirchen	d.	0032	0632	0701	0732	0732	0832	0855	0932	0956	1032	1132	...	1232	1302	1332	1432	1532	1555	1632	1732	1832	1932	2032	2132	2232	2332
61	Schliersee	d.	0101	0701	0727	0801	0801	0901	0923	1001	1023	1101	1201	...	1301	1331	1401	1501	1601	1623	1701	1801	1901	2001	2101	2201	2301	0001
78	**Bayrischzell**	a.	0125	0725	...	0825	0825	0925	...	1025	...	1125	1225	...	1325	1355	1425	1525	1625	...	1725	1825	1925	2025	2125	2225	2325	0025

km																											
					Ⓐ	Ⓐ	©		©					Ⓐ		Ⓐ				Ⓐ							
0	**München** Hbf	d.	0004	0604	0629	0703	0704	0804	0827	0904	0924	1004	1104	1140	1204	1229	1304	1404	1504	1527	1604	1704	1804	1904	2004	2104	2204	2304
37	Holzkirchen	d.	0035	0635	0705	0735	0735	0835	0858	0935	0958	1035	1135	1206	1235	1305	1335	1435	1535	1558	1635	1735	1835	1935	2035	2135	2235	2335
47	Schaftlach	d.	0048	0648	0717	0748	0748	0848	0915	0948	1015	1048	1148	1219	1248	1318	1348	1448	1548	1615	1648	1748	1848	1948	2048	2148	2248	2348
57	Bad Tölz	d.	0100	0700	0730	0800	0800	0900	0927	1000	1027	1100	1200	1232	1300	1330	1400	1500	1600	1627	1700	1800	1900	2000	2100	2200	2300	0000
67	**Lenggries**	a.	0111	0711	0741	0811	0811	0911	0938	1011	1038	1111	1211	1243	1311	1341	1411	1511	1611	1638	1711	1811	1911	2011	2111	2211	2311	0011

km																											
					Ⓐ	Ⓐ	©		©					Ⓐ		Ⓐ				Ⓐ							
0	**München** Hbf	d.	0004	0604	0629	0703	0704	0804	0827	0904	0924	1004	1104	1140	1204	*1229*	1304	1404	1504	1527	1604	1704	1804	1904	2004	2104**b**	2204**r**	2304**r**
37	Holzkirchen	d.	0035	0635	0705	0735	0735	0835	0858	0935	0958	1035	1135	1206	1235	*1305*	1335	1435	1535	1558	1635	1735	1835	1935	2035	2135	2235	2335
47	Schaftlach	d.	0048	0648	0718	0748	0748	0848	0915	0948	1015	1048	1148	1218	1248	1317	1348	1448	1548	1615	1648	1748	1848	1948	2048	2148	2248	2348
59	**Tegernsee**	a.	0109	0709	0738	0809	0809	0909	0936	1009	1036	1109	1209	1239	1309	1338	1409	1509	1609	1636	1709	1809	1909	2009	2109	2209	2309	0009

		Ⓐ	⑥			Ⓐ	©	Ⓐ	Ⓐ	⑥						©	Ⓐ					©					
Bayrischzell	d.	...	...	0449	0532	0607	0632	0634	0705	...	0732	0832	0932	1032	1132	1232	1232	1332**z**	1432	1532	1632	...	1732	1832	1932	2032	2132	2232
Schliersee	d.	0444	0459	0516	0559	0635	0659	0702	0734	0734	0759	0859	0959	1059	1159	1259	1303	1359	1459	1559	1659	1734	1759	1859	1959	2059	2159	2259
Holzkirchen	d.	0510	0528	0544	0628	0705	0728	0732	0804	0804	0828	0928	1028	1128	1228	1328	1332	1428	1528	1628	1728	1804	1828	1928	2028	2128	2228	2328
München Hbf	a.	0535	0555	0612	0653	0736	0753	0758	0831	0833	0856**j**	0957**j**	1054	1154	1255	1354	1358	1454	1557**j**	1656**j**	1757**j**	1832	1854	1954	2054	2154	2254	2354

		Ⓐ	⑥	Ⓐ		Ⓐ	©	Ⓐ	Ⓐ	⑥						©	Ⓐ					©				⊖	
Lenggries	d.	0431	0447	0506	0547	0622	0647	0647	0718	0717	0747	0847	0947	1047	1147	1247	1247	1347	1447	1547	1647	1717	1747	1847	1947	2047	2147	2247
Bad Tölz	d.	0443	0500	0518	0600	0634	0700	0700	0731	0730	0800	0900	1000	1100	1200	1300	1305	1400	1500	1600	1700	1730	1800	1900	2000	2100	2200	2300
Schaftlach	d.	0454	0516	0531	0616	0647	0716	0716	0747	0747	0816	0916	1016	1116	1216	1316	1318	1416	1516	1616	1716	1747	1816	1916	2016	2116	2216	2316
Holzkirchen	d.	0510	0528	0544	0628	0701	0728	0732	0804	0804	0828	0928	1028	1128	1228	1328	1332	1428	1528	1628	1728	1804	1828	1928	2028	2128	2228	2328
München Hbf	a.	0535	0555	0612	0653	0731	0753	0758	0831	0833	0856**j**	0957**j**	1054	1154	1255	1354	1358	1454	1557**j**	1656**j**	1757**j**	1832	1854	1954	2054	2154	2254	2354

			⑥	Ⓐ		Ⓐ	©	Ⓐ	Ⓐ	⑥						©	Ⓐ					©					
Tegernsee	d.	...	0452	0505	0552	0621	0652	0652	0722	0722	0752	0852	0952	1052	1152	1252	1252	1352	1452	1552	1652	1722	1752	1852	1952	2052	2152	2252
Schaftlach	a.	...	0513	0525	0613	0641	0713	0713	0743	0743	0813	0913	1013	1113	1213	1313	1313	1413	1513	1613	1713	1743	1813	1913	2013	2113	2213	2313
Holzkirchen	a.	...	0526	0541	0626	0656	0726	0726	0756	0756	0826	0926	1026	1126	1227	1326	1327	1426	1526	1626	1726	1757	1826	1926	2026	2126	2226	2326
München Hbf	a.	...	0555	0612	0653	0731	0753	0758	0831	0833	0856**j**	0957**j**	1054	1154	1255	1354	1358	1454	1557**j**	1656**j**	1757**j**	1832	1854	1954	2054	2154**b**	...	2354**z**

b – Not ⑥.
j – 2–4 minutes earlier on ©.
r – ⚒ only.
z – © only.
♥ – Change trains at Schliersee on ①–④ (not June 10, 20, Aug. 15, Oct. 3).
⊖ – Change trains at Holzkirchen on ①②③④⑦ (also Nov. 1).

929 PLATTLING - BAYERISCH EISENSTEIN - PLZEŇ

Waldbahn ⊠; ČD; 2nd class only

km																										
				7511			**755**			**759**			**761**			**763**			**767**			**771**			**775**	
				◇§	Ⓐ	Ⓐ	◇	Ⓐ	Ⓐ	◇	Ⓐe	Ⓐe	◇			◇			◇			◇			◇	
0	**Plattling**	d.	0101	...	...	...	...	...	...	...	0520	0629	...	0659	0806	...	0906	1006	...	1106	1206	...	1306	1406	...	1506
9	Deggendorf Hbf	d.	0110	...	...	...	...	...	...	...	0531	0638	...	0709	0816	...	0916	1016	...	1116	1216	...	1316	1416	...	1516
33	Gotteszell	d.	0129	...	...	...	...	...	...	...	0554	0657	...	0733	0835	...	0935	1035	...	1135	1235	...	1335	1435	...	1535
48	Regen	d.	0143	...	...	...	...	...	...	...	0609	0712	...	0748	0848	...	0948	1048	...	1148	1248	...	1348	1448	...	1548
58	Zwiesel (Bay)	d.	0153	...	...	...	...	...	...	...	0623	0725	...	0800	0900	...	1000	1100	...	1200	1300	...	1400	1500	...	1600
72	**Bayerisch Eisenstein** ☆ 🏛	a.	...	...	...	...	...	...	...	...	0636	0738	...	0813	0913	...	1013	1113	...	1213	1313	...	1413	1513	...	1613
72	**Železná Ruda-Alžbětín** ☆ 🏛	d.	...	...	...	0407	...	...	...	*0607*	▬	...	0806	▬	...	*1006*	▬	...	1208	▬	▬	*1402*	▬	...	1608	▬
76	Železná Ruda Město	d.	...	...	...	0414	...	...	...	*0614*	...	...	0813	...	...	*1013*	...	...	1215	...	...	*1409*	...	...	1615	...
79	Špičák	d.	...	...	...	0419	...	...	...	*0619*	...	...	0818	...	...	*1018*	...	...	1220	...	...	*1414*	...	...	1620	...
131	**Klatovy**	a.	...	...	...	0511	...	...	...	*0710*	...	...	0909	...	...	*1109*	Ⓐ	...	1309	Ⓐ	...	*1510*	...	...	1709	...
131	**Klatovy**	d.	...	0400	0448	...	0517	0556	0647	0717	0846	...	0917	1048	...	1117	1246	...	1317	1344	1448	1517	1646	...	1717	1845
141	Švihov u Klatov	d.	...	0412	0457	...	0526	0608	0656	0726	0858	...	0926	1058	...	1126	1258	...	1326	1354	1458	1526	1658	...	1726	1856
170	**Plzeň** hl.n.	a.	...	0500	0543	...	0610	0657	0741	0810	0947	...	1010	1143	...	1210	1343	...	1410	1446	1543	1610	1743	...	1810	1943
	Praha hl.n. **1120**	a.	...	0650	...	...	0750	...	...	0949	...	...	1149	...	...	1349	...	...	1549	...	...	1749	...	...	1949	...

			779								
			◇								
Plattling	d.	1606	...	1706	1806	...	1906	2006	2106	2213	2308
Deggendorf Hbf	d.	1616	...	1716	1816	...	1916	2016	2116	2222	2319
Gotteszell	d.	1635	...	1735	1835	...	1935	2035	2135	2241	2338
Regen	d.	1648	...	1748	1848	...	1948	2048	2148	2254	2350
Zwiesel (Bay)	d.	1700	...	1800	1900	...	2000	2100	2158	2304	0001
Bayerisch Eisenstein ☆ 🏛	a.	1713	...	1813	1913	...	2013	2113	...	...	...
Železná Ruda-Alžbětín ☆ 🏛	d.	...	1808	...	...	2003	...	...	...	...	...
Železná Ruda Město	d.	...	1815	...	...	2009	...	...	...	...	...
Špičák	d.	...	1820	...	...	2014	...	...	...	...	...
Klatovy	a.	...	1909	...	...	2102	...	...	...	...	...
Klatovy	d.	...	1917	...	...	2104	...	...	...	...	...
Švihov u Klatov	d.	...	1926	...	...	2115	...	...	...	...	...
Plzeň hl.n.	a.	...	2010	...	...	2202	...	...	...	...	...
Praha hl.n. **1120**	a.	...	2146	...	...	...	...	...	...	...	...

		Ⓐe	Ⓐe	©z	Ⓐe	©z	Ⓐe		Ⓐ	©
Praha hl.n. **1120**	d.	...	...	...	...	...	...	...	...	...
Plzeň hl.n.	d.	...	...	...	...	...	...	...	0520	0537
Švihov u Klatov	d.	...	...	...	...	...	...	...	0608	0620
Klatovy	a.	...	...	...	...	...	...	...	0618	0629
Klatovy	d.	...	...	...	...	...	...	...	0646	0646
Špičák	d.	...	...	...	...	...	...	...	0740	0740
Železná Ruda Město	d.	...	...	...	...	...	...	...	0745	0745
Železná Ruda-Alžbětín ☆ 🏛	a.	...	...	...	...	...	...	...	0752	0752
Bayerisch Eisenstein ☆ 🏛	d.	...	...	...	...	...	0705	0744**e**	...	...
Zwiesel (Bay)	d.	0415	0529	0559	0621	0652	0722	0759	...	...
Regen	d.	0425	0539	0608	0630	0701	0732	0808	...	...
Gotteszell	d.	0439	0555	0622	0644	0714	0751	0822	...	...
Deggendorf Hbf	d.	0500	0614	0645	0709	0738	0815	0845	...	...
Plattling	a.	0509	0623	0654	0718	0747	0825	0854	...	...

				776			**772**			**770**			**768**				**764**			**760**			**756**			**752**
				◇	Ⓐ		◇	Ⓐ	w	◇		Ⓐ	◇		Ⓐ		◇		Ⓐ	◇	©	Ⓐ	◇			◇
Praha hl.n. **1120**	d.	...	...	0615	...	...	0815	...	...	1015	...	...	1215	...	...	...	1415	...	...	1615	...	...	1815	...	...	2115
Plzeň hl.n.	d.	...	...	0750	0812	...	0950	1012	...	1150	1212	1310	1350	1412	1510	...	1550	1612	1710	1750	1812	1910	1950	...	2113	2247
Švihov u Klatov	d.	...	...	0832	0858	...	1032	1058	...	1232	1258	1354	1432	1458	1554	...	1632	1658	1754	1832	1856	1954	2032	...	2159	2329
Klatovy	a.	...	...	0841	0908	...	1041	1110	...	1241	1308	1403	1441	1510	1603	...	1641	1709	1803	1841	1905	2003	2041	...	2210	2338
Klatovy	d.	...	...	0851	▬	...	*1051*	▬	...	1251	▬	▬	*1451*	▬	*1606*	...	1651	▬	▬	*1851*	▬	▬	▬	2044	...	...
Špičák	d.	...	...	0943	...	...	*1144*	...	...	1343	...	...	*1546*	...	*1701*	...	1743	...	...	*1945*	...	...	...	2140	...	...
Železná Ruda Město	d.	...	...	0948	...	...	*1149*	...	...	1348	...	...	*1551*	...	*1706*	...	1748	...	...	*1950*	...	...	...	2145	...	...
Železná Ruda-Alžbětín ☆ 🏛	a.	...	...	0955	...	...	*1155*	...	...	1355	...	...	*1558*	...	*1713*	...	1754	...	...	*1956*	...	...	...	2151	...	...
Bayerisch Eisenstein ☆ 🏛	d.	0841	0944	...	1041	1141	...	1241	1341	...	1444	1541	...	1641	...	1741	...	1841	1941	...	2041	2141	...	▬	...	...
Zwiesel (Bay)	d.	0859	0959	...	1059	1159	...	1259	1359	...	1459	1559	...	1659	...	1759	...	1859	1959	...	2059	2204**t**	...	...	...	...
Regen	d.	0908	1008	...	1108	1208	...	1308	1408	...	1508	1608	...	1708	...	1808	...	1908	2008	...	2108	2214	...	...	...	...
Gotteszell	d.	0922	1022	...	1122	1222	...	1322	1422	...	1522	1622	...	1722	...	1822	...	1922	2022	...	2122	2228	...	...	...	...
Deggendorf Hbf	d.	0945	1045	...	1145	1245	...	1345	1445	...	1545	1645	...	1745	...	1845	...	1945	2045	...	2145	2251	2329	0038	...	...
Plattling	a.	0954	1054	...	1154	1254	...	1354	1454	...	1554	1654	...	1754	...	1854	...	1954	2054	...	2154	2300	2339	0049	...	...

ZWIESEL - GRAFENAU and BODENMAIS ⊠

ZWIESEL - GRAFENAU *32 km.* Journey time: 47 – 49 minutes.
From Zwiesel (Bay) at 0702 © **z**, 0713 Ⓐ **e**, 0902, 1102, 1304, 1502, 1702 and 1902.
From Grafenau at 0805, 1000, 1200, 1400, 1600, 1800 and 2000.

ZWIESEL - BODENMAIS *15 km.* Journey time: 20 minutes.
From Zwiesel at 0624 Ⓐ **e**, 0802 Ⓐ **e**, 0902, 1002 and hourly until 2002; then 2202.
From Bodenmais at 0558 Ⓐ **e**, 0649 Ⓐ **e**, 0829, 0929 and hourly until 2029.

GOTTESZELL - VIECHTACH *25 km.* Journey time: 40 – 47 minutes.
From Gotteszell at 0450 Ⓐ **e**, 0601 Ⓐ **e**, 0658 Ⓐ **e**, 0739 ⑥, 0751 Ⓐ **e**, 0939, 1039 ⚒ **r**, 1139, 1239 ⚒ **r**, 1336 Ⓐ **e**, 1339 © **z**, 1439, 1539 and hourly until 2039; then 2245.
From Viechtach at 0351 Ⓐ **e**, 0451 Ⓐ **e**, 0600 Ⓐ **e**, 0629 ⑥, 0656 Ⓐ **e**, 0837, 0937 ⚒ **r**, 1037, 1137 ⚒ **r**, 1237, 1328 Ⓐ **e**, 1337 © **z**, 1437, 1537 and hourly until 1937; then 2137.

e – Ⓐ (not June 20, Aug. 15, Nov. 1).
r – Not June 20, Aug. 15, Nov. 1.
t – Arrives 2154.
w – Change trains at Zwiesel on Ⓐ (not June 20, Aug. 15, Nov. 1).
z – Also June 20, Aug. 15, Nov. 1.
◇ – Also conveys 🚲.
§ – Train number **753** Plzeň - Praha.
⊠ – Operated by *Regentalbahn - Die Länderbahn* (under contract from *DB Regio*).
☆ – Bayerisch Eisenstein (German) / Železná Ruda-Alžbětín (Czech) is the same station.

STUTTGART - MÜNCHEN — 930

km	IMPORTANT: SEE NOTE ✣	ICE 619		ICE 893	ICE 993	RE 4205	IC 2291	RE 4205	IC 2097	IC 2097	RJX 63	ICE 699	RE 4207	RE 4207	ICE 991	EC 217	RE 4209	ICE 511	IC 2261	RE 4211	ICE 591	EC 113	RE 4213	ICE 513
				②–⑤		Ⓐt	Ⓐt	Ⓐt	Ⓐs	①g	⑥⑦	①–⑤	Ⓐt	Ⓒx	①–⑤									
				j✕	✕♦	L	🍷	L			✕♦	e✕	L	L	e♦ ✕	🍷♦	L	✕	🍷♦	L	✕♦	✕♦	L	M✕
	Dortmund Hbf **800** d.	2056	...	...	...	...	...	...	...	...	...	...	...	...	...	...	...	0435g	...	...	...	...	...	0637
	Köln Hbf **800 910** d.	2230	...	...	...	...	...	...	...	...	...	...	...	...	...	...	...	0555	...	...	...	...	...	0755
	Frankfurt (Main) Hbf **912** d.	0007	...	...	0225	...	...	...	...	0405	0517	...	...	...	...	...	...	|	...	...	0750	0820	...	|
	Frankfurt Flughafen ✈ **912** d.	0028	...	...	0244	...	...	...	...	|	0539	...	...	...	...	...	...	0652	...	...	|	|	...	0852
	Mannheim Hbf **912** d.	0106	...	...	0328	...	...	...	...	0447	0612	...	...	...	0629	0711	...	0731	...	...	0830	|	...	0931
	Heidelberg Hbf **912** d.	0119	...	...	|	...	...	...	...	0500	|	...	...	...	|	|	...	|	...	...	|	0914	...	|
	Karlsruhe Hbf **931** ▷ d.	0211	...	...	|	...	0455	...	...	|	|	...	...	...	|	|	...	|	0806	...	|	|	...	|
0	**Stuttgart** Hbf **936** d.	0336	...	0512	0512	0542	0553	...	...	0558	0658	0656	0700	0701	0713	0758	0801	0814	0854	0900	0914	0958	1001	1014
22	Plochingen **936** d.	0353	...	|	|	0559	0608	...	...	0616	|	|	0718	0718	|	|	0818	|	0909	0918	|	|	1018	|
42	Göppingen d.	|	...	|	|	0612	0620	←	...	|	|	|	0729	0729	|	|	0829	|	0921	0929	|	|	1029	|
61	Geislingen (Steige) d.	|	...	|	|	0625	|	0626	...	|	|	|	0740	0740	|	|	0840	|	|	0940	|	|	1040	|
94	**Ulm** Hbf **945** d.	0442	...	0612	0612	→	0656	0702	0713	0713	0756	0756	0804	0804	0812	0856	0904	0912	0958	1004	1012	1056	1104	1112
118	Günzburg **945** d.	0458	...	0627	0627	...	0710	...	0735	0735	|	0811	...	...	|	0910	...	|	|	...	|	1110	...	|
180	**Augsburg** Hbf **905** d.	0532	...	0659	0659	...	0742	...	0807	0807	0839	0842	...	...	0855	0942	...	0955	1041	...	1055	1142	...	1155
235	München Pasing **905** a.	0553	...	0721	0721	...	0807	...	0831	0831	0901	0904	...	...	0918	1005b	...	1018	1103	...	1118	1205b	...	1218
242	**München** Hbf **905** a.	0602	...	0732	0732	...	0817c	...	0844	0844	0910	0913	...	...	0927	1011c	...	1027	1112	...	1127	1210c	...	1227
	Salzburg Hbf **890** a.	...	...	...	...	...	...	...	...	...	1058	...	...	...	...	1159	...	...	...	...	...	1359	...	...

IMPORTANT: SEE NOTE ✣	IC 2093	RE 4215	ICE 593	EC 115	RE 4217	ICE 1113	RE 4219	IC 2263	IC 1919	ICE 595	IC 1919	EC 219	RE 4221 4241	ICE 517	RE 4223	IC 2013	ICE 597	EC 117	RE 4225	ICE 519	IC 1269	RE 4227	ICE 599	EC 391
	①–⑥																							
	e🍷	L	B✕	🍷♦	L	G✕		🍷	♦	B✕	♦	🍷♦	L	✕	L	🍷♦	B✕	🍷♦	L	✕	🍷	L	B✕	🍷
Dortmund Hbf **800** d.	...	...	...	...	...	0837	...	...	0724	...	...	...	...	1035	...	0950	...	...	...	1235	...	...	...	...
Köln Hbf **800 910** d.	...	...	...	0818	...	0949d	...	...	0917	...	...	...	...	1155	...	1117	...	...	...	1355	...	...	...	...
Frankfurt (Main) Hbf **912** d.	...	...	0950	|	...	|	...	...	|	1150	...	1220	...	|	...	|	1350	1420	...	|	...	...	1550	1620
Frankfurt Flughafen ✈ **912** d.	...	...	|	|	...	1052	...	...	|	|	...	|	...	1252	...	|	|	|	...	1452	...	...	|	|
Mannheim Hbf **912** d.	...	...	1030	1102	...	1131	...	...	1154	1230	...	|	...	1331	...	1354	1430	|	...	1531	...	...	1630	|
Heidelberg Hbf **912** d.	...	...	|	|	...	|	...	...	1206	|	...	1314	...	|	...	1406	|	1514	...	|	...	...	|	1714
Karlsruhe Hbf **931** ▷ d.	...	...	|	|	...	|	...	1206	|	|	...	|	...	|	...	|	|	|	...	|	1606	...	|	|
tuttgart Hbf **936** d.	1054	1100	1114	1158	1201	1214	1240	1254	1257	1314	...	1359	1401	1414	1454	1458	1514	1558	1601	1614	1654	1700	1714	1758
lochingen **936** d.	1109	1118	|	|	1218	|	1259	1309	|	|	...	|	1418	|	1509	1514	|	|	1618	|	1709	1718	|	|
öppingen d.	1121	1129	|	|	1229	|	1312	1321	1325	|	...	|	1429	|	1521	1528	|	|	1629	|	1721	1729	|	|
eislingen (Steige) d.	|	1140	|	|	1240	|	1327	|	|	|	←	|	1440	|	1532	|	|	|	1640	|	|	1740	|	|
lm Hbf **945** d.	1159	1204	1212	1256	1304	1312	1350	1357	1401	1412	1414	1456	1504	1512	1555	1613	1612	1656	1704	1712	1758	1804	1812	1856
ünzburg **945** d.	|	...	|	1310	...	|	...	|	→	|	|	1510	...	|	...	...	|	1710	...	|	|	...	|	1910
ugsburg Hbf **905** d.	1241	...	1255	1342	...	1355	...	1441	...	1455	1501	1542	...	1555	...	...	1655	1742	...	1755	1840	...	1855	1942
ünchen Pasing **905** a.	1303	...	1318	1405b	...	1418	...	1503	...	1518	...	1605b	...	1618	...	...	1718	1806b	...	1818	1902	...	1918	2004b
ünchen Hbf **905** a.	1312	...	1327	1411c	...	1427	...	1512h	...	1528	...	1611c	...	1627	...	...	1727	1811c	...	1827	1911	...	1927	2011c
Salzburg Hbf **890** a.	...	...	...	1559	...	...	...	...	...	...	...	1759	...	...	...	...	...	1959y	...	...	2100q	...	...	2202q

IMPORTANT: SEE NOTE ✣	RE 4229	ICE 611	IC 2011	IC 2267	RE 4231	ICE 691	TGV 9577	IC 2295	RE 4233	ICE 613	ICE 771	IC 1915	IC 2269	IC 2269	RE 4235	ICE 693	TGV 9579	RB 19279	RE 4237	ICE 615	RB 19281	RB 19283	ICE 895	RE 4239
			①–④				Ⓑq	Ⓑq			⑤f	⑦w	Y	⑦w		Ⓑq	⑥a				⚒t	†z	⑦w	
	L	✕	U	🍷	L	B✕	R🍷	🍷	F	✕	H✕	T			L	B✕	R🍷							
Dortmund Hbf **800** d.	...	1435	...	...	...	...	...	...	...	1635	...	...	...	...	...	...	...	...	...	1835	...	...	...	...
Köln Hbf **800 910** d.	...	1555	1517	...	...	...	...	...	...	1755	...	1717	...	...	...	...	...	...	...	1955	...	...	...	...
Frankfurt (Main) Hbf **912** d.	...	|	|	...	...	1750	...	1819	...	|	1906	|	...	...	...	1950	...	...	...	|	...	...	...	...
Frankfurt Flughafen ✈ **912** d.	...	1652	|	...	...	|	...	|	...	1853	1923	|	...	...	...	|	...	...	...	2052	...	...	...	...
Mannheim Hbf **912** d.	...	1731	1754	...	...	1830	...	|	...	1931	1956	1954	...	...	...	2030	...	...	...	2131	...	...	...	...
Heidelberg Hbf **912** d.	...	|	1806	...	...	|	...	1914	...	|	|	2006	...	...	...	|	...	...	...	|	...	...	...	...
Karlsruhe Hbf **931** ▷ d.	...	|	|	1806	...	|	1828	|	...	|	|	|	2006	2006	...	|	2028	...	...	|	...	...	...	...
tuttgart Hbf **936** d.	1801	1814	1850	1854	1900	1913	1922	1959	2001	2014	2054	2051	2054	2054	2101	2114	2114	2129	2158	2214	2233	2240	2316	2322
lochingen **936** d.	1818	|	1905	1909	1918	|	|	|	2018	|	|	2107	2109	2109	2118	|	|	2147	2217	|	2251	2258	|	2339
öppingen d.	1829	|	...	1921	1929	|	|	|	2029	|	|	...	2121	2121	2129	|	|	2205	2228	|	2310	2317	|	2350
eislingen (Steige) d.	1840	|	...	|	1940	|	|	|	2040	|	|	...	2135	2135	2140	|	|	2229	2240	|	2333	2340	|	0003
lm Hbf **945** d.	1904	1912	...	1959	2004	2012	2020	2057	2104	2112	2200	...	2158	2200	2204	2212	2213	2300	2304	2312	...	...	0015	0035
ünzburg **945** d.	...	|	...	|	...	|	|	2111	...	|	2215	...	...	2215	...	|	|	...	...	|	...	...	0030	...
ugsburg Hbf **905** d.	...	1955	...	2041	...	2055	2106	2143	...	2155	2247	...	...	2247	...	2255	2258	...	...	2355	...	...	0101	...
ünchen Pasing **905** a.	...	2019	...	2103	...	2116	|	2206	...	2216	2309	...	...	2310	...	2320‡	|	...	...	0017	...	...	0123	...
ünchen Hbf **905** a.	...	2028	...	2112	...	2126	2136	2215	...	2226	2319	...	...	2319	...	2329‡	2329	...	...	0027	...	...	0133	...
Salzburg Hbf **890** a.	...	...	...	...	...	...	...	...	...	...	...	...	...	...	...	...	...	...	...	...	...	...	...	...

Regional trains ULM - MÜNCHEN

	Ⓐr		Ⓐr		Ⓐr		Ⓐr																	
lm Hbf d.	...	...	0446	0523	0545	0621	0643	0723	0823	0923	1023	1123	1223	1324	1423	1523	1623	1723	1824	1923	2023	2123	2223	2323
ünzburg d.	...	...	0504	0541	0606	0640	0702	0742	0842	0942	1042	1142	1242	1342	1442	1542	1642	1742	1843	1942	2042	2142	2242	2341
ugsburg Hbf a.	...	...	0559	0630	0658	0733	0802	0833	0933	1033	1133	1233	1333	1433	1533	1633	1733	1833	1933	2033	2133	2233	2333	...
ugsburg Hbf d.	0437	0539	0605	0639	0705	0739	0806	0839	0939	1039	1139	1239	1339	1439	1539	1639	1739	1839	1939	2039	2139	2239	2341	...
ünchen Pasing a.	0511	0613	0641	0714	0745	0813	0847	0913	1013	1113	1213	1313	1413	1514	1613	1713	1813	1913	2014	2122	2222	2315n	0024	...
ünchen Hbf a.	0519	0621	0649	0721	0753	0821	0854k	0921	1022	1121	1221	1321	1421	1521	1622	1721	1822	1921	2022	2131	2231	2324n	0032p	...

– **NOTES** (LISTED BY TRAIN NUMBER)

3 – ⑥⑦ (also June 10). 🚃12 and ✕ Frankfurt - Wien - Budapest. From Oct. 26 departs Frankfurt Hbf 0531 and does not call at Frankfurt Flughafen.

13 – BLAUER ENZIAN – 🚃12 and ✕ Frankfurt - Salzburg - Villach - Klagenfurt; conveys 🚃12 Frankfurt - Villach (**213**) - Ljubljana - Zagreb.

15 – WÖRTHERSEE – 🚃12 and 🍷 Münster - Köln - Koblenz - Salzburg - Villach - Klagenfurt.

17 – SALZACH – 🚃12 and 🍷 Frankfurt - Salzburg - Villach - Klagenfurt.

17 – DACHSTEIN – 🚃12 and 🍷 Saarbrücken - München - Salzburg - Bischofshofen - Selzthal - Graz.

19 – CHIEMGAU – 🚃12 and 🍷 Frankfurt - München - Salzburg - Bischofshofen - Selzthal - Graz.

91 – 🚃12 and ✕ (Hamburg ①–⑤ -) (Hannover ①–⑥ -) Frankfurt - München.

91 – 🚃12 and ✕ Wiesbaden - Mainz - München.

93 – From Frankfurt daily to Sept. 2, ①⑥ from Sept. 7. 🚃12 Berlin (previous day) - Erfurt - Frankfurt - München. Conveys ✕ Ulm - München. Aug. 11 - Oct. 28 departs Frankfurt (Main) Hbf 0250, Mannheim 0337, not calling at Frankfurt Flughafen. From Nov. 2 departs Frankfurt (Main) Hbf 0222.

919 – June 24 - Sept. 8 and Nov. 9 - Dec. 14. 🚃12 Dortmund - München Ost - Berchtesgaden.

013 – ALLGÄU – 🚃12 and 🍷 Dortmund - Köln - Koblenz - Ulm - Kempten - Oberstdorf.

261 – 🚃12 and 🍷 (Basel ①–⑥ **e** -) Karlsruhe - München.

– From Berlin via Erfurt (Table 850).
– To Friedrichshafen (Table 933); see also note ⊠.
– From Hamburg (Table 800). Train number **1211** from Sept. 2.
– From Hamburg (Table 900).
– To Lindau (Table 933); see also note ⊠.
– From Münster (Table 800).
– 🚃12 and 🍷 Paris - Strasbourg - München. 🅡 for international journeys. Runs up to 32 minutes later July 20 - Aug. 4.
– To Nürtingen (a. 2119), Reutlingen Hbf (a. 2138) and Tübingen Hbf (a. 2151).
– ①–④ (not June 10, 19, 20, Oct. 2, 3). To Nürtingen (a. 1917), Reutlingen Hbf (a. 1937) and Tübingen Hbf (a. 1950).
– ①②③④⑦ (not June 9, 19, 20, Oct. 2, 3, 31).

– Also June 9.
– Until July 28.
– From July 29.

d – Until Sept. 1 calls at Köln **Messe/Deutz** (not Hbf); from Sept. 2 calls at Köln Hbf, d. 0955.
e – Not June 10.
f – Also Oct. 2; not Oct. 4.
g – ① (also June 11; not June 10).
h – 1521 on ⑥⑦ to July 28 (also June 10, 20).
j – Not June 7 - Aug. 30.
k – From July 29.
n – On ⑥⑦ July 27 - Sept. 1 arrives München Pasing 2318, München Hbf 2336.
p – 0039 on the mornings ①⑦ July 28 - Sept. 2.
q – Ⓑ (not June 9).
r – Not June 20, Aug. 15, Nov. 1.
s – Not June 20, 21, Aug. 15, Oct. 4, Nov. 1.
t – Not June 20, Nov. 1.
w – Also June 10; not June 9.
x – Also June 20; not Sept. 21 - Nov. 3.
y – From June 13 (until June 12 service is diverted between Rosenheim and Schwarzach, not calling at intermediate stations; see Table 970).
z – Also June 20, Nov. 1.

▷ – Karlsruhe timings may vary by up to 12 minutes July 20 - Aug. 4 and Sept. 14 - Oct. 19 (earlier departures possible).
⊠ – Services between Ulm and Friedrichshafen / Lindau are subject to alteration to July 14 and from Sept. 16.
‡ – On ⑦ July 28 - Sept. 1 does not call at München Pasing and arrives München Hbf 2348.
✣ – Please refer to the shaded engineering work panel on page 369 for details of various alterations affecting services in this table.

930 MÜNCHEN - STUTTGART

IMPORTANT: SEE NOTE ✣	ICE 1018 ⑦ y	ICE 618 ①–⑥ e		ICE 616	RB 19204	RE 4200 Ⓐ t	IC 2268 ① g	IC 2268 ①–⑤ j	IC 2010 ①–⑤ T	RB 19210 © z	RE 4202 Ⓐ t	ICE 614 ✕	RE 4204 L	IC 2294 Ⓐ q 🍷	RB 19214 Ⓐ t	IC 2266 ①–⑥ e 🍷	TGV 9596 ⑦ y R	ICE 692 ①–⑥ e B ✕	RE 4206 4208 L	TGV 9576 ①–⑥ e R	ICE 612 ✕	RE 4210 L	IC 1296 ①–⑥ e 🍷	ICE 690 B ✕
Salzburg Hbf **890** d.	...	...	...	...	...	...	...	...	...	...	...	...	...	...	...	...	...	...	...	...	...	...	0545	...
München Hbf **905** d.	0001◊	0001◊	...	0324§	...	...	0442	...	...	...	...	0522	...	0541	...	0615	0623	0629	...	0646	0728	...	0746**c**	082
München Pasing **905** d.	0009	0009	...	0332§	...	...	0451	...	...	...	...	0530	...	|	...	0624	|	0638	...	|	0736	...	0751**b**	083
Augsburg Hbf **905** d.	0032	0032	...	0357	...	...	0516	...	...	...	...	0601	...	0612	...	0648	0656	0705	...	0716	0803	...	0817	090
Günzburg **945** d.	0102	0102	...	|	...	...	0547	...	...	...	...	|	...	0642	...	0722	|	|	...	|	|	...	0848	|
Ulm Hbf **945** d.	0116	0116	...	0439	0451**t**	0522	0601	0601	...	...	0617	0649	0654	0658	0704	0738	0742	0749	0754	0802	0849	0855	0903	094
Geislingen (Steige) d.	|	|	...	|	0520	0552	0624	0624	...	0621	0644	|	0717	0723	0732	|	|	|	0817	|	|	0918	|	|
Göppingen d.	|	|	...	|	0543	0606	0638	0638	...	0644	0702	|	0729	|	0754	0814	|	|	0829	|	|	0929	|	|
Plochingen **936** d.	0200	0200	...	|	0601	0619	0651	0651	0654	0702	0719	|	0740	0746	0812	|	|	|	0840	|	|	0940	|	|
Stuttgart Hbf **936** a.	0216	0216	...	0536	0619	0637	0705	0705	0709	0721	0736	0745	0756	0800	0830	0837	0839	0845	0856	0900	0945	0956	0959	104
Karlsruhe Hbf **931** ▷ a.	0333	0333	...	|	...	...	0753	0753	|	...	...	|	...	|	...	0928	0930	|	...	0951	|	...	|	|
Heidelberg Hbf **912** a.	0426	0426	...	|	...	...	...	...	0753	...	...	|	...	0844	...	...	...	|	...	...	|	...	1044	|
Mannheim Hbf **912** a.	0438	0438	...	0628	...	...	...	...	0806	...	...	0828	...	|	...	...	...	0929	...	...	1028	...	|	112
Frankfurt Flughafen ✈ **912** a.	0512	0512	...	0706	...	...	...	...	|	...	...	0906	...	|	...	...	...	|	...	...	1106	...	|	|
Frankfurt (Main) Hbf **912** a.	0533	0533	...	|	...	...	...	...	|	...	...	|	...	0940	...	...	...	1008	...	...	|	...	1140	120
Köln Hbf **800 910** a.	0705	0705	...	0805	...	...	...	...	1043	...	...	1005	...	...	...	...	...	...	...	...	1205	...	...	...
Dortmund Hbf **800** a.	0821	0827**k**	...	0921	...	...	...	...	...	...	...	1121	...	...	...	...	...	...	...	...	1321	...	...	...

IMPORTANT: SEE NOTE ✣	RE 4212 L	IC 1268 🍷	ICE 610 ✕	RE 4214 L	EC 390 🍷	ICE 598 B ✕	RE 4216 L	IC 2012 🍷♦	ICE 518 ✕	RE 4218 L	EC 218 🍷♦	IC 1918 ♦	ICE 596 B ✕	IC 1918 ♦	IC 2264 🍷	RE 4220	ICE 516 ✕	RE 4222 L	EC 114 🍷♦	ICE 594 B ✕	RE 4224 L	IC 2362 ①–④ m 🍷	IC 2366 ⑤–⑦ s 🍷	ICE 121 G ✕
Salzburg Hbf **890** d.	...	0642**e**	...	...	0800	...	...	...	...	...	1000	...	...	...	...	...	...	...	1200	...	...	...	...	...
München Hbf **905** d.	...	0847	0928	...	0947**c**	1028	...	...	1128	...	1147**c**	...	1228	...	1246	...	1328	...	1347**c**	1428	...	1447**c**	1447**c**	152
München Pasing **905** d.	...	0856	0936	...	0952**b**	1037	...	...	1136	...	|	1224	1237	...	1255	...	1336	...	1352**b**	1437	...	1456	1456	153
Augsburg Hbf **905** d.	...	0921	1003	...	1017	1103	...	...	1203	...	1217	1249	1302	...	1320	...	1403	...	1417	1503	...	1521	1521	160
Günzburg **945** d.	...	|	|	...	1048	|	...	...	|	...	1248	1327	|	←	|	...	|	...	1448	|	...	|	|	|
Ulm Hbf **945** d.	0956	1004	1048	1055	1103	1149	1154	1157	1249	1255	1303	1344	1349	1356	1404	1411	1449	1455	1503	1549	1556	1604	1604	164
Geislingen (Steige) d.	1019	|	|	1118	|	|	1218	|	|	1318	|	→	|	|	|	1433	|	1518	|	|	1619	|	|	|
Göppingen d.	1031	1038	|	1129	|	|	1229	1235	|	1329	|	...	|	1433	|	1445	|	1529	|	|	1631	|	|	|
Plochingen **936** d.	1042	1050	|	1140	|	|	1240	1249	|	1340	|	...	|	|	1449	1458	|	1540	|	|	1642	1650	1650	|
Stuttgart Hbf **936** a.	1059	1106	1145	1156	1159	1245	1256	1304	1345	1356	1359	...	1445	1500	1503	1515	1545	1556	1600	1645	1658	1703	1704	174
Karlsruhe Hbf **931** ▷ a.	...	1153	|	...	|	|	...	|	|	...	|	...	|	|	1553	...	|	...	|	|	...	1753	1753	|
Heidelberg Hbf **912** a.	...	...	|	...	1244	|	...	1353	|	...	1444	...	|	1553	...	...	|	...	|	|	...	...	...	|
Mannheim Hbf **912** a.	...	...	1228	...	|	1329	...	1406	1428	...	|	...	1529	1606	...	...	1628	...	1656	1729	...	...	...	182
Frankfurt Flughafen ✈ **912** a.	...	...	1306	...	|	|	...	|	1506	...	|	...	|	|	...	...	1706	...	|	|	...	...	...	190
Frankfurt (Main) Hbf **912** a.	...	...	|	...	1340	1408	...	|	|	...	1540	...	1608	|	...	...	|	...	|	1808	...	...	...	|
Köln Hbf **800 910** a.	...	...	1405	...	...	...	...	1643	1605	...	...	...	...	1843	...	...	1805	...	1943	...	...	...	...	2005
Dortmund Hbf **800** a.	...	...	1521	...	...	...	...	1807	1721	...	...	...	...	2007	...	...	1921	...	2103	...	...	...	...	212

IMPORTANT: SEE NOTE ✣	RE 4226 L	EC 112 ✕♦	IC 1910 ⑦ w 🍷	ICE 592 A ✕	IC 1910 ⑦ w 🍷	RE 4228 4230 L	IC 2262 🍷♦	IC 2094 ①–④ ¶	ICE 512 M ✕	RE 4232 L	EC 216 🍷♦	ICE 590 H ✕	RE 4234 L	IC 2092 Ⓑ u 🍷	ICE 1110 ⑤–⑦ y ✕	ICE 510 ★ D ✕	RE 4236 L	RE 4242	ICE 990 N ✕	RJX 66 ⑤⑥ ✕♦	RB 19282 19284	ICE 992 Q B	ICE 992 n ✕	RB 1928 1928
Salzburg Hbf **890** d.	...	1400	...	...	...	...	...	...	...	...	1600	...	...	...	...	...	...	...	...	1856	...	...	...	...
München Hbf **905** d.	...	1548**c**	1618•	1628	...	...	1647**c**	1720**x**	1728	...	1747**c**	1828	...	1844	1928	1928	...	...	2044	2044	...	2151	2151	...
München Pasing **905** d.	...	1553**b**	1627•	1637	...	...	1656	|	1736	...	1753**b**	1837	...	1853	1936	1936	...	...	2053	2053	...	|	|	...
Augsburg Hbf **905** d.	...	1617	1655	1703	...	...	1721	1749	1802	...	1817	1902	...	1918	2003	2003	...	...	2117	2117	...	2220	2220	...
Günzburg **945** d.	...	1648	1728	|	...	...	|	1819	|	...	1848	|	...	1948	|	|	...	...	2147	2147	...	2252	2252	...
Ulm Hbf **945** d.	1655	1703	1742	1749	...	1756	1804	1836	1849	1855	1903	1949	1956	2004	2049	2049	2056	2151	2203	2203	2253	2308	2308	←
Geislingen (Steige) d.	1718	|	1806	|	←	1819	|	...	|	1918	|	|	2019	|	|	|	2119	2213	|	|	2321	|	|	232
Göppingen d.	1729	|	1818	|	1825	1831	1838	...	|	1929	|	|	2031	2038	|	|	2131	2226	|	|	→	|	|	235
Plochingen **936** d.	1740	|	→	|	|	1842	1850	...	|	1940	|	|	2042	2050	|	|	2142	2238	|	|	...	|	|	000
Stuttgart Hbf **936** a.	1756	1759	...	1845	1855	1858	1906	...	1945	1956	1959	2045	2059	2106	2145	2145	2159	2256	2259	2259	...	0006	0006	002
Karlsruhe Hbf **931** ▷ a.	...	|	...	|	|	...	1953	...	|	...	|	|	...	2153	|	|	...	...	|	|	...	|	...	...
Heidelberg Hbf **912** a.	...	1844	...	|	1953	...	...	...	|	...	|	|	...	...	|	|	...	...	|	|	...	|	...	...
Mannheim Hbf **912** a.	...	|	...	1929	2006	...	...	...	2028	...	2048	2129	...	...	2229	2229	...	...	2345	2345	...	0141	...	...
Frankfurt Flughafen ✈ **912** a.	...	|	...	|	|	...	...	...	2106	...	...	|	...	...	2307	2307	...	...	0023	0023	...	0224	...	...
Frankfurt (Main) Hbf **912** a.	...	1940	...	2008	|	...	...	...	|	...	...	2208	...	...	|	...	...	...	0044	0044	...	0240	...	...
Köln Hbf **800 910** a.	...	...	...	...	2243	...	...	...	2205	...	...	...	...	...	0005	...	...	...	...	...	...	...	...	...
Dortmund Hbf **800** a.	...	...	...	...	0002	...	...	...	...	...	...	...	...	...	...	...	...	...	...	...	...	...	...	...

Regional trains MÜNCHEN - ULM

		© v											Ⓐ r	© v										
München Hbf d.	0008**a**	0008**a**	...	...	0529	0636	0735**f**	0835	0935	1035	1135	1235	1335	1335	1435	1534	1635	1735	1835	1935	2035	2100	2200**o**	230(
München Pasing d.	0016	0016	...	...	0536	0644	0743	0843	0943	1043	1143	1243	1343	1343	1443	1542	1643	1743	1843	1943	2043	2107	2207	230
Augsburg Hbf a.	0056	0056	...	...	0619	0720	0819	0919	1019	1119	1219	1319	1419	1419	1519	1619	1719	1819	1919	2019	2122	2148	2248	234
Augsburg Hbf d.	...	0059	...	0522	0623	0724	0825	0925	1025	1125	1222	1325	1425	1425	1525	1625	1725	1825	1925‡	2025	2125	2151	2251	235
Günzburg d.	...	0150	...	0614	0714	0816	0920	1016	1116	1216	1319	1416	1516	1520	1616	1716	1822	1916	2017	2116	2216	2242	2342	004
Ulm Hbf a.	...	0208	...	0633	0733	0835	0939	1035	1135	1235	1337	1435	1535	1539	1635	1735	1840	1935	2037	2135	2235	2302	0002	010

♦ – **NOTES** (LISTED BY TRAIN NUMBER)

66 – ⑤⑥ (also June 9). 🚃 and ✕ Budapest - Wien - Frankfurt.
112 – BLAUER ENZIAN – 🚃 and ✕ Klagenfurt - Villach - Salzburg - Frankfurt; 🚃 Zagreb (**212**) - Ljubljana - Villach (**112**) - Frankfurt.
114 – WÖRTHERSEE – 🚃 and 🍷 Klagenfurt - Villach - Salzburg - Mannheim - Koblenz - Köln - Dortmund.
216 – DACHSTEIN – 🚃 and 🍷 Graz - Selzthal - Bischofshofen - Salzburg - München - Saarbrücken.
218 – CHIEMGAU 🚃 and 🍷 Graz - Selzthal - Bischofshofen - Salzburg - München - Frankfurt (- Erfurt ♣). Arrives Frankfurt 1555 on dates in note ♣.
1918 – June 25 - Sept. 9 and Nov. 10 - Dec. 14. 🚃 Berchtesgaden - München Ost - Dortmund.
2012 – ALLGÄU – 🚃 and 🍷 Oberstdorf - Kempten - Ulm - Köln - Dortmund.
2262 – 🚃 and 🍷 München - Karlsruhe (- Basel Ⓑ **h**).

A – To Leipzig (Table **850**).
B – To Berlin via Erfurt (Table **850**).
D – To Wiesbaden (Table **911**).
G – To Hamburg (Table **800**). Train number **1210** from Sept. 2.
H – To Hamburg on ⑦ (Table **900**).
L – From Lindau (Table **933**). Services between Lindau and Ulm are subject to alteration to July 14 and from Sept. 16.
M – To Münster (Table **800**).
N – ①②③④⑦ (not June 9).
Q – Daily to Sept. 1; ⑤⑦ from Sept. 6.
R – 🚃 and 🍷 München - Strasbourg - Paris. 🅁 for international journeys. Runs up to 22 minutes earlier July 20 - Aug. 4.
T – ①–⑤ (not June 10, 20, 21, Oct. 3, 4, Nov. 1). From Tübingen Hbf (d. 0611), Reutlingen Hbf (d. 0623) and Nürtingen (d. 0642).

a – 0003 on ⑦ July 28 - Sept. 1.
b – Until July 28.
c – From July 29.
d – Until Sept. 1 calls at Köln **Messe/Deutz** (not Hbf); calls at Köln Hbf from Sept. 2.
e – ①–⑥ (not June 10).
f – 0733 until July 28.
g – Also June 11; not June 10.
h – Not June 9, 10.

j – Not June 10, 20, 21, Nov. 1.
k – ⑥ only.
m – Not June 10, 19, 20, Oct. 2, 3, 31.
n – Not Sept. 14, 21, 28, Oct. 5, 12, 19, 26.
o – 2157 on © to July 28 (also June 20).
p – 2254 on ⑥⑦ July 27 - Sept. 1.
q – Not Nov. 1.
r – Not June 20, Aug. 15, Nov. 1.
s – Also June 10, 19, 20, Oct. 2, 3, 31.
t – Ⓐ (not June 20, Nov. 1).
u – Not June 9, 20.
v – Also June 20, Aug. 15, Nov. 1.
w – Also June 10; not June 9.
x – 1714 until July 25.
y – Also June 10.
z – Also June 20, Nov. 1.

¶ – Not June 10, 19, 20, Aug. 14, Oct. 2, 3, 31.
‡ – 1923 until June 23.
◊ – On ①⑦ July 28 - Sept. 2 departs 2354 (the previous da
§ – On ①⑦ July 28 - Sept. 2 departs München Hbf 03 Pasing 0331.
• – Until July 28 departs München Hbf 1614, Pasing 1625.
★ – ①②③④⑦ (not June 9). Train number **1190** on ⑦ (al June 10).
♣ – ①–④ to Aug. 8 (not June 10, 19, 20); ①–④ from Oct. 2
▷ – Karlsruhe timings may vary by up to 21 minutes July 2 Aug. 4 and Sept. 14 - Oct. 19.
✣ – Please refer to the shaded engineering work panel on pa 369 for details of various alterations affecting services this table.

KARLSRUHE - STUTTGART (also local trains HEIDELBERG - STUTTGART) 931

See Table **32** for full details of international *TGV* services from / to Paris. See Table **912** for fast trains Heidelberg - Stuttgart and v.v.

km	km	SEE NOTE ✣	ICE 619	IC 2291	IC 2363	◇	IC 2216	IC 2367	IC 2063	◇	IC 2369	IC 2261	◇	⊙	IC 2065	◇	◇	◇	⊙	IC 2067	IC 2263	◇	◇	⊙	IC 2069	◇
				Ⓐt	①–⑥		Ⓐm	Ⓐm	①–⑥		Ⓐm															
			R	🍷	c		O🍷		eN			B🍷			N					N	🍷				N	
0		**Karlsruhe** Hbf......d.	0211	0455	0559	0602	0637	0658	0706	0733	0741	0806	0805	...	0906	0933	1005	1033	...	1106	1206	1205	1230	...	1306	1405
26		Pforzheim......d.	0233	|	|	0625	|	|	0727	0754	|	|	0826	...	0927	0954	1028	1054	...	1127	|	1228	1254	...	1327	1428
	0	**Heidelberg** Hbf **912** d.	|	|	|	|	|	|	|	|	|	|	|	0835j	|	|	|	|	1036**k**	|	|	|	|	1236**k**	|	|
	33	Bruchsal ...... **912** d.	|	0513	0616	|	0654	0718	|	|	0757	0818	|	0902	|	|	|	|	1100	|	1218	|	|	1300	|	|
39	65	Mühlacker......d.	|	|	|	0633	|	|	0737	0802	|	|	0835	0930	0937	1002	1036	1102	1130	1137	|	1236	1302	1330	1337	1436
47	73	Vaihingen (Enz) .. **912** d.	0247	0531	|	0640	|	|	0746	0808	|	|	0841	0939	0946	1011	1042	1108	1139	1146	|	1242	1310	1339	|	1442
86	112	**Stuttgart** Hbf ..... **912** a.	0320	0548	0648	0657	0725	0750	0802	0826	0827	0849	0900	1012	1002	1028	1100	1126	1212	1202	1249	1300	1328	1412	1359	1500
		München Hbf **930** ..a.	0602	0817**b**	...	...	...	...	...	...	...	1112	...	...	...	...	...	...	...	...	1512**h**	...	...	...	...	...

SEE NOTE ✣	IC 2265	◇	IC 2169	⊙	IC 2161	IC 1269	◇	◇	⊙	IC 2163	IC 2267	◇	TGV 9577	◇	IC 2365	⊙	IC 2165	IC 2269	◇	TGV 9579	◇	⊙	IC 2167	◇	◇	◇
	⑤⑦		⑤f										Ⓑq		⑤f			T		⑥a			Ⓑq			
	v				N	S🍷				N	🍷		P🍷				N	G		P🍷						
Karlsruhe Hbf......d.	1406	1433	1444	...	1506	1606	1604	1633	...	1706	1806	1804	1828	1833	1844	...	1906	2006	2004	2028	2033	...	2106	2133	2205	2315
Pforzheim......d.	|	1454	|	...	1527	|	1627	1654	...	1727	|	1828	|	1854	|	...	1927	|	2028	|	2054	...	2127	2154	2228	2338
Heidelberg Hbf **912** d.	|	|	|	1436**k**	|	|	|	|	1636j	|	|	|	|	|	|	1835j	|	|	|	|	|	2037**k**	|	|	|	|
Bruchsal......**912** d.	1418	|	1457	1500	|	1618	|	|	1700	|	1818	|	|	|	1858	1901	|	2018	|	|	|	2101	|	|	|	|
Mühlacker......d.	|	1502	|	1530	1537	|	1636	1702	1730	1737	|	1836	|	1902	|	1930	1937	|	2036	|	2102	2130	2137	2202	2236	2346
Vaihingen (Enz).... **912** d.	|	1508	|	1539	1546	|	1642	1708	1739	1746	|	1842	|	1908	|	1939	1946	|	2042	|	2108	2139	2146	2210	2245	2352
Stuttgart Hbf...... **912** a.	1449	1526	1530	1612	1602	1649	1700	1726	1812	1802	1849	1900	1904	1928	1930	2012	2002	2049	2100	2104	2127	2212	2202	2225	2303	0022
München Hbf **930**... a.	...	...	...	...	...	1911	...	...	...	...	2112	...	2136	...	...	...	...	2319**w**	...	2329	...	...	...	...	...	...

km	SEE NOTE ✣	◇	ICE 618	IC 2368	◇	◇	◇	IC 2268	◇	IC 2164	IC 2266	TGV 9596	◇	⊙	TGV 9576	◇	IC 2162	◇	◇	⊙	IC 1268	IC 2160	◇	◇	⊙	IC 2168
			1018	Ⓐm	Ⓒz	Ⓐt		Ⓐ		①–⑥	①–⑥	⑦y			①–⑥											⑤f
			R					H		eN	e🍷	P			eP		N				S🍷	N				
	München Hbf **930** .. d.	...	0001‡	...	...	...	...	0442**g**	...	...	0615	0623	...	...	0646	...	...	...	...	...	0847	...	...	...	...	...
0	**Stuttgart** Hbf......**912** d.	0016	0228	0545	0559	0632	0659	0710	0732	0759	0842	0854	0900	0848	0910	0932	0959	1032	1059	1048	1111	1159	1232	1259	1247	1303
29	Vaihingen (Enz) ... **912** d.	0043	0255	0602	0616	0648	0716	|	0748	0816	|	|	0916	0919	|	0948	1016	1048	1116	1119	|	1216	1248	1316	1319	|
	Mühlacker......d.	0049	|	0610	0622	0654	0722	|	0754	0824	|	|	0922	0931	|	0954	1024	1054	1122	1131	|	1224	1254	1322	1331	|
66	Bruchsal......**912** d.	|	|	|	|	|	|	0739	|	|	0912	|	|	0958	|	|	|	|	|	1158	1139	|	|	|	1358	1337
	Heidelberg Hbf **912** a.	|	|	|	|	|	|	|	|	|	|	|	|	1019**k**	|	|	|	|	|	1219**k**	|	|	|	|	1419**k**	|
	Pforzheim......d.	0057	0311	0622	0631	0703	0731	|	0803	0834	|	|	0931	...	|	1003	1034	1103	1131	...	|	1234	1303	1331	...	|
87	**Karlsruhe** Hbf......a.	0120	0333	0645	0654	0726	0755	0753	0826	0853	0928	0930	0954	...	0951	1026	1053	1126	1154	...	1153	1253	1326	1354	...	1352

SEE NOTE ✣	IC 2068	◇	◇	⊙	IC 2264	IC 2066	◇	IC 2313	◇	⊙	IC 2362	IC 2366	IC 2360	IC 2064	◇	◇	⊙	IC 2262	IC 2062	◇	◇	⊙	IC 2092	◇	IC 2060	◇
								Ⓐm			①–④	⑤–⑦	Ⓐm										Ⓑr		Ⓑq	
	N				🍷	N		O🍷			d🍷	u🍷		N				B🍷	N				🍷		N	
München Hbf **930**... d.	...	...	...	...	1246	...	...	...	...	...	1447**x**	1447**x**	...	...	...	...	...	1647**x**	...	...	...	...	1844	...	...	...
Stuttgart Hbf...... **912** d.	1358	1428	1459	1447	1508	1559	1632	1641	1659	1648	1708	1709	1734	1758	1832	1859	1847	1911	1958	2032	2059	2047	2111	2132	2159	2313
Vaihingen (Enz).... **912** d.	1416	1445	1516	1519	|	1616	1648	|	1716	1719	|	|	|	1816	1848	1916	1919	|	2016	2048	2116	2119	|	2148	2217	2331
Mühlacker......d.	1424	1451	1522	1531	|	1624	1654	|	1722	1731	|	|	|	1824	1854	1922	1931	|	2024	2056	2122	2131	|	2154	2224	2340
Bruchsal...... **912** d.	|	|	|	1558	1538	|	|	1712	|	1758	1737	1737	1803	|	|	|	1958	1939	|	|	|	2158	2139	|	|	|
Heidelberg Hbf **912** a.	|	|	|	1619j	|	|	|	|	|	1819j	|	|	|	|	|	|	2019**k**	|	|	|	|	2219**k**	|	|	|	|
Pforzheim......d.	1434	1503	1531	...	|	1634	1703	|	1731	...	|	|	|	1834	1903	1931	...	|	2034	2103	2131	...	|	2203	2234	2348
Karlsruhe Hbf......a.	1453	1526	1554	...	1553	1653	1726	1731	1754	...	1753	1753	1821	1853	1926	1954	...	1953	2053	2126	2154	...	2153	2228	2259	0012

B – From / to Basel on dates in Table **912**.
G – [12] Karlsruhe - Ulm (- München ⑦**w**).
H – ①–⑤ (not June 10, 20, 21, Nov. 1).
[12] (München ①**g** -) Ulm - Karlsruhe.
N – [12] Karlsruhe - Stuttgart - Nürnberg and v.v.
O – To / from Offenburg (Table **916**).
P – [12] and 🍷 München - Stuttgart - Paris and v.v. [R] for international journeys. Runs in amended timings July 20 - Aug. 4.
R – From / to Dortmund or Essen (Tables **800**/**912**).
S – From / to Salzburg (Table **890**).
T – ①②③④⑦ (not June 9, 19, 20, Oct. 2, 3, 31).

a – Also June 9.
b – Until July 26 serves München Pasing (not Hbf).

c – Not June 10, 20.
d – Not June 10, 19, 20, Oct. 2, 3, 31.
e – Not June 10.
f – ⑤ (also June 19, Oct. 2, 31; not June 21, Oct. 4, Nov. 1).
g – ① (also June 11; not June 10).
h – 1521 on ⑥⑦ to July 14 (also June 10, 20).
j – Not July 20 - Sept. 8.
k – Not July 20 - Oct. 20.
m – Not June 20, 21, Oct. 4, Nov. 1.
q – Not June 9.
r – Not June 9, 20.
t – Not June 20, Nov. 1.
u – Also June 10, 19, 20, Oct. 2, 3, 31.
v – Also June 10, 19, Oct. 2, 31; not June 9, Oct. 4, Nov. 1.
w – ⑦ (also June 10; not June 9).

x – Until July 28 departs 9 minutes later from München **Pasing** (not München Hbf).
y – Also June 10.
z – Also June 20, Nov. 1.

‡ – On ①⑦ July 28 - Sept. 2 departs 2354 (the previous day).
✣ – *IC* services via Bruchsal are subject to alteration July 20 - Aug. 4 and Sept. 14 - Oct. 20 (timings may vary by up to 30 minutes and trains do not call at Bruchsal; earlier departures possible).
⊙ – Regional service operated by Abellio Rail Baden-Württemberg.
◇ – Regional service operated by Go-Ahead Verkehrsgesellschaft. Additional trains run Karlsruhe - Stuttgart and v.v. on Ⓐ**t**: **From Karlsruhe** Hbf at 0531, 0633, 0833, 1133, 1333, 1533, 1730 and 1933. **From Stuttgart** Hbf at 0532, 0829, 1132, 1332, 1532, 1730 and 1932.

STUTTGART - STUTTGART FLUGHAFEN / MESSE ✈ 932

S-Bahn 2/3

20 km. Journey time: 27 minutes. On June 20, Nov. 1 services run as on ⑦.

***Warning!** Timings of late evening services (2200 to 0100 the following morning) may vary on June 24, July 8, 22, Aug. 12, 26, Sept. 16, 23, Oct. 14, 21, Nov. 4, 11, 18, Dec. 2*

From Stuttgart Hbf: 0025, 0055, 0455 Ⓐ, 0515 Ⓐ, 0525, 0545 Ⓑ, 0555 ⚒, 0615 Ⓐ, 0625, 0645 Ⓑ, 0655 ⚒, 0715 Ⓐ, 0725, 0745, 0755, 0815, 0825, 0845, 0855 and at 15, 25, 45 and 55 minutes past each hour until 1815, 1825, 1845, 1855; 1915 Ⓐ, 1925, 1945 Ⓐ, 1955, 2015 Ⓐ, 2025, 2045 Ⓐ, 2055, 2115 Ⓐ, 2125, 2145 Ⓐ, 2155, 2215 Ⓐ, 2225, 2245 Ⓐ, 2255, 2315 Ⓐ, 2325, 2355.

From Stuttgart Flughafen ✈: 0008, 0038, 0508, 0518 Ⓐ, 0538 ⚒, 0548 Ⓑ, 0608, 0618 Ⓐ, 0638 ⚒, 0648 Ⓑ, 0708, 0718 Ⓐ, 0738 ⚒, 0748 Ⓑ, 0808, 0818, 0838, 0848 and at 08, 18, 38 and 48 minutes past each hour until 1808, 1818, 1838, 1848, 1908, 1918, 1938, 1948 Ⓐ, 2008, 2018 Ⓐ, 2038, 2048 Ⓐ, 2108, 2118 Ⓐ, 2138, 2148 Ⓐ, 2208, 2218 Ⓐ, 2238, 2248 Ⓐ, 2308, 2318 Ⓐ, 2338, 2348 Ⓐ.

ULM - FRIEDRICHSHAFEN - LINDAU 933

IRE / RE services.

SERVICE JULY 15 - SEPTEMBER 15. Until July 14 services are operated by 🚌 Biberach - Aulendorf (see page 568 for further details). From September 16 to November 3 services are operated by 🚌 Ulm - Laupheim West and Friedrichshafen - Lindau. From November 4 services are operated by 🚌 Biberach - Aulendorf and Friedrichshafen - Lindau.

km		Ⓒ	Ⓐ	F	B			B			B			B			B			B			B			
	Stuttgart Hbf **930** ... d.	...	...	0542**e**	...	0700	0801	...	0900	1001	...	1100	1201	...	...	1401	...	1454	1601	...	1700	1801	...	1900	2001	2101
0	**Ulm** Hbf......d.	0546	0550	0713**h**	0805	0815	0915	1004	1015	1115	1204	1215	1315	1404	...	1515	1604	1614	1715	1804	1815	1915	2004	2015	2115	2215
37	Biberach (Riß)......d.	0615	0619	0736	0825	0838	0938	1025	1038	1138	1225	1238	1338	1425	...	1538	1625	1638	1738	1825	1838	1938	2025	2038	2138	2240
62	Aulendorf......d.	0634	0638	0755	|	0856	0956	|	1056	1156	|	1256	1356	1442	...	1556	|	1656	1756	|	1856	2002	|	2056	2202	2259
84	Ravensburg......d.	0647	0652	0808	0852	0908	1008	1052	1108	1208	1252	1308	1408	1456	...	1608	1652	1708	1808	1852	1908	2015	2052	2108	2215	2311
95	Meckenbeuren......d.	0654	0659	0815	|	0915	1015	|	1115	1215	|	1315	1415	1503	...	1615	|	1715	1815	|	1915	2022	|	2115	2222	2318
99	Friedrichshafen Flug ¶ d.	0658	0704	|	0901	|	|	1101	|	|	1301	|	|	|	...	|	1701	|	|	1901	|	|	2101	|	|	|
103	Friedrichshafen Stadt. a.	0704	0712	0823	0906	0923	1023	1106	1123	1223	1306	1323	1423	1510	...	1623	1706	1723	1823	1906	1923	2030	2106	2123	2230	2326
103	Friedrichshafen Stadt. d.	*0727*	0728	0828	...	0928	1028	...	1128	1228	...	1328	1428	...	1550	1631**t**	...	1728	1828	...	1928	2035	...	2128	*2242*	2331
127	**Lindau** Hbf ⛴......a.	*0752*	0750	0854	...	0952	1055	...	1152	1254	...	1352	1454	...	1625	1655	...	1752	1854	...	1952	2100	...	2156	*2258*	2357

	Ⓒ	Ⓐ		F		B			B			B			B			B			B			B		
Lindau Hbf ⛴......d.	...	0452	0559	0701**v**	0805	...	0905	1005	...	1105	1131	...	1305	1405	...	1505	1605	...	1702	1805	...	1905	2005	...	*2101*	*2205*
Friedrichshafen Stadt. a.	...	0524	0622	0726	0826	...	0926	1026	...	1126	1206	...	1326	1426	...	1527	1626	...	1726	1826	...	1926	2026	...	*2127*	*2231*
Friedrichshafen Stadt. d.	0527	0531	0628	0731	0831	0850	0931	1031	1049	1131	...	1243	1331	1431	1450	1531	1628**k**	1648	1731	1831	1850	1931	2031	2045	2132	2235
Friedrichshafen Flug ¶ d.	|	|	0633**z**	|	|	0855	|	|	1054	|	...	|	|	|	1455	|	|	1655	|	|	1855	|	|	2050	|	2240
Meckenbeuren......d.	0534	0538	0635**k**	0738	0838	|	0938	1038	|	1138	...	1250	1338	1438	|	1538	1638	|	1738	1838	|	1938	2038	|	2138	2245
Ravensburg......d.	0541	0545	0643**k**	0745	0845	0905	0945	1045	1104	1145	...	1258	1345	1445	1505	1545	1645	1705	1745	1845	1905	1945	2045	2059	2146	2253
Aulendorf......d.	0556	0601	0659**k**	0801	0901	|	1001	1101	|	1201	...	1313	1401	1501	|	1601	1701	|	1801	1901	|	2001	2101	2115	2201	2308
Biberach (Riß)......d.	0613	0619	0719	0819	0919	0930	1019	1119	1130	1219	...	1330	1419	1519	1530	1619	1719	1730	1819	1919	1930	2019	2119	2129	2217	2326
Ulm Hbf......a.	0642	0642	0742	0842	0942	0953	1042	1142	1153	1242	...	1353	1442	1542	1553	1644	1742	1753	1842	1942	1953	2042	2142	2153	2246	2357
Stuttgart Hbf **930**.... a.	...	0756	0856	0956	1059	...	1156	1256	...	1356	...	...	1556	1658	...	1756	1858	...	1956	2059	...	2159	...	...	...	...

B – To / from Basel Bad Bf (Table **939**).
F – Change trains at Friedrichshafen Stadt on Ⓒ.
e – Ⓐ only.
h – 0708 on Ⓒ.
k – 2–3 minutes later on Ⓒ.
t – 1628 on Ⓒ.
v – *0656* on Ⓒ.
z – Ⓒ only.
¶ – Friedrichshafen Flughafen ✈.

935 MÜNCHEN, AUGSBURG and ULM - OBERSTDORF and LINDAU *RE / RB services except where shown*

For services to / from Bad Wörishofen see panel at foot of page (also on page 447). For regional services Memmingen - Lindau via Kißlegg see Table **937**.

km		†z		◇ Ⓐe	ALX Ⓐe	ALX Ⓐe	ALX M	◇ Ⓐe	Ⓐe	Ⓐe	Ⓐe	Ⓐe	Ⓒv	Ⓐe	Ⓐe	◇ Ⓒz			Ⓒv	Ⓐe	Ⓐe¶	Ⓒz		◇	m	EC 196 n♥
0	**München** Hbf ⊡ d.	0018	0018	...	0448	0448	0519	...	...	...	...	...	...	...	0552	0552	...	...	...	...	0622	0622	0651	...	...	0714
7	München Pasing d.	0024	0024	...	0455	0455	0527	...	...	...	...	...	...	...	0559	0559	...	...	...	...	0628	0629	0658	...	...	|
42	Geltendorf d.	0050	0050	...	0517	0517	0548	...	...	...	...	...	...	...	0622	0622	...	...	...	...	0649	0649	0721	...	...	|
56	Kaufering d.	0100	0100	...	0526	0526	0558	...	...	...	...	...	...	...	0631	0631	...	...	...	...	0658	0659	0730	...	...	|
	Nürnberg Hbf **905** d.	|	|	...	|	|	|	...	...	...	...	...	...	...	|	|	...	...	...	...	|	|	|	...	...	|
	Augsburg Hbf d.	|	|	0454	|	|	|	...	...	...	...	...	...	0547	|	|	0609	0609	...	0644	|	|	|	0703	...	|
68	Buchloe a.	0109	0109	0528	0534	0534	0606	...	...	...	...	...	...	0621	0639	0638	0642	0642	...	0708	0705c	0709	0738	0735c	...	0756
68	Buchloe d.	0113	...	▬	0536	0536	0607	0615	...	...	...	...	...	0631	0647	0646	0652	0652	...	0712	0713	0711	0739	0747	...	0758
88	Kaufbeuren d.	0125	...	...	0549	0549	0620	0628	...	...	...	...	...	|	|	0658	0703	0703	...	0724	|	|	0751	0800	...	|
94	Biessenhofen d.	0130	...	...	0554	0554	|	0634	...	...	...	...	...	|	|	0703	0707	0707	...	0729	|	|	0757	0806	...	|
100	Marktoberdorf d.	|	...	...	|	|	|	0646	...	...	...	...	...	|	|	0714	|	|	...	|	|	|	|	0816	...	|
131	**Füssen** a.	|	...	...	|	|	|	0726	...	...	...	...	...	|	|	0755	|	|	...	|	|	|	|	0855	...	|
	Türkheim (Bay) d.	|	...	...	|	|	|	▬	...	...	...	...	...	0638	0659f	...	|	|	...	|	0723	0717	|	▬	...	|
	Mindelheim d.	|	...	Ⓒv	|	|	|	...	...	...	...	...	...	0648	0713	...	|	|	...	|	0731	0731	|	Ⓐe	...	|
	Ulm Hbf d.	|	...	0511	|	|	|	...	...	...	...	0548	0613	|	|	...	|	|	0703	|	|	|	|	0658	0658e	|
	Memmingen a.	|	...	0555	|	|	|	...	...	...	...	0643	0701	0709	0733	...	|	|	0740	|	0758	0751	|	0749	0749e	|
	Memmingen **937** d.	|	...	0556	|	|	|	...	0618	...	...	0645	0702	0723	...	...	|	|	0743	|	...	...	|	0800	0800	|
131	**Kempten** Hbf a.	0156	...	0620	0621	0621	0649	ALX	0640	...	...	0717	0726	0757	...	...	0729	0729	0802	0755	...	...	0822	0825	0825	0839
131	**Kempten** Hbf d.	...	...	...	0625	0625	0650	Ⓒz	...	0651	0651	...	...	...	...	...	0731	0731	0805	0800	...	...	...	0827	0827	0841
152	Immenstadt a.	...	...	...	0641	0641	0704	◄	...	0708	0708	...	...	...	...	...	0745	0745	0820	0815	...	...	...	0840	0840	|
152	Immenstadt d.	...	...	...	0645	0656	0708	0712	...	0712	0714	...	...	...	...	...	0748	0751	0830	0821	...	...	...	0842	0850	|
	Sonthofen d.	...	...	...	|	0705	|	0722	...	|	0723	...	...	...	...	...	|	0800	0839	0830	...	...	...	|	0900	|
	Oberstdorf a.	...	...	...	|	0729	|	0740	...	|	0741	...	...	...	...	...	|	0818	0900	0859	...	...	...	|	0918	|
197	Hergatz **937** d.	...	...	...	0724	...	0744	...	...	0753	...	...	...	...	...	...	0820	...	...	...	...	...	...	0923	...	|
203	Wangen (Allgäu) **937** a.	...	...	...	|	...	|	...	...	0758x	...	...	...	...	...	...	|	...	...	...	...	...	...	0927x	...	|
220	**Lindau** Hbf **937** a.	...	...	...	0740	...	0802	...	...	...	...	...	...	...	...	...	0834	...	...	...	...	...	...	...	...	0946

	ALX		◇	◇				◇	ALX	◐	◇ †	◇	◇				Ⓐe	◇	ALX	◐	◇	◇			EC 194 p♥	
München Hbf ⊡ d.	0720	...	...	0752	...	0820	0853	...	0919	...	0941	...	0952	...	1020	1053	...	...	1119	...	...	1152	...	...	1214	1220
München Pasing d.	0727	...	...	0759	...	0827	0900	...	0927	...	0948	...	0959	...	1027	1100	...	...	1127	...	...	1159	...	...	|	1227
Geltendorf d.	|	...	...	0822	...	0849	0922	...	|	...	|	...	1022	...	1049	1121	...	...	|	...	...	1222	...	...	|	1251
Kaufering d.	0756	...	...	0831	...	0900	0931	...	0955	...	|	...	1031	...	1059	1131	...	...	1155	...	...	1231	...	...	|	1259
Nürnberg Hbf **905** d.	|	...	...	|	0716k	|	|	...	|	...	|	...	|	...	|	|	...	...	|	...	...	|	...	...	|	|
Augsburg Hbf d.	|	0730	0815	|	0830	|	|	0903	|	0929	|	1015	|	1030	|	|	...	1103	|	1130	1215	|	1230	1230	|	|
Buchloe a.	0804	0759c	0843	0839	0852	0908	0938	0935c	1003	0959c	|	1043	1038	1051	1108	1139	...	1135c	1203	1159c	1243	1238	1251	1251	1255	1308
Buchloe d.	0807	0818	...	0846	0854	0911	0939	0947	1005	1006	|	...	1046	1054	1112	1141	...	1147	1205	1206	...	1246	1254	1254	1259	1309
Kaufbeuren d.	0821	|	...	0900	0906	|	0951	1000	1018	|	|	...	1058	1106	|	1153	...	1200	1218	|	...	1258	1306	1306	|	|
Biessenhofen d.	|	|	...	0905	|	|	0958	1006	|	|	|	...	1103	|	|	1159	...	1206	|	|	...	1303	|	|	|	|
Marktoberdorf d.	|	|	...	0916	|	|	|	1016	|	|	1047f	...	1114	|	|	|	...	1215	|	|	...	1314	|	|	|	|
Füssen a.	|	|	...	0955	|	|	|	1055	|	|	1126	...	1155	|	|	|	...	1255	|	|	...	1355	|	|	|	|
Türkheim (Bay) d.	|	0825	...	▬	|	0918	|	▬	|	1014	...	...	▬	|	1118	|	...	▬	|	1214	...	▬	|	|	|	1316
Mindelheim d.	|	0835	...	...	|	0930	|	...	|	1032f	...	...	...	|	1131	|	...	...	|	1233j	...	...	|	|	|	1335j
Ulm Hbf d.	|	|	...	0817	|	|	|	0917	|	|	...	...	1017	|	|	|	1117	1117	|	|	...	1217	|	|	|	|
Memmingen a.	|	0856	...	0856	|	0951	|	0954	|	1053	...	...	1054	|	1151	|	1157	1157	|	1255	...	1256	|	|	|	1355
Memmingen **937** d.	|	▬	...	0904	|	▬	|	1001	|	▬	...	...	1104	|	▬	|	1200	1200	|	▬	...	1304	|	|	|	...
Kempten Hbf a.	0848	...	...	0926	0928	...	1022	1026	1046	...	...	...	1126	1128	...	1224	1226	1226	1246	...	...	1326	1328	1328	1340	...
Kempten Hbf d.	0850	ALX	...	...	0932	...	...	1029	1047	ALX	...	...	...	1132	...	...	1227	1227	1247	ALX	...	...	1331	1331	1342	...
Immenstadt a.	0906	◄	...	...	0945	◄	...	1044	1102	◄	...	...	...	1145	◄	...	1242	1242	1302	◄	...	...	1345	1345	|	...
Immenstadt d.	0911	0914	...	...	0947	0951	...	1051	1106	1115	...	...	...	1147	1151	...	1244	1251	1306	1319	...	...	1347	1351	|	...
Sonthofen d.	|	0922	...	...	|	1001	...	1101	|	1123	...	...	...	|	1201	...	|	1300	|	1328	...	...	|	1401	|	...
Oberstdorf a.	|	0939	...	...	|	1022	...	1120	|	1140	...	...	...	|	1219	...	|	1318	|	1351	...	...	|	1419	|	...
Hergatz **937** d.	0946	...	...	...	1020	...	...	...	1144	...	...	...	...	1220	...	...	1325	...	1343	...	...	...	1420	...	|	...
Wangen (Allgäu) **937** a.	|	...	...	...	|	...	...	...	|	...	...	...	...	|	...	...	1329x	...	|	...	...	...	|	...	|	...
Lindau Hbf **937** a.	1003	...	...	...	1034	...	...	...	1200	...	...	...	...	1235	...	...	...	...	1359	...	...	...	1434	...	1446	...

				◇	ALX	◐	◇	◇				◇	Ⓐe		ALX	ALX	RE 2013 A🍷	◐	◇	◇				◇		◐
München Hbf ⊡ d.	...	...	1253	...	1319	...	...	1352	...	1420	1451	...	...	...	1519	1519	...	...	...	1552	...	1620	1651	...	...	...
München Pasing d.	...	...	1300	...	1327	...	...	1359	...	1427	1459	...	...	...	1527	1527	...	...	...	1559	...	1627	1659	...	...	...
Geltendorf d.	...	...	1322	...	|	...	...	1422	...	1449	1521	...	...	...	|	|	...	...	...	1622	...	1649	1721	...	...	...
Kaufering d.	...	...	1331	...	1355	...	...	1431	...	1459	1531	...	...	...	1555	1555	...	...	...	1631	...	1659	1731	...	...	...
Nürnberg Hbf **905** d.	...	...	|	...	|	...	...	|	1313d	|	|	...	...	...	|	|	...	...	...	|	...	|	|	...	...	...
Augsburg Hbf d.	...	...	|	1303	|	1329	1414	|	1430	|	|	1503	...	...	|	|	...	1530	1615	|	1630	|	|	1703	...	1729
Buchloe a.	...	...	1340	1335c	1404	1401c	1443	1438	1452	1508	1538	1535c	...	...	1604	1604	...	1559c	1643	1638	1652	1706	1739	1735c	...	1759
Buchloe d.	...	...	1341	1347	1405	1406	...	1446	1454	1511	1539	1547	...	...	1605	1605	...	1606	...	1646	1654	1709	1740	1747	...	1806
Kaufbeuren d.	...	...	1353	1400	1419	|	...	1458	1506	|	1552	1600	...	...	1619	1619	...	|	...	1658	1706	|	1752	1800	...	|
Biessenhofen d.	...	...	1402	1406	|	|	...	1503	|	|	1559	1606	...	...	|	|	...	|	...	1703	|	|	1757	1806	...	|
Marktoberdorf d.	...	...	|	1416	|	|	...	1514	|	|	|	1616	...	...	|	|	...	|	...	1715	|	|	|	1816	...	|
Füssen a.	...	...	|	1455	|	|	...	1558	|	|	|	1658	...	...	|	|	...	|	...	1755	|	|	|	1855	...	|
Türkheim (Bay) d.	...	...	|	...	|	1414	...	▬	|	1518	|	...	...	...	|	|	...	1614	...	...	|	1716	|	▬	...	1814
Mindelheim d.	...	...	|	...	|	1430f	...	...	|	1531	|	...	...	...	|	|	...	1635j	...	...	|	1734j	|	...	...	1830f
Ulm Hbf d.	1317	1317	|	...	|	|	...	1418	|	|	|	...	1518	1518	|	|	1615	|	...	...	|	|	|	1717	1717	|
Memmingen a.	1355	1355	|	...	|	1451	...	1454	|	1551	|	...	1554	1554	|	|	1643	1655	...	...	|	1754	|	1756	1756	1851
Memmingen **937** d.	1400	1400	|	...	|	▬	...	1504	|	▬	|	...	1600	1600	|	|	1645	...	...	...	|	▬	|	1800	1800	...
Kempten Hbf a.	1425	1425	1427	...	1446	...	...	1526	1529	...	1623	...	1626	1626	1646	1646	1707	...	...	...	1728	...	1822	1826	1826	...
Kempten Hbf d.	1428	1428	...	...	1448	ALX	...	...	1532	...	...	...	1629	1629	1648	1648	1709	...	...	...	1731	...	...	1829	1829	...
Immenstadt a.	1443	1443	...	...	1502	◄	...	...	1545	◄	...	...	1644	1644	1702	1702	1724	...	...	...	1744	◄	...	1844	1844	...
Immenstadt d.	1445	1451	...	...	1506	1514	...	...	1547	1551	...	...	1646	1651	1706	1714	1743	...	...	...	1747	1751	...	1848	1851	...
Sonthofen d.	|	1501	...	...	|	1522	...	...	|	1601	...	...	|	1700	|	1722	1753	...	...	...	|	1801	...	|	1901	...
Oberstdorf a.	|	1519	...	...	|	1539	...	...	|	1619	...	...	|	1719	|	1739	1813	...	...	...	|	1819	...	|	1918	...
Hergatz **937** d.	1520	...	...	...	1543	...	...	...	1620	...	...	...	1722	...	1743	...	...	...	...	...	1818	...	...	1924	...	...
Wangen (Allgäu) **937** a.	|	...	...	...	|	...	...	...	|	...	...	...	|	...	|	...	...	...	...	...	|	...	...	|	...	...
Lindau Hbf **937** a.	1538	...	...	...	1559	...	...	...	1634	...	...	...	1740	...	1800	...	...	...	...	...	1834	...	...	1940	...	...

A – ALLGÄU – [12] (*IC* **2013**) Dortmund - Köln - Stuttgart - Ulm (*RE* **2013**) - Oberstdorf.
M – ⑥ München - Kempten; Ⓒ (also June 20, Aug. 15, Nov. 1) Kempten - Lindau / Oberstdorf.

c – Connects with train in preceding column.
d – Not June 9, 10, 15, 16, 22, 23. 1307 on Ⓐ to June 21.
e – Ⓐ (not June 20, Aug. 15, Nov. 1).
f – Arrives 6 – 8 minutes earlier.
j – Arrives 9 – 11 minutes earlier.
k – 0709 on Ⓐ to June 21; 0620 on Ⓒ to June 23.
m – Not Aug. 15.
n – Not July 22 - Sept. 9.
p – Not July 22 - Sept. 8.
v – Also June 20, Nov. 1.
x – From Sept. 16.
z – Also June 20, Aug. 15, Nov. 1.

◇ – Operated by Bayerische Regiobahn.

◄ – Detached from train in previous column at Immenstadt.
♥ – [12] and ✕ München - Bregenz - St Gallen - Zürich (Table **75**).
◐ – Conveys [12] Augsburg - Türkheim - Bad Wörishofen (see panel below).
¶ – Conveys [12] München - Türkheim - Bad Wörishofen (see panel below).
♣ – Additional journeys Türkheim - Bad Wörishofen: 0020, 0520 Ⓐ**e**, 0557 Ⓐ**e**, 0617 Ⓒ**z**, 0627 Ⓐ**e** and 0700 Ⓐ**e**.
⊡ – Most trains in Table **935** use platforms 27 – 36 at München Hbf (minimum connecting time from other services is 10 minutes).

ALX – Operated by Vogtlandbahn. 🍷.

AUGSBURG - TÜRKHEIM - BAD WÖRISHOFEN

km		Ⓐe	Ⓒz																								
0	**Augsburg** Hbf d.	...	...	...	...	...	0929	...	...	1130	...	...	1329	...	...	1530	...	...	1729	...	...	1930	...	...	...	...	...
40	Buchloe d.	0713	...	...	...	...	1006	...	...	1206	...	...	1406	...	...	1606	...	...	1806	...	...	2006	...	...	...	...	...
48	Türkheim (Bay) ♣ d.	0725	0726	0817	0847	0920	1017	1047	1120	1217	1247	1320	1417	1447	1520	1617	1647	1720	1817	1842	1919	2017	2047	2121	2219	2247	2321
53	**Bad Wörishofen** ♣ a.	0732	0732	0823	0853	0926	1023	1053	1126	1223	1253	1326	1423	1453	1526	1623	1653	1726	1823	1848	1925	2023	2053	2128	2226	2253	2328

RE / RB services except where shown MÜNCHEN, AUGSBURG and ULM - OBERSTDORF and LINDAU 935

For services to / from Bad Wörishofen see panel at foot of page (also on page 446). For regional services Memmingen - Lindau via Kißlegg see Table **937**.

	ALX	ALX	◇	◇	EC 190 p♥					◇	ALX	◐	◇	◇					ALX	◇					ALX	
München Hbf ⊡ d.	1719	1719	...	1752	1815	1820	...	...	1851	...	1919	...	...	1952	...	2020	...	...	2119	...	...	...	2220	...	2319	...
München Pasing d.	1727	1727	...	1759	|	1827	...	...	1859	...	1927	...	...	1959	...	2027	...	...	2127	...	...	...	2227	...	2327	...
Geltendorf d.	|	|	...	1822	|	1852	...	...	1922	...	|	...	...	2022	...	2050	...	...	2148	...	...	...	2250	...	2348	...
Kaufering d.	1755	1755	...	1831	|	1900	...	...	1931	...	1955	...	...	2031	...	2101	...	...	2158	...	...	...	2301	...	2358	...
Nürnberg Hbf **905** d.	|	|	...	|	|	|	1732**y**	1732**y**	|	...	|	...	...	|	...	|	...	...	|	...	...	...	|	...	|	...
Augsburg Hbf d.	|	|	1815	|	|	|	1844	1844	|	1903	|	1930	2014	|	2043	|	...	2130	|	...	...	2233	|	...	|	2327
Buchloe a.	1803	1803	1843	1838	1856	1907	1904**c**	1904	1940	1935**c**	2003	1959**c**	2043	2038	2105	2110**c**	...	2203	2206	...	...	2305	2309**c**	...	0006	2359**c**
Buchloe d.	1805	1805	...	1846	1858	1909	1911	1911	1941	1947	2005	2006	▬	2046	2114	2111	...	2209	2208	...	...	2313	2311	...	0007	0009
Kaufbeuren d.	1818	1818	...	1858	|	|	1925	1925	1953	2000	2018	|	...	2100	2125	|	...	|	2221	2227	...	2324	|	...	0020	|
Biessenhofen d.	|	|	...	1903	|	|	|	|	1958	2006	|	|	...	2105	2130	|	...	|	|	2232	...	2328	|	...	0025	|
Marktoberdorf d.	|	|	...	1914	|	|	|	|	|	2014	|	|	...	2115	|	|	...	|	|	2242	...	|	|	...	|	|
Füssen a.	|	|	...	1955	|	|	|	|	|	2055	|	|	...	2155	|	|	...	|	|	2323	...	|	|	...	|	|
Türkheim (Bay) d.	|	|	...	▬	|	1916	|	|	|	▬	|	2014	...	...	|	2118	...	2217	|	▬	...	|	2318	...	|	0017
Mindelheim d.	|	|	...	...	|	1935**j**	|	|	|	...	|	2030	...	...	|	2130	...	2230	|	...	...	|	2330	...	|	0027
Ulm Hbf d.	|	|	...	1817	|	|	|	|	|	1917	|	|	2017	...	|	|	2117	|	|	...	2217	|	|	2320	|	|
Memmingen a.	|	|	...	1855	|	1954	|	|	|	1954	|	2051	2056	...	|	2151	2200	2251	|	...	2257	|	2350	0003	|	0047
Memmingen **937** d.	|	|	...	1902	|	2005**b**	|	|	|	2000	|	▬	2106	...	|	▬	2201	...	|	...	2305	|	▬	0007	|	...
Kempten Hbf a.	1843	1843	...	1927	1939	|	1947	1947	2025	2029	2046	...	2132	...	2152	...	2227	...	2250	...	2331	2351	...	0033	0052	...
Kempten Hbf d.	1848	1848	...	...	1941	|	1950	1950	2034**h**	...	2048	...	...	...	2155	...	...	...	2254	...	...	2355	...	...	...	...
Immenstadt a.	1903	1903	...	...	|	⊕	2003	2003	2051**h**	...	2103	...	...	...	2210	...	...	...	2310	...	...	0010	...	...	...	...
Immenstadt d.	1907	1915	...	...	|	|	2007	2016	...	...	2106	2110	...	...	2211	2214	...	...	2311	2314	...	0015*	0014	...	...	...
Sonthofen d.	|	1924	...	...	|	|	|	2025	...	...	|	2120	...	...	|	2223	...	...	|	2323	...	|	0023	...	...	...
Oberstdorf a.	|	1941	...	...	|	|	|	2049	...	...	|	2143	...	...	|	2241	...	...	|	2341	...	|	0040	...	...	...
Hergatz **937** d.	1944	...	...	...	|	2103**b**	2039	...	...	...	2144	...	...	...	2250	...	...	...	2348	...	...	0111*	...	...	...	...
Wangen (Allgäu) **937** a.	|	...	...	...	|	2058**b**	|	...	...	...	|	...	...	...	|	...	...	...	|	...	...	|	...	...	...	...
Lindau Hbf **937** a.	2001	...	...	...	2046	2118**b**	2053	...	...	...	2201	...	...	...	2306	...	...	...	0005	...	...	0141*	...	...	...	...

km	km		ALX Ⓐe	ALX ⑥	Ⓐe	Ⓐe		Ⓐe	Ⓐe	Ⓐe	Ⓐe	Ⓒz	Ⓐe	◇ Ⓐe	Ⓒz	Ⓒz	◧ Ⓐe	Ⓒz	Ⓐe	ALX Ⓐe	ALX Ⓐe	ALX Ⓒz	ALX Ⓒz	◧ Ⓒz	Ⓐe	
0		**Lindau** Hbf **937** d.	...	...	...	...	...	...	...	...	...	...	...	...	0516	...	...	...	...	...	0520	...	0555	...	...	...
		Wangen (Allgäu) **937** d.	...	...	...	...	...	...	...	...	...	...	...	...	|	...	...	...	...	...	|	...	|	...	...	...
23		Hergatz **937** d.	...	...	...	...	...	...	...	...	...	...	...	...	0532	...	...	...	...	...	0537	...	0611	...	...	...
	0	**Oberstdorf** d.	...	...	...	...	...	...	...	0452	...	...	...	...	|	0542	...	0542**k**	...	0542	|	0611	|	...	...	...
	13	Sonthofen d.	...	...	...	...	...	...	...	0511	...	...	...	...	|	0600	...	0600**k**	...	0601	|	0630	|	...	...	...
	21	Immenstadt a.	...	...	...	...	...	...	...	0521	...	...	...	...	0609	0609	...	0609**k**	...	0610**c**	0616**c**	0639	0650	...	...	...
	21	Immenstadt d.	...	...	...	...	...	...	...	0528	...	...	...	...	▬	0615	...	0615**k**	0623	0629	0629	0658	0658	...	...	...
	42	**Kempten** Hbf a.	...	...	...	...	...	...	...	0543	...	...	...	...	...	0629	...	0629**k**	0638	0643	0643	0714	0714	...	...	...
	42	**Kempten** Hbf d.	0446	0507	...	0521	0529	0546	...	0544	0601	...	...	...	...	0632	...	0634	0641	0650	0650	0715	0715	...	...	0731**f**
85	77	Memmingen **937** a.	|	|	...	|	0554	|	...	0613	|	...	...	...	...	|	...	0659	0706	|	|	|	|	...	...	0800
85	77	Memmingen d.	|	|	0525	|	0556	|	0549	...	|	0609	0626	...	...	|	0647	0704	0710	|	|	|	|	0707	0739	0804
	129	**Ulm** Hbf a.	|	|	|	|	0641	|	|	...	|	|	|	...	...	|	|	0742	0743	|	|	|	|	|	|	0838
112		Mindelheim d.	|	|	0548	|	▬	|	0610	...	|	0631	0648	...	◇	|	0712	...	...	|	|	|	|	0731	0800	▬
123		Türkheim (Bay) d.	|	|	0557	|	...	|	0620	...	|	0639	0657	...	Ⓒz	|	0724	...	...	|	|	|	|	0747	0809	◇
		Füssen d.	|	|	|	|	...	|	|	...	|	|	|	0600	0600	|	|	...	...	|	|	|	|	|	|	0703
		Marktoberdorf d.	|	|	|	|	...	|	|	...	|	|	|	0643	0643	|	|	...	...	|	|	|	|	|	|	0747
		Biessenhofen d.	0513	0534	|	0548	...	0611	|	...	0627	|	|	0651	0651	0656	|	...	...	|	|	|	|	|	|	0755
		Kaufbeuren d.	0519	0539	|	0553	◇	0616	|	...	0634	|	|	0657	0656	0703	|	...	...	0717	0717	0742	0742	|	|	0800
131		Buchloe a.	0530	0551	0604	0605**c**	Ⓒz	0628	0626**c**	...	0647	0645**c**	0704	0709**c**	0708	0716**c**	0730	...	...	0730**c**	0730**c**	0753	0753	0753	0816	0812**c**
131		Buchloe d.	0532	0552	0610	0607	0613	0629	0640	...	0648	0651	0712	0716	0719	0719	0739	...	...	0733	0733	0755	0755	0800	0817	0825
171		**Augsburg** Hbf a.	*0607*	|	|	0638	0646	|	0712	...	0716	|	|	0745	|	0744	0811	...	...	|	|	|	|	0829	0844	0857
		Nürnberg Hbf **905** a.	|	|	|	...	...	|	...	...	...	|	|	...	|	...	...	...	...	|	|	|	|	...	...	...
		Kaufering d.	0541	0600	0618	...	...	0637	...	...	...	0700	0720	...	0728	...	...	...	...	0742	0742	0803	0803	...	...	...
		Geltendorf d.	|	0610	0628	...	...	0646	...	...	...	0710	0730	...	0739	...	...	...	...	|	|	|	|	...	...	...
		München Pasing a.	0609	0634	0651	...	...	0711	...	...	...	0733	0756	...	0810	...	...	...	...	0809	0809	0833	0833	...	...	...
		München Hbf ⊡ a.	0618	0641	0700	...	...	0719	...	...	...	0741	0804	...	0817	...	...	...	...	0819	0819	0841	0841	...	...	...

						◇	ALX	ALX		Ⓐe			EC 191 p♥				IC 2012 A 🍷	ALX	ALX	Ⓒz						◇
Lindau Hbf **937** d.	...	0707**b**	...	0725	...	...	...	0757	...	...	...	...	0913	...	0928	...	...	...	0958	1016	...	...	...	1125	...	...
Wangen (Allgäu) **937** d.	...	0730**b**	...	|	...	...	...	|	...	0825**v**	...	...	|	...	|	...	...	...	|	|	...	...	...	|	...	...
Hergatz **937** d.	...	0724**b**	...	0740	...	...	...	0814	...	0836	...	...	|	...	0942	...	...	...	1014	1034	...	...	...	1140	...	...
Oberstdorf d.	...	|	0742	|	...	...	0822	|	0841	|	...	...	|	0926	|	...	0951	1008	|	|	1042	...	1142	|	...	...
Sonthofen d.	...	|	0800	|	...	...	0839	|	0900	|	...	...	|	0948	|	...	1012	1031	|	|	1100	...	1201	|	...	...
Immenstadt a.	...	⊕	0809	0814	...	...	0846	0851	0910	0914	...	...	|	1002	1014	...	1021	1039	1051	1112	1110	...	1210	1214	...	...
Immenstadt d.	...	|	0816	0816	...	...	▶	0900	0916	0916	...	...	|	1016	1016	...	1036	▶	1100	1117	1117	...	▶	1216	...	...
Kempten Hbf a.	...	|	0830	0830	...	...	▬	0913	0931	0931	...	...	1019	1029	1029	...	1052	▬	1114	1132	1132	...	▬	1230	...	...
Kempten Hbf d.	0736	|	0832	0832	0834	...	...	0918	0934	0934	0936	...	1021	1032	1032	1034	1055	...	1116	1135	1135	1136	...	1232	1234	...
Memmingen **937** a.	|	0813**b**	|	|	0855	...	◧	|	0959	0959	|	...	|	|	|	1057	1123	◧	|	1158	1158	|	...	|	1255	...
Memmingen d.	|	0817	|	|	0904	...	0907	|	1001	1001	|	1004	|	|	|	1059	1127	1107	|	1204	1204	|	1204	|	1304	...
Ulm Hbf a.	|	|	|	|	0938	...	|	|	1038	1038	|	|	|	|	|	1139	1155	|	|	1239	1239	|	|	|	1340	...
Mindelheim d.	|	0836	|	|	▬	...	0932	|	...	▬	|	1037**j**	|	|	|	▬	▬	1132	|	...	▬	|	1238**j**	|	▬	...
Türkheim (Bay) d.	|	0845	|	|	◇	...	0946	|	...	◇	|	1045	|	|	|	◇	...	1146	|	...	◇	|	1246	|	◇	...
Füssen d.	|	|	|	|	0805	...	|	|	...	0905	|	|	|	|	|	1005	...	|	|	...	1105	|	|	|	1205	...
Marktoberdorf d.	|	|	|	|	0848	...	|	|	...	0947	|	|	|	|	|	1048	...	|	|	...	1147	|	|	|	1248	...
Biessenhofen d.	0800	|	|	|	0856	...	|	|	...	0955	1001	|	|	|	|	1056	...	|	|	...	1155	1200	|	|	1256	...
Kaufbeuren d.	0807	|	0856	0856	0903	...	|	0943	...	1001	1008	|	|	1056	1056	1103	...	|	1143	...	1201	1208	|	1256	1303	...
Buchloe a.	0817	0852	0908	0908	0915	...	0952	0954**c**	...	1015	1019**c**	1052	1100	1108	1108	1115	◇	1152	1154**c**	...	1215	1219**c**	1252	1306	1315	...
Buchloe d.	0820	0853	0909	0909	0918	0918	1000	0955	...	1022	1020	1053	1102	1109	1109	1118	1118	1200	1155	...	1222	1220	1253	1309	1318	1318
Augsburg Hbf a.	|	|	0930	0930	|	0945	1029	|	...	1056	|	|	|	1130	1130	|	1145	1229	|	...	1256	|	|	1330	|	1345
Nürnberg Hbf **905** a.	|	|	1044**r**	1044**r**	|	...	...	|	...	...	|	|	|	...	...	|	...	...	|	...	...	|	|	1446**n**	|	...
Kaufering d.	0829	0902	...	...	0928	...	...	1003	...	...	1028	1101	|	...	...	1128	...	...	1203	...	...	1229	1301	...	1328	...
Geltendorf d.	0838	0911	...	...	0937	...	...	|	...	...	1037	1109	|	...	...	1137	...	...	|	...	...	1238	1311	...	1337	...
München Pasing a.	0857	0933	...	...	0958	...	...	1033	...	...	1058	1132	|	...	...	1158	...	...	1233	...	...	1256	1333	...	1358	...
München Hbf ⊡ a.	0905	0942	...	...	1005	...	...	1040	...	...	1106	1140	1147	...	...	1205	...	...	1241	...	...	1304	1341	...	1405	...

A – ALLGÄU – [12] Oberstdorf - Stuttgart - Dortmund.

b – From Sept. 16.
c – Connects with train in preceding column.
e – Ⓐ (not June 20, Aug. 15, Nov. 1).
f – 0734 on Ⓐ (not June 20, Aug. 15, Nov. 1).
h – ①-④ (not June 10, 20, Aug. 15, Oct. 3).
j – Arrives 12 – 14 minutes earlier.
k – ⑥ only.
n – Not June 9, 10, 15, 16, 22, 23. 1451 on Ⓐ to June 21.

p – Not July 22 - Sept. 8.
r – 1134 on Ⓒ to June 23.
v – From Sept. 16.
y – 1713 on Ⓐ to June 21; 1634 on Ⓒ to June 23.
z – Also June 20, Aug. 15, Nov. 1.

* – By 🚌.
⊕ – Via Kißlegg (Table **937**).

◀ – Detached from train in previous column at Immenstadt.
▶ – Attached to train in the next column at Immenstadt.
♥ – [12] and ✕ München - Bregenz - St Gallen - Zürich and v.v. (Table **75**).
◐ – Conveys [12] Augsburg - Türkheim - Bad Wörishofen (see panel on page 446).
◧ – Conveys [12] Bad Wörishofen - Türkheim - Augsburg (see panel below).
♣ – Other journeys Bad Wörishofen - Türkheim: 0506 Ⓐ **e**, 0545 Ⓐ **e**, 0609 Ⓐ **e**, 0758 Ⓐ **e** and 2301.
◇ – Operated by Bayerische Regiobahn.
⊡ – Most trains in Table **935** use platforms 27 – 36 at München Hbf (minimum connecting time from / to other services is 10 minutes).

BAD WÖRISHOFEN - TÜRKHEIM - AUGSBURG

	Ⓒz	Ⓐe	Ⓐe	Ⓒz																							
Bad Wörishofen ♣ d.	0628	0643	0711	0739	0831	0907	0932	1034	1101	1132	1234	1302	1332	1429	1501	1532	1631	1701	1732	1829	1905	1932	2028	2108	2134	2231	2334
Türkheim (Bay) ♣ a.	0635	0650	0718	0746	0838	0914	0939	1041	1108	1139	1241	1309	1339	1435	1508	1538	1638	1708	1738	1835	1912	1939	2035	2115	2140	2238	2340
Buchloe a.	...	...	0730	0753	...	...	0952	...	...	1152	...	...	1352	...	...	1552	...	...	1752	...	...	1952	...	...	...	...	...
Augsburg Hbf a.	...	...	0811	0829	...	...	1029	...	...	1229	...	...	1429	...	...	1629	...	...	1829	...	...	2027	...	...	...	...	...

935 LINDAU and OBERSTDORF - ULM, AUGSBURG and MÜNCHEN

RE/RB services except where shown

For services from/to Bad Wörishofen see pages 446 and 447. For regional services Lindau - Memmingen via Kißlegg see Table **937**.

	ALX	ALX			Ⓒz	Ⓐe				◇	ALX	ALX		Ⓐe	Ⓒz		EC 195 p♥			◇		ALX	ALX			
Lindau Hbf ... **937** d.	...	1158	...	1217z	...	...	...	1325	...	...	...	1358	...	...	...	...	1513	...	1525	...	...	...	1557	...	1617	...
Wangen (Allgäu) **937** d.	...	|	...	1227a	...	...	...	|	...	...	...	|	...	...	...	...	|	...	|	...	...	...	|	...	|	...
Hergatz ... **937** d.	...	1214	...	1236	...	...	...	1342	...	...	...	1414	...	...	...	...	|	...	1540	...	...	...	1614	...	1635	...
Oberstdorf ... d.	1222	|	1242	|	...	...	1338	|	...	...	1422	|	1442	...	...	...	|	1540	|	...	...	1622	|	1638	|	...
Sonthofen ... d.	1239	|	1300	|	...	...	1401	|	...	...	1439	|	1500	...	...	...	|	1601	|	...	...	1639	|	1700	|	...
Immenstadt ... a.	1247	1251	1310	1314	...	...	1410	1414	...	...	1447	1451	1510	...	...	...	|	1610	1613	...	...	1647	1651	1710	1714	...
Immenstadt ... d.	▶	1300	1316	1316	...	...	▶	1417	...	...	▶	1500	1517	...	...	...	|	1616	1616	...	...	▶	1700	▶	1716	...
Kempten Hbf ... a.	▬	1314	1331	1331	...	...	▬	1430	...	...	▬	1514	1532	...	...	...	1619	1630	1630	...	...	▬	1714	▬	1731	...
Kempten Hbf ... d.	...	1316	1334	1334	1336	1341	...	1432	1435	...	...	1517	1535	1535	1536	...	1621	1631	1631	...	1635	...	1716	...	1733	1736
Memmingen ... **937** a.	◧	|	1400	1400	|	|	...	|	1456	...	◧	|	1558	|	|	...	|	|	|	...	1704	...	|	◧	1759	|
Memmingen ... d.	1307	|	1404	1404	|	|	1408	|	1504	...	1507	|	1602	|	|	1604	|	|	|	...	1705	...	|	1707	1804	|
Ulm Hbf ... a.	|	|	1439	1439	|	|	|	|	1538	...	|	|	1641	|	|	|	|	|	|	...	1738	...	|	|	1839	|
Mindelheim ... d.	1332	|	...	▬	|	|	1430	|	▬	...	1532	|	▬	|	|	1637j	|	|	|	...	▬	◇	|	1731	▬	|
Türkheim (Bay) ... d.	1346	|	...	◇	|	|	1439	|	◇	...	1546	|	◇	|	|	1644	|	|	|	...	...	†w	|	1746	◇	|
Füssen ... d.	|	|	...	1305	|	|	|	|	1405	...	|	|	1505	|	|	|	|	|	|	1605	...	1634	|	|	1705	|
Marktoberdorf ... d.	|	|	...	1347	|	|	|	|	1448	...	|	|	1547	|	|	|	|	|	|	1648	...	1718	|	|	1747	|
Biessenhofen ... d.	|	|	...	1355	1400	1405	|	|	1456	...	|	|	1555	1605	1600	|	|	|	|	1656	...	|	|	|	1755	1805
Kaufbeuren ... d.	|	1343	...	1401	1407	1411	|	1456	1503	...	|	1543	1601	1610	1608	|	|	1655	1655	1703	...	|	1743	|	1801	1810
Buchloe ... a.	1352	1354c	...	1415	1419c	1420	1445	1507	1515	...	1552	1554c	1615	1620	1618	1649	1656	1706	1706	1715	◇	|	1754	1752c	1813	1821
Buchloe ... d.	1400	1355	...	1422	1420	1422	1453	1509	1518	1518	1600	1555	1622	1621	1620	1652	1658	1711	1711	1718	1718	|	1755	1759	1821	1822
Augsburg Hbf ... a.	1429	|	...	1456	|	|	|	1530	|	1545	1629	|	1657	|	|	|	|	1730	1730	|	1745	|	|	1829	1857	|
Nürnberg Hbf **905** ... a.	...	|	...	...	|	|	|	...	|	...	...	|	...	|	|	|	|	...	...	|	...	|	|	...	...	|
Kaufering ... d.	...	1403	...	...	1428	1429	1501	...	1528	...	...	1604	...	1629	1629	1659	|	...	...	1728	...	|	1803	...	...	1830
Geltendorf ... d.	...	|	...	...	1437	1438	1510	...	1537	...	...	|	...	1637	1637	1707	|	...	...	1737	...	|	|	...	...	1840
München Pasing ... a.	...	1433	...	...	1503	1458	1533	...	1557	...	...	1632	...	1658	1658	1733	|	...	...	1758	...	1812	1833	...	...	1909
München Hbf ... ⊡ a.	...	1441	...	...	1509	1509	1541	...	1604	...	...	1640	...	1708	1705	1741	1746	...	...	1805	...	1819	1841	...	...	1916

	Ⓐe					◇	ALX	ALX	Ⓐe		Ⓒz				ALX	ALX		EC 197 q♥	Ⓒz						ALX	
Lindau Hbf ... **937** d.	...	...	...	1725	...	...	...	1758	1817	...	...	...	1908	...	...	1954	...	2016	...	...	2058	...	...	...	2209	...
Wangen (Allgäu) **937** d.	...	...	...	|	...	...	...	|	|	...	...	...	|	...	...	|	...	|	...	...	|	...	...	...	|	...
Hergatz ... **937** d.	...	...	...	1739	...	...	...	1815	1835	...	...	...	1922	...	...	2011	...	|	...	...	2115	...	...	...	2226	...
Oberstdorf ... d.	1705	...	1740	|	...	...	1823	|	|	1839	1859	1920	|	...	2019	|	...	|	...	2123	|	...	...	2220	|	...
Sonthofen ... d.	1730	...	1801	|	...	...	1840	|	|	1901	1924	1942	|	...	2037	|	...	|	...	2142	|	...	...	2241	|	...
Immenstadt ... a.	1739	...	1810	1813	...	...	1848	1853	1914	1910	1931	1950	1955	...	2047	2047	...	|	...	2150	2152	...	...	2250	2305	...
Immenstadt ... d.	1748	...	1816	1816	...	...	▶	1857	1917	1917	1940	▶	1958	...	▶	2055	...	|	...	▶	2156	...	...	▬	2306	...
Kempten Hbf ... a.	1805	...	1830	1830	...	...	▬	1912	1931	1931	1955	▬	2011	...	▬	2110	...	2122	...	▬	2211	...	...	...	2323	...
Kempten Hbf ... d.	1806	...	1832	1832	1834	...	...	1914	1934	1934	1958	...	2012	2031	...	2114	...	2124	2134	...	2214	2236	...	...	2325	2334
Memmingen ... **937** a.	|	...	|	|	1856	...	◧	|	1959	1959	2018	...	|	2056	...	|	...	|	2159	...	|	2300	...	...	|	2400
Memmingen ... d.	|	1807	|	|	1904	...	1907	|	2004	2004t	2020	2008	|	2104‡	...	|	2107	|	2204	2208	|	2301	2307	...	|	0004
Ulm Hbf ... a.	|	|	|	|	1938	...	|	|	2039	2039t	2056	|	|	2200‡	...	|	|	|	2238	|	|	2356	|	...	|	0046
Mindelheim ... d.	|	1831	|	|	▬	...	1932	|	▬	...	...	2030	|	...	...	|	2132	|	▬	2233	|	...	2332	...	|	▬
Türkheim (Bay) ... d.	|	1839	|	|	◇	...	1946	|	◇	...	...	2039	|	...	◇	|	2147	|	◇	2241	|	...	2346	◇	|	...
Füssen ... d.	|	|	|	|	1805	...	|	|	1905	...	...	|	|	...	2033	|	|	|	2133	|	|	...	|	2233	|	...
Marktoberdorf ... d.	|	|	|	|	1848	...	|	|	1947	...	...	|	|	...	2117	|	|	|	2218	|	|	...	|	2317	|	...
Biessenhofen ... d.	1832	|	|	|	1856	...	|	|	1955	...	...	|	|	...	2125	|	|	|	2226	|	2235	...	|	2325	2351	...
Kaufbeuren ... d.	1837	|	1856	1856	1903	...	|	1941	2001	...	...	|	2038	...	2132	2141	|	|	2232	|	2241	...	|	2331	2356	...
Buchloe ... a.	1848	1845c	1908	1908	1915	...	1952	1953c	2015	...	...	2045	2050c	...	...	2153	2152	2203c	...	2248	2251	...	2352	...	0008	←
Buchloe ... d.	1855	1851	1909	1909	1918	1918	2000	1955	2022	...	...	2053	2051	...	...	2155	2215	2205	...	2251	2256	...	0013	...	0009	0013
Augsburg Hbf ... a.	1917	|	1930	1930	|	1945	2027	|	2056	...	...	|	2121	...	...	|	2245	|	...	|	2327	...	→	...	|	0048
Nürnberg Hbf **905** ... a.	...	|	2057r	2057r	|	...	...	|	...	...	...	|	...	...	...	|	...	|	...	|	...	...	...	...	|	...
Kaufering ... d.	...	1859	...	...	1928	...	...	2003	...	...	...	2101	...	...	...	2203	...	|	...	2301	...	...	...	...	0017	...
Geltendorf ... d.	...	1909	...	...	1937	...	...	|	...	...	...	2110	...	...	...	|	...	|	...	2310	...	...	...	...	0027	...
München Pasing ... a.	...	1934	...	...	1958	...	...	2033	...	...	...	2133	...	...	...	2233	...	|	...	2333	...	...	...	...	0049	...
München Hbf ... ⊡ a.	...	1941	...	...	2005	...	...	2041	...	...	...	2141	...	...	...	2241	...	2248	...	2341	...	...	...	...	0057	...

a – Ⓐ from Sept. 16 (not Nov. 1).
c – Connects with train in preceding column.
e – Ⓐ (not June 20, Aug. 15, Nov. 1).
j – Arrives 1625.
p – Not July 22 - Sept. 8.
q – Not July 21 - Sept. 8.
r – 2134 on Ⓒ to June 23.

t – Ⓐ (not June 20, Nov. 1).
w – Also June 20, Aug. 15, Nov. 1.
z – Ⓒ (also June 20, Aug. 15, Nov. 1).

‡ – On Ⓒ (also June 20, Aug. 15, Nov. 1) Memmingen d. 2105, Ulm a. 2138.
▶ – Attached to train in the next column at Immenstadt.
♥ – (12) and ✕ Zürich - St Gallen - Bregenz - München (Table **75**).

◧ – Conveys (12) Bad Wörishofen - Türkheim - Augsburg (see panel on page 447).
◇ – Operated by Bayerische Regiobahn.
⊡ – Most trains in Table **935** use platforms 27 – 36 at München Hbf (minimum connecting time to other services is 10 minutes).

ALX – Operated by Vogtlandbahn. 🍸.

936 STUTTGART - TÜBINGEN - AULENDORF

DB (*IRE*/*RB* services); HzL ◇

km		Ⓐt	2	Ⓐt2	Ⓐt2	Ⓒz2	Ⓐt		2		2		2		2		2		2		2		2		2	
0	**Stuttgart** Hbf ... ☆ d.	...	...	...	...	...	...	...	...	0815	...	1015	...	1215	...	1415	...	1615	...	1815	...	2015	...	...	...	2217
57	Reutlingen ... ☆ d.	...	...	...	...	...	0644	...	...	0850	...	1050	...	1250	...	1450	...	1650	...	1850	...	2050	...	...	...	2251
71	**Tübingen** Hbf ... ☆ d.	...	...	0546	...	0612	0658	0658	0727	0900	0928	1100	1128	1300	1328	1500	1528	1700	1728	1900	1928	2100	2136	...	2236	2310
96	Hechingen ... d.	...	...	0615	...	0638	0719	0719	0753	0920	0952	1120	1152	1320	1352	1520	1552	1720	1752	1920	1952	2120	2204	...	2302	2332
113	Balingen (Württ) ... d.	...	...	0636	...	0652	0734	0734	0808	0935	1007	1135	1207	1335	1407	1535	1607r	1735	1807	1935	2007	2132	2219	...	2317	2345
131	Albstadt-Ebingen ... d.	...	0625	0655	*0658*	0710	0747	0747	0833	0947	1033	1147	1233	1347	1433	1547	1633	1747	1833	1948	2033	2150	2238	...	2336	2358
158	**Sigmaringen** ... a.	...	0654	...	*0721*	...	0811	0811	0858	1011	1058	1211	1258	1411	1458	1611	1658	1811	1858	2011	2058	2216	...	...	...	0020
158	**Sigmaringen** ... **938** d.	0540	0654	...	0727	...	0812	0812	*0911*	1012	*1111*	1212	*1311*	1412	*1511*	1612	*1711*	1813	*1911*	2013	*2104*	2218	...	2303	...	...
175	Herbertingen ... **938** d.	0554	0709	...	0741	...	0828	0828	*0929*	1028	*1129*	1228	*1329*	1428	*1529*	1628	*1729*	1828	*1929*	2028	*2119*	2232	...	2323j	...	...
184	Bad Saulgau ... d.	0605	0724j	...	...	...	0837	0837	*0937*	1037	*1137*	1237	*1337*	1437	*1537*	1637	*1737*	1837	*1937*	2037	*2132*	2241	...	2332	...	...
203	**Aulendorf** ... a.	0621	0739	...	...	...	0852	0852	*0952*	1052	*1152*	1252	*1352*	1452	*1552*	1652	*1752*	1852	*1952*	2052	*2147*	2256	...	2349	...	...

	2	Ⓐt	Ⓒz	Ⓐt2	Ⓐt	Ⓐt2	Ⓒz2	Ⓐt		2		2		2		2		2		2		2		A2	2	
Aulendorf ... d.	...	...	...	...	0546	...	...	0632	0705	*0804*	0904	*1004*	1104	*1204*	1304	*1404*	1504	*1604*	1704	*1804*	1904	*2004*	2115	...	2205	2313
Bad Saulgau ... d.	...	...	...	...	0604	...	...	0647	0721	*0819*	0919	*1019*	1119	*1219*	1319	*1419*	1519	*1619*	1719	*1819*	1919	*2019*	2130	...	2220	2333
Herbertingen ... **938** d.	...	...	...	...	0613	...	...	0656	0730	*0829*	0930	*1029*	1130	*1229*	1330	*1429*	1530	*1629*	1730	*1829*	1930	*2029*	2139	...	2232	2342
Sigmaringen ... **938** a.	...	...	...	...	0627	...	...	0715	0744	*0850*	0948	*1050*	1148	*1250*	1348	*1450*	1548	*1650*	1748	*1849*	1948	*2051*	2152	...	2253	2358
Sigmaringen ... d.	...	0542	0548	...	0629	...	...	...	0750	0903	0950	1103	1150	1305	1350	1503	1550	1703	1750	1905	1950	2105	2153	...	2254	...
Albstadt-Ebingen ... d.	0503	0605	0613	0632	0652	0703	0727	...	0812	0928	1011	1128	1211	1329	1411	1528	1611	1728	1811	1929	2011	2129	2217	2256	2318	...
Balingen (Württ) ... d.	0521	0619	0625	0700	▬	0734	0751	...	0827	0952	1027	1152	1227	1352	1427	1552	1627	1752	1827	1952	2027	2148	2234	2317	...	...
Hechingen ... d.	0536	0634	0637	0718	Ⓐt	0752	0807	...	0839	1007	1039	1207	1239	1407	1439	1607	1639	1807	1840	2007	2039	2204	2246	2331	...	...
Tübingen Hbf ... ☆ a.	0601	0652	0655	0744	0757	0818	0830	...	0857	1030	1057	1230	1257	1430	1457	1630	1657	1830	1857	2030	2057	2229	2304	2356	...	...
Reutlingen ... ☆ a.	...	0707	0708	...	0806	...	...	...	0908	...	1108	...	1308	...	1508	...	1708	...	1908	...	2108	...	...	...	...	...
Stuttgart Hbf ... ☆ a.	...	0743	0743	...	0843	...	...	...	0943	...	1143	...	1343	...	1543	...	1743	...	1943	...	2143	...	...	...	...	...

Other services Stuttgart - Tübingen

km		②–⑦	①		Ⓐt	⑥	Ⓐt	Ⓒz				
0	**Stuttgart** Hbf ... **930** d.	0048	0057	...	0522	*0525*	0616	*0629*	0722	0822		2322
22	Plochingen ... **930** d.	0107	0117	...	0541	0611	0637	0658	0742v	0844	and	2344
35	Nürtingen ... d.	0120	0130	...	0552	0622	0649	0710	0755	0855	hourly	2355
57	Reutlingen Hbf ... d.	0137	0146	...	0608	0641	0706	0728	0812	0912	until	0012
71	**Tübingen** Hbf ... a.	0151	0200	...	0619	0654	0719	0743	0823	0923		0023

	Ⓐt		Ⓒz	Ⓐt						2
Tübingen Hbf ... d.	0506	0535	0622	0625	0737		2037	2136	2236	2313
Reutlingen Hbf ... d.	0517	0547	0632	0636	0748	and	2048	2150	2250	2327
Nürtingen ... d.	0533	0603	0649	0652	0804	hourly	2104	2206	2306	2345
Plochingen ... **930** d.	0547	0618	0700	0704	0818	until	2118	2218	2319	2356
Stuttgart Hbf .. **930** a.	0607	0638	0718	0723	0838		2138	2238	2339	*0024*

A – ⑤⑥ (also June 9, 19, Oct. 2, 31).
j – Arrives 6 – 7 minutes earlier.

r – 1611 on Ⓐ (not June 20, Nov. 1).
t – Not June 20, Nov. 1.
v – 0744 on Ⓒ (also June 20, Nov. 1).

z – Also June 20, Nov. 1.

☆ – See panel below main table for other services.
◇ – Hohenzollerische Landesbahn.

RE / RB services; 2nd class only — MEMMINGEN - LINDAU and AULENDORF — SEE NOTE ⊠ BELOW — 937

km		Ⓐe	Ⓒz							M	
0	**Memmingen** d.	0625	...	...	...	...	...	...	...	2005	...
32	Leutkirch d.	0703	0715	...	...	...	...	...	...	2038	...
	Aulendorf d.	|	|	0908	1108	1308	1508	1708	1908	|	2108
	Bad Waldsee d.	|	|	0916	1116	1316	1516	1716	1916	|	2116
	Kißlegg a.	0711	0723	0932	1132	1332	1532	1732	1932	2047	2132
43	Kißlegg d.	0716	0742	0937	1137	1337	1537	1737	1937	2047	2137
56	Wangen (Allgäu) 935 d.	0731	0753	0953	1153	1352	1553	1753	1953	2058	2150
62	Hergatz 935 d.	0738	0801	0959	1159	1357	1559	1759	1959	2103	2155
85	**Lindau** Hbf 935 a.	0755	0817	1015	1215	1414	1616	1816	2016	2118	2212

	P	Q	M									
Lindau Hbf 935 d.	...	...	0707	0741z	0941	1141	1341	1542	1741	1941	2050	...
Hergatz 935 d.	0608	0653e	0724	0759k	0959	1200	1358	1601	1759	1959	2107	2325
Wangen 935 d.	0613	0658	0730	0809	1009	1209	1408	1609	1809	2009	2112	2333
Kißlegg a.	0623	0709	0740	0819	1019	1219	1419	1619	1819	2019	2122	2343
Kißlegg d.	0623	0717	0741	0826	1027	1227	1427	1627	1827	2027	2137	...
Bad Waldsee d.	|	0733	|	0843	1043	1242	1443	1642	1843	2043	|	...
Aulendorf a.	|	0742	|	0851	1051	1250	1451	1650	1851	2051	|	...
Leutkirch d.	0632	...	0750	...	...	...	...	...	...	...	2146	...
Memmingen a.	0658	...	0813	...	...	...	...	...	...	...	...	...

km											
0	**Memmingen** d.	0900	1100	1300	...	1500	1700	...	1900	...	2100
32	Leutkirch d.	0925	1125	1324	1415	1525	1724	1815	1925	2015	2124
43	Kißlegg d.	0934	1134	1334	1427	1534	1734	1827	1934	2027	2134
63	Bad Waldsee d.	0951	1151	1350	1443	1551	1751	1843	1951	2043	2151
73	**Aulendorf** a.	0958	1158	1358	1451	1558	1758	1851	1958	2051	2158

	Ⓐev											
Aulendorf d.	0555	0802	0908	1002	1108	1202	1402	1508	1602	1802	2002	2315
Bad Waldsee d.	0610	0809	0916	1009	1116	1209	1409	1516	1609	1809	2009	2323
Kißlegg d.	0626	0826	0935	1026	1134	1226	1426	1535	1626	1826	2026	2339
Leutkirch a.	...	0834	0944	1034	1142	1234	1435	1544	1634	1834	2034	...
Memmingen a.	...	0859	...	1058	...	1259t	1459	...	1659	1859	2059	...

M – To / from München (Table 935).
P – Runs 7 – 8 minutes later on Ⓐe
Q – Runs 8 – 13 minutes later on Ⓒz.
e – Ⓐ (not Nov. 1).
k – 0803 on Ⓐ (not Nov. 1).
t – *1316* (change trains at Leutkirch) on Ⓐ (not Oct. 28 - Nov. 1).
v – Continues to Wangen (a. 0643) and Hergatz (a. 0648).
z – Ⓒ (also Nov. 1).
⊠ – Until Oct. 6 services Memmingen - Kißlegg - Lindau and v.v. are subject to alteration with partial 🚌 replacement in operation (see page 568 for timings). Rail services continue to run between Aulendorf and Kißlegg (timings may vary by a few minutes to connect with 🚌 services).

DB (RE / RB services); HzL ◇ — ULM and ROTTWEIL - NEUSTADT - FREIBURG — 938

km		Ⓐe2	2	Ⓐe2	2		Ⓐe			2							2								
0	**Ulm** Hbf d.	...	...	...	...	0603v	0704	0817	0917	...	1017	1117	1217	1317	1417	1517	...	1617	1717	1817	1917	2017	2120	2217	2317
16	Blaubeuren d.	...	...	...	...	0615k	0716	0829	0929	...	1029	1129	1229	1329	1429	1529	...	1629	1729	1829	1929	2029	2133	2232	2335
34	Ehingen (Donau) d.	...	...	...	...	0630	0736	0842	0942	...	1042	1142	1242	1342	1442	1542	...	1642	1742	1842	1942	2042	2145	2246	2351
76	Herbertingen 937 d.	...	...	...	...	0709	0813	0915	1015	...	1115	1215	1315	1415	1515	1615	...	1715	1815	1915	2015	2120	2215	2322	0020
93	**Sigmaringen** 937 a.	...	...	...	...	0724	0829	0931	1029	...	1131	1229	1331	1429	1531	1629	...	1731	1829	1931	2029	2133	2235	2336	0035
93	**Sigmaringen** d.	...	...	...	...	0730k	▬	0934	▬	...	1133	▬	1334	▬	1533	▬	...	1734	▬	1933	▬	2138	▬	▬	▬
135	Tuttlingen d.	...	...	...	...	0813	...	1013	...	...	1213	...	1413	...	1613	...	...	1813	...	2013	...	2216	...	...	...
145	Immendingen 916 d.	...	...	...	...	0821	2	1021	2	...	1221	2	1421	2	1621	2	...	1821	2	2021	2	2224	...	...	2
	Rottweil d.	0515	...	0606	0643	|	0847	|	0947	1047	|	1147	|	1347	|	1547	1647	|	1847	|	2047	|	2148	...	2247
	Trossingen Bahnhof ▲ d.	0529	...	0618	0655	|	0859	|	0959	1059	|	1159	|	1359	|	1559	1659	|	1859	|	2059	|	2206j	Ⓑ	2259
	Villingen (Schwarzw) 916 d.	0548	0620	0635	0720j	|	0925j	|	1025	1125j	|	1225	|	1425	|	1625	1725j	|	1925j	|	2125j	2259§	2225	2313	2325j
164	Donaueschingen 916 a.	0601	0640	0648	0738	0834	0942	1034	1042	1142	1234	1242	1434	1442	1634	1642	1742	1834	1942	2034	2142	2237	2247e	2322	2342
164	Donaueschingen d.	...	0650•	...	0750*	0850*	0950*	...	1050*	1150*	...	1250*	...	1450*	...	1650*	1750*	1850*	1950*	2050*	...	...	...	...	2350*
204	**Neustadt** (Schwarzw) a.	...	0743•	...	0841*	0941*	1041*	...	1141*	1241*	...	1341*	...	1541*	...	1741*	1841*	1941*	2041*	2141*	...	...	...	...	0041*

km		⚒r2	Ⓐe	Ⓐe2	2	Ⓐe	Ⓒz	2	2		2		2		2		2		2		2	2	⊙		
0	**Neustadt** (Schwarzw) d.	...	...	0606*	...	...	...	0721*	0807*	...	0906*	1006*	1106*	1206*	1306*	1406*	1506*	1606*	1706*	1806*	1906*	2006*	...	2106*	...
40	Donaueschingen a.	...	...	0658*	...	...	...	0812*	0858*	...	0957*	1057*	1157*	1257*	1358*	1457*	1557*	1657*	1757*	1857*	1957*	2057*	...	2157*	...
40	Donaueschingen 916 d.	0506	0514	0708	0711z	0717	0721	0815	0915	0922	1015	1122	1215	1322	1415	1522	1615	1722	1815	1922	2015	2115	2122	2239	...
54	Villingen (Schwarzw) 916 d.	0529	0504‡	0724	0734	0705‡	0711‡	0833	0939	|	1033	|	1233	|	1433	|	1633	|	1833	|	2033	2139	|	2259	2319
69	Trossingen Bahnhof ▲ d.	0547	|	▬	0800	|	|	0900	1000	|	1100	|	1300	|	1500	|	1700	|	1900	|	2100	2159	|	...	2332
81	**Rottweil** a.	0558	|	...	0810	|	|	0910	1010	|	1110	|	1310	|	1510	|	1710	|	1910	|	2110	2209	|	...	2343
	Immendingen 916 d.	▬	0529	...	▬	0733	0735	▬	...	0935	▬	1135	▬	1335	▬	1535	▬	1735	▬	1935	...	...	2135	...	...
	Tuttlingen d.	...	0537	...	...	0750j	0746	...	...	0944	...	1144	...	1344	...	1544	...	1744	...	1944	...	...	2147	...	...
	Sigmaringen a.	...	0619	...	...	0826	0823	...	...	1027	...	1226	...	1427	...	1626	...	1827	...	2025	...	...	2229	...	...
	Sigmaringen 937 d.	0522	...	0628	0727	0832	0831	0932	...	1030	1132	1230	1332	1430	1532	1630	1732	1830	1932	2031	...	...	2236	...	...
	Herbertingen 937 d.	0536	...	0641	0742	0844	0844	0944	...	1044	1144	1244	1344	1444	1544	1644	1744	1844	1944	2045	...	...	2249	...	...
	Ehingen (Donau) d.	0607h	...	0714	0813	0913	0913	1013	...	1113	1213	1313	1413	1513	1613	1713	1813	1914	2013	2115	...	...	2318	...	...
	Blaubeuren d.	0626h	...	0731	0830	0929	0929	1029	...	1129	1229	1329	1429	1529	1629	1729	1829	1930	2029	2133	...	...	2336	...	...
	Ulm Hbf a.	0637h	...	0742	0842	0941	0942	1041	...	1141	1241	1341	1441	1541	1641	1741	1841	1941	2041	2144	...	...	2351	...	...

km		Ⓐe	⚒r	Ⓐe	Ⓐe	Ⓒz	Ⓐe	Ⓐe	Ⓑ														
0	**Neustadt** (Schwarzw) d.	0526	0555	0631	0642	0656	...	...	0731	0801	...	0831	...	and at the same	1931	...	2031	...	2131	2226	...	...	...
	Seebrugg d.	|	|	|	|	|	0641	0705	|	|	...	|	0839f	minutes past	|	1939f	|	2021	|	|	...	...	...
5	Titisee d.	0533	0602	0638	0649	0703	0708	0731	0738	0808	...	0838	0908	each hour until	1938	2008	2038	2048	2138	2233	...	...	...
36	**Freiburg** (Brsg) Hbf a.	0612	0640	0718	0730	0741	0749	...	0818	0848	...	0918	0948		2018	2048	2118	...	2218	2315	...	...	...

km		Ⓐe	Ⓐe	Ⓐe	Ⓐe	Ⓒz	Ⓐe	Ⓐe														
0	**Freiburg** (Brsg) Hbf d.	...	0535	...	0640	0638	0710	...	0742	...	0810	0840	and at the same	1810	1840	1910	1940	2010	...	2113	...	2228	2325
31	Titisee d.	0608	0612	0630	0719	0722	0750	0752	0819	...	0849	0919	minutes past	1849	1919	1949	2019	2049	2058	2149	...	2304	0001
50	**Seebrugg** a.	0633	|	0658	|	0749	|	0818	|	...	0916	|	each hour until	1916	|	2015	|	|	|	|	...	|	|
	Neustadt (Schwarzw) a.	...	0618	...	0725	...	0756	...	0825	...	...	0925		...	1925	...	2025	2055	2104	2155	...	2310	0007

e – Ⓐ (not June 20, Nov. 1).
f – 3 minutes **earlier** on † (also June 20, Nov. 1).
h – On Ⓒ (also June 20, Nov. 1) Ehingen d. 0605, Blaubeuren d. 0625, Ulm a. 0642.
j – Arrives 7 – 10 minutes earlier.
k – 2 minutes earlier on Ⓒ (also June 20, Nov. 1).
r – Not June 20, Nov. 1.
v – 0558 on Ⓒ (also June 20, Nov. 1).
z – Ⓒ (also June 20, Nov. 1).
* – Timings until Oct. 31. By 🚌. Through rail service is expected to resume from Nov. 1 in amended timings.
• – Ⓐ (not June 20, Nov. 1). See also note * above.
⊙ – Change trains at Sigmaringen on Ⓐ (not June 20, Nov. 1).
‡ – Starts from Villingen, then Donaueschingen.
§ – Arrival time. Calls after Donaueschingen.
◇ – Hohenzollerische Landesbahn.
▲ – Connecting services run to / from Trossingen Stadt (operated by Hohenzollerische Landesbahn). Journey time: 5 minutes.

IRE / RB services — FRIEDRICHSHAFEN - SINGEN - BASEL — Subject to alteration Sept. 9 - Oct. 25 — 939

km			Ⓐt		Ⓐt	Ⓒz	Ⓐt	Ⓒz																		
	Lindau Hbf ⊡ d.	...	...	...	...	...	...	...	0656z	...	...	...	...	...	...	...	...	...	...	...	...	...	...	...	2205	...
	Ulm Hbf 933 d.	...	...	...	...	...	...	...	|	▽	...	▽	...	▽	...	▽	...	▽	...	▽	...	...	▽	...	|	...
0	**Friedrichshafen** Stadt d.	...	0430	...	0545	0634	0701	0713	0739	0913	0938	1113	1138	1313	1338	1513	1538	1713	1738	1913	1938	2033	2113	2138	2242	2335
34	Überlingen d.	...	0510	...	0619	0711	0730	0733	0813	0933	1013	1133	1213	1333	1413	1533	1613	1733	1813	1933	2013	2110	2133	2213	2317	0010
59	Radolfzell 916 d.	...	0543	...	0647	0734	0751	0752	0842	0952	1042	1153	1242	1353	1442	1553	1642	1753	1842	1953	2042	2139	2153	2246	2342	0033
69	**Singen** 916 a.	...	0554	...	0703r	0747	0758	0800	0856	0959	1056	1200	1256	1400	1456	1600	1656	1800	1856	2000	2056	...	2200	2259	2356	0041
			|				|	|		|		|		|		|		|		|			|			
69	**Singen** 🚋 940 d.	...	0601	0651	...	...	0802	0802	0902	1002	1102	1202	1302	1402	1502	1602	1702	1802	1902	2002	2102	...	2202	2306	0006	...
88	**Schaffhausen** 🚋 940 d.	...	0613	0716	...	...	0816	0816	0916	1016	1116	1216	1316	1416	1516	1616	1716	1816	1916	2016	2116	...	2216	2324	0024	...
107	Erzingen (Baden) 🚋 d.	...	0625	0729	...	...	0829	0829	0929	1029	1129	1229	1329	1429	1529	1629	1729	1829	1930	2029	2129	...	2235	...	...	...
127	Waldshut d.	0610	0641	0742	...	...	0842	0842	0942	1042	1142	1242	1342	1442	1542	1642	1742	1842	1943	2042	2144	...	2252	...	...	...
150	Bad Säckingen d.	0633	0654	0756	...	...	0856	0856	0956	1056	1156	1256	1356	1456	1556	1656	1756	1856	1956	2056	2158	...	2314	...	...	...
167	Rheinfelden (Baden) d.	0649	0704	0806	...	...	0906	0906	1006	1106	1206	1306	1406	1506	1606	1706	1806	1906	2006	2106	2208	...	2329	...	...	...
182	**Basel** Bad Bf a.	0705	0715	0816	...	...	0916	0916	1016	1116	1216	1316	1416	1516	1616	1716	1816	1916	2016	2116	2218	...	2344	...	...	...

					Ⓐ	Ⓒz	Ⓐt																			
Basel Bad Bf d.	...	...	...	...	0510	0617	0635	0742	0842	0942	1042	1142	1242	1342	1442	1542	1642	1742	1842	1942	2042	...	2147	2151	...	2300
Rheinfelden (Baden) d.	...	...	...	...	0525	0632	0645	0751	0851	0951	1051	1151	1251	1351	1451	1551	1651	1751	1851	1951	2051	...	2155	2205	...	2314
Bad Säckingen d.	...	...	...	...	0541	0648	0655	0801	0901	1001	1101	1201	1301	1401	1501	1601	1701	1801	1901	2001	2101	...	2205	2221	...	2330
Waldshut d.	...	...	...	...	0604	0714	0711	0814	0914	1014	1114	1214	1314	1414	1514	1614	1714	1814	1914	2014	2114	...	2218	2252	...	2352
Erzingen (Baden) 🚋 d.	...	...	...	0548	0629	0729	0729	0829	0929	1029	1129	1229	1329	1429	1529	1629	1729	1829	1929	2029	2129	...	2233	2309	...	...
Schaffhausen 🚋 940 d.	...	0528	...	0630	0643	0743	0743	0843	0943	1043	1143	1243	1343	1443	1543	1643	1743	1843	1943	2043	2143	...	2247	2339	0007	...
Singen 🚋 940 a.	...	0547	...	0649	0659	0756	0756	0856	0956	1056	1156	1256	1356	1456	1556	1656	1756	1856	1956	2056	2156	...	2259	...	0025	...
	Ⓐt	Ⓒz	Ⓐt	Ⓒz		|	|		|		|		|		|		|		|		|				
Singen 916 d.	0517	0614	0614	0652k	...	0757	0757	0902	0957	1102	1157	1302	1357	1502	1557	1702	1757	1902	1957	2102	2157	2210	2303k	...	...	...
Radolfzell 916 d.	0525	0622	0622	0710	...	0805	0805	0914	1005	1114	1205	1314	1405	1514	1605	1714	1805	1914	2005	2114	2205	2225	2315	...	...	...
Überlingen d.	0551	0644	0646	0742	...	0822	0822	0942	1023	1142	1222	1342	1422	1542	1622	1742	1822	1942	2022	2142	2222	2247	2343	...	...	...
Friedrichshafen Stadt a.	0623	0723	0724	0821	...	0842	0842	1021	1041	1221	1242	1421	1442	1621	1642	1821	1842	2021	2042	2221	2241	2325	0020	...	...	...
Ulm Hbf 933 a.	|	...	...	|	...	▽	▽	...	▽	...	▽	...	▽	...	▽	...	▽	...	▽	...	|	...	...	...	...	...
Lindau Hbf ⊡ a.	0652	...	...	0854	...	...	...	...	...	...	...	...	...	...	...	...	...	...	...	...	2258	...	...	...	...	...

k – Not July 20 - Sept. 8.
r – *0718* July 22 - Sept. 6.
t – Not June 20, Nov. 1
z – Ⓒ (also June 20, Nov. 1).
▽ – See Table 933 for timings from / to Ulm.
⊡ – See Table 933 for other services Lindau - Friedrichshafen and v.v.

940 STUTTGART - SINGEN - SCHAFFHAUSEN - ZÜRICH

Regional tickets are valid on *IC* trains Stuttgart - Singen and v.v. **Warning!** Services Tuttlingen - Singen and v.v. are subject to alteration July 20 - Sept. 8 and Oct. 26 - Nov. 3.

km		IC 181	IC 1181	RE 4775	IC 2381	IC 183	IC 183	IC 2383	IC 185	IC 2385	IC 187	IC 2387	IC 189	IC 2389	IC 281	IC 281	IC 2281	IC 283	IC 2289	IC 285	IC 2285	RE 4779	RB 17627	IRE 4777	RE 17629	IC 2287
		Ⓐe	©z	©z	Ⓐe	⚒e									Ⓐe	©z				Ⓑd	ⒷjK	⑥K		⑦	⑤⑥	B
0	**Stuttgart** Hbf ..... 942 d.	0617	0617	0703	0716	0829	...	0916	1029	1116	1229	1316	1429	1516	1624	1629	1716	1829	1916	2027	2116	2117	2217	2318	2348	2348
26	Böblingen .... 942 d.	0638	0638	0724	0738	0850	...	0938	1050	1138	1250	1338	1450	1538	1650	1650	1738	1850	1938	2048	2138	2138	2238	2339	0009	0009
42	Herrenberg .... 942 d.	0648	0647	0735	0747	|	...	0947	|	1147	|	1347	|	1547	|	|	1747	|	1947	|	2147	2147	2247	2349	0018	0019
51	Bondorf .... 942 d.	0656	0655	0743	0755	|	...	0955	|	1155	|	1355	|	1555	|	|	1755	|	1955	|	2155	2155	2255	|	0026	0027
67	Horb .... d.	0710	0710	0806f	0807	0914	...	1007	1114	1207	1314	1407	1514	1607	1714	1714	1807	1914	2007	2113	2207	2207	2320	0006	0043	0043
110	Rottweil .... d.	0743	0743	0842	0842	0944	...	1042	1144	1242	1344	1442	1544	1642	1744	1744	1842	1944	2042	2145	2242	2242	2352	0034	0114	0114
138	Tuttlingen .... d.	0801	0801	0859	0859	1001	...	1059	1201	1259	1401	1459	1601	1659	1801	1801	1859	2001	2059	2203	2259	2259	...	0051	...	...
157	Engen .... 916 d.	|	|	0913	0913	|	...	1113	|	1313	|	1513	|	1713	|	|	1913	|	2113	|	2313	2313	...	0104	...	...
172	**Singen** .... 916 a.	0825	0825	0922	0925	1025	...	1125	1225	1325	1425	1525	1625	1725	1825	1825	1925	2025	2125	2225	2325	2325	...	0113	...	...
172	**Singen** .... 939 d.	0832	0832	0932	0932	1032	1032	1132	1232	1332	1432	1532	1632	1732	1832	1832	1932	2032	2132	2232	...	...	...	...	...	...
191	**Schaffhausen** 🚌 939 a.	0845	0845	0945	0945	1045	1045	1145	1245	1345	1445	1545	1645	1745	1845	1845	1945	2045	2145	2245	...	...	...	...	...	...
239	**Zürich** HB .... a.	0923	0923	1023	1023	1123	1123	1223	1323	1423	1523	1623	1723	1823	1923	1923	2023	2123	2223	2323	...	...	...	...	...	...

	RE 17620	RE 17622	IC 2286	RE 17650	RE 17674	IC 1186	IC 2284	RE 4774	IC 284	IC 2288	IC 282	IC 2280	IC 280	IC 2388	IC 188	IC 2386	IC 186	IC 2384	RE 4778	IC 184	IC 2382	IC 182	IC 182	IC 2380	IC 180	IRE 4776
	Ⓐe		A	⚒e	†z	Ⓐe	♠K	⑦K	★										©z			Ⓑb				⑤
Zürich HB .... d.	...	...	...	...	...	...	...	...	0637	0737	0837	0937	1037	1137	1237	1337	1437	1537	...	1637	1737	1837	1837	1937	2037	...
Schaffhausen 🚌 939 d.	...	...	...	...	...	...	...	...	0716	0816	0916	1016	1116	1216	1316	1416	1516	1616	...	1716	1816	1916	1916	2016	2116	2130
Singen .... 939 a.	...	...	...	...	...	...	...	...	0730	0830	0930	1030	1130	1230	1330	1430	1530	1630	...	1730	1830	1930	1930	2030	2130	2149
Singen .... 916 d.	...	...	...	...	...	0551	0629	0629	0737	0835	0937	1035	1137	1235	1337	1435	1537	1635	1712	1737	1835	1937	...	2035	...	2200
Engen .... 916 d.	...	...	...	...	...	0600	0638	0638	|	0844	|	1044	|	1244	|	1444	|	1644	|	|	1844	|	...	2044	...	|
Tuttlingen .... △ d.	...	...	...	...	...	0615	0652	0652	0800	0859	1000	1059	1200	1259	1400	1459	1600	1659	1735	1800	1859	2000	...	2059	...	2223
Rottweil .... d.	...	0511e	0537	0604	0616	0639	0711	0711	0816	0917	1016	1117	1216	1317	1416	1517	1616	1717	1756	1816	1917	2017	...	2117	...	2242
Horb .... d.	0447	0547	0612	0639	0647	0710	0751	0751	0845	0951	1045	1151	1245	1351	1445	1551	1645	1751	1828	1845	1951	2046	...	2151	...	2311
Bondorf .... 942 d.	0503	0602	0630	0702	0702	|	0803	0803	|	1003	|	1203	|	1403	|	1603	|	1803	|	|	2003	|	...	2203	...	|
Herrenberg .... 942 d.	0511	0611	0640	0711	0711	0725	0811	0811	|	1011	|	1211	|	1411	|	1611	|	1811	1843	|	2011	|	...	2211	...	2327
Böblingen .... 942 d.	0521	0621	0649	0721	0721	0737	0822	0822	0911	1022	1111	1222	1311	1422	1511	1622	1711	1822	1853	1911	2022	2111	...	2222	...	2337
Stuttgart Hbf .... 942 a.	0542	0642	0710	0742	0742	0757	0843	0843	0932	1043	1132	1243	1332	1443	1536	1643	1732	1843	1916	1932	2043	2132	...	2243	...	2359

SCHAFFHAUSEN - ZÜRICH (operated by SBB)

km									
0	**Schaffhausen** .... d.	0547	0617	and at the same	2117	2147	2157	2247	2327
28	Bülach .... d.	|	0637	minutes past	2137	|	2228	|	2358
48	**Zürich** HB .... a.	0623	0655	each hour until	2155	2223	2253	2323	0023

Zürich HB .... d.	0005	...	0605	0637	and at the same	2037	2105	2205	2305
Bülach .... d.	0023	...	0623	|	minutes past	|	2123	2223	2323
Schaffhausen .... a.	0044	...	0643	0713	each hour until	2113	2143	2243	2344

A – ①-⑤ (not June 10).
B – ①②③④⑦ (not June 9).
K – To / from Konstanz (Table **916**).
b – Not June 9, 19, Oct. 2, 31.
d – Runs daily from Nov. 24.
e – Ⓐ (not June 20, Nov. 1).
f – Arrives 0757.
j – Not June 9.
z – Also June 20, Nov. 1.
★ – ①-⑥ (daily from Nov. 25).
♠ – ①-⑥ (not June 10).
△ – Certain Tuttlingen departures are up to 8 minutes earlier July 20 - Sept. 8 and Oct. 26 - Nov. 3.

941 TÜBINGEN - HORB - PFORZHEIM - BAD WILDBAD

RB services (2nd class only)

km																				
		Ⓐe	⑥	Ⓐe			©z													
	Tübingen .... ⊡ d.	...	...	...	...	...	0727	...	0927	...	1127	...	1327	...	1527	...	1727	...	1927	2127
0	**Horb** .... ⊡ d.	0434	0607	0604	0651	0758	0758	0851	0958	1051	1158	1251	1358	1451	1558	1651	1758	1851	1958	2200
15	Hochdorf (b. Horb) ..... d.	0447	0620	0620	0702	0808	0808	0902	1009	1102	1209	1302	1409	1502	1609	1702	1809	1902	2009	2220v
25	Nagold .... d.	0504	0632	0632	0719	0820	0820	0913	1020	1113	1220	1313	1420	1513	1620	1713	1820	1913	2021	2232
34	Wildberg (Württ) .... d.	0512	0639	0645	0730	0830	0830	0920	1030	1121	1230	1321	1430	1521	1629	1721	1830	1921	2030	2239
45	Calw .... d.	0522	0649	0656	0740	0840	0840	0934	1040	1134	1240	1334	1440	1534	1639	1734	1840	1934	2040	2249
52	Bad Liebenzell .... d.	0529	0657	0704	0748	0847	0847	0944	1047	1144	1247	1344	1447	1544	1647	1744	1847	1944	2047	2300
71	**Pforzheim** Hbf .... a.	0550	0719	0724	0807	0907	0907	1007	1107	1207	1307	1407	1507	1607	1707	1807	1907	2007	2111	2320

	Ⓐe	Ⓐe	©z	⚒e										Ⓐe		Ⓐe				
Pforzheim Hbf .... d.	0446	0641	0649	0752	0852	0952	1052	1152	1252	1352	1452	1552	1652	1720	1752	1823	1852	1952	2043	2238
Bad Liebenzell .... d.	0506	0708	0712	0813	0913	1012	1114	1213	1314	1413	1514	1613	1714	1744	1813	1848	1914	2013	2104	2258
Calw .... d.	0513	0715	0719	0820	0920	1019	1121	1220	1321	1420	1521	1619	1721	1751	1820	1855	1921	2020	2111	2305
Wildberg (Württ) .... d.	0524	0728	0730	0830	0932	1030	1132	1231	1333	1430	1533	1630	1732	1803	1830	1905	1932	2031	2121	2315
Nagold .... d.	0532	0739	0739	0839	0940	1039	1140	1239	1340	1439	1540	1639	1739	1821	1839	1914	1939	2039	2129	2323
Hochdorf (b. Horb) ...... d.	0543	0750	0751	0851	0951	1051	1151	1250	1351	1451	1550	1651	1751	1832	1851	1925	1950	2051	2148	2340
Horb .... ⊡ a.	...	0802	0802	0902	1002	1102	1202	1302	1402	1502	1602	1702	1802	1843	1902	1937	2002	2101	2159	2351
Tübingen .... ⊡ a.	...	...	0833	...	1033	...	1233	...	1433	...	1633	...	1833	...	...	...	2033	...	2232	...

e – Not June 20, Nov. 1.
v – Arrives 2211.
z – Also June 20, Nov. 1.
⊡ – See panel below main table for full service.
⊠ – The 1217 from Pforzheim and 1205 from Bad Wildbad Kurpark run only on ©z (see also note ▶ below).
▶ – S-Bahn route **S6**. Additional journeys on Ⓐe:
From Pforzheim Hbf at 0645, 1224, 1247, 1347, 1547, 1647, 1747 and 1847.
From Bad Wildbad Kurpark at 0459, 0525, 0635, 0735, 1216, 1335, 1535, 1635 and 1735.

km																									
		Ⓐe	Ⓐe	Ⓐe	Ⓐe	©z						Ⓐe					Ⓐe								
0	**Tübingen** Hbf .... d.	0529	0600	0628	0724	0727	0835	0927	1035	1127	1235	1303	1327	1435	1527	1635	1703	1727	1835	1927	2035	2127	2237	...	...
32	**Horb** .... a.	0600	0633	0705	0755	0754	0909	0954	1109	1154	1309	1336	1354	1509	1554	1709	1737	1755	1909	1954	2109	2156	2307	...	...

		Ⓐe	Ⓐe	©z	Ⓐe	Ⓐe	©z	©z						Ⓐe				Ⓐe		Ⓐe					Ⓐe	©z
Horb .... d.	0455	0613	0644	0652	0725	0805	0806	0849	1006	1049	1206	1249	1406	1424	1449	1606	1649	1717	1806	1824	1849	2006	2049	2203	2248	2248
Tübingen Hbf .... a.	0526	0651	0723	0723	0801	0833	0833	0924	1033	1124	1233	1324	1433	1455	1524	1633	1724	1800	1833	1855	1924	2033	2124	2232	2325	2328

km	SEE NOTE ▶	Ⓐe	⚒e	†z	⚒e	Ⓐe		⊠		
0	**Pforzheim** Hbf .... d.	0507	0607	0707	0717	0747	0817	and	2317	0017
23	**Bad Wildbad** Bf .... d.	0538	0638	0738	0749	0819	0849	hourly	2349	0049
25	**Bad Wildbad** Kurpark a.	0540	0640	0710	0752	0822	0852	until	2352	0052

SEE NOTE ▶	Ⓐe	⑥	Ⓐe	†z	⚒e		⊠		
Bad Wildbad Kurpark...... d.	0559	0647	0705	0747	0805	0905	and	2305	0005
Bad Wildbad Bf .... d.	0602	0651	0708	0751	0809	0909	hourly	2309	0011
Pforzheim Hbf .... a.	0633	0722	0740	0822	0840	0940	until	2340	0040

942 STUTTGART - FREUDENSTADT - OFFENBURG

km																									
		Ⓐe 2			2	†z	†z	⚒e	2		2		2		2		2		2		2			a	©z 2
0	**Stuttgart** Hbf .... 940 d.	0548	0617	...	...	0818	...	0818	...	1018	...	1218	...	1418	...	1618	...	1818	...	2018	...	2217	...	2348	...
26	Böblingen .... 940 d.	0609	0638	...	...	0838	...	0839	...	1039	...	1239	...	1439	...	1639	...	1839	...	2039	...	2238	...	0009	...
42	Herrenberg .... 940 d.	0630	0647	...	...	0847	...	0848	...	1048	...	1248	...	1448	...	1648	...	1848	...	2048	...	2247	2318	0018	...
51	Bondorf .... 940 d.	|	0655	...	0803	0854	...	0856	1003	1056	1203	1256	1403	1456	1603	1656	1803	1856	2003	2056	2204	2255	2326	0026	...
57	Eutingen im Gäu .... d.	0642	0701	0708	0810	0900	0908	0908	1010	1108	1210	1308	1410	1508	1610	1708	1810	1908	2010	2108	2211	2302	2333	0033	0043
62	Hochdorf (b. Horb) ...... d.	0647	...	0712	0814	...	0912	0912	1014	1112	1214	1312	1414	1512	1614	1712	1814	1912	2014	2112	2215	...	2337	...	0047
87	**Freudenstadt** Hbf ...... a.	0713	...	0741	0841	...	0941	0941	1041	1141	1241	1341	1441	1541	1641	1741	1841	1941	2041	2141	2241	...	0003	...	0113

	©z 2	Ⓐe 2		⚒e	†z	2		⚒e	2		2		2		2		2	⚒e	†z	2	⚒e	†z	2		2
Freudenstadt Hbf .... d.	0008	0519	...	0618	0618	0718	0818	0818	0918	1018	1118	1218	1318	1418	1518	1618	1718	1818	1818	1918	2018	2018	2118	2218	...
Hochdorf (b. Horb) .... d.	0034	0547	...	0648	0648	0744	0846	0846	0944	1046	1144	1246	1344	1446	1544	1646	1744	1846	1846	1944	2046	2046	2144	2246	...
Eutingen im Gäu .... d.	0038	0551	0556	0656	0656	0750	0850	0856	0950	1056	1150	1256	1350	1456	1550	1656	1750	1856	1856	1950	2056	2056	2150	2257	...
Bondorf .... 940 a.	...	...	0602	0702	0702	0756	...	0902	0956	1102	1156	1302	1356	1502	1556	1702	1756	1902	1902	1956	2102	2102	2156	2304	...
Herrenberg .... 940 a.	...	...	0610	0710	0710	...	...	0910	...	1110	...	1310	...	1510	...	1710	...	1910	1910	...	2110	2110	...	2311	2316
Böblingen .... 940 a.	...	...	0620	0720	0720	...	...	0920	...	1120	...	1320	...	1520	...	1720	...	1920	1920	...	2120	2120	...	...	2330
Stuttgart Hbf .... 940 a.	...	...	0642	0742	0742	...	...	0942	...	1142	...	1342	...	1542	...	1742	...	1942	1942	...	2142	2142	...	...	2355

FREUDENSTADT - OFFENBURG (operated by Südwestdeutsche Verkehrs-AG; 2nd class only)

km		Ⓐe	⚒e			✣		Ⓐe		
0	**Freudenstadt** Hbf ...... d.	0533	0643	0743	0843	and	2043	2143	...	...
16	Alpirsbach .... d.	0552	0659	0759	0859		2059	2159	...	...
25	Schiltach .... d.	0603	0710	0810	0910	hourly	2110	2210	...	...
35	Wolfach .... d.	0613	0720	0820	0920	until	2120	2221	...	...
39	Hausach .... 916 a.	0618	0725	0825	0925		2125	2225	2235	...
72	**Offenburg** .... 916 a.	0647	0755	0855	0955		2155	...	2300	...

	Ⓐe	⑥	Ⓐe						
Offenburg .... 916 d.	0458	0554	0558	0702	0804	and	2004	...	2226
Hausach .... 916 d.	0525	0627	0627	0732	0832		2032	...	2254
Wolfach .... d.	0530	0632	0632	0737	0837	hourly	2037	...	2259
Schiltach .... d.	0540	0643	0643	0747	0847		2047	...	2309
Alpirsbach .... d.	0551	0701	0701	0800	0900	until	2100	...	2323
Freudenstadt Hbf .... a.	0607	0717	0717	0816	0916		2116	...	2339

a – Not June 9.
e – Not June 20, Nov. 1.
z – Also June 20, Nov. 1.
✣ – The 1243 from Freudenstadt runs on © (daily June 8 – 23, July 27 - Sept. 10, Oct. 26 - Nov. 3). On other dates service is retimed: Freudenstadt d. 1220, Alpirsbach d. 1236, Schiltach d. 1254, Wolfach d. 1305, Hausach a. 1309, Offenburg a. 1345

KARLSRUHE - FREUDENSTADT 943

S-Bahn (2nd class only)

km		Ⓐe	Ⓐe	⑥	Ⓐe	Ⓒz		†w									⑤⑥f						
	Karlsruhe Bahnhofsvorplatz d.	0430	0507	0511	...	0611	0711z	...	0806j	0911	1011	1111		2011	2111	2211	2311		...	...	...	...	...
0	**Karlsruhe** Hbf .... 916 d.	|	|	|	0610	|	0707e	0806	|	|	|	|		|	|	|	|		1010	1210	1410	1610	1810
24	Rastatt .... 916 d.	0503	0533	0538	0633	0638	0738	0829	0838	0938	1038	1138	and	2038	2138	2238	2338	also	1029	1229	1429	1629	1829
40	Gernsbach Bf .... d.	0525	0556	0600	0656	0700	0800	0844	0900	1000	1100	1200		2100	2200	2300	0000		1044	1244	1444	1644	1844
51	Forbach (Schwarzw) .... d.	0544	0613	0618	0718	0718	0818	0900	0918	1018	1118	1218	hourly	2118	2218	2318	0018	faster	1100	1300	1500	1700	1900
61	Schönmünzach .... d.	0556	0624	0631	0729	0729	0829	0911	0929	1029	1129	1229		2129	2229	2329	0034	trains	1111	1311	1511	1711	1911
74	Baiersbronn Bf .... d.	0612	0642	0649	0750	0749	0849	0922	0949	1049	1149	1249	until	2149	2249	2346	0050		1122	1322	1522	1722	1922
79	**Freudenstadt** Stadt .... a.	0620	0650	0657	0758	0757	0857	0930	0957	1057	1157	1257		2157	2257	2354	0058	at	1130	1329	1530	1730	1930
82	**Freudenstadt** Hbf .... a.	0625	0705	0707	0807	0807	0907	0937	1007	1112k	1215n	1307		2207	2307	2400	0104		1137	1337	1537	1737	1937

	Ⓒz	Ⓐe	Ⓐe	⑥	Ⓐe	Ⓐe	Ⓒz	Ⓐe	Ⓐe	Ⓒz	⚒r												Ⓒz
Freudenstadt Hbf .... d.	0006	0443	0524	0601	0614	0648	0653	0720	0745	0753	0823	0853		1953	2053	2153	2253		1023	1223	1423	1623	1823
Freudenstadt Stadt .... d.	0011	0449	0530	0607	0620	0654	0703	0730	0803	0803	0830	0903		2003	2103	2203	2306	also	1030	1230	1430	1630	1830
Baiersbronn Bf .... d.	0018	0458	0539	0616	0628	0702	0711	0738	0811	0811	0838	0911	and	2011	2111	2211	2314		1038	1238	1438	1638	1838
Schönmünzach .... d.	0034	0513	0555	0631	0645	0730	0729	0749	0829	0829	0849	0929		2029	2129	2229	2330	faster	1049	1249	1449	1649	1849
Forbach (Schwarzw) .... d.	0045	0525	0612	0643	0701	0742	0742	0801	0842	0842	0901	0942	hourly	2042	2153t	2254t	2341	trains	1101	1301	1501	1701	1901
Gernsbach Bf .... d.	0101	0541	0631	0659	0728	0800	0800	0815	0900	0900	0915	1000		2100	2211	2311	0000		1115	1315	1515	1715	1915
Rastatt .... 916 d.	0122	0557	0706t	0722	0754	0822	0822	0830	0922	0922	0931	1022	until	2122	2231	2338	0022	at	1130	1330	1530	1730	1931
Karlsruhe Hbf .... 916 a.	|	0614	0728	|	0816	|	|	0849	|	|	0949	|		|	|	|	|		1149	1350	1549	1749	1948
Karlsruhe Bahnhofsvorplatz a.	0146	...	...	0746	...	0846	0846	...	0946	0946	...	1046		2146	2256	0002	0046		...	...	...	...	...

e – Ⓐ (not June 20, Nov. 1).
f – Also June 9, 19, Oct. 2, 31.
j – 0811 on Ⓒ (also June 20, Nov. 1).
k – 1107 on Ⓒ (also June 20, Nov. 1).
n – 1207 on Ⓒ (also June 20, Nov. 1).
r – Not June 20, Nov. 1.
t – Arrives 13 – 14 minutes earlier.
w – Also June 20, Nov. 1.
z – Ⓒ (also June 20, Nov. 1).

MÜNCHEN - PASSAU 944

RE services

km		Ⓐe	⚒e	⚒e	Ⓐe	Ⓐe	Ⓒz																	
0	**München** Hbf .... 878 d.	...	0444	...	0524	0604	0624	0724	0824	0924c	1024	1124	1224	1324	1424	1524	1623	1724	1824	1924	2024	2124	...	2325
42	Freising .... 878 d.	...	0508	...	0549	0628	0649	0749	0849	0949	1049	1149	1249	1349	1449	1549	1650	1749	1849	1949	2049	2149	...	2349
76	Landshut (Bay) Hbf .... 878 d.	...	0527	0543	0613	0651	0715	0815	0915	1015	1115	1215	1315	1416	1515	1615	1715	1815	1915	2015	2115	2215	...	0013
121	Landau (Isar) .... d.	...	...	0625	0701v	0737n	0748	0848	0948	1048	1148	1248	1349	1448	1549	1649	1748	1848	1948	2048	2148	2248	...	0042
139	Plattling .... a.	...	...	0640	0714	0750	0800	0900	1000	1100	1200	1300	1400	1500	1600	1700	1800	1900	2000	2100	2200	2302	...	0055
139	Plattling .... 920 d.	0600	...	0642	0725	0800	0802	0902	1004	1102	1204	1302	1404	1504	1604	1702	1804	1902	2004	2102	2202	2306	...	0057
191	**Passau** Hbf .... 920 a.	0633	...	0718	0800	0835	0837	0937	1039	1137	1239	1337	1439	1539	1639	1737	1839	1937	2039	2139	2237	2341	...	0132

	⚒e		Ⓐe	Ⓒz	Ⓐe																			
Passau Hbf .... 920 d.	0441	0523	0604	0627	0646	0725	0826	0919	1026	1119	1219	1319	1426	1519	1625	1719	1822	1919	2026	2126	...	2313	...	...
Plattling .... 920 a.	0513	0558	0640	0701	0720	0759	0900	0953	1100	1153	1253	1353	1500	1553	1659	1753	1856	1953	2100	2200	...	2347	...	...
Plattling .... d.	0520	0600	0642	0702	0722	0802	0902	1002	1102	1202	1302	1402	1502	1602	1702	1802	1902	2002	2102	2202	...	2357	...	...
Landau (Isar) .... d.	0532	0613	0656	0714	0734	0814	0914	1014	1114	1214	1314	1414	1514	1614	1714	1814	1914	2014	2114	2214	...	0008	...	...
Landshut (Bay) Hbf .... 878 d.	0608	0644	0728	0747	0806	0848	0948	1048	1148	1248	1348	1448	1548	1648	1748	1849	1948	2048	2148	2248	...	0038	...	...
Freising .... 878 d.	0629	0709	0749	0810	0829	0910	1010	1110	1210	1310	1410	1510	1610	1710	1810	1910	2010	2110	2210	2310	...	...	...	...
München Hbf .... 878 a.	0656	0738	0817	0836	0856	0937	1036	1136	1237	1336	1436	1536	1637	1737	1836	1937	2036	2137	2236	2337	...	...	...	...

c – 0922 on ⑥⑦ to Aug. 25.
e – Not June 20, Aug. 15, Nov. 1.
n – Arrives 0729.
v – Arrives 0649.
z – Also June 20, Aug. 15, Nov. 1.

REGENSBURG - INGOLSTADT - DONAUWÖRTH - ULM 945

agilis

On June 20, Aug. 15, Nov. 1 services run as on Ⓒ.

km			Ⓐ	Ⓐ	Ⓐ	Ⓐ	Ⓐ	Ⓐ	Ⓐ	Ⓐ	Ⓐ	Ⓐ	Ⓐ	Ⓐ	Ⓐ	Ⓐ	Ⓐ	Ⓐ	Ⓐ	Ⓐ	Ⓐ	Ⓐ	Ⓐ	Ⓐ	Ⓐ	Ⓐ
0	**Regensburg** Hbf ...... d.	Ⓐ	...	*0405*	*0452*	0508	0534	0608	...	0713	*0741*	0846	*0952*	1046	*1152*	*1246*	*1352*	*1446*	*1552*	1614	*1646*	1728	*1752*	1846	...	1952
46	Neustadt (Donau) ...... d.		...	*0442*	*0534*	0556	0626	0656	...	0803	*0830*	0928	*1029*	1128	*1229*	*1323*	*1429*	*1528*	*1629*	1702	*1731*	1811	*1829*	1928	...	2028
74	**Ingolstadt** Hbf .... a.		...	*0502*	*0553*	0622	0652	0720	...	0826	*0851*	0954	*1050*	1153	*1250*	*1349*	*1450*	*1548*	*1650*	1733	*1755*	1835	*1852*	1949	...	2054
74	**Ingolstadt** Hbf .... d.		...	0507	0607	0632	0702	...	0807	...	0908	1009	1108	1209	1307	1407	1508	1607	1708	1740	1810	1841	1908	...	2047	...
95	Neuburg (Donau) .... d.		...	0527	0627	0648	0729	...	0828	...	0925	1028	1129	1228	1328	1428	1527	1628	1725	1802	1829	1855	1929	...	2108	...
127	**Donauwörth** .... a.		...	0552	0653	0725	0753	...	0852	...	0951	1053	1153	1253	1354	1454	1553	1653	1753	1835j	1853	1920j	1953	...	2137	...
127	**Donauwörth** .... d.		0452	0603	0702	...	0803	...	0901	...	1002	1101	1202	1302	1400	1503	1601	1702	1801	...	1901	...	2001	...	2139	...
153	Dillingen (Donau) .... d.		0513	0632	0724	...	0823	...	0925	...	1023	1121	1223	1330	1423	1525	1623	1725	1823	...	1922	...	2021	...	2204	...
176	Günzburg .... 930 a.		0533	0649	0741	...	0839	...	0940	...	1039	1140	1240	1347	1439	1540	1639	1740	1839	...	1939	...	2037	...	2221	...
200	**Ulm** Hbf .... 930 a.		0554	0710	0808	...	0857	...	0958	...	1057	1158	1310	1410	1457	1558	1657	1758	1857	...	1957	...	2056	...	*2302*	...

	Ⓐ	Ⓐ	Ⓐ			Ⓒ	Ⓒ	Ⓒ	Ⓒ	Ⓒ	Ⓒ	Ⓒ	Ⓒ	Ⓒ	Ⓒ	Ⓒ	Ⓒ	Ⓒ	Ⓒ	Ⓒ	Ⓒ	Ⓒ	Ⓒ	Ⓒ	Ⓒ	Ⓒ
Regensburg Hbf .... d.	2014	2111	2222	...	Ⓒ	0024	...	...	0557	0649	0759	0845	1000	1045	1200	1245	1400	1445	1600	1645	1800	1845	1949	...	2046	2222
Neustadt (Donau) .... d.	2101	2207	2302	...		0108	...	...	0638	0733	0838	0933	1038	1132	1238	1332	1438	1532	1638	1732	1838	1932	2029	...	2132	2302
Ingolstadt Hbf .... a.	2122	2226	2322	...		0129	...	...	0654	0753	0854	0954	1054	1153	1254	1354	1454	1553	1654	1753	1854	1954	2049	...	2152	2322
Ingolstadt Hbf .... d.	2143	2240	2343	...		...	...	0607	0708	0808	0907	1008	1107	1208	1307	1408	1507	1608	1707	1808	1907	2038	...	...	2240	2343
Neuburg (Donau) .... d.	2203	2257	0004	...		...	...	0627	0722	0824	0922	1024	1122	1224	1322	1424	1522	1624	1722	1824	1922	2059	...	...	2257	0004
Donauwörth .... a.	2228	2323	0030	...		...	...	0653	0746	0853	0945	1053	1146	1253	1346	1454	1548	1653	1746	1853	1944	2125	...	...	2323	0030
Donauwörth .... d.	2238	2338	...	...		...	0452	0703	0750	0901	0950	1101	1150	1303	1350	1503	1550	1702	1750	1901	1950	2138	...	2238	2338	...
Dillingen (Donau) .... d.	2302	2358	...	...		...	0513	0723	0807	0925	1006	1121	1206	1324	1406	1525	1606	1725	1806	1922	2007	2159	...	2302	2358	...
Günzburg .... 930 a.	2319	0014	...	...		...	0533	0739	0824	0940	1022	1140	1222	1340	1422	1540	1622	1740	1825	1939	2024	2221	...	2319	0014	...
Ulm Hbf .... 930 a.	2337	0033	...	...		...	0554	0758	0840	0958	1040	1158	1240	1358	1440	1558	1640	1758	1844	1957	2041	*2302*	...	2337	0033	...

		Ⓐ	Ⓐ	Ⓐ	Ⓐ	Ⓐ	Ⓐ	Ⓐ	Ⓐ	Ⓐ	Ⓐ	Ⓐ	Ⓐ	Ⓐ	Ⓐ	Ⓐ	Ⓐ	Ⓐ	Ⓐ	Ⓐ	Ⓐ	Ⓐ	Ⓐ	Ⓐ	Ⓐ	Ⓐ
Ulm Hbf .... 930 d.	Ⓐ	...	...	...	0450	0533	*0545*	0625	...	0745	0848	0948	1048	1148	1248	1348	...	1448	1548	1648	1742	1831	...	1942	...	2048
Günzburg .... 930 d.		...	...	...	0509	0551	0609	0645	...	0804	0913	1006	1115	1206	1314	1406	...	1513	1606	1713	1803	1851	...	2003	...	2115
Dillingen (Donau) .... d.		...	...	...	0524	0608	0634	0701	...	0828	0933	1025	1132	1223	1331	1423	...	1533	1623	1733	1826	1907	...	2021	...	2131
Donauwörth .... a.		...	...	...	0545	0629	0658	0728h	...	0849	0953	1049	1153	1246	1352	1445	...	1553	1647	1753	1848	1932	...	2042	...	2153
Donauwörth .... d.		...	0501	...	0554	0631	0701	0731h	0801	0859	1004	1101	1203	1302	1402	1501	...	1601	1703	1803	1901	1940	2005	2043	2138	...
Neuburg (Donau) .... d.		...	0526	...	0627	0704	0730	0804	0830	0930	1030	1128	1230	1329	1430	1535	...	1630	1735	1828	1930	2008	2029	2108	2205	...
Ingolstadt Hbf .... a.		...	0547	...	0648	0723	0746	0833	0846	0949	1046	1146	1246	1346	1446	1553	...	1648	1750	1849	1946	2023	2046	2127	2223	...
Ingolstadt Hbf .... d.		0521	0600	0628	*0705*	0730	*0805*	...	*0905*	1005	*1105*	1205	*1318*	*1405*	*1505*	*1605*	1624	*1705*	*1805*	*1905*	*2007*	2030	*2108*	2138	2236	...
Neustadt (Donau) .... d.		0545	0622	0655	*0729*	0752	*0828*	...	*0927*	1029	*1127*	1229	*1339*	*1429*	*1527*	*1629*	1651	*1727*	*1829*	*1927*	*2029*	2048	*2133*	2203	2302	...
Regensburg Hbf .... a.		0628	0706	0739	*0807*	0836	*0910*	...	*1007*	1110	*1207*	1310	*1430*	*1510*	*1607*	*1710*	1732	*1807*	*1910*	*2007*	*2111*	2129	*2210*	2252	2345	...

	Ⓐ	Ⓐ	Ⓐ			Ⓒ	Ⓒ	Ⓒ	Ⓒ	Ⓒ	Ⓒ	Ⓒ	Ⓒ	Ⓒ	Ⓒ	Ⓒ	Ⓒ	Ⓒ	Ⓒ	Ⓒ	Ⓒ	Ⓒ	Ⓒ	Ⓒ	Ⓒ	Ⓒ
Ulm Hbf .... 930 d.	...	*2223*	2255	...	Ⓒ	...	...	0555	0718	0745	0918	0948	1118	1148	1318	1348	1518	1550	1718	1742	1918	...	1942	2102	*2223*	2255
Günzburg .... 930 d.	...	2245	2318	...		...	...	0616	0736	0804	0936	1013	1136	1213	1336	1413	1536	1613	1736	1814	1936	...	2003	2120	2245	2318
Dillingen (Donau) .... d.	...	2301	2334	...		...	...	0631	0752	0828	0952	1032	1152	1231	1352	1431	1552	1632	1752	1831	1952	...	2029	2136	2301	2334
Donauwörth .... a.	...	2323	0001	...		...	...	0653	0812	0849	1012	1053	1212	1252	1412	1452	1612	1652	1812	1853	2012	...	2051	2201	2323	0001
Donauwörth .... d.	2238	2338	...	...		0501	...	0701	0814	0904	1014	1101	1214	1302	1414	1501	1614	1702	1814	1901	2012	...	2138	▬	2338	...
Neuburg (Donau) .... d.	2308	0004	...	...		0526	...	0732	0838	0932	1037	1132	1237	1332	1437	1533	1637	1733	1837	1933	2036	...	2205	...	0004	...
Ingolstadt Hbf .... a.	2327	0021	...	...		0546	...	0748	0851	0949	1051	1148	1251	1349	1451	1549	1651	1749	1851	1948	2056	...	2223	Ⓒ	0023	...
Ingolstadt Hbf .... d.	2340	...	...	...		0605	0655	0805	0905	1005	1105	1205	1305	1405	1505	1605	1705	1805	1905	2005	2105	2206	...	2340	...	...
Neustadt (Donau) .... d.	2359	...	...	...		0627	0718	0828	0921	1027	1121	1227	1321	1427	1521	1627	1721	1827	1921	2029	2121	2227	...	2359	...	...
Regensburg Hbf .... a.	0041	...	...	...		0708	0807	0910	0954	1110	1155	1310	1355	1510	1555	1710	1755	1910	1955	2111	2155	2312	...	0041	...	...

h – Until June 21 Donauwörth a. 0727, d. 0728.
j – 2 minutes later until June 21.

ANGERMÜNDE - SZCZECIN 949

German holiday dates apply

km		⚒							E	⑤
	Berlin Gesundbrunnen **845** .. d.	...	0804	...	...	1453	1719	...	...	2104
0	**Angermünde** .... d.	0640	0855	1040	1340	1545	1808	1932	2140	2155
40	Tantow .... d.	0718	0928	1118	1418	1625	1847	2014	2218	2234
59	Szczecin Gumience ▦ .... d.	0733	0943	1133	1433	1639	1907	2028	2233	2249
64	**Szczecin** Głowny .... a.	0744	0949	1139	1439	1645	1913	2034	2239	2255

		⚒				⑤	E		
Szczecin Głowny .... d.	0605	0823	1006	1213	1517	1707	1723	1945	2110
Szczecin Gumience ▦ .... d.	0611	0829	1012	1219	1523	1713	1729	1957	2116
Tantow .... d.	0625	0843	1026	1233	1536	1727	1742	2012	2130
Angermünde .... a.	0705	0922	1104	1312	1616	1805	1821	2044	2209
Berlin Gesundbr. **845** ...... a.	0755	...	1153	...	...	1856	...	2138	...

E – Daily except ⑤.

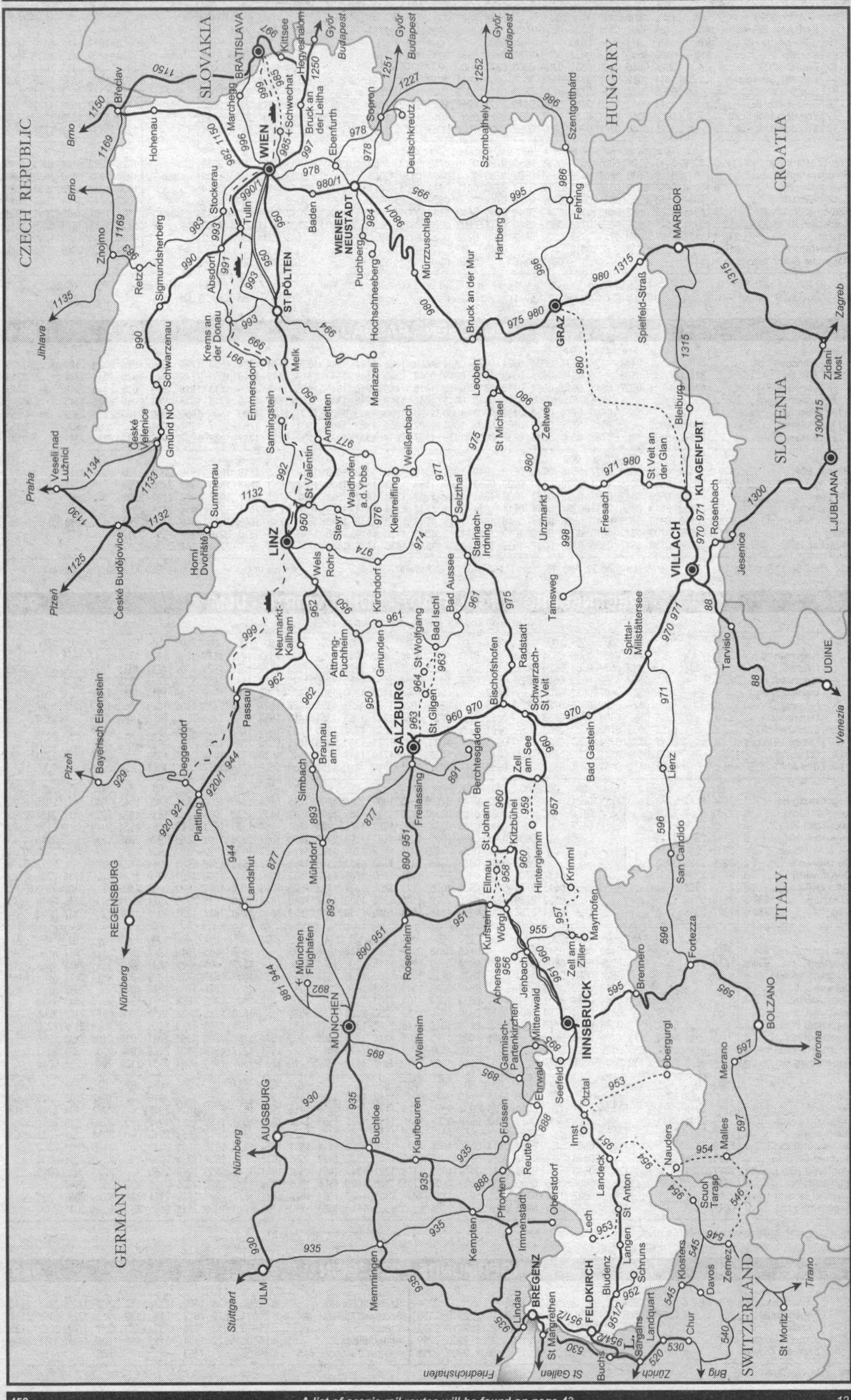

A list of scenic rail routes will be found on page 42

AUSTRIA

Operator: Except where otherwise stated, rail services are operated by Österreichische Bundesbahnen (**ÖBB**) www.oebb.at

Timings: Valid until **December 14**, 2019 unless stated otherwise in individual tables. See page 4 for public holiday dates.

Services: Trains convey both first and second class seating unless footnotes show otherwise or there is a '2' in the train column. Overnight sleeping car (🛏) or couchette (🛏) trains do not necessarily convey seating accommodation - refer to individual footnotes for details. Descriptions of sleeping and couchette cars appear on page 10.

Train categories:

RJX or *RJ*	**Railjet**	Austrian high-speed train. Conveys first and economy (2nd) class. *Business class* also available to first class ticket holders (supplement payable).
ICE	**InterCity Express**	German high-speed train.
EC	**EuroCity**	International express train.
IC	**InterCity**	Internal or international express train.
D	**Schnellzug**	Ordinary fast train.
NJ	**ÖBB nightjet**	Quality overnight express train - see page 10.
EN	**EuroNight**	Other international overnight express train - see page 10.
WB	**Westbahn**	Wien - Salzburg private operator (special fares payable).
REX	**Regional Express**	Semi-fast regional train.
	Regional / S-Bahn	Local stopping trains – no category or train number shown.

Reservations: Seats may be reserved on all express trains (*RJX, RJ, ICE, EC, IC, NJ, D*).

Catering: Three types of catering are indicated in the tables: ✕ – Restaurant car; ⊗ – Bordbistro; 🍸 – At seat trolley service.

FLUGHAFEN WIEN - WIEN - LINZ - SALZBURG — 950

km		RJ 898	RJX 368	RJ 540	RJX 660	RJX 260	ICE 228	RJ 542	RJX 160	RJX 560	RJ 662	RJX 262	RJX 1262	RJ 596	ICE 28	RJX 162	RJX 562	RJ 548	ICE 92	IC 528	RJX 60	RJX 860	RJ 640	ICE 26	RJX 564	RJX 1264
			①–⑥							⚒			⑥Y							Ⓒ						⑥U
		K✕	u✕	✕	✕	✕	Q✕	✕	C✕	L✕	✕	✕	G✕	K✕	Q✕	B✕	L✕	✕	P✕	△🍸	B✕	✕	✕	R✕	✕	G✕
0	**Flughafen Wien** ✈ d.	...	...	...	...	...	...	...	...	0703	0733	0803	...	0833	...	...	0903	...	...	...	...	1003	1033	...	1103	...
17	**Wien** Hbf d.	...	0530	0555	0630	0630	0650	0655	0730	0730	0755	0830	0830	0855	0915	0930	0930	0955	1015	1010	1030	1030	1055	1115	1130	1130
21	**Wien** Meidling d.	...	0537	0602	0637	0637	0657	0702	0737	0737	0802	0837	0837	0902	0922	0937	0937	1002	1022	1017	1037	1037	1102	1122	1137	1137
52	Tullnerfeld 993 d.	...	|	0616	|	|	|	0716	|	|	0816	|	|	0916	|	|	|	1016	|	|	|	|	1116	|	|	|
82	**St Pölten** Hbf 993 d.	...	0600	0630	0700	0700	0724	0730	0800	0800	0830	0900	0900	0930	0946	1000	1000	1030	1046	1051	1100	1100	1130	1146	1200	1200
142	Amstetten d.	...	|	0656	|	|	|	0756	|	|	0856	|	|	0956	|	|	|	1056	|	|	|	|	1156	|	|	|
179	St Valentin 976 d.	...	|	0716	|	|	|	0816	|	|	0916	|	|	1016	|	|	|	1116	|	|	|	|	1216	|	|	|
204	**Linz** Hbf 976 a.	...	0644	0730	0744	0744	0815	0830	0844	0844	0930	0944	0944	1030	1034	1044	1044	1130	1134	1138	1144	1144	1230	1234	1244	1244
204	**Linz** Hbf 962 d.	0632	0646	0732	0746	0746	0817	0832	0846	0846	0932	0946	0946	1032	1036	1046	1046	1132	1136	1140	1146	1146	1232	1236	1246	1246
229	**Wels** Hbf 962 d.	0646	0700	0746	|	|	0833	0846	|	|	0946	|	|	1046	|	|	|	1146	|	1153	|	|	1246	|	|	|
	Passau Hbf 962 🚌 a.	|	|	|	|	|	0922	|	|	|	|	|	|	|	1131	|	|	|	1231	|	|	|	|	1331	|	|
259	Attnang-Puchheim d.	0700	|	0800	|	|	...	0900	|	|	1000	|	|	1100	...	|	|	1200	...	1206	|	|	1300	...	|	|
264	Vöcklabruck d.	0706	|	0806	|	|	...	0906	|	|	1006	|	|	1106	...	|	|	1206	...	...	|	|	1306	...	|	|
329	**Salzburg** Hbf a.	0748	0754	0848	0852	0852	...	0948	0952	0952	1048	1052	1052	1148	...	1152	1152	1248	...	...	1252	1252	1348	...	1352	1352
	München Hbf 890 ★ a.	...	|	...	|	1030	...	...	|	|	|	1230	...	...	...	|	|	...	...	...	1431	|	...	...	|	...
	Innsbruck Hbf 951 a.	...	0944	...	1044	...	...	...	1144	1144	1244	...	...	...	...	1344	1344	...	...	...	...	1444	...	...	1544	...
	Zürich HB 520 a.	...	1320	...	|	...	...	...	1520	...	|	...	...	...	...	1720	...	...	...	...	...	|	...	...	...	...
	Bregenz 951 a.	...	...	...	1317	...	...	...	...	...	1517	...	...	...	...	...	...	...	...	...	...	1717	...	...	...	...

	RJ 642	RJX 62	RJX 862	RJ 644	ICE 90	RJX 166	RJX 566	RJ 646	RJX 64	RJX 864	RJ 698	ICE 22	RJX 168	RJ 740	RJX 66	RJX 866	RJ 742	ICE 20	RJX 760	RJX 1260	RJ 744	RJX 68	RJX 868	RJ 746	RJX 762	RJ 748
																				⑤Z						
	✕	B✕	✕	✕	E✕	✕	L✕	✕	B✕	✕	K✕	R✕	✕	✕	N✕	✕	✕	Q✕	✕	G✕	✕	B✕	✕	✕	✕	✕
Flughafen Wien ✈ d.	...	...	1203	1233	...	...	1303	...	...	1403	1433	...	1503	1533	...	1603	1633	...	1703	...	...	...	1803	1833	1903	...
Wien Hbf d.	1155	1230	1230	1255	1315	1330	1330	1355	1430	1430	1455	1515	1530	1555	1630	1630	1655	1715	1730	1730	1755	1830	1830	1855	1930	1955
Wien Meidling d.	1202	1237	1237	1302	1322	1337	1337	1402	1437	1437	1502	1522	1537	1602	1637	1637	1702	1722	1737	1737	1802	1837	1837	1902	1937	2002
Tullnerfeld 993 d.	1216	|	|	1316	|	|	|	1416	|	|	1516	|	|	1616	|	|	1716	|	|	|	1816	|	|	1916	|	2016
St Pölten Hbf 993 d.	1230	1300	1300	1330	1346	1400	1400	1430	1500	1500	1530	1546	1600	1630	1700	1700	1730	1746	1800	1800	1830	1900	1900	1930	2000	2030
Amstetten d.	1256	|	|	1356	|	|	|	1456	|	|	1556	|	|	1656	|	|	1756	|	|	|	1856	|	|	1956	|	2056
St Valentin 976 d.	1316	|	|	1416	|	|	|	1516	|	|	1616	|	|	1716	|	|	1816	|	|	|	1916	|	|	2016	|	2116
Linz Hbf 976 a.	1330	1344	1344	1430	1434	1444	1444	1530	1544	1544	1630	1634	1644	1730	1744	1744	1830	1834	1844	1844	1930	1944	1944	2030	2044	2130
Linz Hbf 962 d.	1332	1346	1346	1432	1436	1446	1446	1532	1546	1546	1632	1636	1646	1732	1746	1746	1832	1836	1846	1846	1932	1946	1946	2032	2046	2132
Wels Hbf 962 d.	1346	|	|	1446	|	|	|	1546	|	|	1646	|	|	1746	|	|	1846	1850	|	|	1946	|	|	2046	|	2146
Passau Hbf 962 🚌 a.	|	|	|	|	1531	|	|	|	|	|	|	1731	|	|	|	|	|	1934	|	|	|	|	|	|	|	|
Attnang-Puchheim d.	1400	|	|	1500	...	|	|	1600	|	|	1700	...	|	1800	|	|	1900	...	|	|	2000	|	|	2100	|	2200
Vöcklabruck d.	1406	|	|	1506	...	|	|	1606	|	|	1706	...	|	1806	|	|	1906	...	|	|	2006	|	|	2106	|	2206
Salzburg Hbf a.	1448	1452	1452	1548	...	1552	1552	1648	1652	1652	1748	...	1752	1848	1852	1852	1948	...	1952	1952	2048	2052	2052	2148	2152	2248
München Hbf 890 ★ a.	...	1632	|	...	...	|	|	...	1831	|	...	...	|	...	2032	|	...	...	|	...	...	2231	|	...	|	...
Innsbruck Hbf 951 a.	...	...	1644	...	...	1744	1744	...	...	1844	...	...	1944	...	...	2048	...	...	2144	...	...	...	2248b	...	2348	...
Zürich HB 520 a.	...	...	|	...	...	2120	...	...	...	|	...	...	2320	...	...	|	...	...	|	...	...	...	...	...	...	...
Bregenz 951 a.	...	...	1917	...	...	...	...	...	...	2117	...	...	...	...	...	2317	...	...	0013	...	...	...	...	...	...	...

	RJX 42	RJX 664	NJ 490	RJ 840	NJ 466	RJ 820	NJ 246	EN 462	EN 40462
		④⑦							
	B✕	m✕	H♣	✕	A	✕	♥	D♣	⊙
Flughafen Wien ✈ d.	...	2003	...	2033	...	2133	...	...	...
Wien Hbf d.	2030	2030	2041	2055	2127	2155	2255	2325	2325
Wien Meidling d.	2037	2037	2049	2102	2135	2202	2303	2333	2333
Tullnerfeld 993 d.	|	|	|	2116	|	2216	2323	|	|
St Pölten Hbf 993 d.	2100	2100	2120	2130	2202	2230	2341	2359	2359
Amstetten d.	|	|	|	2156	2229	2256	0014	|	|
St Valentin 976 d.	|	|	|	2216	|	2313	0039	|	|
Linz Hbf 976 a.	2144	2144	2214	2230	2255	2327	0054	0048	0048
Linz Hbf 962 d.	2146	2146	2216	2232	2258	...	0056	0103	0103
Wels Hbf 962 d.	2200	2200	2233	2246	2316	...	0112	0118	0118
Passau Hbf 962 🚌 a.	|	|	2320	|	|	...	|	|	|
Attnang-Puchheim d.	|	|	...	2300	2334	...	0134	|	|
Vöcklabruck d.	|	|	...	2306	|	...	0140	|	|
Salzburg Hbf a.	2254	2254	...	2348	0024	...	0221	0213	0213
München Hbf 890 ★ a.	...	...	...	...	|	...	|	0545t	|
Innsbruck Hbf 951 a.	...	...	...	...	0423	...	0519	...	0423
Zürich HB 520 a.	...	...	...	...	0820	...	|	...	0820
Bregenz 951 a.	...	...	...	...	...	...	0829	...	...

	RJ 825	NJ 247	EN 463	EN 40467	RJ 821	RJ 823	NJ 467	RJ 541	NJ 491	RJX 761	RJ 543	RJX 49
	⚒					⚒						①–⑥
	w✕	♥	D♣	⊖	✕	w✕	A	✕	H♣	✕	✕	uB✕
Bregenz 951 d.	...	2140	...	...	...	...	...	...	...	...	...	
Zürich HB 520 d.	...	|	...	2140	...	...	2140	...	...	...	...	...
Innsbruck Hbf 951 d.	...	0044	...	0128	...	...	0128	...	...	...	...	0510
München Hbf 890 ★ d.	...	|	2320t	|	...	...	|	...	...	...	...	|
Salzburg Hbf d.	...	0324	0350	0350	...	...	0436	0512	...	0605	0612	0708
Vöcklabruck d.	...	0405	|	|	...	...	|	0554	...	|	0654	|
Attnang-Puchheim d.	...	0411	|	|	...	...	0525	0600	...	0650	0700	|
Passau Hbf 962 🚌 d.	...	|	|	|	...	...	|	|	0524	|	|	|
Wels Hbf 962 d.	0356e	0429	|	|	...	0556e	0543	0616	0618	|	0716	|
Linz Hbf 962 a.	0408e	0445	0457	0457	...	0608e	0558	0628	0643	0714	0728	0814
Linz Hbf 976 d.	0410	0447	0510	0510	0533	0610	0615	0630	0645	0716	0730	0816
St Valentin 976 d.	|	0504	|	|	0549	|	|	0649	|	|	0749	|
Amstetten d.	0435	0526	|	|	0606	0635	0643	0706	0718	|	0806	|
St Pölten Hbf 993 d.	0502	0610	0602	0602	0632	0702	0712	0732	0753	0802	0832	0902
Tullnerfeld 993 a.	0514	0626	|	|	0643	|	|	0743	|	|	0843	|
Wien Meidling a.	0532	0646	0627	0627	0658	0723	0744	0758	0820	0823	0858	0923
Wien Hbf a.	0539	0654	0635	0635	0705	0730	0755	0805	0827	0830	0905	0930
Flughafen Wien ✈ a.	0557	...	...	...	0727	0757	...	...	...	0857	0927	...

	RJX 949	RJ 545	RJX 763	RJX 265	RJ 547	RJX 861	RJX 61	RJ 549	RJX 765	ICE 21	RJ 691	RJX 863	RJ 63	RJ 643	RJX 161	ICE 23	RJ 645	RJX 1265	RJ 65	RJ 865	RJX 563	ICE 91	RJ 649	RJX 867	RJX 67	ICE 93
																		⑥X								
	✕	✕	✕	✕	✕	✕	B✕	✕	✕	Q✕	K✕	✕	M✕	✕	✕	R✕	✕	G✕	B✕	✕	✕	E✕	✕	✕	B✕	P✕
Bregenz 951 d.	...	...	...	...	...	...	...	...	0548	...	...	0639	...	...	...	...	...	...	...	0840	...	...	...	1040	...	...
Zürich HB 520 d.	...	...	...	...	...	...	...	...	|	...	...	|	...	...	0640	...	...	...	...	|	...	...	...	|	...	...
Innsbruck Hbf 951 d.	0510y	...	0610	...	...	0713	...	...	0817	...	...	0914	...	...	1017	...	...	...	...	1114	1217	...	...	1314	...	...
München Hbf 890 ★ d.	|	...	|	0623	...	|	0723	...	|	...	...	|	0930	...	|	...	...	...	1130h	|	|	...	...	|	1330	...
Salzburg Hbf d.	0708	0712	0808	0808	0812	0908	0908	0912	1008	...	1012	1108	1108	1112	1208	...	1212	1308	1308	1312	1408	...	1412	1508	1508	...
Vöcklabruck d.	|	0754	|	|	0854	|	|	0954	|	...	1054	|	|	1154	|	...	1254	|	|	1354	|	...	1454	|	|	...
Attnang-Puchheim d.	|	0800	|	|	0900	|	|	1000	|	...	1100	|	|	1200	|	...	1300	|	|	1400	|	...	1500	|	|	...
Passau Hbf 962 🚌 d.	|	|	|	|	|	|	|	|	|	1026	|	|	|	|	|	1229	|	|	|	|	|	1429	|	|	|	1529
Wels Hbf 962 d.	|	0816	|	|	0916	|	|	1016	|	1112	1116	|	|	1216	|	|	1316	|	|	1416	|	|	1516	|	|	|
Linz Hbf 962 a.	0814	0828	0914	0914	0928	1014	1014	1028	1114	1124	1128	1214	1214	1228	1314	1324	1328	1414	1414	1428	1514	1524	1528	1614	1614	1624
Linz Hbf 976 d.	0816	0830	0916	0916	0930	1016	1016	1030	1116	1126	1130	1216	1216	1230	1316	1326	1330	1416	1416	1430	1516	1526	1530	1616	1616	1626
St Valentin 976 d.	|	0849	|	|	0949	|	|	1049	|	|	1149	|	|	1249	|	|	1349	|	|	1449	|	|	1549	|	|	|
Amstetten d.	|	0906	|	|	1006	|	|	1106	|	|	1206	|	|	1306	|	|	1406	|	|	1506	|	|	1606	|	|	|
St Pölten Hbf 993 d.	0902	0932	1002	1002	1032	1102	1102	1132	1202	1216	1232	1302	1302	1332	1402	1416	1432	1502	1502	1532	1602	1616	1632	1702	1702	1716
Tullnerfeld 993 a.	|	0943	|	|	1043	|	|	1143	|	|	1243	|	|	1343	|	|	1443	|	|	1543	|	|	1643	|	|	|
Wien Meidling a.	0923	0958	1023	1023	1058	1123	1123	1158	1223	1238	1258	1323	1323	1358	1423	1438	1458	1523	1523	1558	1623	1638	1658	1723	1723	1738
Wien Hbf a.	0930	1005	1030	1030	1105	1130	1130	1205	1230	1245	1305	1330	1330	1405	1430	1445	1505	1530	1530	1605	1630	1645	1705	1730	1730	1745
Flughafen Wien ✈ a.	0957	...	1057	...	1127	1157	...	...	1257	...	1327	1357	...	1427	1457	...	1527	1557	...	...	1657	...	1727	1757	...	...

☛ See page 454 for regional trains Wien Westbf - St Pölten - Melk - Amstetten - Linz, also services Wien - Linz - Salzburg operated by *Westbahn*.

FOR NOTES SEE PAGE 454 →

950 SALZBURG - LINZ - WIEN - FLUGHAFEN WIEN

	RJ 741	RJX 565	RJX 165	ICE 27	RJ 793	RJX 869	RJX 69	IC 725	RJ 745	RJX 167	RJX 567	RJ 1267	ICE 29
								©			●	⑦W	
	✕	L✕	B✕	R✕	K✕	✕	✕	△	✕	C✕	L✕	G✕	Q✕
Bregenz **951** d.	...	...	...	...	...	1240	...	...	...	...	...	...	...
Zürich HB **520** d.	...	...	1040	...	...	│	...	...	...	1240	...	...	...
Innsbruck Hbf **951** d.	...	1417	1417	...	...	1514	...	...	...	1617	1617	...	...
München Hbf **890**★ d.	...	│	│	...	...	│	1530	...	...	│	│	...	...
Salzburg Hbf d.	1512	1608	1608	...	1612	1708	1708	...	1712	1808	1808	1800	...
Vöcklabruck d.	1554	│	│	...	1654	│	│	...	1754	│	│	│	...
Attnang-Puchheim d.	1600	│	│	...	1700	│	│	1754	1800	│	│	│	...
Passau Hbf **962** 🏛 d.	│	│	│	1629	│	│	│	│	│	│	│	│	1829
Wels Hbf **962** d.	1616	│	│	│	1716	│	│	1808	1816	│	│	1857	│
Linz Hbf **962** a.	1628	1714	1714	1724	1728	1814	1814	1820	1828	1914	1914	1918	1924
Linz Hbf **976** d.	1630	1716	1716	1726	1730	1816	1816	1822	1830	1916	1916	1920	1926
St Valentin **976** d.	1649	│	│	│	1749	│	│	│	1849	│	│	│	│
Amstetten d.	1706	│	│	│	1806	│	│	│	1906	│	│	1945	│
St Pölten Hbf **993** d.	1732	1802	1802	1816	1832	1902	1902	1910	1932	2002	2002	2010	2016
Tullnerfeld **993** a.	1743	│	│	│	1843	│	│	│	1943	│	│	2023	│
Wien Meidling a.	1758	1823	1823	1838	1858	1923	1923	1939	1958	2023	2023	2042	2038
Wien Hbf a.	1805	1830	1830	1845	1905	1930	1930	1946	2005	2030	2030	2049	2045
Flughafen Wien ✈ ❦ a.	...	1857	...	...	1927	1957	...	...	...	...	2057	...	...

	RJ 797	RJX 661	RJX 261	RJX 1261	RJ 749	RJ 769	RJX 169	RJ 841	ICE 229	RJX 663	RJ 843	RJX 367	RJ 845
		⑦v		⑥U	⑦v	①-⑥							Ⓑb
	K✕	✕	✕	G✕	✕	d✕	✕	✕	Q✕	✕	✕	✕	✕
Bregenz **951** d.	...	1440	...	...	...	1440	...	...	...	...	...	...	...
Zürich HB **520** d.	...	│	...	...	...	│	1440	...	...	...	...	1640	...
Innsbruck Hbf **951** d.	...	1714	...	...	...	1714	1817	...	...	1914	...	2017	...
München Hbf **890**★ d.	...	│	1730	...	...	│	│	...	...	│	...	│	...
Salzburg Hbf d.	1812	1908	1908	1908	1912	1912	2008	2012	...	2108	2112	2208	2212
Vöcklabruck d.	1854	│	│	│	1954	1954	│	2054	...	│	2154	│	2254
Attnang-Puchheim d.	1900	│	│	│	2000	2000	│	2100	...	│	2200	│	2300
Passau Hbf **962** 🏛 d.	│	│	│	│	│	│	│	│	2038	│	│	│	│
Wels Hbf **962** d.	1916	│	│	│	2016	2016	│	2116	2129	│	2216	2305	2316
Linz Hbf **962** a.	1928	2014	2014	2014	2028	2028	2114	2128	2143	2214	2228	2317	2328
Linz Hbf **976** d.	1930	2016	2016	2016	2030	2030	2116	2130	2145	2216	...	2319	...
St Valentin **976** d.	1949	│	│	│	2049	2049	│	2149	│	│	...	│	...
Amstetten d.	2006	│	│	│	2106	2106	│	2206	│	│	...	│	...
St Pölten Hbf **993** d.	2032	2102	2102	2102	2132	2132	2202	2232	2239	2302	...	0005	...
Tullnerfeld **993** a.	2043	│	│	│	2143	2143	│	2243	│	│	...	│	...
Wien Meidling a.	2058	2123	2123	2123	2158	2158	2223	2258	2302	2323	...	0026	...
Wien Hbf a.	2105	2130	2130	2130	2205	2205	2230	2305	2309	2330	...	0033	...
Flughafen Wien ✈ ❦ a.	2127	...	2157n	2157	2227	2227	...	...	...	...	...	...	...

Regional ÖBB trains **WIEN - MELK - AMSTETTEN - ST VALENTIN - LINZ** (2nd class only)

km‡		©	⚒	ⒶT	⚒			c		S										⊕						
0	**Wien** Westbahnhof d.	0054	...	0424	...	0620	...	...	0720	...	0820	0920	1020	1120	1220	1320	1420	1520	1620	1720	1820	1920	2020	2120	...	2354
6	**Wien** Hütteldorf d.	0100	...	0430	...	0627	...	...	0727	...	0827	0927	1027	1127	1227	1327	1427	1527	1627	1727	1827	1927	2027	2127	...	0000
	Tullnerfeld d.	│	...	│	...	0640	...	...	0740	0812	0840	0940	1040	1140	1240	1340	1440	1540	1640	1740	1840	1940	2040	2140	...	│
61	**St Pölten** Hbf a.	0150	...	0520	...	0654	...	...	0754	0850	0854	0954	1054	1154	1254	1354	1454	1554	1654	1754	1854	1954	2054	2154	...	0055
61	**St Pölten** Hbf d.	0152	0445	0522	0605	0705	0734	...	0805	0853	0905	1005	1105	1205	1305	1405	1505	1605	1705	1805	1905	2005	2105	2205	2235	0100
85	Melk d.	0208	0504	0538	0621	0721	0757		0821	0909	0921	1021	1121	1221	1321	1421	1521	1621	1721	1821	1921	2021	2121	2221	2254	0116
94	Pöchlarn d.	0215	0510	0544	0627	0727	0802	0803	0827	0917	0927	1027	1127	1227	1327	1427	1527	1627	1727	1827	1927	2027	2127	2227	2300	0123
107	Ybbs an der Donau d.	0225	0521	0554	0637	0737	...	0814	0837	0927	0937	1037	1137	1237	1337	1437	1537	1637	1737	1837	1937	2037	2137	2237	2311	0133
124	Amstetten a.	0238	0534	0607	0650	0750	...	0827	0850	0938	0950	1050	1150	1250	1350	1450	1550	1650	1750	1850	1950	2050	2150	2250	2324	0146
124	Amstetten d.	...	0536	*0612*	*0707*	*0807*e	...	...	*0907*	0940	*1007*e	*1107*	*1207*e	*1307*	*1407*e	*1507*	*1607*r	*1707*	1807e	1907	2007e	*2107*	...	2307	...	...
163	**St Valentin** **976** a.	...	0606	*0630*	*0736*	*0836*e	...	...	*0936*	1000	*1036*e	*1136*	*1236*e	*1336*	*1436*e	*1536*	*1636*r	*1736*	1836e	1936	2036e	*2136*	...	2336	...	...
188	**Linz** Hbf **976** a.	...	*0636*	*0649*	...	...	...	...	...	1020	...	...	...	...	...	...	...	...	...	...	...	...	...	...	...	...

			Ⓐ	Ⓐ¶	Ⓐ	F	Ⓐ¶																S	⊗		
Linz Hbf d.	...	...	...	...	...	...	...	...	...	...	...	...	...	...	...	...	...	...	...	...	*1852*	...	1925	...	*2052*	...
St Valentin d.	...	...	...	0447	...	...	0547	*0624*	*0724*	*0824*	*0924*e	*1024*	*1124*e	*1224*	*1324*e	*1424*	*1524*e	*1624*	1724	1824	*1923*	...	1950	*2023*	*2123*	...
Amstetten a.	...	...	...	0516	...	...	0616	*0653*	*0753*	*0853*	*0953*e	*1053*	*1153*e	*1253*	*1353*e	*1453*	*1553*e	*1653*	1753	1853	*1953*	...	2013	*2053*	*2153*	...
Amstetten d.	0419	...	0442	0518	0548	0558	0618	0710	0810	0910	1010	1110	1210	1310	1410	1510	1610	1710	1810	1910	2010	...	2016	2110	2210	...
Ybbs an der Donau d.	0431	...	0454	0530	0600	0611	0630	0722	0822	0922	1022	1122	1222	1322	1422	1522	1622	1722	1822	1922	2022	...	2029	2122	2222	...
Pöchlarn d.	0441	...	0504	0540	0610	0622	0640	0732	0832	0932	1032	1132	1232	1332	1432	1532	1632	1732	1832	1932	2032	...	2041	2132	2232	...
Melk d.	0447	...	0510	0546	0616	0629	0646	0738	0838	0938	1038	1138	1238	1338	1438	1538	1638	1738	1838	1938	2038	...	2050	2138	2238	...
St Pölten Hbf a.	0504	...	0530	0604	0634	0650	0704	0755	0855	0955	1055	1155	1255	1355	1455	1555	1655	1755	1855	1955	2055	...	2107	2156	2255	...
St Pölten Hbf d.	0506	...	0532	0606	0636	...	0706	0806	0906	1006	1106	1206	1306	1406	1506	1606	1706	1806	1906	2006	...	...	2118	2205	...	2305
Tullnerfeld a.	0519	...	0545	0619	0649	...	0719	0819	0919	1019	1119	1219	1319	1419	1519	1619	1719	1819	1919	2019	...	...	2148	│	...	│
Wien Hütteldorf a.	0533	...	0559	0633	0703	...	0733	0833	0933	1033	1133	1233	1333	1433	1533	1633	1733	1833	1933	2033	...	...	...	2328	...	0024
Wien Westbahnhof a.	0540	...	0606	0640	0710	...	0740	0840	0940	1040	1140	1240	1340	1440	1540	1640	1740	1840	1940	2040	...	...	...	2337	...	0032

SERVICES OPERATED BY *WESTBAHN* **WIEN - LINZ - SALZBURG**. Special fares payable (ÖBB tickets not valid). All trains convey 🍸.

km		WB 900	WB 950	WB 902	WB 952	SEE NOTE ⊠	WB 976	WB 928	WB 978	WB 930
			Ⓐq						†	
	Wien Praterstern d.	...	0556	...	0656		1856	...	1956	...
	Wien Mitte d.	...	0559	...	0659	and at	1859	...	1959	...
	Wien Hbf d.	...	0606	...	0706		1906	...	2006	...
	Wien Meidling d.	...	0614	...	0714	the same	1914	...	2014	...
0	**Wien** Westbahnhof d.	0543	│	0643	│		│	1943	│	2043
6	**Wien** Hütteldorf d.	0550	│	0650	│	minutes	│	1950	│	2050
60	**St Pölten** Hbf d.	0610	0638	0710	0738		1938	2010	2038	2110
120	Amstetten d.	0632	0701	0732	0801	past each	2001	2032	2101	2132
182	**Linz** Hbf a.	0656	0726	0756	0826		2026	2056	2126	2156
182	**Linz** Hbf d.	0658	0728	0758	0828	hour until	2028	2058	2128	...
207	Wels Hbf d.	0711	0741	0811	0841		2041	2111	2141	...
237	Attnang-Puchheim d.	0724	0754	0824	0854		2054	2124	2154	...
242	Vöcklabruck d.	0729	0759	0829	0859		2059	2129	2159	...
307	**Salzburg** Hbf a.	0808	0838	0908	0938		2138	2208	2238	...

	WB 901	WB 951	WB 903	WB 953	WB 905	WB 955	SEE NOTE ⊠	WB 979	WB 931	WB 981
	Ⓐ	Ⓐ	⚒	⚒a						†
Salzburg Hbf d.	...	...	0552	0622	0652	0722		1922	1952	2022
Vöcklabruck d.	...	...	0632	0702	0732	0802	and at	2002	2032	2102
Attnang-Puchheim d.	...	...	0637	0707	0737	0807		2007	2037	2107
Wels Hbf d.	...	...	0650	0720	0750	0820	the same	2020	2050	2120
Linz Hbf a.	...	...	0702	0732	0802	0832		2032	2102	2132
Linz Hbf d.	0604	0634	0704	0734	0804	0834	minutes	2034	2104	2134
Amstetten d.	0628	0700	0728	0800	0828	0900		2100	2128	2200
St Pölten Hbf d.	0650	0723	0750	0823	0850	0923	past each	2123	2150	2223
Wien Hütteldorf a.	0710	│	0810	│	0910	│		│	2210	│
Wien Westbf a.	0717	│	0817	│	0917	│	hour until	│	2217	│
Wien Meidling a.	...	0746	...	0846	...	0946		2146	...	2246
Wien Hbf a.	...	0752	...	0852	...	0952		2152	...	2252
Wien Mitte a.	...	0759	...	0859	...	0959		2159	...	2259
Wien Praterstern a.	...	0803	...	0903	...	1003		2203	...	2303

A – 🛏 1, 2 cl., ▬ 2 cl. and (2) Wien - Zürich and v.v.; conveys 🛏 1, 2 cl., ▬ 2 cl. and (2) (*EN* **237**/**236**) Wien - Salzburg - Villach - Tarvisio 🏛 - Venezia and v.v.
B – From / to Budapest (Table **1250**).
C – From / to Bratislava (Table **86**).
D – KÁLMÁN IMRE – 🛏 1, 2 cl., ▬ 2 cl. and (2) Budapest - Wien - München and v.v.
E – (12) and ✕ Hamburg - Hannover - Nürnberg - Regensburg - Passau - Wien and v.v.
F – From Waidhofen a. d. Ybbs (Table **977**).
G – To / from Wörgl via Zell am See (Table **960**).
H – 🛏 1, 2 cl., ▬ 2 cl. and (2) Wien - Hannover - Hamburg and v.v.; 🛏 1, 2 cl., ▬ 2 cl. and (2) (**40490**/**40421**) Wien - Köln - Düsseldorf and v.v.
K – To / from Klagenfurt (Table **970**).
L – To / from Feldkirch on dates in Table **951**.
M – (12) and ✕ (Frankfurt ⑥⑦ **k** -) München - Wien - Budapest.
N – (12) and ✕ Budapest - München (- Frankfurt ⑤⑥ **f**).
P – (12) and ✕ Berlin - Erfurt - Nürnberg - Regensburg - Passau 🏛 - Wien and v.v.
Q – (12) and ✕ Frankfurt - Nürnberg - Regensburg - Passau 🏛 - Wien and v.v.
R – (12) and ✕ Dortmund - Frankfurt - Nürnberg - Regensburg - Passau 🏛 - Wien and v.v.
S – May 1 - Oct. 27. (2) Wien Franz-Josefs-Bf - Passau and v.v.
T – To Kleinreifling (Table **977**).
U – ⑥ Dec. 29 - Apr. 20.
W – ⑦ Dec. 30 - Apr. 14 (also Apr. 22); ⑦ June 30 - Sept. 1.
X – ⑥ Dec. 29 - Apr. 20; ⑥ June 29 - Aug. 31.
Y – ⑥ Dec. 29 - Apr. 20; ⑥ June 29 - Sept. 7.
Z – ⑤ Dec. 28 - Apr. 19; ⑤ June 28 - Sep. 6.

a – Runs daily Linz - Wien.
b – Ⓑ (not Apr. 21, June 9).
c – © only.
d – Also Apr. 21, June 9; not Apr. 22, June 10.
e – Ⓐ only.
f – ⑤⑥ (also Dec. 23, 24, 25, 30, 31, Apr. 18, 21, June 9).
h – 1128 on ⑥ June 29 - July 27.

k – ⑥⑦ (also Dec. 24, 25, 26, 31, Jan. 1, Apr. 19, 22, June 10).
m – Also Apr. 22, June 10, Oct. 30; not May 30, June 20, Aug. 15, Oct. 31.
n – Not ⑥.
q – Also runs on ⑥ Linz - Salzburg.
r – ⚒ only.
t – Mar. 15 - May 15 runs to / from München Ost (not Hbf); see Table **890**.
u – Not Apr. 22, June 10.
v – ⑦ (Also Apr. 22, June 10; not Apr. 21, June 9).
w – Also May 1, Oct. 26.
y – ①⑥ (also Apr. 23, May 30, June 11, 20, Aug. 16, Nov. 1; not Apr. 22, June 1, 10, 22, Nov. 2).

● – ①②③④⑦ (not Apr. 21, June 9).
⊙ – 🛏 1, 2 cl., ▬ 2 cl. and (2) Budapest (**462**) - Salzburg (**466**) - Zürich.
⊖ – 🛏 1, 2 cl., ▬ 2 cl. and (2) Zürich (**467**) - Salzburg (**463**) - Budapest.
♥ – Conveys 🛏 1, 2 cl., ▬ 2 cl. and (2).
△ – SALZKAMMERGUT – (12) Wien - Attnang-Puchheim - Stainach-Irdning and v.v. (Table **961**).
⊕ – Change trains at Amstetten on ©.
⊗ – Change trains at St Pölten on Ⓐ.
¶ – Runs daily St Pölten - Wien.
❦ – See Table **985** for full service from / to Wien Flughafen ✈.
♣ – Ⓡ for journeys to / from Germany.
★ – München timings are subject to alteration Mar. 17 - 26 and Apr. 11 - June 6.
⊠ – Train numbers increase by 2 each hour. From June 2019 (exact date to be confirmed) the following services will run as through trains to / from München Hbf : Wien Westbahnhof departures at 0643, 1143 and 1643 (arriving München Hbf 1106, 1606 and 2115); Wien Westbahnhof arrivals at 1117, 1617 and 2117 (departing München at 0655, 1155 and 1655); see Table **890** for full timings between Salzburg and München.
‡ – Distance via the classic route. Trains calling at Tullnerfeld use the high-speed line between Wien and St Pölten.

SALZBURG and MÜNCHEN - INNSBRUCK - BREGENZ - LINDAU 951

km		NJ 466	EN 40462		NJ 464	NJ 246		RJ 666			RJX 360	RJ 668	IC 118	NJ 421	EC 81	RJX 368			RJX 660	EC 85	RJX 560	RJX 160			RJ 662	EC 87
										⚒				®	¶	①–⑥					⚒					
		N	⊙	2	♦	N	2	✕	2	2	✕	✕	♀♦	♦	A✕	u✕	2	2◧	✕	A✕	F✕	R✕	2	2◧	F✕	A✕
	Wien Hbf **950** d.	2127	2325	...	...	2255	...	...	...	...	...	...	...	...	...	0530	...	...	0630	...	0730	0730	...	...	0755	...
	Linz Hbf **950** d.	2258	0103	...	...	0056	...	...	...	...	...	...	...	...	...	0646	...	...	0746	...	0846	0846	...	...	0932	...
0	**Salzburg** Hbf d.	0230	0230	...	...	0306	...	...	...	...	...	0656	...	...	...	0756	...	...	0856	...	0956	0956	...	...	1056	...
	München Hbf **890** ‡ d.	|	|	...	...	|	...	...	...	...	...	|	...	0729	0734	|	...	...	|	0934	|	|	...	...	|	1134
	München Ost **890** ‡ d.	|	|	...	...	|	...	...	...	...	...	|	...	|	0744	|	...	...	|	0944	|	|	...	...	|	1144
	Rosenheim .. **890** ‡ d.	|	|	...	...	|	...	...	...	...	...	|	...	|	0814	|	...	...	|	1014	|	|	...	...	|	1214
120	Kufstein 🏨 ‡ d.	|	|	...	...	|	0510	...	0612	0636	...	|	...	0828	0836	0909	0936	...	|	1036	1109	1109	...	...	|	1236
134	Wörgl Hbf **960** d.	|	|	...	...	|	0524	...	0629	0649	...	0817	...	0839	0846	0919	0954	...	1015	1046	1119	1119	...	...	1215	1246
159	Jenbach **960** d.	|	|	...	...	|	0546	...	0651	0709	...	0831	...	0855	0901	|	1014	...	1029	1101	|	|	...	...	1229	1301
193	**Innsbruck** Hbf **960** a.	0423	0423	...	...	0519	0620	...	0725	0739	...	0846	...	0914	0918	0944	1040	...	1044	1118	1144	1144	...	...	1244	1318
193	**Innsbruck** Hbf d.	0431	0431	...	0453	0523	...	0642	...	...	0745	▬	0854	...	...	0948	...	0952	1048	...	1148z	1148	...	1152	1248	...
239	Ötztal d.	|	|	...	|	0551	...	0706	...	...	0809	...	0928	...	...	1012	...	1030	|	...	1212z	1212	...	1230	|	...
248	Imst-Pitztal d.	|	|	...	|	0602	...	0716	...	...	0819	...	0939	...	...	|	...	1041	1119	...	|	|	...	1241	1319	...
265	Landeck - Zams d.	|	|	...	0545	0622	...	0730	...	...	0833	...	0954	...	...	1033	...	1056	1133	...	1233z	1233	...	1256	1333	...
293	St Anton am Arlberg d.	|	|	...	0610	0648	...	0754	...	...	0857	...	1022	...	...	1057	...	▬	|	...	1257z	1257	...	...	|	...
304	Langen am Arlberg d.	|	|	...	0621	0659	...	0804	...	...	|	...	1032	...	...	|	...	...	1204	...	|	|	...	...	1404	...
329	Bludenz **952** d.	0625	0625	0630	0706	0735	...	0831	...	...	0931	...	1102	...	...	1131	...	...	1231	...	1331z	1331	...	...	1431	...
350	**Feldkirch** **952** a.	0637	0637	0645	0721	0749	...	0842	...	...	0942	2	1113	...	...	1142	...	2	1242	...	1342z	1342	...	...	1442	...
350	**Feldkirch** **952** d.	0640	0640	0647	0738	0754	...	0847	...	...	0944	0947	1115	...	...	1148	...	1147	1247	...	...	1348	1347	...	1447	...
369	**Buchs** 🏨 **952** a.	0656	0656	|	0753	|	...	|	...	...	0959	|	|	...	...	1206	...	|	|	...	...	1406	|	...	|	...
	Zürich HB **520** a.	0820	0820	|	0920	|	...	|	...	...	1120	|	|	...	...	1320	...	|	|	...	...	1520	|	...	|	...
375	Dornbirn **952** d.	...	...	0709	...	0821	...	0909	...	...	...	1009	1132	...	...	...	...	1209	1309	...	...	...	1409	...	1509	...
387	**Bregenz** 🏨 **952** a.	...	...	0718	...	0829	...	0917	...	...	...	1018	1141	...	...	...	...	1218	1317	...	...	...	1418	...	1517	...
397	**Lindau** Hbf 🏨 **952** a.	...	...	0731	...	*0901*	...	*0932*	...	...	...	1031	1153	...	...	...	...	1231	*1332*	...	...	...	1431	...	*1532*	...

	RJX 562	RJX 162		RJX 860	EC 89	RJ 564	EC 164		RJ 1287	RJX 862	RJ 1287	ICE 1281	EC 83	RJX 166	RJX 566		RJX 864	EC 287	RJX 168	ICE 1285	RJX 866	EC 289	RJX 760	RJX 868	RJX 762	
									⑥C		⑥C	⑥			S					⑤				Ⓑw		
	F✕	B✕	2◧	F✕	A✕	F✕	✕♦	2◧	✕	F✕	✕	✕♦	A✕	✕	F✕	2	F✕	✕	F✕	✕♦	F✕	✕	F✕	F✕	F✕	2
Wien Hbf **950** d.	0930	0930	...	1030	...	1130	...	...	...	1230	...	...	...	1330	1330	...	1430	...	1530	...	1630	...	1730	1830	1930	...
Linz Hbf **950** d.	1046	1046	...	1146	...	1246	...	...	...	1346	...	...	...	1446	1446	...	1546	...	1646	...	1746	...	1846	1946	2046	...
alzburg Hbf d.	1156	1156	...	1256	...	1356	...	...	...	1456	...	...	...	1556	1556	...	1656	...	1756	...	1900	...	1956	2056	2156	...
München Hbf **890** ‡ d.	|	|	...	|	1334	|	...	...	1428	|	...	1521	1534	|	|	...	|	1734	|	1825	|	1934	|	|	|	...
München Ost **890** ‡ d.	|	|	...	|	1344	|	...	...	1437	|	...	|	1544	|	|	...	|	1744	|	1837	|	1944	|	|	|	...
Rosenheim **890** ‡ d.	|	|	...	|	1414	|	...	...	1509	|	...	1600	1614	|	|	...	|	1814	|	1914	|	2014	|	|	|	...
ufstein 🏨 ‡ d.	1309	1309	...	|	1436	1509	...	...	1530	|	...	1622	1636	1709	1709	...	|	1836	1909	1941	|	2036	2109	2209	2309	...
Vörgl Hbf **960** d.	1319	1319	...	1415	1446	1519	1502	...	1544	1615	...	1631	1646	1719	1719	...	1815	1846	1919	1950	2019	2046	2119	2219	2319	...
enbach **960** d.	|	|	...	1429	1501	|	1518	...	1600	1629	...	...	1701	|	|	...	1829	1901	|	▬	2033	2101	|	2233	2333	...
nnsbruck Hbf **960** a.	1344	1344	...	1444	1518	1544	1540	...	1617	1644	...	...	1718	1744	1744	...	1844	1918	1944	...	2048	2118	2144	2248	2348	...
nnsbruck Hbf d.	1348y	1348	1352	1448	...	...	1548	1552	1624	1648	...	...	...	1748	1748	1752	1848	...	1948	...	2051	...	2148	...	...	0005
)tztal d.	1412y	1412	1430	|	...	...	1612	1630	1703	|	←	...	...	1812	1812	1830	|	...	2012	...	|	...	2212	...	...	0057
nst-Pitztal d.	|	|	1441	1519	...	...	|	1641	1712	1719	1723	...	...	|	|	1841	1919	...	2022	...	2122	...	2222	...	...	0107
andeck - Zams d.	1433y	1433	1456	1533	...	...	1633	1656	→	1733	1746	...	...	1833	1833	1856	1933	...	2036	...	2136	...	2236	...	...	0122
t Anton am Arlberg d.	1457y	1457	▬	|	...	...	1657	▬	...	|	1817	...	...	1857	1857	▬	|	...	2100	...	|	...	2300	...	...	...
angen am Arlberg d.	|	|	...	1604	...	...	|	...	...	1804	1828	...	...	|	|	...	2004	...	|	...	2207	...	2310	...	...	...
ludenz **952** d.	1531y	1531	...	1631	...	...	1731	...	...	1831	1904	...	...	1931	1931	...	2031	...	2134	...	2234	...	2337	...	...	...
eldkirch **952** a.	1542y	1542	2	1642	...	...	1742	2	...	1842	1919	...	...	1942	1942	2	2042	...	2145	2	2245	...	2348	...	...	...
eldkirch **952** d.	...	1548	1547	1647	...	...	1744	1747	...	1847	...	...	...	1948	...	1947	2047	...	2148	2150	2247	...	2350	...	...	...
Buchs 🏨 **952** a.	...	1606	|	|	...	...	1759	|	...	|	...	...	...	2006	...	|	|	...	2203	|	|	...	|	...	...	...
Zürich HB **520** a.	...	1720	|	|	...	...	1920	|	...	|	...	...	...	2120	...	|	|	...	2320	|	|	...	|	...	...	...
ornbirn **952** d.	...	...	1609	1709	...	...	...	1809	...	1909	...	...	...	...	...	2009	2109	...	...	2212	2309	...	0005	...	...	...
regenz 🏨 **952** a.	...	...	1618	1717	...	...	...	1818	...	1917	...	...	...	...	...	2018	2117	...	...	2221	2317	...	0013	...	...	...
indau Hbf 🏨 **952** a.	...	...	1631	*1732*	...	...	...	1831	...	*1932*	...	...	...	...	...	2031	*2132*	...	...	2234	*2332*	...	...	...	...	...

km		RJX 49		RJX 763		RJX 861	EC 288	RJX 765	RJX 863	ICE 1280		RJX 161	EC 286	RJ 1286	RJ 865	RJ 1286	ICE 1284		EC 163	RJX 563	EC 88	RJX 867		RJX 165	RJX 565	EC 80
		①–⑥			⚒					⑥				⑥C		⑥C	⑦									
		u B ✕	2	F✕	2	F✕	✕	F✕	F✕	✕♦	2	F✕	✕	✕	✕	✕	✕♦	2	✕♦	F✕	A✕	F✕	2	B✕	F✕	A✕
	Lindau Hbf 🏨 **952** d.		...	...	...	...	...	...	*0624*	...	0727	...	...	...	*0825*	...	...	0925	...	...	...	*1025*	1127	...	...	...
	Bregenz 🏨 **952** d.	...	...	...	...	...	...	0548	0639	...	0740	...	...	...	0840	...	...	0940	...	...	...	1040	1140	...	...	...
	Dornbirn **952** d.	...	...	...	...	...	...	0557	0652	...	0751	...	...	...	0851	...	...	0951	...	...	...	1051	1151	...	...	...
	Zürich HB **520** d.	...	...	...	...	...	...	|	|	...	|	0640	...	...	|	...	...	|	0840	...	...	|	|	1040	...	...
	Buchs 🏨 **952** d.	...	...	...	...	...	...	|	|	...	|	0754	...	...	|	...	...	|	1000	...	...	|	|	1154	...	...
	Feldkirch **952** a.	...	...	...	...	...	...	0611	0712	...	0812	0809	...	...	0912	...	...	1012	1015	...	...	1112	1212	1209	...	...
	Feldkirch **952** d.	...	...	...	...	...	...	0613	0717	...	▬	0817	...	0850	0917	...	...	▬	1017	...	...	1117	▬	1217	1217v	...
	Bludenz **952** d.	...	...	...	...	...	...	0626	0730	...	...	0830	...	0905	0930	...	...	...	1030	...	...	1130	...	1230	1230v	...
	Langen am Arlberg d.	...	...	...	...	...	...	0652	0756	...	...	|	...	0937	0956	...	...	...	|	...	...	1156	...	|	|	...
	St Anton am Arlberg d.	...	...	...	...	...	...	0703	|	...	2△	0903	...	0948	|	...	...	2△	1103	...	...	|	2△	1303	1303v	...
	Landeck - Zams d.	...	0434	...	0604	...	...	0727	0827	...	0901	0927	...	1017	1027	←	...	1101	1127	...	...	1227	1301	1327	1327v	...
	Imst-Pitztal d.	...	0451	...	0619	...	...	0740	0840	...	0917	|	...	1033	1040	1046	...	1118	|	...	...	1240	1318	|	|	...
	Ötztal d.	...	0504	...	0631	...	...	0751	|	...	0931	0948	...	→	|	1107	...	1131	1148	...	...	|	1331	1348	1348v	...
	Innsbruck Hbf a.	...	0553	...	0702	...	...	0814	0911	...	1006	1011	...	...	1111	1136	...	1206	1211	...	...	1311	1406	1411	1411v	...
0	**Innsbruck** Hbf **960** d.	0510	...	0610	...	0713	0717	0817	0914	...	...	1017	1040	...	1114	1140	...	...	1221	1217	1240	1314	...	1417	1417	1440
34	Jenbach **960** d.	0527	...	0627	...	0730	0735	|	0931	...	...	|	1101	...	1131	1201	...	...	1244	|	1301	1331	...	|	|	1501
59	Wörgl Hbf **960** d.	0541	...	0641	...	0745	0749	0843	0945	1025	...	1043	1116	...	1145	1220	1220	...	1258	1243	1316	1345	...	1443	1443	1516
73	Kufstein 🏨 ‡ d.	0551	...	0651	...	|	0759	0853	|	1037	...	1053	1126	...	|	1232	1232	...	...	1253	1326	|	...	1453	1453	1526
107	Rosenheim **890** ‡ a.	|	...	|	...	|	0818	|	|	1057	...	|	1145	...	|	|	1255	...	...	|	1345	|	...	|	|	1545
162	**München** Ost **890** ‡ a.	|	...	|	...	|	0849	|	|	|	...	|	1215	...	|	1322	1328	...	...	|	1415	|	...	|	|	1615
172	**München** Hbf **890** ‡ a.	|	...	|	...	|	0901	|	|	1134	...	|	1226	...	|	1332	1345	...	...	|	1426	|	...	|	|	1626
	Salzburg Hbf a.	0702	...	0802	...	0902	...	1003	1102	...	...	1203	...	...	1302	...	...	...	...	1403	...	1502	...	1603	1603	...
	Linz Hbf **950** a.	0814	...	0914	...	1014	...	1114	1214	...	...	1314	...	...	1428	...	...	...	...	1514	...	1614	...	1714	1714	...
	Wien Hbf **950** a.	0930	...	1030	...	1130	...	1230	1330	...	...	1430	...	...	1605	...	...	...	...	1630	...	1730	...	1830	1830	...

♦ – **NOTES** (LISTED BY TRAIN NUMBER)

18 – [12] Innsbruck - Lindau - Ulm - Stuttgart - Köln - Dortmund. Terminates at Lindau from Mar. 3.

63/4 – TRANSALPIN – [12] and ✕ Zürich - Kitzbühel - Schwarzach - Selzthal - Graz and v.v.

21 – 🛏 1, 2 cl., ▬ 2 cl. and [2] Düsseldorf - Frankfurt - Innsbruck; 🛏 1, 2 cl., ▬ 2 cl. and [2] (**40491**) Hamburg - Hannover - Innsbruck.

64 – 🛏 1, 2 cl., ▬ 2 cl. and [2] Graz - Schwarzach - Zürich; 🛏 1, 2 cl.*, ▬ 2 cl.* and [2] (*EN* **414**) Beograd - Zagreb - Ljubljana - Villach - Schwarzach - Zürich.

280 – ⑥ June 29 - Sept. 7. [12] Schwarzach - Wörgl - München.

281 – ⑥ June 22 - Sept. 7. [12] München - Wörgl - Schwarzach.

284 – ⑦ June 23 - Sept. 8. [12] Schwarzach - Wörgl - München - Flensburg.

285 ⑤ Jun. 28 - Sept. 6. [12] Hamburg - München - Wörgl - Schwarzach.

– To / from Verona, Bologna or Venezia via Brennero (Table **70**).

– From / to Budapest (Table **1250**).

– ⑥ Dec. 29 - Apr. 27; ⑥ June 29 - Sept. 7.

– From / to Wien Flughafen ✈ (Table **950**).

– Conveys 🛏 1, 2 cl., ▬ 2 cl. and [2].

– From Bratislava (Table **86**).

– Daily Wien Flughafen - Innsbruck; Ⓐ Innsbruck - Feldkirch.

u – Not Apr. 22, June 10.

v – ⑥⑦ (also Apr. 22, June 10).

w – Not Apr. 21, June 9.

y – ⑤⑥† (not May 1).

z – ⑤⑥ (also May 30, June 20, Aug. 15).

¶ – Train number **1289** on ⑥⑦.

△ – Runs 5–11 minutes **earlier** on †.

⊙ – 🛏 1, 2 cl., ▬ 2 cl. and [2] Budapest (**462**) - Salzburg (**466**) - Zürich. Also conveys through cars from Praha (see Table **52**).

* – 🛏 1, 2 cl. and ▬ 2 cl. from Zagreb.

◧ – On † departs Ötztal 2 minutes later, Imst-Pitztal 9 minutes later, arrives Landeck 10 minutes later.

‡ – Additional local services run München Ost - Rosenheim - Kufstein and v.v. (branded *Meridian*, operated by Bayerische Oberlandbahn). **Valid until May 15**. Journey time: 1 hr 5 mins - 1 hr 13 mins. **From München Ost** at 0650, 0752, 0852 and hourly until 1752, 1851, 1952. **From Kufstein** at 0601, 0702, 0802, 0903, 1002 and hourly until 1902. Also: Rosenheim to Kufstein at 2135, 2235 and 2335; Kufstein to Rosenheim at 1959, 2058, 2158 and 2258.

951 LINDAU - BREGENZ - INNSBRUCK - MÜNCHEN and SALZBURG

	RJX		RJX	RJX	EC	RJX	RJ		RJX	EC	IC	RJX		RJX	EC	NJ	RJX			RJX		NJ	NJ		EN	NJ
	869		167	567	84	661	769		169	86	119	663		367	82	420	667			369		247	465		40467	467
				E		⑦v	①–⑥								◧	R										
	F✕	2	R✕	F✕	A✕	✕	w✕	2	✕	A✕	🍸	✕	2	✕	A✕	♦	✕	2	2	✕	2	N	♦	2	◇	N
Lindau Hbf 🏛 ..... **952** d.	1225	1327	...	...	...	1425	1425	1525	...	...	1601	...	1727	...	...	...	1825	...	1927	...	...	2104	...	2227	...	...
Bregenz 🏛 .... **952** d.	1240	1340	...	...	...	1440	1440	1540	...	...	1611	...	1740	...	...	...	1840	...	1940	...	...	2140	...	2240	...	...
Dornbirn .... **952** d.	1251	1351	...	...	...	1451	1451	1551	...	...	1621	...	1751	...	...	...	1851	...	1951	...	...	2151	...	2251	...	...
Zürich HB **520** .... d.	|	|	1240	...	...	|	|	|	1440	...	|	...	|	1640	...	...	|	...	|	1840	...	|	2040	|	2140	2140
Buchs 🏛 .... **952** d.	|	|	1354	...	...	|	|	|	1554	...	|	...	|	1800	...	...	|	...	|	1954	...	|	2205	|	2305	2305
Feldkirch .... **952** a.	1312	1412	1409	...	...	1512	1512	1612	1609	...	1638	...	1812	1815	...	...	1912	...	2012	2009	...	2216	2220	2312	2321	2321
Feldkirch .... **952** d.	1317	▬	1417	1417v	...	1517	1517	▬	1617	...	1640	...	▬	1817	...	...	1917	...	...	2017	...	2227	2245	...	2324	2324
Bludenz .... **952** d.	1330	...	1430	1430v	...	1530	1530	...	1630	...	1656	...	...	1830	...	...	1930	...	...	2030	...	2242	2301	...	2340	2340
Langen am Arlberg .... d.	1356	...	|	|	...	1556	1556	...	|	...	1728	...	...	|	...	...	1956	...	...	|	...	2310	2335	...	|	|
St Anton am Arlberg .. d.	|	2△	1503	1503v	...	|	|	2△	1703	...	1738	...	2△	1903	...	...	2007	...	...	2107	...	2320	2345	...	|	|
Landeck - Zams .... d.	1427	1501	1527	1527v	...	1627	1627	1701	1727	...	1805	...	1901	1927	...	...	2031	...	...	2131	...	2348	0009	...	0036	0036
Imst-Pitztal .... d.	1440	1518	|	|	...	1640	1640	1718	|	...	1821	...	1918	1940	...	...	2044	...	...	2144	...	0002	|	...	|	|
Ötztal .... d.	|	1531	1548	1548v	...	|	|	1731	1748	...	1835	...	1931	1951	...	...	2055	...	...	2155	...	0013	|	...	|	|
Innsbruck Hbf .... a.	1511	1606	1611	1611v	...	1711	1711	1806	1811	...	1905	...	2006	2014	...	...	2118	...	...	2218	...	0039	0054	...	0120	0120
Innsbruck Hbf ..... **960** d.	1514	...	1617	1617	1640	1714	1714	...	1817	1840	...	1914	...	2017	2040	2044	...	2135	...	...	2235	0044	...	...	0128	0128
Jenbach .... **960** d.	1531	...	|	|	1701	1731	1731	...	|	1901	...	1931	...	|	2101	2106	...	2209	...	...	2309	|	...	...	|	|
Wörgl Hbf .... **960** d.	1545	...	1643	1643	1716	1745	1745	...	1843	1916	...	1945	...	2043	2116	2123	...	2235	...	...	2335	|	...	...	|	|
Kufstein 🏛 .... ‡ d.	|	...	1653	1653	1726	|	|	...	1853	1926	...	|	...	2053	2126	2135	...	2248	...	...	2348	|	...	...	|	|
Rosenheim .... **890** ‡ a.	|	...	|	|	1745	|	|	...	|	1945	...	|	...	|	2145	2158	...	...	...	...	...	|	...	...	|	|
München Ost **890** ‡ a.	|	...	|	|	1816	|	|	...	|	2014	...	|	...	|	2216	|	...	...	...	...	...	|	...	...	|	|
München Hbf **890** ‡ a.	|	...	|	|	1826	|	|	...	|	2026	...	|	...	|	2226	2238	...	...	...	...	...	|	...	...	|	|
Salzburg Hbf .... a.	1702	...	1803	1803	...	1902	1902	...	2003	...	...	2104	...	2206	...	...	...	...	...	...	...	0258	...	...	0322	0322
Linz Hbf **950** .... a.	1814	...	1914	1914	...	2014	2028	...	2114	...	...	2214	...	2317	...	...	...	...	...	...	...	0445	...	...	0457	0558
Wien Hbf **950** .... a.	1930	...	2030	2030	...	2130	2205	...	2230	...	...	2330	...	0033	...	...	...	...	...	...	...	0654	...	...	0635	0755

♦ – NOTES (LISTED BY TRAIN NUMBER)

420 – 🛏 1, 2 cl., ▬ 2 cl. and (2) Innsbruck - Frankfurt - Düsseldorf;
🛏 1, 2 cl., ▬ 2 cl. and (2) (**40420**) Innsbruck - Hannover - Hamburg.

465 – 🛏 1, 2 cl., ▬ 2 cl. and (2) Zürich - Schwarzach - Graz; ▬ 1, 2 cl.*, ▬ 2 cl.* and (2) (*EN* **40465**) Zürich - Schwarzach - Villach - Ljubljana - Zagreb - Beograd.

A – From Verona or Venezia via Brennero (Table **70**).
E – ①②③④⑦ (not Apr. 21, June 9).
F – To Wien Flughafen ✈ (Table **950**).
N – Conveys 🛏 1, 2 cl., ▬ 2 cl. and (2).
R – To Bratislava (Table **86**).

v – Also Apr. 22, June 10; not Apr. 21, June 9.
w – Also Apr. 21, June 9; not Apr. 22, June 10.

* – 🛏 1, 2 cl. and ▬ 2 cl. to Zagreb.
◇ – 🛏 1, 2 cl., ▬ 2 cl. and (2) Zürich (**467**) - Salzburg (**463**) - Budapest. Also conveys through cars to Praha (see Table **52**).
△ – Runs 5–11 minutes **earlier** on †.
◧ – Train number **1288** on ⑥⑦.
‡ – See note on page 455 for other regional services Kufstein - München.

952 VORARLBERG LOCAL SERVICES

2nd class only (except where shown)

BLUDENZ - BREGENZ - LINDAU ⊖ △

Bludenz ....d.	0039	0439	0600	0630	0730	0800	0900	1000	1009	1200	1209	1300	1400	1409	1500	1539	1600	1609	1700	1800	1809	1900	1939	2009	2039	2209	2239
Feldkirch ....d.	0100	0500	0617	0647	0747	0817	0917	1017	1030	1217	1230	1317	1417	1430	1517	1600	1617	1630	1717	1817	1830	1917	2000	2030	2100	2230	2300
Dornbirn ....d.	0129	0529	0639	0709	0809	0839	0939	1039	1059	1241	1259	1339	1439	1459	1539	1629	1639	1659	1739	1841	1859	1939	2029	2059	2129	2259	2329
Bregenz 🏛.......d.	0144	0545	0649	0719	0819	0849	0949	1049	1115	1251	1320	1349	1449	1520	1549	1645	1648	1720	1749	1851	1920	1948	2045	2120	2145	2320	2344
Lindau Hbf 🏛 ..a.	...	0556	0658	0731	0831	0901	1001	1101	1127	1302	1332	1402	1501	1532	1601	1657	...	1732	1801	1902	1932	...	2057	2132	2157	2332	...

Lindau Hbf 🏛 ..d.	0001	...	0657	0757	0825	0857	...	1001	1053	1157	1225	1257	1357	1425	...	1459	1627	1701	1757	1825	...	1901	1957	2031	2104	2201	2301
Bregenz 🏛.......d.	0014	0614	0710	0810	0844	0910	0944	1014	1106	1210	1244	1310	1410	1444	1510	1514	1640	1714	1810	1844	1910	1914	2010	2044	2114	2214	2314
Dornbirn ....d.	0030	0630	0721	0821	0900	0921	1000	1030	1117	1221	1300	1321	1421	1500	1521	1530	1651	1730	1821	1900	1921	1930	2021	2100	2130	2230	2330
Feldkirch ....d.	0101	0701	0744	0844	0931	0944	1031	1101	1144	1244	1331	1344	1444	1531	1544	1601	1714	1801	1844	1931	1944	2001	2044	2131	2201	2301	0001
Bludenz ....a.	0121	0721	0759	0859	0951	0959	1051	1121	1159	1259	1351	1359	1459	1551	1559	1621	1729	1821	1859	1951	1959	2021	2059	2151	2221	2321	0021

ST MARGRETHEN - BREGENZ - LINDAU ⊡ △

km							*EC* 191							*EC* 195						*EC* 197						
			Ⓒ	Ⓐ			♥							♥						♥						
0	St Margrethen 🏛 ...... d.	0550	0625	0625	0655	0755	0842	0855	0955	1055	1155	1255	1355	1442	1455	1555	1655	1755	1855	1942	1955	2055	2155	2255	...	2355
12	**Bregenz** 🏛.............. a.	0610	0640	0640	0710	0810	0853	0910	1010	1110	1210	1310	1410	1453	1510	1610	1710	1810	1910	1953	2010	2110	2210	2310	...	0010
22	**Lindau** Hbf 🏛........... a.	*0629*e	0650	*0658*	*0731*	*0831*	0905	*0932*	*1031*	*1127*	*1231*	*1332*	*1431*	1505	*1532*	*1631*	*1732*	*1831*	*1932*	2005	*2031*	*2132*	*2234*	*2332*	...	...

							EC 196							*EC* 194									*EC* 190			
				Ⓐ			♥							♥		Ⓐ			Ⓐ				♥			
Lindau Hbf 🏛 .... d.	...	...	*0624*	*0657*	*0727*	*0825*	*0925*	0954	*1025*	*1127*	*1225*	*1327*	*1425*	1454	*1525*	*1601*	*1627*	*1727*	*1757*	*1825*	*1927*	*2031*	2058	*2131*	...	*2227*
Bregenz 🏛............... d.	0542	0617	0647	0717	0747	0849	0947	1006	1047	1147	1247	1347	1449	1506	1547	1617	1647	1747	1817	1847	1949	2047	2110	2147	...	2247
St Margrethen 🏛 .... a.	0559	0634	0704	0734	0804	0904	1004	1018	1104	1204	1304	1404	1504	1518	1604	1634	1704	1804	1834	1904	2004	2104	2122	2204	...	2304

FELDKIRCH - BUCHS ⊖

km		A	A	AB	A	A		A	A	A	A	
0	**Feldkirch**......... d.	0533	0649	0714	0745	0849	...	1612	1645	1715	1815	...
16	Schaan-Vaduz d.	0552	0708	0733	0806	0908	...	1634	1704	1734	1834	...
19	**Buchs** 🏛......... a.	0555	0711	0736	0809	0911	...	1637	1707	1737	1837	...

	A	A	A		A		A	A	A	A	A
Buchs 🏛.............. d.	0617	0716	0819	...	1234	...	1619	1649	1719	1819	1849
Schaan-Vaduz .... d.	0620	0719	0822	...	1237	...	1622	1652	1722	1822	1852
Feldkirch.............. a.	0639	0737	0841	...	1256	...	1641	1711	1741	1841	1911

BLUDENZ - SCHRUNS

Operated by Montafonerbahn. *12 km*. Journey time: 19 minutes.

From Bludenz at 0535 Ⓐ, 0632 ⚒, 0702, 0737, 0805, 0837, 0937, 1037, 1137, 1205 ⚒, 1237, 1305 ⚒, 1337, 1437, 1537, 1605, 1634, 1705, 1737, 1805, 1837, 1937, 2037, 2137, 2245, 2345

From Schruns at 0504 Ⓐ, 0534 ⚒, 0631, 0701, 0736, 0804, 0904, 1004, 1104, 1136 ⚒, 1204, 1236 ⚒, 1304, 1404, 1504, 1536, 1604, 1633, 1704, 1736, 1804, 1904, 2004, 2110, 2210, 2310

A – ①–⑤ (not Apr. 22, May 1, 30, June 10, 20, Oct. 26, Nov. 1).
B – From Bludenz (d. 0647).
e – Ⓐ only.
♥ – (12) and ✕ Zürich - München and v.v. See Table **75**.
⊖ – Selected local trains. See also Table **951**.
⊡ – Additional trains run on Ⓐ.
△ – Austrian holiday dates apply.

953 🚌 IMST - ÖTZTAL - OBERGURGL, ST ANTON - LECH

April 29 - June 21

km	🚌 Route **4194/8352**								Ⓒ	Ⓐ	Ⓐs	t	Ⓒ	Ⓐ	Ⓒ	Ⓐ	Ⓒ	Ⓐ		
0	**Imst** (Terminal Post) .... d.	0605	0632	0805	0850	1000	1115	1155	1230	1235	1340	1400	1450	1510	1530	1610	1630	1645	1800	1915
13	**Ötztal** (Bahnhof) .... a.	0622	0649	0822	0904	1017	1132	1212	1247	1252	1357	1417	1507	1527	1544	1627	1647	1702	1817	1932
13	**Ötztal** (Bahnhof) .... d.	0623	0700	0825	0905	1020	1135	1215	1248	1255	1400	1420	1510	1535	1545	1630	1648	1705	1818	1935
21	Oetz (Gemeindeamt) .... d.	0638	0715	0840	0920	1035	1150	1230	1303	1310	1415	1435	1525	1550	1600	1645	1703	1720	1833	1949
54	Sölden (Postamt).................... d.	0726	0803	0928	1008	1125	1238	1318	1351	1358	1505	1525	1615	1640	1648	1733	1751	1808	1921	2037
58	Zwieselstein (Gh Neue Post) . d.	0734	0811	0936	1016	1133	1246	1326	1359	1406	1513	1533	1623	1648	1656	1741	1759	1816	1929	2045
68	**Obergurgl** (Zentrum) .... a.	0749	0826	0951	1031	1148	1301	1341	1414	1421	1528	1548	1638	1703	1711	1756	1814	1833	1944	2100

🚌 Route **4194/8352**	Ⓐ	s	t						Ⓐ	Ⓒ	Ⓐ	Ⓒ				Ⓒ	Ⓐ			⑥u
Obergurgl (Zentrum) ....d.	...	...	...	0650	0750	0845	1015	1115	1205	1215	1305	1315	1345	1515	1615	1655	1725	1815	1915	...
Zwieselstein (Gh Neue Post) ..d.	...	0548	0548	0705	0805	0900	1030	1130	1220	1230	1320	1330	1400	1530	1630	1710	1740	1830	1930	...
Sölden (Postamt).....................d.	0525	0558	0558	0715	0815	0910	1040	1140	1230	1240	1330	1340	1410	1540	1640	1720	1750	1840	1940	2058
Oetz (Gemeindeamt) ....d.	0612	0645	0645	0807	0907	1002	1132	1232	1322	1332	1424	1432	1502	1632	1732	1812	1842	1932	2032	2150
Ötztal (Bahnhof).....................a.	0623	0656	0656	0819	0918	1013	1143	1244	1334	1344	1433	1443	1513	1643	1744	1824	1854	1943	2043	2201
Ötztal (Bahnhof).....................d.	0625	0700	0700	0820	0920	1015	1145	1245	1335	1345	1435	1445	1515	1645	1745	1825	1855	1945	2045	2201
Imst (Terminal Post)..............a.	...	0715	0715	0835	0935	1030	1200	1300	1350	1400	1450	1500	1530	1700	1800	1840	1910	2000	2100	2223

s – Schooldays only.
t – Daily during school holiday periods.
u – Also days before holidays.

🚌 Route **92**: **ST ANTON AM ARLBERG - LECH** *20 km.* Journey time: 31 minutes.

From St Anton a. A. Terminal West at 0731‡, 0910, 1010‡, 1110, 1310‡, 1510, 1710, 1910‡.

From Lech Postamt at 0810 Ⓒ, 0817 Ⓐ, 1010, 1210‡, 1410, 1610, 1810‡, 2010‡.

Valid until Dec. 14.

☛ All services call at St Christoph am Arlberg and Zürs

‡ – June 19 - Oct. 6.

🚌 LANDECK - NAUDERS - SCUOL and MALLES — 954

Landeck - Nauders and Martina

Route 210											Ⓐ												
Landeck - Zams Bahnhof .... d.	0650	0800	0855	1000	1055	1212	1255	1400	1455	1600	1647	1702	1805	1905	...	...	...	...	...	...	...	...	...
Ried im Oberinntal Trujen ...... d.	0719	0829	0924	1029	1124	1241	1324	1429	1524	1629	1716	1731	1834	1934	...	...	...	...	...	...	...	...	...
Martina cunfin 🏛 .... a.	|	|	0956	|	1156	|	1356	|	1556	|	1756	|	|	|	...	...	...	...	...	...	...	...	...
Nauders Mühle .... a.	0800	0910	...	1110	...	1322	...	1510	...	1710	...	1812	1915	2015	...	...	...	...	...	...	...	...	...
Nauders Mühle .... d.	0607	0644	...	0847	...	1047	...	1247	...	1447	...	1647	...	1847	...	...	...	...	...	...	...	...	...
Martina cunfin 🏛 .... d.	|	|	...	|	1000	|	1200	|	1400	|	1600	|	1800	|	...	...	...	...	...	...	...	...	...
Ried im Oberinntal Trujen ...... d.	0644	0724	...	0924	1029	1124	1229	1324	1429	1524	1629	1724	1829	1924	...	...	...	...	...	...	...	...	...
Landeck - Zams Bahnhof .... a.	0712	0752	...	0952	1057	1152	1257	1352	1457	1552	1657	1752	1857	1952	...	...	...	...	...	...	...	...	...

Scuol Tarasp - Nauders - Malles

		⚒										
Scuol Tarasp Staziun .... d.	0630	...	0730	...	and at	1730	...	1830	...	1930	...	...
Martina cunfin 🏛 .... d.	0655	0705	0755	0805	the same	1755	1805	1855	1910	2003	2010	...
Nauders Mühle 🏛 .... d.	...	0716	...	0816	minutes	...	1816	...	1921	...	2021	...
Reschenpass / Passo di Resia 🏛 ...... d.	...	0720	...	0820	past each	...	1820	...	1925	...	2025	...
Resia .... d.	...	0723	...	0823	hour until	...	1823	...	1928	...	2028	...
Malles Stazione **597** .... a.	...	0753	...	0853		...	1853	...	1958	...	2058	...
	⚒	⚒										
Malles Stazione **597** .... d.	0601	...	0701	...	and at	1801	...	1901	...	2001	...	...
Resia .... d.	0631	...	0731	...	the same	1831	...	1931	...	2031	...	...
Passo di Resia / Reschenpass 🏛 ...... d.	0634	...	0734	...	minutes	1834	...	1934	...	2034	...	...
Nauders Mühle 🏛 .... d.	0638	...	0738	...	past each	1838	...	1938	...	...	...	...
Martina cunfin 🏛 .... d.	0649	0701	0749	0801	hour until	1849	1901	1949	...	...	...	...
Scuol Tarasp Staziun .... a.	...	0728	...	0827		...	1927	...	...	...	...	...

Operators

Landeck - Nauders: Tioler Linien Bus GmbH, Nauders. ✆ +43 (0)664 384 1360.

Scuol Tarasp - Martina: Auto Da Posta, Svizra. CH-7550 Scuol. ✆ +41 (0) 58 453 28 28.

Martina - Nauders - Malles: Servizi Autobus Dolomiti (SAD). Corso Italia 13N, I-39100 Bolzano. ✆ +39 0471 450 111.

JENBACH - MAYRHOFEN — 955

2nd class only Narrow gauge Zillertalbahn *

km																		🚂 A
0	**Jenbach** Zillertalbahnhof § ... d.	0630	0652	0746	0809	0836	0909	0936	and at	1809	1836	1856	...	2007		1042
11	Fügen-Hart .... d.	0646	0709	0804	0825	0854	0924	0954	the same	1824	1852	1912	...	2023		1112
17	Kaltenbach-Stumm .... d.	0656	0720	0815	0836	0905	0935	1005	minutes	1835	1903	1923	...	2033	also	1129
21	Aschau im Zillertal .... d.	0703	0727	0821	0842	0911	0941	1011	past each	1841	1908	1928	...	2038		1144
25	**Zell am Ziller** .... d.	0710	0735	0828	0849	0918	0948	1018	hour until	1848	1915	1935	...	2045		1155
32	**Mayrhofen** .... a.	0722	0747	0839	0900	0929	0959	1029		1859	1926	1946	...	2056		1214

	Ⓒ																🚂 A
Mayrhofen .... d.	0546	0610	0635	0732	0817	0847	and at	1617	1647	1717	1747	1847	1907	1949		433
Zell am Ziller .... d.	0557	0621	0647	0742	0829	0859	the same	1629	1659	1729	1759	1858	1919	2000		1450
Aschau im Zillertal .... d.	0603	0627	0653	0748	0835	0905	minutes	1635	1705	1735	1805	1904	1924	2006	also	1459
Kaltenbach-Stumm................. d.	0610	0634	0659	0755	0841	0911	past each	1641	1711	1741	1811	1910	1931	2012		1515
Fügen-Hart .... d.	0620	0646	0710	0805	0852	0923	hour until	1652	1723	1752	1824	1922	1941	2024		1537
Jenbach Zillertalbahnhof § .... a.	0637	0704	0727	0821	0908	0942		1708	1742	1807	1842	1937	1957	2039		1600

A – ⑥⑦ May 4–26; ③–⑦ May 29 - Oct. 13.

🚂 – Steam train. Special fares apply.

§ – Adjacent to ÖBB station.

* – Zillertaler Vehrkehrsbetriebe, Austraße 1, A-6200 Jenbach. ✆ +43 (0) 5244 606 0.

JENBACH - ACHENSEE — 956

2nd class only *Achenseebahn*

Narrow gauge rack railway operated by steam locomotives (special fares apply). *7 km.* Journey time 42–50 minutes. **Service April 27 - October 27, 2019.**

Operator: Achenseebahn AG, A-6200 Jenbach: ✆ +43 (0) 5244 62243, Fax +43 (0) 5244 622435. Jenbach Achensee Bf is adjacent to the ÖBB station.

Apr. 27 - May 24 and **Oct. 7–27**: **From Jenbach Achensee Bf** at 1100, 1300 and 1500. **From Achensee Seespitz Bahnstation** at 1200, 1400 and 1600.

May 25 - Oct. 6: **From Jenbach Achensee Bf** at 1000, 1045, 1200, 1345, 1500 and 1645. **From Achensee Seespitz Bahnstation** at 1105, 1220, 1405, 1520, 1600, 1740 **a** 1750 **b**.

a – May 26–30 and Oct. 4–7. **b** – May 31 - Oct. 3.

ZELL AM SEE - KRIMML and 🚌 KRIMML - MAYRHOFEN — 957

2nd class only

ZELL AM SEE - KRIMML ⊡

km						Ⓐ				Ⓐ	Ⓒ			S 🚂	T ♣	
0	**Zell am See** Lokalbahn .... d.	0630	0800	and	1600	1650	1700	1800	1900	2000	2050	...		0918	1518	...
29	Mittersill .... d.	0723	0848	hourly	1648	1729	1748	1848	1948	2048	2134	...	also	1108j	1631	...
39	Bramberg................................. d.	0737	0904	until	1704	1740	1804	1904	2004	2104	2148	...		1131	1649	...
53	**Krimml** .... a.	0755	0923		1723	1755	1823	1923	2023	2123	2205	...		1202	1713	...
			Ⓐ	Ⓐ										S 🚂	T ♣	
	Krimml .... d.	0533	0603	0628	0640	0733	and	1533	1633	1733	1833	...		1355	1933	...
	Bramberg................................. d.	0551	0621	0644	0658	0751	hourly	1551	1651	1751	1851	...	also	1422	1951	...
	Mittersill .... d.	0608	0638	0656	0720	0808	until	1608	1708	1808	1908	...		1520j	2008	...
	Zell am See Lokalbahn............ a.	0655	0725	0737	0805	0855		1655	1755	1855	1955	...		1630	2055	...

🚌 Krimml Bahnhof - Krimml Wasserfälle and v.v. Route **670**. *3 km.* Journey time: 5–8 minutes.

From Krimml Bahnhof at 0757, 0929, 1029 and hourly until 1729; then 1829 and 1930 Ⓐ.

From Krimml Wasserfälle at 0537 Ⓐ, 0620 ⚒, 0823, 1023, 1123 and hourly until 1823.

🚌 routes **673** and **4094**: KRIMML - KÖNIGSLEITEN - MAYRHOFEN **Summer service valid June 1 - October 6**

km										
0	**Krimml** Bahnhof.................. d.	...	...	...	...	...	...	...	...	...
3	Krimml Wasserfälle .... d.	...	...	...	...	...	...	...	...	...
16	Königsleiten Almdorf .... d.	...	...	...	...	...	...	...	...	...
25	**Gerlos** Gasthaus Oberwirt.... d.	0701	0821	1010	1110	1245	1505	1610	1715	1741
45	Zell am Ziller Bf .... **955** a.	0736	0852	1047	1147	1322	1542	1647	1752	1818
53	**Mayrhofen** Bahnhof ...... **955** a.	0746	0902	...	1157	...	...	1657	1802	1828

Mayrhofen Bahnhof.... **955** d.	0730	0835	0935	...	...	1440	...	1645	1845
Zell am Ziller Bahnhof . **955** d.	0743	0851	0950	1100	1330	1455	1600	1700	1900
Gerlos Gasthaus Oberwirt . d.	0813	0926	1025	1135	1400	1530	1635	1735	1929
Königsleiten Almdorf .... d.	...	...	...	...	...	...	...	...	...
Krimml Wasserfälle .... a.	...	...	...	...	...	...	...	...	...
Krimml Bahnhof................ a.	...	...	...	...	...	...	...	...	...

S – ③④ May 22 - Sept. 26.
T – ④ Jan. 10 - Mar. 21.

j – Arrives 30 minutes earlier.

🚂 – Steam train with special fares.
♣ – Historic Diesel train. Special fares.

⊡ – Narrow gauge railway. **Operator**: Pinzgauer Lokalbahn. Trains call at Mittersill and Bramberg on request only.

🚌 WÖRGL - ELLMAU - KITZBÜHEL and ST JOHANN — 958

ÖBB-Postbus routes **4006**, **4060**, **4902**

	⚒	Ⓐ¶	⑥	⚒	Ⓐ	⑥	⚒	†	⚒	†b	⚒	†b	Ⓐ	⑥	†	⚒	⚒	†	†b	⚒	Ⓐ	†b	⚒	Ⓐ	†
Wörgl Hauptbahnhof .... d.	...	0545	...	0640	0743	0743	...	...	0905	1050	1120	1210	1210	1210	...	...	1405	...	1610	1610	...	1750	1750	1835	...
Söll (Dorf) .... ♥ d.	...	0605	0612	0659	0805	0810	...	0917	0937	1118	1140	1238	1240	1240	1240	...	1440	1545	1638	1640	...	1818	1820	1905	1905
Scheffau am Wilden Kaiser ★ d.	...	0612	0621	...	0812	0817	...	0927	0947	...	1150	...	1250	1250	1250	...	1450	1555	...	1650	...	...	1830	1913	1913
Ellmau (Dorf) .... d.	0622	0620	0633	...	0820	0825	0900	0940	1000	...	1203	...	1303	1303	1303	1315	1503	1608	...	1703	1715	...	1843	1923	1923
Kitzbühel Bahnhof............ a.	0650	|	|	...	|	|	0924	|	|	...	|	...	|	...	|	1345	|	|	...	|	1745	...	|	|	|
St Johann in Tirol Bahnhof a.	...	0641	0654	...	0841	0847	...	1004	1024	...	1227	...	1327	...	1327	...	1527	1632	...	1727	...	...	1907	1940	1940
	Ⓐ	⚒	z	⚒	†	⚒	†b	⚒	†	⚒	⚒	†b	Ⓐ	⑥	†	⚒	⚒	†b	Ⓐ	†	Ⓐ	⑥	⚒	Ⓐ	Ⓐ
St Johann in Tirol Bahnhof d.	...	0535	...	0725	0750	...	...	0855	1055	1055	...	...	1235	...	1340	1340	1555	...	...	1655	1655	...	1755	...	1907
Kitzbühel Bahnhof............ d.	...	|	...	|	|	0803	...	|	|	|	1215	...	|	...	|	|	|	...	1630	|	|	...	|	1830	|
Ellmau (Dorf) .... d.	...	0552	...	0745	0810	0833	...	0915	1115	1115	1245	...	1300	1305	1400	1400	1615	...	1700	1715	1715	...	1815	1858	1927
Scheffau am Wilden Kaiser ★ d.	...	0559	...	0753	0818	...	...	0923	1123	1123	...	...	1308	1311	1408	1408	1623	...	...	1723	1723	...	1823	...	1935
Söll (Dorf) .... ♥ d.	0545	0615	0710	0810	0832	...	0940	0940	1137	1140	...	1320	1325	1325	1422	1425	1645	1645	...	1737	1745	1745	1840	...	1952
Wörgl Hauptbahnhof .... a.	0615	0645**a**	0745	0840	...	...	1010	1010	*1210***b**	1210	...	1350	1355	1352	...	1455	1715	1715	...	...	1808	1808	1903**a**	...	2015

a – Ⓐ only.
b – Dec. 22 - Mar. 31.
z – 5 minutes later on ⑥.
★ – Scheffau am Wilden Kaiser Am Trattenbach.

¶ – Runs 5–11 minutes later during school holiday periods.

♥ – 🚌 **KUFSTEIN** Bahnhof → **SÖLL** Dorf (journey time: 27–29 minutes): 0540 ⚒, 0639 Ⓐ, 0735 Ⓐ, 0740 ⑥, 0840 Ⓐ, 0845 Ⓒ, 1010, 1110, 1210 Ⓐ, 1300 Ⓒ, 1310 Ⓐ, 1410 Ⓐ, 1510 Ⓒ, 1524 Ⓐ, 1610 ⚒, 1710 Ⓐ, 1738 †, 1740 ⑥, 1810 Ⓐ and 1907 Ⓐ.
🚌 **SÖLL** Dorf → **KUFSTEIN** Bahnhof (journey time: 25–29 minutes): 0610 ⚒, 0706 Ⓐ, 0812 ⚒, 0915 Ⓒ, 0940 Ⓐ, 1040, 1140, 1240 Ⓐ, 1330 Ⓒ, 1337 Ⓐ, 1440 Ⓐ, 1540 Ⓒ, 1551 Ⓐ, 1640 ⑥, 1642 Ⓐ, 1742 Ⓐ, 1805 †, 1840 ⚒ and 1934 Ⓐ.

959 ZELL AM SEE - HINTERGLEMM

ÖBB-Postbus Route 680

km		⚒	E	E		E		E		A		A		A	
0	**Zell am See** Bahnhof d.	0610p	0656	0820	0920	1020	1120	1220	1320	1420	1520	1620	1720	1820	1920
20	Saalbach Schattberg a.	0637	0725	0852	0952	1052	1152	1252	1352	1452	1552	1652	1752	1852	1952
23	**Hinterglemm** Ellmauweg a.	0643	0730	0857	0957	1057	1157	1257	1357	1457	1557	1657	1757	1857	1957

	⚒	E			E		E		E		A		A		A
Hinterglemm Ellmauweg d.	0611	0657	0750	...	0920	1020	1120	1220	1320	1420	1520	1620	1720	1820	1916
Saalbach Schattberg d.	0618	0703	0800	...	0930	1030	1130	1230	1330	1430	1530	1630	1730	1830	1922
Zell am See Bahnhof a.	0646	0732	0830	...	1000	1100	1200	1300	1400	1500	1600	1700	1800	1900	1950

A – Ⓐ (daily to Apr. 26, June 10 - Sept. 27 and from Dec. 2).
E – ⚒ (daily to Apr. 27, June 10 - Sept. 28 and from Dec. 2).
p – Zell am See Postplatz (not Bahnhof).
Information: ✆ +43 (0) 6542 5444-18

960 SALZBURG - SCHWARZACH - INNSBRUCK

km		*NJ* **464** A	2	Ⓐ 2	⚒ 2	2	Ⓒ 2	⑥k 2	Ⓐ 2	*IC* **894** ✕⊖	2	Ⓐ 2	*ICE* **1280** ⑥N ✕	D 2	2	*RJ* **898** ✕⊖	2	Ⓐ 2	*ICE* **1284** ⑦M ✕	D 2	2	*RJ* **111** ✕⊖	2	D 2Ⓐ	*RJ* **1262** ⑥H ✕
	Wien Hbf **950** d.	...	...	...	...	...	...	...	...	...	...	...	...	...	...	...	...	...	...	...	...	...	...	...	0830
0	**Salzburg** Hbf **951 970 975** ‡ d.	...	...	...	...	...	0411	...	0435	0612	...	...	...	0708	...	0812	...	...	...	0908	...	1012	...	1108	1115
29	Golling-Abtenau **970** ‡ d.	...	...	...	...	...	0449	...	0459	0633	...	...	...	0734	...	0833	...	...	...	0934	...	1033	...	1134	1140
53	**Bischofshofen** **970 975** ‡ d.	0158	...	...	...	...	0513	...	0523	0654	...	...	...	0756	...	0854	...	...	...	0956	...	1054	...	1156	1201
61	St Johann im Pongau. **970** ‡ d.	|	...	...	...	...	0523	...	0533	0703	...	...	...	0804	...	0903	...	...	...	1004	...	1103	...	1204	1211
67	**Schwarzach - St Veit**. **970** ‡ a.	0211	...	...	...	...	0529	...	0539	0709	...	...	...	0810	...	0909	...	...	...	1010	...	1109	...	1210	1217
67	**Schwarzach - St Veit** d.	0232	...	...	...	...	0531	...	0541	▬	0712	...	0805	0812	...	...	0912	...	1005	1012	...	...	1112	1212	1223
99	**Zell am See** d.	|	...	...	...	...	0607	...	0617	...	0745	...	0837	0845	...	...	0945	...	1037	1045	...	...	1145	1245	1255
113	Saalfelden d.	|	0401	0450	0517	0534	0619	0625	0630	Ⓐ	0755	...	0848	0855	0914c	...	0955	...	1048	1055	1114c	...	1155	1255	1307
131	Hochfilzen d.	|	0418	0508	0534	0554	▬	0643	0648	2	0813	0835	0904	0913	0933	...	1013	1035	1104	1113	1133	...	1213	1313	|
148	St Johann in Tirol d.	|	0434	0526	0550	0612	...	0700	0705	0751	0828	0853	0922	0928	0951	...	1028	1053	1122	1128	1151	...	1228	1328	1339
157	**Kitzbühel** d.	|	0442	0535	0558	0621	...	0708	0713	0800	0835	0902	0931	0935	1000	...	1035	1102	1131	1135	1200	...	1235	1335	1348
166	Kirchberg in Tirol d.	|	0451	0546	0609	0632	2	0717	0722	0811	0844	0913	0943	0943	1011	...	1044	1113	1143	1143	1211	...	1244	1343	1357
192	Wörgl Hbf **951** a.	|	0518	0615	0635	0701	0729	0742	0747	0840	0909	0942	1007	1008	1040	...	1109	1142	1207	1208	1240	...	1309	1408	1421
217	Jenbach **951** a.	|	0538	0638	*0657*e	*0724*e	0750	*0813*	0808	0913	|	*1013*	...	*1027*	*1059*	...	|	*1213*	...	*1227*	*1259*	...	|	*1427*	...
251	**Innsbruck** Hbf **951** a.	0449	0607	0713	*0717*e	*0810*e	0825	*0840*	0833	0940	*0944*	*1040*	...	*1044*	*1118*	...	*1144*	*1240*	...	*1244*	*1318*	...	*1344*	*1444*	...

	2	*RJ* **596** ✕⊖	*EC* **164** Z✕	Ⓐ 2	D 2	2	*EC* **113** ✕⊖	2	*RJ* **1264** ⑥K ✕	Ⓐ 2	D 2	*EC* **115** ⊗⊖	*IC* **518** ⊡🍷	Ⓐ 2	D 2	2	Ⓐ 2	*RJ* **698** ✕⊖	2	Ⓑ 2	2	*EC* **117** ⊗⊖	2	*RJ* **1260** ⑤J ✕	2
Wien Hbf **950** d.	...	0855	...	...	...	...	...	...	1130	...	...	...	...	...	...	...	...	1455	...	...	...	...	...	1730	...
Salzburg Hbf. **951 970 975** ‡ d.	...	1212	...	...	1308	...	1412	...	1415	...	1508	1612	...	...	1708	...	1743	1812	...	...	1908	2012	...	2015	2215
Golling-Abtenau **970** ‡ d.	...	1233	...	...	1334	...	1433	...	1440	...	1534	1633	...	...	1734	...	1812	1833	...	...	1934	2033	...	2040	2242
Bischofshofen **970 975** ‡ d.	...	1254	1250	...	1356	...	1454	...	1501	...	1556	1654	1650	...	1756	...	1837	1854	...	...	1956	2054	...	2101	2305
St Johann im Pongau .. **970** ‡ d.	...	1303	1259	...	1404	...	1503	...	1511	...	1604	1703	1659	...	1804	...	1847	1903	...	...	2004	2103	...	2111	2314
Schwarzach - St Veit ... **970** ‡ a.	...	1309	1305	...	1410	...	1509	...	1517	...	1610	1709	1705	...	1810	...	1852	1909	...	...	2010	2109	...	2117	2319
Schwarzach - St Veit d.	...	...	1313	...	1412	...	...	1512	1523	...	1612	▬	1713	...	1813	...	1853	...	1912	1912	2012	▬	2112	2123	2321
Zell am See d.	...	...	1344	...	1445	...	...	1545	1555	...	1645	...	1744	...	1846	...	1929	...	1946	1946	2046	⚒	2148	2155	2356
Saalfelden d.	...	...	1354	1416	1455	1514c	...	1555	1607	...	1655	2	1754	...	1856	...	1941	...	1956	1957	2057	2	2200	2207	0005
Hochfilzen d.	1333	...	|	1435	1513	1533	...	1613	|	1635	1713	1733	|	1835	1914	1933	...	...	...	2016	2116	2205	...	|	...
St Johann in Tirol d.	1351	...	1422	1453	1528	1551	...	1628	1639	1653	1728	1751	1822	1853	1929	1951	...	...	...	2030	2130	2223	...	2239	...
Kitzbühel d.	1400	...	1430	1502	1535	1600	...	1635	1648	1702	1735	1800	1830	1902	1936	2000	...	...	...	2038	2138	2232	...	2248	...
Kirchberg in Tirol d.	1411	...	1438	1513	1543	1611	...	1644	1657	1713	1743	1811	1838	1913	1944	2011	...	...	...	2045	2145	2243	...	2257	...
Wörgl Hbf **951** a.	1440	...	1500	1542	1608	1640	...	1709	1721	1740	1808	1840	1900	1942	2009	2040	...	...	...	2110	2210	2312	...	2321	...
Jenbach **951** a.	*1459*	...	1516	*1613*	*1627*	*1659*	...	|	...	*1813*	*1827*	*1859*	1916	*2013*	*2031*	*2059*	...	...	...	|	*2250*	*2331*	...	...	...
Innsbruck Hbf **951** a.	*1518*	...	1540	*1640*	*1644*	*1718*	...	*1744*	...	*1840*	*1844*	*1918*	1940	*2040*	*2048*	*2118*	...	...	...	*2144*	*2325*	*2348*	...	...	...

	NJ **465** A	⚒ 2	2	2	⚒ 2	Ⓑ 2	2	2	*RJ* **691** ✕⊖	2	Ⓐ 2	2	Ⓐ 2	*IC* **515** ⊡🍷	*EC* **114** ⊗⊖	2	*RJ* **1265** ⑥H ✕	E 2	Ⓐ 2	2	*EC* **112** ✕⊖	2	E 2	Ⓐ 2	*EC* **163** Z✕
Innsbruck Hbf **951** d.	0056	...	...	...	*0510*	*0514*e	...	*0610*	...	...	*0620*	*0713*	*0721*	0821	...	...	...	*0914*	*0920*	*1017*	...	*1040*	*1114*	*1120*	1221
Jenbach **951** d.	|	...	...	...	*0527*	*0540*e	...	*0627*	...	...	*0647*	*0730*	*0750*	0844	...	...	...	*0931*	*0947*	|	...	*1101*	*1131*	*1147*	1244
Wörgl Hbf **951** d.	|	...	...	...	0542	0605	...	0649	...	...	0722	0750r	0820	0900	...	0922	0942	0952	1020	1050	...	1122	1152	1220	1300
Kirchberg in Tirol d.	|	...	...	...	0609	0635	...	0714	...	...	0752	0816r	0850	0921	...	0952	1008	1017	1050	1116	...	1152	1217	1250	1321
Kitzbühel d.	|	...	...	...	0620	0646	...	0725	...	...	0803	0825r	0901	0930	...	1003	1017	1025	1101	1125	...	1203	1225	1301	1330
St Johann in Tirol d.	|	...	...	...	0629	0655	...	0732	...	...	0812	0832r	0910	0938	...	1012	1026	1032	1110	1132	...	1212	1232	1310	1338
Hochfilzen d.	|	...	...	...	0646	0713	...	0747	...	...	0830	0847r	0928	|	...	1031	|	1047	1128	1147	...	1230	1247	1328	|
Saalfelden d.	|	0458	0552	0705	0705	0730	0734r	0805	...	0834r	...	0905	...	1006	...	1048c	1058	1105	...	1205	...	...	1305	...	1406
Zell am See d.	|	0508	0602	0715	0715	...	0747r	0815	...	0847r	...	0915	...	1017	...	...	1110	1115	...	1215	...	...	1315	...	1417
Schwarzach - St Veit a.	0317	0541	0637	0748	0748	...	0822	0848	...	0922	...	0948	...	1046	...	...	1140	1149	...	1248	...	...	1348	...	1446
Schwarzach - St Veit ... **970** ‡ d.	0324	0542	0639	0749	0749	...	0824	...	0850	0924	...	0949	...	1056	1052	...	1143	1150	...	...	1252	...	1349	...	1456
St Johann im Pongau .. **970** ‡ d.	|	0548	0646	0755	0755	...	0829	...	0858	0929	...	0955	...	1102	1058	...	1150	1155	...	...	1258	...	1355	...	1502
Bischofshofen **970 975** ‡ d.	0336	0558	0655	0804	0804	...	0840	...	0907	0940	...	1004	...	1110	1107	...	1200	1204	...	...	1307	...	1404	...	1510
Golling-Abtenau **970** ‡ d.	...	0620	0717	0825	0825	...	0904	...	0927	1004	...	1025	...	...	1127	...	1221	1225	...	...	1327	...	1425	...	...
Salzburg Hbf. **951 970 975** ‡ a.	...	0645	0744	0851	0851	...	0940	...	0948	1040	...	1051	...	...	1148	...	1245	1251	...	...	1348	...	1451	...	...
Wien Hbf **950** a.	...	...	...	...	...	...	...	...	1305	...	...	...	...	...	...	...	1530	...	...	...	...	...	...	...	...

	RJ **793** ✕⊖	2	E 2	2	*RJ* **797** ✕⊖	*RJ* **1267** ⑦L ✕	2	*RJ* **1261** ⑥K ✕	E 2	Ⓐ 2	*ICE* **1281** ⑥P ✕	Ⓐ 2	2	*RJ* **110** ✕⊖	2	E 2	Ⓐ 2	2	*IC* **895** ✕⊖	2	Ⓐ 2	*ICE* **1285** ⑤Q ✕	Ⓐ 2	Ⓒ 2	2
Innsbruck Hbf **951** d.	...	*1240*	*1314*	*1417*	...	...	*1440*	...	*1514*	*1520*	...	1600	*1617*	...	*1640*	*1714*	1720	*1817*	...	*1840*	*1914*	...	*2017*	*2017*	*2135*
Jenbach **951** d.	...	*1301*	*1331*	|	...	...	*1501*	...	*1531*	*1547*	...	1625	|	...	*1701*	*1731*	1749	|	...	*1901*	*1931*	...	|	|	*2209*
Wörgl Hbf **951** d.	...	1322	1352	1450	...	1455	1522	1542	1552	1620	1638	1650	1650	...	1722	1752	1820	1850	...	1922	1952	1958	2052	2052	2234
Kirchberg in Tirol d.	...	1352	1417	1516	...	1521	1552	1608	1617	1650	1704	1716	1716	...	1752	1817	1850	1916	...	1952	2017	2024	2117	2122	2304
Kitzbühel d.	...	1403	1425	1525	...	1530	1603	1617	1625	1701	1716	1725	1725	...	1803	1825	1901	1925	...	2003	2026	2036	2125	2133	2315
St Johann in Tirol d.	...	1412	1432	1532	...	1539	1612	1626	1632	1710	1725	1732	1732	...	1812	1832	1910	1932	...	2012	2034	2045	2132	2142	2324
Hochfilzen d.	...	1431	1447	1547	...	|	1630	|	1647	1728	1742	1747	1747	...	1830	1847	1928	1947	...	2031	2049	2102	2147	2200	2342
Saalfelden d.	...	1448	1505	1605	...	1611	...	1658	1705	...	1759	1805	1805	...	...	1905	...	2005	...	2048b	...	2119	2205	2218	2359
Zell am See d.	...	...	1515	1615	...	1623	...	1710	1715	...	1810	1815	1815	...	...	1915	...	2015	...	...	...	2130	2215	2230	...
Schwarzach - St Veit a.	...	...	1548	1648	...	1653	...	1740	1748	...	1840	1848	1848	...	...	1948	...	2048	...	...	...	2200	2248	...	...
Schwarzach - St Veit ... **970** ‡ d.	1452	...	1549	...	1652	1655	...	1743	1749	...	...	...	...	1852	...	1949	...	...	2052	...	...	...	...	...	...
St Johann im Pongau .. **970** ‡ d.	1458	...	1555	...	1658	1701	...	1750	1755	...	...	...	...	1858	...	1955	...	...	2057	...	...	...	...	...	...
Bischofshofen **970 975** ‡ d.	1507	...	1604	...	1707	1711	...	1800	1804	...	...	...	...	1907	...	2004	...	...	2107	...	...	...	...	...	...
Golling-Abtenau **970** ‡ d.	1527	...	1625	...	1727	1731	...	1821	1825	...	...	...	...	1927	...	2025	...	...	2127	...	...	...	...	...	...
Salzburg Hbf. **951 970 975** ‡ a.	1548	...	1651	...	1748	1754	...	1845	1851	...	...	...	...	1948	...	2051	...	...	2148	...	...	...	...	...	...
Wien Hbf **950** a.	1905	...	...	...	2105	2049	...	2130	...	...	...	...	...	...	...	...	...	...	...	...	...	...	...	...	...

A – 🛏 1, 2 cl., 🛌 2 cl. and (2) Graz - Feldkirch - Buchs 🛃 - Zürich and v.v. Conveys from / to Schwarzach 🛏 1, 2 cl.*, 🛌 2 cl.* and (2) (*EN* **414/40465**) Beograd - Zagreb - Ljubljana - Villach - Zürich and v.v.
D – Runs daily Salzburg - Saalfelden, then on Ⓐ Saalfelden - Wörgl (- Innsbruck).
E – Runs on Ⓐ (Innsbruck -) Wörgl - Saalfelden, then daily Saalfelden - Salzburg.
H – ⑥ Dec. 29 - Apr. 20; ⑥ June 29 - Sept. 7.
J – ⑤ Dec. 28 - Apr. 19; ⑤ June 28 - Sept. 6.
K – ⑥ Dec. 29 - Apr. 20.
L – ⑦ Dec. 30 - Apr. 14 (also Apr. 22); ⑦ June 30 - Sept. 8.
M – ⑦ June 23 - Sept. 8. (12) Schwarzach - München - Hamburg - Flensburg.
N – ⑥ Jun. 29 - Sept. 7. (12) Schwarzach - München.
P – ⑥ June. 22 - Sept. 7. (12) München - Schwarzach.
Q – ⑤ June 28 - Sept 6. (12) Hamburg - München - Schwarzach.

Z – TRANSALPIN – (12) and ✕ Graz - Selzthal - Bischofshofen - Innsbruck - Buchs 🛃 - Zürich and v.v.

b – Not ⑥.
c – Ⓒ only.
e – Ⓐ only.
k – Not Oct. 26.
r – ⚒ only.

* – 🛏 1, 2 cl., 🛌 2 cl. from / to Zagreb.
⊡ – From / to Graz (Table **975**).
⊖ – See Table **970** for further details.
‡ – See also adjacent table.

Freilassing **890** d.	0607		2307
Salzburg Hbf **890** d.	0621	and	2321
Golling-Abtenau d.	0659	hourly	2359
Bischofshofen d.	0724	until	0024
St Johann im Pongau d.	0734		0034
Schwarzach - St Veit a.	0739		0039

Schwarzach - St Veit d.	0524		2224
St Johann im Pongau d.	0529	and	2229
Bischofshofen d.	0540	hourly	2240
Golling-Abtenau d.	0604	until	2304
Salzburg Hbf **890** a.	0640		2340
Freilassing **890** a.	0653		2354

2nd class only — ATTNANG-PUCHHEIM - STAINACH-IRDNING — 961

km																								
		⚒			Ⓐ								Ⓐ	ⒸA										
	Wien Hbf 950 d.	...	...	...	...	...	...	...	...	...	...	...	...	1010	...	...	...	...	...	...	...	...	...	...
0	**Attnang-Puchheim** d.	...	...	...	0459	...	0603	0715	0811	0911	1011	1111	1211	1211	1311	1411	1511	1611	1711	1811	1911	2005	...	2111
12	**Gmunden** d.	...	...	...	0515	...	0621	0732	0826	0932	1026	1132	1226	1226	1332	1426	1532	1626	1732	1826	1932	2022	...	2129
17	Altmünster am Traunsee d.	...	...	...	0522	...	0626	0738	0832	0938	1032	1138	1232	1232	1338	1432	1538	1632	1738	1832	1938	2028	...	2136
22	Traunkirchen d.	...	...	...	0528	...	0633	0744	0838	0944	1038	1144	1238	1238	1344	1438	1544	1638	1744	1838	1944	2033	...	2141
27	Ebensee Landungsplatz d.	...	...	...	0534	...	0640	0752	0844	0952	1044	1152	1244	1244	1352	1444	1552	1644	1752	1844	1952	2040	...	2149
28	Ebensee d.	...	...	...	0537	...	0643	0758	0847	0958	1047	1158	1247	1247	1358	1447	1558	1647	1758	1847	1958	2042	...	2152
44	**Bad Ischl** d.	...	...	...	0556	...	0705	0820	0903	1020	1103	1220	1303	1303	1420	1503	1620	1703	1820	1903	2020	2102	...	2213
54	Bad Goisern d.	...	...	...	...	...	0719	0833	0913	1033	1113	1233	1313	1313	1433	1513	1633	1713	1833	1913	2033	2115	...	...
64	Hallstatt ⊡ d.	...	...	...	...	...	0731	0848	0925	1048	1125	1248	1325	1325	1448	1525	1648	1725	1848	|	|	|	...	...
67	Obertraun-Dachsteinhöhlen d.	...	...	...	...	...	0735	0851	0928	1051	1128	1251	1328	1328	1451	1528	1651	1728	1851	1928	2051	2131	...	...
78	**Bad Aussee** d.	0503	...	0632	...	...	0749	...	0942	...	1142	...	1342	1342	...	1542	...	1742	...	1942	2104	2143	...	...
93	Bad Mitterndorf d.	0521	...	0650	...	...	0804	...	0959	...	1159	...	1359	1359	...	1559	...	1759	...	1959	...	...	...	...
108	**Stainach-Irdning** a.	0538	...	0707	...	...	0818	...	1015	...	1215	...	1415	1415	...	1615	...	1815	...	2015	...	...	...	...

			Ⓐ	⚒	⚒										Ⓐ	ⒸB	Ⓒ	Ⓐ				Ⓒ	Ⓐ	
tainach-Irdning d.	...	...	...	...	0611	...	0713	...	0940	...	1140	...	1340	...	1540	1540	...	...	1740	...	...	1940	1940	2047
ad Mitterndorf d.	...	...	...	...	0629	...	0730	...	0959	...	1159	...	1359	...	1559	1559	...	...	1759	...	...	1959	1959	2104
ad Aussee d.	...	0456	...	0603	0650	0650	0810r	...	1016	...	1216	...	1416	...	1616	1616	...	...	1816	...	...	2016	2016	2121
bertraun-Dachsteinhöhlen d.	...	0508	...	0615	0702	0702	0823	0903	1028	1103	1228	1303	1428	1503	1628	1628	1703	1703	1828	1905	...	2028	...	...
allstatt ⊡ d.	...	|	...	|	0706	0706	0828	0907	1032	1107	1232	1307	1432	1507	1632	1632	1707	1707	1832	|	...	|	...	...
ad Goisern d.	...	0523	...	0630	0720	0720	0842	0922	1043	1122	1243	1322	1443	1522	1643	1643	1722	1722	1843	1922	...	2042	...	...
ad Ischl d.	0433	0536	0601	0643	0733	0733	0853	0935	1053	1135	1253	1335	1453	1535	1653	1653	1735	1740	1853	1935	...	2052	...	...
bensee d.	0453	0559	0621	0707	0758	0758	0911	0958	1111	1158	1311	1358	1511	1558	1711	1711	1758	1758	1911	1958	...	2108	...	...
bensee Landungsplatz d.	0456	0601	0624	0710	0800	0800	0913	1001	1113	1201	1313	1401	1513	1601	1713	1713	1801	1801	1913	2001	...	2110	...	...
raunkirchen d.	0503	0609	0633	0718	0808	0808	0919	1009	1119	1209	1319	1409	1519	1609	1719	1719	1809	1809	1919	2009	...	2116	...	...
ltmünster am Traunsee d.	0509	0614	0639	0724	0814	0814	0925	1016	1125	1216	1325	1416	1525	1616	1725	1725	1816	1816	1925	2016	...	2122	...	...
munden d.	0516	0621	0645	0732	0826	0826	0931	1026	1131	1226	1331	1426	1531	1626	1731	1731	1826	1826	1931	2023	...	2129	...	...
ttnang-Puchheim a.	0531	0638	0703	0748	0842	0842	0947	1044	1147	1244	1347	1444	1547	1644	1747	1747	1844	1844	1947	2041	...	2146	...	...
Wien Hbf 950 a.	...	...	...	...	...	...	...	...	...	...	...	...	...	...	...	1946	...	...	...	...	...	...	...	...

– SALZKAMMERGUT – (12) Wien (*IC* **528**) - Attnang-Puchheim - Stainach-Irdning.
– SALZKAMMERGUT – (12) Stainach-Irdning - Attnang-Puchheim (*IC* **725**) - Wien.

– Daily from May 1 - Oct. 26.
– Arrives 0748.

⊡ – services operate Hallstatt Bahnhof - Hallstatt Markt. Journey: 8 minutes. **Operator**: Hallstättersee-Schifffahrt Hemetsberger KG ✆ +43 (0)6134 8228.
From Hallstatt Bahnhof at 0706⚒, 0735⚒, 0830, 0900, 0930, 1035, 1100, 1130, 1235, 1300, 1330, 1435, 1500, 1530, 1635, 1700, 1730 and 1850.
From Hallstatt Markt at 0650⚒, 0715⚒, 0810⚒**d**, 0845, 0915, 1015, 1045, 1215, 1245, 1315, 1415, 1445, 1515, 1615, 1645, 1715 and 1815.

LINZ - PASSAU and SIMBACH — 962

km																									
										ICE 228					*ICE* 28	5914			*ICE* 92			*ICE* 26			
		Ⓐ	⚒			Ⓐ	Ⓐ	Ⓒ	Ⓒ					Ⓐ							⚒				⚒
		2	2	G2	2	A2	2	2	2	✕	2	2	2	2	✕	⊖2	2	2	B✕	2	2	D✕	2	2	2
	Wien Hbf 950 d.	...	...	...	...	...	...	...	...	0650	...	...	...	...	0915	0655f	...	...	1015	...	...	1115	...	...	...
0	**Linz** Hbf 950 d.	...	0452	0540	0558	0655	...	0736	...	0817	0850	...	0950	...	1036	1023	1052	...	1136	1150	...	1236	1250	...	1350
25	**Wels** Hbf 950 d.	0444	0516	0612	0620	0731	...	0755	...	0833	0909	...	1009	...	|	1051j	1109	...	|	1209	...	|	1309	...	1409
54	Neumarkt-Kallham d.	0508	0543	0641	0646	0757	0812	0823	0832	|	0936	0940	1032	1040	|	1115	1140h	1140	|	1232	1240	|	1336	1340	1432
	Ried im Innkreis d.	0529	|	|	0710	|	0831	|	0901h	|	|	1001	|	1101	|	|	1201	|	|	|	1301	|	|	1401	|
	Braunau am Inn a.	0604	|	|	0740	|	0906	|	0941	|	|	1041	|	1141	|	|	1241	|	|	|	1341	|	|	1441	|
	Simbach (Inn) 🏛 893 a.	*0644*	|	|	0744	|	*0945*	|	0945	|	|	1045	|	1145	|	|	1245	|	|	|	1345	|	|	1445	|
92	Schärding d.	...	0615	0714	...	0827	...	0853	...	0910	1009	...	1059	...	|	1141	...	1213	|	1259	...	|	1409	...	1459
106	**Passau** Hbf a.	...	0629	0728	...	0841	...	0907	...	0922	1023	...	1112	...	1131	1154	...	1226	1231	1312	...	1331	1423	...	1512
	Nürnberg Hbf 920 a.	...	...	...	...	...	...	...	...	1127	...	...	...	...	1327	...	...	...	1427	...	...	1527‡	...	...	...
	Frankfurt (Main) Hbf 920 a.	...	...	...	...	...	...	...	...	1336	...	...	...	...	1536	...	...	...	...	...	...	1736	...	...	...

		ICE 90						*ICE* 22							*ICE* 20						*RJ* 748		*NJ* 490	*RJ* 840	
	⚒					⚒	Ⓐ		Ⓐ			Ⓐ	Ⓐ				Ⓐ								
	2	H✕	2	2	2	2	2	D✕	2	2	2	2	2	2	✕	2	2	2	2	2	✕	2	⊡	✕	2
Wien Hbf 950 d.	...	1315	...	...	...	...	...	1515	...	...	...	...	...	...	1715	...	...	...	...	...	1955	...	2041	2055	...
inz Hbf 950 d.	...	1436	1450	...	1550	...	1612	1636	1640	1650	...	1712	1750	1750	1836	1852	...	1950	...	2050	2132	...	2216	2232	...
els Hbf 950 d.	...	|	1509	...	1609	...	1631	|	1655	1709	...	1731	1809	1814k	1850	1909	...	2009	...	2109	2144	2149	2233	2244	2249
eumarkt-Kallham d.	1440	|	1540h	1540	1632	1640	1652	|	1720	1736	1740	1759	1834	1840	|	1936	1940	2036	2040	2136	...	2217	|	...	2316
Ried im Innkreis d.	1501	|	1601	|	|	1701	|	|	1737	|	1801	|	|	1901	|	|	2001	|	2101	|	...	2238	|	...	|
Braunau am Inn a.	1541	|	1641	|	|	1741	|	|	1808	|	1841	|	|	1941	|	|	2041	|	2138	|	...	2313	|	...	|
Simbach (Inn) 🏛 893 a.	1545	|	1645	|	|	1745	|	|	...	|	1845c	|	|	1945	|	|	*2047*	|	2142	|	...	...	|	...	|
chärding d.	...	|	...	1613	1659	...	1717	|	...	1809	...	1834	1901	...	|	2009	...	2109	...	2209	...	...	|	...	2348
assau Hbf a.	...	1531	...	1626	1712	...	...	1731	...	1823	...	1848	1914	...	1934	2023	...	2123	...	2223	...	...	2320	...	...
Nürnberg Hbf 920 a.	...	1729	...	...	...	...	...	1927	...	...	...	...	...	...	2128	...	...	...	...	...	...	...	0127	...	...
Frankfurt (Main) Hbf 920 a.	...	...	...	...	...	...	...	2136	...	...	...	...	...	...	2340	...	...	...	...	...	...	...	...	...	...

km																									
					NJ 491															*ICE* 21					*ICE* 23
		⚒	Ⓐ			⚒	†		⚒	Ⓐ	Ⓐ		⚒	Ⓐ			Ⓒ				Ⓐ				
		2	2	2	⊡	2	2	2	2	2	2	2	2	2	2	2	2	2	2	✕	2	2	2	2	D✕
	Frankfurt (Main) Hbf 920 d.	...	...	...	...	...	...	...	...	...	...	...	...	...	...	...	...	...	...	0621	...	...	...	...	0819v
	Nürnberg Hbf 920 d.	...	...	...	0307	...	...	...	...	...	...	...	...	...	...	...	...	...	...	0830	...	...	...	...	1030
	Passau Hbf d.	...	0410	0419c	0524	...	...	0538	0602	0623	...	...	0649	...	...	0805	...	0934	...	1026	...	1048	...	1137	1229
	Schärding d.	0358	0423	0432	|	...	...	0552	0616	0637	...	...	0703	...	...	0819	...	0948	...	|	...	1102	...	1150	|
0	**Simbach** (Inn) 🏛 893 d.	|	|	|	|	...	...	|	|	|	...	...	|	0717	...	|	0818	|	0918	|	1018	|	1118	|	|
2	**Braunau** am Inn d.	|	|	|	|	0514	0526	|	|	|	0610	0629	|	0723	0754	|	0822	|	0924	|	1024	|	1124	|	|
39	Ried im Innkreis d.	|	|	|	|	0552	0601	|	|	|	0643	0710	|	0755	0831	|	0855	|	1001	|	1101	|	1201	|	|
61	Neumarkt-Kallham d.	0429	0451	0504	|	0613	0619	0624	0644	0706	0709	0730	0736	0812	0849	0853	0912	1019	1024	|	1119	1128	1219	1224	|
90	**Wels** Hbf 950 d.	0456	0515	0531	0618	0637	...	0652	0712	0728	0737	0758z	0807	0837	...	0923	0937	...	1053	1112	...	1153	...	1253	|
115	**Linz** Hbf 950 a.	0519	0532	0554	0643	0652e	...	0708	0743	0747	...	...	0824	0858	...	0940	0958	...	1110	1124	...	1210	...	1310	1324
	Wien Hbf 950 a.	...	...	...	0827	...	...	...	...	...	...	...	...	...	...	...	...	...	...	1245	...	...	...	...	1445

					ICE 91				*ICE* 93		*ICE* 27				5927	*ICE* 29			*RJ* 749 769		*RJ* 841	*ICE* 229			*RJ* 843
	⚒					⚒	⚒					⚒											Ⓐ		
	2	2	2	2	H✕	2	2	2	B✕	2	D✕	2	2	2	⊖2	✕	2	2	✕	2	✕	✕	2	2	
Frankfurt (Main) Hbf 920 d.	...	...	...	...	...	...	...	...	...	...	1221	...	...	...	...	1421	...	...	...	...	...	1621	...	...	...
Nürnberg Hbf 920 d.	...	...	...	...	1230	...	...	...	1332	...	1430	...	...	...	...	1630	...	...	...	...	...	1830	...	...	...
assau Hbf d.	...	1248	1334	...	1429	...	1448	...	1529	1537	1629	...	1648	...	1744	1829	...	1849	...	...	...	2038	...	2053	...
chärding d.	...	1302	1348	...	|	...	1502	...	|	1550	|	...	1702	...	1758	|	...	1902	...	...	...	2052	...	2106	...
Simbach (Inn) 🏛 893 d.	1218e	|	|	1318	|	1418	|	1518	|	|	|	1618	|	1718	|	|	1818	|	...	1918	...	|	*2018*	|	...
Braunau am Inn d.	1224	|	|	1324	|	1424	|	1524	|	|	|	1624	|	1724	|	|	1824	|	...	1924	...	|	2024	|	...
Ried im Innkreis d.	1301	|	|	1401	|	1501	|	1601	|	|	|	1701	|	1801	|	|	1901	|	...	2001	...	|	2101	|	...
eumarkt-Kallham d.	1319	1328	1419	1424	|	1519	1528	1619	|	1624	|	1719	1728	1824	1833	|	1924	1936	...	2024	...	|	2119	2138	...
els Hbf 950 d.	...	1353	...	1453	|	...	1553	...	|	1653	|	...	1753	1853	1904	|	1953	2005	2016	2051	2116	2129	...	2205	2216
nz Hbf 950 a.	...	1410	...	1510	1524	...	1610	...	1624	1708	1724	...	1810	1910	1920	1924	2010	2022c	2028	...	2128	2143	...	...	2228
Wien Hbf 950 a.	...	...	...	...	1645	...	...	...	1745	...	1845	...	...	...	2232f	2045	...	...	2205	...	2305	2309	...	...	*0033*

– From Amstetten (d. 0612) and St Valentin (d. 0635).
– To / from Berlin (Table **850**).
– To / from Dortmund (Table **800**).
– From Garsten (Table **976**).
– To / from Hamburg (Table **900**).
– Ⓒ only.

e – Ⓐ only.
f – Wien **Franz-Josefs-Bahnhof**.
h – Arrives 5 – 7 minutes earlier.
j – Arrives 1036.
k – 1819 on Ⓐ.
v – 0821 on ⑦.

z – † only.
‡ – 2 – 3 minutes later on ⑦.
⊖ – May 1 - Oct. 27. (2) Wien Franz-Josefs-Bf - St Pölten - Passau and v.v.
⊡ – 🛏 1, 2 cl., 🛏 2 cl. and (2) Wien - Nürnberg - Hamburg and v.v.; 🛏 1, 2 cl., 🛏 2 cl. and (2) (**40490/40421**) Wien - Frankfurt - Köln - Düsseldorf and v.v. 🅁 for journeys to / from Germany.

963 SALZBURG and ST WOLFGANG - STROBL - BAD ISCHL

Routes 150, 546

km	Route 150	⚒	†	Ⓐ	⑥k	Ⓐ											Ⓐ		Ⓐ				Ⓐ		
0	**Salzburg** Hbf △ d.	0555	...	0625	0645	0715	0815	0845	0915	0945	1015	1115	1215	1315	1415	1515	1545	1615	1715	1815	1915	...	2015	2215	2315
32	St Gilgen (Busbahnhof) d.	0643	0650	0717	0735	0807	0907	0937	1007	1037	1107	1207	1307	1407	1507	1607	1637	1707	1807	1907	2007	...	2107	2258	2358
45	Strobl (Busbahnhof) d.	0701	0706	0738	0751	0828	0928	0958	1028	1058	1128	1228	1328	1428	1528	1628	1658	1728	1828	1928	2028	...	2128	2313	0013
57	**Bad Ischl** Bahnhof a.	0720	0723	0757	0808	0847	0947	1017	1047	1117	1147	1247	1347	1447	1547	1647	1717	1747	1847	1947	2047	...	2147	2329	0029

Route 150	⚒	Ⓐ	Ⓐ		Ⓐ	⑥k		Ⓑh												Ⓐ			⚒	†	
Bad Ischl Bahnhof d.	0504	0541	0557	0611	0646	0646	0746	0824	0924	1024	1054	1124	1154	1224	1324	1424	1524	1624	1724	1754	1824	1924	2024	2024	2124
Strobl (Busbahnhof) d.	0520	0600	0615	0630	0705	0707	0807	0845	0945	1045	1115	1145	1215	1245	1345	1445	1545	1645	1745	1815	1845	1945	2045	2045	2145
St Gilgen (Busbahnhof) d.	0535	0615	0630	0645	0720	0728	0828	0906	1006	1106	1136	1206	1236	1306	1406	1506	1606	1706	1806	1836	1906	2006	2100	2106	2206
Salzburg Hbf △ a.	0620	0656	0721	0732	0801	0819	0919	0957	1057	1157	1227	1257	1327	1357	1457	1557	1657	1757	1857	1927	1957	2052	*2152*k	2152	2252

km	Route 546	Ⓐ	⚒	⚒	Ⓒ	†	Ⓐ	Ⓐ	Ⓐ		Ⓐ	Ⓒ	Ⓐ		Ⓐ		Ⓐ			Ⓐ	Ⓒ	Ⓐ	Ⓒ		
0	**St Wolfgang** ⊡ ‡ ♥ d.	0500	0600	0648	0735	0735	0740	0753	0900	0913	1013	1013	1100	1213	1318	1413	1513	1613	1713	1713	1813	1813	1828	1913	2003
7	Strobl (Busbahnhof) ♥ d.	0512	0612	0703	0746	0747	|	0804	|	0926	|	1028	|	1228	1333	1428	1528	1628	1726	1728	|	1828	1841	1926	2016
19	**Bad Ischl** Bahnhof a.	0531	0639	0729	...	0806	0811	...	0931	...	1044	1050	1131	1250	1359	1450	1554	1650	...	1754	1844	1850	...	...	...

Route 546	Ⓐ	⚒	⚒		Ⓐ	Ⓐ	Ⓒ	Ⓐ			⚒		Ⓒ	Ⓐ	Ⓐ			Ⓐ			Ⓐ				
Bad Ischl Bahnhof d.	0605	0642	...	0823	0913	...	0913	1023	...	1113	1223	...	1323	1330	1423	...	1513	1623	...	1713	1823	...	1913	...	...
Strobl (Busbahnhof) d.	0630	0706	0806	|	|	0930	0935	1045	1045	1135	1245	1245	1345	1355	1445	1445	1535	1645	1645	1735	1845	1845	|	1930	2043
St Wolfgang ⊡ ‡ a.	0642	0718	0817	0850	0940	0942	0947	1057	1057	1147	1257	1257	1357	1407	1457	1457	1547	1657	1657	1747	1857	1857	1940	1942	2055

c – Ⓒ only.
h – Also Oct 26.
k – ⑥ (not Oct. 26).

△ – All services also call at Mirabellplatz.

⊡ – St Wolfgang Schafbergbahnhof. All services also call at St Wolfgang Markt.
♥ – Additional services St Wolfgang - Strobl: 1028 Ⓐ, 1113 Ⓒ, 1313 Ⓒ and 1513 Ⓒ.
‡ – The **Schafbergbahn** narrow-gauge steam rack railway operates St Wolfgang - Schafbergspitze (*6 km*). Services operate subject to demand and weather conditions **May 11 - Nov. 3**, 2019. 2nd class only. Special fares payable. Journey time: 35 minutes each way. ✆ +43 (0) 6138 2232 0.

964 STROBL - ST GILGEN (WOLFGANGSEE)

June 8 - September 8

			⛴			⛴			⛴			⛴					
Strobl Schiffstation ⊡ d.	...	0845	...	0925	1025	...	1125	1225	...	1325	1425	...	1525	1625	1725	1820	1920
St Wolfgang Markt d.	...	|	...	|	|	1120	1200	1300	1320	1400	1500	1520	1600	1700	1800	1835	1933
St Wolfgang Schafbergbahnhof ‡ d.	0830	0910	0935	0955	1055	1130	1208	1308	1330	1408	1508	1530	1608	1708	1808	1845	1941
St Wolfgang Markt d.	|	0918	0945	1005	1105	|	|	|	|	|	|	|	|	|	|	...	...
St Gilgen Schiffstation ● a.	0855	0955	1015	1045	1145	1210	1245	1345	1410	1445	1545	1610	1645	1745	1845	...	...

					⛴			⛴			⛴			⛴			
St Gilgen Schiffstation ● d.	...	...	0900	1000	1030	1100	1200	1230	1300	1400	1430	1500	1600	1630	1700	1800	1850
St Wolfgang Markt d.	...	...	|	|	|	|	|	|	|	|	|	|	|	|	|	|	1925
St Wolfgang Schafbergbahnhof ‡ d.	0825	0855	0937	1037	1100	1137	1237	1300	1337	1437	1500	1537	1637	1700	1737	1837	1935
St Wolfgang Markt d.	|	0905	0950	1050	1110	1150	1250	1310	1350	1450	1510	1550	1650	1710	1750	1850	...
Strobl Schiffstation ⊡ a.	0840	0920	1015	1115	...	1215	1315	...	1415	1515	...	1615	1715	...	1815	1915	...

‡ – See note under Table **963**.
⊡ – Approximately 400 metres from Strobl Busbahnhof.
● – Approximately 500 metres from St Gilgen Busbahnhof.
⛴ – July 6 - Sept. 1 (subject to weather conditions). Operated by paddle-steamer *Kaiser Franz Josef I*. Supplement payable (€ 1).

969 TAUERN TUNNEL CAR-CARRYING TRAINS

BÖCKSTEIN - MALLNITZ-OBERVELLACH *11 km.* Transit time: 11 minutes. Passengers without cars are also conveyed. ✆ 05-1717. E-mail: autoschleuse.tauernbahn@pv.oebb.
From Böckstein at 0620, 0720 and hourly until 2320. **From Mallnitz-Obervellach** at 0550, 0650 and hourly until 2250.

970 SALZBURG - VILLACH - KLAGENFURT

km		*EN* 50463 R A	*NJ* 237 R ♦	*NJ* 235 2		*EN* 40465 R ♦	2	⚒ 2	2	*IC* 894 ✕	*RJ* 898 L✕	*RJ* 111 ✕	*RJ* 596 ✕	*EC* 113 ✕♦	*EC* 115 ⊗♦	Ⓐ 2	*RJ* 698 ✕		*EC* 117 d ⊗♦	S	*EC* 117 S ⊗♦	Ⓐ 2	*NJ* 295 R ♦
	Wien Hbf **950** d.	...	2127	...	...	...	...	...	...	...	...	...	0855	...	...	...	1455	...	...	...	...	...	...
	München Hbf **890** d.	2320	|	...	...	...	...	...	...	...	...	0817**e**	|	1217**c**	1417**c**	...	|	...	1817**c**	...	1827**o**	...	2010
0	**Salzburg** Hbf **960 975** d.	0140	0140	...	...	...	...	...	...	0612	0812	1012	1212	1412	1612	...	1812	...	2012	2012	|	2115	2201
29	Golling-Abtenau **960** d.	|	|	...	...	...	...	...	...	0633	0833	1033	1233	1433	1633	...	1833	...	2033	2033	|	2140	|
53	**Bischofshofen** **960 975** d.	|	|	...	...	...	...	...	...	0654	0854	1054	1254	1454	1654	...	1854	...	2054	2054	|	2202	|
61	St Johann im Pongau **960** d.	|	|	...	...	...	...	...	...	0703	0903	1103	1303	1503	1703	...	1903	...	2103	2103	|	2210	|
67	**Schwarzach - St Veit** **960** d.	|	|	...	...	0423	...	...	...	0711	0911	1111	1311	1511	1711	...	1911	...	2111	2109	2122	2218	2254
86	Bad Hofgastein d.	|	|	...	...	0441	...	...	...	0729	0929	1129	1329	1529	1729	...	1929	...	2129	...	2140	2234	|
97	Bad Gastein d.	|	|	...	...	0501	...	...	...	0742	0942	1142	1342	1542	1742	...	1942	...	2142	...	2153	2245	|
113	Mallnitz-Obervellach d.	|	|	...	...	0516	...	0647	...	0756	0956	1156	1356	1556	1756	1800	1956	...	2156	...	2207	...	|
146	Spittal-Millstättersee **971** d.	|	|	...	...	0542	...	0717	0729	0820	1020	1220	1420	1620	1820	1830	2020	...	2220	...	2231	...	|
182	**Villach** Hbf **971** a.	0357	0357	...	...	0605	...	...	0753	0843	1043	1243	1443	1643	1843	...	2043	...	2243	...	2254	...	001
182	**Villach** Hbf **971** d.	...	...	0418	...	...	0620	...	0755	0847	1047	1247	1447	1649	1847	...	2047	...	2247	...	2258	...	...
198	Velden am Wörthersee **971** d.	...	...	|	...	...	0634	...	0806	0858	1058	1258	1458	1700	1858	...	2058	...	2258	...	2309	...	...
207	Pörtschach am Wörthersee **971** d.	...	...	|	...	...	0642	...	|	0904	1104	1304	1504	1707	1904	...	2104	...	2304	...	2315	...	...
220	**Klagenfurt** Hbf **971** a.	...	...	0439	...	...	0656	...	0822	0913	1113	1316	1513	1718	1916	...	2116	...	2316	...	2327	...	...

	NJ 236 R ♦	*EN* 498 R A		*NJ* 294 R ♦		Ⓐ 2	⚒ 2	*RJ* 691 ✕	*EC* 114 ⊗♦	*EC* 112 ✕♦		*RJ* 793 ✕	*RJ* 797 ✕	Ⓐ 2	Ⓐ 2	*RJ* 110 ✕	*IC* 895 ✕	2	2	*EN* 414 R ♦		
Klagenfurt Hbf **971** d.	...	...	...	...	...	...	...	0645	0842	1027	...	1245	1445	1532	...	1642	1845	2045	2232	...	...	...
Pörtschach am Wörthersee **971** d.	...	...	...	...	...	...	...	0655	0855	1040	...	1255	1455	1547	...	1655	1855	2055	2247	...	...	...
Velden am Wörthersee **971** d.	...	...	...	...	...	...	...	0702	0902	1047	...	1302	1502	1554	...	1702	1902	2102	2254	...	...	...
Villach Hbf **971** a.	...	...	...	...	...	...	...	0713	0913	1058	...	1313	1513	1609	...	1713	1913	2113	2309	...	...	...
Villach Hbf **971** d.	0150	0150	...	0400	...	...	0529	0716	0916	1116	...	1316	1516	1610	...	1716	1916	2116	...	2320	...	...
Spittal-Millstättersee **971** d.	|	|	...	|	...	...	0604	0740	0940	1140	...	1340	1540	1634	1644	1740	1940	2140	...	2345	...	...
Mallnitz-Obervellach d.	|	|	...	|	...	...	0633	0804	1004	1204	...	1404	1604	...	1714	1804	2004	2204	...	0014	...	...
Bad Gastein d.	|	|	...	|	...	0624	...	0817	1017	1217	...	1417	1617	...	...	1817	2017	2217	...	0030	...	...
Bad Hofgastein d.	|	|	...	|	...	0635	...	0830	1030	1230	...	1430	1630	...	...	1830	2030	2230	...	0042	...	...
Schwarzach - St Veit **960** d.	|	|	...	0520	...	0654	...	0850	1052	1252	...	1452	1652	...	...	1852	2052	2252	...	0058	...	...
St Johann im Pongau **960** a.	|	|	...	|	...	0700	...	0857	1057	1257	...	1457	1657	...	...	1857	2057	2257	...	...	...	...
Bischofshofen **960 975** a.	|	|	...	|	...	0710	...	0905	1105	1305	...	1505	1705	...	...	1905	2105	2305	...	...	...	...
Golling-Abtenau **960** a.	|	|	...	|	...	|	...	0926	1126	1326	...	1526	1726	...	...	1926	2126	2326	...	...	...	...
Salzburg Hbf **960 975** a.	0404	0404	...	0615	...	0750	...	0948	1148	1348	...	1548	1748	...	...	1948	2148	2348	...	...	...	...
München Hbf **890** a.	|	0610	...	0819**g**	...	...	...	|	1341**c**	1541**c**	...	|	|	...	...	2142**h**	...	...	...	...	...	...
Wien Hbf **950** a.	0755	...	...	...	...	...	...	1305	...	...	...	1905	2105	...	...	...	...	...	...	...	...	...

♦ – **NOTES** (LISTED BY TRAIN NUMBER)

112 – [12] and ✕ Klagenfurt - München - Stuttgart - Frankfurt; [12] Zagreb (**212**) - Villach (**112**) - Frankfurt.
113 – [12] and ✕ Frankfurt - Stuttgart - München - Klagenfurt; [12] Frankfurt - Villach (**213**) - Zagreb.
114 – WÖRTHERSEE – [12] and ⊗ Klagenfurt - München - Stuttgart - Köln - Dortmund.
115 – WÖRTHERSEE – [12] and ⊗ Münster - Köln - Stuttgart - München - Klagenfurt.
117 – SALZACH – [12] and ⊗ Frankfurt - Stuttgart - München - Salzburg - Klagenfurt.
236/7 – 🛏 1,2 cl., ▬ 2 cl. and [2] Venezia - Tarvisio ▣ - Villach - Salzburg - Wien and v.v.
294/5 – 🛏 1,2 cl., ▬ 2 cl. and [2] Roma - Firenze - Bologna - München and v.v.; 🛏 1,2 cl., ▬ 2 cl. and [2] (**40235/40295**) Milano - Verona - München and v.v.
414 – [2] Beograd - Zagreb - Ljubljana - Villach - Schwarzach (**464**) - Innsbruck - Feldkirch - Zürich; 🛏 1,2 cl. and ▬ 2 cl. Zagreb - Ljubljana - Villach - Schwarzach (**464**) - Innsbruck - Feldkirch - Zürich.
40465 – [2] Zürich (**465**) - Feldkirch - Innsbruck - Schwarzach (**40465**) - Villach - Ljubljana - Zagreb - Beograd; 🛏 1,2 cl. and ▬ 2 cl. Zürich (**465**) - Feldkirch - Innsbruck - Schwarzach (**40465**) - Villach - Ljubljana - Zagreb.

A – LISINSKI – 🛏 1,2 cl., ▬ 2 cl. and [2] Zagreb - Dobova ▣ - Ljubljana - Jesenice ▣ - Villach - München and v.v.; 🛏 1,2 cl. and [2] (**480/60463**) Rijeka - Ljubljana - München and v.v.; conveys 🛏 1,2 cl., ▬ 2 cl. and [2] (*NJ* **40236/40463**) Venezia - Villach - München and v.v. See Table **890** for amended München timings Mar. 15 - May 15.

L – From Linz (Table **950**).
R – Ⓡ for international journeys.
S – Apr. 11 - June 12.

c – Mar. 15 - July 28 calls at München **Ost**, not Hbf (see Table **890**).
d – Not Apr. 11 - June 12.
e – Not Apr. 11 - June 7.
f – See note △ on Table **890**.
g – See note ▽ on Table **890**.
h – Not Apr. 10 - June 6.
o – München **Ost**.

LIENZ - VILLACH - KLAGENFURT - FRIESACH (- WIEN) 971

	NJ 235		RJ 530					RJ 532				IC 894	RJ 534			RJ 898		RJ 536				RJ 111	RJ 132		
	★	⚒									⚒	◐			⚒	◐				Ⓐ	⚒	◐			Ⓐ
	2	2	✕	U 2	2	2	2	✕	2	2	2	✕	✕	2	2	✕	2	✕	2	2	2	✕	V✕	2	2
ienz d.	...	...	...	...	...	...	0524	...	...	0629	...	...	...	0719	*0824*e	...	0924	...	...	...	1024e	...	...	1124	...
pittal-Millstättersee a.	...	...	...	...	...	...	0627	...	...	0727	...	...	...	0822	*0922*e	...	1022	...	...	...	1122e	...	...	1222	...
pittal-Millstättersee 970 d.	...	...	...	0448r	0530e	*0542*	0630	...	0635e	0729	0732	0820	...	0832	0932	1020	1032	...	...	...	1132	1220	...	1232	...
illach Hbf 970 a.	...	...	...	0520r	0558e	*0605*	0656	...	0708e	0753	0804	0843	...	0904	1004	1043	1104	...	←	...	1204	1243	...	1304p	...
illach Hbf 970 d.	0418	0450	0526	0529	0604	0620	0659e	0714	0720	0755	0820	0847	0914	0920	1020	1047	1120	1114	1120	1150	1220	1247	1314	1320	1350
elden am Wörthersee 970 d.	|	0505	|	0543	|	0634	0711e	0725	0734	0806	0834	0858	|	0934	1034	1058	→	1125	1134	1204	1234	1258	|	1334	1404
örtschach am W'see ⊡ 970 d.	|	0513	|	0551	|	0642	|	|	0742	|	0842	0904	0929	0942	1042	1104	...	|	1142	1212	1242	1304	1329	1342	1412
rumpendorf d.	|	0519	|	0557	|	0648	|	|	0748	|	0848	|	|	0948	1048	|	...	|	1148	1218	1248	1310	|	1348	1418
lagenfurt Hbf 970 a.	0439	0528	0547	0605	0625	0656	0728e	0737	0756	0822	0856	0913	0937	0956	1056	1113	...	1137	1156	1226	1256	1316	1337	1356	1426
lagenfurt Hbf 980 d.	0440	...	0549	0607	0627	0704	...	0739	0804	0823	0904	...	0939	1004	1104	...	...	1139	1204	1228	1304	...	1339	1404	1428
t Veit an der Glan 980 d.	|	...	0602	0627	0640	0724	...	0753	0824	0838	0924	...	0953	1024	1124	...	...	1153	1224	1247	1324	...	1353	1424	1447
riesach 980 a.	|	...	|	0659	0703	0756	...	|	0856	...	0956	...	1015	1056	1156	...	...	|	1256	...	1356	...	1415	1456	...
Wien Hbf 980 a.	0846	...	0935	...	...	...	...	1135	...	...	...	...	1335	...	...	...	...	1535	...	...	...	...	1735	...	...

	D 730		RJ 596	RJ 630			D 732		EC 113		IC 632			D 734		EC 115	RJ 130				RJ 698			EC 117	
	⑦w	⚒	◐			Ⓐ	⑦w	⚒	◐				Ⓐ	⑦w	⚒	◐			⚒	⚒	◐	◇	⚒		
	2	2	✕	✕	2	2	2	2	✕	2	✕	2	2	2	2	⊗	V✕	2	2	2	✕	2	2	◐	2
ienz d.	...	1224e	...	...	1324	...	1453	1424e	...	1524	1553	...	...	...	1624e	...	...	1724	1824e	...	...	1924	2024e	⊗	...
pittal-Millstättersee a.	...	1322e	...	...	1422	...	1542	1522e	...	1622	1642	...	...	...	1722e	...	...	1822	1922e	...	...	2022	2122e	...	...
pittal-Millstättersee 970 d.	...	1332	1420	...	1432	...	1546	1532	1620	1632	1646	...	...	...	1732	1820	...	1832	1932	...	2020	2032	2132	2220	...
illach Hbf 970 a.	...	1404	1443	...	1504p	...	1609	1604	1643	1704	1709	←	...	...	1804	1843	...	1904p	2004	...	2043	2104	2204	2243	...
illach Hbf 970 d.	1414	1420	1447	1514	1520	1550	1614	1620	1649	1720	1714	1720	1750	1814	1820	1847	1914	1920	...	2020	2047	2120	2220	2247	2350
elden am Wörthersee 970 d.	1425	1434	1458	1525	1534	1604	1625	1634	1700	→	|	1734	1804	1825	1834	1858	1925	1934	...	2034	2058	2134	2234	2258	0004
örtschach am W'see ⊡ 970 d.	1431	1442	1504	|	1542	1612	1631	1642	1707	...	1729	1742	1812	1831	1842	1904	|	1942	...	2042	2104	2142	2242	2304	0012
rumpendorf d.	|	1448	|	|	1548	1618	|	1648	1712	...	|	1748	1818	|	1848	1910	|	1948	...	2048	2110	2148	2248	2310	0018
lagenfurt Hbf 970 a.	1439	1456	1513	1537	1556	1626	1639	1656	1718	...	1737	1756	1826	1839	1856	1916	1937	1956	...	2056	2116	2156	2256	2316	0026
lagenfurt Hbf 980 d.	1441	1504	...	1539	1604	1628	1641	1704	...	...	1739	1804	1828	1841	1904	...	1939	2004	...	2104	...	2204	2304	...	0028
t Veit an der Glan 980 d.	1454	1524	...	1553	1624	1647	1654	1724	...	...	1753	1824	1847	1854	1924	...	1953	2024	...	2124	...	2224	2324	...	0047
riesach 980 a.	1518	1556	...	|	1656	...	1718	1756	...	...	1815	1856	...	1918	1956	...	|	2056	...	2156	...	2256	2356	...	...
Wien Hbf 980 a.	1835	...	...	1935	...	...	2035	...	...	...	2135	...	...	2235	...	...	2335	...	...	...	...	...	...	...	...

km						RJ 691				EC 114			RJ 131	EC 112			IC 533			RJ 793			RJ 535	RJ 797	
		⚒	⚒		⚒	◐	⚒	⚒k	◇	◐	⚒			◐	⚒				Ⓐ	◐	⚒			◐	⚒
		2	2	2	2	✕	2	U 2	2	⊗	2	2	V✕	✕	2	2	✕	2	2	✕	2	2	✕	✕	2
	Wien Hbf 980 d.	...	...	...	...	...	...	...	...	...	...	...	0625	...	...	...	0825	...	...	...	...	...	1025	...	...
0	**Friesach** 980 d.	...	...	0508	0545	...	0608	0643	0708	...	0808	0908	|	...	1008	1108	1144	...	...	...	1208	1308	|	...	1408
33	St Veit an der Glan 980 d.	...	0512	0542	0616	...	0642	0718	0742	...	0842	0942	1008	...	1042	1142	1208	...	1212	...	1242	1342	1408	...	1442
53	**Klagenfurt** Hbf 980 a.	...	0530	0600	0631	...	0700	0738	0800	...	0900	1000	1020	...	1100	1200	1220	...	1230	...	1300	1400	1420	...	1500
53	**Klagenfurt** Hbf 970 d.	...	0532	0602	0633	0645	0702	0744	0802	0842	0902	1002	1022	1027	1102	1202	1222	...	1232	1245	1302	1402	1422	1445	1502
60	Krumpendorf d.	...	0541	0611	0643	|	0711	0752	0811	0849	0911	1011	|	1034	1111	1211	|	...	1241	|	1311	1411	|	|	1511
66	Pörtschach am W ⊡ 970 d.	...	0547	0617	0648	0655	0717	0757	0817	0855	0917	1017	|	1040	1117	1217	1232	...	1247	1255	1317	1417	|	1455	1517
75	Velden am Wörthersee 970 d.	...	0554	0624	0654	0702	0724	0804	0824	0902	0924	1024	1036	1047	1124	1224	|	...	1254	1302	1324	1424	1436	1502	1524
91	**Villach** Hbf 970 a.	...	0609	0639	0710	0713	0739	0820	0839	0913	0939	1039	1046p	1058	1139	1239	1246	←	1309	1313	1339	1439	1446p	1513	1539
91	**Villach** Hbf 970 d.	*0529*	0617e	0654	...	0716	0754	...	0854	0916	0954	1054	...	1116	1154	1254	1250	1254	...	1316	1354	1454	...	1516	1554
127	Spittal-Millstättersee 970 a.	*0602*	0650e	0726	...	0738	0826	...	0926	0938	1026	1126	...	1138	1226	→	1314	1326	...	1338	1426	1526	...	1538	1626
127	Spittal-Millstättersee d.	0632	...	0737	...	...	0837e	...	0937	...	1037e	1137	...	...	1237e	...	1316	1337	...	...	1437e	1537	...	...	...
195	**Lienz** a.	0732	...	0837	...	...	0937e	...	1037	...	1137e	1237	...	...	1337e	...	1406	1437	...	...	1537e	1637	...	...	...

			RJ 133			RJ 110		D 737			RJ 539		IC 895		D 739			RJ 631			RJ 633			NJ 233	
	Ⓐ				Ⓐ	◐	⚒	⑤f	Ⓐ			Ⓐ	◐	⚒	⑤b	Ⓐ			⚒					★	
	2	2	V✕	2	2	✕	2	2	2	2	✕	2	✕	2	2	2	2	✕	2	2	✕	2	2	2	2
Wien Hbf 980 d.	...	...	1225	...	...	...	...	1325	...	...	1425	...	...	...	1525	...	...	1625	...	...	1825	...	...	1923	...
riesach 980 d.	...	1508	1544	...	...	...	1608	1639	...	1708	|	...	...	1808	1840	...	1908	1944	2008	2108	|	...	...	2301	...
t Veit an der Glan 980 d.	1512	1542	1608	...	1612	...	1642	1704	1712	1742	1808	1812	...	1842	1905	1912	1942	2008	2042	2142	2208	...	...	|	...
lagenfurt Hbf 980 a.	1530	1600	1620	...	1630	...	1700	1716	1730	1800	1820	1830	...	1900	1917	1930	2000	2020	2100	2200	2220	...	←	2335	...
lagenfurt Hbf 970 d.	1532	1602	1622	...	1632	1642	1702	1717	1732	1802	1822	1832	1845	1902	1921	1932	2002	2022	2102	2232	2222	...	2232	2337	2341
rumpendorf d.	1541	1611	|	...	1641	1649	1711	1726	1741	1811	|	1841	|	1911	|	1941	2011	|	2111	→	|	...	2241	|	2350
örtschach am W'see ⊡ 970 d.	1547	1617	1632	...	1647	1655	1717	1733	1747	1817	|	1847	1855	1917	1930	1947	2017	2032	2117	...	|	...	2247	|	2357
elden am Wörthersee 970 d.	1554	1624	|	...	1654	1702	1724	1740	1754	1824	1836	1854	1902	1924	1937	1954	2024	|	2124	...	2236	...	2254	|	0004
illach Hbf 970 a.	1609	1639	1646	←	1709	1713	1739	1755	1809	1839	1846p	1909	1913	1939	1947	2009	2039	2046p	2139	...	2246	...	2309	0001	0019
illach Hbf 970 d.	1610	1654	...	1654	1710	1716	1754	...	1810	1854	...	...	1916	1954	1950	...	2054	...	2154	...	...	2254	*2320*	...	...
pittal-Millstättersee 970 a.	1634	→	...	1726	1734	1738	1826	...	1834	1926	...	...	1938	2026	2014	...	2126	...	2226	...	...	2326	*2343*	...	...
pittal-Millstättersee d.	1637	...	...	1737	...	...	1837e	...	...	1937	...	...	...	*2037*e	2016	...	2137	...	...	...	...	...	...	...	...
ienz a.	1737	...	...	1837	...	...	1937e	...	...	2037	...	...	...	*2136*e	2106	...	2235	...	...	...	...	...	...	...	...

– To / from Unzmarkt (Table **980**).
– [12] Venezia - Tarvisio ▦ - Villach - Wien and v.v.
– Also May 29, June 19, Aug. 14, Oct. 31; not May 31, June 21, Aug 16, Nov. 1.

e – Ⓐ only.
f – Also May 29, June 19, Aug. 14, Oct. 31; not May 31, June 21, Aug 16, Nov. 1.
k – Change trains at Klagenfurt on Ⓐ to July 5 / from Sept. 9.
p – Connects with train in previous column.
r – ⚒ only.
w – Also Apr. 22, June 10; not Apr. 21, June 9.

◇ – Change trains at Spittal-Millstättersee on Ⓐ.
★ – See Table **980** for through cars to / from Roma and Milano.
◐ – See Table **970** for further details.
⊡ – Pörtschach am Wörthersee.

LINZ - SELZTHAL 974

2nd class only (except *IC* trains)

km								IC 503											IC 601								
		⚒						🍷						Ⓐ			Ⓐ		🍷		Ⓐ						
0	**Linz** Hbf d.	0506	0536	0636	0712	0736	0836	0914	0936	1058	1136	1258	1336	1404	1458	1536	1558	1636	1714	1736	1800	1858	1936	2036	2136	2236	2336
28	Rohr - Bad Hall d.	0539	0609	0709	0736	0809	0909	0935	1009	1121	1209	1321	1409	1429	1521	1609	1622	1709	1735	1809	1825	1921	2009	2109	2209	2309	0009
32	Kremsmünster d.	0545	0615	0715	|	0815	0915	|	1015	1125	1215	1325	1415	1436	1525	1615	1627	1715	|	1815	1829	1925	2015	2115	2215	2315	0015
51	Kirchdorf a. d. Krems d.	0604	0633	0736	0750	0834	0933	0949	1033	1140	1233	1340	1434	1453	1540	1633	1644	1733	1749	1833	1843	1939	2033	2134	2233	2333	0033
68	Hinterstoder d.	0625	...	0757	0807	0856	...	|	...	1201	...	1401	1456c	1514	1601	...	1705	...	|	...	1904	2001	...	2156	...	...	...
82	Windischgarsten d.	0639	...	...	0821	0910	...	1020	...	1215	...	1415	1510c	1528	1615	...	1719	...	1820	...	1918	2015	...	2211	...	...	...
87	Spital am Pyhrn d.	0646	...	...	0827	0916	...	1026	...	1221	...	1421	1516c	1534	1621	...	1725	...	1826	...	1924	2021	...	2218	...	...	...
104	**Selzthal** a.	0702	...	...	0843	...	...	1040	...	1239	...	1439	...	...	1639	...	1743	...	1840	...	...	2039	...	2234	...	...	...
	Liezen 975 a.	...	...	...	0851e	...	...	|	...	1251e	...	1451e	...	...	1648e	...	...	...	|	...	...	...	...	...	...	...	...
	Graz Hbf 975 a.	...	...	...	...	...	...	1214	...	...	...	...	...	...	...	...	...	...	2014	...	...	...	...	...	...	...	...

												IC 502										IC 600					
		Ⓐ		⚒		⚒	Ⓐ	Ⓒ				🍷								Ⓐ		🍷					
Graz Hbf 975 d.	...	...	...	...	...	...	...	...	...	...	...	0745	...	...	...	...	...	...	...	...	...	1545	...	...	...	...	...
Liezen 975 d.	...	...	...	...	...	...	...	...	...	...	...	|	...	...	...	...	1305e	...	1505e	...	...	|	...	...	...	...	...
elzthal d.	...	0428	...	...	...	0547	0615	0615	0721	...	...	0919	...	...	1121	...	1321	...	1521	...	...	1719	...	...	1921	...	...
pital am Pyhrn d.	...	0445	...	...	...	0604	0632	0632	0738	...	...	0934	...	1044	1140	...	1340	...	1540	...	1643	1734	...	...	1940	2043e	...
indischgarsten d.	...	0451	...	...	...	0610	0640	0649f	0744	...	...	0940	...	1050	1146	...	1346	...	1546	...	1649	1740	...	...	1947	2049e	...
interstoder d.	...	0504	...	...	...	0625	0654	0702	0758	0808	...	|	...	1104	1200	...	1400	...	1600	...	1704	|	...	...	2000	2103e	...
rchdorf a. d. Krems d.	0425	0525	0525	0555	0625	0646	0717	0725	0821	0828	0925	1011	1025	1125	1221	1325	1421	1525	1621	1650	1725	1811	1825	1925	2021	2125	2225
remsmünster d.	0445	0545	0545	0615	0645	0703	0731	0745	0836	0845	0945	|	1045	1145	1236	1345	1436	1545	1636	1714	1745	|	1845	1945	2036	2145	2245
ohr - Bad Hall d.	0449	0549	0549	0619	0649	0708	0737	0749	0840	0849	0949	1025	1049	1149	1240	1349	1440	1549	1640	1718	1749	1825	1849	1949	2040	2149	2249
nz Hbf a.	0524	0624	0624	0654	0725	0735	0803	0824	0903	0924	1024	1047	1124	1224	1303	1424	1503	1624	1703	1754	1824	1847	1924	2024	2103	2224	2324

– Kirchdorf - Spital am Pyhrn on Ⓒ only.
e – Ⓐ only.
f – Arrives 0637.

975 SALZBURG - BISCHOFSHOFEN - SELZTHAL - GRAZ

km			NJ 465						IC 719			IC 513	IC 503		RJ 111	IC 515			EC 217			EC 113	EC 163	
		⚒ 2	A	⚒ 2	Ⓐ 2	Ⓐ 2	Ⓐ 2	2	⊗	Ⓐ 2	2	🍷	🍷	2	✕	🍷	Ⓐ 2L	2	G⊗	Ⓐ 2L	Ⓑ 2	✕	Z✕	Ⓐ 2
0	**Salzburg** Hbf ... 960 970 d.	...	...	...	...	...	...	...	0615	...	...	0815	...	...	1012	...	...	...	1215	...	...	1412	...	...
	Innsbruck Hbf 960 ... d.	...	0056	...	...	...	...	...	|	...	...	|	...	...	|	0821	...	...	|	...	...	|	1221	...
53	**Bischofshofen** ... 960 970 a.	...	0336	...	...	...	...	...	0702	...	...	0902	...	...	1052	1110	...	...	1302	...	...	1452	1510	...
53	**Bischofshofen** ... d.	...	0338	...	...	...	...	...	0713	...	0741r	0913	...	...	...	1113	...	...	1313	...	...	...	1513	...
77	Radstadt ... d.	...	|	...	...	...	...	0610	0736	...	0809	0936	...	...	...	1136	...	...	1336	...	...	...	1536	...
94	Schladming ... d.	...	0416	0500	...	...	...	0629	0752	...	0831	0952	...	1031	...	1152	...	1231	1352	...	1431	...	1552	...
133	**Stainach-Irdning** ... d.	0415	0446	0541	...	...	...	0710	0821	...	0912	1021	...	1112	...	1221	...	1312	1421	...	1512	...	1621	...
145	Liezen ... d.	0427	0457	0553	...	...	...	0726	0832	0857	0926	1032	...	1126	...	1232	1305	1326	1432	1505	1526	...	1632	1704
	Linz Hbf 974 ... d.	|	|	|	...	...	...	|	|	|	|	|	0914	|	...	|	|	|	|	|	|	...	|	|
152	**Selzthal** ... a.	0433	0504	0559	...	...	...	0733	0839	0904	0933	1039	1040	1133	...	1239	1312	1333	1439	1512	1533	...	1639	1711
152	**Selzthal** ... d.	0440	0513	0606	...	0716	...	0739	0846	...	0939	1048	1048	1139	...	1248	...	1339	1446	...	1539	...	1648	...
158	Stadt Rottenmann ... d.	0447	|	0613	...	0722	...	0745	0853	...	0945	|	|	1145	...	|	...	1345	1453	...	1545	...	|	...
169	Trieben ... d.	0455	|	0621	...	0729	...	0753	|	...	0953	|	|	1153	...	|	...	1353	|	...	1553	...	|	...
215	St Michael ... a.	0530	0550	0655	...	0802	...	0828	0921	...	1028	1121	1121	1228	...	1321	...	1428	1521	...	1628	...	1721	...
215	St Michael ... 980 d.	0531	0551	0701	0706	0803	...	*0833*	0922	...	*1033*	1122	1122	*1233*	...	1322	...	*1433*	1522	...	*1633*	...	1722	...
225	Leoben Hbf ... 980 d.	0540	0601	0709	0715	0811	0817	*0841*	0930	...	*1041*	1130	1130	*1241*	...	1330	...	*1441*	1530	...	*1641*	...	1730	...
	Bruck a. d. Mur ... 980 a.	|	0612	|	0728	0824	|	*0853*	|	...	*1053*	|	|	*1253*	...	|	...	*1453*	|	...	*1653*	...	|	...
293	**Graz** Hbf ... 980 a.	0633	0700	0802	|	...	0903	...	1014	...	...	1214	1214	...	...	1414	...	...	1614	...	...	...	1814	...

		IC 611	IC 601			EC 219	EC 117		
	2	🍷	🍷	2	Ⓐ 2	F⊗	⊗	2	Ⓑ 2
Salzburg Hbf ... 960 970 d.	...	1615	...	...	*1643*	1815	2012	...	...
Innsbruck Hbf 960 ... d.	...	|	...	...	|	|	|	...	...
Bischofshofen ... 960 970 a.	...	1702	...	...	*1735*	1902	2052	...	...
Bischofshofen ... d.	...	1713	...	...	1741	1913	...	2100	...
Radstadt ... d.	...	1736	...	...	1810	1936	...	2130	...
Schladming ... d.	1631	1752	...	1831	...	1952	...	2149	2155
Stainach-Irdning ... d.	1712	1821	...	1912	...	2021	...	...	2234
Liezen ... d.	1726	1832	...	1926	...	2032	...	...	...
Linz Hbf 974 ... d.	|	|	1714	|	...	|	...	...	...
Selzthal ... a.	1733	1839	1840	1933	...	2039	...	...	...
Selzthal ... d.	1739	1848	1848	1939	...	2046	...	...	...
Stadt Rottenmann ... d.	1745	|	|	1945	...	2053	...	...	...
Trieben ... d.	1753	|	|	1953	...	|	...	...	...
St Michael ... a.	1828	1921	1921	2028	...	2121	...	...	...
St Michael ... 980 d.	*1833*	1922	1922	*2033*	...	2122	...	...	...
Leoben Hbf ... 980 d.	*1841*	1930	1930	*2041*	...	2130	...	...	...
Bruck a. d. Mur ... 980 a.	*1853*	|	|	*2053*	...	|	...	...	...
Graz Hbf ... 980 a.	...	2014	2014	...	...	2214	...	...	...

						EC 218			IC 502	IC 512
	⚒ 2	⚒ 2	2	Ⓐ 2	⚒ 2	F⊗	2	Ⓐ 2L	🍷	🍷
Graz Hbf ... 980 d.	...	...	...	...	...	0536	...	...	0745	074
Bruck a. d. Mur ... 980 d.	...	...	...	*0536*	0613	|	*0706*	...	|	|
Leoben Hbf ... 980 d.	...	...	...	*0549*	0625	0631	*0721*	...	0831	083
St Michael ... 980 a.	...	...	...	*0556*	...	0637	*0728*	...	0837	083
St Michael ... d.	...	...	...	0600	...	0638	0731	...	0838	083
Trieben ... d.	...	...	...	0636	...	|	0805	...	|	|
Stadt Rottenmann ... d.	...	...	...	0644	...	0708	0812	...	|	|
Selzthal ... a.	...	...	...	0650	...	0713	0818	...	0911	091
Selzthal ... d.	...	0544	...	...	...	0719	0823	0844	0919	091
Linz Hbf 974 ... a.	...	|	...	...	...	|	|	|	1047	|
Liezen ... d.	...	0552	...	...	...	0727	0832	0851	...	092
Stainach-Irdning ... d.	...	0604	...	...	...	0737	0845	...	...	093
Schladming ... d.	0506	0648	0648	...	...	0810	0928	...	...	101
Radstadt ... d.	0525	0706	0706	...	...	0826	...	...	...	102
Bischofshofen ... a.	0554	0735	0735	...	...	0848	...	...	...	104
Bischofshofen ... 960 970 d.	*0558*	*0740*	*0740*	...	...	0857	...	...	...	105
Innsbruck Hbf 960 ... a.	...	...	...	...	...	|	...	...	...	|
Salzburg Hbf ... 960 970 a.	*0645*	*0840*	*0840*	...	...	0944	...	...	...	114

		EC 164	EC 112			EC 216			IC 518	RJ 797				IC 600	IC 610						IC 718			NJ 464
	2	Z✕	✕	Ⓑ 2	Ⓐ 2L	G⊗	2	Ⓐ 2L	🍷	✕	2	Ⓐ 2L	⚒ 2	🍷	🍷	Ⓐ 2	⚒ 2	Ⓑ 2	⚒ 2	⚒ 2	⊗	2	⑥ 2	A
Graz Hbf ... 980 d.	...	0945	...	...	...	1145	...	...	1345	...	...	...	1500	1545	1545	...	...	...	1700	...	1745	...	...	222
Bruck a. d. Mur ... 980 d.	*0906*	|	...	*1106*	...	|	*1306*	...	|	...	*1506*	...	|	|	|	...	...	*1706*	|	...	|	*1906*	*1906*	231
Leoben Hbf ... 980 d.	*0921*	1031	...	*1121*	...	1231	*1321*	...	1431	...	*1521*	...	1557	1631	1631	...	...	*1721*	1755	1801	1831	*1921*	*1921*	233
St Michael ... 980 a.	*0928*	1037	...	*1128*	...	1237	*1328*	...	1437	...	*1528*	...	1605	1637	1637	...	...	*1728*	...	1809	1837	*1928*	*1928*	233
St Michael ... d.	0931	1038	...	1131	...	1238	1331	...	1438	...	1531	...	1608	1638	1638	...	...	1731	...	1810	1838	1931	1931	234
Trieben ... d.	1005	|	...	1205	...	|	1405	...	|	...	1605	...	1644	|	|	...	...	1805	...	1846	|	2005	2005	...
Stadt Rottenmann ... d.	1012	|	...	1212	...	1308	1412	...	|	...	1612	...	1652	|	|	...	...	1812	...	1854	1908	2012	2012	...
Selzthal ... a.	1018	1111	...	1218	...	1313	1418	...	1511	...	1618	...	1658	1711	1711	...	...	1818	...	1900	1913	2018	2018	001
Selzthal ... d.	1023	1119	...	1223	1244	1319	1423	1444	1519	...	1623	1641	...	1719	1719	...	1746	1823	...	...	1919	2023	2023	002
Linz Hbf 974 ... a.	|	|	...	|	|	|	|	|	|	...	|	|	...	1847	|	...	|	|	...	...	|	|	|	...
Liezen ... d.	1032	1127	...	1232	1251	1327	1432	1451	1527	...	1632	1648	...	...	1727	...	1753	1832	...	...	1927	2032	2032	003
Stainach-Irdning ... d.	1045	1137	...	1245	...	1337	1445	...	1537	...	1645	...	...	...	1737	...	1806	1845	...	...	1937	2045	2045	004
Schladming ... d.	1128	1210	...	1328	...	1410	1528	...	1610	...	1728	...	...	...	1810	...	1848	1929	...	...	2010	2126	2127	011
Radstadt ... d.	...	1226	...	...	...	1426	...	...	1626	...	...	...	...	...	1826	1920	...	1952	...	...	2026	...	2147	|
Bischofshofen ... a.	...	1248	...	...	...	1448	...	...	1648	...	...	...	...	...	1848	1950	...	...	...	...	2048	...	...	015
Bischofshofen ... 960 970 d.	...	1250	1307	...	...	1457	...	...	1650	1707	...	...	...	...	1857	*2004*	...	...	...	...	2057	...	...	015
Innsbruck Hbf 960 ... a.	...	1540	|	...	...	|	...	...	1940	|	...	...	...	...	|	|	...	...	...	...	|	...	...	044
Salzburg Hbf ... 960 970 a.	...	...	1348	...	...	1544	...	...	...	1748	...	...	...	...	1944	*2051*	...	...	...	...	2144	...	...	...

A – 🛏 1, 2 cl., 🛌 2 cl. and (2) Graz - Innsbruck - Buchs 🏛 - Zürich and v.v.
F – CHIEMGAU – (12) and ⊗ Graz - München - Stuttgart - Frankfurt and v.v.
G – DACHSTEIN – (12) and ⊗ Graz - München - Stuttgart - Saarbrücken and v.v.
L – To / from Linz (Table 974).
Z – TRANSALPIN – (12) and ✕ Zürich - Graz and v.v.

r – ⚒ only.

976 LINZ - STEYR - KLEINREIFLING - WEISSENBACH

2nd class only

km		⚒	Ⓐ		Ⓐ	Ⓒ		Ⓒ	Ⓐ			Ⓒ	Ⓐ			Ⓒ	Ⓐ		Ⓐ		Ⓒ	Ⓐ		Ⓐ		Ⓒ
0	**Linz** Hbf ... 950 992 d.	0433	0514	0619	0649	0649	0752	0752	*0830*	0852	0952	0952	*1030*	1052	1152	1152	1222	1252	1252	1352	1352	1422	1452	*1530*	1552	155
17	Enns ... 992 d.	0450	0532	0637	0707	0707	0810	0810	|	0910	1010	1010	|	1110	1210	1210	1240	1310	1310	1410	1410	1440	1510	|	1610	161
25	St Valentin ... 950 d.	0509	0540	0649	0721	0721	0821	0821	0851	0921	1021	1021	1051	1121	1221	1221	1251	1321	1321	1421	1421	1451	1521	1551	1621	162
45	**Steyr** ... d.	0532	0605	0714	0754t	0754t	0846	0846	0912	0946	1046	1046	1112	1146	1246	1246	1312	1346	1346	1446	1446	1512	1546	1612	1646	164
47	Garsten ... d.	0536	0608	0717	0758	0758	0849	0850	0916	0949	1049	1050	1116	1149	1249	1250	1316	1349	1350	1449	1450	1516	1549	1616	1649	165
67	Losenstein ... d.	0601	...	...	0822	0822	...	0917	0937	...	...	1117	1137	...	...	1317	1337	...	1423	...	1517	1537	...	1640	...	171
89	Kastenreith ... 977 a.	0628	...	...	0848	0852	...	0941	1004	...	...	1141	1204	...	...	1341	1404	...	1447	...	1541	1603	...	1704	...	174
92	**Kleinreifling** ... 977 a.	0633	...	...	0852	0856	...	0946	1008	...	...	1146	1208	...	...	1346	1408	...	1451	...	1546	1607	...	1708	...	174
106	Weißenbach ⊡ .. 977 a.	0648e	...	...	0907	*0916*	...	...	...	...	...	*1216*	...	...	...	*1416*	...	...	...	...	...	1622	...	1723	...	*1816*

	Ⓐ		Ⓐ		Ⓒ	Ⓐ					
Linz Hbf ... 950 992 d.	1622	1652	*1730*	1752	1752	1822	*1852*	1952	*2052*	2152	2252
Enns ... 992 d.	1640	1710	|	1810	1810	1840	*1910*	2010	*2110*	2210	2310
St Valentin ... 950 d.	1651	1721	1751	1821	1821	1851	1921	2021	2121	2221	2321
Steyr ... d.	1712	1746	1812	1846	1846	1912	1946	2045	2146	2246	2346
Garsten ... d.	1716	1749	1816	1849	1850	1916	1949	2048	2149	2249	2349
Losenstein ... d.	1737	...	1841	...	1917	1937	...	2111	...	...	...
Kastenreith ... 977 a.	1803	...	1905	...	1941	2002	...	2135	...	...	...
Kleinreifling ... 977 a.	1807	...	1910	...	1946	2006	...	2139	...	...	...
Weißenbach ⊡ ... 977 a.	1822	...	1924	...	...	...	...	...	...	...	...

	P	Ⓐ	⚒		Ⓐ			Ⓐ	Ⓐ	Ⓒ	
Weißenbach ⊡ .977 d.	...	...	...	...	...	0603e	...	0706	...	...	...
Kleinreifling ... 977 d.	...	0437	0513	...	...	0618	...	0721	0754	0812	...
Kastenreith ... 977 d.	...	0441	0517	...	...	0622	...	0724	0758	0816	...
Losenstein ... d.	...	0505	0540	...	...	0647	...	...	0822	0843	...
Garsten ... d.	0442	0527	0601	0609	0637	0709	0809	...	0843	0909	090
Steyr ... d.	0446	0532	0606	0614	0642	0714	0814	...	0847	0914	091
St Valentin ... 950 a.	0508	0555	0622	0637	0705	0737	0837	...	0907	0937	093
Enns ... 992 a.	0517	0601	0628	0645	0717	0747	0847	...	|	0947	094
Linz Hbf ... 950 992 a.	0536	0617	0640	0701	0738	0808	0908	...	*0930*	1008	100

		Ⓐ	Ⓒ			Ⓐ	Ⓒ			Ⓐ	Ⓒ			Ⓐ	Ⓒ		Ⓐ	Ⓐ		Ⓐ	Ⓒ					
Weißenbach ⊡ ... 977 d.	...	0940	...	...	...	...	...	...	...	1338	*1341*	...	...	...	*1541*	...	...	1639	...	1738	*1747*	...	...	1939	...	...
Kleinreifling ... 977 d.	...	0954	1015	...	...	1154	1215	...	...	1354	1415	...	...	1554	1615	...	...	1654	...	1753	1815	...	...	1953	2021	...
Kastenreith ... 977 d.	...	0958	1019	...	...	1158	1219	...	...	1358	1419	...	...	1558	1619	...	...	1658	...	1757	1819	...	...	...	2025	...
Losenstein ... d.	...	1022	1044	...	...	1222	1244	...	...	1422	1444	...	...	1621	1644	...	...	1744v	...	1821	1844	...	...	...	2050	...
Garsten ... d.	1009	1043	1109	1109	1209	1243	1309	1309	1409	1443	1509	1509	1609	1643	1709	1709	1743	1809	1809	1843	1909	1909	2009	...	2113	220
Steyr ... d.	1014	1047	1114	1114	1214	1247	1314	1314	1414	1447	1514	1514	1614	1647	1714	1714	1747	1814	1814	1847	1914	1914	2014	...	2116	221
St Valentin ... 950 a.	1037	1107	1137	1137	1237	1307	1337	1337	1437	1507	1537	1537	1637	1707	1737	1737	1807	1837	1837	1907	1937	1937	2037	...	2139	223
Enns ... 992 a.	1047	|	1147	1147	1247	|	1347	1347	1447	|	1547	1547	1647	|	1747	1747	|	1847	1847	|	1947	1947	2047	...	2147	224
Linz Hbf ... 950 992 a.	1108	*1130*	1208	1208	1308	*1330*	1408	1408	1508	*1530*	1608	1608	1708	*1730*	1808	1808	*1830*	1908	1908	*1930*	2008	2008	2108	...	2206	230

P – To Passau (Table 962). e – Ⓐ only. k – ⑥ (not Oct. 26). t – Arrives 0745. v – Arrives 1725. ⊡ – Weißenbach-St Gallen.

AMSTETTEN - KLEINREIFLING - SELZTHAL 977

nd class only

km		Ⓐ	⑥k	⚒W		†	Ⓒ	Ⓒ	Ⓐ	Ⓐ	Ⓒ	Ⓐ	Ⓐ	Ⓒ	Ⓐ	Ⓐ	Ⓒ	Ⓐ	Ⓐ	Ⓒ	Ⓐ	†	Ⓐ		Ⓑv	
0	**Amstetten** d.	0514	0523	0611	0705	0705	0805	0905	0905	1005	1105	1105	1209	1309	1309	1409	1509	1509	1609	1709	1709	1809	1809	1909	2009	2109
23	Waidhofen a. d. Ybbs. d.	0549	0548	0710j	0729	0730	0829	0929	0929	1028	1130	1129	1232	1333	1332	1432	1533	1532	1632	1733	1732	1832	1832	1932	2031	2132
41	Weyer d.	0608	0608	0729	...	0748	0850	0947	0947	...	1147	1147	1249	1350	1349	1449	1550	1549	1649	1750	1749	1849	1849	1949	...	...
44	Kastenreith 976 d.	0611	0611	0733	...	0751	0856	0951	0950	...	1151	1151	1253	1354	1353	1453	1554	1553	1653	1754	1753	1853	1853	1953	...	...
47	**Kleinreifling** 976 a.	0615	0615	0736	...	0755	0859	0955	1008	...	1155	1208	1257	1358	1408	1457	1558	1607	1708	1758	1807	1857	1857	1957	...	...
61	Weißenbach ⊡ 976 a.	0648	...	...	...	...	0916	...	...	...	1216t	...	...	1416t	...	...	...	1622	1723	1816k	1822	1912	1924	...	...	...
79	**Selzthal** a.	...	...	...	...	...	1018	...	...	...	...	...	...	...	...	...	...	...	...	...	...	...	...	...	...	...

	⚒	P	ⒶP	Ⓒ	Ⓐ	⚒	Ⓐ		⚒	Ⓐ	Ⓒ	Ⓐ	Ⓐ	Ⓒ	Ⓐ	Ⓐ	Ⓒ	Ⓐ	Ⓐ	Ⓒ	Ⓐ	Ⓐ	Ⓒ	†	Ⓐ	Ⓒ
zthal d.	...	...	...	...	...	...	...	...	...	...	...	...	...	...	...	...	...	...	...	...	...	...	1644	...	...	...
ißenbach ⊡ 976 d.	...	...	...	...	0603	...	0706	...	...	0940	...	...	...	...	...	1338	1341t	...	...	1541	1639	1738	1747	...	1939	1939‡
einreifling 976 d.	...	...	0522	0559	0617	0623	0721	0802	...	0954	1002	...	1154	1204	1304	1354	1404	1504	1554	1604	1654	1753	1804	1904	1957	2004
stenreith 976 d.	...	...	0526	0603	▬	0631	0725	0806	...	1006	1006	...	1208	1208	1308	1408	1408	1508	1608	1608	1708	1808	1808	1908	2008	2008
yer d.	...	...	0529	0607	...	0635	0728	0810	...	1010	1010	...	1213	1213	1313	1413	1413	1513	1613	1613	1713	1813	1813	1913	2013	2013
idhofen a. d. Ybbs. d.	0430	0526	0547	0625	0625	0653	...	0829	0929	1029	1028	1129	1232	1231	1331	1432	1431	1532	1632	1631	1732	1832	1832	1932	2032	2032
nstetten a.	0454	0555	0613	0651	0651	0719	...	0851	0951	1051	1051	1151	1255	1255	1355	1455	1455	1555	1655	1655	1755	1855	1855	1955	2055	2055

- To St Pölten (Table **950**).
- From Wien (Table **950**).

j – Arrives 0647.
k – ⑥ (not Oct. 26).
t – Change trains at Kleinreifling on ⑥. Through train on †.
v – Not Dec. 24, 25, 31, Jan. 5, Apr. 21, 30, May 29, June 9, 19, Aug. 14, Oct. 25, 31.
‡ – Change at Kleinreifling on †.
⊡ – Weißenbach-St Gallen.

WIEN and WIENER NEUSTADT - SOPRON - DEUTSCHKREUTZ 978

nd class only

WIEN - EBENFURTH - SOPRON - DEUTSCHKREUTZ *Operated by GySEV Győr-Sopron-Ebenfurti Vasút (in German Raab-Oedenburg-Ebenfurter Eisenbahn – ROeEE)*

km		Ⓐ	Ⓐ		Ⓐ		Ⓐ		Ⓐ		Ⓐ		Ⓐ		Ⓐ				Ⓑ
	Bratislava-P ⊖ **997** d.	...	...	0611	0715	0815	0915	1015	1115	1215	...	1415	1515	1615c	...	1815c	1915e	...	...
0	**Wien** Hbf d.	0520	0619	0719	0819	0919	1019	1119	1219	1319	1419	1519	1619	1719	1819	1919	2019	...	...
4	**Wien** Meidling d.	0525	0625	0725	0825	0925	1025	1125	1225	1325	1425	1525	1625	1725	1825	1925	2025	...	...
42	Ebenfurth d.	0601	0701	0801	0902	1002	1102	1202	1302	1402	1502	1602	1702	1802	1902	2002	2102	...	2243
74	**Sopron** 🏛 a.	0637	0738	0837	0937	1037	1137	1237	1337	1437	1537	1637	1737	1837	1937	2037	2137	...	2318
83	**Deutschkreutz** a.	0657	0754	0847	0947	1047	1147	1247	1347	1447	1547	1647	1747	1847	1947	2047	2147	...	2331

	Ⓐ	Ⓐ	Ⓐ		Ⓐ		Ⓐ	Ⓐ		Ⓐ		Ⓐ		Ⓐ		Ⓐ		Ⓐ	
utschkreutz d.	0413	0513	0535	0613	0635	0713	0735	0813	0913	1013	1113	1213	1313	1413	1513	1613	1713	1813	1913
pron 🏛 d.	0423	0523	0546	0623	0646	0723	0746	0823	0923	1023	1123	1223	1323	1423	1523	1623	1723	1823	1923
enfurth ▷ d.	0504	0604	0626	0704	0726	0804	0826	0904	1004	1104	1204	1304	1404	1504	1604	1704	1804	1904	2004
en Meidling a.	0535	0635	0700	0735	0800	0835	0900	0935	1035	1135	1235	1335	1435	1535	1635	1735	1835	1935	2035
en Hbf a.	0542	0642	0707	0742	...	0842	0907	0942	1042	1142	1242	1342	1442	1542	1642	1742	1842	1942	2042
Bratislava-P ⊖ **997** a.	...	0744	...	0844	...	0944	...	1044	1144	1244	1344c	1444	1544c	...	1744c	1844	1944	...	2144

c – Ⓒ only.
e – Ⓐ only.
h – Wien Hbf (arrives 7 minutes later).
k – Not Oct. 26.

⊖ – Bratislava-Petržalka.
▷ – Departures may be 2 minutes **earlier** Apr. 13–22, June 29 - Sept. 1 and Nov. 1–3.
⊠ – **Additional journeys** from Wiener Neustadt to Sopron at 1301 Ⓐ, 1337 Ⓒ, 1401 Ⓐ, 1501 Ⓐ, 1537 Ⓒ, 1601 Ⓐ, 1701 Ⓐ, 1801 Ⓐ, 1901 Ⓐ.

WIENER NEUSTADT - SOPRON - DEUTSCHKREUTZ ⊠ *Operated by ÖBB*

km		Ⓐ						Ⓐ			Ⓐ	Ⓐ		Ⓐ	Ⓐ	Ⓒ	Ⓐ	Ⓒ	Ⓐ	Ⓒ	Ⓐ		Ⓐ		Ⓑ	
	Wien Meidling **980/1** d.	...	...	...	...	...	...	...	...	...	...	...	...	...	1600	...	1700	...	1800	...	...	...	...	...	...	...
0	**Wiener Neustadt** Hbf. d.	0503	0603	0703	0739	0837	0937	1037	1137	1237	1331	1431	1437	1531	1631	1637	1731	1737	1831	1837	1931	1937	2037	2137	2233	2237
16	Mattersburg d.	0526	0626	0726	0803	0902	1002	1102	1202	1302	1344	1444	1502	1544	1644	1702	1744	1802	1844	1902	1944	2002	2102	2202	|	2302
33	**Sopron** 🏛 a.	0542	0641	0741	0818	0917	1017	1117	1217	1317	1400	1500	1517	1600	1700	1717	1800	1817	1900	1917	2000	2017	2117	2217	2318	2317
42	**Deutschkreutz** a.	...	...	...	...	...	...	...	...	...	1410	1510	...	1610	1710	...	1810	...	1910	...	2010	...	...	2227e	2331	...

	Ⓐ	Ⓐ	Ⓐ		Ⓐ	⑥		Ⓐ				Ⓐ										Ⓐ			Ⓐ	
utschkreutz d.	...	...	0459	...	0559	0635	...	0659	...	...	...	...	...	...	...	...	...	...	...	...	...	...	...	...	2234	...
pron 🏛 d.	0418	0447	0509	0547	0609	0647	0647	0709	0747	0844	0944	1044	1144	1244	1344	1444	1544	1644	1744	1844	1944	2044	2144	...	2244	2244
ttersburg d.	0434	0503	0527	0603	0627	0703	0703	0727	0803	0902	1002	1102	1202	1302	1402	1502	1602	1702	1802	1902	2002	2102	2202	...	2302	2302
ener Neustadt Hbf a.	0453	0525	0539	0625	0639	0725	0725	0739	0825	0925	1025	1125	1225	1325	1425	1525	1625	1725	1825	1925	2025	2125	2225	...	2325	2325
Vien Meidling **980/1** a.	...	...	0615h	...	0714h	...	...	0815	...	...	...	...	...	...	...	...	...	...	...	...	...	...	...	...	...	...

WIEN and GRAZ - KLAGENFURT (- VILLACH) 980

km					*RJ* **72**			🚌 **951**	*RJ* **551**	*RJ* **554**	🚌 **953**	*RJ* **131**	*RJ* **553**		*EC* **151**	*RJ* **558**	🚌 **955**	*IC* **533**	*RJ* **71**		*RJ* **559**	*EC* **158**	*RJ* **535**	*RJ* **73**	
		⚒ 2	⚒ 2	⚒ 2	✕	2	2	☆	✕	✕	☆	V✕	✕	2	E✕	✕	☆	L✕	P✕	2	✕	✕	✕	P✕	2
	Flughafen Wien ✈ 985 d.	...	...	...	...	...	...	...	...	...	...	...	0633	...	...	...	...	...	...	...	0933	...	...	...	...
0	**Wien** Hbf 981 985 d.	...	...	...	...	...	...	...	0558	...	...	0625	0658	...	0758	...	...	0825	0858	...	0958	...	1025	1058	...
4	**Wien** Meidling 981 d.	...	...	...	...	...	...	...	0605	...	...	0632	0705	...	0805	...	...	0832	0905	...	1005	...	1032	1105	...
49	**Wiener Neustadt** Hbf 981 d.	...	...	...	...	...	...	...	0632	...	...	0657	0732	...	0832	...	...	0857	0932	...	1032	...	1057	1132	...
4	Semmering 981 d.	...	...	...	...	...	...	...	|	...	...	|	|	...	0915	...	...	|	1015	...	1115	...	|	|	...
8	Mürzzuschlag 981 d.	...	0521	...	...	0621r	0621h	...	0730	...	...	|	0830	...	0930	...	...	|	1030	...	1130	...	|	1230	...
	Graz Hbf 975 d.	...	|	0528	0626	|	|	0630	|	0726	0805	|	|	0826	|	0926	1005	|	|	1026	|	1126	|	|	1226
58	**Bruck** an der Mur a.	...	0602	0603	0701	0702r	0702h	|	0756	0801	|	0813	0856	0901	0956	1001	|	1013	1056	1101	1156	1201	1213	1256	1301
58	**Bruck** an der Mur 975 ‡ d.	0436	0607	0613	...	0706	0707	|	0758	...	|	0815	0858	0906	0958	...	|	1015	1058	1106	1158	...	1215	1258	1306
2	**Graz** Hbf ‡ a.	|	0654	|	...	|	0754	|	0833	...	|	|	0933	|	1033	...	|	|	1133	|	1233	...	|	1333	|
4	Leoben Hbf 975 d.	0450	▬	0626	...	0721	...	|	...	...	|	0827	...	0921	...	...	|	1027	...	1121	...	...	1227	...	1321
	St Michael 975 a.	0458	...	|	...	0728	...	|	...	...	|	|	...	0928	...	...	|	|	...	1128	...	...	|	...	1328
	St Michael d.	0507	...	|	...	0734	...	|	...	...	|	|	...	0934	...	...	|	|	...	1134	...	...	|	...	1334
5	Knittelfeld d.	0527	...	0648	...	0752	...	|	...	...	|	0847	...	0952	...	...	|	1047	...	1152	...	...	1247	...	1352
3	Zeltweg d.	0534	⚒	0654	...	0758	...	|	...	...	|	|	...	0958	...	...	|	|	...	1158	...	...	|	...	1358
20	Judenburg d.	0542	2	0702	...	0806	...	|	...	...	|	0859	...	1006	...	...	|	1059	...	1206	...	...	1259	...	1406
9	Unzmarkt d.	0558	0608	0718	...	0822	...	|	...	...	|	0913	...	1022	...	...	|	1113	...	1222	...	...	1313	...	1422
6	Friesach 971 a.	...	0642	...	...	0855	...	|	...	...	|	|	...	1055	...	...	|	1143	...	1255	...	...	|	...	1455
9	St Veit an der Glan 971 a.	...	0716	...	...	...	...	|	...	...	|	1006	...	...	...	...	|	1206	...	...	...	...	1406	...	...
9	**Klagenfurt** Hbf 971 a.	...	0738	...	...	...	...	0830	...	...	1005	1020	...	...	...	...	1205	1220	...	...	...	...	1420	...	...
	Villach Hbf **971** a.	...	0820t	...	...	...	...	...	...	...	...	1046	...	...	...	...	...	1246	...	...	...	...	1446	...	...

	🚌 **957**	*RJ* **653**	*RJ* **656**	🚌 **959**	*RJ* **133**	*RJ* **75**		*D* **737** ⑤f	*RJ* **657**	*RJ* **750**	*RJ* **539**	*RJ* **77**		🚌 **961**	⚒	*EC* **159** ¶	*RJ* **754**	*RJ* **631**	*RJ* **79**		🚌 **963**	Ⓐ	*D* **459** Ⓐ	*RJ* **755** §	
	☆	✕	✕	☆	V✕	P✕	2	2	✕	✕	✕	P✕	2	☆	2	F✕	✕	✕	P✕	2	☆	2	2	✕	2
ghafen Wien ✈ 985 d.	...	1133	...	...	...	...	...	...	1333	...	...	...	...	...	...	...	...	...	...	...	...	...	...	1733	...
n Hbf 981 985 d.	...	1158	...	...	1225	1258	...	1325	1358	...	1425	1458	...	...	...	1558	...	1625	1658	...	...	...	1725	1758	...
n Meidling 981 d.	...	1205	...	...	1232	1305	...	1332	1405	...	1432	1505	...	...	...	1605	...	1632	1705	...	...	...	1732	1805	...
ener Neustadt Hbf 981 d.	...	1232	...	...	1257	1332	...	1357	1432	...	1457	1532	...	...	...	1632	...	1657	1732	...	...	...	1757	1832	...
mmering 981 d.	...	1315	...	...	|	|	...	|	|	...	|	1615	...	...	...	|	...	|	1815	...	...	...	1850	1915	...
zzuschlag 981 d.	...	1330	...	...	|	1430	...	|	1530	...	|	1630	...	...	...	1730	...	|	1830	...	...	...	1903	1930	...
raz Hbf 975 d.	1230	|	1326	1405	|	|	1426	|	|	1526	|	|	1626	1630	1700	|	1726	|	|	1826	1840	1900	...	|	1926
ck an der Mur a.	|	1356	1401	|	1413	1456	1501	1513	1556	1601	1613	1656	1701	|	|	1756	1801	1813	1856	1901	|	|	...	1956	2001
ck an der Mur 975 ‡ d.	|	1358	...	|	1415	1458	1506	1514	1558	...	1615	1658	1706	|	|	1758	...	1815	1858	1906	|	|	...	1958	2006
raz Hbf ‡ a.	|	1433	...	|	|	1533	|	|	1633	...	|	1733	|	|	|	1833	...	|	1933	|	|	|	...	2033	|
ben Hbf 975 d.	|	...	...	|	1427	...	1521	1525	...	...	1627	...	1721	|	1758	...	...	1827	...	1921	|	1956	...	...	2021
t Michael 975 a.	|	...	...	|	|	...	1528	|	...	...	|	...	1728	|	|	...	...	|	...	1928	|	2003	...	...	2028
t Michael d.	|	...	...	|	|	...	1534	|	...	...	|	...	1734	|	|	...	...	|	...	1934	|	2009	...	...	2034
telfeld d.	|	...	...	|	1447	...	1552	1545	...	...	1647	...	1752	|	1821	...	...	1847	...	1952	|	2027	...	...	2052
weg d.	|	...	...	|	|	...	1558	|	...	...	|	...	1758	|	1827	...	...	|	...	1958	|	2034	...	...	2058
enburg d.	|	...	...	|	1459	...	1606	1557	...	...	1659	...	1806	|	1835	...	...	1859	...	2006	|	2042	...	...	2106
markt d.	|	...	...	|	1513	...	1622	|	...	...	1713	...	1822	|	1851	...	...	1913	...	2021	|	2057	...	...	2121
sach 971 a.	|	...	...	|	1543	...	1655	1638	...	...	|	...	1855	|	...	...	...	1943	...	...	|	...	...	...	...
'eit an der Glan 971 a.	|	...	...	|	1606	...	...	1703	...	...	1806	...	...	|	...	...	...	2006	...	...	|	...	...	...	...
genfurt Hbf 971 a.	1430	...	...	1605	1620	...	...	1716	...	...	1820	...	...	1830	...	...	...	2020	...	...	2040	...	...	...	...
illach Hbf **971** a.	...	...	...	...	1646	...	...	1755	...	...	1846	...	...	...	...	...	...	2046	...	...	...	...	...	...	...

R NOTES SEE NEXT PAGE →

980 WIEN and GRAZ - KLAGENFURT (- VILLACH)

	RJ 633	RJ 371		NJ 233	RJ 759		NJ 1237 D	RJ 373	REX 1975
	✕	P✕	2	AR	✕	2	R	P✕	2
Flughafen Wien ✈ ...... **985** d.	...	...	...	...	1933	...	...	...	...
Wien Hbf .... **981 985** d.	1825	1858	...	1923	1958	...	2023	2058	2259
Wien Meidling .... **981** d.	1832	1905	...	1931	2005	...	2031	2105	2305
Wiener Neustadt Hbf ... **981** d.	1857	1932	...	1958	2032	...	2058	2132	2332
Semmering .... **981** d.	|	|	...	|	|	...	|	|	0030
Mürzzuschlag .... **981** d.	|	2030	...	|	2130	...	|	2230	0044
Graz Hbf .... **975** d.	|	|	*2026*	|	|	*2104*r	|	|	...
Bruck an der Mur .... a.	2013	2056	*2101*	2125	2156	*2150*r	2220	2256	...
Bruck an der Mur ...... **975** ‡ d.	2015	2058	2106	2127	2158	2206	2222	2258	...
Graz Hbf .... ‡ a.	|	2133	|	|	2233	|	|	2333	...
Leoben Hbf .... **975** d.	2027	...	2121	2142	...	2219	2236	...	...
St Michael .... **975** a.	|	...	2128	|	...	|	|	...	...
St Michael .... d.	|	...	2134	|	...	|	|	...	...
Knittelfeld .... d.	2047	...	2152	2205	...	2242	|	...	...
Zeltweg .... d.	|	...	2158	|	...	2248	|	...	...
Judenburg .... d.	2059	...	2206	|	...	2256	|	...	...
Unzmarkt .... d.	2113	...	2221	|	...	2311	|	...	...
Friesach .... **971** a.	|	...	...	2300	...	...	|	...	...
St Veit an der Glan .... **971** a.	2206	...	...	|	...	...	|	...	...
Klagenfurt Hbf .... **971** a.	2220	...	...	2335	...	...	0019	...	...
Villach Hbf **971** .... a.	2246	...	...	0001	...	...	0043	...	...

	REX 1956 ©	D 458 Ⓐ	⚒	⚒	RJ 550	NJ 1234 B	NJ 235	⚒	⚒	RJ 72	Ⓐ
	2	2	2	2	✕	R	AR	2	2	P✕	2
Villach Hbf **971** .... d.	...	...	...	...	...	0344	0418	...	...	...	...
Klagenfurt Hbf .... **971** d.	...	...	...	...	...	0409	0440	...	...	...	...
St Veit an der Glan .... **971** d.	...	...	...	...	...	|	|	...	...	...	*050*
Friesach .... **971** d.	...	...	...	...	...	|	|	...	...	...	*052*
Unzmarkt .... d.	...	...	...	0437	...	|	|	0527	0548	...	060
Judenburg .... d.	...	...	...	0453	...	|	|	0543	0604	...	062
Zeltweg .... d.	...	...	...	0501	...	|	|	0552	0612	...	063
Knittelfeld .... d.	...	...	...	0507	...	|	|	0558	0618	...	063
St Michael .... a.	...	...	...	0526	...	|	|	|	|	...	065
St Michael .... **975** d.	...	...	0531	0535	...	|	|	|	|	...	070
Leoben Hbf .... **975** d.	...	...	0540	0543	...	0608	0627	0623	0642	...	071
Graz Hbf .... ‡ d.	...	...	|	|	0528	|	|	|	|	0626	|
Bruck an der Mur ... **975** ‡ a.	...	...	|	0557	0603	0621	0639	|	0654	0701	072
Bruck an der Mur .... d.	...	...	|	...	0605	0624	0641	|	0707	0703	...
Graz Hbf .... **975** a.	...	...	0633	...	|	|	|	0714	0754	|	...
Mürzzuschlag .... **981** d.	0521	0524	...	...	0634	|	|	...	...	0733	...
Semmering .... **981** d.	0537	0538	...	...	|	|	|	...	...	0747	...
Wiener Neustadt Hbf .. **981** d.	0630	0630	...	...	0730	0754	0803	...	...	0832	...
Wien Meidling .... **981** a.	0655	0655	...	...	0755	0905**g**	0839	...	...	0855	...
Wien Hbf .... **981 985** a.	0702	0702	...	...	0802	0915**g**	0846	...	...	0902	...
Flughafen Wien ✈ ... **985** a.	...	...	...	...	0827	...	...	...	...	...	...

	⚒		RJ 530	RJ 551			RJ 74	🚌 950	RJ 532	EC 151	RJ 558	🚌 952		RJ 76	RJ 534	RJ 559	EC 158	🚌 856		RJ 78	RJ 536	RJ 653	RJ 656		RJ 370
	2	2	✕	✕	2	2	P✕	☆	✕	✕	✕	☆	2	P✕	✕	✕	F✕	☆	2	P✕	✕	✕	✕	2	P✕
Villach Hbf **971** .... d.	...	...	0526	...	0529	...	...	...	0714	...	...	...	...	...	0914	...	...	...	...	...	1114	...	...	...	...
Klagenfurt Hbf .... **971** d.	...	...	0549	...	0607	...	...	0720	0739	...	...	0920	...	...	0939	...	...	1120	...	...	1139	...	...	...	...
St Veit an der Glan .... **971** d.	...	*0501*r	0602	...	0627	...	...	|	0753	...	...	|	...	...	0953	...	...	|	...	...	1153	...	...	...	...
Friesach .... **971** d.	...	*0527*r	|	...	0700	...	...	|	|	...	...	|	0903	...	1016	...	...	|	1103	...	|	...	...	1303	...
Unzmarkt .... d.	...	0634	|	...	0733	0737	...	|	0847	...	...	|	0937	...	1047	...	...	|	1137	...	1247	...	...	1337	...
Judenburg .... d.	...	0651	|	...	▬	0753	...	|	0901	...	...	|	0953	...	1101	...	...	|	1153	...	1301	...	...	1353	...
Zeltweg .... d.	...	0658	|	...	...	0801	...	|	|	...	...	|	1001	...	|	...	...	|	1201	...	|	...	...	1401	...
Knittelfeld .... d.	...	0705	|	...	*RJ*	0807	...	|	0914	...	...	|	1007	...	1114	...	...	|	1207	...	1314	...	...	1407	...
St Michael .... a.	...	|	|	...	**554**	0826	...	|	|	...	...	|	1026	...	|	...	...	|	1226	...	|	...	...	1426	...
St Michael .... **975** d.	0701	|	|	...		0833	...	|	|	...	...	|	1033	...	|	...	...	|	1233	...	|	...	...	1433	...
Leoben Hbf .... **975** d.	0709	0728	0734	...	✕	0841	...	|	0934	...	...	|	1041	...	1134	...	...	|	1241	...	1334	...	...	1441	...
Graz Hbf .... ‡ d.	|	|	|	...	0726	|	0826	|	|	...	0926	|	|	1026	|	...	1126	|	|	1226	|	...	1326	|	142
Bruck an der Mur ...... **975** ‡ a.	|	0739	0744	...	0801	0853	0901	|	0944	...	1001	|	1053	1101	1144	...	1201	|	1253	1301	1344	...	1401	1453	150
Bruck an der Mur .... d.	|	...	0746	0758	0803	*0858*	0903	|	0946	0958	1003	|	*1058*	1103	1146	1158	1203	|	*1258*	1303	1346	1358	1403	*1458*	150
Graz Hbf .... **975** a.	0802	...	|	0833	|	*0933*	|	0920	|	1033	|	1120	*1133*	|	|	1233	|	1320	*1333*	|	|	1433	|	*1533*	|
Mürzzuschlag .... **981** d.	...	...	|	...	0833	...	0933	...	|	...	1033	...	...	1133	|	...	1233	...	...	1333	|	...	1433	...	153
Semmering .... **981** d.	...	...	|	...	0847	...	0947	...	|	...	|	...	...	1147	|	...	|	...	...	1347	|	...	|	...	154
Wiener Neustadt Hbf ... **981** d.	...	...	0905	...	0932	...	1032	...	1105	...	1132	...	...	1232	1305	...	1332	...	...	1432	1505	...	1532	...	163
Wien Meidling .... **981** a.	...	...	0928	...	0956	...	1055	...	1128	...	1155	...	...	1255	1328	...	1355	...	...	1455	1528	...	1555	...	165
Wien Hbf .... **981 985** a.	...	...	0935	...	1002	...	1102	...	1135	...	1202	...	...	1302	1335	...	1402	...	...	1502	1535	...	1602	...	170
Flughafen Wien ✈ ...... **985** a.	...	...	...	...	1027	...	...	...	...	...	1227	...	...	...	...	...	...	...	...	...	...	...	1627	...	...

	🚌 956	RJ 132	RJ 657	RJ 750	🚌 958		RJ 372	RJ 630	EC 159 ¶	RJ 754	D 732 ⑦w		RJ 374	🚌 960	IC 632	RJ 755 §	EC 150		D 734 ⑦w	RJ 850	🚌 962	RJ 130	RJ 759	⑤–⑦	
	☆	V✕	✕	✕	☆	2	P✕	✕	✕	✕	2	2	S✕	☆	L✕	✕	E✕	2	2	✕	☆	V✕	✕	2	2
Villach Hbf **971** .... d.	...	1314	...	...	...	...	...	1514	...	...	1614	...	...	...	1714	...	...	...	1814	...	...	1914	...	...	...
Klagenfurt Hbf .... **971** d.	1345	1339	...	...	1520	...	...	1539	...	...	1641	...	...	1745	1739	...	...	...	1841	...	1945	1939	...	...	...
St Veit an der Glan .... **971** d.	|	1353	...	...	|	...	...	1553	...	...	1654	...	...	|	1753	...	...	...	1854	...	|	1953	...	...	...
Friesach .... **971** d.	|	1416	...	...	|	1503	...	|	...	...	1719	1703	...	|	1816	...	...	1903	1919	...	|	|	...	...	...
Unzmarkt .... d.	|	1447	...	...	|	1537	...	1647	...	...	|	1737	...	|	1847	...	...	1937	|	...	|	2047	...	2137	...
Judenburg .... d.	|	1501	...	...	|	1553	...	1701	...	...	1802	1753	...	|	1901	...	...	1953	2002	...	|	2101	...	2153	...
Zeltweg .... d.	|	|	...	...	|	1601	...	|	...	...	|	1801	...	|	|	...	...	2001	|	...	|	|	...	2201	...
Knittelfeld .... d.	|	1514	...	...	|	1607	...	1714	...	...	1814	1807	...	|	1914	...	...	2007	2014	...	|	2114	...	2207	...
St Michael .... a.	|	|	...	...	|	1626	...	|	...	...	|	1826	...	|	|	...	...	2026	|	...	|	|	...	2226	...
St Michael .... **975** d.	|	|	...	...	|	1633	...	|	...	...	|	1833	...	|	|	...	...	2033	|	...	|	|	...	2233	...
Leoben Hbf .... **975** d.	|	1534	...	...	|	1641	...	1734	...	...	1834	1841	...	|	1934	...	...	2041	2034	...	|	2134	...	2241	...
Graz Hbf .... ‡ d.	|	|	...	1526	|	|	1626	|	...	1726	|	|	1826	|	|	...	1926	|	|	2026	|	|	...	|	220
Bruck an der Mur ...... **975** ‡ a.	|	1544	...	1601	|	1653	1701	1744	...	1801	1844	1853	1901	|	1944	...	2001	2053	2044	2101	|	2144	...	2253	225
Bruck an der Mur .... d.	|	1546	1558	1603	|	*1658*	1703	1746	1758	1803	1846	*1858*	1903	|	1946	1958	2003	*2058*	2046	2103	|	2146	2158	*2258*	2308
Graz Hbf .... **975** a.	1545	|	1633	|	1720	*1733*	|	|	1833	|	|	*1933*	|	1945	|	2033	|	*2133*	|	|	2145	|	2233	*2333*	|
Mürzzuschlag .... **981** d.	...	|	...	1633	...	...	1733	|	...	1833	|	...	1933	...	|	...	2033	...	|	2133	...	|	...	...	235
Semmering .... **981** d.	...	|	...	1647	...	...	1747	|	...	1847	|	...	|	...	|	...	|	...	|	|	...	|	...	...	...
Wiener Neustadt Hbf ... **981** d.	...	1705	...	1732	...	...	1832	1905	...	1932	2005	...	2032	...	2105	...	2132	...	2205	2232	...	2305	...	...	...
Wien Meidling .... **981** a.	...	1728	...	1755	...	...	1855	1928	...	1955	2028	...	2055	...	2128	...	2155	...	2228	2255	...	2328	...	...	...
Wien Hbf .... **981 985** a.	...	1735	...	1802	...	...	1902	1935	...	2002	2035	...	2102	...	2135	...	2202	...	2235	2302	...	2335	...	...	...
Flughafen Wien ✈ ...... **985** a.	...	...	...	1827	...	...	...	...	...	2027	...	...	...	...	...	...	...	...	...	...	...	...	...	...	...

Local stopping trains **BRUCK AN DER MUR - GRAZ - SPIELFELD-STRASS** (for international services Graz - Spielfeld Straß - Maribor - Ljubljana / Zagreb see Table **1315**).

km				Ⓐ				◇									◇			⚒			⚒	⚒	
	Bruck a.d. Mur .... d.	0457	0607	0650	*0707*	*0808*	*0908*	0958	1008	*1108*	1208	*1308*	1408	*1508*	1608	*1708*	1758	1808	*1908*	2008	*2108*	2208	2208	2308	...
	Graz Hbf .... a.	0544	0654	0729	*0754*	*0855*	*0955*	1033	1055	*1155*	1255	*1355*	1455	*1555*	1655	*1755*	1833	1855	*1955*	2055	*2155*	2255	2255	2355	...
0	**Graz** Hbf .... **1315** d.	0558	0708	0738	0808	0908	1008	1039	1108	1208	1308	1408	1508	1608	1708	1808	1839	1908	2008	2108	2208	...	2308	...	000
9	Flughafen Graz ✈ .... d.	0610	0720	0750	0820	0920	1020	|	1120	1220	1320	1420	1520	1620	1720	1820	|	1920	2020	2120	2220	...	2320	...	002
35	Leibnitz .... d.	0636	0750	0820	0850	0950	1047	1059	1150	1250	1350	1450	1550	1650	1749	1847	1859	1950	2047	2147	2247	...	2347	...	004
47	**Spielfeld-Straß** .... **1315** a.	0648	0800	0830	0900	1000	1100	1108	1200	1300	1400	1500	1600	1700	1759	1900	1908	2000	2057	2157	2257	...	2357	...	005

	Ⓐ				Ⓐ						◇									◇		⚒		⚒	
Spielfeld-Straß .... **1315** d.	0352	0431	0504	...	0549	0609	0709	0809	0909	1009	1048	1109	1209	1309	1409	1509	1609	1709	1809	1848	1909	2009	2109	2209	...
Leibnitz .... d.	0403	0442	0515	...	0600	0620	0720	0820	0920	1020	1058	1120	1220	1320	1420	1520	1620	1720	1820	1858	1920	2020	2120	2220	...
Flughafen Graz ✈ .... d.	0431	0510	0542	...	0628	0649	0748	0848	0948	1048	|	1148	1248	1348	1448	1548	1648	1748	1848	|	1948	2048	2148	2248	...
Graz Hbf .... **1315** a.	0442	0521	0554	...	0639	0701	0759	0859	0959	1059	1120	1159	1259	1359	1459	1559	1659	1759	1859	1920	1959	2059	2159	2259	...
Graz Hbf .... d.	0445	...	0601**e**	0609	0642	*0708*	*0804*	0904	1004	1104	1126	*1204*	1304	*1404*	1504	*1604*	1704	*1804*	1904	1926	*2004*	2104	*2204*	2304	000
Bruck a.d. Mur .... a.	0531	...	0642**e**	0655	0728	*0754*	*0850*	0950	1050	1150	1201	*1250*	1350	*1450*	1550	*1650*	1750	*1850*	1950	2001	*2050*	2150	*2250*	2350	005

A – 🛏 1,2 cl., 🛌 2 cl. and (2) Milano - Wien and v.v.; 🛏 1,2 cl., 🛌 2 cl. and (2) (**40294/40233**) Roma - Bologna - Venezia - Wien and v.v.

B – From Villach on ⑤⑦ Apr. 14 - Oct. 13 (also Apr. 23, June 11; not May 18,25). Previous night from Livorno. 🛏 1,2 cl., 🛌 2 cl. and (2) Livorno - Pisa - Firenze - Bologna - Wien.

D – ③⑤ Apr. 12 - Oct. 11 (also Apr. 21, June 9; not May 22, 24). 🛏 1,2 cl., 🛌 2 cl. and (2) Wien - Bologna - Firenze - Pisa - Livorno.

E – EMONA – (12) and ✕ Ljubljana - Maribor - Spielfeld-Straß 🏛 - Graz - Wien and v.v.

F – CROATIA – (12) and ✕ Zagreb - Maribor - Spielfeld-Straß 🏛 - Graz - Wien and v.v.

L – LIENZER DOLOMITEN – To / from Lienz (Table **971**).

P – (12) and ✕ Graz - Wien - Břeclav 🏛 - Praha and v.v. (Table **60**).

R – Ⓡ for journeys from / to Italy.

S – (12) and ✕ Graz - Wien - Břeclav 🏛 - Brno (Table **60**).

V – (12) and ✕ Wien - Villach - Tarvisio 🏛 - Udine - Venezia and v.v. (Table **88**).

e – Ⓐ only.

f – Also May 29, June 19, Aug. 14, Oct. 31; not May 31, June 21, Aug 16, Nov. 1.

g – On ⑦ arrives Wien Meidling 0826, Wien Hbf 0832.

h – † only.

r – ⚒ only.

t – Change trains at Klagenfurt on Ⓐ to July 5 / from Sept. 9.

w – Also Apr. 22, June 10; not Apr. 21, June 9.

◇ – *EC* train (see main panel, also Table **1315**).

¶ – Train number **1259** on ©.

§ – Train number **1255** on ©.

‡ – For other local journeys see panel below main table.

◧ – Leoben - St Michael is *10 km*. St Michael - Knittelfeld is *22 km*.

☆ – **ÖBB** *Intercitybus*. Rail tickets valid. 1st and 2nd class. 🍸 in 1st class. Number of seats limited so reservation is recommended.

Local trains WIEN - WIENER NEUSTADT - MÜRZZUSCHLAG 981

WIEN - WIENER NEUSTADT □

km		⚒P			⊖				P
0	**Wien** Floridsdorf d.	0409	0509	0539		2209	2239	2309	2339
5	**Wien** Praterstern d.	0418	0518	0548	and at	2218	2248	2318	2348
7	**Wien** Mitte d.	0422	0522	0552	the same	2222	2252	2322	2352
10	**Wien** Hbf d.	0429	0529	0559	minutes	2229	2259	2329	2359
14	**Wien** Meidling d.	0437	0537	0607	past each	2237	2307	2337	0005
26	Mödling d.	0449	0549	0619	hour until	2249	2319	2349	|
37	Baden d.	0457	0557	0627		2257	2327	2357	0018
59	**Wiener Neustadt** Hbf. a.	0521	0621	0649		2321	2349	0021	0031

		⊖				⊖			P
Wiener Neustadt Hbf d.	0503		0733	0811	0838		2111	2138	2238
Baden d.	0523		0753	0832	0902	and at	2132	2202	2302
Mödling d.	0530	and every	0800	0839	0909	the same	2139	2209	2309
Wien Meidling a.	0542	30 minutes	0812	0853	0923	minutes	2153	2223	2323
Wien Hbf a.	0549	until	0819	0859	0929	past each	2159	2229	2329
Wien Mitte a.	0557		0827	0907	0937	hour until	2207	2237	2337
Wien Praterstern a.	0601		0831	0911	0941		2211	2241	2341
Wien Floridsdorf a.	0610		0840	0919	0949		2219	2249	2349

WIENER NEUSTADT - PAYERBACH-REICHENAU - MÜRZZUSCHLAG □

km		⚒P			⊖				Q	P
0	**Wiener Neustadt** Hbf. d.	0535	0635	0735		2035	2135	2235	2332	0032
14	Neunkirchen NÖ d.	0546	0646	0746	and	2046	2146	2246	2343	0043
27	Gloggnitz d.	0559	0659	0759	hourly	2059	2159	2259	2355	0056
34	Payerbach-Reichenau d.	0608	0708	0808	until	2108	2208	2308	0006	0105
55	Semmering a.	...	...	...		...	...	...	0030	...
69	**Mürzzuschlag** a.	...	...	...		...	...	...	0044	...

		⚒	†	⚒		Ⓒ	Ⓐ	Ⓒ	Ⓐ	Ⓒ	Ⓐ	Ⓒ	ⒶY	Ⓐ	Ⓒ
Wiener Neustadt Hbf. d.	A	...	...	...	...	...	...	...	...	...	...	...	1757	...	...
Neunkirchen NÖ d.	L	...	...	...	...	...	...	...	...	...	...	...	|	...	...
Gloggnitz d.	S	...	...	...	...	...	...	...	...	...	...	...	1813	...	...
Payerbach-Reichenau d.	O	0710	0811	0838	1011	1211	1238	1411	1538	1611	1738	1811	1823	1938	2011
Semmering a.		0733	0840	0907	1040	1240	1307	1440	1607	1640	1807	1840	1849	2007	2040
Mürzzuschlag a.		...	0856	...	1056z	1256	1323	1456	...	1656	...	1856	1903	2023	2056

	ⒶD	ⒶP	ⒶG	ⒸP	⚒P	ⒸR	ⒶW	H	P		⊖		P
ürzzuschlag d.	0345	...	...	...	...	0521	0524	...	*0603*	...		...	...
emmering d.	0400	...	...	...	...	0537	0538	...	*0618*	...		...	...
ayerbach-Reichenau d.	0427	0452	0527	0527	0552	0604	0604	0627	0655	0755	and	1955	2158
loggnitz d.	0436	0501	0536	0536	0601	0612	0612	0636	0704	0804	hourly	2004	2217
eunkirchen NÖ d.	0447	0512	0547	0547	0612	|	|	0647	0715	0815	until	2015	2228
iener Neustadt Hbf a.	0458	0522	0558	0558	0622	0626	0626	0658	0725	0825		2025	2238

		⚒		Ⓒ	Ⓐ	Ⓒ	Ⓐ	Ⓒ	Ⓐ	Ⓒ	Ⓐ	Ⓒ
ürzzuschlag d.	A	...	0907t	1107	...	1307	1337	1507	...	1701	...	1901
emmering d.	L	0752	0922	1122	1152	1322	1352	1522	1652	1717	1852	1917
ayerbach-Reichenau d.	S	0822	0952	1152	1222	1352	1422	1552	1722	1752	1922	1952
loggnitz d.	O	...	...	...	...	...	...	...	...	...	...	...
eunkirchen NÖ d.		...	...	...	...	...	...	...	...	...	...	...
iener Neustadt Hbf a.		...	...	...	...	...	...	...	...	...	...	...

– To Wien Meidling (a. 0529) and Wien Hbf (a. 0536).
– To Wien Meidling (a. 0629) and Wien Hbf (a. 0638).
– On Ⓐ to Wien Meidling (a. 0729). On Ⓒ note P applies.
– [2] Wien Floridsdorf - Wien Hbf - Wiener Neustadt - Payerbach-Reichenau and v.v.
– *REX* 1975. From Wien (Table **980**).

R – *REX* **1956**. To Wien (Table **980**).
W – *D* **458**. To Wien (Table **980**).
Y – *D* **459**. From Wien (Table **980**).
t – † only.
z – Ⓒ only.

⊖ – Note **P** applies on certain services.
□ – Only selected services are shown Wien Floridsdorf - Wiener Neustadt - Payerbach-Reichenau and v.v. Additional journeys Wien Floridsdorf - Wiener Neustadt are shown in Tables **982** and **983**. See Table **980** for long-distance services.

Local trains WIEN - BŘECLAV 982

2nd class only; Austrian Holiday dates apply

See Table **1150** for other fast international services

km		Ⓐ		Ⓐ				Ⓐ		Ⓐ	Ⓐ		Ⓐ	Ⓐ		Ⓐ	Ⓐ	Ⓐ		Ⓑb				
	Wiener Neustadt Hbf. 980/1 d.	...	0516e	0616	0716e	...	0911	1011	1111	1211	1238	1311	1411	1438	1511	1538	1611	1638	1711	1811	1911	2011	...	2138
0	**Wien** Meidling 980/1 d.	0527	0557	0700	0800	...	0954	1054	1154	1254	1324	1354	1454	1524	1554	1624	1654	1724	1754	1854	1954	2054	...	2224
4	**Wien** Hbf 980/1 d.	0533	0603	0706	0806	...	1000	1100	1200	1300	1330	1400	1500	1530	1600	1630	1700	1730	1800	1900	2000	2100	...	2230
7	**Wien** Mitte 981 d.	0541	0611	0714	0814	...	1008	1108	1208	1308	1338	1408	1508	1538	1608	1638	1708	1738	1808	1908	2008	2108	...	2238
9	**Wien** Praterstern 981 d.	0545	0615	0718	0818	...	1012	1112	1212	1312	1342	1412	1512	1542	1612	1642	1712	1742	1812	1912	2012	2112	...	2242
14	**Wien** Floridsdorf 981 d.	0553	0623	0726	0826	...	1020	1120	1220	1320	1350	1420	1520	1550	1620	1650	1720	1750	1820	1920	2020	2120	...	2250
40	Gänserndorf d.	0615	0645	0748	0848	...	1042	1142	1242	1342	1412	1442	1542	1612	1642	1712	1742	1812	1842	1942	2042	2142	...	2314
74	Hohenau 🏛 a.	0647	0717	0816	0920	...	1114	1214	1314	1414	1444	1514	1614	1644	1714	1736	1814	1842	1914	2014	2114	2214	...	2346
92	**Břeclav** 🏛 a.	...	...	...	0935	...	1129	...	...	...	...	1529c	...	1658	1729c	...	...	1857	1929c	...	...	...	...	...

	Ⓐ	Ⓐ		Ⓐ		Ⓐ	⚒							Ⓐ		Ⓐ	Ⓐ		Ⓐ		Ⓐ			
řeclav 🏛 d.	...	...	...	0557	0627k	...	...	...	...	...	1027	...	1227	...	...	...	...	1627c	1727	1827c	1927	2027c	...	...
ohenau 🏛 d.	0442	0512	0542	0612	0642	0712	0742	...	0842	...	1042	...	1242	1342	1442	1516	1542	1642	1742	1842	1942	2042	...	2242
änserndorf d.	0515	0545	0615	0645	0715	0745	0815	...	0915	...	1115	...	1315	1415	1515	1542	1615	1715	1815	1915	2015	2115	...	2315
ien Floridsdorf 981 a.	0538	0608	0638	0708	0738	0808	0838	...	0938	...	1138	...	1338	1438	1538	1608	1638	1738	1838	1938	2038	2138	...	2338
ien Praterstern 981 a.	0547	0617	0647	0717	0747	0817	0847	...	0947	...	1147	...	1347	1447	1547	1617	1647	1747	1847	1947	2047	2147	...	2347
ien Mitte 981 a.	0551	0621	0651	0721	0751	0821	0851	...	0951	...	1151	...	1351	1451	1551	1621	1651	1751	1851	1951	2051	2151	...	2351
ien Hbf 980/1 a.	0558	0628	0658	0728	0758	0828	0858	...	0958	...	1158	...	1358	1458	1558	1628	1658	1758	1858	1958	2058	2158	...	2358
ien Meidling 980/1 a.	0604	0634	0704	0734	0804	0834	0904	...	1004	...	1204	...	1404	1504	1604	1634	1704	1804	1904	2004	2104	2204	...	0004
iener Neustadt Hbf 980/1 a.	0649	0721	0749	0821	0849	0921	0949	...	1049	...	1249	...	1449	1549	1649	1721	1749	1849	1949	2049	2149	2249	...	0031

– Not Dec. 25, Apr. 21, June 9.
c – Ⓒ only.
e – Ⓐ only.
k – ⑥ (not Oct. 26).

WIEN - RETZ - ZNOJMO 983

2nd class only; Austrian holiday dates apply

km		⚒				⑥k									Ⓐ		Ⓐ		Ⓐ		Ⓑ	Ⓐ			
	Wiener Neustadt Hbf 980/1 d.	...	0503	0603	0703	0703	0808r	...	...	...	...	...	...	1508	1535	1608e	1635	1708	1735	1808e	...	1908	...	...	...
0	**Wien** Meidling 980/1 d.	...	0544	0644	0744	0744	0844	0944	1044	1144	1244	1344	1444	1544	1614	1644	1714	1744	1814	1844	...	1944	2044	2151	2314
4	**Wien** Hbf 980/1 d.	...	0550	0650	0750	0750	0850	0950	1050	1150	1250	1350	1450	1550	1620	1650	1720	1750	1820	1850	...	1950	2050	2157	2320
7	**Wien** Mitte 981 d.	...	0558	0658	0758	0758	0858	0958	1058	1158	1258	1358	1458	1558	1628	1658	1728	1758	1828	1858	...	1958	2058	2205	2328
9	**Wien** Praterstern 981 d.	...	0602	0702	0802	0802	0902	1002	1102	1202	1302	1402	1502	1602	1632	1702	1732	1802	1832	1902	...	2002	2102	2209	2332
14	**Wien** Floridsdorf 981 d.	...	0611	0711	0811	0811	0911	1011	1111	1211	1311	1411	1511	1611	1641	1711	1741	1811	1841	1911	...	2011	2111	2218	2341
34	Stockerau d.	...	0628	0728	0828	0828	0928	1028	1128	1228	1328	1428	1528	1628	1701	1728	1801	1828	1901	1928	...	2028	2128	2243	2358
60	Hollabrunn d.	...	0645	0745	0845	0845	0945	1045	1145	1245	1345	1445	1545	1645	1723	1745	1823	1845	1923	1945	...	2045	2145	...	0024
90	**Retz** a.	...	0712	0812	0912	0912	1012	1112	1212	1312	1412	1512	1612	1712	1752	1812	1852	1912	1952	2012	...	2112	2212	...	0050
90	**Retz** 🏛 d.	0618	...	0815	...	0915	...	...	1215	...	1415	...	1615	...	...	1815	...	...	...	...	2015	...	...	...	...
96	Šatov 🏛 d.	0626	...	0823	...	0923	...	...	1223	...	1423	...	1623	...	...	1823	...	...	...	...	2025	...	...	...	...
107	**Znojmo** a.	0636	...	0834	...	0934	...	...	1234	...	1434	...	1634	...	...	1834	...	...	...	...	2036	...	...	...	...

	Ⓐ	Ⓐ	⚒	Ⓒ	Ⓐ	Ⓐ	Ⓐ					⑥k											Ⓑ		Ⓒ
nojmo d.	...	...	...	...	...	0530	...	...	0653r	...	0857	0955	...	...	...	1255	...	1455	...	1655	...	1855	1950	...	...
atov 🏛 d.	...	...	...	...	...	0541	...	0610r	0704r	...	0906	1006	...	...	...	1306	...	1506	...	1706	...	1906	2000	...	...
etz 🏛 a.	...	...	...	...	...	0550	...	0615r	0712r	...	0914	1014	...	...	...	1314	...	1514	...	1714	...	1914	2009	...	...
etz d.	0402	0434	0510	0514a	0530	...	0552	0617	0715	0817	0917	1017	1017	1117	1217	1317	1417	1517	1617	1717	1817	1917	...	2017	2117
ollabrunn d.	0430	0502	0539	0543	0558	...	0620	0645	0745	0845	0945	1045	1045	1145	1245	1345	1445	1545	1645	1745	1845	1945	...	2045	2145
ockerau d.	0447	0527	0556	0615	0625	...	0640	0702	0802	0902	1002	1102	1102	1202	1302	1402	1502	1602	1702	1802	1902	2002	...	2102	2202
ien Floridsdorf 981 a.	0502	0547	0617	0641	0647	...	0659	0717	0817	0917	1017	1117	1117	1217	1317	1417	1517	1617	1717	1817	1917	2017	...	2117	2217
ien Praterstern 981 a.	0511	0557	0627b	0650	0657	...	0708	0727	0827	0927	1027	1127	1127	1227	1327	1427	1527	1627	1727	1827	1927	2027	...	2127	2227
ien Mitte 981 a.	0515	0601	0631b	0654	0701	...	0712	0731	0831	0931	1031	1131	1131	1231	1331	1431	1531	1631	1731	1831	1931	2031	...	2131	2231
ien Hbf 980/1 a.	0522	0608	0638b	0701	0708	...	0719	0738	0838	0938	1038	1138	1138	1238	1338	1438	1538	1638	1738	1838	1938	2038	...	2138	2238
ien Meidling 980/1 a.	0528	0614	0644b	0707	0714	...	0725	0744	0844	0944	1044	1144	1144	1244	1344	1444	1544	1644	1744	1844	1944	2044	...	2144	2244
iener Neustadt Hbf 980/1 a.	0600	0652	0724b	...	0752	...	...	0824r	...	...	...	...	...	...	...	1524e	1624e	1724e	1824e	1924e	...	...	...	...	...

– † only.
– Not ⑥.
e – Ⓐ only.
k – ⑥ (not Oct. 26).
r – ⚒ only.

984 WIENER NEUSTADT - PUCHBERG am Schneeberg - HOCHSCHNEEBERG *2nd class only*

WIENER NEUSTADT - **PUCHBERG** am Schneeberg *28 km.* Journey time: ± 45 minutes.
From Wiener Neustadt at 0043 †, 0737, 0837 and hourly until 2137.
From Puchberg at 0452 Ⓐ, 0522 Ⓐ, 0552 Ⓐ, 0622 Ⓐ, 0636 Ⓒ, 0645 Ⓐ, 0736, 0836 and hourly until 2036.

PUCHBERG am Schneeberg - **HOCHSCHNEEBERG** *Schneebergbahn* (narrow-gauge rack railway). *9 km.* Journey time: ± 40 minutes.
Services run **Apr. 27 - Oct. 27, 2019** subject to demand and weather conditions. **Operator**: NÖ Schneebergbahn GmbH, Bahnhofplatz 1, A-2734 Puchberg. ✆ +43 (0) 2636 3661 20.
From Puchberg at 0900, 1030, 1200, 1400, 1530. **From Hochschneeberg** at 0945, 1115, 1315, 1445, 1615. Additional trains operate during July and August, also at other times when there is sufficient demand. A steam service operates on † June 30 - Sept. 1: Departs Puchberg 1123, departs Hochschneeberg 1517 (extended journey time; special fares apply).

985 FLUGHAFEN WIEN ✈ Schwechat *CAT ★; S-Bahn (2nd class only)*

km																						
		Ⓐ			★		★		★			★		★		★						
0	**Wien** Praterstern d.	0415	0445	0515	...	0545	...	0615	...	0645	and at the same	...	2215	...	2245	...	2315	2345	...	...	...	...
2	**Wien** Mitte d.	0419	0449	0519	0537	0549	0607	0619	0637	0649	minutes past	2207	2219	2237	2249	2307	2319	2349	...	...	...	...
21	**Flughafen Wien** ✈ a.	0442	0512	0542	0553	0612	0623	0642	0653	0712	each hour until	2223	2242	2253	2312	2323	2342	0012	...	...	...	...

		Ⓐ			★		★		★		★		★		★			★		★		★
Flughafen Wien ✈ d.	0018	0448	0518	0548	0609	0618	0639	0645	0709	0718	0739	0745	0809	0818	0839	0848	and at the same	2239	2248	2309	2318	2339
Wien Mitte a.	0044	0514	0544	0614	0625	0644	0655	0711	0725	0744	0755	0811	0825	0844	0855	0914	minutes past	2255	2313	2325	2344	2355
Wien Praterstern a.	0048	0518	0548	0618	...	0648	...	0715	...	0748	...	0815	...	0848	...	0918	each hour until	...	2318	...	2348	...

★ – *City Airport Train (CAT).* Non-stop service with special fares.

RJ trains **Wien Hbf** - **Flughafen Wien** ✈ and v.v. Journey time: 15 – 17 minutes. Most trains run from / to Salzburg, Linz and St Pölten (see Table **950**) or Graz (Table **980**).
From Wien Hbf at 0542, 0612, 0642, 0712, 0740, 0812, 0840, 0912, 0940, 1012, 1040, 1112, 1142, 1212, 1242, 1312, 1342, 1412, 1440, 1512, 1540, 1612, 1640, 1712, 1742, 1812, 1840, 1912, 1940, 2012, 2040, 2112, 2142 and 2212. **From Flughafen Wien** ✈ at 0633, 0703, 0733 and at 03 and 33 minutes past each hour until until 2203, 2233 and 2303.

🚌 *Vienna Airport Lines*: Wien Westbahnhof (Europaplatz) – Flughafen Wien ✈ and v.v. Journey time: 40 minutes.
🚌 From **Wien Westbahnhof**: 0430, 0530 and every 30 minutes until 0000, 0030. 🚌 From **Flughafen Wien** ✈: 0600, 0630 and every 30 minutes until 0000, 0030.

🚌 ÖBB-Postbus / Slovak Lines: **Bratislava**, AS Mlynské nivy (bus station) – **Flughafen Wien** ✈ and v.v. Journey time: 60 minutes.
Reservation recommended ✆ +43 (0) 810 222333-6 or +421 2 55422734. Please note that a much reduced service operates on Dec. 24, 25, 26, 31, Jan. 1.
🚌 From **Bratislava** AS Mlynské nivy at 0400, 0500 and hourly until 2000; then 2200. 🚌 From **Flughafen Wien** ✈ at 0630, 0730 and hourly until 2230; then 2359.

986 GRAZ - SZENTGOTTHÁRD - SZOMBATHELY *ÖBB, GySEV •; 2nd class only*

km																										
		A ✓	W		W				N	Ⓐ		Ⓐ ◇		Ⓐ		Ⓐ	P	Ⓐ ⊡		⚒		Ⓐ		⚒		
0	**Graz** Hbf d.	0608	0708	0808	0908	1008	1108	1208	1308	1308	1408	1438	1508	1538	1608	1638	1708	1738	1808	1838	1908	1938	2008	2108	2213	0008
29	Gleisdorf d.	0650	0750	0850	0950	1050	1150	1250	1350	1350	1450	1513	1550	1613	1650	1713	1750	1813	1850	1913	1950	2013	2050	2150	2253	0047
53	Feldbach d.	0715	0814	0914	1014	1114	1214	1314	1414	1414	1514	1529	1614	1629	1714	1729	1814	1829	1914	1929	2014	2029	2114	2217	2316	011[illegible]
62	Fehring d.	0726	0824	0925	1024	1125	1233t	1325	1424	1430	1525	1542	1624	1638	1725	1738	1824	1842	1925	1941	2024	2040	2125	2227	2326	012[illegible]
82	**Szentgotthárd** ⊞ a.	0746	...	0947	...	1147	1255	1347	...	1451	1547c	1603	...	*1702*	1747c	*1803*	...	1903	1947c	2002e	...	2101	2146	...	...	...

		Ⓐ	Ⓐ		Ⓐ	Ⓐ	⑥k	†	Ⓐ	⚒	Ⓐ H			P		W								N	Ⓐ	B ✓
Szentgotthárd ⊞ d.	...	...	*0445*	0516k	*0532*	...	...	0616	*0619*	0640k	...	...	0816	...	1016	...	1210	1303	1408	*1509*e	1616	1716e	1813	...	...	2147
Fehring d.	0409	0440	0511	0540	0557	0615	0615	0640	0644	0703	0730	0740	0840	0940	1040	1140	1240t	1327	1430	1540	1640	1740	1840	1940	2040	2207
Feldbach d.	0420	0450	0522	0550	0606	0627	0627	0650	0654	0715	0742	0750	0850	0950	1050	1150	1250	1350z	1450z	1550	1650	1750	1850	1950	2050	2217
Gleisdorf d.	0443	0513	0540	0613	0626	0650	0655	0713	0713	0738	0802	0813	0913	1013	1113	1213	1313	1413	1513	1613	1713	1813	1913	2013	2113	2232
Graz Hbf a.	0519	0553	0615	0652	0703	0724	0734	0753	0748	0816	0837	0853	0953	1053	1153	1253	1353	1453	1553	1653	1753	1853	1953	2053	2153	230[illegible]

SZENTGOTTHÁRD - SZOMBATHELY •

km																										
			Ⓐ ⊖				A ✓					Ⓐ												Ⓐ		n
0	**Szentgotthárd** ⊞ d.	0401	0501	0606	0636	0706	0822	0836	1006	...	1206	1236	1306	1406	1436	1536	...	1636	1706	1806	1836	...	2006	2106	...	2236
28	Körmend d.	0425	0525	0630	0700	0730	0841	0900	1030	...	1230	1300	1330	1430	1500	1600	...	1700	1730	1830	1900	...	2030	2131	...	2300
64	**Szombathely** a.	0448	0547	0653	0723	0753	0900	0923	1053	...	1253	1323	1353	1453	1523	1623	...	1723	1753	1853	1923	...	2053	2153	...	232[illegible]
	Sopron **1233** a.	0559	...	...	...	...	...	1017	1150	...	...	1427	...	...	1627e	1727	...	...	1917	...	2056	...	2200	...	...	...

												Ⓐ		Ⓐ					n	Ⓐ ⊖		n	B ✓	n		n
Sopron **1233** d.	...	0410	0455	...	0547	...	...	...	...	...	1108	...	...	...	1343	1443e	1543	1643	...	...	...	...	...	2015	...	...
Szombathely d.	0431	0501	0606	0636	0706	...	0906	...	1106	...	1236	1306	1336	1406	1436	1536	1636	1736	1836	1906	...	2036	2058	2136	...	2236
Körmend d.	0455	0525	0630	0700	0730	...	0930	...	1130	...	1300	1330	1400	1430	1500	1600	1700	1800	1900	1930	...	2100	2118	2200	...	2300
Szentgotthárd ⊞ a.	0519	0549	0654	0724	0754	...	0954	...	1154	...	1324	1354	1424	1454	1524	1624	1724	1824	1924	1954	...	2124	2135	2224	...	232[illegible]

A – 🚃12 Graz (**317**) - Szentgotthárd (*IC* **317**) - Budapest.
B – 🚃12 Budapest (*IC* **318**) - Szentgotthárd (**318**) - Graz.
H – From Hartberg (Table **995**).
N – To / from Wiener Neustadt on dates shown in Table **995**.
P – To / from Wiener Neustadt on Ⓐ (Table **995**).
W – To / from Wiener Neustadt (Table **995**).

c – Ⓒ only.
e – Ⓐ only.
k – ⑥ (not Oct. 26).
n – Not Dec. 24, 31.
t – Arrives 8 – 9 minutes earlier.
z – Arrives 11 – 13 minutes earlier.

◇ – On ⑤ change trains at Fehring (Fehring d. *1546*, Szentgotthárd a. *1607*).
⊡ – Change trains at Fehring on ①–④.
⊖ – *IC* train to / from Budapest (Tables **1250/2**). [R] and supplement payable.
✓ – [R] and supplement payable in Hungary.
• – Szentgotthárd - Szombathely operated by Győr-Sopron-Ebenfurti Vasút.

990 WIEN - GMÜND - ČESKÉ VELENICE *2nd class only*

km																									
			⚒v	Ⓒ G							⑤f			Ⓐ		Ⓒ	Ⓐ		Ⓐ		Ⓒ	D			Ⓑ h
0	**Wien** Franz-Josefs-Bf **991/3** d.	0628	0732	0732	0828	0932	1028	1132	1228	1332	1400	1428	1528	1616	1628	1628	1655	1728	1816	1828	1828	1855	1928	2028	205[illegible]
1	Wien Spittelau ● **991/3** d.	0631	0735	0735	0831	0935	1031	1135	1231	1338	1403	1431	1531	1618	1631	1631	1658	1731	1818	1831	1831	1858	1931	2031	210[illegible]
3	Wien Heiligenstadt △ **991/3** d.	0634	0738	0738	0834	0938	1034	1138	1234	1338	1406	1434	1534	1621	1634	1634	1702	1734	1822	1834	1834	1902	1934	2034	210[illegible]
33	Tulln a. d. Donau **991/3** d.	0656	0759	0759	0856	0959	1056	1159	1256	1359	|	1456	1556	|	1656	1656	1726	1756	1844	1856	1856	1926	1956	2056	212[illegible]
44	Absdorf-Hippersdorf **991** d.	0705	0808	0808	0905	1008	1105	1208	1305	1408	|	1505	1605	|	1705	1705	|	1805	|	1905	1905	|	2005	2105	213[illegible]
79	Eggenburg d.	0734	0838	0838	0934	1038	1134	1238	1334	1438	1454	1534	1638	1715	1734	1734	1802	1837	1913	1934	1934	2002	2038	2134	220[illegible]
89	Sigmundsherberg d.	0742	0846	0846	0942	1046	1142	1246	1342	1446	1502	1542	1648	1723	1741	1742	1812	1846	1923	1941	1942	2014	2046	2142	221[illegible]
121	Göpfritz an der Wild d.	0806	...	0907	1006	...	1206	...	1406	...	1522	1606	1713e	1748	...	1806	1837	1911e	1947	...	2006	2037	2109b	2206	...
138	Schwarzenau im Waldviertel d.	0820	...	0919	1020	...	1220	...	1420	...	1536	1620	1733e	1801	...	1820	1849	1933e	2001	...	2020	2051	2123b	2220	...
162	**Gmünd** NÖ a.	0841	...	0937	1041	...	1241	...	1441	...	1553	1641	1754e	1822	...	1841	1911	1956e	2022	...	2041	2112	2144b	2241	...
162	**Gmünd** NÖ ⊞ d.	0844	...	...	1044	...	1244	...	1444	...	...	1646	...	1826	...	1844	...	...	2026	...	2045	...	...	...	...
164	**České Velenice** ⊞ **1133/4** a.	0848	...	...	1048	...	1248	...	1448	...	...	1650	...	1830	...	1848	...	...	2030	...	2049	...	...	...	...

	Ⓐ	Ⓐ	⚒		Ⓐ	Ⓐ	Ⓐ		Ⓐ											Ⓒ	Ⓐ		†		⑦v
České Velenice ⊞ **1133/4** d.	...	...	...	...	...	...	...	...	...	0602	0707	...	0907	...	1107	...	1307	...	1507	...	...	1705	...	1905	...
Gmünd NÖ ⊞ a.	...	...	...	...	...	...	...	...	...	0606	0711	...	0911	...	1111	...	1311	...	1511	...	...	1709	...	1909	...
Gmünd NÖ d.	...	0350	0359k	...	0440	...	0455	0508	...	0612	0714	...	0914	...	1114	...	1314	...	1514	...	...	1712	...	1912	205[illegible]
Schwarzenau im Waldviertel d.	...	0412	0420k	...	0459	...	0518	0531	...	0633	0735	...	0935	...	1135	...	1335	...	1535	...	...	1733	...	1933	|
Göpfritz an der Wild d.	...	0425	0434k	...	0511	...	0532	0546	...	0646	0749	...	0949	...	1149	...	1349	...	1549	...	...	1748	...	1948	212[illegible]
Sigmundsherberg d.	0410	0449	0457	0509	0532	0539	0557	0610	0640	0710	0814	0909	1014	1109	1214	1309	1414	1509	1614	1709	...	1813	1909	2014	214[illegible]
Eggenburg d.	0419	0457	0506	0518	0540	0548	0606	0619	0649	0718	0822	0918	1022	1118	1222	1318	1422	1518	1622	1718	1718	1821	1918	2022	215[illegible]
Absdorf-Hippersdorf **991** d.	0448	|	0535	0548	|	0617	|	0648	0718	0748	0852	0948	1052	1148	1252	1348	1455	1548	1652	1748	1748	1852	1948	2052	|
Tulln a. d. Donau **991/3** d.	0457	|	0544	0558	|	0627	|	0658	0727	0757	0901	0958	1101	1158	1301	1358	1504	1558	1701	1758	1758	1901	1958	2101	|
Wien Heiligenstadt △ **991/3** a.	0519	0549	0605	0620	0639	0647	0655	0722	0750	0819	0922	1019	1122	1219	1322	1419	1525	1619	1722	1819	1819	1922	2019	2122	224[illegible]
Wien Spittelau ● **991/3** a.	0522	0552	0609	0623	0632	0651	0659	0725	0753	0822	0925	1022	1125	1222	1325	1422	1528	1622	1725	1822	1822	1925	2022	2125	224[illegible]
Wien Franz-Josefs-Bf **991/3** a.	0525	0555	0612	0626	0635	0654	0702	0728	0756	0825	0928	1025	1128	1225	1328	1425	1531	1625	1728	1825	1825	1928	2025	2128	224[illegible]

D – ①–④ (not Dec. 25, 26, Jan. 1, Apr. 22, May 1, 30, June 10, 20, Aug. 15).
G – Ⓒ May 4 - Oct. 27.

b – Sigmundsherberg - Gmünd on ①–④ (not Dec. 24, 25, 26, Jan. 1, Apr. 22, 30, May 1, 29, 30, June 10, 19, 20, Aug. 14, 15, Oct. 31).
e – Sigmundsherberg - Gmünd on Ⓐ only.

f – Not Nov. 1.
h – Not Oct. 25.
k – ⑥ (not Oct. 26).
v – Runs daily Apr. 29 - Oct. 31.
w – Also Apr. 22, June 10; not Apr. 21, June 9.

△ – S-Bahn (Line **S45**) trains run every 10 – 15 minutes from / to Wien Hütteldorf (journey: 21 – 23 minutes).
● – Direct U-Bahn links: Line **U4** – Wien Mitte - Spittelau; Line **U6** – Wien Meidling - Westbahnhof - Spittelau - Floridsdorf.

d class only — WIEN - KREMS an der Donau - EMMERSDORF — 991

m																							
				Ⓐ					Ⓐ	Ⓐ	©	Ⓐ		Ⓐ	Ⓐ	©	Ⓐ		Ⓐ				
0	**Wien** Franz-Josefs-Bf. **990/3** d.	0009	...	0505	0605	0705		1505	1533	1601	1605	1633	1705	1733	1801	1805	1833	1905	1933	2005	2105	2205	2305
1	Wien Spittelau ● **990/3** d.	0011	...	0507	0607	0707	and	1507	1539	1604	1607	1636	1707	1736	1804	1807	1836	1907	1936	2007	2107	2207	2307
3	Wien Heiligenstadt △ **990/3** d.	0015	...	0510	0610	0710	hourly	1510	1539	1608	1610	1639	1710	1739	1808	1810	1839	1910	1939	2010	2110	2210	2310
33	Tulln a. d. Donau **990/3** d.	0052	...	0533	0633	0733		1533	1601	1633	1633	1701	1733	1801	1833	1833	1901	1933	2001	2033	2133	2233	2333
44	Absdorf-Hippersdorf **990** d.	...	...	0541	0641	0741	until	1541	1609	1641	1641	1709	1741	1809	1841	1841	1909	1941	2009	2041	2141	2241	2341
76	**Krems** a. d. Donau a.	...	...	0614	0716	0814		1614	1636	1714	1714	1736	1814	1836	1914	1914	1936	2014	2036	2114	2214	2314	0014

	Ⓐ	⚒	Ⓐ		Ⓐ	Ⓐ		Ⓐ							Ⓐ	©								
ms a. d. Donau d.	0429	0451	0529	0551	0616	0629	0651	0729	0751	0851	0951	1051	1151	1251	1343	1351	1451	1551	1651	1751	1851	1951	2051	2151
dorf-Hippersdorf **990** d.	0454	0523	0554	0623	0642	0654	0723	0754	0823	0923	1023	1123	1223	1323	1423	1423	1523	1623	1723	1823	1923	2023	2123	2223
n a. d. Donau **990/3** d.	0503	0532	0603	0631	0653	0704	0734	0803	0831	0931	1031	1131	1231	1331	1431	1431	1531	1631	1731	1831	1931	2031	2131	2231
n Heiligenstadt △ **990/3** a.	0523	0553	0624	0651	0718	0726	0754	0823	0851	0951	1051	1151	1251	1351	1451	1451	1551	1651	1751	1851	1951	2051	2151	2251
n Spittelau ● **990/3** a.	0527	0556	0628	0655	0721	0729	0757	0827	0855	0955	1055	1155	1255	1355	1455	1455	1555	1655	1755	1855	1955	2055	2155	2255
en Franz-Josefs-Bf **990/3** a.	0530	0559	0631	0658	0724	0732	0800	0830	0858	0958	1058	1158	1258	1358	1458	1458	1558	1658	1758	1858	1958	2058	2158	2258

KREMS - EMMERSDORF ⊠

m		R		R		R		R		
0	**Krems** an der Donau d.	0920	...	1120	...	1320	...	1620	...	...
18	**Spitz** an der Donau d.	0951	...	1151	...	1351	...	1651	...	...
34	**Emmersdorf** an der Donau a.	1012	...	1212	...	1412	...	1712	...	...

	R		R		R		R		
Emmersdorf an der Donau d.	1020	...	1220	...	1450	...	1750	...	...
Spitz an der Donau d.	1042	...	1242	...	1512	...	1812	...	...
Krems an der Donau a.	1112	...	1312	...	1542	...	1842	...	...

© Mar. 30 - Oct. 27 (daily July 1 - Sept. 29). Special fares apply.

● – Direct U-bahn links: Line **U4** – Wien Mitte - Spittelau. Line **U6** – Wien Meidling - Westbahnhof - Spittelau - Floridsdorf.
△ – S-Bahn trains run every 10–15 minutes from / to Wien Hütteldorf (journey: 21–23 minutes).
⊠ – Operated by NÖVOG (Wachaubahn). ✆ +43 (0) 2742 360 990-99. www.wachaubahn.at.

d class only — LINZ and ST VALENTIN - GREIN - SARMINGSTEIN — 992

m																									
		Ⓐ	Ⓐ	⚒						Ⓐ		⚒		Ⓐ	⚒	Ⓐ	Ⓐ		Ⓐ	Ⓐ		Ⓐ	©	Ⓐ	
0	**Linz** Hbf **976** d.	*0433*	0524	*0630*	*0649*	...	0838	...	1038	*1130*	*1230*	*1330*	1438	*1452*	*1530*	*1530*	1608	1638	1708	*1730*	*1752*	1838	*1930*	1938	*2030*
17	Enns **976** d.	*0450*	0538	|	*0707*	...	0850	...	1050	|	|	|	1450	*1510*	|	|	1620	1650	1720	|	*1810*	1850	|	1950	|
	St Valentin d.	0502	|	0649	0719	...	|	...	|	1150	1250	1350	|	1521	1550	1550	|	|	|	1750	1821	|	1950	|	2050
34	Perg d.	0524	0609	0713	0744	...	0914	...	1114	1214	1314	1414	1514	1545	1614	1614	1644	1714	1745	1814	1845	1914	2014	2014	2113
55	Grein-Bad Kreuzen d.	0601	0644	0744	0816	...	0945	...	1145	1248	1345	1445	1545	1613	1644	1645	1714	1745	1816	1845	1915	1945	2043	2043	2142
57	Grein Stadt d.	0604	0648	0747	0819	...	0948	...	1148	1251	1348	1448	1548	...	...	1648	...	1748	1819	1847	1918	1948	2046	2046	...
62	St Nikola-Struden a.	0610	0655	0753	0825	...	0954	...	1154	1257	1354	1454	1554	...	...	1654	...	1754	1825	...	1924	1954	2053	2053	...
65	Sarmingstein a.	0615	...	...	...	...	...	...	...	...	...	...	...	...	...	...	...	...	1830	...	...	1959	2057	2057	...

m																									
		Ⓐ	Ⓐ		Ⓐ	⚒		Ⓐ			Ⓐ	Ⓐ	©	⚒		Ⓐ	Ⓐ	©	Ⓐ	Ⓐ	Ⓐ	©	Ⓐ	Ⓑ	
0	Sarmingstein d.	...	0511	0525	...	...	0627	...	...	...	...	...	...	...	...	...	...	...	...	...	...	...	1858	...	...
3	St Nikola-Struden d.	...	0515	0530	...	...	0632	0703	0803	1003	...	1203	1203	1303	1403	1503	1603	1603	...	1703	1803	1803	1903	...	1933
8	Grein Stadt d.	0401	0522	0537	...	...	0639	0710	0810	1010	1110	1210	1210	1310	1410	1510	1610	1610	...	1710	1810	1810	1910	1910	1940
10	Grein-Bad Kreuzen d.	0405	0526	0540	0601	0612	0644	0714	0815	1015	1115	1215	1215	1315	1415	1515	1615	1615	1644	1715	1815	1815	1915	1915	1945
31	Perg d.	0432	0553	0610	0630	0642	0714	0744	0844	1044	1144	1244	1244	1344	1444	1545	1645	1645	1714	1745	1845	1845	1944	1944	2014
49	**St Valentin** a.	0454	|	0632	|	0706	|	0807	|	|	1207	|	1307	1407	|	|	|	1707	1736	1807	|	1907	2007	2007	2036
	Enns **976** a.	*0517*	0613	*0645*	0652	|	0736	|	0907	1107	|	1307	|	|	1507	1607	1707	|	*1747*	|	1907	|	|	|	*2047*
	Linz Hbf **976** a.	*0536*	0626	*0701*	0705	*0730*	0752	*0830*	0922	1122	*1230*	1322	*1330*	*1430*	1522	1622	1722	*1730*	*1808*	*1830*	1922	*1930*	*2030*	*2030*	*2108*

d class only — ST PÖLTEN - KREMS and TULLN — 993

ST PÖLTEN - KREMS

m																									
		⚒	Ⓐ		Ⓐ					Ⓐ					Ⓐ		Ⓐ		Ⓐ		Ⓐ		Ⓐ		
0	**St Pölten** Hbf d.	0505	0539	0605	0639	0705	0805	0905	1005	1105	1205	1305	1405	1505	1539	1605	1639	1705	1739	1805	1839	1905	2005	2105	2205
0	Herzogenburg d.	0514	0547	0614	0647	0714	0814	0914	1014	1114	1214	1314	1414	1514	1548	1614	1648	1714	1748	1814	1848	1914	2014	2114	2214
0	**Krems** a. d. Donau a.	0541	0625	0641	0727	0741	0841	0941	1041	1141	1241	1341	1442	1541	1612	1641	1712	1741	1812	1841	1914	1941	2041	2141	2241

		⚒	⚒		Ⓐ										Ⓐ	©	Ⓐ								
ms a. d. Donau d.	...	0519	0548	0617	0646	0718	0746	0819	0919	1019	1119	...	1219	1319	1342	1419	1421	1519	1619	1719	1819	1919	2019	2119	2219
zogenburg d.	...	0547	0614	0647	0715	0747	0814	0847	0947	1047	1147	...	1247	1347	1413	1447	1448	1547	1647	1747	1847	1947	2047	2147	2247
ölten Hbf a.	...	0555	0623	0655	0725	0755	0823	0855	0955	1055	1155	...	1255	1355	1423	1455	1457	1555	1655	1755	1855	1955	2055	2155	2255

ST PÖLTEN - TULLN - WIEN

m																									
		⚒	Ⓐ	©	Ⓐ	Ⓐ				ⒶD			ⒶD		ⒶD		Ⓐ	ⒶD			Ⓐ	ⒶD		ⒶD	P
0	**St Pölten** Hbf **950** d.	0404	0512	0519**z**	0545	...	0612	...	0715	0812	0912	1112	1212	1312	1412	1512	...	1612	...	1712	...	1812	1912	2012	2118
0	Herzogenburg d.	0417	0529	0533**z**	0603	...	0629	...	0732	0833	0931	1131	1229	1329	1429	1529	...	1629	...	1731	...	1829	1929	2029	2127
0	Tullnerfeld **950** a.	0449	0608	0611**z**	0638	...	0711	...	0811	0911	1011	1211	1311	1411	1511	1611	...	1711	...	1811	...	1911	2011	2111	2148
0	Tullnerfeld d.	0450	0624	0624	0654	0648	0724	0751	0824	0924	1024	1224	1324	1424	1524	1624	1648	1724	1748	1824	1848	1924	2024	2124	2150
6	**Tulln** Stadt d.	0456	0630	0630	0700	0653	0730	0756	0830	0930	1030	1230	1330	1430	1530	1630	1653	1730	1753	1830	1853	1930	2030	2130	2201
	Absdorf-Hippersdorf ▷ a.	|	|	|	|	0701	|	0803	|	|	|	|	|	|	|	|	1701	|	1801	|	1901	|	|	|	|
	Stockerau ▷ a.	|	|	|	|	0726	|	0826	|	|	|	|	|	|	|	|	1726	|	1826	|	1926	|	|	|	|
7	**Tulln** a. d. Donau **990/1** a.	0458	0632	0632	0702	...	0732	...	0832	0932	1032	1232	1332	1432	1532	1632	...	1732	...	1832	...	1932	2032	2132	|
7	Wien Heiligenstadt **990/1** a.	0545	0714	0715	0745	...	0815	...	0915	1015	1115	1315	1415	1515	1615	1715	...	1815	...	1915	...	2015	2115	2215	2225
9	Wien Spittelau **990/1** a.	0548	0717	0718	0748	...	0818	...	0918	1018	1118	1318	1418	1518	1618	1718	...	1818	...	1918	...	2018	2118	2218	2229
0	**Wien** Franz-Josefs-Bf. **990/1** a.	0551	0720	0721	0751	...	0821	...	0921	1021	1121	1321	1421	1521	1621	1721	...	1821	...	1921	...	2021	2121	2221	2232

	Ⓐ	⚒	Ⓐ	⚒			⚒		P	Ⓐ	ⒶD			ⒶD		ⒶD		ⒶD			Ⓐ	ⒶD		ⒶD	
n Franz-Josefs-Bf **990/1** d.	...	...	...	0509	0539	...	0609	0639	0655	...	0739	0839	1039	1139	1239	1339	1439	1539	...	1639	...	1739	1839	1938	2039
n Spittelau **990/1** d.	...	...	...	0511	0541	...	0611	0641	|	...	0741	0841	1041	1141	1241	1341	1441	1541	...	1641	...	1741	1841	1941	2041
n Heiligenstadt **990/1** d.	...	...	...	0515	0545	...	0615	0645	0703	...	0745	0844	1045	1145	1245	1345	1445	1545	...	1645	...	1745	1845	1946	2045
n a. d. Donau **990/1** d.	0442	0527	...	0557	0627	...	0658	0727	|	...	0827	0927	1127	1227	1327	1427	1527	1627	...	1727	...	1827	1927	2027	2127
ockerau ▷ d.	|	|	0531	|	|	0631	|	|	|	0731	|	|	|	|	|	|	|	|	1631	|	1731	|	|	|	|
osdorf-Hippersdorf ▷ d.	|	|	0558	|	|	0658	|	|	|	0758	|	|	|	|	|	|	|	|	1700	|	1800	|	|	|	|
n Stadt d.	0445	0531	0605	0600	0629	0705	0701	0729	0745	0805	0829	0929	1129	1229	1329	1429	1529	1629	1708	1729	1808	1829	1929	2029	2129
ierfeld a.	0450	0536	0610	0605	0634	0710	0706	0734	0750	0810	0834	0934	1134	1234	1334	1434	1534	1634	1713	1734	1813	1834	1934	2034	2134
ierfeld **950** d.	0451	0551	...	0620	0648	...	0720	0748	0812	...	0848	0948	1148	1248	1348	1448	1548	1648	...	1748	...	1848	1948	2048	...
zogenburg d.	0525	0630	...	0657	0730	...	0753	0830	0841	...	0930	1030	1230	1330	1430	1530	1630	1732	...	1830	...	1930	2030	2130	...
ölten Hbf **950** a.	0538	0649	...	0715	0744	...	0805	0844	0850	...	0944	1044	1249	1349	1449	1549	1649	1749	...	1849	...	1944	2044	2144	...

Runs daily Tullnerfeld - Wien and v.v.
May 1 - Oct. 27. (2) Wien Franz-Josefs-Bf - Linz - Passau and v.v.

z – ⑥ (not Oct. 26).

▷ – Additional local trains run Absdorf-Hippersdorf - Stockerau and v.v.

rrow gauge 2nd class only — ST PÖLTEN - MARIAZELL — 994

				★	C[R]	S[R]					
	St Pölten Hbf d.	0635	0737	0837	0842	0905	1037	1237	1437	1637	1837
2	Ober Grafendorf d.	0654	0754	0854	0904	0924	1054	1254	1454	1654	1854
1	Kirchberg a. d. Pielach d.	0723	0823	0923	0938	1003	1123	1323	1523	1723	1923
3	Frankenfels ⊗ d.	0741	0841	0941	0958	1030	1141	1341	1541	1741	1941
3	Laubenbachmühle d.	0751	0851	0951	1011	1056	1151	1351	1551	1751	1949
7	Gösing ⊗ d.	0819	0919t	1019	1047	1142	1219	1419	1619	1819	...
)	Mitterbach ⊗ d.	0845	0945t	1045	1115	1215	1245	1445	1645	1845	...
4	**Mariazell** a.	0852	0952t	1052	1122	1222	1252	1452	1652	1852	...

						C[R]	S[R]	★		
Mariazell d.	...	0907	1107	1307	1507	1527	1522	1607t	1707	1907
Mitterbach ⊗ d.	...	0913	1113	1313	1513	1533	1529	1613t	1713	1913
Gösing ⊗ d.	...	0938	1138	1338	1538	1600	1600	1638t	1738	1938
Laubenbachmühle d.	0655	1010	1210	1410	1610	1633	1650	1710	1810	2010
Frankenfels ⊗ d.	0702	1017	1217	1417	1617	1642	1659	1717	1817	2017
Kirchberg a. d. Pielach d.	0726	1036	1236	1436	1636	1702	1722	1736	1836	2036
Ober Grafendorf d.	0754	1104	1304	1504	1704	1734	1754	1804	1904	2104
St Pölten Hbf a.	0812	1122	1322	1522	1722	1757	1817	1822	1922	2122

Runs on ⑥ June 1 - Sept. 28. ÖTSCHERBÄR – Traditional loco-hauled electric train with special fares. Conveys (12) and ✕.
Runs on May 12, June 9, July 14, Aug. 11, Sept. 8, Oct. 13, Dec. 1, 8 Steam train with special fares. Conveys (12) and ✕.
May 11 - Oct. 27.

★ – Daily. On © May 11 - Oct. 27 conveys first class panorama cars with special fares ([R]).
⊗ – Trains call on request only.

Operator: NÖVOG. ✆ +43 (0) 2742 360 990 99
www.noevog.at/mariazellerbahn
Additional trains run between St Pölten and Laubenbachmühle.

995 (WIEN -) WIENER NEUSTADT - FEHRING
2nd class o

km		⚒	Ⓐ	Ⓐ		Ⓑ		Ⓐ				⑤⑦r	†w	Ⓐ			Ⓐ	Ⓐ	Ⓐ		Ⓑ	Ⓐ	Ⓑ	
0	**Wien** Meidling ... **980/1** d.	...	...	...	...	...	...	...	...	...	...	...	1435	1600	...	...	1700	1735	1800	...	...	...	...	
44	**Wiener Neustadt** Hbf. **980/1** d.	...	0500	0639	0903	0903	1103	...	1303	...	1503	1503	1503	1633	1703	...	1733	1801	1833	1903	2003	2003	2103	21
99	Friedberg ... d.	...	0628	0802	1002	1002	1202	...	1402	...	1602	1602	1602	1734	1802	...	1837	1857	1931	2002	2059	2100	2200	22
126	Hartberg ... d.	0621	...	0835	1035	1035	1234	1327	1435	...	1634	1635	1635	1812	1835	...	...	1929	...	2035	...	2133	2232	
157	Fürstenfeld ... d.	0653	...	0910	1110	1110	...	1359	1510	...	...	1710	1710	...	1910	...	...	...	...	2110	...	...	...	
177	**Fehring** ... a.	0723	...	0937	1137	1137	...	1426	1537	...	...	1737	1737	...	1937	...	...	...	...	2137	...	...	...	
	Graz Hbf **986** ... a.	0837e	...	1053	...	1253	...	...	...	...	...	...	...	...	2053v	...	...	...	...	...	...	...	...	

	Ⓐ	Ⓐ	Ⓐ	Ⓐ	⚒	Ⓐ	Ⓑ	Ⓐ							Ⓐ					⑤⑦r				†
Graz Hbf **986** ... d.	...	...	...	...	...	...	...	...	...	...	0708	...	0908	...	...	...	...	1308k	...	...	...	...	1708	
Fehring ... d.	...	...	...	...	...	0501	...	...	0622	...	0827	...	1027	...	1227	...	...	1427	...	1627	...	...	1827	18
Fürstenfeld ... d.	...	...	...	...	...	0530	...	...	0653	...	0855	...	1055	...	1255	...	...	1455	...	1655	...	...	1855	18
Hartberg ... d.	...	...	0435	0533	0533	0602	...	...	0724	...	0927	...	1127	...	1327	1327	...	1527	...	1727	1727	...	1929	19
Friedberg ... d.	0347	0428	0509	0607	0607	0636	0636	0700	0758	...	1002	...	1202	...	1402	1402	...	1602	...	1802	1802	...	2002	20
Wiener Neustadt Hbf .. **980/1** a.	0454	0529	0611	0711	0711	0735	0735	0757	0851	...	1057	...	1257	...	1457	1457	...	1657	...	1857	1857	...	2057	20
Wien Meidling ... **980/1** a.	...	0559	0643	0743	...	...	...	...	...	...	...	...	...	...	...	...	...	...	...	...	...	...	...	2
Wien Hbf ... **980/1** a.	...	0606	0651	...	...	...	...	...	...	...	...	...	...	...	...	...	...	...	...	...	...	...	...	2

e – Ⓐ only.
k – ⑥ (not Oct. 26).
r – Also Apr. 22, May 1, 29, 30, June 10, 19, 20, Aug. 14, 15, Oct. 26, 31; not May 31, June 21, Aug. 16.
v – ⑤⑥†.
w – Not Apr. 21, June 9, Oct. 26, Nov. 1.

996 WIEN - BRATISLAVA via Marchegg
2nd class only; Austrian holiday dates ap

km												A		C		
0	**Wien** Hbf ... d.	0516	0616		1716	1816	2016	2216	...	A	1437	...	2042	...	...
4	**Wien** Simmering ⊖ ... d.	0522	0622	and	1722	1822	2022	2222	...	L	|	...	|	...	...
47	Marchegg 🏛 ... d.	0602	0702	hourly	1802	1902	2102	2302	...	S	⊠	...	⊠	...	...
53	Devínska Nová Ves 🏛 ... d.	0610	0710	until	1810	1910	2110	2310	...	O	|	...	|	...	...
66	**Bratislava** hl. st. ... a.	0622	0722		1822	1922	2122	2322	...		1558	...	2151	...	...

										D		B		
Bratislava hl. st. ... d.	0538	0638		1738	1838	2038	2238	...	A	0610	...	1201	...	...
Devínska Nová Ves 🏛 ... d.	0551	0651	and	1751	1851	2051	2251	...	L	|	...	|	...	...
Marchegg 🏛 ... d.	0601	0701	hourly	1801	1901	2101	2301	...	S	⊠	...	⊠	...	...
Wien Simmering ⊖ ... a.	0639	0739	until	1838	1938	2138	2338	...	O	|	...	|	...	...
Wien Hbf ... a.	0645	0745		1844	1944	2144	2344	...		0718	...	1322	...	...

A – *IC* **45** – 🚃 ✕ Wien - Bratislava - Koši (Table **1180**). Ⓡ Bratislava - Košice.
B – *IC* **44** – 🚃 ✕ Košice - Bratislava - Wi (Table **1180**). Ⓡ Košice - Bratislava.
C – *RJX* **167** – 🚃 ✕ Zürich - Bratislava.
D – *RJX* **160** – 🚃 ✕ Bratislava - Zürich.

⊠ – Via Bratislava - Petržalka
⊖ – For U-Bahn connections (line U3) from / Wien Mitte and Wien Westbahnhof.

997 WIEN - BRATISLAVA via Bruck an der Leitha
2nd class only; Austrian holiday dates ap

km					Ⓐ			
0	**Wien** Hbf ... d.	0050	...	0445	0539	0645	and	2245
41	Bruck an der Leitha ... d.	0129	...	0513	0609	0713	hourly	2313
69	Kittsee 🏛 ... a.	0153	...	0538	0634	0738	until	2338
74	**Bratislava** - Petržalka 🏛 ☆ ... a.	0159	...	0544	0641	0744		2344

		Ⓐ		Ⓐ					
Bratislava - Petržalka 🏛 ☆ d.	0427	0515	0611	0646	0715	0815	and	2115	2
Kittsee 🏛 ... d.	0433	0521	0617	0652	0721	0821	hourly	2121	2
Bruck an der Leitha ... d.	0458	0547	0647	0717	0747	0846	until	2146	2
Wien Hbf ... a.	0539	0616	0716	0746	0815	0914		2214	0

☆ – Bus 93 links Petržalka station with Bratislava hlavná every 5 – 10 minutes (journey time ± 12 minutes).

☛ Many services run as through trains from / to Deutschkreutz (Table 9

998 UNZMARKT - TAMSWEG
2nd class only; Narrow gau

km		Ⓐ	H		④B 🚂	Ⓒ 🚌	Ⓐ	②A 🚂		⑦C 🚂	Ⓒ	Ⓐ	Ⓒ 🚌	Ⓐ	Ⓐ 🚌		🚌
0	**Unzmarkt** ... d.	0719	0719	0922	...	1118	1122	...	1322	...	*1518**	1522	1718	1722	...	1922	2125
27	Murau-Stolzalpe ... d.	0759	0800	1000	1015	1200	1200	1250	1400	1410	1600	1600	1800	1758	1805	2000	2200
34	St Lorenzen ... d.	...	0813	1013	1035	1212	1213	1310	1413	1430	1613	1613	1812	...	1816s	2013	2208s
44	Stadl an der Mur ... d.	...	0827	1027	1105	1225	1227	1343	1427	1450	1627	1627	1825	...	1827s	2027	2219s
65	**Tamsweg** ... a.	...	0857	1057	1153	1252	1257	1431	1457	...	1657	1657	1852	...	1850	2057	2240

	Ⓐ	Ⓐ	Ⓒ	Ⓐ	Ⓒ 🚌		Ⓒ 🚌	Ⓐ	④B 🚂	⑦C 🚂	Ⓒ	Ⓐ	②A 🚂		Ⓐ 🚌	Ⓐ 🚌	Ⓒ 🚌
Tamsweg ... d.	...	0650	0703	0903	0910	1103	1310	1303	1335	...	1503	1503	1615	1703	1820	...	1910
Stadl an der Mur ... d.	...	0721	0731	0931	0929	1131	1329	1331	1425	1515	1531	1531	1710	1731	1840	...	1929
St Lorenzen ... d.	...	0738	0745	0945	0943	1145	1343	1345	1446	1535	1545	1545	1732	1745	1853	...	1943
Murau-Stolzalpe ... d.	0631	0802	0802	1002	1000	1202	1400	1402	1500	1550	1559	1602	1745	1804	1905	2002z	2000
Unzmarkt ... a.	0711	0840	0840	1040	1040	1240	1440	1440	...	...	*1640**	1640	...	1842	...	2040	2040

A – June 18 - Sept. 3.
B – June 27 - Sept. 19.
C – July 21 - Aug. 25.
H – Apr. 15 – 19, 23, June 11, Ⓐ July 8 - Sep not Aug. 15.

s – Stops to set down only.
z – Murau **Schulzentrum**.
* – By 🚌.
🚂 – Steam train. Special fares payable.

Operator: Steiermärkische Landesbahnen.

999 Danube shipping: BRATISLAVA - WIEN - LINZ - PASSAU
2019 serv

Hydrofoil services. 🍸	W Ⓡ♠	E Ⓡ♠	ⒸN Ⓡ♠	W Ⓡ♠		Y ⊙	W Ⓡ♠	Z ⊙	
Wien Reichsbrücke ▲ ... d.	...	...	...	...	...	1600	...	1730	...
Wien Schwedenplatz ▲ .. d.	0830	0900	1030	1230	...	|	1630	|	...
Bratislava ... a.	0945	1015	1145	1345	...	1730	1745	1900	...

Hydrofoil services. 🍸	T ⊙		W Ⓡ♠		W Ⓡ♠	E Ⓡ♠		ⒸN Ⓡ♠	Ⓡ
Bratislava ... d.	0900	...	1030	...	1430	1600	...	1800	1
Wien Schwedenplatz ... a.	|	...	1200	...	1600	1730	...	1930	2
Wien Reichsbrücke ▲ ... a.	1045	...	...	...	...	...	...	...	

All sailings convey ✕	C ⊡	B ◐		D ◐	⑦J ◐Ⓡ	D ⊡	D ◐	D ◐	
Wien Reichsbrücke ▲ ... d.	...	...	...	...	0830	...	...	...	...
Tulln ... d.	...	...	...	...	1120	...	...	...	...
Krems an der Donau ... d.	1005	1015	...	1310	1400	1540	1545	...	...
Dürnstein ... d.	1040	1050	...	1340	1430	1610	1620	...	...
Spitz an der Donau ... d.	1140	1145	...	1445	⁝	1700	1720	1730	...
Melk ... a.	1300	1320	...	1605	...	*1730**	...	1850	...
Grein ... d.	...	...	...	...	...	...	...	...	...
Linz Lentos ... a.	...	...	...	...	...	...	...	...	...

All sailings convey ✕	D ◐		C ⊡	B ◐	⑥D ⊖	⑦J ◐Ⓡ	D ⊡	D ◐	
Linz Lentos ... d.	...	...	...	...	0900	...	...	...	
Grein ... d.	...	...	...	...	1200	...	...	...	
Melk ... d.	1100	...	1345	1350	1440	...	...	1625	
Spitz an der Donau ... d.	1200‡	...	1430	1440	1520	...	1705	1710	1
Dürnstein ... d.	1230	...	1500	1510	1600	1640	1730	...	1
Krems an der Donau ... d.	1250	...	1525	1530	1620	1700	1755	...	1
Tulln ... d.	...	...	...	...	...	1900	...	...	
Wien Reichsbrücke ▲ ... a.	...	...	...	...	...	2100	...	...	

All sailings convey ✕	⊖H	⊖D	⊖M
Linz Lentos ... d.	...	...	1420
Schlögen ... d.	...	1425	1800
Obernzell ... d.	...	1615	1935
Passau Liegestelle 11 🏛 d.	1515	1715	2050
Deggendorf ... a.	2030	...	...

All sailings convey ✕	⊖L	⊖D	⊖G
Deggendorf ... d.	...	...	1000
Passau Liegestelle 11 🏛 d.	0900	1200	1400
Obernzell ... d.	0945	1245	...
Schlögen ... a.	1110	1410	...
Linz Lentos ... a.	1410	...	...

B – Apr. 13 - Oct. 27 (also Mar. 30, 31, Apr. 6, 7).
C – Apr. 13 - Oct. 27.
D – Apr. 27 - Oct. 6.
E – ①–④ Apr. 1 – 11; ①–④ Sept. 30 - Oct. 24.
G – ④⑥ June 6 - Sept. 21 (not June 20, 22, July 13).
H – ④ June 6 - Sept. 19 (not June 20, July 11).
J – ⑦ July 28 - Sept. 22 (also July 7; not Sept. 1).
L – ②–⑦ Apr. 26 - Oct. 6 (also Oct. 12, 19, 26).
M – ②③④⑥⑦ Apr. 27 - Oct. 6 (also Oct. 12, 19, 26; not June 19, 20, Aug. 8).
N – Winter service: Ⓒ from Nov. 1.
T – ③–⑦ Apr. 20 - Sept. 1; ⑤–⑦ Sept. 6 - Oct. 20.
W – ⑤–⑦ Mar. 29 - Apr. 7; daily Apr. 12 - Sept. 29; ⑤–⑦ Oct. 4 – 27.
Y – ⑤–⑦ Sept. 6 - Oct. 20.
Z – ③–⑦ Apr. 20 - Sept. 1.

* – By 🚌 from Spitz.
‡ – Arrives 1140.

▲ – DDSG operates Wien sightseeing cruises Schwedenplatz - Reichsbr and v.v. Daily Mar. 30 - Nov. 3.
From Schwedenplatz (duration 1 h 55 m via Schleuse Freudenau) at 1030, 1400 (also 1130, 1500 Apr. 13 - Oct. 6).
From Reichsbrücke (duration 1 h 20 m via Schleuse Nussdorf) at 1230, 1600 (also 1330, 1700 Apr. 13 - Oct. 6).
Also shorter *City Cruise* available daily throughout the year from Schwedenplatz at 1100, 1300, 1430 and 1600 (duration 1 h 15 m).

Operators:
⊡ – Brandner Schiffahrt GmbH, Ufer 15, A-3313 Wallsee. ✆ +43 (0) 7433 25 90 21. www.brandner.at
◐ – DDSG Blue Danube Schiffahrt GmbH, Handelskai 265, A-1020 Wie ✆ +43 (0)1 588 80. www.ddsg-blue-danube.at
⊖ – Wurm und Köck, Höllgasse 26, D-94032 Passau. ✆ +49 (0) 851 92 92 92. www.donauschiffahrt.de
⊙ – SPaP - LOD – Slovenská Plavba a Prístavy - Lodná Osobná Doprava Fajnorovo nábrežie 2, 811 02 Bratislava. Reservation recommende Check-in 15 minutes before departure. Bratislava: ✆ +421 2 529 32 224. www.lod.sk
♠ – *Twin City Liner*. DDSG Blue Danube GmbH, Handelskai 265, A-102 Wien. Check-in 30 minutes before departure. ✆ +43 (0)1 904 88 80. Internet booking: www.twincityliner.com

POLAND

perators: Express services are operated by PKP Intercity www.intercity.pl. Most local trains are operated by Przewozy Regionalne (PR) www.przewozyregionalne.pl. Certain local services are operated by regional companies owned by local government: e.g. Koleje Dolnośląskie, Koleje Mazowieckie, Koleje Śląskie and Koleje Wielkopolskie.

rvices: **PKP InterCity**: Note reservation is compulsory (Ⓡ) on all services operated by PKP InterCity (*EC, EIC, EIP, EN, IC, MP, TLK*):

EC, EIC and *EIP* trains are fast premium-rate trains on long-distance routes (*EC* or *EuroCity* trains run on international routes) - first and second class seats, higher rate of fares apply and a supplement is payable for pass holders. *EC, EIC* and *EIP* trains normally convey ✕ or 🍸 for at least part of the route. *IC* and *TLK* trains are lower-cost long distance trains with first and second class seats (also sleepers and couchettes on nights routes as shown in the tables). *TLK* is short for *Twoje Linie Kolejowe* (Your Railway Lines). Certain trains convey 🍸 but it is not possible to identify these in the tables. *MP* is the classification (within Poland) for other international trains; *TLK* fares apply within Poland. *EN* trains are *EuroNight* services with 'global' fares which include the sleeping accommodation. Descriptions of sleeping (🛏) and couchette (▬) cars appear on page 10.

Przewozy Regionalne and other local operators:

IR (InterRegio) and *RE* (*Regional Express*) trains are semi-fast trains operated by Przewozy Regionalne on longer distance routes, with second class seats. Fares are cheaper than *TLK* services but slightly higher than local *Regio* trains. All other trains are local *R* (*Regio*) trains, second class only, calling at all or most stations en route. No train category is shown in our tables for these trains. They are operated by Przewozy Regionalne unless otherwise shown in the table heading or by a footnote. Fares on *Regio* trains are the cheapest available.

nings: Valid **June 9, 2019 - August 31, 2019** except where shown otherwise. *However, alterations and amendments are possible at any time (particularly on and around public holidays) and readers are advised to check specific dates locally before travelling.* Engineering work can often affect schedules; major changes are shown in the tables where possible but other changes may occur at short notice. A number of long-distance trains running only in high summer (particularly to coastal resorts) are not shown owing to lack of space. Note that train numbers often change en route by one or two digits. In station names, Gł. is short for Główny or Główna, meaning main station.

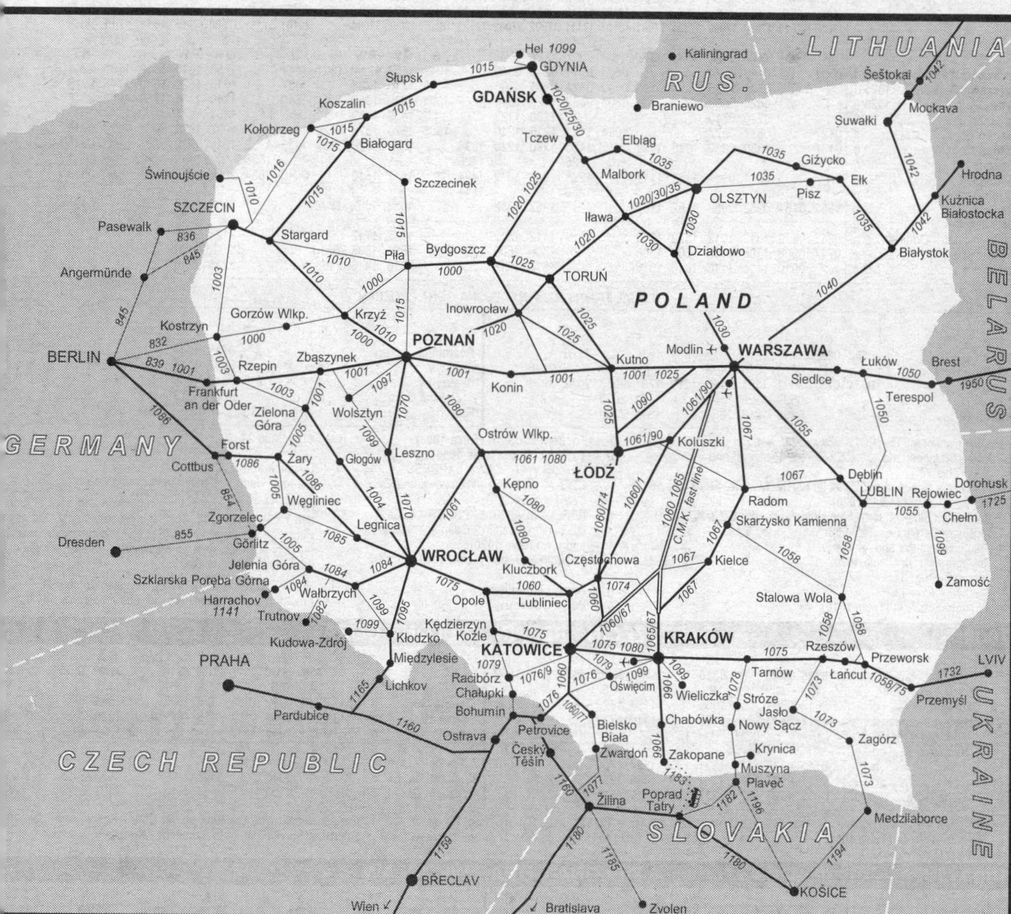

KOSTRZYN - KRZYŻ - POZNAŃ and BYDGOSZCZ 1000

n			TLK 82106 E		2	TLK 85108 G		TLK 82105 S		①–⑥			Ⓑ	TLK 82102 E		Ⓑ							B	①–⑥	
0	**Kostrzyn**	d.	...	...	...	0511	...	0621	...	0824	...	...	1101	...	...	...	...	1344	1502	1545	...	...	1819	2001	...	2123
3	Gorzów Wlkp. ●	d.	...	...	...	0609	0643	0719	...	0927	...	...	1159	...	...	...	...	1444	1607	1643	...	...	1916	2039	...	2225
03	Krzyż **1010**	d.	0450	...	0635	0717	0739	0810	...	1018	1050	...	1249	1254	...	1452	...	1535	1659	1736	1748	...	2007	...	2117	2316
6	**Poznań** **1010**	a.	|	...	|	0840	|	...	...	1151	|	...	...	|	...	|	...	...	▬	1858	|	...	...	...	|	...
3	Piła Gł.	d.	0539	0545	0724	...	0845r	...	1118	...	1139	1151	...	1349	1519	1541	1604	...	1742	...	1839	2010	...	...	2206	...
8	**Bydgoszcz**	a.	...	0658	...	...	0954	...	1228	...	...	1316	...	...	1628	...	1729	...	1906	...	...	2134	...	...	...	...

		①–⑤ B	①–⑤	Ⓑ		⑥⑦ B							TLK 28103 E		①–⑥				TLK 28105 S				TLK 58109 G		TLK 28107 E
goszcz	d.	...	0347	...	...	...	...	0742	...	...	...	...	1140	1149	...	...	...	...	1521	...	1743	...	1823	2006	2050
Gł.	d.	...	0512	0517	...	...	0732	0905	0919	...	1150	...	1247	1313	1343	...	1432	...	1627	1720	1906	...	1943	2130	2216
oznań **1010**	d.	...	▬	|	...	...	|	▬	|	0906	|	1203	...	...	|	...	|	...	...	|	▬	1912	|	...	...
yź **1010**	d.	...	0505	0608	0613	...	0825	0830	1011	1033	1241	1322	...	...	1434	1509	1525	1543	...	1812	1817	2057	2035	...	...
zów Wlkp. ●	d.	0520	0601	...	0709	0820	...	0925	...	1129	...	1418	...	...	...	1604	...	1640	...	...	1912	2155	2130	...	...
strzyn	a.	0559	0657	...	0808	0859	...	1021	...	1235	...	1526	...	...	...	1720	...	1755	...	...	2008	2250	...	...	...

🚌 Berlin - Gorzów Wlkp. and v.v.
To / from Lublin (Table **1055**).

G – To / from Gdynia (Table **1025**).
S – To / from Szczecin (Table **1010**).

r – Arrive 0830.

● – Gorzów Wielkopolski Wschodni.

1001 BERLIN - POZNAŃ - WARSZAWA

km		TLK	EIC	EIC	EC	EC	TLK	TLK	MP	EC	EC	TLK	TLK	EC	EC	TLK	EC	EC	TLK	EC	EC	MP	EC	
		81170	7110	8110	41	41	82100	75111	453	43	43	81107	77137	45	45	71110	55	55	81101	47	47	457	441	
		81171	7111	8111	71000	71000	82101	75110		71002	71002	81106	77136	71004	71004	71111	75000	75000	81100	71006	71006	74010	71010	
			①–⑥	①–⑥	①–⑥	①–⑥			⊠															
		NT		S	PW	QW	U	G		PW	QW	S		PW	QW	S	PX	QX	S	PW	QW	A	B	
0	**Berlin** Hbf ⊖ d.	...	...	...	0543	0543	...	...	0726	0937	0937	...	...	1237	1237	...	1437	1437	...	1643	1643	1841	...	..
5	**Berlin** Ostbahnhof ⊖ d.	...	...	...	0555o	0555o	...	...	0759g	0950	0950	...	...	1250	1250	...	1450	1450	...	1653	1653	1851	1924	..
87	Frankfurt an der Oder 🏛 ⊖ d.	...	...	...	0645	0645	...	...	0855	1045	1045	...	...	1345	1345	...	1545	1545	...	1745	1745	1945	2043	..
98	Kunowice 🏛 ⊖ d.	...	...	...	|	|	...	...	|	|	|	...	...	|	|	...	|	|	...	|	|	|	|	..
110	Rzepin ▷ d.	0008	...	...	0708	0708	...	...	0920	1108	1108	...	...	1408	1408	...	1608	1608	...	1808	1808	2005	2057	..
•58	**Zielona Góra** ▷ d.	|	...	...	|	|	...	0852	|	|	|	...	1243	|	|	1526	|	|	...	|	|	...	|	..
185	Zbąszynek ▷ d.	0056	...	...	0744	0744	0817	0934	|	1147	1147	...	1324	1445	1445	1617	1646	1646	...	1845	1845	...	|	..
191	Zbąszyń ▷ d.	|	...	...	|	|	|	0940	|	|	|	...	1330	|	|	1623	|	|	...	|	|	...	|	..
266	**Poznań** Gł. ▷ a.	0150	...	...	0827	0827	0911	1028	1039	1228	1228	...	1416	1527	1527	1711	1728	1728	...	1926	1927	...	2209	..
266	**Poznań** Gł. d.	0225	0520	0639	0830	0830	0942	...	1043	1231	1231	1326	...	1542	1542	1730	...	...	1834	1930	1930	...	2212	..
366	Konin d.	|	|	|	0916	0916	|	...	|	1317	1317	|	...	1629	1629	|	...	...	|	2017	2017	...	|	..
445	Kutno **1025** d.	0453	0731	0848	0958	1026	1200	...	|	1358	1430	1602	...	1710	1743	1951	...	...	2044	2058	2129	...	|	..
572	**Warszawa** Centralna **1025** a.	0630	0851	1007	1120	1146	1330	...	|	1524	1553	1749	...	1831	1907	2115	...	...	2211	2220	2250	...	|	..
577	**Warszawa** Wschodnia **1025** a.	0646	0921	1041	1141	1156	1346	...	1508	1546	1621	1806	...	1846	1926	2126	...	...	2231	2231	2311	...	0227	..

	EC	MP	EC	EC	EC	EC	TLK	TLK	EC	EC	TLK	TLK	EC	EC	MP	TLK	TLK	EC	EC	EIC	EIC	TLK		
	440	456	46	46	54	54	18100	17110	44	44	77139	18106	42	42	452	28100	57110	40	40	1810	1710	18170		
	17010	47010	17000	17000	57001	57001	18101	17111	17002	17002	77138	18107	17004	17004		28101	57111	17006	17006	1811	1711	18171		
								①–⑥							⊠			Ⓑ	Ⓑ	①–⑤	Ⓑ			
	M	A	QW	PW	PX	QX	S	Y	QW	PW		S	QW	PW		U	G	QW	PW			NT		
Warszawa Wschodnia **1025** d.	0008	...	0449	0524	...	...	0629	0714	0849	0849	...	1049	1159	1214t	1301	1444	...	1559	1615	1619	1709	2204	...	..
Warszawa Centralna **1025** d.	|	...	0506	0535	...	...	0640	0724	0905	0906	...	1115	1210	1225	|	1457	...	1610	1625	1640	1743	2215	...	..
Kutno **1025** d.	|	...	0629	0659	...	...	0807	0852	1023	1040	...	1304	1329	1353	|	1640	...	1740	1751	1759	1908	2348	...	..
Konin d.	|	...	0740	0740	...	...	|	|	1130	1123	...	|	1439	1439	|	|	...	1851	1834	|	|	|	...	..
Poznań Gł. a.	0427	...	0827	0827	...	...	1014	1121	1215	1210	...	1535	1526	1526	1729	1911	...	1937	1920	2001	2123	0215	...	..
Poznań Gł. ▷ d.	0437	...	0830	0830	1029	1029	...	1136	1230	1230	1338	...	1529	1529	1733	1935	1738	1948	1930	...	...	0245	...	..
Zbąszyń ▷ d.	|	...	|	|	|	|	...	1225	|	|	1426	...	|	|	|	|	1826	|	|	...	...	|	...	..
Zbąszynek ▷ d.	|	...	0911	0911	1111	1111	...	1258	1312	1312	1434	...	1612	1612	|	2040	1834	2026	2012	...	...	0338	...	..
Zielona Góra ▷ a.	|	...	|	|	|	|	...	1350	|	|	1514	...	|	|	|	...	1915	|	|	...	...	|	...	..
Rzepin ▷ d.	0552	0751	0952	0952	1152	1152	...	...	1352	1352	...	...	1652	1652	1902	...	...	2105	2052	...	...	0427	...	..
Kunowice 🏛 ⊖ d.	|	|	|	|	|	|	...	...	|	|	...	...	|	|	|	...	...	|	|	...	...	...	...	..
Frankfurt an der Oder 🏛 ⊖ a.	0612	0812	1012	1012	1212	1212	...	...	1412	1412	...	...	1712	1712	|	...	...	2125	2112	...	...	...	...	..
Berlin Ostbahnhof ⊖ a.	0717	0906	1106	1106	1306	1306	...	...	1506	1506	...	...	1806	1806	2021g	...	...	2201o	2201o	...	...	...	...	..
Berlin Hbf ⊖ a.	...	0916	1116	1116	1316	1316	...	...	1516	1516	...	...	1816	1816	2103	...	...	2216	2216	...	...	...	...	..

LOCAL TRAINS RZEPIN / ZIELONA GORA - POZNAŃ

		Ⓐ									
Rzepin d.	0532	0635	...	...	...	1450	1636	...	1920	...	...
Zielona Góra d.	|	|	0719	1036	1405	|	|	1946	|	2146	...
Zbąszynek d.	0634	0737	0801	1121	1458	1552	1737	2033	2022	2231	...
Zbąszyń d.	...	...	0807	1126	1503	...	1742	2038	...	...	...
Poznań Gł. a.	...	...	0858	1218	1603	...	1834	2138	...	...	...

			Ⓐ						
Poznań Gł. d.	...	...	0715	1046	...	1420	1638	...	18
Zbąszyń d.	...	...	0807	1146	...	1512	1729	...	19
Zbąszynek d.	0613	0710	0813	1205	1420	1518	1736	1740	20
Zielona Góra a.	|	|	0857	1313	|	|	1820	|	21
Rzepin a.	0715	0813	...	...	1523	1612	...	1842	..

A – *ÖBB nightjet* METROPOL – [couchette] 1, 2 cl., [sleeper] 2 cl., [2] Berlin - Wien / Budapest and v.v. [2] Berlin - Przemyśl and v.v. See Table **77**.
B – ①⑥ (from Berlin): [couchette] [1] ✕ Ⓡ Berlin - Moskva. See Table **56**.
G – To / from Gdynia (Table **1020**).
M – ⑤⑦ (from Moskva, ⑥① from Warszawa): [couchette] [1] ✕ Ⓡ Moskva - Berlin. See Table **56**.
N – Also conveys [couchette] and / or [sleeper].
O – To / from Olsztyn (Table **1020**).
P – June 24 - Aug. 31.
Q – Mar. 10 - June 23.
S – To / from Szczecin (Table **1010**).
T – To / from Szczecin (Table **1003**).
U – To / from Lublin (Table **1055**).
W – BERLIN WARSZAWA EXPRESS – [12] ✕ Ⓡ, Berlin - Warszawa and v.v. See Table **56**.
X – BERLIN GDANSK EXPRESS – [12] ✕ Ⓡ, Berlin - Poznań - Gdansk - Gdynia and v.v. (Table **1020**).
Y – To / from Białystok (Table **1040**).
g – Berlin **Lichtenberg**.
o – Berlin **Ostkreuz**.
t – 1159 June 24–30.
• – Distance from Zbąszynek.
▷ – For local trains see panel below main table.
⊠ – Paris - Moskva service; for composition and days of runn see Tables **24 / 56 / 95**. Special conditions apply. Journeys within the European Union (e.g. Paris to Berlin) are possib but only bookable through agents of Russian Railways or the Russian rail website.
⊖ – Berlin - Frankfurt an der Oder: see also Table **839**. Frankfurt an der Oder - Rzepin: see also Table **1003**.

1003 SZCZECIN - RZEPIN - ZIELONA GÓRA

km			IC	IC		IC		TLK	IC	MP		TLK
			8305	86109		8310		84101	84102	457		81171
			P	C		P		T	TS	A		W
0	**Szczecin** Gł. d.	...	0612	0804	...	1000	...	1157	1622	...	...	2228
104	Kostrzyn d.	...	0717	0913	...	1107	...	1310	1733	...	...	2335
	Frankfurt / Oder d.	...	|	|	0817	|	1211	|	|	1945	2021	|
	Kunowice 🏛 d.	...	|	|	0828	|	1222	|	|	|	2033	|
136	Rzepin a.	...	0741	0936	0836	1131	1230	1334	1756	2006	2042	0007
136	Rzepin d.	0614	0747	0937	0837	1132	1231	1335	1757	2009	2050	...
207	**Zielona Góra** a.	0714	0832	1022	0939	1217	1333	1421	1841	2056	2151	...

		MP	IC		IC	IC		TLK	IC		TL
		456	48103		48105	3810		68109	3805		18
		A	TS		T	P		C	P		V
Zielona Góra d.	0632	0701	0932	1023	1328	1537	1656	1841	1941	2255	..
Rzepin a.	0733	0745	1016	1124	1413	1621	1757	1926	2026	2355	..
Rzepin d.	0734	0751	1017	1132	1414	1622	1800	1927	2027	...	04
Kunowice 🏛 d.	0742	|	|	1140	|	|	1808	|	|	...	|
Frankfurt / Oder a.	0753	0812	|	1153	|	|	1819	|	|	...	|
Kostrzyn d.	...	...	1043	...	1441	1649	...	1953	2053	...	05
Szczecin Gł. a.	...	...	1153	...	1553	1753	...	2103	2159	...	06

A – See Note **A** in Table **1001**.
C – To / from Wrocław (Table **1004**).
P – To / from Przemyśl (Table **1075**).
S – To / from Kołobrzeg (Table **1015**).
T – To / from Katowice.
W – To / from Warszawa.
For additional trains Frankfurt an der Oder - Rzepin see Table 10
Additional services operate **Szczecin - Kostrzyn** and v.v.

1004 ZIELONA GÓRA - WROCŁAW

km			IC		IC	IC		IC	TLK			IC		MP
			7300		8305	86109		8310	84100			84102		457
			P		P	P		SP	ST			TK		A
0	**Zielona Góra** d.	0537	0620	0645	0833	1023	1137	1226	1423	1557	1755	1842	2010	2057
23	Nowa Sól d.	0559	0636	0705	0848	1038	1156	1242	1439	1616	1815	1858	2030	|
54	Glogów d.	0631	0701	0750	0911	1103	1228	1306	1505	1646	1847	1923	2100	2132
154	**Wrocław** Gł a.	0812	0817	0932	1025	1223	1408	1429	1628	1826	2030	2042	2241	2255
	Kraków **1075** a.	...	1139	...	1342	...	...	1737	...	...	...	...	...	0522

	MP		IC			TLK		IC		TLK		IC	I
	456		48103			48105		3810		68109		3805	37
	A		TK			ST		P		S		SP	
Kraków **1075** d.	2215	...	...	...	...	...	...	1018	...	...	...	1418	16
Wrocław Gł. d.	0510	0556	0725	0744	1040	1122	1255	1342	1501	1624	1701	1743	19
Glogów d.	0623	0735	0847	0924	1214	1241	1432	1456	1636	1740	1835	1856	20
Nowa Sól d.	|	0805	0915	0957	1244	1311	1502	1521	1706	1807	1905	1922	21
Zielona Góra a.	0701	0824	0930	1018	1303	1326	1521	1536	1725	1821	1924	1937	21

A – See Note **A** in Table **1001**.
K – To / from Kołobrzeg (Table **1015**).
P – To / from Przemyśl (Table **1075**).
S – To / from Szczecin (Table **1003**).
T – To / from Katowice (Table **1075**).
y – June 23 - Sept. 1.

1005 ZIELONA GÓRA - WEGLINIEC - JELENIA GÓRA

km		⊖	IC	⊖	⊖			⊖		⊖		⊖
			16170									
0	**Zielona Góra** d.	...	...	...	...	0735	0945	...	1344	...	1547	...
54	Zary **1086** d.	...	...	...	...	0838	1043	...	1441	...	1644	...
67	Żagań **1086** a.	...	...	...	...	|	|	...	|	...	|	...
94	Wegliniec **1085** d.	0501	0609	...	...	0947	1148	...	1547	...	1747	...
118	Zgorzelec Miasto d.	0523	|	...	...	1009	1209	...	1607	...	1809	...
	Görlitz **1085** ✣ d.	|	|	0739	0939	|	|	1539	|	1739	|	1939
120	Zgorzelec **1085** d.	|	|	0744	0944	1014	1214	1544	1614	1744	1814	1944
	Görlitz **1085** a.	|	|	|	|	1018	1219	|	1618	|	1818	|
144	Lubań Śląski d.	0557	0639	0816	1016	...	...	1616	...	1818	...	2016
196	**Jelenia Góra** a.	0704	0739	0918	1118	...	...	1718	...	1916	...	2119

	⊖		⊖		⊖		⊖		⊖	⊖	I
											61
Jelenia Góra d.	0536	...	0748	...	0948	...	1348	...	1748	1948	21
Lubań Śląski d.	0655	...	0856	...	1056	...	1456	...	1856	2056	22
Görlitz **1085** d.	|	0907	|	1107	|	1507	|	1707	|	|	
Zgorzelec **1085** d.	0727	0912	0927	1112	1127	1512	1527	1712	1927	2127	
Görlitz **1085** ✣ a.	0731	|	0931	|	1131	|	1531	|	1931	2131	
Zgorzelec Miasto d.	...	0915	...	1115	...	1515	...	1715	...	...	
Wegliniec **1085** d.	...	0944	...	1145	...	1544	...	1744	...	...	22
Żagań **1086** d.	...	|	...	|	...	|	...	|	...	...	.
Zary **1086** d.	...	1045	...	1237	...	1646	...	1837	...	...	.
Zielona Góra a.	...	1142	...	1336	...	1743	...	1935	...	...	.

⊖ – Operator: Koleje Dolnośląskie.
✣ – Additional journey Görlitz (d. 1339) - Jelenia Góra (a. 1518) and Jelenia Góra (d. 1548) - Görlitz (a. 1731).
☛ [bus] Görlitz Bahnhof - Zgorzelec Miasto and v.v. every 30 minu (journey 22 minutes).

SZCZECIN - POZNAŃ 1010

m																							
		EIC		*TLK*			*TLK*	*IC*			*TLK*	*IC*	*IC*			*IC*			*IC*	*IC*		*TLK*	
		8111		83102			81106	8310			84100	8321	84104			81101			8701	83192		81170	
		8110		83103			81156	8311			84101	8320	84105			81100			8700	83193		81171	
		①–⑥			⚒					Ⓐ				Ⓑ									
				P				P												NP		NB	
	Świnoujście ... d.	...	...	...	...	...	0814j	0829	0744	0949	1120	...	1206	...	1313	...	...	1637h	...	1836	...	2108	...
0	**Szczecin** Gł. ... **1015** d.	0403	...	0602	0635	...	0948	1000	1014	1143	1257	1230	1335	1417	1516	1550	...	1800	1846	2021	...	2300	...
5	Szczecin Dąbie ... **1015** d.	0417	...	0617	0648	...	1005	|	1027	1157	1311	1244	1349	1431	1530	1604	...	1818	1900	2035	...	|	...
40	Stargard ... **1015** d.	0436	...	0640	0711	...	1028	|	1056	1222	1352	1302	1410	1455	1556	1624	...	1842	1918	2054	...	|	...
30	Krzyż ... **1000** d.	0531	...	0758	0823	...	1136	|	1205	1334	1458	1402	1515	1617	1726	1721	...	1952	2020	2154	...	|	...
3	**Poznań** Gł. ... **1000** a.	0629	...	0910	0948	...	1307	|	1323	1455	1625	1458	1615	1741	1845	1819	...	2111	2116	2302	...	0201	...
	Wrocław Gł. **1070** ... a.	|	...	|	...	...	|	1412	...	...	1903	|	1830	...	...	|	...	...	...	|	...	|	...
	Warszawa Cent. **1001** ... a.	1007	...	|	...	...	1749	|	...	...	|	|	|	...	...	2211	...	...	...	|	...	0635	...
	Katowice **1075 1080** ... a.	...	...	|	...	...	...	|	...	...	2128	|	2048	...	...	...	...	...	...	0306	...	...	...
	Kraków Gł **1075 1080** ... a.	...	...	1427	...	...	...	1737	...	...	...	2129	...	...	...	...	...	...	...	0506	...	...	...

	TLK		*IC*		*IC*		*IC*	*IC*	*IC*				*TLK*	*IC*			*TLK*		*EIC*			
	18170		38192		7801		18100	48101	3820				18106	3810			38102		1810			
	18171		38193		7800		18101	48100	3821				18156	3811			38103		1811			
										Ⓑ	⑥								Ⓑ			
	NB		NP											P			P					
raków Gł. **1075 1080** ... d.	...	...	2215	...	...	...	...	...	0637	...	...	...	...	1018	...	...	1311	...	...	...	...	...
atowice **1075 1080** ... d.	...	...	0040	...	...	...	...	0709	|	...	...	...	...	|	...	...	|	...	...	...	...	...
'arszawa Cent. **1001** ... d.	2220	...	|	...	...	...	0640	|	|	...	...	...	1115	|	...	...	|	...	1640	...	...	...
'rocław Gł. **1070** ... d.	|	...	|	...	...	...	|	0939	|	...	...	...	|	1342	...	...	|	...	|	...	...	...
znań Gł. ... **1000** d.	0235	...	0535	0640	0835	1022	1032	1203	1258	1336	1336	...	1602	|	1622	...	1858	...	2026	...	...	...
'yż ... **1000** d.	|	...	0650	0804	0948	1141	1136	1313	1357	1516	1516	...	1711	|	1743	...	1955	...	2141	...	...	...
'gard ... **1015** d.	|	...	0752	0918	1050	1306	1237	1409	1452	1639	1639	...	1809	|	1852	...	2053	...	2234	...	...	...
zecin Dąbie ... **1015** d.	0604	...	0811	0947	1110	1330	1256	1427	1513	1704	1704	...	1827	|	1919	...	2110	...	2254	...	...	...
zecin Gł. ... **1015** a.	0540	...	0824	1001	1123	1347	1310	1441	1526	1717	1717	...	1841	1753	1935	...	2124	...	2308	...	...	...
winoujście ... a.	0717	...	1013	1204	...	1532	...	1614	...	1918	...	...	2025h	1922	2138	...	...	...	...	...	...	...

m											
		Ⓐ	Ⓒ	Ⓐ		Ⓐ					Ⓑ
0	**Świnoujście** ... d.	0445	0542	0616	0744	0949	...	1313	1550	1744	1950
9	Szczecin Dąbie ... a.	0616	0714	0749	0917	1119	...	1442	1722	1914	2121
1	**Szczecin** Gł. ... a.	0629	0728	0804	0931	1133	...	1455	1736	1929	2135

		Ⓐ					Ⓑ			
Szczecin Gł. ... d.	0519	0748	1022	...	1347	1554	1732	...	1955	...
Szczecin Dąbie ... d.	0532	0804	1036	...	1401	1607	1746	...	2009	...
Świnoujście ... a.	0703	0936	1204	...	1532	1736	1918	...	2138	...

m											
			Ⓒ	Ⓐ	88150				①–④	⑤⑦	
					§U						
0	**Szczecin** Gł. ... d.	...	0639	...	0754	1109	...	...	1911	1911	...
2	Szczecin Dąbie ... d.	...	0654	...	0810	1124	...	...	1926	1926	...
7	Stargard ... d.	0444	0722	0722	0839	1150	...	...	1954	1954	...
2	Kalisz Pomorskí ... d.	0600	0846	0846	0945	1259	...	1650	2111	2111	...
6	Wałcz ... d.	0644	0928	0928	1027	1347	...	1739	...	2155	...
6	**Piła** Główna ... a.	0712	0955	0955	1056	1418	...	1807	...	...	...

	①	⑥					80151	⚒	†	
							§U			
Piła Główna ... d.	...	...	0731	...	1318	1539	1703	1938	1938	...
Wałcz ... d.	0344	0344	0800	...	1345	1606	1738	2006	2006	...
Kalisz Pomorskí ... d.	0429	0429	0845	...	1428	1649	1819	2048	2048	...
Stargard ... d.	0541	0542	0959	...	1556	1757	1924	2152	2152	...
Szczecin Dąbie ... d.	...	0608	1025	...	1622	1824	1945	...	2215	...
Szczecin Gł. ... a.	...	0623	1040	...	1637	1842	2001	...	2229	...

To / from Bielsko Biała (Table **1060**).
Also conveys 🛏 and / or 🛏.

P – To / from Przemyśl (Table **1075**).
U – To / from Lublin (Table **1055**).

Y – To / from Białystok (Table **1040**).

h – June 23 - Sept. 1.
j – June 21 - Aug. 31.

§ – *TLK* service.

SZCZECIN - KOSZALIN - GDYNIA - GDAŃSK 1015

m																								
		EIP	*TLK*	*IC*			*TLK*	*TLK*	*TLK*		*TLK*		*TLK*			*IC*	*IC*	*TLK*	*TLK*			*IC*	*IC*	
		8300	85107	85105			86104	81105	48107		48103		85103			3806	80106	83174	85100			4801	80102	
		8301	85106	85104			86105	81104	48157		48102		85102			3807		83175	85101					
		①–⑥	①–⑥												①–⑥									
		K	O	O			W	Y	T		T		O			P	P	PN				T	T	
0	**Szczecin** Gł. ... **1010** d.	...	0445	0654	...	0805	...	1038	...	...	1156	1322	1401	...	1510	...	...	...	1657	...	...	...	...	...
5	Szczecin Dąbie ... **1010** d.	...	0458	0708	...	0820	...	1052	...	...	1210	1335	1415	...	1526	...	...	...	1710	...	...	...	...	...
0	Stargard ... **1010** d.	...	0517	0731	...	0849	...	1111	...	...	1231	1359	1433	...	1558	...	...	...	1732	...	...	...	...	...
1	**Poznań** Gł. ... d.	...	|	|	0540	|	...	|	0941	...	|	|	|	1222	|	1411	1411	...	|	1446	1645	1830	1830	...
5	Piła Gł. ... d.	...	|	|	0743	|	...	|	1116	...	|	|	|	1431	|	1546	1546	...	|	1711	1914	2008	2008	...
4	Szczecinek ... d.	...	|	|	0855	|	...	|	1210	...	|	|	|	1541	|	1639	1639	...	|	1821	2017	2101	2101	...
1	Białogard ... a.	...	0637	0850	1000	1014	...	1240	1302	...	1406	1523	1555	1641	1728	1734	1734	...	1853	1921	2113	2154	2154	...
1	Białogard ... d.	...	0642	0851	1006	1017	...	1241	1303	...	1415	1529	1556	1644	1729	1752	1802	...	1901	1924	2116	2210	2224	...
7	Kołobrzeg ... a.	...	|	|	1042	|	...	|	|	...	1444	|	|	1721	|	1821	|	...	|	|	2153	2241	|	...
3	Kołobrzeg ... d.	0557	|	|	...	|	0955	|	|	...	...	|	|	...	|	...	|	1743	|	|	...	...	|	...
5	**Koszalin** ... d.	0632	0701	0907	...	1053f	1042	1257	1321	...	...	1551	1619	...	1749	...	1823	1845	1928	1942	...	...	2240	...
2	Słupsk ... d.	0712	0754	0948	...	1147	1140	1348	1424	...	...	1640	1700	...	1841	...	1922	2003	2019	...	...	...	2321	...
4	Lębork ... d.	0742	0824	1018	...	...	1211	1429	...	...	...	...	1729	...	...	...	...	2044	2107	...	...	...	...	...
3	**Gdynia** Gł. ... a.	0819	0905	1105	...	...	1303	1512	...	...	...	...	1811	...	...	...	...	2133	2158	...	...	...	...	...
3	**Gdynia** Gł. ... ▷ d.	0821	0928	1123	...	...	1320	1544	...	...	...	...	1826	...	...	...	...	2153	2201	...	...	...	...	...
2	Sopot ... ▷ a.	0829	0936	1131	...	...	1329	1552	...	...	...	...	1834	...	...	...	...	2200	2209	...	...	...	...	...
4	**Gdańsk** Gł. ... ▷ a.	0845	0951	1146	...	...	1344	1608	...	...	...	...	1849	...	...	...	...	2215	2225	...	...	...	...	...
	Warszawa C. **1025/30** ... a.	1145	...	...	...	...	1705	...	...	...	...	...	...	...	...	...	...	...	...	...	...	...	...	...

		IC	*IC*			*TLK*	*IC*	*IC*	*TLK*		*TLK*		*TLK*	*TLK*	*TLK*				*TLK*	*IC*		*TLK*	*EIP*
		88103	8400			58100	88107	8306	38172		58103		84102	84107	18105				68105	58105		58107	3800
						58101		8307	38173		58102		84103	84157	18104				68104	58104		58106	3801
										①–⑤												Ⓑ	Ⓑ
			T				P	P	PN		O		T	T	Y				W	O		O	K
'arszawa C. **1025/30** ... d.	...	...	...	...	...	...	...	...	...	...	...	...	...	...	...	...	...	...	1055	...	...	...	1625
ńsk Gł. ... ▷ d.	...	...	...	...	...	0536	...	...	0622	...	0900	...	...	...	1210	...	...	...	1422	1600	...	1749	1924
ot ... ▷ d.	...	...	...	...	...	0550	...	...	0638	...	0914	...	...	...	1226	...	...	...	1437	1614	...	1803	1940
nia Gł. ... ▷ a.	...	...	...	...	...	0558	...	...	0647	...	0923	...	...	...	1234	...	...	...	1446	1623	...	1812	1948
nia Gł. ... d.	...	...	...	...	...	0601	...	...	0717	...	0950	...	...	...	1246	...	...	...	1501	1633	...	1846	1951
ork ... d.	...	...	...	...	...	0707	...	...	0825	...	1041	...	...	...	1335	...	...	...	1600	1730	...	1938	2030
sk ... d.	...	0430	...	0500	...	0753	0845	...	0856	0953	1120	1220	...	1348	1409	...	1440	...	1639	1802	1909	2019	2103
zalin ... d.	...	0511	...	0548	...	0834	0939	...	0945	1049	1201	1321	...	1430	1452	1503	1551	...	1733	1843	2022	2102	2141
obrzeg ... a.	...	|	...	|	...	|	|	...	1025	|	|	|	...	|	|	|	|	...	1812	|	|	|	2218
obrzeg ... d.	...	|	0500	|	0810	|	|	0930	...	|	|	|	1341	|	|	|	|	1612	...	|	|	|	...
ogard ... a.	...	0525	0531	0608	0846	0848	0953	1004	...	1110	1216	1339	1412	1446	1507	1522	1615	1659	...	1857	2040	2116	...
ogard ... d.	0519	0555	0555	0612	0853	0855	1024	1024	...	1111	1217	1341	1413	1447	1508	1528	1617	1702	...	1858	2041	2120	...
zczecinek ... d.	0627	0715	0715	|	1009	|	1117	1117	...	|	|	|	|	1546	|	1650	|	1820	...	|	|	|	...
a Gł. ... d.	0740	0820	0820	|	1109	|	1209	1209	...	|	|	|	|	1651	|	1753	|	1921	...	|	|	|	...
oznań Gł. ... a.	0938	0955	0955	|	1303	|	1345	1345	...	|	|	|	|	1827	|	1933	|	2103	...	|	|	|	...
gard ... **1010** d.	...	...	...	0745	...	1012	...	...	...	1303	1331	1516	1548	...	1637	...	1744	...	...	2018	2204	2244	...
ecin Dąbie ... **1010** a.	...	...	...	0808	...	1028	...	...	...	1325	1348	1540	1605	...	1655	...	1808	...	...	2035	2227	2301	...
ecin Gł. ... **1010** a.	...	...	...	0822	...	1042	...	...	...	1339	1402	1557	1619	...	1709	...	1822	...	...	2049	2241	2314	...

To / from Kraków (Tables **1065**, **1067**).
Also conveys 🛏 and / or 🛏.
To / from Olsztyn (Table **1035**).
To / from Przemyśl (Table **1075**).

T – To / from Katowice (Tables **1075**, **1080**).
W – To / from Wrocław (Table **1061**).
Y – To / from Białystok (Table **1035**).

f – Arrive 1035.
* – Distance from Białogard.
** – Distance from Koszalin.

◐ – Via Szczecin Goleniów ✈ (Table **1016**).
▷ – Frequent local trains run between Gdynia and Gdansk.

1016 SZCZECIN - KOŁOBRZEG

km		⚒	Ⓒ			Ⓐ		⚒			⑤
0	**Szczecin** Gł. d.	0628	0822	0954	...	1222	1451	1644	1933	...	2135
35	Goleniów ✈ d.	0702	0903	1029	...	1257	1531	1721	2008	...	2211
106	Kołobrzeg a.	0902	1040	1220	...	1500	1727	1915	2203	...	2336

	Ⓐ	Ⓐ	⑥							
Kołobrzeg d.	0352	0438	0446	0629	0952	...	1328	...	1525	17
Goleniów ✈ d.	0523	0622	0622	0826	1146	...	1526	...	1722	19
Szczecin Gł. a.	0602	0657	0658	0900	1222	...	1604	...	1757	20

1020 GDYNIA - GDAŃSK - BYDGOSZCZ - POZNAŃ

km		*TLK* 54102 56150	Ⓐ		*IC* 56106 56107	*TLK* 57104 57105 ①–⑥	*EC* 54 57000 C	Ⓐ	*TLK* 56104 56105	*TLK* 54100 54101 K		*TLK* 53108 53109 PF		*IC* 5600 5601		*TLK* 14103 16105 Y	*TLK* 57110 57111 F		*IC* 5602 5603	Ⓑ	*IC* 57100 57101 Ⓑ	*TLK* 57106 57107	*IC* 5700 5701 Ⓑ	*IC* 55180	*TLK* 54170 54171 NJ
0	**Gdynia** Gł. ▷ d.	...	...	...	0515	...	0705	...	0746	0826	...	...	...	1137	...	...	1330	...	1529	...	...	1732	1857	2037	2207
9	Sopot ▷ d.	...	...	...	0523	...	0713	...	0754	0835	...	...	...	1146	...	...	1338	...	1538	...	...	1740	1905	2045	2216
21	**Gdańsk** Gł. ▷ d.	...	...	...	0541	...	0730	...	0813	0854	...	...	...	1203	...	...	1356	...	1559	...	...	1758	1922	2102	2234
53	Tczew ▷ d.	...	...	...	0600	...	0747	...	0834	0915	...	...	...	1220	...	...	1417	...	1618	...	...	1820	1939	2124	2254
181	**Bydgoszcz** Gł. ▷ a.	...	...	...	0721	...	0859	...	0957	1044	...	...	...	1339	...	...	1542	...	1743	...	...	1945	2052	2246	0016
181	**Bydgoszcz** Gł. d.	0501	0546	...	0726	...	0901	...	1000	1052	1102	...	...	1342	1451	...	1545	...	1756	...	...	1955	2055	...	0019
	Olsztyn Gł. d.	|	|	...	|	0659	|	...	|	|	|	0934	...	|	|	1325	|	...	|	...	1746	|	|	...	|
	Iława d.	|	|	...	|	0756	|	...	|	|	|	1029	...	|	|	1422	|	...	|	...	1831	|	|	...	|
	Toruń Gł. d.	|	|	0651	|	0908	|	0916	|	|	|	1142	1255	|	|	1537	|	1709	|	1905	1950	|	|	...	|
227	Inowrocław d.	0532	0627	0724	0755	0935	0928	0949	1030	1123	1142	1208	1331	1409	1531	1604	1615	1743	1825	1940	2021	2026	2122	...	0050
283	Gniezno d.	0610	0711	0807	0831	1012	0958	1033	1108	1202	1230	1252	1415	1443	1614	1645	1653	1830	1901	2023	2057	2105	2155	...	0126
334	**Poznań** Gł. a.	0640	0758	0854	0857	1042	1023	1130	1138	1233	1318	1322	1502	1508	1659	1715	1723	1917	1928	2112	2129	2135	2220	...	0156
	Wrocław **1070** a.	0918	...	...	1110	...	...	...	1411	1516	...	...	...	1729	...	1938	...	...	2149	...	...	...	...	...	0454

km		*TLK* 45170 45171 NJ	*IC* 55179	*IC* 7500 7501 ①–⑥	⚒	*IC* 75100 75101 ①–⑥	*TLK* 75106 75107		*IC* 6503 6502		*TLK* 41103 61105 Y	*TLK* 75111 75110 F	Ⓐ	*IC* 6501 6500		*TLK* 35108 35104 PF	*TLK* 45101 45100 K		*IC* 65103 65102	*EC* 55 75000 C	*TLK* 75104 75105 Ⓑ		*TLK* 65107 65106		*TLK* 45102 65150
	Wrocław **1070** d.	2338	...	...	...	...	...	...	0638	...	0832	...	...	1044	...	...	1239	...	1354	...	...	...	1652	...	1837
	Poznań Gł. d.	0239	...	0540	0549	0625	0645	0747	0905	0950	1110	1040	1150	1305	1350	1435	1523	1551	1630	1726	1745	1751	1922	1951	2100
	Gniezno d.	0310	...	0606	0636	0655	0716	0834	0933	1037	1141	1117	1237	1331	1437	1506	1554	1638	1702	1752	1817	1837	1953	2038	2131
0	Inowrocław d.	0345	...	0638	0718	0731	0754	0917	1007	1119	1218	1154	1319	1403	1519	1543	1631	1720	1734	1822	1859	1924	2030	2121	2208
35	**Toruń** Gł. d.	|	...	|	0750	0756	|	|	|	1150	1243	|	|	|	1550	1608	|	1752	|	|	1927	|	|	2155	|
129	Iława d.	|	...	|	...	0908	|	|	|	...	1409	|	|	|	...	1719	|	...	|	|	2039	|	|	...	|
198	**Olsztyn** Gł. a.	|	...	|	...	1001	|	|	|	...	1503	|	|	|	...	1838	|	...	|	|	2133	|	|	...	|
	Bydgoszcz Gł. a.	0413	...	0704	...	...	0822	0956	1034	...	...	1222	1358	1429	...	...	1659	...	1800	1847	...	2001	2058	...	2237
	Bydgoszcz Gł. ▷ d.	0416	0510	0707	...	...	0825	...	1037	...	...	1225	...	1432	...	...	1702	...	1806	1850	...	...	2105	...	...
	Tczew ▷ d.	0548	0637	0821	...	...	0959	...	1203	...	...	1347	...	1551	...	...	1832	...	1924	2004	...	...	2230	...	...
	Gdańsk Gł. ▷ a.	0610	0700	0837	...	...	1018	...	1220	...	...	1406	...	1607	...	...	1851	...	1941	2022	...	...	2249	...	...
	Sopot ▷ a.	0628	0716	0853	...	...	1035	...	1238	...	...	1423	...	1622	...	...	1909	...	1958	2040	...	...	2305	...	...
	Gdynia Gł. ▷ a.	0638	0726	0901	...	...	1044	...	1248	...	...	1432	...	1632	...	...	1918	...	2007	2050	...	...	2315	...	...

B – To/from Bielsko Biała (Table **1060**).
C – 🚃12 ✕ Gdynia - Poznań - Berlin and v.v. (Table **1001**).
F – To/from Zielona Góra (Table **1001**).
J – To/from Jelenia Góra/Szklarska Poreba Górna (Table **1084**).
K – To/from Katowice (Table **1075**).
N – Also conveys 🛏 and/or 🛌.
P – To/from Kraków (Table **1075**).
Y – To/from Białystok (Table **1035**).
▷ – See also Table **1025**. Frequent local services run betw Gdynia and Gdansk (see Table **1035**).

1025 GDYNIA - GDAŃSK - BYDGOSZCZ - WARSZAWA/ŁODŹ

km		*TLK* 51122 51123 ①–⑥	*IC* 5130 5131	*TLK* 51160 51161 ①–⑥		*TLK* 54110 54111 ①–⑥	*TLK* 82106 82107 LU	*IC* 51108 51109		*IC* 5136 5137	*IC* 5330 5360	*TLK* 82105 82104 S		*TLK* 51104 51105	*IC* 5420 5421	*TLK* 82102 82103 LU		*IC* 5132 5133	*IC* 5124 5125 Ⓑ		*TLK* 58108 58109 H		*TL* 54 54
0	**Gdynia** Gł. ▷ d.	...	...	...	...	0444	...	...	...	...	0915	...	...	...	1307	...	...	...	1727	...	1610	...	22
9	Sopot ▷ d.	...	...	...	...	0452	...	...	...	...	0923	...	...	...	1315	...	...	...	1735	...	1618	...	22
21	**Gdańsk** Gł. ▷ d.	...	...	...	...	0509	...	...	...	...	0941	...	...	...	1332	...	...	...	1752	...	1635	...	22
53	Tczew ▷ d.	...	...	...	...	0531	...	...	...	...	0958	...	...	...	1349	...	...	...	1812	...	1658	...	22
181	**Bydgoszcz** Gł. ▷ a.	...	...	...	...	0652	...	...	...	...	1116	...	...	...	1506	...	...	...	1931	...	1820	...	00
181	**Bydgoszcz** Gł. d.	0421	0522	0557	...	0707	0731	0910	...	1025	1128	1224	...	1414	1518	1630	...	1838	1943	...	...	...	00
	Inowrocław d.	|	|	|	...	|	0813	|	...	|	|	|	...	|	|	|	...	|	|	...	...	...	00
232	**Toruń** Gł. d.	0503	0603	0640	...	0747	|	0953	...	1106	1209	1307	...	1456	1559	1714	...	1918	2025	...	...	...	
287	Włocławek d.	0541	0638	0720	...	0824	|	1032	...	1141	1244	1345	...	1535	1634	1752	...	1953	2102	...	...	...	
	Poznan Gł d.	|	|	|	...	|	|	|	...	|	|	|	...	|	|	|	...	|	|	...	...	...	02
	Konin d.	|	|	|	...	|	|	|	...	|	|	|	...	|	|	|	...	|	|	...	...	...	
342	Kutno d.	0634	0725	0808	...	0905	0945	1112	...	1224	1326	1425	...	1622	1714	1834	...	2034	2149	...	...	...	
469	**Warszawa** Centralna a.	0806	0847	0937	...	|	1126	1244	...	1345	|	1555	...	1755	|	2006	...	2155	|	...	...	...	
474	**Warszawa** Wschodnia a.	0821	0911	0951	...	|	1146	1301	...	1356	|	1611	...	1821	|	2016	...	2211	|	...	...	...	
413	**Łódź** Widzew a.	...	...	...	...	1021	...	...	...	...	1456	...	...	...	1842	...	...	...	2257	...	...	...	
	Katowice **1060** a.	...	...	...	...	1312	...	...	...	...	|	...	...	...	2129	...	...	...	...	...	...	...	07
	Kraków **1065** a.	...	...	...	...	...	...	...	...	...	1724	...	...	...	...	...	...	...	...	...	...	...	.

	TLK 45170 45171	*IC* 1525 1524 ①–⑥	*TLK* 85108 85109 H		*IC* 1532 1533	*TLK* 28102 28103 LU	*IC* 4521 4520		*TLK* 15104 15105	*TLK* 28104 28105 S	*IC* 3530 3560		*IC* 1536 1537	*IC* 15108 15109		*IC* 1530 1531	*TLK* 28106 28107 LU		*TLK* 45110 45111 Ⓑ	*TLK* 15122 15123		*TLK* 15110 15111 Ⓑ
Kraków **1065** d.	...	...	...	...	...	...	...	...	...	...	1038	...	...	...	...	...	...	...	...	...	...	...
Katowice **1060** d.	2103	...	...	...	...	...	0625	...	...	...	|	...	...	...	...	...	...	...	1456	...	...	...
Łódź Widzew d.	|	0515	...	...	...	...	0933	...	...	...	1322	...	...	...	...	...	...	...	1745	...	...	...
Warszawa Wschodnia d.	|	|	...	...	0539	0744	|	...	1019	1144	|	...	1349	1504	...	1614	1629	...	|	1759	...	1934
Warszawa Centralna d.	|	|	...	...	0552	0805	|	...	1036	1155	|	...	1405	1522	...	1626	1640	...	|	1810	...	1957
Kutno d.	|	0647	...	...	0721	0934	1045	...	1213	1324	1444	...	1527	1656	...	1752	1817	...	1858	1938	...	2126
Konin d.	|	|	...	...	|	|	|	...	|	|	|	...	|	|	...	|	|	...	|	|	...	|
Poznan Gł a.	0205	|	...	...	|	|	|	...	|	|	|	...	|	|	...	|	|	...	|	|	...	|
Włocławek d.	|	0729	...	...	0802	1013	1124	...	1254	1403	1523	...	1609	1737	...	1833	|	...	1940	2020	...	2207
Toruń Gł. d.	|	0806	...	...	0839	1051	1202	...	1331	1440	1600	...	1646	1815	...	1909	|	...	2017	2058	...	2245
Inowrocław d.	0345	|	...	...	|	|	|	...	|	|	|	...	|	|	...	|	1953	...	|	|	...	|
Bydgoszcz Gł a.	0413	0844	...	...	0917	1130	1240	...	1410	1520	1639	...	1724	1855	...	1948	2032	...	2056	2137	...	2324
Bydgoszcz Gł. ▷ d.	0416	0856	0950	...	...	...	1255	...	...	...	1651	...	...	...	...	...	...	...	2111	...	...	...
Tczew ▷ d.	0548	1012	1113	...	...	...	1415	...	...	...	1811	...	...	...	...	...	...	...	2235	...	...	...
Gdańsk Gł. ▷ a.	0610	1031	1133	...	...	...	1431	...	...	...	1828	...	...	...	...	...	...	...	2256	...	...	...
Sopot ▷ a.	0628	1047	1148	...	...	...	1448	...	...	...	1844	...	...	...	...	...	...	...	2312	...	...	...
Gdynia Gł. ▷ a.	0638	1056	1157	...	...	...	1457	...	...	...	1854	...	...	...	...	...	...	...	2322	...	...	...

H – To/from Gorzów Wlkp (Table **1000**).
L – To/from Piła (Table **1000**).
S – To/from Szczecin (Table **1010**).
U – To/from Lublin (Table **1055**).
▷ – See also Table **1020**. Frequent local services run between Gdynia and Gda

GDYNIA - GDAŃSK - (OLSZTYN -) WARSZAWA **1030**

km																													
m		*EIC*	*IC*	*TLK*	*EIP*	*EIP*	*IC*	*EIP*	*EIP*	*IC*	*EIP*	*EIP*	*EC*	*IC*	*EIP*	*EIP*	*TLK*	*EIP*	*IC*	*EIP*	*EIP*	*IC*	*EIP*	*EIP*	*IC*	*TLK*	*EIP*	*TLK*	
		5354	**5324**	**53100**	**5312**	**5314**	**56102**	**5410**	**8300/1**	**5322**	**5302**	**5304**	**54000**	**5320**	**5306**	**5402**	**86104**	**5308**	**5326**	**5404**	**5104**	**5120**	**5310**	**5102**	**5122**	**53170**	**5100**	**83170**	
		5355	**5325**	**53101**	**5313**	**5315**	**56103**	**5110**	**5352/3**	**5323**	**5303**	**5305**	**105**	**5321**	**5307**	**5403**	**86105**	**5309**	**5327**	**5405**	**5105**	**5121**	**5311**	**5103**	**5123**	**53171**	**5101**	**83171**	
		①⑥			①–⑥																								
		H	**K**	**P**	**K**	**K**	**C**	**T**	**K**	**K**	**K**	**D**	**X**	**K**	**K**	**T**	**C**	**R**	**K**	**B**		**L**	**K**		**L**	**Y**		**PN**	
	Kołobrzeg **1015** ..d.	...	...	...	...	...	...	...	0557f	...	...	...	...	...	...	...	0955	...	...	...	...	...	...	...	...	...	...	1825	...
0	**Gdynia** Gł. ▶ d.	0303	...	0455	0510	0603	...	0714	0821	...	0910	1009	1112	...	1210	1317	1320	1410	...	1517	1610	...	1710	1810	...	1801	1920	2201	...
9	Sopot ▶ d.	0312	...	0504	0519	0612	...	0723	0830	...	0919	1018	1120	...	1219	1326	1329	1419	...	1526	1619	...	1719	1819	...	1811	1929	2210	...
21	**Gdańsk** Gł. ▶ d.	0330	...	0522	0537	0630	...	0741	0847	...	0937	1036	1138	...	1237	1344	1347	1437	...	1544	1637	...	1737	1839	...	1831	1947	2228	...
53	Tczew ▶ d.	0348	...	0548	0555	0649	...	0758	0904	...	0954	1053	1155	...	1254	1401	1405	1454	...	1601	1654	...	1754	1856	...	1849	2004	2250	...
72	Malbork ▶ d.	0401	...	0600	0607	0701	...	0811	0916	...	1006	1105	1208	...	1306	1413	1418	1506	...	1613	1706	...	1806	1908	...	1911	2016	2304	...
•	**Olsztyn** ▶ d.	|	0451	|	|	|	0632	|	|	0930	|	|	|	1249	|	|	|	|	1527	|	|	1726	|	|	1917	|	|	...	...
41	Iława Gł. ▶ d.	0449	0537	0700	0652	0746	0733	0849	1001	1015	1052	1152	1249	1335	1352	1449	1504	1552	1612	1650	1752	1811	1852	1950	2008	2003	2053	...	...
01	Działdowo d.	0523	0609	0732	|	|	0809	|	|	1046	|	|	1321	1406	|	|	1537	|	1642	1721	|	1842	|	|	2039	2036	|	...	...
51	Ciechanów d.	0546	0634	0800	|	|	0854	|	|	1110	|	|	|	1431	|	1541	1604	|	1707	|	|	1907	|	2042	2104	2104	|	...	...
05	Modlin ✈ d.	|	0702	0830	|	|	0927	|	|	1138	|	|	|	1458	|	|	1633	|	1734	|	|	1933	|	|	2132	|	|	...	...
45	**Warszawa** Wsch. a.	0641	0728	0858	0827	0925	0958	1035	1137	1205	1232	1328	1427	1523	1527	1627	1702	1728	1801	1827	1928	2000	2028	2135	2157	2202	2227	...	...
50	**Warszawa** Cent. a.	0649	0735	0905	0835	0935	1005	1049	1145	1215	1240	1335	1435	1530	1535	1635	1710	1735	1810	1835	1935	2010	2035	2145	2205	2220	2235	...	...

	TLK	*EIP*	*IC*	*TLK*	*EIP*	*EIP*	*IC*	*EIP*	*EIP*	*IC*	*TLK*	*EIP*	*EIP*	*IC*	*EIP*	*EIP*	*EIP*	*EC*	*EIP*	*EIP*	*IC*	*EIP*	*IC*	*EIP*	*TLK*	*EIP*	*EIC*	*IC*	
	38170	**1500**	**1522**	**35170**	**1518**	**1504**	**1520**	**3510**	**4502**	**3526**	**68105**	**3508**	**4504**	**3520**	**3506**	**3504**	**3502**	**104**	**3552**	**3800**	**3522**	**4510**	**65104**	**3500**	**35100**	**4500**	**3550**	**3524**	
	38171	**1501**	**1523**	**35172**	**1519**	**1505**	**1521**	**3511**	**4503**	**3527**	**68104**	**3509**	**4505**	**3521**	**3507**	**3505**	**3503**	**45000**	**3553**	**3801**	**3523**	**1510**	**65105**	**3501**	**35110**	**4501**	**3554**	**3525**	
		①–⑥																	⑥	Ⓑ						Ⓑ	⑤⑦		
	PN			**Y**			**L**	**K**	**T**	**K**	**C**	**R**	**B**	**K**	**K**	**K**	**K**	**X**	**K**	**K**	**K**	**T**	**C**	**K**	**P**	**B**	**J**	**K**	
arszawa Cent. d.	...	0525	0550	0535	0625	0725	0750	0825	0925	0955	1110	1025	1125	1155	1225	1325	1425	1525	1625	1625	1630	1725	1755	1825	1920	1925	2025	2040	...
arszawa Wsch d.	...	0533	0600	0553	0633	0733	0803	0833	0933	1003	1118	1033	1133	1203	1233	1333	1433	1533	1633	1633	1637	1733	1802	1833	1929	1933	2034	2049	...
odlin ✈ d.	...	|	0625	|	|	|	0829	|	|	1030	1147	|	|	1231	|	|	|	|	|	|	1704	|	1833	|	2003	|	|	2116	...
echanów d.	...	|	0653	0651	0718	|	0854	|	|	1056	1222	|	1218	1258	|	|	|	|	|	|	1731	|	1905	|	2034	|	2123	2143	...
iałdowo d.	...	|	0717	0720	|	|	0919	|	1039	1121	1250	|	|	1322	|	|	|	1640	|	|	1788	|	1945	|	2101	|	|	2208	...
wa Gł. ▶ d.	0504	0708	0750	0754	0811	0908	0952	1011	1111	1153	1323	1209	1311	1355	1411	1512	1608	1713	1808	1808	1828	1910	2021	2008	2133	2108	2215	2242	...
Olsztyn ▶ a.	|	|	0841	|	|	|	1043	|	|	1237	|	|	|	1439	|	|	|	|	|	|	1912	|	2116	|	|	|	|	2327	...
albork ▶ d.	0553	0743	...	0855	0846	0943	...	1055	1146	...	1409	1254	1346	...	1455	1556	1653	1757	1853	1853	...	1946	...	2053	2224	2143	2301	...	...
zew ▶ d.	0611	0755	...	0908	0859	0955	...	1107	1158	...	1422	1306	1358	...	1507	1608	1705	1809	1905	1905	...	1959	...	2105	2237	2155	2313	...	...
dańsk Gł. ▶ a.	0632	0811	...	0924	0915	1011	...	1123	1214	...	1443	1322	1414	...	1524	1624	1721	1826	1921	1921	...	2015	...	2121	2254	2211	2333	...	...
pot ▶ a.	0650	0828	...	0942	0933	1029	...	1142	1232	...	1458	1341	1432	...	1543	1643	1740	1843	1940	1940	...	2033	...	2140	2312	2230	2348	...	...
dynia Gł. ▶ a.	0704	0838	...	0951	0942	1038	...	1150	1241	...	1507	1349	1441	...	1551	1651	1748	1852	1948	1948	...	2042	...	2148	2320	2239	2357	...	...
Kołobrzeg **1015** ... a.	1026	...	...	...	...	...	...	...	...	...	1812	...	...	...	...	...	...	...	...	2218	...	...	...	...	...	...	...	...	...

- To/from Bielsko Biała (Table **1060**).
- To/from Wrocław (Table **1061**).
- To Kraków until May 19 (Table **1065**).
- ①⑥ June 22 - Aug. 31 (also Aug. 15).
- ⑤⑦ June 23 - Aug. 30 (also Aug. 14).
- To/from Kraków (Tables **1065/7**).
- To/from Łódź (Table **1090**).
- Also conveys 🛏 and/or ▬.

P – To/from Przemyśl (Table **1075**).
R – To/from Rzeszów (Table **1075**).
T – To/from Katowice (Table **1060**).
X – SOBIESKI – [12] ✕ Gdynia - Warszawa - Katowice - Wien and v.v.
Y – Dec. 9 - Feb. 23, June 22 - Aug. 31 from Gdynia; Dec. 10 - Feb. 24, June 23 - Sept. 1 from Zakopane: 🛏 1, 2 cl., ▬ 2 cl. [12] Gdynia - Warszawa - Kraków - Zakopane and v.v. (Table **1066**).

f – ①–⑥.

▶ – For additional trains Gdynia - Gdansk - Iława (- Olsztyn) see Table **1035**. Frequent local trains (every 10 - 30 mins.) run between Gdynia and Gdańsk operated by *SKM*.

• – Olsztyn - Działdowo: *84 km*.

GDYNIA - GDAŃSK - EŁBLAG - OLSZTYN - BIAŁYSTOK **1035**

km												
m				*TLK*	*TLK*		*IC*	*TLK*		*IC*	*TLK*	
				53106	**85107**		**85105**	**61105**		**81105**	**85103**	
				53107	**85106**		**85104**	**41103**		**81104**	**85102**	
				K	①–⑥			**C**				
	Szczecin Gł. **1015** .. d.	...	...	...	0445	...	0654	...	...	1038	1401	...
0	**Gdynia** Gł. ▶ d.	0424	0505	0721	0928	1055	1123	...	1255	1544	1826	2107
9	Sopot ▶ d.	0433	0514	0730	0937	1104	1132	...	1303	1553	1835	2116
21	**Gdańsk** Gł. ▶ d.	0447	0528	0749	0954	1119	1149	...	1318	1611	1852	2129
53	Tczew ▶ d.	0514	0553	0810	1019	1145	1210	...	1343	1637	1914	2204
72	Malbork ▶ d.	0534	0616	0824	1035	1205	1224	...	1359	1651	1928	2224
01	**Ełblag** d.	0559	|	0843	1054	1232	1243	...	|	1710	1947	2249
	Iława Gł. ▶ a.	▬	0711	|	|	...	|	...	1458	|	|	...
	Iława Gł. d.	...	0723	|	|	...	|	...	1508	|	|	...
00	**Olsztyn** a.	*IC*	0815	1012	1212	...	1401	...	1558	1841	2107	...
00	**Olsztyn** d.	**5610**	...	1027	...	...	...	1518	...	1901	...	...
49	Giżycko d.	**J**	...	1207	...	...	...	1704	...	2036	...	...
66	Ełk a.	①–⑥	...	1246	...	...	...	1742	...	2115	...	...
66	Ełk d.	0511	...	1259	...	...	...	1743	...	2116	...	...
70	**Białystok** a.	0634	...	1419	...	...	...	1905	...	2244	...	...

		TLK		*IC*	*TLK*	*IC*		*TLK*	*TLK*		*IC*
		58102		**18104**	**16105**	**58105**		**58107**	**35106**		**6510**
		58103		**18105**	**14103**	**58104**		**58106**	**35107**		**J**
					C			Ⓑ	**K**		Ⓑ
Białystok d.	...	...	...	0541	0931	...	...	...	1326	...	2132
Ełk a.	...	...	...	0713	1055	...	...	...	1454	...	2250
Ełk d.	...	...	...	0714	1056	...	...	...	1506	...	▬
Giżycko d.	...	...	...	0753	1135	...	...	...	1547	...	...
Olsztyn a.	...	...	...	0925	1308	...	...	...	1720	...	...
Olsztyn d.	...	0635	0822	0940	▬	1336	...	1526	1735	...	1943
Iława Gł. a.	...	|	0924	|	...	|	...	|	|	...	2035
Iława Gł. ▶ d.	...	|	0934	|	...	|	...	|	|	...	2050
Ełblag d.	0431	0802	|	1110	1248	1504	1548	1652	1854	1940	|
Malbork ▶ d.	0503	0822	1038	1117	1327	1524	1616	1712	1914	2019	2140
Tczew ▶ d.	0524	0836	...	1148	1352	1538	1637	1726	1928	2038	2204
Gdańsk Gł. ▶ a.	0558	0857	...	1207	1428	1557	1713	1746	1947	2112	2226
Sopot ▶ a.	0613	0913	...	1225	1443	1613	1726	1802	2005	2125	2241
Gdynia Gł. ▶ a.	0623	0923	...	1234	1452	1623	1736	1812	2015	2134	2249
Szczecin Gł. **1015** .a.	...	1402	...	1709	...	2049	...	2314	...	...	...

LOCAL SERVICES OLSZTYN - EŁK - BIAŁYSTOK

km													
m		①–⑥	Ⓐ								Ⓑ		
0	**Olsztyn** d.	...	...	0822	0849	...	1353	...	1443	1619	...	1738	2046
45	Szczytno 🚌 d.	...	...	*0907*	|	...	|	...	*1528*	|	...	*1824*	|
2	Pisz 🚌 d.	...	...	1031	|	...	|	...	*1651*	|	...	1948	|
	Giżycko d.	...	...	|	1040	...	1549	...	...	1817	...	|	2238
57	Ełk 🚌 d.	0531	0743	1131	1130	1458	1633	1646	...	1900	1910	2048	2322
1	**Białystok** a.	0711	0915	...	...	1630	...	1824	...	...	2042	...	...

			Ⓐ								Ⓑ	Ⓑ
Białystok d.	...	...	0512	...	1029	...	...	...	1441	...	1658	1842
Ełk 🚌 d.	0358	0507	0652	0731	1201	1207	1215	...	1620	1650	1842	2030
Giżycko d.	|	0552	...	0816	...	1259	|	...	...	1742	...	...
Pisz 🚌 d.	*0459*	|	...	|	...	|	*1316*	*1656*	...	|	...	...
Szczytno 🚌 d.	0629	|	...	|	...	|	1446	1826	...	|	...	...
Olsztyn a.	0710	0741	...	1006	...	1449	1533	1906	...	1933	...	...

- To/from Wrocław (Table **1020**).
- To/from Jelenia Góra (Table **1084**).
- To/from Kraków (Table **1065**).

🚌 – Szczytno - Pisz and v.v.
🚌 – Pisz - Ełk and v.v.
* – *210 km* via Iława.

▶ – For additional trains Gdynia - Gdansk - Iława (- Warszawa) see Table **1030**. Frequent local trains run between Gdynia and Gdańsk operated by *SKM* (every 10 - 30 mins.).

WARSZAWA - BIAŁYSTOK **1040**

km																							
km		*IC*	*IC*	*TLK*	*IC*	*IC*	*IC*	*TLK*		*IC*		*IC*	*IC*		*TLK*	*TLK*	*IC*	*IC*		*TLK*			
		61190	**1102**	**41106**	**6117**	**1156**	**1101**	**35106**		**7112**		**6112**	**1005**		**11114**	**10101**	**6510**	**4112**		**71110**			
		61170	**1103**	**41107**	①–⑥	⑦	**1100**	**35107**		**7113**		**6113**	**1004**		**11115**		**6170**	①–⑤		**71111**			
		J		**V**	**C**		**L**	**H**		**C**		**C**	**L**		**P**		**J**	**B**		**A**			
0	**Warszawa** Cent d.	0605	0650	0755	0850	0850	0950	1045	...	1315	...	1450	1550	...	1715	1815	1905	1950	...	2117	...	...	...
5	**Warszawa** Wsch d.	0613	0657	0802	0857	0857	1000	1055	...	1322	...	1458	1558	...	1725	1823	1914	2000	...	2124	...	...	...
95	Małkinia d.	0717	0805	0909	1001	1001	1100	1156	...	1423	...	1559	1702	...	1825	1933	2026	2101	...	2229	...	...	...
84	**Białystok** a.	0822	0919	1017	1115	1115	1215	1311	...	1526	...	1713	1815	...	1941	2041	2131	2215	...	2344	...	...	...

	TLK	*IC*	*IC*	*IC*	*TLK*	*IC*	*IC*	*IC*		*IC*	*IC*		*TLK*		*IC*	*TLK*		*IC*		*IC*			
	17110	**1412**	**5610**	**1010**	**10110**	**1004**	**1612**	**1052**		**1614**	**1654**		**53106**		**1616**	**14106**		**1002**		**16170**			
	①–⑥	①–⑤	**1670**	**1011**		**1005**	**1613**	⑥		Ⓑ	⑥		**53107**		**1617**	**14107**		**1003**		**16190**			
	A	**B**	**J**	**L**	**P**	**L**	**C**			**C**	**C**		**H**		**C**	**X**		**L**		**J**			
łystok d.	0458	0534	0648	0752	0847	0942	1040	1038	...	1238	1238	...	1434	...	1649	1750	...	1915	...	2056	...	...	...
łkinia d.	0614	0654	0803	0908	0952	1102	1158	1158	...	1358	1358	...	1601	...	1800	1905	...	2027	...	2204	...	...	...
rszawa Wsch a.	0713	0752	0859	1006	1100	1200	1259	1256	...	1454	1454	...	1702	...	1900	2012	...	2129	...	2304	...	...	...
rszawa Cent a.	0720	0810	0910	1015	1110	1210	1310	1310	...	1505	1505	...	1710	...	1910	2020	...	2140	...	2315	...	...	...

- To/from Poznań (Table **1001**).
- To/from Bielsko Biała (Table **1060**).
- To/from Wrocław (Table **1061**).
- To/from Kraków (Table **1065**).

J – To/from Jelenia Góra (Table **1084**).
L – To/from Łódź (Table **1090**).
P – To/from Suwałki (Table **1042**).

V – HAŃCZA – [12] Kraków - Warszawa - Białystok - Suwałki; [2] Kraków - Warszawa - Białystok (**10015**) - Hrodna.
X – HAŃCZA – [12] Suwałki - Białystok - Warszawa - Kraków; [2] Hrodna (**10016**) - Białystok (**14106**) - Warszawa - Kraków.

1042 BIAŁYSTOK - VILNIUS and HRODNA

PKP, BCh, L(

km											
					TLK	IC					TLK
			143		41107	10015		149			99109
		Ⓐ	⑥⑦		V	V		⑤⑥⑦	2		
0	*Warszawa Cent* **1040** d.	...	...	...	0755	0755	...	...	...	...	1745
5	*Warszawa Wsch* **1040** d.	...	...	...	0802	0802	...	...	...	...	1753
184	**Białystok** d.	0621	0828	0940	1050*	1034*	1449	1549	...	1842	2049
225	Sokółka d.	0706	0859	1019	1128	|	1528	1620	...	1920	2125
324	**Suwałki** d.	|	1020	1148	1240	|	1704	1751	...	|	2239
	Mockava ⊞ ◐ § a.	|	|	▬	...	|	...	|	...	|	...
377	Šeštokai § a.	|	|	2	...	|	...	|	...	|	...
471	**Kaunas** **1811** § a.	|	1425	1435	...	|	...	2125	2230	|	...
575	**Vilnius** **1811** § a.	|	...	1553	...	|	...	...	2346	|	...
241	Kuźnica Białostocka ⊞ a.	0722	...	...	...	1122	...	...	...	1936	...
241	Kuźnica Białostocka ⊞ d.	...	...	...	...	1232	...	...	...	...	...
268	**Hrodna** ⊞ ‡ a.	...	...	...	...	1410	...	...	...	...	...

		TLK				IC	TLK			
		10110			141	10016	14106			14
			2		①⑥⑦	X	X	2	Ⓑ	⑥
Hrodna ⊞ ‡ d.	...	...	...	...	...	1531	...	...	...	..
Kuźnica Białostocka ⊞ a.	...	...	...	...	...	1509	...	...	...	..
Kuźnica Białostocka ⊞ d.	0508	...	...	0735	...	1631	...	...	1939	..
Vilnius **1811** § d.	|	...	0707	|	...	|	...	1545	|	..
Kaunas **1811** § d.	|	...	0842	|	0958	|	...	1704	|	17
Šeštokai § d.	|	...	▬	|	|	|	...	▬	|	|
Mockava ⊞ ◐ d.	|	...	Ⓐ	|	|	|	...	...	|	|
Suwałki d.	|	0622	0808	|	1134	|	1540	1800	|	19
Sokółka d.	0525	0739	0936	0751	1313	|	1654	1928	1955	20
Białystok a.	0603	0814	1024	0828f	1342	1718	1730	2015	2043	20
Warszawa Wsch **1040** a.	...	1103	...	...	...	2012	2012	...	...	..
Warszawa Cent **1040** a.	...	1110	...	...	...	2020	2020	...	...	..

V – HAŃCZA – (12) Kraków - Warszawa - Białystok - Suwałki; (2) Kraków - Warszawa - Białystok (**10015**) - Hrodna.
X – HAŃCZA – (12) Suwałki - Białystok - Warszawa - Kraków; (2) Hrodna (**10016**) - Białystok (**14106**) - Warszawa - Kraków.
f – 0844 on ⑥⑦.
* – Arrive 1017.
§ – Lithuanian time.
‡ – Belarus time.
◐ – ⊞ = Trakiszki (Poland) / Mockava (Lithuania); ticketing point is Mockava.

1050 WARSZAWA - TERESPOL - BREST

For Paris / Nice / Berlin - Warszawa - Moskva services see Tables **24 / 25 / 56**

km		TLK	MP	TLK	TLK	TLK	TLK	MP	TLK	MP	TLK	TLK	TLK
		12115	11008	12107	82107	82101	11107	11011	82105	12011	12111	82103	11102
			128					10		68			
		C		C				⊡M	U	A	⑤⑦	U	
0	**Warszawa** Cent. d.	0710	0835	0910	1130	1320	1410	1605	1615	1710	1810	2020	2035
5	**Warszawa** Wsch. d.	0718	0843	0917	1139	1332	1418	1613	1631	1717	1818	2038	2044
93	Siedlce a.	0819	0935	1010	1233	1428	1521	1715	1732	1818	1912	2132	2144
93	Siedlce d.	0820	0936	1011	1234	1429	1522	1717	1733	1819	1913	2133	2145
121	Łuków d.	0910	0953	1054	1310	1504	1539	1734	1810	1905	1949	2209	2203
•	Lublin a.	1026	|	1211	1429	1630	|	|	1935	2030	2117	2324	|
173	Biała Podlaska d.	...	1027	...	...	...	1621	1831	...	...	...	...	2239
210	Terespol ⊞ a.	...	1100	...	...	...	1720	1900	...	...	...	...	2310
217	**Brest** Tsentralny ⊞ ‡ a.	...	1449¦	...	...	...	...	2231¦	...	...	...	...	...

	MP	TLK	TLK	MP	TLK	TLK	TLK	MP	TLK	TLK	TLK	TL
	9	28102	11112	21010	28104	28100	28106	127	21106	21114	99114	21
	10012			67				11018				
	⊡M	U		A	U	U			C	C		⑤
Brest Tsentralny ⊞ ‡ d.	0610¦	...	...	...	...	...	...	1523¦	...	...	...	..
Terespol ⊞ d.	0513	...	0703	...	...	...	...	1457	...	...	1844	..
Biała Podlaska d.	0549	...	0739	...	...	...	...	1532	...	...	1920	..
Lublin d.	|	0435	|	0740	0840	1139	1316	|	1512	1745	|	19
Łuków d.	0624	0615	0814	0923	1029	1333	1506	1606	1706	1925	1955	21
Siedlce a.	0641	0632	0831	0941	1046	1350	1523	1622	1724	1940	2012	21
Siedlce d.	0642	0633	0833	0942	1047	1351	1524	1624	1725	1941	2014	21
Warszawa Wsch. a.	0747	0732	0937	1042	1142	1442	1617	1715	1819	2043	2118	22
Warszawa Cent. a.	0755	0740	0945	1050	1150	1450	1650	1725	1830	2050	2125	22

A – KYÏV EKSPRES / KIEV EXPRESS – 🛏 1, 2 cl. Warszawa (**12100/21100**) - Chelm - Kyïv and v.v. (Table **1725**). International journeys only.
C – To / from Chełm (Table **1055**).
M – To / from Minsk / Moskva (Table **95**).
U – To / from Lublin (Table **1055**).
‡ – Belarus time.
• – Distance from Łuków *111km*.
¦ – 1 hour earlier from Mar. 31.
⊡ – For composition and days of running see Tables **56 / 95**.

TERESPOL - BREST and v.v. local services

Terespol d.	1026	...	2105	Brest ‡ d.	0800	...	17
Brest ‡ a.	1247	...	2326	Terespol a.	0621	...	16

1055 WARSZAWA - LUBLIN - CHEŁM - DOROHUSK

km					TLK	TLK	IC		TLK	IC		TLK	IC	TLK		TLK		MP	IC			TLK		.0IC
					12114	12114	22372		12106	22390		82107	22392	82101		12105		12011	22394			82102		22396
					12115	12115	22373		12107	22391		82106	22393	82100		12104		68	22395			82103		22397
		🚌	2	🚌			🚌	2		🚌	2		🚌		2		2		🚌	2			2	🚌
					Q	P	R			R		A	R	G				X	R					R
0	**Warszawa** Cent d.	...	...	...	0510	0710	...	...	0910	...	...	1140	...	1340	...	1510	...	1705	...	...	...	2050	...	...
5	**Warszawa** Wsch d.	...	...	0525	0518	0718	...	...	0918	...	...	1149	...	1348	...	1518	...	1712	...	...	...	2058	...	...
104	Dęblin d.	0405	...	0824	|	|	0854	...	|	1105	...	|	1356	|	...	|	...	|	1948	...	...	|	...	2205
125	Puławy Miasto d.	0436	...	...	|	|	0957	...	|	1140	...	|	1431	|	...	|	...	|	2023	...	...	|	...	2240
175	**Lublin** a.	0608	...	...	0830	1020	1044	...	1220	1255	...	1518	1546	1642	...	1846	...	2031	2138	...	...	2346	...	2355
175	**Lublin** d.	...	0620	...	0850	1040	...	1115	1247	...	1450	...	...	...	1750	...	1920	2051	...	2137	...	...	2237	...
228	Rejowiec d.	...	0710	...	0929	1118	...	1206	1325	...	1545	...	...	...	1841	...	2016	2131	...	2228	...	...	2332	...
249	Chełm a.	...	0726	...	0944	1133	...	1221	1341	...	1602	...	...	...	1856	...	2032	2149	...	2244	...	...	2349	...
270	**Dorohusk** ⊞ a.	...	...	...	...	...	...	...	...	...	...	...	...	...	...	...	...	2210	...	...	...	...	...	...

		TLK	IC		IC	MP			TLK			TLK	IC		TLK	IC		TLK	IC		TLK				
		28102	22480		22484	67			21104			28100	22488		28106	22492		21106	22432		21114				
		28103	22481		22485	21010			21105			28101	22489		28107	22493		21107	22433		21115				
	Ⓐ		🚌		🚌		Ⓐ				①–⑥		🚌			🚌			🚌						
	2		R	2	R	X	2	2			2	G	R	2	A	R			R	2		2	2		
Dorohusk ⊞ d.	...	...	...	...	...	0557	...	...	...	...	...	...	...	...	...	...	...	...	...	...	...	...	...	...	..
Chełm d.	0352	...	...	0502	...	0619	0705	0758	...	...	1014	...	...	1157	...	...	...	1514	...	1811	1830	2010	...	...	..
Rejowiec d.	0408	...	...	0518	...	0638	0721	0813	...	...	1031	...	...	1214	...	...	...	1530	...	1827	1847	2028	2035	...	..
Lublin a.	0505	...	...	0608	...	0717	0811	0904	...	...	1126	...	...	1310	...	...	...	1609	...	1917	1925	...	2128	...	..
Lublin d.	...	0435	0509	...	0635	0737	...	...	0936	...	...	1135	1235	...	1315	1436	...	1636	1712	...	1945	...	...	...	..
Puławy Miasto d.	...	|	0624	...	0750	|	...	...	|	...	...	|	1350	...	|	1551	...	|	1827	...	|	...	...	...	..
Dęblin d.	...	|	0658	...	0824	|	...	...	|	...	...	|	1424	...	|	1625	...	|	1901	...	|	...	...	...	..
Warszawa Wsch a.	...	0748	...	...	...	1042	...	...	1237	...	...	1443	...	...	1619	...	...	1942	...	...	2244	...	...	...	..
Warszawa Cent a.	...	0756	...	...	...	1050	...	...	1250	...	...	1450	...	...	1635	...	...	1945	...	...	2250	...	...	...	..

A – To / from Piła (Table **1000**).
G – To / from Gorzów Wlkp.
P – June 9 – 20.
Q – June 21 - Aug. 31.
X – KYÏV EKSPRES / KIEV EXPRESS – 🛏 1, 2 cl. Warszawa (**12010/21010**) - Chelm - Kyïv and v.v. (Table **1725**). International journeys only.
Y – From / to Radom (Table **1067**
• – Distance from Dęblin.

1058 LUBLIN - RZESZÓW - PRZEMYŚL

km			IC		IC				TLK		
			23116		13104				13102		
			23117		13105				13103		
	Warszawa Wsch. **1055** d.	...	...	...	0529	...	...	...	1344	...	...
0	*Warszawa Cent.* **1055** d.	...	...	...	0544	...	...	...	1355	...	...
	Lublin d.	...	...	...	◧	...	...	...	◧	...	...
103	Stalowa Wola Rozwadów d.	...	0755	...	1111	...	1434	...	1814	1931	...
132	Tanobrzeg d.	...	0823	...	|	...	1504	...	|	2002	...
204	**Rzeszów** a.	...	0918	...	|	...	1627	...	|	2121	...
	Rzeszów **1075** d.	0739	...	1026	|	1331	...	1700	|	...	2230
178	Przeworsk **1075** d.	0819	...	1058	1223	1407	...	1733	1930	...	2304
193	Jarosław **1075** d.	0830	...	1109	1233	1420	...	1744	1940	...	2315
228	**Przemyśl** **1075** a.	0909	...	1148	1312	1503	...	1823	2019	...	2354

			TLK					IC		IC	
			31102					31104		32116	
			31103	⚒				31105		32117	
Przemyśl **1075** d.	...	0550	0757	0845	...	1429	...	1627	1650	...	19
Jarosław **1075** d.	...	0630	0837	0924	...	1511	...	1706	1729	...	20
Przeworsk **1075** d.	...	0640	0847	0935	...	1523	...	1716	1740	...	20
Rzeszów **1075** a.	...	0714	|	1009	...	1601	...	|	1813	...	20
Rzeszów d.	0510	...	|	...	1234	...	1732	|	...	1840	.
Tanobrzeg d.	0633	...	|	...	1353	...	1849	|	...	1936	.
Stalowa Wola Rozwadów d.	0704	...	0959	...	1432	...	1930	1828	...	2003	.
Lublin a.	...	...	◧	...	...	...	...	◧	...	...	.
Warszawa Cent. **1055** a.	...	...	1350	...	...	...	...	2221	...	...	.
Warszawa Wsch. **1055** a.	...	...	1411	...	...	...	...	2241	...	...	.

◧ – Via Radom (Table **1067**).

WARSZAWA / ŁÓDŹ - KATOWICE and BIELSKO BIAŁA 1060

	EC	IC	IC	EC	IC	EIP	EC	TLK	TLK	EIP		IC	EC	EIC	IC	EIP	EC	IC	IC	EIP	TLK	TLK		TLK
	14000	1460	1410	14002	1412	1452	14004	54110	56102	5410		14006	54000	1408	2400	5402	14008	5420	2402	5404	14100	14106		53170
	116	1461	1411	103	1462	1453	131	54111	56103	5110		112	105	1409	2401	5403	110	5421	2403	5405	14101	14107		53171
		Ⓒ	Ⓐ											Ⓑ	Ⓑ		Ⓑ				Ⓑ			
	Z		B	P	Y		V	G	OW	G		M	S	B	AL	G	Q	G	L	G		D		E
Warszawa Wschodnia ....d.	0514	0604	0604	0619	0804	0839	0849	...	0959	1029	...	1319	1429	1539	1544	1629	1734	...	1744	1829	1949	2019	...	2214
Warszawa Centralna ....d.	0525	0615	0615	0635	0815	0850	0905	...	1010	1045	...	1335	1440	1551	1614	1644	1751	...	1815	1850	2018	2035	...	2225
Łódź Widzew ....d.	|	|	|	|	|	|	|	1021	|	|	...	|	|	|	|	|	|	1842	|	|	|	|	...	|
Koluszki ....d.	|	0712	0712	|	0912	|	|	|	1119	|	...	|	|	|	1707	|	|	|	1912	|	2127	|	...	2337
Piotrków Trybunalski........d.	|	0735	0735	|	0935	|	|	1055	1143	|	...	|	|	|	1731	|	|	1915	1936	|	2151	|	...	0003
Częstochowa..................d.	|	0828	0828	|	1030	|	|	1146	1237	|	...	|	|	|	1824	|	|	2010	2029	|	2246	|	...	0115
Zawiercie .... **1067** d.	0738	0915	0915	0844	1116	|	1110	1226	1317	1232	...	1552	1638	1750	1912	1832	1949	|	2108	|	|	2308	...	...
Sosnowiec Gł. .... **1067** d.	0805	0944	0944	0906	1143	1100	1134	1303	1344	1254	...	1617	1700	1814	1939	1854	2013	|	2135	2100	|	2337	...	...
Katowice .... **1067** a.	0816	0953	0953	0915	1152	1109	1143	1312	1353	1303	...	1626	1709	1823	1948	1903	2022	2129	2144	2109	0011	2346	...	...

	TLK	TLK	IC	EIC	IC	EIC	EC	IC	EIP		EC	EC	TLK	EIP	TLK	EC	IC	IC	EIP	IC	IC	EC	EC	TLK
	41101	41106	4202	4102	4521	4502	111	4200	4504		113	104	65104	4510	45110	130	4112	4162	4500	4110	4160	102	117	35170
	41100	41107	4203	4103	4520	4503	41008	4201	4505		41006	45000	65105	4511	45111	41004	4113	4163	4150	4111	4161	41002	41000	35171
	①–⑥			①–⑥			①–⑥	①–⑥						Ⓑ			Ⓐ	Ⓒ		Ⓐ	Ⓒ			
		C	BL	B	G	G	Q	AL	G		M	S	WO	G	G	V	Y	Y	G			P	Z	F
Katowice .... **1067** d.	0316	0413	0605	0537	0625	0655	0736	0813	0850	...	1133	1233	1403	1450	1456	1614	1604	1604	1650	1808	1808	1837	1950	...
Sosnowiec Gł. .... **1067** d.	|	0422	0614	0546	|	0705	0745	0822	0859	...	1142	1242	1413	1500	1505	1623	1613	1613	1659	1817	1817	1846	2000	...
Zawiercie .... **1067** d.	|	0448	0642	0612	|	0728	0811	0851	|	...	1208	1305	1441	1523	1533	1649	1644	1644	|	1848	1848	1909	2027	...
Częstochowa..................d.	0454	|	0728	|	0806	|	|	0932	|	...	|	|	1525	|	1619	|	1732	1732	|	1934	1934	|	|	0248
Piotrków Trybunalski........d.	0550	|	0819	|	0857	|	|	1023	|	...	|	|	1618	|	1710	|	1824	1824	|	2025	2025	|	|	0343
Koluszki ....d.	0614	|	0843	|	|	|	|	1047	|	...	|	|	1642	|	|	|	1848	1848	|	2048	2048	|	|	0410
Łódź Widzew ....a.	|	|	|	|	0930	|	|	|	|	...	|	|	|	|	1743	|	|	|	|	|	|	|	|	|
Warszawa Centralna ....a.	0725	0737	0941	0810	...	0915	1011	1145	1110	...	1425	1507	1750	1710	...	1855	1945	1945	1912	2145	2145	2108	2235	0520
Warszawa Wschodnia ....a.	0741	0801	1016	0846	...	0931	1021	1216	1131	...	1441	1531	1801	1731	...	1921	1956	1956	1931	2156	2156	2128	2246	0541

	IC		EC	IC	IC	EIP	IC	EC	EIP	TLK		IC		EIC	EIP	IC		EC	EIP	IC		TLK		
	40001		14000	1460	1410	1452	1412	14004	5410	56103		14006		1408	5402	2400		14008	5404	2402		14106		
	101		116	1461	1411	1453	1462	131	5411			112		1409	5403	2401		110	5405	2403		14107		
				Ⓒ	Ⓐ									Ⓑ		Ⓑ		Ⓑ	Ⓑ					
	R		Z				Y	V	G	W		M			G	AL		Q	G	L				
Katowice .... **1075** d.	0505	...	0831	0956	0956	1112	1157	1203	1306	1356	...	1629	...	1827	1906	1954	...	2025	2112	2147	...	2349	...	...
Tychy ....▷ d.	0519	...	0846	1009	1010	1126	1211	1218	|	|	...	1644	...	1842	|	|	...	2039	2126	2201	...	|	...	...
Rybnik ....▷ a.	0545	...	0912	...	|	|	|	1244	|	|	...	1711	...	|	|	|	...	2106	|	|	...	|	...	...
Gliwice .... **1075** a.	...	...	...	...	|	|	|	...	1328	1418	...	...	...	|	1928	2016	...	...	|	|	...	0011	...	...
Bielsko Biała ....▷ a.	...	...	...	...	1044	1201	1246	...	...	...	...	...	...	1916	...	...	...	...	2201	2235	...	...	...	...

	TLK	EIC	IC	EIC	EC	IC	EIP		EC		EIP	EC	IC	IC	EIP	EIP	IC	IC		EC		IC		
	41106	4102	4202	4502	111	4200	4504		113		4510	130	4112	4162	4500	4150	4110	4160		117		100		
	41107	4103	4203	4503	41008	4201	4505		41006		4511	41004	4113	4163	4501	4151	4111	4161		41000		44000		
		①–⑥			①–⑥						Ⓑ		Ⓐ	Ⓒ	Ⓑ	⑥	Ⓐ	Ⓒ						
			L	G	Q	AL	G		M		G	V	Y	Y	G					Z		R		
Bielsko Biała ....▷ d.	...	0438	0514	...	...	...	0758	...	...	...	...	...	1509	...	1558	1558	1711	1711	...	...	...	...	...	...
Gliwice .... **1075** d.	0345	|	|	0628	...	0743	|	...	...	...	1421	...	|	...	|	|	|	|	...	...	...	...	...	...
Rybnik ....▷ d.	|	|	|	|	0650	|	|	...	1048	...	|	1513	|	...	|	|	|	|	...	1847	...	2209	...	...
Tychy ....▷ d.	|	0515	0548	|	0718	|	0833	...	1116	...	|	1540	1546	1546	1633	1633	1745	1745	...	1914	...	2237	...	...
Katowice .... **1075** a.	0410	0531	0602	0652	0733	0808	0847	...	1130	...	1445	1554	1600	1600	1647	1647	1759	1759	...	1928	...	2251	...	...

To / from Racibórz (Table **1076**).

To / from Bielsko Biała.

HAŃCZA – [12] Gliwice - Katowice - Warszawa - Białystok - Suwałki; [2] Gliwice (**41106**) - Katowice - Warszawa - Białystok (**11015**) - Hrodna.

HAŃCZA – [12] Suwałki - Białystok - Warszawa - Katowice - Gliwice; [2] Hrodna (**10016**) - Białystok (**14106**) - Warszawa - Katowice - Gliwice.

Dec. 9 - Feb. 23, June 22 - Aug. 31: [sleeper] 1, 2 cl., [couchette] 2 cl. [12] Gdynia Gł. - Warszawa - Kraków - Zakopane. (Table **1066**).

Dec. 10 - Feb. 24, June 23 - Sept. 1: [sleeper] 1, 2 cl., [couchette] 2 cl. [12] Zakopane - Kraków - Warszawa - Gdynia Gł. (Table **1066**).

G – To / from Gdynia (Tables **1025/30**).

L – To / from Lublin (Table **1055**).

M – PORTA MORAVICA – [12] ✕ Warszawa - Praha and v.v.

O – To / from Olsztyn (Table **1030**).

P – POLONIA – [12] ✕ Warszawa - Wien and v.v.

Q – COMENIUS – [12] ✕ Warszawa - Ostrava and v.v.

R – MORAVIA – [12] ✕ Katowice - Ostrava - Wien and v.v.

S – SOBIESKI – [12] ✕ Gdynia - Warszawa - Wien and v.v.

V – VARSOVIA – [12] ✕ Warszawa - Budapest and v.v.

W – To / from Wrocław (Table **1061**).

Y – To / from Białystok (Table **1040**).

Z – PRAHA – [12] ✕ Warszawa - Praha and v.v.

▷ – For local trains Katowice - Bielsko Biała and Rybnik – see Tables **1077/79**.

WARSZAWA - ŁÓDŹ - WROCŁAW 1061

	IC	EIC	EIC	TLK	IC	IC		IC	IC	EIP	IC	IC	TLK	IC	EIP	IC	TLK	EIC	IC		IC			
	1610	1650	1606	46100	1620	1662		5610	1614	1602	1820	1612	35152	1614	1604	46109	86104	1608	1616		16170			
	1611	1651	1607	48150	1621	1663		1670	1614	1603	1821	1613	45102	1654	1652		86105	1609	1617		16190			
	Ⓐ	Ⓒ	Ⓐ	①–⑥	①–⑥	⑦							Ⓑ			⑤⑦		Ⓑ						
		J						EJ			S	Y		Y			K		Y		YP			
Warszawa Wschodnia ....d.	0504	0549	0549	...	0739	0704	...	0904	1119	1149	1309	1304	...	1459	1549	...	1704	1739	1904	...	2309	...	...	...
Warszawa Centralna ....d.	0515	0605	0605	...	0750	0720	...	0915	1135	1205	1320	1320	...	1510	1605	...	1718	1755	1925	...	2320	...	...	...
Piotrków Trybunalski........d.	|	|	|	...	|	|	...	1038	|	|	|	|	...	1629	|	...	|	|	|	...	0146	...	...	...
Częstochowa ....d.	|	0812**x**	0812**x**	...	|	|	...	1149	|	1404**x**	|	|	...	1728	1804**x**	...	|	2007**x**	|	...	0239	...	...	...
Łódź Widzew ....▷ d.	0641	|	|	...	0914	0836	...	|	|	|	1432	1332	...	|	|	...	1855	|	2044	...	|	...	...	...
Kalisz ....▷ d.	0832	|	|	...	1104	1024	...	|	1418	|	1613	1638	...	|	|	...	2042	|	2242	...	|	...	...	...
Ostrów Wlkp ....▷ d.	0849	|	|	...	1121	1041	...	|	1435	|	...	1657	...	|	|	...	2101	|	2300	...	|	...	...	...
Opole Gł. ....d.	|	0905	0905	0931	|	|	...	1252	|	1458	...	|	1729	1830	1857	1928	|	2102	|	...	0337	...	...	...
Brzeg ....d.	|	|	|	0956	|	|	...	1316	|	|	...	|	1754	1855	1919	1953	|	|	|	...	0357	...	...	...
Wrocław Gł. ....▷ a.	1015	0947	0947	1023	1243	1202	...	1343	1557	1537	...	1834	1821	1920	1940	2020	2224	2143	0027	...	0424	...	...	...

	IC	EIC	EIP	EIP	TLK		IC	TLK	IC	IC	IC	EIC	IC	IC	IC	IC	EIP	TLK	IC	EIC		IC		
	6117	6108	6104	6152	68105		6114	53152	8121	6112	6203	6106	64104	6170	6163	6201	6102	64100	6111	6150		61170		
	6116	6109	6105	6153	68104		6154	54102	8120	6113	6202	6107		6510	6162	6200	6103	64101	6110	6151		61190		
	①–⑥	①–⑥	①–⑥	⑦				①–⑥				①–⑤	⑤⑦		⑥	Ⓑ				Ⓒ				
			J		K		Y		S		L			EJ		L				J		QY		
...cław Gł. ....▷ d.	0404	0509	0619	0619	0613	...	0836	0938	...	1046	1159	1228	1338	1430	1600	1600	1622	1738	1804	1824	...	0038	...	...
...zeg ....d.	|	|	0640	0640	|	...	0902	1005	...	1110	|	|	1407	1457	|	|	|	1805	|	|	...	0103	...	...
...pole Gł. ....d.	|	0551	0703	0703	|	...	0927	1029	...	1131	|	1311	1431	1522	|	|	1703	1829	|	1906	...	0127	...	...
...ów Wlkp ....▷ d.	0532	|	|	|	0736	...	|	...	...	|	1325	|	...	|	1728	1728	|	...	1942	|	...	|	...	...
...z ....▷ d.	0549	|	|	|	0753	...	|	...	1149	|	1343	|	...	|	1746	1746	|	...	2000	|	...	|	...	...
...ź Widzew ....▷ d.	0740	|	|	|	0942	...	|	...	1332	|	1528	|	...	|	1932	1932	|	...	2149	|	...	|	...	...
...stochowa ....d.	|	0645**x**	0756**x**	0756**x**	|	...	1028	...	|	1229	|	1405**x**	...	1627	|	|	1756**x**	...	|	1959**x**	...	0231	...	...
...otrków Trybunalski ....d.	|	|	|	|	|	...	1119	...	|	1322	|	|	...	1718	|	|	|	...	|	|	...	0322	...	...
...szawa Centralna ....a.	0859	0855	0955	0955	1102	...	1240	...	1440	1445	1641	1611	...	1840	2040	2040	1955	...	2314	2207	...	0545	...	...
...szawa Wschodnia ....a.	0911	0926	1011	1011	1116	...	1256	...	1451	1456	1716	1626	...	1856	2051	2116	2011	...	2326	2221	...	0611	...	...

To / from Białystok / Ełk (Tables **1035 / 1040**).

To / from Jelenia Góra (Table **1084**).

To / from Kołobrzeg (Table **1015**).

To / from Lublin (Table **1055**).

P – To Jelenia Góra (arrive 0739) and Szklarska Poreba (0835).

Q – From Szklarska Poreba (depart 2026) and Jelenia Góra (2125).

S – To / from Szczecin (Table **1010**).

Y – To / from Białystok (Table **1040**).

x – Częstochowa **Stradom**.

▷ – For local trains see Table **1080**.

* – *406 km* via CMK.

• – Częstochowa - Opole Gł. *91 km*.

1065 WARSZAWA - KRAKÓW

km																								
		EIP	*EIP*	*TLK*	*EIC*	*EIC*	*EIP*	*EIP*	*TLK*	*EIP*	*EIC*	*TLK*	*EIP*	*EIP*	*EIP*	*EIC*	*EIP*	*EIC*	*TLK*	*EIP*	*EIP*	*IC*	*TLK*	*EIP*
		1302	**1300**	**13100**	**5350**	**1350**	**5312**	**1304**	**53100**	**5314**	**1313**	**13112**	**8300/1**	**5302/3**	**5304**	**1312**	**5306**	**1314**	**53106**	**5308**	**1306**	**14010**	**14106**	**5310**	**1**
		1303	**1301**	**13101**	**5351**	**1351**	**5313**	**1305**	**53101**	**5315**	**1312**	**13113**	**5352/3**	**1352/3**	**5305**	**1313**	**5307**	**1354**	**53107**	**5309**	**1307**	**407**	**14107**	**5311**	**1**
					①⑥		①–⑥	⑦										⑧			⑧				
				P	GU	V	G		GP	G	B	m	T	C	D	E	G	F	H	GR			J	G	
0	**Warszawa** Wsch. d.	0544	0634	0719	0634	0634	0829	0829	0859	0929	1039	1129	1139	1234	1329	1434	1529	1634	1659	1729	1844	1914	2014	2029	2
5	**Warszawa** Cent. d.	0556	0645	0735	0650	0650	0839	0845	0910	0945	1050	1140	1155	1245	1345	1445	1547	1648	1715	1747	1858	1930	2027	2045	2
297	**Kraków** Gł. a.	0830	0908	1030	0925	0925	1106	1106	1251	1206	1326	1442	1416	1506	1605	1716	1809	1924	2040	2008	2126	2220	2338	2307	2

	TLK	*EIP*	*IC*	*EIC*	*TLK*	*EIP*	*EIP*	*EIP*	*EIP*	*EIP*	*TLK*	*EIP*	*EIP*	*TLK*	*EIP*	*EIP*	*EIC*	*EIC*	*EIC*	*EIP*	*TLK*	*EIC*	*IC*
	41106	**3510**	**41010**	**3124**	**35106**	**3508**	**3106**	**3506**	**3504**	**3502**	**31152**	**3800/1**	**3104**	**35100**	**3500**	**3102**	**3112**	**3550**	**3158**	**3100**	**31100**	**3112**	**3108**
	41107	**3511**	**406**	**3154**	**35107**	**3558**	**3107**	**3507**	**3505**	**3503**	**31153**	**3552/3**	**3105**	**35101**	**3501**	**3103**	**3113**	**3551**	**3159**	**3101**	**31101**	**3113**	**3109**
				①–⑥			①–⑥											⑤⑦					
	J	G		L	H	RG		G	G	G		S		PG	G	E	B	GX	W		P	E	
Kraków Gł. d.	0425	0549	0625	0655	0657	0753	0853	0946	1051	1148	1256	1339	1457	1513	1549	1650	1650	1749	1749	1852	1920	1955	2200
Warszawa Centralna a.	0737	0815	0920	0934	1035	1020	1115	1210	1315	1415	1545	1605	1720	1917	1815	1914	1926	2019	2019	2115	2208	2226	0040
Warszawa Wschodnia a.	0801	0831	0941	0946	1056	1031	1126	1231	1331	1431	1556	1631	1731	1926	1831	1926	1936	2025	2025	2126	2221	2241	0050

A – ②③④⑤⑦.
B – From May 20.
C – From Gdynia on ①–⑥ (Table **1030**).
D – Until May 19. From Gdynia (Table **1030**).
E – Until May 19.
F – To Przemyśl on ⑤⑦ (Table **1075**).
G – From/to Gdynia (Table **1030**).
H – From/to Gdynia (Table **1035**).
J – From/to Hrodna and Suwałki (Table **1042**).
K – ①②③④⑥.
L – From Przemyśl on ①⑥ (Table **1075**).
P – To/from Przemyśl (Table **1075**).
R – To Rzeszów (Table **1075**).
S – Daily to Gdynia (Table **1030**). ⑧ to Kołobrzeg (Table **1015**).
T – Daily from Gdynia (Table **1030**). ①–⑥ from Kołobrzeg (Table **1015**).
U – ①⑥ June 22 - Aug. 31 (also Aug. 15).
V – ②③④⑤⑦ June 23 - Aug. 30 (not Aug.
W – ①②③④⑥ June 22 - Aug. 31 (not Aug.
X – ⑤⑦ June 23 - Aug. 30 (also Aug. 14).

1066 KRAKÓW - ZAKOPANE

km		*TLK*			*EIC*	*EIC*		*TLK*		*IC*
		53171			**5351**	**1351**		**13152**		**5360**
		GNK			GS	T		R		K
	Warszawa Cent. **1065** d.	2225	...	...	0650	0650	...	1140	...	...
0	**Kraków** Gł. d.	0327	...	...	0940	0940	...	1511	...	1744
5	Kraków Płaszów d.	|	...	...	|	|	...	|	...	|
68	Sucha Beskidzka Zamek d.	0456	...	...	|	|	...	1638	...	1907
103	Chabówka a.	0532	...	...	1134	1134	...	1713	...	|
103	Chabówka d.	0546	...	...	1148	1148	...	1730	...	|
126	Nowy Targ d.	0615	...	...	1215	1215	...	1805	...	2029
147	**Zakopane** a.	0652	...	...	1239	1239	...	1853	...	2053

	IC		*TLK*		*EIC*	*EIC*		*TLK*
	3560		**31152**		**3550**	**3150**		**35170**
	L		X		GW	V		GNL
Zakopane d.	0632	...	0913	...	1435	1435	...	2101
Nowy Targ d.	0656	...	0941	...	1458	1458	...	2127
Chabówka a.	|	...	1009	...	1525	1525	...	2154
Chabówka d.	|	...	1023	...	1539	1539	...	2209
Sucha Beskidzka Zamek d.	0817	...	1116	...	|	|	...	2245
Kraków Płaszów a.	|	...	|	...	|	|	...	|
Kraków Gł. a.	0937	...	1237	...	1735	1735	...	0009
Warszawa Cent. **1065** a.	...	...	1545	...	2019	2019	...	0520

G – To/from Gdynia (Table **1030**).
K – June 22 - Aug. 31.
L – June 23 - Sept. 1.
N – Also conveys 🛌 and/or 🛏.
R – ⑤⑥⑦ June 22 - Aug. 31.
S – ①⑥ June 22 - Aug. 31 (also Aug. 15).
T – ②③④⑤⑦ June 23 - Aug. 30 (not Aug. 15).
V – ①②③④⑥ June 22 - Aug. 31 (not Aug. 14).
W – ⑤⑦ June 23 - Aug. 30 (also Aug. 1
X – ①⑥⑦ June 23 - Aug. 31 (also Aug

1067 WARSZAWA and LUBLIN - KIELCE - KATOWICE and KRAKÓW

km	*For fast trains to Kraków see Table* **1065**		*TLK*		*IC*	*IC*	*IC*	*IC*			*TLK*		*IC*	*IC*	*IC*	*IC*	*IC*		*IC*	*IC*		
			83170		**22480**	**16110**	**22484**	**5324**			**16112**		**5322**	**22488**	**16114**	**22492**	**5320**		**22432**	**5326**		
			83171		**22481**	**16111**	**22485**	**5325**			**16113**		**5323**	**22489**	**16115**	**22493**	**5321**		**22433**	**5327**		
			Y		🚌	W	🚌	O	🚌	2	W		O	🚌	W	🚌	O	🚌	🚌	O	2	🚌
0	**Warszawa** Wschodnia d.	...	...	...	...	...	...	0729	...	...	...	...	1209	...	...	...	1524	...	...	1804	...	...
4	**Warszawa** Centralna d.	...	...	...	...	...	...	0740	...	...	...	...	1220	...	...	...	1535	...	...	1821	...	...
	Lublin d.	...	...	...	0509	...	0635	|	0722	...	...	...	|	1235	...	1436	|	1535	1712	|	...	1945
•	Dęblin d.	0343	...	...	0659	...	0825	|	0925	0935	...	...	|	1425	...	1626	|	1743	1902	|	2113	2148
107*	Radom d.	0439	...	...	0829	0839	0955	1005	...	1033	1145	...	1443	1555	1605	1756	1806	...	2032	2042	2222	...
148	Skarżysko Kamienna d.	...	...	...	...	0906	...	1031	...	...	1210	...	1509	...	1632	...	1832	...	...	2108	...	...
192	Kielce d.	...	0616	...	...	1004	...	1115	...	...	1302	...	1545	...	1726	...	1908	...	...	2146	...	...
	Zawiercie **1060** d.	...	|	...	...	1143	...	|	...	...	1423	...	|	...	1901	...	|	...	...	|	...	...
	Sosnowiec Gł. **1060** d.	...	|	...	...	1214	...	|	...	...	1452	...	|	...	1929	...	|	...	...	|	...	...
	Katowice **1060** a.	...	|	...	...	1225	...	|	...	...	1504	...	|	...	1943	...	|	...	...	|	...	...
324	**Kraków** Gł. a.	...	0824	...	...	...	...	1253	...	...	...	...	1719	...	...	...	2042	...	...	2318	...	...

km					*IC*	*IC*	*IC*	*IC*		*TLK*	*IC*	*IC*			*TLK*			*IC*	*IC*	*IC*	*IC*	*TLK*
					3526	**22372**	**3520**	**22390**		**61114**	**22392**	**3522**			**61112**			**3524**	**22394**	**61110**	**22396**	**38170**
					3527	**22373**	**3521**	**22391**		**61115**	**22393**	**3523**			**61113**			**3525**	**22395**	**61111**	**22397**	**38171**
																	⑦					
		2	🚌	2	O	🚌	O	🚌		W	🚌	O	2	🚌	W	2	🚌	O	🚌	W	🚌	Y
	Kraków Gł. d.	...	...	...	0440	...	0654	...	...	...	...	1118	...	...	...	...	...	1534	...	...	...	2018
0	**Katowice** **1060** d.	...	...	...	|	...	|	...	...	0856	...	|	...	...	1303	...	...	|	...	1704	...	|
9	Sosnowiec Gł. **1060** d.	...	...	...	|	...	|	...	...	0905	...	|	...	...	1312	...	...	|	...	1713	...	|
44	Zawiercie **1060** d.	...	...	...	|	...	|	...	...	0932	...	|	...	...	1338	...	...	|	...	1740	...	|
161	Kielce d.	...	...	...	0614	...	0826	...	...	1109	...	1254	...	...	1515	...	...	1707	...	1922	...	2150
	Skarżysko Kamienna d.	...	...	...	0650	...	0903	...	...	1119	...	1332	...	...	1553	...	...	1744	...	1959	...	...
	Radom d.	0358	...	0623	0714a	0724	0926a	0935	...	1216	1226	1358a	1438	...	1620	1652	...	1808a	1818	2025	2035	...
	Dęblin d.	0458	0513	0719	|	0854	|	1105	...	...	1356	|	1535	1625	...	1749	1758	|	1948	...	2205	...
	Lublin a.	...	0721	...	|	1044	|	1255	...	...	1546	|	...	1828	...	...	2001	|	2138	...	2355	...
	Warszawa Centralna a.	...	...	...	0944	...	1150	...	...	...	...	1620	...	...	...	...	...	2031	...	...	...	...
	Warszawa Wschodnia a.	...	...	...	1001	...	1201	...	...	...	...	1636	...	...	...	...	...	2046	...	...	...	...

O – To/from Olsztyn (Table **1030**).
W – To/from Wrocław (Tables **1061/75**).
Y – 🛌 1, 2 cl., 🛏 2 cl. and (2) Kołobrzeg - Gdańsk - Kraków - Przemyśl and v.v. (Table **1015**).
a – Arrival time.
• – Lublin - Radom: *12*
* – *161 km* via Dęblin.

1070 POZNAŃ - WROCŁAW

km		*IC*		*TLK*			*IC*	*IC*		*TLK*		*TLK*		*IC*		*IC*	*IC*		*TLK*			*IC*		
		7300		**56150**			**56106**	**8400**		**56104**		**54101**		**8306**		**5600**	**84104**		**16105**			**5602**		
				56151			**56107**			**56105**		**54100**		**8307**		**5601**	**84105**		**14103**			**5603**		
			2		2				2				2					2		2				
		P		A			G	TE		G		GT		EP		G	CT		Y			G		
0	**Poznań** Gł. d.	0555	0600	0650	0744	...	0900	0958	1040	1147	...	1255	1325	1349	...	1511	1618	1640	1718	1831	...	1936	...	...
69	Leszno d.	0710	0721	0801	0913	...	0959	1055	1208	1255	...	1357	1514	1451	...	1623	1717	1821	1823	1948	...	2053	...	...
165	**Wrocław** Gł. a.	0822	0858	0918	1050	...	1110	1209	1340	1411	...	1516	1653	1610	...	1729	1830	1948	1938	2120	...	2208	...	...

	IC			*TLK*	*IC*		*IC*	*IC*	*TLK*			*IC*			*IC*	*TLK*			*TLK*			*IC*		
	6503			**41103**	**48101**		**6501**	**3806**	**45101**			**65103**			**4801**	**65107**			**45102**			**3701**		
	6502			**61105**	**48100**		**6500**	**3807**	**45100**			**65102**				**65106**			**65150**					
		2	2							2			2				2	2		2				
	G			Y	CT		G	P	TG			G			TE	G		Ⓒ	A			P		
Wrocław Gł. d.	0642	0730	0817	0832	0939	...	1044	1142	1239	1245	...	1354	1418	...	1555	1652	1702	1742	1837	1910	...	2004	...	...
Leszno d.	0801	0904	1018	0958	1059	...	1154	1258	1409	1432	...	1505	1613	...	1720	1818	1909	1937	1954	2050	...	2132	...	...
Poznań Gł. a.	0902	1022	1148	1059	1200	...	1259	1400	1512	1558	...	1612	1742	...	1820	1918	2032	2059	2055	2218	...	2234	...	...

A – To/from Bydgoszcz (Table **1020**).
B – To/from Bielsko Biała.
C – To/from Świnoujście (Table **1010**).
E – To/from Kołobrzeg (Table **1015**).
G – To/from Gdynia (Tables **1015/20**).
P – To/from Przemyśl (Table **1075**).
T – To/from Katowice (Table **1075**
Y – To/from Białystok (Table **1035**

RZESZÓW - JASŁO - ZAGÓRZ - MEDZILABORCE 1073

km				TLK 33151						
		2 ①–⑤	2 A	2	2 ⚒	2	①–⑥ 2	①–⑤ 2	2	
0	**Rzeszów** Gł. d.	...	0549	1116	...	1434	1526	1624	1936	...
9	Boguchwała d.	...	0613	1139	...	1451	1549	1640	1957	...
48	Frysztak d.	...	|	1216	...	1544	1633	1725	2044	...
52	Przybówka d.	...	|	|	...	1548	1638	1734	2048	...
71	**Jasło** d.	0716	0721	1311	1520	1608	1658	1753	2109	...
94	Krosno d.	0746	0747	1340	1551	...	...	...	...	...
33	Sanok d.	0840	0837	1458	1651	...	...	...	...	...
39	Nowy Zagórz a.	0848	|	|	1658	...	...	...	...	...
40	**Zagórz** d.	0851	0847	1519	1700	...	...	...	...	...
88	Łupków 🏛 a.	...	0955	1634	...	...	...	...	...	...
04	**Medzilaborce** mesto a.	...	1015	...	...	...	...	...	...	...
06	Medzilaborce a.	...	1020	...	...	...	...	...	...	...

					TLK 33134				
	Ⓐ 2	⚒ 2	①–⑤ 2	2	2	⚒ 2	①–⑥ 2	2 A	
Medzilaborce d.	...	...	...	...	...	...	...	1747	...
Medzilaborce mesto a.	...	...	...	...	...	...	...	1752	...
Łupków 🏛 d.	...	...	...	...	...	...	...	1812	...
Zagórz d.	...	0515	...	...	1331	...	...	1920	...
Nowy Zagórz d.	...	0517	...	...	|	...	...	|	...
Sanok d.	...	0524	...	...	1343	1533	...	1929	...
Krosno d.	...	0625	...	...	1448	1629	...	2219	...
Jasło d.	0502	0656	0730	0906	1533	1701	1712	2111	...
Przybówka d.	0521	...	0749	0926	|	...	1731	|	...
Frysztak d.	0526	...	0753	0930	1555	...	1736	|	...
Boguchwała d.	0610	...	0843	1015	1638	...	1821	2201	...
Rzeszów Gł. a.	0628	...	0908	1039	1647	...	1843	2220	...

- ⑥⑦ June 29 - Aug. 31.

ŁÓDŹ - CZESTOCHOWA - KRAKÓW 1074

km			IC 1321 ①–⑥		TLK 54110 ①–⑥ HT		2		IC 5420 HT	
0	**Łódź** Fabryczna d.	...	0559	...	...	...	1253	...	...	...
15	**Łódź** Widzew d.	...	0607	...	1021	...	1300	...	1842	...
67	Piotrków Trybunalski d.	...	0640	...	1055	...	1356	...	1915	...
53	**Częstochowa** d.	...	0736	...	1145	...	1517	...	2006	...
9*	**Kraków** Gł. a.	...	0915	...	...	...	...	...	...	...

	IC 4521 HT		Ⓐ 2		TLK 45110 Ⓑ T		IC 3120 Ⓑ		
Kraków Gł. d.	...	...	...	...	...	...	1824	...	...
Częstochowa d.	0806	...	1338	...	1619	...	1959	...	...
Piotrków Trybunalski d.	0857	...	1510	...	1710	...	2056	...	...
Łódź Widzew a.	0930	...	1604	...	1743	...	2129	...	...
Łódź Kaliska a.	...	...	1623	...	...	...	2139	...	...

- To/from Gdynia (Table **1025**). T – To/from Katowice (Table **1060**). * – *274 km* via CMK.

WROCŁAW - KATOWICE - KRAKÓW - PRZEMYŚL 1075

For other trains Poznań - Katowice/Kraków see Tables **1080** (via Ostrów Wlkp) and **1025** (via Łódź)

km		MP	IC	TLK	TLK	IC	TLK	TLK	IC	TLK	IC	TLK	TLK	IC	IC	IC	TLK	IC	TLK	EIC	IC	TLC	EIP	IC	IC	IC	
		457	83192	83174	54170	6302	13100	62114	7300	53100	8305	83105	62112	65104	8400	6304	33116	8310	62110	1354	8306	84101	5308	6300	84104	84102	
		74010	83193	83175	54172	6303	13101	62115	7301	53101	8304	83104	62113	65100		6305	33117	8311	62111	1355	8307	84100	5309	6301	84105	84103	
		83192																		⑤⑦							
		A	BN	EN	N		W	L	Z	G	Y	B	L	O	E	J		T	L	W	QE	B	G		B	E	
0	**Wrocław** Gł. 1061 d.	2300	...	...	0537	0634	...	0640	0831	...	1035	...	1051	1138	1238	1233	...	1426	1438	...	1630	1638	...	1835	1840	2100	...
2	Brzeg 1061 d.	|	...	...	0604	0701	...	0709	0856	...	1100	...	1118	1208	1307	1300	...	1450	1505	...	1657	1707	...	1902	1908	2129	...
2	Opole Gł. 1061 d.	2340	...	...	0634	0725	...	0738	0918	...	1122	...	1144	1239	1336	1322	...	1513	1536	...	1720	1736	...	1927	1933	2154	...
2	Gliwice 1060 d.	0215	0242	...	0727	|	...	0830	|	...	|	...	1235	1332	1433	|	...	|	1629	...	|	1831	...	|	2024	2248	...
0	**Katowice** 1060 a.	0239	0307	...	0752	|	...	0854	|	...	|	...	1259	1357	1500	|	...	|	1653	...	|	1857	...	|	2048	2313	...
0	**Katowice** d.	0327	0327	...	...	|	...	...	|	...	|	...	...	...	...	|	...	|	...	...	|	...	...	|	...	...	...
•	Częstochowa Stradom d.	|	|	0500	...	0818	...	...	1014	...	1216	1254	...	...	...	1416	...	1612	...	...	1816	...	...	2025	...	...	...
8	**Kraków** Gł. a.	0532	0532	0803	...	0943	...	...	1139	...	1342	1427	...	...	...	1541	...	1737	...	...	1943	...	...	2154	...	...	...
8	**Kraków** Gł. 1078 d.	0546	0546	0837	...	1002	1057	...	1151	1311	1346	1439	...	...	...	1547	1650	1750	...	1930	2002	...	2011	...	...	...	...
3	Kraków Płaszów 1078 d.	0555	0555	0846	...	1010	|	...	1203	|	1354	1447	...	...	...	1555	|	1758	...	1951	2010	...	2020	...	...	...	...
6	Tarnów 1078 d.	0653	0653	0943	...	1101	1214	...	1255	1433	1445	1544	...	...	...	1647	1800	1852	...	2038	2110	...	2109	...	...	...	...
9	Dębica d.	0714	0714	1004	...	1118	1232	...	1312	1452	1503	1605	...	...	...	1705	1817	1910	...	2056	2128	...	2125	...	...	...	...
6	**Rzeszów** 1058 d.	0745	0745	1039	...	1146	1303	...	1338	1534	1531	1640	...	...	...	1738	1848	1939	...	2125	2201	...	2150	...	...	...	...
3	Przeworsk 1058 d.	0812	0812	1104	...	1211	1330	...	1403	1601	1556	1705	...	...	...	1804	1914	2004	...	|	2227	...	...	...	...	...	...
8	Jarosław 1058 d.	0823	0823	1115	...	1222	1341	...	1414	1612	1607	1716	...	...	...	1815	1925	2015	...	2159	2238	...	...	...	...	...	...
3	**Przemyśl** 1058 a.	0858	0858	1155	...	1300	1414	...	1453	1645	1644	1756	...	...	...	1856	2005	2053	...	2231	2319	...	...	...	...	...	...

	EIC	IC	IC	IC	IC	TLK	EIP	TLK	TLK	IC	IC	IC	TLK	TLK	TLK	IC	TLK	IC	TLK	IC	TLK	TLK	TLK	MP	TLK		
	3154	48103	48101	3600	3806	48105	3508	33138	26110	3810	4801	3604	56102	26112	38102	3804	35100	3700	26114	3602	45170	31100	38172	38192	38192		
	3155	48102	48100	3601	3807	48155	3509	33139	26111	3811		3605	56100	26113	38103	3805	35101	3701	26115	3603	45171	31101	38173	47010	38193		
	①⑥																							456			
	W	E	B		QE	B	G		L	B	E	JB	O	L	B	B	G	Z	L		N	W	EN	A	BN		
emyśl 1058 d.	0400	...	...	...	0422	...	...	0537	...	0653	...	0910	...	...	0949	1102	1152	1309	...	1451	...	1542	1713	1809	1809	...	...
osław 1058 d.	0433	...	...	...	0458	...	...	0620	...	0732	...	0950	...	...	1029	1140	1227	1347	...	1530	...	1613	1753	1845	1845	...	...
eworsk 1058 d.	|	...	...	...	0509	...	...	0630	...	0742	...	1001	...	...	1040	1151	1238	1358	...	1540	...	1624	1804	1856	1856	...	...
eszów 1058 d.	0508	...	...	...	0538	...	0609	0656	...	0809	...	1027	...	...	1107	1218	1309	1425	...	1607	...	1652	1831	1923	1923	...	...
bica d.	0535	...	...	...	0610	...	0635	0728	...	0835	...	1100	...	...	1142	1244	1341	1451	...	1634	...	1719	1906	1955	1955	...	...
nów 1078 d.	0553	...	...	...	0629	...	0652	0746	...	0854	...	1118	...	...	1203	1302	1402	1509	...	1652	...	1758	1927	2015	2015	...	...
ków Płaszów 1078 d.	0639	...	...	...	0726	...	0739	|	...	0942	...	1207	...	...	1257	1351	1455	1557	...	1741	...	|	2021	2115	2115	...	...
ków Gł. 1078 a.	0648	...	...	...	0735	...	0748	0846	...	0949	...	1214	...	...	1304	1358	1504	1604	...	1748	...	1902	2028	2124	2124	...	...
ków Gł. d.	...	...	...	0604	0744	...	...	...	...	1018	...	1217	...	...	1311	1418	...	1616	...	1817	...	...	2102	2139	2139	...	...
Częstochowa Stradom d.	...	...	...	0735	0916	...	...	...	...	1144	...	1344	...	...	1446	1546	...	1745	...	1944	...	...	0002	|	|	...	...
owice a.	...	...	...	|	|	...	...	...	...	|	...	|	...	...	...	|	...	|	...	|	...	...	...	2358	2358	...	...
owice 1060 d.	...	0511	0709	|	|	0907	...	...	1137	|	1259	|	1356	1501	...	|	...	|	1914	|	2103	...	...	0018	0038	...	...
vice 1060 d.	...	0534	0733	|	|	0931	...	...	1200	|	1324	|	1419	1524	...	|	...	|	1937	|	2127	...	...	0043	0103	...	...
ole Gł. 1061 d.	...	0629	0826	0832	1025	1030	...	...	1258	1239	1417	1443	1513	1622	...	1640	...	1839	2028	2038	2221	...	...	0424	...	...	...
eg 1061 d.	...	0654	0852	0858	1047	1055	...	...	1322	1301	1442	1505	1538	1647	...	1702	...	1901	2053	2100	2246	...	...	|	...	...	...
ocław Gł. 1061 a.	...	0722	0919	0925	1116	1123	...	...	1349	1325	1511	1531	1606	1715	...	1726	...	1926	2120	2125	2313	...	...	0505	...	...	...

LOCAL SERVICES KATOWICE - KRAKÓW and v.v.

			⑥	Ⓑ						
owice d.	0533	0801	1155	1221	1424	1532	1649	1826	2015	...
ków Gł. a.	0744	1040	1433	1433	1629	1800	1927	2040	2213	...

		Ⓑ	⑥		Ⓑ	⑥				
Kraków Gł. d.	0316	0458	0458	0717	0934	0934	1139	1435	1631	2120
Katowice a.	0526	0733	0830	0959	1142	1241	1422	1638	1846	2328

ÖBB nightjet METROPOL – 🛏 1, 2 cl., (2) Berlin - Wrocław - Przemyśl and v.v.
To/from Szczecin/Świnoujście (Tables **1010**, **1080**).
To/from Kołobrzeg (Table **1015**).
To/from Gdynia (Tables **1030**, **1065**).
To/from Jelenia Góra (Table **1084**).

L – To/from Lublin (Table **1067**).
N – Also conveys 🛏 and/or 🛏.
O – To/from Olsztyn (Table **1030**).
Q – Conveys 🛏 2 cl., Wrocław - Przemyśl - Lviv and v.v.
T – To/from Szczecin (Table **1003**, **1004**).
W – To/from Warszawa (Table **1065**).

Z – To/from Zielona Góra (Table **1004**).

f – 57 - 59 minutes later on ⑥

• – Wrocław - Kraków Gł. via Częstochową Stradom adds *47 km*.

1076 KATOWICE and KRAKÓW - BOHUMÍN - OSTRAVA

For night trains see Table 99

km	km		*EC* 101 ✕⟋ R	*LE* 400 🍷 K	*EC* 116 ✕⟋ Y	*EC* 103 ✕⟋ P	*EC* 114 ⟋ C	*EC* 131 ✕⟋ V	*EN* 409 ✕⟋ A	*EC* 112 ✕⟋	*EC* 205 ⟋ T	*EC* 105 ✕⟋ S	*EC* 110 ✕⟋ Ⓑ
		Warszawa Cen **1060** d.	...	...	0525	0640	...	0855	1230	1330	...	1440	1747
	0	**Kraków** Gł. ▷ d.	...	0448	|	|	1016	|	|	|	1541	|	|
0		**Katowice** d.	0500	0641	0828	0921	|	1158	|	1626	|	1713	2024
	65	Oświęcim ▷ d.	|	|	|	|	1150	|	|	|	1658	|	|
74	116	Zebrzydowice ⊞ d.	|	0737	|	1016	1305	|	|	|	1810	1816	|
45		Rybnik ▷ d.	0545	|	0912	|	|	1244	|	1711	|	|	2107
82		Racibórz ▷ d.	|	|	|	|	|	|	|	|	|	|	|
102		Chałupki ▷ d.	0620	|	0943	|	|	1316	1717	1742	|	|	2141
∆94		Bohumín ⊞ a.	0626	0754	0949	1036	1325	1322	1723	1748	1828	1836	|
94		Bohumín ⊞ **1160** d.	0651	0756	1006	1051	1406	1351	1800	1806	1851	1851	|
102		**Ostrava** hlavní **1160** a.	0658	0802	1013	1058	1413	1358	|	1813	1858	1858	2154
		Praha hlavní **1160** a.	|	1123	1339	|	1739	|	|	2139	|	|	...
		Wien Hbf **1150** a.	0949	...	...	1349	...	|	2117	...	2149	2149	...
		Budapest Nyugati a.	...	...	...	...	...	1920	...	...	...	...	...

	EC 111 ✕⟋ ①–⑥	*EN* 408 ✕⟋ B	*EC* 113 ✕⟋	*EC* 104 ✕⟋ S	*EC* 204 ⟋ T	*EC* 115 ⟋ C	*EC* 130 ✕⟋ V	*EC* 102 ✕⟋ P	*EC* 117 ✕⟋ Y	*LE* 401 🍷 J	*E*(10 ✕ R
Budapest Nyugati d.	...	...	...	...	...	...	0840	...	...	...	...
Wien Hbf **1150** d.	...	0605	...	0810	0810	...	|	1410	...	...	18
Praha hlavní **1160** d.	...	|	0624	|	|	1024	|	|	1424	1609	|
Ostrava hlavní **1160** d.	0605	|	0950	1102	1102	1350	1402	1702	1752	1935	21
Bohumín ⊞ **1160** a.	|	0914	0957	1109	1109	1357	1409	1709	1759	1942	21
Bohumín ⊞ d.	|	0951	1009	1120	1129	1433	1435	1722	1809	1949	21
Chałupki ▷ d.	0619	1001	1016	|	|	|	1442	|	1816	|	21
Racibórz ▷ d.	|	|	|	|	|	|	|	|	|	|	|
Rybnik ▷ d.	0651	|	1049	|	|	|	1518	|	1848	|	22
Zebrzydowice ⊞ d.	|	|	|	1141	1148	1455	|	1743	|	2008	|
Oświęcim ▷ a.	|	|	|	|	1305	1604	|	|	|	|	|
Katowice a.	0735	|	1132	1230	|	|	1601	1832	1931	2109	22
Kraków Gł. ▷ a.	|	|	|	|	1436	1724	|	|	|	2257	...
Warszawa Cen **1060** a.	1012	1435	1430	1507	...	...	1903	2107	2239	...	..

A – ④ (⑤ from Warszawa): 🛏 1 cl. (lux), 🛏 1, 2 cl. Moskva - Nice. ✕ (PKP) Warszawa - Nice.
B – ⑦ (① from Wien): 🛏 1 cl. (lux), 🛏 1, 2 cl. Nice - Moskva. ✕ (PKP) Nice - Warszawa.
C – CRACOVIA – [12] 🍷 Praha - Kraków and v.v.
J – ⑤⑦ Mar. 22 - June 28, daily June 29 - Sept. 1: LEO EXPRESS – [12] 🍷 Praha - Bohumín - Kraków.
K – ①⑥ Mar. 23 - June 29, daily June 30 - Sept. 2: LEO EXPRESS – [12] 🍷 Kraków - Bohumín - Praha.
P – POLONIA – [12] ✕ Warszawa - Wien and v.v.
R – MORAVIA – [12] ✕ Katowice - Wien and v.v.

S – SOBIESKI – [12] ✕ Gdynia - Warszawa - Wien and v.v.
T – SOBIESKI – [2] Ⓡ Kraków - Wien and v.v.
V – BÁTHORY – [12] ✕ Warszawa - Budapest and v.v.
Y – PRAHA – [12] ✕ Warszawa - Praha and v.v.

⟋ – Supplement payable.
▷ – For local trains see Tables **1079/99**.
∆ – *106 km* via Chałupki.

1077 KATOWICE - BIELSKO BIAŁA - ZWARDOŃ - ŽILINA

Koleje Śląskie, 2nd clas

km				Ⓒ	Ⓐ			Ⓐ							
0	**Katowice** **1060** d.	0431	0535	0723	0733	0936	1133	1239	1324	1441	1542	1642	1735	1935	2131
17	Tychy d.	0449	0554	0739	0751	0954	1151	1257	1342	1459	1600	1701	1754	1954	2150
44	Czechowice Dziedzice d.	0517	0623	0802	0819	1022	1220	1324	1410	1527	1627	1729	1821	2021	2217
55	**Bielsko Biała** Gł. **1060** d.	0535	0641	0814	0837	1040	1238	1343	1428	1545	1647	1750	1840	2041	2236
76	Zywiec a.	0608	0731	0842	0906	1109	1306	1411	1456	1615	1718	1821	1915	2109	2305
113	**Zwardoń** a.	...	0836	0943	1018	1216	1408	1512	1609	1725	1819	1923	2016	2211	0007

	Ⓐ														
Zwardoń d.	...	0347	0447**a**	0525	0628	0740	0945	1143	1333	1430**c**	1514	1615	1744	1941	...
Zywiec d.	0404	0449	0548	0628	0732	0843	1047	1244	1447	1539	1614	1719	1855	2047	...
Bielsko Biała Gł. **1060** d.	0442	0521	0619	0700	0810	0922	1122	1324	1533	1611	1646	1751	1925	2127	...
Czechowice Dziedzice d.	0459	0537	0635	0711	0826	0938	1138	1340	1549	1627	1703	1807	1936	2143	...
Tychy d.	0527	0605	0703	0734	0854	1006	1207	1408	1617	1656	1731	1836	1959	2211	...
Katowice **1060** a.	0546	0624	0721	0750	0913	1024	1224	1426	1636	1714	1750	1854	2029	2229	...

	⚒		Ⓐ				
Czech. Dziedzice d.	0615	...	1436	...	...	...	...
Zebrzydowice d.	0655	...	1516	...	...	...	...
Cieszyn ★ a.	0719	...	1540	...	...	...	...

		⚒		Ⓐ			
Cieszyn ★ d.	...	0407	...	1258	...	...	...
Zebrzydowice d.	...	0438	...	1329	...	...	...
Czech. Dziedzice a.	...	0514	...	1404	...	...	...

a – Ⓐ.
c – Ⓒ.

★ – Cieszyn station (Poland) is situated ± 1500 metres from Český Těšín station (Czech Republic).

ZWARDÓN - ŽILINA

km					Ⓐ	
0	**Zwardoń** ⊞ d.	0350	0642	1542	1642	1952
22	Čadca **1160** a.	0424	0726	1626	1731	2026
52	**Žilina** **1160** a.	0506	0813	1713	1813	2113

	Ⓒ		Ⓐ		
Žilina **1160** d.	0448	1348	1448	1758	2248
Čadca ⊞ **1160** d.	0537	1437	1537	1838	2328
Zwardoń ⊞ a.	0617	1510	1610	1910	2359

1078 KRAKÓW - NOWY SĄCZ - KRYNICA

km		*TLK* 30171 A			□ Ⓒ	*TLK* 30101 ⑥⑦		□	□	□
0	**Kraków** Gł. **1075** d.	0400	0343	0539	0742	1130	...	1550	1646	2019
5	Kraków Płaszów **1075** d.	|	0352	0550	|	|	...	1607	1701	2028
78	Tarnów **1075** a.	0508	0521	0647	0849	1242	...	1702	1759	2143
78	Tarnów d.	0512	0522	0648	0850	1243	1331	1703	1800	2144
136	Stróze d.	0624	0642	0751	0951	1343	1441	1813	1901	2252
167	**Nowy Sącz** d.	0713	0725	0830	1031	1422	1529	1855	1942	2334
217	Muszyna d.	0829	...	0940	1143	1549	1549	...	2055	...
228	**Krynica** a.	0846	...	0957	1200	1606	1606	...	2112	...

	□	□	□			*TLK* 33100 ⑥⑦	□ Ⓒ	Ⓑ	*TL* 331 A
Krynica d.	...	...	0500	0541	1357	1435	1710	...	194
Muszyna d.	...	...	0525	0605	1419	1503	1734	...	201
Nowy Sącz d.	0352	0445	0631	0711	1523	1606	1840	1941	21
Stróze d.	0429	0522	0703	0749	1601	1642	1914	2019	214
Tarnów a.	0537	0630	0804	0858	1711	1750	2009	2128	224
Tarnów **1075** d.	0538	0632	0812	...	1712	1751	2022	2130	224
Kraków Płaszów **1075** a.	0642	0731	|	...	1824	|	2119	2256	233
Kraków Gł. **1075** a.	0655	0741	0920	...	1844	1857	2132	2306	234

A – ⑥⑦ Dec. 9 - Feb. 24, June 29 - Sept. 8.

□ – Operator: Koleje Małopolskie.

1079 LOCAL SERVICES IN SILESIA

2nd clas

KATOWICE - OŚWIECIM

Operator: Koleje Śląski

km		①	Ⓐ					Ⓐ		Ⓐ		
0	Katowice d.	0428	0527	0621	0828	1133	1325	1436	1538	1655	1854	2113
33	Oświęcim d.	0518	0615	0713	0920	1225	1414	1526	1627	1747	1944	2203

	Ⓐ	Ⓐ						Ⓐ		Ⓐ	⑤⑥
Oświęcim d.	0441	0528	0628	0755	0936	1245	1449	1537	1640	1845	19
Katowice a.	0536	0622	0723	0850	1033	1340	1544	1631	1736	1942	20

KATOWICE - RYBNIK - RACIBÓRZ

Operator: Koleje Śląsk

km												
0	Katowice d.	0622	0728	1124	...	1329	1525	...	1940	...	2136	...
45	Rybnik d.	0732	0832	1217	...	1428	1620	...	2035	...	2232	...
81	Racibórz a.	0828	0934	1309	...	1524	1717	...	2129	...	2325	...

Racibórz d.	0435	0524	0734	1000	...	1255	...	1534	...	1727	19
Rybnik d.	0532	0631	0832	1132	...	1347	...	1628	...	1836	20
Katowice a.	0630	0729	0927	1238	...	1439	...	1727	...	1937	21

RACIBÓRZ - BOHUMIN

Operator: Koleje Śląsk

km		Ⓐ				Ⓐ				Ⓐ	Ⓐ		
0	Racibórz d.	0539	...	0745	...	1135	1325	...	1530	1637	...	1951	...
20	Chałupki d.	0559	0602	0806	0820	1156	1346	1354	1551	1657	1726	2011	2119
25	Bohumín a.	...	0608	...	0826	...	...	1400	...	...	1732	...	2125

	Ⓐ			Ⓐ.				Ⓐ		Ⓐ		
Bohumín d.	...	0651	...	...	0847	...	1139	...	1453	...	...	19
Chałupki d.	0459	0657	0702	0813	0853	0902	1145	1219	1500	1600	1904	19
Racibórz a.	0519	...	0722	0832	...	0924	...	1240	1520	1620	1925	.

(WROCŁAW -) OPOLE - KEDZIERZYN-KOŹLE - RACIBÓRZ

Operator: Przewozy Regionalr

km				⑥⑦					Ⓐ		Ⓐ	Ⓒ	
	Wrocław Gł d.	...	...	0748	0949	...	1145	...	...	1454	1645	1650	1858
0	Opole Gł. d.	...	...	0852	1053	...	1249	...	...	1558	1745	1807	2006
42	Kedzierzyn-Koźle d.	0455	0700	0948	1146	1204	1342	1404	1510	1651	1905	1905	2102
74	Racibórz a.	0534	0740	...	...	1244	...	1444	1550	1726	1939	1939	2139

	Ⓐ							Ⓐ	Ⓒ				(
Racibórz d.	0502	0557	...	0929	...	1317	...	1452	1527	...	1735	1949	21
Kedzierzyn-Koźle d.	0539	0640	0810	1007	1012	1355	1417	1530	1605	1624	1813	2029	22
Opole Gł. d.	0640	0740	0922	...	1112	...	1517	...	...	1723	1913	2129	23
Wrocław Gł a.	0752	0843	1025	...	1218	...	1629	...	...	1830	2018	2232	.

POZNAŃ - OSTRÓW - KATOWICE - KRAKÓW 1080

For other trains Poznań - Katowice - Kraków (via Wrocław) see Table **1075**; for Poznań - Kraków via Łódź see Table **1025**

km		⊗	TLK 73102 73103 ①–⑥	TLK 74100 ①–⑥	⊗	TLK 83105 83104 S	⊗	⊗	TLK 53108 53104 A	⊗	TLK 73100 73101	TLK 84106 84156 K	IC 83192 83193 SN
0	**Poznań** Gł. d.	...	0530	0800	...	0930	...	...	1335	...	1739	1830	2314
7	Jarocin d.	...	0612	0842	...	1012	...	...	1417	...	1828	1913	|
4	Ostrów Wlkp. d.	...	0643	0914	...	1043	...	...	1448	...	1902	1945	0023
0	Kępno d.	...	0714	0944	...	1119	...	...	1519	...	1936	2017	|
1	Kluczbork d.	...	0743	1011	...	|	...	...	1544	...	2012	2046	0118
2	Lubliniec d.	0656	0815	1044	1201	|	1409	1529	1617	1949	2046	2119	0149
	Gliwice d.	|	|	|	|	|	|	|	|	|	|	2206	0237
2	Bytom d.	0753	|	1121	1255	|	1509	1628	|	2046	|	|	|
	Częstochowa ✣ d.	|	0838	|	|	1254	|	|	1640	|	2112	|	|
0*	**Katowice** a.	0822	|	1143	1322	|	1535	1652	|	2112	|	2231	0335
8	**Kraków** Gł. a.	...	1011	...	...	1427	...	...	1820	...	2247	...	0522

	IC 38192 38193 SN	TLK 48107 48157 K	⊗	TLK 37100 37101 B	⊗	TLK 35108 35104 A	⊗	⊗	TLK 38102 38103 S	TLK 47101 Ⓑ	TLK 37102 37103 Ⓑ	⊗
Kraków Gł. d.	2215	...	...	0535	...	0929	...	...	1311	...	1759	...
Katowice d.	0040	0536	0604	|	0819	|	1011	1342	|	1625	|	2054
Częstochowa ✣ d.	|	|	|	0716	|	1111	|	|	1453	|	1934	|
Bytom d.	|	|	0628	|	0843	|	1036	1410	|	1648	|	2118
Gliwice d.	0109	0559	|	|	|	|	|	|	|	|	|	|
Lubliniec d.	0156	0640	0725	0741	0946	1133	1140	1510	|	1737	1956	2215
Kluczbork d.	0239	0715	...	0816	...	1207	...	...	|	1818	2030	...
Kępno d.	|	0744	...	0846	...	1232	...	...	1630	1845	2058	...
Ostrów Wlkp. d.	0351	0817	...	0922	...	1303	...	...	1713	1915	2130	...
Jarocin d.	|	0848	...	0957	...	1334	...	...	1745	1946	2201	...
Poznań Gł. a.	0502	0931	...	1044	...	1415	...	...	1827	2028	2242	...

nd class — LOCAL TRAINS POZNAŃ / WROCŁAW - OSTRÓW WLKP - ŁÓDŹ

		♣									
Poznań Gł. d.	...	0549a	0821	...	1235	1347	1516	1655	...	1916	2158
Jarocin d.	...	0652	0918	...	1334	1447	1612	1751	...	2015	2256
Wrocław Gł. **1061** d.	...	|	|	0759	|	|	|	|	1616	|	|
Ostrów Wlkp. **1061** d.	0456	0748	0954	1024	1423	1534	1711	1827	1833	2051	2335
Kalisz **1061** d.	0519	0824	...	1048	1445	1556	1734	...	1858	...	...
Łódź Kaliska **1061** a.	0710	1017	...	1313	1712	1805	1945	...	2120	...	...

(the ♣ mark also stands above the 1916 column)

				♣			♣				
Łódź Kaliska **1061** d.	0432	...	0733	...	0953	1158	...	1514	1700	...	1917
Kalisz **1061** d.	0654	...	0947	...	1202	1426	...	1705	1909	...	2108
Ostrów Wlkp. **1061** d.	0746f	0739	1022	1053	1242	1451	1534	1740	1943	2041	2130
Wrocław Gł. **1061** a.	0934	|	|	|	|	1648	|	|	|	|	...
Jarocin d.	...	0816	1058	1130	1318	...	1612	1816	2019	2120	...
Poznań Gł. a.	...	0912	1154	1228	1433	...	1710	1912	2115	2216	...

– To / from Olsztyn (Table **1020**).
– To / from Słupsk (Table **1015**).
– Also conveys 🛏 and / or 🛌.
– To / from Szczecin / Świnoujście (Table **1010**).

a – Ⓐ.
f – Arrive 0717.

✣ – Częstochowa **Stradom**.
⊗ – Operator: Koleje Śląskie.

♣ – Operator: Koleje Wielkopolskie.
* – *331 km* via Gliwice.

JELENIA GÓRA - TRUTNOV 1082

o winter service

km			S		S		S		S	
0	**Jelenia Góra** d.	...	...	...	...	...	...	...	...	...
27	Sędzisław d.	...	0905	...	1304	...	1704	...	2005	...
43	Lubawka 🏛 d.	...	0929	...	1329	...	1729	...	2029	...
48	Královec 🏛 d.	...	0936	...	1336	...	1736	...	2026	...
65	**Trutnov** hlavní a.	...	1004	...	1404	...	1804	...	2104	...

	S		S		S		S		
Trutnov hlavní d.	0736	...	1134	...	1534	...	1837	...	...
Královec 🏛 d.	0804	...	1204	...	1604	...	1905	...	...
Lubawka 🏛 d.	0811	...	1211	...	1611	...	1912	...	...
Sędzisław d.	0835	...	1235	...	1636	...	1936	...	...
Jelenia Góra a.	...	...	...	...	...	...	...	...	...

– ⑥⑦ June 9 - Aug. 31 (also June 20, July 5, Aug. 15).

Operated by Koleje Dolnośląskie (in Czech Republic by GW Train Regio).

SZKLARSKA POREBA - JELENIA GÓRA - WAŁBRZYCH - WROCŁAW 1084

km		EIP 6104 ①–⑥	IC 66100	IC 6304 P	⊖	IC 6510 6170 M	EIC 6150 Ⓒ	D	TLK 66110 65150	⊖	⊖	TLK 66114 N
0	**Jelenia Góra** d.	0430	0725	1020	1124	1241	1557	1424	1610	1737	1931	2143
7	Sedzisław d.	|	0751	1045	1151	1307	|	1454	1635	1805	1958	2208
7	Wałbrzych Gł. d.	0521r	0808	1103	1212	1325	1647r	1522	1652	1826	2021	2226
8	Jaworzyna Śląska d.	|	0840	1135	1259	1358	1709	1600	1724	1902	2059	2259
7	**Wrocław** Gł. a.	0612	0911	1206	1341	1428	1742	1645	1755	1944	2140	2330
	Warszawa C. △ a.	0955	...	...	...	1840	2007	...	...	...	...	...

	TLK 60115 N	D	TLK 60111 56150	EIC 1651 Ⓒ	IC 5610 1670 M	⊖	IC 3604 P	⊖	IC 60101	EIP 1605 Ⓑ	⊖
Warszawa C. △ d.	...	...	...	0605	0915	...	...	...	...	1605	...
Wrocław Gł. d.	0539	0916	0947	1019	1346	1512	1549	1714	1923	1945	2114
Jaworzyna Śląska d.	0612	0958	1019	1051	1417	1552	1624	1756	1955	|	2200
Wałbrzych Gł. d.	0649	1035	1054	1115r	1452	1626	1700	1831	2032	2037r	2236
Sedzisław d.	0706	1055	1111	|	1510	1647	1717	1852	2050	|	2257
Jelenia Góra a.	0732	1123	1137	1205	1536	1716	1743	1920	2116	2125	2324

km		⊖	N	⊖	D	‡Ⓒ	⊖	⊖	⊖	⊖
0	Jelenia Góra d.	0719	0749	0929	1131	1210	1329	1523	1736	1927
32	Szklarska Poreba Górna a.	0807	0835	1017	1218	1250	1419	1620	1824	2015

	⊖	⊖	⊖	D	⊖	‡Ⓒ	⊖	⊖	N
Szklarska Poreba Górna d.	0627	0837	1035	1328	1431	1506	1631	1837	2026
Jelenia Góra a.	0715	0925	1122	1420	1520	1607	1719	1928	2115

– To / from Poznań (Table **1070**).
– 🚃12 Ełk / Białystok - Warszawa - Jelenia Góra and v.v. (Tables **1040/1061**).

N – Also conveys 🛏 and / or 🛌.
P – To / from Przemyśl (Table **1075**).
r – Wałbrzych **Miasto**.

‡ – *IC* service.
⊖ – Operator: Koleje Dolnośląskie.

△ – **1060** via Katowice; **1070** via Poznań; **1061/1090** via Łódź.

GÖRLITZ - WROCŁAW 1085

km		IC 6113	⊖	⊖		⊖	⊖	⊖		⊖	⊖	IC 61170
	Dresden **855** d.	...	0608	...	...	...	1208	...	...	1808	...	...
0	**Görlitz** 🏛 d.	...	0733	...	0907	...	1333	...	1707	1933	...	...
1	Zgorzelec 🏛 **1005** d.	...	0738	...	0912	...	1338	...	1712	1938	...	...
3	Zgorzelec Miasto d.	...	0741	...	0915	...	1341	...	1715	1941	...	...
28	Węgliniec **1005** d.	0634	0800	0805	0944	0947	1400	1409	1744	2000	2008	2300
	Zary a.	|	...	|	1038	|	...	|	1837	...	|	|
63	Bolesławiec d.	0650	...	0823	...	1005	...	1427	...	...	2026	2316
99	Legnica **1086** d.	0718	...	0852	...	1041	...	1509	...	...	2055	2345
64	**Wrocław** Gł. **1086** a.	0802	...	0938	...	1134	...	1603	...	...	2145	0031

	IC 16170	⊖	⊖	⊖		⊖	⊖	⊖		⊖	⊖	IC 1612	⊖
Wrocław Gł. **1086** d.	0429	0618	...	0749	...	1226	...	1553	...	1827	...	1844	1959
Legnica **1086** d.	0516	0709	...	0845	...	1314	...	1649	...	1915	...	1927	2055
Bolesławiec d.	0544	0743	...	0918	...	1343	...	1723	...	1944	...	1953	2129
Zary d.	|	|	...	|	0838	|	...	|	1644	|	...	|	|
Węgliniec **1005** d.	0559	0801	0806	0936	0947	1401	1406	1741	1747	2001	2006	2006	2146
Zgorzelec Miasto d.	...	...	0826	...	1009	...	1425	...	1809	...	2026	...	...
Zgorzelec 🏛 **1005** d.	...	...	0830	...	1014	...	1430	...	1814	...	2030	...	...
Görlitz 🏛 a.	...	...	0834	...	1018	...	1434	...	1818	...	2034	...	...
Dresden **855** a.	...	...	0956	...	...	...	1556	...	...	...	2156	...	...

– Operator: Koleje Dolnośląskie.

COTTBUS - FORST - WROCŁAW 1086

km		⊖	Ⓐ	⊖ Ⓐ	⊖ Ⓒ	IRE 5835 ⑥K	⊖	⊖	IRE 5837 ⑤K	⊖	Ⓐ	⊖ Ⓒ	⊖ Ⓐ
	Berlin L ❦ d.	...	...	...	...	0825	...	...	1226	...	...	...	...
)	**Cottbus** **854** d.	...	*0607*	...	*0807*	0953	...	...	1349	...	*1607*	*1807*	...
?	Forst 🏛 **854** a.	...	*0626*	...	*0825*	|	...	...	|	...	*1626*	*1825*	...
?	Forst d.	...	0635	...	0830	1011	...	...	1405	...	1638	1830	...
6	Tuplice d.	...	0650	...	0845	|	...	...	|	...	1653	1844	...
7	Záry **1005** d.	0542	0711	0821	0906	1046	1113	1415	1437	1649	1714	1907	1907
)	Zagań **1005** d.	0555	0723	0834	0918	1105	1126	1428	1450	1707	1726	1920	1920
4	Legnica **1085** d.	0708	...	0943	1030	1209	1233	1535	1602	1813	...	2032	2026
)	**Wrocław** Gł. **1085** a.	0757	...	1032	1119	1254	...	...	1648	1902	...	2123	...

	Ⓐ	⊖ Ⓒ	⊖ Ⓐ	⊖	⊖	⊖	Ⓐ	⊖ Ⓐ	⊖ Ⓒ	IRE 5832 ⑦Kf	IRE 5832 ⑤K	⊖
Wrocław Gł. **1085** d.	...	0529	...	...	...	1309	...	...	1517	1718	1718	1934
Legnica **1085** d.	...	0623	0623	0947	1251	1359	...	1600	1618	1804	1804	2027
Zagań **1005** d.	0540	0729	0729	1053	1357	1514	1541	1705	1730	1903	1903	2133
Záry **1005** d.	0552	0743	0741	1105	1409	1526	1553	1718	1742	1916	1916	2145
Tuplice d.	0613	0804	...	...	...	...	1614	...	1803	|	|	...
Forst a.	0628	0819	...	...	...	...	1629	...	1818	1946	1946	...
Forst 🏛 **854** d.	*0633*	*0833*	...	...	...	...	*1633*	...	*1833*	|	|	...
Cottbus **854** a.	*0651*	*0851*	...	...	...	...	*1651*	...	*1851*	2005	2005	...
Berlin L ❦ a.	...	...	...	...	...	...	...	...	...	2130	2130	...

KULTURZUG - 🚃2 Berlin - Wrocław and v.v. For International journeys only. Special fares apply.

f – Also June 10; not June 9.

❦ – Full name: Berlin Lichtenberg.

⊖ – Operator: Koleje Dolnośląskie.

1090 WARSZAWA - ŁÓDŹ

km		IC	IR	IC	IC	♣	TLK	IR	IC	IR	♣	IC	IC	IR	♣	IC	IR	IC	♣	TLK	TLK	IC	♣	TLK	TLK	IC	♣
		1610	**11120**	**1902**	**1620**	**99104**	**19160**	**11126**	**1010**	**11130**	**19102**	**1912**	**1612**	**11140**	**19104**	**19118**	**11148**	**1904**	**99110**	**19108**	**19116**	**1910**	**11104**	**86104**	**19152**	**1900**	**191**
		1611	**11121**	**1903**	**1621**	**99105**	**19161**	**11127**	**1011**	**11131**	**19103**	**1913**	**1613**	**11141**	**19105**	**19119**	**11149**	**1905**	**99111**	**19109**	**19117**	**1911**	**11105**	**86105**	**19153**	**1901**	**191**
		Ⓐ	①–⑥			©		Ⓐ		Ⓐ	©			Ⓐ	©		Ⓐ		©		Ⓐ	Ⓐ	©		Ⓐ		©
		C			**C**				**Y**				**CY**											**CE**			
0	**Warszawa** Wsch d.	0504	0519	0609	0739	...	0844	0914	1009	1039	1109	1204	1304	1314	1334	1404	1414	1504	1519	1603	1639	1649	1649	1704	1709	1814	18
4	**Warszawa** Cent d.	0515	0540	0619	0750	0840	0855	0935	1020	1055	1122	1215	1320	1325	1341	1415	1425	1514	1542	1618	1652	1711	1710	1718	1735	1827	18
70	Skierniewice d.	0554	0628	0704	0828	0915	0941	1018	1109	1139	1155	1254	1400	1410	1416	1503	1514	1554	1616	1708	1750	|	1747	1803	1823	1906	19
109	Koluszki d.	0621	0657	0735	0901	0941	1009	1054	1133	1208	1221	1314	1424	1438	1446	1534	1538	1621	1644	1735	1821	|	1817	1830	1853	1930	20
130	**Łódź** Widzew a.	0634	0710	0747	0912	0956	1022	1114	1151	1225	1232	1332	1444	1457	1456	1552	1555	1634	1657	1759	1846	1827	1827	1844	1912	1950	20
138	**Łódź** Chojny a.	0649	|	|	0924	|	|	|	|	|	|	|	1458	|	|	|	|	|	|	|	|	|	|	1903	|	|	
135	**Łódź Fabryczna** a.	...	0717	0757	...	1000	1030	1118	1159	1233	1240	1342	...	1506	1504	1600	1604	1644	1705	1811	1856	1836	1835	...	1913	2000	20

	IC	♣	IC	♣	IC	IC	IC			
	1616	**19112**	**5120**	**99106**	**1002**	**5122**	**16190**			
	1617	**19113**	**5121**	**99107**	**1003**	**5123**	**16170**			
		©		©						
	CY		**O**		**Y**	**O**	**YJ**			
Warszawa Wsch d.	1904	1939	2004	2109	2134	2159	2309	...	...	...
Warszawa Cent d.	1925	1949	2014	2120	2145	2210	2320	...	...	...
Skierniewice d.	2006	2029	2052	2154	2225	2249	2359	...	...	...
Koluszki d.	2033	2055	2124	2219	2251	2313	0026	...	...	...
Łódź Widzew a.	2044	2109	2135	2235	2309	2331	0037	...	...	...
Łódź Chojny a.	2103	|	|	|	|	|	|	...	...	...
Łódź Fabryczna a.	...	2118	2144	2243	2318	2339	0053	...	...	...

	IC	TLK	TLK	IC	TLK	IC	IC	♣	IR	IC
	61190	**91109**	**91117**	**18155**	**91151**	**1521**	**9111**	**91101**	**10133**	**61**
	61170	**91108**	**91116**	**18154**	**91150**	**1520**	**9110**	**91100**	**10132**	**61**
			Ⓐ	⑥	Ⓐ		Ⓐ	©	Ⓐ	①-
	JY					**O**				**C**
Łódź Fabryczna d.	0415	0441	0459	0459	0530	0614	0626	0628	0639	..
Łódź Chojny d.	|	|	|	|	|	|	|	|	|	07
Łódź Widzew d.	0423	0452	0508	0508	0540	0623	0635	0636	0645	07
Koluszki d.	0436	0510	0525	0525	0557	0637	|	0648	0702	07
Skierniewice d.	0457	0541	0558	0558	0630	0706	|	0717	0736	08
Warszawa Cent a.	0545	0630	0645	0645	0716	0745	0750	0750	0827**x**	08
Warszawa Wsch a.	0611	0641	0656	0656	0726	0756	0811	...	0834	09

km		IC	♣	TLK	IR	♣	IC	IC	IR	♣	IR	♣	IC	♣	IC	IR	IC	♣	IR	IC	♣	IC	IR	IC	IC	
		9101	**91103**	**68105**	**10137**	**91107**	**91161**	**6113**	**10139**	**11109**	**10141**	**99103**	**1005**	**91111**	**91119**	**10143**	**10101**	**91113**	**10145**	**9105**	**91101**	**6121**	**10179**	**6111**	**9107**	
		9100	**91102**	**68104**	**10136**	**91106**	**91160**	**6112**	**10138**	**11108**	**10140**	**99102**	**1004**	**91110**	**91118**	**10142**	**10100**	**91112**	**10144**	**9104**	**91100**	**6120**	**10149**	**6110**	**9106**	
			©		Ⓐ	©			Ⓐ	©	Ⓐ	©		©		Ⓐ		©	Ⓐ		©					
				CE				**C**					**Y**									**C**		**C**		
0	**Łódź Fabryczna** d.	0832	0922	...	1005	1100	1114	...	1207	1319	1346	1407	1416	1516	1522	1606	1630	1704	1758	1812	1918	...	2002	...	2331	...
	Łódź Chojny d.	|	|	0932	|	|	|	1152	|	|	|	|	|	|	|	|	|	|	|	|	|	1931	|	2139	|	...
5	**Łódź** Widzew d.	0841	0928	0942	1012	1107	1121	1203	1214	1326	1353	1414	1424	1523	1529	1614	1639	1711	1804	1820	1925	1943	2009	2149	2338	...
26	Koluszki d.	0853	0941	0958	1029	1118	1138	1218	1230	1340	1411	1427	1439	1534	1546	1630	1653	1722	1818	1832	1936	1955	2022	2201	2353	...
65	Skierniewice d.	0923	1009	1025	1059	1147	1209	1246	1300	1406	1443	1453	1506	1603	1615	1700	1726	1750	1851	1902	2005	2024	2055	2230	0020	...
131	**Warszawa** Cent a.	1003	1043	1102	1145	1220	1250	1325	1344	1439	1530	1530	1545	1643	1658	1742	1808	1824	1935	1941	2039	2103	2137	2314	0057	...
135	**Warszawa** Wsch a.	1026	1051	1116	1156	1241	1301	1341	1356	1451	...	1541	1556	1656	1706	1751	1821	1841	1946	1951	2046	2116	2146	2326	0108	...

C – To / from Wrocław (Table **1061**).
E – To / from Kołobrzeg (Table **1015**).
J – To / from Jelenia Góra / Szklarska Poreba (Tables **1061/84**).
O – To / from Olsztyn (Table **1030**).
Y – To / from Białystok (Table **1040**).
x – Warszawa **Śródmieście**.
♣ – Operator: Łódźka Kolej Aglomeracyjna (ŁKA

1095 WROCŁAW - KŁODZKO

Certain trains continue beyond Kłodzko – see Table **1165**

km		⊖	⊖	⊖			⊖		⊖	⊖		⊖	⊖	⊖	⊖		⊖				⊖		⊖	
		①–⑥		©								Ⓑ		Ⓑ										
0	**Wrocław** Gł. d.	0518	0608	0738	0819	...	0959	...	1226	1309	1414	1518	1552	1630	1650	...	1821	...	1955	...	2125	...	2300	..
72	Kamieniec Ząbkowicki d.	0632	0716	0848	0924	...	1103	...	1325	1412	1519	1625	1656	1720	1754	...	1925	...	2106	...	2229	...	0004	..
94	**Kłodzko** Gł. **1165** a.	0656	0739	0908	0946	...	1127	...	1345	1434	1541	1649	1720	1743	1816	...	1948	...	2131	...	2251	...	0027	..

	⊖	⊖	⊖	⊖		⊖	⊖	⊖	⊖	⊖			⊖		⊖	⊖	⊖			⊖	⊖		
	①–⑥			①–⑥		①–⑥	①–⑥	⑦								©	©			①–⑤			
Kłodzko Gł. **1165** d.	0332	0433	0532	0607	0620	0744	0849	0947	1054	1120	...	1320	1453	...	1658	1740	1811	...	1900	2005	2101	...	..
Kamieniec Ząbkowicki d.	0355	0456	0555	0627	0646	0807	0912	1010	1114	1142	...	1343	1520	...	1723	1759	1831	...	1928	2025	2124	...	..
Wrocław Gł. a.	0502	0603	0702	0733	0802	0915	1022	1121	1215	1249	...	1454	1627	...	1834	1859	1945	...	2034	2132	2230	...	..

⊖ – Operated by Koleje Dolnośląskie.

1099 OTHER LOCAL SERVICES

2nd class on

GDYNIA - HEL Valid June 9 - Aug. 31 *77 km, journey 1 hr 50 mins - 2 hrs*

Gdynia Główna depart: 0510 **A**, 0553 **B**, 0702 **B**, 0708 **A**, 0825 **B**, 0859 **A**, 0905 **B**, 0941 **B**, 1000 **B**, 1040 **A**, 1120 **B**, 1212 **B**, 1239 **A**, 1338 **B**, 1427 **B**, 1430 **A**, 1525 **B**, 1539 **A**, 1648 **B**, 1653 **A**, 1854 **A**, 1900 **B**, 2016 **A**, 2030 **B**, 2122 **A**, 2155 **B**.

Hel depart: 0430 **B**, 0437 **A**, 0542 **A**, 0545 **B**, 0641 **A**, 0740 **B**, 0849 **A**, 0945 **B**, 1040 **B**, 1116 **B**, 1123 **A**, 1220 **B**, 1328 **B**, 1402 **A**, 1431 **B**, 1441 **A**, 1613 **B**, 1615 **A**, 1633 **B**, 1709 **A**, 1721 **B**, 1751 **B**, 1821 **B**, 1827 **A**, 2011 **B**, 2030 **A**, 2120 **B**.

KŁODZKO - KUDOWA-ZDRÓJ *44 km, journey 1 hr 10 mins*

Kłodzko Główne depart: 0750, 0910©, 0958, 1158, 1346, 1557, 1755, 1953Ⓑ.

Kudowa-Zdrój depart: 0613①–⑥, 0938, 1142, 1330, 1535, 1615©, 1733, 1930.

Operator: Koleje Dolnośląskie.

KRAKÓW - LOTNISKO (for Kraków John Paul II Airport ✈)

Kraków Główny depart: 0401, 0451, 0604, 0708, and at the same minutes past each hour until 1604, 1716, 1810, 1920, 2014, 2112, 2215, 2312, 2330.

Kraków Lotnisko depart: 0430, 0530, 0637, 0740 and at the same minutes past each hour until 1542, 1647, 1748, 1836, 1952, 2050, 2145, 2247, 2340, 0020.

12 km, journey 18 mins.

KRAKÓW - OŚWIĘCIM (for Auschwitz-Birkenau Memorial and Museum)

VIA TRZEBINIA *65 km Journey 1 hr 45 mins - 1 hr 50 mins*

Kraków Główny depart: 0613, 0834, 1024, 1118, 1300, 1534, 1710, 1818, 1947, 2222.

Oświęcim depart: 0340, 0414, 0458, 0620, 0941, 1033, 1140, 1330, 1509, 1751.

KRAKÓW - WADOWICE *62 km, journey 1 hr 45 mins*

Kraków Płaszów depart: 0350, 0527, 0952, 1230, 1422, 1626, 1739.

Wadowice depart: 0424, 0829, 1009, 1250, 1528, 1807, 2038.

Wadowice is the birthplace of Pope John Paul II.

KRAKÓW - WIELICZKA (for Salt Mine) *15 km, journey 25–30 mins*

Kraków Główny depart: 0459, 0602, 0704, 0805, 0906, 1006©, 1108©, 1208©, 1259©, 1405©, 1505, 1611, 1711, 1815, 1903, 2013, 2113, 2212, 2312.

Wieliczka Rynek depart: 0423, 0533, 0637, 0737, 0839, 0938©, 1041©, 1141©, 1245©, 1338©, 1438, 1538, 1644, 1744, 1850, 1940, 2046, 2145, 2245.

LESZNO - WOLSZTYN - ZBĄSZYNEK

		Ⓐ	Ⓐ 🚂	©	Ⓐ		Ⓐ 🚂		Ⓐ	
Leszno d.	0500	0538	0815	0821	1015	...	1326	1438	1634	18
Wolsztyn d.	0615	0701	0947	0937	1146	...	1456	1545	1742	20
Zbąszyń d.	0641	...	...	...	1212	...	...	1612	...	..
Zbąszynek a.	0647	...	...	...	1218	...	...	1618	...	..

	Ⓐ 🚂			Ⓐ 🚂	Ⓐ	Ⓐ				
Zbąszynek d.	...	0716	...	...	1235	...	...	1657	...	..
Zbąszyń d.	...	0722	...	...	1241	...	...	1703	...	..
Wolsztyn d.	0613	0759	0952	1133	1308	1509	...	1744	2020	..
Leszno a.	0735	0907	1100	1255	1416	1624	...	1852	2128	..

Operator: Koleje Wielkopolskie.

POZNAN - WOLSZTYN Jan. 19 - Dec. 13. *81 km, journey 1 hr 25 mins - 2 hrs*

Poznan Główny depart: 0617, 0806, 0952Ⓐ, 1023⑥ 🚂, 1149Ⓑ, 1354, 1442Ⓐ, 1552, 1657Ⓐ, 1706⑥ 🚂, 1813Ⓐ, 1952©, 2127Ⓐ.

Wolsztyn depart: 0433Ⓐ, 0539, 0628⑥ 🚂, 0802Ⓑ, 0949, 1148Ⓐ, 1341Ⓑ, 1402⑥ 🚂, 1531, 1649Ⓐ, 1750, 2017.

Operator: Koleje Wielkopolskie.

REJOWIEC - ZAMOŚĆ *63 km, journey 1 hr 20 mins*

Rejowiec depart: 1028, 1431, 1750, 2129Ⓑ.

Zamość depart: 0520①–⑥, 0824, 1214, 1614.

WAŁBRZYCH - KŁODZKO *51 km, journey 1 hr 25 mins*

Wałbrzych Główny depart: 0624Ⓐ, 0841, 1112, 1426, 1629, 1833, 2027.

Kłodzko Główne depart: 0500Ⓐ, 0700, 0915, 1306, 1500, 1703, 1903.

Operator: Koleje Dolnośląskie.

WARSZAWA - WARSZAWA MODLIN AIRPORT ✈ *40 km, journey 40 mins*

Warszawa Centralna depart: 0312, 0400, 0425Ⓐ, 0500, 0600, 0700, 0800, 0911**w**, 1000 1100, 1200, 1300, 1400, 1505, 1600, 1704, 1755, 1900, 2000, 2100, 2200, 2300.

Modlin ✈ depart: 0031, 0421, 0521, 0621, 0721, 0821, 0921, 1026, 1116, 1221, 1321, 14 1516, 1621, 1721, 1821, 1921, 2021, 2121, 2222, 2331.

Operator: Koleje Mazowieckie.

A 🚌 connects the rail station with the terminal. Additional slower trains run Modlin ✈ to Warszawa Gdánska, with metro connection to city centre.

NOTES FOR TABLE 1099 (ALL ROUTES): **A** – June 9 - 19. **B** – June 20 - Aug. 31. **w** – Warszawa **Wschodnia**. 🚂 – Normally operated by steam locomoti

CZECH REPUBLIC

rvices: Operator: České Dráhy (ČD), www.cd.cz. Railway infrastructure and timetables are the responsibility of Správa železniční dopravní cesty (SŽDC), www.szdc.cz. All daytime trains convey first and second classes of travel unless otherwise shown by '2' at the top of the column or by a note (which may be in the table heading).

nings: Valid **June 9 - December 14, 2019** with amendments as received. Certain trains are cancelled during the Christmas / New Year period, particularly the evening of Dec. 24, 31 and the morning of Dec. 25, 26, Jan. 1; passengers travelling during this period are advised to confirm train times before travel.

kets: It is possible to reserve seats on most Express trains. SuperCity (*SC*) tilting trains have a compulsory reservation fee. *Business* class on Railjet (RJ) trains requires a first class ticket and a supplement. Note that ČD tickets, including day passes and Interrail / Eurail passes, are not valid on trains operated by GW Train Regio.

ation names: hlavní nádraží (hl. n.) = main station; západ = west; východ = east; horní = upper; dolní = lower; střed = centre, starý = old; město = town; předměstí = outskirts.

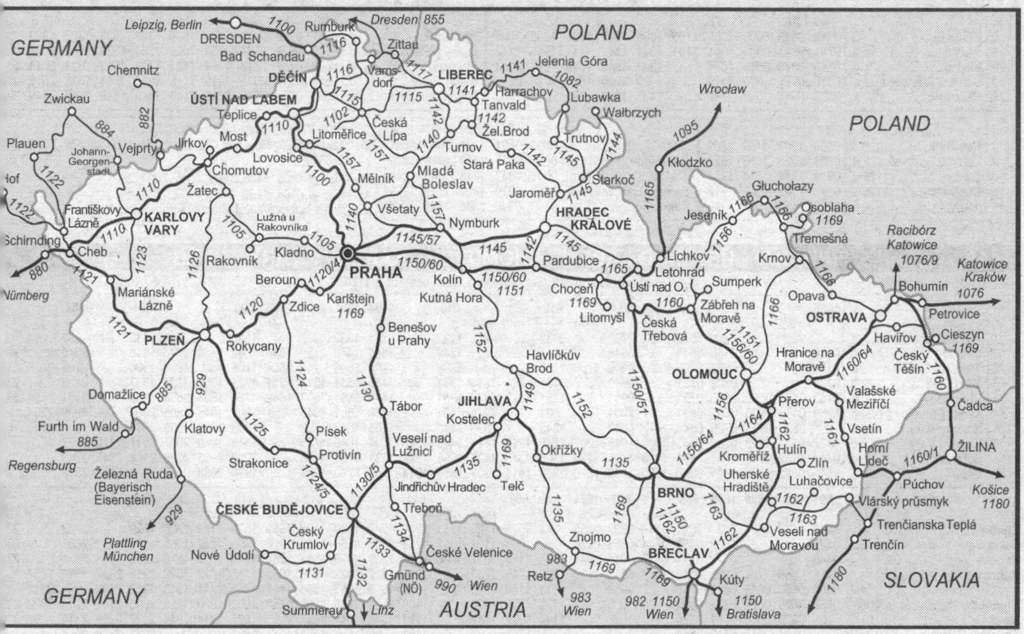

PRAHA - ÚSTÍ NAD LABEM - DĚČÍN - DRESDEN 1100

km		616	EC 178	692	614	5274	EC 176	690	612	EC 174	688	610	EC 378	686	608	EC 172	684	606	5278	682	EC 170	680	604
		Ⓐ	B			W	B			B			B			H			S	Ⓐ	B		
0	**Praha** hlavní nádraží .... d.	...	0522	0632	0651	0732	...	0832	0851	0932	1032	1051	1132	1232	1251	1332	1432	1451	1532	...	1551	1632	1651	1732
3	**Praha** Holešovice .... d.	...	0531	0642	0700	0742	...	0842	0900	0942	1042	1100	1142	1242	1300	1342	1442	1500	1542	...	1600	1642	1700	1742
27	Kralupy nad Vltavou.............. d.	...	0551	|	0720	|	...	|	0920	|	|	1120	|	|	1320	|	|	1520	|	...	1620	|	1720	|
66	Roudnice nad Labem............ d.	0539	0612	|	0744	|	...	|	0944	|	|	1144	|	|	1344	|	|	1544	|	...	1644	|	1744	|
84	Lovosice .... d.	0559	0625	|	0759	|	...	|	0959	|	|	1159	|	|	1359	|	|	1559	|	n	1659	|	1759	|
06	**Ústí nad Labem** hl. n. .... a.	0620	0641	0741	0814	0842	...	0941	1014	1042	1141	1214	1242	1341	1414	1442	1541	1614	1642	1650	1714	1741	1814	1842
06	**Ústí nad Labem** hl. n. ...... ▶ d.	0621	0648	0743	0816	0848	0919	0943	1016	1048	1143	1216	1248	1343	1416	1448	1543	1616	1648	1651	*1727*	1743	1816	1848
	Karlovy Vary **1110**......... ▷ a.	|	0843	|	|	1043	|	|	|	1243	|	|	1443	|	|	1643	|	|	1843	|	|	|	|	2045
29	**Děčín** .... ▶ a.	0637	...	0758	0831	...	0934	0958	1031	...	1158	1231	...	1358	1431	...	1558	1631	...	1708	*1743*	1758	1831	...
29	**Děčín** 🏛 ⊖ .... ⊡ d.	...	...	0802	...	...	0936	1002	...	...	1202	...	...	1402	...	...	1602	...	...	1710	...	1802	...	...
51	Bad Schandau 🏛 ⊖ .... ⊡ d.	...	...	0818	...	...	0952	1018	...	...	1218	...	...	1418	...	...	1618	...	...	1730	...	1818	...	...
91	**Dresden** Hbf .... ⊡ a.	...	...	0843	...	...	1021	1043	...	...	1243	...	...	1443	...	...	1643	...	...	1808	...	1843	...	...

	678	EC 258	EC 258	676	602	674	672		670
	Ⓐ		N			Ⓐ			
aha hlavní nádraží .... d.	1751	1832	1832	1851	1932	1951	2051	2135r	2322
aha Holešovice .... d.	1800	1842	1842	1900	1942	2000	2100	2146	2330
alupy nad Vltavou................ d.	1820	|	|	1920	|	2020	2120	2216	2350
udnice nad Labem............... d.	1844	|	|	1944	|	2044	2144	2251	0014
vosice .... d.	1859	|	|	1959	|	2059	2159	2308	0029
tí nad Labem hl. n............. a.	1914	1941	1941	2014	2042	2114	2214	2328	0044
tí nad Labem hl. n......... ▶ d.	1916	1943	1943	2016	2048	*2122*	2216	2329	0046
Karlovy Vary **1110**.......... ▷ a.	|	|	|	|	c	|	|	|	|
čín .... ▶ a.	1931	1958	1958	2031	...	*2138*	2231	2348	0101
čín 🏛 ⊖ .... ⊡ d.	...	...	2002	...	...	...	...	...	...
d Schandau 🏛 ⊖ .... ⊡ d.	...	...	2018	...	...	...	...	...	...
esden Hbf .... ⊡ a.	...	...	2043	...	...	...	...	...	...

	1993	671	673	601	675	603	677	EC 259	EC 259	679
				Ⓐ	Ⓐ			P		Ⓐ
Dresden Hbf................. ⊡ d.	...	...	...	...	...	...	...	0710	...	...
Bad Schandau 🏛 ⊖ ..... ⊡ d.	...	...	...	...	...	...	...	0737	...	...
Děčín 🏛 ⊖ .... ⊡ a.	...	...	...	...	...	...	...	0753	...	...
Děčín .... ▶ d.	0016	0426	0526	...	0626	...	0726	0758	0758	*0816*
Karlovy Vary **1110** ...... ▷ d.	|	|	|	c	|	c	|	|	|	|
Ústí nad Labem hl. n..... ▶ a.	0031	0440	0540	0607	0640	0709	0740	0813	0813	*0832*
Ústí nad Labem hl. n......... d.	0033	0442	0542	0613	0642	0715	0742	0815	0815	0842
Lovosice .... d.	0050	0459	0559	|	0659	|	0759	|	|	0859
Roudnice nad Labem......... d.	...	0512	0612	|	0712	|	0812	|	|	0912
Kralupy nad Vltavou........... d.	...	0538	0638	|	0738	|	0838	|	|	0938
Praha Holešovice............... a.	...	0559	0659	0715	0759	0815	0859	0915	0915	0959
Praha hlavní nádraží.......... a.	...	0610	0710	0726	0810	0826	0910	0926	0926	1010

	5279	605	681	EC 171	607	683	EC 173	1655	609	685	EC 379	611	687	EC 175	613	689	EC 177	5275	615	691	EC 179	617	693	
	S			B			H	Ⓐ			B			B			B	Wz			B		⑦e	2
esden Hbf .... ⊡ d.	0750	...	...	0910	...	...	1110	...	...	...	1310	...	...	1510	...	...	1710	1735	...	...	1910	...	...	...
d Schandau 🏛 ⊖ .... ⊡ d.	0826	...	...	0937	...	...	1137	...	...	...	1337	...	...	1537	...	...	1737	1804	...	...	1937	...	...	...
čín 🏛 ⊖ .... ⊡ a.	0844	...	...	0953	...	...	1153	...	...	...	1353	...	...	1553	...	...	1753	1820	...	...	1953	...	...	...
čín .... ▶ d.	0846	...	0926	0958	...	1126	1158	*1216*	...	1326	1358	...	1526	1558	...	1726	1758	1822	...	1926	1958	...	2151	*2228*
Karlovy Vary **1110** .... ▷ d.	|	0713	|	|	0915	|	|	|	1115	|	|	1315	|	|	1515	|	|	|	1715	|	|	1915	|	|
tí nad Labem hl. n......... ▶ a.	0903	0909	0940	1013	1109	1140	1213	*1232*	1309	1340	1413	1509	1540	1613	1709	1740	1813	1838	1909	1940	2013	2109	2205	*2257*
tí nad Labem hl. n............. d.	0904	0915	0942	1015	1115	1142	1215	1243	1315	1342	1415	1515	1542	1615	1715	1742	1815	...	1915	1942	2015	2115	2206	2300
vosice .... d.	n	|	0959	|	|	1159	|	1258	|	1359	|	|	1559	|	|	1759	|	...	|	1959	|	2133	2221	2322
udnice nad Labem............... d.	...	|	1012	|	|	1212	|	1311	|	1412	|	|	1612	|	|	1812	|	...	|	2012	|	2144	2233	2335
alupy nad Vltavou.............. d.	...	|	1038	|	|	1238	|	...	|	1438	|	|	1638	|	|	1838	|	...	|	2038	|	2208	2256	...
aha Holešovice .... a.	...	1015	1059	1115	1215	1259	1315	...	1415	1459	1515	1615	1659	1715	1815	1859	1915	...	2015	2059	2115	2226	2315	...
aha hlavní nádraží .... a.	...	1026	1110	1126	1226	1310	1326	...	1426	1510	1526	1626	1710	1726	1826	1910	1926	...	2026	2110	2126	2237	2326	...

- BERLINER - 🅡12 ✕ Praha - Dresden - Berlin and v.v. (Table **60**). Some extend to / from Hamburg.
- HUNGARIA – 🅡12 ✕ Budapest - Brno - Praha - Dresden - Berlin - Hamburg and v.v. (Table **60**).
- PORTA BOHEMICA – ⑧ (not Dec. 24, 25, 31, Apr. 21). 🅡12 ✕ Praha - Dresden - Leipzig.
- PORTA BOHEMICA – ①–⑥ (not Dec. 25, 26, Jan. 1, Apr. 22). 🅡12 ✕ Leipzig - Dresden - Praha.
- ⑥⑦ Mar. 30 - Nov. 3 (also Apr. 19 - 22, May 1, 30, June 10, Oct. 3, 31).
- ⑥⑦ Mar. 30 - Nov. 3 (also Apr. 19 - 22, May 1, 8, July 5, Oct. 28); ⑥⑦ Nov. 30 - Dec. 14.
- To / from Chomutov (Table **1110**).
- Also Dec. 26, Jan. 1, Apr. 22, May 1, 8, Oct. 28; not Dec. 23, 30, Apr. 21, Oct. 27.

n – From / to Litomerice město (d. 1614 / a. 0940).
r – Praha **Masarykovo**.
z – On ⑥⑦ Nov. 30 - Dec. 14 runs two hours earlier (train **5277**).
▶ – Ústí nad Labem - Děčín : see also Table **1115** and foot of Table **1110**.
▷ – Praha - Karlovy Vary trains continue to / from Cheb (Table **1110**).
⊖ – Routeing point for international tickets : Schöna.
⊡ – Local trains run every two hours Děčín - Bad Schandau (Table **1116**) connecting with Bad Schandau - Dresden local trains (Table **857**).

1102 LOVOSICE - LITOMĚŘICE - ČESKÁ LIPA

2nd class

km										
0	Lovosice 1100 d.	0601	0801	1001	1201	1401	1601	1801	2001	2214
8	Litoměřice horní d.	0616	0816	1016	1216	1416	1616	1816	2016	2225
50	Česká Lípa a.	0724	0924	1124	1324	1524	1724	1924	2124	...

		Ⓐ									
Česká Lípa d.	...	0435	0635	0835	1035	1235	1435	1635	1835	2035	...
Litoměřice horní d.	0014	0544	0744	0944	1144	1344	1544	1744	1944	2144	225
Lovosice 1100 a.	0025	0555	0755	0955	1155	1355	1555	1755	1955	2155	230

Also: Lovosice - Litoměřice horní: 0054, 0501, 0630Ⓐ, 0731 and hourly to 1331, 1431Ⓐ, 1442Ⓒ, 1501Ⓐ, 1531, 1631, 1701Ⓐ, 1731, 1831, 1901Ⓐ, 1931, 2031, 2101Ⓐ, 2141, 2241Ⓐ, 23
Litoměřice horní - Lovosice: 0444Ⓐ, 0514, 0614Ⓐ, 0644Ⓐ, 0714Ⓐ, 0814 and hourly to 2114 (also 0844Ⓐ, 1244Ⓐ, 1444Ⓐ, 1644Ⓐ, 1844Ⓐ, 2044Ⓐ, 2211, 2256).

1105 PRAHA - RAKOVNIK - CHOMUTOV - JIRKOV

km			2◧		2◧						P
0	Praha Bubny Vlt. ⊡ d.	0650r	0805	0905	1005	1105	1305	1505	1705	1905	2105
29	Kladno a.	0741	0841	0941	1041	1141	1341	1541	1741	1941	2142
29	Kladno d.	0743	0846	0943	1046	...	1343	1543	1743	1943	2143
62	Lužná u Rakovnika a.	0820	0929	1020	1129	...	1420	1620	1820	2020	2220
71	Rakovník a.	0833	0946	1033	1142	...	1433	1633	1833	2033	2233

	⚒	2			2◐				⑦e	2
Rakovník d.	0517	0618	0723	0923	1008	1323	1523	1723	1923	20
Lužná u Rakovnika d.	0527	0629	0734	0934	1021	1334	1534	1734	1934	20
Kladno a.	0606	0711	0813	1013	1103	1413	1613	1813	2013	21
Kladno d.	0608	0715	0815	1015	1115	1415	1615	1815	2015	21
Praha Bubny Vlt. ⊡ a.	0643	0750	0849	1049	1149	1449	1649	1849	2049	22

km	2nd class	Ⓒ			
0	Rakovnik d.	0808	1008	1409	1809
9	Lužná u Rakovnika d.	0823	1023	1423	1823
50	Žatec 1126 d.	0914	1114	1514	1914
75	Chomutov 1126 a.	0942	1142	1542	1942
81	Jirkov a.	0952	1152	1552	1952

	Ⓐ	Ⓒ			⑦e
Jirkov d.	0607	0801	1201	1601	1801
Chomutov 1126 d.	0617	0810	1210	1610	1810
Žatec 1126 d.	0643	0843	1243	1643	1843
Lužná u Rakovnika a.	0729	0929	1329	1729	1929
Rakovník a.	0746	0946	1346	1746	1946

P – Ⓑ to Kladno; ⑦e to Rakovnik.
e – Also Apr. 22, May 1, 8, Oct. 28; not Dec. 23, 30, Apr. 21, Oct. 2
r – 0705 on Ⓒ.
◧ – Also at 1205, 1405, 1605, 1805, 2005, 2205.
◐ – Also at 0808, 1209, 1409, 1609, 1809.
⊡ – Praha Bubny Vltavská (access from Vltavská metro station).

1110 (PRAHA) - ÚSTI NAD LABEM - CHOMUTOV - KARLOVY VARY - CHEB

For faster journeys Praha - Cheb via Plzeň see Table **1120**

km		1686				616	1670	614		612			610		1694	608		1696	606			604		602		
			2	Ⓐ			2S		Ⓐm		m	Ⓐp			Ⓐ			2Ⓐ		2Ⓒ	Ⓐ					
	Praha hlavní 1100 d.	...	...	...	...	0522	...	0732	...	0932	...	...	1132	...	...	1332	...	...	1532	...	...	1732	...	1932	...	..
0	Ústí nad Labem hl. n. d.	0048	...	...	0458	0648	...	0848	...	1048	...	...	1248	...	1346	1448	...	1546	1648	...	1746	1848	...	2048	...	22
17	Teplice v Čechách d.	0108	...	...	0520	0706	...	0906	...	1106	...	...	1306	...	1404	1506	...	1604	1706	...	1804	1906	...	2106	...	22
46	Most d.	0135	...	...	0602	0731	...	0931	...	1131	...	1213	1331	...	1431	1531	1613	1631	1731	1808	1831	1933	...	2133	...	23
71	Chomutov d.	0153	0404	0509	0625	0751	...	0951	...	1151	...	1233	1351	...	1449	1551	1633	1649	1751	1833	1853	1953	...	2151	2154	23
84	Kadaň-Prunéřov ‡ d.	▬	0419	0520	0635	0801	...	1001	...	1201	...	1245	1401	...	1459	1601	1645	...	1801	1845	1905	2003	...	▬	2204	..
130	Karlovy Vary ⊙ a.	...	0523	0619	0726	0843	...	1043	...	1243	...	1336	1443	...	1605	1643	1739	...	1843	1939	2005	2045	...	...	2258	..
130	Karlovy Vary ⊙ d.	0422	0531	0623	0730	0845	1000	1045	1207	1245	1318	1414	1445	1523	1607	1645	1745	...	1845	1940	2007	2047	2122	2222	...	..
156	Sokolov d.	0443	0552	0647	0751	0906	1018	1106	1229	1306	1340	1437	1506	1544	1631	1706	1806	...	1906	2005	2028	2108	2143	2243	...	..
184	Cheb a.	0513	0622	0720	0821	0930	1050	1130	1300	1330	1411	1509	1530	1614	1702	1730	1836	...	1930	2038	2058	2132	2213	2313	...	..

	601	1691	603	1689	1695	605		607	1671		609			611			613		615			617				
	Ⓐ	Ⓐ	△	Ⓐ	Ⓐ		Ⓒ		2S			Ⓐn	Ⓒ		Ⓐ	Ⓒ		Ⓐd		Ⓒ	Ⓐ				2	2
Cheb d.	...	0403	...	...	0431	0627	0745	0829	0855	...	1029	1125	1143	1229	1247	1329	1429	1559	1629	1713	1726	1829	...	2002	...	22
Sokolov d.	...	0428	...	...	0500	0651	0814	0853	0929	...	1053	1154	1212	1253	1316	1358	1453	1628	1653	1742	1755	1853	...	2031	...	23
Karlovy Vary ⊙ a.	...	0448	...	...	0522	0711	0837	0913	0945	...	1113	1217	1235	1313	1339	1420	1513	1651	1713	1805	1818	1913	...	2054	...	23
Karlovy Vary ⊙ d.	...	0456	0456	...	0558	0713	...	0915	...	1022	1115	1222	...	1315	1422	1422	1515	1652	1715	1822	1822	1915	2022	▬	2257	..
Kadaň-Prunéřov ‡ d.	0453	0550	0550	0615	0649	0756	...	0958	...	1113	1158	1313	...	1358	1513	1513	1558	1742	1758	1913	1913	1958	2132	Ⓐ	0012	..
Chomutov d.	0503	0558	0606	0629	0702	0806	...	1008	...	1125	1208	1325	...	1408	1525	1525	1608	1753	1808	1925	1925	2008	2142	2253	0022	..
Most d.	0522	...	0625	0649	0721	0825	...	1027	...	1144	1227	1349	...	1427	1544	1544	1627	...	1827	1944	1944	2027	2201	2315	...	..
Teplice v Čechách d.	0549	...	0651	0718	0749	0851	...	1051	...	...	1251	...	...	1451	...	...	1651	...	1851	...	...	2051	2234	0001	...	..
Ústí nad Labem hl. n. a.	0607	...	0709	0737	0808	0909	...	1109	...	...	1309	...	...	1509	...	...	1709	...	1909	...	...	2109	2257	0024	...	..
Praha hlavní 1100 a.	0726	...	0826	...	...	1026	...	1226	...	...	1426	...	...	1626	...	...	1826	...	2026	...	...	2237	...	...	...	..

Local trains (2 cl.)								
Děčín d.	0459	0530	and	1930	2042	2124	2228	...
Ústí nad Labem hl. n. d.	0525	0558	hourly	1958	2118	2147	2257	...
Teplice v Čechách d.	...	0620	until	2020	2138	...	...	...
Most a.	...	0654		2054	2207	...	...	...

Local trains (2 cl.)	Ⓐ								Ⓐ	Ⓐ
Most d.	...	0434	0501	and	2001	2101	...	A	...	...
Teplice v Čechách d.	0430	0506	0534	hourly	2034	2134	...	L	...	...
Ústí nad Labem hl. n. d.	0452	0530	0558	until	2058	2157	2227	S	1432	163
Děčín a.	0518	0554	0624		2124	...	2255	O	1456	165

S – Ⓒ June 16 - Sept. 29.
d – Daily Mariánské Lázně (d. 1524) - Cheb - Karlovy Vary. Extends to Chomutov on Ⓐ.
m – To Mariánské Lázně (arrive 1348Ⓐ and 1446).
n – From Mariánské Lázně (depart 1038).
p – Karlovy Vary - Cheb - Plzeň (Table **1121**).
‡ – Local trains run to Kadaň (5 km).
⊙ – Known locally as Karlovy Vary horní (upper).
△ – On Ⓐ conveys 🛏 Cheb (**1691**) - Chomutov (**603**) - Praha

1115 ÚSTÍ NAD LABEM - DĚČÍN - ČESKÁ LIPA - LIBEREC

2nd class

km		1997	1161	1163	1165	1167	1169	1171	1173	1175	1177
			⚒n								
0	Ústí nad Labem hl. § d.	...	0527	0727	0927	1127	1327	1527	1727	1927	2122
23	Děčín § d.	0423	0545	0745	0945	1145	1345	1545	1745	1945	2140
54	Česká Lipa d.	0514	0622	0822	1022	1222	1422	1622	1822	2022	2222
113	Liberec a.	0626	0728	0928	1128	1328	1528	1728	1928	2128	2328

	1176	1174	1172	1170	1168	1166	1164	1162	1160	
	⚒n									
Liberec d.	0427	0628	0828	1028	1228	1428	1628	1828	2028	21
Česká Lipa d.	0537	0738	0938	1138	1338	1538	1738	1938	2135	22
Děčín § d.	0616	0816	1016	1216	1416	1616	1816	2016	2209	23
Ústí nad Labem hl. § a.	0632	0832	1032	1232	1432	1632	1832	2032	2225	...

n – ①–⑥ (not Dec. 24 - 26, Jan. 1, Apr. 20, 22, July 6, Oct. 28).
§ – See also Table **1100** and foot of Table **1110**.

1116 DĚČÍN - RYBNIŠTĚ - RUMBURK / DĚČÍN - SEBNITZ - RUMBURK

km								Ⓐ			
0	Děčín d.	0634	0835	1035	1235	1435	1635	1735	1835	2035	2235
25	Česká Kamenice d.	0706	0906	1106	1306	1506	1706	1806	1906	2106	2306
50	Rybniště a.	0736	0936	1136	1336	1536	1736	1835	1936	2136	2332
61	Rumburk a.	0750	0950	1150	1350	1550	1750	1848	1950	2150	2351

	Ⓐ									G
Rumburk d.	0516	0605	0800	1000	1200	1400	1602	1800	2000	21
Rybniště d.	0528	0618	0813	1013	1213	1413	1615	1813	2013	21
Česká Kamenice d.	0554	0647	0847	1047	1247	1447	1647	1847	2047	21
Děčín a.	0622	0719	0919	1119	1319	1519	1719	1919	2119	22

km		Ⓐn									
0	Děčín ▷ d.	0525	0641	0841	1041	1241	1441	1641	1841	2041	2241
22	Bad Schandau 🏛 ▷ a.	0554	0710	0910	1110	1310	1510	1710	1910	2110	2310
22	Bad Schandau d.	0555	0718	0918	1118	1318	1518	1718	1918	2118	...
37	Sebnitz d.	0628	0741	0941	1141	1341	1541	1741	1941	2141	...
38	Dolní Poustevna 🏛 d.	0632	0745	0945	1145	1345	1545	1745	1945	2145	...
65	Rumburk a.	0712	0834	1026	1226	1427	1634	1834	2026	2225	...

Rumburk d.	0533	0728	0920	1120	1320	1528	1728	1920	2037	..
Dolní Poustevna 🏛 d.	0614	0812	1012	1212	1412	1612	1812	2012	2118	..
Sebnitz d.	0618	0818	1018	1218	1418	1618	1818	2018	2121	..
Bad Schandau a.	0639	0839	1039	1239	1439	1639	1839	2039	...	..
Bad Schandau 🏛 ▷ d.	0648	0848	1048	1248	1448	1648	1848	2048	...	23
Děčín ▷ a.	0716	0916	1116	1316	1516	1716	1916	2116	...	00

G – ⑤⑥ (also Apr. 18 - 21, 30, May 7, July 4, Oct. 27).
n – Runs 12 mins later Sebnitz - Rumburk certain dates.
▷ – See also Table **1100**.

1117 RYBNIŠTĚ - VARNSDORF - ZITTAU - LIBEREC

Die Länderbahn *Trilex* 2nd class

km					d				d					d			d			d					⑤
0	Rybniště ◇ d.	...	0642	...	...	...	0942	...	...	1129	1224	...	1342	...	...	1542	...	...	1742	...	1842	...	2024	...	
11	Varnsdorf 🏛 d.	0557	0700	0730	...	0852	1000	1027	...	1157	1242	1257	1400	...	1500	1600	...	1700	1800	...	1900	2013	2042	2127	23
29	Zittau 🏛 d.	0615	0718	0749	0844	0915	...	1044	1048	1215	...	1315	1418	1444	1518	1617	1644	1718	1817	1844	1918	2041	...	2146	23
56	Liberec a.	0655	0755	0824	0919	0955	...	...	1124	1253	...	1355	1455	1524	1555	...	1715	1755	...	1915	1955	2113	...	2229	23

					d	Ⓐ	Ⓒ		d					d			d				d			⑤⑥	
Liberec d.	0500	0602	0702	0802	0838	0858	...	1002	1038	...	...	1231	1402	1433	1502	1602	1633	...	...	1802	1833	...	2005	2133	22
Zittau 🏛 d.	0537	0642	0742	0847	0911	0942	0942	1042	1114	1131	...	1309	1442	1511	1542	1642	1711	1714	...	1842	1911	1914	2042	2207	23
Varnsdorf 🏛 d.	0555	0659	0759	0904	...	0959	0959	1104	...	1148	1304	1326	1504	...	1559	1704	...	1731	1804	1859	...	1948r	2059	2224	23
Rybniště ◇ a.	0613	...	...	0922	...	...	...	1122	...	1206	1322	...	1522	...	...	1722	...	...	1822	...	...	2006	...	...	..

d – From/to Dresden (Table **855**).
r – Arrive 1931.
◇ – For connections Rybniště - Děčín and v.v. see Table **1116**.
Operator: Die Länderbahn.

PRAHA - BEROUN - PLZEŇ 1120

km		Ex		Ex		Ex		Ex	Ex		IC•	Ex		Ex		Ex		Ex		Ex		Ex	
		778	362	776	562	774	360	772	560	358	770	512	356	768	558	766	354	764	556	762	352	760	554	758
		Ⓐ	M	z	🍷		M	k	🍷	M	z	F🍷	M	k	🍷		M		🍷		M	k	🍷	
	Ostrava hl. n. **1160** d.	...	...	...	...	...	...	...	...	...	...	0715	...	...	...	...	...	...	...	...	...	...	...	...
0	**Praha** hlavní n. **1124** d.	0515	0545	0615	0645	0715	0745	0815	0845	0945	1015	1045	1145	1215	1245	1315	1345	1415	1445	1515	1545	1615	1645	1715
4	Praha Smíchov **1124** d.	0523	0553	0623	0653	0723	0753	0823	0853	0953	1022	1053	1153	1223	1253	1323	1353	1423	1453	1523	1552	1623	1653	1723
3	Beroun **1124** d.	0553	|	0653	|	0753	|	0853	|	|	1053	|	|	1253	|	1353	|	1453	|	1553	|	1653	|	1753
2	Zdice **1124** d.	0602	|	0702	|	0802	|	0902	|	|	1102	|	|	1302	|	1402	|	1502	|	1602	|	1702	|	1802
0	Rokycany d.	0629	|	0729	|	0829	|	0929	|	|	1129	|	|	1329	|	1429	|	1529	|	1629	|	1729	|	1829
7	**Plzeň** hlavní n. a.	0640	0659	0740	0759	0840	0859	0940	0959	1059	1140	1159	1259	1340	1359	1440	1459	1540	1559	1640	1659	1740	1759	1840
	Cheb **1121** a.	...	...	...	0926	...	...	...	1126	...	...	1324	...	...	1526	...	...	...	1726	...	...	...	1926	...

	Ex		IC•		Ex	Ex			
	350	756	504	754	552	550	752	750	
	M		🍷		🍷	Ⓑh	k		
...strava hl. n. **1160** d.	...	...	1515	...	...	...	...	...	...
...ha hlavní n. **1124** d.	1745	1815	1845	1915	1945	2045	2115	2339	...
...a Smíchov **1124** d.	1753	1823	1853	1923	1953	2053	2123	2346	...
...oun **1124** d.	|	1853	|	1953	|	|	2153	0016	...
...e **1124** d.	|	1902	|	2002	|	|	2202	0025	...
...ycany d.	|	1929	|	2029	|	2152	2229	0052	...
...ň hlavní n. a.	1859	1940	1959	2040	2059	2204	2240	0103	...
...heb **1121** a.	...	...	2117	...	...	2332	...	...	...

			Ex		Ex		IC•		Ex
	751	753	551	755	553	757	505	759	351
	Ⓐ		⚒n	k	🍷		🍷	k	M‡
Cheb **1121** d.	...	...	0432	...	...	...	0634	...	...
Plzeň hlavní n. d.	0420	0520	0600	0620	0700	0720	0800	0820	0900
Rokycany d.	0432	0532	|	0632	|	0732	|	0832	|
Zdice **1124** d.	0500	0600	|	0700	|	0800	|	0900	|
Beroun **1124** d.	0510	0610	|	0710	|	0810	|	0910	|
Praha Smíchov **1124** a.	0538	0638	0708	0738	0808	0838	0908	0938	1008
Praha hlavní n. **1124** a.	0549	0650	0719	0750	0819	0849	0919	0949	1019
Ostrava hl. n. **1160** a.	...	...	...	...	...	...	1244	...	...

	Ex		Ex	Ex		Ex		Ex		Ex		IC•		Ex			Ex		Ex		Ex		Ex	
	555	761	353	557	763	355	765	559	767	357	769	515	771	359	773		561	775	361	777	563	779	363	
	🍷	k	M	🍷	k	M		🍷	z	M		F🍷	k	M				z	M			z	M	2
...heb **1121** d.	0833	...	1033	...	...	...	...	1233	...	...	...	1436	...	...	...	...	1633	...	...	...	1833	...	...	...
...ň hlavní n. d.	1000	1020	1100	1200	1220	1300	1320	1400	1420	1500	1520	1600	1620	1700	1720	...	1800	1820	1900	1920	2000	2020	2100	2213
...ycany d.	|	1032	|	|	1232	|	1332	|	1432	|	1532	|	1632	|	1732	...	|	1832	|	1932	|	2032	|	2231
...e **1124** d.	|	1100	|	|	1300	|	1400	|	1500	|	1600	|	1700	|	1800	...	|	1900	|	2000	|	2100	|	...
...oun **1124** d.	|	1110	|	|	1310	|	1410	|	1510	|	1610	|	1710	|	1810	...	|	1910	|	2010	|	2110	|	...
...a Smíchov **1124** a.	1108	1138	1208	1308	1338	1408	1438	1508	1538	1608	1638	1708	1738	1808	1838	...	1908	1938	2008	2038	2108	2138	2208	...
...ha hlavní n. **1124** a.	1119	1149	1219	1319	1349	1419	1449	1520	1549	1619	1649	1719	1749	1819	1849	...	1919	1949	2016	2049	2119	2146	2216	...
...strava hl. n. **1160** a.	...	...	...	...	...	...	...	...	...	...	...	2044	...	...	...	...	...	...	...	...	...	...	...	...

(12) Bohumín - Ostrava - Praha - Plzeň - Cheb - Františkovy Lázně (Table **1121**) and v.v.

ZÁPADNI EXPRES - (12) 🍷 Praha - Plzeň - Regensburg - München and v.v. (Tables **76**, **885**). See warning above.

h – Not Dec. 23 - 25, 31, Apr. 19, 21, July 5, Oct. 27.

k – To / from Klatovy (Table **929**).

n – ①–⑥ (not Dec. 24 - 26, Jan. 1, Apr. 20, 22, July 6, Oct. 28).

z – To / from Železná Ruda via Klatovy (Table **929**).

• – PENDOLINO – classified *SC* Bohumín / Ostrava - Praha and v.v. (🅁 Ostrava - Praha and v.v.)

‡ – Starts from Regensburg on ⑦ (Table **885**).

Praha - Cheb trains are named ZÁPADNI EXPRES.

PLZEŇ - MARIÁNSKÉ LÁZNĚ - CHEB 1121

km		Ex	Ex	Ex	IC•	Ex		Ex	Ex	IC•	Ex
		564	562	560	512	558	1988	556	554	504	550
		⚒n	🍷	🍷	F🍷	🍷	2	🍷	🍷	🍷	Ⓑh
	Ostrava hl. n. **1160** d.	...	...	...	0715	...	...	...	...	1515	...
	Praha hl. n. **1120** d.	...	0645	0845	1045	1245	...	1445	1645	1845	2045
0	**Plzeň** hlavní n. d.	0605	0805	1005	1205	1405	1505	1605	1805	2005	2211
3	Stříbro d.	0631	0831	1031	1231	1431	1537	1631	1831	2028	2237
4	Planá u Marián. Lázní d.	0653	0853	1053	1253	1453	1604	1653	1853	2048	2301
6	Mariánské Lázně ▷ d.	0707	0907	1107	1306	1507	1629	1707	1907	2057	2312
6	**Cheb** ▷ a.	0729	0926	1126	1324	1526	1701	1726	1926	2117	2332
3	Františkovy Lázně **1122** a.	...	...	...	1333	...	...	...	...	...	...

	Ex	IC•	Ex	Ex	Ex	IC•		Ex	Ex	Ex
	551	505	555	557	559	515	1989	561	563	565
	⚒n	🍷	🍷	🍷	🍷	F🍷	2k	🍷	🍷	Ⓑh
Františkovy Lázně **1122** d.	...	...	...	...	...	1427	...	...	...	...
Cheb ▷ d.	0432	0634	0833	1033	1233	1436	1510	1633	1833	1935
Mariánské Lázně ▷ d.	0454	0655	0854	1054	1254	1455	1542	1654	1854	1955
Planá u Marián. Lázní d.	0505	0705	0905	1105	1305	1505	1553	1705	1905	2006
Stříbro d.	0527	0727	0927	1127	1327	1527	1622	1727	1927	2028
Plzeň hlavní n. a.	0554	0754	0954	1154	1354	1554	1653	1754	1954	2055
Praha hl. n. **1120** a.	0719	0919	1119	1319	1520	1719	...	1919	2119	...
Ostrava hl. n. **1160** a.	...	1244	...	...	...	2044	...	...	...	...

(12) Bohumín - Ostrava - Praha - Plzeň - Cheb - Františkovy Lázně and v.v.

Not Dec. 23 - 25, 31, Apr. 19, 21, July 5, Oct. 27.

From Karlovy Vary (Table 1110) on Ⓐ.

①–⑥ (not Dec. 24 - 26, Jan. 1, Apr. 20, 22, July 6, Oct. 28).

PENDOLINO – classified *SC* (with 🅁) Bohumín / Ostrava - Praha and v.v.

▷ – Additional local trains Mariánské Lázně - Cheb and v.v. (journey 30 mins):
From Mariánské Lázně 0455Ⓐ, 0552Ⓐ, 0654Ⓐ, 0747Ⓒ, 0814Ⓐ, 0918Ⓒ, 1038Ⓐ, 1230Ⓒ, 1245Ⓐ, 1431Ⓐ, 1524, 1838Ⓑ h, 2007.
From Cheb 0504⚒, 0546Ⓐ, 0648, 0959, 1148Ⓐ, 1317Ⓐ, 1415, 1806, 2003, 2248Ⓐ.

...d class CHEB - FRANTIŠKOVY LÁZNĚ - HOF / PLAUEN 1122

		⑥						Ⓐ				
	Cheb ◇ d.	0518	0637	0738	0937	1137	1337	1435	1537	1737	1937	2250
	Františkovy Lázně d.	0527	0645	0745	0945	1145	1345	1443	1545	1745	1945	2259
	Aš 🛃 d.	0601	0710	0808	1008	1208	1408	1505	1608	1808	2008	2327
	Hof a.	0640	...	0845	1048	1248	1448	...	1648	1848	2044	0001r

	⚒s	Ⓐ						Ⓐ			
Hof d.	0508	...	0709	0907	1107	1307	1508	...	1707	1907	
Aš d.	0546	0650	0747	0947	1147	1347	1547	1647	1747	1947	2056
Františkovy Lázně d.	0609	0714	0812	1012	1212	1412	1612	1712	1812	2012	2119
Cheb ◇ a.	0616	0721	0819	1019	1219	1419	1619	1719	1819	2019	2126

		Ⓐ	Ⓐ	Ⓒ				b				
	Cheb d.	0527	0548	0803	1003	...	1203	1326	1603	1803	...	...
	Františkovy Lázně d.	0535	0555	0812	1012	...	1212	1333	1612	1812	...	...
	Bad Brambach 🛃 a.	...	0621	0836	1036	...	1236	...	1636	1836	...	...
	Plauen ⊖ a.	...	0727	0927	1127	...	1328	...	1727	1927	...	...

	Ⓐ				b					
Plauen ⊖ d.	...	0830	1030	...	...	1430	...	1630	1830	...
Bad Brambach 🛃 d.	...	0921	1121	...	...	1521	...	1721	1921	...
Františkovy Lázně d.	0617	0945	1145	...	1427	1545	...	1745	1945	...
Cheb a.	0625	0952	1152	...	1434	1552	...	1752	1952	...

IC train (see Table **1121**).

Change at Aš on Ⓑ.

Runs 5 minutes later on ⑥.

⊖ – Trains continue beyond Plauen to / from Zwickau (Hbf and Zentrum).

◇ – Most journeys run Marktredwitz (Table **880**) - Cheb - Hof and v.v.

☛ – There is 🚌 substitution Františkovy Lázně - Bad Brambach and v.v. (in same timings) June 3 - 27.

Operator: Die Länderbahn *Oberpfalzbahn* and *Vogtlandbahn*.

...d class KARLOVY VARY - MARIÁNSKÉ LÁZNĚ 1123

	Karlovy Vary dolní (lower) d.	...	0620	0859	1059	1259	1503	1708	1930	2130
	Bečov nad Teplou d.	0442	0649	0928	1128	1328	1532	1737	1959	2159
	Mariánské Lázně a.	0525	0733	1012	1212	1412	1616	1821	2043	2243

Mariánské Lázně d.	0604	0830	1043	1230	1434	1639	1913	2113	2255
Bečov nad Teplou d.	0649	0914	1128	1314	1518	1723	1959	2159	2338
Karlovy Vary dolní (lower) a.	0718	0944	1157	1344	1548	1753	2028	2228	

Operator: GW TrainRegio. ČD tickets and rail passes are not valid.

...d class PRAHA - BEROUN - PŘÍBRAM - PISEK - ČESKÉ BUDĚJOVICE 1124

		1254	1252	1250		1248	1246	1244	1242	1240
		Ⓐ	①d		◧	Ⓒ§	Ⓐ	⑤f		
	Praha hlavní n. **1120** d.	...	0524	0724	...	0937	1124	1324	1524	1724
	Praha Smíchov **1120** d.	...	0531	0731	...	0944	1131	1331	1531	1731
	Beroun **1120** d.	...	0616	0812	0857	1015	1212	1412	1612	1812
	Zdice **1120** d.	...	0626	0823	0908	1026	1224	1424	1624	1824
	Příbram d.	...	0659	0859	0950	1059	1259	1459	1659	1859
	Březnice d.	...	0717	0917	1018	1117	1317	1517	1717	1917
	Písek d.	0600	0759	0959	1109	1159	1359	1559	1759	1959
	Protivín **1125** d.	0612	0813	1013	1124	1213	1413	1613	1813	2013
	České Budějovice **1125** a.	0642	0845	1045	...	1245	1445	1645	1845	2045x

	1241	1243		1245	1247	1249	1251	635	1253
			◐	⑤f			⑦e	Ⓐ	
České Budějovice **1125** d.	0512z	0712	...	1112	1312	1512	1712	1712	1912
Protivín **1125** d.	0543	0743	1034	1143	1343	1543	1743	1743	1943
Písek d.	0558	0758	1049	1158	1358	1558	1758	1756	1956
Březnice d.	0639	0839	1143	1239	1439	1639	1839	...	...
Příbram d.	0703	0859	1208	1303	1503	1700	1903	...	...
Zdice **1120** d.	0734	0928	1243	1334	1534	1734	1934	...	...
Beroun **1120** d.	0746	0946	1254	1346	1546	1746	1945	...	...
Praha Smíchov **1120** a.	0825	1023	...	1427	1627	1827	2014	...	...
Praha hlavní n. **1120** a.	0837	1036	...	1437	1637	1837	2024	...	...

Also Dec. 27, Jan. 2, Apr. 23, May 2, 9, Oct. 29; not Dec. 24, 31, Apr. 22, Oct. 28.

Also Dec. 26, Jan. 1, Apr. 22, May 1, 8, Oct. 28; not Dec. 23, 30, Apr. 21, Oct. 27.

Also Apr. 18, 30, May 7, July 4; not Apr. 19, July 5. Runs on Ⓐ Písek - České Budějovice and v.v.

⑤–⑦ (also Dec. 25, 26, Jan. 1, Apr. 18, 22, 30, May 1, 7, 8, July 4, Oct. 28).

① (also Dec. 27, Jan. 2, Apr. 23, May 2, 9, Oct. 29; not Dec. 24, Apr. 22, Oct. 28).

◧ – Also at 1101, 1301Ⓐ, 1501Ⓑ, 1701.

◐ – Also at 0834, 1234, 1434Ⓐ, 1634Ⓑ, 1834.

§ – Daily from Písek (train **632** on Ⓐ).

1125 PLZEŇ - ČESKÉ BUDĚJOVICE

km		653	661	663	665	667	669	655	657	659
		⚒n						b		
0	Plzeň hlavní n. d.	...	0603	0803	1003	1203	1403	1603	1803	2003
34	Nepomuk d.	...	0631	0831	1031	1231	1431	1631	1831	2031
59	Horažďovice předměstí d.	...	0652	0852	1052	1252	1452	1652	1852	2052
76	Strakonice d.	0457	0707	0907	1107	1307	1507	1707	1907	2107
99	Protivín 1124 d.	0517	0726	0926	1126	1326	1526	1726	1926	2126
136	**České Budějovice** 1124 a.	0549	0755	0955	1155	1355	1555	1755	1955	2155
	Jihlava 1135 a.	0833	1033	1233z	1433	1633	1833	2027r	...	...
	Brno 1135 a.	1030	1230	1430z	1630	1830	2030	...	...	...

	658	656	654	668	666	664	662	660
			b					
Brno 1135 d.	...	...	...	0727	0927z	1127	1327	1527
Jihlava 1135 d.	...	0525a	0725	0925	1125z	1325	1525	1725
České Budějovice 1124 d.	0604	0804	1004	1204	1404	1604	1804	2004
Protivín 1124 d.	0632	0832	1032	1232	1432	1632	1832	2032
Strakonice d.	0653	0853	1053	1253	1453	1653	1853	2053
Horažďovice předměstí d.	0709	0909	1109	1309	1509	1709	1909	2109
Nepomuk d.	0729	0929	1129	1329	1529	1729	1929	2129
Plzeň hlavní n. a.	0756	0956	1156	1356	1556	1756	1956	2156

a – Ⓐ only.
b – To / from Havlíčkův Brod on dates in Table **1149**.
n – ①–⑥ (not Jan. 1, Apr. 20, 22, July 6, Oct. 28).
r – Ⓑ (not Dec. 23-25, 31, Apr. 19, 21, July 5, Oct. 27).
z – ⑤⑥⑦ (daily May 24 - Sept. 8), also Jan. 1, Apr. 18, 22, 30, May 1, 7, 8, Oct. 28.

June 17-30: departs Plzeň 31-33 mins earlier (by 🚌 Strakonice - Ražice and v.v.). Arrives Plzeň 25-30 mins lat

1126 PLZEŇ - CHOMUTOV - MOST

Operator: GW Train Re

km		1098	1080	1082	1084	1086	1088	1090	1092	1094
		Ⓐ		E						⑦u
0	Plzeň hlavní n. d.	...	0604	0804	1004	1204	1404	1604	1804	2004
59	Blatno u Jesenice d.	0455	0709	0909	1109	1309	1509	1709	1909	2109
107	Žatec 1105 d.	0551	0802	1002	1202	1402	1602	1802	2002	2202
130	Chomutov 1110 d.	0615	0824	1024	1224	1424	1624	1824	2024	2224
155	**Most** 1110 a.	0636	0844	1044	1244	1444	1644	1844	2044	2244

	1081	1083	1085	1087	1089	1091	1093	1099
	⚒n			E				Ⓐ
Most 1110 d.	0509	0709	0909	1109	1309	1509	1709	1909
Chomutov 1110 d.	0530	0730	0930	1130	1330	1530	1730	1930
Žatec 1105 d.	0553	0753	0953	1153	1353	1553	1753	1953
Blatno u Jesenice d.	0645	0845	1045	1245	1445	1645	1845	2046
Plzeň hlavní n. a.	0755	0954	1154	1354	1554	1754	1954	...

E – Ⓒ (daily May 1 - Sept. 15).
n – ①–⑥ (not Dec. 24-26, Jan. 1, Apr. 20, 22, July 6, Oct. 28).
u – Also Jan. 1, Apr. 22, Oct. 28; not Dec. 23, 30, Apr. 21, Oct. 27.

GW Train Regio. ČD tickets and passes not valid

1130 PRAHA - TÁBOR - ČESKÉ BUDĚJOVICE

km		1835	701	Ex 1541	703	705	Ex 531	707	♥ 1059	709	Ex 1543	711	713	715	Ex 1545	717	Ex 533	719	Ex 535	721	721	Ex 537	723
		2	⚒n	🍷	⚒n		K🍷	⚒n	R🍷		🍷	🍷	Ⓐ		🍷		Ⓐ		Ⓐ🍷		⑦z	🍷	
	Praha Holešovice d.	...	...	...	...	0709n	0748n	0820	...	0920	0948	1120	1220	1320	1348	1420	1448	1520	...	1620	1620	1648	1720
0	**Praha** hlavní n. d.	...	0531	0601	0631	0731	0801	0831	0901	0931	1001	1131	1231	1331	1401	1431	1501	1531	1601	1631	1631	1701	1731
49	Benešov u Prahy d.	...	0612	|	0712	0812	|	0912	|	1012	|	1212	1312	1412	|	1512	|	1612	|	1712	1712	|	1812
103	**Tábor** d.	0615	0703	0718	0803	0903	0920	1003	1021	1103	1118	1303	1403	1503	1518	1603	1620	1703	1718	1803	1803	1820	1903
130	Veselí nad Lužnicí ▷ a.	0642	0724	|	0824	0924	|	1024	|	1124	|	1324	1424	1524	|	1624	|	1724	|	1824	1824	|	1924
169	**České Budějovice** ▷ a.	0721	0758	0803	0858	0958	1008	1058	1106	1158	1203	1358	1458	1558	1603	...	1708	1758	1803	...	1858	1908	1958
	Linz Hbf 1132 a.	...	...	1007	...	...	...	...	...	...	1407	...	...	...	1807	...	...	...	...	...	...	...	...

	Ex 1547	725	Ex 539	727	729	731	733	733 8259	
	P🍷		⑦e					2N	
Praha Holešovice d.	1748	1820	...	1920r	...	2148	2320	2320	...
Praha hlavní n. d.	1801	1831	1901	1931	2031	2201	2331	2331	...
Benešov u Prahy d.	|	1912	|	2012	2112	2242	0012	0012	...
Tábor d.	1918	2003	2018	2058	2155	2325	0053	0055	...
Veselí nad Lužnicí ▷ a.	|	2024	|	2119	2216	2346	...	0120	...
České Budějovice ▷ a.	2003	2058	2103	2152	2246	0018	...	0158	...
Linz Hbf 1132 a.	2207	...	...	...	...	...	...	...	...

	732	730	728	728	1834 728	Ex 538	726	Ex 536
	⚒n	⚒n	①d	⚒n	⑦b	Ⓐ🍷		🍷
Linz Hbf 1132 d.	...	...	...	...	...	...	...	...
České Budějovice ▷ d.	...	0455	0501	...	0501	0555	0601	0655
Veselí nad Lužnicí ▷ d.	...	|	0534	0534	0534	|	0634	|
Tábor d.	0506	0540	0602	0602	0602	0640	0702	0742
Benešov u Prahy d.	0549	0619	0649	0649	0649	|	0749	|
Praha hlavní n. a.	0627	0700	0727	0727	0727	0757	0827	0857
Praha Holešovice a.	0646	0710	0746	0746	0746	0810	0846	0910

	724	Ex 534	722	Ex 1540	720	718	716	♥ 1058	714	Ex 1542	712	Ex 532	710	708	Ex 530	706	706	Ex 1544	704	702	700	Ex 1546	
		Ⓐ🍷		P🍷	⚒n		🍷	S🍷	Ⓐ	🍷		K🍷			⑦e	⚒s		🍷				🍷	2
Linz Hbf 1132 d.	...	...	...	0635	...	...	...	...	...	1152	...	...	...	...	...	...	...	1552	...	...	...	1835	...
České Budějovice ▷ d.	...	0755	0801	0855	0903	1001	1203	1255	1301	1355	1401	1455	1501	1603	1653	1701	...	1755	1801	1901	2003	2055	2257
Veselí nad Lužnicí ▷ d.	0734	|	0834	|	0934	1034	1234	|	1334	|	1434	|	1534	1634	|	1734	1734	|	1834	1934	2034	2125	2350
Tábor d.	0802	0842	0902	0940	1002	1102	1302	1340	1402	1440	1502	1542	1602	1702	1740	1802	1802	1840	1902	2002	2102	2143	0018
Benešov u Prahy d.	0849	|	0949	|	1049	1149	1349	|	1449	|	1549	|	1649	1749	|	1849	1849	|	1949	2049	2149	2219	...
Praha hlavní n. a.	0927	0957	1027	1057	1127	1227	1427	1456	1527	1557	1627	1657	1727	1827	1857	1927	1927	1957	2027	2127	2227	2257	...
Praha Holešovice a.	0946	1010	1046	1110	1146	1246	1446	...	...	1610	1646	1710	1746	1846r	...	...	...	...	2046	...	2246h	...	...

K – [12] 🍷 Praha - České Budějovice - Český Krumlov and v.v. (Table **1131**).
N – ⑤⑥⑦ and holidays (also Apr. 18, 30, May 7, July 4).
P – [12] Praha - Linz and v.v.; 🛏 1, 2 cl. Praha - Linz - Salzburg - Innsbruck - Zürich and v.v.; 🍷 Praha - České Budějovice and v.v.
R – [12] Brno - Praha - České Budějovice.
S – [12] České Budějovice - Praha - Bratislava.
b – Also Dec. 24, Apr. 20-22, July 6, Oct. 28.
d – Also Apr. 23, May 2, 9, Oct. 29; not Apr. 22, Oct. 28.
e – Also Dec. 26, Jan. 1, Apr. 22, May 1, 8, Oct. 28; not Dec. 23, 30, Apr. 21, Oct. 27. Conveys 🍷.
h – Ⓑ (not Dec. 23-25, 31, Apr. 19, 21, July 5, Oct. 27).
n – ①–⑥ (not Jan. 1, Apr. 20, 22, July 6, Oct. 28).
r – ①–⑥ (also Dec. 30, Apr. 21, Oct. 27; not Jan. 1, Apr. 22, May 1, 8, Oct. 28).
s – ①–⑥ (not Jan. 1, Apr. 20, 22, May 1, 8, July 6, Oct.
z – Also Apr. 22, Oct. 28; not Dec. 23, 30, Apr. 21, Oct
♥ – Operator: REGIOJET. Separate fare tariff applies.
▷ – See also Table **1135**.

June 8, 9, 15, 16, 22, 23: partial 🚌 substitution with arrivals up to 20 minutes later.

1131 ČESKÉ BUDĚJOVICE - ČESKÝ KRUMLOV - NOVÉ ÚDOLÍ

2nd class (also 1st in

km			S	W	Ex 531	W	S					◇
	Praha hl. n. 1130 d.	...	...	...	0801	...	...	...	...	...	...	...
0	**České Budějovice** d.	0513	0744	0813	1019	1029	1029	1213	1426	1613	1813	2013
31	Český Krumlov d.	0605	0835	0905	1055	1122	1122	1305	1512	1705	1905	2057
68	Horní Planá d.	0658	0937	0959	...	1217	1226	1359	1605	1803	1959	...
88	Černý Kříž a.	0725	1012	1026	...	1243	1258	1424	1631	1828	2025	...
96	**Nové Údolí** a.	0739	1039	1039	...	1256	1311	1438	1644	1841r	...	...

	▽					Ex 532			
Nové Údolí d.	...	...	...	0915	1122	...	1319	1523	1721
Černý Kříž d.	...	0443	0651	0930	1135	...	1332	1538	1736
Horní Planá d.	...	0510	0717	1000	1202	...	1359	1606	1803
Český Krumlov d.	0405	0604	0812	1056	1300	1407	1455	1700	1900
České Budějovice a.	0450	0649	0856	1146	1346	1444	1540	1744	1944
Praha hl. n. 1130 a.	...	...	...	...	...	1657	...	...	...

S – Apr. 29 - Sept. 29.
W – Not Apr. 29 - Sept. 29.
r – Ⓒ (daily Apr. 27 - Sept. 29).
▽ – Also at 0448 Ⓐ.
◇ – Also at 1521 Ⓐ, 2302.

Local trains (no train numbers shown) are operated by GW Train Regio; ČD tickets / rail passes are not valid.

1132 ČESKÉ BUDĚJOVICE - LINZ

km		3801	Ex 1541	3803	Ex 1543	3805	Ex 1545	3807	Ex 1547	
		2		2		2		2	P	2
	Praha hl. n. 1130 d.	...	0601	...	1001	...	1401	...	1801	...
0	**České Budějovice** d.	0600	0808	1003	1208	1403	1608	1803	2008	2257
50	Rybnik a.	0653	0852	1052	1252	1452	1652	1852	2052	2357
72	Lipno nad Vltavou ⊡ a.	*0745*	*0945*	*1145*	*1345*	*1545*	*1744*	*1957*	|	...
64	Summerau 🏛 d.	0712	0909	1112	1309	1512	1709	1912	2109	...
73	Freistadt a.	0721	0917	1121	1317	1521	1717	1921	2117	...
126	**Linz** Hbf a.	0824	1007	1224	1407	1624	1807	2024	2207	...

	Ex 1540	3800	3802	Ex 1542	3804	Ex 1544	3806	Ex 1546
	P	2	2		2		2	
Linz Hbf d.	0635	0752	0935	1152	1335	1552	1735	1835
Freistadt d.	0742	0842	1039	1242	1439	1644	1839	1942
Summerau 🏛 d.	0752	0852	1051	1252	1451	1653	1851	1952
Lipno nad Vltavou ⊡ d.	|	*0814*	*1014*	*1214*	*1414*	*1614*	*1814*	*1919r*
Rybnik d.	0807	0907	1107	1308	1507	1708	1907	2007
České Budějovice a.	0851	0958	1158	1351	1558	1751	1958	2051
Praha hl. n. 1130 a.	1057	...	...	1557	...	1957	...	2257

P – [12] Praha - Linz and v.v.; 🛏 1, 2 cl. Praha - Linz - Salzburg - Innsbruck - Zürich and v.v.
r – Ⓐ (daily Apr. 15 - Oct. 4).
⊡ – Change trains at Rybnik.

TRAIN NAMES: Praha - Linz trains are named JIŽNÍ EXPRES.

1133 ČESKÉ BUDĚJOVICE - ČESKÉ VELENICE

km		Ⓐ	2Ⓐ					2Ⓐ		2Ⓐ		⊡
0	České Budějovice d.	0506	0635	0809	1009	1209	1409	1509	1609	1709	1809	2009
50	České Velenice 🏛 a.	0554	0727	0857	1057	1257	1457	1557	1657	1757	1857	2057

	2	2Ⓐ					2Ⓐ		
České Velenice 🏛 d.	0456	0629	0903	1103	1303	1503	1603	1703	1903
České Budějovice a.	0548	0717	0950	1150	1350	1550	1650	1750	1950

⊡ – Additional journey runs at 2259.

For connections České Velenice - Wien see Table **990**.

☛ 0809-1409 (returning 0903-1503) are subject to alteration June 1

d class VESELÍ NAD LUŽNICÍ - ČESKÉ VELENICE 1134

For connections Praha - Veselí nad Lužnicí see Table **1130**. For connections České Velenice - Wien see Table **990**.

m												
			Ⓐ	Ⓒ			E					Ⓐ
0	Veselí nad Lužnicí	d.	0452	0626	0734	0938	1138	1338	1538	1738	1938	2139	2230
21	Třeboň	d.	0516	0649	0755	0959	1159	1359	1559	1759	1959	2200	2256
55	České Velenice 🚉	a.	0552	0728	0832	1035	1235	1435	1635	1835	2035	2249	2334

		◧	Ⓐn	Ⓒ		E					
České Velenice 🚉	d.	0610	0649	0716	0921	1121	1321	1521	1721	1921	2214
Třeboň	d.	0650	0759r	0759	1000	1200	1400	1600	1800	2000	2254
Veselí nad Lužnicí	a.	0712	0820	0820	1020	1220	1420	1620	1820	2020	2313

- Ⓐ (daily Apr. 15 - Oct. 4). n – Not Dec. 27 - Jan. 2, Feb. 1, Apr. 18, July 1 - Aug. 30, Oct. 29, 30. r – Arrives 0727. ◧ – Additional journeys run at 0328Ⓐ, 0419Ⓐ.

ČESKÉ BUDĚJOVICE - JIHLAVA - BRNO 1135

m			1435	651	653	661	663	665	667	669	2	655
			2Ⓐ	⚒n			H					Ⓑh
	Plzeň **1125**	d.	...	...	...	0603	0803	1003	1203	1403	...	1603
0	**České Budějovice**	d.	...	0415z	0607	0807	1007	1207	1407	1607	...	1807
39	Veselí nad Lužnicí	▷ d.	...	0445z	0640	0840	1040	1240	1440	1640	...	1840
65	Jindřichův Hradec	▷ d.	...	0516z	0716	0916	1116	1316	1516	1716	...	1914
17	Kostelec u Jihlavy	d.	...	0615z	0815	1015	1215	1415	1615	1815	...	2010
32	**Jihlava**	a.	...	0633z	0833	1033	1233	1433	1633	1833	...	2027
32	**Jihlava**	d.	0530	0640	0840	1040	1240	1440	1640	1840	1933	▽
61	Okříšky	d.	0603	0707	0907	1107	1307	1507	1707	1907	2018	...
73	Třebíč	d.	0620	0724	0924	1124	1324	1524	1724	1924	2054	...
36	**Brno** hlavní n.	a.	0738	0830	1030	1230	1430	1630	1830	2030	2210	...

		656	654	668	666	664	662	660	652	650
		Ⓐ			H					Ⓑh
Brno hlavní n.	d.	...	...	0727	0927	1127	1327	1527	1727	1927
Třebíč	d.	...	...	0834	1034	1234	1434	1634	1834	2036
Okříšky	d.	...	...	0847	1047	1247	1447	1647	1847	2051
Jihlava	a.	...	▽	0918	1118	1318	1518	1718	1918	2117
Jihlava	d.	0525	0725	0925	1125	1325	1525	1725	1930r	...
Kostelec u Jihlavy	d.	0542	0742	0942	1142	1342	1542	1742	1948r	...
Jindřichův Hradec	▷ d.	0643	0843	1043	1243	1443	1643	1843	2050r	...
Veselí nad Lužnicí	▷ d.	0716	0916	1116	1316	1516	1716	1916	2118r	...
České Budějovice	a.	0747	0947	1147	1347	1547	1747	1947	2149r	...
Plzeň **1125**	a.	0956	1156	1356	1556	1756	1956	2156	...	...

			Ⓐ	Ⓐ					Ⓑh			⑤u
0	Okříšky	d.	0443	0610	0710	0917	1117	1317	1517	1717	1920	1920
32	Moravské Budějovice	a.	0518	0645	0744	0952	1152	1352	1552	1752	2000	2000
70	Znojmo	a.	*0630*	0730	0847	1047	1247	1447	1647	1847	...	2047

		Ⓐ	⚒n				Ⓐ			⊡
Znojmo	d.	0529	0659	0902	1102	1302	...	1502	1702	1859
Moravské Budějovice	d.	0624	0803	1003	1203	1346	1427	1603	1803	1941
Okříšky	a.	0703	0839	1039	1239	...	1503	1639	1839	2016

⑤⑥⑦ (daily May 24 - Sept. 8), also Oct. 28.
Not Apr. 19, 21, July 5, Oct. 27.
①–⑥ (not Apr. 20, 22, July 6, Oct. 28).
⑤⑦ (also July 4, Oct. 28; not July 5, Oct. 27).
Also Apr. 18, 30, May 7, July 4; not Apr. 19, July 5.
① (also Oct. 29; not Oct. 28).
- To Jihlava, arrive 2105.

▽ – To/from Havlíčkův Brod on dates in Table **1149**.
▷ – Additional trains Veselí nad Lužnicí - Jindřichův Hradec: 0740, 0935, 1135Ⓐ, 1335, 1735, 1935Ⓐ, 2038, 2127, 2225, 2350.
Jindřichův Hradec - Veselí nad Lužnicí: 0550Ⓐ, 0642Ⓒ, 0730, 0947, 1147, 1347Ⓐ, 1553Ⓑ h, 1747, 1947, 2139, 2236Ⓐ. Journey 31-36 mins.

Engineering work June 3 - 16: by 🚌 Brno - Třebic and v.v. Depart Brno 15 mins earlier than shown - turn right out of main entrance for bus stop. Arrivals at Brno (by 🚌 from Třebic) are 15 minutes later than shown.

d class PRAHA - MLADÁ BOLESLAV - TURNOV - (LIBEREC) 1140

n			1148	1574	1146		1144	1142	1944	1140	1940	
			T	ⒸS	T		T	T	Ⓐ			
0	**Praha** Masarykovo	d.	0719	0819r	0919	1147	1319	1519	1619	1719	1919	2047
4	Neratovice	d.	0757	0857	0957	1232	1357	1557	1658	1757	1957	2132
0	Všetaty	d.	0804	0905	1004	1243	1404	1604	1706	1804	2004	2143
2	**Mladá Boleslav**	a.	0831	0945	1031	1321	1431	1631	1746	1831	2033	2218
2	**Mladá Boleslav**	d.	0834	...	1034	*1344*	1434	1634	*1749*	1834	2034	2241
8	Mnichovo Hradiště	d.	0859	...	1059	*1408*	1459	1659	*1813*	1859	2058	2259
2	**Turnov**	a.	0912	...	1112	*1428*	1512	1712	*1833*	1912	2116	2315
	Turnov **1142**	d.	*0921*	...	*1121*	*1440**	*1521*	*1721*	*1840**	*1921*	*2121*	*2319*
	Liberec **1142**	a.	*0955*	...	*1155*	*1524**	*1555*	*1755*	*1924**	*1955*	*2155*	*2355*

		1941	1141	1143		1145	1147	1149	1575	1151	
		Ⓐ		T		T	T	T	ⒸS	T	Ⓒ
Liberec **1142**	d.	*0401*	*0603*	*0803*	*0830**	*1203*	*1403*	*1603*	...	*1803*	*2030*
Turnov **1142**	a.	*0437*	*0639*	*0839*	*0915**	*1239*	*1439*	*1639*	...	*1839*	*2114*
Turnov	d.	0441	0644	0844	*0927*	1244	1444	1644	...	1844	2130
Mnichovo Hradiště	d.	0459	0658	0858	*0945*	1258	1458	1658	...	1858	2148
Mladá Boleslav	a.	0519	0715	0915	*1010*	1315	1515	1715	...	1915	2209
Mladá Boleslav	d.	0521	0723	0923	1037	1323	1523	1723	1812	1923	2221
Všetaty	d.	0550	0750	0950	1123	1350	1550	1750	1840	1950	2300
Neratovice	d.	0558	0759	0958	1136	1358	1558	1758	1849	1958	2308
Praha Masarykovo	a.	0635	0835	1035	1220	1435	1635	1835	1933r	2035	2350r

Ⓒ Mar. 30 - Oct. 28. Heritage DMU operated by KŽC.
To/from Tanvald on dates in Table **1142** (some extend to/from Harrachov on Ⓒ).
r – Praha **hlavní** nádrazi.
* – Also change at Turnov.

d class LIBEREC - TANVALD - HARRACHOV - SZKLARSKA PORĘBA 1141

n																										
				Ⓐ			Ⓐu			Ⓒp					Ⓐu			Ⓒp								
0	**Liberec**	d.	0035	0437	0535	0635	0705	0735	0835	...	0935	1035	1135	1235	1305	1335	1435	...	1535	1635	1735	1835	1935	2035	2135	2235
2	Jablonec nad Nisou	d.	0053	0456	0556	0656	0726	0756	0856	...	0956	1056	1156	1256	1326	1356	1456	...	1556	1656	1756	1856	1956	2056	2156	2256
7	**Tanvald**	a.	0118	0525	0625	0725	0755	0825	0925	1009	1025	1125	1225	1325	1355	1425	1525	1609	1625	1725	1825	1925	2025	2125	2225	2325
9	Harrachov	a.	...	...	...	0753	...	0853	0955	1040	1051	1153s	1251	1353	...	1453	1553	1640	1653	1753	1853	1953r	...	...	...	...
5	**Szklarska Poręba** ‡	a.	...	...	...	0822	...	0922s	1022	...	1122s	1222s	...	1422	...	1522z	1622s	...	1722z	1822	...	2022r	...	...	...	...

						Ⓐv					Ⓒp		Ⓐ		Ⓐ		Ⓐv				Ⓒp					
larska Poręba ‡	d.	...	...	...	...	...	...	0829	0929s	1029	...	1129s	...	1229s	...	...	...	1429	1529z	1629s	...	1729z	1829	...	2029r	...
rachov	d.	...	...	...	...	...	0757x	0857	0957	1057	1106	1157s	...	1257	...	1357	...	1457	1557	1657	1706	1757	1900	1957r	2057r	...
vald	d.	0429	0529	0629	0729	0759	0829	0929	1029	1129	1132	1229	1259	1329	1359	1429	1459	1529	1629	1729	1732	1829	1929	2029	2129	2229
onec nad Nisou	d.	0457	0557	0657	0757	0827	0857	0957	1057	1157	...	1257	1327	1357	1427	1457	1527	1557	1657	1757	...	1857	1957	2057	2157	2257
erec	a.	0518	0618	0718	0818	0848	0918	1018	1118	1218	...	1318	1348	1418	1448	1518	1548	1618	1718	1818	...	1918	2018	2118	2218	2318

From/to Praha (Table **1142**).
Ⓒ Apr. 27 - June 16; daily June 20 - Sept. 1 (also May 2, 3).
Dec. 26 - Jan. 2, Jan. 5, 6, Jan. 12 - Mar. 17; ⑥⑦ Mar. 23 - June 16 (also Apr. 19, 22, May 1, 2, 3, 8); daily June 20 - Sept. 1; ⑥⑦ Sept. 7 - Oct. 27 (also Oct. 28).

u – Also at 0500Ⓐ, 0605Ⓐ, hourly 1405Ⓐ to 1805Ⓐ.
v – Also 0351Ⓐ, 0459Ⓐ, 0559Ⓐ, 0659Ⓐ, 1559Ⓐ, 1659Ⓐ.
x – Ⓒ only.
z – Ⓒ (also May 3, June 20, Aug. 15, Nov. 1, 11).

‡ – Szklarska Poręba Górna.
🚉 Czech Republic/Poland = Jakuszyce.

d class LIBEREC - HRADEC KRÁLOVÉ - PARDUBICE 1142

m			1261	1263		1275	1277
0	**Liberec**	d.	0401	0603		1803	2003
8	Turnov	a.	0437	0639		1839	2039
8	Turnov	d.	0438	0642	and	1842	2042
	Železný Brod	a.	0454	0658	every	1858	2058
2	Železný Brod ★	d.	0455	0659	two	1859	2059
6	Stará Paka	d.	0525	0727	hours	1927	2127
7	Dvůr Králové n. L.	d.	0600	0800	until	2000	2159
2	Jaroměř	d.	0619	0819		2019	2213
9	**Hradec Králové**	a.	0633	0833		2033	2230
9	**Hradec Králové** ▶	d.	0635	0836		2036	2232
1	**Pardubice**	a.	0655	0856		2054	2254

		1276		1262	1260
Pardubice ▶	d.	0502		1903	2103
Hradec Králové ▶	a.	0523		1923	2123
Hradec Králové	d.	0526	and	1926	2126
Jaroměř	d.	0542	every	1943	2144
Dvůr Králové n. L.	d.	0556	two	1956	2158
Stará Paka	d.	0631	hours	2031	2232
Železný Brod ★	a.	0656	until	2056	2257
Železný Brod	d.	0700		2100	2301
Turnov	a.	0718		2118	2318
Turnov	d.	0721		2121	2319
Liberec	a.	0755		2155	2355

		△		Ⓒ	Ⓐ		Ⓑh	Ⓑh
Praha Mas. ◧	d.	...	0719	0919	*0919*	1319	1519	*1719*
Turnov	d.	...	0919	1119	1126	1519	1719	1926
Železný Brod	d.	0701	0936	1136	1145	1536	1736	1946
Tanvald	a.	0727	1003	1203	1210	1603	1803	2012
Harrachov **1141**	a.	...	1040c	...	...	1640c	...	...
		▽	⑥u	Ⓒ	Ⓐ	Ⓒ	d	
Harrachov **1141**	d.	...	...	1106	...	...	...	1706c
Tanvald	d.	0627	0750	1149	1340	1350	1549	1750
Železný Brod	a.	0653	0817	1217	1407	1417	1617	1817
Turnov	a.	...	0835	1235	1436	1435	1635	1835
Praha Mas. ◧	a.	...	1035	1435	*1635*	1635	1835	2035

Ⓒ only.
Change at Turnov on Ⓐ.
Not Dec. 23 - 25, 31, Apr. 19, 21, July 5, Oct. 27.
Ⓐ (daily Apr. 15 - Oct. 4).
⑥ (also ①–⑤ July 1 - Aug. 30), also Apr. 19, May 1, 8; not Apr. 20.
Also 0901, 1101Ⓒ, 1301, 1417Ⓐ, 1501, 1701, 1901, 2101, 2301**s**.
Also 0427⚒, 0527Ⓐ, 0827, 1027, 1227, 1430, 1627, 1827, 2027, 2227**s**.

★ – For Pardubice - Tanvald and v.v. change at Železný Brod (see right hand panel).
◧ – Praha Masarykovo. See Table **1140**.
▶ – Additional trains **Hradec Kralové - Pardubice** and v.v. (journey 20 - 30 minutes):
From Hradec Kralové: 0019, 0431, 0504Ⓐ, 0532Ⓐ, 0545, 0602, 0704, 0731, 0804, 0904, 0937⚒, 1004, 1104, 1137, 1204, 1304, 1337, 1404, 1504, 1537, 1604, 1704, 1737, 1804, 1904, 1937, 2006, 2104, 2207.
From Pardubice: 0105, 0430Ⓐ, 0532, 0605Ⓐ, 0629⚒, 0634Ⓒ, 0719Ⓐ, 0741, 0806, 0837, 0933, 1033, 1133, 1206, 1233, 1333, 1406, 1434, 1534, 1607, 1633, 1733, 1806, 1833, 1933, 2009, 2033, 2144, 2300.

class STARKOČ - WAŁBRZYCH 1144

			S	Ⓒ		S		S		S
Starkoč **1145**	d.	0841	...	1125	...	...	1441	...	1741	...
Náchod	d.	0900	...	1139	1200	...	1500	...	1800	...
Meziměsti 🚉	d.	0942	0956	...	1242	1318	1542	1548	1841	1918
Wałbrzych Gł.	a.	...	1036	...	...	1358	...	1628	...	1959
Wrocław **1084**	a.	...	...	...	...	...	...	...	...	2109

		S	Ⓒ	Ⓒ	S		S		S	
Wrocław **1084**	d.	0646r	...	...	...	...	...	...	...	...
Wałbrzych Gł.	d.	0800	...	...	1100	...	1436	...	1636	...
Meziměsti 🚉	d.	0840	0919	...	1140	1219	1516	1518	1716	1719
Náchod	d.	...	0958	1021	...	1304	...	1605	...	1804
Starkoč **1145**	a.	...	...	1037	...	1318	...	1619	...	1818

⑥⑦ Apr. 27 - Sept. 29 (also May 1, 3, 8, June 20, July 5, Aug. 15). Operated by GW Train Regio; rail passes not valid.
r – 0600 on May 8, July 5.

1145 PRAHA - HRADEC KRÁLOVÉ - TRUTNOV

km		1780	941	1782	921	943	1784	923	945	1786	925	1788	927	947	1790	929	935	1792	931	949	951	1796	953	955	95
			Ⓐ🍷	⑥t	🍷	🍷	2	🍷	🍷	2Ⓐ	🍷	2	🍷	🍷	2	🍷	🍷	2	🍷	🍷	🍷		🍷	🍷	🍷
0	**Praha** hlavní n. d.	...	0506	...	0606	0706	...	0806	0906	...	1006	...	1206	1306	...	1406	1506	...	1606	1706	1806	...	1906	2006	220
55	Nymburk ▷ d.	...	0555	...	0655	0755	...	0855	0955	...	1055	...	1255	1355	...	1455	1555	...	1655	1755	1855	...	1955	2055	225
66	Poděbrady ▷ d.	...	0602	...	0702	0802	...	0902	1002	...	1102	...	1302	1402	...	1502	1602	...	1702	1802	1902	...	2002	2102	230
125	**Hradec Králové** a.	...	0651	...	0751	0851	...	0951	1051	...	1151	...	1351	1451	...	1551	1651	...	1751	1851	1951	...	2051	2151	235
125	**Hradec Králové** d.	0602	...	0703	0804	...	0903	1004	...	1103	1204	1303	1404	...	1503	1604	1705	1703	1804	...	...	2002	...	...	...
142	Jaroměř d.	0619	...	0719	0819	...	0918	1019	...	1118	1219	1318	1419	...	1518	1619	▽	1718	1819	...	...	2020	...	...	...
160	Starkoč d.	0638	...	0740	0840	...	0940	1040	...	1140	1240	1339	1440	...	1540	1640	...	1740	1840	...	...	2040	...	...	...
194	**Trutnov** hlavní n. a.	0720	...	0819	0920	...	1017	1120	...	1218	1320	1417	1520	...	1618	1720	...	1817	1920	...	...	2118	...	...	...

	952	950	1785	934	932	1787	948	930	1789	928	1791	946	926	1793	944	924	1795	942	922	1797	940	920			
	Ⓐ🍷	🍷		🍷	🍷	2	🍷	🍷	2Ⓐ	🍷	2	🍷	🍷	2	🍷	🍷	2	🍷	🍷	2	🍷	🍷	2	2	
Trutnov hlavní n. d.	...	...	0542	...	0642	0743	...	0842	0942	1042	1141	...	1242	1341	...	1442	1541	...	1642	1741	...	1842	2041	...	...
Starkoč d.	...	...	0621	...	0721	0823	...	0921	1023	1121	1223	...	1321	1423	...	1521	1623	...	1721	1823	...	1921	2119	2122	...
Jaroměř d.	...	...	0642	▽	0741	0842	...	0941	1042	1141	1242	...	1341	1442	...	1541	1642	...	1741	1842	...	1941	...	2142	...
Hradec Králové a.	...	...	0659	0653	0755	0856	...	0955	1056	1155	1256	...	1355	1456	...	1555	1656	...	1755	1856	...	1955	...	2200	...
Hradec Králové d.	0508	0608	...	0708	0808	...	0908	1008	...	1208	...	1308	1408	...	1508	1608	...	1708	1808	...	1908	2008	...	...	...
Poděbrady ▷ d.	0554	0654	...	0754	0854	...	0954	1054	...	1254	...	1354	1454	...	1554	1654	...	1754	1854	...	1954	2054	...	...	...
Nymburk ▷ d.	0602	0702	...	0802	0902	...	1002	1102	...	1302	...	1402	1502	...	1602	1702	...	1802	1902	...	2002	2102	...	...	...
Praha hlavní n. a.	0649	0749	...	0849	0949	...	1049	1149	...	1349	...	1449	1549	...	1649	1749	...	1849	1949	...	2049	2149	...	...	...

t – ⑥ (© Apr. 27 - Sept. 29), also Apr. 19; not July 6.
▽ – To / from Letohrad (a. 1830 / d. 0533).
▷ – See also Table **1157**.

HRADEC KRÁLOVÉ - LETOHRAD Journey 80-85 mins
From Hradec Králové 0705©, 0905, 1105, 1305, 1506, 1705, 1905.
From Letohrad 0533, 0729©, 0833, 1133, 1333, 1533, 1733.

1149 HAVLÍČKŮV BROD - JIHLAVA

2nd class

27 km																	
		Ⓐ		R§				Ⓐ		Ⓐ		Ⓐ		ⒷP		Ⓐ	
Havlíčkův Brod ... d.	0448	0603	0648	0700	0805	1005	1205	1313	1405	1513	1605	1712	1805	1902	2005	2105	2208
Jihlava a.	0516	0632	0718	0722	0832	1033	1234	1343	1434	1542	1635	1742	1834	1923	2033	2134	2237

		⚒P		Ⓐ				Ⓐ		Ⓐ		Ⓐ		Ⓐ		S§	
Jihlava d.	0518	0536	0605	0656	0727	0922	1122	1237	1322	1436	1521	1614	1721	1813	1924	2034	2135
Havlíčkův Brod ... a.	0547	0558	0643	0734	0751	0950	1150	1305	1351	1504	1550	1642	1750	1841	1952	2056	2203

P – From / to Praha. For days of running see Table **1152**.
R – ①⑥ also Dec. 27, Jan. 2, Apr. 19, 23, May 1, 2, 8, 9, July Oct. 29; not Dec. 24, 31, Apr. 20-22, July 6, Oct. 28.
S – ⑤⑦ also Dec. 26, Jan. 1, Apr. 18, 22, 30, May 1, 7, 8, July Oct. 28; not Dec. 23, 30, Apr. 19, 21, July 5, Oct. 27.
§ – To / from Plzeň (Table **1135**).

1150 PRAHA - PARDUBICE - BRNO - BŘECLAV - WIEN and BRATISLAVA

FAST TRAINS For semi-fast trains Praha - Brno see Table **1151**

km		*EC* 271	*RJ* 71	♥ 1031	*EC* 273	*EC* 101	*RJ* 73	♥ 1041	*EC* 275	*RJ* 75	♥ 1033	*EC* 277	*EC* 103	*RJ* 77	♥ 1043	*EC* 279	*RJ* 79	*EC* 131	♥ 1035	*EC* 173	*RJ* 371	♥ 1045	*EC* 281	♥ 1037	*R* 37
		✕	✕ ⚒n	🍷 ⚒x	✕	⊡	✕	🍷	✕	✕	🍷	✕	✕ ⊡	✕	🍷	✕	✕	✕ B	🍷	✕ H	✕	🍷	✕	🍷	✕
0	**Praha** hlavní n. △ d.	...	0448	0520	0550	...	0647	0720	0750	0847	0920	0950	...	1047	1120	1150	1247	...	1320	1350	1447	1520	1550	1620	16
62	Kolín △ d.	...	0525	|	0627	...	|	|	0827	|	|	1027	...	|	|	1227	|	...	|	1427	|	|	1627	|	|
104	**Pardubice** △ d.	...	0546	0615	0648	...	0743	0815	0848	0943	1015	1048	...	1143	1215	1248	1343	...	1415	1448	1541	1615	1648	1715	17
164	Česká Třebová △ d.	...	0620	|	0721	...	0817	|	|	1018	|	|	...	1217	|	|	1417	...	|	|	1615	|	|	|	18
253	Brno Židenice d.	...	0716	0742	0816	...	0916	0942	1016	1116	1142	1216	...	1316	1342	1416	1516	...	1542	1616	1716	1742	1816	1842	19
255	**Brno** dolní nádrazí ☆ d.	0624	0724	0749	0824	...	0924	0949	1024	1124	1149	1224	...	1324	1349	1424	1524	...	1549	1624	1724	1749	1824	1849	19
314	Břeclav a.	0652	0752	0818	0852	...	0952	1020	1052	1152	1218	1252	...	1352	1420	1452	1552	...	1618	1652	1752	1820	1852	1918	19
314	Břeclav ▷ d.	0659	0755	0820	0859	0855	0955	1023	1059	1155	1220	1259	1255	1355	1423	1459	1555	1559	1620	1659	1755	1823	1859	1920	19
402	**Wien** Hbf ▷ a.	|	0849	0922	|	0949	1049	|	|	1249	1322	|	1349	1449	|	|	1649	|	1722	|	1849	|	|	2022	20
	Graz **980** a.	|	1133	...	|	...	1333	|	|	1533	...	|	...	1733	|	|	1933	|	...	|	2133	|	|	...	23
332	Kúty 🏛 d.	0713	...	...	0913	...	...	|	1113	...	...	1313	...	...	|	1513	...	1613	...	1713	...	|	1913	...	...
396	**Bratislava** hl. st. a.	0750	...	...	0950	...	...	1112	1150	...	...	1350	...	...	1512	1550	...	1650	...	1750	...	1912	1950	...	...
	Budapest Ny. ‡ **1175** a.	1020	...	...	1220	...	...	...	1420	...	...	1620	...	...	...	1820	...	1920	...	2020	...	...	2220	...	...

	♥ 1047	*EC* 283	*EC* 105	♥ 1049	*RJ* 375	*RJ* 285	♥ 1051	*IC* 573	573 477	*NJ* 457	*IC* 575
	🍷	✕ P	✕ ⊡	🍷 m	✕	✕	🍷 ⊕	✕ ⊕	⊕ M	§ N	✕ ⊕
Praha hlavní n. △ d.	1720	1750	...	1820	1847	1950	2020	2156	2156	...	2350
Kolín △ d.	|	1827	...	|	|	2027	|	2233	2233	...	0027
Pardubice △ d.	1815	1848	...	1915	1943	2048	2113	2258	2258	...	0048
Česká Třebová △ d.	|	|	...	|	2017	2121	|	2338	2338	...	0127
Brno Židenice d.	1942	2016	...	2047	2116	2216	2250	0042	0042	...	0227
Brno dolní nádrazí ☆ d.	1949	2024	...	2052	2124	2224	2254r	0050	0050	...	0233
Břeclav a.	2020	2052	...	...	2152	2252	...	0121	0121	...	...
Břeclav ▷ d.	2023	2059	2055	...	2155	2254	...	...	0459	0549	...
Wien Hbf ▷ a.	|	|	2149	...	2249	|	...	...	|	0700	...
Graz **980** a.	|	|	...	...	...	|	...	...	|	...	...
Kúty 🏛 d.	|	2113	...	...	...	|	...	...	0513	...	...
Bratislava hl. st. a.	2112	2150	...	...	...	2343	...	...	0550	...	...
Budapest Ny. ‡ **1175** a.	...	...	...	...	...	...	...	...	0835k	...	...

	RJ 574	♥ 1040	*IC* 572	♥ 1042	*RJ* 284	♥ 1044	*EC* 282	♥ 1030	*RJ* 70	*E* 10
	✕ ⚒n	🍷 ⊕y	✕	🍷	✕	🍷	✕ P	🍷	✕	✕ ⊡
Budapest N ‡ **1175** d.	...	...	...	...	...	...	...	...	...	...
Bratislava hl. st. d.	...	...	...	...	0510	0545	0610	...	...	...
Kúty 🏛 d.	...	...	...	...	|	|	0649	...	...	...
Graz **980** d.	...	...	...	...	|	|	|	...	...	...
Wien Hbf ▷ d.	...	...	...	...	|	|	|	0639	0710	08
Břeclav ▷ a.	...	...	...	...	0601	0634	0701	0736	0804	09
Břeclav d.	...	...	0502	...	0607	0636	0707	0737	0807	...
Brno dolní nádrazí ☆ d.	0428	0500	0534	0607	0637	0707	0737	0807	0837	.
Brno Židenice d.	0433	0506	0539	0613	0642	0713	0742	0813	0842	.
Česká Třebová △ d.	0539	|	0636	|	0739	|	|	|	0939	.
Pardubice △ d.	0614	0647	0711	0745	0814	0845	0911	0945	1014	.
Kolín △ d.	|	|	0731	|	|	|	0931	|	|	.
Praha hlavní n. △ a.	0707	0743	0807	0843	0907	0942	1007	1042	1107	.

	EC 280	♥ 1046	*RJ* 72	*EC* 172	♥ 1032	*EC* 130	*RJ* 74	*EC* 278	♥ 1048	*RJ* 76	*EC* 102	*EC* 276	♥ 1034	*RJ* 78	♥ 1050	*EC* 274	*RJ* 370	*EC* 100	*EC* 272	♥ 1036	*RJ* 372	*EC* 270	*RJ* 374	476 572	*N* 45
	✕	🍷	✕	✕ H	🍷	✕ B	✕	✕	🍷	✕	✕ ⊡	✕	🍷	✕	🍷	✕	✕	⊡	✕	🍷	✕ ⊕	✕	✕	M	§ N
Budapest Ny. ‡ **1175** d.	0540	...	...	0740	...	0840	...	0940	...	...	...	1140	...	...	...	1340	...	...	1540	...	...	1740	...	1925k	.
Bratislava hl. st. d.	0810	0847	...	1010	...	1110	...	1210	1247	...	...	1410	...	...	1526	1610	...	...	1810	...	...	2010	...	2210	.
Kúty 🏛 d.	0849	|	...	1049	...	1149	...	1249	|	...	...	1449	...	...	|	1649	...	...	1849	...	...	2049	...	2249	.
Graz **980** d.	|	|	0626	|	...	|	0826	|	|	1026	...	|	...	1226	|	|	1426	...	|	...	1626	|	1826	|	.
Wien Hbf ▷ d.	|	|	0910	|	1039	|	1110	|	|	1310	1410	|	1439	1510	|	|	1710	1810	|	1839	1910	|	2110	|	22
Břeclav ▷ a.	0901	0936	1004	1101	1136	1201	1204	1301	1336	1404	1504	1501	1536	1604	1636	1701	1804	1904	1901	1936	2004	2101	2204	2301	23
Břeclav d.	0907	0937	1007	1107	1138	...	1207	1307	1338	1407	...	1507	1538	1607	1638	1707	1807	...	1907	1938	2007	2107	2207	0502	.
Brno dolní nádrazí ☆ d.	0937	1007	1037	1137	1207	...	1237	1337	1407	1437	...	1537	1607	1637	1707	1737	1837	...	1937	2007	2037	2137	2235	0534	.
Brno Židenice d.	0942	1013	1042	1142	1213	...	1242	1342	1413	1442	...	1542	1613	1642	1713	1742	1842	...	1942	2013	2042	2142	...	0539	.
Česká Třebová △ d.	|	|	1139	|	|	...	1339	|	|	1539	...	|	|	1739	|	|	1939	...	2039	|	2145	2239	...	0636	.
Pardubice △ d.	1111	1145	1214	1311	1345	...	1414	1511	1545	1614	...	1711	1745	1814	1845	1911	2014	...	2114	2145	2220	2314	...	0711	.
Kolín △ d.	1131	|	|	1331	|	...	|	1531	|	|	...	1731	|	|	|	1931	|	...	2134	|	2240	2334	...	0731	.
Praha hlavní n. △ a.	1207	1242	1307	1407	1442	...	1507	1607	1642	1707	...	1807	1842	1907	1942	2007	2107	...	2209	2242	2314	0011	...	0807	.

B – BATHORY – 🚃12 ✕ Warszawa - Katowice - Ostrava - Břeclav - Budapest and v.v.
H – HUNGARIA – 🚃12 ✕ Hamburg - Berlin - Dresden - Praha - Bratislava - Budapest and v.v.
M – 🚃12 Praha - Břeclav and v.v.; 🚃12 Břeclav - Budapest and v.v.; 🛏 1, 2 cl., ▬ 2 cl. Praha - Břeclav (**477/6**) - Bratislava - Budapest and v.v. For other cars Břeclav - Budapest and v.v. see Table **99** Warszawa and Kraków - Budapest and Tables **60** / **71** Berlin - Budapest.
N – NIGHTJET – 🛏 1, 2 cl., ▬ 2 cl., 🚃2 Berlin - Ostrava - Břeclav - Wien and v.v.; 🛏 1, 2 cl., 🚃2 Warszawa - Kraków - Ostrava - Břeclav - Wien and v.v. (Table **99**), also ▬ 2 cl. on dates in Table **99**.
P – 🚃12 ✕ Praha - Bratislava and v.v. Conveys on dates in Table **1175**, 🛏 1, 2 cl. Praha (**283/2**) - Bratislava (**873/0**) - Nové Zámky (**801/0**) - Košice - Prešov and v.v.; 🚃12 ✕ Praha - Bratislava (**873/0**) - Nové Zámky and v.v.
k – Budapest **Keleti**.
m – Not Dec. 24-31, Apr. 21, 30, May 7, July 5.
n – ①-⑥ (not Dec. 24-26, Jan. 1, Apr. 20, 22, July 6, Oct. 28).
r – Brno **hlavní** nádraží.
x – ①-⑥ (also Dec. 30; not Dec. 24, 25, 31).
y – ①-⑥ (not Dec. 25 - Jan. 1, Apr. 22, July 5).

♥ – Operated by REGIOJET. Separate fare tariff applies.
⊡ – For origin / destination see Table **99** or **1164**.
▷ – For local trains Břeclav - Wien see Table **982**.
△ – See also Table **1160**.
⊕ – For additional station stops see Table **1151**.
☆ – 🚌 connections available Brno dolní nádraží - Brno hlavní nádraží (see plan on page 31).
§ – Ⓡ for international journeys.
‡ – Budapest **Nyugati**.
RJ – Railjet train (operated by Austrian & Czech Railways). Thr classes of service: Business, First, Economy.

TRAIN NAMES
Praha - Budapest trains are named METROPOLITAN.
Praha - Graz trains are named VINDOBONA.

PRAHA - PARDUBICE - OLOMOUC / BRNO semi-fast trains 1151

For fast trains see Tables **1150** (Praha - Brno) and **1160** (Praha - Olomouc)

m		1973	1975	883	861	885	863	887	865	889	867	1977	891	869	893	871	895	873	897	1051	875	877	899	*IC*573	*IC*575
		⚒n	2Ⓐ	🍷	E	🍷	🍷	⚒n	🍷	🍷	🍷	2Ⓐ	🍷	🍷	🍷	🍷	🍷	🍷	🍷	♥🍷	🍷	Ⓑh	🍷	M	✖
	Praha Smichov d.	...	...	...	...	...	...	...	0946	1041	...	...	1243	1346	1446	1546	1646	1746	1846	...	2013	...	...	...	...
0	**Praha** hlavní n. d.	...	...	...	0558r	0658	0758	0858	0958	1058	1158	...	1258	1358	1458	1558	1658	1758	1858	2020	2024	2050	2124	2156	2350
62	Kolín d.	...	...	⊖	0638r	0738	0838	0938	1038	1138	1238	...	1338	1438	1538	1638	1738	1838	1938	|	2103	2126	2202	2233	0027
04	**Pardubice** d.	...	...	0607	0707	0807	0907	1007	1107	1207	1307	...	1407	1507	1607	1707	1807	1907	2007	2113	2127	2146	2228	2258	0048
39	Choceň d.	...	...	0625	0725	0825	0925	1025	1125	1225	1325	...	1425	1525	1625	1725	1825	1925	2025	|	2144	...	2245	2315	0105
54	Ústí nad Orlicí d.	...	...	0637	0737	0837	0937	1037	1137	1237	1337	...	1437	1537	1637	1737	1837	1937	2037	2139	2156	...	2258	2328	0117
64	**Česká Třebová** d.	0540	0639	0651	0751	0851	0951	1051	1151	1251	1351	1450	1451	1551	1651	1751	1851	1951	2051	|	2205	...	2308	2338	0127
06	Zábřeh na Moravé d.	|	|	|	|	|	|	|	|	|	|	|	|	|	|	|	|	|	|	|	...	...	2330	|	|
52	**Olomouć** a.	|	|	0729	|	0929	|	1129	|	1329	|	|	1529	|	1729	|	1929	|	2129	|	...	...	2351	|	|
31	Svitavy d.	0558	0700	◇	0803	◇	1003	◇	1203	◇	1403	1505	◇	1603	⊡	1803	▽	2003	⊙	2158	...	...	p	2349	0137
08	Letovice d.	0628	0728	...	0822	...	1022	...	1222	...	1422	1532	...	1622	...	1822	...	2022	...	2217	...	...	...	0008	|
33	Blansko d.	0650	0752	...	0841	...	1041	...	1241	...	1441	1553	...	1641	...	1841	...	2041	...	2233	...	...	...	0025	0210
55	**Brno** hlavní n. a.	0716	0816	...	0903	...	1103	...	1303	...	1503	1615	...	1703	...	1903	...	2103	...	2254	...	...	...	|	|
55	**Brno** dolní n. ☆ a.	...	...	...	...	...	...	...	...	...	...	...	...	...	...	...	...	...	...	...	...	...	...	0048	0233

	876	898	*RJ*574	896	1040	874	894	872	892	870	890	868	888	866	886	864	884	1974	862	882	860	860	*Ex*120	*RJ*372	640
	⚒n	🍷	⚒n	⚒n	♥v	B🍷	🍷	🍷	🍷	🍷	🍷	🍷	🍷	🍷	🍷	🍷	🍷	Ⓐb	🍷	🍷	🍷	⑦e	🍷	✖	⑦e
o dolní n. ☆ d.	...	...	0428	...	0500	...	...	...	...	...	...	...	...	...	...	...	...	...	...	...	...	...	...	2037	...
o hlavní n. d.	...	...	|	...	|	0457	...	0654	...	0853	...	1053	...	1253	...	1453	...	1543	1653	...	1853	1853	...	|	...
nsko d.	...	...	0452	...	0525	0520	...	0716	...	0915	...	1115	...	1315	...	1515	...	1608	1716	...	1915	1915	...	2059	...
ovice d.	...	...	0510	...	0544	0539	...	0739	...	0939	...	1139	...	1339	...	1539	...	1631	1739	...	1940	1940	...	2116	...
avy d.	...	p	0528	⊡	0601	0601	⊙	0803	▽	1003	◇	1203	◇	1403	◇	1603	◇	1703	1803	◇	2003	2003	z	2134	u
lomouc d.	...	0429	|	0509	|	|	0631	|	0831	|	1031	|	1231	|	1431	|	1631	|	|	1831	|	|	2009	|	2120
ábřeh na Moravé d.	...	0451	|	0543	|	|	|	|	|	|	|	|	|	|	|	|	|	|	|	|	|	|	2040	|	2143
ská Třebová d.	...	0514	0539	0605	|	0614	0714	0814	0914	1014	1114	1214	1314	1414	1514	1614	1714	1719	1814	1914	2014	2014	2102	2145	2205
nad Orlicí d.	...	0524	|	0614	0619	0624	0724	0824	0924	1024	1124	1224	1324	1424	1524	1624	1724	...	1824	1924	2024	2024	2110	|	2214
oceň d.	...	0536	|	|	|	0636	0736	0836	0936	1036	1136	1236	1336	1436	1536	1636	1736	...	1836	1936	2036	2036	2123	|	2226
dubice d.	0537	0601	0614	0641	0647	0701	0801	0901	1001	1101	1201	1301	1401	1501	1601	1701	1801	...	1901	2001	2055	2101	2141	2220	2245
n d.	0602	0626	|	0702	|	0726	0826	0926	1026	1126	1226	1326	1426	1526	1626	1726	1826	...	1926	2026	...	2126	2204	2240	2307
ha hlavní n. a.	0639	0704	0707	0739	0743	0804	0904	1004	1104	1204	1304	1404	1504	1604	1704	1804	1904	...	2004	2104	...	2204	2239	2314	2344
raha Smichov a.	...	...	...	...	...	0817	0919	...	1120	1216	1316	1416	1516	1616	1716	1816	...	...	...	...	...	...	...	...	...

Ⓐ from Brno; daily from Česká Třebová.
①r from Praha, ⚒n from Pardubice, daily from Česká Třebová.
[12] ✖ Praha - Brno - Břeclav; 🛏 1, 2 cl., 🛏 2 cl. Praha - Budapest (Table **1150**).
2nd class. Additional trains run at 1343Ⓐ, 1743Ⓐ.
⑦ (also Dec. 26, Jan. 1, Apr. 22, May 1, 8, Oct. 28; not Dec. 23, 30, Apr. 21, Oct. 27).

h – Not Dec. 23-25, 31, Apr. 19, 21, July 5, Oct. 27.
n – ①–⑥ (not Dec. 24-26, Jan. 1, Apr. 20, 22, July 6, Oct. 28).
p – To/from Přerov (Table **1162**).
r – ① (also Dec. 27, Jan. 2, Apr. 23, May 2, 9, Oct. 29; not Dec. 24, 31, Apr. 22, Oct. 28).
u – From Bohumín (Table **1160**).
v – ①–⑥ (not Dec. 25 - Jan. 1, Apr. 22, July 5).
z – From Žilina (Table **1160**).

♥ – Operated by REGIOJET. Separate fare tariff applies.
⊡ – To/from Staré Město u Uherské Hradiště (Table **1162**).
▽ – To/from Veseli nad Moravou (Table **1162**).
◇ – To/from Luhačovice (Table **1162**).
⊖ – From Hradec Králové (d. 0545).
⊙ – To/from Zlín (Table **1162**).
☆ – See plan on page 31.

PRAHA - HAVLIČKŮV BROD - BRNO 1152

r Praha - Brno see Table **1150**

		975	977	979	981	983	985	987	961	989	991	963
		⚒n					Ⓐ		Ⓑh		G	
0	**Praha** hlavní n. ▷ d.	0603	0803	1003	1203	1403	1503	1603	1703	1803	1903	2003
2	Kolín ▷ d.	0647	0847	1047	1247	1447	1547	1647	1747	1847	1947	2047
3	Kutná Hora d.	0658	0858	1058	1258	1458	1558	1658	1758	1858	1958	2058
2	Čáslav d.	0708	0908	1108	1308	1508	1608	1708	1808	1908	2008	2108
6	**Havlíčkův Brod** d.	0802	1002	1202	1402	1602	1702	1802	1902	2002	2100	2157
	Jihlava **1149** a.	|	|	|	|	|	|	|	1923	|	|	...
9	Ždár nad Sázavou d.	0829	1029	1229	1429	1629	1729	1829	...	2029	2126	...
6	**Brno** Královo Pole § a.	0928	1128	1328	1528	1728	1828	1928	...	2130	2221	...

	962	960	990	988	986	984	982	980	978	976	972
	⚒n		E						Ⓑh		
Brno Královo Pole § d.	...	...	0531	0631	0831	1031	1231	1431	1531	1631	1831
Ždár nad Sázavou d.	...	...	0632	0732	0932	1132	1332	1532	1632	1732	1932
Jihlava **1149** d.	...	0536n	|	|	|	|	|	|	|	|	|
Havlíčkův Brod d.	0500	0600	0700	0800	1000	1200	1400	1600	1700	1800	2000
Čáslav d.	0550	0650	0750	0850	1050	1250	1450	1650	1750	1850	2050
Kutná Hora d.	0600	0700	0800	0900	1100	1300	1500	1700	1800	1900	2100
Kolín ▷ d.	0611	0711	0811	0911	1111	1311	1511	1711	1811	1911	2111
Praha hlavní n. ▷ a.	0652	0752	0852	0952	1152	1352	1552	1752	1852	1952	2152

①v from Brno Královo Pole, Ⓐ from Ždár nad Sázavou, ⚒n from Havlíčkův Brod.
Ⓑh to Havlíčkův Brod; ⑤ (also Apr. 18, 30, May 7, July 4; not Apr. 19, July 5) to Brno Královo Pole.
Not Dec. 23-25, 31, Apr. 19, 21, July 5, Oct. 27.

n – ①–⑥ (not Dec. 24-26, Jan. 1, Apr. 20, 22, July 6, Oct. 28).
v – Also Jan. 2, Apr. 23, May 2, 9, Oct. 29; not Apr. 22, Oct. 28.
▷ – See also Tables **1150**/**51**/**60**.
§ – Connection by tram route P6 to/from Brno hl. n. (11 km) during partial closure of Brno hl. n. (see city plan page 31).

ADDITIONAL JOURNEYS: Havlíčkův Brod - Králove Pole 0502Ⓐ, 0602, 0802. Králove Pole - Havlíčkův Brod 1731Ⓐ, 2031⚒. Praha - Čáslav (Havlíčkův Brod on ⑤⑥) 2203. Praha - Kutná Hora hourly 1530Ⓐ to 1830Ⓐ. Kutná Hora - Praha 0631Ⓐ, 0731Ⓐ, 0831Ⓐ, 1642Ⓐ.

BRNO - OLOMOUC - ŠUMPERK and JESENÍK 1156

		901	903	905	907	909	909	911	913	915	917
		Ⓐb	Ⓒd			Ⓐ	Ⓒ				E
0	**Brno** Královo Pole ☆ d.	0514	0622	0716u	0914	1114	1114	1314	1514	1714	1914
9	**Brno** Židenice ☆ d.	0525	0633	0727	0925	1125	1125	1325	1525	1725	1925
2	Vyškov na Moravé d.	0559	0702	0759	0959	1159	1159	1359	1559	1759	1959
8	Nezamyslice d.	0620	0720	0820	1020	1220	1220	1420	1620	1820	2020
7	Prostějov d.	0635	0735	0835	1035	1235	1235	1435	1635	1835	2035
7	**Olomouc** a.	0652	0752	0852	1052	1252	1252	1452	1652	1852	2052
7	**Olomouc** ▽ d.	0656	0756	0856	1056	1256	—	1456	1656	1856	2056
3	Zábřeh na Moravé ▽ a.	0722	0822	0922	1122	1322	Ⓒ	1522	1722	1923	2123
3	Zábřeh na Moravé d.	0731	0831	0931	1131	1331	1331	1531	1731	1926	2126
6	**Šumperk** a.	0741r	0841r	0941r	1141r	1341r	|	1541r	1741r	1943	2141
8	Hanušovice a.	0759	0859	0959	1159	1359	1359	1559	1759	*1959*x	...
0	Lipová Lázně a.	0850	0950	1050	1250	1449	1449	1651*	1851	*2053*x	...
4	**Jeseník** a.	0858	0958	1058	1258	1458	1458	1658*	1858	*2100*x	...

	1638	914	912	910	908	1708	906	904	902	900
	Ⓐ	F			Ⓐ	Ⓒ				Ⓒ
Jeseník d.	...	...	0701	0901	1101	1101	1301	1501	1701	*1846*z
Lipová Lázně d.	...	...	0708	0908	1108	1108	1308	1508	1708	*1854*z
Hanušovice d.	...	...	0800	1000	1200	1200	1400	1600	1800	*1953*z
Šumperk d.	0449	0611	0809s	1009s	1209s	|	1409s	1609s	1809s	2015
Zábřeh na Moravé a.	0506	0630	0825	1025	1225	1225	1425	1625	1825	2031
Zábřeh na Moravé ▽ d.	0515	0631	0834	1034	1234	—	1434	1634	1834	2034
Olomouc ▽ a.	0552	0700	0900	1100	1300	Ⓒ	1500	1700	1900	2100
Olomouc d.	0558	0706	0906	1106	1306	1306	1506	1706	1906	2106
Prostějov d.	0616	0723	0923	1123	1323	1323	1523	1723	1923	2123
Nezamyslice d.	0637	0739	0939	1139	1339	1339	1539	1739	1939	2139
Vyškov na Moravé d.	0700	0800	1000	1200	1400	1400	1600	1800	2000	2200
Brno Židenice ☆ a.	0734	0835	1034	1234	1434	1434	1634	1834	2034	2232
Brno Královo Pole ☆ a.	0746	0845	1045	1245	1445	1445	1645	1845	2045	2243

Daily Brno - Olomouc, Ⓑh to Šumperk.
①–⑥ n from Šumperk, daily Olomouc - Brno.
Runs daily Olomouc - Jeseník (no Šumperk portion on Ⓒ).
Runs daily Zábřeh - Jeseník (Šumperk portion runs on Ⓒ).
Not Dec. 23-25, 31, Apr. 19, 21, July 5, Oct. 27.
Not Dec. 24-26, Jan. 1, Apr. 20, 22, July 6, Oct. 28.

r – Šumperk portion detatches at Zabreh (dep. xx26).
s – Šumperk portion attaches at Zabreh (arr. xx22).
u – Brno **hlavní nádrazí** on ①–⑥ **n** (depart 0719).
x – Change at Bludov (a. 1935/d. 1938).
z – Change at Bludov (a. 2016/d. 2022).
* – On ⑦ arrive Lipová Lázně 1657, Jeseník 1716.

▽ – See also Table **1160**.
☆ – Connections by tram to/from central Brno during partial closure of Brno hl. n. (see city plan page 31).

Different train numbers apply Zabreh - Jeseník.

DĚČÍN - ÚSTÍ NAD LABEM - MĚLNÍK - KOLÍN and RUMBURK - KOLÍN 1157

	781	783		793	795
	⚒n				Ⓑh
Ústí n. L západ d.	0447	0647		1647	1847
Ústí n. L Střekov d.	0452	0652		1652	1852
Litoměřice město d.	0512	0712	and	1712	1912
Mělník d.	0540	0740	every	1740	1940
Všetaty d.	0548	0748	**two**	1748	1948
Stará Boleslav d.	0558	0758	hours	1758	1958
Lysá n. Labem ▷ d.	0606	0806	until	1806	2006
Nymburk ▷ d.	0618	0818		1818	2018
Poděbrady ▷ d.	0625	0825		1825	2025
Kolín d.	0640	0840		1840	2040

	794	792		782	780
	⚒n				Ⓑh
Kolín d.	0714	0914		1914	2114
Poděbrady ▷ d.	0729	0929		1929	2129
Nymburk ▷ d.	0737	0937	and	1937	2137
Lysá n. Labem ▷ d.	0748	0948	every	1948	2148
Stará Boleslav d.	0755	0955	**two**	1955	2155
Všetaty d.	0807	1007	hours	2007	2207
Mělník d.	0816	1016	until	2016	2216
Litoměřice město d.	0845	1045		2045	2245
Ústí n. L Střekov a.	0902	1102		2102	2302
Ústí n. L západ a.	0910	1110		2110	2307r

⊖						
Děčín hl. n. d.	0602	0802	1202	1402	1602	1802
Ústí n. L Střekov a.	0644	0844	1244	1444	1644	1844

⊖						
Ústí n. L Střekov d.	0655	0913	1313	1513	1713	1913
Děčín hl. n. a.	0734	0955	1355	1555	1755	1955

RUMBURK - ČESKA LIPÁ - KOLÍN

						E
Rumburk d.	0522a	0714	1114	1314	1514	1714
Česka Lipá d.	0624	0824	1224	1424	1624	1824
Mladá Boleslav d.	0722	0922	1322	1522	1722	1922
Nymburk ▷ d.	0748	0948	1348	1548	1748	1948
Poděbrady ▷ d.	0756	0956	1356	1556	1756	1956
Kolín a.	0810	1010	1410	1610	1810	2010

						E
Kolín d.	0744	0944	1344	1544	1744	1944
Poděbrady ▷ d.	0759	0959	1359	1559	1759	1959
Nymburk ▷ d.	0808	1008	1408	1608	1808	2008
Mladá Boleslav a.	0835	1035	1435	1635	1835	2034
Česka Lipá a.	0933	1133	1533	1733	1933	2132
Rumburk a.	1035	1235	1636	1836	2035	...

⑤⑥† (daily May 24 - Sept. 15), also Jan. 2, Apr. 18, 30, May 7, Oct. 30.
Ⓐ only.

h – Not Dec. 23-25, 31, Apr. 19, 21, July 5, Oct. 27.
n – ①–⑥ (not Dec. 24-26, Jan. 1, Apr. 20, 22, July 6, Oct. 28).
r – Continues to Ústí nad Labem hlavní nádraží, arrive 2315.

▷ – See also Table **1145**.
⊖ – 2nd class only. For Dečín - Ústí nad Labem hl. n. see Table **1100**.

1160 PRAHA - OLOMOUC - OSTRAVA - ŽILINA - (KOŠICE)

FAST TRAINS. For semi-fast trains Praha - Česká Třebová - Olomouc see Table **1151**. For additional trains Přerov - Ostrava - Bohumín see Table **1164**.

km		341	641	641	343	Ex 121	♥ 1001	Ex 113	SC• 241	Ex 123	♥ 1003	LE♠ 1351	EC* 141	AEx 1061	LE♠ 1353	Ex 125	SC• 505	♥ 1005	LE♠ 1355	EC 115	SC• 507	345	Ex 127	♥ 1007
			2	2		🍷	🍷	🍷⊖	R 🍷	🍷	🍷	R 🍷	🍷	♣	R 🍷	🍷	R 🍷	🍷	R 🍷	🍷⊖	R 🍷		✕	🍷
			①g	⚒n			⚒q	♦						D♡			⊕			♦				
0	**Praha** hl. n. ▷ d.	...	0424	...	...	0524	0547	0624	0709	0724	0747	0809	0824	0836	0909	0924	0941	0947	1009	1024	1141	...	1124	1147
62	Kolín ▷ d.	...	0502	...	...	0602	|	0702	0745	0802	|	0846	0902	|	0946	1002	|	|	1046	1102	|	...	1202	|
104	**Pardubice** ▷ d.	...	0523	...	...	0623	0641	0723	0805	0823	0841	0905	0923	0936	1005	1023	1034	1041	1105	1123	1234	...	1223	1241
155	Ústí nad Orlicí město ▷ d.	...	0551c	...	...	|	|	0752	|	|	|	|	0952	|	|	|	|	|	|	1152	|	...	|	|
164	Česká Třebová ▷ d.	...	0601	...	...	0701	0716	0801	0837	0901	0916	|	1001	|	|	1101	|	1116	|	1201	|	...	1301	1316
206	Zábřeh na Moravé d.	...	0623	...	...	0723	0738	0823	|	0923	0938	0958	1023	|	1058	1125	|	1138	1158	1223	|	...	1325	1338
252	**Olomouc** d.	...	0646	0646	...	0753	0802	0846	0916	0953	1002	1020	1046	1104	1120	1153	1145	1202	1220	1246	1345	...	1353	1402
	Přerov **1162** ▽ d.	...	|	|	...	|	|	|	|	|	|	1038	|	1121	1135	|	|	|	1238	|	|	...	|	|
	Staré Město U.H. ‡ a.	...	|	|	...	|	|	|	|	|	|	|	|	1150	1202	|	|	|	|	|	|	...	|	|
303	Hranice na Moravě ▽ d.	...	0718	0718	...	0828	0835	0916	|	1028	1033	1057	1116	...	...	1228	|	1235	1257	1316	|	...	1428	1435
353	Ostrava Svinov ▽ d.	0644	0751	0751	0844	|	0902	0942	1007	|	1100	1127	1142	...	...	|	1236	1302	1327	1342	1436	1444	|	1502
381	Opava východ a.	|	|	|	|	|	|	|	|	|	|	|	|	...	...	|	|	|	|	|	|	|	|	|
358	**Ostrava** hl. n. ▽ d.	0652	0759	0759	0852	|	0910	0950	1015	|	1108	1136	1150	...	...	|	1244	1310	1333	1350	1444	1452	|	1510
376	Havířov d.	|	|	|	|	|	0929	|	|	|	1126	|	|	...	...	|	...	1329	|	|	...	|	|	1529
366	Bohumín ▽ a.	0659	0806	0806	0859	|	...	0957	|	|	|	1143	1157	...	...	|	...	...	1342	1357	...	1459	|	...
366	Bohumín d.	0700	...	...	0900	|	...	1009	|	|	|	1147	1200	...	...	|	...	...	...	1433	...	1500	|	...
	Katowice **1076** a.	|	...	...	|	≋	...	1133	|	≋	|	|	|	...	...	≋	...	...	...	|	...	|	≋	...
	Kraków **1076** a.	|	...	...	|	|	...	...	|	|	|	|	|	...	...	|	...	...	...	1729	...	|	|	...
381	Karviná hl. n. d.	0715	...	...	0915	|	...	...	|	|	|	1202	1215	...	...	|	...	...	...	...	...	1515	|	...
397	**Český Těšín** d.	0733	...	...	0933	|	...	...	1047	|	1144	...	1233	...	...	|	...	...	...	...	...	1533	|	...
405	Trinec centrum d.	0741	...	...	0941	|	...	...	|	|	1152	...	1241	...	...	|	...	...	...	...	...	1541	|	...
417	Návsi d.	0749	...	...	0949	|	...	...	|	|	|	...	1249	...	...	|	...	...	...	...	...	1549	|	...
435	Čadca 🏛 d.	0806	...	...	1006	|	...	...	1111	|	1215	...	1306	...	...	|	...	...	...	...	...	1606	|	...
▵466	**Žilina** a.	0833	...	...	1033	1032	...	...	1133	1232	1237	...	1333	...	...	1432	...	...	...	...	...	1633	1632	...
	Banská Bystrica **1185** a.	1026	...	...	1226	|	...	...	|	|	|	...	|	...	...	|	...	...	...	...	...	1826	|	...
	Zvolen **1185** a.	...	...	...	1255	|	...	...	|	|	|	...	|	...	...	|	...	...	...	...	...	1857	|	...
	Poprad Tatry **1180** a.	...	...	...	...	*1238*r	...	...	1319	*1438*r	1425	...	*1539*s	...	...	*1638*r	...	...	...	...	...	...	*1838*r	...
	Prešov **1196** a.	...	...	...	...	|	...	...	|	|	|	...	|	...	...	|	...	...	...	...	...	...	|	...
	Košice **1180** a.	...	...	...	...	*1353*r	...	...	1427	*1553*r	1546	...	*1648*s	...	...	*1753*r	...	...	...	...	...	...	*1953*r	...

	LE♠ 1357	Ex 143	SC• 509	347	Ex 221	♥ 1009	LE♠ 1359	AEx 1063	IC 511	EC 117	♥ 1011	SC• 243	SC• 243	Ex 129	♥ 1013	LE♠ 401	EC* 145	IC 513	♥ 1015	LE♠ 1363	Ex 521	SC• 515	♥ 1017	LE♠ 1365
	R 🍷	🍷	R 🍷		✕	🍷	R 🍷	♣	R 🍷	✕⊖	🍷	R 🍷	R 🍷	✕	🍷	R 🍷	✕	R 🍷	🍷	R 🍷	✕	R 🍷	🍷	R 🍷
							P	♡	Ⓐ	♦			⑤f		m	W	R				V	⊗		
Praha hl. n. ▷ d.	1209	1224	1341	...	1324	1347	1409	1417	1441	1424	1450	1541	1541	1524	1547	1609	1624	1641	1650	1709	1724	1741	1747	1809
Kolín ▷ d.	1246	1302	|	...	1402	|	1446	|	|	1502	|	|	|	1602	|	1646	1702	|	|	1746	1802	|	|	1846
Pardubice ▷ d.	1305	1323	1434	...	1423	1441	1505	1517	1534	1523	1546	1634	1634	1623	1641	1705	1723	1734	1746	1805	1823	1834	1841	1905
Ústí nad Orlicí město ▷ d.	|	1352	|	...	|	|	|	|	|	1552	|	|	|	|	|	|	1752	|	|	|	|	|	|	|
Česká Třebová ▷ d.	|	1401	|	...	1501	1516	|	|	|	1601	1620	|	|	1701	1716	|	1801	|	1820	|	1901	|	1916	|
Zábřeh na Moravé d.	1358	1423	|	...	1525	1538	1558	|	|	1625	1642	|	|	1725	1738	1758	1825	|	1842	1858	1925	|	1938	1958
Olomouc d.	1420	1446	1545	...	1553	1602	1620	1641	1645	1648	1705	1745	1745	1753	1802	1820	1848	1845	1905	1920	1953	1945	2002	2020
Přerov **1162** ▽ d.	1438	|	|	...	|	|	1638	1659	|	|	|	|	|	|	|	1838	|	|	|	1935	|	|	|	2038
Staré Město U.H. ‡ a.	|	|	|	...	|	|	|	1731	|	|	|	|	|	|	|	|	|	|	|	2002	|	|	|	|
Hranice na Moravě ▽ d.	1457	1516	|	...	1628	1635	1657	...	|	1718	1735	|	|	1828	1835	1857	1918	|	1935	...	2027	|	2035	2057
Ostrava Svinov ▽ d.	1527	1542	1636	1644	|	1702	1727	...	1738	1744	1802	1838	1838	|	1901	1927	1944	1938	2002	...	...	2036	2102	2127
Opava východ a.	|	|	|	|	|	|	|	...	1759	|	|	|	|	|	1921	|	|	1959	|	...	...	|	|	|
Ostrava hl. n. ▽ d.	1533	1550	1644	1652	|	1710	1735	...	...	1752	1810	1846	1846	|	...	1935	1952	...	2010	...	...	2044	2110	2133
Havířov d.	|	|	...	|	|	1729	|	...	...	|	1830	|	|	|	...	|	|	...	2030	...	...	|	2130	|
Bohumín ▽ a.	1542	1557	...	1659	|	...	1742	...	...	1759	|	1852	1852	|	...	1942	1959	...	|	...	...	2052	|	2142
Bohumín d.	...	1600	...	1700	|	...	1747	...	...	1809	|	...	1853	|	...	1949	2000	...	|	...	...	...	|	...
Katowice **1076** a.	...	|	...	|	≋	...	|	...	...	1931	|	...	|	≋	...	2111	|	...	|	...	...	...	|	...
Kraków **1076** a.	...	|	...	|	|	...	|	...	...	...	|	...	|	|	...	2257	|	...	|	...	...	...	|	...
Karviná hl. n. d.	...	1615	...	1715	|	...	1803	...	...	...	|	...	|	|	...	...	2015	...	|	...	...	...	|	...
Český Těšín d.	...	1633	...	1733	|	...	1821	...	...	...	1848	...	1922	|	...	...	2033	...	2048	...	...	...	2148	...
Trinec centrum d.	...	1641	...	1741	|	...	1828	...	...	...	1856	...	|	|	...	...	2041	...	2056	...	...	...	2156	...
Návsi d.	...	1649	...	1749	|	...	|	...	...	...	|	...	|	|	...	...	2049	...	2107	...	...	...	2207	...
Čadca 🏛 d.	...	1706	...	1806	|	...	1855	...	...	...	1920	...	1946	|	...	...	2106	...	...	...	...	...	...	...
Žilina a.	...	1733	...	1833	1832	...	1917	...	...	...	1942	...	2008	2032	...	...	2133	...	...	...	...	...	...	...
Banská Bystrica **1185** a.	...	|	...	2026	|	...	|	...	...	...	|	...	|	|	...	...	...	...	...	...	...	...	...	...
Zvolen **1185** a.	...	|	...	2055	|	...	|	...	...	...	|	...	|	|	...	...	...	...	...	...	...	...	...	...
Poprad Tatry **1180** a.	...	*1935*s	...	...	*2038*r	...	2104	...	...	...	2147	...	2155	*2238*r	...	...	...	...	...	...	...	...	...	...
Prešov **1196** a.	...	|	...	...	|	...	2214	...	...	...	|	...	|	|	...	...	...	...	...	...	...	...	...	...
Košice **1180** a.	...	*2042*s	...	...	*2153*r	...	2242	...	...	...	2256	...	2305	*2353*r	...	...	...	...	...	...	...	...	...	...

	Ex 523	SC• 517	♥ 1019	LE♠ 1367	♥ 1021	IC 501	EN 443	443 406	Ex 547	EN 445
	✕	R 🍷	🍷	R 🍷	🍷	🍷	R	R	R	R
	V			P	♦	©y	♦	K	2H	♦F
Praha hl. n. ▷ d.	1924	1941	1947	2009	2147	2241	2215	2215	2347	2347
Kolín ▷ d.	2002	|	|	2046	|	2317	2258	2258	0021	0037
Pardubice ▷ d.	2023	2034	2041	2105	2242	2336	2325	2325	0042	0100
Ústí nad Orlicí město ▷ d.	|	|	|	|	|	0003	|	|	|	|
Česká Třebová ▷ d.	2101	|	2116	|	|	|	0004	0004	|	|
Zábřeh na Moravé d.	2125	|	2138	2158	2339	|	|	|	|	|
Olomouc d.	2153	2145	2202	2220	0004	0048	0107	0107	0159	0218
Přerov **1162** ▽ d.	|	|	|	2238	|	|	|	|	|	|
Staré Město U.H. ‡ a.	|	|	|	|	|	|	|	|	|	|
Hranice na Moravě ▽ d.	2227	|	2235	2257	0037	|	|	|	|	|
Ostrava Svinov ▽ d.	...	2236	2302	2327	0104	0139	0215	0215	0255	0315
Opava východ a.	...	|	|	|	|	0159	|	|	|	|
Ostrava hl. n. ▽ d.	...	2244	2310	2335	0112	...	0225	0225	0301	0324
Havířov d.	...	|	2330	|	0130	...	|	|	|	|
Bohumín ▽ a.	...	2252	|	2342	|	...	0234	0234	0309	0331
Bohumín d.	...	...	|	2347	|	...	0308	0318	...	0354
Katowice **1076** a.	...	...	|	|	|	...	|	|	...	|
Kraków **1076** a.	...	...	|	|	|	...	|	0616	...	|
Karviná hl. n. d.	...	...	|	0002	|	...	|	...	...	0410
Český Těšín d.	...	...	2348	0018	0148	...	|	...	...	0427
Trinec centrum d.	...	...	2356	0025	0156	...	|	...	...	0434t
Návsi d.	...	...	0007	|	|	...	|	...	...	|
Čadca 🏛 d.	...	...	...	0046	0224	...	|	...	...	|
Žilina a.	...	...	...	0107	0249	...	0434	...	...	0523
Banská Bystrica **1185** a.	...	...	...	|	|	...	|	...	...	|
Zvolen **1185** a.	...	...	...	|	|	...	|	...	...	|
Poprad Tatry **1180** a.	...	...	...	0252	0443	...	0706	...	...	0739
Prešov **1196** a.	...	...	...	0401	|	...	|	...	...	|
Košice **1180** a.	...	...	...	0429	0600	...	0823	...	...	0908

	♥ 1020	EN 444	EN 442	407 442	LE♠ 1350	IC 518	♥ 1000	SC• 516
	🍷	R	R	R	R 🍷	R 🍷	🍷	R 🍷
	♦	♦G	♦	K	P	Ⓐp	⚒v	
Košice **1180** d.	2122	2026	2207	...	2311	...	...	...
Prešov **1196** d.	|	|	|	...	2342	...	...	...
Poprad Tatry **1180** d.	2240	2203	2323	...	0052	...	...	...
Zvolen **1185** d.	|	|	|	...	|	...	...	...
Banská Bystrica **1185** d.	|	|	|	...	|	...	...	...
Žilina d.	0044	0015	0130	...	0238	...	...	...
Čadca 🏛 d.	0108	|	|	...	0300	...	...	...
Návsi d.	|	|	|	...	|	...	...	...
Trinec centrum d.	0133	0105t	|	...	0319	...	...	...
Český Těšín d.	0142	0113	|	...	0326	...	...	...
Karviná hl. n. d.	|	0130	|	...	0342	...	...	...
Kraków **1076** d.	|	|	|	2234	|	...	...	...
Katowice **1076** d.	|	|	|	|	|	...	...	...
Bohumín a.	|	0144	0253	0129	0355	...	...	...
Bohumín ▽ d.	|	0210	0323	0323	0356	...	...	0507
Havířov d.	0204	|	|	|	|	...	...	|
Ostrava hl. n. ▽ d.	0222	0219	0334	0334	0404	...	...	0515
Opava východ d.	|	|	|	|	|	0400	0426	|
Ostrava Svinov ▽ d.	0231	0227	0344	0344	0412	0421	0453	0523
Hranice na Moravě ▽ d.	|	|	|	|	0440	0445	0519	|
Staré Město U.H. ‡ d.	|	|	|	|	|	|	|	|
Přerov **1162** ▽ d.	|	|	|	|	0501	|	|	|
Olomouc d.	0328	0324	0443	0443	0517	0514	0550	0614
Zábřeh na Moravé d.	0352	|	|	|	0539	|	0614	|
Česká Třebová ▷ d.	|	|	0536	0536	|	|	0635	|
Ústí nad Orlicí město ▷ d.	|	|	|	|	|	|	|	|
Pardubice ▷ d.	0452	0457	0617	0617	0629	0623	0712	0723
Kolín ▷ d.	|	|	|	|	0648	|	|	|
Praha hl. n. ▷ a.	0554	0616	0731	0731	0723	0719	0813	0819

♦ – **NOTES** (LISTED BY TRAIN NUMBER)

112/3 – VARSOVIA – (12) Praha - Katowice - Warszawa and v.v.; 🍷 Praha - Ostrava and v.v. Conveys on ③ 🛏 1, 2 cl. Praha - Minsk - Moskva, returning on ① (Table **95**).

114/5 – CRACOVIA – (12) 🍷 Praha - Bohumín - Kraków and v.v.; (2) Praha - Bohumín (*IC* **130/1**) - Katowice - Warszawa and v.v. (Table **99**).

116/7 – VARSOVIA – (12) ✕ Praha - Bohumín - Katowice - Warszawa and v.v.

442/3 – SLOVAKIA – 🛏 1, 2 cl., ▬ 2 cl., (2) Praha - Košice - Humenné and v.v.; 🍷 Praha - Bohumín and v.v.; R Praha - Žilina and v.v.

444/5 – BOHEMIA – 🛏 1, 2 cl., ▬ 2 cl., (2) Praha - Košice and v.v.; 🍷 Praha - Bohu[illegible] and v.v.; R Praha - Žilina and v.v.

1020/1 – 🛏 (1,2,3 berth), ▬ (6 berth), (12) Praha - Košice and v.v.

NOTES CONTINUED ON NEXT PAGE

SC and IC trains are not available for local travel Ostrava Svinov - Ostrava hlavní - Bohumín or v.v.

(KOŠICE) - ŽILINA - OSTRAVA - OLOMOUC - PRAHA 1160

	LE♠ 1352 🅁🍷	♥ 1002 🍷 T	LE♠ 1354 🅁🍷	IC 514 🅁🍷	Ex 544 🍷 U	♥ 1004 🍷	SC• 512 🅁🍷 ⊗	Ex 520 🍴 V	♥ 1006 🍷	LE♠ 400 🅁🍷 Y	EC* 144 🍴	♥ 1008 🍷	Ex 220 🍴	346	IC 508 🅁🍷 ⑥b	SC• 510 🅁🍷 Ⓑd	AEx 1060 ♣ ♡	LE♠ 1358 🅁🍷 P	EC 116 🍴⊖ ♦	♥ 1010 🍷	SC• 242 🅁 ⑥b	Ex 128 🍴	LE♠ 1360 🅁🍷	Ex 142 🍷	♥ 1012 🍷
Košice **1180** d.	...	...	...	...	...	...	...	...	...	...	...	0345	*0407*r	...	...	...	...	0507	...	...	0658	*0607*r	...	...	0745
Prešov **1196** d.	...	...	...	...	...	...	...	...	...	...	...	|	|	...	...	...	...	0538	...	...	|	|	...	...	|
Poprad Tatry **1180** d.	...	...	...	...	...	...	...	...	...	...	...	0454	*0523*r	...	...	...	...	0648	...	...	0804	*0723*r	...	...	0854
Zvolen **1185** d.	...	...	...	...	...	...	...	...	...	...	...	|	|	0502	...	...	...	|	...	...	|	|	...	...	|
Banská Bystrica **1185** d.	...	...	...	...	...	...	...	...	...	...	...	|	|	0534	...	...	...	|	...	...	|	|	...	...	|
ina d.	...	...	...	...	...	...	...	...	...	...	0627n	0644	0728	0727	...	...	...	0838	...	...	0953	0928	...	1027	1044
adca ▦ d.	...	...	...	...	...	...	...	...	...	...	0656n	0708	|	0756	...	...	...	0900	...	...	1017	|	...	1056	1108
ávsi d.	...	0447	...	...	0502	0547	...	...	0647	...	0711	0723	|	0811	...	...	...	|	...	0949x	|	|	...	1111	1123
nec centrum d.	...	0458	...	...	0509	0558	...	...	0658	...	0719	0733	|	0819	...	...	...	0919	...	0959x	|	|	...	1119	1133
eský Těšín d.	...	0506	...	...	0520	0606	...	...	0706	...	0727	0742	|	0827	...	...	...	0926	...	1007x	1040	|	...	1127	1142
arviná hl. n. d.	...	|	...	...	0537	|	...	...	|	...	0744	|	|	0844	...	...	...	0942	...	|	|	|	...	1144	|
Kraków **1076** d.	...	|	...	...	|	|	...	...	|	0433	|	|	≋	|	...	...	...	|	...	|	|	≋	...	|	|
Katowice **1076** d.	...	|	...	...	|	|	...	...	|	0640	|	|	|	|	...	...	...	|	0827	|	|	|	...	|	|
humín a.	...	|	...	...	0551	|	...	...	|	0753	0758	|	|	0858	...	...	...	0955	0949	|	|	|	...	1158	|
humín ▽ d.	...	|	0550	...	0555	|	0707	...	|	0756	0806	|	|	0900	...	0907	...	0956	1006	|	|	|	...	1206	|
Havířov d.	...	0524	|	...	|	0624	|	...	0724	|	|	0824z	|	|	...	|	...	|	|	1024	|	|	...	|	1224z
strava hl. n. ▽ d.	...	0544	0558	...	0604	0644	0715	...	0744	0804	0815	0844	|	0909	...	0915	...	1004	1015	1044	1115	|	...	1215	1245
Opava východ d.	...	|	|	0600	|	|	|	...	|	|	|	|	|	|	0900	|	...	|	|	|	|	|	...	|	|
strava Svinov ▽ d.	...	0553	0606	0623	0613	0653	0723	...	0753	0812	0823	0853	|	0915	0923	0923	...	1012	1023	1053	1123	|	...	1223	1253
anice na Moravě ▽ d.	...	0619	0634	|	0646	0719	|	0733	0819	0840	0848	0919	0933	...	|	|	...	1040	1048	1119	|	1133	...	1248	1319
Staré Město U.H. ‡ d.	0528	|	|	|	|	|	|	|	|	|	|	|	|	...	|	|	0957	|	|	|	|	|	1228	|	|
Přerov **1162** ▽ d.	0601	|	0655	|	|	|	|	|	|	0901	|	|	|	...	|	|	1028	1101	|	|	|	|	1301	|	|
omouc d.	0617	0650	0711	0714	0720	0750	0814	0809	0850	0917	0920	0950	1009	...	1014	1014	1050	1117	1120	1150	1214	1209	1317	1320	1350
břeh na Moravé d.	0639	0714	0736	|	0743	0814	|	0840	0914	0939	0943	1014	1040	...	|	|	|	1139	1143	1214	|	1240	1339	1343	1414
eská Třebová ▷ d.	|	0735	|	|	0805	0835	|	0905	0935	|	1005	1035	1105	...	|	|	|	|	1205	1235	|	1305	|	1405	1435
stí nad Orlicí město ▷ d.	|	|	|	|	0813	|	|	|	|	|	1013	|	|	...	|	|	|	|	1213	|	|	|	|	1413	|
rdubice ▷ d.	0729	0809	0829	0823	0841	0912	0923	0941	1009	1029	1041	1112	1141	...	1123	1123	1220	1229	1241	1312	1323	1341	1429	1441	1512
lín ▷ d.	0748	|	0848	|	0902	|	|	1002	|	1048	1102	|	1202	...	|	|	|	1248	1302	|	|	1402	1448	1502	|
aha hl. n. ▷ a.	0823	0913	0923	0919	0939	1013	1019	1039	1113	1123	1139	1213	1239	...	1219	1218	1326	1323	1339	1413	1419	1439	1523	1539	1613

	LE♠ 1362 🅁🍷	Ex 126 🍴	344	SC• 506 🅁🍷	LE♠ 1364 🅁🍷	EC 114 🍷⊖ ♦	♥ 1014 🍷	SC• 504 🅁🍷 ⊕	Ex 124 🍷	IC 502 🅁🍷 ⑦e	AEx 1062 ♣ E♡	LE♠ 1366 🅁🍷	EC* 140 🍷	♥ 1016 🍷	Ex 122 🍴	342	SC• 500 🅁🍷	Ex 112 🍷⊖ ♦	♥ 1018 🍷	Ex 120 🍷	SC• 240 🅁🍷	640 2 Ⓑh	640 2 ⑦e	340	
Košice **1180** d.	...	*0807*r	...	...	...	...	...	...	*1007*r	...	...	...	*1112*s	...	*1207*r	...	...	...	...	*1407*r	1500	...	...	...	...
Prešov **1196** d.	...	|	...	...	...	...	...	...	|	...	...	...	|	...	|	...	...	...	...	|	|	...	...	...	...
Poprad Tatry **1180** d.	...	*0923*r	...	...	...	...	...	...	*1123*r	...	...	...	*1220*s	...	*1323*r	...	...	...	...	*1523*r	1607	...	...	...	...
Zvolen **1185** d.	...	|	...	...	...	...	...	...	|	...	...	...	|	...	|	...	...	...	...	|	|	...	...	...	...
Banská Bystrica **1185** d.	...	|	0934	...	...	...	...	...	|	...	...	...	|	...	|	1334	...	...	...	|	|	...	...	1734	...
ina d.	...	1128	1127	...	...	...	...	...	1328	...	...	...	1427	...	1528	1527	...	...	...	1728	1754	...	...	1927	...
adca ▦ d.	...	|	1156	...	...	...	...	...	|	...	...	...	1456	...	|	1556	...	...	...	|	1818	...	...	1956	...
ávsi d.	...	|	1211	...	...	...	...	...	|	...	...	...	1511	...	|	1611	...	...	...	|	|	...	...	2011	...
nec centrum d.	...	|	1219	...	...	...	...	...	|	...	...	...	1519	...	|	1619	...	...	...	|	|	...	...	2019	...
eský Těšín d.	...	|	1227	...	...	...	...	...	|	...	...	...	1527	...	|	1627	...	...	...	|	1841	...	...	2027	...
arviná hl. n. d.	1238	|	1244	...	...	...	...	...	|	...	...	...	1544	...	|	1644	...	...	...	|	|	...	...	2044	...
Kraków **1076** d.	|	≋	|	...	...	1022	...	...	≋	...	...	...	|	...	≋	|	...	...	...	≋	|	...	...	|	...
Katowice **1076** d.	|	|	|	...	...	|	...	...	|	...	...	...	|	...	|	|	...	1623	...	|	|	...	...	|	...
humín a.	1252	|	1258	...	...	1325	...	...	|	...	...	...	1558	...	|	1658	...	1748	...	|	|	...	...	2058	...
humín ▽ d.	1256	|	1300	...	1356	1406	...	...	|	...	...	1556	1606	...	|	1700	...	1806	...	|	|	2000	2000	2100	...
Havířov d.	|	|	|	...	|	|	1424	...	|	...	...	|	|	1624	|	|	...	|	1824	|	|	|	|	|	...
strava hl. n. ▽ d.	1304	|	1309	1315	1404	1415	1445	1515	|	...	...	1604	1615	1645	|	1709	1715	1815	1844	|	1915	2009	2009	2109	...
Opava východ d.	|	|	|	|	|	|	|	|	|	1600	...	|	|	|	|	|	|	|	|	|	|	|	|	|	...
strava Svinov ▽ d.	1312	|	1315	1323	1412	1423	1453	1523	|	1622	...	1612	1623	1653	|	1715	1723	1823	1853	|	1923	2017	2017	2115	...
anice na Moravě ▽ d.	1340	1333	...	|	1440	1448	1519	|	1533	|	...	1640	1648	1719	1733	...	|	1848	1919	1933	|	2048	2048	...	...
Staré Město U.H. ‡ d.	|	|	...	|	|	|	|	|	|	|	1559	|	|	|	|	...	|	|	|	|	|	|	|	...	...
Přerov **1162** ▽ d.	1401	|	...	|	1501	|	|	|	|	|	1630	1701	|	|	|	...	|	|	|	|	|	|	|	...	...
omouc d.	1417	1409	...	1414	1517	1520	1550	1614	1609	1714	1650	1717	1720	1750	1809	...	1814	1920	1950	2009	2014	2118	2120	...	...
břeh na Moravé d.	1439	1443	...	|	1539	1543	1614	|	1640	|	|	1739	1743	1814	1840	...	|	1943	2014	2040	|	...	2143	...	...
eská Třebová ▷ d.	|	1505	...	|	|	1605	1635	|	1705	|	|	|	1805	1835	1905	...	|	2005	2035	2102	2053	...	2205	...	...
stí nad Orlicí město ▷ d.	|	|	...	|	|	1613	|	|	|	|	|	|	1813	|	|	...	|	2013	|	2110c	|	...	2214c	...	...
rdubice ▷ d.	1529	1541	...	1523	1629	1641	1712	1723	1741	1824	1820	1829	1841	1912	1941	...	1923	2041	2109	2141	2125	...	2245	...	...
lín ▷ d.	1548	1602	...	|	1648	1702	|	|	1802	|	|	1848	1902	|	2002	...	|	2102	|	2204	2144	...	2307	...	...
aha hl. n. ▷ a.	1623	1639	...	1619	1723	1739	1813	1819	1839	1919	1929	1923	1939	2013	2039	...	2019	2139	2213	2239	2219	...	2344	...	...

TES (CONTINUED FROM PREVIOUS PAGE)

- ⑤⑥ (daily from June 7), also Dec. 31, Apr. 18; not Apr. 20.
- ⑥⑦ (daily from June 8), also Jan. 1, Apr. 19, 22, May 1, 8; not Dec. 23, Apr. 20, 21.
- Dec. 20 - 23, 27 - 30, Jan. 2 - 8, Apr. 16 - 29, May 31 - Sept. 16, Oct. 25 - Nov. 5.
- From Kosice Dec. 19 - 22, 26 - 29, Jan. 1 - 7, Apr. 15 - 28, May 30 - Sept. 15, Oct. 24 - Nov. 4.
- Dec. 9 - 19, 26, Jan. 1, Jan. 9 - Apr. 15, Apr. 30 - May 30, Sept. 17 - Oct. 24, Nov. 6 - Dec. 14.
- 🛏 1, 2 cl., ▬ 2 cl., (2) Praha - Bohumín (**406/7**) - Kraków - Warszawa and v.v.
- (12) Praha - Prešov - Košice and v.v. (Table **1180**). Different train numbers apply between Prešov and Košice.
- Daily to Návsi; Ⓑ **h** to Žilina.
- Daily to Bohumin; Ⓑ **h** to Návsi.
- ①–⑥ **q** from Navsi; daily from Ostrava Svinov. Not Dec. 25, Jan. 1.
- ①–⑥ **n** from Návsi, daily from Bohumín.
- To / from Vsetín (Table **1161**).
- Daily to Bohumín; extends to Kraków via Katowice on ⑤⑦ (daily from June 29).
- From Kraków ①⑥ (daily from June 29); runs daily Bohumín - Praha.
- Also Apr. 19, May 1, 8, July 5; not Apr. 20, July 6.
- Ústí nad Orlicí (not Ústí nad Orlicí město station).
- Also Apr. 20, July 6; not Apr. 19, May 1, 8, July 5.

e – Also Dec. 26, Jan. 1, Apr. 22, May 1, 8, Oct. 28; not Dec. 23, 30, Apr. 21, Oct. 27.
f – Also Apr. 18, 30, May 7, July 4; not Apr. 19, July 5.
g – Also Dec. 27, Jan. 2, Apr. 23, May 2, 9, Oct. 29; not Dec. 24, 31, Apr. 22, Oct. 28.
h – Not Dec. 23 - 25, 31, Apr. 19, 21, July 5, Oct. 27.
m – Not Dec. 24 - 31, Apr. 21, 30, May 7, July 5.
n – ①–⑥ (not Dec. 24 - 26, Jan. 1, Apr. 20, 22, July 6, Oct. 28).
p – Also Dec. 23 - 25, 30, Apr. 20, 21, July 6, Oct. 27.
q – ①–⑥ (not Dec. 24, Apr. 19, July 6, Sept. 28).
r – Change at Púchov (Tables **1161** / **1180**).
s – Change at Žilina (Table **1180**).
t – Trinec (not Trinec centrum).
v – Not Dec. 27 - 31, Apr. 20, July 6, Sept. 28.
x – ⑦ (also Jan. 1, Apr. 19, July 6, Oct. 28; not Dec. 30).
y – ⑥⑦ (also Dec. 24 - 26, Jan. 1, Apr. 19 - 22, May 1, 8, July 5, Oct. 28).
z – Arrives 25 minutes earlier.
♥ – Operated by REGIOJET. Separate fare tariff applies.
♠ – Operated by LEO Express. Separate fare tariff applies.

♣ – Operated by ARRIVA. 2nd class, 🍷. Separate fares.
≋ – Via Vsetín, Horní Lideč and Púchov (Table **1161**).
• – *SUPERCITY PENDOLINO* train, 🅁; reservation fee.
⊕ – From / to Cheb via Plzeň (Table **1120**).
⊗ – From / to Františkovy Lázně via Plzeň (Table **1120**).
♡ – Praha - Trenčin - Nitra and v.v. (Table **1163**).
⊖ – 🅁 for international journeys.
▷ – See also Tables **1150 / 51**.
▽ – See also Table **1164**.
‡ – See Table **1162**.
Δ – *439 km* via Vsetin.
* – Classified *Ex* in Slovakia.

Local trains run hourly Ostrava Svinov - Havířov - Český Těšín

(PRAHA) - OLOMOUC - VSETÍN - HORNÍ LIDEČ - ŽILINA 1161

km		2	*Ex* **121** 🍷	*Ex* **123** 🍷	*Ex* **125** 🍷	*Ex* **127** 🍴	*Ex* **221** 🍴	*Ex* **129** 🍴	*Ex* **521** 🍴	*Ex* **523** 🍴
	Praha hl. n. **1160** d.	...	0524	0724	0924	1124	1324	1524	1724	1924
0	**Olomouc** d.	...	0753	0953	1153	1353	1553	1753	1953	2153
51	Hranice na Moravě d.	0634	0828	1028	1228	1428	1628	1828	2033	2228
77	Valašské Meziříčí d.	0706	0853	1053	1253	1453	1653	1853	2057	2253
96	**Vsetín** d.	0725	0910	1110	1310	1510	1710	1910	2112	2308
114	Horní Lideč ▦ d.	...	0929	1129	1329	1529	1729	1929	...	...
42	**Púchov** a.	...	0952	1152	1352	1552	1752	1952	...	...
	Žilina **1180** a.	...	*1040*r	*1240*r	*1440*r	*1640*r	*1840*r	*2040*r	...	...
	Poprad Tatry **1180** a.	...	*1238*r	*1438*r	*1638*r	*1838*r	*2038*r	*2238*r	...	...
	Košice **1180** a.	...	*1353*r	*1553*r	*1753*r	*1953*r	*2153*r	*2353*r	...	...
42	**Púchov** **1180** d.	...	0953	1153	1353	1553	1753	1953	...	...
53	Považská Bystrica **1180** d.	...	1011	1211	1411	1611	1811	2011	...	...
87	**Žilina** **1180** a.	...	1032	1232	1432	1632	1832	2032	...	...

	Ex **522** 🍴	*Ex* **520** 🍴	*Ex* **220** 🍴	*Ex* **128** 🍴	*Ex* **126** 🍴	*Ex* **124** 🍷	*Ex* **122** 🍷	*Ex* **120** 🍷	2
Žilina **1180** d.	...	...	0728	0928	1128	1328	1528	1728	...
Považská Bystrica **1180** d.	...	...	0749	0949	1149	1349	1549	1749	...
Púchov **1180** a.	...	...	0806	1006	1206	1406	1606	1806	...
Košice **1180** d.	...	...	*0407*r	*0607*r	*0807*r	*1007*r	*1207*r	*1407*r	...
Poprad Tatry **1180** d.	...	...	*0523*r	*0723*r	*0923*r	*1123*r	*1323*r	*1523*r	...
Žilina **1180** d.	...	...	*0720*r	*0920*r	*1120*r	*1320*r	*1520*r	*1722*r	...
Púchov d.	...	...	0808	1008	1208	1408	1608	1808	...
Horní Lideč ▦ d.	...	...	0833	1033	1233	1433	1633	1833	...
Vsetín d.	0452	0650	0852	1052	1252	1452	1652	1852	1950
Valašské Meziříčí d.	0509	0707	0909	1109	1309	1509	1709	1909	2010
Hranice na Moravě d.	0533	0733	0933	1133	1333	1533	1733	1933	2040
Olomouc a.	0607	0807	1007	1207	1407	1607	1807	2007	...
Praha hl. n. **1160** a.	0839	1039	1239	1439	1639	1839	2039	2239	...

Change at Púchov.

☛ For faster trains Praha - Olomouc - Žilina via Ostrava (including through trains Praha - Žilina - Košice) see Table **1160**.

Note partial closure of Brno hlavní nádraží as shown (see plan page 31

1162 OLOMOUC - UHERSKÉ HRADIŠTĚ - BŘECLAV - BRNO / WIEN

km		457	816		881	814	883	*EC* 101	812	885	*AEx* 1061	810	*LE*♠ 1353	887	*EC* 103	808	889	*EC* 131	806	891	*AEx* 1063	804	893	*Ex* 59
		N		2	⚒n	🍷	⊡🍷	M§	🍷	🍷	D♣	🍷	🅁🍷	🍷	P§	🍷	🍷	B§	🍷	🍷	♣	🍷		b
	Praha hl. n. **1151/60** d.	...	...	...	...	...	...	...	...	0658	0836	...	0909	0858n	...	...	1058	...	...	1258	1417	...	1458	..
0	**Olomouc** ▽ d.	...	...	...	0559	0709	0731	...	0909	0931	1104	1109	1120	1131	...	1309	1331	...	1509	1531	1641	1709	1731	..
	Ostrava hl. n. **1164** d.	0230	...	...	|	|	|	0700	|	|	|	|	|	|	1100	|	|	1400	|	|	|	|	|	170
22	Přerov ▽ d.	|	...	0540	0615	0724	0746	0753	0924	0948	1121	1125	1135	1146	1153	1324	1348	1453	1524	1548	1659	1724	1746	175
37	Hulín d.	|	...	0600	0626	0735	0756	|	0935	0959	|	1135	1145	1156	|	1335	1359	|	1535	1559	|	1735	1756	|
50	Otrokovice d.	|	...	0614	0636	0744	0804	0809	0944	1007	1139	1144	1153	1204	1209	1344	1407	1509	1544	1607	1719	1744	1804	180
61	**Zlín** střed ▷ a.	|	...	|	|	|	|	|	|	|	|	|	|	|	|	|	|	|	|	|	|	|	|	|
68	Staré Město U.H. ⊖ a.	|	...	0628	0646	0753	0815	0818	0953	1018	1150	1153	1202	1215	1218	1353	1418	1518	1553	1618	1731	1753	1815	181
68	Staré Město U.H. ⊖ d.	|	...	0632	0656	0756	0827	0819	0956	1027	1151	1156	...	1227	1219	1356	1427	1519	1556	1627	1733	1757	*1823*	181
73	Uherské Hradiště a.	|	...	|	0702	|	0833	|	|	1033	1157	|	...	1233	|	|	1433	|	|	1633	1739	|	*1829*	|
90	Uherský Brod a.	|	...	|	0722	|	0853	|	|	1053	1223	|	...	1253	|	|	1453	|	|	1653	1755	|	...	|
104	**Luhačovice** a.	|	...	|	0745	|	0918	|	|	1118	...	|	...	1318	|	|	1518	|	|	1718	...	|	...	|
102	Hodonin d.	|	0621	0708	...	0828	...	0836	1028	...	...	1228	...	...	1236	1428	...	1536	1628	...	...	1828	...	183
122	Břeclav a.	0410	0635	0726	...	0840	...	0847	1040	...	...	1240	...	...	1247	1440	...	1547	1640	...	...	1840	...	184
122	Břeclav △ d.	0549	0643	...	...	0846	...	0855	1046	...	...	1246	...	...	1255	1446	...	*1555*	1646	...	...	1846	...	...
181	**Brno** dolní nádraží ☆ △ a.	|	0723	...	...	0923	...	|	1123	...	...	1323	...	...	|	1523	...	|	1723	...	...	1923	...	..
210	**Wien** Hbf △ a.	0700	...	...	...	...	...	0949	...	...	...	...	...	...	1349	...	...	*1649*	...	...	...	...	...	..

	409	802	*LE*♠ 1363	895	*EC* 105	800	897		899
	J⑤	🍷	🅁🍷		S§	Ⓑh		2	🍷
Praha hl. n. **1151/60** d.	...	...	1709	1658	...	...	1858	...	2124
Olomouc ▽ d.	...	1909	1920	1931	...	2109	2131	...	2353
Ostrava hl. n. **1164** d.	b	|	|	|	1900	|	|	...	|
Přerov ▽ d.	|	1924	1935	1946	1953	2124	2146	2243	0007
Hulín d.	|	1935	1945	1956	|	2135	2156	2258	...
Otrokovice d.	|	1944	1953	2004	2009	2144	2214	2309	...
Zlín střed ▷ a.	|	|	|	|	|	|	2226	|	...
Staré Město U.H. ⊖ a.	|	1953	2002	2015	2018	2153	...	2325	...
Staré Město U.H. ⊖ d.	|	1956	*2006*	2027	2019	2156	...	...	...
Uherské Hradiště a.	|	|	*2012*	2033	|	|	...	...	...
Uherský Brod a.	|	|	...	v	|	|	...	...	...
Luhačovice a.	|	|	...	...	|	|	...	...	...
Hodonin d.	|	2028	...	...	2036	2215	...	...	...
Břeclav a.	1945	2040	...	...	2047	2227	...	...	...
Břeclav △ d.	2014	2046	...	...	2055	...	...	...	...
Brno dolní nádraží ☆ △ a.	|	2123	...	...	|	...	...	...	...
Wien Hbf △ a.	2117	...	...	...	2149	...	...	...	...

	898	896	*LE*♠ 1352	894	801	*Ex* 590	892	803	40
	🍷	⚒n	🅁🍷		⚒n	b		🍷	J
Wien Hbf △ d.	...	...	...	...	...	...	...	...	06
Brno dolní nádraží ☆ △ d.	...	...	...	...	...	*0624*	...	0636	|
Břeclav △ a.	...	...	...	...	...	*0652*	...	0715	07
Břeclav d.	...	...	...	...	0530	0710	...	0721	07
Hodonin d.	...	...	...	...	0543	0722	...	0743	|
Luhačovice d.	...	...	...	...	|	|	...	|	|
Uherský Brod d.	...	...	...	...	|	|	v	|	|
Uherské Hradiště d.	...	...	...	...	|	|	0725	|	|
Staré Město U.H. ⊖ a.	...	...	...	...	0601	0739	0731	0801	|
Staré Město U.H. ⊖ d.	...	0421	0528	...	0604	0740	0743	0804	|
Zlín střed ▷ d.	...	|	|	0531	|	|	|	|	|
Otrokovice d.	...	0432	0539	0554	0615	0751	0755	0815	|
Hulín d.	...	0441	0547	0603	0624	|	0804	0824	|
Přerov ▽ a.	0413	0451	0557	0613	0633	0806	0813	0833	|
Ostrava hl. n. **1164** a.	|	|	|	|	|	0900	|	|	b
Olomouc ▽ a.	0427	0507	0615	0629	0649	...	0829	0849	...
Praha hl. n. **1151/60** a.	0704	0739	0823	0904	...	...	1104	...	..

	EC 104	890	*AEx* 1060	805	888	807	*LE*♠ 1360	*EC* 130	886	809	*EC* 102	884	*AEx* 1062	811	882	813	880	*EC* 100	815	1777			817	45
	S§	G🍷	♣	🍷	🍷	🍷	🅁	B§	🍷	🍷	P§	🍷	E♣	🍷	🍷	🍷	🍷	M§	🍷	Ⓑh	2	2		N
Wien Hbf △ d.	0810	...	...	...	...	...	...	*1110*	...	...	1410	...	...	...	...	...	...	1810	...	...	...	...	...	22
Brno dolní nádraží ☆ △ d.	|	...	...	0836	...	1036	...	|	...	1236	|	...	...	1436	...	1636	...	|	1836	1936	...	...	2037	|
Břeclav △ a.	0904	...	...	0915	...	1115	...	*1204*	...	1315	1504	...	...	1515	...	1715	...	1904	1915	2017	...	...	2118	230
Břeclav d.	0910	...	...	0921	...	1121	...	1210	...	1321	1510	...	...	1521	...	1721	...	1910	1921	2023	2034	...	2125	235
Hodonin d.	0922	...	...	0943	...	1143	...	1222	...	1343	1522	...	...	1543	...	1743	...	1922	1943	2035	2054	...	2137	|
Luhačovice d.	|	0831	...	|	1031	|	...	|	1231	|	|	1431	...	|	1631	|	1820	|	|	...	|	...	...	|
Uherský Brod d.	|	0910r	0933	|	1110r	|	...	|	1310r	|	|	1510r	1536	|	1710r	|	1840	|	|	...	|	...	...	|
Uherské Hradiště d.	|	0927	0950	|	1127	|	...	|	1327	|	|	1527	1552	|	1727	|	1858	|	|	...	|	...	...	|
Staré Město U.H. ⊖ a.	0939	0933	0956	1001	1133	1201	...	1239	1333	1401	1539	1533	1558	1601	1733	1801	1904	1939	2001	...	2125	...	...	|
Staré Město U.H. ⊖ d.	0940	0943	0957	1004	1143	1204	1228	1240	1343	1404	1540	1543	1559	1604	1743	1804	1915	1940	2004	...	2133	...	...	|
Zlín střed ▷ d.	|	|	|	|	|	|	|	|	|	|	|	|	|	|	|	|	|	|	|	...	|	←	...	|
Otrokovice d.	0951	0955	1009	1015	1155	1215	1239	1251	1355	1415	1551	1555	1611	1615	1755	1815	1927	1951	2015	...	2148	2210	...	|
Hulín d.	|	1004	|	1024	1204	1224	1247	|	1404	1424	|	1604	|	1624	1804	1824	1936	|	2024	...	→	2221	...	|
Přerov ▽ a.	1006	1013	1027	1033	1213	1233	1257	1306	1413	1433	1606	1613	1629	1633	1813	1833	1945	2006	2033	...	...	2235	...	|
Ostrava hl. n. **1164** a.	1100	|	|	|	|	|	|	1400	|	|	1700	|	|	|	|	|	|	2100	|	...	...	...	...	01
Olomouc ▽ a.	...	1029	1045	1049	1229	1249	1315	...	1429	1449	...	1629	1646	1649	1829	1849	2001	...	2049	...	...	...	...	..
Praha hl. n. **1151/60** a.	...	1304	1326	...	1504	...	1523	...	1704	...	...	1904	1929	...	2104	...	...	...	...	...	...	...	...	..

B – BATHORY – [12] ✕ Warszawa - Katowice - Ostrava - Břeclav - Bratislava - Budapest and v.v. (Table **99**).
D – ⑤⑥ (daily from June 7), also Dec. 31, Apr. 18.
E – ⑥⑦ (daily from June 8), also Jan. 1, Apr. 19, 22, May 1, 8; not Dec. 23, Apr. 20, 21.
G – ⚒**n** from Luhačovice, daily from Staré Město U.H.
J – 🛏 1, 2 cl. Moskva - Nice and v.v., for days of running see Table **25**.
M – MORAVIA – [12] ✕ Katowice - Bohumín - Ostrava - Břeclav - Wien and v.v. (Table **99**).
N – NIGHTJET – 🛏 1, 2 cl., 🛌 2 cl., [2] Berlin - Wroclaw - Bohumín - Ostrava - Wien and v.v. (Table **71**); 🛏 1, 2 cl., [2] Warszawa (**407/6**) - Kraków - Bohumín (**457/6**) - Ostrava - Wien and v.v., also 🛌 2 cl. on dates in Table **99**. 🅁 for international journeys.
P – POLONIA – [12] ✕ Warszawa - Katowice - Ostrava - Břeclav - Wien and v.v. (Table **99**).
S – SOBIESKI – [12] ✕ Gdynia - Gdansk - Warszawa - Katowice - Ostrava - Břeclav - Wien and v.v. (Table **99**).
b – From / to Bohumín (Table **1164**).
h – Not Dec. 23-25, 31, Apr. 19, 21, July 5, Oct. 27.
n – ①–⑥ (not Dec. 24-26, Jan. 1, Apr. 20, 22, July 6, Oct. 28).

r – Arrives 20 minutes earlier.
v – To / from Veseli nad Moravou (Table **1163**).
♠ – Operated by LEO Express. Separate fare tariff applies.
♣ – [2] 🍷 Praha - Trenčin - Nitra and v.v. (Table **1163**). Operated ARRIVA. Separate fare tariff applies.
⊖ – Full name: Staré Město u Uherské Hradiště.
☆ – 🚌 connections available Brno dolní nádraží - Brno hl. n. (see p. 3
⊡ – From Hradec Králové via Pardubice (Table **1160**).
△ – For other trains Břeclav - Brno see Table **1150**; for other trains Břeclav - Wien see Table **1150** (also **982** for local trains).
▽ – See also Table **1160**.
▷ – Local trains Otrokovice - Zlín: 1-2 per hour (trolleybus every 10 m
§ – 🅁 for international journeys to / from Poland.

1163 BRNO - UHERSKÉ HRADIŠTĚ - LUHAČOVICE / TRENČIN

2nd clas

km		P						b	b	
0	**Brno** Židenice ☆ d.	...	0736	0932	1132	1332	1532	1732	1932	2132
67	Kyjov d.	...	0832	1032	1232	1432	1632	1832	2032	2232
90	Veselí nad Moravou d.	0711	0902	1102	1302	1502	1702	1902	2102	2258
104	Kunovice a.	|	|	|	|	|	|	1920	2119	...
106	Uherské Hradiště ▷ a.	0724	0920	1120	1320	1520	1720	*1928*	*2123*	...
111	**Staré Město u Uh. H** ▷ a.	0731	0927	1127	1327	1527	1727	*1936*	*2130*	...

	u								P	u
Staré Město u Uh. H ▷ d.	...	*0606*n	0833	1033	1233	1433	1633	*1823*	2027	..
Uherské Hradiště ▷ d.	...	0635	0840	1040	1240	1440	1640	1840	2034	..
Kunovice d.	...	|	|	|	|	|	|	|	|	
Veselí nad Moravou d.	0601	0701	0901	1101	1301	1501	1701	1901	2047	21
Kyjov d.	0628	0728	0928	1128	1328	1528	1728	1928	...	21
Brno Židenice ☆ a.	0728	0829	1028	1228	1428	1628	1828	2028	...	22

km				D♣			♣		b	b
	Praha hl. n. **1160** d.	...	...	0836	...	...	1417	...	...	...
0	**Staré Město u Uh. H** ▷ d.	0936	1136	1151	1336	1536	1733	1823	*1906*r	...
5	Uherské Hradiště ▷ a.	0942	1142	1157	1342	1542	1739	1829	*1912*r	...
5	Uherské Hradiště ▷ d.	0943	1143	1205	1346	1545	1740	1830	*1914*	*2113*
7	Kunovice d.	0947	1147	|	1350	1550	|	1835	1923	2120
22	Uherský Brod ▷ d.	1007	1207	1226	1411	1611	1756	1855	1942	2140
26	Újezdec u Luhačovic a.	1011	1211	|	1414	1614	|	1859	1946	2144
36	**Luhačovice** ▷ a.	*1028*	*1228*	|	*1430*	*1630*	|	*1916*s	*2002*a	*2202*
35	Bojkovice město d.	1028	1228	1243	1446	1645	1811	1920	2002	2202
63	Bylnice d.	...	...	1313	1519a	...	1841	...	2037	2236
68	Vlárský průsmyk 🏛 a.	...	...	|	...	...	|	...	...	...
90	Trenčianska Teplá **1180** a.	...	...	1334	...	...	1903	...	...	...
98	**Trenčin** **1180** a.	...	...	1342	...	...	1910	...	...	...
	Nitra **1177** a.	...	...	1513	...	...	2042	...	...	...

	Ⓒ	Ⓐ	♣				E♣		Ⓒ	
Nitra **1177** d.	...	...	0636	...	...	...	1245	...	...	..
Trenčin **1180** d.	...	...	0806	...	...	...	1412	...	...	...
Trenčianska Teplá **1180** d.	...	...	0814	...	...	...	1420	...	...	17
Vlárský průsmyk 🏛 d.	...	...	|	...	...	...	|	...	...	17
Bylnice d.	...	0650	0838	...	...	...	1444	...	...	18
Bojkovice město d.	0704	0728	0907	0920	1120	1333	1518	1533	1735	18
Luhačovice ▷ d.	*0649*	|	|	*0922*	*1122*	*1332*	|	*1532*	*1736*	*18*
Újezdec u Luhačovic d.	0721	0747	|	0940	1140	1350	|	1550	1752	19
Uherský Brod ▷ d.	0725	0752	0933	0950	1150	1354	1536	1554	1757	19
Kunovice a.	0742	0811	|	1009	1209	1414	|	1614	1814	19
Uherské Hradiště ▷ a.	0745	0814	0949	1012	1212	1417	1551	1617	1817	*19*
Uherské Hradiště ▷ d.	0746	0819	0950	1018	1218	1418	1552	1618	*1829*	*19*
Staré Město u Uh. H ▷ a.	0752	0825	0956	1024	1224	1424	1558	1623	*1835*	*19*
Praha hl. n. **1160** a.	...	...	1326	...	...	...	1929	...	...	

D – ⑤⑥ (daily from Sept. 1), also July 4; not July 6.
E – ⑥⑦ (daily from Sept 1), also July 5; not July 6.
P – To / from Praha (Table **1162**).
a – Ⓐ only.
b – Brno - Bylnice (see both sections of the table).
n – ①–⑥ (not Dec. 24-26, Jan. 1, Apr. 20, 22, July 6, Oct. 28).

r – Ⓑ (not Dec. 23-25, 31, Apr. 19, 21, July 5, Oct. 27).
s – ⑦ (also Apr. 22, May 1, 8; not Apr. 21, Oct. 27).
t – ⑦ (also Jan. 1, Apr. 22, Oct. 28; not Dec. 23, 30, Apr. 21, June 30 - Aug. 25, Oct. 27).
u – To Brno hl. n. (arrive 9 mins later).

♣ – ARRIVA EXPRESS – operated by Arriva. 2nd clas 🍷. ČD tickets and passes not valid.
▷ – See also Table **1162**.
☆ – Tram connection available from Brno hl. n. (see plan page 31).

BRNO - PŘEROV - OSTRAVA - BOHUMÍN 1164

km				Ex			EC			EC				EC					EC				
		821	823	590	408	825	104	827	829	130	831	833	835	102	837	839	841	843	100	845	847	849	456
		⚒n	⚒n		J①	🍷	S	🍷	🍷	B	🍷	🍷	🍷	P	🍷	🍷	🍷	Ⓑh	M	🍷	⑦e	🍷	N
0	**Brno** Královo Pole ☆	**1156** d.	0456	0556	...	...	0656	...	0856	1056	...	1156	1256	1356	...	1456	1556	1656	1756	...	1856	1956	2056	...
9	**Brno** Židenice ☆	**1156** d.	0506	0606	...	...	0706	...	0906	1106	...	1206	1306	1406	...	1506	1606	1706	1806	...	1906	2006	2106	...
52	Vyškov na Moravě	**1156** d.	0540	0640	...	...	0740	...	0940	1140	...	1240	1340	1440	...	1540	1640	1740	1840	...	1940	2040	2140	...
78	Kojetin	d.	0606	0706	...	...	0806	...	1006	1206	...	1306	1406	1506	...	1606	1706	1806	1906	...	2006	2106	2206	...
	Wien Hbf **1150**	d.	|	|	...	0605	|	0810	|	|	...	|	|	|	1410	|	|	|	|	1810	|	|	|	2210
	Břeclav **1162**	d.	|	|	0710	0724	|	0910	|	|	1210	|	|	|	1510	|	|	|	|	1910	|	|	|	2350
95	**Přerov**	**1160** d.	0623	0723	0808	|	0823	1008	1023	1223	1308	1323	1423	1523	1608	1623	1723	1823	1923	2008	2023	2123	2223	|
24	Hranice na Moravě	**1160** d.	0644	0743	0828	|	0843	1028	1044	1243	1328	1343	1443	1543	1628	1643	1743	1843	1943	2028	2043	2143	2243	|
74	Ostrava Svinov	**1160** a.	0715	0815	0852	|	0915	1052	1115	1315	1352	1415	1515	1615	1652	1715	1815	1915	2015	2052	2115	2215	2315	|
79	**Ostrava** hl. n.	**1160** a.	0723	0823	0900	|	0923	1100	1123	1323	1400	1423	1523	1623	1700	1723	1823	1923	2023	2100	2123	2223	2323	0130
87	Bohumín	**1160** a.	0734	0834	0909	0914	0934	1109	1134	1334	1409	1434	1534	1634	1709	1734	1834	1934	2034	2109	2134	2234	2334	0139

					EC				EC			EC				Ex				EC			
		457	848	846	844	101	842	840	838	103	836	834	131	832	830	828	591	826	409	824	105	822	820	
		N	⚒n	⚒n	🍷	M	🍷	🍷	🍷	P	🍷	🍷	B	🍷	🍷	🍷		Ⓑh	J⑤	🍷	S	⑦e	🍷	
humín	**1160** d.	0220	0424	0524	0624	0651	0724	0824	1024	1051	1224	1324	1351	1424	1524	1624	1651	1724	1800	1824	1851	1924	2024	...
strava hl. n.	**1160** d.	0230	0435	0535	0635	0700	0735	0835	1035	1100	1235	1335	1400	1435	1535	1635	1700	1735	|	1835	1900	1935	2035	...
strava Svinov	**1160** d.	|	0443	0543	0643	0708	0743	0843	1043	1108	1243	1343	1408	1443	1543	1643	1708	1743	|	1843	1908	1943	2043	...
anice na Moravě	**1160** d.	|	0515	0615	0715	0733	0815	0915	1115	1133	1315	1415	1433	1515	1615	1715	1733	1815	|	1915	1933	2015	2115	...
erov	**1160** d.	|	0537	0637	0737	0753	0837	0937	1137	1153	1337	1437	1453	1537	1637	1737	1753	1837	|	1937	1953	2037	2137	...
Břeclav **1162**	a.	0410	|	|	|	0847	|	|	|	1247	|	|	1547	|	|	|	1847	|	1945	|	2047	|	|	...
Wien Hbf **1150**	a.	0700	|	|	|	0949	|	|	|	1349	|	|	...	|	|	|	...	|	2117	|	2149	|	|	...
jetin	d.	...	0553	0653	0753	...	0853	0953	1153	...	1353	1453	...	1553	1653	1753	...	1853	...	1953	...	2053	2153	...
škov na Moravě	**1156** d.	...	0617	0717	0817	...	0917	1017	1217	...	1417	1517	...	1617	1717	1817	...	1917	...	2017	...	2117	2217	...
no Židenice ☆	**1156** a.	...	0650	0750	0850	...	0950	1050	1250	...	1450	1550	...	1650	1750	1850	...	1950	...	2050	...	2150	2247	...
no Královo Pole ☆	**1156** a.	...	0701	0801	0901	...	1001	1101	1301	...	1501	1601	...	1701	1801	1901	...	2001	...	2101	...	2201	2258	...

– BATHORY – [12] ✕ Budapest - Bratislava - Ostrava - Katowice - Warszawa and v.v.; [2] [R] Budapest - Bratislava - Ostrava - Bohumín (**115/4**) - Kraków and v.v.
– 🛏 1, 2 cl. Nice - Wien - Moskva and v.v. For days of running see Table **25**.
– MORAVIA – [12] ✕ Wien - Břeclav - Bohumín - Katowice and v.v.
– NIGHTJET – 🛏 1, 2 cl., ▬ 2 cl., [2] Wien - Břeclav - Ostrava - Bohumín - Wroclaw - Berlin and v.v. (Table **71**); 🛏 1, 2 cl., ▬ 2 cl. ⊡, [2] Wien - Břeclav - Ostrava - Bohumín (**406/7**) - Kraków - Warszawa and v.v. (Table **99**); 🛏 1, 2 cl., ▬ 2 cl., [2] Budapest (**476/7**) - Bratislava - Břeclav (**456/7**) - Wroclaw - Berlin and v.v. (Table **71**); 🛏 1, 2 cl., ▬ 2 cl. ⊡, [2] Budapest (**476/7**) - Bratislava - Břeclav (**456/7**) - Bohumín (**406/7**) - Kraków - Warszawa and v.v. [R] for international journeys.

P – POLONIA – [12] ✕ Wien - Břeclav - Ostrava - Bohumín - Katowice - Warszawa and v.v.
S – SOBIESKI – [12] ✕ Wien - Bohumín - Katowice - Warszawa - Gdansk - Gdynia and v.v.
e – Also Dec. 26, Jan. 1, Apr. 22, May 1, 8, Oct. 28; not Dec. 23, 30, Apr. 21, Oct. 27.
h – Not Dec. 23 - 25, 31, Apr. 19, 21, July 5, Oct. 27.
n – ①–⑥ (not Dec. 24 - 26, Jan. 1, Apr. 20, 22, July 6, Oct. 28).
⊡ – For days of running of ▬ 2 cl. see Table **99**.
☆ – Connections by tram to / from central Brno during partial closure of Brno hl. n. (see city plan page 31).

nd class (PRAHA) - ÚSTI NAD ORLICI - LICHKOV - KLODZKO - (WROCJAW) 1165

m				①–⑥	⑦	⑦u	⚒n					
			f	f	f					z		x
	Praha hl. n. **1151**	d.	...	...	...	0758	0858	...	1058	1258	1358	1658
	Pardubice **1151**	d.	0607	...	...	0907	1007	...	1207	1407	1507	1807
0	**Ústi nad Orlici**	d.	0654	...	...	0942	1042	...	1242	1442	1542	1842
14	Letohrad	d.	0716	...	...	1003	1103	...	1303	1503	1603	1903
35	Lichkov	a.	0744	...	...	1027	1127	...	1327	1527	1627	1927
			|			◇	|			◇		◇
35	Lichkov	d.	0746	...	...	1136	1136	...	...	1547	...	1959
44	Miedzylesie 🏛	a.	0755	0800	0844	1145	1145	1218v	...	1556	...	2008
70	**Klodzko** Gl.	⊕ a.	...	0847	0928	...	...	1301	...	1642	...	2056
	Wroclaw **1095**	⊕ a.	...	1024	1100	...	...	1453	...	1839	...	2244

		①–⑥							Ⓐ	Ⓒ		
		b			b			d			b	k
Wroclaw **1095**	⊕ d.	0517	...	...	0817	...	...	1308	...	...	1414	1657
Klodzko Gl.	⊕ d.	0655	...	...	0957	...	...	1440	...	...	1549	1827
Miedzylesie 🏛	d.	0749	0828	...	1041	1221	...	1526	...	...	1639	1916
Lichkov	a.	...	0836	...	...	1230	...	1535	...	...	...	1929
			|			|		◇				◇
Lichkov	d.	...	0837	1035	...	1235	1434	1539	1635	1732	...	1931
Letohrad	d.	...	0902	1102	...	1301	1502	1602	1702	1802	...	2001
Ústi nad Orlici	a.	...	0920	1120	...	1320	1520	1620	1720	1820	...	2019
Pardubice **1151**	a.	...	0955	1155	...	1355	1555	1655	1755	1855	...	2055
Praha hl. n. **1151**	a.	...	1104	1304	...	1504	1704	1804	1904	2004	...	...

- By 🚌 Gorzanów - Miedzylesie July 8 - 29, arr 30 mins later.
- July 8 - 29 Lichkov a. 1610 (by 🚌). Connects with next column.
Subject to alteration July 8 - 29.
- July 8 - 28 Lichkov a. 1958 by 🚌 (no connection at Lichkov).

n – ①–⑥ (not Apr. 20, 22, July 6, Oct. 28).
u – Also Apr. 20, 22, July 6, Oct. 28.
v – 1146 (by 🚌) July 8 - 29.
x – July 8 - 28 Lichkov d. 1924 by 🚌 (no connection).

z – July 8 - 29 Lichkov d. 1513 by 🚌 (no connection).
◇ – Change trains at Lichkov.
⊕ – Polish times are valid June 9 - Aug. 31.

nd class OLOMOUC - KRNOV - OPAVA - OSTRAVA 1166

m											Ⓐ	Ⓐ	Ⓐu
0	**Olomouc**	d.	...	0705r	0901	1105	1305	1505	1705	1906	...	...	...
64	Bruntál	d.	...	0826r	1027	1226	1426	1626	1826	2027	...	...	...
87	Krnov	a.	...	0851r	1051	1251	1451	1651	1851	2052	...	...	...
87	Krnov	d.	0706	0906	1106	1306	1506	1706	1906	2101	...	...	...
16	**Opava** východ ▷	d.	0737	0937	1137	1337	1537	1737	1939	2138	0615	every	1615
44	Ostrava Svinov ▷	a.	0757	0957	1157	1357	1557	1759	2001	...	0639	**two**	1639
49	**Ostrava** hl. n.	a.	0808	...	1208	1408	1608	...	...	...	0653	hours	1653

										Ⓐ	Ⓐ	Ⓐ
Ostrava hl. n.	d.	...	...	0949	...	1349	1549	1749	...	0654	every	1854
Ostrava Svinov ▷	d.	0600	0800	1000	1200	1400	1600	1801	...	0713	**two**	1913
Opava východ ▷	d.	0628	0828	1028	1228	1428	1628	1829	2023	0736	hours	1936
Krnov	a.	0657	0856	1056	1256	1456	1656	1857	2100	...	...	...
Krnov	d.	0705	0905	1105	1305	1505	1705	...	2112	...	...	...
Bruntál	d.	0734	0934	1134	1334	1534	1734	...	2138	...	...	...
Olomouc	a.	0852	1052	1255	1452	1652	1852	...	2304	...	...	...

0	Jesenik	d.	0530	0930	...	1330	...	1730	...
22	Glucholazy (Poland)	d.	0610	1010	...	1410	...	1810	...
43	Tremešná ve Slezsku	d.	0640	1040	1240	1440	1643	1840	2040
60	Krnov	a.	0658	1058	1259	1458	1702	1858	2059

Krnov	d.	0705	0908	1105	1308	1505	1708	1905
Tremešná ve Slezsku	d.	0725	0928	1125	1328	1523	1728	1925
Glucholazy (Poland)	d.	0759	...	1159	...	1559	...	1959
Jesenik	a.	0836	...	1236	...	1636	...	2036

r – ①–⑥ (not Apr. 20, 22, July 6, Oct. 28).
u – Also at 1809 Ⓐ.
▷ – Local trains run hourly (journey 35 mins).

nd class. May vary on holidays. OTHER LOCAL SERVICES 1169

RNO - ZNOJMO *89 km* Journey 2 hours

›m Brno: 0649⑥**t**, 0849Ⓒ, 1254Ⓒ, 1454 **R**, 1654Ⓒ.
›m Znojmo: 0900Ⓒ, 1300Ⓒ, 1500 **R**, 1700Ⓒ.

Change at Miroslav and Hrušovany nad Jevišovkou

ESKÝ TĚŠÍN - CIESZYN (Poland) *3 km* Journey 5 mins

›m Český Těšín: 0522, 0720, 0922, 1222, 1422, 1622, 1820, 2022, 2222.
›m Cieszyn: 0533, 0731, 0933, 1233, 1433, 1633, 1831, 2033, 2233.

HOCEŇ - LITOMYŠL *24 km* Journey 55 minutes

›m Choceň: 0507Ⓐ, 0628, 0839, 1039⚒**n**, 1339Ⓒ, 1429Ⓐ, 1539Ⓒ, 1639Ⓐ, 1839Ⓒ.
›m Litomyšl: 0604Ⓐ, 0719Ⓐ, 0734Ⓒ, 0932⚒**n**, 1232, 1520Ⓐ, 1532, 1732, 1932Ⓒ.
ange at Vysoké Myto město on certain journeys.

NDŘICHŮV HRADEC - NOVÁ BYSTŘICE *33 km* Narrow gauge, 80 mins

›m Jindřichův Hradec: 0725 **S**, 0925, 1044 **G**, 1120, 1320, 1520, 1720 **S**.
›m Nová Bystřice: 0904 **S**, 1103, 1304, 1504, 1515 **G**, 1704, 1855 **S**.
erator: JHMD www.jhmd.cz

OJETIN / HULIN - KROMĚŘÍŽ *8 km* Journey 8 minutes

etin - Kroměříž: approx hourly. *9 km*, journey 12 minutes.
lin - Kroměříž: 1 - 2 trains per hour connecting with trains in Table **1162**.

KOSTELEC U JIHLAVY - TELČ *23 km* Journey 36 minutes

From Kostelec: 0457Ⓐ, 0637Ⓐ, 0820, 1018, 1111Ⓐ, 1316, 1421Ⓐ, 1512Ⓒ, 1522Ⓐ, 1710, 1818⑦**e**, 1907⚒, 2019⑦**e**, 2128Ⓐ.

From Telč: 0404⚒**n**, 0516Ⓐ, 0719Ⓑ, 0803Ⓐ, 0902Ⓒ, 0935Ⓐ, 1205, 1327Ⓐ, 1404Ⓒ, 1441Ⓐ, 1604, 1655⑦**e**, 1823⚒, 1910⑦**e**, 2028Ⓐ.

PRAHA - KARLŠTEJN *33 km* Journey 42 minutes

From Praha hl. n.: 0420, 0520, 0620, 0650, 0720, 0750⚒, 0820, 0850, 0920Ⓒ, 0950, 1020Ⓒ, 1050, 1120Ⓒ, 1150 and every 30 minutes to 1920, 1950Ⓐ, 2020, 2120, 2220, 2320.

From Karlštejn: 0530, 0600, 0630Ⓐ, 0700, 0730, 0800, 0830⚒, 0900, 0930, 1000, 1030Ⓒ, 1100, 1130Ⓒ, 1200, 1230Ⓒ, 1300 and every 30 mins to 2000, 2030Ⓐ, 2100, 2200, 2300.

Trains continue to / from Beroun (journey 10 mins).

TŘEMEŠNÁ VE SLEZSKU - OSOBLAHA *20 km* Narrow gauge, 45 minutes

From Třemešná: 0730⑥**u**, 1045 **b**, 1130, 1525, 1930.
From Osoblaha: 0950, 1350, 1510 **b**, 1750.

ZNOJMO - BŘECLAV *69 km* Journey 80 minutes

From Znojmo: 0458Ⓐ, 0558⚒, 0656, 0900, 1100, 1200Ⓐ, 1300, 1400Ⓐ, 1500, 1600Ⓑ, 1700, 1800Ⓐ, 1803 **E**, 1900.

From Břeclav: 0457Ⓐ, 0557⚒, 0740, 0851 **E**, 0940, 1140, 1244Ⓐ, 1340, 1444Ⓐ, 1540, 1646Ⓐ, 1740, 1940, 2140Ⓑ.

- Ⓒ Apr. 19 - Sept. 29.
- ⑥ May 4 - Sept. 28 (also ①③⑤⑦ June 30 - Aug. 31). Steam hauled journey, ✕. Special fares. 1044 arrives Nová Bystřice 1302; 1515 arr. Jindřichův Hradec 1704.
- Ⓒ Apr. 19 - Sept. 29.

S – June 29 - Sept. 1.
b – ⑥ June 1 - Sept. 21, also ⑦ July 7 - Aug. 25 (also May 8, July 5, Nov. 9). Steam hauled journey, special fares. Journey 75 - 80 minutes.
e – Also May 1, 8, Oct. 28; not Oct. 27.

n – ①–⑥ (not Apr. 20, 22, July 6, Oct. 28).
t – Also Apr. 19, May 1, 8, July 5; not Apr. 20, July 6.
u – Also ①–⑤ July 1 - Aug. 30.

SLOVAKIA

Operator: National railway operator is Železničná spoločnosť Slovensko (ŽSSK), www.slovakrail.sk, which runs on the network of Železnice Slovenskej Republiky (ŽSR), www.zsr.sk

Services: All trains convey first and second class seating, **except** where shown otherwise in footnotes or by '2' in the train column, or where the footnote shows sleeping and/or couchet cars only. Descriptions of sleeping (🛏) and couchette (▬) cars appear on page 10. Note: hl. st. = hlavná stanica = main station.

Timings: Valid **June 9 - December 14, 2019**. Certain trains may be cancelled during the period Dec. 24 - Jan. 1 and these cancellations may not be shown in the tables.

Supplements: A higher level of fares applies to travel by *EC* and *IC* trains. It is possible to reserve seats on most Express trains.

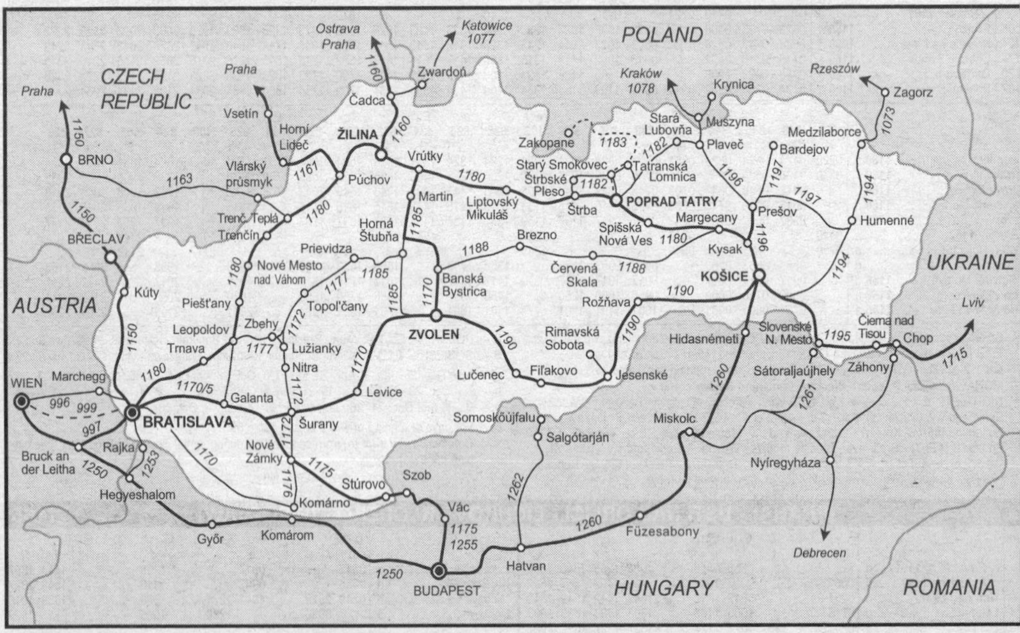

1170 BRATISLAVA - LEVICE - ZVOLEN - BANSKÁ BYSTRICA

km		831	811	835	813	839	1851	815	843	845	847	801
							Ⓐ 2z		Ⓐ z			Ⓑ P
0	**Bratislava** hl. st. ▷ d.	0604	0804	1004	1204	1404	1434	1604	1700	1804	2004	2330
49	Galanta ▷ d.	0638	0838	1038	1238	1438	1516	1638	1733	1838	2038	0008
60	Šaľa ▷ d.	0647	0847	1047	1247	1447	1525	1647	1741	1847	2047	0018
	Nové Zámky ▷ d.	|	|	|	|	|	|	|	|	|	|	0057
89	Šurany d.	0709	0909	1109	1309	1509	1548	1709	1807	1909	2109	0108
132	Levice d.	0748	0948	1148	1348	1548	...	1748	1849	1948	2148	0147
187	Žiar nad Hronom d.	0838	1038	1238	1438	1638	...	1838	1940	2038	2238	0237
209	**Zvolen** osob. a.	0856	1056	1256	1456	1656	...	1856	1958	2056	2256	0256
	Košice **1190** ⊖ a.	|	1437	|	1837	|	...	2235	|	|	|	0648
209	**Zvolen** osob. d.	0902	*1102*r	1302	*1502*r	1702	...	*1902*r	2002	2102	2302	...
230	**Banská Bystrica** a.	0926	*1126*r	1326	*1526*r	1726	...	*1926*r	2026	2126	2326	...

	830	*Ex* 530	832	810	836	812	840	17840	814	816	80
		Ⓐ z						⑦ e			Ⓑ P
Banská Bystrica d.	0431	0535	0631	*0831*r	1031	*1231*r	1431	1512	*1631*r	*1833*r	...
Zvolen osob. a.	0455	0553	0655	*0855*r	1055	*1255*r	1455	1540	*1655*r	*1857*r	...
Košice **1190** ⊖ d.	|	|	|	0523	|	0923	|	|	1323	1523	220
Zvolen osob. d.	0500	0555	0700	0900	1100	1300	1500	1547	1700	1900	015
Žiar nad Hronom d.	0518	0613	0718	0918	1118	1318	1518	1607	1718	1918	02
Levice d.	0612	0658	0812	1012	1212	1412	1612	1709	1812	2012	03
Šurany d.	0651	0739	0851	1051	1251	1451	1651	1756	1851	2051	035
Nové Zámky ▷ d.	|	|	|	|	|	|	|	|	|	|	04
Šaľa ▷ d.	0714	|	0914	1114	1314	1514	1714	1817	1914	2114	044
Galanta ▷ d.	0725	|	0925	1125	1325	1525	1725	1826	1925	2125	045
Bratislava hl. st. ▷ a.	0758	0836	0958	1158	1358	1558	1758	1901	1958	2158	053

ADDITIONAL LOCAL TRAINS ZVOLEN - BANSKÁ BYSTRICA

		▶		Ⓐ			Ⓐ							Ⓐz	⊙	Ⓐz		⊡			Ⓐz				
Zvolen d.	0435	0502	0522	0557	0635	0658	0732	0800	1001	1111	1201	1311	1401	1429	1511	1539	1601	1711	1814	1911	2021	2124	2239	...	...
Banská Bystrica a.	0513	0529	0555	0629	0713	0730	0803	0830	1030	1142	1230	1341	1430	1508	1542	1611	1630	1745	1846	1941	2053	2155	2311	...	...

			Ⓐz	Ⓐz	Ⓐ	Ⓒ	Ⓐz						Ⓐz		Ⓐ	Ⓒ	Ⓐz					▶			
Banská Bystrica d.	0448	0541	0605	0647	0717	0731	0748	0816	0929	1129	1216	1329	1346	1416	1512	1529	1546	1616	1732	1816	1931	2031	2129	2228	...
Zvolen a.	0521	0614	0634	0717	0750	0759	0820	0849	0959	1159	1249	1359	1419	1449	1554	1559	1619	1649	1802	1851	2001	2055	2202	2259	...

P – POĽANA – Ⓑ (not Dec. 23-25, 31, Apr. 19, 21, July 5, Nov. 1).
🛏 1, 2 cl., ▬2 Bratislava - Zvolen - Košice - Prešov and v.v.;
🛏 1, 2 cl. Praha (**283/2**) - Brno - Bratislava (**873/0**) - Nové Zámky (**801/0**) - Zvolen - Košice - Prešov and v.v.

e – Also Apr. 22; not Dec. 23,30, Apr. 21. Additional train on ⑦**e** (not June 30 - Aug. 31) runs two hours later (train **17842**).

n – Not July 1 - Sept. 1.

r – Change at Zvolen (Zvolen - Žilina and v.v. train, Table **1185**).

z – Not Dec. 22 - Jan. 6.

▶ – ▬12 Zvolen - Banská Bystrica - Vrútky - Žilina - Ostrava and v.v. (train **346/347**, Table **1185**).

⊖ – For faster services Bratislava - Košice (via Žilina) see Table **1180**.

▷ – For additional trains see Table **1175**.

⊡ – 10 minutes later on ⑦ (also Apr. 22; not Dec. 23,30, Apr. 21, July 7 - Aug. 25).

⊙ – 10 minutes later on ⑦**e**.

BRATISLAVA - KOMÁRNO via Dunajská Streda

Operator: Regiojet. *94* km. 2nd class. Journey 2h 10m.

From Bratislava hl. st.: 0503Ⓐ, 0605Ⓒ, 0705Ⓐ, 0805, 1005, 1204, 1305**n**, 1405, 1513Ⓐ, 1605Ⓒ, 1613Ⓐ, 1705Ⓒ, 1713Ⓐ, 1805, 2005.

From Komárno: 0348Ⓐ, 0436, 0549Ⓐ, 0643Ⓐ, 0743, 0943, 1143, 1343, 1433Ⓐ, 1543Ⓒ, 1635Ⓐ, 1743Ⓒ, 1839Ⓐ, 1946. *Subject to alteration Dec. 24 - Jan. 6.*

1172 NOVÉ ZAMKY - NITRA - TOPOĽČANY

2nd clas

km						Ⓒ	Ⓐ						Ⓐ			Ⓐ	Ⓐ					Ⓐ	Ⓒ		
0	**Nové Zamky** d.	...	0426	0521	0628	0715	*0725*	0915	1115	1254	1315	1405	1420	1454	1515	1554	1620	1654	1715	1820	1854	1915	1915	2054	225
10	Šurany a.	...	0438	0532	0639	0726	*0736*	0926	1126	1305	1326	1416	1431	1505	1526	1605	1631	1705	1726	1831	1905	1926	1926	2105	231
10	Šurany d.	...	0442	0533	0640	0728	*0740*	0928	1128	...	1328	...	1437	...	1528	...	1637	...	1728	1837	...	1928	1928	2113	231
36	**Nitra** a.	...	0516	0605	0717	0800	*0811*	1000	1200	...	1400	...	1518	...	1600	...	1718	...	1800	1909	...	2000	2000	2146	234
36	**Nitra** 1177 d.	0412	0536	0606**a**	0733	0813	0813	1012	1212	...	1412	...	1529	...	1612	...	1733	...	1812	1933	...	2012	...	*2240*	...
40	Lužianky **1177** d.	0425	0548	0616**a**	0743	0824	0824	1024	1224	...	1424	...	1543	...	1624	...	1743	...	1824	1944	...	2024	...	*2252*	..
69	**Topoľčany** a.	0506	0628	◇	◇	0900	0900	1100	1300	...	1500	...	1618	...	1700	...	...	...	1900	◇	...	2100	...	*2329*	..
	Prievidza **1177** a.	...	0755	...	...	1020	1020	1223	1415	...	1625	...	...	...	1822	...	...	...	...	...	...	...	...	...	..

			Ⓐ	Ⓐ	Ⓒ					Ⓐ			Ⓐ	Ⓐz			Ⓐ			Ⓐ	Ⓒ		Ⓒ	Ⓐ	
Prievidza **1177** d.	...	...	0517	...	...	0623	...	0943	...	...	1136	...	...	...	1340	...	1424	1538	...	...	...	1746	...	...	...
Topoľčany d.	0421	◇	0633	...	◇	0737	0904	1104	...	◇	1304	...	◇	...	1504	...	1533	1704	...	◇	◇	1904	◇	◇	*210*
Lužianky **1177** d.	0502	0619	0709	...	0745	0825	0945	1145	...	*1225*	1345	...	1425	...	1545	...	1625	1745	...	1848	1825	1945	2020	2025	*214*
Nitra **1177** a.	0512	0629	0721	...	0756	0836	0956	1156	...	*1236*	1356	...	1436	...	1556	...	1636	1756	...	1859	1836	1956	2030	2036	22
Nitra d.	0519	0631	▬	0748	0803	▬	1003	1203	...	1255	1403	...	1455	...	1603	...	1655	1803	...	1913	1913	...	2032	2058	225
Šurany a.	0554	0701	Ⓐ	0829	0834	...	1034	1234	...	1326	1434	...	1526	...	1634	...	1726	1834	...	1948	1948	...	2103	2134	233
Šurany d.	0604	0702	0747	0835	0835	0855	1035	1235	1253	1330	1435	1453	1530	1553	1635	1653	1730	1835	1853	1949	1959	...	2111	2135	233
Nové Zamky a.	0615	0713	0759	0846	0846	0906	1046	1246	1308	1341	1446	1508	1541	1608	1646	1708	1741	1846	1908	2000	2010	...	2123	2146	234

a – Ⓐ only.

◇ – To / from Zbehy or Leopoldov (Table **1177**).

z – Not Dec. 22 - Jan. 6.

BRATISLAVA - ŠTÚROVO - BUDAPEST 1175

km		IC 573 477	EC 271	EC 273	EC 275	EC 277	EC 279	EC 131	EC 173	EC 281	283 873
		🅁	✕	✕	✕	✕	✕	✕	✕	✕	✕
		M						B	H		Ⓑb
	Praha hlavní **1150** ..... d.	2156	...	0550	0750	0950	1150	...	1350	1550	1750
	Brno dolní n. **1150** . ☆ d.	0050	0624	0824	1024	1224	1424	...	1624	1824	2024
	Břeclav **1150** .... d.	0459r	0659	0859	1059	1259	1459	1559	1659	1859	2059
0	**Bratislava** hlavná .... d.	0553	0757	0957	1157	1357	1557	1655	1757	1957	2153
91	Nové Zámky .... d.	0645	0852	1052	1252	1452	1652	1752	1852	2052	2254
135	Štúrovo 🏛 .... d.	0714	0920	1120	1320	1520	1720	1820	1920	2120	...
150	Szob 🏛 .... ▷ d.	|	0932	1132	1332	1532	1732	1832	1932	2132	...
163	Nagymaros-Visegrád ¶ ▷ d.	|	0941	1141	1341	1541	1741	1841	1941	2141	...
180	Vác .... ▷ d.	0750	0954	1154	1354	1554	1754	1854	1954	2154	...
214	**Budapest** Nyugati ..... ▷ a.	|	1020	1220	1420	1620	1820	1920	2020	2220	...
223	**Budapest** Keleti .... a.	0835	...	...	...	...	...	...	...	...	...

	870 282	EC 280	EC 172	EC 130	EC 278	EC 276	EC 274	EC 272	EC 270	476 IC 572
	✕	✕	✕	✕	✕	✕	✕	✕	✕	🅁
	⚒d		H	B						M
Budapest Keleti .... d.	...	...	...	...	...	...	...	...	...	1925
Budapest Nyugati ..... ▷ d.	...	0540	0740	0840	0940	1140	1340	1540	1740	|
Vác .... ▷ d.	...	0606	0806	0906	1006	1206	1406	1606	1806	2007
Nagymaros-Visegrád ¶ ▷ d.	...	0619	0819	0919	1019	1219	1419	1619	1819	|
Szob 🏛 .... ▷ d.	...	0629	0829	0929	1029	1229	1429	1629	1829	|
Štúrovo 🏛 .... d.	...	0643	0843	0943	1043	1243	1443	1643	1843	2042
Nové Zámky .... d.	0500	0711	0911	1010	1111	1311	1511	1711	1911	2110
Bratislava hlavná .... a.	0603	0803	1003	1102	1203	1403	1603	1803	2003	2203
Břeclav **1150** .... a.	0701	0901	1101	1201	1301	1501	1701	1901	2101	2301s
Brno dolní n. **1150** .. ☆ a.	0735	0935	1135	...	1335	1535	1735	1935	2135	0532
Praha hlavní **1150** ..... a.	1007	1207	1407	...	1607	1807	2007	2209	...	0807

2nd class — LOCAL TRAINS BRATISLAVA - NOVÉ ZÁMKY

△					Ⓐ	Ⓐ		Ⓐ	Ⓐz			Ⓑn
Bratislava hl .... § d.	0709	0909	1109	1309	1457	1633	1709	1733	1833	1909	2109	2153
Galanta .... § d.	0758	0958	1158	1358	1532	1714	1758	1814	1914	1958	2158	2226
Šal'a .... § d.	0808	1008	1208	1408	1540	1724	1808	1824	1924	2008	2208	2235
Nové Zámky ..... a.	0838	1038	1238	1438	1559	1742	1838	1842	1942	2038	2238	2254

▽		Ⓐ	Ⓐ					Ⓐ		Ⓐz	
Nové Zámky ... d.	0500	0518	0618	0923	1123	1323	1523	1623	1723	1823	1923
Šal'a .... § d.	0521	0539	0639	0953	1153	1353	1553	1653	1754	1854	1953
Galanta .... § d.	0530	0549	0649	1005	1205	1405	1605	1705	1805	1905	2005
Bratislava hl .. § a.	0603	0630	0730	1053	1253	1453	1653	1753	1853	1953	2053

– BATHORY – [12] ✕ Budapest - Bratislava - Ostrava - Katowice - Warszawa and v.v.; [2] 🅁 Budapest - Bratislava - Ostrava - Bohumín (**115/4**) - Kraków and v.v.
– HUNGARIA – [12] ✕ Hamburg - Berlin - Dresden - Praha - Bratislava - Budapest and v.v.
– METROPOL – [12] Břeclav - Budapest and v.v.; 🛏 1, 2 cl., ▬ 2 cl. Praha (*IC* **573/2**) - Břeclav (**477/6**) - Budapest and v.v.; 🛏 1, 2 cl., ▬ 2 cl., [2] Berlin (**457/6**) - Wroclaw - Bohumín - Břeclav (**477/6**) - Budapest and v.v.; 🛏 1, 2 cl., [2] (also ▬ 2 cl. on dates in Table **99**) Warszawa (**407/6**) - Kraków - Bohumín (**457/6**) - Břeclav (**477/6**) - Budapest and v.v.
– Not Dec. 23 - 25, 31, Apr. 19, 21, July 5, Nov. 1.
– ①–⑥ (not Dec. 24 - 26, Jan. 1, Apr. 20, 22, July 6, Nov. 2).
– Arrives 0125.
– Departs 0502.

z – Not Dec. 22 - Jan. 6.
△ – Also at: 0444, 1209Ⓐ, 1409Ⓐ, 1509, 1609Ⓐ, 1809Ⓐ, 2309.
▽ – Also at: 0323, 0428, 0530, 0554, 0656Ⓐ, 0723, 1423Ⓐ.
▷ – For local trains Szob - Budapest and v.v. see Table **1255**.
☆ – 🚌 connections available Brno dolní nádraží - Brno hlavní nádraží (see plan on page 31).
§ – See also Table **1170**.
¶ – A ferry operates across the river to Visegrád.

NAMES: Praha - Budapest trains are named METROPOLITAN.

2nd class — NOVÉ ZÁMKY - KOMÁRNO 1176

km						Ⓐz		Ⓐz		Ⓐz		
0	Nové Zámky .... d.	0702	0902	1102	1302	1402	1502	1602	1702	1802	1902	2102
29	Komárno .... a.	0728	0928	1128	1328	1428	1528	1628	1728	1828	1928	2128

					Ⓐz		Ⓐz		Ⓐz		
Komárno .... d.	0634	0834	1034	1234	1334	1434	1534	1634	1734	1834	2021
Nové Zámky .... a.	0700	0900	1100	1300	1400	1500	1600	1700	1800	1900	2047

– Not Dec. 22 - Jan. 6.

ADDITIONAL TRAINS: from Nové Zámky 0456, 0550Ⓐ**z**, 0734Ⓐ**z**; from Komárno 0421, 0535Ⓐ**z**, 0739Ⓐ**z**.

2nd class — BRATISLAVA - NITRA and PRIEVIDZA 1177

km			1721				1723				1061		1725						1727			1063			
		Ⓐ									P♣			v		Ⓒ	Ⓐ			Ⓒ	Ⓐ	P♣			
0	**Bratislava** hl. .... **1180** d.	...	0636	...	*0813*	*1013*	1036	...	*1213*	...	...	*1413*	1436	...	*1613*	...	*1713*r	*1813*	1836	...	...	...	*2013*	2130	2328
46	Trnava .... **1180** d.	...	0714	...	*0844*	*1044*	1114	...	*1244*	...	...	*1444*	1514	...	*1644*	...	*1744*r	*1844*	1914	...	...	...	*2044*	2219	0018
63	Leopoldov .... **1180** a.	...	0726	...	*0854*	*1054*	1126	...	*1254*	...	...	*1454*	1526	...	*1654*	...	*1754*r	*1854*	1926	...	...	...	*2054*	2233	0032
63	Leopoldov .... d.	0638	0741	...	0907	1107	1141	...	1307	...	1435	1507	1541	...	1707	...	1800	1907	1941	...	...	1956	2107	...	...
87	Zbehy .... d.	0710	0804	0810	0934	1134	1204	1208	1334	1408	|	1534	1606	1608	1734	1804	1840	1934	2006	2008	2008	|	2134	...	...
91	Lužianky .... **1172** a.	0717	|	0816	0941	1141	|	1214	1341	1414	|	1541	|	1614	1741	1810	1847	1941	|	2014	2014	|	2140	...	...
98	**Nitra** .... **1172** a.	0729	|	*0836*	*0956*	*1156*	|	1236	*1356*	1436	1513	*1556*	|	1636	*1756*	1836	1859	*1956*	|	2030	2036	2042	2151	...	...
114	Topol'čany .... ▷ a.	◇	0829	...	...	...	1229	◇	...	◇	...	...	1631	◇	...	◇	◇	...	2031	...	...	...	...	...	...
131	Partizánske .... ▷ a.	...	0854	...	...	...	1254	...	...	...	...	...	1654	...	...	...	...	...	2055	...	...	...	...	...	...
158	**Prievidza** .... ▷ a.	...	0928	...	...	...	1328	...	...	...	...	...	1727	...	...	...	...	...	2128	...	...	...	...	...	...

			1720		1060				1722				1062		1724						1726			17728	
				Ⓐ	P♣		Ⓐ						P♣				Ⓐ	Ⓒ						⑦e	
Prievidza .... ▽ d.	...	...	0432	...	...	...	...	...	0828	...	...	...	...	...	1228	...	...	...	...	...	1628	...	...	1834	...
Partizánske .... ▽ d.	...	...	0504	...	...	...	...	...	0908	...	...	...	...	...	1308	...	...	...	...	...	1708	...	...	1908	...
Topol'čany .... ▽ d.	...	...	0531	...	...	◇	...	...	0931	...	...	...	...	...	1331	...	...	...	...	◇	1731	...	◇	1933	...
Nitra .... **1172** d.	0412	0527	|	0606	0636	0733	...	0933	|	1004	1133	1204	1245	1333	|	1404	*1529*	1533	1604	1733	|	1804	1933	|	2004
Lužianky .... **1172** d.	0428	0539	|	0620	|	0745	...	0944	|	1017	1144	1217	|	1344	|	1417	1543	1543	1617	1744	|	1815	1944	|	2017
Zbehy .... d.	0435	0545	0557	0627	|	0807	...	0950	0958	1024	1150	1224	|	1350	1358	1424	1550	1549	1624	1750	1758	1824	1950	2010	2024
Leopoldov .... a.	0508	...	0618	0653	0721	0834	...	...	1019	1051	...	1251	1321	...	1419	1451	1620	...	1651	...	1819	1851	...	2033	2051
Leopoldov .... **1180** d.	...	...	0633	*0704*	...	...	0839	...	1033	*1104*	...	*1304*	...	...	1433	*1504*	1632	...	*1704*	...	1833	*1904*	...	2035	*2104*
Trnava .... **1180** d.	...	...	0648	*0718*	...	...	0855	...	1048	*1118*	...	*1318*	...	...	1448	*1518*	1646	...	*1718*	...	1848	*1918*	...	2050	*2118*
Bratislava hl. ...... **1180** a.	...	...	0724	*0747*	...	...	0942	...	1124	*1147*	...	*1347*	...	...	1524	*1547*	1724	...	*1747*	...	1924	*1947*	...	2129	*2147*

– Praha - Olomouc - Nitra and v.v. For days of running see Table **1163**.
– Also Apr. 22; not Dec. 23, 30, Apr. 21.
– For days of running see Table **1180**.
– Change at Lužianky on Ⓐ.

z – Not Dec. 22 - Jan. 6.
❦ – Certain journeys run from / to Nové Zamky or Nitra (Table **1172**).
▷ – Local trains Topol'čany - Prievidza (journey 60 - 80 mins) ❦: 0347Ⓐ, 0450, 0547Ⓐ, 0645, 0910, 1110, 1301, 1413Ⓐ**z**, 1512, 1703, 1841Ⓐ, 1910Ⓒ, 2223Ⓐ.

▽ – Local trains Prievidza - Topol'čany (journey 60 - 80 mins) ❦: 0402Ⓐ, 0517, 0623, 0717Ⓐ, 0943, 1136, 1340, 1424Ⓐ, 1538, 1746, 1842Ⓐ, 1915Ⓒ, 2231Ⓐ.
◇ – To / from Nové Zámky (Table **1172**).
♣ – Operated by ARRIVA. ČD tickets / passes not valid.

BRATISLAVA - ŽILINA - POPRAD TATRY - KOŠICE 1180

km			♥			EN	EN			IC		♣			SC•		♥			IC		♣		
		1761	1021	1763	1765	443	445	767	701	521	601	1060	703	603	241	705	1003	605	707	523	607	1062	709	
		2	🍷	✕	2	⊖	⊖	✕		🅁✕	✕	🍷		✕	🅁✕		🍷	✕		🅁✕	✕	🍷		
		Ⓐz	❦	Ⓐ	Ⓐ	♦	B♦		Ⓐ			△	Ⓐ		u				Ⓐ			△	Ⓐ	
	Wien Hbf. **996** .... d.	...	...	...	...	...	...	...	...	...	...	...	...	...	...	...	...	...	...	...	...	...	...	...
0	**Bratislava** hlavná st. ... **1177** d.	...	...	...	...	...	...	...	0513	0601	0613	...	0713	0813	...	0913	...	1013	1113	1159	1213	...	1313	...
46	Trnava .... **1177** d.	...	...	...	...	...	...	...	0544	0626	0644	...	0744	0844	...	0944	...	1044	1144	1225	1244	...	1344	...
63	Leopoldov .... **1177** d.	...	...	...	...	...	...	...	0556	|	0656	0724	0756	0856	...	0956	...	1056	1156	|	1256	1328	1356	...
81	Piešťany .... d.	...	...	...	...	...	...	...	0607	|	0707	0737	0807	0907	...	1007	...	1107	1207	|	1307	1342	1407	...
99	Nové Mesto nad Váhom .... d.	...	...	...	...	...	...	...	0620	|	0720	0750	0820	0920	...	1020	...	1120	1220	|	1320	1356	1420	...
124	**Trenčín** .... d.	...	...	...	...	...	...	0510	0635	0659	0735	0806	0835	0935	...	1035	...	1135	1235	1259	1335	1412	1435	...
132	Trenčianska Teplá .... d.	...	...	...	...	...	...	0517	0643	|	0743	0813	0843	0943	...	1043	...	1143	1243	|	1343	1419	1443	...
	Praha hl. n. **1160** .... d.	...	2147	...	...	2215	2347	|	|	|	|	...	|	*0524**	0709	|	0747	*0724**	|	|	*0924**	...	|	...
159	**Púchov** .... **1161** d.	...	|	...	...	|	|	0543	0659	|	0800	...	0900	1000	|	1100	|	1200	1259	|	1400	...	1500	...
171	Považská Bystrica .... **1161** d.	...	|	...	...	|	|	0601	0719	|	0819	...	0919	1019	|	1119	|	1219	1319	|	1419	...	1519	...
203	**Žilina** .... **1161** a.	...	0249	...	...	0434	0523	0632	0740	0750	0840	...	0940	1040	1133	1140	1237	1240	1340	1350	1440	...	1540	...
203	**Žilina** .... **1185** d.	...	0250	...	...	0500	0540	0636	...	0752	0844	...	...	1044	1134	...	1238	1244	...	1352	1444	...	...	...
224	Vrútky .... **1185** d.	...	0308	...	...	0518	0558	0653	...	0810	0902	...	...	1102	|	...	1255	1302	...	1410	1502	...	...	...
242	Kral'ovany .... d.	...	|	...	...	0535	0611	0706	...	|	0915	...	...	1115	|	...	|	1315	...	|	1515	...	...	...
260	Ružomberok .... d.	...	0336	...	...	0553	0627	0721	...	0836	0930	...	...	1130	1215	...	1321	1330	...	1436	1530	...	...	...
286	Liptovský Mikuláš .... d.	...	0355	...	...	0617	0647	0742	...	0854	0949	...	...	1149	1233	...	1338	1349	...	1454	1549	...	...	...
325	Štrba .... d.	...	0424	...	...	0647	0720	0813	...	|	1018	...	...	1218	1301	...	1406	1418	...	|	1618	...	...	...
344	**Poprad-Tatry** .... d.	0432	0444	0535	0635	0708	0757x	0840	...	0940	1040	...	...	1240	1321	...	1434	1440	...	1540	1640	...	...	...
370	Spišská Nová Ves .... d.	0451	0508	0554	0654	0728	0816	0859	...	0957	1059	...	...	1259	|	...	1452	1459	...	1557	1659	...	...	...
410	Margecany .... d.	0524	0534	0624	0725	0755	|	0926	...	|	1126	...	...	1326	|	...	|	1526	...	|	1726	...	...	...
429	Kysak .... **1196** a.	0539	0547	0638	0739	0809	0853	0939	...	1035	1139	...	...	1339	1414	...	1529	1539	...	1635	1739	...	...	...
	Prešov .... a.	|	|	|	|	|	|	|	...	|	|	...	...	|	|	...	|	|	...	|	|	...	...	...
445	**Košice** .... **1196** a.	0553	0600	0653	0753	0823	0908	0953	...	1048	1153	...	...	1353	1427	...	1546	1553	...	1648	1753	...	...	...
	Humenné **1194** .... a.	...	...	...	...	1033	...	...	...	...	...	...	...	...	...	...	...	...	...	...	...	...	...	...

CONTINUED ON NEXT PAGE

1180 BRATISLAVA - ŽILINA - POPRAD TATRY - KOŠICE

Continued from previous page

	1733	609	711	15711	1737	IC 45	611	LE♠ 1359	713	15713	IC 525	♥ 1011	SC• 243	613	715	15715	17715		717	717 443		719	LE♠ 1367	615
	2	✕			2	[R]✕	✕	🍷[R]			[R]✕	🍷	[R]✕	✕	2	2		2	✕	🛏	2	✕	🍷[R]	2
	Ⓐ		H	⑤f	Ⓐ			P	G	⑤k			⑤n		Ⓐ	⑤a	⑦e			R			P	♦
Wien Hbf. **996** d.	...	...	...	...	...	1437	...	...	...	...	...	...	...	...	...	...	...	...	...	...	...	...	...	...
Bratislava hlavná st. **1177** d.	1336	1413	1513	1513	1536	1606	1613	...	1713	1713	1801	...	...	1813	1913	1913	1913	...	2013	2013	...	2213	...	2248
Trnava **1177** d.	1415	1444	1544	1544	1615	1631	1644	...	1744	1744	1826	...	...	1844	1945	1945	1944	...	2044	2044	...	2244	...	2320
Leopoldov **1177** d.	1428	1456	1556	1556	1628	|	1656	...	1756	1756	|	...	...	1856	1958	1958	1956	...	2056	2056	...	2256	...	2333
Piešťany d.	1441	1507	1607	1607	1651	|	1707	...	1807	1807	|	...	...	1907	2012	2012	2007	...	2107	2107	...	2307	...	2346
Nové Mesto nad Váhom d.	1457	1520	1620	1620	1706	|	1720	...	1820	1820	|	...	...	1920	2025	2025	2019	...	2120	2120	...	2320	...	2359
Trenčín d.	1513	1535	1635	1635	1722	|	1735	...	1835	1835	1859	...	...	1935	2039	2041	2038	...	2135	2135	...	2333	...	0016
Trenčianska Teplá d.	...	1543	1643	1643	...	|	1743	...	1843	1843	|	...	...	1943	...	2049	2045	...	2143	2143	...	...	...	0023
Praha hl. n. **1160** d.	...	*1124**	|	|	...	|	*1324**	1409	|	|	|	1448	1541	*1524**	...	|	|	...	|	|	...	...	2009	|
Púchov **1161** d.	...	1600	1700	1700	...	|	1800	|	1859	1859	|	|	|	2000	...	2109	2100	...	2200	2200	2237	...	|	0043
Považská Bystrica **1161** d.	...	1615	1719	1719	...	|	1819	|	1919	1919	|	|	|	2019	...	2128	2119	...	2219	2219	2254	...	|	0057
Žilina **1161** a.	...	1640	1740	1740	...	1753	1840	1917	1940	1940	1950	1942	2008	2040	...	2149	2140	...	2240	2240	2328	...	0107	0125
Žilina **1185** d.	...	1644	...	1746	...	1755	1844	1919	...	1943	1952	1947	2010	2044	...	...	...	2157	...	0500	...	...	0108	0137
Vrútky **1185** d.	...	1702	...	1804	...	|	1902	1936	...	2000	2010	2016	|	2102	...	...	...	2218	...	0518	...	...	0125	0155
Kraľovany d.	...	1715	...	1828	...	|	1915	|	...	2013	|	|	|	2115	...	...	...	2241	...	0535	...	...	|	0209
Ružomberok d.	...	1730	...	1843	...	|	1930	2002	...	2028	2036	2042	2051	2130	...	...	...	2307	...	0553	...	...	0151	0224
Liptovský Mikuláš d.	...	1749	...	1902	...	|	1949	2019	...	2046	2054	2100	2109	2149	...	...	...	2333	...	0617	...	...	0208	0244
Štrba d.	...	1818	...	1933	...	|	2018	2046	...	2114	|	2128	2137	2218	...	...	...	...	...	0647	...	...	0234	|
Poprad-Tatry d.	...	1840	...	1955	...	1936	2040	2105	...	2146	2140	2148	2157	2240	...	...	...	...	...	0708	...	...	0253	0331
Spišská Nová Ves d.	...	1859	...	2014	...	|	2059	2123	...	2204	2157	2206	|	2259	...	...	...	...	...	0728	...	...	0311	0350
Margecany d.	...	1926	...	2041	...	|	2126	|	...	2230	|	|	|	2326	...	...	...	...	...	0755	...	...	|	0417
Kysak **1196** a.	...	1939	...	|	...	2029	2141	|	...	2244	2236	2244	2252	2341	...	...	...	...	...	0809	...	...	|	0430
Prešov a.	...	|	...	2111	...	|	|	2214	...	|	|	|	|	|	...	...	...	...	...	|	...	...	0401	|
Košice **1196** a.	...	1953	...	|	...	2042	2153	2242	...	2257	2248	2256	2305	2353	...	...	...	...	...	0823	...	...	0429	0444
Humenné **1194** a.	...	...	...	2250	...	...	...	...	...	...	...	...	...	...	...	...	...	...	...	...	...	...	...	0633

	700	1732	702	16702	704		706	1750	♥ 400/1008	600	IC 520	708	LE♠ 1356	602	SC• 242	IC 44	710	♥ 1012	604	712	♣ 1061	606	IC 522	714
	✕	2	✕			2		2	🍷	✕	[R]✕		🍷[R]	✕	[R]✕	[R]✕		🍷	✕		🍷	✕	[R]✕	
	Ⓐz	Ⓐ	Ⓐ	Ⓒ		Ⓐ	Ⓐ	Ⓐz				Ⓐ	P		⑥b		Ⓐ			Ⓑh	△			Ⓑj
Humenné **1194** d.	...	...	...	...	...	...	...	...	...	...	...	...	...	...	...	...	...	...	...	...	...	...	...	...
Košice **1196** d.	...	...	...	...	...	...	...	...	0345	0407	0512	...	0507	0607	0658	0711	...	0745	0807	...	...	1007	1118	...
Prešov d.	...	...	...	...	...	...	...	...	|	|	|	...	0538	|	|	|	...	|	|	...	...	|	|	...
Kysak **1196** d.	...	...	...	...	...	...	...	...	0358	0421	0525	...	|	0621	0710	0724	...	0758	0821	...	...	1021	1131	...
Margecany d.	...	...	...	...	...	...	...	...	|	0437	|	...	|	0637	|	|	...	|	0837	...	...	1037	|	...
Spišska Nová Ves d.	...	...	...	...	...	...	...	...	0436	0504	0602	...	0631	0704	|	|	...	0836	0904	...	...	1104	1209	...
Poprad-Tatry d.	...	...	...	...	...	...	...	...	0454	0523	0620	...	0648	0723	0804	0818	...	0854	0923	...	...	1123	1227	...
Štrba d.	...	...	...	...	...	...	...	...	0514	0543	|	...	0707	0745	0823	|	...	0914	0945	...	...	1145	|	...
Liptovský Mikuláš d.	...	...	...	...	...	0428	...	0527	0541	0613	0706	...	0734	0813	0850	|	...	0941	1013	...	...	1213	1306	...
Ružomberok d.	...	...	...	...	...	0454	...	0547	0559	0631	0725	...	0751	0831	0908	|	...	1000	1031	...	...	1231	1325	...
Kraľovany d.	...	...	...	...	...	0521	...	0604	|	0646	|	...	|	0846	|	|	...	|	1046	...	...	1246	|	...
Vrútky **1185** d.	...	...	...	...	...	0546	...	0620	0626	0700	0751	...	0818	0900	|	|	...	1026	1100	...	...	1300	1351	...
Žilina **1185** a.	...	...	...	...	...	0606	...	0635	0642	0716	0807	...	0834	0916	0948	0959	...	1042	1116	...	...	1316	1407	...
Žilina **1161** d.	...	...	0420	...	0520	▬	0620	▬	0644	0720	0809	0820	0838	0920	0953	1002	1020	1044	1120	1220	...	1320	1409	1420
Považská Bystrica **1161** d.	...	...	0443	...	0542	...	0643	...	|	0743	|	0844	|	0943	|	|	1043	|	1143	1243	...	1343	|	1444
Púchov **1161** d.	...	...	0502	...	0602	...	0702	...	|	0802	|	0902	|	1002	|	|	1102	|	1202	1302	...	1402	|	1502
Praha hl. n. **1160** a.	...	...	|	...	|	2	|	⑥	1213	*1239**	|	|	1323	*1439**	1419	|	|	1613	*1639**	|	...	*1839**	|	|
Trenčianska Teplá d.	...	...	0518	...	0618	Ⓐ	0718	q	...	0818	|	0918	...	1018	...	|	1118	...	1218	1318	1336	1418	|	1518
Trenčín d.	0437	0442	0525	0525	0625	0641	0725	0725	...	0825	0902	0925	...	1025	...	|	1125	...	1225	1325	1344	1425	1503	1525
Nové Mesto nad Váhom d.	0454	0508	0540	0540	0640	0705	0740	0740	...	0840	|	0940	...	1040	...	|	1140	...	1240	1340	1403	1440	|	1540
Piešťany d.	0507	0522	0552	0552	0652	0719	0752	0752	...	0852	|	0952	...	1052	...	|	1152	...	1252	1352	1417	1452	|	1552
Leopoldov **1177** d.	0522	0534	0604	0604	0704	0733	0804	0804	...	0904	|	1004	...	1104	...	|	1204	...	1304	1404	1428	1504	|	1604
Trnava **1177** d.	0538	0549	0618	0618	0718	0747	0818	0818	...	0918	0937	1018	...	1118	...	1134	1218	...	1318	1418	...	1518	1539	1618
Bratislava hlavná st. **1177** a.	0607	0624	0647	0647	0747	0824	0847	0847	...	0947	1000	1047	...	1147	...	1158	1247	...	1347	1447	...	1547	1602	1647
Wien Hbf. **996** a.	...	...	...	...	...	...	...	...	...	...	...	...	...	...	...	1322	...	...	...	...	...	...	...	...

	608	716	17716	17610	610	SC• 240	1760	17718	17612	612	IC 524	1762	17720	17764	764		EN 444	♥ 1020	EN 442	442 704	LE♠ 1348	1730	614	
	✕		2		✕	[R]✕	2	2		✕	[R]✕	2		✕	✕	2	⊖	🍷	⊖	🛏	🍷[R]	2		
		Ⓐ	⑦c	⑦d		u	Ⓐz	⑦e	⑦d			Ⓐ	⑦e	⑦g	⚒y		C♦	≋	♦	S	P	Ⓐ	♦	
Humenné **1194** d.	...	...	...	...	...	...	...	...	1406	...	...	...	...	...	...	...	...	...	1946	...	...	...	2154	...
Košice **1196** d.	1207	...	...	1345	1407	1500	1507	...	|	1607	1712	1718	...	1807	1807	1927	2026	2122	2207	2207	2311	...	2345	...
Prešov d.	|	...	...	|	|	|	|	...	1536	|	|	|	...	|	|	|	|	|	|	|	2342	...	|	...
Kysak **1196** d.	1221	...	...	1359	1421	1512	1521	...	|	1621	1725	1732	...	1821	1821	1945	2040	2136	2221	2221	|	...	2359	...
Margecany d.	1237	...	...	1415	1437	|	1537	...	1607	1637	|	1748	...	1837	1837	2006	|	2151	2236	2236	|	...	0014	...
Spišska Nová Ves d.	1304	...	...	1442	1504	|	1612	...	1637	1704	1802	1822	...	1904	1904	2048	2119	2219	2303	2303	0033	...	0041	...
Poprad-Tatry d.	1323	...	...	1503	1523	1607	1630	...	1700	1723	1820	1841	...	1938	1938	2116	2203	2240	2323	2323	0052	...	0101	...
Štrba d.	1345	...	...	1526	1545	1627	▬	...	1723	1745	|	...	...	2000	2000	▬	2226	2302	2346	2346	0111	...	|	...
Liptovský Mikuláš d.	1413	...	...	1554	1613	1653	...	...	1753	1813	1906	...	...	2028	2028	...	2254	2331	0010	0010	0138	...	0148	...
Ružomberok d.	1431	...	...	1611	1631	1711	...	...	1811	1831	1925	...	...	2047	2047	...	2312	2350	0028	0028	0155	...	0206	...
Kraľovany d.	1446	...	...	1628	1646	|	...	...	1828	1846	|	...	...	2102	2102	...	2329	|	|	|	|	...	0222	...
Vrútky **1185** d.	1500	...	...	1642	1700	|	...	...	1842	1900	1951	...	...	2115	2115	...	2343	0017	|	|	0221	...	0235	...
Žilina **1185** a.	1516	...	...	1658	1716	1752	...	...	1858	1916	2007	...	...	2131	2131	2	2359	0033	0108	0108	0237	...	0251	...
Žilina **1161** d.	1520	1620	1620	1704	1720	1754	♣	1803	1901	1920	2009	...	2020	2139	2141	2241	0015	0044	0130	0520	0238	...	0307	...
Považská Bystrica **1161** d.	1543	1643	1648	1733	1743	|	**1063**	1830	|	1943	|	...	2043	2206	2218	2316	|	|	|	0542	|	...	0333	...
Púchov **1161** d.	1602	1702	1705	1752	1802	|	🍷	1849	|	2002	|	...	2102	2224	2241	2332	|	|	|	0602	|	...	0354	...
Praha hl. n. **1160** a.	*2039**	|	|	|	*2239**	2219	△	|	|	|	|	...	|	|	|	...	0616	0554	0731	|	0723	...	|	...
Trenčianska Teplá d.	1618	1718	1730	1807	1818	...	1904	1912	|	2018	|	...	2118	2247	2304	...	...	...	...	0618	...	...	0411	...
Trenčín d.	1625	1725	1738	1814	1825	...	1911	1921	1956	2025	2102	...	2125	2253	2311	...	...	...	...	0625	...	0348	0419	...
Nové Mesto nad Váhom d.	1640	1740	1758	1829	1840	...	1928	1941	|	2040	|	...	2140	2307	...	...	...	...	...	0640	...	0405	0438	...
Piešťany d.	1652	1752	1812	1840	1852	...	1941	1954	|	2052	|	...	2152	2318	...	...	...	...	...	0652	...	0420	0451	...
Leopoldov **1177** d.	1704	1804	1825	1852	1904	...	1953	2008	|	2104	|	...	2204	2330	...	...	...	...	...	0704	...	0433	0504	...
Trnava **1177** d.	1718	1818	1839	1906	1918	...	...	2022	2036	2118	2137	...	2218	2342	...	...	...	...	...	0718	...	0447	0518	...
Bratislava hlavná st. **1177** a.	1747	1847	1913	1934	1947	...	...	2056	2104	2147	2200	...	2247	0010	...	...	...	...	...	0747	...	0524	0549	...
Wien Hbf. **996** a.	...	...	...	...	...	...	...	...	...	...	...	...	...	...	...	...	...	...	...	...	...	...	...	...

♦ – **NOTES** (LISTED BY TRAIN NUMBERS)

442/3 – SLOVAKIA – 🛏 1, 2 cl., ▬ 2 cl., [2] Praha - Bohumín - Žilina - Košice - Humenné and v.v.

444/5 – BOHEMIA – 🛏 1, 2 cl., ▬ 2 cl., [2] Praha - Bohumín - Žilina - Košice and v.v.

614/5 – ZEMPLÍN – 🛏 1, 2 cl., ▬ 2 cl., [2] Bratislava - Košice - Humenné and v.v. Not Dec. 24, 31.

B – Dec. 20-23, 27-30, Jan. 2-8, Apr. 16-29, May 31 - Sept. 16, Oct. 25 - Nov. 5.
C – Dec. 19-22, 26-29, Jan. 1-7, Apr. 15-28, May 30 - Sept. 15, Oct. 24 - Nov. 4.
G – ①②③④⑦ (also Dec. 28; not Dec. 23-25, Apr. 18, 21, July 4, Oct. 31).
H – ①-④ (also Dec. 28; not Dec. 24-26, Jan. 1, Apr. 18, 22, May 1, 8, July 4, Aug. 29, Oct. 31).
P – [12] Praha - Prešov - Košice and v.v. Train number changes at Prešov.
R – 🛏 1, 2 cl. Bratislava (**717**) - Žilina (**443**) - Košice. Not Dec. 24, 31.
S – 🛏 1, 2 cl. Košice (**442**) - Žilina (**704**) - Bratislava. Not Dec. 24, 31.
a – Also Apr. 18, 30, May 7, July 4, Aug. 28, Oct. 31; not Dec. 28, Jan. 4, Apr. 19, July 5, Nov. 1.
b – Also Apr. 19, May 1, 8, July 5; not Apr. 20, July 6.
c – Also Apr. 22, May 1, 8, Aug. 29; not Dec. 23, 30, Apr. 21.
d – Also Dec. 26, Apr. 22; not Dec. 23, 30, Apr. 21.
e – Also Apr. 22; not Dec. 23, 30, Apr. 21, June 30 - Aug. 31.
f – Also Apr. 18, July 4, Oct. 31; not Dec. 28, Apr. 19, July 5, Nov. 1.
g – Also Jan. 1, Apr. 22; not Dec. 23, 30, Apr. 21.
h – Not Dec. 23-25, Apr. 19, 21, July 5, Nov. 1.
j – Also Apr. 20, July 6, Nov. 2; not Apr. 19, July 5, Nov. 1.
k – Also Apr. 18, July 4, Oct. 31; not Dec. 28, Apr. 19, July 5, Nov. 1.
n – Also Apr. 18, 30, May 7, July 4; not Apr. 19, July 5.
q – Also Jan. 1, Apr. 19, May 1, 8, July 5, Aug. 29, Nov. 1; not Apr. 20, July 6, Nov. 2.
u – Not Dec. 24, 25, 31.
x – Arrives 0739.
y – ①-⑥ (also Dec. 23, 30, Apr. 21; not Jan. 1, Apr. 22).
z – Not Dec. 22 - Jan. 6.
△ – [2] Nitra - Praha and v.v. For days of running see Table **1163**.
⊖ – [R] for international journeys.
• – PENDOLINO KOŠIČAN.
♥ – Operated by REGIOJET. Separate fares.
♠ – Operated by LEO Express. Separate fares.
♣ – Operated by ARRIVA. 🍷. Separate fares.
≋ – 🛏 (1,2,3 berth), ▬ (6 berth), [2].
* – Connection Praha - Púchov or v.v. via Vsetín (Table **1161**).

LOCAL LINES IN POPRAD TATRY AREA 1182

2nd class

km																									
						T						Ⓐz			T	⑦e	Ⓐz	Ⓐz			Ⓐz			
0	**Poprad Tatry** d.	0402	0544	0646	...	0730	0846	...	1046	...	1246	...	1346	1446	...	1527	...	1546	...	1646	...	1746	1846	...	2200
8	Studený Potok a.	0414	0556	0658	0702	|	0858	0904	1058	1104	1258	1304	1358	1458	1504	|	...	1558	1604	1658	1704	1758	1858	1904	2212
17	**Tatranská Lomnica** a.	*0434*	*0611*	|	0713	|	|	0915	|	1115	|	1315	|	|	1515	|	...	|	1615	|	1715	|	|	1915	|
14	Kežmarok a.	0448	0618	0712	...	0751	0914	...	1114	...	1314	...	1412	1514	...	1551	...	1612	...	1714	...	1812	1914	...	2224
44	**Stará Lubovňa** a.	0533	0703**a**	...	...	0834	0957	...	1157**z**	...	1357	...	...	1600	...	1637	1705	...	...	1757	...	...	1957**r**	...	2307
60	Plaveč 🏛 a.	...	...	...	...	0851	...	...	...	...	...	...	...	1619**f**	...	1654	1724	...	...	...	...	...	...	...	...
75	**Muszyna** a.	...	...	...	...	0910	...	...	...	...	...	...	...	...	...	1721	...	...	...	...	...	...	...	...	...

								T			Ⓐz			Ⓐz	⑦e	Ⓐv			Ⓐz	⑤f			T		
uszyna a.	...	...	...	...	...	...	...	0954	...	...	...	...	...	...	...	...	...	...	...	...	...	...	1750	...	...
laveč 🏛 d.	...	...	...	...	...	...	...	1013	...	...	...	...	...	...	...	...	...	...	...	1635	...	1740**e**	1809	...	...
tará Lubovňa d.	...	0458	0558**a**	...	0803	...	1003	1028	...	1203**z**	...	...	1403	...	1453	...	...	1603	...	1653	...	1803	1824	...	2203**r**
ežmarok d.	0446	0548	0650	...	0850	...	1050	1102	...	1250	1350	...	1450	...	1550	1550	...	1650	1750	...	...	1850	1902	...	2254
Tatranská Lomnica d.	*0439*	|	*0643*	0843	|	1043	|	|	1243	|	|	1443	|	1543	|	|	1643	|	|	...	1843	|	|	2158	|
tudený Potok d.	0457	0559	0701	0856	0901	1056	1101	|	1256	1301	1401	1456	1501	1556	1601	1601	1656	1701	1801	...	1856	1901	|	2214	2305
oprad Tatry a.	0510	0612	0714	...	0914	...	1114	1125	...	1314	1414	...	1514	...	1614	1614	...	1714	1814	...	...	1914	1925	2227	2318

oprad Tatry - Starý Smokovec (24 mins, *13* km, narrow gauge): 0502, 0602, 0627Ⓐ, 727**k**, 0827, 0902**E**, 0927, 1002**N**, 1027, 1102**E**, 1127**N**, 1227, 1327, 1427, 1502, 1527, 627, 1727, 1827, 1944, 2044**R**, 2144, 2244. Most continue to Štrbské Pleso (see below).

tarý Smokovec - Štrbské Pleso (41 mins, *16* km, narrow gauge): 0528, 0628, 0659Ⓐ, 759**d**, 0859, 0929**E**, 0959, 1029**N**, 1059, 1129**E**, 1159**N**, 1259, 1359, 1459, 1529, 1559, 659, 1759, 1859, 2013, 2113**R**, 2213, 2309. Most start from Poprad Tatry (see above).

tarý Smokovec - Tatranská Lomnica (14 mins, *6* km, narrow gauge): 0416, 0554, 0658, 802**k**, 0838**S**, 0902**W**, 0914**S**, 1002, 1102, 1202**N**, 1302, 1402, 1502, 1602, 1702, 1802, 902**d**, 2014, 2114, 2214.

trbské Pleso - Štrba (18 mins ⊕): 0520, 0620, 0720, 0815, 0910**E**, 0915, 1015, 1020**E**, 115, 1215, 1300, 1345, 1445, 1545, 1550**E**, 1645, 1650**E**, 1745, 1750**E**, 1845, 1945, 2251.

Starý Smokovec - Poprad Tatry (23 mins, *13* km, narrow gauge): 0437, 0553, 0653, 0733Ⓐ, 0753, 0853, 0953, 1053, 1153**N**, 1253, 1353, 1453, 1533**E**, 1553, 1633**N**, 1653, 1733**E**, 1753, 1853**k**, 2010, 2110, 2210, 2310. Most start from Štrbské Pleso (see below).

Štrbské Pleso - Starý Smokovec (39 mins, *16* km, narrow gauge): 0511, 0612, 0639Ⓐ, 0714, 0811, 0911, 1011, 1111**N**, 1211, 1311, 1411, 1441**E**, 1511, 1541**N**, 1611, 1641**E**, 1711, 1811**d**, 1911, 2021, 2121, 2221. Most continue to Poprad Tatry (see above).

Tatranská Lomnica - Starý Smokovec (14 mins, *6* km, narrow gauge): 0512, 0612, 0716**b**, 0820**S**, 0834**W**, 0856**S**, 0934, 1034, 1134**N**, 1234, 1334, 1434, 1534, 1634, 1734, 1824**k**, 1934, 2044, 2144, 2244.

Štrba - Štrbské Pleso (15 mins ⊕): 0454, 0556, 0658, 0752, 0842, 0847**E**, 0952, 0957**E**, 1042, 1047**E**, 1152, 1242, 1322, 1422, 1522, 1622, 1627**E**, 1722, 1727**E**, 1822, 1922, 2026.

– Ⓒ June 15 - Sept. 22 (daily June 29 - Sept. 1).
– Dec. 9 - Apr. 23, May 13 - Sept. 22.
– May 13 - Sept. 22.
– June 29 - Sept. 1.
– ⑥⑦ June 29 - Sept. 1.
– Not June 29 - Sept. 1.
– Ⓐ only.

b – 0734 on Ⓒ (daily Dec. 24 - Jan. 6, July 1 - Sept. 1).
d – Štrbské Pleso - Starý Smokovec - Tatranská Lomnica and v.v.
e – ⑦ (also Jan. 7, Apr. 23; not Dec. 23 - Jan. 6, Feb. 17, Apr. 21, June 30 - Aug. 25).
f – ⑤ (also Jan. 31, Apr. 17, Oct. 29; not Dec. 28, Jan. 4, Feb. 1, 22, Apr. 19, July 5 - Aug. 30, Nov. 1).
k – Tatranská Lomnica - Starý Smokovec - Poprad Tatry and v.v.

r – Ⓑ (not holidays; runs July 6).
v – Ⓐ (not Dec. 24 - Jan. 6, Apr. 23).
z – Ⓐ (not Dec. 22 - Jan. 6).
⊕ – 5 km, rack line.

POPRAD TATRY - ZAKOPANE 1183

No winter service STRAMA 🚌

	S	S	S	S	V	V
oprad Tatry (Bus Stn stand 4) d.	0850	1150	1650	1750	0850	1650
tarý Smokovec (Bus Station) ... d.	0910	1210	1710	1810	0910	1710
atranská Lomnica (Bus Stn) d.	0924	1224	1724	1824	0924	1724
akopane (Bus Stn) a.	1033	1333	1833	1933	1033	1833
akopane (ul. Balzera Nosal) a.	...	1339	1839	1939	...	1839

	S	S	S	S	V	V
Zakopane (ul. Balzera Nosal) ... d.	0600	0900	...	1600	0600	1500
Zakopane (Bus Stn stand 11) .. d.	0615	0915	1115	1615	0615	1515
Tatranská Lomnica (Bus Stn) ... d.	0727	1027	1227	1727	0727	1627
Starý Smokovec (Bus Station) .. d.	0737	1037	1237	1737	0737	1637
Poprad Tatry (Bus Station) ..... a.	0753	1053	1253	1753	0753	1653

S – June 14 - Sept. 30, 2019.
V – Oct. 1 - 13, 2019.
Rail tickets not valid.
🏛 = Lysa Polana.

us stations at Poprad Tatry and Zakopane are adjacent to railway stations.

ŽILINA - VRÚTKY - MARTIN - BANSKÁ BYSTRICA and ZVOLEN 1185

2nd class ♣

km																									
		941		**943**		**945**		**341**		**343**		**951**				**953**			**345**			**347**			
				Ⓐu	Ⓐu									Ⓐ	Ⓐz			Ⓐz			⚒			⑤⑦ w	n
	Ostrava Svinov **1160** d.	...	...	...	...	...	...	0644	...	0844	...	...	...	...	...	...	...	...	1444	...	...	1644	...		...
	Ostrava hl. n. **1160** d.	...	...	...	...	...	...	0652	...	0852	...	...	...	...	...	...	...	...	1452	...	...	1652	...	...	...
0	**Žilina** **1180** d.	0455	...	0601	*0625*	0655	...	0855	...	1055	...	1255	...	*1352*	*1430*	1455	...	*1554*	1655	...	*1734*	1855	...	...	*2044*
21	Vrútky **1180** a.	0512	...	0618	*0644*	0712	...	0912	...	1112	...	1312	...	*1409*	*1449*	1512	...	*1612*	1712	...	*1753*	1912	...	...	*2100*
21	Vrútky d.	0513	0519	0619	0650	0713	0719	0913	0919	1113	1119	1313	1319	1417	1452	1513	1519	1619	1713	1719	1819	1913	1919	1919	2119
28	**Martin** d.	0520	0528	0627	0659	0720	0728	0920	0928	1120	1128	1320	1328	1426	1500	1520	1528	1628	1720	1728	1828	1920	1928	1928	2128
51	Turčianske Teplice d.	0538	0557	0645	0728	0738	0757	0938	0957	1138	1157	1338	1357	1455	1530	1538	1557	1657	1738	1757	1857	1938	1957	1957	2157
97	**Banská Bystrica** a.	0626	|	0729	|	0826	|	1026	|	1226	|	1426	|	|	|	1626	|	|	1826	|	|	2026	|	|	|
60	Horná Štubňa d.	...	0612	...	0738	|	0807	...	1007	|	1212	...	1417	1505	1540	|	1609	1707	|	1807	1907	|	2007	2014	2207
80	Kremnica d.	...	0637	...	...	|	...	...	...	|	1237	...	◇	...	...	|	1634	...	|	...	...	|	...	2039	...
106	Hronská Dúbrava d.	...	0710	...	...	|	...	...	...	|	1310	...	...	...	...	|	1707	...	|	...	...	|	...	2112	...
117	**Zvolen** osob. ▷ a.	...	0719	...	...	0855	...	...	...	1255	1319	...	...	...	...	1655	1716	...	1857	...	...	2055	...	2121	...

					346			**942**		**344**		**946**				**342**		**950**		**952**			**340**	**956**	
		Ⓐu	Ⓐ	Ⓒ		Ⓐz							Ⓐ	Ⓐu			Ⓐz	Ⓐu			Ⓐz				
volen osob. ▷ d.	...	...	0425	...	0502	...	0619	...	...	...	...	1102	...	...	...	...	...	...	1425	1502	1526	...	...	1902	1905
ronská Dúbrava d.	...	...	0435	...	|	...	0629	...	...	...	...	|	...	...	...	...	...	...	1435	|	1536	...	...	|	1915
remnica d.	...	...	0515	...	|	...	0707	...	◇	...	...	|	...	...	...	...	...	...	1509	|	1609	...	...	|	1948
orná Štubňa d.	0453	0519	0553	0553	|	0653	0753	...	0953	...	1153	|	1253	...	1353	...	1453	...	1553	|	1653	1753	...	|	2022
Banská Bystrica d.	|	|	|	|	0534	|	|	0734	|	0934	|	1134	|	...	|	1334	|	1434	|	1534	|	|	1734	1934	|
určianske Teplice d.	0504	0529	0603	0603	0621	0704	0803	0821	1003	1021	1203	1221	1304	...	1403	1421	1503	1521	1603	1621	1704	1803	1821	2021	2031
artin d.	0533	0558	0633	0633	0640	0733	0833	0840	1033	1040	1233	1240	1333	...	1433	1440	1533	1540	1633	1640	1733	1833	1840	2040	2100
rútky a.	0541	0606	0641	0641	0646	0741	0841	0846	1041	1046	1241	1246	1341	...	1441	1446	1541	1546	1641	1646	1741	1841	1846	2046	2108
rútky **1180** d.	*0546***a**	*0612*	...	...	0648	*0755*	...	0848	...	1048	...	1248	...	1355	...	1448	*1553*	1548	...	1648	*1808*	...	1848	2048	*2120*
lina **1180** a.	*0606***a**	*0631*	...	...	0705	*0814*	...	0905	...	1105	...	1305	...	1414	...	1505	*1612*	1605	...	1705	*1827*	...	1905	2105	*2139*
Ostrava hl. n. **1160** a.	...	...	...	...	0907	...	...	...	...	1307	...	...	...	...	...	1707	...	...	...	...	...	...	2107	...	...
Ostrava Svinov **1160** a.	...	...	...	...	0915	...	...	...	...	1315	...	...	...	...	...	1715	...	...	...	...	...	...	2115	...	...

km						◇					
0	Horná Štubňa d.	0417	0617	0817	1017	1217	1417	1617	1817	2017	...
18	Handlová d.	0440	0640	0840	1040	1240	1440	1640	1840	2040	...
37	Prievidza a.	0511	0711	0911	1111	1311	1511	1711	1911	2111	...

			◇							
Prievidza d.	0438	0641	0841	1041	1241	1441	1641	1841	2141	...
Handlová d.	0521	0717	0917	1117	1317	1517	1717	1917	2221	...
Horná Štubňa a.	0544	0741	0941	1141	1341	1541	1741	1941	2244	...

– Ⓐ only.
– Runs one hour later on ①–⑥.
– Not Dec. 24 - Jan. 6, July 1 - Sept. 1.

w – ⑤⑦ (also Jan. 7, Apr. 18, 23, July 4, Oct. 31; not Jan. 6, Apr. 19, 21, July 5, Nov. 1).
z – Not Dec. 22 - Jan. 6.

◇ – 🚌2 Vrutky - Horná Štubňa - Prievidza and v.v.
▷ – For connections Banská Bystrica - Zvolen see Table **1170**.
♣ – Trains showing a train number also have 1st class.

BANSKÁ BYSTRICA - BREZNO - MARGECANY - (KOŠICE) 1188

2nd class

km		**821**	**825**					**823**			
		Ⓐ	Ⓒ								
0	**Banská Bystrica** ▷ d.	0536	0736	0835	1035	1233	1438	1535	1640	1747	1851
43	Brezno ▷ d.	0626	0831	0935	1135	1334	1538	1626	1745	1902	2002
86	Červená Skala d.	0720	0937	▬	▬	▬	▬	1734	▬	▬	▬
94	Telgárt penzión d.	0728	0945	...	...	...	...	1742	...	...	...
106	Dobšinká L'adová Jas. d.	0741	0958	...	...	...	...	1755	...	1931	...
114	Dedinky d.	0752	1009	...	...	...	...	1806	...	1941	...
139	Nálepkovo d.	0832	1036	1039**r**	1239	1423	1639	1833	1845	2014	...
171	Gelnica d.	0906	1110	1141	1342	1522	1741	1907	1941	2108	2222
179	**Margecany** a.	0915	1119	1153	1353	1533	1753	1916	1953	2120	2233
	Margecany **1180** d.	*0926*	*1126*	...	...	...	...	*1926*	...	...	...
	Košice **1180** a.	*0953*	*1153*	...	...	...	...	*1953*	...	...	...

		820					**822**			
	Ⓐ		Ⓒ							
Košice **1180** d.	...	*0607*	...	...	...	...	*1407*	...	...	...
Margecany **1180** a.	...	*0634*	...	...	...	...	*1434*	...	...	...
Margecany d.	...	0648	0808	1008	1208	1408	1448	1608	1808	2008
Gelnica d.	...	0657	0820	1020	1220	1427	1457	1620	1820	2020
Nálepkovo d.	...	0730	0903	1103**s**	1305	1510	1530	1704	1915	2104
Dedinky d.	...	0807	▬	▬	▬	▬	1556	1742	▬	2137
Dobšinká L'adová Jas. d.	...	0817	...	...	...	...	1606	1753	...	2148
Telgárt penzión d.	...	0829	...	...	...	...	1618	▬	...	▬
Červená Skala d.	...	0837	...	...	...	Ⓑ	1627	...	...	...
Brezno ▽ d.	0816	0936	1108	1218	1418	1509	1720	1812	2024	2214
Banská Bystrica ▽ a.	0923	1026	1210	1324	1526	1619	1814	1920	2124	2318

– 1046 on Ⓒ.
– 1116 on Ⓒ.
– Not Dec. 22 - Jan. 6.

▷ – Also Banská Bystrica - Brezno at 0419, 0613, 1344Ⓐ**z**, 1550Ⓐ**z**, 1948Ⓐ**z**, 2035, 2230.

▽ – Also Brezno - Banská Bystrica at 0409, 0454Ⓐ**z**, 0558, 0724, 0803Ⓒ, 1626⚒.

1190 ZVOLEN - LUČENEC - KOŠICE

2nd class (also 1st in **8xx 9xx**)

For faster services Bratislava - Košice (via Žilina) see Table **1180**

km			931		811		813	17935		815		801
						n		⑦e				ⒷP
	Bratislava **1170** d.	...	*0604*	...	0804	...	1204	...	...	1604	...	2330
0	**Zvolen** osob. d.	0724	0913	0924	1113	1324	1513	1713	1724	1913	2232	0315
54	Lučenec d.	0835	1002	1035	1202	1435	1602	1802	1835	1959	2340	0405
69	Fiľakovo d.	0852	1015	1052	1215	1452	1615	1815	1852	2012	2357	0419
98	Jesenské d.	...	1041	...	1241	...	1641	1841	...	2039	...	0447
162	Rožňava d.	...	1139	...	1339	...	1737	1939	...	2134	...	0546
202	Moldava nad Bodvou d.	...	1212	...	1412	...	1810	2012	...	2207	...	0621
233	**Košice** a.	...	1237	...	1437	...	1837	2037	...	2235	...	0648
	Prešov **1196** a.	...	...	...	...	...	...	...	...	...	...	0742

		810		812		814		816			800
											ⒷP
Prešov **1196** d.	...	...	...	...	...	...	...	...	...	...	2112
Košice d.	...	0523	...	0923	...	1323	...	1523	...	...	2203
Moldava nad Bodvou d.	...	0550	...	0948	...	1348	...	1548	...	...	2231
Rožňava d.	...	0623	...	1019	...	1420	...	1619	...	...	2308
Jesenské d.	...	0719	...	1119	...	1519	...	1719	...	...	0005
Fiľakovo d.	0700	0746	0910	1146	1310	1546	1710	1746	2016	...	0033
Lučenec d.	0728	0800	0928	1200	1328	1600	1728	1800	2033	2236	0047
Zvolen osob a.	0840	0847	1040	1247	1440	1647	1835	1847	...	2344	0144
Bratislava **1170** a.	...	1158	...	1558	...	1958	...	2158	...	...	0530

km												
0	Fiľakovo d.	0600	...	...	0855	1055	...	1455	...	1655	1855	...
29	Jesenské d.	0644	0725	0844	0944	1144	1244	1544	1644	1744	1940	2044
40	Rimavská Sobota a.	0658	0739	0858	0958	1158	1258	1558	1658	1758	1954	2058

				Ⓐz							
Rimavská Sobota d.	0600	0700	0817	1017	1101	1217	1417	1501	1617	1701	1917
Jesenské a.	0614	0714	0831	1031	1115	1231	1431	1515	1631	1715	1931
Fiľakovo a.	0649	...	0908	1108	...	1308	1508	...	1708	...	2008

P – POL'ANA – Ⓑ (not Dec. 23, 24, 25, 31, Apr. 19, 21, July 5, Nov. 1). 🛏 1, 2 cl., 2 Bratislava - Prešov and v.v.; 🛏 1, 2 cl. Praha (**283/2**) - Brno - Bratislava (**873/0**) - Nové Zamky (**801/0**) - Košice - Prešov and v.v.
e – Also Apr. 22; not Dec. 23, 30, Apr. 21, June 30 - Aug. 31.
n – Change at Lučenec on Ⓒ.
z – Not Dec. 22 - Jan. 6.

1194 KOŠICE - HUMENNÉ - MEDZILABORCE

2nd class

km		615	EN 443	1901	1903	1905	1907	1909	1911	1913	1915	
		Z	S		Ⓐ		Ⓐn				b	
	Bratislava **1180** d.	2248	...	...	...	...	...	...	...	...	...	...
0	**Košice** d.	0501	0901	1101	1301	1501	1537	1701	1901	2101	2301	...
68	Trebišov d.	0550	0947	1150	1350	1550	1630	1750	1950	2150	2350	...
88	Michalovce d.	0611	1011	1211	1411	1611	1651	1811	2010	2218	0011	...
112	**Humenné** a.	0633	1033	1233	1433	1633	1713	1833	2033	2240	0033	...

	1900	1902	1904	1906	1908	1910	1912	1914	EN 442	614	
	Ⓐ			Ⓐn		d			S	Z	
Humenné d.	0333	0528	0728	0928	1128	1328	1528	1728	1946	2154	
Michalovce d.	0356	0551	0751	0951	1151	1351	1551	1751	2011	2216	...
Trebišov d.	0418	0613	0813	1013	1213	1413	1613	1813	2032	2238	...
Košice a.	0504	0659	0859	1059	1259	1459	1659	1859	2117	2325	...
Bratislava **1180** a.	...	...	...	...	...	...	...	...	...	0549	...

km						Ⓐ	Ⓐ		Ⓐ			Ⓐ§
0	Humenné d.	0435	0637	0837	1037	1237	1329	1437	1529	1637	1837	2037
41	Medzilaborce a.	0552	0746	0946	1146	1346	1423	1546	1623	1746	1946	2146
43	Medzilaborce mesto a.	0557	0750a	0950	1150	1350	...	1550	...	1750r	1950	...

	Ⓐ					⑦	①–⑥				
Medzilaborce mesto d.	0418	...	0618	0818a	1018r	1206	1223	1417	1617	1818	2018
Medzilaborce d.	0427	0504	0628	0828	1028	1210	1228	1428	1628	1828	2028
Humenné a.	0524	0559	0724	0924	1124	1307	1324	1524	1724	1924	2124

S – SLOVAKIA – 🛏 1, 2 cl., 🛏 2 cl., 2 Praha - Košice - Humenné and v.v.
Z – ZEMPLÍN – 🛏 1, 2 cl., 🛏 2 cl., 2 Bratislava - Košice - Humenné and v.v. Not Dec. 24, 31.
a – Ⓐ only.
b – Runs 12 mins later on ⑤ (also Apr. 18, 30, May 7, July 4; not Apr. 19, July 5).
d – Runs 9 minutes earlier on ⑦.
n – Not Dec. 22 - Jan. 6.
r – Change trains on ⑥⑦ June 29 - Sept. 1.
§ – Additional journey runs daily at 2244.

1195 KOŠICE - ČIERNA NAD TISOU - CHOP - MUKACHEVO

2nd class

km				Ⓐ	r		r			K	Ⓐ△	△
0	**Košice** d.	0506	0706	0806	0910	1006	1201	1206	1416	1510	1716	1906
62	Slovenské N. Mesto d.	0614	0814	0914	|	1114	|	1314	1520	1616	1821	2014
95	Čierna nad Tisou a.	0651	0851	0951	1022	1151	1313	1351	1559	1652	1859	2052
95	Čierna nad Tisou 🏛 d.	...	*0900*	...	1023	...	1314	...	...	1707	...	...
105	Chop 🏛 ⊕ a.	...	*1040*	...	1200	...	1451	...	...	1847	...	...
105	Chop **1715** d.	...	...	...	1241	...	1521	...	...	2056	...	...
146	**Mukachevo** **1715** a.	...	...	...	1400	...	1642	...	...	2155	...	...
	Lviv **1715** a.	...	...	...	...	...	...	...	...	0220	...	...
	Kyiv **1700** a.	...	...	...	...	...	...	...	...	1013	...	...

	▽	Ⓐ		L		▽	r			r	
Kyiv **1700** d.	...	...	...	1830	...	...	...	...	...	...	...
Lviv **1715** d.	...	...	...	0409	...	...	...	...	...	...	...
Mukachevo **1715** d.	...	...	...	0854	...	...	1454	...	...	1820	...
Chop **1715** a.	...	...	...	0946	...	...	1625	...	...	1930	...
Chop 🏛 ⊕ d.	...	...	...	1135	...	...	1655	...	...	2006	210
Čierna nad Tisou a.	...	...	...	1139	...	...	1654	...	...	2005	210
Čierna nad Tisou d.	0701	0801	1001	1201	1404	1501	1658	1804	1954	2018	...
Slovenské N. Mesto d.	0743	0843	1043	1243	1446	1543	|	1846	2035	|	...
Košice a.	0854	0954	1154	1354	1554	1654	1813	1954	2154	2133	...

K – 2 Košice - Chop; 🛏 1, 2 cl. Košice (**8862**) - Chop (**107**) - Lviv (**29**) - Kyiv.
L – 2 Chop - Košice; 🛏 1, 2 cl. Kyïv (**81**) - Lviv - Chop (**8861**) - Košice.
r – From June 9. Ⓡ for domestic journeys within Slovakia.
⊕ – Ukraine time (one hour ahead of Slovakia).
△ – Additional journeys: 1606Ⓒ, 1628Ⓐ, 2106, 2306.
▽ – Additional journeys: 0301, 0401, 0501, 0553, 1601Ⓐ.

1196 KOŠICE - PREŠOV - LIPANY - PLAVEČ

2nd class

km			1356			1930			801										1932			1934		1936	
			♠Ⓡ	Ⓐ	Ⓒ	Ⓐ	Ⓒ	Ⓐ	EP			⑥	Ⓑ	Ⓒ	Ⓐ		Ⓐ		Ⓐ	Ⓑ	⑥	Ⓐ		Ⓐ	Ⓐ
0	**Košice** **1180** d.	0358	0507	0536	0536	0613	0636	0636	0703	0736	0836	*0927*	0936	...	1017	*1127*	1236	1335	1413	1436	1436	1513	1536	1613	1636
16	Kysak **1180** d.	0435	|	0553	0553	0627	0653	0653	0726	0753	0857	0953	0953	1042	1042	1153	1253	1352	1428	1453	1453	1527	1553	1627	1653
33	**Prešov** a.	0457	0535	0618	0618	0642	0716	0723	0742	0815	0919	1015	1015	1105	1105	1215	1315	1415	1443	1517	1517	1542	1615	1642	1715
33	**Prešov** d.	0519	...	0636	...	...	...	0728	...	0821	...	1019	1019	...	...	1219	1319	1419	...	1519	...	...	1619	...	1719
65	Lipany a.	0556	...	0713	...	...	...	0805	...	0858	...	1056	1056	...	...	1256	1356	1456	...	1556	...	...	1656	...	1756
88	**Plaveč** a.	...	...	...	...	...	...	...	...	...	...	...	...	...	...	...	...	...	...	1629x	...	...	...	...	...

									1348	
	Ⓒ			†	⚒			n	♠Ⓡ	①
Košice **1180** d.	1636	1736	1836	*1927*	1936	...	*2127*	2214	2311	...
Kysak **1180** d.	1653	1753	1853	1953	1953	2033	2145	2237	|	0001
Prešov a.	1715	1815	1915	2015	2015	2048	2209	2259	2337	0018
Prešov d.	...	1819	1919	2019	2019	...	...	2300	...	...
Lipany a.	...	1856	1956	2056	2056	...	...	2337	...	...
Plaveč a.	...	...	...	...	...	...	...	...	...	...

		1369			1931			1933		1935
		♠Ⓡ			Ⓐ	Ⓐ	Ⓒ	Ⓐ		Ⓐ
Plaveč d.	...	...	...	...	...	...	...	...	...	...
Lipany d.	...	...	0420	0503	...	0557	...	...	0646	...
Prešov a.	...	...	0457	0540	...	0634	...	...	0726	...
Prešov d.	0342	0404	0458	0542	0600	0642	0642	0705	0742	0819
Kysak **1180** a.	0405	|	0520	0606	0615	0706	0706	0720	0806	0835
Košice **1180** a.	*0438*	0429	0541	0624	0629	0724	...	0733	0831	0848

							1937				1939										800		1361		
				Ⓐ	Ⓒ		Ⓐ	Ⓑ	⑥		Ⓐ	Ⓐ	Ⓒ	Ⓐ	⑥	†					FP		♠Ⓡ	⑦	
Plaveč d.	...	...	...	...	...	...	...	...	...	...	...	...	...	...	...	...	...	1730x	...	...	...	...	...	...	...
Lipany d.	0903	...	1103	1203	...	1303	...	1403	...	1503	...	1603	...	1703	...	1703	...	1803	...	...	...	2029	...	...	...
Prešov a.	0940	...	1140	1240	...	1340	...	1440	...	1540	...	1640	...	1740	...	1740	...	1840	...	...	...	2107	...	...	...
Prešov d.	0942	1044	1142	1242	1242	1342	1417	1443	1443	1542	1617	1642	1642	1742	1742	1742	...	1842	1953	...	2112	2136	2217	2337	...
Kysak **1180** a.	1006	1105	1206	1306	1306	1405	1438	1506	1506	1606	1639	1706	1706	1806	1806	1806	1825	1906	2018	2021	2127	2158	|	2352	...
Košice **1180** a.	1024	...	1224	1324	1324	1422	1451	1524	1524	1624	1653	1724	1724	1824	...	...	1841	1924	...	2037	2140	2222	2242	...	...

E – ①–⑥ (not Dec. 24 - 26, Jan. 1, Apr. 20, 22, July 6, Nov. 2). From Praha / Bratislava previous day.
F – Ⓑ (not Dec. 23 - 25, 31, Apr. 19, 21, July 5, Nov. 1).
P – POL'ANA – 🛏 1, 2 cl., 2 Bratislava - Košice - Prešov and v.v. (Table **1190**); 🛏 1, 2 cl. Praha (**283/2**) - Brno - Bratislava (**873/0**) - Nové Zamky (**801/0**) - Košice - Prešov and v.v.
n – Runs approx 15 minutes later on ⑤ (also Apr. 18, July 4, Oct. 31; not Dec. 28, Apr. 19, July 5, Nov. 1).
x – ⑤⑦ (also Jan. 7, 31, Apr. 17, 23, Oct. 29; not Dec. 23 - Jan. 6, Feb. 1, 17, 22, Apr. 19, 21, June 30 - Aug. 30, Nov. 1). Continues to / from Čirč (a. 1647 / d. 1710).
♠ – Operated by LEO Express, Ⓡ, 🍸. 12 Praha - Prešov - Košice and v.v. (Table **1180**).

1197 PREŠOV - BARDEJOV and HUMENNÉ

2nd class

km		§	Ⓐ	Ⓒ		Ⓐ					§	Ⓑd
0	Prešov d.	0415	0603	0626	0824	1024	1224	1424	1624	1824	2053	2302
45	Bardejov a.	0532	0710	0733	0931	1131	1331	1531	1731	1931	2207	0006

		Ⓐ	Ⓒ		Ⓐ		h			§	d
Bardejov d.	0430	0608	0631	0829	1029	1229	1429	1629	1829	1958	222
Prešov a.	0535	0713	0736	0934	1134	1334	1534	1734	1934	2107	233

km						Ⓐ	Ⓐ					⑤b
0	Prešov d.	0415	0610	0844	1043	1244	1344	1448r	1645	1844	2053	2137
70	Humenné a.	0603	0750	1020	1220	1420	1520	1619	1820	2020	2227	2250

		Ⓐ		△				⑦b			
Humenné d.	0350	0440	0540	0728	0940	1140	1335	1406	1540	1740	193
Prešov a.	0527	0633	0723	0908	1108	1308	1508	1519	1708	1908	210

b – 12 Bratislava - Prešov - Humenné and v.v. For days of running see Table **1180**.
d – Runs approx 15 minutes later on ⑤.
h – On ⑦ d. 1338, a. 1448.
r – 1434 on ⑦ (also Dec. 26, Apr. 22; not Dec. 23, 30, Apr. 21).
△ – Change at Strážske (a. 0737 / d. 0750).
§ – Change at Kapušany.

HUNGARY

Operator: MÁV-START (www.mav-start.hu) running on the network of MÁV (www.mav.hu). Certain services in the west are operated by Györ-Sopron-Ebenfurthi Vasút (GySEV).

Services: All trains convey first and second class seating, except where shown otherwise in footnotes or by '2' in the train column, or where the footnote shows sleeping or couchette cars only. Descriptions of sleeping- (🛏) and couchette (▬) cars appear on page 10. Certain international services, as indicated in the tables, cannot be used for internal journeys.

Timings: Valid **December 9, 2018 - December 14, 2019** with amendments as received. Engineering work may affect travel - it is not always possible to show short-term changes.

Reservations: Most InterCity (*IC*) and Express (*Ex*) trains have **compulsory** reservation, as shown by 🅁 in the tables. *IC* trains also require a supplement; the amount depends on distance of the journey. Higher reservation fees apply at peak times (Friday and Sunday afternoons), and if purchased on day of travel. A supplement is required for **domestic** journeys on **international** *EC* / *IC* / *RJ* / *EN* trains (and seat reservation is compulsory where shown as 🅁 in tables). For **international** journeys on these trains the supplement does not apply but seat reservation is possible (and is **compulsory** where shown in the tables). If a seat reservation or supplement is not paid in advance, a higher supplement is payable on the train: 500 HUF for domestic journeys and 10 EUR (which can be paid in HUF) for international journeys.

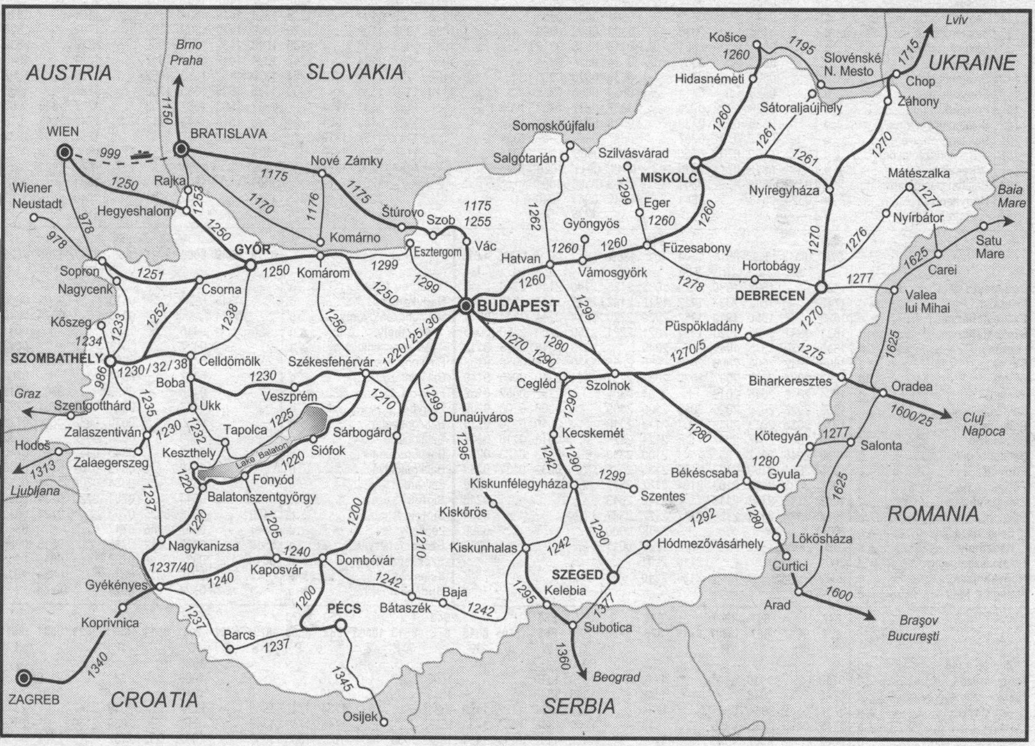

BUDAPEST - DOMBÓVÁR - PÉCS 1200

km			*IC* 800	*IC* 802	*IC*● 802	*IC* 812	*IC* 804	*IC* 814	*IC*● 814	*IC* 806	*IC* 816	*IC*● 816	*IC* 808	*IC* 818	
		2	🅁	🅁	2🅁	🅁	🅁	🅁	🅁	🅁	🅁	🅁	🅁	🅁	2
0	**Budapest** Keleti .... d.	...	0545	0745	0745	0945	1145	1345	1345	1545	1645	1645	1745	1945	2055**d**
13	Kelenföld ⊡ .... d.	...	0559	0759	0759	0959	1159	1359	1359	1559	1659	1659	1759	1959	2102
93	Sárbogárd .... d.	...	0659	0859	0859	1059	1259	1459	1459	1659	|	|	1859	2059	2225
173	Dombóvár .... a.	...	0749	0949	0949	1149	1349	1549	1549	1749	1855	1855	1949	2149	...
173	Dombóvár .... d.	0603	0753	0953	1003	1153	1353	1553	1603	1753	1907	1859	1953	2153	...
	Kaposvár **1240** .... a.	|	|	|	1027	|	|	|	1627	|	|	1923	|	|	...
218	Szentlőrinc .... d.	0646	0826	1026	...	1226	1426	1626	...	1826	1943	**u**	2026	2226	...
237	**Pécs** .... a.	0704	0840	1040	...	1240	1440	1640	...	1840	1957	...	2040	2240	...

		IC 809	*IC* 819	*IC*● 819	*IC* 807	*IC* 817	*IC* 805	*IC* 815	*IC*● 815	*IC* 803	*IC* 801	*IC*● 801	*IC* 811		
	2	🅁	🅁	🅁	🅁	🅁	🅁	🅁	2🅁	🅁	🅁	2🅁	🅁	2	2Ⓑ
Pécs .... d.	...	0514	0602	...	0714	0914	1114	1310	...	1514	1710	...	1914	2045	2247
Szentlőrinc .... d.	...	0528	0616	**u**	0728	0928	1128	1324	...	1528	1724	...	1928	2107	2305
Kaposvár **1240** .... d.	...	|	|	0621	|	|	|	|	1324	|	|	1724	|	|	|
Dombóvár .... a.	...	0601	0647	0645	0801	1001	1201	1354	1348	1601	1754	1748	2001	2150	2348
Dombóvár .... d.	0410	0605	0658	0658	0805	1005	1205	1405	1405	1605	1805	1805	2005	...	...
Sárbogárd .... d.	0522	0659	|	|	0859	1059	1259	1459	1459	1659	1859	1859	2059	...	...
Kelenföld ⊡ .... a.	0636	0758	0858	0858	0958	1158	1358	1558	1558	1758	1958	1958	2158	...	...
Budapest Keleti .... a.	0644**d**	0814	0914	0914	1014	1214	1414	1614	1614	1814	2014	2014	2214	...	...

d – Budapest Déli.
u – To / from Gyékényes (Table **1240**).
⊡ – For metro line 4 from / to Budapest Keleti (see page 31).
● – For train number to / from Kaposvár see Table **1240**.

FONYÓD - PÉCS 1205

km		18803	8803	8873	18801
		S	P	K	⑦S
	Tapolca **1232** ..... d.	1646	1715	1715	...
	Keszthely **1220** ... d.	1723	1748	1748	...
0	**Fonyód** .... ▶ d.	1835	1835	1835	1958
53	Kaposvár .... ▶ a.	1930	1930	1930	2048
82	Dombóvár alsó ...... d.	2005	2005	...	2123
129	Szentlőrinc .... d.	2039	2039	...	2157
148	**Pécs** .... a.	2058	2058	...	2211

	8872	8802	18802		8806
	K	P	S		c
Pécs .... d.	...	0721	0721	...	...
Szentlőrinc .... d.	...	0741	0741	...	...
Dombóvár alsó ...... d.	...	0823	0823	...	...
Kaposvár .... ▶ d.	0857	0857	0857	1520	1715
Fonyód .... ▶ a.	0954	0954	0955	1619	1816
Keszthely **1220** .... a.	1046	1046	1046	...	1921
Tapolca **1232** ...... a.	1124	1124	1124	...	1959

K – Ⓐ to Apr. 26; Ⓐ from Sept. 16.
P – Ⓒ (daily Apr. 27 - June 14, Aug. 26 - Sept. 15).
S – June 15 - Aug. 25.
c – To Celldömölk (- Szombathely Apr. 27 - Sept. 1), Table **1232**.
▶ – **Also**: Fonyód - Kaposvár: 0556, 0751, 0955, 1148, 1341, 1511, 1712, 2141. Kaposvár - Fonyód: 0355Ⓐ, 0605, 0720, 1116, 1310, 1837, 2245.

BUDAPEST - SÁRBOGÁRD - SZEKSZÁRD - BAJA 1210

2nd class (except *Ex* trains)

km		*IR* 8300	*IR* 8302	*IR* 8304		*IR* 8306	*Ex* 1836	*IR* 18308	*Ex* 838	*IR* 8308	8318
		⚒		⚒	Ⓐ		F🅁	Ⓒ	🅁		
0	**Budapest** Keleti .... ▷ d.	...	...	...	...	...	1515**z**	...	1715**z**	...	...
4	Kelenföld ⊡ .... ▷ d.	...	...	...	...	...	1529**z**	...	1729**z**	...	...
84	**Sárbogárd** .... ▷ d.	0702	0902	1102	...	1502	|	1702	|	1902	2102
149	Szekszárd .... a.	0757	0957	1157	1422	1557	1722	1757	1915	1957	2205
168	Bátaszék .... **1242** a.	0818	1018	1218	1441	1618	1741	1818	1932	2018	2249
188	**Baja** .... **1242** a.	0838	1038	1239	1503	1641**r**	1800	1837	1951	2037	2311

	8319	*Ex* 839	*IR* 8307	*IR* 8397	*IR* 8305	*IR* 18305	8313	*Ex* 1833	*IR* 8303	*IR* 8301
	⚒	🅁		⚒		Ⓒ	Ⓐ	🅁G		
Baja .... **1242** d.	0425	0557	0701	0913	1312	1515	1514	1601	1712**v**	1912
Bátaszék .... **1242** d.	0445	0616	0723	0934	1334	1534	1534	1620	1734**v**	1934
Szekszárd .... d.	0545	0636	0759	0959	1357	1559	1620**x**	1637	1759	1959
Sárbogárd .... ▷ a.	0649	|	0854	1054	1454	1654	1733	|	1854	2054
Kelenföld ⊡ .... ▷ a.	...	0828*	...	...	...	...	...	1828*	...	...
Budapest Keleti .... ▷ a.	...	0844*	...	...	...	...	...	1844*	...	...

F – ⑤ (not June 21 - Aug. 30).
G – ⑦ (not June 16 - Sept. 1).
r – Arrive 1654 on ⑦ (except June 16 - Sept. 1).
v – On ⑤ **F** Baja d. 1659, Bátaszék d. 1718.
x – Arrive 1554.
z – 15 mins earlier until July 19.
▷ – For connections see Table **1200**.
⊡ – For metro line 4 from / to Budapest Keleti (see page 31).
* – Approx 20 mins later until July 19.

Sárbogárd - Székesfehérvár *39 km* Journey 53 mins.
From Sárbogárd 0903, 1703Ⓒ, 1741Ⓐ.
From Székesfehérvár 1000, 1600Ⓒ, 1950Ⓐ.

See pages 560/561 for service June 15 - August 25

1220 BUDAPEST - SIÓFOK - FONYÓD - KESZTHELY / NAGYKANIZSA 2nd class

Dec. 9 - June 14 and Aug. 26 - Dec. 14. *For service June 15 - Aug. 25 see page 560*

km		8550	8530	8612	8510	8720	840 870	200	842 872	8872 8802	246	8722	18602	852 862	8624	18704	844 874	8514	854 864	8524	8716	204	8806 18806	8506
		Ⓐ					W	G		P		Y	Z		Ⓐ	J				U	Ⓐ	C	Q	
0	**Budapest** Déli ▶ d.	...	...	...	0405	*0505*	0635	0635	0735	...	0830	...	0835	0935	...	1035	1135	*1230*	1335	*1430*	...	1535	...	1635
4	Kelenföld ⊡ ▶ d.	...	...	...	0412	*0512*	0642	0642	0742	...	0837	...	0842	0942	...	1042	1142	*1237*	1342	*1437*	*1442*	1542	...	1642
67	**Székesfehérvár** ▶ a.	...	...	...	0509	*0609*	0720	0720	0820	...	0915	...	0925	1020	...	1120	1220	*1315*	1420	*1515*	*1540*	1620	...	1720
67	**Székesfehérvár** d.	...	...	...	0525	0635	0721	0721	0821	...	...	0930	0930	1021	...	1121	1221	1320	1421	1520	1600	1621	...	1721
95	Lepsény d.	...	...	...	0550	0703	0740	0740	0840	...	...	0955	0955	1040	...	|	1240	1345	1440	1542	1629	1640	...	1744
115	**Siófok** a.	...	...	...	0615	0727	0755	0755	0855	...	...	1016	1016	1055	...	1205	1255	1406	1455	1606	1650	1655	...	1805
115	**Siófok** d.	...	0435	...	0617	...	0757	0757	0857	...	...	1017	1017	1057	...	1207	1257	1407	1457	1607	...	1657	...	1807
124	Zamárdi d.	...	0447	...	0629	...	0804	0804	0904	...	...	1029	1029	1104	...	1219	1304	1419	1504	1619	...	1704	...	1819
130	Balatonföldvár d.	...	0454	...	0636	...	0809	0809	0909	...	...	1036	1036	1109	...	1226	1309	1426	1509	1626	...	1709	...	1826
139	Balatonszemes d.	...	0504	...	0651	...	0818	0818	0918	...	...	1049	1049	1118	...	1239	1318	1439	1518	1639	...	1718	...	1839
146	Balatonlelle d.	...	0515	...	0659	...	0824	0824	0924	...	...	1057	1057	1124	...	1247	1324	1447	1524	1647	...	1724	...	1847
149	Balatonboglár d.	...	0520	...	0706	...	0830	0830	0930	...	...	1102	1102	1130	...	1251	1330	1452	1530	1652	...	1730	...	1852
157	**Fonyód** a.	...	0528	...	0714	...	0835	0835	0935	...	...	1110	1110	1135	...	1300	1335	1500	1535	1700	...	1735	...	1900
157	**Fonyód** d.	...	0529	0629	0729	...	0837	0837	0937	1000	...	...	1112	1137	1251	...	1337	1503	1537	1703	...	1737	1835	1903
165	Balatonfenyves d.	...	0539	0639	0739	...	0843	0843	0943	1016	...	...	1122	1143	1301	...	1343	1513	1543	1713	...	1743	1845	1913
181	Balatonszentgyörgy a.	...	0557	0701	0757	...	0857	0857	0957	1034	...	...	1141	1157	1319	...	1357	1532	1557	1732	...	1757	1907	1932
181	Balatonszentgyörgy ▲ d.	...	*0600*	0702	*0800*	...	0900*	0900*	1008*	1035	...	...	1146	1208*	1320	...	1408*	...	1608*	...	...	1808*	1910	...
	Keszthely ▲ a.	...	*0612*	0714	*0811*	...	0911*	0911*	1020*	1046	...	...	1157	1220*	1331	...	1420*	...	1620*	...	...	1820*	1921	...
181	Balatonszentgyörgy d.	0438	0601	...	0801	...	0908	0908	1001	...	...	...	...	1201	...	...	1401	...	1601	...	...	1801	...	...
221	**Nagykanizsa** a.	0524	0643	...	0841	...	0947	0947	1040	...	...	...	...	1240	...	...	1440	...	1642	...	...	1840	...	...
352	*Zagreb* **1340** a.	...	...	...	...	...	...	1238	...	...	...	...	...	...	...	...	...	...	...	...	...	2105	...	...

	866 876	18518	18508	8518	1204	848 878	18698		18718	18728	18618
		M	J	N	A 🄡		F		L	L	L
Budapest Déli ▶ d.	1735	...	1805	*1830*	1855**k**	1935	2135	*2140*	2140	2240	2340
Kelenföld ⊡ ▶ d.	1742	...	1812	*1837*	1912	1942	2142	*2147*	2147	2247	2347
Székesfehérvár ▶ a.	1820	...	1855	*1915*	1952	2020	2220	*2244*	2244	2344	0044
Székesfehérvár d.	1821	1851	1920	1920	1954	2021	2221	2250	2250	2350	0050
Lepsény d.	1840	1920	1945	1945	|	2040	|	2315	2315	0015	0112
Siófok a.	1855	1942	2006	2006	2029	2055	2255	2336	2336	0036	0133
Siófok d.	1857	2004	2007	2007	2030	2057	2257	...	2340	0040	0140
Zamárdi d.	1904	2016	2019	2019	|	2104	2304	...	2352	0052	0152
Balatonföldvár d.	1909	2023	2026	2026	2040	2109	2309	...	0000	0100	0200
Balatonszemes d.	1918	2033	2039	2039	|	2118	2318	...	0010	0110	0210
Balatonlelle d.	1924	2041	2047	2047	|	2124	2324	...	0018	0118	0218
Balatonboglár d.	1930	2046	2052	2052	|	2130	2330	...	0023	0123	0227
Fonyód a.	1935	2054	2100	2100	2100	2135	2335	...	0032	0132	0235
Fonyód d.	1937	2103	2103	2103	2101	2137	2337	...	...	...	0236
Balatonfenyves d.	1943	2117	2117	2117	|	2143	2343	...	...	...	0246
Balatonszentgyörgy a.	1957	2136	2136	2136	2117	2157	2357	...	...	...	0304
Balatonszentgyörgy ▲ d.	2008*	...	...	...	|	2208*	0000	...	...	...	0305
Keszthely ▲ a.	2020*	...	...	...	|	2220*	0011	...	...	...	0316
Balatonszentgyörgy d.	2001	...	...	...	2118	2201	...	...	...	...	...
Nagykanizsa a.	2042	...	...	...	2156	2240	...	...	...	...	...
Zagreb **1340** a.	...	...	...	...	0022	...	...	...	...	...	...

	8719	8549	8609	8727	859 869	8747	1205	8529
				Ⓐ		Ⓐ	B 🄡	
Zagreb **1340** d.	...	...	...	...	...	...	0317	...
Nagykanizsa d.	...	0345	...	...	0510	...	0606	0600
Balatonszentgyörgy a.	...	0424	...	...	0548	...	0644	0640
Keszthely ▲ d.	...	...	0415	...	0538*	...	|	*0631*
Balatonszentgyörgy ▲ a.	...	...	0427	...	0549*	...	|	*0643*
Balatonszentgyörgy d.	...	...	0428	...	0602	...	0645	0647
Balatonfenyves d.	...	...	0447	...	0617	...	|	0706
Fonyód a.	...	...	0456	...	0622	...	0700	0715
Fonyód d.	...	...	0457	...	0624	0630	0701	0720
Balatonboglár d.	...	...	0505	...	0630	0638	|	0728
Balatonlelle d.	...	...	0509	...	0634	0642	|	0732
Balatonszemes d.	...	...	0517	...	0640	0652	|	0740
Balatonföldvár d.	...	...	0526	...	0649	0701	0719	0749
Zamárdi d.	...	...	0533	...	0654	0708	|	0756
Siófok a.	...	...	0544	...	0701	0720	0731	0808
Siófok d.	0423	...	0546	0625	0703	...	0733	0815
Lepsény d.	0444	...	0607	0646	0717	...	|	0840
Székesfehérvár a.	0510	...	0633	0712	0736	...	0813	0905
Székesfehérvár ▶ d.	*0514*	...	0634	*0718*	0737	...	0815	*0918*
Kelenföld ⊡ ▶ a.	*0615*	...	0716	*0815*	0816	...	0854	*1015*
Budapest Déli ▶ a.	...	...	0724	...	0824	...	0909**k**	...

	847 877	9657	857 867	8807 18807	8715	845 875	8725	205	855 865	18605	8615	843 873	8513	18603	853 863	8873 8803	18791	8721	201	8511	18691	9621	8531	18611
				R			Ⓐ	G	W	J	K		Ⓐ E	Z		P	⑦ S	T	C		F			L
Zagreb **1340** d.	...	...	...	...	...	...	...	0949	...	...	...	...	...	...	...	...	...	...	1638	...	...	...	...	...
Nagykanizsa d.	0710	...	0910	...	...	1110	...	1310	1310	...	...	1508	...	...	1710	...	...	...	1908	...	...	...	2120	...
Balatonszentgyörgy a.	0748	...	0948	...	...	1148	...	1348	1348	...	...	1548	...	...	1748	...	...	...	1948	...	...	...	2157	...
Keszthely ▲ d.	0734*	0848	0934*	0947	...	1134*	...	1334*	1334*	1422	1422	1534*	...	1622	1734*	1748	1838	...	1934*	...	2048	2147	|	2348
Balatonszentgyörgy ▲ a.	0745*	0859	0945*	0959	...	1145*	...	1345*	1345*	1433	1433	1545*	...	1633	1745*	1759	1849	...	1945*	...	2059	2159	|	2359
Balatonszentgyörgy d.	0802	...	1002	1005	...	1202	...	1402	1402	1434	1434	1602	1634	1634	1802	1805	1850	...	2002	2032	2102	...	2202	0002
Balatonfenyves d.	0817	...	1017	1040	...	1217	...	1417	1417	1453	1453	1617	1653	1653	1817	1824	1912	...	2017	2051	2118	...	2221	0021
Fonyód a.	0822	...	1022	1051	...	1222	...	1422	1422	1502	1502	1622	1702	1702	1822	1834	1921	...	2022	2100	2123	...	2230	0030
Fonyód d.	0824	...	1024	...	...	1224	...	1424	1424	1503	1503	1624	1703	1703	1824	...	1922	...	2024	2103	2124	...	2231	0035
Balatonboglár d.	0830	...	1030	...	...	1230	...	1430	1430	1511	1511	1630	1711	1711	1830	...	1930	...	2030	2111	2130	...	2239	0043
Balatonlelle d.	0834	...	1034	...	...	1234	...	1434	1434	1515	1515	1634	1715	1715	1834	...	1934	...	2034	2115	2134	...	2243	0047
Balatonszemes d.	0840	...	1040	...	...	1240	...	1440	1440	1523	1523	1640	1723	1723	1840	...	1942	...	2040	2123	2140	...	2251	0055
Balatonföldvár d.	0849	...	1049	...	...	1249	...	1449	1449	1532	1532	1649	1732	1732	1849	...	1952	...	2049	2132	2149	...	2300	0109
Zamárdi d.	0854	...	1054	...	...	1254	...	1454	1454	1539	1539	1654	1739	1739	1854	...	1959	...	2054	2139	2154	...	2312	0116
Siófok a.	0901	...	1101	...	...	1301	...	1501	1501	1550	1550	1701	1751	1750	1901	...	2011	...	2101	2150	2201	...	2324	0128
Siófok d.	0903	...	1103	...	1151	1303	1350	1503	1503	1551	1551	1703	...	1751	1903	...	2017	2017	2103	2158	2203	...	...	0130
Lepsény d.	0917	...	1117	...	1212	1317	1412	1517	1517	1612	1612	1717	...	1813	1917	...	2040	2040	2117	2223	|	...	...	0151
Székesfehérvár a.	0936	...	1136	...	1238	1336	1438	1536	1536	1636	1638	1736	...	1836	1936	...	2105	2105	2136	2247	2236	...	...	0211
Székesfehérvár ▶ d.	0937	...	1137	...	*1242*	1337	*1442*	1537	1537	1637	*1642*	1737	...	1837	1937	...	2106	...	2137	2248	2237	...	...	0213
Kelenföld ⊡ ▶ a.	1016	...	1216	...	*1321*	1416	*1521*	1616	1616	1716	*1721*	1816	...	1916	2016	...	2146	...	2216	2345	2316	...	...	0310
Budapest Déli ▶ a.	1024	...	1224	...	*1329*	1424	*1529*	1624	1624	1724	*1729*	1824	...	1924	2024	...	2154	...	2224	2354	2324	...	...	0319

A – ADRIA – June 14 - Sept. 6. 1, 2 cl., 2 cl., [2] Budapest - Zagreb - Split.
B – ADRIA – June 15 - Sept. 7 from Split (next day from Zagreb). 1, 2 cl., 2 cl., [2] Split - Zagreb - Budapest.
C – AGRAM – [12] Budapest - Zagreb and v.v.; [12] Budapest - Keszthely and v.v.
E – Ⓐ to Apr. 26; Ⓐ from Aug. 26.
F – ⑤⑥⑦ and holidays Apr. 26 - June 14.
G – GRADEC – Aug. 26 - Sept. 15. [12] Budapest - Zagreb and v.v.; [12] Budapest - Keszthely and v.v.
J – © Apr. 27 - June 14.
K – Daily except dates in note **J**.
L – June 14 - Aug. 25.
M – Aug. 26 - Sept. 6 (also June 14).
N – Dec. 9 - June 13, Sept. 7 - Dec. 14.
P – Kaposvár - Fonyód - Keszthely - Tapolca and v.v. (Table **1205**). From / to Pécs on © and daily Apr. 27 - Sept. 15.
Q – [2] Kaposvár - Fonyód - Keszthely - Tapolca - Celldömölk (- Szombathely Apr. 27 - Sept 1), Table **1205**.
R – [2] (Szombathely Apr. 27 - Sept 1) - Celldömölk - Tapolca - Keszthely - Fonyód (Table **1205**).
S – ⑦ Apr. 28 - June 10; ⑦ Sept. 1 - 15.
T – Not dates in note **S**.
U – Ⓑ (daily Apr. 27 - June 14).
W – Dec. 9 - June 14, Sept. 16 - Dec. 14.
Y – Not dates in note **Z**.
Z – © Mar. 30 - Apr. 26; daily Apr. 27 - June 14; © Aug. 26 - Nov. 3.
k – Budapest **Keleti**.
⊡ – Connection with metro line 4 (see city plan page 31).
▶ – See also Tables **1225** and **1230**.
▲ – *Italic* times: change at Balatonszentgyörgy. See also Table **1232**.
* – Portion is detached / attached at Balatonszentgyörgy.

1225 BUDAPEST - SZÉKESFEHÉRVÁR - BALATONFÜRED - TAPOLCA 2nd class

Dec. 9 - June 14 and Aug. 26 - Dec. 14. *For service June 15 - Aug. 25 see page 561*

km	*Continued on next page*	9740	9710	9720	900	9712	972	246	9722	1974	904	9714	974	9004	9724	1976	9006	9716	976	906	9726	1978	908	9718	9738
		Ⓐ	⚒							D			H			⑤						⑤ F			
0	**Budapest** Déli ▶ d.	...	...	*0405*	0630	...	0800	0830	0825**z**	1000	1030	...	1200	1230	...	1400	1430	...	1600	1630	...	1800	1830	...	*2140*
4	Kelenföld ▶ d.	...	...	*0412*	0637	...	0807	0837	0832**z**	1007	1037	...	1207	1237	...	1407	1437	...	1607	1637	...	1807	1837	...	*2147*
67	**Székesfehérvár** ▶ a.	...	...	*0509*	0715	...	0845	0915	0912**z**	1045	1115	...	1245	1315	...	1445	1515	...	1645	1715	...	1845	1915	...	*2244*
67	**Székesfehérvár** d.	...	0429	0530	...	0723	0855	...	0924	1055	...	1124	1255	...	1324	1450	▬	1524	1655	...	1724	1855	...	1924	2254
105	Balatonkenese d.	...	0512	0615	...	0810	0929	...	1010	1129	...	1210	1329	...	1410	1529	...	1610	1729	...	1810	1929	...	2010	2339
117	Balalatonalmádi d.	...	0526	0629	...	0827	0943	...	1027	1143	...	1227	1343	...	1427	1543	...	1627	1743	...	1827	1943	...	2027	2352
123	Alsóörs d.	...	0533	0636	...	0834	0949	...	1034	1149	...	1234	1349	...	1434	1549	...	1634	1749	...	1834	1949	...	2034	2359
132	**Balatonfüred** a.	...	0543	0647	...	0846	0958	...	1046	1158	...	1246	1358	...	1446	1558	C	1646	1758	...	1846	1958	...	2046	0010
132	**Balatonfüred** d.	0400	0545	0654	...	0848	1000	...	1048	1200	...	1248	1400	...	1448	1600	1543	1648	1800	...	1848	2000	...	2048	...
157	Révfülöp d.	0437	0627	0730	...	0930	1027	...	1130	1227	...	1330	1427	...	1530	1627	1625	1730	1827	...	1930	2027	...	2125	...
168	Badacsonytomaj d.	0455	0642	0745	...	0945	1038	...	1145	1238	...	1345	1438	...	1545	1638	1638	1745	1838	...	1945	2038	...	2140	...
170	Badacsony d.	0458	0645	0748	...	0948	1041	...	1148	1241	...	1348	1441	...	1548	1641	1641	1748	1841	...	1948	2041	...	2143	...
184	**Tapolca** a.	0516	0703	0810	...	1010	1057	...	1210	1255	...	1410	1457	...	1610	1657	1659	1810	1857	...	2005	2055	...	2200	...

2nd class TAPOLCA - BALATONFÜRED - SZÉKESFEHÉRVÁR - BUDAPEST 1225

Dec. 9 - June 14 and Aug. 26 - Dec. 14. *For service June 15 - Aug. 25 see page 561*

	9739	9719	9069 Ⓐ	9729	979	9729	909	9717	907	9727	19745 C	9715	9005	975 H	9725	247	1973 ⑦N	9713	903	971	9723 E	901	1971 D	9711 Ⓑ	9711 ⑥
apolca d.	...	0435	...	0530	0558	...	...	0750	...	0950	1059	1150	...	1301	1350	...	1503	1550	...	1701	1750	...	1903	2015	2015
adacsony d.	...	0452	...	0547	0613	...	...	0807	...	1007	1114	1207	...	1316	1407	...	1516	1607	...	1716	1807	...	1916	2032	2032
adacsonytomaj d.	...	0455	...	0550	0616	...	...	0810	...	1010	1117	1210	...	1319	1410	...	1519	1610	...	1719	1810	...	1919	2038	2038
évfülöp d.	...	0510	...	0605	0627	...	...	0827	...	1027	1130	1227	...	1330	1427	...	1530	1627	...	1730	1827	...	1930	2052	2052
alatonfüred a.	...	0543	...	0641	0653	←	...	0903	...	1103	1212	1303	...	1357	1503	...	1557	1703	...	1757	1903	...	1957	2125	2125
alatonfüred d.	0345	0544	...	→	0655	0708	...	0908	...	1108	▬	1308	...	1359	1508	...	1559	1708	...	1759	1908	...	1959	2129	▬
sóörs d.	0356	0555	...	...	0703	0719	...	0919	...	1119	...	1319	...	1407	1519	...	1607	1719	...	1807	1919	...	2007	2139	...
alalatonalmádi d.	0403	0602	...	...	0709	0727	...	0927	...	1127	...	1327	...	1413	1527	...	1613	1727	...	1813	1927	...	2013	2147	...
alatonkenese d.	0416	0615	...	...	0723	0743	...	0943	...	1143	...	1343	...	1427	1543	...	1627	1743	...	1827	1943	...	2027	2200	...
zékesfehérvár a.	0505	0700	...	...	0800	0833	...	1033	...	1233	...	1433	...	1502	1633	...	1702	1833	...	1902	2033	...	2102	2244	...
zékesfehérvár ▶ d.	0514	...	0704	...	0812	...	0842	...	1042	...	1242	...	1442	1512	...	1642	1712	1845z	1842	1912	2037	2042	2112	...	2248
elenföld ▶ a.	0615	...	0750	...	0851	...	0921	...	1121	...	1321	...	1521	1551	...	1721	1751	1925z	1921	1951	2116	2121	2151	...	2345
udapest Déli ▶ a.	...	...	0759	...	0859	...	0929	...	1129	...	1329	...	1529	1559	...	1729	1759	1944z	1929	1959	2124	2129	2159	...	2354

– © Apr. 27 - June 10; © Aug. 31 - Oct. 23.
– © Apr. 27 - May 26; daily June 1 - 14, Aug. 26 - 30; © Aug. 31 - Sept. 22.
– Daily to Székesfehérvár; ⑦ to Budapest (train **19723**).
– ⑤ (not Dec. 28, June 21 - Aug. 30).
– Apr. 6 - June 14; Aug. 26 - Oct. 23.
N – ⑦ (also Jan. 1; not Dec. 23, 30, June 16 - Sept. 1), also ⑥ Apr. 27 - June 8.
d – Runs daily Balatonfüred - Tapolca.
z – © Apr. 6 - 28; daily Apr. 29 - June 14; daily Aug. 26 - Sept. 22; © Sept. 28 - Oct. 23.
▶ – See also Tables **1220** and **1230**.

2nd class BUDAPEST - SZÉKESFEHÉRVÁR - ZALAEGERSZEG and SZOMBATHELY 1230

For faster trains Budapest - Szombathely (via Györ) see Table **1252**. The section Szombathely - Porpác (17 km) is operated by GySEV.

km		9510	900	900 9590	960	246 C	246 902	962	904	904 9594		9004	9004 9504	964	9006	9006 9596	966	906	906 956	IC 958 🅁	9518	908	968	9008	9008 1246 R⊖
0	**Budapest** Déli ▶ d.	...	0630	0630	0730	0830	0830	0930	1030	1030	...	1230	1230	1330	1430	1430	1530	1630	1630	1730	...	1830	1930	2030	2030
4	Kelenföld ▶ d.	...	0637	0637	0737	0837	0837	0937	1037	1037	...	1237	1237	1337	1437	1437	1537	1637	1637	1737	...	1837	1937	2037	2037
67	**Székesfehérvár** ▶ d.	...	0716	0716	0816	0916	0916	1016	1116	1116	...	1316	1316	1416	1516	1516	1616	1716	1716	1816	...	1916	2016	2116	2116
90	Várpalota d.	...	0736	0736	0833	0936	0936	1033	1136	1136	...	1336	1336	1433	1536	1536	1633	1736	1736	|	...	1936	2033	2135	2135
112	Veszprém d.	...	0802	0802	0855	1002	1002	1055	1202	1202	...	1402	1402	1455	1602	1602	1655	1802	1802	1854	...	2002	2055	2157	2157
148	Ajka d.	...	0833	0833	...	1033	1033	▬	1233	1233	...	1433	1433	▬	1633	1633	▬	1833	1833	1925	...	2035	▬	2231	2231
	Celldömölk d.	0605	|	|	...	|	|	1205	|	|	1401	|	|	1605	|	|	1801	|	|	|	2005	|	2205	|	|
181	Boba a.	0613	0900	0900	...	1100	1100	1213	1300	1300	1409	1500	1500	1613	1700	1700	1809	1900	1900	|	2013	2108	2213	2302	2302
181	Boba d.	0615	0905	0909	...	1109	1105	1215	1305	1309	1410	1505	1509	1615	1705	1709	1810	1905	1909	|	2015	2109	2215	2306	2317
199	Ukk d.	0635	|	0929	...	1124	|	1235	|	1329	1435	|	1524	1635	|	1724	1835	|	1924	2002	2037	|	2235	|	|
230	Zalaszentiván a.	0705	|	0959	...	1145	|	1305	|	1359	1505	|	1545	1705	|	1759	1905	|	1945	2023	2104	|	2305	|	|
239	**Zalaegerszeg** a.	0714	|	1012	...	1155	|	1314	|	1412	1514	|	1555	1714	|	1812	1914	|	1955	2032	2114	|	2314	|	2357
191	Celldömölk ▷ d.	...	0914	...	...	...	1114	...	1314	...	...	1514	...	...	1714	...	...	1914	...	...	...	2120	...	2316	...
236	**Szombathely** ▷ a.	...	0947	...	...	...	1147	...	1347	...	...	1547	...	...	1747	...	...	1947	...	...	...	2157	...	...	...

	9009	1247 959 R⊖	IC 959 🅁	909	9517	907	957 907	905	9597 905	965	9005	9505 9005	9525	247 C	9003 247	9513	903	953 903	9523	IC🅁 1951 ⑦n	901	9591 901	9511	9021	9521
zombathely ▷ d.	...	...	...	0605	...	0805	...	1005	...	...	1205	...	...	...	1403	...	1605	...	...	...	1805	...	...	2004	...
elldömölk ▷ d.	0440	...	...	0644	...	0843	...	1043	...	...	1243	...	...	...	1444	...	1643	...	...	...	1843	...	...	2048	...
Zalaegerszeg d.	|	0527	0527	|	0646	|	0804	|	0945	...	|	1204	1246	1345	|	1446	|	1604	1646	1716	|	1745	1846	|	2058
Zalaszentiván d.	|	0535	0535	|	0654	|	0812	|	1002	...	|	1212	1254	1402	|	1454	|	1612	1654	|	|	1802	1854	|	2106
Ukk d.	|	0601	0601	|	0723	|	0835	|	1032	...	|	1235	1328	1432	|	1523	|	1635	1729	|	|	1832	1923	|	2133
ba a.	0448	|	|	0652	0740	0851	0851	1051	1051	...	1251	1251	1345	1451	1452	1540	1651	1651	1746	|	1851	1851	1940	2057	2150
ba d.	0449	|	|	0654	0741	0901	0901	1101	1101	...	1301	1301	1346	1501	1501	1541	1701	1701	1747	|	1901	1901	1941	2058	2151
Celldömölk a.	|	|	|	|	0752	|	|	|	|	...	|	|	1357	|	|	1552	|	|	1758	|	|	|	1952	|	2202
ka d.	0524	0635	0635	0723	▬	0926	0926	1126	1126	...	1326	1326	▬	1526	1526	▬	1726	1726	▬	1818	1926	1926	...	2142	...
eszprém d.	0602	0705	0705	0802	0902	1002	1002	1202	1202	1302	1402	1402	1502	1602	1602	1702	1802	1802	1902	1902	2002	2002	...	2223	...
árpalota d.	0624	|	|	0821	0924	1021	1021	1221	1221	1324	1421	1421	1524	1621	1621	1724	1821	1821	1924	1924	2021	2021	...	...	...
zékesfehérvár ▶ d.	0642	0742	0742	0842	0942	1042	1042	1242	1242	1342	1442	1442	1542	1642	1642	1742	1842	1842	1942	1942	2042	2042	...	...	...
elenföld ▶ d.	0721	0821	0821	0921	1021	1121	1121	1321	1321	1421	1521	1521	1621	1721	1721	1821	1921	1921	2021	2021	2121	2121	...	...	...
udapest Déli ▶ a.	0729	0829	0829	0929	1029	1129	1129	1329	1329	1429	1529	1529	1629	1729	1729	1829	1929	1929	2029	2029	2129	2129	...	...	...

– CITTADELLA – 12 Budapest - Zalaegerszeg - Hodoš - Ljubljana and v.v.; conveys June 20 - Aug. 24 12 Budapest - Ljubljana - Koper and v.v., returning June 21 - Aug. 25.
– ISTRIA – from Budapest June 21 - Aug. 30, from Rijeka / Koper June 22 - Aug. 31. 1, 2 cl., 2 cl., 2 Budapest - Ljubljana - Rijeka and v.v.; 2 cl., 2 Budapest - Koper and v.v.
– Not Dec. 23, 30, June 16 - Sept. 1.
▶ – See also Tables **1220** and **1225**.
▷ – See also Tables **1232** and **1238**.
⊖ – 🅁 for domestic journeys within Hungary.

2nd class SZOMBATHELY - CELLDÖMÖLK - UKK - TAPOLCA - KESZTHELY 1232

Dec. 9 - June 14 and Aug. 26 - Dec. 14. *For service June 15 - Aug. 25 see page 561*

km		9639	9619		9637	877	9627	8807 f		9617	19807 E	875		9625	9615	9613	9603		9623	8803 m	9611		9621	
0	**Szombathely** 1230/38 d.	...	...	...	...	...	...	0717s	...	...	0925	...	...	...	...	...	...	...	...	...	...	...	...	...
45	Celldömölk 1230/38 d.	...	0453	...	...	...	0605	0805	...	...	1001	...	...	1205	...	1401	1501	...	1605	...	1801	...	2005	...
55	Boba 1230 d.	...	0502	...	...	...	0615	0816	...	0909	|	...	...	1215	...	1410	1514	...	1615	...	1810	...	2015	...
73	**Ukk** 1230 a.	...	0520	...	...	...	0633	0834	...	0928	1027	...	...	1233	...	1428	1537	...	1633	...	1828	...	2033	...
73	**Ukk** d.	...	0523	...	...	...	0636	0836	...	0931	1032	...	...	1236	...	1436	1538	...	1636	...	1836	...	2036	...
81	Sümeg d.	...	0534	...	...	...	0647	0847	...	0942	1041	...	...	1247	...	1447	1549	...	1647	...	1847	...	2047	...
01	**Tapolca** a.	...	0554	...	...	...	0713	0905	...	1011	1058	...	...	1314	...	1514	1610	...	1713	...	1914	...	2107	...
01	**Tapolca** d.	0447	0559	...	0647	...	...	0906	...	1012	1101	...	...	1315	1420	1515	1620	...	...	1715	1915	...	2110	...
26	**Keszthely** a.	0518	0630	...	0718	...	...	0940	...	1043	1133	...	...	1346	1454	1546	1657	...	...	1746	1946	...	2141	...
26	**Keszthely** 1220 d.	...	0631	...	...	0734	...	0947	...	...	...	1134	...	1347	...	1547	...	...	...	1748	1947	...	2147	...
36	**B'tonszentgyörgy** 1220 a.	...	0643	...	...	0745	...	0959	...	...	...	1145	...	1359	...	1559	...	...	...	1759	1959	...	2159	...

	9610	9630 Ⓐ	9630 ©	9620	9632	9652	870	9612	8802 n	9614	8624 Ⓐ	9624	9616	9626	864	19804 E	9636	9646	8806 k	876	9618	9658	868	9658
onszentgyörgy 1220 d.	...	...	...	0600	...	0800	0900	...	1035	1200	1322	1400	...	1600	1608	...	...	1800	1910	2008	...	2200	2208	...
szthely 1220 a.	...	...	...	0612	...	0811	0911	...	1046	1212	1334	1412	...	1612	1620	...	...	1812	1921	2020	...	2212	2220	...
szthely d.	...	0528	...	0613	0657	...	...	0916	1052	1213	...	1413	1503	1613	...	1639	1703	1813	1929	...	2035	2235	...	2235
polca a.	...	0556	...	0644	0728	...	...	0949	1124	1244	...	1444	1536	1644	...	1707	1735	1844	1959	...	2106	2306	...	2306
polca d.	0445	0600	0600	0645	...	...	...	0950	...	1245	...	1445	1540	1645	...	1715	...	1845	2007	...	...	...	...	...
meg d.	0504	0620	0620	0708	...	...	...	1018	...	1308	...	1508	1608	1708	...	1732	...	1908	2026	...	...	...	...	...
k a.	0515	0631	0631	0720	...	...	...	1030	...	1320	...	1520	1620	1720	...	|	...	1920	2035	...	...	...	...	...
k 1230 d.	0523	0634	0634	0723	...	...	...	1032	...	1328	...	1523	1635	1729	...	|	...	1923	2036	...	...	...	...	...
ba 1230 a.	0540	0653	0653	0740	...	...	...	1051	...	1345	...	1540	1651	1746	...	|	...	1940	2052	...	...	...	...	...
lldömölk 1230/38 a.	0552	0706	0706	0752	...	...	...	...	...	...	...	1552	...	1758	...	1802	...	1952	2104	...	...	...	...	...
ombathely 1230/38 a.	...	...	...	...	...	...	...	...	...	...	...	...	...	...	...	1854	...	...	2142s	...	...	...	...	...

- © Apr. 27 - June 10; daily Aug. 26 - 30; © Aug. 31 - Oct. 23.
To Fonyód (Table **1220**).
From Kaposvár (Table **1205**).
m – To Kaposvár (train **8873**) or Pécs (train **8803**), Table **1205**.
n – From Pécs (train **8802**) or Kaposvár (train **8872**), Table **1205**.
s – Apr. 27 - Sept. 1.

1233 SOPRON - SZOMBATHELY

GySEV. 2nd class

km			P		◇		◇	◇	◇		Ⓐ	
0	**Sopron** d.	0644	0810	0934	1108	1208	1343	1543	1643	1756	1906	2015
38	Bük d.	0718	0837	1007	1140	1240	1415	1615	1715	1828	1945	2047
62	**Szombathely** a.	0737	0854	1026	1159	1259	1433	1633	1733	1851	2002	2105

		◇	◇		Ⓐ		◇			P	◇
Szombathely d.	0700	0927	1100	1238	1330	1435	1635	1713	1825	1910	211
Bük d.	0719	0945	1118	1257	1353	1453	1653	1731	1845	1925	212
Sopron a.	0755	1017	1150	1329	1427	1527	1727	1811	1917	1950	220

P – To/from Pécs (Table **1237**).
◇ – To/from Szentgotthárd (Table **986**).

ADDITIONAL JOURNEYS Sopron - Szombathely: 0410◇, 0455◇, 0547◇, 1443Ⓐ◇, 2230; Szombathely - Sopron: 0425, 0505◇, 0629, 1535Ⓐ◇, 2005◇, 2225.

Subject to alteration June 11 - 21 with 🚌 substitution.

1234 SZOMBATHELY - KÖSZEG

GySEV. 2nd class

From **Szombathely**: 0500, 0606, 0706Ⓐ, 0806, 0906, 1006Ⓐ, 1106, 1206Ⓐ, 1306Ⓒ, 1335Ⓐ, 1430Ⓐ, 1506Ⓒ, 1522Ⓐ, 1606Ⓒ, 1614Ⓐ, 1706, 1806Ⓐ, 1906, 2108, 2236.
From **Köszeg**: 0432, 0526, 0632, 0732Ⓐ, 0832, 0932Ⓐ, 1032, 1132Ⓐ, 1232, 1401Ⓐ, 1432Ⓒ, 1456Ⓐ, 1532Ⓒ, 1548Ⓐ, 1632Ⓒ, 1640Ⓐ, 1732Ⓐ, 1832, 2032, 2208.
18 km Journey time 23 minutes.

1235 SZOMBATHELY - ZALASZENTIVÁN - ZALAEGERSZEG

MÁV-START/GySEV. 2nd class

km		△						△				△		Ⓐ					Ⓐ	△					
	Sopron **1233** d.	...	...	...	...	...	...	0810	...	...	...	...	...	...	...	...	...	...	...	...	...	...	...	...	...
0	**Szombathely** d.	0509	...	0612	...	0702	...	0909	...	1109	...	1305	...	1402	...	1432	1602	...	1637	1707	...	1802	1909	2233	...
24	Vasvár d.	0530	...	0635	...	0725	...	0930	...	1132	...	1328	...	1425	...	1455	1626	...	1700	1730	...	1825	1932	2256	...
49	Zalaszentiván a.	0551	...	0657	...	0747	...	0951	...	1154	...	1351	...	1447	...	1517	1648	...	1727	1751	...	1847	1954	2318	...
49	Zalaszentiván ▶ d.	...	0557	...	0706	...	0812	...	1004	...	1212	...	1404	...	1506	1521	...	1706	...	...	1804	1854	1958	2322	...
58	**Zalaegerszeg** ▶ a.	...	0606	...	0714	...	0821	...	1012	...	1221	...	1412	...	1514	1530	...	1714	...	...	1812	1903	2007	2331	...

								△				△		Ⓐ	Ⓐ	Ⓒ				△			△		
Zalaegerszeg ▶ d.	0348	0446	...	0545	0740	...	0945	...	1135	...	1345	...	1446	...	1535	1535	1646	...	1745	...	1935	2150	...	2243	...
Zalaszentiván ▶ a.	0356	0453	...	0554	0749	...	0954	...	1144	...	1354	...	1453	...	1544	1544	1653	...	1754	...	1944	2159	...	2251	...
Zalaszentiván d.	0400	...	0458	0603	...	0803	...	1003	...	1203	...	1403	...	1503	1603	1603	...	1658	...	1803	2003	...	2203	...	...
Vasvár d.	0423	...	0521	0626	...	0826	...	1025	...	1226	...	1425	...	1526	1626	1626	...	1721	...	1825	2026	...	2225	...	...
Szombathely a.	0445	...	0543	0648	...	0848	...	1045	...	1248	...	1450	...	1548	1655	1648	...	1743	...	1845	2048	...	2251	...	...
Sopron **1233** a.	...	...	...	0755	...	...	...	...	...	...	...	...	...	...	...	...	...	...	...	1950	...	...	...	...	...

△ – To/from Pécs (Table **1237**).
▶ – See also Tables **1230** and **1237**.

1237 ZALAEGERSZEG - NAGYKANIZSA - PÉCS

2nd class

km		8910	8900	8954 Ⓐ	8902	8914	8904	8956 ⚒	18958 ⑦	9876	8906
	Sopron **1233** d.	...	...	...	0810	...	...	...	...	...	...
	Szombathely **1235** d.	...	0509	...	0909	...	1305	...	...	...	1707
0	**Zalaegerszeg** ▷ d.	...	*0545*r	...	*0945*r	...	*1345*r	...	...	1656	*1745*r
9	Zalaszentiván ▷ d.	...	0558	...	1000	...	1400	...	...	1708	1800
61	**Nagykanizsa** a.	...	0648	...	1048	...	1448	...	...	1818	1848
61	**Nagykanizsa** **1240** d.	0415	0651	...	1049	1215	1449	...	...	...	1851
90	Gyékényes **1240** d.	0449	0720	...	1120	1258	1518	...	...	...	1925
145	Barcs d.	0612	0826	1012	1226	1412	1626	1712	1812	...	2031
175	Szigetvár d.	0658	0857	1057	1302	1456	1701	1810	1855	...	2113
190	Szentlőrinc d.	0729	0913	1116	1325	1516	1725	1828	1916	...	2132
209	**Pécs** a.	0749	0936	1138	1342	1539	1742	...	1939	...	2149

	9867	8907	8905	8955	8903	8953	8913	8901	8961	897 Ⓑ
Pécs d.	...	0615	1015	1212	1415	1452	1612	1815	2012	222
Szentlőrinc d.	...	0638	1038	1236	1438	1516	1636	1838	2054	225
Szigetvár d.	...	0654	1054	1258	1454	1534	1658	1854	2112	230
Barcs d.	...	0725	1125	1337	1525	1612	1738	1925	2151	234
Gyékényes **1240** a.	...	0838	1238	...	1637	...	1843	2043	...	...
Nagykanizsa **1240** a.	...	0907	1307	...	1707	...	1940	2111	...	...
Nagykanizsa d.	0608	0910	1310	...	1710	...	...	2112	...	...
Zalaszentiván ▷ a.	0708	0958	1358	...	1758	...	...	2202	...	...
Zalaegerszeg ▷ a.	0721	*1012*r	*1412*r	...	*1812*r	...	...	*2214*r	...	...
Szombathely **1235** a.	...	1045	1450	...	1845	...	...	2251	...	...
Sopron **1233** a.	...	...	...	...	1950	...	...	...	...	...

r – Connecting train Zalaegerszeg - Zalaszentiván and v.v.
▷ – See also Tables **1232** and **1235**.

1238 GYÖR - CELLDÖMÖLK - SZOMBATHELY

km												
0	**Györ** d.	0742	0840	0935	1040	1238	1458	1640	1749	1840	1950	2040
47	Pápa d.	0848	0927	1032	1127	1325	1558	1727	1848	1927	2046	2127
72	Celldömölk a.	0919	0953	1103	1153	1356	1634	1753	1919	1953	2117	2153
72	Celldömölk d.	...	1006	...	1206	...	...	1806	...	2006	...	2206
117	**Szombathely** a.	...	1044	...	1244	...	...	1844	...	2044	...	2242

Szombathely d.	0519	0704	...	...	1304	...	1504	...	1704	...	...
Celldömölk a.	0551	0748	...	...	1351	...	1551	...	1751	...	...
Celldömölk d.	0606	0806	0926	1126	1406	1449	1606	1648	1806	1926	212
Pápa d.	0631	0831	1000	1200	1431	1523	1631	1737	1831	2000	220
Györ a.	0718	0916	1054	1253	1516	1619	1716	1829	1916	2056	225

Additional trains: Györ - Celldömölk 0508, 0636, 1352Ⓐ, 1602; Celldömölk - Györ 0440, 0650, 1250Ⓐ.

Subject to alteration May 18 - June 8.

1240 (BUDAPEST) - DOMBÓVAR - KAPOSVÁR - NAGYKANIZSA

2nd class

km		8250	8212	8907	8222	*IC*• 822 [R]	8214	205 G	8254	8216 Ⓐh	8256	8903	8226 Ⓐ	*IC*• 824 [R]	8236	201 A	8913	8206	8901	*IC*• 828 [R]	8561	8218	8208 Ⓑ	8208 ⑥	
	Budapest Keleti **1200** d.	...	...	...	...	0745z	...	...	...	...	...	...	...	1345z	...	...	...	...	...	1645z	...	...	...	...	...
0	**Dombóvár** d.	0425r	0622	...	0807	1003	...	...	1207	...	1407	...	...	1603	1607	...	...	1807	...	1859	...	2007	2207	2207	...
31	**Kaposvár** a.	0458r	0700	...	0840	1027	...	...	1240	...	1440	...	...	1627	1640	...	...	1831	...	1923	...	2040	2231	2231	...
31	**Kaposvár** d.	0500	0706	...	0849	...	1049	...	1249	1350	1449	...	1555	...	1650	...	...	1845	...	1925	...	2109	2242	...	...
71	Somogyszob d.	0605	0758	...	0940	...	1140	...	1340	1444	1541	...	1650	...	1740	...	...	1940	...	2013	...	2211	2332	...	...
101	Gyékényes a.	0635	0828	...	1011	...	1211	...	1411	1515	1612	...	1721	...	1811	...	...	2015	...	2041	...	2242	0003	...	...
101	Gyékényes **1237** d.	0720	...	0839	...	...	...	1232	1414	...	1615	1637	...	...	...	1834	1904	...	2044	...	2048	...	...	...	...
130	**Nagykanizsa** **1237** a.	0750	...	0907	...	...	...	1256	1444	...	1645	1707	...	...	...	1906	1940	...	2111	...	2118	...	...	...	...

	8219 ⚒	18219 †	8229 Ⓐ	8910	*IC*• 829 [R]	8259	8207	8217	200 G	8902	8215	*IC*• 825 [R]	8914	8225		8253	*IC*• 823 [R]	8263	204 A	8906	8201	8568 Ⓑ	18251 ⑥	8251 Ⓑ	
Nagykanizsa **1237** d.	...	...	...	0415	...	0500	0645	...	0949	1049	...	...	1215	...	...	1455	...	1709	1841	1851	...	1910	2055	2055	...
Gyékényes **1237** a.	...	...	...	0447	...	0530	0715	...	1014	1119	...	...	1257	...	...	1526	...	1739	1903	1924	...	1949	2139	2139	...
Gyékényes d.	0340	...	0422	...	0508	0531	0722	0946	...	...	1146	...	...	1346	...	1527	...	1746	...	...	1932	...	2140	2140	...
Somogyszob d.	0411	...	0456	...	0537	0606	0756	1022	...	...	1222	...	...	1421	...	1602	...	1822	...	...	2013	...	2211	2211	...
Kaposvár a.	0457	...	0542	...	0619	0700	0842	1114	...	...	1314	...	...	1514	...	1648	...	1911	...	...	2059	...	2257	2305	...
Kaposvár d.	0517	0517	...	...	0621	0717	0926	1117	...	...	...	1324	...	1517	...	1655	1724	1925	...	...	2126	...	...	2306	...
Dombóvár a.	0550	0550	...	...	0645	0750	0950	1150	...	...	...	1348	...	1550	...	1728	1748	1958	...	...	2150	...	...	2338	...
Budapest Keleti **1200** a.	...	...	...	...	0914z	...	...	...	...	...	...	1614z	...	...	...	...	2014z	...	...	...	...	...	...	...	...

A – AGRAM – [12] Zagreb - Budapest and v.v.
G – GRADEC, June 15 - Sept. 15. [12] Zagreb - Budapest and v.v. (Table **1220**).
h – Not Dec. 24 - Jan. 2, June 17 - Aug. 30.
r – ⚒ only.
z – Not May 13 - 26 (starts from/terminates at Kelenföld during this period - for timings see Table **1200** on page 559).
• – For train number Budapest - Dombóvár and v.v. see Table **1200** (train divides/joins at Dombóvár).

1242 DOMBÓVAR - BAJA - KISKUNFÉLEGYHÁZA - KECSKEMÉT

2nd class (*Ex* also 1s

km							⑤F	G		[R]	
0	**Dombóvár** d.	...	0606	...	1406	...	1606	1606	1811	...	...
60	Bátaszék **1210** d.	0520	0723	...	1513	...	1719	1732	1920	1933	...
80	**Baja** **1210** a.	0540	0744	...	1538	...	1740	1753	...	1951	...

	⚒	Ⓐ	[R]						Ⓐ	Ⓒ
Baja **1210** d.	0425	...	0557	...	...	1407	1555x	...	1812	181
Bátaszék **1210** d.	0444	0448	0615	0633	...	1429	1633	...	1838	183
Dombóvár a.	...	0554	...	0740	...	1540	1740	...	1945	194

km			Ⓐ						Ⓐr		
0	**Baja** d.	0413	0517	0609	0809	1009	1209	1409	1511	1609	1809
76	Kiskunhalas a.	0520	0630	0720	0920	1120	1320	1520	1630	1720	1920
76	Kiskunhalas d.	0532	0639	0732	0932	1132	1332	1532	...	1732	1932
122	Kiskunfélegyháza **1290** d.	0615	0719	0815	1015	1215	1415	1615	...	1815	2014
147	**Kecskemét** **1290** a.	0636	...	0836	1036	1236	1436	1636	...	1836	...

	Ⓐ						Ⓐ			
Kecskemét **1290** d.	...	0510	0722	0922	1122	1322	...	1522	1722	192
Kiskunfélegyháza **1290** d.	...	0545	0745	0945	1145	1345	1438	1545	1745	194
Kiskunhalas a.	...	0625	0825	1025	1225	1425	1518	1625	1825	202
Kiskunhalas d.	0528	0637	0837	1037	1237	1437	1528r	1637	1837	203
Baja a.	0638	0742	0942	1142	1342	1542	1638r	1742	1942	214

F – ⑤ from Apr. 5 (not June 21 - Aug. 30).
G – Daily to Mar. 31 except dates in note **F**.
r – Not Dec. 24 - Jan. 2, June 17 - Aug. 30.
x – 1611 on ⑦ from Apr. 28 (except June 16 - Sept. 1).

BUDAPEST - GYŐR - WIEN 1250

km				IC	RJX	IC	RJX	IC	EC*	IC	RJX	IC	IC	RJX	IC	IC	RJX	IC	EC*	IC	RJX		IC	EC*	
		9430	346	910	162	930	60	912	140	932	62	922	942	64	914	934	66	924	144	936	68	9304	916	344	9306
		2	Ⓡ	Ⓡ	✕⊖	Ⓡ	✕⊖	Ⓡ	⊖	Ⓡ	✕⊖	Ⓡ	Ⓡ	✕⊖	Ⓡ	Ⓡ	✕⊖	Ⓡ	⊖	Ⓡ	✕⊖	2	Ⓡ	⊖	2
			D		**Z**		**M**		**H**		**M**			**M**			**M f**		**T**		**M**	Ⓐ		**A**	Ⓐ
0	**Budapest** Keleti d.	...	0540	0610	0640	0710	0740	0810	0840	0910	0940	1010	1110	1140	1210	1310	1340	1410	1440	1510	1540	1553	1610	1640	1653
7	Ferencváros d.	...	0549	|	|	|	|	|	|	|	|	|	|	|	|	|	|	|	|	|	|	1601	|	|	1701
13	Kelenföld ☆ d.	...	0555	0625	0655	0725	0755	0825	0855	0925	0955	1025	1125	1155	1225	1325	1355	1425	1455	1525	1555	1610	1625	1655	1710
75	Tatabánya d.	...	0626	0656	0726	0756	0826	0856	0926	0956	1026	1056	1156	1226	1256	1356	1426	1456	1526	1556	1626	1648	1656	1726	1748
83	Tata d.	...	|	0704	|	0804	|	0904	|	1004	|	1104	1204	|	1304	1404	|	1504	|	1604	|	1657	|	|	1757
103	Komárom d.	...	|	0717	|	0817	|	0917	|	1017	|	1117	1217	|	1317	1417	|	1517	|	1617	|	1710	1716	|	1810
140	**Győr** a.	...	0700	0735	0800	0835	0900	0935	1000	1035	1100	1135	1235	1300	1335	1435	1500	1535	1600	1635	1700	1731	1735	1800	1831
140	**Győr** d.	0448	0702	0738	0802	0838	0902	0938	1002	1038	1102	1138	1238	1302	1338	1438	1502	1538	1602	1638	1702	...	1738	1802	...
176	Mosonmagyaróvár d.	0513	0720	△	0820	▽	0920	△	1020	▽	1120	△	▽	1320	△	▽	1520	△	1620	▽	1720	...	△	1820	...
187	Hegyeshalom 🏛 d.	0529	0732	...	0832	...	0932	...	1032	...	1132	...	...	1332	...	...	1532	...	1632	...	1732	...	...	1832	...
256	**Wien** Hbf a.	0624	0821	...	0918	...	1021	...	1121	...	1221	...	...	1421	...	...	1618	...	1721	...	1821	...	...	1921	...

	IC	RJX		IC	EC*	IC	IC	EN		
	946	42	9308	318	148	938	948	462		
	Ⓡ	✕⊖	2	Ⓡ	⊖	Ⓡ	Ⓡ	Ⓡ	2	2
		S	Ⓐ	**G**				**K**	⊡	
Budapest Keleti d.	1710	1740	1753	1810	1840	1910	2010	2040	2120**d**	2320**d**
Ferencváros d.	|	|	1801	|	|	|	|	|	|	|
Kelenföld ☆ d.	1725	1755	1810	1825	1855	1925	2025	2055	2128	2328
Tatabánya d.	1756	1826	1848	1856	1926	1956	2056	2126	2215	0015
Tata d.	1804	|	1857	1904	|	2004	2104	|	2225	0025
Komárom d.	1817	|	1910	1917	|	2017	2117	|	2246	0046
Győr a.	1835	1900	1931	1935	2000	2035	2135	2200	2313	0113
Győr d.	1838	1902	...	1938	2002	2038	...	2202	...	...
Mosonmagyaróvár d.	▽	1920	...	△	2020	▽	...	2220	...	...
Hegyeshalom 🏛 d.	...	1932	...	...	2032	△	...	2232	...	...
Wien Hbf a.	...	2018	...	...	2118	...	...	2321	...	...

			IC			IC	IC	EN	IC	RJX	IC
		9409	949	7701	9407	919	939	463	917	41	937
	2	2	Ⓡ	2	2	Ⓡ	Ⓡ	⊖	Ⓡ	✕⊖	Ⓡ
	⊙	Ⓐ		**c**	Ⓐ			**K**			
Wien Hbf d.	...	...	...	0445	...	...	...	0640	...	0742	...
Hegyeshalom 🏛 d.	...	0505	...	0547	0605	...	...	0728	...	0828	...
Mosonmagyaróvár d.	...	0513	...	...	0613	△	▽	0736	△	0836	▽
Győr a.	...	0540	...	...	0640	0701	0724	0753	0819	0853	0919
Győr d.	0344	0545	0621	...	0645	0703	0726	0756	0821	0856	0921
Komárom d.	0409	0609	0639	...	0709	|	0744	|	0839	|	0939
Tata d.	0429	0622	0652	...	0722	|	0757	|	0852	|	0952
Tatabánya d.	0441	0631	0700	...	0731	|	0805	0830	0900	0930	1000
Kelenföld ☆ a.	0528	0707	0732	...	0807	0812	0837	0902	0932	1002	1032
Ferencváros a.	|	0714	|	...	0814	|	|	|	|	|	|
Budapest Keleti a.	0539**d**	0723	0749	...	0823	0828	0854	0919	0949	1019	1049

	EC*	IC	RJX	IC	EC*	IC	RJX	IC	IC	RJX	IC	EC*	IC	RJX	IC	EC*	IC	RJX	IC	RJX	IC				
	345	317	49	947	143	927	61	945	915	63	933	145	925	65	943	147	913	67	931	165	911	347			
	⊖	Ⓡ	✕⊖	Ⓡ	⊖	Ⓡ	✕⊖	Ⓡ	Ⓡ	✕⊖	Ⓡ	⊖	Ⓡ	✕⊖	Ⓡ	⊖	Ⓡ	✕⊖	Ⓡ	✕⊖	Ⓡ	Ⓡ	2	2**b**	2
	A	**G**	**v**		**T**		**M**			**M f**				**M**		**H**		**M**		**Z**		**D**			
Wien Hbf d.	0842	...	0942	...	1042	...	1140	...	...	1340	...	1442	...	1542	...	1642	...	1740	....	1842	...	1942	...	2045	...
Hegyeshalom 🏛 d.	0928	...	1028	...	1128	...	1228	...	...	1428	...	1528	...	1628	...	1728	...	1828	...	1928	...	2028	...	2147	...
Mosonmagyaróvár d.	0936	△	1036	▽	1136	△	1236	▽	△	1436	▽	1536	△	1636	▽	1736	△	1836	▽	1936	△	2036	...	2155	...
Győr a.	0953	1019	1053	1119	1153	1219	1253	1319	1419	1453	1519	1553	1619	1653	1719	1753	1819	1853	1919	1953	2019	2053	...	2221	...
Győr d.	0956	1021	1056	1121	1156	1221	1256	1321	1421	1456	1521	1556	1621	1656	1721	1756	1821	1856	1921	1956	2021	2056	2139	...	2239
Komárom d.	|	1039	|	1139	|	1239	|	1339	1439	|	1539	|	1639	|	1739	|	1839	|	1939	|	2039	|	2204	...	2304
Tata d.	|	1052	|	1152	|	1252	|	1352	1452	|	1552	|	1652	|	1752	|	1852	|	1952	|	2052	|	2223	...	2323
Tatabánya d.	1030	1100	1130	1200	1230	1300	1330	1400	1500	1530	1600	1630	1700	1730	1800	1830	1900	1930	2000	2030	2100	2130	2234	...	2333
Kelenföld ☆ a.	1102	1132	1202	1232	1302	1332	1402	1432	1532	1602	1632	1702	1732	1802	1832	1902	1932	2002	2032	2102	2132	2202	2321	...	...
Ferencváros a.	|	|	|	|	|	|	|	|	|	|	|	|	|	|	|	|	|	|	|	|	|	2211	|	...	...
Budapest Keleti a.	1119	1149	1219	1249	1319	1349	1419	1449	1549	1619	1649	1719	1749	1819	1849	1919	1949	2019	2049	2119	2149	2220	2329**d**	...	...

A – AVALA – [12] Budapest - Wien and v.v.
D – DACIA – [12] Budapest - Wien and v.v.; 🛏 1, 2 cl., ▬ 2 cl., [2] București - Budapest - Wien and v.v.
G – RÁBA – [12] Budapest - Szombathely - Graz and v.v.
H – HORTOBÁGY – [12] ✕ Záhony - Nyiregyháza - Debrecen - Budapest - Wien and v.v. Conveys 🛏 1, 2 cl. Kyïv - Lviv - Chop - Záhony - Budapest - Wien and v.v. (Table **96**).
K – KÁLMÁN IMRE / WIENER WALZER – 🛏 1, 2 cl., ▬ 2 cl., [2] Budapest - Wien - Salzburg - München and v.v.; 🛏 1, 2 cl., ▬ 2 cl., [2] Budapest - Wien - Salzburg (**466/7**) - Zürich and v.v.
M – [12] and ✕ Budapest - Wien - Salzburg - München and v.v. (Table **65**).
S – [12] and ✕ Budapest - Wien - Salzburg and v.v. (Table **65**).
T – TRANSILVANIA – [12] Cluj Napoca - Oradea - Budapest - Wien and v.v.
Z – [12] ✕ Budapest - Wien - Salzburg - Innsbruck - Zürich and v.v. (Table **86**).
b – Change at Bruck an der Leitha (a. 2112 / d. 2117).

c – Change at Bruck an der Leitha (a. 0512 / d. 0520).
d – Budapest **Déli**.
f – Extended to / from Frankfurt on dates in Tables **912** / **930**.
v – From Innsbruck and Salzburg on dates in Table **86**.
⊖ – Reservation compulsory for domestic journeys in Hungary.
△ – To / from Szombathely (Table **1252**).
▽ – To / from Sopron (Table **1251**).
⊡ – Additional train Budapest Déli - Komárom: 2220.
⊙ – Additional train runs one hour later.
☆ – See also Tables **1200**, **1220**, **1225**, **1230**. Kelenföld is also served by metro line 4 from Budapest Keleti.
* – Classified *D* in Austria.
RJX – *Railjet Express*, 1st and economy class. *Business class* also available to 1st cl. ticket holders (supplement).

Komárom - Székesfehérvár
82 km Journey 1h 25m
From Komárom 0845, 1610.
From Székesfehérvár 1035, 1835.

Győr - Hegyeshalom - Bruck an der Leitha *79 km*
Journey 1h 15m - 1h 22m
From Győr 0448, 0748, 0948, 1148, 1348, 1548, 1748, 1948.
From Bruck an der Leitha 0748, 0948, 1048, 1248, 1448, 1748, 1848, 2117.

GYŐR - SOPRON 1251

Operator: GySEV

km							IC		IC		IC			IC			IC			IC			IC		
		9910	9920	9912	9922	9932	930	9942	932	9914	942	9924	9934	934	9916	9926	936	9936	9946	946	9918	9948	938	9928	9938
			Ⓐ			Ⓐ	Ⓡ		Ⓡ		Ⓡ		Ⓐ	Ⓡ			Ⓡ			Ⓡ		⑦**e**	Ⓡ		
	Budapest Kel. **1250** d.	...	...	...	...	...	0710**z**	...	0910**z**	...	1110**z**	...	...	1310**z**	...	...	1510**z**	...	...	1710**z**	...	...	1910**z**	...	...
0	**Győr** d.	0408	0519	0601	0645	0751	0838	0851	1038	1051	1238	1251	1351	1438	1451	1551	1638	1651	1751	1838	1851	1951	2038	2051	2251
31	Csorna d.	0435	0551	0632	0717	0821	0859	0921	1059	1121	1259	1323	1421	1459	1520	1621	1659	1720	1821	1859	1920	2020	2104	2117	2317
85	**Sopron** a.	0523	0643	0724	0803	0908	0938	1006	1138	1206	1338	1414	1513	1538	1614	1713	1738	1814	1913	1938	2013	2106	2143	2201	0001

				IC				IC		IC		IC		IC				IC			IC				
	9919	9929	9939	939	9917	9927		937	9937	947	9915	945	9925	933		9913	9923	943	9933	9943	931	9911	9921	9931	
				Ⓡ	Ⓐ			Ⓡ		Ⓡ		Ⓡ		Ⓡ		Ⓐ		Ⓡ	Ⓐ		Ⓡ				
Sopron d.	0350	0455	0600	0625	0645	0743	...	0821	0944	1021	1144	1221	1345	1421	...	1446	1545	1621	1646	1746	1821	1846	1944	2229	...
Csorna d.	0435	0546	0647	0703	0735	0834	...	0859	1034	1059	1233	1259	1434	1459	...	1535	1634	1659	1735	1834	1859	1935	2034	2317	...
Győr a.	0501	0617	0717	0724	0806	0906	...	0919	1106	1119	1307	1319	1506	1519	...	1606	1706	1719	1806	1906	1919	2006	2106	2343	...
Budapest Kel. **1250** a.	...	...	...	0854**z**	...	...	...	1049**z**	...	1249**z**	...	1449**z**	...	1649**z**	...	...	...	1849**z**	...	...	2049**z**	...	...	...	...

e – Not Dec. 23, 30, June 16 - Sept. 1.

GYŐR - CSORNA - SZOMBATHELY 1252

For alternative services Budapest - Szombathely via Székesfehérvár see Table **1230**

km		IC	IC	IC	IC	IC	IC	IC	IC	IC
		910	912	922	914	924	916	318	938	918
		Ⓡ	Ⓡ	Ⓡ	Ⓡ	Ⓡ	Ⓡ	Ⓡ	Ⓡ	Ⓡ
	Budapest Keleti **1250** d.	0610	0810	1010	1210	1410	1610	1810	1910	1910
0	**Győr** d.	0738	0938	1138	1338	1538	1738	1938	2038	2038
31	Csorna d.	0759	0959	1159	1359	1559	1759	1959	2058	2112
103	**Szombathely** a.	0849	1049	1249	1449	1649	1849	2049	...	2202
	Graz **986** a.	...	...	...	...	...	...	2300	...	...

	IC	IC	IC	IC	IC	IC	IC	IC	
	919	917	317	927	915	925	913	911	
	Ⓡ	Ⓡ	Ⓡ	Ⓡ	Ⓡ	Ⓡ	Ⓡ	Ⓡ	2
Graz **986** d.	...	...	0608	...	...	...	...	...	...
Szombathely d.	0554	0710	0910	1110	1310	1510	1710	1910	2238
Csorna d.	0641	0759	0959	1159	1359	1559	1759	1959	2346
Győr a.	0701	0819	1019	1219	1419	1619	1819	2019	...
Budapest Keleti **1250** a.	0828	0949	1149	1349	1549	1749	1949	2149	...

GYŐR - RAJKA - BRATISLAVA 1253

Local trains, 2nd class

km			⚒**b**			◇		◇		◇	
0	**Győr** 1250 d.	0548	...	0648	...	1248	...	1448	...	1648	...
36	Mosonmagyaróvár 1250 d.	0613	...	0713	...	1313	...	1513	...	1713	...
47	Hegyeshalom 1250 d.	0623	0633	0733	...	1323	1333	1523	1533	1723	1733
60	Rajka 🏛 d.	...	0649	0746	0749	...	1349	...	1549	...	1749
77	**Bratislava** Petržalka ☆ a.	...	0707	...	0807	...	1407	...	1607	...	1807

	⚒**b**			◇		◇		◇		◇
Bratislava Petržalka ☆ d.	0726	...	0849	...	1449	...	1649	...	1849	...
Rajka 🏛 d.	0744	0809	0909	...	1509	...	1709	...	1909	...
Hegyeshalom 1250 d.	...	0822	0922	0935	1522	1535	1722	1735	1922	1935
Mosonmagyaróvár 1250 d.	...	...	...	0943	...	1543	...	1743	...	1943
Győr 1250 a.	...	...	...	1010	...	1610	...	1810	...	2010

b – ①–⑥ (not Jan. 1, Apr. 19, 20, 22, May 1, 8, July 5, Aug. 29, 31, Nov. 1).
☆ – Bus 93 links Petržalka station with Bratislava hlavná stanica (main station) every 5 - 12 minutes; journey approx 10 minutes.
◇ – For faster connection (Ⓡ) see Table **1250**.

1255 BUDAPEST - VÁC - SZOB

Local trains, 2nd class

km										
0	**Budapest** Nyugati ..... d.	0052	0445	0545	0707	then	2107	2152	2252	2352
34	Vác ..... d.	0134	0534	0634	0734	hourly	2134	2234	2334	0034
51	Nagymaros-Visegrád ¶ d.	0149	0549	0649	0749	⊡	2149	2249	2349	0049
64	**Szob** ..... a.	0205	0605	0705	0805	until	2205	2305	0005	0105

Szob ..... d.	0455	0555	0655	then	1855	2000	2100	2200	2300
Nagymaros-Visegrád ¶ d.	0511	0611	0711	hourly	1911	2016	2116	2216	2316
Vác ..... d.	0528	0628	0728	⊡	1928	2032	2132	2232	2332
Budapest Nyugati ..... a.	0554	0654	0754	until	1954	2114	2214	2314	0014

¶ – A ferry operates across the river to Visegrád.

⊡ – For *EC* trains every two hours (to / from Praha) see Table **1175**.

1260 BUDAPEST - MISKOLC - KOŠICE

2nd class (also 1st in *IC* trains)

For trains Budapest - Debrecen - Nyiregyháza see Table **1270**

km		5520	5030	5040	5500	520	*IC** 182 R⊖	542	*IC* 560 Ⓡ	522	*IC* 502 Ⓡ	552	*IC* •562 Ⓡ	*IC* 512 Ⓡ	544	*IC* 564 Ⓡ	524	*IC* 504 Ⓡ	554	*IC* 566 Ⓡ	526 ⑤⑦	*IC* 514 Ⓡ	546	*IC* 568 Ⓡ	528
0	**Budapest** Keleti ..... d.	...	...	...	...	0500x	0605z	0600x	0705z	0700x	0805z	0800x	0905z	1005z	1000x	1105z	1100x	1205z	1200x	1305z	1300x	1405z	1400x	1505z	1500x
67	Hatvan ..... d.	0405	...	0505	0555	0654	0717	0754	0817	0854	0917	0954	1017	1117	1154	1217	1254	1317	1354	1417	1454	1517	1554	1617	1654
87	Vámosgyörk ⊡ ..... d.	0421	...	0520	0608	0707	|	0807	|	0907	|	1007	|	|	1207	|	1307	|	1407	|	1507	|	1607	|	1707
126	Füzesabony ..... a.	0457	...	0555	0640	0730	0749	0830	0849	0930	0949	1030	1049	1149	1230	1249	1330	1349	1430	1449	1530	1549	1630	1649	1730
126	Füzesabony ..... d.	0504	0503	0603	0650	0733	0751	0831	0851	0933	0951	1031	1051	1151	1231	1251	1333	1351	1431	1451	1533	1551	1632	1651	1733
143	**Eger** ⊙ ..... a.	0523	|	|	0707	|	|	0850	|	|	|	1050	|	|	1250	|	|	|	1450	|	|	|	1650	|	|
139	Mezőkövesd ..... d.	...	0514	0614	...	0744	|	...	|	0944	|	...	|	|	...	|	1344	|	...	|	1544	|	...	|	1744
183	**Miskolc** ..... a.	...	0552	0652	...	0822	0826	...	0926	1022	1026	...	1126	1226	...	1326	1422	1426	...	1526	1622	1626	...	1726	1822
183	**Miskolc** ..... d.	...	...	...	...	0835	0830	...	0930	1035	...	...	1130	...	...	1330	1435	...	...	1530	1635	...	...	1730	1835
	Nyíregyháza **1261** ... a.	...	...	...	...	▽	|	...	1029	▽	...	...	1229	...	...	1429	▽	...	...	1629	▽	...	...	1829	▽
244	Hidasnémeti 🏛 ..... d.	...	...	...	...	...	0937	...	...	...	...	...	...	...	...	...	...	...	...	...	...	...	...	...	...
270	**Košice** ..... a.	...	...	...	...	...	0959	...	...	...	...	...	...	...	...	...	...	...	...	...	...	...	...	...	...

	IC 506 Ⓡ	556	*IC* 586 Ⓡ	5208	*IC** 186 H⊖	5508	*IC* 508 Ⓡ	🚌	5008	5018
Budapest Keleti ..... d.	1605z	1600x	1705z	1700x	1805z	1800x	1905z	1940	2000x	2200x
Hatvan ..... d.	1717	1754	1817	1854	1917	1954	2017	2040	2159	2353
Vámosgyörk ⊡ ..... d.	|	1807	|	1907	|	2009	|	...	2213	0007
Füzesabony ..... a.	1749	1830	1849	1930	1949	2042	2049	...	2243	0041
Füzesabony ..... d.	1751	1831	1851	1933	1951	2052	2051	...	2250	...
Eger ⊙ ..... a.	|	1850	|	|	|	2109	|	...	|	...
Mezőkövesd ..... d.	|	...	|	1944	|	...	|	...	2301	...
Miskolc ..... a.	1826	...	1926	2022	2026	...	2126	...	2340	...
Miskolc ..... d.	...	...	1929	2035	2030	...	...	...	...	...
Nyíregyháza **1261** ..... a.	...	...	2029	▽	|	...	...	...	...	...
Hidasnémeti 🏛 ..... d.	...	...	...	...	2137	...	...	...	...	...
Košice ..... a.	...	...	...	...	2159	...	...	...	...	...

	5009	5509	529	*IC* 519 Ⓡ	547	*IC** 187 H⊖	527	*IC* 682 Ⓡ	557	*IC* 517 Ⓡ	
Košice ..... d.	...	...	...	...	...	0602	...	...	...	...	...
Hidasnémeti 🏛 ..... d.	...	...	...	...	...	0633	...	...	...	...	...
Nyíregyháza **1261** . d.	...	...	▽	0526	...	|	▽	0726	...	...	...
Miskolc ..... a.	...	...	0522	0627	...	0726	0722	0827	...	...	...
Miskolc ..... d.	0328	...	0534	0629	...	0729	0734	0829	...	0929	...
Mezőkövesd ..... d.	0406	...	0610	|	...	|	0812	|	...	|	...
Eger ⊙ ..... d.	|	0435	|	|	0702	|	|	|	0904	|	...
Füzesabony ..... a.	0417	0455	0619	0704	0723	0804	0824	0904	0923	1004	...
Füzesabony ..... d.	0419	0500	0620	0705	0725	0805	0825	0905	0925	1005	...
Vámosgyörk ⊡ ..... d.	0454	0536	0652	|	0751	|	0851	|	0951	|	...
Hatvan ..... a.	0509	0552	0705	0738	0804	0838	0904	0938	1004	1038	...
Budapest Keleti ..... a.	...	0710z	0820z	0858z	1000x	0958z	1100x	1058z	1200x	1158z	...

	525	*IC* 650 Ⓡ	545	*IC* 515 Ⓡ	*IC* 652 Ⓡ	555	*IC* 505 Ⓡ	5205	*IC* 654 Ⓡ	543	*IC* 513 Ⓡ	523 ⑤⑦	*IC* 656 Ⓡ	553	*IC* 503 Ⓡ	*IC* 1521 Ⓡ G	521 E	15201 G	*IC* 658 Ⓡ	541	*IC** 181 R⊖	5203 ①–⑥	15203 ⑦	1511 ⑦	5021
Košice ..... d.	...	...	...	...	...	...	...	...	...	...	...	...	...	...	...	...	...	...	...	...	1802	...	...	...	...
Hidasnémeti 🏛 ..... d.	...	...	...	...	...	...	...	...	...	...	...	...	...	...	...	...	...	...	...	...	1833	...	...	...	...
Nyíregyháza **1261** ... d.	▽	0926	...	...	1126	...	...	▽	1326	...	...	▽	1526	...	...	▽	▽	...	1726	...	|	▽	▽	1926	...
Miskolc ..... a.	0922	1027	...	...	1227	...	...	1322	1427	...	...	1522	1627	...	...	1716	1722	...	1827	...	1926	1922	1922	2029	...
Miskolc ..... d.	0934	1029	...	1129	1229	...	1329	1334	1429	...	1529	1534	1629	...	1729	1729	1734	1734	1829	...	1929	1934	1934	2034	2300
Mezőkövesd ..... d.	1012	|	...	|	|	...	|	1412	|	...	|	1612	|	...	|	|	1812	1812	|	...	|	2012	2012	2112	2338
Eger ⊙ ..... d.	|	|	1104	|	|	1304	|	|	|	1504	|	|	|	1704	|	|	|	|	|	1904	|	|	|	|	|
Füzesabony ..... a.	1024	1104	1123	1204	1304	1323	1404	1424	1504	1523	1604	1624	1704	1723	1804	1804	1824	1824	1904	1920	2004	2024	2024	2124	2350
Füzesabony ..... d.	1025	1105	1128	1205	1305	1325	1405	1425	1505	1525	1605	1625	1705	1725	1805	1805	1825	1825	1905	1925	2005	...	2025	2126	...
Vámosgyörk ⊡ ..... d.	1051	|	1152	|	|	1351	|	1451	|	1551	|	1651	|	1751	|	|	1851	1851	|	1954	|	...	2051	2152	...
Hatvan ..... a.	1104	1138	1204	1238	1338	1404	1438	1504	1538	1604	1638	1704	1738	1804	1838	1838	1904	1904	1938	2007	2038	...	2104	2205	...
Budapest Keleti ..... a.	1300x	1258z	1400x	1358z	1458z	1600x	1558z	1700x	1658z	1800x	1758z	1900x	1858z	2000x	1958z	1958z	2100x	2100x	2058z	2200x	2158z	...	2300x	0015x	...

E – Not dates in note **G**.
G – ⑦ (not Dec. 23, 30, June 16 - Sept. 1).
H – HERNÁD / HORNÁD. R – RÁKÓCZI.
x – Local train Budapest Keleti - Pécel and v.v.; 🚌 Pécel - Hatvan and v.v.
z – By 🚌 Budapest Keleti (Verseny utca bus stop) - Hatvan and v.v.
⊖ – Ⓡ for domestic journeys.

⊙ – Local trains **Füzesabony - Eger** and v.v. (journey 17 mins): **From Füzesabony**: 0422, 0604, 0708Ⓐ, 0808Ⓐ, 0908, 1008Ⓐ, 1108, 1208Ⓐ, 1308, 1408Ⓐ, 1508, 1608Ⓐ, 1708, 1808Ⓐ, 2008Ⓐ, 2208Ⓐ, 2255. **From Eger**: 0322, 0531Ⓐ, 0631, 0731Ⓐ, 0831, 0931Ⓐ, 1031, 1131Ⓐ, 1231, 1331Ⓐ, 1431, 1531Ⓐ, 1631, 1731Ⓐ, 1831, 1931Ⓐ, 2031, 2131Ⓐ, 2231.
▽ – To / from Sátoraljaújhely (Table **1261**).
* – Classified *EC* in Slovakia.

⊡ – Connecting trains **Vámosgyörk - Gyöngyös** and v.v (journey 16 mins): **From Vámosgyörk**: 0522, 0610, 0708, 0908, 1108, 1308, 1408Ⓐ, 1508, 1608, 1708, 1908. **From Gyöngyös**: 0546, 0633, 0732, 0932, 1132, 1332, 1432Ⓐ, 1532, 1632, 1732, 1932.

Engineering work (shown) to last until late 2019

1261 MISKOLC - SÁTORALJAÚJHELY and NYÍREGYHÁZA

2nd class (also 1st in *IC* trains)

For trains Budapest - Debrecen - Nyiregyháza see Table **1270**

km		*IC* 580 Ⓡ ▷	5140 ⊡	510	520	*IC* 560 Ⓡ	522	*IC* 562 Ⓡ	5122	5234	*IC* 564 Ⓡ	5114	524	*IC* 566 Ⓡ	5124	5236 ④–⑦	*IC* 568 Ⓡ	5116	528	*IC* 586 Ⓡ	1528 Ⓡ F	5118	5208	5128	5158 Ⓑ
	Budapest Kel. **1260** .. d.	...	...	...	△	△	△	△	...	...	△	...	△	△	...	△x	△	...	△	△	△	...	△	...	...
0	**Miskolc** ..... d.	0620	0633	0728	0835	0930	1035	1130	1135	1235	1330	1335	1435	1530	1535	1635	1730	1735	1835	1929	1929	1935	2035	2135	2310
38	Szerencs ..... a.	0644	0710	0752	0912	0954	1112	1154	1212	1312	1354	1412	1512	1554	1612	1712	1754	1812	1912	1954	1953	2012	2112	2212	2347
38	Szerencs ..... d.	0645	0711	0753	0914	0955	1114	1155	1216	1314	1355	1416	1514	1555	1616	1714	1755	1816	1914	1955	2014	2016	2114	2216	2348
74	Sárospatak ..... a.	|	*0801*	|	1001	|	1201	|	*1301*	1401	|	*1501*	1601	|	*1701*	1801	|	*1901*	2001	|	2101	*2101*	2201	*2305*	|
84	**Sátoraljaújhely** ..... a.	|	*0812*	|	1012	|	1212	|	*1312*	1412	|	*1512*	1612	|	*1712*	1812	|	*1912*	2012	|	2112	*2112*	2212	*2316*	|
56	Tokaj ..... d.	0657	0729	0806	...	1008	...	1208	1234	*1334*	1408	1434	*1534*	1608	1634	*1734*	1808	1834	*1934*	2008	...	2034	*2134*	2234	0006
88	**Nyíregyháza** ..... a.	0719	0813	0829	...	1029	...	1229	1315	*1415*	1429	1515	*1615*	1629	1715	*1815*	1829	1915	*2015*	2029	...	2115	*2215*	2315	0040
	Debrecen **1270** ..... a.	0801	...	...	...	...	...	...	...	...	...	...	...	...	...	...	...	...	...	...	...	...	...	...	...

	529	*IC* 519 Ⓡ	5139	527	5169	*IC* 682 Ⓡ	525	5117	*IC* 650 Ⓡ	5227	*IC* 652 Ⓡ	5205	5115 ⊙	*IC* 654 Ⓡ	523 5235 ④–⑦	*IC* 656 Ⓡ	*IC* 1521 Ⓡ G	521 E	5113	*IC* 658 Ⓡ	5203 15203	5123	511 1511	5221	5231
Debrecen **1270** ..... d.	...	...	...	...	...	0654	...	...	...	...	...	...	...	...	...	...	...	...	...	...	...	...	...	...	...
Nyíregyháza ..... d.	*0342*	0526	0538	...	0632	0726	...	0838	0926	...	1126	...	1238	1326	...	1526	...	...	1638	1726	...	1838	1926	...	2038
Tokaj ..... d.	*0418*	0548	0620	...	0729	0748	...	0920	0948	...	1148	...	1320	1348	...	1548	...	...	1720	1748	...	1920	1950	...	2120
Sátoraljaújhely ..... d.	0353	|	|	0548	*0648*	|	0748	|	|	0948	|	1148	*1248*	|	1348	|	1548	1548	*1648*	|	1748	*1848*	|	1948	*2048*
Sárospatak ..... d.	0404	|	|	0604	*0704*	|	0804	|	|	1004	|	1204	*1304*	|	1404	|	1604	1604	*1704*	|	1804	*1904*	|	2004	*2104*
Szerencs ..... a.	0443	0601	0639	0643	0739	0801	0843	0939	1001	1043	1201	1243	1339	1401	1443	1601	1643	1643	1739	1801	1843	1939	2003	2043	2139
Szerencs ..... d.	0445	0602	0640	0645	0745	0802	0845	0945	1002	1045	1202	1245	1345	1402	1445	1602	1644	1645	1745	1802	1845	1945	2004	2045	2220
Miskolc ..... a.	0522	0627	0713	0722	0822	0827	0922	1022	1027	1122	1227	1322	1422	1427	1522	1627	1716	1722	1822	1827	1922	2022	2029	2122	2257
Budapest Kel. **1260** ... a.	△	△	...	△	...	△	△	...	△	...	△	△	...	△	△x	△	△	△	...	△	△v	...	△z	...	...

E – Not dates in note **G**.
F – ⑤ (not Dec. 28, June 21 - Aug. 30).
G – ⑦ (not Dec. 23, 30, June 16 - Sept. 1).
v – ⑦ only.

x – ⑤⑦ only (train **526** / **523**).
z – ⑦ only.
⊡ – Similar journeys run at 0535, 0735, 0935.
⊙ – Similar journeys run at 1038, 1438.

▷ – To Budapest Nyugati (Table **1270**).
△ – For engineering work timings until late 2019 Budapest Miskolc and v.v. see Table **1260**.

1262 HATVAN - SALGÓTARJÁN - SOMOSKÖÚJFALU

2nd class

km											
0	Hatvan ..... d.	0410	0610	0810	1013	1213	1410	1610	1813	2013	2213
59	Salgótarján ..... a.	0540	0740	0940	1140	1340	1540	1740	1940	2140	2340
65	Somosköújfalu ..... a.	0551	0751	0951	1151	1351	1551	1751	1951	2151	2351

Somosköújfalu ..... d.	0417	0617	0817	1017	1217	1417	1617	1817	2017	2217
Salgótarján ..... d.	0429	0629	0829	1029	1229	1429	1629	1829	2029	2229
Hatvan ..... a.	0550	0750	0950	1150	1350	1550	1750	1950	2150	2350

Additional trains: Hatvan to Somosköújfalu: 0510Ⓐ, 0710Ⓐ, 1310Ⓐ, 1510Ⓐ, 1910Ⓐ. Somosköújfalu to Hatvan: 0317, 0517Ⓐ, 0717Ⓐ, 1317Ⓐ, 1517Ⓐ.

BUDAPEST - DEBRECEN - NYÍREGYHÁZA - ZÁHONY - CHOP 1270

km		IC	IC	IC	IC	IC	IC	IC	IC	IC	IC	IC	IC	IC	IC	IC	EC	IC								
		682	1650	34	1652	602	1654	604	1656	614	1658	606	616	626	608	618	147	628		6230	6250	6260	6202		6208	6008
		[R]	[R]	⊖	[R]	[R]	[R]	[R]	[R]	[R]	[R]	[R]	[R]	[R]	[R]	[R]	⊖	[R]		2	2	2	2		2	2
				L													H	E								d
0	**Budapest** Nyugati .. ◧ d.	...	0623	0723	0823	0923	1023	1123	1223	1323	1423	1523	1623	1723	1823	1923	1940k	2023		...	...	0503	0628		1828	2028
11	Köbánya Kispest .... ◧ d.	...	0637	0737	0837	0937	1037	1137	1237	1337	1437	1537	1637	1737	1837	1937	|	2037	S	...	...	0518	0642	E	1842	2042
18	Ferihegy ✈ .... ◧ d.	...	0643	0743	0843	0943	1043	1143	1243	1343	1443	1543	1643	1743	1843	1943	|	2043	L	...	...	0527	0648	V	1848	2048
73	Cegléd .... ◧ d.	...	0718	0818	0918	1018	1118	1218	1318	1418	1518	1618	1718	1818	1918	2018	|	2118	O	...	...	0624	0724	E	1924	2130
100	**Szolnok** .... ◧ d.	...	0738	0838	0938	1038	1138	1238	1338	1438	1538	1638	1738	1838	1938	2038	2104	2138	W	...	0550	0650	0750	R	1950	2156
177	Püspökladány .... d.	...	0821	0921	1021	1121	1221	1321	1421	1521	1621	1721	1821	1921	2021	2121	2207	2221		0455	0655	0755	0855	Y	2055	2259
201	Hajdúszoboszló .... d.	...	0837	0937	1037	1137	1237	1337	1437	1537	1637	1737	1837	1937	2037	2137	2226	2237	T	0514	0714	0814	0914		2114	2318
221	**Debrecen** .... a.	...	0852	0952	1052	1152	1252	1352	1452	1552	1652	1752	1852	1952	2052	2152	2241	2252	R	0529	0729	0829	0929	2	2129	2333
221	**Debrecen** .... d.	0654	0854	0954	1054	1154	1254	1354	1454	1554	1654	1757	1854	1954	2054	2154	2243	2254	A	0534	0741	0834	0934		2134	...
270	**Nyíregyháza** .... a.	0724	0924	1024	1124	1224	1324	1424	1524	1624	1724	1827	1924	2024	2124	2224	2313	2324	I	0616	0823	0916	1016	H	2216	...
270	**Nyíregyháza** .... d.	◇	...	1031	...	...	...	...	...	1631	...	1831	1931	2031f	...	...	2318	...	N	0648	0848	0948	1048	O	2248	...
313	Kisvárda .... d.	...	...	1102	Arrivals at Nyíregyháza will be up to 9 minutes later until June 21					1702	...	1902	2002	2102f	...	...	2351	...	S	0732	0932	1032	1132	U	2332	...
335	Záhony .... a.	...	...	1121						1721	...	1921	2021	2121f	...	...	0010	...		0757	0957	1057	1157	R	2357	...
335	Záhony ▦ .... ▶ d.	...	...	1223						...	...	...	...	...	...	...	0110	...		...	...	...	...	S	...	...
341	**Chop** ▦ .... ⊙ ▶ a.	...	...	1340						...	...	...	...	...	...	...	0228	...		...	...	...	...		...	...

	EC	IC	IC	IC	IC	IC	IC	IC	IC	IC	IC	IC	IC	IC	IC	IC	IC									
	140	609	619	580	607	617	1560	605	1562	615	1564	33	1566	603	1568	601	586			6109	6209	6207		6293	6223	6211
	⊖	[R]	[R]	[R]	[R]	[R]	[R]	[R]	[R]	[R]	[R]	⊖	[R]	[R]	[R]	[R]	[R]		2	2	2	2		2	2	2
	H											L				E										h
Chop ▦ .... ⊙ ▶ d.	0328	...	...	...	...	...	Departures may be up to 11 minutes earlier until June 21				...	1410	...	...	...	...	...		...	...	...	...		...	...	...
Záhony ▦ .... ▶ a.	0246	...	...	...	...	...					...	1327	...	...	...	...	...	S	...	...	...	...	E	...	...	...
Záhony .... d.	0341	...	0524	...	0735	...					...	1440	...	1623e	...	1835	...	L	0358	...	0553	0803	V	1603	1703	1803
Kisvárda .... d.	0400	...	0543	...	0754	...					...	1459	...	1642e	...	1854	...	O	0423	...	0618	0828	E	1628	1728	1828
Nyíregyháza .... a.	0433	...	0614	◇	0825	...	...	...	...	...	...	1530	...	1714e	...	1925	◇	W	0507	...	0702	0912	R	1712	1812	1912
Nyíregyháza .... d.	0451	0531	0620	0731	0831	0931	1031	1131	1231	1331	1431	1531	1631	1731	1831	1931	2031		▬	0544	0744	0944	Y	1744	1844	1944
Debrecen .... a.	0521	0601	0653	0801	0901	1001	1101	1201	1301	1401	1501	1601	1701	1801	1901	2001	2101	T	2	0626	0826	1026		1826	1926	2026
Debrecen .... d.	0523	0603	0703	0803	0903	1003	1103	1203	1303	1403	1503	1603	1703	1803	1903	2003	...	R	0414	0631	0831	1031	2	1831	1931	▬
Hajdúszoboszló .... d.	0539	0619	0719	0819	0919	1019	1119	1219	1319	1419	1519	1619	1719	1819	1919	2019	...	A	0430	0647	0847	1047		1847	1947	...
Püspökladány .... d.	0558	0637	0737	0837	0937	1037	1137	1237	1337	1437	1537	1637	1737	1837	1937	2037	...	I	0455	0708	0908	1108	H	1908	2008	2
Szolnok .... ◧ d.	0657	0721	0821	0921	1021	1121	1221	1321	1421	1521	1621	1721	1821	1921	2021	2121	...	N	0605	0815	1015	1215	O	2015	2115	2225
Cegléd .... ◧ d.	|	0743	0843	0943	1043	1143	1243	1343	1443	1543	1643	1743	1843	1943	2043	2143	...	S	0628	0838	1038	1238	U	2038	2148	2250
Ferihegy ✈ .... ◧ d.	|	0815	0915	1015	1115	1215	1315	1415	1515	1615	1715	1815	1915	2015	2115	2215	...		0715	0910	1110	1310	R	2110	2240	2348
Köbánya Kispest ..... ◧ a.	|	0820	0920	1020	1120	1220	1320	1420	1520	1620	1720	1820	1920	2020	2120	2220	...		0720	0915	1115	1315	S	2115	2248	2358
Budapest Nyugati .. ◧ a.	0820k	0837	0937	1037	1137	1237	1337	1437	1537	1637	1737	1837	1937	2037	2137	2237	...		0737	0932	1132	1332		2132	2305	0014

E – ⑤⑦ from Apr. 7 (not June 15 - Sept. 1).
H – HORTOBÁGY – [12] Wien - Budapest - Debrecen - Záhony and v.v.; 🛏 1, 2 cl. Wien - Budapest - Chop - Lviv - Kyïv and v.v. (Table **96**).
L – LATORCA – [12] Budapest - Záhony and v.v.; [2] Budapest - Chop - Mukachevo (Table **1715**) and v.v.; [2] Záhony - Chop and v.v.
d – An additional journey runs two hours later.
e – ⑦ only (train *IC* **1603**).
f – ⑤ only (train *IC* **1626**).
h – Additional journeys run at 1927, 2003.
k – Budapest **Keleti**.

m – [2] Záhony - Chop - Mukachevo (Table **1715**) and v.v.
⊖ – Compulsory reservation [R] for domestic journeys within Hungary.
◇ – To / from Miskolc (Table **1261**). Trains **586** and **682** also continue to / from Budapest Keleti (Table **1260**).
⊙ – Ukrainian (East European) time, one hour ahead of Hungarian time.
◧ – Also **1290** Budapest - Cegléd; **1280** Budapest - Szolnok. Ferihegy ✈ is served by 5 - 6 trains per hour.

▶ – **LOCAL TRAINS ZÁHONY - CHOP** 2nd class (minimum 15 minutes connection time at Záhony required):

				m									m		
Záhony .... d.	0110	0342	0634	0835	1437	1829	2015	Chop ⊙ d.	0530	0822	1025	1625	1803	2022	2220
Chop .. ⊙ a.	0228	0500	0752	0953	1555	1947	2133	Záhony .. a.	0448	0740	0943	1543	1721	1940	2138

BUDAPEST - BIHARKERESZTES - ORADEA 1275

km				IC*				EC*	IC*	
			369	367	6204	365		143	407	
		2		H [R]	2	2	2	T [R]	C [R]	2
	Wien Hbf **1250** .... d.	...	...	...	...	...	...	1042	...	...
0	**Budapest Keleti** .... **1270** d.	...	...	0740	1028n	...	...	1340	1740	...
100	Szolnok .... **1270** d.	0526	...	0903	1150	...	...	1503	1903	...
177	Püspökladány .... **1270** a.	0628	...	0957	1252	...	...	1556	1956	...
177	Püspökladány .... d.	...	0633	1014	...	1313	1513	1613	2018	2125
228	Biharkeresztes .... a.	...	0729	1114	...	1417	1617	1717	2118	2221
228	Biharkeresztes ▦ .... d.	...	0752	1144	...	1437	...	1757	2153	...
241	Episcopia Bihor ▦ .... ⊙ a.	...	0907	1259	...	1552	...	1912	2308	...
241	Episcopia Bihor .... ⊙ d.	...	0923	1317	...	1607	...	1935	2323	...
247	**Oradea** .... ⊙ a.	...	0931	1325	...	1615	...	1943	2331	...
	Cluj Napoca **1600** .... ⊙ a.	...	▽	1608	...	...	...	2225	0203	...
	Braşov **1600** .... ⊙ a.	...	...	2344	...	...	...	...	0953	...

	IC*		EC*					IC*	
	406	6427	144	364	6205		368	366	
	C [R]	⚒	T [R]	2	2	2	2	H [R]	2
Braşov **1600** .... ⊙ d.	1847	...	...	...	...	...	...	0701	...
Cluj Napoca **1600** ..... ⊙ d.	0228	...	0735	...	...	...	▽	1446	...
Oradea .... ⊙ d.	0502	...	1016	1128	...	...	1434	1728	...
Episcopia Bihor .... ⊙ a.	0510	...	1024	1136	...	...	1442	1736	...
Episcopia Bihor ▦ .... ⊙ d.	0533	...	1049	1153	...	...	1457	1759	...
Biharkeresztes ▦ .... a.	0448	...	1004	1108	...	...	1412	1714	...
Biharkeresztes .... d.	0524	0731	1034	1130	...	1337	1437	1747	1943
Püspökladány .... a.	0627	0833	1136	1233	...	1433	1533	1848	2039
Püspökladány .... **1270** d.	0655	...	1203	...	1308	...	...	1903	...
Szolnok .... **1270** d.	0757	...	1257	...	1410	...	...	1957	...
Budapest Keleti .... **1270** a.	0920	...	1420	...	1532n	...	...	2120	...
Wien Hbf **1250** .... a.	...	...	1721	...	...	...	...	...	...

C – CORONA – 🛏 1, 2 cl., ▬ 2 cl., [2] Budapest - Cluj Napoca - Miercurea Ciuc - Braşov and v.v.
H – HARGITA – [12] Budapest - Oradea - Cluj Napoca - Miercurea Ciuc - Braşov and v.v. Conveys [2] Budapest - Cluj Napoca - Târgu Mureş and v.v. on dates in Table **1615**.
T – TRANSILVANIA – [12] Wien - Budapest - Oradea - Cluj Napoca and v.v.

n – Budapest **Nyugati**.
⊙ – Romanian (East European) time, one hour ahead of Hungary.
▽ – To / from Salonta (arrive 1037 / depart 1335).
* – *IR* in Romania.

2nd class DEBRECEN - MÁTÉSZALKA 1276

km									△		Ⓑ	
0	**Debrecen** .... d.	0452	0710	0910	1110	1310	1510	1705	1807	1910	2116	2246
58	Nyírbátor .... d.	0621	0837	1037	1237	1437	1637	1838	1921	2034	2243	0010
78	**Mátészalka** ...... a.	0644	0900	1100	1300	1500	1700	1901	1941	2057	2306	0033

		▽						⑦			
Mátészalka .... d.	0353	0447	0702	0902	1102	1302	1502	1611	1702	1915	2108
Nyírbátor .... d.	0418	0507	0726	0926	1126	1326	1526	1638	1726	1945	2132
Debrecen .... a.	0544	0625	0849	1049	1249	1449	1649	1757	1855	2115	2255

△ – [2] [R] Budapest Nyugati (*IC* **606**) - Debrecen (*IC* **638**) - Mátészalka.
▽ – [2] [R] Mátészalka (*IC* **639**) - Debrecen (*IC* **619**) - Budapest Nyugati.

2nd class DEBRECEN - ORADEA and BAIA MARE and other cross-border services 1277

km		6812	6822	6826
0	**Debrecen** .... d.	0711	0911	1511
30	Nyirábrány .... a.	0751	0951	1551
30	Nyirábrány ▦ .... d.	0806	1006	1631
39	Valea lui Mihai ▦ . ⊙ a.	0921	1121	1746
39	Valea lui Mihai ...... ⊙ d.	0941	1136	1821
105	**Oradea** .... ⊙ a.	1102	|	|
70	Carei .... **1625** ⊙ a.	...	1208	1855
106	Satu Mare .... **1625** ⊙ a.	...	1254	1941
165	**Baia Mare** ... **1625** ⊙ a.	...	...	2150

	6827	6823	6811
Baia Mare ... **1625** ⊙ d.	0433	...	...
Satu Mare .... **1625** ⊙ d.	0621	1500	...
Carei .... **1625** ⊙ d.	0710	1543	...
Oradea .... ⊙ d.	|	|	1635
Valea lui Mihai ...... ⊙ a.	0749	1617	1759
Valea lui Mihai ▦ .. ⊙ d.	0815	1639	1839
Nyirábrány ▦ .... a.	0730	1554	1754
Nyirábrány .... d.	0809	1609	1809
Debrecen .... a.	0849	1649	1849

km			
0	**Békéscsaba** .... **1280** d.	0638	1550
16	Gyula .... **1280** d.	0659	1609
36	Kötegyán .... a.	0727	1633
36	Kötegyán ▦ .... d.	0740	1645
50	**Salonta** ▦ .... ⊙ a.	0900	1805

Salonta ▦ .... ⊙ d.	0940	1830
Kötegyán ▦ .... a.	0900	1750
Kötegyán .... d.	0915	1815
Gyula .... **1280** d.	0950	1854
Békéscsaba ...... **1280** a.	1010	1910

km			
0	**Mátészalka** .... d.	0535	1406
18	Tiborszállás .... a.	0605	1436
18	Tiborszállás ▦ .... d.	0620	1455
33	**Carei** .... ⊙ a.	0746	1621

Carei .... ⊙ d.	0927	1738
Tiborszállás ▦ .... a.	0853	1704
Tiborszállás .... d.	0908	1719
Mátészalka .... a.	0956	1806

⊙ – Romanian (East European) time, one hour ahead of Hungary. For other trains within Romania see Table **1625**.

2nd class DEBRECEN - FÜZESABONY 1278

km										Ⓑ	
0	**Debrecen** .... d.	0435r	0635r	0835r	1035r	1235r	1435r	1635r	1835r	2000r	2252r
42	Hortobágy .... d.	0536	0736	0936	1136	1336	1536	1736	1936	2100	2353
73	Tiszafüred .... d.	0612	0812	1012	1212	1412	1612	1812	2012	2135	0028
103	**Füzesabony** .... a.	0647	0847	1047	1247	1447	1647	1847	2047	...	...

			Ⓐ							
Füzesabony .... d.	0459	0659	...	0859	1059	1259	1459	1659	1859	2253
Tiszafüred .... d.	0535	0735	0827	0935	1135	1335	1535	1735	1935	2328
Hortobágy .... d.	0616	0816	0901	1016	1216	1416	1616	1816	2016	...
Debrecen .... a.	0716r	0916r	1000r	1116r	1316r	1516r	1716r	1916r	2116r	...

r – By 🚌 Debrecen - Balmazújváros and v.v. (27 km) in timings shown until Dec. 14.

1280 BUDAPEST - BÉKÉSCSABA - LÖKÖSHÁZA - ARAD

2nd class except where shown

km			7410	7400	IC* 73	7402	IC* 75	7404	IC 752		7504	754	7506	IC* 79	7406	IC 756	748		IC* 473		17408	347	
					T ⊖		F ⊖		[R]					K ⊖		[R]			B [R]	b	⑤	D [R]	
0	**Budapest** Keleti 1270 d.	...	...	0605	0705	0810	0910	1010	1110	...	1210	1310	1410	1510	1610	1710	1810	...	1910	...	2010	2310	...
100	Szolnok 1270 d.	0445a	0545	0734	0834	0934	1034	1134	1234	...	1334	1434	1534	1634	1734	1834	1934	...	2034	...	2134	0036	...
141	Mezőtúr d.	0529	0629	0759	0859	0959	1059	1159	1259	...	1359	1459	1559	1659	1759	1859	1959	...	2059	...	2159	|	...
159	Gyoma d.	0547	0647	0814	0912	1012	1112	1212	1312	...	1414	1512	1612	1712	1812	1912	2012	...	2112	...	2212	|	...
196	**Békéscsaba** a.	0617	0717	0840	0940	1040	1140	1240	1340	...	1440	1540	1640	1740	1840	1940	2040	...	2140	...	2236	0130	...
196	**Békéscsaba** d.	0635	...	...	0943	...	1143	...	1343	...	1443	1543	1643	1743	...	1943	...	...	2143	2235	*2243*	0134	...
225	Lökösháza a.	0713	...	...	1010	...	1210	...	1410	...	1513	1613	1713	1813	...	2010	...	...	2210	2302	*2310*	0159	...
225	Lökösháza 🏛 d.	...	...	...	1050	...	1250	...	...	...	...	...	...	1853	...	...	...	...	2251	...	...	0239	...
236	Curtici 🏛 ⊙ a.	...	...	...	1200	...	1400	...	...	...	...	...	...	2003	...	...	...	...	0001	...	...	0349	...
236	Curtici ⊙ d.	...	...	...	1230	...	1425	...	...	...	...	...	...	2031	...	...	...	...	0036	...	...	0419	...
253	**Arad** ⊙ a.	...	...	...	1243	...	1439	...	...	...	...	...	...	2045	...	...	...	...	0050	...	...	0433	...
	Timişoara Nord **1625** ⊙ a.	...	...	...	1333	...	|	...	...	...	...	...	...	2135	...	...	...	...	|	...	...	|	...
	Braşov **1600** ⊙ a.	...	...	...	|	...	2338	...	...	...	...	...	...	...	...	...	...	...	0950	...	...	1332	...
	Bucureşti Nord **1600** ⊙ a.	...	...	...	2322	...	...	...	...	...	...	...	...	...	...	...	...	...	1230	...	...	1606	...

	346	7509	IC* 472	IC 759	7507		IC* 78	7407	757	7405		IC 755	7403		IC* 74	IC* 72	IC 753	7501	751		7441	7541	7451
	D [R]		B [R]	[R]			K ⊖					[R]			F ⊖	T ⊖	[R]						
Bucureşti Nord **1600** ⊙ d.	1400	...	1745	...	...	...	...	...	...	...	...	...	...	...	...	0520	...	...	...	...	...	...	...
Braşov **1600** ⊙ d.	1631	...	2025	...	...	...	...	...	...	...	...	...	...	...	0525	|	...	...	...	...	...	...	...
Timişoara Nord **1625** ⊙ d.	|	...	|	...	...	...	0730	...	...	...	...	...	...	...	|	1440	...	...	...	...	...	...	...
Arad ⊙ d.	0122	...	0516	...	...	...	0821	...	...	...	...	...	...	...	1419	1531	...	...	...	...	...	...	...
Curtici ⊙ a.	0135	...	0529	...	...	...	0834	...	...	...	...	...	...	...	1432	1544	...	...	...	...	...	...	...
Curtici 🏛 ⊙ d.	0210	...	0559	...	...	...	0859	...	...	...	...	...	...	...	1458	1609	...	...	...	...	...	...	...
Lökösháza 🏛 a.	0120	...	0509	...	...	...	0809	...	...	...	...	...	...	...	1408	1519	...	...	...	...	...	...	...
Lökösháza d.	0200	0448	0549	0649	0749	...	0849	...	1049	...	...	1249	...	...	1449	1549	1649	1749	1849	...	...	2049	...
Békéscsaba a.	0225	0515	0616	0716	0816	...	0916	...	1116	...	...	1316	...	...	1516	1616	1716	1816	1916	...	...	2116	...
Békéscsaba d.	0229	0532	0619	0719	0819	...	0919	1019	1119	1219	...	1319	1419	...	1519	1619	1719	1819	1919	...	2040	...	2240
Gyoma d.	|	0601	0648	0746	0848	...	0948	1048	1148	1248	...	1346	1448	...	1548	1648	1748	1848	1948	...	2111	...	2311
Mezőtúr d.	|	0616	0701	0801	0901	...	1001	1101	1201	1301	...	1401	1501	...	1601	1701	1801	1901	2001	...	2126	...	2326
Szolnok 1270 d.	0325	0649	0727	0827	0927	...	1027	1127	1227	1327	...	1427	1527	...	1627	1727	1827	1927	2027	2219			
Budapest Keleti 1270 a.	0450	0815	0850	0950	1050	...	1150	1250	1350	1450	...	1550	1650	...	1750	1850	1950	2050	2150	0015	...	...	...

km	♥											
0	Békéscsaba d.	0725	0950	1150	1250	1350	1450	1550	1650	1750	1950	2050
29	Gyula a.	0741	1007	1207	1307	1407	1507	1607	1707	1807	2007	2106

♠											
Gyula d.	0659	0754	0854	0950	1054	1250	1450	1550	1650	1750	1854
Békéscsaba a.	0715	0810	0910	1010	1110	1310	1510	1610	1710	1810	1910

B – ISTER – 🛏 1, 2 cl., ▬ 2 cl., (2) Budapest - Arad - Sibiu - Braşov - Bucureşti and v.v. ⊡
D – DACIA – 🛏 1, 2 cl., ▬ 2 cl., (2) Wien - Budapest - Arad - Sighişoara - Braşov - Bucureşti and v.v.; (2) Budapest - Bucureşti and v.v.
F – FOGARAS – (2) Budapest - Arad - Sibiu - Braşov and v.v. ⊡
K – KÖRÖS / CRIŞ – (2) Budapest - Arad - Timisoara and v.v. ⊡
T – TRAIANUS – (2) Budapest - Arad - Timişoara - Craiova - Bucureşti and v.v. ⊡

a – Ⓐ only.
b – Not ⑤.
* – Classified *IR* in Romania.
♥ – Also from Békéscsaba at 0523, 0638, 1427Ⓐ, 2230 **b**, 2241⑤.
♠ – Also from Gyula at 0459, 0548, 0617Ⓐ, 1950, 2107.
⊡ – Also (2) Budapest - Lökösháza and v.v.
⊙ – Romanian (East European) time, one hour ahead of Hungary.
⊖ – Reservation compulsory for domestic journeys in Hungary ([R] in Romania).

1290 BUDAPEST - KECSKEMÉT - SZEGED

km		7020	*IC* 700	*IC* 702	*IC* 712		*IC* 708	*IC* 718	*IC* 728	7028
		2	[R]	[R]	[R]		[R]	[R]	[R]	2
									⑤⑦	
0	**Budapest** Nyugati ▷ d.	0400	0553	0653	0753	and	1853	1953	2053	2143
11	Kőbánya Kispest ▷ d.	0415	0607	0707	0807	hourly	1907	2007	2107	2158
18	Ferihegy ✈ ▷ d.	0424	0613	0713	0813	until	1913	2013	2113	2207
73	Cegléd ▷ d.	0531	0648	0748	0848		1948	2048	2148	2303
106	**Kecskemét** d.	0605	0711	0811	0911		2011	2111	2211	2332
131	Kiskunfélegyháza d.	0630	0730	0830	0930		2030	2130	2230	...
191	**Szeged** a.	0715	0815	0915	1015		2115	2215	2315	...

	7029	7009	*IC* 709	*IC* 707	*IC* 717		*IC* 701	*IC* 711	*IC* 721
	2	2	[R]	[R]	[R]		[R]	[R]	[R]
									⑤⑦
Szeged d.	...	0434	0547	0645	0745	and	1845	1945	2045
Kiskunfélegyháza d.	...	0521	0631	0731	0831	hourly	1931	2031	2131
Kecskemét d.	0431	0538	0648	0748	0848	until	1948	2048	2148
Cegléd ▷ d.	0508	0608	0713	0813	0913		2013	2113	2214
Ferihegy ✈ ▷ a.	0554	0654	0744	0844	0944		2044	2144	2248
Kőbánya Kispest ▷ a.	0600	0700	0750	0850	0950		2050	2150	2254
Budapest Nyugati ▷ a.	0617	0717	0807	0907	1007		2107	2207	2310

▷ – For additional trains see Table **1270**.

Note : *IC* trains on this line have designated carriages for the use of passengers without seat reservations.

1292 SZEGED - BÉKÉSCSABA

2nd class

km				d	d		Ⓐ				
0	**Szeged** d.	0510r	0610r	0705r	0905r	1105r	1205r	1305r	and	1905r	2025r
31	Hódmezövásárhely d.	0601	0705	0801	1001	1201	1305	1401	hourly	2001	2115
62	Orosháza d.	0631	0731	0831	1031	1231	1331	1431	until	2031	2143
97	**Békéscsaba** a.	0712	0810	0910	1110	1310	1410	1510		2110	...

				h	h	Ⓐ			
Békéscsaba d.	0547	0647	0747	0947	1147	1247	1347	and	1947
Orosháza d.	0632	0732	0832	1032	1232	1332	1432	hourly	2032
Hódmezövásárhely a.	0700	0756	0900	1100	1300	1356	1500	⊡	2100
Szeged a.	0800r	0900r	1000r	1200r	1400r	1500r	1600r	until	2152r

d – Also at 0805Ⓒr, 1005Ⓒr.
h – Also at 0847Ⓒ, 1047Ⓒ.
r – By 🚌 Szeged - Hódmezövásárhely and v.v. (to Dec. 14).
⊡ – At 1445, 1547, 1645, 1747, 1847.

1295 BUDAPEST - KISKUNHALAS - KELEBIA - (BEOGRAD)

2nd class

km		7920	7912	7922	343	7916	7926	7918	7928	3748
					V					
0	**Budapest Keleti** d.	...	0555	0757	1157	1357	1557	1757	1920	2220
7	Ferencváros d.	...	0604	0806	1206	1406	1606	1806	1929	2229
61	Kunszentmiklós-Tass d.	0457	0659	0859	1259	1459	1659	1859	2057	2335
107	Kiskőrös d.	0559	0759	0959	1359	1559	1759	1959	2156	...
134	Kiskunhalas a.	0632	0832	1032	1432	1632	1832	2032	2228	...
163	**Kelebia** 🏛 a.	0711	0911	1111	1511	1711	1911	2111	2259	...
	Subotica **1360** a.	...	...	...	1555	...	...	...	...	...
	Beograd Centar **1360** a.	...	...	...	m	...	...	...	...	...

	7919	3739	7929	7927	7937	7925	342	7923	7911
							V		
Beograd Centar **1360** d.	...	...	...	...	...	...	n	...	...
Subotica **1360** d.	...	...	...	...	...	...	1402	...	...
Kelebia 🏛 d.	0209	...	0448	0646	0846	1246	1446	1646	1846
Kiskunhalas d.	0240	...	0525	0723	0925	1325	1525	1725	1925
Kiskőrös d.	0313	...	0558	0759	0959	1359	1559	1759	1959
Kunszentmiklós-Tass d.	0412	0459	0659	0859	1059	1459	1659	1859	2059
Ferencváros a.	0520	0609	0809	0955	1155	1555	1755	1955	2155
Budapest Keleti a.	0529	0618	0818	1004	1204	1604	1804	2004	2204

V – IVO ANDRIC – (2) Budapest - Novi Sad and v.v. (change at Kelebia).
m – To Novi Sad ❃ (a. 1842).
n – From Novi Sad ❃ (d. 1057).
❃ – No connection to / from Beograd due to trackwork scheduled to last until Dec. 14 (at least).

1299 OTHER LOCAL SERVICES

2nd class

BUDAPEST - DUNAÚJVÁROS — *80 km*, journey approx 100 minutes
From **Budapest** Déli : 0455, 0555, 0655, 0855, 1055, 1255, 1355, 1455, 1555, 1655, 1855, 2055. From **Dunaújváros** : 0329, 0428, 0528, 0628, 0730, 0828, 1033, 1228, 1433, 1533, 1633, 1729, 1833, 2028, 2233.

BUDAPEST - ESZTERGOM — *53 km*, journey 65 - 74 minutes
From **Budapest** Nyugati : 0025, 0401, 0440Ⓐ, 0510, 0540Ⓐ, 0621, 0651 and every 30 mins until 2121, 2215, 2315.
From **Esztergom** : 0504Ⓐ, 0534, 0555Ⓒ, 0604Ⓐ, 0634, 0655Ⓒ, 0707Ⓐ, 0734, 0755Ⓒ, and at 07Ⓐ, 34, 55Ⓒ mins past each hour to 2007Ⓐ, 2034, 2055Ⓒ, 2107Ⓐ, 2134, 2234, 2334.
Ⓒ Mar. 15 - Nov. 3: 0951, 1051, 1251 call at **Vasútmúzeum**, returning 1459, 1559, 1659.

BUDAPEST - SZENTENDRE — *21 km*, journey time 40 minutes
HÉV suburban trains (line H5) from Budapest Batthyány tér (on metro M2), every 12 - 30 mins.

ESZTERGOM - KOMÁROM — *53 km*, journey time 1h 30m
From **Esztergom** : 0700, 1413. From **Komárom** : 0516, 1216.

EGER - SZILVÁSVÁRAD — *34 km*, journey time 65 minute
From **Eger** : 0638 **G**, 0910, 1257, 1638 **G**.
From **Szilvásvárad** : 0753 **G**, 1112, 1512, 1753 **G**.
Via Szilvásvárad-Szalajkavölgy (for the forest railway), 5 minutes before Szilvásvárad.

HATVAN - SZOLNOK — *68 km*, journey 71 - 73 minute
From **Hatvan** : 0402, 0512Ⓐ, 0612, 0712Ⓐ, 0812, 1012, 1212, 1312 **E**, 1412, 1512, 1612, 1712Ⓐ, 1812, 1912Ⓐ, 2012, 2112Ⓐ, 2212.
From **Szolnok** : 0314, 0431, 0531Ⓐ, 0631, 0731Ⓐ, 0831, 1031, 1231, 1331 **E**, 1431, 1531Ⓐ, 1631, 1731Ⓐ, 1831, 1931Ⓐ, 2031, 2131.

KISKUNFÉLEGYHÁZA - CSONGRÁD - SZENTES — *39 km*, journey time 51 minute
From **Kiskunfélegyháza** : 0535Ⓐ, 0735, 0935, 1335, 1535, 1735, 1935, 2135.
From **Szentes** : 0425Ⓐ, 0635, 0835, 1235, 1435, 1635, 1835 (calls Csongrád 17 mins later)

E – Not Dec. 22 - Jan. 2, June 15 - Sept. 1.
G – Apr. 1 - Oct. 23.

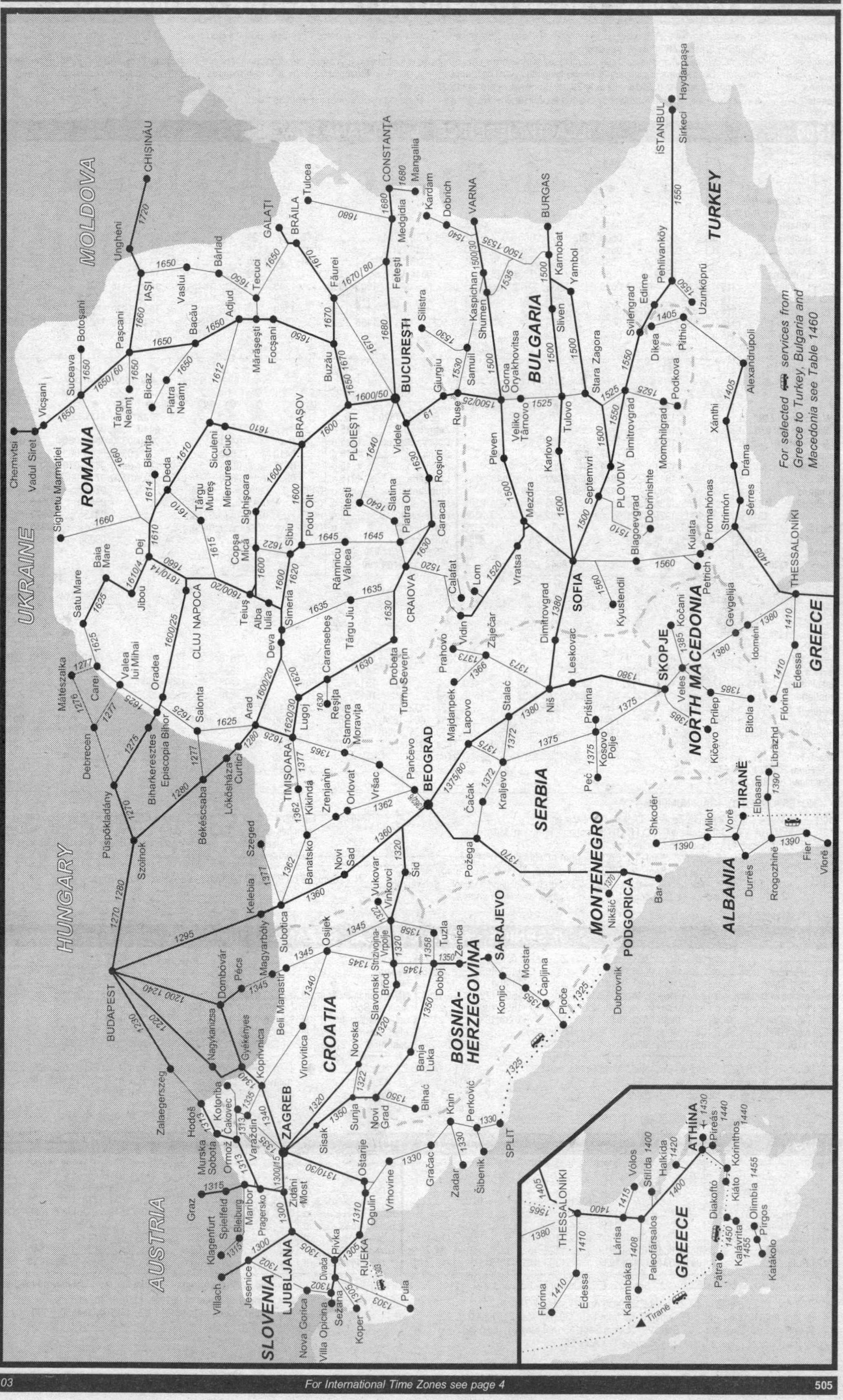
UKRAINE
MOLDOVA
ROMANIA
HUNGARY
AUSTRIA
SLOVENIA
CROATIA
BOSNIA-HERZEGOVINA
SERBIA
MONTENEGRO
ALBANIA
NORTH MACEDONIA
BULGARIA
GREECE
TURKEY
BUDAPEST
BUCUREȘTI
BEOGRAD
SOFIA
ZAGREB
LJUBLJANA
SARAJEVO
SKOPJE
TIRANË
PODGORICA
CHIȘINĂU
ISTANBUL
THESSALONIKI
ATHINA
CONSTANȚA
VARNA
BURGAS
CLUJ NAPOCA
BRAȘOV
CRAIOVA
TIMIȘOARA
PLOVDIV
IAȘI
GALAȚI
RIJEKA
SPLIT
For selected services from Greece to Turkey, Bulgaria and Macedonia see Table 1460

SLOVENIA, CROATIA and BOSNIA-HERZEGOVINA

Operators: Slovenske Železnice (SŽ): www.slo-zeleznice.si; Hrvatske Željeznice (HŽ): www.hzpp.hr; Željeznice Federacije Bosne i Hercegovine (ŽFBH): www.zfbh.ba; and Željeznice Republike Srpske (ŽRS): www.zrs-rs.com.

Services: All trains convey first and second class seating, **except** where shown otherwise in footnotes or by '2' in the train column, or where the footnote shows sleeping and / or couchette cars only. Descriptions of sleeping (🛏) and couchette (▬) cars appear on page 10. In Slovenia, travel by *ICS* train requires reservation and payment of a special fare.

Timings: Valid from **December 9, 2018** until **July 20, 2019** except where indicated otherwise.

Tickets: A supplement is payable for travel by internal express trains. Reservation of seats is possible on most express trains.

1300 VILLACH - JESENICE - LJUBLJANA - ZAGREB

SŽ, HŽ, ÖBB

km		2	2 Ⓐ	2	499 ♦	2	2	2 Ⓐ	2 Ⓐ	415 ♦	2 Ⓐ	2 Ⓐ	2 Ⓒ	2 Ⓐ	2	2 Ⓐ	2 Ⓐ	2	2	626 2 Ⓐ	2 Ⓐ	211 ♦	2 Ⓐ	631 2 Ⓐ	2	2	2 Ⓑ
	München Hbf **890** .d.	...	...	...	2335	...	...	...	...	...	...	...	...	...	...	...	...	...	...	...	...	...	...	...	...	...	...
	Salzburg Hbf **970** ..d.	...	...	...	0140	...	...	...	...	...	...	...	...	...	...	...	...	...	...	...	...	...	...	...	...	...	...
0	**Villach** Hbf. d.	...	...	...	0415	...	...	...	...	0625	...	...	...	...	...	...	...	...	...	...	...	1253	...	...	...	...	...
38	**Jesenice** 🏛 d.	...	0430	...	0503	0533	...	0606	0623	0712	...	0732	0754	...	...	0946	...	1120	...	...	1235	1339	...	...	1423	...	...
51	Lesce-Bled d.	...	0444	...	0515	0547	...	0620	0638	0729	...	0746	0813	...	...	1003	...	1134	...	...	1249	1351	...	...	1437	...	...
74	Kranj d.	...	0508	...	0537	0611	...	0645	0705	0751	...	0813	0838	...	...	1031	...	1158	...	...	1321	1411	...	...	1500	...	...
102	**Ljubljana** a.	...	0539	...	0557	0644	...	0720	0743	0811	...	0844	0908	...	...	1101	...	1228	...	...	1352	1432	...	...	1531	...	...
102	**Ljubljana** **1315** d.	0430f	...	0548	0620	...	0650	...	...	0825	0842	...	...	1003	*1050*	...	1145	...	*1250*	1345	...	1445	1448	1535	...	1550	1650
166	Zidani Most **1315** d.	0604	...	0657	0713	...	0808	...	...	0918	1000	...	...	1110	1200	...	1300	...	1400	1445	...	1545	1610	1635	...	1707	1801
182	Sevnica **1315** d.	0623	...	0715	0729	...	0827	...	...	0934	1020	...	...	1128	1218	...	1319	...	1418	1501	...	1601	1629	1651	...	1726	1820
215	Dobova 🏛 **1315** d.	0654	...	0746	0805	...	0858	...	...	1013	1050	...	...	1156	1246	...	1350	...	1446	1531	...	1640	1700	1721	...	1756	1851
245	**Zagreb** **1315** a.	...	...	...	0835	...	...	...	...	1043	...	...	...	...	...	...	...	...	...	...	...	1710	...	...	...	...	...
	Beograd **1320** a.	...	...	...	...	...	...	...	...	1728	...	...	...	...	...	...	...	...	...	...	...	...	...	...	...	...	...

	2 Ⓐ	2	*EC* 213 ♦	2	2	N 2	315 ♦	411 ♦	2	2 Ⓐ
München Hbf **890** d.	...	...	1217	...	...	...	...	...	...	...
Salzburg Hbf **970** d.	...	...	1412	...	...	...	...	...	...	...
Villach Hbf. d.	...	...	1653	...	...	...	1853	...	...	...
Jesenice 🏛 d.	1531	...	1739	...	1807	1925	1945	...	2035	...
Lesce-Bled d.	1545	...	1751	...	1821	1942	2002	...	2049	...
Kranj d.	1624	...	1812	...	1847	2007	2022	...	2115	...
Ljubljana a.	1653	...	1833	...	1920	2038	2042	...	2147	...
Ljubljana **1315** d.	...	1755	1836	1855	...	...	2105	...	...	2205
Zidani Most **1315** d.	...	1905	1929	2004	...	...	2202	...	...	2308
Sevnica **1315** d.	...	1923	1945	2022	...	...	2218	...	...	2326
Dobova 🏛 **1315** d.	...	1951	2021	2049	...	...	2306	2306	...	2354
Zagreb **1315** a.	...	...	2051	...	...	...	2336	2336	...	...
Beograd **1320** a.	...	...	...	...	...	...	0548	0548	...	...

	2 Ⓐ	2	2 Ⓐ	630 2 Ⓐ	N 2 Ⓒ	2	410 ♦	632 2 Ⓐ	314 ♦	2	2 Ⓐ	2
Beograd **1320** d.	...	...	...	...	...	...	2122	...	2122	...	...	...
Zagreb **1315** d.	...	...	...	...	...	...	0440	...	0440	...	...	...
Dobova 🏛 **1315** d.	...	...	...	0451	...	...	0510	0530	0540	0604	...	0706
Sevnica **1315** d.	...	0410	...	0525	...	...	...	0558	0605	0633	...	0737
Zidani Most **1315** d.	...	0428	...	0544	...	0602	...	0615	0621	0705	...	0807
Ljubljana **1315** a.	...	0530	...	0640	...	0705	...	0710	0718	0807	...	0913
Ljubljana d.	0435	...	0608	...	0652	...	...	...	0726	...	0824	...
Kranj d.	0508	...	0645	...	0723	...	...	...	0751	...	0858	...
Lesce-Bled d.	0547	...	0709	...	0754	...	...	...	0813	...	0922	...
Jesenice 🏛 a.	0600	...	0722	...	0813	...	...	...	0824	...	0935	...
Villach Hbf. a.	...	...	...	...	...	...	...	...	0908	...	...	...
Salzburg Hbf **970** a.	...	...	...	...	...	...	...	...	...	...	...	...
München Hbf **890** a.	...	...	...	...	...	...	...	...	...	...	...	...

	EC 212 ♦	2	2	2 Ⓐ	2	2	2 Ⓐ	2 Ⓐ	2	2	210 ♦	2	2 Ⓐ	2 Ⓐ	2 Ⓐ	2	2 Ⓐ	2	2	2 Ⓑ	2 Ⓐ	2	2	2 Ⓑ	414 ♦	2 Ⓑ	498 ♦
Beograd **1320** d.	...	...	...	...	...	...	...	...	...	...	...	...	...	...	...	...	...	...	...	...	...	...	...	...	1033	...	...
Zagreb **1315** d.	0700	...	...	...	...	...	...	...	...	...	1236	...	...	...	...	...	...	...	...	...	...	...	...	...	1838	...	2120
Dobova 🏛 **1315** d.	0745	...	0913	1019	...	1104	...	1206	...	1312	1339	...	...	1407	...	1510	...	...	1610	...	1706	1806	...	1911	1925	2010	2206
Sevnica **1315** d.	0809	...	0944	1048	...	1135	...	1235	...	1341	1406	...	...	1438	...	1539	...	...	1639	...	1737	1837	...	1942	1949	2029	2232
Zidani Most **1315** d.	0825	...	1005	1112	...	1200	...	1300	...	1400	1422	...	...	1512	...	1609	...	...	1708	...	1800	1900	...	2009	2005	2100	2248
Ljubljana **1315** a.	0916	...	1111	1214	...	1305	...	1402	...	1502	1514	...	...	1618	...	1711	...	...	1810	...	1906	2005	...	2115	2056	2202	2339
Ljubljana d.	0922	1000	...	...	1250	...	1332	...	1445	...	1527	1532	1549	...	1622	...	1718	1754	...	1846	...	...	2043	...	2110	...	2355
Kranj d.	0943	1031	...	...	1321	...	1411	...	1518	...	1552	1604	1624	...	1656	...	1750	1827	...	1919	...	...	2115	...	2131	...	0016
Lesce-Bled d.	1003	1055	...	...	1351	...	1437	...	1545	...	1613	1628	1649	...	1720	...	1821	1851	...	1942	...	...	2139	...	2151	...	0036
Jesenice 🏛 a.	1014	1108	...	...	1404	...	1450	...	1559	...	1624	1641	1703	...	1733	...	1834	1904	...	1955	...	...	2152	...	2202	...	0047
Villach Hbf. a.	1058	...	...	...	...	...	...	...	...	...	1709	...	...	...	...	...	...	...	...	...	...	...	...	...	2243	...	0131
Salzburg Hbf **970** a.	1348	...	...	...	...	...	...	...	...	...	...	...	...	...	...	...	...	...	...	...	...	...	...	...	...	...	0404
München Hbf **890** a.	1541	...	...	...	...	...	...	...	...	...	...	...	...	...	...	...	...	...	...	...	...	...	...	...	...	...	0611

♦ – **NOTES** (LISTED BY TRAIN NUMBER)

210/1 – SAVA – [12] Vinkovci - Zagreb - Ljubljana - Villach and v.v.

212/3 – MIMARA – [12] Zagreb - Villach (**112/3**) - München - Frankfurt and v.v.

314/5 – [12] Villach - Ljubljana - Dobova and v.v.

410 – Dec. 11 - Jan. 14, June 24 - Sept. 17: [12] Beograd - Dobova (**314**) - Ljubljana.

411 – Dec. 10 - Jan. 13, June 23 - Sept. 16: [12] Ljubljana (**315**) - Dobova - Beograd.

414/5 – ALPINE PEARLS – 🛏 1, 2 cl., ▬ 2 cl. and [2] Zagreb - Ljubljana - Villach - Schwarzach (**464/5**) - Zürich and v.v.; [2] Beograd - Zagreb - Ljubljana - Villach and v.v.

498/9 – LISINSKI – 🛏 1, 2 cl., ▬ 2 cl. and [2] Zagreb - Salzburg (**462/3**) - München and v.v.; [2] (also 🛏 1, 2 cl. Apr. 9 - 16, May 25 - Sept. 29 from Rijeka, following day from München): Rijeka (**480/1**) - Ljubljana - München and v.v.

N – Conveys on Ⓒ: [2] Ljubljana - Jesenice - Nova Gorica and v.v.

f – Ⓐ only.

1302 JESENICE - NOVA GORICA - SEŽANA

2nd class only SŽ

km		Ⓐ		Ⓐ	N		Z	Ⓐ	Ⓐ		k	
0	**Jesenice** d.	...	0415	0605	0827	1115	...	...	1432	1651	...	1918
10	Bled Jezero d.	...	0431	0621	0843	1131	...	...	1448	1706	...	1934
28	Bohinjska Bistrica d.	...	0451	0648	0903	1151	...	...	1508	1726	...	1954
56	Most na Soči d.	...	0526	0724	0939	1227	...	...	1553	1801	...	2036
89	Nova Gorica ♣ a.	...	0605	0812	1016	1304	...	...	1632	1838	...	2113
89	Nova Gorica ♣ d.	0455	0608q	0854	...	...	1411	1530	...	...	1850	...
130	**Sežana** a.	0551	0707q	0950	...	...	1512	1626	...	...	1946	...

	Ⓐ				w	Ⓐ		Ⓒ N	Y		Ⓑ y	h
Sežana d.	...	...	0626q	1023a	...	1430	...	...	1624	...	2050	2140
Nova Gorica ♣ a.	...	...	0719q	1116a	...	1522	...	...	1716	...	2143	2232
Nova Gorica ♣ d.	0330	0529	0735	1120	1447	...	1555	1719	...	1956	...	...
Most na Soči d.	0407	0607	0813	1159	1526	...	1634	1803	...	2035	...	...
Bohinjska Bistrica d.	0453	0646	0905	1245	1604	...	1727	1839	...	2114	...	...
Bled Jezero d.	0513	0707	0926	1306	1624	...	1747	1859	...	2133	...	...
Jesenice a.	0529	0722	0942	1322	1640	...	1803	1915	...	2149	...	...

N – Conveys on Ⓒ: [2] Ljubljana - Jesenice - Nova Gorica and v.v.

Y – Runs 11 – 12 minutes later on Ⓐ.

Z – Runs 33 – 38 minutes later on certain dates.

a – Ⓐ.

h – June 22 - Aug. 24.

k – Ⓑ (daily June 22 - Aug. 24).

q – Ⓐ (daily June 22 - Aug. 24).

w – Not Ⓒ June 25 - Sept. 1.

y – Not June 22 - Aug. 24.

♣ – Line **1** 🚌 service operates between Nova Gorica (bus stop 100 metres from station on Italian side) and Gorizia Centrale (Italy) stations. Total journey time ± 20 minutes.

1303 DIVAČA - PULA

2nd class only HŽ, SŽ

km		Ⓐ		w	1272/4 L			z	Ⓐ			
	Ljubljana **1305** d.	...	...	...	0612	...	...	...	...	...	...	...
0	**Divača** d.	...	...	...	0745	1009	...	...	...	1612	...	...
12	Hrpelje-Kozina d.	...	...	...	0804	1021	...	...	...	1626	...	...
30	Rakitovec 🏛 d.	...	...	...	0839	1047	...	...	...	1650	...	...
36	Buzet 🏛 d.	...	0519z	0707	0900	1053	1108	1308	...	1656	1713	1957r
43	Lupoglav ▲ d.	0435	0540	0728	0919	...	1129	1329	1520	...	1734	2018
117	**Pula** a.	0613	0715	0902	1039	...	1303	1511	1659	...	1910	2157

	w	z						Ⓐ	v	1273/5 L	
Pula d.	0455	0637	0905	...	1320	...	1436	1540	1721	1702	1940
Lupoglav ▲ a.	0635	0824	1041	...	1512	...	1631	1716	1902	1829	2121
Buzet 🏛 d.	0658	0842	1059	1119	1530	1705	1649	...	1920r	1855	2139
Rakitovec 🏛 d.	...	...	...	1130	...	1714	...	...	...	1907	...
Hrpelje-Kozina d.	...	...	...	1154	...	1738	...	...	...	1934	...
Divača a.	...	...	...	1209	...	1751	...	...	...	1945	...
Ljubljana **1305** a.	...	...	...	...	...	...	...	...	...	2238	...

L – Ⓒ Apr. 20 - June 16; daily June 22 - Sept. 22: [2] Ljubljana - Pula and v.v.

r – ⑥⑦ Apr. 20 - June 16, June 22 - Sept. 29 (also Apr. 27, May 1, 2).

v – Ⓐ until Apr. 19; daily Apr. 20 - Sept. 29; Ⓐ from Sept. 30 (not May 31, June 22).

w – ⚒ until Apr. 19; daily Apr. 20 - Sept. 29; ⚒ from Sept. 30 (not May 31, June 22).

z – Ⓐ (not Dec. 24 - Jan. 11, Apr. 18 - 26, June 17 - Aug. 30).

▲ – 🚌 service **Lupoglav - Rijeka** and v.v.: Journey 40 minutes.
From Lupoglav at 0639⚒, 1110, 1630, 2120.
From Rijeka at 0555⚒, 1025, 1425Ⓐ, 1545Ⓒ, 1930.

SŽ, HŽ 2nd class only except where shown — LJUBLJANA - RIJEKA, KOPER, SEŽANA and VILLA OPICINA 1305

km		Ⓐ	Ⓐ	1824 U	1274 ♦	1605 ♦	🚌	481 ♦		IC 503		Ⓐ	Ⓐ				483 ♦		1896 T	Ⓐ	IC 509 ♦		Ⓐ	A	
	Maribor **1315** d.	...	...	...	...	0325	...	...	...	...	...	...	...	...	...	...	...	...	...	...	...	...	...	...	...
0	**Ljubljana** d.	0430	0542	0600	0612	0612	...	0635	0815	1021	...	1044	1210	1317	...	1435	1510	1545	1610	1658	1747	1855	1950	...	2103
67	Postojna d.	0532	0644	0656	0709	0709	...	0732	0917	1119	...	1145	1314	1421	...	1537	1611	1649	1708	1803	1845	1958	2052	...	2207
80	Pivka ▲ d.	0545	0657	0709	0722	0722	...	0745	0930	1132	...	1159	1328	1434	...	1550	1623	1703	1721	1817	1858	2011	2106	...	2220
	Ilirska Bistrica 🏛 ▲ d.	|	|	|	|	|	...	0814	|	|	...	|	|	|	...	|	1653	|	|	|	|	|	|	...	|
	Šapjane 🏛 d.	|	|	|	|	|	...	0843	|	|	...	|	|	|	...	|	1721	|	|	|	|	|	|	...	|
	Rijeka a.	|	|	|	|	|	...	0924	|	|	...	|	|	|	...	|	1803	|	|	|	|	|	|	...	|
104	Divača a.	0605	0717	0728	0742	0742	...	...	0950	1153	...	1218	1351	1454	...	1609	...	1723	1739	1838	1919	2031	2126	...	2241
104	Divača d.	0609	0718	0728	0745	0745	0757	...	0951	1154	1157	1219	1352	1455	1538	1610	...	1724	1740	1839	1921	2032	2127	2127	2242
116	Hrpelje-Kozina ⊡ d.	|	|	|	0804	0759	0809	...	|	1207	|	|	|	|	|	|	...	1738	|	|	1934	|	|	|	|
153	**Koper** ⊡ a.	|	|	|	...	0833	0843	...	|	1240	|	|	|	|	|	|	...	1812	|	|	2007	|	|	|	|
113	**Sežana** 🏛 a.	0618	0727	0737	...	...	...	...	1000	...	1207	1228	1402	1505	1548	1620	...	...	1748	1849	...	2042	2136	2136	2252
113	**Sežana** 🏛 d.	0619	...	0737	...	...	...	...	1001	...	...	1229	...	...	...	1627	...	...	1751	...	...	2044	2138	2138	...
120	Villa Opicina **601** a.	0629	...	0747	...	...	...	...	1011	...	...	1239	...	...	...	1637	...	...	1801	...	...	2054	2148	2148	...

km			Ⓐ	Ⓐ	Ⓐ	IC 508 ♦	Ⓐ		Ⓐ	1825 T			482 ♦	Ⓐ	Ⓐ		IC 502	Ⓐ		1897 U	1275 ♦	1604 ♦	480 ♦		B
	Villa Opicina **601** d.	...	...	...	...	...	...	0700	...	0946	1030	...	...	1327	...	...	...	...	1740	1958	...	...	...	2119	2158
	Sežana 🏛 a.	...	...	...	...	...	...	0710	...	0956	1040	...	...	1337	...	...	...	...	1750	2008	...	...	...	2129	2208
	Sežana 🏛 d.	...	0430	0505	0558	...	...	0711	0855	0957	1041	...	...	1338	1433	1516	...	1650	1751	2009	...	...	...	...	...
	Koper ⊡ d.	...	|	|	|	0525	...	|	|	|	|	1003	...	|	|	|	1445	|	|	|	...	2017	...	...	...
	Hrpelje-Kozina ⊡ d.	...	|	|	|	0557	...	|	|	|	|	1035	...	|	|	|	1518	|	|	|	1934	2052	...	...	...
	Divača a.	...	0439	0515	0608	0609	...	0720	0904	1005	1051	1047	...	1347	1443	1526	1529	1659	1800	2017	1945	2104	...	...	...
	Divača d.	...	0440	0516	...	0611	...	0721	0905	1006	...	1059	...	1348	1444	...	1531	1700	1801	2018	2107	2107	...	...	...
0	**Rijeka** d.	...	|	|	...	|	...	|	|	|	...	|	1155	|	|	...	|	|	|	|	|	|	2050	...	...
28	Šapjane 🏛 d.	...	|	|	...	|	...	|	|	|	...	|	1253	|	|	...	|	|	|	|	|	|	2148	...	...
40	Ilirska Bistrica 🏛 ▲ d.	...	|	|	...	|	0632	|	|	|	...	|	1323	|	|	...	|	|	|	|	|	|	2217	...	...
56	Pivka ▲ d.	0410	0502	0539	...	0637	0649	0742	0926	1026	...	1120	1339	1409	1505	...	1553	1723	1823	2038	2129	2129	2233	...	...
	Postojna d.	0423	0515	0553	...	0650	0703	0755	0939	1039	...	1134	1353	1422	1519	...	1604	1737	1836	2051	2141	2141	2246	...	...
	Ljubljana a.	0526	0619	0700	...	0748	0806	0857	1042	1136	...	1236	1448	1526	1625	...	1704	1839	1939	2148	2238	2238	2339	...	...
	Maribor **1315** a.	...	...	...	...	...	...	...	...	...	...	...	...	...	...	...	...	...	...	...	...	0113	...	...	...

♦ – **NOTES** (LISTED BY TRAIN NUMBER)

80/1 – OPATIJA – [12] Rijeka - Ljubljana and v.v.; [2] (also 🛏 1, 2 cl. Apr. 9 - 16, May 25 - Sept. 29 from Rijeka, following day from München): Rijeka - Ljubljana (**498/9**) - München and v.v. Conveys June 22 - Aug. 31 (from Budapest); June 23 - Sept. 1 (from Rijeka): 🛏 1, 2 cl., ▬ 2 cl. and [2] Rijeka - Ljubljana (**1604/5**) - Maribor (**1246/7**) - Budapest.

82/3 – LJUBLJANA – [12] Rijeka - Ljubljana and v.v.

08/9 – [12] Ljubljana - Koper and v.v. Conveys June 21 - Aug. 25 (from Budapest), June 22 - Aug. 26 (from Koper): [12] Budapest (**246/7**) - Ljubljana - Koper and v.v.

274/5 – Ⓒ Apr. 20 - June 16; daily June 22 - Sept. 22: [2] Ljubljana - Pula and v.v. Train number **1272/3** June 22 - Sept. 2.

604 – ISTRA – June 22 - August 31: [2] Koper - Ljubljana - Maribor. Conveys ▬ 2 cl. and [2] Koper - Ljubljana (**1247**) - Hodoš - Budapest; 🛏 1, 2 cl., ▬ 2 cl. and [2] Rijeka (**480**) - Ljubljana - Budapest.

605 – ISTRA – June 22 - August 31: [2] Maribor - Ljubljana - Koper. Conveys (previous day from Budapest): ▬ 2 cl. and [2] Budapest (**1246**) - Hodoš - Maribor - Koper; 🛏 1, 2 cl., ▬ 2 cl. and [2] Budapest - Maribor - Ljubljana (**481**) - Rijeka.

A – Ⓒ Apr. 22 - Sept. 22.
B – Ⓐ (also Ⓒ Apr. 22 - Sept. 22).
T – To/from Trieste (Table **87**).
U – To/from Udine (Table **87**).

▲ – Local services **Pivka - Ilirska Bistrica** and v.v.: Journey 16 minutes.
From Pivka at 0550Ⓐ, 0932Ⓐ, 1201Ⓐ, 1339Ⓐ, 1508Ⓐ, 1724Ⓑ, 1824Ⓑ.
From Ilirska Bistrica at 0523Ⓐ, 0632Ⓐ, 1100Ⓐ, 1413Ⓐ, 1530Ⓐ, 1757Ⓑ, 1952Ⓑ.

⊡ – 🚌 service **Koper - Trieste** and v.v.: Journey 45 minutes.
From Koper at 0600⚒, 0642Ⓐ, 0700Ⓐ, 0730⚒, 1030⚒, 1115Ⓐ, 1215Ⓐ, 1400⚒, 1730⚒. **From Trieste** at 0700⚒, 0900⚒, 1000Ⓐ, 1115Ⓐ, 1230⚒, 1300⚒, 1400Ⓐ, 1530⚒, 1900⚒.
Service is subject to alteration. No service on ⑦, Slovenian and Italian holidays.
Operator: Arriva Slovenija, Meljska cesta 97, 2000 Maribor.

An irregular 🚌 service also operates Trieste - Hrpelje-Kozina and v.v.

HŽ 2nd class only except where shown — RIJEKA - ZAGREB 1310

km			⚒	703			⚒	Ⓐs		Ⓐ	1701		
0	**Rijeka** d.	...	...	0535	0725	...	...	1153	1358	1522	1730	...	1915
61	Delnice d.	...	...	0644	0837	...	...	1309	1512	1635	1837	...	2032
90	Moravice d.	...	0603	0717	0912	...	...	1344	1547	1714	1911	1950	2107
20	Ogulin **1330** d.	0413	0634	0750	0942	1027	1217	1420	1619	1746	1940	2021	2137
26	Oštarije **1330** d.	0420	0641	0759	...	1035	1224	...	1626	...	1948	2028	...
76	Karlovac **1330** d.	0521	0754	0848	...	1136	1327	...	1728	...	2037	2125	...
29	**Zagreb** **1330** a.	0614	0849	0934	...	1230	1420	...	1825	...	2118	2218	...
	Osijek **1340** a.	...	...	1446	...	...	...	...	...	...	...	...	...

		Ⓐ			Ⓐs			Ⓐ		702	Ⓐ	
Osijek **1340** d.	...	...	...	...	...	...	...	...	...	1202	...	...
Zagreb **1330** d.	...	...	0636	0812	...	1314	...	1422	1545	1705	1712	2140
Karlovac **1330** d.	...	...	0725	0905	...	1408	...	1521	1640	1746	1808	2235
Oštarije **1330** d.	...	...	0828	1006	...	1510	...	1627	1744	1833	1907	2335
Ogulin **1330** d.	0420	0600	0834	1026	1405	1516	1601	1633	1752	1841	1913	2341
Moravice d.	0451	0634	...	1057	1435	...	1635	...	1822	1910	...	...
Delnice d.	0525	0714	...	1132	1513	...	1709	...	...	1941	...	...
Rijeka a.	0638	0829	...	1241	1624	...	1819	...	...	2042	...	...

– Not June 17 - Aug. 30.

SŽ, MÁV 2nd class only except where shown — MARIBOR - ČAKOVEC, MURSKA SOBOTA and ZALAEGERSZEG 1313

km		1247 ♦	Ⓐ	Ⓐ		Ⓐ	Ⓐ		Ⓐ	640	247 ♦		Ⓐ	⚒	g	Ⓐ	Ⓐ		Ⓐ				520 Ⓐ			Ⓐ	IC 502	Ⓐ
	Ljubljana **1315** d.	0015	...	...	...	...	...	...	...	...	0825	...	...	...	...	...	...	...	...	...	...	...	...	...	...	...	1715	...
0	**Maribor** **1315** d.	|	...	...	...	...	...	0705	...	0918	|	...	1105	1303	1303	1350	...	1433	...	1527	...	1620	...	...	...	1845	|	2210
19	Pragersko **1315** d.	0225	...	...	...	...	0617	|	...	0944	1114	...	|	|	|	|	...	1503	...	|	...	|	1725	...	...	|	1935	|
37	Ptuj d.	0238	...	...	...	...	0641	0750	...	0959	1126	...	1147	1344	1344	1435	...	1524	...	1610	...	1656	1738	...	...	1926	1951	2252
59	Ormož d.	|	...	0447	...	0530	0708	0812	0814	1015	1141	1150	1211	1410	1410	1457	...	1549	1555	1634	1643	1710	1753	...	1758	1952	2007	2314
	Središče 🏛 a.	|	...	0458	...	|	...	|	0827	|	|	1201	...	|	|	1508	...	|	1606	|	1654	...	|	...	1811	|	|	...
	Čakovec a.	|	...	...	...	|	...	|	0840	|	|	...	...	|	|	...	...	|	—	|	...	...	|	...	1824	|	|	...
98	**Murska Sobota** d.	0319	0330	...	...	0615	...	0854	...	1048	1213	...	...	1451	1451	...	1537	1633	...	1720	...	...	1827	...	...	2035	2054	...
27	Hodoš a.	0338	0356	...	...	...	...	...	...	...	1230	...	...	...	...	...	1603	...	...	...	...	...	1855	...	...	...	2121	...
27	Hodoš 🏛 d.	0353	...	...	0620	...	...	...	...	...	1252	...	...	...	...	...	...	...	1610	...	...	...	...	1930	...	...	...	...
74	**Zalaegerszeg** a.	0431	...	...	0710	...	...	...	...	...	1330	...	...	...	...	...	...	...	1706	...	...	...	...	2020	...	...	...	...
	Budapest D **1230** a.	0844k	...	...	...	...	...	...	...	...	1729	...	...	...	...	...	...	...	...	...	...	...	...	...	...	...	...	...

km		1246 ♦		521 Ⓐ	Ⓐ	Ⓐ		IC 503	Ⓒ	Ⓐ	Ⓐ	Ⓐ	Ⓐ	Ⓐ	246 ♦	Ⓐ	⚒	g	Ⓐ	Ⓐ		1641 g	Ⓐ	1643 g				Ⓐ
	Budapest D **1230** d.	1950k	...	...	...	...	...	...	...	...	...	...	...	...	0830	...	...	...	...	...	...	...	...	...	...	...	...	...
	Zalaegerszeg d.	0012	...	...	...	...	0520	...	...	...	...	...	...	...	1212	...	...	...	...	...	1450	...	...	...	1645	...	1825	...
	Hodoš 🏛 a.	0048	...	...	...	...	0611	...	...	...	...	...	...	...	1250	...	...	...	...	...	1540	...	...	...	1735	...	1916	...
	Hodoš d.	0103	...	0420	...	0545	...	0631	...	...	...	...	...	...	1305	...	...	...	...	...	—	1615	1617	...	—	...	...	2135
	Murska Sobota d.	0122	...	0448	...	0615	...	0652	...	...	0922	...	1220	...	1325	...	1508	1508	...	...	...	1644	1643	1815	...	1855	...	2201
0	**Čakovec** d.	|	...	|	...	|	...	|	...	0930	|	...	|	...	|	...	|	|	...	...	...	|	...	|	1832	|	...	...
12	Središče 🏛 d.	|	0424	|	0537	|	...	|	...	0945	|	...	|	1340	|	1529	|	|	1614	...	1710	|	...	|	1847	|	...	...
22	Ormož d.	|	0436	0520	0550	0655	...	0720	0841	0955	1001	1219	1302	1351	1357	1540	1548	1548	1625	1700	1722	1727	...	1849	1857	1937	...	...
	Ptuj d.	0201	0500	0535	0613	0717	...	0735	0901	...	1026	1242	1325	...	1411	...	1609	1609	...	1723	...	1752	...	1905	...	2005	...	...
	Pragersko **1315** d.	0331t	|	0548	0643	|	...	0754	|	...	1055	|	|	...	1425	...	1640	1640	...	1746	...	1823	...	1926	...	|	...	...
	Maribor **1315** a.	0225	0553	...	0706	0807	...	|	0936	...	1117	1326	1411	...	|	...	1701	1701	...	...	...	|	...	|	...	2050	...	...
	Ljubljana **1315** a.	0550	...	...	...	...	...	1018	...	...	...	...	...	...	1639	...	...	...	...	...	...	2035	...	2136	...	...	...	...

– **NOTES** (LISTED BY TRAIN NUMBER)

6/7 – CITADELLA – [12] Budapest - Ljubljana and v.v. Conveys June 21 - Aug. 25 (from Budapest), June 22 - Aug. 26 (from Koper): [12] Budapest - Ljubljana (**508/9**) - Koper and v.v.

46 – ISTRA – June 22 - Aug. 31: 🛏 1, 2 cl. and [2] Budapest - Hodoš - Maribor (**1605**) - Koper; 🛏 1, 2 cl., ▬ 2 cl. and [2] Budapest - Ljubljana (**481**) - Rijeka.

47 – ISTRA – June 23 - Sept. 1: 🛏 1, 2 cl. and [2] Koper - Ljubljana - Hodoš - Budapest; 🛏 1, 2 cl., ▬ 2 cl. and [2] Rijeka (**480**) - Ljubljana - Budapest.

g – ⑦ Dec. 9 - June 23, Sept. 1 - Dec. 1 (also Jan. 2, Apr. 22; not Dec. 23, 30, Apr. 21, 28).
k – Budapest Keleti.
t – Via Maribor.

1315 LJUBLJANA and ZAGREB - MARIBOR - GRAZ

SŽ, HŽ, ÖBB

km		1247 ♦	2 h	2 Ⓐ	IC 512 🚌	2	14 Ⓡ 🚌	EC 158 ✕ ♦	247 ♦	2	2	IC 18	2	2 Ⓐ	2 ⚒	ICS 20 Ⓡ	2	2	EC 150 ✕ ♦	IC 502 ♦	ICS 26 Ⓡ 🚌	2 ✣	1604 2 ♦	604 2 w		
	Koper 1305 d.	...	...	...	...	...	...	...	...	...	...	...	...	...	...	...	...	...	...	...	...	...	2017	...	...	...
0	**Ljubljana** 1300 d.	0015	0045	...	0545	...	0800	...	0858	1050	...	1312	1250	...	1350	1515	...	...	1545	1715	2012	2050	2250	2250	...	...
*	**Zagreb** 1300 d.	|	|	...	|	...	|	0700	|	|	...	|	|	...	|	|	...	...	|	|	|	|	|	|	...	...
	Dobova 🛃 1300 d.	|	|	...	|	...	|	0757	|	|	...	|	|	...	|	|	...	...	|	|	|	|	|	|	...	...
	Sevnica 1300 d.	|	|	...	|	...	|	0825	|	|	...	|	|	...	|	|	...	...	|	|	|	|	|	|	...	...
64	Zidani Most 1300 d.	0108	0145	...	|	0703	|	|	0953	1157	...	1357	1401	...	1500	1600	...	1604	1642	1815	|	*2200*	2351	2355	...	...
89	Celje d.	0144	0215	...	0700	0737	0910	0920	1032	1231	...	1427	1435	...	1538	1631	...	1631	1719	1852	2127	*2232*	0029	0033	...	...
137	Pragersko 1313 d.	0222	0256	...	0741	0823	...	0959	1111	1317	...	1500	1521	...	1624	1705	...	1723	1756	1933	2159	*2319*	0111	0115	...	...
156	**Maribor** ▲ 1313 a.	...	0307	...	0755	0841	...	1014	...	1335	...	1513	1539	...	1643	1718	...	1743	1812	...	2210	*2337*	0125	0129	...	...
156	**Maribor** d.	...	...	0503	...	...	...	1019	...	...	1335	...	...	1636	...	...	1737	...	1820	...	...	...	...	...	...	...
172	Spielfeld-Straß 🛃 a.	...	...	0525	...	...	...	1036	...	...	1353	...	...	1656	...	...	1757	...	1836	...	...	...	...	...	...	...
172	Spielfeld-Straß 🛃 980 d.	...	...	...	...	...	...	1048	...	...	...	...	...	...	...	...	...	...	1848	...	...	...	...	...	...	...
219	**Graz** Hbf 980 a.	...	...	...	...	...	...	1120	...	...	...	...	...	...	...	...	...	...	1920	...	...	...	...	...	...	...
	Wien Hbf 980 a.	...	...	...	...	...	...	1402	...	...	...	...	...	...	...	...	...	...	2202	...	...	...	...	...	...	...

	2 h ✣	605 2 w	1605 ♦	ICS 11 Ⓡ	2 Ⓐ	IC 503 ♦	2	2 Ⓐ ✣	ICS 17 Ⓡ 🚌	EC 151 ✕ ♦	2 Ⓐ	246 ♦	2 ✣	ICS 19 Ⓡ 🚌	1611 2 g	2 Ⓐ	2 Ⓐ	ICS 21 Ⓡ	1615 2 g	1641 2 ♦	2	2 Ⓐ ✣	1643 2 ♦	EC 159 ✕ ♦	523 🚌	161. 2 g
Wien Hbf 980 d.	...	...	...	...	...	...	...	...	...	0758	...	...	...	...	...	...	...	...	...	...	...	...	...	1558	...	...
Graz Hbf 980 d.	...	...	...	...	...	...	...	...	...	1039	...	...	...	...	...	...	...	...	...	...	...	...	...	1839	...	...
Spielfeld-Straß 980 a.	...	...	...	...	...	...	...	...	...	1108	...	...	...	...	...	...	...	...	...	...	...	...	...	1908	...	...
Spielfeld-Straß d.	...	...	...	...	0545	...	0903	...	...	1120	...	...	*1405*	...	...	...	1710	...	...	...	1803	...	...	1920	...	...
Maribor a.	...	...	...	...	0607	...	0922	...	...	1137	...	...	*1423*	...	...	...	1731	...	...	...	1819	...	...	1937	...	...
Maribor ▲ 1313 d.	0115	0315	0315	0540	...	...	...	0925	1048	1145	1317	...	1427	1517	1615	1615	...	1748	1757	...	...	1824	...	1940	...	195
Pragersko 1313 d.	0133	0331	0331	0554	...	0754	...	0944	1102	1201	1336	1425	1446	1531	1634	1634	...	1801	1813	1823	...	1843	1926	1956	...	201
Celje d.	0218	0415	0415	0630	...	0836	...	*1034*	1139	1241	1434	1505	*1535*	1608	1718	1718	...	1840	1900	1908	...	*1933*	2007	2039	2040	205
Zidani Most 1300 d.	0252	0451	0451	0701	...	0920	...	*1105*	|	1319	1514	1543	*1606*	|	1756	1752	...	|	1938	1941	...	*1959*	2044	|	|	213
Sevnica 1300 d.	|	|	|	|	...	|	...	...	|	|	...	|	|	|	|	...	...	|	|	|	...	...	|	2130	|	|
Dobova 🛃 1300 d.	|	|	|	|	...	|	...	...	|	|	...	|	|	|	|	...	...	|	|	|	...	...	|	2211	|	|
Zagreb 1300 a.	|	|	|	|	...	|	...	...	|	|	...	|	|	|	|	...	...	|	|	|	...	...	|	2241	|	|
Ljubljana 1300 a.	0347	0550	0550	0745	...	1018	...	...	1249	1414	...	1639	...	1716	1847	...	...	1950	2031	2035	...	...	2136	...	2152	222
Koper 1305 a.	...	...	0833	...	...	...	...	...	...	...	...	...	...	...	...	...	...	...	...	...	...	...	...	...	...	...

ADDITIONAL SERVICES MARIBOR - ZIDANI MOST and v.v.: 2nd class only ✣ – By 🚌 Celje - Zidani Most and v.v.

			✣Ⓐ	Ⓐ	✣Ⓐ		✣Ⓐ	Ⓐ	✣		✣Ⓐ	✣	✣Ⓑ
Maribor ▲ d.	0420	0511	0620	0715	0816	1015	1115	1215	1520	1714	1918	2020	2100
Pragersko d.	0440	0530	0639	0734	0835	1034	1134	1234	1539	1733	1938	2040	2119
Celje d.	0526	0620	0728	0820	0924	1123	1225	1320	1628	1820	2026	2128	2207
Zidani Most d.	0600	0654	0802	0854	0956	1154	1256	1354	1659	1852	2053	2155	2234

	✣	Ⓐ	✣Ⓐ	✣Ⓐ	✣Ⓐ	✣Ⓐ	✣Ⓐ	✣	✣Ⓐ	m	✣	✣Ⓐ	✣
Zidani Most d.	0452	0542	0801	0850	1007	1109	1257	1702	1800	1902	2008	2100	220
Celje d.	0527	0620	0838	0930	1041	1146	1332	1738	1832	1936	2040	2132	223
Pragersko d.	0613	0706	0924	1017	1128	1233	1419	1824	1919	2021	2126	2218	231
Maribor ▲ a.	0631	0724	0943	1035	1145	1253	1437	1842	1937	2041	2146	2237	233

♦ – **NOTES** (LISTED BY TRAIN NUMBER)

150/1 – EMONA – [12] ✕ Ljubljana - Wien and v.v.
158/9 – CROATIA – [12] ✕ Zagreb - Wien and v.v.
246/7 – CITADELLA – [12] Budapest - Ljubljana and v.v. Conveys June 21 - Aug. 25 (from Budapest), June 22 - Aug. 26 (from Koper): [12] Budapest - Ljubljana (**508/9**) - Koper and v.v.
503/2 – POHORJE – [12] Ljubljana - Pragersko - Hodoš and v.v.
1247 – ISTRA – June 22 - Aug. 31: ▬ 2 cl., [2] Koper (**1604**) - Ljubljana - Hodoš - Budapest; 🛏 1, 2 cl. ▬ 2 cl. [2] Rijeka (**480**) - Ljubljana - Hodoš - Budapest.
1604 – ISTRA – June 22 - Aug. 31: [2] Koper - Ljubljana - Maribor. Conveys ▬ 2 cl., [2] Koper - Ljubljana (**1247**) - Hodoš - Budapest; 🛏 1, 2 cl., ▬ 2 cl. [2] Rijeka (**480**) - Ljubljana - Hodoš - Budapest.
1605 – ISTRA – June 21 - Aug. 30: [2] Maribor - Ljubljana - Koper. Conveys ▬ 2 cl., [2] Budapest (**1246**) - Hodoš - Maribor - Koper; 🛏 1, 2 cl., ▬ 2 cl. [2] Budapest - Maribor - Ljubljana (**481**) - Rijeka.
1641 – ⑦ Dec. 9 - June 23, Sept. 1 - Dec. 2 (not Oct. 28): [2] Hodoš - Ljubljana.
1643 – ⑦ Dec. 9 - June 23, Sept. 1 - Dec. 2 (not Oct. 28): [2] Murska Sobota - Ljubljana.

B – 🚌 Ljubljana - Celje and v.v.

MARIBOR - BLEIBURG (- KLAGENFURT)

km		Ⓐ	k		Ⓐ	k
0	Maribor d.	0520	1445	*Klagenfurt* d.	*0805*	*163*
87	Bleiburg 🛃 a.	0730	1659	Bleiburg 🛃 d.	0854	172
126	*Klagenfurt* a.	*0839*	*1756*a	Maribor a.	1055	192

Other services are available Bleiburg - Klagenfurt and v.v.

a – Ⓐ only.
g – ⑦ Dec. 9 - June 23, Sept. 1 - Dec. 2 (also Jan. 2, Apr. 22; not Dec. 23, 30, Apr. 21, 8, Oct. 28).
h – Dec. 16 - Jan. 1, June 9 - Sept. 23.
k – Ⓑ (not ⑦ June 23 - Aug. 25). Not Dec. 25, 26, 30, Jan. 1, Apr. 2 May 1, June 25, Aug. 15, Oct. 31, Nov. 1.
m – Runs 15-23 minutes later on ⑦.
w – Not June 22 - Aug. 31.

* – Zagreb - Celje: *104 km*.
▲ – For Maribor - Bleiburg (- Klagenfurt) services see panel above.
✣ – By 🚌 Celje - Zidani Most and v.v.

1320 ZAGREB - VINKOVCI - BEOGRAD

SŽ, HŽ, ŽS

km		741	2	415 ♦	743 ⚒	745	211 ♦	✣ 2 ⚒	747	411 ♦
	Ljubljana 1300 d.	...	...	0825	...	...	1445	...	...	2105
0	**Zagreb** d.	0613	0741	1103	1303	1518	1742	1907	2138	2343
105	Novska d.	0806	1005	1256	1505	1718	1935	2123	2332	0134
191	Slavonski Brod d.	0904	1128	1354	1606	1816	2032	2237	0039	0229
224	Strizivojna-Vrpolje 1345 d.	0923	1157	1413	1626	1835	2052	2307	0104	0248
	Osijek 1345 a.	|	|	|	|	|	|	|	|	|
256	**Vinkovci** d.	0940	1222	1440	1644	1853	2110	2331	0128	0307
288	Šid 🛃 a.	...	...	1518	...	...	...	...	...	0345
407	**Beograd** Centar a.	...	...	1742	...	...	...	...	...	0602

	740	742	✣ 2 ⚒	210 ♦	746	414 ♦	748	2 Ⓐ	410 ♦
Beograd Centar d.	...	...	...	...	...	1035	...	...	210
Šid 🛃 d.	...	...	...	...	...	1346	...	...	002
Vinkovci d.	0255	0545	0740	0855	1145	1444	1716	1945	010
Osijek 1345 d.	|	|	|	|	|	|	|	|	|
Strizivojna-Vrpolje 1345 d.	0320	0604	0757	0914	1203	1503	1740	2010	012
Slavonski Brod d.	0346	0625	0817	0934	1223	1524	1806	2039	014
Novska d.	0451	0727	0911	1028	1318	1622	1911	2156	023
Zagreb a.	0643	0924	1058	1221	1510	1812	2110	0008	042
Ljubljana 1300 a.	...	...	...	1514	...	2056	...	...	071

♦ – **NOTES** (LISTED BY TRAIN NUMBER)

210/1 – SAVA – [12] Vinkovci - Zagreb - Ljubljana - Villach and v.v.
410 – Dec. 10 - Jan. 13, June 23 - Sept. 16: [12] Beograd - Dobova (**314**) - Ljubljana.
411 – Dec. 9 - Jan. 12, June 22 - Sept. 15: [12] Ljubljana (**315**) - Dobova - Beograd.
414/5 – ALPINE PEARLS – 🛏 1, 2 cl., ▬ 2 cl. and [2] Zagreb - Ljubljana - Villach Schwarzach-St Veit (**464/5**) - Zürich and v.v.; [2] Beograd - Zagreb - Ljubljana Villach and v.v.
✣ – Subject to alteration.

1322 LOCAL SERVICES in Croatia (*subject to confirmation*)

2nd class only HŽ

ZAGREB - SISAK CAPRAG: Journey 60–75 minutes. All services call at Sisak (5 minutes from Sisak Caprag).
From Zagreb at 0545Ⓐ, 0633, 0746Ⓐ, 0904, 1111, 1233Ⓐ, 1356, 1455Ⓐ, 1546, 1652Ⓐ, 1759Ⓐ, 1910, 2011, 2123Ⓐ, 2251.
From Sisak Caprag at 0422⚒, 0526, 0603Ⓐ, 0619, 0700Ⓐ, 0804Ⓐ, 1035⚒, 1213, 1415Ⓐ, 1517, 1610Ⓐ, 1658, 1805Ⓐ, 2008, 2128.

SISAK CAPRAG - SUNJA: Journey 30 minutes.
From Sisak Caprag at 0347⚒, 0701Ⓐ, 0736, 0957, 1214, 1450, 1659, 1854Ⓐ, 2009.
From Sunja at 0454⚒, 0547, 0628Ⓐ, 1141, 1256, 1626, 1936, 2056, 2138Ⓐ.

SUNJA - NOVSKA: Journey 70 minutes.
From Sunja at 0808, 1246, 1532Ⓐ **x**, 2047Ⓑ.
From Novska at 0438, 0519Ⓐ, 1032, 1401Ⓐ **x**, 1807Ⓑ.

VINKOVCI - VUKOVAR: Journey 40 minutes.
From Vinkovci at 0403Ⓐ, 0608Ⓐ, 1002Ⓐ, 1204Ⓐ **x**, 1520, 1901
From Vukovar at 0450Ⓐ, 0654Ⓐ, 1101Ⓐ, 1321Ⓐ **x**, 1630, 1950

x – Not June 18 - Aug. 31.

1325 🚌 SPLIT - PLOČE - DUBROVNIK (*subject to confirmation*)

🚌 SPLIT - DUBROVNIK: Up to 18 departures per day. Journey 4 hrs - 5 hrs 10 mins.
🚌 SPLIT - PLOČE: Up to 22 departures per day. Journey 2 hrs - 2 hrs 50 mins.
🚌 PLOČE - DUBROVNIK: Up to 17 departures per day. Journey 2 hrs - 2 hrs 20 mins.

Note: various operators run on these routes; tickets are not interchangeable.
Split and Ploče bus stations are situated adjacent to the railway stations.
Buses pass through Bosnia between Ploče and Dubrovnik (passports required).

HŽ 2nd class only except where shown — ZAGREB - ZADAR, ŠIBENIK and SPLIT — 1330

Knin - Zadar and v.v. 🚌 service is subject to alteration

km	km																									
										ICN 521						ICN 523							821		1204
								🚌	🚌	R					🚌	R								🚌	
			Ⓐ	⚒	Ⓐ		Ⓐq	h	s	🍷	Ⓐ	Ⓐ				🍷	Ⓐ	Ⓐ					♦		♦
0		Zagreb 1310 d.	...	...	...	...	...	...	...	0735	...	...	...	...	...	1520	...	...	...	...	...	...	2256	...	0038
53		Karlovac 1310 d.	...	...	...	...	...	...	...	0811	...	...	...	...	...	1556	...	...	...	...	...	...	2339	...	0116
103		Oštarije 1310 d.	...	...	...	...	...	...	...	0900	...	...	...	...	...	1642	...	...	...	...	...	...	|	...	|
109		**Ogulin** 1310 d.	...	...	...	...	...	...	...	|	...	...	...	...	...	|	...	...	...	...	...	...	0043	...	0226
225		Gospić d.	...	...	...	...	...	...	...	1037	...	...	...	...	...	1816	...	...	...	...	...	...	0251	...	|
269		Gračac d.	...	...	...	...	...	...	...	1110	...	...	...	...	...	1850	...	...	...	...	...	...	0329	...	|
333		Knin a.	...	...	...	...	...	...	...	1200	...	...	...	...	...	1940	...	...	...	...	...	...	0433	...	0622
333	0	Knin d.	...	...	0739	...	...	1111	1200	1211	...	...	1510	...	1715	1941	1955	...	...	0415	...	...	0435	0505	0639
	95	**Zadar** ⊡ a.	...	...	|	...	...	1328	1418	|	...	...	|	...	1933	|	|	...	...	|	...	...	|	0724	|
387	—	Perković a.	...	...	0841	...	...	...	...	1257	...	...	1616	...	...	2035	2058	...	...	0517	...	←	0532	...	0733
387	0	Perković d.	0614	0705	0852	0901	1221	...	...	1258	1301	1513	1631	1640	...	2036	2059	2100	2259	→	0525	0536	0546	...	0734
	22	**Šibenik** ⊡ a.	|	0736	0923	|	|	...	...	|	1332	1543	1702	|	...	|	2130	|	2326	...	|	0607	|	...	|
435		**Split** ⊡ a.	0717	...	...	1005	1321	...	...	1343	...	...	...	1740	...	2121	...	2200	...	...	0628	...	0645	...	0837

							ICN 520						ICN 522					1205						820	
						🚌	R						R	🚌								🚌			
	Ⓐ	⚒					🍷		Ⓐq	Ⓐ		Ⓐ	🍷	h		Ⓐ		♦		Ⓐ				♦	
Split ⊡ d.	...	...	0748	...	...	...	0833	...	1031	...	...	...	1425	...	1528	...	...	1830	...	1947	...	...	...	2144	...
Šibenik ⊡ d.	0453	0624	|	...	0814	...	|	...	|	1106	...	1425	|	...	|	1555	...	|	...	|	2026	...	2212	|	...
Perković a.	0523	0654	0849	...	0844	...	0919	...	1132	1138	...	1455	1511	...	1629	1625	...	1931	...	2052	2056	...	2241	2257	...
Perković d.	0534	...	...	...	0851	...	0920	...	...	...	...	...	1512	...	...	1632	...	1933	...	...	2102	...	...	2258	...
Zadar ⊡ d.	|	...	...	...	|	0735	|	...	...	...	...	...	|	1440	...	|	...	|	...	...	|	2030	...	|	...
Knin a.	0637	...	...	...	0954	0956	1005	...	...	...	...	...	1555	1659	...	1735	...	2042	...	...	2205	2249	...	2356	...
Knin d.	...	...	...	...	...	...	1007	...	...	...	...	...	1556	...	...	...	...	2044	...	...	...	...	...	2357	...
Gračac d.	...	...	...	...	...	...	1111	...	...	...	...	...	1651	...	...	...	...	|	...	...	...	...	...	0110	...
Gospić d.	...	...	...	...	...	...	1145	...	...	...	...	...	1726	...	...	...	...	|	...	...	...	...	...	0148	...
Ogulin 1310 d.	...	...	...	...	...	...	|	...	...	...	...	...	|	...	...	...	...	0105j	...	...	...	...	...	0407	...
Oštarije 1310 d.	...	...	...	...	...	...	1321	...	...	...	...	...	1910	...	...	...	...	|	...	...	...	...	...	|	...
Karlovac 1310 d.	...	...	...	...	...	...	1410	...	...	...	...	...	1957	...	...	...	...	0205	...	...	...	...	...	0504	...
Zagreb 1310 a.	...	...	...	...	...	...	1446	...	...	...	...	...	2036	...	...	...	...	0243	...	...	...	...	...	0549	...

♦ – **NOTES** (LISTED BY TRAIN NUMBER)

820 – 1, 2 cl., 2 cl., [2] Split - Zagreb.

821 – 1, 2 cl., 2 cl., [2] Zagreb - Split.

1204 – ADRIA – June 14 - Sept. 6 (from Budapest, one day later from Zagreb): 1, 2 cl., 2 cl., [2] Budapest - Gyékényes - Zagreb - Split.

1205 – ADRIA – June 15 - Sept. 7: 1, 2 cl., 2 cl., [2] Split - Zagreb - Gyékényes - Budapest.

h – ⚒ (daily June 1 - Sept. 30).

j – Arrive 0026.

q – Not June 17 - Aug. 30.

s – June 1 - Sept. 30.

⊡ – Frequent 🚌 services operate Zadar - Šibenik - Split and v.v.; some continue to Ploče and Dubrovnik (see Table **1325**). Bus station locations: Zadar, Split and Ploče are adjacent to rail station, Šibenik approximately 10 minutes walk.

HŽ, MÁV 2nd class only except where shown — ZAGREB - VARAŽDIN - NAGYKANIZSA — 1335

There is currently no service Kotoriba - Murakeresztúr and v.v.

km																												
																992	770											
		⚒		Ⓐ		Ⓐ			⚒		⚒	⚒	Ⓐ	Ⓐ			♦	Ⓐ			Ⓐ	ⒶV	⚒	V				
0	**Zagreb** d.	...	...	...	...	0541	0733	...	0858	...	1115	...	1308	...	...	1425	1538	...	1536	...	1642	...	1811	...	...	1954	2125	2232
38	Zabok d.	...	...	0544	...	0656	0840	...	1001	...	1228	...	1414	...	...	1525	k	...	1638	...	1742	...	1924	...	...	2103	2228	2330
104	**Varaždin** ▲ d.	0523	0651	0745	...	0839	1022	...	1142	1305	1404	1435	1557	1607	...	1705	1736	1745	1848	1921	1938	2022	2104	2119	2211	2239	0004	0105
115	Čakovec d.	0534	0708	0757	...	0849	1034d	...	...	1322	...	1452	...	1619	...	1717d	...	1805	...	1933	▬	2034	...	2131	2222	...	0014	...
145	Kotoriba 🏛 d.	0614	0746	0839	...	...	1116d	...	...	1400	...	1536	...	1704	...	1756d	...	1850	...	2012	...	2112	...	2213a	2303	...	...	...
151	Murakeresztúr 🏛 d.	...	...	...	0855	...	...	1255	...	...	...	...	...	...	1655	...	...	...	...	...	2100	...	...	...	...	...	...	...
165	**Nagykanizsa** a.	...	...	...	0906	...	...	1306	...	...	...	...	...	...	1706	...	...	...	...	...	2111	...	...	...	...	...	...	...

					991	771															995					
	⚒	⚒	⚒	⚒	⚒	♦		⚒			⚒		Ⓐ	Ⓐ	Ⓐ	⚒	⚒			Q				Ⓐ		Ⓐ	
Nagykanizsa d.	...	...	...	...	...	...	...	...	0652	...	...	1049	...	...	...	...	...	...	1452	...	...	...	...	...	1851	...	...
Murakeresztúr 🏛 d.	...	...	...	...	...	...	...	...	0703	...	...	1100	...	...	...	...	...	...	1503	...	...	...	...	...	1908	...	...
Kotoriba 🏛 d.	...	...	...	0419	...	...	...	0627	...	0807	...	...	1044	...	1155	1241	...	1503d	...	1601	1632	...	1818	1915	...	2119	2231
Čakovec d.	...	...	...	0500	...	...	...	0707	...	0852	...	...	1125	...	1234	1320	...	1543d	...	1640	1718	...	1904	2000	...	2158	2311
Varaždin ▲ d.	0230	0318	0410	0510	0524	0531	0647	0717	...	0902	1045	...	1135	1220	1244	1330	1414	1600	...	1650	1728	1752	1922	2010	...	2208	2321
Zabok d.	0405	0502	0621	...	0655	k	0839	...	...	...	1227	...	...	1410	...	...	1559	1743	...	...	...	1923	2105	...	...	...	...
Zagreb a.	0502	0600	0729	...	0749	0727	0938	...	...	...	1326	...	...	1508	...	...	1704	1842	...	...	...	2021	2203	...	...	...	...

▲ – **VARAŽDIN - KOPRIVNICA** and v.v. 2nd class only except where shown:

km												
			771									
		⚒	ⒶZ		Ⓐ	⚒	⚒		⚒	Q		Ⓐ
0	Varaždin d.	0430	0531	0652	0756	1020	1303	1430	1608	1707	1924	2215
42	Koprivnica a.	0515	0607	0736	0840	1105	1348	1518	1653	1752	2008	2259

	980								770			
	Ⓐ		Ⓐ		⚒	†	Ⓐ		ⒶZ	⑦	ⒶV	V
Koprivnica d.	0432	0543	0813	0903	1123	1303	1435	1542	1700	1800	1918	2029
Varaždin a.	0520	0636	0905	0948	1208	1352	1519	1634	1736	1845	2006	2114

Q – ⑦: [2] Kotoriba - Varaždin - Koprivnica.

V – [2] Koprivnica - Varaždin - Kotoriba and v.v.

Z – Ⓐ: [2] Zagreb - Koprivnica - Varaždin and v.v.

a – Ⓐ only.

d – ⚒ only.

HŽ, MÁV — ZAGREB - KOPRIVNICA - NAGYKANIZSA and OSIJEK — 1340

km		1205	783	205	703		981	770	201	581	973
		♦		♦	♦		2	♦	♦		2
	Rijeka **1310** d.	...	...	...	0535	...	...	...	...	...	...
0	**Zagreb** d.	0317	0652	0949	0949	...	1239	1538	1638	1638	1847
57	Križevci d.	0409	0744	1042	1042	...	1341	1628	1729	1729	1944
88	Koprivnica d.	0449	0814	1122	1117	...	1438	1647	1757	1801	2014
103	Gyékényes 🏛 d.	0540	|	1232	|	...	|	...	1834	|	...
132	**Nagykanizsa** a.	0605	|	1256	|	...	|	...	1906	|	...
	Budapest Keleti **1220** a.	0909	|	1624d	|	...	|	...	2224d	|	...
153	Virovitica d.	...	0929	...	1229	...	1604	...	...	1917	...
225	Našice d.	...	1045	...	1353	...	1737	...	...	2030	...
275	**Osijek** a.	...	1137	...	1446	...	1840	...	...	2121	...

	980	970	771	580	200	702	204	782	1204
	Ⓐt		♦		♦	♦	♦	♦	♦
Osijek d.	0106	...	...	0527	...	1202	...	1618	...
Našice d.	0159	...	...	0618	...	1254	...	1711	...
Virovitica d.	0321	...	...	0734	...	1415	...	1829	...
Budapest Keleti **1220** d.	|	...	...	|	0635d	|	1535d	|	1855
Nagykanizsa d.	|	...	...	|	0949	|	1841	|	2157
Gyékényes 🏛 d.	|	...	...	|	1044	|	1927	|	2255
Koprivnica d.	0428	0444	0619	0845	1108	1531	1953	1953	2313
Križevci d.	...	0519	0638	0907	1138	1551	2014	2014	2334
Zagreb a.	...	0624	0727	0953	1238	1645	2105	2105	0022
Rijeka **1310** a.	...	...	...	...	...	2042	...	...	...

♦ – **NOTES** (LISTED BY TRAIN NUMBER)

200 – GRADEC – June 15 - Sept. 15: [12] Budapest - Zagreb.

201 – AGRAM – [12] Zagreb - Budapest.

204 – AGRAM – [12] Budapest (**204**) - Gyékényes - Koprivnica (**782**) - Zagreb.

205 – GRADEC – June 15 - Sept. 15: [12] Zagreb (**703**) - Koprivnica (**205**) - Gyékényes - Budapest.

702 – [12] Osijek - Zagreb - Rijeka.

703 – [12] Rijeka - Zagreb - Koprivnica - Osijek; [12] Zagreb - Koprivnica (**205**) - Gyékényes - Budapest.

770/1 – Ⓐ: [2] Zagreb - Koprivnica - Varaždin and v.v.

782 – [12] Osijek - Koprivnica - Zagreb; [12] Budapest (**204**) - Gyékényes - Koprivnica - Zagreb.

1204 – ADRIA – June 14 - Sept. 6 (from Budapest, one day later from Zagreb): 1, 2 cl., 2 cl., [2] Budapest - Gyékényes - Zagreb - Split.

1205 – ADRIA – June 15 - Sept. 7: 1, 2 cl., 2 cl., [2] Split - Zagreb - Gyékényes - Budapest.

a – Ⓐ only.

d – Budapest **Déli**.

t – To Varaždin (Table **1335**).

CROATIA and BOSNIA-HERZEGOVINA

1345 PÉCS - OSIJEK - DOBOJ

2nd class only except where shown · HŽ, MÁV, ŽRS

There is currently no service Slavonski Šamac - Šamac - Doboj and v.v.

km																												
		🚌 Ⓐ	⚒	Ⓐ			⚒		⚒		⚒	Ⓐ			⚒	Ⓐ									Ⓑ	Ⓐ		Ⓐ
	Budapest Déli **1200** d.	...	...	...	...	...	...	...	...	...	...	...	...	...	...	...	...	...	...	...	...	...	...	...	...	...	...	...
0	**Pécs** d.	...	...	...	0512	...	...	0655	...	0910	...	...	...	1110	...	...	...	...	1310	1510	...	1710	...	1910	...	...	...	...
36	Villány d.	...	...	...	0558	...	...	0748	...	0955	...	...	...	1155	...	...	...	...	1355	1555	...	1755	...	1955	...	...	...	...
43	Magyarbóly 🛃 d.	...	...	...	0625	...	...	0755	...	1022	...	...	...	1202	...	...	...	...	1422	1602	...	1822	...	2002	...	...	...	...
54	Beli Manastir 🛃 d.	...	...	0553	0636	0700	...	—	0815	1033	...	...	1051	...	1222	...	...	1410	1433	—	1615	1833	1850	—	...	2006	...	2300
82	**Osijek** a.	...	...	0621	...	0728	...	Ⓐ	0843	...	...	...	1119	...	1250	...	...	1438	—	⚒	1643	—	1918	...	...	2034	...	2328
82	**Osijek** d.	...	0440	...	...	...	0748	0815	...	...	1051	1102	...	...	...	1347	1353	...	...	1623	...	1815	...	1955	2027	...	2231	...
	Vinkovci a.	...	|	...	...	...	0829	|	...	...	1132	|	...	...	...	|	1435	...	🚌	1705	...	1856	...	|	2108	...	2311	...
130	Strizivojna-Vrpolje d.	0503	0530	...	...	...	...	0907	...	...	...	1154	...	...	...	1439	...	...	1645	...	...	...	...	2047	...	...	...	...
150	Slavonski Šamac 🛃 d.	0526	...	...	...	...	...	...	...	...	...	...	...	...	...	...	...	...	1708	...	...	...	...	...	...	...	...	...
154	Šamac 🛃 d.	...	...	...	...	...	...	...	...	...	...	...	...	...	...	...	...	...	...	...	...	...	...	...	...	...	...	...
226	**Doboj** a.	...	...	...	...	...	...	...	...	...	...	...	...	...	...	...	...	...	...	...	...	...	...	...	...	...	...	...

km																												
		Ⓐ		Ⓐ	🚌 Ⓐ	⚒	⚒	⚒	⚒		Ⓐ	⚒		Ⓐ				⚒	Ⓐ			🚌	Ⓐ			Ⓑ		Ⓐ
	Doboj d.	...	...	...	...	...	...	...	...	...	...	...	...	...	...	...	...	...	...	...	...	...	...	...	...	...	...	...
	Šamac 🛃 d.	...	...	...	...	...	...	...	...	...	...	...	...	...	...	...	...	...	...	...	...	...	...	...	...	...	...	...
	Slavonski Šamac 🛃 d.	...	...	...	0533	...	...	...	...	...	...	...	...	...	...	...	...	...	...	...	...	1712	...	...	...	...	...	...
	Strizivojna-Vrpolje d.	...	...	0540	0556	0626	...	...	...	...	1005	...	...	1204	...	...	...	...	1648	...	...	1735	...	...	1900	...	2058	...
0	Vinkovci d.	...	...	|	—	|	0640	...	0836	...	|	...	1206	|	...	...	...	1522	|	1723	...	—	...	1904	|	2114	|	...
35	**Osijek** a.	...	...	0631	...	0717	0722	...	0916	...	1056	...	1248	1253	...	...	...	1603	1739	1804	...	...	...	1945	1949	2152	2148	...
	Osijek d.	0515	0626	...	...	...	—	0733	...	1012	—	1141	...	—	1320	...	1528	...	—	...	1813	...	1927	...	...	...	...	2222
	Beli Manastir 🛃 d.	0543	0654	...	...	...	0705	0801	...	1040	1108	1209	...	...	1348	1508	1556	...	...	...	1841	1908	1955	...	...	...	...	2250
	Magyarbóly 🛃 d.	...	...	...	0539	...	0736	...	...	...	1139	...	...	1339	...	1539	...	...	1739	...	...	1939	...	...	...	...	...	...
	Villány a.	...	...	...	0546	...	0743	...	...	...	1146	...	...	1346	...	1546	...	...	1746	...	...	1946	...	...	...	...	...	...
	Pécs a.	...	...	...	*0642*	...	0842	...	...	...	1242	...	...	1442	...	1642	...	...	1842	...	...	2042	...	...	...	...	...	...
	Budapest Déli **1200** a.	...	...	...	...	...	...	...	...	...	...	...	...	...	...	...	...	...	...	...	...	...	...	...	...	...	...	...

The 🚌 service between Slavonski Šamac and Strizivojna-Vrpolje is subject to confirmation.

1350 ZAGREB - DOBOJ - SARAJEVO

2nd class only except where shown · HŽ, ŽFBH, ŽRS

km																										
						715 A						Ⓐ						713 Ⓡ								
0	**Zagreb** d.	...	...	...	...	...	...	...	...	...	...	0545	...	0900	...	...	...	...	...	1356	...	1546	...	...	1910	2251
72	Sunja d.	...	...	...	...	...	...	...	...	...	...	0817j	...	1025	...	...	...	...	...	1522	...	1731	...	...	2041	0017
92	Volinja 🛃 d.	...	...	...	...	...	...	...	...	...	...	0845	...	1053	...	...	...	...	...	1550	...	1759	...	...	2109**a**	0045**c**
98	Dobrljin 🛃 d.	...	...	...	...	...	...	...	...	...	0631	...	...	...	...	...	...	...	1456	...	...	...	...	1832	...	...
	Bihać d.	...	...	...	...	0203	...	...	...	...	|	...	...	...	...	...	...	...	|	...	...	...	...	|	...	...
112	Novi Grad d.	...	...	...	...	0358	0429	...	...	...	0651	...	...	...	...	...	...	...	1515	...	...	...	...	1852	...	...
214	Banja Luka d.	...	...	...	0415	0531	0631	0727	...	...	0844	...	...	...	...	1527	...	1549	1709	...	...	...	1927	2043	...	...
324	**Doboj** a.	...	...	...	0625	0704	...	0929	...	...	...	...	...	...	...	1749	...	1722	...	...	...	...	2128	...	...	...
324	**Doboj** d.	...	...	...	...	0712	...	...	...	...	...	...	...	...	...	...	...	1732	...	...	...	...	...	...	...	...
347	Maglaj d.	...	0448	...	...	0743	...	...	0926	...	...	...	...	...	...	...	1718	1803	...	...	...	...	...	...	...	...
370	Zavidovici d.	...	0520	...	...	0806	...	...	0958	...	...	...	...	...	...	...	1750	1826	...	...	...	...	...	...	...	...
419	Zenica d.	0454	0621	0717	...	0902	...	...	1059	1107	...	...	1528	...	...	...	1851	1917	...	...	1932	...	...	...	...	...
447	Kakanj d.	0531	...	0754	...	0931	...	...	...	1148	...	...	1605	...	1741	...	...	1946	...	...	2009	...	...	...	...	...
465	Visoko d.	0553	...	0820	...	0948	...	...	...	1214	...	...	1631	...	1803	...	...	2003	...	...	2031	...	...	...	...	...
472	Podlugovi d.	0602	...	0829	...	0956	...	...	...	1223	...	...	1639	...	1812	...	...	2011	...	...	2040	...	...	...	...	...
496	**Sarajevo** a.	0638	...	0905	...	1030	...	...	...	1259	...	...	...	...	1848	...	...	2041	...	...	2116	...	...	...	...	...

km																										
		⚒										712 Ⓡ								Ⓐ		714 A				
	Sarajevo d.	...	...	...	...	...	0441	...	...	0708	...	1018	...	...	...	...	1102	...	1515	...	...	1550	...	...	...	1915
	Podlugovi d.	...	...	...	...	...	0518	...	...	0745	...	1049	...	...	...	...	1139	...	1552	...	...	1621	...	1728	...	1952
	Visoko d.	...	...	...	...	...	0527	...	...	0754	...	1057	...	...	...	...	1148	...	1601	...	...	1629	...	1737	...	2005
	Kakanj d.	...	...	...	...	...	0553	...	...	0816	...	1114	...	...	...	...	1210	...	1626	...	...	1646	...	1803	...	2031
	Zenica d.	...	...	...	...	...	0629	...	0715	0852	...	1144	...	...	...	...	1246	1531	...	...	...	1721	...	1839	1923	2107
	Zavidovici d.	...	...	...	...	...	—	...	0816	...	...	1233	...	...	...	...	...	1632	...	...	...	1810	...	...	2024	...
	Maglaj d.	...	...	...	...	...	...	...	0847	...	...	1256	...	...	...	...	...	1703	...	...	...	1833	...	...	2055	...
	Doboj a.	...	...	...	...	...	...	...	...	...	...	1326	...	...	...	...	...	—	...	...	...	1903	...	...	...	...
	Doboj d.	...	...	0429	...	...	...	0728	...	...	...	1331	...	...	...	1528	...	...	...	...	...	1907	1930	...	...	...
	Banja Luka d.	...	0400	0633	0724	...	...	0939	...	...	...	1504	...	1525	...	1749	...	...	...	...	1925	2052	2139	...	...	...
0	Novi Grad d.	...	0601	...	0921	...	...	...	...	...	1345	...	...	1730	...	...	...	...	...	...	2128	2239	...	...	...	...
78	Bihać a.	...	|	...	...	...	...	...	...	...	|	...	...	|	...	...	...	...	...	...	...	0022	...	...	...	...
	Dobrljin 🛃 d.	...	0619	...	...	...	...	...	...	...	1404	...	...	1748	...	...	...	...	...	...	...	...	...	...	...	...
	Volinja 🛃 d.	0425	...	...	...	1104	...	...	...	...	...	...	1557	...	1907	...	...	...	...	2123	...	...	...	...	...	...
	Sunja d.	0454	...	...	...	1132	1254	...	...	...	...	...	1626	...	1936	...	...	2102	...	2230	...	...	...	...	...	...
	Zagreb a.	0619	...	...	...	...	1428	...	...	...	...	...	1755	...	2101	...	...	2228	...	...	...	...	...	...	...	...

A – 🛏 1, 2 cl., (2) Bihać - Sarajevo and v.v. Ⓡ. a – Ⓐ. c – ⚒. j – Arrive 0731.

1355 SARAJEVO - PLOČE

Most services 2nd class only · HŽ, ŽFBH

There is no rail service Čapljina - Metković and v.v. (see note below).

km		🚌 ⚒	🚌 ⚒	723 Ⓡ		1721 Ⓡ S	🚌 Ⓐ	Ⓐ	🚌 ⚒		721 Ⓡ
	Zagreb **1350** d.	...	...	...	...	...	...	...	...	...	...
0	**Sarajevo** d.	...	...	0715	...	1109	...	1543	...	...	1649
67	Konjic d.	...	...	0817	...	1211	...	1705	...	...	1756
129	Mostar d.	...	...	0907	...	1301	...	...	...	...	1846
149	Žitomislići d.	...	...	|	...	|	...	...	...	...	|
163	Čapljina 🛃 d.	...	...	0932	...	1326	...	...	...	...	1911
173	Metković d.	0510	0628	...	...	...	1325	...	1705	...	...
194	**Ploče** a.	0545	0703	...	...	...	1400	...	1740	...	...

	Ⓐ	720 Ⓡ		🚌 ⚒		🚌 Ⓐ		🚌 ⚒	722 Ⓡ	1722 Ⓡ S
Ploče d.	...	...	...	0550	...	1240	...	1420	...	...
Metković d.	...	...	...	0625	...	1315	...	1455	...	...
Čapljina 🛃 d.	...	0612	...	...	...	...	...	...	1638	1925
Žitomislići d.	...	|	...	...	...	...	...	...	|	|
Mostar d.	...	0639	...	...	...	...	...	...	1705	1952
Konjic d.	0529	0728	...	...	...	...	...	...	1754	2041
Sarajevo a.	0651	0833	...	...	...	...	...	...	1855	2142
Zagreb **1350** a.	...	...	...	...	...	...	...	...	...	...

S – May 1 - Aug. 31.

☛ Alternative 🚌 services are available Sarajevo - Mostar - Metković - Dubrovnik and v.v. Connections are possible at Metković to / from Ploče.

1358 LOCAL SERVICES in Bosnia

2nd class only · HŽ, ŽFBH, ŽRS

VINKOVCI - TUZLA

There is currently no service Gunja - Brčko - Tuzla and v.v.

km		Ⓐ						Ⓐ
0	Vinkovci d.	0328	...	0943	...	1500	...	1935
49	Gunja d.	0426	...	1040	...	1558	...	2033
53	Brčko 🛃 d.	...	...	...	...	...	...	...
127	Tuzla a.	...	...	...	...	...	...	...

	Ⓐ						Ⓐ
Tuzla d.	...	...	...	...	...	...	...
Brčko 🛃 d.	...	...	...	...	...	...	...
Gunja d.	0434	...	1045	...	1608	...	2042
Vinkovci a.	0532	...	1143	...	1707	...	2141

TUZLA - DOBOJ

km					Ⓐ			
0	Tuzla d.	0452	1010	...	...	...	1709	...
32	Petrovo Novo d.	0536	1054	...	1412	...	1753	...
60	Doboj a.	0631	1149	...	1505	...	1846	...

			Ⓐ				
Doboj d.	0730	...	1310	1526	...	1932	...
Petrovo Novo d.	0826	...	1405	1621	...	2026	...
Tuzla a.	0909	...	...	1704	...	2109	...

SERBIA, MONTENEGRO and NORTH MACEDONIA

MAP PAGE 505

perators: Železnice Srbije (ŽS): www.zeleznicesrbije.com; Železnice Crne Gore (ŽCG): www.zcg-prevoz.me; Makedonski Železnici (MŽ): www.mztransport.mk; Trainkos (KŽ/HK): www.trainkos.com.

ervices: All trains convey first- and second-class seating, except where shown otherwise in footnotes, by a '2' in the train column, or where the footnote shows that the train conveys sleeping- (🛏) and / or couchette (🛏) cars only. Descriptions of sleeping- and couchette cars are given on page 10.

imings: Valid from **December 9, 2018** except where indicated otherwise.
Services may be amended or cancelled at short notice and passengers are strongly advised to check locally before travelling.

ickets: A supplement is payable for travel by internal express trains. Reservation of seats is possible on most express trains.

isas: Most nationals do not require a visa to enter Serbia and Montenegro, but must obtain an entry stamp in their passport, sight of which will be required by officials on leaving the country. These must be obtained at a border crossing recognised by the authorities - this excludes Kosovo's external borders with Montenegro, North Macedonia and Albania. Note also that Serbia should not be entered from Kosovo unless initial travel into Kosovo was via Serbia. Visas are not required for entry into North Macedonia for most nationals.

urrency: Visitors must declare large amounts of foreign currency upon arrival; currently €2,000 in Montenegro, and €10,000 in Serbia and North Macedonia. It is reported, however, that North Macedonia may now be operating on a threshold of €2,000. A certificate issued by the customs officer must be presented on departure, otherwise any funds held may be confiscated.

ecurity: Following the declaration of independence by Kosovo (which has not been recognised by Serbia) caution should be exercised when travelling in southern Serbia and northern Kosovo. Caution is also advised in the northern and western border regions of North Macedonia.

ŽS (BUDAPEST -) KELEBIA - SUBOTICA - BEOGRAD 1360

❖ Engineering work has caused the suspension of rail services between Novi Sad and Beograd ❖.

❖ Travellers make their own way between Novi Sad and Beograd ❖.

km															343 A	343 A							
	Budapest Keleti **1295** d.	...	...	...	...	...	...	...	...	...	...	...	...	...	1157	...	...	...	...	...	...	...	...
0	**Kelebia** 🏛 d.	...	...	...	...	...	...	...	...	...	...	...	...	...	1511	1541	...	...	...	...	...	...	...
10	**Subotica** 🏛 a.	...	...	...	...	...	...	...	...	...	...	...	...	...	...	1555	...	...	...	...	...	...	...
10	**Subotica** d.	...	0440	...	...	0632	...	...	1023	...	...	1338	...	...	...	1625	...	...	1834	...	...	2048	...
108	Novi Sad a.	...	0700	...	...	0906	...	...	1300	...	...	1614	...	...	...	1842	...	...	2122	...	...	2321	...
108	Novi Sad d.	...	...	...	...	...	...	...	...	...	...	...	...	...	...	...	...	...	...	...	...	...	...
181	Novi Beograd d.	...	...	...	...	...	...	...	...	...	...	...	...	...	...	...	...	...	...	...	...	...	...
186	**Beograd** Centar a.	...	...	...	...	...	...	...	...	...	...	...	...	...	...	...	...	...	...	...	...	...	...

					342 A	342 A																
eograd Centar d.	...	...	...	...	...	...	...	...	...	...	...	...	...	...	...	...	...	...	...	...	...	...
ovi Beograd d.	...	...	...	...	...	...	...	...	...	...	...	...	...	...	...	...	...	...	...	...	...	...
ovi Sad a.	...	...	...	...	...	...	...	...	...	...	...	...	...	...	...	...	...	...	...	...	...	...
ovi Sad d.	0705	0915	...	...	1057	...	...	...	1542	...	...	1707	...	...	2025	...	...	2220	...	...	...	...
ubotica a.	0928	1142	...	...	1328	...	...	...	1815	...	...	1941	...	...	2242	...	...	0054	...	...	...	...
ubotica 🏛 d.	...	...	...	...	1402	...	...	...	...	...	...	...	...	...	...	...	...	...	...	...	...	...
elebia 🏛 a.	...	...	...	...	1416	1446	...	...	...	...	...	...	...	...	...	...	...	...	...	...	...	...
Budapest Keleti **1295** a.	...	...	...	...	...	1804	...	...	...	...	...	...	...	...	...	...	...	...	...	...	...	...

– IVO ANDRIĆ – 2 Budapest - Kelebia and v.v. and 2 Kelebia - Novi Sad and v.v.

❖ – Engineering work is affecting services between Novi Sad and Beograd. Passengers have to use the regular bus service between Novi Sad and Beograd (rail tickets not valid).

ŽS 2nd class only SUBOTICA and KIKINDA - ZRENJANIN - PANČEVO - BEOGRAD 1362

Services on the Zrenjanin - Pančevo - Beograd route have been suspended until December 2019.

km											
	Subotica ⊖ d.	...	...	...	...	0710	...	...	...	...	1445
	Senta ⊖ d.	...	...	...	...	0838	...	...	...	...	1615
	Banatsko Miloševo ⊖ d.	...	...	...	...	0942	...	...	...	...	1719
0	**Kikinda** ⊖ d.	...	0425	...	...	1005	1115	...	...	1650	1742
19	Banatsko Miloševo d.	...	0449	...	...	...	1139	...	...	1714	...
71	**Zrenjanin** d.	...	0639	...	...	...	1329	...	...	1908	...
96	Orlovat stajalište d.	...	...	...	...	...	...	...	...	...	...
145	**Pančevo** glavna **1365/6** d.	...	...	...	...	...	...	...	...	...	...
160	Pančevački most **1365/6** d.	...	...	...	...	...	...	...	...	...	...
161	**Beograd** Dunav **1365** a.	...	...	...	...	...	...	...	...	...	...

Beograd Dunav **1365** d.	...	...	...	...	...	...	...	...	...	...
Pančevački most **1365/6** d.	...	...	...	...	...	...	...	...	...	...
Pančevo glavna **1365/6** d.	...	...	...	...	...	...	...	...	...	...
Orlovat stajalište d.	...	...	...	...	...	...	...	...	...	...
Zrenjanin d.	...	0725	...	...	1415	...	...	...	2020	...
Banatsko Miloševo a.	...	0916	...	...	1606	...	...	...	2215	...
Kikinda ⊖ a.	...	0939	1025	...	1629	1810	...	...	2238	...
Banatsko Miloševo ⊖ d.	...	...	1057	...	...	1840	...	...	...	...
Senta ⊖ d.	...	...	1156	...	...	1938	...	...	...	...
Subotica ⊖ a.	...	...	1315	...	...	2059	...	...	...	...

– For alternative 🚌 services Subotica - Kikinda and v.v. see www.polazak.com.

ŽS local services are subject to confirmation.

ŽS, CFR 2nd class only BEOGRAD - VRŠAC - TIMIŞOARA 1365

There is currently no service Vršac - Stamora Moravita and v.v.

km										
0	**Beograd** Dunav **1362** d.	...	0710	...	1150	...	1510	1625	...	2014
1	Pančevački most **1362/6** d.	...	0716	...	1201	...	1516	1631	...	2020
16	Pančevo glavna **1362/6** d.	...	0740	...	1223	...	1538	1653	...	2038
83	Vršac a.	...	0901	...	1334	...	1649	1804	...	2155
83	Vršac 🏛 d.	...	...	...	...	...	...	...	...	...
103	Stamora Moraviţa 🏛 § a.	...	...	...	...	...	...	...	...	...
103	Stamora Moraviţa § d.	0527	...	1229	...	1648	...	...	2045	...
159	**Timişoara** Nord § a.	0647	...	1344	...	1813	...	...	2200	...

Timişoara Nord § d.	...	...	0749	...	1448	...	1632	...	1901
Stamora Moraviţa § a.	...	...	0902	...	1603	...	1745	...	2018
Stamora Moraviţa 🏛 § d.	...	...	...	...	...	...	...	...	...
Vršac 🏛 a.	...	...	...	...	...	...	...	...	...
Vršac d.	0500	0750	...	0935	...	1422	...	1824	...
Pančevo glavna **1362/6** d.	0617	0901	...	1047	...	1533	...	1936	...
Pančevački most **1362/6** d.	0643	0927	...	1110	...	1602	...	1959	...
Beograd Dunav **1362** a.	0648	0932	...	1115	...	1607	...	2004	...

S local services are subject to confirmation.

§ – Romanian (East European) time.

ŽS 2nd class only NOVI BEOGRAD - PANČEVO 1366

							Ⓐ
ovi Beograd d.	0619	and	1919	...	2104	...	2234
eograd Centar d.	0625	hourly	1925	...	2110	...	2240
ančevački most d.	0634	until	1934	...	2119	...	2249

				Ⓐ						Ⓐ
Pančevački most d.	0608	and	1508	1608	1708	and	2008	2123	2218	2338
Beograd Centar d.	0618	hourly	1518	1618	1718	hourly	2018	2133	2228	2348
Novi Beograd a.	0623	until	1523	1623	1723	until	2023	2138	2233	2353

ančevački most **1362/5** d.	0716	...	1141	1201	...	1516	1631	1743	...	2020
ančevo glavna **1362/5** a.	0733	...	1158	1218	...	1536	1648	1800	...	2037

Pančevo glavna **1362/5** d.	0617	0901	1016	1047	...	1533	1639	...	1936	...
Pančevački most **1362/5** a.	0642	0926	1038	1109	...	1601	1701	...	1958	...

S local services are subject to confirmation.

1370 BEOGRAD and NIKŠIĆ - PODGORICA - BAR — ŽCG, ŽS

km																										
													431							**711**			**433**			**1137**
		2	2	2	2	2			2	2		2		2	2	2	2	2	2		2			2	2	
								K					**B**								**K**		**A**			**P**
0	**Beograd** Centar d.	...	...	...	...	...	...	...	...	...	0730	...	...	...	1230	...	...	...	1515	1704	...	1930	...	...	...	...
	Beograd Topčider d.	...	...	...	...	...	...	...	...	...	|	...	0900	...	|	...	...	...	|	|	...	|	2110	...	...	2110
93	Valjevo d.	...	...	...	...	...	...	...	...	...	0903	...	1016	...	1403	...	...	...	1642	1820	...	2104	2226	...	...	2326
159	Požega d.	...	...	...	...	...	...	0627	...	...	1048	...	1143	...	1546	...	...	...	1827	1953	2050	2233	2353	...	...	0052
185	Užice d.	...	...	...	...	...	...	0700	0705	...	1115	...	1208	...	1613	1625	...	...	1902	2018	2120	2258	0018	...	...	0125
243	Štrpci ▦ d.	...	...	...	...	...	...	...	0841	...	...	...	|	...	...	1759	...	...	2030	...	▬	...	|	...	...	|
292	Prijepolje teretna d.	...	...	...	...	...	...	...	1018	...	...	...	1507	...	...	1936	...	...	2205	...	...	...	0348	...	...	0516
328	Vrbnica ▦ a.	...	...	...	...	...	...	...	...	...	...	...	1548	...	...	...	...	...	...	...	...	...	|	...	...	|
338	Bijelo Polje ▦ d.	0701	...	0937	...	...	...	...	...	...	...	...	1650	...	...	...	...	1928	...	...	...	...	0508	...	...	0640
	Nikšić d.	|	1102	|	...	1412	...	...	...	...	...	1700	|	...	...	...	2000	|	...	...	...	...	|	0620	...	|
	Danilovgrad d.	|	1138	|	...	1447	2	...	...	...	...	1736	|	...	...	...	2036	|	...	...	2	...	|	0656	...	|
468	**Podgorica** a.	0927	1205	1202	...	1514		...	...	...	...	1800	1849	...	...	...	2103	2207	...	...		...	0707	0723	...	0848
468	**Podgorica** d.	0930	...	1209	1300	...	1535	...	...	1650	...	...	1904	1915	...	...	...	2210	...	...	0518	...	0712	...	0755	0854
	Sutomore d.	1019	...	1259	1346	...	1621	...	...	1736	...	...	1944	2004	...	...	...	2255	...	...	0603	...	0756	...	0842	0949
524	**Bar** a.	1031	...	1311	1358	...	1633	...	...	1748	...	...	1956	2016	...	...	...	2307	...	...	0615	...	0808	...	0854	1001

	710									**430**									**1136**				**432**		
		2		2	2	2	2	2	2		2		2	2	2	2	2	2		2	2	2		2	2
				K						**B**							**K**		**P**				**A**		
Bar d.	...	...	...	...	...	0520	0635	...	...	...	0900	0935	...	1138	...	1420	...	...	1538	1650	1652	...	1805	1900	2040	...
Sutomore d.	...	...	...	...	...	0534	0648	...	...	...	0917	0949	...	1151	...	1433	...	...	1551	1705	1706	...	1819	1915	2054	...
Podgorica a.	...	...	...	...	...	0622	0736	...	...	...	0954	1037	...	1235	...	1517	...	...	1639	1743	1754	...	1903	2001	2138	...
Podgorica d.	...	...	...	...	...	0628	...	0800	...	...	1000	...	...	...	1255	...	1530	...	1645	1750	...	1830	1910	2005	...	2140
Danilovgrad d.	...	...	...	...	...	|	...	0829	...	...	|	...	...	...	1324	...	1559	...	|	|	...	1859	|	|	...	2209
Nikšić a.	...	...	...	...	...	|	...	0903	...	...	|	...	...	...	1358	...	1633	...	|	|	...	1933	|	|	...	2243
Bijelo Polje ▦ d.	...	...	...	...	...	0852	...	...	...	...	1225	...	...	...	...	...	...	...	1909	2035	...	...	2130	2243	...	...
Vrbnica ▦ d.	...	...	...	...	...	...	...	...	...	...	1308	...	...	...	...	...	...	...	...	|	...	...	...	|	...	...
Prijepolje teretna d.	...	0330	...	...	0630	...	...	...	1115	...	1355	...	...	...	...	...	...	...	...	2205	...	...	...	0009	...	...
Štrpci ▦ d.	...	0507	...	...	0807	...	...	...	1252	...	|	...	...	...	...	...	...	...	...	|	...	...	...	|	...	...
Užice d.	0455	0634	0640	0740	0945	...	...	...	1431	1440	1701	...	1810	...	...	...	...	2135	...	0119	...	...	...	0310	...	...
Požega d.	0520	...	0706	0810	1011	...	...	...	...	1509	1722	...	1845	...	...	...	...	2205	...	0141	...	...	...	0332	...	...
Valjevo d.	0647	...	0842	...	1155	...	...	...	...	1646	1849	...	2028	...	...	...	...	...	...	0308	...	...	...	0500	...	...
Beograd Topčider a.	|	...	|	...	|	...	...	...	...	|	2005	...	|	...	...	...	...	...	...	0437	...	...	...	0615	...	...
Beograd Centar a.	0800	...	1011	...	1320	...	...	...	...	1814	...	...	2155	...	...	...	...	...	...	...	...	...	...	...	...	...

A – LOVĆEN – 🛏 1, 2 cl., ▬ 2 cl., (2) Beograd - Bar and v.v.
B – TARA – (2) ✕ Beograd - Bar and v.v.
K – To / from Kraljevo (Table **1372**).
P – PANONIJA – June 19 - Sept. 16 (from Subotica); June 20 - Sept. 17 (from Bar): 🛏 1, 2 cl., ▬ 2 cl., (2) Subotica - Bar and v.v.

1372 POŽEGA - KRALJEVO - STALAĆ — 2nd class only ŽS

tariff km		J		U			J			U
0	**Požega** d.	...	...	0830	...	1300	...	1730	...	2240
45	Čačak d.	...	...	0909	...	1339	...	1809	...	2319
83	**Kraljevo** d.	0455	...	0952	1010	1422	1500	1852	...	0002
155	Stalać a.	0735	...	...	1308	...	1740	...	...	...

	U				J			U	J
Stalać d.	...	...	...	...	0948	...	...	...	1953
Kraljevo d.	0440	0625	...	1015	1229	1510	...	1910	2234
Čačak d.	0534	0710	...	1100	...	1555	...	1955	...
Požega a.	0613	0749	...	1139	...	1634	...	2034	...

J – To / from Jagodina (Table **1380**).
U – To / from Užice (Table **1370**).

1373 MAJDANPEK and PRAHOVO - ZAJEČAR - NIŠ — 2nd class only except where shown ŽS

tariff km		⚒									
0	Majdanpek d.	0350	...	...	0848	...	...	...	...	1740	...
★	Prahovo pristanište d.	|	0910	...	|	...	...	1740	...	|	...
97	**Zaječar** d.	0601	1058	...	1111	...	...	1928	...	2003	...
144	Knjaževac d.	...	...	...	...	...	...	...	...	...	...
221	**Niš** a.	...	...	...	...	...	...	...	...	...	...

										A
Niš d.	...	...	...	...	...	...	...	...	...	...
Knjaževac d.	...	...	...	...	...	...	...	...	...	...
Zaječar d.	...	0622	0650	...	...	...	1504	1530	...	2010
Prahovo pristanište a.	...	|	0837	...	...	...	|	1717	...	|
Majdanpek d.	...	0843	...	...	...	...	1725	...	...	2219

A – Ⓑ (not May 1, Nov. 10).
★ – Prahovo - Zaječar: *81 km*.

1375 LAPOVO and PRIŠTINA - KOSOVO POLJE - SKOPJE — 2nd class only ŽS, KŽ

km		Ⓐ					A			B
	Beograd **1380** d.	...	...	...	...	...	...	...	...	...
0	**Lapovo** d.	...	...	...	...	...	1110	...	...	1930
28	**Kragujevac** d.	...	...	...	...	...	1204	...	...	2024
82	Kraljevo d.	0230	...	...	0710	...	1402	...	...	2222
163	Raška d.	0411	...	...	0852	...	...	...	...	...
180	Lešak / Leshak d.	...	...	...	0924	...	...	...	...	...
210	Zvečan / Zveçan ♣ d.	...	...	...	1041	...	...	...	...	...
			891					**761**		
			⊠ h	⊠		⊠⊗		⊠	⊠⊗	
214	Mitrovica / Mitrovicë ♣ d.	...	...	...	...	...	...	...	...	...
	Priština / Prishtinë d.	...	0710	0750	...	...	...	1630	...	...
247	**Kosovo Polje / Fushë Kosovë** ♣ d.	...	0722	0804	...	1600	...	1641	1936	...
*	Peć / Pejë a.	...	|	0953	...	|	...	1826	|	...
276	Uroševac / Ferizaj d.	...	0802	...	...	1644	...	...	2020	...
304	Deneral Janković / Hani I Elezit ▦ a.	...	0900	...	...	1725	...	...	2101	...
331	**Skopje** a.	...	0951	...	...	...	...	...	...	...

				760					**892**
			⊠⊗	⊠			⊠⊗	⊠	⊠ h
Skopje d.	...	...	...	...	...	...	...	...	1610
Deneral Janković / Hani I Elezit ▦ d.	...	...	0548	...	...	...	1050	...	1735
Uroševac / Ferizaj d.	...	...	0632	...	...	...	1135	...	1816
Peć / Pejë d.	...	...	|	0532	...	...	|	1210	|
Kosovo Polje / Fushë Kosovë ♣ d.	...	...	0714	0721	...	...	1219	1359	1908
Priština / Prishtinë a.	...	...	...	0732	...	...	...	1410	1920
Mitrovica / **Mitrovicë** ♣ d.	...	...	...	...	...	...	...	...	...
	Ⓐ	A				B			
Zvečan / Zveçan ♣ d.	...	...	...	...	1106	...	...	...	...
Lešak / Leshak d.	...	...	...	...	1223	...	...	...	...
Raška d.	0440	...	...	...	1256	...	...	...	...
Kraljevo d.	0620	0645	...	...	1436	1455	...	...	...
Kragujevac d.	...	0844	...	...	...	1654	...	...	...
Lapovo a.	...	0937	...	...	...	1747	...	...	...
Beograd **1380** a.	...	...	...	...	...	...	...	...	...

A – Daily. On ②③④⑤⑥⑦ 🚌 Lapovo - Kragujevac and v.v.
B – Daily. On ②③④⑤⑥ 🚌 - Lapovo - Kragujevac and v.v.
h – A change of train may be necessary at Deneral Janković / Hani I Elezit (connection between trains is guaranteed).
⊠ – Service operated by KŽ (see country heading).
⊗ – Service currently suspended.
♣ – Currently no service Zvečan - Mitrovica - Kosovo Polje and v.v.
* – Kosovo Polje - Peć: *82 km*.

1377 MINOR BORDER CROSSINGS — 2nd class only ŽS, MÁV, CFR

SUBOTICA - SZEGED and v.v.: *Service suspended*

km				
0	Subotica d.		Szeged d.	
24	Horgoš ▦ d.		Röszke ▦ d.	
31	Röszke ▦ a.		Horgoš ▦ d.	
43	Szeged a.		Subotica a.	

KIKINDA - JIMBOLIA - TIMISOARA and v.v.:

km							
0	Kikinda d.	...	...	...	...	...	...
19	Jimbolia ▦ § d.	0515	0608	0615	1250	1440	1725
58	Timisoara § a.	0558	0651	0958	1333	1523	1808

Timisoara § d.	0705	0812	1340	1625	1936	2312
Jimbolia ▦ § d.	0748	0855	1423	1708	2019	2355
Kikinda a.	...	...	...	...	...	...

§ – East European time, one hour ahead of Central European time.

ŽS, MŽ, BDŽ

BEOGRAD - NIŠ - SOFIA, SKOPJE and THESSALONÍKI 1380

km									791						1491								793		1335	🚌
		2			2	2		2⚒		K2		2		Y2	B	2			2	2	2	K2		2⚒	H	H
0	**Beograd** Centar d.	...	...	...	...	...	0405	...	0610	...	...	...	0719	...	...	...	...	1330	...	...	...	...	1730	...	...	...
	Beograd Topčider d.	...	...	...	...	...	|	...	|	...	...	...	|	...	0912	...	...	|	...	...	1530	...	|	...	1835	...
110	Lapovo d.	...	0325	...	...	...	0623	...	0803	...	...	...	0942	...	1057	...	...	1549	...	...	1750	...	1922	...	2028	...
135	Jagodina d.	...	0409	...	...	...	0707	...	0843	0850	...	...	1026	...	1138	...	...	1633	...	...	1834	1849	2002	...	2108	...
155	Paraćin d.	...	0427	...	...	...	0724	...	0859	0909	...	...	1044	...	1154	...	...	1651	...	...	1851	1913	2018	...	2124	...
176	Stalać d.	...	0502	...	...	...	0800	...	0934	0947	...	...	1120	...	1230	...	...	1727	...	...	1927	1951	2053	...	2159	...
244	**Niš** a.	...	0646	...	...	...	0937	...	1049	...	...	...	1258	...	1339	...	...	1905	...	...	2105	...	2208	...	2308	...
244	**Niš** d.	...	...	0700	...	0805	...	...	▬	...	1110	...	...	...	1407	...	1555	▬	1900	...	...	...	...	...	2318	...
	Dimitrovgrad d.	...	...	1012	...	|	...	...	...	...	1445	...	...	1535	1718	...	1918	...	|	...	...	...	...	...	|	...
	Dragoman § d.	...	...	...	...	|	...	...	...	...	▬	...	...	1738	1947	...	▬	...	|	...	...	...	...	...	|	...
	Sofia § a.	...	...	...	...	|	...	...	...	...	...	...	...	1900	2030	...	...	...	|	...	...	...	...	...	|	...
288	Leskovac d.	...	...	...	...	0919	...	...	...	...	...	...	...	...	...	...	...	2	2004	...	...	...	...	...	0003	...
392	Preševo d.	...	...	...	...	1150	...	...	...	...	...	...	...	...	...	...	...		2246	...	...	...	...	...	0307	...
401	Tabanovci d.	0515	...	...	0750	...	...	...	2	...	2	...	...	...	...	1740	2	2018	...	...	...	...	...	...	0345	...
462	**Skopje** a.	0609	...	...	0844	...	...	...		...		...	...	...	...	1834		2112	...	...	...	...	...	...	0425	...
462	**Skopje** **1385** d.	0625	...	...	0900	...	...	1320	1430	...	1640	1655	...	...	...	...	2010	...	...	2240	...	...	...	0415	0445	...
511	Veles **1385** d.	0722	...	...	0952	...	...	1412	1520	...	1732	1747	...	...	...	...	2100	...	...	2329	...	...	...	0501	0526	...
638	Gevgelija a.	0908	...	...	...	...	...	...	...	...	...	1938	...	...	...	...	...	...	...	...	...	...	...	...	0650	...
638	Gevgelija d.	...	...	...	...	...	...	...	...	...	...	...	...	...	...	...	...	...	...	...	...	...	...	...	...	0723
641	Idoméni § a.	...	...	...	...	...	...	...	...	...	...	...	...	...	...	...	...	...	...	...	...	...	...	...	...	0828
641	Idoméni § d.	...	...	...	...	...	...	...	...	...	...	...	...	...	...	...	...	...	...	...	...	...	...	...	...	0856
717	**Thessaloníki** § a.	...	...	...	...	...	...	...	...	...	...	...	...	...	...	...	...	...	...	...	...	...	...	...	...	1033

km				790									1490												🚌	1334
			2		2		2	2	2⚒	2		Y2	B	2		K2	2	2	2	2⚒	2	2	2	2	H	H
	Thessaloníki § d.	...	...	...	...	...	...	...	...	...	...	...	...	...	...	...	...	...	...	...	...	...	...	...	1851	...
	Idoméni § a.	...	...	...	...	...	...	...	...	...	...	...	...	...	...	...	...	...	...	...	...	...	...	...	1936	...
	Idoméni § d.	...	...	...	...	...	...	...	...	...	...	...	...	...	...	...	...	...	...	...	...	...	...	...	2011	...
	Gevgelija a.	...	...	...	...	...	...	...	...	...	...	...	...	...	...	...	...	...	...	...	...	...	...	...	1916	...
	Gevgelija d.	...	...	...	...	...	...	...	...	0443	...	...	...	...	...	...	...	...	...	...	...	...	...	1655	...	1948
	Veles **1385** d.	...	...	...	...	...	0503	0540	0610	0635	...	...	...	...	...	...	...	1210	...	1423	1522	...	...	1840	...	2113
	Skopje **1385** a.	...	...	...	...	...	0558	0635	0705	0733	...	...	...	...	...	...	...	1302	...	1520	1614	...	...	1931	...	2154
	Skopje d.	...	0357	...	...	...	0630	▬	...	...	...	...	...	...	...	...	...	▬	...	▬	...	1625	1900	...	...	2219
	Tabanovci d.	...	0456	...	...	...	0724	...	...	...	...	...	...	...	...	...	...	...	...	...	...	1719	1955	...	...	2329
	Preševo d.	...	▬	...	0355	...	...	...	...	...	...	...	...	...	...	...	1210	...	...	...	...	...	...	...	...	0018
	Leskovac d.	...	...	...	0630	...	...	...	...	...	...	...	...	...	...	...	1453	...	...	...	...	...	...	...	...	0254
0	**Sofia** § d.	...	...	...	|	...	...	2	...	...	...	0930	0930	...	...	...	|	...	...	...	...	...	...	...	...	|
42	Dragoman § d.	...	...	...	|	...	...		...	...	...	1016	1016	...	...	...	|	...	...	...	...	...	...	...	...	|
63	Dimitrovgrad d.	...	...	...	|	...	...	0650	...	...	...	1030	1100	1125	...	...	|	**792**	1500	...	...	...	...	...	...	|
161	**Niš** a.	...	K	...	0732	...	...	1009	...	...	...	...	1336	1444	...	...	1553		1820	...	...	...	...	...	...	0338
	Niš d.	0300	2	0640	...	0730	...	...	...	...	1210	...	1410	...	1550	...	...	1720	...	2000	...	...	...	...	...	0357
	Stalać d.	0437	0740	0756	...	0907	...	...	...	...	1347	...	1520	...	1723	1745	...	1836	...	2140	...	...	...	...	...	0507
	Paraćin d.	0501	0807	0817	...	0931	...	...	...	...	1411	...	1541	...	1747	1812	...	1857	...	2204	...	...	...	...	...	0528
	Jagodina d.	0519	0825	0833	...	0948	...	...	...	...	1428	...	1557	...	1805	1830	...	1913	...	2221	...	...	...	...	...	0544
	Lapovo d.	0558	...	0906	...	1027	...	...	...	...	1507	...	1630	...	1849	...	...	1946	...	2255	...	...	...	...	...	0626
	Beograd Topčider a.	0823	...	|	...	|	...	...	...	...	|	...	1818	...	|	...	...	|	...	...	...	...	...	...	...	0814
	Beograd Centar a.	...	...	1100	...	1241	...	...	...	...	1730	...	...	...	2104	...	...	2136	...	...	...	...	...	...	...	...

B – BALKAN – June 14 - Sept. 16: [2] Beograd - Sofia and v.v.

H – HELLAS – June 14 - Sept. 15 from Beograd; June 15 - Sept. 16 from Thessaloníki: 🛏 2 cl., [2] Beograd - Skopje - Gevgelija and v.v. 🚌 Gevgelija - Thessaloníki and v.v.

K – To / from Kraljevo (Table **1372**).

Y – Dec. 9 - June 13, Sept. 17 - Dec. 14.

§ – East European time.

MŽ 2nd class only

BRANCH LINES in North Macedonia 1385

SKOPJE - KOČANI and BITOLA and v.v. :

km					®§		
0	Skopje **1380** d.	0642	1430	1640	1710	2010	...
49	Veles **1380** d.	0748	1524	1734	1752	2113	...
★	Kočani a.	|	|	1926	|	|	...
134	Prilep d.	0934	1710	...	1921	2259	...
178	Bitola a.	1016	1752	...	1956	2338	...

			®§			
Bitola d.	0315	...	0520	1252	1832	...
Prilep d.	0353	...	0556	1334	1928	...
Kočani d.	|	0500	|	|	|	...
Veles **1380** d.	0540	0657	0726	1522	2117	...
Skopje **1380** a.	0635	0750	0807	1614	2205	...

SKOPJE - KIČEVO and v.v. :

km				
0	Skopje d.	...	1715	...
86	Tetovo d.	...	1818	...
163	Kičevo a.	...	1919	...

Kičevo d.	...	0530	...
Tetovo d.	...	0630	...
Skopje a.	...	0732	...

§ – Also conveys [1].

★ – Veles - Kočani: *110 km.*

ALBANIA

SEE MAP PAGE 505

Operator: Hekurudha Shqiptarë (HSH).

Services: Trains convey one class of accommodation only. Tickets are not sold in advance, only for the next available departure.

Timings: Timings have been compiled from the latest information received, but readers should be aware that timetable amendments usually come into effect at short notice, and are advised to check information locally before travelling.

Security: Most visits to Albania are reported to be trouble free, but travellers are advised to avoid the north-east of the country.

HSH One class only

ALBANIAN RAILWAYS 1390

Kashar - central Tiranë and v.v. is operated by 🚌 *(approximately 7.5 km)*

km	km										
	0	**Shkodër** d.	...	...	...	...	0630	...	...	1225	...
	82	Vorë d.	...	...	...	...	|	...	...	|	...
	98	**Tiranë** 🚌 d.	...	...	...	...	|	...	...	|	...
0	—	Kashar 🚌 d.	...	0655	...	...	|	...	...	|	...
9		Vorë d.	...	0707*	...	...	0950*	...	...	1545*	...
31		**Durrës** a.	...	0737	...	...	1020	...	...	1615	...
—	0	**Durrës** d.	...	...	0755	...	...	...	1325	...	...
0	36	Rrogozhinë d.	...	...	0855*	...	...	...	1425*	...	...
	77	Elbasan a.	...	...	1036	...	...	...	1610	...	...
	98	**Librazhd** a.	...	...	...	...	...	...	...	...	...
17		Lushnjë a.	...	...	...	...	...	...	...	...	...
49		Fier a.	...	...	...	...	...	...	...	...	...
83		**Vlorë** a.	...	...	...	...	...	...	...	...	...

Vlorë d.	...	...	...	...	...	...	...	...	...
Fier d.	...	...	...	...	...	...	...	...	...
Lushnjë d.	...	...	...	...	...	...	...	...	...
Librazhd d.	...	...	...	...	...	...	...	...	...
Elbasan d.	...	...	0700	...	...	1337	...	...	...
Rrogozhinë d.	...	...	0843*	...	...	1520*	...	...	...
Durrës a.	...	...	0945	...	...	1620	...	...	...
Durrës d.	0705	...	...	1300	...	...	1635	...	...
Vorë d.	0737*	...	...	1332	...	...	1706*	...	...
Kashar 🚌 a.	|	...	...	|	...	...	1717	...	...
Tiranë 🚌 a.	|	...	...	|	...	...	...	...	...
Vorë d.	|	...	...	|	...	...	...	...	...
Shkodër a.	1055	...	...	1650	...	...	...	...	...

* – Estimated time.

GREECE

SEE MAP PAGE 505

Operator: TRAINOSE S.A., ΤΡΑΙΝΟΣΕ Α.Ε.: www.trainose.gr.

Services: All trains convey first and second class seating except where shown otherwise in footnotes or by '2' in the train column, or where the footnote shows sleeping and/or couchette cars only. Descriptions of sleeping (🛏) and couchette (▬) cars appear on page 10. Services that convey catering may vary from day to day.

Timings: Timings have been compiled from the latest information received. Readers should be aware that timetable amendments may come into effect at short notice, and are advised to check information locally before travelling.

Tickets: Reservation of seats is possible (and recommended) on most express trains. *IC* trains carry a supplement which varies depending upon distance travelled. Break of journey is only permitted when tickets are so endorsed before travel with the station quoted.

1400 ATHÍNA - LÁRISA - THESSALONÍKI

km				*IC* 50		590	884		*IC* 52		3522	*IC* 54			*IC* 56		2596		*IC* 58		1520			600	
		🚌	🚌	✕✗	🚌		🍷	🚌	✕✗	🚌	⑦	✕✗	🚌		🍷✗	🚌		🚌	✕✗	🚌		🚌			
0	**Athína** Lárisa **1420** d.	...	...	0622	...	...	0720	...	0922	...	1021	1222	...	...	1522	...	...	...	1822	...	1921	...	...	2350	...
7	SKA (Acharnon) **1420/40** d.	...	...	|	...	...	0731	...	0931	...	1031	1231	...	...	1531	...	...	...	1831	...	1931	...	...	|	...
61	Inói **1420** d.	...	...	|	...	...	0814	...	1010	...	1110	1310	...	...	1610	...	...	...	1910	...	2010	...	...	0038	...
89	Thíva d.	...	...	|	...	...	0832	...	1025	...	1131	1325	...	...	1625	...	...	...	1925	...	2031	...	...	0057	...
129	Levadiá d.	...	...	|	...	...	0857	...	1045	...	1200	1345	...	...	1645	...	...	...	1945	...	2100	...	...	0124	...
154	Tithoréa d.	...	...	|	...	...	0912	...	|	...	1222	|	...	...	|	...	...	...	|	...	2122	...	...	0139	...
169	Amfíklia d.	...	...	|	...	...	|	...	|	...	1234	|	...	...	|	...	...	...	|	...	2134	...	...	|	...
210	Lianokládi d.	0500	0648	0810	0815	...	0942	0945	1117	1138	1326	1417	1438	...	1717	1738	...	1918	2017	2038	2226	2235	...	0213	...
	Lamia d.	0512	0700	|	0827	...	|	0957	|	1150	...	|	1450	...	|	1750	...	1929	|	2050	...	2246	...	|	...
	Stilída a.	0535	0723	|	0850	...	|	1020	|	1213	...	|	1513	...	|	1813	...	...	|	2113	...	...	...	|	...
276	Domokos d.	...	...	|	...	...	1024	...	|	...	...	|	...	...	|	...	...	...	|	...	...	...	...	0245	...
291	Paleofársalos **1408** d.	...	...	|	...	1037	1034	...	1151	...	...	1451	...	...	1751	...	1825	...	2051	...	...	...	...	0255	...
	Kalambáka **1408** a.	...	...	|	...	|	1131	...	|	...	...	|	...	...	|	...	|	...	|	...	...	...	...	|	...
333	**Lárisa 1415** ▲ d.	...	...	0912	...	1108	...	...	1221	...	...	1521	...	...	1821	...	1856	...	2121	...	...	...	...	0333	...
417	Kateríni ▲ d.	...	...	|	...	1154	...	...	1301	...	...	1601	...	...	1901	...	1942	...	2201	...	...	...	...	0425	...
465	Platí **1410** ▲ d.	...	...	|	...	1217	...	...	1321	...	...	1621	...	...	1921	...	2005	...	2221	...	...	...	...	0452	...
502	**Thessaloníki 1410** ▲ a.	...	...	1032	...	1243	...	...	1345	...	...	1645	...	...	1945	...	2031	...	2245	...	...	...	...	0520	...

km			1521		*IC* 51	1595		*IC* 53			*IC* 55	3523			*IC* 57	591		885		*IC* 59				601	
		🚌		🚌	🍷✗		🚌	✕✗		🚌	✕✗	⑦		🚌	✕✗		🚌	🍷	🚌	✕✗	🚌	2			
	Thessaloníki 1410 ▲ d.	...	...	...	0627	0818	...	0915	...	...	1215	...	...	...	1515	1612	...	...	...	1815	...	...	...	2350	...
	Platí **1410** ▲ d.	...	...	...	|	0845	...	0940	...	...	1240	...	...	...	1540	1639	...	...	...	1840	...	...	...	0018	...
	Kateríni ▲ d.	...	...	...	|	0908	...	1000	...	...	1300	...	...	...	1600	1703	...	...	...	1900	...	...	...	0046	...
	Lárisa 1415 ▲ d.	...	...	...	0748	0954	...	1040	...	...	1340	...	...	...	1640	1748	...	...	...	1940	...	...	...	0140	...
	Kalambáka **1408** d.	...	...	...	|	|	...	|	...	...	|	...	...	...	|	|	...	1715	...	|	...	...	...	|	...
	Paleofársalos **1408** d.	...	...	...	0807	1013	...	1059	...	...	1359	...	...	...	1659	1808	...	1813	...	1959	...	...	...	0204	...
	Domokos d.	...	...	...	|	...	...	|	...	...	|	...	...	...	|	...	...	1823	...	|	...	...	...	0214	...
0	Stilída d.	0545	...	0729	|	...	1035	|	...	1335	|	...	...	1635	|	...	1820	|	...	|	2120	...	...	|	...
17	Lamia d.	0609	...	0753	|	...	1059	|	...	1359	|	...	...	1659	|	...	1844	|	1955	|	2144	2250	...	|	...
23	Lianokládi d.	0620	0624	0804	|	...	1110	1132	...	1410	1432	1524	...	1710	1732	...	1855	1906	2005	2032	2155	2300	...	0251	...
	Amfíklia d.	...	0716	...	|	...	...	|	...	...	|	1616	...	...	|	...	...	|	...	|	...	...	...	|	...
	Tithoréa d.	...	0728	...	|	...	...	|	...	...	|	1628	...	...	|	...	...	1940	...	|	...	...	...	0321	...
	Levadiá d.	...	0749	...	|	...	...	1205	...	...	1505	1650	...	...	1805	...	...	1953	...	2105	...	...	...	0336	...
	Thíva d.	...	0818	...	|	...	...	1223	...	...	1523	1719	...	...	1823	...	...	2018	...	2123	...	...	...	0402	...
	Inói **1420** d.	...	0837	...	|	...	...	1237	...	...	1537	1737	...	...	1837	...	...	2034	...	2137	...	...	...	0419	...
	SKA (Acharnon) **1420/40** d.	...	0915	...	|	...	...	1315	...	...	1615	1816	...	...	1915	...	...	2115	...	2215	...	...	...	|	...
	Athína Lárisa **1420** a.	...	0924	...	1024	...	...	1324	...	...	1624	1825	...	...	1924	...	...	2125	...	2224	...	...	...	0506	...

▲ – Local service Thessaloníki - Litóhoro - Lárisa and v.v.:

Thessaloníki d.	0535	0730	0818	1000	1259	1430	1719	1850	2040
Platí d.	0602	0757	0845	1027	1326	1457	1746	1917	2107
Kateríni d.	0626	0821	0908	1050	1349	1520	1809	1940	2130
Litóhoro ⛰ d.	0634	0829	0917	1059	1358	1529	1818	1949	2139
Lárisa a.	0709	0904	0954	1134	1433	1604	1853	2024	2214

Lárisa d.	0551	0730	0940	1245	1350	1445	1631	2000	2200
Litóhoro ⛰ d.	0628	0807	1017	1322	1427	1522	1708	2037	2237
Kateríni d.	0637	0816	1026	1331	1436	1531	1717	2046	2246
Platí d.	0700	0839	1049	1354	1459	1554	1740	2109	2309
Thessaloníki a.	0726	0905	1115	1420	1525	1620	1806	2235	2335

1405 THESSALONÍKI - ALEXANDRÚPOLI - DÍKEA

OSE

There are currently no cross-border services from / to Turkey

km			1682		600A	1684		*IC* 90	1680	
			2			🚌		✗	🚌	
0	**Thessaloníki** d.	...	...	...	0550	...	...	1508	...	...
42	Kilkís d.	...	...	...	0626	...	...	1541	...	...
97	Rodópoli d.	...	...	...	0721	...	...	1633	...	...
130	Strimón d.	...	...	...	0812	...	...	|	...	...
162	Sérres d.	...	...	...	0845	...	...	1753	...	...
232	Dráma d.	...	...	...	1011	...	...	1912	...	...
327	Xánthi d.	...	...	...	1248	...	...	2146	...	...
374	Komotiní d.	...	...	...	1321	...	...	2214	...	...
443	**Alexandrúpoli** a.	...	...	...	1428	...	...	2319	...	...
443	**Alexandrúpoli** d.	...	0840	...	...	1504	...	...	0040	...
556	Píthio d.	...	1017	...	...	1642	...	...	0218	...
*	*İstanbul Sirkeci* **1550** a.	...	|	...	...	|	...	...	|	...
574	Néa Orestiáda d.	...	1033	...	...	1659	...	...	0235	...
611	Díkea a.	...	1104	...	...	1734	...	...	0310	...

	IC 91		1681		1683	601A		1685	
	✗		🚌		2			🚌	
Díkea d.	...	...	0606	...	1148	...	...	1906	...
Néa Orestiáda d.	...	...	0642	...	1219	...	...	1942	...
İstanbul Sirkeci **1550** d.	...	...	|	...	|	...	...	|	...
Píthio d.	...	...	0659	...	1234	...	...	1959	...
Alexandrúpoli a.	...	...	0837	...	1410	...	...	2137	...
Alexandrúpoli d.	0559	...	...	...	...	1450	...	...	...
Komotiní d.	0705	...	...	...	...	1558	...	...	...
Xánthi d.	0736	...	...	...	...	1633	...	...	...
Dráma d.	1010	...	...	...	...	1913	...	...	...
Sérres d.	1129	...	...	...	...	2037	...	...	...
Strimón d.	|	...	...	...	...	2110	...	...	...
Rodópoli d.	1249	...	...	...	...	2201	...	...	...
Kilkís d.	1341	...	...	...	...	2256	...	...	...
Thessaloníki a.	1412	...	...	...	...	2330	...	...	...

✗ – R with supplement payable. *Icity* train.

⛰ – Station for Mount Ólimbos.

* – Píthio - İstanbul: *268 km*.

1408 LÁRISA - PALEOFÁRSALOS - KALAMBÁKA

km		880		882		884		886	888
		2		2		🍷		2	2
	Thessaloníki **1400** d.	...	...	...	...	...	...	...	...
	Athína **1400** d.	...	...	...	...	0720	...	...	...
	Lárisa 1400 d.	...	...	...	...	|	...	...	...
0	Paleofársalos **1400** d.	0310	...	0818	...	1034	...	1820	2100
31	Karditsa d.	0331	...	0839	...	1054	...	1841	2121
60	Tríkala d.	0351	...	0859	...	1115	...	1901	2141
82	**Kalambáka 1400** ⊡ a.	0406	...	0914	...	1131	...	1916	2156

	881	883		885		887		891
	2	2		🍷		2		2
Kalambáka 1400 ⊡ d.	0700	0928	...	1715	...	1940	...	2204
Tríkala d.	0716	0944	...	1731	...	1956	...	2220
Karditsa d.	0737	1005	...	1752	...	2017	...	2241
Paleofársalos **1400** a.	0757	1025	...	1813	...	2037	...	2301
Lárisa 1400 a.	...	...	...	|	...	...	...	...
Athína **1400** a.	...	...	...	2125	...	...	...	...
Thessaloníki **1400** a.	...	...	...	...	...	...	...	...

✗ – R with supplement payable. *Icity* train.

⊡ – An infrequent bus service operates Kalambáka - Igumenítsa and v.v. (approximately *250 km*).

THESSALONÍKI - ÉDESSA - FLÓRINA 1410

km		81	83	733	85	735
		2	2	2	2	2
0	**Thessaloníki 1400/05** d.	0646	1321	1540	1915	2200
38	Platí **1400** d.	0714	1349	1608	1943	2228
69	Véria d.	0736	1411	1637	2005	2257
97	Skídra d.	0756	1431	1700	2025	2320
112	**Édessa** d.	0812	1446	1713	2040	2333
162	Amíndeo d.	0855	1529	...	2123	...
196	**Flórina** a.	0924	1558	...	2152	...

	730	82	84	86	734
	2	2	2	2	2
Flórina d.	...	0655	1020	1609	...
Amíndeo d.	...	0726	1051	1640	...
Édessa d.	0505	0811	1135	1723	2040
Skídra d.	0520	0826	1149	1737	2055
Véria d.	0542	0846	1209	1757	2117
Platí **1400** d.	0611	0907	1238	1819	2146
Thessaloníki 1400/05 a.	0639	0935	1306	1847	2214

LÁRISA - VÓLOS 1415

km						A				B		
0	Lárisa **1400** d.	0553	0743	0935	1245	1445	1535	1647	1845	2045	2135	2245	...
61	Vólos a.	0641	0831	1023	1333	1533	1635	1735	1933	2133	2235	2333	...

	C			A		A						
Vólos d.	0600	0650	0837	0925	1140	1225	1340	1540	1740	1940	2140	2340
Lárisa **1400** a.	0700	0738	0925	1025	1228	1325	1428	1628	1828	2028	2228	0028

A – ①-⑥. 🚌. B – ⑥. 🚌. C – ①-⑤. 🚌.

PIREÁS - ATHÍNA - HALKÍDA 1420

km					Ⓐ						❖				❖								
0	Pireás d.	...		0525	...	0625	...	...	0725	0825	...	and at	1725	1825	...	...	1925	2025	...	2125	...	...	2225
10	**Athína** Lárisa **1400** ▲ d.	...	0451	0543	0551	0643	0651	...	0743	0843	0851	the same	1743	1843	1851	...	1943	2043	2051	2143	2151	...	2243
15	Káto Acharnai **1430/40** d.	...	0500	...	0600	...	0700	...	...	...	0900	minutes	...	...	1900	...	...	...	2100	...	2200	...	...
17	SKA (Acharnon) **1400/30** d.	...	0502	...	0602	...	0702	...	...	...	0902	past each	...	...	1902	...	...	...	2102	...	2202	...	...
71	Inói **1400** d.	0500	0549	...	0649	...	0749	...	...	...	0949	hour	...	...	1949	...	...	...	2149	...	2249	...	...
94	**Halkída** a.	0519	0610	...	0710	...	0810	...	...	...	1010	until	...	...	2010	...	...	...	2210	...	2310	...	...

						Ⓐ			❖				❖										
Halkída d.	...	0526	...	0626	...	0726	...	...	0826	...	...	and at	1826	...	...	...	2026	...	...	...	2226	...	2327
Inói **1400** d.	...	0548	...	0648	...	0748	...	...	0848	...	...	the same	1848	...	...	...	2048	...	...	...	2248	...	2346
SKA (Acharnon) **1400/30** d.	...	0633	...	0733	...	0833	...	...	0933	...	...	minutes	1933	...	...	...	2133	...	...	...	2333	...	...
Káto Acharnai **1430/40** d.	...	0635	...	0735	...	0835	...	...	0935	...	...	past each	1935	...	...	...	2135	...	...	...	2335	...	...
Athína Lárisa **1400** ▲ a.	0558	0643	0658	0743	0758	0843	0858	...	0943	0958	1058	hour	1943	1958	2058	...	2143	2158	2303	...	2343	...	...
Pireás a.	0616	...	0716	...	0816	...	0916	...	...	1016	1116	until	...	2016	2116	...	...	2216	2321	...	...	...	...

❖ – Every two hours.

▲ – See below Table **1440** for summary of Metro services.

ATHÍNA - ATHÍNA AIRPORT ✈ 1430

km									
0	**Athína** Lárisa **1400** ▲ d.	0503	0603	...	0703	...	and at	2103	...
5	Káto Acharnai **1420/40** d.	0512	0612	...	0712	...	the same	2112	...
	SKA (Acharnon) **1400/20** d.	|	|	0635	|	0735	minutes	|	2135
11	Neratziótissa ▲ d.	0522	0623	0643	0723	0743	past each	2123	2143
36	**Athína Airport** ✈ ▲ a.	0548	0647	0706	0747	0806	hour until	2147	2206

Athína Airport ✈ ▲ d.	0552	0609	0652	0709	and at	2052	2109	2209
Neratziótissa ▲ d.	0617	0634	0717	0734	the same	2117	2134	2234
SKA (Acharnon) **1400/20** d.	0623	|	0723	|	minutes	2123	|	|
Káto Acharnai **1420/40** d.	...	0642	...	0742	past each	...	2142	2242
Athína Lárisa **1400** ▲ a.	...	0652	...	0752	hour until	...	2152	2255

▲ – See below Table **1440** for summary of Metro services.

ATHÍNA - KÓRINTHOS - KIÁTO 1440

km					and at				
0	**Athína** Lárisa **1400** ▲ d.	0536	...	0636	the same	2136	...	2236	...
5	Káto Acharnai **1420/30** d.	0544	...	0644	minutes	2144	...	2244	...
80	**Kórinthos** d.	0639	...	0739	past each	2239	...	2339	...
101	**Kiáto 1450** a.	0655	...	0755	hour until	2255	...	2355	...

				and at				
Kiáto 1450 d.	0459	...	0559	the same	1959	...	2059	2159
Kórinthos d.	0514	...	0614	minutes	2014	...	2114	2214
Káto Acharnai **1420/30** d.	0608	...	0708	past each	2108	...	2208	2308
Athína Lárisa **1400** ▲ a.	0619	...	0719	hour until	2119	...	2219	2319

▲ – Frequent Metro services operate as follows:
Line 1 (green): Pireás - Monastiraki - Omónia - Attiki - Neratziótissa - Kifissia.
Line 2 (red): Elliniko - Syntagma - Omónia - Athína Lárisa (for **Athína** mainline station) - Attiki - Anthoupoli.
Line 3 (blue): Agia Marina - Monastiraki - Syntagma - Athína Airport ✈.
Operators: ISAP Line 1; Attiko Metro Lines 2 and 3.

KIÁTO - PÁTRA 🚌 services 1450

	🚌	🚌	🚌	🚌	🚌	🚌	🚌	🚌	🚌	🚌
Kiáto **1440** d.	0805	1005	1205	1405	1605	1705	1805	1905	2005	2105
Diakoftó **1455** d.	|	1050	|	|	1650	|	|	1950	|	|
Pátra a.	0930	1140	1330	1530	1740	1830	1930	2040	2130	2230

	🚌	🚌	🚌	🚌	🚌	🚌	🚌	🚌	🚌	🚌
Pátra d.	0625	0805	1015	1225	1425	1525	1615	1725	1825	1925
Diakoftó **1455** d.	|	0855	1105	|	|	|	1705	|	|	|
Kiáto 1440 a.	0750	0940	1150	1350	1550	1650	1750	1850	1950	2050

PELOPÓNNISOS narrow-gauge branches 1455

Diakoftó – Kalávrita

2nd class only, rack railway

km				Ⓒ		Ⓒ
0	Diakoftó **1450** d.	0905	1130	1249	1405	1530
23	Kalávrita a.	1010	1235	1354	1510	1635

			Ⓒ		Ⓒ
Kalávrita d.	1017	1243	1403	1528	1723
Diakoftó **1450** a.	1122	1348	1508	1633	1828

⊗ – Service currently suspended.

Katákolo – Pírgos – Olimbía

2nd class only

km					⊗	⊗			⊗	⊗	⊗
0	Katákolo d.	...	0840	...	1030	1211	...	...	1405	1550	1730
12	Pírgos a.	0700	0904	...	1050	1233	1235	...	1425	1610	1752
33	Olimbía a.	0728	0932	...	1112	...	1303	...	1447	1632	...

		⊗		⊗			⊗	⊗	⊗	
Olimbía d.	0733	...	0937	1120	...	1308	...	1500	1637	...
Pírgos d.	0804	1000	1005	1144	...	1336	1338	1524	1701	...
Katákolo a.	0826	1018	...	1202	...	...	1400	1542	1719	...

🚌 INTERNATIONAL BUS SERVICES 1460

A number of operators run long-distance 🚌 services to and from Greece, and selected services are listed below. Details should be checked with the relevant operator before travel. Rail tickets and passes are not valid. Further details about travelling to Greece by bus can be found on www.europebyrail.eu

ATHÍNA - ISTANBUL: Depart Athína 1700. Depart Istanbul 1800. Journey 16 hours. Operator: Metro www.metroturizm.com.tr

THESSALONIKI - ISTANBUL: Depart Thessaloniki 2100. Depart Istanbul 2100. Journey 10 hours. Operator: Simeonidis Tours www.simeonidistours.gr
Depart Thessaloniki 1000, 2200, 2330. Depart Istanbul 1000, 1800, 2200. Journey 10 - 11 hours. Operator: Metro www.metroturizm.com.tr

THESSALONIKI - SKOPJE: Depart Thessaloniki 0830, 1730. Depart Skopje 0600, 1700. Journey 3½ - 4 hours. Operator: Simeonidis Tours www.simeonidistours.gr

THESSALONIKI - SOFIA: Coach services are operated by Union Ivkoni (www.union-ivkoni.com) as follows:

Pireás (0730) → Athína (0830) → Thessaloniki (1530) → Sofia (2030) → Varna (0500).
Varna (2345) → Sofia (0800) → Thessaloniki (1300) → Athína (2000) → Pireás (2100).
Kórinthos → Pireás → Athína (1900) → Thessaloniki (0130) → Sofia (0645) → Plovdiv → Burgas.
Burgas → Plovdiv → Sofia (2000) → Thessaloniki (0100) → Athína (0800) → Pireás → Kórinthos.

BULGARIA and TURKEY IN EUROPE

SEE MAP PAGE 505

Operators: Bâlgarski Dârzhavni Zheleznitsi (BDZh) www.bdz.bg
Türkiye Cumhuryeti Devlet Demiryolları (TCDD) www.tcdd.gov.tr

Services: Trains convey first- and second-class seating, except where shown otherwise in footnotes or by '2' in the train column, or where the footnote shows sleeping and/or couchette cars only. Descriptions of sleeping (🛏) and couchette (▬) cars appear on page 10. Seat reservation is possible on most long-distance trains (compulsory on express trains).

Timings: BDŽ schedules valid **until December 14**, 2019. **Timetable amendments are possible at short notice so it is advisable to confirm timings locally before travelling.** Subject to alteration on and around public holiday dates. Please refer to Tables **61**, **98** and **99** for international through cars to/from Burgas and Varna (summer only). TCDD schedules are the latest available. For services in Asian Turkey see pages 518–520.

1500 SOFIA - RUSE, BURGAS and VARNA

km	km				2655	8631	8661	8601	2601	3621	460/2	2611	8651			2613	8613	3623	3601	2615	8641	2641	9647	8637	2627	8627	3637
			2	2				⚡[R] 🍷	⚡[R]		[R] A2			2	2				⚡[R] ⑤			⚡[R]	L	Z	Z	Z	Z D
0	0	**Sofia** 1520 d.	...	...	...	...	...	0630	0700	0700	0900	1000	1010	...	...	1300	1310	1319	1545	1600	1610	1800	2000	...	2240	2250	2305
	103	Septemvri d.	...	...	...	...	...	0816	|	|	|	|	1214	...	...	|	1514	|	|	|	1814	|	|	...	|	0049	|
	119	Pazardzhik d.	...	...	...	...	...	0826	|	|	|	|	1225	...	...	|	1525	|	|	|	1825	|	|	...	|	0102	|
	156	**Plovdiv** a.	...	...	...	...	...	0848	|	|	|	|	1250	...	...	|	1550	|	|	|	1850	|	|	...	|	0130	|
	156	**Plovdiv** d.	...	...	...	0730	...	0900	|	|	|	|	1300	...	1350	|	1600	|	|	|	1900	|	|	2355	|	0140	|
	262	Stara Zagora d.	...	...	...	0914	...	1041	|	|	|	|	1450	...	1610r	|	1755	|	|	|	2045	|	|	0138	|	0329	|
	340	Yambol d.	...	0605	...	1000	...	1126	|	|	|	|	1535	...	1722	|	1851	|	|	|	▬	|	|	0224	|	0418	|
		Karlovo d.	...	|	...	|	...	|	|	0931	|	|	|	...	|	|	|	1556	1825	|	...	|	|	|	|	|	0132
		Kazanlak d.	...	|	...	|	...	|	|	1032	|	|	|	...	|	|	|	1655	1922	|	...	|	|	|	|	|	0229
		Tulovo d.	...	|	...	|	...	|	|	1046	|	|	|	...	|	|	|	1709	1936	|	...	|	|	|	|	|	0243
		Sliven d.	0500	|	...	|	...	|	|	1155	|	|	|	...	|	|	|	1818	2042	|	...	|	|	|	|	|	0355
	389	Karnobat 1535 d.	0553	0648	...	1036	1100	1200	|	1236	|	|	1612	1615	1809	|	1927	1900	2122	|	...	|	|	0301	|	0458	0437
	450	**Burgas** 1535 a.	0655	0750	...	|	1140	1236	|	1316	|	|	|	1717	1911	|	2007	1940	2208	|	...	|	|	|	|	0543	|
88		Mezdra 1520 d.	▬	▬	...	|	...	...	0826	▬	1029	1129	|	▬	...	1429	...	...	...	1729	...	1930	2150	|	0026	...	|
194		Pleven d.	...	...	0650	|	...	...	0943	...	1147	1246	|	...	...	1545	...	...	...	1848	...	2044	2307	|	0145	...	|
239		Levski d.	...	...	0722	|	...	...	1013	...	1216	1315	|	...	...	1615	...	...	...	1916	**4640**	2112	2337	|	0216	...	|
294		Gorna Oryakhovitsa a.	...	...	0803	|	...	...	1053	...	1255	1353	|	...	...	1653	...	...	...	1953	T	2151	0015	|	0255	...	|
294		Gorna Oryakhovitsa d.	...	...	0808	|	...	...	1103	...	1315	1403	|	...	...	1703	...	...	...	2003	2013	...	0025	|	0300	...	|
405		**Ruse** 🏛 a.	2	2	|	|	...	...	|	Ⓐ2	1515	|	|	2	...	|	...	...	...	|	2218	...	0224	|	|	...	|
435		Shumen 1530/5 d.	0520	0707	0957	|	...	...	1252	1420	...	1552	|	1718	...	1852	...	...	...	2154	...	...	...	|	0454	...	|
459		Kaspichan 1530/5 d.	0548	0735	1017	|	...	...	1312	1448	...	1612	|	1746	...	1912	...	...	...	2214	...	...	...	|	0513	...	|
518		Povelyanovo 1530/5 d.	0659	0845	1116	1235	...	...	1411	1559	...	1711	1811	1858	...	2010	...	...	...	2314	...	...	...	0507	0611	...	0651
543	546	**Varna** 1530/5 a.	0730	0915	1140	1300	...	...	1435	1630	...	1735	1835	1928	...	2034	...	...	...	2338	...	...	...	0531	0635	...	0715

km		2640	8640	4641	2610	8610		2602	8660	8650	2612	2642	2614		3624	8602	461/3		8632		2654		8626	3636	9646	2626	8636
		⚡[R]		T			2	⚡[R]				⚡[R]		Ⓐ 2		⚡[R] 🍷	[R] A2	2		2		2	Z	Z D	N	Z	Z
	Varna 1530/5 d.	...	...	...	0425	...	0615	0730	...	0830	1030	...	1330	1415	...	...	...	...	1630	1645	1730	1940	...	2130	...	2200	2300
	Povelyanovo 1530/5 d.	...	...	...	|	...	0647	0755	...	0855	1055	...	1355	1447	...	...	...	...	1655	1719	1758	2012	...	2214j	...	2226	2325
	Kaspichan 1530/5 d.	...	...	...	0545	...	0756	0851	...	|	1151	...	1451	1556	...	...	...	...	|	1827	1857	2121	...	|	...	2323	|
	Shumen 1530/5 d.	...	...	...	0603	...	0822	0910	...	|	1210	...	1509	1622	...	...	...	...	|	1853	1915	2147	...	|	...	2343	|
	Ruse 🏛 d.	...	...	0550	|	...	▬	|	...	|	|	...	|	▬	...	...	1625	...	|	▬	|	▬	...	|	2332	|	|
	Gorna Oryakhovitsa a.	...	...	0745	0750	...	...	1055	...	|	1355	...	1655	...	...	...	1820	...	|	...	2108	...	...	|	0126	0132	|
	Gorna Oryakhovitsa d.	0505	...	▬	0805	...	...	1105	...	|	1405	1600	1705	...	...	...	1830	...	|	...	2113	...	...	|	0155	0155	|
	Levski d.	0543	...	**3602**	0843	...	**3622**	1143	...	|	1443	1638	1743	...	...	...	1909	...	|	...	2154	...	...	|	0237	0237	|
	Pleven d.	0612	...	⚡[R]	0912	...		1212	...	|	1512	1707	1812	...	...	...	1938	...	|	...	2223	...	...	|	0309	0309	|
	Mezdra 1520 d.	0726	...	⑥	1026	...		1326	...	|	1626	1824	1925	2	...	...	2053	...	|	2	...	2	...	|	0429	0429	|
0	**Burgas** 1535 d.	|	...	0525	|	0710	0820	|	0950	|	|	|	|	1350	1430	1630	|	1750	|	←	...	1950	2250	|	|	|	|
61	Karnobat 1535 d.	|	...	0612	|	0753	0904	|	1030	1050	|	|	|	1453	1513	1708	|	1851	1856	1907	...	2055	2339	0023	|	|	0135
119	Sliven d.	|	...	0652	|	|	0943	|	...	|	|	|	|	|	1553	|	|	→	|	1955	...	|	|	0106	|	|	|
195	Tulovo d.	|	...	0803	|	|	1053	|	...	|	|	|	|	|	1708	|	|	...	|	...	...	|	|	|	|	|	|
210	Kazanlak d.	|	...	0817	|	|	1107	|	...	|	|	|	|	|	1722	|	|	...	|	...	...	|	|	0230	|	|	|
269	Karlovo d.	|	...	0916	|	|	1207	|	...	|	|	|	|	|	1824	|	|	...	|	...	...	|	|	0330	|	|	|
	Yambol d.	|	...	|	|	0827	|	|	...	1125	|	|	|	1603	|	1740	|	...	1932	...	...	2138	0016	|	|	|	0215
	Stara Zagora d.	|	0610	|	|	0916	|	|	...	1211	|	|	|	1716	|	1822	|	...	2028	...	...	...	0115	|	|	|	0309
	Plovdiv a.	|	0750	|	|	1057	|	|	...	1350	|	|	|	...	|	1957	|	...	2205	...	...	...	0304	|	|	|	0456
	Plovdiv d.	|	0800	|	|	1100	|	|	...	1400	|	|	|	...	|	2000	|	...	...	...	...	...	0311	|	|	|	...
	Pazardzhik d.	|	0825	|	|	1125	|	|	...	1425	|	|	|	...	|	2022	|	...	...	...	...	...	0338	|	|	|	...
	Septemvri d.	|	0835	|	|	1135	|	|	...	1435	|	|	|	...	|	2031	|	...	...	...	...	...	0349	|	|	|	...
418	**Sofia** 1520 a.	0852	1038	1144	1154	1338	1440	1454	...	1642	1753	1950	2053	...	2054	2225	2220	...	...	...	...	...	0552	0610	0600	0600	...

Other trains **SOFIA - PLOVDIV**

	1611			1613		1625	493/1493
	S	Ⓐ2	2	S	2		B¶
Sofia d.	0810	1210	1410	1510	1715	1810	2110
Septemvri d.	1014	1428	1614	1714	1933	2009	2307
Pazardzhik d.	1025	1445	1629	1725	1950	2020	2318
Plovdiv a.	1050	1525	1702	1750	2030	2045	2343

		494/1492	1622		1624		1614
		B		2		2	S
Plovdiv d.	0445	0600	0700	0900	1300	1520	1800
Pazardzhik d.	0518	0625	0725	0942	1325	1557	1825
Septemvri d.	0536	0635	0735	1010	1335	1614	1835
Sofia a.	0807	0838	0938	1240	1538	1840	2038

Other local trains **GORNA ORYAKHOVITSA - RUSE**

	Ⓐ2	2	2	2	2
Gorna Oryakhovitsa d.	0450	0825	1125	1425	1725
Ruse a.	0716	1040	1340	1650	1952

	Ⓐ2	2	2	2	2
Ruse d.	0625	0825	1125	1425	1825
Gorna Oryakhovitsa a.	0855	1045	1345	1644	204

A – To/from Bucureşti June 7 - Oct. 7 (Table **61**).
B – BALKAN EXPRESS – 2 Sofia - Svilengrad and v.v.; 🛏 and ▬ Sofia - Halkalı and v.v. (Table **1550**).
D – Conveys 🛏 and 2 Sofia - Povelyanovo - Dobrich and v.v. (Table **1540**).
L – ▬ and 2 Sofia - Ruse - Silistra (Table **1530**).
N – ▬ and 2 Silistra - Ruse - Gorna (**2626**) - Sofia.
S – To/from Svilengrad (Table **1550**).
T – To/from Stara Zagora (Table **1525**).
Z – Conveys 🛏 and 12 .
j – Arrives 2154.
r – Arrives 1555.
¶ – 20–24 minutes later June 1 - Oct. 7
⚡ – Express train. Higher fare payable.

1510 SEPTEMVRI - DOBRINISHTE

Narrow gauge; 2nd class only

SERVICE FROM JUNE 16. Timings may change at short notice.

km										
0	**Septemvri** d.	0220	...	0845	...	1225	...	1650	...	...
39	Velingrad d.	0408	...	1017	...	1356	...	1832	...	...
119	Bansko d.	0728	...	1325	...	1653	...	2148	...	...
125	**Dobrinishte** a.	0740	...	1337	...	1705	...	2200	...	...

	Ⓐ								
Dobrinishte d.	...	...	0538	...	0920	...	1505	...	1740	...
Bansko d.	...	...	0556	...	0937	...	1522	...	1758	...
Velingrad d.	0455	...	0853	...	1229	...	1825	...	2100	...
Septemvri a.	0623	...	1030	...	1405	...	1950	...	2227	...

1520 SOFIA - VIDIN - CRAIOVA

km				7620		7622				7624		7630
		2	2		2		2	Ⓑ2	2		2	Ⓑ
0	**Sofia** 1500 d.	...	...	0725	...	1145	...	...	...	1700	...	1900
88	Mezdra 1500 d.	0440	...	|	...	1332	...	1705	...	1843	...	2106
106	Vratsa d.	0459	...	0909	...	1348	...	1724	...	1859	...	2122
	Boychinovtsi a.	0543	...	0948	...	1429	...	1812	...	1939	...	2201
182	Brusartsi ⊖ a.	0624	0630	1025	1030	1507	1520	1852	1905	2017	2025	2239
204	Lom ⊖ a.	|	0657	|	1058	|	1548	|	1933	|	2053	2309
269	**Vidin** a.	0815	...	1201	...	1647	...	2044	...	2200	...	...

	2660	7631		7621					7623				762
	2	⚒	2		2	2	Ⓐ2	2		Ⓑ2	Ⓑ2	2	
Vidin d.	...	...	...	0450	...	0600	...	...	1210	...	1535	...	172
Lom ⊖ d.	...	0445	0540	|	0712	|	1110	1310	|	1653	|	1820	|
Brusartsi ⊖ d.	...	0514	0605	0626	0738	0743	1137	1337	1349	1720	1729	1847	185
Boychinovtsi d.	...	0558	...	0706	...	0822	1216	...	1428	...	1810	...	193
Vratsa d.	0525	0640	...	0746	...	0907	1302	...	1507	...	1857	...	201
Mezdra 1500 a.	0539	0655	...	0801	...	0925	1320	...	|	...	1915	...	|
Sofia 1500 a.	0730	0845	...	0946	...	...	...	...	1648	...	...	...	220

km		①–⑥			
	Vidin 🏛 d.	...	...	...	1245
0	**Calafat** d.	0325	0610	...	|
107	**Craiova** a.	0632	0927	...	1550

km					Ⓑ
0	**Craiova** d.	0810	...	1646	1925
	Calafat a.	|	...	2010	2239
119	**Vidin** 🏛 a.	1123	...	...	...

⊖ – Other services Brusartsi - Lom and v.v.: **From Brusartsi** at 0800, 1210 Ⓐ, 135 and 1733 Ⓑ. **From Lom** at 0945, 1438 and 1945.

RUSE - STARA ZAGORA - DIMITROVGRAD - MOMCHILGRAD - PODKOVA 1525

km				4641					465	
		2	Ⓐ2		2	2	2	2	B2	2
0	**Ruse** 1500 d.	...	...	0550	...	...	...	...	...	...
111	**Gorna Oryakhovitsa** 1500 d.	0515	0725	0815	...	1120	1420	1725	2025	2120
125	Veliko Târnovo d.	0533	0744	0832	...	1141	1440	1744	2042	2140
226	Tulovo a.	0748	...	1040	...	1356	1654	...	|	...
226	Tulovo d.	0749	...	1057	...	1357	1710	...	|	...
253	Stara Zagora d.	0823	...	1130	1350	1433	1743	...	2310	...
310	**Dimitrovgrad** a.	...	...	...	1510	...	...	...	0015	...

		464					4640		
	2	B2	2	2	2	Ⓐ2		2	2
Dimitrovgrad d.	...	0555	...	0925	...	...	...	...	...
Stara Zagora d.	...	0710	1000	1043	1305	...	1620	...	1850
Tulovo a.	...	0745	1035	...	1342	...	1657	...	1927
Tulovo d.	...	0746	1036	...	1346	...	1658	...	1945
Veliko Târnovo d.	0700	1001	1309	...	1611	1807	1922	2020	2206
Gorna Oryakhovitsa 1500 a.	0720	1020	1330	...	1630	1825	1940	2043	2225
Ruse 1500 a.	...	...	...	...	...	...	2218	...	...

km		2	2	2	2
0	**Dimitrovgrad** d.	0500	...	...	1525
23	Haskovo d.	0528	...	...	1551
87	Kârdzhali d.	0707	0730	1310	1740
101	**Momchilgrad** a.	...	0750	1330	1800
119	**Podkova** a.	...	0814	1355	1823

		2	2	2	P2
Podkova d.	0620	...	0820	1400	...
Momchilgrad d.	0644	...	0844	1422	1705
Kârdzhali d.	0703	0712	0903	...	1735
Haskovo d.	...	0853	...	...	1914
Dimitrovgrad a.	...	0920	...	...	1940

B – (2) Gorna - Dimitrovgrad and v.v. See Table **61** for seasonal through cars Bucureşti - Ruse - Svilengrad - Kapıkule - Halkalı and v.v.
P – To Plovdiv (Table **1550**).

RUSE - SILISTRA and VARNA 1530

km		9647		9621		2655			9623		
		H	2		2		2			2	2
0	**Ruse** d.	0229	...	0605	0725	...	...	...	1620	1830	...
5	Ruse Razpr d.	0247	...	0614	0734	...	...	...	1625	1839	...
71	Razgrad d.	0349	...	0715	0844	...	...	...	1730	1951	...
93	Samuil d.	0435f	0515	0736	0906	...	1000	...	1751	2013	2030
	Silistra a.	0706←	|	|	|	...	1240	...	|	...	2310
142	Kaspichan 1500 a.	...	0617	0828	1007	1017	...	...	1845	...	...
	Shumen 1500 a.	...	...	|	1055	|	...	...	|	...	...
201	Povelyanovo 1500 a.	...	...	0926	...	1115	...	...	1944	...	...
226	**Varna** 1500 a.	...	...	0950	...	1140	...	...	2008	...	...

km				2610		9620				9622	9646
		2	2		2		Ⓐ2	2	2		D
	Varna 1500 d.	...	...	0425	...	0900	1415	...	...	1810	...
	Povelyanovo 1500 d.	...	...	|	...	0925	1447	...	...	1835	...
	Shumen 1500 d.	...	...	|	...	|	|	...	1605	|	...
	Kaspichan 1500 d.	...	...	0544	0630	1022	1555	...	1650f	1933	...
0	**Silistra** d.	...	0430	...	|	|	...	1440	|	|	1905
113	Samuil d.	0500	0715	...	0737	1117	...	1720	1752	2027	2153f
	Razgrad d.	0521	...	...	0759	1137	...	...	1814	2047	2213
	Ruse Razpr a.	0637	...	...	0916	1235	...	...	1930	2146	2311
	Ruse a.	0648	...	...	0926	1245	...	...	1939	2155	2329

H – and (2) Sofia - Ruse - Silistra.
D – and (2) Silistra - Gorna Oryakhovitsa (**2626**) - Sofia.
f – Arrives 18 – 25 minutes earlier.

VARNA and SHUMEN - BURGAS 1535

km				8650	8661				8632	3623		
		2	2			2	2	2			2	2
	Varna 1500 d.	...	0650	0830	...	1040	...	...	1630	...	...	1840
	Povelyanovo 1500 d.	...	0723	0855	...	1112	...	...	1655	...	...	1911
0	**Shumen** d.	0457	|	|	...	|	...	1400	|	...	1900	|
50	Komunari d.	0555	0817	0936	...	1209	...	1500	1739	...	2000	2008
133	Karnobat 1500 d.	...	1018r	1049	1100	1350	1453	...	1855	1900	...	2148
194	**Burgas** 1500 a.	...	1120	...	1140	...	1555	...	...	1940	...	...

				8660	8631			3624	8651	
	2	2	2			2	2			
Burgas 1500 d.	...	...	0750	0950	...	...	*1350*	1430	...	...
Karnobat 1500 d.	0345	...	0905r	1030	1036	...	1500	1512	1612	...
Komunari d.	0529	0605	1057	...	1152	1515	1643	...	1728	2012
Shumen a.	|	0702	|	...	|	1615	|	...	|	2112
Povelyanovo 1500 d.	0625	...	1153	...	1235	...	1747	...	1811	...
Varna 1500 a.	0655	...	1223	...	1300	...	1817	...	1835	...

r – Arrives 13 – 15 minutes earlier.

VARNA - DOBRICH - KARDAM 1540

km		2	D	2		2	2	2		2	
0	**Varna** 1500 d.	0600	...	...	...	1240	1540	...	...	1950	...
	Sofia 1500 d.	|	2305	...	...	|	|	...	...	|	...
25	Povelyanovo 1500 d.	0632	0710	...	...	1312	1612	...	...	2024	...
93	**Dobrich** a.	0752	0835	0845	...	1427	1733	1738	...	2148	...
131	Kardam a.	...	...	0950	...	...	...	1842	...	...	...

	2		2	2	2		2		2	E
Kardam d.	...	...	...	1040	...	...	...	...	1910	...
Dobrich d.	0610	...	0910	1145	1210	...	1510	...	2014	2027
Povelyanovo 1500 a.	0734	...	1034	...	1333	...	1634	...	...	2147
Sofia 1500 a.	|	...	|	...	|	...	|	...	...	0610
Varna 1500 a.	0805	...	1105	...	1405	...	1705	...	...	...

D – and (2) Sofia (**3637**) - Povelyanovo (**2637**) - Dobrich.
E – and (2) Dobrich (**2636**) - Povelyanovo (**3636**) - Sofia.

BDŽ; TCDD

(SOFIA -) PLOVDIV - SVILENGRAD - İSTANBUL 1550

km	*Bulgarian train number*					1611		1613		493	493	1493
	Turkish train number	12701		❖						81031	81031	81031
			2	⑥⑦	2		2		2	AB	AC	AD
0	*Sofia* 1500 d.	...	...	...	...	0810	...	1510	...	2110	2110	2130
156	**Plovdiv** ▷ d.	...	0610	0840	0910	1110	1410	1810	2200	2355	2355	0017
202	Parvomaj ▷ d.	...	0655	⊖	0950	1145	1452	1848	2246	0023	0023	0045
234	Dimitrovgrad ▷ a.	...	0719	⊖	1015	1202	1520	1906	2319	0041	0041	0103
234	Dimitrovgrad d.	...	0724	⊖	1017	1204	*1530*	1907	...	0044	0044	0136
299	Svilengrad a.	...	0815	⊖	1108	1255	*1631*	2000	...	0132	0130	0223
299	Svilengrad 🏛 d.	...	▬	⊖	...	...	...	...	...	0209	0205	0300
318	**Kapıkule** 🏛 a.	...	...	⊖	...	...	...	...	...	0225	0325	0316
318	**Kapıkule** d.	0725	**12703**	⊖	...	...	...	...	...	0252	0410	0350
338	Edirne d.	0743		1300	...	...	...	...	...	0309	0427	0407
	Uzunköprü d.	|	1540	...	...	...	...	...	...	|	|	|
385	Pehlivanköy d.	0815	1558	...	...	...	...	...	...	|	|	|
406	Alpullu d.	0835	1618	...	...	...	...	...	...	0359	0517	0457
506	Çerkezköy d.	1005	1748	...	...	...	...	...	...	0517	0635	0613
593	Halkalı 1570 a.	1126	1915	...	...	...	...	...	...	0649	0810	0740
621	**İstanbul** Sirkeci a.	◇	◇	...	...	...	...	...	...	◇	◇	◇

Turkish train number	81032	81032			12704						12702
Bulgarian train number	1492	492/4					1614			❖	
	AD	AE	2	2		2		2	M2	⑥⑦	
İstanbul Sirkeci d.	◇	◇	...	...	◇	...	...	...	...	...	◇
Halkalı 1570 d.	2140	2240	...	...	0840	...	...	...	...	...	1800
Çerkezköy d.	2310	0014	...	...	1004	...	...	...	...	...	1932
Alpullu d.	0029	0135	...	...	1130	...	...	...	...	...	2101
Pehlivanköy d.	|	|	...	...	1147	...	...	...	...	...	2118
Uzunköprü a.	|	|	...	...	1202	...	...	...	...	...	|
Edirne d.	0116	0221	...	...	▬	...	...	...	...	1700	2152
Kapıkule a.	0132	0237	...	...	...	...	...	...	...	⊖	2208
Kapıkule 🏛 d.	0230	0315r	...	...	...	...	...	...	...	⊖	...
Svilengrad 🏛 a.	0250	0335	...	...	...	...	...	...	...	⊖	...
Svilengrad d.	0325	0405	0520	...	...	1415	1610	1730	...	⊖	...
Dimitrovgrad a.	0415	0451	0620	...	2	1508	1700	1824	...	⊖	...
Dimitrovgrad ▷ d.	0435	0452	0621	0930	1125	1535	1702	1830	1941	⊖	...
Parvomaj ▷ d.	0452	0509	0654	1004	1158	1602	1720	1900	2011	⊖	...
Plovdiv ▷ a.	0528	0545	0744	1048	1245	1643	1755	1944	2055	2120	...
Sofia 1500 a.	0838	0838	...	...	...	...	2038	...	...	...	...

– SOFIA-İSTANBUL EXPRESS/BALKAN – (2) Sofia - Svilengrad and v.v. and Sofia - Halkalı and v.v. [R]. See Table **61** for seasonal through cars from/to Bucureşti.
– Mar. 31 - May 31 and Oct. 8 – 26.
– To Mar. 30 and from Oct. 27.
– June 1 - Oct. 7.
– To May 31 and from Oct. 8.
– From Momchilgrad (Table **1525**).

r – 0415 (Turkish time) to Mar. 30 and from Oct. 27.
▷ – Additional trains Plovdiv - Dimitrovgrad and v.v.: **From Plovdiv** at 1610. **From Dimitrovgrad** at 0520.
❖ – Subject to confirmation.
⊖ – Intermediate timings to be confirmed.
◇ – Frequent suburban services (at least every 10 minutes) operate between Halkalı and İstanbul Sirkeci (journey time: 38 minutes).

Most trains 2nd class only

SOFIA - KYUSTENDIL, PETRICH, KULATA and THESSALONÍKI 1560

km				5621	6621		5623		361		5611		5625
									[R]				
0	**Sofia** d.	...	0520	0740	0800	1000	1200	...	1500	...	1700	*1900*	2020
33	Pernik d.	...	0612	0824	0902	1048	1245	1318	1548	...	1747	1955	2110
48	Radomir d.	...	0641	0841	0918	1106	1301	1338	1603	1615	1803	2015	2126
102	**Kyustendil** a.	...	|	|	1052	|	|	1520	|	1750	|	2147	|
91	Dupnitsa d.	0625	0741	0919	▬	1155	1346	▬	1643	▬	1847	▬	2204
123	**Blagoevgrad** a.	0703	0818	0950	...	1236	1414	...	1711	...	1920	...	2235
123	**Blagoevgrad** d.	0710	▬	*0957*	...	...	*1419*	...	1712	...	1921	...	...
186	Sandanski d.	0826	...	*1116*	...	...	*1530*	...	1808	...	2023	...	...
197	General Todorov. a.	0838	...	*1128*	...	...	*1542*	...	1818	...	2035	...	...
197	General Todorov. d.	0839	0850	*1140*	1142	...	*1554*	1600	1819	1825	2047	2050	...
207	**Petrich** a.	|	0903	*1153*	|	...	*1610*	|	|	1838	2100	|	...
210	Kulata a.	0853	...	...	1156	...	...	1614	1830	...	...	2104	...
210	Kulata 🏛 d.	...	...	...	...	...	...	...	1905‡	...	...	...	...
354	**Thessaloníki** a.	...	...	...	...	...	...	...	2222‡	...	...	...	...

		5610				360		5622		5624	
						[R]					
Thessaloníki d.	...	...	...	...	...	0655‡	...	...	...	...	...
Kulata 🏛 a.	...	...	...	...	...	1010‡	...	...	...	...	...
Kulata d.	0530	...	0645	...	...	1050	1400	...	1720	...	1900
Petrich d.	|	0530	|	0640	1040	|	|	*1405*	|	*1725*	*1900*t
General Todorov a.	0543	0543	0658	0654	1053	1101	1413	*1419*	1733	*1739*	1914
General Todorov d.	▬	0553	▬	0706	▬	1102	▬	*1431*	▬	*1752*	1920
Sandanski d.	**5620**	0604	...	0720	...	1114	...	*1444*	...	*1810*	1934
Blagoevgrad a.		0707	...	0832	...	1211	...	*1600*	...	*1919*	2055
Blagoevgrad d.	0525	0708	**6620**	0833	0920	1212	1350	1610	**6622**	1930	2056
Dupnitsa d.	0559	0739		0910	1009	1242	1430	1645		2002	2135
Kyustendil d.	|	|	0708	...	|	|	|	|	1755	|	...
Radomir d.	0640	0822	0837	...	1105	1323	1520	1723	1924	2042	...
Pernik d.	0700	0840	0900	...	1135	1340	1540	1745	1940	2100	...
Sofia a.	0751	0930	0950	...	1233	1422	1630	1832	2031	2152	...

☛ Additional journeys Radomir - Kyustendil and v.v.: **From Radomir** at 0715, 1110 and 1807. **From Kyustendil** at 0438, 0908, 1108, 1338 and 1608.

– Change trains at General Todorov. ‡ – The cross-border section of line between Kulata and Strimón (15km south of Kulata) is operated by 🚌 until further notice.

TURKEY IN ASIA

Operator: Türkiye Cumhuryeti Devlet Demiryolları (TCDD).

Services: *YHT* (high-speed) trains convey first and second class seating. Long distance trains convey a single class of seating known locally as 'Pullman' (shown as [1] in footnotes) which are gender specific and may also convey sleeping and/or couchette cars. Local trains convey 2nd class seating, shown as '2' in the train column. Descriptions of sleeping (🛏) and couchette (▬) cars appear on page 10. Reservation of seats (free of charge) is required for *YHT* and express trains.

Timings: Schedules are the latest available. Timetable amendments are possible at short notice so please confirm timings locally before travelling. A shaded column indicates that the service is currently suspended.

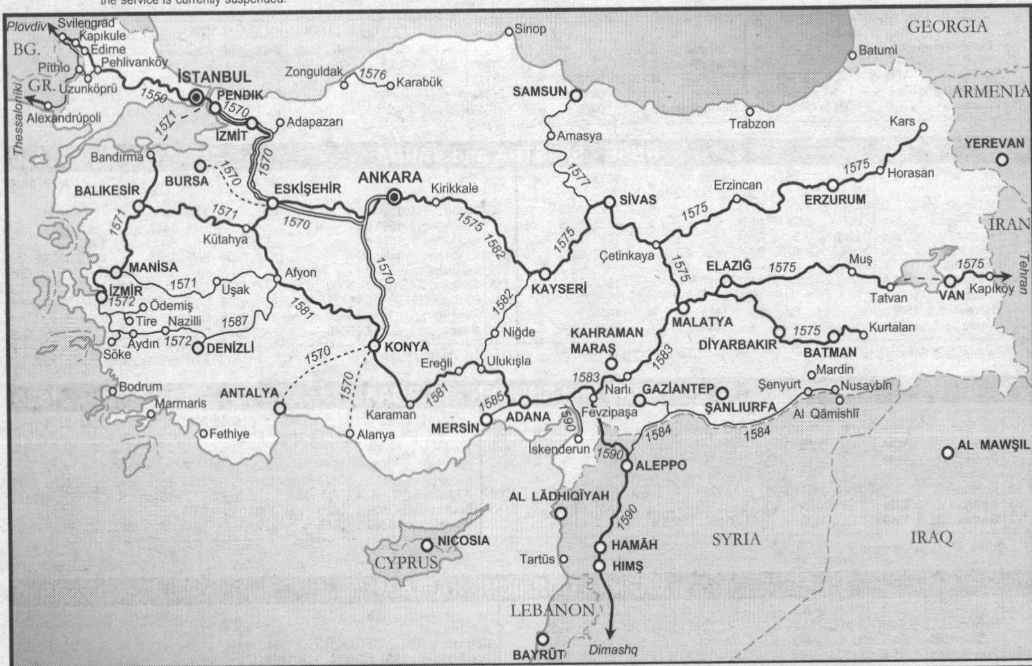

1570 İSTANBUL - ESKİŞEHIR - KONYA and ANKARA — TCDD

km	All trains 🅁 and 🍷	YHT 81052	YHT 81202	YHT 81054	YHT 81204	YHT 81002	YHT 81206	YHT 81302	YHT 81004	YHT 81208	YHT 81056	YHT 81006	YHT 81210	YHT 81304	YHT 81008	YHT 81212	YHT 81010	YHT 81058	YHT 81214	YHT 81012	YHT 81014	YHT 81060	YHT 81216	YHT 81306	YHT 81016
	Halkalı .... 1550 d.	...	...	...	...	0600	...	0625	...	...	...	...	...	...	1155	...	...	...	...	...	...	...	...	...	...
	İstanbul Söğütlüçeşme d.	...	...	...	...	0647	...	0712	0830	...	...	1040	...	1220	1242	...	1335	...	...	1600	1750	...	...	1850	1915
	İstanbul Pendik..... ▽ d.	...	...	...	...	0718	...	0743	0901	...	...	1114	...	1256	1313	...	1405	...	...	1631	1821	...	...	1921	1946
	Gebze .... ▽ d.	...	...	...	...	0738	...	0803	0921	...	...	1136	...	1316	1333	...	1422	...	...	1651	1841	...	...	1941	2015
	Izmit .... ▽ d.	...	...	...	...	0810	...	0835	0953	...	...	1208	...	1348	1405	...	1454	...	...	1723	1913	...	...	2013	2047
	Arifiye .... ▽ d.	...	...	...	...	0830	...	0855	|	...	...	1228	...	1408	|	...	1514	...	...	|	1933	...	...	2033	2107
	Bilecik........................d.	...	...	...	...	0911	...	0936	|	...	...	1309	...	1449	|	...	1555	...	...	1823	2014	...	...	2114	|
	Bozüyük ....d.	...	...	...	...	0936	...	1000	|	...	...	1333	...	1513	|	...	1619	...	...	|	2038	...	...	2138	|
0	**Eskişehir** ....d.	0620	...	0845	...	0957	...	1020	1132	...	1310	1353	...	1533	1544	...	1639	1750	...	1905	2058	2115	...	2158	2228
355	**Konya**.....................a.	|	...	|	...	|	...	1202	|	...	|	|	...	1715	|	...	|	|	...	|	|	|	...	2340	|
	Konya.....................d.	|	0630	|	0910	|	1100	...	|	1230	|	|	1430	...	|	1600	|	|	1750	|	|	|	2110	...	|
156	Polatli YHT ....d.	0709	0736	0936	|	1047	1206	...	|	1336	1359	1441	|	...	|	1706	1727	1839	|	|	2146	2204	2221	...	|
220	Sincan ▲ ....d.	0734	0801	1001	1037	1112	1231	...	1248	1401	1424	1506	1557	...	1654	1731	1752	1904	1921	2015	2211	2229	2246	...	2338
245	**Ankara**......................a.	0750	0817	1017	1053	1128	1247	...	1304	1417	1440	1522	1613	...	1710	1747	1808	1920	1937	2031	2227	2245	2302	...	2354

km	All trains 🅁 and 🍷	YHT 81001	YHT 81201	YHT 81051	YHT 81301	YHT 81003	YHT 81203	YHT 81205	YHT 81005	YHT 81053	YHT 81207	YHT 81007	YHT 81303	YHT 81209	YHT 81009	YHT 81211	YHT 81055	YHT 81011	YHT 81013	YHT 81213	YHT 81057	YHT 81305	YHT 81015	YHT 81059	YHT 81215
0	**Ankara**......................d.	0600	0620	0640	...	0810	0830	0950	1010	1055	1135	1220	...	1330	1350	1520	1545	1610	1745	1805	1825	...	1910	2055	2115
25	Sincan ▲ ....d.	0618	0638	0658	...	0828	0848	1008	1028	1113	1154	1238	...	1348	1408	1538	1603	1628	1803	1823	1843	...	1928	2113	2133
89	Polatllı YHT ....d.	0641	0702	0722	...	|	0912	1032	1051	1137	|	|	...	1412	1431	|	1627	|	1826	1847	1907	...	|	2137	2157
309	**Konya**.....................a.	|	0808	|	...	|	1018	1138	|	|	1321	|	...	1518	|	1704	|	|	|	1953	|	...	|	|	2303
	Konya.....................d.	|	...	|	0655	|	...	...	|	|	...	|	1310	...	|	...	|	|	|	...	|	1825	|	|	...
245	**Eskişehir** ....d.	0731	...	0807	0841	0938	...	...	1141	1222	...	1348	1455	...	1521	...	1712	1738	1916	...	1952	2010	2038	2222	...
	Bozüyük ....d.	0747	...	...	0857	|	...	...	1157	...	...	|	1512	...	1537	...	...	|	1932	...	...	2026	|	...	...
	Bilecik........................d.	0809	...	...	0919	|	...	...	1219	...	...	|	1534	...	1559	...	...	|	1954	...	...	2048	|	...	...
	Arifiye .... ▽ d.	0851	...	...	1001	|	...	...	1301	...	...	|	1616	...	1641	...	...	|	2036	...	...	2130	2153	...	...
	Izmit .... ▽ d.	0913	...	...	1023	1114	...	...	1323	..	..	1524	1638	...	1703	...	...	1914	2058	...	...	2152	2215	...	...
	Gebze .... ▽ d.	0944	...	...	1054	|	...	...	1355	...	...	|	1709	...	1734	...	...	|	2129	...	...	2223	2246	...	...
506	**İstanbul** Pendik..... ▽ a.	1006	...	...	1115	1206	...	...	1426	...	...	1616	1731	...	1756	...	...	2006	2151	...	...	2244	2308	...	...
529	**İstanbul** Söğütlüçeşme a.	1038	...	...	1142	1233	...	...	1453	...	...	1652	1800	...	1833	...	...	2038	2218	...	...	2317	2335	...	...
	Halkalı .... 1550 a.	1120	...	...	...	...	...	...	...	...	...	...	...	...	...	...	...	2120	...	...	...	2359	...	...	...

🚌 CONNECTIONS

km											
0	Eskişehir.....................d.	0802	0950	1152	1343	1531	1727	1806	1921	2010	2048
	Bursa..........................a.	1017	1205	1407	1558	1746	1942	2021	2136	2225	2303

Bursa..........................d.	0555	0715	0859	1025	1102	1246	1402	1505	1557	1815
Eskişehir.....................a.	0810	0930	1114	1240	1317	1501	1617	1720	1817	2030

km											
0	Konya..........................d.	0000	...	0900	...	1145	1330	1530	1730	1820	...
	Alanya ....a.	|	...	1400	...	|	|	|	|	2320	...
	Antalya.....................a.	0515	...	...	...	1700	1845	2045	0045	...	...

Antalya.................d.	0100	...	0700	...	0900	...	...	...	...	...
Alanya ....d.	|	...	|	...	|	1000	...	1200	...	1630
Konya ....a.	0615	...	1215	...	1415	1520	...	1720	...	2050

İSTANBUL - ARIFIYE - ADAPAZARI ★

km		12602	12604	12606	12608
0	**İstanbul** Pendik ... d.	0815	1225	1730	2050
19	Gebze.................. d.	0833	1243	1755	2108
66	Izmit..................... d.	0910	1320	1832	2145
107	**Arifiye** .... d.	0948	1358	1910	2223
115	Adapazarı .... a.	0954	1404	1916	2229

	12601	12603	12605	12607
Adapazarı.......... d.	0555	0900	1500	1755
Arifiye .... d.	0611	0916	1516	1815
Izmit................... d.	0640	0945	1545	1845
Gebze................. d.	0715	1020	1620	1920
İstanbul Pendik a.	0737	1036	1641	1940

★ – ADA EKSPRES TRENİ – Conveys [1].
▽ – See also İstanbul - Arifiye - Adapazarı panel below main table.
▲ – **Warning!** Trains currently call at Eryaman station instead of Sincan station.

Suburban services run Halkalı - İstanbul - Gebze via the 1.4 km Marmaray Tunnel at least every 10 minutes 0600 - 2200. Route (with journey time): Halkalı (0) - Kazlıçeşme (31) - Sirkeci (38) - Söğütlüçeşme (51) - Pendik (90) - Gebze (120).

TCDD — ESKIŞEHIR, BANDIRMA and AFYON - IZMIR — 1571

km		32606	32006 B	32010 F	32602	32002 C	32608	32012 E	32604	32004 D	72610
	Ankara **1570** d.	...	...	...	...	...	...	...	...	...	...
0	**Eskişehir** ♧ d.	...	2206	...	...	...	...	...	...	...	...
77	Kütahya ♧ d.	...	2332	...	...	...	...	...	...	...	1630
128	Tavşanllı ♧ d.	...	0043	...	...	...	...	...	...	...	1730
‡	**Bandirma** Şehir d.	...	|	...	...	0735	...	...	...	1600	|
‡	**Bandirma** Gar d.	...	|	...	...	0740	...	...	...	1605	|
331	Ballıkesir d.	...	0505	0530	...	0932	...	1400	...	1756	2149
	Savaştepe d.	...	0604	|	...	1031	...	1502	...	1901	—
413	Soma d.	...	0632	0702	...	1101	...	1530	...	1929	**32008**
454	Akhisar d.	...	0715	0747	...	1149	...	1620	...	2021	**A**
◇	**Afyon** Ali Çetinkaya d.	...	|	|	...	|	...	|	...	|	2331
◇	Uşak d.	...	|	|	0620	|	...	|	1605	|	0154
◇	Alaşehir d.	0515	|	|	0857	|	1540	|	1840	|	0409
506	Manisa d.	0702	0808	0850	1106	1246	1726	1730	2053	2117	0548
572	**Izmir** Basmane a.	0836	0936	1024	1238	1412	...	1902	2225	2239	0712

	32011 E	32601	32001 C	32605	32003 D	32603	32607	32009 F	32005 B	32007 A
Izmir Basmane d.	0640	0740	0830	1100	1400	1500	...	1715	1805	2015
Manisa d.	0807	0914	0955	1234	1526	1633	1830	1838	1930	2149
Alaşehir d.	|	1122	|	1417	|	1841	2014	|	|	2326
Uşak d.	|	1405	|	...	|	2124	...	|	|	0153
Afyon Ali Çetinkaya a.	|	...	|	...	|	...	...	|	|	0415
Akhisar d.	0910	...	1047	...	1621	...	...	1931	2022	—
Soma d.	0958	...	1131	...	1705	...	...	2016	2104	**72609**
Savaştepe d.	1029	...	1158	...	1735	...	...	2043	2132	
Ballıkesir d.	1127	...	1256	...	1838	...	...	2143	2247	0715
Bandirma Gar a.	...	...	1449	...	2034	...	...	...	|	|
Bandirma Şehir a.	...	...	1453	...	2038	...	...	...	|	|
Tavşanllı ♧ d.	...	...	...	...	...	...	...	...	0307	1137
Kütahya ♧ d.	...	...	...	...	...	...	...	...	0402	1232
Eskişehir ♧ a.	...	...	...	...	...	...	...	...	0532	...
Ankara **1570** a.	...	...	...	...	...	...	...	...	...	...

Istanbul - Bandirma

İstanbul Deniz Otobüsleri*

km							⑦	⑤⑦	●		
0	**İstanbul** Yenikapi d.	0700	...	...	...	1230	1530	1830	1915	...	...
	Bandirma Şehir a.	0930	...	...	...	1500	1800	2100	2145	...	...

	①–⑤	⑥⑦					♥	⑤⑦		
Bandirma Şehir d.	0745	0930	...	...	1530	...	1830	2130	...	...
İstanbul Yenikapi a.	1015	1200	...	...	1800	...	2100	0000	...	...

- KONYA MAVI TRENI – 🛏, [1] and ✕ Konya - Izmir Basmane and v.v.
- IZMIR MAVI TRENI – 🛏, [1] and ✕ Izmir - Eskişehir and v.v.
- 6 EYLÜL EKSPRESI – [1].
- 17 EYLÜL EKSPRESI – [1].
- EGE EKSPRESI – [1].
- KARESI EKSPRESI – [1].

● – ①②③④⑥.
♥ – Daily except ⑤.
♧ – For local services see Table **1581**.
‡ – Bandirma Sehir - Bandirma Gar: *1 km*. Bandirma Sehir - Ballıkesir *101 km*.
◇ – Afyon - Manisa: *355 km*. Usak - Manisa: *220 km*. Alaşehir - Manisa: *122 km*.
* – İstanbul Deniz Otobüsleri ✆ +90 (212) 455 6900. www.ido.com.tr

TCDD 2nd class — IZMIR - TIRE, ÖDEMIŞ, SÖKE and DENIZLI — 1572

km		32759	32721	32701	32703	32323	32747	32751	32705	32725	32749	32713	32753
0	**Izmir** Basmane ⊡ d.	...	0620	0742	0853	0920	...	0954	1130	1230	...	1341	1353
18	Adnan Menderes ⊡ d.	...	0639	0806	0918	0944	...	1019	1155	1254	...	1406	1419
49	Torballı d.	...	0714	0836	0948	1015	...	1048	1225	1324	...	1435	1448
86	Çatal d.	0555	0757	|	|	1052	...	1133	|	1408	...	|	1525
96	**Tire** a.	0606	|	|	|	|	...	1145	|	|	...	|	1537
11	**Ödemiş** Gar a.	—	0823	|	|	1113	...	...	|	1434	...	|	...
12	**Ödemiş** Şehir a.	**32743**	0828	|	|	1118	...	...	|	1439	...	|	...
77	Selçuk d.		...	0909	1017	...	...	...	1253	...	...	1503	...
	Söke d.	0635	...	|	|	...	1045	...	|	...	1400	|	...
00	Ortaklar d.	0706	...	0942	1049	...	1114	...	1325	...	1428	1534	...
30	Aydin d.	0738	...	1013	1127	...	1146	...	1356	...	1500	1605	...
75	Nazilli d.	0836	...	1105	1222	...	1236	...	1445	...	1550	1659	...
251	Goncali **1587** d.	0947	...	1216	1337	...	...	...	1558	...	...	...	...
260	**Denizli** **1587** a.	0958	...	1227	1348	...	...	...	1609	...	...	...	...

	32745	32727	32707	32755	32709	32729	32337	32711	32757	32741	32731	32733
Izmir Basmane ⊡ d.	...	1505	1530	1605	1641	1705	...	1754	1906	1930	2030	2205
Adnan Menderes ⊡ d.	...	1531	1555	1630	1706	1731	...	1819	1931	1955	2054	2230
Torballı d.	...	1605	1625	1703	1737	1803	...	1850	2002	2027	2124	2300
Çatal d.	...	1648	|	1743	|	1850	1855	|	2039	|	2201	2336
Tire a.	...	|	|	1755	|	|	1906	|	2051	|	|	|
Ödemiş Gar a.	...	1709	|	...	|	1916	...	|	...	|	2222	2357
Ödemiş Şehir a.	...	1714	|	...	|	1921	...	|	...	|	2224	0002
Selçuk d.	...	...	1655	...	1805	...	...	1920	...	2056	...	...
Söke d.	1555	...	|	...	|	...	...	|	...	2154h	...	...
Ortaklar d.	1623	...	1727	...	1836	...	...	1957	...	2128	...	...
Aydin d.	1657	...	1804	...	1909	...	...	2033	...	...	...	...
Nazilli d.	1748	...	1859	...	1958	...	...	2121	...	...	...	...
Goncali **1587** d.	1858	...	2008	...	2107	...	...	2230	...	...	...	...
Denizli **1587** a.	1909	...	2019	...	2118	...	...	2241	...	...	...	...

km		32722	32752	32742	32702	32724	32754	32704	32726	32744	
0	**Denizli** **1587** d.	...	...	...	0420	...	...	0550	...	0645	...
9	Goncali **1587** d.	...	...	...	0434	...	...	0604	...	0659	...
85	Nazilli d.	...	...	...	0545	...	...	0715	...	0810	...
30	Aydin d.	...	...	...	0634	...	...	0805	...	0908	...
60	Ortaklar d.	...	...	0618	0705	...	...	0836	...	0943	...
83	**Söke** a.	...	...	0550j	|	...	...	|	...	1009	...
83	Selçuk d.	...	...	0649	0736	...	...	0908	...	...	...
	Ödemiş Şehir d.	0520	...	|	|	0705	...	|	0845	...	...
	Ödemiş Gar d.	0524	...	|	|	0709	...	|	0849	...	...
	Tire d.	|	0610	|	|	|	0740	|	|	...	...
	Çatal d.	0553	0623	|	|	0733	0758	|	0911	...	...
11	Torballı d.	0639	0659	0714	0805	0824	0839	0939	0951	...	...
42	Adnan Menderes ⊡ a.	0709	0732	0748	0837	0856	0909	1009	1020	...	...
60	**Izmir** Basmane ⊡ a.	0733	0756	0812	0902	0919	0933	1033	1045	...	...

	32706	32756	32728	32746	32748		32730	32708	32758	32710	32750	32732	32714	32712
Denizli **1587** d.	0825	...	...	1030	...	...	...	1245	...	1435	...	...	...	1730
Goncali **1587** d.	0839	...	...	1044	...	...	...	1259	...	1449	...	...	...	1745
Nazilli d.	0951	...	...	1156	1300	...	...	1411	...	1600	1710	...	1750	1900
Aydin d.	1043	...	...	1253	1355	...	...	1501	...	1654	1805	...	1847	1952
Ortaklar d.	1115	...	...	1326	1427	...	...	1535	...	1726	1837	...	1917	2023
Söke a.	|	...	...	1352	1453	...	...	|	...	|	1903	...	|	|
Selçuk d.	1146	...	...	...	...	...	...	1606	...	1757	...	...	1948	2055
Ödemiş Şehir d.	|	...	1200	...	...	...	1450	|	...	|	...	1755	|	|
Ödemiş Gar d.	|	...	1204	...	...	...	1454	|	...	|	...	1759	|	|
Tire d.	|	1150	|	...	...	...	|	|	1635	|	...	|	|	|
Çatal d.	|	1203	1231	...	...	...	1524	|	1649	|	...	1828	|	|
Torballı d.	1214	1238	1316	...	...	...	1604	1634	1738	1827	...	1916	2016	2126
Adnan Menderes ⊡ a.	1244	1308	1345	...	...	...	1633	1706	1808	1857	...	1945	2045	2156
Izmir Basmane ⊡ a.	1309	1333	1409	...	...	...	1657	1730	1832	1921	...	2009	2109	2221

h – Arrival time. Calls after Ortaklar.
j – Departure time. Calls before Ortaklar.
⊡ – Frequent local trains operate 0600 - 2300.

TCDD — ANKARA - SIVAS, KARS, KURTALAN, TATVAN and TEHRAN — 1575

km		42602	42604	42606	22012	22014	42608	51516	22010	21124	21206
					②⑦	△		②			
		2	2	2	B	C	2	G	D	E ❋	F ❋
0	**Ankara** **1582** d.	...	...	...	1100	1100	...	...	1800	1900	2005
43	Elmadağ **1582** d.	...	...	...	1151	1151	...	...	1851	1952	2056
92	Kirikkale **1582** d.	...	...	...	1245	1245	...	...	1944	2046	2146
03	Yerköy **1582** d.	...	...	...	1434	1434	...	...	2128	2229	2339
79	Kayseri d.	...	...	...	1750	1750	...	...	0039	0136	...
02	**Sivas** a.	...	...	...	2109•	2109•	...	...	0409•	0456	...
02	**Sivas** d.	0801	1600	1810	2125•	2125•	...	...	0413•	0512	...
10	Çetinkaya d.	0925	1824	1948	2306	2306	...	...	0551	0702	...
79	Divrigi d.	1041	1949	2106	|	|	0530	...	0716	|	...
35	Erzincan d.	—	...	—	|	|	0836	...	1026	|	...
50	Erzurum d.	...	...	...	|	|	—	...	1422	|	...
35	Horasan d.	...	...	...	|	|	...	...	1541	|	...
07	Sarkamiş d.	...	...	...	|	|	...	...	1715	|	...
65	**Kars** a.	...	...	...	|	|	...	...	1813	|	...
54	Malatya d.	**52604**	...	**52606**	0154	0154	...	...	...	0925	...
49	Yolçatı d.	2		2	0405	0405	...	...	...	...	...
07	Diyarbakir d.	0840	...	1750	|	0728	**52602**	...	...	...	...
98	Batman d.	1024	...	1933	|	0918	②⑤⑦	...	...	...	...
67	**Kurtalan** a.	...	...	...	|	1035	2	...	...	...	...
73	Elâzig d.	...	...	...	0439	...	0705	...	...	...	...
01	Mus d.	...	...	...	0905	...	1132	...	...	...	...
95	**Tatvan** Gar a.	...	...	...	1046	...	1302	...	...	...	...
00	**Tatvan** Iskele a.	...	...	...	...	...	...	...	...	...	...
0	**Van** Iskele d.	...	...	...	...	...	...	...	...	...	...
3	**Van** Gar d.	...	...	...	...	...	...	2100	...	...	...
14	Kapiköy 🛃 d.	...	...	...	...	...	...	0030	...	...	...
20	Razi d.	...	...	...	...	...	...	0340	...	...	...
42	Tabriz a.	...	...	...	...	...	...	0725	...	...	...
42	Tabriz **4630** ¶ d.	...	...	...	...	...	...	...	...	...	...
78	**Tehran** **4630** ¶ a.	...	...	...	...	...	...	...	...	...	...

	42601	51515	52603	52601	51123	21205	52013	52011	42009	52505
		①		①③⑥			▽	②④		
	2	G	2	2	E ❋	F ❋	C	B	D	2
Tehran **4630** ¶ d.	...	...	...	...	...	...	...	...	...	...
Tabriz **4630** ¶ a.	...	...	...	...	...	...	...	...	...	...
Tabriz d.	...	2330	...	...	...	...	...	...	...	...
Razi d.	...	0435	...	...	...	...	...	...	...	...
Kapiköy 🛃 d.	...	0445	...	...	...	...	...	...	...	...
Van Gar a.	...	0612	...	...	...	...	...	...	...	...
Van Iskele a.	...	—	...	...	...	...	...	...	...	...
Tatvan Iskele d.	...	...	...	...	...	...	...	...	...	...
Tatvan Gar d.	...	...	...	0735	...	...	...	0755	...	...
Mus d.	...	...	...	0904	...	...	...	0926	...	...
Elâzig d.	...	...	...	1315	...	...	...	1401	...	...
Kurtalan d.	...	...	...	—	...	...	0800	|	...	...
Batman d.	...	...	0530	...	...	...	0922	|	...	1500
Diyarbakir d.	...	...	0715	...	...	...	1111	|	...	1645
Yolçatı d.	...	...	—	...	...	...	1429	1429	...	...
Malatya d.	...	...	...	...	1530	...	1645	1645	...	...
Kars d.	...	...	...	...	|	...	|	|	0800	...
Sarkamiş d.	...	...	...	...	|	...	|	|	0903	...
Horasan d.	...	...	...	**42607**	|	...	|	|	1028	...
Erzurum d.	...	**42603**	**42605**	2	|	...	|	|	1159	...
Erzincan d.	...	2	2	1430	|	...	|	|	1558	...
Divrigi d.	0600	0635	1615	1734	|	...	|	|	1903	...
Çetinkaya d.	0720	0758	1733	...	1757	...	1912	1912	2024	...
Sivas a.	0848	0959	1858	...	1937	...	2042•	2042•	2154•	...
Sivas d.	...	...	...	...	1947	...	2052•	2052•	2206•	...
Kayseri d.	...	...	...	...	2318	...	0029	0029	0138	...
Yerköy **1582** d.	...	...	...	...	0229	0350	0337	0337	0441	...
Kirikkale **1582** d.	...	...	...	...	0415	0539	0528	0528	0629	...
Elmadağ **1582** a.	...	...	...	...	|	0640	0634	0634	0734	...
Ankara **1582** a.	...	...	...	...	0610	0735	0722	0722	0822	...

- VAN GÖLÜ EKSPRESI – 🛏 🛏 and [2] Ankara - Tatvan and v.v.
- GÜNEY KURTALAN EKSPRESI – 🛏 🛏 and [2] Ankara - Kurtalan and v.v.
- DOĞU EKSPRESI – 🛏 [12] Ankara - Kars and v.v.
- 4 EYLÜL MAVI – [12] 🛏 and ✕ Ankara - Malatya and v.v.
- CÜKUROVA MAVI – 🛏 🛏 and [2] ✕ Ankara - Adana and v.v.
- 🛏 and 🍸 Tabriz(**494**/**495**) - Kapiköy(**51515**/**51516**) - Van and v.v.

△ – ①③④⑤⑥.
▽ – ①③⑤⑥⑦.
❋ – Service currently suspended.
¶ – Table **4630** appears in the Summer (June) and Winter (December) editions.
• – Journeys to / from Sivas are subject to alteration until November 2019 with 🚌 replacement services connecting with trains at alternative stations (please check locally for amended timings).

1576 KARABÜK - ZONGULDAK TCDD

km		22626	22630	22632	22636
0	**Karabük** ..... d.	0705	1250	1600	1810
59	Gokçebey ... d.	0826	1414	1721	1933
75	Çaycuma .... d.	0847	1439	1741	1954
96	Filyos .... d.	0921	1511	1813	2026
120	**Zonguldak** . a.	1003	1552	1859	2107

	22621	22625	22627	22633
Zonguldak ... d.	0730	1130	1325	1825
Filyos .... d.	0815	1214	1408	1917
Çaykuma .... d.	0848	1247	1440	1953
Gokçebey ..... d.	0909	1308	1501	2014
Karabük .... a.	1033	1428	1621	2135

Additional local trains run Zonguldak - Gokçebey and v.v.
From Zonguldak at 0930, 1625, 1730 and 2030.
From Gokçebey at 0540, 0635, 1225 and 1825.

1577 SIVAS - AMASYA - SAMSUN TCDD

Service suspended until further notice

km					
0	**Sivas** .... d.	...	...	...	...
53	Yildizeli .... d.	...	...	...	...
205	Turhal .... d.	...	...	...	...
268	**Amasya** .... d.	...	...	...	...
295	Suluova .... d.	...	...	...	...
315	Havza .... d.	...	...	...	...
401	**Samsun** .... a.	...	...	...	...

Samsun .... d.	...	...	...
Havza .... d.	...	...	...
Suluova .... d.	...	...	...
Amasya .... d.	...	...	...
Turhal .... d.	...	...	...
Yildizeli .... d.	...	...	...
Sivas .... a.	...	...	...

1581 ESKIŞEHIR - AFYON - KONYA - ADANA TCDD

For YHT (high-speed) services between Eskisehir and Konya, see Table **1570**.

km		32007	72442	72444	72602	72014	62006	72604	72608	72606	72006
		F	2	2	2	H	J	2		2	C
			❋	❋							
0	**Eskişehir** .... **1571** d.	...	...	...	0930	1025	...	1425	1830	2000	2206
77	Kütahya .... **1571** d.	...	...	...	1059	1202	...	1601	2003	2131	2332
	Tavşanllı .... **1571** a.	...	...	...	...	|	...	...	|	2226	0025
163	**Afyon** .... d.	0424	...	...	...	1357	...	...	2147	...	...
261	Akşehir .... d.	0554	0630	1220	...	...	...	...	...	...	...
435	**Konya** .... d.	0837	0902	1452	...	...	1530	...	...	...	...
537	Karaman .... d.	...	...	...	...	...	1701	...	...	...	...
624	Ereğli .... d.	...	...	...	...	...	1810	...	...	...	...
672	Ulukışla .... **1582** d.	...	...	...	...	...	1905	...	...	...	...
781	Yenice .... **1582** d.	...	...	...	...	...	2052	...	...	...	...
804	**Adana** .... **1582** d.	...	...	...	...	...	2117	...	...	...	...

	72005	72601	72607	72603	72441	62005	72013	72605	72443	7200[8]
	C	2		2	2	J	H	2	2	F
					❋				❋	
Adana .... **1582** d.	...	...	...	...	...	0745	...	...	...	...
Yenice .... **1582** d.	...	...	...	...	...	0813	...	...	...	...
Ulukışla .... **1582** d.	...	...	...	...	...	1019	...	...	...	...
Ereğli .... d.	...	...	...	...	...	1102	...	...	...	...
Karaman .... d.	...	...	...	...	...	1217	...	...	...	...
Konya .... d.	...	...	...	...	0920	1348	...	...	1730	1915
Akşehir .... d.	...	...	...	...	1150	...	...	...	2000	2200
Afyon .... d.	...	...	0755	...	...	...	1239	...	...	2324
Tavşanllı .... d.	0307	0600	|	...	...	...	|	...	...	...
Kütahya .... **1571** d.	0402	0655	0945	1130	...	...	1455	1640	...	...
Eskişehir .... **1571** a.	0532	0823	1115	1301	...	...	1614	1807	...	...

km		62702		62704				62706			
			🚌		🚌	🚌			🚌	🚌	
0	Konya .... **1570** d.	0550	0700	0920	1210	1340	...	1730	1840	2030	...
102	Karaman .... d.	0709	0830	1038	1340	1510	...	1848	2010	2200	...

	62701					62703				6270[…]
		🚌	🚌	🚌			🚌	🚌		
Karaman .... d.	0735	0935	1050	1215	...	1440	1540	1715	...	1930
Konya .... **1570** d.	0852	1105	1220	1345	...	1604	1710	1845	...	2050

C – IZMIR MAVI TRENI – 🛏, [1] and ✕ Izmir - Eskişehir and v.v.
F – KONYA MAVI TRENI – 🛏, [1] and ✕ Konya - Izmir Basmane and v.v.
H – PAMUKKALE EKSPRESİ – [1] and ✕ Eskişehir - Denizli and v.v.
J – TOROS EKSPRESİ – [2] Adana - Konya and v.v.
❋ – **Service currently suspended.**

1582 ANKARA - KAYSERI - ADANA TCDD

km		22002	22012	22014	22010	62006	21124	21206		
		G	B	C	D	J	E	F		
			△	▽			❋	❋		
0	**Ankara** .... **1575** d.	...	1100	1100	1800	...	1900	2005	...	...
43	Elmadağ .... **1575** d.	...	1151	1151	1851	...	1952	2056	...	...
92	Kirikkale .... **1575** d.	...	1245	1245	1944	...	2056	2148	...	...
203	Yerköy .... **1575** d.	...	1434	1434	2128	...	2229	2339	...	...
379	**Kayseri** .... **1575** d.	0700	1739	1739	0025	...	0136	|	...	...
479	Niğde .... d.	0908	...	...	...	...	...	0351	...	...
542	Ulukışla .... **1581** d.	1017	...	...	...	1905	...	0504	...	...
651	Yenice .... **1581** d.	1205	...	...	...	2052	...	0706	...	...
674	**Adana** .... **1581** d.	1232	...	...	...	2117	...	0725	...	...

	62005	62001	21123	21205	22011	22013	22009		
	J	G	E	F	B	C	D		
			❋	❋	△	▽			
Adana .... **1581** d.	0745	1630	...	1930	...	...	...	...	...
Yenice .... **1581** d.	0813	1700	...	1951	...	...	...	...	...
Ulukışla .... **1581** d.	1015	1907	...	2220	...	...	...	...	...
Niğde .... d.	...	2014	...	2321	...	...	...	...	...
Kayseri .... **1575** d.	...	2221	2318	|	0029	0029	0138	...	...
Yerköy .... **1575** d.	...	...	2346	0350	0337	0337	0441	...	...
Kirikkale .... **1575** d.	...	...	0415	0539	0528	0528	0629	...	...
Elmadağ .... **1575** a.	...	...	|	0640	0634	0634	0734	...	...
Ankara .... **1575** a.	...	...	0610	0735	0722	0722	0822	...	...

B – VAN GÖLÜ EKSPRESI – 🛏 ▬ and [2] ✕ Ankara - Tatvan and v.v.
C – GÜNEY KURTALAN EKSPRESI – 🛏 ▬ and [2] ✕ Ankara - Kurtalan and v.v.
D – DOĞU EKSPRESI – 🛏 ▬ and [2] ✕ Ankara - Kars and v.v.
E – 4 EYLÜL MAVI – ▬ and [2] ✕ Ankara - Malatya and v.v.
F – CÜKUROVA MAVI – 🛏 ▬ and [2] ✕ Ankara - Adana and v.v.
G – ERCIYES EKSPRESI – [2] Kayseri - Adana and v.v.
J – TOROS EKSPRESİ – [2] Adana - Konya and v.v.
△ – Runs on ②⑦ from Ankara. Runs on ②④ from Tatvan.
▽ – Runs on ①③④⑤⑥ from Ankara. Runs on ①③⑤⑥⑦ from Kurtalan.
❋ – **Service currently suspended.**

1583 ADANA - MALATYA - ELAZIĞ TCDD

km		52608	62004
			L
0	**Adana** .... d.	...	0835
78	Toprakkale .... d.	...	0943
141	Fevzipaşa .... d.	...	1113
210	Narlı .... d.	...	1218
335	Doğansehir .... d.	...	1442
392	**Malatya** .... d.	0645	1557
487	Yolçatı .... d.	0833	1748
511	**Elazığ** .... a.	0851	1807

	52003	52609
	L	
Elazığ .... d.	0810	1810
Yolçatı .... d.	0834	1829
Malatya .... d.	1046	2021
Doğansehir .... d.	1154	...
Narlı .... d.	1413	...
Fevzipaşa .... d.	1529	...
Toprakkale .... d.	1641	...
Adana .... a.	1746	...

L – FIRAT EKSPRESİ – [1] Elazig - Adana and v.v.

1584 GAZIANTEP - ALEPPO & NUSAYBIN TCDD

km			
0	**Gaziantep** .... d.	...	...
49	Nizip .... d.	...	...
88	Karkamiş .... d.	...	...
143	Çobanbey .... 🏛 d.	...	...
218	**Aleppo** .... a.	...	...
356	Şenyurt .... d.	...	...
381	**Nusaybin** .... a.	...	...

Nusaybin .... d.	...	...
Şenyurt .... d.	...	...
Aleppo .... d.	...	...
Çobanbey .... 🏛 d.	...	...
Karkamiş .... d.	...	...
Nizipden .... d.	...	...
Gaziantep .... a.	...	...

SERVICE SUSPENDED.

1585 MERSIN - ADANA TCDD

km				K														K		J							
0	**Mersin** .... d.	0545	0610	0630	0700	0730	0800	0830	0915	1000	1045	1145	1215	1300	1345	1430	1515	1630	1700	1730	1800	1830	1900	1935	2030	2130	223[…]
26	Tarsus .... d.	0613	0641	0703	0733	0758	0829	0858	0948	1033	1113	1213	1248	1333	1413	1458	1544	1703	1733	1808	1833	1903	1933	2003	2058	2204	230[…]
43	Yenice .... d.	0628	0656	0719	0749	0814	0844	0913	1003	1048	1128	1228	1303	1348	1428	1513	1559	1719	1748	1826	1848	1918	1948	2018	2113	2220	231[…]
68	**Adana** .... a.	0648	0718	0742	0811	0836	0906	0935	1025	1110	1150	1250	1325	1410	1450	1535	1621	1742	1810	1852	1910	1940	2010	2040	2135	2242	234[…]

								K	J													K					
Adana .... d.	0550	0615	0645	0705	0730	0815	0900	0925	1000	1100	1145	1230	1315	1400	1445	1530	1615	1650	1715	1745	1815	1840	1915	2000	2045	2130	223[…]
Yenice .... d.	0611	0639	0709	0731	0754	0839	0924	0949	1029	1124	1209	1254	1339	1424	1509	1554	1639	1714	1739	1809	1839	1905	1941	2026	2109	2154	225[…]
Tarsus .... d.	0627	0655	0725	0747	0810	0855	0940	1005	1047	1140	1225	1310	1355	1440	1525	1610	1655	1730	1755	1825	1855	1921	1957	2042	2125	2210	231[…]
Mersin .... a.	0651	0726	0756	0818	0835	0919	1005	1033	1120	1204	1256	1341	1426	1504	1550	1634	1726	1801	1826	1856	1926	1952	2021	2106	2149	2238	234[…]

J – [1] Islahiye - Adana - Mersin and v.v.
K – [1] Iskenderun - Adana - Mersin and v.v.

1587 AFYON - BURDUR, ISPARTA & DENIZLI TCDD

km		72014	⊙	⊙
		H	🚌	🚌
	Eskişehir ◇ . d.	1025	...	...
0	**Afyon** .... d.	1401	...	...
114	Karakuyu .... d.	1610	...	...
129	Dinar .... d.	1628	1640	1640
	Burdur .... a.	|	1740	|
	Isparta ...... a.	|	...	1740
254	Goncali .... d.	1838	...	...
263	**Denizli** .... a.	1851	...	...

	⊙	⊙	72013
	🚌	🚌	H
Denizli ... **1572** d.	...	...	0750
Goncali ... **1572** d.	...	...	0801e
Isparta ...... d.	0830	...	|
Burdur .... d.	|	0830	|
Dinar .... d.	0930	0930	1013
Karakuyu .... d.	...	...	1033
Afyon .... a.	...	...	1238
Eskişehir ◇ . a.	...	...	1614

H – PAMUKKALE EKSPRESİ – [1] and ✕ Eskişehir - Denizli and v.v.
e – Goncali Muselles.
◇ – See Table **1581**.
⊙ – Subject to confirmation.

1590 ADANA - ISLAHIYE / ISKENDERUN TCDD

All trains in Syria are believed to have been withdrawn

km		2 K	2 K	2 J
0	**Adana** .... d.	0743	1747	1854
78	Toprakkale ...... d.	0852	1856	2002
137	Iskenderun ... a.	0940	1943	|
141	Fevzipaşa .... d.	...	...	2123
	Islahiye .... d.	...	...	2134
179	Meydan Ekbez 🏛 a.	...	...	...
274	**Aleppo** .... a.	...	...	...
418	Hamāh .... d.	...	...	...
479	Himş II .... d.	...	...	...
623	**Dimashq** Kadem a.	...	...	...

	2 K	2 J	2 K
Dimashq Kadem . d.	...	...	...
Himş II .... d.	...	...	...
Hamāh .... d.	...	...	...
Aleppo .... d.	...	...	...
Meydan Ekbez 🏛 d.	...	...	...
Islahiye .... d.	...	0725	...
Fevzipaşa .... d.	...	0740	...
Iskenderun ... a.	0715	|	164[…]
Toprakkale ...... d.	0805	0854	173[…]
Adana .... a.	0924	0958	183[…]

J – [1] Islahiye - Adana - Mersin and v.v.
K – [1] Iskenderun - Adana - Mersin and v.v.

ROMANIA

SEE MAP PAGE 505

Operator: Societatea Naţională de Transport Feroviar de Călători (CFR Călători): www.cfrcalatori.ro. Certain services are operated by private companies as shown in relevant tables.

Services: Trains convey 1st- and 2nd-class seating accommodation unless otherwise indicated. Sleeping- (🛏) and couchette (▬) cars are described on page 10. Most long-distance trains are classified *IR* (Interregio), shown in our tables with just the train number.

Timings: Valid **December 9, 2018 - December 14, 2019.** Minor alterations to schedules are possible at any time.

Tickets: Reservation is obligatory for travel by all CFR Călători services for which a train number is shown in the tables, and passengers boarding without a prior reservation are surcharged. CFR trains shown without numbers are slow stopping-services calling at all, or most, stations.

BUCUREŞTI - BRAŞOV - CLUJ NAPOCA / ORADEA / SIBIU / ARAD (- BUDAPEST) ° 1600

km		144		1739	74		72	366	1745	1586	1623		1645 1539	346		406	1529 1929*	472	1741	⊡ 1945	1931	1641 1941*	1641 1639	1924	1821 1921*
		T	2	⑥–①	F	2	S	H				2	Ln	D	2	C	n	R	⊕	J⊕	J⊕	⊗	⊗	J	⊕
	Mangalia **1680** d.	...	...	...	...	...	...	...	...	...	...	...	...	...	...	...	...	...	...	1517	1600	1545x	1545x	1829	1927r
	Constanţa **1680** d.	...	...	...	...	...	...	...	...	0520	...	...	...	...	...	...	1400s	...	...	1710	1800	1755x	1755x	2008	2104r
0	**Bucureşti** Nord ▷ d.	...	...	...	...	...	0520	...	0605	0805	0955	...	1215	1400	...	...	1638	1745	1845	1928b	2030b	2105	2105	2258	2340
59	Ploieşti Vest ▷ d.	...	...	...	...	...	|	...	0647	0846	1041	...	1257	1439	...	...	1725	1825	1928	2016	2120	2147	2147	|	|
121	Sinaia ▷ d.	...	...	...	...	...	|	...	0744	0935	1135	...	1347	1524	...	...	1817	1910	2020	2107	2214	2240	2240	|	|
140	Predeal ▷ d.	...	...	...	...	...	|	...	0810	1001	1202	...	1414	1544	...	...	1843	1933	2047	2132	2241	2306	2306	|	|
166	**Braşov** ▷ a.	...	...	...	...	...	|	...	0849	1040	1241	...	1455	1623	...	...	1921	2010	2126	2211	2320	2344	2344	|	|
166	**Braşov** d.	...	...	...	0525	0600	|	0701z	0859	...	1257	1435	1508	1631	1747	1847	1933	2025	2138	2223	2332	2355	2355	|	|
294	**Sighişoara** **1622** d.	...	0531	...	|	|	|	|	1148	...	|	|	1752	1911	|	|	|	|	0027	|	0221	|	|	|	|
330	Mediaş **1622** d.	...	0615	v	|	|	|	|	1222	...	|	|	1825	1939	|	|	|	|	0102	|	0257	|	|	|	|
340	Copşa Mică **1622** d.	...	0629	0720	|	|	|	|	1233	...	|	|	1837	|	|	|	|	|	0118	|	0310	|	|	|	|
370	Blaj d.	...	0710	0751	|	|	◧	◐	1306	...	|	|	1905	2017	|	◐	|	|	0147	◐	0340	◐	◐	△	▽
392	Teiuş **1620** d.	...	0754	0819	|	|	|	|	1336	...	|	|	1935	|	|	|	|	|	0220	|	0410	|	|	|	|
405	Aiud **1620** d.	...	0807	0833	|	|	|	|	1350	...	|	|	1950	|	|	|	|	|	0236	|	0426	|	|	|	|
425	Războieni **1620** d.	...	0844	0902	|	|	|	|	1413	...	|	|	2014	|	|	|	|	|	0259	|	0449	|	|	|	|
442	Câmpia Turzii **1620** d.	...	0903	0920	|	|	|	|	1429	...	|	|	2031	|	|	|	|	|	0317	|	0506	|	|	|	|
494	**Cluj Napoca** **1620** a.	...	1020	1025	|	|	|	1423	1533	...	|	|	2135	|	|	0216	|	|	0422	|	0609	|	0737	|	|
494	**Cluj Napoca** **1625** d.	0735	...	...	|	|	|	1446	1554	...	|	|	...	|	|	0228	|	|	0439	|	0631	|	...	|	|
543	Huedin **1625** d.	0826	...	...	|	|	|	1538	|	...	|	|	...	|	|	0321	|	|	0536	|	0727	|	...	|	|
646	**Oradea** **1625** a.	1011	...	...	|	|	|	1723	|	...	|	|	...	|	|	0457	|	|	0724	|	0915	|	...	|	|
	Baia Mare **1610/14** a.	|	...	...	|	|	|	|	2006	...	|	|	...	|	|	|	|	|	|	0846	...	0926	...	|	|
	Satu Mare **1610/25** a.	|	...	...	|	|	|	|	...	...	|	|	...	|	|	|	|	|	0937	1013	...	...	...	|	|
•65	Făgăraş d.	|	...	...	0641	0737	|	|	...	...	1408	1612	...	|	1924	|	2104	2138	...	...	...	...	...	|	|
•127	Podu Olt **1645** d.	|	...	...	|	0912	|	|	...	...	1510	1803	...	|	2057	|	|	|	...	...	...	...	...	0657	|
•149	**Sibiu** **1645** d.	|	...	...	0806	0954	|	|	...	...	1538	1843	...	|	2137	|	2248	2302	...	...	...	...	...	0725	|
•223	Sebeş Alba d.	|	...	...	0935	...	|	|	...	...	...	...	...	|	...	|	...	0029	...	...	...	...	...	...	|
	Alba Iulia d.	|	...	...	|	...	|	|	...				...	2101	...	|	...	|	...	...	...	...	...	...	|
•232	Vinţu de Jos d.	|	...	...	0948	...	|	|	...				...	|	...	|	...	0043	...	...	...	...	...	...	|
•276	Simeria **1620** d.	|	...	...	1055	...	|	|	...				...	2205	...	|	...	0149	...	...	...	...	...	...	0801
•285	Deva **1620** d.	|	...	...	1111	...	|	|	...				...	2222	...	|	...	0206	...	...	...	...	...	...	0818
•433	**Arad** **1620** a.	|	...	...	1417	...	1528	|	...				...	0119	...	|	...	0513	...	...	...	...	...	...	1131
	Budapest Keleti **1280** ‡ a.	1420	...	...	1750	...	1850	2120	...				...	0450	...	0920	...	0850	...	...	...	...	...	...	...

May 13 - 26: for revised times in Hungary see page 560

	73	1923	367	75	1738		⊡ 1944	1932	1642 1942*	1638 1642	1822 1922*	1742	143	1528 1928*	407	473	1634	347	1636		1746		1646	1624	1538
	S	K	H	F	⑤–⑦	2	K⊕	K⊕	⊗	⊗	⊕	⊕	T	n	C	R	2n	D		2		2	Mn		n
Budapest Keleti **1280** ‡ d.	0705	...	0740	0910	...	...	...	...	...	...	...	...	1340	...	1740	1910	...	2310	...	...	...	...	...	...	...
Arad **1620** d.	1245	...	|	1441	...	...	...	...	...	...	1840	...	|	...	|	0100	...	0436	...	...	...	...	...	...	...
Deva **1620** d.	|	...	|	1748	...	...	...	...	...	...	2147	...	|	...	|	0415	...	0735	...	...	...	...	...	...	...
Simeria **1620** d.	|	...	|	1816	...	...	...	...	...	...	2213	...	|	...	|	0442	...	0800	...	...	...	...	...	...	...
Vinţu de Jos d.	|	...	|	1904	...	...	...	...	...	...	|	...	|	...	|	0527	...	|	...	...	...	...	...	...	...
Alba Iulia d.	|	...	|	|	...	...	...	...	...	...	|	...	|	...	|	|	...	0859	...	...	...	...	...	...	...
Sebeş Alba d.	|	...	|	1917	...	...	...	...	...	...	|	...	|	...	|	0539	...	|	...	...	...	...	...	...	...
Sibiu **1645** d.	|	1836	|	2051	...	...	...	...	...	...	|	...	|	0400	|	0712	...	|	...	1155	...	1435	...	1640	...
Podu Olt **1645** d.	|	1909	|	|	...	...	...	...	...	...	|	...	|	|	|	|	...	|	...	1236	...	1522	...	1712	...
Făgăraş d.	|	|	|	2226	...	...	...	...	...	...	|	...	|	0539	|	0838	...	|	...	1411	...	1653	...	1819	...
Satu Mare **1610/25** d.	|	|	|	|	...	...	1321	...	...	...	|	1700	|	|	|	|	...	|	...	|	...	|	...	|	...
Baia Mare **1610/14** d.	|	|	|	|	...	...	1500	...	1752	...	|	|	|	|	|	|	...	|	...	|	0540	|	...	|	...
Oradea **1625** d.	|	|	1332	|	...	...	|	1625	|	...	|	1924	1948	|	2336	|	...	|	...	|	|	|	...	|	...
Huedin **1625** d.	|	|	1516	|	...	...	|	1819	|	...	|	2106	2134	|	0115	|	...	|	...	|	|	|	...	|	...
Cluj Napoca **1625** a.	|	|	1608	|	...	...	|	1909	|	...	|	2158	2225	|	0203	|	...	|	...	|	1002	|	...	|	...
Cluj Napoca **1620** d.	|	|	1623	|	1613	1650	|	1924	|	1917	|	2214	...	|	0215	|	...	|	...	|	1014	|	...	|	1340
Câmpia Turzii **1620** d.	|	|	|	|	1714	1814	|	2028	|	|	|	2319	...	|	|	|	...	|	...	|	1117	|	...	|	1444
Războieni **1620** d.	|	|	|	|	1741	1836	|	2046	|	|	|	2336	...	|	|	|	...	|	...	|	1134	|	...	|	1501
Aiud **1620** d.	|	|	|	|	1801	1910	|	2109	|	|	|	2359	...	|	|	|	...	|	...	|	1155	|	...	|	1524
Teiuş **1620** d.	|	|	|	|	1815	1932	|	2126	|	|	|	0019	...	|	|	|	...	|	...	|	1213	|	...	|	1543
Blaj d.	◧	△	◐	|	1839	2019	◐	2153	◐	◐	▽	0049	...	|	◐	|	...	0947	...	|	1240	|	...	|	1609
Copşa Mică **1622** d.	|	|	|	|	1908	2106	|	2220	|	|	|	0119	...	|	|	|	...	|	...	|	1306	|	...	|	1637
Mediaş **1622** d.	|	|	|	|	v	2121	|	2233	|	|	|	0133	...	|	|	|	...	1022	...	|	1318	|	...	|	1650
Sighişoara **1622** d.	|	|	|	|	...	2205	|	2312	|	|	|	0212	...	|	|	|	...	1054	...	|	1355	|	...	|	1728
Braşov a.	|	|	2344	2338	...	...	0133	0159	0320	0320	|	0457	...	0719	0953	0950	...	1332	...	1552	1641	1831	...	1931	2011
Braşov ▷ d.	|	|	...	...	...	...	0146	0214	0332	0332	|	0510	...	0735	...	1002	1120	1340	1415	...	1653	...	1920	1945	2019
Predeal ▷ d.	|	|	...	...	...	...	0232	0259	0409	0409	|	0554	...	0814	...	1039	1158	1417	1453	...	1737	...	1958	2023	2056
Sinaia ▷ d.	|	|	...	...	...	...	0300	0328	0431	0431	|	0622	...	0843	...	1101	1225	1437	1519	...	1804	...	2025	2050	2122
Ploieşti Vest ▷ d.	|	|	...	...	...	...	0353	0424	0524	0524	|	0717	...	0940	...	1147	1322	1525	1617	...	1858	...	2115	2144	2212
Bucureşti Nord ▷ a.	2322	0311	...	...	...	...	0442b	0525b	0611	0611	0616	0803	...	1026	...	1230	1404	1606	1704	...	1943	...	2200	2231	2253
Constanţa **1680** a.	...	0610	...	...	...	...	0718	0758	0920x	0920x	0906r	...	...	1258s	...	...	...	...	...	...	...	...	...	...	...
Mangalia **1680** a.	...	0800	...	...	...	...	0912	1008	1108x	1108x	1043r	...	...	...	...	...	...	...	...	...	...	...	...	...	...

ADDITIONAL TRAINS BUCUREŞTI - BRAŞOV

	1631	◇	♥	1732	♥	1937	◇	1633	1643	♣	♥
	n	2	c		cd	2J	2	2	⊗e	Jm	c
Constanţa **1680** d.	...	...	...	...	...	1015	...	...	...	1609	...
Bucureşti Nord d.	0700	0740	0923	g	1020	1255	1450	1510	1800	1818b	1924
Ploieşti Vest d.	0742	0823	1002	1019	1100	1336	1533	1547	1842	1908	2006
Sinaia d.	0832	0911	1051	1110	1149	1424	1621	1635	1938	2001	2056
Predeal d.	0858	0936	1116	1136	1214	1448	1646	1658	2004	2027	2122
Braşov a.	0937	1014	1155	1215	1252	1527	1725	1736	2041	2105	2201

	1630	1644	♥	♣	1632	◇	1936	♥	♥	1731	◇
	2Ⓐ	⊗e	c	Jm	2	2	2J	c	cd		2
Braşov d.	0450	0527	0650	0720	0840	1035	1230	1455	1545	1730	1800
Predeal d.	0528	0605	0727	0758	0917	1113	1307	1531	1622	1808	1836
Sinaia d.	0554	0635	0753	0823	0940	1140	1328	1556	1647	1835	1900
Ploieşti Vest d.	0652	0736	0845	0921	1029	1231	1417	1646	1736	1927	1950
Bucureşti Nord a.	0739	0823	0928	1012b	1110	1316	1500	1728	1818	g	2035
Constanţa **1680** a.	...	...	...	1216	...	...	1736	...	...	...	...

– CORONA – 🛏 1, 2 cl., ▬ 2 cl., (2) Braşov - Cluj Napoca - Budapest and v.v.
– DACIA – 🛏 1, 2 cl., ▬ 2 cl., (2) Bucureşti - Arad - Budapest - Wien and v.v.; (2) Bucureşti - Budapest and v.v.
– FAGARAS – (2) Braşov - Arad - Budapest and v.v.
– HARGHITA – (12) Braşov - Miercurea Ciuc - Cluj Napoca - Budapest and v.v. Conveys (2) Târgu Mures (**1748/9**) - Cluj Napoca - Budapest and v.v. on dates in Table **1615**.
– June 15 - Sept. 8.
– June 14 - Sept. 7.
– (12) Bucureşti - Braşov - Târgu Mureş (Table **1610**); (12) Bucureşti - Braşov (**1539**) - Cluj Napoca.
– (12) Târgu Mureş (Table **1610**) - Braşov - Bucureşti.
– ISTER – 🛏 1, 2 cl., ▬ 2 cl., (2) Bucureşti - Budapest and v.v.
– TRAIANUS – (2) Bucureşti - Craiova - Timişoara - Arad - Budapest and v.v.

T – TRANSILVANIA – (12) Cluj Napoca - Oradea - Budapest - Wien and v.v.
b – Bucureşti **Băneasa**.
c – From / to Craiova (Table **1630**).
d – Not Apr. 15 - Sept. 15.
e – To / from Beclean pe Someş (Table **1610**).
g – From / to Galaţi via Ploieşti Sud (Table **1670**).
m – From / to Mangalia (Table **1680**).
n – Not Dec. 25, Apr. 28, June 16.
r – Apr. 26 - May 1, June 15 - Sept. 8.
s – June 29 - Sept. 8.
v – From / to Râmnicu Vâlcea via Sibiu (Table **1622**).
x – Apr. 26 - May 1 only.
z – 0636 June 10 - July 31.
◐ – Via Miercurea Ciuc (Table **1610**).

◧ – Via Craiova and Timişoara (Table **1630**).
▷ – For additional trains Bucureşti - Braşov and v.v. see panel below main table.
△ – Via Râmnicu Vâlcea (Table **1645**).
▽ – Via Craiova and Târgu Jiu (Tables **1630/35**).
⊡ – For Mangalia - Cluj Napoca and v.v. portion see Table **1610**.
♥ – Operated by Softrans S. R. L.
♣ – Operated by Regiotrans.
◇ – Operated by Astra Trans Carpatic S. R. L.
⊕ – 🛏 1, 2 cl., ▬ 2 cl., (12)
⊗ – 🛏 1, 2 cl., ▬ 2 cl., (2)
‡ – Table **1275** for trains via Oradea.
• – Distance from Braşov.
* – Train number apples when extended to / from Constanţa or Mangalia.

1610 BRAŞOV - MIERCUREA CIUC - TÂRGU MUREŞ / CLUJ / BAIA MARE

For other trains from Bucureşti and Braşov to Cluj Napoca and Baia Mare / Satu Mare see Table **1600**

km		366				1645	406	1643	1945 1949	1641	1641 1639
		H⊡	2	2⚒	2	n	C	⊗	J	⊗	⊗d
	Bucureşti N **1600** d.	...	...	...	...	1215	...	1800	1928**b**	2105	2105
0	**Braşov** d.	0701	...	1246	...	1511	1847	2053	2223	2355	2355
32	Sfântu Gheorghe d.	0731	...	1322	...	1541	1917	2123	2253	0024	0024
95	**Miercurea Ciuc** d.	0834	1227	1434	1541	1644	2019	2238	0008	0126	0126
103	Siculeni d.	0843	1240	1446	1553	1657	2028	2251	0019	0137	0137
150	Gheorghieni d.	0933	1344	1558	1702	1807	2129	2352	0117	0229	0229
184	Topliţa d.	1007	1427	...	1749	1846	2203	0037	0203	0303	0303
228	Deda a.	1104	1550	...	1900	1953	2301	0143	0302	0400	0400
228	Deda ▷ d.	1105	*1635*	...	1913	2013	2303	0146	0313	0404	0404
250	Reghin ▷ d.	|	*1714*	...	2007	2044	|	|	0400*	|	|
282	**Târgu Mureş** ▷ a.	|	*1758*	...	2050	2118	|	|	0435*	|	|
275	Sărăţel d.	1203	...	...	...	...	2359	0243	0411	0512	0512
285	Bistriţa Nord a.	|	...	...	...	...	|	|	|	|	0534*
300	Beclean pe Someş d.	1229	...	...	...	...	0024	0307	0445	0538	0538
324	Dej Călători **1614** d.	1313	...	...	...	...	0107	...	0533	0641	0627
383	**Cluj Napoca** a.	1423	...	...	...	...	0216	...	0727*	|	0737
	Budapest Kel. **1275** a.	2120	...	...	...	...	0920	...	|	|	...
401	Jibou **1614** a.	...	...	...	...	...	...	...	0711	0820	...
458	**Baia Mare** **1614** a.	...	...	...	...	...	...	...	0846	0926	...
	Satu Mare **1625** a.	...	...	...	...	...	...	...	1013	...	...

	407			1646		367	1944 1948	1642	1638 1642	1644
	C	2	2	n	2	H	K	⊗	⊗	⊗d
Satu Mare **1625** d.	...	...	...	...	...	...	1321	...	...	...
Baia Mare **1614** d.	...	...	...	...	...	...	1500	1752	...	...
Jibou **1614** d.	...	...	...	...	...	...	1613	1907	...	...
Budapest Kel. **1275** d.	1740	...	...	...	...	0740	|	|	...	...
Cluj Napoca d.	0215	...	...	...	...	1623	1600*	|	1917	...
Dej Călători **1614** d.	0331	...	...	...	...	1739	1828	2059	2059	...
Beclean pe Someş d.	0406	...	...	...	...	1814	1903	2135	2135	2245
Bistriţa Nord d.	|	...	...	...	...	|	|	|	|	2230*
Sărăţel d.	0431	...	...	...	...	1839	1939	2201	2201	2329
Târgu Mureş ▷ d.	|	...	*1040*	1333	*1430*	|	1905*	|	|	|
Reghin ▷ d.	|	...	*1127*	1410	*1516*	|	1948*	|	|	|
Deda ▷ a.	0533	...	*1157*	1432	*1546*	1937	2035	2256	2256	0038
Deda d.	0534	...	1313	1444	1620	1938	2102	2302	2302	0046
Topliţa d.	0631	...	1428	1541	1732	2035	2204	2358	2358	0144
Gheorghieni d.	0706	1248	1512	1616	1821	2110	2239	0035	0035	0230
Siculeni d.	0759	1414	1622	1720	1929	2204	2335	0140	0140	0331
Miercurea Ciuc d.	0809	1435	1645	1730	1944	2215	2345	0150	0150	0341
Sfântu Gheorghe d.	0924	1606	1807	1832	2124	2318	0105	0252	0252	0444
Braşov a.	0953	1703	1844	1908	2202	2344	0133	0320	0320	0512
Bucureşti N **1600** a.	...	...	...	2200	...	...	0442**b**	0611	0611	0823

C – CORONA – 1, 2 cl., 2 cl., 2 Braşov - Budapest and v.v.
H – HARGHITA – 12 Braşov - Cluj Napoca - Budapest and v.v.
J – June 15 - Sept. 8. 1, 2 cl., 2 cl., 12 Mangalia - Constanţa - Bucureşti Băneasa - Târgu Mureş / Cluj Napoca / Satu Mare.
K – June 14 - Sept. 7. 1, 2 cl., 2 cl., 12 Satu Mare / Cluj Napoca / Târgu Mureş - Bucureşti Băneasa - Constanţa - Mangalia.
b – Bucureşti **Băneasa**.
d – Conveys 2 cl., 2 Bucureşti - Bistriţa Nord and v.v.
n – Not Dec. 25, Apr. 28, June 16.
▷ – Additional trains: Deda - Târgu Mureş at 0417, 0516, 0915, 1206, 1721; Târgu Mureş - Deda at 0313, 0720, 1430, 1540, 1920, 2235. Journey 1h 20m.
⊗ – 1, 2 cl., 2 cl., 2
⊡ – Runs up to 25 mins earlier June 10 - July 31.
* – Separate portion of train.

1612 ADJUD - COMĂNEŞTI - MIERCUREA CIUC

2nd class

km											
0	**Adjud** d.	...	0503	0651	0922	1308	1509	1801	1945	2205	...
39	Oneşti d.	...	0553	0748	1017	1402	1559	1855	2038	2330	...
75	Comăneşti d.	0418	0655	0851	1116	1511	1659	1959	2137	0028	...
109	Ghimeş d.	0507	0744	0942	...	1559	1744	2048	...	...	...
150	Siculeni a.	0611	0859	1046	...	...	1848	2151	...	...	...
158	**Miercuria Ciuc** a.	0627	0908	1102	...	...	1858	...	...	...	...

Miercuria Ciuc d.	...	...	0725	...	...	1213	...	...	1608	1956
Siculeni d.	...	0425	0734	...	...	1228	...	...	1623	2006
Ghimeş d.	...	0534	0835	...	...	1328	...	1615	1724	2115
Comăneşti d.	0424	0630	0936	0955	1250	1425	...	1719	1829	2212
Oneşti d.	0525	0736	...	1103	1415	1524	1545	1820	1941	2325
Adjud a.	0617	0828	...	1155	1507	...	1637	1912	2033	0017

1614 CLUJ NAPOCA - DEJ - BAIA MARE / BISTRIŢA

km				1546				1745	♧	1544	
		2	2	n	2Ⓐ	2Ⓒ	2	b	2Ⓐ	Ⓐ	2
0	**Cluj Napoca** ▷ d.	0610	1101	1405	1510	1535	...	1554	1805	1825	1936
59	Dej Călători **1610** d.	0745	1236	1519	1635	1708	...	1721	1928	1944	2120
136	Jibou **1610** d.	0940	|	1709	|	|	...	1905	|	2133	|
193	**Baia Mare** **1610** a.	...	|	1827	|	|	...	2006	|	2237	|
84	Beclean pe Someş ▷ d.	...	1320	...	1719	1753	...	...	2012	...	2213
134	Sărăţel d.	...	1354	...	1753	1831	1840	...	2046	...	2247
144	**Bistriţa** Nord a.	...	1411	...	1809	1846	1855	...	2059	...	2305

		1746		1545	♧			1543	♧	
	2	b	2	n	2Ⓐ	2	2	⑦	2	2
Bistriţa Nord d.	0312	...	0740	...	1211	1530	...	...	1900	1920
Sărăţel d.	0327	...	0757	...	1225	1547	...	...	1915	1937
Beclean pe Someş ▷ d.	0402	...	0838	...	1300	1621	...	...	1951	2011
Baia Mare **1610** d.	|	0540	|	0848	|	|	1525	1710	|	|
Jibou **1610** d.	|	0653	|	1029	|	|	1638	1820	|	|
Dej Călători **1610** d.	0451	0851	0935	1215	1345	1706	1839	2013	2036	2056
Cluj Napoca ▷ a.	0620	1002	1102	1323	1502	1835	2004	2120	2154	...

b – From / to Bucureşti (Table **1600**).
n – Not Dec. 25, Apr. 28, June 16.
▷ – For additional trains Cluj Napoca - Dej Călători - Beclean pe Someş and v.v. see Table **1660**.
♧ – Operated by Interregional SA.

1615 CLUJ NAPOCA - RĂZBOIENI - TÂRGU MUREŞ

km						1746		1818			1748	
		2	2	2	2		2	2n	2Ⓐ	2	B	2
0	**Cluj Napoca** **1620** d.	...	*0341*	0515	...	1014	...	...	1525	...	1635	...
51	Câmpia Turzii **1620** d.	...	*0444*	0631	...	1117	...	...	1643	...	1737	...
69	Războieni **1620** d.	...	*0500*	0648	...	1133	...	...	1703	...	1753	...
69	Războieni d.	0408	0505	...	0653	...	1145	1221	...	1708	1808	1948
88	Luduş d.	0432	0530	...	0717	...	1217	1241	...	1734	1826	2018
128	**Târgu Mureş** a.	0529	0626	...	0812	...	1314	1326	...	1832	1910	2120

			1739	1749				1819		1766	
	2	2	⑥–①	B	2	2	2	2n	2	2	2
Târgu Mureş d.	0312	0715	...	1129	1435	1537	...	1622	1922	...	2220
Luduş d.	0406	0817	...	1216	1533	1633	...	1706	2017	...	2330
Râzboieni a.	0435	0838	...	1242	1556	1657	...	1733	2039	...	2359
Râzboieni **1620** d.	*0532*	...	0902	1257	...	...	1702	...	...	2047	0017
Câmpia Turzii **1620** d.	*0551*	...	0920	1314	...	...	1722	...	...	2104	t
Cluj Napoca **1620** a.	*0708*	...	1025	1418	...	...	1840	...	...	2208	...

B – Conveys 2 Budapest (**366/7**) - Cluj Napoca (**1748/9**) - Târgu Mureş Dec. 21 - Jan. 5, Apr. 18 - 22, June 1 - Sept. 7, Oct. 31 - Nov. 3, returning next day. Subject to alteration June 10 - July 30.
n – Not Dec. 25, Apr. 28, June 16.
t – To Teiuş (arrive 0101).

1620 CLUJ NAPOCA - SIMERIA - ARAD and TIMIŞOARA

km		1811		1837		1836			1738	1819		1765
		n	2	⊗	2		2Ⓑ	2	⑤–⑦	n	2	⊡e
	Iaşi **1660** d.	...	...	1830	...	...	...	...	...	...	...	1525
	Suceava **1660** d.	...	...	2036	...	...	...	...	...	...	...	1734
0	**Cluj Napoca** **1615** d.	...	...	0341	0515	0725	1135	...	1613	...	1941	0056
51	Câmpia Turzii **1615** d.	...	...	0444	0631	0831	1254	...	1714	...	2102	0200
	Târgu Mureş **1615** d.	...	0312	|	|	|	|	1537	|	1622	|	|
69	Războieni **1615** a.	...	0435	0500	0648	0847	1314	1657	1730	1733	2122	0215
69	Războieni d.	...	0437	0503	0651	0848	1315	1658	1741	1735	2123	0216
89	Aiud d.	...	0506	0528	0721	0911	1345	1727	1801	1755	2153	0238
102	Teiuş d.	...	0532	0547	0750	0930	1400	1742	1815	1812	2209	0256
121	**Alba Iulia** d.	...	0614	0621	0832	1004	▬	▬	|	1847	2256	0326
•	**Sibiu** **1600** d.	0325	|	|	|	|	...	...	△	|	...	|
131	Vinţu de Jos **1600** d.	0511	0625	0635	0849	1015	...	...	|	1905	...	0337
•	**Sibiu** a.	|	0905	|	|	|	...	...	2008	|	...	|
175	**Simeria** a.	0606	...	0736	0950	1113	2	2	v	2014	...	0428
175	**Simeria** **1600** d.	0609	...	0752	...	1134	1216	1612	...	2015	...	0433
184	Deva **1600** d.	0624	...	0809	...	b	1234	1629	...	2030	...	0450
332	**Arad** **1600** a.	|	...	|	...	...	1639	2027	...	|	...	0822
290	Lugoj d.	0854	...	1025	...	...	...	...	...	2254	...	|
349	**Timişoara** Nord a.	1001	...	1132	...	...	...	...	...	0001	...	0937

		1739		1818				1766	1812	1838	1835
	2	⑥–①	2	n	2	2	2	⊡e	n	⊗	
Timişoara Nord a.	...	...	...	0615	...	...	...	1335	1600	1720	...
Lugoj d.	...	...	...	0725	...	...	...	|	1709	1832	...
Arad **1600** d.	...	...	...	*0545*r	...	*0835*	...	1455	|	|	...
Deva **1600** d.	...	...	...	0944	...	*1233*	...	1803	1917	2051	b
Simeria **1600** a.	...	...	...	0959	...	*1250*	...	1819	1932	2105	0038
Simeria d.	...	v	...	1002	...	1423	...	1827	1935	2117	0057
Sibiu d.	...	0623	...	|	...	|	1544	|	|	|	|
Vinţu de Jos **1600** d.	...	|	...	1058	...	1524	1800	1923	2032	2211	015
Sibiu **1600** a.	...	△	...	|	...	|	|	|	2226	|	|
Alba Iulia d.	...	|	...	1110	...	1536	1813	1936	...	2222	020
Teiuş d.	0606	0819	1050	1144	1413	1620	1859	2009	...	2252	023
Aiud d.	0619	0833	1103	1157	1426	1633	1912	2022	...	2305	024
Războieni a.	0647	0856	1131	1220	1454	1701	1940	2045	...	2327	030
Războieni **1615** d.	0653	0902	1132	1221	1455	1702	1948	2047	...	2328	031
Târgu Mureş **1615** a.	0812	|	|	1326	|	|	2120	|	...	|	|
Câmpia Turzii **1615** d.	...	0920	1151	...	1516	1722	...	2104	...	2345	032
Cluj Napoca **1615** a.	...	1025	1310	...	1634	1840	...	2208	...	0049	043
Suceava **1660** a.	...	...	...	...	...	...	...	0538	...	0800	...
Iaşi **1660** a.	...	...	...	...	...	...	...	0746	...	1005	...

b – To / from Bucureşti via Târgu Jiu and Craiova (Table **1635**).
e – Conveys 2 Botoşani - Vereşti - Timişoara and v.v. (Table **1660**).
n – Not Dec. 25, Apr. 28, June 16.
r – Change at Ilia (a. 0847 / d. 0909).
v – To / from Râmnicu Vâlcea (Table **1645**).
△ – Via Copşa Mică.
⊗ – 1, 2 cl., 2 cl., 2
⊡ – 2 cl., 2
• – Sibiu - Vinţu de Jos = *83 km*.

1622 SIGHISOARA - SIBIU

km			⚒		1745		Ⓐ		346		
0	**Sighisoara** **1600** d.	...	...	0615	1148	...	...	1525	1911	...	...
39	Mediaş **1600** d.	0425	0515	0659	1220	1231	...	1610	1938	2002	...
50	Copşa Mică **1600** d.	0440	0530	0717	...	1245	1541	1626	...	2016	...
95	**Sibiu** a.	0557	0652	0904	...	1403	1702	1748	...	2140	...

		347		Ⓐ					Ⓑ	
Sibiu d.	0730	...	1205	1416	1549	1712	1939	...	2317	...
Copşa Mică **1600** d.	0850	...	1337	1531	1710	1838	2100	2106	0032	...
Mediaş **1600** d.	0903	1022	1350	...	1723	1901	2113	2121	0046	...
Sighisoara **1600** a.	...	1052	1433	...	...	1953	...	2205	...	...

TIMIŞOARA - ARAD - ORADEA - CLUJ NAPOCA / BAIA MARE 1625

For Timişoara - Cluj Napoca via Simeria and Teiuş see Table **1620**

km			1532	1741		◇	1834	78		♡					1534	1766		72	1743			1736	1536		
		2⚒		⊕	2	e	2n	K	2		2	2	2	2	n	D	2	T	n	2	2	⑦	⚒	2	2⊡
0	**Timişoara** Nord d.	...	...	...	0511	0539	0638	0730	0820	...	...	...	...	1304	...	1335	1355	1440	1555	...	1629	1712	1712	1741	1946
57	**Arad** a.	...	...	...	0621	0648	0734	0818	0933	...	...	...	...	1413	...	1432	1507	1528	1646	...	1741	1801	1801	1854	2108
57	**Arad** d.	...	...	...	0629	▬	0748	▬	▬	...	...	...	...	1431	...	1455	...	...	1655	...	...	1806	1816	1910	▬
139	Salonta d.	...	...	...	0819	...	0913	...	...	...	...	...	...	1612	...	|	...	...	1817	...	...	1938	1938	2134	...
178	**Oradea** a.	...	...	b	0908	...	0952	...	♡	...	...	...	...	1705	...	◐	...	...	1905	...	...	2017	2017	2218	...
178	**Oradea** 1600 d.	0255	0600	0734	▬	...	0959	...	1253	1520	1530	1635	...	...	1710	|	...	...	1916	1941	...	2025	2025	...	...
281	Huedin 1600 d.	|	0752	|	...	...	1143	...	1451	1721	|	|	...	...	1903	|	...	...	|	|	...	2210	2225	...	...
330	**Cluj Napoca** 1600 a.	|	0840	|	...	2d	1234	...	1545	1817	|	|	d	...	1958	2208	...	...	|	|	...	2259	2314	...	...
244	Valea lui Mihai d.	0435	▬	0839	...	1136	u	...	...	▬	1721	1759	1821	...	...	...	...	...	2023	2126	...	...	...	...	...
275	Carei d.	0511	...	0904	...	1209	...	...	...	...	1804	d	1856	...	...	...	...	...	2045	2158	...	...	...	...	...
311	**Satu Mare** a.	0556	2	0937	2Ⓐ	1254	...	✾	...	2	1848	...	1941	...	...	...	...	...	2115	2243	...	...	...	...	Ⓐ
311	**Satu Mare** d.	...	0745	...	1120	...	...	1321	...	1602	...	...	2003	...	...	...	...	...	2120	...	...	...	...	...	0445
370	**Baia Mare** a.	...	0937	...	1305	...	...	1446	...	1742	...	...	2150	...	...	...	...	...	2232	...	...	...	...	...	0635

		1744		1765		1531					♡		1945	1535			79	1833		1742					1537
	2□	m	2	D	2⚒		2	2	2	2	⚒	2	✾	n	2Ⓐ	2	K	2n	2	⊕	2	2N	2	2Ⓐ	2
Baia Mare d.	...	0045	...	...	...	...	0433	...	...	...	...	0745	0900	...	1226	...	...	...	...	...	1540	...	...	2015	...
Satu Mare a.	...	0159	...	...	...	...	0606	...	...	...	...	0929	1013	...	1411	...	...	...	...	...	1725	...	...	2200	...
Satu Mare d.	...	0206	...	...	0330	...	0621	0742	...	...	...	▬	▬	...	▬	1500	...	...	1545	1700	▬	...	1959	...	...
Carei d.	...	0239	...	...	0402	...	0710	0832	d	...	...	...	...	...	...	1543	...	...	1629	1737	...	...	2047	...	...
Valea lui Mihai d.	...	0303	...	...	0432	...	0749	0918	0941	...	...	...	...	...	...	1617	...	u	1702	1805	♡	...	2125	...	...
Cluj Napoca 1600 d.	...	|	...	0056	|	0550	d	▬	|	...	0854	...	...	1333	...	d	...	1539	|	|	1613	...	|	...	2040
Huedin 1600 d.	...	|	...	|	|	0638	▬	...	|	...	0950	...	...	1429	...	...	...	1633	|	|	1709	...	|	...	2132
Oradea 1600 a.	...	0410	...	|	0552	0826	...	...	1102	...	1155	...	2	1625	...	...	...	1823	1825	1909	1935	...	2246	...	2329
Oradea d.	...	0420	0504	◐	...	0829	...	...	...	...	▬	...	1603	...	...	...	...	1827	...	b	...	1956	...	...	...
Salonta d.	...	0505	0551	|	...	0914	73	...	...	...	...	...	1651	...	◇	...	...	1908	...	...	...	2051	...	...	...
Arad a.	...	0626	0735	0822	...	1035	T	2	...	...	2	2	1852	...	e	...	...	2036	...	...	...	2312	...	...	...
Arad d.	0439	0632	0750	0845	...	1038	1245	1333	...	1448	1651	1802	1855	...	1930	...	2047	2052	...	...	...	2330	...	...	...
Timişoara Nord a.	0610	0729	0920	0937	...	1126	1333	1448	...	1604	1804	1914	2009	...	2017	...	2135	2143	...	...	...	0038	...	...	...

- ▬ 2 cl., (2) Timişoara - Arad - Cluj Napoca - Iaşi and v.v.; (2) Timişoara - Arad - Cluj Napoca - Vereşti (**5565/0**) - Botoşani and v.v.
- CRIŞ – (12) Timişoara - Arad - Budapest and v.v. (Table **1280**).
- Ⓑ (daily Oradea - Arad).
- TRAIANUS – (2) Bucureşti - Craiova - Timişoara - Arad - Budapest and v.v.
- From / to Bucureşti (Table **1600**).

d – From / to Debrecen (Table **1277**).
e – From / to Bucureşti (Table **1630**).
m – Not Dec. 26, Apr. 29, June 17.
n – Not Dec. 25, Apr. 28, June 16.
u – To / from Iaşi (Table **1660**).
◐ – Via Alba Iulia and Teiuş (Table **1620**).

✾ – Summer only – see Table **1610**.
⊕ – 🛏 1, 2 cl., ▬ 2 cl., (12).
◇ – Operated by Astra Trans Carpatic S. R. L.
♡ – Operated by Transferoviar Grup SA.
⊡ – Also at 2338.
□ – Also at 0541.

BUCUREŞTI - CRAIOVA - TIMIŞOARA 1630

km		1699		1991	72	1591	1823		1521	♥	1691	1595	1825	1693	1835	1593 1993*	♥	♥	♥	1597	◇	1695 1995*	1821 1921*	
		Ⓐ	2	J⊕	T	n	2n	2	n	d	2✕	2n				n	d	Rd	S		⊗	⊗h	⊕	
	Mangalia 1680 d.	...	...	1958	...	...	...	...	...	...	...	...	...	...	...	1240s	...	...	...	...	...	1630x	1927r	...
	Constanţa 1680 d.	...	...	2145	...	...	...	...	...	...	...	...	...	...	...	1440s	...	...	1550	...	1720z	1817x	2104r	...
0	**Bucureşti** Nord d.	...	...	0022b	0520	0630	0848	...	0932	1000	1105	1345	1445	1545	1625	1725	1742	1830	1830	1945	2006	2120	2340	...
1	Videle d.	...	...	0117	0615	0721	0946	...	1023	1103	1156	1436	1537	1636	1716	1816	1833	1932	1932	2036	2057	2212	0031	...
0	Roşiori Nord d.	...	...	0204	0702	0808	1040	...	1108	1152	1243	1523	1624	1723	1804	1904	1920	2020	2020	2129	2144	2300	0118	...
5	Caracal d.	...	...	0257	0755	0901	1140	...	1201	1246	1338	1700	1719	1815	1900	2000	2012	2114	2114	2225	2237	2353	0214	...
9	**Craiova** a.	...	...	0338	0837	0942	1221	...	v	1329	1418	...	1800	1857	1942	2042	2053	2155	2155	2306	2317	0035	0255	...
9	**Craiova** 1635 d.	...	...	0350	0845	0948	1236	...	...	...	1425	...	1805	1905	1950	...	...	...	...	...	2324	0045	0305	...
5	Filiaşi 1635 d.	...	...	0415	0913	1016	1255	...	...	...	1452	...	1833	1932	2017	...	...	...	...	...	2351	0112	0332	...
3	Drobeta Turnu Severin d.	...	...	0558	1045	1148	u	...	...	...	1632	...	u	2104	t	...	...	...	...	...	0127	0252	|	...
7	Orşova d.	...	...	0630	1117	...	...	1357	...	...	1704	...	...	2136	...	...	...	...	...	...	0203	0324	|	...
4	Băile Herculane d.	...	...	0651	1138	...	...	1420	...	...	1726	...	...	2158	...	...	...	...	...	...	0227	0346	◐	...
5	Caransebeş d.	0635	0745	0837	1303	...	...	1624	...	...	1852	...	...	2325	...	...	...	...	...	...	0355	0520	|	...
4	Lugoj d.	0713	0837	0912	1338	...	...	1718	...	...	1927	...	...	0003	...	...	...	...	...	...	0433	0556	|	...
3	**Timişoara** Nord a.	0807	0946	1004	1436	...	...	1831	...	...	2019	...	...	0055	...	...	...	...	...	...	0532	0655	|	...
	Arad 1625 a.	...	...	...	1528	...	...	...	...	...	...	...	...	...	...	...	...	...	...	...	0648	...	1131	...

	♥	♥	♥	1826	1692	1824		1596	♥	1522	1590	1836	73	1698		1992			◇	1822 1922*	1592	1594 1994*	1696 1996*	
	d	Rd	S			n	2	n	d	n	n		T	Ⓐ	2	K⊕	2	2	⊗	⊕		n	⊗h	
Arad 1625 d.	...	...	...	...	...	...	...	...	...	...	...	...	1245	...	...	...	...	...	1930	1840	...	...	...	...
Timişoara Nord d.	...	...	...	...	0520	...	0835	...	...	...	...	...	1400	1622	1628	1749	...	1939	2020	|	...	...	2227	...
Lugoj d.	...	...	...	...	0614	...	0956	...	...	...	...	...	1454	1717	1737*	1849	...	2055	2112	|	...	...	2321	...
Caransebeş d.	...	...	...	...	0650	...	1046	...	...	...	...	...	1531	1752	1829	1948	1956	2144	2150	|	...	...	0016	...
Băile Herculane d.	...	...	...	...	0816	...	...	...	...	...	...	...	1702	...	...	2112	2159	...	2322	◐	...	...	0140	...
Orşova d.	...	...	...	...	0838	...	...	...	...	...	...	...	1731	...	...	2137	2220	...	2344	|	...	...	0202	...
Drobeta Turnu Severin d.	...	...	...	u	0912	u	...	...	...	...	1425	t	1805	...	...	2215	...	...	0018	|	...	...	0240	...
Filiaşi 1635 d.	...	...	...	0642	1101	1150	...	...	...	...	1605	1630	1947	...	...	|	...	...	0156	0225	...	...	0420	...
Craiova 1635 a.	...	...	...	0707	1127	1215	...	...	...	...	1630	1655	2012	...	...	0025	...	...	0223	0251	...	...	0445	...
Craiova d.	0610	0640	0640	0715	1135	1225	...	1410	1558	v	1638	1710	2020	...	...	0045	...	...	0230	0300	0310	0425	0458	...
Caracal d.	0648	0718	0718	0756	1215	1305	...	1450	1637	1652	1718	1808	2058	...	...	0125	...	...	0309	0340	0352	0505	0548	...
Roşiori Nord d.	0735	0807	0807	0850	1305	1355	...	1540	1724	1742	1805	1905	2145	...	...	0215	...	...	0356	0430	0448	0600	0638	...
Videle d.	0822	0853	0853	0938	1351	1442	...	1630	1810	1839	1852	2002	2231	...	...	0303	...	...	0444	0517	0547	0651	0725	...
Bucureşti Nord a.	0913	0951	0951	1030	1442	1543	...	1722	1902	1937	1944	2103	2322	...	...	0358b	...	...	0535	0616	0647	0745	0825	...
Constanţa 1680 a.	...	...	1231	...	...	...	...	...	...	...	...	...	...	...	...	0640	...	...	0841z	0906r	...	1040s	1115x	...
Mangalia 1680 a.	...	...	...	...	...	...	...	...	...	...	...	...	...	...	...	0836	...	...	...	1043r	...	1258s	1310x	...

June 15 - Sept. 8.
June 14 - Sept. 7.
June 16 - Sept. 9.
Not Apr. 15 - Sept. 15.
Apr. 15 - Sept. 15.
TRAIANUS – (2) Bucureşti - Craiova - Timişoara - Arad - Budapest and v.v.
Bucureşti **Băneasa**.
From / to Braşov (Table **1600**).
Conveys (2) to / from Reşiţa Sud (a. 0713 / d. 2215).

n – Not Dec. 25, Apr. 28, June 16.
r – Apr. 26 - May 1, June 15 - Sept. 8.
s – June 29 - Sept. 8.
t – To / from Cluj Napoca via Târgu Jiu (Table **1635**).
u – To / from Târgu Jiu (Table **1635**).
v – To / from Râmnicu Vâlcea (Table **1645**).
x – Apr. 26 - May 1 only.
z – June 16 - Sept. 16.
⊕ – 🛏 1, 2 cl., ▬ 2 cl., (12).
⊗ – 🛏 1, 2 cl., ▬ 2 cl., (2).

♥ – Operated by Softrans S. R. L.
◇ – Operated by Astra Trans Carpatic S. R. L.
◐ – Via Târgu Jiu and Simeria (Table **1635**).
* – Train number apples when extended to / from Constanţa or Mangalia.

CARANSEBEŞ - REŞIŢA SUD (journey 64 - 73 mins):
From Caransebeş: 0358, 0600, 0717, 0853 **L**, 1333Ⓐ, 1631, 1935. From Reşiţa Sud: 0525, 0845, 1317, 1505Ⓐ, 1758, 2215.

CRAIOVA - TÂRGU JIU - DEVA 1635

	1821		1727	1729	1823			1825		1835
	⊕s	2	①–④	⑤–⑦	n	2Ⓑ	2		2	
Bucureşti N 1630 d.	2340	...	...	...	0848	...	...	1445	...	1625
Craiova 1630 d.	0305	0545	0800	0800	1226	1430	1620	1805	...	1950
Filiaşi 1630 d.	0332	0630	0827	0827	1255	1541	1718	1833	...	2017
Târgu Jiu a.	0445	0804	0949	0949	1422	1720	1855	1957	...	2131
Târgu Jiu d.	0447	0815a	...	0955	...	1722	1910	...	2118	2140
Petroşani a.	0556	0955a	...	1115	...	1849	2041	...	2243	2250
Petroşani d.	0601	...	...	...	...	*1854*	...	...	2301	2254
Simeria 1620 d.	0801	...	...	...	...	*2108*	...	...	0050	0057
Deva 1620 a.	0816	...	...	...	...	...	...	...	...	|
Cluj Napoca 1620 a.	|	...	...	...	...	...	...	...	...	0434
Arad 1600 a.	1131	...	...	...	...	...	...	...	...	...

	1826		1824	1726	1728	1836				1822
		2	n	①–④	⑤–⑦		2	2Ⓑ	2	⊕s
Arad 1600 d.	...	...	...	...	...	...	...	...	...	1840
Cluj Napoca 1620 d.	...	...	...	...	...	0725	...	...	...	|
Deva 1620 d.	...	...	...	...	...	|	...	...	...	2147
Simeria 1620 d.	...	...	0720	...	...	1134	...	...	1958	2213
Petroşani a.	...	...	0919	...	...	1330	...	...	2208	2356
Petroşani d.	...	0805	0925	...	1240	1335	1430a	1915	2236	0001
Târgu Jiu a.	...	0935	1033	...	1350	1445	1559a	2044	0002	0109
Târgu Jiu d.	0510	0951	1035	1352	1352	1505	1612	2052	...	0111
Filiaşi 1630 a.	0642	1125	1150	1513	1513	1629	1754	2233	...	0225
Craiova 1630 a.	0707	1212	1215	1539	1539	1655	1841	2318	...	0251
Bucureşti N 1630 a.	1030	...	1543	...	...	2103	...	...	...	0616

Ⓐ only.
Not Dec. 25, Apr. 28, June 16.

s – Extended from / to Mangalia and Constanţa on dates in Table **1630** (numbered **1921/2**).

⊕ – 🛏 1, 2 cl., ▬ 2 cl. and (12).

1640 BUCUREŞTI - PITEŞTI - CRAIOVA

km		1891	1781	1783	1785	1893	1787	1895	1789	1897	1791	1793
			2	2	2				2		2	2u
0	**Bucureşti** Nord .... d.	0545	0730	0930	1130	1330	1430	1530	1630	1730	1830	1930
108	Piteşti .... d.	0808	0933	1137	1327	1539	1640	1736	1826	1940	2029	2129
189	Slatina .... d.	0942	...	...	...	1724	...	1910	...	2111	...	...
206	Piatra Olt .... **1645** a.	1001	...	...	...	1742	...	1929	...	2129	...	...
250	**Craiova** .... **1645** a.	1045	...	...	...	1845	...	2015	...	2213	...	...

	1782	1890	1784	1892	1786	1788	1790	1894	1792	1794	189
	2		2		2	2	2		2	2	
Craiova .... **1645** d.	...	0420	...	0720	...	...	...	1220	...	...	162
Piatra Olt .... **1645** d.	...	0504	...	0804	...	...	...	1305	...	...	170
Slatina .... d.	...	0525	...	0825	...	...	...	1326	...	...	172
Piteşti .... d.	0600	0700	0800	1000	1100	1300	1400	1500	1600	1700	190
Bucureşti Nord .... a.	0749	0848	0941	1148	1241	1454	1541	1641	1749	1856	204

u – An additional journey runs one hour later.

1645 SIBIU - RÂMNICU VÂLCEA - CRAIOVA / BUCUREŞTI

km		1722		1720		1522			1725	1923	1738
		n	2	n	2⚒	n	2	2		K	E
0	**Sibiu** .... **1600** d.	0234	0307	0700	0743	...	...	1602	1708	1836	2013
22	Podu Olt .... **1600** d.	│	0343	0729	0828	...	1305	1642	1739	1909	│
83	Călimăneşti .... d.	0440	0534	0900	1025	1430	1452	1845	1921	2048	2212
99	**Râmnicu Vâlcea** .... d.	0500	0600	0920	1054	1453	1520	1910	1942	2108	2230
186	Piatra Olt .... **1640** d.	0627	0807	1038	...	1612	1733	2203	2059	2305	...
230	**Craiova** ...... **1640** a.	│	│	1130	...	│	...	...	2142	│	...
•32	Caracal .... **1630** a.	0703	*0900*	...	...	1650	...	...	...	│	...
•17	Slatina .... d.	...	...	...	...	│	...	...	...	2328	...
•98	Piteşti .... d.	...	...	...	...	△	...	...	...	0130	...
•206	**Bucureşti** Nord . **1630** a.	...	...	...	...	1937	...	...	...	0311	...
	Constanţa **1680** .... a.	...	...	...	...	...	...	...	...	0610	...
	Mangalia **1680** .... a.	...	...	...	...	...	...	...	...	0800	...

	1739	1924				1724	1521		1721	172
	F	J	2	2	2		n	2	n	n
Mangalia **1680** .... d.	...	1829	...	...	...	...	...	...	...	...
Constanţa **1680** .... d.	...	2008	...	...	...	...	...	...	...	...
Bucureşti N ... **1630** d.	...	2258	...	...	...	...	0932	...	...	...
Piteşti .... d.	...	0120	...	...	...	...	△	...	...	...
Slatina .... d.	...	0252	...	...	...	...	│	...	...	...
Caracal .... **1630** d.	...	│	...	...	...	...	1202	...	...	181
Craiova ... **1640** d.	...	│	...	...	0505	0805	│	...	1505	│
Piatra Olt .... **1640** d.	...	0330	0342	...	0632	0910	1238	...	1614	190
Râmnicu Vâlcea .... d.	0410	0503	0630	...	0903	1037	1359	1605	1741	203
Călimăneşti .... d.	0427	0521	0656	...	0927	1054	1414	1629	1758	205
Podu Olt .... **1600** a.	│	0656	0907	0912	1111	1227	...	1817	│	│
Sibiu .... **1600** a.	0620	0725	...	0954	1152	1253	...	1858	2012	230

E – ⑤–⑦. From Cluj Napoca (Table **1620**).
F – ⑥–①. To Cluj Napoca (Tables **1620**).
J – June 15 - Sept. 8.
K – June 14 - Sept. 7.
n – Not Dec. 25, Apr. 28, June 16.
△ – Via Roşiori Nord (Table **1630**).
• – Distance from Piatra Olt.

1650 BUCUREŞTI - BUZĂU - BACĂU - IAŞI and SUCEAVA

km ☆		1861 1857	1861	1961	1953	1831	1661	380	1655	♣	♡	1751	1663	♡	1866	1753	1657	1665	1755	1553	402	1559	1653	1667	175
		K⊙	K⊙	J⊙	J⊙		n	2Y	n	⑥–①			2		n		2n	n		Ⓑ	P	n	⊕m	⊕	⊙n
0	**Bucureşti** Nord ...... **1600/70** d.	...	...	...	...	...	0555	0615	0715	b	1012	1050	1155	1240	...	1345	1500	1605	1700	1852	1915	2010	2135	2250	232
59	Ploieşti Sud .... **1600/70** d.	...	...	...	...	...	0649	0709	0811	0933	1120	1141	1247	1343	...	1438	1553	1657	1747	1945	2012	2108	2225	2342	001
	Mangalia **1680** .... d.	2015x	2015x	2027	2130	...	│	│	│	│	│	│	│	│	...	│	│	│	│	...	│	│	│	│	│
	Constanţa **1680** .... d.	2215	2215	2215	2315	...	│	│	│	│	│	│	│	│	...	│	│	│	│	...	│	│	│	│	│
	Făurei .... **1670** d.	0044	0044	│	0145	...	│	│	│	│	│	│	│	│	...	│	│	│	│	...	│	│	│	│	│
128	**Buzău** .... **1670** d.	0142	0142	│	0250	...	0755	0821	0922	1041	1230	1251	1356	1452	...	1551	1704	1807	1855	...	2127	2216	2337	0053	012
161	Râmnicu Sărat .... d.	0215	0215	│	0324	...	0828	0855	0955	1113	...	1323	1429	...	...	1625	1737	1840	│	...	2200	...	0011	0127	015
199	Focşani .... d.	0255	0255	△	0404	...	0907	0935	1035	1153	...	1402	1509	...	...	1705	1817	1920	2005	...	2240	...	0051	0207	023
219	Mărăşeşti .... d.	0330	0332	│	0428	...	│	0959	1059	1222	...	1425	│	...	...	1729	1841	│	2029	...	2304	...	0115	│	025
244	Adjud .... d.	0359	│	│	0457	...	│	1028	1128	│	...	1453	│	...	...	1757	1909	│	2058	...	2333	...	0144	│	032
303	**Bacău** .... d.	0439	│	│	0538	...	│	1114	1205	│	...	1539	│	...	...	1848	1947	│	2144	...	0026	...	0230	│	041
346	Roman .... d.	0510	│	│	0609	...	│	1144	▬	│	...	1609	│	...	...	1918	...	│	2214	...	0101	...	0300	│	044
	Galaţi .... d.	│	│	│	│	0630	│	│	...	│	...	│	│	...	1640	│	...	│	│	...	│	...	│	│	│
238	Tecuci .... d.	│	0357t	0356	│	0808	1003	│	...	1247t	...	│	1605	...	1826	│	...	2016	│	...	│	...	│	0306	│
288	Bârlad .... d.	│	0439	0439	│	0849	1044	│	...	1329	...	│	1654	...	1914	│	...	2058	│	...	│	...	│	0347	│
340	Vaslui .... d.	│	0524	0524	│	0935	1126	│	...	1414	...	│	1745	...	2004	│	...	2144	│	...	│	...	│	0432	│
408	**Iaşi** .... a.	│	0633	0633	│	1044	1230	│	...	1534	...	│	1854	...	2112	│	...	2252	│	...	0239	...	│	0540	│
538	*Chişinău* **1720** .... MD a.	│	...	...	│	c	...	│	...	...	...	│	...	...	...	│	...	...	│	...	0845	...	│	...	│
387	Paşcani .... **1660** d.	0539	...	...	0640	...	...	1213	...	...	...	1637	...	...	...	1947	...	...	2242	...	...	...	0329	...	051
432	Vereşti .... **1660** a.	0611	...	...	0718	...	...	1245	...	...	...	1709	...	...	...	2019	...	...	│	...	...	...	0401	...	054
476	Botoşani .... a.	│	...	...	│	...	...	│	...	...	...	1835r	...	...	...	│	...	...	│	...	...	...	│	...	071
448	**Suceava** .... **1660** a.	0623	...	...	0728	...	...	1257	2	...	...	1729	...	...	...	2031	...	...	2324	...	...	...	0414	...	060
450	**Suceava** Nord .... a.	0632	...	...	0737	...	...	1307	Y	...	...	...	...	...	...	2040	...	...	...	...	...	...	v	...	...
499	Vadul Siret .... 🏛 ▲ UA a.	...	...	...	...	...	...	1541	1743	...	...	...	...	...	...	...	...	...	...	...	...	...	...	...	...
539	**Chernivtsi** .... UA a.	...	...	...	...	...	...	...	1910	...	...	...	...	...	...	...	...	...	...	...	...	...	...	...	...

	1654	1558	1658	1750	1660	1752	1863	♡	♡	1754	1556	1656 1662	1662	♣		381	1664	1832	1756	1952	1962	1862	1856 1862	401	166
	⊕n	u	2n		n		n				Ⓐ	n		⑤–⑦	2Y	2Y	n		⊙m	L⊙	L⊙	M⊙	M⊙	P	⊗
Chernivtsi .... UA d.	...	...	...	...	...	...	...	...	...	...	...	...	...	...	0925	...	...	...	...	...	...	...	...	...	...
Vadul Siret .... 🏛 ▲ UA d.	...	...	...	...	...	...	...	...	...	...	...	...	...	...	1108	1340	...	...	...	...	...	...	...	...	...
Suceava Nord .... d.	v	...	...	...	...	0845	...	...	...	...	...	...	...	...	...	1553	...	...	...	2025	...	...	2245	...	...
Suceava .... **1660** d.	0038	...	...	0520	...	0852	...	...	...	1240	...	...	...	...	...	1601	...	...	2217	2035	...	...	2252	...	...
Botoşani .... d.	│	...	...	│	...	│	...	...	...	1119r	...	...	...	...	...	│	...	...	2107r	│	...	...	│	...	...
Vereşti .... **1660** d.	0051	...	...	│	...	0905	...	...	...	1307	...	...	...	...	...	1614	...	...	2243	2049	...	...	2306	...	...
Paşcani .... **1660** d.	0128	...	...	0604	...	0942	...	...	...	1344	...	...	...	...	...	1650	...	...	2322	2127	...	...	2343	...	...
Chişinău **1720** .... MD d.	│	...	...	│	...	│	...	...	...	│	...	...	...	...	...	│	...	c	│	│	...	...	│	1656	...
Iaşi .... d.	│	...	...	│	0559	│	0757	...	...	│	...	...	1406	1534	...	│	1640	1851	│	│	2115	2228	│	2243	231
Vaslui .... d.	│	...	...	│	0712	│	0908	...	...	│	...	...	1519	1651	...	│	1744	2003	│	│	2229	2342	│	│	003
Bârlad .... d.	│	...	...	│	0802	│	0957	...	...	│	...	...	1609	1738	...	│	1830	2057	│	│	2319	0034	│	│	012
Tecuci .... d.	│	...	...	│	0911	│	1054	...	...	│	...	...	1651t	1823t	...	│	1925	2142	│	│	0002	0116t	│	│	022
Galaţi .... a.	│	...	...	│	│	│	1230	...	...	│	...	...	│	│	...	│	│	2319	│	│	│	│	│	│	│
Roman .... d.	0157	...	...	0632	│	1010	...	...	...	1412	...	...	│	│	...	1718	│	...	2350	2156	│	│	0012	0028	│
Bacău .... d.	0235	...	0437	0702	│	1053	...	...	...	1450	...	1610	│	│	...	1754	│	...	0034	2228	│	│	0043	0110	│
Adjud .... d.	0315	...	0517	0742	│	1134	...	...	...	1531	...	1651	│	│	...	1835	│	...	0116	2309	│	│	0123	0158	│
Mărăşeşti .... d.	0344	...	0545	0810	│	1203	...	...	...	1559	...	1732	1732	1854	...	1904	│	...	0145	2338	│	0202	0202	0228	│
Focşani .... d.	0407	...	0609	0834	0957	1227	...	...	...	1623	...	1755	1755	1919	...	1929	2012	...	0210	0002	△	0226	0226	0254	03
Râmnicu Sărat .... d.	0445	...	0647	│	1035	1306	...	...	...	1700	...	1833	1833	1957	...	2007	2050	...	0249	0040	│	0304	0304	0333	03
Buzău .... **1670** d.	0518	0645	0720	0941	1108	1339	...	1452	1710	1733	...	1905	1905	2031	...	2040	2124	...	0323	0131	│	0355	0355	0413	04
Făurei .... **1670** a.	│	│	│	│	│	│	...	│	│	│	...	│	│	│	...	│	│	...	│	0209	│	0432	0432	│	│
Constanţa **1680** .... a.	│	│	│	│	│	│	...	│	│	│	...	│	│	│	...	│	│	...	│	0416	0511	0653	0653	│	│
Mangalia **1680** .... a.	│	│	│	│	│	│	...	│	│	│	...	│	│	│	...	│	│	...	│	0557	0653	0849x	0849x	│	│
Ploieşti Sud .... **1600/70** d.	0629	0754	0829	1047	1217	1451	...	1600	1825	1842	1928	2013	2013	2144	...	2150	2233	...	0437	...	...	...	...	0521	05
Bucureşti Nord ...... **1600/70** a.	0729	0854	0922	1140	1310	1547	...	1657	1927	1935	2029	2106	2106	d	...	2243	2323	...	0531	...	...	...	...	0620	06

BACĂU - PIATRA NEAMŢ - BICAZ

km							Ⓑ	⑥			
	Bucureşti Nord ⊡ ...... d.	...	...	...	...	...	...	...	1345	1700	...
0	**Bacău** .... d.	0410	0511	0709	...	1446	1642	1642	1912	2200	...
60	Piatra Neamţ .... a.	0551	0649	0851	...	1618	1820	1820	2050	2312	...
86	**Bicaz** .... a.	0632	...	...	...	...	1902	...	2132	...	...

								Ⓑ		
Bicaz .... d.	...	0657	...	...	...	...	...	1925	...	22
Piatra Neamţ .... d.	0502	0735	0910	...	1428	1632	1733	2004	...	22
Bacău .... a.	0632	0905	1023	...	1605	1802	1908	2134	...	23
Bucureşti Nord ⊡ . a.	...	...	1547	...	...	...	...	...	...	05

J – June 15 - Sept. 8.
K – Not June 15 - Sept. 8
L – June 14 - Sept. 7.
M – Not June 14 - Sept. 7.
P – PRIETENIA – 🛏 1, 2 cl., [2] Bucureşti - Ungheni (**106/5**) - Chişinău and v.v.
Y – Daily. On ⑦ conveys 🛏 1, 2 cl. Bucureşti - Vadul Siret - Chernivtsi - Kyïv, returning from Kyïv ⑤ (Table **1700**).
b – From Braşov (d. 0700).
c – To / from Cluj Napoca via Suceava (Table **1660**).
d – To Braşov (a. 0029).
m – Not Dec. 24, Apr. 27, June 15.
n – Not Dec. 25, Apr. 28, June 16.

r – Portion attached / detached to main train at Vereşti.
t – Tecuci **Nord**.
u – Not Dec. 26, Apr. 29, June 17.
v – To / from Vatra Dornei Băi (Table **1660**).
x – Apr. 26 - May 1 only.
⊕ – 🛏 1, 2 cl., ▬ 2 cl., [12].
⊗ – 🛏 1, 2 cl., ▬ 2 cl., [2].
⊙ – ▬ 2 cl., [12].
△ – Via Brăila.
⊡ – See main table above. Portion attached / detached from main train at Bacău.
☆ – Tecuci - Galaţi *85 km*; Iaşi - Roman *114 km*.
♡ – Operated by Transferoviar Grup SA.

♣ – Operated by Regiotrans. 2nd class.
▲ – 🏛 : Vicşani (RO) / Vadul Siret (UA).
MD Moldova. RO Romania. UA Ukraine.

PAŞCANI - TÂRGU NEAMT *31 km*, ± 45 mins
From Paşcani : 0429, 0715, 1641, 1916.
From Târgu Neamt : 0535, 1054, 1745, 2023.

VEREŞTI - BOTOŞANI *44 km*, ± 75 mins
From Vereşti : 0607, 0636, 0836, 1316, 1729, 1900, 2048.
From Botoşani : 0445, 0855, 1119, 1455, 1929, 2107.

IAŞI - SUCEAVA - DEJ - CLUJ NAPOCA 1660

km			1653	1833	1831			4136	1765	1837
		2	⊕m	2n	g	2⚒	2⑦	2z	□e	⊗
0	**Iaşi**	d.	...	b	0606	1100	...	x	...	1525	1830
76	Paşcani **1650**	d.	...	0329	0712	1206	...	...	...	1631	1936
22	Vereşti **1650**	d.	...	0402	0745	1239	...	...	...	1704	2009
37	**Suceava** **1650**	a.	...	0414	0757	1251	...	...	...	1716	2021
37	**Suceava**	d.	...	0429	0809	1303	...	...	...	1734	2036
87	Gura Humorului Oraş	d.	...	0523	0856	1350	...	...	...	1824	2123
19	Câmpulung Moldovenesc	d.	...	0606	0941	1433	...	...	...	1910	2209
257	Vatra Dornei Băi	d.	...	0710	1046	1539	...	...	...	2015	2315
351	Năsăud	d.	...	...	1242	1736	...	...	...	2208	0106
18	**Sighetu Marmaţiei**	d.	0045	...	|	|	1425	1425	1718	|	|
61	Vişeu de Jos	d.	0302	...	|	|	1630	1633	1939	|	|
357	Salva	d.	0513	...	1251	1745	...	1821	2115	2216	0114
379	Beclean pe Someş **1610/4**	d.	0548	...	1316	1811	...	1856	2201	2241	0139
402	Dej Călători **1610/4**	d.	0636	...	1400	1859	...	1946	2246	2336	0221
460	**Cluj Napoca** **1610/4**	a.	0758	...	1510	2009	...	2105	...	0044	0329
	Oradea **1600/25**	a.	...	...	1823	...	...	...	...	|	|
	Timişoara N **1620/25**	a.	...	...	2143	...	...	...	...	0937	1132

		1838	4133		1832		1834		1654	1766
		⊗	2z	2	g		2n	2	⊕m	□f
Timişoara N **1620/25**	d.	1720	...	...	...	...	0638	...	...	1335
Oradea **1600/25**	d.	|	...	...	...	...	0959	...	...	|
Cluj Napoca **1610/4**	d.	0101	...	0510	0930	...	1248	1430	...	2224
Dej Călători **1610/4**	d.	0222	0234	0636	1045	...	1404	1606	...	2345
Beclean pe Someş **1610/4**	d.	0257	0330	0730	1120	...	1439	1649	...	0028
Salva	d.	0320	0405	0812	1143	...	1502	1748	...	0052
Vişeu de Jos	a.	|	0538	0946	|	...	|	1927	...	|
Sighetu Marmaţiei	a.	|	0740	1208	|	...	|	2136	...	|
Năsăud	d.	0328	...	...	1152	...	1511	...	...	0107
Vatra Dornei Băi	d.	0526	...	...	1351	...	1714	...	2150	0304
Câmpulung Moldovenesc	d.	0630	...	...	1457	...	1819	...	2256	0410
Gura Humorului Oraş	d.	0715	...	...	1542	...	1909	...	2339	0453
Suceava	a.	0800	...	...	1627	...	1954	...	0024	0538
Suceava **1650**	d.	0812	...	...	1639	...	2006	...	0038	0553
Vereşti **1650**	d.	0825	...	...	1652	...	2019	...	0051	0606
Paşcani **1650**	d.	0902	...	...	1729	...	2056	...	0126	0643
Iaşi	a.	1005	...	...	1832	...	2159	...	b	0746

– From/to Bucureşti (Table **1650**).
– Conveys [2] Botoşani (d. 1455) - Vereşti - Timişoara.
– Conveys [2] Timişoara - Vereşti - Botoşani (a. 0749).
– From/to Galaţi (Table **1650**).

m – Not Dec. 24, Apr. 27, June 15.
n – Not Dec. 25, Apr. 28, June 16.
x – Not Jan. 6, Feb. 3, Apr. 21, 28, June 16 - Sept. 8.
z – Conveys 🛏 ▬ to/from Timişoara (for train **1765**/from **1838**).

⊕ – 🛏 1, 2 cl., ▬ 2 cl., [12]
⊗ – 🛏 1, 2 cl., ▬ 2 cl., [2]
□ – ▬ 2 cl., [2]
Δ – Distance from Salva.

BUCUREŞTI - GALAŢI 1670

km			1571	1771	1573	1575	1773	♡	1971	1579	1731	1775
			2⑧		2n	n		2	S	⑧		N
0	**Bucureşti Nord** **1650**	d.	0520	0635	0825	1310	1522	1520	...	1817	b	1920
	Ploieşti Sud **1650**	d.	0619	|	0919	1402	|	1616	...	1914	1934	|
**	Buzău **1650**	d.	0735	|	1034	1512	|	1724	...	2023	2047	|
71	Urziceni	d.	|	0743	|	|	1636	|	c	|	|	2028
Δ	Feteşti	d.	|	|	|	|	|	|	1927	|	|	|
138	Făurei	d.	0815	0855	1115	1550	1746	1809	|	2104	2126	2147
198	Brăila	d.	0904	0942	1205	1639	1834	1857	2141	2153	2215	2235
229	**Galaţi**	a.	0941	1018	1242	1716	1910	1938	2218	2230	2252	2312

		1770	1970	1570	1732	♡	1574	1772	1576	1578	1774
			S	⚒		2	n		2n	2⑧	①-⑥
Galaţi	d.	0500	0530	0540	0650	0717	0830	1200	1430	1730	1940
Brăila	d.	0537	0609	0618	0728	0803	0908	1237	1508	1808	2019
Făurei	d.	0624	|	0705	0816	0850	0955	1324	1555	1855	2112
Feteşti	a.	|	0807	|	|	|	|	|	|	|	|
Urziceni	d.	0735	c	|	|	|	|	1433	|	|	2225
Buzău **1650**	d.	|	...	0750	0903	0929	1037	|	1635	1935	|
Ploieşti Sud **1650**	d.	|	...	0859	1010	1037	1150	|	1746	2050	|
Bucureşti Nord **1650**	a.	0845	...	0957	b	1130	1247	1543	1839	2143	2332

– ①②③④⑥.
– June 29 - Sept. 8.

b – From/to Braşov (Table **1600**).
c – From/to Constanţa (Table **1680**).

n – Not Dec. 25, Apr. 28, June 16.
♡ – Operated by Transferoviar Grup SA.

** – Buzău - Făurei: *40 km*.
Δ – Feteşti - Făurei: *89 km*.

BUCUREŞTI - CONSTANŢA - MANGALIA 1680

km			1952	1962		1923	1987		1992	1862	1964		1944	1932	◇	1589	1922	1970	1942	1581	1983			◇	◇	◇
			⊙	⊙	2			2	⊕	⊙	⊙	2	⊕	⊕	⊗		⊕		⊗			2	2			
			J•	J•	Ke	J•	X	J	J•	K•	X•	Kf	J•	J•	B•	U	L•	S	X•	T	S	⑧K	Kf	A	J	P
		From:	*Suc*	*Iaşi*		*Ram*			*Tim*	*Ia/S*	*Ia/S*		*Sat*	*Ora*	*Ara*		*Tar*	*Gal*	*Bai*							
0	Bucureşti Nord	d.	|	|	...	0330	0330	...	0407r	|	|	...	0446r	0525r	0605	0615	0631	|	0640	0710	0710	...	...	0745	0745	0745
146	Feteşti	d.	0320	0409	...	0503	0503	...	0529	0553	0553	...	0609	0652	0738	0752	0800	0809	0814	0831	0831	...	...	0919	0919	0919
190	Medgidia	d.	0353	0443	...	0538	0538	0550	0606	0626	0627	...	0645	0724	0816	0855	0833	0845	0847	0904	0904	0915	...	0956	0956	0956
334	**Tulcea** Oraş	a.	|	|	...	|	|	0901	|	|	|	...	|	|	|	1156	|	|	|	|	|	1216	...	|	|	|
225	**Constanţa**	a.	0416	0511	...	0610	0610	...	0640	0653	0701	...	0718	0758	0841	...	0906	0908	0920	0927	0927	...	...	1021	1021	1021
225	**Constanţa**	d.	0431	0530	0613	0626	0633	...	0700	...	0714	0735	0736	0830	...	...	0922	...	0945	...	0950	...	0955	...	1039	1026
239	Eforie Nord	▷ d.	0456	0555	0637	0656	0704	...	0728	...	0747	0759	0809	0859	...	...	0946	...	1010	...	1028	...	1018	...	1105	1052
268	**Mangalia**	a.	0557	0653	0723	0800	0816	...	0836	...	0849	0846	0912	1008	...	...	1043	...	1108	...	1135	...	1103	...	1205	1158

		1994	1996	1681		♣	♥	1928			1583				1936	1683				1585	1989					1587
			⊗	2	2				2	2		2	2	2	2	2	2	2	2			2	2	2	2	
		S	X•	n	Kf	J	E	S	J	K		J		K	J	n	J	X	Kf		X	⚒h	Kf	J	⑧F	
	From:	*Cra*	*Tim*			*Bra*	*Cra*	*Sib*							*Bra*											
Bucureşti Nord	d.	0815	0840	0930	...	1012r	1016	1045	...	...	1400	...	...	...	1520	1600	...	...	...	1700	1700	...	...	...	...	2010
Feteşti	d.	0940	1016	|	...	1124	1134	1206	...	...	1522	...	...	...	1640	|	...	...	...	1825	1825	...	...	...	...	2135
Medgidia	d.	1016	1051	|	...	|	1208	|	...	...	1555	...	1630	...	1713	|	...	...	...	1858	1858	1910	...	...	...	2208
Tulcea Oraş	a.	|	|	|	...	|	|	|	...	...	|	...	1941	...	|	|	...	...	...	|	|	|	...	...	...	|
Constanţa	a.	1040	1115	1128	...	1216	1231	1258	...	...	1618	...	...	...	1736	1758	...	...	...	1922	1922	1940	...	...	...	2231
Constanţa	d.	1109	1141	...	1216	1228	...	...	1405	1420	...	1624	...	1630	...	...	1807	1815	1823	...	1948	...	1948	2005	2045	...
Eforie Nord	▷ d.	1147	1206	...	1246	1255	...	...	1431	1451	...	1650	...	1652	...	...	1835	1839	1854	...	2015	...	2012	2042	2112	...
Mangalia	a.	1258	1310	...	1331	1355	...	...	1536	1538	...	1742	...	1737	...	...	1945	1932	1940	...	2121	...	2057	2148	2157	...

		1586					1580	1986				1937				1682	1582	1929	1993	◇	◇	◇			♥	
			2	2	2	2			2	2	2	2	2	2	2	2		2					2	2		
			J	K	⚒K			Y	J	Ke	W	J	J	J	K	n	T	S	S	A	P	J	Kf	Nh	E	
Mangalia	d.	...	0445	0525	0628	...	...	0630	0636	0745	0830	...	0852	1023	1140	...	...	...	1240	...	1315	1335	1400	...	...	...
Eforie Nord	▷ d.	...	0557	0611	0721	...	...	0729	0750	0842	0935	...	1004	1127	1226	...	...	...	1354	...	1419	1448	1448	...	...	...
Constanţa	a.	...	0625	0635	0745	...	...	0758	0817	0904	1004	...	1029	1149	1248	...	...	...	1420	...	1440	1509	1512	...	...	...
Constanţa	d.	0520	...	...	...	...	0825	0825	...	...	...	1015	...	...	...	1300	1400	1400	1440	1520	1520	1520	...	1530	1550	...
Tulcea Oraş	d.	|	...	...	...	0519	|	|	...	...	...	|	...	...	...	|	|	|	|	|	|	|	...	|	|	...
Medgidia	d.	0544	...	...	...	0827	0849	0849	...	...	...	1040	...	...	...	|	1424	1424	1506	1545	1545	1545	...	1602	1613	...
Feteşti	d.	0616	...	...	...	...	0921	0921	...	...	...	1113	...	...	...	|	1457	1457	1536	1618	1618	1618	...	...	1646	...
Bucureşti Nord	a.	0739	...	...	...	...	1041	1041	...	...	...	1233	...	...	...	1456	1617	1617	1656	1741	1741	1741	...	...	1759	...
	To:	*Bra*										*Bra*						*Sib*	*Cra*						*Cra*	

		♣	1588	1584	1945	◇	1941		1931	1995	1971		1684	1984		1988	1924	1921	1991		1861	1963	1961	1953		
					⊕	⊗	⊗	2	⊕	⊗		2	2		2				⊕	2	⊙	⊙	⊙	⊙		
		J	V		J	B	X	Kf	J	X	S	G	n	S	Kf	X	J	L	J	Kf	K	X	J	J		
Mangalia	d.	1430	...	...	1517	...	1545	1602	1600	1630	...	...	...	1723	1805	1829	1829	1927	1958	2000	...	2015	2027	2130	...	...
Eforie Nord	▷ d.	1529	...	...	1627	...	1655	1655	1708	1739	...	...	...	1837	1851	1930	1930	2024	2102	2055	...	2128	2136	2232	...	...
Constanţa	a.	1555	...	...	1653	...	1724	1717	1733	1801	...	...	...	1905	1915	1953	1953	2046	2124	2118	...	2151	2158	2254	...	...
Constanţa	d.	1609	...	1700	1710	1720	1755	...	1800	1817	1830	...	1857	1925	...	2008	2008	2104	2145	...	2215	2215	2215	2315	...	...
Tulcea Oraş	d.	|	1317	|	|	|	|	...	|	|	|	1600	|	|	...	|	|	|	|	...	|	|	|	|	...	...
Medgidia	d.	|	1640	1724	1736	1747	1822	...	1827	1844	1855	1908	1920	1951	...	2034	2034	2128	2211	...	2241	2241	2241	2342	...	...
Feteşti	d.	1700	1718	1757	1809	1820	1858	...	1905	1920	1927	...	|	2024	...	2108	2108	2158	2248	...	2315	2315	2326	0017	...	...
Bucureşti Nord	a.	1818r	1855	1915	1928r	1951	2032	...	2030r	2104	|	...	2056	2145	...	2242	2242	2321	0022r	...	|	|	|	|	...	...
	To:	*Bra*			*Sat*	*Ara*	*Bai*		*Ora*	*Tim*	*Gal*						*Ram*	*Tar*	*Tim*		*Ia/S*	*Ia/S*	*Iaşi*	*Suc*		

/From:
– Arad via Craiova, Timişoara (Table **1630**).
– Baia Mare and Cluj Napoca (Tables **1600/10**).
– Braşov (Table **1600**).
– Craiova (Table **1630**).
– Galaţi (Table **1670**).
– Iaşi (Table **1650**).
S – Iaşi and Suceava (Table **1650**).
– Oradea via Cluj Napoca (Table **1600**).
– Sibiu via Râmnicu Vâlcea (Table **1645**).
– Satu Mare via Baia Mare (Tables **1600/10**).
– Sibiu via Braşov (Table **1600**).
– Suceava (Table **1650**).
– Arad via Târgu Jiu (Tables **1600/35**).
– Timişoara via Craiova (Table **1630**).

A – Apr. 1 - Dec. 14.
B – June 16 - Sept. 16.
E – Apr. 15 - Sept. 15.
F – To June 13/from Sept. 8 (dep. 2107 on Sept. 8).
G – ⚒ (daily June 14 - Sept. 7). Not Sept. 8.
J – June 15 - Sept. 8.
K – To June 14/from Sept. 9.
L – Apr. 26 - May 1, June 15 - Sept. 8.
N – Not June 16 - Sept. 9.
P – Sept. 9 - 15.
S – June 29 - Sept. 8.
T – To June 28/from Sept. 9.
U – ⑥ (daily June 15 - Sept. 8).
V – ⑦ (daily June 15 - Sept. 8).

W – Apr. 26 - May 2 only.
X – Apr. 26 - May 1 only.
Y – Apr. 27 - May 2 only.
e – Not Apr. 26 - May 2.
f – Not Apr. 26 - May 1.
h – [2] Constanţa - Medgidia - Tulcea and v.v.
n – Not Dec. 25, Apr. 28, June 16.
r – Bucureşti **Băneasa**.
◇ – Operated by Astra Trans Carpatic S.R.L.
♥ – Operated by Softrans S.R.L.
♣ – Operated by Regiotrans.

⊕ – 🛏 1, 2 cl., ▬ 2 cl., [12]
⊗ – 🛏 1, 2 cl., ▬ 2 cl., [2]
⊙ – ▬ 2 cl., [12]
• – Previous day from point of origin.
▷ – Trains also call at Eforie Sud (7-9 mins south of Eforie Nord) and Costineşti (25-35 mins south of Eforie Nord).

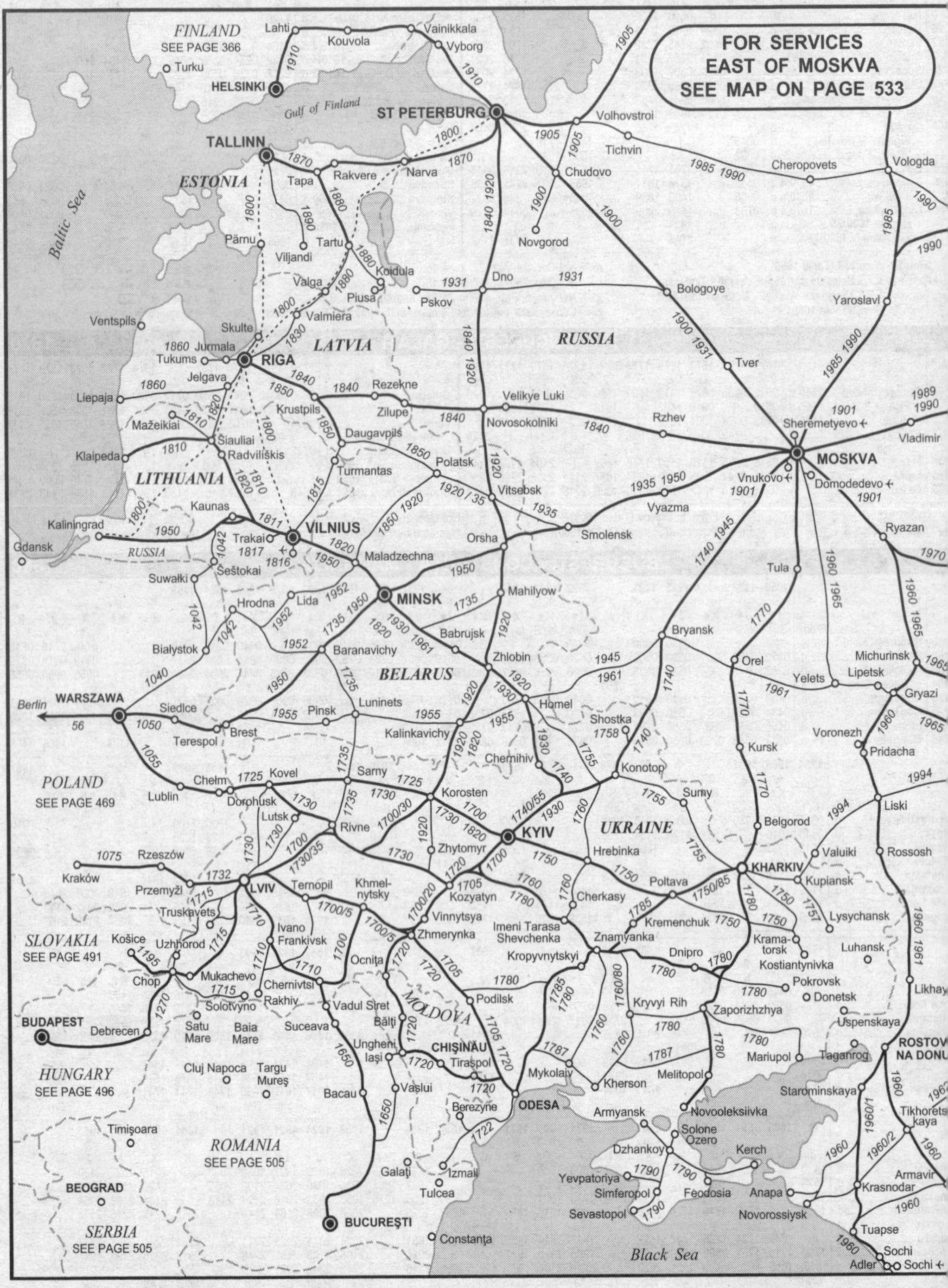

UKRAINE and MOLDOVA

Operators: **UZ**: Ukrzaliznytsya, www.uz.gov.ua **CFM**: Calea Ferată din Moldova, www.railway.md Other operators as indicated in the table headings and notes.

Services: Overnight trains convey sleeping and couchette cars and may not convey seating accommodation. Prior reservation is necessary except for travel by purely local trains. See also panel on page 534.

Timings: Valid from **March 31, 2019** with amendments as received.

Time zones: Local time is used throughout: East European Time for Ukraine and Moldova (UTC+2 winter, UTC+3 summer). Times within European Russia are in the Moskva time zone (UTC+3 all year) unless otherwise shown. As Russia and Belarus do not put their clocks forward in summer (daylight saving time), trains running between Ukraine or Moldova Russia or Belarus change their timings by approximately one hour when clocks change (last Sunday in March and October) as shown in the tables.

Z, CFM KYIV - KOROSTEN / VINNYTSYA - LVIV 1700

For Kyiv - Vinnytsya - Zhmerynka - Odesa / Chişinău see Table **1720**. For Dnipro - Kozyatyn - Lviv and Odesa - Zhmerynka - Lviv see Table **1705**

km		73AJ ★●	73AJ ☆●	IC 705	IC 715	111 ●	138	55MJ ❦ ■(3)	IC 749 H	357	IC 747 E	IC 743	13 S	81 k	43	117 B	49	143 E	29	17 ■	7	91	46	771	15 ●	2 ■(3)
	Moskva Kiy. **1740** d.	1559	1559	...	...	...	...	1742	...	...	...	...	...	...	...	...	...	...	...	...	...	...	...	...	...	...
	Kharkiv **1750** d.	|	|	...	...	2009	2230	|	...	...	...	...	...	...	...	...	...	...	...	1510	...	...	1237	...	1844	2118
0	**Kyiv** d.	0432	0538	0600	0650	0515	0636	0712	1407	1428	1641	1733	1711	1830	1906	2005	2012	2019	2108	2209	2222	2237	2247	2344	0117	0402
59	Kozyatyn 1 d.	0628	0734	|	|	0742	0903	0942	|	|	1823	|	|	2055	|	2210	2219	2230	|	|	|	|	|	0145	|	|
56	Korosten d.	|	|	* 0733	|	|	|	|	|	|	|	1907	|	|	2101	|	|	|	▽	|	|	|	0103	|	|	|
	Shepetivka d.	|	|	|	|	|	|	|	|	|	|	|	2148	|	2319	|	|	|	|	|	|	|	0338	|	|	|
21	**Vinnytsya** d.	0726	0829	|	0911	0919	1002	1044	|	1739	1916	|	|	2152	|	2307	2316	2331	|	|	|	|	|	0243	|	|
68	Zhmerynka d.	|	|	|	|	1045	|	1205	|	|	|	|	|	|	|	|	|	|	|	|	|	|	|	0350	|	|
67	Khmelnytsky d.	0933	1105	|	1049	1218	1204	1334	|	2005	2110	|	|	2356	|	0100	0109	0148	|	|	|	|	|	0513	|	|
	Kamianets-Pod. a.	|	|	|	|	|	...	...	|	|	|	|	|	|	|	0343	|	|	|	|	|	|	|	...	|	|
	Chernivtsi a.	|	|	|	|	|	...	...	|	|	|	|	|	|	|	0757	|	|	|	|	|	|	|	...	|	|
36	Ternopil d.	1132	1316	|	1214	1418	...	...	|	2156	2242	|	|	0147	|	...	0249	0358	|	|	|	|	|	...	|	|
27	**Lviv** a.	1331	1516	1109	1345	1626	...	...	1957	♡	...	2243	0218	0342	0249	...	0438	0615	0356	0450	0503	0600	0807	...	0739	1021
	Przemysl **1732** a.	...	...	1225	1458	...	...	...	|	...	...	...	|	|	|	...	t	|	|	|	|	...	|	...	|	|
	Ivano-Frank. **1710** a.	...	...	...	...	...	...	...	2216	...	...	...	|	|	0543	...	...	0856	|	|	0735	...	|	...	1019	1308
	Chop **1715** a.	...	...	...	...	...	...	...	0140c	...	...	...	0830	0946	...	...	...	v	|	|	...	...	|	...	♡	...
	Uzhhorod **1715** a.	...	...	...	...	...	...	...	...	...	...	...	0755r	1040	...	...	...	...	0920	1030	...	...	1423	...	...	...

	43	770	13 S	7	IC 748 F	29 k	45	IC 744	74LJ ★ ■(1)	74LJ ☆ ■(1)	IC 749 H	772	138	56 ❦ ●	IC 715	112 ■(3)	IC 705	17 ●	144 F	16 ■(3)	1 ●	358	81	92	50	118 B
Uzhhorod **1715** d.	...	...	1938r	...	...	2200	2100	...			...	...	...	...	...	...	...	1320	...	...	...	...	1600	...	...	...
Chop **1715** d.	...	...	1853	...	...	|	|	...	...	...	0527c	...	...	...	...	...	...	|	v	♡	...	...	1658	...	...	...
Ivano-Frank. **1710** d.	2155	...	|	2349	...	|	|	...	...	...	0905	...	...	...	...	...	...	|	1658	1922	1922	...	|	...	...	...
Przemysl **1732** d.	|	...	|	|	...	|	|	...	...	...	|	...	...	...	1310	...	1545	|	|	|	|	...	|	...	t	...
Lviv d.	0101	...	0138	0222	...	0313	0323	0605	0945	1000	1126	...	...	...	1612	1740	1846	1904	2005	2200	2200	♡	2251	2319	2308	...
Ternopil d.	|	...	|	|	0404	|	|	|	1147	1222	|	...	...	...	1743	1952	|	|	2214	|	|	2346	0042	|	0059	...
Chernivtsi d.	|	...	|	|	|	|	|	|	|	|	|	...	...	...	|	|	|	|	|	|	|	|	|	|	|	1946
Kamianets-Pod. d.	|	0100	|	|	|	|	|	|	|	|	|	...	...	...	|	|	|	|	|	|	|	|	|	|	|	2357
Khmelnytsky d.	|	0342	|	|	0545	|	|	|	1342	1434	|	1424	1714	1834	1911	2158	|	|	0023	|	|	0140	0230	|	0244	0255
Zhmerynka d.	|	0531	|	|	|	|	|	|	|	|	|	1559	|	2050	|	2347	|	|	|	|	|	|	|	|	|	|
Vinnytsya d.	|	0614	|	|	0730	|	|	|	1537	1629	|	1643	1941	2144	2049	0035	|	|	0224	|	|	0332	0421	|	0433	0453
Shepetivka d.	0432	|	0601	|	|	|	0709	|	|	|	|	|	|	|	|	|	|	|	|	|	|	|	|	|	|	|
Korosten d.	0640	|	|	|	|	▽	0926	0944	|	|	|	|	|	|	|	|	2223	|	|	|	|	|	|	|	|	|
Kozyatyn 1 d.	|	0704	|	|	0817	|	|	|	1629	1721	|	1735	2038	2239	|	0133	|	|	0319	|	|	|	0513	|	0524	0551
Kyiv a.	0848	0920	1046	0907	1003	1013	1146	1117	1836	1935	1721	1941	2252	0046	2308	0338	2353	0136	0528	0415	0415	0632	0727	0644	0733	0806
Kharkiv **1750** a.	...	...	...	...	...	...	2207	...	|	|	...	...	0752	|	...	1328	...	0839	...	1116	1116	...	...	...	...	...
Moskva Kiy. **1740** a.	...	...	...	...	...	...	...	...	1041	1041	...	...	...	1430	...	...	...	...	...	...	...	...	...	...	...	...

Daily Kyiv - Chernivtsi and v.v. Conveys on ⑤ 🛏 1, 2 cl.
Kyiv - Chernivtsi - Bucuresti (Table **1670**), returning on ⑦.
Uneven dates (even dates in June, July, Sept., Oct.).
Even dates (uneven dates in June, July, Sept., Oct.).
Kyiv - Lviv - Ivano-Frankivsk and v.v. Conveys 🛏 1, 2 cl.
Kyiv - Chop - Záhony - Budapest - Wien and v.v. (Table **96**).
Kyiv - Lviv - Sambir - Chop - Solotvyno and v.v. (Table **1715**).

c – Through 🛏 only (see note **H** and Table **1715**).
k – Conveys 🛏 1, 2 cl. Kyiv - Chop - Cierna nad Tisou - Košice and v.v. (see Table **1195**).
r – Calls before Chop (after Chop towards Kyiv).
t – To / from Truskavets (Table **1715**).
v – To / from Vorokhta (Table **1710**).
❦ – Approx one hour earlier in Ukraine Oct. 27 - Dec. 14.

☆ – Mar. 31 - Oct. 26 (summer time in Ukraine).
★ – Oct. 27 - Dec. 14 (provisional times).
● – Even dates (see page 534).
■ – Uneven dates (see page 534).
♡ – To / from Rakhiv (Table **1710**).
▽ – Via Berdychiv (Kyiv - Lviv = *566 km*).
* – *572 km* via Korosten.

ODESSA / DNIPRO - ZHMERYNKA - LVIV 1705

km		109 K	41	12	108	120 Z	86 N●	70 M	136 ♡	36	26 ■
0	**Odesa** Holovna d.	...	...	2204	2116	...	...	...	1644	1825	1825
6	Podilsk d.	...	...	|	0021	...	...	...	1939	2113	2113
	Dnipro **1780** d.	...	1426	|	|	...	1800	2251	|	|	|
	Kozyatyn 1 ▷ d.	0013	0030	|	|	...	0442	0930	|	|	|
	Vinnytsya ▷ d.	0108	0130	|	|	...	0549	1034	|	|	|
7	Zhmerynka ▷ d.	0216	0245	0257	0410	0652	0710	1146	2250	0053	0053
6	Khmelnytsky ▷ d.	0358	0431	0423	0547	0831	0847	1322	0027	0226	0226
5	Ternopil ▷ d.	0613	0627	0606	0740	1030	1046	1520	0223	0423	0423
6	**Lviv** ▷ a.	0824	0834	0758	0945	1239	1249	1727	0421	0635	0635
	Przemysl **1732** ⊡ a.	...	t	...	u	...	...	...	|	0950	|
	Ivano-Frankivsk **1710** a.	...	...	...	...	...	...	...	0723	...	0940
	Chernivtsi **1710** a.	...	...	...	...	...	...	...	1020	...	...

	70 M	107	86 N●	120 Z	42	110 K	136 ♧	12	36	26 ●
Chernivtsi **1710** d.	...	...	...	...	...	...	1537	...	...	...
Ivano-Frankivsk **1710** d.	...	...	...	...	...	...	1824	...	...	2025
Przemysl **1732** ⊡ d.	...	u	...	...	t	...	|	...	1839	|
Lviv ▷ d.	0115	0253	1110	1359	1522	1539	2140	2216	2328	2328
Ternopil ▷ d.	0327	0459	1329	1613	1748	1817	2357	0018	0134	0134
Khmelnytsky ▷ d.	0531	0701	1528	1819	1953	2021	0156	0214	0334	0334
Zhmerynka ▷ d.	0739	0855	1713	1953	2138	2212	0344	0400	0520	0520
Vinnytsya ▷ d.	0826	|	1803	...	2229	2300	|	|	|	|
Kozyatyn 1 ▷ a.	0923	|	1855	...	2323	2351	|	|	|	|
Dnipro **1780** a.	1943	|	0518	...	0922	...	|	|	|	|
Podilsk d.	...	1212	...	...	...	...	0719	|	0842	0842
Odesa Holovna a.	...	1449	...	...	...	...	0958	0847	1116	1116

Kherson (Table **1760**) - Mykolaiv - Lviv and v.v.
Mariupol (Table **1780**) - Dnipro - Lviv and v.v.
Novooleksiivka (Table **1780**) - Melitopol - Dnipro - Lviv and v.v.
Zaporizhzhya (Table **1780**) - Kryvyi Rih - Lviv and v.v.

t – To / from Truskavets (Table **1715**).
u – To / from Uzhhorod (Table **1715**).
♡ – Not May 2 - Oct. 1.
♧ – Not May 1 - Sept. 30.

▷ – See also Tables **1700** and **1720**.
⊡ – Subject to alteration May 26 - 30.
● – Even dates (see page 534).
■ – Uneven dates (see page 534).

See also Table 1700 LVIV - IVANO-FRANKIVSK - CHERNIVTSI 1710

	357	668	43	136 ♡	7	143 ⊡	26 ●	15 ●	606	702 G	IC 749
Kharkiv **1750** d.	...	...	...	...	...	...	...	1844	...	...	...
Kyiv **1700** d.	1428	k	1906	d	2222	2019	...	0117	...	...	1407
Lviv d.	|	0101	0311	0453	0523	0635	0708	0804	1546	1809	2017
Ivano-Frankivsk a.	|	0408	0543	0723	0735	0856	0940	1019	1847	2011	2216
Kolomyia a.	0537	0547	...	0853	...	|	|	|	|	2056	...
Vorokhta a.	0803	|	...	|	...	1156	1233	1244	2205	|	...
Rakhiv a.	0943	|	...	|	...	...	1417	1417	2350	|	...
Chernivtsi a.	...	0737	...	1020	...	...	...	...	...	2202	...

	606	702 H	IC 749	144 ⊙	358	136 ♧	16 ■(3)	26 ●	43	668	7
Chernivtsi d.	...	0604	...	...	...	1537	...	...	...	2025	...
Rakhiv d.	0032	|	...	...	1217	|	1520	1620	...	|	...
Vorokhta d.	0223	|	...	1346	1418	|	1658	1801	...	|	...
Kolomyia d.	|	0712	...	|	1620	1706	|	|	...	2210	...
Ivano-Frankivsk d.	0503	0802	0905	1658	|	1824	1922	2025	2155	2335	2349
Lviv a.	0830	0951	1106	1945	|	2119	2140	2259	0041	0214	0202
Kyiv **1700** a.	...	...	1721	0528	0632	d	0415	...	0848	k	0907
Kharkiv **1750** a.	...	...	...	...	...	...	1116	...	...	...	...

Daily except ③.
Daily except ④.

d – From / to Odesa (Table **1705**).
k – From / to Kovel (Table **1730**).

⊡ – ■ (● in June, July, Sept., Oct.).
⊙ – ● (■ in June, July, Sept., Oct.).

● ■ – See Table **1700**.
♡ ♧ – See Table **1705**.

LVIV - CHOP - UZHHOROD 1715

	13	81 k	29	17 ■v	IC 33 L	46 v	108 s	2	829	145	749 H
Kyiv **1700** d.	1711	1830	2108	2209	...	2247	...	...	...	...	1407
Lviv d.	0244	0409	0422	0519	...	0833	1011	...	1644	2100	2100
Mukachevo... **1195** d.	|	0854	0809	0910	1230	1258	1438	1620	2047	0054	0054
Chop ⊖ **1195** a.	0830	0946	|	|	1340	|	1531	1730	2141	0140	0140
Uzhhorod a.	0755r	1040	0920	1030	|	1423	1631	z	2222	0235	|
Solotvyno 1 a.	1310	...	...	...	|	...	...	...	...	...	|
Budapest K **1270** a.	...	...	...	...	1837n	...	...	...	...	...	0820

	145	147 J	829	2	17 ●v	IC 34 L	81	13	107 sk	45 v	29
Budapest K **1270** d.	...	1940	...	...	...	0723n	...	...	...	...	...
Solotvyno 1 d.	...	|	...	...	...	|	...	1430	...	...	...
Uzhhorod d.	0429	|	0513	z	1320	|	1600	1938r	2000	2100	2200
Chop ⊖ **1195** d.	0527	0527	0552	1023	|	1410	1658	1853	2056	|	|
Mukachevo... **1195** d.	0624	0624	0656	1133	1448	1520	1802	|	2200	2238	2319
Lviv a.	1014	1014	1101	...	1844	...	2220	0115	0220	0303	0253
Kyiv **1700** a.	...	1721	...	...	0136	...	0727	1046	...	1146	1013

🛏 1, 2 cl. Kyiv (*IC*749) - Lviv (**145**) - Chop (**140**) - Záhony - Budapest Keleti - Wien (Table **96**).
🛏 1, 2 cl. Wien (**147**) - Záhony - Chop (**145**) - Lviv (*IC*749) - Kyïv (Table **96**).
LATORCA – (2) Budapest - Mukachevo and v.v.
From / to Dnipro (Table **1780** / **1705**).
Conveys 🛏 1, 2 cl. Kyiv - Lviv - Chop - Cierna nad Tisou - Košice and v.v. (Table **1195**).

n – Budapest Nyugati.
r – Calls before Chop (after Chop towards Kyiv).
s – From / to Odesa (Table **1705**).
v – From / to Kharkiv (Table **1750**).
z – To / from Záhony (Table **1270**).
⊖ – customs for trains to / from Hungary and Slovakia.
● ■ See Table **1700**.

km		49	41 d
	Kyiv **1700** d.	2012	...
0	**Lviv** d.	0501	0858
78	Sambir d.	0640	|
121	Drohobych a.	0733	1029
133	**Truskavets** a.	0802	1111

	42 d	50
Truskavets d.	1236	1949
Drohobych d.	1323	2016
Sambir d.	|	2129
Lviv a.	1457	2246
Kyiv **1700** a.		0733

1720 KYIV - ZHMERYNKA - ODESA and CHIŞINĂU — UZ, CFM

km		58	94	94	65MJ	65MJ	822	1064	642	47MZ	47MZ	23MJ	23MJ	IC763	145	61MZ	61MZ	797	106		105	341FJ	1062	341F
		R	V	V	●	●	⑤–⑦		⑤–⑦	J	J	●	●			■(4)	■(4)	G	B	①–⑥				
			★	☆	★	☆				★	☆	★	☆			★	☆					★		☆
	Moskva Kiyev. **1740** d.	...	...	...	1630	1630	...	...	...	2016	2016	2059	2059	...	...	...	...	...	...	...	...	1044	...	104
	St P'burg Vit. **1920** d.	...	...	...	|	|	...	...	...	|	|	|	|	...	...	2040	2040	...	...	...	...	|	...	|
	Orsha Tsent. **1920** d.	...	...	...	|	|	...	...	...	|	|	|	|	...	...	0714	0714	...	...	...	...	|	...	|
	Minsk **1930** d.	...	1413	1413	|	|	...	...	...	|	|	|	|	...	...	|	|	...	...	...	...	|	...	|
0	**Kyiv** **1700** d.	...	0124	0220	0522	0610	...	...	...	0839	0955	0921	1034	1630	1740	|	|	...	...	...	2115	2351	...	004
157	Kozyatyn 1 **1700** d.	0216	0339	0433	|	|	...	...	...	1050	1202	1146	1248	|	2008	1925	2025	...	...	...	|	0158	...	025
221	**Vinnytsya** **1700** d.	0319	0436	0530	0829	0932	...	...	...	1147	1256	1243	1344	1855	2110	2037	2121	2239	...	...	0026	0305	...	040
268	Zhmerynka UA **1700** d.	0414	0543	0634	0933	1039	...	...	...	1254	1401	1349	1447	1932	2214	2145	2234	2335	...	...	|	0417	...	052
469	Podilsk ▷ d.	0735	0852	0945	|	|	...	...	...	|	|	1649	1749	2140	0135	|	|	0237	...	...	0344	|	...	|
655	**Odesa** Holovna ▷ a.	1008	1126	1215	|	|	...	...	1845	|	|	1950	2029	2345	0400	|	|	0456	...	...	0558	|	...	|
*627	Tiraspol MD d.	...	▬	...	1553	1648	...	...	2105	|	|	...	...	▬	z	|	|	...	...	...	...	|	...	|
640	Bender 2 d.	...	...	...	1639	1734	...	...	2122	|	|	...	...	...	...	|	|	...	...	...	...	|	...	|
422	Ocniţa MD d.	...	...	...	|	|	...	...	|	1803	1859	...	...	...	...	0202	0300	...	...	...	...	1010	...	105
520	Bălţi Oraş d.	...	1647	...	|	|	...	...	|	2017	2113	...	...	...	...	0419	0528	...	...	*0441*	...	1232	...	132
	Iaşi RO d.	...	|	...	|	|	1742**s**	1826	|	|	|	...	...	...	...	|	|	...	0300	|	...	|	1311	|
598	Ungheni 🛃 a.	...	1930	...	|	|	1859	2015	|	|	|	...	...	...	...	|	|	...	0443	*0736*	...	1418	1505	151
598	Ungheni d.	...	...	...	|	|	1941	...	|	|	|	...	...	0350	...	|	|	...	0637	0845	...	1449	...	154
*705	**Chişinău** a.	...	...	...	1819	1917	2127	...	2228	0006	0055	...	...	0650	...	0754	0900	...	0845	1127	...	1733	...	182

	1061	821	642	6825	47SZ	47SZ	106	1063		105	6831	146	66SZ	66SZ	61SZ	61SZ	IC764	341MZ	341MZ	798	94	94	24SH	24SH	84
		⑤–⑦	⑤–⑦	Ⓑ	K	K				B			■(3)	■(3)	■§	■§				G	W	W	■(1)	■(1)	R
					★	☆							★	☆	★	☆		★	☆		★	☆	★	☆	
Chişinău d.	...	0610	0657	0903	1052	1151	...	...	...	1656	1744	...	2314	2330	2205	2230	...	2116	2146	...	...	...	...	...	...
Ungheni a.	...	0814	|	1156	|	|	...	...	...	1902	2044	...	|	|	|	|	...	2349	0016	...	...	...	...	...	...
Ungheni 🛃 d.	0706	0852	|	...	|	|	...	1614	1628	2050	...	...	|	|	|	|	...	0016	0047	...	...	...	...	...	...
Iaşi RO a.	0844	1015**s**	|	...	|	|	...	1747	|	2221	...	...	|	|	|	|	...	|	|	...	...	...	...	...	...
Bălţi Oraş d.	...	...	|	...	1449	1543	...	...	1917	...	...	...	|	|	0149	0220	...	0220	0254	...	...	...	...	...	...
Ocniţa MD d.	...	...	|	...	1713	1807	...	...	...	...	...	...	|	|	0422	0504	...	0505	0543	...	...	...	...	...	...
Bender 2 d.	...	...	0806	...	|	|	...	...	...	...	...	...	0134	0150	|	|	...	|	|	...	...	...	...	...	...
Tiraspol MD d.	...	...	0825	...	|	|	...	...	...	...	...	z	0158	0214	|	|	...	|	|	...	...	...	...	...	...
Odesa Holovna ▷ d.	...	...	1045	...	|	|	2225	...	...	...	...	2330	|	|	|	|	0540	|	|	1303	1459	1540	1509	1601	181
Podilsk ▷ d.	...	...	...	...	|	|	0039	...	...	...	...	0222	|	|	|	|	0743	|	|	1532	1741	1820	1747	1834	205
Zhmerynka UA **1700** d.	...	...	...	...	2220	2320	|	...	...	...	...	0540	0819	0836	0840	0934	0956	1010	1105	1830	2052	2128	2104	2200	001
Vinnytsya **1700** d.	...	...	...	...	2312	0012	0358	...	...	...	...	0634	0907	0933	0937	1044	1032	1100	1156	1920	2140	2216	2153	2248	011
Kozyatyn 1 **1700** d.	...	...	...	...	0004	0104	|	...	...	...	...	0726	|	|	1052	1153	|	1154	1254	...	2232	2317	2246	2345	021
Kyiv **1700** a.	...	...	...	...	0203	0303	0710	...	...	...	...	0955	1208	1304	|	|	1246	1403	1503	...	0035	0123	0054	0150	...
Minsk **1930** a.	...	...	...	...	|	|	...	...	...	...	...	...	|	|	|	|	...	|	|	...	1344	1344	|	|	...
Orsha Tsent. **1920** a.	...	...	...	...	|	|	...	...	...	...	...	...	|	|	0026	0026	...	|	|	...	...	...	|	|	...
St P'burg Vit. **1920** a.	...	...	...	...	|	|	...	...	...	...	...	...	|	|	1144	1144	...	|	|	...	...	...	|	|	...
Moskva Kiyev. **1740** a.	...	...	...	...	1650	1650	...	...	...	...	...	...	0508	0508	...	...	...	0524	0524	...	...	...	1530	1530	...

B – PRIETENIA – 🛏 1, 2 cl., ▭2 Bucureşti (**402/1**) - Ungheni (**106/5**) - Chişinău and v.v. (Table **1650**).
G – Daily except ②.
J – ①③⑤⑦ (daily from Apr. 7).
K – ②④⑥⑦ (daily from Apr. 7).
R – From / to Kovel; for days of running see Table **1730**.
V – ②⑤ (daily June 1 - Sept. 19).
W – ③⑥ (daily June 2 - Sept. 20).

s – Iaşi **Socola** (broad gauge station, 5 km from Iaşi).
z – To / from Izmaïl (Table **1722**).
● – Even dates (see page 534).
■ – Uneven dates (see page 534).
§ – ■ [.. *27, 1* ..] (see page 534).
☆ – Mar. 31 - Oct. 26 (summer time in Ukraine / Moldova).
★ – Oct. 27 - Dec. 14 (provisional times).

▷ – Zhmerynka - Odesa and v.v.: see also Table **1705**.
* – Odessa - Tiraspol *120 km*. Chişinău via Tiraspol *698 km*.
MD – Moldova RO – Romania UA – Ukraine (all are UTC + 2 in winter, UTC + 3 in summer).
Note that Tiraspol and Bender (formerly Tighina) are locat in the *de facto* autonomous region of Transnistria.

1722 ODESA - BEREZYNE and IZMAÏL — UZ

km		145	145	
			⑤⑥	
	Kyiv **1720** d.	1740	1740	...
0	**Odesa** Holovna d.	0435	0435	...
85	Bilhorod-Dnistrovsky d.	0708	0708	...
175	Artsyz a.	0841	0841	...
210	Berezyne a.	|	1106	...
282	**Izmaïl** a.	1058	...	...

	146	688	
		⑥⑦	
Izmaïl d.	1659	...	...
Berezyne d.	|	1646	...
Artsyz d.	1917	1917	...
Bilhorod-Dnistrovsky d.	2058	2058	...
Odesa Holovna a.	2254	2254	...
Kyiv **1720** a.	0955	0955	...

1725 KYIV - CHELM - WARSZAWA — UZ, PKP

km		751	67	
			K Ⓡ	
0	**Kyiv** **1730** d.	...	1913r	...
	Rivne **1730** d.	0843	|	...
526	Kovel **1730** d.	1120	|	...
632	**Chelm** PL ⊡ a.	1307	0615	...
	Lublin **1055** a.	...	0717	...
	Warszawa C **1055** a.	...	1050	...

	752	68	
		K Ⓡ	
Warszawa C **1055** d.	...	1705	...
Lublin **1055** d.	...	2051	...
Chelm PL ⊡ d.	1435	2154	...
Kovel **1730** a.	1830	|	...
Rivne **1730** a.	2053	|	...
Kyiv **1730** a.	...	1103	...

NOTES FOR TABLES **1722** AND **1725**
K – KYÏV EKSPRES / KIEV EXPRESS – 🛏 1, 2 cl. Kyiv - Warszawa and v.v.
r – Board train by 1848 for customs control.
⊡ – 🛃 = Yahodyn (UA) / Dorohusk (PL). Ukraine is one hour ahead of Poland.

1730 KYIV and LVIV - RIVNE - KOVEL — UZ

km		58	86	127		73	73	122	885	142	97	
		R	■(3)	■(3)		●	●					
			‡	‡		★m	☆m					
	Moskva § **1740** d.	...	...	...	...	1559	1559	...	...	n	...	...
0	**Kyiv** d.	...	...	...	...	0447	0547	0732	1217	1336	2122	...
156	Korosten d.	...	...	...	...	0652	0804	|	|	1825	2322	...
311	Sarny d.	▽	△	k	...	|	|	⊡	|	2153	⊡	...
*234	Kozyatyn 1 d.	0237	0512	0512	...	|	|	|	1517	|	|	...
383	**Rivne** d.	0648	0940	0940	...	1122	1221	1435	2018	|	0345	...
461	Lutsk d.	0830	1128	1128	...	1255	1352	...	...	|	0531	...
545	Kovel d.	1050	1336	1336	...	1452	1542	...	...	0033	0732	...
744	**Lviv** a.	...	...	...	...	...	...	...	...	0430	...	...

	78	88	78	88	122	128		58	142	98	
	■(1)	●	■(1)	●		●		S			
	★m	☆	☆m	★							
Lviv d.	...	...	...	...	...	...	...	...	1424	...	...
Kovel d.	0935	0935	1014	1014	...	1414	...	1810	1827	2010	...
Lutsk d.	1210	1210	1233	1234	...	1629	...	2033	|	2221	...
Rivne d.	1328	1325	1349	1352	1525	1803	...	2154	|	2354	...
Kozyatyn 1 a.	|	1807	|	1814	|	2225	...	0145	|	|	...
Sarny d.	|	△	|	△	⊡	k	...	▽	2102	⊡	...
Korosten d.	1704	...	1747	...	|	...	...	...	0055	0356	...
Kyiv a.	1905	...	1958	...	2151	...	...	...	0540	0551	...
Moskva § **1740**. a.	1041	...	1041	...	...	...	...	...	n	...	...

km		804	806	668
		①–⑥	Ⓑ	
	Chernivtsi **1710** d.	...	...	2025
0	**Lviv** **1735** d.	0950	1631	0239
207	Rivne **1735** a.	1235	1916	|
176	Lutsk a.	...	...	0736
260	**Kovel** a.	...	...	1012

	804	806	668
	①–⑥	Ⓑ	
Kovel d.	...	...	1713
Lutsk d.	...	...	1929
Rivne **1735** d.	0645	1315	|
Lviv **1735** a.	0935	1612	0032
Chernivtsi **1710** a.	...	...	0737

R – From Odesa ● (daily June 1 - Sept. 17).
S – ■(1) (daily May 31 - Sept. 16).
k – From / to Kharkiv (d. 1517 / a. 1212).
m – Moskva (**73/4**) - Kyïv (**77/8**) - Kovel and v.v.
n – From / to Kharkiv (d. 0401 / a. 1425).
☆ – Mar. 31 - Oct. 26 (summer time in Ukraine).
★ – Oct. 27 - Dec. 14 (provisional times).
⊡ – Via Shepetivka.

● – Even dates (see page 534).
■ – Uneven dates (see page 534).
△ – From / to Novooleksiivka via Dnipro (Table **1780**).
▽ – To / from Odesa (Table **1720**).
‡ – Next day from Kozyatyn.
§ – Moskva Kiyevskaya.
* – Distance from Rivne.

1732 PRZEMYSL - LVIV — UZ, PKP

km	⚜	8306 51	89	IC 715	IC 705	35
		z	E			
	Wrocław **1075** d.	1645	...	...	...	...
	Kraków Gł. **1075** d.	2034	...	...	...	...
	Przemyśl **1075** a.	2350	...	...	...	...
0	**Przemyśl** ⊖ PL d.	0046	1015	1310	1545	1839
98	**Lviv** UA a.	0610	1345	1602	1836	2239
	Kyiv **1700** a.	...	...	2308	2353	|
	Odesa **1705** a.	...	...	...	...	1116

⚜	36	IC 705	IC 715	89	51 3806
				E	z
Odesa **1705** d.	1825	...	...	...	...
Kyiv **1700** d.	|	0600	0650	...	...
Lviv UA d.	0755	1120	1355	1600	2340
Przemyśl ⊖ PL a.	0950	1225	1458	1746	0310
Przemyśl **1075** d.	...	...	...	...	0412
Kraków Gł. **1075** a.	...	...	...	...	0730
Wrocław **1075** a.	...	...	...	...	1112

1735 MINSK - LVIV

km		371
		■(1)
0	Mahilyow d.	1540
243	**Minsk** a.	1916
243	**Minsk** d.	1944
384	Baranavichy Pol. d.	2235
500	Luninets BY d.	0039
607	Sarny ‡ UA d.	0414r
694	Rivne **1730** d.	0607r
901	**Lviv** **1730** a.	1000r

	37
	●
Lviv **1730** d.	17
Rivne **1730** d.	21
Sarny ‡ UA d.	235
Luninets BY d.	04
Baranavichy Pol. d.	07
Minsk a.	09
Minsk d.	09
Mahilyow a.	13

NOTES FOR TABLES 1732 AND 1735
E – For days of running see Table **77**.
r – Oct. 26 - Dec. 14 Sarny d. 0320, Rivne d. 0513, Lviv a. 0847 (⊕).
s – 2319 Oct. 27 - Dec. 14 (⊕).

z – 🛏 2 cl. only.
⊖ – 🛃 = Medyka / Mostiska II.
⊕ – Provisional times.
● – Even dates (see page 534).
■ – Uneven dates (see page 534).

⚜ – Timings within Poland are valid June 9 - Aug. 31
‡ – 🛃 : Horyn (BY) / Udrytsk (UA).
BY – Belarus (UTC + 3 all year).
PL – Poland (UTC + 1 winter, UTC + 2 summer).
UA – Ukraine (UTC + 2 winter, UTC + 3 summer).

RZhD, UZ — MOSKVA - BRYANSK - KONOTOP - KYIV — 1740

km		737AJ	131MJ	341FJ	341FJ	739AJ	121VJ	61KH	61KH	73AJ	73AJ	65MJ	65MJ	107MJ	55MJ	55MJ	741VJ	5JA	5JA	47MZ	47MZ	23MJ	23MJ	85CH
							●(4)	■(3)	■(3)	●	●	●	●		■(3)	■(3)				J	J	●	●	
				★	☆			★	☆	★n	☆n	★	☆		★	☆		★	☆	★	☆	★	☆	
0	**Moskva** Kiyevskaya ..... d.	0656	0939	1044	1044	1326	1533	1533	1533	1559	1559	1630	1630	1717	1742	1742	1914	1935	1935	2016	2016	2059	2059	2244
387	Bryansk Orlovski .... d.	1058	1452	1719	1719	1728	2030	2120	2120	2211	2211	2226	2226	2145	2320z	2320z	2322	0131	0131	0222	0222	0315	0315	0428
504	Suzemka .... RU d.	...	...	|	|	...	...	2346	2346	|	|	0044	0044	...	0142	0142	...	|	|	|	|	|	|	...
519	Zernove................. UA d.	...	...	|	|	...	...	2349	0049	|	|	|	|	...	|	|	...	|	|	|	|	|	|	...
651	Konotop ....d.	...	...	2037	2137	...	...	0138	0238	0130	0230	0234	0331	...	0317	0417	...	0418	0508	0532	0632	0612	0708	...
829	Chernihiv ....a.	...	...	|	|	...	...	△	△	|	|	|	|	...	|	|	...	|	|	|	|	|	|	...
872	**Kyiv**..............................a.	...	...	2321	0028	...	...	...	...	0412	0512	0507	0600	...	0600	0702	...	0652	0752	0816	0935	0856	0954	...
	Odesa **1720** ....a.	...	...	|	|	...	...	...	...	|	|	|	|	...	▽	▽	...	...	...	|	|	1950	2029	...
	Chişinău **1720**...........a.	...	...	1733	1828	...	...	...	...	|	|	1819	1917	...	...	...	...	...	...	0006	0055	...	...	...
	Lviv **1700**...................a.	...	...	...	...	...	...	...	...	1331	1516	...	...	...	...	...	...	...	...	...	...	...	...	...

	738AJ	56KJ	56KJ	24SH	24SH	122VJ	47SZ	47SZ	740AJ	108MJ	132MJ	742VJ	66SZ	66SZ	341MZ	341MZ	86CH	6KJ	6KJ	74LJ	74LJ	62SH	62SH	
		●	●‡	■(1)	■(1)	■(5)	K	K					■(3)	■(3)						■(1)	■(1)	●	●‡	
		★	☆	★	☆		★	☆					★	☆	★	☆		★	☆	★n	☆n	★	☆	
Lviv **1700** .... d.	...	...	...	...	...	...	...	...	...	...	...	...	...	...	...	...	...	...	...	0945	1000	...	...	...
Chişinău **1720**........... d.	...	...	...	...	...	...	1052	1151	...	...	...	...	2314	2330	2116	2146	...	...	...	|	|	...	...	...
Odesa **1720**.............. d.	...	▽	▽	1509	1601	...	|	|	...	...	...	...	|	|	|	|	...	...	...	|	|	...	...	...
yiv .... d.	...	2359	0059	0119	0215	...	0218	0318	...	...	...	...	1235	1331	1423	1524	...	1936	2032	1948	2038	...	...	...
Chernihiv .... d.	...	|	|	|	|	...	|	|	...	...	...	...	|	|	|	|	...	|	|	|	|	△	△	...
onotop......................... d.	...	0306	0406	0425	0525	...	0513	0613	...	...	...	...	1552	1650	1725	1825	...	2242	2340	2250	2348	2328	0026	...
ernove .... UA d.	...	|	|	|	|	...	|	|	...	...	...	...	|	|	|	|	...	|	|	|	|	0221	0321	...
uzemka .... RU d.	...	0658	0658	0809	0809	...	0942	0952	...	...	...	...	2044	2044	|	|	...	|	|	0340	0340	|	|	...
ryansk Orlovski .... d.	0706	0840	0840	0950	0950	1029	1122	1122	1326	1700	1742	1910	2248	2248	2341	2341	0015	0420	0420	0456z	0456z	0541	0541	...
oskva Kiyevskaya ..... a.	1108	1430	1430	1530	1530	1500	1650	1650	1728	2107	2252	2312	0508	0508	0524	0524	0609	1009	1009	1041	1041	1112	1112	...

– ①③⑤⑦ (daily from Apr. 7).
– ②④⑥⑦ (daily from Apr. 7).
– Also conveys Moskva - Kyiv - Kovel and v.v. (Table **1730**).
– Bryansk **Lgovski**.
– To/from Khmelnytsky (Table **1700**).

△ – To/from Mykolaiv and Kherson (Table **1760**).
☆ – Mar. 31 - Oct. 26 (summer time in Ukraine and Moldova).
★ – Oct. 27 - Dec. 14 (provisional times).
● – Even dates (see page 534).
■ – Uneven dates (see page 534).

‡ – Next day at stations in this table.
RU – Russia (Moskva Time UTC+3).
UA – Ukraine (UTC+2 in winter, UTC+3 in summer).

UZ — KYIV - POLTAVA - KHARKIV and KOSTIANTYNIVKA — 1750

km		17	112	16	1	IC 722	IC 724	720	IC 726	64	138
		●	■(3)	■(3)	●						
		u		v	L						K
	Lviv **1700** .... d.	1904	1740	2200	2200	...	...	...	...	...	...
0	**Kyiv** .... d.	0156	0406	0435	0435	0645	1325	1540	1802	2305	2312
150	Hrebinka...................... d.	|	0621	|	|	|	|	1724	|	|	0131
335	**Poltava** Kyivska .... a.	0603	1015	0834	0834	0955	1635	1944	2111	0318	0458
335	**Poltava** Kyivska **1785** d.	0623	1048	0900	0900	0957	1637	2015	2113	0338	0518
493	**Kharkiv**............**1785** a.	0839	1328	1116	1116	1134	1813	2219	2247	0557	0752

	IC 725	719	IC 723	17	IC 721	15	111	2	138	63
				■		●	●	■(3)		
				u		v		L	K	
Kharkiv ....**1785** d.	0722	0840	1315	1510	1838	1844	2009	2118	2230	2213
Poltava Kyivska **1785** a.	0858	1046	1451	1715	2014	2047	2257	2328	0102	0026
Poltava Kyivska........ d.	0900	1106	1453	1735	2016	2112	2317	2348	0122	0046
Hrebinka .... d.	|	1322	|	|	|	|	0246	|	0421	|
Kyiv............................ a.	1207	1510	1800	2149	2327	0102	0438	0342	0614	0505
Lviv **1700**................ a.	...	...	...	0450	...	0739	1626	1021	...	...

km		IC 712	126	124	1
					●‡
					L
0	**Kyiv** .... d.	0612	2220	2120	0435
150	Hrebinka .... d.	|	0028	▽	|
335	**Poltava** Kyïvska . d.	0925	0359	|	0900
493	**Kharkiv**........... d.	|	|	0708	1137
635	Slovyansk .... a.	1212	0909	1055r	1447r
649	Kramatorsk .... a.	1223	0929	1124	1516
679	Kostiantynivka..... a.	1248	1010	1201	1555
744	**Donetsk** ◇......... a.	...	...	...	...

	IC 712	2	124	126
		■(3)		
		L		
Donetsk ◇ ....d.	...	...	...	...
Kostiantynivka......d.	1620	1641	1740	2145
Kramatorsk ....d.	1641	1716	1816	2220
Slovyansk ....d.	1653	1744r	1848r	2242
Kharkiv..............a.	|	2058	2215	|
Poltava Kyïvska...d.	1945	2348	|	0427
Hrebinka ....d.	|	|	▽	0727
Kyiv.....................a.	2305	0342	0816	0948

K – Khmelnytsky (Table **1700**) - Kyiv - Kharkiv - Lysychansk and v.v.
L – Ivano Frankivsk (Table **1700**) - Lviv - Kyïv - Kostiantynivka and v.v.
r – Slovyansk **Kurort**.
u – From/to Uzhhorod (Table **1715**).
v – From/to Rakhiv via Ivano-Frankivsk (Table **1710**).
▽ – Via Sumy (Table **1755**).
● – Even dates (see page 534).
■ – Uneven dates (see page 534).
‡ – Following day from Kyïv.
◇ – Service suspended.

UZ — KYÏV - SUMY - KHARKIV — 1755

km		776	53*	53*	45		100	100	780	124	
			●	●			●	R			
			★	☆	u		★	☆			
	St Peterburg **1930**.. d.	...	1610	1610	...	...	...	...	...	...	...
	Minsk **1930**............ d.	...	|	|	...	...	0744	0744	...	...	...
	Homel **1930**............ d.	...	0759	0759	...	...	1250	1250	...	...	...
	Lviv **1700** .... d.	...	|	|	0323	...	|	|	...	...	...
0	**Kyiv** .... d.	0020	|	|	1206	...	|	|	1707	2120	...
221	Konotop..................... d.	0314	1316	1417	1524	...	1759	1859	1935	0029	...
350	Sumy......................... d.	0553	1622	1721	1830	...	2054	2156	2134	0319	...
552	**Kharkiv** .... a.	0900	1957	2054	2207	...	0019	0124	...	0642	...
	Lysychansk **1757**.... a.	...	...	...	0415	...	⊡	⊡	...	△	...

	124	779	100	100	143	143		46	775	
			●(4)	S	■(1)	■(1)				
			★	☆	★	☆		u		
Lysychansk **1757**... d.	△	...	⊡	⊡	...	...	...	0653	...	...
Kharkiv .... d.	2241	...	0520	0617	0621	0645	...	1237	2107	...
Sumy .... d.	0233	0535	0906	1001	0956	1038	...	1640	0030	...
Konotop .... d.	0516	0738	1149	1248	1235	1331	...	1919	0248	...
Kyiv.............................. a.	0816	1000	|	|	|	|	...	2227	0534	...
Lviv **1700**................. a.	...	...	|	|	|	|	...	0807	...	...
Homel **1930**............. a.	...	...	1832	1832	2014	2014	...	...	...	...
Minsk **1930**............. a.	...	...	2350	2350	|	|	...	...	...	...
St Peterburg **1930** . a.	...	...	...	...	1221	1221	...	...	...	...

– Even dates (daily June 1 - Sept. 21).
– From Kharkiv on even dates ●(4) (daily June 3 - Sept. 23).
– From/to Uzhhorod (Table **1715**).

⊡ – To/from Zaporizhzhya or Novooleksiivka (Table **1780**).
☆ – Mar. 31 - Oct. 26 (summer time in Ukraine).
★ – Oct. 27 - Dec. 14 (provisional times).

● – Even dates (see page 534).
■ – Uneven dates (see page 534).
△ – To/from Kostiantynivka (Table **1750**).
* – Numbered **144** Chernihiv - Kharkiv.

UZ — KHARKIV - LYSYCHANSK — 1757

km		138	140	45
		k		u
0	**Kharkiv**.................... d.	0820	1219	2245
29	Kupiansk-Vuslov...... d.	1056	1702	0130
54	Lysychansk .... a.	1345	2010	0415
82	**Luhansk** ◇............. a.	...	...	...

	46	138	140
	u	k	
Luhansk ◇ ....d.	...	...	...
Lysychansk.............d.	0653	1650	2136
Kupiansk-Vuslov .....d.	0957	1953	0040
Kharkiv..................a.	1204	2205	0507

UZ — KYIV - SHOSTKA — 1758

km		786	778	784
0	**Kyiv** .... d.	0721	1338	2058
197	Bakhmach Pas. .... d.	0955	1617	2331
221	Konotop.................. d.	1018	1640	0007
302	**Shostka** .... a.	1127	1754	0118

	784	786	778
Shostka ....d.	0416	1214	1842
Konotop..................d.	0526	1323	1952
Bakhmach Pas. ......d.	0609	1346	2016
Kyiv ....a.	0840	1615	2243

– From/to Khmelnytsky and Kyiv (Tablea **1700/50**). u – From/to Uzhhorod and Lviv (Tables **1710**, **1700**). ◇ – Service suspended.

UZ — KYIV - MYKOLAIV - KHERSON — 1760

km		375	766	61KH	61KH	148	782	102	122	110	133
				■(3)	■(3)						
				★	☆		E				⊙
	Lviv 1705................ d.	...	...	...	...	...	...	...	...	1539	1913
	Kozyatyn 1 .... d.	...	...	...	...	...	...	...	...	2353	0255
0	**Kyiv** .... d.	...	0714	...	...	1546	2000	1937	2214	|	|
	Moskva Kiyev. **1740** . d.	...	|	1533	1533	|	|	|	|	|	|
	Konotop..................... d.	...	|	0138	0238	|	◧	|	|	|	|
	Cherkasy.................... d.	...	|	0722	0824	2013	2334	|	|	|	|
16	Im. T. Shevchenka .... d.	⊡	|	0825	0946	2051	...	2327	0158	0439	0713
08	Znamyanka................. d.	0416	|	1016	1143	♡	...	|	|	|	|
48	Kryvyi Rih.................. d.	0751	|	|	|	...	...	0409	|	|	1222
51	**Mykolaiv** .... a.	1202	1341	1440	1547	...	...	|	0718	0943	1736r
06	Kherson...................... a.	1332	1427	1647	1747	...	...	0815	...	1056	1629

	148	781	62SH	62SH	109	134	375	765	122	102
			●‡	●‡						
		E	★	☆		⊙				
Kherson ....d.	...	...	0814	0915	1233	1359s	1528	1552	...	1929
Mykolaiv ....d.	...	...	1003	1110	1349	1244	1710	1639	2138	|
Kryvyi Rih....................d.	...	...	|	|	|	1839	2146	|	|	2338
Znamyanka...................d.	♡	...	1449	1551	|	|	0130	|	|	|
Im. T. Shevchenka ....d.	0407	...	1637	1745	1947	2321	⊡	|	0344	0407
Cherkasy ....d.	0505	0621	1720	1837	|	|	...	|	|	|
Konotop.......................a.	|	◧	2322	0016	|	|	...	|	|	|
Moskva Kiyev. **1740**.a.	|	|	1112	1112	|	|	...	|	|	|
Kyiv..............................a.	0924	1007	...	...	|	|	...	2314	0650	0656
Kozyatyn 1 ....a.	...	...	...	...	0011	0327	...	...	...	...
Lviv 1705.....................a.	...	...	...	...	0824	1049	...	...	...	...

– Daily except ③.
Calls after Kherson.
Calls after Mykolaiv.
– Via Im. T. Shevchenka (**782** a. 2259/**781** d. 0720).

☆ – Mar. 31 - Oct. 26 (summer time in Ukraine).
★ – Oct. 27 - Dec. 14 (provisional times).
⊡ – From/to Kharkiv (Table **1785**).
⊙ – Via Shepetivka between Lviv and Kozyatyn.

♡ – To/from Odesa via Voznesensk (a. 0514/d. 1941).
● – Even dates (see page 534).
■ – Uneven dates (see page 534).
‡ – Train number **957** Kherson - Mykolaiv.

1770 MOSKVA - OREL - BELGOROD - KHARKIV — RZhD, U…

km		745	725	119AJ	741	719	73JA	743	723		57VJ	19	141VJ	71VJ	81AJ	
			≋			≋	d		≋			● p				
	St Peterburg Gl. **1900** d.	...	...	0011	...	...	...	...	...	...	...	...	...	...	2006	...
0	**Moskva** Kurskaya d.	0650	0830	1012	1200	1410	1500	1600	1745	...	2139	2144	2226	2300	0342	...
194	Tula I d.	0848	1029	1252	1358	1626	1840	1758	1947	...	0004	0014	0117	0137	0555	...
383	Orel d.	1033	1216	1618	1548	1820	2120	1942	2138	...	0217	0237	0500	0357	0742	...
537	Kursk d.	1203	...	1838	1723	...	2343	2114	2323	...	0416	0426	0726	0550	0915	...
697	Belgorod a.	1350	...	2054	1916	...	0203	2255	...	...	s	0630	...	0815	1130	...
697	Belgorod § RU d.	...	...	...	...	...	0305	...	...	...	...	0730	...	...	...	...
781	**Kharkiv** § UA a.	...	...	...	...	...	0323z	...	...	...	...	0751z	...	...	...	...

	720	722	744	120VJ	742		726	746	82VJ	98MJ	72VJ	57CH	20		74	
	≋	≋					≋						■(1) p		d	
Kharkiv § UA d.	...	...	...	...	...	...	...	...	...	...	...	...	2116r	...	2244z	...
Belgorod § RU a.	...	...	...	...	...	...	...	...	...	...	...	...	2335	...	0104	...
Belgorod d.	...	...	0730	0940	1223	...	...	1640	1855	...	2100	s	0035	...	0204	...
Kursk d.	...	0626	0915	1229	1421	...	...	1831	2109	2130	2340	0030	0251	...	0416	...
Orel d.	0700	0807	1047	1515	1557	...	1847	2003	2240	0059*	0127	0220	0453	...	0616	...
Tula I d.	0857	1000	1232	1801	1747	...	2043	2148	0029	0329	0337	0434	0708	...	0836	...
Moskva Kurskaya a.	1110	1158	1430	2114	1945	...	2245	2345	0233	0631	0656	0710	0952	...	1125	...
St Peterburg Gl. **1900** a.	...	...	...	0730x	...	...	...	...	1024	...	...	...	...	...	...	...

d – To/from Kryvyi Rih and Dnipro (Table **178**…
p – Conveys portion to/from Poltava (Table **1785**).
r – Dep. 2216 Mar. 31 - Oct. 26. Passengers must board by 2046 (2146 Mar. 31 - Oct. 2…
s – To/from Stary Oskol (a. 0820/d. 2005).
x – St Peterburg **Ladozhski**.
z – One hour later Mar. 31 - Oct. 26 (summer time in Ukraine).

≋ – *Lastochka* (Swallow) fast day train.
● – Even dates (see page 534).
■ – Uneven dates (see page 534).
§ – 🏛 : Krasny Khutor (RU)/Kozacha Lopan (UA).
* – Arrives 2359.

RU – Russia (Moskva Time UTC+3).
UA – Ukraine (UTC+2 winter, UTC+3 summer…

1780 KYIV and KHARKIV - DNIPRO - ZAPORIZHZHYA - MELITOPOL — U…

km		140	IC 732	IC 738	70	IC 736	84	IC 740	IC 734	81	100	100	12	116	104	72	86	86	76	80	54	42	73JA	73JA	12…
						L		F		G	● ★	P ☆					● ☆n	● ★n				△	★	☆	
	Lviv **1705** d.	...	...	...	0115	...	...	...	...	...	...	...	...	...	...	...	1110	1110	...	...	...	1522	...	...	135…
•	Kozyatyn 1 **1705** d.	...	...	...	0925	...	...	...	...	...	...	...	...	...	...	...	1857	1857	...	...	...	2325	...	...	|
0	**Kyiv** d.	...	0707	1239	|	1411	1632	1722	1734	...	...	...	1922	1915	2006	2012	|	|	2128	2318	...	|	...	...	|
216	Im. Tar. Shevchenka d.	...	0924	|	1415	1628	1957	|	1951	...	...	...	2208	2215	|	2307	0026	0014	0103	|	...	0403	...	...	|
	Odesa Holovna ▷ d.	...	|	|	|	|	|	|	|	...	...	...	|	|	|	|	|	|	|	|	2151	|	...	...	|
	Kropyvnytskyi ▷ d.	...	|	|	|	|	|	|	|	...	...	...	|	|	|	|	|	|	|	|	0318	|	...	...	040…
308	Znamyanka ▷ d.	...	1025	|	1537	1729	2111	|	2052	...	...	...	2319	2334	0004	|	0148	0136	0224	0304	0427	0529	...	...	050…
353	Oleksandria d.	...	1053	|	1618	1757	2149	|	2120	...	...	...	2357	0013	0042	|	0227	0215	0306	0339	0510	0608	...	...	055…
490	**Kryvyi Rih** Hol. a.	...	|	|	|	|	|	2258	|	...	...	...	|	|	|	0316	|	|	0610	|	1010x	|	...	...	093…
	Moskva Kurs. **1770** d.	...	|	|	|	|	|	...	|	...	...	...	|	|	|	|	|	|	...	|	|	|	1500	1500	|
	Minsk **1930** d.	v	|	|	|	|	|	...	|	...	0744	0744	|	|	|	|	|	|	...	|	|	|	|	|	|
•	**Kharkiv** d.	0537	|	|	|	|	|	...	|	2334	0041	0146	|	|	|	|	|	|	...	|	|	|	0413	0513	|
496	Kamianske d.	|	1226	|	1906	1931	0006	...	2253	|	|	|	0211	0232	|	|	0444	0434	...	0559	0812	0848	|	|	|
534	**Dnipro** Hol. a.	1028	1252	1908	1943	1957	0038	...	2319	|	|	|	0245	0306	0329	|	0450	0507	...	0640	0850	0922	0920r	1036r	|
534	**Dnipro** Hol. d.	...	1302	1913	2003	2007	0105	...	2329	|	|	|	0310	0336	0356	|	0515	0523	...	...	...	...	|	|	|
735	Pokrovsk a.	...	|	|	|	|	|	...	0143	|	|	|	|	|	|	|	|	|	...	...	...	...	|	|	|
658	**Zaporizhzhya** I a.	...	1425	2042	2159	2129	0256	...	...	0350	0511	0617	0455	0545	0553	0749	0714	0725	...	...	...	...	0856	0955	143…
658	**Zaporizhzhya** I d.	...	...	...	2204	...	0316	...	...	0355	...	0642	0503	0652	0558	...	0720	0731	...	...	...	...	0926	1025	...
843	Kryvyi Rih Hol. a.	...	...	...	|	...	|	...	...	|	...	|	|	b	|	...	|	|	...	...	...	...	1338	1435	...
1033	Mariupol a.	...	...	...	0630	...	1105	...	...	|	...	|	|	...	1300	...	|	|	...	...	...	...	...	...	...
770	**Melitopol** a.	...	...	...	...	...	...	...	...	0544	...	0825	0639	...	...	...	0907	0917	...	...	...	...	...	...	...
861	Novooleksiivka a.	...	...	...	...	...	...	...	...	0715	...	0952	0748	...	...	...	1050	1100	...	...	...	...	...	...	...

	IC 739	IC 733	140	IC 738	41	IC 732	120	74	74	86	86	53	76	72	70	80	104	IC 736	12	116	100	100	82	84
	E				△			★	☆	■(3) ☆k	■(3) ★k							L			●(4) ★	R ☆	H	
Novooleksiivka d.	...	...	...	...	...	...	...	...	...	1224	1224	...	...	...	...	...	...	...	2031	...	...	2138	2208	...
Melitopol d.	...	...	...	...	...	...	...	...	...	1415	1415	...	...	...	...	...	...	...	2152	...	...	2322	2350	...
Mariupol d.	...	...	...	...	...	...	...	...	...	|	|	...	...	...	1250	...	1450	...	|	...	...	|	|	1847
Kryvyi Rih Hol. d.	...	...	...	...	...	...	...	1104	1152	|	|	...	...	...	|	...	|	...	|	b	...	|	|	|
Zaporizhzhya I a.	...	...	...	...	...	...	...	1519	1619	1552	1552	...	...	...	2014	...	2145	...	2317	2310	...	0053	0120	0207
Zaporizhzhya I d.	...	...	...	0818	...	1535	1220	1604	1649	1556	1556	...	...	1820	2034	...	2149	2250	2325	2340	0033	0108	0125	0212
Pokrovsk d.	...	0439	...	|	...	|	|	|	|	|	|	...	...	|	|	...	|	|	|	|	|	|	|	|
Dnipro Hol. a.	...	0653	...	0950	...	1657	|	|	|	1740	1740	...	...	|	2226	...	2327	0012	0103	0137	|	|	|	0406
Dnipro Hol. d.	...	0703	0708	0955	1426	1707	|	1548s	1700s	1800	1800	1915	...	|	2251	2344	2352	0022	0128	0230	|	|	|	0430
Kamianske d.	...	0731	|	|	1500	1735	|	|	|	1840	1840	1953	...	|	2326	0018	|	0050	0203	0308	|	|	|	0504
Kharkiv a.	...	|	1149	|	|	|	|	2145	2245	|	|	|	...	|	|	|	|	|	|	|	0452	0550	0559	|
Minsk **1930** a.	...	|	v	|	|	|	|	|	|	|	|	|	...	|	|	|	|	|	|	|	2350	2350	...	|
Moskva Kurs. **1770** a.	...	|	...	|	|	|	|	1125	1125	|	|	|	...	|	|	|	|	|	|	|	...	...	...	|
Kryvyi Rih Hol. d.	0616	|	...	|	|	|	1707	...	...	|	|	1809z	2059	2247	|	|	|	|	|	|	...	...	...	|
Oleksandria d.	|	0902	...	|	1736	1906	2013	...	...	2136	2142	2253	0006	|	0216	0240	0256	0221	0419	0539	...	...	...	0733
Znamyanka ▷ d.	|	0932	...	|	1822	1936	2112	...	...	2225	2227	2353	0053	|	0258	0320	0347	0251	0459	0627	...	...	...	0817
Kropyvnytskyi ▷ d.	|	|	...	|	|	|	2205	...	...	|	|	0044	|	|	|	|	|	|	|	|	...	...	...	|
Odesa Holovna ▷ a.	|	|	...	|	|	|	|	...	...	|	|	0618	|	|	|	|	|	|	|	|	...	...	...	|
Im. Tar. Shevchenka d.	|	1032	...	|	2001	2036	|	...	...	0023	0023	...	0207	0300	0435	|	|	0351	0610	0747	...	...	...	0948
Kyiv a.	1152	1248	...	1627	|	2253	|	...	...	|	|	...	0458	0552	|	0708	0805	0607	0915	1100	...	...	...	1238
Kozyatyn 1 **1705** a.	...	...	...	...	0018	...	|	...	...	0440	0440	...	...	...	0928	...	...	...	...	...	...	...	...	...
Lviv **1705** a.	...	...	...	...	0834	...	1239	...	...	1249	1249	...	...	...	1727	...	...	...	...	...	...	...	...	...

E – Uneven dates (even dates in June, July, Sept., Oct.).
F – Even dates (uneven dates in June, July, Sept., Oct.).
G – Uneven dates (daily from Apr. 20).
H – Even dates (daily from Apr. 21).
J – Daily except ②.
L – ①③④⑤⑦.
P – To Zaporizhzhya on even dates (daily June 1 - Sept. 21); to Novooleksiivka daily June 1 - Sept. 21.
R – From Novooleksiivka June 2 - Sept. 22; from Zaporizhzhya (next day) on even dates ●(4) (daily June 3 - Sept. 23).
b – To/from Berdiansk (a. 1150/d. 1800).
k – Conveys portion for Kovel via Kozyatyn (Table **1730**).

n – Conveys portion from Kovel (Table **1730**), Zozyatyn d. 1836.
r – Moskva - Dnipro portion (train **106**).
s – Dnipro - Moskva portion (train **106**).
v – From/to Lysychansk (Table **1757**).
x – Odesa - Kryvyi Rih portion.
z – Kryvyi Rih - Odesa portion (train **564**).

● – Even dates (see page 534).
■ – Uneven dates (see page 534).
☆ – Mar. 31 - Oct. 26 (summer time in Ukraine).
★ – Oct. 27 - Dec. 14 (provisional times).

ADDITIONAL TRAIN KHARKIV - ZAPORIZHZHYA

	797 J			798 J
Kharkiv d.	0920	...	**Zaporizhzhya** d.	1450
Zaporizhzhya a.	1343	...	**Kharkiv** a.	1920

△ – From/to Truskavets (Table **1715**).
▷ – For additional train see Table **1785**.
• – Kozyatyn - Im. Tarasa Shevchenka *304 km*; Kharkiv - Zaporizhzhya *327 km*.

1785 KHARKIV - KREMENCHUK - ODESA — UZ

km		19	19	127	59	791	375
		★●	☆●	●	⊕		
	Moskva K. **1770** d.	2144	2144	...	...	...	...
0	**Kharkiv** d.	0946	1017	1517	1704	...	1939
140	Poltava Pivdenna a.	1203	1235	1800	1939	...	2237
259	**Kremenchuk** a.	...	...	2035	2141	2357	0133
353	Znamyanka a.	...	...	2249	2337	0113	0353
	Kyiv a.	...	...	n	|	0518	k
407	Kropyvnytskyi a.	...	...	...	0025	...	...
765	**Odesa** Holovna a.	...	...	...	0608	...	...

	60	375	128	92	92	792
	⊗		■‡	★■	☆■	
Odesa Holovna d.	1921	...	...	...	...	...
Kropyvnytskyi d.	0108	...	...	...	...	...
Kyiv d.	|	k	n	...	...	1742
Znamyanka d.	0217	0157	0448	...	...	2141
Kremenchuk d.	0417	0424	0653	...	...	2258
Poltava Pivdenna d.	0612	0727	0934	1735	1804	...
Kharkiv a.	0821	1008	1212	1950	2022	...
Moskva K. **1770** a.	...	...	...	0952	0952	...

k – To/from Kherson (Table **1760**).
n – To/from Kovel (Table **1730**).
● – Even dates (see page 534).
■ – Uneven dates (see page 534).
☆ – Mar. 31 - Oct. 26 (summer time in Ukraine).
★ – Oct. 27 - Dec. 14 (provisional times).
⊕ – ● (■ in Oct.); daily Apr. 25 - Sept. 30.
⊗ – ■ (● in Oct.); daily Apr. 26 - Oct. 1.
‡ – Next day in this table.

1787 ODESA - MARIUPOL — U…

km		318	142
		■(3)	●
0	**Odesa** Hol. d.	1417	2235
232	Mykolaiv d.	1930	0301
287	Kherson d.	2054	0416
643	**Zapor.** 1 ⊡ a.	0534	1110
643	**Zapor.** 1 ⊡ d.	0608	1120
1018	Mariupol a.	|	1902
769	**Dnipro** Hol. a.	0821	...

	618 317	1…
	●	■
Dnipro Hol d.	1548	.
Mariupol d.	|	2…
Zapor. 1 ⊡ a.	1805	04…
Zapor. 1 ⊡ d.	1930	04…
Kherson d.	0438	11…
Mykolaiv d.	0552	13…
Odesa Hol. a.	1059	17…

⊡ – Zaporizhzhya 1.

CRIMEAN PENINSULA — 1790

mean Railway. UTC+3

Simferopol d.	0525 0830 1500 1750
Sevastopol a.	0715 1022 1650 1940

Sevastopol d.	0520 0830 1220 1750
Simferopol a.	0710 1020 1410 1940

km		
0	Simferopol d.	0550 0730 0910 1440 1800
79	Yevpatoria a.	0734 0910 1046 1628 1949

Yevpatoriya d.	0535 0800 1110 1320 1900
Simferopol a.	0724 0947 1245 1455 2048

						k			f		
Armyansk d.	...	...	...	...	0705	...	...	...	...	1505	...
Dzhankoy d.	0250	...	0640	...	0920	...	1435	...	...	1640	1725
Vladyslavivka d.	0503	0639	0900	0920	1125	1155	1652	1655	1900	...	1939
Feodosia a.	|	0720	|	1000	1203	|	|	1735	1938	...	2015
Kerch a.	0714	...	1118	...	...	1354	1908	...	...	...	...

			k					f			
Kerch d.	...	...	...	0830	...	1435	...	1625	...	...	2030
Feodosia d.	0620	0805	1040	|	1520	|	...	|	1810	2050	|
Vladyslavivka d.	0703	0845	1110	1132*	1600	1653	...	1826	1855	2130	2247
Dzhankoy a.	0917	...	...	1342	...	1915	1935	...	2100	...	0055
Armyansk a.	1120	...	...	...	...	...	2110	...	...	...	...

Solone Ozero d.	...	0605	0905	...	1500	...	2005
Dzhankoy d.	0525	0633	0935	1210	1530	1720	2034
Simferopol a.	0710	0801	1120	1355	1715	1905	2205

Simferopol d.	0600	0855	1205	1500	1740	1840	2030
Dzhankoy d.	0810	1042	1355	1645	1913	2030	2215
Solone Ozero a.	0835	...	1420	...	1938	2055	...

f – Kerch - Feodosia.
k – Feodosia - Kerch
* – Arrive 1050.

Summer service from June 2, 2019.
Subject to alteration.

LITHUANIA, LATVIA and ESTONIA

SEE MAP PAGE 526

ators: Lithuania: **LG** (Lietuvos Geležinkeliai), www.litrail.lt Latvia: **LDz** (Latvijas Dzelzcelš), www.ldz.lv Estonia: **Elron** www.elron.ee
ices: Trains convey first- and second-class seating unless indicated otherwise. International trains to and from Belarus, Russia and Ukraine are composed of Russian-style sleeping-cars (for details of train types and classes of travel see the panel on page **534**).
ngs: Valid from **December 9, 2018**. Amendments are included as received. Timings are expressed in local time at the station concerned (time comparison chart: page 4).
rvations: Reservation is compulsory for travel by international services to/from Russia.

RIGA - TALLINN, ST PETERBURG, VILNIUS and KALININGRAD — 1800

RIGA - PÄRNU - TALLINN ⊡
ey time: 4 hours 25 mins.
Riga: 0305, 0700, 0800, 0900, 1000, 1230; hourly 1400 - 1900.
Tallinn: hourly 0600 - 1000; 1130, 1230, 1500, 1600, 1700, 1800, 2230.

RIGA - ST PETERBURG ⊡
Journey time: approx 11 - 12 hours.
From Riga: 0305, 0855, 0900, 1000, 1130, 1800, 1845, 1900, 2245, 2355.
From St Peterburg: 0645, 0800, 0815, 1030, 1115, 1600, 1945, 2100, 2315, 2335.

RIGA - VILNIUS ⊡
Journey time: 4h 10m - 4h 30m
From Riga: 0255, 0700, 0830, 0930, 1200, 1245, 1345, 1500, 1630, 1730, 1845, 2250.
From Vilnius: 0230, 0645, 0730, 0900, 1000, 1200, 1330, 1430, 1630, 1730, 1845, 2300.

RIGA - KALININGRAD ⊙
Journey time: 7 hours 40 mins.
From Riga: 2330.
From Kaliningrad: 2230◇.
Daytime service available certain days ⊡.

Operator: Lux Express (www.luxexpress.eu).
Operator: Ecolines (ecolines.net).
◇ – One hour earlier when Latvia is on summer time (Mar. 31 - Oct. 26).
Riga and Vilnius coach stations are close to the railway stations. Tallinn coach station is 3 km from the railway station (by tram).

VILNIUS - ŠIAULIAI - KLAIPEDA — 1810

1,2 class ♥

		Ⓐ		⑥	⑥G				⑤F		
Vilnius 1811 d.	...	0510	0650	0658	0723	0950	...	1415	1600	1645	1740
Kaišiadorys 1811 d.	...	|	0732	0745	|	|	...	1500	|	|	1822
Radviliškis d.	0540	|	0854	0911	|	|	1605	1626	|	|	1948
Šiauliai d.	0613	0725	0912	0930	|	1200	1649	1645	|	1855	2006
Klaipeda a.	0909	0919	1106	...	1123	1347	1948	...	2006	2033	2200

	Ⓐ	⑥				⑥		⑦H		⑦	⑥⑦
Klaipeda d.	0510	...	0640	0805	1030	...	1555	1700	...	1755	1720
Šiauliai d.	0701	0800	0830	1102	1215	1220	1752	|	1900	1943	2020
Radviliškis d.	|	0820	0847	1134	|	1240	1809	|	1920	|	2052
Kaišiadorys 1811 d.	0840	0957	1010	...	|	1408	1939	|	2051	|	...
Vilnius 1811 a.	0922	1043	1052	...	1428	1454	2021	2100	2137	2156	...

	Ⓐ	Ⓒ			⑤⑦		
Kaunas d.	...	...	...	...	1530	...	...
Radviliškis d.	0600	...	1400	1555	1720	...	...
Šiauliai d.	0620	0900	1432	1635	1741	1800	2030
Mažeikiai a.	0734	1014	1545	1750	...	1913	2145

	Ⓐ	Ⓒ			⑤⑦		
Mažeikiai d.	0535	0735	1040	1555	...	1805	1930
Šiauliai d.	0649	0849	1154	1706	1810	1922	2044
Radviliškis a.	...	...	1226	...	1831	...	2116
Kaunas a.	...	...	...	...	2031	...	...

F – ⑤ May 31 - Aug. 23 (also Oct. 31).
G – ⑥ June 1 - Aug. 24 (also Nov. 1).
H – ⑦ June 2 - Aug. 25 (also June 24; not June 23).
♥ – Local trains are 3rd class only.

VILNIUS - KAUNAS — 1811

1,2 class May 22 - Aug. 31

	Ⓐb	Ⓐ		b			b	b		b	b		b		b		b			b				
Vilnius 1810 d.	0405	0445	0532	0556	0705	0827	0935	1035	1140	1245	1340	1437	1535	1610	1730	1755	1855	1935	2042	2200	...	...	...	...
Kaišiadorys 1810 d.	0455	0544	0631	0641	0804	0926	1026	1124	1238	1333	1428	1535	1623	1709	1813	1855	1945	2034	2141	2251	...	...	...	...
Palemonas a.	0512	0605	0653	0700	0825	0947	1046	1142	1300	1351	1446	1557	1642	1730	1830	1921	2002	2055	2202	2310	...	...	...	...
Kaunas (rail stn) a.	△	△	△	*0745*r	△	△	△	*1227*r	△	*1436*r	*1531*r	△	*1727*r	△	*1915*r	△	△	△	△	△	...	...	...	...

	Ⓐ		Ⓐb		b				b	b		b			b		b			b
nas (rail stn) d.	△	△	*0547*r	△	*0649*r	△	△	*1003*r	*1059*r	△	△	*1403*r	△	△	*1710*r	△	△	△	△	△
ıonas d.	0444	0529	0632	0654	0734	0851	0949	1048	1144	1237	1353	1448	1559	1644	1800	1808	1923	2004	2122	2249
dorys 1810 d.	0509	0554	0654	0720	0756	0916	1017	1113	1207	1301	1418	1510	1624	1709	1821	1833	1944	2029	2147	2310
s 1810 a.	0613	0703	0738	0824	0844	1019	1121	1217	1258	1351	1522	1559	1728	1813	1913	1937	2034	2132	2251	2359

Trains terminate at Palemonas due to Rail Baltica construction work

Semi-fast train (other trains call at all stations). r – Connection by rail-replacement 🚌 (rail tickets valid). △ – Connections available by local city 🚌 (rail tickets not valid).

VILNIUS - TURMANTAS - DAUGAVPILS — 1815

3rd class

	Ⓐ	Ⓒ		Ⓐ	Ⓒ		Ⓐ	⑥	Ⓑ		
Vilnius d.	0542	0542	0740	1145	1145	1510	1631	1734	1734	1943	2126
Ignalina d.	0724	0724	0922	1331	1331	1648	1812	1919	1919	2128	2256
Turmantas 🏛 a.	0807	0807	1006	1414	1414	1731	...	2002	2002	...	2333
Daugavpils a.	...	0828	...	...	1435	...	...	2023	...	...	...

				Ⓐ	Ⓒ	Ⓐ	Ⓐ	Ⓒ		Ⓐ	⑥
Daugavpils d.	...	...	...	...	0858	...	...	1542	...	...	2113
Turmantas 🏛 d.	0430	0518	...	0921	0921	1205	1605	1605	1753	...	2135
Ignalina d.	0506	0559	0641	1002	1002	1248	1648	1648	1836	2045	...
Vilnius a.	0633	0738	0830	1139	1139	1427	1825	1825	2013	2209	...

VILNIUS - VILNIUS AIRPORT — 1816

3rd class

/ilnius: 0540, 0754, 0838, 0907, 0940, 1025, 1100, 1134, 1210, 1240, 1340, 1420, 1605, 1745, 1926, 2030, 2217.
/ilnius Airport (*Oro uostas* in Lithuanian): 0716, 0809, 0852, 0920, 0955, 1040, 1115, 1225, 1300, 1400, 1547, 1620, 1712, 1907, 1941, 2151, 2232.
y time 7 - 8 minutes. *4 km.*

VILNIUS - TRAKAI — 1817

3rd class

/ilnius: 0548, 0710, 0816, 1130**S**, 1230, 1430, 1625, 1720, 1840, 2035, 2210.
rakai: 0605, 0644, 0800, 0908, 1230**S**, 1330, 1533, 1730, 1845, 1930, 2140.
y time 33 - 36 minutes. *27 km.*
ar. 31 - Aug. 31.

KYÏV - MINSK - VILNIUS - RIGA — 1820

	31*KJ* D
Kyïv d.	1315r
Kalinkavichy d.	1943
Zhlobin d.	2054
Minsk a.	2335
Minsk d.	0002
Maladzechna d.	0107
Vilnius d.	0330
Siauliai d.	0551
Riga a.	0808

	31*RJ* E
Riga d.	1010
Siauliai d.	1227
Vilnius d.	1453
Maladzechna d.	1913
Minsk a.	2016
Minsk d.	2047
Zhlobin d.	2339
Kalinkavichy d.	0106
Kyïv a.	0520

D – Every four days Feb. 4 - 28, Mar. 2 - 30, Apr. 4 - 28, May 2 - 30, June 4 - 28, July 2 - 30, Aug. 4 - 28, Sept. 2 - 30, Oct. 4 - 28, Nov. 2 - 30, Dec. 4.
E – Every four days Feb. 5 - Mar. 1, Mar. 3 - 31, Apr. 5 - 29, May 3 - 31, June 5 - 29, July 3 - 27, Aug. 5 - 29, Sept. 3 - Oct. 1, Oct. 5 - 29, Nov. 3 - 27, Dec. 1, 5.
r – Board train by 1250 for customs.

🏛 at Slovechno (Ukraine / Belarus), Kena (Belarus / Lithuania), Yonishkis (Lithuania / Latvia).
For other trains: Kyïv - Minsk via Homel see Table **1930**, Minsk - Vilnius see Table **1950**.

RIGA - VALMIERA - VALGA — 1830

										Ⓐ	
Riga d.	0621	0755	1034	1230	1400	1542	1727	1810	1849	1942	2135
Sigulda d.	0741	0909	1144	1344	1514	1656	1841	1903	2000	2056	2249
Cesis d.	0823	...	1225	...	...	...	...	1935	2042	...	...
Valmiera d.	0854	...	1257	...	...	...	...	2002	2113	...	...
Lugaži 🏛 LV a.	...	...	1341	...	...	...	...	2046	...	...	...
Valga 🏛 EE a.	...	...	1347	...	...	...	...	2052	...	...	...

								Ⓐ		Ⓒ	
Valga 🏛 EE d.	...	0516	...	...	...	...	...	1440	...	1641	...
Lugaži 🏛 LV d.	...	0523	...	...	...	...	...	1447	...	1648	...
Valmiera d.	0503	0605	...	...	0953	...	...	1532	...	1733	...
Cesis d.	0535	0631	...	...	1025	...	...	1604	...	1804	...
Sigulda d.	0617	0702	0805	0922	1107	1402	1537	1646	1713	1846	2136
Riga a.	0725	0754	0916	1033	1215	1513	1648	1738	1824	1948	2247

stonia. LV – Latvia. ☛ For trains Valga - Tallinn see Table **1880**.

1840 RIGA - REZEKNE - ST PETERBURG and MOSKVA

LDz, RZ

km		808	662*AJ* 664*AJ*	702	*Fir* 2*RJ*	2*TJ* 83*BJ*	816	*Fir* 2*RJ*	2*RJ* 83*BJ*	
			M	©	L	B		L	B	
					★	★		☆	☆	
0	**Riga** 1850 d.	0950	...	1138	1650	1650	1700	1730	1730	...
51	Lielvarde 1850 d.	1040	...	|	|	|	1750	|	|	...
129	Krustpils ⊡ 1850 d.	1151	...	1315	1837	1837	1857	1918	1918	...
224	**Rezekne 2** d.	1323	...	1420	2002	2002	2029	2055	2055	...
279	Zilupe 🏛 LV d.	1426	...	...	2137	2137	2132	2237	2237	...
306	Sebezh 🏛 RU d.	...	...	...	2355	2355	...	2355	2355	...
417	Novosokolniki d.	...	...	...	0224	0335	...	0224	0335	...
593	Dno d.	...	...	...	|	0606	...	|	0606	...
838	**St Peterburg** Vitebski a.	...	...	...	|	0930	...	|	0930	...
446	**Velikiye Luki** d.	...	2130	...	0259	...	...	0259	...	...
687	Rzhev d.	...	0218	...	0602	...	...	0602	...	...
922	**Moskva** Rizhskaya a.	...	0643	...	1017	...	...	1017	...	...

	815	*Fir* 1*RJ*	83*AJ* 1*RJ*	*Fir* 1*RJ*	83*AJ* 1*RJ*		661*AJ* 663*RJ*	701	8
		L	B	L	B		N	©	
		★	★	☆	☆				
Moskva Rizhskaya d.	...	1705	...	1705	...	...	1956	...	
Rzhev d.	...	2105	...	2105	...	...	0035	...	
Velikiye Luki d.	...	0035	...	0035	...	...	0600	...	
St Peterburg Vitebski d.	...	|	1720	|	1720	...	...	...	
Dno d.	...	|	2057	|	2057	...	...	...	
Novosokolniki d.	...	0135	0135	0135	0135	...	...	...	
Sebezh 🏛 RU d.	...	0415	0415	0415	0415	...	...	...	
Zilupe 🏛 LV d.	0345	0427	0427	0527	0527	...	...	...	1
Rezekne 2 d.	0450	0530	0530	0627	0627	...	...	1510	1
Krustpils ⊡ 1850 d.	0620	0642	0642	0739	0739	...	...	1618	1
Lielvarde 1850 d.	0731	|	|	|	|	...	...	|	1
Riga 1850 a.	0820	0828	0828	0911	0911	...	...	1753	2

B – BALTIJA – 🛏 1, 2 cl. [R]
L – LATVIJAS EKSPRESIS – 🛏 1, 2 cl. [R]
M – ②③④⑤⑦.
N – ①③④⑤⑦.
☆ – Mar. 31 - Oct. 26 (summer time in Latvia).
★ – Oct. 27 - Dec. 14 (provisional times).
⊡ – Station for Jekabpils.
LV – Latvia (UTC + 2 winter, UTC + 3 summer).
RU – Russia (Moskva Time UTC + 3).

1850 RIGA - DAUGAVPILS - MINSK

See also Table 1820. LDz, B

km		802	806	808	810	814	704	818	*Sko* 88*BJ*	*Sko* 88*BJ*	822
			©		⑤–⑦				❦ ★	❦ ☆	
0	**Riga** ▷ d.	0740	0821	0950	1302	1523	1619	1738	1920	2000	2110
51	Lielvarde ▷ d.	0830	0919	1040	1351	1619	|	1824	|	|	2214
129	Krustpils ⊡ ▷ d.	0948	1039	1151	1500	1739	1754	1941	2100	2145	2331
218	**Daugavpils** LV d.	1107	...	...	1630	...	1858	2058	2225	2322	...
379	Polatsk § BY d.	...	...	...	...	...	...	...	0324	0324	...
578	Maladzechna d.	...	...	...	...	...	...	...	0638	0638	...
655	**Minsk** a.	...	...	...	...	...	...	...	0745	0745	...

	821	*Sko* 87*BJ*	*Sko* 87*BJ*	703	817	805	801		809
		❦ ★	❦ ☆			©	⑤–⑦		
Minsk d.	...	2038	2038	...	...	...	...	...	...
Maladzechna d.	...	2216	2216	...	...	...	...	...	...
Polatsk § BY d.	...	0124	0124	...	...	...	...	...	...
Daugavpils LV d.	...	0430	0530	0618	0730	...	1310	...	1738
Krustpils ⊡ ▷ d.	0450	0539	0641	0721	0852	1154	1432	...	1907
Lielvarde ▷ d.	0611	|	|	|	1008	1315	1548	1648	2022
Riga ▷ a.	0716	0729	0828	0900	1055	1411	1635	1746	2108

⊡ – Station for Jekabpils.
★ – Dec. 9 - Mar. 30.
☆ – Mar. 31 - Oct. 26 (summer time in Latvia).
❦ – Runs approx every four days.
▷ – See also Table **1840**. Local trains run Riga - Lielvarde.
§ – 🏛 : Indra (LV) / Bihosava (BY).
LV – Latvia (UTC + 2 winter, UTC + 3 summer).
BY – Belarus (UTC + 3 all year).

1860 RIGA - LIEPAJA, TUKUMS and SAULKRASTI

km		⑤		⑦
0	**Riga** ▷ d.	1825	**Liepaja** d.	1728
43	Jelgava ▷ d.	1905	Saldus d.	1848
125	Saldus d.	2020	Jelgava ▷ d.	2002
223	**Liepaja** a.	2140	**Riga** ▷ a.	2038

RIGA - JURMALA ◧ - TUKUMS *65 km* Journey 1h 25m

From **Riga**: 0544, 0736, 0920, 1300, 1419, 1556, 1706, 1859, 2142, 2240, 2336. From **Tukums** II: 0445, 0549, 0619, 0720Ⓐ, 0810, 0925, 1118, 1455, 1634, 1744, 1936, 2106.

Riga - Jurmala (Sloka) ◧ 1 - 2 trains per hour. journey ± 50 mins.

RIGA - SAULKRASTI *48 km* Journey 1 hour

From **Riga**: 0615, 0720, 0811, 1018, 1220, 1445, 1558Ⓐ, 1737, 1831, 1932, 2037, 2238. From **Saulkrasti**: 0505, 064 0746, 0837, 0946, 1153, 1351, 1623, 1708Ⓐ, 1804, 1919,

Certain trains continue to / from Skulte, *56 km* ± 70 minutes

▷ – Riga - Jelgava: 1 - 2 trains per hour.
◧ – Jurmala's 33 km coastline has several stations; principal stations are Majori (*22 km*) and Sloka (*32 km*). There is no station called Jurn

1870 TALLINN - ST PETERBURG - MOSKVA

Elron, GoRail, R

km		220	20	222		34*VJ*	34*VJ*		224	226
			⊖			A ★	A ☆			
0	**Tallinn** 1880 d.	0700	1141	1512	...	1600	1648	...	1715	2141
77	Tapa 1880 d.	0758	1230	1610	...	1654	1740	...	1813	2239
104	Rakvere d.	0819	1254	1631	...	|	|	...	1834	2300z
165	Jõhvi d.	0912	1339	1724	...	1756	1851	...	1935	...
209	Narva 🏛 EE d.	0944	1407	1756	...	1915	2015	...	2020	...
380	**St Peterburg** Glavni RU a.	...	...	...	...	2358	2358	...	...	...
633	Bologoye 1900 a.	...	...	...	...	0525	0525	...	...	...
797	Tver 1900 a.	...	...	...	...	0719	0719	...	...	...
964	**Moskva** Oktyabrskaya 1900 a.	...	...	...	...	0930	0930	...	...	...

	221	223	21		34*AJ*	34*AJ*		225
			⊖		A ★	A ☆		
Moskva Oktyabrskaya 1900 d.	...	...	...	...	2215	2215	...	...
Tver 1900 d.	...	...	...	...	0031	0031	...	...
Bologoye 1900 d.	...	...	...	...	|	|	...	...
St Peterburg Glavni RU d.	...	...	...	...	0625	0625	...	...
Narva 🏛 EE d.	...	0705	1000	...	1015	1115	...	1422
Jõhvi d.	...	0738	1028	...	1051	1153	...	1454
Rakvere d.	0608z	0833	1112	...	|	|	...	1546
Tapa 1880 d.	0632	0857	1134	...	1153	1301	...	1610
Tallinn 1880 a.	0734	0955	1223	...	1245	1352	...	1708

Lux Express (www.luxexpress.eu) 🚌 TALLINN - ST PETERBURG Reservation compul

🚌	Ⓑ								
Tallinn coach station ◇ d.	0600	0700	0800	1135	1430	1545	1700	2300	2359
St Peterburg coach station ¶ a.	1325*	1525*	1550*	1925*	2220*	2310*	0215*	0700*	0850*

🚌							Ⓑ		
St Peterburg coach stn ¶ d.	0730	0845	1100	1130	1315	1545	1715	1815	2315
Tallinn coach station ◇ a.	1300r	1430r	1810r	2000r	1915r	2130r	2305r	0015r	0505r

A – 🛏 1, 2 cl. [R]. Operated by Go Rail.
r – One hour later Mar. 31 - Oct. 26.
z – By 🚌 (a. 2323 / d. 0542) certain dates.
¶ – Also calls at Baltiski station.
☆ – Mar. 31 - Oct. 26 (summer time in Latvia).
★ – Oct. 27 - Dec. 14 (provisional times).
◇ – 3 km by tram from railway station.
⊖ – Classified *Ekspress* (higher fares).
* – One hour earlier Mar. 31 - Oct. 26.
EE – Estonia (UTC + 2 winter, UTC summer).
RU – Russia (Moskva Time UTC +

1880 TALLINN - TARTU - VALGA

km		210	10	12	14	212	16	214	18	216	60	
			⊖	⊖	⊖		⊖		⊖		⊖	
0	**Tallinn** 1870 d.	0617	0813	1005	1305	1354	1531	1626	1748	1907	2023	...
77	Tapa 1870 d.	0715	0902	1054	1354	1452	1620	1724	1837	2005	2112	...
142	Jõgeva d.	0804	0941	1133	1433	1538	1701	1812	1917	2051	2151	...
190	**Tartu** a.	0837	1008	1201	1501	1613	1728	1845	1944	2124	2218	...

	211	11	13	15	213	17	19	215	61	217
		⊖	⊖	⊖		⊖	⊖		⊖	
Tartu d.	0626	0735	0838	1215	1321	1528	1631	1736	1847	2002
Jõgeva d.	0702	0805	0907	1244	1355	1557	1701	1812	1917	2036
Tapa 1870 d.	0750	0844	0950	1323	1444	1636	1729	1848	1945	2113
Tallinn 1870 a.	0848	0933	1039	1412	1542	1725	1829	1958	2046	2226

km					
0	*Tallinn* § d.	0813	1305	1531	1748
190	**Tartu** d.	1011	1504	1731	1947
215	Elva d.	1038	1531	1758	2014
273	**Valga** a.	1123	1616	1845	2059
	Valga △ d.	*1440*a	*1641*c	...	...
	Riga △ a.	*1738*a	*1948*c	...	...

Riga △ d.	...	...	*1034*	...	...
Valga △ a.	...	...	*1347*	...	...
Valga d.	0620	0718	1411	1729	...
Elva d.	0706	0804	1457	1816	...
Tartu a.	0732	0830	1525	1843	...
Tallinn § a.	0933	1039	1725	2046	...

km	☆		©	Ⓐ	©
	Tallinn § d.	0813	1305	1531	1626
0	Tartu d.	1013	1518	1734	1855
43	Põlva d.	1056	1601	1817	1938
72	Orava d.	1120	1625	1841	2002
85	Koidula d.	1137	1642	1851	2012
92	Piusa a.	1145	1650	...	...

☆	Ⓐ	©	©	Ⓐ
Piusa d.	...	...	1335	1448
Koidula d.	0609	0712	1350	1503
Orava d.	0619	0722	1400	1513
Põlva d.	0643	0746	1424	1537
Tartu a.	0727	0830	1508	1621
Tallinn § a.	0933	1039	1725	1829

a – Ⓐ only.
c – © only.
△ – See Table **1830**.
☆ – Service Apr. 27 - Sept. 29.
⊖ – Classified *Ekspress* Tallinn - Tartu (higher fares apply).
§ – See panel above. For 🚌 Tallinn - Riga see Table **1800**.

1890 TALLINN - VILJANDI

km											⊖	
0	**Tallinn** d.	0738	0836	1009	1145	1300	1443	1632	1734	1916	2019	2227
54	Rapla d.	0836	0934	1110	1236	1358	1535	1731	1826	2019	2111	2326
98	Türi d.	0915	...	1148	1315	...	1614	1809	1906	2057	2143	0004
151	**Viljandi** a.	0956	...	...	1356	...	1655	...	1947	...	2216	...

				⊖						
Viljandi d.	...	0624	...	0841	1114	...	...	1445	...	1823
Türi d.	0600	0706	0756	0915	1156	1321	...	1527	...	1905
Rapla d.	0639	0745	0836	0947	1236	1400	1500	1607	1830	1944
Tallinn a.	0730	0835	0937	1035	1326	1459	1559	1658	1931	2034

⊖ – Classified *Ekspress* (higher fares).

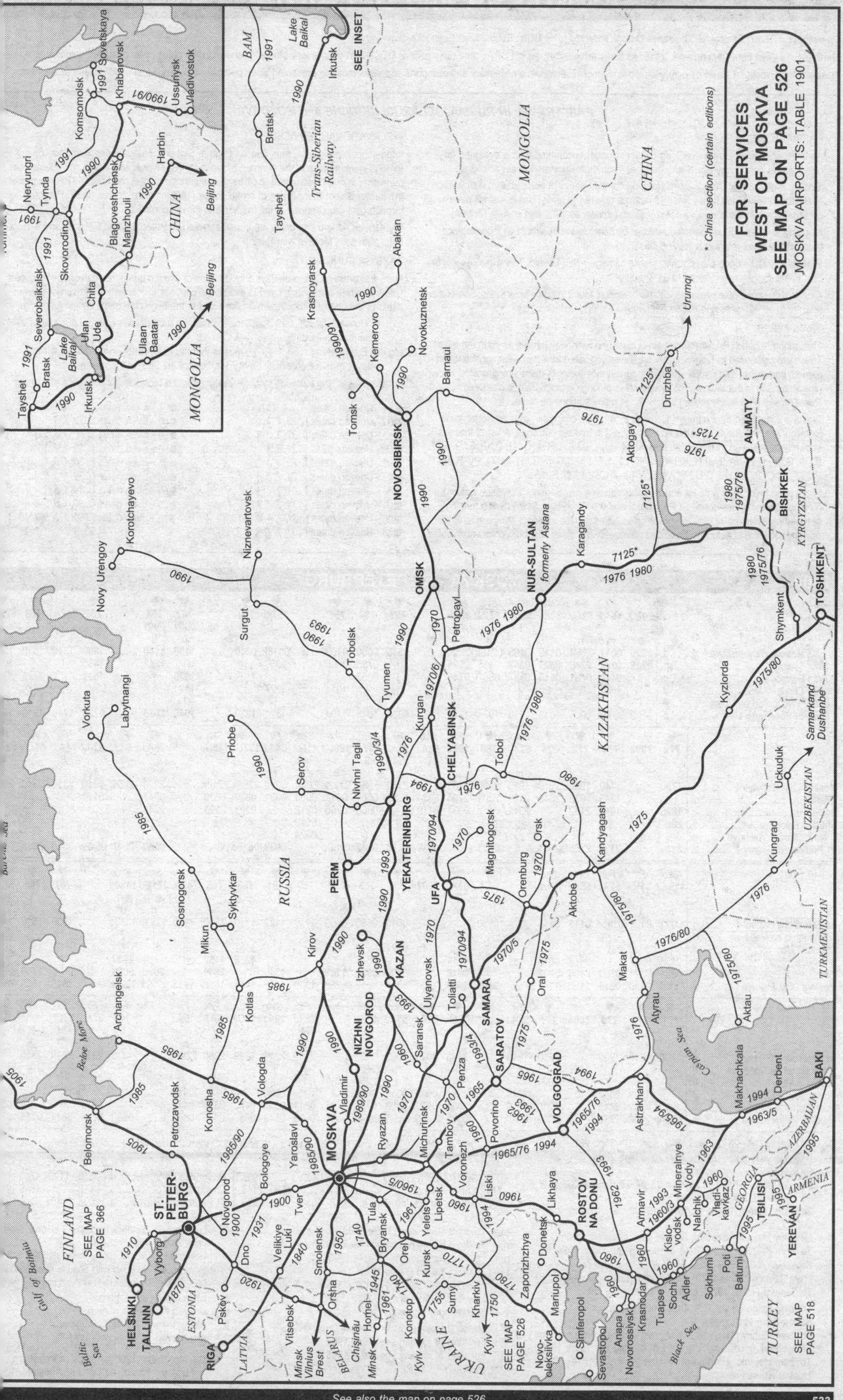
FOR SERVICES
WEST OF MOSKVA
SEE MAP ON PAGE 526
MOSKVA AIRPORTS: TABLE 1901
* China section (certain editions)
SEE INSET
Trans-Siberian Railway
BAM
MONGOLIA
CHINA
RUSSIA
KAZAKHSTAN
UZBEKISTAN
TURKMENISTAN
KYRGYZSTAN
FINLAND
SEE MAP PAGE 366
ESTONIA
LATVIA
BELARUS
UKRAINE
SEE MAP PAGE 526
GEORGIA
ARMENIA
AZERBAIJAN
TURKEY
SEE MAP PAGE 518
Black Sea
Caspian Sea
Baltic Sea
Gulf of Bothnia
Beloe More
Lake Baikal
MOSKVA
ST. PETER-BURG
HELSINKI
TALLINN
RIGA
NIZHNI NOVGOROD
KAZAN
PERM
YEKATERINBURG
UFA
SAMARA
SARATOV
VOLGOGRAD
ROSTOV NA DONU
CHELYABINSK
OMSK
NOVOSIBIRSK
NUR-SULTAN
formerly Astana
ALMATY
BISHKEK
TOSHKENT
TBILISI
YEREVAN
BAKI
Vorkuta
Labytnangi
Novy Urengoy
Korotchayevo
Niznevartovsk
Surgut
Tobolsk
Tyumen
Priobe
Serov
Nivhni Tagil
Kurgan
Petropavl
Sosnogorsk
Syktyvkar
Mikun
Kotlas
Archangelsk
Kirov
Izhevsk
Konosha
Vologda
Belomorsk
Petrozavodsk
Vyborg
Novgorod
Bologoye
Yaroslavl
Tver
Pskov
Dno
Velikiye Luki
Vitsebsk
Smolensk
Orsha
Minsk
Vilnius
Brest
Chişinău
Homel
Bryansk
Tula
Orel
Kursk
Konotop
Kyiv
Sumy
Kharkiv
Yelets
Lipetsk
Voronezh
Liski
Michurinsk
Tambov
Povorino
Ryazan
Vladimir
Penza
Saransk
Ulyanovsk
Toliatti
Oral
Orenburg
Orsk
Magnitogorsk
Aktobe
Kandyagash
Tobol
Karagandy
Aktogay
Druzhba
Urumqi
Barnaul
Tomsk
Kemerovo
Novokuznetsk
Krasnoyarsk
Abakan
Tayshet
Bratsk
Irkutsk
Zaporizhzhya
Donetsk
Mariupol
Novo-oleksiivka
Simferopol
Sevastopol
Likhaya
Anapa
Novorossiysk
Krasnodar
Tuapse
Sochi
Adler
Sokhumi
Poti
Batumi
Armavir
Mineralnye Vody
Kislo-vodsk
Nalchik
Vladi-kavkaz
Astrakhan
Makhachkala
Derbent
Atyrau
Makat
Aktau
Kungrad
Uckuduk
Samarkand
Dushanbe
Kyzlorda
Shymkent
Severobaikalsk
Ulan Ude
Ulaan Baatar
Beijing
Chita
Skovorodino
Tynda
Neryungri
Komsomolsk
Sovetskaya
Khabarovsk
Blagoveshchensk
Manzhouli
Harbin
Ussuriysk
Vladivostok

RUSSIA and BELARUS

SEE MAPS PAGES 526/53

Operators: **RZhD**: Rossiskiye Zheleznye Dorogi, www.rzd.ru **BCh**: Belaruskaya Chyhunka, www.rw.by

Timings: Valid from **December 9, 2018**. All times are now shown in LOCAL time (time zone is UTC+3 all year unless otherwise shown in the notes or by a shaded column).

Tickets: Except for travel by purely local trains, prior reservation is necessary and passports and visas must be presented when purchasing tickets. Most nationalities require visas.

RAIL TRAVEL IN RUSSIA, BELARUS, UKRAINE and MOLDOVA

CARRIAGE TYPES

As trains generally operate over long distances, most accommodation is designed for overnight as well as day use. Carriage types (with their Russian names) are:

Spálny vagón SV or СВ – 2-berth sleeping compartments (9 per carriage) with wash basin, found only in the best trains. Sometimes referred to as 1st class. A small number of named trains also have *de luxe* carriages (also known as *VIP*) with ensuite facilities.

Kupéiny К – 4-berth compartments (9 per carriage) found in almost all long-distance trains. Sometimes referred to as 2nd class.

Platskártny ПЛ – open-plan dormitory-style carriage with 54 bunks, found in all except the best trains. Sometimes referred to as 3rd class.

Óbshchi О – open-plan carriages with hard seating, found in some slow trains. Sometimes referred to as 4th class and not recommended for long-distance travel.

TRAIN TYPES

The top grade of fast long-distance train is classified *Firménny* (shown as *Fir* in the tables). These are composed of higher-quality carriages dedicated to a particular service (often named) and higher fares apply. Normal long-distance express trains are classified *Skóry* (shown as *Sko* in the tables). The lowest class of long-distance train is classified *Passazhírsky* (*Pas* in the tables) which call at many stations en-route.

Trains are identified by a number, followed by a cyrillic character, or a two-letter transliteration which is shown in some tables to assist in making bookings. A list of these is shown here, followed by the cyrillic equivalent: AJ А, BJ Б, CH Ч, CJ Ц, DJ Д, EI Э, EJ Е, FJ Ф, GJ Г, IJ И, JA Я, JI Й, KH Х, KJ К, LJ Л, MJ М, MZ Ь, NJ Н, OJ О, PC П, RJ Р, SH Ш, SJ С, SZ Щ, TJ Т, UJ У, VJ В, Y Ы, ZH Ж, ZJ З.

High-speed train types with 1st and 2nd class seating are *Sapsan* (Peregrine Falcon) running between Moskva and St Peterburg, and the Talgo-built *Strizh* (Swift) running between Moskva and Nizhny Novgorod (also with 1st class sleeping compartments for daytime use). Fast *Lastochka* (Swallow) trains with 2nd class seats run on several routes.

INTERNATIONAL SERVICES

International services to, from and via Poland, Slovakia, Hungary and Romania convey through sleeping cars of the normal European ('RIC') types, with single and double compartments in first class, and 3- or 4-berth compartments in second class. The railways of the former Soviet Union being of broad gauge (1520mm), the bogies (trucks) of these through cars are changed at the frontier with these countries.

High-speed *Allegro* day trains are in use between St Peterburg and Helsinki, and a Talgo hotel train links Moskva with Berlin.

DAYS OF RUNNING

Many trains run on alternate days only, on even or uneven numbered dates. The examples below illustrate the system used to indicate exceptions to the pattern of even or uneven dates at the end of a month with 31 days and at the beginning of the month following:

e.g. "Uneven dates [... *29, 1* ...]" means that the train does not run on the 31st of a month with 31 days.

e.g. "Even dates [... *30, 1, 4* ...]" means that the train, **following a month with 31 days**, runs exceptionally on the 1st, but not the 2nd, of the month.

In these cases, the following symbols are used in the tables to indicate days of running:

■ – Uneven dates.
■(1) – Uneven dates [.. *29, 1* ..]
■(2) – Uneven dates [.. *31, 2, 3* ..]
■(3) – Uneven dates [.. *31, 3* ..]
■(4) – Uneven dates [.. *29, 3* ..]
■(5) – Uneven dates [.. *31, 2, 5* ..]
■(6) – Uneven dates [.. *31, 2, 7* ..]
■(7) – Uneven dates [.. *31, 2, 4, 7* ..]
■(8) – Uneven dates [.. *31, 2, 4, 6, 8, 10, 11* ..]
■(9) – Uneven dates [.. *31, 2, 4, 6, 9* ..]

● – Even dates.
●(2) – Even dates [.. *30, 2* ..]
●(3) – Even dates [.. *30, 1, 3, 8* ..]
●(4) – Even dates [.. *30, 1, 4* ..]
●(5) – Even dates [.. *30, 1, 3, 4* ..]
●(6) – Even dates [.. *30, 1, 3, 6* ..]
●(7) – Even dates [.. *30, 1, 6* ..]
●(8) – Even dates [.. *30, 1, 3, 5, 8* ..]
●(9) – Even dates [.. *30, 1, 3, 5, 7, 10* ..]

1900 MOSKVA - ST PETERBURG RZ

km		Fir	Fir	Sko	Sko	Sko	Sko		♥	♥	♥		♥	♥		♥	♥		♥	♤	♥	♥
		20UJ	16AJ	59GJ	30AJ	162AJ	82VJ	89ZH		752	754	756		757/8	760		762	764		766	748AJ	768	77
						F		▷									⑥⑦	⑥⑦					
		◐	m	n			b							n			u	u					
0	**Moskva** Oktyabrskaya § d.	0020	0041	0044k	0115	0153	0248k	0333k	...	0545	0650	0700	...	0918k	0940	...	1130	1140	...	1330	1340	1530	15
167	Tver d.	0216	0232	0240	0303	0342	0435	0525	...	|	0755	0805	...	1030	|	...	|	1242	...	1435	|	|	16
331	Bologoye d.	|	0440	0431	0448	0537	0607	0749	...	|	0852	|	...	|	1139	...	1323	|	...	1532	|	1723	
532	Chudovo Mos. d.	|	|	|	|	|	|	|	...	|	|	1014	...	1227	|	...	1424	|	...	|	|	1824	
606	Novgorod na Volkhove a.	|	|	|	|	|	|	|	...	|	|	|	...	|	|	...	|	|	...	|	|	|	
650	**St Peterburg** Glavny ‡ a.	0859	0913c	0905	1018	1035	1024	1225	...	0915	1045	1104	...	1320	1330	...	1516	1526	...	1725	1745	1916	19

	♥		♥	♥	♥	Sko	♥	Fir	Sko	Fir	Fir	Sko	Sko	Fir	Sko	Sko		Fir	Fir	Fir	Fir	Fir	F
	772	7003	774	776	778	92AJ	780	18AJ	56AJ	26AJ	107JI	120VJ	41GJ	34AJ	132GJ	146UJ		28AJ	6AJ	32AJ	4AJ	54CH	2
						△		∅	C	M	S		n								E	⊠	
						m		p				b	∅	t	d	d			⊙	h	∅	∅	
Moskva Oktyabrskaya § d.	1730	...	1740	1930	1940	1950	2100	2105	2124	2150	2149k	2142k	2154k	2215	2216k	2216k	...	2228	2250	2310	2330	2340	23
Tver d.	|	...	1845	2035	2045	2139	2201	2256	2334	2353	0001	0018	0009	0031	0039	0039	...	0047	|	0111	|	|	
Bologoye d.	1926	...	1942	2132	|	2342	|	0031	0119	|	0205	0255	0212	|	0223	0223	...	0248	|	|	|	|	
Chudovo Mos. d.	2027	2145	|	|	2257	...	|	...	|	|	|	|	0510	|	|	|	...	|	|	|	|	|	
Novgorod na Volkhove a.	|	2308	|	|	|	...	|	...	|	|	|	|	0624	|	|	|	...	|	|	|	|	|	
St Peterburg Glavny ‡ a.	2116	...	2135	2325	2344	...	0035	...	0519	0606	0532	0730c	...	0539	0616c	0616c	...	0640	0647	0549c	0830	0836	07

	Sko	Fir	Fir	Sko	Sko		♥	Sko		♥	♥	♥	♥	♥	♥	♥	♤	Sko	Sko		♥	♥	F
	119AJ	34VJ	31AJ	55AJ	161AJ		751	91AJ	7002	753	755	757	759	761	763	765	747AJ	131GJ	145AJ		767	769	10
				D	G			△						⑥⑦	⑥⑦		Ⓑ	●(4)	■(2)				■
	b	t	h					m						u	u			d	d				
St Peterburg Glavny ‡ d.	0011	0105	0153c	0115	0145	...	0530	...	...	0640	0650	0900	0910	1100	1110	1300	1310	1333c	1333c	...	1500	1510	14
Novgorod na Volkhove d.	|	|	|	|	|	...	|	...	0610	|	|	|	|	|	|	|	|	|	|	...	|	|	
Chudovo Mos. d.	|	|	|	|	|	...	|	...,	0716	0727	|	|	|	|	1157	|	|	|	|	...	|	1557	
Bologoye d.	0433	0527	|	0648	0633	...	|	0614	...	|	0847	1052	|	|	1258	1452	|	1734	1734	...	|	|	19
Tver d.	0631	0721	0700	0856	0905	...	|	0848	...	0936	0947	1149	|	1340	|	1549	|	2028	2028	...	|	1756	20
Moskva Oktyabrskaya § a.	0943k	0930	0919	1120	1147	...	0900	1036	...	1043	1052	1258	1305	1446	1456	1658	1715	2227k	2227k	...	1845	1859	23

	♥	♥	♥		♥	Fir		♥	Sko	Sko	Sko		Fir	Sko		Fir	Fir		Fir	Fir	Fir	Fir	F
	771	773	775	7004	777	59AJ		779	81AJ	89AJ	42CH		25AJ	29AJ	19UJ	5AJ	15AJ		3AJ	27AJ	53CH	1AJ	17
										▷	n		M						E		⊠	R	
	n					n			b		∅				◐	⊙	m		∅		∅	∅	
St Peterburg Glavny ‡ d.	1700	1710	1900	...	1910	1915	...	2100	2006	2032	...	...	2155	2211	2229	2250	2241c	...	2330	2336	2349	2355	
Novgorod na Volkhove d.	|	|	|	1806	|	|	...	|	|	|	2120	...	|	|	|	|	|	...	|	|	|	|	
Chudovo Mos. d.	|	1757	|	1923	2001	|	...	|	|	|	2254	...	|	|	|	|	|	...	|	|	|	|	
Bologoye d.	|	1903	2052	...	|	2245	...	|	0008	0030	0059	...	|	0209	|	|	0311	...	|	|	|	|	0
Tver d.	1940	|	2149	...	2210	0016	...	2334	0139	0209	0235	...	0341	0355	0402	0433	0444	...	|	0502	|	|	0
Moskva Oktyabrskaya § a.	2054k	2102	2258	...	2313	0210k	...	0035	0327k	0412k	0450k	...	0606	0549	0557	0645	0650	...	0830	0719	0814	0755	0

C – ⑤⑦ (daily Dec. 25 - 29, Jan. 1 - 9, Apr. 26 - Sept. 23).
D – ①⑥ (daily Dec. 25 - Jan. 9, Apr. 26 - Sept. 23).
E – EKSPRESS.
F – Dec. 29, Jan. 3, 4, 6, 7, 9, May 24, 25, 27, 28, June 1 - 3, 5, 7, 9, 10, 12, 14 - 30, July 1 - Aug. 30.
G – Jan. 5, 8, June 8, 10, 12, 14, 15, 17, 19 - 30, July 1 - Aug. 31, Sept. 2, 3.
M – Ⓑ (daily May 26 - Sept. 6). Double deck sleeping cars.
N – To/from Kaliningrad. For days of running see Table **1920**.
R – KRASNAYA STRELA (RED ARROW).
S – From Samara (Table **1970**), depart ■(1), journey 2 nights.
T – To Samara (Table **1970**), journey 2 nights.
b – From/to Belgorod via Tula, Orel (Table **1770**).
c – St Peterburg **Ladozhski**.
d – To/from Nizhny Novgorod, Kirov (then alternate days to/from Chelyabinsk or Izhevsk). For days of running see Table **1990**.
h – To/from Helsinki. For days of running see Table **1910**.
k – Moskva **Kurskaya**.

ST PETERBURG - NOVGOROD NA VOLKHOVE

km			N					N		
0	**St Peterburg** Glavny d.	0726	1226v	...	1932	**Novgorod** na Volkhove d.	0610	1128	1743	1
118	Chudovo Mos. d.	0904	|	1550	2145	Chudovo Mos. a.	0716	|	1856	1
192	**Novgorod** na Volkhove a.	1018	1538	1656	2308	**St Peterburg** Glavny a.	0938	1448v	...	2

m – To/from Murmansk (Table **1905**).
n – To/from Nizhni Novgorod (Table **1990**).
p – To/from Petrozavodsk (Table **1905**).
t – To/from Tallinn (Table **1870**).
u – Also Dec. 28 - Jan. 8, Feb. 22 - 25, Mar. 7, 8, Apr. 30, May 1 - 3, 8 - 10, June 11, 12.
v – St Peterburg **Vitebski**.
♥ – *Sapsan* high-speed train, special fares. ✕ Ⓡ.
△ – For days of running see Table **1905**.
▷ – For days of running see Table **1965**.
♤ – NEVSKIY EKSPRESS. 1st class only.

⊙ – Low-cost double deck train, 🛏 2 cl. only, food drink included in fare.
⊠ – GRAND EXPRESS luxury train (also 🛏 1, 2
∅ – Includes 🛏 de Luxe with ensuite shower/toile
◐ – MEGAPOLIS - operated by Tverskoy Express
● – Even dates (see page 534).
■ – Uneven dates (see page 534).
§ – Also known as *Leningradski vokzal.*
‡ – Also known as *Moskovski vokzal.*

See also Table **1960** for trains St Peterburg - Moskva - Rostov na Donu and beyond.

MOSKVA AIRPORTS ✈ 1901

MOSKVA DOMODEDOVO AIRPORT ✈
Aeroexpress rail service Moskva Paveletskaya - Moskva Domodedovo ✈. *35 km* Journey time 47 minutes.
From **Moskva Paveletskaya**: 0530, 0600 and every 30 minutes (not 1230 on Ⓐ) until 2330, 0000, 0030.
From **Domodedovo ✈**: 0515, 0600, 0630 and every 30 minutes (not 1230 on Ⓐ) until 2330, 0000.

MOSKVA SHEREMETYEVO AIRPORT ✈
Aeroexpress rail service Moskva Belorusskaya - Moskva Sheremetyevo ✈. *35 km* Journey time 35 minutes.
From **Moskva Belorusskaya**: 0530, 0600 and every 30 minutes until 2330, 0000, 0030.
From **Sheremetyevo ✈**: 0500, 0600, 0630 and every 30 minutes until 2330, 0000, 0030.

MOSKVA VNUKOVO AIRPORT ✈
Aeroexpress rail service Moskva Kiyevskaya - Moskva Vnukovo ✈. *28 km* Journey time 35 - 40 minutes.
From **Moskva Kiyevskaya**: 0600 and hourly (also 1530, 1730, 1930) until 2300, 0000.
From **Vnukovo ✈**: 0600 and hourly (also 0938, 1630, 1830) until 2300, 0000.

(MOSKVA) - ST PETERBURG - PETROZAVODSK - MURMANSK 1905

ZhD

km		Fir 18AJ ∅	Sko 92AJ E	❦ 804CH	Fir 16AJ	❦ 806CH	Sko 22CH	Sko 12AJ G	
	Moskva Oktyabrskaya 1900 d.	2105	1950	...	0041	...	...	...	...
0	**St Peterburg** Ladozhski d.	|	|	0632	0950	1800	2121	2320	...
14	Volkhovstroi 1 d.	0428v	0415v	0817	1157	1925	2311	0131	...
94	**Petrozavodsk** d.	0855	0943	1150	1714	2257	0325	0650	...
73	Belomorsk d.	...	1844	...	2347	...	0954	...	...
51	Kandalaksha d.	...	0250	...	0633	...	1648	...	...
38	**Murmansk** a.	...	0903	...	1144	...	2150	...	...

	Sko 21CH	❦ 803CH	Fir 15AJ	❦ 805CH	Fir 17AJ ∅	Sko 91AJ F	Sko 11AJ G	
Murmansk d.	0952	...	1930	...	...	2110	...	...
Kandalaksha d.	1459	...	0122	...	...	0340	...	...
Belomorsk d.	2136	...	0800	...	...	1128	...	...
Petrozavodsk d.	0406	0636	1520	1800	2100	2110	2240	...
Volkhovstroi 1 d.	0805	1011	2017	2134	0128v	0142v	0428	...
St Peterburg Ladozhski a.	1010	1200	2216	2256	|	|	0624	...
Moskva Oktyabrskaya 1900 a.	...	...	0650	...	0853	1036	...	...

②③④⑤⑦ (daily Dec. 18 - Jan. 11, Apr. 23 - Sept. 1).
②④⑤⑥⑦ (daily Dec. 20 - Jan. 13, Apr. 25 - Sept. 8).
G – Ⓑ (daily May 2 - Sept. 6).
v – Volkhovstroi 2.
❦ – *Lastochka* (Swallow) fast day train.
* – Moskva - Vokhovstroi: *641 km.*
∅ – Includes 🛏 de Luxe with ensuite shower/toilet.

MOSKVA - ST PETERBURG - HELSINKI 1910

ZhD, VR

km		SUMMER 781 AE30 A ☆	Fir 32AJ Lb ☆	783 AE34 A ☆	785 AE36 A ☆	787 AE38 A ☆	WINTER 781 AE30 A ★	Fir 32AJ Lb ★	783 AE34 A ★	785 AE36 A ★	787 AE38 A ★
	Moskva Okt. § d.	...	2310	...	...	...	...	2310	...	...	...
	Tver d.	...	0111	...	...	...	...	0111	...	...	...
*	**St Peterburg** Lad. ‡ d.	...	0601	...	...	...	...	0601	...	...	...
0	**St Peterburg** Fin. ‡ d.	0640	|	1130	1530	2030	0640	|	1130	1530	2030
9	Vyborg a.	0735	0754	1225	1625	2125	0735	0754	1225	1625	2125
9	Vyborg 🏛 RU d.	0745	0834	1235	1635	2135	0745	0834	1235	1635	2135
9	Vainikkala 🏛 FIN a.	0807	0914	1257	1657	2157	0707	0814	1157	1557	2057
9	Vainikkala d.	0814	1014	1304	1704	2204	0714	0914	1204	1604	2104
2	**Kouvola** 797 a.	0853	1108	1343	1743	2243	0753	1009	1243	1643	2143
2	Lahti 797 a.	0919	1153	1409	1809	2309	0819	1049	1309	1709	2209
0	Tikkurila 797 a.	0953	1245	1443	1843	2343	0853	1145	1343	1743	2243
3	Pasila 797 a.	|	1323	|	|	|	|	1223	|	|	|
5	**Helsinki** 797 a.	1007	1330	1457	1857	2357	0907	1230	1357	1757	2257

	SUMMER AE33 782 A ☆	AE35 784 A ☆	AE37 786 A ☆	Fir 31AJ Lb ☆	AE39 788 A ☆	WINTER AE33 782 A ★	AE35 784 A ★	AE37 786 A ★	Fir 31AJ Lb ★	AE39 788 A ★
Helsinki 797 d.	0720	1100	1600	1844	2000	0620	1000	1500	1744	1900
Pasila 797 d.	|	|	|	1850	|	|	|	|	1750	|
Tikkurila 797 d.	0733	1113	1613	1901	2013	0633	1013	1513	1801	1913
Lahti 797 d.	0807	1147	1647	1954	2047	0707	1047	1547	1853	1947
Kouvola 797 d.	0833	1213	1713	2034	2113	0733	1113	1613	1934	2013
Vainikkala a.	0913	1253	1753	2130	2153	0813	1153	1653	2030	2053
Vainikkala 🏛 FIN d.	0920	1300	1800	2215	2200	0820	1200	1700	2115	2100
Vyborg 🏛 RU a.	0941	1321	1821	2256	2221	0941	1321	1821	2256	2221
Vyborg d.	0946	1326	1826	2336	2226	0946	1326	1826	2336	2226
St Peterburg Fin. ‡ a.	1047	1427	1927	|	2327	1047	1427	1927	|	2327
St Peterburg Lad. ‡ a.	...	...	...	0118	...	...	...	...	0118	...
Tver a.	...	...	...	0659	...	...	...	...	0659	...
Moskva Okt. § a.	...	...	...	0919	...	...	...	...	0919	...

Allegro (12) ✕ Ⓡ St Peterburg - Helsinki and v.v. International journeys only.
LEV TOLSTOI – 🛏 1 cl. (ensuite), 🛏 1, 2 cl., ✕. Not for domestic journeys within Finland.
b – Ⓑ (daily Dec. 16 - 30, Jan. 1 - 11, Apr. 21 - May 17, May 26 - Sept. 6), also Mar. 9; not Dec. 31, Mar. 8.
☆ – Mar. 31 - Oct. 26 (summer time in Finland).
★ – Oct. 27 - Dec. 14 (provisional times).
§ – Moskva Oktyabrskaya, also known as Leningradski.
‡ – Lad. = Ladozhski; Fin. = Finlyandski.
** – *143 km* St Peterburg Ladozhski - Vyborg.
FIN – Finland (UTC + 2 in winter, UTC + 3 in summer).
RU – Russia (Moskva Time UTC + 3).

ST PETERBURG - HOMEL and KOZYATYN 1920

ZhD, BCh, UZ

	Sko 249BJ A	Sko 79CH K	Fir 53AJ ● ♡	Sko 83AJ	Sko 83AJ ■(4)	Fir 55BJ ◇	Fir 51BJ	Sko 61MZ ■(4) ★	Sko 61MZ ■(4) ☆
St Peterburg Vitebski d.	1426	1226	1610	1720	1720	...	1823	2040	2040
Novgorod na Volkhove d.	|	1625	|	|	|	...	|	|	|
Dno d.	1820	1911	1946	2057	2057	...	2149	0004	0004
Novosokolniki RU d.	2120	2213	2239	0003	0003	...	0033	0321	0321
Vitsebsk ⊖ BY d.	0010	0054	0100	0230	0230	...	0314	0534	0534
Polatsk d.	|	0242	|	|	|	...	|	|	|
Maladzechnia a.	|	0519	|	|	|	...	|	|	|
Moskva Bel. 1950 d.	|	▽	|	|	|	2122	|	|	|
Orsha Tsentralnaya a.	0138	...	0214	0344	0344	0344	0426	0651	0651
Orsha Tsentralnaya 1950 d.	0204	...	0236	0406	0412	0416	0448	0714	0714
Minsk 1950 a.	0532	...	|	|	0633	|	0725	|	|
Hrodna 1952 a.	...	...	|	|	1148	|	|	|	|
Brest Tsent. 1950 a.	...	...	|	|	...	|	1156	|	|
Mahilyow 1 d.	...	...	0356	0544	...	0616	...	0840	0840
Zhlobin 1930 d.	...	...	0610	0738	...	0823	...	1100	1100
Homel 1930 a.	...	...	0736	0858	...	0942	...	|	|
Kyiv 1930 a.	...	...	1358r	...	...	...	...	|	|
Kalinkavichy BY d.	...	...	...	...	...	...	...	1242	1242
Korosten ⊡ UA d.	...	...	...	...	...	...	...	1546	1645
Zhytomyr d.	...	...	...	...	...	...	...	1729	1837
Kozyatyn 1 a.	...	...	...	...	...	...	...	1901	2003
Chișinău 1720 a.	...	...	...	...	...	...	...	0754	0900

	Fir 52BJ	Sko 250BJ B	Sko 83BJ	Sko 80CH K	Fir 55MZ ◇	674BJ 8BJ ● ‡	Sko 61SZ ■§ ★	Sko 61SZ ■§ ☆	Sko 54KJ ■(1) ♡
Chișinău 1720 d.	...	...	...	...	...	...	2205	2230	...
Kozyatyn 1 d.	...	...	...	...	...	...	1052	1153	...
Zhytomyr d.	...	...	...	...	...	...	1220	1320	...
Korosten UA d.	...	...	...	...	...	...	1402	1504	...
Kalinkavichy ⊡ BY d.	...	...	...	...	...	...	1906	1906	...
Kyiv 1930 d.	...	...	...	...	...	...	|	|	1351s
Homel 1930 d.	...	...	1716	...	1823	...	|	|	2039
Zhlobin 1930 d.	...	...	1834	...	1953	...	2104	2104	2210
Mahilyow 1 d.	...	...	2140	...	2220	...	2306	2306	0039
Brest Tsent. 1950 d.	1410	...	|	...	|	...	|	|	|
Hrodna 1952 d.	|	...	|	...	|	1533	|	|	|
Minsk 1950 d.	1845	1822	|	...	|	2130	|	|	|
Orsha Tsentralnaya 1950 a.	2117	2136	2250	...	2337	2355	0026	0026	0151
Orsha Tsentralnaya d.	2140	2200	2312	...	2359	0050	0050	0050	0213
Moskva Bel. 1950 a.	|	|	|	▽	0653	|	|	|	|
Maladzechnia d.	|	|	|	2036	...	|	|	|	|
Polatsk d.	|	|	|	2356	...	|	|	|	|
Vitsebsk BY d.	2302	2333	0043	0157	...	0221	0221	0221	0341
Novosokolniki ⊖ RU d.	0157	0257	0335	0449	...	0531	0531	0531	0628
Dno d.	0419	0536	0606	0733	...	0813	0813	0813	0902
Novgorod na Volkhove a.	|	|	|	1027	...	|	|	|	|
St Peterburg Vitebski a.	0755	0916	0930	1448	...	1144	1144	1144	1221

Dec. 21 - Jan. 15, Feb. 22 - 25, Mar. 7 - 12, Mar. 22 - Apr. 1, Apr. 26 - May 13, May 31 - Sept. 2, Oct. 25 - Nov. 11.
Dec. 20 - Jan. 14, Feb. 21 - 24, Mar. 6 - 11, Mar. 21 - 31, Apr. 25 - May 12, May 30 - Sept. 1, Oct. 24 - Nov. 10.
For days of running see Table **1950**.
Arrive 1257 Oct. 27 - Dec. 14 (provisional time).
Depart 1245 Oct. 27 - Dec. 14 (provisional time).
☆ – Mar. 31 - Oct. 26 (summer time in Ukraine / Moldova).
★ – Oct. 27 - Dec. 14 (provisional times).
▽ – To / from Vilnius and Kaliningrad (Table **1950**).
♡ – For St Peterburg - Kharkiv portion see Tables **1930** / **1755**.
◇ – For Moskva - Homel via Bryansk see Table **1945**.
● – Even dates (see page 534).
■ – Uneven dates (see page 534).
⊖ – 🏛 : Yezyaryshcha (BY) / Zaverezhye (RU).
⊡ – 🏛 : Slovechno (BY) / Berezhest (UA).
‡ – Even dates [.. *28*, *2*..]
§ – ■ [.. *27*, *1*..] (see page 534).
BY – Belarus (UTC + 3)
RU – Russia (Moskva Time UTC + 3).
UA – Ukraine (UTC + 2 winter, UTC + 3 summer).

MINSK - HOMEL - KYIV 1930

BCh, UZ

	716	Sko 100FJ K	Sko 94BJ E	718 Ⓑ	648	708	Fir 86BJ	632	Fir 53AJ ●	53AJ 143 ●
St P'burg Vit. 1920 d.	...	...	...	...	...	...	...	...	1610	1610
Minsk d.	0708	0744	1413	1457	1627	1900	2240	2356	|	|
Babruysk d.	0838	0953	1654	1634	1827	|	0036	0206	|	|
Zhlobin 1920 d.	0921	1106	1746	1716	1923	|	0128	0326	0610	0610
Homel 1920 a.	1021	1222	1859	1814	2042	2154	0245	0754	0736	0736
Homel BY d.	...	1250	1926	...	...	...	0309	...	0759	0759
Chernihiv § UA d.	...	|	2319r	...	...	...	|	...	1109r	1109r
Kyiv a.	...	|	0155r	...	...	...	0859r	...	1358r	
Kharkiv 1755 a.	...	0124r	...	...	...	...	...	...	...	2054r
Odesa 1720 a.	...	▽	1215r	...	...	...	...	...	...	...

	647	707	Sko 94SH F	715	Sko 100DJ L	Fir 54KJ ■(1)	143 54KJ ■(1)	621	Fir 86KJ ⊕
Odesa 1720 d.	...	...	1540r	...	▽	...	...	...	...
Kharkiv 1755 d.	...	...	|	...	0617r	...	0645r	...	...
Kyiv d.	...	...	0203r	...	|	1351r	|	...	2237r
Chernihiv § UA d.	...	...	0506r	...	|	1737r	1737r	...	|
Homel BY a.	...	...	0843	...	1832	2014	2014	...	0416
Homel 1920 d.	0630	0700	0906	1905	1915	2039	2039	2206	0448
Zhlobin 1920 d.	0756	...	1023	2001	2110	2210	2210	0226	0556
Babruysk d.	0858	...	1127	2046	2202	|	|	0330	0653
Minsk a.	1057	0954	1344	2219	2350	|	|	0548	0838
St P'burg Vit. 1920 a.	...	...	...	...	...	1221	1221	...	...

②⑤ (daily June 1 - Sept. 19).
③⑥ (daily June 2 - Sept. 20).
Even dates (daily June 1 - Sept. 21).
Even dates ●(4) (daily June 3 - Sept. 23).
r – Approximately one hour earlier from Oct. 27 (winter time in Ukraine).
● – Even dates (see page 534).
■ – Uneven dates (see page 534).
▽ – To / from Zaporizhzhya or Novooleksiivka (Table **1780**).
⊕ – Board train at Kyiv by 2212r for customs.
§ – 🏛 : Teryukha (BY) / Hornostayivka (UA).
BY – Belarus (UTC + 3).
UA – Ukraine (UTC + 2 winter, UTC + 3 summer).

1931 MOSKVA - PSKOV

km		Fir 10AJ		Fir 10CH
0	**Moskva** Okt. ▷ d.	2023	**Pskov** d.	1930
167	Tver ▷ d.	2238	Dno d.	2118
331	Bologoye ▷ d.	0100	Bologoye ▷ d.	0224
588	Dno d.	0624	Tver ▷ d.	0410
687	**Pskov** a.	0805	**Moskva** Okt. ▷ a.	0614

▷ – See also Table **1900**.

1935 MOSKVA - POLATSK

km		Fir 39SZ		Fir 39BJ
0	**Moskva** Bel. d.	2337	**Polatsk** BY d.	2016
243	Vyazma d.	0301	Vitsebsk ‡ RU d.	2218
419	Smolensk d.	0552	Smolensk d.	0106
560	Vitsebsk ‡ RU d.	0818	Vyazma d.	0346
662	**Polatsk** BY a.	0951	**Moskva** Bel. a.	0642

‡ – 🏛: Rudnya (RU) / Zavolsha (BY)
BY Belarus (UTC+3). RU Russia (UTC+3).

1945 MOSKVA - HOMEL

km		Sko 75BJ ▽		Sk 76 ▽
0	**Moskva** Bel. d.	1525	**Homel** d.	20
485	Bryansk Orlov d.	2359	Dobrush BY d.	20
713	Zlynka RU d.	0407	Zlynka RU d.	21
739	Dobrush BY d.	0433	Bryansk Orlov d.	03
764	**Homel** a.	0501	**Moskva** Bel. a.	11

▽ – Conveys portion to / from Brest (Table **1955**).
BY RU see Table **1935**. For train via Orsha see Table 19

1950 MOSKVA - MINSK - VILNIUS, KALININGRAD and BREST

RZhD, BCh, L

km		❦ 727BJ ☆	❦ 727BJ ★	Pas 803BJ	Pas 607BJ	❦ 725BJ	❦ 729	Sko 25BJ	13MJ ☆ B	13MJ ★ B	❦ 731	❦ 701BJ	Pas 360SJ D	❦ 733	Sko 9SZ ☆ P	Sko 9SZ ★ P	Sko 27BJ	Fir 29CH	❦ 735	Sko 21EJ ☆ ①V	Sko 21EJ ★ ①V	Sko 23JI ☆ ②T	Sko 23JI ★ ②T	Sko 17BJ ☆ ④N	Sk 17 ★ ④
0	**Moskva** Belorusskaya d.	...	...	...	...	...	0710	0945	1017	1155	1138	...	...	1340	1421	1551	1459	1724	1820	1814	1912	1814	1912	1814	19
243	Vyazma d.	...	...	...	...	...	0924	1311	|	|	1352	...	...	1554	1735	1835	1804	2036	2104	2129	2219	2129	2219	2129	22
419	**Smolensk** RU d.	...	...	...	...	...	1106	1505	1440	1544	1534	...	1700	1736	1920	2020	1956	2232	2245	2311	0009	2311	0009	2311	00
	St Peterburg Vit. ◐ d.	...	...	...	...	...	...	|	|	|	▬	...	|	...	|	|	|	|	...	|	|	|	|	|	|
538	Orsha Tsent. BY a.	...	...	...	...	...	...	1628	1548	1651	...	...	1822	...	2031	2131	2106	2351	...	0021	0120	0021	0120	0021	01
538	Orsha Tsent. **1920** d.	...	...	...	...	...	...	1645	1603	1706	**807**	...	1839	...	2047	2147	2123	0015	...	0038	0137	0038	0137	0038	01
750	**Minsk** **1920** a.	...	...	...	...	...	...	1943	1811	1914		...	2127	...	2309	0013	2353	0245	...	0259	0400	0259	0400	0259	04
750	**Minsk** d.	0950	1057	1030	1330	1523	...	...	1824	1927	1930	1937	2150	...	2343	0043	0026	0259	...	0312	0414	0312	0414	0312	04
827	Maladzechna BY d.	|	|	1125	|	|	...	...	|	|	2021	|	2255	...	|	|	|	0400	...	|	|	|	|	|	
943	**Vilnius** LT a.	|	|	1230r	|	|	...	...	|	|	2103r	|	0133r	...	|	|	|	0624r	...	|	|	|	|	|	
943	**Vilnius** LT d.	|	|	...	|	|	...	...	|	|	...	|	0138r	...	|	|	|	0629r	...	|	|	|	|	|	
1285	**Kaliningrad** Ka a.	|	|	...	|	|	...	...	|	|	...	|	0808	...	|	|	|	1233	...	|	|	|	|	|	
892	Baranavichy Tsent. d.	1123	1233	...	1524	|	...	...	|	|	...	2108	...	...	0121	0221	0245	...	...	0451	0555	0451	0555	0451	05
1094	**Brest** Tsentralny a.	1338	1431	...	1801	1833	...	...	2133	2235	...	2304	...	...	0310	0410	0540	...	...	0642	0810	0642	0810	0642	08
	Warszawa Wsch. **1050** a.	*1724c*	*1724c*	...	...	...	...	...	2349	2349	...	...	...	...	0755c	0755c	...	...	...	1150	1150	1150	1150	1150	11

	Sko 79CH ■(3) ⊕	Fir 55BJ	Sko 3BJ ♤	Pas 805BJ	Fir 51BJ	Sko 95BJ	Fir 1BJ	Sko 147CH F	Sko 131BJ Y	
Moskva Belorusskaya d.	...	2122	2203	...	...	2028	2211	2310	2330	...
Vyazma d.	...	0027	0105	...	...	0003	0124	0225	0242	...
Smolensk RU d.	...	0228	|	...	...	0258	0320	0425	0443	...
St Peterburg Vit ◐ d.	1226	|	|	...	1823	|	|	|	|	...
Orsha Tsent. BY a.	|	0344	0355	...	0426	0415	0439	0544	0611	...
Orsha Tsent. **1920** d.	⊡	0416	0412	...	0448	0432	0456	0601	0633	...
Minsk **1920** a.	|	△	0633	...	0725	0754	0734	0836	0921	...
Minsk d.	|	...	0651	0735	0755	0807	...	0858	0936	...
Maladzechna BY d.	0542	...	|	0827	|	|	...	1003	|	...
Vilnius LT a.	0823r	...	|	0918r	|	|	...	1217r	|	...
Vilnius LT d.	0829r	...	|	...	|	|	...	1222r	|	...
Kaliningrad Ka a.	1507	...	|	...	|	|	...	1839	|	...
Baranavichy Tsent d.	...	...	0836	...	0935	1041p	...	...	1125	...
Brest Tsentralny a.	...	...	1041	...	1156	1329	...	...	1352	...
Warszawa Wsch. **1050** a.	...	...	...	...	...	...	...	...	...	...

	Sko 132BJ Y	❦ 702BJ	Pas 804TJ	Pas 608BJ	❦ 716 Z	14MJ ☆ B	14MJ ★ B	❦ 736	Fir 52BJ
Warszawa Wsch. **1050** d.	...	...	...	...	...	0320	0320	...	...
Brest Tsentralny d.	0428	0620	...	0628	...	0753	0845	...	1410
Baranavichy Tsent. d.	0700	|	...	0908	...	|	|	...	1640
Kaliningrad Ka d.	|	|	...	|	...	|	|	...	|
Vilnius LT a.	|	|	...	|	...	|	|	...	|
Vilnius LT d.	|	|	0615r	|	...	|	|	...	|
Maladzechna d.	|	|	0900	|	...	|	|	...	|
Minsk a.	0855	0930	0953	1052	...	1113	1213	...	1823
Minsk **1920** d.	0923	...	...	...	...	1127	1227	...	1845
Orsha Tsent. **1920** a.	1234	...	...	...	...	1349	1449	...	2117
Orsha Tsent. BY d.	1252	...	...	...	...	1404	1504	...	2140
St Peterburg Vit. ◐ a.	|	...	...	...	...	|	|	...	0755
Smolensk RU d.	1433	...	...	...	1607	1518	1618	1932	...
Vyazma d.	1708	...	...	...	1755	|	|	2120	...
Moskva Belorusskaya a.	2003	...	...	...	2008	1943	2008	2333	...

	❦ 728BJ ☆	❦ 728BJ ★	Pas 808TJ	Sko 26BJ	Sko 80CH ■ ⊕	Fir 55MZ	Sko 8BJ ♡	Pas 806TJ	Fir 2BJ	❦ 726BJ	Sko 28BJ	Fir 30CH	Sko 18BJ ☆ ①M	Sko 18BJ ★ ①M	Sko 22AJ ☆ ③W	Sko 22AJ ★ ③W	Sko 24JI ☆ ⑤U	Sko 24JI ★ ⑤U	❦ 730	Sko 10SZ ☆ P	Sko 10SZ ★ P	Sko 148CH G	Sko 96BJ	Pas 360CH ● E	❦ 7
Warszawa Wsch. **1050** d.	*0835c*	*0835c*	...	...	...	...	...	...	...	...	...	...	1536	1536	1536	1536	1536	1536	...	1605c	1605c	...	...	...	
Brest Tsentralny d.	1423	1515	...	...	...	...	1730	...	...	1858	1925	...	2223	2323	2223	2323	2223	2323	...	2338	0038	...	2353	...	
Baranavichy Tsent. d.	1635	1716	...	...	...	...	1930	...	...	2100	2157	...	0025	0125	0025	0125	0025	0125	...	0139	0239	...	0315p	...	
Kaliningrad Ka d.	|	|	...	...	0913	...	|	...	...	|	|	1303	|	|	|	|	|	|	...	|	|	1603	|	1807	
Vilnius LT a.	|	|	...	...	1533r	...	|	...	...	|	|	1853r	|	|	|	|	|	|	...	|	|	2224r	|	0026r	
Vilnius LT d.	|	|	1505r	...	1538r	...	|	1830r	...	|	|	1858r	|	|	|	|	|	|	...	|	|	2229r	|	0031r	
Maladzechna d.	|	|	1806	...	2036	...	|	2111	...	|	|	2320	|	|	|	|	|	|	...	|	|	0302	|	0504	
Minsk a.	1805	1846	1900	...	|	...	2110	2200	...	2230	2331	0023	0205	0304	0205	0304	0205	0304	...	0311	0411	0408	0516	0610	
Minsk **1920** d.	...	...	...	1924	|	△	2130	...	2208	...	0001	0036	0219	0318	0219	0318	0219	0318	...	0341	0441	0432	0540	0634	
Orsha Tsent. **1920** a.	...	...	...	2208	⊡	2337	2355	...	0026	...	0226	0255	0436	0536	0436	0536	0436	0536	...	0603	0704	0723	0817	0928	
Orsha Tsent. BY d.	...	...	...	2225	|	2359	0011	...	0041	...	0243	0319	0453	0553	0453	0553	0453	0553	...	0620	0720	0740	0831	0943	
St Peterburg Vit. ◐ a.	...	...	...	|	1448	|	|	...	|	...	|	|	|	|	|	|	|	|	...	|	|	|	|	|	
Smolensk RU d.	...	...	...	2352	...	0138	|	...	0203	...	0407	0438	0616	0716	0616	0716	0616	0716	0749	0739	0839	0909	1017	1059	13
Vyazma d.	...	...	...	0219	...	0409	0357	...	0433	...	0632	0621	0822	0922	0822	0922	0822	0922	0938	0946	1046	1210	1304	...	14
Moskva Belorusskaya a.	...	...	...	0529	...	0653	0647	...	0807	...	0914	0909	1058	1145	1058	1145	1058	1145	1150	1225	1311	1530	1617	...	17

B – ⑤⑦ from Moskva; ①⑥ from Berlin. 🛏 1 cl (lux), 🛏 1, 2 cl., 🚃 Moskva - Warszawa - Berlin and v.v. (Table **56**). *Strizh* (Swift) Talgo train.
D – Alternate days. From Adler ■(5) via Sochi and Rostov (Table **1960**). Via Bryansk Orl d. 1119. Depart Smolensk on 3rd day.
E – To Adler via Rostov, Sochi (Table **1960**) arrive 4th day. Via Bryansk Orl d. 1649.
F – Dec. 28 - 30, Jan. 1 - 4, 6 - 9, Mar. 7, 11, Apr. 29, 30, May 5, 8, 12, 13, 24, 27; ①②⑤ May 31 - Aug. 30 (also Sept. 3, 7).
G – Dec. 27 - 31, Jan. 1 - 4, 6 - 8, Mar. 6, 10, Apr. 28, 29, May 4, 5, 11, 12, 23, 26; ①④⑦ May 30 - Sept. 1 (also Sept. 5, 8, Oct. 31, Nov. 4).
M – ⑦ from Nice, arrive Moskva ②. 🛏 1 cl (lux), 🛏 1, 2 cl. Nice - Milano - Katowice - Warszawa - Moskva (Table **25**); ✕ Brest - Moskva.
N – ④ from Moskva, arrive Nice ⑥. 🛏 1 cl (lux), 🛏 1, 2 cl. Moskva - Warszawa - Katowice - Milano - Nice (Table **25**); ✕ Moskva - Brest.
P – POLONEZ – ①③⑤ from Moskva; ②④⑥ from Warszawa. 🛏 1, 2 cl., 🍷 Moskva - Warszawa and v.v. (Table **95**); ✕ Moskva - Brest and v.v.
T – ② from Moskva, arrive Paris ④. 🛏 1, 2 cl. Moskva (**23**) - Brest (**452**) - Berlin - Paris (Table **24**); ✕ Moskva - Brest.
U – ④ from Paris, arrive Moskva ⑥. 🛏 1, 2 cl. Paris (**453**) - Berlin - Brest (**24**) - Moskva (Table **24**); ✕ Brest - Moskva.
V – VLTAVA – ① from Moskva, arrive Praha ②. 🛏 1, 2 cl. Moskva (**21** / **404**) - Warszawa - Katowice - Bohumín (**112**) - Praha (Table **95**); ✕ Moskva - Brest.
W – VLTAVA – ③ from Praha, arrive Moskva ④. 🛏 1, 2 cl. Praha (**113**) - Bohumín (**405** / **22**) - Katowice - Warszawa - Moskva (Table **95**); ✕ Brest - Moskva.

Y – Dec. 22 - Jan. 14, Feb. 22 - 25, Mar. 7 - 11, Mar. 22 - Apr. 1, Apr. 26 - May 13, May 31 - Sept. 1, Oct. 25 - Nov. 11.
Z – ①③④⑤⑥.

c – Warszawa **Centralna**.
p – Baranavichy Polesskiye.
r – One hour later Mar. 31 - Oct. 26 (summer time in Lithuania).

☆ – Mar. 31 - Oct. 26 (summer time in Lithuania / Poland).
★ – Oct. 27 - Dec. 14 (provisional times).
△ – To / from Homel (Table **1920**).
⊡ – Via Novgorod na Volkhove, Vitsebsk (Table **1920**).
♤ – Not 31st of month. Train *7MJ* on uneven dates.
♡ – Not 31st of month. Train *4BJ* on uneven dates.
⊕ – Days of running may vary at certain times.
❦ – Fast day train.
◐ – See Table **1920**.
● – Even dates (see page 534).
■ – Uneven dates (see page 534).

BY – Belarus (UTC+3).
Ka – Kaliningrad region of Russia (UTC+2). Local time.
LT – Lithuania (UTC+2 in winter, UTC+3 in summer).
RU – Russia (Moskva Time UTC+3

BORDER CROSSINGS

Between Smolensk and Orsha: Krasnoye (RU) / Osinovka (BY).
Between Maladzechna and Vilnius: Hudahai (BY) / Kena (LT).
Between Vilnius and Kaliningrad: Kybartai (LT) / Nesterov (Ka).

OTHER NAMED TRAINS

1/2 BELORUSSIYA / BELARU
3/4 MINSK
7/8 SLAVYANSKI EKSPRESS
29/30 YANTAR

1952 MINSK - HRODNA

BCh

km		673BJ S	731FJ	629BJ	631BJ		732FJ	674BJ S	634BJ	628BJ
0	**Minsk** d.	0702	1530	1709	2314	**Hrodna** d.	0639	1533	1645	2347
77	Maladzechna d.	0813	1630	1816	|	Baranavichy Pol. d.	|	|	|	0520
205	Lida d.	1003	1807	2018	|	Lida d.	0811	1718	1901	|
141	Baranavichy Pol. d.	|	|	|	0157	Maladzechna d.	0946	1859	2118	|
*337	**Hrodna** a.	1148	1938	2208	0637	**Minsk** a.	1042	2002	2233	0728

S – Daily. Conveys St Peterburg - Minsk - Hrodna and v.v. alternate days (see Table **1920**).
* – *361 km via Baranavichy.*

1955 HOMEL - BREST

B

km		675FJ	603BJ		676FJ	6
	Moskva Bel. d.	1524r	...	**Brest** Tsentralny d.	1018	1
0	**Homel** d.	0815	2011	Luninets d.	1430	0
128	Kalinkavichy d.	1023	2244	Kalinkavichy d.	1733	0
305	Luninets d.	1311	0154	**Homel** a.	1934	0
533	**Brest** Tsentralny a.	1650	0557	*Moskva Bel.* a.	1140r	

r – Train **75/76** (Table **1945**).

MOSKVA - VORONEZH - ROSTOV NA DONU - SOCHI - ADLER 1960

km	Time zone: UTC+3	87GJ Fir E	49AJ Sko L	35AJ Fir ◇ Q	302BJ Pas y	37AJ Sko G	740ZH ⊙	4MJ Fir	121AJ Sko m	115AJ Sko J	12MJ Fir ∅	104VJ Fir ◇	102MJ Fir ∅ C	30SJ Fir ∅	738ZH ⊙	20SJ Fir ∅	140NJ Sko U	360CH Pas ●	306MJ Pas S‡	34SJ Sko	146EI Fir ● ∅	25JA Fir	77CH Sko ◧	62CH Sko
	St Peterburg Glavny .. d.	...	1332	2013	...	2000	...	...	1632	2033x	...	...	...	...	...	...	...	...	...	...	...	...	...	...
	Bologoye .... d.	...	1719	0015	...	0022	...	...	2212	0037	...	...	...	...	...	...	...	...	...	...	...	...	...	...
	Tver .... d.	g	1902	0147	...	0202	...	...	0112	0218	...	...	...	...	...	...	...	...	...	...	...	...	...	...
0	**Moskva** Kazanskaya ...... d.	|	2152k	|	...	|	0814	0822	0329k	0433k	1042	1052	1410	1420	1652	1842	...	...	1950	2150	2318	2104p	2114p	2218
198	Ryazan 2 .... d.	0435	|	0648	...	0715	1029	1048	|	|	1301	1311	1653	1703	1907	2127	...	...	2254	0111	0211	|	|	0122
408	Michurinsk Uralski .... d.	0734	|	|	...	|	|	|	⊕	▽	|	|	|	|	|	|	...	...	|	0420	|	|	0518	|
412	Michurinsk Voronezhski .. d.	|	|	0948	⊡	1014	1236	1306	|	|	1519	1534	1916	1931	2114	2340	...	...	0135	|	0446	|	|	0417
426	Yelets .... d.	|	0615	|	0757	|	|	|	1132	1214	|	|	|	|	|	|	...	...	|	|	|	0457	|	|
504	Lipetsk .... d.	|	0730	|	0913	|	|	|	1324	1406	|	|	|	|	|	|	...	...	|	|	|	0615	|	|
469	Gryazi Voronezhski .... d.	0838	|	1040	|	1113	1321	1348	|	|	1604	1620	2000	2014	2159	0023	...	e	0226	0520	0530	|	0623	0507
588	**Voronezh** 1 .... d.	|	|	1250	1215	1305	1434	|	|	|	|	|	|	|	2312	|	...	0410	0520	|	0755	0830	|	0924
591	**Voronezh** Pridacha .... d.	1040	1107	|	|	...	...	1518	1711	1725	1739	1753	2130	2143	...	0155	d	|	|	0748	|	...	0840	|
667	Liski .... d.	1212	1225	1437	1446	...	...	1628	1915	1837	1853	1904	2242	2254	...	0305	0449	0616	0800	0918	0937	...	0955	1114
786	Rossosh .... d.	1434	1507	1632	1652	...	...	1814	2151	2049	2027	2037	0015	0027	...	0438	0711	0823	1023	1140	1154	...	1348	1305
062	Likhaya .... d.	|	1940	2030	2120	...	...	|	0204	0137	|	|	|	|	...	0815	1141	1237	1445	1630	1620	...	1835	1754
226	**Rostov na Donu** .... a.	2218	2250	2308	0044	...	...	2340	0506	0456	0151	0201	0539	0552	...	1036	1452	1620	1756	1942	1912	...	2200	2150
226	**Rostov na Donu** .... d.	2239	2309	2326	0101	...	...	2357	0528	0519	0206	0216	0603	0613	...	...	1527	1638	1814	2013	1943	...	2223	2208
405	Tikhoretskaya .... d.	|	0202	|	|	...	...	0214	0755	|	|	|	|	|	...	...	1818	|	|	2305	2208	...	0102	0034
332	Starominskaya Tim. .... d.	0007	|	|	0231	...	...	|	|	|	|	|	|	|	...	...	|	1759	1948	|	|	...	u	|
510	**Krasnodar** 1 .... d.	0255	|	0307	0505	...	...	|	|	1259	|	0543	|	0959	...	...	|	2147	2238	|	|	...	...	|
545	Novorossiysk .... a.	|	|	|	|	...	...	|	|	|	|	|	|	1255	...	...	|	|	|	|	|	...	...	|
536	Anapa .... a.	|	|	|	|	...	...	|	|	|	0945	|	|	...	...	...	|	|	|	|	|	...	...	|
533	Armavir Rostovski .... d.	|	0435	|	|	...	...	0401	1013	|	...	|	|	...	...	...	2127t	|	|	0136	0043	...	...	0300
721	Mineralnye Vody .... d.	|	0800	|	|	...	...	0644	1231	|	...	|	|	...	...	...	|	|	|	0445	0340	...	...	0641
747	Pyatigorsk .... d.	|	0836	|	|	...	...	0721	...	|	...	|	|	...	...	...	|	|	|	v	z	...	...	n
785	**Kislovodsk** .... a.	|	0928	|	|	...	...	0814	...	|	...	|	|	...	...	...	|	|	|	...	...	...	...	...
558	Tuapse .... d.	0647	...	0712	0920	...	...	...	...	1647	...	0823	1140	...	...	...	0238	0215	0251	...	...	...	...	...
738	**Sochi** .... a.	0854	...	0923	1156	...	...	...	...	1840	...	1007	1324	...	...	...	0435	0412	0443	...	...	...	...	...
761	**Adler** .... a.	0940	...	1004	1234	...	...	...	...	1921	...	1049	1402	...	...	...	0513	0451	0521	...	...	...	...	...
300	Gagra ◐ .... a.	...	...	...	...	...	...	...	...	...	...	...	...	...	...	...	...	...	0839	...	...	...	...	...
373	**Sukhumi** ◐ .... a.	...	...	...	...	...	...	...	...	...	...	...	...	...	...	...	...	...	1049	...	...	...	...	...

Time zone: UTC+3	49CH Sko M	104ZH Fir ◇	30JI Fir ∅	88SJ Fir F	36SJ Fir ◇ R	302SJ Pas ■(3)	102SJ Fir ∅ D	3SJ Fir	739ZH ⊙	140SJ Sko V	77SJ Sko ◧	37VJ Sko H	306SJ Pas T‡	33SJ Sko	61SJ Sko	145SJ Fir ●(4) ∅	25VJ Fir	360SJ Pas ■(5)	19SJ Fir ∅	121SJ Sko q	11EI Fir ∅	737ZH ⊙	116SJ Sko K	
Sukhumi ◐ .... d.	...	...	...	...	...	...	...	...	...	...	...	...	1405	...	...	...	...	...	...	...	...	...	...	...
Gagra ◐ .... d.	...	...	...	...	...	...	...	...	...	...	...	...	1616	...	...	...	...	...	...	...	...	...	...	...
ller .... d.	...	1832	...	1524	1735	1601	2034	...	...	1357	...	...	1941	...	...	...	...	2129	...	...	...	...	0836	...
chi .... d.	...	1912	...	1609	1813	1640	2109	...	...	1434	...	...	2018	...	...	...	...	2208	...	...	...	...	0924	...
apse .... d.	...	2102	...	1832	2031	1912	2300	...	...	1640	...	...	2232	...	...	...	...	0030	...	...	...	...	1213	...
Kislovodsk .... d.	1345	|	...	|	|	|	|	2009	...	|	...	...	|	...	...	...	...	|	...	...	...	...	|	...
Pyatigorsk .... d.	1445	|	...	|	|	|	|	2106	...	|	...	...	|	v	n	z	...	|	...	...	...	...	|	...
Mineralnye Vody .... d.	1555	|	...	|	|	|	|	2150	...	|	...	...	|	2230	2330	0318	...	|	...	1118	...	...	|	...
Armavir Rostovski .... d.	1829	|	...	|	|	|	|	0013	...	2241t	...	...	|	0114	0159	0544	...	|	...	1356	...	...	|	...
Anapa .... d.	|	|	...	|	|	|	|	|	...	|	...	...	|	|	|	|	...	|	...	|	1345	...	|	...
Novorossiysk .... d.	|	|	2100	|	|	|	|	|	...	|	...	...	|	|	|	|	...	|	...	|	|	...	|	...
asnodar 1 .... d.	|	2325	2335	2301	2355	2312	|	|	...	|	...	...	0128	|	|	|	...	0511	...	|	|	...	1632	...
Starominskaya Tim. ...... d.	|	|	|	0228	|	0238	|	|	...	|	u	...	0442	|	|	|	...	0830	...	|	|	...	|	...
horetskaya .... d.	2041	|	|	|	|	|	|	0205	...	0132	0150	...	|	0327	0358	0759	...	|	...	1618	|	...	|	...
stov na Donu .... a.	2327	0244	0254	0353	0343	0408	0428	0436	...	0446	0502	...	0611	0636	0627	1018	...	0953	...	1846	2047	...	2240	...
stov na Donu .... d.	2345	0259	0309	0411	0401	0426	0443	0453	...	0507	0528	...	0639	0717	0707	1041	...	1015	1522	1909	2107	...	2259	...
naya .... d.	0302	|	|	|	0712	0808	|	|	...	0820	0840	...	1041	1122	1112	1347	...	1414	1753	2234	|	...	0228	...
ssosh .... d.	0721	0831	0841	1125	1114	1259	1013	1023	...	1340	1311	...	1523	1629	1535	1742	...	1850	2133	0313	0240	...	0650	...
ki .... d.	0916	1011	1022	1302	1251	1527	1155	1205	...	1549	1518	...	1655	1820	1722	1915	...	2027	2313	0500	0420	...	0833	...
ronezh Pridacha .... d.	1142	1112	1127	1423	|	|	1302	1316	...	b	1625	...	|	1939	|	|	...	|	0014	0612	0522	...	1019	...
ronezh 1 .... d.	|	|	|	|	1457	1820	|	|	1626	...	|	1900	1937	|	2008	2118	2030	2257	|	|	|	0733	|	...
azi Voronezhski .... d.	|	1246	1259	1633	1644	|	|	|	1743	...	1828	2045	2125	2234	2246	2300	|	f	0148	|	0658	0850	|	...
ipetsk .... d.	1515	|	|	|	|	2113	|	|	|	...	|	|	|	|	|	|	2303	...	|	0944	|	|	1438	...
elets .... d.	1710	|	|	|	|	2310	|	|	|	...	|	|	|	|	|	|	0041	...	|	1134	|	|	1628	...
hurinsk Voronezhski ... d.	|	1331	1346	|	1747	⊡	1524	1541	1824	...	|	2145	2230	|	2343	0005	|	...	0230	|	0757	0931	|	...
hurinsk Uralski .... d.	|	|	|	1831	|	...	|	|	|	...	2009	|	|	0014	|	|	|	...	|	⊗	|	|	△	...
azan 2 .... d.	|	1556	1606	2127	2058	...	1755	1805	2033	...	|	0058	0128	0312	0214	0240	|	...	0450	|	1027	1140	|	...
skva Kazanskaya .... a.	0202k	1823	1833	|	|	...	2015	2025	2246	...	0500p	|	0452	0630	0523	0607	0750p	...	0735	2044k	1338	1353	2336k	...
ver .... d.	0415	...	...	h	0224	...	...	...	...	...	...	0616	...	...	...	...	...	...	...	2340	...	...	0206	...
ologoye .... d.	0554	...	...	...	0408	...	...	...	...	...	...	0813	...	...	...	...	...	...	...	0125	...	...	0354	...
t Peterburg Glavny .... a.	1140	...	...	...	0743	...	...	...	...	...	...	1230	...	...	...	...	...	...	...	0501	...	...	0952x	...

Uneven dates ■(3) (daily Apr. 27 - May 13, June 1 - Sept. 29, from Nov. 1).
Uneven dates ■(1) (daily Apr. 25 - May 11, from May 29).
From Nizhni Novgorod on uneven dates ■(3) (daily May 25 - Oct. 11).
Uneven dates ■(5) (daily May 27 - Oct. 12).
Even dates (daily Apr. 28 - May 14, May 26 - Sept. 2).
Uneven dates ■(1) (daily Apr. 27 - May 13, May 25 - Sept. 1).
Uneven dates (even dates Apr. 2 - 22, daily May 1 - 13, June 2 - Oct. 3).
Uneven dates (even dates Apr. 2 - 20, daily Apr. 27 - May 11, June 1 - Sept. 30).
②④⑤⑦ (daily Dec. 20 - Jan. 8, Apr. 25 - Sept. 22).
②④⑥⑦ (daily Dec. 22 - Jan. 10, Apr. 27 - Sept. 24).
Even dates (uneven dates Apr. 1 - 20, daily Apr. 26 - Nov. 4).
Even dates (uneven dates Apr. 1 - 21, daily Apr. 28 - Nov. 6).
Uneven dates ■(1) (daily Apr. 19 - Oct. 30).
Uneven dates ■(3) (daily Apr. 21 - Oct. 4).
From Novosibirsk on even dates (daily May 26 - Sept. 10).
Even dates ●(6) (daily May 30 - Sept. 14).
Uneven dates ■(3) (daily Dec. 23 - Jan. 11, Apr. 25 - May 13, May 25 - Nov. 5).
Even dates (daily Dec. 24 - Jan. 12, Apr. 26 - May 14, May 26 - Nov. 6).
Every four days Mar. 2 - 30, Apr. 4 - 28, May 2 - 30; even dates June 4 - Sept. 16; every 4 days Sept. 20 - 28, Oct. 2 - 30, Nov. 4 - 28, Dec. 2 - 30.

Z – Every four days Mar. 1 - 29, Apr. 7 - 27 (also Apr. 2), May 1 - 29 (also June 2); uneven dates ■(5) June 7 - Sept. 19; every four days Sept. 23 - 27, Oct. 1 - 29 (also Nov. 2), Nov. 7 - 27, Dec. 1 - 29.
b – To Novosibirsk (Table **1990**). Via Penza (d. 0305 3rd day), Saransk (d. 0613 3rd day). Arrive Novosibirsk 5th day.
d – From Novosibirsk (Table **1990**). Via Saransk (1436 3rd day), Penza (1810 3rd day). Departs Liski 4th day, arrive Adler 5th day.
e – From Kaliningrad ● via Vilnius (Table **1950**). Bryansk Orl d. 1649. Depart Voronezh on 3rd day.
f – To Vilnius and Kaliningrad (Table **1950**). Via Bryansk Orl d. 1119.
g – From Nizhni Novgorod (d. 2018) via Vladimir (d. 2305).
h – To Nizhni Novgorod (a. 0716) via Vladimir (a. 0351).
k – Moskva **Kurskaya**.
m – Train 121AJ on ●(4) to Vladikavkaz a. 1745; train 135AJ on ■(5) to Makhachkala a. 2200.
n – To/from Nal'chik (arrive 0953/depart 1915).
p – Moskva **Paveletskaya**.
q – Train 121SJ on ● from Vladikavkaz (d. 0630); train 135SJ on ● from Makhachkala (d. 1937), next day from Mineralnye Vody.
t – Armavir **Tuapsinkii**.
u – To/from Stavropol (arrive 0557; depart 2117).
v – To/from Vladikavkaz (arrive 0958/depart 1756).

x – St Peterburg **Ladozhski**.
y – ■(1) from Minsk, next day from Yelets (Table **1961**).
z – To/from Nazran (arrive 0649/depart 2325).
◐ – Abkhazia Autonomous Region (🚌 = Veseloe/Tsandryphsh).
∅ – Includes De Luxe sleeping car with ensuite shower/toilet.
⊡ – From/to Minsk (Table **1961**).
◧ – Runs 2-3 times per week.
◇ – Double-deck sleeping cars.
⊙ – Double-deck day train.
▽ – Via Tula (depart 0720).
△ – Via Tula (depart 2105).
⊕ – Via Tula (depart 0617).
⊗ – Via Tula (depart 1723).
‡ – Journey 2 nights.
● – Even dates. See page 534.
■ – Uneven dates. See page 534.
BY – Belarus (UTC+3).
RU – Russia (Moskva time UTC+3).

MINSK - ADLER 1961

n	UTC+3	302BJ ■(1)		302SJ ■(3)
0	**Minsk** ..... 1930 d.	1220	**Adler** .... d.	1601
6	Homel .... BY d.	1740	Sochi .... d.	1640
7	Bryansk O. . RU d.	0058	**Rostov na D.** .. d.	0426
3	Yelets .... d.	0757	Yelets .... d.	2310
7	**Rostov na D.** ... a.	0044	Bryansk O. . RU d.	0715
3	Sochi .... a.	1156	Homel .... BY a.	1217
	Adler .... a.	1234	**Minsk** ...... 1930 a.	1737

Uneven dates, see page 534. For further stations between Yelets and Adler see Table **1960**.

SARATOV - ADLER 1962

km	UTC+3	14ZH W		14SJ X
0	**Saratov** 1 .... ♡ d.	1051	**Adler** .... d.	1824
429	Volgograd 1 ♡ d.	1754	Sochi .... d.	1902
964	Tikhoretskaya .. d.	0233	Tuapse .... d.	2118
1100	**Krasnodar** 1 ... d.	0524	**Krasnodar** 1 ... d.	0045
1248	Tuapse .... d.	0937	Tikhoretskaya .. d.	0328
1328	Sochi .... a.	1131	Volgograd 1 . ♡ d.	1506
1351	**Adler** .... a.	1212	**Saratov** 1 .... ♡ a.	2146

♡ – UTC+4 (local time shown).
FOR OTHER NOTES SEE TABLE **1960**.

ROSTOV - BAKI 1963

km	UTC+3	392SJ Y		391SZ Z
0	**Rostov na D.** .. d.	1807	**Baki** .... AZ d.	0325
307	Armavir Rost. ... d.	2327	Derbent .... d.	1058
495	Mineralnye Vody d.	0226	Makhachkala .... d.	1346
773	Gudermes .... d.	0954	Gudermes .... d.	1759
896	Makhachkala ... d.	1401	Mineralnye Vody d.	0137
1025	Derbent .... d.	1633	Armavir Rost. ... d.	0408
1286	**Baki** .... AZ a.	0215	**Rostov na D.** ... a.	0909

AZ – Azerbaijan (UTC+4). 🚌 = Yalama.
FOR OTHER NOTES SEE TABLE **1960**.

1965 MOSKVA - SARATOV, VOLGOGRAD and BAKI

km	Times are local time	time zone UTC+	89AJ Sko B	1IJ Fir	9GJ Fir ∅	17MJ Fir	15JI Sko	55CH Sko ⑥t	86VJ Sko	31CH Fir	5GJ Fir
	St Peterburg Gl. ... d.	+3	2032	...	...	...	...	...	...	...	...
	Tver ... d.	+3	0209	...	...	...	...	...	...	...	...
0	**Moskva** Pavelets ... d.	+3	0453r	1405	1813	2000	2009	2237r	2114k	2200	2359
198	Ryazan 2 ... d.	+3	|	|	|	|	|	△	0043	|	|
408	Michurinsk Uralski ... d.	+3	|	2008v	0110	0331	0400v	|	0402	0612	0908
426	Yelets ... d.	+3	1336	|	|	|	|	0635	|	|	|
504	Lipetsk ... d.	+3	1501	|	|	|	|	0807	|	|	|
541	Gryazi Voronezhski ... d.	+3	1625	2135	|	|	0523	0930	|	|	|
481	Tambov 1 ... d.	+3	|	|	0222	0444	|	|	0525	0730	1026
861	**Saratov** 1 ... a.	+4	|	|	0929	1238	|	|	1303	...	1834
778	Povorino ... d.	+3	2230	0156	...	...	1010	1350	|	|	|
1145	**Volgograd** 1 ... a.	+4	0558	0915	...	...	1752	2156	|	...	|
1595	Astrakhan 1 ... a.	+4	...	...	...	...	...	0605	0042	...	0630
⊡	Makhachkala ... a.	+3	...	...	...	...	...	1525	1235	...	...
2212	Derbent ... a.	+3	...	...	...	...	...	1822	...	...	...
2473	**Baki** ... AZ a.	+4	...	...	...	...	...	0410	...	...	...

Times are local time	time zone UTC+	9ZH Fir ∅	1ZH Fir	17ZH Fir	15ZH Sko	5ZH Fir	89ZH Sko C	55SZ Sko ④t	85SJ Sko	31 Fi
Baki ... AZ d.	+4	...	...	...	...	...	...	0135	...	..
Derbent ... d.	+3	...	...	...	...	...	...	0902	...	..
Makhachkala ... d.	+3	...	...	...	...	...	...	1134	1445	..
Astrakhan 1 ... d.	+4	...	...	...	...	1140	...	2155	0245	..
Volgograd 1 ... d.	+4	...	1630	...	1813	|	0207	0606	|	
Povorino ... d.	+3	...	2210	...	2357	|	0830	1240	|	
Saratov 1 ... d.	+4	1804	|	2006	|	2355	|	|	1441	..
Tambov 1 ... d.	+3	2304	|	0153	|	0530	|	|	2032	212
Gryazi Voronezhski ... d.	+3	|	0222	|	0436	|	1450	1755	|	|
Lipetsk ... d.	+3	|	|	|	|	|	1544	1842	|	|
Yelets ... d.	+3	|	|	|	|	|	1800	2023	|	|
Michurinsk Uralski ... d.	+3	0045	0313v	0336	0540v	0714	|	|	2242	23
Ryazan 2 ... d.	+3	|	|	|	|	|	|	▽	0224	|
Moskva Pavelets ... a.	+3	0722	0930	1029	1400	1437	0256r	0322r	0530k	0
Tver ... a.	+3	...	...	...	...	...	0523	...	...	..
St Peterburg Gl. ... a.	+3	...	...	...	...	...	1225	...	...	..

B – Even dates (daily Dec. 22 - Jan. 9, Apr. 22 - May 10, May 24 - Sept. 8). Note ⊕.
C – Uneven dates ■(3) (daily Dec. 23 - Jan. 10, Apr. 23 - May 12, May 25 - Sept. 9). Note ⊕.
k – Moskva **Kazanskaya**.
r – Moska **Kurskaya**.
t – Journey 3 nights.
v – Michurinsk **Voronezhski**.
● – Even dates. See page 534.
■ – Uneven dates. See page 534.
△ – Via Tula 1 (d. 0154).
▽ – Via Tula 1 (d. 0058).
⊡ – 1537 km (2083 km via Volgograd).
∅ – Includes Luxe 🛏 with ensuite shower/toi
⊕ – Days of running may vary.
AZ – Azerbaijan (UTC+4).

1970 MOSKVA - SAMARA - UFA - CHELYABINSK - OMSK

km	Times are local time	time zone UTC+	116JI Sko	132UJ Sko	120MJ Sko	66JI Sko	138JI Sko	50MJ Sko	22JI Fir	90UJ Sko ■(5)	10JI Fir ∅	52JI Fir ∅	14EJ Fir	14EJ 675EI Fir ♡	124VJ Sko E	110JI Fir	42JI Fir ∅		6FJ Sko T	18SZ Sko B	84CJ Sko A	102JI Sko ●	107ZH Fir ■(3)
	St Peterburg **1900** ... d.	+3	...	...	...	...	...	...	...	...	...	...	...	...	...	...	...	...	...	...	...	...	1431
0	**Moskva** Kazanskaya ... d.	+3	1226	1510	1522	1708	1716	1808	1908	1920	2008	2040	2122	2122	...	...	2132	...	2240	2240	2250	...	0014k
197	Ryazan 1 ... d.	+3	1531	1833r	1817	2024	2034	2101	2235	|	2259	2342	0037	0037	...	...	0049	...	0146	0146	0208	...	0502
601	Ruzayevka ... d.	+3	2216	|	2314	0222	0254	0237	0412	|	0346	0453	0546	0546	...	...	0629	...	0836	0836	0903	...	1202
627	Saransk ... a.	+3	|	|	2341	|	|	|	|	|	|	|	|	|	...	...	0705	...	|	|	|	|	|
710	**Penza** 1 ... d.	+3	|	0527	...	|	|	|	|	|	|	0735	|	|	0606	0708	|	...	|	|	|	1326	1535
712	Inza ... d.	+4	0125	|	...	0456	0551	0508	0720	|	|	...	0816	0816	|	|	|	...	1111	1111	|	|	|
873	Ulyanovsk ... d.	+4	0501	|	...	|	|	|	1000	|	|	...	|	|	|	|	|	...	|	|	|	|	|
908	Syzran 1 ... d.	+4	|	1046	...	0804	0859	0751	...	|	0838	...	1039	1039	1027	1101	|	...	|	|	1438	1848	2024
1044	**Samara** ... a.	+4	|	1305	...	t	1133	0947	...	❦	1011	...	1220	1220	1255	1234	|	...	1618	1618	1654	2110	2300
1044	**Samara** ... d.	+4	|	1350	...	...	1218	...	...	|	...	...	1309	1309	1415	...	|	...	1708	1708	1739	2204	...
1216	Buzuluk' ... d.	+5	|	1826	...	...	1637	...	...	|	...	...	|	|	|	...	|	...	2122	2122	|	...	...
1462	Orenburg ... a.	+5	|	2240	...	...	2025	...	...	|	...	...	|	|	|	...	|	...	0111	0111	|	...	...
1567	**Ufa** ... d.	+5	1847	n	...	...	...	...	...	|	...	...	2227	2245	0025	...	...	...	...	...	0337	0823	...
1933	Magnitogorsk ... a.	+5	...	...	...	...	...	...	...	|	...	...	|	0737	|	...	...	...	...	...	|	|	...
2048	**Chelyabinsk** ... a.	+5	...	...	...	...	...	...	...	|	...	...	0705	...	1023	...	...	...	...	...	1300	1810	...
2306	Kurgan ... d.	+5	...	...	...	...	...	...	...	0630	...	...	...	...	1415	...	...	...	...	...	1638	e	...
2573	Petropavl ... KA d.	+6	...	...	...	...	...	...	...	1220	...	...	...	...	1945	...	...	...	...	...	2215	...	...
2846	**Omsk** ... a.	+6	...	...	...	...	...	...	...	...	...	...	...	...	2351	...	...	...	...	...	...	...	...

Times are local time	time zone UTC+	115JI Sko	89UJ Sko ■(1)	101JI Sko ●	49JI Sko	41JI Fir ∅	13UJ Fir	676UJ 13UJ ♡	9JI Fir ∅	52MJ Fir ∅	21JI Fir	131UJ Sko		137UJ Sko	109JI Fir	66EI Sko	17SZ Sko B	5FJ Sko T	119JI Sko	83CJ Sko A	107JI Fir ■(1)	123NJ Sko F
Omsk ... d.	+6	...	...	...	...	...	...	...	...	...	...	...	...	...	...	...	...	...	...	...	...	2245
Petropavl ... KA d.	+6	...	1640	...	...	...	...	...	...	...	...	...	...	...	...	...	...	...	...	2045	...	0350
Kurgan ... d.	+5	...	2119	e	...	...	...	...	...	...	...	...	...	...	...	...	...	...	...	0042	...	0713
Chelyabinsk ... d.	+5	...	|	1836	...	...	2310	...	...	...	...	...	...	...	...	...	...	...	...	0450	...	1140
Magnitogorsk ... d.	+5	...	|	|	...	...	|	2145	...	...	...	...	...	...	...	...	...	...	...	|	...	|
Ufa ... d.	+5	0147	|	0413	...	...	0853	0853	...	...	...	n	...	...	...	...	...	...	...	1441	...	2134
Orenburg ... d.	+5	|	|	|	...	...	|	|	...	...	...	0518	...	1120	...	...	1256	1256	...	|	...	|
Buzuluk' ... d.	+5	|	|	|	...	...	|	|	...	...	...	0948	...	1540	...	...	1708	1708	...	|	...	|
Samara ... a.	+4	|	|	1142	...	...	1607	1607	...	...	...	1158	...	1740	...	...	1911	1911	...	2234	...	0503
Samara ... d.	+4	|	❦	1253	1524	...	1655	1655	1950	...	...	1243	...	1838	1848	t	2016	2016	...	2335	2317	0551
Syzran 1 ... d.	+4	|	|	1513	1742	...	1918	1918	2138	...	...	1526	...	2055	2031	2121	2252	2252	...	0224	0156	0824
Ulyanovsk ... d.	+4	1425	|	|	|	...	|	|	|	...	2049	|	...	|	|	|	|	|	...	|	|	|
Inza ... d.	+4	1810	|	|	2028	...	2134	2134	|	...	2357	|	...	0004	|	0016	0128	0128	...	|	|	|
Penza 1 ... d.	+3	|	|	1810	|	...	|	|	|	2135	|	1920	...	|	2222	|	|	|	...	|	0507	1130
Saransk ... d.	+3	|	|	...	|	2043	|	|	|	|	|	|	...	|	|	|	|	|	0640	|	|	|
Ruzayevka ... d.	+3	1919	|	...	2112	2125	2215	2215	0025	0015	0041	|	...	0123	...	0108	0215	0215	0710	0545	0837	|
Ryazan 1 ... d.	+3	0148	|	...	0233	0253	0303	0303	0501	0511	0541	0556r	...	0653	...	0643	0806	0806	1203	1228	1457	|
Moskva Kazanskaya ... a.	+3	0512	0538	...	0545	0600	0622	0622	0753	0823	0908	0938	...	1029	...	1008	1115	1115	1425	1522	2133k	|
St Peterburg **1900** ... a.	+3	...	...	...	...	...	...	...	...	...	...	...	...	...	...	...	...	...	...	...	0532	...

A – To / from Astana and Karagandy (for days of running see Table **1976**).
B – To / from Bishkek (for days of running see Table **1975**).
E – From Belgorod ■(7) (daily June 4 - Sept. 25), next day from Penza. Belgorod d. 0910, Voronezh 1 d. 1804, Tambov 1 d. 2315. To Novosibirsk *UTC+7* (a. 0922).
F – ■(3) (daily June 1 - Sept. 21). From Novosibirsk *UTC+7* (d. 1555). To Tambov 1 (a. 1825), Voronezh 1 (a. 0020), Belgorod (a. 0920).
T – To / from Toshkent (for days of running see Table **1975**). Train **150** / **149** on certain dates (to / from Toshkent and Andizhan, Table **1975**).
e – To / from Yekaterinburg *UTC+5* (a. 2255 / d. 1303).
k – Moskva **Kurskaya**.
n – To / from Orsk *UTC+5* (a. 0505 / d. 2245).
r – Ryazan 2.
t – To / from Toliatti *UTC+4* (a. 1050 / d. 1818).
∅ – Includes De Luxe sleeping car with ensuite shower/toilet.
♡ – Uneven dates Jan., Apr., May, Aug., Nov.; even dates Dec., F Mar., June, July, Sept., Oct.
❦ – Via Kazan and Yekaterinburg (Table **1990**). Journey 2 nights
● – Even dates. See page 534.
■ – Uneven dates. See page 534.
KA – Kazakhstan.

1975 SAMARA / SARATOV - AKTOBE - TOSHKENT / BISHKEK / ALMATY

km	Times are local time	time zone UTC+	381EI Pas G	18SZ Sko ④⑥	150EI Sko A	6FJ Sko C	24CJ Sko ■(1)	8KH Sko ●	310KH Pas	34TJ Sko
0	*Moskva Kaz* **1970** ... d.	+3	...	2240	2240	2240	...	...	...	...
1044	**Samara** ... d.	+4	...	1708	1708	1708	...	...	...	...
•681	Ufa ... d.	+5	1315	|	|	|	...	...	...	...
1462	Orenburg ... d.	+5	2238	0156	0156	0156	...	...	...	...
•894	**Saratov** ... d.	+4	|	|	|	|	...	1951	...	...
•459	Oral / Uralsk ... KA d.	+5	|	|	|	|	...	0825	...	...
1734	Aktobe ... KA a.	+5	0729	1005	1005	1005	...	1845	...	...
1734	Aktobe ... KA d.	+5	0754	1025	1025	1025	1455	1925	2135	2235
1828	Kandyagash ... KA d.	+5	0939	1159	1159	1159	1634	2114	2343	0019
2924	Mangystau ⊙ ... KA a.	+5	|	|	|	|	|	|	0400*	|
2767	Kyzlorda ... KA d.	+5	0326	0348	0348	0348	0957	1344	...	1729
3315	**Toshkent** ... UZ a.	+5	1827	|	1650	1650	|	|	...	|
3738	Andizhan ... UZ a.	+5	...	|	0056	...	|	|	...	|
3240	Shymkent ... KA d.	+6	...	1357	...	...	2037	2301	...	0356
3729	**Bishkek** 2 ... KY a.	+6	...	0210	...	...	|	|	...	|
4001	**Almaty** 1 ... KA a.	+6	...	...	...	...	1102	1216	...	1803
4010	**Almaty** 2 ... KA a.	+6	...	...	...	...	...	1243	...	...

Times are local time	time zone UTC+	149FJ Sko B	5FJ Sko D	17SZ Sko ①③	23KH Sko ■(3)	381MZ Pas H	309KH Pas	33CJ Sko	7 S ●
Almaty 2 ... KA d.	+6	...	...	...	...	...	...	...	00
Almaty 1 ... KA d.	+6	...	...	...	1409	...	...	2242	0
Bishkek 2 ... KY d.	+6	...	...	1234	|	...	...	|	
Shymkent ... KA d.	+6	...	...	0108	0354	...	...	1207	1
Andizhan ... UZ d.	+5	1210	|	|	|	...	...	|	
Toshkent ... UZ d.	+5	1905	1905	|	|	0148	...	|	
Kyzlorda ... KA d.	+5	0921	0921	0921	1257	1737	...	2109	2
Mangystau ⊙ ... KA d.	+5	|	|	|	|	|	1011	|	
Kandyagash ... KA d.	+5	0140	0140	0140	0700	1207	1331*	1410	1
Aktobe ... KA a.	+5	0305	0305	0305	0825	1338	1514	1540	1
Aktobe ... KA d.	+5	0325	0325	0325	...	1403	...	...	1
Oral / Uralsk ... KA a.	+5	|	|	|	...	|	...	...	0
Saratov ... a.	+4	|	|	|	...	|	...	...	1
Orenburg ... d.	+5	1256	1256	1256	...	0002	...	...	
Ufa ... a.	+5	|	|	|	...	0830	...	...	
Samara ... a.	+4	1911	1911	1911	...	...	...	...	
Moskva Kaz **1970** ... a.	+3	1115	1115	1115	...	...	...	...	

A – ③ (also ⑤ Feb. 8 - May 31, Sept. 6 - Nov. 29).
B – ⑦ (also ② Feb. 5 - May 28).
C – ⑦ (also ② Feb. 5 - July 2, Oct. 8 - 29).
D – ④ (also ⑥ Feb. 2 - June 29).
G – ⑥ (also ② Feb. 5 - May 28, Sept. 3 - Dec. 3).
H – ④ (also ⑦ Feb. 3 - May 26).
n – Even dates [.. *28, 31, 2*..]
● – Even dates. See page 534.
⊙ – Station for Aktau (15 km).
* – More than 24 hrs after previous time shown.
• – Distance from Aktobe.
KA – Kazakhstan (Almaty = UTC+6, western zone = UTC+5
KY – Kyrgyzstan (UTC+6).
UZ – Uzbekistan (UTC+5).

ee also Table **1980**

SAMARA / KAZAN - NUR-SULTAN - ALMATY / TOSHKENT 1976

km	Times are local time	time zone UTC+	90UJ	706TJ	84CJ	16TJ	39TJ	316FJ	304CJ	304CJ 306SZ
			■(5)		●(4)	■‡	■(3)	②	⑤	⑤
0	*Moskva Kaz* **1970** d.	+3	1920	...	2250	...	...	...	...	...
44	**Samara** d.	+4	|	...	1739	...	...	...	...	...
48	Chelyabinsk d.	+5	|	...	1310	...	1205	...	...	...
	Kazan ▷ d.	+3	0755	...	|	...	|	2355	2355	2355
	Yekaterinburg ▷ d.	+5	0018	...	|	...	|	1858	1858	1858
06	Kurgan d.	+5	0630	...	1638	...	⊡	0151	0151	0151
73	Petropavl KA d.	+6	1220	1454	2315	2355	|	0910	0910	0910
64	**Nur-Sultan** 1 KA a.	+6	...	2053	0736	0749	1038n	1748	1748	1748
64	**Nur-Sultan** 1 KA d.	+6	...	2113	0820	0820	...	1822	1822	1822
05	Karagandy KA d.	+6	...	2351	1214	1249	...	0044	0044	0044
	Almaty 1 KA a.	+6	...	|	...	0445	...	|	2201	|
07	**Almaty** 2 KA a.	+6	...	1022	...	0518	...	|	2300	|
56	Bishkek 2 KY a.	+6	...	...	...	...	...	|	...	2208
22	Shymkent KA a.	+6	...	...	...	...	...	2150	...	...
55	**Toshkent** UZ a.	+5	...	...	...	...	...	0500	...	...

Times are local time	time zone UTC+	83CJ	15TJ	39CJ	315FJ	303CJ	305SZ 303CJ	705TJ	89UJ
		●	●§	●	⑥	②	②		■(3)
Toshkent UZ d.	+5	...	...	...	0350	...	...	...	...
Shymkent KA d.	+6	...	...	...	1327	...	...	...	...
Bishkek 2 KY d.	+6	...	...	...	|	...	1456	...	...
Almaty 2 KA d.	+6	...	1535	...	|	1543	|	1812	...
Almaty 1 KA d.	+6	...	1608	...	|	1618	|	|	...
Karagandy KA d.	+6	0623	0950	...	1407*	1407	1407	0506	...
Nur-Sultan 1 KA a.	+6	1022	1339	...	1833	1833	1833	0736	...
Nur-Sultan 1 KA d.	+6	1100	1407	1450n	1913	1913	1913	0756	...
Petropavl KA d.	+6	2045	2214	|	0556	0556	0556	1349	1640
Kurgan d.	+5	0044	...	⊡	1100	1100	1100	...	2119
Yekaterinburg ▷ a.	+5	|	...	|	1659	1659	1659	...	0300
Kazan ▷ a.	+3	|	...	|	0610	0610	0610	...	1625
Chelyabinsk d.	+5	0442	...	1035	...	...	...	...	|
Samara a.	+4	2234	...	...	...	...	...	...	|
Moskva Kaz **1970** a.	+3	1522	...	...	...	...	...	...	0538

MOSKVA - MAKAT - TOSHKENT / DUSHANBE

m	Times are local	zone UTC+	350MJ E	330CH ③⑥
0	**Moskva** Kaz d.	+3	1216	1216
98	Ryazan 2 d.	+3	1530	1530
11	Michurinsk Vor d.	+3	1834	1834
75	**Volgograd** d.	+4	1310	1310
04	Atyrau KA d.	+5	0710	0710
34	Makat KA d.	+5	1022	1022
41	Kungrad UZ d.	+5	0218	|
48	Urgench UZ d.	+5	1045	|
65	Bukhara UZ a.	+5	1650	|
58	Navoi UZ a.	+5	1823	|
44	Samarkand UZ a.	+5	2006	|
57	**Toshkent** UZ a.	+5	0055	|
74	Karshi UZ a.	+5	...	1958*
46	Termez UZ a.	+5	...	1024
71	**Dushanbe** 1 TA a.	+5	...	1616

Times are local	329ZJ ②⑥	350FJ E
Dushanbe 1 TA d.	0221	...
Termez UZ d.	0756	...
Karshi UZ d.	2141	...
Toshkent UZ d.	|	1520
Samarkand UZ d.	|	1945
Navoi UZ d.	|	2134
Bukhara UZ d.	|	0011
Urgench UZ d.	|	0731
Kungrad UZ d.	|	1517
Makat KA d.	0738*	0738
Atyrau KA d.	1018	1018
Volgograd d.	0352	0352
Michurinsk Vor d.	1658	1658
Ryazan 2 d.	2048	2048
Moskva Kaz a.	0001	0001

From Moskva ② Dec. 18 - Apr. 2, ② Oct. 8 - Dec. 10; from Toshkent ⑤ Dec. 14 - Mar. 29, ⑤ Oct. 5 - Dec. 13. For Moskva - Toshkent via Aktobe see Table **1975**.

NOVOSIBIRSK - ALMATY / TOSHKENT

km	Times are local	zone UTC+	369NJ J	301NJ ●(7)	1KH R
0	**Novosibirsk** d.	+7	1831	1831	...
228	Barnaul d.	+7	0038	0038	...
1121	Aktogay KA d.	+6	2055	2055	...
	Almaty 2 KA d.	+6	|	|	1932
1678	**Almaty** 1 KA a.	+6	0741	0741	1950
1678	**Almaty** 1 KA d.	+6	0811	0811	2000
1687	**Almaty** 2 KA d.	+6	|	0833	|
2424	Shymkent KA d.	+6	2346	...	0653
2657	**Toshkent** UZ a.	+5	0704	...	1154

Times are local	1MZ S	301CJ ●§	369FJ J
Toshkent UZ d.	1412	...	1715
Shymkent KA d.	2105	...	0241
Almaty 2 KA d.	|	1713	|
Almaty 1 KA a.	0742	1735	1730
Almaty 1 KA d.	0752	1805	1805
Almaty 2 KA a.	0810	|	|
Aktogay KA d.	...	0550	0550
Barnaul d.	...	0336	0336
Novosibirsk a.	...	0858	0858

J – Runs approx every 4-8 days.
R – ①③⑥. Talgo train.
S – ②④⑦. Talgo train.
n – Nur-Sultan **Nurly Zhol**.
● – Even dates. See page 534.
■ – Uneven dates. See page 534.
▷ – See also Table **1990**.
⊡ – Via Tobol.

§ – Even dates [.. *30, 4* ..] (see page 534).
‡ – Uneven dates [.. *31, 5* ..] (see page 534).
* – More than 24 hrs after previous time shown.
KA – Kazakhstan (Almaty zone = UTC+6).
TA – Tajikistan (UTC+5).
UZ – Uzbekistan (UTC+5).
☛ Nur-Sultan is the new name for Astana.

ee also Tables **1975/6**

KAZAKHSTAN and UZBEKISTAN 1980

UTC+6	86CJ	4TJ	708CJ	92CJ	712CJ	21CJ	50KH	29TJ	10TJ	25TJ
				■	●		■h	■		b
-Sultan 1 d.	1025n	1632n	1914n	1950n	1950n	...	2156	...	2010n	...
agandy d.	1444	1912	2154	2230	2230	...	0038	...	2357	...
aty 1 a.	|	0654	|	|	|	1052	|	...	1440	...
aty 2 a.	|	0722	0848	|	|	|	1135	1703	...	2208
mkent a.	0933	...	...	1216	1216	2352	...	0307	...	1002
orda ♡ a.	...	...	...	1809	...	0749	...	0952	...	...
au ♡ a.	...	...	...	...	...	...	...	0553	...	...

UTC+6	3TJ	712KH	707CJ	49KH	9TJ	29KH	26TJ	85CJ	22TJ	92TJ
		■		●k		■	d			●
au ♡ d.	...	...	...	...	...	0832	...	...	...	...
orda ♡ d.	...	...	...	...	...	0358	...	...	1455	2050
mkent d.	...	1346	...	...	...	1205	1735	1955	0032	0521
aty 2 d.	1524	|	1852	2159	...	2248	0555	|	|	|
aty 1 d.	1552	|	|	|	1738	...	...	|	1405	|
agandy d.	0357	0419	0606	0914	0921	...	...	1707	...	2015
Sultan 1 a.	0634n	0707n	0840n	1151	1234n	...	...	2115n	...	2249n

KA UTC+6 (♡+5)	95CJ	49KH	47CJ	37KH
	●	■u	■(3)	●(4)
Nur-Sultan 1 d.	1150n	1215	2033n	2117n
Tobol d.	2056	2056	1222	1010
Kandyagash ♡ d.	|	|	0007	2147
Aktobe 1 ♡ a.	0604	0604	|	|
Oral / Uralsk ♡ a.	1309	1309	|	|
Atyrau ♡ a.	...	...	0930	|
Mangistau ⊙ ♡ a.	...	...	...	2031

KA UTC+6 (♡+5)	37TJ	96CJ	50KH	47TJ
	●	■(3)	●(4)	■(1)
Mangistau ⊙ ♡ d.	1600	...	v	...
Atyrau ♡ d.	|	...	...	2150
Oral / Uralsk ♡ d.	|	1809	1809	|
Aktobe 1 ♡ d.	|	0114	0114	|
Kandyagash ♡ d.	1321	|	|	0829
Tobol d.	0303	1332	1332	2127
Nur-Sultan 1 a.	1447n	2155n	2130	1325n

UZ UTC+5	762‡	758/60 ‡	766‡	56/58 E	72FJ ⑦–④
Toshkent d.	0728	0800	1850	2030	2220
Samarkand d.	0950	1016	2108	0039	0222
Karshi a.	|	1120	|	|	|
Navoi d.	1042	...	2201	0247	0441
Bukhara 1 a.	1119	...	2239	0349	0619
Urgench a.	...	...	...	1007	...
Khiva a.	...	...	...	1052	...

UZ UTC+5	765‡	761‡	757/9 ‡	71FJ ①–⑤	56/58 F
Khiva d.	...	...	...	...	1428
Urgench d.	...	...	...	...	1618
Bukhara 1 d.	0455	1550	...	2146	2300
Navoi d.	0535	1629	...	2350	0039
Karshi d.	|	|	1648	|	|
Samarkand d.	0637	1728	1800	0200	0304
Toshkent a.	0847	1944	2010	0559	0658

②③⑤⑦ (daily to Urgench).
①③④⑥ (daily from Urgench).
On ■ d. 2108, a. 0719 (train **71**TJ).
On ● d. 1948, a. 0623 (train **72**TJ).
From Oral (right hand panel, dep. ●).

k – To Oral (right hand panel).
n – Nur-Sultan **Nurly Zhol**.
u – From Almaty (left hand panel, dep. ●).
v – To Almaty (left hand panel).

⊙ – Station for Aktau (15 km).
♡ – UTC+5 (Kazakhstan western zone, local time is shown).
● – Even dates. See page 534.
■ – Uneven dates. See page 534.

‡ – AFROSIYOB – high-speed Talgo train.
KA UZ See Table **1976**.

Nur-Sultan is the new name for Astana

MOSKVA - ARCHANGELSK, LABYTNANGI and VORKUTA 1985

	Local time (UTC+3)	16MJ Sko	34JA Fir	90GJ Sko	78JA Sko	10JA Sko	108JA Sko	118MJ Fir	22JA Fir	42VJ Fir
			F	●	H	D		⊡	②⑤§	
0	**Moskva** Yarolslavsk. ▷ d.	1005	1305	...	...	...	1705	2020	2035	2150
2	Yaroslavl ▷ d.	1516	1746	...	...	...	2052	0059	0049	0211
	St Peterburg Lad. ▷ d.	|	|	...	1020	1454	|	|	|	|
5	Vologda 1 ▷ d.	1922	2143	...	|	|	2353	0503	0447	0617
7	Konosha 1 d.	2244	0050	...	0125	0504	...	0829	0804	0946
4	**Archangelsk** a.	0600	|	...	|	1320	...	1812	|	|
5	Velsk d.	▬	0247	n	0340	...	...	...	1003	1158
4	**Kotlas** Yuzhny d.	...	0730z	0905	1012	...	...	...	1509	1702
5	Mikun a.	...	1130	1312	1358	...	...	...	1832	2057
2	**Syktyvkar** a.	...	1340	|	1918x	...	...	...	|	|
1	Sosnogorsk a.	**653/5**	...	1807	1926	...	...	...	2254	0117
6	Labytnangi *UTC+5* a.	1245	...	|	|	...	...	...	1840	|
7	**Vorkuta** a.	2104	...	0820	0950	...	...	...	...	1435

Local time (UTC+3)	117JA Fir	34MJ Fir	41MJ Fir	89GJ Sko	107JA Sko	77JA Sko	15JA Sko	9AJ Sko	21NJ Fir	653 655
	⊙	F		●(4)		K		E‡	①⑤§	■
Vorkuta d.	...	...	1635	1905	...	2027	...	...	...	0915
Labytnangi *UTC+5* d.	...	...	|	|	...	|	...	...	0950	0011v
Sosnogorsk d.	...	...	0551	0854	...	0929	...	...	0057	...
Syktyvkar d.	...	0808	|	|	...	0922x	...	...	|	...
Mikun d.	...	1013	1112	1337	...	1428	...	...	0531	...
Kotlas Yuzhny d.	...	1447z	1537	1816	...	1921	...	...	1015	...
Velsk d.	...	1931	2034	u	...	0110	...	...	1501	...
Archangelsk d.	0725	|	|	...	...	|	2025	2120	|	...
Konosha 1 d.	1737	2158	2248	...	...	0336	0454	0556	1716	...
Vologda 1 ▷ d.	2121	0054	0155	...	0509	|	0821	|	2012	...
St Peterburg Lad. ▷ a.	|	|	|	...	|	1845	|	2055	|	...
Yaroslavl ▷ d.	0153	0514	0609	...	0816	...	1229	...	0031	...
Moskva Yarolslavsk. ▷ a.	0623	0912	0958	...	1145	...	1643	...	0446	...

①④⑤ (days may vary).
②⑤⑥ (days may vary).
Approx every 3 days (June - Aug also runs as *Sko* **224**CH, **228**JA).
■(5) (approx every 3 days Jan. 13 - Apr. 24 and Sept. 1 - Dec. 5).
Daily to Mikun and Syktyvkar May - Aug. (train **98**JA other days).
■(3) (approx every 3 days Jan. 13 - Apr. 24 and Sept. 1 - Dec. 5).
Daily from Syktyvkar and Mikun May - Aug. (train **97**VJ other days).
From Nizhni Novgorod (1610), Kirov (2356).
To Kirov (0140), Nizhni Novgorod (0915).

v – Arrive 2218 on uneven dates.
x – Syktyvkar portion: **305**JA and **304**JA.
z – Kotlas **Uzlovoy**.
▷ – See also Table **1990**.
● – Even dates. See page 534.
■ – Uneven dates. See page 534.
⊡ – **116**MJ on ● (Archangelsk a. 1739).
⊙ – **115**JA on ●(4) (Archangelsk d. 0800).
‡ – Train **289**AJ on certain dates.

km	143JA/371JA	♡	371CH/144JA	♧
0	**Murmansk** d.	0615	**Archangelsk** d.	1625
277	Kandalaksha d.	1150	Belomorsk d.	0443
665	Belomorsk d.	1917	Kandalaksha d.	1235
1151	**Archangelsk** a.	0900	**Murmansk** a.	1800

§ – 2-3 times per week June - Sept.
♡ – Every 4 days (● May / Aug; ■ June / July / Sept. 1-13).
♧ – Every 4 days (● May / Aug; ■ June / July / Sept. 1-11).

MOSKVA - NIZHNI NOVGOROD fast day trains 1989

For other trains see Table **1990**. Train number suffix is *NJ (GJ* for *Lastochka* trains)

Time zone: UTC+3	702 ♠	728 ❦	730 ❦	704 ♠	706 ♠	708 ♠	732 ❦	734 ❦	710 ♠	771 ♥
St Peterburg **1900** d.	...	...	...	...	...	...	...	...	...	1700
Moskva Kurskaya d.	0635	0715	0930	1100	1400	1540	1635	1835	2020	2108
Vladimir d.	0816	0858	1116	1241	1541	1721	1821	2018	2201	2306
Nizhni Novgorod d.	1010	1102	1333	1443	1743	1923	2038	2222	2359	0103

Time zone: UTC+3	757 ♥	701 ♠	727 ❦	729 ❦	703 ♠	731 ❦	705 ♠	733 ❦	707 ♠	709 ♠
Nizhni Novgorod d.	0505	0638	0739	0940	1050	1336	1553	1755	1858	2011
Vladimir d.	0704	0839	0945	1201	1257	1549	1759	2016	2054	2217
Moskva Kurskaya a.	0903	1020	1126	1345	1440	1730	1941	2210	2235	2358
St Peterburg **1900** a.	1320	...	...	...	...	...	...	...	...	...

Sapsan high-speed train. ✕ Ⓡ.
♠ – *Strizh* (Swift) fast Talgo day train.
❦ – *Lastochka* (Swallow) fast day train.

1990 MOSKVA - YEKATERINBURG - NOVOSIBIRSK - IRKUTSK - VLADIVOSTOK

km	*All times are local time*	time zone UTC+	72EJ Fir	140SJ Sko Q	36EI Fir	100EI Sko ◇	59AJ Fir	64BJ Sko D	42CH Fir d Ø	6EI Fir Ø	76EI Sko ■(7)	82IJ Sko ●(6)	84MJ Fir ♤	12JA Fir ♡	70CH Sko	51GJ Fir	56Y Fir ■(7)	92IJ Sko ●(6)	60UJ Fir ♤	16EJ Fir ♡	8EJ Fir	26GJ Sko	96 S ▽
	St Peterburg Ladozhski d.	+3	1709	...	...	...	1915g	...	...	...	...	...	...	...	...	...	...	...	...	...	...	...	.
	Vologda 1 d.	+3	0459	...	...	...	△	...	...	...	...	...	...	...	...	...	...	...	...	...	...	...	.
0	**Moskva** Yaroslavskaya d.	+3	|	...	0010	0035	|	...	...	...	...	...	1335	1335	1350	...	1620	1620	...	...	1650	...	.
	Moskva Kazanskaya d.	+3	|	...	|	|	0225k	0314r	0501k	...	1310	1310	|	|	|	...	|	|	1638	1638	|	1738	18
282	Yaroslavl ▷ d.	+3	|	...	|	0459	|	|	|	...	|	|	|	|	1820	...	|	|	|	|	|	|	
210	Vladimir ▶ d.	+3	|	...	0326	|	0433	0636	0730	...	|	|	1650	1650	|	...	1956	1956	|	|	2026	|	
461	**Nizhni Novgorod** ▶ d.	+3	|	...	0631	|	0742	1120	0959	...	|	|	2011	2011	|	2048	2312	2312	|	|	2322	|	
917	**Kirov** d.	+3	1500	...	...	1832	...	1842	...	...	|	|	0228	0228	0551	|	0514	0514	|	|	0524	|	
1397	Perm 2 d.	+5	0043	...	...	0540	...	0550	...	...	|	|	|	|	1559	|	1548	1548	|	|	1528	|	
	Murom 1 d.	+3	|	a	...	|	...	|	...	...	1754	1754	y	w	|	|	|	|	2112	2112	...	2222	00
	Kazan d.	+3	|	1555	...	|	...	|	...	...	0213	0213	...	|	|	0550	|	|	0540	0540	...	0530	07
	Sarapul d.	+4	|	2301	...	|	...	|	...	...	0858	0858	...	|	|	v	|	|	1158	1158	...	v	14
1778	**Yekaterinburg** a.	+5	0612	0759	...	1116	...	1125	...	...	1759	1759	...	2351	2116	...	2108	2108	2015	2015	...	...	23
1778	**Yekaterinburg** d.	+5	...	0827	...	1210	...	1200	...	...	1842	1842	...	0027	2149	...	2140	2140	2130	...	...	...	00
2104	Tyumen d.	+5	...	1419	...	1727	...	1717	...	...	0015	0015	...	0636	0251	...	0241	0241	0403	...	...	...	05
2676	**Omsk** a.	+6	...	2315	...	0216	...	0204	...	...	0856	0856	...	t	1112	...	1046	1046	n	...	...	...	14
2676	**Omsk** d.	+6	...	2357	...	0232	...	0222	...	...	0914	0914	...	...	1128	...	1102	1102	...	...	...	...	15
3303	**Novosibirsk** a.	+7	...	0859	...	1146	...	1134	...	...	1806	1806	...	...	2007	...	1951	1951	...	...	...	...	
3303	**Novosibirsk** d.	+7	...	...	...	1242	...	...	...	...	1856	1856	...	...	2026	...	2046	2046	...	...	...	...	
3534	Tayga d.	+7	...	...	...	1605	...	...	...	...	2238	2238	...	...	0007	...	0019	0019	...	...	...	...	
4065	**Krasnoyarsk** d.	+7	...	...	...	0056	...	...	...	...	0722	0722	...	...	1049	...	0850	0925	...	...	...	...	
4483	Tayshet d.	+8	...	...	...	0903	...	...	...	...	1554	1517	...	...	1858	...	...	1801	...	...	...	...	
5152	**Irkutsk** a.	+8	...	...	...	2031	...	...	...	...	u	0321	...	...	0622	...	...	x	...	...	...	...	
5152	**Irkutsk** d.	+8	...	...	...	2106	...	...	...	...	...	0358	...	...	0657	...	...	...	...	...	...	...	
5608	Ulan Ude d.	+8	...	...	...	0516	...	...	...	...	...	1158	...	...	1657	...	...	...	...	...	...	...	
6165	Chita 2 d.	+9	...	...	...	1729	...	...	...	...	...	...	...	...	0530	...	...	...	...	...	...	...	
7274	Skovorodino d.	+9	...	...	...	1644	...	...	...	...	...	...	...	...	...	...	...	...	...	...	...	...	
8492	**Khabarovsk** d.	+10	...	...	...	1630	...	...	...	2045	...	...	...	...	...	...	...	...	...	...	...	...	
9147	Ussuriysk d.	+10	...	...	...	0402	...	...	...	0632	...	...	...	...	...	...	...	...	...	...	...	...	
9258	**Vladivostok** a.	+10	...	...	...	0603	...	...	...	0827	...	...	...	...	...	...	...	...	...	...	...	...	

All times are local time	time zone UTC+	118NJ Sko ●(4)	90UJ Sko ■(5)	32GJ Fir	2JI Fir Ø	145AJ Sko ■(2)	131GJ Sko ●(4)	110EI Sko	38NJ Fir ●(4)	38NJ Fir ●(4)	74EJ Sko ■(3)	74EJ 110 ■(3)	14NJ Fir ●(4)	24MJ Fir	68Y Sko		2SZ Fir ■(1) R			2SZ 20CH ⑥ V	8UJ Sko ⊙	4ZJ Sko ② B	6 Sk
St Peterburg Ladozhski d.	+3	...	...	...	...	1333	1333	...	...	...	1530	1530	1530	...	...	...	...		...	...	...	...	
Vologda 1 d.	+3	...	...	...	...	△	△	...	...	...	0251	0251	0251	...	...	...	...		...	...	...	...	
Moskva Yaroslavskaya d.	+3	...	...	2005	...	|	|	2235	2250	2250	|	|	|	...	2305	...	2345	*day 1*	...	2345	...	2355	2
Moskva Kazanskaya d.	+3	1920	1920	|	2050	2255k	2255k	|	|	|	|	|	|	2308	|	...	|		...	|	...	|	
Yaroslavl ▷ d.	+3	|	|	|	|	|	|	|	|	|	|	|	|	|	0312	...	|		...	|	...	|	
Vladimir ▶ d.	+3	|	|	2330	|	0139	0139	0149	0159	0159	|	|	|	|	|	...	0252	*day 2*	...	0252	...	0302	0
Nizhni Novgorod ▶ d.	+3	|	|	0225	|	0440	0440	0450	0500	0500	|	|	|	|	|	...	0549	*day 2*	...	0549	...	0559	0
Kirov d.	+3	|	|	0833	|	1233	1233	1138	1148	1148	1243	1243	1243	|	1450	...	1203	*day 2*	...	1203	...	1213	1
Perm 2 d.	+5	|	|	...	|	2251	v	2231	2221	2221	2241	2241	2241	|	0030	...	2201	*day 2*	...	2201	...	2211	2
Murom 1 d.	+3	0017	0017	...	0109	|	...	|	|	|	|	|	|	0302	|	...	|		...	|	...	|	
Kazan d.	+3	0755	0755	...	0800	|	...	|	|	|	|	|	|	1043	|	...	|		...	|	...	|	
Sarapul d.	+4	1423	1423	...	...	|	...	|	|	|	|	|	|	...	|	...	|		...	|	...	|	
Yekaterinburg a.	+5	2324	2324	...	...	0406	...	0335	0322	0322	0357	0357	0357	...	0534	...	0304	*day 3*	...	0304	...	0312	0
Yekaterinburg d.	+5	0018	0018	...	...	0452	...	0418	0350	0350	0426	0426	0426	...	0602	...	0332	*day 3*	...	0332	...	0340	0
Tyumen d.	+5	0541	p	...	...	c	...	1027	0831	0831	0920	1027	0940	...	1159	...	0810	*day 3*	...	0810	...	0820	0
Omsk a.	+6	1445	...	...	...	...	...	s	1653	1653	...	s	1844	...	2115	...	1620	*day 3*	...	1620	...	1636	1
Omsk d.	+6	1501	...	...	...	...	...	...	1710	1710	...	...	1934	...	2131	...	1701	*day 3*	...	1701	...	1652	1
Novosibirsk a.	+7	2322	...	...	...	...	...	...	0219	0219	...	...	0417	...	0600	...	0126	*day 4*	...	0126	...	0107	0
Novosibirsk d.	+7	0014	...	...	...	...	...	...	0309	0320	...	...	0507	...	0651	...	0144	*day 4*	...	0144	2354	0125	0
Tayga d.	+7	o	...	...	...	...	...	...	m	0737	...	...	o	...	1030	...	0506	*day 4*	...	0506	0420	|	
Krasnoyarsk d.	+7	...	...	...	...	...	...	...	...	z	...	...	...	...	q	...	1320	*day 4*	...	1320	1330	1259	1
Tayshet d.	+8	...	...	...	...	...	...	...	...	...	...	...	...	...	...	...	2057	*day 4*	...	2057	2127	|	
Irkutsk a.	+8	...	...	...	...	...	...	...	...	...	...	...	...	...	...	...	0740	*day 5*	...	0740	0828	0750	0
Irkutsk d.	+8	...							...	...	...	...	...	...	...	...	0803	*day 5*	...	0803	0857	0820	0
Ulan Ude d.	+8	...							...	...	...	...	...	...	...	...	1502	*day 5*	...	1502	1647	1547	1
Chita 2 d.	+9	...							...	...	...	...	...	...	...	...	0147	*day 6*	...	0057	0503	...	
Skovorodino d.	+9	...							...	...	...	...	...	...	...	...	2228	*day 6*	...	...	0333	...	
Khabarovsk d.	+10	...							...	...	...	...	...	...	...	...	1931	*day 7*	...	...	0209	...	
Ussuriysk d.	+10	...							...	...	...	...	...	...	...	...	0516	*day 8*	...	...	1238	...	
Vladivostok a.	+10	...	...	...	...	...	...	...	...	...	...	...	...	...	...	...	0707	*day 8*	...	...	1432	...	

For fast day trains Moskva - Nizhni Novgorod and *Sapsan* St Peterburg - Moskva - Nizhni Novgorod see Table **1989**

MOSKVA - BEIJING via Ulaan Baatar

km	*Trans-Mongolian route*	time zone UTC+	306IJ Pas ①⑤	306Y Pas § ②	4ZJ Sko ②B	6SZ Sko § ③A	24 Exp ④◧
0	*Moskva Yar. (above)* d.	+3	...	...	2355 ②	2355 ③	...
3303	*Novosibirsk (above)* d.	+7	...	...	0125 ⑤	0125 ⑥	...
5152	**Irkutsk** d.	+8	0820	0820	0820 ⑥	0820 ⑦	...
5608	Ulan Ude d.	+8	1547	1547	1547 ⑥	1547 ⑦	...
5863	Naushki 🏛 d.	+8	2147	2147	2147 ⑥	2147 ⑦	...
5886	Suche Bator 🏛 MO d.	+8	0014	0014	0014 ⑦	0014 ①	...
6265	**Ulaan Baatar** MO a.	+8	0650	0650	0650 ⑦	0650 ①	...
6265	**Ulaan Baatar** MO d.	+8	...	...	0730 ⑦	...	0730 ④
6770	Dzamin Uud 🏛 MO d.	+8	...	...	2035 ⑦	...	2035 ④
6780	Erlan 🏛 CH a.	+8	...	...	2100 ⑦	...	2100 ④
7622	**Beijing** CH a.	+8	...	...	1435 ①	...	1435 ⑤

MOSKVA - BEIJING via Harbin

km	*Trans-Manchurian route*	time zone UTC+	2SZ 20SZ ⑥V	602CH 684CH ④⑥	602 P
0	*Moskva Yar. (above)* d.	+3	2345 ⑥	...	.
1778	*Yekaterinburg (above)* d.	+5	0332 ①	...	.
3303	*Novosibirsk (above)* d.	+7	0144 ②	...	.
5152	**Irkutsk** d.	+8	0803 ③	...	.
6165	Chita 2 d.	+9	0209 ④	1935	19
6626	Zabaikalsk 🏛 d.	+9	1905 ④	1135	07
6638	Manzhouli 🏛 CH d.	+8	2359 ④	1100	
7573	Harbin CH a.	+8	1229 ⑤	...	
8122	Shenyang CH a.	+8	1926 ⑤	...	
8849	Tianjin CH a.	+8	0352 ⑥	...	
8986	**Beijing** CH a.	+8	0549 ⑥	...	

A – To Ulaanbaatar (see panel below main table). Runs alternate ③ Dec. 19, Jan. 2, 16, 30, Feb. 13, 27, Mar. 13, 27, Apr. 10, 24, May 8, 22, June 5, 19.
B – To Ulaanbaatar and Beijing (see panel below main table).
D – ② from Brest (d. 1142, train **104***BJ*), ②⑤ from Minsk (d. 1623), Smolensk (d. 2108), Moskva next day.
Q – From Adler on even dates ●(6) (daily May 30 - Sept. 14). Depart Yekaterinburg on 4th day. To Barnaul *UTC+7* (a. 1433).
R – ROSSIYA.
V – VOSTOK – to Beijing via Harbin (see panel below main table). Runs on ⑥. Combined with train **2** Moskva - Chita on alternate ⑥.

a – From Adler, Sochi, Rostov (Table **1960**).
b – To Barnaul *UTC+7* (a. 0831). Train **136** (note ▽) Barnaul a. 0530.
c – To Chelyabinsk *UTC+5* (a. 0925).
d – From Novgorod na Volkhove (Table **1900**).
g – St Peterburg **Glavni**.
k – Moskva **Kurskaya**.
m – To Kemerovo *UTC+7* (a. 0820).
n – To Tobolsk *UTC+5* (a. 0751), Surgut *UTC+5* (a. 1715) and Niznevartovsk *UTC+5* (a. 2240).
o – To Novokuznetsk *UTC+7* (train **14** a. 1216; train **118** a. 0754).
p – To Petropavl (Table **1976**), also Chelyabinsk *UTC+5* (a. 0623).
q – To Abakan *UTC+7* (a. 0545).
r – Moskva **Belorusskaya**.
s – To Tobolsk *UTC+5* (a. 1359), Surgut *UTC+5* (a. 2253), Korotchayevo *UTC+5* (a. 1245), Novy Urengoy *UTC+5* (a. 1450).
t – To Tobolsk *UTC+5* (a. 1003), Surgut *UTC+5* (a. 1834), Korotchayevo *UTC+5* (a. 0801), Novy Urengoy *UTC+5* (a. 1000).
u – To Neryungri (Table **1991**).
v – To Izhevsk *UTC+4* (train **26** a. 1126, **51** a. 1153, **131** a. 2054).
w – Via Nivhni Tagil *UTC+5* (d. 2136).
x – To Severobaikalsk (Table **1991**).
y – To Serov *UTC+5* (a. 0118), Priobe *UTC+5* (a. 1333).
z – To Tomsk 2 *UTC+7* (a. 0930) via Tomsk 1 (a. 0901).
♡ – Uneven dates Jan., Apr., May, Aug., Nov.; even dates Dec., Feb., Mar., June, July, Sept., Oct.
♤ – Even dates Jan., Apr., May, Aug., Nov.; uneven dates Dec., Feb., Mar., June, July, Sept., Oct.
◇ – Arrives on 7th day. Conveys 🛏 Moskva - Ussuriysk - Tumangan (N. Korea) on 1st, 5th, 12th, 17th, 21st, 26th of month (train **100***SZ*, arrives 1145 on 8th day; connection to Pyongyang a. 2200 9th day; departures on 12th, 26th have through carriage to Pyongyang).
▷ – Fast day trains run from Moskva Yaroslavskaya to Yaroslavl at 0735, 1445, 1905 (journey 3h 20m).

◧ – ④ all year. Operator: June 2 May 2019 Mongolian Railway June 2019 - May 2020 Chine Railways. Also runs late-June late-September, ⑥ in 2019 (' golian), on ⑤ in 2020 (Chine
△ – Via Tver (Table **1900**).
▽ – Train **136** *MJ* on even dates
⊙ – Numbered **8***NJ* alternate day Conveys portion for Neryung dates in Table **1991**.
Ø – Includes De Luxe sleeping ca with ensuite shower/toilet.
§ – Operated by Mongolian Railw
▶ – For fast day trains Moskva - N Novgorod see Table **1989**.
● – Even dates (see page 534).
■ – Uneven dates (see page 534
CH – China (UTC+8).
MO – Mongolia (UTC+8).

VLADIVOSTOK - IRKUTSK - NOVOSIBIRSK - YEKATERINBURG - MOSKVA 1990

All times are local time	time zone UTC+	67Y Sko	3ZJ Sko B	5SZ Sko§ A	51EI Fir		1MJ Fir ●(8) R			19CH 319CH V	37NJ Fir ●(2)	29NJ 37NJ ●(2)	146UJ Sko ■	132GJ Sko ●	140NJ Sko Q	69CH Sko	71EJ Fir	63BJ Sko ② C	103NJ Sko ⑥ D	73EJ Sko ■(1)	13NJ Fir ■(1)	5EI Fir Ø	7EI Sko ⊙
divostok d.	+10	...	...	...	...	...	1910	day 1	...	...	...	...	...	...	...	...	...	...	...	...	...	2045	2152
uriysk d.	+10	...	...	...	...	...	2121	day 1	...	...	...	...	...	...	...	...	...	...	...	...	...	2254	2353
abarovsk d.	+10	...	...	...	...	...	0820	day 2	...	...	...	...	...	...	...	...	...	...	...	...	...	0821	1034
vorodino d.	+9	...	...	...	...	...	0243	day 3	...	...	...	...	...	...	...	...	...	...	...	...	...	...	0612
ta 2 d.	+9	...	...	...	...	...	0015	day 4	...	0015	...	...	...	...	...	2109	...	...	...	...	...	...	0514
n Ude d.	+8	...	0705	0705	...	...	0855	day 4	...	0855	...	...	...	...	...	0747	...	...	...	...	...	...	1450
tsk a.	+8	...	1452	1452	...	...	1531	day 4	...	1531	...	...	...	...	...	1559	...	...	...	...	...	...	2223
tsk d.	+8	...	1522	1522	...	...	1554	day 4	...	1554	...	...	...	...	...	1639	...	...	...	...	...	...	2252
shet d.	+8	...	|	|	...	...	0235	day 5	...	0235	...	...	...	...	...	0414	...	...	...	...	...	...	1005
snoyarsk d.	+7	q	0811	0811	...	...	0821	day 5	...	0821	z	...	...	...	...	1044	...	...	...	...	...	...	1628
ga d.	+7	1253	|	|	...	...	1637	day 5	...	1637	1511	m	...	...	...	2052	...	...	...	...	o	...	0208
vosibirsk a.	+7	1615	1951	1951	...	...	1939	day 5	...	1939	1854	1908	...	...	...	0006	...	...	...	...	0305	...	0521
vosibirsk d.	+7	1700	2009	2009	...	...	1957	day 5	...	1957	2020	2020	...	...	2138	0109	...	0407	0407	...	0357	...	...
sk a.	+6	0007	0226	0226	...	...	0215	day 6	...	0215	0254	0254	...	...	0519	0900	...	1054	1054	...	1018	...	...
sk d.	+6	0023	0242	0242	...	...	0252	day 6	...	0252	0310	0310	...	...	0555	0918	...	1110	1110	...	1100	...	...
men d.	+5	0702	0850	0850	...	...	0900	day 6	...	0900	0912	0912	c	...	1228	1637	...	1757	1757	1747	1747	...	...
aterinburg a.	+5	1259	1328	1328	...	...	1336	day 6	...	1336	1344	1344	1651	...	1749	2155	...	2311	2311	2303	2303	...	...
aterinburg d.	+5	1337	1358	1358	...	...	1406	day 6	...	1406	1416	1416	1733	...	1817	2322	2312	2346	2346	2335	2335	...	...
arapul d.	+4	|	|	|	v	...	|		...	|	|	|	|	...	0102	|	|	|	|	|	|	...	...
azan d.	+3	|	|	|	2205	...	|		...	|	|	|	|	...	0516	|	|	|	|	|	|	...	...
urom 1 d.	+3	|	|	|	|	...	|		...	|	|	|	|	...	a	|	|	|	|	|	|	...	...
m 2 d.	+5	1930	1940	1940	|	...	1950	day 6	...	1950	2035	2035	2330	v	...	0512	0503	0543	0543	0535	0535	...	...
ov d.	+3	0105	0115	0115	|	...	0125	day 7	...	0125	0327	0327	0714	0714	...	1116	1106	1156	1156	1146	1146	...	...
ni Novgorod ▶ d.	+3	|	0702	0702	0652	...	0748	day 7	...	0748	0947	0947	1354	1354	...	|	|	1818	1818	|	|	...	...
dimir ▶ d.	+3	|	1100	1100	...	...	1110	day 7	...	1110	1305	1305	1730	1730	...	|	|	2230	2230	|	|	...	...
aroslavl ▷ d.	+3	1240	|	|	...	...	|		...	|	|	|	|	|	...	0011	|	|	|	|	|	...	...
skva Kazanskaya a.	+3	|	|	|	...	...	|		...	|	|	|	2151k	2151k	...	|	|	0115r	0115r	|	|	...	...
skva Yaroslavskaya a.	+3	1658	1358	1358	...	...	1413	day 7	...	1413	1558	1558	|	|	...	0411	|	...	...	|	|	...	...
ologda 1 d.	+3	...	...	...	...	...	...		...	...	...	...	△	△	...	...	2110	...	...	2233	2233	...	...
t Peterburg Ladozhski a.	+3	...	...	...	...	...	...		...	...	...	...	0616	0616	...	...	0838	...	...	1000	1000	...	...

All times are local time	time zone UTC+	41GJ Fir d Ø	59GJ Fir	75EI Sko ●(2)	81IJ Sko ●(2)	89UJ Sko ■(3)	689Y 89UJ ■(3)	117NJ Sko ■(1)	95NJ Sko ▽	7EJ Fir	55Y Fir ●(4)	91IJ Sko ●(2)	35GJ Fir	23GJ Fir	1GJ Fir Ø	99EI Sko ◇	25GJ Sko	59EJ Fir ♡	15EJ Fir ♡	31GJ Fir	109MJ Sko	84EJ Fir ♤	11EJ Fir ♤
divostok d.	+10	...	...	...	...	...	...	...	...	...	...	...	...	...	...	0051	...	...	...	...	...	...	...
uriysk d.	+10	...	...	...	...	...	...	...	...	...	...	...	...	...	...	0312	...	...	...	...	...	...	...
barovsk d.	+10	...	...	...	...	...	...	...	...	...	...	...	...	...	...	1500	...						
vorodino d.	+9	...	...	...	...	...	...	...	...	...	...	...	...	...	...	1051	...						
a 2 d.	+9	...	...	...	...	...	...	...	...	...	...	...	...	...	...	0924	...						
Ude d.	+8	...	...	...	1555	...	...	...	...	...	...	...	...	...	...	1915	...						
tsk a.	+8	...	...	...	2310	...	...	...	...	...	...	...	...	...	...	0307	...						
tsk d.	+8	...	...	u	2355	...	...	...	...	...	...	x	...	...	...	0337	...						
shet d.	+8	...	...	1144	1144	...	...	...	...	...	...	1411	...	...	...	1448	...	...	...	...	...	...	...
snoyarsk d.	+7	...	...	1804	1804	...	...	...	...	...	2030	2030	...	...	...	2112	...	...	...	...	...	...	...
ga d.	+7	...	...	0241	0241	...	...	o	...	...	0534	0534	...	...	...	0549	...	...	...	...	...	...	...
osibirsk a.	+7	...	...	0612	0612	...	...	0657	...	...	0839	0839	...	...	...	0909	...	...	...	...	...	...	...
osibirsk d.	+7	...	...	0702	0702	...	...	0749	b	...	0924	0924	...	...	...	1008	...	...	...	...	...	...	...
sk a.	+6	...	...	1423	1423	...	...	1433	1320	...	1705	1705	...	...	...	1742	...	...	...	...	...	...	...
sk d.	+6	...	...	1447	1447	...	...	1510	1414	...	1745	1745	...	...	...	1804	...	n	...	...	s	...	t
men d.	+5	...	...	2137	2137	p	c	2158	2147	...	0024	0024	...	...	...	0034	...	0323	...	...	0044	...	2127
aterinburg a.	+5	...	...	0251	0251	0300	0150	0309	0322	...	0452	0452	...	...	...	0500	...	0923	...	...	0508	...	0330
aterinburg d.	+5	...	...	0319	0319	0404	0404	0404	0354	...	0524	0524	...	...	...	0532	...	1012	1012	...	0644	...	0419
arapul d.	+4	...	...	1115	1115	1125	1125	1125	1135	...	|	|	...	...	...	|	v	1358	1658	...	|	...	|
azan d.	+3	...	...	1615	1615	1630	1630	1630	1642	...	|	|	...	1811	2000	|	2203	2215	2215	...	|	...	|
urom 1 d.	+3	...	...	0031	0031	0055	0055	0055	0107	...	|	|	...	0208	0301	|	0458	0510	0510	...	|	y	w
n 2 d.	+5	...	...	|	|	|	|	|	|	1124	1133	1133	...	|	|	1144	|	|	|	...	1450	|	|
v d.	+3	...	...	|	|	|	|	|	|	1716	1726	1726	...	|	|	1743	|	|	|	2030	2118	2128	2128
ni Novgorod ▶ d.	+3	1625	1906	|	|	|	|	|	|	2310	2324	2324	2335	|	|	|	|	|	|	0302	0312	0320	0320
imir ▶ d.	+3	1853	2156	|	|	|	|	|	|	0204	0240	0240	0325	|	|	|	|	|	|	0627	0712	0722	0722
aroslavl ▷ d.	+3	|	|	|	|	|	|	|	|	|	|	|	|	|	|	0648	|	|	|	|	|	|	|
kva Kazanskaya a.	+3	2138k	0029k	0457	0457	0538	0538	0538	0546	|	|	|	|	0637	0710	|	0923	0930	0930	|	|	|	|
kva Yaroslavskaya a.	+3	...	|	...	...	...	...	...	...	0522	0552	0552	0629	...	...	1113	...	...	...	0943	1030	1038	1038
logda 1 d.	+3	...	△	...	...	...	...	...	...	...	...	...	...	...	...	...	...	...	...	...	...	...	...
Peterburg Ladozhski a.	+3	...	0905g	...	...	...	...	...	...	...	...	...	...	...	...	...	...	...	...	...	...	...	...

For fast day trains Nizhni Novgorod - Moskva see Table **1989** also *Sapsan* Nizhni Novgorod - Moskva - St Peterburg

BEIJING - MOSKVA via Ulaan Baatar

km	Trans-Mongolian route	time zone UTC+	305Y Pas § ⑦	305IJ Pas ②⑥	23 Exp ◧	3ZJ Sko ③B	5SZ Sko § ⑤A
0	**Beijing** CH d.	+8	...	...	0727	0727 ③	...
42	Erlan 🏛 CH d.	+8	...	...	0059	0059 ④	...
52	Dzamin Uud 🏛 MO d.	+8	...	...	0240	0240 ④	...
56	**Ulaan Baatar** MO a.	+8	...	...	1435	1435 ④	...
56	**Ulaan Baatar** MO d.	+8	1522	1522	...	1522 ④	1522 ⑤
35	Suche Bator 🏛 MO d.	+8	2329	2329	...	2329 ④	2329 ⑤
58	Naushki 🏛 d.	+8	0204	0204	...	0204 ⑤	0204 ⑥
13	Ulan Ude d.	+8	0705	0705	...	0705 ⑤	0705 ⑥
69	**Irkutsk** a.	+8	1452	1452	...	1452 ⑤	1452 ⑥
19	*Novosibirsk (above)* a.	+7	...	...	...	1951 ⑥	1951 ⑦
22	*Moskva Yar. (above)* a.	+3	...	...	...	1358 ①	1358 ②

BEIJING - MOSKVA via Harbin

km	Trans-Manchurian route	time zone UTC+	19CH Sko ⑥V	653CH 683CH ⑤⑦	683CH
0	**Beijing** CH d.	+8	2300 ⑥	...	...
137	Tianjin CH d.	+8	0041 ⑦	...	...
864	Shenyang CH d.	+8	0855 ⑦	...	...
1413	Harbin CH d.	+8	1555 ⑦	...	...
2348	Manzhouli 🏛 CH d.	+8	0701 ①	1400	...
2360	Zabaikalsk 🏛 d.	+9	1332 ①	2015e	2015
2820	Chita 2 d.	+9	0015 ②	0752	0752
3833	**Irkutsk** a.	+8	1531 ②	...	...
5683	*Novosibirsk (above)* a.	+7	1939 ③	...	...
7208	*Yekaterinburg (above)* a.	+5	1336 ④	...	...
8986	*Moskva Yar. (above)* a.	+3	1413 ⑤	...	...

From Ulaanbaatar (see below main table). Runs alternate ⑤ Dec. 14, 28, Jan. 11, 25, Feb. 8, 22, Mar. 8, 22, Apr. 5, 19, May 3, 17, 31, June 14, 28.
From Beijing on ③, Ulaanbaatar ④ (see panel below main table). To Smolensk a. 0645 ④ and Minsk a. 1122 ④.
To Smolensk a. 0645 ①, Minsk a. 1122 ①, Brest a. 1616 ①.
Even dates (daily May 26 - Sept. 10). Arrive Adler on 5th day.
From Barnaul *UTC+7* d. 1444.
ROSSIYA.
VOSTOK – from Beijing via Harbin (see below main table). From Beijing on ⑥ (Chita on ②). On certain dates is numbered **319***CH* and combined with train **1** *MJ* between Chita and Moskva.
To Rostov, Sochi, Adler (Table **1960**).
From Barnaul *UTC+7* (d. 0030● train **136**, 2153 ● train **95**).
From Chelyabinsk *UTC+5* (train **146** d. 1230, train **689** d. 2027).
To Novgorod na Volkhove (Table **1900**).
Arrives 1525.
St Peterburg **Glavni**.
Moskva **Kurskaya**.
From Kemerovo *UTC+7* (d. 1348).
From Niznevartovsk *UTC+5* (d. 0645), Surgut *UTC+5* (d. 1253), Tobolsk *UTC+5* (d. 2247). Next day from Yekaterinberg.
From Novokuznetsk *UTC+7* (train **13** d. 2026; train **117** d. 2203).

p – From Petropavl (Table **1976**). Next day from Yekaterinburg.
q – From Abakan *UTC+7* (d. 1820).
r – Moskva **Belorusskaya**.
s – From Novy Urengoy *UTC+5* (d. 1650), Korotchayevo (d. 1855), Surgut (d. 0927 2nd day), Tobolsk *UTC+5* (d. 2000 2nd day).
t – From Novy Urengoy *UTC+5* (d. 1200), Korotchayevo (d. 1427), Surgut (d. 0547 2nd day), Tobolsk *UTC+5* (d. 1621 2nd day).
u – From Neryungri (Table **1991**), departs Tayshet on 3rd day.
v – From Izhevsk *UTC+4* (train **25** d. 1740, **51** d. 1730, **132** d. 2305).
w – Via Nivhni Tagil *UTC+5* (d. 0649).
x – From Severobaikalsk on ● (Table **1991**), next day from Tayshet.
y – From Priobe *UTC+5* (d. 1621), Serov *UTC+5* (d. 0355). Departs Kirov on 2nd day.
z – From Tomsk 2 *UTC+7* (d. 1230) via Tomsk 1 (d. 1302).
♡ – Uneven dates Jan., Apr., May, Aug., Nov.; even dates Dec., Feb., Mar., June, July, Sept., Oct.
♤ – Even dates Jan., Apr., May, Aug., Nov.; uneven dates Dec., Feb., Mar., June, July, Sept., Oct.
◇ – Journey 7 nights Vladivostok - Moskva. Also conveys 🛏 Pyongyang (North Korea) - Tumangan - Ussuriysk - Moskva twice monthly, Tumangan - Ussuriysk - Moskva four times monthly (with connection from Pyongyang).
▽ – Train **136***NJ* on alternate days.

△ – Via Tver (Table **1900**).
▷ – Fast day trains run Yaroslavl to Moskva Yaroslavskaya at 0703, 1355, 1943 (journey 3 h 20 m).
◧ – ⑥ June 9, 2018 - May 30, 2019 (§), ② June 2019 - May 2020 (Chinese Railways); Also runs late-June to late-September, in 2019 on ① (Mongolian Railways), in 2020 on ② (Chinese Railways).
⊙ – Numbered **7***NJ* alternate days. Conveys Neryungri - Novosibirsk on dates in Table **1991**.
Ø – Includes De Luxe sleeping cars with ensuite shower/toilet.
§ – Operated by Mongolian Railways.
▶ – For fast day trains Nizhni Novgorod - Moskva see Table **1989**.
● – Even dates (see page 534).
■ – Uneven dates (see page 534).
CH – China (UTC+8).
MO – Mongolia (UTC+8).

1991 NOVOSIBIRSK - SEVEROBAIKALSK - TYNDA - NERYUNGRI - TOMMOT

Baikal - Amur Magistrale (BAM) line

km	Times are local times	time zone UTC+	87IJ 348Y ●	348Y Pas ●	71IJ Sko ■(1)	76EI Sko ■(7) n	92IJ Sko ●(6) n	324JI Pas	8UJ 687NJ ■(4)	
	Moskva Yar. **1990** d.	+3	...	...	...	1310r	1620	...	...	...
0	**Novosibirsk** **1990** d.	+7	...	...	...	1856	2046	...	2354	...
762	Krasnoyarsk **1990** d.	+7	...	2117	...	0722	0925	...	1330	...
	Ulan Ude **1990** d.	+8	...	|	1555	|	|	...	|	...
	Irkutsk **1990** d.	+8	1933	|	2345	|	|	...	|	...
1180	**Tayshet** a.	+8	0703	0705	1105	1514	1731	...	2124	...
1180	**Tayshet** d.	+8	0815	0840	1140	1554	1801	...	2127	...
1473	Bratsk d.	+8	1809	1809	1809	2201	0023	...	|	...
2243	**Severobaikalsk** d.	+8	1010	1010	1010	1217	1410	...	▽	...
3972	Skovorodino d.	+9	...	...	...	|	...	...	0414x	...
3528	**Tynda** a.	+9	...	...	...	1627*	...	...	0907	...
∆	**Tynda** d.	+9	...	...	...	1808	...	...	1009	...
3757	Neryungri d.	+9	...	...	...	2322	...	0756	1510	...
4125	Tommot a.	+9	...	...	...	...	...	1545	...	...
4493	Nizhny Bestyakh ⊕ a.	+9	...	...	...	...	...	...	...	...

Times are local times	time zone UTC+	323JI	75EI Sko ● u	91IJ Sko ● s	687EI 7EI ■(6)	71Y Sko ■(3)	347Y 87Y ●(4)	347Y Pas ●(4)	
Nizhny Bestyakh ⊕ d.	+9	...	...	...	...	...	...	...	...
Tommot d.	+9	1906	...	...	...	...	...	...	...
Neryungri d.	+9	0317	0457	...	1801	...	...	...	...
Tynda a.	+9	...	1007	...	2241	...	...	...	...
Tynda d.	+9	...	1210	...	2331	...	...	...	...
Skovorodino d.	+9	...	|	...	0612	...	...	...	...
Severobaikalsk d.	+8	...	1512*	1718	▽	2225	2225	2225	...
Bratsk d.	+8	...	0442	0713	|	1251	1325	1325	...
Tayshet a.	+8	...	1042	1341	1002z	1837	2309	2352	...
Tayshet d.	+8	...	1144	1411	1005z	1912	0024	0122	...
Irkutsk **1990** a.	+8	...	|	|	|	0612	1155	|	...
Ulan Ude **1990** a.	+8	...	|	|	|	1355	...	|	...
Krasnoyarsk **1990** a.	+7	...	1722	1955	1548	...	...	0931	...
Novosibirsk **1990** a.	+7	...	0612	0839	0521	...	...	...	...
Moskva Yar. **1990** a.	+3	...	0457r	0552	...	...	...	...	...

	Times are local	UTC+	364EI
0	**Tynda** d.	+9	1700
669	Fevralsk d.	+9	0833
951	Novy Urgal a.	+10	1603
951	Novy Urgal d.	+10	1643
1469	**Komsomolsk** a.	+10	0628

Times are local	UTC+	363EI
Komsomolsk d.	+10	1820
Novy Urgal a.	+10	0817
Novy Urgal d.	+10	0857
Fevralsk d.	+9	1500
Tynda a.	+9	0620

	Times are local	UTC+	351EI	667EI
0	**Vladivostok** **1990** d.	+10	1720	...
111	Ussuriysk **1990** d.	+10	1949	...
766	**Khabarovsk** **1990** d.	+10	0810	2102
1155	Komsomolsk a.	+10	1750	0610
1618	Sovetskaya Gavan a.	+10	0901	...

Times are local	UTC+	351JI	667
Sovetskaya Gavan d.	+10	1725	...
Komsomolsk d.	+10	0806	210
Khabarovsk **1990** a.	+10	1830	061
Ussuriysk **1990** a.	+10	0645	...
Vladivostok **1990** a.	+10	0909	...

n – Novosibirsk on 3rd day, Severobaikalsk on 5th day.
r – Moskva Kazanskaya.
s – Novosibirsk 3rd day, Moskva 5th day.
u – Novosibirsk 4th day, Moskva 6th day.
x – 5th day.

z – 4th day.
▽ – Via Irkutsk (Table **1990**).
● – Even dates. See page 534.
■ – Uneven dates. See page 534.

∆ – *4182* via Skovorodino.
⊕ – Under construction. In summer a ferry (15 km from station) r… to Yakutsk.
* – Following day (more than 24 hours after previous time show…

1993 YEKATERINBURG - KAZAN - SARATOV - VOLGOGRAD

km	Local times	time zone UTC+	45EJ Fir ■(3)	125GJ Sko
0	**Yekaterinburg** d.	+5	0130	...
515	Sarapul d.	+4	1103	...
875	**Kazan** d.	+3	1658	2120
1121	Ulyanovsk d.	+4	0043	0328
1407	**Samara** a.	+4	|	0840
1576	**Saratov 1** d.	+4	1031	...
2005	Volgograd 1 d.	+4	1850	...
2665	Armavir Ros. d.	+3	0810	...
2853	Mineralnye Vody d.	+3	1159	...
2879	Pyatigorsk d.	+3	1236	...
2917	**Kislovodsk** a.	+3	1328	...

Local times	time zone UTC+	45SJ Fir ■(5)	125JI Sko
Kislovodsk d.	+3	2203	...
Pyatigorsk d.	+3	2300	...
Mineralnye Vody d.	+3	0007	...
Armavir Ros. d.	+3	0241	...
Volgograd 1 d.	+4	1658	...
Saratov 1 d.	+4	0047	...
Samara d.	+4	|	2026
Ulyanovsk d.	+4	1014	0220
Kazan d.	+3	1456	0620
Sarapul d.	+4	2129	...
Yekaterinburg a.	+5	0603	...

km	Local times	time zone UTC+	87JI Sko ●(4)	105EJ Sko
0	**Niznevartovsk** d.	+5	1040	2200
216	Surgut d.	+5	1631	0230
692	Tobolsk d.	+5	0209	1159
921	Tyumen d.	+5	0652	1617
1247	**Yekaterinburg** d.	+5	1303	2233
1762	Sarapul d.	+4	|	0600
2122	**Kazan** d.	+3	◇	1221
2368	Ulyanovsk d.	+4	|	1920
2654	**Samara** a.	+4	1142	|
2823	**Saratov 1** d.	+4	...	0601
3252	**Volgograd 1** d.	+4	...	1248

Local times	time zone UTC+	105ZH Sko	88 Sk ■
Volgograd 1 d.	+4	0010	..
Saratov 1 d.	+4	0800	.
Samara d.	+4	|	22
Ulyanovsk d.	+4	1810	|
Kazan d.	+3	2345	◇
Sarapul d.	+4	0636	|
Yekaterinburg d.	+5	1658	00
Tyumen d.	+5	2255	06
Tobolsk a.	+5	0221	10
Surgut a.	+5	1136	19
Niznevartovsk a.	+5	1631	00

● – Even dates (see page 534). ■ – Uneven dates (see page 534). ◇ – Via Ufa (Table **1994**). For Moskva - Niznevartovsk see Table **1990**.

1994 YEKATERINBURG - SAMARA - SATATOV and KYIV - BAKI

km	Local times	time zone UTC+	87JI Sko ⊡	373EJ Pas ●
0	**Tyumen** d.	+5	0652	2040
326	**Yekaterinburg** d.	+5	1303	0301
578	Chelyabinsk d.	+5	1836	1010
1059	Ufa d.	+5	0413	2019
1582	**Samara** d.	+4	1142	0432
2019	**Saratov 1** a.	+4	...	1312
2019	**Saratov 1** d.	+4	...	1400
2695	Astrakhan 1 d.	+4	...	0224
3183	**Makhachkala** a.	+3	...	1121

Local times	time zone UTC+	373SJ Pas ■(5)	88JI Sko ⊡
Makhachkala d.	+3	1635	...
Astrakhan 1 d.	+4	0350	...
Saratov 1 a.	+4	1609	...
Saratov 1 d.	+4	1657	...
Samara d.	+4	0221	2204
Ufa d.	+5	1251	0823
Chelyabinsk d.	+5	2247	1810
Yekaterinburg a.	+5	0518	2255
Tyumen a.	+5	1119	0541

km	Local times	time zone UTC+	370 Pas ①
0	**Kyiv** UA d.	♡	1450r
335	Poltava K UA d.	♡	2015r
493	**Kharkiv** UA d.	♡	2326r
861	Liski d.	+3	0906
1453	Volgograd d.	+4	2243
1903	Astrakhan 1 d.	+4	0651
2391	Makhachkala d.	+3	1600
2520	Derbent d.	+3	1835
2765	**Baki** AZ a.	+4	0410

Local times	time zone UTC+	36 Pa ⑥
Baki AZ d.	+4	013
Derbent d.	+3	090
Makhachkala d.	+3	113
Astrakhan 1 d.	+4	215
Volgograd d.	+4	060
Liski d.	+3	171
Kharkiv UA a.	♡	020
Poltava K UA a.	♡	051
Kyiv UA a.	♡	113

r – Up to one hour earlier from Oct. 27 (winter time in Ukraine).
● – Even dates (see page 534).
■ – Uneven dates (see page 534).

♡ – UTC+2 winter, UTC+3 summer.
⊡ – Alternate days (see Table **1993**).

AZ – Azerbaijan (UTC+4).
UA – Ukraine (UTC+2 winter, UTC+3 summer).

1995 GEORGIA

Time zone: UTC…

km		614	898 ☆	802	870	872	852 ☆	12	698	18	808 ☆	684	678	804	874	602	654	812 A	202 S
0	**Tbilisi** d.	...	...	0800	0810	0830	0850	0900	...	0900	1030	...	1550	1735	1750	2145	2145	0035	0045
221	Kutaisi a.	...	0805	|	|	|	|	|	1345	1430	|	1750	2100	|	|	|	|	|	|
317	Zugdidi a.	...	|	|	1345	|	|	|	1705	...	|	|	...	|	|	0605	|	|	|
312	Poti a.	...	|	|	...	1339	|	|	...	...	|	|	...	|	2252	...	|	|	|
	Ozurgeti a.	0755	|	|	...	...	|	1710	...	...	|	|	...	|	...	...	0620	|	|
348	**Batumi** a.	1000	1101	1300	...	...	1430	...	...	...	1530	2152	...	2235	...	...	...	0550	0710

	677	697	803	683	873	11	17	201 S	809 ☆	801	871	869	613	851 ☆	897 ☆	811 A	601	653	
Batumi d.	...	...	0755	0815	...	...	...	1540	1710	1800	...	...	1820	1910	2100	0045	...	...	...
Ozurgeti d.	...	...	|	|	...	0905	...	|	|	|	...	...	2025	|	|	|	...	2135	...
Poti d.	...	...	|	|	0830	|	...	|	|	|	1830	...	...	|	|	|	...	|	...
Zugdidi d.	...	0800	|	|	|	|	|	|	|	|	|	1815	...	|	|	|	2215	|	...
Kutaisi d.	0455	1125	|	1220	|	|	1225	|	|	|	|	|	...	|	2355	|	|	|	...
Tbilisi a.	1020	...	1250	...	1335	1725	1725	2145	2205	2300	2340	2352	...	0028	...	0555	0635	0635	...

A – Every second day (seats on…
S – June 15 - Oct. 1. 🛏 Batum… Tbilisi - Yerevan and v.v.
W – Uneven dates ■(3) except when train **S** runs.
Y – Even dates (not when **S** run…
■ – See page 534.
☆ – June 15 - Oct. 1 (approx da…

AR – Armenia (UTC+4).
AZ – Azerbaijan (UTC+4).

TBILISI AIRPORT

From Tibilisi: 0750, 1655.
From Airport: 0835, 1740.
Journey 35 minutes

km		37 🛏	
0	Tbilisi d.	2035	...
551	Baki AZ a.	0850	...

	38 🛏	
Baki AZ d.	2040	...
Tbilisi a.	0855	...

km	🛏	372 W	201 S	
	Batumi d.	...	1540	...
0	Tbilisi d.	2020	2216	...
374	Yerevan AR a.	0655	0725	...

🛏	202 S	371 Y
Yerevan AR d.	1530	2130
Tbilisi a.	0012	0750
Batumi a.	0710	...

Timings in Georgia are valid from January 5, 2019

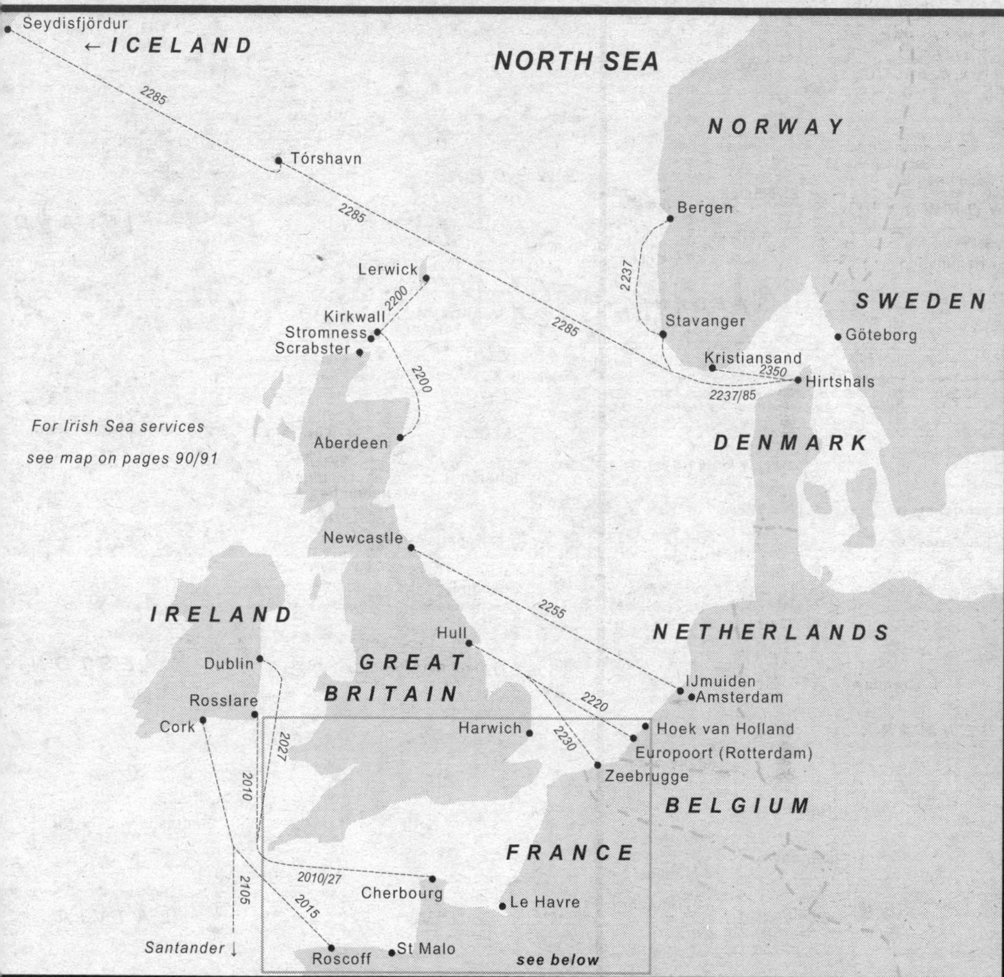
Seydisfjördur
← ICELAND
NORTH SEA
2285
Tórshavn
2285
NORWAY
Bergen
2237
Lerwick
2200
Kirkwall
Stromness
Scrabster
2200
2285
Stavanger
SWEDEN
Göteborg
Kristiansand
2350
Hirtshals
2237/85
For Irish Sea services
see map on pages 90/91
Aberdeen
DENMARK
Newcastle
2255
IRELAND
NETHERLANDS
Hull
GREAT
BRITAIN
Dublin
IJmuiden
Amsterdam
Rosslare
2220
Cork
Harwich
Hoek van Holland
2027
2230
Europoort (Rotterdam)
2010
Zeebrugge
BELGIUM
FRANCE
2010/27
2105
Cherbourg
2015
Le Havre
Santander ↓
Roscoff
St Malo
see below

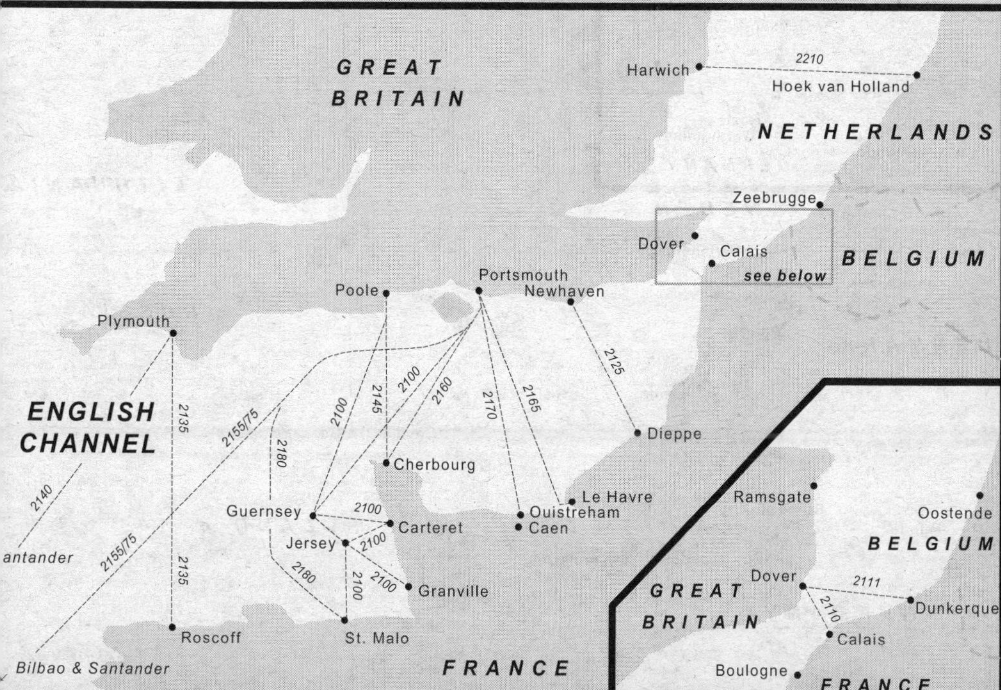
GREAT
BRITAIN
Harwich
2210
Hoek van Holland
NETHERLANDS
Zeebrugge
Dover
Calais
see below
BELGIUM
Portsmouth
Poole
Newhaven
Plymouth
2125
2100
2145
2160
2170
2165
ENGLISH
CHANNEL
2135
2155/75
2180
Dieppe
Cherbourg
2140
Le Havre
Guernsey
2100
Ouistreham
Carteret
Caen
Jersey
2100
antander
2155/75
2135
2180
2100
2100
Granville
Roscoff
St. Malo
Bilbao & Santander
FRANCE
Ramsgate
Oostende
BELGIUM
Dover
2111
GREAT
2110
Dunkerque
BRITAIN
Calais
Boulogne
FRANCE

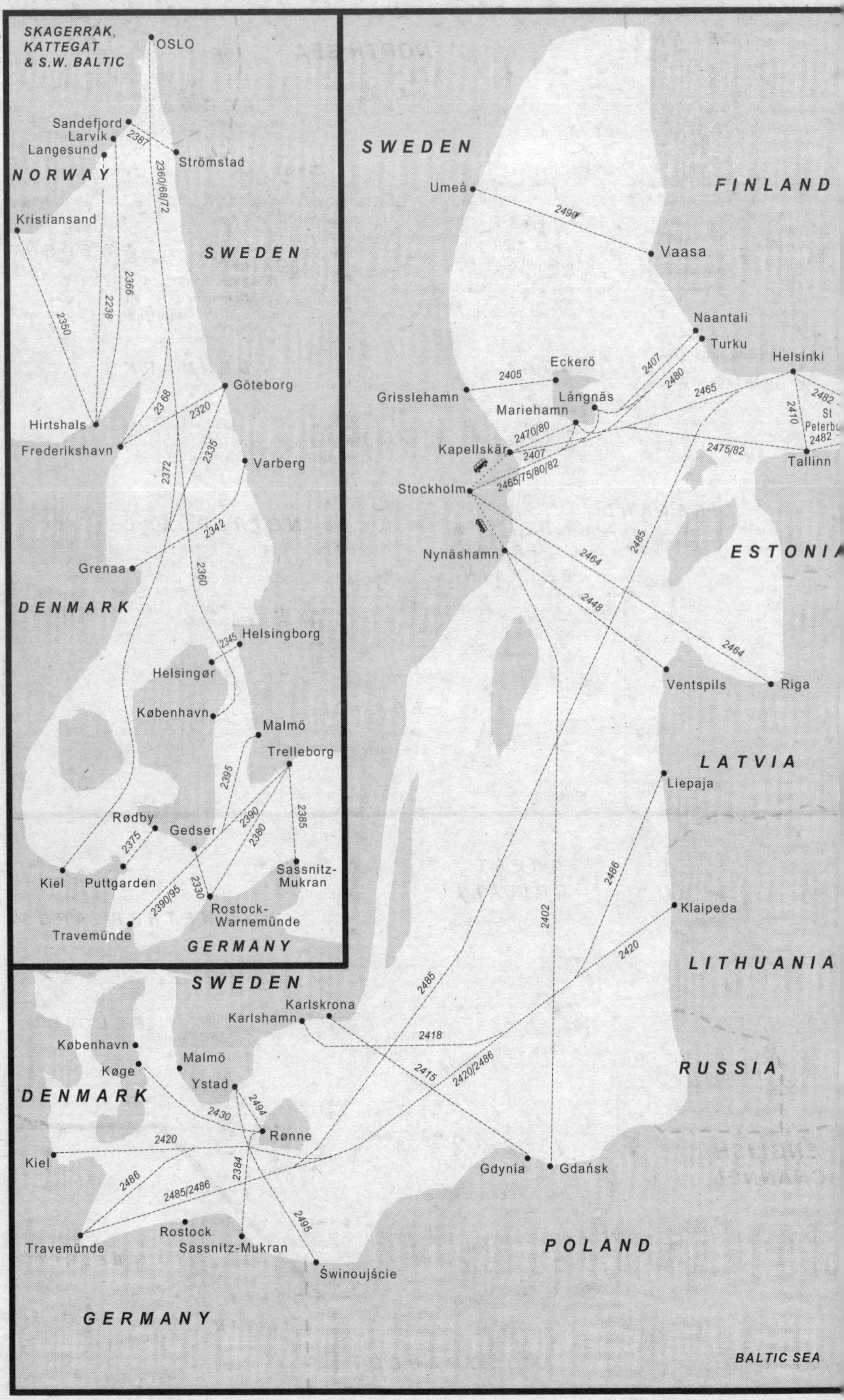
SKAGERRAK, KATTEGAT & S.W. BALTIC
OSLO
Sandefjord
Larvik
Langesund
Strömstad
2387
2360/68/72
NORWAY
Kristiansand
SWEDEN
2350
2238
2366
Göteborg
2368
2320
Hirtshals
Frederikshavn
2335
Varberg
2372
2342
Grenaa
2360
DENMARK
2345
Helsingborg
Helsingør
København
Malmö
Trelleborg
2395
2390
2380
2385
Rødby
Gedser
2375
Kiel
Puttgarden
2330
Sassnitz-Mukran
2390/95
Rostock-Warnemünde
Travemünde
GERMANY
SWEDEN
Karlskrona
Karlshamn
København
Køge
Malmö
Ystad
DENMARK
2494
2430
Rønne
2420
Kiel
2486
2384
2485/2486
Rostock
Sassnitz-Mukran
Travemünde
2495
Świnoujście
GERMANY
SWEDEN
FINLAND
Umeå
2490
Vaasa
Naantali
Turku
Helsinki
2407
2480
Eckerö
2405
Grisslehamn
Långnäs
2465
2482
Mariehamn
2410
St Peterbu
2482
2470/80
Kapellskär
2407
2475/82
Tallinn
2465/75/80/82
Stockholm
2485
Nynäshamn
ESTONIA
2464
2448
2464
Ventspils
Riga
LATVIA
Liepaja
2486
Klaipeda
2402
2420
LITHUANIA
2485
2418
RUSSIA
2415
2420/2486
Gdynia
Gdańsk
POLAND
BALTIC SEA

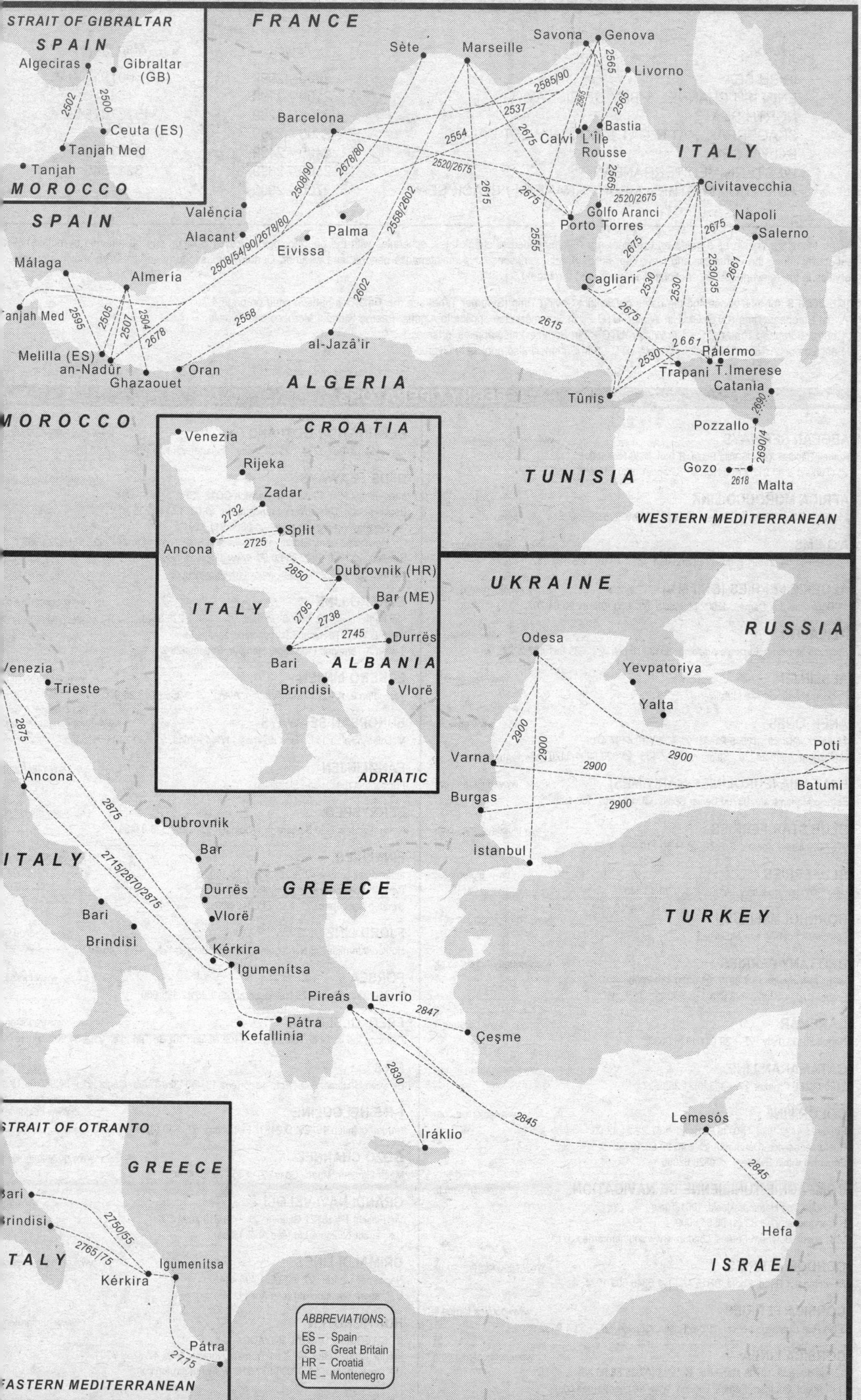
STRAIT OF GIBRALTAR
SPAIN
Algeciras
Gibraltar (GB)
2502
2500
Ceuta (ES)
Tanjah Med
Tanjah
MOROCCO
FRANCE
Sète
Marseille
Savona
Genova
2565
Livorno
2585/90
2537
Barcelona
2554
2675
Calvi
L'Île Rousse
Bastia
ITALY
2520/2675
2615
2565
Civitavecchia
2508/90
2678/80
2520/2675
València
Golfo Aranci
Porto Torres
Napoli
Salerno
SPAIN
Alacant
Palma
Eivissa
2558/2602
2555
2675
2508/54/90/2678/80
2530/35
2661
Málaga
Almeria
Cagliari
2530
2530
2602
2558
2615
2675
2595
2505
2507
2504
2678
2661
Palermo
Tanjah Med
Melilla (ES)
an-Nadûr
Ghazaouet
Oran
al-Jazâ'ir
2530
Trapani
T.Imerese
Catania
ALGERIA
Tûnis
MOROCCO
2690/4
Pozzallo
CROATIA
Venezia
Rijeka
Zadar
2732
Split
2725
Ancona
2850
Dubrovnik (HR)
ITALY
2795
2738
Bar (ME)
2745
Durrës
Bari
ALBANIA
Brindisi
Vlorë
ADRIATIC
TUNISIA
Gozo
2618
Malta
WESTERN MEDITERRANEAN
UKRAINE
RUSSIA
Odesa
Yevpatoriya
Yalta
Venezia
Trieste
2875
2900
2900
Poti
2900
Varna
2900
Batumi
Ancona
2875
Burgas
2900
Dubrovnik
Istanbul
Bar
ITALY
2715/2870/2875
Durrës
GREECE
TURKEY
Bari
Vlorë
Brindisi
Kérkira
Igumenitsa
Pireás
Lavrio
2847
Pátra
Kefallinia
Çeşme
2830
2845
Lemesós
Iráklio
2845
STRAIT OF OTRANTO
GREECE
Bari
Brindisi
2750/55
2765/75
ITALY
Kérkira
Igumenitsa
Hefa
ISRAEL
ABBREVIATIONS:
ES – Spain
GB – Great Britain
HR – Croatia
ME – Montenegro
Pátra
2775
EASTERN MEDITERRANEAN

FERRY SERVICES

Section	*Tables*	*Map page*
IRISH SEA	2000 - 2099	90/91
ENGLISH CHANNEL & BAY OF BISCAY	2100 - 2199	543
NORTH SEA	2200 - 2299	343/370/543
SKAGERRAK, KATTEGAT & SOUTH WEST BALTIC	2300 - 2399	544
BALTIC SEA	2400 - 2499	343/544
WESTERN MEDITERRANEAN	2500 - 2699	321/545
ADRIATIC / EASTERN MEDITERRANEAN / BLACK SEA	2700 - 2900	545

Sailing times are shown as a guide and readers are recommended to check latest schedules with the operator before travel. Sailings can be affected by public holida (especially during the Christmas and New Year holiday), tidal variations, ship maintenance periods, and weather. Certain domestic ferry services are shown alongside services in the relevent country sections (see maps and the Index).

TIME ZONES: for time zones and the dates of Daylight Saving Time (Summer Time) see the Time Comparison chart on page 4.
West European Time (UTC/GMT in Winter, UTC+1 in Summer) also applies to Algeria, Faeroe Islands, Morocco and Tunisia.
Central European Time (UTC+1 in Winter, UTC+2 in Summer) also applies in Israel.
East European Time (UTC +2 in Winter, UTC+3 in Summer) also applies in Cyprus.

FERRY OPERATORS

AEGEAN SEAWAYS www.aegeanseaways.com
Rumeli Caddesi No: 4/6 Villa Plaza, B Blok D:30 Nisantasi.
✆ (Turkey) +90 212 219 9495. ✆ (Greece) +30 21 0408 2150.

AFRICA MOROCCO LINK www.aml.ma
21, BD Pasteur Etage 2, Tanger ✆ +212 539 322253.

A G EMS www.ag-ems.de
Postfach 11 54, 26691 Emden-Außenhafen ✆ +49 (0)1805 180 182.

ALGERIE FERRIES (E N T M V) www.algerieferries.dz
58 Boulevard des Dames, 13002 Marseille ✆ +33 (0)4 91 90 64 70.

ALILAURO www.alilauro.it
Stazione Marittima, Piazzale Angioino, 80133 Napoli ✆ +39 081 497 2222.

ALSLINJEN www.faergen.dk
For contact details see Molslinjen.

ANEK LINES www.anek.gr
24 Akti Kondili Str., 18545 Pireás: ✆ +30 210 4197 470.
U.K. agent: Viamare Ltd., Stanmore, HA7 1JS ✆ 020 8206 3420 www.viamare.com

BALEÀRIA (EUROLÍNIES MARÍTIMES) www.balearia.com
Estació Marítima s/n, 03700 Dénia, Spain ✆ +34 902 160 180.

BLUE STAR FERRIES www.bluestarferries.com
17674 Kallithea, Athína, Greece ✆ +30 210 891 9800.

BLUFERRIES www.bluferries.it
Villa San Giovanni, Italy. ✆ +39 340 98 48 540.

BORNHOLMSLINJEN www.bornholmslinjen.com
For contact details see Molslinjen.

BRITTANY FERRIES www.brittany-ferries.co.uk
Millbay, Plymouth, PL1 3EW ✆ 0330 159 7000.
France: ✆ +33 825 828 828.

CAREMAR www.caremar.it
Napoli 80133, Italy ✆ +39 081 1896 6690.

CATAMARAN LINE www.catamaran-line.hr
21000 Split, Croatia. ✆ +385 (0)21 352 527.

COLOR LINE www.colorline.com
Postboks 1422 Vika, N-0115 Oslo ✆ +47 22 94 42 00.
Customer service (Denmark): ✆ +45 99 56 19 00.
Enquiries within Sweden: ✆ 0526 62000.

COMPAGNIE TUNISIENNE DE NAVIGATION www.ctn.com.tn
5 Avenue Dag Hammarskjoeld, 1001 Tûnis
Reservations: ✆ +33 (1) 86 65 0000.
U.K. agent: Southern Ferries, London www.southernferries.co.uk

CONDOR FERRIES www.condorferries.co.uk
New Harbour Road, Poole, BH15 4AJ ✆ 0845 609 1024

CORSICA FERRIES www.corsica-ferries.fr
5 bis Rue Chanoine Leschi, 20296 Bastia, Corsica ✆ +33 4 9532 9595.

CORSICA LINEA www.corsicalinea.com
42 rue de Ruffi, 13003 Marseille ✆ +33 (0)825 88 80 88.
U.K. agent: Southern Ferries, London www.southernferries.co.uk

DESTINATION GOTLAND www.destinationgotland.
Korsgatan 2, Box 1234, 621 23 Visby, Gotland ✆ +46 (0)498 20 18 00.

DFDS SEAWAYS www.dfdsseaways.co.
International Port, Parkeston, Harwich CO12 4SR.
Bookings from UK: Dover - France route: ✆ 0871 574 7235
Newhaven - Dieppe route: ✆ 0800 917 1201
Newcastle - Amsterdam, also Baltic and Scandinavian routes: ✆ 0871 522 9955
Sweden: ✆ +46 (0)42 26 60 00 www.dfdsseaways.se
Norway: ✆ +47 2162 1340 www.dfdsseaways.no

ECKERÖ LINE www.eckeroline.co
Mannerheimintie 10, 00100 Helsinki: ✆ +358 9 228 8544. www.eckerolinjen.
Helsinki West Terminal T2: Tyynenmerenkatu 14
Tallinn A-Terminal: Passenger Harbour, Sadama 25-2

ECKERÖ LINJEN www.eckerolinjen.
Torggatan 2, AX-22101 Mariehamn, Åland ✆ +358 (0)18 28 000.

EUROPEAN SEAWAYS www.europeanseaways.co
Machis Analatou 111, Neos Kosmos 117 44 Athína ✆ +30 210 9561630

FANØLINJEN www.faergen.
For contact details see Molslinjen.

FERRYSPED www.navbul.co
Navigation Maritime Bulgare (Navibulgar) ✆ +359 526 83409.

FINNLINES www.finnlines.co
Finland call centre: ✆ +358 9 231 43 100
Germany call centre: ✆ +49 451 1507 443
Sweden call centre: ✆ +46 771 340 900

FJORD LINE www.fjordline.c
Hurtigruteterminalen, Nøstegaten 30, 5010 Bergen ✆ +47 51 46 40 99

FORSEA www.forsea.
Knutpunkten 43, 252 78 Helsingborg ✆ +46 42 186 000

FRED. OLSEN S.A. www.fredolsen
Polígono Industrial de Añaza s/n, 38109 Santa Cruz de Tenerife ✆ +34 902 100 107

F R S www.frs
Estación Maritima. P.O./Apto de correos 13, E-11380 Tarifa-Cádiz ✆ +34 956 68 18 3

F R S HELGOLINE www.helgoline
Norderhofenden 19-20, D 24937 Flensburg ✆ +49 (0)461 86444.

GOZO CHANNEL www.gozochannel.c
Mgarr Harbour, Mgarr, Gozo ✆ +356 2210 9000.

GRANDI NAVI VELOCI www.gn
Via Fieschi 17, 16121 Genova ✆ +39 010 2094 591.
U.K. agent: Viamare Ltd (see Anek Lines)

GRIMALDI LINES www.grimaldi-lines.c
Napoli call centre: ✆ +39 081 496 444.
U.K. agent: Viamare Ltd (see Anek Lines)

HURTIGRUTEN www.hurtigruten
NORWEGIAN COASTAL VOYAGE
Fredrik Langes gate 14, 9291 Tromsø, Norway ✆ +47 7759 7201.
U.K. reservations: ✆ 02035 532 516 www.hurtigruten.com

TER SHIPPING www.intershipping.es
ain: ✆ +34 956 68 47 29, +34 956 66 29 56.
orocco: ✆ +212 539 34 38 34.

ISH FERRIES www.irishferries.com
O. Box 19, Alexandra Road, Dublin 1 ✆ +353 818 300 400.
. reservations (Liverpool): ✆ 08717 300 400.
ance reservations: ✆ +33 1 70 72 03 26.

LE OF MAN STEAM PACKET CO. www.steam-packet.com
a Terminal, Douglas, Isle of Man IM1 2RF. ✆ (Isle of Man) 661 661.
K. reservations: ✆ 08722 992 992.
land: ✆ +44 8722 992 992.

LES OF SCILLY STEAMSHIP CO. www.islesofscilly-travel.co.uk
uay Street, Penzance, TR18 4BZ ✆ +44 (0)1736 334220

ADROLINIJA www.jadrolinija.hr
va 16, 51000 Rijeka ✆ +385 51 666 111.
K. agent: Viamare (see Anek Lines).

APETAN LUKA www.krilo.hr
B. Kapetan Luka, Poljička cesta 4, 21314 Jesenice ✆ +385 21 645 476.

BERTY LINES www.libertylines.it
a Serraino Vulpitta 5, 91100 Trapani ✆ +39 0923 873813.

ANCHE ÎLES EXPRESS www.manche-iles.com
bert Quay, St Helier, Jersey ✆ 01534 880 756.
ernsey: ✆ 01481 701 316.
ance: ✆ 0825 131 050.

EDMAR www.medmargroup.it
rminal Porta di Massa, Napoli ✆ +39 (0)81 333 44 11

INOAN LINES www.minoan.gr
, 25th August Street, 712 02 Heraklion, Crete ✆ +30 2810 399899.
K. agent: Viamare (see Anek Lines).

OBY LINES www.mobylines.com
thin Italy: ✆ 199 30 30 40.
ernational call centre: ✆ +49 (0)611 14020.
K. agent: Viamare (see Anek Lines).

OLSLINJEN www.molslinjen.dk
eensgade 4, 8000 Aarhus ✆ +45 70 10 14 18.

AVIERA ARMAS www.navieraarmas.com
008 Las Palmas de Gran Canaria, Spain ✆ +34 902 456 500.

AVIGAZIONE LIBERA del GOLFO www.navlib.it
olo Beverello, 80133 Napoli ✆ +39 081 552 07 63.

ORDLANDEKSPRESSEN www.177nordland.no
rdland Fylkeskommune, Fylkeshuset, 8048 Bodø, Norway ✆ +47 9100 9600.

ORTHLINK FERRIES www.northlinkferries.co.uk
rry Road, Stromness, KW16 3BH, Orkney ✆ 0845 6000 449.

B M www.pbm.bg
B Management, Burgas, Bulgaria ✆ +359 56 871 628.

& O FERRIES www.poferries.com
annel House, Channel View Road, Dover, CT17 9TJ ✆ +44 (0)1304 44 88 88.
public of Ireland: ✆ +353 1 686 9467.

OLFERRIES www.polferries.com
lish Baltic Shipping Co., Portowa 41, 78 100 Kolobrzeg ✆ +48 94 35 52 102.

EEDEREI CASSEN EILS www.cassen-eils.de
i der Alten Liebe 12, 27472 Cuxhaven ✆ +49 (0)4721 667 600.

T PETER LINE www.stpeterline.com
ul. Karavannaya, St Peterburg ✆ +7 (812) 337 20 60.
lsinki: ✆ +358 9 6187 2000
llinn: ✆ +372 6660 800

AMSØLINJEN www.faergen.dk
r contact details see Molslinjen.

ARDINIA FERRIES www.corsica-ferries.fr
is Rue Chanoine Leschi, 20296 Bastia ✆ +33 4 95 32 95 95.

CANDLINES www.scandlines.com
rvice centre Germany (Rostock): ✆ +49 (0)381 7788 7766.
rvice centre Denmark (Odense): ✆ +45 33 15 15 15.

SMYRIL LINE www.smyrilline.com
Yviri Vid Strond 1, Postboks 370, FO-110 Tórshavn, Faroe Islands
Call centre: ✆ +298 34 59 00.
Iceland: ✆ +354 570 8600.
Denmark (Hirtshals): ✆ +45 96 55 85 00.

SNAV www.snav.it
Stazione Marittima, Molo Angioino, 80133 Napoli ✆ +39 081 428 55 55.
U.K. agent: Viamare (see Anek Lines).

STENA LINE (U.K.) www.stenaline.co.uk
Stena House, Station Approach, Holyhead, LL65 1DQ ✆ 08447 70 70 70.
Northern Ireland (Belfast): ✆ +44 (0)8447 70 70 70.
Ireland (Rosslare): ✆ +353 (0)1 907 5555.

STENA LINE www.stenaline.com
SE-405 19 Göteborg, Sweden. Ferry bookings: ✆ +46 (0)770 57 57 00.
Denmark (Frederikshavn): ✆ +45 96 200 200.
Germany: ✆ +49 (0)180 602 0100.
Netherlands: ✆ +31 (0)174 389 333.
Norway: ✆ +47 02010.
Poland: ✆ +48 58 660 92 00.

SUPERFAST FERRIES www.superfast.com
17674 Kallithea, Athína, Greece.
Call centre (Ancona route): +30 210 8919 700.
Call centre (Bari route): +30 210 8919 130.
U.K. Agent: Viamare (see Anek Lines).

TALLINK SILJA www.tallinksilja.com
Tyynenmerenkatu 9, 00220 Helsinki, Finland ✆ +358 9 180 41.
International call centre (Hamburg): ✆ +49 (0)40 547 541 222.
Tallinn Sales Centre: ✆ +372 640 9808.

TIRRENIA www.tirrenia.it
Head office: Napoli, Italy.
Reservation Centre for Europe: +49 611 14020.
Calls from within Italy: ✆ 199 30 30 40.

TOREMAR www.toremar.it
Reservation Centre for Europe: +49 611 14020.
Calls from within Italy: ✆ 199 11 77 33.

TORGHATTEN NORD www.torghatten-nord.no
Kirkegata 4, 9008 Tromsø ✆ +47 906 20 700.

TRASMEDITERRANEA www.trasmediterranea.es
Avda. de Europa 10, Parque Empresarial La Moraleja, C.P. 28108 Alcobendas, Madrid
Contact Centre: ✆ +34(0) 902 454 645.
Calls from Morocco: ✆ 0801 00 35 36.
U.K. agent: Southern Ferries, London www.southernferries.co.uk

TT-LINE www.ttline.com
Zum Hafenplatz 1, 23570 Lübeck-Travemünde ✆ +49 (0)4502 801 81.

UKR FERRY www.ukrferry.com
26 Baba Rada, Varna 9000, Bulgaria ✆ +359 52 602012.

UNITY LINE www.unityline.eu
Plac Rodła 8, 70-419, Szczecin ✆ +48 (0)91 88 02 909.
Reservations: ✆ +48 801 989 771.

VENEZIA LINES www.venezialines.com
Zagrebačka 7, 52440 Poreč, Croatia ✆ +385 52 422 896.

VENTOURIS FERRIES www.ventourisferries.com
17 Gr. Lampraki Str., 18533 Pireás ✆ +30 210 482 8001.
UK agent: Viamare (see Anek Lines).

VIKING LINE www.vikingline.com
Head office (Finland): ✆ +358 18 270 00.
Call centre: ✆ +358 (0)600 41577.

VIRTU FERRIES LTD www.virtuferries.com
Passenger Terminal, Marsa, MRS 1917, Malta ✆ +356 2206 9022.
Catania: ✆ +39 095 7031211.

WASALINE www.wasaline.com
Vaasanlaivat, Laivanvarustajankatu 3, FIN-65170 Vaasa.
Reservations (Finland): ✆ +358 (0)207 716 810.
Sweden: ✆ +46 090 185 200.

IRISH SEA

2002 BELFAST - CAIRNRYAN

Stena Line

Belfast		Cairnryan		Cairnryan		Belfast	
0330§	→	0555	②–⑥	0345§	→	0600	②–⑥
0730	→	0955		0600	→	0845	⑦
1130	→	1355		0730	→	0945	①–⑥
1530	→	1755		1130	→	1345	
1930	→	2155		1530	→	1745	
2300§	→	0145		1930	→	2145	
				2300§	→	0145	

§ – No foot passengers conveyed. 2300 sailings departs at 2330 on certain days.

2005 CAIRNRYAN - LARNE

P & O Ferries Journey 2 hours

Depart Cairnryan and Larne: 0400①–⑥, 0730, 1030**E**, 1330, 1630, 2000, 2359⑦–⑤.

E – ①–⑥ (daily June 30 - Aug. 18).

2010 CHERBOURG - ROSSLARE

Stena Line

Cherbourg		Rosslare	Rosslare		Cherbourg
1500⑦	→	0815①	1630⑥	→	1030⑦
2030⑤	→	1230⑥	2030④	→	1600⑤
2100③	→	1530④	2130②	→	1615③

2015 CORK - ROSCOFF

Brittany Ferries **To Nov. 2, 2019. No winter service**

Sailings from Cork (Ringaskiddy) and Roscoff

Cork		Roscoff	
1600⑥	→	0700⑦	Not Nov. 10 - Mar. 23.

Roscoff		Cork	
2030⑤	→	0930⑥	Not Nov. 9 - Mar. 22. Certain sailings depart one hour later.

2020 DOUGLAS - BELFAST

Isle Of Man Steam Packet Co. Journey 2 hrs 45 minutes

Infrequent sailings (6 - 9 sailings per month April to September only). No winter service.

2025 DOUGLAS - DUBLIN

Isle Of Man Steam Packet Co. High-speed car ferry Journey 2 hrs 55 mins

Infrequent sailings (2 - 8 sailings per month mid-April to mid-September). No winter service.

2027 DUBLIN - CHERBOURG

Irish Ferries **June - December, 2019**

Dublin		Cherbourg	
1600	→	1100	Even dates June 2 - 30 and July 2 - 30, uneven dates Aug. 1 - 31, even dates Sept. 2 - 14, also Sept. 17, 19, 21, 24, 26, 28.
1600	→	1200	⑥ Oct. 5 - Dec. 21.
1830	→	1430	②④ Oct. 1 - Dec. 19 (also Dec. 31).

Cherbourg		Dublin	
1700	→	1015	Uneven dates June 1 - 29 and July 1 - 31, even dates Aug. 2 - 30 (‡), uneven dates Sept. 1 - 15, also Sept. 18, 20, 22, 25, 27, 29.
1730	→	1130	⑦ Oct. 6 - Dec. 22.
1830	→	1230	③⑤ Oct. 2 - Dec. 20.

‡ – Departs 1545 on Aug. 30.

2030 FISHGUARD - ROSSLARE

Stena Line **by ship**

Fishguard		Rosslare	Rosslare		Fishguard
1310	→	1625	0800	→	1115
2345	→	0400	1810	→	2125

2035 HEYSHAM - DOUGLAS

Isle Of Man Steam Packet Co. **2019 service**

Heysham		Douglas		Douglas		Heysham	
0215	→	0600		0845	→	1230	See note **F**.
1415	→	1800	See note **E**	1945	→	2330	

E – On ⑥⑦ to Mar. 24 and ⑥⑦ from Nov. 9 departs Birkenhead (1400) not Heysham.
F – On ⑥⑦ to Mar. 24 and ⑥⑦ from Nov. 9 departs Douglas 0800 and sails to Birkenhead not Heysham.

Timings may vary, and departures are cancelled on certain dates

2040 HOLYHEAD - DUBLIN

Irish Ferries **by ship**

Sailings from Holyhead and Dublin Ferryport.

Holyhead		Dublin		Dublin		Holyhead	
0240	→	0555		0200§	→	0515	
0815§	→	1145		0730	→	0945	Mar. 14 - Sept. 30 ⊕
1040	→	1255	Mar. 14 - Sept. 30 ⊕.	0805	→	1130	
1410	→	1725		1350	→	1605	Mar. 14 - Sept. 30 ⊕
1645	→	1900	Mar. 14 - Sept. 30 ⊕.	1430§	→	1800	
2015§	→	2330		2055	→	0020	

§ – Foot passengers are not normally conveyed.
⊕ – Service by *Dublin Swift* fast ferry.

Sailing times may vary owing to tidal conditions.

🚌 Dublin Ferryport - Dublin Busaras (Central Bus Station).

Continued in next column

Stena Line **by ship**

Sailings from Holyhead and Dublin Ferryport.

Holyhead		Dublin	Dublin		Holyhead
0230	→	0545	0215	→	0545
0855	→	1210	0810	→	1140
1400	→	1715	1450	→	1820
2030	→	2345	2040	→	2400

2050 BIRKENHEAD (LIVERPOOL) - BELFAST

Stena Line

Sailings from Birkenhead Twelve Quays Terminal and Belfast Victoria Terminal 2.

Birkenhead		Belfast		Belfast		Birkenhead	
1030	→	1830	②–⑦	1030	→	1830	②–⑦
2200	→	0630	①	2200	→	0630	①
2230	→	0630	②–⑦	2230	→	0630	②–⑦

2052 LIVERPOOL - DUBLIN

P & O Ferries

Conveys passengers with vehicles only. Limited passenger facilities onboard.

Liverpool		Dublin		Dublin		Liverpool	
0300	→	1030	①–⑥	0900	→	1700	②–⑥
0930	→	1730	②–⑥	1500	→	2330	⑦–⑤
2100	→	0500		2130	→	0530	

Subject to alteration Dec. 24 - Jan. 7

2053 LIVERPOOL - DOUGLAS

Isle Of Man Steam Packet Co. High-speed car ferry

Sailings from Liverpool Landing Stage and Douglas

Liverpool		Douglas	
1915	→	2200	Mar. 29 - Nov. 3. No winter service. See note **R**.

Douglas		Liverpool	
1500	→	1745	Mar. 29 - Nov. 3. No winter service. See note **R**.

R – Times may vary by several hours on certain dates - please check with operator.

For sailings Birkenhead - Douglas see footnote in Table 2035

2055 PEMBROKE - ROSSLARE

Irish Ferries

Pembroke		Rosslare	Rosslare		Pembroke
0245	→	0645	0845	→	1245
1445	→	1845	2045	→	0045

Sailing times may vary owing to tidal conditions

ENGLISH CHANNEL
AND BAY OF BISCAY

2100 CHANNEL ISLAND SERVICES

Condor Ferries *Departure times vary owing to tidal conditions*

POOLE - GUERNSEY by fast ferry

From Poole and Guernsey: sailings all year - contact operator for details.

POOLE - JERSEY by fast ferry

From Poole and Jersey: sailings all year - contact operator for details.

PORTSMOUTH - GUERNSEY by ship

From Portsmouth Continental Ferry Port and St Peter Port: sailings all year - contact operator for details.

PORTSMOUTH - JERSEY by ship

From Portsmouth Continental Ferry Port and St Helier: sailings all year - contact operator fo details.

ST MALO - GUERNSEY by fast ferry

From St Malo and Guernsey: sailings all year - contact operator for details.

ST MALO - JERSEY by fast ferry

From St Malo and Jersey: sailings all year - contact operator for details.

GUERNSEY - JERSEY by fast ferry

From Guernsey and Jersey: sailings all year - contact operator for details.

OTHER SERVICES:

Manche îles Express operate catamaran services in summer from Jersey to Cartere Granville, Sark and Guernsey, and from Guernsey to Alderney and Diélette.

 For international ferry maps – see pages 543 - 545

CORK - SANTANDER 2105

rittany Ferries — Nov. 2018 - Oct. 2019

Cork		Santander			Santander		Cork
2330①	→	0800③	Nov. 5 - Feb. 25.		1730④	→	1900⑤
2330⑤	→	0800⑦	Nov. 9 - Mar. 1.		1200⑦	→	1500①
1100③	→	1430④	Mar. 6 - Oct. 30.				
2230⑤	→	0800⑦	Mar. 8 - Nov. 1.				

DOVER - CALAIS 2110

FDS Seaways by ship

Sailings from Dover Eastern Docks and Calais Maritime. Journey 90 minutes

Conveys passengers with vehicles only.

)epart Dover: 0045, 0240①–⑥, 0410①–⑥, 0550①–⑥, 0740, 0910, 1040①–⑥, 1215, 1345, 1515, 1650, 1820, 1955, 2135⑦–⑤, 2305⑦–⑤.

)epart Calais: 0105①–⑥, 0230①–⑥, 0415①–⑥, 0610, 0740, 0920①–⑥, 1055, 1225, 1355, 1530, 1700, 1830, 2010⑦–⑤, 2140⑦–⑤, 2315.

& O Ferries Journey 90 minutes

Sailings from Dover Eastern Docks and Calais Maritime.

On night services, conveys passengers with vehicles only (foot passengers may travel 0825 - 1915 from Dover, 0945 - 2145 from Calais). Timings subject to variation.

)epart Dover: 0100, 0205, 0320, 0420, 0640, 0725, 0825, 0925, 1015, 1110, 1205, 1255, 1355, 1445, 1540, 1640, 1725, 1835, 1915, 2015, 2120, 2205, 2315.

epart Calais: 0030, 0135, 0245, 0330, 0445, 0545, 0645, 0745, 0840, 0950, 1045, 1135, 1235, 1325, 1420, 1520, 1605, 1715, 1755, 1850, 1955, 2035, 2145, 2335.

🚌 connections:

Calais Port - Calais Ville station 1100 – 1745; Calais Ville station - Calais Port 1030 – 1800.

DOVER - DUNKERQUE 2111

FDS Seaways by ship

ailings from Dover Eastern Docks and Dunkerque. Journey 2 hours

Conveys passengers with vehicles only

epart Dover: 0200①–⑥, 0400①–⑥ **b**, 0600①–⑥, 0800, 1000①–⑥ **b**, 1200, 1400, 1600 **b**, 1800, 2000⑦–⑤, 2200 **b**, 2359⑦–⑤.

epart Dunkerque: 0200①–⑥ **b**, 0400①–⑥ **b**, 0600, 0800①–⑥ **b**, 1000, 1200, 1400 **b**, 1600, 1800⑦–⑤, 2000 **b**, 2200⑦–⑤, 2359⑦–⑤.

– Cancelled on certain dates.

NEWHAVEN - DIEPPE 2125

FDS Seaways

Sailings from Newhaven and Dieppe.

Newhaven		Dieppe	Dieppe		Newhaven
October - April					
1000	→	1500	0530	→	0830
2300	→	0400	1800	→	2100
May - September					
0900	→	1400	1230	→	1530
1730	→	2230	1800	→	2100
2300	→	0500	2359	→	0400

Newhaven ferry terminal is adjacent to Newhaven Town rail station (Table **102**).

Departure times may vary owing to tidal conditions.

PENZANCE - ST. MARY'S 2130

sles Of Scilly Steamship Co. — 2019 service (no winter service)

ailings from Penzance Lighthouse Pier (South Pier) and St Mary's.

rom Penzance and St Mary's: sailings on: ①③⑤ Mar. 18 - 29; ①–⑤ Apr. 1 - June 28 (also May 18; not Apr. 30, May 2, 3, 31; ⑥ July 1 - Sept. 20, also Sept. 23 - 27.

Departure times vary owing to tidal conditions (most sailings Penzance depart 0915, St Mary's depart 1630).

PLYMOUTH - ROSCOFF 2135

rittany Ferries — Oct. 1, 2018 - Nov. 3, 2019

Sailings from Plymouth Millbay and Roscoff.

rom Plymouth: Daily Oct. 1 - 31, Nov. 2 - 4; ②④⑤⑦ Dec. 14 - 23 (also Dec. 26, 28); ②④⑤⑦ Feb. 8 - Mar. 22; daily Mar. 24 - Nov. 3.

rom Roscoff: ①②③④⑥⑦ Oct. 1 - Nov. 4; ①③⑤⑥ Dec. 14 - 22 (also Dec. 26, 27); ①③⑤⑥ Feb. 8 - Mar. 23 (also Mar. 25 - 28); most dates Mar. 30 - Nov. 3.

eparture times vary. Sailing time approx 6 - 9 hours.

PLYMOUTH - SANTANDER 2140

rittany Ferries — Service to Nov. 3, 2019

Sailings from Plymouth Millbay and Santander — No regular winter service

Plymouth		Santander	
1545⑦	→	1215①	Not Nov. 4 - Mar. 24. Departs 1615 Aug. 4 - Sept. 1.
antander		**Plymouth**	
2115③	→	1615④	Not Nov. 7 - Mar. 20.

POOLE - CHERBOURG 2145

rittany Ferries — Oct. 1, 2018 - Nov. 3, 2019

Poole		Cherbourg	Cherbourg		Poole	
0830	→	1345	1830	→	2145	See note **P**.
			2215	→	0700	See note **Q**.

P – Not dates in note **Q**.
Q – ②③ Oct. 2 - 31; ①②③ Nov. 5 - July 10; ①②③ Sept. 3 - Oct. 30.

Varies at Christmas. 🚌 Cherbourg Port - Cherbourg station (operated by Zéphir).

PORTSMOUTH - BILBAO 2155

Brittany Ferries — Service to Nov. 3, 2019

Portsmouth		Bilbao	
0845②	→	1415③	Not Nov. 6 - Jan. 29, Mar. 12 - 28.
1200③	→	1245④	Not Feb. 6 - Mar. 6
2230⑦	→	0745②	Not Dec. 23, 30, Feb. 3 - Mar. 10.
Bilbao		**Portsmouth**	
1030②	→	0915③	Not Dec. 25, Jan. 1, Feb. 5 - Mar. 12.
1530④	→	1415⑤	Not Dec. 6, Feb. 7 - Mar. 7.
1715③	→	2045④	Not Nov. 7 - Jan. 30, Mar. 13 - 27,

PORTSMOUTH - CHERBOURG 2160

Brittany Ferries by fast ferry — May 2 - Sept. 10, 2019

Sailings from Portsmouth Continental Ferry Port and Cherbourg. **No regular winter service**

Portsmouth		Cherbourg	
0730	→	1130	May 24 - 26, May 31 - June 2, ⑤⑥ July 26 - Aug. 31 (also Aug. 4).
0900	→	1300	May 3 - Sept. 10 (except dates of 0730 and 1515 sailings).
1515	→	1915	May 24 - 26, May 31 - June 2, ⑤⑥ July 26 - Aug. 31 (also Aug. 4).
Cherbourg		**Portsmouth**	
1230	→	1430	May 24 - 26, May 31 - June 2, ⑤⑥ July 26 - Aug. 31 (also Aug. 4).
1700	→	1900	May 3 - Sept. 10 (except dates of 1230 and 2030 sailings).
2030	→	2230	May 24 - 26, May 31 - June 2, ⑤⑥ July 26 - Aug. 31 (also Aug. 4).

🚌 Cherbourg Port - Cherbourg station (operated by Zéphir).

PORTSMOUTH - LE HAVRE 2165

Brittany Ferries — Oct. 1, 2018 - Nov. 3, 2019

Sailings from Portsmouth Continental Ferry Port and Le Havre Terminal de la Citadelle

Portsmouth		Le Havre	
2330	→	0830	Not Nov. 18 - 25, Dec. 24, 25, Feb. 8, 9, 15, 16, 22, 23, Mar. 1 - 17, 22 - 24. Departs 2245 on July 8; 2145 on ⑤ July 26 - Aug. 23.
Le Havre		**Portsmouth**	
1700	→	2130	①②③⑥⑦. Not Oct. 1, Nov. 19 - 25, Dec. 24, 25, 31, Jan. 1, Feb. 9, 10, 16, 17, 23, 24, Mar. 2 - 18, 25.
2200	→	0600	⑤ (not Nov. 23, Mar. 1 - 22).
2200	→	0715	④ (not Nov. 22, Mar. 7 - 28).

A shuttle 🚌 service operates between the terminal and railway station

PORTSMOUTH - OUISTREHAM (CAEN) 2170

Brittany Ferries — Oct. 1, 2018 - Nov. 3, 2019 (not Dec. 25)

Sailings from Portsmouth Continental Ferry Port and Ouistreham

Portsmouth		Ouistreham	
0815	→	1500	Daily (not Dec. 25, 26, Jan. 1, 2).
1445	→	2130	①②④⑤⑥⑦ Oct. 1 - Nov. 6; ①②③④⑥⑦ Nov. 7 - Apr. 2 (not Feb. 7, Mar. 27); ①②④⑤⑥⑦ Apr. 6 - Nov. 3.
2200	→	0645	③ Oct. 3 - 31; ⑤ Nov. 9 - Mar. 8; ③ Mar. 13 - Oct. 30.
2245	→	0645	①④⑤⑥⑦ Oct. 1 - Nov. 5; ①②③⑥⑦ Nov. 6 - Mar. 11 (not Dec. 24, 25); ①④⑤⑥⑦ Mar. 9 - Nov. 3 (not July 8).
2245	→	0730	② Oct. 2 - 30; ④ Nov. 8 - Mar. 7 (not Nov. 15); ② Mar. 12 - Oct. 29.
Ouistreham		**Portsmouth**	
0830	→	1315	①②④⑤⑥⑦ Oct. 1 - Nov. 6; ①②③④⑥⑦ Nov. 7 - Mar. 12; ①②④⑤⑥⑦ Mar. 14 - Nov. 3 (not Jan. 1, 3, Mar. 25, 31, Apr. 1).
1400	→	1915	③ Oct. 3 - 31; ⑤ Nov. 9 - Mar. 8 (not Nov. 16); ③ Mar. 13 - Oct. 30.
1630	→	2115	①②④⑤⑥⑦ Oct. 1 - Nov. 6; ①②③④⑥⑦ Nov. 7 - Mar. 12 (not Dec. 25, 31); ①②④⑤⑥⑦ Mar. 14 - Nov. 3.
2300	→	0645	Daily (not Dec. 24, 25, 31, Jan. 1, Feb. 7).

🚌 Ouistreham - Caen station (journey 45 minutes) to connect with most sailings.

PORTSMOUTH - SANTANDER 2175

Brittany Ferries — Service to Nov. 3, 2019

Sailings from Portsmouth Continental Ferry Port and Santander

Portsmouth		Santander	
0845⑥	→	1415⑦	Also ② Nov. 6 - Jan. 29, also Mar. 12; not Dec. 25, Jan. 1.
1700⑤	→	1730⑥	Not Dec. 7, Feb. 8 - Mar. 8, Mar. 29.
1715②	→	1815③	Not Nov. 13 - Mar. 19.
Santander		**Portsmouth**	
1515①	→	1415②	Not Nov. 5 - Mar. 25.
1715⑦	→	2045①	Also ③ Nov. 7 - Jan. 30, also Mar. 13; not Dec. 23, 30.
2030⑥	→	1945⑦	Not Dec. 22, 30, Feb. 8 - Mar. 9.

PORTSMOUTH - ST MALO 2180

Brittany Ferries — Oct. 1, 2018 - Nov. 3, 2019

Sailings from Portsmouth Continental Ferry Port and St. Malo Terminal Ferry du Naye

From Portsmouth: ①③④⑤⑥⑦ Oct. 1 - 31; ①③⑤⑦ Nov. 5 - Mar. 24; ①③④⑤⑥⑦ Mar. 27 - Nov. 3 (daily July 3 - Sept. 2); not Apr. 25, May 2.

From St. Malo: ①②④⑤⑥⑦ Oct. 1 - Nov. 2; ①②④⑥ Nov. 5 - Mar. 30; ①②④⑤⑥⑦ Mar. 31 - Nov. 3 (daily July 4 - Sept. 3); not Apr. 26, May 3.

Departure times vary: most sailings Portsmouth d. 2015 (St. Malo a. 0815); St. Malo d. 1030 (Portsmouth a. 1820). Dates vary at Christmas and New Year.

NORTH SEA

2200 ABERDEEN - KIRKWALL - LERWICK

NorthLink Ferries **2019 service**

Aberdeen		Kirkwall		Kirkwall		Lerwick
January 2 - March 28 and November 1 - December 30						
1700④⑥⑦	→	2300④⑥⑦	→	2345④⑥⑦	→	0730⑤⑦①
1900①②③⑤	→	→	→	→	→	0730②③④⑥
March 29 - October 31						
1700②④⑥⑦	→	2300②④⑥⑦	→	2345②④⑥⑦	→	0730③⑤⑦①
1900①③⑤	→	→	→	→	→	0730②④⑥

Lerwick		Kirkwall		Kirkwall		Aberdeen
January 2 - March 28 and November 1 - December 30						
1730③⑤	→	2300③⑤	→	2345③⑤	→	0700④⑥
1900①②④⑥⑦	→	→	→	→	→	0700②③⑤⑦①
March 29 - October 31						
1730①③⑤	→	2300①③⑤	→	2345①③⑤	→	0700②④⑥
1900②④⑥⑦	→	→	→	→	→	0700③⑤⑦①

Subject to alteration during ship maintenance (January to March)

A 🚌 transfer service is available Kirkwall - Stromness and v.v. in conjunction with evening sailings.

2210 HARWICH - HOEK VAN HOLLAND

Stena Line **by ship**

Sailings from Harwich International Port and Hoek van Holland.

Harwich		Hoek		Hoek		Harwich	
0900	→	1715	①–⑥	1345	→	1945	⑦
1000	→	1815	⑦	1415	→	1945	①–⑥
2300	→	0800		2200	→	0630	

See Table **15** for connecting rail services London - Harwich and v.v.
Connections Hoek van Holland - Rotterdam are currently by 🚌 (by metro from late 2019) – see Table **497**

2220 HULL - ROTTERDAM

P & O Ferries

Sailings from Hull King George Dock and Rotterdam Europoort.

Hull		Rotterdam		Rotterdam		Hull	
2030	→	0815	①–⑤	2030	→	0800	⑥⑦
2030	→	0900	⑥⑦	2100	→	0730	①–⑤

🚌 connections (reservation recommended):
Hull (Paragon Interchange, depart 1700) - King George Dock and v.v.
Rotterdam (Centraal Station, depart 1700) - Europoort and v.v.
Amsterdam (Prins Hedrikkade 25, depart 1700) - Europoort and v.v.

2230 HULL - ZEEBRUGGE

P & O Ferries

Sailings from Hull King George Dock and Zeebrugge Leopold II Dam.

Hull		Zeebrugge		Zeebrugge		Hull	
1830	→	0845	①–⑤	1900	→	0830	①–⑤
1830	→	0930	⑥⑦	1900	→	0900	⑥⑦

🚌 connections, reservation recommended: Hull (Paragon Interchange, depart 1700) - King George Dock and v.v.; Brugge Station - Zeebrugge ferry terminal and v.v.

2237 HIRTSHALS - STAVANGER - BERGEN

Fjord Line

Hirtshals		Stavanger		Bergen		Stavanger		Hirtshals
2000	→	0630/0700	→	1230/1330	→	1900/2000	→	0800 **b**

b – Arrive 0730 June 1 - Aug. 31.

Cancellations: no departure from Hirtshals on Apr. 8 or from Bergen on Apr. 9.
Subject to alteration in January due to scheduled maintenace.

🚌 connection available between Hirtshals railway station and ferry terminal.

2238 HIRTSHALS - LANGESUND

Fjord Line

Hirtshals		Langesund	Langesund		Hirtshals
0900	→	1330	1430	→	1900

No service Apr. 8, Sept. 18, 25, Dec. 24, 25

2239 LOFOTEN ISLANDS (map page 343)

Nordlandekspressen **fast ferry (route NEX 2)** **Service to Jan. 31, 2020**

BODØ - SVOLVÆR

Bodø		Svolvær		Svolvær		Bodø	
1800	→	2125	①–⑥	0600	→	0920	①–⑤
1900	→	2225	⑦	0755	→	1115	⑥
				1245	→	1600	⑦

Torghatten Nord **by ship** Most sailings 3 hours 15 mins

BODØ - MOSKENES

From Bodø and Moskenes: 1 - 2 sailings daily (up to 6 sailings daily June to August).

2240 NORWEGIAN COASTAL SERVICES (map page 34

Hurtigruten **2019 servic**

BERGEN - TRONDHEIM - TROMSØ - KIRKENES

Daily	NORTHBOUND WINTER arrive	depart	SUMMER ☆ arrive	depart	day	SOUTHBOUND ALL YEAR	arrive	depart	d
Bergen ♣	...	2230	...	2000	A	**Kirkenes**	...	1230	A
Florø	0430	0445	0200	0215	B	Vadsø	|	|	
Måløy	0715	0730	0415	0430	B	Vardø	1545	1645	A
Torvik	1030	1045	0715	0730	B	Båtsfjord	1945	2015	A
Ålesund	1200	1500	0845	0930	B	Berlevåg	2145	2200	A
Geiranger ▲	|	|	1325 **s**	1330 **s**	B	Mehamn	0045	0100	
Ålesund	1200	1500	1815 ¶	1900	B	Kjøllefjord	0245	0300	
Molde	1800	1830	2145	2215	B	**Honningsvåg**	0530	0545	
Kristiansund	2215	2300	0145	0200	B/C	Havøysund	0745	0800	
Trondheim	0600	1200	0830	1200	C	**Hammerfest**	1045	1245 §	
Rørvik	2045	2115	2045	2115	C	Øksfjord	1530 §	1545 §	
Brønnøysund	0045	0100	0045	0100	D	Skjervøy	1915 △	1945 △	
Sandnessjøen	0345	0415	0345	0415	D	**Tromsø**	2345	0130	B
Nesna	0525	0530	0525	0530	D	Finnsnes	0415	0445	
Ørnes	0915	0930	0915	0930	D	**Harstad**	0750	0830	
Bodø	1230	1500	1230	1500	D	Risøyhamn	1045	1100	
Stamsund	1900	1930	1900	1930	D	Sortland	1230	1300	
Svolvaer	2100	2200	2100	2200	D	Stokmarknes	1415	1515	
Stokmarknes	0100	0115	0100	0115	E	**Svolvaer**	1830	2030	
Sortland	0245	0300	0245	0300	E	Stamsund	2200	2230	
Risøyhamn	0415	0430	0415	0430	E	**Bodø**	0230	0415	
Harstad	0645	0745	0645	0745	E	Ørnes	0700	0715	
Finnsnes	1100	1130	1100	1130	E	Nesna	1100	1115	
Tromsø	1415	1830	1415	1830	E	Sandnessjøen	1230	1300	
Skjervøy	2230	2245	2230	2245	E	Brønnøysund	1545	1700	
Øksfjord	0200	0215	0200	0215	F	Rørvik	2030	2130	
Hammerfest	0515	0600	0515	0600	F	**Trondheim**	0630	1000	
Havøysund	0845	0915	0845	0915	F	Kristiansund	1630	1700	
Honningsvåg	1115	1445	1115	1445	F	Molde	2100	2130	
Kjøllefjord	1700	1715	1700	1715	F	Ålesund	0030	0100	
Mehamn	1915	1930	1915	1930	F	Geiranger ▲	|	|	
Berlevåg	2200	2215	2200	2215	F	Ålesund	0030	0100	
Båtsfjord	2345	0015	2345	0015	F/G	Torvik	0215	0230	
Vardø	0315	0330	0315	0330	G	Måløy	0515	0545	
Vadsø	0645	0715	0645	0715	G	Florø	0745	0815	
Kirkenes	0900	....	0900	...	G	**Bergen** ♣	1430		

A – 1st day .... **G** – 7th day.
s – June 1 - Aug. 31.
△ – 75 minutes earlier Apr. 1 - May 31.
¶ – Via Hjørundfjorden Sept. 1 - Oct. 31 (Ålesund a. 1700).
§ – 60 minutes earlier Apr. 1 - May 31.
♣ – Sailings from Bergen Frilenesset.
☆ – June 1 - Oct. 31.
▲ – Embarkation and disembarkation take place by tender - passengers are required to be at the quay 30 minutes before departure.

2242 HELGOLAND (Germany) services

From:		Operato
BREMERHAVEN	May - Sept.	**Reederei Cassen Ei**
BÜSUM	Apr. - Oct.	**Adler & Ei**
CUXHAVEN	Mar. - Oct.	**FRS Helgolir**
	All year service	**Reederei Cassen Ei**
HAMBURG	Mar. - Oct.	**FRS Helgolir**

2255 NEWCASTLE - IJMUIDEN (AMSTERDAM)

DFDS Seaways

Sailings from Newcastle International Passenger Terminal (Royal Quays, North Shields) and IJmuiden Felison Terminal.

Newcastle		IJmuiden	IJmuiden		Newcastle
1700	→	0945	1730	→	0915

DFDS 🚌 connections:
Newcastle rail station (Bewick St, depart 1445, 1545) - Ferry Terminal, return after ship arriv
Amsterdam Centraal station - IJmuiden and v.v. (reservation recommended, depart Amsterd every 15 minutes 1500 - 1600; depart ferry terminal following arrival of ship).

2280 STROMNESS - SCRABSTER

NorthLink Ferries Journey 90 minutes

Off-peak timetable (not dates in note **S**):
From Stromness 0630Ⓐ, 0900Ⓒ, 1645; from Scrabster 0845Ⓐ, 1200Ⓒ, 1900.

Peak timetable (dates in note **S**):
From Stromness 0630, 1100, 1645; from Scrabster 0845, 1315, 1900.

S – Apr. 6, 20, ①–⑥ May 18 - Sept. 2 (also Aug. 11, ⑥ Sept. 7 - 28, Oct. 12, 19, 26).

ICELAND and the FAEROE ISLANDS 2285

nyril Line Aug. 25, 2018 - Dec. 22, 2019

August 25, 2018 - June 6, 2019 ▲

irtshals		Tórshavn		Seydisfjördur		Tórshavn		Hirtshals
1500⑥	→	0500①/1400①	→	0900②/2000③	→	1500④/2100④	→	1000⑥

June 8, 2019 - August 23, 2019 △

irtshals		Tórshavn		Seydisfjördur		Tórshavn		Hirtshals
1130②	→	1730③/1800③	→	0830④/1030④	→	0300⑤/0330⑤	→	1230⑥
1530⑥	→	2230⑦	→	→	→	2330⑦	→	0930②

August 24, 2019 - December 22, 2019 ▽

irtshals		Tórshavn		Seydisfjördur		Tórshavn		Hirtshals
1500⑥	→	0500①/1400①	→	0900②/2000③	→	1500④/2100④	→	1000⑥

▲ – Arriving Hirtshals on June 8. No service Dec. 24 - Jan. 3 (ship lays over in Tórshavn).
△ – Arriving Hirtshals on Aug. 24.
▽ – On Aug. 24 Hirtshals d. 1630. No service Dec. 23 - 31 (ship lays over in Tórshavn).

n poor weather conditions sailings may dock at Frederikshavn or Hanstholm (for Hirtshals) nd Klaksvik or Kollafjördur (for Tórshavn). In winter sailings between Tórshavn and Seydisfjördur can be advanced, delayed or (in rare cases) cancelled due to adverse weather conditions.

SKAGERRAK, KATTEGAT & SOUTH WEST BALTIC

BØJDEN - FYNSHAV 2304

s-Linjen (Molslinjen) Journey 50 minutes

om Bøjden and Fynshav: approximately every two hours (additional sailings in summer).

EBELTOFT - SJÆLLANDS ODDE 2310

olsLinjen by catamaran

om Ebeltoft and Sjællands Odde: 6 - 13 sailings daily. Journey 65 minutes.

ESBJERG - FANØ 2312

anøLinjen (Molslinjen) Journey 12 minutes

om Esbjerg and Fanø: Frequent service (up to 3 departures hourly).

FREDERIKSHAVN - GÖTEBORG 2320

ena Line Journey 3½ hours

ailings from Frederikshavn (Færgehavnsvej) and Göteborg (Danmarksterminalen).

om Frederikshavn and Göteborg: 6 sailings daily.

GEDSER - ROSTOCK 2330

candlines Journey 2 hours

om Gedser and Rostock International Port: up to 10 sailings daily.

🚌 services connect with most sailings:

GÖTEBORG - KIEL 2335

ena Line Journey 14½ - 15½ hours

ailings from Kiel (Schwedenkai) and Göteborg (Elof Lindälvs Gata)

Göteborg		Kiel	Kiel		Göteborg
1745⑥⑦	→	0915⑦①	1745⑥⑦	→	0915⑦①
1845①–⑤	→	0915②–⑥	1845①–⑤	→	0915②–⑥

GRENAA - VARBERG 2342

ena Line Journey 4½ - 5½ hours

om Grenaa and Varberg: 2 sailings per day (3 in peak summer).

renaa port is located approximately 3 km from the railway station, which is due to be nked with Aarhus by the new *Letbanan* light rail line, due to open spring 2019.

HELSINGØR - HELSINGBORG 2345

rSea Journey 20 minutes

om Helsingør and Helsingborg: sailings approximately every 15 minutes (every 30 minutes at night).

HIRTSHALS - KRISTIANSAND 2350

olor Line by ship Journey 3 hours 15 mins

om Hirtshals and Kristiansand: 2 sailings daily (normally 1215, 2045 from Hirtshals, 0800, 1630 from Kristiansand, but timings may vary particularly Jan. 1 - 13, Mar. 25 - Apr. 4).

ord Line by catamaran Apr. 12 - Oct. 6, 2019 (no winter service)

rtshals		Kristiansand		Kristiansand		Hirtshals	
April 12 - June 27 and August 12 - October 6							
1145	→	1400	See note **P**.	0830	→	1045	
1800	→	2015		1500	→	1715	See note **P**.
June 28 - August 11							
1000	→	1215		0645	→	0900	
1700	→	1915		1330	→	1545	
2330	→	0145	See note **Q**.	2015	→	2230	See note **Q**.

– Not Apr. 16 or ②③ Apr. 23 - May 28, ②③ June 4 - 12, ②③ Aug. 20 - Sept. 4, ①–④ Sept. 9 - Oct. 3.
– Not July 2, 3, 9, 10, 16, 17, 30, 31, Aug. 6, 7.

KALUNDBORG - SAMSØ 2355

SamsøLinjen

From Kalundborg and Ballen (Samsø): 3 - 5 sailings daily in summer; 2 - 3 sailings daily in winter. Journey 80 - 90 minutes.

KØBENHAVN - OSLO 2360

DFDS Seaways

Sailings from København Dampfærgevej and Oslo Vippetangen (Akershusstranda 31).

København		Oslo	Oslo		København
1630	→	0945	1630	→	0945

DFDS shuttle bus links København port with the city centre.

LARVIK - HIRTSHALS 2366

Color Line Journey 3 hours 45 mins

From Larvik and Hirtshals: 1 - 2 sailings daily. Departure times vary.

OSLO - FREDERIKSHAVN 2368

Stena Line Journey 9½ - 13 hours

Sailings from Oslo (Akershustranda) and Frederikshavn (Færgehavnsvej)

From Oslo: 1930 ②–⑦ (arrives 0730).
From Frederikshavn: 0845 ③–⑦ (arrives 1830), 1830 ① (arrives 0730 ②).

OSLO - KIEL 2372

Color Line

Sailings from Oslo Color Line Terminalen (Filipstadveien 25) and Kiel Norwegenkai.

Oslo		Kiel	Kiel		Oslo
1400	→	1000	1400	→	1000

PUTTGARDEN - RØDBY 2375

Scandlines Journey 45 minutes

Departures every 30 minutes (at 15 and 45 minutes past each hour). Sailing times between 2215 and 0415 may vary.

ROSTOCK - TRELLEBORG 2380

Stena Line

Sailings from Rostock (Überseehafen) and Trelleborg (Kontinentplan).

Rostock		Trelleborg	Trelleborg		Rostock
0730	→	1330	0730	→	1330
1510	→	2110	1500	→	2100
2230	→	0540	2255	→	0610

Timings may vary. Additional sailings operate on certain dates

TT Line Journey 6 - 6½ hours

Sailings from Rostock Überseehafen and Trelleborg: 1 - 3 sailings per day. Timings vary.

SASSNITZ-MUKRAN - RØNNE 2384

Bornholmslinjen Journey 3 hours 20 mins

From Sassnitz : sailing at 1150 ④⑥⑦ in winter (also certain ⑤), daily in summer (also 1400 on summer ⑥⑦).
From Rønne : sailing at 0800 ④⑥⑦ in winter (also certain ⑤), daily in summer (also 0900 on summer ⑥⑦).

SASSNITZ-MUKRAN - TRELLEBORG 2385

Stena Line Journey 4¼ hours

Sailings from Fährhafen Sassnitz-Mukran and Trelleborg: twice daily in summer; infrequent sailings in winter.

For alternative route see Rostock - Trelleborg (Table **2380**).

STRÖMSTAD - SANDEFJORD 2387

Color Line Journey 2½ hours

From Strømstad: 1000, 1340, 1700, 2000.
From Sandefjord: 0700, 1000, 1330, 1700.

Fjord Line Journey 2½ hours

Strømstad		Sandefjord		Sandefjord		Strømstad	
1200	→	1430		0830	→	1100	
1830	→	2100	Not Apr. 2.	1520	→	1750	Not Apr. 2.

TRAVEMÜNDE - TRELLEBORG 2390

TT Line

Sailings from Travemünde Skandinavienkai and Trelleborg: 3 - 4 sailings per day.

🚌 connection available Trelleborg - Malmö railway station and v.v. for certain sailings.

TRAVEMÜNDE - MALMÖ 2395

Finnlines

Travemünde		Malmö	Malmö		Travemünde
0100⑦	→	1030⑦	1000②③④	→	1900②③④
0230②–⑤	→	1115②–⑤	1000⑤⑥	→	1915⑤⑥
0230①	→	1145①	1330⑥	→	2300⑥
0300⑥	→	1200⑥	1600①–⑤	→	0045②–⑥
1000②–⑤	→	1915②–⑤	1600⑦	→	0115①
1100⑥	→	2000⑥	2200①②⑤	→	0700②③⑥
2145②③	→	0715③④	2200③④⑦	→	0715④⑤①
2200①④⑤	→	0715②⑤⑥	2230⑥	→	0830⑦
2200⑥⑦	→	0730⑦①			

BALTIC SEA

2402 GDAŃSK - NYNÄSHAMN

Polferries

Gdańsk		Nynäshamn		Nynäshamn		Gdańsk	
1800	→	1200	See note **A**.	1800	→	1200	See note **A**.

A – Runs 4-6 times per week, not ⑦ (daily June 17 - Aug. 17).

Suburban rail service operates every 30 mins (60 mins on ©) Nynäshamn - Stockholm

2405 GRISSLEHAMN - ECKERÖ

Eckerö Linjen

Grisslehamn		Eckerö		Eckerö		Grisslehamn	
1000	→	1300		0830	→	0915	See note **B**.
1500	→	1800		1330	→	1430	
2000	→	2245	See note **A**.	1830	→	1930	

A – ④⑤⑥⑦ (daily June 14 - Aug. 18).
B – ①⑤⑥⑦ (daily June 14 - Aug. 18).

2407 NAANTALI - KAPELLSKÄR via Långnäs

Finnlines

Naantali		Långnäs		Kapellskär		Kapellskär		Långnäs		Naantali	
1045	→	1545	→	1815	Daily	0915	→	1405	→	1910	①-⑥
2230	→	0355	→	0615	Daily	0945	→	1430	→	1930	⑦
						2130	→	0220	→	0715	Daily

Conveys passengers with vehicles only

2410 HELSINKI - TALLINN

Eckerö Line by ship

Sailings from Helsinki Länsiterminaali 2 and Tallinn A-terminal.

Helsinki		Tallinn		Tallinn		Helsinki	
0900	→	1115		0600	→	0815	Not ⑦.
1515	→	1730		1200	→	1415	
2140	→	2350	Not ⑥.	1830	→	2100	

No sailings Apr. 21 at 2140, Apr. 22 at 0600. Subject to alteration Dec. 23 - Jan. 1.

Distance between Länsiterminaali terminals approximately 700 metres

Connection: Tram route 9 Helsinki railway station - Länsiterminaali

Tallink Silja by ship **Jan. 22 - Dec. 18, 2019**

Sailings from Helsinki Länsiterminaali 2 (§ – Länsiterminaali 1) and Tallinn D-terminal.
Journey 2 hours (§ – 3½ hours)

Depart Helsinki: 0730, 1030, 1330 **A**, 1630, 1830 §, 1930 **A**, 2030 **B**, 2230 ③–①, 2330 **D**.
Depart Tallinn: 0730, 1030, 1230 §, 1330 **E**, 1630, 1930 **E**, 2030 **B**, 2230 ③–①, 2330 **D**.

A – ③–① (daily Mar. 25 - Dec. 18).
B – ② Feb. 5 - Mar. 19.
D – ② Jan. 22-29, ② Mar. 26 - Dec. 17.
E – Not on ② Feb. 5 - Mar. 19.

Jan. 8 - 21: from Helsinki 1030, 1630, 1830 §, 2230; from Tallinn 0730, 1230 §, 1330, 1930.

Distance between Länsiterminaali terminals approximately 700 metres

Connection: Tram route 9 Helsinki railway sation - Länsiterminaali

Viking Line by ship Journey 2½ hours

Sailings from Helsinki Katajanokka terminal and Tallinn Reisisdam:
2-3 sailings daily. Departure times vary.

2415 KARLSKRONA - GDYNIA

Stena Line Journey 10½ - 12 hours

From Karlskrona and Gdynia: 3-4 sailings daily. Departure times vary.

2418 KARLSHAMN - KLAIPEDA

DFDS Seaways

Sailings from Karlshamn Ferry Terminal and Klaipeda International Ferry Port.

Karlshamn		Klaipeda	Klaipeda		Karlsham
1900	→	0900	2100	→	0900

2420 KIEL - KLAIPEDA

DFDS Seaways

Sailings from Kiel Ostuferhafen and Klaipeda International Ferry Port.

Kiel		Klaipeda	Klaipeda		Kiel
2100	→	1730	2200	→	1700

2430 KØGE - RØNNE

Bornholmslinjen

Køge		Rønne	Rønne		Køge
0030	→	0600	1700	→	2230

2445 NYNÄSHAMN - VISBY

Destination Gotland

Sailings Nynäshamn - Visby and v.v.: 1-4 sailings daily (4-6 sailings in high summer). Departure times vary. Journey 3 hrs 15 mins to 3 hrs 30 mins.

All sailings have 🚌 connection Stockholm City Terminal - Nynäshamn and v.v.

Suburban rail service operates every 30 mins (60 mins on ©) Nynäshamn - Stockholm.

2448 NYNÄSHAMN - VENTSPILS

Stena Line Journey 8½ hours

From Nynäshamn and Ventspils: 1-2 sailings daily. Contact operator for sailing times.

Suburban rail service operates every 30 mins (60 mins on ©) Nynäshamn - Stockholm.

2450 OSKARSHAMN - VISBY

Destination Gotland

From Oskarshamn and Visby: 1-2 sailings daily (January - March runs 6 days per week). Departure times vary.

2464 STOCKHOLM - RIGA

Tallink Silja

Sailings from Stockholm Värtahamnen terminal and Riga passenger terminal.

Stockholm		Riga	Riga		Stockholm
1700	→	1100	1730	→	1030

Dry docking: no service from Stockholm Mar. 25, 27, 29, 32, Apr. 2, 4; no service from Riga Mar. 24, 26, 28, 30, Apr. 1, 3.

2465 STOCKHOLM - MARIEHAMN - HELSINKI

Tallink Silja

Sailings from Stockholm Värtahamnen terminal and Helsinki Olympiaterminaali.

Stockholm		Mariehamn		Helsinki	Helsinki		Mariehamn		Stockholm
1645	→	2355	→	1030	1700	→	0420	→	0945

Subject to alteration in January and November for dry docking.

🚌 transfer links Stockholm Värtahamnen with city centre.
Stockholm Värtahamnen is 500 metres from Gärdet metro station.

Viking Line **Service to Dec. 31, 20**

Sailings from Stockholm Stadsgården and Helsinki Katajanokka.

Stockholm		Mariehamn		Helsinki	Helsinki		Mariehamn		Stockholm
Until June 12 and from August 12									
0745	→	1410					1425	→	1855
1630	→	2345	→	1010	1715	→	0430	→	1000
1800	→	0715					0900	→	1515
June 13 - August 11									
1600	→	2255	→	0915	1800	→	0430	→	0950
1730	→	0715					0900	→	1500

Viking Line 🚌: Stockholm Cityterminalen (near Central station) - Viking Line terminal.

2470 (STOCKHOLM -) KAPELLSKÄR - MARIEHAMN

Viking Line Journey 2½ hours

Sailings from Kapellskär and Mariehamn: 2-3 sailings per day (timings vary).

Connecting 🚌 service: Stockholm Cityterminalen (near Central station) - Kapellskär. Overall journey time Stockholm - Mariehamn by 🚌 and ferry is 4 to 4½ hours.

2475 STOCKHOLM - MARIEHAMN - TALLINN

Tallink Silja

Sailings from Stockholm Värtahamnen terminal and Tallinn D-terminal.

Stockholm		Mariehamn		Tallinn	Tallinn		Mariehamn		Stockholm
1730	→	0100	→	1045 **b**	1800	→	0500	→	1015

b – 1000 Mar. 28 - Nov. 5.

No service from Stockholm uneven dates Jan. 7 - 31, Mar. 5 - 17, even dates Feb. 2 - 16; no service from Tallinn even dates Jan. 6 - 30, Mar. 4 - 16, uneven dates Feb. 1 - 15.

2480 STOCKHOLM - MARIEHAMN - TURKU

Tallink Silja Timings may vary in Jan. and Feb. (also May 24 - 27).

Sailings from Stockholm Värtahamnen and Turku.

Stockholm		Mariehamn		Långnäs §		Turku
0710	→	1345	→	→	→	1915
1930	→	→	→	0255	→	0700
Turku		**Långnäs §**		**Mariehamn**		**Stockholm**
0820	→	→	→	1345	→	1815
2015	→	0045	→	→	→	0610

§ – Långnäs is 28km from Mariehamn.

Stockholm Värtahamnen is 500 metres from Gärdet metro station.

Viking Line

Sailings from Stockholm Stadsgården and Turku Linnansatama.

Stockholm		Mariehamn		Långnäs §		Turku
0745	→	1425	→	→	→	1950
2000	→	→	→	0320	→	0735
Turku		**Långnäs §**		**Mariehamn**		**Stockholm**
0845	→	→	→	1425	→	1855
2055	→	0110	→	→	→	0630

§ – Långnäs is 28km from Mariehamn.

Viking Line 🚌: Stockholm Cityterminalen (near Central station) - Viking Line terminal.
In Turku 🚌 number 1 runs between city centre and the harbour.

2482 ST PETERBURG - TALLINN - STOCKHOLM

St Peter Line **2019 servi**

Sailings operate on a two-week cycle as shown below; first sailing Mar. 25 from St Peterburg, last arrival Dec. 30 at St Peterburg. Two-week cycle commences Mar. 25, Apr. 8, 22, May 6, 20, June 3, 17, July 1, 15, 29, Aug. 12, 26, Sept. 9, 23, Oct. 7, 21, Nov. 4, 18, Dec. 2, 16. Subject to alteration Apr. 28 - May 12.

St Peterburg		Helsinki		Tallinn		Stockholm		Helsinki		St Peterburg
1900①	→	→	→	1830② **b**	→	1730③ **c**	→	1900④ **d**	→	0900⑤
1900⑤	→	1800⑥ **e**	→	→	→	→	→	→	→	0900⑦
1800⑦	→	0830①	→	1830① **f**	→	1730② **c**	→	1900③ **d**	→	0900④
1900④	→	1800⑤ **e**	→	→	→	→	→	→	→	0900⑥
1900⑥	→	1800⑦ **e**	→	→	→	→	→	→	→	0900①

b – Arr. 0900. **c** – Arr. 0930. **d** – Arr. 1130. **e** – Arr. 0800. **f** – Arr. 1230.

 For international ferry maps – see pages 543 - 545

TRAVEMÜNDE - HELSINKI 2485

Finnlines

Sailings from Travemünde Skandinavienkai and Helsinki Vuosaaren satama.

Travemünde		Helsinki	Helsinki		Travemünde
0300⑦–⑤	→	0900①–⑥	1700	→	2130
0330⑥	→	0930⑦			

Note Vuosaari harbour (Vuosaaren satama) is located approx 18 km east of Helsinki - can be reached by metro to Vuosaari then 🚌 route 90.

TRAVEMÜNDE - LIEPAJA 2486

Stena Line Journey 21-26 hours

From Travemünde and Liepaja: 4–5 sailings per week. Departure times vary.

VAASA - UMEÅ (HOLMSUND) 2490

Wasaline Journey 4½ hours

From Vaasa and Umeå: 1–2 sailings daily. Departure times vary.

YSTAD - RØNNE 2494

Bornholmslinjen by fast ferry

4-8 sailings daily, departure times vary, journey 80 minutes.

YSTAD - ŚWINOUJŚCIE 2495

Polferries Timings may vary

Ystad		Świnoujście	Świnoujście		Ystad
1345	→	1945	0115	→	0915

Connecting 🚌 operates København railway station - Polferries Terminal and v.v.

Unity Line

Ystad		Świnoujście	Świnoujście		Ystad
1330	→	2000	1300	→	2015
2230	→	0645	2300	→	0630

Subject to alteration due to ship maintenance

Connecting minibus service: Świnoujście terminal - Szczecin Hotel Radisson Blu. Świnoujście d. 0730 and 2030; Szczecin d. 1000 and 1945 (journey 1½ – 2 hours).

WESTERN MEDITERRANEAN

ALGECIRAS - CEUTA 2500

Baleària (Eurolínies Marítimes)

Journey 1¼ - 1½ hours

Depart Algeciras: 0600, 0800, 0930, 1230, 1400, 1600, 1800, 1900, 2145, 2330.
Depart Ceuta: 0600, 0730, 1100, 1130, 1430, 1600, 1730, 2000, 2030, 2330.

Trasmediterranea by fast ferry

Journey 70 minutes

Depart Algeciras: 0750, 1130, 1430, 1730, 2100.
Depart Ceuta: 0930, 1300, 1545, 1915, 2230.

ALGECIRAS - TANJAH (TANGIERS) MED 2502

Africa Morocco Link Journey 1½ hours

From Algeciras and Tanjah Med: 3–4 sailings daily, departure times vary.

Baleària (Eurolínies Marítimes) Journey 1½ hours

From Algeciras and Tanjah Med: 4–7 sailings daily, departure times vary.

FRS Journey 1½ hours

From Algeciras and Tanjah Med: 4–7 sailings daily, departure times vary.

Inter Shipping Journey 1½ hours

From Algeciras and Tanjah Med: 3 sailings daily, departure times vary.

Trasmediterranea Journey 1½ hours

April 1 - May 4
From Algeciras: 0200⑦, 0800, 1100, 1400, 1700, 2000.
From Tanjah Med: 0700⑦, 1000, 1300, 1600, 1900, 2200.

May 5 - June 30
From Algeciras: 0200⑦, 0800, 1100, 1400, 1700, 2000.
From Tanjah Med: 0400⑦, 0900, 1200, 1500, 1800, 2100.

July 1 - September 10
From Algeciras: 0200⑦, 0800, 1100, 1400, 1700, 2000, 2300.
From Tanjah Med: 0400⑦, 0700, 1000, 1300, 1600, 1900, 2200.

September 11 - December 31
From Algeciras: 0200⑦, 0800, 1100, 1400, 1700, 2000.
From Tanjah Med: 0400⑦, 1000, 1300, 1600, 1900, 2200.

Tanjah (Tangiers) Med port is located approximately 45 km east of Tanjah. A connecting 🚌 operates between Tanjah Med and Tanjah.

ALMERÍA - GHAZAOUET 2504

Trasmediterranea Service to Sept. 2019

Almeria		Ghazaouet	
2359	→	0800	① Jan. 7 - June 17; ①③⑤ June 24 - Aug. 9.
1200	→	1900	②④⑥ Aug. 13 - Sept. 14.
Ghazaouet		**Almeria**	
1200	→	2000	② Jan. 8 - June 18
1300	→	2200	②④⑥ June 25 - Aug. 10.
2300	→	0800	②④⑥ Aug. 13 - Sept. 14.

ALMERÍA - MELILLA 2505

Baleària (Eurolínies Marítimes)

From Almeria and Melilla: up to 7 sailings per week, journey 4-4½ hours.

Trasmediterranea Journey 6-8 hours

Depart Almería: 1700①, 2359②–⑦.
Depart Melilla: 0930①, 1400⑤, 1500②③④⑥⑦.

Times may vary (particularly in August and September).

ALMERÍA - AN-NADÛR (NADOR) 2507

Trasmediterranea Journey 5-8 hours

From Almeria and an-Nadûr: Jan. - June: daily sailings; July - Aug.: up to 3 sailings daily; Oct. - Dec.: daily sailings.

BARCELONA - TANJAH (TANGIERS) MED 2508

Grandi Navi Veloci Departure times vary. Journey 31 hours

From Barcelona and Tanjah Med: up to 2 sailings per week.

Tanjah (Tangiers) Med port is located approximately 45 km east of Tanjah. A connecting 🚌 operates between Tanjah Med and Tanjah.

Grimaldi Lines

Barcelona		Tanjah Med	Tanjah Med		Barcelona
2000⑥	→	2300⑦	1500①	→	1900②

Tanjah (Tangiers) Med port is located approximately 45 km east of Tanjah. A connecting 🚌 operates between Tanjah Med and Tanjah.

BALEARIC ISLANDS 2510

(map page 321)

Baleària (Eurolínies Marítimes)

BARCELONA - CIUTADELLA (MENORCA)

From Barcelona and Ciutadella: 6 sailings per week (daily June 10 - Sept. 28), journey 8½ - 9½ hours. Times vary but most sailings depart Barcelona at 2200 and Ciutadella at 1000.

BARCELONA - EIVISSA (IBIZA)

From Barcelona and Eivissa: 5-6 sailings per week (daily June 25 - Sept. 21), journey 8¼ hours. Times vary but most sailings depart Barcelona at 2200 and Eivissa at 1000.

BARCELONA - PALMA

From Barcelona and Palma: 6 sailings per week (daily June 10 - Sept. 28), journey 6 - 8 hours. Times may vary but most sailings depart Barcelona at 2300 and Palma at 1230.

DÉNIA - EIVISSA (IBIZA) - PALMA

Dénia		Eivissa		Palma	Palma		Eivissa		Dénia
1700	→	2000/2100	→	2359	0800	→	1100/1200	→	1500

VALENCIA - PALMA

Valencia		Palma	
2215	→	0600	⑦–⑤.
Palma		**Valencia**	
1130	→	1900	①–⑥.

Additional sailings run via Eivissa.

Trasmediterranea Service to Sept. 30, 2019

Departure times may vary. All routes subject to alteration on and around holidays.

BARCELONA - EIVISSA (IBIZA) by ship Journey 8-14 hours
Depart Barcelona: 2200①–⑤ (also ⑥ June 15 - Sept. 14).
Depart Ibiza: 1030②–⑤ (also ⑥ June 15 - Sept. 14), 2200⑦.

BARCELONA - MAÓ-MAHÓN (MENORCA) by ship Journey 8-9 hours
Depart Barcelona: 2245①–⑤ (daily June 17 - Sept. 20).
Depart Maó-Mahón: 1200②–⑤ (daily June 18 - Sept. 20), 2200⑦ (not June 18 - Sept. 20).
Timings vary Aug. 3, 4, 15-18, 25, 26, Sept. 1, 2.

BARCELONA - PALMA (MALLORCA) by ship Journey 7½ - 8 hours
Depart Barcelona: 1300①–⑤, 2300.
Depart Palma: 1200①–⑤, 2300⑦, 2330⑥, 2355①–⑤.

PALMA (MALLORCA) - MAÓ-MAHÓN (MENORCA) by ship Journey 5½ - 6 hours
Depart Palma: 0800⑦.
Depart Maó-Mahón: 1715⑦.

VALÈNCIA - MAÓ-MAHÓN (MENORCA) via Palma by ship Journey 14-15 hours
Depart València: 2300⑥.
Depart Maó-Mahón: 1715⑦.

VALÈNCIA - PALMA (MALLORCA) by ship Journey 8 hours
Depart València: 1930⑦, 2300①–⑥.
Depart Palma: 1030①, 1130②–⑥, 2345⑦.

2512 CANARY ISLANDS

Fred. Olsen **Inter-Island services**

Playa Blanca (Lanzarote) - Corralejo (Fuerteventura), journey 25 minutes;
Morro del Jable (Fuerteventura) - Las Palmas de Gran Canaria (Gran Canaria), journey 120 minutes;
Agaete (Gran Canaria) - Santa Cruz de Tenerife (Tenerife), journey 80 minutes;
Los Cristianos (Tenerife) - San Sebastián de la Gomera (La Gomera), journey 50 minutes;
Santa Cruz de La Palma (La Palma) - Los Cristianos (Tenerife), journey 170 minutes.

Naviera Armas

Huelva - Arrecife (Lanzarote) - Las Palmas (Gran Canaria) - Santa Cruz (Tenerife): 1 sailing per week.

Inter-Island services

Corralejo (Fuerteventura) - Playa Blanca (Lanzarote)	5–6 sailings daily.
Las Palmas (Gran Canaria) - Arrecife (Lanzarote)	5 sailings per week.
Las Palmas (Gran Canaria) - Morro Jable (Fuerteventura)	1 sailing daily.
Las Palmas (Gran Canaria) - Puerto del Rosario (Fuerteventura)	3 sailings per week.
Las Palmas (Gran Canaria) - Santa Cruz (Tenerife)	2–3 sailings daily.
Los Cristianos (Tenerife) - San Sebastián (La Gomera)	1–3 sailings daily.
Los Cristianos (Tenerife) - Valverde (El Hierro)	3 sailings per week.
Santa Cruz (Tenerife) - Arrecife (Lanzarote)	4 sailings per week.

Sailing frequencies may change

Trasmediterranea

CÁDIZ - LANZAROTE - GRAN CANARIA - TENERIFE - PALMA

Cádiz		Lanzarote (Arrecife)		Gran Canaria (Las Palmas)		Tenerife (Santa Cruz)		Palma (Santa Cruz)
1700②	→	2300/2359③	→	0800/1300④	→	1700/2359④	→	0800⑤
Palma (Santa Cruz)		**Tenerife (Santa Cruz)**		**Gran Canaria (Las Palmas)**		**Lanzarote (Arrecife)**		**Cádiz**
1600⑤	→	2130/2359⑤	→	0800/1400⑥	→	2330⑥/0100⑦	→	1230①

2520 CIVITAVECCHIA - BARCELONA

Grimaldi Lines

Civitavecchia		Barcelona		Barcelona		Civitavecchia
2215①	→	1900②		2215①	→	1900②
2300②–⑤	→	1900③–⑥		2300②–⑤	→	1900③–⑥
2359⑥	→	2000⑦		2359⑥	→	2000⑦

2530 CIVITAVECCHIA - SICILY - TÛNIS

Grandi Navi Veloci

Civitavecchia		Palermo		Tûnis		Palermo		Civitavecchia
1900⑤	→	0800⑥/1100⑥	→	2100⑥/2300⑥	→	0900⑦/1800⑦	→	0900①

Timings vary (sample timings shown) - please check with operator

Grimaldi Lines

Civitavecchia		Trapani		Tûnis		Trapani		Civitavecchia
1855③	→		→	1500④/1830②	→		→	1400③

2535 CIVITAVECCHIA - TERMINI IMERESE

Grandi Navi Veloci Departure times vary. Journey 14 hours

From Civitavecchia and Termini Imerese (for Palermo): up to 5 sailings per week.

2537 GENOVA - BARCELONA

Grandi Navi Veloci Departure times vary. Journey 20-21 hours

From Genova and Barcelona: up to 3 sailings per week.

2547 GENOVA - PALERMO

Grandi Navi Veloci Departure times vary. Journey 20½ hours

From Genova and Palermo: up to 7 sailings per week.

2554 GENOVA - TANJAH (TANGIERS) MED

Grandi Navi Veloci Departure times vary. Journey 49-53 hours

From Genova and Tanjah Med: up to 3 sailings per week.

Tanjah (Tangiers) Med port is located approximately 45 km east of Tanjah.
A connecting 🚌 operates between Tanjah Med and Tanjah.
All sailings via Barcelona (see Table **2508**)

2555 GENOVA - TÛNIS

Grandi Navi Veloci Departure times vary. Journey 25½ hours

From Genova and Tûnis: up to 3 sailings per week.

2558 MARSEILLE - ORAN

Algérie Ferries (E N T M V) Departure times vary. Journey 24-25 hours

From Marseille and Oran: 3-6 sailings per month.

Other services operate from Marseille to Sakîkdah / Skikda

2560 GULF OF NAPOLI (including Gulf of Salerno and Ponziane Islands)

Alilauro

Napoli Beverello - Forio: up to 5 sailings daily (summer only). Sailings via Ischia in winter.
Napoli Beverello or Mergellina - Ischia: up to 15 sailings daily.
Napoli Beverello - Sorrento: 5 sailings daily.
Salerno - Capri: daily sailing.
Sorrento - Capri: up to 8 sailings daily (summer only).

Additional infrequent services to Capri operate (summer only) from Ischia, Castellammare di Stábia, Positano and Amalfi.

Sailing frequencies may change

Caremar

Napoli - Capri: 3 sailings daily by catamaran, 3 sailings by ship (4 / 3 in summer).
Napoli - Ischia: 5 sailings daily by catamaran, 7 sailings by ship (6 / 8 in summer).
Napoli - Procida: 7 sailings daily by catamaran, 6 sailings by ship (8 / 7 in summer).
Pozzuoli - Procida: 1 sailing by catamaran, 5 sailings by ship (1 / 4 in summer).
Procida - Ischia: 5 sailings daily by catamaran, 7 - 10 sailings by ship.
Sorrento - Capri: 4 sailings daily by catamaran.

Medmar

Napoli - Ischia: 3 sailings daily (additional sailings on ⑤⑥⑦).
Ischia - Pozzuoli: up to 8–9 sailings daily.

Additional infrequent services operate between Pozzuoli, Procida and Ischia.

Navigazione Libera del Golfo by ***Linea Jet***

Napoli (Molo Beverello) - Capri: up to 10 sailings daily (more in summer). Journey 40 minutes.
Sorrento - Capri: 2 sailings daily (more in summer). Journey 25 minutes.

Additional services operate (summer only) between Castellammare di Stábia and Capri.

SNAV

NAPOLI - CAPRI By hydrofoil, journey 40 minutes

From Napoli (Beverello): 0700, 0805, 0910, 1010, 1110, 1400, 1600, 1810 **S**, 2000 **N**.
From Capri: 0650 **N**, 0805, 0910, 1010, 1215, 1450, 1710, 1810, 1910 **S**.

N – April - Sept only. **S** – Mid June to end Sept.

SORRENTO - CAPRI By hydrofoil, journey 30 minutes

From Sorrento: 0820, 1125, 1405, 1640①–⑤.
From Capri: 0735①–⑤, 0915, 1210, 1555, 1735①–⑤.

2565 CORSICA

Sailings from mainland FRANCE (map page 171

MARSEILLE - AJACCIO

Corsica Linea Journey 12 hours

From Marseille and Ajaccio: daily sailings.
Most sailings depart 1900 from Marseille and Ajaccio.

MARSEILLE - BASTIA

Corsica Linea Journey 11 - 13 hours

From Marseille and Bastia: daily sailings.
Most sailings depart 1900 from Marseille, 1830 from Bastia.

MARSEILLE - L'ÎLE ROUSSE

Corsica Linea Journey 12 - 13 hours

From Marseille: sailings on most ①③⑤ (additional sailings in high-summer).
From L'Île Rousse: sailings on most ②④⑥ (additional sailings in high-summer).
Most sailings depart 1930 from Marseille, 1900 from L'Île Rousse.

MARSEILLE - PORTO VECCHIO

Corsica Linea Journey 14 hours

From Marseille: sailings on most ①③⑤.
From Porto Vecchio: sailings on most ②④⑥.
Most sailings depart 1800 from Marseille and Porto Vecchio.

MARSEILLE - PROPRIANO

Corsica Linea Journey 9½ - 12½ hours

From Marseille: sailings on most ①③⑤.
From Propriano: sailings on ②④⑥.
Most sailings depart 1830 from Marseille, 1900 from Propriano.

NICE - AJACCIO

Corsica Ferries Journey 4½ - 9 hours

From Nice and Ajaccio: Apr. - June: 5 – 11 sailings per month; July - Aug.: 14 – 19 sailings per month; Sept. - Mar.: irregular sailings.
Most sailings by day, departure times vary.

NICE - BASTIA

Corsica Ferries Journey 5 - 6 hours

From Nice and Bastia: 3 – 5 sailings per week (daily July / Aug.).
Most sailings by day, departure times vary.

NICE - L'ÎLE ROUSSE

Corsica Ferries Journey 5 - 5½ hours

From Nice and L'Île Rousse: Winter: occasional sailings; July - Aug.: 2 - 3 sailings per week.
Most sailings by day, departure times vary.

TOULON - AJACCIO

Corsica Ferries Journey 6 - 10 hours

From Toulon and Ajaccio: 1 – 2 sailings daily (including daily night sailing).
Departure times vary.

ULON - BASTIA

orsica Ferries Journey 9 - 10 hours

om Toulon and Bastia: 1 – 2 sailings daily (including daily night sailing).
Most sailings by night. Departure times vary.

ULON - L'ÎLE ROUSSE

orsica Ferries Journey 6 - 7 hours

om Toulon and L'Île Rousse: Apr. - May: 1 - 2 sailings per week; June: 2 - 3 sailings per week; July - Aug.: 3 – 6 sailings per week; Sept.: 1 – 3 sailings per week; Oct. - Mar.: occasional sailings.
All sailings by day, departure times vary.

Other sailings available from Nice and Toulon to Porto Vecchio.
Moby Lines also has sailings from Piombino to Bastia.

Sailings from ITALY

ENOVA - BASTIA

oby Lines Journey 6 - 7 hours (night sailings 9 - 10 hours)

om Genova and Bastia: summer only: day and night sailings.

VORNO - BASTIA

orsica Ferries Journey 4 hours (night sailings 7½ hours)

om Livorno and Bastia: 1 sailing per day (up to 3 sailings per day in July / Aug).
Most sailings by day, departure times vary.

oby Lines Journey 4 hours

om Livorno and Bastia: summer only: 5 – 7 sailings per week (1 – 2 sailings per day in peak summer).

AVONA - BASTIA

orsica Ferries Journey 6 - 10 hours. Departure times vary.

om Savona and Bastia: Winter: irregular sailings; June: 1 – 2 sailings daily; July – Sept.: 2 – 3 sailings daily.

Other sailings available from Livorno and Savona to L'Île Rousse.

CORSICA - SARDINIA 2566

nap page 287)

ONIFACIO - SANTA TERESA DI GALLURA

oby Lines Journey 50 minutes

om Bonifacio and Santa Teresa di Gallura: 3 – 4 sailings daily.

ORTO VECCHIO - GOLFO ARANCI

orsica Ferries / Sardinia Ferries

om Porto Vecchio and Golfo Aranci: June - Sept.: up to 3 sailings per week.

ITALIAN ISLAND SERVICES 2570
(Egadi, Eolie, Pantelleria, Pelagie and Ustica Islands)

nap page 287)

ilauro **Summer only**

apoli Mergellina - Stromboli - Panarea - Salina - Vulcano - Lipari and v.v.:
Daily sailings late May to early September. Additional sailing on ⑤⑥⑦ July / August (not serving Salina and Vulcano).

berty Lines by hydrofoil

GADI & EOLIAN ISLANDS and USTICA

he Sicilian ports of Messina, Milazzo, Palermo and Trapani are linked by island-hopping ervices serving Alicudi, Favignana, Filicudi, Levanzo, Lipari, Marettimo, Panarea, Rinella, alina, Stromboli, Ustica and Vulcano.

Services operate to differing frequencies (additional sailings in summer).

ILAZZO - PALERMO by hydrofoil Journey 2½ hours

Milazzo		Palermo		Milazzo	
0630	→	1145 / 1430	→	1950	June 20 - Sept. 3, 2019

ILAZZO - VULCANO by hydrofoil Journey 50 minutes

om Milazzo and Vulcano: 10 - 15 departures daily.

THER SERVICES:

nter-island sailings operate, also from mainland Sicily to the islands. Services operate to iffering frequencies (additional sailings in summer).

OLIE ISLANDS:

licudi to Filicudi, Lipari, Milazzo, Rinella, Salina and Vulcano.
ilicudi to Alicudi, Lipari, Milazzo, Rinella, Salina and Vulcano.
inostra to Lipari, Milazzo, and Panarea.
ipari to Alicudi, Filicudi, Ginostra, Milazzo, Panarea, Rinella, Salina, Stromboli and Vulcano.
ilazzo to Alicudi, Filicudi, Ginostra, Lipari, Panarea, Rinella, Salina, Stromboli and Vulcano.
anarea to Filicudi, Ginostra, Lipari, Milazzo, Rinella, Salina, Stromboli and Vulcano.
inella to Alicudi, Filicudi, Lipari, Milazzo, Panarea, Salina, Stromboli and Vulcano.
alina to Alicudi, Filicudi, Lipari, Milazzo, Panarea, Rinella, Stromboli and Vulcano.
tromboli to Alicudi, Filicudi, Lipari, Milazzo, Panarea, Rinella, Salina and Vulcano.
ulcano to Alicudi, Filicudi, Lipari, Milazzo, Panarea, Rinella, Salina and Stromboli.

GADI ISLANDS:

avignana to Levanzo, Marettimo and Trapani.
evanzo to Favignana, Marettimo, and Trapani.
arettimo to Favignana, Levanzo and Trapani.
rapani to Favignana, Levanzo and Marettimo.

NTELLERIA ISLAND:

rapani - Pantelleria and v.v.

LAGIE ISLANDS:

orto Empedocle (Agrigento) - Linosa - Lampedusa and v.v.

STICA ISLAND:

alermo - Ustica and v.v.

SAVONA - BARCELONA 2585

Grimaldi Lines

Savona		Barcelona	Barcelona		Savona
0030⑥	→	1730⑥	2300②	→	1900③

SAVONA - TANJAH (TANGIERS) MED 2590

Grimaldi Lines

Savona		Tanjah Med	Tanjah Med		Savona
0030⑥	→	2300⑦	1500①	→	1900③

Tanjah (Tangiers) Med port is located approximately 45 km east of Tanjah.
A connecting 🚌 operates between Tanjah Med and Tanjah.

MÁLAGA - MELILLA 2595

Baleària (Eurolínies Marítimes) Journey 7 hours. Departure times may vary

From Málaga: sailings most days departing 2230 or 2300.
From Melilla: sailings most days departing 1300 or 1400.

Trasmediterranea Journey 6 - 8 hours. Departure times vary Apr. 11 - 22.

From Málaga: 1500②–⑥, 2300⑦, 2359①.
From Melilla: 1400①, 2359①–⑥.

MARSEILLE - AL-JAZÂ'IR (ALGIERS) 2602

Algérie Ferries (ENTMV)

Marseille		al-Jazâ'ir	
1200	→	1000	5 - 9 sailings per month (14 - 16 July - Sept.). Days and times vary.
al-Jazâ'ir		**Marseille**	
1200	→	1000	5 - 9 sailings per month (14 - 16 July - Sept.). Days and times vary.

Other services operate from Marseille to Sakîkdah / Skikda.

MARSEILLE - TÛNIS 2615

Compagnie Tunisienne de Navigation / Corsica Linea

Until June 23 and from September 22

Marseille		Tunis	
1100⑥	→	1200⑦	Operated by Corsica Linea. Times may vary.
1600③	→	1500④	Operated by CTN. Runs May 16; not May 15. Times may vary.
Tunis		**Marseille**	
1100②	→	1000②	Operated by CTN. Times may vary.
1600⑦	→	1500①	Operated by Corsica Linea. Times may vary.

June 24 - September 21
Sailings on most days (departure times vary).

CIRKEWWA (Malta) - MGARR (Gozo) 2618

Gozo Channel Co.

Sailings Cirkewwa (Malta) - Mgarr (Gozo) and v.v.: every 45 minutes (approx every 90 mins early morning and late evening). Journey 25 minutes.

Frequent 🚌 services serve both ferry terminals.

NAPOLI - PALERMO 2625

Grandi Navi Veloci Journey 10½ hours

From Napoli and Palermo: up to 6 sailings per week. Departure times vary.

Tirrenia

Napoli		Palermo	Palermo		Napoli
2015	→	0645	2015	→	0645

NAPOLI - TRAPANI 2630

Liberty Lines by hydrofoil **June 30 - September 8, 2018. No winter service**

⑥: Napoli 1500 → Ustica 1905 / 1925 → Favignana 2125 / 2135 → Trapani 2200.
⑥: Trapani 0615 → Favignana 0635 / 0640 → Ustica 0840 / 0900 → Napoli 1315

SALERNO - PALERMO - TÛNIS 2661

Grimaldi Lines

Salerno		Palermo		Tûnis
0030⑥	→	1000⑥ / 1230⑥	→	2230⑥
1230①	→	2300① / 0200②	→	1430②
Tûnis		**Palermo**		**Salerno**
0300⑦	→	1530⑦ / 1900⑦	→	0700①
1830④	→	0700⑤ / 1030⑤	→	2000⑤

2675 SARDINIA

Sailings from FRANCE

MARSEILLE - PORTO TORRES

Corsica Linea Journey 10 - 11 hours
From Marseille and Porto Torres: infrequent sailings.

TOULON / NICE - GOLFO ARANCI

Sardinia Ferries Journey 16 hours
From Toulon or Nice and Golfo Aranci: weekly in winter; up to 3 sailings per week summer. Most sailings by night, departure times vary. Winter sailings mostly serve Toulon.

Sailings from mainland ITALY (map page 287)

CIVITAVECCHIA - ARBATAX

Tirrenia Journey 9 - 10 hours
From Civitavecchia and Arbatax: sailings most days (by night). Departure time usually 1900 or 1930 from Civitavecchia, 2359 from Arbatax.

CIVITAVECCHIA - CAGLIARI

Tirrenia
From Civitavecchia and Cagliari: 3 sailings per week (daily in summer). All sailings are overnight. Departure times vary; journey 10½ – 15½ hours.

CIVITAVECCHIA - OLBIA

Grimaldi Lines **June 14 - Sept. 30, 2019 (no winter service)**

Civitavecchia		Olbia	Olbia		Civitavecchia
2245	→	0630	1230	→	2015

Moby Lines Journey 7 hours (day sailings 5½ hours). Departure times vary.
From Civitavecchia and Olbia: daily dailing overnight (most depart 2230 from Civitavecchia, 2300 from Olbia). Additional day sailing (depart 0830) runs on certain days in summer.

Tirrenia Journey 7 hours (day sailings 5½ hours)
From Civitavecchia and Olbia: night sailing every day (most depart 2230 from Civitavecchia, 2300 from Olbia). 1 - 2 additional day sailings June - August.

CIVITAVECCHIA - PORTO TORRES

Grimaldi Lines Journey 7¼ hours. Departure times vary.
From Civitavecchia and Porto Torres: 2 sailings per week in winter (4 - 5 sailings per week June to mid-September).

GENOVA - ARBATAX

Tirrenia Journey 15½ hours **No winter service**
From Genova and Arbatax: infrequent sailings July / August only. Departure time usually 2130 from Genova, 1400 from Arbatax.

GENOVA - OLBIA

Grandi Navi Veloci Journey 12¼ hours. Most departures at 2030.
From Genova and Olbia: 3 - 4 sailings per week. New service from May 25, 2019.

Moby Lines Journey 10½ – 12¼ hours. Departure times vary.
From Genova and Olbia: 3 sailings per week in winter (1 - 2 sailings per day June - Sept.)

Tirrenia Journey 10 hours (night sailings 10½ – 12¼ hours). Departure times vary.
From Genova and Olbia: 3 - 4 sailings per week in winter (daily July / August).

GENOVA - PORTO TORRES

Grandi Navi Veloci Journey 11½ hours
From Genova and Porto Torres: Infrequent sailings in winter; daily in summer. Departure times vary; most sailings overnight.

Tirrenia Journey 9½ - 12 hours
From Genova: daily sailings (depart 2030 / 2130).
From Porto Torres: daily sailings (depart 2030 / 2130 in winter, 0930 June 2 - Aug. 15).

LIVORNO - GOLFO ARANCI

Sardinia Ferries Journey 7 – 12 hours. Departure times vary.
From Livorno and Golfo Aranci: Nightly sailings (also day sailings May - September).

LIVORNO - OLBIA

Grimaldi Lines

Livorno		Olbia	Olbia		Livorno	
1000①-⑤	→	1800①-⑤	1000①-⑤	→	1800①-⑤	
1000⑥⑦	→	1800⑥⑦	1000⑥⑦	→	1800⑥⑦	June 8 - Sept. 30.
2130	→	0615	2130	→	0615	

Moby Lines Journey 6½ – 8 hours (night sailings 7 – 9 hours).
From Livorno and Olbia: daily sailing (by night); additional daytime sailing on certain dates. Departure times vary.

NAPOLI - CAGLIARI

Tirrenia Journey 14½ hours
From Napoli and Cagliari: Infrequent sailings. Departure times vary.

PIOMBINO - OLBIA

Moby Lines Journey 5 – 5¼ hours
From Piombino and Olbia: June - September: up to 4 – 6 sailings per week.

Sailings from SICILY (map page 28…

PALERMO - CAGLIARI

Tirrenia Journey 13 hours
From Palermo and Cagliari: Infrequent sailings. Departure times vary.

Sailings from SPAIN

BARCELONA - PORTO TORRES **2019 servic…**

Grimaldi Lines Journey 12¼ hours
From Barcelona: ②⑥ Jan. 14 - Mar. 3, ①⑤ Mar. 4 - June 2, ①④⑤⑥ June 3 - July 7, ①②④⑤⑥ July 8 - Sept. 15, ②⑤ Sept. 16 - Dec. 21 (departs 2215①, 2300②④⑤, 2359⑥).
From Porto Torres: ④⑥ Jan. 14 - Mar. 3, ③⑦ Mar. 4 - Apr. 14, ⑤⑦ Apr. 15 - 24, ③⑦ Apr. 22 - June 2, ②⑤⑥⑦ June 3 - July 7, ②③⑤⑥⑦ July 8 - Sept. 15, ③⑥ Sept. 16 - Dec. 21 (departs 0615②, 0700③, 0715④⑤⑥, 0830⑦).

2678 SÈTE - AN-NADÛR (NADOR)

Grandi Navi Veloci Departure times vary. Journey 40 – 43 hours
From Sète and an-Nadûr: up to 2 sailings per week.

2680 SÈTE - TANJAH (TANGIERS) MED

Grandi Navi Veloci Departure times vary. Journey ±49 hours
From Sète and Tanjah Med: Infrequent sailings.

Tanjah (Tangiers) Med port is located approximately 45 km east of Tanjah. A connecting 🚌 operates between Tanjah Med and Tanjah.

2690 VALLETTA - CATANIA

Virtu Ferries **by catamaran** Departure times vary. Journey 4¼ hours.
From Valletta and Catania: May - September only: 4 - 6 sailings per week Valletta - Pozzallo and v.v. (Table **2694**) with 🚌 connection to / from Catania. No service on ③.

2694 VALLETTA - POZZALLO

Virtu Ferries **by catamaran** Journey 1 hr 45 min
From Valletta and Pozzallo: 1 – 2 sailings per day, departure times vary.

2695 STRETTO DI MESSINA

MESSINA - REGGIO DI CALABRIA

Bluferries **by hydrofoil** Journey 30 minutes
From Messina:
①-⑤: 0600, 0700, 0730, 0830, 0900, 1025, 1130, 1305, 1340, 1430, 1505, 1600, 1630, 1740, 1900, 2020.
⑥⑦: 0800, 0930, 1100, 1340, 1530, 1700.
From Reggio di Calabria:
①-⑤: 0645, 0745, 0810, 0910, 0940, 1105, 1210, 1345, 1420, 1510, 1545, 1640, 1710, 1820, 1940, 2055.
⑥⑦: 0840, 1010, 1140, 1420, 1610, 1740.

MESSINA - VILLA SAN GIOVANNI

Caronte & Tourist Journey 30 minutes
From Messina: every 40 minutes 0520 - 2320 (also night service 0000 - 0440).
From Villa San Giovanni: every 40 minutes 0520 - 2320 (also night service 0000 - 0440).

Bluferries **by hydrofoil** Journey 20 minutes
From Messina:
①-⑤: 0620, 0740, 0925, 1120, 1230, 1500, 1640, 1805, 1915, 2100.
⑥⑦: 0620, 0925, 1230, 1500, 1640, 1915, 2100.
From Villa San Giovanni:
①-⑤: 0710, 0810, 1000, 1150, 1350, 1540, 1710, 1840, 2020, 2220.
⑥⑦: 0710, 1000, 1350, 1540, 1710, 2020, 2220.

2699 OTHER SERVICES

Corsica Ferries **by fast ferry**
From Piombino and Portoferraio (Elba): June - Sept.: up to 7 sailings daily; journey time 4… minutes.

Moby Lines
Piombino - Portoferraio (Elba): up to 15 sailings daily in high-summer, less frequent at other times; journey time 1 hour.

Toremar
Services operate from Piombino to Cavo, Pianosa, Portoferraio and Rio Marina; from Livorno to Capraia and Gorgona; from Porto Santo Stefano to Isola del Giglio.

ADRIATIC / EASTERN MEDITERRANEAN

ANCONA - PÁTRA via Kérkira / Igumenítsa 2715

Anek Lines / Superfast Ferries — 2019 service

January 1 - June 27 and September 9 - December 31

Ancona		Igumenítsa		Pátra
1330②③④⑤	→	0800③④⑤⑥	→	1430③④⑤⑥
1630⑥⑦	→	0930⑦①	→	1500⑦①

Pátra		Igumenítsa		Ancona
1730⑤⑥	→	2315⑤⑥	→	1400⑥⑦
1730①②③⑦	→	2359①②③⑦	→	1630②③④①

June 28 - September 8

Ancona		Kérkira (Corfu)		Igumenítsa		Pátra
330①③⑤⑥⑦	→	→	→	0630②④⑥⑦①	→	1200②④⑥⑦①
1330②	→	0530③	→	0645③	...	...
1500④	→	0700⑤	→	0815⑤	...	...
1630②④⑥	→	→	→	0930③⑤⑦	→	1500③⑤⑦

Pátra		Igumenítsa		Kérkira (Corfu)		Ancona
...	...	1930③⑤	→	2045③⑤	→	1045④⑥
430①②④⑥⑦	→	2015①②④⑥⑦	→	→	→	1100②③⑤⑦①
1730③	→	→	→	→	→	1200④
1730①⑤	→	2315①⑤	→	→	→	1400②⑥

🚐 connection Pátra - Pireás - Athína and v.v. operates most days in summer.

For international journeys only

Grimaldi Lines / Minoan Lines — 2019 service

January 1 - June 30 and September 9 - December 31

Ancona		Igumenítsa		Pátra	Pátra		Igumenítsa		Ancona
1830①	→	1100②	→	1630②	1900①	→	0100②	→	1600②
1400③	→	0800④	→	1400④	1900②	→	0100③	→	1600③
1400④	→	0800⑤	→	1400⑤	1630④	→	2230④	→	1330⑤
1700⑤	→	1000⑥	→	1600⑥	1630⑤	→	2230⑤	→	1330⑥
1700⑥	→	1000⑦	→	1600⑦	1800⑥	→	2359⑥	→	1500⑦
1830⑦	→	1100①	→	1700①	1800⑦	→	2359⑦	→	1500①

July 1 - September 8

Ancona		Igumenítsa		Pátra	Pátra		Igumenítsa		Ancona
1800①	→	1100②	→	1630②	1930①	→	0130②	→	1700②
1400③	→	1000④		...	1900②	→	0100③	→	1630③
1400④	→	1000⑤		...	...		2100④	→	1330⑤
1700⑤	→	1000⑥	→	1530⑥	...		2100⑤	→	1330⑥
1700⑥	→	1030⑦	→	1600⑦	1800⑥	→	2359⑥	→	1500⑦
1830⑦	→	1130①	→	1700①	1800⑦	→	2359⑦	→	1500①

ANCONA - SPLIT 2725

SNAV — April - October 2019 (No winter service)

Ancona		Split		Split		Ancona	
1100	→	2000	Sept. 1, 8	1100	→	2000	⑥
2000	→	0700	①③⑤	2000	→	0700	②④⑦
2200	→	0900	⑥	2200	→	0900	July 30, 31

Timings and dates vary in July / August. Please confirm all timings with operator.

Jadrolinija — 2019 service

January 1 - March 29 and November 3 - December 31

Ancona		Split		Split		Ancona	
1945	→	0700	②⑤	2000	→	0700	③⑦

March 31 - August 1 and August 26 - November 1

Ancona		Split		Split		Ancona	
1945	→	0700	①③⑤	2000	→	0700	②④⑦

August 2 - 16

Ancona		Split		Split		Ancona	
1945	→	0600	⑤	1430	→	2230	⑥
1945	→	0700	①③	2000	→	0700	②④⑦
2359	→	1030	⑥				

August 17 - 25

Ancona		Split		Split		Ancona	
1030	→	1930	⑦	2000	→	0700	②④
1945	→	0700	①③⑤	2130	→	0830	⑥⑦

ANCONA - ZADAR 2732

Jadrolinija — 2019 service (no winter sailings)

June 3 - July 2 and September 6 - 21

Ancona		Zadar		Zadar		Ancona	
2200	→	0700	②⑥	2200	→	0700	①⑤

July 3 - 11 and August 30 - September 5

Ancona		Zadar		Zadar		Ancona	
2200	→	0700	②④⑥	2200	→	0700	①③⑤

July 12 - 25

Ancona		Zadar		Zadar		Ancona	
2200	→	0700	②④⑤⑥	1130	→	1800	⑤⑥
				2200	→	0700	①③

July 27 - August 29

Ancona		Zadar		Zadar		Ancona	
1600	→	2200	⑥	0800	→	1400	⑥
2200	→	0530	⑤	1130	→	1800	⑤
2200	→	0700	②④⑦	2200	→	0700	①③
				2345	→	0800	⑥

BAR - BARI 2738

Jadrolinija — 2019 service (no winter sailings)

May 21 - July 11 and September 7 - November 28

Bar		Bari	Bari		Bar
2100③	→	0800④	2100②	→	0800③

July 12 - 23

Bar		Bari	Bari		Bar
1200⑥	→	1930⑥	2100②	→	0800③
2100③	→	0800④	2200⑤	→	0800⑥

July 24 - August 18

Bar		Bari	Bari		Bar
1200③⑤	→	1930③⑤	2100②	→	0800③
			2200④	→	0800⑤

August 19, 20

Bar		Bari	Bari		Bar
1200②	→	1930②	2200①	→	0800②

August 21 - September 6

Bar		Bari	Bari		Bar
2200①④	→	0800②⑤	1200①④	→	1930①④

BARI - DURRËS 2745

Grandi Navi Veloci / Adria Ferries — 2019 service

From Bari and Durrës: nightly sailings at 2200. Journey 11 hours.

Ventouris Ferries — 2019 service

From Bari and Durrës: 1-2 sailings per day, July 1 - Sept. 30 only. Journey 9 hours.

BARI - IGUMENÍTSA via Kérkira (Corfu) 2750

Ventouris Ferries — 2019 service (no winter sailings)

Bari		Kérkira (Corfu)		Igumenítsa	
1700	→	0445		...	July 22, 29, Aug. 5, 12, 20, 26, Sept. 3.
1900	→	0645 / 0715	→	0830	July 4, 6, 8, 10, 12, 14, 16, 18, 20, 24, 26, 31, Aug. 2, 7, 9, 14, 16, 18, 22, 24, 28, 30, Sept. 1, 5, 7.
...		0715	→	0830	July 27, Aug. 3, 10. To Bari.
1900	→	0815 / 0845	→	1015	July 3, 5, 7, 9, 11, 13, 15, 17, 19, 21, 23, 25, 30, Aug. 1, 6, 8, 13, 15, 17, 19, 21, 23, 25, 27, 29, 31, Sept. 2, 4, 6.
2359	→	1145 / 1215	→	1330	July 27, Aug. 3, 10.
2359	→	1315 / 1345	→	1515	July 28, Aug. 4, 11.

Igumenítsa		Kérkira (Corfu)		Bari	
0100	→	→	→	1130	July 31, Aug. 7, 14, 22, 28, Sept. 5.
1000	→	→	→	2030	July 27, Aug. 3, 10. From Kérkira.
2000	→	2115 / 2145	→	0730	July 3, 5, 7, 9, 11, 13, 15, 17, 19, 21, 25, 28, Aug. 1, 4, 8, 11, 15, 17, 19, 23, 25, 29, 31, Sept. 2, 6, 8.
2000	→	2130 / 2200	→	0915	July 4, 6, 8, 10, 12, 14, 16, 18, 20, 22, 24, 26, 29, 31, Aug. 2, 5, 7, 9, 12, 14, 16, 18, 20, 22, 24, 26, 28, 30, Sept. 1, 3, 5, 7

BARI - PÁTRA via Kérkira and Igumenítsa 2755

Anek Lines / Superfast Ferries — 2019 service

January 1 - May 29 and October 1 - December 31

Bari		Kérkira (Corfu)		Igumenítsa		Pátra
1330⑦	→	→	→	2300⑦	→	0700①
1930①–⑥	→	→	→	0530②–⑦	→	1300②–⑦

May 30 - June 27 and September 16 - 30

Bari		Kérkira (Corfu)		Igumenítsa		Pátra
1330⑦	→	→	→	2300⑦	→	0700①
1930①②③⑤⑥	→	→	→	0530②③④⑥⑦	→	1300②③④⑥⑦
1930④	→	0430⑤	→	0600⑤	→	1300⑤

June 28 - July 21 and August 30 - September 15

Bari		Kérkira (Corfu)		Igumenítsa		Pátra
1330⑦	→	→	→	2300⑦	→	0700①
1930①②③	→	→	→	0530②③④	→	1300②③④
1930④⑤⑥	→	0430⑤⑥⑦	→	0600⑤⑥⑦	→	1300⑤⑥⑦

July 22 - August 11

Bari		Kérkira (Corfu)		Igumenítsa		Pátra
1300⑤⑥	→	2200⑤⑥	→	2330⑤⑥	...	...
1330⑦	→	→	→	2300⑦	→	0700①
1930①②③⑥	→	→	→	0530②③④⑦	→	1300②③④⑦
1930④	→	0430⑤	→	0600⑤	→	1300⑤

August 12 - 29

Bari		Kérkira (Corfu)		Igumenítsa		Pátra
1300③	→	→	→	2300③	...	...
1300⑤⑥	→	2200⑤⑥	→	2330⑤⑥	...	...
1330⑦	→	→	→	2300⑦	→	0700①
1930①②④⑥	→	→	→	0530②③⑤⑦	→	1300②③⑤⑦

January 1 - May 29 and October 1 - December 31

Pátra		Igumenítsa		Kérkira (Corfu)		Bari
1800	→	0030	→	→	→	0930

May 30 - June 27 and September 16 - 30

Pátra		Igumenítsa		Kérkira (Corfu)		Bari
1800①②④⑤⑥⑦	→	0030②③⑤⑥⑦①	→	→	→	0930②③⑤⑥⑦①
1800③	→	0030④	→	0200④	→	1000④

June 28 - July 21 and August 30 - September 15

Pátra		Igumenítsa		Kérkira (Corfu)		Bari
1800①②④⑤	→	0030②③⑤⑥	→	→	→	0930②③⑤⑥
1800③⑥⑦	→	0030④⑦①	→	0200④⑦①	→	1000④⑦①

July 22 - August 11

Pátra		Igumenítsa		Kérkira (Corfu)		Bari
1800⑤	→	→	→	→	→	0800⑥
1800①②③④⑦	→	0030②③④⑤①	→	→	→	0930②③④⑤①
...	...	0200⑥⑦	→	0330⑥⑦	→	1030⑥⑦

August 12 - 29

Pátra		Igumenítsa		Kérkira (Corfu)		Bari
1800①②⑤⑦	→	0030②③⑥①	→	→	→	0930②③⑥①
1800③	→	0030④	→	0200④	→	1000④
...	...	0030⑥	→	0330⑥	→	1030⑥
...	...	0200④⑦	→	0330④⑦	→	1030④⑦

Subject to alteration during ship maintenance periods

🚐 connection Pátra - Pireás - Athína and v.v.

2765 BRINDISI - IGUMENÍTSA

Grimaldi Lines — **2019 service**

Brindisi		Igumenítsa	Igumenítsa		Brindisi
January 1 - June 9 and September 10 - December 31					
1300	→	2200	0030①③⑤	→	0730②④⑥
2100①③⑤⑥	→	0600②④⑥⑦	1200⑥	→	1900⑥
			2359	→	0700
June 10 - September 9					
1300	→	2230	0030①③⑤⑥	→	0730②④⑥⑦
2100①③⑤⑥	→	0600②④⑥⑦	1200⑥	→	1900⑦
			2359⑦–④	→	0700①–⑤

2775 BRINDISI - PÁTRA

Grimaldi Lines — **2019 service**

Brindisi		Pátra	Pátra		Brindisi
2100①③⑥	→	1400②④⑦	1700②④⑦	→	0800③⑤①

2795 DUBROVNIK - BARI

Jadrolinija — **2019 service (no winter sailings)**

Dubrovnik		Bari	Bari		Dubrovnik
April 15 - May 20					
2200①③	→	0800②④	2100②④	→	0800③⑤
May 23 - June 8 and October 7 - November 2					
2200①⑤	→	0800②⑥	2100④⑥	→	0800⑤⑦
June 9 - July 11 and September 7 - October 5					
1200⑦	→	1930⑦	2100④⑥	→	0800⑤⑦
2200①⑤	→	0800②⑥	2200⑦	→	0800①
July 12 - 23					
1200⑤⑦	→	1930⑤⑦	2100④	→	0800⑤
2200①	→	0800②	2200⑥⑦	→	0800⑦①
July 24 - August 18					
1200④⑥⑦	→	1930④⑥⑦	2200③⑤⑥⑦	→	0800④⑥⑦①
2200①	→	0800②			
August 19 - 20					
1200①	→	1930①	2200②	→	0800③
August 21 - September 6					
2200③⑤⑥⑦	→	0800④⑥⑦①	1200⑤⑥⑦	→	1930⑤⑥⑦
			2100②	→	0800③
November 3 - 28					
2200⑦	→	0800①	2100④	→	0800⑤

2800 GREEK ISLANDS

Summary table of regular ferry services to the Greek Islands.

Routes are operated by various ferry companies to differing schedules.
Additional inter-island routes are operated at less regular intervals.

Pireás to Égina, Póros, Ídra, Spétses, Kíthira, Andikíthira.
Pireás to Sérifos, Sífnos, Mílos, Folégandros.
Pireás to Páros, Íos, Thíra (Santorini), Iráklio.
Pireás to Náxos, Amorgós, Astipálea.
Pireás to Pátmos, Léros, Kálimnos, Kos, Nísiros, Tílos, Sími, Ródos, Kárpathos, Kásos.
Pireás to Ikaría, Sámos, Híos, Lésvos.
Pireás and **Rafína** to Síros, Dílos, Míkonos, Tínos, Ándros.
Pátra to Zákinthos (Zante), Kefallinía, Itháki, Kérkira (Corfu), Igumenítsa.
Vólos, Ágios Konstantínos and **Kími** to Skiathos, Skópelos, Alónissos, Skíros.
Kavála to Thásos, Samothráki, Límnos.

2830 PIREÁS - IRÁKLIO

Minoan Lines — **2019 service**

Pireás		Iráklio		Iráklio		Pireás	
2030	→	0730	To Feb. 20.	2030	→	0715	To Feb. 20.
2100	→	0630	From Feb 21.	2100	→	0630	From Feb. 21.

Anek Lines / Blue Star Ferries — **2019 service**

Pireás		Iráklio	Iráklio		Pireás
2100	→	0600	2100	→	0600

Additional day sailings operate on certain dates in July / August

2845 PIREÁS / LAVRIO - LEMESÓS (LIMASSOL) - HEFA

Salamis Shipping

Pireás - Lemesós - Hefa: weekly freight sailings with limited passenger accommodation

2847 LAVRIO - ÇEŞME

Aegean Seaways

Lavrio		Çeşme		Çeşme		Lavrio	
2200	→	0600	①③⑤	2200	→	0600	②④⑥
1100	→	1900	⑦	2359	→	0800	⑦

Bus connections: Patras - Athína - Lavrio and v.v.
Çeşme - Kuşadasi - Bodrum and v.v.

2850 SPLIT - DUBROVNIK

Jadrolinija — **2019 service (no winter sailings)**

Split		Hvar		Korčula		Dubrovnik	
1530	→	1755	→	1925	→	2125	May 31 - Sept. 30.
Dubrovnik		**Korčula**		**Hvar**		**Split**	
0700	→	0915	→	1050	→	1255	May 31 - Sept. 30.

Catamaran services Spilt → Hvar run 5 - 6 times daily June to September.

Kapetan Luka — **2019 service (no winter sailings)**

Split		Hvar		Korčula		Dubrovnik	
0740	→	0850	→	1010	→	1205	Daily Apr. 8 - Oct. 20; ①③⑥ Oct. 21 - 26.
Dubrovnik		**Korčula**		**Hvar**		**Split**	
1630	→	1835	→	1950	→	2055	Daily Apr. 8 - Aug. 31.
1600	→	1805	→	1920	→	2025	Daily Sept. 1 - Oct. 20; ①③⑥ Oct. 21 - 26.

2875 VENEZIA - PÁTRA via Ancona / Igumenítsa

Anek Lines / Superfast Ferries — **2019 service**

Venezia		Igumenítsa		Pátra	Pátra		Igumenítsa		Venezia
January 1 - May 18 and September 28 - December 31									
1200③	→	1430④	→	2100④	2359①	→	0630②	→	0700③
1330⑥	→	1600⑦	→	2230⑦	2359④	→	0630⑤	→	0700⑥
1200⑦	→	1430①	→	2100①	2359⑤	→	0630⑥	→	0700⑦
May 19 - June 27 and September 9 - 27									
1200③	→	1430④	→	2100④	2359①	→	0630②	→	0700③
1330⑥	→	1600⑦	→	2230⑦	2359④	→	0630⑤	→	0700⑥
1200⑦	→	1500①c	→	2130①	2359⑤	→	0630⑥c	→	0730⑦
June 28 - September 8									
1200③	→	1430④	→	2100④	2359④	→	0630⑤	→	0700⑥
1330⑥	→	1600⑦	→	2230⑦	0059①	→	0730①	→	0800②

c – via Corfu (1345 towards Pátra, 0745 towards Venezia).

For international journeys only

Grimaldi Lines / Minoan Lines — **2019 service**

Venezia		Ancona		Igumenítsa		Pátra
0430③④	→	1400③④	→	0800④⑤	→	1400④⑤
Pátra		**Igumenítsa**		**Ancona**		**Venezia**
1900①②	→	0100②③	→	1600②③	→	0130③④

Subject to variation. For full service Ancona - Igumenítsa - Pátra and v.v. see Table **2715**.

2899 CROATIAN COASTAL SERVICES

Catamaran Line

Runs Pula - Mali Lošinj - Zadar, Šibenik - Kaprije - Žirje, and Split - Split (Resnik) airport.

Jadrolinija

Local services operate from Rijeka, Zadar, Šibenik and Dubrovnik to the Islands.

Venezia Lines

Catamaran services run May to September linking Venezia with destinations on Croatia's Istrian Peninsula (Poreč, Pula, Rovinj and Umag), also with Piran in Slovenia. Journey time 2 hours 30 mins to 4 hours.

2900 BLACK SEA services

Irregular services operate on the following routes (freight services; also carry passengers):

Istanbul - Odesa	**Ukrferry**	
Burgas - Batumi	**PBM**	Certain sailings call at Novorossiysk
Varna - Batumi	**Ferrysped**	
Varna - Poti	**Ferrysped**	
Varna - Odesa	**Ferrysped**	
Odesa - Batumi	**Ferrysped / Ukrferry**	Certain sailings call at Samsun
Odesa - Poti	**Ferrysped / Ukrferry**	

Odesa's ferry terminal is at Chornomorsk, 20km from Odesa.

For international ferry maps – see pages 543 - 545

Extracts from the May 2019 digitial edition Newslines

AIRPORT LINKS

Roma Ciampino airport has a new bus service, *Ciampino Airlink*, operating direct to Ciampino railway station which has a frequent rail service to Roma Termini. The overall bus/rail journey takes 30 – 35 minutes.

INTERNATIONAL

Thalys will introduce a new non-stop service between Brussels and Bordeaux on summer Saturdays with a journey time of just over four hours (see Table **11** of our Summer International Supplement).

Train **301**/**300** *Berlin Night Express* Berlin – Malmö will run on three days a week during the summer (Table **50**).

Train **1335**/**1334** *Hellas* will run between Beograd and Thessaloníki from June 14 to September 16 but passengers will be conveyed by bus between Gevgelija and Thessaloníki (Table **61**).

The twice weekly Leo Express train **401**/**400** Praha – Kraków will run daily from June 29 (Table **99**).

SWITZERLAND

The service between Lausanne and Payerne is disrupted from May 23 to September 15 when bus replacement will be in operation on the section between Palézieux and Moudon. An additional timetable panel has been added to Table **504** showing the amended timings.

SPAIN

Direct high-speed *AVE* services between Madrid and Granada are due to start next month, possibly on June 3 (Table **660**). The two cities have been without a direct service via Antequera since April 7, 2015. Remarkably, at the time the service was suspended we reported that the line was expected to reopen in August 2015! Clearly that was a tad optimistic! Once the high-speed service starts it is unclear if the direct *Talgo* service via Linares-Baeza will continue running (Table **661**).

GERMANY

The latest phase of work to fully electrify the line between München and Lindau via Memmingen started in mid-April resulting in the temporary closure of the section between Aichstetten (21 kilometres west of Memmingen) and Hergatz until September 15. The section between Kißlegg and Hergatz will also remain closed from September 16 to October 6. A special version of Table **937** will be found on page 568 with details of the replacement bus services operating during the closure.

Independent operator Flixtrain is expected to start operating services between Köln and Berlin from May 23. However, owing to engineering work taking place at various locations along the route, the schedules will initially be rather complex. Despite this, we are planning to show outline timings in a revamped version of our Flixtrain table on page 369 in next month's Summer edition.

TURKEY

Further timing alterations affecting Turkish high-speed services are scheduled from May 2 and Table **1570** has been updated accordingly. This latest timetable change sees journey times from and to İstanbul extended by approximately 30 minutes. Regular readers of this column will be aware that timings on this route have changed frequently in recent months so it is advisable to check timings locally before travelling.

The Marmaray project is now complete meaning frequent suburban services now operate between Halkalı and Gebze via central İstanbul.

Journeys to and from Sivas on trains between Ankara and eastern Turkey are subject to alteration until November 2019 due to construction work on the future high-speed line between Ankara and Sivas (Table **1575**). The affected trains are diverted via a freight route avoiding Sivas altogether with bus services provided to connect with these trains at alternative stations.

LITHUANIA

The construction phase of the Rail Baltica scheme has now begun. This new standard gauge high-speed line will eventually link all three Baltic States with Poland and beyond, the line from Kaunas across the Polish border having already opened in 2015. The immediate effect of the preparatory work is that from May 22 train services from Vilnius to Kaunas (Table **1811**) will no longer be able to access Kaunas station but will terminate in the suburbs at Palemonas, where bus connections will be available to and from central Kaunas. Revised timings were not available as we went to press.

BEYOND EUROPE

VIA Rail of Canada has advised that the only major change is the scheduling of *The Canadian* from May 1 (which we previously reported in our Winter edition). This includes an additional weekly service in each direction between Edmonton and Vancouver (Table **9050**).

Amtrak has made some alterations, mainly to its Northeast Corridor services in Table **9215** and Pacific Surfliner services in Table **9320**. As well as some timing changes on the Northeast Corridor route, extra weekend ACELA services have been added together with additional trains to and from Norfolk. Readers should note that ongoing infrastructure works along the Northeast Corridor will have an effect on timings as noted in Table **9215**.

There is some uncertainty regarding the future of the *Hoosier State* service between Indianapolis and Chicago so we have added a suitable warning in Table **9250**.

1220 BUDAPEST - SIÓFOK - FONYÓD - KESZTHELY / NAGYKANIZSA

2nd class (**C**/**G** also 1st)

SUMMER SERVICE June 15 - August 25. *For service to June 14/from Aug. 26 see page 498*

km	*June 15 - Aug 25*	8520 Ⓐ	18520 Ⓒ	18612	18510	18720	200 G	200 870	18542 Ⓐ	18700 Ⓒ	*Ex* 1842 Ⓡ	18802 P	1687 Ⓒ	18502	*Ex* 1862 Ⓡ	18502	18702 Ⓒ	*Ex* 1852 Ⓡ	*Ex* 15607 Ⓡ	*Ex* 16709 Ⓡ	18404	*Ex* 1864 Ⓡ	*Ex* 1787 ⒸⓇ	18404	18704 Ⓒ
0	**Budapest** Déli ▶ d.	...	0220	...	0405	*0505*	0635	0635	...	0705	0735	...	s	0805	0835	...	0905	0935	m	x	1005	1035	u	...	1105
4	Kelenföld ⊡ ▶ d.	...	0227	...	0412	*0512*	0642	0642	...	0712	0742	...	0803	0812	0842	...	0912	0942	0930	|	1012	1042	|	...	1112
67	**Székesfehérvár** ▶ a.	...	0324	...	0509	*0609*	0720	0720	...	|	0820	...	0844	0851	0920	...	|	1020	1024	1043	1051	1120	1124	...	|
67	**Székesfehérvár** d.	...	0340	...	0525	0635	0721	0721	...	|	0821	...	0845	0852	0921	...	|	1021	1025	1044	1052	1121	1125	...	|
95	Lepsény d.	...	|	...	0550	0703	0740	0740	...	|	0840	...	|	0920	|	←	|	1040	|	|	1120	|	|	←	|
115	**Siófok** a.	...	0419	...	0615	0727	0755	0755	...	0823	0855	...	0921	0946	0955	0946	1023	1055	1104	1128	1146	1155	1200	1146	1223
115	**Siófok** d.	0435	0435	...	0617	...	0757	0757	0802	0827	0857	...	0923	1002	0957	1002	1027	1057	1105	1132	1203	1157	1201	1203	1227
124	Zamárdi d.	0447	0447	...	0629	...	0804	0804	0815	|	0904	...	|	→	1004	1015	|	1104	1114	1145	→	1204	1209	1215	|
130	Balatonföldvár d.	0454	0454	...	0636	...	0809	0809	0823	|	0909	...	0937	...	1009	1023	|	1109	1122	1154	...	1209	1215	1223	|
139	Balatonszemes d.	0504	0504	...	0651	...	0818	0818	0833	0849	0918	...	0949	...	1018	1033	1049	1118	1133	1204	...	1218	|	1233	1249
146	Balatonlelle d.	0515	0515	...	0659	...	0824	0824	0844	0857	0924	...	0955	...	1024	1044	1057	1124	1141	1212	...	1224	1239	1244	1257
149	Balatonboglár d.	0520	0520	...	0706	...	0830	0830	0849	0911	0930	...	1000	...	1030	1049	1111	1130	1146	1216	...	1230	1243	1249	1311
157	**Fonyód** a.	0528	0528	...	0714	...	0835	0835	0857	0919	0935	...	1009	...	1035	1057	1119	1135	1155	1224	...	1235	1250	1257	1319
157	**Fonyód** d.	0529	0529	0629	0729	...	0837	0837	0901	0923	0937	1000	...	...	1037	1101	...	1137	1200	1227	...	1237	1254	1301a	1323
165	Balatonfenyves d.	0539	0539	0639	0739	...	0843	0843	0916	0931	0943	1016	...	...	1043	1116	...	1143	1216	1245	...	1243	|	1316a	1331
181	Balatonszentgyörgy a.	0557	0557	0701	0757	...	0857	0857	0936	0953	0957	1034	...	...	1057	1136	...	1157	1234	1302	...	1257	|	1336a	1350
181	Balatonszentgyörgy ▲ d.	*0600*	*0600*	0702	*0800*	...	|	0900	...	...	*1000*	1035	...	...	1100	|	...	*1200*	1235	1307	...	1300	|	...	...
	Keszthely ▲ a.	*0612*	*0612*	0714	*0811*	...	|	0911	...	...	*1012*	1046	...	...	1111	|	...	*1212*	1246	1319	...	1311	1326	...	...
181	Balatonszentgyörgy d.	0601	0601	...	0801	...	0908	...	...	...	1001	...	...	...	...	1226	...	1201	...	...	...	...	...	...	...
221	**Nagykanizsa** a.	0643	0643	...	0841	...	0947	...	...	...	1040	...	...	...	...	1304	...	1240	...	...	...	...	...	...	...
352	*Zagreb* **1340** a.	...	...	...	...	...	1238	...	...	...	...	...	...	...	...	...	...	...	...	...	...	...	...	...	...

June 15 - Aug 25	*Ex* 1844 Ⓡ	18504	*Ex* 1874 Ⓡ	18504	*Ex* 1854 Ⓡ	18406 ⊕	*Ex* 1866 Ⓡ	18406 ⊕	204 C ⊖	18746	18506	*Ex* 1876 Ⓡ	18896 Q	18506	*Ex* 1856 Ⓡ	18608	*Ex* 1868 Ⓡ	1204 A Ⓡ	18608	*Ex* 1848 Ⓡ	18708	*Ex* 1878 Ⓡ	18718	18728 E	18618 E
Budapest Déli ▶ d.	1135	1205	1235	...	1335	1405	1435	...	1535	...	1605	1635	...	...	1735	1805	1835	1855k	...	1935	2005	2135	2140	2240	2340
Kelenföld ⊡ ▶ d.	1142	1212	1242	...	1342	1412	1442	...	1542	...	1612	1642	...	...	1742	1812	1842	1912	...	1942	2012	2142	2147	2247	2347
Székesfehérvár ▶ a.	1220	1251	1320	...	1420	1451	1520	...	1620	...	1651	1720	...	...	1820	1851	1920	1952	...	2020	2051	2220	2244	2344	0044
Székesfehérvár d.	1221	1252	1321	...	1421	1452	1521	...	1621	...	1652	1721	...	...	1821	1852	1921	1954	...	2021	2055	2221	2250	2350	0050
Lepsény d.	1240	1320	|	←	1440	1520	|	←	1640	...	1720	|	...	←	1840	1920	|	|	←	2040	2120	|	2315	0015	0112
Siófok a.	1255	1346	1355	1346	1455	1546	1555	1546	1655	...	1746	1755	...	1746	1855	1946	1955	2029	1946	2055	2146	2255	2336	0036	0133
Siófok d.	1257	1402	1357	1402	1457	1602	1557	1602	1657	1713	1802	1757	...	1802	1857	2002	1957	2030	2002	2057	2152	2257	2340	0040	0140
Zamárdi d.	1304	→	1404	1415	1504	→	1604	1615	1704	1726	→	1804	...	1815	1904	→	2004	|	2015	2104	2205	2304	2352	0052	0152
Balatonföldvár d.	1309	...	1409	1423	1509	...	1609	1623	1709	1737	...	1809	...	1823	1909	...	2009	2040	2023	2109	2213	2309	0000	0100	0200
Balatonszemes d.	1318	...	1418	1433	1518	...	1618	1633	1718	1749	...	1818	...	1833	1918	...	2018	|	2033	2118	2223	2318	0010	0110	0210
Balatonlelle d.	1324	...	1424	1444	1524	...	1624	1644	1724	1756	...	1824	...	1844	1924	...	2024	|	2044	2124	2231	2324	0018	0118	0218
Balatonboglár d.	1330	...	1430	1449	1530	...	1630	1649	1730	1804	...	1830	...	1849	1930	...	2030	|	2049	2130	2239	2330	0023	0123	0227
Fonyód a.	1335	...	1435	1457	1535	...	1635	1657	1735	1814	...	1835	...	1857	1935	...	2035	2100	2057	2135	2247	2335	0032	0132	0235
Fonyód d.	1337	...	1437	1501	1537	...	1637	1703	1737	...	...	1837	1840	1903	1937	...	2037	2101	2103	2137	...	2337	...	...	0236
Balatonfenyves d.	1343	...	1443	1516	1543	...	1643	1716	1743	...	...	1843	1855	1916	1943	...	2043	|	2117	2143	...	2343	...	...	0246
Balatonszentgyörgy a.	1357	...	1457	1542	1557	...	1657	1736	1757	...	...	1857	1916	1936	1957	...	2057	2117	2136	2157	...	2357	...	...	0304
Balatonszentgyörgy ▲ d.	*1400*	...	1500	...	*1600*	...	1700	...	*1800*	...	...	1900	1917	...	*2000*	...	2100	*2119*	2200	*2200*	...	0000	...	...	0305
Keszthely ▲ a.	*1412*	...	1511	...	*1612*	...	1711	...	*1812*	...	...	1911	1928	...	*2012*	...	2111	*2130*	2212	*2212*	...	0011	...	...	0316
Balatonszentgyörgy d.	1401	...	...	...	1601	...	...	...	1801	...	...	...	...	...	2001	...	...	2118	...	2201	...	...	...	...	...
Nagykanizsa a.	1440	...	...	...	1642	...	...	...	1840	...	...	...	...	...	2042	...	...	2156	...	2240	...	...	...	...	...
Zagreb **1340** a.	...	...	...	...	...	...	...	...	2105	...	...	...	...	...	...	...	...	0022	...	...	...	...	...	...	...

June 15 - Aug 25	18729 F	18719	18559	18609	*Ex* 1859 Ⓡ	18747	1205 A Ⓡ	18529	*Ex* 1867 Ⓡ	18529	*Ex* 1847 Ⓡ	18407	*Ex* 1877 Ⓡ	18407	*Ex* 1857 Ⓡ	18507 ⊕	18897 Q	*Ex* 1865 Ⓡ	18507 ⊕	*Ex* 1845 Ⓡ	18405	*Ex* 1875 Ⓡ	18405	205 G ⊖	18705 Ⓒ
Zagreb **1340** d.	...	...	...	...	...	...	0317	...	...	...	...	...	...	...	...	...	...	...	...	...	...	...	...	0949	...
Nagykanizsa d.	...	...	0345	...	0519	...	0606	0600	...	...	0719	0740	...	...	0919	...	...	...	...	1119	1140	...	...	1319	...
Balatonszentgyörgy a.	...	...	0424	...	0557	...	0644	0640	...	...	0757	0818	...	...	0957	...	...	...	...	1157	1218	...	...	1357	...
Keszthely ▲ d.	...	...	...	0415	*0548*	...	|	*0631*	0648	...	*0747*	|	0848	...	*0948*	...	1014	1048	...	*1147*	|	1248	...	*1347*	...
Balatonszentgyörgy ▲ a.	...	...	...	0427	*0559*	...	|	*0643*	0659	...	*0759*	|	0859	...	*0959*	...	1026	1059	...	*1159*	|	1259	...	*1359*	...
Balatonszentgyörgy d.	...	...	...	0428	0602	...	0645	0647	0702	...	0802	0819	0902	...	1002	1015	1035	1102	...	1202	1219	1302	...	1402	1410
Balatonfenyves d.	...	...	...	0447	0617	...	|	0706	0717	...	0817	0843	0917	...	1017	1043	1120	1117	...	1217	1243	1317	...	1417	1428
Fonyód a.	...	...	...	0456	0622	...	0700	0715	0722	...	0822	0854	0922	...	1022	1054	1132	1122	...	1222	1254	1322	...	1422	1437
Fonyód d.	0220	0335	...	0457	0624	0630	0701	0716	0724	...	0824	0903	0924	...	1024	1103	...	1124	...	1224	1303	1324	...	1424	1439
Balatonboglár d.	0228	0343	...	0505	0630	0638	|	0724	0730	...	0830	0912	0930	...	1030	1112	...	1130	...	1230	1312	1330	...	1430	1452
Balatonlelle d.	0232	0347	...	0509	0634	0642	|	0728	0734	...	0834	0916	0934	...	1034	1116	...	1134	...	1234	1316	1334	...	1434	1456
Balatonszemes d.	0240	0355	...	0517	0640	0652	|	0736	0740	←	0840	0924	0940	...	1040	1124	...	1140	...	1240	1324	1340	...	1440	1504
Balatonföldvár d.	0249	0404	...	0526	0649	0701	0719	0745	0749	0745	0849	0933	0949	...	1049	1133	...	1149	...	1249	1333	1349	...	1449	|
Zamárdi d.	0256	0411	...	0533	0654	0708	|	→	0754	0757	0854	0940	0954	←	1054	1140	...	1154	←	1254	1340	1354	←	1454	|
Siófok a.	0307	0422	...	0544	0701	0720	0731	...	0801	0809	0901	0954	1001	0954	1101	1154	...	1201	1154	1301	1354	1401	1354	1501	1526
Siófok d.	0310	0426	...	0546	0703	...	0733	...	0803	0815	0903	1015	1003	1015	1103	1215	...	1203	1215	1303	1415	1403	1415	1503	1532
Lepsény d.	0331	0447	...	0607	0717	...	|	...	|	0840	0917	→	|	1044	1117	→	...	|	1240	1317	→	|	1440	1517	|
Székesfehérvár a.	0351	0513	...	0633	0736	...	0813	...	0836	0905	0936	...	1036	1104	1136	...	...	1236	1305	1336	...	1436	1505	1536	|
Székesfehérvár ▶ d.	0353	0527	...	0634	0737	...	0815	...	0837	*0918*	0937	...	1037	1106	1137	...	...	1237	1306	1337	...	1437	1506	1537	|
Kelenföld ⊡ ▶ a.	0450	0611	...	0716	0816	...	0854	...	0916	*1015*	1016	...	1116	1146	1216	...	...	1316	1346	1416	...	1516	1546	1616	1646
Budapest Déli ▶ a.	0459	0619	...	0724	0824	...	0909k	...	0924	...	1024	...	1124	1154	1224	...	...	1324	1354	1424	...	1524	1554	1624	1654

June 15 - Aug 25	18505	*Ex* 1863 Ⓡ	18505	*Ex* 16706 Ⓡ	*Ex* 15606 Ⓡ	*Ex* 1843 Ⓡ	18703 Ⓒ	*Ex* 1786 ⒸⓇ	18403	*Ex* 1873 Ⓡ	18403	1686 Ⓒ	18803 P	*Ex* 1853 Ⓡ	18701 Ⓒ	18501	*Ex* 1861 Ⓡ	18501	201 C	18511	*Ex* 1871 Ⓡ	18511	8531 ①–④	8531 ⑤–⑦	18611 E
Zagreb **1340** d.	...	...	...	...	...	...	...	...	...	...	...	...	...	...	...	...	...	...	1638	...	...	...	...	...	...
Nagykanizsa d.	...	...	...	...	...	1517	...	...	...	...	...	...	...	1719	...	...	...	...	1917	...	...	...	2120	2120	...
Balatonszentgyörgy a.	...	...	...	...	...	1557	...	...	...	...	...	...	...	1757	...	...	...	...	1957	...	...	...	2157	2157	...
Keszthely ▲ d.	...	1448	...	1435	1513	*1547*	...	1630	...	1648	...	...	1723	*1747*	...	...	1848	...	*1947*	...	2048	...	*2147*	*2147*	2348
Balatonszentgyörgy ▲ a.	...	1459	...	1446	1524	*1559*	...	|	...	1659	...	...	1734	*1759*	...	...	1859	...	*1959*	...	2059	...	*2159*	*2159*	2359
Balatonszentgyörgy d.	1418a	1502	...	1457	1525	1602	...	|	1618	1702	...	...	1737	1802	1810	1818a	1902	...	2002	2018	2102	...	2202	2202	0002
Balatonfenyves d.	1443a	1517	...	1520	1543	1617	...	|	1643	1717	...	...	1807	1817	1828	1850a	1917	...	2017	2043	2118	...	2221	2221	0021
Fonyód a.	1454a	1522	...	1529	1550	1622	...	1700	1654	1722	...	...	1817	1822	1837	1901a	1922	...	2022	2054	2123	...	2230	2230	0030
Fonyód d.	1503	1524	...	1535	1551	1624	1639	1701	1703	1724	...	1755	...	1824	1839	1903	1924	...	2024	2103	2124	...	2231	2231	0035
Balatonboglár d.	1512	1530	...	1543	1559	1630	1652	1707	1712	1730	...	1804	...	1830	1852	1912	1930	...	2030	2112	2130	...	2239	2239	0043
Balatonlelle d.	1516	1534	...	1547	1604	1634	1656	1710	1716	1734	...	1808	...	1834	1856	1916	1934	...	2034	2116	2134	...	2243	2243	0047
Balatonszemes d.	1524	1540	...	1555	1617	1640	1704	|	1724	1740	...	1818	...	1840	1904	1924	1940	...	2040	2124	2140	...	2251	2251	0055
Balatonföldvár d.	1533	1549	...	1603	1632	1649	|	1726	1733	1749	...	1830	...	1849	|	1933	1949	...	2049	2134	2149	...	2300	2300	0109
Zamárdi d.	1540	1554	←	1613	1640	1654	|	1735	1740	1754	←	|	...	1854	|	1940	1954	←	2054	2142	2154	...	2312	2312	0116
Siófok a.	1554	1601	1554	1623	1648	1701	1726	1743	1754	1801	1754	1840	...	1901	1926	1954	2001	1954	2101	2156	2201	...	2324	2324	0128
Siófok d.	1615	1603	1615	1628	1649	1703	1732	1755	1815	1803	1815	1841	...	1903	1932	2015	2003	2015	2103	2158	2203	←	...	2330	0130
Lepsény d.	→	|	1640	|	|	1717	|	|	→	|	1840	|	...	1917	|	→	|	2040	2117	2223	|	2223	...	|	0151
Székesfehérvár a.	...	1636	1705	1710	1733	1736	|	1831	...	1836	1905	1920	...	1936	|	...	2036	2105	2136	→	2236	2247	...	0010	0211
Székesfehérvár ▶ d.	...	1637	1706	|	1734	1737	|	1832	...	1837	1906	1927	...	1937	|	...	2037	2106	2137	...	2237	2248	...	0012	0213
Kelenföld ⊡ ▶ a.	...	1716	1746	|	1824	1816	1846	|	...	1916	1946	2025	...	2016	2046	...	2116	2146	2216	...	2316	2345	...	0100	0310
Budapest Déli ▶ a.	...	1724	1754	z	n	1824	1854	v	...	1924	1954	t	...	2024	2054	...	2124	2154	2224	...	2324	2354	...	0109	0319

A – ADRIA – June 14 - Sept. 6 Budapest - Split; June 15 - Sept. 7 Split (next day from Zagreb) - Budapest. 1, 2 cl., 2 cl., (2) Budapest - Zagreb - Split and v.v.
C – AGRAM – (12) Budapest - Zagreb and v.v.
E – ④⑤⑥ (also July 3, 7, Aug. 18 - 21).
F – ⑤⑥⑦ (also July 4, 8, Aug. 19 - 22).
G – GRADEC – (12) Budapest - Zagreb and v.v.
P – Pécs - Fonyód - Keszthely - Tapolca and v.v. (Table **1205**).
Q – Kaposvár - Fonyód - Keszthely - Tapolca - Celldömölk - Szombathely and v.v. (Table **1205**).

a – Ⓐ only.
k – Budapest **Keleti**.
m – From Miskolc d. 0654, Hatvan d. 0825.
n – To Hatvan a. 1927, Miskolc a. 2054.
s – From Szolnok (d. 0645), Ferihegy ✈ (d. 0740).
t – To Ferihegy ✈ (a. 2053), Szolnok (a. 2155).
u – From Szeged (d. 0757), Ferihegy ✈ (d. 1009).
v – To Ferihegy ✈ (a. 1948), Szeged (a. 2205).
x – From Záhony (0459), Nyiregyháza (0627), Debrecen (0712), Szolnok (0845), Ferihegy ✈ (0940).

z – To Ferihegy ✈ (1818), Szolnok (1914), Debrecen (2100), Nyiregyháza (2146), Záhony (2257).

⊖ – Ⓡ for domestic journeys within Hungary.
⊡ – Connection with metro line 4 (see city plan page 29).
⊕ – Change at Fonyód on Ⓒ.
▶ – See also Tables **1225** and **1230**.
▲ – See also Table **1232**. *Italics* = change trains.

BUDAPEST - SZÉKESFEHÉRVÁR - BALATONFÜRED - TAPOLCA — 1225

2nd class

SUMMER SERVICE June 15 - August 25. *For service to June 14/from Aug. 26 see pages 498/499*

km	June 15 - Aug. 25	9710	19720	19750	19700	1972	19752	19702	19792	19754	19794	16907	19764	19704	19756	19606	19748	19796	19766	19706	1978	19758	19708	19798	9738
									Ⓒ					⊕			Ⓒ	⑤			⑤				
0	**Budapest** Déli ▶ d.	...	0405	0615	0700	0800	0825	0900	1000	1025	1100	b	1225	1300	1415	1500	...	1600	1615	1700	1800	1815	1900	2035	2140
4	Kelenföld ▶ d.	...	0412	0633	0707	0807	0833	0907	1007	1033	1107	1207	1233	1307	1433	1507	...	1607	1633	1707	1807	1833	1907	2042	2147
67	**Székesfehérvár** ▶ a.	...	0509	0712	0745	0848	0912	0945	1048	1112	1145	1248	1312	1345	1512	1545	...	1647	1712	1745	1846	1912	1945	2120	2244
67	**Székesfehérvár** d.	0429	0530	0715	0757	0900	0915	0957	1100	1115	1157	1300	1315	1357	1515	1557	...	1700	1715	1757	1900	1915	1957	2133	2254
105	Balatonkenese d.	0512	0615	0813	|	0945	1013	|	1145	1213	|	1345	1413	|	1613	|	...	1745	1813	|	1945	2013	|	2212	2339
117	Balalatonalmádi d.	0526	0629	0827	0845	0959	1027	1045	1159	1227	1245	1359	1427	1445	1627	1645	...	1759	1827	1845	1959	2027	2045	2226	2352
123	Alsóörs d.	0533	0636	0835	|	1006	1035	|	1206	1235	|	1406	1435	|	1635	|	...	1806	1835	|	2006	2035	|	2234	2359
132	**Balatonfüred** a.	0543	0647	0848	0859	1014	1048	1059	1214	1248	1259	1414	1448	1459	1648	1659	...	1814	1848	1859	2014	2048	2059	2246	0010
132	**Balatonfüred** d.	0544	0703	...	0903	1016	...	1103	1216	...	1303	1416	...	1503	...	1703	1814	1816	...	1903	2016	...	2103	2249	...
157	Révfülöp d.	0627	0743	...	0943	1049	...	1143	1249	...	1343	1449	...	1543	...	1743	1920	1849	...	1943	2049	...	2143	2325	...
168	Badacsonytomaj d.	0642	0801	...	1001	1100	...	1201	1300	...	1401	1500	...	1601	...	1801	1934	1900	...	2001	2100	...	2201	2339	...
170	Badacsony d.	0645	0805	...	1005	1105	...	1205	1305	...	1405	1505	...	1605	...	1805	1937	1905	...	2005	2105	...	2205	2342	...
184	**Tapolca** a.	0703	0822	...	1022	1119	...	1222	1319	...	1422	1519	...	1622	...	1822	2001	1919	...	2022	2119	...	2222	2359	...
	Szombathely **1232** a.	...	...	...	...	...	...	...	...	...	...	...	...	...	...	1956	...	...	...	...	...	...	...	...	...

June 15 - Aug. 25	9739	19719	979	19707	19757	19747	19607	19755	19705	19765	16906	19795	19753	1975	19793	19703	19763	1973	19701	19751	1971	19731	19761	19791	19741
						Ⓒ								Ⓒ	⑦						⑤–⑦			⑦	
Szombathely **1232** d.	...	...	...	...	...	...	0759	...	...	...	...	...	...	...	...	...	...	...	...	...	...	...	...	...	...
Tapolca d.	...	0435	0558	0740	...	0845	0940	...	1140	...	1238	1340	...	1438	...	1540	...	1638	1740	...	1838	1940	...	2038	2225
Badacsony d.	...	0452	0613	0757	...	0901	0957	...	1157	...	1253	1357	...	1453	...	1557	...	1653	1757	...	1853	1957	...	2053	2242
Badacsonytomaj d.	...	0455	0616	0801	...	0904	1001	...	1201	...	1259	1401	...	1459	...	1601	...	1659	1801	...	1859	2001	...	2059	2245
Révfülöp d.	...	0510	0627	0816	...	0918	1016	...	1216	...	1310	1416	...	1510	...	1616	...	1710	1816	...	1910	2016	...	2110	2259
Balatonfüred a.	...	0543	0653	0855	...	0956	1055	...	1255	...	1338	1455	...	1538	...	1655	...	1738	1855	...	1938	2055	...	2138	2340
Balatonfüred d.	0345	0544	0655	0900	0911	...	1100	1111	1300	1311	1340	1500	1511	1540	1620	1700	1711	1740	1900	1911	1940	...	2111	2140	2345
Alsóörs d.	0356	0555	0703	|	0923	...	|	1123	|	1323	1349	|	1523	1549	1635	|	1723	1749	|	1923	1949	...	2123	2149	2359
Balalatonalmádi d.	0403	0602	0709	0913	0931	...	1113	1131	1313	1331	1359	1513	1531	1559	1645	1713	1731	1759	1913	1931	1959	...	2131	2156	0007
Balatonkenese d.	0416	0615	0723	|	0945	...	|	1145	|	1345	1413	|	1545	1613	1659	|	1745	1813	|	1945	2013	...	2145	2212	0021
Székesfehérvár a.	0505	0700	0800	1000	1043	...	1200	1243	1400	1443	1457	1600	1643	1657	1745	1800	1843	1857	2000	2043	2057	...	2233	2248	0101
Székesfehérvár ▶ d.	0527	0712	0812	1012	1045	...	1212	1245	1412	1445	1509	1612	1645	1709	1746	1812	1845	1909	2012	2045	2109	...	2241	2300	...
Kelenföld ▶ a.	0611	0751	0851	1051	1125	...	1251	1325	1451	1525	1551	1651	1725	1751	1835	1851	1925	1951	2051	2125	2151	...	2321	2339	...
Budapest Déli ▶ a.	0619	0759	0859	1059	1134	...	1259	1334	1459	1544	d	1659	1734	1759	1844	1859	1944	1959	2059	2134	2159	...	2334	2349	...

b – From Záhony d. 0703, Nyiregyháza d. 0814, Debrecen d. 0858, Szolnok d. 1045, Ferihegy ✈ d. 1140.
d – To Ferihegy ✈ a. 1618, Snolnok a. 1715, Debrecen a. 1901, Nyiregyháza a. 1946, Záhony a. 2057.
▶ – See also Tables **1220** and **1230**.
⊕ – Additional train runs at 1400 on ⑤.

SZOMBATHELY - CELLDÖMÖLK - UKK - TAPOLCA - KESZTHELY — 1232

2nd class

SUMMER SERVICE June 15 - August 25. *For service to June 14/from Aug. 26 see page 499*

km	June 15 - Aug. 25	19639	19619	19627	19627	18897	19607	19617	*Ex* 19809	19897	19655	19635	19625	19645	19613	19603	18803	19623	19643	19611	19641	19621	19631	
						k	B		Ⓡ								n							
0	**Szombathely** 1230/38 d.	...	...	...	...	0717	0759	...	...	0925	...	...	...	...	...	...	...	...	...	...	...	...	...	...
	Györ 1238 d.	...	...	...	...	|	|	...	0807	|	...	...	...	...	...	...	...	...	...	...	...	...	...	...
45	Celldömölk 1230/38 d.	...	0453	0605	...	0805	0847	...	|	1001	...	...	1205	...	1401	1501	...	1605	...	1801	...	2005	...	...
55	Boba 1230 d.	...	0502	0615	...	0816	0856	...	0950	|	...	...	1215	...	1410	1514	...	1615	...	1810	...	2015	...	...
73	**Ukk** 1230 a.	...	0520	0633	...	0834	|	...	|	1027	...	...	1233	...	1428	1537	...	1633	...	1828	...	2033	...	...
73	**Ukk** d.	...	0523	0636	0800	0836	|	0931	|	1032	...	...	1236	...	1436	1538	...	1636	...	1836	...	2036	...	...
81	Sümeg d.	...	0534	0647	0810	0847	0919	0942	1018	1041	...	...	1247	...	1447	1549	...	1647	...	1847	...	2047	...	...
101	**Tapolca** a.	...	0554	0714	0828	0905	0937	1009	1037	1058	...	...	1314	...	1514	1609	...	1713	...	1914	...	2107	...	...
101	**Tapolca** d.	0447	0559	0715	0830	0910	...	1014	1040	1101	...	1246	1315	1446	1515	...	1646	1715	1846	1915	2028	2110	2228	...
126	**Keszthely** a.	0518	0630	0746	0900	0944	...	1044	1109	1130	...	1322	1346	1522	1546	...	1722	1746	1922	1946	2059	2141	2258	...
126	**Keszthely** 1220 d.	0548	0631	0747	...	1014	...	...	...	...	1147	...	1347	...	1547	...	1723	1747	...	1947	...	2147	...	...
136	**B'tonszentgyörgy** 1220 a.	0559	0643	0759	...	1026	...	...	...	...	1159	...	1359	...	1559	...	1734	1759	...	1959	...	2159	...	...

June 15 - Aug. 25	19610	9630	19630	19620	19632	19652	19662	19612	19642	18802	19614	19634	19624	19616	19626	19894	19636	19606	19646	*Ex* 19808	18896	19618	19628	19658
		Ⓐ	Ⓒ							n								D		Ⓡ	k			
B'tonszentgyörgy 1220 d.	...	...	...	0600	...	0800	...	...	1000	1035	1200	...	1400	...	1600	...	...	...	1800	...	1917	2000	2119	2200
Keszthely 1220 a.	...	...	...	0612	...	0811	...	...	1012	1046	1212	...	1412	...	1612	...	...	...	1812	...	1928	2012	2130	2212
Keszthely d.	0405	0528	...	0613	0703	0817	0903	0923	1025	1052	1213	1303	1413	1503	1613	1639	1748	...	1813	1843	1929	2037	2145	2237
Tapolca a.	0434	0556	...	0644	0735	0850	0934	0956	1059	1124	1244	1335	1444	1536	1644	1707	1819	...	1844	1910	1959	2111	2216	2311
Tapolca d.	0445	0600	0600	0645	...	0851	...	0957	...	...	1245	...	1445	1540	1645	1715	...	1825	1845	1916	2007	...	2225	...
Sümeg d.	0504	0620	0620	0708	...	0919	...	1018	...	...	1308	...	1508	1608	1708	1732	...	1847	1908	1932	2026	...	2244	...
Ukk a.	0515	0631	0631	0720	...	0928	...	1030	...	...	1320	...	1520	1620	1720	|	...	|	1920	|	2035	...	2254	...
Ukk 1230 d.	0523	0634	0634	0723	...	...	...	1032	...	...	1328	...	1523	1635	1729	|	...	|	1923	|	2036	...	2255	...
Boba 1230 a.	0540	0653	0653	0740	...	...	...	1051	...	...	1345	...	1540	1651	1746	|	...	1908	1940	1952	2052	...	2312	...
Celldömölk 1230/38 a.	0552	0706	0706	0752	...	...	...	...	...	...	1357	...	1552	...	1758	1802	...	1919	1952	|	2104	...	2324	...
Györ 1238 a.	...	...	...	...	...	...	...	...	...	...	...	...	...	...	...	|	...	|	...	2119	|	...	...	...
Szombathely 1230/38 a.	...	...	...	...	...	...	...	...	...	...	...	...	...	...	...	1854	...	1956	...	...	2142	...	...	...

B – To Budapest (Table **1225**).
D – From Budapest (Table **1225**).
k – Szombathely - Keszthely - Fonyód - Kaposvár and v.v. (Table **1205**).
n – Tapolca - Keszthely - Fonyód - Kaposvár - Pécs and v.v. (Table **1205**).

FRANCE - ADDITIONAL TABLE

AMIENS - ROUEN — 268

Service until June 28. *For service June 29 - September 15 see page 177*

km		①	Ⓐ		⑥	†		Ⓐ	Ⓐ	⑥	†		①–④	⑤	①–④	†	⑥		Ⓐ	Ⓐ	Ⓒ			
		g						b	b				n		n									
	Lille Flandres **256** d.	...	0602	...	0802	...	...	...	...	...	...	...	...	...	...	...	...	...	1702	...	1802	...	...	...
0	**Amiens** d.	0555	0719	...	0927	0926	...	1027	1235	1244	1425	...	1655	1655	1725	1725	1733	...	1826	1905	1927	...	...	...
31	Poix de Picardie d.	0614	0737	...	0945	0944	...	1109	1317	1305	1443	...	1718	1717	1744	1744	1755	...	1844	1927	1944	...	...	...
52	Abancourt d.	0626	0749	...	0957	0956	...	1140	1348	1320	1455	...	1733	1732	1756	1756	1810	...	1856	1942	1956	...	...	...
73	Serqueux d.	0642	0803	...	1012	1014	...	1210	1418	1336	1512	...	1749	1749	1813	1813	1826	...	1913	1957	2011	...	...	...
121	**Rouen** Rive-Droite a.	0724	0833	...	1046	1047	...	1312	1520	1423	1543	...	...	1822	1842	1842	1907	...	1942	...	2043	...	...	...

	Ⓐ		Ⓐ	Ⓐ		⑥		†	Ⓐ		⑥	⑤	⑤	①–④		Ⓐ			Ⓐ		⑤†			
									b				b	bn										
Rouen Rive-Droite d.	...	...	0617	0717	...	0817	...	0915	0934	...	1217	1217	...	1217	...	1617	...	1816	1834	...	1917	...	...	...
Serqueux d.	0611	...	0647	0747	...	0847	...	0948	1036	...	1248	1247	1300	1319	...	1650	...	1850	1916	...	1950	...	...	...
Abancourt d.	0625	...	0703	0802	...	0901	...	1002	1106	...	1301	...	1330	1349	...	1703	...	1903	1932	...	2003	...	...	...
Poix de Picardie d.	0640	...	0714	0814	...	0914	...	1014	1137	...	1314	...	1401	1420	...	1715	...	1915	...	...	2015	...	...	...
Amiens a.	0705	...	0734	0834	...	0934	...	1034	1219	...	1333	...	1443	1502	...	1734	...	1935	...	...	2035	...	...	...
Lille Flandres **256** a.	...	...	0859	...	...	1058	...	...	...	...	...	...	...	...	...	...	...	2059	...	...	...	...	...	...

b – By 🚌.
g – Also June 11; not June 10.
n – Not holidays.

545 RHÄTISCHE BAHN (RhB) services — Narrow gauge

REVISED TIMINGS UNTIL SEPTEMBER 7. During this period all services Susch - Scuol-Tarasp and v.v. are operated by 🚌.
See page 274 for service from September 8 (also for timings Klosters - Davos - Filisur).

DISENTIS / MUSTÉR - CHUR - LANDQUART - KLOSTERS - SCUOL TARASP

km		Ⓐ M	⚒ D	⚒	⚒	Ⓐ D			D		⚒	M	D			✣ M	D			✣ M	D		Ⓐ M	D	
0	**Disentis / Mustér** d.	...	...	...	...	...	...	0544	...	...	0615	...	...	0644	...	...	...	0744		...	...	1544	...	...	1644
12	Trun d.	...	...	...	...	...	...	0602	...	...	0631	...	...	0702	...	...	...	0802		...	...	1602	...	...	1702
30	Ilanz d.	...	...	...	...	...	...	0624	...	...	0653	...	...	0724	...	...	...	0824	and at	...	...	1624	...	...	1724
49	Reichenau-Tamins d.	...	...	...	0534	...	...	0649	...	...	0718	...	...	0750	...	...	...	0849		...	...	1649	...	...	1749
59	**Chur** a.	...	...	...	0548	...	...	0703	...	...	0733	...	...	0803	...	...	...	0901	the same	...	...	1701	...	...	1801
59	**Chur** 520 534 d.	...	...	...	0550	...	...	0721	...	...	...	...	...	0821	...	...	...	0921		...	...	1721	...	...	1821
73	**Landquart** 520 534 a.	...	...	...	0610	...	...	0741	...	...	...	...	...	0841	...	...	...	0942	minutes	...	...	1742	...	...	1842
73	**Landquart** d.	0455	0512	0534	...	0620	0647	...	0747	0750	...	0820	0847	...	0850	0920	0947	0950		1720	1747	1750	1820	1847	1850
94	Küblis d.	0515	0538	0608	...	0646	0714	...	0810	0814	...	0844	0910	...	0914	0944	1010	1014	past each	1744	1810	1814	1844	1910	1914
103	Klosters Dorf d.	|	0554	0623	...	0659	0727	...	0823	|	...	|	0923	...	|	|	1023	|		|	1823	|	|	1923	|
105	**Klosters** Platz d.	0530	0557	0630	...	0702	0733	...	0826	0833	...	0901	0926	...	0933	1001	1026	1033	hour until	1801	1826	1833	1901	1926	1933
127	Susch a.	0550	...	0654	...	...	0751	...	...	0853	...	0920	...	...	0953	1019	...	1053		1819	...	1853	1919	...	1953
136	Ardez 🚌 ‡ a.	0619*	...	|	...	...	|	...	...	|	...	...	...	...	|	...	...	|		...	...	|	...	...	|
144	**Scuol-Tarasp** 🚌 a.	0628*	...	0725*	...	...	0825*	...	...	0925*	...	...	...	...	1025*	...	...	1125*		...	...	1925*	...	...	2025*

	D		D	⑤ f		D		D		D	
Disentis / Mustér d.	...	1744	...	...	1844	...	1944	...	2044	...	2221
Trun d.	...	1802	...	...	1902	...	2002	...	2102	...	2237
Ilanz d.	...	1824	...	...	1924	...	2024	...	2123	...	2257
Reichenau-Tamins d.	...	1849	...	...	1949	...	2049	...	2149	...	2323
Chur a.	...	1901	...	...	2001	...	2101	...	2202	...	2333
Chur 520 534 d.	...	1921	...	...	▬	...	▬	...	▬	...	▬
Landquart 520 534 a.	...	1941	...	...	...	...	...	...	...	...	...
Landquart d.	1920	...	1947	1950	...	2047	...	2147	...	2247	...
Küblis d.	1944	...	2013	2017	...	2113	...	2213	...	2313	⑤⑥
Klosters Dorf d.	|	...	2027	2031	...	2127	...	2227	...	2327	z
Klosters Platz d.	2000	...	2029	2035	2035	2129	2134	2229	2234	2329	2332
Susch a.	...	...	...	2053	2053	...	2152	...	2251	...	2349
Ardez 🚌 ‡ a.	...	...	...	|	|	...	|	...	|	...	0008*
Scuol-Tarasp 🚌 a.	...	...	...	2125*	2125*	...	2225*	...	2325*	...	0020*

	⚒	⚒ D	⚒	⚒	D		Ⓐ D		D		D
Scuol-Tarasp 🚌 d.	...	...	...	0524*	...	...	...	0630*	...	...	...
Ardez 🚌 ‡ d.	...	...	...	0535*	...	...	...	|	...	...	...
Susch d.	...	...	...	0602	...	...	...	0703	...	...	...
Klosters Platz d.	...	0529	...	0622	0628	...	0655	0723	0728	...	0758
Klosters Dorf d.	...	0532	...	▬	0631	...	0659	...	0731	...	|
Küblis d.	...	0545	...	...	0645	...	0714	...	0745	...	0815
Landquart a.	...	0613	...	...	0713	...	0739	...	0813	...	0836
Landquart 520 534 d.	...	...	0617	...	...	0717	...	...	...	0817	...
Chur 520 534 a.	...	...	0637	...	...	0736	...	...	...	0836	...
Chur d.	0609	...	0653	0653	...	0756	...	...	...	0856	...
Reichenau-Tamins d.	0623	...	0703	0703	...	0805	...	...	...	0905	...
Ilanz d.	0654	...	0733	0733	...	0833	...	...	...	0933	...
Trun d.	0715	...	0754	0754	...	0854	...	...	...	0954	...
Disentis / Mustér a.	0731	...	0811	0811	...	0911	...	...	...	1011	...

		D		D	✣ M			D	✣ M		D	M		D	M		D		D				D		⑤⑥ z
Scuol-Tarasp 🚌 d.	0730*	...	0830*	...	...		1430*	...	...	1530*	...	...	1630*	...	...	1730*	...	1830*	...	1930*	...	2030*	...	2130*	2230*
Ardez 🚌 ‡ d.	|	...	|	...	...		|	...	...	|	...	...	|	...	...	|	...	|	...	|	...	|	...	|	|
Susch d.	0803	...	0903	...	0937	and at	1503	...	1537	1603	...	1635	1703	...	1737	1803	...	1903	...	2003	...	2103	...	2203	2301
Klosters Platz d.	0825	0831	0925	0931	0957		1525	1531	1557	1625	1631	1657	1725	1731	1757	1825	1831	1925	1931	2029	...	2123	2129	2223	2321
Klosters Dorf d.	|	0835	|	0935	|	the same	|	1535	|	|	1635	|	|	1735	|	|	1835	|	1935	2032	...	▬	2132	2226	...
Küblis d.	0844	0850	0944	0950	1016		1544	1550	1616	1644	1650	1715	1744	1750	1816	1844	1850	1944	1950	2046	...	...	2146	2239	...
Landquart a.	0910	0913	1010	1013	1036	minutes	1610	1613	1636	1710	1713	1736	1810	1813	1836	1910	1913	2010	2013	2113	...	...	2213	2305	...
Landquart 520 534 d.	...	0917	1017	...	...		1617	...	...	1717	...	▬	1817	...	...	1917	...	...	▬	...	...	...	...	...	...
Chur 520 534 a.	...	0936	1036	...	...	past each	1636	...	...	1736	...	...	1836	...	...	1936	...	...	...	...	...	...	...	...	...
Chur d.	...	0956	1056	...	...		1656	...	...	1756	...	1825	1856	...	...	1956	...	...	2059	...	2159	2259	...	...	...
Reichenau-Tamins d.	...	1005	1105	...	...	hour until	1705	...	...	1805	...	|	1905	...	...	2005	...	...	2113	...	2211	2311	...	...	...
Ilanz d.	...	1033	1133	...	...		1733	...	...	1833	...	1902	1933	...	...	2033	...	...	2140	...	2234	2334	...	...	...
Trun d.	...	1054	1154	...	...		1754	...	...	1854	...	1924	1954	...	...	2054	...	...	2200	...	...	...	...	...	...
Disentis / Mustér a.	...	1111	1211	...	...		1811	...	...	1911	...	1940	2011	...	...	2111	...	...	2215	...	...	...	...	...	...

SCUOL TARASP and KLOSTERS - ST MORITZ and PONTRESINA

km		⚒	†	Ⓐ		⚒ 🚌	⚒	🚌	⚒	†			🚌		🚌			🚌		✣	🚌			✣	🚌	
0	**Scuol-Tarasp** 🚌 d.	...	...	...	...	0548	...	0630	...	...	...	...	0730	...	0830	...	...	0930	...	...	1030	...	and at	...	1830	...
	Landquart d.	...	...	0455	...	|	...	|	0534	...	...	...	|	0647	|	0750	0820	|	0850	0920	|	0950		1720	|	1750
	Klosters Platz 🚗 d.	...	...	0530	...	|	...	|	0630	...	...	...	|	0733	|	0833	0901	|	0933	1001	|	1033	the same	1801	|	1833
17	Sagliains ⊗ 🚗 d.	...	...	|	...	|	...	|	|	...	...	...	|	|	|	|	|	|	|	|	|	|		|	|	|
19	Susch d.	...	...	0554	...	0621	...	0655	0705	0705	...	...	0755	0806	0855	0858	0921	0955	0958	1019	1055	1058	minutes	1819	1855	1858
25	Zernez ⊖ d.	...	...	0603	...	0630	0632	...	0713	0713	...	...	...	0813	...	0907	0930	...	1007	1026	...	1107		1826	...	1907
42	Zuoz d.	...	...	0623	0633d	...	0654	...	0733	0733	...	0757d	...	0834	...	0928	0954	...	1028	1046	...	1128	past each	1846	...	1928
52	Samedan a.	...	...	0634	0646d	...	0708	...	0746	0746	...	0811d	...	0848	...	0942	1008	...	1042	1057	...	1142		1857	...	1942
52	Samedan d.	0530	0545	0636	0648	...	0710	...	0748	0748	0749	0812	...	0849	...	0948	1009	...	1048	1100	...	1148	hour until	1900	...	1948
	St Moritz a.	|	|	0644	|	...	0717	...	|	|	0757	0819	...	|	...	|	1016	...	|	1109	...	|		1909	...	|
57	**Pontresina** a.	0536	0551	...	0655	...	...	...	0755	0755	...	...	...	0856	...	0955	...	...	1055	...	...	1155		...	...	1955

	Ⓐ	🚌		Ⓐ	🚌		🚌		🚌		
Scuol-Tarasp 🚌 d.	...	1930	...	...	2030	...	2130	...	2230	...	...
Landquart d.	1820	|	1850	...	|	1950f	|	...	|	...	...
Klosters Platz 🚗 d.	1901	|	1933	2002	|	2035	|	2134	|	2234	...
Sagliains ⊗ 🚗 d.	|	|	|	|	|	|	|	|	|	|	...
Susch d.	1919	1955	1958	2022	2055	2059	2155	2200	2255	2300	...
Zernez ⊖ d.	1926	...	2007	2032	...	2106	...	2209	...	2307	...
Zuoz d.	1946	...	2028	2054	...	2127	...	2233	...	2327	...
Samedan a.	2000	...	2042	2107	...	2140	...	2246	...	2340	...
Samedan d.	2001	...	2048	...	...	2150	...	2250	...	2341	...
St Moritz a.	2009	...	|	...	...	|	...	|	...	2349	...
Pontresina a.	...	...	2055	...	...	2156	...	2256	...	...	...

	Ⓐ	⚒	⚒	⚒	†	†		🚌		🚌	⚒
Pontresina d.	...	...	...	0542	...	0558	...	...	0702	...	...
St Moritz d.	...	0445	0541	|	0558	|	...	...	|	...	0723
Samedan a.	...	0451	0548	0548	0605	0605	...	...	0708	...	0730
Samedan d.	0453	0513	▬	0553	...	0608	0608	...	0713	...	0730
Zuoz d.	0506	0526	⚒	0607	...	0622	0622	...	0727	...	0744
Zernez ⊖ d.	0526	0547	🚌	...	...	0646	0646	...	0747	...	...
Susch a.	0532	0553	0557	...	...	0653	0653	0700	0753	0800	...
Sagliains ⊗ 🚗 a.	|	|	|	...	...	|	|	|	|	|	...
Klosters Platz 🚗 a.	0551	0622	|	...	...	0723	0723	|	0823	|	...
Landquart a.	0643	...	|	...	...	...	...	|	0910	|	...
Scuol-Tarasp 🚌 a.	...	...	0628	...	...	...	...	0725	...	0825	...

		🚌	✣			🚌	✣		🚌			🚌			🚌		🚌		🚌		🚌		🚌	⑤⑥ z		
Pontresina d.	0802	...	...	and at	1402	...	...	1502	...	...	1602	...	...	1702	...	1802	...	1902	...	2002	...	2102	...	2202	2202	2302
St Moritz d.	|	...	0847		|	...	1447	|	...	1538	|	...	1647	|	...	|	...	|	...	|	...	|	...	|	|	|
Samedan a.	0808	...	0855	the same	1408	...	1455	1508	...	1545	1608	...	1655	1708	...	1808	...	1908	...	2008	...	2108	...	2208	2208	2309
Samedan d.	0813	...	0858		1413	...	1458	1513	...	1545	1613	...	1658	1713	...	1813	...	1913	...	2013	...	2113	...	2213	2213	▬
Zuoz d.	0827	...	0910	minutes	1427	...	1510	1527	...	1559	1627	...	1710	1727	...	1827	...	1927	...	2027	...	2127	...	2227	2227	...
Zernez ⊖ d.	0849	...	0930		1449	...	1530	1549	...	1628	1649	...	1730	1749	...	1849	...	1949	...	2049	...	2149	...	2249	2249	🚌
Susch a.	0856	0900	0936	past each	1456	1500	1536	1556	1600	1634	1656	1700	1736	1756	1800	1856	1900	1956	2000	2055	2100	2155	2200	2255	2255	2300
Sagliains ⊗ 🚗 a.	|	|	|		|	|	|	|	|	|	|	|	|	|	|	|	|	|	|	|	|	|	|	|	...	|
Klosters Platz 🚗 a.	0923	|	0956	hour until	1523	|	1556	1623	|	1654	1723	|	1756	1823	|	1923	|	2023	|	2123	|	2222	|	2321	...	|
Landquart a.	1010	|	1036		1610	|	1636	1710	|	1736	1810	|	1836	1910	|	2010	|	2113	|	...	|	2305	|	...	...	|
Scuol-Tarasp 🚌 a.	...	0925	...		...	1525	...	...	1625	...	...	1725	...	...	1825	...	1925	...	2025	...	2125	...	2225	...	...	2325

D – [12] Davos - Landquart and v.v.
M – [12] St Moritz - Landquart and v.v.

d – ⚒ only.
f – ⑤ (not Apr. 19).
z – Also Apr. 18, May 29, July 31; not Apr. 19.

* – By 🚌 from / to Susch.
⊗ – No regular passenger service during engineering work.
✣ – Runs every **two** hours.
‡ – Please check locally for 🚌 connections to / from Ardez.
⊖ – See page 275.
🚗 – Car-carrying shuttle available Klosters Selfranga - Sagliains and v.v. ✆ +41 (0) 81 288 37 37. www.rhb.ch/en/car-transporter

Products for sale from European Rail Timetable Limited

2nd Edition of the
Rail Map Europe.
£11.99 + p&p

Subscribe to the ERT from
£100

15th Edition of the
Europe by Rail guidebook.
£15.99 + p&p

Reprint of the 1873 edition of
Cook's Continental Time Tables & Tourist's Hand Book.
£13.99 + p&p

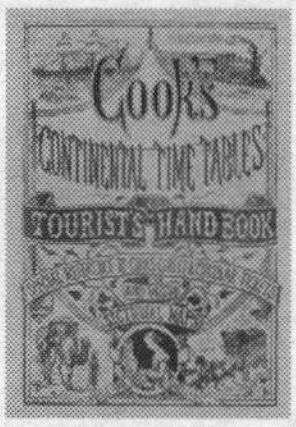

Order on-line at **www.europeanrailtimetable.eu**
Telephone **01832 270198**

European Rail Timetable Price List

☐ Regular printed edition (excluding Summer and Winter): £17.99

☐ Printed Summer or Winter edition: £19.99

☐ Monthly digital edition: £11.99 (January - May, July - November), £13.99 (Summer or Winter)

Postage and packaging rates for a single printed copy are as follows:

☐ UK	£2.48	Delivery in 2 – 5 working days
☐ Europe	£5.68	Delivery in 3 – 10 working days
☐ Rest of the World	£7.98 – £8.43	Delivery in 5 – 21 working days

Subscription rates for 6 printed editions (price includes postage and packaging):

☐ UK £114 ☐ Europe £135 ☐ Rest of the World £150

Annual subscription for 12 digital editions: ☐ £100

Subscription rates for 6 printed issues and 12 digital editions (price includes postage and packaging):

☐ UK £174 ☐ Europe £195 ☐ Rest of the World £210

Order on-line at **www.europeanrailtimetable.eu**

By post to: 28 Monson Way, Oundle, Northamptonshire, PE8 4QG (cheques payable to European Rail Timetable Limited)

✆ +44 (0) 1832 270198 (Monday to Friday 0900 – 1700)

810 HAMM and BAD BENTHEIM - HANNOVER - BERLIN

SERVICE FROM OCTOBER 12. See page 384 for service to October 11.

km		ICE 949	–	ICE 649	–	IC 2447	ICE 841	–	IC 2241	ICE 541	ICE 1041	–	IC 2445	ICE 843	ICE 853	IC 2343	IC 245	ICE 543	ICE 553	IC 2443	ICE 845	ICE 1045	ICE 855	IC 222
				Ⓐ		①	①–⑥		①–⑥	①–⑥	⑦		①–⑥		①–⑥	⑦	①–⑥		①–⑥	①–⑥	①–⑤	⑥⑦		①–
		♥		✕		D 🍷	L ✕		M 🍷	✕	✕		D	✕	✕	N 🍷	🍷	✕	K	D 🍷	✕	✕	✕	V
	Köln Hbf **800** d.	2245	...	...	...	...	...	...	...	0428	...	...	0513	0528	0544	...	...	0626	0648	0712	...	0727	0748	...
	Wuppertal Hbf **800** d.	|	...	...	...	...	...	...	...	|	...	...	0544	|	0617	...	...	|	0716	0744	⊙	|	0816	...
	Düsseldorf Hbf **800** d.	2341	...	...	...	...	...	...	...	0451	...	...	|	0552	|	...	...	0652	|	|	0752	0752	|	...
	Dortmund Hbf **800** d.	0032	...	...	...	...	...	...	...	0546	...	...	0628	0648	|	...	...	0748	|	0828	0848	0848	|	091
0	**Hamm** (Westf) **802** d.	0049	...	...	...	...	...	...	...	0603	...	...	0644	0711	0711	...	...	0811	0811	0844	0911	0911	0911	093
50	Gütersloh Hbf **802** d.	0109	...	...	...	...	...	...	...	0629	...	...	0707	|	|	...	...	|	|	0907	|	|	|	095
67	**Bielefeld** Hbf **802 811** d.	0122	...	...	...	0519	...	...	...	0640	...	...	0719	0738	0738	...	...	0838	0838	0919	0938	0938	0938	100
81	Herford **811** d.	|	...	...	...	0528	...	...	...	|	...	...	0728	|	|	...	...	|	|	0928	|	|	|	101
	Amsterdam C **22** d.	|	...	...	...	|	...	...	...	|	...	...	|	|	|	...	...	|	|	|	|	|	|	|
	Bad Bentheim 🏛 **811** d.	|	...	...	...	|	...	...	...	|	...	...	|	|	|	...	0721	|	|	|	|	|	|	|
	Rheine **811** d.	|	...	...	...	|	...	...	...	|	...	...	|	|	|	...	0735	|	|	|	|	|	|	|
	Osnabrück Hbf **811** d.	|	...	...	...	|	...	...	0604	|	...	...	|	|	|	0804	0805	|	|	|	|	|	|	|
	Bünde (Westf) **811** d.	|	...	...	...	|	...	...	0627	|	...	...	|	|	|	0827	0826	|	|	|	|	|	|	|
97	Bad Oeynhausen **811** d.	|	...	...	...	|	...	...	0638	|	...	...	|	|	|	0839	0839	|	|	|	|	|	|	|
112	Minden (Westf) **811** d.	0151	...	...	...	0547	...	...	0647	|	...	...	0746	|	|	0848	0848	|	|	0946	|	|	|	|
177	**Hannover** Hbf **811** a.	0223	...	...	...	0619	...	...	0718	0728	...	...	0818	0828	0828	0918	0918	0928	0928	1018	1028	1028	1028	110
177	**Hannover** Hbf d.	0240	...	0527	...	0637	0631	...	0722	0731	0731	...	0837	0831	0831	0922	0922	0931	0931	1037	1031	1031	1031	110
	Magdeburg Hbf **866** a.	0401	...	▽	...	0754	|	...	|	|	|	...	0954	|	|	|	|	|	|	1154	|	|	|	|
	Leipzig Hbf **866** a.	|	...	|	...	0915	|	...	|	|	|	...	1115	|	|	|	|	|	|	1315	|	|	|	|
252	Wolfsburg **902** d.	|	...	0620	...	...	0705	...	0754	|	0804	...	...	0905	0905	0954	0954	|	|	...	1105	1105	1105	113
327	Stendal **838** d.	|	...	0646	...	...	0733	...	0826	|	0832	...	...	|	|	1026	1026	|	|	...	|	|	|	|
419	**Berlin** Spandau **838 902** a.	|	...	0722	...	...	0809	...	0904	0854	0906	...	...	0958	0958	1104	1104	1054	1054	...	1158	1158	1158	123
435	**Berlin** Hbf **838 902** a.	0536	...	0732	...	...	0825	...	0922	0906	0917	...	...	1010	1010	1122	1122	1105	1105	...	1210	1210	1210	125
440	**Berlin** Ostbahnhof **838 902** a.	0547	...	...	...	...	...	...	0934	...	...	...	...	...	...	1134	1134	...	...	...	...	...	...	...

	IC 141	ICE 545	ICE 555	IC 2441	ICE 847	ICE 857	IC 143	ICE 547	ICE 557	IC 2049	ICE 849	ICE 859	IC 145	ICE 549	ICE 559	IC 2047	ICE 941	ICE 1051	IC 1922	IC 147	ICE 641	ICE 651	IC 2326	IC 192
																Ⓑ b			⑤⑦				⑦	①–
	🍷	✕	✕	D 🍷	✕	✕	🍷	✕	✕	D 🍷	✕	✕	🍷	✕	A ✕	D 🍷	✕	✕	S 🍷	🍷	✕	✕	R 🍷	🍷
Köln Hbf **800** d.	...	0828	0848	0913	0928c	0948	...	...	1048	1113	...	1148	...	...	1248	1313	...	1348	1346	...	...	1448	1438	143
Wuppertal Hbf **800** d.	...	|	0916	0944	|	1016	...	...	1116	1144	...	1216	...	...	1316	1344	...	1416	|	...	...	1516	|	|
Düsseldorf Hbf **800** d.	...	0852	|	|	0952	|	...	1052	|	|	1152	|	...	1252	|	|	1352	|	1414	...	1452	|	1509	150
Dortmund Hbf **800** d.	...	0948	|	1028	1048	|	...	1148	|	1228	1248	|	...	1348	|	1428	1448	|	1512	...	1548	|	|	|
Hamm (Westf) **802** d.	...	1011	1011	1044	1111	1111	...	1211	1211	1244	1311	1311	...	1411	1411	1444	1511	1511	1534	...	1611	1611	|	|
Gütersloh Hbf **802** d.	...	|	|	1107	|	|	...	|	|	1307	|	|	...	|	|	1507	|	|	1555	...	|	|	|	|
Bielefeld Hbf **802 811** d.	...	1038	1038	1119	1138	1138	...	1238	1238	1319	1338	1338	...	1438	1438	1519	1538	1538	1606	...	1638	1638	|	|
Herford **811** d.	...	|	|	1128	|	|	...	|	|	1328	|	|	...	|	|	1528	|	|	1615	...	|	|	◧	◧
Amsterdam C **22** d.	0700	|	|	|	|	|	0900	|	|	|	|	|	1100	|	|	|	|	|	|	1300	|	|	|	|
Bad Bentheim 🏛 **811** d.	0928	|	|	|	|	|	1128	|	|	|	|	|	1328	|	|	|	|	|	|	1528	|	|	|	|
Rheine **811** d.	0942	|	|	|	|	|	1142	|	|	|	|	|	1342	|	|	|	|	|	|	1542	|	|	|	|
Osnabrück Hbf **811** d.	1008	|	|	|	|	|	1208	|	|	|	|	|	1408	|	|	|	|	|	|	1608	|	|	1657	165
Bünde (Westf) **811** d.	|	|	|	|	|	|	1228	|	|	|	|	|	|	|	|	|	|	|	|	1628	|	|	|	|
Bad Oeynhausen **811** d.	1037	|	|	|	|	|	|	|	|	|	|	|	1437	|	|	|	|	|	|	|	|	|	|	|
Minden (Westf) **811** d.	1047	|	|	1146	|	|	1247	|	|	1346	|	|	1447	|	|	1546	|	|	|	1647	|	|	|	|
Hannover Hbf **811** a.	1118	1128	1128	1218	1228	1228	1318	1328	1328	1418	1428	1428	1518	1528	1528	1618	1628	1628	1701	1718	1728	1728	1802	180
Hannover Hbf d.	1122	1131	1131	1237	1231	1231	1322	1331	1331	1437	1431	1431	1522	1531	1531	1637	1631	1631	1704	1722	1731	1731	1805	180
Magdeburg Hbf **866** a.	|	|	|	1354	|	|	|	|	|	1554	|	|	|	|	|	1754	|	|	|	|	|	|	|	|
Leipzig Hbf **866** a.	|	|	|	1515	|	|	|	|	|	1722	|	|	|	|	|	1915	|	|	|	|	|	|	|	|
Wolfsburg **902** d.	1154	|	|	...	1305	1305	1354	|	|	...	1505	1505	1554	|	|	...	1705	1705	1738	1754	|	|	1839	183
Stendal **838** d.	1226	|	|	...	|	|	1426	|	|	...	|	|	1626	|	|	...	|	|	|	1826	|	|	|	|
Berlin Spandau **838 902** a.	1304	1255	1255	...	1358	1358	1504	1454	1454	...	1558	1558	1704	1654	1654	...	1800	1800	1838	1904	1854	1854	1938	193
Berlin Hbf **838 902** a.	1322	1306	1306	...	1410	1410	1522	1505	1505	...	1610	1610	1722	1706	1706	...	1810	1810	1854	1922	1905	1905	1953	195
Berlin Ostbahnhof **838 902** a.	1334	...	...	...	...	...	1534	...	...	...	...	...	1734	...	...	...	...	...	1905	1934	...	...	...	200

	IC 2045	ICE 943	ICE 1053	IC 149	ICE 643	ICE 653	IC 2043	IC 2043	IC 2043	ICE 945	ICE 1055	IC 241	IC 241	ICE 645	ICE 655	IC 2041	ICE 947	ICE 1057	–	IC 243	ICE 657	–	ICE 102	ICE 110
	Ⓑ		Ⓑ					Ⓑ	⑦	Ⓑ		B	⑦			⑦		⑤⑦		⑦	⑦		Ⓑ	⑥
	D 🍷	✕	✕	🍷	✕	✕	🍷	🍷	🍷	✕	✕	🍷	🍷	✕	✕	🍷	✕	✕		🍷	A ✕		Q	Q
Köln Hbf **800** d.	1513	...	1548	...	...	1648	1713	1713	1713	...	1748	...	...	...	1848	1913	1927y	1948	...	...	2048	...	2111	211
Wuppertal Hbf **800** d.	1544	...	1616	...	...	1716	1744	1744	1744	...	1816	...	...	...	1916	1944	|	2016	...	...	2116	...	2142	|
Düsseldorf Hbf **800** d.	|	1552	|	...	1652	|	|	|	|	1752	|	...	...	1852	|	|	1952	|	...	...	|	...	|	213
Dortmund Hbf **800** d.	1628	1648	|	...	1748	|	1828	1828	1828	1848	|	...	...	1948	|	2028	2048	|	...	...	|	...	2228	222
Hamm (Westf) **802** d.	1644	1711	1711	...	1811	1811	1844	1844	1844	1911	1911	...	...	2011	2011	2044	2111	2111	...	...	2210	...	2249	224
Gütersloh Hbf **802** d.	1707	|	|	...	|	|	1907	1907	1907	|	|	...	...	|	|	2107	|	|	...	...	|	...	2311	231
Bielefeld Hbf **802 811** d.	1719	1738	1738	...	1838	1838	1919	1919	1919	1938	1938	...	...	2038	2038	2119	2138	2138	...	...	2238	...	2321	232
Herford **811** d.	1728	|	|	...	|	|	1928	1928	1928	|	|	...	...	|	|	2128	|	|	...	...	|	...	2330	233
Amsterdam C **22** d.	|	|	|	1500	|	|	|	|	|	|	|	1700	1700	|	|	|	|	|	...	1900	|	...	|	|
Bad Bentheim 🏛 **811** d.	|	|	|	1728	|	|	|	|	|	|	|	1928	1928	|	|	|	|	|	...	2128	|	...	|	|
Rheine **811** d.	|	|	|	1742	|	|	|	|	|	|	|	1942	1942	|	|	|	|	|	...	2142	|	...	|	|
Osnabrück Hbf **811** d.	|	|	|	1808	|	|	|	|	|	|	|	2008	2008	|	|	|	|	|	...	2208	|	...	|	|
Bünde (Westf) **811** d.	|	|	|	|	|	|	|	|	|	|	|	2028	2028	|	|	|	|	|	...	|	|	...	|	|
Bad Oeynhausen **811** d.	|	|	|	1837	|	|	|	|	|	|	|	|	|	|	|	|	|	|	...	2237	|	...	|	|
Minden (Westf) **811** d.	1746	|	|	1847	|	|	1946	1946	1946	|	|	2047	2047	|	|	2146	|	|	...	2247	|	...	2347	234
Hannover Hbf **811** a.	1818	1828	1828	1918	1928	1928	2018	2018	2018	2028	2028	2118	2118	2128	2128	2218	2228	2228	...	2321	2328	...	0018	001
Hannover Hbf d.	1837	1831	1831	1922	1931	1931	...	2037	2037	2031	2031	...	2122	2131	2131	...	2231	2231	...	...	2331	...	...	...
Magdeburg Hbf **866** a.	1954	|	|	|	|	|	...	2154	2154	|	|	...	|	|	|	...	|	|	...	...	|	...	...	...
Leipzig Hbf **866** a.	2115	|	|	|	|	|	...	...	2318	|	|	...	|	|	|	...	|	|	...	...	|	...	...	...
Wolfsburg **902** d.	...	1905	1905	1954	|	|	...	...	...	2105	2105	...	2154	|	|	...	2305	2305	...	...	0004	...	...	...
Stendal **838** d.	...	|	|	2026	|	|	...	...	...	2132	2132	...	2226	|	|	...	|	|	...	...	|	...	...	...
Berlin Spandau **838 902** a.	...	1958	1958	2104	2054	2054	...	...	...	2207	2207	...	2304	2254	2254	...	2358	2358	...	...	0100	...	...	...
Berlin Hbf **838 902** a.	...	2010	2010	2122	2105	2105	...	...	...	2218	2218	...	2322	2306	2306	...	0010	0010	...	...	0110	...	...	...
Berlin Ostbahnhof **838 902** a.	...	...	...	2134	...	...	...	...	...	...	...	...	2334	...	...	...	...	...	...	...	...	...	...	...

A – From Bonn on ①–⑥ (Table **800**).
B – Daily to Nov. 1; Ⓑ from Nov. 3
D – To Dresden (Table **842**).
K – From Koblenz (Table **800**).
L – [12] and ✕ (Oldenburg - Bremen ①⑥ -) Hannover - Berlin.
M – From Münster (Westf) Hbf (d. 0538).
N – From Münster (Westf) Hbf (d. 0738).
Q – [12] and 🍷 Basel - Karlsruhe - Köln - Hannover.
R – To Rostock (Table **835**).
S – ⑤⑦ (also Oct. 31; not Nov. 1). From Stuttgart (Tables **911** and **912**).
V – KAROLINGER – From Aachen Hbf (d. 0707), Rheydt Hbf (d. 0748), Mönchengladbach Hbf (d. 0755), Viersen (d. 0803) and Krefeld Hbf (d. 0816).

b – Also Oct. 26, Nov. 2.
c – ⑥⑦ only.
y – ①②③④⑥.

♥ – Also calls at Braunschweig Hbf (a. 0314), Brandenburg Hbf (a. 0444), Potsdam Hbf (a. 0504), Berlin Wannsee (a. 0513) and Berlin Zoo (a. 0529).
⊙ – From Köln/Bonn Flughafen (Table **800**).
◧ – Via Münster (Table **800**).
▽ – Via Braunschweig Hbf (d. 0601).

BERLIN - HANNOVER - HAMM and BAD BENTHEIM 810

SERVICE FROM OCTOBER 12. See page 385 for service to October 11.

km		ICE	ICE	ICE	IC	ICE	ICE	IC	IC	IC	ICE	ICE	IC	IC	ICE	ICE	IC	IC	ICE	ICE	IC	ICE	ICE	IC
		103	**656**	**646**	**242**	**1056**	**946**	**2042**	**2042**	**2042**	**654**	**644**	**240**	**240**	**1054**	**944**	**2044**	**1929**	**652**	**642**	**148**	**1052**	**942**	**2046**
			Ⓐ	Ⓐ	①–⑥	①–⑥	①–⑥		①–⑥	①		①–⑥	E	①–⑥	①–⑥		①–⑥	①–⑤						①–⑥
		L ✕	✕	✕	🍷	✕	✕	🍷	🍷	🍷	✕	✕	🍷	🍷	✕	✕	D 🍷	🍷	✕	✕	🍷	✕	✕	D 🍷
0	**Berlin** Ostbahnhof . **838 902** d.	...	...	...	...	...	...	...	...	...	...	...	...	0622	...	...	...	0748	...	...	0822	...	...	...
5	**Berlin** Hbf .... **838 902** d.	...	0430	0430	...	0540	0540	...	...	...	0650	0650	...	0634	0749	0749	...	0759	0850	0850	0834	0950	0950	...
21	**Berlin** Spandau ...... **838 902** d.	...	0442	0442	...	0550	0550	...	...	...	0702	0702	...	0651	0800	0800	...	0814	0902	0902	0851	1000	1000	...
113	Stendal .... **838** d.	...	0514	0514	...	0625	0625	...	...	...	|	|	...	0732	|	|	...	|	|	|	0932	|	|	...
188	Wolfsburg .... **902** d.	...	0548	0548	...	0653	0653	...	...	...	0753	0753	...	0801	0853	0853	...	0920	|	|	1001	1053	1053	...
	Leipzig Hbf **866** ....d.	...	|	|	...	|	|	...	...	0439	|	|	...	|	|	|	0636	|	|	|	|	|	|	0836
	Magdeburg Hbf **866**...........d.	...	|	|	...	|	|	...	0601	0601	|	|	...	|	|	|	0803	|	|	|	|	|	|	1003
263	**Hannover** Hbf ....a.	...	0618	0618	...	0728	0728	...	0723	0723	0828	0828	...	0836	0928	0928	0923	0953	1028	1028	1036	1128	1128	1123
263	**Hannover** Hbf .... **811** d.	0540	0621	0621	0640	0731	0731	0740	0740	0740	0831	0831	0840	0840	0931	0931	0940	0956	1031	1031	1040	1131	1131	1140
328	Minden (Westf).............. **811** d.	0612	0650	0650	0711	|	|	0814	0814	0814	|	|	0911	0911	|	|	1014	|	|	|	1111	|	|	1214
343	Bad Oeynhausen .... **811** d.	|	|	|	0722	|	|	|	|	|	|	|	|	|	|	|	|	|	|	|	1122	|	|	|
359	Bünde (Westf)............ **811** d.	|	|	|	|	|	|	|	|	|	|	|	0932	0932	|	|	|	|	|	|	|	|	|	|
396	**Osnabrück** Hbf.......... **811** d.	|	|	|	0753	|	|	|	|	|	|	|	0953	0953	|	|	|	1108	|	|	1153	|	|	|
444	Rheine .... **811** d.	|	|	|	0821	|	|	|	|	|	|	|	1021	1021	|	|	|	|	|	|	1221	|	|	|
465	Bad Bentheim 🏦 .... **811** a.	|	|	|	0834	|	|	|	|	|	|	|	1034	1034	|	|	|	|	|	|	1234	|	|	|
647	*Amsterdam C* **22**...........a.	|	|	|	1100	|	|	|	|	|	|	|	1300	1300	|	|	|	|	|	|	1500	|	|	|
	Herford .... **811** d.	0632	0711	0711	...	|	|	0832	0832	0832	|	|	...	...	|	|	1032	◧	|	|	...	|	|	1232
	Bielefeld Hbf.......... **802 811** d.	0641	0721	0721	...	0822	0822	0841	0841	0841	0922	0922	...	...	1022	1022	1041	|	1122	1122	...	1222	1222	1241
	Gütersloh Hbf .... **802** d.	0651	|	|	...	|	|	0852	0852	0852	|	|	...	...	|	|	1052	|	|	|	...	|	|	1252
	Hamm (Westf) .... **802** a.	0713	0748	0748	...	0848	0848	0914	0914	0914	0948	0948	...	...	1048	1048	1114	|	1148	1148	...	1248	1248	1314
	Dortmund Hbf **800**............a.	0732	|	0809	...	|	0909	0932	0932	0932	|	1009	...	...	|	1109	1132	|	|	1209	...	|	1309	1332
	Düsseldorf Hbf **800**...........a.	|	|	0906	...	|	1006	|	|	|	|	1110	...	...	|	1206	|	1250	|	1311	...	|	1406	|
	Wuppertal Hbf **800**.........a.	0813	0838	.:.	...	0938	...	1012	1012	1012	1038	...	...	...	1138	...	1212	|	1238	...	...	1338	...	1412
	Köln Hbf **800** ....a.	0846	0909	...	...	1009	...	1046	1046	1046	1109	...	...	...	1209	...	1246	1318	1309	...	...	1409	...	1446

	ICE	ICE	IC	ICE	ICE	IC	IC	ICE	ICE	IC		ICE	ICE	IC	IC	IC	ICE	ICE	IC		ICE	ICE	ICE	IC
	650	**640**	**146**	**1050**	**940**	**2048**	**1915**	**558**	**548**	**144**		**858**	**848**	**2440**	**1917**	**2223**	**556**	**546**	**142**		**856**	**846**	**1046**	**2442**
							⑤⑦								⑦	①–⑤						♣	⑤	Ⓑ
	✕	✕	🍷	✕	✕	D 🍷	S 🍷	✕	✕	🍷		✕	✕	D 🍷	K 🍷	◇	T ✕	✕	🍷		✕	✕	G ✕	D 🍷
erlin Ostbahnhof .. **838 902** d.	...	...	1022	...	...	...	1150	...	...	1222	...	...	...	...	...	...	...	...	1422	...	...	...	...	...
erlin Hbf .... **838 902** d.	1050	1050	1034	1149	1149	...	1201	1250	1250	1234	...	1349	1349	...	1355	1355	1451	1451	1434	...	1549	1549	1549	...
erlin Spandau .... **838 902** d.	1102	1102	1051	1200	1200	...	1216	1302	1302	1251	...	1359	1359	...	1405	1405	1502	1502	1451	...	1600	1600	1600	...
endal .... **838** d.	|	|	1132	|	|	...	|	|	|	1332	...	|	|	...	1442	1446	|	|	1532	...	|	|	|	...
'olfsburg .... **902** d.	|	|	1201	1253	1253	...	1321	|	|	1401	...	1453	1453	...	1520	1520	|	|	1601	...	1653	1653	1653	...
Leipzig Hbf **866** ....d.	|	|	|	|	|	1036	|	|	|	|	...	|	|	1236	|	|	|	|	|	...	|	|	|	1436
Magdeburg Hbf **866**...........d.	|	|	|	|	|	1203	|	|	|	|	...	|	|	1403	|	|	|	|	|	...	|	|	|	1603
annover Hbf ....a.	1228	1228	1236	1328	1328	1323	1353	1428	1428	1436	...	1528	1528	1523	1553	1553	1628	1628	1636	...	1728	1728	1728	1723
annover Hbf .... **811** d.	1231	1231	1240	1331	1331	1340	1356	1431	1431	1440	...	1531	1531	1540	1556	1556	1631	1631	1640	...	1731	1731	1731	1740
inden (Westf).............. **811** d.	|	|	1311	|	|	1414	|	|	|	1511	...	|	|	1614	|	|	|	|	1711	...	|	|	|	1814
ad Oeynhausen .... **811** d.	|	|	|	|	|	|	|	|	|	1522	...	|	|	|	|	1633	|	|	|	...	|	|	|	|
Bünde (Westf)............ **811** d.	|	|	1332	|	|	|	|	|	|	|	...	|	|	|	|	|	|	|	1732	...	|	|	|	|
Osnabrück Hbf.......... **811** d.	|	|	1353	|	|	|	|	|	|	1553	...	|	|	|	|	|	|	|	1753	...	|	|	|	|
Rheine .... **811** d.	|	|	1421	|	|	|	|	|	|	1621	...	|	|	|	|	|	|	|	1821	...	|	|	|	|
Bad Bentheim 🏦 .... **811** a.	|	|	1434	|	|	|	|	|	|	1634	...	|	|	|	|	|	|	|	1834	...	|	|	|	|
Amsterdam C **22**............a.	|	|	1700	|	|	|	|	|	|	1900	...	|	|	|	|	|	|	|	2100	...	|	|	|	|
erford .... **811** d.	|	|	...	|	|	1432	1444	|	|	...	...	|	|	1632	1644	|	|	|	...	...	|	|	|	1832
ielefeld Hbf.......... **802 811** d.	1322	1322	...	1422	1422	1441	1453	1522	1522	...	...	1622	1622	1641	1653	1653	1722	1722	...	...	1822	1822	1822	1841
ütersloh Hbf .... **802** d.	|	|	...	|	|	1452	1503	|	|	...	...	|	|	1652	1703	1703	|	|	...	...	|	|	|	1852
amm (Westf)................ **802** a.	1348	1348	...	1448	1448	1514	1524	1548	1548	...	...	1648	1648	1714	1724	1724	1748	1748	...	...	1848	1848	1848	1914
Dortmund Hbf **800**.............a.	|	1409	...	|	1509	1532	|	|	1609	...	...	|	1709	1732	|	1748	|	1809	...	...	|	1909	1909	1932
Düsseldorf Hbf **800**............a.	|	1506	...	|	1606	|	|	|	1711	...	...	|	1806	|	|	...	|	1910	...	...	|	2006	2016	|
Wuppertal Hbf **800**..........a.	1438	...	...	1538	...	1612	1629	1638	...	...	...	1738	|	1812	1828	...	1838	...	...	...	1938	|	...	2012
Köln Hbf **800** ....a.	1509	...	...	1609	...	1646	1712	1709	...	...	...	1809	1832z	1846	1912	...	1909	...	...	...	2009	2036	...	2046

	ICE	ICE	IC	ICE	ICE	IC	ICE	ICE	IC		IC	ICE	ICE	ICE	IC	IC		IC	ICE	IC	ICE	ICE		ICE
	554	**544**	**140**	**854**	**844**	**2444**	**552**	**542**	**2242**		**1932**	**852**	**842**	**832**	**2446**	**1932**		**2240**	**540**	**2240**	**840**	**840**		**948**
				Ⓑ		Ⓑ					⑦	⑦		⑤	⑦	⑦		⑦	⑦	⑦		⑤–⑦		
	✕	✕	🍷	U ✕	✕	D 🍷	✕	✕	M		R	✕	✕	O ✕	D 🍷	R		N 🍷	✕	N 🍷	✕			♥
erlin Ostbahnhof .. **838 902** d.	...	...	1622	...	...	...	...	...	1822	...	...	...	...	...	...	...	...	2022	...	...	...	...	...	2341
erlin Hbf .... **838 902** d.	1650	1650	1634	1749	1749	...	1850	1850	1834	...	...	1949	1949	1949	...	...	...	2034	2050	...	2122	2122	...	2352
erlin Spandau .... **838 902** d.	1702	1702	1651	1800	1800	...	1902	1902	1851	...	1954	2000	2000	2000	...	←	...	2051	2102	←	2135	2135	...	|
endal .... **838** d.	|	|	1732	|	|	...	|	|	1932	...	2030	|	|	|	...	2031	...	2131	|	2132	2217	2217	...	|
olfsburg .... **902** d.	|	|	1801	1853	1853	...	|	|	2001	...	→	2053	2053	2053	...	2104	...	→	2155	2201	2249	2249	...	|
Leipzig Hbf **866** ....d.	|	|	|	|	|	1636	|	|	|	...	...	|	|	|	1836	|	...	...	|	|	|	|	...	|
Magdeburg Hbf **866**...........d.	|	|	|	|	|	1803	|	|	|	...	...	|	|	|	2003	|	...	...	|	|	|	|	...	0149
annover Hbf ....a.	1828	1828	1836	1928	1928	1923	2028	2028	2036	...	...	2128	2128	2128	2123	2140	...	...	2225	2236	2322	2322	...	0309
annover Hbf .... **811** d.	1831	1831	1840	1931	1931	1940	2031	2031	2040	...	...	2131	2131	...	2140	...	...	...	...	2240	...	2331	...	0340
inden (Westf).............. **811** d.	|	|	1911	|	|	2014	|	|	2111	...	...	|	|	...	2214	...	...	...	...	2311	...	|	...	0411
ad Oeynhausen .... **811** d.	|	|	1922	|	|	|	|	|	2122	...	...	|	|	...	|	...	...	...	...	2322	...	|	...	|
Bünde (Westf)............ **811** d.	|	|	|	|	|	|	|	|	2135	2146	...	|	|	...	|	...	...	...	...	2335	...	|	...	|
Osnabrück Hbf.......... **811** d.	|	|	1953	|	|	|	|	|	2159	2214	...	|	|	...	|	...	...	...	...	2357	...	|	...	|
Rheine .... **811** d.	|	|	2021	|	|	|	|	|	...	2248	...	|	|	...	|	...	...	...	...	...	...	|	...	|
Bad Bentheim 🏦 .... **811** a.	|	|	2034	|	|	|	|	|	...	2303	...	|	|	...	|	...	...	...	...	...	...	|	...	|
Amsterdam C **22**............a.	|	|	2300	|	|	|	|	|	...	...	...	|	|	...	|	...	...	...	...	...	...	|	...	|
erford .... **811** d.	|	|	...	|	|	2031	|	|	...	...	...	|	|	...	2231	...	...	...	...	...	...	0018	...	|
ielefeld Hbf.......... **802 811** d.	1922	1922	...	2022	2022	2040	2122	2122	...	...	...	2222	2222	...	2240	...	...	...	...	...	...	0029	...	0436
ütersloh Hbf .... **802** d.	|	|	...	|	|	2050	|	|	...	...	...	|	|	...	2250	...	...	...	...	...	...	0039	...	0446
amm (Westf)................ **802** a.	1948	1948	...	2048	2048	2113	2148	2148	...	...	...	2248	2248	...	2312	...	...	...	...	...	...	0058	...	0509
Dortmund Hbf **800**.............a.	|	2009	...	|	2109	2132	|	2209	...	...	...	|	2309	...	2332	...	...	...	...	...	...	0118	...	0530
Düsseldorf Hbf **800**............a.	|	2106	...	|	2206	|	|	2306	...	...	...	|	0006	...	|	...	...	...	...	...	...	0215	...	0630
Wuppertal Hbf **800**..........a.	2038	|	...	2138	|	2212	2238	|	...	...	...	2338	|	...	0012	...	...	...	...	...	...	|	...	|
Köln Hbf **800** ....a.	2109	2141	...	2209	2231	2246	2313	2330	...	...	...	0009	0030	...	0046	...	...	...	...	...	...	0242	...	0657

– From Dresden (Table **842**).
– Daily to Nov. 2; ①–⑥ from Nov. 4.
– To Neuss Hbf (a. 2029) and Mönchengladbach Hbf (a. 2043).
– To Karlsruhe (Tables **911** and **912**).
– To Basel (Table **912**).
– To Münster (Westf) Hbf (a. 2225). Conveys 🍷 on Ⓑ.
– To Münster (Westf) Hbf (a. 0025).
– To Oldenburg via Bremen (Table **813**).
– 12 Stralsund - Berlin Gesundbrunnen - Bremen - Oldenburg.
– ⑤⑦ (also Oct. 31; not Nov. 1). To Stuttgart (Tables **911** and **912**).
– To Koblenz on ①–⑤ (Table **800**).
– To Koblenz on ⑦ (Table **800**).

z – ⑥ (not Oct. 26).

♣ – Not ⑤.
◇ – KAROLINGER – To Krefeld Hbf (a. 1844), Viersen (a. 1856), Mönchengladbach Hbf (a. 1905), Rheydt Hbf (a. 1910) and Aachen Hbf (a. 1950).
◧ – Via Münster (Table **800**).
♥ – Also calls at Berlin Zoo (d. 2359), Berlin Wannsee (d. 0039), Potsdam Hbf (d. 0047), Brandenburg Hbf (d. 0108) and Braunschweig Hbf (d. 0236).

GERMANY - Additional tables

850 BERLIN - HALLE / LEIPZIG - ERFURT - FRANKFURT / NÜRNBERG

SERVICE AUGUST 10 - OCTOBER 27 (see page 401 for service to August 9 and from October 28). See Table **902** for other fast services Berlin - Frankfurt via Braunschweig.

Other regional services: Table **845** Berlin - Lutherstadt Wittenberg. Table **848** Lutherstadt Wittenberg - Bitterfeld - Leipzig / Halle. Table **849** Leipzig / Halle - Weimar - Erfurt - Eisenach.

km		IC 1950	IC 1950		ICE 1646		ICE 1501	ICE 1656	ICE 501		ICE 593	ICE 1701	ICE 1001	ICE 1638	ICE 1654	ICE 503	ICE 1636	ICE 595	ICE 701	ICE 1003	ICE 1652	ICE 505	ICE 1634
		①	Ⓐ		Ⓐ		Ⓐ	①–⑥	①–⑥			Ⓐ	①–⑥	Ⓐ	①–⑥								
		g	m				L				M							M					
		⊙			✕		✕	✕	✕		✕	✕	✕	✕	✕	✕	✕	✕	✕	✕	✕	✕	✕
	Hamburg Hbf **840** d.	...	...	...	...	...	...	...	...	...	...	...	...	...	...	...	...	...	0527a	...	...	0635e	...
0	**Berlin** Hbf d.	0026	...	...	...	...	...	...	0428	...	0528	0534	0601	0601	...	0630	0704	0728	0737	0805	...	0830	0904
6	**Berlin** Südkreuz d.	0033	...	...	...	...	...	...	0435	...	0535	0541	0607	0607	...	0637	0711	0735	0744	0811	...	0837	0911
97	Lutherstadt Wittenberg d.	0113	...	...	...	...	...	...	0512	...	0611	|	|	|	...	0712	|	0811	|	|	...	0912	|
134	Bitterfeld d.	0130	...	...	...	...	...	...	|	...	|	0634	|	|	...	|	|	|	0834	|	...	|	|
	Halle (Saale) Hbf d.	0151	...	...	...	...	...	...	|	...	|	0652	0712	0712	...	|	0815	|	0852	0918	...	|	1015
	Dresden Hbf **842** d.	|	...	...	...	...	...	...	|	...	|	|	|	|	0610	|	|	|	|	|	0810	|	|
167	**Leipzig** Hbf a.	0215	...	...	...	...	...	...	0542	...	0642	|	|	|	0718	0742	|	0842	|	|	0920	0942	|
167	**Leipzig** Hbf d.	0230	...	...	...	...	...	0533	0548	...	0648	|	|	|	0733	0748	|	0848	|	|	0933	0948	|
287	**Erfurt** Hbf a.	0351	...	...	...	...	...	0615	0628	...	0728	0724p	0740	0740	0815	0829	0848	0928	0924p	0945	1015	1029	1048
287	**Erfurt** Hbf **849a** d.	0400	0400	...	0503	...	...	0617	0630	...	0730	0732	0745	0750	0817	0831	0850	0930	0932	0947	1017	1031	1050
	Coburg **875** d.	|	|	...	|	...	...	|	0704	...	|	|	|	|	|	|	|	|	|	|	|	|	|
	Bamberg **875** d.	|	|	...	|	...	0642	|	0728	...	|	0818	|	|	|	0917	|	|	1017	|	|	1117	|
	Erlangen **875** d.	|	|	...	|	...	0708	|	0753	...	|	|	|	|	|	0937	|	|	|	|	|	1137	|
	Nürnberg Hbf **875** a.	|	|	...	|	...	0725	|	0808	...	|	0852	0856	|	|	0952	|	|	1052	1056	|	1152	|
	München Hbf **904 905** a.	|	|	...	|	...	0839	|	0917	...	|	1043	1001	|	|	1100	|	|	1242	1203	|	1302	|
315	Gotha **849a** d.	0416	0416	...	0519	...	...	0633	...	...	|	...	...	|	0833	...	▽	|	...	...	1033	...	▽
344	**Eisenach** **849a** d.	0432	0432	...	0542	...	...	0648	...	...	|	...	...	0815	0848	...	|	|	...	...	1048	...	|
401	Bad Hersfeld d.	0503	0503	...	0613	...	...	0716	...	...	|	...	...	▽	0916	...	|	|	...	...	1116	...	|
443	Fulda **900/1/2** d.	0540	0540	...	0645	...	...	0801	...	...	0852	...	...	0951	1001	...	|	1052	...	...	1201	...	|
543	**Frankfurt** (Main) Süd **901** a.	|	|	...	0739	...	...	0852‡	...	...	|	...	...	|	|	...	|	|	...	...	|	...	|
547	**Frankfurt** (Main) Hbf **900/1/2** a.	0640	0640	...	...	...	...	0910‡	...	...	0944	...	...	1044	1056	...	1140	1144	...	...	1256	...	1340
	Frankfurt Flughafen ✈ § a.	...	...	...	...	...	...	...	...	...	|	...	...	...	...	...	...	|	...	...	...	...	...
	Wiesbaden Hbf **911** a.	...	...	...	...	...	...	...	...	...	|	...	...	...	...	...	...	|	...	...	...	...	...
	Stuttgart Hbf **912** a.	...	...	...	...	...	...	...	...	...	1108	...	...	...	...	...	...	1308	...	...	...	...	...

	ICE 597	ICE 703	ICE 93	ICE 1650	ICE 507	ICE 1632	ICE 599	ICE 1005	ICE 1558	ICE 509	ICE 1630	IC 1956	ICE 691	IC 1956	ICE 707	ICE 1727	ICE 1556	ICE 1601	ICE 1711	ICE 1538	ICE 693	ICE 709	ICE 1007
												⑦		⑦		⑥⑦							
	M		A				M					G	M	G		uR			O		M		
	✕	✕	✕	🍷	✕	✕	✕	✕	✕	✕	✕	♣	✕		✕	✕	✕	✕	✕	✕	✕	✕	✕
Hamburg Hbf **840** d.	...	0738c	...	...	0835	...	0936	...	...	...	...	...	...	...	1136	...	...	1235	...	...	...	1338	...
Berlin Hbf d.	0928	0937	1005	...	1030	1104	1128	1205	...	1230	1304	...	1328	...	1337	1405	...	1430	1430	1504	1527	1537	1605
Berlin Südkreuz d.	0935	0944	1011	...	1037	1111	1135	1211	...	1237	1311	...	1335	...	1344	1411	...	1437	1437	1511	1534	1544	1611
Lutherstadt Wittenberg d.	1011	|	|	...	1112	|	|	|	...	1312	|	...	1411	...	|	|	...	1512	1512	|	1611	|	|
Bitterfeld d.	|	1034•	|	...	|	|	1225	|	...	|	|	...	|	...	1434	|	...	|	|	|	|	1634	|
Halle (Saale) Hbf d.	|	1052	1118	...	|	1215	|	1318	...	|	1415	...	|	...	1452	1518	...	|	|	1615	|	1652	1718
Dresden Hbf **842** d.	|	|	|	1010	|	|	|	|	1210	|	|	...	|	...	|	|	1410	|	|	|	|	|	|
Leipzig Hbf a.	1042	|	|	1120	1142	|	1242	|	1320	1342	|	...	1442	...	|	|	1520	1542	1542	|	1642	|	|
Leipzig Hbf d.	1048	|	|	1133	1148	|	1248	|	1333	1348	|	1344	1448	...	|	|	1533	1548	1548	|	1648	|	|
Erfurt Hbf a.	1128	1124p	1152	1215	1229	1248	1328	1345	1415	1428	1448	1516	1528	...	1524p	1552	1615	1629	1629	1648	1728	1724p	1745
Erfurt Hbf **849a** d.	1130	1132	1154	1217	1231	1250	1330	1347	1417	1431	1450	1519	1530	...	1532	1554	1617	1631	1631	1650	1730	1732	1747
Coburg **875** d.	|	|	1229	|	|	|	|	|	|	|	|	|	|	...	|	|	|	|	|	|	|	|	|
Bamberg **875** d.	|	1217	|	|	1317	|	|	|	|	1517	|	|	|	...	1617	1643	|	|	|	|	|	1817	|
Erlangen **875** d.	|	|	|	|	1337	|	|	|	|	1537	|	|	|	...	|	1708	|	1737	1737	|	|	|	|
Nürnberg Hbf **875** a.	|	1250	1324	|	1352	|	|	1456	|	1551	|	|	|	...	1652	1724	|	1753	1753	|	|	1852	1856
München Hbf **904 905** a.	|	1405	...	|	1543	|	|	1602	|	1700	|	|	|	...	1843	1837	|	1906	1906	|	|	2042	2001
Gotha **849a** d.	|	...	...	1233	...	|	|	...	1433	...	▽	1536	|	←	...	...	1633	...	...	|	|	...	...
Eisenach **849a** d.	|	...	...	1248	...	1315	|	...	1448	...	|	1551	|	1600	...	...	1648	...	...	1715	|	...	...
Bad Hersfeld d.	|	...	...	1316	...	▽	|	...	1516	...	|	→	|	|	...	...	1716	...	...	▽	|	...	...
Fulda **900/1/2** d.	1252	...	...	1401	...	1447	1452	...	1601	...	|	...	1652	1700	...	...	1801	...	...	1848	1852	...	...
Frankfurt (Main) Süd **901** a.	|	...	...	|	...	1539	|	...	|	...	1739	...	|	1758n	...	...	|	...	...	|	|	...	...
Frankfurt (Main) Hbf **900/1/2** a.	1344	...	...	1456	...	|	1544	...	1656	...	|	...	1744	...	...	...	1856	...	...	1940	1944	...	...
Frankfurt Flughafen ✈ § a.	|	...	...	...	...	1551y	|	...	...	...	1751y	...	|	...	...	...	...	...	...	...	|	...	...
Wiesbaden Hbf **911** a.	|	...	...	...	...	...	|	...	...	...	...	...	|	...	...	...	...	...	...	...	|	...	...
Stuttgart Hbf **912** a.	1508	...	...	...	...	...	1708	...	...	...	...	...	1907	...	...	...	...	...	...	...	2108	...	...

	ICE 1554	ICE 603	ICE 1536	ICE 1736	ICE 695	ICE 801	ICE 801	ICE 1009		ICE 1552	ICE 1715	ICE 1605	ICE 1705		ICE 1617	ICE 1627		ICE 1607		EN 452		ICE 993	ICE 993
			Ⓑ	⑥			B	Ⓑ			⑥	Ⓑ	Ⓑ					Ⓑ		③		E	D
	S			R		K	K				O		J			◇				★		M	
	✕	✕	✕	✕	✕	✕	✕	✕		✕	✕	✕	✕		✕	✕		✕		🅁			✕
Hamburg Hbf **840** d.	...	1435	...	...	...	1537	1537	...	...	...	...	1635	1635	...	...	...	...	1835	...	...	...	1936	1936
Berlin Hbf d.	...	1630	1704	1704	1728	1737	1737	1805	...	...	1830	1830	1830	...	1928	1928	...	2030	...	2103	...	2128	2128
Berlin Südkreuz d.	...	1637	1711	1711	1735	1744	1744	1811	...	...	1837	1837	1837	...	1935	1935	...	2037	...	|	...	2135	2135
Lutherstadt Wittenberg d.	...	1712	|	|	1811	|	|	|	...	...	1912	1912	1912	...	|	|	...	2112	...	|	...	2211	2211
Bitterfeld d.	...	|	|	|	|	1834	1834	|	...	...	|	|	|	...	2025	2030	...	|	...	|	...	2229	2229
Halle (Saale) Hbf d.	...	|	1815	1815	|	1852	1852	1918	...	...	|	|	|	...	|	2052	...	|	...	2217	...	|	|
Dresden Hbf **842** d.	1610	|	|	|	|	|	|	|	...	1810	|	|	|	...	|	|	...	|	...	|	...	|	|
Leipzig Hbf a.	1718	1742	|	|	1842	|	|	|	...	1920	1942	1942	1942	...	2042	|	...	2142	...	|	...	2247	2247
Leipzig Hbf d.	1733	1748	|	|	1848	|	|	|	...	1933	1948	1948	...	...	2048	|	...	2148	...	|	...	2253	...
Erfurt Hbf a.	1815	1828	1848	1848	1928	1924p	1924	1945	...	2015	2029	2029	...	...	2129	2125p	...	2232	...	|	...	2333	...
Erfurt Hbf **849a** d.	1817	1831	1850	1850	1930	...	1932	1947	...	2017	2031	2031	...	...	2131	2133	...	...	...	|	...	2341	...
Coburg **875** d.	|	|	|	|	|	...	|	|	...	|	|	|	...	...	2206	|	...	...	...	|	...	|	...
Bamberg **875** d.	|	1917	|	|	|	...	2017	|	...	|	|	|	...	...	2229	|	...	...	...	|	...	|	...
Erlangen **875** d.	|	1937	|	|	|	...	|	|	...	|	2137	2137	...	...	2251	|	...	...	...	|	...	|	...
Nürnberg Hbf **875** a.	|	1952	|	|	|	...	2052	2056	...	|	2152	2152	...	...	2308	|	...	...	...	|	...	|	...
München Hbf **904 905** a.	|	2105	|	|	|	...	2243	2201	...	|	2302f	2302f	...	...	0022v	|	...	...	...	|	...	|	...
Gotha **849a** d.	1833	...	|	|	|	...	...	...	...	2033	...	...	...	...	...	2149	...	...	...	|	...	|	...
Eisenach **849a** d.	1848	...	|	|	|	...	...	...	...	2048	...	...	...	...	...	2203	...	...	...	|	...	|	...
Bad Hersfeld d.	1916	...	|	|	|	...	...	...	...	2116	...	...	...	...	...	2232	...	...	...	|	...	|	...
Fulda **900/1/2** d.	2001	...	2021	2021	2052	...	...	...	...	2201	...	...	...	...	...	2303	...	...	...	|	...	|	...
Frankfurt (Main) Süd **901** a.	|	...	|	|	|	...	...	...	...	|	...	...	...	...	...	|	...	...	...	0250	...	|	...
Frankfurt (Main) Hbf **900/1/2** a.	2056	...	2132	2132	2144	...	...	...	...	2256	...	...	...	...	...	2400	...	...	...	...	...	0244	...
Frankfurt Flughafen ✈ § a.	...	...	...	...	|	...	...	...	...	...	...	...	...	...	...	...	...	...	...	...	...	|	...
Wiesbaden Hbf **911** a.	...	...	...	...	|	...	...	...	...	...	...	...	...	...	...	...	...	...	...	...	...	|	...
Stuttgart Hbf **912** a.	...	...	...	...	2308	...	...	...	...	...	...	...	...	...	...	...	...	...	...	...	...	0444	...

A – BEROLINA – To Wien via Passau (Tables **920** and **950**).
B – Daily to Sept. 6; Ⓑ from Sept. 8 (also Oct. 5).
D – Daily to Sept. 6; Ⓑ from Sept. 8.
E – Daily to Sept. 1; ⑤⑦ from Sept. 6.
J – To Jena (Table **849a**).
K – From Kiel (Table **820**).
L – From Lichtenfels (d. 0624).
M – To München via Ulm (Table **930**).
O – From Ostseebad Binz (Tables **844**/**845**).
R – From Warnemünde via Rostock (Table **835**).
S – To Saarbrücken on Ⓑ (Table **919**).

a – ①–⑤ only.
c – ⑥⑦ only.
e – ①–⑥ only.
f – 2328 on ⑥ Aug. 10 – 31 (train **1715**), ⑦ Aug. 11 - Sept. 1 (train **1605**).
g – Not Sept. 30 - Oct. 21.
m – Not Oct. 4.
n – 1752 Oct. 6 – 27.
p – Connects with train in previous column.
u – Also Oct. 3; not Oct. 5.
v – 0051 on the mornings of ①⑦ Aug. 11 - Sept. 2.
y – Not Oct. 26, 27.

⊙ – Also calls at Weimar (d. 0337).
◇ – Also calls at Hanau Hbf (a. 2341).
▽ – Diverted via Kassel Wilhelmshöhe.
‡ – On ⑥ Aug. 10 - Sept. 28 does not call at Frankfurt (Main) Süd and arrives Frankfurt (Main) Hbf 0856.
♣ – Via Weimar (see Table **849a**).
★ – 🛏 1, 2 cl. Moskva - Warszawa - Berlin - Strasbourg - Paris. See Table **24**. Operated by Russian Railways. Special fares.

FRANKFURT and NÜRNBERG - ERFURT - LEIPZIG / HALLE - BERLIN 850

SERVICE AUGUST 10 - OCTOBER 27 (see page 402 for service to August 9 and from October 28). See Table **902** for other services Frankfurt - Berlin via Braunschweig.

Other regional services: Table **845** Lutherstadt Wittenberg - Berlin. Table **848** Leipzig / Halle - Bitterfeld - Lutherstadt Wittenberg. Table **849** Eisenach - Erfurt - Weimar - Leipzig / Halle.

km		ICE 1618	EN 453	ICE 1606	ICE 992	ICE 892	ICE 806	ICE 806	ICE 1531	ICE 1604	ICE 1604	ICE 1704	ICE 1714	ICE 1553	ICE 1008	ICE 804	ICE 696	ICE 696	ICE 1533	ICE 602	ICE 1555	ICE 1006	ICE 802
		Ⓐ	⑤	①–⑥		②–⑤	①–⑤		①–⑥	Ⓐ	Ⓑ	①–⑤	⑥	⑥	Ⓐ	⑥	①–⑥		Ⓐ				
			★		E	F			R			J	J O	u		k	H	H					
		🍷	[R]	✕	✕	✕	✕	✕	✕	✕	✕	✕	✕	🍷	✕	✕	✕	✕	✕	✕	✕	✕	✕
	Stuttgart Hbf **912** d.	...	...	...	0012	...	...	...	...	...	...	...	...	...	...	...	...	...	...	...	...	...	...
	Wiesbaden Hbf **911** d.	...	...	...	|	...	...	...	...	...	...	...	...	...	...	...	...	...	...	...	...	...	...
	Frankfurt Flughafen ✈ § d.	...	...	...	0230	...	...	...	...	...	...	...	...	...	...	...	...	...	...	...	...	...	...
	Frankfurt (Main) Hbf **900/1/2** d.	...	...	...	0247	...	...	...	...	...	...	...	...	...	...	...	0614	...	0617	...	0700	...	...
	Frankfurt (Main) Süd **901** d.	...	0137	...	|	...	...	...	...	...	...	...	...	...	...	...	|	...	|	...	|	...	...
	Fulda **900/1/2** d.	...	|	...	|	...	...	...	...	...	...	...	...	...	...	...	0709	...	▽	...	0757	...	...
	Bad Hersfeld d.	...	|	...	|	...	...	...	...	...	...	...	...	...	...	...	|	...	|	...	0839	...	...
	Eisenach **849a** d.	...	|	...	|	...	0553	...	0638	...	...	...	...	...	...	...	0803	...	0844	...	0909	...	...
	Gotha **849a** d.	...	|	...	|	...	0611	...	0653	...	...	...	...	...	...	...	|	...	|	...	0923	...	...
	München Hbf **904 905** d.	...	|	...	|	...	|	...	|	...	...	...	...	...	0557	0547	|	...	|	0657	|	0752	0713
0	**Nürnberg** Hbf **875** d.	...	|	...	|	...	|	...	|	0545	...	...	...	...	0701	0703	|	...	|	0804	|	0858	0905
24	Erlangen **875** d.	...	|	...	|	...	|	...	|	0600	...	...	...	...	|	0718	|	...	|	0819	|	|	|
62	**Bamberg** **875** d.	...	|	...	|	...	|	...	|	0622	...	...	...	...	|	0740	|	...	|	0842	|	|	0940
	Coburg **875** d.	...	|	...	|	...	|	...	|	0644	...	...	...	...	|	|	|	...	|	|	|	|	|
190	**Erfurt** Hbf **849a** a.	...	|	...	0605	...	0626	...	0708	0724	...	...	...	...	0809	0824	0826**p**	...	0907	0926	0938	1009	1024
190	**Erfurt** Hbf d.	...	|	...	0607	...	0628	...	0710	0727	...	...	...	0741	0811	0832	0828	0828	0909	0928	0940	1011	1032
	Leipzig Hbf a.	...	|	...	|	...	0710	...	|	0810	...	...	...	0825	|	|	0910	0910	|	1010	1024	|	|
	Leipzig Hbf d.	0508	|	0616	|	...	0716	0716	|	0818	0818	0818	0818	0831	|	|	0916	0916	|	1016	1031	|	|
	Dresden Hbf **842** a.	|	|	|	|	...	|	|	|	|	|	|	|	0939	|	|	|	|	|	|	1139	|	|
284	**Halle** (Saale) Hbf d.	|	0606	|	0640	0640	|	|	0745	|	|	|	|	...	0840	0906	|	|	0945	|	...	1040	1106
314	Bitterfeld d.	0530	|	|	0658	0658	|	|	0803	|	|	|	|	...	|	0924	|	|	|	|	...	|	1124
351	Lutherstadt Wittenberg d.	0547	|	0648	|	|	0748	0748	|	0848	0848	0848	0848	...	|	|	0948	0948	|	1048	...	|	|
442	**Berlin** Südkreuz a.	0622	|	0722	0751	0751	0825	0825	0851	0923	0923	0923	0923	...	0944	1017	1022	1022	1048	1122	...	1144	1217
448	**Berlin** Hbf a.	0629	0721	0729	0758	0758	0832	0832	0858	0930	0930	0930	0930	...	0951	1024	1029	1029	1055	1129	...	1151	1224
	Hamburg Hbf **840** a.	...	...	0924	...	...	1021	1021	...	1124	1124	1124	...	...	...	...	1221	1221	...	1324	...	...	1421

	ICE 694	ICE 1535	ICE 1600	ICE 1710	ICE 1557	ICE 1724	ICE 1584	ICE 800	ICE 692	ICE 1537	ICE 508	ICE 1559	ICE 1004	ICE 690	ICE 1539	ICE 506	ICE 1651	ICE 92	ICE 706	ICE 598	ICE 1631	ICE 504	ICE 1653
						⑥	⑦																
				O		k R			M					M				A		M			
	✕	✕	✕	✕	✕	✕	✕	✕	✕	✕	✕	✕	✕	✕	✕	✕	✕	✕	✕	✕	✕	✕	✕
Stuttgart Hbf **912** d.	0651	...	...	...	...	...	...	...	0851	...	...	...	...	1051	...	...	...	...	...	1251	...	...	...
Wiesbaden Hbf **911** d.	|	...	...	...	...	...	...	...	|	...	...	...	...	|	...	...	...	...	...	|	...	...	...
Frankfurt Flughafen ✈ § d.	|	0809**y**	...	...	...	...	...	...	|	...	...	...	...	|	...	...	...	...	...	|	...	...	...
rankfurt (Main) Hbf **900/1/2** d.	0814	|	...	...	0902	...	...	...	1014	1018	...	1102	...	1214	1218	...	1302	...	...	1414	1418	...	1502
rankfurt (Main) Süd **901** d.	|	0820	...	...	|	...	...	...	|	|	...	|	...	|	|	...	|	...	...	|	|	...	|
ulda **900/1/2** d.	0909	0913	...	...	0957	...	...	...	1109	|	...	1157	...	1309	1312	...	1357	...	...	1509	|	...	1557
ad Hersfeld d.	|	▽	...	...	1039	...	...	...	|	|	...	1239	...	|	▽	...	1439	...	...	|	|	...	1639
isenach **849a** d.	|	1045	...	...	1109	...	...	...	|	|	...	1309	...	|	1445	...	1509	...	...	|	|	...	1709
otha **849a** d.	|	|	...	...	1123	...	...	...	|	▽	...	1323	...	|	|	...	1523	...	...	|	▽	...	1723
München Hbf **904 905** d.	|	|	0856	0856	|	0919	0921	0954	|	|	1013	|	1157	|	|	1255	|	...	1355	|	|	1456	|
Nürnberg Hbf **875** d.	|	|	1005	1005	|	1036	1036	1106	|	|	1204	|	1301	|	|	1404	|	1437	1506	|	|	1604	|
Erlangen **875** d.	|	|	1019	1019	|	|	|	|	|	|	1219	|	|	|	|	1419	|	|	|	|	|	1619	|
Bamberg **875** d.	|	|	|	|	|	|	|	1140	|	|	1242	|	|	|	|	1442	|	|	1540	|	|	1642	|
Coburg **875** d.	|	|	|	|	|	1129	1129	|	|	|	|	|	|	|	|	|	|	1529	|	|	|	|	|
rfurt Hbf **849a** a.	1026**p**	1107	1126	1126	1138	1202	1202	1224	1226**p**	1307	1326	1338	1409	1426	1507	1526	1538	1602	1624	1626**p**	1707	1726	1738
rfurt Hbf d.	1028	1109	1128	1128	1140	1204	1204	1232	1228	1309	1328	1340	1411	1428	1509	1528	1540	1604	1632	1628	1709	1728	1740
Leipzig Hbf a.	1110	|	1210	1210	1224	|	|	|	1310	|	1410	1424	|	1510	|	1610	1624	|	|	1710	|	1810	1824
Leipzig Hbf d.	1116	|	1216	1216	1231	|	|	|	1316	|	1416	1431	|	1516	|	1616	1631	|	|	1716	|	1816	1831
Dresden Hbf **842** a.	|	|	|	|	1339	|	|	|	|	|	|	1539	|	|	|	|	1739	|	|	|	|	|	1939
alle (Saale) Hbf d.	|	1145	|	|	...	1240	1240	1306	|	1345	|	...	1440	|	1545	|	...	1640	1706	|	1745	|	...
itterfeld d.	|	|	|	|	...	|	|	1324	|	|	|	...	|	1535	|	|	...	|	1724	|	|	|	...
utherstadt Wittenberg d.	1148	|	1248	1248	...	|	|	|	1348	|	1448	...	|	|	|	1648	...	|	|	1748	|	1848	...
erlin Südkreuz a.	1222	1248	1322	1322	...	1348	1348	1417	1422	1448	1522	...	1544	1622	1651	1722	...	1751	1817	1822	1851	1922	...
erlin Hbf a.	1229	1255	1329	1329	...	1355	1355	1424	1429	1455	1529	...	1551	1629	1659	1729	...	1758	1826	1829	1858	1929	...
Hamburg Hbf **840** a.	...	...	1525	...	...	...	...	1621	...	...	1724	...	...	1822	...	1924	...	...	2023	...	...	2124	...

	ICE 1002	ICE 704	IC 1957	ICE 596	IC 1957	ICE 1633	ICE 502	ICE 1655	ICE 1000	ICE 702	ICE 702	ICE 594	ICE 1635	ICE 500	ICE 1657	ICE 592	ICE 1700	ICE 1500	ICE 1510	ICE 592		ICE 1659	ICE 1659
			⑤ f		⑤ f	Ⓑ			Ⓑ	B	⑤⑦		Ⓑ		Ⓑ			⑦	①–④	⑤⑥		Ⓑ	⑤⑦
				M							f	M				M			m	M			v
	✕	✕		✕	♣	✕	✕	🍷	✕	✕	✕	✕	✕	✕	✕	✕	✕			✕		✕§	✕§
Stuttgart Hbf **912** d.	...	...	...	1451	...	...	...	...	...	...	...	1651	...	...	...	1851	...	...	...	...	...	...	...
Wiesbaden Hbf **911** d.	...	...	...	|	...	...	...	...	...	...	...	|	...	...	...	|	...	...	...	...	...	...	...
Frankfurt Flughafen ✈ § d.	...	...	...	|	...	1609**y**	...	...	...	...	...	|	1809**y**	...	...	|	...	...	...	...	...	...	...
rankfurt (Main) Hbf **900/1/2** d.	...	...	1520	1613	...	|	...	1702	...	...	...	1814	|	...	1902	2014	...	...	...	...	...	2102	2102
rankfurt (Main) Süd **901** d.	...	...	|	|	...	1620	...	|	...	...	...	|	1820	...	|	|	...	...	...	...	...	|	|
ulda **900/1/2** d.	...	...	1619	1709	...	1713	...	1757	...	...	...	1909	|	...	1957	2109	...	...	...	...	...	2157	2157
ad Hersfeld d.	...	...	1703	|	...	▽	...	1839	...	...	...	|	|	...	2039	2139	...	...	...	...	...	2239	2239
isenach **849a** d.	...	...	1752	|	←	1849	...	1909	...	...	...	|	|	...	2109	2209	...	...	...	...	...	2309	2309
otha **849a** d.	...	...	1805	|	1807	|	...	1923	...	...	...	|	▽	...	2123	2223	...	...	...	...	...	2323	2323
München Hbf **904 905** d.	1556	1514	→	|	|	|	1655	|	1757	1705	1705	|	|	1856	|	|	1955	1955	1955	...	...	|	|
Nürnberg Hbf **875** d.	1701	1705	...	|	|	|	1804	|	1901	1905	1905	|	|	2004	|	|	2105	2105	2105	...	...	|	|
Erlangen **875** d.	|	|	...	|	|	|	1819	|	|	|	|	|	|	2019	|	|	2120	2120	2120	...	...	|	|
Bamberg **875** d.	|	1740	...	|	|	|	1842	|	|	1940	1940	|	|	2042	|	|	2143	2143	2143	...	...	|	|
Coburg **875** d.	|	|	...	|	|	|	|	|	|	|	|	|	|	|	|	|	2206	2206	2206	←	...	|	|
rfurt Hbf **849a** a.	1809	1824	...	1826**p**	1838	1913	1926	1938	2009	2024	2024	2026**p**	2107	2126	2138	2238	2238	2238	2238	2238	...	2338	2338
rfurt Hbf d.	1811	1832	...	1828	1842	1915	1928	1940	2011	2032	2032	2028	2109	2128	2140•	→	2242	2246	2246	2246	...	...	2340
Leipzig Hbf a.	|	|	...	1910	2016	|	2010	2024	|	|	|	2110	|	2210	2225	...	|	2329	2336	2329	...	...	0024
Leipzig Hbf d.	|	|	...	1916	...	|	2016	2031	|	|	|	2116	|	2216	2231	...	|	...	...	...	...	...	...
Dresden Hbf **842** a.	|	|	...	|	...	|	|	2138	|	|	|	|	|	|	2338	...	|	...	...	...	...	...	...
alle (Saale) Hbf d.	1840	1906	...	|	...	1945	|	...	2040	2106	2106	|	2145	|	...	...	2317	...	...	...	...	...	...
tterfeld d.	|	1924	...	|	...	|	|	...	|	2124	2124	|	|	2234	...	...	|	...	...	...	...	...	...
utherstadt Wittenberg d.	|	|	...	1948	...	|	2048	...	|	|	|	2148	|	2251	...	...	2347	...	...	...	...	...	...
erlin Südkreuz a.	1944	2017	...	2022	...	2048	2122	...	2144	2217	2217	2222	2250	2326	...	...	0023	...	...	...	...	...	...
erlin Hbf a.	1951	2026	...	2029	...	2055	2129	...	2151	2224	2224	2229	2258	2335	...	...	0031	...	...	...	...	...	...
Hamburg Hbf **840** a.	...	2221**b**	...	...	...	...	2333**x**	...	...	...	0033	...	...	...	...	...	...	...	...	...	...	...	...

– BEROLINA – From Wien (Tables **950** and **920**). To Rostock (Table **835**) on ⑤**f**.
– Daily to Sept. 6; Ⓑ from Sept. 8 (also Oct. 5).
– Daily to Sept. 2; ①⑥ from Sept. 7. [12] München (d. 2151 previous day) - Stuttgart - Frankfurt - Berlin. ✕ Erfurt - Berlin.
– From Sept. 3.
– [12] and ✕ (Karlsruhe ① -) (Frankfurt ①–⑥ -) Erfurt - Leipzig - Hamburg - Kiel.
– From Jena (Table **849a**).
– From München via Ulm (Table **930**).
– To Ostseebad Binz (Tables **844**/**845**).
– To Warnemünde via Rostock on dates in Table **835**.

– Ⓑ (not Oct. 3).
– Also Oct. 2; not Oct. 4.
– Also Oct. 3.

m – Not Oct. 2.
p – Connects with train in previous column.
u – Also Oct. 3; not Oct. 5.
v – Also Oct. 2.
x – ⑤–⑦ to Aug. 25; daily from Aug. 30.
y – Not Oct. 26, 27.

• – 2142 on ⑤ (also Oct. 2; not Oct. 4).
▽ – Diverted via Kassel Wilhelmshöhe.
♣ – Via Weimar (see Table **849a**).
§ – ✕ Wiesbaden - Fulda.
★ – 🛏 1, 2 cl. Paris - Berlin - Warszawa - Moskva. See Table **24**. Operated by Russian Railways. Special fares.

874 LEIPZIG - CHEMNITZ

Mitteldeutsche Regiobahn

SERVICE UNTIL SEPTEMBER 19. All services are operated by 🚌 Chemnitz Küchwald - Chemnitz Hbf and v.v. (see note ⊠). See page 410 for service from September 20.

km			⚒				△
0	**Leipzig** Hbf	d.	0518	0620	0720	and hourly until	2220	2337
33	Bad Lausick	d.	0547	0647	0747		2247	0000
44	Geithain	d.	0556	0656	0756		2256	0009
66	Burgstädt	d.	0613	0713	0813		2313	0026
78	Chemnitz Küchwald	a.	0622	0722	0822		2322	0035
81	**Chemnitz** Hbf 🚌	a.	*0642*	*0742*	*0842*		*2342*	*0055*

			⚒				
Chemnitz Hbf 🚌	d.	*0404*	*0513*	*0613*	and hourly until	*2113*	*2213*
Chemnitz Küchwald	d.	0424	0533	0633		2133	2233
Burgstädt	d.	0433	0543	0643		2143	2243
Geithain	d.	0451	0600	0700		2200	2300
Bad Lausick	d.	0500	0609	0709		2209	2309
Leipzig Hbf	a.	0525	0629	0729		2229	2333

△ – 7 minutes later on ①–④.
⊠ – Normal service resumes on the evening of Sept. 19 (1920 from Leipzig / 2031 from Chemnitz).

933 ULM - FRIEDRICHSHAFEN - LINDAU

IRE / *RE* services

SERVICE UNTIL JULY 14. All services are operated by 🚌 Biberach - Aulendorf and v.v. (shaded timings). On June 20 services run as on ⑦. See page 445 for service July 15 - Sept. 15.

km			Ⓒ	Ⓐ	Ⓒ	Ⓐ				⊡																
0	**Ulm** Hbf	d.	0511	0511	0633	0633	0713	0742	0815	and at the same minutes past each hour until	1215	1242	1315	1342**a**	1442	1515	1542	1642	1715	1742	1843	1915	1942	2015	2142	2215
37	Biberach (Riß)	a.	0544	0544	0705	0708	0742**k**	0808	0844		1244	1309	1347	1400**a**	1508	1547	1609	1708	1744	1808	1909	1944	2008	2044	2208	2246
37	Biberach (Riß) 🚌	d.	0548	0548	0709	0712	0746**k**	0812	0849		1249	1313	1352	1413**a**	1512	1552	1613	1712	1749	1812	1914	1949	2012	2049	2212	2251
62	Aulendorf 🚌	a.	0631	0631	0752	0752	0832	0852	0932		1332	1353	1435	1453**a**	1552	1635	1653	1752	1832	1852	1957	2032	2052	2132	2255	2334
62	Aulendorf	d.	0636	0638	0755	0756	0837	0856	0937		1337	1356	1442	1456	1556	1639	1656	1756	1837	1856	2002	2037	2056	2137	2259	2340
84	Ravensburg	d.	0649	0652	0808	0808	0850	0908	0950		1350	1408	1456	1508	1608	1652	1708	1808	1850	1908	2015	2050	2108	2150	2311	2359
95	Meckenbeuren	d.	0656	0659	0816	0816	0857	0915	0957		1357	1415	1503	1515	1615	1659	1715	1815	1857	1915	2022	2057	2115	2157	2318	0009
99	Friedrichshafen Flug ¶	d.	0700	0704	|	|	0901	|	|		|	|	|	|	|	1703	|	|	1901	|	|	2101	|	|	|	0015
103	Friedrichshafen Stadt	a.	0704	0712	0823	0823	0906	0923	1005		1405	1423	1510	1523	1623	1708	1723	1823	1906	1923	2030	2106	2123	2205	2326	0020
103	Friedrichshafen Stadt	d.	*0727*	0728	*0828*	0828	▽	0928	...		...	1428	▽	1535	1631**t**	▽	1728	1828	▽	1928	2035	▽	2128	*2242*	2331	...
127	**Lindau** Hbf 🏛	a.	*0752*	0751	*0854*	0854	...	0952	...		...	1454	...	1554	1655	...	1752	1854	...	1952	2100	...	2156	*2258*	2357	...

		Ⓐ																									
Lindau Hbf 🏛	d.	0445	...	0559	0701**e**	0804	...	0905	1005	...	1105	...	1202	...	1305	1405	...	1505	1605	...	1702	1805	...	1905	2005	...	*2101*
Friedrichshafen Stadt	a.	0517	...	0622	0726**e**	0826	▽	0926	1026	▽	1126	...	1220	▽	1326	1426	▽	1527	1624**k**	▽	1726	1826	▽	1926	2026	▽	*2127*
Friedrichshafen Stadt	d.	0523	0546	0628	0731	0831	0848	0931	1031	1048	1131	1150	1231	1243	1331	1431	1448	1531	1628**k**	1648	1731	1831	1848	1931	2031	2045	2132
Friedrichshafen Flug ¶	d.	|	0552	0633**z**	|	|	0853	|	|	1053	|	|	|	|	|	|	1453	|	|	1655	|	|	1853	|	|	2050	|
Meckenbeuren	d.	0531	0558	0635**k**	0738	0838	0857	0938	1038	1057	1138	1157	1238	1250	1338	1438	1458	1538	1638	|	1738	1838	1857	1938	2038	|	2138
Ravensburg	d.	0538	0605	0643**k**	0745	0845	0905	0945	1045	1105	1145	1204	1245	1258	1345	1445	1505	1545	1645	1705	1745	1845	1905	1945	2045	2059	2146
Aulendorf	a.	0552	0620	0658**k**	0758	0858	0919	0958	1058	1119	1158	1219	1259	1312	1358	1458	1519	1558	1658	1719	1758	1858	1919	1958	2058	2111	2200
Aulendorf 🚌	d.	0556	0626	0702	0802	0902	0924	1002	1102	1124	1202	1223	1304**a**	1320	1402	1502	1524	1602	1702	1724	1802	1902	1924	2002	2102	2116	2205
Biberach (Riß) 🚌	a.	0636	0706**k**	0742	0842	0942	1007	1042	1142	1207	1242	1306	1344**a**	1403	1442	1542	1607	1642	1742	1807	1842	1942	2007	2042	2142	2159	2248
Biberach (Riß)	d.	0640	0710**k**	0746	0846	0946	1012	1046	1146	1212	1246	1310**k**	1348**a**	1412	1446	1548	1612	1646	1746	1812	1846	1946	2012	2046	2146**v**	2214	2253
Ulm Hbf	a.	0718	0742	0813	0913	1013	1042	1113	1213	1242	1319**r**	1341	1414**a**	1442	1513	1614	1644	1713	1813	1842	1913	2013	2042	2113	2213**v**	2246	2323

a – Ⓐ only.
e – Ⓐ only. Connecting service on Ⓒ: Lindau d. *0656*, Friedrichshafen a. *0727*.
k – 2–3 minutes later on Ⓒ.
r – 1313 on Ⓒ.
t – 1628 on Ⓒ.
v – ①③⑤⑥⑦.
z – Ⓒ only.
▽ – To / from Basel Bad Bf (Table **933**).
¶ – Friedrichshafen Flughafen ✈.
⊡ – Certain timings Aulendorf - Lindau may vary by up to 3 minutes. The 1037 and 1237 from Aulendorf continue to Basel Bad Bf (Table **933**).

937 MEMMINGEN - LINDAU

Special service **valid until September 15** during electrification work. See page 449 for rail service Kißlegg - Aulendorf and v.v. On June 20 services run as on ⑦.
From September 16 to October 6 rail services resume between Aichstetten and Kißlegg (please check locally for timings). Normal service is expected from October 7.

		🚌	🚌	🚌	🚌	🚌	🚌	🚌	🚌	🚌	🚌	🚌	🚌	🚌	🚌	🚌	🚌	🚌	🚌	🚌	🚌	🚌	🚌	🚌	🚌	🚌
		Ⓒ	Ⓐ	Ⓐ	Ⓐ		Ⓒ	Ⓐ		Ⓐd				Ⓐd				Ⓐd				Ⓐd				Ⓐd
Memmingen	d.	...	...	*0624**	...	...	*0706**	*0714**	...	*0806**	...	*0902**	...	*1006**	...	*1102**	...	*1206**	...	*1302**	...	*1405**	...	*1502**	...	*1606**
Aichstetten	d.	...	...	0644	0644	...	0726	0736	...	0828	...	0923	...	1028	...	1123	...	1228	...	1323	...	1428	...	1523	...	1628
Leutkirch	d.	...	0525	0703	0703	...	0745	0800	*0800*	0847	*0905*	0942	*1000*	1047	*1105*	1142	*1200*	1247	*1305*	1342	*1400*	1447	*1505*	1542	*1600*	1647
Kißlegg	a.	...	0548	|	0724	...	|	0825	*0825*	|	*0930*	|	*1025*	|	*1130*	|	*1225*	|	*1330*	|	*1425*	|	*1530*	|	*1625*	|
Kißlegg	d.	0518	0549	|	0725	...	|	...	0830	|	0933	|	1030	|	1133	|	1230	|	1333	|	1430	|	1533	|	1630	|
Wangen (Allgäu)	d.	0540	0611	0734	0750	0755	0816	...	0855	0922	0955	1013	1055	1120	1155	1213	1255	1320	1355	1413	1455	1520	1555	1613	1655	1720
Hergatz **935**	a.	0555	|	|	...	0810	|	...	...	0937	1010	|	...	1135	1210	|	...	1335	1410	|	...	1535	1610	|	...	1735
Lindau Hbf **935**	a.	...	0655	0814	...	...	0856	...	...	...	...	1053	...	...	...	1253	...	...	...	1453	...	...	...	1653	...	...

		🚌	🚌	🚌	🚌	🚌	🚌	🚌	🚌	🚌	🚌
					Ⓐ						
Memmingen	d.	...	*1706**	...	*1805**	...	*1904**	...	2004	...	*2104**
Aichstetten	d.	...	1725	...	1827	...	1925	...	2038	...	2125
Leutkirch	d.	*1705*	1744	*1800*	1846	*1905*	1944	*2000*	2057	*2105*	2144
Kißlegg	a.	*1730*	|	*1825*	|	*1930*	|	*2025*	|	*2130*	2207
Kißlegg	d.	1733	|	1830	|	1933	|	2030	|	2133	2208
Wangen (Allgäu)	d.	1755	1815	1905	1916	1955	2015	2058	2128	2205	2231
Hergatz **935**	d.	1810	|	1917	...	|	2030	2110	|	2217	2246
Lindau Hbf **935**	a.	...	1855	...	...	2035	...	...	2208	...	...

		🚌	🚌	🚌	🚌	🚌	🚌	🚌	🚌	🚌	🚌
			Ⓒ	Ⓐ	Ⓐ	Ⓒ			Ⓐd		
Lindau Hbf **935**	d.	...	...	...	0540	0544	0706	...	...	...	0906
Hergatz **935**	d.	...	...	...	0612	|	|	0749**c**	0825	...	|
Wangen (Allgäu)	d.	0524	0524	0551	0623	0623	0745	0800	0838	0905	0945
Kißlegg	a.	0547	0547	|	0646	0645	|	0825	|	0930	|
Kißlegg	d.	0548	0548	|	0647	0646	|	*0830*	|	*0934*	|
Leutkirch	d.	0613	0613	0622	0712	0710	0816	*0855*	0909	*0959*	1016
Aichstetten	a.	...	0635	0643	0733	0728	0837	...	0930	...	1037
Memmingen	a.	...	*0658**	*0705**	*0753**	0759	*0858**	...	*0952**	...	*1058**

		🚌	🚌	🚌	🚌	🚌	🚌	🚌	🚌	🚌	🚌	🚌	🚌	🚌	🚌	🚌	🚌	🚌	🚌	🚌	🚌	🚌	🚌	🚌	🚌	🚌
			Ⓐd				Ⓐd				Ⓐd				Ⓐd											
Lindau Hbf **935**	d.	...	...	...	1106	...	...	...	1306	...	...	...	1506	...	...	...	1706	...	...	...	1906	...	...	...	2106	...
Hergatz **935**	d.	0949	1025	...	|	1149	1225	...	|	1349	1425	...	|	1549	1623	...	|	1749	1823	...	|	1949	...	2045	|	2230
Wangen (Allgäu)	d.	1000	1038	1105	1145	1200	1238	1305	1345	1400	1438	1505	1545	1600	1636	1705	1745	1800	1835	1905	1945	2000	...	2105	2145	2242
Kißlegg	a.	1025	|	1130	|	1225	|	1330	|	1425	|	1530	|	1625	|	1730	|	1825	...	1930	|	2025	...	2130	|	...
Kißlegg	d.	*1030*	|	*1134*	|	*1230*	|	*1334*	|	*1430*	|	*1534*	|	*1630*	|	*1734*	|	*1830*	...	*1934*	|	...	2030	*2134*	|	...
Leutkirch	d.	*1055*	1109	*1159*	1216	*1255*	1309	*1359*	1416	*1455*	1509	*1559*	1616	*1655*	1707	*1759*	1816	*1855*	...	*1959*	2016	...	2054	*2159*	2215	...
Aichstetten	a.	...	1130	...	1237	...	1330	...	1437	...	1530	...	1637	...	1728	...	1837	...	...	...	2037	...	2115	...	...	...
Memmingen	a.	...	*1152**	...	*1258**	...	*1352**	...	*1458**	...	*1550**	...	*1658**	...	*1751**	...	*1858**	...	...	...	*2058**	...	*2143**	...	...	...

c – Ⓒ only.
d – Runs daily Wangen - Hergatz and v.v.
* – By Train Memmingen - Aichstetten and v.v.

Products for sale from European Rail Timetable Limited

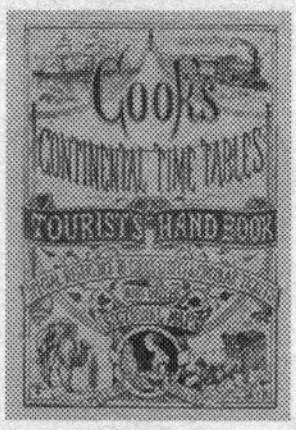

2nd Edition of the
Rail Map Europe.
£11.99 + p&p

Subscribe to the ERT from
£100

15th Edition of the
Europe by Rail guidebook.
£15.99 + p&p

Reprint of the 1873 edition of
Cook's Continental Time Tables & Tourist's Hand Book.
£13.99 + p&p

Order on-line at **www.europeanrailtimetable.eu**
Telephone **01832 270198**

European Rail Timetable Price List

☐ Regular printed edition (excluding Summer and Winter): £17.99

☐ Printed Summer or Winter edition: £19.99

☐ Monthly digital edition: £11.99 (January - May, July - November), £13.99 (Summer or Winter)

Postage and packaging rates for a single printed copy are as follows:

☐ UK	£2.48	Delivery in 2 – 5 working days
☐ Europe	£5.68	Delivery in 3 – 10 working days
☐ Rest of the World	£7.98 – £8.43	Delivery in 5 – 21 working days

Subscription rates for 6 printed editions (price includes postage and packaging):

☐ UK £114 ☐ Europe £135 ☐ Rest of the World £150

Annual subscription for 12 digital editions: ☐ £100

Subscription rates for 6 printed issues and 12 digital editions (price includes postage and packaging):

☐ UK £174 ☐ Europe £195 ☐ Rest of the World £210

Order on-line at **www.europeanrailtimetable.eu**

By post to: 28 Monson Way, Oundle, Northamptonshire, PE8 4QG (cheques payable to European Rail Timetable Limited)

✆ +44 (0) 1832 270198 (Monday to Friday 0900 – 1700)

BEYOND EUROPE

Africa and the Middle East

Introduction

TThe Beyond Europe section covers principal rail services in a different area of the world each month. There are six areas, each appearing as follows:

Winter (December) and Summer (June):	Africa and The Middle East along with all other Beyond Europe sections.
January and July (digital only):	India.
February and August:	South East Asia, Australia and New Zealand; India; North America.
March and September (digital only):	China.
April and October:	Japan; China; South America; South Korea.
May and November (digital only):	North America.

The months have been chosen so that we can bring you up-to-date information for those countries which make seasonal changes.

Contents

INDEX OF PLACES

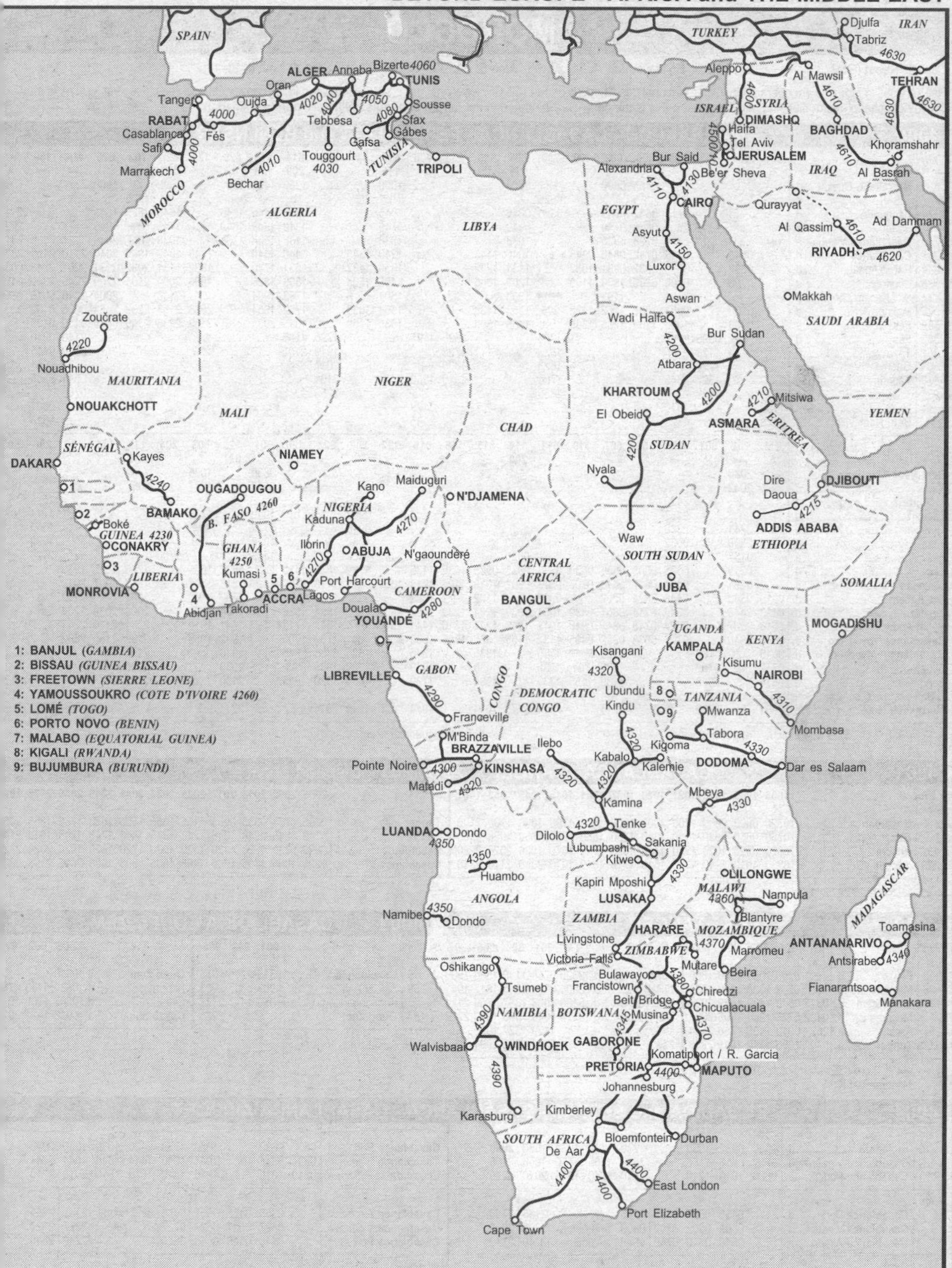

LUXURY and CRUISE TRAINS

HE BLUE TRAIN:

luxury cruise train running between Pretoria and Cape Town with excursions along the way. The service departs on selected ①③⑤ throughout the year. Also occasional trips from Pretoria to loedspruit. ✆ +27 12 334 8459. Fax +27 12 334 8464. www.bluetrain.co.za. Also agents in the US: Truemarketing ✆ +1 973 832 4384, UK: Ethos Marketing ✆ +44 1403243619, Australia: fricareps ✆ +61 41 022 5580'

OVOS RAIL:

uxury cruise train running regularly between: Pretoria and Cape Town, Pretoria and Victoria Falls and Pretoria and Durban. Also occasional trips with excursions Pretoria and Walvis Bay) days) and Cape Town and Dar es Salaam (15 days). Most tours feature haulage by the company's preserved steam locomotives. ✆ +27 12 315 8242. Fax +27 12 323 0843. www.rovos.com.

HONGOLOLO EXPRESS:

arious 12/15 day train journeys throughout Southern Africa with excursions along the way. Tours between Pretoria and Cape Town, Pretoria and Victoria Falls and Pretoria and Swakopmund. ✆ +27 12 315 8242.. www.shongololo.com. Note: now operated by Rovos Rail.

MOROCCO

Capital: **Rabat** (GMT + 1). 2019 Public Holidays: Jan. 1, 11, May 1, June 5, July 30, Aug. 12, 20, 21, Sept. 1, Nov. 6, 10, 18.

Rail services in Morocco are operated by Office National des Chemins de Fer (ONCF. www.oncf.ma). Unless indicated trains convey 1st and 2nd class seating. Trains may als convey couchette and/or sleeping cars and where this is the case it will be noted in the tables. **Schedules will vary during Ramadan.** •

4000 MARRAKECH - CASABLANCA - FÈS - OUJDA and BENI NSAR ONCF

km		502	101 ⚒	203	103	600 ⚒	602	109	700	606 111	113	253	506	610 115	117	207	614 209	618 123	620 ⑦	125	622 127	702	626 131	MA 🛏	139 🛏	MT A
0	**Marrakech** Guéliz ..... d.	...	...	...	...	0455	0600	...	...	0800	...	...	...	1000	...	...	1200	1400	1500	...	1600	...	1800	...	...	2030
*	**Safi** ..... d.	...	...	...	...	|	|	...	0625	|	...	...	...	|	...	...	|	|	|	...	|	1625	|	...	...	|
74	Benguerir ..... d.	...	...	...	...	0542	0645	...	0825	0845	...	...	...	1045	...	...	1245	1445	1545	...	1645	1825	1845	...	...	2117
174	Settat ..... d.	...	...	...	...	0646	0749	...	...	0949	...	...	...	1149	...	...	1349	1549	1649	...	1749	▬	1949	...	...	2223
257	**Casablanca** V'geurs . a.	...	...	...	...	0738	0838	...	...	1038	...	...	...	1238	...	...	1438	1638	1738	...	1838	**129**	2038	...	...	2318
257	**Casablanca** V'geurs . d.	...	0545	...	0640	0740	0840	0945	...	1040	1145	...	...	1240	1345	...	1440	1640	...	1745	1840	1945	2040	2110	2150	2324
346	Rabat Agdal ..... d.	...	0632	...	0730	0832	0931	1032	...	1131	1232	...	...	1330	1432	...	1531	1730	...	1832	1931	2032	2131	2204	2248	0036
386	Kenitra ..... d.	...	0705	...	0806	0905	1009	1105	...	1209	1305	...	...	1406	1505	...	1609	1806	...	1905	2009	2105	2209	2243	2319	0123
471	Sidi Kacem ..... d.	...	|	...	0904	|	1103	|	▬	1303	|	...	...	1504	|	...	1703	1904	...	|	2103	|	2304	2340	0013	0350
526	Meknes Amir ..... d.	...	0838	...	0954	1038	1152	1238	**205**	1352	1438	...	...	1554	1638	...	1752	1954	...	2038	2152	2238	2354	0035	0102	...
582	**Fès** ..... a.	...	0909	...	1035	1109	1235	1309		1435	1509	...	...	1635	1709	...	1835	2035	...	2109	2235	2309	0035	0110	0135	...
582	**Fès** ..... d.	...	...	0925	▬	...	...	...	1325	...	...	1525	1525	...	...	1725	*1855*	...	...	...	...	...	...	0140	0210	...
701	Taza ..... d.	...	...	1125	**504**	...	...	...	1523	...	...	1728	|	...	...	1919	*2102*	...	...	...	...	...	...	0340	0415	...
	Guercif ..... d.	...	...	1226		...	...	...	1623	...	...	1835	|	...	...	2017	...	...	...	...	...	...	...	0432	0504	...
818	Taourirt ..... d.	0920	...	1307	1345	...	...	...	1704	...	...	1920	1950	...	...	2101	...	...	...	...	...	...	...	0511	0555	...
935	**Oujda** ..... a.	|	...	1448	|	...	...	...	1855	...	...	...	|	...	...	2255	...	...	...	...	...	...	...	0705	|	...
	Nador ..... a.	1102	...	...	1510	...	...	...	...	...	...	...	2129	...	...	...	...	...	...	...	...	...	...	...	0801	...
	Beni Nsar Ville ..... a.	1120	...	...	1525	...	...	...	...	...	...	...	2145	...	...	...	...	...	...	...	...	...	...	...	0815	...

	TM A	102 🛏	601 ⚒	AM 🛏	104 ⚒	607	110 ⚒	611	114 200	615	118	619	122	202	623	126	501	128 627	503	204	132 631	134	136	206	505
Beni Nsar Ville ..... d.	...	2030	...	...	...	...	...	...	...	...	...	...	...	...	...	...	0830	...	1035	...	...	...	...	...	1645
Nador ..... d.	...	2042	...	...	...	...	...	...	...	...	...	...	...	...	...	...	0842	...	1047	...	...	...	...	...	1655
Oujda ..... d.	...	|	...	2120	...	...	...	...	...	...	...	...	...	0720	...	...	|	...	|	1120	...	...	...	1520	|
Taourirt ..... d.	...	|	...	2257	...	...	...	...	...	...	...	...	...	0902	...	...	1040	...	1225	1313	...	...	...	1714	1828
Guercif ..... d.	...	2241	...	2338	...	...	...	...	...	...	...	...	...	0946	...	...	1122	...	▬	1354	...	...	...	1803	...
Taza ..... d.	...	2338	...	0032	...	...	...	...	*0620*	...	...	...	...	1050	...	...	1228	...	**130**	1451	...	...	...	1922	...
Fès ..... a.	...	0137	...	0250	...	...	...	...	*0820*	...	...	...	...	1300	...	...	1443	...		1700	...	...	...	2125	...
Fès ..... d.	...	0215	...	0325	0505	0535	0630	0735	0835	0935	1035	1135	1235	▬	1335	1435	...	1535	1635	...	1735	1835	1935	...	...
Meknes Amir ..... d.	...	0251	...	0401	0537	0613	0707	0813	0907	1013	1107	1213	1307	...	1413	1507	...	1613	1707	...	1813	1907	2013	...	...
Sidi Kacem ..... d.	0310	0342	...	0448	0624	0702	|	0902	|	1102	|	1302	|	...	1502	|	...	1702	|	...	1902	|	2102	...	...
Kenitra ..... d.	0423	0440	...	0542	0714	0804	0839	1004	1039	1204	1239	1404	1439	...	1604	1639	...	1804	1839	...	2004	2039	2204	...	...
Rabat Agdal ..... d.	0513	0537	...	0624	0748	0841	0910	1041	1110	1241	1310	1441	1510	**621**	1641	1710	...	1841	1910	...	2041	2110	2241	...	...
Casablanca Voyageurs ..... a.	0610	0640	...	0725	0838	0932	0955	1132	1155	1332	1355	1532	1555	⑦	1732	1755	...	1932	1955	...	2132	2155	2332	...	...
Casablanca Voyageurs ..... d.	0615	...	0700	...	...	0935	▬	1135	...	1335	...	1535	...	1625	1735	▬	...	1935	...	...	2135	...	...	...	...
Settat ..... d.	0712	...	0752	...	...	1030	**701**	1230	...	1430	...	1630	...	1730	1830	**703**	...	2030	...	...	2230	...	...	...	...
Benguerir ..... d.	0816	...	0855	...	...	1130	1155	1330	...	1530	...	1730	...	1830	1930	1955	...	2130	...	...	2330	...	...	...	...
Safi ..... a.	|	...	|	...	...	|	1355	|	...	|	...	|	...	|	|	2155	...	|	...	...	|	...	...	...	...
Marrakech Guéliz ..... a.	0901	...	0939	...	...	1214	...	1414	...	1614	...	1814	...	1914	2014	...	...	2214	...	...	0014	...	...	...	...

A – 🛏 1, 2 cl., (12) Marrakech - Tanger and v.v.

* – Safi - Benguerir: *142 km.*

4001 CASABLANCA - TANGER *Al Boraq* high-speed service. ONCF

km		1005 ⚒	1009	1013	1021	1029	1037	1041	1045	1049 ⑦	1053	1061
0	**Casablanca** V ⊡ ..... d.	0700	0800	0900	1100	1300	1500	1600	1700	1800	1900	2100
	Rabat Agdal ..... d.	0750	0850	0950	1150	1350	1550	1650	1750	1850	1950	2150
137	Kenitra ..... d.	0820	0920	1020	1220	1420	1620	1720	1820	1920	2020	2220
323	**Tanger** Ville ..... a.	0910	1010	1110	1310	1510	1710	1810	1910	2010	2110	2310

	2005 ⚒	2009	2013	2017	2025	2033	2041	2045 ⑦	2049	2053	206
Tanger Ville ..... d.	0655	0755	0855	0955	1155	1355	1555	1655	1755	1855	205
Kenitra ..... d.	0748	0848	0948	1048	1248	1448	1648	1748	1848	1948	214
Rabat Agdal ..... d.	0820	0920	1020	1120	1320	1520	1720	1820	1920	2020	222
Casablanca V ⊡ .. a.	0905	1005	1105	1205	1405	1605	1805	1905	2005	2105	230

⊡ – Casablanca Voyageurs.

4002 FÈS - TANGER ONCF

km		MT A	300	302	304	306
0	**Fès** ..... d.	...	*0505*	1000	1400	1800
56	Meknes Amir. d.	...	*0537*	1038	1438	1838
111	Sidi Kacem ... d.	0345	0640	1129	1529	1929
	Mechraa BK ‡ d.	0432	0725	1206	1606	2006
264	Asilah ..... a.	0622	0919	1400	1758	2154
312	**Tanger** Ville .. a.	0700	1005	1440	1845	2235

	TM A	301	303	305	307
Tanger Ville... d.	2320	0735	1130	1530	1900
Asilah ..... d.	0003	0821	1216	1617	1941
Mechraa BK ‡ d.	0150	1003	1357	1759	2124
Sidi Kacem .... d.	0228	1040	1438	1840	2202
Meknes Amir . d.	...	1129	1527	1929	...
Fès ..... a.	...	1204	1602	2004	...

A – 🛏 1, 2 cl., (12) Marrakech - Tanger and v.v.

‡ – Mechraa Bel Ksir.

4003 CASABLANCA - OUED ZEM ONCF

km		901	903	905
0	**Casablanca** V ⊡ ... d.	0815	1215	1855
58	Sidi El Aidi ..... d.	0904	1307	2003
	Khouribga ..... a.	1050	1447	2147
187	**Oued Zem** ..... a.	...	...	2235

	900	902	904
Oued Zem ..... d.	0540	...	...
Khouribga ..... d.	0630	1135	173
Sidi El Aidi ..... d.	0807	1308	191
Casablanca V ⊡ a.	0913	1421	202

⊡ – Casablanca Voyageurs.

4004 EL JADIDA and SETTAT - CASABLANCA - CASABLANCA AIRPORT ONCF

km		⚒									
0	**El Jadida** ..... d.	0630	0830	1030	...	1230	1430	1630	1830	2030	...
123	**Casablanca** V'geurs ... a.	0752	0956	1156	...	1356	1556	1756	1956	2156	...
	Casablanca Port ..... a.	0806	1010	1210	...	1410	1610	1810	2010	2210	...

	⚒									
Casablanca Port ..... d.	0630	0830	...	1030	1230	1430	1630	1830	2030	...
Casablanca V'geurs d.	0644	0844	...	1044	1240	1444	1644	1844	2044	...
El Jadida ..... a.	0810	1010	...	1210	1410	1610	1810	2010	2210	...

km										
0	**Casablanca** Port ..... d.	...	0455	0555	0655	0755		2155	2255	...
	Casablanca V'geurs ... d.	...	0509	0609	0709	0809	and hourly	2209	2309	...
	Casablanca Airport .... a.	...	0540	0640	0740	0840	until	2240	2340	...

Casablanca Airport .. d.	...	0355	0455	0555	0655	and hourly	2155	2255	...
Casablanca V'geurs a.	...	0427	0527	0627	0727	until	2227	2327	...
Casablanca Port ..... a.	...	0440	0540	0640	0640		2240	2340	...

km		⚒	⚒								
0	**Settat** ..... d.	0615	0820	1020	...	1220	1420	1620	1820	2020	...
83	**Casablanca** V'geurs ... a.	0717	0922	1122	...	1322	1522	1722	1922	2122	...
	Casablanca Port ..... a.	0730	0935	1135	...	1335	1535	1735	1935	2135	...

	⚒	⚒								
Casablanca Port ..... d.	0615	0845	...	1045	1245	1445	1645	1745	2045	...
Casablanca V'geurs d.	0628	0858	...	1058	1258	1458	1658	1759	2058	...
Settat ..... a.	0732	1003	...	1203	1403	1603	1803	1903	2203	..

4005 CASABLANCA - RABAT - KENITRA ONCI

	↓		⚒		⚒		A																
93	**Casablanca** Port ..... d.	...	0620	0700	0725	0800	0825	0900		1500	1525	1600	1625	1700	1725	1800	1825	1900	2000	2025	2125	2200	...
	Ain Seeba ..... d.	...	0631	0711	0736	0811	0836	0911	and hourly	1511	1536	1611	1636	1711	1736	1811	1836	1911	2011	2036	2136	2211	...
0	**Rabat** Ville ..... d.	...	0728	0811	0828	0911	0917a	1011	until	1611	1624	1711	1724	1811	1824	1911	1924	2011	2111	2124	2224	2259	...
7	Salé Ville ..... d.	...	0735	0818	0835	0918	...	1018		1618	1631	1718	1731	1824	1831	1918	1931	2018	2118	2131	2231	2306	...
40	**Kenitra** ..... a.	...	0756	0839	0856	0939	...	1039		1639	1652	1739	1752	1839	1852	1939	1952	2039	2139	2152	2252	2327	...

↓		⚒		⚒															B		
Kenitra ..... d.	...	0555	0620	0655	0720	0755	0820	0855	0955		1555	1620	1655	1720	1755	1820	1855	1920	1955	...	2120	...
Salé Ville ..... d.	...	0619	0644	0719	0744	0819	0844	0919	1019	and hourly	1619	1644	1719	1744	1819	1844	1919	1944	2019	...	2144	...
Rabat Ville ..... d.	...	0628	0653	0728	0753	0828	0853	0928	1028	until	1628	1653	1728	1753	1828	1853	1928	1953	2028	2055a	2153	...
Ain Seeba ..... a.	...	0725	0750	0825	0850	0918	0940	1025	1115		1718	1740	1825	1840	1918	1940	2025	2040	2118	2140	2240	...
Casablanca Port ..... a.	...	0735	0800	0835	0900	0928	0950	1035	1125		1728	1750	1835	1850	1928	1950	2035	2050	2128	2150	2250	...

A – Additional services: 0925, 1025, 1225, 1425, 1925.

a – **Rabat** Agdal.

B – Additional services: 0955, 1155, 1355, 1555.

ALGERIA

Capital: **Alger** (GMT +1). 2019 Public Holidays: Jan. 1, May 1, June 5, July 5, Aug. 12, 33, Sept. 1, 9, Nov. 1, 10.

Rail services are operated Société Nationale des Transports Ferroviaires (SNTF. www.sntf.dz). Unless otherwise noted, trains convey first and second class seated accommodation. Long distance overnight trains may convey sleeping cars and/or couchettes and where this is the case it will be shown in the footnotes. Timings are the most recent available and are subject to alteration at any time.

SNTF 2nd class unless indicated — ORAN - GHAZAOUET and BÉCHAR — 4010

km		2✕	2		2	2	2		✕A	
0	**Oran** d.	0830	1250	...	1600	1600	1645	...	2330	...
76	Sidi bel Abbès d.	0935	1355	...	1705	1711	1756	...	0034	...
163	Tlemcen d.	1100	1512	1700	...	1832	1917	...	|	...
219	Maghnia d.	1209	1622	1823	...	...	...	...	|	...
284	**Ghazaouet** d.	...	...	...	...	...	...	...	|	...
350	Naâma a.	...	...	...	...	...	...	...	0430	...
676	**Béchar** a.	...	...	...	...	...	...	...	0846	...

	✕A	2	✕A	2	2	2	2	2	
Béchar d.	1900	...	2300	...	...	...	...	...	...
Naâma d.	2309	...	0309	...	...	...	...	...	...
Ghazout d.	|	...	|	...	...	...	...	...	...
Maghnia d.	|	...	|	...	0650	...	0850	1405	...
Tlemcen d.	|	...	|	0610	0811	...	0955	1510	...
Sidi bel Abbès d.	0330	0540	0642	0728	...	1028	1120	1629	...
Oran a.	0500	0658	0748	0843	...	1137	1222	1726	...

A – 🛏, (12) and ✕ Oran - Béchar and v.v.

SNTF — ORAN - ALGER — 4020

km			2		2B		✕		2	2	✕	2
0	**Oran** d.	...	...	0610	...	0800	1000	1230	...	1615	1700	1730
77	Mohammadia d.	...	...	0701	0700	0851	|	1322	...	1700	|	1829
	Mostaganem a.	...	...	|	0751	|	|	|	...	|	|	|
126	Relizane d.	...	...	0734	...	0924	1115	1356	...	1731	1815	1903
213	Chlef d.	...	0505	0829	...	1019	1200	1453	1720	1835	1900	...
303	Khémis Miliana d.	...	0611	0939	...	1129	|	1610	1833	...	|	...
354	El Affroun ☆ d.	0615	0654	1023	...	1213	|	1703	...	...	|	...
372	Blida ☆ d.	0629	0710	1036	...	1226	1336	1716	...	...	2036	...
421	**Alger** Agha ☆ a.	0718	0756	1115	...	1305	1407	1754	...	...	2107	...

	2	2C	2✕	2	✕		✕		✕	2	2
Alger Agha ☆ d.	...	...	...	...	0610	0800	1000	1230	1500	1723	1803
Blida ☆ d.	...	...	...	...	0646	0842	1029	1306	1532	1802	1854
El Affroun ☆ d.	...	...	...	...	0659	0857	|	1319	|	1814	1910
Khémis Miliana d.	...	...	...	0545	0741	0943	|	1408	|	1859	...
Chlef d.	...	...	0650	0727	0845	1052	1213	1512	1705	2003	...
Relizane d.	0640	...	0752	...	0956	1205	1300	1625	1753	...	...
Mostaganem d.	|	0530	|	...	|	|	|	|	|	...	...
Mohammadia d.	0714	0621	0827	...	1029	1238	|	1658	|	...	...
Oran a.	0822	...	0915	...	1125	1334	1409	1754	1900	...	...

☆ – Additional local trains available. **B** – Additional trips: 1330, 1800. **C** – Additional trips: 1100, 1640.

SNTF — TEBESSA, TOUGGOURT and M'SILA — 4030

km		F	2	2	2
0	**Constantine** d.	...	0545	...	2345
49	Aïn M'Lila d.	...	|	...	0028
115	Oum el Bouaghi d.	...	|	...	|
212	Sidi Yahia d.	...	|	...	|
258	**Tebessa** a.	...	|	...	|
118	Batna d.	2315	0724	...	0121
151	Aïn Touta d.	2340	|	...	0158
238	Biskra d.	|	0921	1530	0329
403	Djamâa d.	|	...	1843	0502
455	**Touggourt** a.	|	...	1946	0533
202	Barika d.	|	...	...	...
299	**M'Sila** a.	0136	...	...	...

	2	2	2	F
M'Sila d.	...	...	...	1642
Barika d.	...	...	...	|
Touggourt d.	2300	...	...	|
Djamâa d.	2328	...	...	|
Biskra d.	0058	...	1625	|
Aïn Touta d.	0230	...	1756	1843
Batna d.	0255	...	1821	1909
Tebessa d.	|	...	|	...
Sidi Yahia d.	|	...	|	...
Oum el Bouaghi d.	|	...	|	...
Aïn M'Lila d.	0353	...	|	...
Constantine a.	0438	...	2006	...

SNTF — ANNABA - TEBESSA — 4035

km		2	2	2	
0	**Annaba** d.	...	...	1640	...
55	Bouchegouf d.	...	...	1752	...
90	Mechrouha d.	...	...	1848	...
107	Souk Ahras d.	0600	1335	1910	...
156	**Sidi El Hémissi** a.	0709	1444	|	...
131	Dreá d.	...	...	1957	...
163	Oued Kéberit d.	...	...	2036	...
231	**Tebessa** a.	...	...	2149	...

		2	2	2
Tebessa d.	...	0430	...	...
Oued Kéberit d.	...	0541	...	...
Dreá d.	...	0618	0719	1602
Sidi El Hémissi d.	...	|	0828	1714
Souk Ahras d.	...	0656	...	...
Mechrouha d.	...	0722	...	...
Bouchegouf d.	...	0810	...	...
Annaba a.	...	0932	...	...

SNTF 2nd class unless indicated — ALGER - CONSTANTINE - ANNABA — 4040

km						✕D	F	2		2		✕E
0	**Alger** ☆ d.	...	...	...	...	0915	1230	1430	1530	1645	...	2130
54	Thénia ☆ d.	...	...	...	...	1001	|	|	|	1736	...	2216
123	Bouira d.	...	...	...	...	1116	1412	1614	1717	1906	...	2328
	Béjaïa d.	...	...	...	...	|	|	|	|	...	1840	|
171	Beni Mansour d.	...	0535	...	1040	1201	1451	1659	1759	...	2034	0015
259	**Béjaïa** a.	...	0723		1229	|	|	1838	|	...	|	|
237	Bordj Bou Arreridj d.	0550	...	...	...	1309	1553	...	1859	...	2138	0120
289	**M'Sila** a.	0638	...	...	...	|	1642	...	|	...	|	|
308	Setif d.	▬	...	▬	...	1404	...	...	1947	...	2230	0211
464	**Constantine** a.	...	...	...	...	1606	...	...	...	...	...	0441
464	**Constantine** d.	0605	...	0718	...	...	...	...	...	...	...	0441
521	El Harrouch d.	0659	...	|	...	...	...	...	...	...	...	0544
582	El Milia d.	|	...	|	...	...	...	...	...	...	...	|
620	**Jijel** a.	|	...	|	...	...	...	...	...	...	...	|
532	Ramdane Djamel d.	0714	...	0823	...	...	...	...	...	...	...	0600
550	**Skikda** a.	0738	...	0845	...	...	...	...	...	...	...	|
557	Azzaba d.	...	...	...	...	...	...	...	...	...	...	0625
631	**Annaba** a.	...	...	...	...	...	...	...	...	...	...	0713

	✕E			2		F	✕D				
Annaba d.	2130	...	...	...	...	...	...	...	...	...	...
Azzaba d.	2226	...	...	...	...	...	...	...	...	...	...
Skikda d.	|	...	...	...	...	...	...	...	...	1720	1820
Ramdane Djamal d.	2351	...	...	...	...	...	...	...	...	1742	1841
Jijel d.	|	...	...	...	...	...	...	...	...	|	|
El Milia d.	|	...	...	...	...	...	...	...	...	|	|
El Harrouch d.	2307	...	...	...	...	...	...	...	...	|	1901
Constantine a.	0004	...	...	...	...	...	...	...	..	1852	2006
Constantine d.	0004	...	...	...	...	...	0825	0741	...	▬	▬
Setif d.	0229	...	0540	...	0600	...	1041	1007	...	...	...
M'Sila d.	|	...	|	...	|	0136	|	|	...	...	1700
Bordj Bou Arreridj d.	0321	...	0626	...	0649	0225	1122	1050	...	...	1748
Béjaïa d.	|	0800	|	0630	|	|	|	▬	1515	1700	...
Beni Mansour d.	0436	1007	0728	0808	0800	0329	1234	...	1648	1859	...
Béjaïa d.	|	▬	|	|	0949	|	|	...	|	...	...
Bouira d.	0528	0535	0757	0853	...	0418	1318	1650	1730	...	...
Thénia ☆ d.	0651	0700	|	|	...	|	1401	1804	1836	...	...
Alger ☆ a.	0750	0753	1001	1044	...	0600	1513	1850a	1922	...	...

D – (1) and ✕ Alger - Constantine and v.v. **E** – 🛏 (12) and ✕ Alger - Annaba and v.v. **F** – (12) and ✕ Alger - Batna and v.v. **a** – Alger Agha.
☆ – Additional local trains available.

TUNISIA

Capital: **Tunis** (GMT +1). 2019 Public Holidays: Jan. 1, 14, Mar. 20 Apr. 9, May 1, June 5, July 25, Aug. 12, Sept. 1, Oct. 15, Nov. 10.

Rail services are operated Société Nationale des Chemins de Fer Tunisiens (SNCFT. www.sncft.com). Unless otherwise noted, trains convey first and second class seated accommodation. Long distance overnight trains may convey sleeping cars and/or couchettes and where this is the case it will be shown in the footnotes. Timings are the most recent available and are subject to alteration at any time especially during Ramadan.

SNCFT offers the **Carte Bleue** pass. The pass allows unlimited travel on all scheduled SNCFT services (except the Lézard Rouge tourist train) for a period of 7, 15, or 21 days, and are available for each of the three classes of accommodation. Supplements are payable in advance for using certain services. For more information, please visit the website of the European agent www.fahrplancenter.com Prices (in Euros): Grand Confort Class 7 days 31.00, 15 days 62.00, 21 days 93.00. First Class 7 days 28.00, 15 days 56.00, 21 days, 84.00. Second Class 7 days 20,00, 15 days 40.00, 21 days 60.00.

SNCFT — GHARDIMAOU - TUNIS — 4050

km		①–⑥	①–⑥				A ②④⑦			
167	**Annaba** d.	...	...	...	...	...	0800	...	...	...
0	**Ghardimaou** a.	...	...	...	...	...	1230	...	...	...
0	**Ghardimaou** d.	...	...	0500	1005	1225	1325	1535	...	...
34	Jendouba d.	...	...	0527	1034	1248	1350	1600	...	...
92	Béja d.	...	0520	0621	1127	1334	1436	1649	...	...
177	Tebourba d.	0545	|	0747	1247	|	|	1707	...	...
186	Jedeïa d.	0554	0652	0757	1258	1458	|	1818	...	...
211	**Tunis** Ville a.	0632	0733	0839	1343	1538	1618	1918	...	...

			A ①③⑤			⑥			①–⑤
Tunis Ville d.	...	0550	0825	0955	1300	1625	1710	...	1840
Jedeïa d.	...	0633	0856	1035	1342	1705	1754	...	1922
Tebourba d.	...	0642	|	1043	1351	1713	1805	...	1932
Béja d.	...	0801	1009	1158	1509	1822	1930	...	2041
Jendouba d.	...	0849	1047	1247	1601	...	2024	...	...
Ghardimaou a.	...	0910	1121	1307	1627	...	2050	...	...
Ghardimaou d.	...	...	1300	...	...	...	...	...	...
Annaba d.	...	...	1630	...	...	...	...	...	...

A – Subject to confirmation.

SNCFT — BIZERTE - TUNIS — 4060

km		⚒			Ⓐ					
0	**Bizerte** d.	0455	0745	1430	1810	...	...	...	...	...
34	Mateur d.	0540	0818	1503	1844	...	...	...	...	...
73	Jedeïda d.	0632	0854	1544	1929	...	...	...	...	...
98	**Tunis** Ville a.	0712	0936	1624	2009	...	...	...	...	...

	⚒		⑥	⑦–①	Ⓐ				
Tunis Ville d.	0510	1215	1500	1540	1820	...	...	...	...
Jedeïda d.	0550	1259	1543	1625	1900	...	...	...	...
Mateur d.	0632	1334	1624	1705	1936	...	...	...	...
Bizerte a.	0703	1405	1656	1737	2007	...	...	...	...

4070 KALAÂ KASBAH - TUNIS — SNCFT

km			⊡			⊡	1	1	⚒⊡		
0	**Tunis** Ville	d.	0550	0900	...	1400	1550	1635	1815	...	...
63	Pont du Fahs	d.	0708	0956	...	1516	1650	1731	1929	...	...
120	Gaafour	d.	0758	1033	...	1609	1730	1808	2018	...	...
166	Le Sers	d.	0855	1118	...	1705	1815	1853	2113	...	...
191	Dahmani	d.	0924	1140	...	1735	|	1915	2140	...	...
214	Jerissa	d.	|	...	...	|	|	1951	...	...	...
224	**Tajerouine**	a.	|	...	...	|	|	2010	...	...	...
235	**Kalaâ Kasbah**	a.	1026	...	...	1835	|	...	...	...	...
202	**El Kef**	a.	...	...	...	...	1851	...	...	...	...

		⚒⊡	⚒	⚒	⊡		†	†		
El Kef	d.	...	0505	...	...	...	1315	...	...	
Kalaâ Kasbah	d.	...	|	...	0555	...	|	...	1400	...
Tajerouine	d.	...	|	0505	|	...	|	1340	|	...
Jerissa	d.		|	0525	|	...	|	1400	|	...
Dahmani	d.	0400	|	0559	0658	1255	|	1435	1504	...
Le Sers	d.	0428	0540	0617	0726	1313	1352	1453	1533	...
Gaafour	d.	0531	0628	0706	0826	1359	1440	1538	1634	...
Pont du Fahs	d.	0623	0707	|	0916	1436	1517	1616	1732	...
Tunis Ville	a.	0742	0800	0837	1036	1536	1611	1713	1847	...

⊡ – Supplement payable.

4080 TUNIS - SOUSSE - SFAX - TOZEUR — SNCFT

km				⊡		⊡		⊡		⊡	⊡		①-④	⚒⊡	1			⚒	⊡	⊡		⊡		⊡	🚌
0	**Tunis** Ville	d.	...	0545	...	0835	...	0930	...	1220	1305	...	...	1535	1620	...	1720	1745	1800	1845	...	2035	...	2145	...
23	Borj Cédria	◇ d.	0650	|	...	|	0930	|	1045	|	|	1350	1615	|	|	1715	|	1815	|	|	1945	|	...	|	...
59	Bir Bou Rekba	◇ d.	0731	0644	...	0937	1003	1028	1126	1313	1400	1423	1648	1634	|	1752	1814	1850	1858	1949	2022	2132	...	2241	...
64	Hammamet	◇ d.	0736	|	...	|	1008	|	1131	|	|	1428	1653	|	|	1757	|	1855	|	|	2027	|	...	|	...
76	**Nabeul**	◇ a.	0757	|	...	|	1029	|	1152	|	|	1449	1714	|	|	1818	|	1916	|	|	2048	|	...	|	...
142	Kalaâ Séghira	d.	...	0745	...	|	...	1128	...	|	1458	...	...	1743	1802	...	1904	...	2000	2054	...	|	...	|	...
149	**Sousse**	d.	...	0805	...	1055	...	|	...	1429	|	...	...	1752	|	...	|	...	|	2102	...	2250	...	0000	...
174	Monastir	d.	...	|	...	|	...	1202	...	1509	|	...	...	...	|	...	1945	...	|	...	...	|	...	|	...
217	**Mahdia**	a.	...	|	...	|	...	...	...	...	|	...	...	...	|	...	2035	...	2117	...	...	|	...	|	...
215	El Jem	d.	...	0903	...	1154	...	...	...	...	1551	...	...	...	|	...	...	...	2206	...	...	2348	...	0103	...
278	**Sfax**	d.	...	1000	...	1300	...	...	...	...	1643	...	...	...	1935	...	...	...	...	...	...	0040	...	2000	...
340	Ghraïba	d.	...	1052	...	1356	...	...	...	...	1735	...	...	...	|	...	...	...	...	...	...	0134	...	|	...
422	**Gabès**	a.	...	1204	...	|	...	...	...	...	1843	...	...	...	2125	...	...	...	...	...	...	|	...	0400	0410
	Tataouine	a.	...	...	...	|	...	...	...	...	...	...	...	...	...	...	...	...	...	...	...	|	...	...	0632
482	Gafsa	d.	...	...	...	1632	...	...	...	...	...	...	...	...	...	...	...	...	...	...	...	0347	0645	...	...
521	Metlaoui	d.	...	...	...	1710	...	...	...	...	...	...	...	...	...	...	...	...	...	...	...	0424	0720	...	...
574	**Tozeur**	a.	...	...	...	1758	...	...	...	...	...	...	...	...	...	...	...	...	...	...	...	0512	0808	...	...

			⊡	🚌	⊡	⚒	⚒⊡	⊡			⊡	1					⊡		⊡		⊡	①-④	1		
Tozeur	d.	...	2030	...	...	...	...	...	...	...	...	...	...	...	...	...	...	...	0830	...	...	...	...	...	1830
Metlaoui	d.	...	2121	...	...	...	...	...	...	...	...	...	...	...	...	...	...	...	0922	...	...	...	...	...	1919
Gafsa	d.	...	2200	...	...	...	...	...	...	...	...	...	...	...	...	...	...	...	1001	...	...	...	...	...	1954
Tataouine	d.	...	|	2100	...	...	...	...	...	...	...	...	...	...	...	...	...	...	|	...	...	...	...	...	...
Gàbes	d.	...	|	2355	0005	...	...	...	...	...	...	0500	...	...	...	...	1000	...	|	...	...	...	1515	...	...
Ghraïba	d.	...	0011	...	|	...	...	...	...	...	...	|	...	...	...	...	1118	...	1212	...	...	...	1628	...	...
Sfax	d.	...	0105	...	0215	...	...	...	...	...	0530	0653	...	...	...	...	1215	...	1320	...	...	...	1725	...	...
El Jem	d.	...	0157	...	0303	...	...	...	...	...	0639	|	...	...	...	...	1303	...	1410	...	...	...	1814	...	...
Mahdia	d.	...	|	...	|	...	...	...	...	0537	|	|	...	...	...	...	|	...	|	...	...	...	|	...	...
Monastir	d.	...	|	...	|	...	...	...	...	0635	|	|	...	...	...	1235	|	...	|	...	1640	...	|	...	...
Sousse	d.	...	0305	...	0410	...	0455	0550	...	|	0730	0840	...	...	...	1330	|	...	1515	...	1730	...	|	...	...
Kalaâ Seghira	d.	...	|	...	|	...	0503	0559	...	0706	|	|	...	...	...	|	1354	...	|	...	|	...	1907	...	...
Nabeul	◇ d.	...	|	...	|	0530	|	|	0705	|	|	|	0820	...	1220	|	|	1510	|	1610	|	1725	|	1825	...
Hammamet	◇ d.	...	|	...	|	0549	|	|	0724	|	|	|	0839	...	1239	|	|	1529	|	1629	|	1744	|	1844	...
Bir Bou Rekba	◇ d.	...	0410	...	0513	0556	0611	0659	0731	0753	0835	0943	0847	...	1245	1439	1454	1536	1621	1636	1838	1750	2009	1852	...
Borj Cédria	◇ d.	...	|	...	|	0631	0647	0730	0805	0822	0904	|	0921	...	1318	|	|	1609	|	1709	|	...	|	1925	...
Tunis Ville	a.	...	0512	...	0610	0702	0715	0757	0830	0849	0933	1038	...	...	...	1540	1552	...	1724	...	1941	...	2111	...	...

⊡ – Supplement payable. ◇ – Additional services available with connections from/to Tunis. Depart Borj Cédria: 1210. Depart Nabeul: 0530, 1100.

4090 SOUSSE - MONASTIR AIRPORT - MAHDIA — SNCFT

km			501 ⚒	505 ⚒	507	509 ⚒	511	513 ⚒	517	519 ⚒	521	523	523	527	529	531	533	535	537	539	541	543	545	547	549
0	**Sousse** Bab El Jedid	d.	0455	0545	0630	0710	0750	0830	0910	0950	1030	1100	1150	1230	1310	1350	1420	1510	1550	1635	1710	1750	1835	1930	2000
3	**Sousse** Sud	d.	0501	0551	0636	0716	0756	0836	0916	0956	1036	1106	1156	1236	1316	1356	1426	1516	1556	1641	1716	1756	1841	1936	2006
15	Monastir Airport ✈	d.	0515	0605	0650	0730	0810	0850	0930	1010	1050	1120	1210	1250	1330	1410	1440	1530	1610	1655	1730	1810	1855	1950	2020
24	Monastir	d.	0530	0620	0705	0745	0825	0900	0945	1025	1105	1135	1225	1305	1345	1425	1500	1545	1630	1710	1750	1830	1910	2010	2041
47	Moknine	d.	0607	0652	0736	0819	0901	...	1016	1057	1137	1216	1256	1338	1416	1459	1530	1618	1701	1744	1824	1905	1946	2041	2111
73	**Mahdia**	a.	0645	0730	0815	0855	0935	...	1050	...	1210	1250	1330	...	1451	1534	...	1652	1736	1817	1858	1939	2020	2114	2144

		506 ⚒	508	510 ⚒	512 ⚒	514 ⚒	516	518	522	524	528	530 ⚒	532	534	536	538	540	542	544	546		548	550	552	554
Mahdia	d.	0440	0510	0555	0615	...	0700	0745	0825	0905	1020	...	1140	1220	1300	...	1420	...	1545	1620	...	1705	1745	1825	1910
Moknine	d.	0513	0542	0630	0657	0717	0733	0820	0900	0940	1100	1136	1216	1255	1335	1415	1457	1545	1620	1657	...	1743	1823	1906	1944
Monastir	d.	0550	0625	0710	0740	0800	0815	0900	0940	1020	1140	1220	1255	1335	1415	1455	1535	1625	1700	1735	...	1825	1900	1946	2020
Monastir Airport ✈	d.	0600	0635	0720	0750	0810	0825	0910	0950	1030	1150	1229	1304	1345	1425	1505	1545	1634	1710	1745	...	1835	1910	1956	2030
Sousse Sud	d.	0615	0652	0735	0805	0825	0840	0925	1005	1045	1205	1245	1320	1400	1440	1520	1600	1651	1725	1800	...	1850	1925	2011	2045
Sousse Bab El Jedid	a.	0620	0657	0740	0810	0830	0845	0930	1010	1050	1210	1250	1325	1405	1445	1525	1605	1656	1730	1805	...	1855	1930	2016	2050

EGYPT

Capital: **Cairo** (GMT +2). 2019 Public Holidays: Jan. 7, 25, Apr. 25, 28, 29, May 1, June 5 - 7, 30, July 23, Aug. 11 - 15, Sept. 1, Oct. 6, Nov. 10.

Rail services are operated Egyptian National Railways (ENR. www.enr.gov.eg). Unless otherwise noted, trains convey first and second class seated accommodation. Long distance overnight trains may convey sleeping cars and/or couchettes and where this is the case it will be shown in the footnotes. Timings are the most recent available and are subject to alteration at any time.

4100 MERSA MATRUH - CAIRO and ALEXANDRIA — Egyptian National Railways

km			2	A	2	774					
0	**Mersa Matruh**	d.	0705	1335	1545	2200	...	...	...	...	...
84	El Alamein	d.	1024	1620	1830	|	...	...	...	...	...
311	**Alexandria**	a.	1330	|	2115	|	...	...	...	...	...
509	**Cairo** Main	a.	...	2135	...	0540	...	...	...	...	...

		2	A	2	773					
Cairo Main	d.	...	0640	...	2330	...	...	...	...	...
Alexandria	d.	0640	|	1330	|	...	...	...	...	...
El Alamein	d.	0924	1145	1717	|	...	...	...	...	...
Mersa Matruh	a.	1205	1415	2020	0645	...	...	...	...	...

773/4 – 🛏 (1, 2 class). July - Sept. From Mersa on ②④⑦, from Cairo on ①③⑥. see www.wataniasleepingtrains.com. **A** – June – Sept. only.

4110 CAIRO - ALEXANDRIA — Egyptian National Railways

km			941	1205	903	945	965	905	901	909	911	89	913	949	917	919	955	2001	1915	915	923	925	959	921	927	931	935
0	**Cairo** Main	d.	0515	0530	0600	0610	0730	0800	0810	0900	1000	1100	1230	1320	1400	1425	1440	1500	1510	1520	1600	1700	1710	1800	2000	2015	2230
45	Benha	d.	0608	0614	0640	0948	0810	|	0850	|	1040	|	1308	1406	|	1505	1528	|	1548	1600	1640	1740	1754	|	|	2056	|
86	Tanta	d.	...	0659	0727	...	0850	|	0927	|	1118	1208	1341	1450	|	1609	...	|	...	1638	1728	1827	...	1907	|	2143	2337
147	Damanhūr	d.	...	...	0829	...	...	|	1017	|	1209	|	1426	...	|	1709	...	|	...	1729	1829	1924	...	|	|	2239	|
208	**Alexandria**	a.	...	...	0920	...	...	1025	1110	1145	1300	1335	1515	...	1625	1800	...	1725	...	1820	1925	2015	...	2035	2230	2330	0105

		936	944	946	948	1904	902	906	952	904	900	912	1208	914	916	956	918	966	922	928	88	994	926	2008	930	934
Alexandria	d.	...	...	...	...	...	0600	0700	...	0800	0815	1130	...	1300	1400	...	1500	...	1530	1600	1700	...	1945	2000	2010	2200
Damanhūr	d.	...	...	...	...	...	0656	|	...	|	0912	1226	1318	1356	|	...	|	...	1628	|	|	...	|	|	2106	|
Tanta	d.	0600	...	...	0655	0710	0754	|	...	|	1000	1315	1405	1455	|	...	|	1640	1725	1737	1833	1900	|	2128	2200	2343
Benha	d.	0651	0651	0711	0740	0755	0840	|	0906	|	1035	1400	1450	1540	|	1640	|	1725	1803	|	|	1945	|	|	2235	|
Cairo Main	a.	0725	0735	0800	0825	0835	0920	0930	0950	1025	1115	1440	1535	1620	1630	1725	1740	1805	1845	1845	1935	2025	2225	2230	2315	0045

ALEXANDRIA and CAIRO - DUMYAT 4120

Egyptian National Railways 2nd class only

km																				
240	**Alexandria** d.	...	...	1815	...	...	...	...	...	...	**Dumyat** d.	0640	0715	1315	1615	...	...	...	...	...
205	**Cairo** Main d.	0515	0730	|	1935	...	...	...	...	...	**Cairo** Main a.	1005	|	1810	2025	...	...	...	...	...
0	**Dumyat** a.	1015	1130	2255	2355	...	...	...	...	...	**Alexandria** a.	...	1220	...	...	...	...	...	...	...

All services are subject to confirmation.

ALEXANDRIA and CAIRO - BÛR SA'ÎD 4130

Egyptian National Railways 2nd class only

km																				
			12	12			12							12		12	12			
334	**Alexandria** d.	...	0430	...	...	1610	...	...	...	...	**Bûr Sa'îd** d.	0530	0725	0930	1300	1730	1815	1815	...	...
236	**Cairo** Main d.	0610	|	1345	1440	|	1945	...	...	...	**Cairo** Main a.	0950	|	1335	1725	2135	|	0050	...	...
0	**Bûr Sa'îd** a.	1030	1110	1800	1905	2225	2350	...	...	...	**Alexandria** a.	...	1325	...	...	...	0045	...	...	...

All services are subject to confirmation.

CAIRO - EL SUWEIS 4140

Egyptian National Railways 2nd class only

km																				
0	**Cairo** Ain Shams d.	0630	0510**n**	0920	1310	1615	1845	2145	...	...	**El Suweis** d.	0600	1010	1310	1525	1550	1900	2125	...	...
127	**El Suweis** a.	0840	0950	1135	1520	1830	2100	2400	...	...	**Cairo** Ain Shams a.	0815	1215	1525	2005**n**	1805	2110	2335	...	...

All services are subject to confirmation.

n – Cairo Main.

CAIRO - ASWÂN 4150

Egyptian National Railways

km		1902	934	980	982	986	86 B	988	88	996	2008
0	**Cairo** Main ◇ d.	0015	0110	0800	1200	1300	1945	1900	2000	2200	2300
13	El Giza ◇ d.	0045	0140	0825	1225	1325	2015	1925	2025	2230	2330
124	Béni Suef ◇ d.	|	0259	0943	1349	1442	|	2044	2147	2348	|
247	El Menya ◇ d.	|	0435	1120	1520	1620	|	2220	2330	|	|
375	Asyût ◇ d.	0505	0630	1310	1715	1825	|	0010	0135	0310	0350
467	Sohâg ◇ d.	0650	0800	1455	1905	2000	|	0130	0300	0435	0510
609	Qena ◇ d.	0850	1000	1720	2130	2230	|	0330	0540	0640	0715
671	Luxor ◇ d.	0945	1045	1825	2235	2340	0545	0430	0645	0735	0815
879	**Aswân** a.	1245	...	2150	0150	...	0850	0730	1010	1040	1110

	981	983	935	2007	1903	87 B	997	89	989	987
Aswân d.	0530	0730	...	1500	1645	1700	2015	2030	2200	...
Luxor ◇ d.	0910	1055	1230	1820	2000	2010	2335	2359	0115	0415
Qena ◇ d.	1015	1200	1325	1915	2050	|	0030	0105	0205	0600
Sohâg ◇ d.	1255	1435	1535	2135	2300	|	0240	0340	0410	0840
Asyût ◇ d.	1435	1625	1700	2305	0040	|	0405	0510	0535	1015
El Menya ◇ d.	1625	1820	1855	0055	|	|	0600	0705	0725	1220
Béni Suef ◇ d.	1754	1948	2019	|	|	|	0730	0835	0854	1354
El Giza ◇ d.	|	2110	|	|	0500	0530	0855	|	1020	1515
Cairo Main ◇ a.	1935	2130	2205	0400	0520	0550	0915	1025	1040	1535

B – (1, 2 class). www.wataniasleepingtrains.com.

◇ – Additional services available.

OTHER AFRICAN STATES

For details of capital cities and public holiday dates please see individual tables.

Unless otherwise noted, trains convey first and second class seated accommodation. Some operators also offer third class seating. This will not normally be mentioned in the tables, and where it is the only class available will be noted as second class. Long distance overnight trains may convey sleeping cars and/or couchettes. As a general rule, first class sleepers have two berths per cabin, whilst second class has four. The standard of accommodation varies widely with no two countries beng the same. Timings are the latest available and are valid until further notice, but may change at any time so we suggest you confirm them locally before travelling. In Muslim countries a different timetable may be operated during the festival of Ramadan.

SUDAN and SOUTH SUDAN 4200

Sudan Railways Corporation

Sudan: **Khartoum** (GMT +2). 2019 Public Holidays: Jan. 1, 8, Apr. 28, June 5, 30, Aug. 12, Sept. 1, Nov. 10.
South Sudan: **Juba** (GMT +3). 2019 Public Holidays: Jan. 1, 9, May 1, 16, June 5, July 9, 30, Aug. 12, Dec. 25, 28, 31.

km		222	101	212	551	202	D01			
		②	④A	E	B	④C	④D			
926	**Wadi Halfa** d.	1800**b**	...	...	...	0200**d**	...	...	...	...
576	Abu Hamed d.	0600**c**	...	...	...	0800**e**	...	...	...	...
551	Dagash d.	...	...	...	...	1030**e**	...	...	...	...
351	Berber d.	...	...	...	...	2300**e**	...	...	...	...
810	**Bûr Sûdan** d.	...	1530**d**	...	...	|	...	...	...	...
	Sinkat d.	...	2000**d**	...	...	|	...	...	...	...
720	Gebeit d.	...	2240**d**	...	...	|	...	...	...	...
620	Haiya Junction d.	...	0445**e**	...	...	|	...	...	...	...
310	**Atbara** a.	...	1255**e**	...	...	2345**e**	...	...	...	...
310	**Atbara** d.	...	...	2130	...	0200**f**	...	...	...	...
295	Ed Dâmer d.	...	...	2300	...	0300**g**	...	...	...	...
170	Shendî d.	...	...	0300	...	0930**g**	...	...	...	...
0	**Khartoum** Bahri a.	...	...	0730	...	1700**g**	...	...	...	...
0	**Khartoum** Bahri d.	...	...	...	...	...	2000**d**	...	...	...
270	Sennâr Junction d.	...	...	...	...	...	0600**e**	...	...	...
383	Kôsti d.	...	...	...	...	...	1030**e**	...	...	...
470	Tendelti d.	...	...	...	...	...	1500**e**	...	...	...
605	Er Rahad d.	...	...	...	⊖	...	2100**e**	...	...	...
629	**El Obeid** a.	...	...	...	|	...	2230**e**	...	...	...
983	Babanusa d.	...	...	...	⊖	...	...	...	...	...
	El Daien d.	...	...	...	⊖	...	...	...	...	...
1318	**Nyâlâ** a.	...	...	...	⊖	...	...	...	...	...

	552	221	201	502	102	211			
	B	④	①C	①D	①A	E			
Nyâlâ d.	⊖	...	...	...	...	...	...	...	...
El Daien d.	⊖	...	...	...	...	...	...	...	...
Babanusa d.	⊖	...	...	...	...	...	...	...	...
El Obeid d.	|	...	...	0700**a**	...	...	...	...	...
Er Rahad d.	⊖	...	...	0830**a**	...	...	...	...	...
Tendelti d.	...	...	...	1445**a**	...	...	...	...	...
Kôsti d.	...	...	...	1930**a**	...	...	...	...	...
Sennâr Junction d.	...	...	...	0000**b**	...	...	...	...	...
Khartoum Bahri a.	...	...	...	1030**b**	...	...	...	...	...
Khartoum Bahri d.	...	...	0800**a**	...	...	2130	...	...	...
Shendî d.	...	...	1545**a**	...	...	0200	...	...	...
Ed Dâmer d.	...	...	2200**a**	...	...	0600	...	...	...
Atbara a.	...	...	2300**a**	...	...	0730	...	...	...
Atbara d.	...	...	0100**b**	...	2000**a**	...	...	...	...
Haiya Junction d.	...	...	|	...	0415**b**	...	...	...	...
Gebeit d.	...	...	|	...	1015**b**	...	...	...	...
Sinkat d.	...	...	|	...	1120**b**	...	...	...	...
Bûr Sûdan a.	...	...	|	...	1545**b**	...	...	...	...
Berber d.	...	...	0345**b**	...	...	...	...	...	...
Dagash d.	...	...	1530**b**	...	...	...	...	...	...
Abu Hamed d.	...	1730**d**	1745**b**	...	...	...	...	...	...
Wadi Halfa a.	...	0545**e**	2230**b**	...	...	...	...	...	...

A – 12 From Bûr Sûdan 1st and 3rd ④ of each month, from Atbara on following ①. Service temporarily withdrawn March 2014.
B – 1 cl., 2 . From El Rahad/ Nyâlâ every two weeks day and time not fixed.
C – 1 cl., 2 . From Khartoum on 1st and 3rd ① of each month, from Wadi Halfa on following ④. Service temporarily withdrawn March 2014.
D – 1 cl., 2 cl., 3 and . From Khartoum on 2nd ④ of each month, from El Obeid on following ①. Service temporarily withdrawn March 2014. Not operated by SRC.
E – 1 cl., 23 .

a – ①. **b** – ②. **c** – ③. **d** – ④. **e** – ⑤. **f** – ⑥. **g** – ⑦.

⊖ – No timings available.

ERITREA 4210

Chemins de Fer d'Eritrea

km		①–⑥ 2	A	⑦ B		①–⑥ 2	A	⑦ B
0	**Mitsiwa** d.	⊖	A	...	**Asmara** d.	...	A	0800
5	Otumlo d.	⊖	|	...	Nefasit d.	...	A	0915
8	Moncullo d.	...	A	...	Ghinda d.	...	A	...
70	Ghinda d.	...	A	...	Moncullo d.	...	A	...
92	Nefasit d.	...	A	1000	Otumlo d.	⊖	|	...
118	**Asmara** a.	...	A	1200	**Mitsiwa** a.	⊖	A	...

Capital: **Asmara** (GMT +3). 2019 Public Holidays: Jan. 1, 7, Mar. 8, Apr. 19, 21, May 24, June 5, 20, Aug. 12, Sept. 1, 12, 27, Nov. 10, Dec. 25.

A – No regular service. Charter service available. **B** – Minimum 10 passengers required.
⊖ – No information available.

ETHIOPIA 4215

Chemins de Fer Djibouti Ethiopien

km		A			B	
0	**Addis Abeba** Sebeta d.	⊗	...	**Djibouti** Nagad d.	0800	...
	Addis Abeba Lebu d.	0800	...	Ali Sabieh d.	0856	...
115	Adama d.	0951	...	Dewelé a.	1000	...
	Mieso d.	⊗	...	**Diré Daoua** a.	1229	...
	Diré Daoua a.	1438	...	**Diré Daoua** d.	1239	...
	Diré Daoua d.	1448	...	Mieso d.	⊗	...
	Dewelé a.	1800	...	Adama d.	1636	...
	Ali Sabieh d.	1830	...	**Addis Abeba** Lebu d.	1917	...
752	**Djibouti** Nagad a.	1753	...	**Addis Abeba** Sebeta a.	⊗	...

Capital: **Addis Abeba** (GMT +3). 2019 Public Holidays: Jan. 7, 20, Mar. 2, Apr. 26, 28, May 1, 5, 28, June 5, Aug. 12, Sept. 12, 27, Nov. 10.

A – Runs on odd numbered dates except the 31st.
B – Runs on even numbered dates.

⊗ – Schedules not available at publication date.

MAURITANIA 4220

SNIM 2nd class only

km						
0	**Nouadhibou** d.	1450	...	**Zouèrate** d.	1215	...
652	**Zouèrate** a.	0540	...	**Nouadhibou** a.	0618	...

Capital: **Nouakchott** (GMT +0). 2019 Public Holidays: Jan. 1, May 1, 25, June 5, Aug. 12, Sept. 1, Nov. 10, 28. SNIM – Société Nationale Industrielle et Minière.

4230 GUINEA

2nd class only — Chemins de Fer Guinea, Chemins de Fer de Boké

km		①–⑤	①–⑤	①–⑤
0	**Conakry** Portovoya d.	...	0847	1725
	Simbaya d.	0600	0940	1829
36	**Halte Km 36** a.	0640	...	1906

	①–⑤	①–⑤	①–⑤
Halte Km 36 d.	0645	...	1916
Simbaya d.	0730	1630	1950
Conakry P'voya a.	0837	1710	...

km		B		
0	**Kamsar** d.	0930	...	...
55	Boké d.	1135	...	...
136	**Sangaredi** a.	1355	...	...

	B		
Sangaredi d.	1430	...	...
Boké d.	1615	...	...
Kamsar a.	1855	...	...

Capital: **Conakry** (GMT +0).

2019 Public Holidays: Apr. 22, May 1, 25, 31, June 5, Aug. 12, 15, Oct. 2, Nov. 10, Dec. 2

B – ①④⑤⑦.

4240 MALI

2nd class only — Transrail

km		B		
0	**Kayes** d.	0715	...	...
160	Bafoulabé d.	1130	...	...
308	Kita d.	1805	...	...
468	Kati d.	2250	...	...
493	**Bamako** a.	2345	...	...

	A		
Bamako d.	0715	...	...
Kati d.	0815	...	...
Kita d.	1300	...	...
Bafoulabé d.	1935	...	...
Kayes d.	2350	...	...

Capital: **Bamako** (GMT +0).

2019 Public Holidays: Mar. 26, Apr. 22, May 1, 25, June 5, 10, Aug. 12, Sept. 22, Nov. 1
Dec. 25.

A – ①②④⑥.
B – ②③⑤⑦.

4250 GHANA

Ghana Railway Corporation

km		A		
0	**Takoradi** d.	2030	...	...
276	**Kumasi** a.	0930a	...	...

	A		
Kumasi d.	2030	...	...
Takoradi a.	0930a	...	...

km		2B	2B	2B
0	**Accra** d.	0740	1000	1400
40	**Nsawam** a.	0920	1140	1540

	2B	2B	2B
Nsawam d.	0600	1140	1220
Accra a.	0740	1320	1400

A – Service suspended. a – Approximate timings.
B – ①–⑥. Additional trains from Accra at 1900, from Nsawam at 1730.

km		①–⑥	①–⑥	①–⑥
0	**Accra** d.	0500	1215	1700
	Asoprochona a.	0558	1313	1759
	Tema a.	0625	...	1825

	①–⑥	①–⑥	①-⑥
Tema d.	0630	...	1830
Asoprochona d.	0655	1415	1855
Accra a.	0755	1515	1955

Capital: **Accra** (GMT +0).

2019 Public Holidays: Jan. 1, Mar. 6, Apr. 19, 22, May, 1, 25, 27, June 5, Aug. 12, Sept. 21, 2
Dec. 6, 25, 26.

4260 BURKINA FASO - CÔTE D'IVOIRE

Sitarail

km		②④⑥ 2	⑥ A
0	**Ouagadougou** d.	...	⊖
93	Koudougou d.	...	⊖
349	Bobo Dioulasso d.	...	1400
446	Banfora d.	...	1715
495	Niangoloko 🏛 d.	...	2030
539	Ouangolodougou d.	...	2200
576	Ferkessédougou d.	...	2310
658	Tafiré d.	...	0125
769	Katiola d.	...	0430
820	Bouaké d.	...	0645
958	Dimbokro d.	0900	0955
1064	Agboville d.	1255	1219
1115	Anyama d.	1515	1344
1141	**Abidjan** Plateau a.	1610	|
1143	**Abidjan** Treichville a.	1625	1430

	①③⑤ 2	④ A
Abidjan Treichville d.	0900	0700
Abidjan Plateau d.	0920	|
Anyama d.	1015	0755
Agboville d.	1240	0918
Dimbokro d.	1615	1140
Bouaké d.	...	1515
Katiola d.	...	1730
Tafiré d.	...	2020
Ferkessédougou d.	...	2235
Ouangolodougou d.	...	2345
Niangoloko 🏛 d.	...	0215
Banfora d.	...	0345
Bobo Dioulasso d.	...	0700
Koudougou d.	...	⊖
Ouagadougou a.	...	⊖

Capitals: **Ouagadougou** (Burkina Faso, GMT +0), **Yamoussoukro** (Côte d'Ivoire, GMT +0
2019 Public Holidays:
Burkina Faso: Jan. 1, Apr. 22, May 1, 10, June 5, Aug. 12, 15, Nov. 1, 10, Dec. 25.
Côte d'Ivoire: Jan. 1, Apr. 22, May 1, 30, 31, June 5, 10, Aug. 7, 12, Nov. 1, 10, 15, Dec. 2

A – (12) and 🍷 Abidjan - Ouagadougou and v.v. Journey time 43 - 48 hours.
⊖ – No timings available.

4270 NIGERIA

Nigerian Railways Corporation

Capital: **Abuja** (GMT +1). 2019 Public Holidays: Jan. 1, Apr. 19, 22, May 1, 29, Jun. 5, 6, Aug. 12, 13, Oct. 1, Nov. 10, Dec. 25, 26.

km		⑤A	⑤B	②⑤⑥
0	**Lagos** Terminal d.	1200	...	0900
14	Agege d.	⊖	...	⊖
91	Abeokuta d.	⊖	...	⊖
193	Ibadan d.	⊖	...	⊖
280	Ede d.	⊖	...	⊖
295	Oshogbo d.	⊖	...	⊖
391	Ilorin d.	⊖	...	1834
488	Jebba d.	⊖	...	...
685	Zungeru d.	⊖	...	...
744	Minna d.	⊖	...	...
902	**Kaduna** Junction d.	⊖	⊖	...
986	Zaria d.	⊖	⊖	...
1126	**Kano** a.	1701a	⊖	...

	①A	⑤B	③⑥⑦
Kano d.	0900	⊖	...
Zaria d.	⊖	⊖	...
Kaduna Junction d.	⊖	⊖	...
Minna d.	⊖	...	...
Zungeru d.	⊖	...	...
Jebba d.	⊖	...	...
Ilorin d.	⊖	...	0900
Oshogbo d.	⊖	...	⊖
Ede d.	⊖	...	⊖
Ibadan d.	⊖	...	⊖
Abeokuta d.	⊖	...	⊖
Agege d.	⊖	...	⊖
Lagos Terminal a.	1424a	...	2059

km		C	⑤B
0	**Port Harcourt** New d.	⊖	⊖
63	Aba d.	⊖	⊖
113	Umuahia Ibeku d.	⊖	⊖
243	Enugu d.	⊖	⊖
375	Oturkpo d.	⊖	⊖
463	Makurdi d.	⊖	⊖
565	Lafia d.	⊖	⊖
737	Kafanchan d.	⊖	⊖
916	**Kaduna** Junction d.	⊖	⊖
1333	Bauchi d.	⊖	...
1499	Gombe d.	⊖	...
1658	Buni d.	⊖	...
1801	**Maiduguri** a.	⊖	...

	C	⑤B
Maiduguri d.	⊖	...
Buni d.	⊖	...
Gombe d.	⊖	...
Bauchi d.	⊖	...
Kaduna Junction d.	⊖	⊖
Kafanchan d.	⊖	⊖
Lafia d.	⊖	⊖
Makurdi d.	⊖	⊖
Oturkpo d.	⊖	⊖
Enugu d.	⊖	⊖
Umuahia Ibeku d.	⊖	⊖
Aba d.	⊖	⊖
P Harcourt New a.	⊖	⊖

A – Conveys 🛏 (1 cl.), (2) and ✕.
B – Port Harcourt - Kaduna - Kano and v.v.
C – Port Harcourt - Kaduna - Maiduguri and v.v. Once per week in each direction. Subject to confirmation.
a – Next day.
⊖ – No timings available.

4280 CAMEROON

Camrail

Capital: **Youandé** (GMT +1). 2019 Public Holidays: Jan. 1, Feb. 11, Apr. 19, May 1, 20, 30, Jun. 5, Aug. 12, 15, Nov. 10, Dec. 25.

km		151 A	181	103 ①③⑤	191 B	153 A	113 ②④⑥				
0	**Douala** Bessengué d.	0600	0730	0900	...	1445	...	...	...	...	...
72	Edéa d.	|	0910	1210	...	|	...	...	...	...	...
152	Eséka d.	|	1050	1510	...	|	...	...	...	...	...
220	Ngoumou d.	|	1230	1720	...	|	...	...	...	...	...
263	**Yaoundé** d.	0945	1315	1820	1910	1830	...	...	...	...	...
477	Nanga Eboko d.	...	...	...	2300	...	...	...	...	...	...
582	Belabo d.	...	...	...	0230	...	0830	...	...	...	...
686	Mbitom d.	...	...	...	0450	...	1115	...	...	...	...
910	**N'gaoundéré** a.	...	...	...	1000	...	1800	...	...	...	...

	184	112 ①③⑤	104 ②④⑥	192 B	152 A	154 A			
N'gaoundéré d.	...	0800	...	1915	...	...	...	...	...
Mbitom d.	...	1140	...	0000	...	...	...	...	...
Belabo d.	...	1730	...	0230	...	...	...	...	...
Nanga Eboko d.	...	...	...	0600	...	...	...	...	...
Yaoundé d.	0800	...	0915	1000	1025	1920	...	...	...
Ngoumou d.	0855	...	1030	...	|	|	...	...	...
Eséka d.	1045	...	1250	...	|	|	...	...	...
Edéa d.	1225	...	1600	...	|	|	...	...	...
Douala Bessengué a.	1350	...	1910	...	1410	2305	...	...	...

km				173	175	177					
	Douala Bonaberi d.	...	...	...	...	...	...	...	...	...	...
	Mbanga d.	...	...	0920	1300	1730	...	...	...	...	...
	Kumba a.	...	...	1030	1410	1840	...	...	...	...	...

				172	174	176			
Kumba d.	...	...	...	0750	1130	1530	...	...	...
Mbanga d.	...	...	...	0900	1240	1640	...	...	...
Douala Bonaberi a.	...	...	...	...	...	...	...	...	...

A – Conveys (1) and ✕. B – Conveys (12), 🛏 2 cl. (2 & 4 berth) and 🍷. ☛ – Note: All intermediate and arrival times are approximate.

4290 GABON

Chemins de Fer Trans Gabonnais

Capital: **Libreville** (GMT +1). 2019 Public Holidays: Jan. 1, Apr. 17, 21, 22, May 1, June 5, Aug. 12, 15, 16, 17. Nov. 1, Dec. 25.

km				B ③⑦		A ②⑤				
0	**Owendo** (Libreville) d.	...	...	1830	...	1900	...	...	...	...
183	Ndjole d.	...	...	2200	...	2210	...	...	...	...
340	Booué d.	...	...	0125	...	0200	...	...	...	...
485	Lastourville d.	...	...	0405	...	0430	...	...	...	...
625	Moanda d.	...	...	0640	...	0640	...	...	...	...
670	**Franceville** a.	...	...	0720	...	0720	...	...	...	...

			B ②⑤		A ④⑦				
Franceville d.	...	...	1800	...	1915	...	...	...	...
Moanda d.	...	...	1845	...	2000	...	...	...	...
Lastourville d.	...	...	2115	...	2220	...	...	...	...
Booué d.	...	...	2355	...	0115	...	...	...	...
Ndjole d.	...	...	0312	...	0420	...	...	...	...
Owendo (Libreville) a.	...	...	0640	...	0725	...	...	...	...

A – Trans-Ogooué Conveys VIP, (12), ✕. B – L'Equateur Conveys (12), ✕. Note: Services may be less frequent than shown.

Chemins de Fer Congo Océan — CONGO — 4300

km		①③⑤ A⊠	③⑦ B	⑥	②⑤ M
0	**Brazzaville** d.	0700	...	...	...
137	Mindouli d.	1000	...	...	...
190	Loutété d.	1130	0800	...	...
261	Nkayi d.	1255	1015	...	...
342	Dolisie d.	1530	1345	...	0330
382	M'Voui d.	|	1515	1800	|
509	**Pointe Noire** a.	1915	2045	2230	1130

	②④⑦ A⊠	⑥	②⑥ B	①④ M
Pointe Noire d.	0700	1000	0800	0900
M'Vouti d.	|	1500	1330	|
Dolisie d.	1130	...	1500	1730
Nkayi d.	1335	...	1830	...
Loutété d.	1520	...	2045	...
Mindouli d.	1650	...	...	...
Brazzaville a.	1950	...	...	...

Capital: **Brazzaville** (GMT +1).
2019 Public Holidays: Jan. 1, Apr. 21, 22, May 1, 30, June 10, Aug. 15, Nov. 1, Dec. 25.

A – GAZELLE – 🛏 [12] and ✕. ⊠
B – OCEAN – [12] and ✕.
M – Mixed train.

⊠ – Currently suspended.

Kenya Railways — KENYA — 4310

km		A	A	①③⑤ ⊠
0	**Mombasa** d.	0800	1515	...
	Voi d.	0947	|	...
	Mtito Andei d.	1056	|	...
	Emali d.	1212	|	...
485	**Nairobi S** a.	1342	2014	...
0	**Nairobi** d.	...	...	1830
183	Nakuru d.	...	...	0105
400	**Kisumu** a.	...	...	0920

	②④⑦ ⊠	A	A
Kisumu d.	1830	...	...
Nakuru d.	0255	...	...
Nairobi a.	0900	...	...
Nairobi S d.	...	0820	1435
Emali d.	...	0951	|
Mtito Andei d.	...	1124	|
Voi d.	...	1233	|
Mombasa a.	...	1418	1918

Capital: **Nairobi** (GMT +3).
2019 Public Holidays: Jan. 1, Apr. 19, 22, May 1, June 6, Aug. 12, Oct. 10, 20, 21, Dec. 12, 25, 26.

A – MADARAKA EXPRESS – [12] and ✕.
S – Nairobi Syokimau. Connections available from Nairobi Central.

⊠ – Currently suspended.

Société Nationale des Chemins de Fer du Congo — DEMOCRATIC CONGO — 4320

Capital: **Kinshasa** (GMT +1). 2019 Public Holidays: Jan. 1, 4, 16, 17, Apr. 30, May 1, 17, June 29, Aug. 1, Dec. 25.

km		2A	C	B	2D	2④	2			
255	**Sakania** d.	...	...	...	...	0800	...	...	...	...
0	Lubumbashi d.	0300	0700	0700	1300	2000	...	...	...	...
237	Tenke d.	1500	2000	2000	0200	...	...	...	...	...
757	**Dilolo** d.	|	|	|	2200	...	...	...	...	...
600	Kamina d.	1300	1600	2000	...	...	...	...	...	...
1047	Kabalo d.	2000	|	|	...	...	⊖	...	...	...
1583	Kindu a.	...	|	|	...	...	⊖	...	...	...
1320	Kalemie a.	...	|	|	...	...	...	...	...	...
913	Mwene Ditu d.	...	1000	2000	...	...	...	...	...	...
1156	Kananga d.	...	...	2200	...	...	...	...	...	...
1578	**Ilebo** a.	...	...	0900	...	...	...	...	...	...

	2D	C	B	2A	2③	2			
Ilebo d.	...	...	1600	...	...	...	...	...	...
Kananga d.	...	...	0500	...	...	...	...	...	...
Mwene Ditu d.	...	1600	0700	...	...	...	...	...	...
Kalemie d.	...	|	|	...	...	...	...	...	...
Kindu d.	...	|	|	...	...	⊖	...	...	...
Kabalo d.	...	|	|	0600	...	⊖	...	...	...
Kamina d.	...	1100	1100	1400	...	...	...	...	...
Dilolo d.	1500	|	|	|	...	...	...	...	...
Tenke d.	1400	1200	1400	1600	...	...	...	...	...
Lubumbashi a.	0300	1900	2100	2300	0800	...	...	...	...
Sakania a.	...	...	...	...	2000	...	...	...	...

km		⑥2					⑦2	
0	**Kinshasa** Est d.	0730	...	...	**Matadi** d.	...	0715	...
366	**Matadi** a.	1500	...	...	**Kinshasa** Est a.	...	1445	...

km		2③				2④		
0	**Kisangani** d.	0700	...	...	**Ubundu** d.	1700	...	...
125	**Ubundu** a.	1700	...	...	**Kisangani** a.	0700	...	...

☛ All timings are approximate.
A – From Lubumbashi 2nd and 4th ⑥ of each month. From Kabalo 1st and 3rd ④.
B – From Lubumbashi 1st ⑥ of each month. From Ilebo on following ①.
C – From Lubumbashi 1st and 3rd ① of each month. From Mwene on following ④.
D – From Lubumbashi 1st and 3rd ④. From Dilolo on following ⑦.
⊖ – No information available.

Tanzania Railways, TAZARA, Zambian Railways — TANZANIA and ZAMBIA — 4330

Capitals: **Dodoma** (Tanzania, GMT +3), **Lusaka** (Zambia, GMT +2).
2019 Public Holidays: Tanzania: Jan. 1, 12, Apr. 7, 19, 22, 26, May 1, June 5, July 7, Aug. 8, 12, Oct. 14, Nov. 10, Dec. 9, 25, 26.
2019 Public Holidays: Zambia: Jan. 1, Mar. 8, 12, Apr. 19, 22, May 1, 25, July 1, 2, Oct. 24, Dec. 25.

km	②⑤⑦ A	③⑥	①③⑥	④ B		*Tanzania Railways*		⑥ B	④⑦	②④⑦	②④⑦ A
0	2100	...	...	0800	↓	**Dar es Salaam** ◧ d.	↑	1730	...	...	0745
78	2332	...	...	1005		Ruvu d.		1525	...	...	⊖
203	2200	...	...	1330	↓	Morogoro d.	↑	1215	...	...	1945
290	⊖	...	...	|		Kilosa d.		|	...	...	⊖
465	0550	...	...	2000	↓	Dodoma d.	↑	0535	...	...	1810
578	⊖	...	...	|		Manyoni d.		|	...	...	⊖
637	⊖	...	...	|	↓	Itigi d.	↑	|	...	...	⊖
840	1625	...	...	0530		**Tabora** a.		1920	...	...	0640
840	1830	2100	1700	0630	↓	**Tabora** d.	↑	1820	0245	2100	0400
975	⊖	|	|	|		Kaliua d.		|	|	|	⊖
1051	|	1030	|	|	↓	**Mpanda** a.	↑	|	1300	|	|
	|	...	0530	|		**Mwanza** a.		|	...	1500	|
1144	⊖	...	...	|	↓	Uvinza d.	↑	|	...	...	⊖
1256	0620	...	...	1700		**Kigoma** a.		0800	...	...	1600

km	*TAZARA*	② C	⑤ D		⑤ D	② C
0	**Dar es Salaam** ◧ d.	1550	1350	**New Kapiri Mposhi** ⊡ d.	1400	1600
226	Kisaki d.	2013	1910	Mkushi Boma d.	⊖	⊖
360	Ifakara d.	2258	2230	Serenje d.	1817	1947
496	Mlimba d.	0152	0140	Mpika d.	2329	0010
652	Makambako d.	0746	0803	Kasama d.	0309	0329
849	Mbeya d.	1323	1440	Nakonde ▦ a.	0915	0839
969	Tunduma d.	1717	1853	Nakonde ▦ d.	0925	0909
970	Nakonde ▦ a.	1622	1758	Tunduma d.	1045	1029
970	Nakonde ▦ d.	1647	1813	Mbeya d.	1500	1428
1226	Kasama d.	2227	0031	Makambako d.	2129	2030
1412	Mpika d.	0148	0445	Mlimba d.	0351	0208
1652	Serenje d.	0556	0931	Ifakara d.	0628	0512
1761	Mkushi Boma d.	⊖	⊖	Kisaki d.	1035	0757
1852	**New Kapiri Mposhi** ⊡ a.	0926	1337	**Dar es Salaam** ◧ a.	1546	1210

km	*Zambia Railways*	① 2	⑤ E	●		●	① E	⑤ 2
0	**Kitwe** Nkana d.	1600	1600	...	**Livingstone** d.	1800	2000	2000
66	Ndola d.	1855	1855	...	Kalomo d.	2131	0100	0100
199	Kapiri Mposhi ⊡ d.	2357	2357	...	Choma d.	2311	0345	0345
262	Kabwe d.	0255	0255	...	Pemba d.	0054	0609	0609
331	Chisamba d.	0500	0500	...	Monze d.	0153	0749	0749
384	**Lusaka** a.	0656	0656	...	Mazabuka d.	0333	1015	1015
384	**Lusaka** d.	0736	0736	1800	Kafue d.	0515	1244	1244
432	Kafue d.	0946	0946	1942	**Lusaka** a.	0627	1424	1424
481	Mazabuka d.	1155	1155	2104	**Lusaka** d.	...	1524	1524
540	Monze d.	1417	1417	2244	Chisamba d.	...	1656	1656
577	Pemba d.	1558	1558	0021	Kabwe d.	...	1946	1946
643	Choma d.	1834	1834	0145	Kapiri Mposhi ⊡ d.	...	2216	2216
713	Kalomo d.	2108	2108	0301	Ndola d.	...	0336	0336
851	**Livingstone** a.	0200	0200	0627	**Kitwe** Nkana a.	...	0600	0600

km	*Zambia Railways*	③⑥ 2				②⑤ 2	
0	**Mulobezi** d.	1200	...	...	**Livingstone** d.	1400	...
85	Ngwezi d.	⊖	...	...	Ngwezi d.	⊖	...
163	**Livingstone** a.	0200	...	...	**Mulobezi** a.	0200	...

A – 🛏 1, 2 cl., [2] and ✕ Dar es Salaam - Kigoma and v.v.
B – 🛏 2 cl. [23] and ✕. Dar es Salaam - Kigoma and v.v.
C – 🛏 1, 2 cl., 🛏 1, 2 cl., [2] and ✕. Kilimanjaro/Mukuba Express Train.
D – 🛏 1cl. 🛏 1 cl, [12] and ✕. Kilimanjaro/Mukuba Ordinary Train.
E – 🛏 3 and 6 berth [12] and ✕. Zambezi Train.

◧ – Stations are approximately 8 km from each other.
⊡ – Stations are approximately 2 km from each other.
⊖ – No information available.
● – Charter service only.

Chemins de Fer Fianarantsoa-Côte Est / Madarail — MADAGASCAR — 4340

Capital: **Antananarivo** (GMT +3). 2019 Public Holidays: Jan. 1, Mar. 29, Apr. 22, May 1, 30, June 10, 26, Aug. 15, Nov. 1, Dec, 11, 25.

km	*Madarail*	⑤ 2	② 2		① 2	④ 2
0	**Toamasina** d.	...	0820	**Moramanga** d.	0700	1500
43	Tampolo d.	...	0951	Andasibe ◇ d.	0830	1600
86	Ambila-Lemaitso d.	0800	1125	Lohariandava d.	1050	1820
162	Lohariandava d.	1150	1515	Ambila-Lemaitso d.	1340	2200
223	Andasibe ◇ d.	1515	1725	Tampolo d.	1520	...
249	**Moramanga** a.	1740	1855	**Toamasina** a.	1650	...

km	*CFFCE*	②④⑥			③⑤⑦	
0	**Fianarantsoa** d.	0700	...	**Manakara** d.	0645	...
39	Ranomena d.	0855	...	Sahasinaka d.	0900	...
62	Tolongoina d.	1015	...	Manampatrana d.	1130	...
79	Manampatrana d.	1110	...	Tolongoina d.	1225	...
118	Sahasinaka d.	1330	...	Ranomena d.	1355	...
163	**Manakara** a.	1600	...	**Fianarantsoa** a.	1600	...

◇ – Special tour trains using Michelin railcars run Andasibe - Antananarivo and v.v. For dates contact operator.

Botswana Railways — BOTSWANA — 4345

km		502	812		811	501
0	**Francistown** 4380 d.	2100	...	**Lobatse** d.	0530	1950
235	Mahalapye d.	0216	...	Gaborone d.	0649	2135
435	Gaborone d.	0605	1800	Mahalapye d.	...	0103
507	**Lobatse** a.	0736	1928	**Francistown** 4380 a.	...	0610

Capital: **Gaborone** (GMT +2).
2019 Public Holidays: Jan. 1, 2, Apr. 19, 20, 22, May 1, 30, July 1, 15, 16, Sept. 30, Dec, 25, 26.

501/502 – 🛏, [2] and ✕.

4350 ANGOLA

INCFA

km		①–⑤	①–⑤	③	⑥	①–⑤	②	⑥	⑥	①–⑤
0	**Luanda** Textang ⊗ d.	0500a	...	...	0730a	0721	0744	0750	1525	1640
23	Viana ⊗ d.	0528	0700	0700	0755	0803	0855	0834	1610	1732
65	Catete d.	...	0740	0747	0844	0909	|	0927	1704	1827
135	Zenza d.	...	0839	0859	0950	...	1055	...	...	...
190	**Dondo** (Cuanza) a.	...	|	|	1050	...	1155	...	...	...
241	N'dalatando d.	...	1200	1227	...	...	...	...	...	...
424	**Malange** a.	...	1625	1652	...	...	...	...	...	...

	①–⑤	⑥	②	⑥	②⑦	①–⑤	④	⑥	①–⑤
Malange d.	...	...	...	...	0730	...	0730	...	...
N'dalatando d.	...	...	...	...	1215	...	1215	...	...
Dondo (Cuanza) d.	...	...	1320	1340	|	...	|	...	...
Zenza d.	...	...	1418	1450	1516	...	1538	...	...
Catete d.	1000	1020	|	1600	1615	...	1647	1730	1850
Viana ⊗ d.	1052	1110	1620	1649	1655	1708	1730	1822	1945
Luanda Textang ⊗ a.	1137	1149	1701	1720a	...	1750	...	1855a	2021a

km		①–⑤	①	②	①–⑤	③
0	**Lobita** ◧ d.	...	...	...	...	0530
33	Benguela ◧ a.	...	...	...	...	|
355	**Caála** d.	0650	...	...	...	|
368	Dango d.	0730	...	...	...	|
383	**Huambo** a.	0755	...	...	...	1714
0	**Huambo** d.	...	0900	...	1000	▬
30	Cambuio d.	...	|	...	1100	...
77	**Katchiungo** a.	...	1055	...	1200	...
202	Kuito d.	...	1314	0430	...	③
593	Luena d.	...	...	1258	...	0600
909	Luau a.	...	...	...	...	1235

	⑥	①–⑤	⑤	①–⑤	④
Luau d.	...	...	...	...	0600
Luena d.	...	...	0500	...	1240
Kuito d.	0800	...	1330	...	▬
Katchiungo d.	1024	1300	...	...	...
Cambuio d.	|	1400	...	...	...
Huambo a.	1220	1500	...	...	⑤
Huambo d.	...	...	...	1700	0600
Dango d.	...	...	...	1730	|
Caála a.	...	...	...	1810	|
Benguela ◧ d.	...	...	...	...	|
Lobita ◧ a.	...	...	...	...	1648

km			
0	**Namibe** d.	⊖	...
162	Bibala d.	⊖	...
246	Lubango d.	⊖	...
424	Matala d.	⊖	...
509	**Dondo** (Lubango) a.	|	...
756	Menongue a.	⊖	...

Menongue d.	...	⊖
Dondo (Lubango) a.	...	|
Matala d.	...	⊖
Lubango d.	...	⊖
Bibala d.	...	⊖
Namibe a.	...	⊖

Capital: **Luanda** (GMT +1). 2019 Public Holidays: Jan. 1, Feb. 4, Mar. 8, Apr. 4, 19, May 1, Sept. 17, Nov. 2, 11, Dec. 25.

a – Luanda Muceques.
⊗ – Additional local trains available. ⊖ – Timings unavailable.
◧ – Services dep. Lobita and Benguela at 0600, 1700. Journey time 65 minutes

4360 MALAWI

2nd class only Central East African Railway

km		⑥	④	⑤	③
22	Bilila d.	...	0730	...	1625
0	**Balaka** d.	...	0940	0600	1735
16	Nkaya d.	...	1030	0840	...
42	Liwonde d.	...	1115	|	...
114	**Nayuchi** a.	...	1427	|	...
104	Blantyre d.	...	...	1640	...
112	Limbe d.	0900	...	1737	...
233	**Makhanga** a.	1715	...	...	...

	④	③	⑦	④
Makhanga d.	...	...	0700	...
Limbe d.	...	0700	1645	...
Blantyre d.	...	0745	...	...
Nayuchi d.	...	|	...	1500
Liwonde d.	...	|	...	1800
Nkaya d.	...	1315	...	1900
Balaka d.	0600	1453	...	1940
Bilila a.	0710	1605	...	...

Capital: **Lilongwe** (GMT +2).
2019 Public Holidays: Jan. 1, 15, Mar. 3, Apr. 19, 22, May 1, 14, June 5, 14, July 6, Dec. 25.

4370 MOÇAMBIQUE

2nd class only CD do Norte / CF Moçambique

Capital: **Maputo** (GMT +2). 2019 Public Holidays: Jan. 1, Feb. 3, Apr. 7, 19, May 1, June 25, Sep. 7, 25, Oct. 4, Dec. 25.

km		②⑥	④	
0	**Nampula** d.	0400	...	...
173	Iapala d.	0851	...	...
252	Malema d.	1142	...	...
302	Mutuáli d.	1333	...	...
356	Cuamba d.	1526	0600	...
464	Mitande d.	...	⊖	...
541	**Nayuci** a.	...	0900	...

	④⑦	1500	
Nayuci d.	...	⊖	...
Mitande d.	...	1800	...
Cuamba d.	0500	...	...
Mutuáli d.	0735	...	...
Malema d.	0833	...	...
Iapala d.	1120	...	...
Nampula a.	1626	...	...

km		⑥	②	
0	**Beira** d.	0600	1100	...
28	Dondo d.	0731	1224	...
120	Muanza d.	1021	1509	...
187	Inhaminga d.	1208	1656	...
214	Inhamitanga d.	1259	1742	...
302	Marromeu a.	1600	|	...
320	**Nhamalabue** a.	...	2125	...
577	Maotize a.	...	0526	...

	⑦		③
Moatize d.	...	...	1600
Nhamalabue d.	...	...	0011
Marromeu d.	0800	...	|
Inhamitanga d.	1108	...	0426
Inhaminga d.	1159	...	0517
Muanza d.	1346	...	0705
Dondo d.	1639	...	0935
Beira a.	1800	...	1150

km		⑥⑦	⑥	③
0	**Maputo** d.	0730	0955	1300
208	Chókwe d.	1216	1910	1950
534	**Chicualacuala** a.	...	0349	0342

	④	⑦	⑥⑦
Chicualacuala d.	1300	1015	...
Chókwe d.	2323	2020	1420
Maputo a.	0549	0810	1909

km		①–⑤	⑥⑦	⑦–⑤
0	**Maputo** d.	0745	0800	1815
53	Moambe d.	0927	0952	2032
88	**Ressano Garcia** a.	1020	1045	2124

	①–⑥	①–⑤	⑥⑦
Ressano Garcia d.	0346	1205	1225
Moambe d.	0506	1317	1346
Maputo a.	0645	1511	1540

⊖ – No information available.

4380 ZIMBABWE

National Railways of Zimbabwe

Capital: **Harare** (GMT +2). 2019 Public Holidays: Jan. 1, Apr. 18, 19, 22, May 1, 25, Aug. 12, 13, Dec. 22, 25, 26.

km		①④⑥ A		
0	**Mutare** d.	2100	...	...
77	Nyazura d.	2307	...	...
99	Rusape d.	0010	...	...
166	Macheke d.	0239	...	...
201	Marondera d.	0345	...	...
273	**Harare** a.	0605	...	...

	③⑤⑦ A		
Harare d.	2130	...	...
Marondera d.	2345	...	...
Macheke d.	0100	...	...
Rusape d.	0320	...	...
Nyazura d.	0409	...	...
Mutare a.	0600	...	...

km		B		
0	**Bulawayo** d.	1930	...	...
126	Gwayi d.	2310	...	...
266	Dete d.	0200	...	...
339	Hwange d.	0347	...	...
351	Thomson Junction d.	0455	...	...
472	**Victoria Falls** a.	0800	...	...

	B		
Victoria Falls d.	1900	...	...
Thomson Jct d.	2230	...	...
Hwange d.	2303	...	...
Dete d.	0110	...	...
Gwayi d.	0340	...	...
Bulawayo a.	0805	...	...

km		②⑤⑦ A	①③⑤ ⊠	
0	**Harare** d.	2000	...	...
44	Norton d.	2100	...	...
127	Chegutu d.	2310	...	...
160	Kadoma d.	0001	...	...
237	Kwekwe d.	0210	...	...
**	Masvingo d.	|	2000	...
302	Gweru d.	0500	0345	...
336	Somabhula d.	0533	...	...
369	Shangani d.	0630	...	...
486	**Bulawayo** a.	0840	...	...

	①④⑥ A	①③⑤ ⊠	
Bulawayo d.	2000	...	...
Shangani d.	2240	...	...
Somabhula d.	2330	...	...
Gweru d.	0130	0245	...
Masvingo a.	|	0955	...
Kwekwe d.	0337	...	...
Kadoma d.	0520	...	...
Chegutu d.	0605	...	...
Norton d.	0823	...	...
Harare a.	0930	...	...

km		③ A	⑦ A	
0	**Bulawayo** d.	1215	1730	...
113	Shangani d.	1457	2016	...
150	Somabhula d.	1607	2108	...
229	Bannockburn d.	1848	2345	...
309	Ngezi d.	2106	0205	...
401	Rutenga d.	0050	0545	...
433	Lundi d.	|	0934	...
	Sango Halt a.	0625	|	...
500	**Chicualacuala** a.	0706a	|	...
499	Triangle d.	...	1120	...
523	**Chiredzi** a.	...	1200	...

	④ A	① A	
Chiredzi d.	...	1530	...
Triangle d.	...	1620	...
Chicualacuala d.	1500a	|	...
Sango Halt d	1520	|	...
Lundi d.	|	1727	...
Rutenga d.	2145	2145	...
Ngezi d.	0036	0036	...
Bannockburn d.	0339	0339	...
Somabhula d.	0700	0700	...
Shangani d.	0810	0810	...
Bulawayo a.	1100	1100	...

km	⊠	④⑦ 2		
0	**Bulawayo** d.	1800	...	...
317	**Beit Bridge** a.	0540	...	...

⊠	①⑤ 2		
Beit Bridge d.	2100	...	...
Bulawayo a.	0845	...	...

km		802 2	
0	**Bulawayo** ‡ d.	1415	...
	Plumtree d.	1749	...
196	**Francistown** ‡ **4345** a.	1945	...

	801 2	
Francistown ‡ **4345** d.	0700	...
Plumtree d.	0945	...
Bulawayo ‡ a.	1230	...

A – 🛏 1, 2 cl. and 🚃2 Ⓡ. a – 🏛 Sango Halt. ⊖ – No information available. ‡ – 🏛 is Plumtree.
B – 🛏 1 cl., ▬ 2 cl. and 🚃2. ** – Masvingo - Gweru *199 km*. ⊠ Service suspended

4390 NAMIBIA

Starline

Capital: **Windhoek** (GMT +2). 2019 Public Holidays: Jan. 1, Mar. 21, Apr. 19, 22, May 1, 4, 10, 25, Aug. 26, Dec. 10, 25, 26.

km	①–⑤ 12	⑥ A				⑤ A	①–⑤ 12
412	1900	...	↓	d.**Walvisbaai** a.	↑	...	0715
373	2045	1500	↓	d.Swakopmund d.		1000	0530
222	0045	|	↓	d.Usakos d.	↑	|	0150
419	|	|		d. **Otjiwarongo** d.		|	|
282	|	|	↓	d. Omaruru d.	↑	|	|
210	0135	|		d.Kranzberg d.		|	0130
191	0220	|	↓	d.Karibib d.	↑	|	0040
70	0510	|		d.Okahandja d.		|	2205
0	0700	1030	↓	a.**Windhoek** d.	↑	1200a	1915

km	Ⓑ b	③⑥				④⑦	Ⓑ c
0	1940	...	↓	d.**Windhoek** a.	↑	...	0700
97	2210	...	↓	d.Rehobeth d.	↑	...	0425
192	2400	...	↓	d.Kalkrand d.	↑	...	0230
274	0220	...	↓	d.Mariental d.	↑	...	0020
423	0510	...	↓	d.Tses d.	↑	...	2040
505	0700	...		a.**Keetmanshoop** d.		...	1850
505	...	0850	↓	d.**Keetmanshoop** a.	↑	1630	...
681	...	1310	↓	d.Grünau d.	↑	1225	...
732	...	1430	↓	a.**Karasburg** d.	↑	1120	...

km	①–⑥	⑦				①–⑥	⑦
0	0850	1120	↓	d.**Oshikango** ♣ a.	↑	1640	1805
60	1010	1235	↓	a.**Ondangwa** ♠ d.	↑	1520	1650
	1120	1320	↓	d.**Ondangwa** ♠ a.	↑	1420	1647
	1317	1515	↓	d.Omuthiya ♥ d.	↑	1212	1505
	1443	1631	↓	d.Oshivelo d.	↑	1056	1326
306	1640	1840	↓	a.**Tsumeb** d.	↑	0850	1120

♣ – Rev. Theofelus Hamutumbangela.
♠ – Nehale Lya Mpingana. ♥ – Sam Nujoma.

A – DESERT EXPRESS – 🛏, 🚃1 and ✕. Special service including meals and excursions.
a – Departs 1300 in the summer.
b – Also conveys ▬ 2 cl. on ①③⑤.
c – Also conveys ▬ 2 cl. on ②④⑦.

Gautrain / Shosholoza Meyl

SOUTH AFRICA 4400

Capital: **Pretoria** (GMT +2). 2019 Public Holidays: Jan. 1, Mar. 21, Apr. 19, 22, 27, May 1, June 16, 17, Aug. 9, Sep. 24, Dec. 16, 25, 26.

km			③⑤⑦	③⑤⑦	③⑤⑦	¶②	¶⑤	④	③⑤⑦		
			A	B	C	2	2	E	D	...	...
0	**Johannesburg** d.	...	1230	1315	1420	...	...	1030	1840	...	...
14	Germiston d.	...	|	1350	1452	...	...	|	1918	...	...
172	Standerton d.	...	|	|	|	...	...	|	|	...	...
315	Newcastle d.	...	|	|	|	...	...	|	0027	...	...
438	Ladysmith d.	...	|	|	|	...	...	|	0245	...	...
617	Pietermaritzburg d.	...	|	|	|	...	...	|	0632	...	...
722	**Durban** a.	...	|	|	|	...	...	|	0910	...	...
75	Vereeniging d.	...	|	1455	1600	...	...	|	...	...	...
210	Kroonstad d.	...	|	1725	1832	...	...	|	...	...	...
407	**Bloemfontein** a.	...	|	2020	2115	...	...	|	...	...	...
407	**Bloemfontein** d.	...	|	2030	2135	...	...	|	...	...	.....
664	Burgersdorp d.	...	|	|	0305	...	...	|	...	...	...
809	Queenstown d.	...	|	|	0610	1445	1445	|	...	...	...
023	**East London** a.	...	|	|	1020	1000↑	|	|	...	...	...
835	Cradock d.	...	|	0445	...	|	|	|	...	...	...
112	**Port Elizabeth** a.	...	|	0910	...	|	|	|	...	...	...
186	Klerksdorp d.	...	1625	...	...	|	|	|	...	...	...
495	Kimberley d.	...	2120	...	...	|	|	1907	...	...	...
908	De Aar d.	...	0135	...	...	0100	0100	2305	...	...	...
988	Beaufort West d.	...	0600	...	...	0500	0500	0340	...	...	...
355	Worcester d.	...	1205	...	...	1055	1055	|	...	...	...
511	Bellville d.	...	1500	...	...	1345	1345	|	...	...	...
530	**Cape Town** a.	...	1530	...	...	1410	1410	1240	...	...	...

				③⑤⑦	③⑤⑦	③⑤⑦	②		¶⑦	¶④
				B	D	C	E	A	2	2
Cape Town d.	...	...	...	...	...	...	0905	1000	1025	1025
Belleville d.	...	...	...	...	...	...	|	1035	1105	1105
Worcester d.	...	...	...	...	...	...	|	1330	1355	1355
Beaufort West d.	...	...	...	...	...	...	1845	1950	2005	2005
De Aar d.	...	...	...	...	...	...	2235	2345	0010	0010
Kimberley d.	...	...	...	...	...	...	0300	0346	|	|
Klerksdorp d.	...	...	...	...	...	...	|	0826	|	|
Port Elizabeth d.	...	...	...	1100	...	...	|	|	|	|
Cradock d.	...	...	...	1615	...	...	|	|	|	|
East London d.	...	...	...	|	...	1415	|	|	1425↓	|
Queenstown d.	...	...	...	|	...	1914	|	|	1012	1005
Burgersdorp d.	...	...	...	|	...	2215	|	|	...	...
Bloemfontein a.	...	...	...	0135	...	0307	|	|	...	...
Bloemfontein d.	...	...	...	0205	...	0337	|	|	...	...
Kroonstad d.	...	...	...	0523	...	0659	|	|	...	...
Vereeniging d.	...	...	...	1749	...	0928	|	|	...	...
Durban d.	...	...	...	|	1915	|	|	|	...	...
Pietermaritzburg d.	...	...	...	|	2153	|	|	|	...	...
Ladysmith d.	...	...	...	|	0145	|	|	|	...	...
Newcastle d.	...	...	...	|	0407	|	|	|	...	...
Standerton d.	...	...	...	|	|	|	|	|	...	...
Germiston d.	...	...	...	0855	0917	1040	|	|	...	...
Johannesburg a.	...	...	...	0918	0935	1103	1103	1215	...	...

km		⑤		⑤
		H		J
0	**Johannesburg** d.	1810	...	1900
14	Germiston d.	1827	...	⊖
70	Pretoria d.	1940	...	⊖
183	Witbank d.	2225	...	|
218	Middelburg d.	2320	...	|
422	Nelspruit d.	0415	...	|
461	Kaapmuiden d.	0515	...	|
530	**Komatipoort** ▼ a.	0638	...	|
292	Mokopane d.	...	...	⊖
357	Polokwane d.	...	...	0344
504	Makhado d.	...	...	⊖
633	**Musina** ► a.	...	...	1110

	⑦	⑦	
	H	J	
Musina ► d.	...	1525	...
Makhado d.	...	⊖	...
Polokwane d.	...	2235	...
Mokopane d.	...	⊖	...
Komatipoort ▼ d.	1800	|	...
Kaapmuiden d.	1936	|	...
Nelspruit d.	2040	|	...
Middelburg d.	0139	|	...
Witbank d.	0219	|	...
Pretoria d.	0500	|	...
Germiston d.	0557	⊖	...
Johannesburg a.	0616	0544	...

Johannesburg - Pretoria and v.v. 56 km. Journey 36 mins. Operator: Gautrain.

From **Johannesburg** Park: Train call at Sandton* 8 mins later.

Ⓐ: 0530, 0550, 0610, 0620, 0630, 0640, 0650, 0700, 0710, 0720, 0730, 0740, 0750, 0800, 0810, 0820, 0830, 0840, 0900, 0920, 0938, 0958, 1018, and every 20 mins until 1438, 1458, 1508, then every 10 mins until 1828, 1848, 1910, 1930, 1950, 2010, 2030.

Ⓒ: 0530, 0600 and every 30 mins until 2030.

From **Pretoria**: Trains call at Sandton* 27 mins later.

Ⓐ: 0512, 0532, 0552, 0602, 0612, 0622, 0632, 0642, 0652, 0702, 0712, 0722, 0732, 0742, 0752, 0802, 0812, 0822, 0832, 0842, 0852, 0911 and every 20 mins until 1531, 1541, 1551, 1611, then every 10 mins until 1831, 1843, 1903, 1923, 1943, 2003, 2023, 2043.

Ⓒ: 0533, 0603 and every 30 mins until 2003, 2037.

⊖ – Timings not available.
* – Frequent services run throughout the day to/from Sandon and OR Tambo Airport.

– TRANS KAROO – 🛏, (T2) (car) and ✕ Johannesburg - Cape Town and v.v. From Johannesburg ②③⑤⑦ (No (2) on ②). From Cape Town ③⑤⑥⑦ (No (2) on ⑥).
– ALGOA – 🛏, (T2) and ✕ Johannesburg - Port Elizabeth and v.v.
– AMATOLA – 🛏, (T2) and ✕ Johannesburg - East London and v.v.
– TRANS NATAL – 🛏, (T2) (car) and ✕ Durban - Johannesburg and v.v. - on ⑤ conveys PREMIER CLASSE – 🛏 (1 cl.) (1) and ✕ Johannesburg - Durban and v.v.
– PREMIER CLASSE – 🛏 (1 cl.) (1) and ✕ Johannesburg - Cape Town and v.v. Note: Intermediate stops are operational only.
– KOMATI – (T2) and 🍷 Johannesburg - Komatipoort and v.v. **J** – (T2) and 🍷 Johannesburg - Polokwane/Musina and v.v.
– Subject to confirmation.
OTE: These are the published schedules in some cases the actual timings could vary.
► – Musina - Beit Bridge (Zimbabwe): *12 km.* ▼ – Komatipoort - Ressano Garcia (Mozambique): *5 km. See Table* **4370**.
rain Classes: (1) Premier Class coaches consist of one or two berth deluxe compartments that convert to sleeper accommodation at night and can accomodate up to 14 passengers.
(T) Tourist Class coaches consist of two or four berth compartments that convert to sleeper accommodation at night and can accomodate up to 28 passengers.
(2) Economy Class consitsts of sitting accommodation only and hold up to 72 passengers.

ISRAEL

apital: **Jerusalem** (GMT +2, add 1 hour in summer). 2019 Public Holidays: Apr. 20, 26, May 9, June 9, Sept. 30, Oct. 1, 9, 14, 21.

ail services are operated Israel Railways (www.rail.co.il). All services convey a single class of seated accommodation. Timings are the most recent available and are subject to lteration at any time, particularly around religious holidays. Tickets and reservations may be purchased up to 7 days in advance of travel at stations or through the website.

Israel Railways

NAHARIYYA - TEL AVIV - BEN GURION AIRPORT - MODI'IN 4500

km		⑦–④	⑤	⑦–④	⑤	⑦–④	⑤	⑦–④	⑤	⑦–④	⑤	⑦–④	⑦–④	⑤	⑦–④	⑤	⑦–④	⑤		⑦–④	⑤	⑤	⑦–④	⑦–④
0	**Nahariyya** d.	0013	0013	0113	0113	0213	0213	0313	0313	0349	0349	...	0448	0451	0515	0527	0548	0551		1215	1227	1251	1248	1315
	Akko d.	0021	0021	0121	0121	0221	0221	0321	0321	0357	0357	...	0455	0458	0522	0534	0555	0558		1222	1234	1258	1255	1322
20	Qiryat Motzkin d.	0032	0032	0132	0132	0232	0232	0332	0332	0407	0407	...	0505	0508	0532	0544	0605	0608	and at	1232	1244	1308	1305	1332
38	Haifa Hof HaKarmel d.	0052	0052	0152	0152	0252	0252	0352	0352	0426	0426	0503	0536	0539	0603	0613	0636	0639	the same	1303	1313	1339	1336	1403
71	Binyamina d.	0112	0112	0212	0212	0312	0312	0412	0412	0446	0446	0526	0556	0602	0626	0632	0656	0702	minutes	1326	1332	1402	1356	1426
123	**Tel Aviv** Savidor Center d.	0156	0154	0256	0254	0356	0354	0456	0454	0530	0530	0601	0631	0635	0701	0704	0731	0735	past each	1401	1404	1435	1431	1501
	Tel Aviv HaHagana d.	0201	...	0301	...	0401	...	0501	...	0537	...	0609	0639	...	0709	...	0739	...	hour until	1409	...	...	1439	1509
137	Ben Gurion Airport a.	0212	...	0312	...	0412	...	0512	...	0548	...	0619	0649	...	0719	...	0749	...		1419	...	...	1449	1519
158	**Modi'in** Center a.	...	...	...	...	...	...	...	...	...	...	0644	0714	...	0744	...	0814	...		1444	...	...	1514	1544

	⑤	⑦–④	⑤	⑦–④	⑤	⑦–④	⑤	⑦–④	⑤	⑦–④	⑦–④	⑦–④		⑦–④	⑦–④	⑦–④	⑦–④			⑥		⑥		⑥
Nahariyya d.	1327	1348	1351	1415	1427	1448	1451	1515	1525	1548	1615	1648		2015	2048	2148	2313	❖	...	2055	...	2151	...	2313
Akko d.	1334	1355	1358	1422	1434	1455	1458	1522	1532	1555	1622	1655		2022	2055	2155	2321		...	2102	...	2158	...	2321
Qiryat Motzkin d.	1344	1405	1408	1432	1444	1505	1508	1532	1542	1605	1632	1705	and at	2032	2105	2205	2332		...	2112	...	2208	...	2332
Haifa Hof HaKarmel d.	1413	1436	1439	1503	1513	1536	1539	1603	1610	1636	1703	1736	the same	2103	2136	2236	2352	⑥	...	2139	...	2239	...	2352
Binyamina d.	1432	1456	1502	1526	1532	1556	1602	1626	1632	1656	1726	1756	minutes	2126	2156	2256	0012		...	2202	...	2302	...	0012
Tel Aviv Savidor Center a.	1504	1531	1535	1601	1604	1631	1635	1701	1704	1731	1801	1831	past each	2201	2231	2350	0056		...	2235	...	2335	...	0054
Tel Aviv HaHagana d.	...	1539	...	1609	...	1639	...	1709	...	1739	1809	1839	hour until	2209	2239	2357	0101		...	2246	...	2346	...	0101
Ben Gurion Airport a.	...	1549	...	1619	...	1649	...	1719	...	1749	1819	1849		2219	2249	0007	0112	❖	...	2256	...	2356	...	0114
Modi'in Center a.	...	1614	...	1644	...	1714	...	1744	...	1814	1844	1914		2244	2314	0032	...		...	2320	...	0050	...	...

	⑦–④	⑤	⑦–④	⑤	⑦–④	⑤	⑦–④	⑤	⑦–④	⑤	⑤	⑦–④	⑤	⑦–④		⑤	⑦–④	⑤	⑦–④	⑦–④	⑤	⑤	⑦–④
Modi'in Center d.	...	...	...	...	...	...	...	...	...	...	...	0518	...	0548		...	1218	...	1248	1318	...	...	1348
Ben Gurion Airport d.	0035	...	0135	...	0235	...	0335	...	0435	...	...	0535	...	0605		...	1235	...	1305	1335	...	...	1405
Tel Aviv HaHagana d.	0044	...	0144	...	0244	...	0344	...	0444	...	...	0547	...	0617	and at	...	1247	...	1317	1347	...	...	1417
Tel Aviv Savidor Center d.	0053	0053	0153	0153	0253	0253	0353	0353	0453	0453	0550	0558	0622	0628	the same	1250	1258	1322	1328	1358	1350	1422	1428
Binyamina d.	0132	0132	0232	0232	0332	0332	0432	0432	0532	0532	0623	0630	0653	0700	minutes	1323	1330	1353	1400	1430	1423	1453	1500
Haifa Hof HaKarme d.	0151	0151	0251	0251	0351	0351	0451	0451	0555	0555	0647	0649	0712	0724	past each	1347	1349	1412	1424	1449	1447	1512	1524
Qiryat Motzkin d.	0212	0212	0312	0312	0412	0412	0514	0514	0625	0625	0718	0720	0742	0755	hour until	1418	1420	1442	1455	1520	1518	1542	1555
Akko d.	0221	0221	0321	0321	0421	0421	0523	0523	0635	0635	0727	0729	0751	0804		1427	1429	1451	1504	1529	1527	1551	1604
Nahariyya a.	0231	0231	0331	0331	0431	0431	0533	0533	0645	0645	0736	0739	0800	0813		1436	1439	1500	1513	1539	1536	1600	1613

	⑤	⑦–④	⑤	⑦–④	⑦–④	⑦–④		⑦–④	⑦–④	⑦–④	⑦–④	⑦–④	⑦–④	⑦–④	⑦–④	⑦–④			⑥	⑥	⑥	⑥	⑥
Modi'in Center d.	...	1418	...	1448	1518	1548		1818	1848	1918	1948	2018	2048	2115	2218	2318	...	❖	...	...	2108	2208	2307
Ben Gurion Airport d.	...	1435	...	1505	1535	1605	and at	1835	1905	1935	2005	2035	2105	2135	2235	2335	...		...	...	2127	2227	2325
Tel Aviv HaHagana a.	...	1447	...	1517	1547	1617	the same	1847	1919	1947	2026	2047	2117	2147	2247	2347	...		2046	2113	2138	2238	2336
Tel Aviv Savidor Center d.	1450	1458	1522	1528	1558	1628	minutes	1858	1928	1958	2029	2058	2128	2158	2258	2358	...	⑥	2055	2122	2150	2250	2347
Binyamina d.	1523	1530	1553	1600	1630	1700	past each	1930	2000	2030	2100	2130	2200	2230	2347	0047	...		2125	2153	2223	2323	0037
Haifa Hof HaKarme a.	1547	1549	1612	1624	1649	1724	hour until	1949	2024	2049	2124	2149	2224	2249	0005	0105	...		2144	2212	2247	2347	0101
Qiryat Motzkin d.	1618	1620	1642	1655	1720	1755		2020	2055	2120	...	2220	2252	2317	0032	0132	...		2214	2241	2318	0018	0132
Akko a.	1627	1629	1651	1704	1729	1804		2029	2104	2129	...	2229	2301	2326	0041	0141	...	❖	2224	2250	2327	0027	0141
Nahariyya a.	1636	1639	1700	1713	1739	1813		2039	2113	2139	...	2239	2311	2335	0051	0151	...		2234	2259	2336	0036	0150

❖ – Because of electrification works services on ⑥ will be suspended from June 1 until further notice.
☛ For additional services Nahariyya – Tel Aviv and v.v and connections to/from Be'er Sheva see Table **4510**.

4510 NAHARIYYA - TEL AVIV - BE'ER SHEVA — Israel Railways

km			⑦-④	⑦-④	⑤	⑦-④	⑦-④	⑤	⑤	⑦-④	⑦-④	⑤	⑤	⑦-④	⑦-④	⑤	⑤	⑦-④	⑦-④	⑤	⑤	⑦-④	⑤	⑤	⑦-④	⑤	⑤
0	**Nahariyya**	d.	...	...	...	0527	...	...	...	0627	...	...	...	0727	...	...	...	0827	...	...	...	0927	...	...	...	...	...
	Akko	d.	...	...	...	0534	...	...	...	0634	...	...	...	0737	...	...	...	0834	...	...	...	0934	...	...	...	...	...
20	Qiryat Motzkin	d.	...	...	...	0544	0619	...	...	0644	0719	...	...	0744	0819	...	...	0844	0919	...	...	0944	...	...	...	...	...
38	Haifa Hof HaKarmel	d.	...	...	...	0611	0645	...	...	0711	0745	...	...	0811	0845	...	...	0911	0946	...	...	1011	...	...	...	...	...
71	Binyamina	d.	...	...	...	|	|	...	...	|	|	...	...	|	|	...	...	|	|	...	...	|	...	...	...	...	...
123	**Tel Aviv** Savidor Ctr	d.	0607	0637	...	0707	0737	...	...	0807	0837	...	...	0907	0937	...	...	1007	1037	...	...	1107	...	...	1207	...	...
	Tel Aviv HaHagana	d.	0614	0644	...	0714	0744	...	...	0814	0844	...	...	0914	0944	...	...	1017	1044	...	...	1114	...	...	1214	...	...
143	Lod	d.	0627	0658	0728	0727	0758	0807	0826	0827	0858	0907	0928	0927	0958	1007	1028	1027	1058	1107	1128	1127	1207	1228	1227	1307	1328
186	Kiryat Gat	d.	0602	0722	0759	0802	0822	0830	0859	0802	0922	0930	0959	1002	1022	1030	1059	1102	1122	1130	1159	1202	1230	1259	1302	1330	1359
230	**Be'er Sheva** Center	a.	0738	0755	0836	0838	0855**a**	0906	0936	0938	0955**a**	1006	1036	1038	1055**a**	1106	1136	1138	1155	1206	1236	1238	1306	1336	1338	1406	1436

		⑦-④	⑤	⑤	⑦-④	⑤	⑤	⑦-④	⑤	⑤	⑦-④	⑦-④	⑦-④	⑦-④	⑦-④	⑦-④	⑦-④	⑦-④	⑦-④	⑦-④	⑦-④	⑦-④		⑥	⑥	⑥
Nahariyya	d.	...	...	...	...	...	...	...	...	...	...	...	1527	...	1627	...	1727	...	1827	1927	...	...	✣	2043	2129	2229
Akko	d.	...	...	...	...	...	...	...	...	...	...	...	1534	...	1634	...	1734	...	1834	1934	...	...		2050	2136	2236
Qiryat Motzkin	d.	...	...	...	...	...	...	...	...	...	...	1519	1544	1619	1644	1719	1744	1819	1844	1944	...	...		2100	2146	2249
Haifa Hof HaKarmel	d.	...	...	...	...	...	...	...	...	...	1511	1545	1611	1645	1711	1745	1811	1845	1911	2011	...	...		2131	2213	2313
Binyamina	d.	...	...	...	...	...	...	...	...	...	|	|	|	|	|	|	|	|	|	|	...	...		2151	2232	2332
Tel Aviv Savidor Centre	d.	1307	...	...	1407	...	...	1507	...	...	1607	1637	1707	1737	1807	1837	1907	1937	2007	2107	2207	2307	⑥	2230	2305	0023
Tel Aviv HaHagana	d.	1402	...	...	1414	...	...	1514	...	...	1614	1644	1714	1744	1914	1844	1914	1944	2014	2114	2214	2314		2239	2314	0032
Lod	d.	1327	1407	1428	1427	1507	1528	1527	1607	1628	1627	1658	1727	1758	1827	1858	1927	1958	2027	2127	2227	2327		2253	2328	0045
Kiryat Gat	d.	1358	1430	1459	1502	1530	1559	1602	1630	1659	1702	1722	1802	1822	1902	1922	2002	2022	2102	2202	2302	0002	✣	2324	0001	0117
Be'er Sheva Center	a.	1438	1506	1536	1537	1606	1636	1638	1706	1736	1738	1755	1838	1855	1938	1955	2038	2055	2138	2238	2338	0038		2359	0038	0146

		⑦-④	⑤	⑦-④	⑤	⑤	⑦-④	⑦-④	⑤	⑤	⑦-④	⑦-④	⑤	⑤	⑦-④	⑦-④	⑤	⑤	⑦-④	⑤	⑤	⑦-④	⑤	⑤	⑦-④	⑤
Be'er Sheva Center	d.	0453	0455	0553	0555	0628	0634	0653	0655	0728	0734	0753	0755	0828	0834	0853	0855	0928	0953	0955	1028	1053	1055	1128	1153	1155
Kiryat Gat	d.	0525	0528	0625	0627	0702	0703	0725	0728	0801	0803	0825	0827	0902	0903	0925	0927	1002	1024	1028	1102	1124	1128	1212	1225	1227
Lod	d.	0559	0559	0659	0659	0726	0728	0759	0759	0826	0828	0859	0859	0926	0928	0959	0959	1026	1059	1059	1126	1159	1159	1226	1259	1259
Tel Aviv HaHagana	d.	0612	...	0712	...	...	0741	0812	...	...	0841	0912	...	...	0941	1012	...	...	1112	...	...	1212	...	...	1312	...
Tel Aviv Savidor Centre	d.	0622	...	0722	...	...	0752	0822	...	...	0852	0922	...	...	0952	1020	...	...	1120	...	...	1220	...	...	1320	...
Binyamina	d.	|	...	|	...	...	|	|	...	...	|	|	...	...	|	...	...	...	...	...	...	...	...	...	...	...
Haifa Hof HaKarmel	d.	0711	...	0811	...	...	0840	0911	...	...	0940	1011	...	...	1040	...	...	...	...	...	...	...	...	...	...	...
Qiryat Motzkin	d.	0738	...	0838	...	...	0906	0938	...	...	1006	1038	...	...	1106	...	...	...	...	...	...	...	...	...	...	...
Akko	d.	0748	...	0848	...	...	...	0948	...	...	...	1048	...	...	...	...	...	...	...	...	...	...	...	...	...	...
Nahariyya	a.	0758	...	0858	...	...	...	0958	...	...	...	1058	...	...	...	...	...	...	...	...	...	...	...	...	...	...

		⑤	⑦-④	⑤	⑤	⑦-④	⑤	⑦-④	⑦-④	⑤	⑦-④	⑦-④	⑦-④	⑦-④	⑦-④	⑦-④	⑦-④	⑦-④	⑦-④	⑦-④	⑦-④	⑦-④		⑥	⑥	⑥
Be'er Sheva Center	d.	1228	1253	1255	1328	1353	1355	1434	1453	1455	1531	1553	1634	1653	1731	1753	1834	1853	1953	2053	2153	2253	✣	1858	1952	2058
Kiryat Gat	d.	1302	1325	1328	1402	1425	1428	1503	1525	1528	1603	1625	1703	1725	1803	1824	1903	1925	2025	2125	2225	2325		1931	2025	2131
Lod	d.	1326	1359	1359	1426	1459	1459	1528	1559	1559	1628	1659	1728	1759	1828	1859	1928	1959	2059	2159	2259	2359		2003	2056	2203
Tel Aviv HaHagana	d.	...	1412	...	...	1512	...	1541	1612	...	1641	1712	1741	1812	1841	1912	1941	2012	2112	2212	2312	0012		2016	2109	2216
Tel Aviv Savidor Centre	d.	...	1422	...	...	1522	...	1552	1622	...	1652	1722	1752	1822	1852	1922	1952	2022	2120	2220	2320	0020		2025	2120	2225
Binyamina	d.	...	|	...	...	|	...	|	|	...	|	|	|	|	|	|	|	|	...	...	...	...	⑥	2056	2207	2256
Haifa Hof HaKarmel	d.	...	1511	...	...	1611	...	1640	1711	...	1740	1811	1840	1911	1940	2011	2040	2111	...	...	...	...		2115	2225	2315
Qiryat Motzkin	d.	...	1538	...	...	1638	...	1706	1738	...	1806	1838	1906	1938	2006	2038	...	2138	...	...	...	...		2144	*2328*	2344
Akko	d.	...	1548	...	...	1648	...	...	1748	...	...	1848	...	1948	...	2048	...	2148	...	...	...	...	✣	2153	*2337*	2353
Nahariyya	a.	...	1558	...	...	1658	...	...	1758	...	...	1858	...	1958	...	2058	...	2158	...	...	...	...		2202	*2346*	0002

a – Arrives 5 minutes later on ①.

✣ – Because of electrification works services on ⑥ will be **suspended** from June 1 until further notice.

☛ For additional services Nahariyya – Tel Aviv and v.v and connections to/from Nahariyya see Table **4500**.

4513 BEIT SHE'AN - HAIFA Hof HaKarmel — Israel Railways

km			⑦-④	⑦-④	⑦-④		⑦-④	⑦-④		⑦-④														
0	Beit She'an	d.	0531	0601	0631	...	0702	0731	and hourly	2131	...	...	...	⑤	0635	0735	and hourly	1635	...	⑥	...	2108	2208	...
60	Haifa Hof HaKarmel	a.	0629	*0703*	0729	...	*0803*	0829	until	2229	...	...	...		0733	0833	until	1733	...		...	2206	2306	...

		⑦-④	⑦-④		⑦-④	⑦-④	⑦-④	⑦-④	⑦-④	⑦-④	⑦-④	⑦-④											
Haifa Hof HaKarmel	d.	0603	0703	and hourly	1603	*1624*	1703	1803	*1824*	1903	2003	2103	⑤	0619	0719	and hourly	1619	...	⑥	...	2153	2253	...
Beit She'an	a.	0701	0801	until	1701	1729	1801	1901	1929	2001	2101	2201		0721	0821	until	1721	...		...	2254	2354	...

4514 TEL AVIV - BEN GURION AIRPORT - JERUSALEM — Israel Railways

km				⑦-④	⑦-④	⑦-④	⑦-④	⑦-④		⑦-④	⑦-④	⑦-④	⑦-④	⑦-④	⑦-④	⑦-④	⑦-④					
0	**Tel Aviv**	d.	...	...	...	...	...	...	and every 30	...	...	...	...	...	...	...	...	...	⑥	...	...	...
	Ben Gurion Airport	d.	...	0631	0701	0731	0801	0831	minutes	1731	1801	1831	1901	1931	2001	2101	2131	...		2206	2306	...
56	**Jerusalem** Yitzhak Navon	a.	...	0655	0725	0755	0825	0855	until	1755	1825	1855	1925	1955	2025	2125	2155	...		2230	2330	...

			⑦-④	⑦-④	⑦-④	⑦-④	⑦-④		⑦-④	⑦-④	⑦-④	⑦-④	⑦-④	⑦-④	⑦-④	⑦-④	⑦-④				
Jerusalem Yitzhak Navon	d.	...	0630	0700	0730	0800	0830	and every 30	1730	1800	1830	1900	1930	2000	2030	2100	2130	⑥	2154	2254	...
Ben Gurion Airport	d.	...	0653	0723	0753	0823	0853	minutes	1753	1823	1853	1923	1953	2023	2053	2123	2153		2217	2317	...
Tel Aviv	a.	...	...	...	...	...	...	until	...	...	...	...	...	...	...	...	...		...	...	...

4515 HERTSLIYYA - TEL AVIV - BET SHEMESH - JERUSALEM — Israel Railways

km			⑦-④	⑦-④	⑦-④	⑦-④		⑦-④	⑦-④	⑦-④	⑦-④	⑦-④	⑦-④	⑦-④	⑦-④	⑦-④	⑦-④		⑤	⑤		⑤		⑥	⑥
	Hertsliyya	d.	*0519*	0635	0735	0835		1336	1436	1535	1635	1735	1835	1935	2036	2136	2236		...	...		...		1943	214
0	**Tel Aviv** Savidor C	d.	0556**a**	0649	0749	0849	and hourly	1349	1449	1549	1649	1749	1849	1949	2049	2149	2249	⑤	...	...	and hourly	...	⑥	1956	215
20	Lod	d.	0611	0711	0811	0911	until	1411	1511	1611	1711	1811	1911	2011	2111	2211	2311		0736	0836	until	1536		*2040*	*223*
51	**Bet Shemesh**	a.	0638	0738	0838	0938		1438	1538	1638	1738	1838	1938	2038	2138	2238	2338		0801	0901		1601		*2107*	*230*

		⑦-④	⑦-④	⑦-④	⑦-④		⑦-④	⑦-④	⑦-④	⑦-④	⑦-④	⑦-④	⑦-④	⑦-④	⑦-④		⑤	⑤		⑤	⑤		⑥	
Bet Shemesh	d.	0549	0649	0749	0849		1349	1449	1549	1649	1749	1849	1949	2049	2154		0627	0727		1527	1636		2221	...
Lod	d.	0614	0714	0814	0914	and hourly	1414	1514	1614	1714	1814	1914	2014	2114	2220	⑤	0653	0753	and hourly	1553	1702	⑥	2247	...
Tel Aviv Savidor C	a.	0640	0740	0840	0940	until	1440	1541	1641	1740	1840	1940	2040	2140	*2248*		...	...	until	...	...		2309	...
Hertsliyya	a.	0651	0751	0851	0953		1451	1551	1651	1751	1851	1953	2053	2153	*2308*		...	...		...	...		*2330*	...

km			⑦-④	⑤		⑤	⑦-④	⑤	⑤		⑤	⑦-④	⑤	⑦-④	⑤	⑦-④	⑤		⑦-④	⑦-④				⑥			
0	**Bet Shemesh**	d.	0750	0746	...	0846	0950	0946	1046	...	1146	1150	1309	1350	1409	1550	1509	...	1750	1950	...	...	⑥	2305	...	...	...
31	**Jerusalem** Malha	a.	0832	0827	...	0924	1032	1027	1127	...	1227	1232	1348	1432	1448	1630	1548	...	1830	2030	...	...		2346	...	...	...

		⑦-④	⑤		⑤	⑦-④	⑤	⑤	⑦-④	⑤	⑦-④	⑤	⑤	⑦-④	⑤	⑤	⑦-④	⑦-④	⑦-④				⑥			
Jerusalem Malha	d.	0657	0737	...	0837	0857	0937	1037	1057	1137	1253	1258	1358	1453	1458	1556	1653	1853	2115	...	...	⑥	2143	...	...	...
Bet Shemesh	d.	0736	0820	...	0920	0936	1120	1120	1136	1220	1336	1343	1443	1536	1543	1636	1736	1936	2154	...	...		2221	...	...	...

a – Tel Aviv HaHagana.

SYRIA 4600

Chemins de fer Syriens Services suspended due to hostilities

Capital: **Dimashq** (GMT +2, add 1 hour in summer). 2019 Public Holidays: Jan. 1, Mar. 8, Apr. 17, 28, May 1, 6, June 5, Aug. 12, Sept. 1, Oct. 6, Nov. 10, Dec. 25.

km								
0	**Al Qamishli** d.	...	...	...	**Dimashq** Kadem d.	...	...	...
81	Al Hasakah d.	...	...	...	Hims 2 d.	...	...	...
210	Dayr az Zawr d.	...	...	...	Hamah d.	...	...	...
346	Ar Raqqah d.	...	...	...	**Aleppo** (Halab) d.	...	...	...
550	**Aleppo** (Halab) d.	...	...	...	Ar Raqqah d.	...	...	...
694	Hamah d.	...	...	...	Dayr az Zawr d.	...	...	...
755	Hims 2 d.	...	...	...	Al Hasakah d.	...	...	...
899	**Dimashq** Kadem a.	...	...	...	**Al Qamishli** a.	...	...	...

km								
0	**Aleppo** (Halab) d.	...	...	...	**Dimashq** Kadem d.	...	...	...
68	Bismaron d.	...	...	...	Hims 2 d.	...	...	...
95	Jisr ash Shughur d.	...	...	...	Tartus d.	...	...	...
199	**Al Ladhiqyah** d.	...	...	...	**Al Ladhiqyah** d.	...	...	...
280	Tartus d.	...	...	...	Jisr ash Shughur d.	...	...	...
382	Hims 2 d.	...	...	...	Bismaron d.	...	...	...
526	**Dimashq** Kadem a.	...	...	...	**Aleppo** (Halab) a.	...	...	...

IRAQ 4610

Iraq Railways

km		2C	21 B		20 B	12 A
609	Umm Qasr d.	1130	...	**Al Mawsil** d.	...	1900
541	**Al Basrah** Ma'qil d.	1400	2100	Ba'iji d.	...	|
370	An Nasiriyah (for Ur) d.	▬	|	Tikrit d.	...	|
182	Ad Dawanyah d.	...	|	Samarra d.	...	0400
107	Al Hillah (for Babylon) d.	**11**	|	**Baghdad** Central a.	...	0800
0	**Baghdad** Central a.	**A**	0915	**Baghdad** Central d.	1700	▬
0	**Baghdad** Central d.	1920	...	Al Hillah (for Babylon) d.	|	...
117	Samarra d.	2310	...	Ad Dawanyah d.	|	...
171	Tikrit d.	|	...	An Nasiriyah (for Ur) d.	|	**2C**
211	Ba'iji d.	|	...	**Al Basrah** Ma'qil a.	0520	0800
406	**Al Mawsil** a.	0755	...	Umm Qasr a.	...	1025

Capital: **Baghdad** (GMT +3).

2019 Public Holidays: Jan. 1, 6, May 1, June 5 - 7, July 14, Aug. 12 - 15, Sept. 1, 10, Oct. 3, Nov. 10, Dec. 25.

Rail services in Iraq are operated by Iraq Railways. Trains convey second class seating and also sleeping cars where indicated. Information regarding rail services is still very hard to obtain and the schedules shown should be treated as subject to confirmation.

A – 🛏 2 cl. Runs when required.
B – 🛏 2 cl.
C – Runs once per week. Days of operation unknown.

SAUDI ARABIA 4620

Saudi Railways Organization

Capital: **Riyadh** (GMT +3). 2019 Public Holidays: June 5 - 8, Aug. 12, Sep. 23.

Rail services are operated by either: the Saudi Railways Organization (SRO) (www.saudirailways.org) or Saudi Railway Company (SAR) (www.sar.com.sa). SRO operate services to Ad Dammam and the 300km/h Harmain High-Speed Rail (HHR) between Makkaht and Madinah. The Ad Damman service has two types of trains: Modern (shown as **M** in the tables) and Regular (shown as **R**). **M** trains convey first (called Premium and includes refreshments in the waiting rooms) and second class (Standard) seating. **R** trains convey first (called Al-Rihab), second (called Al-Taleaa) and ordinary class (called Al Qafela) seating. HHR services offer business or economy class seating. SAR operate services to Qurayyat. Their day train conveys business and economy classes and the night train also conveys 93 berths in 24 sleeping compartments. Reservations are available from 6 months until 1 hour before departure. **Schedules vary during Ramadan and Eid-al-Fitr.**

km		M	R ⑦–④	M	R ⑦–④	M ④⑥	M	M	M	M	R ⑥–④
0	**Ad Dammam** d.	0345	0510	0805	1013	1143	1335	1542	1748	1955	2144
74	Abqaiq d.	0426	0554	0846	1057	|	1416	1623	1829	2036	2228
139	Al Hufuf d.	0510	0630	0930	1133	|	1500	1707	1913	2120	2304
449	**Ar Riyad** a.	0722	...	1142	...	1503	1712	1919	2125	2332	...

	R ⑦–④	M	R ⑥–④	M	R ⑥–④	M	M	M	M ④⑥	M
Ar Riyad d.	...	0759	...	1118	...	1325	1531	1738	1947	2100
Al Hufuf d.	0515	1019	1144	1338	1407	1545	1751	1958	|	2320
Abqaiq d.	0553	1056	1222	1415	1451	1622	1828	2035	|	2357
Ad Dammam a.	0635	1135	1304	1545	1533	1701	1907	2114	2305	0036

km		④–⑦	④–⑦	④–⑦	④–⑦		④–⑦	④–⑦	④–⑦	④–⑦
0	**Makkah** d.	0800	1000	1230	1700	**Madinah** d.	0800	1230	1430	1700
78	Jeddah d.	0846	1046	|	1746	KAEC ◇ d.	0935	|	|	1835
	KAEC ◇ d.	0933	|	|	1833	Jeddah d.	1022	1449	|	1922
450	**Madinah** a.	1005	1302	1525	2005	**Makkah** a.	1105	1532	1725	2005

◇ – King Abdullah Economic City.

km		B	B ④⑥	A ⑥		B	B ④⑥	A ③
0	**Qurayyat** d.	...	...	...	**Ar Riyad** d.	0930	1730	2130
	Al Jouf d.	...	...	2330	Majma'ah d.	1054	1859	|
	Hail d.	1530	...	0225	**Al Qassim** d.	1206	2001	0015
	Al Qassim d.	1745	2100	0449	Hail d.	1401	...	0235
	Majma'ah d.	1852	2207	|	Al Jouf d.	...	...	0520
1242	**Ar Riyad** a.	2011	2326	0729	**Qurayyat** a.	...	...	...

A – 🛏 (12) ✕.
B – (12) ✕.

IRAN 4630

Raja Trains

Capital: **Tehran** (GMT +3.5, add 1 hour in summer).
2019 Public Holidays: Feb. 9, 11, Mar. 20, Apr. 3, 21, May 26, June 5, 6, 29, Aug. 12, 20, Sept. 9, Oct. 20, 28, 29, Nov. 15.

Rail services in Iran are provided by 11 different private companies. The ticket sales system is centralised (www.iranrail.net), but every company issues its own tickets. All trains convey sleeping cars which convert to seating for daytime travel, except Pardis high-speed and Saba double deck trains, shown as **P** and **S** in the tables. For services to/from Turkey see Table **1575**.

km			P	P	●	S	P	P●	P			S●	●		P		●			●				
0	**Tehran** d.	0030	0705	0720	0840	0920	1150	1155	1505	1545	1605	1615	1755	1755	1910	2015	2210	2150	2200	2315	2335	2359	...	...
926	**Mashhad** a.	1210	1530	1545	1940	2155	2100	2015	0130	0205	0210	0220	0425	0348	0515	0610	0900	0730	0755	0925	0925	1140	...	...

			S	P	P	S	S	●	P				●										
Mashhad d.	...	0035	0050	0520	0600	0710	0755	1025	1140	1215	1255	1540	1350	1655	1730	1830	2005	2040	2210	2235	2315	...	...
Tehran a.	...	1050	1215	1335	1350	1930	1920	2111	1950	2305	2340	0206	0023	0346	0320	0410	0605	0800	0945	1005	1030	...	...

km										
	Mashad d.	...	...	0650	1535	**Tabriz** d.	1030	1455	1730	2110
0	**Tehran** d.	1800	1920	1738	0214	**Tehran** a.	2308	0256	0555	0945
736	**Tabriz** a.	0625	0800	0635	1455	Mashad a.	0955	1445	...	...

km							
0	**Tehran** d.	...	1405	1645	**Khorramshahr** d.	...	1245	...
816	Ahvaz d.	...	0513	0840	Ahvaz d.	1200	1433	1630
939	**Khorramshahr** a.	...	0730	...	**Tehran** a.	0330	0655	0810

km		A				A		
0	**Tabriz** d.	0830	...	...	**Djulfa** d.	1830	...	...
146	**Djulfa** a.	1135	...	...	**Tabriz** a.	2120	...	...

km		P		P	●				●		P	P
0	**Tehran** d.	0605	1125	1550	1715	1955	**Zahedan** d.	...	...	1300	...	...
	Yadz d.	1215	1844	2155	0046	0401	Kerman d.	1610	1930	2047	...	...
	Kerman d.	...	0130	...	0710	1010	Yadz d.	2149	0135	0234	0630	1500
1658	**Zahedan** a.	...	0930	...	...	...	**Tehran** a.	0625	1020	1125	1225	2110

km				●				●
0	**Tehran** d.	1215	1315	1610	**Bandar e Abbas** d.	1155	1305	1550
	Yadz d.	1935	2050	2334	Yadz d.	2314	0045	0306
1483	**Bandar e Abbas** a.	0845	0945	1105	**Tehran** a.	0745	0930	1115

km		S	S		S	S
0	**Mashhad** d.	1005	2030	**Sarakhs** d.	0540	1520
165	**Sarakhs** a.	1245	2310	**Mashhad** a.	0820	1810

km		●	●	●	●		●	●		●
0	**Tehran** d.	1610	1805	1915	2245	**Shiraz** d.	...	1410	1715	1910
494	**Eşfahan** d.	|	|	|	0615	**Eşfahan** d.	1930	|	|	|
1074	**Shiraz** a.	0705	0905	1055	...	**Tehran** a.	0305	0510	0840	1020

km						
0	**Mashhad** d.	1445	1655	**Eşfahan** d.	1620	1810
1484	**Eşfahan** a.	0935	1120	**Mashhad** a.	1035	1230

km		●	●	●			●	●	●	
0	**Mashhad** d.	1150	1300	2045	2359	**Qom** d.	1250	1455	1605	2359
	Tehran d.	2234	2351	0734	1033	Tehran d.	1625	1722	1820	0230
1106	**Qom** a.	0105	0201	1005	1305	**Mashhad** a.	0200	0410	0525	1325

A – ②④⑤⑦. Note: conveys 2nd class seats only.
● – Every other day.
▲ – Odd dated days.

ZAHEDAN - QUETTA 4640

km		404 A			403 B	
0	**Zahedan** d.	1000	...	**Quetta** d.	0800	...
84	Mirjawa 🏛 a.	1220	...	Spezand d.	0920	...
84	Mirjawa 🏛 d.	1300	...	Wali Khan d.	1016	...
100	Kuhi Taftan a.	1550	...	Nushki d.	1510	...
100	Kuhi Taftan d.	1700	...	Dalbandin d.	2240	...
222	Nok Kundi d.	2157	...	Nok Kundi d.	0557	...
389	Dalbandin d.	0540	...	Kuhi Taftan a.	1100	...
578	Nushki d.	1257	...	Kuhi Taftan d.	1230	...
689	Wali Khan d.	1740	...	Mirjawa 🏛 a.	1505	...
712	Spezand d.	1930	...	Mirjawa 🏛 d.	1515	...
737	**Quetta** a.	2025	...	**Zahedan** a.	1740	...

NOTE: Pakistan Railways and Raja Trains give different schedules for this train. This table shows the Pakistan Railways version. The Raja version is: Quetta d. 0830 - Zahedan a. 1335 / Zahedan d. 0800 - Quetta a. 1515.

A – (12) departs on 3rd and 17th of the month. **B** – (12) departs on 1st and 15th of the month.

QUETTA - AMRITSAR 4650

km		23 A	402 ①④	14002 ①④		14001 ①④	401 ①④	24 A
0	**Quetta** d.	1015	...	...	**Amritsar** d.	0650	...	...
131	Sibi d.	1520	...	...	Atari 🏛 a.	0715	...	...
296	Jacobabad d.	1820	...	...	Atari 🏛 d.	...	1100	...
385	Rohri d.	2045	...	...	Wagah a.	...	1410	...
840	Khanewal d.	0720	...	...	Wagah d.	...	1610	...
1127	**Lahore** Junction a.	0955	...	...	**Lahore** Junction a.	...	1645	...
1127	**Lahore** Junction d.	...	0800	...	**Lahore** Junction d.	...	...	1700
	Wagah a.	...	0835	...	Khanewal d.	...	...	2250
	Wagah d.	...	1130	...	Rohri d.	...	...	0630
1147	Atari 🏛 a.	...	1150	...	Jacobabad d.	...	...	0840
1147	Atari 🏛 d.	...	...	2000	Sibi d.	...	...	1155
1173	**Amritsar** a.	...	...	2037	**Quetta** a.	...	...	1700

A – AKBAR EXPRESS operated by Pakistan Railways.

NOTE: Timings are subject to confirmation and connections are not guaranteed.

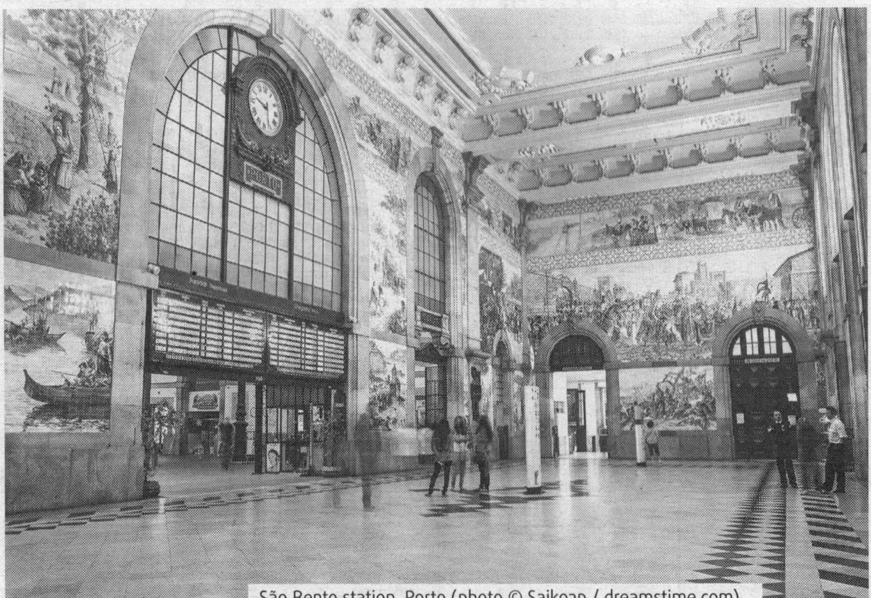

São Bento station, Porto (photo © Saiko3p / dreamstime.com)

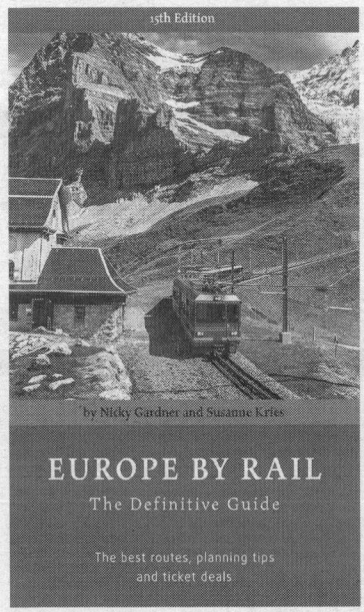

As an added extra for readers of this seasonal Summer edition we are including the remaining BEYOND EUROPE sections, in addition to the pages for **Africa and the Middle East** which appear in the preceding pages.

The tables covering **India, South East Asia, Australia and New Zealand**, **China**, **Japan**, **North America**, **South America** and **South Korea** previously appeared in our monthly editions from January to May 2019. Limited updates have been made to these tables for this seasonal edition.

BEYOND EUROPE
India

Introduction

The Beyond Europe section covers principal rail services in a different area of the world each month. There are six areas, each appearing as follows:

Winter (December) and Summer (June):	Africa and The Middle East along with all other Beyond Europe sections.
January and July (digital only):	India.
February and August:	South East Asia, Australia and New Zealand; India; North America.
March and September (digital only):	China.
April and October:	Japan; China; South America; South Korea.
May and November (digital only):	North America.

The months have been chosen so that we can bring you up-to-date information for those countries which make seasonal changes.

Contents

INDEX OF PLACES

INDIA

Capital: **New Delhi** (GMT +5.5). 2019 Public Holidays: Jan. 26, Mar. 4, Apr. 17, 19, May 18, Aug. 12, 15, 24, Sept. 10, Oct. 2, 8, 27, Nov. 10, 12, Dec. 25.

Rail services in India are operated by Indian Railways. Most trains convey a selection of first and second class accommodation from the several available. Trains which conv second class only are noted in either the column head or footnotes. Note that Rajdhani and Shatabdi trains convey first class accommodation only. The exact carriage typ available on each train varies. A brief summary of train types and accommodation follows:

Rajdhani (shown as *RDi* in column heads). Air-conditioned first class night trains. Special fares payable. Conveys First Class 2 or 4-berth sleepers (code 1A); two-tier (code 2 or three-tier (code 3A) first class open plan berths. **Shatabdi** (shown as *SDi* in column heads). Air-conditioned first class daytime trains. Special fares payable. Conveys Cha Class seats (code CC); Executive Chair Class. **Jan Shatabdi** (shown as *jSDi* in column heads) as Shatabdi but also conveys 2 berth sleepers (code 2S)**Duronto** (shown column heads as *Duro*). Some non-stop trains, some very limited stop trains. Conveys first class sleeping accommodation (codes 1A, 2A, 3A as above); second class non a conditioned 6-berth (code SL). **Express** (shown in column heads as *Exp*). Most services convey first class air conditioned two-tier (code 2A) or three-tier (code 3A) open pl berths; second class 'Sleeper Class' non air-conditioned six-berth (code SL); non air-conditioned second class seats (code 2S). **Yuva** (shown in column heads as *Yuva*). Lo cost air-conditioned train. Seating accommodation only. During the day, all sleepers and berths convert to seated accommodation. The codes shown are those used by Indi Railways.

Timings are valid until further notice. Short notice changes are possible, especially around religious festivals and during monsoon seasons. Tickets can be purchased fro stations or through authorised agents. Reservations are required for travel on all trains shown in this section.

Unfortunately Indian Railways have recently stopped issuing all their rail passes. For help with tickets and travel arrangements on Indian Railways contact SD Enterprise info@indiarail.co.uk.

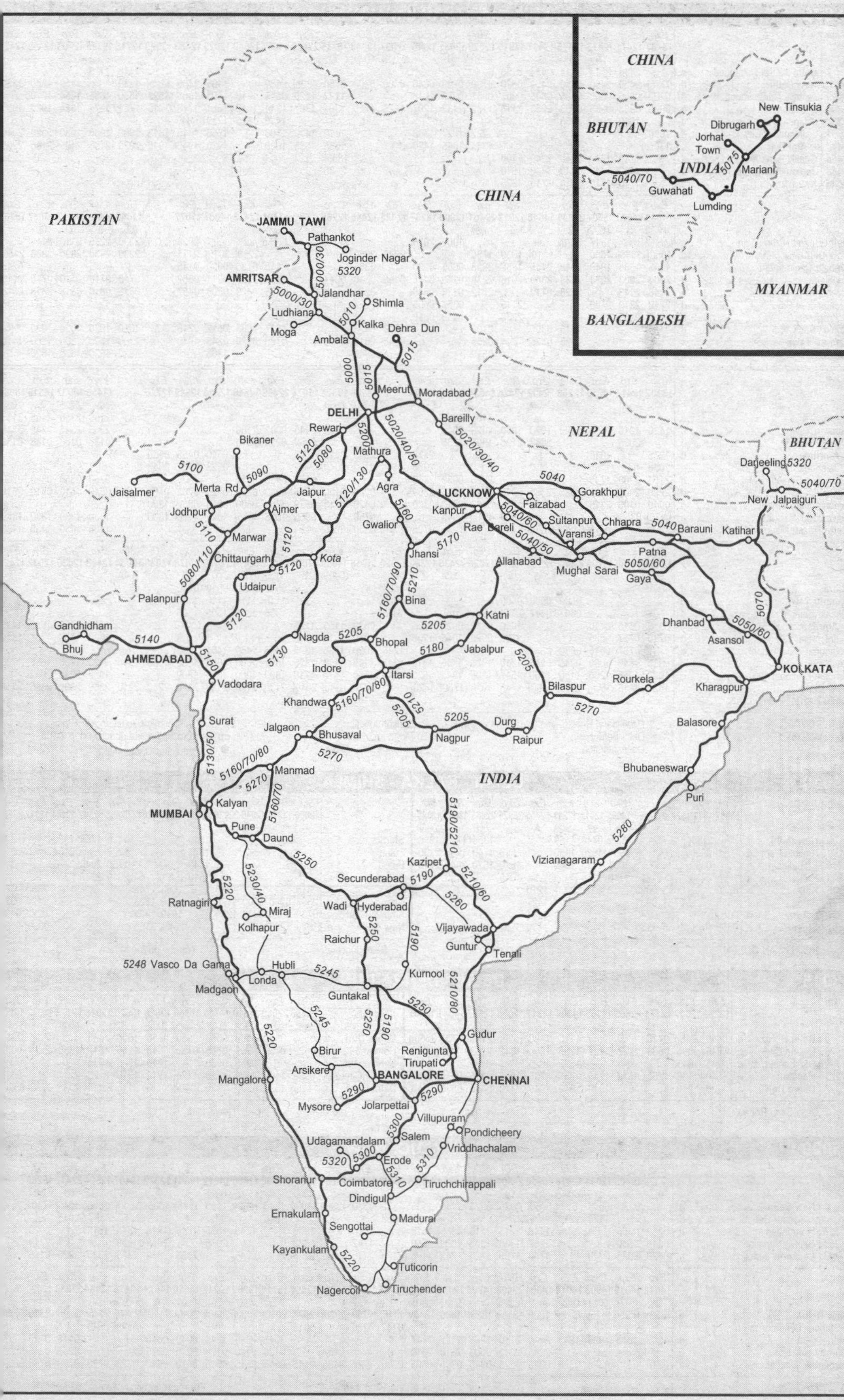
CHINA
BHUTAN
INDIA
New Tinsukia
Dibrugarh
Jorhat Town
5075
Mariani
5040/70
Guwahati
Lumding
MYANMAR
BANGLADESH
PAKISTAN
CHINA
JAMMU TAWI
Pathankot
Joginder Nagar
5320
5000/30
AMRITSAR
Jalandhar
5000/30
Ludhiana
Moga
5010
Shimla
Kalka
Ambala
Dehra Dun
5015
5000
5015
Meerut
Moradabad
DELHI
Rewari
Bareilly
5200
5020/40/50
5020/30/40
NEPAL
BHUTAN
Darjeeling
5320
5040/70
New Jalpaiguri
Bikaner
5100
Jaisalmer
Merta Rd
5090
5120
5080
Mathura
Jaipur
5120/130
Agra
LUCKNOW
5040
Gorakhpur
Faizabad
Jodhpur
Ajmer
Kanpur
5040/60
Sultanpur
Chhapra
5040
Barauni
Katihar
5110
Marwar
5120
Gwalior
5160
Rae Bareli
Varansi
5040/50
Patna
Chittaurgarh
5120
Kota
Jhansi
5170
Allahabad
Mughal Sarai
5050/60
Gaya
5080/110
Udaipur
5160/70/90
5210
Palanpur
Bina
Katni
5070
Dhanbad
5050/60
5120
5205
Asansol
Gandhidham
Bhuj
5140
AHMEDABAD
5150
Nagda
5205
Bhopal
Jabalpur
5180
5205
KOLKATA
5130
Indore
Itarsi
Rourkela
Vadodara
Bilaspur
Kharagpur
Khandwa
5160/70/80
5210
5205
5270
Surat
5205
Durg
Balasore
Jalgaon
Bhusaval
Nagpur
Raipur
5130/50
5270
5160/70/80
Manmad
INDIA
5270
Bhubaneswar
5160/70
Puri
MUMBAI
Kalyan
5190/5210
Pune
Daund
5280
5250
Vizianagaram
Kazipet
5220
5230/40
Secunderabad
5190
5210/60
Ratnagiri
Wadi
Hyderabad
5260
Miraj
Kolhapur
5250
5190
Vijayawada
Raichur
Guntur
Tenali
5248 Vasco Da Gama
Hubli
5245
Kurnool
Madgaon
Londa
5210/80
Guntakal
5250
5245
5250
5190
Gudur
5220
Birur
Renigunta
Tirupati
Arsikere
BANGALORE
CHENNAI
Mangalore
5290
5290
Mysore
Jolarpettai
Villupuram
5300
Pondicheery
Salem
Vriddhachalam
Udagamandalam
5320
5300
Erode
5310
5310
Shoranur
Coimbatore
Tiruchchirappali
Dindigul
Ernakulam
Madurai
Sengottai
Kayankulam
5220
Tuticorin
Nagercoil
Tiruchender

5000 DELHI - AMRITSAR and JAMMU TAWI

Indian Railways

km		Exp	Exp	Exp	Exp	Exp	Exp	SDi	SDi	Exp	SDi	SDi	Exp	Exp	Exp	Exp	Exp	Exp	Exp	Exp	Exp	Exp	Exp	Exp
		15707	**12471**	**12473**	**12475**	**12477**	**12919**	**12029**	**12031**	**12497**	**12037**	**12043**	**18215**	**22429**	**11057**	**12549**	**12925**	**12483**	**12379**	**12715**	**19325**	**12203**	**12459**	**1242**
			A	⑦	④	③		ex④	④		ex①⑥	①⑥	④	ex④		③		⑤	⑥		③⑥	①②⑤		④
7	**Delhi** Hazrat Nizamuddin d.	...	0414	0414	0414	0414	0438	...	...	...	...	...	...	...	0343	0940**f**	1005	1042	...	1148	1125	...	...	...
0	**New Delhi** d.	0325**j**	0450	0450	0450	0450	0520	0720	0720	0640	0700	0700	0750	0825**j**	0430	|	1105	1150	1225**j**	1230	|	1410	1340	133
199	Ambala Cantonment d.	0700	0805	0805	0805	0805	0905	0957	0957	1015	|	|	1122	1120	0940	1310	1455	1505	1525	1550	1635	1654	1720	|
304	Ludhiana d.	0930	0953	0953	0953	0953	1113	1132	1132	1207	1225	1225	1307	1307	1344	1510	1651	1716	1716	1751	1834	1834	1920	193
356	Jalandhar Cantonment d.	|	1050	1050	1050	1050	1205	|	|	|	...	**m**	|	|	1445	1615	1739	|	|	|	|	|	|	|
361	Jalandhar City d.	1040	|	|	|	|	|	1227	1227	1303	...	...	1410	1410	1505	|	1758	1815	1815	1900	1930	1930	2025	204
440	**Amritsar** a.	1305	|	|	|	|	|	1345	1345	1420	...	...	1535	1535	1630	|	1920	1945	1945	2020	2105	2105	2145	220
468	Chakki Bank ♥ d.	...	1240	1240	1240	1240	1400	...	...	...	...	...	1855**k**	**p**	...	|	...	...	...	...	...	...	...	...
568	**Jammu Tawi** a.	...	1440	1440	1440	1440	1610	...	...	...	...	...	2135	...	...	2110	...	...	...	...	...	...	...	...
646	**Katra** a.	...	1710	1710	1710	1710	1825	...	...	...	...	...	...	...	...	...	...	...	...	...	...	...	...	...

	Exp	Exp	Exp	Exp	Exp	SDi	Exp	Exp	Exp	RDi	Exp	Duro		Exp	Exp	Exp	Exp		Exp	Exp	Exp	Exp	Exp
	14649	**14673**	**18507**	**22941**	**14645**	**12013**	**22461**	**12903**	**18237**	**12425**	**12445**	**12265**		**22401**	**12413**	**14033**	**11077**		**11449**	**16031**	**16317**	**16687**	**1810**
	①③⑥	**B**	③⑥⑦	②			ex④					②⑤⑦		①③⑥					②	①④⑤	⑦	③	
Delhi Hazrat Nizamuddin d.	...	...	1417	1420**f**	...	...	...	1900	2035	...	...	2215**a**	...	2215**a**	...	...	2028	...	2235	2235	2110	2110	...
New Delhi d.	1050**j**	1050**j**	1500	|	1610**j**	1630	1730	|	|	2040	2050	|	...	|	2230**j**	2010**j**	2115	...	2330	2330	2330	2330	215
Ambala Cantonment d.	1535	1535	1840	1840	2145	1852	2028	0055	0230	|	2355	|	...	0110	0135	0020	0145	...	|	|	|	|	024
Ludhiana d.	2003	2003	2033	2033	2359	2018	2215	0245	0446	0106	0140	0247	...	0257	0325	0211	0352	...	0710	0710	0710	0710	051
Jalandhar Cantonment d.	2148	2148	|	2128	0110	|	2312	0338	0545	|	0235	|	...	0355	0420	0308	0457	...	0818	0818	0818	0818	061
Jalandhar City d.	2210	2210	2150	|	|	2115	|	0357	0605	|	|	|	...	|	|	|	|	...	|	|	|	|	063
Amritsar a.	2355	2355	2330	|	|	2230	|	0530	0810	|	|	|	...	|	|	|	|	...	|	|	|	|	075
Chakki Bank ♥ d.	...	...	...	2315	0305	...	0100	...	...	0340	0425	|	...	0537	0605	0512	0715	...	1020	1020	1020	1020	|
Jammu Tawi a.	...	...	...	0125	0525	...	0255	...	...	0545	0615	0725	...	0725	0820	0845	1010	...	1300	1300	1300	1300	141
Katra a.	...	...	...	...	...	...	0510	...	...	...	0840	...	...	...	...	1105	...	...	1520	1520	1520	1520	...

	Exp	Exp	Exp	Duro	Exp	RDi	Exp	Exp	Exp		Exp	Exp	Exp	Exp	Exp	Exp	SDi	Exp		Exp	Exp	Exp	Exp
	18102	**12414**	**18238**	**12266**	**22402**	**12426**	**14034**	**12446**	**12904**		**18508**	**19326**	**11078**	**22462**	**14646**	**12204**	**12014**	**12716**		**11450**	**16032**	**16318**	**1668**
				①③⑥	②④⑦						③⑥⑦	③⑥				③⑥⑦				③	②⑤⑥	①	④
Katra d.	...	...	...	...	...	...	1435	1855	...	...	...	...	...	2305	...	...	...	...	...	2155	2155	2155	2155
Jammu Tawi d.	1420	1810	...	1920	1920	1940	1625	2043	...	...	...	...	2145	0043	2100	...	...	...	...	2345	2345	2345	2345
Chakki Bank ♥ d.	|	2005	...	|	2053	2125	1905	2235	...	...	...	...	2350	0220	2310	...	...	...	...	0138	0138	0138	0138
Amritsar d.	1935	|	1610	|	|	|	|	|	2125	...	2345	2315	|	|	|	0410	0455	0530	...	|	|	|	|
Jalandhar City d.	2058	|	1735	|	|	|	|	|	2238	...	0100	0040	|	|	|	0523	0602	0643	...	|	|	|	|
Jalandhar Cantonment d.	2108	2200	1746	|	2232	|	2215	0030	2248	...	|	|	0150	0430	0115	|	|	|	...	0350	0350	0350	035
Ludhiana d.	2220	2305	1925	2325	2325	0015	2345	0135	2359	...	0220	0150	0315	0550	0235	0620	0702	0755	...	0510	0510	0510	051
Ambala Cantonment d.	0040	0100	2215	|	0120	|	0150	0340	0200	...	0420	0413	0550	0757	0500	0810	0832	1000	...	|	|	|	|
New Delhi a.	0430**j**	0355**j**	|	|	|	0500	0545**j**	0645	|	...	0750	|	0955	1035	1055**j**	1045	1100	1300	...	1330	1330	1330	133
Delhi Hazrat Nizamuddin a.	...	...	0415	0420**a**	0420**a**	...	...	...	0705	...	0830	0945	...	...	...	...	...	...	...	1428	1430	1430	143

	Exp	Exp	Exp	Exp	Exp	Exp	Exp	Exp	Exp	Exp	Exp	Exp	Exp	Exp	Exp	Exp	Exp	SDi	SDi	Exp	SDi	SDi	Exp
	12484	**12460**	**15708**	**22942**	**12550**	**18216**	**12926**	**22430**	**12380**	**12920**	**11058**	**14650**	**14674**	**12472**	**12474**	**12476**	**12478**	**12038**	**12044**	**12498**	**12030**	**12032**	**1242**
	⑦			③	④	⑤		ex⑤	⑦			①③⑥	**B**	**C**	④	①	⑦	ex①⑥	①⑥		ex ④	④	①
Katra d.	...	...	...	...	...	...	...	...	...	0655	...	...	...	0910	0910	0910	0910	...	...	...	...	...	...
Jammu Tawi d.	...	...	...	0500	0500	0500	...	...	...	0900	...	...	...	1115	1115	1115	1115	...	...	...	...	...	...
Chakki Bank ♥ d.	...	...	...	0647	0647	0702**k**	...	**pp**	...	1045	...	...	...	1305	1305	1305	1305	...	...	...	...	...	...
Amritsar d.	0555	0615	0710	|	|	1040	0810	0930	1055	|	0830	1155	1155	|	|	|	|	...	...	1510	1650	1650	143
Jalandhar City d.	0710	0727	0835	|	|	1208	0920	1045	1205	|	1010	1315	1315	|	|	|	|	...	...	1620	1757	1757	154
Jalandhar Cantonment d.	|	0737	0845	0830	0830	|	0930	|	|	1243	1020	1325	1325	1455	1455	1455	1455	...	**n**	|	|	|	|
Ludhiana d.	0815	0840	1000	0945	0945	1310	1035	1155	1310	1345	1145	1435	1435	1600	1600	1600	1600	1640	1640	1723	1855	1855	170
Ambala Cantonment d.	1020	1055	1200	1150	1150	1517	1305	1345	1520	1540	1550	1710	1710	1800	1800	1800	1800	|	|	1928	2032	2032	|
New Delhi a.	1320	1415	1504**j**	1500**f**	1500**f**	1845	1625	1700**j**	1820**j**	1855	2020	2040**j**	2040**j**	2130	2130	2130	2130	2210	2210	2250	2305	2305	231
Delhi Hazrat Nizamuddin a.	1353	...	...	...	...	...	...	...	...	...	2101	...	...	...	...	...	...	...	...	...	...	...	...

A – ①②⑤⑥.
B – ②④⑤⑦.
C – ②③⑤⑥.

a – Delhi Sarai Rohilla.
f – Delhi Safdarjang.
j – Delhi Junction.

k – Pathankot Junction.
m – To Moga arr. 1405.
n – From Moga dep. 1500.

p – To Pathankot Junction arr. 1830.
pp – From Pathankot Junction dep. 0700.
♥ – Pathankot Cantonment.

5010 DELHI - KALKA - SHIMLA

Indian Railways

km		Exp	Exp	Exp	Exp	Exp	SDi	Exp	Exp	Exp	Exp	SDi	SDi
		52457	**12311**	**52451**	**52453**	**14095**	**12011**	**12217**	**52455**	**22925**	**22685**	**12005**	**12045**
						A		①③	**A**		③⑥		①–⑥
0	**New Delhi** d.	...	2130**j**	...	...	0535**a**	0740	1150	...	...	1355	1715	1915
199	Ambala Cant d.	...	0220	...	...	0950	1030	1450	...	1515	1740	1958	2200
268	Chandigarh d.	...	0350	...	...	1033	1113	1545	...	1610	1820	2048	2245
305	**Kalka** a.	...	0430	...	...	1110	1145	...	...	1645	...	2120	...
305	**Kalka** ¶ d.	0330	...	0545	0620	...	...	...	1210	...	...	...	...
347	Barog ¶ d.	0555	...	0751	0831	...	...	...	1427	...	...	...	...
351	Solan ¶ d.	0609	...	|	0845	...	...	...	1441	...	...	...	...
401	**Shimla** ¶ a.	0855	...	1035	1135	...	...	...	1730	...	...	...	...

	SDi	Exp	SDi	Exp	Exp	Exp	SDi	Exp	Exp	Exp	Exp	Exp
	12006	**12218**	**12046**	**22926**	**52456**	**14096**	**12012**	**52458**	**52542**	**52454**	**12312**	**2268**
		③⑤	①–⑥		**A**	**A**						②⑥
Shimla ¶ d.	...	...	...	...	1040	...	...	1420	1750	1830	...	...
Solan ¶ d.	...	...	...	...	1321	...	...	1729	|	2104	...	...
Barog ¶ d.	...	...	...	...	1346	...	...	1750	2040	2120	...	...
Kalka ¶ a.	...	...	...	...	1610	...	...	2010	2245	2330	...	...
Kalka d.	0615	...	...	1020	...	1655	1745	...	...	...	2355	...
Chandigarh d.	0653	0930	1200	1120	...	1735	1823	...	...	...	0120	032
Ambala Cant. d.	0738	1020	1242	1205	...	1830	1905	...	...	...	0220	042
New Delhi a.	1020	1320	1525	...	...	2240**a**	2155	...	...	...	0630**j**	075

A – HIMALAYAN QUEEN.
a – Delhi Sarai Rohilla.
j – Delhi Junction.
¶ – Narrow gauge railway.

5015 DELHI - DEHRA DUN

Indian Railways

km		Exp	SDi	Exp	Exp	Exp	Exp	Exp	jSDi	Exp	Exp	Exp
		19019	**12017**	**12171**	**22659**	**19565**	**14309**	**14317**	**12055**	**12687**	**14041**	**12205**
				②⑤	⑦	⑥	④⑤	①⑦		②⑤		
0	**Delhi** H. Niz. d.	0540	0645**n**	0710	1055	1055**n**	1125	1130	1520**n**	2110	2225**j**	2350**n**
76	Meerut City d.	0815	0805	0838	1227	1227	1255	1255	1642	2253	|	0110
190	Saharanpur d.	1245	1015	|	|	|	1525	1525	|	0130	|	|
271	Haridwar d.	1510	1135	1255	1610	1735	1735	1735	1955	0315	0635	0357
323	**Dehra Dun** a.	1735	1250	...	1805	1940	1940	1940	2110	0445	0830	0540

	jSDi	Exp	Exp	Exp	Exp	Exp	Exp	SDi	Exp	Exp	Exp
	12056	**22660**	**14310**	**14318**	**19566**	**12688**	**19020**	**12018**	**12172**	**14042**	**1220**
		①	②③	⑤⑥	⑦	①⑤			②⑤		
Dehra Dun d.	0505	0550	0550	0550	0550	0650	1000	1655	...	2125	233
Haridwar d.	0622	0755	0755	0755	0750	0845	1230	1812	1830	2325	005
Saharanpur d.	|	|	0955	0955	|	1045	1605	1955	|	|	|
Meerut City d.	0929	1129	1129	1126	1126	1212	1910	2125	2144	|	033
Delhi H. Niz. a.	1115**n**	1320	1320	1320	1310**n**	1410	2115	2250**n**	2315	0725**j**	0520

a – Delhi Sarai Rohilla.
j – Delhi Junction.
n – New Delhi.

5020 DELHI - LUCKNOW

Indian Railways

km		Exp	Exp	SDi	Exp	Exp	RDi	RDi	Exp	Exp	Exp	Exp	Exp	Exp	Exp	Exp	Exp	Exp	Exp	Exp	Exp	Exp	Exp	
		12328	**19403**	**12004**	**12876**	**15910**	**20504**	**20506**	**12204**	**14258**	**12420**	**12392**	**13258**	**12584**	**15706**	**12558**	**14312**	**19601**	**12372**	**19407**	**12524**	**22412**	**15280**	
		④⑦	③		②⑤⑦		②	④⑦	③⑥⑦					⑤⑦	②⑤		①③⑤	⑥	④	⑤	③⑦	⑦	①⑤	
0	**New Delhi** d.	...	0020**j**	0610	0630**v**	0750**j**	0925	0925	1115	1135	1225	1310	1330**v**	1405**v**	1345	1450**v**	1455	1505**j**	1505**j**	1505**j**	1505	1545	1710**v**	...
	Kanpur Central d.	...	|	1125	1240	|	|	|	|	|	1955	|	|	|	1915	|	|	|	|	|	|	2045	|	...
167	Moradabad d.	0253	0355	|	|	1118	1215	1215	1355	1510	|	1610	1641	1658	|	1745	1835	1815	1815	1815	1815	|	2023	...
258	Bareilly Junction d.	0418	0530	|	|	1257	1348	1348	1520	1650	|	1742	|	1832	|	|	2035	|	1959	1959	|	|	2210	...
493	**Lucknow** Junction a.	0820	0925	1240	1415	1750	1725	1725	1842	2105	2125	2115	2150	2225	2040	2240	...	2335	2335	2335	2335	2220	0155	...

	Exp	Exp	Exp	Exp	Exp	Exp	Exp	Exp	Exp	Exp	Exp	Exp	Exp	Exp	Exp	Exp	Exp	Exp	Exp	Exp	Exp	Exp	
	14018	**14016**	**14008**	**14014**	**14004**	**22408**	**14206**	**22418**	**22420**	**12226**	**12554**	**14208**	**12556**	**15716**	**19269**	**12212**	**14650**	**14674**	**13414**	**13484**	**12230**	**12430**	
	③	⑤⑦	②④	①⑥	④⑦	①③⑤		①③⑤	②④⑥					①②④	⑤⑥	③	①③⑥	**A**	①③⑥	**A**			
New Delhi d.	1625**v**	1625**v**	1625**v**	1625**v**	1800	1815**v**	1825**j**	1835	1845**v**	1915**j**	1950	1950**j**	2025	2030**j**	2030**j**	2040**v**	2110**j**	2110**j**	2140**j**	2140**j**	2205	2325	...
Kanpur Central d.	|	|	|	|	|	|	|	|	|	0142	0220	|	0315	|	|	|	|	|	0545	0545	|	|	...
Moradabad d.	1943	1943	1938	1943	2110	2110	2205	2147	2147	|	...	2310	|	2345	2345	2345	0040	0040	|	|	0115	0220	...
Bareilly Junction d.	|	|	|	|	2245	2245	0003	2310	2310	|	...	0053	|	0120	0120	0120	0225	0225	|	|	0255	0345	...
Lucknow Junction a.	0210	0210	0325	0325	0225	0225	0345	0305	0305	0300	...	0435	0445	0515	0515	0515	0610	0610	0720	0720	0700	0730	...

A – ②④⑤⑦.
j – Delhi Junction.
v – Delhi Anand Vihar Terminal.

For return service see next page ▷ ▷ ▷

ndian Railways — LUCKNOW - DELHI — 5020

km			Exp 22407 ①③⑤	Exp 12371 ②	Exp 13257		Exp 22411 ④	Exp 14311 ④⑤⑦	Exp 15705 ②⑤		Exp 12523 ③⑦	Exp 19602 ②	Exp 15279 ①⑤	Exp 12211 ⑥	Exp 19270 ①②	Exp 15715 ①③⑥	Exp 12583 ⑤⑦	Exp 12203 ①②⑤	Exp 12419	Exp 14003 ③⑦	Exp 15909	RDi 20503 ⑥	RDi 20505 ③⑦	Exp 12327 ③⑥
0	**Lucknow** Junction d.	...	0110	0110	0225	...	0410	...	0420	...	0320	0320	0320	0440	0440	0455	0455	0610	0600	0620	0540	0610	0610	0735
	Bareilly Junction d.	...	0440	0440	|	...	|	0635	|	...	|	|	0702	0814	0814	0826	0826	0935	|	0948	1005	0935	0935	1115
	Moradabad d.	...	0630	0630	0728	...	|	0823	|	...	0850	0850	0850	0953	0953	1008	1008	1107	|	1128	1225	1107	1107	1247
72	Kanpur Central d.	...	|	|	|	...	0615	|	0815	...	|	|	|	|	|	|	|	|	0740	|	|	|	|	...
511	**New Delhi** a.	...	0935v	0950j	1025v	...	1130	1140j	1150j	...	1200	1205j	1145v	1235v	1250j	1310j	1255v	1355	1505	1435	1555j	1355	1355	...

	Exp 12875 ①③⑥	SDi 12003		Exp 14017 ⑤	Exp 14007 ④⑥	Exp 14015 ①③	Exp 14013 ②⑦	Exp 13413 ②⑤⑦	Exp 13483 B	Exp 14205	Exp 12391	Exp 14257	Exp 19408 ⑥	Exp 19404 ③	Exp 14207	Exp 12555	Exp 12229	Exp 12553	Exp 12225	Exp 12429	Exp 12557	Exp 22417 ③⑤⑦	Exp 22419 ②④⑥
ucknow Junction d.	1345	1535	...	1830	1830	1830	1830	1913	1910	2000	2013	2028	2135	2135	2155	2145	2200	...	2315	2330	2345	2358	2358
areilly Junction d.	|	|	...	|	|	|	|	|	|	2342	2355	0025	0120	0120	0138	|	0150	...	|	0257	|	0322	0322
oradabad d.	|	|	...	0055	0055	0055	0055	|	|	0123	0140	0210	0305	0305	0320	|	0338	...	|	0435	0450	0502	0502
Kanpur Central d.	1525	1655	...	|	|	|	|	2115	2115	|	|	|	|	|	|	2328	|	2350	0050	|	|	|	|
ew Delhi a.	2135	2215	...	0400v	0400v	0400v	0400v	0450j	0450j	0430j	0445	0540	0615j	0615j	0630j	0550	0650	0645	0710j	0730	0740v	0820	0800v

– ②④⑤⑦. B – ①③④⑥. j – Delhi Junction. v – Delhi Anand Vihar Terminal.

ndian Railways — JAMMU TAWI and AMRITSAR - LUCKNOW — 5030

km		jSDi 12054 ex④		HExp 22318 ③	Exp 18104 ③⑤	Exp 14650 ①③⑥	Exp 14674 A	Exp 12238	Exp 15934 ⑤	Exp 13050	Exp 13006	Exp 12356 ③⑦		Exp 12588 ⑥	Exp 15652 ③	Exp 15654 ⑤	Exp 15098 ②	Exp 12332 ①④⑦	Exp 13152	Exp 12204 ③⑥⑦	Exp 12326 ⑥	Exp 12318 ②⑤	Exp 12358 ①④	
0	**Jammu Tawi** d.	...	...	0725	...	...	...	1400	...	...	...	2010	...	2245	2245	2245	2245	2245	1855	...	...	...	...	...
100	Chakki Bank ♥ d.	...	...	|	...	...	...	1540	...	...	...	2150	...	0030	0030	0030	0030	0025	2205	...	...	...	...	...
**	**Amritsar** d.	0650	...	|	1235	1155	1155	|	1545	1810	1840	|	...	|	|	|	|	|	|	0410	...	0555	0555	...
**	Jalandhar City d.	0802	...	|	1348	1315	1315	|	1658	1930	1957	|	...	|	|	|	|	|	|	0523	...	0710	0710	...
213	Jalandhar Cantonment d.	|	...	|	|	1325	1325	1730	|	1940	2007	2330	...	0220	0220	0220	0220	0215	0010	|	...	|	|	...
265	Ludhiana d.	0903	...	1215	1505	1435	1435	1835	1810	2050	2115	0035	...	0330	0330	0330	0330	0330	0205	0620	...	0815	0815	...
378	Ambala Cantonment d.	1105	...	1400	1655	1710	1710	2100	2025	2310	2330	0235	...	0525	0525	0525	0525	0525	0427	0810	1010	1010	1010	...
460	Saharanpur d.	1228	...	1515	1820	D	D	2225	2155	0055	0115	0400	...	0700	0700	0700	0700	0700	0605	D	1135	1135	1135	...
652	Moradabad d.	a	...	1815	2130	0030	0030	0133	0055	0423	0455	0705	...	1018	1018	1018	1018	1018	1035	1355	1455	1455	1455	...
743	Bareilly Junction d.	...	...	1942	2300	0207	0207	|	0238	|	0633	0830	...	1142	1142	1142	1142	1140	1222	1520	1630	1630	|	...
978	**Lucknow** Junction a.	...	...	2315	0250	0610	0610	0710	0625	1145	1035	1225	...	1520	1520	1520	1520	1520	1705	1842	2005	2005	2005	...

	Exp 12325 ⑤	Exp 12317 ①④	Exp 12357 ③⑦	Exp 12203 ①②⑤	Exp 15933 ④	jSDi 12053 ex④	Exp 14649 ①③⑥	Exp 14673 A	HExp 22317 ②	Exp 13151	Exp 18103 ②④	Exp 13005	Exp 13049	Exp 12355 ②⑥	Exp 12237			Exp 12331 ③⑥⑦	Exp 15097 ⑤	Exp 15651 ②	Exp 15653 ④	Exp 12587 ①	
ucknow Junction d.	0253	0253	0253	0610	0610	...	0055	0055	0620	1255	1520	1600	1620	1735	1800	...	...	1945	1945	1945	1945	1945	...
areilly Junction d.	0619	0619	|	0935	0935	...	0426	0426	0948	1727	1923	2010	|	2111	|	...	...	2323	2323	2323	2323	2323	...
oradabad d.	0758	0758	0758	1107	1110	b	0618	0618	1128	1923	2108	2200	2253	2300	2313	...	...	0103	0103	0103	0103	0103	...
aharanpur d.	1130	1130	1130	D	1515	1625	D	D	1515	2340	0035	0145	0320	0210	0230	...	...	0425	0425	0425	0425	0425	...
mbala Cantonment d.	1245	1250	1250	1652	1635	1750	1535	1535	1635	0115	0210	0320	0452	0335	0352	...	...	0549	0549	0549	0549	0545	...
udhiana d.	...	1442	1452	1835	1815	1935	2003	2003	1820	0339	0405	0545	0725	0535	0555	...	...	0740	0740	0740	0740	0740	...
landhar Cantonment d.	...	|	|	|	|	|	2148	2148	|	0445	|	0649	0825	0638	0705	...	...	0845	0845	0845	0845	0845	...
Jalandhar City d.	...	1545	1545	1930	1930	2040	2210	2210	|	|	0513	0707	0845	|	|	...	...	|	|	|	|	|	...
Amritsar a.	...	1720	1720	2105	2105	2205	2355	2355	|	|	0630	0855	1020	|	|	...	...	|	|	|	|	|	...
hakki Bank ♥ d.	...	...	...	...	...	...	...	...	|	0700	...	...	...	0825	0855	...	...	1040	1040	1040	1040	1040	...
mmu Tawi a.	...	...	...	...	...	...	...	...	2330	0925	...	...	...	1030	1110	...	...	1235	1235	1235	1235	1235	...

– ②④⑤⑦. a – To Haridwar arr. 1355. ♥ – Pathankot Cantonment.
– Via Table **5000**. b – From Haridwar dep. 1445. ** – Amritsar - Jalandhar Cantonment: *84 km*. Jalandhar City - Jalandhar Cantonment: *5 km*.

ndian Railways — DELHI - GUWAHATI — 5040

km	km		Exp 15934 ⑥	Exp 15910	RDi 20506 ④⑦	RDi 20504 ②	Exp 12204 ③⑥⑦	RDi 12424	Exp 15708	RDi 20502 ③	Exp 12502 ③⑦	Exp 12370 E
0	0	**New Delhi** d.	...	0750j	0925	0925	1105	1610	1519j	1950v	2345	...
	167	Moradabad d.	...	1118	1215	1215	1355	|	|	|	|	0258
	258	Bareilly Junction d.	...	1257	1348	1348	1520	|	|	|	|	0418
	493	Lucknow Junction d.	0640	1810	1735	1735	1852	|	|	|	|	0830
	772	Gorakhpur Junct d.	|	2345	|	|	0015	|	0600	|	|	|
	776	Varanasi d.	1550	|	2225	2225	|	|	|	|	|	1305
	981	Chhapra d.	2040	0400	0155	0155	0320	|	0950	|	|	|
440		Kanpur Central d.	|	|	|	|	|	2110	2300↑	0034	0615	|
634		Allahabad d.	|	|	|	|	|	2314	|	|	0855	|
787		Mughal Sarai * d.	|	|	|	|	|	0133	|	0443	1158	1423
999		Patna Junction d.	|	|	|	|	|	0430p	|	0805p	1455p	1700
109	1128	Barauni d.	2358	0855	0500	|	0735	0645	1525	1025	|	...
288	1308	Katihar d.	0400	1355	0845	0845	...	1020	2010	1455	2105	...
471	1491	New Jalpaiguri d.	0755	1755	1205	1205	...	1330	...	1815	0030	...
723	1742	New Bongaigaon d.	1245	2330	1620	1620	...	1725	...	|	0522	...
879	1899	**Guwahati** a.	1555	0300	1900	1900	...	1950	...	0030	0845	...

	RDi 20503 ⑤	RDi 20505 ②⑥	Exp 12203 ①④⑦	Exp 12501 ③⑥	Exp 12369 F	RDi 12423	RDi 20501 ③	Exp 15933 ②	Exp 15909	Exp 15707
Guwahati d.	0540	0540	...	0615	...	0700	0725	1955	2200	...
New Bongaigaon d.	0810	0810	...	0910	...	0922	|	2330	0115	...
New Jalpaiguri d.	1215	1215	...	1300	...	1315	1345	0420	0615	...
Katihar d.	1525	1525	...	1710	...	1635	1730	0915	1055	2245
Barauni d.	|	1900	1700	|	...	1915	2010	1250	1425	0310
Patna Junction d.	|	|	|	2225p	2045	2150p	2300p	|	|	|
Mughal Sarai * d.	|	|	|	0158	0044	0104	0230	|	|	|
Allahabad d.	|	|	|	0418	|	0256	|	|	|	|
Kanpur Central d.	|	|	|	0650	|	0505	0630	|	|	2000↓
Chhapra d.	2155	2155	2120	|	|	|	|	1710	1940	0845
Varanasi d.	0140	0140	|	|	|	|	|	2235	|	|
Gorakhpur Junct d.	|	|	0040	|	|	|	|	|	2355	1235
Lucknow Junction d.	0610	0610	0610	|	0715	|	|	0600	0540	|
Bareilly Junction d.	0935	0935	0935	|	...	|	|	...	1005	|
Moradabad d.	1107	1107	1107	|	...	|	|	...	1215	|
New Delhi a.	1355	1355	1355	1300	...	1015	1120v	...	1555j	0250j

– ①②③⑤⑥. j – Delhi Junction. v – Delhi Anand Vihar Terminal.
– ①③④⑥⑦. p – Patliputra. * – Mughal Sarai is now PT Deen Dayal Upadhyaya Jct.

ndian Railways — DELHI - PATNA - KOLKATA — 5050

km		Exp 12324 ④⑦	Duro 12282 ④	Duro 12274 ②⑥	Exp 12312	Exp 12488	Exp 15484		Exp 12322	Exp 12368	SDi 12034 ①–⑥	RDi 20840 ①⑤	RDi 12454 ①⑤	RDi 12302 ⑥–④	RDi 12314	RDi 12306 ⑤	jSDi 12024 ①–⑥	Exp 12570 ②⑥	Exp 22406 ①③⑤	Exp 12316 ①		RDi 22824 K		RDI 12310
0	**New Delhi** d.	0705v	1255	1255	0700j	0730v	0635j	...	...	1440v	1550	1600	1600	1655	1625	1655	...	1655v	1655v	...	...	1705	...	1715
440	Kanpur Central d.	1340	1753	1753	1435	1355	1520	...	...	2035	2045	2100	2100	2140	2120	2140	...	2217	2217	2005	...	2150	...	2200
634	Allahabad Junction d.	1640	|	|	1720	1650	1805	...	...	|	...	|	|	2342	|	2342	...	0018	0018	2245	...	|	...	0005
787	Mughal Sarai * d.	1940	2200	2220	2025	1958	2113	...	2335	0318	...	0125	0115	0154	0145	0153	...	0230	0230	0253	...	0155	...	0213
998	**Patna** Junction a.	|	G	1035	|	2300p	0020	...	|	0620	...	|	...	|	|	0440	0530	0535	0535	0600	...	|	...	0500
992	Gaya d.	2210	...	|	2313	...	...	...	0225	...	...	0323	...	0350	0340	|	|	...	...	|	...	0358	...	...
189	Dhanbad d.	0150	...	|	0322	...	...	...	0649	...	...	...	...	0640	0623	|	|	...	...	|	...	...	...	...
247	Asansol d.	0300	...	0736	0436	...	...	...	0830	...	...	...	...	0730	0713	|	1047	...	...	1203	...	...	...	...
447	**Kolkata** Howrah a.	0610	...	1040	0805	...	...	...	1200	...	...	...	...	0950	1010e	1215	1325	...	...	1510e	...	...	...	...

	Exp 12394	Exp 12304 A	Exp 12382 ①②⑤	Exp 12320 ⑤	Exp 22410 ⑥	Exp 12330 ③	Exp 12380 ⑦	Yuva 12250 ⑦	Duro 12260 C	SDi 12020 ①–⑤	Exp 11106 ⑥	Exp 12818 ①④⑥	Exp 12402	Exp 12802	Duro 12276 ③⑤⑦	Exp 14056	Exp 12350 ②	Exp 13132	Exp 12360 ③⑤⑦	Duro 22214 ②④⑥	Exp 12352		Exp 12334
ew Delhi d.	1725	1735	1735	...	1910v	1910v	1905j	1950v	1940	...	...	1940v	2000	2225	2215	2340j	2345	...	...	...	...	...	...
anpur Central d.	2233	2310	2310	0120	0135	0135	0135	0034	0034	...	0125	0155	0235	0400	|	0555	0615	...	...	...	...	...	...
ahabad Junction d.	|	0125	0235	|	0405	|	|	0236	|	...	0405	0430	0510	0715	0620	0835	0855	...	...	...	...	...	1540a
ughal Sarai * d.	0338	0428	0630	0650	0645	0645	0645	0438	0443	...	0713	0700	0753	1035	...	1143	1158	...	...	...	...	...	1908
atna Junction d.	0650	0740	|	|	|	|	|	|	|	...	1020	|	1125	|	...	1430	1440	1645	2005	2040	2115b	...	2245
Gaya d.	...	|	0908	0922	1000	|	0910	|	|	...	|	0948	...	1310	...	...	...	|	|	|	|	...	|
Dhanbad d.	...	|	1218	1232	...	1235	1232	0903	0905	1748	|	...	...	...	...	...	...	|	|	|	|	...	|
sansol d.	...	1341	1341	1357	...	1357	1357	1000	|	1842	1710	...	...	...	...	...	...	0247	0201	0201	0330	...	0424
olkata Howrah a.	...	1715	1715	1720k	...	1730e	1730e	1250	1245e	2130	2209k	...	...	...	...	...	...	0725	0515k	0540h	0640	...	0740

– ③④⑥⑦. G – To Bhubaneswar arr. ⑤ 1115 a – Allahabad City. h – Kolkata Shalimar. v – Delhi Anand Vihar Terminal.
– ①②⑤⑥. H – From Bhubaneswar dep. ③ 0735 b – Patna Saheb. j – Delhi Junction. * – Mughal Sarai is now PT Deen Dayal Upadhyaya Jct.
– ①②④⑤. J – Runs as **20817** on ⑦, **22811** on ①④. c – Kolkata Chitpur. k – Kolkata.
– ①③④⑦. K – Runs as **20818** on ⑦, **22812** on ①⑤. e – Kolkata Sealdah. p – Patliputra.

For return service see next page ▷ ▷ ▷

5050 KOLKATA - PATNA - DELHI   Indian Railway

km		Exp	Duro	Duro	Duro	Exp	SDI	Exp	Exp	Exp		RDi	Exp	Exp	Exp	Exp		Exp	Exp	Exp	Exp	Exp	jSDI	
		12801	**12273**	**12281**	**12275**	**14055**	**12019**	**11105**	**12303**	**12381**		**12309**	**12367**	**12393**	**12569**	**22405**		**22409**	**12329**	**12379**	**12319**	**12315**	**12023**	
			①⑤	③	②④⑥		①–⑤	⑦	**B**	③④⑦					①⑤	②④⑥		⑦	②	⑤	③	④	①–⑥	
0	**Kolkata** Howrah d.	...	0845	...	...	...	0605	0725**k**	0800	0815	...	...	...	...	...	...	...	...	1310**e**	1310**e**	1310**k**	1310**k**	1405	...
200	Asansol d.	...	1100	...	...	...	0824	1140	1037	1053	...	...	...	...	...	...	...	...	1607	1607	1607	1607	1642	...
	Dhanbad d.	...	|	...	...	...	0925	|	|	1205	...	...	...	...	...	...	...	...	1715	1715	1715	|	|	...
	Gaya d.	1402	1630	...	...	...	...	|	|	1455	...	...	...	...	...	...	...	1930	|	2017	2017	|	|	...
532	**Patna** Junction d.	|	|	**H**	...	1250	...	1820	1610	|	...	1925	1700	1800	1853	1855	...	|	|	|	|	2140	2245	...
744	Mughal Sarai * d.	1720	2023	2057	...	1654	...	2306	1944	1758	...	2222	2043	2119	2244	2244	...	2310	2310	2310	2310	0202	...	...
896	Allahabad Junction d.	1950	|	|	2220	1925	...	0115	2145	2140	...	0017	|	|	0044	0044	...	0125	|	|	|	0418	...	...
1091	Kanpur Central d.	2210	0045	0055	|	2245	...	0340	0010	0010	...	0225	0148	0121	0255	0255	...	0355	0355	0355	0400	0645	...	...
1530	**New Delhi** a.	0420	0615	0615	0615	0605**j**	...	...	0605	0605	...	0740	0810**v**	0750	0820**v**	0820**v**	...	1155	1155**v**	1210**j**	...	...	...	...

	RDI	RDI	RDi	RDi	RDi	RDi	SDi	Yuva	Duro		Exp	Exp	Exp	Exp	Exp	Exp	Exp	Exp	Exp	Exp	Exp	Exp	Dur
	12305	**12301**	**12313**	**22823**	**12453**	**20839**	**12033**	**12249**	**12259**		**12401**	**12349**	**12817**	**12323**	**15483**	**12311**	**13131**	**12333**	**12359**	**12487**	**12351**	**12321**	**2221**
	⑦	①–⑥		**J**	⑤	③⑥	①–⑥	⑥	**D**			①	③⑤⑦	②⑤					②④⑥				①③
Kolkata Howrah d.	1405	1650	1650**e**	...	...	...	...	1840	1830**e**	...	...	...	...	1850	...	1940	1950	2000	2005	...	2035	2200	2205
Asansol d.	|	1859	1920	...	...	...	...	2052	|	...	...	...	...	2118	...	2222	2348	2239	2251	...	2322	0046	011
Dhanbad d.	|	2000	2025	...	...	...	...	2156	2156	...	...	...	...	2250	...	2336	|	|	|	...	|	0210	|
Gaya d.	|	2237	2254	2306	...	2324	...	|	|	...	...	...	2135	0210	...	0300	|	|	|	...	|	0524	|
Patna Junction d.	2110	|	|	|	...	|	...	|	|	...	1745	2220	|	|	0140	|	0945	0410	0530	0525**p**	0520**b**	|	064
Mughal Sarai * d.	0052	0055	0112	0127	0149	0155	...	0230	0230	...	2204	0158	0210	0520	0542	0630	...	0839	...	0929	...	0810	...
Allahabad Junction d.	0245	0245	|	|	|	|	...	0420	|	...	0100	0418	0440	0750	0855	0910	...	1200**a**	...	1155	...	...	...
Kanpur Central d.	0455	0455	0515	0525	0550	0550	0600	0630	0630	...	0325	0650	0720	1035	1225	1245	...	...	...	1425	...	...	...
New Delhi a.	1000	1000	1035	1045	1055	1055	1120	1120	1130	...	1150	1300	1355**v**	1705	2240**j**	2100**j**	...	...	...	2100**v**	...	...	...

For footnotes and return service see previous page. * – Mughal Sarai is now PT Deen Dayal Upadhyaya Jct.

5060 LUCKNOW - MUGHAL SARAI - PATNA - KOLKATA   Indian Railways

km		Exp	Exp	Exp	Exp	Exp	Exp	Exp	Exp	Exp	Exp	Exp	Exp	Exp	Exp	Exp	Exp	Exp	Exp	Exp	Exp	Exp	Exp	Exp	HExp	Exp	Exp
		12354	**22408**	**18104**	**22418**	**14014**	**12238**	**12328**	**12370**	**13010**	**19403**	**13006**	**12356**	**12876**	**13168**	**12332**	**12358**	**12318**	**12326**	**13050**	**13152**	**12392**	**14258**	**13258**	**22318**	**12372**	**194**
		⑦	②④⑦	④⑥	①③⑤	②⑦		③⑥	ex③⑥		③		①④	②⑤⑦	⑥	①②⑤	①④	②⑤	⑥						③	④	⑤
493	Haridwar d.	...	...	...	...	...	...	2350**p**	2350	2220**q**	...	...	...	...	...	...	...	...	...	...	...	...	...	...	...	...	...
0	**Lucknow** Jct d.	0125	0235	0305	0315	0220	0720	0825	0825	0845	0935	1050	1235	1430	1430	1530	2015	2015	2015	1210	172	2125	2100	2200	2325	2345	234
77	Rae Bareli d.	0240	0406	|	|	|	|	|	|	|	|	1216	1402	1553	1553	|	|	|	|	|	|	|	2318	|	|	0105	|
127	Faizabad d.	|	|	0505	|	|	|	|	|	1110	|	|	|	|	|	|	|	|	|	|	2046	|	|	|	|	|	|
140	Sultanpur d.	|	|	|	0518	0610	0935	1038	1040	|	1205	|	|	|	|	1735	|	2213	|	1435	|	2335	|	|	|	|	021
283	Varanasi Jct d.	0720	0805	1005	0825	...	1230	1305	1305	1615	...	1655	1855	2010	2010	2105	0115	0115	0115	1915	0130	0239	0435	0300	0555	0520	054
300	***Mughal Sarai*** * d.	0835	...	1135	...	...	...	1423	1423	1730	...	1813	1948	2120	2120	2213	0220	0233	0233	2033	0300	0335	...	0402	0655	0635	...
512	**Patna** Junction d.	|	...	|	...	...	...	1730	1730	|	...	2140	2245	|	|	0125	|	0600	0600	0150	|	0705	...	0730**f**	|	|	...
***	Gaya d.	1100	...	1415	...	...	...	|	|	|	...	|	...	0015	0020	|	0439	|	|	|	0610	...	...	...	0950	0850	...
***	Dhanbad d.	1430	...	...	...	...	...	|	|	0110	...	|	...	...	0340	|	0727	|	|	|	1021	...	...	...	1310	1216	...
843	Asansol d.	1544	...	...	...	...	...	2358	2358	0230	...	0404	...	...	0510	0815	0825	1203	1203	1105	1145	...	...	...	1424	1322	...
1055	**Kolkata** Howrah a.	1855	...	...	...	...	...	0320	0320	0700	...	0730	...	...	0900	1130	1135**k**	1515**k**	1515**k**	1550	1545**k**	...	...	...	1805	1655	...

	Exp	Exp	Exp	Exp	Exp	Exp	Exp	Exp	Exp	Exp	Exp	Exp	HExp	Exp	Exp	Exp	Exp	Exp	Exp	Exp	Exp	Exp	Exp	Exp	Exp	Exp
	22417	**12353**	**12371**	**22407**	**13257**	**12317**	**12325**	**12357**	**13167**	**12327**	**12369**	**13151**	**22317**	**12875**	**18103**	**13005**	**13049**	**13009**	**12355**	**12237**	**14013**	**14257**	**12331**	**12391**	**19408**	**194**
	②④⑥	⑤	①	②④⑦		③⑦	④	②⑥	④	②⑤	ex③⑤		①	①③⑥	②④				②⑥		②⑦		②⑤⑥		⑥	③
Kolkata Howrah d.	...	0815	0815	...	...	0740**k**	0740**k**	1210**k**	1210	1300	1300	1145**k**	1310**e**	...	...	1910	1350	2025	...	...	...	...	2355	...	...	...
Asansol d.	...	1053	1053	...	...	1037	1037	1452	1452	1534	1534	1520	1807	...	...	2156	1813	0011	...	...	...	...	0223	...	...	...
Dhanbad d.	...	1205	1205	...	...	|	|	1602	1612	|	|	1655	1715	...	...	|	|	0130	...	...	...	...	|	...	...	...
Gaya d.	...	1455	1455	...	...	|	|	1843	1905	|	|	2110	2017	0315	0400	|	|	0500	...	...	...	...	|	...	...	...
Patna Junction d.	...	|	|	...	1545**f**	1610	1610	|	|	2045	2045	|	|	|	|	0350	0215	|	0724	...	...	...	1010	1028	...	...
Mughal Sarai * d.	...	1810	1810	...	1907	1944	1944	2120	2305	0044	0044	0145	0015	0637	0715	0824	0734	0930	1044	...	...	...	1359	1424	...	...
Varanasi Junction d.	1855	1930	1930	1930	2000	2040	2040	2211	2358	0155	0155	0245	0115	0738	0815	0927	0840	1030	1140	1240	...	1350	1447	1512	1535	...
Sultanpur d.	2108	|	|	|	|	2248	|	|	|	0400	0400	|	|	|	|	|	1200	|	|	1455	1530	|	1648	1712	1750	175
Faizabad d.	|	|	|	|	|	|	|	|	|	|	|	0741	|	|	1145	|	|	1431	|	|	|	|	|	|	|	|
Rae Barali d.	|	|	2320	2320	|	|	|	|	0332	|	|	|	|	1113	|	1315	|	|	1519	|	|	1800	|	|	|	|
Lucknow Junction a.	2348	0100	0100	0100	0210	0243	0243	0243	0540	0715	0715	1240	0610	1330	1505	1525	1550	1800	1720	1750	1820	2018	1935	2003	2120	212
Haridwar a.	...	...	...	...	...	...	...	...	...	1550**l**	1615	...	...	...	...	...	...	0455**n**	...	...	...	...	...	...	...	...

f – Danapur. **l** – To Dehra Dun arr. 1805. **n** – To Dehra Dun arr. 0735. **p** – From Dehra Dun dep. 2210. **q** – From Dehra Dun dep. 2000.
*** – Mughal Sarai - Dhanbad: *402 km*. Gaya - Dhandab: *199 km* Dhanbad - Asansol: *58 km*
* – Mughal Sarai is now PT Deen Dayal Upadhyaya Jct.

5070 KOLKATA - NEW JALPAIGURI - GUWAHATI   Indian Railway

km		Exp	Exp	SDi	Exp	Exp	Exp	Exp	Exp	Exp	Exp
		13173	**12509**	**12041**	**12507**	**22501**	**12345**	**15959**	**12525**	**12517**	**22511**
		C	**A**	①–⑥	④	③			③	④⑦	④
0	**Kolkata** Howrah d.	0635**e**	1115	1415	1425	1425	1550	1735	2140**k**	2140**k**	2139
213	Rampurhat d.	1032	1428	|	1728	1728	1858	|	|	|	0159
335	Malda Town d.	1355	1730	1915	2015	2015	2145	0210	0410	0410	0520
480	Kishanganj d.	1639	1932	2112	2205	2205	2337	0425	|	0602	|
567	**New Jalpaiguri** d.	1835	2140	2230	0005	2350	0200	0635	0755	0755	0910
819	New Bongaigaon d.	0040	0225	...	0435	0525	0630	1150	1237	1237	1545
975	**Guwahati** a.	0400	0600	...	0810	0845	0955	1535	1555	1555	1825**c**

	Exp	Exp	Exp	Exp	Exp	SDi	Exp	Exp	Exp	Exp
	22502	**12508**	**12510**	**15960**	**12346**	**12042**	**22512**	**12526**	**12518**	**131**
	⑥	⑤	**B**			①–⑥	⑥	②	③⑥	**D**
Guwahati d.	0525	0620	0620	0745	1230	...	1800**c**	2100	2100	225
New Bongaigaon d.	0825	0945	0945	1145	1525	...	2100	2355	2355	022
New Jalpaiguri d.	1425	1425	1425	1705	1925	0530	0330	0400	0400	075
Kishanganj d.	1538	1538	1538	1820	2042	0635	|	|	0506	090
Malda Town d.	1840	1840	1840	2210	2340	0850	0745	0825	0825	123
Rampurhat d.	2105	2105	2105	|	0151	|	1026	|	|	150
Kolkata Howrah a.	0045	0045	0045	0600	0520	1335	1410	1500**k**	1500**k**	192

A – ①②⑤⑥⑦. Runs as **12513** on ① and as **12515** on ②.
B – ①②③④⑦. Runs as **12514** on ④ and as **12516** on ③.
C – Runs as **13175** on ①③⑥.
D – Runs as **13176** on ①③⑥.
c – Kamakhya Junction.

5075 GUWAHATI - DIBRUGARH   Indian Railway

km		Exp	jSDi	Exp	SDi	Exp	Exp	Exp	RDi	RDi	Exp	RDi
		15910	**12067**	**22501**	**12085**	**14056**	**15934**	**15959**	**20504**	**20506**	**15905**	**12424**
				④	②④⑦		⑦		③	①⑤	⑦	
0	**Guwahati** d.	0315	0630	0905	1210	1500	1610	1550	1920	1920	1925	2010
87	Chaparmukh d.	0516	0755	|	1335	1647	1750	1719	|	|	|	2147
184	Lumding d.	0715	0930	1250	1510	1925	1945	2015	2232	2232	2235	2327
250	Dimapur d.	0900	1048	1420	1653	2045	2105	2145	2357	2357	2357	0110
323	Furkating d.	1057	1204	1545	1755	2300	2325	0010	|	|	0152	|
358	Mariani d.	1140	1247	1630	1830	2356	0020	0115	0235	0235	0235	0310
513	New Tinsukia d.	1445	**a**	2045↓	|	0310	0345	0435	|	0510	0510	0600
561	**Dibrugarh** a.	1555	...	1910	2115	0425	0455	0555	0515	0615	0640	0700

	Exp	Exp	Exp	jSDi	Exp	RDi	RDi	RDi	Exp	Exp	Ex
	15903	**15933**	**15909**	**12068**	**22502**	**20505**	**20503**	**12423**	**15960**	**15906**	**140**
	①⑤	②			⑤	①⑤	④			⑥	
Dibrugarh d.	0700	0700	0935	...	1900	1920	1950	2035	1825	2305	232
New Tinsukia d.	0805	0805	1040	**b**	1755↑	2025	|	2140	1935	0012	002
Mariani d.	1100	1100	1356	1508	2145	2235	2235	0012	2310	0310	035
Furkating d.	1147	1147	1452	1547	2235	|	|	|	0015	0400	044
Dimapur d.	1330	1330	1610	1656	2352	0035	0035	0213	0152	0518	061
Lumding d.	1520	1520	1735	1815	0130	0200	0200	0327	0330	0705	080
Chaparmukh d.	|	1743	1910	1945	|	|	|	0445	0525	|	102
Guwahati a.	1935	1935	2145	2120	0515	0525	0525	0640	0730	1130	123

a – To Jorhat Town arr.1320.
b – From Jorhat Town dep. 1430.

5080 DELHI - JAIPUR - AHMEDABAD   Indian Railway

km	Exp	Exp	SDi	Exp	Exp	Exp	Exp	Exp	Exp	RDi	Exp	Exp	
	19708	**12414**	**12015**	**19408**	**19264**	**12215**	**14311**	**19270**	**12916**	**12958**	**16209**	**19032**	
				E ④⑦	①④	**A**	④⑤⑦	①②			①⑤⑦		↓
0	...	0425	0605**n**	0640	0820**r**	0920**r**	1150	1305	1520	1955**n**	**C**	2230	**Delhi** Junction d.
83	...	0615	0747	0832	1005	1052	1352	1458	1707	|	...	0030	Rewari d.
157	...	0716	0842	0927	1111	1148	1455	1557	1806	|	...	0139	Alwar d.
308	0840	1010	1045	1145	1325	1420	1730	1830	2035	0030	...	0425	**Jaipur** d.
444	1110	1220	1245	1410	1600	1640	2015	2140	2250	0229	0530	0650	Ajmer d.
581	1327	...	...	1612	1855	|	2215	2359	|	|	0740	0910	Marwar Junction d.
749	1650	...	...	1855	2203	2120	0123	0245	0400	0608	1020	1200	Abu Road d.
801	1825	...	...	2037	2317	2217	0247	0410	0502	0712	1152	1318	Palanpur d.
866	1942	...	...	2150	0031	|	0350	|	0558	0805	1307	1422	Mahesana d.
934	2200	...	...	2355	0210	0110	0625	0715	0740	0940	1435	1710	**Ahmedabad** a.

↑	Exp	RDi	Exp	Exp	Exp	Exp	Exp	Exp	Exp	SDI	Exp	Ex
	19031	**12957**	**12915**	**12216**	**14312**	**19407**	**19263**	**19269**	**12413**	**12016**	**19707**	**162**
				B	②④⑦	④	③⑦	⑤⑥				④⑥
Delhi Junction d.	0505	0730**n**	1010	1215**r**	1435	1445	1935**r**	2000	2200	2240**n**	...	**D**
Rewari d.	0320	|	0825	1050	1235	1255	1802	1802	2017	2102	....	...
Alwar d.	0141	|	0643	0917	1111	1134	1543	1543	1842	1852	...	..
Jaipur d.	2315	0300	0440	0720	0850	0910	1320	1320	1625	1750	1900	..
Ajmer d.	2050	0100	0230	0500	0615	0633	1105	1105	1405	1545	1635	174
Marwar Junction d.	1740	|	|	|	0322	0357	0820	0820	...	...	1240	143
Abu Road d.	1450	2050	2210	2345	0040	0115	0535	0535	...	...	0940	115
Palanpur d.	1357	2004	2109	2250	2342	0004	0410	0410	...	...	0843	105
Mahesana d.	1155	1847	1950	|	2148	2212	0216	|	...	...	0644	090
Ahmedabad a.	0955	1740	1830	1940	2020	2100	0050	0050	...	...	0450	070

A – ①②④⑥. **B** – ②③⑤⑦. **C** – Runs as **16531** on ①. **D** – Runs as **16532** on ⑦. **E** – Runs as **19404** on ④.

e – Kolkata Sealdah. **k** – Kolkata. **n** – New Delhi. **r** – Delhi Sarai Rohilla.

Indian Railways DELHI - JODHPUR 5090

km	Exp 15014	Exp 14659	Exp 12461	Exp 12463 ③⑤⑦		Exp 15013	Exp 12464 ②④⑥	Exp 12462	Exp 14660
0	0440	1735	2115	2225r	d.**Delhi** Junction ...... a.	2110	0540r	0640	1115
83	0645	1945	2322	|	d.Rewari ...... d.	1855	|	0455	0915
157	0755	2055	0017	0052	d.Alwar ...... d.	1659	0233	0310	0717
308	1110	2345	0245	0315	d.Jaipur ...... d.	1436	0025	0100	0500
471	|	0248	0511	0544	d.Degana ...... d.	|	2140	2154	0141
516	|	0326	0555	0638	d.Merta Road ...... d.	|	2105	2118	0054
620	1745	0500	0800	0835	a.**Jodhpur** ...... d.	0620	1915	1945	2325

Indian Railways JODHPUR - JAISALMER 5100

km	Exp 14659	Exp 22931 ⑥	Exp 15014	Exp 14810		Exp 15013	Exp 14809	Exp 14660	Exp 22932 ⑥
0	0530	0725	1800	2340	d.**Jodhpur** ...... a.	0545	1300	2245	2348
65	0641	0820	1914	0050	d.Osian ...... d.	0421	1102	2051	2238
137	0800	0920	2015	0156	d.Phalodi ...... d.	0325	1000	1943	2141
184	0839	1017	2055	0236	d.Ramdevra ...... d.	0238	0910	1857	2051
194	0920	|	|	0316	d.Pokaran ...... d.	|	0855	1840	|
198	0928	|	2107	0324	d.Ashapura ...... d.	0227	0826	1809	|
301	1145	1250	2325	0610	a.**Jaisalmer** ...... d.	0100	0700	1645	1920

Indian Railways JODHPUR - AHMEDABAD 5110

km	Exp 16311 ③	Exp 19028 ②	Exp 16507 ④⑥	Exp 16533 ③	Exp 19224	Exp 14707	Exp 12489 ②⑥	Exp 12479	Exp 22966 ⑥	Exp 22473 ①	Exp 17038 D⑤⑦	Exp 22932 ⑥	
277	2140	...	...	...	0045	0930	1340	...	...	1450	1600	...	d. Bikaner Junction
0	0300	0320	0510	0530b	0555	1430	1830	1845	1940b	1930	2115	2358	d.**Jodhpur**
31	0330	0351	0555	0555	0626	1501	1900	1915	|	2003	2146	0030	d.Luni
103	0512	0538	0740	0740	0810	1657	2135f	2032	2138	2138	2315	0202	d.Marwar Junction
268	0745	0825	1020	1023	1050	1937	|	2327	0040	0040	0210	0440	d.Abu Road
321	0907	0952	1152	|	1217	2135	0125	0100	|	0155	0327	0557	d.Palanpur
386	1020	1105	1307	|	1331	2237	0216	0151	0304	0304	0420	0708	d.Mahesana
459	1230	1310	1435	1435	1500	0035	0400	0330	0435	0435	0635	0910	a.**Ahmedabad**

	Exp 14708	Exp 17037 ④⑤	Exp 22663 ①	Exp 16312 ①	Exp 16508 ③⑤	Exp 16534 ②	Exp 22965 ⑥	Exp 19223	Exp 19027 ⑥	Exp 12480	Exp 12490 ③⑦	Exp 22931 C②⑤
Bikaner Junction a.	1530	1650	...	2145	...	...	...	0135	...	...	1310	...
Jodhpur a.	0936	1045	1000	1630	1650	1645b	1650b	2005	0430	0630	0735	0715
Luni d.	0856	1010	0920	1552	1552	1552	|	1915	0353	0543	0700	0641
Marwar Junction d.	0740	0910	0810	1450	1450	1450	1515	1812	0250	0440	0426f	0540
Abu Road d.	0435	0605	0500	1150	1150	1150	1235	1530	2345	0130	|	0250
Palanpur d.	0328	0503	0410	1056	1056	|	|	1428	2250	0033	0155	0155
Mahesana d.	0151	0304	0216	0908	0908	|	1000	1241	2122	2235	2345	2345
Ahmedabad d.	0015	0110	0050	0725	0705	0705	0805	1120	1955	2125	2225	2225

b – Bhagat Ki Koth. f – Marwar Bhinmal. C – Runs as **22474** on ② to Bikaner arr. 1235. D – Also runs from Jodhpur as **22664** on ① dep. 2135.

Indian Railways DELHI and JAIPUR - UDAIPUR - AHMEDABAD 5120

km		Exp 12992	Exp 12315 ⑤	Exp 19602 ②	Exp 15715 ①③⑥	jSDi 12066 ⑤⑦	Exp 12986	Exp 19665	Exp 12963 A	Exp 12981	52927 ⊖	Exp 19943 ⊖
0	**Delhi** SR ...... d.	...	...	1230j	1352	1620	1735	...	1900z	1940	...	...
83	Rewari ...... d.	...	...	1522	1522	1750	|	...	|	2107	...	...
**	**Jaipur** ...... d.	1400	1745	1920	1920	|	2205	2300	|	|	...	...
373	Ajmer ...... d.	1610	2030	2150	2145	2225	...	0125	|	0215	...	...
559	Chittaurgarh ...... d.	1925	0020	0145	...	...	...	0425	0508	0535	...	...
673	**Udaipur** City ...... d.	2130	0245	0355	...	...	...	0635	0720	0750	0810	1745
883	Himmatnagar ...... d.	...	...	...	...	...	...	...	...	...	1810	0155
971	**Ahmedabad** ...... a.	...	...	...	...	...	...	...	...	...	2125	0425

	Exp 12316 ①	jSDi 12065 ⑤⑦	Exp 19601 ⑥	Exp 15716 ①②④	Exp 12991	Exp 19944 ⊖	Exp 12982	Exp 12964 B	52928 ⊖	Exp 19666	Exp 12985
Ahmedabad ...... d.	...	...	...	...	...	2300	...	...	0710	...	...
Himmatnagar ...... d.	...	...	...	...	...	0150	...	...	1030	...	...
Udaipur City ...... d.	0020	...	0020	...	0600	0920	1715	1815	1900	2220	...
Chittaurgarh ...... d.	0235	...	0235	...	0820	...	1930	2045	...	0030	...
Ajmer ...... d.	0630	0540	0633	1105	1125	...	2237	|	...	0340	...
Jaipur ...... a.	0845	|	0910	1320	1335	...	|	|	...	0545	0600
Rewari ...... d.	...	1010	1255	1802	...	...	0335	|	...	...	|
Delhi SR ...... a.	...	1135	1445j	1933	...	...	0505	0635z	...	...	1030

A – Via Mathura (d. 2110), Sawai Madhopur (d. 2358) and Kota (d. 0125). B – Via Kota (d. 2335), Sawai Madhopur (d. 0050) and Mathura (d. 0430). j – Delhi Junction. z – Delhi Hazrat Nizamuddin. ** – Jaipur - Ajmer: *136 km*. ⊖ – Cancelled for gauge conversion.

Indian Railways DELHI and JAIPUR - MUMBAI and AHMEDABAD 5130

km		Exp 12904	Exp 19708	Exp 22934 ②	Exp 12956	Exp 12215 D	Duro 12264 ①④	jSDi 12060	Exp 12918 ②④⑥	Exp 12910 ③⑤⑦	RDi 12952	Yuva 12248 ⑥	RDi 12954	Duro 12240 ②④	Exp 12980 ①③⑤	Exp 12926	Duro 22210 ②⑥	Exp 12908 ①④	Exp 12472 A	Exp 12478 ⑦E	Exp 19024	Exp 19020
0	**Delhi z** ...... d.	0720	...	...	...	0920r	1055	1315	1355	1535	1625n	1535	1650	...	...	1645n	2325n	2135	2150n	2150n	1330n	2150
124	Mathura ...... d.	0950	...	...	...	|	|	1520	1605	1712	|	1712	1840	...	...	1915	|	|	0010	0010	1700	0130
	Jaipur ...... d.	|	0840	1250	1400	1420	|	|	|	|	|	|	|	1910	2025	|	|	|	|	|	|	|
340	Sawai Madhopur d.	1255	|	1530	1610	|	|	1807	|	|	|	|	2038	2105	2245	2205	|	|	0229	0229	2108	0525
448	Kota Junction .. d.	1425	△	1655	1735	△	1530	2000	1955	2015	2110	2015	2144	|	0010	2340	0425	0310	0355	0355	2320	0740
673	Nagda ...... d.	1757	|	2022	2105	|	|	...	|	|	2337	|	|	|	0308	0320	|	|	0725	0722	0435	1315
714	Ratlam ...... d.	1905	|	2125	2150	|	1845	...	2350	2325	0008	2325	0055	0155	0410	0430	0740	|	0815	0815	0540	1425
976	Vadodara ...... d.	2303	0028	0135	0144	0313	2238	...	0415	0307	0334	0307	0426	0530	0810	0830	1120	1111	1216	1225	1040	2007
1075	**Ahmedabad** a.	|	|	|	|	|	P	...	0615	|	|	|	|	|	|	|	|	|	|	1415	|	|
1104	Surat ...... d.	0102	0222	0327	0335	0451	...	...	...	0451	0503	0520	0605	|	1008	1025	|	|	1410	...	1335	2217
1340	Borivali ...... d.	0406	0543	0657	0644	0730	...	...	...	0723	0729	|	0856	|	1329	1357	|	1551	1719	...	1843	0332
1360	**Mumbai** Bandra a.	0505c	0635	0735	0740c	0810	...	...	...	0810	0815c	0920	0945c	1050c	1420	1445	1615c	1635	1805	...	1940c	0420

km		Exp 19019	Exp 19023	Exp 12471 B	Exp 12477 ②F	Exp 12925	Exp 12216 C	Duro 12263 ②⑤	Exp 12979 ②④⑥	Exp 22933 ①	RDi 12951	Exp 12907 ③⑦	Exp 12909 ②④⑥	Yuva 12247 ⑤	Exp 12917 ①③⑤	RDi 12953	jSDi 12059	Exp 12955	Exp 19707	Exp 12903	Duro 12239 ②⑦	Duro 22209 ①⑤
0	**Mumbai** Bandra d.	0005	0725c	0755	...	1200	1245	...	1615	1615	1700c	1635	1635	1635	...	1740c	...	1850c	2055	2125c	2315c	2315c
19	Borivali ...... d.	0040	0807	0828	...	1237	1313	...	1649	1649	1732	1709	1709	|	...	1819	...	1930	2132	2201	|	|
252	Surat ...... d.	0445	1337	1147	...	1620	1600	...	2038	2038	1958	|	2010	2010	...	2055	...	2245	0052	0105	|	|
	Ahmedabad .. d.	|	|	|	1130	|	|	P	|	|	|	|	|	|	1705	|	...	|	|	|	|	|
381	Vadodara ...... d.	0655	1606	1343	1335	1813	1737	1844	2240	2240	2128	2312	2146	2146	1908	2231	...	0044	0245	0259	0405	0405
642	Ratlam ...... d.	1230	2055	1800	1800	2230	|	2215	0245	0245	0040	|	0110	0110	2335	0220	...	0440	|	0715	0740	0740
684	Nagda ...... d.	1415	2205	1900	1900	2325	△	|	0355	0355	0120	|	|	|	|	|	...	0538	△	0810	|	|
909	Kota Junction .. d.	1925	0135	2145	2145	0220	|	0110	0635	0635	0325	0630	0350	0350	0300	0520	0555	0855	|	1105	|	1030
1017	Sawai Madhopur d.	2110	0315	2300	2300	0350	|	|	0845	0845	|	|	|	|	|	0628	0705	1040	|	1230	1225	|
1148	**Jaipur** ...... a.	|	|	|	|	|	0705	|	1045	1045	|	|	|	|	|	|	|	1245	1900	|	1435	|
	Mathura ...... d.	0225	0935	0205	0205	0750	|	|	...	...	|	|	0727	0727	0802	0902	1020	...	...	1620	...	|
	Delhi z ...... a.	0525	1245n	0412	0412	1003	1215r	0655	...	...	0835n	1345	0940	0940	1040	1055	1230	...	...	1845	...	1630n

Notes for TABLES **5130 - 5150**

- A – ②③⑤⑥.
- B – ①④⑤⑦.
- C – ②③⑤⑦.
- D – ①②④⑥.
- E – Runs as **12476** on ①. Also as **12474** on ④.
- F – Runs as **12475** on ③. Also as **12473** on ⑥.
- G – Runs as **12960** on ②⑤.
- H – Runs as **22474** on ②.
- J – Runs as **16507** on ④⑥, **16209** on ⑤⑦, **16533** on ③, **16505** on ②, **16531** on ①.
- L – Runs as **16508** on ②④, **16210** on ③⑤, **16534** on ①, **16506** on ⑦, **16532** on ⑥.
- P – To / from Pune (Table **5160**).
- k Kalyan.
- z – Delhi Hazrat Nizamuddin.
- △ – Via Ahmedabad (Tables **5080, 5150**).

Indian Railways GANDHIDHAM - AHMEDABAD 5140

km		Exp 16335 ⑤	Exp 22952 ④	Exp 16505 ②	Exp 11091 ③	Exp 14312 ②④⑦	Exp 15667 ⑥	Exp 22904 ①④⑥	Exp 12960 ①④	Exp 22956	Exp 12993 ⑤	Exp 19116
58	Bhuj ...... d.	...	...	...	0855	1240	...	1555	1830	2015	...	2225
0	**Gandhidham** ...... d.	0720	0650	0900	1025	1415	1340	1715	1950	2145	2245	2355
53	Samakhiali ...... d.	0815	0747	0950	1118	1508	1439	1803	2043	2240	2340	0048
94	Maliya Miyana ... d.	0849	0827	|	|	1542	1528	|	|	2312	|	0122
170	Dhrangadhra ...... d.	0954	|	1133	1248	1700	|	|	|	0018	0116	0228
236	Viramgam ...... d.	1115	1245	1305	1412	1823	1955	|	|	0138	|	0350
301	**Ahmedabad** ...... a.	1240	1355	1435	1530	1945	2110	2155	0400	0250	0400	0515

	Exp 22955	Exp 14311 ①⑤⑥	Exp 16336 ④	Exp 16506 ①	Exp 12994 ③	Exp 11092 ②	Exp 22903 ①④⑥	Exp 22951 ⑤	Exp 12959 ③⑥	Exp 15668 ⑤	Exp 19115
Ahmedabad .. d.	0205	0655	0725	0705	0745	0805	0645	0815	0815	1840	2359
Viramgam ...... d.	0301	0755	0833	0803	|	0912	|	0922	|	1938	0056
Dhrangadhra .. d.	0403	0900	0940	0906	0940	1014	|	|	|	|	0157
Maliya Miyana d.	0510	1007	1041	|	|	|	|	1343	|	0044	0307
Samakhiali ...... d.	0605	1059	1152	1108	1150	1205	1025	1420	1500	0132	0405
Gandhidham .a.	0705	1200	1300	1230	1300	1305	1115	1530	1600	0240	0510
Bhuj ...... a.	0850	1400	...	...	...	1520	1240	...	1750	...	0700

Indian Railways AHMEDABAD - MUMBAI 5150

km		Exp 12972	Exp 12215 C	Exp 22452 ①④	Exp 14707	Exp 22956	Exp 12479	Exp 12489 C G	Exp 12934	Exp 12990 ①④⑥	Exp 22966 ⑦	Exp 22473 ②	Exp 12932 ①–⑥	Exp 19116	Exp 22954	Exp 22932 ⑦	Exp 16507 J	SDi 12010 ①–⑥	Exp 19028 ②	Exp 22952 ④	Exp 19218	Exp 22928	Duro 12268	Exp 12902	Exp 22904 ①④⑥	Exp 19708	Exp 22946
0	**Ahmedabad** ... d.	2359	0130	0130	0100	0310	0355	0420	0455	0455	0455	0455	0600	0535	0700	0930	1445	1445	1400	1415	2035	2110	2340	2200	2220	2230	2300
64	Anand ...... d.	0106	|	0228	0206	0416	0459	0541	0601	0616	|	0616	0702	0645	0819	1046	1604	1542	1530	|	2152	2238	|	2316	|	2342	0005
100	Vadodara ...... d.	0152	0313	0313	0252	0502	0545	0627	0647	0702	0702	0702	0748	0739	0905	1140	1657	1623	1635	1635	2246	2324	|	0012	0006	0028	0051
229	Surat ...... d.	0350	0451	0520	0442	0700	0743	0820	0840	0855	0855	0855	0927	0955	1115	1350	1915	1803	1835	1830	0050	0122	|	0210	0145	0222	0238
462	Borivali ...... d.	0752	0723	0830	0850	1041	1049	1123	1150	1159	1159	1159	1217	1310	1502	1647	0102k	2035	2146	2146	0452	0503	|	0516	0435	0543	0607
480	**Mumbai** Bandra a.	0835	0810	0920	0940	1125	1135	1200d	1235c	1240d	1245	1245	1300c	1345	1555c	1730	...	2120c	2225	2225	0540	0550	0600c	0625c	0515	0635	0710c

	Exp 12959 ③⑥	SDi 12009 ①–⑥	Exp 22953	Exp 19027 ⑥	Exp 22451 ①④	Exp 12216 C	Exp 12480	Exp 12933	Exp 12931 ①–⑥	Exp 12490 ③⑦	Exp 12989 ①④⑥	Exp 22931 H②⑤	Exp 19115	Exp 14708	Exp 22955	Exp 19217	Exp 22927	Exp 19707	Exp 12971	Exp 22945	Duro 12267	Exp 12901	Exp 16508 L	Exp 22965 ⑤	Exp 22951 ④	Exp 22903 ③⑤⑦
Mumbai Bandra ...... d.	0005d	0625c	0545c	1215	1215	1245	1330	1340c	1420c	1435d	1435d	1435	1500d	1505	1745	1710	1940	2055	2130	2135c	2325c	2205c	...	2355	2355	2345
Borivali ...... d.	0036	0659	0627	1250	1250	1313	1400	1417	1457	1506	1506	1506	1531	1540	1820	1747	2019	2132	2206	2221	|	2253	2130k	0027	0027	0020
Surat ...... d.	0420	0936	1028	1600	1600	1600	1720	1740	1800	1823	1823	1823	1850	1925	2200	2142	0027	0052	0120	0135	|	0215	0255	0355	0420	0318
Vadodara ...... d.	0608	1108	1236	1748	1748	1737	1918	1931	1938	2017	2017	2017	2133	2150	2357	0003	0226	0245	0306	0326	|	0426	0452	0548	0608	0448
Anand ...... d.	0643	1137	1309	1820	1820	|	1950	2007	2015	2054	2054	2054	2206	2227	0033	0039	0259	0318	0340	0403	|	0503	0525	|	|	|
Ahmedabad ...... a.	0755	1245	1440	1930	1930	1920	2105	2125	2140	2205	2205	2205	2340	2355	0145	0200	0420	0430	0455	0535	0555	0635	0655	0745	0755	0625

5160 DELHI - PUNE and MUMBAI

Indian Railways

km		Exp 12172 ③⑥	Exp 12138	Duro 12264 ①④	Exp 12148 ④	Exp 12782 ①	Exp 12630 A	Exp 11078	Exp 12780	Exp 22110 ③	Exp 11058
0	**Delhi** H Nizamuddin .. d.	0010	0515n	1055	0550	0550	0845	1015n	1500	1545	2105
134	Mathura Junction d.	|	0740	|	0756	0756	|	1240	1645	|	2340
188	Agra Cantonment d.	0300	0835	|	0850	0850	|	1335	1735	1751	0040
306	Gwalior d.	|	1036	|	1105	1105	|	1536	1940	1911	0300
403	Jhansi d.	0625	1235	|	1250	1250	1505	1730	2122	2027	0500
556	Bina d.	|	1450	|	1505	1505	|	2015	|	|	0855
694	Bhopal d.	1040	1655	|	1715	1715	1925	2230	0110	2345	1120
786	Itarsi d.	|	1850	▽	1905	1905	|	0025	0250	|	1330
969	Khandwa d.	|	2140	|	2200	2200	|	0325	0535	|	1645
1093	Bhusaval d.	1645	2335	|	2355	2355	|	0530	0730	0525	1855
1277	Manmad d.	|	0155	|	0235	0235	|	0815	0950	|	2150
1513	Daund d.	|	|	|	0755	0755	|	1310	1500	|	|
1589	**Pune** a.	|	|	0710	0915	0915	1105	1515	1620	|	|
1484	Kalyan d.	2255	0625	...	...	...	...	...	...	1050	0245
1521	**Mumbai** LTT a.	2345	0735h	...	...	...	...	...	...	1145	0405h

	Exp 11057	Exp 12779	Exp 12171 ①④	Duro 12263 ②⑤	Exp 22109 ②	Exp 12629 B	Exp 12147 ②	Exp 12781 ⑥	Exp 11077	Exp 12137
Mumbai LTT d.	2330h	...	0755	...	1430	...	...	...	...	1935h
Kalyan d.	0033	...	0830	...	1507	...	...	...	...	2037
Pune d.	|	0410	|	1110	|	0900	1610	1610	1720	|
Daund d.	|	0550	|	|	|	|	1745	1745	1850	|
Manmad d.	0405	1020	|	|	|	1525	2155	2155	2325	0025
Bhusaval d.	0655	1300	1415	|	2020	1800	0025	0025	0200	0250
Khandwa d.	0930	1500	|	|	|	|	0220	0220	0430	0500
Itarsi d.	1250	1735	|	▽	|	|	0445	0450	0715	0745
Bhopal d.	1505	1935	2040	|	0210	0045	0630	0630	0910	0940
Bina d.	1745	|	|	|	|	|	0825	0825	1120	1205
Jhansi d.	2040	2358	0038	|	0531	0610	1038	1038	1347	1430
Gwalior d.	2215	0115	|	|	0632	|	1157	1157	1520	1600
Agra Cantonment d.	0010	0305	0405	|	0757	|	1405	1405	1712	1808
Mathura Junction d.	0108	0402	|	|	|	|	1500	1500	1805	1858
Delhi H Nizamuddin a.	0345	0620	0655	0655	1025	1300	1710	1710	2026	2056

A – ②③⑤⑥ Runs as **22686** on ②⑥. B – ③④⑤⑦ Runs as **22685** on ④⑦. ▽ – Via Kota and Vadodara, see Table **5130**.

5170 LUCKNOW - PUNE and MUMBAI

Indian Railways

km		Exp 11016	Exp 12541	Exp 12144 ②	Exp 12174 ②④	Exp 12104 ⑦	Exp 15101 ③	Exp 12597 ②	Exp 12533	Exp 15029 ④	Exp 12108 ②④⑦
0	**Lucknow** Junction d.	0050a	0353a	0235	0550	0630	0625a	1335	1945	2255	2245
72	Kanpur Central d.	0225	0536	0425	0800	0800	0800	1515	2130	0040	0020
292	Jhansi d.	0715	0941	1020	1155	1155	1155	1905	0140	0435	0345
445	Bina d.	0950	|	1250	|	1410	|	|	|	0710	|
583	Bhopal d.	1200	1356	1445	1635	1635	1635	2320	0600	0940	0820
674	Itarsi d.	1400	1536	|	|	1825	1825	0100	0750	1155	|
858	Khandwa d.	1720	1821	1840	|	2105	2105	|	1025	1450	|
981	Bhusaval d.	1920	2006	2025	2255	2255	2255	0515	1220	1700	1450
1166	Manmad d.	2220	|	2245	|	0125	0108	|	1419	1950	|
1402	Daund d.	|	|	|	|	0620	|	|	|	|	|
1477	**Pune** a.	|	|	|	|	0805	|	|	|	0405	|
1372	Kalyan d.	0315	|	|	0503	...	|	1100	1830	...	2154
1409	**Mumbai** LTT a.	0420	0401	0410	0600	...	0615j	1215j	1950h	...	2300

	Exp 12534	Exp 12542	Exp 15030 ⑥	Exp 12598 ③	Exp 15102 ⑤	Exp 12173 ②⑦	Exp 12107 ①③⑥	Exp 12103 ⑤	Exp 12143 ⑦	Exp 11015
Mumbai LTT d.	0825h	1110	...	1420h	1535h	1625	1625	...	1640	2245
Kalyan d.	0913	|	...	1510	1633	1709	1709	...	|	2328
Pune d.	|	|	1045	|	|	|	|	1615	|	|
Daund d.	|	|	|	|	|	|	|	1745	|	|
Manmad d.	1245	|	1725	|	2015	|	|	2155	2145	0315
Bhusaval d.	1510	1750	2000	2055	2325	2300	2300	0025	0025	0605
Khandwa d.	1715	2105	2345	|	0235	|	|	0220	0235	0900
Itarsi d.	1914	2335	0220	0135	0515	|	|	0505	|	1155
Bhopal d.	2105	0115	0430	0330	0720	0500	0500	0655	0720	1400
Bina d.	|	|	0645	|	|	|	|	0900	0940	1630
Jhansi d.	0208	0525	0855	0735	1145	0920	0920	1110	1155	1920
Kanpur Central d.	0700	1000	1330	1135	1715	1335	1350	1545	1545	0020
Lucknow Junction a.	0840	1127a	1455	1310	1915a	1455	1510	1710	1715	0142a

5180 PATNA - MUGHAL SARAI, VARANASI and ALLAHABAD - MUMBAI

Indian Railways

km		Exp 11062	Exp 22104 ③	Exp 15267 ⑦	Exp 12545 ⑤	Exp 12361 ①	Exp 15547 ②	Exp 22972 ③	Exp 12321	Exp 13201	Exp 18609 ④	Exp 12168	Exp 11094	Duro 12294 ②⑥	Exp 12142	Exp 11060 ①④⑥	Exp 11056 E	Exp 15018	Exp 12335 ②⑤⑦	Exp 15646 ①④	Exp 15648 ③	Exp 22130 ①③Z	Exp 11068 ④⑦	Exp 12166 ②⑤⑥	Exp 11072 X
	Patna Junction d.	...	...	...	0055	0045	0045	2310	...	0020	...	...	...	...	1045p	...	...	...	1400	1335	1400		...		...
	Mughal Sarai * d.	...	...	...	0529	0529	0529	0307	0830	0419	0645	...	...	...	1447	...	...	...	1752	1752	1752	...	...	...	...
	Varanasi d.	2325	...	0345	|	|	|	|	|	|	0800	1025	1120	...	|	...	...	1120	|	|	|	...	...	2020	1550
0	**Allahabad** Junction d.	0305	0700	0740	|	|	|	|	|	|	1220	|	|	1930	|	1705	1705	1615	|	|	|	1845	2100	2330	1940
103	Manikpur d.	0510	0900	|	|	|	|	|	1335	1050	|	1430	1710	|	|	|	|	1832	|	|	|	2035	2300	|	2135
178	Satna d.	0625	1020	1100	1100	1100	1100	0800	1500	1220	1515	1545	1825	2220	2015	2040	2040	2000	2310	2310	2310	|	0015	0220	2245
278	Katni d.	0740	1130	1215	1215	1215	1215	0915	1620	1340	1640	1700	1950	|	|	|	|	2115	0030	0030	0030	|	0115	0328	0025
369	Jabalpur d.	0950	1305	1350	1350	1350	1350	1110	1755	1520	1900	1830	2120	|	2320	2335	2335	2250	0200	0200	0200	|	0310	0500	|
614	Itarsi d.	1405	1720	|	1810	1810	1810	1450	2225	2045	2345	2320	0135	|	|	0330	0330	0430	0720	0720	0720	0855	0800	0905	0935
791	Khandwa d.	1700	|	2045	2045	2045	2045	|	0105	0030	0235	0305	0405	|	|	|	|	0815	1005	1005	1005	1155	1130	|	1250
915	Bhusaval d.	1900	2140	2230	2230	2230	2230	1930	0300	0235	0420	0455	0615	0900	0740	0810	0810	1020	1155	1155	1155	1345	1335	1345	1445
1099	Manmad d.	2125	|	|	0050	0050	0050	|	0535	0455	0640	|	0840	|	0955	|	|	1245	1405	1405	1405	1600	1600	1600	1730
1306	Kalyan d.	0235	0330	0503	0503	0503	0630	|	1015	1025	1100	1125	1300	|	1415	1510	1510	1710	1900	1900	1900	2025	2025	2025	2150
1349	**Mumbai** LTT a.	0340	0500	0600	0600	0615h	0730h	0735b	1125h	1130	1205	1225	1415h	1455	1515	1615	1615	1805	2000	2000	2000	2130	2130	2130	2250

	Exp 12167	Exp 11093	Exp 11067 ③⑥	Exp 12165 ①④⑤	Exp 15017	Exp 22129 ②⑦Y	Exp 12336 ②④⑦	Exp 15645 ③⑥	Exp 15647 ⑤	Exp 11055 B	Exp 11059 ②④⑥	Exp 12362 ③	Exp 12546 ①	Exp 15548 ④	Exp 11061	Exp 22103 ①	Duro 12293 ①⑤	Exp 11071 W	Exp 22971 ①	Exp 15268 ②	Exp 18610 ⑥	Exp 12322	Exp 12141	Exp 13202
Mumbai LTT d.	0035	0010h	0523	0523	0635	0523	0805	0805	0805	1055	1055	1105h	1120	1120	1215	1430	1725	1240	1635b	1550	1550	2130h	2325	2215
Kalyan d.	0123	0115	0608	0608	0722	0606	0840	0840	0840	1137	1137	1200	1200	1200	1300	1507	|	1325	|	1632	1632	2235	0021	2304
Manmad d.	|	0455	0940	0940	1105	0940	1215	1215	1215	|	|	1550	1550	1550	1630	|	|	1655	|	|	2015	0213	0400	0300
Bhusaval d.	0735	0730	1205	1205	1345	1205	1440	1440	1440	1740	1740	1815	1815	1815	1910	2030	2305	1925	0420	2325	2325	0440	0625	0545
Khandwa d.	1015	1000	1420	|	1635	1420	1730	1730	1730	|	|	2040	2040	2040	2130	|	|	2150	|	0235	0235	0655	|	0805
Itarsi d.	1310	1250	1710	1710	2120	1700	2009	2009	2009	2230	2230	2315	2315	2315	0015	0125	|	0030	0920	|	0520	0940	|	1140
Jabalpur d.	1640	1620	2105	2105	0105	|	2330	2330	2330	0155	0155	0240	0240	0240	0330	0455	|	|	1250	0900	0900	1320	1435	1610
Katni d.	1745	1740	2220	2220	0230	|	0045	0045	0045	|	|	0355	0355	0355	0515	0610	|	1010	1405	1030	1030	1445	|	1730
Satna d.	1947	1930	2355	2355	0400	|	0207	0207	0207	0457	0457	0517	0517	0517	0652	0735	0850	1140	1537	1200	1200	1620	1730	1902
Manikpur d.	2212	2155	0145	|	0555	0650	|	|	|	|	|	|	|	|	0855	0937	|	1335	|	|	|	1805	|	2110
Allahabad Junction a.	|	|	0349	0350	0825	0850	|	|	|	1000	1000	|	|	|	1045	1140	1235	1540	|	1600	1600	|	|	|
Varanasi a.	0345	0440	...	0705	1255	...	|	|	|	...	...	|	|	|	1355	...	...	1925	|	1945	1945	|	|	|
Mughal Sarai * a.	...	...	...	...	...	...	0853	0855	0855	...	...	1213	1213	1213	...	...	...	...	2150	...	2040	2315	0037	0353
Patna Junction a.	...	...	...	...	...	...	1230	1230	1230	...	...	1520	1520	1520	...	...	...	...	0205	...	...	...	0445p	1000

Notes for Tables **5170** and **5180**.
B – ①③⑤⑦. E – ②③⑤⑦.
W – Via Bhopal (d. 0235) and Bina (d. 0535).
X – Via Bina (d. 0535) and Bhopal (d. 0740).
Y – Via Bhopal (d. 1845), Bina (d. 2140) and Jhansi (d. 0030).
Z – Via Jhansi (d. 0210), Bina (d. 0425) and Bhopal (d. 0705).
a – Lucknow Aishbagh.
* – Mughal Sarai is now PT Deen Dayal Upadhyaya Jct.

5190 DELHI - SECUNDERABAD - TIRUPATI and BANGALORE

Indian Railways

km		Duro 12245 ex②⑤	Exp 12650 A	Exp 12708 ③⑤⑦	Exp 12648 ③	Duro 12286 ①⑤	RDi 12438 ⑦	Exp 12724	RDi 22692	Duro 12214 ①	Exp 12722
0	**Delhi** H Nizamuddin .. d.	...	0625	0710	0835	1545	1555	1725n	2045	2300r	2300
135	Mathura Junction d.	...	|	|	1020	|	|	1925	|	|	0100
189	Agra Cantonment d.	...	|	|	1115	|	|	2013	2251	|	0200
307	Gwalior d.	...	|	|	1305	|	|	2200	|	|	0348
404	Jhansi d.	...	1215	1355	1440	2027	2043	2335	0125	0425	0535
557	Bina d.	...	|	|	1705	|	|	|	|	|	0800
695	Bhopal d.	...	1620	1800	1910	|	0005	0330	0445	|	1020
788	Itarsi d.	...	|	|	2105	|	|	|	|	|	1225
1085	Nagpur d.	...	2220	0015	0150	0520	0535	0945	1010	|	1745
1298	Balharshah d.	...	0140	0335	0515	0815	0820	1330	1310	1700	2150
1528	Kazipet d.	...	|	0650	0925	|	1127	1647	1607	|	0140
1660	**Secunderabad** a.	...	|	|	|	1400	1400	1900	1825	2115	0405
***	**Secunderabad** d.	...	|	|	|	...	...	1905a	1840	2130	0410c
1666	Kacheguda d.	...	0707	1000	1230	...	...	...	|	|	...
1772	Mahabubnagar d.	...	|	1140	1400	...	...	...	|	|	...
1902	Kurnool Town d.	...	1107	1338	1610	...	...	...	|	|	...
1951	Raichur d.	...	|	|	|	...	...	...	2300	|	...
1956	Dhone d.	...	|	1500	1730	...	...	...	|	|	...
2292	Renigunta d.	1015	|	2102	|	...	...	...	|	|	...
2302	**Tirupati** a.	|	|	2135	|	...	...	...	|	|	...
	Guntakal d.	|	|	...	|	...	...	...	|	0300	...
2101	Dharmavaram d.	|	1520	...	2055	...	...	...	0325	|	...
2306*	**Bangalore** City a.	1600y	1935y	...	0030y	...	...	...	0640	0755y	...

	Duro 12246 ex③⑥	RDI 22691	Duro 12213 ⑥	Exp 12723	Exp 12649 B	RDi 12437 ③	Duro 12285 ④⑦	Exp 12647 ⑦	Exp 12707 ①③⑤	Exp 12721
Bangalore City d.	1100y	2000	2340y	...	2200y	...	...	2340y	...	...
Dharmavaram d.	|	2320	|	...	0040	...	...	0240	...	...
Guntakal d.	|	0110	0350	...	|	...	...	|	...	...
Tirupati d.	|	|	|	...	|	...	...	|	0540	...
Renigunta d.	1650	|	|	...	|	...	...	|	0605	...
Dhone d.	...	|	|	...	|	...	...	0540	1200	...
Raichur d,	...	0245	|	...	|	...	...	|	|	...
Kurnool Town d.	...	|	|	...	0427	...	...	0635	1304	...
Mahabubnagar d.	...	|	|	...	|	...	...	0835	1506	...
Kacheguda d.	...	|	|	...	0821	...	...	1040	1715	...
Secunderabad a.	...	0735	0855	0645e	|	...	...	|	|	2255
Secunderabad d.	...	0750	0910	0650	|	1245	1310	|	|	2300
Kazipet d.	...	0930	|	0842	|	1447	|	1320	1940	0130
Balharshah d.	...	1255	1345	1235	1413	1800	1815	1735	2315	0530
Nagpur d.	...	1530	|	1550	1715	2045	2105	2110	0210	0915
Itarsi d.	...	|	|	|	|	|	|	0145	|	1455
Bhopal d.	...	2130	|	2200	2303	0210	|	0330	0815	1650
Bina d.	...	|	|	|	|	|	|	0525	|	1905
Jhansi d.	...	0056	0106	0220	0300	0531	0550	0745	1210	2130
Gwalior d.	...	|	|	0333	|	|	|	0920	|	2257
Agra Cantonment d.	...	0330	|	0523	|	|	|	1124	|	0050
Mathura Junction d.	...	|	|	0609	|	|	|	1215	|	0139
Delhi H Nizamuddin a.	...	0555	0700r	0835	0915	1025	1035	1415	1800	0405

A – ①②④⑥⑦. B – ①③⑤⑥⑦.
a – To Hyderabad Decan arr. 1935. c – To Hyderabad Decan arr. 0500.
e – From Hyderabad Decan d. 0625. f – From Hyderabad Decan d. 2230.
r – Delhi Sarai Rohilla. y – Bangalore Yesvantpur Junction.
* – *2385 Kms* via Raichur. *** – Secunderabad - Kacheguda: 7 *km*

ndian Railways — DELHI - AGRA — 5200

km		Exp 12172 ③⑥	SDi 12002	Exp 18238	Exp 12138	Exp 12148 ④	Exp 12644 ⑤	Exp 12646 ②	Exp 12782 ①	Exp 12804 ③⑦	Exp 12280	Exp 12642 ①⑥		Exp 12808 A	Exp 18508 ①④⑦	Exp 13008	Exp 12618	Exp 11078	Exp 12626	Exp 18478	Exp 14624	Exp 19326 ④⑦	Exp 12716	Exp 14310 ②③
7	**New Delhi** d.	...	0600	...	0515	...	...	...	...	...	0645	...	...	...	0810	0710	...	1015	1125	...	1220r	...	1320	...
0	**Delhi** Hazrat Nizamuddin d.	0010	|	0430	|	0550	0550	0550	0550	0550	0700	0710	...	0835	0845	|	0915	|	|	1205	|	1005	|	1340
34	Mathura Junction d.	|	0724	0700	0740	0756	0756	0756	0756	0456	0850	|	...	1020	1032	1025	1110	1240	1320	1420	1520	1158	1533	1550
88	**Agra** Cantonment a.	0255	0757	0815	0830	0845	0845	0845	0845	0845	0940	1002	...	1110	1125	1150	1205	1330	1405	1515	1605	1250	1620	1640

	Exp 14318 ⑤⑥	Exp 12191	Exp 12780	Exp 11450 ④	Exp 16032 ③⑥⑦	Exp 16318 ②	Exp 12688 ①⑤	Exp 16688 ⑤	Exp 12550 ④	Exp 12190	Exp 12724	Exp 12616	Exp 14212	Exp 12920	Exp 12448	Exp 12156	Exp 12628	Exp 11058	Exp 12622	Exp 12722	Exp 12422 ①	Exp 12486 ②⑤⑥	Exp 22404 ⑦
ew Delhi d.	...	...	...	1415	1415	1415	...	1415	1510f	...	1725	1840	1735	1915	...	...	2115	2045	2230	...	2345	2345	2345
elhi Hazrat Nizamuddin d.	1340	1420	1500	1430	1430	1430	1430	1438	|	1605	|	|	1757	|	2010	2055	|	2103	|	2300	|	|	|
athura Junction d.	1550	1613	1645	1707	1707	|	|	|	|	1813	1925	2045	2031	2140	2200	|	2303	2340	|	0100	|	0135	0135
gra Cantonment a.	1640	1657	1730	1812	1812	1812	1812	1840	1840	1907	2011	2135	2220	2225	2305	2321	2348	0035	0100	0155	0220	0220	0220

	Exp 11057	Exp 12721	Exp 12919	Exp 12447	Exp 12615	Exp 14623	Exp 12779	Exp 12621	Exp 12171 ②⑤	Exp 12155	Exp 12723	Exp 12549 ③	Exp 14211	Exp 12627	Exp 14309 ④⑤	Exp 14317 ①⑦	Exp 19325 ③⑥	Exp 12192	Exp 12189	Exp 12715	Exp 12485 ①②⑤		Exp 12421 ④
gra Cantonment d.	0010	0050	0125	0225	0250	0155	0305	0353	0405	0450	0523	0535	0550	0645	0705	0705	0620	0735	0815	0840	0915	...	0915
athura Junction d.	0108	0139	0215	0311	0350	0242	0402	|	|	|	0609	|	0650	0737	0810	0810	0810	0830	0920	0930	1010	...	|
elhi Hazrat Nizamuddin a.	0341	0405	0436	0525	0600	|	0620	0642	0655	0800	0838	|	0947	0955	1110	1110	1110	|	1140	1146	|	...	|
ew Delhi a.	0415	...	0505	...	0630	0615r	...	0705	...	...	0905	0930f	1020	1030	...	...	...	1135	...	1210	1300	...	1300

	Exp 12617	Exp 12625	Exp 18477	Exp 12647 ②	Exp 18507 ③⑥⑦	Exp 12807 B	Exp 12781 ⑦	Exp 12643 ④	Exp 12803 ②⑥	Exp 12147 ③	Exp 12645 ①	Exp 12641 ⑤⑦	Exp 13007	Exp 18237	Exp 11077	Exp 12687 ⑤		Exp 12137	Exp 16031 ①④⑤	Exp 11449 ②	Exp 12279	SDi 12001	Exp 22403 ④
gra Cantonment d.	1015	1025	1050	1124	1129	1344	1405	1405	1405	1405	1405	1515	1520	1630	1712	1730	...	1808	1830	1830	1855	2115	2300
athura Junction d.	1102	1113	1150	1214	1214	1435	1500	1500	1500	1500	1500	|	1640	1728	1805	|	...	1858	2000	2000	1946	2150	2350
elhi Hazrat Nizamuddin a.	1315	1321	1440	1415	1415	1645	1710	1710	1710	1710	1710	1800	1912	2020	2026	2040	...	2056	2215	2215	2205	|	|
ew Delhi a.	...	1345	...	...	1440	...	...	...	...	...	...	...	1940	...	2100	...	...	2125	2300	2300	...	2330	0210

– ①②④⑤⑥. Also runs as **12648** on ③.
– ①③④⑤⑦.

f – Delhi Safdarjang.
r – Delhi Sarai Rohilla.

ndian Railways — DELHI - BILASPUR — 5205

km	km		SDi 12002	Exp 18508 ①④⑦	Exp 18478	Exp 18238	Exp 12410 A	Exp 12550 ④	Exp 12824 ②⑤⑦	RDi 12442 ②⑥	Exp 12920
0	0	**Delhi** Hazrat Nizamuddin d.	0600	0845	1205	0430	1520	1510f	1725	1545n	1915n.
35	135	Mathura Junction d.	0724	1032	1420	0700	1730	|	|	|	2140
89	189	Agra Cantonment d.	0802	1130	1520	0818	1830	1845	|	|	2230
307	307	Gwalior d.	0933	1322	1736	1010	2030	|	|	1925	0035
04	404	Jhansi d.	1050	1505	1925	1320	2200	2240	2325	2043	0245
57	557	Bina d.	|	|	|	1640	0015	|	|	|	0515
	632	Saugor d.	|	1850	2320	|	|	0200	0240	|	|
	819	Katni Murwara d.	|	2205	0350	|	|	0535	0605	|	|
	985	Anupper d.	|	0115	0745	|	|	0835	0900	|	|
95		Bhopal d.	1355	|	|	1855	0215	|	|	0005	0740
		Indore Junction a.	...	|	|	|	|	|	|	|	1250
88		Itarsi d.	...	|	|	2120	0405	|	|	|	...
085		Nagpur d.	...	|	|	0340	0935	|	|	0545	...
215		Gondia d.	...	|	|	0601	1129	|	|	0727	...
349		Durg d.	...	|	|	0855	1330	1420↓	1510↓	0930	...
387		Raipur Junction d.	...	|	|	0955	1415	1320↓	1415↓	1015	...
98	1136	**Bilaspur** a.	...	0425	1100	1215	1645	1115	1155	1200	...

	Exp 12409 B	Exp 12823 ①④⑥	Exp 12549 ②	RDi 12441 ①④	Exp 18477	Exp 18507 ②⑤⑥	Exp 18237	SDi 12001	Exp 12919
Bilaspur d.	0555	1450	1450	1400	1535	1910	1415	...	...
Raipur Junction d.	0745	1240↑	1240↑	1540	|	|	1620	...	...
Durg d.	0845	1200↑	1200↑	1630	|	|	1715	...	...
Gondia d.	1039	|	|	1824	|	|	1927	...	...
Nagpur d.	1300	|	|	2045	|	|	2205	...	...
Itarsi d.	1750	|	|	|	|	|	0415	...	...
Indore Junction d.	|	|	|	|	|	|	|	...	1225
Bhopal d.	1950	|	|	0210	|	|	0620	1515	1735
Anupper d.	|	1720	1720	|	1840	2137	|	|	|
Katni Murwara d.	|	2045	2045	|	2310	0110	|	|	|
Saugor d.	|	2315	2315	|	0150	0335	|	|	|
Bina d.	2205	|	|	|	|	|	0920	|	1940
Jhansi d.	0050	0240	0240	0531	0640	0755	1230	1840	2205
Gwalior d.	0230	|	|	0630	0805	0920	1405	1945	2333
Agra Cantonment d.	0418	|	0535	|	1050	1129	1630	2115	0125
Mathura Junction d.	0510	|	|	|	1150	1214	1728	2150	0215
Delhi Hazrat Nizamuddin a.	0730	0905	0930f	1055n	1440	1415	2020	2330	0436

– ①②③④⑥.
– ①③④⑤⑥.

f – Delhi Safdarjang.
n – New Delhi.

ndian Railways — DELHI - NAGPUR - TIRUPATI and CHENNAI — 5210

km		Exp 12804 ③⑦	Exp 12644 ⑤	Exp 12646 ②	Exp 12280	Exp 12642 ①⑥	Exp 12652 ②④	Exp 16115	SDi 12050 ex ⑤	Exp 12808 ex③⑦	Exp 12626	Duro 12270 ②⑥	RDi 12434 ③⑤	Exp 12612 ①	jSDi 12078 ex②	Exp 12688 ①⑤	Exp 16318 ②	Exp 16688 ⑤	Exp 12867 ②	Exp 16032 ③⑥⑦	Exp 12616	Exp 12622	Exp 12898 ③	Exp 22404 ⑦
0	**Delhi** H Nizamuddin d.	0550	0550	0550	0700	0710	0710	...	0810	0835	1125n	1545	1555	1555	...	1430	1430	1438	...	1430	1840n	2230n	...	2345n
135	Mathura Junction d.	0756	0756	0756	0850	|	|	...	|	1020	1320	|	|	|	...	|	|	|	...	1707	2045	|	...	0135
189	Agra Cantonment d.	0850	0850	0850	0945	1007	|	...	0950	1115	1410	|	1802	1802	...	1817	1817	1845	...	1817	2140	0102	...	0225
307	Gwalior d.	1105	1105	1105	1200	|	|	...	1115	1305	1610	1911	1925	1925	...	2015	2015	2053	...	2015	2331	0235	...	|
404	Jhansi d.	1250	1250	1250	1410	1350	1350	...	1235	1440	1750	2027	2043	2043	...	2145	2145	2240	...	2145	0105	0410	...	0555
557	Bina d.	1505	1505	1505	...	|	|	...	...	1705	1955	|	|	|	...	|	|	|	...	0110	0320	|	...	|
695	Bhopal d.	1715	1715	1715	...	1800	1800	...	...	1910	2155	|	0005	0005	...	0155	0155	0310	...	0310	0530	0800	...	1046
788	Itarsi d.	1905	1905	1905	...	1940	|	...	...	2105	2355	|	|	|	...	|	0335	0530	...	0530	0735	0945	...	1251
085	**Nagpur** d.	2325	2325	2325	...	0015	0015	...	...	0140	0410	0519	0535	0535	...	0840	0840	1045	...	1045	1230	1410	...	1845
298	Balharshah d.	0300	0300	0300	...	0335	0335	...	...	...	0750	0815	0820	0820	...	1200	1200	1440	...	1440	1605	1740	...	2240
543	Warangal d.	0632	0632	0632	...	|	|	...	...	...	1107	|	1126	|	...	1538	1538	1843	...	1843	1935	2050	...	0302
752	Vijayawada d.	1105	1000	1040	...	1035	1025	...	...	...	1455	1427	1430	1430	1520	1920	1910	2340	...	0100	2320	0025	...	0720
046	Gudur d.	...	1430	1432	...	1455	|	...	...	...	1905	|	|	1820	2010	|	2320	0415	...	0740	0355	|	...	1150
22	Renigunta a.	...	1600	1600	...	|	|	...	...	...	2035	|	|	|	|	|	0055	0545	...	|	|	|	...	|
32	**Tirupati** a.	...	1630	1630	...	|	|	...	...	...	2058	|	|	|	|	|	0118	0609	0120	|	|	|	...	|
184	**Chennai** Central a.	...	...	...	...	1805e	1805e	1810e	...	...	...	2040	2015	2040	2235	0210	...	...	|	1020	0620	0710	0845e	1425e
384	Pondicherry a.	...	...	...	...	...	...	2225	...	...	...	...	...	...	...	...	...	...	0850	...	...	...	1315	1755

	Exp 22403 ③	Exp 12868 ③	Exp 12615	Exp 12621	Exp 12897 ③	RDi 12433 ⑤⑦	Exp 12611 ⑥	Duro 12269 ①⑤	Exp 12625	Exp 12807 ex①⑤	Exp 12643 ③	Exp 12645 ⑦	Exp 12803 ①⑤	jSDi 12077 ex②	Exp 12641 ④⑥	Exp 12651 ②⑦	Exp 16687 ②	Exp 16317 ⑥	Exp 16116	Exp 12687 ①④	Exp 16031 ③④⑦	SDi 12049 ex ⑤	Exp 12279
ondicherry d.	0915	1230	...	...	1840	...	...	...	...	...	...	...	...	...	...	...	...	...	0535	...	...	...	...
hennai Central d.	1300e	|	1915	2200	2205e	0605	0605	0640	...	...	...	...	...	0735	0905e	0905e	...	...	0930e	1000	0515	...	...
Tirupati d.	|	1930	|	|	...	|	|	|	0350	...	0730	0730	...	|	|	|	0930	0930	...	|	|	...	...
Renigunta d.	|	...	|	|	...	|	|	|	0420	...	0800	0800	...	|	|	|	1000	1000	...	|	|	...	...
udur d.	1535	...	2130	|	...	|	0750	|	0545	...	0920	0920	...	0935	|	|	1125	1125	...	|	0740	...	...
ayawada d.	2015	...	0155	0410	...	1155	1155	1230	1010	...	1425	1425	1435	1445	1600	1605	1620	1620	...	1650	1455	...	...
arangal d.	2345	...	0500	0705	...	1440	|	|	1305	...	1735	1735	1735	...	|	|	1945	1945	...	2025	1808	...	...
alharshah d.	0420	...	0855	1110	...	1800	1800	1815	1710	...	2125	2125	2125	...	2315	|	2340	2340	...	0040	2250	...	...
agpur d.	0745	...	1225	1420	...	2045	2045	2105	2015	2250	0030	0030	0030	...	0210	0210	0255	0255	...	0350	0245	...	...
rsi d.	1300	...	1720	1845	...	|	|	|	0110	0400	0450	0450	0450	...	0630	|	0730	0730	...	|	0815	...	...
opal d.	1445	...	1925	2025	...	0210	0210	|	0300	0600	0630	0630	0630	...	0815	0815	0920	0920	...	0950	1000	...	...
na d.	|	...	2130	|	...	|	|	|	0500	0810	0825	0825	0825	...	|	|	|	|	...	|	1235	...	...
ansi d.	1935	...	2340	0025	...	0531	0531	0550	0705	1028	1038	1038	1038	...	1210	1210	1410	1410	...	1412	1455	1505	1520
walior d.	|	...	0055	0137	...	0632	0632	|	0825	1142	1157	1157	1157	...	|	|	1535	1535	...	1535	1625	1607	1650
gra Cantonment d.	2300	...	0250	0353	...	0757	0757	|	1025	1344	1405	1405	1405	...	1515	|	1730	1730	...	1730	1830	1750	1855
athura Junction d.	2350	...	0350	|	...	|	|	|	1113	1435	1500	1500	1500	...	|	|	|	|	...	|	2000	|	1946
elhi H Nizamuddin a.	0210n	...	0600	0642	...	1025	1025	1035	1321	1645	1710	1710	1710	...	1800	1800	2040	2040	...	2040	2215	1930	2205

– ①②⑤⑥.
– ①②④⑤.

e – Chennai Egmore.
n – New Delhi.

5220 DELHI, AHMEDABAD and MUMBAI - GOA - MANGALORE - TRIVANDRUM

Indian Railways

km		Exp 22150 ③⑦ A	Exp 12133	Exp 16333 ④	Exp 16335 ⑤	Exp 16311 ③	Exp 16348	Exp 10111	Exp 16603	Exp 16630	RDi 12432 ②③⑦	Exp 12450 ①⑥	jSDi 12051	Exp 10103	Exp 12218 ③⑤	Exp 12484 ⑦	Exp 22660 ①	Exp 16649	Exp 16345	Exp 19578 ⑥⑦	Exp 16605	Duro 12284 ⑥	Exp 12619	Exp 12201 ①⑤	jSDi 12075	Dur 1222 ②⑥
0	**Delhi** Hazrat Nizamuddin. d.	...	...	...	...	...	...	...	...	...	1055	0642	...	...	1355	1355	1355	...	...	...	...	2135	...	...	...	...
458	Kota Junction d.	...	...	...	...	...	...	...	...	...	1530	1325	...	...	1955	1955	1955	...	...	...	...	0310	...	...	...	...
****	**Ahmedabad** d.	...	...	1300	1300	1300	...	...	...	...	|	|	...	...	|	|	|	...	...	0330	...	|	...	...	...	...
986	Vadodara Junction d.	...	...	1507	1507	1507	...	...	...	...	2238	2136	...	...	0409	0409	0409	...	...	0535	...	1130	...	...	...	...
***	**Mumbai** CSMT d.	...	2202	|	|	|	...	2305	...	...	|	|	0525d	0710	|	|	|	...	1140t	|	...	|	1520t	1655t	...	205
1397	Panvel d.	2125	2315	2205	2205	2205	...	0030	...	...	0438	0500	0638	0830	1210	1215	1215	...	1255	1315	...	1800	1625	1810	...	|
1678	Ratnagiri d.	0200	0345	0255	0255	0255	...	0530	...	...	0910	0945	1035	1320	1750	1750	1750	...	1825	1915	...	2305	2135	2305	...	020
1917	**Madgaon** d.	0555	0715	0735	0735	0735	...	1045	...	...	1240	1445	1410	1900	2110	2110	2110	...	2255	2335	...	0225	0135	0225	...	055
2166	Udupi d.	0940	1111	1156	1156	1156	...	...	...	...	1620	...	...	...	0040	0140	0140	...	0302	0402	...	|	0540	0622	...	|
2234	**Mangalore** Junction d.	1120	1310	1400	1400	1400	1420c	...	1745c	1815c	1800	...	...	...	0226	0310	0310	0555c	0445	0615	0720c	0810	0730c	0810	...	102
2365	Cannanore d.	1320	...	1605	1605	1605	1705	...	2015	2110	1955	...	...	...	0432	0510	0510	0725	0645	0825	0945	|	...	1015	...	|
2455	Calicut d.	1445	...	1740	1740	1740	1840	...	2155	2245	2120	...	...	...	0552	0620	0620	0905	0835	0955	1120	1135	...	1135	1345	133
2541	Shoranur d.	1620	...	1950	1950	1950	2100	...	2355	0110	2235	...	...	...	0805	0820	0820	1130	1035	1150	1345	|	...	1315	1500	|
2574	Trichur d.	1700	...	2045	2045	2045	2210	...	0050	0200	2325	...	...	...	0835	0910	0900	1215	1120	1225	1430	|	...	1400	1545	|
2645	**Ernakulam** Town d.	1920j	...	2210	2210	2210	2340	...	0225j	0340	0055j	...	...	...	1035j	1110j	1035	1400	1310j	1410j	1625j	1610j	...	1525	1725j	182
2762	Kayankulam d.	...	...	|	0020	0020	0210	...	0440	0600	|	...	...	...	1300	1300	|	1635	1520	1610	1840	...	...	1800	1910	...
2789	Quilon d.	...	...	0120	0120	0120	0320	...	0600	0705	0330	...	...	...	1350	1355	1355	1720	1620	1710	1945	...	...	1910	1955	...
2866	**Trivandrum** Central a.	...	...	0305	0240	0305k	0515	...	0755	0930	0525	...	...	...	1515k	1545k	1545k	1900	1825	1835	2100	...	...	2055k	2135	...
2937	Nagercoil a.	...	...	...	0500	...	...	...	...	...	...	...	...	...	...	...	...	2125	...	2008	2345	...	...	...	...	...

	Duro 12224 ③⑦	Exp 10104	RDi 12431 ②④⑤	Exp 12449 ②③	Exp 16312 ⑥	Exp 16336 ②	Exp 16334 ①	Duro 12283 ②	Exp 16604	Exp 16629	Exp 16347	jSDi 12052	Exp 10112	Exp 22149 ②⑤ B	Exp 12134	Exp 12620	Exp 16606	jSDi 12076	Exp 16650	Exp 12202 ④⑦	Exp 22659 ⑤	Exp 12217 ①⑥	Exp 12483 ③	Exp 19577 ①②	Exp 1634
Nagercoil d.	...	...	...	...	...	1445	...	...	...	...	...	...	...	...	...	...	0200	...	0415	...	...	...	...	0905	...
Trivandrum Central d.	...	...	1915	...	1545k	1605	1545	...	1845	1900	2030	...	...	...	...	...	0335	0600	0620	0845k	0845k	0915k	0915k	1055	094
Quilon d.	...	...	2009	...	1645	1710	1645	...	2015	2030	2155	...	...	...	...	...	0435	0700	0735	0940	0940	1010	1010	1155	103
Kayankulam d.	...	...	|	...	1715	1750	|	...	2115	2125	2245	...	...	...	...	...	0530	0740	0825	1015	|	1050	1050	1230	112
Ernakulam Town d.	2130j	...	2240j	...	2025	2035	2025	2330j	2335j	0005	0135	...	...	0515j	...	...	0750j	0930j	1115	1300	1300	1300j	1300j	1450j	140
Trichur d.	|	...	2357	...	2150	2150	2150	|	0100	0125	0255	...	...	0623	...	...	0925	1040	1255	1405	1405	1400	1405	1605	154
Shoranur d.	|	...	0050	...	2250	2250	2250	|	0200	0310	0415	...	...	0720	...	...	1035	1135	1415	1505	1505	1505	1505	1700	164
Calicut d.	0055	...	0205	...	0020	0040	0040	0250	0340	0525	0620	...	...	0850	...	...	1230	1320	1610	1625	1625	1625	1625	1825	184
Cannanore d.	|	...	0320	...	0145	0215	0215	|	0520	0730	0810	...	...	1015	...	...	1410	...	1740	1755	1755	1755	1755	1955	201
Mangalore Junction d.	0410	...	0525	...	0435	0445	0445	0615	0830c	1100c	1140c	...	...	1215	1355	1425c	1735c	...	2100c	2015	2015	2015	2015	2210	231
Udupi d.	|	...	0650	...	0622	0622	0622	|	...	...	...	...	...	1350	1459	1550	...	...	...	2146	2146	2146	2146	2338	005
Madgaon d.	0855	0915	1010	1120	1130	1130	1130	1210	...	...	...	1430	1800	1720	1850	2040	...	...	...	0130	0130	0130	0130	0400	044
Ratnagiri d.	1245	1405	1330	1505	1615	1615	1615	1655	...	...	...	1755	2305	2100	2220	0030	...	...	...	0505	0505	0505	0505	0810	091
Panvel d.	|	1935	1810	1955	2125	2125	2125	2220	...	...	...	2205	0410	0230	0250	0515	...	...	...	1015	1100	1100	1100	1340	151
Mumbai CSMT a.	1815t	2140	|	|	|	|	|	|	...	...	...	2315d	0550	...	0425	0635t	...	...	...	1145t	|	|	|	|	164
Vadodara Junction d.	...	...	0026	0221	0519	0519	0519	0531	...	...	...	...	...	...	...	...	...	...	...	...	1910	1756	1850	2052	...
Ahmedabad a.	...	...	|	|	0715	0715	0715	|	...	...	...	...	...	...	...	...	...	...	...	...	|	|	|	2300	...
Kota Junction d.	...	...	0655	1000	...	...	...	1250	...	...	...	...	...	...	...	...	...	...	...	...	0300	0300	0300	...	...
Delhi Hazrat Nizamuddin a.	...	...	1240	1655	...	...	...	1940	...	...	...	...	...	...	...	...	...	...	...	...	1053	1058	1040	...	...

A – From Pune (d. 1845 ③⑦). B – To Pune (a. 0550 ③⑥). c – Mangalore Central. d – Mumbai Dadar. j – Ernakulam Junction. k – Trivandrum Kochuveli. t – Mumbai Lokmaniya Tilak Terminus. *** – Mumbai CST - Panvel: 68 km. **** – Ahmedabad - Vadodara: 100 km.

5230 MUMBAI - PUNE - KOLHAPUR

Indian Railways

km		Duro 12297 ②⑤⑦	Exp 11049 ⑦	Exp 22105	Exp 12148 ⑤	Exp 12127	Exp 11007	Exp 11301	Exp 11029	Exp 16331 A	Exp 17031	Exp 11041	Exp 11009	Exp 11019	Exp 16381	Exp 11046 ③	Exp 12125	Exp 12123	Exp 11023	Exp 17411	Exp 22107	Exp 12701	Exp 12115	Exp 11027	Exp 1104
0	**Mumbai** CSMT d.	2230x	1925x	0540	...	0640	0700	0810	0840	1210	1245	1400	1430	1510	1545	...	1625	1710	1750	2020	2100	2150	2245	2345	...
54	Kalyan d.	|	0450	0635	...	|	0755	0905	0935	1308	1340	1500	1530	1608	1640	...	|	|	1850	2123	2152	2240	2345	0040	...
192	**Pune** a.	0710	0750	0905	0930	0957	1105	1140	1240	1545	1630	1805	1840	1900	1915	1923	1950	2025	2155	0010	0030	0120	0210	0325	050
471	Miraj d.	...	1400	...	1500	...	...	...	1910	...	...	...	...	...	...	0215	...	...	0445	0555	...	...	...	...	112
518	**Kolhapur** a.	...	1525	...	1620	...	...	...	2025	...	...	...	...	...	...	0335	...	...	0605	0725	...	...	...	...	130

	Exp 16382	Exp 12702	Exp 12116	Exp 17412	Exp 22108	Exp 11010	Exp 12124	Exp 12126	Exp 11024	Exp 11045 ④	Exp 17032	Exp 11042	Exp 11008	Exp 11302	Exp 11030	Exp 12147 ②	Exp 16332 B	Exp 12128	Exp 22106	Exp 11050 ⑥	Duro 12298 ①④⑥	Exp 11039	Exp 11028	Exp 1102
Kolhapur d.	...	...	...	2030	...	...	...	...	2250	2345	...	...	...	...	0755	0905	...	...	...	1250	...	1530	...	...
Miraj d.	...	...	...	2140	...	...	...	...	0005	0045	...	...	...	...	0910	1020	...	...	...	1345	...	1640	...	...
Pune d.	0050	0115	0305	0335	0415	0605	0715	0750	0700	0725	0910	0935	1515	1600	1545	1555	1645	1755	1835	1950	2135	2305	2335	235
Kalyan d.	0325	0343	0540	0610	0645	0847	|	|	1035	...	1150	1220	1805	1855	1850	...	1930	|	2052	2217	|	...	0230	024
Mumbai CSMT a.	0440	0455	0650	0725	0755	0953	1025	1115	1150	...	1305	1335	1917	2015	2005	...	2050	2105	2200	0745x	0630x	...	0345	035

A – Runs as **16339** on ③④⑤⑦ and as **16351** on ②⑥. B – Runs as **16340** on ②③④⑥ and as **16352** on ①⑤. x – Time at Ahmedabad, NOT Mumbai.

5240 MUMBAI - KALYAN - PUNE - HUBLI

Indian Railways

km		Exp 16531 ②	Exp 16533 ④	Exp 16209 ①⑥	Exp 16507 ⑤⑦	Exp 16505 ③	Exp 11005 ①⑤⑦	Exp 11035 ④	Exp 11021 ②③⑥	Exp 12782 ②	Exp 12630 A	Exp 12780
0	**Mumbai** Dadar d.	...	...	...	...	...	2130	2130	2130	...	...	...
54	Kalyan d.	0105	0105	0105	0105	0105	2213	2213	2213	...	...	...
192	**Pune** d.	0420	0420	0420	0420	0420	0105	0100	0100	0930	1120	1635
338	Satara d.	0715	0715	0715	0715	0715	0400	0400	0400	1210	|	1920
472	Miraj d.	1025	1025	1025	1025	1025	0645	0650	0650	1500	1645	2230
610	Belgaum d.	1310	1310	1310	1310	1310	0905	0905	0905	1710	1850	0050
661	Londa d.	1417	1417	1417	1417	1417	1000	1000	1000	|	|	0205
731	Dharwad d.	1555	1555	1555	1555	1555	1127	1127	1127	1920	2140	...
751	**Hubli** a.	1645	1645	1700	1700	1700	1228	1228	1228	2020	2210	...

	Exp 12781 ⑥	Exp 16532 ⑥	Exp 16534 ①	Exp 16210 ③⑤	Exp 16506 ⑦	Exp 16508 ②④	Exp 11006 ①③④	Exp 11036 ⑦	Exp 11022 ②⑤⑥	Exp 12779	Exp 1262 B
Hubli d.	0440	0635	0635	0635	0635	0635	1510	1510	1510	...	215
Dharwad d.	0505	0700	0700	0700	0700	0700	1540	1540	1540	...	222
Londa d.	|	0825	0825	0825	0825	0825	1710	1705	1705	1845	|
Belgaum d.	0720	0940	0940	0940	0940	0940	1805	1805	1805	1950	003
Miraj d.	1020	1245	1245	1245	1245	1245	2052	2050	2050	2230	032
Satara d.	1240	1505	1505	1505	1505	1505	2310	2310	2310	0040	|
Pune d.	1555	1845	1850	1850	1850	1850	0215	0215	0210	0355	084
Kalyan a.	...	2127	2127	2127	2127	2127	0450	0450	0450	...	...
Mumbai Dadar a.	...	...	...	...	...	...	0540	0540	0540	...	...

A – ③④⑥⑦. Runs as **22686** on ③⑦. B – ②③④⑥. Runs as **22685** on ③⑥.

5245 HUBLI - BANGALORE - MYSORE

Indian Railways

km		Exp 17310 ②⑦	Exp 12726	Exp 12777 ③	Exp 11005 ①②⑥	Exp 11021 ③④⑦	Exp 11035 ⑤	ySDi 12080	Exp 17315 ①	Exp 16507 ⑤⑦	Exp 16505 ③	Exp 16209 ①⑥	Exp 16531 ②	Exp 16533 ④	Exp 14806 ⑥	Exp 12782 ②	Exp 17312 ④	Exp 22697 ⑥	Exp 16591	Exp 17302	Exp 12630 A	Exp 16590	Exp 16536	
0	**Hubli** d.	0330	0600	0645	1238	1238	1238	1400	1440	1710	1710	1710	1655	1655	1820	2025	2015	2025	1820	2140	2220	2240	2300	...
129	Harihar d.	0605	0802	0850	1445	1445	1445	1555	|	1935	1935	1935	|	|	|	2235	2235	2235	|	2355	|	0035	0105	...
258	Birur d.	0815	1007	1050	1705	1705	1705	1750	1900	2150	2150	2150	|	|	|	0035	0035	0035	|	0150	|	0235	0310	...
303	Arsikere d.	0910	1100	1150	1805	1810	1805	1840	1955	2255	2255	2255	G	G	0002	0140	0140	0140	G	0310	0300	0335	0415	...
393	Tumkur d.	1000	1230	1320	1928	1930	|	2000	2140	0110	0110	0110	|	|	0140	|	0325	0325	|	|	0445	0520	0610	...
469	**Bangalore** City a.	1230y	1405	1510y	2130y	2130y	|	2125	2310y	0315	0315	0315	0445	0445	0315y	|	0500y	0500y	0610	|	0620y	0645	0800	...
614	**Mysore** a.	...	...	...	...	...	2140	...	...	...	...	0600	...	...	...	0455	...	...	0910	0705	...	...	1100	...

	Exp 12778 ⑤	jSDi 12079	Exp 11006 ①③④	Exp 11022 ②⑤⑥	Exp 11036 ⑦	Exp 14805 ①	Exp 12629 B	Exp 12725	Exp 17309 ②⑦	Exp 17316 ③	Exp 16535	Exp 12781 ⑤	Exp 16589	Exp 16532 ⑤	Exp 16534 ⑦	Exp 17311 ⑤	Exp 22698 ⑦	Exp 16508 ①③	Exp 16210 ②④	Exp 16506 ⑥	Exp 17301	Exp 16592	
Mysore d.	...	...	...	...	0615	...	...	...	...	...	1530	2010	...	...	...	...	...	...	1830	...	2230	1900	...
Bangalore City d.	0440y	0600	0515b	0320b	|	1030y	1345y	1300	1430y	1430y	1850	|	2115	1700	1700	2155y	2155y	2150	2150	2150	|	2205	...
Tumkur d.	0535	0705	0730	0730	|	1120	1450	1405	1535	1535	2020	|	2227	|	|	2305	2305	2305	2305	2305	|	|	...
Arsikere d.	0720	0835	0915	0915	0915	1305	1620	1540	1700	1700	2150	2310	0010	G	G	0045	0045	0045	0045	0045	0135	G	...
Birur d.	0805	0915	1005	1005	1005	|	|	1627	1745	1745	2235	2350	0056	|	|	0130	0130	0130	0130	0130	0220	|	...
Harihar d.	1010	1105	1210	1210	1210	|	|	1840	1950	|	0030	0155	0255	|	|	0330	0330	0330	0330	0330	0425	|	...
Hubli a.	1240	1325	1505	1505	1505	1930	2140	2114	2345	2345	03200	0430	0535	0630	0625	0653	0620	0630	0630	0625	0715	1040	...

A – ③④⑥⑦. Runs as **22686** on ③⑦. B – ②③④⑥. Runs as **22685** on ③⑥. G – Via Guntakal. y – Bangalore Yesvantpur Junction. b – Bangalore Banaswadi.

Indian Railways

VASCO DA GAMA - MADGAON - HUBLI 5248

km		Exp 18048 A	56962	Exp 17315 ①	Exp 17420 ⑤	56964	Exp 17312 ④	Exp 12779	56966	Exp 12741 ③	Exp 17310 ①⑥
0	**Vasco Da Gama** d.	0710	0735	0900	0900	1310	1430	1510	1730	1905	2120
28	**Madgaon** d.	0750	0815	0935	0935	1347	1520	1550	1815	1940	2200
62	Kulem d.	0830	0905	1025	1025	1500	1610	1635	1910	...	2300
146	Londa d.	1005	...	1205	1205	...	1750	1835	...	...	0032
236	**Hubli** a.	1220	...	1430	1430	...	2005	...	...	...	0320

	Exp 17309 ②⑦	Exp 17316 ③	Exp 17419 ⑤	Exp 12780	56961	Exp 12742 ①	Exp 17311 ⑥	56963	Exp 18047 B	56965
Hubli d.	2350	2350	2350	...	...	...	0655	...	0900	...
Londa d.	0145	0145	0145	0215	...	...	0840	...	1040	...
Kulem d.	0415	0415	0415	0440	0630	...	1105	1220	1300	1715
Madgaon d.	0520	0520	0520	0545	0730	0820	1200	1315	1400	1810
Vasco Da Gama a.	0600	0600	0600	0630	0820	0855	1300	1405	1545	1900

A – ②④⑤⑥. B – ①③④⑥.

Indian Railways

MUMBAI - PUNE - SECUNDERABAD, BANGALORE and CHENNAI 5250

km		Exp 11301	Exp 11017 ⑥	Exp 16331 ①	Exp 16339 A	Exp 16351 ②⑥	Exp 17222 ④⑦	Exp 17031	Exp 11073 ①	Exp 11041	Exp 11019	Exp 16381	Exp 19568 ⑤	Exp 16613 ⑦	Exp 17203 ⑥	Exp 17017 ①③④	Exp 19202 ②	Exp 12163	Exp 12701	Exp 11013	Duro 12219 ③⑥	Exp 12115	Exp 11043 ⑤	Exp 11027	SDi 12025 ③–①
0	**Mumbai** CSMT d.	0810	1205t	1210	1210	1210	1225t	1245	1320t	1400	1510	1545	...	...	...	...	...	2030d	2150	2235t	2305t	2245	0015t	2345	...
54	Kalyan d.	0905	1255	1308	1308	1308	|	1340	1408	1500	1608	1640	1945	1945	1945	1945	1945	2110	2240	2318	|	2345	0100	0040	...
192	**Pune** d.	1145	1535	1550	1550	1550	1535	1635	1645	1810	1905	1925	2230	2230	2230	2230	2230	0010	0125	0155	0210	0220	0355	0335	0550
263	Daund d.	1310	|	1705	1705	1705	|	1815	|	1930	2040	2055	|	2355	2355	2355	2355	|	|	|	|	0335	0530	0505	|
456	Solapur d.	1615	1945	2025	2025	2025	1945	2225	2110	2315	0025	0055	0300	0300	0300	0300	0300	0405	0545	0635	0600	0650	0845	0940	0913
568	Gulbarga d.	1844	2155	2230	2230	2230	2155	0030	2310	0110	0233	0300	0453	0453	0453	0453	0453	0610	0720	0848	|	...	1055	1148	1042
605	Wadi d.	1945	2240	2320	2320	2320	2240	0135	0025	0225	0400	0420	0600	0600	0600	0600	0600	0710	0840	1000	|	...	1205	1255	1130
717	Vikarabad d.	|	|	|	|	|	|	0355	|	|	|	|	|	|	0800	|	|	|	1032	|	|	...	|	|	1255
800	**Secunderabad** a.	|	|	|	|	|	0150	0555c	|	|	0745	|	|	|	1015	1030	1030	|	1210c	|	1105	...	|	|	1420
713	Raichur d.	2140	0015	0120	0120	0120	...	...	0210	0410	...	0625	0735	0735	...	...	...	0850	...	1140	...	...	1340	1450	...
783	Adoni d.	2250	|	0220	0220	0220	...	...	0320	0510	...	0730	0839	0840	...	...	...	0950	...	1250	...	...	1450	1620	...
834	Guntakal d.	2345	0210	0330	0330	0330	...	...	0420	0625	...	0845	0950	0950	...	...	...	1110	...	1400	...	...	1600	1750	...
863	Gooty d.	0015	0240	0400	0400	0400	...	...	0450	0655	...	0915	|	1030	...	...	...	1135	...	1430	...	...	1641	1820	...
913	Anantapur d.	0240	|	0530	0530	|	...	...	|	|	...	|	1129	1135	...	...	...	|	...	1535	...	...	|	|	...
942	Dharmavaram d.	0405	|	0640	0640	|	...	...	|	|	...	|	1252	1300	...	...	...	|	...	1650	...	...	|	|	...
1041	Hindupur d.	0545	|	0820	0820	|	...	...	|	|	...	|	1412	1420	...	...	...	|	...	1820	...	...	|	|	...
1147	**Bangalore** City a.	0850	|	1028k	1028k	|	...	...	|	|	...	|	1623k	1620k	...	...	...	|	...	2150	...	...	|	|	...
1017	Cuddapah d.	...	0515	...	...	0645	...	...	0720	0940	...	1200	...	...	...	...	...	1400	...	...	...	...	1925	2055	...
1142	Renigunta d.	...	0800	...	...	0948	...	...	1005	1255	...	1435	...	...	...	...	...	1640	...	...	...	...	2200	0020	...
1152	**Tirupati** a.	...	|	...	...	|	...	...	|	|	...	1510	...	...	...	...	...	|	...	...	...	...	|	|	...
1214	Arakkonam d.	...	0910	...	...	...	...	...	1115	1435	...	...	...	...	...	...	...	1745	...	...	...	...	2325	0200	...
1283	**Chennai** Central a.	...	1055e	...	...	...	...	...	1255	1620	...	...	...	...	...	...	...	1945e	...	...	...	...	...	0330	...

	Exp 11018 ①	Exp 11028	Exp 11020	SDi 12026 ③–①	Exp 16382	Exp 12702	Exp 19201 ③	Exp 17018 ①②⑥	Exp 17204 ④	Exp 16614 ⑤	Exp 11044 ⑦	Exp 12164	Exp 12116	Exp 19567 ①	Exp 17221 ③⑥	Duro 12220 ②⑤	Exp 17032	Exp 11042	Exp 11014	Exp 11074 ②	Exp 11302	Exp 16332 ⑥	Exp 16340 B	Exp 16352 ④⑦
Chennai Central d.	2200e	2355	...	...	...	...	...	...	...	...	...	0645e	...	...	...	...	...	1220	...	1515	...	...	...	...
Arakkonam d.	2345	0110	...	...	...	...	...	...	...	...	0320	|	...	...	...	...	...	1325	...	1620	...	...	...	...
Tirupati d.	|	|	...	...	0320	...	...	...	...	...	|	|	...	...	...	...	...	|	...	|	...	...	...	...
Renigunta d.	0130	0240	...	...	0350	...	...	...	...	...	0700	0925	...	...	...	...	...	1505	...	1800	...	...	...	2245
Cuddapah d.	0340	0450	...	...	0600	...	...	...	...	...	0915	1115	...	...	...	...	...	1700	...	1945	...	...	...	0045
Bangalore City d.	|	|	...	...	|	...	...	...	...	0715k	|	|	...	1110k	...	...	...	|	1600	|	2045	2130k	2130k	|
Hindupur d.	|	|	...	...	|	...	...	...	...	0930	|	|	...	1305	...	...	...	|	1810	|	2235	2330	2330	|
Dharmavaram d.	|	|	...	...	|	...	...	...	...	1145	|	|	...	1435	...	...	...	|	2015	|	0025	0125	0125	|
Anantapur d.	|	|	...	...	|	...	...	...	...	1220	|	|	...	1510	...	...	...	|	2055	|	0110	0215	0215	|
Gooty d.	0610	0750	...	...	0845	...	...	...	...	1320	1145	1340	...	|	...	...	...	1955	2210	2230	0240	0345	0345	0300
Guntakal d.	0700	0825	...	...	0940	...	...	...	...	1410	1240	1430	...	1715	...	...	...	2040	2245	2310	0320	0420	0420	0330
Adoni d.	|	0915	...	...	1015	...	...	...	...	1500	1325	1510	...	1800	...	...	...	2125	2325	2355	0400	0500	0500	0415
Raichur d.	0910	1025	...	...	1130	...	...	...	...	1610	1430	1630	...	1915	...	...	...	2230	0030	0105	0520	0610	0610	0535
Secunderabad d.	|	|	1140	1445	|	1445c	1500	1500	1500	|	|	|	...	|	2025	2305	2040c	|	|	|	|	|	|	|
Vikarabad d.	|	|	|	1545	|	1602	|	|	1619	|	|	|	...	|	...	|	2210	|	|	|	|	|	|	|
Wadi d.	1220	1500	1600	1722	1740	1805	1845	1845	1845	1845	1845	1910	...	2145	0035	|	0050	0145	0305	0405	0800	0905	0905	0905
Gulbarga d.	1255	1545	1635	1756	1813	1845	1925	1925	1925	1925	1925	1950	...	2220	0111	|	0130	0225	0343	0440	0845	0943	0943	0943
Solapur d.	1500	1820	1855	1940	2015	2050	2125	2125	2125	2125	2125	2200	2240	0015	0310	0400	0350	0440	0600	0650	1120	1150	1150	1150
Daund d.	|	2155	2230	|	2320	|	0030	0030	0030	0030	0030	|	0142	|	|	|	0735	0805	0930	|	1425	1520	1520	1520
Pune d.	1955	2335	2350	2310	0050	0115	0205	0205	0205	0205	0205	0230	0305	0505	0755	0755	0910	0945	1045	1200	1600	1645	1645	1645
Kalyan d.	2230	0230	0240	...	0325	0343	0437	0437	0437	0437	0440	0500	0540	0747	|	|	1150	1220	1315	1505	1855	1930	1930	1930
Mumbai CSMT a.	2345t	0345	0355	...	0440	0455	...	...	...	...	0545	0600d	0650	...	1105t	1105t	1305	1335	1430t	1600t	2015	2050	2050	2050

A – ③④⑤⑦. B – ①②③⑤. c – Hyderabad Decan. d – Mumbai Dadar. e – Chennai Egmore. k – Bangalore Krishnarajapuram.

Indian Railways

HYDERABAD - SECUNDERABAD - TIRUPATI and CHENNAI 5260

km		Exp 17406	Exp 18646	Exp 17230	Exp 12839	Exp 12704	Exp 12604	Exp 12734	Exp 12764 A	Exp 12760	Exp 12710
	Hyderabad Decan d.	...	0950	1115	...	...	1650	...	...	1830	...
0	**Secunderabad** d.	0605	1020	1140	...	1555	1715	1805	1830	1855	2255
281	Guntur d.	|	|	1720	...	2035	2225	2310	|	|	|
132	Kazipet d.	0820	1240	|	...	|	|	|	2025	2055	0050
351	Vijayawada d.	1305	1630	|	2030	2138	|	|	0030	0105	0435
382*	Tenali d.	1350	...	1805	2100	...	2312	0002	0108	0138	0505
643	Gudur d.	1915	...	2205	0120	...	0320	0415	0455	0530	0915
726	Renigunta d.	2045	...	2340	|	...	|	0532	0627	...	...
736	**Tirupati** a.	2125	...	0005	|	...	|	0605	0700	...	...
793	**Chennai** Central a.	...	...	...	0350	...	0555	...	...	0815	...

	Exp 12603	Exp 12709	Exp 12763 B	Exp 12733	Exp 12759	Exp 12703	Exp 12840	Exp 17229	Exp 18645	Exp 17405
Chennai Central d.	1645	...	...	...	1810	...	2345	...	...	...
Tirupati d.	|	...	1700	1825	|	...	|	0035	...	0525
Renigunta d.	|	...	1717	1842	|	...	|	0100	...	0545
Gudur d.	1915	1850	1855	2010	2035	...	0152	0235	...	0730
Tenali d.	2317	2205	2208	0010	0005	...	0516	0630	...	1150
Vijayawada d.	|	2325	2340	|	0115	0325	0625	|	1115	1320
Kazipet d.	|	0235	0250	|	0442	|	...	|	1430	1720
Guntur d.	0015	|	|	0105	|	0420	...	0720	|	|
Secunderabad a.	0515	0540	0550	0625	0715	0915	...	1215	1710	2040
Hyderabad Decan a.	0545	...	...	...	0800	...	...	1255	1755	...

A – ①②④⑤⑦. B – ①②③⑤⑥. * – *311 km* via Guntur.

Indian Railways

MUMBAI and PUNE - KOLKATA 5270

km		Exp 12859	Exp 12869 ⑦	Duro 12261 C	Duro 12221 ①⑥	Exp 22511 ③	Duro 12289	Exp 12101 A	Exp 12129	Exp 12809	jSDi 12070 ex⑥	Exp 18029
0	**Mumbai** CSMT d.	0600	1105	1715	...	1130t	2015	2035t	...	2035	...	2200t
53	Kalyan d.	0655	1200	|	...	1210	|	2117	...	2132	...	2250
*	**Pune** d.	|	|	|	1515	|	|	|	1825	|	...	|
260	Manmad d.	|	|	|	|	1620	|	|	0035	0115	...	0245
420	Jalgaon d.	1200	|	|	2033	|	|	|	0240	0310	...	0440
441	Bhusaval d.	1250	1815	2305	2245	1845	0205	0300	0330	0350	...	0515
584	Akola d.	1455	2040	|	|	2040	|	0450	0525	0610	...	0755
663	Badnera d.	1615	2205	|	|	|	|	0645	0700	0745	...	0945
759	Wardha d.	1722	|	|	|	|	|	|	0840	0922	...	1120
837	Nagpur d.	1900	0140	0415	0415	0140	0720	1000	1010	1115	...	1325
967	Gondia d.	2048	0327	|	|	0327	...	1142	1212	1320	1500	1600
1101	Durg d.	2250	0518	|	|	|	...	1343	1408	1521	1710	1845
1139	Raipur Junction d.	2335	0559	|	|	0558	...	1430	1452	1605	1750	1950
1250	Bilaspur d.	0130	0759	1005	1005	0805	...	1625	1645	1808	1950	2215
1383	Raigarh d.	0305	|	|	|	0958	...	|	1829	2008	2200	0025
1454	Jharsuguda d.	0427	1107	|	|	1152	...	1930	2002	2140	...	0200
1554	Raurkela d.	0549	1225	|	|	1309	...	2048	2133	2259	...	0342
1718	Tatanagar d.	0825	1500	1605	1605	1630	...	2325	0005	0142	...	0703
1853	Kharagpur d.	1025	1655	|	|	1917	...	0130	0158	0340	...	0930
1969	**Kolkata** Howrah a.	1230	1930	1950	1950	2130	...	0337	0415	0550	...	1220h

	Duro 12262 D	Duro 12222 ④⑥	Exp 12860	Exp 22512 ⑦	Exp 12870 ⑤	Exp 18030	Exp 12810	jSDi 12069 ex⑦	Exp 12130	Exp 12102 B	Duro 12290
Kolkata Howrah d.	0820	0820	1354	1435	1435	1500h	2000	...	2145	2251	...
Kharagpur d.	|	|	1525	1625	1625	1740	2145	...	2335	0035	...
Tatanagar d.	1148	1148	1722	1815	1815	2005	2340	...	0127	0230	...
Raurkela d.	|	|	1955	2050	2050	2315	0216	...	0400	0457	...
Jharsuguda d.	|	|	2143	2225	2220	0100	0400	...	0547	0630	...
Raigarh d.	|	|	2233	2315	|	0203	0456	0620	0647	|	...
Bilaspur d.	1745	1745	0045	0130	0130	0445	0725	0850	0910	0940	...
Raipur Junction d.	|	|	0225	0310	0310	0645	0910	1030	1045	1125	...
Durg d.	|	|	0325	|	0410	0755	1005	1125	1140	1220	...
Gondia d.	|	|	0519	0602	0600	1015	1200	1325	1339	1415	...
Nagpur d.	2325	2325	0730	0830	0830	1340	1420	...	1550	1630	2040
Wardha d.	|	|	0835	|	|	1505	1533	...	1646	|	|
Badnera d.	|	|	1010	|	1123	1700	1743	...	1825	1910	|
Akola d.	|	|	1115	1224	1224	1805	1845	...	1925	2005	|
Bhusaval d.	0347	0347	1320	1425	1425	2045	2115	...	2130	2200	0125
Jalgaon d.	|	|	1345	|	|	2110	2140	...	2155	|	|
Manmad d.	|	0603	|	1630	|	2315	2340	...	2355	|	|
Pune a.	|	1145	|	|	|	|	|	...	0650	|	|
Kalyan d.	|	...	2005	2205	2205	0350	0410	...	...	0453	|
Mumbai CSMT a.	1030	...	2120	2315	2315	0450t	0520	...	...	0550t	0805

A – ①②⑤⑥. B – ①③④⑦. C – ②③④⑦. D – ①②③⑤. * – *314 km* from Manmad.

5280 KOLKATA - PURI, SECUNDERABAD, TIRUPATI and CHENNAI

Indian Railways

km			Exp	Exp	Exp	Duro	Exp	Exp	Duro	Exp	Exp	Exp	jSDi	SDi	Exp	Exp	Duro	Exp	Exp	Exp	Exp	Exp	Exp	Exp	Exp	Exp	Exp
			12514	**12510**	**12821**	**22203**	**12703**	**11020**	**12245**	**18645**	**22825**	**22849**	**12073**	**12277**	**12841**	**12665**	**22201**	**18409**	**12863**	**12881**	**12837**	**22642**	**12660**	**15228**	**15644**	**12867**	**1283**
			⑤	**A**		②④⑦	**K**		ex①④	**K**	②	③				**C**	①③⑤			**F**		②⑦	③	①	⑤	⑦	**K**
0	**Kolkata** Howrah	d.	0105	0105	0600	...	0725	...	1055	1145	1210**h**	1210**h**	1325	1425	1450	1610	2000**d**	1900	2035	2055	2235	2305**h**	2305**h**	2315	2315	2330	2345
116	Kharagpur	d.	0300	0300	0745	...	0910	...	|	1353	1405	1405	1520	1615	1635	1755	2220	2055	2230	2250	0023	0145	0110	0145	0115	0115	0130
232	Balasore	d.	0427	0427	0934	...	1037	...	|	1550	1540	1540	1646	1742	1804	1921	|	2305	2356	0028	0153	0323	0323	0320	|	0242	0300
409	Cuttack	d.	0711	0711	1220	...	1323	...	|	1910	1820	1820	1937	2010	2050	2208	|	0210	0245	0325	0445	0605	0605	0605	0527	|	0535
437	Bhubaneswar	d.	0755	0755	1305	...	1410	1525	1700	1955	1905	1905	2020	2050	2135	2255	|	0300	0330	0410	0538	0650	0650	0650	0610	0610	0635
456	Khurda Road	d.	0840	0840	1335	...	1500	1555	|	2030	1945	1945	...	|	2225	2335	|	0335	0410	0440	0610	0740	0730	0740	0640	0655	0715
500	**Puri**	a.	|	|	1430	...	|	|	|	|	|	|	...	2205	|	|	0435	0455	|	0550	0720	|	|	|	0750	|	|
819	Vizianagram	d.	1410	1410	...	...	2005	2115	2210	0233	0050	0050	...	...	|	|	...	...	0920	...	...	1305	1305	1305	...	1139	1245
879	Visakhapatanam	d.	1550	1550	...	1945	2125	2235	|	0405	0210	0210	...	...	0420	0555	...	...	1100	...	...	1425	1424	1425	...	1255	1410
1081	Rajahmundry	d.	1840	1855	...	|	0031	0150	|	0802	0457	0512	...	...	0706	0852	...	...	1350	...	...	1745	1730	1745	...	|	1716
1259	Vijayawada	d.	2135	2145	...	0055	0325	0520	0425	1115	0805	0805	...	...	1010	1225	...	...	1700	...	...	2020	2015	2020	...	1855	2030
1574	**Secunderabad**	a.	0400	|	...	0615	0915	1130	|	1710	|	1425	...	...	|	|	...	...	|	...	...	|	|	|	...	|	|
1637	Renigunta	d.	...	|	...	...	...	...	1010	...	|	...	...	...	|	|	...	...	2240	...	...	|	0300	|	...	0100	|
1647	**Tirupati**	a.	...	|	...	...	...	...	...	...	|	...	...	...	|	|	...	...	2300	...	...	|	0323	|	...	0118	|
1691	**Chennai** Central	a.	...	0435**p**	...	...	...	...	...	...	1535	...	...	...	1700	1955**e**	...	...	...	...	...	0345**p**	...	0345**p**	...	...	0350

		Exp	Duro	Exp	Exp	Exp	Exp	Exp	Exp	Exp	Exp	Exp	Exp	Exp	jSDi	SDi	Exp	Exp	Exp	Exp	Duro	Exp	Duro	Exp	Exp	Exp
		12666	**22202**	**12840**	**12838**	**12864**	**12882**	**15643**	**18410**	**22850**	**12509**	**12513**	**11019**	**12842**	**12074**	**12278**	**12659**	**12507**	**15227**	**18646**	**12246**	**12704**	**22204**	**12822**	**22826**	**1286**
		D	②④⑥	**K**			**G**	⑥		⑤	**B**	⑦			①–⑥		①	③	**E**	**K**	ex③⑥	**K**	①③⑥		④	③
Chennai Central	d.	2230**e**	...	2345	...	...	...	...	...	...	0535**p**	...	...	0845	...	...	...	1000	0710**p**	...	...	...	...	...	1625	...
Tirupati	d.	|	...	|	...	0230	...	...	...	...	|	...	...	|	...	...	0930	|	|	...	...	...	...	...	|	1935
Renigunta	d.	|	...	|	...	0300	...	...	...	...	|	...	...	|	...	...	1000	|	|	...	1700	...	...	...	|	2005
Secunderabad	d.	|	...	|	...	|	...	...	...	0540	|	0730	0800	|	...	...	|	|	|	1020	|	1555	2015	...	|	|
Vijayawada	d.	0525	...	0635	...	0935	...	...	...	1120	1315	1315	1405	1515	...	...	1615	1700	1615	1645	2235	2145	0115	...	2335	0250
Rajahmundry	d.	0742	...	0910	...	1205	...	...	...	1328	1529	1527	1625	1730	...	...	1845	1912	1845	1917	|	0003	|	...	0158	|
Visakhapatanam	d.	1205	...	1320	...	1615	...	...	...	1750	1930	1930	2110	2210	...	...	2305	2305	2305	2355	|	0350	0630	...	0635	0850
Vizianagram	d.	|	...	1420	...	1715	...	...	...	1855	2033	2032	2213	|	...	...	0005	0005	0005	0105	0440	0457	...	...	0740	0950
Puri	d.	|	1920	|	2010	|	2210	2210	2225	|	|	|	|	|	...	0545	|	|	|	|	|	|	...	1135	|	|
Khurda Road	d.	1840	|	2025	2120	2245	2305	2305	2320	0030	0210	0210	0355	0415	...	|	0530	0530	0530	0730	|	1025	...	1225	1335	1510
Bhubaneswar	d.	1912	|	2058	2152	2318	2336	2336	2350	0100	0240	0240	0435	0448	0600	0649	0610	0610	0610	0803	1000	1058	...	1258	1408	1542
Cuttack	d.	1954	|	2138	2233	2358	0012	0011	0036	0142	0320	0320	...	0528	0632	0720	0650	0650	0645	0847	|	1138	...	1338	1438	|
Balasore	d.	2249	|	0010	0115	0232	0251	|	0330	0437	0617	0617	...	0807	0904	1002	0944	0944	0944	1144	|	1404	...	1621	1727	1844
Kharagpur	d.	0100	0115	0148	0250	0410	0445	0450	0555	0620	0830	0830	...	0950	1050	1145	1135	1135	1135	1348	|	1540	...	1810	1925	2033
Kolkata Howrah	a.	0310	0415**d**	0400	0450	0625	0705	0705	0810	0905**h**	1055	1055	...	1155	1240	1340	1350**h**	1355	1355	1610	1645	1755	...	2015	2130**h**	2240

A – ①②③④⑥. Runs as **12516** on ④, **12508** on ⑥.
B – ①④⑤⑥. Runs as **12515** on ①.
C – ①④⑦. Runs as **12663** on ④⑦.
D – ②⑤⑥. Runs as **12664** on ②⑤.
E – ④⑤⑦. Runs as **22641** on ⑤⑦ but arrives Kolkata Shalimar at 1350.
F – ①②④⑤. Runs as **12887** on ①, **12895** on ⑤. Also as **22835** on ③ but departs from Kolkata Shalimar.
G – ①③④⑦. Runs as **12896** on ④, **12888** on ⑦. Also as **22836** on ② but arrives Kolkata Shalimar at 0720.
K – See Table **5260**.
a – Arakkonam.

5290 CHENNAI - BANGALORE - MYSORE

Indian Railways

km			Exp	Exp	SDi	Exp	Exp	Exp	Exp	Exp	Exp	Exp	Exp	Exp	Exp	Exp	Exp	SDi		Exp	Exp	Exp	Exp	Exp	Exp	Exp
			15228	**12510**	**12007**	**22625**	**12639**	**12614**	**12552**	**12609**	**12296**	**16517**	**22351**	**12577**	**17311**	**22698**	**12607**	**12027**		**16218**	**16021**	**12657**	**12691**	**22682**	**12292**	**1659**
			③	②③④	④–②				⑤				⑦	④	⑤	⑦		③–①		④			⑤	④	⑥	
0	**Chennai** Central	d.	0355**p**	0445**p**	0600	0725	0750	...	1140	1335	1355	...	1445	1445	1500	1500	1535	1730	...	...	2115	2315	2330	2330	2330	...
68	Arakkonam	d.	0500	0550	|	0820	0850	...	|	1440	1455	...	1545	1545	1600	1555	1635	|	...	...	2230	0015	0030	0030	0030	...
130	Katpadi	d.	0610	0640	0740	0910	0945	...	1330	1545	1550	...	1630	1630	1650	1645	17350	1910	...	...	2330	0105	0125	0120	|	...
214	Jolarpettai	d.	0740	0820	|	1035	1105	...	1500	1715	1730	...	1755	1755	1815	1812	1855	|	...	...	0055	0225	0245	0245	0245	...
350	Krishnarajapuram	d.	1000	1040	|	1220	1250	...	|	1915	1930	...	1950	|	2010	2010	2045	|	...	...	0240	|	0445	0445	0445	...
361	**Bangalore** City	a.	1150**y**	1140**z**	1050	1310	1400	1515	1825**y**	2005	2020	2030	2055**y**	2040	2135**y**	2135**y**	2135	2230	...	0330	0350	0510	0525	0525	0600**y**	0620
506	**Mysore**	a.	...	...	1300	...	...	1745	...	...	...	2305	...	2330	...	...	...	...	...	0600	0640	...	...	0810	...	0910

		SDi	Exp	Exp	Exp	Exp	Exp	Exp	Exp	Exp	Exp	Exp	Exp	Exp	Exp	SDi		Exp	Exp	Exp	Exp	Exp	Exp	Exp	Exp
		12028	**17312**	**22697**	**12608**	**16217**	**12610**	**16518**	**12551**	**12295**	**22352**	**12578**	**12613**	**22626**	**12640**	**12008**		**16592**	**12658**	**12291**	**12692**	**22681**	**12509**	**16022**	**1522**
		③–①	⑤	⑦		①			⑥		①	⑥				④–②				⑤	⑦	③	③④⑤		③
Mysore	d.	...	...	...	...	0530	...	0515	...	...	...	0720	1130	...	...	1415	...	1900	...	...	...	2010	...	2100	...
Bangalore City	d.	0600	0530**y**	0530**y**	0633	0800	0802	0800	0830**y**	0900	0955**y**	1005	1400	1430	1500	1625	...	2155	2240	2245**y**	2300	2300	2340**z**	2350	2355**y**
Krishnarajapuram	d.	|	0610	0610	0653	...	0825	...	|	0923	1034	|	...	1453	1523	|	...	...	|	2323	2323	2323	2353	0010	0035
Jolarpettai	d.	|	0815	0815	0845	...	1030	...	1115	1130	1230	1230	...	1645	1715	|	...	...	0100	0132	0132	0132	0210	0250	0335
Katpadi	d.	0900	0925	0925	0955	...	1150	...	1225	1240	1340	1340	...	1800	1835	1925	...	...	0210	|	0245	0245	0330	0405	0510
Arakkonam	d.	|	1015	1015	1055	...	1300	...	|	1335	1430	1430	...	1850	1925	|	...	...	0300	0340	0340	0340	0420	0515	0610
Chennai Central	a.	1100	1145	1145	1235	...	1430	...	1535	1515	1555	1555	...	2030	2105	2140	...	...	0435	0515	0515	0515	0525**p**	0700	0700**p**

5300 CHENNAI and BANGALORE - TRIVANDRUM

Indian Railways

km			Exp	Exp	SDi	Exp	Exp	Exp	Exp	Exp	Exp	Exp	Exp	Exp	Exp	Exp	Exp	Exp	Exp	Exp	Exp	Exp	Exp	Exp	Exp	Exp
			22642	**12516**	**12243**	**22619**	**16331**	**22207**	**15906**	**12697**	**12777**	**12695**	**16315**	**16381**	**12644**	**12646**	**12623**	**12257**	**16526**	**12626**	**22645**	**12511**	**22647**	**17230**	**16318**	**1266**
			②④	⑤⑦**A**	③–①	③	②	②⑤	②	⑦	③				⑥	③		②④⑦			②	①⑤⑥	④⑦		④	⑤
0	**Chennai** Central	d.	0355**p**	0445**p**	0710	...	...	1625	...	1515	...	1525	...	...	...	...	1945	...	...	...	2350	2350	2350	...	...	...
	Tirupati	d.	|	|	|	...	...	|	...	|	...	|	...	1515	1635	1635	|	...	...	2100	|	|	|	0010	0120	0325
130	Katpadi	d.	0610	0650	0854	1120	...	1805	1610	1700	...	1715	...	1745	1920	1920	2125	...	...	2312	0140	0140	0140	0235	0335	0540
214	Jolarpettai	d.	0720	0820	1006	1240	...	|	1755	1820	...	1830	...	1930	|	2035	|	...	...	0040	0310	0310	0310	0400	0505	0655
	Bangalore City	d.	|	|	|	|	...	|	|	|	1520**y**	|	1650	|	|	|	|	2100**y**	2000	|	|	|	|	|	|	|
	Krishanrajapuram	d.	|	|	|	|	1030	|	|	|	|	|	1716	|	|	|	|	|	2024	|	|	|	|	|	|	|
	Bangarapet	d.	|	|	|	|	1205	|	|	|	1640	|	1805	|	|	|	|	|	2125	|	|	|	|	|	|	|
335	Salem Junction	d.	0905	0955	1125	1420	1530	2040	1940	1945	1930	2015	2110	2105	2210	2210	0010	0112	0020	0215	0445	0445	0445	0530	0630	0820
394	Erode Junction	d.	1020	1120	1225	1540	1700	2135	2040	2045	2030	2120	2220	2200	2320	2320	0110	0220	0120	0315	0610	0610	0610	0640	0815	0945
494	Coimbatore Junction	d.	1200	1325	1415	1720	1850	2300	2235	|	|	2310	2359	2335	0120	0120	0250	0350	0305	0505	0740	0740	0740	0825	1000	1120
548	Palghat Junction	d.	1305	1440	...	1830	2010	0005	2345	2325	2325	0025	0130	0105	0230	0230	0400	0510	0430	0625	0855	0855	0855	0950	1110	1240
626	Trichur	d.	1415	1610	...	1950	2130	0130	0105	0040	0040	0145	0255	0245	0355	0355	0518	0620	0550	0735	1055	1055	1055	1200	1235	1345
697	Ernakulam Town	d.	1600**j**	1745	...	2125**j**	2300**j**	0300**j**	0230	0200	0200	0310	0425**j**	0510	0540**j**	0600**j**	0650	0820	0740	0925	1230	1230	1230	1320	1420	1525
814	Kayankulam	d.	1830	2010	...	2330	0055	|	|	|	|	0525	0630	0740	0900	...	0920	1050	1025	1215	1505	1505	1505	1600	1645	1800
842	Quilon	d.	1935	2105	...	0010	0150	0525	0535	0515	0515	0615	0720	0850	1005	...	1020	1135	1115	1315	1605	1605	1605	1650	1740	1910
919	**Trivandrum** Central	a.	2115	2240	...	0115	0350	0715	0710	0705	0635**k**	0805	0920**k**	1010	1135	...	1215	1315**k**	1325	1515	1720	1720	1720	1855	1915	1955
	Nagercoil	a.	...	...	...	0302	...	...	0915	...	...	...	...	1205	...	...	...	...	1700	...	...	...	...	...	2130	2155

km			Exp	Exp	Exp	SDi	Exp	Exp	Exp	Exp	Exp	Exp	Exp	Exp	Exp	Exp	Exp	Exp	Exp	Exp	Exp	Exp	Exp	Exp	Exp	Exp
			15905	**22620**	**16332**	**12244**	**22646**	**22648**	**17229**	**16382**	**12625**	**12778**	**12515**	**16525**	**12645**	**12643**	**12624**	**16316**	**16317**	**12659**	**22641**	**12258**	**12507**	**12696**	**22208**	**1269**
			④	⑦	⑥	③–①	**B**	①④				④	⑦		⑥	②		②④⑥	⑤	⑦	④⑥	①③⑤	②		③⑦	⑥
72	Nagercoil	d.	2335	0230	...	...	...	...	...	0700	...	...	...	1025	...	...	...	...	1445	1445	...		...	...	...	...
0	**Trivandrum** Central	d.	0045	0425	0425	...	0615	0615	0715	0855	1115	1250**k**	1240	1245	...	1415	1455	1645**k**	1605	1605	1655	1700**k**	1655	1715	2125	2020
77	Quilon	d.	0145	0530	0530	...	0715	0715	0820	1020	1225	1340	1340	1410	...	1515	1555	1740	1710	1710	1755	1755	1755	1830	2225	2125
105	Kayankulam	d.	|	0610	0610	...	0750	0750	0900	1110	1300	|	1420	1500	...	1550	1640	1825	1750	1750	1840	1840	1840	1906	|	|
222	Ernakulam Town	d.	0525	0825**j**	0825**j**	...	1015**j**	1044	1150	1340	1550	1700	1710	1805	1900**j**	1900**j**	1930	2035**j**	2035	2035	2110**j**	2125	2125	2145	0040**j**	0044
293	Trichur	d.	0630	0950	0950	...	1135	1210	1305	1525	1715	1810	1825	1940	2010	2010	2040	2205	2215	2215	2245	2245	2245	2310	0150	0200
371	Palghat Junction	d.	0815	1200	1200	...	1400	1400	1535	1645	1845	1935	1955	2115	2130	2130	2205	2335	2350	2350	0010	0010	0010	0045	0330	0330
425	Coimbatore Junction	d.	0930	1335	1330	1505	1530	1530	1645	1815	2000	|	2130	2250	2320	2315	2350	0100	0125	0125	0120	0125	0120	0200	0445	|
525	Erode Junction	d.	1100	1510	1510	1615	1710	1710	1830	2000	2200	2210	2310	0030	0055	0050	0115	0245	0330	0315	0305	0315	0305	0340	0615	0600
584	Salem Junction	d.	1200	1600	1600	1710	1810	1810	1930	2055	2300	2310	2358	0125	0145	0150	0215	0340	0430	0412	0350	0415	0350	0440	0715	0655
	Bangarapet	d.	|	|	1950	|	|	|	|	|	|	0235	|	0510	|	|	|	0635	|	|	|	|	|	|	|	|
	Krishnarajapuram	d.	|	|	2120	|	|	|	|	|	|	|	|	0620	|	|	|	0735	|	|	|	|	|	|	|	|
853	**Bangalore** City	a.	|	|	...	|	|	|	|	|	|	0430**y**	|	0725	|	|	|	0835	|	|	|	0930**y**	|	|	|	|
705	Jolarpettai	d.	1355	1755	...	1855	1950	1950	2120	2320	0045	...	0155	...	0345	|	|	...	0610	0600	0600	...	0600	0625	|	0850
789	Katpadi	d.	1500	1900	...	2000	2055	2055	2240	0050	0202	...	0320	...	0530	0530	0505	...	0725	0725	0710	...	0710	0740	1000	1004
912	**Tirupati**	a.	...	...	...	|	|	|	0030	0315	0348	...	|	...	0730	0730	|	...	0920	0920	|	...	|	|	|	|
919	**Chennai** Central	a.	...	...	...	2215	2305	2305	...	...	...	...	0525**p**	...	...	...	0740	...	...	...	0855**p**	...	0935	1000	1200	1225

Notes for Tables **5290** and **5300**:
A – ⑤⑦. Runs as **12516** on ⑤ and as **12508** on ⑦.
B – ②③⑥⑦. Runs as **12512** on ②③⑦ and as **22646** on ⑥.
j – Ernakulam Junction.
k – Trivandrum Kochuveli.
y – Bangalore Yesvantpur Junction.
z – Bangalore Cantonment.

Indian Railways — CHENNAI - SENGOTTAI, TUTICORIN, TIRUCHENDER and NAGERCOIL — 5310

km		Exp 12688 ③⑦	56768 2	Exp 16127	56735 2	Exp 12635	Exp 22620 ⑦	Exp 12633	Exp 22668	Exp 22670	Exp 16105	Exp 12667 ④	Exp 12642 ②⑦	Exp 12652 ③⑤	Exp 12693	Exp 16723	Exp 12631	Exp 12665 ②	Exp 12661	Exp 12637	Duro 22205 ①③	56731 2	56767 2	Exp 16236	Exp 22623 ⑤⑦	56733 2
0	**Chennai** Egmore d.	0235**c**	...	0815	...	1340	...	1715	...	...	1600	1855	1815	1825	1930	1950	2010	2020	2105	2140	2230**c**	...	...	...	2250	...
56	Chengalpattu d.	|	...	0915	...	1440	...	1815	...	...	1700	1950	1925	1925	2030	2050	2110	2120	2200	2240	|	...	...	...	0050	...
159	Villupuram d.	**A**	...	1055	...	1555	...	1955	...	...	1850	2135	2100	2100	2210	2230	2245	2255	2325	2358	**C**	...	...	...	0235	...
214	Vriddhachalam Jct d.	|	...	1137	...	1630	...	2037	...	...	|	2227	2142	2142	2251	2312	2327	2340	0014	0040	|	...	...	...	|	...
340	Tiruchchirappalli Jct d.	|	...	1335	...	1835	...	2230	...	...	2335	0030	2345	2345	0050	0115	0130	0155	0215	0245	|	...	...	...	0320	...
433	Dindigul d.	1115	...	1450	...	2005	...	0005	2315	...	0050	0130	0115	0115	0210	0230	0240	0315	0330	0420	|	...	...	0615	0840	...
495*	Madurai Junction d.	1245	...	1615	1700	2120	...	0105	0010	...	0145	0235	0220	0325	0320	0415	0400	0430	0510	0545	0710	0715	...	0730	1000	1115
538	Virudunagar d.	▬	...	1655	1805	▬	...	0202	0100	...	0225	0315	0300	▬	0402	0455	0440	0515	0555	▬	▬	0805	...	0815	...	1215
662	Tenkasi d.	**56765**	...	|	2011	**56741**	...	|	|	...	|	|	|	**56761**	|	|	|	|	0740	**56742**	**56763**	1010	...	|	...	1420
670	**Sengottai** a.	2	...	|	2135	2	...	|	|	...	|	|	|	2	|	|	|	|	0850	2	2	1055	...	|	...	1510
623	Vanchi Maniyachchi d.	...	1720	1840	...	1905	...	|	0235	0315	0400	|	0414	...	0525	0625	|	0645	...	0825	...	...	1000	1000	...	...
656	**Tuticorin** a.	...	1830	|	...	|	...	|	|	0355	|	|	|	...	0640	|	|	|	...	0935	...	...	|	1115	...	...
652	Tirunelveli Junction d.	1835	...	1935	...	2035	0115	0405	0315	...	0615	0545	0525	0710	...	0800	0705	0825	...	...	0930	...	1115	...	...	...
714	**Tiruchender** a.	2030	...	|	...	...	|	|	|	...	0810	|	|	0855	...	|	...	|	...	...	1100	...	1310	...	...	...
726	**Nagercoil** Junction a.	...	...	2130	...	...	0227	0530	0455	...	...	0755	0655	...	...	0930	...	1020	...	...	...	...	...	...	...	...

	56734 2	56736 2	56768 2	Exp 16235	56741 2	56764 2	Exp 12668 ⑤	Exp 12662	Exp 12634	Exp 12632	Duro 22206 ②④	56766	Exp 12694	Exp 16724	Exp 12641 ③⑤	Exp 12651 ②⑦	Exp 12687 ③⑦	Exp 16106	Exp 22669	Exp 22667	Exp 22619 ④	56732 2	Exp 16128	56742 2	56767 2	56762 2
Nagercoil Junction d.	...	...	...	...	...	...	1705	...	1740	...	...	...	...	1800	1940	...	...	...	...	2130	0305	...	0615	...	...	...
Tiruchender d.	...	...	1420	...	...	1625	|	...	|	...	...	1800	...	|	|	...	...	1900	...	|	|	...	|	...	...	0710
Tirunelveli Junction d.	...	...	1610	...	...	1800	1820	...	1905	1945	...	1940	...	1955	2115	...	...	2030	...	2240	0520	...	0835	0730	...	0905
Tuticorin d.	...	...	|	1625	1750	...	|	...	|	|	...	▬	2000	|	|	...	...	|	2235	|	...	...	|	|	0845	▬
Vanchi Maniyachchi d.	...	...	1705	1710	1850	...	|	...	|	|	...	*Exp*	2030	2040	2141	...	...	2100	2310	2330	▬	...	0935	0815	0945	**56732**
Sengottai d.	1150	1555	...	|	▬	...	|	1815	|	|	...	**22624**	|	|	|	...	...	|	...	|	*Exp*	0630	|	...	...	0330
Tenkasi d.	1205	1610	...	|	*Exp*	...	|	1830	|	|	...	④⑥	|	|	|	...	...	|	...	|	**12636**	0645	|	...	...	0645
Virudunagar d.	1425	1805	...	1830	**12638**	...	2017	2027	2105	2120	...		2155	2210	2307	...	...	2220	...	0049		0920	1105	...	...	0920
Madurai Junction d.	1540	1935	...	1945	2040	...	2115	2144	2205	2220	2245	2105	2250	2305	0030	0030	2335	2350	...	0150	0700	1040	1215	...	...	1040
Dindigul d.	...	...	...	2110	2145	...	2212	2245	2305	2320	|	2202	2350	0010	0127	0127	0035	0110	...	0255	0755	...	1317	...	...	...
Tiruchchirappalli Jct d.	...	...	...	...	2310	...	2345	0010	0035	0105	|	2330	0135	0155	0305	0305	|	0320	...	...	0905	...	1445	...	...	...
Vriddhachalam Jct d.	...	...	...	...	0042	...	0127	0155	0225	0247	**D**	|	0327	0345	0500	0500	**B**	|	...	...	1040	...	1647	...	...	...
Villupuram d.	...	...	...	...	0205	...	0230	0300	0320	0350	|	0420	0435	0450	0555	0555	|	0825	...	...	1150	...	1745	...	...	...
Chengalpattu d.	...	...	...	...	0330	...	0410	0440	0500	0525	|	0600	0620	0645	0735	0735	|	1000	...	...	1320	...	1920	...	...	...
Chennai Egmore a.	...	...	...	...	0455	...	0520	0605	0625	0645	0720**c**	0715	0740	0810	0850	0850	0920**c**	1125	...	...	1435	...	2045	...	...	...

A – Via Katpadi (d. 0420), Salem (d. 0730) and Erode (d. 0850).
B – Via Erode (d.0305), Salem (d. 0350) and Katpadi (d. 0705).
C – Via Salem d. 0305.
D – Via Salem d. 0220.
c – Chennai Central.
* – *596 km* via Salem.

Indian Railways — HILL and MOUNTAIN RAILWAYS — 5320

¶ DARJEELING HIMALAYAN RAILWAY ¶

km	¶	52541	52587	52591	52592 🚂	52593 🚂	52595 🚂	52597	52571 🚂 ②④⑦	52559 🚂	52599
0	**New Jalpaiguri** Jct d.	0830	...	...	...	...	...	...	...	...	...
8	Siliguri Junction d.	0900	...	...	...	...	...	...	...	1030	...
18	Sukna d.	0932	...	...	...	...	...	...	...	1120	...
26	Rangtong d.	1005	...	...	...	...	...	...	...	1150	...
32	Chunbhati d.	|	...	...	...	...	...	...	...	...	...
38	Tindharia d.	1112	...	...	...	...	...	...	...	...	...
50	Mahanadi d.	1214	...	...	...	...	...	...	...	...	...
57	Kurseong d.	1255	0700	...	...	...	...	...	1400	**52598**	...
65	Tung d.	1326	0734	...	...	...	...	...	1445	🚂	...
73	Sonada d.	1405	0815	...	...	...	...	...	1550		...
82	Ghum d.	1455	0900	0840	1055	1100	1330	1355	1655	1725	1730
88	**Darjeeling** a.	1535	0935	0925	1135	1140	1410	1430	1745	1805	1820

¶	52591	52570 🚂 ②④⑥	52592 🚂	52540	52593 🚂	52595 🚂	52597	52598 🚂	52588	52599
Darjeeling d.	0740	0910	0930	0800	0940	1210	1245	1605	1600	1620
Ghum d.	0820	1010	1020	0835	1030	1300	1325	1655	1635	1700
Sonada d.	...	1100	...	0916	...	...	...	...	1717	...
Tung d.	...	1150	...	0955	...	...	...	...	1758	...
Kurseong d.	...	1230	...	1040	...	...	...	...	1830	...
Mahanadi d.	...	...	...	1111	...	...	...	...	▬	...
Tindharia d.	...	...	...	1220	...	...	...	...	**52559**	...
Chunbhati d.	...	...	...	|	...	...	...	...	🚂	...
Rangtong d.	...	...	...	1326	...	...	...	...	1220	...
Sukna d.	...	...	...	1358	...	...	...	...	1255	...
Siliguri Junction d.	...	...	...	1435	...	...	...	...	1335	...
New Jalpaiguri Jct a.	...	...	...	1510	...	...	...	...	...	...

KANGRA VALLEY RAILWAY

km		52464 2	52466 2	18102	52472 2	14034	52468 2	52474 2	14036 ②④⑥	52470 2
0	**Joginder Nagar** d.	...	...	...	0720	...	...	1220	...	...
23	Baijnath Paprola d.	0400	0720	...	1050	...	1410	1555	...	1735
37	Palampur Himachal d.	0438	0800	...	1130	...	1451	1641	...	1813
66	Kangra Mandir d.	0550	0946	...	1246	...	1605	1756	...	1946
164	**Pathankot Junction** a.	1050	1420	...	1730	...	2025	2235	...	2355
164	Pathankot Junction ‡ d.	...	...	1645	...	1905**a**	...	...	2320	...
653	Delhi Junction ‡ a.	...	...	0430	...	0545	...	...	1025**r**	...

	52471 2	52463 2	14033	52465 2	14035 ①③⑤	52473 2	18101	52467 2	52469 2
Delhi Junction ‡ d.	...	...	2010	...	2315**r**	...	2150	...	...
Pathankot Junction ‡ d.	...	...	0508**a**	...	0825	...	1100	...	...
Pathankot Junction d.	0215	0400	...	0645	...	1000	...	1320	1550
Kangra Mandir d.	0647	0843	...	1110	...	1503	...	1858	2032
Palampur Himachal d.	0806	1001	...	1310	...	1634	...	2014	2139
Baijnath Paprola d.	0950	1045	...	1400	...	1805	...	2055	2230
Joginder Nagar a.	1125	...	...	...	...	1945	...	...	...

MATHERAN HILL RAILWAY

km		96003 2		52101	11007	52103	11029	95107 2	92105	95119 2	
90	Mumbai CSMT ♥ d.	0550**k**	...	...	0700	...	0840	1001**k**	...	1554**k**	...
0	Neral Junction ♥ a.	0626	...	...	0825	...	1004	1051	...	1627	...
0	**Neral Junction** ♣ d.	...	...	0720	...	0850	...	...	1420	...	...
21	**Matheran** ♣ a.	...	...	1000	...	1130	...	...	1700	...	...

		11024	52102	95122 2		95128 2	52104	95132	52106	95138
Matheran ♣ d.	...	...	0920	...	...	...	1445	...	1620	...
Neral Junction ♣ a.	...	...	1200	...	...	...	1730	...	1900	...
Neral Junctiom ♥ d.	...	1000	...	1217	...	1543	...	1749	...	2001
Mumbai CSMT ♥ a.	...	1150	...	1251**k**	...	1617**k**	...	1927**k**	...	2140**k**

NILGIRI MOUNTAIN RAILWAY

km		56141	12671	56136		56143		56138		
0	Chennai Central ‡ d.	...	2105	...	...	...	...	...	...	...
530	Mettupalaiyam ‡ a.	...	0615	...	...	...	...	...	...	...
0	**Mettupalaiyam** d.	...	...	0710	...	...	...	...	...	...
28	Coonor d.	0745	...	1040	...	1235	...	1600	...	...
46	**Udagamandalam** (Ooty) a.	0905	...	1200	...	1350	...	1715	...	...

	56139	56142	56137	12672	56140				
Udagamandalam (Ooty) d.	0915	1215	1400	...	1730	...	...	...	...
Coonor d.	1025	1320	1515	...	1840	...	...	...	...
Mettupalaiyam a.	...	...	1735	...	...	...	...	...	...
Mettupalaiyam ‡ d.	...	...	...	1945	...	...	...	...	...
Chennai Central ‡ a.	...	...	...	0505	...	...	...	...	...

a – Chakki Bank.
k – Time at Kalyan Junction.
r – Delhi Sarai Rohilla.
‡ – By main-line train (*Exp*) See also Table **5000**.
♣ – Services normally suspended during Monsoon season. Due to a derailment service is suspended.
♥ – By main-line train. Frequent additional trains (2 cl. only) are available to/from Kalyan. Journey 1½ – 2 hours.
¶ – For up-to-date information see www.dhrs.org

Indian / Pakistan Rlys — LAHORE - DELHI — 5400

km		402 ①④	Exp 14002 ①④
0	**Lahore** Jct d.	0800	...
	Wagah a.	0835	...
	Wagah d.	1130	...
20	Atari 🏛 a.	1150	...
20	Atari 🏛 d.	...	2000
46	**Delhi** Junction a.	...	0320

	Exp 14001 ③⑦	401 ①④
Delhi Junction d.	2310	...
Atari 🏛 a.	0715	...
Atari 🏛 d.	...	1100
Wagah a.	...	1410
Wagah d.	...	1610
Lahore Jct a.	...	1645

NOTE: Timings are subject to confirmation and connections are not guaranteed.

Bangladesh / Indian Rlys — KOLKATA - DHAKA — 5450

km		Exp 13108 ①⑥	Exp 13109 ②⑤
0	**Kolkata** Chitpur ♠ d.	0710	0710
122	Gede ♠ a.	|	|
122	Gede d.	|	|
	Darsana 🏛 a.	|	|
540	**Dhaka** Cantonment a.	1605	1605

	Exp 13107 ⑤⑦	Exp 13110 ③⑥
Dhaka Cantonment d.	0815	0815
Darsana 🏛 d.	|	|
Gede a.	|	|
Gede ♠ d.	|	|
Kolkata Chitpur ♠ a.	1600	1600

♠ – Local services operate Kolkata - Gede and v.v.
NOTE: Timings are subject to confirmation.

BEYOND EUROPE
South East Asia, Australia and New Zealand

Introduction

The Beyond Europe section covers principal rail services in a different area of the world each month. There are six areas, each appearing as follows:

Winter (December) and Summer (June):	Africa and The Middle East along with all other Beyond Europe sections.
January and July (digital only):	India.
February and August:	South East Asia, Australia and New Zealand; India; North America.
March and September (digital only):	China.
April and October:	Japan; China; South America; South Korea.
May and November (digital only):	North America.

The months have been chosen so that we can bring you up-to-date information for those countries which make seasonal changes.

Contents

INDEX OF PLACES

by table number

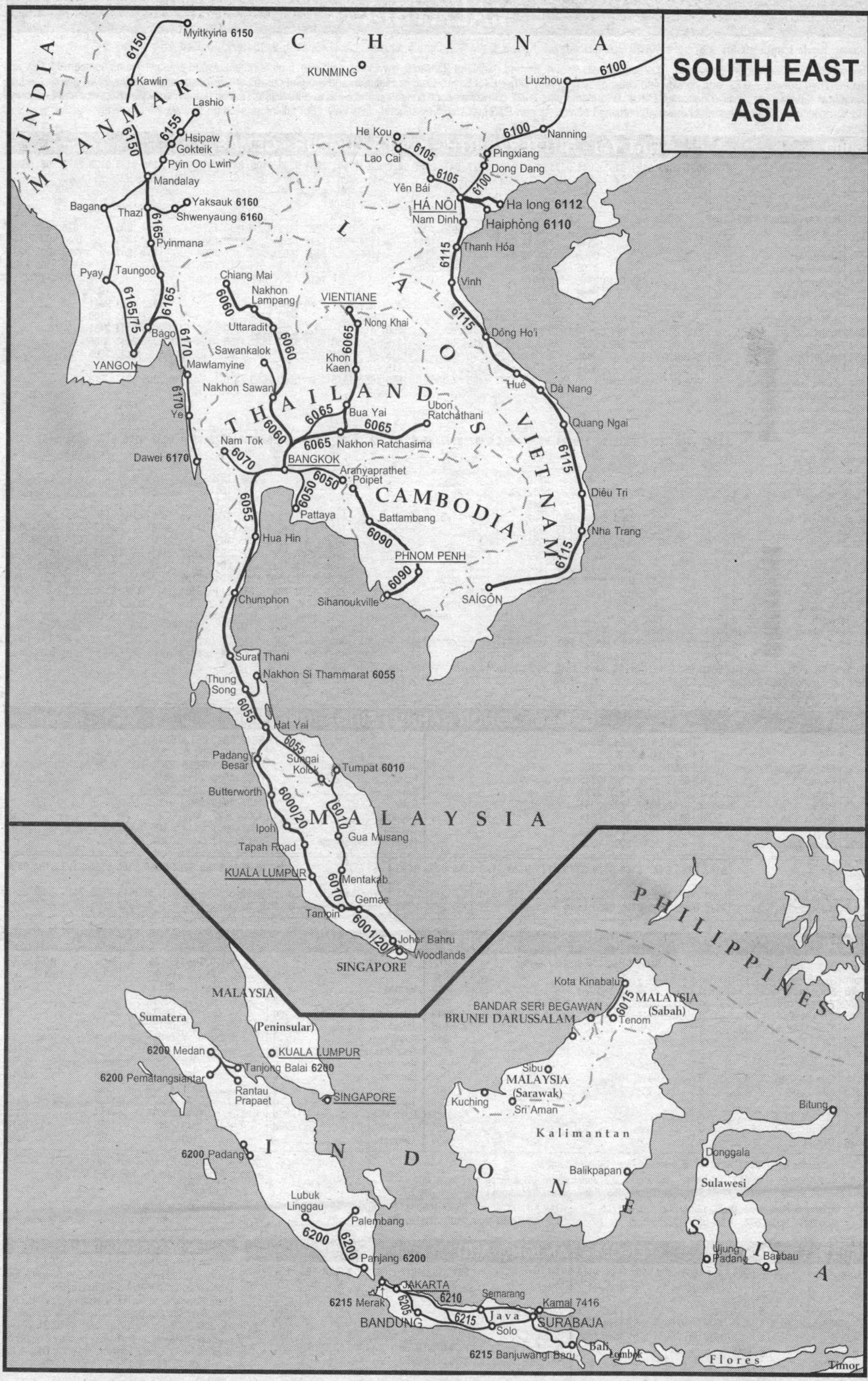
SOUTH EAST ASIA
CHINA
INDIA
MYANMAR
LAOS
THAILAND
CAMBODIA
VIETNAM
MALAYSIA
PHILIPPINES
INDONESIA
Myitkyina 6150
Kawlin
Lashio
Hsipaw
Gokteik
Pyin Oo Lwin
Mandalay
Bagan
Thazi
Yaksauk 6160
Shwenyaung 6160
Pyinmana
Pyay
Taungoo
Bago
YANGON
Mawlamyine
Ye
Dawei 6170
KUNMING
Liuzhou
Nanning
He Kou
Lao Cai
Pingxiang
Dong Dang
Yên Bái
HÀ NỘI
Nam Dinh
Ha long 6112
Haiphòng 6110
Thanh Hóa
Vinh
Dông Ho'i
Huê
Dà Nang
Quang Ngai
Diêu Tri
Nha Trang
SAIGÒN
Chiang Mai
Nakhon Lampang
Uttaradit
Sawankalok
Nakhon Sawan
VIENTIANE
Nong Khai
Khon Kaen
Bua Yai
Ubon Ratchathani
Nakhon Ratchasima
Nam Tok
BANGKOK
Aranyaprathet
Poipet
Pattaya
Battambang
PHNOM PENH
Sihanoukville
Hua Hin
Chumphon
Surat Thani
Nakhon Si Thammarat 6055
Thung Song
Hat Yai
Padang Besar
Sungai Kolok
Tumpat 6010
Butterworth
Ipoh
Gua Musang
Tapah Road
KUALA LUMPUR
Mentakab
Gemas
Tampin
Johor Bahru
Woodlands
SINGAPORE
6150
6155
6165
6165/75
6170
6100
6105
6115
6060
6065
6070
6050
6090
6055
6000/20
6010
6001/20
MALAYSIA
(Peninsular)
Sumatera
6200 Medan
Tanjong Balai 6200
6200 Pematangsiantar
Rantau Prapaet
6200 Padang
Lubuk Linggau
Palembang
Panjang 6200
6200
6215 Merak
JAKARTA
6205
6210
6215
Semarang
Kamal 7416
BANDUNG
Java
Solo
SURABAJA
6215 Banjuwangi Baru
Bali
Lombok
Flores
Timor
Kota Kinabalu
6015
MALAYSIA (Sabah)
BANDAR SERI BEGAWAN
BRUNEI DARUSSALAM
Tenom
Sibu
MALAYSIA (Sarawak)
Kuching
Sri Aman
Kalimantan
Balikpapan
Bitung
Donggala
Sulawesi
Ujung Padang
Baubau

MALAYSIA

Capital: **Kuala Lumpur** (GMT +8). 2019 Public Holidays: Feb. 5, 6, May 1, June 5, 6, Aug. 12, 31, Sept. 1, 9, 16, Nov. 10, Dec. 25.

Rail services in Malaysia are operated by Keretapi Tanah Melayu Berhad (Malayan Railways, www.ktmb.com.my), a government owned agency. Trains numbered **9XXX** are *Electric Train Service – ETS* and convey one class of seating only either ETS Silver, Gold or Platinum and a buffet car, all are air-conditioned. Trains **29XX** are classed as Commuter service and use air-conditioned EMUs. Overnight trains **26/27** convey air-conditioned second class and thirdclass seating (known locally as Superior and Economy) and air-conditioned couchettes which have 40 curtained bunks. All non *ETS* trains convey second class only. For full information go to www.ktmb.com.my.

6000 HAT YAI - BUTTERWORTH - KUALA LUMPUR - GEMAS

Keretapi Tanah Melayu Berhad

km		9051	9023	9121	9103	2941	9321	2945	9221	9027	947	2957	9029	9201	45	2961	9203	9105	949	2967	9037	9205	9425	9123	2977	2981	2985
		R	R	R	R	2	R	2	R	R	2	2	R	R	R	2	R	R	2	2	R	R	R	R	2	2	2
						A									♦												
	Bangkok **6055** d.	...	...	...	...	...	...	...	...	...	...	...	...	...	1510t	...	...	...	...	...	...	...	...	...	...	...	...
0	**Hat Yai** Junction **6055** d.	...	...	...	...	...	...	...	...	...	0730t	...	...	...	0758t	...	...	...	1305t	...	...	...	...	...	...	...	...
45	Padang Besar 🏛 d.	...	...	...	...	0525	...	0625	0747	...	0925	1025	...	1115	0953	1225	1420	...	1500	1525	...	1713	1805	...	1825	1925	2125
76	Arau d.	...	...	...	...	0544	...	0644	0806	...	...	1044	...	1134	▬	1244	1439	...	▬	1544	...	1732	1824	...	1844	1944	2144
114	Alor Setar d.	...	...	...	...	0608	...	0708	0829	...	...	1108	...	1155	...	1308	1503	...	...	1608	...	1754	1847	...	1908	2008	2208
205	Bukit Mertajam d.	...	...	...	...	0705	...	0805	|	...	...	1205	...	|	...	1405	|	...	...	1705	...	|	|	...	2005	2105	2305
216	**Butterworth** d.	...	...	0458	0613	0716	0725	0816	|	...	...	1216	...	|	...	1416	|	1623	...	1716	...	|	|	1945	2016	2116	2316
227	Bukit Mertajam d.	...	...	0509	0624	▬	0735	...	|	...	...	...	...	|	...	...	|	1634	...	...	...	|	|	1956	...	...	...
312	Taiping d.	...	...	0554	0709	**9025**	0820	...	1002	...	...	...	...	1324	**9031**	...	1634	1719	**9035**	...	...	1923	2021	2041	...	...	...
344	Kuala Kangsar d.	...	...	0613	0728	R	0839	...	1021	...	...	...	...	1343	R	...	1653	1738	R	...	...	1942	2041	2100	...	...	...
398	**Ipoh** d.	0505	0625	0644	0759	0810	0910	...	1053	1145	...	...	1300	1414	1525	...	1724	1809	1830	...	1940	2014	2114	2131	...	...	...
434	Kampar d.	0530	0650	0708	0823	0835	0935	...	1117	1210	...	...	1325	1437	1550	...	1747	1832	1855	...	2005	2037	2138	2155	...	...	...
450	Tapah Road d.	0540	0700	0718	|	0845	0946	...	1128	1220	...	...	1335	|	1600	...	|	|	1905	...	2015	|	2149	2205	...	...	...
517	Tanjong Malim d.	0623	0740	0756	|	0925	1026	...	1208	1300	...	...	1415	|	1640	...	|	|	1945	...	2055	|	2229	2243	...	...	...
604	**Kuala Lumpur** Sentral d.	0805	0915	0930	1040	1100	1203	...	1347	1435	...	...	1550	1655	1815	...	2005	2050	2120	...	2230	2255	0011	0013	...	...	...
677	Seremban d.	...	...	...	...	...	1327	...	...	...	...	...	...	...	...	...	...	...	...	...	...	...	0131	...	...	...	...
726	Pulau Sebang/Tampin d.	...	...	...	...	...	1400	...	...	...	...	...	...	...	...	...	...	...	...	...	...	...	0204	...	...	...	...
779	**Gemas** d.	...	...	...	...	...	1438	...	...	...	...	...	...	...	...	...	...	...	...	...	...	...	0240	...	...	...	...

	2948	948	2956	9222	9022	9024	9420	2964	9202	9102	2968	46	2972	9026	9104	9028	9030	9322	9204	9032	9106	9122	9034	9052	9224
	2	2	2	R	R	R	R	2	R	R	2	R	2	R	R	R	R	R	R	R	R	R	R	R	R
	B											♦													
Gemas d.	...	...	...	...	...	...	0740	...	...	...	...	...	...	...	...	...	...	1510	...	...	...	...	...	...	...
Pulau Sebang/Tampin d.	...	...	...	...	...	...	0812	...	...	...	...	...	...	...	...	...	...	1541	...	...	...	...	...	...	...
Seremban d.	...	...	...	...	...	...	0845	...	...	...	...	...	...	...	...	...	...	1614	...	...	...	...	...	...	...
Kuala Lumpur Sentral d.	...	...	...	0700	0835	0950	1004	...	1055	1125	...	...	...	1150	1440	1505	1620	1729	1800	1855	2040	2150	2215	2305	2330
Tanjong Malim d.	...	...	...	0822	0858	1113	1131	...	|	|	...	...	...	1313	|	1628	1743	1859	|	2018	|	2312	2338	0036	0052
Tapah Road d.	...	...	...	0902	1040	1155	1211	...	|	|	...	...	...	1355	|	1710	1825	1939	|	2100	|	2352	0020	0120	0132
Kampar d.	...	...	...	0913	1051	1206	1222	...	1304	1332	...	...	...	1406	1647	1721	1836	1950	2007	2111	2247	0015	0031	0131	0143
Ipoh d.	...	...	...	0939	1115	1230	1248	...	1328	1356	...	...	...	1430	1711	1745	1900	2015	2031	2135	2311	0029	0055	0155	0209
Kuala Kangsar d.	...	...	...	1010	▬	▬	1320	...	1359	1426	...	...	...	▬	1741	▬	▬	2047	2102	...	2341	0100	...	...	0240
Taiping d.	...	...	...	1029	**2960**	...	1340	...	1418	1445	...	...	...	**2976**	1800	**2980**	**2984**	2106	2121	...	0000	0120	...	...	0259
Bukit Mertajam d.	...	...	...	|	2	...	|	...	|	1530	...	...	...	2	1845	2	2	2152	|	...	0045	0205	...	...	|
Butterworth d.	0725	...	1025	|	1225	...	|	1425	|	1540	1625	...	1725	1825	1855	1925	2125	2203	|	...	0055	0215	...	...	|
Bukit Mertajam d.	0736	...	1036	|	1236	...	|	1436	|	...	1636	...	1736	1836	...	1936	2136	...	|	...	...	...	...	...	|
Alor Setar d.	0833	...	1133	1202	1333	**950**	1512	1533	1547	...	1733	...	1833	1933	...	2033	2133	...	2250	...	...	...	...	...	0432
Arau d.	0857	...	1157	1225	1357	2	1535	1557	1609	...	1757	...	1857	1957	...	2057	2157	...	2312	...	...	...	...	...	0455
Padang Besar 🏛 d.	0916	0955	1216	1245	1416	1540	1555	1616	1630	...	1816	1840	1916	2016	...	2116	2316	...	2330	...	...	...	...	...	0515
Hat Yai Junction **6055** a.	...	0950t	...	...	...	1535t	...	...	...	...	...	1810t	...	...	...	...	...	...	...	...	...	...	...	...	...
Bangkok **6055** a.	...	...	...	...	...	...	...	...	...	...	...	1010t	...	...	...	...	...	...	...	...	...	...	...	...	...

6001 GEMAS - JOHOR BAHRU - SINGAPORE

Keretapi Tanah Melayu Berhad

km		ES41	ERT27	ES43	ES45					
		2	R ♦	2	2					
53	Pulau Sebang/Tampin d.	0500	...	1450	2100	...	...	...	...	...
0	**Gemas** d.	0545	0659	1535	2145	...	...	...	...	...
26	Segamat d.	0621	0736	1611	2221	...	...	...	...	...
85	Paloh d.	0742	0859	1732	2351	...	...	...	...	...
112	Kluang d.	0819	0930	1808	0041	...	...	...	...	...
163	Kulai d.	0940	1053	1917	0149	...	...	...	...	...
195	**Johor Bahru** Sentral a.	1029	1147	2006	0238	...	...	...	...	...

	ES40	ES42	ERT26	ES44					
	2	2	R ♦	2					
Johor Bahru Sentral d.	0845	1415	2015	2240	...	...	...	...	...
Kulai d.	0935	1506	2111	2331	...	...	...	...	...
Kluang d.	1106	1614	2234	0039	...	...	...	...	...
Paloh d.	1137	1645	2305	0110	...	...	...	...	...
Segamat d.	1303	1822	0028	0236	...	...	...	...	...
Gemas d.	1342	1901	0113	0315	...	...	...	...	...
Pulau Sebang/Tampin d.	1422	1941	...	0355	...	...	...	...	...

km	◄	ST63	ST65	ST67	ST69	ST71	ST73	ST79	ST83	ST85	ST89	ST93	ST95
		C											
0	**Johor Bahru** Sentral d.	0530	0600	0630	0700	0730	0845	1245	1515	1630	1900	2130	2245
4	**Woodlands** ◇ a.	0535	0605	0635	0705	0735	0850	1250	1520	1635	1905	2135	2250

◄	ST72	ST74	ST80	ST84	ST86	ST88	ST90	ST92	ST94	ST96
	D									
Woodlands ◇ d.	0830	0945	1345	1615	1730	1845	2000	2115	2230	2345
Johor Bahru Sentral d.	0835	0950	1350	1620	1735	1850	2005	2120	2235	2350

6010 TUMPAT - GEMAS

Keretapi Tanah Melayu Berhad

km			SH51	SH53	SH55	SH57	SH59			ERT27
			3	3	3	3	3			R ♦
0	**Tumpat** d.	...	0410	...	1020	1445	...	...	...	1815
14	Wakaf Bharu d.	...	0429	...	1038	1503	...	...	...	1833
25	Pasir Mas d.	...	0447	...	1055	1522	...	...	...	1849
53	Tanah Merah d.	...	0519	...	1127	1557	...	...	...	1916
85	Krai d.	...	0558	...	1301	1637	...	...	...	1953
135	Dabong d.	...	0737	...	1435	1805	...	...	...	2107
	Kemubu d.	...	0751	...	...	1819	...	...	...	|
206	**Gua Masang** d.	...	0947	1010	...	2015	2020	...	...	2253
300	Kuala Lipis d.	...	...	1240	...	...	2250	...	...	0107
353	Jerantut d.	...	...	...	...	...	...	...	...	0229
406	Mentakab d.	...	...	...	...	...	...	...	...	0343
492	Bahau d.	...	...	...	...	...	...	...	...	0601
528	**Gemas** a.	...	...	...	...	...	...	...	...	0659

		SH50	SH52	ERT26		SH56		SH58	SH60
		3	3	R ♦		3		3	3
Gemas d.	...	...	...	0113	...	...	...	...	...
Bahau d.	...	...	...	0204	...	...	...	...	...
Mentakab d.	...	...	...	0503	...	...	...	...	...
Jerantut d.	...	...	...	0618	...	...	...	...	...
Kuala Lipis d.	...	0300	...	0755	...	...	...	1530	...
Gua Masang d.	...	0516	0522	0957	...	...	...	1746	1752
Kemubu d.	...	...	0719	|	...	...	...	...	2004
Dabong d.	...	...	0745	1136	...	1500	...	...	2018
Krai d.	...	...	0901	1250	...	1642	...	...	2201
Tanah Merah d.	...	...	0939	1327	...	1722	...	...	2240
Pasir Mas d.	...	...	1014	1354	...	1757	...	...	2312
Wakaf Bharu d.	...	...	1045	1410	...	1835	...	...	2329
Tumpat a.	...	...	1100	1426	...	1853	...	...	2346

Notes for Tables **6000**, **6001**, **6010**. ♦ – Notes, listed by train number.

26/27 – EKSPRES RAKYAT TIMURAN – 🛏 2 cl., (23) Johor Bahru - Gua Musang -Tumpat and v.v.
45/46 – INTERNATIONAL EXPRESS – See Table **6055**. For connections to/from Butterworth use *ETS* services.

A – Additional trips: 0725, 0825, 1325, 1425, 1625, 1725.
B – Additional trips: 0525, 0625, 0825, 0925, 1525.
C – Additional trips: 0500, 1000, 1130, 1400, 1745, 2015.
D – Additional trips: 1100, 1230, 1500.

2XXX – Komuter Electric Train Service (2).
9XXX – Electric Train Service (2) 🍸.
t – Thai time.
◇ – Border point with Singapore.
◄ – Connections with intercity trains are not guaranteed.

6015 TENOM - TANJONG ARU

JKNS

km		201	401	505	502	508	504	504A
			①–⑥	⑦		⑦	①–⑥	①–⑥
0	**Tenom** d.	...	...	...	0730	1230	1300	...
	Halogilat d.	...	0600	0810	0854	1353	1444	1740
49	Beaufort a.	...	0658	0911	0951	1455	1545	1839
49	Beaufort d.	0500	...	...	1101	...	...	...
101	Papar d.	0611	...	...	1216	...	...	...
134	**Tanjong Aru** ◐ a.	0657	...	...	1310	...	...	...

	301	303	101A	101	106A	102A	103	104	104
	①–⑥	⑦			⑦	①–⑥	①–⑥	⑦	①–⑥
Tanjong Aru ◐ d.	...	...	...	0745	...	...	...	1706	1736
Papar d.	...	...	...	0829	...	...	...	1750	1823
Beaufort a.	...	...	...	0940	...	...	...	1900	1934
Beaufort d.	0500	0700	0750	...	1300	1330	1630	...	...
Halogilat d.	0556	0758	0853	...	1444	1444	1730	...	...
Tenom a.	...	...	1013	...	1555	1555	...	...	...

◐ – Kota Kinabalu.
Operator: Jabatan Keretapi Negeri Sabah (Sabah State Railways).

6020 BANGKOK - WOODLANDS EOE

The EASTERN AND ORIENTAL EXPRESS is a luxury cruise train operating between Bangkok and Woodlands ◇. 2019/20 departure dates:
From **Bangkok** depart 1750, journey 3 nights on Sept. 8, 17, 26, Oct. 8, 20, 28, Nov. 9, 18, 27, Dec. 8, 25, Jan. 3, 25, Feb. 3, 12, 21, Mar. 1, 10, 21, 29.
From **Woodlands** depart 1500, journey 2 nights on Sept. 2, 13, 22, Oct. 2, 25, Nov. 1, 14, 23, Dec. 1, 21, Jan. 8, 18, 30, Feb. 8, 17, 26, Mar. 6, 15, 26.
Operator: Eastern and Oriental Express
✆ UK 0845 077 2222.
◇ – Border point with Singapore.

THAILAND

Capital: **Bangkok** (GMT +7). 2019 Public Holidays: Jan. 1, Feb. 19, Apr. 5, 6, 13–17, May 1, July 17, 28, Aug. 12, Oct. 13, 23, Dec. 5, 10, 31.

Rail services are operated by State Railway of Thailand (www.railway.co.th). Trains may convey any combination of first, second or third class seating as shown in either columns or footnotes. Overnight trains may also convey sleeping cars or couchettes. Sleeping cars have lockable two berth compartments which convert into seats during the day. Couchettes are arranged 'open plan' along the coach and during the day the bottom bunks are used as seats. Dining cars are operated on all important trains. The Thailand Rail Pass offers twenty days unlimted travel in seated accommodation. Two passes are available. Pass A costs 1550 Baht and does not include supplements for express trains or sleeping cars. Pass B costs 3000 Baht and includes all supplements.

State Railway of Thailand — BANGKOK - BAN PLU TA LUANG and ARANYAPRATHET — 6050

km	3rd class only		275	283	281	367	389	279	277	391	371
										A	
0	**Bangkok** Hua Lampong	d.	0555	0655	0800	1010	1210	1305	1525	1655	1740
5	Makkasan	d.	0620	0716	0816	1030	1228	1317	1545	1713	1802
31	Hua Takhe ‡	d.	0703	0814	0857	1109	1304	1348	1618	1753	1842
61	Chachoengsao Junction	d.	0740	0859	0932	1145	1330	1421	1644	1825	1924
131	Si Racha Junction	d.	|	1013a	|	...	...	|	|	...	|
155	Pattaya	d.	|	1035a	|	...	...	|	|	...	|
184	**Ban Plu Ta Luang**	a.	|	1120a	|	...	...	|	|	...	|
122	Prachin Buri	d.	0858	...	1046	...	...	1522	1741	...	2032
161	Kabin Buri	d.	0948	...	1135	...	...	1612	1820	...	...
255	**Aranyaprathet**	a.	1135	...	...	...	...	1735	...	...	...

3rd class only		372	278	280	368	390	282	284	276	
						B				
Aranyaprathet	d.	...	...	0640	...	...	...	...	1355	...
Kabin Buri	d.	...	0630	0823	...	...	1325	...	1539	...
Prachin Buri	d.	0500	0719	0921	...	...	1416	...	1630	...
Ban Plu Ta Luang	d.	|	|	|	...	...	|	1335a	|	...
Pattaya	d.	|	|	|	...	...	|	1421a	|	...
Si Racha Junction	d.	|	|	|	...	...	|	1452a	|	...
Chachoengsao Junction	d.	0619	0831	1022	1235	1405	1534	1620	1800	...
Hua Takhe ‡	d.	0701	0911	1107	1316	1435	1609	1706	1842	...
Makkasan	d.	0751	0958	1148	1354	1512	1655	1801	1925	...
Bangkok Hua Lampong	a.	0815	1015	1205	1410	1525	1715	1815	1940	...

A – Also at 1825.
B – Also at 0545 Ⓐ, 0705.
a – ①–⑤ only.
‡ – For Suvarnabhumi International Airport.

State Railway of Thailand — BANGKOK - HAT YAI - SUNGAI KOLOK — 6055

km			453	175	43	261		171	31	37	463	169	451		83	173	447	167	85	39	41		455	445	
			3	23	2🍷	3		C	B	A	3	C	3		B	C	3	C	B	2🍷	2🍷		3	3	
0	**Bangkok** Hua Lampong	d.	...	...	0805	0920	...	1300	1445	1510	...	1535	...	...	1705	1735	...	1830	1930	2250	2250	...	...	...	...
64	Nakhon Pathom	d.	...	...	0922	1048	...	1437	1611	1638	...	1715	...	...	1833	1912	...	1958	2059	0009	0009	...	...	...	...
117	Rachaburi	d.	...	...	1004	1145	...	1526	1701	1730	...	1820	...	...	1924	2007	...	2050	2150	0052	0052	...	...	...	...
229	Hua Hin	d.	...	...	1129	1335	...	1717	1845	1913	...	2010	...	...	2110	2154	...	2234	2336	0224	0224	...	...	...	...
377	Bang Saphan Yai	d.	...	...	1321	...	...	1946	2107	2143	...	2249	...	...	2341	0048	...	0111	0232	0433	0433	...	...	...	...
485	Chumphon	d.	...	...	1441	...	...	2121	2245	2324	...	0052	...	...	0127	0258	...	0328	0423	0559	0559	...	...	0630	...
651	Surat Thani ♥	d.	...	...	1645	...	...	0027	0126	0203	...	0348	...	...	0427	0603	0600	0628	0716	0805	0815	...	...	0946	...
773	Thung Song Junction	d.	...	...	...	...	...	0239	0322	0400	...	0556	...	...	0635	0832	0848	0855	0932	...	0954	...	...	1219	...
832	**Nakhon Si Thammarat**	a.	...	...	...	...	...	|	|	|	...	|	0600	...	|	0955	|	|	1055	...	|	...	0958	|	...
845	Trang	a.	...	...	...	...	...	|	|	|	...	|	|	...	0805	...	|	1036	...	...	|	...	|	|	...
866	**Kantang**	a.	...	...	...	...	...	|	|	|	...	|	|	...	...	...	|	1120	...	...	|	...	|	|	...
862	Phatthalung	d.	...	...	...	...	...	0422	0506	0548	0602	0738	0822	...	...	...	1039	...	...	...	1112	...	1224	1420	...
943	Hat Yai Junction	d.	...	0630	...	...	...	0645	0635	0735	0755	0930	1018	...	...	...	1233	...	...	...	1250	...	1433	1650	...
1009	Pattani	d.	...	0739	...	...	...	0810	...	0858	0919	1050	1145	...	...	...	1431	...	...	...	1404	...	1616	...	...
1055	Yala	d.	0630	0806	...	...	...	0848	...	0929	0958	1120	1227	...	...	...	1525	...	...	...	1430	...	1710	...	...
1159	**Sungai Kolok**	a.	0840	1000	...	...	...	1045	...	1120	1210	...	1450	...	...	...	1735	...	...	...	...	...	...	...	...

			262	40	446		174	456	168	448		86	452	170	42	44		84	172	464		38	176	32	454
			3	2🍷	2		C	3	C	3		B	3	C	2🍷	2🍷		B	C	3		A	2	B	2
Sungai Kolok	d.	...	...	...	...	...	...	...	...	0630	...	...	0900	...	...	...	...	...	1130	1225	...	1420	1455	...	1525
Yala	d.	...	...	...	...	...	...	0635	...	0828	...	...	1122	1235	1455	...	...	...	1326	1432	...	1609	1637	...	1740
Pattani	d.	...	...	...	...	...	...	0716	...	0920	...	...	1206	1306	1519	...	...	...	1405	1528	...	1640	1704	...	...
Hat Yai Junction	d.	...	...	...	0640	...	...	0918	...	1058	...	...	1350	1445	1623	...	...	...	1539	1705	...	1810	1815	1845	...
Phatthalung	d.	...	...	...	0853	...	...	1118	...	1300	...	...	1534	1623	1736	...	...	...	1713	1850	...	1947	...	2019	...
Kantang	d.	...	...	...	|	...	...	|	1240	|	...	...	|	|	|	...	...	...	|	...	...	|	...	|	...
Trang	d.	...	...	...	|	...	...	|	1329	|	...	...	|	|	|	...	...	1725	|	...	...	|	...	|	...
Nakhon Si Thammarat	d.	...	...	...	|	...	1300	1355	|	|	...	1500	1805	|	|	...	...	|	|	...	...	|	...	|	...
Thung Song Junction	d.	...	...	...	1058	...	1424	...	1517	1531	...	1620	...	1813	1903	...	...	1912	1927	...	...	2138	...	2207	...
Surat Thani ♥	d.	...	...	1040	1325	...	1647	...	1738	1755	...	1837	...	2014	2041	2041	...	2104	2126	...	...	2328	...	2357	...
Chumphon	d.	...	...	1246	1630	...	1936	...	2031	...	...	2122	...	2323	2249	2249	...	2359	0044	...	...	0206	...	0234	...
Bang Saphan Yai	d.	...	...	1407	...	...	2128	...	2216	...	...	2308	...	0109	0019	0019	...	0148	0219	...	...	0336	...	0404	...
Hua Hin	d.	...	1410	1601	...	...	0045	...	0116	...	...	0147	...	0406	0222	0222	...	0415	0456	...	...	0605	...	0629	...
Rachaburi	d.	...	1600	1741	...	...	0244	...	0306	...	...	0404	...	0625	0350	0350	...	0608	0649	...	...	0749	...	0813	...
Nakhon Pathom	d.	...	1716	1826	...	...	0340	...	0405	...	...	0500	...	0726	0438	0438	...	0704	0744	...	...	0842	...	0903	...
Bangkok Hua Lampong	a.	...	1900	1945	...	...	0510	...	0535	...	...	0630	...	0900	0555	0555	...	0835	0915	...	...	1010	...	1030	...

A – INTERNATIONAL EXPRESS – 🛏 1, 2 cl. and ✕ Bangkok (**37/38**) - Hat Yai – Sungai Kolok and v.v.; 🛏 2 cl. Hat Yai (**45/46**) - Padang Besar – Bangkok and v.v. **Note**: Train **45/46** is combined with train **37/38** between Bangkok an Hat Yai.
B – 🛏 1, 2 cl., [23]. **Note**: Trains **31/32** convey new Chinese sleepers.
C – 🛏 2 cl., [23].
♥ – Station is at Phun Phin, 13 km away.

State Railway of Thailand — BANGKOK - CHIANG MAI — 6060

km			403	407	401	303	409	111	7	201	3		209	211	109	207	301	317	9	13	107	105		51	
			3	3	3	3	3	23✕	2🍷	23	2🍷		3	23	B✕	3	3	3	A✕	A✕	B✕	23🍷		B✕	
0	**Bangkok** Hualampong	d.	...	...	...	0420	...	0700	0830	0925	1050	...	1120	1255	1345	1405	1630	1725	1810	1935	2010	2100	...	2200	...
58	Bang Pa In	d.	...	...	...	0536	...	0825	|	1114	|	...	1251	1419	|	1543	1816	1900	|	|	|	2211	...	|	...
71	Ayutthaya	d.	...	...	...	0550	0600	0838	0948	1128	1216	...	1305	1432	1519	1558	1833	1914	1945	2107	2144	2223	...	2236	...
133	Lop Buri	d.	...	...	0600	0705	0715	0944	1029	1241	1300	...	1423	1538	1623	1727	2000	2020	2042	2200	2239	2316	...	0031	...
246	Nakhon Sawan	d.	...	0500	0811	...	...	1124	1140	1511	1407	...	...	1753	1827	1935	...	...	2217	2331	0006	0050	...	0224	...
319	Taphan Hin	d.	...	0617	0936	...	...	1242	1226	1640	1457	...	...	1915	1937	...	...	...	|	|	0130	0210	...	0337	...
389	Phitsanulok	d.	0555	0729	1055	...	...	1345	1322	1755	1604	...	...	...	2037	...	...	...	0018	0149	0238	0309	...	0440	...
485	Uttaradit	d.	0737	0907	...	...	...	1524	1427	...	1912	...	...	...	2223	...	...	...	|	0308	0405	0436	...	0606	...
488	Sila At	d.	0740	0917	...	...	...	1529	1433	...	1915	...	...	...	2237	...	...	...	0154	0321	0418	0440	...	0620	...
534	Den Chai	d.	...	1013	...	...	...	1630	1524	...	...	...	...	...	2342	...	...	...	0251	0419	0515	...	...	0720	...
642	Nakhon Lampang	d.	...	1236	...	...	...	...	1733	...	...	...	...	...	0204	...	...	...	0501	0633	...	...	...	1001	...
683	Khun Tan	d.	...	1330	...	...	...	...	1823	...	...	...	...	...	0258	...	...	...	0606	0737	...	...	...	1105	...
729	Lamphun	d.	...	1415	...	...	...	...	1915	...	...	...	...	...	0344	...	...	...	0651	0821	...	...	...	1150	...
751	**Chiang Mai**	a.	...	1435	...	...	...	...	1930	...	...	...	...	...	0405	...	...	...	0715	0840	...	...	...	1210	...

		318	208	304	212	202	106	112	210		102	8	402		408	410	4		108	52	14	10	302	
		3	3	3	3	23	23🍷	23✕	3		B✕	2🍷	3		3	3	2🍷		B✕	B✕	A✕	A✕		
Chiang Mai	d.	...	...	...	...	...	...	...	...	...	0630	0850	...	...	0930	...	...	...	...	1530	1700	1800	...	...
Lamphun	d.	...	...	...	...	...	...	...	...	...	0652	0905	...	...	1000	...	...	...	...	1548	1720	1820	...	...
Khun Tan	d.	...	...	...	...	...	...	...	...	...	0736	0947	...	...	1103	...	...	...	...	1650	1824	1921	...	...
Nakhon Lampang	d.	...	...	...	...	...	...	...	...	...	0837	1041	...	...	1202	...	...	...	...	1804	1927	2017	...	...
Den Chai	d.	...	...	...	...	...	...	0730	...	...	1046	1239	...	...	1419	...	...	...	1905	2026	2141	2236	...	...
Sila At	d.	...	...	...	...	...	0730	0827	...	...	1147	1326	...	...	1533	1630	1950	...	2012	2130	2236	2333	...	...
Uttaradit	d.	...	...	...	...	...	0735	0833	...	...	1153	1332	...	...	1538	1633	2000	...	2019	2137	2242	|	...	...
Phitsanulok	d.	...	...	...	...	0605	0855	1003	...	...	1318	1444	1345	...	1724	1810	2140	...	2209	2301	0001	0050	...	...
Taphan Hin	d.	...	...	...	0530	0718	0952	1112	...	...	1428	1532	1458	...	1842	...	2239	...	2320	0007	|	|	...	...
Nakhon Sawan	d.	...	0500	...	0701	0835	1048	1242	...	...	1556	1622	1630	...	1955	...	0006	...	0048	0114	0159	0241	...	...
Lop Buri	d.	0600	0706	0800	0918	1056	1220	1439	1732	...	1806	1728	1845	...	...	...	0130	...	0228	0245	0324	0405	0440	...
Ayutthaya	d.	0711	0826	0901	1027	1248	1311	1559	1848	...	1916	1806	...	...	...	...	0227	...	0321	0339	0424	0459	0608	...
Bang Pa In	d.	0722	0840	0912	1039	1229	1323	1616	1903	...	|	|	...	...	...	...	|	...	|	|	|	|	0623	...
Bangkok Hualampong	a.	0905	1020	1035	1210	1405	1440	1800	2035	...	2110	1925	...	...	...	...	0400	...	0510	0525	0615	0650	0815	...

A – Conveys 🛏 1, 2 cl.
B – Conveys 🛏 2 cl., [23].

6065 BANGKOK - UBON RATCHATHANI and NONG KHAI
State Railway of Thailand

km	425	421	21	419	135	71	427	233	145	139	23	67	141		234	424	72	428	136	146	426	22	142	24	420	68	140
	3	3	2🍸	3	23	23🍸	3	3	23✕	B	C	A	23✕	↓ ↑	3	3	23🍸	3	23✕	23✕	3	2🍸	23🍸	C	3	A	B
0	...	...	0545	...	0640	1005	...	1140	1520	1855	2030	2130	2245	d.**Bangkok** Hua .... a.	1415	...	1455	...	1840	2110	...	2255	0500	0515	...	0640	0720
71	...	...	0659	...	0826	1125	...	1307	1657	2026	2153	2251	0017	d.Ayutthaya .... d.	1240	...	1317	...	1637	1925	...	2142	0313	0342	...	0458	0531
113	...	...	0734	...	0910	1204	...	1353	1801	2110	|	2333	0059	d.Saraburi .... d.	1151	...	1241	...	1545	1813	...	2106	0232	|	...	0354	0441
125	...	...	0745	...	0923	1216	...	1406	1815	2124	|	2346	0115	d.Kaeng Khoi Jct ..... d.	1136	...	1228	...	1530	1750	...	2053	0216	|	...	0335	0425
180	...	...	0856	...	1056	1327	...	1524	1949	2249	0010	0105	0259	d.Pak Chong .... d.	1009	...	1127	...	1400	1656	...	1948	0103	0131	...	0217	0303
264	...	0610	1011	1115	1224	1443	1420	1705	2125	0023	0146	0246	0429	d.Nakhon Ratchasima . d.	0822	0950	1018	1145	1233	1523	1825	1847	2325	2359	...	0036	0142
376	...	0810	1137	1317	1422	1617	1635	1916	2341	0226	0334	0429	0634	d.Buri Ram .... d.	0606	0756	0835	0953	1027	1307	1615	1715	2117	2204	...	2245	2344
420	0538	0910	1211	1403	1510	1711	1723	2000	0032	0317	0414	0510	0729	d.Surin .... d.	0520	0703	0749	0905	0939	1217	1528	1641	2022	2123	2120	2201	2256
515	0718	1107	1320	1550	1703	1843	1906	...	0221	0509	0539	0644	0908	d.Si Sa Ket .... d.	...	...	0624	0716	0804	1038	1344	1531	1841	1956	1948	2028	2124
575	0830	1215	1400	1645	1800	1950	2015	...	0335	0615	0636	0750	1020	a.**Ubon Ratchathani** . d.	...	...	0540	0620	0700	0930	1235	1450	1735	1900	1845	1930	2030

km		415	431	75	417	77	25	913	133	917
		3	3	23🍸		23🍸	C	23	3	23
0	**Bangkok** Hua .... d.	...	...	0820	...	1835	2000	...	2045	...
71	Ayutthaya .... d.	...	...	0942	...	2002	2141	...	2218	...
113	Saraburi .... d.	...	...	1018	...	2040	2233	...	2302	...
125	Kaeng Khoi Junction .... d.	...	0500	1030	...	2051	2235	...	2315	...
180	Pak Chong .... d.	...	0618	|	...	2158	|	...	|	...
264	Nakhon Ratchasima .... d.	0620	0829	|	1600	2333	|	...	|	...
346	Bua Yai Junction .... d.	0758	1009	1414	1742	0048	0250	...	0357	...
450	Khon Kaen .... d.	0938	1155	1527	1917	0206	0419	...	0525	...
569	Udon Thani .... d.	1133	...	1710	2140	0336	0558	...	0740	...
621	**Nong Khai** .... a.	1220	...	1745	...	0415	0645	0730	0835	1445
627	**Tha Na Laeng** (Laos) .... a.	...	...	...	...	...	...	0745	...	1500

	416	76	432	914	418	918	78	134	26
	3	23🍸	3	23	3	23	23✕	3	C
Tha Na Laeng (Laos) .... d.	...	...	...	1000	...	1730	...	...	...
Nong Khai .... d.	...	0700	...	1015	1255	1745	1815	1830	1910
Udon Thani .... d.	0555	0738	...	...	1340	...	1852	1919	1959
Khon Kaen .... d.	0757	0912	1355	...	1536	...	2019	2106	2138
Bua Yai Junction .... d.	0938	1045	1546	...	1714	...	2136	2246	2317
Nakhon Ratchasima .... d.	1125	|	1740	...	1900	...	2304	|	|
Pak Chong .... d.	...	|	1914	...	...	...	0042	|	|
Kaeng Khoi Junction .... d.	...	1444	2030	...	...	...	0222	0237	0308
Saraburi .... d.	...	1455	...	...	...	...	0235	0252	0321
Ayutthaya .... d.	...	1535	...	...	...	...	0315	0348	0404
Bangkok Hua Lampong .... a.	...	1710	...	...	...	...	0500	0545	0600

A – Conveys 🛏 1, 2 cl., [23] ✕. B – Conveys 🛏 2 cl., [23] ✕. C – Conveys 🛏 1, 2 cl., ✕.

6070 BANGKOK - NAM TOK
State Railway of Thailand

km	485	909	257	259	3rd class only	260	258	910	486
		Ⓒ A						A	
0	...	0630h	0750	1335	↓ **Bangkok** Thon Buri . d. ↑	1025	1740	1925h	...
64	...	0820	0902	1503	Nakhon Pathom .... d.	0921	1631	1809	...
82	0435	0836	0922	1522	↓ Nong Pla Duk Jct ..... d. ↑	0835	1602	1755	1850
133	0607	0927	1035	1626	Kanchanaburi .... d.	0719	1448	1653	1741
210	0820	...	1235	1830	↓ **Nam Tok** .... a. ↑	0520	1255	1425	1530

A – Tourist train to River Khwae Bridge (a. 0935) and allied war cemetery at Kanchanaburi. Conveys [23]. Ⓡ. Special fare payable. 740 Baht.
h – Bangkok Hua Lampong.

6075 SUVARNABHUMI INTERNATIONAL AIRPORT

City Line.

Bangkok Makksan - Suvarnabhumi International Airport (journey 22 minutes): 0608 Ⓒ, 0610Ⓐ and at least 4 journeys per hour until 2348Ⓐ, 2349Ⓒ, 0004.
Services depart Phaya Thai station 4 mins earlier

Suvarnabhumi International Airport - Bangkok Makksan (journey 22 minutes): 0605Ⓐ, 0610Ⓒ and at least 4 journeys per hour until 2343Ⓐ, 2345Ⓒ, 0000.
Services arrive Phaya Thai station 4 mins later.

CAMBODIA

Capital: **Phnom Penh** (GMT +7). 2019 Public Holidays: Jan. 1, 7, Feb. 19, Mar. 8, May 1, 18, 20, 22, June 1, Sept. 24, Oct. 15, 29, Nov. 9, Dec. 10.

Rail services are operated by Royal Railway, www.royal-railway.com. Trains convey one class of accommodation also car and motorcycle carriers.

6090 PHNOM PENH - SIHANOUVILLE
Royal Railway

km		⑥	⑦	⑤	⑦		①	⑥	⑦	⑦
0	**Phnom Penh** ..... d.	0700	0700	1500	1600	**Sihanoukville** .. d.	0700	0700	0700	1600
75	Takeo .... d.	0830	0830	1630	1730	Kampot .... d.	0840	0840	0840	1740
166	Kampot .... d.	1140	1140	1940	2040	Takeo .... d.	1150	1150	1150	2000
263	**Sihanoukville** ..... a.	1400	1400	2200	2300	**Phnom Penh** ... a.	1400	1400	1400	2200

6091 PHNOM PENH - POIPET
Royal Railway

km			A				A	
0	**Phnom Penh** .... d.	...	0700	...	**Poipet** .... d.	...	0700	...
166	Pursat .... d.	...	1200	...	Battambang .... d.	...	1015	...
273	Battambang .... d.	...	1535	...	Pursat .... d.	...	1310	...
384	**Poipet** .... a.	...	1840	...	**Phnom Penh** ...... a.	...	1845	...

A – Runs weekly. In May 2019 it was ③ from Phnom Penh and ④ from Poipet.

VIÊT NAM

Capital: **Há Nôi** (GMT +7). 2019 Public Holidays: Jan. 1, Feb. 4 - 9, Apr. 14, 30, May 1, Sept. 2.

Rail services are operated by Duóng Sát Viêt Nam (Viêt Nam Railways, www.vr.com.vn). Unless stated trains convey first and second class accommodation. First class has four berth compartments, whilst second class has six. Dining facilities (meals brought to your seats) are provided on some trains.

6100 HÁ NOI - BEIJING
Duóng Sát Viêt Nam

km				MR1	T8702	Z6	Z286			DD5
				BC	BC	C				
0	**Há Nôi** Gia Lam .... d.	...	...	2140	...	...	...	...	...	0705
162	Dong Dang .... a.	...	...	0155	...	...	...	...	...	1140
162	Dong Dang ▦ .... d.	...	...	0250	...	...	...	...	...	...
207	Pingxiang ▦ .... a.	...	...	0431	...	...	...	...	...	...
207	Pingxiang .... d.	...	...	...	0615	...	...	...	...	...
430	Nanning .... a.	...	...	...	1007	...	...	...	...	...
430	Nanning .... d.	...	...	...	...	1055	1735	...	...	...
861	Guilin .... d.	...	...	...	...	1422	2130a	...	...	...
1409	Changsha .... d.	...	...	...	...	1942	0251	...	...	...
1771	Wuhan Wuchang .... d.	...	...	...	...	2311	0618	...	...	...
2307	Zhengzhou .... d.	...	...	...	...	0352	1110	...	...	...
2996	**Beijing** xi .... a.	...	...	...	...	0948	1703	...	...	...

	Z5	T8701	MR2	Z285				DD6	
	D	BD	BD						
Beijing xi .... d.	1609	...	...	2110	...	...	...	...	...
Zhengzhou .... d.	2212	...	...	0309	...	...	...	...	...
Wuhan Wuchang .... d.	0258	...	...	0755	...	...	...	...	...
Changsha .... d.	0619	...	...	1123	...	...	...	...	...
Guilin .... d.	1139	...	...	1629a	...	...	...	...	...
Nanning .... a.	1535	...	...	2102	...	...	...	...	...
Nanning .... d.	...	1805	...	...	...	...	...	...	...
Pingxiang .... a.	...	2210	...	...	...	...	...	...	...
Pingxiang ▦ .... d.	...	...	2241	...	...	...	...	...	...
Dong Dang ▦ .... a.	...	...	2322	...	...	...	...	...	...
Dong Dang .... d.	...	...	0022	...	...	...	...	1530	...
Há Nôi Gia Lam .... a.	...	...	0520	...	...	...	...	1946	...

B – Conveys 🛏 1 cl. Nanning (**T8701/2**) - Pingxiang (**MR2/1**) - Há Nôi and v.v.
C – Runs daily. On ②⑤ (from Há Nôi) conveys 🛏 1 cl. Há Nôi – Beijing (2 nights).
D – Runs daily. On ④⑦ (from Beijing) conveys 🛏 1 cl. Beijing - Há Nôi (2 nights).
a – Guilin bei.

6105 HÁ NOI - LÂO CAÍ
Duóng Sát Viêt Nam

km		YB3	SP1	SP3	SP7			
			AB	A	AC			
0	**Há Nôi** .... d.	0610	2135	2200	2230	...	...	...
6	**Há Nôi** Gia Lâm .... d.	0632	2150	2218	2248	...	...	...
155	Yên Bái .... d.	1040	0140	0220	0246	...	...	...
262	Phố Lu .... d.	...	0431	0506	0535	...	...	...
296	**Lâo Caí** .... a.	...	0530	0605	0633	...	...	...

	SP8			SP2	SP4	YB4		
	AC			AB	A			
Lâo Caí .... d.	2010	...	...	2055	2140	...	...	...
Phố Lu .... d.	2106	...	...	2151	2236	...	...	...
Yên Bái .... d.	2358	...	...	0038	0128	1445	...	...
Há Nôi Gia Lâm .... a.	0356	...	...	0414	0512	1858	...	...
Há Nôi .... a.	0411	...	...	0432	0530	1920	...	...

A – 🛏 1, 2 cl., [12] Há Nôi - Lâo Caí and v.v. B – Conveys private sleeping cars operated by Livitrans: www.livitrans.com C – Peak periods only.

6110 HÁ NOI - HAI PHÒNG
Duóng Sát Viêt Nam

km		HP1	LP3	LP5	LP7		LP2	LP6	LP8	HP2
				2				2		
0	**Há Nôi** Long Bien ..... d.	0600h	0928	1527	1823	**Hai Phòng** .... d.	0610	0905	1500	1840
6	**Há Nôi** Gia Lâm .... d.	0616	0948	1545	1846	Phú Thái .... d.	0646	0941	1537	1916
57	Hai Duong .... d.	0720	1053	1652	1949	Hai Duong .... d.	0718	1008	1605	1946
76	Phú Thái .... d.	0748	1121	1721	2017	Gia Lâm .... d.	0827	1121	1719	2051
102	**Hai Phòng** .... a.	0825	1200	1800	2055	**Há Nôi** Long Bien .... a.	0835	1129	1727	2106h

h – Há Nôi.

6112 HÁ NOI - HA LONG
Duóng Sát Viêt Nam

km		51501			51502	
		2⑤			2⑤	
0	**Há Nôi** Yen Vien .... d.	0455	...	**Ha Long** .... d.	1350	...
58	Kép .... d.	0716	...	Mao Khê .... d.	1600	...
116	Mao Khê .... d.	0950	...	Kép .... d.	1847	...
164	**Ha Long** .... a.	1141	...	**Há Nôi** Yen Vien .. a.	2031	...

Duóng Sát Viêt Nam

HÁ NÔI - SAÍ GÔN 6115

km		SE5 A	SPT1	SE9 B	SNT1	SQN1	SE21	SE3 A	SE19	SE1 A	SE7 A♣
0	**Há Nôi** d.	0900	...	1430	...	...	...	1930	2010	2220	0600
87	Nam Dinh d.	1042	...	1627	...	...	...	2110	2147	2356	0739
116	Ninh Binh d.	1117	...	1716	...	...	...	2144	2222	|	0814
175	Thanh Hóa d.	1231	...	1830	...	...	...	2252	2331	0125	0925
319	Vinh d.	1500	...	2102	...	...	...	0116	0202	0342	1202
522	Dông Ho'i d.	1915	...	0136	...	...	...	0520	0559	0749	1622
688	Hué d.	2221	...	0455	...	...	0700	0830	0926	1052	1946
791	Dà Nang d.	0106	...	0750	...	...	0955	1108	1220	1326	2221
928	Quang Ngai d.	0351	...	1035	...	...	1307	1422	...	1556	0129
1095	Diêu Tri d.	0642	...	1344	...	1515	1615	1716	...	1836	0417
1315	Nha Trang d.	1044	...	1819	1920	2010	2043	2105	...	2219	0824
	Phan Thiet d.	|	1305	|	|	|	|	|	...	|	|
1551	Binh Thuan d.	1507	1316	2232	|	|	0149	0108	...	0232	1228
1726	**Saí Gôn** (Ho Chi Minh) a.	1838	1703	0247	0335	0400	0520	0445	...	0545	1610

	SE8 A♣	SPT4	SE6 A	SE22	SE10 B	SQN4	SE4 A	SNT2	SE2 A	SE20 A
Saí Gôn (Ho Chi Minh) d.	0600	0715	0900	1150	1440	1900	1945	2030	2155	...
Binh Thuan d.	0931	1050	1225	1555	1842	2235	2320	|	0110	...
Phan Thiet a.	|	1101	|	|	|	|	|	|	|	...
Nha Trang d.	1333	...	1623	2004	2351	0252	0321	0535	0454	...
Diêu Tri d.	1727	...	2058	0022	0348	0733	0711	...	0841	...
Quang Ngai d.	2024	...	2347	0326	0703	...	1004	...	1122	...
Dà Nang d.	2304	...	0223	0630	1003	...	1245	...	1353	1845
Hué d.	0139	...	0500	1010	1305	...	1531	...	1626	2131
Dông Ho'i d.	0455	...	0842	...	1625	...	1840	...	1940	0053
Vinh d.	0928	...	1251	...	2058	...	2247	...	2342	0541
Thanh Hóa d.	1156	...	1535	...	0011	...	0128	...	0217	0801
Ninh Binh d.	1312	...	1651	...	|	...	|	...	0320	0924
Nam Dinh d.	1347	...	1727	...	0216	...	0307	...	0352	1005
Há Nôi a.	1530	...	1912	...	0355	...	0450	...	0530	1155

A – Conveys 🛏 1,2 cl., [1] and ✕. B – Conveys 🛏 2 cl., [2]. ♣ – Runs only at peak periods.

MYANMAR

Capital: **Yangon** (GMT +6½). 2019 Public Holidays: Jan. 4, 13, Feb. 12, Mar. 3, 27, May 1, July 19, Dec. 25, 26.

Rail service in Myanmar is provided by Myanmar Railways Corporation (MRC). Unless noted all trains convey first and second class seating (known locallly as upper and ordinary). All seating is allocated on purchase of tickets. Sleeping cars are operated on overnight trains and bedding is supplied. Sleepers have 6 compartments comprising 4 x 4-berth and 2 x 2-berth.

Myanmar Railways

MYITKYINA - MANDALAY 6150

km		42	56 B	54	38	58				
0	**Myitkyina** d.	0640	0830	...	1200	1600	...	...	...	...
299	Kawlin d.	2320	2000	2215	2015	0435	...	...	...	...
	Shwebo d.	0520	0030	0200	0026	0921	...	...	...	...
529	Sagaing d.	|	|	|	|	|	...	...	...	...
539	**Mandalay** a.	0540	0345	0445	0800	1320	...	...	...	...

	57	37	53	55 B	41 B				
Mandalay d.	0900	1130	1530	1600	1740	...	...	...	...
Sagaing d.	|	|	|	|	|	...	...	...	...
Shwebo d.	1155	1426	1803	1839	2145	...	...	...	...
Kawlin d.	1650	1852	2150	2323	0540	...	...	...	...
Myitkyina a.	0540	0630	...	1115	2025	...	...	...	...

B – 🛏 and [12] Myitkyina - Mandalay and v.v. ◧ – This service is reported as suspended.

Myanmar Railways

LASHIO - MANDALAY 6155

km		132	
0	**Lashio** d.	0500	...
74	Hsipaw d.	0940	...
	Kyaukme d.	1125	...
	Gokteik d.	1325	...
213	Pyin Oo Lwin a.	1605	...
213	Pyin Oo Lwin d.	1740	...
280	**Mandalay** a.	2240	...

	131	
Mandalay d.	0400	...
Pyin Oo Lwin a.	0752	...
Pyin Oo Lwin d.	0822	...
Gokteik d.	1108	...
Kyaukme d.	1339	...
Hsipaw d.	1515	...
Lashio a.	1935	...

Myanmar Railways

THAZI - YAKSAUK 6160

km		141 z	143 ◧
0	**Thazi** d.	0700	0500
197	Kalaw d.	1330	1140
	Aungban d.	1420	1230
	Heho d.	1540	1345
247	Shwenyaung a.	1700	1450
	Shwenyaung d.	...	1520
	Yaksauk a.	...	1930

	142 z	144 ◧
Yaksauk d.	...	0600
Shwenyaung a.	...	0910
Shwenyaung d.	0800	0940
Heho d.	0920	1110
Aungban d.	1050	1235
Kalaw d.	1145	1325
Thazi a.	1900	2045

z – From/to Naypyitaw (Table **6165**).
◧ – This service is reported as suspended.

Myanmar Railways

MANDALAY - BAGAN - YANGON 6165

km		8	6	4 A	120	62 B	10/142	32	12	118
0	**Mandalay** d.	...	1500	1700	2100	...	z	...	0600	0720
129	Thazi d.	...	1749	1949	|	...	2200	...	0854	|
	Naypyitaw d.	2000	2036	2251	|	...	0209	0800	1154	|
***	**Bagan** a.	|	|	|	0450	...	|	|	|	1845
***	**Bagan** d.	|	|	|	...	0700	|	|	|	...
335	Taungoo d.	2235	2318	0127	...	|	0536	1059	1451	...
548	Bago d.	0258	0316	0549	...	|	1211	1523	1859	...
622	**Yangon** a.	0435	0500	0745	...	1030	1440	1700	2100	...

	11	31	9/141	5	61 B	3 A	7	119	117
Yangon d.	0600	0800	1100	1500	1600	1700	2030	...	...
Bago d.	0748	0943	1313	1644	|	1848	2213	...	...
Taungoo d.	1231	1410	1937	2059	|	2325	0223	...	...
Bagan a.	|	|	|	|	0931	|	|	...	...
Bagan d.	|	|	|	|	...	|	|	0700	0400
Naypyitaw d.	1522	1700	2255	2332	...	0157	0500	|	|
Thazi d.	1815	...	0330	0211	...	0458	...	|	|
Mandalay a.	2100	...	z	0500	...	0745	...	1430	1555

A – 🛏 and [12] Yangon - Mandalay and v.v.
B – 🛏 and [12] Runs via Pyay line.
y – From Shwenyaung (Table **6160**).
z – To Shwenyaung (Table **6160**).
*** – Yangon - Bagan: *644 km*. Mandalay - Bagan: *179 km*.

Myanmar Railways

YANGON - MAWLAMYINE - DAWEI 6170

km			89	175	35		
0	**Yangon** d.	...	0715	1825	2000	...	...
78	Bago d.	...	0904	2019	2250	...	...
	Kyaikto d.	...	1157	2320	0130	...	...
281	**Mawlamyine** a.	...	1650	0400	0600	...	...
281	**Mawlamyine** d.	...	...	0430	...	...	...
	Ye d.	...	...	1025	...	...	...
	Dawei Port a.	...	...	1900	...	...	...

	90		36	176		
Dawei Port d.	...	...	...	0540	...	...
Ye d.	...	...	...	1438	...	...
Mawlamyine a.	...	...	...	2025	...	...
Mawlamyine d.	0800	...	1930	2055	...	...
Kyaikto d.	1233	...	2355	0130	...	...
Bago d.	1524	...	0245	0413	...	...
Yangon a.	1730	...	0420	0620	...	...

MRC

YANGON - PYAY 6175

km		63 *	75 *	71			
0	**Yangon** d.	0700	1100	1300	...	...	...
257	**Pyay** a.	1800	2215	2130	...	...	...

			76 *	64 *	72		
Pyay d.	...	...	0200	0615	2330	...	...
Yangoon a.	...	...	1340	1730	0750	...	...

⊖ – Information unavailable at press date. * – Trains **63, 64, 75, 76** use Rangoon Kyemyindine station.

INDONESIA

Capital: **Jakarta** (GMT +7). 2019 Public Holidays: Jan. 1, Feb. 5, Mar. 7, Apr. 3, 19, May 1, 19, Jun. 1, 5, 6, Aug. 12, 17, Sept. 1, Nov. 10, Dec. 25.

Rail services in Indonesia are operated by PT Kereta Api (Indonesian Railways, www.kereta-api.co.id). Trains may convey any of three classes of seated accommodation which are known locally as Eksekutif, Bisnis and Ekonomi, shown in the tables as 1, 2 and 3.

PT Kereta Api

SUMATRA 6200

Medan - Pematangsiantar: *127 km* Journey 4 hours
Medan depart: 1400◐.
Pematangsiantar depart: 0620◐.

Medan - Rantau Prapat: *266 km* Journey 5½ - 6 hours
Medan depart: 0752, 1030, 1505, 2230.
Rantau Prapat depart: 0720, 1430, 1725, 2310.

Medan - Tanjung Balai: *173 km* Journey 4½ hours
Medan depart: 0630◐, 1215◐, 1710◐.
Tanjung Balai depart: 0655◐, 1210◐, 1925◐.

Padang - Pariaman: Journey 2 hours.
Padang depart: 0600◐, 0910◐, 1400◐, 1640◐.
Pariaman depart: 0545◐, 0850◐, 1415◐, 1620◐.

Palembang - Lubuk Linggau: *305 km* Journey 7 - 8½ hours
Palembang Kertapati depart: 0930, 2000.
Lubuk Linggau depart: 0930, 2000.

Palembang - Panjang ♠: *401 km* Journey 8 - 8½ hours
Palembang Kertapati depart: 0830◐, 2100.
Panjang depart: 0830◐, 2100.

◐ – Conveys 3rd class only. ♠ – Panjang is also known as Tanjungkarang Telukbetang.

6205 JAKARTA - BANDUNG

PT Kereta Api

km		20		22	24	32	34	26	28	30
		12		12	12	12	12	12	12	12
0	**Jakarta** Gambir d.	0525	...	0845	1030	1130	1235	1530	1845	2000
12	**Jakarta** Jatinegara d.	|	...	|	|	|	|	|	|	|
173	**Bandung** a.	0852	...	1201	1339	1453	1600	1839	2154	2314

	19	21	31	33		23	25	27	29
	12	12	12	12		12	12	12	12
Bandung d.	0500	0630	0735	0835	...	1135	1445	1610	1940
Jakarta Jatinegara a.	|	|	1034	|	...	|	|	|	|
Jakarta Gambir a.	0815	0945	1050	1150	...	1457	1803	1927	2256

6210 JAKARTA - SEMARANG - SURABAJA

PT Kereta Api

km		202	162	70	14	98	2		62	64	144	68	178	78	56	12	18	176	66	48	150		4	74
		3		12	1	12	1		12	12	3	12	3	12	1	1	1	3	12	1	3		1	12
	Bandung d.	...	...	...	...	0615	...	...	...	...	...	...	...	...	...	...	...	...	...	...	...	...	...	2125
	Jakarta Kota d.	...	...	...	...	|	...	...	...	...	...	...	...	...	...	...	...	...	...	...	...	...	...	|
	Jakarta Gambir d.	...	...	2220	0700	|	0930	...	0940	1100	...	1210	...	...	1500	1615	1720	...	1945	1915	...	...	2130	|
	Jakarta Pasar Senen d.	2300	...	|	|	|	|	...	|	|	1300	|	1400	1545	|	|	|	1700	|	|	2030	...	|	|
0	**Jakarta** Jatinegara d.	|	...	|	|	|	|	...	|	|	|	|	|	|	|	|	|	|	|	|	|	...	|	|
212	Cirebon d.	0227p	...	0127	0958	1035	1215	...	1254	1426	1613p	1518	1720p	1854	1754	1912	2016	2021p	2300	2217	2339p	...	0020	0146
288	Tegal d.	0349	...	...	1059	1138	|	...	1410	1547	1717	...	1831	1959	1857	2014	...	2125	0021	2323	0045	...	|	0253
348	Pekalongan d.	0450	...	...	1147	1229	1352	...	...	...	1812	...	1924	2119	1951	2101	...	...	...	0014	0205	...	|	0342
443	**Semarang** Tawang d.	0615n	0811	...	1300	1345	1509	...	...	...	1942n	...	2108	2250	2119	2215	...	...	...	0145	0325	...	0309	0525
644	Madiun d.	...	|	...	...	...	|	...	...	...	|	...	|	|	0104	...	...	...	...	|	...	...	|	|
737	Kediri d.	...	|	...	...	...	|	...	...	...	|	...	|	|	|	...	...	...	...	|	...	...	|	|
573	Cepu d.	...	1019	...	...	...	|	...	...	...	2156	...	2328	0054	♣	...	...	...	...	0340	...	...	|	0728
610	Bojonegoro d.	...	1052	...	...	...	|	...	...	...	2230	...	0003	0127	|	...	...	...	...	0414	...	...	|	0802
713	**Surabaja** Pasar Turi a.	...	1224	...	...	...	1830	...	...	...	0005	...	0140	0304	0330b	...	...	...	...	0543	...	...	0630	0937
881	**Malang** a.	...	...	...	...	...	...	...	...	...	0242	...	...	...	...	...	...	...	...	...	...	...	...	...

	61		171		161	11	69	149	17	1	97	63	65	13	201	143	77	175	55	73	47	3	177
	12		3			1	12	3	1	1	13	12	12	1	3	3	12	3	1	12	1	1	3
Malang d.	...	...	...	...	...	...	...	...	...	...	...	...	...	...	...	1145	...	...	...	...	...	...	...
Surabaja Pasar Turi d.	...	...	...	...	1310	...	...	...	...	0800	...	...	...	...	...	1415	1530	...	1600b	1630	1750	2000	2100
Bojonegoro d.	...	...	...	...	1445	...	...	...	...	|	...	...	...	...	...	1550	1707	...	|	1807	1922	|	2238
Cepu d.	...	...	...	...	1518	...	...	...	...	|	...	...	...	...	...	1626	1746	...	♥	1843	1957	|	2313
Kediri d.	...	...	...	...	|	...	...	...	...	|	...	...	...	...	...	|	|	...	|	|	|	|	|
Madiun d.	...	...	...	...	|	...	...	...	...	|	...	...	...	...	...	|	|	...	1844	|	|	|	|
Semarang Tawang d.	...	...	0237	...	1715	0600	...	0800	...	1130	1735	...	...	1600	1315n	1851n	1955	2112	2239	2057	2200	2330	0142
Pekalongan d.	...	...	0400	...	...	0713	...	0922	...	1240	1901	...	...	1713	1440	2012	2113	2236	2357	2214	2318	|	0318
Tegal d.	0540	...	0458	...	...	0804	...	1024	...	|	1957	1450	1700	1805	1545	2114	2221	2335	0055	2307	0015	|	0420
Cirebon d.	0725	...	0610p	...	...	0907	0830	1133p	1350	1423	2100	1605	1830	1909	1700p	|	2332	0050p	0159	0015	0120	0217	0530p
Jakarta Jatinegara a.	1011	...	0908	...	...	1143	1120	1418	1611	1645	|	1854	2117	2149	|	0121	0218	0342	0433	|	0357	0442	|
Jakarta Pasar Senen a.	|	...	0920	...	...	|	|	1430	|	|	|	|	|	|	2010	0134	0231	0354	|	|	|	|	0840
Jakarta Gambir a.	1029	...	...	...	...	1200	1137	...	1649	1700	|	1912	2135	2208	...	...	...	...	0500	|	0415	0500	...
Jakarta Kota a.	...	...	...	...	...	...	...	...	...	...	|	...	...	...	...	...	...	...	...	|	...	...	...
Bandung a.	...	...	...	...	...	...	...	...	...	...	0111	...	...	...	...	...	...	...	...	0411	...	...	...

b – Surabaya Gubeng. n – Semerang Poncol. p – Cirebon Prujakan. ♣ – Via Jombang (d. 0228). ♥ – Via Jombang (d. 1704).

6215 JAKARTA - YOGYAKARTA - SURABAJA

PT Kereta Api

km		192	205	118	154	10	122	52	86	89	174	156	44	42	176	142	8	54	120	152	116	58	87	84
		3	3	2	3	1	12	1	12	12	3	3	1	1	3	3	1	1	2	3	2	12	12	12
	Jakarta Kota d.	...	...	...	...	...	...	...	...	...	...	♠	...	...	...	...	...	...	...	...	...	...	...	...
	Jakarta Gambir d.	...	...	...	...	0800	...	0830	...	...	...	...	1630	1740	...	...	2015	2045	...	...	...	2205	...	...
	Jakarta Pasar Senen d.	0525	...	0615	0645	|	0815	|	...	...	1015	1225	|	|	1700	1815	|	|	1900	2145	2200	|	...	...
0	**Jakarta** Jatinegara d.	|	...	|	|	|	|	|	...	...	|	|	|	|	|	|	|	|	|	|	|	|	...	...
212	Cirebon d.	0845p	...	0919	0940p	1058	1112	1140	...	...	1340p	1607	1934	2039	2021p	2108p	2312	2348	2158	0044p	0056	0108	...	...
343	Purwokerto d.	1058	...	1132	1149	1312	1329	1350	...	...	1600	1818	2136	2249	|	2325	0123	0151	0005	0249	0314	0330	...	...
370	Kroya d.	1139	...	1210	1236	|	1405	|	...	...	|	1847	|	|	◄	2356	|	|	|	0323	|	0358	...	...
445	Kutoarjo d.	1309	...	1335	1357	1447	1519	1532	...	...	1810	2025	|	0055	|	0134	0256	0324	|	0444	0500	...	...	...
508	**Yogyakarta** d.	...	...	1435	1500l	1544	...	1625	1640	...	1930l	2138l	0052	0200	|	|	0353	0415	0313	0552l	0600	...	...	0645
568	Solo Balapan d.	...	...	...	...	1635	...	...	1735	...	|	|	0144	0255	0308j	0330j	0445	...	...	...	0655	...	...	0741
663	Madiun d.	...	...	...	...	...	...	...	1933	...	2259	0030	0315	0430	0450	0519	...	...	...	...	...	...	...	0911
756	Kediri d.	...	...	...	...	...	...	...	|	...	|	0217	|	0621	0638	0703	...	...	...	...	...	...	...	|
826	Blitar d.	...	...	...	...	...	...	...	|	...	|	...	|	0725	...	0813	...	...	...	...	...	...	...	|
900	**Malang** a.	...	1605	...	...	...	...	...	|	...	|	...	0815	0906	...	1005	...	...	...	...	...	...	...	|
750	Jombang d.	...	|	...	...	...	...	...	2053	...	0026	...	0436↑	...	...	...	...	...	...	...	...	...	...	1035
831	**Surabaja** Gubeng a.	...	|	...	...	...	...	...	2155	2200	0135	...	0620↑	...	...	...	...	...	...	...	...	...	0900	1137
	Jember d.	...	2100	...	...	...	...	...	...	0150	...	...	...	...	...	...	...	...	...	...	...	...	1257	...
1140	**Banyuwangi Baru** a.	...	2350	...	...	...	...	...	...	0415	...	...	...	...	...	...	...	...	...	...	...	...	1520	...

		121	117	51	206	7	151	90		83	155	57	191	173	175	123	119	153	115	53	41	9	88	43	85
		12	2	1	3	1	3	12		12	3	12	3	3	3	1	2	3	2	1	1	1	12	1	12
Banyuwangi Baru d.	...	...	...	...	0500	...	...	2200	...	...	♦	...	...	...	...	...	...	...	...	...	...	...	0900	...	...
Jember d.	...	...	...	...	0740	...	...	0032	...	...	...	...	...	...	...	...	...	...	...	...	...	...	1130	...	...
Surabaja Gubeng d.	...	...	...	...	|	...	...	0417	...	0730	...	...	...	1200	...	...	...	...	...	...	...	...	1517	1700	1725
Jombang d.	...	...	...	...	|	...	...	...	...	0843	...	...	...	1311	...	...	...	...	...	...	...	...	...	1805	1830
Malang d.	...	...	...	...	1235	...	...	...	...	|	...	...	...	|	...	...	...	...	...	...	1330	...	...	1425↑	|
Blitar d.	...	...	...	...	...	...	...	...	...	|	...	...	...	|	...	...	...	...	...	...	1514	...	...	|	|
Kediri d.	...	...	...	...	...	...	...	...	...	|	0751	...	...	|	1404	...	...	...	...	...	1615	...	...	|	|
Madiun d.	...	...	...	...	...	...	...	...	...	1030	0950	...	...	1435	1603	...	...	...	...	...	1812	...	...	1938	2020
Solo Balapan d.	...	...	...	...	...	0800	...	...	...	1153	|	...	...	|	1835j	...	...	...	1730	...	1935	2000	...	2058	2145
Yogyakarta d.	...	...	0700	0800	...	0857	0900l	...	...	1245	1247l	...	...	|	|	...	1745	1800l	1840	2000	2030	2057	...	2200	2232
Kutoarjo d.	...	0700	0802	0856	...	0953	1014	...	...	...	1355	...	1700	1817	►	1900	|	1910	1940	2056	2126	2155	...	|	...
Kroya d.	...	0830	|	1006	...	|	1137	...	...	...	|	1530	|	|	|	2029	|	2040	2105	2205	|	|	...	|	...
Purwokerto d.	...	0910	0945	1043	...	1135	1225	...	...	...	1636	1610	1927	2024	|	2108	2052	2124	2146	2240	2324	2340	...	0038	...
Cirebon d.	...	1124	1200	1246	...	1337	1432p	...	...	...	1916	1815	2142p	2236p	0050p	2324	2305	2344p	2358	0045	0131	0144	...	0242	...
Jakarta Jatinegara a.	...	1406	1450	1523	...	1611	1717	...	...	...	|	2100	0043	0142	|	0204	0152	|	0241	0327	0409	0419	...	0525	...
Jakarta Pasar Senen a.	...	1418	1502	|	...	|	1729	...	...	...	2233	|	0056	0155	0354	0217	0205	0243	0254	|	|	|	...	|	...
Jakarta Gambir a.	...	...	...	1542	...	1627	...	...	...	...	...	2115	...	...	...	...	...	...	...	0345	0427	0437	...	0543	...
Jakarta Kota a.	...	...	...	...	...	...	...	...	...	...	...	...	...	...	...	...	...	...	...	...	...	...	...	...	...

j – Solo Jebres. l – Yogyakarta Lempuyangan. p – Cirebon Prujakan. ♠ – From Merak dep. 0830. ♦ – To Merak arr. 0235. ► – Via Semarang Tawang (d. 2112) and Tegal (d. 2335). ◄ – Via Tegal (d. 2134) and Semarang Twang (d. 0005).

6220 BANDUNG - SURABAYA

PT Kereta Api

km		180	80	6	92	112	82	50	94	96
			12	1	2	123	12	1	13	13
0	**Bandung** d.	...	0720	0830	1545	1650	1855	1930		
124	Tasikmalaya d.	0842	1016	1115	1849	2000	2154	2220	...	...
156	Banjar d.	1000	1115	1211	1942	2100	2254	2318	...	...
249	Kroya d.	|	|	1350	2118	2239	0033	0115	...	...
324	Kutoarjo d.	1322	1415	1500	2309	0031	0158	0233	...	...
387	**Yogyakarta** d.	1435l	1520	1600	0005	0138	0305	0330	0745	2045
447	Solo Balapan d.	|	1615	1651	0057	0235	0358	0424	0852	2142
542	Madiun d.	1735	...	1810	0235	0358	...	0548	1040	2320
635	Kediri d.	|	...	|	0427	0552	...	|	1237	0108
705	Blitar d.	|	...	|	0524	|	...	|	1350	0210
779	**Malang** a.	|	...	|	0705	0938	...	|	1543	0349
629	Jombang d.	2033	...	1924	...	...	...	0710	...	...
710	**Surabaya** Gubeng a.	2142	...	2019	...	...	...	0814	...	...

	79	5	179	93	81	49	91	111	95
	12	1	3	13	12	1	2	123	13
Surabaya Gubeng d.	...	0700	0810	...	...	1630	...	...	...
Jombang d.	...	0757	0920	...	...	1735	...	...	...
Malang d.	...	|	|	0820	...	|	1600	1630	2010
Blitar d.	...	|	|	1013	...	|	1747	|	2153
Kediri d.	...	|	|	1113	...	|	1850	|	2256
Madiun d.	...	0909	1108	1315	...	1912	2059	2153	0110
Solo Balapan d.	0710	1030	|	1345	1910	2032	2236	2313	0240
Yogyakarta d.	0808	1125	1410l	1438	2008	2125	2330	0015	0325
Kutoarjo d.	0910	1225	1530	1540	2108	2219	0029	0118	...
Kroya d.	|	1345	|	1708	2226	2356	0230	0306	...
Banjar d.	1208	1520	1840	...	0029	0130	0403	0440	...
Tasikmalaya d.	1300	1621	1938	...	0121	0222	0500	0537	...
Bandung a.	1548	1906	...	...	0415	0504	0748	0833	...

AUSTRALIA

Capital: **Canberra** (GMT +10). 2019 Public Holidays: Jan. 1, 26, 28, Mar. 4(WA), 11(VIC, TAS) Apr. 19, 20(not TAS, WA), 21, 25, June 3(WA), 10 (not Qld, WA), Dec. 25, 26.

Interstate trains are operated by Great Southern Rail (GSR) (www.gsr.com.au). Intrastate services are operated by Government owned agencies NSW Train Link (New South Wales, www.transportnsw.info), Queensland Rail (QR) (Queensland, www.qr.com.au), V/Line (Victoria, www.vline.com.au) and Transwa (Western Australia, www.transwa.wa.gov.au). Unless indicated all trains convey first and second class seated accommodation. On GSR and some overnight trains the first class accommodation is usually a private compartment which converts to sleeping berths for night time travel. The exact offering varies by operator and by train. Most longer distance trains also convey a refreshment facility. Due to the low frequency of trains reservations are recommended, even if they are not always compulsory. NSW Train Link offer the Discovery Pass which gives either 14 day, 1 month, 3 months or 6 months unlimited travel on their rail and coach network and are available for travel in either economy or premium. Prices range from AU$ 232 for a 14 day economy pass to AU$ 550 for a 6 month premium pass. QR have the Explorer Pass which offers either 1 month (AU$ 299) or 2 months (AU$ 389) unlimited travel on their services. They also offer the Costal Pass for unlimited travel in one direction between Brisbane and Cairns or vice versa. Prices 1 month AU$ 209, 2 months AU$ 289. Reservations are required for all journeys and supplements may also be payable. See www.acprail.com

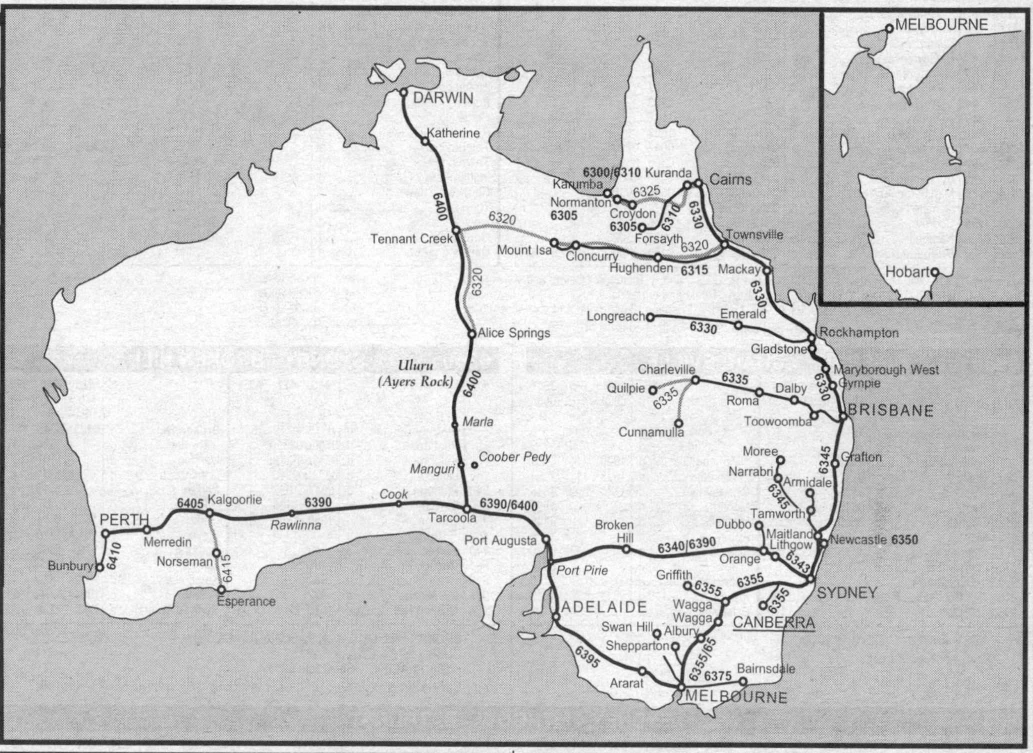

Queensland Rail — CAIRNS - KURANDA — 6300

km		3K30 2a	3K32 2a		3C61 2a	3C65 2a
0	**Cairns** d.	0830	0930	**Kuranda** d.	1400	1530
	Freshwater d.	0850	0950	Freshwater d.	1532	1702
33	**Kuranda** a.	1025	1125	**Cairns** a.	1555	1725

a – Not May 2, 3, June 13, 14, 20, 21, Oct. 17, 18, 31, Nov. 1, 7, 8.

Queensland Rail — NORMANTON - CROYDON — 6305

km		③ A			④ A	
0	**Normanton** d.	0830	...	**Croydon** d.	0830	...
90	Blackbull a.	1115	...	Blackbull a.	1015	...
152	**Croydon** a.	1330	...	**Normanton** a.	1330	...

A – GULFLANDER – (2) Services usually suspended mid Dec. - mid Feb.

CKST — CAIRNS - FORSAYTH — 6310

km		4 ③B	4 ④B		5 ⑤B	5 ⑥B
0	**Cairns** d.	0630	...	**Forsayth** d.	0830	...
33	Kuranda d.	0810	...	Einasleigh d.	1215	...
74	Mareeba d.	0930	...	Mount Suprise a.	1415	...
194	Almaden a.	1315	...	Mount Suprise d.	...	0815
194	Almaden d.	...	0800	Almaden a.	...	1145
302	Mount Suprise a.	...	1130	Almaden d.	...	1215
302	Mount Suprise d.	...	1215	Mareeba d.	...	|
357	Einasleigh d.	...	1445	Kuranda a.	...	1650
423	**Forsayth** a.	...	1730	**Cairns** a.	...	1830

B – SAVANNAHLANDER – (2). Mar. 1 - Dec. 13.
Operator: Cairns Kuranda Steam Ltd ✆ +61 7 4053 6848.

Queensland Rail — TOWNSVILLE - MOUNT ISA — 6315

km		3M34 ③⑥C			3231 ④⑦C	
0	**Townsville** d.	1240	...	**Mount Isa** d.	1330	...
138	Charters Towers d.	1540	...	Duchess d.	1515	...
388	Hughenden d.	2020	...	Cl oncurry d.	1745	...
502	Richmond d.	2245	...	Julia Creek d.	2100	...
648	Julia Creek d.	0210	...	Richmond d.	0005	...
780	Cloncurry d.	0520	...	Hughenden d.	0240	...
890	Duchess d.	0745	...	Charters Towers d.	0705	...
977	**Mount Isa** a.	0935	...	**Townsville** a.	1010	...

C – INLANDER – (2) and 🍸 Townsville - Mount Isa and v.v. Ⓡ.

Greyhound — TOWNSVILLE - TENNANT CREEK — 6320

km		489 🚌③	882 D		880 E	849 🚌④
0	**Townsville** d.	0700	...	**Alice Springs** d.	0715	...
135	Charters Towers d.	0830	...	Barrow Creek d	1105	...
378	Hughenden d.	1205	...	**Tennant Creek** d.	1350	1415
490	Richmond d.	1325	...	Barkly Homestead d.	...	1720
634	Julia Creek d.	1455	...	Camooweal d.	...	2120
768	Cloncurry d.	1625	...	**Mount Isa** a.	...	2320
886	**Mount Isa** a.	1755	...	**Mount Isa** d.	...	2320
886	**Mount Isa** d.	1835	...	Cloncurry d.	...	0050
1074	Camooweal d.	2035	...	Julia Creek d.	...	0220
1353	Barkly Homestead d.	2345	...	Richmond d.	...	0355
1547	**Tennant Creek** a.	0215	0310	Hughenden d.	...	0555
1771	Barrow Creek d.	...	0530	Charters Towers d.	...	0850
2072	**Alice Springs** a.	...	0915	**Townsville** a.	...	1025

D – From Darwin dep. 1140. E – To Darwin arr. 1720.
Operator: Greyhound Australia ✆ 07 3258 1600.

Trans North Bus — CAIRNS - KARUMBA — 6325

km		🚌 ①③⑤			🚌 ②④⑥	
0	**Cairns** Central ◇ d.	0630	...	**Karumba** d.	0630	...
33	Kuranda ◇ d.	0705	...	Normanton d.	0725	...
75	Mareeba d.	0740	...	Croydon d.	0925	...
109	Atherton d.	0820	...	Georgetown d.	1055	...
140	Herberton d.	0835	...	Mount Surprise d.	1240	...
160	Ravenshoe d.	0945	...	Undara d.	1305	...
211	Mount Garnet d.	1015	...	Mount Garnet d.	1355	...
287	Undara d.	1105	...	Ravenshoe d.	1450	...
321	Mount Surprise d.	1130	...	Herberton d.	1520	...
422	Georgetown d.	1325	...	Atherton d.	1540	...
579	Croydon d.	1505	...	Mareeba d.	1615	...
744	Normanton d.	1645	...	Kuranda ◇ d.	1640	...
820	**Karumba** a.	1730	...	**Cairns** Central ◇ a.	1730	...

◇ – Additional service available Cairns – Kuranda and v.v.
Operator: Trans North Bus and Coach ✆ 07 4095 8644.

6330 CAIRNS, TOWNSVILLE and LONGREACH - BRISBANE

Queensland Rail

km	km			V9Q4	Q904		A960	Q902			
				◄	⊡		①④				
				A	B		C	B			
0		**Cairns**	d.	0835	...	...	...	...	...	...	...
23		Gordonvale	d.	0901	...	...	...	...	...	...	...
87		Innisfail	d.	1018	...	...	...	...	...	...	...
135		Tully	d.	1125	...	...	...	...	...	...	...
178		Cardwell	d.	1209	...	...	...	...	...	...	...
232		Ingham	d.	1301	...	...	...	...	...	...	...
340		**Townsville**	a.	1439	...	...	...	...	...	...	...
340		**Townsville**	d.	1454	...	...	...	...	...	...	...
421		Ayr	d.	1557	...	...	...	...	...	...	...
432		Home Hill	d.	1614	...	...	...	...	...	...	...
531		Bowen	d.	1720	...	...	...	...	...	...	...
596		Proserpine	d.	1811	...	...	...	...	...	...	...
717		Mackay	d.	1956	...	...	...	...	...	...	...
754		Sarina	d.	2027	...	...	...	...	...	...	...
869		St Lawrence	d.	2150	...	...	...	...	...	...	...
	0	**Longreach**	d.	|	...	...	1000	...	...	...	...
	108	Barcaldine	d.	|	...	...	1227	...	...	...	...
	194	Jericho	d.	|	...	...	1403	...	...	...	...
	249	Alpha	d.	|	...	...	1518	...	...	...	...
	422	Emerald	d.	|	...	...	1933	...	...	...	...
1042	687	Rockhampton	d.	0039	...	...	0017	0710	...	...	...
1152	797	Gladstone	d.	0202	...	...	0308	0826	...	...	...
1330	975	Bundaberg	d.	0352	0515	...	0526	1005	...	...	...
1414	1059	Maryborough West	d.	0450	0601	...	0635	1058	...	...	...
1507	1152	Gympie North	d.	0608	0701	...	0811	1205	...	...	...
1550	1195	Cooroy	d.	0642	0737	...	0856	1240	...	...	...
1575	1220	Nambour	d.	0705	0757	...	0925	1302	...	...	...
1681	1326	**Brisbane** Roma St	a.	0920	0955	...	1155	1450	...	...	...

		Q301		AW57	VCQ5			Q303	AW57	
		◇		⑥	►	②⑦		☆	②	
		B		C	A	B		B	C	
Brisbane Roma St	d.	1100	...	1355	1545	1655	...	1655	1810	...
Nambour	d.	1235	...	1619	1731	1838	...	1838	2023	...
Cooroy	d.	1258	...	1649	1754	1858	...	1858	2049	...
Gympie North	d.	1337	...	1745	1828	1929	...	1929	2145	...
Maryborough West	d.	1440	...	1905	1929	2028	...	2028	2305	...
Bundaberg	d.	1531	...	2036	2022	2125	...	2125	0013	...
Gladstone	d.	1712	...	2309	2223	2317	...	...	0246	...
Rockhampton	d.	1845	...	0103	0011	0030	...	...	0440	...
Emerald	d.	...	...	0602	|	...	...	...	0940	...
Alpha	d.	...	...	1012	|	...	...	...	1350	...
Jericho	d.	...	...	1121	|	...	...	...	1459	...
Barcaldine	d.	...	...	1316	|	...	...	...	1655	...
Longreach	a.	...	...	1540	|	...	...	...	1920	...
St Lawrence	d.	...	...	...	0230	...	...	...	...	...
Sarina	d.	...	...	...	0400	...	...	...	...	...
Mackay	d.	...	...	...	0454	...	...	...	...	...
Prosperine	d.	...	...	...	0632	...	...	...	...	...
Bowen	d.	...	...	...	0709	...	...	...	...	...
Home Hill	d.	...	...	...	0818	...	...	...	...	...
Ayr	d.	...	...	...	0832	...	...	...	...	...
Townsville	a.	...	...	...	0938	...	...	...	...	...
Townsville	d.	...	...	...	0953	...	...	...	...	...
Ingham	d.	...	...	...	1126	...	...	...	...	...
Cardwell	d.	...	...	...	1300	...	...	...	...	...
Tully	d.	...	...	...	1357	...	...	...	...	...
Innisfail	d.	...	...	...	1446	...	...	...	...	...
Gordonvale	d.	...	...	...	1601	...	...	...	...	...
Cairns	a.	...	...	...	1630	...	...	...	...	...

A – SPIRIT OF QUEENSLAND TILT TRAIN – R, (2) and 🍸 Brisbane - Cairns and v.v.
B – TILT TRAIN – (12) and 🍸 Brisbane - Bundaberg, Rockhampton and v.v.
C – SPIRIT OF THE OUTBACK – 1cl ✕, (2) and 🍸 Brisbane - Longreach and v.v.
R – RailBed – This is a seat by day and converts to a lie-flat bed at night.

► – ①②③⑤⑥.
◄ – ①③④⑤⑦.
⊡ – ①②④⑤⑥.
☆ – ①③④⑤.
◇ – ①②④⑤⑥⑦.

6335 BRISBANE - CHARLEVILLE

Queensland Rail

km			9386	🚌	🚌
			②④	③⑤	③⑤
			D		
0	**Brisbane** ‡	d.	1915	...	...
38	Ipswich	d.	2013	...	...
161	Toowoomba	d.	2325	...	...
244	Dalby	d.	0117	...	...
371	Miles	d.	0325	...	...
512	Roma	d.	0615	...	...
597	Mitchell	d.	0805	...	...
687	Morven	d.	0955	...	...
777	**Charleville**	a.	1145	1155	1155
875	Wyandra	a.	...	1315	|
972	Cunnamulla	a.	...	1425	|
876	Cooladdi	a.	...	...	1305
998	Quilpie	a.	...	...	1430

		🚌	🚌	3907
		③⑤	③⑤	③⑤
				D
Quilpie	d.	...	1500	...
Cooladdi	d.	...	1640	...
Cunnamulla	d.	1500	|	...
Wyandra	d.	1625	|	...
Charleville	d.	1735	1740	1815
Morven	d.	...	...	1955
Mitchell	d.	...	...	2145
Roma	d.	...	...	2335
Miles	d.	...	...	0210
Dalby	d.	...	...	0447
Toowoomba	d.	...	...	0700
Ipswich	d.	...	...	1012
Brisbane ‡	a.	...	...	1125

D – WESTLANDER – (2) and 🍸. R.
‡ – Brisbane **Roma Street**.

6340 SYDNEY - BROKEN HILL

NSW Train Link

km			445	427	WE1
			①		③
			E	F	G
0	**Sydney** Central	d.	0618	0719	1500
	Penrith	d.	0705u	0805u	|
	Katoomba	d.	0759u	0900u	|
155	Lithgow	d.	0839u	0940	|
240	Bathurst	d.	0947	1052	|
290	Blayney	d.	1035	1138	|
323	Orange	d.	1059	1202	|
462	**Dubbo**	a.	|	1345	|
446	Parkes	d.	1248	|	|
546	Condobolin	d.	1400	|	|
816	Ivanhoe	d.	1631	|	|
1017	Menindee	d.	1822	|	|
1125	**Broken Hill**	a.	1910	2245*	0600

		428	446	WE2
			②	②
		F	E	G
Broken Hill	d.	0345*	0745	1855
Menindee	d.	|	0924	|
Ivanhoe	d.	|	1107	|
Condobolin	d.	|	1341	|
Parkes	d.	|	1443	|
Dubbo	d.	1415	|	|
Orange	d.	1552	1644	|
Blayney	d.	1619	1716	|
Bathurst	d.	1705	1802	|
Lithgow	d.	1820	1921s	|
Katoomba	d.	1902s	2002s	|
Penrith	d.	1954s	2054s	|
Sydney Central	a.	2048	2138	1200

E – BROKEN HILL OUTBACK EXPLORER – (2) and 🍸.
F – DUBBO XPT – (12) and 🍸.
G – INDIAN PACIFIC – See Table **6390**.
s – Calls to set down only. **u** – Calls to pick up only. * – Connection by 🚌.

6343 SYDNEY - LITHGOW - BATHURST

Sydney Trains, NSW Train Link

km			505	507		509	529	525	527	503	501	533	4501
			Ⓐ	Ⓐ		Ⓐ	Ⓒ	Ⓐ	†	†	Ⓐ	Ⓐ	
					A								
0	**Sydney** Central	d.	0423	0848	1018	1218	1224	1418	1424	1624	1617	1717	1747
55	Penrith **u**	d.	0510	0936	1106	1305	1314	1505	1513	1713	1706	1806	1843
110	Katoomba	d.	0621	1032	1217	1416	1425	1616	1624	1824	1810	1910	1938
127	Mount Victoria	d.	0641	1050	1237	1436	1445	1636	1644	1844	1830	1932	1958
155	**Lithgow**	a.	0710	1117	1305	1505	1515	1705	1715	1915	1829	2004	2024
240	**Bathurst**	a.	0815*	1227*	...	1625*	1625*	1820*	1820*	2020*	2005*	2119*	2132

			4502	504		502	506	508	534	536	538	548
		Ⓐ	Ⓐ	Ⓐ	Ⓒ	Ⓐ	Ⓐ	Ⓐ	Ⓐ	†	Ⓐ	†
		B										
Bathurst	d.	...	0546	0539*	0740	0809*	1005*	1155*	1410*	1435*	1815*	1750*
Lithgow	d.	0300	0655	0724	0847	0924	1124	1318	1530	1548	1930	1948
Mount Victoria	d.	0331	0723	0754	0915	0954	1154	1346	1600	1617	2000	2017
Katoomba	d.	0350	0740	0813	0932	1013	1213	1403	1619	1637	2019	2037
Penrith	d.	0500	0838s	0924	1028s	1123	1323	1459	1729	1750	2129	2151
Sydney Central	a.	0551	0927	1015	1118	1215	1415	1548	1821	1841	2221	2241

A – Additional services: Ⓐ 0018, 0623, 0818, 1518, 1833, 2018, 2218; Ⓒ 0024, 0424, 0624, 0824, 1024, 1424, 1624, 1824, 2024, 2224.
B – Additional services: Ⓐ 0415, 0508, 0538, 0608, 1318, 1330, 1730, 2130; Ⓒ 0349, 0549, 0648, 0748, 0948, 1148, 1348, 1548, 1748, 1948, 2219.
Note: Additional services operate between Sydney and Katoomba and Sydney and Mount Victoria.
s – Calls to set down only. **u** – Calls to pick up only. * – Connection by 🚌.

6345 BRISBANE, ARMIDALE and MOREE - SYDNEY

NSW Train Link

km	km			036	244	224	032	2144	034	2138	2142
								Ⓐ		Ⓐ	
				H	J	K	L		M		b
0		**Brisbane** Roma Street	d.	...	...	...	0555	...	1500*	...	...
182		Casino	d.	...	...	...	0820	...	1930	...	...
291		Grafton City	d.	0515	...	...	0953	...	2058	...	...
379		Coffs Harbour	d.	0626	...	...	1105	...	2210	...	...
		Nambucca Heads	d.	0708	...	...	1147	...	2251r	...	...
		Macksville	d.	0721	...	...	1200	...	2305r	...	...
483		Kempsey	d.	0805	...	...	1243	...	2347	...	...
532		Wauchope	d.	0844	...	...	1322	...	0024	...	...
608		Taree	d.	0952	...	...	1441	...	0131	...	...
	0	**Armidale**	d.	|	...	0840	|	...	|	...	...
	124	Tamworth	d.	|	...	1027	|	...	|	...	...
	◐	**Moree**	d.	|	0805	|	|	...	|	...	...
	◐	Narrabri	d.	|	0910	|	|	...	|	...	...
	◐	Gunnedah	d.	|	1014	|	|	...	|	...	...
	168	Werris Creek	d.	|	1107	1107	|	...	|	...	...
	264	Scone	d.	|	1228	1228	|	...	|	...	...
	290	Muswellbrook	d.	|	1248	1248	|	...	|	...	...
794	387	Maitland	d.	1253	1355	1355	1730	...	0412	...	...
824	416	Broadmeadow	d.	1319	1418	1418	1752	1839	0434	0930	1030
897	499	Gosford	d.	1420s	1520s	1520s	1857s	1959s	0540s	1037s	1137s
953	545	Hornsby	d.	1504s	1603s	1603s	1938s	2049s	0622s	1122s	1222s
987	579	**Sydney** Central	a.	1544	1639a	1639a	2012	2126	0701	1159	1259

		033	243	223	035	031		2157		
		M	J	K	H	L		Ⓐ		
Sydney Central	d.	0708	0930	0930	1141	1441	...	1515	...	...
Hornsby	d.	0747u	1003u	1003u	1216u	1517u	...	1551u	...	...
Gosford	d.	0829u	1044u	1044u	1258u	1600u	...	1634u	...	...
Broadmeadow	d.	0933	1145	1145	1404	1704	...	1741	...	...
Maitland	d.	0959	1210	1210	1430	1727	...	...	...	...
Muswellbrook	d.	|	1316	1316	|	|	...	...	...	...
Scone	d.	|	1337	1337	|	|	...	...	...	...
Werris Creek	d.	|	1507	1457	|	|	...	...	...	...
Gunnedah	d.	|	1545	|	|	|	...	...	...	...
Narrabri	a.	|	1652	|	|	|	...	...	...	...
Moree	a.	|	1800	|	|	|	...	...	...	...
Tamworth	a.	|	...	1537	|	|	...	...	...	...
Armidale	a.	|	...	1735	|	|	...	...	...	...
Taree	d.	1241	...	...	1725	2008	...	...	...	...
Wauchope	d.	1348	...	...	1831	2113	...	...	...	...
Kempsey	d.	1426	...	...	1910	2152	...	...	...	...
Macksville	d.	1507	...	...	1955	2234	...	...	...	...
Nambucca Heads	a.	1519	...	...	2009	2305*	...	...	...	...
Coffs Harbour	a.	1558	...	...	2050	2335	...	...	...	...
Grafton City	d.	1712	...	...	2215	0049	...	...	...	...
Casino	a.	1841	...	...	...	0219	...	...	...	...
Brisbane Roma Street	a.	2234*	...	...	...	0453	...	...	...	...

H – GRAFTON XPT – (12). R.
J – MOREE EXPLORER – (12) and 🍸. R.
K – ARMIDALE XPLORER – (12) and 🍸. R.
L – BRISBANE XPT – (2) Brisbane - Sydney; 1 cl., (2) Sydney - Brisbane. R.
M – CASINO XPT – 1 cl., (2) Casino - Sydney; (12) Sydney - Casino. R.

a – Arrives 1645 on Ⓒ. **b** – Runs 30 mins later on Ⓒ. **r** – Calls on request.
s – Calls to set down only. **u** – Calls to pick up only. * – Connection by 🚌.
Note: During NSW Daylight Savings services will arrive and depart QLD locations 1 hour earlier than shown.
◐ – Moree - Narrabri: *97 km*. Moree - Gunnedah: *190 km*. Moree - Werris Creek: *255 km*

NEWCASTLE - SYDNEY 6350

Sydney Trains

km			Ⓐ	Ⓐ	Ⓐ	Ⓐ	Ⓐ	Ⓐ	Ⓐ	Ⓐ	Ⓐ	Ⓐ	Ⓐ		Ⓐ	Ⓐ	Ⓐ	Ⓐ	Ⓐ	Ⓐ	Ⓐ	Ⓐ	Ⓐ	Ⓐ	Ⓐ
0	**Newcastle** Interchange d.	Ⓐ	0230	0423	0502	0520	0548	0620	0642	0724	0735	0824	0835	and at the same	1324	1334	1420	1434	1512	1534	1624	1634	1724	1824	1834
	Hamilton d.		0232	0426	0504	0523	0550	0623	0645	0727	0738	0827	0838	minutes	1327	1337	1422	1438	1515	1537	1627	1638	1727	1827	1838
88	Gosford d.		0358	0537	0609	0634	0704	0734	0807	0837	0902	0937	1002	past each	1437	1501	1533	1602	1638	1701	1738	1802	1838	1937	2005
168	**Sydney Central** a.		0528	0657	0726	0757	0827	0857	0928	0959	1029	1059	1129	hour until	1557	1629	1659	1729	1759	1829	1859	1929	1959	2059	2129

	Ⓐ	Ⓐ	Ⓐ	Ⓐ		Ⓒ	Ⓒ	Ⓒ	Ⓒ	Ⓒ	Ⓒ	Ⓒ	Ⓒ	Ⓒ	Ⓒ	Ⓒ	Ⓒ	Ⓒ	Ⓒ	⑥	⑦	Ⓒ	Ⓒ	Ⓒ	Ⓒ	Ⓒ
Newcastle Interchange d.	1924	1945	2046	2141	Ⓒ	0246	0348	0453	0543	0653	0743	0853	0943	1053	1143	1253	1343	1453	1543	1653	1656	1755	1853	1929	2029	2156
Hamilton d.	1927	1948	2048	2144		0248	0350	0455	0545	0655	0745	0855	0945	1055	1145	1255	1345	1455	1545	1655	1658	1757	1855	1931	2031	2158
Gosford d.	2038	2114	2213	2310		0414	0512	0607	0706	0807	0906	1006	1106	1206	1306	1406	1506	1606	1706	1806	1807	1918	2014	2057	2157	2324
Sydney Central a.	2159	2239	2339	0039		0544	0644	0729	0829	0929	1029	1129	1229	1329	1429	1529	1629	1729	1829	1929	1929	2035	2129	2229	2329	0101

		Ⓐ	Ⓐ	Ⓐ	Ⓐ	Ⓐ	Ⓐ	Ⓐ	Ⓐ	Ⓐ	Ⓐ		Ⓐ	Ⓐ	Ⓐ	Ⓐ	Ⓐ	Ⓐ	Ⓐ	Ⓐ	Ⓐ	Ⓐ	Ⓐ	Ⓐ
Sydney Central d.	Ⓐ	0147	0345	0445	0515	0545	0615	0645	0715	0745	0815	and at the same	1315	1345	1415	1515	1550	1620	1635	1720	1750	1820	1915	2015
Gosford d.		0311	0512	0612	0635	0713	0736	0813	0840	0914	0936	minutes	1436	1514	1537	1636	1707	1741	1800	1839	1910	1941	2036	2136
Hamilton a.		0436	0636	0736	0746	0837	0859	0937	0955	1038	1046	past each	1559	1642	1704	1746	1808	1850	1926	1951	2025	2053	2158	2258
Newcastle Interchange a.		0440	0640	0740	0750	0841	0903	0941	0959	1042	1051	hour until	1602	1645	1708	1749	1817	1855	1930	1955	2029	2057	2201	2302

	Ⓐ	Ⓐ	Ⓐ	Ⓐ		⑥	Ⓒ	Ⓒ	Ⓒ	Ⓒ	Ⓒ	Ⓒ	Ⓒ	Ⓒ	Ⓒ	Ⓒ	Ⓒ	Ⓒ	Ⓒ	Ⓒ	Ⓒ	Ⓒ	Ⓒ	Ⓒ	Ⓒ
Sydney Central d.	2115	2148	2248	2348	Ⓒ	0147	0448	0546	0716	0818	0918	1018	1118	1218	1318	1418	1518	1618	1716	1818	1918	2018	2148	2248	2348
Gosford d.	2236	2316	0019	0117		0311	0618	0713	0839	0939	1039	1139	1239	1339	1439	1539	1639	1739	1839	1939	2039	2144	2316	0016	0116
Hamilton a.	2358	0042	0146	0244		0436	0743	...	0950	1100	1150	1300	1350	1500	1550	1700	1750	1900	1950	2100	2155	2310	0040	0140	0240
Newcastle Interchange a.	0001	0046	0150	0248		0440	0747	...	0954	1104	1154	1304	1354	1504	1554	1704	1754	1904	1954	2104	2159	2314	0044	0144	0244

Operator: Sydney Trains ✆ 02 4907 7500.

SYDNEY - CANBERRA, GRIFFITH and MELBOURNE 6355

NSW Train Link/Vline

km		631 ⑥⑦A	641 ⑥B	631 ⒶA	Vline 🚌	NSW 🚌	623 C	633 ⒶA	633 ⑥⑦A	635 ⑥⑦A	635 ⒶA	621 D
0	**Sydney** Central d.	0705	0705	0712	...	...	0740	1201	1206	1736	1742	2042b
143	Moss Vale d.	0847	0847	0854	...	...	0922b	1343	1348	1918	1940	2224b
222	Goulburn d.	0939	0954	0944	...	...	1013b	1432	1437	2007	2029	2314
318	Queanbeyan d.	1101	|	1104	...	...	|	1553	1558	2128	2150	|
326	**Canberra** a.	1116	|	1120	0800t	0937t	|	1608	1613	2143	2203	|
320	Yass Junction d.	...	1103	...	0845u	1045	1120	...	...	...	...	0022r
383	Harden d.	...	1153r	...	|	1153	1211r	...	...	...	...	0112r
427	Cootamundra d.	...	1226	...	|	1222	1244	...	...	...	...	0147
483	Junee d.	...	1307	...	|	|	1325	...	...	...	...	0225
580	Narrandera d.	...	1421	...	g	▬	|	...	...	...	...	|
658	**Griffith** a.	...	1525	...	|	Vline	|	...	...	...	...	|
518	Wagga Wagga a.	...	...	...	|	...	1354	...	...	...	...	0252
547	The Rock d.	...	...	...	|	...	1414r	...	...	...	...	0310r
594	Culcairn d.	...	...	...	|	...	1441r	...	...	...	...	0334r
643	**Albury** 6365 a.	...	...	...	1235v	1254v	1511	...	...	...	...	0408
727	Wangaratta 6365 d.	...	...	...	...	1339	1553	...	...	...	...	0450
765	Benalla 6365 d.	...	...	...	...	1404	1617	...	...	...	...	0514
961	**Melbourne** S Cross a.	...	...	...	...	1640	1830	...	...	...	...	0730

	632 A	642 ⑦B	634 ⑦A	634 ⒶA	Vline 🚌	Vline	624 C	NSW 🚌	636 ⑥⑦A	636 ⒶA	622 D
Melbourne S Cross d.	...	...	...	...	0705	...	0830	...	...	...	1950
Benalla 6365 d.	...	...	...	...	0930	...	1041	...	...	...	2154
Wangaratta 6365 d.	...	...	...	...	0955	...	1106	...	...	...	2220
Albury 6365 d.	...	...	...	...	1037v	1100v	1149	...	...	...	2305
Culcairn d.	...	...	...	...	...	|	1221r	...	...	...	2334r
The Rock d.	...	...	...	...	...	|	1249r	...	...	...	0002r
Wagga Wagga d.	...	...	...	...	...	|	1307	...	...	...	0022
Griffith d.	...	0730	...	...	...	|	|	...	...	...	|
Narrandera d.	...	0832	...	...	...	g	|	...	...	...	|
Junee d.	...	0949	...	...	...	|	1351	...	...	...	0048
Cootamundra d.	...	1040	...	...	...	|	1438	1450	...	...	0135
Harden d.	...	1116	...	...	...	|	1514r	1521	...	...	0214r
Yass Junction d.	...	1207	...	...	...	1450s	1605	1620	...	...	0305r
Canberra d.	0645	|	1150	1200	...	1535t	|	1722t	1715	1729	|
Queanbeyan d.	0654	|	1159	1209	...	...	|	...	1724	1738	|
Goulburn d.	0812	1320	1317	1327	...	...	1715	...	1842	1856	0413
Moss Vale d.	0904	1419	1419	1419	...	...	1805	...	1934	1948	0504
Sydney Central a.	1101b	1615	1615	1615	...	...	1959	...	2131	2143	0659

A – CANBERRA XPLORER – [12] and 🍸.
B – GRIFFITH XPLORER – [12] and 🍸.
C – MELBOURNE XPT – [12] and 🍸.
D – MELBOURNE XPT – 🛏 1 cl., [12] and ✕.
b – 3 - 5 mins earlier on ⑥⑦.
g – Via Gundagai.
r – Calls on request.
t – Canberra Civic Centre.
v – Timings at Wodonga.

MELBOURNE - SHEPPARTON 6360

V/Line

km		①–⑤	⑥⑦	①–⑤	①–⑤	⑥⑦	①–⑤	⑥⑦ A	①–⑤	①–⑤	⑥⑦
0	**Melbourne** S Cross d.	0553	0912	0933	1252	1252	1432	1632	1631	1908	1832
99	Seymour ☛ a.	0726	1034	1055	1411	1413	1554	1752	1807	2030	1952
99	Seymour d.	0736	1039	1100	1416	1418	*1610**	*1800**	1812	2035	1957
147	Murchison East d.	0811	1114	1135	1451	1453	*1700**	|	1847	2110	2032
	Murchison d.	|	|	|	|	|	*1703**	*1851**	|	|	|
182	**Shepparton** a.	0843	1149	1210	1525	1528	*1735**	*1925**	1924	2144	2107

	①–⑤	①–⑤	⑥⑦	①–⑤ B	①–⑤	⑥⑦	①–⑤	⑥⑦	①–⑤	⑤
Shepparton d.	0510	0625	0713	*0825**	*1040**	1234	1246	1602	1603	*1840**
Murchison d.	|	|	|	*0855**	*1107**	|	|	|	|	*1912**
Murchison East d.	0538	0653	0741	|	|	1302	1313	1630	1630	|
Seymour a.	0615	0730	0818	*0955**	*1200**	1339	1350	1707	1707	*2005**
Seymour ☛ d.	0617	0732	0820	1014	1214	1341	1352	1708	1709	2020
Melbourne S Cross a.	0759	0910	0947	1134	1335	1509	1515	1829	1835	2144

☛ Additional trains are available Melbourne - Seymour and v.v.
A – Additional trips on ①–⑤: 0711, 1032, 1737.
B – Additional trips on ①–⑤: 0735, 1655. ⑥⑦ 0810, 1430.
* – By 🚌.

MELBOURNE - ALBURY 6365

V/Line

km			C		①–⑤		D				
0	**Melbourne** S Cross d.	0705	0830	1205	1432	1802	1950	...	...	...	...
99	Seymour ☛ a.	0824	|	1319	1554	1930	|	...	...	...	...
99	Seymour d.	0826	0948u	1321	*1605**	1932	2059u	...	...	...	...
196	Benalla d.	0930	1041	1425	*1720**	2036	2154	...	...	...	...
234	Wangaratta d.	0955	1106	1450	*1755**	2101	2220	...	...	...	...
301	Wodonga d.	1039	|	1534	*1840**	2145	|	...	...	...	...
318	**Albury** a.	1100	1149	1555	*1850**	2205	2305	...	...	...	...

	D		①–⑤		C					
Albury d.	0403	0635	*0900**	1245	1511	1720	...	...	...	...
Wodonga d.	|	0644	*0910**	1254	|	1729	...	...	...	...
Wangaratta d.	0445	0729	*1000**	1339	1553	1814	...	...	...	...
Benalla d.	0509	0754	*1035**	1404	1617	1839	...	...	...	...
Seymour a.	|	0857	*1200**	1507	|	1942	...	...	...	...
Seymour ☛ d.	0605s	0859	1214	1509	1711s	1944	...	...	...	...
Melbourne S Cross a.	0725	1035	1335	1640	1830	2145	...	...	...	...

C – MELBOURNE XPT – [12] and 🍸 Sydney Central - Melbourne Southern Cross and v.v.
D – MELBOURNE XPT – 🛏 1 cl., [12] and ✕ Sydney Central - Melbourne Southern Cross and v.v.
* – By 🚌.
☛ Additional trains are available Melbourne - Seymour and v.v.

MELBOURNE - WARRNAMBOOL 6370

V/Line

km		⑥⑦	①–⑤		⑥⑦	①–⑤		①–⑤	①–⑤	⑥⑦	①–⑤
0	**Melbourne** S Cross d.	0700	0730	...	1300	1305	...	1510	1713	1900	1913
73	Geelong ☛ a.	0811	0829	...	1406	1403	...	1608	1818	1958	2013
73	Geelong d.	0816	0831	...	1411	1408	...	1620*	1820	2003	2018
133	Colac d.	0917	0934	...	1514	1517	...	1747*	1925	2104	2123
267	**Warrnambool** a.	1047	1109	...	1635	1637	...	...	2058	2225	2248

	①–⑤	①–⑤	⑥⑦	①–⑤	⑥⑦	①–⑤			⑥⑦	①–⑤
Warrnambool d.	...	0606	0737	0925	1147	1207	...	...	1734	1742
Colac d.	0615*	0723	0853	1047	1303	1323	...	...	1850	1858
Geelong a.	0748	0830	1010	1154	1410	1427	...	...	1958	2014
Geelong ☛ d.	0750	0832	1012	1156	1412	1429	...	...	2000	2016
Melbourne S Cross a.	0848	0931	1121	1255	1523	1525	...	...	2109	2115

☛ Additional trains are available Melbourne - Geelong and v.v.
* – By 🚌.

MELBOURNE - TRARALGON - BAIRNSDALE 6375

V/Line

km		①–⑤ Ⓡ	⑥ Ⓡ	⑦ Ⓡ	⑦ Ⓡ C	⑥ Ⓡ	①–⑤ Ⓡ	⑥⑦	①–⑤	⑥⑦ Ⓡ	①–⑤ Ⓡ
0	**Melbourne** S Cross d.	0720	0725	0804	1025	1156	1320	1356	1520	1816	1834
32	Dandenong d.	0805u	0800u	0840u	1101u	1239u	1403u	1439u	1603u	1859u	1916u
101	Warragul d.	0857	0859	0930	1153	1333	1452	1534	1658	1952	2010
131	Moe d.	0916	0918	0949	1214	1352	1506	1553	1716	2011	2029
145	Morwell d.	0931	0931	1002	1224	1404	1526	1604	1731	2024	2043
159	**Traralgon** ☛ d.	0942	0941	1015	1238	1416	1538	*1635**	*1750**	2037	2055
207	Sale d.	1017	1019	1050	*1400**	1451	1613	*1725**	*1835**	2112	2130
276	**Bairnsdale** a.	1111	1112	1143	*1500**	1541	1707	...	...	2205	2222

	①–⑤ Ⓡ	⑥ Ⓡ	①–⑤ B	⑦ Ⓡ	⑥ Ⓡ	①–⑤ Ⓡ	⑦ Ⓡ A	⑥	⑥⑦ Ⓡ	①–⑤ Ⓡ
Bairnsdale d.	0608	0628	...	0741	1222	1245	1255*	...	1637	1818
Sale d.	0657	0718	0755*	0831	1312	1335	1411	1530*	1727	1908
Traralgon ☛ d.	0734	0753	0919	0908	1348	1414	1451	1639	1803	1945
Morwell d.	0745	0804	0928	0919	1357	1423	1500	1648	1812	1954
Moe d.	0757	0815	0938	0930	1413	1432	1511	1657	1828	2004
Warragul d.	0816	0834	0957	0949	1432	1455	1533	1719	1847	2022
Dandenong d.	0909s	0929s	1049s	1045s	1524s	1549s	1626s	1819s	1939s	2121s
Melbourne S Cross a.	0957	1006	1137	1130	1610	1635	1710	1900	2019	2208

A – Additional trips on ①–⑤: 0435, 1510.
B – Additional trip on ①–⑤: 0920.
C – Additional trips on ①–⑤: 0813, 1658.
* – By 🚌.
☛ Additional trains are available Melbourne - Traralgon and v.v.

6380 MELBOURNE - BENDIGO - SWAN HILL and ECHUCA — V/Line

km		①-⑤	①-⑤ R🍷	⑥⑦ R🍷	⑥⑦ R	①-⑤	⑥⑦	①-⑤	⑥⑦	①-⑤	①③⑤ 🚌	②④ 🚌	①-⑤ R	⑥⑦	①-⑤ R🍷	⑥⑦ R🍷	①-⑤	⑤ 🚌	①-⑤	⑥⑦	①-⑤	⑥	①-⑤	⑥⑦	①-⑤	⑥
0	**Melbourne** S Cross .. d.	0616	0741	0800	0902	1020	1022	1220	1222	1320	...	...	1520	1720	1825	1835	1902	...	2022	2025	2102	2125	2152	2225	2352	2355
38	Sunbury d.	0652	|	|	0933	1051	1053	1251	1253	1351	...	...	1551	1751	|	|	1933	...	2053	2055	2133	2155	2233	2255	0023	0025
78	Woodend d.	0720	0847	0904	1001	1112	1121	1312	1321	1419	...	...	1619	1819	1932	1942	2001	...	2121	2123	2201	2223	2252	2323	0051	0053
92	Kyneton d.	0728	0857	0914	1008	1120	1128	1320	1328	1426	...	...	1626	1826	1942	1952	2008	...	2128	2130	2208	2230	2258	2330	0058	0100
125	Castlemaine d.	0747	0926	0940	1028	1137	1148	1337	1334	1445	...	...	1647	1846	2006	2014	2026	...	2147	2149	2227	2249	2315	2349	0117	0118
162	**Bendigo** ☛ a.	0816	0956	1005	1053	1207	1212	1403	1412	1506	1525	1525	1710	1909	2034	2038	2051	2105	2208	2214	2250	2314	2336	0014	0142	0144
289	Kerang a.	|	1135	1144	|	1406*	1406*	|	|	...	|	1745	|	|	2213	2217	...	2315	...	...	...	...	...	...	...	...
345	**Swan Hill** a.	|	1223	1232	|	1448*	1448*	|	|	...	1835	1830	|	|	2301	2305	...	2359	...	...	...	...	...	...	...	...
222	Rochester a.	0940*	...	...	1156	...	...	1510*	1515*	...	...	...	1813	2012	...	...	...	...	...	...	...	...	...	...	...	...
248	**Echuca** a.	1003*	...	...	1221	...	...	1533*	1538*	...	...	...	1838	2037	..	...	...	...	...	...	...	...	...	...	...	...

	⑥	①-⑤	⑦	⑥ R	①-⑤ R	⑥⑦ R🍷	①-⑤ R🍷	⑥	⑦ R	①-⑤	①③⑤ 🚌	②④ 🚌	①-⑤	⑥	①-⑤ R	⑦	①-⑤	⑦	①-⑤ R🍷	⑥ R🍷	⑥⑦ R	⑥	⑦ R🍷	①-⑤ R	⑦	①-⑤
Echuca d.	...	...	...	0701	0716	...	...	0855*	0854	0855*	...	...	...	...	...	1250*	1255*	...	...	...	1558	...	...	...	...	...
Rochester d.	...	...	...	0724	0739	...	...	0920*	0917	0920*	...	...	...	...	...	1315*	1320*	...	...	...	1621	...	...	...	...	...
Swan Hill d.	...	...	...	|	|	0651	0658	|	|	|	0850	0850	...	0940*	1055*	|	|	1235*	1254	1314	|	...	1613	1535a	...	...
Kerang d.	...	...	...	|	|	0734	0741	|	|	|	|	0940	...	1026*	1141*	|	|	1321*	1337	1357	|	...	1656	1615a	...	...
Bendigo ☛ d.	0730	0745	0800	0827	0845	0916	0922	1022	1022	1030	1205	1205	1230	1225	1336	1425	1438	1525	1518	1539	1725	1842	1838	1847	2046	2120
Castlemaine d.	0752	0806	0821	0848	0908	0940	0948	1044	1044	1051	...	...	1251	1247	1357	1447	1501	1547	1547	1605	1747	1908	1905	1909	2107	2144
Kyneton d.	0812	0825	0841	0908	0930	1005	1013	1105	1105	1111	...	...	1311	1308	1416	1508	1521	1608	1611	1628	1808	1929	1933	1931	2127	2205
Woodend d.	0820	0833	0849	0916	0939	1016	1024	1113	1113	1120	...	...	1320	1316	1425	1516	1530	1616	1621	1638	1816	1937	1943	1939	2135	2213
Sunbury d.	0851	0858	0919	0948	1011	|	|	1145	1145	1152	...	...	1352	1348	1450	1548	1602	1648	|	|	1848	2002	|	2011	2208	2245
Melbourne S Cross ... a.	0924	0928	0951	1021	1043	1123	1134	1218	1218	1223	...	...	1423	1420	1522	1620	1633	1720	1725	1744	1920	2033	2044	2043	2240	2315

☛ Additional trains are available Melbourne - Bendigo and v.v. a – Connection by 🚌 on ⑤ only. * – By 🚌.

6385 MELBOURNE - MARYBOROUGH and ARARAT — V/Line

km		⑥⑦ R	①-⑤	②⑥ A	①-⑤	①-⑤ 🚌	⑥⑦	⑥ 🚌	①-⑤ R	⑥⑦	①-⑤	①②④ 🚌	①-⑤	⑦	①-⑤	①-⑤ 🚌	①-⑤	⑤ 🚌	①-⑤	⑥⑦ R	⑥⑦	①-⑤ R	⑦	①-⑤	E 🚌	①-⑤
0	**Melbourne** S Cross .. d.	0816	0816	0805	0916	...	0916	...	1216	1216	1316	...	1416	1516	1633	...	1654	...	1750	1816	...	1823	1916	2030	2110	2355
41	Melton d.	0849	0847	|	0947	...	0949	...	1247	1249	1347	...	1447	1549	|	...	|	...	|	1849	...	1852	1949	2102	|	0027
53	Bacchus Marsh d.	0901	0857	|	0957	...	1001	...	1257	1301	1357	...	1457	1601	1721	...	1727	...	1822	1901	...	1859	2001	2110	|	0035
82	Ballan d.	0918	0914	|	1014	...	1017	...	1314	1318	1414	...	1414	1618	|	...	1744	...	1840	1918	...	1916	2018	2127	|	0052
122	**Ballarat** ☛ a.	0940	0939	|	1039	1100	1040	1055	1339	1340	1439	1500	1539	1635	1738	1750	1800	1810	1857	1935	1942	1933	2036	2150	2240	1009
180	**Maryborough** a.	|	|	|	1138	|	...	1201	|	|	...	1607	|	|	1838	|	...	1917	|	|	2035	|	|	...	2358	...
210	**Ararat** a.	1041	1039	1113	...	1216	...	...	1439	1439	...	...	1639	1820*	...	1909	...	...	2021*	2036	...	2033	2205*	...	...	...

	①-⑥ 🚌	①-⑤	①-⑤	①-⑤	①-⑤	⑥	⑥ R	⑦		D 🚌	①-⑤	⑥	⑥	①-⑤	⑥	⑦	①-⑤	①-⑤	①-⑤	①⑤ A	⑥⑦	①-⑤	①-⑤	⑦	⑥⑦	①-⑤
Ararat d.	...	...	0618	...	0715	...	0715	...	0815b	...	0807*	0830*	0922*	1046*	1108	1115	1226	...	1449	1535	1610	1649	1730*	1745*	...	...
Maryborough d.	0410	...	|	0711	|	0710	|	0810	|	0824	|	|	|	|	|	|	|	1446	|	|	|	|	|	|	...	...
Ballarat ☛ d.	0503a	0519	0721	0802	0818	0801	0817	0901	0918	0933	1018	1018	1118	1218	1218	1218	1318	1537	1552	|	1713	1801	1909	1912	2115	2245
Ballan d.	|	0538	0738	...	0834	...	0835	...	0935	...	1035	1035	1135	1235	1235	1235	1335	...	1609	|	1735	1822	1932	1935	2132	2307
Bacchus Marsh d.	|	0555	0755	...	0851	...	0852	...	0952	...	1052	1052	1152	1252	1252	1252	1352	...	1625	|	1752	1843	1949	1952	2153	2324
Melton d.	|	0603	|	...	0900	...	0901	...	1001	...	1100	1101	1201	1300	1301	1301	1400	...	1635	|	1801	1852	2001	2001	2200	2336
Melbourne S Cross ... a.	0705	0635	0836	...	0939	...	0940	...	1040	...	1140	1140	1240	1340	1340	1340	1440	...	1716	1850	1840	1927	2040	2040	2239	0015

☛ Additional trains are available Melbourne - Ballarat and v.v. A – See Table 6395. D – ①②④⑤⑥. E – ①②③④⑤⑦. a – Arrive. b – ⑦ only. * – By 🚌.

6390 SYDNEY - PERTH — Great Southern Rail

km		WE1 R ③A	
0	**Sydney** Central d.	1500	③
1125	Broken Hill ◇ a.	◇	④
1688	**Adelaide** Parklands ◇ a.	1515	④
1688	**Adelaide** Parklands ◇ d.	2140	④
	Cook a.	◇	⑤
	Nullarbor d.	◇	⑤
4343	East **Perth** a.	1500	⑥

	WE2 R ⑦A	
East **Perth** d.	1000	⑦
Kalgoorlie ◇ a.	2050	:
Nullarbor d.	◇	①
Adelaide Parklands ◇ a.	0720	②
Adelaide Parklands d.	1015	:
Broken Hill d.	◇	:
Sydney Central a.	1200a	③

A – INDIAN PACIFIC – 🛏 P 1 cl., and ✕ Sydney - Adelaide - Perth and v.v. From Sydney on ③. From Perth on ⑦.
◇ – Off train excursion **Note**: Train **WE2** has a additional off train excursion at Cook on ①.
a – Blue Mountain Excursion available arrive in Sydney at 1515.

6400 DARWIN - ADELAIDE — Great Southern Rail

km		8506 R ③D	
0	**Darwin** △ d.	1000	③
310	Katherine ◇ d.	◇	:
	Newcastle Waters d.	|	:
947	Tennant Creek a.	|	:
947	Tennant Creek d.	|	:
1414	**Alice Springs** a.	0910	④
1414	**Alice Springs** d.	1245	④
2661	Port Augusta a.	|	:
2661	Port Augusta d.	|	:
2751	Manguri ◇ d.	◇	④
2775	Crystal Brook d.	|	:
2827	Snowtown d.	|	:
2973	**Adelaide** Parklands a.	1300	⑤

	8505 R ⑦C	
Adelaide Parklands d.	1215	⑦
Snowtown d.	|	:
Crystal Brook d.	|	:
Maria ◇ d.	◇	①
Port Augusta a.	|	:
Port Augusta d.	|	:
Alice Springs a.	1345	①
Alice Springs d.	1815	①
Tennant Creek a.	|	:
Tennant Creek d.	|	:
Newcastle Waters d.	|	:
Katherine ◇ a.	◇	②
Darwin △ a.	1730	②

C – THE GHAN – 🛏 P, 1 cl., ✕ and 🍷 Adelaide - Darwin. From Adelaide on ⑦ service will also stop at Maria and Katherine for an off train excursion. Between June and Aug. 2019 an additional service departs Adelaide on ③ at 1210 and arrives Darwin on ⑤ at 1930.
D – THE GHAN – 🛏 P, 1 cl., ✕ and 🍷 Darwin - Adelaide. From Darwin on ③ until Feb. 2019 also Nov. 2019 and Feb. 2020, service will also stop at Katherine and Manguri for an off train excursion. There will be a special timetable operating March 2019, Apr. - Oct. 2019 and Mar. 2020. Service departs Darwin on ③ at 1000 arriving Adelaide on ⑥ at 1050 and has an extended stop at Coober Pedy on ⑤. Between June and Aug. 2019 an additional service departs Darwin on ⑥ at 0900 arriving Adelaide on ② at 1135.

The Ghan will not operate between Dec. 16, 2018 and Jan. 12, 2019. or Dec - Jan. 2020.

△ – Darwin station is in the suburb of Berrimah. 🚌 connections to and from Darwin city centre are provided by the operator.
◇ – Off train Excursion.

6395 MELBOURNE - ADELAIDE — Great Southern Rail

km		8701 R B ②⑥	
0	**Melbourne** S Cross d.	0805	...
74	Geelong North Shore d.	0915	...
265	Ararat d.	1115	...
381	Horsham d.	1231	...
416	Dimboola d.	1300	...
454	Nhill d.	1327	...
734	Murray Bridge d.	1550	...
828	**Adelaide** Parklands a.	1740	...

	8702 R B ①⑤	
Adelaide Parklands d.	0745	...
Murray Bridge d.	0950	...
Nhill d.	1317	...
Dimboola d.	1350	...
Horsham d.	1417	...
Ararat d.	1535	...
Geelong North Shore d.	1739	...
Melbourne S Cross a.	1850	...

B – THE OVERLAND – (12) and 🍷 Melbourne - Adelaide and v.v.

6405 KALGOORLIE - PERTH — All trains 2 cl. and R — TransWA

km		AVO2 ①-⑤	PL02 ①③⑤	PA02 ②④⑥	MO2 ⑤	MO2 ①	MO2 ③		PA56 ⑦	PA52 ①	PA54 ⑤
0	**Kalgoorlie** d.	...	0705	0705	...	...	...	...	1405	1500	1500
250	Southern Cross d.	...	0912	0912	...	...	...	...	1612	1707	1715
371	Merredin d.	...	1023	1023	1305	1310	1310	...	1723	1818	1829
427	Kellerberrin d.	...	1102s	1102	1336	1341	1341	...	1802	1857	1908
531	Northam d.	0630	1209	1209	1441	1446	1454	...	1907	2002	2013
641	Midland d.	0750	1323	1323	1555	1600	1610	...	2020	2115	2125
653	East **Perth** a.	...	1345	1345	1620	1620	1630	...	2040	2135	2145

	PL01 ①③⑤	PA01 ②④⑥		M01 ①③⑤		PA55 ⑦	PA51 ①		PA53 ⑤	AVO1 ①-⑤
East **Perth** d.	0710	0710	...	0855	...	1410	1515	...	1515	...
Midland d.	0727	0727	...	0912	...	1427	1533	...	1532	1750
Northam d.	0850	0850	...	1027	...	1547	1645	...	1655	1910
Kellerberrin d.	0956u	0956	...	1138	...	1653	1750	...	1800	...
Merredin d.	1027	1027	...	1210	...	1728	1821	...	1831	...
Southern Cross d.	1144	1144	...	...	...	1845	1938	...	1948	...
Kalgoorlie a.	1400	1400	...	...	...	2100	2150	...	2205	...

s – Set down only. u – Pick up only. NOTE: Trains will only call at intermediate stations if bookings are made in advance.

6410 PERTH - BUNBURY — All trains 2 cl — TransWA

km		B03 R	B55 R	
0	**Perth** City d.	0930	1755	...
30	Armadale d.	0956	1825	...
85	Pinjarra d.	1042	1911	...
111	Waroona d.	1100	1929	...
136	Harvey d.	1121	1950	...
157	Brunswick Junction d.	1136	2005	...
183	**Bunbury** a.	1155	2025	...

	B02 R	B56 R	
Bunbury d.	0600	1445	...
Brunswick Junction d.	0617	1502	...
Harvey d.	0632	1517	...
Waroona d.	0656	1538	...
Pinjarra d.	0712	1555	...
Armadale d.	0755	1639	...
Perth City a.	0830	1715	...

NOTE: Trains will only call at intermediate stations if bookings are made in advance.

6415 KALGOORLIE - ESPERANCE — TransWA

km		671 🚌 ①③	651 🚌 ⑤	
0	**Kalgoorlie** d.	1430	1430	...
208	Norseman d.	1715	1730	...
409	**Esperance** a.	1930	1945	...

	700 🚌 ⑦	690 🚌 ③⑤	
Esperance d.	0800	0835	...
Norseman d.	1045	1120	...
Kalgoorlie a.	1315	1335	...

NEW ZEALAND

Capital: **Wellington** (GMT +12, add one hour in Summer). 2019 public holidays: Jan. 1, 2, Feb. 6, Apr. 19, 22, 25, June 3, Oct. 28, Dec. 25, 26.

ong distance rail services are operated by Tranz Scenic (www.tranzscenic.co.nz). Only one class of accommodation is offered, which is referred to in the tables as second lass. All services operated by TranzScenic require compulsory reservation. There are two types of Scenic Rail Passes; the Fixed Pass offers unlimited travel on the TranzScenic etwork (not the Capital Connection) and also allows one journey on the Interislander ferry service. Adult prices: 7 days NZ$599, 14 days NZ$699, 21 days NZ$799. The reedom Pass offers flexible travel from 3 to 10 days. Adult prices: 3 days NZ$ 417 to 10 days NZ$ 1290. For full information go to www.kiwirailscenic.co.nz. **All Rail Passes are urrently unavailable for sale because The Coastal Pacific is currently out of service due to the recent earthquake in Kaikoura.**

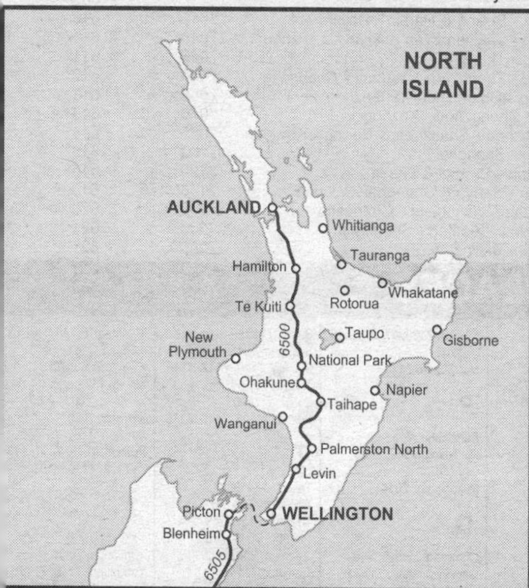

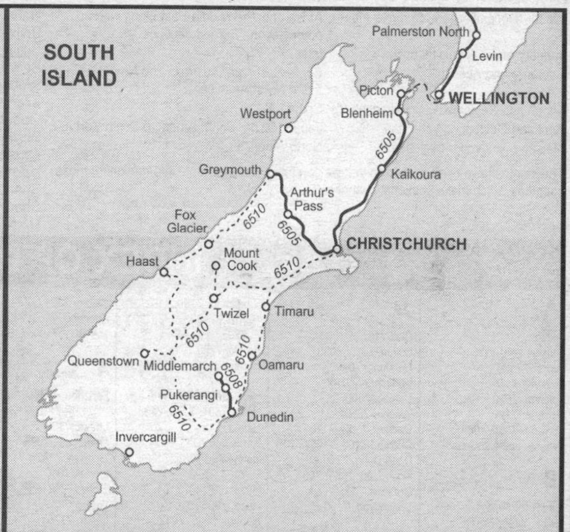

AUCKLAND - WELLINGTON 6500

KiwiRail Scenic

km		1203	0201		0200	1205
			R		R	
		①–⑤	①④⑥		③⑤⑦	①–⑤
		B	A		A	B
0	**Auckland** Strand........ d.	...	0745	**Wellington** .... ⊡ d.	0755	1715
34	Papakura........ d.	...	0840	Paraparaumu........ d.	0845	1803
139	Hamilton........ d.	...	1015	Levin........ d.	|	1842
183	Otorohanga........ d.	...	1054	**Palmerston North**........ d.	1000	1920
334	National Park........ d.	...	1315	Ohakune........ d.	1245	...
364	Ohakune........ d.	...	1345	National Park........ d.	1315	...
544	**Palmerston North**........ d.	0615	1620	Otorohanga........ d.	1545	...
590	Levin........ d.	0653	|	Hamilton........ d.	1630	...
632	Paraparaumu........ d.	0732	1730	Papakura........ d.	1755	...
681	**Wellington**........ ⊡ a.	0820	1825	**Auckland** Strand........ a.	1850	...

ote: Trains are permitted to depart from intermediate stations earlier than advertised provided that all pre-booked passengers are on board.
– NORTHERN EXPLORER – ② and 🍸. Not Dec. 25, 28, 29.
– CAPITAL CONNECTION – ② and 🍸. Not public holidays or Dec. 25 - Jan 4.
– Calls to set down only.
– Calls to pick up only.

PICTON - CHRISTCHURCH 6505

KiwiRail Scenic

km		803	0701		0700	0804
		R	R		R	R
		D	C		C	D
0	**Picton**........ ⊡ d.	...	1350	**Greymouth**........ d.	...	1405
28	Blenheim........ d.	...	1421	Brunner........ d.	...	|
157	Kaikoura........ d.	...	1647	Moana........ d.	...	1503
285	Waipara........ d.	...	|	Otira........ d.	...	1551
318	Rangiora........ d.	...	1927	Arthur's Pass........ d.	...	1628
348	**Christchurch**........ a.	...	2015	Springfield........ d.	...	1739
348	**Christchurch**........ d.	0815	...	**Christchurch**........ a.	...	1831
417	Springfield........ d.	0920	...	**Christchurch**........ d.	0700	...
484	Arthur's Pass........ d.	1052	...	Rangiora........ d.	0730	...
498	Otira........ d.	1126	...	Waipara........ d.	|	...
	Moana........ d.	1206	...	Kaikoura........ d.	1016	...
565	Brunner........ d.	|	...	Blenheim........ d.	1233	...
579	**Greymouth**........ a.	1305	...	**Picton**........ ⊡ a.	1315	...

Note: Trains are permitted to depart from intermediate stations earlier than advertised provided that all pre-booked passengers are on board.
C – COASTAL PACIFIC – ② and 🍸. Dec. 1, 2018 - Apr. 28, 2019. Note: **Timings may be affected by speed restrictions so please allow for delays of up to one hour.**
D – THE TRANZALPINE – ② and 🍸. Not Dec. 25.

] – Wellington - Picton ⛴ service ('Interislander'). Journey 3 - 3½ hours.
here are normally daily sailing from both Wellington and Picton. The timings given are a guide only, to get accurate sailing times you need to contact the operator.

Operator: Interislander ✆ +64 4 498 3302. https://www.greatjourneysofnz.co.nz/interislander
From Wellington: 0330, 0900, 1445, 1700, 2030.
From Picton: 0905, 1045, 1415, 1845, 2215.

DUNEDIN - PUKERANGI - MIDDLEMARCH 6508

Taieri Gorge Railway

eparting from Dunedin the Taieri Gorge Railway begins its scenic journey into some of New ealand's spectacular and iconic scenery. The train travels through the southern parts of Dunedin ty until it arrives at Wingatui Junction where it turns off onto the Taieri branch. From here the train neaks across the Taieri Plains and climbs into the Taieri Gorge, a narrow and deep gorge carved ut over aeons by the ancient Taieri River. The train travels through ten tunnels and over ountless bridges and viaducts on its 58km journey to Pukerangi.

ww.dunedinrailways.co.nz ✆ +64 3 477 4449.

km		S	SW	W	S		S	W	SW	S
		a	b	①–⑥			a	①–⑥	b	
0	**Dunedin**........ d.	0930	0930	1230	1430	Middlemarch........ d.	...	...	1300	...
58	Pukerangi........ a.	1135	|	1435	1635	**Pukerangi**........ d.	1145	1445	|	1645
77	Middlemarch........ a.	...	1200	...	...	**Dunedin**........ a.	1330	1630	1525	1830

S – Summer timings October to April. **W** – Winter timings May to October.
a – Generally runs ①②③④⑥. **b** – Generally runs ⑤⑦. For exact days of running see website.

SELECTED SOUTH ISLAND BUS SERVICES 6510

km	Operator	IC	AS	IC	AS	IC	Operator	IC	AS	IC	AS	IC
0	**Christchurch** d.	0745	0800	1400	1500	1715	**Dunedin**..... d.	0745	0800	1250	1430	1715
82	Ashburton..... d.	0915	0920	1525	1630	1850	Oamaru....... d.	0930	1000	1500	1635	1855
'60	Timaru......... d.	1030	1025	1700	1800	2030	Timaru........ d.	1120	1110	1620	1740	2030
'40	Oamaru........ d.	1205	1200	1815	1910	2135	Ashburton ... d.	1225	1210	1730	1845	2135
'66	**Dunedin**...... a.	1340	1350	1950	2045	2305	**Christchurch** a.	1345	1350	1855	2000	2250

km	Operator	AS	IC	NM	Operator	NM	IC	AS
0	**Christchurch**. d.	0730	0730	0830	**Queenstown**. d.	0805	0745	1500
82	Ashburton....... d.	0845	0850	0950	Cromwell....... d.	0910	0920	1555
144	Geraldine........ d.	0925	1000	1045	Twizel........... d.	1110	1130	1805
191	Fairlie............ d.	1000	1025	1125	**Mount Cook**.. d.	|	1345	|
341	**Mount Cook**.. d.	|	1425	|	Fairlie............ d.	1315	1550	1920
281	Twizel............. d.	1120	1515	1330	Geraldine....... d.	1410	1655	2000
435	Cromwell........ d.	1340	1715	1530	Ashburton...... d.	1455	1735	2040
496	**Queenstown**.. a.	1430	1830	1630	**Christchurch** a.	1630	1910	2145

km	Operator		IC	AS	AS	Operator	AS	IC	AS	
0	**Queenstown**........ d.	...	0745	0915	1500	**Dunedin**........ d.	1000	1355	1530	...
61	Cromwell........ d.	...	0850	1015	1555	Milton........ d.	1040	1445	1620	...
92	Alexandra........ d.	...	0920	1050	1930	Roxburgh........ d.	1220	1605	1740	...
'34	Roxburgh........ d.	...	0955	1120	1715	Alexandra........ d.	1250	1640	1805	...
'24	Milton........ d.	...	1130	1240	1830	Cromwell........ d.	1340	1705	1830	...
'80	**Dunedin**........ a.	...	1235	1345	1930	**Queenstown**........ a.	1430	1815	1935	...

km	Operator	AS	IC		Operator	IC	AS	
0	**Greymouth**.... d.	...	*1330*	...	**Queenstown**. d.	...	0810	...
41	Hokitika.......... d.	...	*1455*	...	Wanaka......... d.	...	0945	...
189	Franz Josef.... d.	0800	*1705*	...	Haast............. d.	...	1250	...
213	**Fox Glacier**.... d.	0845	*1740*	...	Paringa.......... d.	...	1435	...
	Paringa........... d.	1005	...	...	**Fox Glacier**... d.	0830	1525	...
334	Haast............. d.	1120	...	...	Franz Josef.... d.	0915	1610	...
476	Wanaka.......... d.	1435	...	...	Hokitika......... d.	1230	...	...
593	**Queenstown**.. a.	1615	...	...	**Greymouth**... a.	1315	...	...

S – Atomic Travel. ✆ 03 349 0697. *IC* – Intercity Coachlines. ✆ 09 583 5780. *NM* – Newmans. ✆ 09 583 5780.

BEYOND EUROPE
China

Introduction

The Beyond Europe section covers principal rail services in a different area of the world each month. There are six areas, each appearing as follows:

Winter (December) and Summer (June):	Africa and The Middle East along with all other Beyond Europe sections.
January and July (digital only):	India.
February and August:	South East Asia, Australia and New Zealand; India; North America.
March and September (digital only):	China.
April and October:	Japan; China; South America; South Korea.
May and November (digital only):	North America.

The months have been chosen so that we can bring you up-to-date information for those countries which make seasonal changes.

Contents

INDEX OF PLACES

China

Capital: Beijing (GMT + 8). 2019 Public Holidays: Jan. 1, Feb. 4, 5, 6, Apr. 5, May 1, June 7, Sept. 13, Oct. 1, 2, 3.

Rail services in the People's Republic are generally operated by Chinese Railways. High-speed services are operated by China Rail High Speed. All times shown are Beijing time unless otherwise stated. Schedules in this section are as per the latest information available and are liable to change at any time.

Trains are numbered using a combination of letters and numbers, with the letter indicating the type of train. The fastest trains carry prefixes **C** and **G**. These use the new high speed railways and run at speeds up to 350 km/h on routes Beijing to Tianjin and Beijing to Shanghai and up to 300 km/h on routes such as Wuhan to Guangzhou. Other high speed trains running at speeds of up to 200 km/h are prefixed with the letter **D** and **Z**. These trains use both dedicated high-speed railways and normal lines. Ordinary long distance trains are prefixed **T** or **K**. **T** trains make fewer stops and thus are considerably quicker than **K** trains. Most **K** trains in this section are only shown to highlight additional connections between major points and may not be shown in their entirety. Also shown are a few trains without prefix letters.

Train classes are shown in the chart below. It should be noted that not all classes will be available on every train and that the exact train compositions are **not** shown in the tables. Hard seats are cheapest class available and are often very busy as Standing ticket holders can stand in the aisles. Soft seats are larger and generally can be reclined. Second class seats have five seats per row. First class has four seats per row. Business and VIP seats have three seats per row. Hard sleepers consist of open cabins of six berths (upper, middle and lower), with three beds on either side. Soft sleepers have four berths and a sliding door. Deluxe Soft cabins have two berths and an en-suite bathroom.

High-Speed	Business Class	VIP Class	1st Class	2nd Class	Soft Sleepers	Deluxe Sleeper
G	Yes	Yes	Yes	Yes	No	Yes
D	No	No	Yes	Yes	Certain trains	No
C	No	No	Yes	Yes	No	No

Regular	Hard Seats	Soft Seats	Hard Sleepers	Soft Sleepers	Deluxe Sleeper
Z	No	No	No	Yes	Yes
T	Yes	Yes	Yes	Yes	No
K	Yes	Yes	Yes	Yes	No

All travel should be reserved in advance either at stations or through an agent. At many stations you may find it possible to only book for trains calling there, however in major cities such as Beijing, Shanghai and Guangzhou you may be able to purchase all tickets. Some major stations may have English speakers available at ticket desks. Reservations for **Z** and **D** usually open 10 - 21 days in advance. Other classes of train are only usually available 7 - 10 days before departure. In peak seasons such as Spring Festival holiday reservations may only open 5 days before departure. Identity documents, such as passports for most foreigners or ID cards for Chinese citizens, are required to buy tickets for and to board **C, D** and **G** trains.

Because of space restrictions we are only able to show selected services in certain tables. Additional services and other information can be found in the footnotes. More comprehensive train schedules are available (in Chinese!) from Chinese Railways official website: www.12306.cn/index/. Other unofficial websites such as http://trains.ctrip.com www.travelchinaguide.com and www.chinahighlights.com have more detailed class information with photographs, timetable search facilities in English and can arrange tickets. A comprehensive printed English language timetable is available from Duncan Peattie (CTT) 29 Watford Field Road, Watford UK, WD18 0BG or see www.chinatt.org.

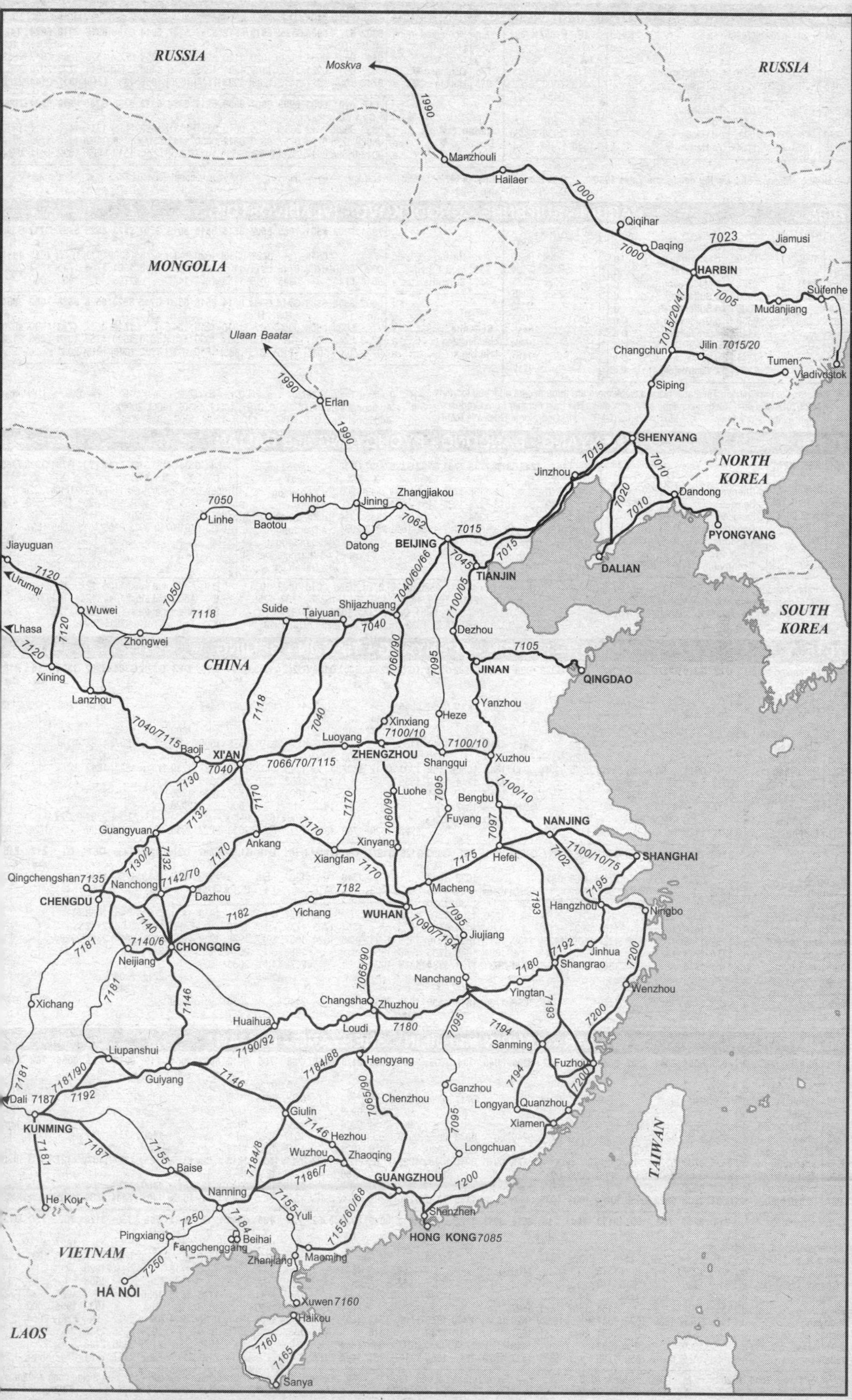
RUSSIA
Moskva
1990
Manzhouli
Hailaer
7000
Qiqihar
Daqing
7023
Jiamusi
HARBIN
7005
Suifenhe
Mudanjiang
7015/20/47
Changchun
Jilin 7015/20
Tumen
Vladivostok
Siping
SHENYANG
MONGOLIA
Ulaan Baatar
Erlan
7015
7010
Jinzhou
NORTH KOREA
Dandong
7020
PYONGYANG
DALIAN
7050
Linhe
Baotou
Hohhot
Jining
Zhangjiakou
7062
Datong
BEIJING
TIANJIN
7045
Jiayuguan
Urumqi
7120
Lhasa
Wuwei
Zhongwei
7118
Suide
Taiyuan
Shijiazhuang
7040/60/66
7100/05
Dezhou
SOUTH KOREA
7105
JINAN
QINGDAO
CHINA
Xining
Lanzhou
7060/90
7095
Yanzhou
Heze
Xinxiang
7100/10
7040/7115
Baoji
XI'AN
7040
7066/70/7115
Luoyang
ZHENGZHOU
Shangqui
Xuzhou
7130
7132
7170
Luohe
Bengbu
Fuyang
7097
NANJING
Guangyuan
Ankang
Xinyang
7102
7100/10/75
SHANGHAI
7130/2
Xiangfan
Hefei
7175
Qingchengshan 7135
Nanchong
7142/70
Dazhou
7182
Macheng
7195
CHENGDU
Yichang
WUHAN
7193
Hangzhou
Ningbo
7140
7140/6
CHONGQING
7090/7194
Jiujiang
7192
Jinhua
Neijiang
7181
7065/90
Shangrao
7200
Nanchang
7180
Yingtan
Wenzhou
Xichang
7146
Changsha
Zhuzhou
Huaihua
Loudi
7194
Sanming
Liupanshui
7190/92
Hengyang
7184/88
Fuzhou
7181/90
Guiyang
Ganzhou
Chenzhou
Longyan
Quanzhou
Dali 7187
Xiamen
KUNMING
Giulin
Hezhou
TAIWAN
7187
7155
7184/8
Wuzhou
Zhaoqing
Longchuan
Baise
7186/7
GUANGZHOU
Nanning
7155/60/68
Shenzhen
He Kou
7250
Yuli
HONG KONG 7085
Pingxiang
Fangchenggang
Beihai
VIETNAM
Zhanjiang
Maoming
HÀ NÔI
Xuwen 7160
Haikou
LAOS
7165
Sanya

7000 MANZHOULI and QIQHAR - HARBIN

Chinese Railways, China Rail High Speed

km	20 ⑤ A	K7092	K7058	Read Down / Read Up	19 ⑦ A	K7057	K7091
0	2359	1710	2038	d.**Manzhouli** a.	0417	0812	0903
186	0215	1921	2258	d.Hailaer d.	0213	0600	0702
268	|	2035	0009	d.Yakeshi d.	|	0434	0541
396	0519	|	0205	d.Boketu d.	2251	0236	|
693	|	|	0729	d. Qiqihar a.	|	2207	|
776	|	|	0922	d.Daqing d.	|	1956	2236d
935	1238	0602	1154x	a.**Harbin** ♥ d.	1540	1748x	2024

km	Unmarked trains prefix 'D'	6902	5373 D	6906	G1262	6910	6912	5383 D	5387	6914	G786	6916	6918	6924	T48 C
0	Qiqihar d.	0549	0604	0838	0929n	1020	1120	1255	1338	1356	1505n	1526	1642	1942	1853
776	Daqing xi ♥ d.	0627	0637	0921	1002	1109	1204	1339	1416	1438	1544d	1614	1725	2026	2005
935	**Harbin** xi ♥ a.	0742	0748j	1027	1113	1209j	1323	1444j	1520j	1558	1639	1718j	1837	2144	2202

	T47 C	6901	6903	6905	6907	6909	6911	5384 D	6913	5388	G785	6919	6921	G1261
Harbin xi ♥ d.	0633	0522	0612	0655j	0705	0810	0854j	1031j	1053	1135j	1317	1420	1617	1937
Daqing xi ♥ d.	0808	0622d	0728	0757	0833	0912	0950	1142	1144d	1236	1408d	1540	1730	2044
Qiqihar a.	0913	0659n	0817	0828n	0909n	0953n	1037	1221	81226n	1312	1455n	1622	1811	2115n

A – Beijing - Moscow and v.v. For details see Table **1990**.
C – 🛏 1, 2 cl. Beijing(**T47/48**) - Qiqihar and v.v.
D – To/from Table **7023**.
j – Harbin.
♥ – Additional services Daqing xi - Harbin and v.v.

7005 HARBIN - SUIFENHE - GRODEKOVO - (VLADIVOSTOK)

Chinese Railways

km	K7023	402 2	A ③⑥	Read Down / Read Up	401 2	K7024	A ①④
0	1930	...	1930	d.**Harbin dong** a.	...	0620	0620
161	0026	...	0026	d.Yimianpo d.	...	0255	0255e
355	0331	...	0331	d.Mudanjiang d.	...	2325	2325
548	0505	...	0505	a.**Suifenhe** d.	...	2056	2056
548	...	1000	1000	d.**Suifenhe** 🛃 a.	1714	...	1714c
569	...	0630	0630	a.**Grodekovo** ◐ d.	1043	...	1043
569	...	...	1115	d.**Grodekovo** ◐ a.	...	...	0415
766	...	...	1245	a.Ussruiysk ◐ d.	...	...	0240c
766	...	...	2241	d.Ussruiysk ◐ a.	...	...	1410
878	...	...	0100f	a.**Vladivostok** ◐ d.	...	...	1215

km		7961	7963	8501 k	7965	8507	8513	8515	8519	G707 H	8523	8525	5387	G717 H	G393 H
0	**Harbin** xi d.	..	...	0515	...	0723j	0930j	1020	1134j	1245	1430j	1508j	1547j	1645	1834
307	Mudanjiang a.	0520	0640	0702	0743	0911	1101	1224	1344	1446	1601	1708	1745	1857	2035
444	**Suifenhe** a.	0618	0743	...	0845	1019	1159	1327	1447	...	1703	...	1853	2000	...

	8502 m	8506	5388	G714 H	G394 H	8514	8518	8520	G716 H	8524	8526	8528	7962	7964
Suifenhe d.	...	0638	0806	0908	...	1040	1219	1347	...	1510	...	1723	1930	2020
Mudanjiang a.	0533	0749	0917	1018	1030	1051	1330	1452	1510	1620	1750	1828	2033	2122
Harbin xi a.	0733	1000	1015j	1215	1243	1353j	1510	1637j	1720	1816j	1918j	2031	...	...

A – Accordng to the Chinese Timetable twice a week there are through cars attached to trains **K7023/7024** and **401/402** that continue to Vladivostok. The train number from Grodekovo to Vladivostok is unknown. ◐ – Moscow time (GMT +3). Operator in Russia is **RZhD**.
H – To/from Table **7015/20**. a – ④⑦. c – ②⑤. e – ③⑥. f – ①⑤. j – Harbin.
k – Additional trips: 0640, 0730, 0757, 1050j, 1330j, 1906j, 2000j.
m – Additional trips: 0722j, 0900j, 1100j, 1258j, 1600, 1838, 2056.

7010 SHENYANG - DANDONG - PYONGYANG and DALIAN

China Rail High Speed, Chinese Railways

km	K27 A	K27		K28 A	K28
0	0340	0340	d.**Shenyang** a.	2207	2207
84	0448	0448	d.Benxi d.	2106	2106
217	0633	0633	d.Fengcheng d.	1921	1921
277	0722	0722	a.**Dandong** d.	1831	1831
277	0935	...	d.**Dandong** a.	1623	...
282	1346	...	d.Sinuiji 🛃 ⊗ a.	|	...
506	1930	...	a.**Pyongyang** ⊗ d.	1010	...

km	7641 B	7742 E	G8108 X	7743 F	7751	G782 X	G395 X	G397 X	G786 X	Unmarked trains prefix 'D'	7604 C	G398 X	G8103 X	G788 X	7741	7737 D	G781 X	G396 X	7753
0	0616	...	1430	1155	1300	1414	1431n	1849	1908	d.**Shenyang** a.	0809	0829	0906b	1039b	1117	1225	1710b	1722n	...
76	0649	...	1513	1228	1339	1451	1457	1922	1942	d.Benxi d.	0737	0751	0816	1003	1040	1252	1645	1658	...
178	0721	...	|	1304	|	|	|	1955	2014	d.Fengcheng dong d.	0652	0719	0737	0930	|	1114	|	|	...
223	0738	...	1603	1321	1427	1534	1546	2012	2031	a.**Dandong** d.	0633	0701	0719	0912	0950	1055	1555	1607	...
223	...	0756	...	1341	1447	...	...	...	...	d.**Dandong** a.	...	...	...	...	0931	1035	...	...	2035
371	...	0910	...	1445	1559	...	...	...	...	d.Zhuanghe bei d.	...	...	...	...	0813	0927	...	...	1933
517	...	1041	...	1608	1732	...	...	...	...	a.**Dalian** bei d.	...	...	...	...	0623	0818	...	...	1758

⊗ – Korean Standard Time (GMT +9, 1 hour ahead of Chinese time). Times in North Korea are subject to confirmation.
A – ①③④⑥. Beijing(**K27/28**) - Dandong(**6/5**) - Pyongyang and v.v.
B – Additional trips: 0526, 0628, 0724, 0853, 0919, 1002, 1031, 1138, 1221**b**, 1250, 1345, 1449, 1522, 1636**b**, 1722, 1756.
C – Additional trips: 0801, 0829, 0927, 1035, 1155, 1228, 1328, 1422, 1436, 1533, 1632, 1710, 1725, 1913, 1949.
D – Additional trips: 1104, 1220, 1628.
E – Additional trips: 1041, 1244, 1630, 1804.
F – Additional trips: 0755, 1559, 1705.
X – To/from Tables **7015/7020**.

7015 QIQHAR - HARBIN - SHENYANG - TIANJIN - BEIJING

China Rail High Speed, Chinese Railways

km	Unmarked trains prefix 'D'	D12 ♠	G218	G1226	G398 X	D2	D24	G238	D28	G1206	G1202	G1276	D26 J	G240	D20	D102	G1262	G1238	G394 M	D30	D22	G396 X	G384	G382	G374	Z16 🛏	Z18 🛏
293	Qiqihar d.	...	...	...	...	...	...	...	...	...	...	...	...	...	...	...	0929	...	...	1246n	...	...	...	...	...	...	...
0	**Harbin** xi d.	...	...	...	...	...	...	...	0705	0806	0821	0856	0945	...	...	1043	1116	1204	1247	1447	r	...	...	1616	1703	2120	2133
**	Jilin d.	...	...	...	...	...	...	...	|	|	|	|	|	1044	...	|	|	|	|	|	1515	...	1602	|	|	|	|
**	Changchun d.	...	...	...	...	...	...	...	|	|	|	|	|	1127	1113	|	|	|	|	|	1600	...	1645	|	|	|	|
240	Changchun xi d.	...	...	...	...	...	0752	...	0813	0919	0933	1010	1105	|	|	1202	1228	1316	1355	1600	|	...	1657	1722	1808	|	|
358	Siping dong d.	...	...	...	...	...	0825	...	|	|	|	1039	|	|	1200	|	|	|	|	|	1640	...	|	1750	1836	|	|
538	**Shenyang** bei d.	0709	0811	0804	0832y	0911y	0925	0957y	0949	1041	1056	1132	1231	1242	1307	1335	1343	1432	1505	1727	1739	1742n	1826	1842	1936	|	|
761	Jinzhou nan d.	0833	|	|	0958	1036	|	|	|	1212	1214	1249	1359	|	|	1453	1502	1550	1624	1846	|	|	|	|	2100	|	|
926	Shanhaiguan d.	0914	|	1101	1054	|	|	|	|	1312	1318	1351	|	|	|	|	1605	|	1727	1944	1955	|	|	2109	|	|	|
964	Beidaihe d.	1014	|	1130	|	|	|	|	1249	|	1342	|	|	|	|	1623	|	|	1800	|	2026	|	|	|	|	|	|
	Tianjin a.	|	|	1252x	1238x	|	|	|	|	1448x	1501x	1529x	|	|	|	|	1806x	1836x	1947x	|	|	2145x	2215x	2252	2327x	|	|
1241	**Beijing** a.	1217	1158	...	1318	1408	1414	1359	1451	...	...	...	1728	1629	1753	1831	...	...	2033	2222	2230	2230	2253n	2338n	...	0724	0753

	G373	D29	D21	G383	G381	G395 X	D17	G1205	G1237	D25 J	G393 M	G1261	G1275	D9	G1221	D101	D19	G1204	G397 X	D27	D23	G239	D51	D1	Z17 🛏	Z15 🛏
Beijing ♠ d.	...	0634	0639	0735n	0755n	0905	0915	...	...	1028	1050	...	...	1319	...	1352	1418	...	1350	1515	1533	1700	1713	1808	2115	2121
Tianjin d.	0802	|	|	0821x	0842	0949	|	1037x	1046x	|	1135	1225x	1408	|	1418	|	|	1522x	1429x	|	|	|	|	|	|	|
Beidaihe d.	0918	|	0842	0954	|	1101	1121	|	|	1236	1300		|	|	|	|	1624	1643	|	1721	|	|	|	2017	|	|
Shanhaiguan d.	|	|	0922	|	|	|	|	|	1239	1309	1355	1432	1545	|	|	1637	|	|	1630	1801	|	|	2008	|	|	|
Jinzhou nan d.	|	1014	1028	|	1108	1234	|	|	|	1410	1437	1529	|	1653	1703	1739	|	1810	|	|	1913	|	2112	|	|	|
Shenyang bei ♠ d.	1156	1149	1208	1246	1230	1409n	1423y	1439	1511	1552	1610	1658	1803	1813	1824	1857	1917	1930	1949	2029	2036	2051	2317	2328y	|	|
Siping dong d.	1257	1243	1323	|	|	...	...	|	1604	1645	1705	1750	1855	...	...	1956	|	2024	...	|	2141	|	...	...	|	|
Changchun xi d.	1325	1316	|	|	1346	...	...	1600	1633	1724	1734	1819	1924	...	...	2028	|	2053	...	|	|	|	...	...	|	|
Changchun a.	|	|	1404	1412	|	...	...	|	|	|	|	|	|	...	...	|	2045	|	...	|	2211	2205	...	...	|	|
Jilin a.	|	|	1447	1455	|	...	...	|	|	|	|	|	|	...	...	|	...	|	...	|	...	2245	...	...	|	|
Harbin xi a.	1422	1440	ra	...	1449	...	...	1656	1730	1846	1830	1929	2033	...	...	2140	...	2156	...	2250	...	...	...	...	0712	0725
Qiqihar a.	...	1632n	...	...	...	...	...	...	...	...	...	2115n	...	...	...	...	...	...	...	...	...	...	...	...	...	...

7020 QIQHAR - HARBIN and JILIN - SHENYANG - DALIAN

China Rail High Speed

km	All trains prefix 'G'	8070	8068	8042	8002	8046	8004	702	8006	8048	704	706	48	8008	8128 ta	8050	708	766	8010	8052	8054	710	8012	712	8056	782 X	8108 X
	Qiqihar nan d.	...	...	...	...	...	...	...	...	...	...	...	...	...	...	...	...	0720	...	...	...	...	...	...	...	...	...
0	**Harbin** xi d.	...	...	...	...	...	...	0616	...	...	0717	0754	0830	...	...	...	0905	0915	...	...	...	1034	...	1142	...	1155	...
**	**Jilin** d.	...	...	...	...	...	0610	|	...	...	|	|	|	0851	0903	...	|	|	...	...	...	|	...	|	...	|	1214
**	Changchun d.	...	...	...	0605	...	0653	|	0728	...	|	|	|	0934	0946	...	|	|	1036	...	...	|	...	|	...	|	1257
240	Changchun xi d.	...	...	...	|	...	0704	0722	0740	...	0823	0852	0926	|	0959	...	1017	1023	|	...	...	1146	1211	1247	...	1253	|
358	Siping dong d.	...	...	...	0639	...	0737	|	|	...	0851	0920	|	1010	1028	...	1045	1052	1118	...	...	|	|	|	...	|	|
538	**Shenyang** bei d.	0635	0708	0725	0742y	0821y	0824y	0841y	0906y	0915	0940	1018y	1033	1107y	1126y	1122	1144y	1150y	1213	1239y	1310y	1305y	1327	1407y	1427	1403	1430y
638	Anshan xi d.	0724	|	0807	0814	0900	0906	0913	0938	|	|	1105	|	|	1158	|	1217	1230	1249	|	1355	|	|	|	|	...	...
715	Yinkou dong d.	|	0807	|	|	|	|	|	1001	|	|	|	|	1209	|	|	1246	1259	1312	|	|	1400	1430	|	|	...	...
921	**Dalian** bei a.	0851	0908	0922	0936	1020v	1031	1035	1112v	1124v	1138	1220	1206	1301	1333v	1346v	1346	1400	1424v	1452v	1522v	1453	1541v	1601	1622v	...	...

All trains prefix 'G'	714	8014	752 J	50	8130	764	718 J	8016	8058	3722	720	8018	8060	8020	8062	724	786 X	8044	772 J	8024	716 M	730	8126 t	722	728	D122
Qiqihar nan d.	...	...	...	...	...	...	...	...	...	...	...	...	...	...	...	...	1505	...	...	...	...	...	...	1627	...	...
Harbin xi d.	1219	...	1254	1321	...	1329	1340	...	...	...	1429	...	...	...	...	1542	1642	...	1649	...	1723	1749	...	1815	1832	2120
Jilin d.	|	1237	|	|	1336	|	|	1409	...	...	|	1458	...	1545	...	|	|	...	|	1718	|	|	1820	|	|	|
Changchun d.	|	1320	|	|	1419	|	|	1452	...	...	|	1542	...	1628	...	|	|	...	|	1802	|	|	1903	|	|	|
Changchun xi d.	1323	|	1403	1419	|	1439	1452	|	...	...	1534	|	...	|	...	1647	1741	...	1748	1815	1835	1854	|	1927	1932	2227
Siping dong d.	1351	|	|	|	1454	1507	1521	1527	...	...	|	|	...	1704	...	|	1810	...	1816	|	193	|	1939	1955	2000	...
Shenyang bei d.	1438	1455y	1508	1526	1547	1605y	1612y	1620	1634y	1647y	1655	1716y	1742	1803	1808y	1813y	1908	1914y	1919y	1944	2001y	2012	2036y	2053y	2054	...
Anshan xi d.	|	1527	...	|	1631	1644	1651	1657	1714	1732	1739	|	1818	|	1847	1857	...	1946	1959	|	2039	2055	2116	|	2138	...
Yinkou dong d.	|	1549	...	|	1652	...	|	1718	|	1754	|	1817	|	1849	|	|	...	|	2021	|	2108	2116	2138	|	2200	...
Dalian bei a.	1635	1655	...	1659	1745	...	1805	1817	1829	1847	1854	1934v	1933	1942	2013v	2019	...	2114	2121	2145v	2202	2217	2231	2247	2253	...

Notes for Tables **7015**, **7020**.
J – To/from Table **7023**.
M – To/from Table **7005**.
X – To/from Table **7010**.
r – To Tumen bei arr 1658.
ra – From Tumen bei dep. 1308.
ta – From Tumen bei. dep. 0701.
t – From Tumen bei dep. 1611.
v – Dalian.
y – Shenyang.
** – Changhcun *0 km* - Jilin 111 km - Siping dong *130 km*.
♥ – Additional services **Shenyang** bei – **Beijing** and v.v.

China Rail High Speed — DALIAN - SHENYANG - JILIN and HARBIN — 7020

All trains prefix 'G'	701	8041	8001	703	771	8103	8003	705	8125	707	47	788	8045	8005	709	8007	711	8047	8009	8049	713	8011	3721	8013	8051
					J	X			t	M		X													
Dalian bei d.	0557	0616	0611	0645	0651	...	0657	0730	0735	0802	0830	...	0832v	0836	0912	0917v	0942	0949v	1024	1040v	1107	1108v	1114	1133v	1202a
Yinkou dong d.	0652	|	0730	0740	0752	...	0813	0833	0845	|	|	...	0941	0931	|	|	1044	1058	|	|	|	|	1209	1256	1310
Anshan xi d.	|	|	0753	0802	0814	...	|	|	0907	0913	|	...	1010	|	1028	|	|	1117	|	1204	|	|	|	1319	|
Shenyang bei d.	0753y	0756y	0826y	0852	0858	0909	0925y	0927y	0944	0946y	1006	1042	1051	1030	1058y	1131	1132y	1204y	1214y	1235	1257y	1311y	1304y	1356	1359
Siping dong d.	|	...	0923	0938	0949	1001	1011	|	|	1056	|	1135	...	|	1209	1211	1227	...	1304	...	|	1408	—	1456	...
Changchun xi d.	0911	...	|	1007	1017	|	1040	1045	1105	1131	1112	1204	...	|	1238	|	1256	...	1332	...	1420	|	D121	|	...
Changchun a.	|	...	0954	|	|	1035	1051	|	1122	|	|	|	...	1150	|	1254	|	...	1345	...	|	1441	1447	1536	...
Jilin a.	|	...	...	|	|	1115	1134	|	1159	|	|	|	...	...	|	1337	|	...	1427	...	|	1522	|	1618	...
Harbin xi a.	1009	...	...	1115	1130	...	...	1150	t	1242	1206	1317	...	...	1342	...	1405	...	...	...	1523	...	1604	...	...
Qiqihar nan a.	...	...	...	...	...	...	...		...	...	...	1445	...	...	...	...	1559	...	...	...	...	...	...	...	...

All trains prefix 'G'	717	719	49	8015	753	8053	723	8127	781	8017	8055	725	765	8057	8019	727	8059	8147	729	8067	8023	731	8069	8061	8043
	M				J		J	ta	X																
Dalian bei d.	1222	1244	1330	1338	...	1353v	1413	1416	...	1444v	1514v	1535	1547	1548v	1602v	1639	1647v	1735	1752	1805v	1845	1903	1925	1953	2035
Yinkou dong d.	|	1344	|	1433	...	|	1519	1532	...	|	1631	|	|	1656	|	1740	1754	1837	1901	|	|	|	|	|	2148
Anshan xi d.	|	1412	|	|	...	1523	|	|	...	|	|	1659	1704	|	1731	|	1816	1859	|	0941	|	|	2035	2103	2210
Shenyang bei d.	1423	1445y	1506	1528y	1546	1553y	1620y	1627y	1730	1704	1721	1742	1743y	1748y	1817y	1842y	1852y	1945y	1955y	2022	2044	2104	2122	2137	2250
Siping dong d.	|	|	|	1618	1632	...	1711	1721	|	1757	...	|	|	...	1913	1945	...	...	2052	...	|	2157	...	...	...
Changchun xi d.	1537	1617	1612	|	1700	...	1739	1751	1851	|	...	1901	1910	...	|	2014	...	...	2120	...	|	2233	...	...	...
Changchun a.	|	|	|	1659	|	...	|	1805	|	1838	...	|	|	...	1948	|	...	...	|	...	2207	|	...	...	...
Jilin a.	|	|	|	1739	|	...	|	1851	|	1919	...	|	|	...	2028	|	...	...	|	...	...	|	...	...	...
Harbin xi a.	1636	1722	1706	...	1817	...	1846	ta	1954	...	...	2005	2021	...	...	2118	...	...	2218	...	...	2330	...	...	...
Qiqihar nan a.	...	...	...	...	...	...	...	...	...	...	...	...	2215	...	...	...	...	...	...	...	...	...	...	...	...

J – To/from Table **7023**. **M** – To/from Table **7005**. **X** – To/from Table **7010**. **t** – To Tumen bei arr. 1415. **ta** – To Tumen bei arr. 2053. **v** – Dalian. **y** – Shenyang.

China Rail High Speed — HARBIN - JIAMUSI — 7023

km	All trains prefix 'D'	7801	7803	7805	7807	7809	5373	7811	7813	7815	G771	7817	7819	7821	5383	121	7823	7825	G753	G723	25	7827	G755
							F				K				F				K	K	K		
0	**Harbin** xi d.	0534	0601	0620	0655	0722	0808	0922h	1000h	1100h	1136	1215h	1300h	1426h	1504h	1604	1632	1712	1820	1843	1854	1920h	1943h
350	**Jiamusi** a.	0800	0837	0852	0935	1004	1030	1120	1224	1323	1358	1441	1524	1624	1730	1826	1909	1940	2041	2104	2119	2130	2141

All trains prefix 'D'	7802	7804	26	5384	7806	7808	7810	G752	G718	G754	7812	7814	7816	G772	7818	7820	7822	7824	122	7826	7828	7830
			K	F				K	K					J								
Jiamusi d.	0527	0611	0715	0747	0840	0912	0942	1023	1100	1132	1145	1259	1400	1420	1518	1552	1720	1759	1850	1946	2107	2201
Harbin xi a.	0742h	0836h	0941	1011h	1038h	1121h	1203h	1251	1337	1400	1410h	1533	1614	1646	1716h	1818h	1951	2043	2117	2214	2325	2359h

F – To/from Table **7000**. **K** – To/from Tables **7015/20**. **h** – Harbin.

Chinese Railways — BEIJING - BADALING — 7035

km		S203	S287	S205	S209	S211	S213	S217	S219	S221	
			⑤–①				⑤–①			⑤–①	...
0	**Beijing** ▽ d.	0745	0808	0909	1132	1240	1308	1535	1653	1720	...
82	**Badaling** △ a.	0852	0924	1015	1247	1353	1419	1652	1759	1826	...

	S204	S208	S210	S286	S214	S216	S218	S222	S224	S228
				⑤–①			⑤–①			⑤–①
Badaling △ d.	0727	0955	1104	1121	1334	1454	1525	1739	1901	1939
Beijing ▽ a.	0840	1111	1217	1234	1503	1607	1638	1901	2026	2101

△ – For Great Wall of China. ▽ – Services now depart from Huangtudian station.

China Rail High Speed — BEIJING - TAIYUAN - XI'AN & LANZHOU — 7040

km		D2501	D2567	D2561	G601	D2519	G91	D1963	D2563	G603	D2569	G605	G607	G609	D2565	G611	D2525	D2003	G613	G615	D2533	D2005	G683	G619	G621	G623	G625
		A				E															D						
0	**Beijing** xi d.	...	...	...	0721	...	0840	...	...	1010	...	1028	1114	1133	...	1238	...	1316	1410	1503	...	1529	1658	1802	1807	1845	2005
281	Shijiazhuang d.	...	...	...	0853	...	...	...	...	1132	...	1155	1243	1254	...	1415	...	1514	1538	1636	...	1722	1820	1924	1939	2020	2115
384	Yangquan bei d.	...	...	...	0936	...	|	...	...	|	...	1238	|	1339	...	|	...	1559	1620	1718	...	1810	|	2007	2023	2104	|
513	**Taiyuan** nan d.	0700	0750	0935	1022	1102	1107	1147	1215	1255	1333	1349	1405	1425	1502	1538	1628	1657	1706	1804	1913	1902	1941	2053	2110	2150	2237
746	Linfen xi d.	0819	|	1102	...	|	...	1322	|	...	1516	1532	...	...	1629	...	1747	1832	...	...	|	2052	...	...	...	...	...
869	Yuncheng bei d.	0906	|	|	...	1326	...	1401	|	...	|	1617	...	...	1716	...	1827	1925	...	...	|	...	...	...	...	...	...
1092	**Xi'an** bei a.	1025	1134	1301	...	1445	...	1527	1549	...	1722	...	...	...	1828	...	1946	...	...	...	2239	...	...	...	...	...	...

	G602	G606	G684	G92	D2002	G610	D2004	G612	D2504	D2508	D2536	G614	G616	G618	G620	D2566	G622	D2570	G624	G626	D2562	D2530	D2568	D2564	D2534	D1906
									F	C	B															
Xi'an bei d.	...	...	...	...	...	...	...	...	0808	0915	1000	...	...	...	...	1156	...	1417	...	...	1609	1743	1814	1850	1905	1949
Yuncheng bei d.	...	...	...	...	...	...	0810	...	|	1036	|	...	1153	...	...	|	...	|	...	...	1742	1911	1936	|	2027	|
Linfen xi d.	...	...	...	...	0740	...	0912	...	1016	1122	|	...	1240	...	...	1404	...	1610	...	...	1837	|	|	|	|	2133
Taiyuan nan d.	0648	0805	0824	0833	0927	1100	1109	1140	1149	1256	1327	1332	1429	1458	1523	1531	1650	1728	1807	1850	2003	2115	2148	2224	2231	2251
Yangquan bei d.	|	0853	0922	|	1021	|	1158	1231	...	...	...	1423	1518	1546	1614	...	1738	...	|	1940	...	...	...	...	...	...
Shijiazhuang d.	0817	0935	1009	|	1102	1224	1251	1314	...	...	...	1505	1605	1629	1658	...	1821	...	1934	2035	...	...	...	...	...	...
Beijing xi a.	0935	1054	1141	1100	1252	1344	1501	1436	...	...	...	1633	1728	1741	1817	...	1943	...	2057	2154	...	...	...	...	...	...

km	All trains prefix 'D'	6801	2671	2651	2653	6807	2679	6809	G427	2567	2657	G2023	G1833	2659	2561	G1970	6817	G671	G1875	G96	G429	2569	2565	2665	2667	G673	G844
			Z						X				V			V		X		Y	X					X	Y
0	**Xi'an** bei ♥ d.	0725	0736	0800	0838	0900	1020	1030	1115	1142	1202	1214	1232	1245	1310	1330	1400	1424	1455	1636	1630	1730	1835	1925	2000	2048	2112
167	**Baoji** nan ♥ a.	0832	0837	0901	0933	1007	1115	1131	1210	1238	1257	1309	1327	1340	1405	1425	1510	1531	1553	|	1731	1826	1930	2024	2055	2155	|
568	**Lanzhou** xi ♥ a.	...	1056	1116	1149	...	1330	...	1424	1452	1512	1523	1546	1555	...	1641	...	...	1803	1924	1955	2039	2137	2234	2308	...	2351

All trains prefix 'D'	G672	6802	6806	G834	2654	2566	G642	2656	6812	G430	G1972	G854	G1876	G428	2562	6818	G674	2672	2556	2568	2664	2564	2666	G2024	2674	2670
	X			Y						X	V	Y	V	X			X									
Lanzhou xi ♥ d.	...	...	...	0805	0833	0838	0849	0912	...	0954	1039	1051	1202	1317	...	...	...	1416	1435	1500	1512	...	1535	1545	1837	1900
Baoji nan ♥ d.	0800	0855	0946	1018	1044	1049	1055	1117	1200	1211	1248	1259	1419	1521	1500	1533	1600	1635	1646	1710	1715	1730	1745	1757	2043	2109
Xi'an bei ♥ a.	0907	1009	1042	1119	1140	1145	1150	1212	1257	1307	1350	1400	1520	1610	1601	1634	1710	1730	1747	1805	1810	1837	1842	1852	2153	2210

A – Additional trips: 0720, 0825, 0921, 1244, 1325, 1742, 1807.
B – Additional trips: 1145, 1335.
C – Additional trips: 1041, 1108, 1210, 1530, 1725.
D – Additional trips: 1002, 1521, 1720, 1839.
E – Additional trips: 0628, 0800, 1028.
F – Additional trips: 0733, 0907, 0946, 1250, 1500.
V – To/from Table **7070/7100**. **X** – To/from Table **7066**.
Y – To/from Table **7065**. **Z** – To/from Table **7120**.
♥ – Additional services available.

China Rail High Speed — BEIJING - TIANJIN — 7045

High-speed '**C**' trains (numbers **C20xx**, **C21xx** and **C22xx C25xx**). *120 km*. Journey 30 - 37 minutes.

Beijing nan depart: 0602, 0607, 0617, 0622, 0632, 0643, 0648, 0653, 0658, 0710, 0722, 0732, 0737, 0743, 0810, 0825, 0830, 0835, 0847, 0852, 0904, 0909, 0923, 0936, 0946, 0951, 1013, 1018, 1023, 1029, 1039, 1051, 1056. 1108, 1121, 1126, 1100, 1145, 1202, 1210, 1226, 1240, 1245, 1250, 1310, 1317, 1322, 1341, 1347, 1402, 1418, 1442, 1451, 1500, 1512, 1532, 1545, 1550, 1602, 1608, 1619, 1632, 1641, 1649, 1709, 1723, 1731, 1745, 1752, 1806, 1825, 1835, 1840, 1852, 1906, 1926, 1942, 2002, 2008, 2015, 20026, 2034, 2056, 2107, 2126, 2150, 2218, 2243, 2305.

Tianjin depart: 0618, 0630, 0638, 0652, 0700, 0715, 0728, 0744, 0802, 0811, 0823, 0838, 0851, 0907, 0912, 0923, 0937, 0951, 0957, 1002, 1014, 1029, 1039, 1047, 1105, 1114, 1135, 1140, 1155, 1207, 1213, 1219, 1225, 1236, 1247, 1302, 1315, 1338, 1350, 1406, 1429, 1441, 1447, 1505, 1517, 1525, 1531, 1539, 1609, 1623, 1633, 1645, 1706, 1718, 1723, 1735, 1741, 1747, 1801, 1810, 1815, 1823, 1841, 1859, 1917, 1930, 1938, 1955, 2009, 2018, 2019, 2031, 2046, 2054, 2103, 2111, 2127, 2139, 2153, 2203, 2209, 2233, 2252.

Chinese Railways — HARBIN - TIANJIN and BEIJING — 7047

km	Z188 ♦	K28 ♦	T122 ♦	Z238 ♦	T48 ♦	Read Down ↓ / Read Up ↑	K27 ♦	T47 ♦	Z237 ♦	T121 ♦	Z187 ♦
0	...	...	...	2139	2204x	d.**Harbin** a.	...	0612	0649x	...	...
242	...	...	2128	|	|	d.Changchun d.	...	|	|	0649	...
546	...	...	0012	0159	0257	a.**Shenyang** bei d.	...	0124	0233	0400	...
546	1735	2224y	0019	0205	0303	d.**Shenyang** bei a.	0318y	0116	0227	0350	0530
934	2338	0304	0406	|	|	d.Shanhaiguan d.	2242	|	|	2303	2327
972	|	|	|	|	|	d.Beidaihe d.	|	2124	|	|	|
1235	0303	0649	0800	0750	|	a. **Tianjin** d.	1909	|	2040	1935	2013
1249	...	0840	...	...	0914	a.**Beijing** d.	1727	1857	...	...	...

Chinese Railways — HOHHOT - LANZHOU — 7050

km		K41 ♦	K888 ♦	Z311	Z179 ♦	Read Down ↓ / Read Up ↑	Z180 ♦	K887 ♦	K42 ♦		Z312
0	...	0651	0927	1733h	2359	d.**Hohhot** dong a.	0033	0105	0946	...	1411
165	...	0856	1219	1940	0205	d.Baotou d.	2246	2255	0711	...	1220
383	...	1113	1454	2204	0422	d.Linhe d.	2014	2033	0452	...	0953
838	...	1824	2226	0512	1009	d.Zhongwei d.	1421	1434	2153	...	0205
1095	...	2207	|	|	1341	a. **Wuwei** d.	1047	|	1800	...	|
1562	...	0347	|	|	1822	a. Jiayuguan d.	0554	|	1214	...	|
970	...	...	|	0723	...	d.Jingtai d.	...	1217	...	...	2323
1057	...	...	|	0852	...	d.Beiyin xi d.	...	1013	...	...	2129
1144	...	...	0542	1109	...	a.**Lanzhou** xi d.	...	0738	...	...	1941

K27/28 – ①③④⑥. Beijing(**K27/28**) - Dandong(**6/5**) - Pyongyang and v.v.
K42/41 – Jiayuggan(**K42/41**) - Beijing.
T47/48 – 🛏 1, 2 cl.Qiqihar(**T48/47**) - Beijing.
T121/122 – Changchun(**T122/21**) - Tianjin(**T123/24**) - Guangzhou and v.v.
Z179/180 – Beijing(**Z178/180**) - Urümqi and v.v.
Z187/188 – Shenyang bei(**Z188/87**) - Tianjin(**Z185/86**) - Shenzhen and v.v.
Z237/238 – Harbin(**Z238/37**) - Tianjin(**Z235/36**) - Guangzhou and v.v.
K887/88 – Beijing(**K887/88**) - Lanzhou and v.v.
h – Hohhot. **y** – Shenyang.

7060 BEIJING - ZHENGZHOU - WUHAN - CHANGSHA(- GUANGZHOU)

China Rail High Speed

km	All trains prefix 'G'	93	551	D295	541	850	423 D	507	485	529 D	73	71	531	309	83	98	820	81	421 D	511	79	824	834	65	545	557
0	**Beijing** xi ♣ d.	...	...	...	...	...	...	0642	0703	0708	...	0727	...	0823	0855	...	...	0900	0905	0927	1000	...	...	1033	...	1107
281	Shijiazhuang d.	...	...	...	...	...	0753	0816	0832	0846	...	0859	0915	0955	1005	...	...	1010	1035	1050	1109	...	...	1159	...	1229
403	Xingtai dong d.	...	...	...	...	...	|	|	0902	0923	...	0935	0949	|	|	...	...	|	|	1120	|	...	...	1236	...	|
456	Handan dong d.	...	...	...	...	...	0845	0858	0920	0944	...	0954	|	1053	|	...	...	|	1116	1145	|	...	...	|	...	|
516	Anyang dong d.	...	...	...	...	...	|	0917	0939	|	1003	|	1022	1112	|	...	...	|	1135	1204	|	...	...	1306	...	1330
626	Xinxiang dong d.	...	...	...	...	...	0932	|	|	|	|	1041	1049	|	|	...	...	|	|	1232	|	...	...	|	...	1358
	Xi'an bei **7070** d.	...	...	...	...	...	|	|	|	|	|	|	|	|	|	0957	0935	|	|	|	|	1103	1130	|	...	|
693	**Zhengzhou** dong ♣ a.	...	...	...	...	...	0954	1007	1021	1038	1045	1102	1111	1154	1126	1147z	1159z	1131	1218	1253	1231	1312z	1340z	1348	...	1419
693	**Zhengzhou** dong ♣ d.	0756	...	0824z	0825	0931	0959	1010	1026	1043	1048	1106	1114	1157	1129	1150z	1202z	1134	1221	1256	1234	1315z	1346z	1351	1405	1423
848	Luohe xi d.	|	0800	0922	0901	|	1036	|	|	|	1130	|	|	|	|	|	1254	|	1305	1331	|	1401	|	|	1444	1505
1030	Xinyang dong d.	|	0854	1015	0949	1046	1123	1129	1145	1205	1210	|	1240	|	|	|	1339	|	1352	|	|	1452	|	1508	|	1646
1229	**Wuhan** ♣ a.	0955	0951	1119h	1033	1130	1207	1220h	1229	1249	1254	1305	1331	1349h	1316	1348	1423	1321	1436	1455h	1417	1540	1605	1552	1613	1746
1438	Yueyang dong d.	|	|	...	|	1227	1315	...	1331	1412	|	|	|	...	|	|	1518	|	1535	...	|	1632	|		|	...
1576	**Changsha** nan **7065** a.	1116	1130	...	1204	1308	1349	...	1408	1446	1420	1426	1501	...	1438	1511	1554	1442	1609	...	1538	1706	1739	1729	1744	...
	Guangzhou nan **7065** a.	1350	1424	...	1456	1555	...	...	...	...	1701	1713	1751	...	...	1739	1837	...	...	...	1801	1954	2026	2016	2035	...
	Shenzhen bei **7065** a.	...	1500	...	...	...	...	...	...	...	1734	1803f	1825	...	...	...	1918	...	...	...	1846k	2035	...	...	...	...

All trains prefix 'G'	553	75	838	828	842	555	67	517	491	533	69	547	519	503	858	587	521	505	573	585	523	561	525	563	527
Beijing xi ♣ d.	...	...	...	...	...	1256	1213	1219	1233	1301	1306	...	1405	1441	...	1448	1523	1540	1618	1623	1630	1653	1714	1719	1814
Shijiazhuang d.	...	...	...	...	...	1406	1341	1348	1355	1411	1448	...	1531	1606	...	1611	1652	1703	1742	1758	1753	1815	1836	1848	1936
Xingtai dong d.	...	...	...	...	...	|	1418	|	1436	|	|	...	|	|	...	1648	|	1733	|	1828	1823	1847	1906	1918	|
Handan dong d.	...	...	...	...	...	|	1447	1429	1454	|	|	...	|	|	...	|	1734	1751	|	1848	|	1906	1917	1936	|
Anyang dong d.	...	...	...	...	...	|	|	|	|	|	|	...	1631	|	...	1718	1753	|	|	1907	1853	1925	1936	1955	|
Xinxiang dong d.	...	...	...	...	...	|	1527	|	1543	|	|	...	1659	|	...	1753	|	|	1905	1935	1921	1953	|	2023	|
Xi'an bei **7070** d.	...	...	1232	1239	1320	|	|	|	|	|	|	...	|	|	1518	|	|	|	|	|	|	|	|	|	|
Zhengzhou dong ♣ a.	...	...	1442z	1501z	1533z	1527	1548	1522	1605	1532	1617	...	1720	1742	1722z	1815	1836	1854	1926	1956	1943	2014	2025	2037	2103
Zhengzhou dong ♣ d.	...	1410	1447z	1504z	1536z	1530	1551	1540	1611	1535	1620	1644	1723	1744	1726z	1817	1847	1857	1929	2000	1946	...	2029	...	2107
Luohe xi d.	...	1458	|	1550	|	|	1633	|	|	|	|	|	|	1826	|	1911	1936	|	|	2043	2025	...	2111	...	|
Xinyang dong d.	1530	1559	1613	|	|	|	1715	|	1721	|	|	1815	1846	|	1904	1951	2030	|	2044	2126	2114	...	2158	...	|
Wuhan ♣ a.	1625	1648	1657	1725	1749	1720h	1800	1737	1805	1720	1817	1859	1930	1943	1948	2035	2128h	2056	2128	2211	2159	...	2249h	...	2252
Yueyang dong d.	1723	1739	1755	1829	|	...	1855	...	...	|	1912	2005	...	|	...	...	...	2158	...	...	...	...	...	...	...
Changsha nan **7065** a.	1756	1813	1829	1859	1921	...	1929	...	...	1841	1953	2028	...	2114	...	...	...	2232	...	...	...	...	...	...	...
Guangzhou nan **7065** a.	2045	2100	2117	2149	2208	...	2219	...	...	...	2229	2315	...	...	...	...	...	...	...	...	...	...	...	...	...
Shenzhen bei **7065** a.	...	2140	...	2235	2243	...	...	...	...	...	...	...	...	...	...	...	...	...	...	...	...	...	...	...	...

All trains prefix 'G'	565	509	567	807	D901 A	D903 A	D909 A	D921 C	D927 A	D923 A
Beijing xi ♣ d.	1828	1900	1916	2000	2010	2015	2020	2030	2025	2035
Shijiazhuang d.	1951	2009	2038	|	2135	2140	2145	2201	2156	2206
Xingtai dong d.	|	|	2108	|	|	|	2217	|	|	|
Handan dong d.	2053	|	2126	|	|	2225	|	|	|	|
Anyang dong d.	|	|	|	|	2236	|	|	|	|	|
Xinxiang dong d.	2136	|	2218	|	|	|	|	|	|	|
Xi'an bei **7070** d.	|	|	|	|	|	|	|	|	|	|
Zhengzhou dong ♣ a.	2157	2131	2239	2225	|	2327	2332	2342	2337	2347
Zhengzhou dong ♣ d.	...	2134	...	...	|	2332	2337	2347	2342	2352
Luohe xi d.	...	|	...	...	|	|	|	|	|	|
Xinyang dong d.	...	|	...	...	|	|	|	|	|	|
Wuhan ♣ a.	...	2324h	...	...	|	|	|	|	|	|
Yueyang dong d.	...	...	...	...	|	|	|	|	|	|
Changsha nan **7065** a.	...	...	...	...	|	|	|	|	|	|
Guangzhou nan **7065** a.	...	...	...	...	0628	0633	0638	0653	0659	0643
Shenzhen bei **7065** a.	...	...	...	...	0706	0711	0716	...	0742	...

All trains prefix 'G'	520	562	508	564	510	588	502	512	84	586
Shenzhen bei **7065** d.	...	...	...	...	...	...	...	...	...	...
Guangzhou nan **7065** d.	...	...	...	...	...	...	...	...	...	...
Changsha nan **7065** d.	...	...	...	...	...	...	0736	...	0900	...
Yueyang dong d.	...	...	...	...	...	...	|	...	|	...
Wuhan ♣ d.	0700h	...	0710h	...	0810	0830	0911	0921h	1020	1042
Xinyang dong d.	|	...	0801	...	0855	|	|	1014	|	|
Luohe xi d.	|	...	0848	...	0953	|	|	|	|	|
Zhengzhou dong ♣ a.	0851	...	0929	...	1030	1015	1059	1129	1205	1230
Zhengzhou dong ♣ d.	0854	0919	0932	0948	1034	1017	1103	1132	1208	1231
Xi'an bei **7070** a.	|	|	|	|	|	|	|	|	|	|
Xinxiang dong d.	|	|	|	|	1057	|	1132	|	|	|
Anyang dong d.	|	1005	|	1034	|	|	|	1222	|	|
Handan dong d.	|	|	1035	1053	1137	|	|	|	|	|
Xingtai dong d.	|	1035	|	|	|	|	1228	1252	|	|
Shijiazhuang d.	1018	1110	1116	1140	1219	|	1258	1324	1332	1401
Beijing xi ♣ a.	1126	1232	1228	1314	1339	1242	1424	1456	1441	1521

All trains prefix 'G'	572	514	94	556	832	96		518	82	516	552	72	80	74	66	542	818	404	532	822	524	68	836	422 D	310
Shenzhen bei **7065** d.	...	...	...	...	...	...	...	...	...	...	...	0700f	0827k	0842	...	...	0935	...	0940	1000	...	...	...	...	...
Guangzhou nan **7065** d.	...	...	0739	...	0711	0855	...	...	...	...	0932	0746	0900	0922	1000	0945	1016	...	1022	1039	...	1113	1124	...	...
Changsha nan **7065** d.	...	...	1020	...	0956	1115	...	...	1138	...	1230	1034	1120	1207	1220	1235	1257	1303	1308	1325	...	1400	1417	1422	...
Yueyang dong d.	...	...	|	...	1032		...	...	|	...	1305	1118	|	1253	|	1310	|	|	1344	1400		1435	1452	1457	
Wuhan ♣ d.	1031	0953	1152	1040h	1128	1236	...	1245	1258	1330	1359	1220	1241	1349	1341	1405	1435	1425	1440	1455	1520	1534	1546	1601	1610h
Xinyang dong d.	1116	|	|	1134	|	|	...	1341	|	|	1453	|	|	1434	|	1450	1520	|	1525	1541	1614	1619	1631	1646	|
Luohe xi d.	1203	1148	|	|	|	|	...	|	|	|	...	1420	|	1521	|	1542	1600	|	1607	|	1655	1706	1719	|	|
Zhengzhou dong ♣ a.	1240	1241	1343	1306	1344z	1433z	...	1451	1447	1514	...	1456	1425	1602	1525	1621	1653z	1610	1641	1703z	1730	1741	1800z	1803	1818
Zhengzhou dong ♣ d.	1240	1248	...	1312	1355z	1439z	...	1454	1448	1517	...	1459	1428	...	1528	...	1700z	1612	1644	1708z	1734	1753	1803z	1806	1824
Xi'an bei **7070** a.	|	|	...	|	1608	1631	...	|	|	|	...	|	|	...	|	...	1913	|	|	1930	|	|	2009	|	|
Xinxiang dong d.	|	|	...	1334	...	...	...	|	|	|	...	|	|	...	|	...	...	|	1706	...	|	|	...	1846	1846
Anyang dong d.	1331	1339	...	1409	...	...	...	|	|	|	...	1543	|	...	|	...	...	|	|	...	1824	1847	...	|	1914
Handan dong d.	|	1359	...	|	...	...	...	|	|	|	...	|	|	...	|	...	...	|	1756	...	|	|	...	|	|
Xingtai dong d.	|	|	...	1439	...	...	...	|	|	|	...	1630	|	...	|	...	...	|	|	...	|	|	...	1919	1944
Shijiazhuang d.	1426	1448	...	1522	...	...	...	1634	1614	1642	...	1703	1554	...	1653	...	...	1737	1845	...	1919	1950	...	1941	2016
Beijing xi ♣ a.	1554	1609	...	1646	...	...	...	1746	1721	1750	...	1822	1701	...	1800	...	...	1845	...	...	2043	2110	...	2053	2142

All trains prefix 'G'	486	402	424 D	506	808	844	70	530 D	492	826	528	840	558	544	406	546	D296	76	548	D922 C	D924 A	D902 A	D904 A	D910 A	D928 A
Shenzhen bei **7065** d.	...	...	...	...	...	...	...	...	...	1249	...	1300	...	...	...	...	...	1546	...	...	...	1940	1945	1950	1955
Guangzhou nan **7065** d.	...	...	...	...	...	1230	1250	...	...	1330	...	1345	...	1356	...	1413	...	1625	1630	2005	2010	2015	2020	2025	2030
Changsha nan **7065** d.	1427	1441	1501	1505	...	1517	1538	1548	...	1617	...	1532	...	1647	1705	1710	...	1915	1923	|	2303	|	2313	2318	2323
Yueyang dong d.	|	|	1536	1541	...	1553	|	1623	...	|	...	|	...	1723	|	|	...	|	1959	|	|	|	|	|	
Wuhan ♣ d.	1611	1621	1639	1644	...	1651	1707	1720	1726	1748	1759	1807	1810	1831	1836	1846	1727	2041	2056	|	|	|	|	|	|
Xinyang dong d.	1656	1706	1724	1729	...	1737	1752	1805	1813	1833	1844	1853	1902	|	|	1935	1928	2126	2151	|	|	|	|	|	|
Luohe xi d.	1735	1755	1804	1809	...	|	|	1857	|	1929	|	|	1954	2007	|	2030	2020	2206	|	|	|	|	|	|	|
Zhengzhou dong ♣ a.	1811	1830	1838	1843	...	1914z	1906	1938	1921	2030z	2002	2020z	2040	2041	2024	2113	2114	2248	2307	|	|	|	|	|	|
Zhengzhou dong ♣ d.	1814	1834	1841	1848	1908	1916z	1914	1943	1924	2041z	2006	2027z	2041	...	2030	...	...	...	...	|	|	|	|	|	|
Xi'an bei **7070** a.	|	|	|	|	|	2112	|	|	|	2249	|	2232	|	...	|	...	...	...	...	|	|	|	|	|	|
Xinxiang dong d.	|	1856	1908	|	|	...	|	|	1947	...	|	...	|	...	|	...	...	...	...	|	|	|	|	|	|
Anyang dong d.	1857	1924	1951	|	|	...	1957	|	|	...	|	...	|	...	|	...	...	...	...	|	|	|	|	|	|
Handan dong d.	1917	1944	|	2000	|	...	2016	|	2032	...	2115	...	|	...	|	...	...	...	...	|	|	|	|	|	0501
Xingtai dong d.	|	|	2023	|	|	...	|	2057	|	...	|	...	|	...	|	...	...	...	...	|	|	|	|	0509	|
Shijiazhuang d.	2000	2040	2051	2044	|	...	2100	2130	2115	...	2156	...	2222	...	2206	...	...	...	...	0518	0523	0528	0533	0544	0550
Beijing xi ♣ a.	2126	2159	...	2204	2135	...	2228	2258	2243	...	2322	...	2334	...	2318	...	...	...	...	0640	0651	0656	0701	0713	0718

A – Conveys 🛏 1cl, 🚃 Runs ①⑤⑥⑦ only.
C – ①⑤⑥⑦ 🛏 1cl, 🚃 Beijing - Zhanjiang and v.v.
D – To/from Table **7184**.
f – Shenzhen Futian
h – Wuhan Hankou.
k – To/from West Kowloon see Table **6065**.
z – Zhengzhou.
♣ – Additional services operate Beijing – Zhengzhou – Wuhan and v.v.

7062 BEIJING - HOHHOT - BAOTOU

China Rail High Speed, Chinese Railways

km	K263	D6775 X	K617	K395	Z179 ♦	D6751 X	K573	K597	K41 ♦	K89	Z317	K888 ♦			D6770 X	K618	K42 ♦	Z318	K598	D6788 X	K90	K574	K264	K396	Z180 ♦	K887 ♦
0	0925	...	1024x	1107x	1500	...	2035x	2128x	2045	2217x	2250	2343	↓	d.**Beijing** a. ↑	...	1935x	1942	2150	0454x	...	0725x	0858x	0821	0955x	0949	1205
190	|	...	|	|	|	...	|	|	|	|	|	|	↓	d. Zhangjiakou nan . d. ↑	...	|	|	|	|	...	|	|	|	|	|	|
368	1607	...	1807	1717	2109	...	0253	0346	0319	0427	0503	0602	↓	d.Datong d. ↑	...	1300	1326	1538	2303	...	0139	0303	0157	0355	0337	0504
374	1752	...	2009	1904	2251	...	0438	0527	0509	0610	0646	0745	↓	d.Jining nan d. ↑	...	1057	1131	1349	2110	...	2335	0022	0007	0137	0152	0140
524*	1918h	1921	2233h	2104h	2359	0619	0621	0701	0651	0755	0826h	0927	↓	a.**Hohhot** dong d. ↑	0754	0915	0946	1225h	1933	2126	2200	2252	2330	0007	0033	0103
697	2131	2040	...	2347	0205	0736	0854	0911	0856	...	1012	1219	↓	a.Baotou d. ↑	0630	...	0711	1045	1715	2007	...	2021	1945	2152	2246	...

♦ – **NOTES** by train number
K41/42 – Jiayuggan(**K41/42**) - Beijing.
Z179/180 – Beijing(**Z179/180**) - Urümqi and v.v.
K887/88 – Beijing(**K887/88**) - Lanzhou and v.v.
X – Regular high-speed services run throughout the day.
h – Hohhot.
x – Beijing xi.
* – 645km via Datong.

China Rail High Speed — (BEIJING -) XIA'N - WUHAN - CHANGSHA - GUANGZHOU - SHENZHEN — 7065

km	71	98	79	824	65	834 X	838	828	842	854 X	67	69	All trains 'G'	832	72	96 X	80	66	818	822	68	836	844 X	70	840
1229	0727	...	1000	...	1033	...	...	...	...	...	1213	1306	d.*Beijing xi* **7060**..... a.	...	1822	...	1701	1800	...	...	2110	...		2228	...
1050	|	0957	|	1103	|	1130	1232	1239	1320	1414	|	|	d.**Xi'an** bei .... a.	1608	|	1631	|	|	1913	1930	|	2009	2106	|	2232
929	|	|	|	1135	|	1202	1305	1322	1400	|	|	|	d.Huashan bei........ d.	1538	|	|	|	|	1843	|	|	|	|	|	|
793	|	|	|	|	|	|	|	1350	|	1515	|	|	d.Sanmenxia nan ... d.	1509	|	|	|	|	1807	1828	|	|	|	|	2141
670	|	|	|	1234	|	1303	1406	1423	1454	1548	|	|	d.Luoyang Longmen d.	1436	|	|	|	|	|	1749	|	1844	|	|	2108
536	1106	1150**z**	1234	1315**z**	1351	1346**z**	1447**z**	1504**z**	1536**z**	1629**z**	1551	1620	d.Zhengzhou dong . d.	1355**z**	1459	1439**x**	1428	1528	1700**z**	1708**z**	1753	1803**z**	1916**z**	1914	2027**z**
0	1308	1351	1420	1540	1557	1612	1704	1733	1749	1935	1803	1821	d.**Wuhan**............... d.	1128	1220	1236	1241	1341	1435	1455	1534	1546	1651	1707	1805
209	|	|	|	1632	1655	|	1755	|	|	...	1855	1912	d.Yueyang dong..... d.	1032	1118	|	|	|	|	1400	1435	1452	1553	|	|
347	1429	1515	1541	1710	1732	1743	1833	1908	1924	...	1934	1956	d.**Changsha** nan.... d.	0956	1034	1115	1120	1220	1257	1325	1400	1417	1517	1538	1632
387	|	|	|	|	|	|	|	|	|	...	|	|	d.Zhuzhou xi .... d.	|	|	|	|	|	|	|	1336	1355	1453	|	|
496	1508	|	|	1749	|	1822	1912	1940	|	...	|	2035	d.Hengyang dong... d.	0912	0951	|	|	|	|	1242	|	1325	|	|	1546
628	|	|	|	1824	1846	1857	1947	|	|	...	2048	|	d.Chenzhou xi .... d.	|	0916	|	|	|	1142	1207	|	1243	|	1416	1511
758	1616	|	|	1857	|	|	|	2051	2105	...	|	|	d.Shaoguan............ d.	|	0839	|	|	|	|	|	1206	|	1323	1343	1438
968	1713	1739	1801	1954	2016	2026	2117	2148	2209	...	2218	2229	a.**Guangzhou** nan . d.	0711	0746	0955	0900	1000	1016	1040	1113	1124	1230	1250	1345
1070	1803**f**	...	1839	2035	...	...	...	2235	2243	...	...	...	a.**Shenzhen** bei ..... d.	...	0700**f**	...	0824	...	0935	1000	...	...	...	...	1300
1110	...	...	1858	...	...	...	...	...	...	...	...	...	a.**West Kowloon** ... d.	...	...	...	0805	...	...	...	...	...	...	...	...

km	All trains prefix 'G'	8905	6011	6101	6013	6113	6015	1001	1105	1003	1005	77	1158	1007	1009	551	93	2924 G	1035 C	85 A	541	633	1031 C	6037	1013	1148 C
0	**Wuhan** ♥ **7060** .... d.	...	...		...	...	...	0725	0737	0755	0812	0900	0910	0930	0941	0951	0956	...	1019	...	1039	...	1140	...	1207	1225
209	Yueyang dong........... d.	...	...		...	...	...	|	0828	|	0910	|	1008	1028	1033	|	|	...	1135	...	|	...	1238	...	1300	1323
347	**Changsha** nan ♥..... d.	...	0700	0711	0728	0738	0755	0854	0912	0923	0947	1021	1045	1107	1111	1130	1120	...	1218	1228	1207	1241	1316	1332	1341	1401
387	Zhuzhou xi .... d.	...	|	0728	|	0755	|	|	|	|	|	|	|	1124	1135	1148	|	...	|	|	|	1258	|	1349	1358	1418
496	Hengyang dong......... d.	0647	|		|	|	0834	0933	0951	|	|	|	|	1153	1204	1217	1159	...	1257	|	1246	|	1355	1418	1427	1447
628	Chenzhou xi.............. d.	|	0807		0842	0859	|	|	1026	|	|	|	1159	1232	1239	1251	|	...	1340	|	1321	|	1430	1453	|	1522
758	Shaoguan .... d.	|	0840	0858	0915	0931	0942	|	|	|	|	|	1232	|	|	|	|	...	1413	|	1359	|	1504	|	|	1556
968	**Guangzhou** nan ♥... a.	0844	0951	1002	1014	1032	1038	1131	1156	1200	1224	1243	1329	1402	1410	1423	|	1435	1510	1451	1456	1525	1601	1616	1628	1653
1070	**Shenzhen** bei ♥....... a.	0918	1034	...	1052	1104	1111	1212	...	1241	1300	1316	...	1441	1445	1500	1350	1504	1556	...	...	1606	1644	1656	1705	...
1110	**West Kowloon**........ a.	...	...	...	...	1126	...	...	...	...	...	...	...	...	...	...	...	...	...	...	...	...	...	...	...	...

All trains prefix 'G'	G311 G	73	6001	531	1015	6031	820	1017	1301 A	275	1314 C	1019	1129	545	553	2055	75	1021	99 A	2928 G	6027	1133	1135	1305 A	547
Wuhan ♥ **7060**............... d.	...	1301	...	1336	1345	...	1427	1439	...	1502	1512	1545	1550	1619	1630	1643	1648	1658	...	...	...	1758	1808	...	1907
Yueyang dong .... d.	...	|	...	|	1447	...	1518	1530	...	|	|	1637	|	|	1723	|	1739	1800	...	...	1850	1904	|	...	2005
Changsha nan ♥.............. d.	...	1424	1500	1505	1526	1551	1601	1607	1612	1624	1655	1716	1721	1748	1800	1805	1816	1838	1858	...	1930	1945	1940	2047	2042
Zhuzhou xi........................ d.	...	|	|	|	|	|	|	|	|	|	1712	|	1738	|	|	1822	1833	|	|	...	|	|	1957	|	|
Hengyang dong .... d.	...	|	|	|	1606	1634	1640	1646	1658	1704	1741	1746	1807	1827	|	1851	1902	1917	|	...	2010	2031	2026	2133	2122
Chenzhou xi .... d.	...	1531	|	1612	1646	|	|	|	1733	1745	1816	|	|	1902	|	|	|	1952	|	...	2045	2110	|	2208	|
Shaoguan .... d.	...	1604	|	|	1719	1746	|	1754	1806	1819	1849	1902	|	|	1947	1952	2003	|	2035	...	|	|	2127	2241	|
Guangzhou nan ♥ .... a.	1602	1701	1723	1751	1816	1842	1837	1851	1903	1915	1945	2000	2011	2031	2045	2049	2100	2122	2132	2159	2214	2240	2224	2338	2315
Shenzhen bei ♥ .... a.	1632	1734	1758	1825	1852	1924	1918	1931	...	...	2025	2040	...	...	...	...	2140	2202	2209	2230	2249	...	...	...	...
West Kowloon................... a.	1655	...	...	...	...	...	...	...	...	...	...	...	...	...	...	...	...	...	2229	...	...	...	...	...	...

All trains prefix 'G'	1102	1002	94	6012	86 A	2056	280	1312 C	2926 G	1004	74	552	542	6032	1006	532	1110	1112	1008	1114	6016	100 A	1010	6018	G312 G
West Kowloon................... d.	...	...	...	...	...	...	...	...	...	...	...	...	...	...	...	...	...	...	...	...	...	1110	...	...	1206
Shenzhen bei ♥ .... d.	...	0700	...	0715	...	...	0743	0738	0758	0832	0842	...	...	0902	0930	0940	...	...	1024	...	1103	1132	1125	1205	1228
Guangzhou nan ♥ .... d.	0700	0734	0739	0754	0800	0805	0815	0810	0827	0911	0922	0932	0946	0954	1011	1020	1025	1046	1056	1101	1142	1205	1159	1245	1305
Shaogun.............................. d.	|	|	|	0845	|	0856	0908	0903	...	|	|	1033	1039	1054	1104	1114	1119	1139	1149	1201	1235	1269	1252	1338	...
Chenzhou xi .... d.	|	0853	0859	|	|	0931	|	0936	...	1030	1049	1106	1116	|	|	1147	1152	1212	1222	|	1308	|	1329	1411	...
Hengyang dong .... d.	0854	0928	0934	|	|	|	|	|	...	1105	|	|	|	|	|	|	1227	1247	|	1302	1343	|	|	|	...
Zhuzhou xi........................... d.	|	|	|	|	|	|	|	1033	...	|	|	1206	|	|	|	|	|	1315	1320	|	1412	|	|	1508	...
Changsha nan ♥................ d.	0945	1013	1020	1035	1021	1044	1102	1057	...	1148	1207	1230	1235	1237	1252	1308	1313	1340	1345	1350	1430	1434	1456	1528	...
Yueyang dong .... d.	1021	1048	|	...	...	|	|	|	...	|	1253	1305	1310	...	|	1344	1349	|	1420	1425	...	...	|	...	...
Wuhan ♥............................ a.	1118	1138	1152	...	...	1204	1227	1218	...	1320	1343	1355	1401	...	1417	1434	1446	1501	1522	1518	...	...	1623	...	...

All trains prefix 'G'	1304 A	1032 C	826	1012	544	546	6020	554	1146 C	1130	6002	1306 A	1018	1036 C	1014	2922 G	76	548	1162	1020	1134	6130	1022	6114	6122
West Kowloon................... d.	...	...	...	...	...	...	...	...	...	...	...	...	...	...	...	...	...	...	...	...	...	...	...	1718	...
Shenzhen bei ♥ .... d.	...	1239	1249	1310	...	...	1405	1329	...	...	1500	...	1505	1510	1521	1527	1546	...	...	1625	...	...	1708	1740	...
Guangzhou nan ♥ .... d.	1324	1319	1330	1351	1356	1413	1445	1409	1501	1526	1533	1538	1544	1549	1601	1601	1625	1630	1647	1705	1729	1745	1750	1813	2100
Shaogun.............................. d.	1428	|	1423	1444	1449	1506	|	|	|	1631	|	|	1637	1643	1654	...	|	|	1740	|	1822	|	|	1906	2153
Chenzhou xi .... d.	1501	1445	1456	1517	1522	1539	1611	1529	1621	1704	|	1657	1710	1716	1727	...	1752	|	1813	1831	1855	1911	1916	1939	|
Hengyang dong .... d.	1536	1527	1532	1552	1557	1618	1646	1604	1657	1739	|	|	1745	1751	1802	...	1827	|	1846	1906	1930	1946	|	2014	2254
Zhuzhou xi........................... d.	|	|	|	|	|	1647	1715	|	|	|	|	|	|	1820	1931	...	|	|	|	|	|	2015	|	2043	|
Changsha nan ♥................ d.	1617	1611	1617	1637	1646	1710	1734	1654	1743	1825	1755	1808	1831	1842	1853	...	1915	1924	1933	1950	2016	2035	2043	2103	2336
Yueyang dong .... d.	...	1646	|	1713	1723	|	...	1749	1818	1900	...	...	1913	|	1928	...	|	1959	|	2026	2052	...	2125	...	...
Wuhan ♥............................ a.	...	1749	1743	1804	1825	1837	...	1915	1910	1957	...	...	2003	2015	2021	...	2041	2056	2106	2123	2142	...	2215	...	...

China Rail High Speed — BEIJING - ZHENGZHOU - XI'AN — 7066

km	427 X	89 H	671 X	571 H	429 X	659	87	673 X	663	665	669	25	All trains prefix 'G'	26	672 X	656	662	660	430 X	88	574 H	664	428 X	674 X	90 H
0	0620	0653	0815	0922	1045	1153	1400	1428	1545	1600	1708	1855	d.**Beijing** xi ♣........ a.	1350	1511	1533	1641	1651	1853	1755	1953	2020	2149	2310	2252
281	0736	0802	0946	1045	1212	1328	|	1556	1708	1730	1841	2004	d.Shijiazhuang........ d.	1241	1345	1414	1510	1535	1726	1648	1827	1900	2030	2149	2144
403	|	|	|	|	1242	1358	|	1626	1739	1800	1910	|	d.Xingtai dong........ d.	|	1315	1342	1433	|	1655	|	1752	1828	|	2118	|
456	|	|	1027	1130	|	|	|	1652	1758	|	1929	|	d.Handan dong ...... d.	|	1257	|	|	1450	|	|	|	|	1938	|	|
516	|	|	|	1157	1312	1428	|	1711	|	1830	|	|	d.Anyang dong....... d.	|	|	|	1403	1424	|	|	1718	1758	1919	|	|
626	|	|	|	1225	1340	|	|	1746	|	1858	|	|	d.Xinxiang dong ..... d.	|	1201	|	1326	1350	1602	|	|	1730	1851	|	|
693	0910	0932	1151	1254	1410	1524	1630	1816	1903	1928	2035	2132	d.**Zhengzhou** dong d.	1111	1139	1225	1304	1328	1540	1523	1628	1708	1818	1950	2017
836	0949	|	1230	|	1448	|	|	1854	1941	2013	2120	|	d.Luoyang Longmen d.	|	|	1144	1220	1247	1447	|	1543	1612	1740	1905	|
959	|	|	1303	1400	|	1635	|	|	2019	2046	|	|	d.Sanmenxia nan ... d.	|	1023	1109	1147	|	|	|	|	|	|	1829	|
1095	|	|	1331	1429	|	1705	|	|	2048	|	|	|	d.Huashan bei........ d.	|	0953	|	1117	1146	1347	|	1441	1511	|	1801	|
1216	1106	1124	1416	1503	1620	1735	1820	2026	2118	2146	2237	2321	a.**Xi'an** Bei ♣ .... d.	0918	0911	1003	1043	1113	1315	1330	1409	1438	1621	1721	1824

China Rail High Speed — XI'AN - ZHENGZHOU - XUZHOU — 7070

km	Prefix 'G' unless noted	1914 D	1900	1844	2002	1896	362 D	1918 D	1922 D	1904	2204 H	1926 D	1856	1282 H	1884	1836 E	1972 Da	1888	1938	1876 X	1942	1880 E	1832	2210 H	D305 D	2212
0	**Xi'an** Bei.................. d.	0626	0730	0742	0810	0840	0849	0923	1023	1057	1210	1225	1256	1309	1340	1345	1356	1614	1513	1523	1550	1626	1659	1934	1944	2058
121	Huashan bei.............. d.	0706	0810	0831	0901	0928	|	1003	|	|	1244	1258	|	|	1412	1417	1436	1648	|	1556	|	1706	|	|	2028	|
257	Sanmenxia nan......... d.	0734	0838	0906	|	0956	|	1031	|	|	|	|	|	|	|	1445	|	1716	|	1624	|	|	1801	2035	2102	|
380	Luoyang Longmen .... d.	|	0912	0939	0951	1035	|	1104	1150	1226	|	1352	1430	1435	1513	1518	1535	1749	1633	1658	1719	1801	1839	2115	2141	2225
523	**Zhengzhou** dong...... d.	0843	0953	1035	1029	1123	1043	1147	1238	1310	1423	1452	1515	1534	1554	1606	1622	1837	1714	1741	1808	1844	1920	2200	2232	2304
713	Shangqui .... d.	|	1052	1143	...	1229	|	1246	1345	1410	...	|	1614	...	1650	1713	1721	1836	|	1835	1914	1943	2019	...	|	...
883	**Xuzhou** dong............ a.	1029	1144	1232	...	1321	1213	1338	1436	1502	...	1629	1730	...	1742	1819	1820	2030	1845	1927	2008	2035	2121	...	0021**x**	...

Prefix 'G' unless noted	D307 D	2201 H	2001	2023	1833 E	1879 E	1831	1970 Da	1887	1875	1975 DH	361 D	1701	1883	1921	1835	1895	1903	2211	1925 D	1929	1933	1711	1937 D	1941
Xuzhou dong. .... d.	...	...	...	...	0830	0836	0845	0907	0941	1022	1034	1106	...	1148	1225	1304	1404	1430	...	1441	1616	1700	...	1901	1943
Shangqui.............................. d.	...	...	...	0827	0924	|	0942	1009	1036	1117	1129	|	...	|	|	|	1457	1524	...	1539	|	|	...	|	2029
Zhengzhou dong................. d.	0720	0710	0813**x**	0941	1017	1039	1046	1105	1136	1218	1223	1244	1312	1341	1415	1445	1559	1637	1616	1646	1811	1834	2010	2059	2137
Luoyang Longmen .... d.	0806	0749	0840	|	1057	1118	1131	1150	1216	1256	1302	|	1357	1421	|	|	1644	1716	|	|	1849	1913	2053	|	|
Sanmenxia nan...................... d.	0845	0823	0912	1052	|	1150	|	1223	|	1333	|	|	|	|	1526	1550	1717	|	|	1758	|	|	2126	2203	2242
Huashan bei .... d.	0919	|	0941	1121	|	1220	1227	|	1320	1408	|	|	|	1524	1555	1619	1756	|	1816	1827	1945	|	2155	|	|
Xi'an Bei .... a.	1002	0927	1024	1200	1225	1252	1310	1322	1403	1448	1426	1432	1519	1555	1625	1654	1834	1842	1858	1906	2019	2031	2225	2254	2333

– To/from Table **7192**. D – Shanghai - Zhengzhou - Xi'an bei. G – To /from Table **7187**. f – Shenzhen Futian. x – Xuzhou. z – Zhengzhou.
– To/from Table **7168**. Da – Shanghai - Zhengzhou - Xi'an - Lanzhou. H – To/from Table **7132**. ♥ – Additional services operate Wuhan/Changsha – Guangzhou/Shenzhen and v.v.
– To/from Table **7182**. E – To/from Table **7097**. X – To/from Table **7040**. ♣ – Additional services operate Beijing - Xi'an and v.v.

7085 BEIJING, SHANGHAI and GUANGZHOU - SHENZHEN and HONG KONG

GUANGZHOU DONG - SHENZHEN via Dongguan — China Rail High Speed

High-speed 'C' trains (**C70xx** and **C71xx**). *139 km.* Journey 70 minutes. Trains call at **Dongguan** 34–37 minutes after Guangzhou dong and 28–32 minutes after Shenzhen. Also calls at Guangzhou.

Guangzhou dong depart: 0612*, 0622, 0630, 0640, 0648, 0700*, 0716, 0724, 0740*, 0758, 0810, 0818, 0830, 0842*, 0854, 0902, 0911, 0928, 0937, 0954*, 1003, 1018, 1033, 1042, 1048*, 1105, 1112, 1118, 1136*, 1153, 1201, 1210, 1225, 1240, 1255, 1305*, 1321, 1331, 1342, 1400, 1415, 1424, 1432*, 1447, 1502, 1516, 1530, 1540*, 1558, 1616, 1632, 1648*, 1658, 1715, 1726, 1743, 1758*, 1811, 1824*, 1849, 1858, 1907*, 1916, 1932, 1941, 1952*, 2012, 2027, 2036, 2051, 2100*, 2126*, 2152, 2205, 2223, 2238*.

Shenzhen depart: 0612, 0630, 0645*, 0702, 0713, 0724, 0743*, 0804, 0821, 0832, 0846*, 0908, 0928, 0940, 0957, 1017, 1025, 1033, 1044, 1058*, 1110, 1122, 1134, 1150, 1201, 1212, 1218, 1237*, 1245, 1303, 1311, 1324, 1336*, 1345, 1400, 1407, 1423, 1437, 1447*, 1458, 1513, 1531, 1547, 1556*, 1609, 1622*, 1641, 1650, 1659*, 1713, 1729, 1751*, 1800, 1820, 1829, 1849, 1901*, 1921, 1928*, 1948, 2000, 2019, 2024, 2035, 2043*, 2114, 2122, 2145, 2158, 2209, 2230, 2240.

GUANGZHOU NAN - SHENZHEN BEI — China Rail High Speed

High-speed 'G' trains (**G62xx G63xx, G89XX**)*102 km.* Journey 29 - 44 minutes.

Guangzhou nan depart: 0705, 0718, 0728, 0735, 0740, 0746, 0824, 0841, 0847, 0902, 0915, 0927, 1012, 1018, 1044, 1049, 1103, 1107, 1118, 1131, 1136, 1144, 1150, 1200. 1205, 1231, 1236, 1241, 1247, 1252, 1302, 1322, 1334, 1344, 1354, 1400, 1415, 1425, 1440, 1450, 1455, 1508, 1535, 1541, 1546, 1646, 1710, 1801, 1811, 1816, 1944, 1954, 2031, 2036, 2049, 2058, 2121, 2230.

Shenzhen bei depart: 0721, 0816, 0821, 0837, 0847, 0914, 0925, 0950, 1033, 1045, 1050, 1145, 1150, 1155. 1200, 1234, 1334, 1340, 1400, 1410, 1420, 1426, 1430, 1436, 1442, 1555, 1615, 1620, 1632, 1652, 1729, 1805, 1820, 1829, 1836, 1842, 1847, 1857, 1902, 1914, 1919, 1929, 2012, 2026, 2041, 2046, 2056, 2107, 2129, 2212, 2225, 2250, 2300.

GUANGZHOU NAN - SHENZHEN BEI - WEST KOWLOON (HONG KONG) — China Rail High Speed, MTR Corporation

High-speed 'G' trains (**G65xx**)*142 km.* Journey 55 – 75 minutes. ** Non-stop Journey 47 minutes. Trains call at **Shenzhen** 39– 52 minutes after Guangzhou and 19–24 minutes after West Kowloon

Guangzhou nan depart: , 0648, 0723, 0755, 0805, 0830, 0856, 0922, 0949, 1000**, 1028, 1053, 1113, 1123, 1155, 1213, 1226, 1310, 1349, 1420, 1500**, 1525, 1551, 1612, 1652, 1735**, 1743 1827, 1837, 1904, 2025.

West Kowloon depart: 0830, 0851, 0916, 0949, 1000**, 1034, 1044, 1117, 1149, 1222, 1245, 1324, 1355, 1430, 1500**, 1535, 1617, 1622, 1705, 1710, 1735**, 1838, 1902, 1936, 1958, 2009, 2023, 2031, 2058, 2250.

GUANGZHOU - KOWLOON — MTR Corporation

km		Z801	Z807	Z813	Z823	Z817	Z809	Z825	Z815	Z803	Z819	Z827	Z811
0	**Guangzhou** dong .... d.	0819	0904	0955	1037	1203	1404	1538	1614	1733	1820	2030	2132
82	Dongguan (Changping) ..... d.	0903	0948	1039	1121	|	1448	1622	1658	1817	1904	2114	|
174	**Kowloon** Hung Hom .... a.	1017	1102	1153	1233	1356	1602	1734	1812	1931	2018	2226	2325

		Z812	Z824	Z820	Z804	Z808	Z814	Z826	Z818	Z810	Z828	Z816	Z802
Kowloon Hung Hom .... d.	...	0725	0815	0924	1052	1132	1223	1311	1432	1635	1800	1844	2001
Dongguan (Changping) ...... d.	...	0839	0927	1038	1204	|	|	1420	1546	1749	1912	1958	2115
Guangzhou dong .... a.	...	0924	1012	1123	1251	1326	1417	1508	1631	1834	1957	2043	2200

BEIJING & SHANGHAI - KOWLOON — Chinese Railways

	Z97 A	Z99 B
Beijing xi .... d.	1240	...
Shanghai .... d.	|	1745
Kowloon Hung Hom . a.	1301	1301

	Z100 A	Z98 B
Kowloon Hung Hom d.	1515	1515
Shanghai .... a.	1037	|
Beijing xi .... a.	...	1530

Note: Trains make no intermediate passenger stops.

A – Odd dates in (2019): Jan., Apr., May, Aug., Nov., Dec.
Even dates in (2019): Feb., Mar., June, July, Sept., Oct.

B – Odd dates in (2019): Feb., Mar., June, July, Sept., Oct.
Even dates in (2019): Jan., Apr., May, Aug., Nov., Dec.

7090 BEIJING and TIANJIN - WUHAN - NANCHANG and GUANGZHOU — Chinese Railways

km		T126 ♦	Z49 C	Z35	Z235 ♦	Z189	T123 ♦	T145	Z97	Z161 ♦	Z89	T167	Z13	T9 C	Z5 ♦	T253	Z77 ♦	Z3 C	Z151 ♦	Z201 ♦	T179	Z121	Z167 ♦	Z285 ♦	Z137 ♦
0	**Beijing** xi .... d.	...	1128	1149	...	...	...	1237**b**	1240	1234	...	1416	...	1505	1609	...	1615	1748	1603	1754	...	...	...	2110	...
	Tianjin .... d.	...	|	|	0758	...	0824	|	|	|	...	|	1443	|	|	1233	|	|	|	|	...	...	...	|	...
281	Shijiazhuang .... d.	...	1404	|	1146	...	1236	1537	|	1508	1646	1712	1820	1746	1838	1715	1844	2018	1832	2024	...	...	...	2340	...
689	Zhengzhou .... d.	...	1736	1742	1558	1640	1703	2010	1831	1847	2032	2136	2206	2229	2212	2246	2218	|	A	2353	...	...	0151	0309	0449
1225	**Wuhan** Wuchang ...... d.	1542	2215**h**	2229	2059	2159	2323	0147	2311	2333	0134	0330	0252	...	0258	0417	0304	0411**h**	...	0438	0428	0713	0701	0755	0956
1587	Changsha .... d.	|	...	0151	0021	0129	0255	0537	0236	0255	0455	|	0613	...	0613	0751	0615	...	...	0807	0823	1101	1040	1117	1323
1639	Zhuzhou .... d.	|	...	|	0100	|	0333	0623	|	...	|	|	|	...	...	0833	...	...	...	|	0904	|	1119	...	1403
2006	**Nanchang** .... a.	1919	...	|	|	|	|	1034	|	...	|	0708	|	...	...	|	...	...	...	|	|	|	|	...	|
2297	**Guangzhou** .... a.	...	...	0916	0830**d**	0923	1048	...	1004**d**	...	1226	...	1350**d**	...	...	1551	...	...	...	1543	1630	1822	1852**d**	...	2122

km		Z138 ♦	Z202 ♦	Z162 ♦	T146	Z50 C	Z4 C	T10 C	T168	Z6 ♦	Z78 ♦	Z90	T128 ♦	Z190	Z36	Z14	Z98	T124 ♦	Z286 ♦	Z236 ♦	T254	Z152 ♦	T180	Z122	Z168 ♦
0	**Guangzhou** .... d.	0822	0828	...	...	...	...	...	...	...	...	1350	...	1541	1620	1712**d**	1806**d**	1737	...	1950**d**	1930	...	2012	2202	2252**d**
	Nanchang .... d.	|	|	...	1210	...	...	...	1920	...	...	|	2126	|	|	|	|	|	...	|	|	...	|	|	|
655	Zhuzhou .... d.	1533	|	...	1631	...	...	...	|	...	...	|	|	|	|	|	|	0039	...	0311	|	...	0322	|	0621
707	Changsha .... d.	1618	1626	1636	1728	...	...	...	|	1940	2148	2120	|	2315	2343	0048	0135	0125	0251	0400	0320	...	0407	0530	0710
1069	**Wuhan** Wuchang ...... d.	2021	2004	2015	2128	2328**h**	2335**h**	...	2342	2306	0126	0113	0056	0242	0310	0421	0500	0522	0618	0742	0702	...	0744	0913**h**	1056
1605	Zhenghzou .... d.	0115	0052	0058	0308	|	|	0431	0532	0352	0609	0603	...	0756	0758	0917	0944	1131	1110	1256	1221	B	...	...	1619
2017	Shijiazhuang .... d.	...	0416	0422	0749	0723	0730	0831	0949	0716	0935	1002	...	...	|	1241	|	1542	1433	1657	1628	1148	...	...	...
2436	**Tianjin** .... a.	...	|	|	|	|	|	|	|	|	|	...	...	...	|	1557	|	1925	|	2032	2200	|	...	...	...
2297	**Beijing** xi .... a.	...	0646	0652	1118**b**	1002	1010	1112	1305	0948	1210	...	...	...	1344	...	1530	...	1703	...	...	1426	...	...	...

7095 BEIJING - NANCHANG - SHENZHEN — Chinese Railways

km			Z133	Z65	Z107	Z67	K105	Z185 ♦	K1619	T127 ♦
0	**Beijing** xi .... d.	...	1915	1947	1953	1959	2316	...	...	...
	Tianjin .... d.	...	|	|	|	|	|	0312	2220	...
426	Liaocheng .... d.	...	2252	|	2336	|	0422	0742	0335	...
582	Heze .... d.	...	0003	|	0047	|	0552	0853	0508	...
687	Shangqiu nan .... d.	...	|	|	|	|	0716	1000	0627	...
855	Fuyang .... d.	...	|	|	0312	|	0929	1154	0849	...
1091	Macheng .... d.	...	|	|	|	|	1208	1408	1229	...
1314	Jiujiang .... d.	...	0625	0644	|	0655	1425	1613	|	...
1449	**Nanchang** .... d.	...	0739**x**	0747	0826	0759	1613	1735	1744	1941
1675	Ji'an .... d.	...	0943	...	1041	...	1840	1952	2018	2159
1861	Ganzhou .... d.	...	...	...	1234	...	2048	2143	2221	2352
2248	Huizhou .... d.	...	...	...	1653	...	0217	0225	0407	0441
2310	Dongguan dong .... d.	...	...	...	|	...	0330	0338	0504	0525
2372	**Shenzhen** .... a.	...	...	...	1810	...	0420	0428	0621**d**	...

	Z66	Z68	Z134	T128 ♦	K1620	Z108	K106		Z186 ♦
Shenzhen .... d.	...	...	...	...	0828**d**	1448	1031	...	1950
Dongguan dong .... d.	...	...	...	1140	0916	|	1126	...	2036
Huizhou .... d.	...	...	...	1227	1004	1614	1215	...	2122
Ganzhou .... d.	...	...	...	1701	1527	2032	1746	...	0205
Ji'an .... d.	...	...	1738	1855	1749	2226	1948	...	0402
Nanchang .... d.	1935	1942	1953**x**	2105	2025**x**	0103	2248	...	0619**x**
Jiujiang .... d.	2042	2049	2102	...	2208	|	|	...	0728
Macheng .... d.	|	|	|	...	0100	|	|	...	0931
Fuyang .... d.	|	|	|	...	0439	0605	0637	...	1150
Shangqiu nan .... d.	|	|	|	...	0655	|	0836	...	1325
Heze .... d.	|	|	|	...	0804	0825	0951	...	1421
Liaocheng .... d.	|	|	|	...	1009	0936	1131	...	1538
Tianjin .... a.	|	|	|	...	1533	|	|	...	2005
Beijing xi .... a.	0740	0749	0803	...	...	1317	1627	...	...

♦ – **NOTES** (by train number) Tables **7090/7095**:

Z5/6 – Beijing(**Z5/6**) - Nanning and v.v. **Z77/78** – Beijing xi (**Z77/78**) - Guiyang and v.v.
T123/124 – Changchun (**T122/121**) - Tianjin (**T123/124**) - Guangzhou and v.v.
Z151/152 – Beijing xi (**Z151/152**) - Xining xi and v.v.
T127/28 – Chengdu (**T126/25**) - Wuhan Wuchang (**T127/28**) - Dongguan dong and v.v.
Z137/38 – Urumqi (**Z136/35**) - Zhengzhou (**Z137/38**) - Guangzhou and v.v.
Z168/70 – Guangzhou dong (**Z168/67**) - Jinan (**Z169/70**) - Qingdao and v.v.
Z161/62 – Beijing (**Z161/62**) - Kunming and v.v. **Z201/02** –Beijing(**Z201/02**) - Sanya and v.v.
Z185/86 – Shenyang bei(**Z188/87**) - Tianjin(**Z185/86**) - Shenzhen and v.v.
Z263/264 – Lhasa (**Z266/265**) - Zhengzhou (**Z263/64**) - Guangzhou and v.v.
Z285/286 – Beijing (**Z285/286**) - Nanning and v.v.

A – Via Xi'an (Table **7115**. a. 0345).
B – Via Xi'an (Table **7115**. d. 0226).
C – Beijing - Chongqing bei and v.v.

b – Beijing. **f** – To Shenzhen, a. 0852. **g** – From Shenzhen, d. 1730. **h** – Hankou.

7097 BEIJING - BENGBU - HEFEI — China Rail High Speed

km	All trains prefix **'G'** ↓	1833 E	1669 C	7409	345 C	433	261	265	355 C	263	27 C	244 CD	323 C	301 C	325 C	303 C	23	248 D	161	351	29	267	1880 E	269	454 D
0	**Beijing** nan .... d.	...	...	...	...	...	0708	0745	0840	0845	0945	...	1010	1030	1205	1230	1300	...	1515	1530	1600	1731	...	1915	...
406	Jinan xi .... d.	0643	...	...	0655	0813	0856	0936	1042	1031	1134	1029**j**	1158	1233	1354	1418	1433	1609**j**	1656	1718	1724	1920	...	2105	2135
692	Xuzhou dong .... d.	0809	0658	0738	0823	0944	1008	1050	1200	1143	|	1236	1317	1352	1459	1540	|	1733	1809	1841	|	2043	2038	|	2306
848	**Bengbu** nan .... d.	...	0743	0823	0909	...	1049	1130	1240	|	|	|	1356	1430	1548	1622	|	1834	1858	1920	|	2133	2123	|	...
891	Huainan dong .... d.	...	|	0841	|	...	1107	|	|	|	|	1344	|	|	1606	1640	|	1852	1916	|	|	2151	2141	2300	...
980	**Hefei** nan .... a.	...	0840	0937**h**	1005	...	1202**h**	1227	1340	1312	1352	1422	1452	1527	1644	1716	1644	1930	2001	2020	1935	2230	2220	2339	...

All trains prefix **'G'** ↓	453 D	246 D	1879 E	262	266	352	302 C	24	162	7410	28 C	264	322 C	242 CD	324 C	270	304 C	356 C	1836 DE	434	272	348 C	30	1670 C
Hefei nan .... d.	...	0640	0654	0705	0907	0958	1124	1142	1202	2030	1333	1338	1343	1403	1514	1625	1637	1710	...	...	1817	1921	1956	2115
Huainan dong .... d.	...	0720	0734	0745	0935	|	|	|	1242	2106	|	|	|	1443	|	1705	1717	1757	...	...	|	|	|	2157
Bengbu nan .... d.	...	0740	0754	0804	0955	1050	1223	1234	1303	2120	|	|	|	1504	1613	1724	1736	1816	...	...	|	2013	|	2225
Xuzhou dong .... d.	0635	0826	0831	0849	1048	1129	1310	|	1342	2216	|	|	1527	1544	1713	1802	1834	1855	1838	1920	|	2115	|	2302
Jinan xi .... d.	0808**j**	0949**j**	...	0958	1157	1243	1422	1401	1503	...	1600	1404	1640	1745**j**	1833	1927	1956	|	2000**j**	2043	2057	2240	2209	...
Beijing nan .... a.	...	...	...	1146	1358	1433	1633	1528	1663	...	1753	1758	1838	...	2013	2108	2148	2224	...	...	2240	...	2333	...

C – To/from Table **7193**. **D** – To/from Table **7105**. **E** – To/from Table **7070**. **h** – Hefei. **j** – Jinan.

China Rail High Speed

BEIJING, ZHENGZHOU and NANJING - SHANGHAI and HANGZHOU — 7100

km		D3125	G7349	D2281	G1377	D3135	G7589	G7291	G7599	G297	G101	G5	G105	G143	G1914	G221	G107	G111	G1	G113	G211	G41	G362	G115	G117	G7	G119
		A		A	B	A	a		A						E	Q							E				
0	**Beijing** nan..... d.	...	...	...	...	...	...	...	...	...	0643	0700	0720	0750	...	...	0805	0835	0900	0850	0931T	0915	...	0920	0925	1000	1005
314	Dezhou dong .. d.	...	...	...	...	...	...	...	...	...	0813	|	0843	|	...	...	0922	0950	|	1019	|	|	...	1043	1109	|	1120
406	Jinan xi.......... d.	...	...	...	...	...	...	...	...	0718	0841	0832	0911	0939	...	0952	0948	1017	1024	1047	1051	1058	...	1109	1138	1124	1146
	Zhengzhou dong d.	...	...	...	...	...	...	...	...	|	|	|	|	|	0843	|	|	|	|	|	|	|	1043	|	|	|	|
	Shangqiu........ d.	...	...	...	...	...	...	...	...	|	|	|	|	|	|	|	|	|	|	|	|	|	|	|	|	|	|
692	Xuzhou dong... d.	...	...	...	...	...	0653	0753	0743	0845	|	|	1030	|	1034	1107	1100	|	|	1153	|	|	1220	|	|	|	1306
848	Bengbu nan .... d.	...	...	...	...	...	0738	0838	0828	0924	|	|	|	|	|	|	|	|	|	|	|	1247	|	|	|	|	|
1023	**Nanjing** nan ... d.	0625f	0730	0746f	0739	0809f	0846	0938	0932	1009	1116	1032	1153	1157	1201	1233	1218	1257	1226	1311	1316	1331	1337	1341	1408	1325	1424
1088	Zhenjiang nan . d.	|	0751	0820	0800	0834	0909	|	0956	1029	1137	|	|	|	|	|	1243	|	|	|	|	1256	|	1401	|	|	1446
1153	Changzhou bei d.	0729c	0810	0853c	0819	0906c	|	1012	1016	|	|	|	1239	1231	1238	1307	|	|	|	|	|	|	|	|	|	|	|
1210	Wuxi dong....... d.	0746	0829	0910	0839	0933	|	1031	1035	1101	|	|	|	|	|	1327	|	1349	|	|	1405	|	|	|	|	|	1517
1237	Suzhou bei...... d.	0803g	0842	0929g	0852	1002g	0956	|	|	1117	1215	|	|	|	1309	|	1321	|	|	1410	1417	|	|	|	1506	|	|
1318	**Shanghai** Hongqiao a.	0846	0907	1028	0922	1037	1028	1103h	1104	1140	1240	1140h	1308	1312	1341	1358	1346	1422	1328	1433	1441	1449	1445	1459	1537	1428	1547
1477	Hangzhou dong a.	1009	1004	1131	...	1212	1141	...	1203	...	...	...	...	...	...	...	...	...	...	...	...	1548	...	...	...	...	...

	G232	G213	G121	G1918	G125	G411	G9	G1922	G131	G133	G135	G139	G3	1926	G43	G141	G215	G228	G145	G1202	G11	G155	G147	1972	G169	G151
	Q			E				E						E				Q						E		
Beijing nan .... d.	...	1042T	1020	...	1110	1120	1200	...	1220	1250	1305	1345	1400	...	1405	1410	1446T	...	1435	1453T	1500	1545	1550	...	1640	1645
Dezhou dong .... d.	...	1136	1153	...	1232	1249	|	...	|	1423	1428	1515	|	...	1520	1525	1541	...	|	|	|	1715	1723	...	1806	1815
Jinan xi.................... d.	1202j	1203	1229	...	1258	1315	1332	...	1402	1450	1454	1541	1524	...	1546	1551	1608	1630j	1632	1641	1624	1743	1751	...	1837	1841
Zhengzhou dong ... d.	|	|	|	1147	|	|	|	1238	|	|	|	|	|	1452	|	|	|	|	|	|	|	|	|	1622	|	|
Shangqiu.................. d.	|	|	|	1246	|	|	|	1345	|	|	|	|	|	|	|	|	|	|	|	|	|	|	|	1721	|	|
Xuzhou dong .... d.	1337	1333	1342	1347	|	1438	|	1446	1531	|	|	1653	|	1631	1658	1703	1729	1756	1739	1801	|	1850	|	1828	1956	1000
Bengbu nan .... d.	|	|	|	1426	1442	1516	|	|	|	1627	1649	1735	|	1719	|	1750	|	1835	|	1840	|	|	|	1913	|	2043
Nanjing nan .... d.	1454	1449	1500	1510	1525	1559	1532	1609	1654	1713	1732	1836	1725	1804	1818	1841	1901	1919	1905	1921	1825	2006	2028	1956	2113	2140
Zhenjiang nan .... d.	|	|	|	|	1551	|	|	|	|	|	1753	|	|	|	1843	1902	|	1940	|	1946	|	|	2053	2017	|	|
Changzhou bei .... d.	|	1526	|	|	1611	|	|	1613	|	|	|	|	|	|	|	1921	1935	2000	1946	2006	|	2041	|	2037	|	2215
Wuxi dong .... d.	|	|	1548	|	|	1646	|	|	1747	|	1829	1929	|	1917	|	|	|	|	|	2025	|	2102	2124	|	2159	|
Suzhou bei .... d.	1546	1551	1600	1615	|	1701	|	1715	|	1809	|	|	|	|	1922	1945	1954	2031	2010	2037	|	2016	2137	|	2212	2239
Shanghai Hongqiao .. a.	1612	1617	1625	1645	1659	1725	1636	1738	1816	1840	1859	2005	1828	1947	1943	2009	2023	2104	2033	2100	1928	2141	2200	2126	2235	2302
Hangzhou dong ...... a.	...	...	...	...	...	...	...	...	...	...	...	...	...	...	2047	...	...	...	...	...	...	...	...	...	...	...

	G13	G153	G157	G236	G15	G17	G21	D701	D705	D305
				Q						E
Beijing nan ....d.	1700	1715	1736	...	1800	1900	1908	1922	2121	...
Dezhou dong ....d.	|	|	1859	...	|	|	|	|	|	...
Jinan xi.......................d.	1824	1858	1938	1906j	1932	|	2032	|	|	...
Zhengzhou dong .....d.	|	|	|	|	|	|	|	|	|	2232
Shangqiu.....................d.	|	|	|	|	|	|	|	|	|	|
Xuzhou dong ....d.	|	2010	2050	2028	|	|	|	|	|	0026d
Bengbu nan ....d.	|	2055	|	|	|	|	|	|	|	|
Nanjing nan ....d.	2024	2145	2207	2151	2132	2215	2233	0457f	0651f	0328f
Zhenjiang nan..............d.	|	|	|	|	|	|	|	|	0724	|
Changzhou bei ....d.	|	2222	2246	|	|	|	|	|	|	|
Wuxi dong ....d.	|	2242	|	2237	2210	|	|	|	|	|
Suzhou bei ....d.	2111	|	2316	|	|	|	|	0636g	|	0527g
Shanghai Hongqiao ....a.	2136	2311	2340	2310	2243	2318	2336	0725h	0920h	0626h
Hangzhou dong........a.	...	...	...	...	...	...	...	...	...	...

	G1970	G102	G221	G104	G6	G106	G1975	G110	G120	G8
	E		Q				E			
Hangzhou dong ....d.	...	...	...	...	...	...	...	...	...	...
Shanghai Hongqiao...........d.	0610	0626	0705	0638	0700h	0712	0717	0728	0751	0800
Suzhou bei.........................d.	0635	|	0735	|	0727	0739	0744	0800	|	|
Wuxi dong ....d.	|	0656	|	0709	|	|	0756	|	0824	|
Changzhou bei....................d.	0658	0715	|	|	|	|	0815	0835	0843	|
Zhenjiang nan ....d.	0718	|	|	0741	|	|	|	0854	|	|
Nanjing nan ....d.	0739	0748	0825	0802	0813	0837	0849	0916	0921	0902
Bengbu nan ....d.	0824	0839	|	0853	|	|	0944	|	|	|
Xuzhou dong..........................d.	0909	0929	0946	0937	0909	1016	1034	1044	1040	|
Shangqiu ....d.	1009	|	|	|	|	|	1129	|	|	|
Zhengzhou dong ....a.	1100	|	|	|	|	|	1220	|	|	|
Jinan xi ....d.	...	1039	1055j	1047	1013	1130	...	1150	1146	1059
Dezhou dong ....d.	...	|	...	|	|	|	...	|	|	|
Beijing nan..........................a.	...	1229	...	1233	1138	1313	...	1338	1333	1224

	G2	G112	G114	G212	G361	G231	G116	G1204	G118	G10	G42	G122	G124	G126	G130	G1925	G12	G132	G412	G134	G138	G140	G4	G227	G142	G146
					E	Q										E								Q		
Hangzhou dong... d.	...	...	...	...	...	...	...	...	...	...	0924	...	...	...	...	...	...	...	...	...	...	...	...	...	...	...
Shanghai Hongqiao .. d.	0900	0805	0815	0842	0836	0852	0934	0939	0952	1000	1026	1041	1059	1105	1115h	1140	1200	1217	1228	1300	1329	1334	1400	1420	1410	1452
Suzhou bei .... d.	|	0830	|	0907	|	|	0959	1004	|	|	|	1106	|	1130	|	1205	|	1242	|	|	1354	1359	|	|	1438	|
Wuxi dong .... d.	|	0842	0853	0924	|	0936	|	|	|	|	1058	1118	|	|	1155	1220	|	|	1258	1337	|	|	|	|	|	|
Changzhou bei .... d.	|	|	|	0943	|	0955	1023	1039	|	|	|	|	|	1154	|	1242	|	1306	|	|	|	1423	|	|	|	|
Zhenjiang nan .... d.	|	|	0929	|	|	1015	1046	1055	1104	|	1128	|	|	|	1227	|	|	|	|	|	|	1446	|	|	|	|
Nanjing nan .... d.	1002	0935	0950	1020	0946	1038	1109	1122	1132	1101	1149	1215	1210	1227	1248	1317	1310	1340	1351	1424	1451	1506	1502	1543	1528	1624
Bengbu nan .... d.	|	|	1041	|	|	1123	1153	|	|	|	|	1258	|	1311	|	1401	|	|	|	1511	1540	|	|	1627	|	|
Xuzhou dong .... d.	|	1107	1120	1148	1104	1207	1232	1244	|	|	1315	1338	1328	1350	1423	1441	|	1506	1520	1552	|	|	|	1717	1651	1746
Shangqiu................. d.	|	|	|	|	|	|	|	|	|	|	|	|	|	|	|	1539	|	|	|	|	|	|	|	|	|	|
Zhengzhou dong ... a.	|	|	|	|	1234	|	|	|	|	|	|	|	|	|	|	1643	|	|	|	|	|	|	|	|	|	|
Jinan xi.................... d.	1201	1214	1233	1309	...	1323j	1345	1403	1412	1301	1428	1457	1444	1519	1544	...	1510	1632	1649	1711	1739	1743	1701	1841j	1821	1905
Dezhou dong .... d.	|	1240	|	1336	...	...	|	|	|	|	|	|	|	1545	|	...	|	|	1726	1737	|	1809	|	...	1858	|
Beijing nan .... a.	1328	1408	1413	1426T	...	...	1523	1518T	1558	1428	1608	1643	1618	1705	1729	...	1638	1832	1848	1858	1928	1941	1828	...	2018	2048

	G14	G214	G148	G170	G150	G152	1937	G235	G216	G16	G154	G44	G158	G7292	G298	D3136	G18	G7600	D3126	G7590	G1378	G22	D702	D706	D2282	D306
							E	Q								A		A	A	b	B				A	E
Hangzhou dong... d.	...	...	...	...	...	...	...	...	...	...	...	1615	...	...	...	1641	...	1706	1730	1745	1828	...	...	...	2001	...
Shanghai Hongqiao .. d.	1500	1505	1523	1552	1605	1618	1612	1632	1637	1700	1713	1723	1734	1746	1809	1745	1755	1828	1847	1852	1928	1900	1909h	2118h	2126	2255h
Suzhou bei .... d.	|	|	1548	|	|	1643	1637	|	1702	|	1738	1748	|	1819	1834	1849g	|	1900	1944g	1929	1953	|	|	|	2157g	2341g
Wuxi dong .... d.	|	1542	|	1623	1635	|	|	1702	|	|	|	1800	1811	1832	1846	1906	|	1912	2001	1945	205	|	|	2226	2214	|
Changzhou bei .... d.	|	|	1612	1642	|	|	1704	|	|	|	1802	|	|	1850	1905	1933c	|	1937	2018c	2004	2024	|	|	|	2231c	|
Zhenjiang nan........... d.	|	1614	1632	|	1707	|	|	|	1745	|	|	1832	|	|	|	2005	|	1957	2053	|	2044	|	2103	|	|	|
Nanjing nan .... d.	1602	1638	1653	1715	1727	1734	1741	1747	1806	1801	1836	1852	1907	1927	1943	2028f	1901	2021	2116f	2042	2104	2002	2146f	2357f	2314	0149f
Bengbu nan .... d.	|	|	|	|	|	|	|	|	1850	|	|	|	1951	2017	2048	...	1942	2116	...	2136	...	|	|	|	...	|
Xuzhou dong .... d.	|	1754	1817	|	1843	1851	1901	1903	1928	1910	|	2015	|	2101	2136	...	|	2157	...	2221	...	|	|	|	...	0524d
Shangqiu.................. d.	|	|	|	|	|	|	|	|	|	|	|	|	|	...	|	...	|	...	...	...	...	|	|	|	...	|
Zhengzhou............ a.	|	|	|	|	|	|	2045	|	|	|	|	|	|	...	|	...	|	...	...	...	...	|	|	|	...	0715
Jinan xi.................... d.	1801	1913	1933	1938	2021	2025	...	2024j	2042	2009	2114	2128	2142	...	2254	...	2109	...	...	...	...	|	|	|	...	...
Dezhou dong .... d.	|	|	|	2003	2047	2051	...	...	|	|	|	|	|	...	|	...	|	...	...	...	...	|	|	|	...	...
Beijing nan .... a.	1936	2016T	2113	2118	2200	2212	...	...	2200T	2136	2248	2308	2329	...	...	...	2236	...	...	...	...	2318	0712	0924	...	...

China Rail High Speed

BEIJING and NANJING - HANGZHOU and NINGBO — 7102

km	All trains prefix 'G'	1667	1505	1503	7611	7691	61	63	51	1481	57	19	55	31	7609	1483	1222	167	D655	59	7603	35	1861	45	D2224	37	39
		C	B	B			B	A		B			A			B		A	D					B	D		
0	**Beijing** nan..... d.	...	...	...	...	...	...	...	0700T	...	0715	0800	0810	1100	...	...	1214T	1245	...	1340	...	1510	...	1525	...	1605	1904
314	Dezhou dong .. d.	...	...	...	...	...	...	...	0800	...	0838	|	0926	|	...	...	1316	1414	...	1509	...	|	1601	1647	...	1737	|
406	Jinan xi.......... d.	...	...	...	...	...	0706	0723j	0837	...	0906	0924	0955	1224	...	...	1343	1444	...	1535	...	1651	1700	1713	...	1803	|
692	Xuzhou dong... d.	...	...	...	0705	...	0834	0857	0950	...	1025	|	1121	1323	...	...	1455	1552	...	1648	...	1805	1823	1837	...	1908	|
1023	**Nanjing** nan ... d.	0657	0720	0832	0848	0937	1002	1029	1112	1132	1149	1126	1237	1433	1353	1515	1613	1715	1731	1812	1850	1932	1940	1954	2008	2044	2219
1152	Yixing............. d.	0742	0810	0915	0931	1026	1045	1105	1148	1220	1225	|	|	|	1435	1557	1656	|	1823	1848	1939	|	2023	2037	2059	2127	|
1208	Huzhou .... d.	0807	0835	0933	0956	1044	1103	|	|	1248	|	1215	1332	|	1500	1622	1714	1817	1846	1906	1957	2033	|	2055	2125	2146	|
1279	**Hangzhou** dong a.	0835	0903	0956	1024	1119	1125	1153	1223	1310	1305	1238	1353	1535	1521	1650	1735	1838	1910	1927	2018	2055	2110	2123	2154	2207	2322
1439	Ningbo .... a.	...	...	...	1127	...	...	1248	1324	...	1409	...	1455	...	1620	...	1838	1940	2039	2031	...	...	...	...	...	...	...

All trains prefix 'G'	34	1862	D2223	20	D656	1221	58	36	46	168	7602	56	32	1482	7608	1676	52	166	60	1484	62	64	40	1504	7630	1506
		Q	D		D				B	A		A		B		C				B	B	A		B		B
Ningbo.......................... d.	...	...	...	...	0645	0734	0745	...	...	1033	...	1155	...	...	1258	...	1350	...	1438	...	...	1704	...	...	...	...
Hangzhou dong .... d.	0701	0631k	0742	0748	0810	0831	0850	0905	0950	1139	1209	1246	1300	1329	1400	1415	1447	1512	1543	1621	1736	1800	1900	2042	2131	2147
Huzhou...................... d.	0724	0707	|	0811	0844	0854	|	0935	1013	1209	1239	1309	|	1359	1423	1445	1510	1535	|	1651	1806	1825	|	2105	2201	2210
Yixing .... d.	0744	0726	0847	|	0904	0913	|	|	1039	1228	1258	|	|	|	1449	1511	1536	1601	|	1720	1825	1851	|	2131	|	2229
Nanjing nan .... d.	0833	0819	0937	0858	0959	0955	1011	1029	1117	1322	1330	1430	1404	1500	1530	1550	1620	1643	1703	1801	1922	1933	2006	2210	2252	2308
Xuzhou dong .... d.	1009	0950	...	|	...	1133	1132	1154	1236	1458	...	1548	|	...	...	...	1742	1758	1830	...	2052	2124	|	...	...	...
Jinan xi........................ d.	1124	1121j	...	1057	...	1252	1305	1313	1349	1620	...	1705	1612	...	...	...	1849	1918	1950	...	2231	2245	|	...	...	...
Dezhou dong .... d.	|	...	...	|	...	|	1331	1340	|	1646	...	|	|	...	...	...	1916	|	|	...	...	...	|	...	...	...
Beijing nan .... a.	1303	...	...	1220	...	1414T	1443	1453	1543	1813	...	1853	1739	...	...	...	2005T	2056	2129	...	...	...	2323	...	...	...

A – To/from Table 7200. B – To/from Table 7192. C – To/from Table 7193. D – To/from Table 7182. E – Shanghai - Zhengzhou - Xi'an bei and v.v. Q – To/from Qingdao (Table 7105).
T – Time at Tianjin xi not Beijing. a – To Ningbo a. 1237. b – From Ningbo d. 1642. c – Changzhou. d – Xuzhou. f – Nanjing. g – Suzhou. h – Shanghai. j – Jinan. k – Hangzhou.

7105 BEIJING - JINAN - QINGDAO

Chinese Railways, China Rail High Speed

km	All unmarked trains prefix 'D'	Z169 A	6001	6003	G6901	G6903	G453 D	G175	G6909	G481	G6911	G246 D	G221 S	G255 S	G179	G171	G181	1631	G6915	G231 S	G183	G185	G187	G173	G289	G189	G120
426	**Beijing** nan ..... d.	...	...	...	...	...	...	0621	...	0725	...	...	...	...	0935	...	1040	...	...	...	1148	1225	1240	...	...	1320	...
304	**Tianjin** nan . d.	...	...	...	...	...	...	|	...	0801	...	...	...	...	|	1047**x**	1118	...	...	...	|	|	1318	1347**x**	...	|	1458**x**
122	Dezhou dong .. d.	...	...	...	...	...	...	0747	...	0847	...	...	...	...	1050	|	1214	1159	...	...	1312	|	1404	1442	...	1447	|
0	**Jinan** ♥ .... d.	0140	0553	0707	0725**d**	0750**d**	0808	0833	0835**x**	0928**d**	0931**x**	0952	1057	1123	1136	1237	1259	1310	1315**d**	1326	1401	1433	1440**d**	1527	1538	1548	1641
130	Zibo .... d.	0247	0643	0751	0756**b**	0823**b**	0858	0922	|	0953**b**	1031**b**	1038	1142	1208	1220	1327	1345	1355	1340**b**	1410	1447	1522	1505**b**	1611	1622	1634	1726
230	Weifang .... d.	0348	0727	0828	0832**b**	0854**b**	0948	1000	1015**b**	1022**b**	1100**b**	1115	1219	1245	1258	|	1422	1432	1425**b**	1447	1524	1606	1534**b**	1654	1705	1711	1809
413*	**Qingdao** ♥ .... a.	0522	0900	0954	0933**b**	0948**b**	1045	1115	1121**b**	1112**b**	1201**b**	1229	1322	1401	1413	1524	1536	1529	1520**b**	1601	1644	1720	1620**b**	1809	1826	1832	1911**b**

	G191	G6919	G193	G242 D	G195	G6963	G227 S	6011	G197	G199	1836 D	G235 S
Beijing nan ......d.	1420	...	1440	...	1610	...	...	...	1650	1721	...	...
Tianjin nan ...d.	|	...	1532	...	|	...	...	...	1733	1757	...	...
Dezhou dong ....d.	1535	...	|	...	1733	...	...	...	1819	1843	...	...
Jinan ♥ ....d.	1621	1640**d**	1703	1745	1817	1839**x**	1844	1853	1908	1941	2008	2023**x**
Zibo ....d.	1711	1714**b**	1747	1829	1906	1941**b**	1931	1937	1954	|	2052	2124**b**
Weifang ....d.	1748	1753**b**	|	1906	1947	2017**b**	2010	2016	2033	2108	2135	2153**b**
Qingdao ♥ ......a.	1920	1848**b**	1945	2026	2101	2117**b**	2125	2136	2153	2228	2232	2303

	6002	G1208	G2086	G221 S	G6902	G178	G180	G182	G244 D	6004	G172	G232 S
Qingdao ♥ ..d.	0537	0612**b**	0632	0703	0705**b**	0656	0830**b**	0815	0739	0849	0900	0912
Weifang ....d.	0654	0715	0740**b**	0811**b**	0752**b**	0815	0917**b**	0932	0857	1023	1012	1030
Zibo ....d.	0742	0753	0810**b**	0841**b**	0822**b**	0852	0946**b**	1009	0940	1101	1049	1113
Jinan ♥ ....d.	0829	0848	0846**d**	0952**x**	0920**x**	0947	1011**d**	1058	1027	1154	1145	1200
Dezhou dong d.	...	0943	0938	...	...	|	1048	|	...	...	|	...
Tianjin nana.	...	1033**x**	|	...	...	1121	|	|	...	...	1326**x**	...
Beijing nan ..a.	...	...	1058	...	...	1158	1203	1258	...	...	...	...

	G184	6006	G6904	G186	G188	G190	G192	G6906	Z170 A	G248 D	1612	6008	G228 S	G6908	G194	G6910	G256	G260	1632	G174	G196	G236 S	G198	G200	G454 D	6012
Qingdao ♥ .... d.	0926	0939	1000**b**	1020	1125	1205	1255**b**	1312	1403	1320	1323	1327	1358	1410**b**	1433	1435**b**	1436	1527	1558	1604	1557	1622	1710	1834	1843	1943
Weifang .... d.	1043	1106	1101**b**	1137	1242	1323	1356**b**	1454**b**	1601	1439	1427	|	1455	1504**b**	1549	1526**b**	1548	1633	1656	1722	1716	1733	1831	1951	2000	2100
Zibo .... d.	1127	1150	1144**b**	1221	1321	1401	1440**b**	|	1647	1520	1512	1528	1541	1549**b**	|	1559**b**	1632	1711	1734	1804	1754	1810	1909	2028	2038	2149
Jinan ♥ .... d.	1218	1239	1221**d**	1311	1414	1450	1511**d**	1627**x**	1742	1607	1638	1615	1628	1711**x**	1711	1622**d**	1719	1759	1827	1853	1843	1903	1958	2125	2133	2245
Dezhou dong .... d.	|	...	...	|	1507	1540	|	...	...	...	...	...	...	...	|	...	...	...	1947	|	|	...	|	2231	...	...
Tianjin nan .... a.	|	...	...	1434	|	1624	|	...	...	...	...	...	...	...	1837	...	...	...	...	2039**x**	2006	...	|	|	...	...
Beijing nan .... a.	1418	...	...	1508	1622	1700	1714	...	...	...	...	...	...	...	1913	...	...	...	...	...	2040	...	2156	2343	...	...

A – Guangzhou dong(**Z168/67**) - Jinan(**Z169/70**) - Qingdao and v.v.
D – To/from Table **7097**.
S – To/from Table **7100/7102**.
* – 344 kms via new high-speed line.
♥ – Additional trips Jinan - Qingdao.

7110 SHANGHAI - NANJING - ZHENGZHOU

Chinese Railways

km		K290 ♦	T112 ♦	Z167 ♦	T116 ♦	Z252 ♦	K152	Z40 ♦	Z164 ♦		K282 ♦
0	**Shanghai** .... d.	0851	A	...	1532	1552	1631	1941	2010	...	2028
84	Suzhou .... d.	0958	1312	...	1635	1643	1735	2036	2058	...	2134
126	Wuxi .... d.	1031	|	...	|	1709	|	2102	2123	...	2206
165	Changzhou .... d.	1101	|	...	1730	1736	|	2127	|	...	2236
301	**Nanjing** .... d.	1247	1540	...	1903	1909	2044	2250	2305	...	0040
485	Bengbu .... d.	1514	1751	...	2048	2054	0009	0027	0040	...	0254
***	**Jinan** .... d.	|	|	1808	|	|	|	|	|	...	|
649	Xuzhou .... d.	1741	1942	2214	2224	2230	|	0206	0220	...	0503
795	Shangqiu .... d.	1924	|	2340	2357	2349	0500	|	|	...	0653
998	**Zhengzhou** .... a.	2153	2254	0136	0149	0142	0727	0453	0507	...	0909

	Z163 ♦	Z39 ♦	Z254 ♦	T115 ♦	T111 ♦	Z168 ♦	K289 ♦	K151	K284 ♦	
Zhengzhou .... d.	0258	0305	0347	0313	0609	1637	1750	1813	1920	...
Shangqiu .... d.	|	|	0525	0503	|	1837	2006	2050	2155	...
Xuzhou .... d.	0558	0604	0656	0640	0925	2014	2157	|	2342	...
Jinan .... a.	|	|	|	|	|	0128	|	|	|	...
Bengbu .... d.	0722	0728	0832	0846	1105	...	2347	0046	0129	...
Nanjing .... d.	0900	0906	1010	1033	1309	...	0152	0250	0351	...
Changzhou .... d.	|	1011	|	|	1438	...	0322	|	|	...
Wuxi .... d.	1030	1036	1139	1206	1510	...	0353	|	0539	...
Suzhou .... d.	1101	1107	1205	1235	1541	...	0429	0540	|	...
Shanghai .... a.	1151	1157	1256	1330	B	...	0534	0641	0706	...

For footnotes see Table **7120**.

7115 ZHENGZHOU - XI'AN - LANZHOU

Chinese Railways

km	G1970	Z135 ♦	T117 ♦	Z252 ♦		Z165 ♦	Z41 ♦	T197 ♦	Z151 ♦	T113 ♦	Z323 ♦	Z223 ♦	Read Down / Read Up	Z254 ♦	T118 ♦	Z42 ♦	Z166 ♦	Z136 ♦		T114 ♦	T198 ♦	Z152 ♦	Z324 ♦	Z224 ♦	G197
0	1105	0123	0210	0150	...	0514	0500	2054	...	2302	...	...	↓ d. **Zhengzhou** .... a. ↑	0340	0242	0257	0250	0439	...	0601	0705	...	...	...	1613
124	1150	0250	0337	|	...	|	0624	2234	...	0035	...	...	d. Luoyang .... d.	|	|	|	|	0318	...	0436	0532	0647	...	...	1535
512	1322	0724	0812	0757	...	1114	1100	0331	0345	0509	...	...	↓ a. **Xi'an** .... d. ↑	2135	2015	2050	2044	2241	...	2352	0040	0217	...	...	1350
512	1322	0734	0824	...	...	1124	1110	0339	0357	0519	...	...	d. **Xi'an** .... a.	...	2003	2040	2034	2233	...	2339	0030	0201	...	...	1343
685	1430	0918	1020	...	...	|	1249	0548	0535	0706	0240**g**	0240**g**	↓ d. Baoji .... d. ↑	...	1824	1910	|	2054	...	2132	2251	|	0123**g**	0123**g**	1248
840	1516	1058	1202	...	...	|	1435	0739	0712	0851	|	|	d. Tianshui .... d.	...	1542	1628	|	1810	...	1847	2010	2159	|	|	1204
1188	1641	1502	1604	...	...	1817	1824	1148	1119	1258	0910	0910	↓ a. **Lanzhou** .... d. ↑	...	1115	1218	1226	1334	...	1415	1545	1727	1853	1853	1039

For ♦ footnotes see Table **7120**. g – Time at Guangyuan.

7118 BEIJING - LANZHOU

Chinese Railways

km		Z69 ♦	T175 ♦	T41	Z55	Z151 ♦	T7 ♦	Z21 ♦		
0	**Beijing** xi .... d.	1000	1305	1422	1458	1603	1640	2000	...	...
291	Shijiazhuang bei .... d.	1307	1601	1728	1757	1832	2003	2237	...	...
395	Yangquan bei .... d.	1404	|	|	1904	|	|	|	...	...
516	**Taiyuan** .... d.	1509**n**	1829	1954	2001**n**	|	2215	0025	...	...
701	Lvliang .... d.	1640	2031	2209	|	|	2358	|	...	...
790	Suide .... d.	1736	2128	2342	|	|	|	|	...	...
1283	**Xi'an** .... a.	|	|	0535	|	0345	0621	|	...	...
1267	Zhongwei .... d.	2243	0227	...	0236	|	...	0716	...	...
1524	**Wuwei** .... a.	0212	|	...	|	|	...	|	...	...
1573	**Lanzhou** .... a.	...	0744	...	0734	1124	...	1217	...	...

	Z22 ♦	T42	T176 ♦	T8 ♦	Z152 ♦	Z56	Z70 ♦		
Lanzhou .... d.	1617	...	1507	...	1727	2040	...	...	...
Wuwei .... d.	|	...	|	...	|	|	0505	...	...
Zhongwei .... d.	2131	...	2038	...	|	0217	0837	...	...
Xi'an .... d.	|	1939	|	2247	0217	|	|	...	...
Suide .... d.	|	0139	0200	|	|	|	1254	...	...
Lvliang .... d.	|	0239	0300	|	|	|	1352	...	...
Taiyuan .... d.	0351	0427	0448	0727	|	0847**n**	1533**n**	...	...
Yangquan bei .... d.	|	|	|	0832	|	|	1641	...	...
Shijiazhuang bei .... d.	0548	0626	0645	0941	1148	1107	1744	...	...
Beijing xi .... a.	0820	0931	0935	1231	1426	1336	2022	...	...

7120 LANZHOU - ÜRÜMQI and LHASA

Chinese Railways, China Rail High Speed

km		D2701	D2703	D2711 C	D2569 X		Z179 ♦	T197 ♦	Z135 ♦	T295	Z41 ♦	Z69 ♦
	Zhongwei .....d.	...	...	...	...	...	1009	...	...	...	...	2243
0	**Lanzhou** ....d.	0750**x**	0820**x**	1040**x**	2046**x**	...	|	1203	1518	1747	1841	|
188	Xining ....d.	0914	0944	1202	2158	...	|	|	1711	|	|	|
303	Wuwei ....d.	|	|	|	...	...	1341	1511	|	2100	2150	0219
770	Jiayuguan ....d.	1224**n**	1301**n**	1535**n**	...	...	1822	1948	2135	0140	0205	0651
1067	Liuyuan ....d.	1418**n**	1458**n**	1732**n**	...	...	2121	2255	0035	0442	|	0958
1339	Hami ....d.	1558	1630	1910	...	...	0011	0418	0350	0752	0711	1304
1749	Turpan ....d.	1803**b**	1833**b**	2118**b**	...	...	0429	0722**b**	0640**b**	1139	0946**b**	1552**b**
1892	**Ürümqi** nan ......a.	1906	1941	2227	...	...	0618	0846	0806**a**	1306	1115	1711

	Z70 ♦	T296	Z180 ♦	Z42 ♦	T198 ♦	Z136 ♦		D2570 X	D2706	D2712 D	D270
Ürümqi nan ...d.	1410	1441	1910	1951	1907	1949**a**	...	...	0944	1045	1209
Turpan ....d.	1526**b**	1615	2078	2126**b**	2031**b**	2138**b**	...	...	1038**b**	1148**b**	1312**b**
Hami ....d.	1825	2005	0014	0020	0025	0037	...	...	1302	1403	1522
Liuyuan ....d.	2128	2308	0257	0315	0437	0340	...	...	1431**n**	1538**n**	1651**n**
Jiayuguan ......d.	0032	0218	0554	0609	0733	0652	...	...	1625**n**	1743**n**	1848**n**
Wuwei ....d.	0505	0711	1047	|	1226	|	...	...	|	|	|
Xining ....d.	|	|	|	1007	|	|	...	0930	1947	2115	2206
Lanzhou ....a.	|	1024	|	1203	1530	1315	...	1049	2059**x**	2227**x**	2318
Zhongwei ..a.	0822	...	1421	...	...	...	...	...	...	...	...

km		D2741	D2743	D2745 E	D2671 X	T175 ♦	Z323 Z223 ♦	Z151 ♦	Z21 ♦		D2757 X	Z165 ♦
0	**Zhongwei** ....d.	...	...	...	...	0227		...	0716	...	...	...
306	**Lanzhou** ....d.	0725**x**	0755	0838	1100	0802	0927	1138	1233	...	1703	1834
534	Xining ....d.	0841	0929	0959	1321	1041	1227	1417	1521	...	1836	2132
	Jiayuguan nan .a.	1200	1238	1307	1624	...	|	...	|	...	2209	|
1352	Golmud ....d.	...	...	...	...	...	1949	...	2235	...	...	0451
2172	Naqu ....d.	...	...	...	...	...	0552	...	0824	...	...	1451
2449	**Lhasa** ....a.	...	...	...	...	...	0955	...	1220	...	...	1917

	Z166 ♦		T176 ♦	Z22 ♦	Z152 ♦	Z324 Z224 ♦	D2672 X	D2744 F	D2748	D2674 X	D275
Lhasa ....d.	1115	...	...	1530	...	1820	...	...	...	...	...
Naqu ....d.	1455	...	...	1855	...	2147	...	...	...	...	...
Golmud ....d.	0148	...	...	0554	...	0830	...	...	...	...	...
Jiayuguan nan .a.	|	...	...	|	...	|	0828	0837	1222	1305	1854
Xining ....d.	0915	...	1205	1322	1430	1539	1159	1207	1537	1629	2202
Lanzhou ....a.	1211	...	1447	1600	1712	1837	1318**x**	1326**x**	1705	1747**x**	2307
Zhongwei ......a.	...	...	2025	2121	...	...	...	...	...	...	...

♦ – **NOTES** for Tables **7110**, **7115 7118** and **7120** (by train number):

- **T7/8** – Beijing xi(**T7/8**) - Chengdu and v.v.
- **Z21/22** – Beijing xi(**Z21/22**) - Lhasa and v.v.
- **Z39/41** – Urumqi(**Z42/41**) - Zhengzhou(**Z39/40**) - Shanghai and v.v.
- **Z69/70** – Beijing xi(**Z69/70**) - Urumqi and v.v.
- **T111/114** – Lanzhou(**T114/13**) - Zhengzhou(**T111/12**) - Hangzhou and v.v.
- **T115/118** – Lanzhou(**T118/17**) - Zhengzhou(**T115/16**) - Shanghai and v.v.
- **Z135/36** – Urumqi(**Z136/35**) - Zhengzhou(**Z137/38**) - Guangzhou and v.v.
- **Z151/152** – Beijing xi(**Z151/152**) - Xining and v.v.
- **Z163/166** – Lhasa(**Z166/165**) - Zhengzhou(**Z163/164**) - Shanghai and v.v.
- **Z168/70** – Guangzhou dong(**Z168/67**) - Jinan(**Z169/70**) - Qingdao and v.v.
- **T175/76** – Beijing xi(**T175/76**) - Xining xi and v.v.
- **Z179/180** – Beijing(**Z179/80**) - Urumqi and v.v.
- **T193/194** – Zhengzhou(**T193/194**) - Urumqi and v.v.
- **T197/198** – Zhengzhou(**T197/198**) - Urumqi and v.v.
- **Z223/224** – Lhasa(**T224/223**) - Chongqing and v.v. See note **G**.
- **Z252/54** – Xian(**Z254/252**) - Zhengzhou - Shanghai and v.v.
- **K282/284** – Shanghai(**K282/284**) - Zhengzhou(**K283/281**) – Chengdu and v.v.
- **K289/290** – Shanghai(**K290/289**) - Zhengzhou(**K291/292**) – Chengdu and v.v.
- **Z323/24** – Chengdu(**Z322/21**) - Lanzhou(**Z323/24**) - Lhasa and v.v. See note **G**.

A – From Hangzhou dep. 1023.
B – To Hangzhou arr. 1853.
C – Additional trips: 0836.
D – Additional trip: 0856.
E – Additional trips: 1200, 1346, 1410, 1703, 1813, 1827.
F – Additional trips: 0859, 1331, 1645, 1705, 1910.
G – Runs alternate days only.
X – To/from Xi'an.
a – **Ürümqi**.
*** – Jinan *0 km* - Xuzhou *319 km*

ÜRÜMQI - ALMATY - NUR-SULTAN 7125

km		5801	13 *CJ* ①	13/53 ①
0	**Ürümqi** d.	2242	2333	2333
144	Shihezi d.	0129	|	|
241	Kuitun d.	0259	|	|
477	Alashankou a.	0727	0800	0800
477	Alashankou 🛃 d.	...	1100	1100
493	Druzhba 🛃 a.	...	0920	0920
493	Druzhba d.	...	1240	1240
654	Beskol' d.	...	1621	1621
797	**Aktogay** a.	...	1828	1828
797	**Aktogay** d.	...	1858	1935
1051	Ush Tobe d.	...	2311	|
1283	Kapchagay d.	...	0345	|
1354	**Almaty** 1 a.	...	0454	|
1363	**Almaty** 2 a.	...	0545	|
1657	Karagandy a.	...	...	0809
1898	**Nur-Sultan** a.	...	...	1301

	5802	54/14 ⑥	13 *KH* ⑦
Nur-Sultan d.	...	1658	...
Karagandy d.	...	2119	...
Almaty 2 d.	...	|	0022
Almaty 1 d.	...	|	0113
Kapchagay d.	...	|	0225
Ush Tobe d.	...	|	0654
Aktogay a.	...	1030	1053
Aktogay d.	...	1123	1123
Beskol' d.	...	1346	1346
Druzhba d.	...	1635	1635
Druzhba 🛃 a.	...	1950	1950
Alashankou 🛃 a.	...	2210	2210
Alashankou d.	2312	2350	2350
Kuitun d.	0409	|	|
Shihezi d.	0550	|	|
Ürümqi a.	0835	0854	0854

)perators: Chinese Railways and Kazakstan Temir Zholy.

XI'AN - CHENGDU 7130

Chinese Railways

km		K291 C	K245	T7 A	K1363	Z324 B	Z224 E	K282 C	K165 D	K195
	Zhengzhou d.	2202	2335	...	...	...	...	0927	...	...
0	**Xi'an** d.	|	0701	0641	1320	...	...	|	2210	2240
173	Baoji d.	c	0938	0843	1546	...	...	c	0034	0103
523	Guangyuan d.	|	1811	1546	0016	0157	0207	0624	0917	0944
727	Mianyang d.	|	2133	1908	0336	|	a	0945	|	1310
842	**Chengdu** a.	1830	2315	2036	0512	0700	...	1120	1413	1438

	T8 A	K166 D	K196	K284 C	K292 C	Z223 E	Z323 B	K246	K1364
Chengdu d.	0900	1326	1610	1822	2131	...	2137	2120	2200
Mianyang d.	1039	1505	|	1950	|	e	|	|	2346
Guangyuan d.	1421	1857	2106	2329	c	0240	0240	0250	0337
Baoji d.	2048	0430	0546	|	|	...	...	1046	1148
Xi'an a.	2227	0630	0753	|	0906n	...	...	1242	1351
Zhengzhou a.	...	...	...	1920	1740	...	...	1934	...

A – Bejing xi(**T7/8**) - Chengdu and v.v.
B – Chengdu(**X323/21**) - Lanzhou(**Z323/24**) - Lhasa and v.v. Runs alternate days only.
C – Shanghai - Zhengzhou – Chengdu and v.v. **c** – Via Table **7170**
D – Xi'an(**K165/66**) - Kunming and v.v.
E – Lhasa(**Z224/23**) - Chongqing. Runs alternate days only.
a – To Chongqing arr. 0623.
e – From Chongqing dep. 2225.

XI'AN - CHENGDU - CHONGQING 7132

China Rail High Speed

km		D1911 B	D1913 A	D1701	D1917	G2201 Z	G89 Z	D1979 F	D1975 Z	G571 Z	G2211 Z
0	**Xi'an** bei d.	0711	0750	0800	0900	0934	1129	1200	1442	1509	1907
	Guangyuan d.	0928	1007	1031	1057	1141	|	1423	1642	1711	2115
	Mianyang d.	1028	|	|	|	1235	|	|	1742	1824	2211
658	**Chengdu** dong a.	1118	1151	|	1223	1319	1438	|	1843	1904	2305
	Nanchong bei d.	...	...	|	...	...	...	1559	|	|	...
977	**Chongqing** bei a.	...	..	1318x	..	...	...	1707	2017	2048x	...

	D1912 D	G2204 Z	D1918 E	G1282 Z	G574 Z	G90 Z	G2210 Z	D1965	D1969 G	D1707
Chongqing bei d.	...	...	...	...	0815x	...	...	0841	0905	1823
Nanchong bei d.	...	...	...	...	|	...	...	|	1016	1936
Chengdu dong d.	0728	0808	0900	0906	0955	1502	1529	|	|	|
Mianyang d.	0812	0859	|	0955	1040	|	|	|	|	|
Guangyuan d.	0920	0956	1028	1052	1151	|	1714	1132	1147	2108
Xi'an bei a.	1143	1203	1225	1300	1405	1816	1930	13521	1410	2311

– Additional trips: 0818, 0958, 1106, 1303, 1400, 1434, 1515.
– Additional trips: 0920, 0926, 1033, 1140, 1214, 1316, 1618, 1723, 1800, 1815, 1847.
D – Additional trips: 0747, 0828, 0919, 1002, 1257, 1431, 1539, 1657, 1733, 1756, 1858.
E – Additional trips: 1211, 1249, 1351, 1400, 1507, 1639, 1807.
F – Additional trips: 1251, 1458, 1752.
G – Additional trips: 1309, 1416, 1804, 1832.
Z – To/from Table **7066** and **7070**.

CHENGDU - QINGCHENGSHAN 7135

China Rail High Speed

igh-speed '**C**' trains (numbers **C61xx**). *65km 50km from Xipu.* Journey 40 - 50 minutes. * – To/from Xipu.

hengdu depart: 0602, 0753*, 0908*, 0935*, 1028*, 1140, 1304*, 1641, 1943*, 2119*, 2217*. **Qingchengshan** depart : 0655*, 0834*, 0954*, 1018*, 1115*, 1350*, 1742, 2018*, 2119, 2254.

CHENGDU - CHONGQING 7140

China Rail High Speed

km	All unmarked trains prefix 'D'	1841	2244 C	638 C	1854	G8541 B	2224 C	354	2208 C	G8683	2256 C	2264 C	2238 C	1820	2374	G8505	2260 C	G8705	368 C	G8547	G8507	634 C	G8509	G8519
0	**Chengdu** dong d.	0639	0643	0712	0718	0742	0735	0811	0815	0825	0825	0905	0911	0918	0929	1002	1020	1051	1055	1159	1228	1333	1335	1351
146	Suining d.	|	0742	|	0817	|	|	|	0922	|	|	|	|	|	1030	|	|	|	|	|	|	1437	|	|
198	Tongnan d.	|	|	0829	0849	|	0858	|	|	|	|	|	|	1038	1101	|	1136	|	1212	|	|	1508	|	|
247	Hechuan d.	|	0834	|	|	|	0925	|	|	|	1016	|	|	1105	1128	|	|	|	1239	|	|	|	|	|
313	**Chongqing** bei **7182** a.	0831x	0900	0931	0948x	0924y	0950	1024	1029	0959x	1036	1100	1124	1141	1153	1143	1221	1239	1304	1326y	1415	1552	1508	1523y

ll trains prefix 'D'	G8511	G8713	G8717	G8557	5102	G8517	G8595	C6001	G2231
hengdu dong d.	1433	1500	1548	1814	1836	1936	1952	2000	2138
uining d.	|	|	|	|	|	|	|	|	|
ongnan d.	|	|	|	|	1954	|	|	|	|
echuan d.	|	|	|	|	2021	|	|	|	|
hongqing bei **7182** a.	1606	1626	1730	1956y	2046	2117	2130	2211	2310

All unmarked trains prefix 'D'	G8542	5105	G8702 A	C6002	G8508	G8546	G8504	G8548	G8508
Chongqing bei **7182** d.	0729	0758	0819	0823	0911	0957y	0958	1116y	1211
Hechuan d.	|	|	|	|	|	|	|	|	|
Tongnan d.	|	|	|	|	|	|	|	|	|
Suining d.	|	0915	|	|	|	|	|	|	|
Chengdu dong a.	0912	1012	1000	1023	1059	1128	1143	1253	1359

ll trains prefix 'D'	G8550	G8596	632 C	G8552	366 C	G8516	2373 C	2259	G8710	G8556	353	2255 C	1822	2236 C	637 C	953	2207 C	G8560	2223 C	2242 C	1827	2263	1835	G8522
hongqing bei **7182** d.	1239y	1318	1358	1424y	1508	1527	1652	1720	1735	1758y	1811	1844	1900	1854	1904	1931	1945	1954y	1957	2000	2026	2107	2117	2159
echuan d.	|	|	1426	|	1535	|	1719	|	|	|	|	1911	|	1921	|	|	2013	|	2024	2027	|	2134	2146	|
ongnan d.	|	|	1453	|	1603	|	1746	1805	|	|	1858	1939	|	|	|	|	2040	|	2055	2055	|	2201	|	|
uining d.	|	|	1525	|	|	|	1820	1836	|	|	1931	|	|	2013	|	|	|	|	|	|	|	2230	|	|
hengdu dong a.	1429	1455	1628h	1558	1728	1701	1917	1933	1917	1934	2027	2054	2059	2112	2101	2128	2201	2128	2210	2211	2217	2331	2323	2334

– Additional trips: 0652, 0754, 1033, 1338, 1400, 1452, 1551, 1621, 1635, 1715, 1848, 1930, 2103.
– Additional trips: 0837, 0903**y**, 0950, 1033**y**, 1130, 1152, 1307, 1521**y**, 1618, 1632**y**, 1723, 1752**y**, 2041.
C – To/from Table **7182**.
h – Chengdu.
y – To/from Shapingba.
Note: Trains numbered **G8XXX** go via Neijiang.

CHENGDU - DAZHOU 7142

China Rail High Speed

km	All trains prefix 'D'	5182	5184	5196	5162	5174 A	5154	5188 E	5192	5156	5194
0	**Chengdu** dong d.	0801h	0931h	1026	1219h	1230	1349h	1435	1656	1844	2003
146	Suining d.	0908	|	|	|	1330	|	|	1756	1951	2103
213	Nanchong d.	0945	1105	1156	1352	1408	1522	|	1833	2025	2141
372	**Dazhou** a.	1103	1228	1319	...	...	...	1710	1952	...	2305

All trains prefix 'D'	5171 B	5181	5185	5161 C	5187	5197	6195	5191	5193	5195 D
Dazhou d.	...	0736	1121	...	1247	1336	...	1732	1927	2011
Nanchong d.	0807	0912	1243	1415	|	1509	1642	1909	|	2146
Suining d.	0840	|	|	|	|	|	|	|	2133	2220
Chengdu dong a.	0946	1037	1413	1540	1533	1635	1814h	2033	2235h	2322h

– Additional trips: 0728, 0748, 1143, 1329, 1542.
– Additional trips: 0939, 1304, 1917.
C – Additional trips: 1146, 1509, 1647.
D – Additional trip: 0908.
E – Additional trip: 1609.
h – Chengdu.

CHENGDU - CHONGQING - GUIYANG - GUILIN - GUANGZHOU 7146

China Rail High Speed

km	All trains prefix 'D'	211	1861	G2924 YZ	1841	2815	G1334 X	1863	1865	G311 YZ	1801	1854	1867	1859	1338 X	1820	2825	1824	G2934 Y	1871	1875	1825	G2928 Y	1851	1877	1833
519	**Chengdu** dong d.	...	...	...	0639	...	...	...	...	...	0727	0718	...	0832	...	0918	...	1039	...	...	...	1238	...	1323	...	1413
	Suining d.	...	...	...	|	...	...	...	...	...	|	0817	...	|	...	|	...	|	...	...	...	|	...	|	...	|
345	**Chongqing** xi d.	...	0720	...	0831	...	0848	0844	0890	...	0941	0948	0954	1100	1136	1141	...	1307	...	1342	1448	1501	...	1531	1610	1618
	Zunyi d.	...	0852	...	0959	...	1015	1004	|	...	1107	|	|	1226	1301	1308	...	1445n	...	1514	|	|	...	1651	1736	|
0	**Guiyang** bei ♠ d.	0800	0944d	1014	1050	1052	1113	1104d	1114d	1126	1159d	1207d	1218d	1326d	1349	1410d	1434	1540d	1650	1614d	1709d	1721d	1736	1749d	1829d	1643d
408	**Guilin** xi d.	|	1159	|	1308	|	...	1327	1346	1336	1407	1437	|	1619	...	1642	1702	1807	|	1858	1929	1956	|	2019	2052	2109
593	Hezhou d.	|	1317	|	1411	|	...	1425	1450	|	|	1550	1555	1725	...	1755	1808	1919	|	1957	2041	|	|	2124	2157	2214
778	Zhaoqing dong d.	|	1420	|	1508	|	...	|	1547	|	|	1653	|	1822	...	1858	1911	2022	|	2100	|	|	|	|	2255	2313
854	**Guangzhou** nan ♠ a.	1210	1455	1428	1554	1540	...	1612	1622	1557	1651	1738	1745	1911	...	1940	1952	2058	2105	2136	2209	2221	2159	2301	2331	2355

ll trains prefix 'D'	1862	1849	G2932 Y	1864	1806	1842	G2926 YZ	1810	1853	1822	1868	G1337 X	1826	1857	G312 YZ	1834	212	1872	1874	G2930	1876	1878	G2922 YZ	G1333 X	2840
uangzhou nan ♠ d.	0700	0726	0754	0800	0818	0848	0836	0920	0943	1100	1151	...	1230	1250	1308	1318	1400	1426	1510	1529	1538	1601	1607	...	1711
haoqing dong d.	0736	0807	|	|	0901	|	|	1003	|	|	1233	...	1313	|	|	|	|	1509	1553	1612	|	|	|	...	|
ezhou d.	0832	|	|	0942	1003	1032	|	1100	1129	1240	1331	...	1415	1436	|	1453	|	1618	|	|	1719	|	|	...	|
uilin xi a.	0940	1028	|	1052	1125	1146	|	1207	1235	1347	1433	...	1522	1538	1530	1600	|	1721	1755	1801	1824	1854	|	...	1937
uiyang bei ♠ a.	1200d	1240d	1213	1328d	1347b	1414	1256	1445d	1508d	1631d	1654d	1730	1750d	1806	1737	1842d	1814	1941d	2037	2015	2058d	2105	2032	2118	2205
unyi d.	1257	1337	...	1417n	1438	|	...	1542	1603n	|	|	|	1847	|	...	1940	...	2038	2135	...	2149	2156	...	2209	...
hongqing xi d.	1423	1529	...	1551	1610	1637	...	1727	1736	1900	1905	1939	2026	2038	...	2117	...	2216	2303	...	2309	2316	...	2329	...
uining d.	...	|	...	...	|	|	...	|	1851	|	...	...	|	2212	...	|	...	...	...	...	...	...	...	...	...
hengdu dong a.	...	1721	...	...	1828	1836	...	1927	1955	2059	...	...	2217	2310	...	2323	...	...	...	...	...	...	...	...	...

– To/from Table **7192**. **Y** – To/from Table **7187**. **Z** – To from Table **7065**. ♠ – Additional stopping services available Guangzhou nan – Guiyang bei and v.v.

7155 NANNING - GUANGZHOU Chinese Railways

km		K366	K1206	K232
	Kunming d.	0750	0853	1652
	Baise d.	|	1808	|
0	**Nanning** d.	2034	2156	0712
263	Yuli d.	2351	0205	1045
438	Maoming d.	0306	0632	1401
700	Zhaoqing d.	0612	0938	1739
787	Fuoshan d.	0812	1114	1933
809	**Guangzhou** a.	0845	1155	2011

	K231	K365	K1205
Guangzhou d.	0532	0950	1723
Fuoshan d.	0611	1020	1753
Zhaoqing d.	0736	1137	1910
Maoming d.	1215	1525	2256
Yuli d.	1520	1827	0200
Nanning a.	1945	2209	0550
Baise d.	|	|	0920
Kunming a.	1007	1113	2108

7160 GUANGZHOU - SANYA Chinese Railways

km		K385	K511	Z201	Z111
			C	B	
0	**Guangzhou** d.	0524	1733	1603	2130
22	Fuoshan d.	0551	1803	1632	2201
109	Zhaoqing d.	0701	1918	1743	2313
361	Maoming d.	1020	2259	2120	0203
488	Zhanjiang xi d.	1112	0006	2215	0258
601	Xunwen d.	|	|	0025	0505
794	Haikou a.	1630	0600	0350	0846
1157	**Sanya** a.	2000	...	0812	...

	K386	Z112	K512	Z20
			C	B
Sanya d.	0710	...	...	173
Haikou d.	1035	1730	1930	210
Xunwen d.	|	2103	2311	|
Zhanjiang xi d.	1535	2247	0042	014
Maoming d.	1630	0014	0201	024
Zhaoqing d.	1954	0356	0623	054
Fuoshan d.	2112	0633	0811	072
Guangzhou a.	2225	0737	0850	080

B – Beijing(**Z201/02**) - Sanya and v.v. C – Shanghai(**K511/12**) - Haikou and v.v.

7165 HAIKOU - SANYA China Rail High Speed

High-speed '**D**' trains (numbers **D73xx**). *308 km from Haikou, 284km from Haikou dong* (Eastern Ring) . Journey 2 - 2¼ hours. * – Also To/from Haikou.

Haikou dong depart: 0640, 0709*, 0722*, 0740, 0900, 0917*, 1000, 1021, 1105, 1120, 1150, 1207, 1305, 1355, 1410, 1449, 1520*, 1540, 1555, 1638, 1755, 1810*, 1900, 1925, 2023, 2025 2126*, 2030, 2115.

Sanya depart : 0635*, 0705, 0719, 0740, 0800*, 0820, 0845, 0910, 0919, 0940, 0947, 1050, 1102, 1121, 1149, 1207, 1215, 1310, 1326, 1348, 1415, 1556, 1623, 1630, 1651, 1802, 1840, 1908 1945, 2010, 2105, 2138.

7168 GUANGZHOU - ZHANJIANG China Rail High Speed

km		D921	D9451	D931	D7493	D7461	D9467	D9471	D7495	D7483	D7587
		A		C							
0	**Guangzhou** nan ♥ d.	0700	0710	0742	0836	1014	1134	1300	1610	1735	2000
	Yangjiang d.	0832	0843	0916	|	1201	1321	1429	1751	1904	2139
	Maoming d.	0917	0940	1001	1115	1252	1418	1514	1842	1949	2224
	Zhanjiang xi ♥ d.	0953	1020	1037	1149	1326	1452	1548	1922	2023	2258

	D7452	D7462	D7468	D7474	D932	D922	D7484	D7486	D7492	D749
					C	A				
Zhanjiang xi ♥ d.	0720	1057	1314	1436	1607	1703	1748	1837	1919	2057
Maoming d.	0754	1137	1348	1516	1641	1737	1822	1917	1953	2131
Yangjiang d.	0845	1228	1433	|	1726	1822	1907	2002	2050	2216
Guangzhou nan ♥ d.	1028	1405	1603	1745	1904	2000	2039	2152	2225	2352

A – ①⑤⑥⑦ 1cl, 2 Beijing(**D921/22**) - Zhanjiang and v.v. C – ①⑤⑥⑦ 1cl, 2 Shanghai(**D931/22**) - Zhanjiang and v.v. ♥ – Additional services operate.

7170 ZHENGZHOU and WUHAN - CHENGDU and CHONGQING Chinese Railways

km		Z3	K389	K290	K205	K805	Z49	K283	T247	K15	T125	K117	T9	K357
		D		B			D	B			C	E	D	
	d. **Zhengzhou**	...	...	2205	0609	...	1736	0927	...	1628	...	2100	2255	...
0	d. **Wuhan** Wu	0434h	0604	|	|	1050	2220h	|	1925	|	0127	|	|	2236
165	d. Suizhou	|	0803	|	|	1339	|	|	2116	|	|	|	|	|
334	d. Xiangyang	|	1023d	|	1337	1615d	|	|	2308d	2348	0419d	0428	0517	|
500	d. Shiyan	|	1232	|	1545	1850	|	1919	0116	0148	0638	|	0709	|
702	d. Ankang	y	1523	0816	1818	2226	|	2152	0342	0409	0901	0842	0930	|
978	d. Dazhou	|	|	1304	|	0228	|	|	0716	0757	1258	1220	1317	1352
1137	d. Nanchong	|	|	1532	|	|	|	|	|	|	1521	1400	|	|
1204	d. Suining	|	|	1625	|	|	0720	|	0947	|	1617	|	|	|
1375	a. **Chengdu**	|	0439	1830	0840	|	0839	1120	1120d	|	1749	1702	|	|
1233	a. **Chongqing** bei	1156	...	...	...	0510	0545↑	...	...	1100	...	...	1614	1633

	Z50	Z4	K806	K358	K390	T248	K292	K206	K284	T126	K118	T10	K16
	D	D		♦			B		B	C	E	D	
Zhengzhou a.	0328	...	...			...	1750	1842	1858		2108	0410	0617
Wuhan Wu a.	2259h	2308	0219	1535	0821	0455	|	|	|	1512	|	|	|
Suizhou d.	|	|	2256	|	|	0254	|	|	|	1258	|	|	|
Xiangyang d.	|	|	2115d	|	0331	0137d	|	1154	1138	1142d	1342	2153	2339
Shiyan d.	|	|	1822	|	0114	2330	|	0856	0904	0938	|	1928	2057
Ankang d.	|	|	1531	|	2237	2046	0620	0607	0613	0647	0806	1640	1816
Dazhou d.	|	|	1156	0210	|	1739	0250	|	|	0330	0456	1335	1508
Nanchong d.	|	|	|	|	|	1530	0014	|	|	0128	0248	|	|
Suining d.	1304	|	|	|	|	1415	2321	|	|	0034	0148	|	|
Chengdu d.	1142	|	|	|	0819	1245	2131	1620	1822	2245	2359	|	|
Chongqing bei d.	1444↑	1528	0811	2333	...	...	...	...	...	...	...	1042	1220

B – Shanghai - Zhengzhou - Chengdu and v.v.
C – Chengdu (**T126/25**) - Wuhan Wuchang (**T127/28**) - Dongguan dong and v.v.
D – Beijing - Chongqing bei and v.v.
E – Zhengzhou(**K117/18**) - Panzhihua and v.v.
h – Wuhan Hankou.
y – Via Yichang dong.

7175 SHANGHAI - NANJING - WUHAN China Rail High Speed

km	All trains prefix '**D**'	3077	637	G1772	2207	3073	3057	2213	G598	3064	G577	G677	2216	3022	3091	3061	3069	G1724	3081	3027	3007	3011	3033	3015	G1728	3043	3047
		A	A		A	A							A														
0	**Shanghai** ♣ d.	...	0633	0647	0658	0703	0719	0737	0746	0820	0824	0830	0842	0915	1012	0946	1018	1146	...	1327	1353	1441	1516	1607	1651	1647	1753
84	Suzhou d.	...	0713	071bb	0735	0740	0755	0811	|	0859	0850b	0859b	0918	0945	1055b	1037	1054	1211b	...	1354	1432	1517	1552	1643	1720b	1737	1832
126	Wuxi d.	...	0728	|	0752	0757	0812	0828	|	0922	0905d	0911d	0935	1002	1110d	1055	1111	|	...	1420	1445	1535	1609	1701	|	1755	1850
165	Changzhou d.	...	0745	0736b	0809	0814	0835	0848	|	0939	|	0940b	0952	1019	|	1121	1128	|	...	1437	1507	1552	|	1718	|	1812	1907
237	Zhenjiang d.	...	0812	|	0841	0846	|	0923	|	1006	0937n	|	1035	1055	|	1155	1146	|	...	1503	1533	1618	|	1750	|	1838	|
311	**Nanjing** nan d.	0754	0878	0815	0915	0920	0932	0955	0900	1037	1002	1020	1106	1127	1213	1228	1233	1303	1443	1537	1604	1652	1724	1826	1812	1912	2003
468	Hefei nan d.	0858	0957	0919	1018	1023	1037	1102	1003	1142	1119	1127	1207	1235	1311	1326	1331	1401	1541	1644	1718	1803	1833	1931	1912	2020	2106
555	Liuan d.	0924	1028	0945	1044	1049	1104	1140	|	|	1145	1156	1233	1301	1337	1352	1357	|	1607	|	|	1829	1859	1957	|	2046	2132
827	**Wuhan** Hankou a.	1059	1151	1119	1210	1215	1225	1313	1144	1343	1330	1336	1420	1520g	1516	1521	1530	1542	1750	1851	1926	1957	2046	2135	2047	2227	2306
1119	*Yichang dong* **7182** a.	1304	1354	a	1425	1449	...	1525	...	...	a	...	1625	...	...	...	...	...	1957	2059	2132	...	...	...	...	...	...

All trains prefix '**D**'	3028	3016	G1722	G1738	3034	3008	3054	3044	G1730	3082	3048	3058	G678	2214	G600	G1774	2218	3092	3074	3024	G1726	G578	638	3004	3078	2208
										A							A		A				A		A	A
Yichang dong **7182** d.	...	...	...	...	...	0640	0802	...	...	0922	...	...	...	1132	...	a	1256	...	1332	...	...	a	1414	...	1517	1455
Wuhan Hankou d.	0731	0759	0800	0825	0900	0905	1007	1013	1105	1126	1125g	1305	1335	1356	1500	1510	1514	1536	1541	1605	1615	1632	1641	1725	1731	1720
Liuan d.	0920	0939	|	1000	1027	1101	1129	1152	1221	1256	1346	1444	1455	1529	|	1631	1647	1657	1702	1745	|	|	1810	1851	1904	1844
Hefei nan d.	0953	1015	0938	1031	1104	1135	1203	1223	1250	1329	1427	1520	1525	1601	1649	1704	1719	1735	1745	1827	1801	1816	1852	1932	1942	1922
Nanjing nan d.	1056	1116	1036	1127	1209	1246	1304	1328	1345	1422	1523	1628	1621	1703	1743	1759	1823	1849	1858	1922	1856	1910	2003	2027	2035	2018
Zhenjiang d.	|	1147	|	1152n	1239	1325	1343n	1358	1407	...	|	1655	1643n	1733	|	|	|	1920n	1928	|	|	1932n	2033	2057	...	2048
Changzhou d.	1152	1213	|	|	1325	1357	1413b	1433	1437	...	1626	1730	1713b	1810	|	|	1919	1956b	2004	2014	|	1951b	2105	2133	...	2115
Wuxi d.	1209	1230	|	1223d	1352	1414	1437d	1452	1458	...	1643	1757	|	1836	|	1903d	1936	|	2023	2042	|	|	2122	2150	...	2132
Suzhou d.	1232	1248	1128b	1236b	1419	1432	1450b	1524	1511b	...	1701	1811	1738b	1853	|	1916b	1954	2024b	2046	2101	1949b	2016b	2140	2207	...	2150
Shanghai Hongqiao a.	1306	1322	1153	1317	1448	1515	1516	1559	1541	...	1729	1841	1808	1927	1855	1939	2028	2050	2120	2135	2013	2046	2214	2241	...	2224

A – To/from Table **7182**. a – To/from Changsha Nan. g – Wuhan Wuchang. h – Wuhan. ♣ – **Shanghai** Hongqiao.

7180 SHANGHAI - ZHUZHOU - GUANGZHOU Chinese Railways

km		T169	T77		T81		K79	K527	K511	K739
			B		A		D		C	E
0	**Shanghai** nan d.	1050	1127	...	1606	...	1826	1915	1921	1936
80	Jiaxing d.	1135	1212	...	1652	...	1933	2004	2017	2034
188	Hangzhou dong d.	1246	1319	...	1804	...	2052	2118	2132	2156
312	Yiwu d.	1352	1428	...	1919	...	2210	2256	2302	2320
446	Quzhou d.	1529	1601	...	2056	...	0004	0047	0132	0147
557	Shangrao d.	1645	1717	...	2209	...	0134	0313	0306	|
673	Yingtan d.	1752	1825	...	2317	...	0305	0431	0424	0514
1044	Pingxiang d.	|	|	...	|	...	0712	0859	0816	0923
1125	**Zhuzhou** d.	|	2226	...	0428	...	0846	1040	0932	1105
1259	Hengyang d.	|	0040	...	0604	...	...	1213	1113	...
1406	Chenzhou d.	|	...	...	...	...	...	1400	1257	...
1559	Shaoguan dong d.	0247	...	...	...	...	...	1545	1442	...
1780	**Guangzhou** a.	0524	...	...	...	...	...	1830	1720	...

	K528		K80	K512	T170	K740		T82	T78
			D	C		E		A	B
Guangzhou d.	0745	...	...	0910	1455	...	...	...	...
Shaogun dong d.	1010	...	...	1201	1717	...	...	...	...
Chenzhou d.	1154	...	...	1358	|	...	...	...	...
Hengyang d.	1351	...	...	1549	|	...	...	0034	1948
Zhuzhou d.	1533	...	1546	1748	|	2320	...	0220	|
Pingxiang d.	1630	...	1642	|	|	|	...	0311	|
Yingtan d.	2043	...	2047	2248	0111	0441	...	0633	|
Shangrao d.	2155	...	2201	0009	|	0608	...	|	|
Quzhou d.	2313	...	2344	|	|	0817	...	0843	0515
Yiwu d.	0055	...	|	0444	0516	1023	...	1012	0643
Hangzhou nan d.	0218	...	0255	0619	0712	1157	...	1135	0758
Jiaxing d.	|	...	0402	0743	0812	1300	...	1232	0905
Shanghai nan a.	0406	...	0516	0849	0912	1433	...	1327	1018

A – Shanghai nan(**T81/82**) - Nanning and v.v. C – Shanghai(**K511/12**) - Haikou and v.v. E – Shanghai nan(**K739/40**) - Kunming and v.v. a – Shanghai.
B – Shanghai nan(**T77/78**) - Nanning and v.v. D – Shanghai nan(**K79/80**) - Kunming and v.v.

7181 CHENGDU - KUNMING - HEKOU Chinese Railways

km		K853	T8869	K113	K145	K165	K117	K6140	K9832	K9826	K9822	K9816
						D	E					
0	**Chengdu** d.	0854	0910	1300	1428	1457	1728	...	...	...	...	...
219	Neijiang d.	1248	|	|	|	|	|	...	...	...	...	...
557	Xichang d.	|	1857	2312	0018	0053	0205	...	...	...	...	...
738	Liupanshui d.	0035	|	|	|		|	...	...	...	...	...
749	Panzhihua d.	|	2201	0215	0402	0422	0451	...	...	...	...	...
1100	**Kunming** a.	0528	...	0734	0901	0954	...	0819	1102	1230	1541	2255
1500	**Hekou** bei a.	...	...	...	...	...	...	1521	1623	1849	2128	0605

	K114	T8870	K854	K146	K166	K118	K9818	K9828	K6142	K9694	K982
					D	E					
Hekou bei d.	...	...	...	...	...	...	0700	0935	1130	1705	2255
Kunming d.	0825	...	1013	1739	2003	...	1234	1545	1716	2218	065
Panzhihua d.	1400	0808	|	2311	0036	1154	...	...	...	...	...
Lipanshui d.	|	|	1505	|	|	|	...	...	...	...	...
Xichang d.	1646	1102	|	0414	0342	1441	...	...	...	...	...
Neijiang d.	|	|	0131	|	|	|	...	...	...	...	...
Chengdu a.	0403	2024	0526	1324	1251	2330	...	...	...	...	...

D – Xi'an(**K165/66**) - Kunming and v.v. E – Zhengzhou(**K117/18**) - Panzhihua and v.v.

China Rail High Speed

WUHAN - YICHANG - CHONGQING 7182

km	All unmarked trains prefix 'D'	632	2251	2277	366	2373	3077	2255	2236	637	2207	3073	G1312	2223	2242	2213	G309	656	2216	2271	2232	2226	G318	3081	3027	3007
		D			D	D		D	BD	D			C	AD	BD			A			B	B				
	Shanghai **7175** d.	...	...	...	...	...	...	...	...	0633	0658	0706	...	...	...	0737	...	...	0842	...	...	...	...	...	1327	1353
	Nanjing nan **7175** d.	...	...	...	...	0716	0754	0820	...	0848	0915	0920	...	0945	...	0955	...	1012	1106	1132	...	...	...	1443	1537	|
	Nanchang **7194** d.	...	...	...	...	|	|	|	0840	|	|	|	...	|	1032x	|	...	|	|	|	1224x	1237x	...	|	|	|
0	**Wuhan** Hankou d.	0700	0749	0836	0803	1019	1109	1142	1206	1159	1216	1239	1225h	1252	1313	1320	1355	1335	1432	1528	1535	1545	1554	1750	1857	1933
83	Tianmen nan d.	0737	|	0913	0840	|	|	|	|	|	|	1316	|	1336	|	|	|	|	|	1609	1619	1628	1637	1827	|	|
34	Qianjiang (Hubei) d.	|	0842	0935	0900	|	|	1241	1259	|	1309	1338	1404	|	1413	1422	|	1504	|	1631	1641	1650	1659	1847	1943	|
204	Jingzhou d.	0821	0910	1003	0928	1140	1230	1309	1328	1319	1337	1414	1432	1423	1441	1450	1522	|	1550	1659	|	1718	1728	1917	2028	2058
292	**Yichang** dong d.	0910	0956	1042	1007	1219	1304	1349	1407	1354	1433	1449	1515	1506	1523	1532	1601	1611	1635	1738	1744	1807	1812	1957	2059	2132
567	Lichuan d.	1149	1229	1317	1247	1450	...	1624	1645	1633	1718	...	1741	1753	1804	1814	1831	1841	1914	2023	2013	2040	|	...	...	...
845	**Chongqing** bei **7140** a.	1346	1441	1514	1451	1641	...	1824	1854	1842	1924	...	1933	1943	1954	2011	2028	2036	2112	2221	2210	2238	2231	...	...	...

unmarked trains prefix 'D'	3008	3082	3258	2214	655	2234	G1314	2272	2218	2228	3074	G310	2264	2244	638	2224	2208	3078	2256	2238	2260	368	2278	2252	634
					A	B	C			B			D	BD	D	AD	D		D	BD		D			D
hongqing bei **7140** d.	...	...	...	0715	0727	0743	0750	0829	0838	0859	...	0934	1118	0907	0938	0959	1045	...	1057	1120	1234	1314	1323	1520	1604
chuan d.	...	...	...	0910	|	|	0950	1024	1034	|	...	|	|	1110	1146	1157	|	...	|	|	|	|	|	1727	|
chang dong d.	0640	0922	0900	1132	1142	1206	1215	1250	1256	1320	1332	1400	1538	1345	1414	1422	1455	1517	1533	1553	1653	1739	1751	1954	2035
gzhou d.	0722	0958	0937	1208	1224	1245	1254	1330	1339	1356	1408	1440	1620	1427	1450	1504	1532	1553	1610	1630	1729	1815	1828	2030	2112
anjiang (Hubei) d.	0749	|	1004	|	|	1312	1321	1357	1405	1423	1435	|	1647	|	1517	|	|	1620	|	1657	1756	1842	|	|	|
anmen nan d.	0817	|	|	|	|	1334	1343	1419	1429	|	|	1524	1709	|	|	1553	|	|	1659	|	1824	1904	|	2113	|
uhan Hankou a.	0853	1123	1107	1350	1337	1440	1504h	1456	1506	1519	1533	1603	1752	1556	1621	1634	1705	1725	1736	1802	1901	2000	1955	2150	2235
Nanchang **7194** a.	|	|	1416	|	|	1740	...	|	|	1822x	|	...	|	1859x	|	|	|	|	|	2114	...	...	...	...	...
Nanjing nan **7175** a.	1240	1422	...	1700	1725	...	...	1801	1820	...	1855	...	2124	...	2003	2004	2010	2035	2106	...	...	...	...	...	...
Shanghai Hongqiao **7175** a.	1515	...	...	1927	...	...	...	...	2028	...	2120	...	...	...	2214	...	2224	...	...	...	...	...	...	...	...

km	All unmarked trains prefix 'D'	7080	5817	5989	5762	5819	5972	5996	7083	7062	5992	5853	5752		5766	5955	5862	5772	5977	G555	G1032	5866	5776	G1146	7071	G1036
																					C			C		C
0	**Wuhan** Hankou d.	0603	0645	0714	0725c	0757	0818	0848	0904	0914	0947	0957	1020c	...	1224c	1341	1618	1621c	1640	1725	1754h	1839	1916	1921h	1950	2024h
83	Tianmen nan d.	|	|	|	0813	|	0901	|	0941	0951	1024	1035	1107	...	|	|	1655	|	1729	1802	1856	|	2003	|	2027	2123
34	Qianjiang (Hubei) d.	|	|	0813	|	0851	|	0943	1004	1013	|	|	|	...	1329	1442	1718	1734	1754	|	|	1948	|	2039	2049	|
04	Jingzhou d.	|	0800	0841	0901	0919	0951	1012	|	1041	1110	1119	1151	...	1357	|	1746	1804	1822	1847	1942	2016	2049	2109	2117	2207
92	**Yichang** dong a.	0752	0834	0915	0935	0955	1025	1046	1100	1121	1150	1159	1231	...	1431	1539	1820	1838	1856	1921	2016	2104	2123	2143	2151	2241

unmarked trains prefix 'D'	5854	G1035	G556	G1031	5858	G1148	5876	G516	5982	5956	5864	5990		5868	5820	5778	5998	5994	7064	5954	5826	5774	5978	7082	7072
		C		C		C																			
chang dong d.	0615	0733	0818	0837	0909	0945	1021	1038	1047	1116	1225	1339	...	1522	1609	1624	1631	1642	1711	1658	1840	1858	1920	2005	2130
gzhou d.	0657	0810	0900	0919	0946	1021	1103	1114	1123	1152	1303	1417	...	1605	1645	1701	1713	1719	1753	1742	1917	1940	1957	2048	2208
anjiang (Hubei) d.	0724	0837	0927	0946	|	|	|	|	|	|	1330	1444	...	|	|	1728	|	1746	1820	1809	|	|	2024	|	|
anmen nan d.	0752	0900	0949	1008	|	1105	1146	1157	1206	1237	1252	|	...	1648	|	17504	1802	1811	|	1833	2000	|	|	2131	|
uhan Hankou a.	0834	1013h	1031	1117h	1100	1212h	1250	1236	1242	1320	1450	1551	...	1729	1807	1844c	1843	1855	1921	1915	2037	2107c	2123	2215	2320

- Wuchang. **h** – Wuhan. **x** – Nanchang xi. **A** – To/from Table **7102**. **B** – To/from Table **7194**. **C** – To/from Table **7065**. **D** – To/from Table **7140**.

China Rail High Speed

CHANGSHA - GUILIN - NANNING - BEIHAI and FANGCHENGGANG 7184

km	D8262	431	D8266	423	1505	1503	529	1501	D8271	421	433		All unmarked trains prefix 'G'		434	422	424	1502	530	D8268	1504	1506	D8272	432	D8280
				A	B	B	A h	B		A						A	A	B	A j		B	B			
362	...	0706	...	1214	...	...	1255	...	...	1444	1449	↓	d.Wuhan a.	↑	1457	1600	1633	...	1715	...	...	...	...	2250	...
0	...	0848	...	1352	1412	1440	1450	1531	...	1617	1632	↓	d.**Changsha** nan a.	↑	1316	1422	1458	1523	1543	...	1604	1700	...	2117	...
177	...	0927	...	1438	1453	1520	1530	1610	...	1708	1714	↓	d.Hengyang dong d.	↑	1235	1330	1414	1434	1501	...	1516	1607	...	2025	...
*	0806	|	1402	|	|	|	|	|	1749	|	|	↓	d. Hezhou a.	↑	|	|	|	|	|	1336	|	|	1717	|	2226
519	0943	1225	1532	1718	1725	1809	1825	1905	1928	1952	1959	↓	d.**Guilin** d.	↑	0958	1057	1126	1145	1210	1203	1229	1328	1600b	1735	2055
675	1058	1334	1647	1828	1833	1924	1946	2019	2037	2103	2114	↓	d.Liuzhou d.	↑	0848	0948	1007	1028	1056	1044	1113	1219	1430	1614	1935
887	1214	1445	1757	1938	1943	2023	2050h	2129	2147	2219	2224	↓	a.**Nanning** dong d.	↑	0740	0835	0900	0915	0943j	0930	1010	1105	1310	1505	1820

km	8403	8451	8203	3561	3563	8409	8453	8211	1779	8411	3571		All trains prefix 'D'		8202	3572	1780	8404	8452	3568	8214	3570	8454	8416	8218
	G							E			C				F	D		H							
	...	...	...	0718	0818	...	...	...	1155d	...	1440		d.**Guiyang** bei a.		...	1340	1600	...	...	2123	...	2248	...	...	...
0	0759	0904	0821	1006	1100b	1152	1321	1406	1448	1509	1744	↓	d.**Guilin** a.	↑	1003	1039	1313	1439	2124	1833b	2140	2011b	225	2306	2312
156	0908	1018	0945	1121	1215	1301	1432	1527	1602	1624	1902		d.Liuzhou d.		0856	0929	1203	1317	2021	1654	2041	1840	2057	2201	2207
368	1023	1132	1101	1243	1331	1428	1546	1643	1725	1655	2019	↓	a.**Nanning** dong d.	↑	0750	0820	1050	1155	1848a	1540	1915	1718a	1950	2038	2052
368	1038	1142	...	1307	1338	1437	1610	...	1728	1701	...	↓	d.**Nanning** dong a.	↑	...	...	1045	1151	1826a	1530	...	1705a	1948	2032	...
496	1122	|	...	1351	1422	1521	|	...	1813	|	...	↓	d.Qinzhou dong d.	↑	...	...	0917	1012	|	1354	...	1608	|	1901	...
587	1158	|	...	1427	1505	1604	|	...	1856	1915	...	↓	a.Beihai d.	↑	...	...	0840	0929	|	1311	...	1525	|	1824	...
539	...	1242	...	...	...	...	1710	...	...	...	...	↓	a.Fangchenggang bei d.	↑	...	...	...	...	1717	...	...	...	1806	...	...

– To/from Table **7060**.
– To/from Table **7192**.
– Additional trip: 1616.
D – Additional trips: 0925, 1014.
E – Additional trips: 1038, 1609, 1846, 1943, 2017.
F – Additional trips: 0825. 0855, 1140, 1738, 2001.
G – Additional trips: 0814, 0935, 1240, 1549, 1658.
H – Additional trips: 0834, 1030, 1130, 1226, 1608, 1753.
a – Nanning.
h – To Beihai arr. 2230.
j – From Beihai dep. 0742.
* – *185* km from Guilin.

China Rail High Speed

BEIHAI - NANNING - GUANGZHOU 7186

km	All unmarked trains prefix 'D'	3603	3605	3607	G2911	201	3615	3708	3684	3712	G2913	3685	203	3625	3627	205	3717	3639	3724	3728	3789	G2915	3869	3732	207	3853
		A																								
	Fangchenggang bei d.	...	...	...	...	...	...	...	0913	...	...	1035	...	...	...	...	...	...	...	...	...	...	...	...	...	...
0	**Beihai** ▶ d.	...	...	...	...	...	...	0810	|	0917	...	|	...	...	...	...	1318	...	1453	1519	...	...	...	1704	...	...
91	Qinzhou dong d.	...	...	...	...	...	...	0849	|	1000	...	|	...	...	...	...	1401	...	1536	1557	...	...	1720	1746	...	...
97	**Nanning** dong ▶ d.	0708	0718	0742	0803	0831	0850	0956	1035	1103	1138	1156	1340	1322a	1352	1500	1505	1616	1646	1705	1736	1802	1823	1850	1902	1936
	Guigang d.	|	0808	0832	|	|	|	1046	1123	1153	1228	|	|	|	1443	|	|	1706	|	|	1826	1853	1920	1951	|	2026
	Wuzhou nan d.	0909	0927	0948	0955	|	1102	1205	1236	1315	1335	1359	|	1538	1559	|	1708	1826	1851	1914	1940	2000	2051	2116	|	2146
	Zhaoqing dong d.	|	1035	1102	|	|	1209	1315	1340	|	|	|	|	|	|	|	1819	1927	|	2022	2051	2102	|	2225	|	|
73	**Guangzhou** nan a.	1111	1117	1139	1127	1146	1258	1358	1417	1503	1520	1545	1656	1722	1740	1820	1904	2010	2036	2111	2134	2144	2246	2308	2218	2336
62	Shenzhen bei a.	...	...	...	1201	...	...	...	...	...	1549	...	...	...	...	...	...	...	...	...	...	2224	...	...	...	...

unmarked trains prefix 'D'	3602	G2912	2362	2364	2366	3604	3706	202	3710	3830	3618	3702	3682	204	3622	G2914	3714	3690	206	3722	3726	3686	G2916	3632	208	3650
			B																							
Shenzhen bei d.	...	0705	...	...	...	...	...	...	...	...	...	...	...	...	...	1222	...	...	...	...	...	...	1625	...	...	...
uangzhou nan d.	0745	0737	0806	0817	0848	0912	0906	1006	0924	1042	1144	1112	1136	1208	1214	1302	1302	1350	1420	1524	1555	1613	1647	1737	1830	1946
aoqing dong a.	0826	0814	|	0902	|	0950	|	|	1008	|	1227	|	|	|	1258	|	1353	|	|	1608	|	|	1728	1815	|	2031
uzhou nan d.	0931	0920	0955	1009	1038	1101	1048	|	1111	1230	1343	1331	1324	|	1409	1445	1504	1542	|	1713	1745	1803	1829	1925	|	2136
uigang d.	|	1020	1104	1124	|	1204	|	|	|	1339	1453	|	|	|	1524	1548	|	1657	|	1828	1900	1912	|	2028	|	2245
anning dong ▶ a.	1132	1113	1202	1216	1250	1256	1250	1325	1308	1430	1545	1550	1530	1526	1616	1636	1705	1800	1739	1921	2000	2012	2016	2126	2149	2337
nzhou dong d.	...	...	...	...	...	...	1345	...	1411	...	...	1637	1619	...	...	...	|	|	...	2030	2103	|	...	...	...	...
eihai ▶ a.	...	...	...	...	...	...	1421	...	1454	...	...	1720	...	...	...	...	1836	|	...	2106	2145	|	...	...	...	...
angchenggang bei a.	...	...	...	...	...	...	...	...	...	...	...	...	...	...	...	...	...	1913	...	...	...	2130	...	...	...	...

– Additional trips: 0730, 0750, 0754, 0818, 0902, 0913, 0926, 0936, 0946, 1150, 1224, 1243, 1410, 1454, 1525, 1547, 1657, 1947.
– Additional trips: 0918, 0954, 1018, 1030, 1054, 1137, 1405, 1443, 1619, 1628, 1718, 1724, 1804, 1836, 1842, 1852, 1858, 1910, 1935.
a – Nanning.
▶ – Additional trains Nanning dong – Beihai and v.v.

China Rail High Speed

DALI - KUNMING - NANNING - GUANGZHOU 7187

km	All trains prefix 'D'	G2924	3812	G311	3816	3828	3844	3848	3852	G2934	G2928	3856
		H		H	C						H	
0	Dali d.	...	...	...	...	...	1005	...	1113	...	...	1153
56	**Kunming** nan d.	0753	0906	0921	0926	1037	1248	1310	1359	1445	1523	1433
	Baise d.	|	1217	|	1233	1335	1551	1617	1706	|	|	1737
65	**Nanning** dong d.	|	1426	|	1431	1537	1747	1812	1920	|	|	1936
	Guigang d.	G	1521	G	|	1627	|	|	2016	G	G	2027
	Wuzhou nan d.	|	1650	|	1631	1749	1952	2021	2136	|	|	2146
	Zhaoqing dong d.	|	|	|	1748	|	2114	2147	|	|	|	|
38	**Guangzhou** nan a.	1428	1842	1556	1831	1933	2203	2230	2325	2105	2154	2336

	3802	G2932	3814	G2926	3818	3830	3838	G312	3854	3858	G2922
				H		D		H			H
Guangzhou nan d.	0654	0754	0828	0836	0842	1042	1124	1308	1314	1345	1607
Zhaoqing dong d.	0738	|	|	|	0920	|	1208	|	|	1423	|
Wuzhou nan d.	0849	|	1020	|	1030	1230	1313	|	1510	1532	|
Guigang d.	0951	G	1129	G	1133	1339	|	G	1625	|	G
Nanning dong d.	1046	|	1223	|	1240	1432	1522	|	1718	1734	|
Baise d.	1246	|	1409	|	1451	1619	1722	|	1905	1930	|
Kunming nan a.	1614	1417	1730	1502	1825	1923	2020	1947	2155	2208	2246
Dali a.	1827	...	1935	...	2037	...	...	...	...	...	...

– Additional trips: 1016, 1056, 1119, 1214, 1335. **D** – Additional trips: 0724, 0942, 0954, 1106, 1156. **G** – Via Guiyang bei Table **7146**. **H** – To/from Table **7065**. **a** – Nanning.

7188 CHANGSHA/ZHUZHOU - NANNING Chinese Railways

km	T81 A	T77 B	Z5 C	Z285 D				T78 B	Z6 C	T82 A	Z286 D
0	...	...	...	...	↓	d.**Nanchang** d.		...	...	...	...
231	...	...	...	...		d.Pingxiang a.	↑	...	...	0307	...
* *	...	...	0619	1123	↓	d. **Changsha 7090** a.		...	1934	|	0241
312	0428	...	|	|		d.**Zhuzhou** a.	↑	...	|	0156	|
437	|	...	|	|	↓	d.Loudi d.		...	|	|	|
446	0604	0041	0820	1323		d. Hengyang d.	↑	1948	1728	0034	0050
808	|	0425**b**	1138	1629**b**	↓	d.Guilin d.		1550	1422	|	2130**b**
989	|	0615	1314	1838		d.Liuzhou d.	↑	1314	1252	|	1945
1124	1646	|	|	|		d.Litang d.		|	|	1241	|
1244	1846	0850	1534	2104	↓	a.**Nanning** a.	↑	1000	1052	1105	1735

A – Shanghai nan(**T81/82**) - Nanning and v.v.
B – Shanghai nan(**T77/78**) - Guilin and v.v.
C – Beijing(**Z5/6**) - Nanning and v.v.
D – Beijing(**Z285/6**) - Nanning and v.v.
b – Guilin bei.
* * – Changsha *0 km* - Zhuzhou *52 km*.

7190 CHANGSHA/ZHUZHOU - KUNMING Chinese Railways

km	Z161 G	Z77 F	K79 H	K739 E				K80 H	Z162 G	Z78 F	K74 E
* *	0301	0620	...	...	↓	d.**Changsha** a.		...	1630	2140	...
0	|	|	0848	1105		d. **Zhuzhou** a.	↑	1529	|	|	230
145	0505	0820	1029	1249	↓	d.Loudi d.		1336	1423	1934	203
440	0916	1228	1459	1712		d.Huaihua d.	↑	0932	1020	1535	160
709	1259	1610	1855	|		d.Kaili d.		|	|	1144	112
917	1529	1836	2141	2356	↓	d.**Guiyang** d.	↑	0304	0408	0920	084
948	|	...	2259	|		d.Anshun d.		0134	|	...	070
1146	1855	...	0133	0335	↓	d.Liupanshui d.	↑	2336	0058	...	043
1378	2114	...	0435	0644		d.Qujing d.		2050	2231	...	011
1525	2232	...	0609	0823	↓	a.**Kunming** a.	↑	1910	2105	...	233

E – Shanghai nan(**K739/40**) - Kunming and v.v.
F – Beijing xi(**Z77/78**) - Guiyang and v.
G – Beijing(**Z161/62**) - Kunming and v.v.
H – Shanghai nan(**K79/80**) - Kunming and v.
* * – Changsha *0 km* - Loudi *177 km*.

7192 SHANGHAI - HANGZHOU - NANCHANG - CHANGSHA – GUIYANG – KUNMING China Rail High Speed

km	All trains prefix 'G'	1421	1383 G	1371	1341 E	85 C	1505 AB	1337 D	1373	1503 AB	1377 A	1347	1501 B	61 A	1301 C	1375	1333 D	1481 A	1387	1369	1329	99 C	1305 C	1483 A	1361	1365	45 A
0	**Shanghai** ♥ d.	...	0645	0722	0732	0800	...	0825	0855	...	0928	0951	1003	...	1023	1115	1139	...	1220	1240	1341	1410	1525	...	1642	1738	...
84	Jiaxing nan d.	...	0715	0753	0808	|	...	0854	|	...	1004	|	1033	...	1055	1144	|	...	1250	|	1410	|	|	...	1718	1808	...
159	**Hangzhou** ♣ d.	0731	0748	0825	0835	0847	0919	0926	0944	0959	1031	1053	1103	1134	1130	1210	1241	1312	1323	1342	1442	1501	1614	1652	1745	1842	213
268	Yiwu d.	0812	0829	0859	0909	|	0954	1007	|	1040	1105	|	|	|	1207	1251	1326	|	1357	1423	|	|	|	1727	1819	|	221
320	Jinhua d.	0830	|	0918	0930	|	1012	1025	1030	1058	|	1145	1155	1221	1226	|	1344	1358	|	|	1535	1547	1700	|	1837	1927	223
398	Quzhou d.	|	|	0946	0953	|	1035	1051	|	1121	|	|	|	1244	|	1332	|	1422	|	|	|	|	|	1808	1900	|	225
500	Shangrao d.	0929	0935	1015	1025	|	1107	1124	|	1151	1212	|	1247	1313	1319	1411	1429	|	1502	1520	1623	1634	1750	1837	1930	2019	...
604	Yingtan bei d.	|	1003	1043	|	|	1135	1152	1141	1220	|	1259	|	1341	1347	|	1457	1520	1530	1548	1651	|	|	1905	1958	|	...
744	**Nanchang** xi a.	1025	1053	1118	1128	1100	1221	1227	1216	1308	1319	1334	1343	1417	1422	1521	1532	1602	1613	1623	1726	1735	1846	1945	2033	2122	...
1086	**Changsha** nan a.	1205	...	1251	1312	1225	1405	1410	1351	1435	1502	1517	1525	...	1609	1715	1725	1749	...	1816	1915	1855	2039	2141	2213	2301	...
1211	Loudi nan d.	1252	...	1339	...	...	...	|	1431	...	1546	...	...	...	...	|	1809	1837	...	1911	1956	...	...	...	...	...	...
1418	Huaihua nan d.	1401	...	1441	...	...	...	1547	1527	...	1648	...	...	...	...	1900	1911	1939	...	2017	2058	...	...	...	...	...	...
1586	**Guiyang** bei a.	1547	...	1630	...	...	...	1722	1714	...	1847	...	...	...	...	2048	2106	2127	...	...	2237	...	...	...	...	...	...
2252	**Kunming** nan a.	1830	...	1923	...	...	...	...	1934	...	2120	...	...	...	...	2301	...	...	...	...	...	...	...	...	...	...	...

All trains prefix 'G'	46 A	1382	1384 H	1342	1346 F	1482 A	1348	86 C	1370	1354	1484 A	1322	62 A	1378 D	100 C	1372	1334 D	1502 B	1328	1504 AB	1374	1304 C	1376	1506 AB	1338 D	130 C
Kunming nan d.	...	...	...	...	...	...	...	...	...	...	...	...	...	0736	...	0814	...	...	...	...	1008	...	1037	...	...	...
Guiyang bei d.	...	...	...	...	...	...	...	...	...	...	0758	0907	...	1008	...	1049	1121	...	1154	...	1235	...	1311	...	1401	...
Huaihua nan d.	...	...	...	...	...	...	...	...	0918	...	0946	1102	...	1204	...	1245	1336	...	1351	...	1431	...	1501	...	1547	...
Loudi nan d.	...	...	...	...	...	...	...	...	1018	...	1047	|	...	1304	...	1345	1438	...	1451	...	|	...	|	...	|	...
Changsha nan d.	...	...	...	0706	0800	0840	0900	1024	1104	1140	1125	1249	...	1346	1441	1435	1522	1527	1532	1609	1614	1621	1655	1705	1733	181
Nanchang xi d.	...	0722	0815	0843	0936	1026	1033	1147	1237	1319	1324	1428	1436	1538	1604	1622	1658	1707	1717	1749	1820	1800	1834	1841	1917	194
Yingtan bei d.	...	0815	0851	|	1020	|	|	|	|	|	1400	1505	1519	1614	|	1700	1734	1743	1802	1825	1857	1843	|	1925	1954	|
Shangrao d.	...	0843	0939	|	|	1135	|	|	1349	1417	1428	1533	1547	1642	1702	|	1802	1811	1830	1853	1925	1912	1939	1953	2021	|
Quzhou d.	0816	0913	|	1003	1110	|	|	|	1419	|	1458	1603	1617	|	|	|	1832	|	1907	|	1955	|	2047	2023	|	210
Jinhua d.	0846	0936	1032	|	|	1226	1209	|	1442	1511	1522	|	1640	1742	1749	1806	1855	1904	1938	1948	2025	1959	2111	2053	2116	212
Yiwu d.	0904	|	1050	|	1144	1244	|	|	1500	1529	1540	1639	1658	|	|	1825	1913	1922	1956	2006	2043	2017	2129	2111	2134	214
Hangzhou dong d.	0944	1031	1124	1113	1219	1325	1255	1402	1535	1603	1613	1716	1732	1828	1839	1859	1956	2010	2036	2039	2120	2055	2210	2144	2215	222
Jiaxing nan d.	...	|	1149	1150	|	...	|	|	|	1635	...	|	...	|	|	|	|	2036	2113	...	2147	2121	|	...	|	|
Shanghai Hongqiao a.	...	1131	1218	1214	1318	...	1341	1450	1638	1703	...	1822	...	1922	1927	1945	2056	2115	2142	...	2216	2151	2256	...	2300	231

A – To/from Table **7100/2**.
B – To/from Table **7184**.
C – To/from Table **7065**.
D – To/from Table **7146**.
E – Additional trips: 0712, 1048, 1325, 1347, 1501, 1537, 1709.
F – Additional trips: 0730, 0927,1030, 1325, 1343, 1640, 1710.
G – Additional trips: 1310, 1632, 1828.
H – Additional trip: 1341.
♥ – Shanghai Hongqiao
♣ – Hangzhou dong.

7193 BEIJING - HEFEI and SHANGHAI - HANGZHOU - FUZHOU - XIAMEN China Rail High Speed

km	All trains prefix 'G'	1651	1611	1667	1631	1653	1669 A	1655	1601	345 A	1657	1633	1659	355 A	27 A	244 A	1635	323 A	301 A	1637	325 A	303 A	1639	7381	7383	739
	Beijing nan d.	...	...	...	...	...	...	...	...	...	...	...	...	0840	0945	...	...	1010	1030	...	1205	1230	...	...	...	...
	Xuzhou dong d.	...	...	...	...	...	0658	...	...	0823	...	...	...	1200	|	1236	...	1317	1352	...	1459	1540	...	...	...	...
	Hefei nan d.	...	0821	...	...	...	0848	...	0925	1010	...	...	...	1344	1358	1429	...	1459	1531	...	1651	1723	...	...	...	...
0	**Shanghai** Hongqiao d.	0655	|	...	0754	0815	|	0923	|	|	1018	1225	1257	|	|	|	1435	|	|	1513	|	|	1722	1911	2044	193
84	Jiaxing nan d.	|	|	...	|	|	|	0952	|	|	1048	|	1326	|	|	|	1506	|	|	1552	|	|	|	1942	2121	|
159	**Hangzhou** dong d.	0803	|	0839	0852	0904	|	1026	|	|	1120	1328	1353	|	|	|	1538	|	|	1625	|	|	1832	2021	2153	203
304	Yiwu d.	0844	|	0919	|	|	|	1100	|	|	|	1402	1428	|	|	|	1612	|	|	1659	|	|	|	2102	2234	212
352	Jinhua d.	0902	|	0937	0944	|	|	|	|	|	1206	1421	|	|	|	|	|	|	|	1717	|	|	|	2121	2252	213
438	Quzhou d.	|	|	1006	|	|	|	|	|	|	|	|	|	|	|	|	1646	|	|	|	|	|	|	2150	2314	220
549	Shangrao d.	0954	1103	1042	1033	|	1121	1206	1216	1244	1305	1511	|	1626	1603	1709	1721	1749	1814	1827	1920	1958	2016	...	...	...
768	Nanping bei d.	|	1203	1149	1134	|	1228	1314	1323	|	1403	1633	|	|	|	1809	1822	|	|	1935	|	2107	2137	...	...	...
889	**Fuzhou** d.	**S**	1258	1246	1215	1159	1317	1407	1412	1429	1457	1718	1654	1816	1733	1859	1900	**S**	1957	2020	2100	2144	2215	...	...	...
1063	Quanzhou d.	|	1413	1402	...	|	1433	1519	1529	...	1621	...	|	1932	...	2014	...	|	...	...	|	...	...	...	...	...
1134	**Xiamen** bei a.	1339	1440	1428	...	1331	1459	1543	1554	...	1647	...	1820	1958	...	2041	...	2142	...	...	2300	...	...	...	...	...

All trains prefix 'G'	7372	7382	302 A	1632	1634	322 A	242 A	28 A	1652	1676	324 A	304 A	1636	1638	356 A	1642	348 A	1654	1662	1656	1670 A	1668	1640	1658	166
Xiamen bei d.	...	...	...	...	...	0657	0745	...	0921	0812	0857	...	...	...	1059	...	...	1312	1317	1411	1452	1536	...	1617	170
Quanzhou d.	...	...	...	...	...	|	0818	...	|	0846	0930	...	...	...	1126	...	...	|	1344	1438	1525	1603	...	1650	173
Fuzhou d.	...	...	0701	0759	0901	**S**	0934	0952	1051	1032	1058	1215	1226	1245	1252	1445	1454	**S**	1509	1556	1645	1732	1755	1811	184
Nanping bei d.	...	...	0738	08422	0944	|	1010	|	|	1124	|	1251	1309	1321	|	1521	|	|	1545	1633	1721	|	|	1847	193
Shangrao d.	...	...	0848	0953	1045	1050	1111	1124	|	1227	1240	1400	1409	1438	1428	1634	1639	1725	1649	1748	1836	1916	1943	1956	204
Quzhou d.	0640	0715	|	1031	|	|	|	|	|	|	|	|	|	1510	|	1708	|	1809	1737	1827	|	1949	2015	2031	|
Jinhua d.	0710	0745	|	|	1152	|	|	|	|	1320	|	|	1506	|	|	1739	|	1839	1801	1850	|	2012	2040	2101	213
Yiwu d.	0728	0803	|	1107	|	|	|	|	|	1338	|	|	|	1545	|	1758	|	1857	1819	1908	|	2030	2058	2119	214
Hangzhou dong d.	0811	0853	|	1142	1245	|	|	|	1344	1411	|	|	1554	1627	|	1832	|	1932	1855	1944	|	2104	2150	2155	223
Jiaxing nan d.	0850	|	|	1207	|	|	|	|	|	...	|	|	1620	1653	|	...	|	|	...	2009	|	...	2215	2220	|
Shanghai Hongqiao a.	0925	0954	|	1235	1337	|	|	|	1432	...	|	|	1655	1721	|	...	|	2025	...	2038	|	...	2243	2247	232
Hefei nan a.	1230	...	1120	...	...	1335	1356	1330	...	...	1508	1635	...	...	1705	...	1917	...	...	...	2108	...	...	...	...
Xuzhou dong d.	...	...	1310	...	...	1527	1542	|	...	...	1713	1834	...	...	1855	...	2115	...	...	...	2302	...	...	...	...
Beijing nan a.	...	...	1633	...	...	1838	...	1753	...	...	2013	2148	...	...	2224	...	...	...	...	...	...	...	...	...	...

7194 WUHAN - NANCHANG - FUZHOU and XIAMEN China Rail High Speed

km	All trains prefix 'D'	6521	6501	6523	6525	6503	6527	6505	3262	G1643	3276	6529	6507	3286	295	2378	6509	3272	3245	6531	3265	2234 B	2228 B	6511	2244 B	223 B
0	**Wuhan** ⊕ d.	...	...	...	...	...	...	...	0836	0907	0855	...	...	1050	1214	1247	...	1307	1446	...	1455	1518	1554	...	1641	184
118	Huangshi bei d.	...	...	...	...	...	...	...	0918	0947	0937	...	...	1134	|	1325	...	1345	1525	...	1535	|	|	...	|	191
368	**Nanchang** xi⊕ d.	0714**h**	0747**h**	0853	0909**h**	0946**h**	0950	1030**h**	1105	|	1131	1242**h**	1353**h**	1332	1441	1507	1447	1544	1711**h**	1729**h**	1731	1741	1822	1917**h**	1905	2108
732	Sanming bei d.	0959	1026	1118	1142	1231	1213	1307	1329	|	1355	1528	1618	1552	1704	1738	1715	1808	...	2015	1959	2006	2046	2148	2122	...
927	**Fuzhou** a.	|	1147	|	|	1346	|	1423	1438	1528	|	|	1727	|	1826	|	1838	|	...	|	2109	|	2208	2257	2245	...
1068	**Xiamen** bei a.	1220	...	1321	1358	...	1416	...	...	...	1608	1740	...	1801	...	2006	...	2023	...	2240**z**	...	2214	...	...	...	...

All trains prefix 'D'	2236 B	2242 B	3266	2232 B	6502	2226 B	2376	6522	6524	3274	296	3246	3288	6504	6506	6508	6526	3264	3278	6528	6530	6510	6512	6532	653
Xiamen bei d.	...	...	...	0739	...	...	0813	0834**z**	0846	0817	...	...	1028	...	...	...	1422	...	1445	1548**z**	1646	...	...	1815	184
Fuzhou d.	...	0648	0808	|	0829	0848	|	|	|	|	1046	...	|	1311	1407	1440	|	1536	|	|	|	1747	1910	|	|
Sanming bei d.	...	0805	0925	0957	0946	1007	1053	1113	1125	1042	1207	...	1245	1428	1524	1601	1632	1652	1709	1821	1851	1904	2021	2048	211
Nanchang xi ⊕ d.	0840**h**	1026	1157	1224	1221**h**	1237	1310	1337	1347	1329	1436	1513	1523	1657**h**	1741	1837	1902**h**	1918	1929	2036	2112	2145**h**	2252**h**	2326**h**	234
Huangshi d.	1047	|	1356	1411	...	1434	1454	...	...	1530	|	|	1724	...	...	...	...	2103	2126	...	...	...	...	...	...
Wuhan ⊕ a.	1124	1230	1434	1504	...	1512	1530	...	...	1618	1727	1744	1800	...	...	...	...	2147	2211	...	...	...	...	...	...

Notes for Tables **7193/4**. A – Via Table **7097**. B – Via Table **7182**. S – Via Sanming bei and Longyan. h – Nanchang. z – Xiamen. ⊕ – Additional services availab

China Rail High Speed

SHANGHAI - HANGZHOU - FUZHOU - XIAMEN - SHENZHEN and LONGYAN 7200

km	All trains prefix D	3111	3145	3131	2287	3125	2285	3107	2281	3135	2283	931
				S		Z			Z	NZ		A
	Nanjing d.	...	...	...	...	0637	...	...	0741	0809	...	...
0	Shanghai ♥ d.	...	0640	0737	0746	0849	0905	0940	1028	1042	1124	2000
84	Jiaxing nan d.	...	0710	0813	0842	0934	0946	1027	1105	1132	1154	|
159	Hangzhou ♣ d.	0733	0743	0842	0909	1014	1020	1125	1135	1215	1229	2100
314	Ningbo d.	0849	0908	0952	1017	1125	1131	1226	1236	1325	1339	2203
466	Taizhou d.	0951	1010	|	|	1226	1233	1328	1344	1427	1435	|
589	Wenzhou nan d.	1042	1100	1150	1209	1318	1329	1424	1442	1519	1531	|
883	Fuzhou nan d.	1253	1316	1355	1413	1529	1535	1622	1640	1729	1746	|
038	Quanzhou d.	1356	1420	1456	1512	1628	1634	1727	1739	|	1839	|
109	Xiamen bei d.	1427	1453	1526	1549	1657	1703	1756	1809	1913	1908	|
151	Zhangzhou d.	1448	|	|	1610	|	1725	1817	1836	1935	1929	|
	Longyan a.	|	1559	1635	|	|	|	|	|	2019	|	|
318	Chaoshan d.	1555	...	...	|	1824	1836	1923	1945	...	2041	|
567	Huizhou nan d.	1743	...	...	|	2002	2009	|	2122	...	|	|
623	Shenzhen bei a.	1814	...	...	1914	2033	2040	2131	2153	...	2245	0639

All trains prefix D	3136	3126	3108	3132	2284	2282	3146	2286	2288	3112	932
	GZ	Z		H		Z					A
Shenzhen bei d.	...	0710	0822	...	0846	0921	...	0954	1042	1124	2014
Huizhou nan d.	...	0738	|	...	|	0949	...	1024	|	1158	|
Chaoshan d.	...	0922	1031	...	1107	1130	...	1215	1251	1343	|
Longyan d.	0818	|	|	1058	|	|	1255	|	|	|	|
Zhangzhou d.	0912	|	|	1148	1220	1247	|	1328	|	1451	|
Xiamen bei d.	0934	1046	1158	1211	1248	1312	1357	1351	1438	1516	|
Quanzhou d.	|	1113	1226	1239	1321	1339	1425	1419	1512	1545	|
Fuzhou nan d.	1119	1214	1337	1352	1427	1442	1532	1547	1619	1647	|
Wenzhou nan d.	1327	1428	1545	1600	1624	1650	1740	1749	1832	1901	|
Taizhou d.	1423	|	1636	1656	1720	1741	1830	|	|	|	|
Ningbo d.	1522	1621	1745	1758	1829	1846	1938	1954	2023	2050	|
Hangzhou ♣ d.	1641	1730	1904	1922	1939	2001	2050	2110	2140	2201	0600
Jiaxing nan d.	1713	|	1930	|	2014	|	2131	2142	|	...	|
Shanghai ♥ a.	1742	1843	1959	2034	2044	2120	2200	2212	2235	...	0650
Nanjing nan a.	2028k	2116k	...	...	...	2314k	...	...	...	...	...

km	All unmarked trains prefix 'D'	6201	3231	G7501	379	G7543	G7505	3201	3295	G7581	3205	G7587	G63	G7599	3215	G1673	G7511	G7539	G55	3217	381	3101	G7545	3103	G7521	G167
		R		P									Y	Z					Y							Y
	Nanjing nan d.	...	...	...	...	...	0713	...	0745	0647	...	0748	1029	0932	...	...	...	...	1237	...	...	...	...	...	...	1715
0	Shanghai Hongqiao d.	...	...	0650	0702	0707	0900	0820	|	0916	0935	0958	|	1110	...	1156	1208	1415	|	...	1445	1508	1547	1557	1647	|
84	Jiaxing nan d.	...	...	0726	0743	0738	0929	0901	|	0957	1009	|	|	1139	...	1226	|	|	|	...	1535	|	|	|	1723	|
159	Hangzhou dong d.	...	0716	0758	0813	0808	0959	0931	0941	1036	1041	1058	1156	1205	...	1302	1257	1516	1406	1558	1619	1630	1650	1700	1755	1841
314	Ningbo d.	...	0833	0856	0921	0913	1059	1047	1058	1136	1200	1205	1251	1312	1414	1426	1353	1615	1457	1711	1722	1751	1807	1813	1907	1952
466	Taizhou d.	...	|	0958	1023	1015	...	|	1206	1244	1302	1313	1353	|	|	1528	1455	1723	1559	1813	|	1859	1904	1915	2009	2054
589	Wenzhou nan d.	...	1025	1046	1125	1105	...	1233	1256	1339	1358	1409	1449	1457	1612	1618	1557	1824	1649	1909	1922	1945	1959	2007	2058	2149
883	Fuzhou nan d.	0639	1236	...	1324	...	...	1450	1502	...	1602	...	...	...	1822	1835	...	...	1857f	2117	2122	2151f	...	2213	...	...
038	Quanzhou d.	0744	1338	...	1425	...	...	1603	1614	...	|	...	...	...	1933	1943	...	...	...	|	...	...	...	...	...	...
109	Xiamen bei a.	0831	1403	...	1451	...	...	1629	1639	...	1721	...	...	...	1959	2008	...	...	...	2241	...	...	...	...	...	...

All unmarked trains prefix 'D	G7504	G7572	G7506	G168	G7540	3102	G56	382	3104	3234	3216	6204	G7546	G7516	3218	3208	3296	G7600	G64	3206	3202	378	3308	G7536	3232
	T			Y			Y					Q						Z	Y						
Xiamen bei d.	...	...	...	...	...	...	...	...	...	0651x	0800	0829	...	...	0841	0956	0950	...	...	1254	1322	1427	...	...	1557
Quanzhou d.	...	...	...	...	...	...	...	...	...	0741	0834	0902	...	...	0914	|	1038	..	...	1327	1350	1500	...	...	|
Fuzhou nan d.	...	...	...	...	...	0740f	0753f	0737	0830	0849	0955	1007	...	...	1034	1130	1143	...	...	1436	1502	1607	1704f	...	1743
Wenzhou nan d.	0629	0649	0732	0833	0900	0955	1002	0944	1038	1058	1201	...	1120	1217	1227	1338	1357	1402	1510	1637	1711	1821	1912	1922	1945
Taizhou d.	0719	0745	0827	0930	1002	1040	1052	1035	|	|	1251	...	1222	1307	1324	1429	1447	1452	1600	|	|	|	2003	2024	2042
Ningbo d.	0823	0855	0925	1033	1107	1149	1155	1133	1234	1246	1352	...	1326	1417	1429	1533	1548	1558	1704	1835	1906	2013	2112	2127	2140
Hangzhou dong d.	0919	0957	1036	1139	1202	1300	1241	1238	1339	1343	...	...	1431	1519	1533	1648	1700	1706	1800	1951	2020	2130	2209	2230	2238
Jiaxing nan d.	0944	|	1108	|	1234	|	|	1304	1424	...	...	...	|	1551	...	1723	|	|	|	2019	2108	2157	...	|	...
Shanghai Hongqiao a.	1020	1106	1133	|	1308	1414	|	1354	1524	...	...	...	1530	1620	...	1805	|	1812	|	2048	2147	2227	...	2318	...
Nanjing nan a.	...	1321	...	1315	...	...	1420	...	...	...	...	...	...	...	...	...	1844	2017	1931	...	...	...	...	...	...

km	All trains prefix 'D'	G6389	2315	G3001	689	2327	2311	G1609	9961	2297	6409	G3003	6407	6591	2325	3339	2331	G3007	6381	G1601	2307	3295	G3005	2353	671	6417	6419
		F					E				C																
	Fuzhou d.	...	...	0825	...	...	...	...	...	...	0800	...	0925	...	1022	...	1225	...	...	1412	...	...	...	1648	...	1829	2005
0	Fuzhou nan d.	...	...	|	...	0710	0757	0816	0805	...	0818	...	0943	1012	|	1051	1243	...	1342	|	1456	1502	...	1712	1816	1850	2025
155	Quanzhou d.	...	0713	0936	...	0827	|	0928	|	...	|	...	|	1112	1140	1206	1349	...	1447	1529	1557	1614	...	1811	1920	2008	2134
226	Xiamen bei d.	...	0742	1003	0831	0908	0931	0959	0952	1043	0947	1015	1108	1142	1216	1244	1420	1453	1517	1601	1624	1647	1709	1842	1956	|	|
268	Zhangzhou d.	...	0803	|	0852	|	0951	|	1038	1105	1008	1050	1129	1203	|	|	|	1527	1538	1621	1647	|	1750	1910	|	2053	2217
382	Longyan a.	...	|	|	|	|	|	|	1131	|	1100	|	1219	1251	|	|	|	|	1627	|	|	1751	|	|	|	2138	2300
435	Chaoshan d.	0839	0908	1121	1001	1038	1100	1127	...	1206	...	1156	...	...	1347	1424	1549	1633	...	1727	1759	...	1858	2025	2125	...	...
582	Huizhou nan d.	|	|	|	1139	|	1227	|	...	1343	...	1330	...	...	1524	1602	1733	1815	...	1859	|	...	2034	|	|	...	...
740	Shenzhen bei a.	1113	1118	1341	1209	1243	1258	1337	...	1417	...	1427	...	...	1555	1633	1804	1906	...	1930	2008	...	2123	2234	2322	...	...
.	West Kowloon a.	1132	...	1400	...	...	...	a	...	...	...	1446	...	...	...	...	...	1925	...	...	...	...	2142	...	...	...	...

All trains prefix 'D'	G6382	6383	3296	682	6577	2308	G1602	G1663	G3006	2310	3146	6437	6439	684	2324	G3002	2304	6445	G3004	G1610	672	2326	6449	686	2332	G3008
	K									D			B													
West Kowloon d.	0723	...	...	...	...	...	...	...	0845	...	...	...	...	...	...	1424	...	...	1517	aa.	...	...	...	...	...	1947
Shenzhen bei d.	0808	...	...	0640	...	0839	0854	...	0926	0948	...	...	...	1220	1403	1510	1453	...	1602	1547	1617	1621	...	1830	1836	2007
Huizhou nan d.	0836	...	...	|	...	|	0928	...	0954	1022	...	...	...	|	1431	|	|	...	1630	1615	|	|	...	|	1904	2053
Chaoshan d.	1009	...	...	0830	...	|	1113	...	1135	1205	...	...	...	1422	1615	1706	1701	...	1814	1757	1836	1848	...	2034	2046	|
Longyan d.	...	0708	0836	|	1021	|	|	1149	|	|	1254	1302	1350	|	|	|	|	1733	|	|	|	|	1954	|	|	|
Zhangzhou d.	...	0758	0927	|	1112	1201	1214	1252	1242	1313	|	1352	1435	1529	1735	|	|	1833	1915	1901	|	1958	2044	|	2156	|
Xiamen bei d.	...	0823	0950	1015	1136	1225	1240	1317	1315x	1340	1357	1417	1510	1603x	1810	1827	1846	1859	1955x	1926	2011	2021	2114	2202	2218	2352
Quanzhou d.	...	0857	|	...	1203	|	1307	1344	...	1407	1425	1455	1539	...	1848	1854	1922	1933	...	1955	2038	|	2141	...	...	...
Fuzhou nan a.	...	1002	1120	...	1300	1401	1413	1448	...	1512	1527	|	1637	...	...	|	2030	|	...	|	2141	2156	2250	...	...	...
Fuzhou a.	...	...	...	...	1319	...	1429	1509	...	...	...	1609	1701	...	...	2003	2051	2043	...	2105	...	...	2310	...	...	...

China Rail High Speed

SHANGHAI - HANGZHOU - NINGBO 7202

km	All trains prefix 'G'	7331	7333	7317	7349	7351	7301	7365	7303	7325	7555	7355
		U										
0	Shanghai ♥ d.	0617	0629	0836	0910	1134	1330	1607	1622	1727	2105	2130
84	Jiaxing nan d.	0646	|	0911	0940	1210	|	1637	1658	1803	2141	2159
69	Hangzhou d.	0716d	0721d	0946d	1004	1249	1437	1703	1732d	1833d	2208d	2228

All trains 'G'	7556	7558	7302	7330	7354	7304	7308	7360	7318	7336	7312
			V								
Hangzhou d.	0650d	0713d	0758	0907d	1004	1130	1452	1537	1553	1653d	1800
Jiaxing nan d.	0729	0749	0836	|	1045	1212	|	1615	1625	1718	1832
Shanghai ♥ d.	0803	0812	0910	1007	1119	1239	1551	1650	1659	1752	1900

km	All trains prefix 'G'	7503	7505	7507	7509	7511	7595	7515	7517	7519	7525	7527
		W										
0	Shanghai ♥ d.	0804	0900	1013	1058	1208	1304	1400	1456	1552	1758	2021
84	Jiaxing nan d.	0834	0929	1043	1127	|	1344	1429	1525	|	1828	|
59	Hangzhou dong d.	0859	0958	1108	1200	1257	1411	1501	1551	1655	1903	2124
314	Ningbo a.	0952	1059	1208	1253	1349	1509	1555	1651	1755	2003	2231

	7502	7504	7572	7506	7510	7512	7514	7518	7520	7522	7524
	X										
Ningbo d.	0706	0823	0855	0925	1124	1228	1314	1528	1616	1715	1814
Hangzhou dong d.	0823	0919	0957	1036	1226	1323	1419	1626	1725	1823	1917
Jiaxing nan d.	0855	0944	|	1108	1259	1355	1452	1658	1758	1858	|
Shanghai ♥ a.	0929	1020	1106	1136	1327	1432	1520	1725	1832	1926	2017

otes for Tables **7200** and **7202**.

– ①⑤⑥⑦ 🛏 1cl, 2 Shanghai(**D931/22**) - Zhanjiang and v.v.
– Additional trips: 1510, 1659. **C** – Additional trip: 1630.
– Additional trips: 0725, 0819, 0849. 1203, 1306, 1448, 1530, 1644
– Additional trips: 0645, 0919, 0936, 0955, 1017, 1407, 1546.
– Additional trips: 1043, 1248, 1732, 1956.
– Additional trip: 0659. **H** – Additional trip: 0849.
– Additional trips: 0909, 1154, 1413, 1640.
– Additional trip: 1112.
– Additional trips: 1129, 1419, 1612, 1714, 1758, 1901, 1916.

Q – Additional trips: 0739, 0854**x**, 1001**x**, 1152, 1204, 1229, 1328, 1345, 1524, 1531**x**, 1703, 1715**x**, 1810**x**, 1946, 2049, 2108.
R – Additional trips: 0710**f**, 0805, 0851**f**, 0924, 0949, 1013, 1119, 1210, 1305, 1408, 1419**f**, 1525**f**, 1608, 1628, 1709, 1720, 1751, 1948.
S – Additional trip: 1215.
T – Additional trips: 0742, 0748, 1234, 1536, 1613, 1618, 1838.
U – Additional trips: 0830, 1230, 1807, 1848.
V – Additional trips: 0610, 1902, 2000.
W – Additional trips: 0810, 0958, 1034, 1129, 1440, 1612, 1928, 2035.
X – Additional trips: 0729, 0830, 1028, 1107, 1417, 1642, 1735, 2031.

Y – To/from Beijing, Table **7102**.
Z – To/from Table **7100**.

a – To Guangzhou nan a.1415.
aa – From Guangzhou nan d.1455.
d – Hangzhou dong.
f – Fuzhou. **h** – Hangzhou.
k – Nanjing. **x** – Xiamen.

♥ – Shanghai Hongqiao.
♣ – Hangzhou dong.

Chinese Railways, Duóng Sát Việt Nam

HÁ NOI - BEIJING 7250

km		MR1	T8702	Z6	Z286	DD5
		BC	BC	C		
0	Há Nôi Gia Lam d.	2140	...	...	...	0705
162	Dong Dang a.	0155	...	...	...	1140
162	Dong Dang 🏛 d.	0250	...	...	...	...
207	Pingxiang 🏛 a.	0431	...	...	...	...
207	Pingxiang d.	...	0615	...	...	...
430	Nanning a.	...	1007	...	...	...
430	Nanning d.	...	...	1055	1735	...
861	Guilin d.	...	...	1422	2130a	...
409	Changsha d.	...	...	1940	0251	...
771	Wuhan Wuchang d.	...	...	2306	0618	...
307	Zhengzhou d.	...	...	0352	1110	...
996	Beijing xi a.	...	...	0948	1703	...

	Z5	T8701	MR2	Z285	DD6
	D	BD	BD		
Beijing xi d.	1609	...	...	2110	...
Zhengzhou d.	2212	...	...	0309	...
Wuhan Wuchang d.	0258	...	...	0755	...
Changsha d.	0619	...	...	1123	...
Guilin d.	1138	...	...	1629a	...
Nanning a.	1535	...	...	2102	...
Nanning d.	...	1805	...	...	...
Pingxiang a.	...	2210	...	...	...
Pingxiang 🏛 d.	...	...	2241	...	...
Dong Dang 🏛 a.	...	...	2322	...	...
Dong Dang d.	...	...	0022	...	1530
Há Nôi Gia Lam a.	...	...	0520	...	1946

B – Conveys 🛏 1 cl. Nanning(**T8701/2**) - Pingxiang (**MR2/1**) - Há Nôi and v.v.
C – Runs daily. On ②⑤ (from Há Nôi) conveys 🛏 1 cl. Há Nôi – Beijing (2 nights).
D – Runs daily. On ④⑦ (from Beijing) conveys 🛏 1 cl. Beijing - Há Nôi (2 nights).

a – Guilin bei.

BEYOND EUROPE
Japan

Introduction

The Beyond Europe section covers principal rail services in a different area of the world each month. There are six areas, each appearing as follows:

Winter (December) and Summer (June):	Africa and The Middle East along with all other Beyond Europe sections.
January and July (digital only):	India.
February and August:	South East Asia, Australia and New Zealand; India; North America.
March and September (digital only):	China.
April and October:	Japan; China; South America; South Korea.
May and November (digital only):	North America.

The months have been chosen so that we can bring you up-to-date information for those countries which make seasonal changes.

Contents

INDEX OF PLACES

by table number

JAPAN

Capital: Tokyo (GMT + 9). 2019 Public Holidays: Jan. 1, 14, Feb. 11, Mar. 21, Apr. 29. 30, May 1 - 6 , July 15, Aug. 11, 12, Sep. 16, 23, Oct. 14, 22, Nov. 3, 4, 2:

Operators: Most rail services in Japan are operated by the six private regional railway companies which are marketed as a whole as Japan Railways (JR); there are also a number of private railways, some quite large, which are not shown in this section. The six regional operators are JR Central (jr-central.co.jp), JR Ea (www.jreast.co.jp), JR Hokkaido (www.jrhokkaido.co.jp), JR Kyushu (www.jrkyushu.co.jp), JR Shikoku (www.jr-shikoku.co.jp) and JR West (www.westjr.co.jp

Services: Except where noted, all trains convey first and second class seated accommodation (known locally as "Green" and "Standard" respectively). Seat reservatic is obligatory in first class and a supplement must be paid. No train convey restaurant cars, but some main-line services have some kind of refreshment servic available, often in form of box-meals or in vending machines. The few remaining overnight trains have one berth in first class and 1 or 2 berths in second. Trains are very punctual and delays are rare.

Timings: The latest available timings are shown. The availability of english language timetable information varies by operator. An english language booklet of timetable for high-speed and principal long distance trains is available on application from the Japan National Tourism Organization in London (✆ 020 7398 5678 c www.seejapan.co.uk), however it does not list all stations. Much more detailed information can be obtained using the Hyperdia Timetable and Route Searc website, which is also available in english (www.hyperdia.com/en).

Tickets: Tickets can be purchased from windows or machines at stations. A basic one-class fare structure applies according to the distance travelled. Rural lines have slightly higher fare. Supplements are payable for travel on high-speed and express services, for the use of first class, and in some cases where a JR group tra uses the line of a private operator.

Passes: The Japanese Railways Group offers the Japan Rail Pass (www.japanrailpass.net). To qualify for a pass you must enter the country under the status of "temporary visitor" and your passport must be endorsed with this stamp. When you purchase your pass you will receive an Exchange Order which must b exchanged, within 3 months, for an actual pass. This is done at any of 63 JR stations (most of which do not open until 1000) and Chubu Central Japan International Airport. The pass can now be purchased in Japan at 54 JR stations, Chubu Central Japan International Airport and Sendai Airport. (see www.japanrailpass.net/en/exchange.html). The JR Pass is not valid on Nozomi and Mizuho trains and a supplement is payable for any sleeping berth but it is valid for all other JR Group Railways, some JR buses and the JR ferry from Miyajima to Miyajimaguchi. You can travel in a higher class by paying th relevant supplements. The pass is valid from the date it is first used. Ages for the child pass are from 6 to 11.

Prices: Adult first (Green) class 7 Day ¥44000/14 Day ¥ 71000/21 Day ¥90000, Adult second (Ordinary) class 7 Day ¥33000/14 Day ¥52000/21 Day ¥6500 Child first (Green) class 7 Day ¥22000/14 Day ¥35500/21 Day ¥45000, Child second (Ordinary) class 7 Day ¥16500/14 Day ¥26000/21 Day ¥32500.

A variety of more region specific passes are also available.

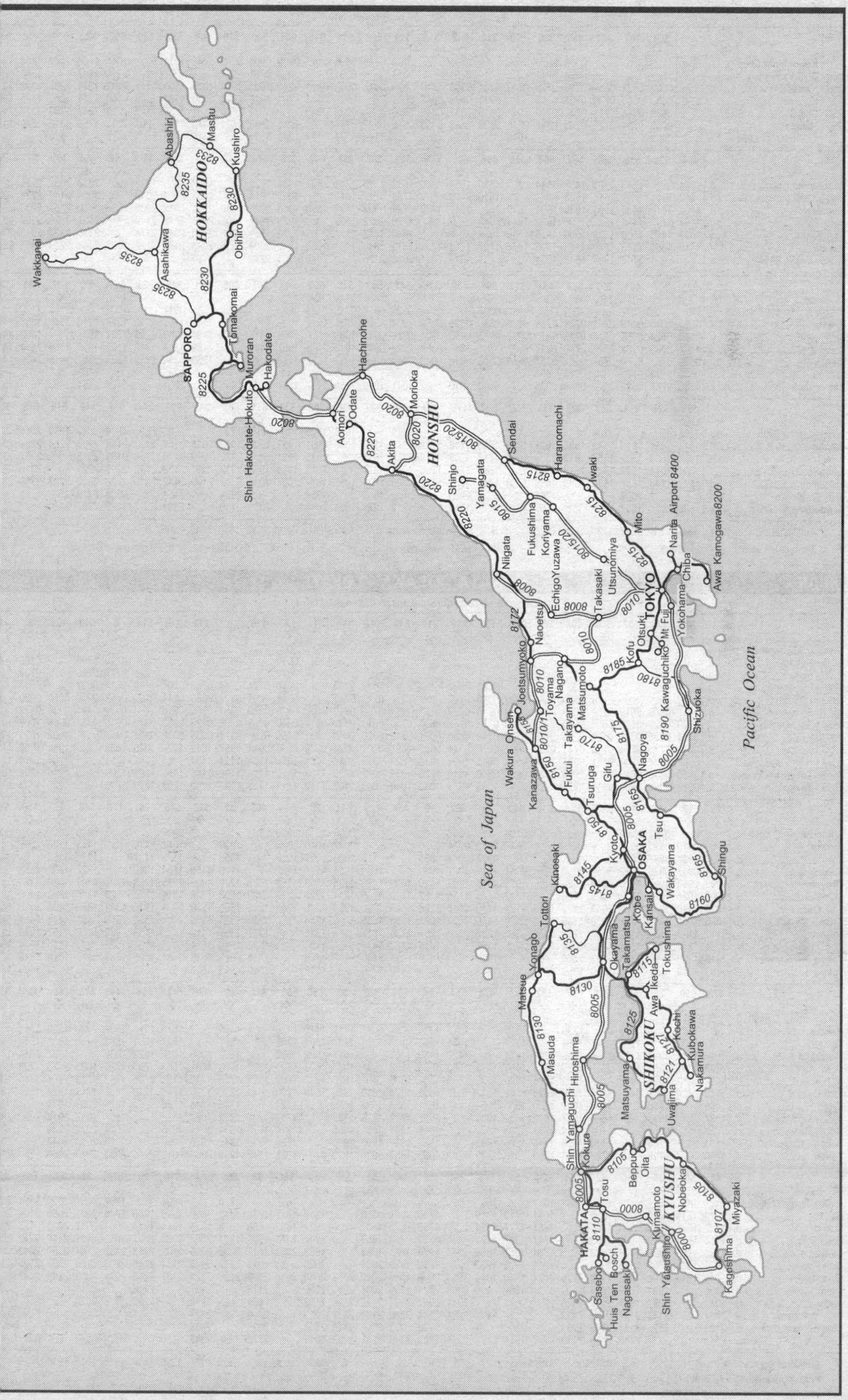
HOKKAIDO
Wakkanai
Asahikawa
Abashiri
Mashu
Kushiro
Obihiro
SAPPORO
Tomakomai
Muroran
Hakodate
Shin Hakodate-Hokuto
HONSHU
Aomori
Hachinohe
Odate
Morioka
Akita
Shinjo
Yamagata
Sendai
Haranomachi
Iwaki
Fukushima
Koriyama
Niigata
Mito
Narita Airport 8400
Chiba
Awa Kamogawa 8200
TOKYO
Yokohama
Utsunomiya
Takasaki
Echigo Yuzawa
Naoetsu
Joetsumyoko
Nagano
Toyama
Wakura Onsen
Kanazawa
Takayama
Matsumoto
Kofu
Otsuki
Mt Fuji
Kawaguchiko
Shizuoka
Nagoya
Gifu
Fukui
Tsuruga
Kyoto
OSAKA
Tsu
Shingu
Wakayama
Kobe
Kansai
Kinosaki
Tottori
Yonago
Matsue
Okayama
Takamatsu
Tokushima
Awa Ikeda
Kochi
Kubokawa
Nakamura
Uwajima
Matsuyama
SHIKOKU
Masuda
Hiroshima
Shin Yamaguchi
Kokura
KYUSHU
HAKATA
Tosu
Beppu
Oita
Nobeoka
Miyazaki
Kumamoto
Shin Yatsushiro
Kagoshima
Sasebo
Huis Ten Bosch
Nagasaki
Sea of Japan
Pacific Ocean

8000 KAGOSHIMA - HAKATA

JR Kyush

Kyushu Shinkansen high-speed line

km		540	302	304	400	308	600	310	542	312	314	602	544	316	604	546	318	548	550	320	552	322	554	402	55
			A				✣					✣			✣										
0	**Kagoshima** Chuo d.	...	...	...	0608	0626	0702	...	0706	...	0730	0800	0806	...	0900	0906	...	0948	1011	...	1048	1106	1147	1204	124
126	Shin Yatsushiro d.	...	...	...	0654	0711	|	...	0751	...	0817	|	0851	...	|	0951	...	|	1057	...	|	1152	|	1250	|
158	Kumamoto d.	0601	0621	0637	0706	0723	0743	0734	0803	0810	0829	0848	0903	0911	0943	1003	1011	1035	1109	1111	1135	1211	1235	1302	133
224	Kurume d.	0633	0653	0709	0728	0755	|	0811	0828	0842	0901	|	0927	0943	1004	1028	1044	1056	1131	1143	1156	1243	1256	1323	135
230	Shin Tosu d.	0638	0658	0713	0732	0759	|	0816	0832	0846	0906	|	0932	0948	|	1032	1048	1101	1136	1148	1200	1247	1300	1327	140
256	**Hakata** a.	0650	0711	0727	0745	0812	0818	0829	0845	0858	0919	0922	0945	1001	1018	1045	1101	1113	1149	1201	1213	1259	1313	1340	141
	Shin Osaka **8005** a.	0953	...	...	...	...	1048	...	1124	...	...	1148	1224	...	1248	1324	...	1348	1424	...	1448	...	1548	...	164

	404	326	558	560	562	564	330	406	606	608	566	568	338	610	570	572	342	408	344	346	612	458	348	350	41
									✣	✣				✣							✣	a			
Kagoshima Chuo d.	1304	...	1348	1403	1437	1514	...	1530	1557	16032	1637	1716	1733	1804	1807	1829	...	1907	...	1933	1951	2013	2052	2138	22
Shin Yatsushiro d.	1349	...	|	1448	1523	|	...	1616	|	|	1723	|	1819	|	1852	1914	...	1953	...	2019	|	2058	2140	2224	23
Kumamoto d.	1402	1410	1435	1501	1535	1601	1610	1628	1641	1720	1735	1802	1831	1850	1904	1926	1930	2004	2012	2038	2035	2110	2153	2236	231
Kurume d.	1423	1442	1456	1522	1556	1622	1641	1649	|	|	1756	1822	1903	|	1925	1947	2002	2025	2045	2110	|	2131	2225	2308	233
Shin Tosu d.	1428	1446	1500	1526	1600	1626	1646	1654	|	|	1800	1827	1907	|	1929	1951	2006	2030	2049	2114	|	2135	2230	2313	234
Hakata a.	1440	1500	1513	1539	1613	1639	1658	1707	1714	1755	1813	1840	1920	1923	1942	2004	2018	2043	2101	2127	2107	2148	2243	2325	235
Shin Osaka **8005** a.	...	...	1748	1824	1848	1924	...	...	1944	2024	2048	2125	...	2147	2221	2249	...	...	...	...	2337	...	...	...	...

	305	307	401	309	403	451	313	601	405	315	541	543	545	603	547	407	605	321	549	323	551	409	607	553	32
				B		a		✣						✣			✣						✣		
Shin Osaka **8005** d.	...	...	...	...	...	...	...	0600	...	...	0625	0650	0715	0753	0804	...	0859	...	0917	...	1008	...	1108	1120	...
Hakata d.	...	0610	0645	0701	0721	0759	0809	0830	0839	0850	0904	0929	0954	1019	1039	1101	1125	1141	1156	1230	1243	1318	1340	1356	140
Shin Tosu d.	...	0624	0658	0714	0736	0813	0822	|	0853	0904	0918	0943	1008	|	1053	1115	|	1154	1209	1243	1257	1331	|	1409	141
Kurume d.	...	0629	0703	0719	0740	0817	0827	|	0857	0909	0923	0947	1012	|	1057	1119	|	1159	1214	1248	1302	1336	1355	1414	142
Kumamoto d.	0639	0701	0724	0751	0801	0837	0858	0903	0918	0940	0944	1008	1033	1052	1118	1140	1156	1230	1234	1319	1323	1357	1416	1435	145
Shin Yatsushiro d.	0650	0713	0735	...	0813	0850	...	|	0931	...	0956	...	1045	|	|	1152	|	...	1246	...	|	1409	|	|	150
Kagoshima Chuo a.	0735	0758	0820	...	0858	0935	...	0946	1016	...	1041	1055	1129	1137	1204	1236	1241	...	1331	...	1409	1454	1458	1521	155

	555	327	411	557	329	413	559	331	415	333	561	563	609	565	339	611	567	343	569	347	571	349	613	573	35
													✣			✣							✣		
Shin Osaka **8005** d.	1208	...	...	1308	...	...	1408	...	...	...	1508	1520	1608	1620	...	1708	1720	...	1808	...	1908	...	1959	2016	...
Hakata d.	1443	1456	1518	1543	1559	1621	1643	1659	1718	1732	1743	1800	1839	1901	1917	1939	1959	2015	2100	2123	2146	2203	2224	2254	231
Shin Tosu d.	1457	1509	1532	1557	1613	1634	1657	1713	1731	1745	1758	1813	|	1915	1931	|	2012	2029	2113	2138	2159	2216	|	2307	232
Kurume d.	1501	1514	1536	1602	1618	1639	1702	1718	1735	1750	1803	1817	|	1919	1936	1954	2017	2034	2118	2142	2205	2221	|	2312	232
Kumamoto d.	1522	1545	1557	1622	1648	1659	1722	1749	1757	1821	1826	1838	1912	1944	2007	2015	2042	2106	2142	2213	2226	2300	2257	2343	235
Shin Yatsushiro d.	|	...	1609	|	...	1711	|	...	1809	...	|	1850	|	1956	...	|	2054	...	2154	...	2238	2313	|	...	...
Kagoshima Chuo a.	1609	...	1654	1709	...	1757	1810	...	1854	...	1912	1935	1959	2040	...	2058	2138	...	2239	...	2322	2357	2340	...	...

A – Additional services: 0711, 1310, 1510, 1657, 1738, 1806, 1908.

B – Additional services: 0734, 0940, 1042, 1230, 1818, 1846, 1946, 2036.

a – To/from Hiroshima see Table **8005**.

✣ – NOT available to holders of Japan Rail Pass. To use these trains you must pay the full fare.

8005 HAKATA - OSAKA - TOKYO

JR Central, JR We

Sanyo and *Tokaido Shinkansen* high-speed lines

km		200	100	102	504	104	208	106	108	110	214	510	112	114	512	2	116	4	118	120	514	6	540	122	8	51
		✣ D	✣	✣	E	✣	✣	✣	✣	✣	✣		✣	✣		✣	✣	✣	✣	✣		✣	k	✣	✣	
	Kagoshima C **8000** d.	...	...	...	...	...	...	...	...	...	...	...	...	...	...	...	...	...	...	...	...	...	...	...	...	
0	**Hakata** d.	...	...	...	...	...	...	...	...	...	...	...	...	...	...	0610	...	0636	...	...	...	0710	0700	...	0736	
56	Kokura d.	...	...	...	...	...	...	...	...	...	...	...	...	...	...	0627	...	0653	...	...	...	0727	0720	...	0753	
248	Hiroshima d.	...	...	...	...	...	...	...	0603	0622	...	...	0639	0703	...	0718	0724	0744	0753	0806	...	0817	0827	...	0839	
393	Okayama d.	...	...	...	...	0600	...	0620	0645	0702	...	...	0719	0745	...	0754	0803	0821	0833	0841	...	0853	0909	0859	0920	
521	Shin Kobe d.	...	0609	0619	...	0636	...	0656	0719	0739	...	...	0756	0819	...	0826	0839	0853	0906	0918	...	0926	0941	0938	0952	
554	Shin **Osaka** d.	0600	0623	0633	0608	0650	0703	0710	0733	0753	0806	0730	0810	0833	0817	0840	0853	0906	0920	0933	0916	0940	0953	0953	1006	10
593	Kyoto d.	0614	0638	0648	0623	0705	0718	0726	0748	0808	0821	0745	0826	0848	0832	0856	0908	0921	0935	0948	0932	0956	...	1008	1021	10
727	Nagoya d.	0649	0715	0724	0718	0742	0753	0802	0824	0844	0857	0837	0902	0924	0926	0933	0944	0957	1012	1024	1026	1033	...	1044	1057	11
1044	Shin Yokohama a.	0805	0834	0844	0851	0904	0914	0925	0945	1004	1014	1022	1025	1045	1051	1054	1104	1114	1134	1145	1151	1154	...	1204	1214	12
1063	**Tokyo** Shinagawa a.	0816	0846	0856	0903	0916	0926	0936	0956	1016	1026	1033	1036	1056	1103	1106	1116	1126	1146	1156	1203	1206	...	1216	1226	13
1069	**Tokyo** a.	0823	0853	0903	0910	0923	0933	0943	1003	1023	1033	1040	1043	1103	1110	1113	1123	1133	1153	1203	1210	1213	...	1223	1233	13

	10	12	600	14	464	124	518	542	16	602	18	466	126	544	20	604	468	22	128	546	24	470	548	26	130	52
	✣	✣	✣	✣		✣			✣	✣	✣		✣		✣	✣		✣	✣		✣			✣	✣	
Kagoshima C **8000** d.	...	...	0702	...	...	...	...	0706	...	0800	...	...	...	0806	...	0900	...	...	...	0906	...	...	0948	...	...	
Hakata d.	0750	0810	0820	0836	...	...	...	0847	0910	0924	0936	...	...	0947	1010	1020	...	1036	...	1047	1110	...	1115	1136	...	
Kokura d.	0807	0827	0837	0853	...	...	...	0904	0927	0941	0953	...	...	1003	1027	1036	...	1053	...	1103	1127	...	1132	1153	...	
Hiroshima d.	0857	0917	0926	0939	...	0950	...	0954	1017	1027	1039	...	1050	1054	1117	1122	...	1139	1150	1154	1218	...	1222	1239	1253	
Okayama d.	0933	0953	1003	1020	0917	1028	...	1035	1053	1103	1120	1023	1128	1135	1153	1159	1123	1220	1228	1235	1253	1223	1303	1320	1328	
Shin Kobe d.	1006	1026	1035	1052	1029	1106	...	1112	1126	1135	1152	1129	1206	1211	1226	1235	1229	1252	1306	1311	1326	1329	1335	1352	1406	
Shin **Osaka** d.	1020	1040	1048	1106	1043	1120	1116	1124	1140	1148	1206	1143	1220	1224	1240	1248	1243	1306	1320	1324	1340	1343	1348	1406	1420	14
Kyoto d.	1035	1056	...	1121	1059	1135	1132	...	1156	...	1221	1158	1235	...	1256	...	1259	1321	1335	...	1356	1358	...	1421	1435	14
Nagoya d.	1112	1133	...	1157	1137	1212	1226	...	1232	...	1257	1235	1312	...	1333	...	1337	1357	1412	...	1433	1435	...	1457	1512	15
Shin Yokohama a.	1234	1254	...	1314	1322	1334	1351	...	1355	...	1414	1422	1434	...	1454	...	1522	1514	1534	...	1554	1622	...	1614	1634	16
Tokyo Shinagawa a.	1246	1306	...	1326	1333	1346	1403	...	1406	...	1426	1433	1446	...	1506	...	1533	1526	1546	...	1606	1633	...	1626	1646	17
Tokyo a.	1253	1313	...	1333	1340	1353	1410	...	1413	...	1433	1440	1453	...	1513	...	1540	1533	1553	...	1613	1640	...	1633	1653	17

	472	550	28	552	232	30	132	32	474	554	34	134	528	36	556	38	476	40	136	42	558	44	478	46	560	13
			✣		✣	✣	✣	✣			✣	✣		✣		✣		✣	✣	✣		✣		✣		
Kagoshima C **8000** d.	...	1011	...	1048	...	...	...	...	...	1147	...	...	...	...	1248	...	...	...	...	...	1348	...	...	...	1403	
Hakata d.	...	1151	1210	1215	...	1236	...	1310	...	1315	1336	...	...	1410	1415	1436	...	1450	...	1510	1515	1536	...	1550	1541	
Kokura d.	...	1207	1227	1231	...	1253	...	1327	...	1331	1353	...	...	1427	1431	1453	...	1507	...	1527	1531	1553	...	1607	1558	
Hiroshima d.	...	1256	1317	1322	...	1339	1353	1417	...	1422	1439	1453	...	1517	1522	1539	...	1557	1606	1617	1622	1639	...	1657	1644	170
Okayama d.	1323	1337	1353	1358	...	1420	1428	1453	1423	1503	1520	1528	...	1553	1603	1620	1523	1633	1642	1653	1703	1720	1623	1733	1728	17
Shin Kobe d.	1429	1411	1426	1435	...	1452	1506	1526	1529	1535	1552	1606	...	1626	1635	1652	1629	1706	1719	1726	1735	1752	1729	1806	1810	18
Shin **Osaka** d.	1443	1424	1440	1448	1453	1506	1520	1540	1543	1548	1606	1620	1616	1640	1648	1706	1643	1720	1733	1740	1748	1806	1743	1820	1824	18
Kyoto d.	1459	...	1456	...	1508	1521	1535	1556	1559	...	1621	1635	1632	1656	...	1721	1659	1735	1748	1756	...	1821	1759	1835	...	18
Nagoya d.	1537	...	1533	...	1544	1557	1612	1632	1637	...	1657	1712	1726	1732	...	1757	1737	1812	1824	1832	...	1857	1837	1912	...	19
Shin Yokohama a.	1722	...	1654	...	1704	1714	1734	1755	1822	...	1814	1834	1851	1855	...	1914	1922	1934	1945	1955	...	2014	2022	2034	...	20
Tokyo Shinagawa a.	1733	...	1706	...	1716	1726	1746	1806	1833	...	1826	1846	1903	1906	...	1926	1933	1946	1956	2006	...	2026	2033	2048	...	20
Tokyo a.	1740	...	1713	...	1723	1733	1753	1813	1840	...	1833	1853	1910	1913	...	1933	1940	1953	2003	2013	...	2033	2040	2053	...	21

	48	562	50	480	52	534	564	54	606	254	56	482	58	538	60	566	62	568	64	610	96	570	98	572	612	45
	✣		✣		✣			✣	✣	✣	✣		✣		✣		✣		✣	✣	✣		✣		✣	
Kagoshima C **8000** d.	...	1437	...	...	...	...	1514	...	1557	...	...	...	...	...	...	1637	...	1716	...	1804	...	1807	...	1829	1951	20
Hakata d.	1610	1615	1636	...	1650	...	1641	1710	1716	...	1736	...	1750	...	1810	1815	1833	1842	1859	1925	1930	1944	2001	2006	2109	21
Kokura d.	1627	1631	1653	...	1707	...	1657	1727	1734	...	1753	...	1807	...	1827	1832	1850	1858	1915	1941	1947	2001	2017	2023	2125	22
Hiroshima d.	1717	1722	1739	...	1752	...	1747	1817	1821	...	1839	...	1857	...	1917	1922	1936	1951	2001	2027	2037	2052	2103	2119	2212	22
Okayama d.	1753	1803	1820	1723	1828	...	1834	1853	1858	...	1920	1823	1933	...	1953	2003	2012	2032	2036	2102	2113	2132	2144	2200	2248	...
Shin Kobe d.	1826	1835	1852	1829	1905	...	1911	1925	1932	...	1952	1929	2006	...	2026	2035	2049	2112	2108	2134	2146	2208	2216	2237	2325	...
Shin **Osaka** d.	1840	1848	1906	1843	1920	1916	1924	1940	1944	1953	2006	1943	2020	2037	2040	2048	2103	2125	2123	2147	2200	2221	2230	2249	2337	...
Kyoto d.	1856	...	1921	1859	1935	1932	...	1956	...	2008	2021	1959	2035	2053	2056	...	2118	...	2137	...	2215	...	2246	...	...	...
Nagoya d.	1932	...	1957	1937	2012	2026	...	2033	...	2044	2057	2037	2112	2129	2132	...	2154	...	2212	...	2250	...	2320	...	...	...
Shin Yokohama a.	2054	...	2114	2122	2134	2152	...	2154	...	2204	2214	2222	2234	2307	2253	...	2314	...	2327	...	...	...	...	...	...	...
Tokyo Shinagawa a.	2106	...	2126	2133	2146	2203	...	2206	...	2216	2226	2233	2246	2319	2304	...	2325	...	2338	...	...	...	...	...	...	...
Tokyo a.	2113	...	2133	2140	2153	2210	...	2213	...	2223	2233	2240	2253	2326	2311	...	2332	...	2345	...	...	...	...	...	...	...

D – Additional services: 0603, 0616, 1053, 1153, 1253, 1353, 1510, 1553, 1610, 1653, 1710, 1810.

E – Additional services: 0626, 0716, 1216, 1316, 1516, 1716, 1816, 2026.

k – From Kumamoto (Table **8000**).

✣ – NOT available to holders of Japan Rail Pass. To use these trains you must pay the full fare.

For return service see next page ▷ ▷ ▷

JR Central, JR West

HAKATA - OSAKA - TOKYO

8005

Sanyo and *Tokaido Shinkansen* high-speed lines

	451	601	541	543	95	545	603	97	547	99	1	3	605	501	5	549	7	203	461	9	11	551	101	13	463	15
		❖			❖		❖	❖		❖	❖	❖		B	❖		❖	A❖		❖	❖		❖	❖		❖
okyo d.	...	...	...	...	...	...	...	...	...	...	0600	0616	...	0626	0630	...	0650	0700	0703	0710	0730	...	0740	0750	0803	0810
okyo Shinagawa d.	...	...	...	...	...	...	...	...	...	0600	0607	0623	...	0634	0637	...	0657	0707	0710	0717	0737	...	0747	0757	0810	0817
hin Yokohama d.	...	...	...	...	...	...	...	...	...	0611	0618	0634	...	0646	0649	...	0709	0719	0721	0729	0749	...	0759	0809	0821	0829
agoya d.	...	...	...	...	0620	...	...	0706	...	0729	0735	0752	...	0820	0813	...	0836	0843	0908	0849	0913	...	0921	0933	1008	0948
yoto d.	...	...	...	...	0656	...	...	0743	...	0803	0809	0827	...	0916	0849	...	0913	0919	0946	0924	0949	...	0957	1010	1046	1024
hin **Osaka** d.	...	0600	0625	0650	0712	0715	0753	0759	0804	0818	0824	0842	0859	0930	0905	0917	0929	0933	1002	0939	1005	1008	1013	1025	1102	1039
hin Kobe d.	...	0613	0638	0703	0725	0728	0806	0813	0817	0832	0837	0855	0913	...	0918	0931	0943	...	1015	0952	1018	1022	1026	1038	1115	1052
kayama d.	...	0651	0715	0741	0757	0805	0838	0845	0854	0905	0910	0928	0946	...	0951	1008	1020	...	1117	1025	1051	1055	1103	1112	1219	1124
iroshima d.	0644	0726	0756	0822	0838	0846	0914	0921	0934	0942	0950	1004	1022	...	1032	1048	1056	...	...	1105	1127	1135	1138	1148	...	1205
okura d.	0741	0812	0847	0911	0925	0937	1001	1012	1021	1031	1037	1054	1108	...	1118	1138	1142	...	...	1152	1217	1226	...	1238	...	1252
akata a.	0756	0828	0902	0927	0940	0952	1017	1027	1037	1046	1052	1110	1123	...	1133	1154	1157	...	...	1207	1233	1241	...	1253	...	1307
Kagoshima C **8000** a.	0933	0946	1041	1055	...	1129	1137	...	1204	...	...	...	1241	...	...	1331	...	...	...	...	...	1409	...	...	...	...

	17	607	553	103	465	19	21	555	105	467	23	25	557	107	469	27	29	559	109	227	471	31	33	561	513	563
	❖	❖		❖		❖	❖		❖		❖	❖		❖		❖	❖		❖	❖		❖	❖			
okyo d.	0830	...	...	0850	0903	0910	0930	...	0950	1003	1010	1030	...	1050	1103	1110	1130	...	1150	1200	1203	1210	1230	...	1233	...
okyo Shinagawa d.	0837	...	...	0857	0910	0917	0937	...	0957	1010	1017	1037	...	1057	1110	1117	1137	...	1157	1207	1210	1217	1237	...	1240	...
hin Yokohama d.	0849	...	...	0909	0921	0929	0949	...	1009	1021	1029	1049	...	1109	1121	1129	1149	...	1209	1219	1221	1229	1249	...	1252	...
agoya d.	1013	...	...	1033	1108	1048	1113	...	1133	1208	1148	1213	...	1233	1308	1248	1313	...	1333	1343	1408	1348	1413	...	1418	...
yoto d.	1049	...	...	1110	1146	1124	1149	...	1210	1246	1224	1249	...	1310	1346	1324	1349	...	1410	1419	1446	1424	1449	...	1513	...
hin **Osaka** d.	1105	1108	1120	1125	1202	1139	1205	1208	1225	1302	1239	1305	1308	1325	1402	1339	1405	1408	1425	1433	1502	1439	1505	1508	1526	1520
hin Kobe d.	1118	1131	1133	1138	1215	1152	1218	1222	1238	1315	1252	1318	1322	1338	1415	1352	1418	1422	1438	...	1515	1452	1518	1522	...	1533
kayama d.	1151	1158	1206	1215	1319	1224	1251	1255	1315	1419	1324	1351	1355	1415	1519	1424	1451	1455	1515	...	1619	1524	1551	1555	...	1606
iroshima d.	1227	1235	1247	1250	...	1305	1327	1335	1350	...	1405	1427	1435	1450	...	1505	1527	1535	1550	...	...	1605	1627	1635	...	1658
okura d.	1318	1322	1338	...	...	1352	1418	1426	...	...	1452	1517	1526	...	...	1552	1617	1626	...	...	...	1652	1717	1726	...	1740
akata a.	1333	1338	1354	...	...	1407	1433	1441	...	...	1507	1533	1541	...	...	1607	1633	1641	...	...	...	1707	1733	1741	...	1758
Kagoshima C **8000** a.	...	1458	1521	...	...	...	...	1609	...	...	...	...	1709	...	...	...	...	1810	...	...	...	...	...	1912	...	1935

	111	473	35	37	609	565	515	113	475	39	41	611	567	115	233	477	43	45	569	117	237	479	47	49	571	521
	❖		❖	❖				❖		❖	❖			❖			❖	❖		❖			❖	❖		
okyo d.	1250	1303	1310	1330	...	...	1333	1350	1403	1410	1430	...	...	1450	1500	1503	1510	1530	...	1550	1600	1603	1610	1630	...	1633
okyo Shinagawa d.	1257	1310	1317	1337	...	...	1340	1357	1410	1417	1437	...	...	1457	1507	1510	1517	1537	...	1557	1607	1610	1617	1637	...	1640
hin Yokohama d.	1309	1321	1329	1349	...	...	1352	1409	1421	1429	1449	...	...	1509	1519	1521	1529	1549	...	1609	1619	1621	1629	1649	...	1652
agoya d.	1433	1508	1448	1513	...	...	1518	1533	1608	1548	1613	...	...	1633	1643	1708	1648	1713	...	1733	1743	1808	1748	1813	...	1819
yoto d.	1510	1546	1524	1549	...	...	1613	1610	1646	1624	1649	...	...	1710	1719	1746	1724	1749	...	1810	1819	1846	1824	1849	...	1913
hin **Osaka** d.	1525	1602	1539	1605	1608	1620	1626	1625	1702	1639	1705	1708	1720	1725	1733	1802	1739	1805	1808	1825	1833	1902	1839	1905	1908	1926
hin Kobe d.	1538	1615	1552	1618	1622	1633	...	1638	1715	1652	1718	1722	1733	1738	...	1815	1752	1818	1822	1838	...	1915	1852	1918	1922	...
kayama d.	1615	1719	1624	1651	1655	1709	...	1715	1819	1724	1751	1758	1809	1815	...	1919	1824	1851	1858	1915	...	2019	1924	1951	1958	...
iroshima d.	1650	...	1705	1727	1731	1754	...	1750	...	1805	1827	1835	1850	1854	...	...	1900	1927	1950	1954	...	...	2000	2027	2038	...
okura d.	...	...	1752	1817	1822	1844	...	...	...	1852	1917	1922	1941	...	...	...	1952	2018	2041	...	...	...	2052	2117	2128	...
akata a.	...	...	1807	1833	1837	1859	...	...	...	1907	1933	1937	1957	...	...	...	2007	2033	2058	...	...	...	2107	2133	2145	...
Kagoshima C **8000** a.	...	...	...	...	1959	2040	...	...	...	...	...	2058	2138	...	...	...	...	...	2239	...	...	...	...	...	2322	...

	51	481	53	613	55	573	523	119	121	525	57	123	527	59	529	125	127	531	129	257	533	131	133	135	263	265
	❖		❖	❖	❖	k		❖	❖		❖	❖		❖		❖	❖		❖	❖		❖	❖	❖	❖	❖
okyo d.	1650	1703	1710	...	1730	...	1733	1750	1800	1803	1810	1830	1833	1850	1903	1910	1930	1933	1950	2000	2003	2010	2030	2050	2110	2123
okyo Shinagawa d.	1657	1710	1717	...	1737	...	1740	1757	1807	1810	1817	1837	1840	1857	1910	1917	1937	1940	1957	2007	2010	2017	2037	2057	2117	2130
hin Yokohama d.	1709	1721	1729	...	1749	...	1752	1809	1819	1821	1829	1849	1852	1909	1921	1929	1949	1952	2009	2019	2021	2029	2049	2109	2129	2142
agoya d.	1833	1908	1848	...	1913	...	1919	1933	1943	2008	1948	2013	2018	2033	2108	2048	2113	2118	2133	2143	2208	2148	2213	2233	2248	2258
yoto d.	1910	1946	1924	...	1949	...	2013	2010	2019	2100	2024	2049	2113	2110	2200	2124	2149	2213	2210	2219	2300	2224	2249	2310	2322	2332
hin **Osaka** d.	1925	2002	1939	1959	2005	2016	2026	2025	2035	2113	2039	2105	2126	2126	2213	2139	2205	2226	2226	2233	2313	2239	2306	2325	2336	2345
hin Kobe d.	1938	2015	1952	2012	2018	2029	...	2038	2048	...	2052	2118	...	2139	...	2152	2219	...	2239	...	...	2252	2319	2339	...	...
kayama d.	2015	2117	2024	2044	2051	2102	...	2115	2119	...	2125	2154	...	2212	...	2228	2254	...	2315	...	...	2328	2355	...	...	...
iroshima d.	2052	...	2105	2119	2127	2144	...	2154	...	...	2201	2234	...	2249	...	2308	...	...	2355	...	...	...	...	...	...	...
okura d.	2138	...	2152	2207	2217	2236	...	...	...	...	2251	...	...	2340	...	...	...	...	...	...	...	...	...	...	...	...
akata a.	2153	...	2207	2222	2233	2252	...	...	...	...	2307	...	...	2354	...	...	...	...	...	...	...	...	...	...	...	...
Kagoshima C **8000** a.	...	...	...	2340	...	...	...	...	...	...	...	...	...	...	...	...	...	...	...	...	...	...	...	...	...	...

– Additional services: 0800, 0900, 0940, 1000, 1100, 1300, 1400, 1620, 1700, 1720, 1820, 1900, 1920, 2020, 2100. B – Additional services: 0733, 0833, 0933, 1033, 1433, 1533.

– To Kumamoto (Table **8000**).

– NOT available to holders of Japan Rail Pass. To use these trains you must pay the full fare.

JR East JR West

TOKYO - ECHIGO YUZAWA - NIIGATA

8008

Joetsu Shinkansen high-speed line

km		481	301	401	303	471	305	403	307	309	311	313	315	317	319	321	323	325	327	329	331	333	405	335
						⚒																		
0	**Tokyo** **8010/15/20** d.	...	0608	0636	0704	0712	0748	0804	0824	0852	0912	0928	1016	1040	1140	1240	1340	1440	1516	1540	1616	1640	1708	1716
4	**Tokyo** Ueno **8010/15/20** d.	...	0614	0642	0710	0718	0754	0810	0830	0858	|	0934	1022	1046	1146	1246	1346	1446	1522	1546	1622	1646	1714	1722
31	Omiya **8010/15/20** d.	...	0634	0702	0730	0738	0814	0830	0850	0917	0935	0954	1042	1106	1206	1306	1406	1506	1542	1606	1642	1706	1734	1742
109	Takasaki d.	...	0659	0737	|	0813	0839	0906	0919	0949	|	1026	1106	1134	1231	1331	1431	1530	|	1631	1713	1731	1806	1816
183	**Echigo Yuzawa** d.	0700	0725	0806	0815	...	0909	0935	0945	1023	|	1051	1136	|	1301	1402	1501	1600	|	1701	|	1801	1835	|
245	Nagaoka d.	0726	0750	...	0840	...	0933	...	1005	1048	|	1112	1201	1216	1326	1427	1526	1625	1645	1726	1754	1825	...	1857
269	Tsubame Sanjo d.	0736	0800	...	0850	...	0943	...	1015	1058	|	1122	1211	1226	1336	1437	1536	1635	|	1736	1804	1835	...	|
301	**Niigata** a.	0749	0813	...	0902	...	0956	...	1028	1111	1049	1134	1224	1239	1348	1449	1548	1647	1704	1748	1816	1848	...	1915

	337	407	339	409	411	341	413	343	415	345	347	349	473	351	417	475
okyo **8010/15/20** d.	1740	1752	1812	1816	1832	1852	1912	1936	1952	2004	2024	2052	2112	2140	2228	2300
okyo Ueno **8010/15/20** d.	1746	1758	1818	1822	1838	1858	1918	1942	1958	2010	2030	2058	2118	2146	2234	2306
miya **8010/15/20** d.	1806	1818	1838	1842	1858	1918	1938	2002	2018	2030	2050	2118	2138	2206	2254	2326
akasaki d.	1832	1855	1902	1917	1931	1950	2013	2031	2057	|	2122	2147	2210	2239	2326	2358
chigo Yuzawa d.	1857	1924	1929	1946	2000	2017	2042	2057	2126	|	2148	2217	...	2309	2355	...
agaoka d.	1922	...	1950	...	...	2042	...	2117	...	2134	2213	2238	...	2333	...	...
subame Sanjo d.	1932	...	2000	...	...	2052	...	2127	...	2144	2323	|	...	2343	...	...
igata a.	1944	...	2012	...	...	2105	...	2140	...	2156	2236	2257	...	2356	...	...

	470	400	472	300	474	402	302	304	404	306	308	310	312	406	314	408	316	410	318	320	322	324	326
					Ⓐ																		
igata d.	...	...	...	0607	...	...	0633	0656	...	0719	0749	0825	0904	...	0923	...	1017	...	1119	1235	1319	1413	1419
subame Sanjo d.	...	...	...	0620	...	...	0645	0709	...	0731	0802	0837	|	...	0935	...	1029	...	1131	1247	1331	|	1431
agaoka d.	...	...	...	0630	...	...	0656	0720	...	0742	0813	0848	|	...	0946	...	1040	...	1142	1258	1342	1432	1442
chigo Yuzawa d.	...	0607	...	|	...	0708	0722	|	0748	0808	0840	0909	|	0928	1012	1030	1106	1130	1208	1324	1408	|	1508
akasaki d.	0617	0637	0653	0715	0721	0738	0748	0802	0817	0838	0911	0934	|	1003	1037	1102	1135	1202	1238	1354	1438	|	1538
miya **8010/15/20** d.	0651	0710	0727	0747	0754	0815	0823	0835	0851	0915	0939	1003	1020	1035	1103	1135	1203	1235	1303	1419	1503	1535	1603
okyo Ueno **8010/15/20** d.	0711	0731	0747	0807	0815	0835	0843	0855	0911	0935	0959	1023	|	1055	1123	1155	1223	1255	1323	1439	1523	1555	1623
okyo **8010/15/20** a.	0716	0736	0752	0812	0820	0840	0848	0900	0916	0940	1004	1028	1043	1100	1128	1200	1228	1300	1328	1444	1528	1600	1628

	328	412	330	332	334	336	338	340	342	414	344	346		348	416	350
igata d.	1509	...	1537	1609	1622	1659	1723	1744	1812	...	1856	1936	...	2020	...	2135
subame Sanjo d.	1521	...	|	1622	1636	|	1735	1756	1824	...	1908	1948	...	2032	...	2147
agaoka d.	1532	...	1556	1633	1647	1716	1746	1807	1835	...	1919	1959	...	2043	...	2158
chigo Yuzawa d.	|	1601	1622	|	1713	1737	1812	1828	1901	1913	1940	2025	...	2109	2140	2224
akasaki d.	|	1630	1647	|	1742	1803	1842	1858	|	1942	2010	2054	...	2138	2210	2250
miya **8010/15/20** d.	1635	1703	1715	1735	1815	1835	1915	1927	1947	2015	2035	2127	...	2203	2243	2315
okyo Ueno **8010/15/20** d.	1655	1723	1735	1755	1835	1855	1935	1947	2007	2035	2055	2147	...	2223	2303	2335
okyo **8010/15/20** a.	1700	1728	1740	1800	1840	1900	1940	1952	2012	2040	2100	2152	...	2228	2308	2340

8010 TOKYO - NAGANO - TOYAMA - KANAZAWA

JR East JR West

Hokuriku Shinkansen high-speed line

km		591	501 R	551	601	503 R	603	553		505 R	555	507 R	557	607	509 R	559	609	561	611	563	613	565	615	567
0	**Tokyo** 8008/15/20 d.	...	0616	0628	0652	0720	0724	0752	...	0836	0844	0920	0932	0944	1024	1032	1104	1124	1204	1224	1304	1324	1404	142
4	**Tokyo** Ueno 8008/15/20 d.	...	0622	0634	0658	0726	0730	0758	...	0842	0850	0926	0938	0950	|	1038	1110	1130	1210	1230	1310	1330	1410	143
31	Omiya 8008/15/20 d.	...	0642	0654	0718	0746	0750	0818	...	0902	0909	0946	0958	1010	1048	1058	1130	1150	1230	1250	1330	1350	1430	145
109	Takasaki d.	...	|	0719	0746	|	0823	0843	...	|	0934	|	|	1042	|	1123	1202	1216	1302	1316	1402	1416	1502	151
151	Karuizawa d.	...	|	0735	0808	|	0844	0900	...	|	0950	|	1035	1103	|	1140	1218	|	1323	|	1418	|	1523	|
194	Ueda d.	...	|	0754	0827	|	0902	0918	...	|	1009	|	1054	1121	|	1155	1237	|	1341	|	1437	|	1541	|
226	**Nagano** d.	0611	0740	0808	0838	0845	0914	0932	...	1001	1022	1048	1107	1133	1146	1209	1248	1254	1353	1358	1448	1454	1553	155
285	Joetsumyoko d.	0635	|	0831	...	|	...	0958	...	|	1045	|	1126	...	|	1235	...	1317	...	1417	...	1517	...	161
392	**Toyama** d.	0716	0827	0912	...	0932	...	1039	...	1047	1126	1135	1207	...	1233	1317	...	1358	...	1458	...	1558	...	165
412	Shin Takaoka d.	0725	|	0921	...	|	...	1048	...	|	1135	|	1216	...	|	1325	...	1407	...	1507	...	1607	...	170
454	**Kanazawa** 8150 a.	0738	0846	0935	...	0951	...	1102	...	1106	1149	1154	1230	...	1252	1339	...	1420	...	1520	...	1620	...	172

		617	569	619	511 R	571	621	513 R	623	573	515 R	625	575	517 R	627	539 R ⑤⑦	577	629	519 R	631	633		
Tokyo 8008/15/020 d.	...	1504	1524	1552	1624	1632	1652	1724	1732	1804	1824	1840	1904	1924	1932	1956	2012	2036	2104	2128	2208	...	...
Tokyo Ueno 8008/15/20 d.	...	1510	1530	1558	1630	1638	1658	1730	1738	1810	1830	1846	1910	1930	1938	2002	2018	2042	2110	2134	2214	...	...
Omiya 8008/15/20 d.	...	1530	1550	1618	1650	1658	1718	1750	1758	1830	1850	1906	1930	1950	1958	2022	2038	2102	2130	2154	2234	...	...
Takasaki d.	...	1602	1616	1650	|	1723	1750	|	1827	|	|	1934	1956	|	2023	|	2104	2127	|	2222	2302	...	...
Karuizawa d.	...	1618	1632	1711	|	1739	1809	|	1848	1911	|	1955	2013	|	2044	|	2121	2149	|	2243	2323	...	...
Ueda d.	...	1637	|	1730	|	1758	1828	|	1906	1931	|	2014	2032	|	2103	|	2140	2206	|	2302	2342	...	...
Nagano d.	...	1649	1657	1742	1748	1812	1840	1851	1918	1952	1948	2026	2052	2048	2114	2121	2154	2218	2228	2313	2353	...	...
Joetsumyoko d.	...	...	1720	...	|	1835	...	|	...	2015	|	...	2115	|	...	|	2217	...	|	...	...	...	...
Toyama d.	...	...	1801	...	1835	1916	...	1938	...	2056	2035	...	2156	2135	...	2208	2258	...	2316	...	...	...	...
Shin Takaoka d.	...	...	1810	...	|	1925	...	|	...	2105	|	...	2205	|	...	2216	2307	...	|	...	...	...	...
Kanazawa 8150 a.	...	...	1824	...	1854	1938	...	1958	...	2119	2055	...	2219	2154	...	2230	2321	...	2335	...	...	...	...

	600	602	604	500 R	606	608	552	502 R	520 R ⑥	610	504 R	554	612	506 R	556	508 R	558	614	560	616	562	618	564
Kanazawa 8150 d.	...	...	...	0600	...	...	0613	0700	0708	...	0748	0723	...	0848	0823	0946	0921	...	1056	...	1156	...	125
Shin Takaoka d.	...	...	...	|	...	...	0627	|	0722	...	|	0737	...	|	0837	|	0936	...	1110	...	1210	...	131
Toyama d.	...	...	...	0619	...	...	0637	0719	0732	...	0807	0747	...	0907	0847	1005	0945	...	1119	...	1219	...	131
Joetsumyoko d.	...	...	...	|	...	...	0717	|	|	...	|	0827	...	|	0927	|	1025	...	1159	...	1259	...	135
Nagano d.	0602	0618	0642	0707	0711	0722	0742	0807	0820	0824	0855	0859	0926	0955	0959	1053	1059	1126	1224	1227	1320	1323	142
Ueda d.	0614	|	0654	|	0723	0734	0754	|	|	0836	|	0911	0939	|	1011	|	1111	1138	|	1239	|	1336	|
Karuizawa d.	0634	0642	0714	|	0742	0754	0814	|	|	0856	|	0930	0959	|	1032	|	1130	1158	|	1259	|	1355	|
Takasaki d.	0650	0702	0734	|	0758	0814	0830	|	|	0915	|	0946	1019	|	|	|	1146	1218	1301	1315	1401	1415	150
Omiya 8008/15/20 d.	0715	0735	0759	0807	0827	0843	0855	0907	0919	0947	0955	1011	1047	1055	1111	1155	1211	1247	1327	1347	1427	1447	152
Tokyo Ueno 8008/15/20 d.	0735	0755	0819	0827	0847	0903	0915	0927	0939	1007	1015	1031	1107	1115	1131	1215	1231	1307	1347	1407	1447	1507	154
Tokyo 8008/15/20 a.	0740	0800	0824	0832	0852	0908	0920	0932	0944	1012	1020	1036	1112	1120	1136	1220	1236	1312	1352	1412	1452	1512	155

	620	644 ©	566	622	568	626	510 R	628	570	512 R	572	514 R	630	574	576	516 R		632	578	518 R	590		
Kanazawa 8150 d.	...	...	1356	...	1446	...	1555	...	1609	1647	1650	1755	...	1809	1902	1918	...	...	2017	2100	2135	...	...
Shin Takaoka d.	...	...	1410	...	1500	...	|	...	1623	|	1704	|	...	1823	1916	|	...	...	2031	|	2149	...	...
Toyama d.	...	...	1419	...	1510	...	1615	...	1633	1707	1713	1815	...	1832	1925	1937	...	...	2041	2120	2158	...	...
Joetsumyoko d.	...	...	1459	...	1553	...	|	...	1713	|	1757	|	...	1913	2009	|	...	...	2121	|	2238	...	...
Nagano d.	1427	1500	1520	1523	1618	1623	1703	1709	1734	1755	1822	1903	1908	1938	2034	2026	...	2115	2146	2208	2302	...	...
Ueda d.	1439	1512	|	1536	1630	1636	|	1721	1746	|	1834	|	1920	1950	2046	|	...	2127	2158	|	...	...	...
Karuizawa d.	1459	1532	|	1555	1646	1655	|	1740	1806	|	1854	|	1940	2009	2105	|	...	2147	2218	|	...	...	...
Takasaki d.	1515	1549	1601	1615	1702	1715	|	1800	1822	|	1910	|	1959	2026	2121	|	...	2207	2234	|	...	...	...
Omiya 8008/15/20 d.	1547	1615	1627	1647	1727	1747	1803	1827	1847	1855	1935	2000	2027	2051	2147	2131	...	2235	2259	2307	...	...	...
Tokyo Ueno 8008/15/20 d.	1607	1635	1647	1707	1747	1807	1823	1847	1907	1915	1955	|	2047	2111	2207	|	...	2255	2319	2327	...	...	...
Tokyo 8008/15/20 a.	1612	1640	1652	1712	1752	1812	1828	1852	1912	1920	2000	2023	2052	2116	2212	2156	...	2300	2324	2332	...	...	...

Additional services TOYAMA - KANAZAWA and v.v.

km		701	703	705	707	709	711	713	715	717	719	721		723	725	727	729	731	733	735			
0	**Toyama** d.	0612	0642	0733	0750	0832	1022	1112	1246	1343	1417	1517	...	1618	1711	1820	1942	2016	2139	2333	...	...	...
19	Shin Takaoka d.	0621	0651	0742	0759	0841	1031	1121	1255	1352	1426	1526	...	1627	1720	1829	1952	2025	2148	2342	...	...	...
59	**Kanazawa** a.	0635	0705	0756	0813	0854	1045	1135	1309	1406	1439	1540	...	1640	1734	1843	2006	2038	2201	2356	...	...	...

		700	702	704	706	708	710	712	714	716	718		720	722	724	726	728	730	732	734		
Kanazawa d.	...	0650	0758	0949	1034	1128	1231	1328	1431	1504	1539	...	1735	1838	1924	2025	2106	2219	2306	2337	...	...
Shin Takaoka d.	...	0705	0812	1003	1048	1142	1245	1342	1446	1519	1553	...	1750	1852	1938	2039	2120	2233	2320	2351	...	...
Toyama d.	...	0713	0821	1012	1057	1151	1254	1351	1454	1527	1602	...	1758	1901	1946	2048	2129	2242	2329	2359	...	...

8015 TOKYO - SHINJO and MORIOKA

JR East

Yamagata and *Tohoku Shinkansen* high-speed line

km		41	121	201	203	123	123	125	205 A	127	127	43	129	131	131	45	133	133		47	135	135	49	137	137	51
0	**Tokyo** 8010/20 d.	0604	0612	0620	0640	0708	0708	0732	0744	0808	0808	0848	0856	0924	0924	0940	1000	1000	...	1036	1100	1100	1136	1200	1200	123
4	**Tokyo** Ueno 8010/20 d.	0610	0618	0626	0646	0714	0714	0738	0750	0814	0814	0854	0902	|	|	0946	1006	1006	...	1042	1106	1106	1142	1206	1206	124
31	Omiya 8010/20 d.	0630	0638	0646	0706	0734	0734	0758	0810	0834	0834	0914	0922	0948	0948	1006	1026	1026	...	1102	1126	1126	1202	1226	1226	130
109	Utsunomiya d.	0654	0702	0719	0737	0803	0803	0824	0844	0905	0905	0939	0946	|	|	1031	1052	1052	...	1131	1150	1150	1229	1250	1250	133
214	Koriyama d.	0725	0731	0757	0824	0831	0831	0856	0926	0933	0933	1007	1017	|	|	1059	1120	1120	...	1200	1219	1219	1257	1319	1319	140
255	Fukushima d.	0739	0748	0815	0838	0848	0853	0916	0940	0949	0950	1025	1033	1048	1051	1114	1135	1138	...	1217	1235	1238	1317	1335	1338	141
295	Yonezawa d.	|	0820	|	|	0926	|	|	|	1025	|	|	1105	1121	|	|	1210	|	...	|	1307	|	|	1409	|	|
342	Yamagata d.	|	0859	|	|	1008	|	|	|	1104	|	|	1137	1152	|	|	1246	|	...	|	1344	|	|	1444	|	|
369	Murayama d.	|	0927	|	|	1031	|	|	|	...	|	|	...	1212	|	|	1308	|	...	|	...	|	|	1507	|	|
404	**Shinjo** a.	|	0955	|	|	1054	|	|	|	...	|	|	...	1235	|	|	1331	|	...	|	...	|	|	1530	|	|
325	Sendai (Honshu) d.	0801	...	0843	0859	...	0919	0938	1006	...	1011	1049	...	...	1114	1136	...	1204	...	1239	...	1304	1339	...	1404	143
497	**Morioka** a.	0919	...	...	...	...	...	...	...	...	...	1207	...	...	...	1254	...	...	...	1354	...	...	1454	...	...	155

	139	139	53	141	141	55	143	143	57	145	145	147	149	149	151	153	153	157	157	219	59	159	159	221	22
Tokyo 8010 8020 d.	1300	1300	1336	1400	1400	1436	1500	1500	1536	1600	1600	1636	1700	1700	1728	1800	1800	1916	1916	1928	2020	2044	2044	2056	214
Tokyo Ueno 8010 8020 d.	1306	1306	1342	1406	1406	1442	1506	1506	1542	1606	1606	1642	1706	1706	1734	1806	1806	1922	1922	1934	2026	2050	2050	2102	215
Omiya 8010 8020 d.	1326	1326	1402	1426	1426	1502	1526	1526	1602	1626	1626	1702	1726	1726	1754	1826	1826	1942	1942	1954	2046	2110	2110	2122	221
Utsunomiya d.	1350	1350	1431	1450	1450	1531	1550	1550	1631	1650	1650	1731	1750	1750	1818	1850	1850	2008	2008	2026	2110	2134	2134	2150	223
Koriyama d.	1419	1419	1502	1519	1519	1602	1619	1619	1702	1719	1719	1803	1819	1819	1855	1919	1919	2038	2038	2103	2138	2203	2203	2228	230
Fukushima d.	1435	1438	1517	1535	1538	1616	1635	1638	1717	1735	1738	1817	1836	1838	1917	1937	1938	2056	2057	2117	2156	2219	2220	2243	232
Yonezawa d.	1512	|	|	1611	|	|	1707	|	|	1808	|	|	1909	|	|	2012	|	2128	|	|	|	2251	|	|	|
Yamagata d.	1550	|	|	1650	|	|	1746	|	|	1844	|	|	1945	|	|	2047	|	2159	|	|	|	2326	|	|	|
Murayama d.	...	|	|	1714	|	|	...	|	|	1906	|	|	...	|	|	...	|	2221	|	|	|	...	|	|	|
Shinjo a.	...	|	|	1741	|	|	...	|	|	1929	|	|	...	|	|	...	|	2245	|	|	|	...	|	|	|
Sendai (Honshu) d.	...	1504	1539	...	1604	1639	...	1704	1739	...	1804	1841	...	1904	1937	...	1959	...	2123	2143	2220	...	2246	2303	234
Morioka a.	...	...	1654	...	...	1754	...	...	1854	...	...	...	...	...	...	...	...	...	...	...	2331	...	...	...	...

A – Additional trips: 0856, 1012, 1212, 1412, 1612, 1736, 1828, 1836.

For return service see next page ▷ ▷

	202	204	206 C	[illegible]	[illegible]	[illegible]	[illegible]	[illegible]	[illegible]	[illegible]	[illegible]	[illegible]	[illegible]	[illegible]	[illegible]	[illegible]	[illegible]	[illegible]	[illegible]	[illegible]	[illegible]	[illegible]	[illegible]	[illegible]	[illegible]	[illegible]
Morioka d.	...	...	...	...	...	[illegible]	[illegible]	[illegible]	[illegible]	[illegible]	[illegible]	[illegible]	[illegible]	[illegible]	[illegible]	[illegible]	[illegible]	[illegible]	[illegible]	[illegible]	[illegible]	[illegible]	[illegible]	[illegible]	[illegible]	[illegible]
Sendai (Honshu) d.	0606	0624	0650	...	0711	[illegible]	[illegible]	[illegible]	[illegible]	[illegible]	[illegible]	[illegible]	[illegible]	[illegible]	[illegible]	[illegible]	[illegible]	[illegible]	[illegible]	[illegible]	[illegible]	[illegible]	[illegible]	[illegible]	[illegible]	[illegible]
Shinjo d.	|	|	|	0540	|	...	[illegible]	[illegible]	[illegible]	[illegible]	[illegible]	[illegible]	[illegible]	[illegible]	[illegible]	[illegible]	[illegible]	[illegible]	[illegible]	[illegible]	[illegible]	[illegible]	[illegible]	[illegible]	[illegible]	[illegible]
Murayama d.	|	|	|	0603	|	...	|	[illegible]	[illegible]	[illegible]	[illegible]	[illegible]	[illegible]	[illegible]	[illegible]	[illegible]	[illegible]	[illegible]	[illegible]	[illegible]	[illegible]	[illegible]	[illegible]	[illegible]	[illegible]	[illegible]
Yamagata d.	|	|	|	0625	|	0708	|	|	[illegible]	[illegible]	[illegible]	[illegible]	[illegible]	[illegible]	[illegible]	[illegible]	[illegible]	[illegible]	[illegible]	[illegible]	[illegible]	[illegible]	[illegible]	[illegible]	[illegible]	[illegible]
Yonezawa d.	|	|	|	0702	|	0738	|	|	[illegible]	[illegible]	[illegible]	[illegible]	[illegible]	[illegible]	[illegible]	[illegible]	[illegible]	[illegible]	[illegible]	[illegible]	[illegible]	[illegible]	[illegible]	[illegible]	[illegible]	[illegible]
Fukushima d.	0633	0646	0716	0739	0739	0814	0814	0835	0842	[illegible]	[illegible]	[illegible]	[illegible]	[illegible]	[illegible]	[illegible]	[illegible]	[illegible]	[illegible]	[illegible]	[illegible]	[illegible]	[illegible]	[illegible]	[illegible]	[illegible]
Koriyama d.	0647	0704	0730	0753	0753	|	|	0849	0856	0930	[illegible]	[illegible]	[illegible]	[illegible]	[illegible]	[illegible]	[illegible]	[illegible]	[illegible]	[illegible]	[illegible]	[illegible]	[illegible]	[illegible]	[illegible]
Utsunomiya d.	0723	0742	0810	0822	0822	|	|	0918	0933	0958	[illegible]	[illegible]	[illegible]	[illegible]	[illegible]	[illegible]	[illegible]	[illegible]	[illegible]	[illegible]	[illegible]	[illegible]	1358	1358	1434
Omiya 8010/20 d.	0751	0811	0839	0847	0847	0913	0913	0943	0959	1023	1023	[illegible]	[illegible]	[illegible]	[illegible]	[illegible]	[illegible]	[illegible]	1259	1323	1323	1351	1359	1423	1423	1459
Tokyo Ueno 8010/20 d.	0811	0831	0859	0907	0907	|	|	1003	1019	1043	1043	1111	1119	1143	1143	1219	1243	1243	1319	1343	1343	1411	1419	1443	1443	1519
Tokyo 8010/20 a.	0816	0836	0904	0912	0912	0935	0935	1008	1024	1048	1048	1116	1124	1148	1148	1224	1248	1248	1324	1348	1348	1416	1424	1448	1448	1524

	[illegible]	142	214	48	144	144	50	146	146	216	52	148	148	150	150	154	154	156	156	54	56	158	158	58	160	60
Morioka d.	...	...	...	[illegible]	[illegible]	...	1407	...	[illegible]	...	1507	...	...	...	...	...	...	...	...	1754	1840	...	...	1940	...	2029
Sendai (Honshu) d.	[illegible]	[illegible]	[illegible]	1424	...	1444	1524	...	1545	[illegible]	1624	...	1634	...	1644	...	1743	...	1843	1910	2000	...	2017	2054	...	2147
Shinjo d.	...	|	|	|	1318	|	|	...	|	|	|	...	|	1517	|	...	|	1712	|	|	|	1843	|	|	1957	|
Murayama d.	...	|	|	|	1342	|	|	...	|	|	|	...	|	1542	|	...	|	1737	|	|	|	1906	|	|	2021	|
Yamagata d.	1304	|	|	|	1404	|	|	1503	|	|	|	1546	|	1607	|	1705	|	1804	|	|	|	1931	|	|	2043	|
Yonezawa d.	1340	|	|	|	1438	|	|	1540	|	|	|	1623	|	1638	|	1741	|	1838	|	|	|	2013	|	|	2117	|
Fukushima d.	1416	1416	1422	1450	1516	1516	1550	1616	1615	1623	1650	1701	1701	1716	1716	1816	1816	1916	1916	1933	2023	2049	2049	2124	2155	2209
Koriyama d.	1430	1430	1436	1505	1530	1530	1605	1630	1629	1639	1705	1715	1715	1730	1730	1830	1830	1930	1930	1947	2042	2104	2104	2138	2209	2224
Utsunomiya d.	1458	1458	1520	1534	1558	1558	1634	1657	1657	1720	1734	1746	1716	1758	1758	1859	1859	1959	1959	2022	2110	2134	2134	2206	2238	2253
Omiya 8010/20 d.	1523	1523	1551	1559	1623	1623	1659	1723	1723	1732	1759	1811	1811	1823	1823	1923	1923	2023	2023	2047	2135	2159	2159	2231	2303	2319
Tokyo Ueno 8010/20 d.	1543	1543	1611	1619	1643	1643	1719	1743	1743	1811	1819	1831	1831	1843	1843	1943	1943	2043	2043	2107	2155	2219	2219	2251	2323	2339
Tokyo 8010/20 a.	1548	1548	1616	1624	1648	1648	1724	1748	1748	1816	1824	1836	1836	1848	1848	1948	1948	2048	2048	2112	2200	2224	2224	2256	2328	2344

– Additional trips: 0734, 1725, 1811, 1917, 2037.

For return service see previous page.

TOKYO - AKITA and AOMORI - HAKODATE 8020

Akita, Tohoku and Hokkaido Shinkansen high-speed lines

km		91 [R]	93 [R]	95 [R]	95 [R]	1 [R]	1 [R]	101 [R]	3 [R]	3 [R]	103 [R]	5 [R]	7 [R]	7 [R]	9 [R]	9 [R]	11 [R]	13 [R]	15 [R]	15 [R]	17 [R]	19 [R]	19 [R]	
0	**Tokyo** 8010 8015 d.	...	...	...	...	0632	0632	0716	0736	0736	0756	0820	0840	0840	0908	0908	0936	1004	1020	1020	1044	1120	1120	...
4	**Tokyo** Ueno 8010 8015 d.	...	...	...	...	0638	0638	0722	0742	0742	0802	|	0846	0846	0914	0914	|	1010	1026	1026	1050	1126	1126	...
31	Omiya 8010 8015 d.	...	...	...	...	0658	0658	0742	0802	0802	0822	0844	0906	0906	0933	0933	1000	1030	1046	1046	1110	1146	1146	...
325	Sendai (Honshu) d.	...	...	0640	0640	0806	0806	0849	0912	0912	0936	0952	1016	1016	1042	1042	1108	1139	1154	1154	1217	1254	1254	...
497	Morioka d.	...	0654	0758	0759	0849	0848	1001	0954	0956	1049	1032	1057	1059	1123	1125	1148	...	1235	1237	1325	1335	1337	...
537	Tazawako d.	...	|	0831	|	|	0921	...	1026	|	...	|	1128	|	1202	|	|	...	1311	|	|	1407	|	...
555	Kakunodate d.	...	|	0845	|	|	0935	...	1040	|	...	|	1142	|	1218	|	|	...	1325	|	|	1421	|	...
572	Omagari d.	...	|	0859	|	|	0948	...	1052	|	...	|	1154	|	1231	|	|	...	1337	|	|	1433	|	...
624	**Akita** a.	...	|	0932	|	|	1024	...	1125	|	...	|	1230	|	1302	|	|	...	1408	|	|	1504	|	...
593	Hachinohe d.	...	0726	...	0835	0922	...	...	...	1032	...	|	...	1127	...	1202	|	...	...	1305	1334	...	1414	...
675	Shin **Aomori** d.	0632	0756	...	0904	0951	...	...	...	1100	...	1121	...	1151	...	1229	1237	...	...	1331	1358	...	1443	...
824	Shin **Hakodate Hokuto** ♥ a.	0734	0858	...	1001	1053	...	...	...	...	...	1218	...	...	...	...	1334	...	...	1433	...	...	...	...
842	*Hakodate* ♥ 8225 a.	*0807*	*0934*	...	*1030*	*1125*	...	...	...	...	...	*1251*	...	...	...	...	*1402*	...	...	*1502*	...	...	...	...

	21 [R]	21 [R]		23 [R]	23 [R]	25 [R]	25 [R]	27 [R]	27 [R]	31 [R]	31 [R]	105 [R]	33 [R]	33 [R]	107 [R]	35 [R]	35 [R]	109 [R]	37 [R]	37 [R]	111 [R]	39 [R]	39 [R]	41 [R]
Tokyo 8010 8015 d.	1220	1220	...	1320	1320	1420	1420	1520	1520	1620	1620	1656	1720	1720	1756	1820	1820	1856	1920	1920	1940	2016	2016	2136
Tokyo Ueno 8010 8015 d.	1226	1226	...	1326	1326	1426	1426	1526	1526	1626	1626	1702	1726	1726	1802	1826	1826	1902	1926	1926	1946	|	|	|
Omiya 8010 8015 d.	1246	1246	...	1346	1346	1446	1446	1546	1546	1646	1646	1722	1746	1746	1822	1846	1846	1922	1946	1946	2006	2040	2040	2200
Sendai (Honshu) d.	1354	1354	...	1454	1454	1554	1554	1654	1654	1754	1754	1831	1854	1854	1931	1954	1954	2030	2055	2055	2115	2148	2148	2307
Morioka d.	1435	1437	...	1535	1537	1635	1637	1735	1737	1835	1837	1944	1935	1937	2044	2035	2037	2144	2136	2138	2223	2230	2231	...
Tazawako d.	1511	|	...	1607	|	1712	|	1809	|	1912	|	...	2007	|	...	2111	|	...	2206	|	...	|	|	...
Kakunodate d.	1525	|	...	1621	|	1728	|	1823	|	1927	|	...	2021	|	...	2124	|	...	2219	|	...	|	|	...
Omagari d.	1537	|	...	1633	|	1741	|	1835	|	1941	|	...	2033	|	...	2136	|	...	2232	|	...	2323	|	...
Akita a.	1608	|	...	1708	|	1812	|	1906	|	2012	|	...	2104	|	...	2207	|	...	2302	|	...	2353	|	...
Hachinohe d.	...	1505	...	...	1614	...	1705	...	1814	...	1909	...	...	2013	...	...	2109	...	...	2206	...	...	2308	...
Shin **Aomori** d.	...	1531	...	...	1645	...	1731	...	1845	...	1937	...	...	2041	...	...	2137	...	...	2232a	...	...	2336	...
Shin **Hakodate Hokuto** ♥ a.	...	1630	...	...	1747	...	1828	...	1947	...	...	...	...	2144	...	...	...	...	...	2329a	...	...	...	...
Hakodate ♥ 8225 a.	...	*1705*	...	...	*1820*	...	*1853*	...	*2015*	...	...	...	...	*2213*	...	...	...	...	...	*2359*	...	...	...	...

	2 [R]	102 [R]	4 [R]	104 [R]	6 [R]	6 [R]	8 [R]	106 [R]	10 [R]	10 [R]		108 [R]	12 [R]	12 [R]	14 [R]	14 [R]	16 [R]	16 [R]	18 [R]	18 [R]	20 [R]	20 [R]		22 [R]
Hakodate ♥ 8225 d.	...	...	...	...	...	...	...	...	...	*0607*	...	...	...	*0659*	...	...	...	*0848*	...	*1018*	...	...	...	...
Shin **Hakodate Hokuto** ♥ d.	...	...	...	...	...	...	...	...	...	0639	...	...	...	0738	...	...	...	0935	...	1053	...	...	...	...
Shin **Aomori** d.	...	...	0617	...	...	...	0649	...	...	0743	...	...	...	0837	...	0952	...	1039	...	1152	...	1239	...	1315
Hachinohe d.	...	...	0641	...	...	...	0717	...	...	0811	...	...	...	0905	...	1016	...	1107	...	1216	...	1307	...	1339
Akita d.	...	...	|	...	0608	...	|	...	0716	|	...	...	0811	|	0912	|	1007	|	1107	|	1213	|	...	|
Omagari d.	...	...	|	...	0640	...	|	...	0748	|	...	...	0843	|	0950	|	1039	|	1140	|	1246	|	...	|
Kakunodate d.	...	...	|	...	|	...	|	...	0758	|	...	...	0856	|	1000	|	1054	|	1156	|	1257	|	...	|
Tazawako d.	...	...	|	...	|	...	|	...	0812	|	...	...	0909	|	1013	|	1108	|	1212	|	1311	|	...	|
Morioka d.	...	0610	0711	0727	0736	0736	0801	0810	0850	0850	...	0907	0950	0950	1050	1050	1150	1150	1250	1250	1350	1350	...	1416
Sendai (Honshu) d.	0636	0721	0752	0844	0816	0816	0856	0921	0930	0930	...	1021	1030	1030	1130	1130	1230	1230	1330	1330	1430	1430	...	1457
Omiya 8010 8015 d.	0743	0831	0900	0951	0925	0925	1007	1030	1039	1039	...	1131	1139	1139	1239	1239	1339	1339	1438	1439	1539	1539	...	1607
Tokyo Ueno 8010 8015 d.	|	0851	|	1011	|	|	1027	1050	1059	1059	...	1151	1159	1159	1259	1259	1359	1359	1458	1459	1559	1559	...	1627
Tokyo 8010 8015 a.	0807	0856	0923	1016	0947	0947	1032	1056	1104	1104	...	1156	1204	1204	1304	1304	1404	1404	1504	1504	1604	1604	...	1632

•	24 [R]	24 [R]	26 [R]	28 [R]	28 [R]	110 [R]	30 [R]	30 [R]	112 [R]	32 [R]	32 [R]	34 [R]	34 [R]	36 [R]	36 [R]	38 [R]	40 [R]	40 [R]	42 [R]	42 [R]	96 [R]	96 [R]	98 [R]	100 [R]
Hakodate ♥ 8225 d.	...	*1202*	...	...	*1302*	...	...	*1409*	...	...	...	...	*1545*	...	...	*1654*	...	...	...	*1808*	...	*1906*	*2006*	*2117*
Shin **Hakodate Hokuto** ♥ d.	...	1248	...	...	1339	...	...	1448	...	...	...	...	1620	...	...	1725	...	...	...	1840	...	1941	2043	2157a
Shin **Aomori** d.	...	1352	...	...	1438	...	...	1552	...	...	1638	...	1722	...	1744	1824	...	1838	...	1944	...	2040	2147	2305a
Hachinohe d.	...	1416	...	...	1506	...	...	1616	...	...	1706	...	|	...	1812	|	...	1906	...	2012	...	2108	2215	...
Akita d.	1306	|	...	1414	|	...	1506	|	...	1612	|	1634	|	1710	|	|	1816	|	1910	|	2014	|	|	...
Omagari d.	1339	|	...	1447	|	...	1539	|	...	1647	|	1708	|	1743	|	|	1848	|	1943	|	2047	|	|	...
Kakunodate d.	1350	|	...	1458	|	...	1551	|	...	1658	|	1718	|	1754	|	|	1858	|	1953	|	2057	|	|	...
Tazawako d.	1408	|	...	1512	|	...	1608	|	...	1712	|	1734	|	1810	|	|	1912	|	2009	|	2111	|	|	...
Morioka d.	1450	1450	...	1550	1550	1607	1650	1650	1707	1750	1750	1815	1815	1850	1850	1913	1950	1950	2050	2050	2151	2151	2248	...
Sendai (Honshu) d.	1530	1530	1557	1630	1630	1721	1730	1730	1821	1830	1830	1857	1857	1930	1930	1953	2030	2030	2130	2130	2301	2301	...	...
Omiya 8010 8015 d.	1639	1639	1707	1739	1739	1830	1839	1839	1930	1939	1939	2007	2007	2039	2039	2100	2139	2139	2239	2239	...	...	...	...
Tokyo Ueno 8010 8015 d.	1659	1659	1727	1759	1759	1850	1859	1859	1950	1959	1959	2027	2027	2059	2059	|	2159	2159	2259	2259	...	...	...	...
Tokyo 8010 8015 a.	1704	1704	1732	1804	1804	1856	1904	1904	1956	2004	2004	2032	2032	2104	2104	2123	2204	2204	2304	2304	...	...	...	...

On ⑦ from June 9 until July 28 no service between Shin Aomori and Shin Hakodate Hokuto.

– Services to/from Hakodate change at Shin Hakodate Hokuto. NOT [R]. For non-connecting services see Table **8225**.

me trains run on a different schedule on ©.

BEYOND E…

8105

JR Kyushu

km																		
		0731	0802	0822	0901	…	0921	0957										
		…	0800	0833	0857	0917	0948	…	1009	1039	…	1019	1057	…	1119	1157		
		0833	…	0922	0951	1014	1034	1057	…	1128	1150	…	1109	1139	…	1209	1239	1219
0	Hakata	0749	0816	0844	0910	0932	1007	1024	1044	1106	1110	1138	1200	1206	1236	1258	1304	1336 1359 1406 143…
67	Koku…	0604	0912	…	1028	…	1105	…	1208	…	…	1309	…	1225	1249	…	1327	1349 … 1309
186	Be…	0601	0832	0916	1019	…	1136	…	1210	…	1310	…	…	1413	1408	…	1512	… 1428
198	O… a.	0633	0814	0842	0930	1030	…	1147	…	1220	…	1318	…	1422	1515	1524	1624	1634 … 1612 1723 1732
322																		
40…																		

Hakata d.	1257	…	1319	1357	…	1419	1457	…	1519	1557	…	1619	1657	…	1719	1757	…	1819	1857	1919	1959	2019	2103	2205	230…			
Kokura d.	1339	…	1409	1439	…	1509	1541	…	1608	1641	…	1709	1741	…	1808	1841	…	1911	1941	2012	2047	2110	2153	2304	…			
Beppu d.	1449	…	1525	1550	…	1627	1650	…	1726	1752	…	1827	1852	…	1925	1953	…	2035	2052	2136	2205	2228	2314	…				
Oita d.	1500	1504	1535	1600	1605	1636	1700	1706	1736	1802	1805	1837	1904	…	1935	200…	2018	2041	2102	2145	2216	2238	…					
Nobeoka d.	…	1731	…	…	1818	…	…	1910	…	…	2017	…	…	2127	…	…	2227	…	…	…	…	…	…					
Miyazaki d.	…	1837	…	…	1925	…	…	2017	…	…	2128	…	…	2236	…	…	2334	…	…	…	…	…	…					
Miyazaki Airport a.	…	1846	…	…	1937	…	…	…	…	…	…	…	…	…	…	…	…	…	…	…	…	…	…					

Miyazaki Airport d.	…	- -	…	…	…	…	…	…	…	…	…	…	…	…	…	…	…	…	…	…	…	1020	…	…	1126	…
Miyazaki d.	…	- -	…	…	…	…	…	…	0555	…	…	0658	…	…	0806	…	…	…	0925	…	…	1031	…	…	1136	…
Nobeoka d.	…	…	…	…	…	…	…	…	0706	…	…	0806	…	…	0910	…	…	…	1036	…	…	…	…	…	…	…
Oita d.	…	0518	0556	0640	0714	0746	0810	0841	0909	0911	0939	1007	1011	1045	1108	1110	1145	1210	1238	1245	1311	1340	1345	1411	1439	144…
Beppu d.	…	0527	0604	0648	0722	0755	0819	0851	…	0919	0947	…	1020	1053	…	1119	1154	1218	…	1253	1320	…	1353	1420	…	145…
Kokura d.	0613	0650	0731	0810	0844	0919	0939	1005	…	1041	1105	…	1141	1205	…	1241	1305	1341	…	1405	1441	…	1505	1539	…	160…
Hakata a.	0716a	0749a	0830b	0856a	0940a	1003	1022c	1047e	…	1128	1148	…	1228	1247	…	1328	1346	1428	…	1446	1528	…	1547	1628	…	164…

Miyazaki Airport d.	…	1215	…	…	1320	…	…	1422	…	…	1525	…	1623	…	…	1719	1752	…	1825	1930	2023	…	…			
Miyazaki d.	…	1229	…	…	1331	…	…	1433	…	…	1535	…	1637	…	…	1731	1803	…	1842	1943	2040	…	2119			
Nobeoka d.	…	1338	…	…	1437	…	…	1539	…	…	1641	…	1744	…	…	1844	1918	…	1948	2054	2146	…	2130			
Oita d.	1511	1542	1545	1610	1641	1645	1710	1741	1744	1811	1842	1911	1939	1942	2012	2055	…	2143	…	…	…	…	2238		2235	234…
Beppu d.	1520	…	1553	1618	…	1653	1718	…	1753	1820	1851	1919	…	1950	2020	2104	…	2151	…	…	…	…	…		2348	005…
Kokura d.	1639	…	1705	1739	…	1805	1839	…	1905	1943	2009	2041	…	2113	2139	2231	…	2311	…	…	…	…	…	2255	…	
Hakata a.	1728	…	1749	1830	…	1848	1930	…	1948	2030	2057	2128	…	2201	2227	2325	…	2359	…	…	…	…	…	2305	…	

a – Arrival time 2–3 minutes earlier on Ⓒ. b – Arrival time 0819 on Ⓒ. c – Arrival time 1023 on Ⓒ. e – Arrival time 1050 on Ⓒ.

8107 MIYAZAKI - KAGOSHIMA

JR Kyushu

km											
0	Miyazaki d.	0555	0716	0815	0920	1015	1226	1416	1621	1736	1855
79	Kirishima-Jingu d.	0717	0836	0936	1038	1137	1343	1538	1740	1856	2022
95	Hayato d.	0733	0853	0953	1056	1154	1400	1553	1758	1913	2041
123	Kagoshima d.	0803	0922	1020	1123	1221	1424	1619	1826	1938	2110
126	Kagoshima Chuo a.	0808	0926	1025	1127	1226	1428	1623	1831	1943	2115

Kagoshima Chuo d.	0559	0737	0849	0959	1150	1419	1618	1717	1828	202…
Kagoshima d.	0604	0741	0853	1003	1154	1424	1622	1722	1832	202…
Hayato d.	0634	0819	0921	1032	1222	1448	1649	1749	1905	205…
Kirishima-Jingu d.	0652	0836	0936	1050	1239	1505	1706	1806	1921	21…
Miyazaki a.	0823	1000	1056	1209	1402	1620	1826	1935	2038	22…

8110 HAKATA - SASEBO and NAGASAKI

JR Kyushu

km						Ⓐ		A			A			A			A				A		A	
0	Hakata d.	0555	0633	0717	0729	0753	0814	0834	0857	0915	0931	0955	1015	1032	1055	1115	1131	1155	1231	1255	1331	1355	1431	…
29	Tosu d.	0618	0655	0740	0758	0816	0838	0857	0917	0938	0956	1016	1038	1058	1115	1139	1158	1215	1258	1315	1358	1415	1458	…
31	Shin Tosu d.	0622	0659	0744	0802	0820	0842	0901	0921	0942	1000	1020	1042	1102	1121	1143	1202	1219	1302	1320	1402	1429	1502	…
54	Saga d.	0636	0712	0801	0815	0833	0856	0915	0934	0956	1016	1033	1056	1117	1134	1157	1217	1233	1317	1333	1416	1433	1516	…
108	Haiki d.	|	|	|	0916	|	…	1015	|	|	1114	|	|	1215	|	|	1315	|	1415	|	1515	|	1617	…
117	Sasebo a.	|	|	|	0927	|	…	1026	|	|	1125	|	|	1225	|	|	1325	|	1426	|	1526	|	1628	…
154	Nagasaki a.	0801	0835	0927	…	0950	…	…	1050	1124	…	1150	1219	…	1249	1324	…	1350	…	1450	…	1550	…	…

Hakata d.	1455	1515	1531	1555	1615	1631	1655	1715	1731	1755	1815	1833	1855	1915	1933	1955	2033	2100	2133	…	2211	2234	2334
Tosu d.	1515	1538	1558	1615	1638	1658	1716	1739	1758	1816	1837	1858	1917	1942	1957	2017	2058	2121	2157	…	2230	2256	2357
Shin Tosu d.	1519	1542	1602	1619	1642	1702	1720	1743	1802	1820	1842	1902	1921	1946	2001	2022	2102	2126	2202	…	2235	2300	0001
Saga d.	1533	1556	1617	1633	1656	1716	1734	1756	1816	1834	1858	1916	1935	2000	2017	2037	2116	2139	2218	…	2248	2313	0015
Haiki d.	|	|	1715	|	|	1816	|	|	1916	|	|	2012	|	|	2123	|	2215	|	2315	…	|	0007	…
Sasebo a.	|	|	1724	|	|	1825	|	|	1925	|	|	2023	|	|	2132	|	2225	|	2324	…	|	0016	…
Nagasaki a.	1650	1723	…	1755	1825	…	1852	1925	…	1952	2026	…	2054	2123	…	2157	…	2257	…	…	2359	…	…

		Ⓒ	Ⓐ	Ⓒ	Ⓐ	Ⓒ	Ⓐ	Ⓐ	Ⓒ	Ⓐ	Ⓒ	Ⓐ		Ⓒ		Ⓐ							A		
Nagasaki d.	…	…	…	0558	0558	…	…	…	0625	0625	…	…	0728	…	…	…	0828	…	0846	0920	…	0947	1020	…	1047	11…
Sasebo d.	…	…	…	|	|	0621	0621	…	|	|	0708	0708	|	…	0806	…	|	0847	|	|	0942	|	|	1040	|	
Haiki d.	…	…	…	|	|	0636	0636	…	|	|	0723	0723	|	…	0821	…	|	0902	|	|	0958	|	|	1059	|	
Saga d.	0625	0705	0705	0717	0717	0729	0729	0737	0756	0756	0819	0819	0845	0859	0912	0925	0945	0953	1013	1034	1053	1113	1136	1153	1213	12…
Shin Tosu d.	0640	0717	0717	0730	0730	0743	0743	0753	0809	0809	0834	0834	0858	0914	0925	0939	0958	1006	1026	1047	1107	1126	1149	1206	1226	12…
Tosu d.	0644	0721	0721	0734	0734	0747	0747	0803	0813	0813	0839	0839	0902	0918	0932	0943	1002	1011	1031	1052	1111	1130	1152	1211	1230	12…
Hakata a.	0707	0743	0747	0756	0758	0809	0815	0824	0830	0836	0903	0906	0920	0938	0953	1005	1021	1034	1053	1113	1134	1152	1213	1234	1253	13…

	A		A				A			A			A												
Nagasaki d.	…	1220	…	1320	…	1420	…	1446	1520	…	1547	1620	…	1646	1720	…	1751	1818	…	1853	1918	…	1956	2050	…	21…
Sasebo d.	1142	|	1242	|	1342	|	1442	|	|	1544	|	|	1642	|	|	1743	|	|	1845	|	|	1952	|	|	2043	
Haiki d.	1159	|	1259	|	1400	|	1500	|	|	1602	|	|	1700	|	|	1800	|	|	1901	|	|	2008	|	|	2100	
Saga d.	1252	1334	1353	1435	1452	1535	1553	1612	1635	1654	1713	1736	1753	1814	1836	1853	1914	1937	1954	2016	2039	2057	2117	2213	2149	23…
Shin Tosu d.	1306	1347	1406	1447	1506	1547	1608	1626	1647	1707	1426	1749	1807	1827	1848	1907	1926	1949	2008	2030	2052	2110	2130	2226	2203	23…
Tosu d.	1311	1351	1411	1452	1512	1552	1613	1630	1652	1712	1730	1753	1812	1831	1852	1912	1931	1953	2013	2035	2056	2114	2134	2229	2205	23…
Hakata a.	1334	1412	1434	1513	1534	1613	1636	1651	1713	1734	1753	1814	1835	1852	1914	1935	1952	2014	2038	2056	2116	2136	2158	2251	2227	23…

km				Ⓒ		Ⓒ						
	Hakata ⊙ d.	0834	0931	1032	*1032*	1131	*1131*	*1231*	1331	1431	*1531*	…
0	Haiki d.	1016	1117	1213	1224	1313	1325	1424	1516	1619	1739	…
14	Huis Ten Bosch a.	1022	1122	1219	1229	1319	1331	1429	1521	1624	1744	…

				Ⓒ		Ⓒ		Ⓒ				Ⓒ	
Huis Ten Bosch d.	1043	1145	1234	1246	1336	1347	1434	1446	1547	1646	1723	1747	20…
Haiki a.	1059	1159	1239	1259	1342	1400	1440	1500	1602	1700	1728	1800	20…
Hakata ⊙ a.	1234	1334	*1434*	1434	*1534*	1534	*1636*	1636	1734	1835	*1935*	1935	2…

A – Conveys (12) Hakata - Haiki - Huis Ten Bosch and v.v. See panel below main table for timings. ⊙ – See main table for intermediate timings Hakata - Haiki and v.v.

8115 TAKAMATSU - TOKUSHIMA

JR Shikoku

km									a											a			
0	Takamatsu d.	0612	0705	0824	0911	1010	…	1106	1206	1312	…	1412	1512	1612	…	1715	1813	…	1917	2005	2121	…	2224
10	Yashima d.	0622	0714	0833	0921	1022	…	1117	|	1323	…	1423	1522	1622	…	1725	1822	…	1927	2016	2131	…	2234
64	Ikenotani d.	|	0804	0924	1009	1116	…	1206	|	1407	…	|	1612	|	…	1814	|	…	2017	2106	2225	…	|
75	Tokushima a.	0731	0814	0936	1018	1125	…	1215	1304	1415	…	1520	1620	1716	…	1823	1924	…	2027	2115	2233	…	2334

				b											b							
Tokushima d.	0541	0700	…	0823	0923	…	1028	1131	1224	…	1325	1427	…	1528	1646	1728	…	1830	1932	2034	…	2202
Ikenotani d.	0552	0711	…	0834	0932	…	|	1141	1233	…	|	1436	…	1537	|	1737	…	1838	|	|	…	2211
Yashima d.	0645	0804	…	0920	1022	…	|	|	1322	…	1423	1522	…	1622	|	1822	…	1927	2029	2131	…	2310
Takamatsu a.	0654	0813	…	0931	1031	…	1137	1234	1331	…	1433	1531	…	1632	1744	1832	…	1936	2038	2140	…	2320

a – From Okayama (depart 1 hour earlier). b – To Okayama (arrive 1 hour later).

8118 TOKUSHIMA - AWA IKEDA

JR Shikoku

km		LEX	LEX	A	LEX		LEX		LEX	LEX		LEX	
0	Tokushima d.	0647	0901	1145	1201	1317	1501	1627	1757	1905	1927	2017	2106
74	Awa Ikeda a.	0810	1015	1346	1316	1515	1616	1838	1916	2022	2117	2134	2253

	LEX	B	LEX		LEX		LEX		LEX	LEX		
Awa Ikeda d.	0647	0652	0833	0948	1027	1237	1333	1539	1632	1950	2009	2…
Tokushima a.	0802	0852	0947	1128	1138	1422	1445	1720	1745	2104	2159	2…

A – Additional trips: 0539, 0609, 0721, 0950, 1433, 1532, 1759, 2238. B – Additional trips: 0547, 0622, 0753, 1126, 1429, 1654, 1747, 1847Ⓐ.

Shikoku — UWAJIMA - KUBOKAWA — 8121

km											
0	**Uwajima** ‡ d.	...	0604	0939	1139	1535	1730	1835	...	...	...
2	**Kubokawa** ‡ a.	...	0809	1145	1422	1750	1938	2043	...	...	...

Kubokawa ‡ d.	0622	0940	1319	1501	1658	1843	...	...	...	...
Uwajima ‡ d.	0828	1223	1534	1724	1915	2047	...	...	...	...

Japan Rail Pass holders must pay a supplement to travel between these stations.

Shikoku — OKAYAMA and TAKAMATSU - MATSYUAMA and UWAJIMA — 8125

km																									
'2	**Okayama** d.	...	...	...	...	...	...	...	0722	...	...	0832	...	...	0925	...	...	1035	...	...	1135	...	...	1235	...
0	**Takamatsu** d.	...	...	...	0517	...	0600	...	|	0737	...	|	0845	...	|	0942	...	|	1047	...	|	1150	...	|	1250
'6	Utazu d.	...	...	...	|	...	0618	...	0801	0801	...	0913	0913	...	1006	1006	...	1113	1113	...	1213	1213	...	1314	1314
4	Imabari d.	...	...	0630	0711	...	0756	...	0930	0930	...	1041	1041	...	1136	1136	...	1241	1241	...	1339	1339	...	1443	1443
'4	**Matsuyama** a.	0548	0648	0711	0758	0809	0836	0903	1006	1006	1015	1115	1115	1126	1210	1210	1224	1315	1315	1324	1413	1413	1428	1517	1517
'1	**Uwajima** a.	0713	0813	...	...	0930	...	1026	...	...	1133	...	...	1247	...	...	1350	...	...	1446	...	...	1551	...	...

ayama d.	...	1335	...	...	1435	...	...	1535	...	...	1635	...	...	1735	...	1835	...	...	1935	...	...	2039	...	2200	...
akamatsu d.	...	|	1350	...	|	1450	...	|	1550	...	|	1650	...	|	1750	|	1858	...	|	1952	...	|	2059	|	2220
zu d.	...	1414	1414	...	1515	1515	...	1615	1615	...	1715	1715	...	1809	1813	1910	1917	...	2009	2012	...	2115	2118	2236	2239
bari d.	...	1541	1541	...	1644	1644	...	1745	1745	...	1847	1847	...	1948	1948	2053	2053	...	2157	2157	...	2256	2256	0021	0021
suyama a.	1527	1616	1616	1632	1724	1724	1730	1826	1826	1843	1923	1923	1936	2028	2028	2132	2132	2149	2237	2237	2248	2333	2333	0056	0056
ajima a.	1650	...	...	1751	...	...	1856	...	...	2009	...	...	2057	*2205*	*2205*	...	...	2308	...	...	0008	...	...	...	...

ajima d.	...	...	...	...	...	...	0533	...	...	0635	0635	0738	...	...	0840	...	...	0950	...	...	1044	...	...	1150	...
suyama d.	...	0505	0505	...	0613	0613	0658	0720	0720	0810	0810	0903	0915	0915	1008	1021	1021	1118	1123	1123	1212	1221	1221	1316	...
bari d.	...	0541	0541	...	0650	0650	...	0756	0756	0847	0847	...	0957	0957	...	1059	1059	...	1202	1202	...	1259	1259	...	...
zu d.	...	0715	0714	0753	0827	0826	...	0926	0925	1019	1020	...	1134	1133	...	1234	1233	...	1335	1334	...	1435	1434	...	...
akamatsu a.	...	|	0736	0811	|	0844	...	|	0946	1039	|	...	|	1154	...	|	1254	...	|	1355	...	|	1455	...	...
yama a.	...	0751	...	...	0900	...	...	0959	...	...	1058	...	1210	...	...	1310	...	...	1410	...	...	1511	...	...	...

ajima d.	...	...	1255	...	...	1359	...	...	1456	...	...	1603	...	...	1709	...	...	1808	...	1907	...	2016	...	2116	...
suyama d.	1326	1326	1414	1423	1423	1520	1528	1528	1618	1627	1627	1727	1737	1737	1835	1839	1839	1928	1932	2030	2036	2136	2140	2239	2306
bari d.	1405	1405	...	1501	1501	...	1606	1606	...	1704	1704	...	1813	1813	...	1919	1919	...	2008	...	2113	...	2217	...	2344
zu d.	1535	1534	...	1634	1635	...	1735	1736	...	1836	1837	...	1938	1939	...	2053	2052	...	|	...	|	...	2345	...	...
akamatsu a.	|	1554	...	1654	|	...	1757	|	...	1854	|	...	1956	|	...	|	2111	...	2155	...	2256	...	0003	...	...
yama a.	1611	...	...	...	1711	...	...	1811	...	...	1911	...	...	2012	...	2129	...	...	...	...	...	...	...	...	...

Shikoku — OKAYAMA and TAKAMATSU - KOCHI - NAKAMURA — 8127

km																											
0	**Okayama** d.	...	...	0708	...	...	0852	...	1005	1105	...	1205	1305	...	1405	1505	1605	...	1705	...	...	1805	1905	...	2005	...	2139
	Takamatsu d.	0604	0723	|	...	0825	|	...	|	|	...	|	|	...	|	|	|	...	|	...	1828	|	|	...	|	2028	|
7	Awa Ikeda d.	0706	0829	0829	...	0924	1020	...	1122	1234	...	1332	1425	...	1523	1630	1734	...	1834	...	1935	1935	2029	...	2138	2138	2259
9	**Kochi** a.	0818	0939	0939	0953	1037	1130	1139	1229	1341	1349	1442	1539	1543	1639	1741	1848	1855	1943	1953	2050	2050	2146	2153	2251	2251	0006
1	Kubokawa ‡ d.	0927	...	...	1057	...	...	1249	...	...	1454	...	...	1651	*1806*	...	...	2010	...	2104	...	...	...	2300	...	...	...
4	**Nakamura** ‡ a.	1004	...	...	1132	...	...	1324	...	...	1531	...	...	1727	*1846*	...	...	2049	...	2139	...	...	...	2336	...	...	...

km																											
	Nakamura ‡ d.	...	...	...	...	0608	0700	...	...	0924	...	...	1111	...	...	1324	...	...	1510	...	...	1647	...	1745	...	...	1934
	Kubokawa ‡ d.	...	...	...	...	0648	0741	...	...	1004	...	...	1157	...	...	1402	...	...	1551	...	...	1728	...	1824	...	...	2012
0	**Kochi** d.	0451	0600	0700	0700	0801	0904	0913	1013	1106	1113	1213	1302	1313	1413	1504	1513	1613	1659	1713	1713	1834	1836	1928	1931	1931	2120
2	Awa Ikeda d.	0600	0709	0813	0813	0907	...	1020	1122	...	1223	1322	...	1424	1523	...	1620	1719	...	1824	1824	...	1946	...	2040	2040	2228
3	**Takamatsu** a.	0702	|	0921	|	|	...	|	|	...	|	|	...	|	|	...	|	|	...	|	1925	...	|	...	2142	|	2326
	Okayama a.	...	0838	...	0938	1033	...	1140	1240	...	1340	1441	...	1541	1641	...	1741	1847	...	1941	...	...	2111	...	...	2157	...

West — TOTTORI and OKAYAMA - IZUMOSHI - YAMAGUCHI — 8130

Tottori d.	...	0704	...	0824	...	0944	...	...	1140	...	...	1337	...	...	1508	...	...	1742	...	1842	...	...	2049	...	...
Kurayoshi d.	...	0733	...	0858	...	1012	...	...	1209	...	...	1408	...	...	1539	...	...	1811	...	1913	...	...	2122	...	...
Okayama d.	...	|	0705	|	0804	|	0904	1004	|	1104	1204	|	1304	1404	|	1504	1604	|	1704	|	1804	1904	|	2005	2140
Niimi d.	...	|	0810	|	0908	|	1011	1107	|	1207	1312	|	1413	1508	|	1610	1707	|	1807	|	1907	2008	|	2111	2243
Yonago d.	0550	0811	0917	0930	1016	1048	1118	121/	1241	1318	1418	1439	1520	1620	1613	1723	1823	1849	1921	1947	2027	2122	2156	2220	2350
Matsue d.	0613	0835	0942	...	1040	1110	1141	1241	1303	1340	1444	1503	1544	1644	1637	1745	1847	1916	1946	...	2050	2145	...	2243	0013
Izumoshi d.	0639	0904	1010	...	1104	1136	1209	1307	1326	1408	1510	1528	1609	1716	1707	1813	1920	1942	2018	...	2115	2210	...	2308	0037
Hamada d.	0758	1016	...	...	...	1250	...	...	1438	▬	...	1641	...	...	1824	...	...	2051	...	...	...	...	...	...	...
Masuda d.	0840	1051	...	...	...	1324	...	...	1514	1615	...	1718	...	...	1902	...	...	2122	...	...	...	...	...	...	...
Tsuwano d.	0911	*1206*	...	...	...	1355	...	...	...	1655	...	1750	...	...	...	...	...	...	...	...	...	...	...	...	...
Yamaguchi a.	1001	*1336*	...	...	...	1443	...	...	...	1816	...	1838	...	...	...	...	...	...	...	...	...	...	...	...	...
Shin **Yamaguchi** a.	1015	*1359*	...	...	...	1457	...	...	...	1841	...	1851	...	...	...	...	...	...	...	...	...	...	...	...	...

Shin **Yamaguchi** d.	...	...	...	...	...	...	...	...	...	...	...	...	0852	...	*0913*	...	...	...	1253	...	*1333*	...	...	1712	...
Yamaguchi d.	...	...	...	...	...	...	...	...	...	...	...	...	0908	...	0947	...	...	...	1307	...	1358	...	...	1727	...
Tsuwano d.	...	...	...	...	...	...	...	...	...	...	...	...	0958	...	1109	...	...	...	1355	...	1517	...	...	1815	...
Masuda d.	...	...	...	...	...	0550	...	0700	...	...	...	...	1031	...	1150	1217	...	...	1430	...	1558	1607	...	1851	...
Hamada d.	...	...	...	...	...	0621	...	0736	...	...	...	...	1103	...	▬	1250	...	...	1503	...	▬	1640	...	1924	...
Izumoshi d.	0442	0530	...	0627	0722	0732	0831	0854	0934	1032	...	1134	1210	1234	1331	1359	1433	1530	1614	1630	1717	1748	1827	2035	...
Matsue d.	0507	0555	...	0658	0751	0758	0857	0924	1002	1057	...	1201	1235	1301	1400	1424	1459	1558	1645	1659	1743	1816	1907	2104	...
Yonago d.	0532	0621	0658	0723	0819	0825	0922	0950	1026	1125	1216	1226	1303	1325	1428	1450	1527	1625	1711	1726	1815	1841	1923	2127	2040
Niimi d.	0640	0729	|	0834	0934	|	1036	|	1136	1235	|	1337	...	1438	1537	|	1637	1737	|	1837	1925	|	2033	...	|
Okayama a.	0741	0834	|	0938	1035	|	1138	|	1238	1338	|	1438	...	1539	1638	|	1738	1838	|	1938	2024	|	2136	...	|
Kurayoshi d.	...	...	0733	...	...	0858	...	1025	...	...	1255	...	...	...	...	1521	...	...	1742	...	...	1914	...	...	2112
Tottori a.	...	...	0803	...	...	0927	...	1058	...	...	1324	...	...	...	...	1552	...	...	1816	...	...	1942	...	...	2140

West — KYOTO - KURAYOSHI — 8135

	1	3	5	7		9	11	13	
Kyoto d.	0706	0850	1054	1252	...	1452	1656	1935	...
Shin Osaka d.	0730	0915	1118	1316	...	1516	1719	2000	...
Osaka d.	0736	0925	1124	1324	...	1524	1726	2006	...
Himeji d.	0836	1022	1220	1421	...	1620	1822	2108	...
Kamigori ‡ d.	0902	1048	1244	1444	...	1644	1845	2131	...
Chizu ‡ d.	0944	1130	1323	1524	...	1724	1931	2214	...
Tottori d.	1013	1159	1353	1553	...	1752	2002	2242	...
Kurayoshi a.	1043	1230	1420	1620	...	...	2033	...	...

	2	4	6	8	10		12	14	
Kurayoshi d.	0608	0812	1013	1219	1423	...	1622	*1742*	...
Tottori d.	0639	0853	1046	1254	1454	...	1654	1840	...
Chizu ‡ d.	0708	0921	1115	1323	1523	...	1724	1908	...
Kamigori ‡ d.	0751	1003	1202	1401	1601	...	1804	1947	...
Himeji d.	0814	1025	1225	1424	1624	...	1828	2009	...
Osaka d.	0924	1120	1321	1521	1719	...	1936	2107	...
Shin Osaka d.	0929	1124	1326	1526	1724	...	1942	2113	...
Kyoto a.	0953	1147	1348	1548	1748	...	2006	2137	...

West — OKAYAMA - TOTTORI — 8140

Okayama d.	0647	0913	1105	1343	1724	1946	...	...	...
Kamigori ‡ d.	0725	0950	1142	1419	1803	2022	...	...	...
Chizu ‡ d.	0811	1035	1226	1501	1845	2104	...	...	...
Tottori a.	0838	1104	1253	1533	1917	2131	...	...	...

Tottori d.	0705	1002	1400	1621	1857	2035	...	...	...
Chizu ‡ d.	0734	1033	1427	1652	1932	2103	...	...	...
Kamigori ‡ d.	0820	1115	1511	1733	2014	2148	...	...	...
Okayama a.	0857	1148	1545	1811	2048	2222	...	...	...

Japan Rail Pass holders must pay a supplement to travel between these stations.

8145 KYOTO and OSAKA - KINOSAKI

JR We

km																								
0	**Kyoto** d.	0732	0836	0924	1025	1125	...	1225	1325	...	1425	1525	...	1625	1728	...	1828	1928	...	2037	...	2137	...	..
76	Ayabe d.	0839	0946	1031	1136	1231	...	1340	1431	...	1535	1631	...	1735	1843	...	1949	2050	...	2149	...	2243	...	..
89	Fukuchiyama d.	0849	0954	1040	1145	1244	...	1349	1444	...	1544	1640	...	1743	1856	...	1958	2059	...	2159	...	2252	...	..
148	Toyooka d.	0943	...	...	...	1340	...	...	1541	...	...	...	...	...	1957	...	...	...	...	...	...	...	...	..
158	**Kinosaki** Onsen a.	0952	...	...	...	1349	...	...	1550	...	...	...	...	...	...	...	...	...	...	...	...	...	...	..
	Kinosaki Onsen d.	...	...	...	...	...	...	...	...	...	1039	...	...	1232	...	...	...	...	...	1631	...	...	...	..
	Toyooka d.	...	...	...	...	0742	...	...	...	...	1049	...	...	1242	...	...	...	...	...	1641	...	...	...	..
	Fukuchiyama d.	...	0602	0657	0743	0838	...	0945	1044	...	1145	1244	...	1346	1444	...	1543	1644	...	1749	1854	...	2003	..
	Ayabe d.	...	0612	0712	0753	0855	...	0955	1100	...	1156	1300	...	1356	1459	...	1556	1659	...	1759	1910	...	2013	..
	Kyoto a.	...	0718	0821	0903	1007	...	1107	1207	...	1307	1407	...	1507	1607	...	1707	1808	...	1909	2021	...	2119	..

km																								
0	Shin **Osaka** d.	0808	...	0904	1005	...	1105	...	1205	1305	...	1405	...	1505	1705	...	1801	...	1906	2006	...	2105	...	22
4	**Osaka** d.	0814	...	0910	1012	...	1111	...	1211	1311	...	1411	...	1511	1711	...	1811	...	1912	2012	...	2112	...	22
118	Fukuchiyama d.	0955	...	1046	1146	...	1242	...	1350	1442	...	1546	...	1647	1854	...	2002	...	2058	2156	...	2259	...	23
178	Toyooka d.	1049	...	1143	1242	...	...	...	1445	...	...	1641	...	1751	...	...	2059	...	...	...	...	...	...	..
188	**Kinosaki** Onsen a.	1058	...	1152	1250	...	...	...	1454	...	...	1650	...	1800	...	...	...	...	...	...	...	...	...	..
	Kinosaki Onsen d.	...	...	...	...	...	...	...	...	...	0933	...	1133	...	1329	...	1435	...	1530	...	...	1741	1853	..
	Toyooka d.	...	...	...	...	...	...	...	...	...	0943	...	1143	...	1339	...	1445	...	1540	...	...	1752	1903	..
	Fukuchiyama d.	...	0549	0652	...	0745	0840	...	0950	...	1046	...	1246	1344	1442	...	1545	...	1646	...	1759	1857	2001	..
	Osaka a.	...	0735	0839	...	0926	1021	...	1123	...	1223	...	1424	1524	1622	...	1722	...	1822	...	1937	2037	2136	..
	Shin **Osaka** a.	...	0741	0846	...	0932	1027	...	1129	...	1229	...	1429	1530	1628	...	1727	...	1828	...	1944	2044	2144	..

8150 OSAKA and NAGOYA - KANAZAWA

JR We

km																									
				Ⓐ							a								b						
0	**Osaka** d.	...	...	...	...	0630	0700	...	0740	...	0758	0810	0840	...	...	0912	0942	...	1012	1042	...	1142	...	1212	12
4	Shin **Osaka** d.	...	...	...	...	0634	0704	...	0744	...	0803	0814	0844	...	...	0917	0946	...	1016	1046	...	1146	...	1216	12
43	Kyoto d.	...	...	...	...	0659	0729	...	0810	...	0831	0841	0909	...	...	0942	1009	...	1040	1110	...	1210	...	1240	13
	Nagoya 8175 d.	...	...	...	...	|	|	...	|	0750	|	|	|	...	0850	|	|	0948	|	|	...	|	1148	|	
	Gifu 8170 d.	...	...	...	...	|	|	...	|	0810	0956	|	|	...	0911	|	|	1012	|	|	...	|	1212	|	
	Maibara d.	...	...	...	...	|	|	0809	|	0857	0922↑	|	|	...	0956	|	|	1056	|	|	1156	|	1256	|	
137	Tsuruga d.	...	...	0643	...	0758	0822	0840	0902	0926	...	0938	|	...	1026	1035	1103	1125	1133	1202	1225	1303	1326	|	14
191	Fukui d.	0600	0650	0720	0743	0831	0855	0915	0938	1001	...	1013	1032	...	1101	1111	1136	1201	1208	1235	1301	1338	1401	1407	14
268	**Kanazawa** 8010 a.	0647	0737	0809	0832	0913	0938	1005	1025	1048	...	1102	1114	...	1148	1158	1220	1248	1256	1320	1348	1423	1449	1455	15

km																									
	Osaka d.	...	1342	...	1442	...	1512	1542	...	1642	...	1712	1742	...	1812	1842	...	1912	1927	...	2007	...	2054	...	..
	Shin **Osaka** d.	...	1346	...	1446	...	1516	1546	...	1646	...	1716	1746	...	1816	1846	...	1916	1931	...	2012	...	2058	...	..
	Kyoto d.	...	1410	...	1510	...	1540	1610	...	1709	...	1740	1809	...	1840	1910	...	1940	1954	...	2038	...	2121	...	..
0	**Nagoya** 8175 d.	...	|	1348	|	...	|	|	1548	|	...	|	|	1748	|	|	...	|	|	1948	|	...	|	...	..
30	Gifu 8170 d.	...	|	1412	|	...	|	|	1611	|	...	|	|	1811	|	|	...	|	|	2012	|	...	|	...	..
80	Maibara d.	1355	|	1456	|	1556	|	|	1656	|	1756	|	|	1856	|	|	1956	|	|	2056	|	...	|	2156	22
126	Tsuruga d.	1425	1502	1525	1602	1626	1632	1703	1724	1801	1825	1834	|	1926	1933	2007	2025	|	2049	2125	2133	...	2215	2226	23
180	Fukui d.	1500	1540	1601	1636	1702	1708	1740	1800	1833	1900	1909	1930	2002	2008	2039	2100	2107	2125	2201	2208	...	2248	2301	23
257	**Kanazawa** 8010 a.	1547	1630	1650	1726	1750	1755	1827	1847	1916	1949	1955	2013	2050	2056	2123	2148	2153	2209	2250	2256	...	2329	2348	00

																		b						
Kanazawa 8010 d.	0500	0535	0548	0607	0648	...	0645	0715	0748	0805	...	0815	0848	0902	0948	0954	1048	1056	1124	1148	1214	1248	1320	13
Fukui d.	0549	0620	0639	0701	0739	...	0729	0803	0838	0848	...	0905	0936	0944	1036	1042	1136	1143	1209	1236	1306	1336	1409	14
Tsuruga d.	0622	0653	0712	0737	0812	...	0801	0838	0912	|	...	0939	-1010	1016	1110	1116	1210	1216	|	1310	1342	1410	1442	15
Maibara d.	0656	|	0752	|	0844	...	|	|	0950	|	...	|	1045	|	1152	|	1245	|	|	1351	|	1445	|	15
Gifu 8170 d.	...	|	0829	|	...	...	|	|	1026	|	...	|	...	|	1227	|	...	|	|	1427	|	...	|	16
Nagoya 8175 a.	...	|	0851	|	...	...	|	|	1049	|	...	|	...	|	1248	|	...	|	|	1448	|	...	|	16
Kyoto a.	...	0751	...	0837	...	...	0855	0934	...	1011	...	1037	...	1109	...	1209	...	1309	1337	...	1437	...	1536	.
Shin **Osaka** a.	...	0817	...	0901	...	...	0918	0958	...	1035	...	1102	...	1132	...	1232	...	1332	1400	...	1500	...	1559	.
Osaka a.	...	0822	...	0906	...	...	0922	1003	...	1039	...	1106	...	1137	...	1237	...	1337	1405	...	1505	...	1604	.

											a											Ⓐ		
Kanazawa 8010 d.	1354	1420	1448	1457	1519	1548	1600	1629	1648	1655	...	1731	1748	1754	1842	1853	1905	1947	2006	2047	2108	2140	2210	23
Fukui d.	1442	1507	1535	1543	1608	1636	1644	1722	1736	1744	...	1815	1837	1841	1928	1942	1952	2034	2055	2132	2156	2231	2257	00
Tsuruga d.	1516	1541	1609	|	1642	1710	1715	1756	1810	1816	...	|	1910	1916	2001	2016	|	2108	2129	2204	...	2307	...	.
Maibara d.	|	|	1650	|	|	1744	|	|	1850	|	1823↓	|	1944	|	|	2055	|	|	2201	|	...	...	...	.
Gifu 8170 d.	|	|	1726	|	|	...	|	|	1925	|	1743	|	...	|	|	2129	|	|	...	|	...	...	...	.
Nagoya 8175 a.	|	|	1749	|	|	...	|	|	1946	|	|	|	...	|	|	2154	|	|	...	|	...	...	...	.
Kyoto a.	1609	1637	...	1707	1739	...	1809	1853	...	1909	1918	1938	...	2009	2054	...	2119	2202	...	2259	...	...	...	.
Shin **Osaka** a.	1632	1701	...	1731	1803	...	1833	1916	...	1933	1944	2003	...	2034	2118	...	2144	2226	...	2323	...	...	...	.
Osaka a.	1637	1706	...	1736	1809	...	1839	1921	...	1938	1950	2009	...	2038	2123	...	2149	2231	...	2328	...	...	...	.

a – To/from Takayama see Table **8170**. **b** – To/from Wakura Onsen see Table **8155**.

8155 KANAZAWA - WAKURA ONSEN

JR Cent

km				c							
0	**Kanazawa** 8150 d.	0856	1123	1309	...	1500	1835	2009	...	...	...
66	Nanao d.	0948	1217	1402	...	1552	1932	2107	...	...	...
71	**Wakura Onsen** a.	0954	1222	1407	...	1558	1938	2112	...	...	...

			c							
Wakura Onsen d.	0701	0841	1014	1430	...	1730	...	...	...	.
Nanao d.	0707	0848	1020	1436	...	1737	...	...	...	.
Kanazawa 8150 a.	0805	0945	1118	1543	...	1831	...	...	...	.

c – To/from Osaka see Table **8150**.

8160 OSAKA - SHINGU

JR W

km		1	3	5		7	9	11		13	15	17		19	21	23	25	27	29	31		33		3
39	Kyoto d.	*0703*	*0830*	*0900*	...	*0945*	*1045*	*1145*	...	*1245*	*1345*	*1445*	...	*1545*	*1644*	1747	...	*1844*	*1944*	*2044*	...	...	...	*22*
0	Shin **Osaka** d.	0733	0903	0932	...	1015	1115	1215	...	1315	1415	1515	...	1615	1715	1815	1845	1915	2015	2115	...	2146	...	22
14	**Osaka** Tennoji d.	0759	0921	0949	...	1033	1132	1232	...	1332	1432	1532	...	1632	1735	1835	1905	1936	2036	2136	...	2206	...	23
75	Wakayama d.	0850	1006	1035	...	1118	1216	1317	...	1418	1516	1616	...	1718	1822	1926	1953	2025	2125	2223	...	2253	...	23
181	Shirahama d.	1011	1137	1200	...	1248	1338	1445	...	1541	1640	1740	...	1845	1947	2055	...	2156	2253	...	...	...	...	
234	Kushimoto d.	1103	...	1255	...	...	...	1540	...	...	...	1835	...	...	2037	...	...	2258	...	...	...	...	...	
261	**Kii Katsuura** d.	1134	...	1333	...	...	...	1615	...	...	...	1909	...	...	2111	...	...	2334	...	...	...	...	...	
276	**Shingu** a.	1149	...	1352	...	...	...	1638	...	...	...	1926	...	...	2126	...	...	2351	...	...	...	...	...	

	2	4Ⓐ	4Ⓒ	6Ⓐ	6Ⓒ	8	10	12	14	16	18	20	22		24	26			28	30	32	34	36
Shingu d.	...	...	...	...	...	...	...	0630	...	0837	...	1028	...	...	1250	...	...	...	...	1506	...	...	1744
Kii Katsuura d.	...	...	...	...	...	...	...	0648	...	0853	...	1045	...	...	1305	...	...	...	...	1524	...	...	1802
Kushimoto d.	...	...	...	...	...	...	...	0721	...	0926	...	1120	...	...	1337	...	...	...	...	1558	...	...	1835
Shirahama d.	...	...	...	...	...	0640	0712	0821	0919	1029	1118	1227	1316	...	1434	1519	...	...	1621	1657	1726	1819	1934
Wakayama d.	0514	0603	0605	0626	0638	0809	0843	0950	1049	1150	1249	1350	1448	...	1551	1649	...	...	1747	1820	1849	1949	2102
Osaka Tennoji d.	0602	0701	0701	0725	0731	0901	0934	1034	1135	1235	1335	1435	1535	...	1635	1734	...	...	1834	1904	1934	2034	2151
Shin **Osaka** a.	0621	0721	0721	0750	0750	0922	0950	1050	1151	1250	1350	1450	1550	...	1650	1750	...	...	1850	1920	1950	2050	2206
Kyoto a.	*0658*	*0805*	*0805*	*0835*	*0829*	*0953*	*1029*	1117	*1229*	*1329*	*1429*	*1529*	*1629*	...	*1729*	*1829*	...	...	*1929*	*1953*	*2029*	*2137*	*2249*

Central — NAGOYA - SHINGU — 8165

	1	3	5	7						
Nagoya d.	0805	1001	1258	1947	...	...	...	...	...	...
Yokkaichi ‡ d.	0837	1037	1337	2019	...	...	...	...	...	...
Suzuka ‡ d.	0846	1046	1345	2027	...	...	...	...	...	...
Tsu ‡ d.	0901	1101	1400	2042	...	...	...	...	...	...
Matsusaka d.	0916	1116	1416	2057	...	...	...	...	...	...
Taki d.	0924	1129	1424	2105	...	...	...	...	...	...
Kumano Shi d.	1114	1318	1605	2254	...	...	...	...	...	...
Shingu a.	1134	1337	1624	2314	...	...	...	...	...	...
Kii Katsuura a.	1156	1358	1642	...	...	...	...	...	...	...

	2	4	6	8						
Kii Katsuura d.	...	0855	1224	1710	...	...	...	...	...	...
Shingu d.	0620	0913	1244	1731	...	...	...	...	...	...
Kumano Shi d.	0640	0933	1305	1750	...	...	...	...	...	...
Taki d.	0819	1118	1449	1931	...	...	...	...	...	...
Matsusaka d.	0826	1126	1456	1938	...	...	...	...	...	...
Tsu ‡ d.	0841	1142	1512	1954	...	...	...	...	...	...
Suzuka ‡ d.	0854	1154	1525	2006	...	...	...	...	...	...
Yokkaichi ‡ d.	0904	1205	1534	2015	...	...	...	...	...	...
Nagoya a.	0941	1241	1610	2049	...	...	...	...	...	...

Japan Rail Pass holders must pay a supplement to travel between these stations.

Central, JR West — NAGOYA - TOYAMA — 8170

			a							
Nagoya d.	0745	0843	0939	1048	1143	1248	1448	1648	1813	2018
Gifu **8150** d.	0805	0903	1011	1108	1206	1308	1508	1708	1839	2042
Mino Ota d.	0827	0923	1032	1129	1225	1328	1530	1735	1900	2102
Gero d.	0927	1015	1133	1227	1330	1425	1631	1834	2003	2203
Takayama d.	1016	1101	1229	1315	1418	1512	1719	1923	2049	2249
Hida Furukawa d.	...	1116	1242	1330	...	1526	1732	...	...	...
Toyama a.	...	1230	...	1447	...	1639	1852	...	...	...

								b		
Toyama d.	...	...	0800	0952	...	...	1302	...	...	1714
Hida Furukawa d.	...	...	0918	1107	...	1311	1419	...	...	1826
Takayama d.	0646	0800	0938	1132	1233	1329	1440	1538	1636	1847
Gero d.	0732	0846	1027	1220	1319	1414	1527	1624	1721	1929
Mino Ota d.	0827	0948	1119	1315	1418	1519	1620	1717	1819	2022
Gifu **8150** d.	0851	1012	1141	1341	1441	1541	1641	1741	1840	2043
Nagoya a.	0912	1034	1204	1404	1504	1604	1704	1806	1906	2103

(12) Nagoya – Hida Furukawa, (2) Osaka (Table **8150**) – Takayama. b – (12) Takayama – Nagoya, (2) Takayama – Osaka(Table **8150**).

East — NIIGATA - NAOETSU - JOETSUMYOKO — 8172

	LEX	*LEX*	*LEX*			*LEX*		*LEX*	Ⓡ	
Niigata d.	0737	1021	1306	...	1701	1624	...	2000	2057	...
Nagaoka d.	0828	1119	1355	...	1803	1716	...	2052	2203	...
Naoetsu d.	0925	1213	1451	...	1916	1810	...	2147	2303	...
Joetsumyoko ‡ a.	0939	1226	1506	...	1933	1823	...	2200	...	...

	Ⓡ	*LEX*			*LEX*	*LEX*	*LEX*		*LEX*	
Joetsumyoko ‡d.	...	0725	...	...	1033	1307	1727	*1824*	2024	...
Naoetsu d.	0615	0741	...	...	1047	1322	1741	1843	2037	...
Nagaoka d.	0722	0835	...	...	1140	1415	1834	1955	2131	...
Niigata a.	0835	0928	...	...	1230	1506	1926	2055	2223	...

Japan Rail Pass holders must pay a supplement to travel between these stations.

Central — NAGOYA - NAGANO — 8175

	A										
Nagoya **8150** d.	0700	0800	1000	1100	1200	1300	1500	1600	1740	1840	1940
Nakatsugawa d.	0749	0850	1049	1149	1249	1350	1549	1649	1830	1930	2032
Kiso Fukushima d.	0829	0925	1125	1225	1325	1425	1625	1725	1907	2007	2110
Shiojiri d.	0859	0957	1155	1255	1354	1454	1655	1755	1937	2035	2138
Matsumoto d.	0909	1007	1206	1306	1404	1505	1705	1805	1947	2046	2149
Nagano a.	1001	1058	1254	1353	1456	1555	1753	1858	2039	2134	2238

	B										
Nagano d.	0609	0745	0900	1000	1201	1404	1500	1600	1700	1811	1940
Matsumoto d.	0704	0836	0950	1050	1253	1453	1553	1653	1752	1907	2031
Shiojiri d.	0714	0846	1003	1103	1303	1503	1603	1703	1803	1919	2041
Kiso Fukushima d.	0743	0913	1030	1130	1330	1530	1630	1730	1830	1948	2108
Nakatsugawa d.	0822	0950	1106	1206	1406	1608	1710	1810	1910	2026	2144
Nagoya **8150** a.	0917	1052	1201	1301	1501	1701	1805	1905	2005	2121	2234

Additional trips: 0900, 1400. B – Additional trips: 1100, 1300.

Central — SHIZUOKA - KOFU — 8180

Shizuoka d.	0817	0941	1141	1339	1540	1740	1940	...	...	...
Fuji d.	0844	1013	1211	1411	1611	1811	2011	...	...	...
Kofu a.	1030	1205	1402	1603	1803	1959	2204	...	...	...

Kofu d.	0622	0845	1044	1237	1436	1634	1836	...	...	...
Fuji d.	0814	1037	1234	1429	1629	1828	2031	...	...	...
Shizuoka a.	0842	1102	1302	1456	1656	1855	2058	...	...	...

East — TOKYO - KOFU - MATSUMOTO — 8185

All trains Ⓡ		B																						
Tokyo Shinjuku d.	0700	0730	0800	0830	0900	1000	1100	1130	1200	1300	1400	1500	1600	...	1700	1730	1800	...	1900	...	2000	2100	...	...
Hachioji d.	0729	0802	0833	0908	0939	1033	1129	1202	1231	1331	1431	1531	1631	...	1732	1806	1835	...	1936	...	2034	2134	...	...
Otsuki d.	0756	0831	|	0938	|	|	|	1229	|	|	|	|	|	...	|	1833	|	...	|	...	|	2201	...	...
Kofu d.	0828	0908	0929	1014	1036	1129	1224	1300	1328	1427	1526	1627	1728	...	1829	1905	1932	...	2034	...	2130	2232	...	...
Chino d.	0908	0952	1007	...	1111	1206	1300	1339	1403	1507	1607	1707	1804	...	1906	1946	2011	...	2111	...	2208	2314	...	...
Kami Suwa d.	0913	0957	1012	...	1117	1212	|	1345	1410	1512	1613	1713	1809	...	1912	1952	2017	...	2117	...	2213	2320	...	...
Shiojiri d.	0928	1013	1028	...	|	1227	|	1402	|	1528	1628	1728	|	...	1927	2017	2031	...	2132	...	2229	2336	...	...
Matsumoto a.	0938	1027	1037	...	1139	1236	1325	1411	1431	1537	1638	1737	1834	...	1937	2016	2041	...	2142	...	2238	2346	...	...

ains Ⓡ																	A							
umoto d.	...	0625	0650	0800	0840	...	0910	1010	1110	1210	...	1310	1345	...	1450	1510	1550	1630	...	1718	1840	...	1928	2010
iri d.	...	0633	0658	|	0849	...	0918	|	1118	1218	...	1318	1355	...	|	1520	1558	1638	...	1728	|	...	1937	2018
Suwa d.	...	0649	0713	0821	0905	...	0933	|	1133	1233	...	1333	1410	...	1512	1536	1613	1653	...	1746	1901	...	1952	2033
o d.	...	0655	0719	0827	0910	...	0939	1035	1139	1239	...	1339	1416	...	1518	1542	1619	1659	...	1752	1906	...	1958	2039
d.	...	0739	0756	0904	0947	...	1017	1111	1217	1316	...	1416	1454	...	1554	1631	1701	1736	...	1835	1942	2004	2036	2116
ki d.	...	|	|	|	|	...	1046	|	|	|	...	|	|	...	|	|	|	|	...	1905	|	2038	|	|
ioji d.	...	0834	0851	0958	1043	...	1114	1205	1311	1410	...	1510	1549	...	1650	1730	1801	1831	...	1933	2036	2105	2135	2213
o Shinjuku a.	...	0914	0926	1032	1119	...	1145	1233	1342	1441	...	1541	1624	...	1726	1804	1836	1906	...	2010	2106	2137	2207	2245

All trains Ⓡ											
Tokyo Shinjuku d.	0930	1030	1230	1330	1430	1530	1630	1830	1930	2200	2300
Hachioji d.	1009	1102	1302	1401	1502	1602	1703	1906	2008	2235	2335
Otsuki d.	1038	1129	1328	1428	1529	1630	1730	1932	2034	2301	0001
Kofu a.	1114	1205	1403	1503	1604	1705	1806	2012	2111	2337	0037

All trains Ⓡ											
Kofu d.	0718	0818	0924	1132	1232	1332	1430	1512	1611	1745	1902
Otsuki d.	0752	0852	0957	1206	1306	1406	1506	1555	1647	1828	2036
Hachioji d.	0822	0919	1025	1233	1333	1433	1533	1624	1714	1855	2003
Tokyo Shinjuku a.	0904	0956	1059	1304	1404	1504	1603	1658	1751	1927	2037

Some trains run on a slightly different schedule on Ⓒ. **A** – From Minami Otari dep. 1422. **B** – To Minami Otari arr. 1142.

East, Fujikyu Railway — TOKYO - MOUNT FUJI - KAWAGUCHIKO — 8190

	Ⓡ Ⓒ	Ⓡ	D Ⓡ	Ⓡ	F	E	D Ⓡ	F	E Ⓐ	E Ⓒ
Tokyo Shinjuku d.	0735	0830	...	0930	...	...	...	...	...	...
Hachioji d.	0810	0908	...	1009	...	...	...	...	...	...
Otsuki ‡ ◧ d.	0852	0942	0951	1042	1144	1246	1338	1440	1550	1554
Mt Fuji ⊖ d.	0934	1017	1045	1117	1226	1329	1426	1526	1631	1639
Kawaguchiko ‡ ◧ a.	0939	1022	1051	1122	1232	1335	1431	1532	1637	1645

	D Ⓡ	F	E	D Ⓡ	F	E	Ⓡ	Ⓡ Ⓒ		Ⓡ
Kawaguchiko ‡ ◧ d.	0837	0941	1107	1205	1308	1403	1505	1600	...	1738
Mt Fuji ⊖ d.	0845	0949	1116	1213	1316	1411	1513	1609	...	1746
Otsuki ‡ ◧ d.	0940	1034	1155	1257	1357	1450	1555	1651	...	1828
Hachioji d.	...	...	...	...	...	...	1624	1725	...	1855
Tokyo Shinjuku a.	...	...	...	...	...	...	1658	1759	...	1927

Fuji Tozan Densha. Japan Rail Pass not valid.
Fujisan Express. Japan Rail Pass not valid.
Fujisan View Express. Japan Rail Pass not valid.
◧ – Frequent additional local services available.
‡ – Japan Rail Pass not valid between Otsuki and Kawaguchiko.
⊖ – Altitude is 809 m. Bus service to Fuji-Subaru Line 5th Station (Altitude 2305 m) is available.

East — TOKYO - IZUKYU SHIMODA and SHUZENJI — 8195

			Ⓡ E		ⒸB	ⒸD	Ⓡ			Ⓡ
Tokyo d.	0900	0900	0925j	1000	1030	1030	1100	1200	1200	1300
Yokohama d.	0924	0924	0959	1023	1054	1054	1124	1224	1224	1324
Odawara d.	1002	1002	|	1102	1132	1132	|	1301	1301	|
Atami d.	1023	1025	1056	1122	1154	1156	1218	1323	1325	1419
Ito ‡ d.	1046	|	1118	1146	1225	|	1238	1346	|	1442
Izukyu Shimoda ‡ a.	1146	|	1212	1236	1325	|	1329	1447	|	1542
Mishima ‡ d.	...	1040	...	...	...	1211	...	...	1340	...
Shuzenji ‡ a.	...	1108	...	...	...	1239	...	...	1406	...

	Ⓒ	Ⓡ				Ⓡ		C	Ⓡ	Ⓒ
Shuzenji ‡ d.	...	...	...	1235	...	...	...	1539	...	A
Mishima ‡ d.	...	...	...	1305	...	...	...	1606	...	...
Izukyu Shimoda ‡ d.	...	1004	1213	|	1303	1410	1506	|	1607	1650
Ito ‡ d.	1004	1105	1305	|	1406	1510	1602	|	1700	1754
Atami d.	1032	1128	1332	1333	1429	1533	1629	1629	1726	1825
Odawara d.	1050	1146	1349	1350	1449	|	1646	1646	|	1846
Yokohama d.	1127	1222	1426	1427	1526	1627	1723	1723	1824	1932
Tokyo a.	1150	1241	1449	1449	1549	1649	1746	1746	1856j	1958

Additional trips on Ⓒ at 1125Ⓡ, 1344, on ⑦ at 1433Ⓡ.
Additional trips on ⑥ at 1130Ⓡ, on Ⓒ at 1330.
Additional trips on ⑦ at 0946, on Ⓒ at 1418.
D – Additional trip on ⑥ at 1330.
E – Additional trip on Ⓒ at 0830.
j – Tokyo **Shinjuku**.
‡ – Japan Rail Pass holders must pay a supplement to travel between these stations.

8200 TOKYO - AWA KAMOGAWA — JR E

km									A			
0	**Tokyo** d.	0715	0900	1000	1100	1300	1500	1702	1800	1900	2100	2201
43	Soga d.	0753	0935	1033	1134	1334	1534	1734	1834	1935	2134	2233
62	Oami d.	0805	0947	1047	1146	1346	1546	1747	1849	1949	2148	2247
74	Mobara d.	0813	0955	1055	1155	1354	1554	1755	1857	1957	2158	2254
82	Kazusa Ichinomiya d.	0820	1002	1106	1202	1401	1601	1802	1904	2008	2206	2301
110	Katsuura a.	0846	1028	1130	1227	1426	1627	1827	...	2034	2230	2326
133	**Awa Kamogawa** a.	...	1053	1156	1252	1452	...	...	...	...	...	...

Awa Kamogawa d.	...	0739	0839	...	1137	1406	1534	1636	...	...
Katsuura d.	0726	0808	0906	1035	1205	1436	1559	1703	1815	...
Kazusa Ichinomiya d.	0753	0833	0932	1101	1234	1502	1631	1738	1840	1930
Mobara d.	0759	0839	0939	1108	1241	1508	1638	1744	1846	1936
Oami d.	0809	0847	0946	1116	1249	1516	1646	1752	1854	1948
Soga d.	0824	0902	1002	1130	1302	1531	1700	1805	1908	2001
Tokyo a.	0901	0934	1036	1205	1335	1603	1734	1840	1940	2034

A – Additional trip: Ⓐ 2000. Note: Some trains run on a slightly different schedule on Ⓒ.

8205 TOKYO - NAGANOHARA KASATSUGUCHI and MAEBASHI — JR E

km		Ⓒ			Ⓐ	Ⓐ[R]A	a[R]	a[R]	Ⓐ[R]	Ⓐ[R]	Ⓐ[R]
0	**Tokyo** Ueno d.	0900	1000	1212	1803	1830	1900	2000	2100	2200	2250
27	Omiya d.	0926	1026	1237	1831	1856	1925	2025	2124	2225	2315
62	Kumagaya d.	0952	1051	1302	1909	1926	1951	2053	2153	2254	2343
102	**Takasaki** d.	1020	1119	1333	2001	*2019*h	2025	2126	2223	2326	0013
164	**Naganohara Kusatsuguchi** a.	1122	1218	1434	|	|	|	|	|	|	...
112	**Maebashi** a.	...	...	...	2015	*2037*	*2053*	2136	*2247*	2337	...

	Ⓐ[R]	Ⓐ[R]	Ⓐ[R]	Ⓒ	Ⓐ[R]	Ⓒ	Ⓒ	
Maebashi d.	...	*0717*	*0749*	*0749*	0835	0908	...	...
Naganohara Kusatsuguchi d.	...	|	|	|	|	|	1204	1307
Takasaki d.	...	0740	0810	0810	0848	0922	1306	1405
Kumagaya d.	0606	0810	0842	0842	0920	0953	1333	1434
Omiya d.	0640	0841	0912	0912	0950	1022	1401	1500
Tokyo Ueno a.	0705	0911j	0939	0939	1013	1054j	1424	1526

A – Additional trip: 1930. a – [R] on Ⓐ only. h – Change trains at Honjo. j – Tokyo **Shinjuku**. k – Change trains at Takasaki.

8210 TOKYO - NIKKO — JR E

km		[R]	[R]	[R]	[R]						
0	**Tokyo** Shinjuku d.	0730	1031	1300	1732	...	...	...	...	...	...
27	Omiya d.	0802	1102	1330	1802	...	...	...	...	...	...
135	Tobu **Nikko** ‡ d.	0928	|	|	|	...	...	...	...	...	...
140	**Kinugawa** Onsen ‡ a.	...	1238	1507	1940	...	...	...	...	...	...

	[R]	[R]	[R]	[R]					
Kinugawa Onsen ‡ d.	0810	1041	1505	...	...	...	...	...	...
Tobu **Nikko** ‡ d.	|	|	|	1639	...	...	...	...	...
Omiya d.	0949	1217	1646	1804	...	...	...	...	...
Tokyo Shinjuku a.	1018	1247	1719	1836	...	...	...	...	...

‡ – Japan Rail Pass holders must pay a supplement to travel to/from this station.
NOTE: Tobu Railway (http://www.tobu.co.jp/foreign/en/) operate regular services between Tokyo Skytree and Tobi Nikko and Kinugawa Onsen.

8215 TOKYO - IWAKI - SENDAI — JR E

km	All trains [R]					Ⓐ	Ⓒ																		
	Tokyo Shinagawa d.	0645	0715	...	...	...	0845	...	0945	1015	1045	1115	1145	1215	1245	1315	1345	1415	1445	1515	1545	1615	1645	1715	1745
0	**Tokyo** Ueno d.	0700	0730	0800	0830	0900	0900	0930	1000	1030	1100	1130	1200	1230	1300	1330	1400	1430	1500	1530	1600	1630	1700	1730	1800
67	Tsuchiura d.	0742	0816	0850	0917	|	|	1016	|	1115	|	1215	|	1313	|	1413	|	1513	|	1614	|	1711	|	1816	*1907*
118	Mito d.	0811	0850	0919	0950	1016	1016	1048	1106	1148	1207	1248	1307	1345	1407	1445	1507	1546	1607	1647	1706	1744	1808	1848	1909
124	Katsuta d.	0817	0855	0925	0955	1021	1021	1053	1111	1153	1212	1252	1312	1350	1412	1450	1512	1551	1612	1652	1712	1749	1813	1853	1914
150	Hitachi d.	0834	0915	0941	...	1040	1040	...	1126	...	1232	...	1327	...	1430	1511	1527	...	1630	...	1730	...	1831	...	1932
212	**Iwaki** △ a.	0918	...	1023	...	1124	1124	...	1207	...	1315	...	1409	...	1514	...	1609	...	1714	...	1811	...	1915	...	2015
290	Haranomachi △ d.	...	...	...	...	...	...	...	...	...	...	...	...	...	...	...	...	...	...	...	...	...	...	...	...
361	**Sendai** (Honshu) △ a.	...	...	...	...	...	...	...	...	...	...	...	...	...	...	...	...	...	...	...	...	...	...	...	...

All trains [R]										
Tokyo Shinagawa d.	1845	1915	1945	...	2015	2045	2115	2145	2215	2245
Tokyo Ueno d.	1900	1930	2000	2015	2030	2100	2130	2200	2230	2300
Tsuchiura d.	*2010*	2018	|	2107	2117	2142	2221	2242	2319	2351
Mito d.	2008	2052	2108	2142	2150	2211	2255	2314	2353	0024
Katsuta d.	2014	2057	2113	2147	2156	2217	2300	2319	2358	0029
Hitachi d.	2032	...	2131	...	2214	2235	...	2338	...	...
Iwaki △ a.	2116	...	2214	...	2256	2319	...	...	...	...
Haranomachi △ d.	...	...	...	...	...	...	...	...	...	...
Sendai (Honshu) △ a.	...	...	...	...	...	...	...	...	...	...

All trains [R]			Ⓐ						
Sendai (Honshu) △ d.	...	...	...	...	...	...	...	...	...
Haranomachi △ d.	...	...	...	...	...	...	...	...	...
Iwaki △ d.	...	...	...	...	...	0614	...	0703	0739
Hitachi d.	...	...	...	0556	...	0701	0719	0745	0822
Katsuta d.	...	0539	0601	0616	0700	0720	0739	0804	0841
Mito d.	...	0545	0607	0622	0706	0726	0745	0810	0848
Tsuchiura d.	0606	0620	0640	0656	0739	0758	0819	0839	0920
Tokyo Ueno a.	0705	0723	0742	0759	0843	0858	0915	0933	1006
Tokyo Shinagawa a.	...	...	...	0813	...	0913	0931	0949	1021

All trains [R]																									
Sendai (Honshu) △ d.	...	...	...	...	...	...	...	...	...	...	...	...	...	...	...	...	...	...	...	...	...	...	...	...	...
Haranomachi △ d.	...	...	...	...	...	...	...	...	...	...	...	...	...	...	...	...	...	...	...	...	...	...	...	...	...
Iwaki △ d.	0818	...	0920	...	1017	...	1120	...	1218	...	1323	...	1418	...	1518	...	1618	...	1721	...	1816	...	1918	...	2016
Hitachi d.	0901	...	1002	1027	1102	...	1202	...	1302	...	1405	...	1502	...	1602	1626	1702	...	1803	...	1900	...	2000	...	2100
Katsuta d.	0921	0947	1021	1047	1121	1147	1221	1247	1321	1347	1421	1447	1521	1547	1621	1647	1721	1747	1821	1847	1921	1947	2021	2047	2121
Mito d.	0927	0953	1027	1053	1127	1153	1227	1253	1327	1353	1427	1453	1527	1553	1627	1653	1727	1753	1827	1853	1927	1953	2027	2053	2127
Tsuchiura d.	|	1025	|	1125	|	1225	|	1325	|	1425	|	1525	|	1625	|	1725	|	1824	|	1924	|	2024	|	2124	2156
Tokyo Ueno a.	1037	1108	1137	1208	1237	1308	1337	1408	1437	1509	1537	1609	1639	1708	1738	1808	1838	1908	1938	2010	2037	2109	2139	2208	2238
Tokyo Shinagawa a.	1051	1122	1151	1222	1251	1322	1351	1422	1451	1522	1551	1623	1653	1723	1752	1823	1851	1922	1952	2023	2052	2123	2154	2223	2253

△ – LEX services Iwaki - Sendai and v.v. are suspended due to earthquake damage. Some local services may be available. Note: Some trains run on a slightly different schedule on Ⓒ.

8220 NIIGATA - AOMORI — JR E

km			A	*LEX*		*LEX*	*LEX*	*LEX* C	*LEX*	*LEX*	*LEX*	
0	**Niigata** d.	...		...	...	0822	...	1057	1232	1457	...	...
168	Sakata d.	...	0634	...	...	1037	...	1304	1441	1712	...	...
273	Akita d.	...	0828	0837	...	1203	1239	...	1604	1841	1552	1920
377	Odate d.	...	...	1004	...	...	1409	...	...	...	1724	2055
421	Hirosaki d.	...	...	1042	...	...	1447	...	...	...	1802	2131
455	Shin Aomori d.	...	...	1112	...	...	1515	...	...	...	1831	2207
459	**Aomori** a.	...	...	1117	...	...	1520	...	...	...	1837	2213

	LEX D	*LEX*	*LEX*	*LEX*		*LEX*	*LEX*	*LEX*		B
Aomori d.	...	...	0905	...	...	1242	...	1557	...	...
Shin Aomori d.	...	...	0911	...	...	1248	...	1604	...	...
Hirosaki d.	...	...	0940	...	...	1320	...	1633	...	...
Odate d.	...	...	1017	...	...	1357	...	1710	...	...
Akita d.	...	1035	1144	1300	...	1528	1635	1840	...	2049
Sakata d.	0528	1201	...	1430	...	...	1804	...	...	2231
Niigata a.	0731	1405	...	1636	...	...	2009	...	...	...

A – Additional trips: 0535, 0755, 0935, 1229, 1537, 1630, 1750, 1908, 2125.
B – Additional trips: 0538, 0650, 0913, 1208, 1516, 1644, 1803, 1919.
C – Additional trips: 1715, 1855, 2113.
D – Additional trips: 0645, 0904, 1556.

8225 HAKODATE and MURORAN - SAPPORO — JR Hokka

km		1	3	1	5		3		5	7	9	7	11	13	9	15	11	17		19	21	23
0	**Hakodate** d.	...	...	0602	...	...	0737	0747	0855	1005	1048	...	1215	1353	...	1453	...	1637	1728	1751	1849	1954
18	Shin **Hakodate Hokuto** 8020 d.	...	...	0620	...	...	0757	0809	0915	1024	1109	...	1234	1412	...	1512	...	1655	1750	1811	1910	2013
50	Mori d.	...	...	0648	...	...	0824	...	0942	1053	1137	...	1302	1441	...	1543	...	1725	...	1838	1936	2041
112	Oshamambe d.	...	...	0729	...	...	0906	...	1020	1134	1220	...	1343	1523	...	1625	...	1808	...	1918	2016	2122
154	Toya d.	...	...	0756	...	...	0931	...	1045	1157	1246	...	1409	1548	...	1650	...	1834	...	1943	2042	2148
	Muroran d.	0527	0656	|	...	...	|	...	|	|	|	1348	|	|	1626	|	1812	|	...	|	|	|
190	Higashi-Muroran d.	0541	0710	0824	0923	...	0959	...	1113	1223	1313	1400	1437	1615	1638	1717	1824	1905	...	2011	2110	2215
207	Noboribetsu d.	0556	0724	0837	0937	...	1012	...	1125	1235	1326	1415	1450	1628	1653	1729	1839	1918	...	2023	2122	2228
248	Tomakomai d.	0622	0749	0900	1002	...	1036	...	1151	1259	1352	1441	1514	1652	1719	1754	1904	1943	...	2046	2146	2251
275	Minami Chitose d.	0641	0807	0916	1022	...	1053	...	1208	1316	1410	1459	1530	1708	1737	1811	1923	2000	...	2103	2203	|
319	**Sapporo** a.	0714	0838	0948	1101	...	1127	...	1241	1346	1441	1534	1604	1741	1811	1841	1955	2033	...	2135	2233	2340

km				2	4	2	6	8	10	4	12	6	14		16	18	8	20	22	10	24	12
0	**Sapporo** d.	...	...	0600	0653	0730	0839	0932	1044	1124	1216	1355	1332	...	1445	1539	1602	1639	1808	1854	2000	2200
44	Minami Chitose d.	...	...	0628	0722	0759	0911	1000	1115	1159	1245	1427	1401	...	1515	1611	1632	1711	1841	1927	2028	2234
71	Tomakomai d.	...	...	0644	0739	0818	0928	1017	1132	1219	1302	1445	1418	...	1533	1627	1651	1728	1858	1945	2044	2253
112	Noboribetsu d.	...	...	|	0804	0845	0951	1043	1155	1245	1327	1509	1442	...	1557	1654	1722	1751	1924	2011	2108	2319
129	Higashi-Muroran d.	...	...	0718	0817	0859	1004	1057	1209	1300	1340	1524	1455	...	1610	1708	1738	1804	1937	2026	2120	2334
136	**Muroran** a.	...	...	|	|	...	|	|	|	1311	|	1536	|	...	|	|	1749	|	|	2037	|	2346
	Toya d.	...	...	|	0844	...	1031	1124	1235	...	1407	...	1522	...	1637	1734	...	1833	2005	...	2147	...
	Oshamambe d.	...	...	0806	0911	...	1057	1152	1302	...	1435	...	1548	...	1701	1802	...	1903	2032	...	2214	...
	Mori d.	...	...	0845	0954	...	1138	1234	1344	...	1517	...	1628	...	1742	1842	...	1944	2113	...	2257	...
	Shin **Hakodate Hokuto** 8020 a.	0654	0814	0913	1022	...	1207	1306	1412	...	1549	...	1655	1730	1809	1908	...	2011	2139	...	2323	...
	Hakodate a.	0713	0833	0929	1038	...	1223	1323	1427	...	1605	...	1710	1749	1825	1924	...	2027	2156	...	2338	...

SAPPORO - KUSHIRO 8230

Hokkaido

Sapporo d.	0657	0754	0854	1024	1153	1416	1608	1724	1832	1940	2104
Minami Chitose d.	0727	0826	0926	1057	1226	1448	1641	1756	1905	2011	2132
Tomamu d.	0833	0933	1040	1212	1329	1600	1758	1918	2020	2126	2246
Obihiro d.	0927	1036	1140	1310	1422	1659	1900	2018	2121	2220	2341
Kushiro a.	1059	...	1320	...	1556	1839	...	2159	...	2355	...

Kushiro d.	...	0626	...	0820	...	1124	...	1339	1614	...	1900
Obihiro d.	0645	0802	0848	0957	1110	1257	1330	1520	1747	1922	2034
Tomamu d.	0741	0903	0955	1051	1212	1358	1432	1613	1839	2020	2126
Minami Chitose d.	0900	1014	1108	1153	1324	1507	1544	1722	1944	2143	2228
Sapporo a.	0933	1045	1140	1226	1356	1541	1618	1756	2015	2215	2258

KUSHIRO - ABASHIRI 8233

Hokkaido

Kushiro d.	...	...	0603	0857	1414	1605	1732	1852	2216
Mashu d.	...	...	0727	1011	1531	1723	1924	2011	2331
Shiretoko-Shari d.	0645	0728	0834	1112	1633	1855	...	2122	...
Abashiri a.	0731	0817	0919	1153	1717	1945	...	2203	...

Abashiri d.	...	...	0641	1024	1510	1617	1852	2029	2112
Shiretoko-Shari d.	...	...	0726	1111	1557	1730	1939	2115	2253
Mashu d.	0542	0635	0836	1216	1723	1832	2055	...	...
Kushiro a.	0708	0753	1000	1333	1846	1955	2215	...	...

SAPPORO - WAKKANAI and ABASHIRI 8235

Hokkaido

			A	A	A		A			
Sapporo d.	0656	0730	*1100*	*1200*	*1530*	1730	*1830*	...	...	...
Takikawa d.	0755	0824	*1152*	*1252*	*1622*	1829	*1922*	...	...	...
Asahikawa 8240 a.	0832	0858	*1225*	*1325*	*1655*	1905	*1955*	...	...	...
Asahikawa 8240 d.	0835	0900	1241	1335	1705	1908	2006	...	...	...
Nayoro d.	|	0956	|	1431	|	|	2103	...	...	...
Wakkanai a.	|	1240	|	1723	|	|	2347	...	...	...
Kamikawa d.	0917	...	1327	...	1745	1949	...	...	...	...
Abashiri a.	1218	...	1635	...	2049	2300	...	...	...	...

		A	A	A	A					
Abashiri d.	0556	...	0806	1235	...	1725	...	...	...	...
Kamikawa d.	0901	...	1111	1540	...	2036	...	...	...	...
Wakkanai d.	|	0636	|	|	1301	|	1746	...	...	...
Nayoro d.	|	0925	|	|	1548	|	2032	...	...	...
Asahikawa 8240 a.	0944	1019	1150	1619	1648	2114	2126	...	...	...
Asahikawa 8240 d.	0947	*1030*	*1200*	*1630*	*1700*	2117	2130	...	...	...
Takikawa d.	1022	*1102*	*1232*	*1702*	*1733*	2152	2204	...	...	...
Sapporo a.	1118	*1155*	*1325*	*1755*	*1825*	2253	2257	...	...	...

Change trains at Asahikawa.

SAPPORO - ASAHIKAWA 8240

Hokkaido

Sapporo d.	0635	0749	0830	0900	0930	1000	1100	1200	1300	1400	1430	1500	1530	1600	1630	1700	1800	1830	1900	1930	2000	2100	2200	2305
Takikawa d.	0727	0841	0922	0952	1022	1052	1152	1252	1352	1452	1522	1552	1622	1652	1722	1752	1852	1922	1952	2022	2052	2152	2252	2357
Asahikawa 8235 a.	0800	0914	0955	1025	1055	1125	1225	1325	1425	1525	1555	1625	1655	1725	1754	1825	1925	1955	2025	2055	2125	2225	2325	0030
ikawa 8235 d.	0518	0600	0645	0718	0755	0830	0900	1000	1030	1100	1200	1300	1400	1430	1500	1600	1630	1700	1730	1800	1830	1900	2000	2200
kawa d.	0550	0632	0717	0750	0827	0902	0932	1032	1102	1132	1232	1332	1432	1502	1532	1632	1702	1732	1802	1832	1902	1932	2032	2232
poro a.	0643	0733	0826	0846	0920	0955	1025	1125	1155	1225	1325	1425	1525	1555	1625	1725	1755	1825	1855	1925	1955	2025	2125	2325

SUMMARY OF OVERNIGHT TRAINS 8300

km										
			A [R]	B [R]						
	Takamatsu d.	...	...	2126	...	...	...	...	...	
	Kojima d.	...	...	2201	...	...	...	...	...	
0	**Izumoshi** d.	...	1851	|	...	...	...	...	...	
33	Matsue d.	...	1927	|	...	...	...	...	...	
62	Yonago d.	...	1956	|	...	...	...	...	...	
140	Niimi d.	...	2120	|	...	...	...	...	...	
221	**Okayama** d.	...	2234	2234	...	...	...	...	...	
397	Osaka d.	...	0034	0034	...	...	...	...	...	
773	Shizuoka d.	...	0440	0440	...	...	...	...	...	
925	Yokohama d.	...	0645	0645	...	...	...	...	...	
954	**Tokyo** a.	...	0708	0708	...	...	...	...	...	

					B [R]	A [R]			
Tokyo d.	...	...	...	...	2200	2200	...	...	...
Yokohama d.	...	...	...	...	2224	2224	...	...	...
Shiuoka a.	...	...	...	...	0020	0020	...	...	...
Osaka d.	...	...	...	...	|	|	...	...	...
Okayama d.	...	...	...	...	0631	0634	...	...	...
Niimi d.	...	...	...	...	|	0744	...	...	...
Yonago d.	...	...	...	...	|	0905	...	...	...
Matsue d.	...	...	...	...	|	0931	...	...	...
Izumoshi a.	...	...	...	...	|	0958	...	...	...
Kojima d.	...	...	...	...	0653	...	...	...	...
Takamatsu a.	...	...	...	...	0727	...	...	...	...

SUNRISE IZUMO 1, 2 cl., (2) Izumoshi - Tokyo and v.v. B – SUNRISE SETO 1, 2 cl., (2) Takamatsu - Tokyo and v.v.
As well as De-lux, single and twin berth compartments both trains have *Nobinobi* – open-plan sleeping areas categorised as seats.

AIRPORT RAIL LINKS 8400

BU CENTRAL JAPAN INTERNATIONAL AIRPORT

' Limited Express [R] service Meitetsu Nagoya - Central Japan International Airport and v.v. *44 km.* Journey 30 minutes. (Frequent additional slower trains are available, not [R]). Operator: tsu.

Meitetsu Nagoya at 0600Ⓐ, 0602Ⓒ, 0628Ⓐ, 0630Ⓒ, 0648Ⓐ, 0653Ⓒ, 0720, 0750Ⓒ, 0751Ⓐ, 0820Ⓒ, 0823Ⓐ, 0850, 0920, 0950, 1020, 1050, 1120, 1150, 1220, 1250, 1320, 1350, 1420, , 1520, 1550, 1620, 1650, 1719Ⓐ, 1720Ⓒ, 1749Ⓐ, 1750Ⓒ, 1819Ⓐ, 1820Ⓒ, 1849Ⓐ, 1850Ⓒ, 1919Ⓐ, 1920Ⓒ, 1949Ⓐ, 1950Ⓒ, 2019Ⓐ, 2020Ⓒ, 2049Ⓐ, 2050Ⓒ, 2119Ⓐ, 2120Ⓒ.

Central Japan International Airport at 0703Ⓐ, 0713Ⓒ, 0726Ⓐ, 0729Ⓒ, 0759Ⓒ, 0800Ⓐ, 0829Ⓒ, 0834Ⓐ, 0907, 0937, 1007, 1037, 1107, 1137, 1207, 1237, 1307, 1337, 1407, 1437, 1507, , 1607, 1637, 1706Ⓐ, 1707Ⓒ, 1736Ⓐ, 1737Ⓒ, 1806Ⓐ, 1807Ⓒ, 1836Ⓐ, 1837Ⓒ, 1906Ⓐ, 1907Ⓒ, 1936Ⓐ, 1937Ⓒ, 2007, 2037, 2107, 2137, 2207.

SAI AIRPORT

UKA' Limited Express service Kyoto - Shin Osaka ■ - Kansai Airport and v.v. *100 km.* Journey 80 - 90 minutes. Operator: JR West.

Kyoto at 0545, 0621, 0644, 0713, 0745, 0817, 0848, 0930, 1000, 1030, 1100, 1130, 1200, 1230, 1300, 1330, 1400, 1430, 1500, 1530, 1600, 1630, 1700, 1730, 1800, 1830, 1900, 1930, 2000,

Kansai Airport at 0630, 0727, 0755, 0845, 0916, 0946, 1016, 1046, 1114, 1144 and ½ hourly until 1614, 1644, 1716, 1746, 1816, 1846, 1916, 1946, 2016, 2046, 2125, 2216.

Trains call at Shin Osaka 28 - 33 minutes after Kyoto and 45 - 50 minutes after Kansai Airport.

YO HANEDA AIRPORT

ed Express service Tokyo Shinagawa - Haneda Airport International Terminal △ and v.v. *14 km.* Journey 20 minutes. Operator: Keikyu Railway.

Tokyo Shinagawa at 0552 and every 10 - 15 minutes until 2300.

Haneda Airport International Terminal at 0530 and every 10 - 15 minutes until 2330.

Most trains continue to/from Haneda Aiport Domestic Terminal, journey 3 minutes.

ORAIL service Tokyo Hamamatsucho – Haneda Airport International Terminal□ and v.v. (JR pass valid) *14 km.* Journey 13 minutes(Haneda Express), 15 minutes, (rapid) 24 minutes (stopping). Operator: Tokyo Monorail Co Ltd.

Tokyo Hamamatsucho at 0459 and every 3 - 10 minutes until 0001.

Haneda Airport International Terminal at 0518 and every 3 - 10 minutes until 0010.

All trains continue to/from Haneda Aiport Domestic Terminal 1, journey 3 - 5 minutes and Aiport Domestic Terminal 2, journey 5 - 7 minutes.

YO NARITA AIRPORT

TA EXPRESS' Limited Express [R] service Tokyo - Narita Airport Terminal 1 ▽ and v.v. *79 km.* Journey 55 minutes. Operator: JR East.

Tokyo at 0618, 0700, 0715, 0731, 0755, 0830, 0900, 1003, 1033, 1103, 1133, 1203, 1233, 1303, 1333, 1403, 1433, 1503, 1533, 1603, 1633, 1703, 1733, 1803, 1833, 1903, 2003.

Narita T1 at 0744, 0813, 0850, 0915, 0945, 1015, 1045, 1114, 1145, 1220, 1245, 1314, 1345, 1418, 1444, 1514, 1544, 1619, 1644, 1716, 1744, 1815, 1848, 1912, 1946, 2044, 2144.

Trains also call at Narita Aiport Terminal two, 2/3 minutes before/after Terminal one. Additional slower trains(not [R]) are available about hourly each direction.

INER' Limited Express [R] service Tokyo Ueno Keisei - Narita Airport Terminal one ▷ and v.v. *69 km.* Journey 45 minutes. Operator: Keisei Electric Railway.

Tokyo Ueno Keisei at 0558, 0620, 0640, 0700, 0720, 0740, 0800, 0825, 0850, 0920, 1000, 1040, 1120, 1200, 1240, 1320, 1400, 1420, 1440, 1500, 1520, 1540, 1600, 1620, 1640, 1700, Ⓒ, 1725Ⓐ, 1740Ⓒ, 1750Ⓐ, 1820.

Narita Airport Terminal 1 at 0726Ⓐ, 0729Ⓒ, 0820Ⓐ, 0825Ⓒ, 0911Ⓐ, 0915Ⓒ, 0959, 1039, 1119, 1159, 1239, 1319, 1359, 1419, 1439, 1459, 1519, 1539, 1559, 1619, 1639, 1659, 1719, 1759Ⓒ, 1805Ⓐ, 1830Ⓒ, 1833Ⓐ, 1858Ⓒ, 1900Ⓐ, 1930Ⓐ, 1938Ⓒ, 2005Ⓐ, 2008Ⓒ, 2038Ⓒ, 2044Ⓐ, 2108Ⓐ, 2109Ⓒ, 2149Ⓐ, 2150Ⓒ, 2230.

Trains also call at Narita Airport Terminal two, 3/5 minutes before/after Terminal one. Additional slower trains are available.

ORO SHIN CHITOSE AIRPORT

and Rapid service Sapporo - Shin Chitose Airport and v.v. *47 km* Journey 48 minutes(local*) 38 minutes (rapid). All services call at Minami-Chitose 3/4 minutes before/after Shin Chitose t. Operator: JR Hokkaido.

Sapporo at 0602*, 0616, 0631, 0643, 0702, 0716, 0733, 0748, 0805, 0820, 0835, 0850, 0905, 0920, 0935, 0950, 1005, 1020, 1035, 1050 and at the same minutes past the hour until 1805, 1835, 1850, 1905, 1920, 1935, 1950, 2005*, 2025, 2045, 2110*, 2137*, 2151*.

Shin Chitose Airport at 0656*, 0704*, 0723*, 0734*, 0748*, 0815, 0830, 0845, 0900, 0915, 0930, 0945, 1000, 1015, 1030, 1045 and at the same minutes past the hour until 2000, 2015, 2030, 2104, 2116, 2130, 2150, 2205, 2215, 2235, 2253.

BEYOND EUROPE
North America

Introduction

The Beyond Europe section covers principal rail services in a different area of the world each month. There are six areas, each appearing as follows:

Winter (December) and Summer (June):	Africa and The Middle East along with all other Beyond Europe sections.
January and July (digital only):	India.
February and August:	South East Asia, Australia and New Zealand; India; North America.
March and September (digital only):	China.
April and October:	Japan; China; South America; South Korea.
May and November (digital only):	North America.

The months have been chosen so that we can bring you up-to-date information for those countries which make seasonal changes.

Contents

INDEX OF PLACES

CANADA

ital : **Ottawa** (GMT -5 add one hour in summer: not Saskatchewan). 2019 Public Holidays : Jan. 1, Apr. 19, 22 (NB, NT, NU,QC), May 20 (not NS, PE, QC), July 1, Sept. 2, . 14 (not NB, NS, PE), Nov. 11 (not MB, NS, ON, QC), Dec. 25.

principal operator in Canada is Via Rail (Via Rail ✆ 1 888 842 7245. www.viarail.ca). Timings shown are the most recently available and are subject to alteration at any time, especially around public holidays. Details of other operators can be found in relevant tables. Unless otherwise noted all trains carry first and second class seated omodation. In Canada first class is called 'Business' and second class is called 'Economy'. Most very long distance trains convey sleeping cars called 'Sleeper Plus' which two berths per compartment, some of which are en-suite, The *Canadian* also offers 'Prestige Class' and one to four berth 'Sleeper Plus' compartments some of which are en-. Most trains also convey some form of catering, but again the actual service offered varies considerably. Tickets are available from staffed stations, websites and through orised ticketing agents. A reservation is neccessary for travel on very long distance Via Rail trains, but generally not for corridor services such as Montréal - Ottawa/Toronto Toronto - Windsor/London/Sarnia.

Rail offers the CANRAIL PASS which is a convenient and flexible pass that allows you to choose between 7, 10 or unlimited one-way trips to a destination of your choice. You the choice of travelling between Quebec and Ontario for 21 consecutive days with the Corridor pass, or across Canada for 60 consecutive days with the System Pass. The *SE PASS* for Economy or Escape fare tickets costs: - **Corridor**, $355 for 7 one-way tickets, $474 for 10 one-way tickets. **System**, $522 for 7 one-way tickets, $1068 for 10 -way tickets. Note: these have limited seat availability. *EXTRA PASS* for Economy or Escape fare tickets and Economy Plus fare seats booked the day before departure costs **orridor**, $438 for 7 one-way tickets, $593 for 10 one-way tickets. **System**, $914 for 7 one-way tickets, $1187 for 10 one-way tickets. The unlimited **Corridor** pass costs $831 nlimited travel over 21 consecutive days and the unlimited **System** pass costs $1543 for unlimited travel over 60 consecutive days. There are reductions for 60+, students youths. For conditions see www.viarail.ca.

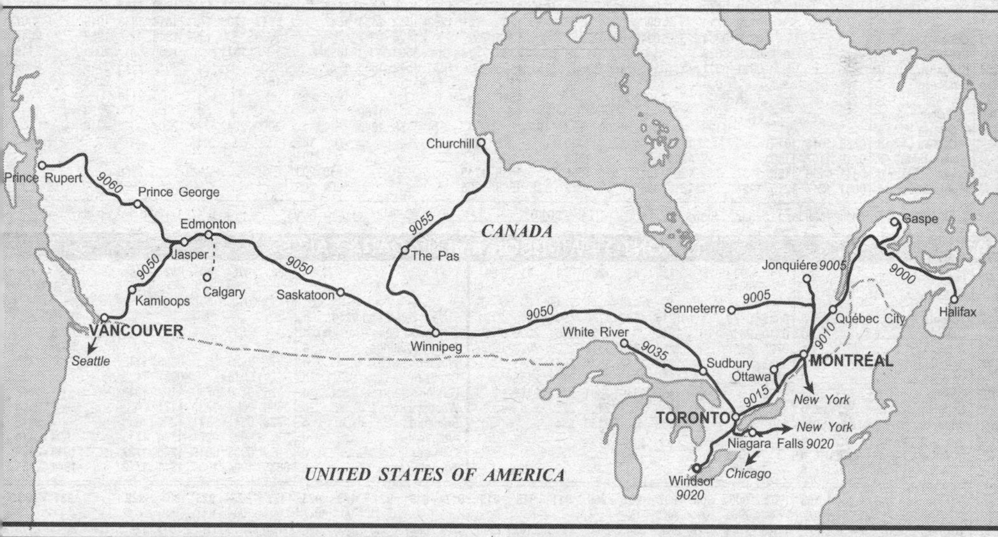

GASPÉ and HALIFAX — 9000

Rail

n		15	17
		R	R
		③⑤⑦	③⑤⑦
		A	Z B
9	**Halifax** d.	1300	...
6	Truro d.	1431	...
2	Amherst d.	1608	...
5	**Moncton** d.	1717	...
5	**Moncton** d.	1732	...
6	Miramichi d.	1937	...
	Bathurst d.	2128	...
4	Campbellton d.	2318	...
0	**Gaspé** d.	|	1520
7	Percé d.	|	1639
3	Bonaventure d.	|	1930
5	Matapédia d.	2252	2252
5	Mont Joli d.	0126	0126
6	Rimouski d.	0201	0201
2	Rivière du Loup d.	0353	0352
0	**Sainte Foy 9010** a.	0613	0613
	Montréal Central **9010** a.	1003	1003

	16	14
	R	R
	③⑤⑦	③⑤⑦
	Z B	A
Montréal Central **9010** d.	1900	1900
Sainte Foy 9010 d.	2249	2249
Rivière du Loup d.	0113	0113
Rimouski d.	0301	0301
Mont Joli d.	0339	0339
Matapédia d.	0610	0610
Bonaventure d.	0909	|
Percé d.	1158	|
Gaspé a.	1317	|
Campbellton d.	...	0748
Bathurst d.	...	0937
Miramichi d.	...	1123
Moncton a.	...	1323
Moncton d.	...	1338
Amherst d.	...	1442
Truro d.	...	1622
Halifax a.	...	1751

OCEAN – 🛏 [2] Montréal - Halifax and v.v.
[2] Montréal - Gaspé and v.v.
During infrastructure work currently in progress, trains 16 and 17 will not be operating and train services between Matapédia and Gaspé will be suspended. As an alternative you can travel on trains 14 and 15 between Montréal and Matapédia.
Orleans Express (https://www.orleansexpress.com/en/our-schedules/) operate buses every day between Rimouski and Gaspé but they do not connect with *Via Rail services.*

JONQUIÈRE and SENNETERRE — 9005

Via Rail

km		604	606	600	602		
		R 2	R 2	R 2	R 2		
		②④	⑦	②④	⑦		
717	**Senneterre** d.	0545	0845	...	...	...	...
561	Clova d.	0750	1050	...	...	...	...
495	Parent d.	0850	0110	...	...	...	...
	Weymont d.	1001	1301	...	...	...	...
297	La Tuque d.	1153	1453	...	...	...	...
510	**Jonquière** d.	|	|	0810	1110	...	...
444	Chambord d.	|	|	0911	1211	...	...
341	Lac Édouard d.	|	|	1105	1405	...	...
251	Rivière à Pierre d.	|	|	1240	1540	...	...
217	**Hervey** a.	1325	1625	1350	1650	...	...
217	**Hervey** d.	1400	1700	1400	1700	...	...
170	Shawinigan d.	1448	1748	1448	1748	...	...
0	**Montréal** Central a.	1715	2015	1715	2015	...	...

		601		603			
		R 2		R 2			
		①③⑤		①③⑤			
Montréal Central d.	...	0815	...	0815	...	...	...
Shawinigan d.	...	1043	...	1043	...	...	...
Hervey a.	...	1130	...	1130	...	...	...
Hervey d.	...	1140	...	1200	...	...	...
Rivière à Pierre d.	...	1234	...	|	...	...	...
Lac Édouard d.	...	1408	...	|	...	...	...
Chambord d.	...	1605	...	|	...	...	...
Jonquière a.	...	1710	...	|	...	...	...
La Tuque d.	...	...	...	1318	...	...	...
Weymont d.	...	...	...	1504	...	...	...
Parent d.	...	...	...	1625	...	...	...
Clova d.	...	...	...	1721	...	...	...
Senneterre a.	...	...	...	1940	...	...	...

QUÉBEC CITY - MONTRÉAL — 9010

Rail

	33	15	17	35	37	25	637	39	29
		2	2						
	①–⑤	①④⑥	①④⑥		①–⑤	⑥	⑦	⑦–⑤	
	C	A *	ZB *	C	C		C	C	
Québec City Palais ▽ d.	0525	...	...	0815	1300	1300	1300	1500	1745
Ste. Foy ▽ d.	0552	0628	0628	0841	1326	1326	1326	1526	1811
Charny ▽ d.	|	|	|	0849	|	|	|	|	|
Drummondville d.	0715	0836	0836	1031	1509	1509	1509	1654	1943
St. Hyacinthe d.	0758	0915	0915	1109	|	|	|	|	2021
St. Lambert ▽ d.	0824	0950	0950	1138	1603	1604	1603	1800	2049
Montréal Central ▽ a.	0835	1003	1003	1149	1614	1615	1614	1811	2100

	20	22	622	624	24	26	28	16	14
								2	2
	①–⑤	①–⑤	⑥⑦	⑥⑦	①–⑤		⑦–⑤	③⑤⑦	③⑤⑦
		C		C	C	C	C	ZB *	A *
Montréal Central ▽ d.	0620	0856	0906	1245	1245	1640	1825	1900	1900
St. Lambert ▽ d.	0633	0918	0918	1308	1308	1702	1848	1925	1925
St. Hyacinthe d.	0700	|	0943	|	|	1729	1916	1958	1958
Drummondville d.	0729	1012	1012	1401	1401	1815	1955	2047	2047
Charny ▽ d.	|	|	|	1556	1556	|	|	|	|
Ste. Foy ▽ d.	0919	1158	1157	1604	1604	2000	2130	2204a	2234a
Québec City Palais ▽ a.	0943	1222	1222	1628	1628	2024	2154	...	...

OCEAN – 🛏 [2] Montréal Central - Halifax and v.v. (Table **9000**).
[2] Montréal Central - Gaspé and v.v. (Table **9000**).
[12] Québec City Palais - Montréal Central - Ottawa Union and v.v. (Table **9015**).
During infrastructure work currently in progress, trains 16 and 17 will not be operating and train services between Matapédia and Gaspé will be suspended.

a – Arrival time.
s – Calls to set down only.
u – Request stop. Calls to pick up only.
* – A shuttle operates between Sainte-Foy and Québec City Palais R required.
▽ – Local traffic not carried Montréal Cenrtal - St Lambert and v.v., or Québec City Palais - Charny and v.v.

9015 MONTRÉAL - OTTAWA - TORONTO

Via F

km		41	641	43	51	61	643	63	633	33	45	53	65	47	35	645	55	635	67	69	647	59	37	637	669	39	651
										A					A								A	A		A	2
		①–⑤	⑥	①–⑤	①–⑤	①–⑥	⑥⑦		⑥⑦	①–⑤							⑦–⑤	⑦–⑤		⑦–⑤	⑦–⑤		①–⑤	⑦		⑦–⑤	①–⑤
0	**Montréal** Central d.	...	...	...	0620	0642	...	0855	0900	0900	...	...	1100	...	1204	...	...	1420	1435	1625	...	...	1650	1650	1830	1850	
19	Dorval d.	...	...	...	0644	0709	...	0920	0924	0934	...	...	1126	...	1239	...	...	1446	1458	1649	...	...	1724	1724	1855	1924	
100	Alexandria d.	...	...	...	0728	|	...	|	1011	1022	...	...	|	...	1327	...	...	|	|	|	...	...	1809	1809	|	2018	
187	**Ottawa** Union a.	...	...	...	0820	|	...	|	1104	1114	...	...	|	...	1415	...	...	1614	|	|	...	...	1853	1853	|	2102	
187	**Ottawa** Union d.	0530	0640	0720	0835	|	0840	|	...	...	1027	1140	|	1228	...	1430	1530	...	|	|	1720	1826	...	...	|		
253	Smiths Falls d.	0622	0726	|	0924	|	0929	|	...	...	|	|	|	|	...	|	|	...	|	|	|	1925	...	...	|		
	Cornwall d.	|	|	|	|	0800	|	1010	...	...	|	|	1217	|	...	|	|	...	1549	|	|	|	...	...	1948		
298	Brockville d.	0651	0755	|	0953	|	0958	|	...	...	|	|	|	1356	...	|	1654	...	|	1819	|	1958	...	...	|		
378	**Kingston** d.	0734	0838	0913	1036	0929	1041	1143	...	...	1226	1339	1345	1445	...	1635	1738	...	1716	1902	1920	2041	...	...	2115		0532
451	Belleville d.	0816	0919	|	|	1007	1125	|	...	...	|	1421	1427	1528	...	1716	1818	...	|	|	|	2122	...	...	|		0616
520	Cobourg d.	0851	0954	|	1136	|	1203	|	...	...	|	|	1504	|	...	|	1852	...	|	|	|	2200	...	...	|		0700
581	Oshawa d.	0927	1029	|	|	1116	1243	1355	...	...	|	1529	1539	1638	...	1823	1925	...	1900	2046	2112	2233	...	...	2304		0740
633	**Toronto** Union a.	1002	1102	1125	1252	1146	1316	1407	...	...	1448	1603	1617	1715	...	1905	1957	...	1929	2115	2145	2307	...	...	2333		0825

km		22	624	24	60	50	34	62	52	26	40	64	28	42	644	44	66	38	46	646	68	54	668	48		650
		A	A	A						A			A													
		①–⑤	⑥⑦	①–⑤	①–⑥	①–⑥							⑦–⑤						⑦–⑤	⑦–⑤	⑦–⑤	①–⑤				⑦–⑤
0	**Toronto** Union d.	...	...	...	0640	0640	...	0835	0835	...	1040	1130	...	1220	1320	1420	1515	...	1540	1635	1700	1740	1757	1840	...	1935
51	Oshawa d.	...	...	...	0719	0719	...	0908	0928	...	|	1208	...	1252	1353	1454	1547	...	1617	1706	1731	1814	1833	1916	...	2007
113	Cobourg d.	...	...	...	0754	0754	...	0940	0940	...	|	1245	...	|	1426	|	|	...	1650	|	1802	1848	|	1953	...	2042
182	Belleville d.	...	...	...	0829	0829	...	|	|	...	|	1326	...	|	1503	|	1653	...	|	1811	|	1930	|	2036	...	2119
254	**Kingston** d.	...	...	...	0911	0911	...	1053	1053	...	1251	1408	...	1434	1542	1636	1732	...	1802	|	|	2012	2018	2116	...	2156
335	Brockville d.	...	...	...	|	1008	...	|	1148	...	|	1457	...	|	|	1720	|	...	1847	|	1954	|	|	2203	...	...
428	Cornwall d.	...	...	...	1048	|	...	1226	|	...	|	1546	...	|	|	|	1859	...	|	|	|	|	2146	|	...	...
380	Smiths Falls d.	...	...	...	|	1039	...	|	|	...	|	|	...	|	|	1750	|	...	|	|	|	|	|	2233	...	...
446	**Ottawa** Union a.	...	...	...	|	1129	...	|	1309	...	1457	|	...	1634	1758	1846	|	...	2009	2042	|	2207	|	2316	...	...
	Ottawa Union d.	0630	1015	1017	|	...	1120	|	...	1420	...	|	1615	...	...	...	|	1855	...	...	|	...	|	...	...	...
	Alexandria d.	0718	1107	1110	|	...	1211	|	...	1508	...	|	|	...	...	...	|	1946	...	...	|	...	|	...	...	...
520	Dorval d.	0811	1156	1155	1137	...	1257	1315	...	1555	...	1638	1745	...	...	...	1948	2037	...	...	2129	...	2236	...	...	...
539	**Montréal** Central a.	0831	1217	1215	1157	...	1316	1335	...	1615	...	1658	1805	...	...	...	2009	2057	...	...	2149	...	2256	...	...	....

A – (12) Québec City Palais - Montréal Central - Ottawa Union and v.v. (Table **9010**).

s – Calls to set down only.

u – Calls to pick up only.

9020 TORONTO - WINDSOR and NIAGARA FALLS

GO Transit, Via F

km	Via Rail	71	97		73	83	75	79	81	69
			R B							
						①–⑤		⑦–⑤	⑥	⑦–⑤
0	**Toronto** Union d.	0645	0820	...	1215	1635	1730	1945	1945	2134
34	Oakville d.	0710	0844	...	1240	|	1756	2009	2009	2157
56	Aldershot d.	0725	0857	...	1258	1713	1812	2023	2023	2209
96	Brantford d.	0753	|	...	1327	1743	1844	2051	2051	...
139	Woodstock d.	0825	|	...	1355	1812	1914	2118	2118	...
185	London d.	0905	|	...	1430	1849	2001	2157	2152	...
290	Chatham d.	1013	|	...	1539	...	2104	2259	...	...
360	**Windsor** a.	1102	|	...	1630	...	2156	2344	...	...
114	St. Catharines d.	...	0954	...	...	...	...	...	...	...
133	**Niagara Falls** (Canada) a.	...	1016	...	...	...	...	...	...	...
	New York Penn **9210** a.	...	2150	...	...	...	...	...	...	....

Via Rail	82	70	80	72	76		98	78
							R B	
	①–⑤	①–⑥	⑦					
New York Penn **9210** d.	...	...	...	...	...	...	0715	...
Niagara Falls (Canada) d.	...	...	...	...	...	...	1745	...
St. Catharines d.	...	...	...	...	...	...	1808	...
Windsor d.	...	0530	...	0905	1345	...	|	1745
Chatham d.	...	0618	...	0951	1430	...	|	1832
London d.	0625	0730	0730	1102	1543	...	|	1942
Woodstock d.	0656	0807	0807	1131	|	...	|	2014
Brantford d.	0728	0841	0841	1202	1640	...	|	2045
Aldershot d.	|	0921	0921	1234	1713	...	1904	2115
Oakville d.	|	0938	0938	1248	1727	...	1918	2129
Toronto Union a.	0835	1004	1004	1311	1752	...	1941	2151

km	GO Transit - 2nd class.	703	903	905	905	907	907	909	911	913	915	917	919	921	473	923	477	925	925	927	929		931	933
		Ⓐ		⑥⑦	Ⓐ	⑥⑦	Ⓐ							⑥⑦	Ⓐ	⑥⑦	Ⓐ	Ⓐ	⑥⑦					
0	**Toronto** Union ☛ d.	0613	0643	0743	0748	0843	0848	0943	1043	1143	1243	1343	1443	1543	1600	1643	1700	1740	1743	1843	1943	...	2043	2143
34	Oakville d.	0651	0724	0824	0829	0924	0929	1024	1124	1224	1324	1424	1524	1624	1631	1724	1731	1821	1824	1924	2024	...	2124	2224
51	Burlington ☛ a.	0710	0744	0844	0849	0944	0949	1044	1144	1244	1344	1444	1544	1644	1651	1744	1751	1841	1844	1944	2044	...	2144	2244
114	St. Catharines a.	*0820**	*0854**	*0959**	*0959**	*1059**	*1059**	*1159**	*1254**	*1354**	*1459**	*1559**	*1659**	*1754**	*1816**	*1854**	*1911**	*1956**	*1954**	*2059**	*2154**	...	*2254**	*2354**
133	**Niagara Falls** (Canada) a.	...	*0924**	*1024**	*1034**	*1129**	*1134**	*1229**	*1329**	*1429**	*1529**	*1629**	*1729**	*1829**	*1841**	*1924**	*1936**	*2016**	*2024**	*2119**	*2219**	...	*2319**	*0019**

GO Transit - 2nd class.	900	470	704	906	706	708	908	910	910	912	914	916	918	920	922	922	924	926	928	730	930	930	932	934	936
	Ⓐ	Ⓐ	Ⓐ	⑥⑦	Ⓐ	Ⓐ	⑥⑦	⑥⑦	Ⓐ	Ⓐ					⑥⑦	①–⑤				Ⓐ	⑥⑦	Ⓐ			
Niagara Falls (Canada) d.	...	*0449**	*0519**	*0522**	...	*0604**	*0622**	*0717**	*0707**	*0812**	*0912**	*1012**	*1112**	*1207**	*1307**	*1304**	*1402**	*1502**	*1602**	...	*1702**	*1712**	*1812**	*1917**	*2017**
St. Catharines d.	...	*0514**	*0544**	*0552**	*0614**	*0634**	*0652**	*0747**	*0742**	*0847**	*0947**	*1047**	*1147**	*1247**	*1347**	*1339**	*1442**	*1542**	*1642**	*1722**	*1742**	*1747**	*1847**	*1942**	*2047**
Burlington ☛ d.	0539	0629	0659	0707	0729	0759	0807	0907	0912	1012	1107	1207	1307	1407	1507	1504	1607	1707	1807	1842	1907	1907	2007	2107	2207
Oakville d.	0557	0647	0717	0726	0747	0817	0834	0926	0931	1031	1126	1226	1326	1426	1526	1523	1626	1726	1826	1901	1926	1926	2026	2126	2226
Toronto Union ☛ a.	0640	0720	0750	0810	0820	0850	0910	1010	1016	1116	1211	1311	1411	1511	1610	1608	1711	1810	1911	1946	2010	2011	2111	2211	2311

B – THE MAPLE LEAF – (12) and 🍸 Toronto (**97/98**) - Niagara Falls (**64/63**) - New York and v.v. (Table **9210**).

☛ – Additional trains are available Toronto – Burlington and v.

* – Connection by 🚌 (Route 12).

9025 TORONTO - COCHRANE

Ontario Northland

km		421	🚌
		①–⑤	
		C 🍸	
0	**Toronto** Bay Street d.	...	0915
143	Washago d.	...	1145
164	Gravenhurst d.	...	1205
219	Huntsville d.	...	1315
351	**North Bay** a.	...	1450
351	**North Bay** d.	...	1625*
513	Cobalt d.	...	1805
529	New Liskeard d.	...	1835
571	Engleheart d.	...	1930
643	Swastika d.	...	2025**r**
677	Matheson d.	...	2115*
754	**Cochrane** a.	...	2225
754	**Cochrane** d.	0900	...
	Fraserdale d.	1045**r**	...
	Moose River d.	1235**r**	...
1053	**Moosonee** a.	1350	...

	🚌	422
		①–⑤
		C 🍸
Moosonee d.	...	1700
Moose River d.	...	1807**r**
Fraserdale d.	...	1957**r**
Cochrane a.	...	2145
Cochrane d.	0855	...
Matheson d.	1005*	...
Swastika d.	1105**r**	...
Engleheart d.	1200	...
New Liskeard d.	1255	...
Cobalt d.	1315	...
North Bay a.	1515	...
North Bay d.	1620*	...
Huntsville d.	1740	...
Gravenhurst d.	1855	...
Washago d.	1910	...
Toronto Union a.	2145	...

C – POLAR BEAR EXPRESS – (2) Cochrane - Moosonee and v.v. R. Also ⑦ in summer.

r – Calls on request.

* – Change buses.

9030 TORONTO - SARNIA

2nd class Via F

km		85	87
0	**Toronto** Union d.	1055	1740
34	Brampton d.	1129	1814
47	Georgetown d.	1140	1826
79	Guelph d.	1206	1851
101	Kitchener d.	1232	1918
143	Stratford d.	1309	1955
195	London d.	1417	2114
290	**Sarnia** a.	...	2220

	84
Sarnia d.	0610
London d.	0732
Stratford d.	0840
Kitchener d.	0918
Guelph d.	0944
Georgetown d.	1010
Brampton d.	1020
Toronto Union a.	1053

9035 WHITE RIVER - SUDBURY

2nd class Via F

km		186	
		2	
		③⑤⑦	
0	**White River** d.	0700	...
79	Franz d.	0820	...
209	Chapleau d.	1045	...
341	Biscotasing d.	1245	...
484	**Sudbury** § a.	1550	...

	185
	2
	②④⑥
Sudbury § d.	0900
Biscotasing d.	1120
Chapleau d.	1335
Franz d.	1550
White River a.	1705

§ – Sudbury is 10 km from Sudbury Junction (Table **9050**).

9040 HEARST - SAULT STE MARIE

km		AC	
0	**Hearst** d.	...	...
82	Oba d.	...	...
126	Mosher d.	...	...
162	Franz d.	...	...
211	Hawk Junction d.	...	...
282	Eton d.	...	...
292	Agawa Canyon d.	1400	...
475	**Sault Ste. Marie** a.	1800	...

	AC	
Sault Ste. Marie d.	0800	...
Agawa Canyon d.	1200	...
Eton d.	...	...
Hawk Junction d.	...	...
Franz d.	...	...
Mosher d.	...	...
Oba d.	...	...
Hearst a.	...	...

AC – Agawa Canyon Tour Train. Service operates daily from June 18 until October 15. www.agawatrain.com

9045 THE PAS - PUKATAWAGAN

Keewatin Rail

km		291	
		F	
		①④	
0	**The Pas** **9055** d.	1115	...
88	Cranberry Portage d.	1355	...
251	**Pukatawagan** a.	1845	...

	290
	F
	②⑤
Pukatawagan d.	1000
Cranberry Portage d.	1515
The Pas **9055** a.	1730

F – Operated by Keewatin Railway Company. To book ✆ 204 623 5255.

a Rail TORONTO - VANCOUVER 9050

n		1 ® A	A	® C	C
0	**Toronto** Union d.	0930	③⑦	...	...
3	Washago d.	1210	:	...	...
1	Parry Sound d.	1412	:	...	...
2	Sudbury Junction § d.	1642	:	...	...
4	**Capreol** a.	1707	:	...	...
4	**Capreol** d.	1737	:	...	...
3	Foleyet d.	2229	:	...	...
9	Oba d.	0123	④①	...	...
1	Hornepayne d.	0254	:	...	...
4	Longlac d.	0519	:	...	...
7	Sioux Lookout d.	1140	:	...	...
2	Red Lake Road d.	1326	:	...	...
3	**Winnipeg** a.	1930	:	...	...
3	**Winnipeg** d.	2130	:	...	...
2	Portage la Prairie d.	2304	:	...	...
3	Rivers d.	0131	⑤②	...	...
4	Melville d.	0604	:	...	...
2	**Saskatoon** a.	1050	:	...	...
2	**Saskatoon** d.	1150	:	...	...
2	Biggar d.	1339	:	...	...
7	Wainwright d.	1633	:	...	...
1	**Edmonton** a.	2050	⑤②	...	...
1	**Edmonton** d.	0001	⑥③	0001	⑤
0	Edson d.	0252	:	0252	:
	Hinton d.	0358	:	0358	:
0	**Jasper** a.	0630	:	0630	:
0	**Jasper** d.	0930	:	0930	:
1	Valemount d.	1050	:	1050	:
2	**Kamloops** North a.	1828	:	1828	:
2	**Kamloops** North d.	1903	:	1903	:
0	Hope d.	0201	⑦④	0201	⑥
6	**Vancouver** Pacific a.	0800	⑦④	0800	⑥

	2 ® A		® E	E
Vancouver Pacific a.	1500	①⑤	1500	②
Agassiz d.	1703	:	1703	:
Kamloops North a.	0017	②⑥	0017	③
Kamloops North d.	0635	:	0052	:
Valemount d.	0701	:	0701	:
Jasper a.	1100	:	1100	:
Jasper d.	1230	:	1230	:
Hinton d.	1345	:	1345	:
Edson d.	1519	:	1519	:
Edmonton a.	1850	②⑥	1850	③
Edmonton d.	1950	②⑥	...	...
Wainwright d.	0014	③⑦	...	...
Biggar d.	0431	:	...	...
Saskatoon a.	0657	:	...	...
Saskatoon d.	0757	:	...	...
Melville d.	1357	:	...	...
Rivers d.	1722	:	...	...
Portage la Prairie d.	1915	:	...	...
Winnipeg a.	2200	:	...	...
Winnipeg d.	0001	④①	...	...
Red Lake Road d.	0422	:	...	...
Sioux Lookout d.	0722	:	...	...
Longlac d.	1442	:	...	...
Hornepayne d.	1910	:	...	...
Oba d.	2001	:	...	...
Foleyet d.	2258	:	...	...
Capreol a.	0418	⑤②	...	...
Capreol d.	0448	:	...	...
Sudbury Junction § d.	0520	:	...	...
Parry Sound d.	0913	:	...	...
Washago d.	1130	:	...	...
Toronto Union a.	1500	⑤②	...	...

THE CANADIAN – 🛏 P cl., 🛏, [2] and ✕ Toronto - Vancouver and v.v.

An additional service runs Edmonton - Vancouver on ⑤ May 3 - Oct. 11.

E – An additional service runs Vancouver - Edmonton on ② Apr. 30 - Oct. 8.

§ – Sudbury Junction is 10 km from Sudbury (Table **9035**).

Via Rail WINNIPEG - CHURCHILL 9055

km		691/3 ® B			690/2 ® B	
0	**Winnipeg** d.	1205	②⑦	**Churchill** d.	1930	②④⑥
88	Portage la Prairie d.	1315r	:	Herchmer d.	0003	③⑤⑦
283	Dauphin d.	1706r	:	Giliam (Nelson River) d.	0530	③⑤⑦
484	Canora **a** d.	1946	:	**Thompson** a.	1130	③⑤⑦
549	Endeavour **a** d.	2054r	:	**Thompson** d.	1400	③⑤⑦
635	Hudson Bay **a** d.	2232r	:	Thicket Potage d.	1622	:
777	**The Pas** 9045 a.	0145	①③	Wabowden d.	1811	:
777	**The Pas** 9045 d.	0230	①③⑤	Cormorant d.	2147	:
843	Cormorant d.	0412	:	**The Pas** 9045 a.	2330	③⑤⑦
996	Wabowden d.	0748	:	**The Pas** 9045 d.	0315	⑥①
1073	Thicket Potage d.	0937	:	Hudson Bay **a** d.	r	:
1149	**Thompson** a.	1200	①③⑤	Endeavour **a** d.	r	:
1149	**Thompson** d.	1700	①③⑤	Canora **a** d.	0818	:
1401	Giliam (Nelson River) a.	2300	①③⑤	Dauphin d.	1206	:
1540	Herchmer d.	0426	②④⑥	Portage la Prairie d.	1537r	:
1697	**Churchill** a.	0900	②④⑥	**Winnipeg** a.	1645	②

B – 🛏, [2] and ✕ Churchill - Winnipeg and v.v.

a – Saskatchewan, always standard time. r – Request stop.

Via Rail PRINCE RUPERT - JASPER 9060

km		5 ® ③⑤⑦			6 ® ③⑤⑦	
0	**Jasper** d.	1245	③⑤⑦	**Prince Rupert** d.	0800	③⑤⑦
174	McBride d.	1444	:	Terrace (Kitimat) d.	1025	:
409	**Prince George** a.	1908	:	New Hazelton d.	1230r	:
409	**Prince George** d.	0800	④⑥①	Smithers d.	1424	:
560	Fort Fraser d.	1032r	:	Fort Fraser d.	1757r	:
795	Smithers d.	1420	:	**Prince George** a.	2029	:
869	New Hazelton d.	1537r	:	**Prince George** d.	0945	④⑥①
1007	Terrace (Kitimat) d.	1805	:	McBride d.	1348	:
1160	**Prince Rupert** a.	2025	:	**Jasper** a.	1830	:

Compulsory overnight stop in **Prince George**. Passengers must arrange their own accommodation.

r – Request stop.

MR ROCKY MOUNTAINEER TOURS 9065

	D	E	G	H
attle d.	...	...	...	1510
ncouver ‡ a.	...	...	...	2045
ncouver ‡ d.	0730	0730	...	...
I. Vancouver d.	|	|	0740	...
Vhistler ♥ a.	|	|	1130	...
Vhistler ♥ d.	|	|	0710	...
uesnel ♥ a.	|	|	1930	...
uesnel ♥ d.	|	|	0710	...
mloops ♥ a.	1730	1730	|	...
mloops ♥ d.	0625	0745	|	...
asper a.	|	1800	2030	...
e Louise a.	1830	...	...	...
nff a.	1930	...	...	...

	H	E	D	G
Banff d.	...	...	0740	...
Lake Louise d.	...	...	0900	...
Jasper d.	...	0810	|	0655
Kamloops ♥ a.	...	1700	1815	|
Kamloops ♥ d.	...	0735	0735	|
Quesnel ♥ a.	...	|	|	1930
Quesnel ♥ d.	...	|	|	0710
Whistler ♥ a.	...	|	|	1930
Whistler ♥ d.	...	|	|	1510
N. Vancouver a.	...	|	|	1900
Vancover ‡ a.	...	1730	1730	...
Vancouver ‡ d.	0810	...	...	...
Seattle a.	1315	...	...	...

FIRST PASSAGE TO THE WEST – For 2019 dates contact operator.◀
JOURNEY THROUGH THE CLOUDS – For 2019 dates contact operator. ◀
RAINFOREST TO GOLD RUSH – For 2019 dates contact operator. ★
COASTAL PASSAGE – For 2019 dates contact operator. ★
- Services operate on selected dates from mid April to early October.
- Services opeate on selected dates from late April to early October.
Vancouver Cottrell Street.
Compulsory overnight stop, arrival times are flexible.
erator: Rocky Mountaineer Railtours (www.rockymountaineer.com)

West Coast VANCOUVER - MISSION CITY 9070

km		①-⑤	①-⑤		①-⑤	①-⑤		①-⑤	
0	**Vancouver** Waterfront d.	1550	1620	...	1650	1730	...	1820	...
26	Coquitlam d.	1619	1649	...	1719	1759	...	1849	...
68	**Mission City** a.	1705	1735	...	1805	1845	...	1935	...

		①-⑤	①-⑤		①-⑤	①-⑤		①-⑤	
Mission City d.	...	0525	0555	...	0625	0655	...	0725	...
Coquitlam d.	...	0610	0640	...	0710	0740	...	0810	...
Vancouver Waterfront a.	...	0640	0710	...	0740	0810	...	0840	...

Operator: West Coast Express ✆ 604 488 8906.

Red Arrow 🚌 CALGARY - EDMONTON 🚌 9090

km		Ⓐ	a ⚒	a ⑦	a	a Ⓐ		a	
0	**Calgary** d.	0600	0800	1000	1200	1400	1630	1830	...
303	**Edmonton** a.	0920	1150	1405	1605	1805	1950	2215	...

		Ⓐ	a ⚒	a ⑦	a	a Ⓐ		a	
Edmonton d.	...	0600	0800	1000	1200	1400	1630	1830	...
Calgary a.	...	0920	1205	1405	1605	1805	1950	2200	...

a – Also calls at Red Deer. www.redarrow.ca

UNITED STATES OF AMERICA

ital: **Washington DC** (GMT -5, add one hour in summer). 2019 Public Holidays: Jan. 1, 21, Feb. 18, May 27, July 4, Sep. 1, Oct. 14, Nov. 11, 28, Dec. 25.

principal operator in the USA is Amtrak (✆ 1 800 872 7245. www.amtrak.com). Details of other operators can be found in relevant tables. Unless otherwise noted all trains y first and second class seated accomodation known as 'Business' and 'Coach' class respectively. Acela Express trains running between Boston, New York and Washington vey business class and an enhanced seated accommodation, confusingly called 'First Class'. Most very long distance trains convey sleeping cars, and where this is the case detailed in the footnotes. Almost all sleeping car accommodation in North America has two berths per compartment, some of which are en-suite, although the exact product ring varies by operator and route. Most trains also convey some form of catering, but again the actual service offered varies considerably. Timings shown are the latest ilable and are subject to alteration around public holidays and it is recommended that you confirm all timings locally as short notice changes are possible. Tickets are available n staffed stations, websites and through authorised ticketing agents. Amtrak requires reservations on practically all of its services, and also requires that you have identity uments available for inspection.

rak offers the 'USA Rail Pass' It is available to both US citizens and foreign nationals and has the option of three validity periods: 15 day/8 segments of travel, 30 day/12 ments of travel and 45 day/18 segments of travel. The adult prices are $459 for 8 segments, $689 for 12 segments and $899 for 18 segments, 50% reduction for children d 2 - 12. The pass is valid in coach class on the entire Amtrak system. Be warned though: this program is now revenue/capacity managed and may not be available on all ns all the time. The pass is not valid on the Autotrain, Acela Express trains, Thruway buses numbered 7000 – 7999 and the Canadian portion of trains operated jointly by rak and VIA Rail Canada. The pass alone is not valid for travel; tickets and, where neccessary, reservations must be obtained for each segment of travel. Upgrades to higher ls of accommodation may be possible subject to capacity and the payment of relevant supplements. Travel is limited to no more than four one-way journeys over any given e segment. A segment is any time you get on and then get off a train or bus, regardless of the length of that journey. A 7 day Califorina Rail Pass is also available. For full ils on both passes see the Amtrak website (www.amtrak.com).

ite Pass and Yukon Railroad SKAGWAY - WHITEHORSE 9100

m		1 A	C	①-⑥ D	🚌
0	**Skagway** Shops d.	0730	0740	1240	1430
22	White Pass ▶ 🏛 d.	|	|	|	|
41	Fraser a.	0900	0945	1445	1530
41	Fraser d.	0900	...	...	1535
65	Bennett a.	1015	...	...	|
65	Bennett d.	1100	...	...	|
08	Carcross a.	1230	...	...	1630
08	Carcross d.	...	...	...	1635
77	**Whitehorse** a.	...	...	...	1800

	🚌	C	①-⑥ D	2 B
Whitehorse d.	0745	...	...	...
Carcross a.	0845	...	...	...
Carcross d.	0900	...	...	1300
Bennett a.	|	...	...	1430
Bennett d.	|	...	...	1515
Fraser a.	1015	...	...	1600
Fraser d.	1015	1040	1530	1600
White Pass ▶ 🏛 d.	|	|	|	|
Skagway Shops a.	1130	1220	1720	1745

☛ For services crossing the US/Canadian border passengers must provide proof of citizenship. All services ®. All times shown are Alaska time.

▶ – Between Apr. 29 and Oct. 3 a White Pass Summit round trip excursion operates **c**. Services departs Skagway on most days at 0900 and 1300 (ex ③) but times do vary on some dates. Additional services operate at 1515 on ①②③ and 1615 on ②③ between May and early September. Contact operator for exact details.

c – Not May 1, 5, 6, Sept. 27, 30, Oct. 2.

Operator: White Pass & Yukon Railroad ✆ Skagway 907 983 2217. www.wpyr.com

May 21 - Sept. 14. From Skagway ②③④⑤⑦.
May 21 - Sept. 14. From Carcross ②③④⑥⑦.
Apr. 29 - Oct. 3 (not May 1, 5, 6, Sept. 27 - 30, Oct. 2). Note: Services on ②③ are not available on-line, phone for availability.
May. 7 - Oct. 1 (not May 9, Sept. 27 - 30.) Note: Services on ②③ are not available on-line, phone for availability.

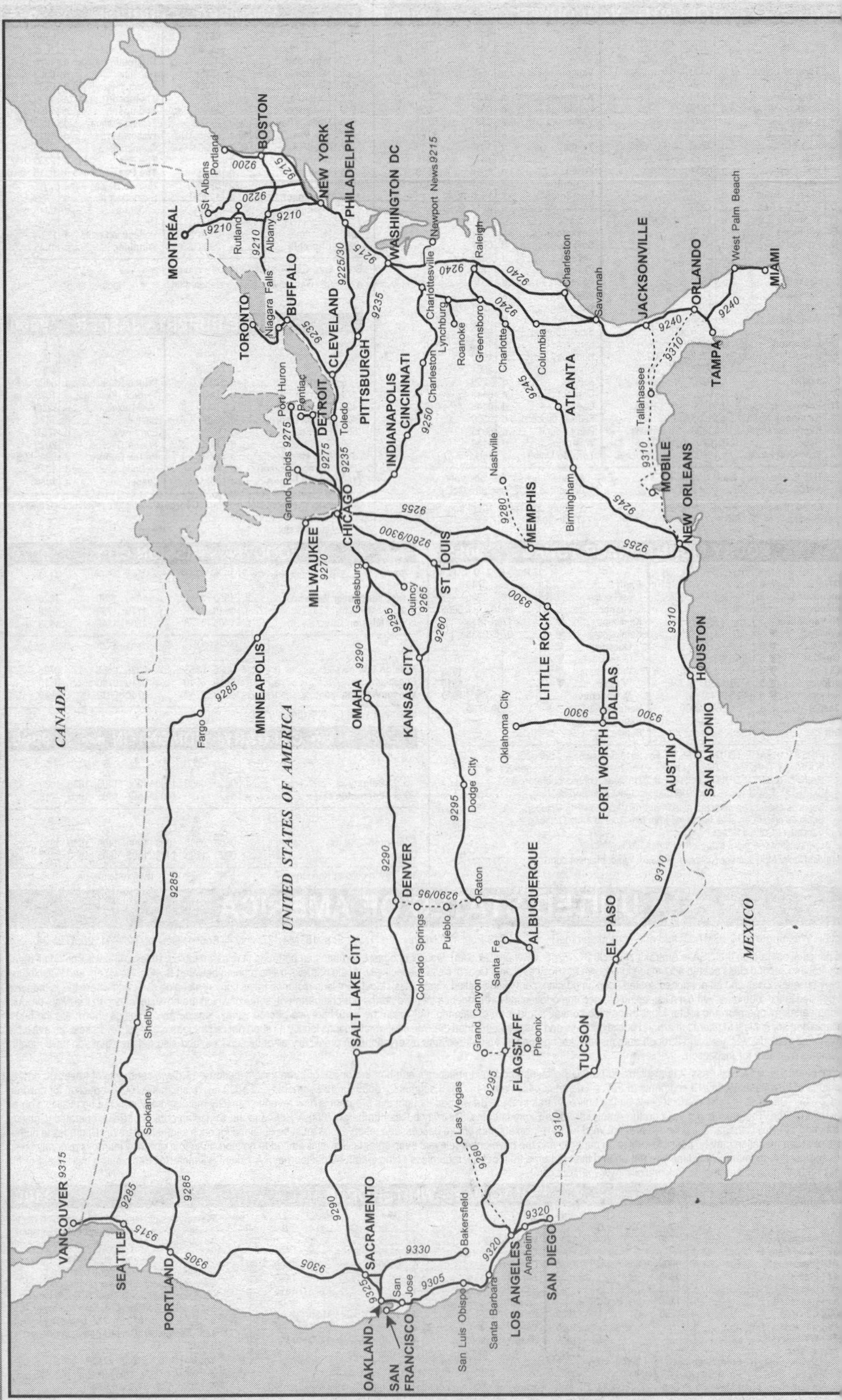
CANADA
UNITED STATES OF AMERICA
MEXICO
MONTRÉAL
St Albans
Portland
BOSTON
NEW YORK
PHILADELPHIA
WASHINGTON DC
Newport News
Rutland
Albany
BUFFALO
Niagara Falls
TORONTO
CLEVELAND
PITTSBURGH
Charlottesville
Raleigh
Lynchburg
Roanoke
Greensboro
Charlotte
Charleston
Savannah
Columbia
JACKSONVILLE
ORLANDO
West Palm Beach
MIAMI
TAMPA
Tallahassee
ATLANTA
Birmingham
MOBILE
NEW ORLEANS
Port Huron
Pontiac
DETROIT
Toledo
INDIANAPOLIS
CINCINNATI
Charleston
Nashville
MEMPHIS
Grand Rapids
CHICAGO
MILWAUKEE
Galesburg
Quincy
ST LOUIS
LITTLE ROCK
KANSAS CITY
MINNEAPOLIS
OMAHA
Fargo
HOUSTON
DALLAS
FORT WORTH
Oklahoma City
AUSTIN
SAN ANTONIO
Dodge City
Raton
DENVER
Colorado Springs
Pueblo
ALBUQUERQUE
Santa Fe
EL PASO
SALT LAKE CITY
Grand Canyon
FLAGSTAFF
Pheonix
TUCSON
Shelby
Spokane
Las Vegas
VANCOUVER
SEATTLE
PORTLAND
SACRAMENTO
OAKLAND
SAN FRANCISCO
San Jose
Bakersfield
San Luis Obispo
Santa Barbara
LOS ANGELES
Anaheim
SAN DIEGO
9200
9210
9215
9220
9225/30
9235
9240
9245
9250
9255
9260
9260/9300
9265
9270
9275
9280
9285
9290
9290/95
9295
9300
9305
9310
9315
9320
9325
9330

ALASKA — 9105

ska Railroad

	E	F	Ab	C ④	Bf ⑦	D ④–①
Fairbanks d.	...	...	0815	...	0830	...
Denali d.	...	...	1230	...	1230	...
Hurricane d.	...	...	|	1445	1445	1630
Talkeetna d.	...	...	1655	1650	1650	1915
Wasilla d.	...	...	1820e	1825	1825	...
Anchorage a.	...	...	2000	2000	2000	...
Anchorage d.	0645	0945	...	...	...	...
Girdwood d.	0800e	1100	...	...	...	...
Portage a.	|	1130	...	...	...	...
Whittier d.	|	1245	...	...	...	...
Portage d.	|	1325	...	...	...	...
Spencer a.	|	1345	...	...	...	...
Spencer d.	|	1355	...	...	...	...
Grandview a.	|	1520a	...	...	...	...
Seward a.	1105	...	...	...	...	...

	Aa	Bd ⑥	C ④	D ④–①	F	E
Seward d.	...	...	...	...	...	1800
Grandview d.	...	...	...	...	1530a	|
Spencer a.	...	...	...	...	1630	|
Spencer d.	...	...	...	...	1640	|
Portage a.	...	...	...	...	1715	|
Whittier d.	...	...	...	...	1845	|
Portage d.	...	...	...	...	1920	|
Girdwood d.	...	...	...	...	1940	2055e
Anchorage a.	...	...	...	...	2115	2215
Anchorage d.	0815	0830	0830	...	...	...
Wasilla d.	0935e	0950	0950	...	...	...
Talkeetna d.	1120	1125	1125	1300	...	...
Hurricane a.	|	1340	1340	1530	...	...
Denali d.	1600	1555	...	...	...	...
Fairbanks a.	2000	2000	...	...	...	...

DENALI STAR – [2] and ✕ (**Aa** – May 11 - Sept. 16. **Ab** – May 12 - Sept. 17).
AURORA – [2] and ✕ Sept. 22, 2018 - May 5, 2019 (**Bd** – Also Nov. 21, Dec. 26, 28, Jan. 2, Feb. 6, 8, 13, 20, 27, Mar. 1, 6, 8, 13, 15, 20, 22, 27, 29; **Bf** – Also Nov. 20, Dec. 25, 27, Jan. 1, Feb. 5, 7, 12, 19, 26, 28, Mar. 5, 7, 12, 14, 19, 21, 26, 28).
HURRICANE TURN (WINTER) – [2] 1st ④ of every month Oct. 4, 2018 - May 30, 2019.
HURRICANE TURN (SUMMER) – [2] May 16 - Sept. 16.

E – COASTAL CLASSIC – [2] and ✕ May 11 - Sept. 16.
F – GLACIER DISCOVERY – [2] and ✕ May 25 - Sept. 16.

a – From June 5.
p – Kms from Portage.

Operator : Alaska Railroad ✆ Anchorage 907 265 2620. Fax 907 265 2323.

BRUNSWICK - PORTLAND - BOSTON — 9200

trak

	680 Ⓐ	690 Ⓒ	682 Ⓐ	692 Ⓒ	684 Ⓐ	694 Ⓒ	686 Ⓐ	696 Ⓒ	688 Ⓐ	698 Ⓒ
Brunswick d.	0430	0600	0730	0730	1110	1120	1330	...	1725	1805
Freeport d.	0443	0613	0743	0743	1123	1133	1343	...	1738	1818
Portland d.	0520	0650	0820	0820	1155	1215	1420	1530	1815	1855
Old Orchard Beach ≪≪ d.	|	|	|	|	|	|	1435	|	|	|
Saco d.	0542	0712	0841	0842	1222	1237	1442	1552	1837	1917
Wells d.	0559	0729	0858	0859	1239	1254	1459	1609	1855	1934
Dover d.	0617	0747	0916	0917	1257	1312	1517	1627	1913	1952
Durham d.	0625	0754	0924	0925	1305	1320	1525	1635	1921	2000
Exeter d.	0639	0807	0938	0938	1319	1334	1539	1649	1935	2014
Haverhill d.	0700	0827	0959	1000	1340	1355	1600	1710	1956	2035
Boston North a.	0750	0915	1050	1050	1430	1445	1650	1800	2045	2125

	681 Ⓐ	691 Ⓒ	693 Ⓒ	683 Ⓐ	695 Ⓒ	685 Ⓐ	687 Ⓐ	697 Ⓒ	689* Ⓐ	699* Ⓒ
ton North d.	0905	1020	1210	1305	1645	1700	1815	1935	2230	2230
erhill d.	0953	1108	1258	1353	1733	1748	1902	2023	2318r	2318r
er d.	1014	1129	1319	1414	1754	1809	1922	2044	2339r	2339r
am d.	1027	1142	1340	1427	1807	1822	1943	2057	2352r	2352r
er d.	1035	1150	1348	1435	1815	1830	1951	2105	2359r	0000r
s d.	1053	1208	1406	1453	1833	1848	2009	2123	0018r	0018r
) d.	1110	1225	1423	1510	1850	1905	2026	2140	0035r	0035r
Orchard Beach ≪≪ d.	|	|	|	|	|	|	|	|	|	|
land a.	1135	1255	1445	1535	1915	1925	2050	2205	0055	0055r
port d.	1210r	1330r	...	1610r	1950r	2000r	2125r	2240r	0130r	0130r
nswick a.	1225	1345	...	1625	2005	2015	2140	2255	0145	0145

Calls on request. ≪≪– Seasonal stop. Station open mid-June to mid-October only.
* – To accommodate special events in Boston a special train will depart Boston North at 2325.

NEW YORK - ALBANY - RUTLAND, MONTREÁL and NIAGARA FALLS — 9210

trak

Note: June 28 - Sept. 2 train **69** will combine with and run in the regular time slot of train **63** between New York and Albany.

	63 F	69 2H	281 J	233	283 J	255 ⑤	291 ①–④ K	235 Ⓐ	295 Ⓒ K	49 G	237 Ⓐ	253 Ⓒ	239 ①–④	293 ⑤ K	241	243 Ⓐ	259 Ⓒ	245 Ⓐ	261 Ⓒ
New York Penn Station ▼ d.	0715	0915	1020	1120	1320	1420	1420	1515	1515	1540	1640	1715	1747	1747	1915	2055	2115	2245	2335
Yonkers ▼ d.	0744	0844	|	1144	1344	1444	1444	1539	1539	|	|	1739	|	|	1939	2119	2139	|	|
Croton Harmon ▼ d.	0803	0903	1101	1203	1403	1503	1503	1558	1558	1626	|	1758	1832	1832	1958	2138	2158	2326	0016
Poughkeepsie ▼ d.	0845	0945	1143	1245	1445	1545	1545	1640	1640	1710	|	1840	1922	1922	2040	2220	2240	0008	0058
Rhinecliff Kingston d.	0900	1001	1158	1300	1500	1600	1600	1655	1655	1727e	1811e	1855	1937e	1937	2055e	2236e	2255e	0023e	0113e
Hudson d.	0921	1021	1220	1320	1522	1620	1620	1715	1716	|	1832e	1915	1957e	1957	2115e	2256e	2315e	0043e	0134e
Albany Rensselaer a.	0950	1047	1245	1150	1545	1650	1650	1745	1745	1820	1900	1945	2020	2020	2145	2325	2345	0115	0205
Albany Rensselaer d.	1000	1110	1300	...	1600	...	1705	...	1800	1905	...	...	...	2030	...	...	...	...	...
Schenectady d.	1024	1133	1323	...	1623	...	1728	...	1824	1932	...	...	...	2054	...	...	...	...	...
Saratoga Springs d.	|	1202	|	...	|	...	1754	...	1850	|	...	...	...	2123	...	...	...	...	...
Rutland a.	|	|	|	...	|	...	1952	...	2048	|	...	...	...	2318	...	...	...	...	...
Westport d.	|	1402	|	...	|	...	...	...	...	|	...	...	...	...	...	...	...	...	...
Plattsburgh d.	|	1520	|	...	|	...	...	...	...	|	...	...	...	...	...	...	...	...	...
Montréal Central a.	|	1911	|	...	|	...	...	...	...	|	...	...	...	...	...	...	...	...	...
Utica d.	1141	...	1440	...	1741	...	...	...	...	2049	...	...	...	...	...	...	...	...	...
Syracuse d.	1243	...	1545	...	1844	...	...	...	...	2152	...	...	...	...	...	...	...	...	...
Rochester d.	1357	...	1659	...	1958	...	...	...	...	2312	...	...	...	...	...	...	...	...	...
Buffalo Exchange St. a.	1514	...	1824e	...	2123e	...	...	...	...	0020d	...	...	...	...	...	...	...	...	...
Niagara Falls USA a.	1928	...	1911	...	2211	...	...	...	...	...	...	...	...	...	...	...	...	...	...
Toronto Union **9020** a.	1941	...	...	...	...	...	...	...	...	...	...	...	...	...	...	...	...	...	...

	230 Ⓐ	232 Ⓐ	250 Ⓒ	234 Ⓐ	252 ⑥	260 Ⓒ	236 Ⓐ	280 J	254 ⑦	290 Ⓐ K	238	284 J	256 Ⓒ	292 ⑥ K	242 Ⓐ	48 G	244	68 2H	64 F	296 ⑦ K	288 ⑦
ronto Union **9020** d.	...	...	...	...	...	...	...	...	...	...	...	...	...	...	...	...	...	...	0820	...	...
ara Falls USA d.	...	...	...	...	...	...	...	0352	...	...	...	0647	...	...	...	...	...	...	1212	...	149
alo Exchange St d.	...	...	...	...	...	...	...	0430	...	...	...	0725	...	...	...	0854d	...	...	1250	...	1537
hester d.	...	...	...	...	...	...	...	0541	...	...	...	0836	...	...	...	0953	...	...	1358	...	1648
cuse d.	...	...	...	...	...	...	...	0701	...	...	...	0956	...	...	...	1123	...	...	1514	...	1808
a d.	...	...	...	...	...	...	...	0756	...	...	...	1051	...	...	...	1220	...	...	1615	...	1903
ontréal Central d.	...	...	...	...	...	...	...	|	...	...	...	|	...	...	...	|	...	1020	|	...	|
attsburgh d.	...	...	...	...	...	...	...	|	...	...	...	|	...	...	...	|	...	1325	|	...	|
estport d.	...	...	...	...	...	...	...	|	...	...	...	|	...	...	...	|	...	1429	|	...	|
Rutland d.	...	...	...	...	...	...	...	|	...	0815	...	|	...	1115	...	|	...	|	|	1705	|
aratoga Springs d.	...	...	...	...	...	...	...	|	...	0952	...	|	...	1251	...	|	...	1645	|	1847	|
enectady d.	...	...	...	...	...	...	...	0920	...	1028	...	1216	...	1332	...	1359	...	1718	1813	1923	2035
ny Rensselaer a.	...	...	...	...	...	...	...	0941	...	1050	...	1237	...	1355	...	1431	...	1740	1835	1945	2055
ny Rensselaer d.	0510	0555	0615	0700	0715	0810	0825	1005	1010	1110	1210	1305	1410	1410	1515	1545	1610	1815	1915	2015	2115
son d.	0432	0617	0637	0722	0737	0832	0847	1028	1032	1131	1231	1328	1431	1432	1536	|	1631	1838	1937	2037	2137
cliff Kingston d.	0555	0639	0659	0744	0759	0854	0909	1051	1054	1153	1252	1351	1452	1454	1557	1633	1652	1900	1959	2059	2159
ghkeepsie ▼ d.	|	|	0710	|	0810	0910	0920	1110	1110	1210	1310	1410	1510	1510	1615	1652	1710	1915	2015	2115	2217
on Harmon ▼ d.	0643	0731	0750	|	0850	0950	0959	1150	1150	1250	1350	1450	1550	1550	1655	1738	1750	1956	2056	2155	2257
kers ▼ d.	|	|	0811	|	0911	1011	1021	|	|	1311	1411	1511	1611	1611	1716	|	|	2017	2116	2216	|
York Penn Station ▼ a.	0719	0814	0844	0918	0944	1039	1049	1244	1244	1345	1444	1544	1644	1645	1745	1822	1844	2050	2150	2250	2344

THE MAPLE LEAF – [12] and 🍸 Toronto (**97/98**) - Niagara Falls (**64/63**) - New York and v.v. (Table **9020**).
LAKE SHORE LIMITED – 🛏 1, 2 cl., [2] and ✕ Boston - Albany - Chicago and v.v.
ADIRONDACK – [2] and 🍸 New York - Montréal and v.v.
EMPIRE SERVICE – [12] and 🍸 New York - Niagara Falls and v.v.
ETHAN ALLEN EXPRESS – [12] and 🍸 New York - Rutland and v.v.

d – Buffalo **Depew**.
NOTE: Until June 29 some services will arrive up to 15 minutes later at Albany and/or New York
▼ – Local traffic not carried. Frequent services are operated by Metro North Railroad.

9215 BOSTON - NEW YORK - WASHINGTON - NEWPORT NEWS

Most trains 🍸 Amt

km		65	67	151	111	2103	89	89	131	51	2107	183	79	79	2109	2203	153	185	451	2151	2205	155	141	2153
						Acela					Acela				Acela	Acela				Acela	Acela			Acela
		⑤⑥	⑦–④	①–⑤	①–⑤	①–⑤	⑥⑦	①–⑤	⑥⑦	③⑤⑦	①–⑤	①–⑤	⑥⑦	①–⑤	①–⑤	⑥	⑥⑦	①–⑤	①–⑤	①–⑤	⑦	⑥⑦	①–⑤	①–⑤
							♦	♦		♦			♦	♦					2					
0	**Boston** South.....d.	2130	2130	...	...	...	...	...	...	...	...	...	...	...	...	...	...	...	...	0500	...	...	...	0600
69	Providence.....d.	2222	2222	...	...	...	...	...	...	...	...	...	...	...	...	...	...	...	...	0535	...	...	...	0638
169	New London.....d.	2331	2331	...	...	...	...	...	...	...	...	...	...	...	...	...	...	...	...	0619	...	...	...	|
	Springfield MA.....d.	|	|	...	...	...	...	...	...	...	...	...	...	...	...	...	...	...	0515	|	...	...	0555	|
	Hartford.....d.	|	|	...	...	...	...	...	...	...	...	...	...	...	...	...	...	...	0548	|	...	...	0631	|
251	New Haven.....d.	0050	0050	...	...	...	...	...	...	...	...	...	...	...	...	...	...	...	0635	0704	...	...	0737	0809
301	Stamford.....d.	0136	0136	...	...	...	...	...	...	...	...	...	...	...	...	...	...	...	...	0754	...	...	0827	0858
373	**New York** Penn.....a.	0230	0230	...	...	...	...	...	...	...	...	...	...	...	...	...	...	...	...	0850	...	...	0921	0950
373	**New York** Penn.....d.	0300	0325	0440	0530	0600	0602	0551	0645	0645	0700	0705	0717	0725	0800	0800	0805	0810	...	0903	0900	0905	0935	1003
389	Newark NJ.....d.	0320	0345	0457u	0546u	0615u	0619u	0608u	0702	0705u	0715u	0722	0739u	0744u	0815u	0814	0822	0827	...	0918	0914u	0922	0952	1018
519	**Philadelphia** 30th St..d.	0432	0500	0614	0703	0720	0732u	0733u	0817	0815u	0820	0835	0854	0854	0918	0918	0936	0946	...	1015	1017	1034	1119	1115
670	Baltimore Penn.....d.	0543	0610	0737	0810	0824	0845u	0844u	0934	0930u	0925	0942	1007	1009	1022	1022	1049	1057	...	1121	1120	1149	1231	1220
687	BWI Airport.....d.	0556	0625	0750	0826	|	0858u	0857	0948	|	|	0956	|	|	|	1035	1102	1110	...	1135	1133	1202	1245	1234
735	**Washington** Union.....a.	0630	0700	0822	0856	0901	0930u	0924u	1024	1100u	0959	1032	1046	1048	1058	1101	1133	1142	...	1159	1201	1234	1321	1300
735	**Washington** Union.....d.	0700	0720	...	...	...	1005u	1005u	...	1100u	...	...	1108	1108	...	...	...	...	...	...	...	...	...	...
822	Fredricksburg.....d.	0805	0826	...	...	...	|	|	...	|	...	...	1219	1219										
911	Richmond.....d.	0908	0934	...	...	...	1216	1216	...	|	...	...	1327	1327										
1042	**Newport News**.....a.	1115	1133	...	...	...	...	...	...	|	...	...	...	...										
1092	Norfolk.....a.	*1215**	*1250**	...	...	...	...	...	...	|	...	...	...	...										
	Virgina Beach.....a.	*1255**	*1330**	...	...	...	...	...	...	|	...	...	...	...										
915	Charlottesville.....d.	...	...	...	...	...	...	...	...	1352	...	...	...	...										
1012	**Lynchburg**.....a.	...	...	...	...	...	...	...	...	...	...	...	...	...	...	...	...	...	...	...	...	...	...	...

Due to track and infrastructure improvements being performed alo the Northeast Corridor (that started on April 14) scheduled departu and arrival times of Acela Express and Northeast Regional trains m vary by up to 15 minutes in both directions between Boston, New Yo Washington DC and Roanoke.

	143	495	95	2155	91	405	195	125	2117	2251	2213	157	147	145	471	171	99	2159	2215	133	2121		93
				Acela					Acela	Acela	Acela							Acela	Acela		Acela		
	⑥⑦	①–⑤	①–⑤	①–⑤		⑥⑦	⑥⑦	①–⑤	①–⑤	⑥	⑦	⑦	⑥	⑦	①–⑤	①–⑤	⑥⑦	①–⑤	⑦	⑤	①–⑤		①–⑤
		2			♦	2									2								
Boston South.....d.	...	...	0610	0715	...	...	0630	...	...	0800	...	...	...	...	...	0810	0840	0900	...	...	...	...	0930
Providence.....d.	...	...	0650	0751	...	...	0711	...	...	0835	...	...	...	...	...	0853	0919	0936	...	...	...	...	1011
New London.....d.	...	...	0745	|	...	...	0808	...	...	|	...	...	...	...	...	0947	1020	|	...	...	...	...	1112
Springfield MA.....d.	0600	0705	|	|	...	0725	|	...	...	|	...	0758	0835	...	0855	|	|	|	...	...	...	...	|
Hartford.....d.	0634	0739	|	|	...	0759	|	...	...	|	...	0833	0910	...	0929	|	|	|	...	...	...	...	|
New Haven.....d.	0740	0827	0843	|	...	0847	0905	...	...	1009	...	0939	1018	...	1018	1036	1109	1106	...	...	...	...	1209
Stamford.....d.	0830	...	0930	1001	...	...	0959	...	...	1058	...	1025	1111	...	...	1129	1158	1156	...	...	...	...	1258
New York Penn.....a.	0926	...	1022	1059	...	...	1051	...	...	1147	...	1125	1213	...	...	1221	1303	1247	...	...	...	...	1348
New York Penn.....d.	0947	...	1035	1113	1102	...	1105	1135	1200	1200	1200	1205	1250	1255	...	1235	1317	1300	1300	1309	1400	...	1402
Newark NJ.....d.	1004	...	1053	1128	1122u	...	1123	1152	1215u	1214	1214u	1222	1307	1312	...	1252	1335	1315	1316u	1325u	1415u	...	1419
Philadelphia 30th Street.....d.	1118	...	1202	1234	1235u	...	1234	1307	1318	1315	1318	1333	1421	1422	...	1414	1450	1413	1417	1424	1514	...	1530
Baltimore Penn.....d.	1232	...	1317	1340	1355u	...	1343	1424	1422	1420	1423	1448	1531	1532	...	1530	1558	1518	1521	1547	1619	...	1638
BWI Airport.....d.	1245	...	1330	|	|	...	1356	1438	|	1433	1436	1501	1544	1545	...	1545	1611	1533	1534	1602	1632	...	1651
Washington Union.....a.	1321	...	1358	1413	1505u	...	1428	1510	1457	1503	1503	1533	1617	1617	...	1620	1639	1600	1600	1634	1658	...	1720
Washington Union.....d.	...	...	1430	...	1505u	...	1450	1555	...	...	...	1600	1635	1650	...	1650	1700	...	...	...	...	...	1750
Fredricksburg.....d.	...	...	1540	...	|	...	1601	1712	...	...	...	1710	|	|	...	|	1808	...	...	...	...	...	1902
Richmond.....d.	...	...	1649	...	1707	...	1704	1828	...	...	...	1822	|	|	...	|	1913	...	...	...	...	...	2017
Newport News.....a.	...	...	|	...	...	...	...	|	...	...	...	|	|	|	...	|	2106	...	...	...	...	...	|
Norfolk.....a.	...	...	1904	...	...	...	...	2020	...	...	...	2036	|	|	...	|	*2155**	...	...	...	...	...	2231
Virgina Beach.....a.	...	...	...	...	...	...	...	...	...	...	...	...	|	|	...	|	*2225**	...	...	...	...	...	...
Charlottesville.....d.	...	...	...	...	...	...	...	...	...	...	...	...	1901	1916	...	1923	...	...	...	...	...	...	...
Lynchburg.....a.	...	...	...	...	...	...	...	...	...	...	...	...	2014	2029	...	2036	...	...	...	...	...	...	...
Roanoke.....a.		...	...	...	...	...	...	...	...	...	...	...	2133	2148	...	2155	...	...	...	...	...	...	...

	461	161	19	2163	2253	85	87		97	473	173	2261	2165	189	463	163	129	2167	2255	159	409	149	193	2119
				Acela	Acela							Acela	Acela					Acela	Acela					Acela
	⑥⑦	⑥⑦		①–⑤	⑥⑦	①–⑤	⑥⑦			①–⑤	①–⑤	⑦	①–⑤	⑦	⑥	⑥	①–⑤	①–⑤	⑥⑦	⑥	⑦	⑦	①–⑤	①–⑤
	2		♦						♦	2					2						2			
Boston South.....d.	...	0935	...	1100	1105	...	...	...	...	...	1110	1200	1205	...	...	1140	...	1300	1300	...	...	1215	...	...
Providence.....d.	...	1015	...	1143	1140	...	...	...	...	...	1154	1236	1242	...	...	1220	...	1336	1336	...	...	1257	...	...
New London.....d.	...	1110	...	|	|	...	...	...	...	...	1246	|	|	...	...	1320	...	|	|	...	...	1354	...	...
Springfield MA.....d.	1035	|	...	|	|	...	...	...	...	1205	|	|	|	...	1230	|	...	|	|	...	1310	|	...	...
Hartford.....d.	1109	|	...	|	|	...	...	...	...	1239	|	|	|	...	1305	|	...	|	|	...	1344	|	...	...
New Haven.....d.	1157	1205	...	1309	1308	...	...	...	...	1328	1340	1408	1411	...	1352	1409	...	1511	1513	...	1430	1443	...	...
Stamford.....d.	...	1257	...	1357	1357	...	...	...	...	...	1429	1457	1458	...	...	1458	...	1558	1558	...	...	1531	...	...
New York Penn.....a.	...	1351	...	1451	1447	...	...	...	...	...	1522	1547	1552	...	...	1552	...	1650	1647	...	...	1633	...	...
New York Penn.....d.	...	1405	1415	1504	1500	1505	1504	...	1515	...	1535	1600	1602	1605	...	1605	1635	1700	1700	1705	...	1705	1727	1800
Newark NJ.....d.	...	1422	1437u	1519	1514	1522	1521u	...	1538u	...	1553	1614u	1617	1622	...	1622	1652	1715	1714	1722	...	1722	1744	1815u
Philadelphia 30th Street.....d.	...	1537	1555u	1618	1615	1631	1635	...	1654u	...	1705	1714	1714	1735	...	1735	1814	1812	1815	1837	...	1837	1854	1914
Baltimore Penn.....d.	...	1651	1708u	1724	1721	1747	1750	...	1812u	...	1823	1819	1820	1848	...	1854	1930	1918	1920	1953	...	1952	2008	2018
BWI Airport.....d.	...	1704	|	1737	1734	1801	1802	...	|	...	1837	1832	1833	1901	...	1908	1944	1931	1933	2006	...	2006	2021	2031
Washington Union.....a.	...	1736	1756u	1804	1802	1830	1835	...	1850u	...	1907	1900	1601	1939	...	1942	2015	2000	2001	2039	...	2042	2053	2058
Washington Union.....d.	...	...	1830u	...	...	1905	1900	...	1925u	...	...	...	...	...	...	...	...	...	...	...	...	...	...	...
Fredricksburg.....d.	...	...	|	...	...	2017	2012	...	2033	...	...	...	...	...	...	...	...	...	...	...	...	...	...	...
Richmond.....d.	...	...	|	...	...	2121	2122	...	2134	...	...	...	...	...	...	...	...	...	...	...	...	...	...	...
Newport News.....a.	...	...	|	...	...	...	|	...	...	...	...	...	...	...	...	...	...	...	...	...	...	...	...	...
Norfolk.....a.	...	...	|	...	...	...	2336	...	...	...	...	...	...	...	...	...	...	...	...	...	...	...	...	...
Virgina Beach.....a.	...	...	|	...	...	...	...	...	...	...	...	...	...	...	...	...	...	...	...	...	...	...	...	...
Charlottesville.....d.	...	...	2052	...	...	...	...	...	...	...	...	...	...	...	...	...	...	...	...	...	...	...	...	...
Lynchburg.....a.	...	...	2200	...	...	...	...	...	...	...	...	...	...	...	...	...	...	...	...	...	...	...	...	...

	137	55	2257	2171	57	465	165	475	175	2259	2173	467	167	2275	123	417	2175	187	177	139	497	169	479
			Acela	Acela						Acela	Acela			Acela			Acela						
	①–⑤	①–⑤	⑦	①–⑤	⑥⑦	⑦	⑥⑦	①–⑤	①–⑤	⑦	①–⑤	⑥	⑥	⑦	⑦	①–⑤	①–⑤	①–⑤	①–⑤	⑦	⑦	⑥⑦	①–⑤
		♦			♦	2		2				2				2					2		2
Boston South.....d.	1330	...	1500	1505	...	...	1505	...	1515	1600	1610	...	1605	1650	...	...	1720	...	1735	1730	...	1825	...
Providence.....d.	1415	...	1538	1543	...	...	1545	...	1556	1635	1649	...	1644	1729	...	...	1755	...	1814	1810	...	1905	...
New London.....d.	1510	...	|	|	...	...	1644	...	1652	|	|	...	1750	|	...	...	|	...	1915	1906	...	2003	...
Springfield MA.....d.	|	1450	|	|	1450	1555	|	1555	|	|	|	1730	|	|	...	1745	|	...	|	|	1935	|	1925
Hartford.....d.	|	1527	|	|	1527	1629	|	1629	|	|	|	1805	|	|	...	1820	|	...	|	|	2011	|	1959
New Haven.....d.	1559	1639	1708	1710	1639	1718	1736	1718	1741	1810	1818	1852	1911	1909	...	1908	1920	...	2006	2007	2058	2108	2048
Stamford.....d.	1655	1728	1757	1759	1728	...	1830	...	1832	1857	1906	...	1959	1958	...	...	2005	...	2101	2059	...	2158	...
New York Penn.....a.	1756	1825	1847	1851	1825	...	1930	...	1921	1947	2002	...	2053	2047	...	...	2056	...	2151	2152	...	2255	...
New York Penn.....d.	1825	1845	1900	1904	1901	...	2001	...	1940	2000	2015	...	2109	2100	2109	...	2105	2110	2205	2205	...	2309	...
Newark NJ.....d.	1842	1903	1914	1919	1918	...	2018	...	1958	2014	2030	...	2128	2114	2128	...	2122	2127	2222	2222	...	2328	...
Philadelphia 30th Street.....d.	1956	2019	2015	2016	2033	...	2131	...	2116	2115	2133	...	2244	2212	2245	...	2220	2240	2330	2336	...	0038	...
Baltimore Penn.....d.	2104	2129	2121	2123	2144	...	2242	...	2229	2221	2239	...	2355	2320	2353	...	2327	2351	0042	0049	...	0151	...
BWI Airport.....d.	2117	|	2134	2136	2157	...	2256	...	2243	2234	|	...	0008	|	0006	...	|	0004	0056	0103	...	0159	...
Washington Union.....a.	2153	2208	2202	2205	2229	...	2332	...	2314	2302	2315	...	0045	2355	0040	...	2359	0035	0134	0139	...	0241	...
Washington Union.....d.	...	...	...	...	...	...	...	...	...	...	...	...	...	...	...	...	...	...	...	...	...	...	...
Fredricksburg.....d.	...	...	...	...	...	...	...	...	...	...	...	...	...	...	...	...	...	...	...	...	...	...	...
Richmond.....d.	...	...	...	...	...	...	...	...	...	...	...	...	...	...	...	...	...	...	...	...	...	...	...
Newport News.....a.	...	...	...	...	...	...	...	...	...	...	...	...	...	...	...	...	...	...	...	...	...	...	...
Norfolk.....a.	...	...	...	...	...	...	...	...	...	...	...	...	...	...	...	...	...	...	...	...	...	...	...
Virgina Beach.....a.	...	...	...	...	...	...	...	...	...	...	...	...	...	...	...	...	...	...	...	...	...	...	...
Charlottesville.....d.	...	...	...	...	...	...	...	...	...	...	...	...	...	...	...	...	...	...	...	...	...	...	...
Lynchburg.....a.	...	...	...	...	...	...	...	...	...	...	...	...	...	...	...	...	...	...	...	...	...	...	...

♦ – **NOTES**, LISTED BY TRAIN NUMBER:

19/20 – CRESCENT – 🛏 1, 2 cl., [2] and ✕ New York - Washington - New Orleans and v.v.

50/51 – CARDINAL – 🛏 1, 2 cl., [2] and 🍸 Chicago - Washington - New York and v.v.

54/55 – VERMONTER – [12] and 🍸 Washington - New York - New Haven - St Albans and

56/57 – VERMONTER – [12] and 🍸 Washington - New York - New Haven - St Albans and

79/80 – CAROLINIAN – [12] and 🍸 New York - Washington - Charlotte and v.v.

s – Calls to set down only. u – Calls to pick up only.

trak Most trains 🍸

NEWPORT NEWS - WASHINGTON - NEW YORK - BOSTON 9215

n		66	*Acela* 2190	190	490	150	450	*Acela* 2150	*Acela* 2290	170	470	160	460	180	*Acela* 2100	162	130	*Acela* 2154	172	98	54
			①-⑤	①-⑤	①-⑤	⑥⑦	⑥⑦	①-⑤	⑥	①-⑤	①-⑤	⑥⑦	⑥⑦	①-⑤	①-⑤	⑥⑦	①-⑤	①-⑤	①-⑤		⑥⑦
					2		2				2									♦	♦
	Lynchburg d.	...	...	...	...	...	...	...	...	...	...	...	...	...	...	...	...	...	...	...	...
	Charlottesville d.	...	...	...	...	...	...	...	...	...	...	...	...	...	...	...	...	...	...	...	...
	Virginia Beach d.	*1430**	...	...	...	...	...	...	...	...	...	...	...	...	...	...	...	...	...	...	...
	Norfolk d.	*1515**	...	...	...	...	...	...	...	...	...	...	...	...	...	...	...	...	...	...	...
	Newport News d.	1650	...	...	...	...	...	...	...	...	...	...	...	...	...	...	...	...	...	...	...
	Richmond d.	1830	...	...	...	...	...	...	...	...	...	...	...	...	...	...	...	...	...	0432	...
	Fredericksburg d.	1927	...	...	...	...	...	...	...	...	...	...	...	...	...	...	...	...	...	0526	...
	Washington Union a.	2054	...	...	...	...	...	...	...	...	...	...	...	...	...	...	...	...	...	0707**s**	...
	Washington Union d.	2140	...	0310	...	0310	...	0450	...	0435	...	0520	...	0520	0600	0610	0620	0700	0715	0707**s**	0720
	BWI Airport d.	2208	...	0335	...	0335	...	|	...	0505	...	0548	...	0549	0623	0638	0649	0721	0743	|	0747
	Baltimore Penn d.	2225	...	0350	...	0350	...	0522	...	0524	...	0605	...	0605	0636	0655	0706	0734	0759	0812**s**	0804
	Philadelphia 30th Street d.	2344	...	0509	...	0514	...	0627	...	0642	...	0717	...	0722	0741	0816	0825	0836	0914	0930**s**	0915
	Newark NJ d.	0102	...	0623	...	0622	...	0728	...	0758	...	0827	...	0825**s**	0846**s**	0926	0941	0932	1026	1040**s**	1027
	New York Penn a.	0125	...	0641	...	0640	...	0745	...	0816	...	0845	...	0844	0908	0945	0959	0951	1044	1100	1045
	New York Penn d.	0240	0615	0655	...	0700	...	0800	0800	0830	...	0900	...	...	...	1000	...	1003	1100	...	1130
	Stamford d.	0327	0701	0747	...	0748	...	0847	0846	0919	...	0948	...	...	...	1048	...	1048	1148	...	1218
0	New Haven d.	0442	0802	0843	0900	0840	0850	0940	0940	1017	1025	1047	1100	...	...	1146	...	1142	1245	...	1330
0	Hartford d.	|	|	|	0945	|	0935	|	|	|	1109	|	1146	...	...	|	...	|	|	...	1411
1	**Springfield** MA a.	|	|	|	1024	|	1013	|	|	|	1148	|	1223	...	...	|	...	|	|	...	1455
	New London d.	0534	0842**e**	0934	...	0929	...	|	|	1109	...	1132	...	...	...	1233	...	|	1335	...	...
	Providence d.	0656	0927	1029	...	1025	...	1105	1104	1208	...	1232	...	...	...	1330	...	1303	1432	...	...
	Boston South a.	0758	1015	1123	...	1115	...	1154	1155	1308	...	1325	...	...	...	1422	...	1405	1524	...	...

	Acela 2104	*Acela* 2248	56	152	86	*Acela* 2250	*Acela* 2158	182	164	464	20	*Acela* 2160	*Acela* 2208	174	464	82	154	*Acela* 2110	*Acela* 2252	84	88	488	*Acela* 2164
	①-⑤	⑥	①-⑤	⑥⑦	①-⑤	⑦	①-⑤	①-⑤	⑥⑦	⑥⑦		①-⑤	⑥	①-⑤	①-⑤	⑥	⑦	①-⑤	⑥⑦	①-⑤	⑥⑦	⑥⑦	①-⑤
			♦								♦												
ynchburg d.	...	...	...	...	...	...	...	...	...	...	0556	...	...	...	...	...	...	...	...	...	...	...	...
harlottesville d.	...	...	...	...	...	...	...	...	...	...	0709	...	...	...	...	...	...	...	...	...	...	...	...
nia Beach d.	...	...	...	...	...	...	...	...	...	...	|	...	...	...	...	...	...	...	...	...	...	...	...
olk d.	...	...	...	...	...	...	...	...	...	...	|	...	...	...	...	...	...	...	...	0615	0615	...	...
port News d.	...	...	...	...	...	...	...	...	...	...	|	...	...	0520	...	...	...	...	...	|	|	...	...
mond d.	...	...	...	...	0600	...	...	...	0635	...	|	...	...	0710	...	0735	...	...	...	0825	0825	...	...
ericksburg d.	...	...	...	...	0656	...	...	...	0733	...	|	...	...	0810	...	0832	...	...	...	0925	0925	...	...
shington Union a.	...	...	...	...	0815	...	...	...	0900	...	0953**s**	...	...	0941	...	0944	...	...	...	1045	1055	...	...
shington Union d.	0750	0750	0755	0845	0840	0850	0850	0910	0920	...	0953**s**	0950	0950	1010	...	1010	1010	1050	1050	1110	1120	...	1150
Airport d.	0811	0813	0822	0845	0908	0913	0911	0938	0948	...	|	1013	1013	1037	...	1040	1039	1113	1113	1138	1148	...	|
more Penn d.	0827	0826	0839	0902	0928	0926	0926	0956	1005	...	1055**s**	1026	1026	1053	...	1056	1056	1126	1126	1154	1203	...	1222
adelphia 30th Street d.	0931	0934	0853	1027	1042	1034	1031	1110	1118	...	1208**s**	1131	1134	1205	...	1213	1213	1231	1234	1307	1317	...	1327
ark NJ d.	1030**s**	1036	1103	1140	1152	1136	1130	1222	1229	...	1325**s**	1230	1233**s**	1315	...	1328	1328	1330**s**	1336	1415	1428	...	1430
York Penn a.	1048	1053	1121	1159	1215	1153	1150	1240	1247	...	1346	1246	1255	1339	...	1346	1346	1350	1353	1437	1446	...	1446
York Penn d.	...	1108	1133	...	1230	1205	1203	...	1300	...	...	1303	...	1400	...	1416	...	...	1403	...	1500	...	1500
nford d.	...	1156	1218	...	1318	1253	1248	...	1348	...	...	1348	...	1448	...	1505	...	...	1448	...	1548	...	1545
Haven d.	...	1252	1330	...	1410	1343	1345	...	1446	1455	...	1444	...	1544	1600	1607	...	...	1538	...	1647	1700	|
artford d.	...	|	1411	...	|	|	|	...	|	1542	...	|	...	|	1646	|	...	...	|	...	|	1745	|
pringfield MA a.	...	|	1455	...	|	|	|	...	|	1619	...	|	...	|	1725	|	...	...	|	...	|	1824	|
London d.	...	|	...	...	1454	|	|	...	1534	...	...	|	...	1635	...	1657	...	...	|	...	1736	...	|
idence d.	...	1430	...	...	1555	1503	1509	...	1636	...	...	1609	...	1734	...	1751	...	...	1723	...	1835	...	1758
ton South a.	...	1525	...	...	1647	1555	1603	...	1732	...	...	1704	...	1836	...	1841	...	...	1815	...	1928	...	1846

	176	476	140	*Acela* 2166	*Acela* 2254	184	194	96	*Acela* 2168	*Acela* 2260	94	494	156	*Acela* 2170	*Acela* 2218	*Acela* 2256	416	136	196	92	168	132	432	134
	①-⑤	①-⑤	⑥⑦	①-⑤	⑥⑦	①-⑤	⑥	⑦	①-⑤	⑥	①-⑤	①-⑤	⑥⑦	①-⑤	⑥	⑦	⑦	⑤	①-④		⑥	⑦	⑦	④⑤
																				♦				
oanoke d.	0619	...	...	...	...	...	...	...	...	...	...	...	0840	...	...	...	...	...	...	...	...	...	...	...
ynchburg d.	0738	...	...	...	...	...	...	...	...	...	...	...	0959	...	...	...	...	...	...	...	...	...	...	...
harlottesville d.	0852	...	...	...	...	...	...	...	...	...	...	...	1113	...	...	...	...	...	...	...	...	...	...	...
nia Beach d.	|	...	...	...	...	...	*0610**	*0610**	...	...	...	...	|	...	...	...	...	...	...	...	...	...	...	...
olk d.	|	...	...	...	...	...	*0650**	*0650**	...	...	0900	...	|	...	...	...	...	...	...	...	...	...	...	...
port News d.	|	...	...	...	...	...	0830	0830	...	...	|	...	|	...	...	...	...	...	...	...	...	...	...	...
mond d.	|	...	...	...	...	...	1019	1019	...	...	1108	...	|	...	...	...	...	...	...	1216	...	...	...	...
ericksburg d.	|	...	...	...	...	...	1117	1117	...	...	1209	...	|	...	...	...	...	...	...	|	...	...	...	...
hington Union a.	1120	...	...	...	...	...	1235	1235	...	...	1327	...	1336	...	...	...	...	...	...	1438**s**	...	...	...	...
hington Union d.	1155	...	1215	1250	1250	1255	1305	1315	1350	1350	1400	...	1415	1450	1450	1450	...	1455	1455	1438**s**	1520	1520	...	1525
Airport d.	1224	...	1244	|	1313	1324	1332	1344	|	1413	1428	...	1443	1513	1511	1513	...	1524	1524	|	1548	1548	...	1551
more Penn d.	1239	...	1300	1322	1326	1339	1352	1403	1422	1426	1443	...	1500	1526	1524	1526	...	1540	1540	1550**s**	1604	1604	...	1606
adelphia 30th Street d.	1353	...	1413	1427	1434	1458	1508	1518	1528	1534	1558	...	1617	1631	1633	1634	...	1655	1655	1705**s**	1715	1716	...	1729
ark NJ d.	1459	...	1528	1530	1536	1614	1620	1630	1630	1635	1705	...	1727	1730	1736**s**	1736	...	1810	1810	1830**s**	1828	1828	...	1837**s**
York Penn a.	1517	...	1546	1546	1553	1632	1641	1648	1646	1653	1724	...	1748	1746	1750	1753	...	1830	1830	1850	1846	1846	...	1856
York Penn d.	1530	...	1630	1600	1603	...	1700	1725	1700	1703	1738	...	...	1800	...	1803	...	1845	...	...	1900	1930	...	...
nford d.	1618	...	1718	|	1648	...	1748	1813	1748	1748	1829	...	...	1847	...	1848	...	1935	...	...	1948	2018	...	...
Haven d.	1735**a**	1725	1826	1733	1741	...	1843	1903	1841	1841	1937**c**	1935	...	1936	...	1938	1945	2044	...	...	2046	2116	2125	...
artford d.	|	1809	1912	|	|	...	|	|	|	|	|	2020	...	|	...	|	2030	2134	...	...	|	|	2210	...
pringfield MA a.	|	1848	1955	|	|	...	|	|	|	|	|	2059	...	|	...	|	2108	2213	...	...	|	|	2248	...
London d.	1825	...	...	|	|	...	1945	1953	|	|	2024	...	...	|	...	|	...	...	...	...	2137	2209	...	...
idence d.	1929	...	...	1904	1906	...	2050	2046	2006	2005	2122	...	...	2101	...	2100	...	...	...	...	2239	2308	...	...
ton South a.	2025	...	...	1954	1956	...	2149	2144	2055	2058	2219	...	...	2154	...	2155	...	...	...	...	2333	0003	...	...

	Acela 2172	412	*Acela* 2258	178	478	126	146	80	*Acela* 2122	*Acela* 2222	148	166	192	*Acela* 2124	*Acela* 2224	138	50	158	*Acela* 2126	186	124	*Acela* 2128	*Acela* 2228	90
	①-⑤	①-④	⑦	①-⑤	①-⑤	⑦	⑥		①-⑤	⑦	①-⑤	⑦	⑥	①-⑤	⑦	①-⑤	③⑤⑦	⑥⑦	①-⑤	①-⑤	⑥⑦	①-⑤	⑦	
					2			♦									♦							♦
ynchburg d.	...	...	...	...	...	...	...	...	...	...	...	...	...	...	...	...	...	...	...	...	...	...	...	...
harlottesville d.	...	...	...	...	...	...	...	...	...	...	...	...	...	...	...	...	1519	...	...	...	...	...	...	...
nia Beach d.	...	...	...	...	...	...	...	...	...	...	...	...	...	...	...	...	|	...	...	...	...	...	...	...
olk d.	...	...	...	...	...	...	...	...	...	...	...	...	...	...	...	...	|	...	...	...	...	...	...	...
port News d.	...	...	...	...	...	...	...	...	...	...	...	...	...	...	...	...	|	...	...	...	...	...	...	...
mond d.	...	...	...	...	...	...	...	1411	...	...	...	...	...	...	...	...	|	...	...	...	...	...	...	1714
ericksburg d.	...	...	...	...	...	...	...	1507	...	...	...	...	...	...	...	...	|	...	...	...	...	...	...	|
hington Union a.	...	...	...	...	...	...	...	1630**s**	...	...	...	...	...	...	...	...	1819**s**	...	...	...	...	...	...	1942**s**
hington Union d.	1550	...	1550	1555	...	1615	1615	1630**s**	1650	1650	1655	1717	1720	1750	1750	1755	1819**s**	1810	1900	1905	1910	2000	2000	2030**s**
Airport d.	|	...	1613	1626	...	1643	1644	|	|	1713	1724	1745	1748	|	1813	1825	|	1838	|	1933	1939	|	2021	2057
more Penn d.	1622	...	1626	1643	...	1659	1700	1747**s**	1722	1726	1742	1802	1805	1822	1827	1842	1916**s**	1855	1930	1950	1956	2030	2036	2115**s**
adelphia 30th Street d.	1727	...	1734	1757	...	1813	1814	1900**s**	1827	1834	1857	1918	1921	1928	1934	1956	2026**s**	2010	2035	2111	2115	2135	2141	2228**s**
ark NJ d.	1830	...	1837	1905	...	1923**s**	1926	2012**s**	1930**s**	1935**s**	2022	2027	2032	2030**s**	2035**s**	2112	2138**s**	2124**s**	2133**s**	2224**s**	2226	2234**s**	2237**s**	2336**s**
York Penn a.	1849	...	1853	1923	...	1945	1946	2038	1949	1959	2041	2045	2050	2049	2059	2130	2158	2145	2155	2244	2249	2255	2259	2358
York Penn d.	1900	...	1903	1950	...	...	2000	...	...	...	2057	2100	...	...	...	...	...	...	...	...	...	...	...	...
nford d.	1945	...	1948	2045	...	...	2048	...	...	...	2149	2148	...											
Haven d.	2043	2051	2038	2142	2155	...	2154	...	...	...	2259	2243	...											
artford d.	|	2136	|	|	2240	...	2240	...	...	...	2346	|	...											
ringfield MA a.	|	2215	|	|	2318	...	2322	...	...	...	0030	|	...											
London d.	2122**e**	...	|	2232	...	...	...	...	...	...	...	2333	...											
idence d.	2211	...	2202	2331	...	...	...	...	...	...	...	0025	...											
ton South a.	2300	...	2255	0026	...	...	...	...	...	...	...	0118	...	...	...	...	...	...	...	...	...	...	...	...

Due to track and infrastructure improvements being performed along the Northeast Corridor (that started on April 14) scheduled departures and arrival times of Acela Express and Northeast Regional trains may vary by up to 15 minutes in both directions between Boston, New York, Washington DC and Roanoke.

0 – PALMETTO – [12] and 🍸 New York - Washington - Savannah and v.v.
2 – SILVER STAR – 🛏 1, 2 cl., [2] and ✕ New York - Washington - Tampa - Miami and v.v.
8 – SILVER METEOR – 🛏 1, 2 cl., [2] and ✕ New York - Washington - Orlando - Miami and v.v.

a – Arrives at 1712.
c – Arrives at 1927.
* – Connection by 🚌.

9220 ST ALBANS - SPRINGFIELD — Amtrak

km		55	57		54	56
		①-⑤	⑥⑦		⑥⑦	①-⑤
		A	A		A	A
0	**St. Albans** d.	0915	0915	*Washington U* **9215** d.	0720	0755
38	Burlington Essex Jct. d.	0944	0944	*New York P* **9215** d.	1130	1133
70	Waterbury d.	1010	1010	**Springfield** MA d.	1515	1515
90	Montpelier d.	1025	1025	Northampton d.	1557	1557
133	Randolph d.	1059	1059	Brattleboro d.	1656	1656
189	White River Jct. d.	1137	1137	Bellows Falls d.	1726	1726
205	Windsor VT d.	1156	1156	Claremont d.	1747	1747
225	Claremont d.	1206	1206	Windsor VT d.	1756	1756
252	Bellows Falls d.	1230	1230	White River Jct. d.	1818	1818
291	Brattleboro d.	1302	1302	Randolph d.	1856	1856
360	Northampton d.	1401	1401	Montpelier d.	1934	1934
397	**Springfield** MA a.	1435	1435	Waterbury d.	1950	1950
609	*New York Penn* **9215** a.	1825	1825	Burlington Essex Jct. d.	2018	2018
974	*Washington U* **9215** a.	2208	2229	**St. Albans** a.	2050	2050

9225 HARRISBURG - PITTSBURGH — Amtrak

km		43			42
		B			B
	New York Penn **9230** d.	1052	...	**Pittsburgh 9235** d.	0730
	Philadelphia **9230** d.	1242	...	Greensburg d.	0810
0	**Harrisburg** d.	1436	...	Latrobe d.	0820**r**
95	Lewistown d.	1546	...	Johnstown d.	0903
154	Huntingdon d.	1623	...	Altoona d.	1001
186	Tyrone d.	1649**r**	...	Tyrone d.	1018**r**
213	Altoona d.	1713	...	Huntingdon d.	1045
275	Johnstown d.	1810	...	Lewistown d.	1124
334	Latrobe d.	1851**r**	...	**Harrisburg** a.	1253
346	Greensburg d.	1902	...	*Philadelphia* **9230** a.	1455
401	**Pittsburgh 9235** a.	1959	...	*New York Penn* **9230** a.	1656

Notes for Tables 9220 and 9225.
A – VERMONTER – [12] and 🍸 Washington - New York - New Haven - St Albans and
B – PENNSYLVANIAN – [12] and 🍸 Pittsburgh - Harrisburg - New York and v.v.

9230 NEW YORK - PHILADELPHIA - HARRISBURG — Amtrak

NOTE: Due to track work schedules will be subject to alteration until September 2.

km		601s	605	607s	611	661	641s	663	643s	43s	645s	615	609	665	647	649s	667	651	653s	669	655s	671	619s	639
		Ⓐ	Ⓐ	Ⓐ	⑥	Ⓒ	Ⓐ	Ⓒ	Ⓐ	B	Ⓐ	⑦	Ⓐ	Ⓒ	Ⓐ	Ⓐ	Ⓒ	Ⓐ	Ⓐ	Ⓒ	Ⓐ	Ⓒ	Ⓐ	Ⓐ
0	**New York** Penn **9215** d.	*0325*	*0440*	*0530*	*0300*	0700	0717	0909	0930	1052	1205	*1205*	1254	1305	1411	1444	1513	1603	1647	1717	1835	1953	*2110*	2315
16	Newark NJ **9215** d.	*0345*	*0457***u**	*0546***u**	*0320*	0717**u**	0734**u**	0927**u**	0946**u**	1109**u**	1222**u**	*1222*	1310**u**	1323**u**	1428	1459	1532**u**	1620**u**	1704	1734**u**	1852	2009**u**	*2127*	2332
146	**Philadelphia** 30th St a.	*0452*	*0611*	*0701*	*0427*	0820	0846	1035	1050	1215	1325	*1333*	1417	1426	1533	1612	1638	1723	1812	1836	2000	2015	*2237*	0040
146	**Philadelphia** 30th St d.	0520	0620	0725	0725	0830	0856	1055	1100	1242	1335	1355	1445	1445	1545	1645	1655	1735	1842	1855	2015	2135	2259	...
178	Paoli d.	0546	0646	0752	0750	0855	0919	1115	1123	1312	1359	1420	1510	1510	1610	1711	1721	1802	1907	1921	2040	2200	2324**f**	...
255	Lancaster d.	0632	0735	0834	0837	0942	1006	1203	1211	1352	1446	1506	1558	1558	1655	1802	1808	1851	1955	2008	2128	2250	0012**f**	...
300	Elizabethtown d.	0649	0752	0850	0853	0958	1023	1220	1228	1406	1503	1523	1615	1614	1709	1818	1824	1907	2012	2024	2144	2306	0028**f**	...
315	**Harrisburg** a.	0710	0815	0910	0915	1020	1046	1245	1250	1426	1525	1542	1640	1635	1730	1840	1845	1930	2035	2045	2205	2330	0050	...

	640s	642	600s	660	644s	662	646	664	648s	666	650s	42s	670	652s	654s	672	656	618s	658s	674	610	612	620
	Ⓐ	Ⓐ	Ⓐ	Ⓒ	Ⓐ	⑥	Ⓐ	Ⓒ	Ⓐ	Ⓒ	Ⓐ	B	Ⓒ	Ⓐ	Ⓐ	Ⓒ	Ⓐ	①-④	⑤	⑦	⑥	⑦	Ⓐ
Harrisburg d.	0500	0555	0645	0720	0755	0830	0900	0930	1005	1120	1205	1305	1405	1515	1630	1705	1735	1840	1840	1905	1905	2020	2030
Elizabethtown d.	0517	0612	0702	0737	0811	0847	0917	0947	1021	1137	1222	1323	1422	1532	1647	1722	1752	1857	1857	1922	1922	2037	2047
Lancaster d.	0535	0630	0721	0755	0827	0905	0933	1005	1037	1155	1241	1340	1440	1552	1705	1740	1810	1912	1912	1940	1940	2055	2102
Paoli d.	0619	0723	0809	0841	0905	0951	1018	1049	1116	1241	1322	1424	1528	1636	1750	1825	1855	1955	1955	2025	2025	2140	2143
Philadelphia 30th St a.	0645	0750	0835	0905	0930	1015	1040	1115	1141	1305	1352	1455	1555	1705	1825	1850	1923	2020	2020	2050	2050	2210	2210
Philadelphia 30th St d.	0700	0805	0850	0923	0945	1030	1055	1125	1155	1330	1405	1525	1610	1718	1850	1910	1940	*2111*	2036	2110	*2115*	*2344*	...
Newark NJ d.	0812	0906**e**	0950**s**	1031	1047**e**	1142**e**	1157**e**	1231**e**	1256**s**	1440**e**	1508**e**	1636**s**	1713**e**	1833**e**	1954**e**	2014**e**	2045**e**	*2224***s**	2142**e**	2214**e**	*2226***s**	*0120*	...
New York Penn a.	0830	0926	1011	1049	1105	1159	1215	1249	1315	1457	1526	1656	1732	1853	2012	2034	2103	2244	2200	2234	*2249*	*0125*	...

B – PENNSYLVANIAN – see Table **9225**.   NOTE: On weekdays during periods of severe weather trains MAY operate on a special schedule when only trains marked **XXX s** will oper

9235 BOSTON - CHICAGO — Amtrak

km		29	449	49		30	48	448
		E	C	D		E	D	C
0	**Boston** South d.	...	1250**a**	...	**Chicago** Union d.	1840	2130	2130
70	Worcester d.	...	1403**a**	...	South Bend d.	2109	2359	2359
157	Springfield MA d.	...	1523**a**	...	Elkhart d.	2129	0027	0027
242	Pittsfield d.	...	1639**a**	...	Waterloo d.	2023	0120	0120
	New York **9205** d.	...	|	1540	Toledo d.	2349	0315	0315
320	**Albany** R'laer a.	...	1810**a**	1820	Sandusky d.	0040	0407	0407
320	**Albany** R'laer d.	...	1905	1905	**Cleveland** d.	0154	0550	0550
349	Schenectady d.	...	1933	1933	Alliance d.	0305	|	|
558	Syracuse d.	...	2152	2152	Pittsburgh **9225** d.	0520	|	|
686	Rochester d.	...	2312	2312	Cumberland d.	0932	|	|
784	Buffalo Depew d.	...	0020	0020	Martinsburg d.	1101	|	|
931	Erie d.	...	0154	0154	Harper's Ferry d.	1131	|	|
0	**Washington** U d.	1605	|	|	**Washington** U a.	1305	|	|
88	Harper's Ferry d.	1716	|	|	Erie d.	...	0720	0720
118	Martinsburg d.	1745	|	|	Buffalo Depew d.	...	0854	0854
234	Cumberland d.	1924	|	|	Rochester d.	...	0953	0953
478	Pittsburgh **9225** d.	2359	|	|	Syracuse d.	...	1123	1123
613	Alliance d.	0139	|	|	Schenectady d.	...	1359	1359
1083*	**Cleveland** d.	0259	0345	0345	**Albany** R'laer a.	...	1431	1431
1179	Sandusky d.	0402	0455	0455	**Albany** R'laer d.	...	1545	1505**b**
1254	Toledo d.	0522	0615	0615	*New York* **9205** a.	...	1823	...
1379	Waterloo d.	0636	0733	0733	Pittsfield d.	...	...	1609**b**
1467	Elkhart d.	0729	0825	0825	Springfield MA d.	...	...	1733**b**
1494	South Bend d.	0751	0849	0849	Worcester d.	...	...	1844**b**
1629	**Chicago** Union a.	0845	0950	0950	**Boston** South a.	...	...	2001**b**

9240 WASHINGTON - MIAMI — Amtrak

km		89	91	97		98	92
		F	G	H		H	G
0	**New York** Penn d.	0551**v**	1102	1515	**Miami** Amtrak d.	0810	1150
146	Philadelphia 30th St d.	0732	1235**u**	1654**u**	Fort Lauderdale d.	0850**u**	1230**u**
297	Baltimore Penn d.	0844	1355**u**	1812**u**	West Palm Beach d.	0947**u**	1327**u**
362	**Washington** Union d.	1005	1505**u**	1925**u**	Sebring d.	1123	1502
536	Richmond d.	1229	1717	2144	Winter Haven d.	1207	1548
581	Petersburg d.	1307	1751	2218	**Tampa** d.	|	1727
738	Rocky Mount d.	1429	1921	2350	Kissimmee d.	1256	1848
852	**Raleigh** d.	|	2101	|	Orlando d.	1335	1932
882	Fayetteville d.	1605	|	0122	Winter Park d.	1352	1949
1015	Florence d.	1744	|	0313	**Jacksonville** a.	1647	2243
1167	Charleston SC d.	1919	|	0451	**Jacksonville** d.	1707	2303
1176	Columbia d.	|	0138	|	Savannah d.	1931	0122
1328	Savannah d.	2104	0418	0640	Columbia d.	|	0401
1565	**Jacksonville** a.	...	0639	0909	Charleston SC d.	2117	|
1565	**Jacksonville** d.	...	0659	0934	Florence d.	2312	|
1792	Winter Park d.	...	0943	1226	Fayetteville d.	0037	|
1800	Orlando d.	...	1020	1304	**Raleigh** d.	|	0845
1829	Kissimmee d.	...	1044	1326	Rocky Mount d.	0209	1003
1959	**Tampa** d.	...	1237	|	Petersburg d.	0333	1128
	Winter Haven d.	...	1335	1413	Richmond d.	0432	1216
1955	Sebring d.	...	1416	1454	**Washington** Union a.	0707**s**	1438**s**
2120	West Palm Beach a.	...	1617**s**	1647**s**	Baltimore Penn a.	0812**s**	1550**s**
2189	Fort Lauderdale a.	...	1717**s**	1743**s**	Philadelphia 30th St a.	0930**s**	1705**s**
2224	**Miami** Amtrak a.	...	1758	1839	**New York** Penn a.	1100	1850

NOTES for Table **9235** and **9240**.
C – 🛏 1, 2 cl., [seat] and 🍸 Boston(**449/448**) - Albany(**48/49**) - Chicago and v.v.
D – LAKE SHORE LIMITED – 🛏 1, 2 cl., [seat] and ✕ New York(**49/48**) - Albany(**49/48**) - Chicago and v.v.; conveys 🛏 1, 2 cl., [seat] and 🍸 Boston(**449/448**) - Albany(**48/49**) - Chicago and v.v.
E – CAPITOL LIMITED – 🛏 1, 2 cl., [seat] and ✕ Washington - Chicago and v.v.
F – PALMETTO – [12] and 🍸 New York - Washington - Savannah and v.v.
G – SILVER STAR – 🛏 1, 2 cl., [seat] and ✕ New York - Washington - Tampa - Miami and v.v.
H – SILVER METEOR – 🛏 1, 2 cl., [seat] and ✕ New York - Washingto Orlando - Miami and v.v.
a – By 🚌 June 2, 9, 15, 23, 30 July 7, 14, 21, 28.
b – By 🚌 June 3–6, 10–13, 17–20, 24–27, July 1–3, 8–11, 15–18, 22–25, 29–31, Aug 1.
v – 0602 on ⑥⑦.
* – Washington - Cleveland *702 km*.

9245 WASHINGTON - CHARLOTTE - NEW ORLEANS — Amtrak

km		73	75*	77*	79	19		20	80	74*	76*	78
		C	C	C	A	B		B	A	C	C	C
	New York Penn **9215** d.	...	...	...	0725**a**	1415	**New Orleans** d.	0700	...	...	...	...
0	**Washington** Union d.	...	...	...	1108	1830	Hattiesburg d.	0930	...	...	...	...
174	Richmond d.	...	...	...	1336	|	Meridian d.	1107	...	...	...	...
219	Petersburg d.	...	...	...	1413	|	Tuscaloosa d.	1244	...	...	...	...
376	Rocky Mount d.	...	...	...	1536	|	Birmingham d.	1424	...	...	...	...
490	**Raleigh** d.	0630	1000	1500	1716	|	Anniston d.	1559	...	...	...	...
619	Greensboro d.	0803	1133	1633	1902	0022	**Atlanta** d.	2004	...	...	...	...
645	High Point d.	0819	1149	1649	1918	0039	Gainesville d.	2059	...	...	...	...
699	Salisbury d.	0853	1223	1723	1952	0117	Greenville d.	2258	...	...	...	...
766	**Charlotte** a.	0940	1310	1810	2042	0220	Spartanburg d.	2339	...	...	...	...
890	Spartanburg d.	...	...	...	...	0414	**Charlotte** d.	0146	0645	1030	1515	1900
940	Greenville d.	...	...	...	...	0501	Salisbury d.	0232	0728	1111	1556	1941
1102	Gainesville d.	...	...	...	...	0658	High Point d.	0316	0802	1144	1629	2014
1179	**Atlanta** d.	...	...	...	...	0838	Greensboro d.	0344	0824	1203	1648	2033
1344	Anniston d.	...	...	...	...	1000	**Raleigh** d.	|	1013	1341	1826	2210
1447	Birmingham d.	...	...	...	...	1208	Rocky Mount d.	|	1140	...	...	...
1536	Tuscaloosa d.	...	...	...	...	1307	Petersburg d.	|	1311	...	...	...
1692	Meridian d.	...	...	...	...	1504	Richmond d.	|	1411	...	...	...
1829	Hattiesburg d.	...	...	...	...	1638	**Washington** Union a.	0953	1630	...	...	...
2018	**New Orleans** a.	...	...	...	...	1932	*New York Penn* **9215** a.	1346	2038	...	...	...

A – CAROLINIAN – [12] and 🍸 New York - Washington - Charlotte and v.v.
B – CRESCENT – 🛏 1, 2 cl., [seat] and ✕ New York - Washington - New Orleans and v.v.
C – PIEDMONT – [seat] and 🍸 Raleigh - Charlotte and v.v. * Will not operate June 10, 11, 24, 25, July 1, 2, 9.
a – 0717 ⑥⑦.

9248 FLORIDA — Virgin Trains U

km		①-⑤	⑥⑦	①-⑤	①-⑤
0	**Miami** ⊡ d.	0640	1010	1540	1640
35	Fort Lauderdale ⊡ d.	0712	1042	1612	1712
104	**West Palm Beach** ⊡ a.	0755	1125	1655	1755
424	Orlando a.	...	...	...	...

	①-⑤	①-⑤	①-⑤	①-⑤	⑤
Miami ⊡ d.	1740	2040	2140	2310	2328
Fort Lauderdale ⊡ d.	1812	2112	2212	2342	2358
West Palm Beach ⊡ a.	1855	2155	2255	0025	0042
Orlando a.	...	...	...	...	...

	①-⑤	①-⑤	①-⑤	①-⑤	⑥⑦
Orlando d.	...	...	...	...	...
West Palm Beach ⊙ d.	0500	0600	0630	0700	0800
Fort Lauderdale ⊙ a.	0539	0639	0709	0739	0839
Miami ⊙ a.	0615	0715	0745	0815	0915

	①-⑤	①-⑤	①-⑤	⑥⑦	①-⑤
Orlando d.	...	...	...	...	...
West Palm Beach ⊙ d.	0930	1030	1130	2000	2130
Fort Lauderdale ⊙ a.	1009	1109	1209	2039	2209
Miami ⊙ a.	1045	1445	1245	2115	2245

⊡ – Additional trips from Miami: ①-⑤ 0740 and hourly until 1 1840, 1940. ⑥⑦ 1210, 1310, 1410, 1610, 1810, 2010, 2
⊙ – Additional trips from W P Beach: ①-⑤ 0730, 1330 and ho until 1930. ⑥⑦ 1000, 1100, 1200, 1400, 1500, 1600, 1

 e – May leave before time shown.   r – Calls on request.   s – Calls to set down only.   u – Calls to pick up only.

rak WASHINGTON - CHICAGO 9250

	51	851
	③⑤⑦	
	A	B
New York P **9215** d.	0645	...
Washington Union d.	1100	...
Culpeper d.	1225	...
Charlottesville d.	1352	...
Clifton Forge d.	1613	...
White Sulpher Springs d.	1705	...
Charleston WV d.	2029	...
Huntington d.	2151	...
South Portsmouth d.	2257	...
Cincinnati d.	0141	...
Indianapolis a.	0515	...
Indianapolis d.	0600	0600
Crawfordsville d.	0658	0658
Lafayette d.	0736	0736
Chicago Union a.	1000	1000

	50	851
	②④⑥	
	A	B
Chicago Union d.	1745	1745
Lafayette d.	2146	2146
Crawfordsville d.	2220	2220
Indianapolis a.	2339	2339
Indianapolis d.	2359	...
Cincinnati d.	0327	...
South Portsmouth d.	0545	...
Huntington d.	0716	...
Charleston WV d.	0821	...
White Sulpher Spings d.	1139	...
Clifton Forge d.	1244	...
Charlottesville d.	1519	...
Culpepper d.	1635	...
Washington Union a.	1819	...
New York P **9215** a.	2158	...

CARDINAL – 🛏 1, 2 cl., (2) and 🍷 Chicago - New York and v.v.
HOOSIER STATE – (2) Chicago - Indianapolis and v.v. Runs on days Trains **50**/**51** do not operate. Amtrak recently stated that they were going to amend the HOOSIER STATE schedules with train 851 leaving later than the current 0600 departure and train 850 arriving earlier than the present 2339 timing. However, its website now indicates that, due to Indiana's state budget not including funding for this service, the HOOSIER STATE has been removed from the reservation system for journeys after July 1.

Amtrak CHICAGO - NEW ORLEANS 9255

km		391	393	59
		D	E	C
0	**Chicago** Union d.	0815	1605	2005
92	Kankakee d.	0922	1712	2123**r**
208	Champaign ‡ d.	1025	1815	2234
323	Effingham d.	1129	1919	2337**r**
408	Centralia d.	1216	2006	0025**r**
498	Carbondale d.	1345	2135	0126
725	Newbern d.	...	...	0356**r**
850	Memphis d.	...	...	0640
1051	Greenwood d.	...	...	0900
1136	Yazoo City d.	...	...	0951**r**
1207	Jackson d.	...	...	1120
1334	McComb d.	...	...	1240**r**
1419	Hammond d.	...	...	1328
1503	**New Orleans** a.	...	...	1547

	58	390	392
	C	D	E
New Orleans d.	1345	...	...
Hammond d.	1445	...	...
McComb d.	1532**r**	...	...
Jackson d.	1744	...	...
Yazoo City d.	1842**r**	...	...
Greenwood d.	1937	...	...
Memphis d.	2240	...	...
Newbern d.	0022**r**	...	...
Carbondale d.	0316	0730	1615
Centralia d.	0410**r**	0823	1708
Effingham d.	0457**r**	0907	1752
Champaign ‡ d.	0615	1014	1859
Kankakee d.	0718**r**	1115	2000
Chicago Union a.	0920	1300	2145

C – CITY OF NEW ORLEANS – 🛏 1, 2 cl., (2) and ✕ Chicago - New Orleans and v.v.
NOTE: Until further notice the rail service between Jackson and New Orleans is operated by 🚌. The northbound journey will depart New Orleans at 1215.
D – SALUKI – (12) and 🍷 Chicago - Carbondale and v.v.
E – ILLINI – (12) and 🍷 Chicago - Carbondale and v.v.
‡ – Champaign Urbana.

rak CHICAGO - ST. LOUIS - KANSAS CITY 9260

	311	301	303	313	21	3	305	307	
	F	G	G	F	H	J	G	G	
Chicago Union d.	...	0700	0925	...	1345	1450	1715	1900	...
Joliet Union d.	...	0757	1015	...	1440**u**	|	1805	1950	...
Pontiac d.	...	|	1106	...	1527	|	1856	2041	...
Bloomington d.	...	0914	1139	...	1604	|	1929	2114	...
Lincoln d.	...	|	1210	...	1637	|	2002	2147	...
Springfield IL d.	...	1015	1250	...	1714	|	2039	2224	...
Carlinville d.	...	|	1328	...	1749**r**	|	2119	2304	...
Alton d.	...	1120	1357	...	1820	|	2148	2333	...
St. Louis d.	0915	1220	1500	1600	1921	|	2245	0030	...
Kirkwood d.	0944	...	...	1629	...	|	...	...	...
Washington MO d.	1021	...	...	1706	...	|	...	...	...
Jefferson City d.	1136	...	...	1822	...	|	...	...	...
Sedalia d.	1246	...	...	1939	...	|	...	...	...
Lee's Summit d.	1404	...	...	2050	...	|	...	...	...
Independence d.	1420	...	...	2106	...	|	...	...	...
Kansas City a.	1455	...	...	2140	...	2200	...	...	...

	300	302	22	4	314	304	306	316	
	G	G	H	J	F	G	G	F	
Kansas City d.	...	...	...	0728	0815	...	...	1600	...
Independence d.	...	...	...	|	0834	...	...	1619	...
Lee's Summit d.	...	...	...	|	0851	...	...	1636	...
Sedalia d.	...	...	...	|	1004	...	...	1749	...
Jefferson City d.	...	...	...	|	1118	...	...	1903	...
Washington MO d.	...	...	...	|	1231	...	...	2016	...
Kirkwood d.	...	...	...	|	1313	...	...	2058	...
St. Louis d.	0435	0640	0755	|	1355	1500	1730	2140	...
Alton d.	0522	0727	0845	|	...	1547	1817	...	...
Carlinville d.	0550	0755	0915**r**	|	...	1614	1845	...	...
Springfield IL d.	0632	0837	0955	|	...	1656	1932	...	...
Lincoln d.	0700	0905	1025	|	...	1724	2000	...	...
Bloomington d.	0731	0946	1108	|	...	1756	2036	...	...
Pontiac d.	0759	1014	1139	|	...	1823	2104	...	...
Joliet Union d.	0859	1119	1256**s**	|	...	1926	2202	...	
Chicago Union a.	1000	1220	1352	1450	...	2040	2310	...	

RIVER RUNNER – (12) and 🍷 St Louis - Kansas City and v.v.
LINCOLN SERVICE – (12) and 🍷 Chicago - St. Louis and v.v.
H – TEXAS EAGLE. See Table **9300**.
J – SOUTHWEST CHIEF. See Table **9295**.

rak CHICAGO - QUINCY 9265

	381	5	3	383					
	A	C	D	B					
Chicago Union d.	0735	1400	1500	1755	...	...	...	...	...
Princeton d.	0921	1544	1646	1941	...	...	...	...	...
Galesburg d.	1018	1638	1738	2038	...	...	...	...	...
Quincy a.	1158	...	...	2218	...	...	...	...	...

	380	4	382						
	B	D	A						
Quincy d.	0612	...	1730	...	...	...	...	...	...
Galesburg d.	0738	1208	1856	...	...	...	...	...	...
Princeton d.	0831	1258	1949	...	...	...	...	...	...
Chicago Union a.	1035	1515	2153	...	...	...	...	...	...

CARL SANDBURG – (12) and 🍷 Chicago Union - Quincy and v.v.
ILLINOIS ZEPHYR – (12) and 🍷 Chicago Union - Quincy and v.v.
C – CALIFONIA ZEPHYR – See Table **9290**.
D – SOUTHWEST CHIEF – See Table **9295**.

rak 2nd class CHICAGO - MILWAUKEE 9270

HIAWATHA SERVICE

	329	331	333	335	337	339	341	8307	343
	①–⑤							🚌	⑤
Chicago Union d.	0610	0825	1105	1305	1515	1708	2005	2115	2325
Sturtevant d.	0710	0925	1205	1405	1615	1814	2105	|	0025
Milwaukee Airport a.	0724	0939	1219	1419	1629	1828	2119	|	0029
Milwaukee a.	0739	0954	1234	1434	1644	1845	2134	2340	0054

		330	332	334	336	338	340	342	
		①–⑥							
Milwaukee d.	...	0615	0805	1100	1305	1500	1745	1935	...
Milwaukee Airport d.	...	0626	0815	1110	1315	1510	1755	1945	...
Sturtevant d.	...	0643	0828	1123	1328	1523	1808	1958	...
Chicago Union a.	...	0757	0934	1229	1434	1629	1914	2104	...

trak CHICAGO - GRAND RAPIDS, PORT HURON, DETROIT and PONTIAC 9275

	8465	350	8150	352	8365	364	354	370	8354	8356
	🚌		🚌		🚌				🚌	🚌
		K		K	P	L	K	M		
Chicago Union CT d.	...	0720	...	1325	...	1600	1750	1830	...	2235
Benton Harbour ET d.	...	|	...	|	...	|	|	2114	...	|
Grand Rapids ET a.	0723	|	...	|	1633**d**	|	|	2334	...	|
Michigan City CT d.	|	0828	...	|	|	|	1853	...	...	|
Niles ET d.	|	1004	...	1602	|	1832	2024	...	...	|
Kalamazoo a.	0900	1047	...	1636	1735	1911	2058	...	2200**d**	0245
Battle Creek a.	...	1113	1150**d**	1702	...	1938	2124	...	|	|
East Lansing d.	...	|	1325	|	...	2047	|	...	0025	|
Durand d.	...	|	|	|	...	2124	|	...	|	|
Flint d.	...	|	1545	|	...	2155	|	...	0125	|
Port Huron a.	...	|	...	|	...	2331	|	...	...	|
Jackson d.	...	1206	...	1755	...	...	2218	...	...	|
Ann Arbor d.	...	1248	...	1834	...	...	2255	...	...	|
Dearborn d.	...	1317**e**	...	1908**e**	...	...	2324**e**	...	...	0520
Detroit d.	...	1340**e**	...	1933**e**	...	...	2354**e**	...	...	0555
Pontiac a.	...	1439	...	2032	...	...	0055	...	...	f

	371	351	365	8351	8353	8364	353	8555	355	8651
				🚌	🚌	🚌		🚌		🚌
	M	K	L	R			K		K	
Pontiac d.	...	0550	...	...	...	...	1000	...	1735	g
Detroit d.	...	0633	...	...	...	...	1045	...	1818	|
Dearborn d.	...	0651	...	...	...	...	1103	...	1836	|
Ann Arbor d.	...	0720	...	...	...	...	1132	...	1905	|
Jackson d.	...	0756	...	...	...	...	1213	...	1942	|
Port Huron d.	...	|	0620	...	...	...	|	...	|	|
Flint d.	...	|	0732	...	0720	...	|	1550	|	|
Durand d.	...	|	0804	...	|	...	|	|	|	|
East Lansing d.	...	|	0845	...	0830	...	|	1800	|	|
Battle Creek d.	...	0851	0952	...	1030	...	1307	|	2036	|
Kalamazoo d.	...	0916	1019	0835	1115	1415	1331	2040	2100	|
Niles ET d.	...	|	1104	|	...	|	1404	...	2142	|
Michigan City CT d.	...	|	|	|	...	|	|	...	2112	|
Grand Rapids ET d.	0600	|	|	0940	...	1510	|	...	|	|
Benton Harbour ET d.	0810	|	|	...	...	...	|	...	|	|
Chicago Union CT a.	0908	1032	1145	...	...	...	1505	...	2240	0605

WOLVERINE – (12) and 🍷 Chicago - Pontiac and v.v.
BLUE WATER – (12) and 🍷 Chicago - Port Huron and v.v.
PERE MARQUETTE – (2) Chicago - Grand Rapids and v.v.
P – Additional trip: 1912.
R – Additional trip: 2200.
d – Departure time.
e – Can leave before time shown.
f – To Toronto arr. 1305.
g – From Toronto dep. 1830.
CT – Central Time.
ET – Eastern Time.

yhound SELECTED BUS ROUTES 9280

Greyhound 🚌 *service*	1529	1535	1539	1537	1511				
Nashville d.	0315	0645	1125	1720	2235	...	...	...	...
Memphis a.	0700	1045	1525	2125	0220	...	...	...	...

Greyhound 🚌 *service*	1502	1510	1514	1508	1504				
Memphis d.	0515	0920	1355	2005	2300	...	...	...	...
Nashville a.	0910	1325	1755	2350	0255	...	...	...	...

Greyhound 🚌	6001	1683	6021	6023	6005	6019	6009	1675	6013	6017	6025
										⑦	
Las Vegas NV d.	0135	0345	0700	0800	0915	1030	1201	1540	1645	1930	0001
Los Angeles a.	0825	0910	1515	1330	1600	1610	1720	2225	2230	0105	0500

Greyhound 🚌	6034	6002	1682	6008	6006	6012	6010	6014	6044	1384	6048
									⑤		
Los Angeles d.	0030	0615	0815	08360	1015	1215	1355	1500	1815	1840	2300
Las Vegas NV a.	0530	1410	1325	1340	1710	1730	2130	2045	2330	0035	0430

9285 CHICAGO - SEATTLE Amtrak

km			7 A	27 B	🚌 8948			🚌 8909	28 B	8 A
0	Chicago Union	d.	1415	...	...	Vancouver BC	d.	1130	...	...
137	Milwaukee	d.	1552u	...	...	Portland	d.	|	1645	...
241	Columbus	d.	1702	...	...	Vancouver WA	d.	|	1707	...
285	Portage WI	d.	1731	...	...	Pasco	d.	|	2057	...
314	Wisconsin Dells	d.	1749	...	...	Seattle King St.	d.	1530	|	1640
386	Tomah	d.	1827	...	...	Everett	d.	...	|	1739
452	La Crosse	d.	1911	...	...	Wenatchee	d.	...	|	2042
673	Minneapolis / St Paul	a.	2203	...	...	Spokane	a.	...	0013	0040
673	Minneapolis / St Paul	d.	2220	...	...	Spokane	d.	...	...	0125
773	St. Cloud	d.	0024	...	...	Sandpoint	d.	...	...	0230
1058	Fargo	d.	0324	...	...	Whitefish	d.	...	...	0741
1194	Grand Forks	d.	0441	...	...	Essex	d.	...	...	0850r
1332	Devils Lake	d.	0602	...	...	Shelby	d.	...	...	1133
1522	Minot	d.	0906	...	...	Havre	d.	...	...	1322
1958	Glasgow	d.	1226	...	...	Malta	d.	...	...	1442
2072	Malta	d.	1325	...	...	Glasgow	d.	...	...	1537
2212	Havre	d.	1504	...	...	Minot	d.	...	...	2147
2381	Shelby	d.	1722	...	...	Devils Lake	d.	...	...	2337
2537	Essex	d.	1941r	...	...	Grand Forks	d.	...	...	0102
2624	Whitefish	d.	2116	...	...	Fargo	d.	...	...	0218
2924	Sandpoint	d.	2349	...	...	St. Cloud	d.	...	...	0519
3030	Spokane	a.	0140	...	...	Minneapolis / St Paul	a.	...	...	0743
3030	Spokane	d.	0215	0245	...	Minneapolis / St Paul	d.	...	...	0800
3306	Wenatchee	d.	0535	|	...	La Crosse	d.	...	...	1047
3501	Everett	d.	0838	|	...	Tomah	d.	...	...	1126
3554	Seattle King St.	a.	1025	|	1045	Wisconsin Dells	d.	...	...	1208
3265	Pasco	d.	...	0535	|	Portage WI	d.	...	...	1227
3621	Vancouver WA	d.	...	0918	|	Columbus	d.	...	...	1257
3638	Portland	a.	...	1010	|	Milwaukee	d.	...	...	1407s
	Vancouver BC	a	...	...	1415	Chicago Union	a.	...	...	1555

A – EMPIRE BUILDER – 🛏 1, 2 cl., (2) and 🍸 Chicago - Spokane - Seattle and v.v.
B – EMPIRE BUILDER – 🛏 1, 2 cl., (2) Chicago - Spokane - Portland and v.v.

9290 CHICAGO - SAN FRANCISCO An

km			5 C	D			🚌
0	Chicago Union	d.	1400	...	San Francisco ‡	d.	0750
261	Galesburg	d.	1638	...	Emeryville	d.	0825
330	Burlington	d.	1725	...	Martinez	d.	▬
450	Ottumwa	d.	1853	...	Sacramento	d.	D
806	Omaha	a.	2255	...	Truckee	d.	...
806	Omaha	d.	2305	...	Reno	d.	...
892	Lincoln	d.	0014	...	Winnemucca	d.	...
1049	Hastings	d.	0147	...	Elko	d.	...
1261	McCook	d.	0343	...	Salt Lake City	a.	...
1668	Denver Union ◇	a.	0715	...	Salt Lake City	d.	...
1668	Denver Union ◇	d.	0805	0700	Provo	d.	...
1770	Winter Park	d.	1007	0900	Green River	d.	...
1791	Granby	d.	1037	...	Grand Junction	d.	...
1966	Glenwood Springs	d.	1353	...	Glenwood Springs	d.	...
2109	Grand Junction	d.	1610	...	Granby	d.	...
2279	Green River	d.	1758	▬	Winter Park	d.	1630
2516	Provo	d.	2126	...	Denver Union ◇	a.	1840
2587	Salt Lake City	a.	2305	🚌	Denver Union ◇	d.	...
2587	Salt Lake City	d.	2330		McCook	d.	...
3010	Elko	d.	0303		Hastings	d.	...
3232	Winnemucca	d.	0540		Lincoln	d.	...
3514	Reno	d.	0836		Omaha	a.	...
3569	Truckee	d.	0937		Omaha	d.	...
3785	Sacramento	d.	1413s	...	Ottumwa	d.	...
3879	Martinez	d.	1526s	...	Burlington	d.	...
3922	Emeryville	a.	1610	1625	Galesburg	d.	...
3936	San Francisco ‡	a.	...	1700	Chicago Union	a.	...

C – CALIFORNIA ZEPHYR – 🛏 1, 2 cl., (2) and 🍸 Chicago - Emeryville and v.v.
D – WINTER PARK EXPRESS: operates ⑥⑦ Jan. 5 until March 31 also Jan 4, 11, Feb. 1, 8, Mar, 1, 8.
◇ – Thruway buses operate to/from Raton (T9295) via Colorado Springs and Pueblo.
‡ – San Francisco Transbay Temporary Terminal.

9295 CHICAGO - LOS ANGELES Amtrak

km			3 D				4 D	
0	Chicago Union	d.	1450	...	Los Angeles Union	d.	1800	...
261	Galesburg	d.	1726	...	San Bernardino	d.	1944	...
329	Fort Madison	d.	1830	...	Victorville	d.	2055	...
677	Kansas City	a.	2200	...	Barstow	d.	2141	...
677	Kansas City	d.	2242	...	Needles	d.	0008	...
783	Topeka	d.	0029	...	Kingman *	d.	0120*	...
1001	Newton	d.	0245	...	Williams Junction *	d.	|	...
1247	Dodge City	d.	0519	...	Flagstaff * ⊙	d.	0415*	...
1488	Lamar	d.	0638	...	Winslow *	d.	0515*	...
1572	La Junta	d.	0804	...	Gallup	d.	0801	...
1704	Trinidad	d.	0924	...	Abuquerque ⊡	a.	1120	...
1741	Raton ◇	d.	1030	...	Abuquerque ⊡	d.	1148	...
1918	Las Vegas NM	d.	1212	...	Lamy	d.	1302	...
2022	Lamy	d.	1358	...	Las Vegas NM	d.	1451	...
2132	Abuquerque ⊡	a.	1529	...	Raton ◇	d.	1642	...
2132	Abuquerque ⊡	d.	1619	...	Trinidad	d.	1741	...
2391	Gallup	d.	1846	...	La Junta	d.	1929	...
2595	Winslow *	d.	1930*	...	Lamar	d.	2223	...
2690	Flagstaff * ⊙	d.	2038*	...	Dodge City	d.	2347	...
2768	Williams Junction *	d.	|	...	Newton	d.	0219	...
2967	Kingman *	d.	2328*	...	Topeka	d.	0440	...
3067	Needles	d.	0031	...	Kansas City	a.	0653	...
3337	Barstow	d.	0345	...	Kansas City	d.	0728	...
3398	Victorville	d.	0424	...	Fort Madison	d.	1049	...
3472	San Bernardino	d.	0542	...	Galesburg	d.	1148	...
3588	Los Angeles Union	a.	0800	...	Chicago Union	a.	1450	...

D – SOUTHWEST CHIEF – 🛏 1, 2 cl., (2) and 🍸 Chicago - Los Angeles and v.v.
⊙ – Thruway buses operate to/from the Grand Canyon and Phoenix.
⊡ – New Mexice Rail Runner operate services between Abuquerque and Santa Fe. For schedules see www.riometro.org or www.nmrailrunner.com
◇ – Thruway buses operate to/from Denver (T9290) via Colorado Springs and Pueblo.
* – Do not observe DST, schedule times will be one hour later from November 3 2019.

9300 CHICAGO - SAN ANTONIO Am

km			821 2 E	21 F			22 F
0	Chicago Union	d.	...	1345	Los Angeles Union	d.	2200b
148	Pontiac	d.	...	1527	San Antonio	a.	0450b
298	Springfield IL	d.	...	1714	San Antonio	d.	0700
457	St. Louis	a.	...	1921	San Marcos	d.	0832
457	St. Louis	d.	...	1955	Austin	d.	0931
717	Poplar Bluff	d.	...	2342	Taylor	d.	1022
813	Walnut Ridge	d.	...	0037	Temple	d.	1125
1007	Little Rock	d.	...	0310	Fort Worth	a.	1358
1127	Arkadelphia	d.	...	0420	Fort Worth	d.	1420
1240	Texarkana	d.	...	0558	Gainesville	d.	|
1384	Longview	d.	...	0828	Ardmore	d.	|
1588	Dallas	a.	...	1130	Oklahoma City	d.	|
1588	Dallas	d.	...	1150	Dallas	a.	1520
336c	Oklahoma City	d.	0825	|	Dallas	d.	1540
172c	Ardmore	d.	1024	|	Longview	d.	1815
109c	Gainesville	d.	1110	|	Texarkana	d.	2043
1638	Fort Worth	a.	1227	1325	Arkadelphia	d.	2202
1638	Fort Worth	d.	...	1410	Little Rock	d.	2339
1844	Temple	d.	...	1643	Walnut Ridge	d.	0141
1906	Taylor	d.	...	1736	Poplar Bluff	d.	0244
1962	Austin	d.	...	1830	St. Louis	a.	0724
2011	San Marcos	d.	...	1912	St. Louis	d.	0755
2060	San Antonio	a.	...	2155	Springfield IL	d.	0955
2060	San Antonio	d.	...	0245a	Pontiac	d.	1139
4389	Los Angeles Union	a.	...	0535a	Chicago Union	a.	1352

E – HEARTLAND FLYER – (2) 🍸.
F – TEXAS EAGLE – 🛏 1, 2 cl., (2) and ✕ 🍸 Chicago (21/22) - San Antonio (421/4 Los Angeles and v.v.
a – San Antonio - Los Angeles ②④⑦ only. Arrives Los Angeles ①③⑤. See Table 93
b – Los Angeles - San Antonio ③⑤⑦ only. Arrives San Antonio ①④⑥. See Table 93
c – km from Fort Worth.

9305 SEATTLE - LOS ANGELES Amtrak

km			🚌	11 G	🚌 5011			🚌 5014	14 G	🚌 6014
	Vancouver BC	d.	0530	...	...	Los Angeles ◐	d.	...	1010	...
0	Seattle King St.	d.	0900	0945	...	Santa Barbara	d.	...	1240	...
64	Tacoma	d.	▬	1037	...	San Luis Obispo	d.	...	1535	...
114	Olympia	d.	...	1127	...	Paso Robles	d.	...	1637	...
151	Centralia	d.	...	1151	...	Salinas	d.	...	1828	...
219	Kelso Longview	d.	...	1235	...	San Jose	d.	...	2023	...
282	Vancouver WA	d.	...	1318	...	Oakland	a.	...	2124	...
298	Portland	a.	...	1400	...	Oakland	d.	...	2139	2135
298	Portland	d.	...	1425	...	San Francisco ‡	d.	2110	|	2205
382	Salem	d.	...	1537	...	Emeryville	a.	2145	2154	▬
496	Eugene	d.	...	1710	...	Emeryville	d.	...	2204	...
691	Chemult	d.	...	2008	...	Martinez	d.	...	2246	...
808	Klamath Falls	d.	...	2200	...	Sacramento	d.	...	2359	...
976	Dunsmuir	d.	...	0035	...	Chico	d.	...	0147	...
1067	Redding	d.	...	0221	...	Redding	d.	...	0306	...
1186	Chico	d.	...	0350	...	Dunsmuir	d.	...	0456	...
1320	Sacramento	d.	...	0635	...	Klamath Falls	d.	...	0817	...
1397	Martinez	d.	...	0734	...	Chemult	d.	...	0932	...
1441	Emeryville	a.	🚌	0810	...	Eugene	d.	...	1236	...
1441	Emeryville	d.	6011	0820	0825	Salem	d.	...	1355	...
	San Francisco ‡	a.	0745	|	0855	Portland	a.	...	1532	...
1449	Oakland	a.	0825	0835	...	Portland	d.	...	1556	...
1449	Oakland	d.	...	0850	...	Vancouver WA	d.	...	1616	...
1573	San Jose	d.	...	1007	...	Kelso Longview	d.	...	1651	...
1624	Salinas	d.	...	1148	...	Centralia	d.	...	1736	...
1780	Paso Robles	d.	...	1338	...	Olympia	d.	...	1801	...
1835	San Luis Obispo	d.	...	1520	...	Tacoma	d.	...	1850	🚌
2025	Santa Barbara	d.	...	1802	...	Seattle King St.	a.	...	1956	2100
2190	Los Angeles ◐	a.	...	2100	...	Vancouver BC	a.	...	...	0015

G – COAST STARLIGHT – 🛏 1, 2 cl., (2) and 🍸 Seattle - Los Angeles and v.v.
‡ – San Francisco Transbay Temporary Terminal.
◐ – Los Angeles Union.
NOTE: Due to extensive trackwork schedules are subject to change.

9310 NEW ORLEANS - LOS ANGELES Am

km			1257 🚌 J	1 ①③⑥ H			2 ③⑤⑦ H
0	Orlando	d.	1855	...	Los Angeles Union	d.	2200
235	Jacksonville	d.	2145	...	Pomona	d.	2241
509	Tallahasse	d.	0115	...	Palm Springs	d.	0036
998	Mobile	d.	0535	...	Yuma *	d.	0247*
1230	New Orleans	a.	0755	...	Maricopa *	d.	0540*
1230	New Orleans	d.	...	0900	Tucson *	d.	0815*
1434	New Iberia	d.	...	1156	Benson *	d.	0915*
1462	Lafeyette	d.	...	1224	Lordsburg	d.	1215
1581	Lake Charles	d.	...	1355	El Paso	a.	1510
1678	Beaumont	d.	...	1548	El Paso	d.	1535
1810	Houston	d.	...	1855	Alpine	d.	2045
2146	San Antonio	a.	...	0005	Del Rio	d.	0102
2146	San Antonio	d.	...	0245	San Antonio	a.	0450
2418	Del Rio	d.	...	0549	San Antonio	d.	0625
2765	Alpine	d.	...	1038	Houston	d.	1210
3114	El Paso	a.	...	1322	Beaumont	d.	1405
3114	El Paso	d.	...	1347	Lake Charles	d.	1529
3350	Lordsburg	d.	...	1613	Lafeyette	d.	1715
3539	Benson*	d.	...	1718*	New Iberia	d.	1741
3619	Tucson*	d.	...	1935*	New Orleans	a.	2140
3757	Maricopa*	d.	...	2102*	New Orleans	d.	...
4021	Yuma*	d.	...	2349*	Mobile	a.	...
4253	Palm Springs	d.	...	0202	Tallahasse	a.	...
4371	Pomona	d.	...	0404s	Jacksonville	a.	
4422	Los Angeles Union	a.	...	0535	Orlando	a.	...

H – SUNSET LIMITED – 🛏 1, 2 cl., (2) and ✕ 🍸; conveys TEXAS EAGLE (421/ San Antonio - Los Angeles and v.v.
J – Operated by Greyhound USA. Change at Mobile.
* – Do not observe DST, schedule times will be one hour later from November 3 201

VANCOUVER - SEATTLE - PORTLAND - EUGENE 9315

trak Most trains 🍸

	🚌	511	501	🚌	13	11	517	505	507	🚌	519
		①-⑤		①-⑤	Ⓒ						
	D	A	A	D	A	B	A	A	A		A
Vancouver (Canada) d.	...	...	...	...	...	*0530**	0635	*0900**	*1130**	1600	1745
Bellingham d.	...	...	...	...	...	|	0834	|	|	|	19447
Mount Vernon d.	...	...	...	...	...	|	0903	|	|	|	2013
Everett d.	...	...	...	...	...	|	0953	|	|	|	2107
Seattle King Street a.	...	...	...	...	...	*0900**	1100	*1245**	*1530**	1945	2210
Seattle King Street d.	...	...	0725	...	...	0945	1130	1420	1810	...	...
Tukwila ✈ d.	...	...	0739	...	...	|	1144	1434	1824	...	...
Tacoma d.	...	...	0808	...	...	1037	1213	1503	1853	...	...
Olympia d.	...	...	0845	...	...	1127	1250	1540	1930	...	...
Centralia d.	...	...	0906	...	...	1151	1311	1601	1951	...	...
Kelso Longview d.	...	...	0947	...	...	1235	1352	1642	2032	...	...
Vancouver WA d.	...	...	1025	...	...	1318	1430	1720	2110	...	...
Portland a.	...	...	1055	...	...	1400	1500	1750	2140	...	...
Portland d.	0700	0945	*1110**	1225	1230	1425	*1515**	1805	*2200**	...	...
Salem d.	0815	1051	*1215**	1345	1336	1537	*1620**	1911	*2255*t	...	...
Albany d.	0850	1120	*1255**	1415	1405	1610	*1715**	1940	*2335*t	...	...
Eugene a.	0940	1220	*1345**	1505	1505	1703	*1805**	2040	*0010**	...	...

	516	🚌	500	502	🚌	504/6	518	14	🚌	508
			①-⑤	Ⓒ						
	A		A	A		A	A	B	C	A
Eugene d.	...	...	0530	*0530*c	0730	0900a	*1155*e	1236	1315f	1630
Albany d.	...	...	0611	*0620**	0820	0943a	1245*	1322	1405	1711
Salem d.	...	...	0641	*0655**	0855	1012a	1325*	1355	1440	1741
Portland a.	...	...	0805	*0805**	1015	1135a	1440*	1532	1550	1905
Portland d.	...	...	0820	0820	—	1200	1500	1556	...	1920
Vancouver WA d.	...	...	0838	0838	...	1218	1518	1616	...	1938
Kelso Longview d.	...	...	0911	0911	...	1251	1551	1651	...	2011
Centralia d.	...	...	0952	0952	...	1332	1632	1736	...	2052
Olympia d.	...	...	1013	1013	...	1353	1653	1801	...	2113
Tacoma d.	...	...	1055	1053	...	1435	1735	1850	...	2155
Tukwila ✈ d.	...	...	1123	1123	...	1503	1803	|	...	2223
Seattle King Street a.	...	...	1150	1150	🚌	1530	1830	1956	...	2250
Seattle King Street d.	0745	1045	...	*1215**	1345	*1645*b	1900	*2100**	...	...
Everett d.	0836	|	...	*1300**	|	|	1952	|	...	...
Mount Vernon d.	0922	|	...	*1345**	|	|	2035	|	...	...
Bellingham d.	0952	|	...	*1415**	|	|	2105	|	...	...
Vancouver (Canada) a.	1145	1415	...	...	1715	*2015*b	2300	*0015**	...	...

CASCADES – (12) and 🍸.
COAST STARLIGHT – Table **9305**.
Additional trips: 1430, 1745.
Additional trip: 1330Ⓒ, 1900.

a – By 🚌 on ①–⑤ timings Eugene 0825, Albany 0920, Salem 1000 arrive Portland 1115.
b – Connection by 🚌 ⑥⑦ only.
c – Connection by 🚌 (departs 0515 until Sept. 30).
e – Connection by 🚌 (departs 1055 until Sept. 30).

f – 1215 until Sept. 30.
t – Paid ticket required to board.

✈ – Sea Tac Airport.
* – Connection by 🚌.

SAN LUIS OBISPO - LOS ANGELES - SAN DIEGO 9320

trak Most trains 🍸

PACIFIC SURFLINER

	5818	562	1564	564	1566	566			🚌	768	572	1572	774	🚌	580	🚌	782	584	1584	1590	590	🚌	792		796
	🚌		Ⓒ	Ⓐ	Ⓒ	Ⓐ					Ⓐ	Ⓒ.		R				Ⓐ	Ⓒ	Ⓒ	Ⓐ				
San Luis Obispo d.	...	...	...	...	...	...	...	...	0400	...	...	...	0655	...	...	0920	...	...	...	...	...	1335	...	...	1615
Santa Maria d.	...	...	...	...	...	...	...	...	0440	...	...	...	0731a	...	...	1010u	...	...	...	...	...	1415	...	...	1651a
Santa Barbara d.	...	...	...	...	...	...	...	...	0630	0649	...	...	0927	1140	...	1230	1249	...	...	...	...	1615	1640	...	1902
Oxnard **9354** d.	...	...	...	...	...	...	...	...	...	0743	...	...	1018	1235	...	...	1342	...	...	...	...	...	1740	...	1954
Los Angeles Union a.	...	...	...	...	...	...	...	...	...	0935	...	...	1215	1420	...	...	1535	...	...	...	...	...	1947	...	2148
Los Angeles Union d.	0315	0605	0652	0702	0819	0833	...	...	...	0955	1040	1120	1233	...	1458	...	1608	1715	1715	1846	1921	...	2015	...	2222
Anaheim d.	|	0645	0731	0741	0858	0912	...	...	...	1034	1119	1159	1312	...	1537	...	1647	1756	1756	1926	2000	...	2054	...	2301
San Juan Capistrano d.	0440s	0723	0809	0822	0931	0946	...	...	...	1109	1201	1241	1349	...	1614	...	1724	1832	1832	2000	2038	...	2130	...	2336
Oceanside **9364/6** d.	0515s	0802	0842	0855	1019	1028	...	...	...	1147	1238	1315	1424	...	1652	...	1801	1906	1906	2045	2111	...	2205	...	0010
Solana Beach d.	0535s	0818	0901	0914	1038	1042	...	...	...	1208	1254	1331	1443	...	1713	...	1820	1923	1920	2059	2135	...	2219	...	0026
San Diego a.	0600	0858	0948	1001	1121	1123	...	...	...	1250	1338	1413	1528	...	1750	...	1907	2009	2014	2146	2216	...	2303	...	0115

	759	🚌	561	1761	🚌	763	1565	565	1767	767	🚌	569	1569	1573	573	777	1579	579	583	785	🚌		591	🚌	595	5811
	Ⓐ		Ⓐ	Ⓒ			Ⓒ	Ⓐ	Ⓒ	Ⓐ		Ⓐ	Ⓒ	Ⓒ	Ⓐ		Ⓒ	Ⓐ								🚌 R
Diego d.	...	...	0400	0440	...	0555	0645	0657	0807	0825	...	0943	0943	1051	1115	1205	1330	1335	1450	1558	...	...	1843	...	2057	2140
na Beach d.	...	...	0437	0517	...	0633	0725	0737	0846	0902	...	1023	1023	1131	1152	1243	1411	1416	1531	1636	...	...	1923	...	2135	2210
anside **9366** d.	...	...	0453	0537	...	0657	0743	0755	0908	0923	...	1040	1040	1151	1216	1300	1429	1436	1548	1653	...	...	1943	...	2153	2240
Juan Capistrano d.	...	...	0525	0609	...	0730	0818	0830	0944	1001	...	1117	1121	1222	1253	1333	1501	1508	1625	1734	...	...	2016	...	2226	2315
heim d.	...	...	0602	0648	...	0808	0855	0907	1019	1036	...	1151	1155	1257	1328	1408	1536	1543	1705	1810	...	...	2051	...	2301	|
Angeles Union a.	...	...	0703	0730	...	0851	0944	0956	1108	1125	...	1234	1238	1346	1415	1451	1629	1636	1754	1857	...	...	2135	...	2350	0055
Angeles Union d.	0409	...	...	0750	...	0911	...	...	1148	1148	...	...	...	...	...	1506	...	...	...	1916	...	...	...	2150	...	...
ard **9354** d.	0558	...	...	0921	...	1044	...	...	1316	1316	...	...	...	...	...	1639	...	...	...	2047	...	...	...	2345	...	...
a Barbara a.	0647	0655	...	1019	1030	1141	...	...	1413	1413	1425	...	...	...	...	1741	...	...	...	2151	2200	...	...	0035	...	...
a Maria d.	...	0825	...	...	1200	1344a	...	...	...	...	1550	...	...	...	...	1938a	...	...	...	...	2330	...	...	...	...	...
Luis Obispo a.	...	0910	...	...	1245	1430	...	...	...	...	1635	...	...	...	...	2036	...	...	...	...	0020	...	...	...	...	...

Guadalupe - Santa Maria.

s – Calls to set down only.

SAN JOSE and SAN FRANCISCO - SACRAMENTO 9325

trak 2nd class Most trains 🍸

CAPITOL CORRIDOR

	520	522	524	720	724	528	728	530	532	732	534	734	536	736	538	540	738	542	544	742	546	744	548	550	748
	Ⓐ	Ⓐ	Ⓐ	Ⓒ	Ⓒ	Ⓐ	Ⓒ	Ⓐ	Ⓐ	Ⓒ	Ⓐ	Ⓒ	Ⓐ	Ⓒ	Ⓐ	Ⓐ	Ⓒ	Ⓐ	Ⓐ	Ⓒ	Ⓐ	Ⓒ	Ⓐ	Ⓐ	Ⓒ
San Jose d.	...	...	0640	...	0815	0918	1010	...	1220	1305	...	...	...	A	1510	...	1610	1620	...	1710	1750	1840	1915	...	2110
Oakland JLS ¶ d.	0520	0625	0743	0815	0920	1022	1114	1215	1323	1408	1450	1500	1535	1610	1614	1650	1713	1723	1810	1817	1854	1943	2022	2208	2213
San Francisco ‡ d.	*0455*e	*0555*e	*0710*e	*0745*e	*0845*e	*0950*e	*1040*e	*1145*e	*1250*e	*1335*e	*1420*e	*1430*e	*1500*e	*1540*e	*1540*e	*1620*e	*1635*e	*1640*e	*1735*e	*1740*e	*1810*e	*1900*e	*1950*e	*2135*e	*2140*e
Emeryville d.	0529	0634	0752	0824	0929	1031	1123	1224	1331	1417	1459	1509	1544	1619	1623	1659	1722	1732	1819	1826	1903	1952	2031	2217	2222
Martinez d.	0606	0711	0829	0901	1008	1108	1200	1301	1409	1454	1536	1546	1621	1656	1700	1736	1759	1809	1856	1903	1940	2029	2108	2254	2259
Sacramento a.	0720	0825	0949	1015	1124	1232	1319	1415	1529	1614	1650	1700	1722	1810	1824	1850	1919	1929	2010	2004	2059	2149	2229	0009	0019

	521	523	723	525	527	529	727	531	729	535	733	537	737	541	741	543	743	545	745	747	547	549	749	551	751	553
	Ⓐ	Ⓐ	Ⓒ	Ⓐ	Ⓐ	Ⓐ	Ⓒ	Ⓐ	Ⓒ	Ⓐ	Ⓒ	Ⓐ	Ⓒ	Ⓐ	Ⓒ	Ⓐ	Ⓒ	Ⓐ	Ⓒ	Ⓒ	Ⓐ	Ⓐ	Ⓒ	Ⓐ	Ⓒ	Ⓐ
ramento d.	0430	0530	0610	0620	0705	0733	0810	0845	0913	1010	1030	1210	1210	1410	1410	1535	1555	1645	1655	1740	1755	1855	1935	2110	2230	2230
inez d.	0531	0631	0711	0721	0806	0834	0911	0946	1014	1111	1131	1311	1311	1511	1511	1636	1656	1746	1756	1841	1856	1956	2036	2211	2321	2331
ryville d.	0610	0710	0750	0800	0845	0913	0950	1025	1053	1150	1210	1350	1350	1550	1550	1715	1735	1825	1835	1920	1935	2035	2115	2250	0010	0010
an Francisco ‡ a.	*0640*e	*0750*e	*0820*e	*0835*e	*0920*e	*0945*e	*1020*e	*1055*e	*1125*e	*1220*e	*1240*e	*1420*e	*1420*e	*1620*e	*1620*e	*1745*e	*1805*e	*1855*e	*1905*e	*1950*e	*2005*e	*2100*e	*2140*e	*2315*e	*0035*e	*0035*e
and JLS ¶ a.	0618	0718	0758	0810	0853	0936	0958	1033	1101	1158	1218	1358	1358	1609	1558	1724	1743	1844	1854	1928	1943	2043	2134	2309	0029	0029
Jose a.	0738	0838	0918	0928	1018	...	1118	...	1225	...	...	1518	1518	...	1718	1848	1908	...	...	2048	2113	*2340*b	*2340*b	...	...	...

Also Train **746** on Ⓒ departs Oakland 2030.
Connection by 🚌, change at **Emeryville**.
Connection by 🚌 San Francisco - Emeryville and v.v.

‡ – San Francisco Transbay Temporary Terminal.
¶ – Oakland Jack London Square.

OAKLAND and SAN FRANCISCO - BAKERSFIELD 9330

trak 2nd class 🍸

SAN JOAQUIN

	🚌 5872	710	712	714	702	716	704	718	🚌	1718
								⑦–④		⑤⑥
Oakland JLS ¶ d.	x	0535	0735	0935	...	1435	...	1755	...	1755
San Francisco ‡ d.	...	*0505*e	*0705*e	*0905*e	...	*1405*e	...	*1640*e	...	*1640*e
Emeryville d.	...	0545	0745	0945	...	1445	...	1805	...	1805
Martinez d.	...	0624	0824	1024	...	1524	...	1844	...	1844
Sacramento d.	...	*0620*f	*0805*f	*1000*f	1241	*1505*f	1730	*1825*f	...	*1825*f
Lodi d.	...	|	|	|	1319	|	1808	|	...	|
Stockton San Joaquin d.	...	0728	0925	1122	1337d	1622	1826d	1939	...	1939
Modesto d.	...	0759	0958	1152	1410	1650	1859	2011	...	2011
Merced d.	...	0840	1042	1239	1453	1735	1936	2051	...	2051
Madera d.	...	0908	1110	1309	1521	1808	2007	2124	...	2124
Fresno d.	0530	0943	1139	1340	1553	1845	2040	2157	2300	2156
Hanford d.	0620	1018	1214	1415	1627	1920	2116	...	|	2232
Bakersfield a.	0805	1152	1344	1549	1806	2053	2245	...	0040	2358
Los Angeles a.	1015	*1420**	*1610**	*1815**	*2030**	*2315**	*0105**	...	0305	*0210**

	701	711	703	713	1701	715	717	719	🚌 5877	
	Ⓐ				Ⓒ					
Los Angeles d.	*2310**	*0110**	*0255**	*0625**	*0740**	*0925**	*1410**	*1410**	1600	...
Bakersfield d.	*0140**	0420	0600	0900	1015	1200	1500	1710	1815	...
Hanford d.	*0320**	0538	0717	1024	1133	1322	1622	1830	1955	...
Fresno d.	0445	0613	0753	1104	1208	1402	1701	1910	2045	...
Madera d.	0510	0638	0821	1132	1233	1427	1726	1937	...	...
Merced d.	0540	0713	0858	1205	1303	1506	1800	2015	...	...
Modesto d.	0617	0748	0936	1242	1340	1541	1835	2055	...	...
Stockton S.Joaquin d.	0650d	0828	1009d	1317	1413d	1615	1911	2131	...	...
Lodi d.	0705	|	1024	|	1428	|	|	|	...	...
Sacramento a.	0801	*1015*f	1115	*1425*f	1524	*1745*f	*2035*f	*2235*f	...	...
Martinez d.	...	0924	...	1413	...	1709	2009	2224	...	...
Emeryville d.	...	1004s	...	1458s	...	1753s	2054s	2311s	...	...
San Francisco ‡ a.	...	*1035*e	...	*1530*e	...	*1825*e	*2125*e	*2340*e	...	...
Oakland JLS ¶ a.	...	1021	...	1510	...	1805	2108	2323	...	...

Stockton **Downtown**. Also known as ACE station.
Connection by 🚌 San Francisco - Emeryville and v.v.
Connection by 🚌 Sacramento - Stockton (**d**) and v.v.

s – Calls to set down only.
x – On Ⓒ runs 30 minutes later.

* – Connection by 🚌.
‡ – San Francisco Transbay Temporary Terminal.
¶ – Oakland Jack London Square.

CALIFORNIA

This section is intended to give a brief overview of rail services in California that are not operated by Amtrak. All services in this section are operated using modern air-conditi rolling stock and convey a single class of accommodation, known locally as coach class, equivalent to European 2nd class. Timings are the latest available and may chan any time. Tickets must be purchased separately for each network and are generally not valid on parallel Amtrak services.

9350 SAN FRANCISCO - SAN JOSE Calt

km			ex①	Ⓐ B	Ⓐ	Ⓐ	Ⓐ	Ⓐ	Ⓐ	Ⓐ	Ⓐ	Ⓐ	Ⓐ	Ⓐ	Ⓐ	Ⓐ	Ⓐ	Ⓐ	Ⓐ		Ⓐ	Ⓐ	Ⓐ	Ⓐ
0	**San Francisco** △ ▽ . d.	Ⓐ	0005	0455	0525	0605	0635	0645	0659	0705	0715	0735	0745	0759	0805	0815	0835	0845	0900	and	1500	1534	1612	1623
22	Millbrae d.		0033	0518	0548	0622	0652	0704	0716	|	0739	0752	0804	0816	|	0839	0852	0902	0925	at the	1527	1553	1628	|
44	Redwood City d.		0059	0541	0615	0644	0711	0723	0731	|	0806	0811	0823	0831	|	0906	0911	0923	0951	same	1554	1618	|	|
47	Menlo Park d.		0104	0547	0620	0650	0717	0729	|	0748	|	0817	0829	|	0848	|	0917	0929	0956	minutes	1559	1624	|	|
55	Palo Alto d.		0108	0551	0624	0654	0721	0733	0737	0752	0814	0821	0833	0837	0852	0914	0921	0933	1000	past each	1604	1628	1647	1706
58	Mountain View d.		0120	0604	0637	0704	0728	0746	0750	0759	|	0828	0846	0850	0859	|	0928	0946	1013	hour	1617	1640	1656	1717
71	Santa Clara d.		0134	0622	0651	|	|	0803	|	|	0827	|	0903	|	|	0927	|	1003	1027	until	1632	1655	|	1729
75	**San Jose** Diridon a.		0142	0631	0705	0721	0743	0812	0805	0820	0836	0843	0912	0905	0920	0936	0943	1011	1035		1644	1705	1712	1737

	Ⓐ	Ⓐ	Ⓐ	Ⓐ	Ⓐ	Ⓐ	Ⓐ	Ⓐ	Ⓐ	Ⓐ	Ⓐ	Ⓐ	Ⓐ	Ⓐ	Ⓐ	Ⓐ		Ⓒ	Ⓒ	Ⓒ	Ⓒ	Ⓒ D	Ⓒ	Ⓒ	⑥
San Francisco △ ▽ . d.	1638	1658	1716	1723	1732	1738	1758	1816	1823	1832	1838	1858	1930	2030	2130	2230	Ⓒ	0807	0937	1107	1204	1237	1707	1934	2250
Millbrae d.	1655	1717	1734	|	1800	1755	1817	1834	|	1900	1855	1917	1956	2056	2156	2256		0834	1004	1134	1219	1304	1734	1949	2316
Redwood City d.	1710	1735	|	|	1828	1810	1835	|	|	1928	1910	1935	2023	2123	2223	2323		0904	1034	1204	1238	1334	1804	2008	2347
Menlo Park d.	|	1741	|	|	1834	|	1841	|	|	1934	|	1941	2028	2128	2228	2328		0912	1042	1212	|	1342	1812	|	2355
Palo Alto d.	1717	1745	1756	1806	|	1817	1845	1856	1906	|	1917	1945	2032	2132	2232	2332		0916	1046	1216	1245	1346	1816	2015	0003
Mountain View d.	|	1757	1803	1817	1842	|	1857	1903	1917	1943	|	1957	2044	2144	2244	2344		0929	1059	1229	1254	1359	1829	2024	0012
Santa Clara d.	|	1815	|	1829	1857	|	1914	|	|	1955	|	2013	2058	2158	2258	2358		0944	1114	1244	|	1414	1844	|	0027
San Jose Diridon a.	1746	1826	1818	1837	1906	1846	1926	1919	1935	2004	1946	2024	2106	2206	2306	0006		0952	1122	1252	1313	1422	1852	2043	0035

		Ⓐ A	Ⓐ	Ⓐ	Ⓐ	Ⓐ	Ⓐ	Ⓐ	Ⓐ	Ⓐ	Ⓐ	Ⓐ	Ⓐ	Ⓐ	Ⓐ	Ⓐ	Ⓐ		Ⓐ	Ⓐ	Ⓐ	Ⓐ	Ⓐ	Ⓐ
San Jose Diridon d.	Ⓐ	0428	0503	0545	0559	0604	0649	0654	0659	0704	0723	0749	0754	0759	0804	0823	0913	and	1413	1424	1513	1540	1612	1624
Santa Clara d.		0433	0508	|	0606	|	|	|	0706	|	0728	|	|	0808	|	0828	0918	at the	1418	1429	1520	1545	1618	|
Mountain View d.		0448	0523	0601	0625	|	0705	0712	0725	|	0746	0805	0812	0827	|	0842	0934	same	1433	1444	1535	1602	|	1638
Palo Alto d.		0501	0536	0609	0638	0627	0713	0722	0738	0728	|	0813	0822	0840	0828	|	0947	minutes	1446	1456	1547	1615	1633	1646
Menlo Park d.		0504	0539	|	0641	|	|	|	0741	|	0756	|	|	0843	|	0851	0950	past each	1449	1459	1551	1619	|	1649
Redwood City d.		0510	0544	|	0647	0633	|	|	0747	0735	0802	|	|	0849	0835	0857	0957	hour	1455	1505	1556	1624	1640	1655
Millbrae d.		0536	0611	0628	0703	0652	0731	|	0803	0753	0829	0834	|	0906	0853	0924	1023	until	1523	1532	1625	1642	1705	1712
San Francisco △ ▽ . a.		0603	0638	0647	0724	0709	0752	0808	0824	0813	0900	0854	0908	0929	0913	0952	1052		1552	1557	1653	1702	1738	1733

	Ⓐ	Ⓐ	Ⓐ	Ⓐ	Ⓐ	Ⓐ	Ⓐ	Ⓐ	Ⓐ	Ⓐ	Ⓐ	Ⓐ	Ⓐ	Ⓐ	Ⓐ	Ⓐ		⑥	Ⓒ	Ⓒ	Ⓒ C	Ⓒ	Ⓒ	Ⓒ	Ⓒ
San Jose Diridon d.	1640	1645	1710	1720	1730	1740	1745	1810	1820	1835	1845	1907	1945	2045	2145	2230		0708	0838	0951	1008	1138	1308	1438	1721
Santa Clara d.	1646	|	1716	|	|	1746	|	1816	|	|	|	1912	1950	2050	2150	2235	Ⓒ	0713	0843	|	1013	1143	1313	1443	|
Mountain View d.	1705	1659	|	1734	1748	1805	1759	|	1834	1854	1903	1927	2005	2105	2205	2250		0729	0859	1006	1029	1159	1329	1459	1736
Palo Alto d.	1720	1707	1731	1742	1756	1820	1807	1831	1842	1902	1913	1940	2017	2117	2217	2304		0742	0912	1013	1042	1212	1342	1512	1743
Menlo Park d.	1723	|	|	1745	1759	1923	|	|	1845	1905	1916	1943	2020	2120	2220	2307		0745	0915	|	1045	1215	1345	1515	|
Redwood City d.	1729	1713	1738	1751	|	1829	1813	1838	1851	|	1922	1949	2027	2127	2227	2313		0753	0923	1020	1053	1223	1353	1523	1750
Millbrae d.	1748	1732	1803	1808	|	1848	1832	1903	1908	|	1943	2015	2052	2152	2252	2338		0823	0953	1040	1123	1253	1423	1553	1810
San Francisco △▽ .. a.	1806	1753	1835	1829	1844	1906	1853	1935	1929	1950	2004	2042	2120	2220	2320	0005		0852	1022	1100	1152	1322	1452	1622	1830

△ – San Francisco 4th and King Street.
▽ – On June 1, 2, 22, 23 buses will replace trains between San Francisco & Bayshore.
A – Additional trips: 0623, 0839, 0950.
B – Additional trips: 0615, 0943, 1443.
C – Additional trips: 1608, 1738, 1908, 2038,
D – Additional trips: 1407, 1537, 1837, 2113.

9352 SAN JOSE - STOCKTON Altamont Corridor Expr

km		①-⑤	①-⑤	①-⑤	①-⑤						
0	**San Jose** Diridon d.	1535	1635	1735	1838	...	...	...	...	...	...
	Santa Clara d.	1540	1640	1740	1843	...	...	...	...	...	...
	Great America d.	1549	1649	1749	1852	...	...	...	...	...	...
	Fremont d.	1605	1705	1805	1908	...	...	...	...	...	...
	Pleasanton d.	1628	1728	1828	1931	...	...	...	...	...	...
	Livermore d.	1637	1737	1837	1940	...	...	...	...	...	...
	Tracy d.	1711	1811a	1911a	2014a	...	...	...	...	...	...
125	**Stockton** Downtown a.	1747	1847	1947	2050	...	...	...	...	...	...

	①-⑤	①-⑤	①-⑤	①-⑤						
Stockton Downtown d.	0420	0535	0640	0705	...	...	...	...	...	...
Tracy d.	0451	0606	0711	0736	...	...	...	...	...	...
Livermore d.	0525	0640	0745	0810	...	...	...	...	...	...
Pleasanton d.	0533	0648	0753	0818	...	...	...	...	...	...
Fremont d.	0555	0710	0815	0840	...	...	...	...	...	...
Great America d.	0613	0728	0833	0858	...	...	...	...	...	...
Santa Clara d.	0620a	0735a	0840a	0905a	...	...	...	...	...	...
San Jose Diridon a.	0632	0747	0852	0917	...	...	...	...	...	...

a – Trains may leave early after all passengers have exited.

9354 OXNARD - LOS ANGELES Metrol

km		①-⑤	①-⑤	①-⑤	①-⑤	①-⑤		①-⑤	①-⑤	①-⑤ A		⑥⑦ B	①-⑤	①-⑤	B	①-⑤	B	①-⑤	①-⑤	①-⑤	①-⑤	①-⑤		B	①-⑤
0	**Oxnard** d.	...	...	0535	0615	0652	...	...	...	0743	...	0743	...	...	1018	...	1342	...	...	...	...	...	...	1740	...
32	Moorpark d.	0502	...	0557	0637	0714	...	...	...	0808	...	0808	0828	...	|	...	1407	1419	...	...	...	1709	...	1825	...
62	Chatsworth d.	0526	...	0622	0701	0738	...	...	0828	0840	...	0840	0854	1100	1114	...	1439	1446	...	...	1639	1736	...	1857	...
77	Van Nuys d.	0540	...	0635	0715	0752	...	...	0843	0856	...	0856	0909	1114	1128	...	1453	1500	...	...	1653	1754	...	1909	...
86	Burbank Airport South ✈ d.	0547	0614	0643	0724	0759	...	0839	0850	0904	...	0904	0917	1122	1135	1230	1501	1507	1541	1556	1700	1801	...	1917	2031
92	Downtown Burbank d.	0555	0619	0648	0732	0804	...	0845	0855	0909	...	|	0922	1127	|	1235	|	1513	1546	1601	1705	1806	...	|	2036
107	**Los Angeles** Union a.	0615	0638	0713	0751	0833	...	0904	0917	0935	...	0935	0941	1149	1215	1255	1535	1536	1605	1621	1726	1827	...	1947	2055

	①-⑤ A	①-⑤	①-⑤	①-⑤	⑥⑦ B	①-⑤		①-⑤	①-⑤	B	①-⑤	①-⑤	B	①-⑤	①-⑤	B	①-⑤	①-⑤		①-⑤	①-⑤	①-⑤	①-⑤	B
Los Angeles Union d.	0409	0538	0651	0716	0750	0800	...	0823	0855	0911	0952	1140	1148	1243	1448	1506	1514	1537	...	1628	1710	1752	1850	1916
Downtown Burbank d.	|	0554	0709	0734	|	0818	...	0841	0914	|	1010	1158	|	1301	1506	|	1532	1555	...	1646	1728	1810	1910	|
Burbank Airport South ✈ d.	0434	0603	0715	0740	0812	0825	...	0848	0921	0933	1016	1205	1210	1307	1513	1528	1538	1600	...	1652	1734	1815	1916	1938
Van Nuys d.	0444	...	0725	0748	0821	...	...	...	...	0943	1024	...	1220	1316	...	1538	1546	1608	...	1659	1741	1823	1923	1948
Chatsworth d.	0506	...	0739	0811	0833	...	...	...	...	0955	1041	...	1232	1331	...	1550	1603	1622	...	1713	1800	1838	1937	2000
Moorpark d.	0531	...	0806	...	0857	...	...	...	...	|	...	...	1236	1400	...	|	...	1651	...	1741	1826	1907	2002	|
Oxnard a.	0558	...	...	...	0921	...	...	...	...	1044	...	...	1316	...	...	1639	...	...	...	1803	1848	...	2023	2047

A – Operated by Amtrak. Metrolink tickets valid on this service.

9356 LANCASTER - LOS ANGELES Metrol

km		①-⑤	①-⑤	①-⑤	①-⑤		①-⑤	⑥⑦	①-⑤	①-⑤		⑥⑦	①-⑤	①-⑤	⑥⑦		①-⑤	⑥⑦	①-⑤	①-⑤		①-⑤	⑥⑦	①-⑤	⑥⑦
0	**Lancaster** d.	0344	0446	0516	...	...	0558	0622	0648	...	...	0857	0901	...	1115	...	1135	1240	...	1345	...	...	1423	...	1820
	Via Princessa d.	0442	0544	0615	...	...	0656	0717	0747	0905	...	0957	0959	1126	1209	...	1234	1336	1351	1443	...	1525	1521	...	1920
82	Santa Clarita d.	0448	0550	0621	0648	...	0702	0723	0755	0911	...	1004	1005	1132	1215	...	1240	1342	1357	1449	...	1532	1527	1711	1926
	Burbank Airport North ✈ d.	0522	0624	0700	|	...	0740	0755	0831	0947	...	1036	1044	1208	1251	...	1318	1414	1433	1529	...	1610	1601	1747	2000
106	Downtown Burbank d.	0528	0630	0705	0722	...	0745	0801	0837	0952	...	1042	1049	1213	1257	...	1323	1420	1439	1535	...	1621	1606	1752	2006
121	**Los Angeles** Union a.	0553	0655	0725	0740	...	0806	0825	0857	1013	...	1105	1108	1234	1323	...	1343	1443	1501	1555	...	1641	1630	1814	2028

	①-⑤	①-⑤	①-⑤	⑥⑦		①-⑤	①-⑤	⑥⑦	①-⑤		①-⑤	⑥⑦	①-⑤	⑥⑦		①-⑤	①-⑤	⑥⑦	①-⑤		①-⑤	①-⑤	①-⑤	⑥⑦
Los Angeles Union d.	0619	0729	0829	0845	...	0942	1106	1137	1158	...	1355	1410	1528	1550	...	1550	1644	1725	1734	...	1758	1838	1936	2053
Downtown Burbank d.	0638	0749	0848	0902	...	1001	1125	1154	1218	...	1414	1437	1548	1607	...	1609	1704	1742	1751	...	1818	1857	1955	2111
Burbank Airport North ✈ d.	0644	0755	0854	0906	...	1007	1131	1158	1224	...	1420	1431	1554		...	1616	1710	1746	|	...	1823	1903	2001	2115
Santa Clarita d.	0726	0833	0932	0941	...	1048	1211	1234	1302	...	1451	1507	1632	1643	...	1652	1749	1823	1825	...	1900	1943	2038	2150
Via Princessa d.	0733	0842	0910	0947	...	1055	1218	1240	1312	...	1506	1514	1639	1649	...	...	1756	1829	...	...	1907	1950	2045	2157
Lancaster a.	0835	...	1046	1055	...	...	1320	1350	...	...	...	1618	1741	1755	...	...	1858	1930	...	...	2012	2054	2149	2300

rolink LOS ANGELES - SAN BERNARDINO 9358

	⑥	①–⑤ A	①–⑤	⑥⑦	①–⑤	⑦	⑥	①–⑤	⑥⑦	①–⑤	⑥⑦	①–⑤	①–⑤	⑥⑦	①–⑤	①–⑤	⑥⑦	①–⑤	①–⑤	⑥	①–⑤	⑥⑦	①–⑤	⑤⑥
Los Angeles Union .... d.	0615	0725	0906	0900	1019	1010	1035	1106	1210	1242	1345	1356	1502	1600	1556	1656	1735	1739	1825	1910	1930	2100	2149	2330
El Monte .... d.	0635	0759	0935	0920	1042	1031	1057	1136	1232	1311	1407	1420	1526	1621	1620	1722	1757	1804	1848	1932	1952	2121	2211	2350
Covina .... d.	0651	0822	0953	0938	1100	1050	1115	1153	1250	1329	1425	1437	1543	1638	1637	1740	1815	1823	1906	1950	2010	2139	2229	0007
Pomona North..................... d.	0702	0835	1006	0950	1113	1059	1127	1206	1302	1342	1436	1450	1556	1649	1650	1753	1827	1836	1919	2002	2023	2150	2242	0021
San Bernardino Depot .... a.	0754	0928	1050	1045	1158	1152	1222	1252	1400	1426	1530	1536	1644	1745	1743	1839	1922	1921	2012	2054	2105	2240	2326	0105

	①–⑤ B	①–⑤	①–⑤	⑥⑦	①–⑤	⑥	①–⑤	⑥⑦	①–⑤	⑥⑦	①–⑤	⑦	①–⑤	⑥	①–⑤	⑥⑦	①–⑤	⑥⑦	①–⑤	⑥	①–⑤	①–⑤	⑥⑦	①–⑤	⑥	⑤
Bernardino Depot d.	0603	0626	0702	0700	0803	0825	0850	0950	1002	1130	1137	1230	1231	1305	1338	1407	1515	1535	1606	1655	1720	1818	1830	1948	2120	2134
na North .... d.	0648	0710	0746	0741	0847	0906	0938	1034	1047	1213	1223	1308	1317	1349	1423	1449	1601	1618	1650	1739	1813	1918	1914	2033	2205	2217
na .... d.	0659	0722	0757	0751	0858	0916	0949	1044	1058	1223	1234	1317	1329	1359	1435	1459	1612	1628	1702	1749	1824	1930	1924	2044	2215	2227
nte.................... d.	0716	0738	0814	0807	0915	0935	1006	1101	1115	1243	1251	1332	1345	1419	1451	1514	1632	1649	1723	1809	1848	1952	1944	2102	2235	2247
Angeles Union ... a.	0740	0802	0836	0835	0939	1005	1030	1130	1139	1315	1315	1400	1408	1450	1514	1540	1700	1715	1753	1840	1910	2014	2015	2127	2300	2312

Also from Los Angeles Union on ①–⑤ at 0546, 1534, 1625, 1716, 1806, 2042. **B** – Also from San Bernardino Depot on ①–⑤ at 0352, 0424, 0443, 0516, 0542.

rolink LOS ANGELES - RIVERSIDE 9360

	①–⑤	①–⑤	①–⑤	①–⑤	①–⑤	①–⑤				
Los Angeles Union.... d.	1320	1615	1700	1730	1800	1835	...	...	...	...
Industry .... d.	1355	1650	1735	1805	1835	1910	...	...	...	...
Downtown Pomona.... d.	1404	1659	1744	1814	1844	1919	...	...	...	...
Riverside Downtown .. a.	1448	1742	1827	1858	1925	2002	...	...	...	...

	①–⑤	①–⑤	①–⑤	①–⑤	①–⑤	①–⑤				
Riverside Downtown d.	0447	0542	0615	0650	0810	1507	...	...	...	...
Downtown Pomona . d.	0520	0615	0648	0723	0843	1540	...	...	...	...
Industry.................. d.	0529	0624	0657	0732	0852	1549	...	...	...	...
Los Angeles Union . a.	0610	0707	0735	0815	0935	1635	...	...	...	...

	①–⑤	①–⑤	①–⑤	①–⑤	⑥⑦	①–⑤	①–⑤	①–⑤	①–⑤	⑥⑦
Los Angeles Union.... d.	0545	...	...	...	1515	1535	1620	1730	1850	1912
Fullerton .... d.	0619	...	...	...	1549	1609	1654	1804	1924	1946
West Corona .... d.	0643	...	...	...	1613	1635	1718	1828	1948	2010
Riverside Downtown .. a.	0715	0810	1200	1453	1652	1703	1745	1855	2025	2052
Perris Downtown......... a.	...	0846	1236	1529	...	1739	1821	1931	...	...

	①–⑤	①–⑤	①–⑤	①–⑤	⑥⑦	⑥⑦	①–⑤	①–⑤	①–⑤	
Perris Downtown....... d.	0447	0516	0552	0655	...	...	1040	1355	...	...
Riverside Downown d.	0527	0556	0632	0735	0750	0900	1120	1435	1807	...
West Corona............ d.	0551	0618	0656	...	0814	0924	...	...	1831	...
Fullerton .... d.	0618	0643	0721	...	0839	0949	...	...	1854	...
Los Angeles Union . a.	0705	0732	0810	...	0930	1040	...	...	1945	...

trolink SAN BERNARDINO - RIVERSIDE - OCEANSIDE 9362

	①–⑤	①–⑤	①–⑤	①–⑤	⑥⑦	①–⑤	⑥⑦	①–⑤	①–⑤	①–⑤
San Bernardino a...... d.	0436	0523	0559	...	0705	...	0900	...	1224	...
Riverside Downtown .. d.	0455	0539	0616	0659	0725	0728	0920	1018	1240	1501
West Corona .... d.	0518	0604	0639	0722	0749	0752	0944	1041	1304	1526
Anaheim Canyon .... d.	0536	0625	0659	0742	0811	0812	1007	1059	1325	1545
Orange .... d.	0544	0633	0707	0753	0822	0822	1017	1106	1334	1554
Santa Ana .... d.	0553	0638	0712	0758	0827	0828	1023	1111	1340	1600
Irvine .... d.	0607	0655	0726	0813	0842	0842	1039	1127	1354	1615
San Juan Capistrano .. d.	0626	...	...	...	0903	...	1100	...	1409	...
San Clemente.............. d.	0636	...	...	...	0913	...	1110	...	1418	...
Oceanside .... a.	0703	...	...	...	0955	...	1150	...	1453	...

	①–⑤	①–⑤	①–⑤	①–⑤	⑥⑦	①–⑤	①–⑤	⑥⑦	①–⑤	①–⑤
Oceanside .... d.	0739	...	...	...	1451	...	...	1628	1625	...
San Clemente.......... d.	0802	...	...	...	1514	...	...	1650	1646	...
San Juan C'strano ... d.	0811	...	...	...	1529	...	...	1700	1657	...
Irvine .... d.	0827	0923	1250	1537	1548	1606	1655	1718	1728	1845
Santa Ana................. d.	0839	0935	1303	1550	1601	1619	1707	1730	1741	1857
Orange .... d.	0844	0940	1308	1557	1607	1624	1712	1735	1746	1902
Anaheim Canyon ..... d.	0851	0946	1314	1603	1616	1631	1719	1742	1753	1909
West Corona............ d.	0909	1004	1334	1622	1638	1652	1738	1804	1811	1930
Riverside D'town..... a.	0944	1029	1410	1657	1708	1717	1806	1833	1837	2005
San Bernardino a... a.	...	1046	...	...	1723	1732	1821	1848	1853	...

San Bernardino Depot.

trolink LOS ANGELES - OCEANSIDE 9364

	①–⑤	①–⑤	⑥⑦		①–⑤	⑥⑦	①–⑤		⑥⑦	①–⑤	①–⑤		①–⑤	①–⑤	①–⑤		⑥⑦	①–⑤	①–⑤		①–⑤	①–⑤		①–⑤	
Los Angeles Union ... d.	0646	0758	0840	...	...	1050	...	...	1400	1411	1519	...	1547	...	1630	...	1640	1650	1746	...	1840	*1850*	...	...	...
Fullerton .... d.	0721	0833	0915	...	1000	1125	1340	...	1435	1446	1556	...	1625	1655	1710	...	1715	1725	1823	...	1916	1935	...	2210	...
Anaheim .... d.	0729	0840	0922	...	1007	1132	1347	...	1442	1454	1603	...	1633	1702	1717	...	1722	1733	1831	...	1923	1943	...	2218	...
Orange .... d.	0735	0845	0927	...	1012	1137	1352	...	1447	1459	1608	...	1638	1707	1722	...	1727	1739	1837	...	1928	1947	...	2223	...
Santa Ana................. d.	0741	0850	0932	...	1017	1142	1357	...	1452	1505	1613	...	1643	1712	1727	...	1732	1745	1842	...	1933	1952	...	2227	...
Irvine .... d.	0758	0904	0946	...	1031	1156	1411	...	1506	1521	1627	...	1702	1726	1741	...	1746	1801	1856	...	1947	2005	...	2241	...
San Juan Capistrano.. d.	...	0920	1001	...	...	1213	...	...	1521	...	1646	...	...	...	1757	...	1801	...	1912	...	2004	...	...	2258	...
San Clemente............ d.	...	0930	1012	...	...	1225	...	...	1534	...	1659	...	...	...	1806	...	1815	...	1922	...	2017	...	...	2307	...
Oceanside .... a.	...	1001	1052	...	...	1300	...	...	1615	...	1728	...	...	...	1837	...	1855	...	1954	...	2046	...	...	2335	...

	①–⑤	①–⑤	①–⑤		①–⑤	①–⑤	①–⑤		①–⑤	①–⑤	⑥⑦		①–⑤	①–⑤	⑥⑦		⑥⑦	①–⑤	①–⑤		①–⑤	①–⑤	⑥⑦		①–⑤
anside .... d.	...	0438	0516	...	0542	...	0634	...	...	...	0815	...	...	...	1124	...	1324	1459	1526	...	...	...	1736	...	...
Clemente.......................... d.	...	0501	0538	...	0604	...	0656	...	...	...	0838	...	...	...	1150	...	1346	1521	1548	...	...	...	1758	...	...
Juan Capistrano .... d.	...	0511	0547	...	0613	...	0705	...	...	...	0850	...	...	...	1200	...	1400	1531	1557	...	...	...	1811	...	...
e .... d.	0415	0527	0603	...	0629	0710	0722	...	0813	0854	0908	...	0908	1140	1219	...	1417	1550	1619	...	1717	1805	1829	...	2100
a Ana .... d.	0427	0539	0616	...	0643	0722	0734	...	0825	0906	0920	...	0920	1152	1231	...	1429	1604	1633	...	1729	1817	1841	...	2112
ge .... d.	0432	0547	0621	...	0649	0727	0739	...	0830	0911	0925	...	0925	1157	1236	...	1434	1609	1638	...	1734	1822	1846	...	2117
eim .... d.	0436	0552	0626	...	0655	0732	0744	...	0835	0916	0930	...	0929	1201	1241	...	1439	1614	1644	...	1739	1827	1851	...	2122
rton .... d.	0443	0559	0635	...	0702	0741	0751	...	0842	0925	0937	...	0941	1215	1248	...	1446	1624	1651	...	1746	1840	1858	...	2135
Angeles Union .... a.	0525	0640	0720	...	0745	0819	0840	...	0926	1004	1030	...	...	...	1337	...	1539	...	1731	...	1827	*1945*	1956	...	...

aster OCEANSIDE - SAN DIEGO 9366

	Ⓐ	Ⓐ	Ⓐ	Ⓐ	Ⓐ	Ⓒ	Ⓐ	Ⓐ	Ⓒ	Ⓒ	Ⓐ	Ⓐ	⑥	Ⓐ	Ⓒ	Ⓐ	⑥	⑤	⑤			
Oceanside .... 9320 d.	0503	0602	0633	0715	0740	0820	0937	1108	1108	1400	1442	1532	1533	1711	1721	1741	1825	1842	2151	...	...	...
Carlsbad Village............................. d.	0507	0606	0637	0720	0744	0825	0942	1113	1113	1405	1447	1536	1538	1716	1726	1746	1830	1848	2156	...	...	...
Encinitas... d.	0519	0618	0650	0732	0756	0836	0954	1125	1125	1416	1500	1549	1550	1727	1737	1756	1841	1859	2207	...	...	...
Solana Beach .... d.	0525	0623	0657	0739	0801	0842	1000	1133	1133	1424	1505	1554	1556	1734	1744	1801	1847	1905	2313	...	...	...
Sorrento Valley .... d.	0535	0640	0708	0749	0812	0851	1011	1142	1142	1433	1514	1603	1605	1743	1753	1811	1856	1915	2222	...	...	...
San Diego Old Town...................... a.	0557	0704	0730	0812	0835	0913	1033	1207	1207	1454	1536	1628	1629	1807	1814	1837	1924	1942	2243	...	...	...
San Diego SF Depot............ 9320 a.	0605	0711	0738	0820	0843	0921	1040	1214	1214	1502	1544	1635	1636	1815	1823	1845	1930	1950	2251	...	...	...

			Ⓐ	Ⓐ	Ⓐ	Ⓒ	Ⓒ	Ⓐ	Ⓐ	Ⓒ	Ⓐ	Ⓐ	Ⓐ	⑥	Ⓐ	Ⓐ	Ⓒ	Ⓐ	⑤	⑥	⑤		
Diego SF Depot............. 9320 d.	...	...	0615	0739	0918	0935	1225	1249	1356	1536	1536	1621	1653	1656	1738	1826	1910	1913	2012	2314	2315	...	...
Diego Old Town......................... d.	...	...	0623	0747	0916	0942	1233	1257	1404	1544	1544	1629	1701	1703	1746	1834	1918	1921	2018	2321	2321	...	...
ento Valley .... d.	...	...	0645	0810	0948	1004	1257	1319	1426	1606	1606	1651	1724	1725	1808	1856	1943	1943	2040	2342	2343	...	...
na Beach .... d.	...	...	0657	0823	0959	1013	1306	1330	1436	1617	1617	1700	1734	1735	1820	1906	1953	1953	2050	2352	2353	...	...
nitas... d.	...	...	0703	0830	1005	1019	1311	1336	1442	1623	1623	1708	1740	1742	1826	1912	1958	1959	2056	2358	2359	...	...
sbad Village.................................. d.	...	...	0715	0842	1016	1033	1321	1347	1454	1635	1635	1721	1752	1754	1838	1924	2010	2011	2108	0011	0011	...	...
nside .... 9320 a.	...	...	0720	0847	1023	1039	1327	1354	1500	1641	1641	1728	1758	1800	1845	1930	2016	2018	2115	0019	0020	...	...

: Coaster Day Pass and Monthly Passes are now valid on all Amtrak services between Oceanside and San Diego.

rinter OCEANSIDE - ESCONDIDO 9368

	D	D	D	D		D	D	D	D
Oceanside .... d.	0533	0633	0733	0833	and at	1733	1833	1933	2033
Vista Transit Center .... d.	0556	0656	0756	0856	the same	1756	1856	1956	2056
San Marcos Civic Ctr .. d.	0613	0713	0813	0913	minutes past each	1813	1913	2013	2113
Escondido .... a.	0626	0726	0826	0926	hour until	1826	1926	2026	2126

	D	D	D	D		D	D	D	D
Escondido .... d.	0533	0633	0733	0833	and at	1733	1833	1933	2033
S. Marcos Civic Ctr .. d.	0544	0644	0744	0844	the same	1744	1844	1944	2044
Vista Transit Center . d.	0557	0657	0757	0857	minutes past each	1757	1857	1957	2057
Oceanside .... a.	0626	0726	0826	0926	hour until	1826	1926	2026	2126

Additional services: from **Oceanside** at 0403 ①–⑤ and hourly until 1003 ①–⑤, 1103 and hourly until 1803, 1903 ①–⑤, 2003 ①–⑤; from **Escondido** at 0403 ①–⑤ and hourly until 0903 ①–⑤, 1003 and hourly until 1703, 1803 ①–⑤, 1903 ①–⑤, 2003 ①–⑤. Additional later evening services are available on ⑤⑥.

9900 MEXICO — Ferromex

km		①④⑥			②⑤⑦	
		A	B		A	B
0	**Chihuahua** d.	...	0600	**Los Mochis** d.	1500	0600
132	Cuauhtémoc d.	...	0825	El Fuerte d.	1750	0819
295	Creel d.	0600	1147	Témoris d.	|	1124
355	Divisadero d.	0730	1341	Bahuichivo d.	|	1224
358	Posada Barrancas d.	|	1352	San Rafael d.	|	1315
370	San Rafael d.	|	1416	Posada Barrancas d.	|	1346
400	Bahuichivo d.	|	1512	Divisadero d.	2330	1425
440	Témoris d.	|	1612	Creel d.	0055	1539
570	El Fuerte d.	1300	1919	Cuauhtémoc d.	...	1907
655	**Los Mochis** a.	1505	2130	**Chihuahua** a.	...	2130

km		⑥	⑥		⑥	⑥
		C	🚌		C	🚌
0	**Guadalajara** d.	0900	0930	**Tequila** d.	1800	1830
	Tequila a.	1100	1030	**Guadalajara** a.	2000	2000

A – EL CHEPE EXPRESS – 12 and ✕. B – EL CHEPE REGIONAL – 2 and ✕.
C – JOSÉ CUERYO EXPRESS – 12 Outward by train, return by 🚌 or v.v.

9905 HONDURAS — FC de Hondura

km					①–⑤	①–⑤	①–⑤	①–⑤	①–⑤	①–
0	**S Pedro Sula** Est d.	...	...	...	1240	1335	1430	1530	1630	173
3	**S Pedro Sula** Central a.	...	...	...	1300	1355	1450	1550	1650	175

		①–⑤	①–⑤	①–⑤	①–⑤	①–⑤	①–⑤			
S Pedro Sula Central d.	...	1305	1400	1500	1600	1700	1755	...	...	...
S Pedro Sula Est a.	...	1325	1420	1520	1620	1720	1815	...	...	...

All services subject to confirmation.

9910 PANAMA — Panama Canal R

km		①–⑤			①–⑤	
0	**Ciudad Panama** d.	0715	...	**Colon** d.	1715	..
77	**Colon** a.	0815	...	**Ciudad Panama** a.	1815	..

9915 COSTA RICA — INCOFE

km			①–⑤	①–⑤	①–⑤	①–⑤		①–⑤	①–⑤	①–⑤	①–⑤	①–⑤	①–⑤	①–⑤
0	**San José** Pacifico d.	...	0515	0632	0705	0716	...	1500	1510	1520	1620	1643	1703	1832
3	Pavas Metropolis III d.	...	0545	0702	0735	0746	...	1530	1540	1550	1650	1713	1733	1902
10	**S Antonio de Belén** a.	...	0555	0712	...	0756	...	1540	...	1600	...	1723	1743	1912

			①–⑤	①–⑤	①–⑤	①–⑤		①–⑤	①–⑤	①–⑤	①–⑤	①–⑤	①–⑤	①–⑤
S Antonio de Belén d.	...	...	0610	0720	...	0804	...	1548	...	1608	...	1723	1751	1920
Pavas Metropolis III d.	...	...	0620	0730	0739	0814	...	1558	1544	1618	1654	1733	1801	1930
San José Pacifico a.	...	...	0655	0805	0814	0849	...	1633	1619	1653	1729	1808	1836	2005

km		①–⑤				
0	**Freses de Curidabat** d.	0605	...	...	...	..
4	Universidad Costa Rica d.	0613	...	...	...	..
15	**San José** Pacifico a.	0632	...	...	...	..

				①–⑤	①–⑤	
San José Pacifico d.	...	...	...	1619	1729	...
Universidad Costa Rica d.	...	...	...	1644	1754	...
Freses de Curidabat a.	...	...	...	1652	1802	..

km		①–⑤	①–⑤	⑥	①–⑤	⑥a	⑥	⑥	⑥	①–⑤	①–⑤
0	**San José** Atlantico ▲d.	0445	0645	0630	0800	0730	0830	0930	1030	1530	1730
10	**Heredia** ▲a.	0512	0712	0657	0827	0757	0857	0957	1057	1557	1757
22	Alajuela a.	0535	0735	0720	0850	0820	0920	1020	1120	1620	1820

	①–⑤	⑥⑤	⑥	①–⑤	⑥	⑥c	⑥	⑥	①–⑤	①–
Alajuela d.	0545	0630	0730	0745	0830	0930	1030	1130	1630	18
Heredia ▲d.	0609	0654	0754	0809	0854	0954	1054	1154	1654	18
San José Atlantico ▲a.	0635	0720	0820	0835	0920	1020	1120	1220	1720	19

a – Also: ⑥ 1130, 1230. c – Also: ⑥ 1230, 1330. ▲ – Additional services operate **San José** Atlantico - **Heredia** and v.v.

9920 CUBA — Unión de los Ferrocarriles Cubanc

km		⊡	9		17	15	13	7	5	⊡	73
					1	1	1	1	🍸12		⊠
		◧	⊠		◧	◧	◧	⊠	▶	◧	⊡
0	**Habana** La Coubre d.	...	...	...	1800	1853	1925	2121	2240	...	0715a
90	Matanzas d.	...	...	...	1950	2034	2108	2354	§	...	|
	Varadero d.	...	...	...	|	|	|	|	|	0815	|
286	Santa Clara d.	...	1425	...	2319	2329	0042	0524	§	|	|
	Cienfuegos d.	...	|	...	|	|	|	|	|	1325	1335
	Trinidad d.	0800	|	...	|	|	|	|	|	1500	1745
	Sancti Spiritus d.	0925	|	...	|	|	|	0833	|	...	▬
436	Ciego de Avila d.	1045	§	...	|	0300	0400	...	§	...	...
538	Camagüey d.	1240	2126	...	0707	0450	0524	...	§	...	...
714	Bayamo d.	|	|	...	|	|	1017	...	|	...	...
770	**Manzanillo** a.	|	|	...	|	|	1150	...	|	...	...
652	Las Tunas d.	1440	|	...	|	§	...	...	§	...	...
729	Cacocúm d.	|	§	...	|	1015	...	...	§	...	⊡
	Holguim d.	1555	§	...	|	|	...	...	1130	...	◧
	Baracoa d.	|	|	...	|	|	...	...	...	...	1330
884	**Guantanamo** a.	|	|	...	|	1238	...	...	...	...	1640
854	**Santiago de Cuba** a.	1925	0605	...	1156	...	...	...	...	...	1820

	⊡	14	16	8	6	⊡	18		10	
	2	1	1	2	🍸12	◧	◧			
	◧	◧	◧	⊠	▶				⊠	◧
Santiago de Cuba d.	0735	...	...	...	...	1930	1330	...	0700	..
Guantanamo d.	0930	...	0850	...	...	|	|	...	|	..
Baracoa a.	1235	...	|	...	...	|	|	...	|	..
Holguim d.	▬	...	|	...	1930	2035	|	...	|	.
Cacocúm d.	...	...	1300	...	§	|	§	...	|	.
Las Tunas d.	...	...	|	...	§	0020	|	...	|	.
Manzanillo d.	...	2026	|	...	|	|	|	...	|	..
Bayamo d.	...	2211	|	...	|	|	|	...	|	..
Camagüey d.	...	0346	1655	...	§	0220	§	...	1552	..
Ciego de Avila d.	**74**	§	1916	...	§	0415	§	...	|	..
Sancti Spiritus d.	⊠	|	|	2045	|	0535	|	...	|	..
Trinidad a.	⊡	|	|	|	|	0655	|	...	|	15
Cienfuegos d.	0700	|	|	|	|	...	|	...	|	16
Santa Clara d.	|	0852	2147	0025	§	...	§	...	2243	
Valadero a.	|	|	|	|	|	...	|	...	...	21
Matanzas d.	|	1158	0045	0526	§	...	§	...	...	.
Habana La Coubre a.	1730a	1350	0233	0755	0845	...	§	...	...	.

a – Havana Tulipan. Note: Services run: ◧ every fourth day, ⊠ every third day, ⊖ every second day and **ALL are subject to confirmation, please check locally**.
§ – Timings unknown. ⊡ – Service not confirmed. ▶ – Service due to start mid June 2019 runs every third day.

9925 VENEZUELA — IF

km		①–⑤	①–⑤	①–⑤		①–⑤		⑥⑦		⑥⑦		
0	**Caracas** d.	0514	0534	0554	and every	2224	...	0456	and every	2222	...	...
24	Charallave Norte d.	0531	0551	0611	20 minutes	2241	...	0513	30 minutes	2239	...	...
32	Charallave Sur d.	0536	0556	0616	until	2246	...	0518	until	2244	...	...
41	**Cúa** a.	0545	0605	0625		2255	...	0527		2353	...	...

		①–⑤	①–⑤	①–⑤		①–⑥		⑥⑦		⑥⑦		
Cúa d.	...	0430	0450	0510	and every	2144	...	0500	and every	2141	...	...
Charallave Sur d.	...	0439	0459	0519	20 minutes	2153	..	0509	30 minutes	2149	...	...
Charallave Norte d.	...	0444	0504	0524	until	2158	...	0514	until	2154	...	...
Caracas a.	...	0501	0521	0541		2215	....	1051		2211	...	...

km		Ⓐ	Ⓒ	Ⓐ	Ⓐ	Ⓐ	Ⓒ	Ⓐ
0	**Puerto Cabello** d.	...	...	...	...	...	...	...
140	Yaritagua d.	0610	0755	0900	0948	1500	1605	1700
168	San Jacinto a.	0652	0835	0930	1030	1530	1635	1730
174	**Barquisimeto** a.	0705	0845	0940	1045	1540	1645	1740

		Ⓐ	Ⓐ	Ⓒ	Ⓐ	Ⓐ	Ⓒ	(
Barquisimeto d.	...	0640	0710	0850	1250	1540	1650	18
San Jacinto d.	...	0652	0732	0900	1300	1550	1700	18
Yaritagua d.	...	0722	0812	0938	1330	1620	1738	18
Puerto Cabello a.	...	...	...		...		...	

9930 COLOMBIA

BARRANCABERMEJA — Coopsercol Ltda

km										
0	**Puerto Parra** d.	...	...	0510	...	...	...	...	...	1655
65	Barrancabermeja d.	0600	...	0725	...	1130	...	1430	1700	1910
95	**García Cardena** a.	0700	...	...	...	1230	...	1530	1800	...

García Cardena d.	...	0700	...	...	...	1230	...	1530	...	1800
Barrancabermeja d.	0500	0800	...	1300	...	1330	...	1630	...	1900
Puerto Parra a.	0715	...	...	1515	...	...	...	...	...	...

All services subject to confirmation, please check locally.

BOGOTÁ - ZAPAQUIRÁ — Turistr

km		Ⓒ			Ⓒ	
0	**Bogotá Sabana** d.	0815	...	**Zapaquirá** d.	1235	
15	Usaquen d.	0915	...	Cajicá d.	1305	15
34	La Caro d.	1015	...	La Caro d.	...	15
40	Cajicá d.	|	...	Usaquen d.	...	16
53	**Zapaquirá** a.	1105	...	**Bogotá** Sabana a.	...	17

9935 ECUADOR — FC del Ecua

km	All trains Ⓡ		②		All trains Ⓡ			③
0	**Quito** d.	...	0800	...	**Latacunga** d.	...	...	...
45	Machachi d.	...	1010	...	Lasso d.	...	...	...
62	Cotopaxi d.	...	1100	...	Cotopaxi d.	...	...	1500
80	Lasso d.	...	...	...	Machachi d.	...	...	1550
110	**Latacunga** a.	...	...	...	**Quito** a.	...	...	1756

km	All trains Ⓡ	40	31		All trains Ⓡ	32	🚌	43
		④–⑦	⑤–⑦			⑤–⑦	⑤–⑦	④–⑦
0	**Otavalo** a.	...	0800	...	**Salinas** d.	1510	...	1445
30	**Ibarra** d.	1030	1122	...	**Ibarra** a.	1705	1705	1615
61	**Salinas** a.	1200	1315	...	**Otavalo** d.	...	1755	...

km	All trains Ⓡ	A	★	
		②–⑦	②–⑤	②–⑦
0	**Riobamba** d.	...	0630	...
41	Colta d.	...	0730	...
98	Alausi d.	0800	1040	1100
111	Sibambe d.	0900	...	1200
154	**Bucay** a.	...	...	...
		④–⑦		
87	**Bucay** d.	1440	...	...
21	Yaguachi d.	1645	...	...
0	**Duran** a.	1800	...	...

All trains Ⓡ	④–⑦		
Duran d.	0800	...	
Yaguachi d.	0910	...	
Bucay a.	1135	...	
		B	
	②–⑦	②–⑦	②
Bucay d.	...	...	
Sibambe d.	1000	1300	
Alausi d.	1030	1330	1
Colta d.	...	...	1
Riobamba a.	...	...	1

A – Additional trip 1400. B – Additional trip 1600. ★ – Suspended.

PERU 9940

POROY - MACHU PICCHU — Inca Rail / Perurail

km		81	41	301	61	83	601	33	501	31	203	11	43	43	91		73	303	603	45	
		B	I E	A	I D	B	A	B	A	A	A	C	I 1E	I E	G	I D	B	A	A	I E	I E
0	**Poroy** △ d.	...	...	...	0555	...	U	0640	...	0735	0825	0905	0928	...	Ua	...	...	...	...	...	...
8	Ollantaytambo d.	0610	0640	0705	0722	0745	0800	0829	0853	0915	1032	|	1115	1130	|	1236	1255	1327	1537	1636	1927
6	**Machu Picchu** a.	0740	0801	0827	0848	0915	0925	0954	1029	1052	1211	1224	1241	1306	1334	1400	1425	1450	1702	1809	2100

	50	72	42		302	204	44	34	304	64	504	32	604	12	606	84	46	92	86	
	B	B	I E	I D	A	A	I E	B	A	I D	AB	A	A	C	A	B	I 1E	G	Bx	I E
chu Picchu d.	0535	0853	0830	1032	1055	1337	1430	1520	1548	1612	1622	1643	1723	1750	1810	1820	1900	1930	2050	2130
antaytambo d.	0744	1052	1010	1212	1232	1504	1556	1705	1729	1750	1810	1831	1902	|	1951	2005	2032	|	2220	2254
roy △ a.	...	...	...	...	...	...	...	1905	U	1939	...	1905	2052	2116	...	...	2236	Ua	...	...

A – VISTADOME – [1] and 🍸. Perurail.
B – EXPEDITION – [2] and 🍸. Perurail
C – HIRAM BINGHAM – [1] and ✕. Does not operate on the last ⑦ each month.
G – SACRED VALLEY – [1] and ✕. Does not operate on the first ⑦ each month.
I – Inca Rail. Conveys: 1 - First Class ✕, D – 360 ✕, E – Voyager 🍸. www.incarail.com
U – To / from Urubamba dep. 0650, arr. 1843.
Ua – To / from Urubamba dep. 1030, arr. 2237.
△ – Poroy is *13 km* from **Cusco**, connection by bus.
x – Additional trips: 1455, 2150.

CUSCO - PUNO

ICACA TRAIN. *338 km. Journey 10½ hours.*
m Cusco at 0710 ③⑤⑦.
m Puno at 0730. ①④⑥
ins convey [1] and ✕. Operator: Perurail.
e BELMOND ANDEAN EXPLORER operates ween CUSCO and PUNO / AREQUIPA.
· details see www.perurail.com

LIMA - HUANCAYO

TREN DE LA SIERRA. *332 km. Journey 12 hours.*
From Lima at 0700 on dates in note **E** but may vary.
From Huancayo at 0700 on dates in note **F** but may vary.
Trains convey [12] and ✕. Operator: FC Central Andino.
E – 2019: June 28, July 26, Aug. 30, Sept. 20, Oct. 5, 31, Nov. 22.
F – 2019: May 4, July 1, 29, Sept. 1, 22, Oct. 8, Nov 3, 25.

TACNA - ARICA

62 km. Journey 1¼ hours. 2nd class.
From Tacna. 0600, 1630
From Arica. 0800, 1815
Operator: FC Tacna Arica.

HUANCAYO - HUANCAVELICA

EL TREN MACHO
127 km. Journey 5¼ hours.
From Huancayo. ①③⑤ 0630.
From Huancavelica. ②④⑥ 0630
Operator: FC HH.

BOLIVIA 9945

erroviária Andina / Ferroviária Oriental

PUERTO QUIJARRO - SANTA CRUZ DA LA SIERRA — FO

m			13 ②④⑦	7 ①③⑤			14 ①③⑤	8 ②④⑥
0	**Puerto Quijarro** d.	...	1300	1800	**SC da la Sierra** d.	...	1320	1800
25	Rivero Torrez d.	...	1537	2010	Pozo del Tigre d.	...	1626	|
40	Roboré d.	...	1854	2245	San José Chiquitos d.	...	1930	2308
74	San José Chiquitos d.	...	2304	0150	Roboré d.	...	2342	0212
	Pozo del Tigre d.	...	0229	|	Rivero Torrez d.	...	0309	0448
40	**SC da la Sierra** a.	...	0540	0700	**Puerto Quijarro** a.	...	0602	0700

SANTA CRUZ DE LA SIERRA - YACUIBA — FO

km		64 ④				63 ⑤		
0	**SC de la Sierra** a.	1530	...	...	**Yacuiba** d.	1700	...	...
115	Cabezas d.	1945	...	...	Villa Montes d.	1948	...	...
239	Charaguá d.	2322	...	...	Boyuibe d.	2235	...	...
360	Boyuibe d.	0229	...	...	Charaguá d.	0135	...	...
434	Villa Montes d.	0513	...	...	Cabezas d.	0535	...	...
533	**Yacuiba** a.	0805	...	...	**SC de la Sierra** a.	0955	...	...

OURO - VILLAZÓN — FCA

m		2 ②⑤	16 ③⑦	68 ①④		1 ③⑥	15 ①④	67 ①④
0	**Oruro** d.	1430	1900	...	**Villazón** ⊡ d.	1530	1530	...
13	Uyuni ⊡ d.	2140	0250	0800	Tupiza d.	1825	1905	...
91	**Avaroa** a.	|	|	1430	Atocha d.	2145	2300	...
04	Atocha d.	2355	0520	...	**Avaroa** d.	|	|	1630
01	Tupiza d.	0310	0905	...	Uyuni ⊡ d.	2352	0145	2359
02	**Villazón** ⊡ a.	0605	1205	...	**Oruro** a.	0705	0845	...

· Train services currently suspended bus connections are available at different timings.

OTHER SERVICES IN BOLIVIA — FA

km	②④⑥		③⑤⑦	km	①④		②⑤
0	0800	d.**Cochabamba** d.	1645	0	0800	d.**Viacha** d.	1410
216	1645	a.**Aiquille** a.	0800	208	1420	a.**Charaña** a.	0800
km	⚘		⚘	km	A		A
0	...	d.**Potosí** d.	...	0	0800	d.**El Alto** d.	1820
171	...	a.**Sucre** El Tejar a.	...	77	1320	a.**Guaqui** a.	1600

⚘ – Service suspended.
A – 2nd Sunday of every month.

BRAZIL 9950

strada de Ferro do Carajás / Estrada de Ferro Vitória a Minas

SÃO LUIS - PARAUAPEBAS — EFC

km		①④⑥ 12✕		②⑤⑦ 12✕	
0	...	0800	d.**São Luis** a.	2200	...
26	...	1016	d.Arari d.	1941	...
45	...	1040	d.Vitória do Mearim d.	1913	...
13	...	1156	d.Santa Inês d.	1804	...
64	...	1256	d.Alto Alegre d.	1659	...
81	...	1319	d.Mineirinho d.	1634	...
99	...	1340	d.Auzilândia d.	1613	...
15	...	1402	d.Altamira d.	1551	...
34	...	1430	d.Presa de Porco d.	1525	...
84	...	1526	d.Nova Vida d.	1429	...
13	...	1741	d.Acailandia d.	1219	...
50	...	1957	d.São Pedro d.	0956	...
38	...	2131	d.Marabá d.	0829	...
85	...	2222	d.Itainopolis d.	0731	...
61	...	2350	a.**Parauapebas** d.	0600	...

BELO HORIZONTE - VITÓRIA — EFVM

km		12		12	
0	...	0730	d.**Belo Horizonte** a.	2010	...
71	...	0903	d.Dois Irmãos d.	1830	...
97	...	1002	d.Rio Piracicaba d.	1732	...
149	...	1048	d.Drumond d.	1639	...
173	...	1116	d.Antonio Dias d.	1605	...
	...	1152	d.Mario Carvalho d.	1532	...
286	...	1315	d.Periquito d.	1405	...
339	...	1420	d.G Valadares d.	1314	...
415	...	1547	d.Conselheiro Pena d.	1125	...
484	...	1704	d.Aimorés d.	1026	...
532	...	1804	d.Colatina d.	0927	...
588	...	1859	d.Piraqueacú d.	0829	...
612	...	1926	d.Fundão d.	0802	...
657	...	2012	d.Flexal d.	0715	...
664	...	2030	a.**Vitória** d.	0700	...

DRUMOND - ITABIRA — EFVM

km		2		2	
0	...	1645	d.**Drumond** a.	1026	...
35	...	1741	a.**Itabira** d.	0930	...

PORTO SANTANA - SERRA DO NÁVIO

km		②④⑦ 2	Temporarily suspended.	①③⑥ 2	
0	...	1000	d.**Porto Santana** a.	1205	...
	...	1320	d.Porto Grande d.	0847	...
130	...	1403	d.Dona Maria d.	0807	...
150	...	1445	d.Cupixi d.	0725	...
162	...	1505	d.Munquba d.	0705	...
179	...	1540	d.Pedra Branca do Amapari d.	0630	...
194	...	1610	a.**Serra do Návio** d.	0600	...

URUGUAY 9955

errocarriles del Estado

m		①-⑤	①-⑤	⑥	⑥	①-⑤	①-⑤	⑥	①-⑤	⑥	①-⑤	①-⑤
0	**Montevideo** ◧ d.	0655	1015	1035	1330	1500	1545	1550	1750	1810	1845	1950
8	Sayago d.	0709	1029	1048	1343	1514	1600	1604	1804	1824	1900	2004
9	Las Piedras d.	0730	1050	1111	1406	1535	1627	1629	1827	1845	1923	2025
26	Progreso d.	0743	1103	1124	1419	1548	1641	1643	1841	1858	1937	2038
42	Canalones d.	...	...	...	...	...	...	1707	1904	1916	2000	...
53	**25 de Augosto** a.	...	...	...	...	...	...	1737	1934	1940	2029	...

	①-⑤	⑥	①-⑤	①-⑤	⑥	①-⑤	①-⑤	⑥	①-⑤	⑥	①-⑤
25 de Augosto d.	0435	0530	0530	...	0635	...	...	...	...	...	...
Canalones d.	0504	0600	0559	...	0705	...	...	...	...	...	...
Progreso d.	0529	0623	0623	0715	0728	0755	1120	1135	1555	1555	1700
Las Piedras d.	0544	0638	0638	0731	0743	0807	1132	1147	1607	1609	1714
Sayago d.	0607	0701	0702	0754	0806	0829	1154	1209	1628	1631	1738
Montevideo ◧ a.	0622	0716	0717	0809	0821	0843	1208	1223	1642	1645	1753

- Montevideo Nueva Terminal.

ARGENTINA 9960

OFSE — BUENOS AIRES - MAR DEL PLATA — 9960A

km		301 ▲	303 ⑦	303 ⑥	303 ①-⑤	6071 ⑦x	6071 ①-⑥x		
0	**Buenos Aires** ‡ d.	0622	1520	1528	1529	1818	1828	...	...
14	Chascomús d.	|	1703	1711	1712	2023	2030	...	...
52	Lezama d.	|	1730	1738	1739	2058	2105	...	...
204	Dolores d.	|	1842	1850	1851	...	...	...	...
271	Maipú d.	|	2003	2011	212	...	...	...	...
346	**Pinamar** a.	|	|	|	|	...	...	...	...
399	**Mar del Plata** a.	1155	2146	2154	2155	...	...	...	...

		304 ⑥	304 ⑦-①	6702 ⑦x	6702 ①-⑥x	302 ▲	
ar del Plata d.	...	2328	2330	...	...	1314	...
Pinamar d.	...	|	|	...	...	|	...
aipú d.	...	0112	0114	...	...	|	...
olores d.	...	0233	0235	...	...	|	...
zama d.	...	0347	0349	0532	0536	|	...
nascomús d.	...	0414	0416	0608	0612	|	...
uenos Aires ‡ a.	...	0611	0613	0829	0833	1845	...

	⑥⑦	⑤-⑦		⑤-⑦			①-⑤	⑥⑦	⑤-⑦		
ienos Aires ‡ d.	A	A	A	A	A	Chascomús d.	0604	0804	1103	1400	2024
ejandro Korn d.	0608	0856	1200	1640	1830	Alejandro Korn d.	0728	0928	1227	1524	2148
nascomús d.	0731	1019	1323	1803	1953	**Buenos Aires** ‡ d.	A	A	A	A	A

- Connections available to / from Buenos Aires. Additional services ⑤-⑦.
Suspended. ▲ – On request.

SOFSE — ALTA CÓRDOBA - COSQUÍN — 9960B

km								
0	d.**Alta Córdoba** d.	0825	1040	1140	d.**Cosquín** d.	0800	1500	1600
55	d.**Cosquín** a.	1049	1303	1403	d.**Alta Córdoba** a.	1024	1723	1823

SOFSE — BUENOS AIRES - BAHÍA BLANCA / TANDIL — 9960C

km	c ⓒ	a ①-⑤	6303 ①-⑤	133 ①③⑤		134 ②④⑦	6302 ①-⑤	b ①⑤	d ⓒ
0	...	...	1846	1952	d.**Buenos Aires** ‡ a.	1002	0901	...	...
64	0725	1840	2011	|	d.Cañuelas d.	|	0737	1151	1916
107	0826	1941	...	2205	d.Monte d.	0749	...	1050	1815
179	...	...	...	2332	d.Las Flores d.	0622	...	...	...
269	...	...	...	|	d. Rauch d.	|	...	...	...
330	...	...	...	|	a. **Tandil** d.	|	...	...	...
374	...	...	...	|	a. Vela d.	|	...	...	...
289	...	...	...	0129	d.Azul d.	0425	...	...	...
332	...	...	...	0250	d.Olavarria d.	0304	...	...	...
420	...	...	...	|	d. Laprida d.	|	...	...	...
490	...	...	...	|	d. Pringles d.	|	...	...	...
488	...	...	...	0525	d.Coronel Suárez d.	0029	...	...	...
538	...	...	...	0619	d.Pigüé d.	2335	...	...	...
	...	...	...	0718	d.Tornquist d.	2236	...	...	...
680*	...	...	...	0843	a.**Bahía Blanca** Sud d.	2112	...	...	...

Additional trips: **a** – 0432, 0901, 1512. **b** – 0609, 1706, 2021. **c** – 1608. **d** – 0920.
* – *640 km* via Pringles. ‡ – Buenos Aires Plaza Constitución.

9960 ARGENTINA

9960D BUENOS AIRES - LINCOLN / REALICÓ / PEHUAJO — Ferrobaires / SOFS

km					151 ①⑤				
0	Buenos Aires Once	d.	...	...	1841	...	...	...	...
98	Mercedes DFS	d.	...	...	2100	...	...	...	...
158	Chivilcoy Sud	d.	...	...	2228	...	...	...	...
209	Bragado	d.	...	...	...	...	...	...	...
261	9 de Julio	d.	...	...	...	...	...	...	...
310	Carlos Casares	a.	...	...	...	...	...	...	...
363	**Pehuajo**	a.	...	...	...	...	...	...	...
523	Catriló	a.	...	...	...	...	...	...	...
606	Santa Rosa	a.	...	...	...	...	...	...	...
263	Los Toldos	d.	...	...	...	...	...	...	...
313	**Lincoln**	d.	...	...	...	...	...	...	...
336	General Pinto	d.	...	...	...	...	...	...	...
446	General Villegas	d.	...	...	...	...	...	...	...
559	**Realicó**	a.	...	...	...	...	...	...	...
644	General Pico	a.	...	...	...	...	...	...	...

				152 ①	154 ②			
General Pico	d.	...	...	...	...	...	...	...
Realicó	d.	...	...	...	...	...	...	...
General Villegas	d.	...	...	...	...	...	...	...
General Pinto	d.	...	...	...	...	...	...	...
Lincoln	d.	...	...	...	...	...	...	...
Los Toldos	d.	...	...	...	...	...	...	...
Santa Rosa	d.	...	...	...	...	...	...	...
Catriló	a.	...	...	...	...	...	...	...
Pehuajo	d.	...	...	...	...	...	...	...
Carlos Casares	d.	...	...	...	...	...	...	...
9 de Julio	d.	...	...	...	...	...	...	...
Bragado	d.	...	...	...	...	...	...	...
Chivilcoy Sud	d.	...	...	0305	0645	...	...	...
Mercedes DFS	d.	...	...	0438	0818	...	...	...
Buenos Aires Once	a.	...	...	0700	1040	...	...	...

9960E BUENOS AIRES - GENERAL ALVEAR — SOFSE

Service suspended

km			383 ⑦	381 ⑤				384 ①	382 ⑥
0	...	...	...	...	↓	d.**B. Aires** P Constitución a.	↑	...	...
17	...	...	1830	2002	↓	d.Temperley a.	↑	1015	1344
98	...	...	2020	2140	↓	d.Empalme Lobos d.	↑	0837	1159
136	...	...	2153	2312	↓	d.Roque Pérez d.	↑	0703	1025
185	...	...	2330	0050	↓	a.Saladillo d.	↑	0525	0847
233	...	...	0143	0303	↓	a.**General Alvear** d.	↑	0313	0635
205	...	...	...	...	↓	a. **25 de Mayo** d.	↑	...	...

9960F BASAVILBASO - CONCORDIA — SOFSE

km	Service suspended		613 ①-⑤		Service suspended		614 ①-⑤	
0	**Basavilbaso**	d.	0700	...	**Concordia**	d.	...	...
56	Villaguay Este	d.	0828	...	Villaguay Este	d.	...	...
61	Villaguay Central	d.	...	...	Villaguay Central	d.	...	...
56	Villaguay Este	d.	...	...	Villaguay Este	d.	1643	...
171	**Concordia**	a.	...	...	**Basavilbaso**	a.	1812	...

9960G BUENOS AIRES - TUCUMÁN — SOFSE

km			265 ①④	277				266 ③⑥		278
0	**B. Aires** Retiro	d.	1330	1730	...	**Tucumán**	d.	1300	...	...
92	Zárate	d.	|	1934	...	La Banda	d.	1840	...	...
294	Rosario Sur	d.	|	2311	...	Colonia Dora	d.	2300	...	...
314	Rosario Norte	d.	1955	2355	...	Pinto	d.	0104	...	...
523	Rafaela	d.	0115	...	...	Ceres	d.	0404	...	...
684	Ceres	d.	0542	...	...	Rafaela	d.	0823	...	...
791	Pinto	d.	0831	...	...	Rosario Norte	d.	1451	...	0100
858	Colonia Dora	d.	1052	...	...	Rosario Sur	d.	|	...	0151
1020	La Banda	d.	1811	...	...	Zárate	d.	|	...	0537
1170	**Tucumán**	a.	2045	...	...	**B. Aires** Retiro	a.	2010	...	0728

9960H BUENOS AIRES - CÓRDOBA — SOFSE

km			215 ①②	215 ⑥	269 ①⑤			268 ④⑦		216 ①⑤⑦
0	**B. Aires** Retiro	d.	*	**	2000	**Córdoba** Mitre	d.	1430	...	1800
314	Rosario Norte	d.	...	...	0329	Villa Maria	d.	1913	...	2230
384	Cañada de Gómez	d.	...	...	0553	C de Gómez	d.	0052	...	...
566	Villa Maria	d.	0500	0700	1129	Rosario Norte	d.	0312	...	...
708	**Córdoba** Mitre	a.	0930	1130	1633	**B. Aires** Retiro	a.	0930	...	...

*– Not on holiday ①. **– Runs on holiday ①.

9960J VILLA BALLESTER - ZÁRATE — SOFSE

km			2501 ①-⑤	2501 ⑥⑦	2503 ①-⑤	2503 ⑥⑦a			2500 ①-⑤	2500 ⑥⑦b	2502 ①-⑤	2502 ⑥⑦
0	**Villa Ballester**	d.	0230	0346	0500	0700	**Zárate**	d.	0504	0600	0706	0904
52	Escobar	d.	0323	0439	0543	0753	Escobar	d.	0554	0652	0758	0956
92	**Zárate**	a.	0415	0531	0645	0845	**Villa Ballester**	a.	0643	0742	0900	1046

a – Additional trips: ①-⑤ 0709, 0942, 1230, 1506, 1800, 2046. ⑥⑦ 0950, 1306, 1640, 1900.
b – Additional trips: ①-⑤ 0913, 1145, 1435, 1710, 2004, 2250. ⑥⑦ 1205, 1515, 1845, 2106.

9960K SÁENZ PEÑA - CHOROTOS — SOFSE

km			813				814	
0	**Sáenz Peña**	d.	1450	...	**Chorotis**	d.	0355	...
119	General Pinedo	d.	1820	...	General Pinedo	d.	0650	...
187	**Chorotis**	a.	2136	...	**Sáenz Peña**	a.	1010	...

9960L VIEDMA - BARILOCHE — T

km			371 ③		363 ⑤				372 ③	3
0	**Viedma** ◧	d.	...	...	1800	**Bariloche**	d.	...	1700	1
189	San Antonio Oeste	d.	...	...	2220	Ing Jacobacci	d.	...	2145	2
625	Ing Jacobacci	d.	0530	...	0730	S Antonio Oeste	d.	...	...	0
819	**Bariloche**	a.	1010	...	1228	**Viedma** ◧	a.	...	...	1

◧ – 🚌 connections available to / from B. Blanca and Buenos Aires (operator El Pingu

9960M PARANÁ - CONCEPCIÓN DEL URUGUAY — SOFS

km	Service suspended		①③⑤	2302 ⑤	Service suspended		①③⑤	2
0	**Paraná**	d.	...	1300	**C del Uruguay**	d.	1230	1
46	Crespo	d.	...	1415	Basavilbaso	d.	1400	1
120	Nogoyá	d.	...	1600	Nogoyá	d.	...	1
216	Basavilbaso	d.	0600	1830	Crespo	d.	...	1
280	**C del Uruguay**	a.	0735	2010	**Paraná**	a.	...	2

9960N BUENOS AIRES - ALBERDI - RUFINO — SOF

km				565 ⑤					566 ①
0	**B. Aires** Retiro	d.	...	1820a	...	**Rufino**	d.	...	...
111	Mercedes	d.	...	|	...	**Alberdi**	d.	...	...
209	Chacabuco	d.	...	2201	...	Junin	d.	...	0410
255	Junin	a.	...	2253	...	Chacabuco	d.	...	0502
336	**Alberdi**	a.	...	...	...	Mercedes	d.	...	|
421	**Rufino**	a.	...	...	...	**B. Aires** Retiro	a.	...	0910a

a – Until mid 2019 will depart/arrive at Caseros.

9960P SALTA - SOCOMPA — Tren a las Nub

km			809 ✕a				810 ✕a	
0	**Salta**	d.	0700b	🚌	**Socompa**	d.	...	
53	Alfarcito	d.	1035	🚌	Viaducto La Polvorilla	d.	1330	
	San Antonio de los Cobres	d.	1200	...	San Antonio de los Cobres	a.	1500	
218	Viaducto La Polvorilla	a.	1300	...	Tastil	d.	1800	🚌
570	**Socompa**	a.	...	...	**Salta**	a.	2000	🚌

a – Operates ⑥ also ②④ in July, Aug, Sept, Oct. plus additional dates see http://www trenalasnubes.com.ar/ for exact dates. b – Passengers should arrive at 0615.

9960Q SALTA - GÜEMES — SOFS

km				2802 ①-⑥	2804 ①-⑤			2801 ①-⑥		28 ①
0	**Salta**	d.	...	1230	1930	**Güemes**	d.	0630	...	1
46	**Güemes**	a.	...	1359	2059	**Salta**	a.	0759	...	1

9960R RESISTENCIA - LOS AMORES — SOF

km									
	Resistencia	d.	...	...	...	**Los Amores**	d.	...	0053
0	Cacui	d.	...	1346	...	La Sabana	d.	...	0210
120	La Sabana	d.	...	1812	...	Cacui	a.	...	0635
147	**Los Amores**	a.	...	1928	...	**Resistencia**	a.	...	...

9960S EL TREN DEL FIN DEL MUNDO

km	a	b	c					a	b	c	
0	0930	1000	1200	1500	↓	d.**Fin Del Mundo** a.	↑	1140	1155	1410	17
8	1030	1050	1300	1600	↓	a.**Parque Nacional** d.	↑	1040	1115	1310	16

a – Sept. 1 - Apr. 30. b – May 1 - Aug. 31. c – Departs 30 minutes later May 1 - Aug.

9965 CHILE

Empresa de los Ferrocarriles del Esta

SANTIAGO - CHILLÁN — EFE

km		22001	22003	22007 ⑤				22202 Ⓑ	22204 Ⓑ	22206 ⑦	
0	...	0830	1730	1825	↓	d.**Santiago** Alameda a.	↑	1231	1931	2131	...
	...	0843	1743	1838	↓	d.San Bernardo d.	↑	1219	1919	2119	...
85	...	0923	1823	1918	↓	d.Rancagua d.	↑	1139	1839	2039	...
138	...	0957	1857	1952	↓	d.San Fernando d.	↑	1105	1805	2005	...
191	...	1031	1929	2024	↓	d.Curicó d.	↑	1032	1732	1932	...
	...	1044	1942	2037	↓	d.Molina d.	↑	1019	1719	1919	...
258	...	1114	2012	2107	↓	**d.Talca** d.	↑	0949	1649	1849	...
278	...	1128	2026	2121	↓	d.San Javier d.	↑	0935	1635	1835	...
308	...	1151	2049	2144	↓	d.Linares d.	↑	0912	1612	1812	...
348	...	1219	2117	2212	↓	d.Parral d.	↑	0844	1544	1744	...
382	...	1245	2143	2238	↓	d.San Carlos d.	↑	0818	1518	1718	...
400	...	1302	2200	2255	↓	a.**Chillán** d.	↑	0800	1500	1700	...

VICTORIA - TEMUCO

km			22931 ①-⑤	22933	22935			22932 ①-⑤	22934	22
0	**Victoria**	d.	0630	1140	1820	**Temuco**	d.	0930	1645	20
44	Lautaro	d.	0718	1228	1908	Lautaro	d.	1010	1725	20
73	**Temuco**	a.	0801	1311	1951	**Victoria**	a.	1101	1816	2

TALCA - CONSTITUCIÓN

km			20701		20703			20702		20
0	**Talca**	d.	0740	...	1610	**Constitución**	d.	0715	...	1
	Gonzalez Bastias	d.	0907	...	1737	Gonzalez Bastias	d.	0905	...	1
89	**Constitución**	a.	1052	...	1922	**Talca**	a.	1027	...	18

SANTIAGO - SAN FERNANDO — Ferrobair

km			501 Ⓐ a	503 ⚒	505	509	513	517	523	525	529	533 Ⓑ
0	**Santiago** Alameda	d.	0650	0800	0900	1100	1300	1500	1700	1800	1900	2030
	San Bernardo	d.	0704	0814	0914	1114	1314	1514	1714	1814	1910	2044
85	Rancagua	a.	0800	0910	1000	1210	1410	1610	1810	1910	2010	2100
138	**San Fernando**	a.	...	...	...	...	...	...	...	...	...	...

		500 Ⓐ b	502 Ⓐ	508 Ⓐ	514	520 ⚒	522	526 Ⓐ	528 Ⓑ	530 Ⓑ	5
San Fernando	d.	...	...	...	...	...	...	...	...	...	...
Rancagua	d.	0530	0600	0730	1100	1400	1500	1700	1800	1900	1
San Bernardo	d.	0637	0657	0827	1157	1457	1557	1757	1857	1957	2
Santiago Alameda	a.	0640	0710	0840	1210	1510	1610	1810	1910	2010	20

a – Additional trips: 1000Ⓐ, 1200Ⓐ, 1400Ⓐ, 1600Ⓐ, 1630Ⓑ, 1830Ⓑ, 1930Ⓑ. b – Additional trips: 0800⑥, 0900Ⓐ, 0930Ⓒ, 1000Ⓐ, 1200Ⓑ, 1230⑥, 1300Ⓑ, 1600Ⓐ, 1630Ⓒ, 173

South Korea

il services in South Korea are operated by Korea National Railways under the brand names 'Korail', 'Supreme Railways' and 'AREX'. All services convey at least Economy ss seating (shown in the tables as '2nd class') with many trains (and all KTX and SRT high-speed services) also conveying 1st class accommodation. Timings shown are the est available.
rail offer the *KORAIL PASS* which allows foreign visitors to take almost all trains operated by *Korail*. It cannot be used on SRT services, metro and temporary tourist trains. ult prices: 138,000KRW for a 3 consecutive day pass; 210,000KRW for a 5 consecutive day pass; 121,000 KRW for a 2 day select pass; 193,000 KRW for a 4 day select pass. lect passes can be used over a 10 day period. Discounts for children (6 - 12) and groups of 2 to 5 persons are available for all passes. www.letskorail.com

orail — SEOUL - BUSAN — 9970

m	*KTX/SRT high-speed*	101 H	103 A	303 D	291 201	107	309	111 C	313	115	231	117	251 B	121	233	123	327	125	127	129	131	337	135	293 203	137	295 205
0	**Seoul** Main....... 9971 d.	0515	0530	0600e	0605	0635	0705e	0730	0800e	0800	0757	0900	0945	1000	1017	1030	1050e	1100	1200	1230	1300	1330e	1330	1355	1400	1415
6	Cheonan Asan.. 9971 d.	│	0608	0633	0644	│	0744	│	│	│	│	│	1024	1039	│	1106	1118	1139	1239	│	│	│	1409	│	│	│
0	Daejeon........... 9971 d.	0612	0632	0657	0714	0733	0814	0830	0854	0900	0940	0952	1050	1103	1159	1135	1147	1203	1303	1333	1403	1428	1433	1452	1502	1513
3	Dongdaegu....... 9971 d.	0658	0724	0743	0806	0823	0900	0921	0938	0944	1024	1036	1136	1149	1245	1226	1233	1249	1349	1419	1457	1514	1519	1541	1547	1554
'2	Ulsan.......................d.	0729	0753	│	0832	0854	0926	│	1004	1015	│	│	│	1220	1311	1252	1304	1320	1420	1444	│	1538	1549	│	│	│
3*	**Busan**......................a.	0751	0817	0825	0854	0916	0947	1002	1026	1037	1104	1115	1248	1242	1334	1314	1327	1342	1442	1507	1545	1600	1610	1622	1627	1632

X/SRT high-speed	141	143	347	235	149	255	151	153	155	157	361	159	211 Ⓒ	367	161	213 Ⓒ	163	215 Ⓒ	371	167	169	375	171	173	217 Ⓒ	281
oul Main........9971 d.	1500	1540	1600e	1611	1700	1715	1725	1800	1815	1830	1840e	1900	1920	1930e	1935	1955	2000	2015	2030e	2100	2130	2130e	2200	2230	2250	2300
eonan Asan...9971 d.	1538	│	│	│	│	│	1804	1834	│	1904	1916	1938	│	│	│	2033	2039	2053	2108	2138	│	│	2238	2309	│	2339
ejeon............9971 d.	1608	1642	1651	1752	1802	1812	1828	1858	1917	1934	1941	2008	2020	2028	2033	2058	2108	2117	2137	2203	2232	2225	2302	2333	2347	0008
ngdaegu........9971 d.	1654	1728	1737	1837	1854	1858	1914	1948	2002	2020	2032	2052	2106	2113	2123	2144	2153	2202	2226	2249	2318	2311	2349	0017	0033	0058
an........................d.	1719	1753	1802	1902	1919	│	1945	2013	2029	2051	│	│	2132	│	2148	│	2217	│	│	2314	2349	2336	0014	0042	│	...
san......................a.	1742	1816	1824	1924	1942	2012	2007	2035	2050	2113	2119	2139	2154	2200	2210	2229	2237	2242	2311	2337	0012	2359	0037	0103	0115	...

X/SRT high-speed	302 G	102	104 F	106 ①–⑤	108	204 Ⓒ	110	112 N	312	114	232	254	116	120	122	124	324	126	272 Ⓒ	128	132	134	210 Ⓒ	256 E	338	136
san......................d.	0500	0510	0520	0545	0610	0630	0700	0730	0745	0810	0820	0817	0840	0905	0935	1000	1010	1015	1005	1100	1230	1310	1325	1323	1340	1400
an........................d.	0523	0533	│	0608	0633	0653	0723	0753	│	0834	0844	│	0903	0929	│	│	│	1038	│	1123	1253	1333	│	│	│	1423
ngdaegu........9971 d.	0550	0600	0610	0635	0706	0725	0750	0826	0831	0901	0911	0929	0935	0956	1015	1045	1100	1111	1117	1150	1325	1400	1411	1442	1425	1450
ejeon............9971 d.	0632	0647	0653	0717	0754	0807	0838	0908	0913	0948	0853	1011	1018	1038	1057	1127	1142	1153	1205	1236	1407	1442	1454	1524	1507	1538
eonan Asan...9971 d.	0657	0712	│	0746	0824	│	│	0933	0943	1013	│	│	│	1108	│	1153	│	│	│	│	│	1510	1522	1554	│	1608
oul Main........9971 a.	0736e	0751	0757	0827	0903	0910	0937	1014	1015e	1049	1135	1116	1122	1147	1151	1231	1239e	1257	1304	1342	1511	1548	1604	1634	1605e	1645

X/SRT high-speed	138	140	142	346	144	352	146	214 Ⓒ	148	152	236	154	360	156	158	364	220 Ⓒ	238	162	166	262	168	376	172	174	222 Ⓒ
san......................d.	1420	1455	1510	1530	1545	1600	1620	1630	1645	1720	1745	1800	1810	1830	1900	1930	1945	1955	2005	2100	2045	2130	2200	2215	2225	2250
an........................d.	│	│	│	1553	1608	1623	│	│	1708	1743	1809	1824	1833	1853	1923	1953	│	│	2028	2124	│	2153	│	2238	│	2313
ngdaegu........9971 d.	1510	1535	1550	1620	1635	1656	1710	1717	1740	1815	1842	1851	1900	1925	1950	2020	2035	2040	2100	2151	2201	2226	2242	2305	2315	2340
ejeon............9971 d.	1553	1615	1632	1702	1717	1738	1758	1805	1822	1857	1924	1939	1947	2012	2033	2103	2117	2122	2142	2239	2244	2309	2323	2351	2356	0022
eonan Asan...9971 d.	│	│	│	│	1742	1807	│	1830	1847	1922	│	2009	│	│	│	2128	2142	│	2207	│	│	│	│	0016	0025	0046
oul Main........9971 a.	1654	1712	1725	1755e	1823	1840e	1902	1909	1927	2002	2109	2048	2045	2117	2140	2206e	2221	2308	2249	2342	2349	0009	0015e	0054	0100	0124

- Additional trips: 0600, 0700, 1430, 1630, 1840.
- Additional trips: 1305, 1525Ⓒ, 2110, 2135.
- Additional trips: 0750, 1320, 1445Ⓒ, 1600, 1855, 2030.
- Additional trips: 0530, 0630, 0700, 0730, 0805, 0900, 0905, 0920, 1000, 1030, 1210, 1230, 1255, 1300, 1400, 1430, 1500, 1530, 1625, 1640, 1700, 1730, 1800, 1830, 1900, 1920, 2000, 2100, 2200, 2240.

E – Additional trips: 0950, 1535, 1630, 1715, 1840.
F – Additional trips: 0855, 1320, 2210
G – Additional trips: 0530, 0600, 0650, 0720, 0800, 0830, 0900, 0915, 0945, 1030, 1045, 1210, 1245, 1300, 1330, 1410, 1425, 1500, 1540, 1555, 1635, 1730, 1740, 1855, 2000, 2020, 2030, 2050, 2120, 2230, 2300.
H – Additional trip: 0935.

N – Additional trips: 0750Ⓒ, 1200, 1700, 2040.
e – Seoul Suseo.
Note: Services running to/from Seoul Suseo are operated by SRT and have different stopping patterns (but all services call at Daejeon and Dongdaegu).
* – *409km* via Miryang.

orail — SEOUL - MASAN - JINJU — 9971

km	*KTX high-speed*	401 E	403 D	407	409	411	413	415	419	421	423
0	**Seoul** Main........ 9970 d.	0505	0540	0905	1005	1250	1345	1620	1810	2040	2215
96	Cheonan Asan... 9970 d.	│	0618	0944	1043	│	1418	│	1844	2118	│
50	Daejeon............ 9970 d.	0601	0648	1008	1108	1352	1441	1722	1908	2147	2308
93	Dongdaegu........ 9970 d.	0647	0737	1059	1159	1438	1527	1811	1955	2235	2359
48	Miryang............ 9970 d.	0719	0813	1130	1231	│	1559	1842	2028	│	0031
37	Changwon Jungang....d.	0747	0839	│	1256	1537	1625	1910	2054	2332	│
97	Changwon..................d.	0755	│	1203	│	1545	│	│	│	2340	0102
01	**Masan**.......................a.	0800	0849	1208	1230	1550	1635	1920	2104	2346	0107
50	Jinju ....a.	...	0915	...	1332	...	1701	...	...	0012	...

KTX high-speed	402	404	406	408	412	414	416	418	422 C	424
Jinju.........................d.	...	0620	...	1000	1250	1430	...	1745	...	...
Masan......................d.	0505	0647	0905	1026	1317	1455	1650	1811	2110	2150
Changwon ....d.	0511	0652	│	1031	1323	│	1656	│	│	2156
Changwon Jungang .d.	0519	│	0917	1040	1331	1506	1704	1823	│	│
Miryang.......... 9970 d.	0548	0724	0945	1104	│	1530	│	1845	│	2225
Dongdaegu..... 9970 d.	0630	0801	1025	1145	1430	1604	1804	1919	2219	2259
Daejeon.......... 9970 d.	0712	0849	1107	1227	1518	1647	1852	2001	2301	2341
Cheonan Asan 9970 d.	│	│	│	1253	│	│	1916	│	2326	│
Seoul Main..... 9970 a.	0813	0953	1206	1333	1624	1748	1957	2100	0030	0045

- Additional trips: 1240, 2000. D – Additional trip: 0825. E – Additional trip: 1735.

orail — SEOUL - GWANGJU - MOKPO — 9972

m	*KTX/SRT high-speed*	651 G	501	503	505	653	507	541 E	509	605 H	575	511	513	515	517	519	521	661	523	581	525	615	527	529	667	531
0	**Seoul** Yongsan. 9973 d.	0510e	0510	0550	0630	0640e	0749	0923	0820	0830e	0930	1035	1220	1245	1335	1455	1535	1615e	1645	1710	1745	1805e	1940	2035	2110e	2225
3	Cheonan Asan.. 9973 d.	│	│	0627	│	0717	│	│	0854	│	1007	│	1257	│	1413	1532	│	│	1722	│	│	1839	│	2112	2144	2302
'1	Osong........................d.	│	0554	0639	0714	0729	│	│	0906	│	│	1123	│	1325	│	1545	1620	│	│	│	1826	│	2024	2124	│	2315
'0	Iksan .... 9973 d.	0612	0622	0708	0742	0757	0904	1029	0935	0950	1134	1151	1341	1353	1450	1619	1649	1726	1806	1909	1854	1922	2058	2153	2227	2344
7	Jeongeup..................d.	0628	0638	0724	0758	0813	0920	│	0951	1006	1150	1207	│	1409	1506	1635	│	│	1822	│	│	1938	2114	2209	2256	0000
'7	**Gwangju** Songjeong.. d.	0647	0656	0743	0817	0832	0939	1056	1010	1023	1209	1226	1410	1428	1525	1654	1718	1755	1841	1938	1923	1955	2133	2228	2307	0019
5	**Mokpo**.......................a.	0724	0730	0820	0854	0909	1016	...	1047	...	1245	1303	1447	1502	1602	1728	1755	1832	1918	2014	2000	...	2210	2305	2333	0056

X/SRT high-speed	602 J	542	502	572	652 K	504	506	508	510	544 F	512	514	658	516	518	614	520	522	582	524	526	528	666	530	532	668
kpo.......................d.	...	...	0527	0605	0630	0710	0825	0910	1000	...	1100	1255	1310	1350	1425	...	1600	1655	1717	1800	1845	2000	2030	2055	2200	2230
angju Songjeong.. d.	0520	0530	0607	│	0709	0750	0905	0951	1036	1125	1140	1335	1349	1429	1502	1555	1639	1724	1754	1840	1924	2040	2109	2131	2239	2309
ongeup..................d.	0538	0548	0625	│	│	0808	0923	│	│	1143	│	1353	1407	1447	1520	│	1657	1753	1813	1858	1942	2058	2127	2149	│	2327
an.................9973 d.	0554	0604	0645	0715	0738	0824	0939	1026	1105	1159	1216	1409	1423	1503	1545	1624	1713	1816	1830	1914	1958	2114	2143	2213	2308	2343
ong.......................d.	0621	0631	0720	│	│	0858	1006	│	│	│	1243	1438	1451	1538	│	│	│	│	1945	1949	│	2150	2219	2241	│	│
eonan Asan...9973 d.	0635	0645	│	0838	0815	│	1020	│	│	1243	1257	│	1505	│	│	│	1757	1853	1959	2003	│	│	│	2255	│	0020
oul Yongsan..9973 a.	0709e	0723	0806	0917	0854e	0946	1058	1137	1215	1318	1335	1526	1538e	1625	1702	1733e	1833	1931	2037	2042	2110	2238	2256e	2330	0017	0053e

- Additional trips: 1610, 1835, 2120.
- Additional trips: 1825, 2100.
- Additional trips: 0940, 1100, 1315, 1710, 1910.
- Additional trips: 0540, 0740, 1020, 1220, 1410, 1520, 1940, 2225, 2300.
- Additional trips: 0620, 0800, 1015, 1120, 1300, 1630, 1830, 2030, 2200.

K – Additional trips: 0800, 1005, 1400, 1650, 1900.
e – Seoul Suseo.

Note: Services running to/from Seoul Suseo are operated by SRT and have different stopping patterns (but all services call at Iksan and Gwangju Songjeong).

orail — SEOUL - YEOSU — 9973

km	*KTX high-speed*	701 B	703	705	709	713	783	715	719	721	723
0	**Seoul** Yongsan.. 9972 d.	0510	0715	0840	1055	1410	1440	1645	1850	2005	2150
93	Cheonan Asan... 9972 d.	│	0752	│	1133	│	1517	1722	1927	2043	│
	Osong ....d.	0554	0804	0924	1145	1454	│	│	│	│	│
40	Iksan .... 9972 d.	0626	0839	0958	1220	1528	1641	1808	2010	2120	2258
66	Jeonju ....d.	0642	0856	1014	1236	1545	1658	1824	2026	2136	2314
26	Namwon.......................d.	0708	0922	1040	1302	1611	1724	1850	2052	2202	2340
94	Suncheon ....d.	0739	0956	1118	1337	1643	1758	1926	2126	2236	0011
34	**Yeosu** Expo ....a.	0801	1018	1140	1359	1704	1817	1947	2147	2258	0030

KTX high-speed	702	704	706	708 A	710	714	718	784	722	724
Yeosu Expo............d.	0506	0720	0840	1030	1200	1405	1635	1847	2030	2150
Suncheon ....d.	0527	0742	0902	1052	1222	1427	1657	1910	2051	2210
Namwon ....d.	0601	0815	0936	1126	1255	1500	1731	1943	2124	2240
Jeonju.......................d.	0627	0842	1003	1153	1322	1527	1758	2009	2151	2307
Iksan.............. 9972 d.	0645	0858	1026	1216	1338	1545	1816	2026	2213	2323
Osong.......................d.	0720	0933	│	1243	│	│	│	│	2241	2351
Cheonan Asan 9972 d.	│	0947	│	1257	1422	│	1853	2150	2255	│
Seoul Yongsan9972 a.	0806	1026	1137	1335	1457	1702	1931	2229	2330	0038

Additional trips: 1210, 1305, 1500, 1800. B – Additional trips: 0745, 0955, 1220, 1745.

9974 SEOUL - POHANG Kora

km	KTX high-speed	451 A	453	455	457	459	461	491	467	469	473
0	**Seoul** Main .... **9971** d.	0540	0645	0815	0925	1045	1300	1510	1620	1735	2220
96	Cheonan Asan ... **9971** d.	0618	0723	0850	|	1123	|	|	|	|	|
160	Daejeon .... **9971** d.	0648	0747	0919	1028	1153	1403	1613	1722	1837	2322
293	Dongdaegu .... **9971** d.	0734	0833	1005	1114	1239	1454	1659	1808	1928	0008
374	**Pohang** .... a.	0808	0908	1040	1149	1313	1529	1736	1843	2003	0043

KTX high-speed	452	454	456	458 B	462	464	468	492	472	47
Pohang .... d.	0550	0720	0945	1015	1235	1400	1625	1855	1920	213
Dongdaegu ..... **9971** d.	0630	0801	1025	1051	1313	1442	1702	1932	2001	221
Daejeon .... **9971** d.	0712	0849	1107	1133	1401	1524	1750	2020	2043	230
Cheonan Asan **9971** d.	|	|	|	1203	|	1554	|	|	2113	232
Seoul Main ..... **9971** a.	0813	0953	1206	1241	1505	1634	1855	2125	2154	000

A – Additional trips: 1240, 1435, 2040. **B** – Additional trips: 1105, 1530, 1800.

9975 SEOUL - GANGNEUNG Kora

km	KTX high-speed	801 A	807	809	813	815	819	821	823	827	833	835
	Seoul C .... d.	0532	0822	0922	1122	1222	1422	1522	1622	1822	2122	2222
0	Manjong .... d.	0623	|	1011	|	1311	|	1611	|	1911	|	2308
59	Pyeongchang .... d.	0645	0937	|	1232	|	1533	|	|	|	2236	|
116	**Gangneung** ..... a.	0708	0958	1057	1259	1353	1555	1702	1753	1957	2258	2350

KTX high-speed	802	804	808	812	814	816	818	820	824	834	83
Gangneung ... d.	0530	0630	0830	1030	1130	1230	1330	1430	1630	2130	223
Pyeongchang . d.	|	0659	|	|	1154	|	1359	|	1659	|	225
Manjong .... d.	0614	0724	|	1120	|	1319	|	1520	|	|	231
Seoul C .... a.	0702	0813	1005	1208	1303	1407	1509	1608	1809	2306	000

A – Additional trips: 0622, 0722, 1022, 1322, 1722, 1922, 2022. **B** – Additional trips: 0730, 0930, 1530, 1730, 1830, 1925, 2030. **C** – **Seoul** Cheongnyangni.

9976 SEOUL - ANDONG and DAEGU - BUSAN Kora

km		1601	1621 2B	1603	1605	1607	1609	1623 2B	
0	**Seoul** Cheongnyangni .... d.	0640	0738	1033	1300	1538	1913	2103	...
105	Wonju .... d.	0754	0855	1143	1412	1649	2079	2211	...
155	Jecheon .... d.	0837	0941	1226	1456	1733	2133	2255	...
219	Yeongju .... **9978** d.	0942	1047	1333	1601	1838	2237	2354	...
256	**Andong** .... **9978** d.	1011	1116	1404	1630	1910	2307	0023	...

	1602 2	1622 2B	1604 2	1606 2	1608 2	1610 2	1624 2B	
Andong .... **9978** d.	0713	1119	1408	1503	1710	1925	0221	...
Yeongju .... **9978** d.	0751	1156	1445	1539	1750	2001	0254	...
Jecheon .... **9977** d.	0848	1254	1548	1641	1852	2059	0359	...
Wonju .... **9977** d.	0936	1339	1634	1726	1940	2146	0442	...
Seoul Cheongnyangni .... **9977** a.	1048	1449	1743	1850	2049	2252	0550	...

km		1773 2C	1775 2	1779 2	1781 2	1621 2B	1783 2	1681 2A	1791 2	1795 2	1623 2B
	Andong .... **9978** d.	...	...	...	...	1118	...	1735		...	0023
0	**Dongdaegu** .... **9978** d.	0730	0831	1030	1135	|	1350	|	1905	2128	|
	Gyeongju .... d.	0842	0948	1148	1248	1325	1500	1937	2023	2254	0220
	Taehwagang (Ulsan) ... d.	0917	1023	1226	1328	1406	1541	2019	2106	2331	0257
	ShinHaeundu .... d.	1009	1118	1321	1425	1503	1636	2113	2202	0025	0347
185	**Busan** Bujeon .... a.	1023	1136	1339	1440	1520	1651	2130	2220	0042	0402

	1774 2D	1622 2B	1776 2	1682 2A	1780 2	1784 2	1788 2	1790 2	1794 2	162 2B
Busan Bujeon .... d.	0600	0720	0745	0910	1130	1357	1535	1640	2014	224
ShinHaeundu .... d.	0619	0738	0803	0928	1150	1415	1553	1656	2033	225
Taehwagang (Ulsan) d.	0714	0834	0857	1024	1244	1507	1648	1748	2129	235
Gyeongju .... d.	0755	0916	0936	1106	1327	1546	1732	1824	2213	002
Dongdaegu **9978** a.	0911	|	1050	|	1441	1711	1845	1942	2325	|
Andong .... **9978** a.	...	1117	...	1253	...	...	...	...	...	02

A – To/from Donghae (Table **9978**). **B** – **Seoul** Cheongnyangni – Andong – Bujeon and v.v. **C** – Additional trips: 0930, 1700, 2000. **D** – Additional trips: 1300, 1735, 210

9977 SEOUL - DONGHAE Kora

km		1631	1633	1635	1637	1639	1641		
0	**Seoul** Cheongnyangni .... **9976** d.	0705	0934	1236	1430	1636	2320	...	...
105	Wonju .... **9976** d.	0837	1045	1357	1534	1746	0031	...	...
155	Jecheon .... **9976** d.	0928	1138	1441	1617	1829	0111	...	...
	Yemi .... d.	1022	1234	1538	1716	1924	0205	...	...
	Mindungsan .... d.	1045	1259	1601	1742	1946	0227	...	...
	Taebaek .... d.	1117	1331	1635	1823	2020	0300	...	...
	Dogye .... d.	1150	1359	1705	1858	2049	0331	...	...
315	**Donghae** .... a.	1233	1439	1751	1940	2130	0413	...	...
	Jeongdongjin .... a.	1300	1511	1823	2010	2200	0442	...	...
	Gangneung .... a.	1319	1529	1843	2027	2217	0459	...	...

		1632	1634	1636	1638	1640	1642	
Gangneung .... d.	...	0428	0643	0813	1000	1410	1623	...
Jeongdongjin .... d.	...	0445	0700	0830	1018	1427	1640	...
Donghae .... d.	...	0514	0729	0859	1048	1456	1711	...
Dogye .... d.	...	0559	0812	0941	1134	1537	1754	...
Taebaek .... d.	...	0629	0841	1011	1205	1603	1823	...
Mindungsan .... d.	...	0701	0915	1044	1238	1638	1856	...
Yemi .... d.	...	0723	0938	1106	1302	1726	1925	...
Jecheon .... **9976** d.	...	0822	1035	1200	1359	1801	2019	...
Wonju .... **9976** d.	...	0912	1119	1243	1440	1854	2102	...
Seoul Cheongnyangni .... **9976** a.	...	1021	1242	1353	1547	2005	2218	...

9978 DAEGU - DONGHAE Korail 2nd class

km		1672	1682 2A	1674	
0	**Dongdaegu** **9976** d.	0600	...	1630	...
127	Andong .... **9976** d.	0747	1254	1821	...
164	Yeongju .... **9976** d.	0826	1326	1859	...
	Cheoram .... d.	1011	1518	2047	...
	Dogye .... d.	1040	1554	2117	...
348	**Donghae** .... a.	1127	1634	2200	...
	Gangneung .... a.	1217	1721	2245	...

	1671	1681 2A		1673
Gangneung .... d.	0609	1300	...	1646
Donghae .... d.	0655	1349	...	1733
Dogye .... d.	0736	1433	...	1823
Cheoram .... d.	0803	1503	...	1851
Yeongju ... **9976** d.	0955	1658	...	2045
Andong .... **9976** d.	1025	1732	...	2116
Dongdaegu **9976** a.	1239	...	...	2300

A – To/from Busan Bujeon (Table **9976**).

9979 DAEGU - POHANG Korail 2nd clas

km		1751	1753	1755	1757
0	**Dongdaegu** .... d.	0545	0900	1500	1830
	Yeongcheon .... d.	0618	0935	1535	1907
103	**Pohang** .... a.	0737	1052	1651	2035

	1752	1754	1756	17
Pohang .... d.	0619	1125	1425	19
Yeongcheon ..... d.	0735	1249	1553	20
Dongdaegu ...... a.	0808	1321	1629	21

9980 DAEGU - MASAN Korail 2nd clas

km		1901	1903	1031	1905	1907	1909	1231	1911 2	1033 2
	Seoul .... d.			0853				1544	...	1914
0	**Dongdaegu** .... d.	0640	0920	1222	1400	1710	1832	1939	2155	2247
57	Miryang .... d.	0724	1007	1256	1446	1756	1919	2020	2240	2319
	Changwon Jungang .... d.	0757	1039	1324	1522	1831	1957	2058	2315	2350
	Changwon .... d.	0805	1048	1333	1530	1841	2006	2107	2324	2539
105	**Masan** .... a.	0810	1053	1337	1536	1846	2011	2111	2329	0004

	1902	1232	1904	1032	1906	1908	1034	1910	19
Masan .... d.	0550	0730	0830	0941	1157	1555	1638	1844	210
Changwon .... d.	0556	0736	0836	0947	1203	1601	1644	1850	210
Changwon Jungang .... d.	0606	0745	0845	0957	1213	1611	1654	1859	211
Miryang .... d.	0643	0814	0916	1024	1247	1646	1722	1930	214
Dongdaegu .... a.	0744	0853	1003	1055	1337	1737	1753	2017	224
Seoul .... a.	...	1253	...	1431	...	...	2122	...	

9981 MOKPO - BUSAN Korail 2nd clas

km		1944	1972	1952	1954	1441	1942	1974
0	**Mokpo** .... d.	...	...	...	0934			
	Gwangju Songjeong .... d.	...	0613		1033			1918
85	Seogwangju .... d.	...	0622		1042	1349		1928
	Boseong .... d.	...	0737		1151	1500		2035
206	**Suncheon** .... d.	0630	0838	0910	1249	1556	1720	2130
284	Jinju .... d.	0729		1010	1351		1822	
350	Masan .... d.	0819		1055	1435		1906	
354	Changwon .... d.	0825		1101	1441		1912	
	Changwon Jungang .... d.	0834		1111	1450		1922	
385	Samnangjin .... d.	0901		1139	1516		1946	
433	**Busan** Bujeon .... a.	0943		1227	1603		2037	

	1971	1442	1951	1941	1953	1973	1943
Busan Bujeon .... d.	...	...	0614	1035	1346	...	1844
Samnangjin .... d.	...	...	0707	1121	1435	...	1933
Changwon Jungang .... d.	...	...	0736	1148	1502	...	2004
Changwon .... d.	...	...	0745	1157	1511	...	2013
Masan .... d.	...	...	0752	1204	1518	...	2020
Jinju .... d.	...	...	0839	1251	1604	...	2104
Suncheon .... d.	0555	0702	0938	1347	1700	1735	2200
Boseong .... d.	0650	0800	1036	...	...	1831	...
Seogwangju .... d.	0803	0909	1150	...	...	1941	...
Gwangju Songjeong .... a.	0812		1149	...	...	1951	...
Mokpo .... a.	...	...	1259	...	...	...	...

9983 SEOUL - CHUNCHEON 2nd class Kora

Seoul Yongsan - **Namchuncheon** and v.v. *93 km*. Journey 69 – 78 minutes.

From **Seoul** Yongsan. Most trains call at **Gapyeong** 56 – 64 mins later: ①–⑤ 0600, 0700, 0752, 0852, 0955, 1058, 1200, 1258, 1400, 1510, 1600, 1700, 1800, 1856, 1956, 2032, 2120, 2248; ⑥⑦ at 0615, 06 0755, 0820, 0845, 0919, 0950, 1020, 1100, 1130, 1157, 1256, 1330, 1415, 1447, 1514, 1547, 1628, 1656, 1730, 1800, 1826, 1900, 1930, 2008. 2035, 2120, 2140⑥, 2215.

From **Namchuncheon**. Most trains call at **Gapyeong** 15 – 19 minutes later: ①–⑤ 0612, 0706, 0740, 0814, 0915, 1027, 1118, 1213, 1318, 1414, 1526, 1618, 1709, 1817, 1850, 1942, 2113, 2218; ⑥⑦ at 06 0711, 0742⑥, 0808, 0851, 0931, 0956, 1021, 1057⑥, 1118, 1202⑥, 1231, 1313, 1342, 1406, 1455, 1516, 1556, 1622, 1656, 1730, 1759, 1831, 1904, 1938, 2004, 2037, 2113, 2152, 2217.

9984 INCHEON AIRPORT ✈ - SEOUL ARE

Incheon Airport ✈ - **Seoul** Main and v.v. *61 km*. 2nd class only. Journey 45 minutes.

From **Incheon Airport** ✈ at 0520, 0600, 0630, 0720, 0802, 0835, 0920, 0954, 1032, 1056, 1130, 1156, 1230, 1301, 1332, 1400, 1434, 1500, 1526, 1607, 1641, 1715, 1759, 1847, 1915, 1954, 2016, 2100, 21
Frequent additional slower services (calling at Gimpo Airport ✈) run 5 – 6 times per hour 0523 – 2342 (journey 55 – 60 minutes Incheon - Seoul).

From **Seoul** Main at 0600, 0626, 0700, 0734, 0816, 0900, 0938, 1027, 1106, 1135, 1158, 1228, 1257, 1337, 1405, 1428, 1511, 1530, 1602, 1635, 1720, 1745, 1820, 1901, 1943, 2026, 2050, 2121, 2200.
Frequent additional slower services (calling at Gimpo Airport ✈) run 5 – 6 times per hour 0520 – 2338 (journey 55 – 60 minutes Seoul - Incheon).

RAIL *EXTRA* is an additional feature to be found in our Summer and Winter editions, giving the Editorial team an opportunity to include further information on rail travel throughout Europe to supplement the timetables in our regular editions. In particular we have selected a number of tourist and heritage lines from the many hundreds on offer, with timetable details where possible (though it's always best to check before travel in case of late changes). We would also encourage readers to seek out the many museum and heritage lines which we cannot show for space reasons, many of which include steam operation.

AUSTRIA

RAIL TRAVEL

See Tables **950 - 999**. Most trains are operated by Österreichische Bundesbahnen (ÖBB) www.oebb.at. For train types see page 453. Scenic highlights include the Semmeringbahn (Table **980**), the Arlberg route (**951**) and the Salzburg to Villach Tauern line. Many minor routes are also scenic.

Opening of the Wien to St Pölten high-speed line in 2012, along with upgrading elsewhere, has led to significant journey time improvements on the key east to west 'Westbahn' route linking Wien with Linz and Salzburg. ÖBB's latest high-quality *Railjet* trains take advantage of this, running at up to 230 km/h. Private operator *Westbahn* competes with ÖBB on the route. A recent development is the introduction by ÖBB of the *Nightjet* brand for night trains, with a network of both international and domestic routes.

Services in and through Wien (Vienna) have been revolutionised in recent years by the opening of the new Hauptbahnhof (central station), which allows through services on a site (the old Südbahnhof) where previously all trains had to terminate. A notable feature of the new station is the diamond shaped roof employing 25,000 square metres of translucent glass and steel. The Westbahnhof is now less important for long-distance services.

Several local lines are run by private operators, and a small selection of tourist and heritage lines is shown below.

MARIAZELLERBAHN

Niederösterreichische Verkehrsorganisationsgesellschaft (NÖVOG) run several local lines including the 84 km narrow gauge Mariazellerbahn from St Pölten Hbf to Mariazell. Full details are shown in Table **994**.

The electrified Mariazellerbahn is widely recognised as one of the most attractive railway journeys in the Alps and an excursion is highly recommended. There are 21 tunnels and 75 bridges or viaducts along the route and the highest point (892m) is actually situated in the 2368m Gösing Tunnel. Between Kirchberg and Laubenbachmühle the line passes through the spectacular gorge of the River Pielach and at Winterbach there are some particularly fine views. On Summer Saturdays a heritage electric train runs one trip each way, whilst a steam hauled journey runs on several dates.

STEYRTAL-MUSEUMSBAHN

A 10 minute walk from Steyr station (Table **976**) takes you to the Lokalbahn station from where the 17 km line operated by ÖGEG www.oegeg.at takes you to Grünburg. Opened in 1889, the Steyrtalbahn is the oldest narrow gauge (760mm) line in Austria. Passing through the scenic Steyr valley, it has been operating as a heritage line since 1986 using steam traction.

The main operating season is ⑥⑦ July to September, also ⑦ in June. From Grünburg 0830, 1200, 1700 (1100, 1700 on ⑥ in July / August), from Steyr Lokalbahn at 1000, 1400, 1830 (1400, 1830 on ⑥ in July / August). Journey time is 60 minutes each way.

NIEDERÖSTERREICHISCHE SCHNEEBERGBAHN

This 9.8 km narrow gauge rack railway runs from Puchberg am Schneeberg to Hochschneeberg. Timings, which include a steam service on Sundays in high summer, can be found in Table **984**.

Construction was completed in 1897. The journey to the summit provides wonderful views of the Schneeberg mountain range, with Hochschneeberg station being the highest in Austria at 1795m above sea-level.

WALDVIERTLER SCHMALSPURBAHNEN

A narrow gauge (760mm) network based on Gmünd NÖ close to the Czech border, running through enchanting, densely wooded landscapes. The line runs for 68 km Groß Gerungs - Gmünd - Alt Nagelberg - Litschau. It has enjoyed a revival since being taken over from ÖBB in 2001 and operated as a tourist railway by NÖVOG www.noevog.at

Gmünd to Groß Gerungs runs Apr. 27 - Oct. 27 as follows. Operated by railcars, except on ③⑥ when trains are hauled by heritage diesels (steam on 1st / 3rd ⑥ of the month).

	†	③A	⑥	†	B
Gmünd NÖ .d.	0900	1100	1315	1315	1400
Weitra.........d.	0925	1130	1345	1340	1425
G. Gerungs .a.	1030	1245	1510	1445	1530

	†	③A	†	B	⑥
G. Gerungs d.	1115	1500	1530	1700	1700
Weitra........ d.	1219	1605	1629	1804	1815
Gmünd NÖ a.	1245	1635	1655	1830	1845

Gmünd to Litschau runs May 1 - Sept. 29 as follows. Operated by railcars ①–⑥. On † trains are steam hauled on 1st / 3rd ⑦ of the month, otherwise heritage diesel.

	B	③D	③D	③D	⑥E	⑥E	†	†
Gmünd NÖ ....d.	1000	0850	1250	1650	1000	1430	1000	1430
Alt Nagelberg............... ▷ d.	1030	0920	1320	1720	1030	1540	1030	1500
Litschau...........................a.	1055	0945	1345	1745	1055	1525	1055	1525
	B	**③D**	**③D**	**③D**	**⑥E**	**⑥E**	**†**	**†**
Litschau...........................d.	1245	1000	1400	1800	1300	1600	1300	1600
Alt Nagelberg............... ▷ d.	1317	1032	1432	1832	1332	1632	1332	1632
Gmünd NÖ ....a.	1340	1055	1455	1855	1355	1655	1355	1655

A – May 8 - Sept. 25.
B – ①②④⑤ July 1 - Sept. 6.
D – June 5 - Sept. 25.
E – June 1 - Sept. 28.
▷ – Connecting heritage trains run Alt Nagelberg - Heidenreichstein on ③⑥⑦ July 13 - Sept. 1. From Alt Nagelberg 1030, 1500, 1720③; from Heidenreichstein 0945③, 1345③, 1545③, 1245©, 1545©. Journey 40 minutes. www.wsv.or.at

ACHENSEEBAHN

This short (6.8 km) narrow gauge steam-operated rack railway runs from Jenbach, adjacent to the ÖBB station, to Seespitz-Bahnstation. The timetable is shown in Table **956**. The line climbs from Jenbach (532m) to the southern tip of the Achensee (931m), the departure point for Achensee boat excursions.

RAILWAY MUSEUMS

One of Austria's principal railway museums is the Eisenbahnmuseum Strasshof, also known as *Das Heizhaus*, situated adjacent to Silberwald station on the Wien to Břeclav line and served by local trains. Open ②–⑦ Apr. 1 - Oct. 26 (also winter weekends, not Dec. 24 - Jan. 31). Sundays are the best time to visit when certain locomotives are running. Steam is in operation within the large site on several dates between April and October.

Another large railway museum is the Lokpark Ampflwang, operated by ÖGEG. Steam / diesel trips run on ⑦ July - Sept. on the 11 km line which links the museum with Timelkam, which is served by local trains from Linz.

Austrian Railways *CityJet* suburban service, Wien

BELGIUM

RAIL TRAVEL

See Tables **400 - 439**. Operated by NMBS (in Dutch) / SNCB (in French) www.b-rail.be. With over 3,500 km of lines, Belgium is well served by frequent rail services, mostly running to regular-interval timetables at the same minutes past each hour (with some peak hour extras). Note, however, that timetables and the route network can vary on Saturdays and Sundays, as shown in our tables. The most scenic lines are those in the Ardennes region, for example Liège to Gouvy and on to Luxembourg.

The two principal stations in Brussels, Midi/Zuid (south) and Nord, were long ago linked by a cross-city line, including the uninspiring Central station with its underground platforms, and most trains run through Brussels by way of this line, many also serving Brussels Airport. However, a further line serves Luxembourg and Schuman stations in the European quarter of Brussels, and this too has a link to the airport via a recently opened tunnel.

Journeys between Brussels and Liège (Table **400**), as well as international journeys to Germany, were considerably speeded up by the opening of the high-speed line in 2002, and from Liège to Aachen in 2009. Other high-speed lines are used by *Eurostar* trains to London and by trains to the Netherlands.

Belgium's coastal resorts are linked with each other not by the national rail system but by a frequent coastal tramway (the *Kusttram*) operated by De Lijn. For details see Table **406**.

Heritage lines include Stoomtrein Dendermonde-Puurs www.stoomtrein.be, Stoomcentrum Maldegem, which links Eeklo (Table **413**) with Maldegem (see www.stoomtreinmaldegem.be), and the historic Tramway Vicinal des Grottes de Han (see www.tramdehan.net). However, the most significant heritage operation is the 'Three Valleys' CFV3V, detailed below.

Brussels also has a recently opened railway museum close to Schaerbeek station. See www.trainworld.be for further details. Closed on Mondays.

CHEMIN DE FER À VAPEUR DES TROIS VALLÉES (CFV3V)

This 14 km line runs from Mariembourg (800m from the SNCB/NMBS station in Table **421**) to Treignes, where there is a railway museum on the site of the old international station building. See www.cfv3v.eu for details.

Trains run on ⑥⑦ Apr. to Oct. (also June 10, ②③④ July / Aug., ⑤ July 19 - Aug. 9, Nov. 1). There are three return services departing Mariembourg 1110, 1420 and 1700 (1730 certain dates) returning from Treignes 1310, 1620 (1550 on certain dates) and 1810. Many dates include steam-hauled journeys but check the website for details. Journey time is 30 minutes each way by diesel railcar or 40 minutes by steam train. A special steam festival takes place each September (in 2019 on Sept. 21/22) and special timetables run on a handful of other dates.

BULGARIA

RAIL TRAVEL

See Tables **1500 - 1560**. Bulgarian State Railways (BDZ) www.bdz.bg run on a network of a little over 4,000 km, the principal lines of which link the capital Sofia with the Black Sea resorts of Burgas and Varna. Trains are often crowded and reservations are recommended for long-distance travel (and are obligatory for certain express trains). Signs at stations are in Cyrillic, although the website does have an English version.

BDZ has one narrow gauge line, running 125 km from Septemvri to Dobrinishte, serving en route the winter resort town of Bansko. Timings for this (very slow) line are in Table **1510**.

The National Railway Museum is in a former railway station in the outskirts of Ruse (see link foot of http://fan.bdz.bg). There is little else in the form of heritage lines, although there are occasional steam specials, and Plovdiv has a 600mm gauge Children's Railway (formerly Pioneer Railway).

CROATIA

RAIL TRAVEL

See Tables **1300 - 1359**. National railway company is Hrvatske Željeznice (HŽ) www.hzpp.hr. The network is centered on the capital Zagreb, but services are generally infrequent, even on the main lines to Rijeka and Split. The Zagreb to Split line (Table **1330**) is particularly scenic; the day trains on this line are operated by modern diesel units, with compulsory reservation. Sadly, connections from Knin to Zadar are no longer by train but provided by bus, although the route is still considered part of the rail network for ticketing purposes. Buses along the coast from Split to Ploče and Dubrovnik are, however, privately operated - brief details are given in Table **1325**.

The Croatian Railway Museum consists of an outdoor collection of exhibits in Zagreb, accessed from Ulica grada Vukovara 47, with limited opening hours (see http://muzej.hzinfra.hr). It is currently closed for reconstruction.

CZECH REPUBLIC

RAIL TRAVEL

See Tables **1100 - 1169**. National rail company is České Dráhy (ČD) (www.cd.cz), whilst the railway infrastructure is administered by SŽDC (www.szdc.cz). An extensive network of over 9,000 km is operated, with many branch lines serving towns and villages away from the main lines, making it possible to visit almost anywhere by rail. If you like to explore on slow, winding, country branch lines, this is definitely a country to visit. With a rail pass or day ticket you can hop on and off trains at will, since the only trains requiring advance reservation are the handful of *SC* (*SuperCity*) Pendolino trains, which run mainly on the Praha - Ostrava route (reservation fee varies up to a maximum of CZK 250).

Other high-quality trains are classified *IC*, *EC* or *Ex*, whilst *Railjet* trains also run on the Praha - Wien axis (whilst *Railjet* is an Austrian train type, there are also some in the colours of Czech Railways). Regular fast trains are classified *R* (for rychlík) or *Rx* and are shown in our tables with just the train number. Seats can be reserved on all of these train types (recommended at busy times), and many convey buffet cars. Semi-fast trains are *Sp* or spešný. Local trains, which can be very slow, are *Os* or osobný.

Other operators compete with ČD on several major routes, principally Regiojet from Praha to Ostrava, Bratislava, Košice and Wien, and Leo Express to Ostrava and Košice. Tickets are not interchangeable with those of ČD. Some branch lines are also operated by private companies.

In Praha, most services are concentrated on Praha hlavní nádraží (which means main station) though some services of a more local nature leave from the nearby Masarykovo station (10 mins walk). Trains to Rakovník (Table **1105**) are currently leaving from Bubny-Vltavská due to work on the viaduct. Holešovice station has been of less importance since 2008 when a new line opened enabling all through trains to serve hlavní nádraží.

Chomutov depository: Czech loco 498.106 built by Škoda in 1955

As with many countries in this listing, it is possible to book tickets online (with an account) and to print tickets at home. Although Praha airport is not rail connected, the Airport Express (AE) bus between the airport and Praha hlavní is included in ČD's ticket system so it is possible to print your own ticket from the airport to rail stations in the Czech Republic - very handy for a quick getaway and avoiding ticket office queues!

HERITAGE LINES

Heritage operations mainly consist of special trains on parts of the Czech rail system, and these are shown in ČD's own timetable (some in a special section at the end, listed on their website as ZVL). Many of these trains are run by KŽC (www.kzc.cz) with heritage diesel railcars or locos, mainly on summer weekends.

Recommended is a short 30 minute trip from Praha hlavní nad. over the scenic so-called *Prague Semmering* line to Praha-Zličín. Operated by KŽC and known as *Pražský motoráček*, it is included in the Prague public transport tariff. Departures are on ⑥⑦ at 0841, 1036, 1229 and 1436, returning at 0948, 1148, 1348, 1548 (or by tram from adjacent terminus).

Another popular journey is the scenic *Posázavsky Pacifik* line from Praha to Čerčany via Vrané nad Vltavou. As well as ČD local trains, KŽC runs heritage journeys in summer (Apr. to Oct.) from Praha to Čerčany at 0739⑥ and 1226⑦, returning at 1205⑥ and 1734⑦.

ČD's only narrow gauge line is also worth a mention, running to the village of Osoblaha close to the Polish border - see Table **1169** for brief details.

The principal railway museum is at Lužna u Rakovnika, 64 km from Praha (Table **1105**), open ⑥⑦ Apr. to Oct. (②–⑦ June - Aug). Steam trips operate on certain summer weekends to and from Lužna (for example from Praha or Chomutov). The museum's website is www.cdmuzeum.cz - click on the ČD Nostalgie link for a document listing many heritage events and trips throughout the year.

The National Technical Museum also has a large railway depository in Chomutov, open ④–⑦ Mar. 30 - Oct. 28. www.muzeum-chomutov.cz. Approx 1.4 km on foot from Chomutov station via Globus car park.

JHMD - JINDŘICHOHRADECKÉ MÍSTNÍ DRÁHY

This privately operated narrow gauge railway runs from Jindřichův Hradec (Table **1135**) for 33 km to the small town of Nová Bystřice, close to the Austrian border. A steam hauled train with buffet runs in summer. For timings see Table **1169**. www.jhmd.cz

JHMD also operates a second narrow gauge line from Jindřichův Hradec, which runs for 46 km in a northerly direction to Obrataň (which is also served by a local ČD line from Tábor to Horní Cerekev). Trains run approximately every two hours, taking around 90 minutes for the journey. Aimed mostly at local travellers, it provides plenty of atmosphere for those who relish slow local lines. For the tourists, a steam train with buffet runs 21 km from Jindřichův Hradec to Kamenice nad Lipou on ②④ July 2 - Aug. 29, leaving at 0930 and returning at 1510.

DENMARK

RAIL TRAVEL

See Tables **700 - 728**. Operator is Danske Statsbaner (DSB) www.dsb.dk. There are also some independent lines, and certain former DSB services in Jutland are now operated by private company ArrivaTog www.arriva.dk. See page 344 for further information.

Principal trains linking København with the rest of Denmark are classified InterCity (*IC*) and InterCityLyn (*Lyn*), travelling at up to 200 km/h. Reservations are recommended but not compulsory, and can be made by telephone ✆ 70 13 14 15 as well as online and on the DSB app.

Travel from Sjælland (the island on which København sits) to the rest of the country (Fyn and Jylland) is by way of the impressive 18 km Great Belt Fixed Link (Storebælt), consisting of a bridge and a tunnel, with an island inbetween. Prior to 1997 trains were conveyed on board ferries to make the crossing. On the other side of København, the equally impressive 16 km Øresund Bridge, opened in 2000, links the city with Malmø in Sweden, with a frequent rail service which also serves København's Kastrup Airport en route. The airport is also linked to the city by metro.

There are also plans for a Fehmarn Belt fixed link between Denmark and Germany (an undersea tunnel between Rødby and Puttgarden), although it's several years away. Trains to Germany still need to go on board ferries for now, but will be rerouted via Padborg from December 2019.

Denmark's railway museum is situated in Odense, adjacent to the railway station and open daily all year. www.jernbanemuseet.dk

MUSEUMSBANEN MARIBO-BANDHOLM

Starting at Maribo on the privately operated Nykøbing to Nakskov line (see footnote in Table **720**), this short museum line in the south of Denmark heads 8 km north to Bandholm. After pausing for 20 minutes at Bandholm station, where the railway is based, the train continues for a further 400 metres to a platform adjacent to the harbour. www.museumsbanan.dk

Trains run ⑦ June 16 - Aug. 18 (also ③ July 3 - Aug. 7, ④ July 4 - Aug. 8, also Oct. 16, 17). Trains are steam hauled on certain dates.

Maribo	d.	1005	1305	1505	Bandholm havn	d.	1110	1410	1610
Bandholm	a.	1032	1332	1532	Bandholm	d.	1125	1425	1625
Bandholm havn	a.	1055	1355	1555	Maribo	a.	1152	1452	1652

ESTONIA

RAIL TRAVEL

See Tables **1870 - 1890**. Local services are run by the state owned railway company under the name Elron www.elron.ee using modern diesel multiple units on broad gauge tracks. The most important route links Tallinn with the country's second largest city, Tartu (Table **1880**).

The only international service is that to St Peterburg and Moskva (Table **1870**), which is operated by GoRail (www.gorail.ee). There are good bus links to Latvia's capital Riga (Table **1800**), and to St Peterburg (Table **1870**), whilst those determined to reach Riga by rail (taking much longer) can do so at certain times by changing at Valga (Tables **1880 / 1830**). Note that Tallinn's bus station is 3 km from the railway station, linked by tram. A new standard gauge rail project known as *Rail Baltica* will eventually link Tallinn with the other Baltic States and Poland, possibly by 2026.

Tallinn's proximity to Helsinki means that many tourists combine a trip to both cities. The various ferry routes linking the two cities are shown in our Ferry section (Table **2410**).

There is a railway museum in the impressive former station at Haapsalu, which can no longer be reached by rail (1h 45m by bus). Open daily June 1 - Aug. 31 (also ③–⑦ May, ⑤–⑦ Sept. - Apr.); see the Raudtee ja Sidemuuseum link on www.salm.ee. There is also a narrow gauge railway museum at Lavassaare, 17 km from Pärnu. www.museumrailway.ee

FINLAND

RAIL TRAVEL

See Tables **790 - 799**. Trains are run by national rail company VR www.vr.fi. Long distance day trains are generally high-speed tilting Pendolinos (up to 220 km/h) or modern double-deck trains. Trains are spacious, helped by the wider 'Russian' track gauge of 1524mm. Fares depend on train type - for further information on train types and ticketing see the introduction to the Finland section on page 366.

Focal point of the rail system is Helsinki's iconic 19-platform central rail station, designed by Eliel Saarinen in *Art Nouveau* style and incorporating four giant granite figures on the frontage. No fewer than 10 tracks head north for 3 km to Pasila, where lines start to divide.

Helsinki's Vantaa airport was added to the rail network in 2015 and can be reached either way around a loop, the anti-clockwise service (lettered 'I') being slightly quicker than the clockwise service ('P').

JOKIOINEN MUSEUM RAILWAY

Finland's only 750mm gauge railway (www.jokioistenmuseorautatie.fi) starts from Humppila on the Turku to Tampere line (Table **795**) and runs for 14 km to Jokioinen. The line also features a collection of preserved Finnish narrow gauge engines and rolling stock at Minkiö station, where the museum is open ②–⑥ in July / Aug (also ①–⑤ May 13 - June 28).

Trains run ⑦ June 2 - July 28 and ⑥ July 27 - Aug. 24 (also Sept. 7) as ahown below. A special timetable applies on June 30, during the Minkiö Steam Festival on July 27, 28, and on Sept. 7. Most trains are steam hauled.

	⑦**b**	⑦**b**	⑦**b**		⑦**b**	⑦**b**	⑦**b**	⑦**z**
Humppila .... d.	1025	1310	1600	Jokioinen.......... d.	...	1150	1440	1700
Minkiö.............. a.	1049	1334	1624	Minkiö .... a.	...	1208	1458	1717
Minkiö.............. d.	1115	1410	1635**z**	Minkiö .... d.	0945	1225	1520	...
Jokioinen .... a.	1134	1429	1652**z**	Humppila.......... a.	1011	1251	1546	...
	⑥**d**	⑥**d**	⑥**d**		⑥**d**	⑥**d**		
Humppila .... d.	...	1405	1700	Jokioinen.......... d.	1240	1530	...	...
Minkiö.............. a.	...	1429	1724	Minkiö .... a.	1258	1548	...	...
Minkiö.............. d.	1210	1500	...	Minkiö .... d.	1325	1615	...	...
Jokioinen .... a.	1229	1519	...	Humppila.......... a.	1351	1641	...	...

b – ⑦ June 2 - July 21. **d** – ⑥ Aug. 3 - 24. **z** – June 30 - July 21.

FINNISH RAILWAY MUSEUM

Rail enthusiasts will find the 59 km trip from Helsinki to Hyvinkää worthwhile, served by half-hourly regional trains (Table **790**). A short walk from the station is the excellent Finnish Railway Museum, open most days (but not Mondays Sept. to May). The museum is closed on Bank Holidays, including the Midsummer holiday June 21 - 23. www.rautatiemuseo.fi

Finnish Railway Museum

FRANCE

RAIL TRAVEL

See Tables **250 - 399**. The national operator is SNCF - Société Nationale des Chemins de fer Français. www.sncf.com www.oui.sncf
Within France, the premium rate customer service line is ✆ 36 35.

Since the 1980s France has built up an excellent network of dedicated high-speed lines, fanning out in all directions from Paris. The longest is that to Marseille, with the 750 km being covered in 3h 20m. The latest extensions opened in July 2017: *TGV Océane* Tours to Bordeaux and *TGV Bretagne-Pays de la Loire* from Le Mans to Rennes. The line to the north is of international significance, with *Thalys* trains to Brussels and Amsterdam, and *Eurostar* trains through the Channel Tunnel to London, whilst other high-speed lines include services to Germany, Switzerland and Spain. Speeds of up to 320 km/h (200 mph) are attained, with many trains continuing on conventional track to serve most parts of France.

The high-speed *TGV* trains (*TGV* stands for Train à Grande Vitesse) are in the course of being rebranded *TGV inOui*, whilst *Ouigo* is a name used for a network of special low-cost high-speed services, which is set to further expand in the future.

TGV trains require compulsory reservation, but there are exceptions for journeys between Lille and the coast (Calais, Boulogne, Dunkerque), see Tables **264/5** for details. Although reservations can often be made at the last minute, space permitting, it does make it difficult to make last-minute travel decisions. It also increases the cost for rail pass holders, who need to take into account the cost of reservation fees (for normal tickets the reservation fee is included in the ticket price). Light refreshments are available on *TGV* trains, except on short routes such as Paris to Lille.

On other lines, most local and regional trains (outside Paris) are branded *TER* (Transport Express Régional), organised in conjunction with regional authorities. Off-peak services are often infrequent. Some departures may be provided by bus - if the bus uses the *TER* branding and is running on a route normally provided by train then rail tickets and passes are valid.

With France being western Europe's largest country, with much long-distance travel, there are huge peaks in travel demand, notably on Friday afternoons and Sunday evenings. Fares are higher at these times, known as white periods, as well as during the normal Monday to Friday peaks. When summer holiday and winter sports peaks are also taken into account, this leads to many complications in the timetables. Most public holidays are on fixed dates which also leads to timetable variations (with extra demand either side of holidays too). Note that when engineering work affects schedules, it is not uncommon for trains to leave earlier than normal, so a last-minute check of timings is recommended.

Note that domestic night trains in France have all but disappeared, apart from a handful of socially necessary services.

Terminal stations in Paris are scattered around the periphery of the city centre (see page 33), linked by metro lines, or in some cases by *RER* services which are cross-city outer suburban routes. Beware of pickpockets operating on these lines, which can be very crowded.

CHEMIN DE FER TOURISTIQUE DU VERMANDOIS

On Sundays in July and August a heritage train runs from the SNCF station at St Quentin (Tables **255/7/8**) to Origny-Ste Benoîte (22 km). The train departs at 1415, arriving back at 1715. www.cftv.fr

A luxurious dining car experience can also be had on the *Restaurant Art-Deco Express* which operates on May 26, June 16, July 7, Aug. 25 and Oct. 27 with an authentic restaurant car built in 1928.

CHEMIN DE FER DE LA BAIE DE SOMME

As the name suggests, the line runs around the Somme Bay, an area north of Abbeville on the Picardy coast noted for its varied flora and fauna. Operated by historic narrow gauge steam trains, the line runs for 27 km on the route Le Crotoy - Noyelles - St.Valery - Cayeux. At Noyelles-sur-Mer connections can be made with SNCF trains (Table **261**). www.cfbs.eu

The following timetable applies from Apr. 6 to Nov. 2:

	n		**n**				**n**		**n**
St Valery .... d.	1100	1430	1600	1730	Le Crotoy .... d.	1100	1430	1600	1730
Noyelles .... d.	1135	1505	1635	1805	Noyelles .... d.	1135	1505	1635	1805
Le Crotoy........ a.	1200	1530	1700	1830	St Valery .... a.	1200	1530	1700	1830

n – © (daily May 30 - Sept. 15). Operated by diesel train (steam on peak dates).

A reduced service also operates ②③④⑥⑦ in October and on certain other winter dates. A connecting diesel service from St.Valery to Cayeux on the south side of the bay operates in summer taking 35 minutes:

⑦ June 2 - Sept. 22; ⑥ July 13 - Aug. 31, ②③④ July 9 - Aug. 29 (see website for other dates): From St.Valery: 1225, 1545, 1745. From Cayeux: 1025, 1355, 1645.

TRAIN THUR DOLLER ALSACE

Situated west of Mulhouse, this 14 km standard-gauge line runs from Cernay St André to Sentheim. The station at Cernay is approximately 2 km from the SNCF station, which is served by trains on the Mulhouse - Thann line. Certain journeys are steam hauled. www.train-doller.org

Splendid scenery and varied wildlife are features of the trip along this line. Some of the railway's rolling stock dates back to 1892 and includes traditional wooden-bodied coaches. The French National Railway Museum (Cité du Train, see below) is situated nearby in Mulhouse.

On ⑦ June to September (also Aug. 15) trains depart Cernay at 1030 and

1500 (journey 90 mins) returning from Sentheim at 1330 and 1730 (journey 60 mins). On ③ in July and August trains depart Cernay at 1000 and 1430 (journey 80 mins) returning from Sentheim at 1300 and 1645 (journey 50 mins).

CHEMIN DE FER DE LA VENDÉE

Situated in the Pays de la Loire region, Mortagne-sur-Sèvre is 10 km from Cholet (Table **299**). This tourist line, normally steam hauled, runs for 22 km on the route Mortagne-sur-Sèvre - Les Épesses - Les Herbiers, noted for its three spectacular viaducts. Les Herbiers station features a 1930s period style bar.

The train runs ⑦ June 3 - Sept. 29, also ③⑤ July 3 - Aug. 30, departing Mortagne at 1530 for the one hour journey to Les Herbiers. Arrival back at Mortagne is at 1800. www.vendeetrain.fr

Special *Grands Express* restaurant car services also operate most ④⑥⑦ May to October, departing Mortagne at 1200 for a three-hour dining experience. Bookings can be made online.

LE PETIT TRAIN DE LA RHUNE

This vintage rack railway with panoramic views takes passengers to the summit of La Rhune, a mountain in the Basque country close to the Spanish border. The electrified metre-gauge line is 4.2 km long and climbs to a height of 905 metres. www.rhune.com

The start point is Col de St Ignace (11 km from St Jean de Luz, Table **305**) which can be reached by bus. Trains run daily Apr. 7 to Nov. 3. Low Season departures from Col de St Ignace are at 0930, 1000, 1040, 1120, 1200, 1400, 1440, 1520 and 1600. High Season departures (July 8 - Sept. 1) are at 0820, 0850 then every 40 minutes until 1730.

Opened in 1924, the line uses traditional wooden-bodied coaches. The journey to the summit takes 35 minutes at a leisurely speed of 8 km/h. The wonderful scenery of the western Pyrenees can be enjoyed during the journey and the views at the summit are spectacular. A return journey takes approx two hours. There are a number of scenic walking routes from the summit station including a signed route back to Col de St Ignace.

LIGNE DE CERDAGNE (SNCF)

Also known as *Le Petit Train Jaune* (the little yellow train), this narrow gauge line is part of the SNCF (French Railways) system and runs for 63 km from Latour de Carol to Villefranche. Timings are shown in Table **354**.

Construction of this steeply graded line was completed as late as 1929 and it provides some fine views of the Pyrenees. The bright yellow trains are electrically powered using a third rail system and during the summer most trains include open sightseeing carriages. Rail or bus connections are available at both ends of the line - at Latour de Carol for Toulouse (Table **312**) and at Villefranche for Perpignan (Table **354**).

TRAIN À VAPEUR DES CÉVENNES

Based at Anduze in the foothills of the Cévennes mountains in southern France, this standard gauge line runs for 14 km to St Jean du Gard. The nearest SNCF station is Alès (Table **333**), about 15 km from Anduze.

The 40 minute journey includes some fine panoramas as the line crosses a number of spectacular viaducts. A notable nearby attraction is the *Bambouseraie* botanical gardens, originally created in 1855.

The high-season timetable runs from July 15 to Aug. 30 with departures from Anduze at 0930, 1130, 1430 and 1630, returning from St Jean du Gard at 1030, 1330, 1530 and 1730. Trains are steam hauled except for the 0930 from Anduze and 1730 from St Jean du Gard.

There is also a low-season service on most days from Apr. 7 to July 14 and Aug. 31 to Oct. 31, but note that the line is closed on certain days in Apr., May, Sept. Oct. Departures from Anduze are at 1130, 1500 and 1700, returning at 1030, 1400, 1600, with the last journey in each direction being diesel hauled. www.trainavapeur.com

CITÉ DU TRAIN - MULHOUSE RAILWAY MUSEUM

One of the largest railway museums in the world, Cité du Train (the French National Railway Museum) is situated in Mulhouse in eastern France. It is open every day except Christmas day and is served by the *Musées* stop on tram line 3 from Mulhouse railway station. www.citedutrain.com

Thalys TGV trains at Paris Nord

GERMANY

RAIL TRAVEL

See Tables **800 - 949**. National operator is Deutsche Bahn (DB) www.bahn.de. Telephone enquiries: ✆ 01806 99 66 33 (24 hrs), also information in English is available on ✆ 0044 (0) 8718 80 80 66.

The vast rail network of over 33,000 km covers all parts of Germany, with dedicated high-speed lines in various parts of the country helping to speed up long distance journeys, whether they be north to south or east to west. The sleek white *ICE* trains (InterCity Express) provide the fastest service, and whilst they have higher fares, reservation is not compulsory, and therefore there is no extra charge for pass holders either. Several other train categories are in use, and these are explained at the start of the German section on page 369.

The latest addition to the high-speed network opened in December 2017 and runs for 123 km south from Erfurt towards Nürnberg, complete with 22 tunnels and 29 bridges. This completes the upgrade of the important 623 km Berlin - München route, with a mix of upgraded and new lines, bringing the journey time down to under four hours for the fastest trains.

In addition to DB, there are a large number of private operators running local lines. Also, services are increasingly being franchised out to other operators, including certain *S-Bahn* networks, which are suburban services in large cities. Most urban areas have integrated ticketing, with day and period tickets being valid on all modes of public transport.

A common abbreviation in timetables is Hbf. which refers to the main station (Hauptbahnhof), whilst a mere station is simply Bf. In most cities, principal rail services are concentrated on a single main station. Since 2006 this has included Berlin, with its impressive Hauptbahnhof, with east to west and north to south lines on two different levels.

Several major airports are rail connected, that at Frankfurt having long-distance trains to various parts of the country, as well as local services.

Readers interested in the many museum and heritage lines in Germany may find the following website useful: www.vdmt.de.

DB has its own museum in Nürnberg (closed Mondays), 750m west of the main station: www.dbmuseum.de.

HARZER SCHMALSPURBAHNEN

With a total length of 140 km this system of narrow gauge lines is one of the most extensive in Europe with scheduled steam and diesel services running throughout the year. It has the added advantage of being easily accessible with no less than three interchanges with the DB network. The journey to the 1125m summit at Brocken, the highest point in northern Germany, is particularly impressive (weather permitting) passing through the scenic Hochharz National Park. Three and five day tickets are available for unlimited travel over the whole network. www.hsb-wr.de

Timings are shown in Table **867**. Routes operated are as follows:

Nordhausen Nord - Eisfelder Talmühle - Drei Annen Hohne - Wernigerode (61 km - *Die Harzquerbahn*).

Eisfelder Talmühle - Stieger - Alexisbad - Quedlinburg, also Stiege - Hasselfelde and Alexisbad - Harzgerode (60 km - *Die Selketalbahn*).

Drei Annen Hohne - Brocken (19 km - *Die Brockenbahn*).

Connections with DB services are made at Nordhausen (Tables **865/9**), Wernigerode (Table **860**) and Quedlinburg (Table **862**).

SÄCHSISCH-OBERLAUSITZER EISENBAHNGESELLSCHAFT

A narrow gauge steam operated line situated close to the Polish and Czech border with services running throughout the year. The line, which is 16 km in total, runs from Zittau to a junction at Bertsdorf, from where trains continue to Kurort Oybin or Kurort Jonsdorf. The timetable features simultaneous steam departures from Bertsdorf to Oybin and Jonsdorf which create an impressive sight! www.zittauer-schmalspurbahn.de

Timings are shown in Table **853**, and Zittau can be reached by means of Tables **854**, **855** and **1117**.

LÖSSNITZGRUNDBAHN

Operated by Sächsische Dampfeisenbahngesellschaft mbH, this steam-operated narrow gauge line starts in the unlikely setting of the Dresden suburbs at Radebeul Ost, running for 16.6 km via Moritzburg to Radeburg. Radebeul Ost can be reached by train (Tables **842** and **857**) and the narrow gauge service runs daily throughout the year (see Table **853** for timings). The main tourist attraction in the area is the impressive Moritzburg Castle. www.loessnitzgrundbahn.de

DAMPFBAHN FRÄNKISCHE SCHWEIZ

From Forchheim in the area known as Upper Franconia (Oberfranken) in northern Bavaria, an hourly train service (VGN route R22) brings you 20 minutes later to Ebermannstadt. From there the steam railway (sometimes diesel) runs 16 km to Behringersmühle.

Trains run on ⑦ May to October, also June 10, 20, Aug. 1, 15, Oct. 3, Nov. 30. Departures from Ebermannstadt are at 1000, 1400, 1600, returning from Behringersmühle at 1100, 1500, 1700. The first two journeys are generally steam operated, otherwise journeys are behind a diesel locomotive. Journey time is 45 minutes each way. There are also Christmas specials in December. Steam trains convey a buffet car. www.dfs.ebermannstadt.de

RÜGENSCHE BÄDERBAHN

This well-known 26.7 km narrow gauge (750 mm) line nicknamed *Rasender Roland* runs on the route Lauterbach (Mole) - Putbus - Binz - Göhren on the island of Rügen in north-eastern Germany. Timings are shown in Table **844a**. Connections with DB trains are made at Putbus where there is a service from Bergen auf Rügen (also in Table **844a**). The Lokalbahn station in Binz, however, is over 2 km from DB's Ostseebad Binz station. www.ruegensche-baederbahn.de

Services operate throughout the year with steam traction. However, the Putbus to Lauterbach narrow gauge section is seasonal.

ÖCHSLE MUSEUMS-SCHMALSPURBAHN

A 19 km narrow gauge steam railway running from Warthausen to Ochsenhausen. Warthausen is located 34 km south of Ulm and 3 km north of Biberach (Table **933**) and is served by the adjacent Warthausen station. Note, however, that most trains in Table **933** do not call at Warthausen (suggested DB connections are shown below). www.oechsle-bahn.de

Trains run on ⑦ May 5 to Oct. 6 (also ⑥ May 4, 18, June 1, 15, 22, July 6, 20, Aug. 3, 17, Sept. 7, 21, Oct. 5), also ④ July 4 - Sept. 5.

Ulm Hbf (DB)	d.	*0942*	*1315*	Ochsenhausen	d.	1200	1615
Biberach (DB)	d.	*1012*	*1412*	Warthausen	a.	1310	1725
Warthausen	d.	1030	1445	*Biberach* (DB)	a.	*1347*	*1744*
Ochsenhausen	a.	1140	1555	*Ulm Hbf* (DB)	a.	*1341*	*1842*

Completed in 1899, the Öchsle Museums-Schmalspurbahn was one of five narrow gauge railways built by the old *Königlich Württembergischen Staats-Eisenbahnen*. Passenger traffic ceased in 1964, although freight traffic continued to use the line for a further 19 years. Tourist trains have been running since 1985.

BUCKOWER KLEINBAHN

This short standard gauge electric railway is situated in the picturesque *Märkische Schweiz* region, approximately 50 km east of Berlin. The railway's museum at Buckow station has a number of exhibits charting the region's railway heritage. The line runs 5 km from its base at Buckow to Müncheberg. Connecting trains from Berlin Ostkreuz or Lichtenberg to Müncheberg run hourly, as shown in Table **832**.

The Kleinbahn runs on Ⓒ Apr. 27 - Oct. 6 with departures from Buckow at 0955, 1055, 1155, 1425, 1525, 1625 and 1725; from Müncheberg 1020, 1120, 1220, 1450, 1550, 1650 and 1750. Journey time is 12 – 13 minutes each way. www.buckower-kleinbahn.de

GREAT BRITAIN

RAIL TRAVEL

See Tables **100 - 229**. Rail services in Great Britain are franchised out to a number of different train operating companies - a list is provided in the introduction to the Great Britain section on page 92, and codes are used in our tables to show the operator. Collectively the railway companies work together as National Rail (www.nationalrail.co.uk) which means that timetable enquiries are available irrespective of operator, as are full price tickets, which are available between any two stations. A 24-hour national telephone enquiry line is available ✆ 03457 48 49 50.

The railway infrastructure is in the hands of publicly owned Network Rail (www.networkrail.co.uk), which also runs major stations.

Best value advance purchase tickets are usually only valid on a specified train, and some other tickets may be restricted to a particular operator. Many ticket types have complex time restrictions, and there can be vast differences in the price of tickets (travelling to or from London in the rush hour can be particularly expensive).

The network of over 15,000 km of lines covers most parts of Britain, although closures in the 1960s and 1970s has left some gaps in coverage. Services are particularly dense in the south-east, where outer suburban lines from London stretch right to the coast. Kent has also benefitted from high-speed services on the line (known as HS1) to the Channel Tunnel. A dense network also operates around the northern conurbations, notably Manchester and Liverpool. Key long distance routes are the East Coast Main Line from London King's Cross to Leeds, Newcastle and Edinburgh, and the West Coast Main Line from London Euston to Birmingham, Manchester, Liverpool and Glasgow. A new high-speed line (HS2) from London to Birmingham and beyond is planned.

All major airports have good rail links (see Table **100** for London airports). London's stations are mostly terminals linked by London Underground lines, but there are also north-south through services known as Thameslink (Tables **103 / 185**). Crossrail is a major project to build an east-west line in tunnel through the centre of London for cross-city suburban trains, also serving Heathrow Airport. The line will be known as the Elizabeth Line and is expected to open late 2020 or early 2021.

When major engineering work takes place it is usually at weekends and at times when commuting is at its lowest (for example Christmas and Easter), and buses may replace trains.

HERITAGE AND TOURIST RAILWAYS

There are numerous heritage railway operations up and down Great Britain, many with steam locomotives, and only a small number can be described below. In addition, contact details for the following will be found in our Great Britain section: Isle of Wight Steam Railway, Table **107**; Dartmouth Steam Railway, Table **111**; Dean Forest Railway, Table **117**; Ravenglass and Eskdale Railway, Table **159**; Ecclesbourne Valley and Peak Rail, Table **172**; North Norfolk Railway and Bure Valley Railway, Table **203**. A useful independent website is www.heritage-railways.com.

Several organisations run occasional heritage trains on the main line network - see www.uksteam.info for further details.

The National Railway Museum at York is a major tourist attraction and is free of charge (www.railwaymuseum.org.uk). There is also an offshoot at Shildon (Table **212**), known as *Locomotion* (www.locomotion.org.uk). Many of the heritage railways also have their own small museums.

WEST SOMERSET RAILWAY

Based in Minehead, the West Somerset Railway runs for 32 km to Bishops Lydeard, with no fewer than eight intermediate stations. This former Great Western Railway country branch line is now one of the largest tourist attractions in south-west England. From Minehead the line runs close to the coastline through Dunster, Blue Anchor and Watchet before turning inland at Williton. The railway continues alongside the Quantock Hills before arriving at Bishops Lydeard. Most services are steam-hauled and a buffet car is conveyed on most trains. www.west-somerset-railway.co.uk

The heritage railway runs daily June to Sept. (also most dates in May / Oct. and specials in December), with between four and seven journeys each way. The journey takes approximately 80 minutes. Bishops Lydeard can be reached in around 30 minutes by First Bus route 28 from Taunton bus station, also calling at Taunton railway station (Tables **110**, **115**, **116**).

SEVERN VALLEY RAILWAY

Connected to the National Rail network at Kidderminster (Tables **126 / 8**), the long-established Severn Valley Railway is within easy reach of Birmingham and the West Midlands. The line runs for 25 km to the attractive Shropshire town of Bridgnorth, serving four beautifully restored intermediate stations en route, which are ideal starting points for walks around the surrounding area. The railway is based at the first of these stations, Bewdley. Refreshments are available at most stations and on most trains, and a full dining car service operates most weekends, for which advance booking is required. www.svr.co.uk

Trains run daily from Apr. 13 to Sept. 29, and on Ⓒ in Mar., Apr., Oct., Nov., with at least six journeys each way (eight on peak dates). Trains are hauled by a steam loco or heritage diesel, the journey taking 70 - 80 minutes each way. As with most heritage lines, there are also 'Santa Specials' in December.

BLUEBELL RAILWAY

Making a connection with National Rail services at the West Sussex town of East Grinstead (48 km south of London, Table **102**) the well known Bluebell Railway runs for 17.7 km via Horsted Keynes to Sheffield Park, where the railway has its main base. Stations have been restored to show how they would have been at various points in history, that at Sheffield Park having a Victorian ambience. The line has featured in many films and TV programmes including Downton Abbey. Most trains are steam hauled.

The timetable features between 3 and 7 journeys each way depending on the date. On summer Ⓒ (and summer school holiday) trains leave Sheffield Park at 0930, 1045, 1200, 1315, 1430, 1600 (also 1715 on ⑥ in July / Aug.), returning approximately one hour later from East Grinstead. The journey takes 40 - 50 minutes each way. www.bluebell-railway.com

KEIGHLEY & WORTH VALLEY RAILWAY

Starting at Keighley, where it shares the station with the famously scenic Leeds - Settle - Carlisle rail line (Tables **173/4**, also **176**), this attractive heritage railway runs to Haworth and Oxenhope in 'Brontë Country'. Along the way is the *Rail Story* museum at Ingrow. Trains run daily June to August, on ⑥⑦ throughout the year, and on various winter dates (including most ③, not Nov. to Jan.). Timetables vary according to the date, with between four and nine return trips. Trains are steam or diesel hauled. www.kwvr.co.uk

Another popular line is the Great Central Railway, a double track main line heritage railway from Loughborough to Leicester. This *Standard 5* was built at Doncaster in 1956.

NORTH YORKSHIRE MOORS RAILWAY

Running through the North Yorkshire Moors National Park, this 29 km standard gauge line runs from Pickering to Grosmont, passing through the villages of Levisham and Goathland along the way. Grosmont is a station on the National Rail line between Middlesbrough and Whitby (Table **211**). Indeed some of the heritage line's steam trains continue on this line to the popular resort of Whitby, with the through journey taking up to two hours.

Most trains are steam hauled and convey refreshment facilities. Trains run daily from April to October, with a limited winter timetable on certain dates outside this period. www.nymr.co.uk

Details of the summer timings can be found in Table **211**. Pickering can be reached by *Yorkshire Coastliner* bus from Leeds and York.

FFESTINIOG RAILWAY

The Ffestiniog Railway, a former industrial narrow gauge line, starts on the Cambrian coast at Porthmadog, before heading inland for 22 km through the magnificent scenery of the Snowdonia National Park. The 75 minute journey ends at Blaenau Ffestiniog by which time the line has climbed over 200m. The huge slate mines clearly visible at Blaenau Ffestiniog provide a reminder of this line's original purpose when built back in 1832. Indeed, the railway can claim to be the oldest railway company in the world still operating trains. Most trains are steam-hauled, with some locomotives being over 150 years old. www.festrail.co.uk

Trains run daily from May 1 to November 3 and timings are shown in Table **160**. Porthmadog station is a short walk from the town's station on the Welsh Coast line to Pwllheli (Table **148**), and interchange is also possible at Minffordd. At Blaenau Ffestiniog there are connections with the National Rail service to Llandudno on the North Wales coast (Table **160**).

WELSH HIGHLAND RAILWAY

Also running from Porthmadog, and operated by the same company as the Ffestiniog Railway, the recently reopened Welsh Highland Railway is the UK's longest heritage line, running for 39 km across stunning landscape to Caernarfon. The journey across Snowdonia takes a little over two hours. At Porthmadog the railway shares a newly rebuilt station with the Ffestiniog Railway, whilst Caernarfon can be reached by bus from Bangor (Table **160**) on the Chester - Holyhead line.

WHR trains run daily May 1 to Nov. 2, apart from some ① and ⑤ in May, June and Oct. Timings can be found in Table **160**. www.festrail.co.uk

SNOWDON MOUNTAIN RAILWAY

Yet another line in Wales, this narrow gauge (800mm) railway to the summit of Snowdon dates back to the 1890s and is Britain's only public rack and pinion railway. Starting from Llanberis, Summit station is reached after an arduous 7.5 km climb with the steepest gradient being 1 in 5.5. A return trip takes two and a half hours, which includes approximately 30 minutes at the summit (single tickets are also available for those who wish to walk down). www.snowdonrailway.co.uk

Trains, which may be steam or diesel operated, run from May to October at regular intervals, subject to demand. There is also a service in March and April to the unsheltered Clogwyn station, which may also be the destination at times of high winds. Advance reservation is recommended during the summer months and during school holiday periods.

The nearest railhead is Bangor on the Chester to Holyhead line (Table **160**). Bus number 85 operated by Gwynfor Coaches runs every two hours or so from Bangor to Llanberis taking 55 minutes.

VALE OF RHEIDOL RAILWAY

The final Welsh line in our listing is the 19 km narrow gauge steam line from Aberystwyth (adjacent to the mainline station in Table **147**) to Devil's Bridge. Opened in 1902, it has operated continuously since then, and unusually remained part of the nationalised British Rail network until being privatised in 1989.

The journey through the spectacular Rheidol Valley to Devil's Bridge takes 60 minutes. From there it is possible to walk to the Mynach Falls, Jacob's Ladder, and Devil's Punch Bowl. www.rheidolrailway.co.uk

Trains run daily Mar. 30 to Nov. 1 (and on certain dates in Feb / Mar) with departures from Aberystwyth at 1030 and 1400, taking one hour to Devil's Bridge and returning at 1230 and 1600 (1615 on certain days). Two or three additional journeys run on certain dates, mostly midweek. A train also runs on ⑦ Nov. 3 - 24 at 1100, returning at 1400.

STRATHSPEY RAILWAY

Representing Scotland in our listing, the Strathspey Railway runs from Aviemore, where connections can be made with trains on the Edinburgh to Inverness line (Table **223**), to Broomhill via Boat of Garten. The 14 km standard gauge line is mainly steam operated.

Trains run daily in July and August, and ③–⑦ in June and September (also various dates in winter). A round trip takes 1h 40m, with trains leaving Aviemore at 1030, 1230, 1445. An additional dining car service leaves at 1300 on ⑦ Mar. 31 - Oct. 27, and evening dining trips run on ⑤ June 7 - Aug. 30 leaving at 1900. www.strathspeyrailway.co.uk

ISLE OF MAN RAILWAYS

Situated in the Irish Sea some two or three hours by ferry from Heysham or Liverpool, the Isle of Man is a self-governing British dependency which is synonymous with heritage transport, and a mecca for enthusiasts and tourists alike. The main transport attractions consist of:

Isle of Man Steam Railway: Douglas - Port Erin (25 km)

Manx Electric Railway: Douglas - Laxey - Ramsey (29 km)

Snaefell Mountain Railway: Laxey - Snaefell Summit (8 km)

In Douglas, the famous horse drawn trams (dating from 1876) run along the promenade linking the town centre Sea Terminal with the Electric Railway station. In 2019 they are expected to run late May to Nov. 3.

The Manx Electric Railway serves Laxey station en route where there is interchange with the Snaefell Mountain Railway. The original electric trains, dating back to 1895, are used for the journey to Snaefell Summit from where it is possible to see England, Wales, Scotland and Ireland on a clear day. Go Explore travelcards give unlimited travel on all scheduled rail and bus services for 1 / 3 / 5 / 7 days.

Further details: see Table **229**. www.iombusandrail.info

The Electric Railway has a small museum in Douglas open on Sundays, whilst the Steam Railway has a museum in Port Erin. Further attractions on the island (not included on the Go Explore ticket) are the steam operated Groudle Glen Railway (www.ggr.org.uk) and the miniscule Great Laxey Mine Railway (www.laxeyminerailway.im). An annual heritage transport festival takes place in July (in 2019: July 24 - 28).

NORTHERN IRELAND

In Northern Ireland, trains are operated by Northern Ireland Railways (NIR), part of Translink, and are not administered by National Rail.

Apart from the line across the border to Dublin, the principal line runs from Belfast to Londonderry, with a branch to Portrush (Table **231**). Local lines run from Belfast to Bangor and Larne.

✆ +44 (0)28 90 66 66 30 www.translink.co.uk

Tourist railways in Northern Ireland include the 914mm gauge (3 foot) Giant's Causeway and Bushmills Railway, which is a great way to visit the famous Giant's Causeway on the County Antrim coast, with its thousands of interlocking basalt columns, a major tourist attraction. Running at weekends Easter to October and daily in July and August, the 3.2 km line starts from Bushmills, which can be reached by bus from Portrush. Trains leave Giant's Causeway at 1200, 1400, 1600, and from Bushmills 30 minutes later. www.freewebs.com/giantscausewayrailway

Located adjacent to Cultra Halt on the Belfast - Bangor line (Table **233**), the Ulster Folk and Transport Museum houses one of Europe's largest transport collections. Closed Mondays. www.nmni.com

Snaefell Mountain Railway, Isle of Man. This car was built in 1895.

GREECE

RAIL TRAVEL

See Tables **1400 - 1460**. Trains in Greece are operated by TrainOSE S.A., which was state owned until 2017 but has now been privatised and is a subsidiary of Italian Railways. www.trainose.gr Call centre for reservations and information (0600-2300 daily, english spoken): ✆ 14 511.

The network of a little over 2,200 km is centered on the 500 km main line between Athína (Athens) and Thessaloníki (Table **1400**). Daytime services on the route are operated by modern InterCity trains, on which reservation is compulsory and a supplement is payable. The line has recently been electrified and upgraded with daytime trains now taking around 4 hours 20 mins, and there is also a night train taking 5½ hours.

International services consist of the summer *Hellas* Beograd - Skopje - Thessaloniki (Table **1380**), and a daytime train Sofia - Thessaloniki (Table **1560**). However, many travellers arrive by sea from one of several ports in Italy, arriving at Pátra (Patras) in the northern Peloponnese; for schedules see our ferry section. Patras, Greece's third largest city, is a destination in itself, but for those continuing to Athens there is a frequent bus service. Alternatively there are OSE buses to Kiáto (Table **1450**), connecting with trains to Athens (Table **1440**). Athens airport is also rail connected.

As well as at major stations (principally Athens, Thessaloniki, Larissa and Volos), rail tickets can be purchased at the TrainOSE Travel and Tourism office at 18 Aristotelous Square in Thessaloniki (①③ 0900-1800, ②④⑤ 0900-2100, ⑥ 0900-1500 hrs). Tickets can also be purchased online.

DIAKOFTÓ - KALÁVRITA RAILWAY (OSE)

Also known as the Odontotos Rack Railway, this historic 750mm gauge rack line runs for 22 km through spectacular Peloponnese scenery. Starting at Diakoftó, its climb to Kalávrita involves numerous bridges and tunnels and a height difference of 700m. Shortly after departure the line turns inland and enters the dramatic canyon of the Vouraikos river.

Operated by OSE (Greek Railways), the line runs daily throughout the year. Timings are shown in Table **1455**. www.odontotos.com

Diakoftó can be reached by OSE bus from Patra or Kiáto as shown in Table **1450**; rail services operate between Athína and Kiáto (Table **1440**).

THE PELION RAILWAY

The 16 km narrow gauge (600 mm) mountainous line from Ano Lehonia to Milies closed in 1971 but was resurrected as a museum line in 1996, operated by OSE. The scenic route, with two tunnels and nine bridges, affords spectacular views over Pagasitikos Bay. The nearest OSE station is Vólos (Table **1415**). www.trainose.gr

Trains run on ⑥⑦ April 13 - Oct. 27 (also June 17, July 18, 19, 25, 26; daily in August) leaving Ano Lehonia at 1000 for the 90 minute journey. Return from Milies is at 1500. A 15 minute stop is made at Ano Gatzea in both directions. On ⑥⑦ there is also 1200 from Milies, 1330 from Ano Lehonia.

Services are operated using a diesel locomotive disguised to look somewhat like a steam loco, with historic wooden carriages.

HUNGARY

RAIL TRAVEL

See Tables **1200 - 1299**. A comprehensive network of over 7,000 km is operated by Hungarian State Railways (MÁV) www.mav.hu. Principal cities are connected by *IC* trains, with compulsory reservation (see the introduction to the Hungary section on page 497 for further information about reservations and supplements).

The main holiday area is around Lake Balaton, and services in the area have different schedules from mid June to late August. Northern Hungary around Eger and Miskolc is another popular area for tourism, and some of the forest railways that we have selected below are situated in this region.

The three main stations in Budapest are named after points of the compass: Keleti (East), Nyugati (West) and Déli (South). However, don't take this as an indication of the direction of travel; trains from Nyugati can go north and east, and as some international trains serve Keleti your train from the 'East' station might well be heading west! Note, however, that the day trains to Bratislava, Praha and beyond have switched from Keleti to Nyugati giving a shorter route.

A curiosity is that hourly *IC* trains leave Budapest Keleti, circumnativate Eastern Hungary via Miskolc and Debrecen, ending up back in Budapest at Nyugati station (Tables **1260** and **1270**), though the circle is currently broken due to engineering work (a regular feature of MÁV schedules). Main stations are connected by metro as shown on the city plan, page 31.

Apart from the metro and MÁV lines, suburban rail services in Budapest include several unconnected lines known as the HÉV, which have only recently become the responsibility of MÁV, through a subsidiary company. Day tickets for Budapest are, however, valid on almost all transport, including some MÁV lines.

BUDAPEST CHILDREN'S RAILWAY (GYERMEKVASÚT)

Running through the Buda hills on the outskirts of Budapest, this charming and popular diesel operated narrow gauge line, formerly known as the Pioneer Railway, runs for 12 km from Hüvösvölgy to Széchenyihegy. Apart from the engine drivers, it is operated mainly by children, who stand and salute as the train leaves the station.

The intermediate station of Jánoshegy is close to the highest point of Budapest where there is a look-out tower, and is only a short walk from the chair lift (Libegö) which offers excellent views of Budapest on the way down to Zugliget (connected by bus 291 to/from Nyugati station).

The Hüvösvölgy end of the line can be reached by taking metro line M2 to Széll Kálmán tér, then tram 61 to Hüvösvölgy terminus.

To reach the southern end of the line at Széchenyihegy take tram 59 or 61 two stops from Széll Kálmán tér to Városmajor, then the rack railway (route 60) which terminates 250m from the Children's Railway.

Trains run throughout the year (except winter Mondays), hourly 0910 to 1610 from Hüvösvölgy, and 1003 to 1703 from Széchenyihegy, increasing to every 45 minutes in summer. Journey time is 40 – 50 minutes each way. Diesel trains are the norm, but there are steam hauled journeys on certain weekends. Full timings are available from www.gyermekvasut.hu

NAGYCENK MUSEUM RAILWAY

Nagycenki Széchenyi Múzeumvasút is a 3.6 km narrow gauge tourist railway situated in the north-western corner of Hungary on the GySEV operated Sopron to Győr line (Table **1251**). The museum line starts from Fertőboz which is 11 km from Sopron (certain Sopron trains call there).

The route is Fertőboz - Barátság - Kastély (Nagycenk), so named because Kastély (Castle) station is located close to Nagycenk village and is about 25 minutes walk from Nagycenk station on the Sopron - Szombathely line (12 km from Sopron, most trains in Table **1233** call there). The Kastély terminus of this 760mm gauge light railway is adjacent to the Schloss Széchenyi, a major tourist attraction in this area. The station also features an outdoor display of plinthed narrow gauge steam locomotives.

The museum line is operated by GySEV. As the line is currently being reconstructed, trains may only be running between Kastély and Barátság and details should be verified from the GySEV website www2.gysev.hu.

ÁLLAMI ERDEI VASUTAK *HUNGARIAN FOREST RAILWAYS*

There are a number of narrow gauge forest railways in Hungary, mostly operated by ÁEV using diminutive diesel locomotives. Timings are available on www.kisvasut.hu. For this feature we have selected the following lines in the scenic Matra mountains area in north-eastern Hungary, which are of particular interest to tourists:

ÁEV SZILVÁSVÁRAD *Forest Railway - see above*

Route: Szalajka Fatelep - Szalajka Fátyolvizesés (5 km). Szalajka-Fatelep is situated 2 km from Szilvásvárad-Szalajkavölgy station, on the Eger - Szilvásvárad line (one stop from Szilvásvárad, Table **1299**).

Apr. 1 - Nov. 3: from Szalajka-Fatelep 1030, 1130, 1300, 1400, 1500 (also 0830© July / Aug.; 0930, 1600 May - Sept.; 1700, 1800© June - Aug). Trains return from Szalajka-Fátyolvizesés 30 mins later. Journey 16 mins. Limited winter service. Note that timings for 2019 are unconfirmed.

ÁEV MÁTRAVASÚT *Forest Railway - see above*

Route: Gyöngyös - Mátrafüred (7 km). Connections with MÁV are made at Gyöngyös (Table **1260**); from the station approach road turn right, then about 400 metres to the ÁEV station. Trains run daily Apr. 2 - Oct. 31. Journey time is 22 mins. Timings and dates are unconfirmed for 2019.

Depart Gyöngyös: 0830 **E**, 1000, 1200, 1400, 1600, 1730 **E**.
Depart Mátrafüred: 0915 **E**, 1045, 1245, 1445, 1645, 1815 **E**.

E – © May 1 - Oct. 23 (daily June 18 - Sept. 2). Provisional dates / times.

ÁEV also runs between Gyöngyös and Szalajkaház (13 km) on summer weekends, and on certain other days mid-June to late August.

ÁEV LILLAFÜRED *Forest Railway - see above*

Route: Miskolc (Dorottya utca) - Papírgyár - Lillafüred - Garadna (13 km). From Miskolc station (Tables **1260/1**) take tram number 1 towards Felső-Majláth and alight at Dorottya utca (approx. 8 km).

The 13 km journey takes approximately one hour. Timings can be found on www.kisvasut.hu (click on Lillafüred then Menetrend).

HUNGARIAN RAILWAY MUSEUM

Based at a 34-track roundhouse built in 1911, this extensive railway museum opened in the year 2000. www.vasuttortenetipark.hu

Located at Tatai út 95 in the northern suburbs of Budapest, it is open Apr. 9 to Oct. 28 daily except Mondays. During opening times, certain trains on the Budapest - Esztergom line make a special stop at *Vasútmúzeum* - see Table **1299** for timings. Otherwise, access is by bus or tram to the Rokolya utca stop. The urban transport museum at Szentendre also has some railway exhibits (21 km from Budapest by HÉV train).

Budapest's impressive Keleti (East) station

IRELAND

RAIL TRAVEL

See Tables **230 - 246**. Rail services are operated by Iarnród Éireann (IÉ) www.irishrail.ie. Telephone enquiries can be made 0830-1800 Mondays to Fridays on ✆ +353 (0)1 836 6222.

Running on a network of nearly 2,000 km based on Dublin, many services are operated by modern diesel multiple units, with loco-hauled trains on the Dublin - Cork and Dublin - Belfast routes. The trains to Belfast, branded *Enterprise*, are operated jointly with Northern Ireland Railways (for NIR see separate section under Great Britain). The local IÉ north-south electric line in Dublin is called DART (Dublin Area Rapid Transit). Tracks in Ireland are built to the 'Irish gauge' of 1600mm (5ft 3in), not found elsewhere in Europe.

A scenic highlight of the Irish rail system is the Dublin to Wexford line, particularly the section between Dun Loaghaire (pronounced Dun Leery) and Greystones where the line hugs the coast.

The two railway stations in Dublin are named Connolly and Heuston. Both gained their current names in 1966 on the 50th anniversary of the Easter Rising and are named after James Connolly and Sean Heuston, both of whom were executed following the Rising. The two stations are linked by the frequent red line service of Dublin's LUAS tram system.

WATERFORD & SUIR VALLEY RAILWAY

Part of the abandoned Waterford to Dungarvan track bed was used to build this 8.5 km narrow gauge heritage railway, which runs mostly along the picturesque banks of the River Suir. A restored Simplex locomotive pulls two partially open carriages travelling at 15 km/h on a 40 - 50 minute round trip. www.wsvrailway.ie

Situated 12 km from Waterford, and sadly not accessible by public transport, trains run daily April to September leaving Kilmeaden hourly 1100-1500, also 1600 May to Aug. On ⑦ these times are one hour later.

Other short heritage lines in Ireland include the Fintown Railway, the Cavan & Leitrim Railway, and the West Clare Railway.

ITALY

RAIL TRAVEL

See Tables **580 - 648**. The national operator is Trenitalia, a division of Ferrovie dello Stato (FS) www.trenitalia.com. A 24-hour telephone line is available for information and reservation changes: ✆ 89 20 21 (calls from abroad can be made 0700-2359 daily on ✆ +39 06 6847 5475). The network exceeds 16,000 km, most of which is electrified.

Dedicated high-speed lines have been a major feature of the Italian rail network since the Roma - Firenze *Direttissima* was opened in 1977. Backbone of the system is the high-speed line stretching for nearly a thousand kilometres from Torino in the north via Milano, Bologna, Firenze, Roma and Napoli to Salerno in the south (Table **600**). Headline journey time for the Milano - Roma journey is just 2h 55m. High-speed trains are branded *Frecciarossa* (Red Arrow), whilst those which divert off the line to other desinations are *Frecciargento* (Silver Arrow). Best trains on the traditional network are another colour of arrow, this time white, being branded *Frecciabianca*. Reservation is required on all high-speed trains. For other train categories see the start of the Italian section on page 288.

Whilst several countries these days have competing operators on their main lines (thanks to EU rules which favour liberalisation), Italy is unique in having an 'open access' competitor running high-speed trains. In fact, NTV (Nuovo Trasporto Viaggiatori) runs over the entire length of the core high-speed line; timings can be found on the first page of Table **600**.

Private operators are also found on a multitude of local lines across the country, whilst local services in Lombardy (the Milano region) are handled by *Trenord*, jointly owned by Trenitalia and FNM (Ferrovie Nord Milano).

Italy's vast coastline, along with its Appennine mountain range stretching for over 1,000 km along the spine of the country, means that there is no shortage of scenic railway lines. For example, much of the line from the French border at Ventimiglia to La Spezia follows the coast, although a newly opened route has taken part of the line inland. Bear in mind that the most scenic routes across the mountains are by the slower conventional routes, as the high-speed line is constantly in and out of tunnels.

There are often long queues at stations, but tickets and reservations can also be made at travel agencies displaying the FS symbol.

TRENINO VERDE DELLA SARDEGNA

As well as the Trenitalia services in Table **629**, Sardinia is blessed with a network of scenic narrow gauge tourist railways (the 'green' trains) running on five different routes during the summer. Services have been cut back over the years and now run on just a few days per week on the following routes: Tempio to Palau (59 km), Mandas to Laconi (37 km), Mandas to Sadali (58 km), Arbatax to Gairo (62 km) and Sindai to Bosa (33 km). Services are diesel hauled or use diesel railcars. Details can be found on www.treninoverde.com.

PIETRARSA RAILWAY MUSEUM

Italy's principal railway museum is located in the suburbs of Naples in the old works adjacent to Pietrarsa station. Recently reopened following redevelopment work, the museum is open Friday to Sunday (also 1400-2000 on Thursdays). www.museopietrarsa.it

LATVIA

RAIL TRAVEL

See Tables **1800** and **1830 - 1860**. Trains in Latvia are operated by LDZ (www.ldz.lv) using the 'Russian' track gauge of 1520mm. Hub of the network is Riga's centrally located station. Services to other Latvian cities, such as Daugavpils, are not very frequent. However, good local services run from Riga to the nearby coastal resorts.

Until the *Rail Baltica* scheme is complete (see under Estonia), there are no international trains to Lithuania or Estonia, apart from occasional connections at Valga for Tallinn and a weekend service from Daugavpils to Vilnius. However, good express bus services (Table **1800**) leave from Riga's busy coach station a few hundred metres from the railway station. International trains to Russia and Belarus consist of a nightly train to Moskva and St Peterburg, and a train to Minsk on alternate days.

Riga has an interesting railway museum open on Tuesdays to Saturdays, a short tram ride from the city centre on the other side of the river (alight at Nacionala biblioteka). www.railwaymuseum.lv

GULBENE - ALUKSNE

Catering for both locals and tourists this 33 km narrow gauge (750 mm) line is situated in the north east of the country. Gulbene is no longer linked to the rest of the rail network (except by special trains) but there is a bus service from Riga. Trains leave Gulbene twice daily at 1300 and 1800 for the 1h 25m journey to Aluksne, returning at 1525 and 1955. The 1300 from Gulbene and 1525 from Aluksne are steam hauled on certain dates, taking 1h 50m (in 2019: June 1, 15, 29, July 13, 27, Aug. 10, 24, Sept. 7, 21, Oct. 5, 19, Nov. 9, and Dec. 21). www.banitis.lv

LITHUANIA

RAIL TRAVEL

See Tables **1800 - 1818**, **1950**. Services are operated by Lithuanian Railways (www.litrail.lt) using the 'Russian' track gauge of 1520mm. ✆ +370 700 55111. A good service is run from Vilnius to Kaunas, Lithuania's second city (fans of old funicular railways will enjoy a visit there); trains to Klaipeda are infrequent. Vilnius Airport is rail connected.

Vilnius sits astride the main line linking Russia with its detached federal outpost, Kaliningrad (Table **1950**), and Vilnius also has reasonably good services to Minsk, capital of Belarus, served by the same line.

The *Rail Baltica* project to link Lithuania (and ultimately the other Baltic States) to Poland with a standard-gauge line has been slow off the ground, but a limited service runs across the border between Bialystok and Kaunas (Tables **93** and **1042**). There are plans to eventually reach Tallinn, and possibly even Helsinki. In the meantime, travel between Lithuania and its northern neighbours is by bus (Table **1800**).

A small indoor railway museum is located within the station building at Vilnius, and some outdoor exhibits are stabled in an adjacent siding.

A train from Vilnius having arrived at Kaunas

LUXEMBOURG

RAIL TRAVEL

See Tables **445/6/9** (also **384**, **390**, **915**). Operator is Société Nationale des Chemins de fer Luxembourgeois (CFL) www.cfl.lu. Telephone enquiry line: ✆ +352 2489 2489.

This small country has a rail network of only 275 km, but services are fairly frequent, and there are good international links, including *TGV* services to Paris and hourly trains to Brussels and Koblenz.

The country is heavily forested, with some attractive scenery, particularly on the main line to the north. One of the attractions of exploring the country by rail is its excellent value day ticket, valid on trains and local buses (only €4, or €5 if purchased on board the train) and in fact travel will be free from 2020. Most rail stations are small with few facilities.

AMTF TRAIN 1900

Luxembourg's only preserved steam railway is situated close to the French and Belgian borders, operated by Assoc. des Musée et Tourisme Ferroviaires (AMTF). The line runs from Pétange to Bois-de-Rodange, pausing at Fond-de-Gras where the railway is based. www.train1900.lu

Pétange can be reached by regular CFL local train (Table **449**) whilst Rodange CFL station is approximately 2 km from Bois-de-Rodange.

Trains run on ⑦ and holidays May to September. Services marked 🚂 are known as *Le Train 1900* and are hauled by an historic steam locomotive. Other services are operated by a diesel railcar.

			🚂		🚂		🚂	
Pétange-TRAIN 1900...... d.	...	1320	1415	1510	1615	1710	1820	1900
Fond-de-Gras .... a.	...	1350	1442	1534	1642	1734	1855	1922
Fond-de-Gras .... d.	...	1410	1510	1610	1720	1810	1900	...
Bois-de-Rodange .... a.	...	1415	1515	1615	1725	1815	1905	...
		🚂		🚂		🚂		🚂
Bois-de-Rodange .... d.	...	...	1420	1520	1620	1730	1820	1910
Fond-de-Gras .... a.	...	...	1425	1525	1626	1736	1826	1915
Fond-de-Gras .... d.	1250	1325	1445	1535	1645	1740	1830	...
Pétange-TRAIN 1900...... a.	1314	1352	1506	1600	1706	1805	1853	...

NETHERLANDS

RAIL TRAVEL

See Tables **450 - 499**. National rail company is Nederlandse Spoorwegen (NS) www.ns.nl ✆ +31 30 751 5155.

A comprehensive network of over 3,000 km provides frequent regular-interval services linking most towns and cities. Most services are provided by NS, although other operators, notably Arriva, are contracted to run local train services in some parts of the north and east.

Fast domestic trains, calling only at principal stations, are classified *Intercity*, whilst local stopping trains are known as *Sprinter* services. A further category is *Intercity direct* for which a supplement is payable - these use the *HSL-Zuid* high-speed line which opened in 2009 linking Amsterdam and Schiphol Airport with the Belgian border and on to Antwerpen. Through services to Paris via Brussels are provided by *Thalys* trains, and *Eurostar* trains now link London with Amsterdam, although travel in the other direction currently involves a change of train at Brussels, where customs formalities are carried out. Schiphol airport is well served by rail services, not only to Amsterdam but to other parts of the country.

Through tickets can be purchased between all stations in the Netherlands, regardless of operator. A national stored-value smartcard scheme operates throughout the country known as OV-Chipcard, used on trains and most public transport (for further information see the introduction to the Netherlands section on page 248). Cycle hire and cycle and baggage storage are usually available at larger stations. Smaller stations are usually unstaffed, but all stations have ticket vending machines. Seat reservations are not available for domestic journeys.

A recent development is the conversion of the Hoek van Holland to Rotterdam line, once traversed by many long distance trains connecting with ferries, into a metro line, due to reopen later this year as part of Rotterdam's metro system.

MUSEUMSPOORLIJN S.T.A.R.

Located in the north-eastern corner of the Netherlands, this former NS line runs from Veendam to Stadskanaal, where the railway is based. Veendam can be reached by local train from Groningen (Table **498**). Trains can be steam or diesel hauled. www.stadskanaalrail.nl

Trains run on June 9, 10, 15, 23, ⑦ July 7 - Aug. 25 (also ③ July 10 - Aug. 28), Sept. 21, 22, 28, 29, Oct. 19, 20, 22, 23, 27 plus occasional winter dates. On the majority of these dates the timetable is as shown below:

Stadskanaal	d.	1045	1330	1600	Veendam	d.	1200	1445	1710
Veendam	a.	1125	1410	1640	Stadskanaal	a.	1240	1525	1750

VELUWSCHE STOOMTREIN MAATSCHAPPIJ (VSM)

Running on the route Apeldoorn - Eerbeek - Dieren (22 km), this line connects with NS services at both ends: Apeldoorn (Tables **480** / **498**) and Dieren (Table **475**). It runs through the Veluwe nature area and, on dates in note **A**, a ride on the train can be combined with a boat trip along the River IJssel between Dieren and Zutphen (boats are scheduled to connect with the trains). The journey back to Apeldoorn can be completed by train from Zutphen (Table **498**). Special tickets are available for this interesting day trip known as *De Veluwe-IJssel-Boemel*. www.stoomtrein.org

		A	A	B			A	A	B ⊙
Apeldoorn	d.	1030	1400	1145	**Dieren**	d.	1220	1550	...
Eerbeek	d.	1119	1449	1234	Eerbeek	d.	1246	1616	1255
Dieren	a.	1145	1515	...	**Apeldoorn**	a.	1335	1705	1425

A – ②③④ July 16 - Aug. 29.
B – ⑦ Apr. 1 - Oct. 27; ①⑤ July 15 - Aug. 30, also June 10, Oct. 22 - 24.
⊙ – Includes a 45 minute stop at Beekbergen (for the railway's museum and depot).

MUSEUMSTOOMTRAM HOORN - MEDEMBLIK

This long-established standard gauge line runs for 20 km between Hoorn and Medemblik and is easily accessible from Amsterdam (Table **461**/**470**). All trains are operated by steam traction. A popular triangular journey (known locally as *De Historische Driehoek*) uses the boat between Medemblik and Enkhuizen (see below), returning to Hoorn or Amsterdam by rail. A day ticket valid on steam tram and boat services is available. The station at Hoorn includes a steam tram museum. www.stoomtram.nl

		A	B				A		
Hoorn	d.	1040	1140	...	Enkhuizen	d.	1040	...	...
Medemblik	a.	1200	1310	...	Medemblik	a.	1155	...	...
			A				A	B	
Medemblik	d.	...	1320	...	Medemblik	d.	1320	1520	...
Enkhuizen	a.	...	1450	...	Hoorn	a.	1440	1645	...

A – ②–⑦ Apr. 2 - Sept. 29 (daily July 1 - Aug. 31), also ⑥⑦ Oct. 1 - Nov. 16 (also Oct. 21 - 25).
B – July 13 - Aug. 31 (also Apr. 27 - May 5, May 30, June 9, 10, Oct. 20 - 27).

NARROW GAUGE

Fans of narrow gauge trains will enjoy the Stoomtrein Katwijk Leiden along the shore of Lake Valkenburg, along with the associated museum. Open summer weekends (also ②④ July 23 - Aug. 29). Reach by bus from Den Haag or Leiden. www.stoomtreinkatwijkleiden.nl

A further narrow gauge line and museum is the RTM Ouddorp situated in Zeeland and reached by bus from Roterdam's Spikenisse metro station to Port Zelande, which is part way along this short line. Runs July to September on ③④⑥. www.rtm-ouddorp.nl

MUSEUM STOOMTREIN GOES - BORSELE

Evoking railways of the 1930's, this standard gauge line runs for 16 km across the beautiful landscape of the province of Zeeland. Starting from Goes (a short walk from the NS station, Table **450**) steam trains run for 40 minutes to the scenic village of Hoedekenskerke calling at Kwadendamme. Departures from Goes are at 1100 and 1400, returning at 1240 and 1620. Main operating days are ⑦ Apr. 7 - Oct. 20 (also ①–④ July 8 - Aug. 29). An additional diesel service runs the full length of the line to Baarland on most ⑦ (also ②③④ July / Aug). www.destoomtrein.nl.

UTRECHT RAILWAY MUSEUM

The National Railway Museum is located in the former Maliebaan railway station in Utrecht, open ②–⑦ (also ① in school holidays). The museum has a dedicated hourly railway service from Utrecht Centraal (or 1.6 km on foot). www.spoorwegmuseum.nl

A London to Amsterdam *Eurostar* train at Rotterdam

NORWAY

RAIL TRAVEL

See Tables **770 - 789**. Most trains are operated by the Vy Group (using the name Vy), owned by the Norwegian government and prior to April 2019 known as NSB (Norges Statsbaner). www.vy.no. ✆ +47 61 05 19 10.

As you might expect, a high proportion of the country's 4,000 km rail network can be regarded as scenic. For those touring the country by rail, a circular route can often be arranged by including buses or boats in the itinerary. Trips to the far north can also be extended by catching the bus from Bodø to Narvik (Table **787**) and returning through Sweden. Since Norway also has a border with Russia, our Lapland bus table (**789**) even includes a service to Murmansk.

Trains convey 2nd-class seating, whilst most medium- and long-distance trains also convey *Komfort* accommodation, a dedicated area with complimentary tea/coffee and newspapers (supplement payable). Sleeping cars have one- and two-berth compartments; a sleeper supplement is payable per compartment (for two people travelling together, or sole use for single travellers). Long-distance trains convey a bistro car serving hot and cold meals, drinks and snacks. Reservation is possible (and recommended) on all long-distance trains. Reserved seats may not be marked, but your confirmation specifies carriage and seat/berth numbers.

FLÅMSBANA

Branching off the Olso to Bergen line (Table **781**), this is undoubtedly one of Europe's most spectacular railway journeys. Trains descend from an altitude of 865m at Myrdal to sea-level at Flåm in just 20 km. In between the 20 tunnels there is some breathtaking scenery and, to reassure passengers, the trains have no less than five sets of brakes, each of which can stop the train on the extremely steep inclines! Timings are shown in Table **781**. This journey can be included as part of various circular excursions, such as the *Norway in a Nutshell* tour (see Table **781a** for boat and bus connections). For further details see www.visitflam.com

KRØDERBANEN

This former NSB line (originally built as narrow gauge but rebuilt to 1435mm in 1909) closed to passengers in 1958 but was resurrected as a museum line in the 1980s. Operated by the Norwegian Railway Club, it is Norway's longest museum railway at 26 km and makes an ideal day trip from Oslo. It runs from the railway's base at Krøderen to Vikersund, which is situated between Drammen and Hønefoss (Table **780**). However, operations are currently limited to the Krøderen - Kløftefoss section due to track reconstruction (though a vintage bus runs to Vikersund). Trains run on ⑦ June 30 - Sept. 1. For timings see www.njk.no.

GAMLE VOSSEBANEN

Also operated by the Norsk Jernbaneklubb, the 18 km 'Old Voss Steam Railway' runs from Garnes to Midttun, crossing the Bergen to Voss line (Table **781**) at Arna, where the station is 300m from the old station on the steam railway. Both ends of the line can also be reached by bus from Bergen bus station.

Services are hauled by one of the original steam locomotives built for the Bergen Railway in 1913 and the restored teak coaches are from the same period. Until 1964 the line was actually part of the main Oslo - Bergen railway. www.njk.no. Trains run on ⑦ June 16 - Sept. 1 as follows:

Garnes	d.	1130	1430	...	Midttun	d.	1230	1540	...
Arna (old station)	d.	1140	1440	...	Arna (old station)	d.	1310	1620	...
Midttun	a.	1220	1520	...	Garnes	a.	1320	1630	...

Connecting trains: Bergen - Arna at 1059, 1359; Arna - Bergen at 1548, 1648.

NORWEGIAN RAILWAY MUSEUM

The museum is located 3 km from the centre of Hamar, on the Oslo - Lillehammer - Trondheim line (Table **785**), and is open daily except Mondays (daily July / August). Bus number 1 runs from the railway station. www.jernbanemuseet.no.

POLAND

RAIL TRAVEL

See Tables **1000 - 1099**. Long-distance trains are operated by PKP Intercity (www.intercity.pl). The best trains on the principal routes are classified *EIP* (Express InterCity Premium), which are operated with the latest sleek *Pendolino* type trains. Other fast trains are *EIC* or *IC* (along with international *EC* trains), plus the cheaper *TLK* trains which make more stops. Reservation is compulsory on all trains operated by PKP Intercity, whose trains are shown in red on PKP timetables and station departure sheets. See page 469 for further details of train classifications.

Trains on the Warszawa - Berlin route are operated jointly with German Railways and are branded *Berlin-Warszawa Express*, whilst Russian Railways operate several trains to or through Warszawa (including the Berlin - Moscow *Talgo* train).

Things get more complicated when it comes to local trains. Przewozy Regionalne is the main operator, using the name PolRegio (polregio.pl), with train categories *RE* or *R* (local trains are shown without numbers in our tables). However, several local authorities have set up their own railway organisations, such as Koleje Wielkopolskie and Koleje Śląskie. Outer suburban services in the Warsaw area come under Koleje Mazowieckie, whilst local electric services in the Tricity area (Gdansk, Sopot, Gdynia) have long been the preserve of PKP subsidiary SKM Trojmiasto. Ticket inter-availability between operators is complex.

Poland is a large country with many scenic rail routes, notably in the more hilly areas in the south of the country. In addition to the standard gauge network, the country used to be covered with hundreds of kilometres of narrow gauge lines, and some of these survived in PKP ownership as late as 2001. Since closure, many sections have resurfaced as museum lines, some with regular summer operation, others with only occasional trains. Although timings are not up to date, further information can be found on www.narrowrail.net, and two of the lines are included below.

WOLSZTYN

Wolsztyn (Table **1099**) is located some 80 km south-west of Poznań and is famous for its steam depot running the last regularly timetabled steam hauled passenger services on a main line in Europe. Although these ceased in 2014, a service was resurrected in May 2017 running between Wolsztyn and Poznań on Saturdays as shown below. The Monday to Friday trains between Wolsztyn and Leszno may not be currently running.

		⑥	⑥				⑥	⑥	
Wolsztyn	d.	0629	1331	...	Poznań	d.	0939	1656	...
Leszno	a.	|	|	...	Leszno	d.	|	|	...
Poznań	a.	0822	1520	...	Wolsztyn	a.	1146	1917	...

Latest timings can be found on www.koleje-wielkopolskie.com.pl
The atmospheric steam depot at Wolsztyn is a short walk from the station and can be visited for a small fee.

WARSAW RAILWAY MUSEUM

Warsaw's railway museum is located in the former Warszawa Główna terminus in the city centre, between Centralna and Zachodnia stations in ul.Towarowa. There is an extensive outdoor display of rolling stock as well as indoor exhibits. Open daily. www.stacjamuzeum.pl

SOCHACZEW MUSEUM RAILWAY

A short walk from Sochaczew station (local trains approximately hourly from Warszawa Wschodnia) is the narrow gauge station which has been made into a museum with a large collection of narrow gauge rolling stock, open daily except Mondays. See www.stacjamuzeum.pl (link top right).

On ⑥⑦ Apr. 27 - Sept. 30 (also ⑥ Oct. 5 - 19) a steam hauled 'Retro' train leaves the museum at 1030 for a trip to Wilcze Tułowskie in the Kampinos Forest. The itinerary includes a guided forest walk, and arrival back at Sochaczew is at 1520. It also runs ③ July 3 - Aug. 28 with diesel traction.

ZNINSKA KOLEJ POWIATOWA

The 12 km Znin - Gasawa railway is the last remaining section of a much larger narrow gauge (600mm) network in this area which, by 1913, had reached 79 km in length. Regular passenger services were withdrawn in 1962 but since 1976 tourist trains have been running regularly between Znin and Gasawa. Znin can be reached by bus from Bydgoszcz.

A varied collection of narrow gauge rolling stock is situated adjacent to Wenecja Muzeum station, where trains arrive 10 - 15 minutes before the time shown. www.muzeumznin.pl

Trains run daily May 1 - Sept. 1 (no service June 24 - 28), also during the Archeological Festival Sept. 14 - 22.

						S							S
Znin	d.	0900	1030	1205	1350	1535	Gasawa	d.	1030	1205	1345	1530	1710
Wenecja §	d.	0940	1110	1250	1435	1615	Wenecja §	d.	1110	1250	1435	1620	1755
Gasawa	a.	1015	1150	1330	1515	1655	Znin	a.	1140	1320	1505	1650	1825

S – ⑥⑦ July and August (also May 1 - 5, June 21 - 23, Aug. 15 - 18, Sept. 14 - 22).
§ – Wenecja Muzeum.

CHABÓWKA AND JAWORZYNA ŚLĄSKA

The 'Skansen' at Chabówka is an extensive open air railway museum, located on the scenic Kraków - Zakopane line (Table **1066**). Steam trips run on several summer dates June - August from the Skansen to Kasina Wielka. www.parowozy.pl

Another railway museum is located at Jaworzyna Śląska on the Wroclaw - Jelenia Góra line (Table **1084**), open daily. www.muzeumtechniki.pl

PORTUGAL

RAIL TRAVEL

See Tables **690 - 699**. Operator is Comboios de Portugal (CP) www.cp.pt
Telephone enquiries (24 hours): ✆ 707 210 220.

The network is approximately 2,500 km, and as with Spain, trains run on tracks of 'Iberian' gauge, 1668 mm. Backbone of the network is the 337 km line between Lisboa and Porto, with the longest distance trains running all the way from Faro in the south to Porto in the north. The best trains are the modern *AP* (Alfa Pendular) trains, which along with *IC* and international trains require advance reservation. Lines in the north of the country are particularly scenic, especially the Duoro Valley line to Régua and Pocinho (see Table **694** and the tourist train below).

Lisboa's traditional terminus at Santa Apolónia was joined by an impressive through station in 1998 called Oriente, located 6 km north of the centre. Noted for its metal and glass roof, it is part of a major transport hub including metro and bus links. Trains to Cascais, however, leave from Cais do Sodre station, whilst Rossio is the city centre terminus for trains to Sintra (see city plan on page 32).

Another impressive feature of Lisbon's transport network is the *25 de Abril* bridge across the Tagus, to which railway tracks were added under the road in 1999, and which is sometimes compared to San Francisco's Golden Gate Bridge. As well as CP trains to the south, it carries local trains of private operator *Fertagus*.

The national railway museum is located at Entroncamento, open on ②–⑦ 10.00 to 18.00. www.fmnf.pt Access is from Rua Ferreira de Mesquita on the north side of the tracks across the footbridge. There are also several small regional railway museums.

COMBOIO HISTÓRICO

This steam hauled tourist train runs in summer on the scenic Douro line between Régua and Tua. Details of dates and timings can be found in Table **694**. The train is operated by CP at special fares.

Polish EIP (Express InterCity Premium) *Pendolino* train

Photos in this Rail Extra feature are by
Brendan Fox - pages 653 - 655, 657, 658, 660 - 662
Graham Benbow - pages 656, 659, 663, 664

ROMANIA

RAIL TRAVEL

See Tables **1600 - 1680**. State railway Căile Ferate Române (CFR) operates an extensive network of over 10,000 km, and trains of its passenger subsidiary CFR Călători link all major towns. www.cfrcalatori.ro Telephone information is available on ✆ 021 9521 for domestic traffic or ✆ 021 314 5528 for international services.

Most main lines are electrified and quite fast, but branch line services are very slow. Trains are fairly punctual and very cheap. Except for local trains, reserve and pay a speed supplement in advance (tickets issued abroad include the supplement). Cheapest are *regio* (very slow), then *Interregio*, and finally *IC* trains, whose prices approach Western levels. Food and drink is normally available only on *IC* and some *IR* trains. Couchette (*cuşeta*) or sleeper (*vagon de dormit*) accommodation is inexpensive. An increasing number of services are now operated by private operators, such as Regiotrans, Transferoviar Grup SA, and Softrans S.R.L., as indicated in relevant tables.

CFF VIŞEU DE SUS

Situated in the north of Romania, the Vaser Valley forest railway has been transporting wood to a processing plant in Vişeu de Sus since its opening in 1932, and claims to be the last European forestry railway. The 22 km narrow gauge railway also started running steam hauled tourist trains in the year 2000. Visitors can enjoy the remote mountain scenery during the very leisurely two hour journey from Vişeu de Sus along the winding valley to Paltin, where there is a break before the return journey.

Vişeu de Sus is situated 7 km from the CFR station at Vişeu de Jos (Table **1660**) and it can also be reached by bus from Baia Mare or Sighetu Marmatiei. The train runs on ④–⑦ Mar. 21 - Nov. 17 (daily June 3 - Sept. 29) leaving Vişeu de Sus at 0900, arriving back at approximately 1430 (one hour later June 3 - Sept. 29). www.cffviseu.com

RUSSIA

RAIL TRAVEL

Operator of this vast system is RZhD www.rzd.ru. Flagship trains are those running between Moskva and St Peterburg (Table **1900**), which consist of high-speed *Sapsan* trains by day, taking under four hours, and a variety of night trains to suit every budget, from low-cost double deck trains to expresses offering the height of luxury. Modern high-speed trains are also found on the St Peterburg - Helsinki route, branded *Allegro*. Russian trains are spacious and run on broad gauge tracks (1520mm).

Our tables also include the famous Trans-Siberian Railway (Table **1990**), with the *Rossiya* running over 9,000 km between Moskva and Vladivostok, as well as trains to Beijing, either via Mongolia or the Trans-Manchurian route. The more northerly 'BAM' route is shown in Table **1991**.

Details of the various types of accommodation to be found on Russian trains will be found on page 534. Many trains in Russia run on alternate days, and this page also explains our system for what happens to trains running on even or uneven dates at the end of months with 31 days.

All times in Russia are now shown in local time. Russia and Belarus do not observe daylight saving time, so complications arise when countries to the west change their clocks on the last Sundays in March and October; this is handled in our tables with footnotes or duplicate columns.

SERBIA

RAIL TRAVEL

See Tables **1360 - 1380**. The 3,300 km network is operated by state railway company Železnice Srbije (ŽS). www.zeleznicesrbije.com There is also an English language website, www.serbianrailways.com.

Both daytime and nightime international services link Beograd with Ljubljana, Zagreb and Budapest, whilst Sofia has one daytime train. There is also a night train on the lengthy run to Thessaloniki via Skopje, whilst travel to Timisoara in Romania involves trains of a more local nature, changing at Vršac.

Scenic highlight, however, is the line from Beograd to neighbouring Montenegro, passing through its capital Podgorica before continuing to the coast at Bar. Opened as late as 1976, this winding 524 km line (Table **1370**) involves no fewer than 435 bridges and 254 tunnels!

There is an indoor railway museum in Beograd at 6 Nemanjina Street, open on Mondays to Fridays 0900-1500 hrs., and a narrow gauge section near Pozega station. For details see the *Museum* link on the ŽS website.

ŠARGANSKA OSMICA (*ŠARGAN EIGHT)*

Threading its way through the scenic Mokra Gora mountain region, close to the border with Bosnia, this line was originally part of a narrow gauge route between Beograd and Sarajevo which was closed in 1974. Between 1999 and 2003 the line was rebuilt as a tourist railway using diesel or steam traction. www.zeleznicesrbije.com

The 15.4 km narrow gauge (760 mm) line runs from Mokra Gora to Šargan Vitasi, passing through 22 tunnels and over five bridges. The nearest mainline ŽS station is Užice on the Beograd - Bar main line (Table **1370**). The 40 km journey from Užice to Mokra Gora can be made by bus or taxi.

Trains run daily April 1 - October 31, departing Mokra Gora at 1030 and 1330 (also 1610 April 1 - September 30). Total journey time for a return trip is approximately 2½ hours.

SLOVAKIA

RAIL TRAVEL

See Tables **1170 - 1199**. The national rail operator is Železničná spoločnosť (ŽSSK) www.slovakrail.sk. Track and infrastructure is managed by ŽSR www.zsr.sk. Call centre (24h) is ✆ 18 188, or from abroad ✆ +421 24 48 58 188.

An efficient network of 3,600 km is operated, with the fastest trains being the handful of *IC* trains on the principal route between Bratislava and Košice (Table **1180**). On the international Praha (Prague) to Košice route, the state railways compete for passengers with two other companies, Regiojet and Leo Express. Arriva also has cross border services running from Praha to Nitra, one of the oldest cities in Slovakia.

Trains are cheap, but often crowded. In fact most resident children, seniors and students qualify for free travel (except on *IC* trains or cross-border services) in a recently introduced scheme. Qualifying EU citizens may also be entitled to register for the scheme (especially children under 15 and seniors of 62 or over).

Apart from the small number of *EC* and *IC* trains, for which higher fares apply, the fastest trains are *expresný* (*Ex*) and *Rýchlik* (*R*, usually those with three-digit train numbers). Cheaper are *zrýchlený* (semi-fast) and *osobný* (very slow). Sleeping cars and couchettes are provided on most overnight trains (reserve at all main stations, well in advance in summer). Seat reservations may be made at station counters marked R, and are recommended for express trains.

The most scenic areas are close to the Tatra mountains, particularly the High Tatras (Vysoké Tatry) where a network of electrified narrow gauge lines is run by ŽSR subsidiary TEŽ (Table **1182**). Most lines in the centre of the country, radiating from Banská Bystrica, are also scenic, particularly the line following the River Hron (Table **1188**).

ČIERNOHRONSKÁ ŽELEZNICA

After closure in 1982, enthusiasts eventually managed to save this narrow gauge (760 mm) forestry railway and transform it into a tourist railway. It is the last remaining section of a once extensive system in central Slovakia.

The line starts at Chvatimech, which is served by all trains between Banská Bystrica and Brezno (Table **1188**, eight minutes before Brezno). The first 7 km to Šánske is, however, currently being rebuilt. 5 km further on is Čierny Balog, the railway's headquarters, where the line continues 4 km to Dobroč, and there is also a 4 km branch to Vydrovo. www.chz.sk

Chvatimech - Šánske - currently no service.

Čierny Balog - Šánske: ⑥ Apr. 20 - June 22; daily June 29 - Sept. 1. From Čierny Balog: 1100, 1500. From Šánske: 1130, 1530. Journey time 20 minutes; steam hauled in high-season.

Čierny Balog - Vydrovo Konečná: daily April 20 - September 15. From Čierny Balog: 0900, 1000, 1100, 1300, 1400, 1500, 1600, 1700, returning 20 mins later.

Čierny Balog - Dobroč: ⑥ Apr. 20 - June 22; daily June 29 - Sept. 1. From Čierny Balog: 1000, 1200, 1400, 1600. From Dobroč: 1030, 1230, 1430, 1630. Journey time 20 minutes; steam hauled in high season.

DETSKÁ ŽELEZNICA KOŠICE

This short railway in Košice was completed in 1956 as one of the Pioneer Railways in the former Czechoslovakia. The line was built to allow children to learn how railways operate, so most of the railway's functions were performed by children. Some of the railway's rolling stock dates from as far back as 1884. www.detskazeleznica.sk

The 4.2 km narrow gauge line runs from Čermel' to Alpinka. Čermel' can be reached from the main station by tram 2 to Havlíčkova then bus 14.

Trains run on © May to Oct. (daily in July and August) with between four and six journeys each way.

A long-distance train at Bratislava Hlavná Stanica (main station)

NATIONAL RAILWAY MUSEUM

This is located at Bratislava Vychod depot and is open daily Apr. 15 to Oct. 15 (1000-1700). Nearest station is Bratislava Rača, served by local trains on the line to Trnava, and 1.6 km from the museum. The website (www.mdc.sk) also has a list of special heritage trains running on the Slovak network on various dates throughout the year. A special annual *Rendez* event takes place at the museum in June (in 2019 June 15 / 16).

There is also an indoor transport museum near Bratislava hlavná station at Šancová 1/A, closed on Mondays. www.muzeumdopravy.com.

SLOVENIA

RAIL TRAVEL

See Tables **1300 - 1320**. Slovenia's relatively small network of 1,200 km is operated by Slovenske Železnice (SŽ) www.slo-zeleznice.si. Telephone information is available from within Slovenia on ✆ 080 81 11.

Hub of the network is the capital Ljubljana. The best trains are the *IC* trains on the Maribor route, and the *EC* trains which continue beyond Maribor into Austria. Other international links include those to München, Budapest and Beograd, all with a choice of daytime or overnight timings, except that the night train to Budapest runs only in high summer.

LJUBLJANA RAILWAY MUSEUM

Ljubljana has a railway museum in a former roundhouse at Parmova 35, open daily except Mondays from 1000 to 1800.

Steam-hauled heritage trains run between Jesenice and Nova Gorica on the scenic Bohinj line, which can also be booked as part of a guided tour. Operating two to four times per month from May to October, the train leaves Jesenice at 0903, returning at 1953. Details: www.slo-zeleznice.si

SPAIN

RAIL TRAVEL

See Tables **650 - 689**. National rail company is Red Nacional de los Ferrocarriles Españoles (RENFE) www.renfe.es. ✆ 912 320 320.

The opening of the Madrid - Sevilla high-speed line in 1992 was just the start of what is now one of Europe's longest high-speed networks. Particularly important is the 620 km Madrid - Barcelona line, which also continues northwards into France, and which has taken a large market share away from the airlines. Another principal route runs from Madrid to Valencia and Alicante, and in fact travel to just about any area of Spain can benefit from a high-speed train for at least part of the way. Trains which run purely on these lines are classified *AVE* (Alta Velocidad Española). For other train categories see the introduction to the Spanish section on page 322.

The traditional network is built to the 'Iberian' track gauge of 1668 mm, whereas the new high-speed network is standard gauge (1435 mm). Trains which switch between the two networks, such as the *Altaria* and *Alvia* trains, therefore have to have gauge changing equipment.

Spain also has around 1,200 km of narrow gauge lines, built to metre gauge, and in the main these are in the hands of a separate division of RENFE known as FEVE. These are largely in coastal areas, and particularly interesting is the long and scenic narrow gauge line along the north coast of Spain (Table **687**), along with the associated Bilbao to León line (Table **683**). Several narrow gauge lines are run by other operators, such as Euskotren, FGC, and FGV.

Reservation is compulsory on all services for which a train category (*AVE*, *IC* etc) is shown in the timing columns of this timetable. RENFE attaches a high degree of importance to punctuality and has a comprehensive scheme of refunds if trains run late.

VALL DE NÚRIA

A 12.5 km rack railway operated by Ferrocarrils de la Generalitat de Catalunya (FGC) runs from Ribes Enllaç to Núria. The train climbs from 905m at Ribes to 1967m at Nuria and passes through some fine scenery. At one point the train is travelling above the narrow gorge of the River Nuria. Table **658** has the timings. www.valldenuria.cat

Ribes Enllaç station is adjacent to RENFE's Ribes de Freser station on the Barcelona to Latour de Carol line (Table **656**).

CERCEDILLA - COTOS MOUNTAIN RAILWAY

Apart from the FEVE network, RENFE has a narrow gauge line of its own. It runs from Cercedilla to Cotos and is actually part of Madrid's suburban network, allocated route number **C9**. The 18 km journey through the scenic *Sierra de Guadarrama* region takes around 45 minutes (25 minutes Cercedilla to Puerto de Navacerrada). This is excellent walking country and a number of marked routes are available at stations en-route.

Regular services (at least hourly) operate between central Madrid and Cercedilla (line **C8** - journey 80 minutes from Atocha or 70 mins from Chamartín). Special *C9* return fares are available between any station on the Cercanías network and any station on the narrow gauge line. See www.renfe.com under the heading 'Viajeros' then 'Cercanias' (suburban).

Trains run from Cercedilla at 0935, 1135, 1335, 1535, 1735, returning from Cotos at 1043, 1243, 1443, 1643, 1843.

FERROCARRIL DE SÓLLER

Opened in 1912, the line from Mallorca's capital Palma to the northern town of Sóller is operated by historic electric traction and runs through the scenic *Sierra de Tramuntana* region. The 28 km line is built to the unusual gauge of 914mm (one yard).

From Sóller a narrow gauge tramway runs for 5 km to Port de Sóller. Further details of both lines are in Table **674**. www.trendesoller.com

A modern RENFE suburban train at Bilbao Abando station, previously known as Estación del Norte

SWEDEN

RAIL TRAVEL

See Tables **730 - 768**. National rail company is SJ AB www.sj.se. The company was formed when Statens Järnvägar (SJ) was split into different companies. Telephone enquiries: ✆ +46 771 75 75 75 (daily 0600-2200, but ticket purchase only available Mon-Fri 0800-1700).

The best services are operated by high-speed trains (*Snabbtåg*, shown as *Sn* in our tables) running at up to 200 km/h and using either SJ 2000 trains (formerly known as X2000) or the newer SJ 3000 units. Supplements are required on *Snabbtåg*. Some local lines are run by regional authorities or private companies such as Norrtåg www.norrtag.se; see page 351 for other operators.

Sleeping-cars have one or two berths in 2nd class, couchettes have six berths; female-only compartments are available. 1st-class sleeping-cars with en-suite shower and WC run on many overnight services; 2nd-class compartments have washbasins, while a shower and WC are at the end of the carriage. Long-distance trains have a refreshment service. Many trains have a family coach with a playroom, and facilities for the disabled. Seat reservations are compulsory on *Sn* and night trains. *Sn* services also operate between Sweden and Copenhagen via the Öresund bridge and tunnel but it is better to use the frequent local trains for short journeys.

'C' (for Central) in timetables etc. means the town's main station. *Biljetter* indicates the station ticket office, often with limited opening hours, but ticket machines are also widely in use.

Journeys north from Stockhom along the coast to Umeå and beyond have been revolutionised by the *Botniabanan* which opened in 2010. An interesting alternative route to the far north of Sweden, albeit much slower, is the privately operated *Inlandsbanan*, with a single train each way in summer taking all day for the 746 km journey between Östersund and Gälllivare (Table **766**).

UPPSALA - LENNA JERNVÄG

Starting at Uppsala (Tables **760 / 761**), head for tracks 9/10 at the Central station from where this narrow gauge heritage line runs for 33 km east to Faringe. The focal point of the railway is Marielund station, where trains often pass and steam trains refill their water tanks. A popular station café is also located there. The railway's collection of rollling stock is based at the Faringe engine sheds. Track gauge is 891mm (Swedish 'three foot'), unique to Sweden.

Trains run on ⑦ June 2 - Sept. 15, ⑥ June 22 - Sept. 14, and ③④ June 26 - Aug. 8, also June 6. There are five to seven departures from Uppsala depending on the date, with some journeys hauled by steam. A round trip takes three to four hours. For timings see www.lennakatten.se

ÖSTRA SÖDERMANSLAND JÄRNVÄG

Mariefred - Läggesta - Taxinge is the route of this 11 km narrow gauge (600mm) museum line. Läggesta nedre station is a 500m walk from the SJ station in Table **732**, located west of Stockholm on the line to Eskilstuna. The narrow gauge line offers some great views of Lake Mälaren. Starting on the north side of the lake at Mariefred, trains reverse at Läggesta nedre with several services continuing along the south shore to Taxinge.

On summer weekends it is possible to cross the lake by steamer between Mariefred and Taxinge (round trip fares are available), giving an ideal day out from Stockholm.

Trains run on ⑥⑦ May 11 - Sept. 8 (daily July 6 - Aug. 4), also Aug. 6 - 8, 14, with several trains each day. Timings, including boat schedules and connections from Stockholm, can be found at www.oslj.nu.

SWITZERLAND

RAIL TRAVEL

See Tables **500 - 578**. The principal rail carrier is Swiss Federal Railways (SBB / CFF / FFS) www.sbb.ch. A 24 hour premium rate helpline is available on ✆ 0848 44 66 88 (German, French, Italian, English spoken).

As might be expected, there are a large number of scenic routes and mountain lines, with endless possibilities for exciting days out. Rail travel can often be combined with other modes such as lake steamers, buses, funicular railways and even cable cars to complete a round trip. Several examples are given on the official tourism site www.myswitzerland.com.

The Swiss rail system is characterised by the large number of rail operators other than SBB. Many of these are narrow gauge, notably the Rhätische Bahn (RhB), which has a large network in the south-east, and the Matterhorn-Gotthard-Bahn (MGB) in the south-west. Together these two railways provide the famous *Glacier Express* running for 290 km from St Moritz to Zermatt (Table **575**). This requires a supplement and advance reservation, but of course the exact same lines can also be traversed with a series of local trains (Tables **576** and **545**).

Other services very popular with tourists include the *Bernina Express* from Chur to Tirano, just across the border in Italy (Table **545**), MOB's *Golden Pass* trains from Montreux to Zweizimmen, some of which have panorama cars (Table **566**), and Zentralbahn's Luzern to Interlaken route with its many lakeside views (Table **561**). Some other highlights are mentioned below, but there are many more. The Swiss rail network is, of course, synonymous with punctuality and spotlessly clean trains.

CHEMIN DE FER - MUSÉE BLONAY - CHAMBY (BC)

Situated in the south-west corner of Switzerland close to Lake Geneva, this narrow gauge railway museum has an extensive collection of rolling stock. Trains run from Blonay to Chamby (3 km) before changing direction to reach the nearby Chaulin museum. Trains leaving the museum return to either Chamby or Blonay. Both steam and electric trains are operated. Passengers are treated to fine views over Lake Geneva during the short journey. Rail connections are available at both Blonay (regular trains from Vevey) and Chamby (Table **566**). www.blonay-chamby.ch

Trains run on ⑥⑦ May 4 - Oct. 27 (also June 10).

		b		⑦	🚂		🚂		🚂	
Blonay ....d.	1005	1105	1205	1305	1405	1440	1520	1605	1705	...
Chamby ....d.	1021	1121	1221	1321	1423	1458	1538	1621	1721	...
Musée ....a.	1025	1125	1225	1325	1427	1502	1542	1625	1725	...
Musée ....d.	...	1350	...	1646	...	...	...	...	...	...
Chamby ....a.	...	1354	...	1650	...	...	...	...	...	...
	b		⑦	🚂		🚂		🚂		
Musée ....d.	1035	1135	1235	1335	1420	1455	1535	1635	1745	...
Blonay ....a.	1050	1150	1250	1350	1435	1510	1550	1650	1800	...

b – 🚂 on ⑦ (also Aug. 1).   🚂 – Steam train.

BRIENZ ROTHORN BAHN (BRB)

Within easy reach of Interlaken by rail (Table **561**) or boat (Table **506**), this narrow gauge (800mm) mountain rack railway from Brienz can claim the unusual fact that its lowest and highest stations have the greatest height difference of any railway in Switzerland. With stunning views, the distance to the summit at Rothorn (2244m) is 7.6 km, and the journey takes about one hour. Built in 1892, an added attraction is that most trips are steam operated, since it is one of the very few non-electrified routes in Switzerland. Trains run between June and October - timings are shown in Table **553**. www.brienz-rothorn-bahn.ch

DAMPFBAHN FURKA-BERGSTRECKE (DFB)

This tortuous narrow gauge mountain route is the original main line over the Furkapass which was closed in 1982 following the opening of the Furka base tunnel. Since 1992 the line has reopened in stages as a spectacular tourist route, the final section between Gletsch and Oberwald being completed in 2010. Steam-hauled journeys over the full 18 km route from Realp to Oberwald via Furka take over two hours (reservation is compulsory), whilst shorter diesel hauled journeys are available between Oberwald and Gletsch taking 25 minutes. Itineraries are also available using both steam and diesel services with a break of journey at Gletsch, near to the Rhone Glacier.

Trains run on ⑤⑥⑦ June 22 - Oct 6 (daily July 8 - Aug. 18), with the most intensive service running on ⑥⑦ July 27 - Aug. 25. For timings and reservations see www.dfb.ch.

Both ends of the route can be reached by means of the hourly MGB trains between Brig and Andermatt in Table **576**. In Realp the DFB station is a 10 minute walk from the MGB station.

RIGI-BAHNEN (RB)

There are two electrified rack railways to the Rigi-Kulm summit (1750m), an 8.5 km line from Arth Goldau on the Gotthard main line, and a 7 km line from Vitznau by the lake. Opening in 1871, the latter was Europe's first rack railway, and is the more scenic of the two routes. The lines are also notable for being the highest standard gauge railway in Europe. At the summit, one of the finest Swiss panoramas, overlooking the *Vierwaldstättersee*, awaits the visitor. www.rigi.ch

Trains run hourly all year on both routes, but evening services run only in summer; timings are shown in Table **553**.

Arth-Goldau, where the RB station is adjacent to the main line station, can be reached by means of rail services in Tables **525** and **550**. In Vitznau the station is by the quayside (lake steamer services: Table **506**).

PILATUS BAHN (PB)

The world's steepest rack railway runs from Alpnachstad, south-west of Lake Luzern, to the mountain's summit at Pilatus Kulm, a distance of 4.6 km, reaching a height of 2070m. The 800mm gauge line was first opened in 1889 and uses an unusual rack system with teeth on either side of a horizontal rail. The line has been electrified since the 1930s.

Alpnachstad is 13 km from Luzern on the line to Interlaken (Table **561**). A popular excursion from Luzern is to take the train or boat to Alpnachstad, rack railway to Pilatus Kulm, cable-car and gondolas down to Kriens, then trolleybus route **1** back to central Luzern.

The Pilatus Bahn runs early-May to mid-November; there is no winter service - see Table **553** for timings. www.pilatus.ch

JUNGFRAUBAHNEN (JB)

Reached from Interlaken by two different routes (Table **564**), Kleine Scheidegg is the start point for the Jungfraubahn, which burrows through the Mönch and the Eiger to reach Europe's highest station at Jungfraujoch (3454m). The 9.3 km electrified narrow gauge rack railway is mostly in tunnel but stops twice on the way up at Eigerwand and Eismeer from where there are spectacular views through windows incorporated into the mountain side. On a clear day the views from the summit are breathtaking. Visitors are strongly advised to check weather conditions at the summit before travelling. www.jungfrau.ch

The line runs all year, up to every 30 minutes, but may sometimes be affected by snowfall in winter. The journey takes 35 minutes. See Table **564** for timings.

GORNERGRAT BAHN (GGB)

Starting from Zermatt, western terminus of the famous *Glacier Express* (Table **575**, also local services in Table **576**), the Gornergratbahn runs for 9.4 km to the summit at 3089m. Gornergrat is the highest open-air station in Europe, since the higher Jungfraujoch station described above is actually situated inside the mountain! www.gornergratbahn.ch

The journey on this electrified narrow gauge rack railway takes 33 minutes (44 downhill) and initially provides a birds-eye view of Zermatt followed by fine views of the Matterhorn. From Zermatt sit on the right-hand side for the best views. The GGB station at Zermatt is close to the MGB station, at right angles to it. The service runs all year; see Table **578** for timings.

SWISS MUSEUM OF TRANSPORT

Known as the Verkehrshaus, the museum is located eight minutes by local train from Luzern station (route S3 to the Verkehrshaus stop), and can also be reached by bus or boat. It is open daily. www.verkehrshaus.ch

TURKEY

RAIL TRAVEL

See Tables **1570 - 1590** (also **1550** for European Turkey). Operator is TCDD (Turkish State Railways) www.tcdd.gov.tr. The principal Istanbul - Ankara route has been revolutionised in recent years by the opening of a new high-speed line via Eskişehir, with another high-speed section linking these cities with Konya. Further lines are under construction or planned for the future. Traditional routes are tortuous and slow, but the coaching stock is generally comfortable.

The Marmaray Tunnel under the Bosphorus opened in 2013, joining the Asian and European parts of Istanbul by local rail service for the first time. Following a period when the high-speed trains from Istanbul to Ankara were starting from Pendik in the suburbs, these trains now use the more centrally located Söğütlüçeşme station, with certain trains starting from Halkali on the European side and using the tunnel (Table **1570**). The neoclassical pseudo-castle Haydarpasa station building on the Asian side of the Bosphorus is sadly out of use.

UKRAINE

RAIL TRAVEL

See Tables **1700 - 1790**, which also include neighbouring Moldova. Ukrainian Railways goes under the initials UZ. www.uz.gov.ua

This vast 1520mm gauge railway network links all major towns and many small ones, and the introduction of modern diesel multiple units in recent years has seen a new *InterCity* category of train, giving fast links on key routes. The most scenic routes are in the south west of the country.

Determined railfans may find the remaining narrow gauge lines of interest, although services are sparse, time consuming to access, and information scarse. One of the lines, that between Rudnytsia and Holovanivs'k, is actually Europe's longest 750mm gauge line at 130 km, but its future is far from certain.

There are no through trains to the Crimea, and the continuing conflict in the Donbass region means there are no trains to Donetsk or Luhansk.

Robert Foster's Column

Robert Foster is a long-standing customer and supporter of the European Rail Timetable who played a key role in its rebirth in 2014. In an occasional column Robert shares some of his personal thoughts based on his recent travel experiences.

When discussing this column with the Editor-in-chief, he asked if I would be upbeat. Other than being upbeat about the European Rail Timetable (ERT), as you will see, it is difficult to be upbeat about the development of the European railway system. However, one bright point is that trains between Italy and Slovenia have been reintroduced after a gap of five years following withdrawal of the daytime and overnight trains between Budapest and Venezia. This is the route, taken until its final demise in 1977, of the Direct Orient Express from Calais and Paris to Istanbul and Athens. In Serbia, it was the train on which lunch was taken in the restaurant car by Sean Connery and his adversary in 'From Russia with Love'. Eastbound, the train left Paris Gare de Lyon at 2353 but was painfully slow, and indeed it was possible to catch it up by leaving Paris next day at 0746 from Gare de l'Est on the train to Wien, named the 'Mozart', changing at Munchen into the 1727 Tauern-Orient Express, some coaches of which next morning combined with the Direct Orient Express at Beograd.

However the timings of the new trains are abysmal (ERT Table **87**). To get from Venezia, the principal traffic source in eastern Italy, to Ljubljana requires a start by local train at 0641 with a change at Trieste, the journey taking five hours. The only later possibility is at 1641 from Venezia, arriving Ljubljana at 2148, too late for the typical tourist who might wish to use this route. In the other direction the start from Ljubljana is at the ridiculous time of 0600, the second train departing at 1610 and reaching Venezia at 2120, again much too late. The eight kilometres between the border at Villa Opicina and departure from Trieste consumes more than an hour in each direction.

A train is capable of running between Ljubljana and Venezia in 3 hours 45 minutes, by cutting out the Trieste detour, calling at the new Trieste Airport station and then running fast to Venezia Mestre. Looking now at ERT Table **1300**, the 0700 Zagreb – München – Frankfurt arrives Ljubljana at 0916. What should happen is a train from Ljubljana to Venezia at 0930, arriving Venezia Santa Lucia at 1315. In the reverse direction, the Frankfurt – Zagreb train leaves Ljubljana at 1836. So have the train from Venezia into Ljubljana at 1815, which gives a departure from Venezia at 1430, giving a very adequate turnaround time at Venezia of 75 minutes. A train at these times would be of real benefit to tourists in that area.

While discussing this route, there has for some years been spectacular missed connections at Villach, where the same 0700 from Zagreb fails by 8 minutes to connect with the 0625 Wien – Venezia, but that is a much longer route. The 1225 from Wien plus the 0955 and 1555 from Venezia – there are only two each way per day – at Villach all miss the Ljubljana/Zagreb train by about 20 minutes.

It is 25 years since the Channel Tunnel opened. A regular columnist in RAIL magazine laments the insular attitude of Eurostar and comments that it operates as if it were an airline. It now advises passengers to arrive up to 60 minutes before departure – negating much of the natural advantage of rail – most of which is spent in the departure lounge below platform level where you don't see anything of the splendid trainshed of St Pancras before the scramble up to the platform when this is announced a mere 20 minutes before departure. Onward travel by connection from Lille has always been entirely haphazard, made worse by the fact that some trains direct from the south and west of France use Lille Flandres instead of Lille Europe. It is almost always quicker, and cheaper, to go via and changing stations in Paris. A particular irritation to me is the gap on most days of the week in the otherwise hourly Paris service between 1024 and 1224 outward and between 1303 and 1503 on the return, both of which incidentally are 12 minutes slower than their previous xx15 departure time from Gare du Nord. Eurostar is taking a backward step this year in discontinuing the Sparpreis tickets to German destinations available from www.bahn.de. For €59, €99 in first-class, you could go to any destination in Germany. As Mark Smith of www.seat61.com says, this is a major backward step in international rail travel from and to the UK.

However, the really backward step this year is the extension of the SNCF Ouigo low-cost network. These trains require a 30 minute check-in, and in Paris Gare de Lyon herd passengers down to the below ground Halle 3, with the result that when recently taking the 0719 Paris – Nice, it took 22 minutes from arrival at the station to reaching the coach, just 50 metres from where we had entered the station and having walked almost half a kilometre. The airline trick of making you pay for luggage applies to these trains, but whereas airlines offer a comprehensive range of food and drink, Ouigo offers nothing as the buffet car is sealed off: to Nice this is a 6-hour journey, itself between 15 and 40 minutes slower than 10 years ago. Seating, all second class, is three and one in the lower level of the TGV Duplex, instead of the conventional two and two. You cannot print out tickets until they are sent by email only four days before departure.

I experienced Italian trains – poor once away the main Torino – Milano – Roma – Napoli spine route – at their worst this year, but the ERT came to the rescue. Travelling from Bern to Domodossola, for some inexplicable and unexplained reason trains were limited to 30 km/h all the way from the Italian border inside the Simplon tunnel to Domodossola and so missed the intended connection to Locarno over the charming Centovalli route (Table **551**) which in any event had no trains running on it. So we boarded the 0739 Geneve – Milano, running 50 minutes late, as far as Gallarate from where we made our way across to Lugano. Two of the party required the PostAuto to Thusis (Table **544**) and the detour meant rescheduling. Table **544** of the ERT conflicted with the SBB website, but the ERT was correct! On my annual pilgrimage in May via Chur and the Bernina line (Table **545**) to Bellagio on Lake Como, with 16 people in tow, the 1708 from Tirano to Varenna was two hours late for no announced reason other than 'a problem on the line'. The restaurant opposite the pier at Bellagio where we always dine kept open and served us at 10 p.m. On the return three days later we took the hydrofoil to Como (Table **599**) intending to take the 0847 from Como SG over the Gotthard pass to Erstfeld (Tables **550** and **550a**). As this was shown first as 10, then 15 minutes late, I made the last-minute decision to board a stopping train to Lugano. Here our intended train was now shown as 35 minutes late and so we took the 1043 ICN to Bellinzona, and what a good thing that was, as the 0847 was cancelled. Of course I was relying on the ERT, not a website which would have been almost useless.

Last year and again this year, apart from our group, there were fewer than five passengers on the 4-car train. Surely it cannot be long before SBB bow to the inevitable and close this magnificently engineered line, now that all other passenger and freight traffic uses the Gotthard base tunnel, slightly longer than the Channel Tunnel, opened in December 2016.

EUROPEAN RAIL PASSES

ail passes represent excellent value for train travellers who are touring ·round Europe (or parts of it) or making a number of journeys within a hort period. They can offer substantial savings over point-to-point ckets, as well as greater flexibility.

he principal pass schemes for Europe are **Interrail** for residents of urope, and **Eurail** for those resident outside Europe. Both schemes ave a choice of **Global** passes covering 31 countries, or **One Country asses** for individual countries. Note, however, that you cannot use the ass in your country of residence.

Passes either cover a specified number of consecutive days, or are of the *flexi* type where you get so many 'travel days' within a specified period (there are boxes on the pass where you write each date). Free travel requires the use of a travel day, whereas discounted travel does not.

Passes generally cover the ordinary services of the national rail companies, but supplements often have to be paid for travel on high-speed services, night trains, and 'global price' trains. Independent rail operators may not accept passes but may give discounts to passholders. Extra charges always apply for travel in sleeping cars or couchettes.

Interrail and Eurail

Europe-wide or single-country passes

website: www.interrail.eu www.eurail.com

nyone of any age can buy a pass, either for pretty much the whole of urope, or for an individual country. **Global** passes cover 31 countries of urope and can either be *Continuous* passes for a set number of onsecutive days or months, or *Flexi* passes for a certain number of avel days within a period of one or two months (you choose the travel ays as you go along, writing the date on the pass). **One Country asses** are all flexi passes for a certain number of days within one month sometimes there is more than one country, as with the Benelux pass).

he two pass schemes (Interrail and Eurail) are now very similar, but terrail passes are for residents of Europe, whilst Eurail passes are for ose resident outside Europe. Turkey, Russia and the CIS countries ount as Europe for this purpose. You may need proof of residence.

asses can be purchased up to eleven months before travel begins. It's est to buy the pass online or in your own country before travelling, though most passes can also be purchased at major stations in Europe. ote, however, that the new 3 day Global pass cannot be purchased from tations. Recommended retail prices are now the same for both Interrail nd Eurail and are in Euros as shown below, but prices may vary etween different outlets. At certain times of year special offer prices may e available. All passes are either for second class or first class travel (of ourse first class passes can also be used to travel in second class).

asses come with a travel diary which has to be filled in with each urney. You cannot use the pass in your own country of residence. owever, with an Interrail Global Pass you can make one outbound and ne inbound journey in your country of residence (see next page).

ITERRAIL / EURAIL GLOBAL PASS - valid in 31 countries:
ustria, Belgium, Bosnia-Herzegovina, Bulgaria, Croatia, Czech Repub-:, Denmark, Finland, France, Germany, Great Britain, Greece, Hungary, eland (including Northern Ireland), Italy, Lithuania, Luxembourg, lontenegro, Netherlands, North Macedonia, Norway, Poland, Portugal, omania, Serbia, Slovakia, Slovenia, Spain, Sweden, Switzerland and urkey. Note that Lithuania is NEW for 2019.

OT VALID in the passholder's country of residence.

RICES - INTERRAIL / EURAIL GLOBAL PASS - FIRST CLASS

2019 prices	Adult (28-59) 1st cl.	Senior (60+) 1st cl.	Youth (12-27) 1st cl.	Child * (under 12) 1st cl.
LEXI PASSES:				
days within 1 month	€291	€262	€224	€0
days within 1 month	€376	€338	€289	€0
days within 1 month	€446	€401	€343	€0
) days within 2 months	€534	€481	€411	€0
5 days within 2 months	€657	€591	€505	€0
ONTINUOUS DAYS:				
5 days	€590	€531	€454	€0
2 days	€690	€621	€530	€0
month	€893	€804	€686	€0
months	€975	€878	€750	€0
months	€1202	€1082	€924	€0

RICES - INTERRAIL / EURAIL GLOBAL PASS - SECOND CLASS

2019 prices	Adult (28-59) 2nd cl.	Senior (60+) 2nd cl.	Youth (12-27) 2nd cl.	Child * (under 12) 2nd cl.
LEXI PASSES:				
days within 1 month	€218	€196	€168	€0
days within 1 month	€282	€254	€217	€0
days within 1 month	€335	€302	€258	€0
) days within 2 months	€401	€361	€308	€0
5 days within 2 months	€493	€444	€379	€0
ONTINUOUS DAYS:				
5 days	€443	€399	€341	€0
2 days	€518	€466	€398	€0
month	€670	€603	€515	€0
months	€731	€658	€562	€0
months	€902	€812	€693	€0

Child: two children per fare paying Adult (not Senior) travel free.

INTERRAIL / EURAIL ONE COUNTRY PASS

Covers any one of the participating countries below. **NOT** available for the passholder's country of residence. Note that Benelux passes (also the Eurail Scandinavia pass) actually cover more than one country. As with the Global pass, two children per fare paying Adult travel free.

There are some variations between Interrail and Eurail One Country Passes (where they differ, details are shown below). For example, Great Britain and Germany have their own pass schemes for overseas visitors (Britrail and the German Rail Pass), hence there is no Eurail One Country Pass for these countries.

Interrail: Germany or Great Britain
Eurail: Scandinavia (Norway, Sweden, Denmark, Finland combined)

	Adult 1st cl.	Senior 1st cl.	Youth 1st cl.	Adult 2nd cl.	Senior 2nd cl.	Youth 2nd cl.
3 days within 1 month	€256	€230	€205	€192	€173	€166
4 days within 1 month	€291	€262	€233	€218	€196	€189
5 days within 1 month	€321	€289	€257	€241	€217	€209
6 days within 1 month	€349	€314	€279	€262	€236	€227
8 days within 1 month	€396	€356	€317	€297	€267	€257

Norway, Spain or Sweden

	Adult 1st cl.	Senior 1st cl.	Youth 1st cl.	Adult 2nd cl.	Senior 2nd cl.	Youth 2nd cl.
3 days within 1 month	€227	€204	€182	€170	€153	€148
4 days within 1 month	€263	€237	€210	€197	€177	€171
5 days within 1 month	€294	€265	€235	€221	€199	€191
6 days within 1 month	€323	€291	€258	€242	€218	€210
8 days within 1 month	€374	€337	€299	€281	€253	€243

Interrail: Austria, France or Switzerland
Eurail: Austria or France

Eurail France Pass: 1, 2 and 7 day passes also for sale outside Europe

	Adult 1st cl.	Senior 1st cl.	Youth 1st cl.	Adult 2nd cl.	Senior 2nd cl.	Youth 2nd cl.
3 days within 1 month	€195	€176	€156	€146	€131	€127
4 days within 1 month	€230	€207	€184	€173	€156	€150
5 days within 1 month	€262	€236	€210	€197	€177	€170
6 days within 1 month	€291	€262	€233	€218	€196	€189
8 days within 1 month	€344	€310	€275	€258	€232	€224

Benelux, Denmark, Finland, Ireland or Italy*

Benelux is Belgium, Netherlands and Luxembourg combined
Ireland includes Northern Ireland
** Prices for the Italy Pass are 5% higher than shown*

	Adult 1st cl.	Senior 1st cl.	Youth 1st cl.	Adult 2nd cl.	Senior 2nd cl.	Youth 2nd cl.
3 days within 1 month	€161	€145	€129	€121	€109	€105
4 days within 1 month	€194	€175	€155	€146	€131	€126
5 days within 1 month	€225	€203	€180	€169	€152	€146
6 days within 1 month	€253	€228	€202	€190	€171	€164
8 days within 1 month	€305	€275	€244	€229	€206	€198

Greece, Hungary, Portugal or Romania

	Adult 1st cl.	Senior 1st cl.	Youth 1st cl.	Adult 2nd cl.	Senior 2nd cl.	Youth 2nd cl.
3 days within 1 month	€123	€111	€98	€92	€83	€80
4 days within 1 month	€152	€137	€122	€114	€103	€99
5 days within 1 month	€179	€161	€143	€134	€121	€116
6 days within 1 month	€205	€185	€164	€154	€139	€133
8 days within 1 month	€253	€228	€202	€190	€171	€164

Bulgaria, Croatia, Czech Republic, Lithuania, North Macedonia, Poland, Serbia, Slovakia, Slovenia or Turkey

	Adult 1st cl.	Senior 1st cl.	Youth 1st cl.	Adult 2nd cl.	Senior 2nd cl.	Youth 2nd cl.
3 days within 1 month	€78	€70	€62	€59	€53	€51
4 days within 1 month	€99	€89	€79	€74	€67	€64
5 days within 1 month	€119	€107	€95	€89	€80	€77
6 days within 1 month	€139	€125	€111	€104	€94	€90
8 days within 1 month	€176	€158	€141	€132	€119	€114

See next page for the Greek Islands Pass

Interrail and Eurail - continued

GREEK ISLANDS PASS

This is a special ferry pass now available in both the Interrail and Eurail schemes. It is valid on ferries operated by the Attica Group, which includes Superfast Ferries, Blue Star Ferries and Hellenic Seaways. The 5 trip pass is valid for five domestic trips on ferries within Greece. The 6 trip pass is valid for two international trips between Italy and Greece plus four domestic trips in Greece. The 6 trip pass includes accommodation in either 1st or 2nd class, also rail / bus transfers between Patras and Piraeus. Both passes give 30% discount on additional ferry trips.

	Adult 1st cl.	Senior 1st cl.	Youth 1st cl.	Adult 2nd cl.	Senior 2nd cl.	Youth 2nd cl.
5 trips within 1 month	N/A	N/A	N/A	€ 90	€ 81	€ 68
6 trips within 1 month	€ 208	€ 187	€ 182	€ 176	€ 159	€ 155

OVERNIGHT TRAVEL

Passes do not include supplements for travel in sleeping car or couchette accommodation and these have to be purchased separately. Many overnight trains have a *global* price where the ticket price includes the sleeping accommodation - in these cases pass holders pay a specified supplement or passholder fare (see below for further details).

Holders of flexi passes travelling overnight and leaving before midnight need to write the date of departure on the pass, and of course the pass can be used for the whole of that day. Pass holders will not need to activate a second day on their pass for the day of arrival unless they board a second train (but the day of arrival does need to be within the overall validity of the pass). The rule can also be used for late evening trains arriving after midnight. If you need to use a connecting train having arrived overnight it may be worth buying a regular ticket to avoid having to use a travel day.

Note that this is a new rule for 2019 and replaces the previous 7pm rule whereby pass holders had to write the day of arrival on their passes, rather than the day of departure, for night trains departing after 7pm.

FREE TRAVEL TO THE BORDER, AIRPORT OR SEAPORT

Although it is not possible to purchase an Interrail pass for the holder's own country of residence, a Global pass entitles the holder to two free journeys (one outbound, one inbound) between any station in their country of residence and its border, an airport or seaport. Each journey must be completed in one day (no overnight stops allowed), at any time within the overall validity of the pass, or include a travel day if using a flexi pass. Details must be entered in the travel diary.

SUPPLEMENTS AND RESERVATION FEES

Required for certain types of high-speed or 'global price' train.

International day train examples, 2nd class (subject to change): France - Italy *TGV* € 38; *Berlin - Warszawa Express* € 4.50; *EC Switzerland - Italy* € 11; *Eurostar* passholder fare € 30 (€ 38 in standard premier with 1st class pass); *TGV / ICE* France - Germany € 13; *TGV Lyria* (France - Switzerland) € 34; *Thalys* € 20 - € 30; *TGV* Brussels - France € 20; *SJ Snabbtåg* Stockholm - København € 7.50. *IC bus* Klagenfurt - Venezia € 15 - 29.

Domestic examples (subject to alteration): **Croatia** *IC / ICN* € 3.60. **Czech Republic** *SC* € 8. **Finland** *Pendolino* € 9. **France** *TGV* € 10 limited allocation (otherwise € 20), *Intercités* with compulsory reservatic € 10. **Hungary** *IC* € 3. **Italy** *FA*, *FB* and *FR* € 10, *IC* € 3. **Norway** lon distance trains € 6.3. **Poland** *EIP* € 10, *EIC / TLK* free. **Portugal** *AP /* € 5. **Romania** *IC/IR* € 1 - 4. **Slovakia** *IC* € 4. **Slovenia** *ICS* € 3.4 **Spain** *AVE* € 10, most other long-distance trains € 6.50, *MD* € 4.5 **Sweden** *Snabbtåg* € 7.

Night trains: sleeping accommodation is typically € 15 to € 75 for couchette, and € 35 to € 155 for a berth in a sleeping car. Some trai also include reclining seats. Many night trains are globally priced ar fares for passholders vary widely.

As some of the supplements / passholder fares can be rather high, i worth checking whether a regular advance purchase ticket might be better option, particularly if booked a month or two ahead. Supplemen can often be avoided altogether by taking slower regional trains.

VALIDITY ON PRIVATE RAILWAYS

Passes are valid on the national railway companies in each country, plu many privately run railways (some give discounts). For details se www.interrail.eu, www.eurail.com, or the Traveller's Guide that com with your pass.

Selected details are as follows (subject to change): **Austria**: free trav on WESTbahn and ROeEE. **Czech Republic**: valid on Leo Express ar RegioJet. **Denmark**: free travel on Arriva and DSB-Øresund, 50 discount on Nordjyske Jernbaner (Hjørring - Hirtshals and Frederikshav - Skagen). **France**: SNCF bus services included. **Germany**: free c most regional services and many private companies. **Hungary**: GySE services are included. **Italy**: free travel on Trenord and Leonarc Express. **Netherlands**: privately run regional lines are include **Norway**: Flåmsbana (Myrdal - Flåm) gives 30% discount. **Polan** valid on Koleje Dolnośląskie, Koleje Mazowieckie and PR. **Spain**: FEV is included. FGC gives 50% discount. **Sweden**: most private operato are included. **Switzerland**: free travel on BLS, FART/MGB, MOB, Rh SOB, SSIF, THURBO, TMR and ZB. Many others offer 25 - 50 discount, including AB, ASM, CJ, FB, LAF, LEB, MBC, MRV, NStC RA, RB, RBS, SZU, TPC, TPF, TRN, WB, WSB. Discounted fare c William Tell Express (rail and boat tour).

VALIDITY ON FERRY AND BUS SERVICES

Global passes includes free deck passage between Italy and Greece c SuperFast Ferries (you pay port taxes and possibly a fuel surcharge free air-type seats for 1st class pass holders. Many other ferry compani offer discounts (not usually on cabins), for example: Balearia 20 Finnlines 50%, Fjord Line 20% (10% high-season), Grimaldi 20%, Iris Ferries 30%, Stena Line 30%, Tallink Silja 20% (high-season), 40% (lo season), Viking Line 50%. Note that Minoan Ferries no longer accep passes.

Most Swiss lakes give 50% discount, as does Fjord1 on Norwegia Fjords. Certain bus services in Scandinavia are included, including Lul - Haparanda - Tornio - Kemi.

Other benefits are often available, such as hotel discounts, bike hi discounts, free entry to railway museums, and access to railway stati lounges.

Where to Buy your Pass

Sources of rail passes (and point to point tickets) include the following:

ACP Rail - see www.acprail.com

Deutsche Bahn UK (German Railways)
UK Booking Centre ✆ 08718 80 80 66 www.bahn.com

Eurail – buy on www.eurail.com or see www.eurailgroup.org for a list of sales partners. All participating European railway companies sell passes.

Ffestiniog Travel
Former St Mary's Church, Tremadog, Porthmadog, Gwynedd LL49 9RA
✆ 01766 512400 www.ffestiniogtravel.com

French Railways – see www.oui.sncf

International Rail
PO Box 153, Alresford, Hampshire SO24 4AQ
✆ 0871 231 0790 www.internationalrail.com
London Rail Desk is situated at STA Travel, 52 Grosvenor Gardens, London SW1W 0AU, open Mon-Fri, book appointment online.

Interrail – see www.interrail.eu. All participating railway companies sell passes.

Interrail by National Rail – see www.myinterrail.co.uk

Loco 2 – see www.loco2.com

Rail Canterbury
39 Palace Street, Canterbury, Kent CT1 2DZ
✆ 01227 450088 www.rail-canterbury.co.uk

Rail Europe Inc (USA)
44 South Broadway, White Plains, NY 10601, USA
www.raileurope.com

Rail Europe, Canada
www.raileurope.ca

RailTourGuide
Suite 42, 7 - 15 Pink Lane, Newcastle upon Tyne, NE1 5DW
✆ 0191 246 0708 www.railtourguide.com

Real Russia
Unit 5, The Ivories, Northampton Street, Islington, London, N1 2HY
✆ 0207 100 7370 www.realrussia.co.uk

STA Travel
Numerous branches throughout the UK
✆ 0333 321 0099 www.statravel.co.uk

Switzerland Travel Centre
30 Bedford Street, 1st floor, London WC2E 9ED
✆ 0207 420 4934 www.stc.co.uk

Trainseurope
4 Station Approach, March, Cambs PE15 8SJ
✆ 0871 700 7722 www.trainseurope.co.uk

Other useful websites:

www.seat61.com
www.ricksteves.com.

BritRail

ritRail is a pass for overseas visitors to Great Britain, allowing unlimited avel on the national rail network in England, Scotland and Wales. It is ot available to residents of Great Britain, Northern Ireland, the Isle of lan or the Channel Islands. Passes must be purchased before arriving in ritain. Youth prices apply to ages 16 to 25, senior applies to 60+. All asses are available for First or Standard class. For further details see ww.britrail.com or www.acprail.com.

RITRAIL CONSECUTIVE PASS

JSD prices)	Adult 1st cl.	Youth 1st cl.	Senior 1st cl.	Adult Std cl.	Youth Std cl.	Senior Std cl.
days	178	107	151	118	71	101
days	266	160	226	176	106	150
days	331	199	281	218	131	186
days	471	283	401	317	171	269
5 days	696	418	592	471	283	401
2 days	884	531	752	589	354	501
month	1047	629	890	696	418	592

RITRAIL FLEXIPASS

JSD prices)	Adult 1st cl.	Youth 1st cl.	Senior 1st cl.	Adult Std cl.	Youth Std cl.	Senior Std cl.
days within 1 month	222	133	188	150	91	128
days within 1 month	331	199	281	224	135	190
days within 1 month	407	244	346	280	168	238
days within 1 month	598	359	508	401	241	341
5 days within 2 months	893	536	759	603	362	513

RITRAIL ENGLAND PASSES

he Britrail England Pass excludes Wales and Scotland, giving a saving f approximately 20%. A Britrail South West pass is also available. Both re available in Consecutive and Flexi versions (no 2-day passes).

BRITRAIL LONDON PLUS PASS

This 'flexi' pass allows unlimited rail travel in London and the surrounding area. You can visit such places as Canterbury, Salisbury, Bristol, Bath, Oxford, Cambridge, Stratford-Upon-Avon, Worcester, and anywhere on the coast between Harwich to Weymouth.

(USD prices)	Adult 1st cl.	Youth 1st cl.	Senior 1st cl.	Adult Std cl.	Youth Std cl.	Senior Std cl.
3 days within 1 month	192	125	164	137	89	117
4 days within 1 month	222	145	189	167	109	142
8 days within 1 month	315	205	268	232	151	197

BRITRAIL SCOTLAND PASSES

Three different passes are available, all standard class adult passes: Spirit of Scotland covers the whole country; available as 4 days within 8 days, or 8 days within 15 days. The other areas are Central Scotland (3 days consecutive), and Highlands (4 days within 8 days).

M-PASS

The Britrail England Consecutive Pass is available as a mobile ticket on your mobile phone (saving shipping cost) - see www.acprail.com.

DISCOUNTS

Saver Discount: groups of 3 to 9 people receive a discount of up to 20%. Passes must be of the same type and duration and the party must travel together at all times. Cannot be combined with the family discount.

Family Discount: if any adult or senior pass is purchased, one accompanying child (aged 5-15) may receive a free pass of the same type and duration. Any further children travelling receive a 50% discount. All children under 5 travel free.

Other International Passes

3ALKAN FLEXIPASS

Jnlimited travel in Bosnia & Herzegovina, Bulgaria, Greece, Montenegro, lorth Macedonia, Serbia and Turkey (also trains operated by Regiotrans ı Romania). Not available to residents of these countries. Valid for any /5/7/10/15 days in two months: 1st class €127/180/243/314/378; nd class €91/134/183/233/280. 40% discount for under 26s, 20% for ver 60s, 50% for children (4-12). Supplements for *IC* trains.

lso allows travel on Superfast Ferries/ANEK Lines routes from Patras ɔ Ancona and Bari (port taxes and high season supplements apply); 30% iscount on Attica Group (Blue Star Ferries and Hellenic Seaways) routes vithin Greece. Note that if purchased from one of the above countries the ass allows only a return journey from place of issue to the border of a eighbouring participating country before unlimited travel is possible.

3ODENSEE TICKET

Jnlimited travel by rail, bus and ferry in border region Austria/Germany/ witzerland surrounding the Bodensee (Lake Constance). One day 6 CHF/€27, 3 days 57 CHF/€42. Discounts for children and families. lot valid on ICE/IC/EC trains In Germany or on Friedrichshafen - onstanz catamarans. Zonal versions also available for smaller areas.

EUREGIO TICKET MAAS-RHEIN

)ne days unlimited travel in border region Belgium/Netherlands/ Germany by rail and bus (covers Liège, Hasselt, Maastricht, Roermond, achen, Düren). In Germany and Belgium covers only local trains and uses. Price €19. At weekends/public holidays valid as a family ticket (2 dults plus 3 children under 12).

EUROPEAN EAST PASS

)ffers unlimited rail travel throughout Austria, Czech Republic, Hungary nd Slovakia for any 5 to 10 days within a month. Valid also on direct ervices through Germany between Kufstein and Salzburg (the assholder cannot leave the train). Available to European residents except those from countries where the ticket is valid) as well as non- uropean residents. 1st class €266 (5 days) to €396 (10 days); 2nd lass €183 (5 days) to €303 (10 days). Children aged 4-11 half price.)iscounts available on river cruises, Children's Railway etc.

ÖRESUND RUNDT

Two days unlimited travel on trains and buses in the København, Malmö and Helsingborg area (includes the metro in København). The Öresund can only be crossed by rail in one direction; the Helsingborg - Helsingør ferry (included) must be used in the other direction. Available in Denmark from København Tourist Office (price 249 DKK) and in Sweden from Skånetrafiken (price 299 SEK); children 7-15 half price.

PASS ALSACE-RHEIN-NECKAR

A day ticket valid on Saturdays, Sundays and public holidays covering local trains (2nd class), buses and trams in the Rhein-Neckar area (VRN) centered on Mannheim and Heidelberg, the Karlsruhe area (KVV), plus local trains in the Bas Rhin area of France centered on Strasbourg. Price €19 for one person or €31.50 for a group of 2-5 people.

PASSBASK

One day's travel in the area between Bayonne in France and San Sebastian in Spain on SNCF trains (includes *TGV* but not night trains) and EuskoTren services. A barrier pass for EuskoTren should be obtained at Hendaye station. Price €12, child aged 4-12 €8.

SAAR-LOR-LUX TICKET

One day's unlimited 2nd class travel on Saturday or Sunday throughout Saarland (i.e. Saarbrücken area of Germany, local trains only), Lorraine (i.e. Metz, Nancy, Épinal area of France) and all CFL trains in Luxembourg. Price €26; for groups of 2-5 people add €10 per extra person. Not valid on *TGV* or *ICE* trains.

OTHER PASSES

A range of day tickets is available covering areas of the Czech Republic and adjoining countries, i.e. **Euro-Neisse Ticket** (Liberec, Jelenia Góra, Zittau, Görlitz area; www.zvon.de); **EgroNet-Ticket** (Cheb, Karlovy Vary, Plauen, Zwickau, Hof, Bayreuth; www.egronet.de); **Bayern-Böhmen Ticket** (border areas of Bavaria/Bohemia); **Sachsen-Böhmen Ticket** (Liberec, Děčín, Dresden area); **Elbe-Labe Ticket** (Chomutov, Ústí nad Labem, Dresden area).

Railplus

ailplus cards are valid for one year and offer a discount of 15% on ross-border rail travel (excluding supplements) between the participating ountries, which are Austria, Belgium, Bosnia-Herzegovina, Bulgaria, zech Republic, Denmark, Finland, Germany, Greece, Hungary, Italy, atvia, Lithuania, Luxembourg, Montenegro, Netherlands, North Mace- onia, Poland, Romania, Serbia, Slovakia, Slovenia and Switzerland.

In addition, Norway, Spain and Sweden grant discounts to youth (12-25) and seniors (60+) only. There are no discounts on Eurostar or Thalys services. Cards are not available for sale in all participating countries, and you may be required to hold a national railcard for the country where you buy the pass, in addition to the Railplus card.

This extended Rail Passes Feature appears in the Summer and Winter editions of the European Rail Timetable (published in June and December). All editions of the European Rail Timetable include details of Interrail and Eurail passes as well as Britrail and other international passes.

Passes for Domestic Travel

Every effort has been made to show latest prices, but some may have changed. Most cities offer day tickets valid on public transport (some include local trains). Larger cities often have Visitor Cards (some are shown below) which include tourist attractions as well as public transport; these are available from airports and tourist information offices, often also from hotels and online.

AUSTRIA

See separate sections for Interrail / Eurail Global and One Country passes, European East Pass, Bodensee Ticket.

Einfach-Raus-Ticket: one day's 2nd class travel (until 0300 hrs the following day) on regional and local trains in Austria (except Vorarlberg) for groups of 2 to 5 people, € 34 - 46. On Mon to Fri not valid before 0900 hrs. Add €9 to include bicycles.

Vorteilscard annual discount card gives 45-50% discount; the *Classic* version (€99) is available to all but there are cheaper cards for families, seniors and those under 26.

ÖBB Österreichcard gives unlimited travel on Austrian Railways for one year, € 1,889 (1st class € 2,839). Cheaper cards for families, seniors and those under 26.

Wien all public transport (not airport): day ticket € 5.80; 24 / 48 / 72 hours € 8 / 14.10 / 17.10; weekly ticket (starts Monday, photo required) € 17.10; any 8 days (not necessarily consecutive, transferable) € 40.80.

Vienna City Card: unlimited travel on local transport (excludes airport) plus discounted museum entry, 24 / 48 / 72 hours € 17 / 25 / 29. One child under 15 free. Similar **Easy City Pass Vienna** also available.

Other visitor cards giving local travel plus museum / sights discounts for 24 / 48 / 72 hours: **Salzburg Card** € 29 / 38 / 44 (reduced by € 3 - 5 low season Nov. to Apr.); **Innsbruck Card** € 43 / 50 / 59. Children half price.

BELARUS

Minsk: 10, 15 and 30-day public transport passes are available from metro stations (bus only or bus / tram passes also available).

BELGIUM

See separate sections for Interrail / Eurail Global and Benelux passes, Euregio Ticket Maas-Rhein.

Netabonnement / Abonnement Réseau : unlimited travel on rail network; 1 month € 310 / 477 (2nd / 1st class), 3 months € 867 / 1335, 1 year € 3097 / 4770. Add-ons for city transport also available.

Tickets available on NMBS/SNCB rail network include: **Rail Pass** (age 26 +) allows 10 single journeys within Belgium for € 83 2nd class, € 128 1st class, valid 1 year. **Go Pass 10** is under 26 version, € 53 2nd class. **Weekend Ticket**: gives 50% discount, from Friday 1900 hrs. **Senior Ticket** (65 +), flat fare of €6.80 2nd class, €14.40 1st class, from 0900 Mon-Fri, not Sat/Sun mid-July to mid-August.

Brussels: **Jump ticket** covers all transport in greater Brussels (De Lijn, NMBS/SNCB, MIVB/STIB and TEC) 24 / 48 / 72 hrs € 7.50 / 14 / 18. Personal Mobib or Mobib Basic card required (€ 5). STIB also has a contactless day ticket for € 7.50, no Mobib card required.

De Lijn has 1 / 3 / 5-day system passes (€ 7 / 14 / 20) for its trams and buses; includes coastal tram. Buy in advance; the day pass may also be purchased on the bus or tram for € 9.

De Lijn 7-day **West Flanders** pass also available (includes coastal tram and buses), € 26 for 1 person, € 40 for 2 people.

BOSNIA-HERZEGOVINA

See separate sections for Interrail / Eurail Global pass, Balkan Flexipass.

BULGARIA

See separate sections for Interrail / Eurail Global and One Country passes, Balkan Flexipass.

Sofia: metro, tram and bus: 1 day 4 BGN, 3 days 10 BGN (the 3 day card requires an electronic card, cost 2 BGN). A 10-trip card costs 12 BGN.

CROATIA

See separate section for Interrail / Eurail Global and One Country passes.

Zagreb: day ticket (dnevna karta) all ZET tram / bus (zone 1): 30 HRK, available as paper ticket. Also multi-day tickets (višednevne karte): 3 / 7 / 15 / 30 days, 70 / 150 / 200 / 400 HRK, requires stored value card.

Zagreb Card adds museums, discounts, 24 hrs 98 HRK, 72 hrs 135 HRK.

CZECH REPUBLIC

See separate sections for Interrail / Eurail Global and One Country passes, European East Pass. See also under *Other International Passes* for a range of passes covering border areas.

Day ticket (Celodenní Jízdenka): 2nd class travel on whole rail networ 579 CZK (reservation payable on *SC* trains, up to 250 CZK). 13 regiona areas also available, 159 - 239 CZK. Certain regions also have day ticket including border areas of Germany or Poland, 250 - 300 CZK. Other da tickets cover specific cross-border areas: Vltava-Dunaj (4 days 566 CZK) EgroNet (200 CZK), Labe-Elbe (270 CZK), Euro-Nisa (160 CZK); most have discounts for groups of two or more. Day tickets (also Interrail / Eurail passes) are not valid on services operated by GW Train Regio.

Group Weekend ticket (Skupinová víkendová jízdenka): 2nd class travel on whole network on Sat. or Sun. for 2 adults and up to 3 childrer 679 CZK (829 CZK including local transport in Praha). Reservation fee payable on *SC* trains. Valid cross-border to first station on local trains (except Austria). Regional areas also available, 229 - 319 CZK. Version for Czech Republic plus border areas of Germany or Poland, including regional areas, are also available.

Summer Ticket: unlimited rail travel for 7 or 14 days during July and August only, 7 days 790 CZK, 14 days 1190 CZK.

Praha: all public transport (including most trains): 24 hrs 110 CZK, 3 days (72 hrs) 310 CZK, 30 days 670 CZK. Wider areas available. **Pragu Card**: 2 / 3 / 4 day admission card, includes public transport, € 62 - 83 (student € 46 - 61). Most cities have day tickets for city transport.

DENMARK

See separate sections for Interrail / Eurail Global and One Country passes, Eurail Scandinavia pass, Öresund Rundt.

Fares based on national zonal system; 30-day **Pendlerkort** is availabl (photocard required) including all-zones version. 10-journey tickets alsc available. **Rejsekortet** is a new pre-pay travel card aimed at Danish residents, but a **Rejsekort Anonymt** may be purchased by anyone (car costs 80 DKK, plus an initial amount for travel purposes).

København: **City Pass** zones 1 - 4 (includes airport) on bus, metro an train 24 - 120 hrs 80 - 300 DKK (child half price).

Copenhagen Card: greater København public transport (zones 1 - 99) free entry to over 80 attractions, 24 / 48 / 72 / 120 hrs € 54 / 80 / 99 / 133 (two children under 10 free).

ESTONIA

Estonian Railways: a zonal system operates; there is no network pass

Tallinn: tram / bus / trolley-bus **Ühiskaart** pre-pay travel card (deposit € 2) available for 1 / 3 / 5 / 30 days: € 3 / 5 / 6 / 23 (supplement on expres buses); one hour ticket € 1.10.

Tallinn Card: public transport plus over 40 museums and attractions, 2 hrs € 26, 48 hrs € 39, 72 hrs € 47, under 18s € 15 / 20 / 24. **Tallinn Car PLUS** adds free bus tour of city, € 36 / 49 / 58.

FINLAND

See separate sections for Interrail / Eurail Global and One Country passes, also Eurail Scandinavia pass.

Helsinki: single-charge electronic cards for all public transport includin local trains: 1 / 2 / 3 days € 8 / 12 / 16; 7 days € 32 (1 - 7 days available).

Helsinki Card: public transport plus free entry to 25 + attractions and bu tour, 24 / 48 / 72 hrs €49 / 61 / 71, child 7-16 half price; Region version includes airport for €5 - 8 extra.

FRANCE

See separate sections for Interrail / Eurail Global and One Country passes, Pass Alsace - Rhein-Neckar, Passbask, Saar-Lor-Lux Ticket.

Annual railcards: **Carte Jeune** (ages 12 - 27, € 50), **Carte Senior +** (over 60, € 60) and **Carte Enfant +** (child under 12 plus up to 4 companions, € 75) all give 25% discount off normal rail fares for one yea including certain international journeys, and 10% off Prem's tickets. **Cart Week-End** (all ages, € 75) gives same discounts at weekends.

Regional Tickets: several regions offer day tickets on TER (local) train at weekends and holidays. Conditions vary and some only valid in summer. Details generally available on TER website www.ter.sncf.com

Alsa Plus 24h: a zonal day pass (24 hours) for the Alsace region, whic includes Strasbourg, Colmar and Mulhouse. Valid on train, bus and tram € 36.90 for the whole region; group ticket (2-5 people) available at weekends for € 38.10. Smaller areas are also available.

Paris Visite: public transport within Paris including metro, RER, SNCF suburban trains, bus and tram. Available for two areas: zones 1 - 3 (central Paris) or zones 1 - 5 which includes airports and trains to Versailles and Disneyland. Prices for zone 1 - 3 are € 13.20 / 21.50 / 29.4 for 1 / 2 / 3 days, € 42.20 for 5 days. Prices for zones 1 - 5 are € 27.80, 42.20 / 59.20 for 1 / 2 / 3 days, € 72.40 for 5 days. Child 4 - 11 half price

Paris Passlib' includes the Paris Visite zone 1 - 3 pass above, plus various museums and attractions. 2 / 3 / 5 days € 65 / 70 / 90, children aged 4 - 11 € 35 / 39 / 47.

obilis: Paris one-day public transport ticket (excludes airport services), :7.50 (zones 1-2) to €17.80 (zones 1-5). **Navigo** weekly and monthly ckets also available; all zones 7 day (Mon to Sun) ticket costs €22.80; hotocard required at extra cost; two zone version also available.

ille City Pass: local public transport (metro, tram, bus) plus museums nd attractions, 24/48/72 hrs, €25/35/45. The 72-hour pass includes ER trains in regional area for 24 hours (includes Dunkerque) and dditional attractions in the wider area.

ost cities have day tickets for urban bus and tram services, e.g. **Lyon**: 4/48/72 hrs €6/11.50/15.50; **Lille** 1 to 5 days, €4.46 to €13.86.

ERMANY

ee separate sections for Interrail/Eurail Global pass, Interrail One ountry pass, Bodensee Ticket, Euregio Ticket Mass-Rhein, Sar-Lor-Lux icket. Note that Eurail does not have a One Country pass for Germany s German Railways (DB) has its own pass for non-European residents, s shown below.

erman Rail Pass is available only to non-European residents and gives nlimited travel on DB trains in Germany, also to certain destinations in witzerland, Austria and Italy. Includes IC Bus. Available in flexi and onsecutive versions as shown below. No supplements on *ICE*, *EC*. outh passes apply to those aged 12 to 27. All versions are also available r 4 days within 1 month and 4 consecutive days. A **Twin Pass** offers a scount of approx 50% for a second adult. Accompanied children aged - 11 get a free pass (two with an adult pass, four with a twin pass).

	Adult 1st cl.	Adult 2nd cl.	Youth 1st cl.	Youth 2nd cl.
LEXI PASSES:				
days within 1 month	€270	€200	€215	€160
days within 1 month	€310	€230	€245	€185
days within 1 month	€380	€280	€310	€225
) days within 1 month	€490	€360	€390	€290
5 days within 1 month	€690	€450	€550	€410
ONSECUTIVE DAYS:				
days	€260	€190	€210	€155
days	€300	€220	€240	€180
days	€365	€270	€295	€215
) days	€435	€320	€350	€260
5 days	€610	€450	€490	€360

uer-durchs-Land-Ticket: one day's unlimited travel (not before 0900 on. - Fri., but valid until 0300 following day) on local trains (IRE/RE/RB/ -Bahn), 2nd class. Valid for up to 5 people. €44 for one person, then dd €8 for each additional person in the group (€76 for a group of five).

chönes-Wochenende-Ticket: withdrawn from June 2019.

egional tickets (Länder-Tickets): one day's unlimited 2nd class travel r up to 5 people on DB local trains (not before 0900 on Mon.-Fri., valid 0300 the following day). Buy on the day. First class versions also vailable for some regions. Some tickets include other public transport. egions available:

aden-Württemberg: 1 person €24 (add €6 per additional person).
ayern: 1 person €25 (add €7 for each additional person).
randenburg-Berlin: €29 (up to 5 passengers).
essen: €36 (up to 5 passengers).
lecklenburg-Vorpommern: 1 person €23 (add €4 per person).
iedersachsen: 1 person €24 (add €5 for each additional person).
ordrhein-Westfalen (SchönerTag Ticket NRW): 1 person €31, - 5 people €46.
heinland-Pfalz: 1 person €25 (add €5 for each additional person).
aarland: 1 person €25 (add €5 for each additional person).
achsen: 1 person €25 (add €7 for each additional person).
achsen-Anhalt: 1 person €25 (add €7 for each additional person).
chleswig-Holstein: 1 person €29 (add €3 for each additional person). cludes public transport in Hamburg.
hüringen: 1 person €25 (add €7 for each additional person).

nnual Railcards: **Bahncard 25/50**: gives discounts of 25% or 50% on l national DB trains for €62/255 in 2nd class (1st class €125/515). A outh Bahncard 25 is available for those aged 6 to 18, price €10 (valid r 1st and 2nd class). **Bahncard 100** gives unlimited travel for one year, :4,395 in 2nd class, €7,435 in 1st class, passport photo required. All dult Bahncards entitle the holder to discounts on flexible fares between ermany and up to 26 European countries.

arz: HSB narrow gauge railway, 3/5 days €90/135; children aged - 14 pay €54/81.

ageskarte (day ticket): most urban areas offer 24/48/72 hour tickets alid on most public transport; generally a zonal system operates.

/elcome Tickets: most public transport in selected cities, also includes ee or reduced entry to many museums and visitor attractions. Buy from ourist Information, main stations, some airports and hotels. Examples:

erlin Welcome Card: one adult and up to 3 children aged 3-14; 48 hrs 23, 72 hrs €32, 4 days €37, 5 days €42, 6 days €47. Covers zones , B, C (includes Potsdam) and includes DB trains; cheaper version vailable for Berlin only (zones A, B). Also available 72 hrs + Museum land €48, 72 hrs + 30 free admissions (zones A, B, C) €105.

Dresden City Card: 1 day €12, 2 days €17, 3 days €25; family card also available for 2 adults and up to 4 children under 15 €15/25/33.

Frankfurt Card: 1 day €10.50, 2 days €15.50; group ticket (up to 5 people) €22/€32. Includes travel from/to the airport.

Hamburg Card: Day Ticket €10.50, also 2-5 days €19.90 - 42.50; group version (up to 5 people) €18.50 one day, €33.50-75.50 for 2-5 days. **Hannover Card**: 1 day €10, 2 days €16, 3 days €19, group ticket (up to 5 people) €21/28/36. **Köln Card**: 24/48 hrs €9/18, group ticket (up to 5 people) €19/38. **Leipzig Card**: 1 day €12.40, 3 days €24.40, 3 day group ticket (2 adults and up to 3 children under 14) €44.90. **Nürnberg Card**: 2 days €28 (children aged 6-11 €6).

GREAT BRITAIN

See separate sections for Interrail/Eurail Global pass, Interrail One Country pass, Britrail.

Railcards: annual cards giving 34% discount on most rail fares; 16-25 Railcard, 26-30 Railcard, Two Together Railcard, Family & Friends Railcard, Senior Railcard: all £30; Disabled Persons £20. Some have 3-year versions (£70 online). Network Railcard gives off-peak discount in South East England, £30. New from September 2019 will be a 16-17 Railcard giving 50% discount.

All-Line Rail Rover: covers whole National Rail network. 1st/standard class £796/526 (7 days), £1216/796 (14 days), children 5-15 half price. 34% discount for holders of Senior/Disabled/Two Together railcard, and (standard class only) 16-25, 26-30 and Family & Friends railcards. Some restrictions before 1000 Mon.-Fri. Not valid on Eurostar, Heathrow Express, London Underground. Valid on Ffestiniog Railway but not other private railways.

Spirit of Scotland Travelpass: all rail services in Scotland (includes Carlisle and Berwick) plus Caledonian MacBrayne ferry services and some buses. Standard class only. Valid 4 out of 8 days £149, or 8 out of 15 days £189; not before 0915 Mon. to Fri. (except on Glasgow - Oban/Mallaig/Stranraer services and north of Inverness). 34% discount with most annual railcards. 50% discount for children (5-15). 20% discount on Northlink Ferries to Orkney and Shetland. Smaller areas also available: **Highland Rover**, 4 out of 8 days £89; **Central Scotland Rover** 3 days (consecutive) £49.

Explore Wales Pass: standard class rail travel on any 4 days out of 8 (not valid before 0930 Mon.-Fri.), price £99, children half price. Tickets available from staffed stations and on the train. Other areas available: **South Wales** £69, **North and Mid Wales** £69.

A range of **Rover** tickets is available covering various areas, typically for 7 days, 3 in 7 days, 4 in 8 days, or 8 in 15 days. Most not valid until after the morning peak on Mon. to Fri. Examples: Anglia Plus, Coast and Peaks, Devon & Cornwall, East Midlands, Heart of England, Kent, North Country, North East, North Wales, North West, Severn & Solent, South West, Thames.

Ranger day tickets also available: e.g. Cheshire, Cotswolds, Cumbria, Cumbian Coast, Devon, East Midlands, Isle of Wight, Lakes, Lancashire, Lincolnshire, North Downs, Oxfordshire, South Pennines, Thames Branches, Tyne & Tees, West Midlands, West Yorkshire, Yorkshire Coast. Details: www.nationalrail.co.uk or www.railrover.org.

London: Day Travelcards cover almost all transport (Underground, bus and rail) in the London area; peak version from £13.10 (central London, zones 1-4) to £18.60 (zones 1-6), off-peak version (not before 0930 Mon.-Fri.) £13.10 (zones 1-6). 7-day tickets from £35.10 (zones 1-2) to £64.20 (zones 1-6), no off-peak version. Wider zones also available. For single journeys contactless debit and credit cards, or stored-value Oyster cards offer the best value as prices are capped. Visitor Oyster cards are available preloaded from £10 to £50 (plus £5 fee, non-refundable). Children under 11 travel free on buses and trams (also on Tube, DLR and some rail services) when accompanied by a fare paying adult.

All-day tickets (some off-peak) covering local rail and most buses are available in Derbyshire, Glasgow, Greater Manchester, Merseyside, South Yorkshire, West Yorkshire, Tyneside and West Midlands.

Isle of Man: Go Explore card: all buses and trains, Douglas horse trams (excludes Groudle Glen Railway, Great Laxey Mine Railway), 1/3/5/7 days, £17/34/41/50 (add £2 for card), children aged 5-15 half price. Family card: 2 adults and up to 3 children, £41.50/80/100/122.

GREECE

See separate sections for Interrail/Eurail Global, One Country and Greek Islands passes, Balkan Flexipass.

Athens: 24-hour ticket valid on metro, tram and bus (excludes airport) €4.50, 5 days €9 (airport is €10 single). 3-day tourist ticket including metro or bus to/from airport (one journey each way) €22.

Athens Card gives entrance to various museums and includes 5 days public transport. Silver and Gold versions, prices €125 to €230.

Passes for Domestic Travel

HUNGARY

See separate sections for Interrail / Eurail Global and One Country passes, European East Pass.

Travel by rail and local transport is free for over-65s with an EU passport or ID card.

START Klub Card: gives 50% discount on 2nd class travel. Valid for either 6 months or one year: HUF 19900 / 34900 (HUF 14900 / 24900 under 26 years). Requires passport style photograph. Cardholders may obtain 50% discount for a second person on Saturday.

Budapest: tram / metro / bus / rail, 24 hr travelcard HUF 1,650, 72 hrs HUF 4,150, 7 days HUF 4,950. Also 24 hr group (1 - 5 people), HUF 3,300.

Budapest Card also includes museums, walking tour and discounts: 24 hrs HUF 6,490, 48 hrs HUF 9,900, 72 hrs HUF 12,900. Also for 96 / 120 hrs (HUF 15,990 / 18,990); 72 hr has Junior version for 9,900.

IRELAND

See separate sections for Interrail / Eurail Global and One Country passes. Interrail and Eurail passes valid in the Republic of Ireland are also valid in Northern Ireland.

REPUBLIC OF IRELAND ONLY:

Irish Explorer: any 5 days in 15 on IÉ rail services, € 160 (child € 80), standard class. **Trekker** gives 4 consecutive days on Irish Rail for €110.

Dublin area: **Leap Visitor Card**: smartcard 24 hrs € 10, 72 hrs €19.50, 7 days (168 hrs) € 40. Includes rail in Short Hop zone, Luas tram and bus (also Airlink); purchase at airport or tourist offices (not railway stations). Can top up with additional periods. Luas **Flexi** ticket (tram only): 1 day € 7.30, zonal tickets available for 7 days. **Leap** cards are also available for Cork, Galway, Limerick and Waterford bus networks.

NORTHERN IRELAND ONLY:

iLink Travel Card: unlimited bus and rail travel on Translink services (Northern Ireland Railways, Ulsterbus and Belfast Citybus). Zone 4 covers the whole of Northern Ireland: 1 day £ 16.50, 7 days £ 60, 1 month £ 205. Zone 1 covers Belfast city (£ 5 / 19 / 67). Children half price. North West zone: £ 13.50 / 51 / 180. Initial £1 fee for card (waived online).

Belfast Visitor Pass: local public transport (includes rail to Cultra; not bus to Belfast International Airport) plus visitor discounts: 1 / 2 / 3 days, adult £ 6 / 11 / 14.50, child £ 3.50 / 6 / 7.75.

ITALY

See separate sections for Interrail / Eurail Global and One Country passes.

Mobilcard Südtirol: regional trains, buses, funiculars and cable cars in Bolzano, Malles, Brennero area: 1 / 3 / 7 days; € 15 / 23 / 28 (child under 14 € 7.50 / 11.50 / 14).

Roma: Roma Tourist Ticket covers rail / metro / bus in urban area (excludes Fiumicino Airport), 24 / 48 / 72 hrs, € 7 / 12.50 / 18; 7-day ticket (CIS) € 24.

Roma Pass: 48 hr / 72 hr transport pass (€ 28 / 38.50) with museum discounts.

Milano: 24 hour ticket (abbonamento giornaliero): ATM city services plus local Trenitalia, Trenord rail services, € 4.50. Also 48 hour ticket € 8.25.

Napoli: 'Campania > artecard' is a 3-day transport + museum visitors card, allowing free entry or disounts. Two areas available, Napoli (€ 21 adult, € 12 for ages 18 - 25) and wider Campania area (€ 32 / 25).

Venezia: Travel cards for ACTV buses and boats: 1 / 2 / 3 / 7 days € 20 / 30 / 40 / 60. Each card is also available with airport transfer add-on (€ 6 single or €12 return).

LATVIA

Latvian Railways: tickets are available for 1 / 3 / 4 / 5 days for unlimited travel between specified stations, but there are no network passes.

Riga: trams and buses 24 hrs €5, 3 / 5 days €10 / 15. **Riga Pass**: public transport, bus tour, plus free / discounted museum entry, € 25 / 30 / 35 for 24 / 48 / 72 hours.

LITHUANIA

See separate section for Interrail / Eurail Global and One Country passes.

Vilnius: 1 / 3 / 10 day tickets available on local VVT buses / trolleybuses; € 5 / 8 / 15. **Vilnius Pass** includes public transport, free entry to museums and various discounts, 72 hrs, € 40.

LUXEMBOURG

See separate sections for Interrail / Eurail Global and Benelux passes, Sar-Lor-Lux Ticket.

Note that there are plans to make all public transport free of charge throughout the country from the start of 2020.

Dagesbilljee / Billet longue durée: unlimited travel on all public transport throughout the country for one day (until 0400 hrs following morning), not valid to border points, 2nd class € 4, 1st class € 6 (add € if bought on board the train). Booklet of 5 day tickets (2nd class) € 16. Tickets for 2 and 3 days travel also available for € 8 / 12 (2nd class).

Oeko Pass: network season ticket, valid one month, € 50 2nd class, € 7 1st class; from CFL offices.

Luxembourg Card: unlimited 2nd class travel on trains and buses throughout the country, plus free entry to 70 attractions. 1 day € 13, 2 days € 20, 3 days € 28. Family pass for 2 - 5 people (max 2 adults) for 1 2 / 3 days: € 28 / 48 / 68.

MONTENEGRO

See separate sections for Interrail / Eurail Global pass, Balkan Flexipass

NETHERLANDS

See separate sections for Interrail / Eurail Global and Benelux passes, Euregio Ticket Maas-Rhein.

A national stored-value OV-chipkaart is used for public transport, initia cost € 7.50, which can be loaded with day tickets. A single-use chipcar or e-ticket may be used by less frequent travellers. Supplements payab on IC Direct trains. **Railrunner**: Children aged 4 - 11 travel for a flat rate € 2.50 each, valid all day.

Day ticket: unlimited rail travel (NS and other carriers) for one day; 1s class € 87.46, 2nd class € 53.

Holland Travel Ticket: valid one day on all public transport (not Thalys includes 2nd class on all NS and private operators' trains, tram, bus an metro, € 61 all day, or Off-Peak version (not 0630 - 0900 Mon-Fri) € 4

Amsterdam: GVB tram / bus / metro 24 / 48 / 72 hrs € 8 / 13.50 / 19. Also available for 4 / 5 / 6 / 7 days (€ 24.50 to € 36.50).

Amsterdam Travel Ticket: adds local NS trains (includes Schiphol airport): 1 / 2 / 3 days € 17 / 22.50 / 28, valid to 0400 next day.

Amsterdam & Region Travel Ticket: as above but covers wider area (e.g. trains to Haarlem, Lelystad) 1 / 2 / 3 days € 19.50 / 28 / 36.50.

I amsterdam Card: GVB tram / bus / metro, canal tour, plus discounted c free entry to 70 + attractions; 24 / 48 / 72 / 96 hrs, € 60 / 80 / 95 / 105.

South Holland: **Tourist Day Ticket** gives tram / bus / metro / waterbus throughout Rotterdam and Den Haag area, €14.50. Excludes NS trains

NORTH MACEDONIA

See separate sections for Interrail / Eurail Global and One Country passes, Balkan Flexipass.

NORWAY

See separate section for Interrail / Eurail Global and One Country passe Eurail Scandinavia pass.

Oslo: 24 hour ticket for all 'Ruter' public transport in zone 1, 108 NOK, 7 days 285 NOK; all zones (includes airport) 246 NOK, 7 days 761 NOK Children, youth (18 - 19) and seniors (67 +) half price.

Oslo Pass: all public transport including NSB local trains (zones 1 - 2, excludes airport), free entry to 30 attractions, discounts on sightseeing buses / boats: 24 / 48 / 72 hours 445 / 655 / 820 NOK (child approx 50%).

Bergen Card: local bus and tram travel plus free or discounted entry various attractions; 24 / 48 / 72 hrs, 280 / 360 / 430 NOK (child 3 - 15 pay 35%). Student / Senior version (also Eurail holders) 224 / 288 / 344 NOK

POLAND

See separate section for Interrail / Eurail Global and One Country passe

PKP Intercity operates *EIC, EIP, IC, TLK* trains and offers the followin passes for its trains: **Bilet Weekendowy** (weekend ticket): valid 1900 F to 0600 Mon. (extended if Thu. or Mon. is a public holiday), version val only in *TLK* and *IC* trains 81 / 111 PLN 2nd / 1st class. **Weekendowy MA** is also valid in *EIC, EIP* trains: 164 PLN 2nd class, 264 PLN 1st class (supplement of 10 PLN for each *EIP* journey). Seat reservations free (b not compulsory). Both the above also available from train conductor (except on *EIP* trains). **Bilety Sieciowe** (network tickets): 1 month 1,650 PLN 2nd class, 2,250 PLN 1st class, also available for longer periods up to one year. Bearer version with unnamed holder also available at additional cost.

Polregio operates REGIO and IR trains: **Bilety Sieciowe** (network tickets) are weekly or monthly tickets. **REGIOpass**: valid for any 3 day out of 2 months, 75 PLN (Polregio plus most other regional operators) c 65 PLN for Polregio REGIO trains only; validate ticket before travel.

Bilet Turystyczny (tourist ticket): valid 1800 Fri. to 0600 Mon., 45 PL (Polregio plus most other regional operators); or 39 PLN for Polregio REGIO trains only. **Bilet Turystyczny + Czechy** adds border area of Czech Republic, 55 PLN.

Koleje Mazowieckie (KM) trains: wide area around Warsaw, 24 hr and 3 ay passes are available.

Warsaw ZTM tram / bus / metro / rail (includes Chopin airport): 1 day zone only, 15 PLN; zones 1 & 2, 26 PLN (3-day ticket €36 / 57). Weekend cket valid 1900 Fri. - 0800 Mon. in zones 1 & 2, 24 PLN (group ticket for p to 5 people, 40 PLN).

PORTUGAL

See separate section for Interrail / Eurail Global and One Country passes.

ntra-Rail: for ages 12 - 30, rail travel with free nights at youth hostels; *XCape* version valid 3 days € 58 (€ 64 without youth card). *XPlore* ersion valid 7 days € 127 (€ 146 without youth card). Not valid on *AP* rains. Buy at main stations. Show Card and ID to obtain free travel ticket.

Lisboa: Carris tram / bus / metro - one-day ticket (bilhete diário 24 h) € 6.40; with Transtejo (Cacilhas) included € 9.50. Carris, metro and local CP trains € 10.55. Includes the funiculars and lift.

Lisboa Card: public transport plus free / discounted attractions: 24 / 48 / 72 hrs, € 20 / 34 / 42 (children aged 4 - 15: € 13 / 19 / 22.50).

Porto: *Andante Tour Card* gives metro + STCP bus + local rail, all zones, 24 hrs € 7, 72 hrs € 15. **Porto Card** also includes free / discounted entry o museums etc, 1 day € 13, 2 days € 20, 3 days € 25, 4 days € 33.

Coimbra: day ticket on SMTUC local buses € 3.50.

ROMANIA

See separate section for Interrail / Eurail Global and One Country passes.

Bucureşti: STB tram, bus and trolleybus network (not express buses): 1 / 7 / 15 days, 8 / 17 / 25 RON, fares are loaded onto an 'Activ' smartcard. A free 3-day **Bucharest City Card** is available giving tourist discounts.

RUSSIA

Moskva: smartcards for unlimited number of metro journeys, 1 day 230 RUB, 3 days 438 RUB. Card for 60 trips 1900 RUB. Monthly *yediniy bilyet* covers bus / tram / metro (limited to 70 metro trips) 2770 RUB. A City Pass is available which includes attractions and 15 transport rides.

St Peterburg: passes for 10 / 20 / 40 metro journeys available. All modes one month pass 2900 RUB. **St Petersburg Card** includes museums and other discounts for 2 / 3 / 5 / 7 days, approx € 60 / 78 / 96 / 109.

SERBIA

See separate sections for Interrail / Eurail Global and One Country passes, Balkan Flexipass.

SLOVAKIA

See separate sections for Interrail / Eurail Global and One Country passes, European East Pass.

Zero fare rail tickets for most trains can be obtained by EU citizens under 16 and over 62. Supplements on *EC* and *SC*.

Bratislava: urban trams, buses and local trains, 24 hrs € 3.50, 3 days € 8, 7 days € 11.40. **Bratislava Card** includes many discounts, 24 hrs € 18, 48 hrs € 22, 72 hrs € 25, available online or from tourist offices.

SLOVENIA

See separate section for Interrail / Eurail Global and One Country passes.

Ljubljana Card: city buses, castle funicular, tourist boat and museums, valid for 24, 48 or 72 hours, € 27.90 / 35.10 / 40.50, child 6 - 14 years € 16.20 / 20.70 / 24.30 (online prices including 10% discount).

SPAIN

See separate sections for Interrail / Eurail Global and One Country passes, Passbask.

RENFE Spain Pass: for people resident outside Spain giving 4, 6, 8 or 10 individual journeys. Tickets must be obtained in advance using the pass; reservations are compulsory but free. Valid 1 month from first journey. Can be purchased and printed online (www.renfe.com).

Madrid: **Abono Turístico** (Tourist Ticket) gives all public transport in zone A, 1 / 2 / 3 days € 8.40 / 14.20 / 18.40, also 5 / 7 days € 26.80 / 35.40, children under 11 years 50%. Available for wider area (zone T) at double the price. Various museum passes are available but these exclude public transport.

Barcelona T-Dia ticket: valid 1 day on metro / TMB bus / tram / local rail, € 8.60 (zone 1, includes airport), wider areas available. **Hola Barcelona** zone 1 travelcard available for 2 / 3 / 4 / 5 days, approx € 15 / 22 / 29 / 35. **Barcelona Card**: adds free or discounted museums, 3 to 5 days € 46 / 56 / 61 (children 4 - 12 years € 22 / 28 / 33).

SWEDEN

See separate sections for Interrail / Eurail Global and One Country passes, Eurail Scandinavia pass, Öresund Rundt.

Stockholm: Travelcards give all SL public transport in Greater Stockholm, 24 / 72 hours 130 / 260 SEK, 7 days 335 SEK; SL Access smartcard required (20 SEK). Discount for under 20s / 65 +. **Stockholm Pass** gives bus / boat tour plus free museums, 1 / 2 / 3 / 5 days (645 - 1345 SEK); add Travelcard (above) to include public transport.

SWITZERLAND

See separate sections for Interrail / Eurail Global pass, Interrail One Country pass, Bodensee Ticket.

Swiss Travel Pass: available to all non-Swiss residents. Consecutive days on Swiss Railways, boats and most alpine postbuses and city buses. Valid for 3, 4, 8 or 15 days; 1st class 369 / 447 / 663 / 810 CHF, 2nd class 232 / 281 / 418 / 513 CHF. Youth Pass (16 - 25 years) gives approximately 15% reduction. All versions give up to 50% reduction on most funicular and mountain railways. Includes free admission to over 500 tourist sites. Children aged 6 - 15 travel free with a Family Card if accompanied by a parent (not other relatives), otherwise half fare.

Swiss Travel Pass Flex: as above but for 3 / 4 / 8 / 15 days within 1 month. Prices 1st / 2nd class: 424 / 267 CHF (3 days), 514 / 323 CHF (4 days), 742 / 467 CHF (8 days), 890 / 563 CHF (15 days). Youth version (16 - 25 years) gives approximately 15% reduction.

Swiss Half Fare Card: discount card offering up to 50% off most public transport, valid for 1 month, 120 CHF. For non-Swiss residents.

Holders of the Swiss Half Fare Card can purchase a **1-day Travelpass** for 75 CHF 2nd class or 127 CHF 1st class, valid on most trains and public transport. A **Saver Day Pass** is also available but is more restrictive, from 29 CHF (or from 52 CHF without a Half Fare Card); prices vary according to when it is purchased, passes may sell out.

Bernese Oberland Regional Pass: valid April to October. Available for 3, 4, 6, 8 or 10 days unlimited travel in the area; 210 - 390 CHF 2nd class, 252 - 468 CHF 1st class. Flat fare of 30 CHF for children under 16.

Regional Passes: other areas available include Lake Geneva - Alps and Tell-Pass (Central Switzerland).

Jungfrau Travel Pass: valid 13 April to 27 October for 3 / 4 / 5 / 6 days travel, 180 / 205 / 230 / 255 CHF (7 / 8 days 280 / 305 CHF). Covers most routes in area; connecting ticket for Jungfraujoch € 61 (or € 74 June to August). 5 to 8 day passes include boats on Lakes Brienz and Thun. Reduced fare for holders of Travel Pass or Half Fare Card. **Summer Season Pass** covers similar area, gives unlimited travel Apr. 13 - Dec. 1 for 560 CHF (380 CHF with Half Fare Card). Not available in Switzerland.

Bern: day ticket for city area (2 zone) 7.90 CHF. **Bern Ticket** is issued to overnight guests offering free LIBERO bus and tram travel within city zones 100/101. Also includes Gurten and Marzilibahn funiculars.

Genève: Day ticket (Carte 24 Heures) includes buses, trams, trains and boats: 10 CHF (valid for 2 people at weekends). **Carte 9 h** is valid from 0900 hrs, 8 CHF. Day ticket for wider regional area 18.50 CHF (13.20 CHF after 0900). The **Geneva Transport Card** is given to those staying at a hotel or youth hostel in the city and allows unrestricted travel on all public transport for the duration of the stay.

Zürich: ZVV Tageskarte gives 24 hours on all transport including SBB trains, 14.60 / 8.80 CHF 1st / 2nd class (central zone only); all zones in Canton 56.80 / 34.40 CHF. Off-peak version is 9-UhrPass, all zones, not before 0900 Mon. - Fri., 42.80 / 26 CHF. **Zürich Card** includes most museums and other discounts: 24 hours 27 CHF, 72 hours 53 CHF (children 19 / 37 CHF), includes airport.

TURKEY

See separate sections for Interrail / Eurail Global and One Country passes, Balkan Flexipass.

Gezgin Paketi: this 30 day network pass is proposed but may not yet be available. Covering travel in standard class and couchettes, price is expected to be around 800 TRY (640 TRY youth under 27). **Gezgin Plus Paketi** is the proposed version for business class travel (1120 / 896 TRY).

UKRAINE

Kyïv: unlimited use passes valid for one calendar month are available for the various modes of travel (including one for metro, tram and bus). Cheaper if purchased after the 15th of the month. **Kyiv Pass** gives metro trips and various museums, 24 / 48 / 72 hours, € 15 / 25 / 35.